AD MAJOREM DEI GLORIAM

THE

American Catalogue

UNDER THE DIRECTION OF

F. LEYPOLDT

AUTHOR AND TITLE ENTRIES

OF BOOKS IN PRINT AND FOR SALE (INCLUDING REPRINTS AND IMPORTATIONS)
JULY 1, 1876

COMPILED BY

LYNDS E. JONES

NEW YORK
PETER SMITH
1941

Reprinted, 1941
By special arrangement with
R. R. BOWKER CO.

PRINTED IN THE UNITED STATES OF AMERICA

PREFACE.

THE AMERICAN CATALOGUE, an undertaking long since planned and often cherished by the undersigned, and as often laid aside for lack of encouragement and opportunity, becomes an accomplished fact with the completion of this first volume, in which the materials for the second are comprised. It was projected as the culmination of the series of book-trade helps, of which "The Publishers' Weekly" and "The Publishers' Trade List Annual" are the other chief factors, and as the foundation for a more methodical, continuous and comprehensive system of trade bibliography than had before been practicable for America. It was not until 1872 that there was hope of sufficient support to warrant the risk its publication would involve, but the discussions of that year in "The Publishers' Weekly" led to the announcement, in 1873, that the work would positively be undertaken should the interest of the trade take the practical shape of subscriptions for the necessary number of copies. This guarantee fund, in that year and in 1874, reached but half the amount then thought necessary, but it was determined in the latter part of 1875 to assume the risk, and the work was accordingly begun in 1876. It thus happened that THE AMERICAN CATALOGUE became one of the several important enterprises originated with the centennial year.

It is necessary to say a few words as to the position of the undersigned at the time when this undertaking was finally determined upon, in order that its limitations and his own subsequent relations to the execution of the work may be better understood. Limited as to both means and time, it was with apprehension and reluctance that he renewed a plan so often given up before. Cheerfully would he have yielded the task to other and more able hands, but there were none to take it up, and the need was pressing. Trübner showed no sign of reviving his admirable "Guide to American Literature;" Roorbach dead; and Kelly disheartened by the lack of support with which his patience and industry were received, there was no prospect for the continuation of the American catalogues known by their names and which, for the periods covered by them, had rendered so valuable service.

These and the few other bibliographical aids in existence had long ceased to answer the daily needs of the bookseller. The accumulating literature during the most productive years the country had known, in addition to the constant shifting of the older books from list to list, so peculiar to the American publishing trade (due partly to the early practice of stereotyping and partly to the frequent business changes), made an entirely new catalogue an imperative demand. Circumstances and a growing sense of duty seemed accordingly to force the undertaking upon the undersigned as necessarily within the scope of his work.

With whatever favor this Catalogue, during its issue in parts, has been received by librarians, bibliographers and other workers with books, its origin and consequent shaping must, nevertheless, be borne in mind. The wants of the trade, from which came the pressure for it, and whose support was its main dependence, were and have remained the first consideration. Clearly defined and properly designated as a "Finding List for the Trade," the Catalogue was necessarily limited to what was considered the living substance of the trade, viz.: *books in print and for sale.* The line drawn was a practical necessity, as has been fully proved by the results. It has been only through strict adherence to this plan, resisting the temptation to yield to the cry for something still more comprehensive, and the conviction that it was safer and better to meet the immediate needs of the many, rather than to satisfy the more ambitious desires or specific wants of the few, that the work has been carried through to what may be considered practically a successful conclusion.

The original design was to prepare what is known as a dictionary catalogue, comprising in one continuous alphabet entries under authors, titles and specific subjects. This was subsequently modified so as to include the author and title entries in one alphabet, and the subject entries in a second, and in this form the work is printing, each alphabet in a volume by itself. It was thought that by this method not only could a portion of the Catalogue (complete in itself and securing the entire material) be more quickly prepared and so made use of, but that, as the purpose of the two volumes is so distinct, reference to them would be facilitated if they were separate. The compilation of the second volume, for which the material is thus gathered fully in the first, will present but secondary difficulties.

The first volume now makes its appearance fully two years later than, with the most liberal margin, was anticipated at the outset. This startling miscalculation, which almost proved disastrous to the completion of the work, was due less to the vastness of material than to the condition in which it was found. The impracticability of re-working previous bibliographical material, and the necessity of relying entirely on direct information from the publishers, soon made themselves evident, and every estimate proved inadequate to cover the unexpected labor involved in the mere process of collecting and verifying. Indeed the avowal must be made that, had it been possible to gauge approximately the dimensions that the compilation was to assume and the difficulties that were to beset it, the work would not have been begun. In its present limitations the undertaking was growing so much beyond the strength and resources of its originator, that he was finally forced to seek the coöperation of another publisher, who had faith enough in the soundness of the enterprise to lend his aid.

This plain statement of hard facts is made necessary, partly in explanation of unavoidable bibliographical shortcomings of the work, partly in extenuation of the tax imposed on the patience and generosity of those to whose early encouragement and substantial coöperation, by advance subscription, the work owes its beginning.

The principal features of the work have been adopted with the approval of competent bibliographers; the details, fully explained in the introduction, have been the results of careful consideration, chiefly in consultation with Mr. L. E. Jones, to whose capable management and careful execution, and Mr. R. R. Bowker, to whose active interest and untiring efforts, personally and editorially, the work is as much indebted for its existence as to those who have supported it pecuniarily.

F. LEYPOLDT.

NEW YORK, March, 1880.

INTRODUCTION.

Upon the final determination of the plan of the Catalogue the compilation of this volume was begun early in 1876. The difficulty met at the outset was the difficulty which has followed the work throughout: the absence of any preliminary basis, of any official record of titles, of even an approximately complete list of publishers. Thus the material had to be collected *de novo*. Lists of presumable publishers were made from every discoverable source, and circulars and letters addressed to them to obtain (in case they proved book publishers) *data* of their publications. The greater part of these met with no response, thus rendering a second, a third, often a fourth (registered) letter necessary, to be followed by an application to some neighboring bookseller for the needed information, or, as a last resource, by search among the archives of the Copyright Office at Washington. Appeals to the trade were frequently made through the columns of "The Publishers' Weekly;" and in the "Publishers' Trade List Annual," for 1876, the entire list of publishers as it then stood was printed, and corrections and additions solicited. Such information as was not obtained directly from the publisher, but from some other dealer, from advertisements, from the records of this office, or from Washington, was inserted with the sign (?) added, to show that it was given on other authority than that of the publisher. Perhaps it should not be a cause for surprise that the subscription houses showed the least willingness to have their books recorded, some vigorously declining to afford the slightest assistance towards obtaining the requisite *data*. All of this took time. Publication of the Catalogue was retarded not less than a year by the correspondence required to obtain publishers' lists, and by the delay in their receipt. Some lists have been received even since this volume was printed, and hence have had to be inserted in the *Errata and Addenda*.[1] A second difficulty, scarcely less serious than the former, and the cause of almost as great a delay, was the incomplete and inaccurate condition in which many lists were sent. Frequently they had to be returned with a statement of their uselessness, and a request for something a little less unsatisfactory. More frequently they could only be used as a basis for a prolonged correspondence with the publisher, or a continued research in the authorities at command, or in the Copyright Office at Washington. Scarcely any but required some supplementing, though there were a few houses who took sufficient care and pains in especially preparing the material for the purpose to render further application unnecessary, excepting on points which neither compilers nor publishers could anticipate. The verification of all titles thus received was manifestly impossible. The record of the publisher had to be accepted as correct, unless on its face it suggested incompleteness or inaccuracy, in which case it was investigated, though not always with satisfactory results. The effect of this has been not only many errors and omissions, but a lack of consistency in the relative fulness of titles, in the method of entering names of authors, and in the descriptive details added to the title proper, — and this especially as to sizes and bindings. The responsibility for this must rest chiefly with the publishers, on whose records the Catalogue is primarily based. All reasonable precautions have been taken in the transcription and printing of titles, so that it is felt that the number of such editorial errors does not greatly exceed the minimum unavoidable in a work of this character and magnitude.

The Catalogue aims to include all books (with certain exceptions) published in the United States which were in print, and for sale to the general public, July 1, 1876. The exceptions were local directories, periodicals, sheet music, books chiefly blank, unbound maps, tracts, and other low-priced pamphlets, the reasons for the exclusion of which are obvious. It embraces reprints, such importations also as are kept in stock, publications of learned societies (when for sale), the works of general importance issued by the various departments of the national government (without price), and the full law reports of the courts of the different States (all of which are generally for sale, though some have no fixed price). To secure uniformity it was evidently necessary to set a date after which the titles of new books or changes in prices or publishers could not be recorded, and this date it was found could not be made later than July, 1876, without still further delaying the publication. The interval which has elapsed since then has, of course, seen many new books and new editions issued, some works go out of print, others change prices or owners. This is unavoidable with any large catalogue. The number of such changes compared with the total number of entries in the Catalogue (about 70,000, representing the publications of over 900 houses) is, however, small, and the clue furnished of former price and publisher will direct the inquirer, so that he need have but little difficulty in ascertaining the present *status* of any desired work. This

---

[1] It should be noted here that a number of houses who replied to the circulars and letters sent them that they were not publishers were afterwards discovered to have issued one or more books each.

difficulty is still further lessened by the notes of firm changes in the list of publishers revised to date, and by the changes of price, etc., recorded in the Appendix.

In the Appendix will also be found the new books and new editions issued since July, 1876, of the leading houses, thus largely remedying the evil of the delay. It is to be regretted that all houses of prominence, whose books are included in the body of the Catalogue, could not enter into the arrangement by means of which the Catalogue, as regards the more important books, is virtually brought down to date.

Strict adherence to bibliographical rule has not been possible where not a score of titles have been taken from the books themselves; but it is believed the approximate accuracy amply suffices for a work whose first purpose is to serve as a *trade tool*, a finding-list to enable its user to learn where and at what price a given book can be obtained. For this purpose simplicity of method and clearness of style, with a reasonable fulness of title and of description, were recognized as the chief *desiderata*. The chief labor of the compilation was the endeavor to remedy what still remain the most serious deficiencies of the Catalogue: the frequent lack of dates of publication, the imperfect titles of some important historical and scientific works, the absence of contents to the collected writings of many authors, and the anonymous entry of books, of which publishers failed to supply names of authors. The publication of the volume in parts has fortunately led to the discovery of many errors which have accordingly been noted in the accompanying list of *Errata*. In the subject volume additional dates of publication and contents of collections of important works will be inserted as far as practicable without delaying the work.

The mode of entry is generally in conformity with the custom of this country, following largely the rules of the American Library Association. The chief exception is in regard to the Bible. While, in accordance with library usage, the separate parts are placed with the complete work, under the heading "Bible," commentaries, whether with or without text, are entered under the names of their editors, unless the notes are clearly subsidiary and the text of main importance. The reason for this deviation is that such editions are almost invariably known and quoted by the names of the commentators, and hence would first be looked for under their names, where, moreover, they could be more readily found than in the confusingly large collection which would result if all were gathered together. Since in the subject volume all works relating to the Bible will be grouped together, a repetition is avoided by the arrangement here adopted. [See also Note, p. 7.] A further exception to the library rule is in entering under the name of a society only its transactions, proceedings, journals, reports, etc., of which the society may be regarded as the author, and in placing the writings of individual members (although published by the society) under their names. As it was not desirable to repeat these under both headings, this method was thought to be the more useful of the two. Similarly in regard to such series and collections (*e. g.*, Harper's library of select novels, French's standard and minor drama) as were too large to be enumerated twice, the series entry was made without contents and the specifications given in the author entries. In all cases, however, where the collection was not too extensive, or where there was a sufficiently marked connection between included works, full record was made under each heading. For finding purposes, the author and title entries were indispensable, the series one was not. The chief remaining deviation is in not designating the compilers of music collections, school readers and speakers, as editors (*ed.*), but in entering them, as they essentially are, as authors, — the distinction being most immaterial and one often difficult to make. In other respects the American custom has generally been followed. Entries under titles have not been limited to strictly popular works (as novels, juveniles, poems, plays), but include all which do not clearly indicate the subject, or which (even when the subject is expressed) have distinguishing titles. It has been thought better, for facilitating reference, to be liberal rather than sparing in their use.

In submitting the completed volume to subscribers, it is hoped that the patience which has awaited the work during its compilation and publication may be extended over the shorter period required for the preparation of the subject volume. That volume, it is thought, can be safely promised within a year. For the varied assistance received from the trade and librarians during the progress of their work the compilers would express their grateful acknowledgment. But for the practical encouragement of booksellers and publishers the work would not have been undertaken; and it has only been sustained by the continuance of that cordial support. Not less do they appreciate the prompt courtesy with which their inquiries to librarians have been met, and the readiness with which so many library catalogues have been placed at their service. They would especially mention, in recognition of their value, the publications of Mr. Spofford (Library of Congress), Prof. Winsor (Boston Public Library, now of Harvard University), and Mr. Cutter (Boston Athenæum), to whom they are also under personal obligations for assistance and advice. They also avail themselves of this opportunity of publicly recognizing the zeal and interest displayed by Miss Jennie Walker, the chief assistant, who has been engaged upon the work throughout, as well as their indebtedness to the others who have been connected with the work.

LYNDS E. JONES.

NEW YORK, March, 1880.

NOTE ON BIBLE.

Bible manufacture is carried to such an extent within the United States, and the various styles in which the ordinary versions are published differ so slightly except as regards binding, typography, paper, etc. (*i.e.*, in what relates to the manufacture solely), that an enumeration of their varieties in the body of the Catalogue would present a result too confusing to be of any practical use, while seriously retarding reference to those editions that have distinctive literary features of their own. The entries under the heading Bible, in the Catalogue, have, therefore, been restricted to texts differing from the ordinary versions, or possessing individual characteristics; and a brief summary is presented here of the lines issued by houses making their manufacture a specialty, and which are not entered in the Catalogue.

The *Am. Baptist Pub. Soc.* (Phila.) has a Sunday-school edition of the Bible (12°, 40c.) and of the New Testament (32°, pap., 10c.), and also the Testament and Psalms together (8°, $1.25; $1.50).

The *Am. Bible Soc.* (N.Y.) furnishes all of its publications at cost. Those in English include over one hundred styles of the complete Bible (ranging from imp. 4°, "great primer," mor., $30, to 32°, "diamond," cl., 30c.), some fifty of the New Testament (from 4 v., roy. 8°, "great primer," $5, to 64°, "diamond," roan, 15c.), twenty-five of the New Testament and Psalms bound together (8°, $4.50, to 64°, 20c.), and a number of the books separately (from $1.25 to 4c.) Its cheapest Bible is an "agate," 24°, 25c., and its cheapest New Testament a "pearl," 32°, at 5c. Its foreign editions cover most of the living languages (including three African and ten Indian dialects), besides the Latin, Greek and Hebrew. In most of these are printed both the complete Bible and the New Testament separately, a few having only the Testament or the Testament and Psalms together, and some only the Bible. A number have also an edition containing both the vernacular and English texts in parallel columns. Single books (generally the Gospels and Psalms) appear in the Spanish, Micronesian, African, Indian and various other languages. The prices of the Bibles vary from 50c. to $9, averaging about $2.50; of the Testaments from 12c. to $2, averaging about 50c.; and of the other parts from 8c. to 40c. It also publishes the Bible for the blind in 8 v. ($20) and in 16 v. ($28), the Testament in 2 v. ($5) and in 4 v. ($7), and the Psalms ($1.50) and Gospel of John ($2) each in 1 v.

The *Am. Bible Union* (N.Y.), in addition to the Bibles on sale, has the Testament and Psalms together (8°) at from $2.50 to $7, and revised texts of Genesis, Job, Psalms, Proverbs, Ruth, New Testament, and each of the Gospels and Epistles, some of which are accompanied by the old version and by notes. They range in price from $6.50 (Test., 8°, mor.) to 25c. (Ruth, 8°, pap.), averaging about $2.50.

The *Am. Family Bible Pub. Co.* (Cincinnati), in addition to that entered in the Catalogue, issues a family Bible (4°), at from $5 to $24, containing tables, histories, indexes, etc., and also Luther's German version, with dictionary, etc., at from $6 to $22.

The *Am. Tract Soc.* (N.Y.), in addition to the Bibles and Testaments entered in the Catalogue, publishes the Psalms in 48° at 25c. and 30c.

W. T. Amies (Phila.) has an illustrated Bible for the young, with histories of the books, biographies of the Apostles, Gospel harmony, etc. (4°, $5–$7.50); a popular family Bible, illustrated, and containing the Apocrypha, a concordance, metrical Psalms, Bible dictionary, life of Christ, etc. (4°, $8–$12); Brown's Self-interpreting family Bible, with notes, reflections, references and readings (steel engravings, 4°, $25–$40); and a Catholic family Bible (Douay and Rheims version), with annotations, index, notes, etc., revised by J. G. Shea, and with illuminations, illustrations and places for photographs (4°, $14–$17).

John Baer's Sons (Lancaster, Pa.) has Luther's German version of the New Testament, with parallel references, etc., in 12°, at $1.50.

The *Bible Assoc. of Friends in America* (Phila.) issues a reference Bible, containing a concordance, index, etc., in five different styles (8°), at from $1.75 to $4.50; a medium Bible, without concordance, etc. (8°), at $1; a school Bible in four styles (18°), at from 50c. to $2; the New Testament, in seven styles (18° and 12°), at from 15c. to 50c.; and the Testament and Psalms together in two styles (18° and 12°), at 20c. and 40c.

Ira Bradley & Co. (Boston), besides the London editions of Eyre and Spottiswoode imported by them, have various styles of quarto Bibles of their own, usually with illustrations, references, concordances, tables, etc. ($2–$13). The London editions range from $1 (24°, "minion") to $40 (imp. 4°, "great primer," mor.), and are also to be had in sheets at from $2.75 to $20.

Bridgman & Childs (Northampton, Mass.) publish a "pearl" edition of the New Testament in 48° at 75c.

The *Claremont Manufacturing Co.* (Claremont, N.H.) issues the New Testament in 12° at 25c., and in 32° ("pearl" ed.) at 15c. and ("polyglot" ed.) at 40c.

Clark & Maynard (N.Y.) have a school edition of the New Testament in 18° at 38c.

Collins & Bro. (N.Y.), in addition to the one entered in the Catalogue, publish a small octavo Testament at $1.

Eugene Cummiskey (Phila.) has the Catholic Testament in 12° at $1 and $4.

The *Evangelical Assoc.* (Cleveland, Ohio), in addition to the German Bible entered in the Catalogue, issues a German New Testament in 24° at 30c. and 35c.

A. J. Holman & Co.'s (Phila.) list includes six editions of different size type of family, pulpit and reference Bibles, large and small pica, antique type, English and crown reference, tetx or pulpit, without reference. Most of them (excepting those for pulpit use) are illustrated and include family records, concordances and Psalms. A number have also Bible dictionaries, histories, etc. ($1.75 to $35), and Luther's German Bible, with references and readings ($3.50 to $7). The New Testament, 8°, at 60c. to $1.10; Smith's Bible dictionary, 8°, illustrated, at $1.35 to $1.75.

H. J. Johnson (N.Y.), in addition to the (Protestant) Bible entered in the Catalogue, has the Douay and Rheims Catholic version with annotations, references and index, in 4° at from $23 to $26.

P. J. Kenedy (N.Y.) publishes the Catholic Bible in imperial and royal 8° at from $2.50 to $10.50.

Ignatius Kohler (Phila.), in addition to the Bibles entered in the Catalogue, has the New Testament in German (8°) at 75c. and $1.

J. B. Lippincott & Co. (Phila.), in addition to those entered in the Catalogue, include in their list three editions of Bagster's Comprehensive Bible (student's miniature 4°, med. 4° and roy. 4°) at from $5.50 to $30, besides a variety of imported Oxford and Cambridge pulpit and family Bibles ($2.50–$60) and a number in smaller type and size (33c.–$3), with the Testament, in various styles, at from 30c. to $3.75.

Louis Lloyd & Co. (Chicago) and the *St. Louis Bible Pub. Co.* (St. Louis) publish (by subscription) three varieties of family Bibles, containing biblical histories, biographical sketches, dictionaries, etc., edited by Rev. Alfred Nevin, Prof. A. L. Rawson, T. H. Horne and others (4°, $4–$20); and also Luther's German version, with concordance, indexes, tables, etc. (4°, $7–$20).

Mayfield, Rogers & Co. (Nashville, Tenn.) have the Testament separately in 32° at 15c. and in 12° at 60c., and the Testament and Psalms together in 8° at $1.50.

The *Methodist Book Concern* (N.Y.), in addition to the Bibles and Testaments entered in the Catalogue, issues the Testament and Psalms together in 8° at $1.75.

Thos. Nelson & Sons (N.Y.) publish a fac-simile series of Bagster's polyglot Bibles, comprising the "miniature" edition (16°, $5), the "medium" edition (f'cap 8°, $6.50; with Cruden's Concordance, $7.50) and the "large print" edition (8°, $7.50; with Cruden's Concordance, $8). These are all bound in flexible morocco and contain references, tables, indexes, etc.

P. O'Shea (N.Y.), in addition to those entered in the Catalogue, has the Catholic Bible in f°, imp. 4° and 12° ($3.50–$50) and a pocket Testament in 24°, at from 40c. to $2.25.

Moses Polock (Phila.) publishes the Psalms in 48° at 25c.

John E. Potter & Co. (Phila.), in addition to these entered in the Catalogue, issue reference Bibles with notes in 8° (3.50–$10) and 16° ($2–$5), a pictorial family Bible with concordance, tables, etc. (4°, $10–$20), a standard Bible (18°, $1.50–$3.50) and a pocket Bible (32°, $1.25–$3); and also a similar series of Testaments priced from 30c. to $3.50. These usually have the Psalms in metre, paraphrases, etc. The 16°, 18° and 32° Bibles have each an illustrated dictionary and teacher's aids.

The *Presbyterian Bd. of Pub.* (Phila.) in addition to the Gospels and Epistles and Proverbs entered in the Catalogue, has the Psalms in 32° at 40c.

Geo. Routledge & Sons (N.Y.), in addition to those entered in the Catalogue, keep in stock most of the Bibles and Testaments published by Wm. Collins, Sons & Co., London. These include texts in a variety of sizes and styles (50c.–$10), reference and self-explanatory Bibles ($1–$18), pulpit and family Bibles, with maps, commentaries, etc. ($12–$50), a number of Testaments (25c.–$5) and the Testament and Psalms together ($1–$3).

D. & J. Sadlier & Co. (N.Y.), in addition to those entered in the Catalogue, have various styles of the Catholic Bible from folio ($18–$38) to post 4° ($4–$8), and the New Testament in 12° and 18° (63c.–$3).

Thompson, Brown & Co. (Boston), in addition to the polyglot Bible and Testament entered in the Catalogue, publish the Testament in 48° at 30c.

The *United Presbyterian Bd. of Pub.* (Pittsburgh, Pa.), in addition to those entered in the Catalogue, issues Bagster's reference Bible, with tables, metrical Psalms, Gospel harmony, etc. (16°, 80c.–$3); his small reference Bible (18°, 75c.–$2.75); the Testament with Psalms in 32°, 24° and 8° (25c.–$2.50); and the revised Psalms in 48°, 32°, 18° and 12° (10c.–$2.50).

John Wiley & Sons (N.Y.), in addition to those entered in the Catalogue, keep in stock full lines of the various combinations of Bagster's polyglot Bibles. Those in English include interleaved editions, editions with margins for MS. notes, the Comprehensive Bible (in different styles and sizes), etc., ranging in price from $4 to $35, and in numbers of vols. from 1 to 29; a translation of the Septuagint Old Testament (2 v., $7); various editions of the New Testament (hexapla, reprints of early editions, critical versions, etc.), at from $1.12 to $23; and the Apocrypha, Gospels, Epistles, Psalms (including metrical versions, psalters, etc.), Proverbs and other single books (by various translators), priced from 25c. to $3. The foreign versions consist usually of the complete Bible with separate editions of the New Testament and Psalms, and occasionally of the Gospels, Apocrypha and some single books. They comprise editions in most of the well-known languages, with a variety of combinations of two together (as French and German, Hebrew and Italian, etc.), besides the polyglots proper in from three to nine languages. The prices of the polyglots are from $1.75 (octoglot psalter) to $100 (polyglot Bible cabinet, 11 v.); of those in two languages usually $5 or $6.25; and of the single versions from $2 25 to $3. Many of these are interpaged, a number contain notes, and some are by special translators.

ARRANGEMENT.

Imprint Entries (chiefly by author). Works are arranged under names of *authors* when known, — under *initials* and *pseudonyms* when the real names have not been ascertained, — under names of *editors* of collections, — and under *governments* and names of *societies.* Anonymous works are entered under the *first word* of the title not an article; translations under the author (or, if anonymous, under the first word of the title when known) of the original work. The writings of a few popular authors, known chiefly by their assumed names, are, however, arranged under their pseudonyms (as George Eliot, Marion Harland), and anonymous biographies are entered under the family name of the subject. Law reports of a given court are placed under the country or State (as England. Common law reports. — New York. Supreme Court reports), with references from names of the reporters; reports of various courts and digests of reports are placed under names of compilers, with references from the countries. Laws are placed under the countries or States; treatises or commentaries under names of their authors. Transactions, journals, reports and collections of a society are entered under its name; works by individual members, although published by the society, are placed under names of authors. Church constitutions, hymn books, liturgies, prayer books, etc., when official, appear under the name of the church society, otherwise under the title; individual churches under the name of the place.

Initials and pseudonyms, used as headings, are regarded as real names; the last part being placed first (as A., S. F. — Holm, Saxe). Married ladies are entered under their *latest* name, excepting when that is but little known (as Brontë, Charlotte). English compound names are usually entered under the last part of the name; foreign ones under the first part. French and English names beginning with a prefix (excepting the French de or d') are entered under the prefix; in all other languages (and in case of the French de or d') they are entered under the part of the name following the prefix. The German diphthongs, ä, ö, ü, are so spelt (excepting when, like Goethe, the author himself used ae, oe, ue), and are arranged as a, o, u. In general, the vernacular usage of the language has been followed, excepting when there was special reason for deviation. In doubtful cases, cross-references indicate the proper heading.

Reference (Title) Entries. — Novels, juveniles, plays and other popular books having characteristic titles, are also entered in brief under the first word of the title not an article; fuller information than is here given will be found in the author-entry. Additional entries of such series and libraries as are commonly quoted in sets are made under the series-titles. References (to a partial extent) are also made from the significant (when not the first) words of popular titles.

A single dash indicates the repetition of the preceding heading (author or title); two dashes indicate the repetition of the preceding double heading (two joint authors, or two titles), or of the preceding main and subordinate headings (author and title; title and edition), etc. Under Bible, the first dash is in place of the word Bible, the second, third, etc., in place of the division (Old Test., Acts, etc.), language, version (Catholic, etc.), or edition. A dash (—) in a title separates different editions of the work. A shorter dash (-) between prices indicates various prices and bindings ranging between those given. In cross-references a (; —) separates alphabetical headwords; a (;) subordinate headings (or titles) under the same alphabetical heading. Brackets enclose words added to, or altered in, the title. Brackets after a proper name enclose the real name of a pseudonymous writer, the family name of a nobleman, the present name of an authoress; the pseudonym (in quotation marks) of a writer entered under real name, the title (in italics) of a nobleman entered under family name.

A name in parentheses, following the size, indicates (as Bagster, Bohn, Lond., Weale) the foreign imprint, or (as Westfield) the place of local publication. A parenthesized date preceding the number of the edition is the year of the first edition; the date following the size, that of the current edition. Dates of publication separated by a dash are the years of publication of the first and last volumes of the work or series. In law reports and digests the dates following the volume-numbers indicate the years covered by the reports. An asterisk before the price indicates that the edition is sold only by subscription. Absence of binding indicates cloth or want of mention in publisher's record. The sign (?) in place of initials or price indicates failure to obtain the information.

The abbreviations are usually self-explanatory, and follow as a rule the recommendations of the American Library Association. [*Library Journal*, March, 1878.] A colon after initial designates the most usual given name, as: — A: (August, Augustus); B: (Benjamin); C: (Carl, Charles); D: (David); E: (Edouard, Eduard, Edward); F: (Frederic, Friedrich); G: (Georg, George); H: (Heinrich, Henry); I: (Isaac); J: (John, Johann, Jean, masc.); K: (Karl); L: (Louis, Ludwig); M: (Marc, Mark); N: (Nicolas, Nicolaus, Nicole); O: (Otto); P: (Peter); R: (Richard); S: (Samuel); T: (Thomas); U: (Ulrich); W: (William, Willem, Wilhelm.)

The less evident abbreviations are adv.(anced), anc.(ient), ann.(ual), app.(endix), comb.(ining). comp.(iled), conc.(erning), const.(itution), disc.(overy), doc.(ument), doct.(rine), Hom.(œopathic), imp, (erial), incl.(uding), Leis.(ure), lib.(rary), lit.(eral), man.(ual), mod.(ern), obs.(ervations), o. p.(out of print), pop.(ular), por.(trait), pref.(ace), prep.(ared), quest.(ion), resp.(ecting), roxb.(urgh), roy.(al), ser.(ies), sel.(ected), S.(Sunday), sup.(er).

KEY TO ABBREVIATIONS

OF NAMES OF PUBLISHERS WHOSE BOOKS ARE INCLUDED IN THE AMERICAN CATALOGUE

WITH NOTES OF SUBSEQUENT CHANGES.

The sign (?) with the name of a publisher indicates that the information concerning his publications could not be obtained from the publisher himself, and is given on other authority. When appearing in the record of any particular book in the body of the Catalogue, though omitted in this Key, it signifies that the data of *that* book were not sent by the publisher, but were obtained elsewhere.

Acad. of Nat. Sci. Academy of Natural Sciences, cor. 19th and Race Sts., Phila.

Academy of Natural Sciences. See *Dav. Acad. Nat. Sci.*

Academy of Sci. of St. Louis. See *St. L.*

Adair. Adair, D. L., Hawesville, Ky.

Adams, Geo. H., & Son. See *Asher.*

Adams & Bishop. See *Williams, H. T.*

Adams, B. & L. Adams, Blackmer & Lyon Pub. Co., 147 and 149 5th Ave., Chicago.

Adams, V. & Co. Adams, Victor & Co., 98 William St., New York.

Advocate Pub. House. See *S. W. Bk. & Pub.*

Agar. Agar, Alex., 110 and 112 William St., New York.

Ala. Med. Medical Assoc. of State of Alabama, B. H. Riggs, Sec., Selma, Ala.

Albany.(?) Albany Institute, Albany, N. Y.

Allegan Co. Democrat Assoc. See *N. W. Bible.*

Allen. Allen, Lane & Scott, 229–231 South 5th St., Phila.

Allen, H. S. Allen, Henry S., 13 Astor Pl., New York.

Allison. Allison, Wm. L., 128 Nassau St., New York.

Allyn. Allyn, John, 30 Franklin St., Boston.

Alvord.(?) Alvord, C. A., New York.

Am. Acad. of A. and S. American Acad. of Arts and Sciences, Austin Holden, Sub-Lib'n, Boston.

Am. Acad. Dent. Sci. American Acad. of Dental Science, G. T. Moffatt, Sec., Boston.

Am. Antiq. American Antiquarian Soc., Worcester, Mass.

Am. Assoc. Adv. Sci. American Assoc. for the Advancement of Science, F. W. Putnam, Perm. Sec., Salem, Mass.

Am. Bapt. American Baptist Pub. Soc., 1420 Chestnut St., Phila.

Am. Berk. American Berkshire Assoc., Springfield, Ill.

Am. Bib. Soc. American Bible Soc., 4 Bible House, New York.

Am. Bib. Un. American Bible Union, 32 Great Jones St., New York.

Am. Eth. Soc. American Ethnological Soc., Henry T. Drowne, Pres't, 52 Wall St., N. Y.

Am. Fam. American Family Bible Pub. Co., 177 W. 4th St., Cincinnati.

Am. Indust. American Industrial Pub. Co., 381 and 383 Pearl St., New York.

Am. Inst. Arch. American Institute of Architects, C. F. McKim, Sec., 128 Broadway, N. Y.

Am. Inst. M. E. American Inst. of Mining Engineers, T. M. Drown, Sec., Lafayette College, Easton, Pa.

Am. Iron. American Iron and Steel Assoc., 265 S. 4th St., Phila.

Am. Jew. American Jewish Pub. Soc., Sol. Weil, Agent, 248 W. 36th St., New York.

American Lloyds. See *Hartshorne.*

Am. Med. American Medical Assoc., W. B. Atkinson, Perm. Sec., 1400 Pine St., Phila.

Am. News. American News Co., 39 and 41 Chambers St., New York.

Am. Orient. American Oriental Soc., Addison Van Name, New Haven, Conn.

Am. Pharm. American Pharmaceutical Assoc., Jno. M. Maisch, Perm. Sec., 145 N. 10th St., Phila.

Am. Philol. American Philological Assoc., Prof. Charles R. Lanman, Sec., Johns Hopkins Univ., Baltimore.

Am. Philos. Soc. American Philosophical Soc., T. P. Lesley, Lib'n, 104 S. 5th St., Phila.

Am. Print.(?) American Printing Co., Waterbury, Conn.

Am. Pub. American Pub. Co., 284 Asylum St., Hartford, Conn.

Am. Railroad.(?) American Railroad Co., New York.

American Social Science Assoc.
Embraced in list of A. Williams & Co.

Am. Soc. of C. E. American Soc. of Civil Engineers, Jno. Bogart, Sec., 104 E. 20th St., N. Y.

Am. S.S. American Sunday-School Union, 1122 Chestnut St., Phila.

Am. Swed. American Swedenborg Print. & Pub. Co., 20 Cooper Union, New York.

Am. Tr.	American Tract Soc., 150 Nassau St., New York. See also Boston Am. Tr. Soc.
Am. Unit.	American Unitarian Assoc., 7 Tremont Pl., Boston.
Ames.	Ames, A. D., Clyde, Ohio.
Anderson.	Anderson & Lawson, 87 and 89 Franklin St., Chicago. *Now* John Anderson & Co.
Andrè.(?)	Andrè, G., & Co., Phila. Books now included in list of Ditson.
Andrews.	Andrews, A. H., & Co., 211 and 213 Wabash Ave., Chicago.
Andrews, I. N.	Andrews, Isaac N., Nashua, N. H.
Andrus.	Andrus, McChain & Co., Ithaca, N. Y. *Now* Andrus & Church.
Anglim.(?)	Anglim, James, 1424 F St., Washington. *Now* E. V. Anglim, 349 Park Ave., Wash.
Appleton.	Appleton, D., & Co., 1, 3 and 5 Bond St., New York.
Argus.	Argus (The) Co., Albany, N. Y.
	Armstrong, A. C., & Son. See *Mason.*
Arnold.	Arnold, J. M., & Co., 189 Woodward Ave., Detroit, Mich. *Now* Arnold & Willyoung.
Arthur.	Arthur, T. S., & Son, 227 S. 6th St., Phila.
Asher.	Asher & Adams, 59 Beekman St., N. Y. *Now* Geo. H. Adams & Son.
Ashmead.(?)	Ashmead, Duffield, Phila.
Atlantic.	Atlantic Pub. and Engr. Co., 9 Murray St., New York.
Atwood.	Atwood & Culver, Madison, Wis.
Austin.	Austin, Jackson & Co., Dansville, Livingston Co., N. Y.
Authors.	Authors' Pub. Co., 27 Bond St., New York.
Babbitt.	Babbitt & Co., 5 Clinton Pl., New York.
Bachelder.(?)	Bachelder, J. B., Boston.
Baer.	Baer's (John) Sons, Lancaster, Pa.
Bailey.	Bailey & Noyes, 68 Exchange St., Portland, Me.
Baird.	Baird, Henry C., & Co., 810 Walnut St., Phila.
	Baker, Davis & Co. See *Davis, C. H.*
Baker, P. & Co.	Baker, Pratt & Co., 142 and 144 Grand St., New York.
Baker, V. & Co.	Baker, Voorhis & Co., 66 Nassau St., New York.
	Ball, R. H. See *Sample.*
	Baltzer, A. See *Germ. Ev. Syn. of West.*
Bancroft.	Bancroft, A. L., & Co., 721 Market St., San Francisco.
	Bancroft, J. A., & Co. See *Keystone.*
	Banker's Magazine Office. See *Homans.*
Banks.	Banks & Bros., 144 Nassau St., New York.
Barclay.	Barclay & Co., 21 N. 7th St., Phila.
Bardeen.	Bardeen, C. W., Syracuse, N. Y. *Now* Davis, Bardeen & Co.
Barnard.	Barnard, Dr. Henry, 28 Main St., Hartford, Conn.
Barnes.	Barnes, A. S., & Co., 111 William St., New York.
Barnet.	Barnet, James, 160 Newberry Ave., Chicago.
Barrett & B.	Barrett & Brown, 109 Commerce St., Montgomery, Ala.
Barry.	Barry & Colesworthy, 66 Cornhill, Bost. *Now* D. C. Colesworthy.
Barthel.	Barthel, M. C. (Ag't Germ. Evang. Luth. Synod of Mo., Ohio and other States), cor. Miami St. and Indiana Ave., St. Louis.
Bartlett.	Bartlett, Levi, Warner, Merrimac Co., N. H.
Batcheller, C. J.	Batcheller, Chas. J., East Douglass, Worcester Co., Mass.
Beadle.	Beadle & Adams, 98 William St., New York.
Beal.	Beal, N. S. R., Macedon, N. Y. *Now* at Lima, Allen Co., Ohio.
Beal, R. A.	Beal, R. A., Ann Arbor, Mich.
Belknap.	Belknap, Thomas, Hartford, Conn.
Bell.	Bell, J. P., & Co., Lynchburg, Va.
Belmont.(?)	Belmont Pub. Co., Philadelphia.
	Bendel, Aug. ("Der Pilger.") See *Pilger.*
Benerman.	Bennerman & Wilson, 116 N. 7th St., Phila. *Now* Edward L. Wilson.
Benham.	Benham, H. L., 158 W. 4th St., Cincinnati.
Benjamin.	Benjamin, E. B., 10 Barclay St., N. Y.
Benner.	Benner, Samuel, Dundas, Vinton Co., O.
Bennett, D. M.	Bennett, D. M., 141 Eighth St., N. Y.
Bennett, P. & Co.	Bennett, Penniwell & Co., 323 Market St., Phila.
Benziger.	Benziger Bros., 311 B'way, New York.
Berendsohn.	Berendsohn Bros., 202 William St., New York. *Now* Rudolph Berendsohn, 11½ College Pl.
Berkey.	Berkey, Wm. A., Grand Rapids, Mich.
Berry.	Berry, Mrs. M. E., 3 Beacon St., Boston.
Besser.	Besser (Ernst) & Bro., 510 Main St., Buffalo, N. Y.
Betts.	Betts (James) & Co., Hartford, Conn.
	Bible Association of Friends in America, Jno. S. Stokes, Ag't, 116 N. 4th St., Phila.
Bicknell.	Bicknell, A. J., & Co., 27 Warren St., New York. *Now* Bicknell & Comstock.
Bidwell.	Bidwell, Geo. H., 33 Park Row, New York.
Bien.	Bien, Julius, 16 Park Pl., New York.
Biglow.	Biglow & Main, 76 E. 9th St., New York.
Bill, L.	Bill, Ledyard, Worcester, Mass.
Black.	Black, Austin ("Manufacturer and Builder"), 37 Park Row, New York.
Blackall.	Blackall, C. R., 61 Washington St., Chicago. *Now* at 9 Murray St., N. Y.
Bliss, F. C.	Bliss, F. C., & Co., 910 Broad St., Newark, N. J.
Bliss, J. W.	Bliss, John W., 81 Elm St., Hartford, Conn.
Bliss, T.	Bliss (Theodore) & Co., 507 North St., Phila.
Bloch.	Bloch & Co., 169 Elm St., Cincinnati.
	Blun, E. N. See *Phillips, H. G.*
Boericke.	Boericke & Tafel, 145 Grand St., New York.
Bolling.	Bolling, R. R., & Co., 181 Fourth St., Louisville, Ky.
	Booth, Walter L. See *Leonard.*
Bost. Am. Tr.	Boston Amer. Tract Soc. *Now* care of Am. Tr. Soc., N. Y.
Bost. Soc. Nat. Hist.	Boston Soc. of Natural History, Boston.

Bouton.	Bouton, J. W., 706 Broadway, New York.
Bradburn.(?)	Bradburn, J., N. Y.
Bradley, I.	Bradley (Ira) & Co., 162 Washington St., Boston.
Bradley, M.	Bradley (Milton) & Co., Springfield, Mass.
Bradley & G.(?)	Bradley, Garretson & Co., 66 N. 4th St., Phila. *Now* Wm. Garretson & Co.
Brainard.	Brainard's (S.) Sons, 341 Euclid Ave., Cleveland, Ohio.
Brentano.	Brentano, August, Jr., 39 Union Sq., New York. *Now* Brentano's Literary Emporium.
	Brewer & Tileston. See *Ware.*
Bridgman.	Bridgman & Childs, Northampton, Mass.
Bright.	Bright, Louis J., & Co., 129 and 131 Gravier St., New Orleans.
Brinton.	Brinton, D. G., 115 S. 7th St., Phila.
Brobst.	Brobst, S. K., & Co., Allentown, Pa. *Now* Brobst, Diehl & Co.
Brockmann.	Brockmann, Rev. John H., Watertown, Wis.
Bromhall.(?)	Bromhall, A., Muscatine, Iowa.
Brown, C. R.(?)	Brown, C. R., Kalamazoo, Mich.
Brown, H.D. (?)	Brown, H. D., & Co., 144 Tremont St., Boston.
Brown, E. & Co.	Brown (T. J.), Eager & Co., Toledo, Ohio.
Brown & F.	Brown & Faunce, 115 Summit St., Toledo, Ohio. *Now* Geo. B. Brown.
Brown & G.	Brown & Gross, 77 and 79 Asylum St., Hartford, Conn.
Brumbaugh.	Brumbaugh, H. B., & Bro., Box 50, Huntingdon, Pa. *Now* Quinter & Brumbaugh Bros.
Brumder.	Brumder, George, 306 West Water St., Milwaukee, Wis.
Bryan, C. W.(?)	Bryan (The C. W.) Co., Springfield, Mass.
Bryant.	Bryant, J. C., 179 Washington St., Buffalo, N. Y.
Buckeye.	Buckeye Pub. Co., Marysville, Ohio.
Buckman.(?)	Buckman, Benj. E., New York.
Buffalo Soc. Nat. Sci.	Buffalo Soc. of Natural Sciences, Buffalo, N. Y.
Burbank.	Burbank, Jas. P., Salem, Mass.
Burgheim.	Burgheim, M. & R., 484 Vine St., Cincinnati.
Burke.	Burke, J. W., & Co., Macon, Ga.
Burley.	Burley, S. W., 152 S. 4th St., Phila.
Burnham.	Burnham, T. O. H. P., 68 School St., Boston.
Burns.	Burns & Co., 24 Clinton Pl., New York.
Burnton.	Burnton, Jas. S., 149 Grand St., New York.
Burr.	Burr (J. B.) Pub. Co., Hartford, Conn.
Bus. Wom. Un.	Business Women's Union, 80 Willoughby St., Brooklyn, N. Y.
Butler.	Butler, J. H., & Co., 723 Chestnut St., Phila.
Cal. Acad. Sci.	California Acad. of Sciences, C. Troyer, Lib'n, cor. California and Dupont Sts., San Francisco.
Cal. Med.	California State Medical Soc., G. G. Tyrrell, Perm. Sec., cor. Jay and 5th Sts., Sacramento.
Callaghan.	Callaghan & Co., 161 Clark St., Chicago.
Campbell & Co.	Campbell & Co., 78 Nassau St., New York. *Formerly* McDivitt, Campbell & Co.
Campbell, A. J.	Campbell, A. J., Cleveland, Ohio.
Campbell, Jas.	Campbell, James, 17 Franklin St., Boston. *Now* N. R. Campbell & Co.
Campbell, J., & Son.	Campbell, John, & Son, 740 Sansom St., Phila.
Campbell, R. A.	Campbell, Robert A., cor. Olive and 5th Streets, St. Louis.
Carle.(?)	Carle & Grener, 23 Un. Sq., New York.
Carleton.	Carleton, Geo. W., & Co., Madison Sq., New York.
Carmany.	Carmany, J. H., & Co., 409 Wash'n St., San Francisco.
Carroll, D. H.	Carroll, D. H. (Meth. Episc. Bk. Depos.), 168 W. Baltimore St., Baltimore.
Carroll, R. W.	Carroll, R. W., & Co., 233 W. 4th St., Cincinnati.
Carter.	Carter (Robert) & Bros., 530 B'way, New York.
Carter, H. H.	Carter, H. H., 3 Beacon St., Boston. *Formerly* Carter & Pettee.
Case.	Case, Lockwood & Brainard Co., Hartford, Conn.
Case, O. D.	Case, O. D., & Co., Hartford.
Cassell.	Cassell, Petter & Galpin, 596 Broadway, New York. *Now* Cassell, Petter, Galpin & Co.
	Cassino, S. E. See *Nat. Agcy.*
Cath. Pub.	Catholic Pub. Soc. Co., 9 Barclay St., New York.
Cen. Bk.	Central Book Concern, Oskaloosa, Iowa.
Cen. Pub.	Central Pub. Co., 628 Olive Street, St. Louis.
Challen.	Challen, Howard, 237 S. 3d St., Phila.
Champlin.	Champlin, H. L., Chelsea Station, Bost.
	Chapman, J. J. See *Solomons.*
Chase.	Chase & Hall, 180 Elm St., Cincinnati. *Now* J. B. Hall & Co.
Cheney.	Cheney & Clapp, Brattleborough, Vt.
Chew.	Chew, Sinnickson, cor. Front and Market Sts., Camden, N. J.
Chic. Leg. News.(?)	Chicago Legal News Co., Chicago.
Chr. Sci.	Christian Scientist Pub. Co., Boston.
Christern.	Christern, F. W., 180 Fifth Ave., N. Y.
Church.	Church, John, & Co., 66 W. 4th St., Cincinnati.
Church, W. C. & F. P.	Church, W. C. & F. P., 240 Broadway, New York.
Cin. Meth. Bk. Conc.	Cincinnati Meth. Bk. Conc. (Hitchcock & Walden), 190 W. 4th St., Cin.
Clapp, D.	Clapp (David) & Son, 564 Washington St., Boston.
Clapp, E.	Clapp, Ebenezer, 7 School St., Boston.
Clapp, O.	Clapp (Otis) & Son, 3 Albion St., Boston.
Claremont.	Claremont M'f'g Co., Claremont, N. H.
Clark, J. A.	Clark, John A., Wadsworth, Ohio.
Clark & M.	Clark & Maynard, 5 Barclay St., N. Y.
Clarke.	Clarke (Robert) & Co., 65 W. 4th St., Cincinnati.
Clarke, J. B.	Clarke, John B., Manchester, N. H.
Clarke, S. A.	Clarke, S. A., & Co., 115 Wood St., Pittsburgh, Pa.
Clauder.	Clauder, Henry T., 88 Main St., Bethlehem, Pa.

Claxton. Claxton, Remsen & Haffelfinger, 624 Market St., Phila.

Clayton. Clayton, Chas. H., & Co., 157 and 159 Pearl St., New York.

Cleary. Cleary, Wm. P., 319 B'way, New York.

Clifford. Clifford & Co., 23 School St., Boston.

Coates. Coates, J. H., & Co., 822 Chestnut St., Philadelphia.
Books now included in list of Porter & Coates.

Cobb. Cobb, Andrews & Co., 315 and 317 Euclid Ave., Cleveland, Ohio.

Cockcroft. Cockcroft & Co., 146 Wooster St., N. Y.

Coddington. Coddington, Robert, 246 4th Ave., New York.

Colby. Colby & Rich, 9 Montgomery Pl., Bost.

Coleman. Coleman, H. R., 721 Market St., San Francisco.

Colesworthy, D. C. See *Barry*.

College of Physicians of Phila. See *Phila. Coll. Phy.*

Collin & S. Collin & Small, 59 Beekman St., New York.
Now J. B. Collin & Co.

Collins, R. H. Collins, Richard H., Louisville, Ky.

Collins & Bro. Collins & Bro., 414 B'way, New York.

Collins & McL. Collins & McLeester, 705 Jayne St., Phila.

Collins Print. Collins Printing House, J. W. Huff, Att'y and Sup't, 705 Jayne St., Phila.

Col. Bk. Columbian Book Co., Hartford, Conn.

Combs. Combs, W. S., St. Paul, Minn.

Combs, W. & Co. (?) Combs, Whitney & Co., Leavenworth, Kansas.

Cong. Pub. Congregational Pub. Soc., cor. Beacon and Somerset Sts., Boston.

Conn. Acad. of A. & S. Connecticut Acad. of Arts and Sciences, Addison Van Name, New Haven, Conn.

Conn. Med. Connecticut Medical Soc., C. W. Chamberlain, Sec., Hartford, Conn.

Conn. Pub. Connecticut Pub. Co., 91 Asylum St., Hartford, Conn.

Conway. Conway, J. D., 180 Chestnut St., Lawrence, Mass.

Cook. Cook, Son & Jenkins, 261 B'way, New York.

Cook, E. A. Cook, Ezra A., & Co., 7 to 13 Wabash Ave., Chicago.

Coolidge. Coolidge, Geo. A., 220 Devonshire St., Boston.

Cope. (?) Cope, Geo. F., Virginia City, Montana.

Cornick. Cornick & Cornick, Knoxville, Tenn.

Cowan. (?) Cowan & Co., 139 Eighth St., New York.

Cowperthwait. Cowperthwait & Co., 628 Chestnut St., Phila.

Cramer. Cramer, Aikens & Cramer ("Evening Wisconsin"), Milwaukee, Wis.

Crandall. Crandall, J. C., Friendship, Allegany Co., N. Y.
Now disposed of all but music books. Plates chiefly sold to authors.

Crittenden. (?) Crittenden, S. H., & Co., cor. 12th and Chestnut Sts., Phila.

Crocker. Crocker & Brewster, 51 Wash'n St., Boston.
Books now incl. in list of Houghton, O. & Co.

Crosby. Crosby, S. S., 421 Wash'n St., Boston.

Crowell. Crowell, Thos. Y., 744 B'way, New York.
Formerly Warren & Wyman.

Cumberland. (?) Cumberland Presbyterian Board of Pub., Nashville, Tenn.

Cummiskey. Cummiskey Eugene, 909 Arch St., Phila.

Cunningham. Cunningham, Peter F., & Son, 817 Arch St., Phila.

Currie. Currie, G. E., 153 B'way, New York.

Curtiss & C. Curtiss & Childs, Utica, N. Y.

Cushing, E. H. Cushing, E. H., 5 and 7 Franklin St., Houston, Texas.
Now deceased.

Cushing, T., & Co. Cushing, Thomas & Co., 163 and 165 Dearborn St., Chicago.

Cushings & B. Cushings & Bailey, 262 Baltimore St., Baltimore.

Daily Advertiser. (?) Daily Advertiser Office, Newark, N. J.

Dana. Dana, Wm. B., & Co., 79 William St., New York.

Dando. Dando, T. S., 307 Walnut St., Phila.

Darrow. Darrow, E., 67 E. Main St., Rochester, N. Y.

Daughaday. (?) Daughaday, J. W., & Co., 723 Chestnut St., Phila.

Dav. Acad. Nat. Sci. Davenport Acad. of Nat. Science, J. D. Putnam, Corr. Sec., Davenport, Iowa.

Davidson. (?) Davidson, G., Albany, N. Y.

Davis, A. J. Davis, A. J., & Co., 24 E. 4th St., New York.
Books now included in list of Colby & Rich.

Davis, C. H. Davis, Chas. H., & Co., 1114 Arch St., Phila.
Formerly Baker, Davis & Co., *now* T. Ellwood Zell, Davis & Co.

Davis, R. S. (B.) Davis, Robert S., & Co., 36 Bromfield St., Boston.

Davis, R. S. (P.) Davis, Robert S., & Co., cor. 5th Ave. and Wood St., Pittsburgh, Pa.
Now Jas. M. Wilkinson.

Davis, T. H. Davis, T. H., & Co., Phila.

Davis, Bardeen & Co. See *Bardeen*.

Dawley. (?) Dawley, T. R., 31 Beekman St., New York.

Day. Day, Egbert & Fidlar, Davenport, Iowa.
Now Egbert, Fidlar & Chambers.

Denham. Denham, Alex., 706 Broadway, New York.

Dennet. Dennet, W. H., 260 Wash'n St., Boston.

Dennis. Dennis, Martin R., & Co., 739 Broad St., Newark, N. J.

Denton. Denton, Wm., Wellesley, Mass.

De Selding. De Selding, Edw. F., 400 Fulton St., Brooklyn.
Formerly De Selding & Bolles.

Des Forges. Des Forges, J. P., 3 St. Paul St., Balt.

Desilver. Desilver, Chas., & Sons, 1701 Chestnut St., Phila.

Dette. Dette, Fred., 710 Franklin Ave., St. Louis.

Dewey. Dewey, D. M., 8 Arcade Hall, Rochester, N. Y.

De Witt. De Witt, Robert M., 33 Rose St., N. Y.

Dick & F. Dick & Fitzgerald, 18 Ann St., N. Y.

Dillingham. Dillingham, Chas. T., 678 B'way, N. Y.
Formerly Lee, Shepard & Dillingham.

Diossy, Geo. S. See *Ward*.

Disturnell. Disturnell, J., 137 8th St., New York.
Now deceased.

Ditson. Ditson (Oliver) & Co., 451 Washington St., Boston.

Dockham. Dockham, C. A., 242 Wash'n St., Bost.

Dod, A. F.	Dod, A. F., & Co., 379½ Main St., Memphis, Tenn. *Now* deceased.
Dodd.	Dodd, Mead & Co., 751 Broadway, N. Y.
Doe.	Doe, Rev. W. P., Providence, R. I.
Doerflinger.	Doerflinger, Carl, Milwaukee, Wis.
Donnell. (?)	Donnell, J. C., & Co., Boston.
Donnelley.	Donnelley, Gassette & Loyd, Lakeside Bldg., Chicago.
Dooley.	Dooley, K. A., 182 River St., Troy, N. Y. *Formerly* P. J. Dooley.
Dorch. Antiq.	Dorchester Antiquarian and Hist. Soc., care E. Clapp, 7 School St., Boston.
Douglas.	Douglas, J. S., Milwaukee, Wis. *Now* deceased.
	Douglas & Co. See *Fiske & D.*
Dowling.	Dowling, L. H., 216 N. 8th St., St. Louis.
Draper.	Draper, Warren F., Andover, Mass.
Dreka.	Dreka, Louis, 1121 Chestnut St., Phila.
Dresser.	Dresser, McLellan & Co., Portland, Me.
Drew, C.	Drew, Columbus, Jacksonville, Fla.
Duffie.	Duffie, W. J., Columbia, S. C.
Dulany.	Dulany, Wm. J. C., & Co., 332 W. Baltimore St., Baltimore.
Durrie.	Durrie, Dan. S., Madison, Wis.
Durston.	Durston, T. W., & Co., Syracuse, N. Y.
Dustin.	Dustin, Gilman & Co., 350 Asylum St., Hartford, Conn. *Now* ceased publishing.
Dutton.	Dutton, E. P. & Co., 713 Broadway, New York.
Earl, B.	Earl (Benjamin) & Son, Fall River, Mass.
Earle.	Earle, James H., 20 Hawley St., Boston.
Eastman.	Eastman, Edson C., Concord, N. H.
Eaton.	Eaton, C. W., Wakefield, Mass.
	Egbert, Fidlar & Chambers. See *Day.*
Eldredge.	Eldredge & Bro., 17 N. 7th St., Phila.
Elliott. (?)	Elliott & Noyes, Boston.
Ellis.	Ellis, Geo. H., 101 Milk St., Boston.
Ellyson.	Ellyson, J. T., 112 Main St., Richmond. *Now* J. A. Yancey & Co.
Elmira.	Elmira Farmer's Club, Elmira, N. Y.
Emerson. (?)	Emerson, S., Chicago.
Enderis.	Enderis, H., 132 Lake St., Chicago.
Engberg.	Engberg, Holmberg & Lindell, 119 Chicago Ave., Chicago. *Now* Germ. Bk. & News Co., 128 and 130 Lake St.
English.	English, A. H., & Co., 98 4th Ave., Pittsburgh, Pa. *Now* H. I. Gourley.
Ennis.	Ennis Bros., 42 Dey St., New York.
Essex.	Essex Institute, Geo. M. Whipple, Sec., Salem, Mass.
Estes.	Estes & Lauriat, 301 Wash'n St., Boston.
Eureka.	Eureka Pub. Co., 717½ Olive Street, St. Louis.
Ev. Assoc.	Evangelical Assoc., Lauer and Yost, Ag'ts, 214–220 Woodland Avenue, Cleveland, Ohio.
	Evangelisch lutherische Synode von Iowa. See *Germ. Ev. Luth. Syn. of Iowa.*
Evans. (?)	Evans, T. W., Philadelphia.
Eyrich.	Eyrich, J. C., 130 Canal St., New Orleans.
Faxon.	Faxon, C. A., 228 Wash'n St., Boston.
Fergus.	Fergus Printing Co., 244 Illinois St., Chicago.
Ferry.	Ferry, J. Milton, 586 B'way, New York. *Now* ceased publishing.
Fillmore.	Fillmore Bros., 8 E. 4th St., Cincinnati.
Finch.	Finch & Apgar, 60 State St., Ithaca, N.Y.
Firelands.	Firelands Hist. Soc., Horatio Barr, Sec., Norwalk, Ohio.
Fisher.	Fisher, A. J., 24 Vesey St., New York.
Fisk, D. E.	Fisk, D. E., & Co., Springfield, Mass.
Fiske & D.	Fiske & Douglas, Ann Arbor, Mich. *Now* Douglas & Co.
Fitch.	Fitch, J. Patten, 284 Asylum St., Hartford, Conn.
Fleming.	Fleming, Howard, Philadelphia.
Flint.	Flint, Wm., 623 Sansom St., Phila.
	Foote, E. B. See *Murray.*
Ford.	Ford, J. B., & Co., 27 Park Pl., New York. *Now* Fords, Howard & Hulbert.
For. Dir. (?)	Foreign Directory Co., 2 Wall St., N. Y.
Forest.	Forest and Stream Pub. Co., 111 Fulton St., New York.
Fortescue.	Fortescue, W. S., & Co., 811 Arch St., Philadelphia.
Foster.	Foster, Jos. H., Portsmouth, N. H. *Now* Willis G. Myers.
Fox.	Fox, Patrick, 14 S. 5th St., St. Louis.
Fox, O. L. (?)	Fox, O. L., Chicago.
Francis. (?)	Francis, D. G., Astor Pl., New York.
Frank.	Frank, L. H., & Co., 32½ Bowery, N. Y. *Now* H. Sakolski, 53 Division St.
Franklin Inst.	Franklin Institute, E. Hildebrand, Lib'n, 15 S. 7th St., Phila.
	Franklin Pub. House. See *Hopkins.*
	Frederick, G. W. See *Luth. Bk. St.*
Free Rel.	Free Religious Assoc., 1 Tremont Pl., Boston.
Freeman.	Freeman, E. L., & Co., Central Falls, R.I.
Freewill.	Freewill Baptist Print. Establishment, Dover, N. H.
French.	French (Samuel) & Son, 38 E. 14th St., New York.
	Friends' Bible Assoc. of Am. *See* Bible Assoc. of Friends in Am.
Friends Bk. Assoc.	Friends' Book Assoc., 706 Arch St., Phila.
Friends Bk. St.	Friends' Book Store, Jacob Smedley, Ag't, 304 Arch St., Phila.
Friends Pub. H.	Friends' Pub. House, New Vienna, Clinton Co., Ohio.
Fuller.	Fuller, Horace B., 14 Bromfield St., Boston.
Ga. Hist.	Georgia Historical Soc., Wm. Harden, Lib'n, Savannah, Ga.
Ga. Med.	Medical Assoc. of Georgia, Jas. B. Baird, Sec., Atlanta, Ga.
Galbraith.	Galbraith, T., 106 W. 19th St., N. Y.
	Garretson, Wm., & Co. See *Bradley & G.*
Garrett.	Garrett, P., & Co., 708 Chestnut St., Phila.
Garrigues.	Garrigues Bros., 608 Arch St., Phila.
Gebbie.	Gebbie & Barrie, 615 Sansom St., Phila.
Gen. Assembly.	General Assembly of the Presb. Church, E. F. Hatfield, Stated Clerk, 23 Centre St., New York.
Geringer.	Geringer, Aug., 463 S. Canal St., Chicago.
German, E. S.	German, E. S., 28 South Second St., Harrisburg, Pa. *Now* E. S. German's Sons.

Germ. Bapt.	German Baptist Pub. Soc., 957 and 959 Payne Ave., Cleveland, Ohio.
	German Bk. & News Co. See *Engberg.*
Germ. Ev. Luth. Syn. of Iowa.	German Evangelical Luth. Synod of Iowa, F. Richter, Mendota, La Salle Co., Ill.
	German Evang. Luth. Synod of Mo., Ohio and other States. See *Barthel*
German Ev. Syn. of the West.	German Evang. Synod of the West, A. Baltzer, Ag't, St. Charles, Mo.
Gibbens.	Gibbens Bros., Parkersburg, West Va.
Gilbert.	Gilbert, W. J., 209 N. 4th St., St. Louis.
Gill, J. D.	Gill, James D., Springfield, Mass.
Gill, W.	Gill, Watson, 12 W. Railroad St., Syracuse, N. Y.
Gill, W. F.	Gill, Wm. F., & Co., 309 Washington St., Boston. *Now* ceased publishing.
Ginn.	Ginn Bros., 13 Tremont Pl., Boston. *Now* Ginn & Heath.
Gleason.	Gleason, Geo. W., 69 S. High St., Columbus, Ohio.
Goodenough.	Goodenough, Edward, 122 Nassau St., New York.
Goodman.	Goodman, J. S., 142 LaSalle St., Chicago.
Goodrich.	Goodrich, E. J., Oberlin, Ohio.
Goodspeed. (?)	Goodspeed, H. S., & Co., 173 Greenwich St., New York.
Goodyear.	Goodyear Rubber Curler Co., 697 Broadway, New York.
Gootee. (?)	Gootee, H. P., & Co., Phila.
Gordon.	Gordon, S. T., & Son, 13 E. 14th St., New York.
	Gorton, A., & Co. See *Scofield, F.*
Gospel.	Gospel Book and Tract Depository, 2 Hamilton Pl., Boston.
Gould.	Gould, Wm., & Sons, 68 State St., Albany, N. Y.
	Gourley, H. I. See *English.*
Graham.	Graham, Andrew J., 61 Bible House, New York.
Graves.	Graves, A. F., 23 Franklin St., Boston. *Now* Graves, Locke & Co.
Gray.	Gray, Baker & Co., 407 N. 4th St., St. Louis. *Now* Hugh R. Hildreth Printing Co.
Greenough.	Greenough & Co., 22 School St., Boston.
Griffiths.	Griffiths, John W., Box 5125, New York.
Griggs.	Griggs, S. C., & Co., 25 Washington St., Chicago.
Gross.	Gross, Wm. L., Springfield, Ill.
Haas. (?)	Haas & Klein, Buffalo, N. Y. *Formerly* Haas & Nauert.
Hadley.	Hadley Bros. & Co., 63 and 65 Washington St., Chicago. *Now* S. S. Hadley.
Hale.	Hale, E. J., & Son, 17 Murray St., New York.
Hall, A. J.	Hall, A. J., & Co., 1010 Locust Street, St. Louis.
	Hall, J. B., & Co. See *Chase.*
Hall, T. J.	Hall, T. J., 814 Broadway, New York. Books now included in list of Ditson.
Halsey. (?)	Halsey, C. S., Chicago.
Halsted.	Halsted, Oliver S., Lyons Farms, N. J. *Now* deceased.
Hamersley.	Hamersley & Co., Hartford, Conn. Most of their books now included in lists of Brown & Gross, and J. W. Bliss.

Hamilton.	Hamilton, Turner, 1407½ Chestnut St., Phila.
Hamilton, D. H.	Hamilton, D. H., Lewiston, Me.
Hammett, C. E.	Hammett, Chas. E., Jr., 124 Thames St., Newport, R. I.
Hammond.	Hammond, James, 1224 Chestnut St., Phila.
Haney.	Haney (Jesse) & Co., 119 Nassau St., New York.
	Hannibal Print Co. See *Winchell.*
	Hanson, J. W. See *N. W. Univ.*
Happy.	Happy Hours Co., O. A. Roorbach, 5 Beekman St., New York.
Harding.	Harding, Wm. W., 630 Chestnut St., Phila. Books now included in list of A. J. Holman.
Hardy.	Hardy (Edward) & Co., Hanover, N. H. *Formerly* J. B. Parker; *now* Storrs & Foster.
Harpel.	Harpel, O. H., Lockland, Ohio.
Harper.	Harper & Bros., 331 Pearl St., N. Y.
	Harrison, S., & Co. See *Hope.*
Hart.	Hart (Francis) & Co., 65 Murray St., New York.
Hartshorne.	Hartshorne, Richard T. (American Lloyds), 26 Burling Slip, N. Y. *Now* Meyers & Salter.
	Harvard Coll. Mus. of Comp. Zool. See *Mus. of Comp. Zool.*
Harv. Coll. Ob.	Harvard College Observatory, Edw. C. Pickering, Cambridge, Mass.
Hastings.	Hastings, H. L., Scriptural Tract Repository, 47 Cornhill, Boston.
	Hatfield, E. F. See *Gen. Assembly.*
Hauser.	Hauser, I. L., & Co., 136 Spring St., Milwaukee, Wis.
Haverty.	Haverty, P. M., 218 Sixth Ave., N. Y.
Hayden. (?)	Hayden, Miller & Maltbie, Hartford, Conn.
Held. (?)	Held & Clark, New York.
Henkel.	Henkel & Co., New Market, Va.
Henry Bill.	Henry Bill Pub. Co., 43 and 45 Shetucket St., Norwich, Conn.
	Herald. See *N. Y. Herald.*
Herder.	Herder, Benjamin, 19 S. 5th Street, St. Louis.
Herrick.	Herrick, Avery, Albany, N. Y.
Hersey, C. (?)	Hersey, Charles, Worcester, Mass.
Hickey.	Hickey & Co., 11 Barclay St., New York.
Hicks.	Hicks, Thomas F., Wernersville, Berks Co., Pa.
	Hildreth (H. R.) Print. Co. See *Gray.*
Hine.	Hine, C. C., "Insurance Monitor" Office, 161 Broadway, New York.
Hinton.	Hinton, H. L., & Co., 204 Broadway, New York.
	Historical Soc. of Penna. See *Penn. Hist.*
	Hitchcock & Walden. See *Cin. Meth. Bk. Conc.*
Hoeger.	Hoeger, J. B., & Sons, 449 and 451 E. Water St., Milwaukee, Wis.
Hoffmann.	Hoffmann Brothers, 413 E. Water St., Milwaukee, Wis.
	Holbrook, M. L. See *Wood & H.*
Holden.	Holden, Geo. H., 9 Bowdoin Sq., Boston.
Holland. (?)	Holland, W. J., Cleveland, Ohio.
	Holman, A. J., & Co., 930 Arch St., Phila.
Holmes.	Holmes, D. S., 89 4th St., Brooklyn, E. D.
Holt.	Holt (Henry) & Co., 12 E. 23d St., N.Y. *Formerly* Leypoldt & Holt.

Holt Bros	Holt Bros., 151 William St., New York. *Now* Chauncey Holt, 119 and 121 Nassau St.
Homans.	Homans, I. Smith, 521 B'way, New York. *Now* Banker's Magazine Office.
	Homœopathic Med. Soc. See *N. Y. Hom. Med.*
Hope.	Hope Pub. Co., 200 Montague St., Brooklyn. *Formerly* S. Harrison & Co.
Hopkins.	Hopkins, I. A., & Sons (Franklin Pub. House), 121 Penna. Ave., Washington.
	Houghton, H. O., & Co. See *Hurd & H.*
	Houghton, Osgood & Co. See *Hurd & H.;* also *Osgood.*
Howard.	Howard, Geo. W., 10 South St., Baltimore.
Howe.(?)	Howe, Prof. D. P., Union Coll., Boston.
Hoyt.	Hoyt, Henry, 25 Bromfield St., Boston. Books *formerly* pub. by him now included in list of Ira Bradley & Co.
Hoyt, F. & D.	Hoyt, Fogg & Donham, 193 Middle St., Portland, Me.
Hubbard.	Hubbard Bros., 723 Sansom St., Phila.
Hubbell.	Hubbell, John H., & Co., 24 Park Pl., New York.
Humphrey.	Humphrey, Charles, 41 Maumee St., Adrian, Mich.
Hunt.	Hunt, John P., 29 S. 9th St., Phila.
Hunter.	Hunter & Co., Hinsdale, N. H.
Hunter, S. J.	Hunter, Samuel J., Savannah, Mo.
Hunter, T.	Hunter, Thomas, 716 Filbert St., Phila.
Huntington.	Huntington, F. J., & Co., 107 Duane St., New York. *Now* at Hartford, Conn.
Hurd & H.	Hurd & Houghton [H. O. Houghton & Co., Boston; Riverside Press, Cambridge], Astor Pl., New York. *Now* Houghton, Osgood & Co., 41 Franklin St., Boston.
Hurlburt.	Hurlburt, C. T., 15 E. 19th St., New York.
Hurst.	Hurst & Co., 122 Nassau St., New York.
Hyatt.(?)	Hyatt, H. S., St. Louis.
Ill. Hort.	Illinois State Horticultural Soc., O. B. Galusha, Sec., Morris, Grundy Co., Illinois.
	Indianapolis Journal Co. See *Journal Co.*
Indust.	Industrial Pub. Co., 14 Dey St., N. Y.
Ingham.	Ingham, Clarke & Co., 217 Superior St., Cleveland, Ohio.
Intern.	International Pub. Co., 407 N. 4th Street, St. Louis.
Intern. Fr. Tr.	International Free Trade Alliance, care A. D. F. Randolph & Co., 900 B'way, New York. *Now* care of G. P. Putnam's Sons.
Island Review.(?)	Island Review, Nantucket, Mass.
Ivison.	Ivison, Blakeman, Taylor & Co., 140 Grand St., New York.
Jaggars.(?)	Jaggars, J. F., Philadelphia.
James, T. P.	James, T. P., Brattleborough, Vt.
James, U. P.	James, U. P., 177 Race St., Cincinnati.
James & W.	James & Webb, 224 Market St., Wilmington, Del.
Jansen.	Jansen, McClurg & Co., 117 and 119 State St., Chicago.
Jenkins.	Jenkins, E. O., 20 N. William St., New York.
Johnson, A. J.(?)	Johnson, A. J., & Co., 11 Great Jones St., New York.
Johnson, T. & J. W.	Johnson, T. & J. W., & Co., 535 Chestnut St., Philadelphia.
Johnson & M.	Johnson & Miles, 27 Beekman St., New York. *Now* Henry J. Johnson.
Jones.	Jones Bros. & Co., 141–143 Race St., Cincinnati, Ohio.
Jones, E.	Jones (Elliott) & Co., Columbus, Ohio.
Jones, G. I.	Jones, G. I., & Co., 208 S. 4th Street, St. Louis.
Journal Co. (?)	Journal Co., Indianapolis, Ind.
Judd.	Judd (Orange) Co., 245 Broadway, N.Y.
Judd & W.	Judd & White, New Haven, Conn. *Now* Edw. P. Judd.
Kalamazoo. (?)	Kalamazoo Pub. Co., Kalamazoo, Mich.
	Kansas Democrat Office. See *Peacock.*
	Kansas Pub. House. See *Martin.*
Kay.	Kay & Bro., 17 and 19 S. 6th St., Phila.
Keen.	Keen (W. B.), Cooke & Co., 113 State St., Chicago. *Now* ceased publishing.
Keep.	Keep, John R., Hartford, Ct.
	Kehoe, Lawrence. See *Cath. Pub.*
Kelly, T.	Kelly, Thomas, 17 Barclay St., N. Y.
Kelly, P. & Co.	Kelly, Piet & Co., 174 W. Baltimore St., Baltimore. *Now* John B. Piet.
Kendall.(?)	Kendall, A. J., 361 E. 124th St., New York.
Kenedy.	Kenedy, P. J., 5 Barclay St., New York.
Kewand.(?)	Kewand & Towers, Washington.
Keystone.	Keystone School and Church Furn. Co. (A. F. Old, Manager), 518 Arch St., Phila. *Formerly* J. A. Bancroft & Co.
King.	King, Homer A., 70 Bible House, New York.
King, L. L. & M.	King (L. L. & Moses), 104 N. 3d Street, St. Louis.
	Kirchner, Geo., & Co. See *Stroefer.*
Knœfel.	Knœfel, Henry, 68 W. Market St., Louisville, Ky.
Knowlton.	Knowlton, Chas. B., Buffalo, N. Y.
Kohler.	Kohler, Ignatius, 911 Arch St., Phila.
Krebs.	Krebs Lithographing Co., cor. 4th and Walnut Sts., Cincinnati.
Kreuzer.	Kreuzer Bros., 30 North St., Baltimore.
Lapsley.(?)	Lapsley & Bazley, New York.
	Lauer & Yost. See *Ev. Assoc.*
Law.	Law, James, Cornell Univ., Ithaca, N. Y.
Lea.	Lea, Henry C., 706 Sansom St., Phila. *Now* Henry C. Lea's Son & Co.
Leary.	Leary & Co., cor. 5th and Walnut Sts., Phila.
Lee, J. V.	Lee, J. V., Columbus, Ohio.
Lee & S.	Lee & Shepard, 41 Franklin St., Boston.
	Lee & Walker. Books included in list of Ditson.
Leffel.	Leffel (James) & Co., Springfield, Ohio.
Leighton.	Leighton Pub. Co., care Jas. A. Moore, 1224 Sansom St., Phila. *Now* ceased publishing.
Lent.	Lent (De Witt C.) & Co., 446 Broome St., New York. *Now* out of business.

Leonard. — Leonard & Booth, Rochester, Minn. *Now* Walter S. Booth.

Leslie. (?) — Leslie, Frank, New York. *Now* deceased.

Leypoldt, F. See *Publishers' Weekly;* also *Holt.*

Lindemann. — Lindemann, Wm., 32 Ave. A, N. Y.

Lindsay. — Lindsay & Blakiston, 25 S. 6th St., Phila.

Lippincott. — Lippincott, J. B., & Co., 717 Market St., Phila.

Lit. and Art. Pub. (?) — Literary and Art Pub. Co., New York.

Littell & G. — Littell & Gay, 17 Bromfield St., Boston. *Now* Littell & Co.

Little, L. — Little, L., & Co., Ridgway, Pa.

Little, W. C. — Little, W. C., & Co., 525 B'way, Albany.

Little, B. & Co. — Little, Brown & Co., 254 Wash'n St., Boston.

Lloyd. — Lloyd (Louis) & Co., 93 Wash'n St., Chicago.

Locke. — Locke, J. S., & Co., 23 Franklin St., Boston. *Now* Graves, Locke & Co.

Locke & J. (?) — Locke & Jones, Toledo, Ohio.

Lockwood, G. R. — Lockwood, G. R., 812 B'way, New York.

Lockwood, H. — Lockwood, Howard, 74 Duane St., N. Y.

Lockwood, I. (?) — Lockwood, Ingersoll, 128 B'way, New York.

Lockwood, B. & Co. — Lockwood, Brooks & Co., 381 Wash'n St., Boston. Part of their plates sold, Sept., 1878, to different houses.

L. I. Hist. — Long Island Historical Soc., Geo. Hannah, Lib'n, Brooklyn.

Longstreth. (?) — Longstreth, Henry, 738 Sansom St., Phila.

Loring. — Loring, A. K., 369 Wash'n St., Boston.

Loring, S. & H. — Loring, Short & Harmon, 208 Middle St., Portland, Me.

Lothrop. — Lothrop, D., & Co., 32 Franklin St., Boston.

Lovell, A. A. (?) — Lovell, A. A., Worcester, Mass.

Ludwig. — Ludwig, Henry, 39 Centre St., New York. Books now pub. by Luth. Pub. Soc., 180 Chatham St.

Lunt. — Lunt, Wm. Parsons, 42 Congress St., Boston.

Luth. Bk. St. — Lutheran Book Store, G. W. Frederick, 117 N. 6th St., Phila.

Luth. Pub. (?) — Lutheran Pub. Soc., J. K. Shryock, Sup't, 42 N. 9th St., Phila.

Lutheran Pub. Soc. (N. Y.) See *Ludwig.*

Lynch. (?) — Lynch, Cole & Meehan, New York.

McCaskey. — McCaskey, J. P., & Co., Lancaster, Pa.

McCauley. — McCauley, Richard, 1309 Chestnut St., Phila. *Now* James McCauley.

M'Cormick. — M'Cormick, F. L., 41 First St., Portland, Oregon. *Formerly* S. J. M'Cormick.

McCurdy. — McCurdy, J. C., & Co., 26 S. 7th St., Phila.

McDivitt, Campbell & Co. See *Campbell & Co.*

Mac Donald. (?) — Mac Donald, Geo., & Co., Chicago.

McDowell. — McDowell, Geo., & Co., 253 Market St., Phila.

McGee. — McGee, J. A., 7 Barclay St., New York.

Machris. (?) — Machris & Aveling, Detroit, Mich.

McIntyre. — McIntyre, J. W., 614½ Olive Street, St. Louis.

McKennie. — McKennie, M., & Son, Univ. of Va. (P. O.), Va.

Mackey. (?) — Mackey, Jos., New York.

McKinney. — McKinney, Henry N., & Co., 725 Sansom St., Phila. *Now* out of business.

McKnight. — McKnight, Charles, Pittsburgh, Pa. *Formerly* People's Monthly Pub. Co.

Maclean. — Maclean, Geo., & Co., S. E. cor. 6th and Locust Sts. (Box 2495), Phila. *Now* ceased publishing. Most of their books now included in list of J. M. Stoddart & Co.

McLoughlin. (?) — McLoughlin Bros., 71 and 73 Duane St., New York.

Macmillan. — Macmillan & Co., 22 Bond St., New York.

McMorris. — McMorris & Gans, 713 Sansom St., Phila.

Macoy. — Macoy, Robert, 4 Barclay St., New York.

Magee, James P. See *N. E. Meth.*

Magee, R. — Magee, R., & Son, 808 Chestnut St., Phila.

Marcy. (?) — Marcy, L. J., 1340 Chestnut St., Phila.

Martien. (?) — Martien, Alfred, 21 S. 7th St., Phila.

Martin. — Martin, Geo. W. (Kansas Pub. House), Topeka, Shawnee Co., Kansas.

Martindale. — Martindale, Jas. B., 293 Broadway, N. Y.

Marvin. — Marvin, T. R., & Son, 49 Federal St., Boston.

Mason. — Mason, Albert, care Hurd & Houghton, Astor Pl., New York. Books now for sale by A. C. Armstrong & Son, 714 Broadway, N.Y.

Mason, P. — Mason (Perry) & Co., 41 Temple Pl., Boston.

Masonic. — Masonic Pub. Co. (W. T. Anderson), 3 E. 4th St., New York.

Mass. Hist. — Massachusetts Hist. Soc., Dr. S. A. Green, Lib'n, 30 Tremont St., Bost.

Masury. — Masury, John W., & Son, 111 Duane St., New York.

Md. Hist. — Maryland Historical Soc., Jno. G. Gatchell, Ass't Lib'n, Athenæum Bldg., Baltimore.

Me. Hist. — Maine Historical Society, A. S. Packard, Lib'n, Brunswick, Me.

Mayfield, Rogers & Co. See *So. Bapt.*

Meagher. (?) — Meagher, Thos. F., 34 Park Row, N. Y.

Mearns. (?) — Mearns, Endler & Co., 183 Greenwich St., New York.

Medical Assoc. of Alabama. See *Ala. Med.*

Medical Assoc. of Georgia. See *Ga. Med.*

Medical Soc. of N. Y. See *N. Y. Med. Soc.*

Medical Soc. of Penn. See *Pa. Med.*

Medical Soc. of Va. See *Va. Med.*

Mendenhall. — Mendenhall, E., 157 Main St., Cincin.

Mendum. — Mendum, J. P., Paine Memorial Bldg., Boston.

Mercantile and Statistical Agency. See *Murphy, J. A.*

Merriam. — Merriam, G. & C., 110 State St., Springfield, Mass.

Merriam, E. D. — Merriam, E. D., Greenfield, Mass. *Now* ceased publishing.

Merrill. — Merrill, Hubbard & Co., 5 E. Wash'n St., Indianapolis, Ind.

Meth. Bk. Conc. Methodist Book Concern (Nelson & Phillips; *now* Phillips & Hunt), 805 B'way, New York.
See also *Cin. Meth. Bk. Conc.*

Meth. Epis. Methodist Episcopal Book and Pub. House, 1018 Arch St., Phila.

Methodist Episcopal Bk. Dep. See *Carroll, D. H.*

Meyer, L. Meyer, Louis, 1413 Chestnut St., Phila.
Now ceased publishing.

Meyers & Salter. See *Hartshorne.*

Mich. Med. Mich. State Medical Soc., Geo. E. Ranney, Sec., Lansing, Mich.

Miller. Miller, James, 779 B'way, New York.

Mills. Mills & Co., Des Moines, Iowa.

Minn. Hist. Minnesota Historical Soc., St. Paul.

Minn. Med. Minnesota State Medical Soc., C. H. Boardman, M. D., Sec., St. Paul, Minn.

Monroe, J. R. Monroe, J. R., Seymour, Ind.

Moore, A. Moore (Alexander) & Co., 3 School St., Boston.

Moore, J. A. Moore, J. A., 1224 Sansom St., Phila.

Morgan. Morgan, Rev. Henry, 81 Shawmut Ave., Boston.

Morris. (?) Morris, F. W., Springfield, Mass.

Morrison. Morrison, W. H. & O. H., 475 Penna. Ave., Washington.

Morton. Morton, John P., & Co., 156 and 158 W. Main St., Louisville, Ky.

Morton & D. Morton & Dumont, 160 Fulton St., N.Y.

Morwitz. Morwitz & Co., 614 Chestnut St., Phila.

Moss. Moss & Co., 432 Chestnut St., Phila.

Munn, H. N. Munn, H. N., 37 Park Row, New York.

Munn & Co. Munn & Co., 37 Park Row, New York.

Munro. Munro, George, 17–27 Vandewater St., N. Y.

Munsell. Munsell, Joel, 82 State St., Albany, N. Y.
Now deceased.

Murphy. Murphy, John, & Co., 182 Baltimore St., Baltimore.

Murphy, J. A. Murphy (J. Arthurs) & Co., 5 and 7 Dey St., New York.
Now Merc. and Stat. Ag'cy.

Murphy, M. Murphy, M., 715 Sansom St., Phila.

Murray. Murray Hill Pub. Co. (E. B. Foote), 129 E. 28th St., New York.

Mus. Comp. Zool. Museum of Comparative Zoology, Cambridge, Mass.

Myers, E. B. Myers, E. B., 121 Monroe St., Chicago.

Myers, Willis G. See *Foster.*

Nagle. (?) Nagle, John R., & Co., Phila.
Books now pub. by Schüllerman & Co., 608 Chestnut St., Phila.

Narragansett Club.
Books pub. by Tibbitts & Randall.

N. A. of Wool Man. National Assoc. of Wool Manufacturers, John L. Hayes, Boston.

Nat. Agcy. Naturalists' Agency (S. E. Cassino), Salem, Mass.
Now at 299 Washington St., Boston.

Nat. Ed. National Educ. Assoc., Peoria, Ill.

Nat. Pub. National Pub. Co., 724 Cherry St., Phila.

Nat. R. W. Pub. National Railway Pub. Co., 46 Bond St., N.Y.; 229–231 South 5th St., Phila.

Nat. Temp. National Temperance Soc. and Pub. House, 58 Reade St., New York.

Nelson. Nelson (Thomas) & Sons, 42 Bleecker St., New York.

Nelson, E. Nelson, Edwin, Amherst, Mass.

Nelson & Phillips. See *Meth. Bk. Conc.*

New Ch. New Church Board of Pub., E. H. Swinney, 20 Cooper Un., New York.

N. E. Agri. New Eng. Agri. Soc., Boston.

N. E. Hist. Gen. New Eng. Historic, Genealogical Soc., J. W. Dean, 18 Somerset St., Boston.

N. E. Meth. New England Methodist Book Depos., Jas. P. Magee, Ag't, 38 Bromfield St., Boston.

New England Pub. Co. See *Walker, J. B. R.*

N. H. Agri. New Hampshire Bd. of Agri., J. O. Adams, Sec., Concord, N. H.

N. H. Hist. New Hampshire Hist. Soc., S. C. Eastman, Lib'n, Concord, N. H.

N. Hav. Hist. New Haven Colony Hist. Soc., W. G. Andrews, Sec., New Haven, Conn.

N. J. Hist. New Jersey Hist. Soc., W. A. Whitehead, Corr. Sec., Newark, N. J.

New World. New World Pub. Co., 811 Arch St., Phila.

N. Y. Acad. Med. New York Acad. of Medicine, Laurence Johnson, Lib'n, 12 W. 31st St., New York.

N. Y. & H. Pub. New York and Hartford Pub. Co., 55 Dey St., New York.

N. Y. Bk. Conc. New York Book Concern, 7 Warren St., New York.

N. Y. Herald. (?) Herald Office, New York.

N. Y. Hom. Med. Homœopathic Medical Soc. of N. Y., W. H. Vanderzee, Sec., 127 Madison Ave., Albany, N. Y.

N. Y. Med. Medical Soc. of State of N. Y., Dr. C. H. Porter, Treas., 55 Eagle St., Albany, N. Y.

N. Y. News. New York News Co., 18 Beekman St., New York.

N. Y. Ref. Ch. Bd. Reformed Church Bd. of Pub., 34 Vesey St., New York.

N. Y. Times. (?) New York Times, New York.

N. Y. Tribune. N. Y. Tribune Assoc., New York.

N. Y. World. (?) World Office, New York.

Newark Daily Advertiser. See *Daily Advertiser.*

Newton. Newton, W. H., St. Georges, Del.

Nichols, C. A. Nichols, C. A., & Co., 203 Main St., Springfield, Mass.

Nichols & H. Nichols & Hall, 32 Bromfield St., Bost.

Nims. Nims, H. B., & Co., Troy, N. Y.

Niver. Niver, D. R., 20 N. Pearl St., Albany, N. Y.

Noonan. Noonan, Thomas B., & Co., 23 and 25 Boylston St., Boston.

Normal Pub. House. See *Perrine.*

North. North, F. A., & Co., 1308 Chestnut St., Phila.

N. W. Bible. North Western Bible and Pub. Soc., Allegan, Mich.
Now Allegan Co. Democrat Assoc.

N. W. Univ. North West Universalist Pub. House ("New Covenant"), cor. Dearborn and Randolph Sts., Chicago.

Novello & Ewer.
Books included in list of Ditson.

Numismatic and Antiq. Soc. of Phila. See *Phila. Num.*

Nuttall. Nuttall Ornithological Club, R. Dean, Corr. Sec., Cambridge, Mass.

O'Brien. O'Brien & O'Mahony, 206 Henry St. (Box 4070), New York.

O'Kane. (?) O'Kane, Thomas, 130 Nassau St., New York.

Oneida. Oneida Community, Oneida, N. Y.

Osgood. Osgood, Jas. R., & Co., 41 Franklin St., Boston.
Now Houghton, Osgood & Co.
Note. The plates, copyrights, etc., of those books which are entered with an asterisk before the name of Osgood were disposed of by auction in the spring of 1876. Though no longer now in the hands of this house, they had not been reprinted on July 1, 1876, and at that date, therefore, the Osgood edition was still the edition in the market.

O'Shea. O'Shea, P., 37 Barclay St., New York.

Osman. Osman & Hapeman, 18 La Salle St., Ottawa, Ill.

Otis. Otis, H. H., Buffalo, N. Y.

Otley, Rogers & Co., 22 N. Cherry St., Nashville, Tenn. See *So. Bapt.*

Pa. Med. Medical Soc. of State of Penna., W. B. Atkinson, Perm. Sec., 1400 Pine St., Phila.

Packard. Packard, S. S., 805 B'way, New York.

Palmer. Palmer, W. C., Jr., 11 Bible House, New York.

Park Pub. (?) Park Pub. Co., Hartford, Conn.

Parker, J. B. See *Hardy.*

Parson. Parson & Co., 716 N. 4th St., St. Louis.

Parsons, J. D. Parsons, John D., Jr., Albany, N. Y.

Patterson. Patterson, F. B., 27 Park Row, New York.
Now ceased publishing.

Paul. Paul (Peter) & Bro., Buffalo, N. Y.

Paxon. (?) Paxon, J. H., New York.

Payot. Payot, Upham & Co., 204 Sansome St., San Francisco.

Peabody Acad. of Sci. Peabody Acad. of Science, A. S. Packard, Jr., Director, Salem, Mass.

Peabody Med. Peabody Medical Inst., 4 Bulfinch St., Boston.

Peabody Mus. Am. Arch. Peabody Mus. of Am. Arch. and Eth., F. W. Putnam, Curator, Harvard Univ., Cambridge, Mass.

Peace. Peace Assoc. of Friends in America (Daniel Hill), New Vienna, Clinton Co., Ohio.

Peacock. Peacock, T. B. ("Kansas Democrat"), Topeka, Kansas.

Peale. Peale, R. S., & Co., Des Moines, Iowa.

Peck. Peck, Henry H., 346 Chapel St., New Haven, Conn.

Peckham. Peckham, W. L., Waterford, Conn.

Penn. Hist. Historical Soc. of Penn., F. D. Stone, Lib'n, 820 Spruce St., Philadelphia.

Pennsylvania School Supply Co. See *Keystone.*

People's Monthly Pub. Co. See *McKnight.*

Perine, G. E. Perine, Geo. E., 100 Nassau St., N.Y.

Perkinpine. Perkinpine & Higgins, 914 Arch St., Philadelphia.

Perley. Perley, M. V. B., Springfield, Mass.

Perrine. Perrine, B. F. (Normal Pub. House), Valparaiso, Ind.

Peters. Peters, J. L., 843 B'way, New York.
Books now included in list of Ditson.

Peterson. Peterson, T. B., & Bros., 306 Chestnut St., Philadelphia.

Peterson, H. Peterson (Henry) & Co., 319 Walnut St., Philadelphia.
Now ceased publishing.

Pettengill. Pettengill, S. M., & Co., 37 Park Row, New York.

Philadelphia Acad. of Nat. Sci. See *Acad. of Nat. Sci.*

Phila. Cath. Philadelphia Cath. Pub. Co., 724 Sansom St., Philadelphia.

Phila. Coll. Phy. College of Physicians, R. Bridges, Lib'n, cor. 13th and Locust Sts., Philadelphia.

Phila. Num. Numismatic and Antiquarian Soc. of Philadelphia, Henry Phillips, Jr., Corr. Sec., 428 Library St., Phila.

Philes. Philes, Geo. P., 704 B'way, New York.

Phillips, H. G. Phillips, H. G., New Haven, Conn.
Now E. N. Blun.

Phillips, J. S. Phillips, J. S., 702 California St., San Francisco.

Phillips, A. & Co. (?) Phillips, Andrade & Co., New York.
Now W. Phillips & Co., 81 Nassau St.

Phillips & Hunt. See *Meth. Bk. Conc.*

Pierce. Pierce, R. V., World's Dispensary, Buffalo, N. Y.

Piet, J. B. See *Kelly, P. & Co.*

Pilger. Pilger-Buchhandlung (A. Bendel), Reading, Pa.

Pitman. Pitman, Benn, Cincinnati.

Poland. (?) Poland, J. & J. M., Montpelier, Vt.

Polock. Polock, Moses, 406 Commerce St., Phila.

Pond. Pond, Wm. A., & Co., 25 Union Sq., New York.

Poor. Poor, H. V. & H. W., 68 Broadway, New York.

Porter. Porter & Coates, S.W. cor. 9th and Chestnut Sts., Phila.

Pott. Pott, Young & Co., 6 Cooper Un., N. Y.

Potter, J. E. Potter, John E., & Co., 617 Sansom St., Phila.

Potter, A. & Co. Potter, Ainsworth & Co., 35 and 37 Park Pl., New York.

Poughkeepsie Soc. of Nat. Sci. Poughkeepsie Soc. of Nat. Science, E. H. Parker, Sec., Poughkeepsie, N. Y.

Pounsford. Pounsford, A. H., & Co., 9 and 11 W. 4th St., Cincinnati.

Power & B. Power & Barksdale, Jackson, Miss.

Powers, J. H. Powers (J. Hale) & Co., 131 W. 4th St., Cincinnati.

Prang. Prang, L., & Co., 286 Roxbury St., Bost.

Pratt, F. (?) Pratt, Foster, Grand Sec. Grand Lodge of F. and A. Masons, Kalamazoo, Mich.

Pratt & B. (?) Pratt & Battle, Oberlin, Ohio.

Pres. Bd. Presb. Bd. of Pub., 1334 Chestnut St., Phila.

Presb. Church, Gen. Assembly. See *Gen. Assembly.*

Pres. Com. Presb. Com. of Pub., J. L. Shotwell, 1001 Main St., Richmond.
Now Presb. Pub. Co.

Procter. Procter Bros., Gloucester, Mass.

Publishers' Weekly. Publishers' Weekly Office, 13 and 15 Park Row, New York.
Books now published by F. Leypoldt.

Pustet. Pustet, Fr., 52 Barclay St., New York.

Putnam. Putnam's (G. P.) Sons, 182 5th Ave., New York.

Putnam & D. Putnam & Davis, Worcester, Mass.

Quak. City.	Quaker City Pub. Co., 217 and 219 Quince St., Phila.
	Quinter & Brumbaugh Bros. See *Brumbaugh.*
R. R. Gazette.	Railroad Gazette, 73 B'way, New York.
Radde.	Radde, William, 548 Pearl St., New York.
Ramaley.	Ramaley & Cunningham, St. Paul, Minn.
Ramsey. (?)	Ramsey, T. N., Raleigh, N. C.
Randall.	Randall & Co., Columbus, Ohio. *Now* A. H. Smythe.
Randolph.	Randolph, A. D. F., & Co., 900 B'way, New York.
Randolph, J. W.	Randolph, J. W., & English, 1302–1304 Main St., Richmond.
Redding.	Redding & Co., 731 B'way, New York.
Redfield.	Redfield, J. S., New York. *Now* ceased publishing.
Reed.	Reed, Geo. B., 37 Brattle St., Boston.
Reed, F. M. (?)	Reed, F. M., New York.
	Reformed Church Bd. of Pub. (N. Y.) See *N. Y. Ref. Ch. Bd.*
Ref. Ch. Pub.	Reformed Church Pub. Bd. (Phila.), 907 Arch St., Philadelphia.
Rel. Phil.	Religio-Philosophical Pub. House, cor. LaSalle and Washington Sts., Chicago.
Revell.	Revell, F. H., 91 Wash'n St., Chicago.
Rice.	Rice, D., & Co., 508 Minor St., Phila.
Richards.	Richards & Co., 372 Larimer St., Denver, Col. *Now* Stone & Co.
Richmond.	Richmond, Backus & Co., 183 Jefferson Ave., Detroit, Mich.
	Richter, F. See *Germ. Ev. Luth. Syn. of Iowa.*
Rider.	Rider, Sidney S., 17 Westminster St., Providence, R. I.
	Riverside Press. See *Hurd & H.*
Roberts.	Roberts Brothers, 299 Washington St., Boston.
Robertson.	Robertson, L. D., 12 Barclay St., N. Y.
Robinson. (?)	Robinson, J. W., Indianapolis, Ind.
Robson.	Robson, Chas., 1123 Chestnut St., Phila.
Rockwell. (?)	Rockwell, Baker & Hill, Buffalo, N. Y.
Rodgers. (?)	Rodgers, Jas. B., & Co., Phila.
Roe.	Roe, Edward P., Cornwall, N. Y.
Roeslein.	Roeslein, Fred., 22 S. 4th St., St. Louis.
Roman.	Roman, A., & Co., San Francisco.
	Roorbach, O. A. See *Happy.*
Ropp.	Ropp, C., Jr., Bloomington, Ill.
Routledge.	Routledge, Geo., & Sons, 416 Broome St., New York.
Rowell.	Rowell, G. P., & Co., 10 Spruce St., N. Y.
Rural.	Rural New Yorker Co., 78 Duane St., New York. Books now incl. in list of Orange Judd Co.
Rural Home. (?)	Rural Home Pub. Co., Rochester, N. Y.
Russell.	Russell, B. B., & Co., 57 Cornhill, Boston.
Russell, G. D.	Russell, G. D., & Co., Boston. Books *formerly* pub. by them now included in list of Ditson.
Ruttenber.	Ruttenber, E. M., & Son, 54 Water St., Newburgh, N. Y.
Rutter.	Rutter, Wm., & Co., cor. 7th and Cherry Sts., Philadelphia.
Ryan.	Ryan, P. J., Springfield, Mass.

S. C. Med.	South Carolina Med. Assoc., H. D. Fraser, Sec., Charleston, S. C.
S. W. Bk. & Pub.	South Western Book and Pub. Co., 415 N. 6th Street, St. Louis. *Now* Advocate Pub. House, 113 N. 8th St.
Sabin.	Sabin, J., & Sons, 64 Nassau St., New York. *Now* J. Sabin's Son.
Sadlier.	Sadlier, D. & J., & Co., 31 Barclay St., New York.
Sadlier, W. H.	Sadlier, W. H., 11 Barclay St., New York.
St. L. Acad. of Sci.	Academy of Science of St. Louis, Nath. Holmes, Corr. Sec., St. Louis.
St. L. B. & B. Pub.	St. Louis Book and Bible Pub. Co., J. H. Chambers, Manager, 305 Locust St., St. Louis.
	Sakolski, H. See *Frank.*
Sample.	Sample, Jas. G., & Co., 705 Sansom St., Philadelphia. *Now* R. H. Ball.
Samuels.	Samuels, E. A., 125 Tremont St., Boston.
	San Francisco News Co. See *White & B.*
Sanborn.	Sanborn, B. W., & Co., Concord, N. H.
Scammell.	Scammell & Co., 210 and 212 N. 3d Street, St. Louis.
Schäfer.	Schäfer & Koradi, S. W. cor. 4th and Wood Sts., Phila.
Schermerhorn.	Schermerhorn, J. W., & Co., 30 E. 14th St., New York. Plates and editions of many of their books now sold to different houses.
Schirmer.	Schirmer, G., 701 B'way, New York.
Schmidt.	Schmidt, L. W., 7 Barclay St., New York. *Now* ceased publishing.
Schmidt, C.	Schmidt, Christian, 39 Centre St., New York.
Schober. (?)	Schober & Co., Detroit, Mich.
Schoenhof.	Schoenhof & Moeller, 40 Winter St., Boston. *Now* Carl Schoenhof.
Schofield, W. J.	Schofield, W. J., 19 Summer St., Boston.
Schuberth.	Schuberth, Ed., & Co., 23 Union Sq., New York.
	Schüllerman & Co. See *Nagle.*
Scofield, F.	Scofield, Fred., & Co., 26 S. 7th St., Phila. *Now* A. Gorton & Co.
Scott, D. W.	Scott, D. W., & Co., Galena, Ill.
Scott, J. W.	Scott, J. W., & Co., 146 Fulton St., New York.
Scranton.	Scranton, S. S., & Co., 281 Asylum St., Hartford, Conn.
Scribner.	Scribner, Armstrong & Co., 745 Broadway, New York. *Now* Charles Scribner's Sons.
Scribner, W. & A.	Scribner, Welford & Armstrong, 745 Broadway, New York. *Now* Scribner & Welford.
	Scriptural Tract Repos. See *Hastings.*
Searcy.	Searcy, Geo. A., Tuscaloosa, Ala.
Searle.	Searle, Frederick A., 262 Washington St., Boston.
Sebald. (?)	Sebald, Hugo, Phila.
Setliff.	Setliff, A., 108 Church St., Nashville, Tenn.
Sev. Day Adv.	Seventh Day Adventists, Battle Creek, Mich.
Sever.	Sever, C. W., Cambridge, Mass.
Shankland. (?)	Shankland, Mrs. E. R., Dubuque, Iowa.

Shea.	Shea, John G., 537 Pearl St., New York.
Sheehan.	Sheehan & Co., Ann Arbor, Mich.
Sheffield. (?)	Sheffield, Henry, Nashville, Tenn.
Sheldon.	Sheldon & Co., 8 Murray St., New York.
Shepard. (?)	Shepard, Henry L., & Co., Boston.
Sherwood.	Sherwood, Geo., & Co., 130 Adams St., Chicago.
Shorey.	Shorey, John L., 36 Bromfield St., Boston.
	Shuey, W. J. See *Un. B. Pub.*
Sibole.	Sibole & Stellwagen, 109 S. 15th St., Phila. *Now* ceased publishing.
Sickels.	Sickels, D., & Co., 2 Bleecker St., New York.
Siemon.	Siemon & Bro., Fort Wayne, Ind.
Simmons, H. E.	Simmons, H. E., 150 Nassau St., New York.
Simon, J. K.	Simon, James K., 29 S. 6th St., Phila.
	Skelly, J. P., & Co., Phila. Books included in lists of Martien and J. A. Moore.
Skinner. (?)	Skinner, H. N., 281 Greenwich St., New York.
Slaughter.	Slaughter, Rev. Philip, Mitchell's Station, Va.
Slote. (?)	Slote, Woodman & Co., 119 William St., New York. *Now* D. Slote & Co.
Smith, E. A.	Smith, E. A., 516 Pine Street, St. Louis, and 346 Broadway, New York.
Smith, Dr. E. A.	Smith, Dr. E. A., Tuscaloosa, Ala. Books now pub. by Barrett & Brown, Montgomery, Ala.
Smith, E. B.	Smith, E. B., & Co., 116 Woodward Ave., Detroit, Mich.
Smith, G. W.	Smith, Geo. W., & Co., 95 Nassau St., New York. *Now* S. A. Wilder.
Smith, W. R.	Smith, W. R., Tuscaloosa, Ala.
Smith, E. & Co.	Smith, English & Co., 710 Arch St., Phila.
Smith. Inst.	Smithsonian Institution, Washington.
	Smythe, A. H. See *Randall.*
Solomon, F. (?)	Solomon, Felix, Baltimore.
Solomons.	Solomons & Chapman, Washington. *Now* Jas. J. Chapman.
Somerby.	Somerby, Charles P., 18 Bond St., New York.
Souder.	Souder, S. T., & Co., 721 Sansom St., Phila.
Soule.	Soule, Thomas & Wentworth, 208 S. 4th Street, St. Louis. *Now* F. H. Thomas & Co.
So. Bapt.	Southern Baptist Pub. Soc., 361 Main St., Memphis, Tenn. *Now* Mayfield, Rogers & Co., Nashville, Tenn.
So. Meth.	Southern Methodist Pub. House, Nashville, Tenn.
So. Pub.	Southern Pub. Co., Atlanta, Ga.
Sower.	Sower, Potts & Co., 530 Market St., Phila.
Spear.	Spear, Henry, 82 Wall St., N. Y.
Spectator.	Spectator Co., F. Hargan, Manager, 16 Dey St., New York.
Spon.	Spon, E. & F. N., 446 Broome St., New York.
Starr.	Starr, Frank, 41 Platt St., New York.
State.	Published by state government.
	Stearns, J. N. See *Nat. Temp.*

Stechert. (?)	Stechert & Wolff, 766 Broadway, New York. *Now* Gustav E. Stechert.
Steiger.	Steiger, E., 25 Park Pl., New York.
Stevens.	Stevens, Geo. E., 39 W. 4th St., Cincinnati.
Stevenson. (?)	Stevenson, J. M., New York.
Stiles.	Stiles, Ed. H., Ottumwa, Wapello Co., Iowa.
Stoddard, S. R.	Stoddard, S. R., 22 Elm St., Glens Falls, N. Y.
Stoddart, J. M.	Stoddart, J. M., & Co., 727 Chestnut St., Phila.
Stone.	Stone, Livingston. Books for sale at Cold Spring Trout Ponds, Charlestown, N. H.
	Stone & Co. See *Richards.*
	Storrs & Foster. See *Hardy.*
Stratton.	Stratton, Geo. W., & Co., 21 Hanover St., Boston.
Strickland.	Strickland & Co., 1061 B'way, Oakland, Cal.
Stroefer.	Stroefer & Kirchner, 865 B'way, New York. *Now* Geo. Kirchner & Co.
Strong.	Strong, Thos. W., 599 B'way, New York. Books now included in lists of T. Kelly and of P. J. Kenedy.
Studer.	Studer, Jacob H., & Co., Columbus, Ohio.
	Sutton & Scott. See *West. Tr.*
Swallow.	Swallow, G. C., Columbia, Mo.
Syckelmoore. (?)	Syckelmoore, Wm., 1420 Chestnut St., Phila.
Symonds.	Symonds, J. H., 68 Devonshire St., Boston.
Taintor.	Taintor Bros., Merrill & Co., 758 B'way, New York.
Tavel. (?)	Tavel, Eastman & Howells, Nashville, Tenn.
Taylor, M.	Taylor (Martin) & Co., 22 W. Eagle St., Buffalo, N. Y.
Taylor, W. A.	Taylor, W. A., 145 Wood St., Pittsburgh, Pa.
Tenn. Agri.	Tennessee Bureau of Agriculture, Statistics and Mines, J. B. Killebrew, Com'r, Nashville, Tenn.
Thomas, D.	Thomas, Dion, 16 New Church St., New York.
	Thomas, F. H., & Co. See *Soule.*
Thomas, F. W.	Thomas, F. W., & Sons, 7th St., below Chestnut, Phila.
Thomas, J. H.	Thomas, John H., 10 E. 3d St., Dayton, Ohio.
Thompson.	Thompson, Brown & Co., 23 Hawley St., Boston.
Tibbals.	Tibbals, N., & Sons, 37 Park Row, N.Y.
Tibbitts.	Tibbitts & Randall, 21 Westminster St., Providence, R. I.
Tilton.	Tilton, S. W., & Co., 333 Wash'n St., Boston.
	Times. See *N. Y. Times.*
Tinsley.	Tinsley & Morgan, Syracuse, N. Y.
Tompkins.	Tompkins, K., 16 Cedar St., New York. *Now* ceased publishing.
Torrey Bot.	Torrey Botanical Club, Wm. H. Leggett, 54 E. 81st St., New York.
Townsend.	Townsend, W. A., 177 B'way, New York.
Townsend & Co. (?)	Townsend & Co., Phila.

Tr. P. & P. Co.	Transylvania Print. and Pub. Co., 49 and 51 E. Main St., Lexington, Ky.
Tracy. (?)	Tracy, Siemering & Co., Austin, Texas.
Treat.	Treat, E. B., 805 B'way, New York.
	Tribune Assoc. See *N. Y. Tribune.*
Tucker, B. R.	Tucker, B. R., New Bedford, Mass.
Tucker, L.	Tucker (Luther) & Son, 395 B'way, Albany, N. Y.
Tumbridge.	Tumbridge & Co., 2 Wall St., New York.
Turf, F. & F.	Turf, Field and Farm Assoc., 37 Park Row, New York.
Turnbull.	Turnbull Bros., 8 N. Charles St., Baltimore. *Now* ceased publishing.
Tuttle.	Tuttle & Co., Rutland, Vt.
Tyler.	Tyler, R. D. S., & Co., Detroit, Mich.
U. P. Bd. of Pub.	United Presbyterian Bd. of Publication, 55 9th St., Pittsburgh, Pa.
U. S. C. Pub.	United States Central Pub. Co., 171 and 173 Greenwich St., New York.
U. S. Govt.	Published by the United States government.
U. S. Pub.	United States Pub. Co., 13 University Pl., New York.
Un. B. Pub.	United Breth. Pub. House (W. J. Shuey), cor. Main and Fourth Sts., Dayton, Ohio.
Un. Bk. Conc.	Union Book Concern, 163 Randolph St., Chicago.
Un. Pub. Co.	Union Pub. Co., 725 Broad St., Newark, N. J.
Un. S. S.	Unitarian Sunday School Soc., 7 Tremont Pl., Boston.
Univ. Pub.	University Pub. Co., 19 Murray St., New York.
Universalist.	Universalist Pub. House, 16 Bromfield St., Boston.
Urick. (?)	Urick & Gehring, Kutztown, Pa.
	Van Antwerp, Bragg & Co. See *Wilson, H. & Co.*
Va. Med.	Medical Soc. of Virginia, L. B. Edwards, M. D., Sec., Richmond, Va.
Van Benthuysen. (?)	Van Benthuysen Print. House, Albany, N. Y.
Van Evrie.	Van Evrie & Co., 60 Beekman St., New York.
Van Loan.	Van Loan & Van Gordon, Catskill, Greene Co., New York. *Now* Walter Van Loan.
Van Nostrand.	Van Nostrand, D., 23 Murray St., New York.
Van Siclen.	Van Siclen, H. K., 95 Fifth Ave., New York.
Vent.	Vent, C. F., 51 W. 4th St., Cincinnati.
Vering.	Vering, Hermann, 305 Convent St., St. Louis.
Vt. Hist.	Vermont Historical Soc., M. D. Gilman, Lib'n, Montpelier, Vt.
Vt. Med.	Vermont Medical Soc., S. S. Clark, Sec., St. Albans, Vt.
Vick.	Vick, James, Rochester, N. Y.
Virtue.	Virtue & Yorston, 12 Dey St., N. Y. *Now* J. S. Virtue & Co.
Volkening.	Volkening, Louis, 904 N. 5th Street, St. Louis.
Vose.	Vose, Reuben, 34 Liberty St., New York. *Now* deceased.
Wagenseller.	Wagenseller, J. A., 23 N. 6th St., Phila.
Waggener.	Waggener, D. B., & Co., 420 Walnut St., Phila.
Waggoner, J. F.	Waggoner, J. Fred., 8 Lakeside Bldg., Chicago.
Waldo.	Waldo, J. Curtiss, 90 Camp St., New Orleans.
Waldteufel.	Waldteufel, A., San Jose, Cal.
Walker, E.	Walker, Edward, care C. H. Jones & Co., 114 Fulton St., New York.
Walker, J. B. R.	Walker, J. B. R. (New Eng. Pub. Co.), 284 Asylum St., Hartford, Conn.
Walker, S.	Walker, Samuel, & Co., 18 Arch St., Boston.
Walker, W. & Co. (?)	Walker, Wise & Co., Boston.
Wallace, A.	Wallace, Adam, 14 N. 7th St., Phila.
Wallace, J. M. P.	Wallace, J. M. Power, 132 S. 6th St., Phila.
	Wallingford Print. Co., Wallingford, Conn. Branch of Oneida Community; *now* dissolved.
Ward.	Ward, U. D., 116 Nassau St., New York. *Now* Ward & Drummond.
Ward & P.	Ward & Peloubet, 80 Nassau St., New York. *Now* Geo. S. Diossy.
Ware.	Ware, Wm., & Co., 47 Franklin St., Boston. *Formerly* Brewer & Tileston.
Ware, I. D.	Ware, Isaac D., 414 Arch St., Phila.
Warner.	Warner & Beers, 64 W. Lake St., Chicago.
	Warren & Wyman. See *Crowell.*
Waters, W. W.	Waters, W. W., 198 Penna. Ave., Pittsburgh, Pa.
Watson. (?)	Watson, Jas., New York.
Watson, G. (?)	Watson, Gaylord, 16 Beekman St., New York.
Watts.	Watts (The H. C.) Co., 504 Minor St., Phila.
Waverley.	Waverley Pub. Co., 60 S. Salina St., Syracuse, N. Y. *Now* ceased publishing.
Weed.	Weed, Parsons & Co., Albany, N. Y.
Wells.	Wells, S. R., & Co., 737 Broadway, New York.
Wells, J. G.	Wells, Jno. G., 13 E. Houston St., N.Y. *Formerly* Wells Pub. Co.
Welsh.	Welsh (Rees) & Co., N. W. cor. 6th and Walnut Sts., Phila.
Wendell.	Wendell, Rufus, 480 B'way, Albany, N.Y.
Weppner.	Weppner, Miss Margaretha, care L. S. L. Jordan, Cooper Union, New York.
West, J. B.	West, John B., & Co., St. Paul, Minn. *Now* West Pub. Co.
West, J. & Co.	West, Johnston & Co., 911 Main St., Richmond.
West. News. (?)	Western News Co., Chicago.
West. Pub.	Western Pub. House, 72, 73 and 80 Ashland Block, Chicago.
West. Tr.	Western Tract Soc. (Sutton & Scott), 176 Elm St., Cincinnati.
West. Un. Tel. (?)	Western Union Telegraph Co., New York.
Westermann.	Westermann, B., & Co., 838 Broadway, New York.
Wheaton.	Wheaton, W. F., 18 William St., New Bedford, Mass.
Wheildon.	Wheildon, W. W., Concord, Mass.

White, J.	White, Joel, 20 Market St., Montgomery, Ala.
White & B. (?)	White & Bauer, San Francisco. *Now* San Francisco News Co.
Whiting, I. N.	Whiting, I. N., Columbus, Ohio.
Whitman.	Whitman, Walt, 431 Stevens St., Camden, N. J.
Whitney, S.	Whitney (Sumner) & Co., 613 Clay St., San Francisco.
Whitney, W. W.	Whitney, W. W., 111 Summit St., Toledo, Ohio.
Whitney & A.	Whitney & Adams, Springfield, Mass.
Whittaker.	Whittaker, Thos., 2 Bible House, N. Y.
Whittett.	Whittet & Shepperson, Richmond, Va.
Widdleton.	Widdleton, W. J., 714 Broadway, N. Y. Part of his books now in the hands of A. C. Armstrong & Son.
Wiebusch.	Wiebusch, Aug., & Son, 631 S. 4th Street, St. Louis.
	Wilder, S. A. See *Smith, G. W.*
Wiley.	Wiley, John, & Sons, 15 Astor Pl., N. Y.
	Wilkinson, James M. See *Davis, R. S.*
Willard.	Willard Tract Repository, Beacon Hill Pl., Boston.
Williams.	Williams, A., & Co., 283 Wash'n St., Boston.
Williams, H. L. (?)	Williams, Henry L., New York.
Williams, H. T.	Williams, Henry T., 46 Beekman St., New York. *Now* Adams & Bishop.
Williams, N. B.	Williams (N. Bangs) & Co., 52 Westminster St., Providence, R. I.
Williamson.	Williamson & Cantwell Pub. Co., 213 W. 4th St., Cincinnati.
Willig.	Willig, Geo., & Co., 1 North Charles St., Baltimore.
Wilson, A.	Wilson, Archibald, 8 Liberty St., Poughkeepsie, N. Y.
	Wilson, Edw. L. See *Benerman.*
Wilson, E. A.	Wilson, Edwin A., & Co., Springfield, Ill.
Wilson & Co. (?)	Wilson & Co., New Haven, Conn.
Wilson, H. & Co.	Wilson, Hinkle & Co., 137 Walnut St., Cincinnati. *Now* Van Antwerp, Bragg & Co.
Wilstach.	Wilstach, Baldwin & Co., 141 Race St., Cincinnati.
Winchell.	Winchell & Elbert Print. and Lith. Co., Hannibal, Mo. *Now* Hannibal Print Co., cor. 3d and Centre Sts.
Wis. Med.	Wisconsin State Medical Soc., J. T. Reeve, Sec., Appleton, Wis.
Wise.	Wise, Isaac M., "Israelite and Deborah" Office, Cincinnati.
Witter.	Witter, Conrad, 21 S. 4th St., St. Louis.
Wom. Cent. (?)	Women's Centennial Executive Committee, Phila.
Wood, W.	Wood, Wm., & Co., 27 Gt. Jones St., New York.
Wood & H.	Wood & Holbrook, 13 and 15 Laight St., New York. *Now* M. L. Holbrook.
Woodbury. (?)	Woodbury, C. J., & Co., Rockford, Ill.
Woodhouse.	Woodhouse & Parham, 1107 Main St., Richmond.
Woodward.	Woodward, Geo. E., & Co., 31 Broome St., New York. Books now included in lists of Am. News Co. and Orange Judd Co.
Woodward & P. (?)	Woodward & Palmer, Haverhill, Mass.
	World. See *N. Y. World.*
World Pub.	World Pub. House, 139 8th St., New York. Entire stock of plates sold, Sept. 1878, to different houses.
Worthington, A. D.	Worthington, A. D., Hartford, Conn.
Worthington, R.	Worthington, R., 750 Broadway, New York.
Wright.	Wright & Potter, 97 Milk St., Boston.
Wynkoop.	Wynkoop & Hallenbeck, 113 Fulton St., New York.
Y. S. of F. Arts.	Yale School of Fine Arts, New Haven, Conn.
	Yancey, J. A. See *Ellyson.*
Young, H. A.	Young, Henry A., & Co., 13 Bromfield St., Boston.
Young, Hiram.	Young, Hiram, York, Pa.
Young, W. H.	Young, Wm. H., 8 and 9 First St., Troy, New York.
	Zell (T. Ellwood), Davis & Co. See *Davis, C. H.*
Zickel.	Zickel, Solomon, 19 Dey St., New York.
Ziegler.	Ziegler, P. W., & Co., 1000 Arch St., Phila.

ERRATA AND ADDENDA

PAGE

3 *After* **Abbott**, J: S. C. French revolution, *insert*
— History of Austria. 12°. $2 .... *Russell.*
— History of Christianity. pl. and maps. 8°. '72. *$2.50; hf. mor., $3 .... *Russell.*
— History of the empire of Russia. pl. 8°. '72. $2 .... *Russell.*
— History of Ohio. 8°. '74. $4–$8 .... *Tyler.*
— Prussia and the Franco-Prussian war. pl. and maps. 12°. '71. $1.50; $2 .... *Russell.*
— *Germ.* Preussen und der französisch-preussische Krieg; a. d. Engl. v. F. Stähli. pl. and maps. 12°. '71. $1.50; $2 .... *Russell.*

For **Abelons**, *read* **Abelous**.

4 *Insert* **Adair**, D. L. Annals of bee culture, 1869–'72. 8°. $1.75 .... *Adair.*
— Progressive bee culture; or, apine instincts illustrated and defined on a new theory. 8°. '72. pap., 25c. .... *Adair.*

For **Adam**, S., *read* **Adlam**, S.

6 *For* **Adams**, W. H. Land of the Nile, *read* **Adams**, W: H. D. Land of the Nile.

7 *After* **Adler**, G: J. Progressive Germ. reader, *insert* — *See also* Ollendorff, H. G.

8 **Adventures** of Leo Rembrandt. *For* Hoffman, F., *read* Hoffmann, F.

10 **Agreeable** surprise. *For* O'Keefe, J., *read* O'Keeffe, J.

11 *Insert* **Aiken**, A. *See* Vermont, Supreme Court reports.

12 **Alabama** geol. survey. *For* bienniel, *read* biennial.

15 **Ali Bey**, Mohamed. Before *Pres. Com.*, insert *N. Y. Ref. Ch. Bd.*

16 **Alice** Dunbar. *For* Spottswood, L., *read* Spottswood, L. A.

20 *Insert* **American** conflict (The). Greeley, H. 2 v. ea., $5 .... *O. D. Case.*

21 *Insert* **American** Lloyd's register of Am. and foreign shipping. [Annual.] 4°. mor., $15. *Hartshorne.*

24 *After* **Anderson**, R. B., Norse mythology, *insert* — Norske Maalsag (Den); [also] Han Per og ho Bergit, af Kristofer Janson. 16°. '74. 50c.; bds., 30c. .... *Anderson.*

25 *After* **Angell**, Jos. K. Treatise on limitations of actions, etc., *insert* — *See also* Rhode Island, Sup. Ct. reports.

After **Andrews**, Fanny, *insert* ["Elzey Hay."]

26 **Annals** of Quodlibet. *For* Kennedy, J. P. $1.75. *Lippincott*, read *See* Kennedy, J. P.

27 *After* **Anthon**, J: Law student, *insert* — *See also* New York State, Sup. Ct. reports.

28 **Arabesques**. *For* Greenough, R. S., *read* Greenough, S. D.

29 *Insert* **Archer**, J. T. *See* Florida, Supreme Court reports.

Insert **Ariel** (*pseud.*) *See* Payne, Buckner H.

30 *After* **Arndt**, J: Sechs Bücher, etc., *insert* — — *Same.* 8°. $2.50; (fine pap. ed.) leath., $5; mor., $8 .... *Kohler.*

PAGE

32 *After* **Arthur**, *Rev.* W: Italy in transition, *insert* — Model merchant (The): memoir of Samuel Budgett; abridg. by Mrs. S. A. Myers. 12°. 70c. *Pres. Bd.*

35 **Atlantic** lib. *For* Lances of Linwood, *read* Lances of Lynwood.

36 *After* **Augustine**, *St.* Life, *insert* — *Same.* 18°. 55c.; 60c. .... *Dutton.*

Insert **Aunt** Abbie (*pseud.*) My class; or, stories on the elements of Christian character. 18°. 45c.; 55c. .... *Am. Bapt.*

37 **Aunt** Saidee's cow. *For* Prichard, S. J., *read* Pritchard, S. J.

38 *After* **Avery**, Jane G., *insert* (*pseud.*)

40 **Bachelor's** bed-room. *For* Mathews, A. J., *read* Mathews, C. J.

Backwoodsman (The). *For* Wraxhall, *Sir* C. F. L., *read* Wraxhall, *Sir* F. C. L.

45 **Ballard**, E: *For* Topham, *read* Popham.

46 **Bampton** lectures, 1866. Before *Pott;* insert *Dutton.*

47 *Insert* **Banks**, Elliot N. *See* Kansas, Sup. Court reports.

48 *For* **Barbier** (Il) di Seviglia, *read* **Barbiere** (Il) di Siviglia.

Barbour, Ol. L. *For* New York, Supreme Court reports, *read* New York State, Chancery reports; Supreme Court reports.

49 **Barnard**, H: *For* — Oral training, etc., *read* **Barnard**, H: Oral training, etc.

Note. Not by Dr. Barnard, author of "Military schools."

Barnard, H: *Insert* — Armsmear: memorial of S: Colt. 8°. $5.50 .... *Barnard.*
— Common schools, as they were before 1800; — as they were in 1870. 8°. ea., $1 ...... *Barnard.*
— Common schools in Connecticut, 1838–'42. 8°. $1. *Barnard.*
— Compulsory school attendance. 8°. $1 .. *Barnard.*
— Connecticut educational institutions. 8°. $3.50. *Barnard.*
— Documents on popular education. 4 v. 8°. ea., $1 .... *Barnard.*
— Education in Europe in 1854. 8°. $1.50 .. *Barnard.*
— Educational activity. 8°. $3.50 .... *Barnard.*
— Educational aphorisms and suggestions. 8°. $3.50. *Barnard.*
— Educational associations, national and state. 8°. $3.50 .... *Barnard.*
— Educational biography. 6 v. 8°. ea., $3.50. *Barnard.*

Cont.: American teachers, 2 v., por. — Benefactors of Am. educ., por. — German educ. reformers and teachers. — English, French and other teachers. — Swiss teachers and educators.

— Elementary and secondary schools. 4 v. 8°. ea., $5.50 .... *Barnard.*

Cont.: 1. German states. — 2. Continental European states. — 3. Great Britain. — 4. American states.

— Ezekiel Cheever, and the free schools of New Eng. 8°. $1 .... *Barnard.*
— Object teaching: oral and other methods of instruction. 8°. $3.50 .... *Barnard.*

PAGE

49 **Barnard**, H: *continued.*

— [Pedagogy.] 6 v. 8°. ea., $3.50....... *Barnard.*
Cont.: American pedagogy. — English, 2 v. — German. — French. — Swiss.

— Professional and special schools. 5 v. 8°. ea., $5.50. *Barnard.*
Cont.: 1. Science and national industries. — 2. Military schools and education. — 3. Normal schools and professional training. — 4. Female schools and education. — 5. Reformatory and preventive agencies.
Note. v. 1 is also sold in two parts: 1. Great Britain, $2.50. — 2. United States, $3.

— Public schools of Rhode Island, 1843-'49. 8°. $3.50 .... *Barnard.*

— Report [on common schools of Connecticut]. 8°. $4.50 .... *Barnard.*

— Report [on public schools of Rhode Island]. 8°. $4.50 .... *Barnard.*

— School architecture. 500 ill. 8°. $5.50.. *Barnard.*

— School codes, state, municipal, institutional. 8°. $3.50 .... *Barnard.*

— School status of freedmen and colored children. 8°. $1.......................... *Barnard.*

— Studies and conduct. 8°. $3.50........ *Barnard.*

— Superior instruction. New ed. 2 v. 8°. '75. $7. *Barnard.*
Cont.: 1. Historical development, $2.50. — 2. Superior instruction as organized, $5.50.

— Supplementary schools and agencies. 8°. $5.50. *Barnard.*

— Tribute to Gallaudet: discourse on life, etc., of Rev. T. H. Gallaudet; with history of deaf mute instruction and institutions, etc. 8°. '52. $3. *J. W. Bliss.*

— *Same.* 8°. $2.50..................... *Barnard.*

— *See also* United States, *Bureau of Educ.*
Note. The above are by Dr. Barnard, author of "Military schools."

50 *After* **Barnes**, W: H. Body politic, *insert* — Fortieth Congress of the U. S., historical and biographical. 2 v. por. 8°. '69. ea., $15. *G. E. Perine.*

51 *For* **Barry**, *Mrs.* Martha E., *read* **Berry**, *Mrs.* Martha E.

54 *After* **Bates**, *Mrs.* Sa. B. Margie Hopkins, *insert* — Lucy Randolph; or, present doing and patient waiting. ('65.) New ed. ill. 16°. '75. $1.15. *Hoyt.*

Battle, W: H. After *See also* North Carolina, Reports, *insert*; Revisal of public statutes.

55 *Insert* **Bay**, E. H. *See* South Carolina, Superior Court reports.

After **Beach**, Ha. Mar., *insert (pseud.)*

56 **Bearing** our burdens. *For* McLean, M. W., *read* McLain, M. W.

Insert **Beasley**, M. *See* New Jersey, Court of Chancery reports.

60 **Belcher**, Jos. *For* Baptists martyr, *read* Baptist martyrs.

Insert **Bell**, Alex. Melville. Class-primer of Eng. visible speech: diagrams and read. exercises of "English visible speech." 4°. '67. pap., 20c. *Burbank.*

— English visible speech for the million; for teaching exact pronunc. of the lang. to native, foreign, or illiterate learners; with diagrams, etc. 4°. '67. pap., 40c.......................... *Burbank.*

— Explanatory lecture on visible speech, Roy. Coll. of Preceptors, Feb., 1870. 12°. '70. pap., 15c. *Burbank.*

— Lecture on art of delivery and influence of school discipline on public oratory. 12°. '60. pap., 15c. *Burbank.*

— Observations of stammering; with notes of cases. 32°. '60. pap., 15c................ *Burbank.*

— Sermon-reading and memoriter delivery: [lecture], New Coll. of Edin. 12°. '60. pap., 15c. *Burbank.*

— Standard elocutionist: extracts in prose and poetry for reading and recitations; [with] principles of eloc., etc. 12°. '60. $1.50........... *Burbank.*

PAGE

60 **Belcher**, Jos. *continued.*

— Treatise on art of reading. 12°. '45. pap., 20c. *Burbank.*

— Universal line-writing and stenography; on the basis of "Visible speech." 8°. '69. 85c.; in 5 pts., ea., 20c.......................... *Burbank.*

— Visible speech: the science of universal alphabetics; or, self-interpreting physiol. letters for writing all lang. in one alphabet and for teaching the deaf and dumb to speak; [with] tables, diagrams, etc. 4°. '67. $5........... *Burbank.*

— *See also* Protestant Episc. Church, Emphasized liturgy.

63 *After* **Bennett**, Edm. H., *and* Heard, F. F. Selection of leading cases, etc., *insert* — — Digest of Massachusetts Supreme Court reports, 1804-'57. 2 v. 8°. '62-'63.......................... *State.*

— *and* Holland, H: W. Digest of Mass. Supreme Court reports, 1857-'69. 4°. '72.......... *State.*

66 **Bertrand** et Raton. *For* Scribe, A. E., *read* Scribe, E.

73 *For* **Bigelow** papers, *read* **Biglow** papers.

Insert **Bill**, Ledyard. History of the Bill family. 8°. '67. $7.......................... *L. Bill.*

— Minnesota: its character and climate; with sketches of other resorts favorable to invalids. 12°. '71. $1.25 .... *Wood & H.*

— Pen pictures of the war: lyrics, incidents and sketches of the rebellion. 12°. '64. $2.25.. *L. Bill.*

74 *After* **Birch**, S: Records of the past, etc., *insert* — *Same.* 4 v. 16°. ea., $1.75.. *Scribner, W. & A.*
Cont.: Assyrian texts, 2 v. — Egyptian texts, 2 v.

75 *Insert* **Birthday** present. *See* Present for my darling lib.

Insert **Birthday** wishes. *See* Little Willie's lib.

76 *Insert* **Black**, C: Cp. Michael Angelo Buonarroti, sculptor, painter, architect: his life and labours, with bibliog. of Michael Angelo and his works. photos. roy. 8°. $12 .... *Macmillan.*

After **Black**, J. R. The ten laws of health, *insert* — *and* Hicks, T: H. Alcohol as a medicine, and how its use affects the temperance cause: discussion. 8°. '70. 50c.; pap., 25c. .... *Hicks.*

Black panther. *For* Wraxhall, *Sir* C. F. L., *read* Wraxhall, *Sir* F. C. L.

79 *Insert* **Bleckley**, L. E. *See* Georgia, Supreme Court reports.

82 **Bohn**, H. G. (*ed.*) Chronicles of the crusades. Before *Scribner, W. & A.*, insert *Lippincott.*

84 *For* **Bonnie** ærie. L., L., *read* **Bonnie** Aerie! Pratt, I. L.

Book about boys. *For* Moncrieff, A. R. H., *read* Moncrieff, R. H.

Book about dominoes. *For* Moncrieff, A. R. H., *read* Moncrieff, R. H.

Book (The) and its story. *For* R., L. N., *read* Ranyard, Ellen.

86 *After* **Borgo**, C: Novena to the sacred heart of Jesus, *insert* — Meditations on sacred heart of Jesus. *See* Nouet, J., Life of Christ.

91 **Boys'** own guide. *For* Simonds, W. A., *read* Simonds, W.

Brace, C: Loring. *Insert* — Dangerous classes of N. Y. [City], and twenty years' work among them. ill. 8°. '72. $2.................... *Wynkoop.*

93 *Insert* **Bradley**, C. S. *See* Rhode Island, Sup. Court reports.

Insert **Branch**, J. *See* Florida, Supreme Court reports.

Branches of palm. *For* L., L., *read* Pratt, I. L.

94 **Brazen** gates. *For* [Juvenile.] 12°, *read* Smith, F. N.

Breach of promise. *For* [Fiction.] 8°. pap., 50c., *read* Smythies, G. 50c.

PAGE

94 **Breaking** the rules. *For* 60c., *read* 90c.

95 *Insert* **Breese**, S. *See* Illinois, Supreme Court reports.

After **Brenda** (*pseud.*) Froggy's little brother, *insert* — Nothing to nobody. ill. 16°. '74. 90c. *Dodd.*

97 *After* **Brightwell**, C. L. Palissy, etc., *insert* — *Same.* 18°. 85c. .... *Am. S. S.*

98 *After* **Brock**, *Mrs.* Carey. Rectory and the manor, etc., *insert* — Stepping stones. ('73.) 3d ed. 16°. '76. 75c. .... *So. Meth.*

— *Same.* ('63.) New ed. ill. 16°. '68. $1.15 .. *Hoyt.*

— Village missionaries; or, to every one his work. ill. 12°. $1.50 .... *Nelson.*

99 *After* **Brockett**, Linus Pierpont. Year of battles, *insert* — *and* Vaughan, *Mrs.* Ma. C. Woman's work in the civil war: a record of heroism, patriotism and patience. 8°. '67. $3 ...... *Ziegler.*

Broken fetters. *For* L., L., *read* Pratt, I. L.

Broken idols. *For* McLean, M. W., *read* McLain, M. W.

101 *After* **Brown**, C: R. Government of Mich., etc., *insert* — *See also* Michigan, Nisi prius reports.

Insert **Brown**, G. A. *See* Nebraska, Statutes.

106 **Buck**, Ruth. *For* How Charlie helped, etc., *read See* Lamb, *Mrs.* Jos.

107 *After* **Bulfinch**, Mar. H. Frank Stirling's choice, etc., *insert* — Margie: a Christmas story. 18°. 50c. .... *Dutton.*

108 **Bull** in a china shop. *For* Matthews, C., *read* Mathews, C. J.

109 *After* **Bungener**, L. L: Fél. Rome and the council, etc., *insert* — Three days in the life of a father. 18°. '67. 40c .... *Randolph.*

115 *Insert* **Bush**, —. Digest of Florida laws, 1846–'72. 8° .... *State.*

117 *After* **Byerly**, T: *and* Roberts, Ja. Craigie. Percy anecdotes, etc., *insert* — — *Same.* New [chp.] ed. 2 v. sm. 8°. $3.50; cf., $10 ... *Appleton.*

— — *Same*; with Am. anecdotes. 8°. $2; shp., $2.50. *Harper.*

118 *Insert* **Byron** as a detective. *See* Pinkerton, A.

After **Caddell**, Cecilia Ma. Blind Agnes, etc., *insert* — Miner's daughter. 16°. 60c.; $1 .. *Sadlier.*

119 *Insert* **Caines**, G. Cases in court for trial of impeachments and a correction of errors in N. Y., 1804–5. 8°. 1810 .... *State.*

— *See also* New York State, Supreme Court reports.

120 **Call**, D. *After* Circuit Court reports, *insert*; Virginia, Court of Appeals reports.

122 **Camp-fires** of Napoleon. *For* ill. 8°, *read* Watson, H. C.

123 **Captain** Christie's granddaughter. *For* Lamb, R. B., *read* Lamb, *Mrs.* Jos.

124 *For* **Card-drawing**, *read* **Card-drawer.**

125 *Insert* **Caroline** Howard (*pseud.*) *See* Jervey, *Mrs.* C. H.

126 **Carpenter**, Jos. E. Sacred songster. *Transfer the Note to below* Standard reciter.

Carré, Michel. Faust and Marguerite. After *De Witt*, insert; *French.*

127 *Insert* **Casas**, Bart. de las. Life of Las C.; or, opening chapter of the early missionary hist. of Am.; ed. by one of the Dominican fathers of N. Y. 12°. $1 .... *O'Shea.*

128 **Castle** of Andalusia. *For* O'Keefe, *read* O'Keeffe.

129 *Insert* **Catherine**, *St.* Life. *See* Winefrida, *St.*, Life.

Catherine Howard. *For* Suter, W. D., *read* Suter, W. E.

136 *After* **Charles**, *Mrs.* E. H., *insert* [*formerly Miss* Emily Hawthorne].

PAGE

137 *Insert* **Charlton**, R. M. *See* Georgia, Superior court reports.

Insert **Charlton**, T. U. P. *See* Georgia, Superior court reports.

138 *Insert* **Chatfield**, Pl. Tin trumpet; or, heads and tales for the wise and waggish. 12°. $1.50; pap., 50c .... *Appleton.*

141 **Child-life.** *For* Richenau, *read* Reichenau.

Children of the east. *For* Jessup, H. A., *read* Jessup, H. H.

Children of elfland. *For* Paul, H. B., *read* Paull, H. B.

Children of the great king. *For* ill. 16°, *read* Horsburgh, M.

144 *Insert* **Choctaw** girl. *See* Haymakers.

146 **Christian** hero (The), etc. *Correct so as to read* Christian hero (The). Macpherson, J. 90c. *Hoyt.*

Christianity and discipline. *For* Monad, *read* Monod.

148 *Insert* **Christus** judex. Roth, E. $1 .. *I. N. Andrews.*

Chronicles of Cosynook. *For* Hall, S. C., *read* Hall, A. M.

149 **Churton**, H: (*pseud.*) For *See* Tourjee, A. W., read *See* Tourgee, A. W.

150 *Insert* **Cincinnati** [Ohio]. Superior Court reports, 1854–'56; by R. D. and J. H. Handy. 2 v. 8°. '55–56 .... *State.*

151 **Clark**, Alex. *For* Work for Christianity, *read* Workday Christianity.

For **Clark**, Alvan, *read* **Clark**, Alva.

Insert **Coan**, A. Four memorable years at Hilo: narrative of missionary labor in the Sandwich Islands. 16°. '75. pap., 10c .... *Hicks.*

154 *Insert* **Claver**, P: Sketch of his life and labors in behalf of the African slave. 16°. '66. 75c. *Cath. Pub.*

156 *After* **Cobb**, Ja. Paul and Virginia, etc., *insert* — Siege of Belgrade: opera. 16°. pap., 15c. *French.*

After **Cobb**, T. R. R. Inquiry into law, etc., *insert* — *See also* Georgia, Supreme Court reports.

158 *Insert* **Coldwell**, T. H. *See* Tennessee, Supreme Court reports.

Insert **Coleman**, W. *See* New York, Supreme Court reports.

160 *After* **Collins**, T: *insert* [" Iconoclast."]

161 **Col.** Thorpe's scenes in Arkansaw. *For* Thorpe, J. B., *read* Thorpe, T. B.

162 *Insert* **Comet** (The); or, the earth in its varied phases, etc. 12°. $2.25 .... *Hale.*

165 *Insert* **Conner**, J. Digest of So. Car. Court of Appeals reports, 1835–'54. 8°. '55 .... *State.*

— *See also* Simonton, C. H., *and* Conner, J.

166 **Constance** Aylmer. *For* P., H. F., *read* Parker, H. F.

168 *Take out* **Cooke**, Anna B. Queen (A). 18°. 75c. *Dutton.*

Insert **Cooke**, W. W. *See* Tennessee, Law reports.

170 *Insert* **Corbin**, D. T. *See* South Carolina, Revised statutes.

171 *After* **Corner**, Jla. China, pictorial, etc., *insert* — India, pictorial, descriptive and historical. ill. and maps. 12°. (Bohn.) $1.75 .. *Little, B. & Co.*

— *Same.* ill. and maps. 12°. (Bohn.) $2. *Lippincott; Scribner, W. & A.*

Take out **Cornet** (The); or, the earth in its varied phases, etc. 12°. $2.25 .... *Hale.*

174 *Insert* **Cousin** Kate (*pseud.*) My first pennies. 16°. $1.15 .... *Cong. Pub.*

Insert **Cowen**, E. *See* New York State, Supreme Court reports.

PAGE

176 *After* **Coyne**, Jos. Stirling. Little rebel, etc., *insert* — Our clerks; or, No. 3 Fig-tree Court, Temple: farce. 16°. pap., 15c. . . . . *De Witt.*

Cozy house stories. Winnie and her grandfather, etc. *For* S. P. Martyn, *read* S. T. Martyn.

After **Craik**, *Mrs.* Dinah Mar. Little Sunshine's holiday, etc., *insert* — Michael, the miner: Hungarian story. ill. 18°. 45c. . . . . . *Bost. Am. Tr.*

— *Same.* ill. 18°. '67. 50c. *N. Y. Ref. Ch. Bd.; Pres. Com.*

— *Same*, and other tales. 18°. 70c. . . . . . . *Pres. Bd.*

178 **Creation.** *For* Haydn, J., *read* Haydn, F. J.

For **Crichton**, A., *and* Wharton, H., *read* **Crichton**, A., *and* Wheaton, H.

182 *For* **Cummings**, M. S., *read* **Cummins**, Mar. S.

183 *Insert* **Curry**, T. *See* Louisiana, Supreme Court reports.

184 **Cushman**, J: F. For *See* Mississippi, High Court of Error and Appeals report, read *See* Mississippi, Law reports.

For **Cymberline**, *read* **Cymbeline.**

185 *Insert* **Dacre**, B. Brand (*Lady*). Winifred, Countess of Nithsdale. 16°. $1; $1.50. *Sadlier.*

Daddy Dacre's school. *For* Hall, S. C., *read* Hall, A. M.

Daily governess. *For* Hall, S. C., *read* Hall, A. M.

187 *Insert* **Dana, J.** *See* Kentucky, Court of Appeals reports.

For **Dangerous** guest; by author of "Gilbert Rugge." 8°. pap., 50c., *read* **Dangerous** guest. Jackson, H. 50c.

193 **Dawson**, H: B. *For* Fœderalist, *read* Federalist.

Day after the holidays. *For* Moncrieff, A. R. H., *read* Moncrieff. R. H.

194 *Insert* **Dayton**, W. L. *See* New Jersey, Statutes.

Insert **Dean**, J. F. *See* Vermont, Supreme Court reports.

195 *After* **De Costa**, B: F., *insert* ["W: Hickling."]

198 **Dennery**, A. P., *and* Clairville, L. F. N. My wife's diary. Insert *De Witt;* before *French.*

Denton, *Prof.* W. *For* Man's true savior, *read* Man's true saviors.

201 *Insert* **Dewey**, Ja. S. Compiled laws of Mich., 1871. 2 v. 8°. '72. . . . . *State.*

202 *After* **Dibdin**, T: Of age tomorrow: farce, *insert* — Past ten o'clock: farce. 16°. pap., 15c. *French.*

Insert **Dick**, W: Brisbane. Modern pocket Hoyle: games of skill and chance, and field games. 16°. $1.25; pap., 50c.; bds., 75c. . . . . *Dick & F.*

205 *Insert* **Didier**, the vagabond. *See* Little Willie's lib.

207 *Insert* **Dixon**, Fs. B. Handbook of marine insurance and average. ('62.) 2d ed. 8°. '66. $4. *Spear.*

— Law of shipping, and merchants and shipmasters' guide. ('59.) 3d ed. 8°. '73. $8 . . . . . . *Spear.*

— Practical treatise on adjustment of general average in the U. S. and other countries. 8°. '67. $6. *Spear.*

— Synopsis of law of general average: sup. to "Law of shipping." 8°. '74. $1 . . . . *Spear.*

Dr. Howell's family. *For* Goodwin, H. R., *read* Talcott, H. B.

208 *Insert* **Doctor's** visit. *See* Little Rosy's travels.

212 *Insert* **Douglass**, S. T. *See* Michigan, Supreme Court reports.

214 *Insert* **Drew**, J. B. C. *See* Florida, Supreme Court reports.

Insert **Drinker**, Anna. *See* May, Edith (*pseud.*)

215 *Insert* **Ducks** and the pigs. *See* Little Rosy's travels.

Insert **Dudley**, G. M. *See* Georgia, Superior Court reports.

PAGE

219 *Insert* **Durchhülfe** (Die): e. Geschichte f. Knaben. 18°. 50c.; 75c . . . . *Ev. Assoc.*

After **Durfee**, T: *See* Angell, J. K., *and* Durfee, T., *insert*; — Rhode Island, Sup. Court reports.

After **Durrie**, Dan. Steele. *See also* Davis, W. B., *and* Durrie, D. S., *insert*; — Tuttle, C: R., *and* Durrie, D. S.

Insert **Dutcher**, A. *See* New Jersey, Supreme Court reports.

220 **Duyckinck**, E. A. Lives and portraits of presidents of U. S. *For* mor., $1, *read* mor., $10.

Take out **Dying** Savior and the gipsy girl. *See* Sibree, M.

222 *For* **Eastwood**, Fs., *read* **Eastwood**, Fes.

For **Eaton**, T. E., *read* **Eaton**, T. T.

223 *Insert* **Echo.** *See* Happy voices.

225 *For* **Edwards**, Jona. (*the younger*). Christian love, etc., *read* — Christian love, etc.

Note. This is by the elder Edwards, whose works are given just above.

After **Edwards**, Tryon. Sketches for the fireside, etc., *insert* — The world's laconics: best thoughts of the best authors in prose and verse. 12°. '52. $1.75 . . . . *Dodd.*

231 *Insert* **Emery**, E. Myself: a romance of New England life. 12°. '72. $2 . . . . *Lippincott.*

238 **Eugenie**, *Sister.* For *See* Sister Eugenie, *read* Life and letters of a Sister of Charity [Sister Eugenie]. 18°. '73. $1; $1.50 . . . . *Murphy.*

Eulenspiegel (Der). *For* Wiederstandene, *read* Wiedererstandene.

239 **Evening** rest. *For* L., L., *read* Pratt, I. L.

242 **Facts** and fancies for school-day reading. *For* Sedgwick, C. A., *read* Sedgwick, C. M.

243 *Insert* **Faith.** *See* Little Willie's lib.

246 **Farmer.** *For* O'Keefe, *read* O'Keeffe.

Insert **Farrand**, *Miss* H. A. Moravian Indian boy. 18°. 75c . . . . *Pres. Bd.*

250 *After* **Feuillet**, Octave. Led astray, *insert* — *Same:* drama; tr. 16°. pap., 15c. . . *French.*

260 **Fontainebleau.** *For* O'Keefe, *read* O'Keeffe.

261 **For** a woman's sake. *For* Wackenhusen, *read* Wachenhusen.

After **Foresti**, F. Italian reader, *insert* — *See also* Ollendorff, H. G.

267 *Insert* **Franks**, Mary B. New names; or, what I wish I were. 18°. 30c . . . . *Dutton.*

269 **Fresh** leaves from the book, and its story. *For* R., L. N., *read* Ranyard, Ellen.

273 **Fünf** hundert tausend Thaler. *For* Pittawall, *read* Pitawall.

274 **Gabriele** das Weib, etc. *For* Pitawall, C., *read* Pitawall, E.

275 *Insert* **Gands**, P. *See* Ollendorff, H. G.

277 **Gatty**, *Mrs.* M. Motes in the sunbeam. After *Carter*, insert *; Dutton.*

278 **Gay** cottage stories. Our Charlie. *For* Mrs. A. S. Southworth, *read* Mrs. S. A. Southworth.

279 **Gentle** life ser. Concordance to Milton's poems. *For* D. Cleveland, *read* C. D. Cleveland.

280 *Insert* **Georgia** Medical Assoc. *See* Medical Assoc. of Georgia.

281 **Gerstäcker**, F. Franctireurs. *For* Pitawall, C., *read* Pitawall, E.

290 **Golden** hair. *For* Wraxhall, *Sir* L., *read* Wraxhall, *Sir* F. C. L.

291 **Goldsmith**, Christabel. For *See* Smith, Julie P., read *See* Smith, Fannie N.

297 *After* **Graham**, Ma. Grandfather's last work, *insert* — Nellie West from ten to twenty. 16°. $1. *Am. S. S.*

PAGE

299 **Gray**, Asa. Dried plants. *For* Gilliss, J. W., *read* Gilliss, J. M.

301 *Insert* **Greeley**, Hor. American conflict: hist. of the great rebellion in the U. S., 1860–4. 2 v. 8°. '64–'66. ea., $5 .... *O. D. Case.*

302 *Insert* **Greene**, G. W. *See* Ollendorff, H. G.

310 **Guyot**, Arn. *See also* Barnard, etc. *For* Hewitt, E. C. A, *read* Hewitt, E. C.

312 *After* **Hale**, E: Everett. Ingham papers, *insert* — Lost palace, and other stories. 8°. '75. pap., 25c .... *Lockwood.*

— Nicolette and Aucassin. 8°. '75. pap., 25c. *Lockwood, B. & Co.*

— Spoons in a wherry, and other stories. 8°. '75. pap., 25c. .... *Lockwood, B. & Co.*

— Stand and wait, and other stories. ('74.) New ed. 8°. '75. pap., 25c. .. *Lockwood, B. & Co.*

— Tale (A) of the Simplon, and other stories. 8°. '75. pap., 25c. .... *Lockwood, B. & Co.*

— Ten times one is ten. ('70.) New ed. 8°. '75. pap., 25c. .... *Lockwood, B. & Co.*

314 *After* **Hall**, Marie. Dying Saviour and the gipsy girl, *insert* — *Same.* 18°. '70. 50c. *Meth. Bk. Conc.*

— *Same.* sq. 18°. 50c. .... *Claxton.*

315 **Hallock**, W: A. *Insert* — Memoir of Harlan Page. ill. 18°. '35. 45c .... *Am. Tr.*

After **Hamilton**, *Mrs.* Celia V. Ropes of sand, *insert* — Six months hence: passages from the life of Maria (neé) Secretan. [Fiction.] 8°. $1.25; pap., 75c .... *Estes.*

317 *Insert* **Han** Per og ho Bergit. *See* Janson, K.

321 **Harland**, Marion. [Novels.] *After* Empty heart, *insert* [first pub. under title of "Husks"].

324 **Harte**, Bret. *For* Mrs. Skagg's husband, *read* Mrs. Skaggs' husbands.

326 **Haverfield**, T. T. Old oak farm. *For* 60c., *read* 90c.

327 *For* **Haws**, Jl., *read* **Hawes**, Jl.

After **Hay**, F: Lame excuse, *insert* — Lodgers and dodgers: farce. 16°. pap., 15c. ... *French.*

328 *Insert* **Hayes**, Alb. H. Diseases of the nervous system; or, pathology of the nerves and nervous maladies. 8°. '73. $2 .... *Peabody Med.*

— Science of life; or, self-preservation. 12°. '68. $1 .... *Peabody Med.*

329 *Insert* **He** who is not for me. *See* Little Willie's lib.

333 **Helen** of the glen. *For* Pollok, R. 35c. *N. Y. Ref. Ch. Bd.*, read *See* Pollok, Rob.

For **Helping** hand, *read* **Helping** hands.

334 *Insert* **Henderson**, Knud. National-og Selskabs-Sange med Musik. obl. 16°. '76. bds., $1. *Anderson.*

337 **Herbert's** keys. *For* 60c., *read* 90c.

339 *Insert* **Hetzel**, Pierre-Jules. *See* Stahl, P.-J. (*pseud.*)

340 *Insert* **Hicks**, T: F. Golden hygienic rules: health advice to young men. 12°. '75. 50c.; pap., 25c .... *Hicks.*

— *See also* Black, J. R., *and* Hicks, T: F.

Insert **Hicks**, W. J. Tennessee manual of chancery practice. 8°. '70. leath., $8; — with addenda, $10. — Addenda. $2 .... *Cormick.*

High and low. *For* 60c., *read* 90c.

Highland reel. *For* O'Keefe, *read* O'Keeffe.

342 *Insert* **Hilles**, W: S. Letters to a Unitarian. 16°. pap., 10c .... *Hicks.*

354 **Hooper**, Lucy. *Correct so as to read* **Hooper**, Lucy (*ed.*) Lady's book of flowers, etc.

Hooper, Lucy Hamilton. Poems, etc.

PAGE

355 **Hope**, Ascott Rob. *For* Moncrieff, A. R. H., *read* Moncrieff, R. H.

Hopkins, M: *Insert* — Educational labors and views. 8°. $1 .... *Barnard.*

361 **Howard**, V. E. For *See* Mississippi, High Court of Errors and Appeals reports, read *See* Mississippi, Law reports.

363 **Huggins**, W. *See* Roscoe, H. E., etc. *For* Lockyer, J. W., *read* Lockyer, J. N.

Hughes, *Abp.* J: *For* Kirwin, *read* Kirwan.

365 **Human** temperaments. *For* Powell, W. P., *read* Powell, W. B.

368 *Insert* **Husks**. *See* Harland, M. Empty heart.

371 **Illinois** geol. survey. Palæontology. *For* Newbury, *read* Newberry.

Illustrated lib. of wonders. *For* Egypt 3300 years ago. — Rameses the Great, by F. de Lanoye, *read* Rameses the Great; or, Egypt 3300 years ago, by F. D. Lanoye.

Immen-See. *For* Storme, T., *read* Storm, T.

372 *After* **Inchbald**, *Mrs.* Eliz. Simpson. Child of nature, *insert* — Midnight hour: farce. 16°. pap., 15c. .... *French.*

374 **Inn** of the Guardian Angel. *For* Ségur, S., *read* Ségur, *Comtesse* E. de.

376 **Iron** age of Germany. For *Luth. Pub.*, read (?) *Luth. Pub.*

Insert **Irreparable** loss. *See* Little Willie's lib.

Irving, Wash. Lighter works. *For* Knickerbocker. — Hist. of N. Y., *read* Knickerbocker's Hist. of N. Y.

Insert **Janson**, Kristofer. Han Per og ho Bergit. *See* Anderson, R. B., Norske Maalsag (Den).

386 *Insert* **Jewett**, J. L. *See* Ollendorff, H. G.

387 *Insert* **John** *the Evangelist, St.* Life. 12°. '75. $2 .... *Cath. Pub.*

Insert **John** of the Rackets. *See* Little Willie's lib.

391 *After* **Jonquil** (*pseud.*) Was she engaged, *insert* — Queen Krinaleen's plagues; or, how a simple people were destroyed: discourse in the 22d century. sm. 12°. pap., 50c. ..... *Lippincott.*

396 *After* **Keary**, *Miss* Annie. Janet's home, *insert* — Mia and Charlie. 18°. 75c... *Carter; Dutton.*

— Sidney Grey. 18°. 75c........ *Carter; Dutton.*

397 *Insert* **Keep**, J: R. First lessons for the deaf and dumb. 16°. '62. bds., 40c .... *Keep.*

— School stories, with questions. 16°. '72. bds., 40c. .... *Keep.*

402 **King**, T: Starr. The White Hills, etc., *Correct so as to read* ('59.) 10th ed. cr. 8°. '74. $3. *I. N. Andrews; Gill.*

403 **King's** pine apple. *For* R., E., *read* Reed, E.

408 *After* **Köhler**, F: Dictionary of the Eng.-Germ. and Germ.-Eng. lang., *insert* — *and* Witter, C. Neues Taschenwörterbuch den engl. u. deutschen Sprache. sm. 8°. '74. $1.50 ...... *Witter.*

— — Pocket dict. of the Germ. and Eng. lang. sm. 8°. '74. $1.50 .... *Witter.*

414 **Land** of the Nile. *For* Adams, W. H., *read* Adams, W. H. D.

415 **Lange**, J: P: (*ed.*) Comment. on Scriptures, v. 2. *For* S. Osgood, *read* H. Osgood.

416 *After* **La** Rochefoucauld, François (*Duc*) de. Reflections and moral maxims, etc., *insert* — *Same.* 16°. $1.25 .... *Scribner, W. & A.*

417 *For* **Lathes**, *Mrs.* Stanley, *read* **Leathes**, *Mrs.* Stanley.

After **Lathrop**, *Mrs.* H: Elm Grove cottage, etc., *insert* — School girls of Elverly. 16°. '75. $1.25 .... *H. A. Young.*

PAGE

418 **Law** library. *For* Dearsley (Criminal process), *read* Dearsly; *for* Parson (Wills), *read* Parsons; *for* Brown (Comment. on common law), *read* Broom; *for* Bucknell (Criminal lunacy), *read* Bucknill.

424 *After* **Leigh**, Larrie, *insert* [*pseud.* of L. T. Warner].

428 **Lewis**, *Mrs.* Ma. *For* Mtea, *read* Meta.

445 **Locke**, J: Some thoughts conc. education. *Insert — Same.* 8°. $1 .... *Barnard.*

Lockroy, —, *and* Michel, M. Tompkins, the troubadour, etc. After *De Witt;* insert *French.*

465 *For* **Macleod**, Xav. Don. Memoir of Norman Macleod, etc., *read* **Macleod**, Don. Memoir of Norman Macleod, etc.

Note. The other entries under Macleod, Xav. Don., are correct.

466 *Insert* Macpherson, J. The Christian hero; or, Robert Annan. New ed. '74. 90c...... *Hoyt.*

471 **Mann**, Hor. Lectures and annual reports. *Insert — Same.* 8°. $5.50.......... *Barnard.*

476 **Marsh**, *Miss* Caro. Victory won. After *N. Y. Ref. Ch. Bd.*, insert *; Pres. Com.*

480 **Mary** Elton. *For* Paul, H. B., *read* Paull, H. B.

After **Maryland**. Code: supplement [to 1867], *insert* — — *Same*, 1868. 8° '68. $4.. *Murphy.*

— — *Same*, 1870. 8°. '71. $3 .... *Murphy.*

488 *Insert* **Medical** Assoc. of Georgia. Transactions. 8°. [Annual.] pap., $1.......... *Ga. Med.*

Insert **Medical** Soc. of the State of Pennsylvania. Transactions, 1850–'76. 27 v. 8°. pap... *Pa. Med.*

Note. The v. vary in price, averaging $1.50.

Insert **Medical** Soc. of Virginia. Transactions, 1871–'76. 6 v. 8°. ea., pap., 50c...... *Va. Med.*

489 **Meiklejohn**, J. M. D. *For* Sonnenschein, R., *read* Sonnenschein, A.

Melinda, the caboceer. *For* Sketchly, J. A., *read* Skertchly, J. A.

499 *Insert* **Minnesota** State Medical Soc. Transactions, 1870–6. 7 v. 8°. ea., pap., 50c. *Minn. Med.*

501 **Mistletoe** bough. *For* Somerset, C., *read* Somerset, C. A.

503 **Modern** British essayists. *For* J. Stephens, *read* Sir J. Stephen.

504 *After* **Molière**, J: Bapt. P. de. Rogueries of Scapin, *insert — Same.* 18°. 40c.......... *Sadlier.*

Molière, J: Bapt. de. *For* Tartuffe, *read* Tartufe.

507 *After* **Moore**, Fk. Portrait gallery, etc., *insert* — Rebellion record: diary of events, Dec., 1860–[1865]; with official reports of Federal and Confederate state officers, etc. 12 v. ill., por. and maps. roy. 8°. '61–'69. shp., $72; hf. cf., $78; hf. mor., $84.......... *Van Nostrand.*

509 *After* **More**, Ha. Shepherd of Salisbury Plain, etc., *insert — Same.* 18°. '66. 35c. *N. Y. Ref. Ch. Bd.; Pres. Com.*

534 *Insert* **Niemeyer**, A. H. Aphorisms [on education]. 8°. $2.50.......... *Barnard.*

PAGE

538 *Insert* **Northend**, E. Normal schools and teachers' seminaries. 8°. '54. $2........ *Barnard.*

542 **Ohio**. Supreme Court reports. *For* A. M. Stanton, *read* E. M. Stanton.

551 *For* **Osgood**, S: On Leviticus, *read* **Osgood**, H. Introduction to Leviticus.

552 *For* **Ottalie's** stories, *read* **Ottilie's** stories.

553 **Our** Charlie. *For* Southworth, *Mrs.* A. S., *read* Southworth, *Mrs.* S. A.

557 *Take out* **Page**, Harlan. Memoir of W: A. Hallock.

565 *After* **Patrick**, *St.* Life, *insert — Same;* by an Irish priest. 16°. $1; $1.50 .... *Sadlier.*

574 *Insert* **Pestalozzi**, J: H: Leonard and Gertrude. 8°. $1 .... *Barnard.*

— Memoir. por. 8°. $1.50.......... *Barnard.*

— Pestalozzi and pestalozzianism. 8°. $3.50. *Barnard.*

582 **Pioneer** lib. Counsels to young men. *For* Haws, *read* Hawes.

604 **Queens** of society. *For* Wharton, G. *and* P., *read* Thomson, K. B. *and* J. C.

609 *Insert* **Raumer**, K: v. German universities. 8°. $2.50 .... *Barnard.*

— Ratich, Comenius and Basedow. 8°. $1. *Barnard.*

638 *Insert* **Russell**, W: Normal training. 8°. $1.50. *Barnard.*

648 *For* **Schabalie**, Ph., *read* **Schabalie**, J: Ph.

664 *For* **Shabalie**, J: Ph., *read* **Schabalie**, J: Ph.

681 **Smith**, Ha. Little Meg's children. sq. 18°. '69. 60c. For *Am. Bapt.*, read *Am. Tr.*

742 **Toinette**. *For* Tourjee, A. W., *read* Tourgee, A. W.

744 *For* **Tourjee**, Albion W., *read* **Tourgee**, Albion W.

752 *Take out* **Tryon**, Edwards. The world's laconics, etc.

764 **United States**. *Insert — Bureau of Education.* Report of H: Barnard, Com'r, 1867–8. 8°. $5.50 .... *Barnard.*

— — Special reports on Dist. of Columbia; — on national systems; — on technical educ.; by H. Barnard. 8°. ea., $5.50 .... *Barnard.*

770 *Insert* **Vaughan**, *Mrs.* Ma. C. *See* Brockett, L. P., *and* Vaughan, *Mrs.* M. C.

771 *Insert* **Vermont** Medical Soc. Transactions. 8°. [Annual.] ea., pap., 50c. .... *Vt. Med.*

776 *Insert* **Virginia** Medical Soc. *See* Medical Soc. of Va.

785 *Insert* Warner, L. T. *See* Leigh, Larrie.

789 *After* **Watson**, H: C. Camp-fires of the revolution, *insert* — Camp-fires of Napoleon. 8°. $2.50 .... *T. Bliss.*

808 *For* **Williams**, C: K., *read* **Williams**, Chauncey K.

815 *Insert* **Wisconsin** State Medical Soc. Transactions, 1870–'76. 7 v. 8°. ea., pap., 50c. *Wis. Med.*

818 *Insert* **Woman's** work in the civil war. Brockett, L. P., *and* Vaughan, *Mrs.* M. C. $3.. *Ziegler.*

824 **World's** laconics. *For* Tryon, E., *read* Edwards, T.

PAGE

10 Insert *Barhyte.* Barhyte, James H., 111 State St., Schenectady, N. Y.

61 **Belle** France (La). *For* Parkes, B. R., *read* Belloc, B. P.

62 *After* **Belloc,** Bessie Parkes. Peoples of the world, *insert* — Essays on woman's work. 16°. $1.50. *Routledge.*

— La belle France. ill. 8°. $3 .... *Routledge.*

— Vignettes: 12 biog. sketches. cr. 8°. $2.50. *Routledge.*

64 *For* **Berchman,** J: *read* **Berchmann,** J:

84 *After* **Bonnechose,** Émile de. History of France, etc., *insert* — Hero of Brittany. *See* Popular library of history.

85 **Books** about wonderful and curious things. *After* Elder Park garden, *read* by A. Payne.

86 *For* **Borgo,** —., *read* **Borgo,** C:

141 **Child** of prayer. *For* a father's memorial, etc., *read* Tyng, S. H. 50c. .... *Randolph.*

219 **Dutton,** Amy. *For* Streets and lakes of a city, *read* Streets and lanes of a city.

227 **Elder** Park; or, scenes in our garden. *For* ('67.) New ed. 16°. '73, *read* Payne, A.

Elder Park series. *After* Elder Park, *read* by A. Payne.

241 *For* **Ewing,** F. Historical memoirs, etc., *read* Ewing, R. C. Historical memoirs, etc.

Note. The Lectures are by F. Ewing.

286 **Gladstone,** W: Ewart. Speeches of Pius IX. *For* $1.75, *read* pap., 25c.

301 **Great** question. *For* essay. 16°. '56, *read* White, L.

315 **Hamersly,** L. R. Records of living officers, etc. After *Lippincott;* insert *Van Nostrand.*

316 *Take out* **Hammersly,** L. B. Records of living officers, etc.

332 **Heisler,** D. Y. Gift book for the million, etc. For *Ref. Ch. Bd.*, read *Ref. Ch. Pub.*

337 **Hero** of Brittany. For *See* Popular library of history, read *See* Bonnechose, É. de.

340 **Higginson,** T: W. *Insert* — Army life in a black regiment. 16°. $1.50 .... *Lee & S.*

— Atlantic essays. 12°. $1.50 .... *Lee & S.*

— Malbone: an Oldport romance. 16°. $1.50 .. *Lee & S.*

— Oldport days. ill. 12°. $2 .... *Lee & S.*

— Out-door papers. 16°. $1.50 .... *Lee & S.*

348 *After* **Holbeach,** H: *insert* (*pseud.*)

349 *For* **Hollen,** J. C., *read* **Hotten,** J: C.

378 *Insert* **Jackson,** I. W. Elementary treatise on mechanics. 8°. '74. bds., $2.50 .... *Barhyte.*

— Elements of trigonometry, plane and spherical. 8°. '74. pap., 50c. .... *Barhyte.*

380 **James,** H: Substance and shadow. *For* mortality, *read* morality.

382 *For* **Jaques,** D. H., *read* **Jacques,** D. H.

429 **Lewis,** Tayler. *Insert* — The Bible and science; or, the world problem. 12°. '56. $1.50 .. *Barhyte.*

479 *Take out* **Martyn,** H: Memoir of J. Sargent, etc.

PAGE

504 *For* **Mohan,** Milo, *read* **Mahan,** Milo.

505 **Monroe,** Lew. B. *Insert* — Miscellaneous readings in prose and verse; for home, school and public readings. 12°. '72. $1.50 .... *Lee & S.*

518 *For* **Murrel,** J: A., *read* **Murel,** J: A.

526 *Take out* **Neiremurg,** E. Treatise on difference between temporal and eternal. $2 .... *O'Shea.*

562 *Take out* **Parkes,** Bessie Raynor. Essays on woman's work. 16°. $1.50 .... *Routledge.*

— La belle France. ill. 8°. $3 .... *Routledge.*

— Vignettes: 12 biog. sketches. cr. 8°. $2.50. *Routledge.*

567 *Insert* **Payne,** *Mrs.* Alfred. Elder Park; or, scenes in our garden. ('67.) New ed. 16°. '73. 90c. .. *Hoyt.*

— — *See also* Books about wonderful and curious things.

590 **Popular** library of history. *After* Hero of Brittany, *read* by É. de Bonnechose.

608 *Insert* **Rands,** W. B. *See* Holbeach, H:

628 *For* **Rochsa,** N. C., *read* **Bochsa,** N. C:

641 **Sage** es Jesu. *For* 18°, *read* Shipton, A.

646 *Insert* **Sargent,** J: Memoir of H: Martyn. '34. 60c. *Am. Tr.*

649 *Take out* **Schenck,** B. S. Mercersburg theology inconsistent with Protestant and reformed doctrine. 12°. $1.25 .... *Lippincott.*

652 *After* **Schneck,** B: S. Mercersburger Theologie, etc., *insert* — Mercersburg theology inconsistent with Protestant and reformed doctrine. 12°. $1.25. *Lippincott.*

671 **Shipton,** Anna. *After* Tell Jesus, etc., *Insert* — *Germ.* Sage es Jesu. 18°. 45c. ..... *Ev. Assoc.*

675 *Take out* **Simons,** J: W. Comparison of Egyptian symbols with those of the Hebrews; tr. by F. Portal. 12°. '75. $1 .... *Masonic.*

683 *Take out* **Smith,** Mirah. The seven trumpets. 16°. '75. pap., 15c. .... *Sev. Day Adv.*

684 **Smith,** Uriah. *After* — Nature and destiny of man, etc., *insert* — The seven trumpets. 16°. '75. pap., 15c. .... *Sev. Day Adv.*

709 *For* **Streets** and lakes of a city, *read* Streets and lanes of a city.

724 *For* **Taylor,** *Rev.* C. B., *read* **Tayler,** C: B.

725 **Taylor,** I: *For* The world of mine, *read* The world of mind.

759 **Tyng,** Ste. H. *Insert* — Child of prayer: a father's memorial of D. A. Tyng. 32°. '66. 50c. .. *Randolph.*

774 **Vignettes.** *For* Parkes, B. R., *read* Belloc, B. P.

800 *Insert* **White,** L. Great question: essay. 16°. '56. 50c. .... *Meth. Bk. Conc.*

806 *After* **Wilkinson,** W: Cleaver. Free lance in field of life and letters. 12°. '74. $1.50, *insert* *Mason.*

811 **Wilson,** H: *Transfer* — — *Same.* por. 8°. $1.50. *Morton to below* Wilson, H: *and* Caulfield, J. Book of wonderful characters, etc.

825 *For* **Wreck,** F: *read* **Wieck,** F.

THE AMERICAN CATALOGUE

OF BOOKS IN PRINT AND FOR SALE, JULY 1, 1876.

AUTHORS AND TITLES.

A., A. Miriam's trial. ill. 18°. 50c.............*Pott.*

A., E. Bible class guide: lessons on the four Gospels in harmony. 18°. '60. bds., 40c.....*Whittaker.*

A., F. C. Looking up. ill. 18°. 50c.............*Pott.*

A., F. S. (*pseud.*) *See* Flint, *Miss* S. A.

A., L. L. (*pseud.*) *See* Adams, *Mrs.* G. M.

A., S. F. Great success. 16°. '71. $1.50..*H. A. Young.*

A., S. M. How to study the Old Test., in a series of questions. 1st ser.: Genesis to Samuel. sq. 18°. '73. 40c.; 75c.; bds., 25c...........*Randolph.*

A B C-bok för minstabegynnare. 12°. bds., 10c. *Engberg.*

A B C Buch, u. Lese-Schreib- u. Denkübungen, od. erstes Buch. 16°. bds., 15c............*Ludwig.*

A B C (Das) in Bildern u. Bibelsprüchen. [Germ. and Eng.] 12°. pap., 10c...............*Radde.*

A B C of life. Child, A. B. 25c. ....*Colby.*

A B C of whist. W., J. R. 25c...*Scribner, W. & A.*

A B C- u. Bilderbuch. 12°. pap., 10c.; 15c....*Radde.*

A B C- u. Buchstabir-Büchlein. ill. 32°. '60. 10c. *Am. Tr.*

A B C- u. erstes Unterrichtsbuch f. Sonntagschulen. 16°. bds., 20c. ....*Ev. Assoc.*

A. L. O. E. (*pseud.*) *See* Tucker, *Mrs.* C.

A. S. S.: farce. 16°. pap., 15c. ....*French.*

Aarbergs (The). Hervey, R. $1.75......*Macmillan.*

Abaddon and Mahanaim. Bergh, J. F. $1. *Perkinpine.*

Abandoned. *See* Verne, Jules.

Abbe, F: R. The temple rebuilt: poem of Christian faith. 16°. '72. $1.50......*Lockwood, B. & Co.*

Abbé Tigrane. Fabre, F. $1.50 ....*Ford.*

Abbeokuta. Tucker, E. 75c...............*Carter.*

Abbey, A. J. *See* Ogden, W. A., *and* Abbey, A. J.

Abbey, H: Ballads of good deeds, and other verses. 12°. $1.25 ....*Appleton.*

Abbey, R: Apostolic succession: letters to Bp. Green. Rev. and enl. 12°. '50. 75c. ....*So. Meth.*

— Baptismal demonstrations. ('56.) 10th ed. 8°. '76. pap., 20c...........................*So. Meth.*

— Call to the ministry. 8°. '58. pap., 10c. ...*So. Meth.*

— Church and ministry. 18°. '60. 60c. ......*So. Meth.*

— City of God and the church makers: examination into structural Christianity, and criticism of Christian scribes and doctors of the law. cr. 8°. '72. $1.50 ....*Hurd & H.*

— Creed of all men; ed. by T. O. Summers. ('55.) 2d ed. 18°. '75. 40c. ....*So. Meth.*

— Diuturnity; or, the comparative age of the world. 12°. '66. $1.75....................*Pounsford.*

Abbey, R: *continued.*

— Divine assessment for the support of the ministry; ed. by T. O. Summers. 12°. '57. pap., 20c. *So. Meth.*

— Ecce ecclesia; showing the essential identity of the church in all ages. ('68.) 4th ed. 12°. '75. $1.75.............................*So. Meth.*

— Ecclesiastical constitution: origin and character of the church of Christ and the Gospel ministry. ('56.) 2d ed. 12°. '60. $1.50.........*So. Meth.*

— Strictures on church government; ed. by T. O. Summers. 12°. '60. pap., 10c. ....*So. Meth.*

— *See also* Yerger, —, Smedes, —, *and* Abbey, R.

Abbey; or, taking it easy. 18°. 45c. ......*Am. S. S.*

Abbey of Innismoyle. Kennedy, G. 25c. ..*Peterson.*

Abbey of Ross. Burke, O. J. 50c.; 75c. ...*Sadlier.*

Abbot, Ezra. Bibliography of works rel. to nature, etc., of the soul. *See* Alger, W. R., Critical hist. of doct. of a future life.

— *See also* Hudson, C. F., Critical Gk. and Eng. concord. to New Test.; — Orme, W., Memoir of controversy resp. three heavenly witnesses; — Smith, W: Bible dictionary.

Abbot, Fs. E. *See* McQuaid, B. J., *and* Abbot, F. E.

Abbot, H: L. Siege artillery in the campaign against Richmond. pl. 8°. '68. $3.50.... *Van Nostrand.*

— — *See also* United States, *Corps of Eng.*

Abbot (The). *See* Scott, *Sir* W.

Abbott, A. O. Prison life in the south, 1864–5. ill. 12°. $2.............................*Harper.*

Abbott, Abbott A. Life of A. Lincoln. 12°. '64. pap., 25c. ....(?)*Dawley.*

Abbott, Austin. Legal remembrancer: concise statements of law of N. Y. on subjects of importance. 12°. $2.50 ....*Baker, V. & Co.*

— *See also* Abbott, B. V. *and* A.; — New York, Court of Appeals reports; Reports of practice cases; Statutes rel. to partnership; — Tilton, T., *vs.* Beecher, H. W.; — United States, District Court.

Abbott, *Mrs.* Belle Kendrick. Leah Mordecai. [Fiction.] 12°. '75. $1.50........*Baker, P. & Co.*

Abbott, B: V. Digest of decisions of the various courts within the U. S., [1658]–1870. 1st ser. 14 v. roy. 8°. '74–'76. shp., $84..*Little, B. & Co.*

Note. A re-arrangement of the United States digest.

— *Same.* New ser. [Annual.] v. 1–6 (1870–'75). roy. 8°. '72–'76. ea., shp., $6..*Little, B. & Co.*

— Digest of U. S. courts reports and of acts of Congress [1789]–1875. ('67.) 2d ed. 6 v. roy. 8°. '75. shp., $45......................*Ward & P.*

— Treatise upon the U. S. courts and their practice. ('69.) 2d ed. 2 v. roy. 8°. '76. $15..*Ward & P.*

Abbott, B: V., *continued.*
— *See also* New York, Reports of practice cases; — United States, Circuit and District Court reports; District Court reports.
— *and* Austin. Clerks and conveyancers' assistant: forms of conveyancing, contracts and legal proceedings. 8°. shp., $5 .... *Baker, V. & Co.*
— — Collection of forms of practice and pleading. New ed. 2 v. 8°. shp., $10 .... *Baker, V. & Co.*
— — Digest of the law of corporations. roy. 8°. shp., $8.50 .... *Baker, V. & Co.*
— — Digest of New York statutes and reports to 1873; with add. to 1876. 6 v. roy. 8°. ea., shp., $6.50. *Baker, V. & Co.*
Abbott, E: Baby's (The) things: a Christmas story in verse. ill. 4°. '71. 75c.; pap., 35c. *Randolph.*
— Dialogues of Christ. 32°. 60c. .... *Cong. Pub.*
— Paragraph hist. of Am. revolution. sq. 18°. '76. 50c. *Roberts.*
— Paragraph hist. of U. S. sq. 18°. '75. 50c... *Roberts.*
Abbott, Edn. Abbott. Bible lessons. 2d ed. 12°. '71. $1.50 .... *Macmillan.*
— Child's Christmas sheaf from the Bible fields. ill. 16°. $1 .... *Bost. Am. Tr.*
— Concordance to works of Alexander Pope. 8°. $4. *Appleton.*
— Good voices: a child's guide to the Bible. ill. 16°. '71. $1 .... *Dutton.*
— *Same.* ill. 12°. '72. $1.25 .... *Macmillan.*
— How to write clearly: rules and exercises on English composition. 16°. '75. 60c. .... *Roberts.*
— Latin prose [composition] through Eng. idiom; with add. by E. R. Humphreys. 18°. $1 ...... *Allyn.*
— Parables for children. ill. 12°. '73. $1.25. *Macmillan.*
— Sermons preached before the Univ. of Cambridge. 8°. '75. $2 .... *Macmillan.*
— Shakespearian grammar: ill. of the differences between Elizabethan and modern Eng. New ed., enl. 12°. '74. $2 .... *Macmillan.*
— *and* Seeley, J. R. English lessons for English people. 16°. '71. $1.50 .... *Roberts.*
Abbott, G. S. Baptist question book. 18°. 15c. *Am. Bapt.*
Abbott, Jac. Aboriginal America. ill. 16°. $1.25. *Sheldon.*
— August stories. 4 v. 16°. '71–'72. ea., $1.50.. *Dodd.*
Cont.: August and Elvie. — Hunter and Tom. — Schooner Mary Ann. — Granville valley.
— Discovery of America. ill. 16°. $1.25 ..... *Sheldon.*
— Florence stories. 6 v. ill. 16°. $6 .... *Sheldon.*
Cont.: Florence and John. — Grimkie. — Isle of Wight. — Orkney Islands. — English Channel. — Florence's return.
— Franconia stories. 10 v. ill. 16°. ea., 90c... *Harper.*
Cont.: Malleville. — Mary Bell. — Ellen Linn. — Wallace. — Beechnut. — Stuyvesant. — Agnes. — Mary Erskine. — Rodolphus. — Caroline.
— Gentle measures in training the young. ill. 12°. $1.75 .... *Harper.*
— Harlie stories. 6 v. sq. 16°. $3 .... *Sheldon.*
Cont.: The new shoes; or, productive work with little hands. — The French flower; or, be kind and obliging to your teacher. — Harlie's letter; or, how to learn with little teaching. — Wild Peggie; or, charity with discretion. — The sea-shore; or, how to plan picnics and excursions. — Friskie the pony; or, do no harm to harmless animals.
— Harper's story books. 36 v. ill. sq. 4°. ea., 90c. Same: in 12 v. ea., $1.75 .... *Harper.*
Cont.: Bruno. — Willie and the mortgage. — The strait gate. — The little Louvre. — Prank. — Emma. — Virginia. — Timboo and Joliba. — Timboo and Fanny. — Harper establishment. — Franklin. — The studio. — Story of ancient hist. — Story of Eng. hist. — Story of Am. hist. — John True. — Elfred. — The museum. — The engineer. — Rambles among the Alps. — Three gold dollars. — Gibraltar gallery — The alcove. — Dialogues. — The great elm. — Aunt Margaret. — Vernon. — Carl and Jocko. — Lapstone. — Orkney. — Judge Justin. — Minigo. — Jasper. — Congo. — Viola. — Little Paul.
— John Gay; or, work for boys. 4 v. ill. 18°. '75. $4. *Hurd & H.*
— Jonas books. ('39.) New ed. 6 v. ill. 18°. '75. $4.50 .... *Clark & M.*

Abbott, Jac., *continued.*
Cont.: Jonas' stories. — Jonas a judge. — Jonas on a farm, winter. — Jonas on a farm, summer. — Caleb in town. — Caleb in the country.
— Juno stories. 4 v. ill. 16°. '70. ea., $1 ..... *Dodd.*
Cont.: Juno and Georgie. — Mary Osborn. — Hubert. — Juno on a journey.
— Little learner series. 5 v. ill. 16°. ea., 90c... *Harper.*
Cont.: Learning to talk — to think — to read — about common things — about right and wrong.
— Lucy books. ('41.) New ed. 6 v. ill. 18°. '75. $4.50 .... *Clark & M.*
Cont.: Lucy's stories — conversations — studies. — Lucy at play — on the sea-shore — on the mountains.
— Marco Paul's voyages and travels in pursuit of knowledge. 6 v. ill. 16°. ea., 90c. .... *Harper.*
Cont.: In New York. — On the Erie canal. — In the forests of Maine. — In Vermont. — In Boston. — At the Springfield armory.
— Mary Gay; or, work for girls. 4 v. ill. 18°. '75. $4 .... *Hurd & H.*
— Northern colonies (The). ill. 16°. $1.25... *Sheldon.*
— Rainbow and Lucky series. 5 v. ill. 16°. ea., 90c. *Harper.*
Cont.: Handie. — Rainbow's journey. — The Three Pines. — Selling Lucky. — Up the river.
— Revolt of the colonies. ill. 16°. $1.25 ..... *Sheldon.*
— Rollo books. 14 v. ill. 16°. $14; — chp. ed. 18°. $8.75 .... *Sheldon.*
Cont.: Rollo learning to walk — to read — at work — at play — at school. — Rollo's vacation — experiments — museum — travels — correspondence — philosophy, water — philosophy, air — philosophy, fire — philosophy, sky.
— Rollo code of morals. 18°. '41. 50c.; bds., 40c. *Crocker.*
— Rollo story books. 12 v. ill. 18°. $4 ..... *Sheldon.*
Cont.: Trouble on the mountain. — Causey building. — Apple gathering. — Two wheel-barrows. — Blueberrying. — The freshet. — Georgie. — Rollo in the woods. — Rollo's garden. — The steeple trap. — Labor lost. — Lucy's visit.
— Rollo's tour in Europe. 10 v. ill. 16°. $9... *Sheldon.*
Cont.: Rollo on the Atlantic — in Paris — in Switzerland — in London — on the Rhine — in Scotland — in Geneva — in Holland — in Naples — in Rome.
— Science for the young. 4 v. ill. 12°. ea., $1.50. *Harper.*
Cont.: Heat. — Light. — Water and land. — Force.
— Southern colonies (The). ill. 16°. $1.25.. *Sheldon.*
— Summer (A) in Scotland. ill. 12°. $1.75.. *Harper.*
— Teacher (The): moral influence in the instruction and government of the young. ill. 12°. $1.75. *Harper.*
— Visit to the mountains. 18°. '43. 50c. .... *Crocker.*
— War of the revolution. ill. 16°. $1.25 ..... *Sheldon.*
— Wars of the colonies. ill. 16°. $1.25 ..... *Sheldon.*
— Washington. ill. 16°. $1.25 .... *Sheldon.*
— William Gay; or, play for boys. 4 v. ill. 18°. '69. $2.50 .... *Hurd & H.*
— Young Christian (The). ill. 12°. (cop. '32.) '34. 80c. .... *Am. Tr.*
— Young Christian series. 4 v. ill. 12°. ea., $1.75. *Harper.*
Cont: The young Christian. — The corner stone. — Way to do good. — Hoaryhead and M'Donner.
— *See also* Abercrombie, J.
— *and* J: S. C. Biographical histories. 32 v. ill. 16°. ea., $1 .... *Harper.*
Cont.: Cyrus the Great. — Darius the Great. — Xerxes. — Alexander the Great. — Romulus. — Hannibal. — Pyrrhus. — Julius Cæsar. — Cleopatra. — Nero. — Alfred the Great. — William the Conqueror. — Richard I. — Richard II. — Richard III. — Margaret of Anjou. — Mary, queen of Scots. — Queen Elizabeth. — Charles I. — Charles II. — Hernando Cortez. — Henry IV. — Louis XIV. — Maria Antoinette. — Madam Roland. — Josephine. — Joseph Bonaparte. — Hortense. — Louis Philippe. — Genghis Khan. — King Philip. — Peter the Great.
— — New Test., with notes. 12°. '41. $1.50.. *Crocker.*
Abbott, J: L. Home-book of wonders in nature, science and art. ill. 12°. '70. *$5 .... *Case.*
Abbott, J: S. C. American pioneers and patriots; ill. early hist. and settlement of Am. 12 v. ill. 12°. '73–'76. ea., $1.50 .... *Dodd.*
Cont.: Adventures of de La Salle and his companions. — Capt. Wm. Kidd and other pirates or buccaneers. — Daniel Boone, the pioneer of Kentucky. — David Crockett. — Ferdinand De Soto, the discoverer of the Mississippi. — George Washington. — Kit Carson, the pioneer of the far west. — Life and

Abbott, J: S. C., *continued.*
adventures of John Paul Jones. — Life of Ben. Franklin. — Life of Christopher Columbus. — Miles Standish, the Puritan captain. — Peter Stuyvesant, the last Dutch governor of New Amsterdam.

— Child (The) at home; or, principles of filial duty. ill. 16°. $1 .... *Harper.*
— *Same.* (cop. '33.) New ed. ill. 18°. '35. 45c. *Am. Tr.*
— *German.* Das Kind im elterlichen Hause. ill. 18°. '45. 40c. .... *Am. Tr.*
— French revolution (The) of 1789 in the light of republican institutions. ill. 8°. $5; shp., $5.50; hf. cf., $7.25 .... *Harper.*
— History of the civil war in Am. [*In* Eng. *or* Germ.] 2 v. ill. 8°. ea., *$3.50; leath., $4; — in 1 v. *$5; leath., $5.50 .... *C. A. Nichols.*
— *Same.* ('63.) New ed. 2 v. ill. 8°. '75. *$6; $7; $8 .... *Henry Bill.*
— History of Frederick the Great. ill. 8°. $5; hf. cf., $7.25 .... *Harper.*
— History of Maine; from [its] discovery by the Northmen. ill. 8°. *$3.50; hf. mor., $4.25; shp., $4.50 .... *Russell.*
— History of Napoleon Bonaparte. 2 v. maps, ill., etc. 8°. $10; shp., $11; hf. cf., $14.50 .... *Harper.*
— Italy and the war for Ital. independence; incl. sketch of Pius IX., etc. por. and maps. 8°. *$2.50; $3 .... *Russell.*
— Kings and queens; or, life in the palace: hist. sketches. ill. 12°. $1.75 .... *Harper.*
— Life of Napoleon III. ill. roy. 8°. *$3.50; mor., $4.50 .... *Russell.*
— Life of U. S. Grant. ill. and maps. 12°. *$1.50; mor., $2 .... *Russell.*
— Lives of the presidents of the U. S.; [with account of] the hundred years' progress of the republic. ill. 8°. *$3.50; hf. mor., $4.25; shp., $4.50. *Russell.*
— Mother (The) at home; or, the principles of maternal duty. ill. 16°. $1 .... *Harper.*
— *Same.* 18°. '33. 40c. .... *Am. Tr.*
— *German.* Die Familienmutter. 18°. '75. 40c. *Am. Tr.*
— Napoleon at St. Helena. ill. 8°. $5; shp., $5.50; hf. cf., $7.25 .... *Harper.*
— Practical Christianity. 16°. $1 .... *Harper.*
— Romance of Spanish hist. ill. 12°. $2 .... *Harper.*
— *See also* Abbott, J. *and* J. S. C.

Abbott, Lyman. Acts; with notes and comments. maps and ill. 8°. '76. $1.75 .... *Barnes.*
— Jesus of Nazareth: his life and teachings. ill. cr. 8°. $3.50; shp., $4; hf. cf., $5.75 ..... *Harper.*
— Layman's (A) story; or, the experiences of John Laicus and his wife in a country parish. 16°. '73. $1.25 .... *Dodd.*
— New Testament with notes and comments: Matthew and Mark. maps and ill. 8°. '75. $2.50. *Barnes.*
— *Same.* ill. roy. 8°. '76. *$3.50; shp., $4.50; hf. cf., $6.50 .... *Barnes.*
— Old Test. shadows of New Test. truths. ill. 8°. $3; $3.50; hf. cf., $5.25 .... *Harper.*
— *and* Conant, T. C. (*ed.*) Dictionary of religious knowledge. maps and ill. roy. 8°. *$6; shp., $7; hf. mor., $8.50 .... *Harper.*

Abbott, *Rev.* O. Peep into sacred tradition. 2d ed., rev. 16°. '67. pap., 50c. .... (?) *Emerson.*

Abbott, Rosa (*pseud.*) *See* Parker, R. A.

Abbott, Waldo. Our Sunday school, and how we conduct it. ('63.) New ed. 16°. '72. $1.15 .. *Hoyt.*

Abdallah. Laboulaye, E. $1.25 .... *Scribner, W. & A.*

A'Beckett, Gilb. A. [Plays.] 12 v. 16°. ea., pap., 15c. .... *French.*
Cont.: Angelo; or, the actress of Padua. — Clear case: farce. — Figaro in London: farce. — Glitter: comedy. — Lending a hand: comedy. — Man with the carpet-bag: farce. — Manfred: burlesque. — Mendicant. — Roof scrambler: opera. — Siamese twins: farce. — Turned head: farce. — Unfortunate Miss Bailey.

A'Beckett, Gilb. A., *continued.*
— Comic Blackstone. ill. 16°. $1.50 ...... *Lippincott.*
— Comic hist. of Eng. ill. by J. Leech. 8°. $6. *Appleton; Lippincott; Scribner, W. & A.*
— *Same;* [also] Comic hist. of Rome. ill. by J. Leech. 2 v. 8°. hf. cf., $14 .... *Lippincott.*
— Comic hist. of Rome. ill. by J. Leech. 8°. $3.75. *Appleton; Lippincott; Scribner, W. & A.*
— Lending a hand: comedy. 16°. pap., 15c. .. *Lee & S.*

Abednego, the money lender. *See* Gore, *Mrs.* C. G.

Abeel, Gst., Murdoch, D., *and* McKee, J. Memorials of Rev. James Scott. [Sermons.] 8°. pap., 50c. *N. Y. Ref. Ch. Bd.*

Abeille (L') pour les enfans; ou, leçons françaises. pt. 1. 18°. 30c. .... *Fortescue.*

Abel Drake's wife. Saunders, J. 75c. ...... *Harper.*

Abel Gray. 18°. 75c. .... *Tilton.*
— *Same.* 18°. '60. 60c. .... *Am. Tr.*

Abell, *Mrs.* L. G. Skillful housewife: guide to cookery, taste, comfort, economy, etc. 12°. 75c. ... *Judd.*

Abellino. *See* Zschokke, H.

Abellino, d. grosse Bandit. 12°. pap., 15c. *Radde; F. W. Thomas.*

Abelons, L: D: Gustavus Adolphus, the hero of the reformation; tr. by Mrs. C. A. Lacroix. ill. 12°. '71. $1 .... *Meth. Bk. Conc.*
— William the Taciturn; tr. by J. L. Lacroix. ill. 12°. '72. $1.25 .... *Meth. Bk. Conc.*

Abenteuer (Das) der Neujahrsnacht. *See* Zschokke, H.

Abercrombie, J. Contest (The) and armor. 32°. 50c. *Carter.*
— Inquiries conc. the intellectual powers; with questions. 18°. 75c. .... *Harper.*
— *Same;* with add., etc., by J. Abbott. New ed. 12°. '74. $1.05 .... *Collins & Bro.*
— Miscellaneous essays. 18°. 75c. .... *Harper.*
— Philosophy of the moral feelings; with questions. 18°. 75c. .... *Harper.*
— *Same;* [ed. by] J. Abbott. New ed. 12°. '74. $1.05. *Collins & Bro.*

Abercrombie, R. M. Prayer-book and its story. 18°. $1.25 .... *Dutton.*

Abiding comforter. Atwood, A. $1.25 ... *A. Wallace.*

Abijah. 18°. 18c. .... *Am. S. S.*

Able to save; or, encouragement to patient waiting; by author of "The pathway to promise." 16°. $1 .... *Carter; Routledge.*

Abnakis (The) and their hist. Vetromile, E. $1.25. *Strong.*

Abney, A. H. Life and adventures of L. D. Lafferty. 12°. '75. $1 .... (?) *Goodspeed.*

Abode of snow. Wilson, A. $2.25 ...... *Putnam.*

Abominations (The) of modern society. Talmage, T. De W. $1.50 .... *Adams, V. & Co.*

Abou Ben Adhem. Locke, D. R. $1.50 .... *Lee & S.*

Abou Hassan. Talfourd, F. 15c. .... *French.*

About, Edmond. Hand-book of social economy; or, the worker's ABC. 12°. $2 .... *Appleton.*
— Man (The) with the broken ear; tr. by H. Holt. ('67.) New ed. (Leis. hour ser.) 16°. '76. $1.25. *Holt.*
— Notary's (The) nose; tr. (Leis. hour ser.) 16°. '74. $1.25 .... *Holt.*
— Rouge et noir: a tale of Baden-Baden; tr. by E. R. 12°. '73. $1.50; pap., $1 .... *Claxton.*
— *See also* Brette, P. H. E., *and* Masson, G.

About common wonders. *See* Sunberry Dale lib.

About in the world. Friswell, J. H. $3. *Scribner, W. & A.*

About men and things. Henry, C. S. 75c.; $1.50. *Whittaker.*

Above and below. Reed, R. P. $1.25 ... *Cong. Pub.*

Above the breakers. Onley, M. 75c. ...... *Nelson.*

Above rubies. *See* Brightwell, C. L.
Above suspicion. Riddell, J. H. $1.25; 75c...*Estes.*
Above tempest and tide. Verena, S. $1.50. *McKinney.*
Abraham. Leben. 18°. 40c............*Ev. Assoc.*
Abraham the patriarch. 18°. 35c.........*Am. S. S.*
Abraham Page, Esq. Holt, J. S. $1.50..*Lippincott.*
Abrantès, *Duchesse* d'. Memoirs of Napoleon, his court and family. 2 v. por. 8°. $5; hf. cf., $10. *Appleton.*
Abroad. Brown, H. E. $1.25.......*Bost. Am. Tr.*
Ab-sa-ra-ka, home of the crows: experience of an officer's wife on the plains. ill. 12°. $2. *Lippincott.*
Absent man: comedietta. 16°. pap., 15c.....*French.*
Absentee. *See* Edgeworth, M.
Absolute money. Hill, B. A. $1; 50c.......*Gray.*
Abyssinian boy (The). ('57.) 2d ed. 18°. '69. 50c. *So. Meth.*
Academic atlas of modern and classical geog. 4°. '75. $2.50...........................*Putnam.*
Academic speaker. 12°. pap., 15c.........*De Witt.*
Academy of Natural Sciences of Phila. Journal, 1817-'39. 8 v. 8°. $48......*Acad. of Nat. Sci.*
— *Same.* 2d ser. v. 1-7 (1847-'74); v. 8, pt. 1. 4°. v. 1-7, ea., $12.50; v. 8, pt. 1, $3.75 *Acad. of Nat. Sci.*
— Proceedings, 1841-'76. 28 v. 8°. v. 1-22, ea., $3.75; v. 23-28, ea., $6.25..........*Acad. of Nat. Sci.*
Academy of Science of St. Louis. Transactions. v. 1-2 (1856-'68); v. 3, nos. 1-3. ill. 8°. v. 1, $4; v. 2, $3; v. 3, nos. 1-3, ea., pap., $1. *St. L. Acad. of Sci.*
Academy of stars: Ethiop. drama. 16°. pap., 15c. *French.*
Academy vocalist. Root, G. F., *and* Mason, L. $1. *Ditson.*
Acadia. Cozzens, F. S. $1.50...........*Hurd & H.*
Accelerate. Caldor, M. T. 15c............*Lee & S.*
Accidents of childhood; or, cautionary stories for heedless children. ill. 16° 50c........*Routledge.*
Accordion at home; with easy method of instruction. obl. 8°. '58. pap., 75c..................*Ditson.*
Accordion songster. *See* Howe, E.; — Winner, S.
Accusing spirit. Suter, W. E. 15c..........*French.*
Achard, Amédée. Belle Rose; tr. by Mrs. M. L. Johnson. 8°. '72. pap., $1.................*Claxton.*
— Clos-pommier (Le); [also] Les prisonniers du Caucase, par X. De Maistre. ('69.) New ed. 12°. '76. 90c................................*Holt.*
Achard, Émile. History of my friends; or, home life with animals; tr. by A. Putnam. ill. 12°. '75. $1.50 ....*Putnam.*
Acharnians. *See* Aristophanes.
Acheson, D: Life. 18°. '53. 35c...........*Am. Tr.*
Achilleïs. *See* Goethe, J. W. v.
Achilles' wrath. *See* Homer.
Achsah. Round, W. M. F. $1.50.......(?)*Lee & S.*
Acht und sechzig biblische Bilder. 4°. $2....*Kohler.*
Acis and Galatea: extravaganza. 16°. pap., 15c. *French.*
Acis and Galatea: burlesque. Burnand, F. C. 15c. *French.*
Acis and Galatea: opera. Gay, H. 15c......*French.*
Ackerman, A. First book in natural hist. ('46.) New ed. ill. 12°. '76. $1.............*Clark & M.*
Ackermann, G. C. B. On the Christian element in Plato; tr. by S. R. Ashbury. 8°. $3.75. *Scribner, W. & A.*
Ackland, *Rev.* T. S. The story of creation as told by theology and science. 16°. 75c...........*Pott.*
Acolyte (The). Hughes, T. $1.50....*Cunningham.*
Acrelius, Israel. History of New Sweden; or, the settlements on the river Delaware; tr. from the Swed., with introd. and notes, by W. M. Reynolds. 8°. $4.....................*Lippincott.*
— — *See also* Hist. Soc. of Penna.
Across America. Rusling, J. F. $2.......*Sheldon.*
Across America and Asia. Pumpelly, R. $5; $2.50. *Holt.*
Across the Atlantic. Haeseler, C. H. $2..*Peterson.*
Across the continent. Bowles, S. $1.50; $2. *Hurd & H.*
Across the desert. Campbell, S. M. $1.50..*Pres. Bd.*
Across Mexico in 1864-5. Bullock, W. H. $2.50. *Macmillan.*
Across the sea. Chard, T. S. $1............*Jansen.*
Across the sea. Clarke, B. $1..............*Nelson.*
Acté. *See* Dumas, A., Convert of St. Paul.
Acting drama. nos. 1-50. 16°. ea., pap., 15c. *Happy.*
Acting plays of Edwin Booth. *See* Hinton, H. L.
Actions and words. *See* Sunbeam series.
Actions speak louder than words. Neely, K. J. $1. *Lee & S.*
Active Christian (The). Harris, J. 25c.; 40c.; $1. *Lothrop.*
Acton, *Lord.* *See* Gladstone, W. E., Vatican decrees.
Acton, *Miss* Eliza. Modern cookery; rev. by Mrs. S. J. Hale; with index. ill. 12°. $1.75...*J. E. Potter.*
Acton, W: Functions and disorders of the reproductive organs; in their physiological, social and moral relations. 4th Am. from 5th Lond. ed., rev. and enl. 8°. '75. $3...........*Lindsay.*
— Prostitution; in its moral, social and sanitary aspects. 2d ed., enl. 8°. '70. $5.............*Lindsay.*
Actor and singer: Ethiop. drama. 16°. pap., 15c. *French; Happy.*
Actor's retreat. Brough, W., *and* Halliday, A. 15c. *French.*
Acts. *See* Bible.
Acts and monuments of the church. *See* Fox, John.
Acts of the early martyrs. 4 v. 12°. ea., $1.50..*Sadlier.*
Acts of Parliament. *See* England, Law reports.
Ad clerum. Parker, J. $1.50..............*Roberts.*
Ad fidem. Burr, E. F. $2......*Lockwood, B. & Co.*
Ada and Gerty. Gray, L. M. $1.25........*Am. Tr.*
Ada Arundel. Reynolds, G. W. M. 50c.....*De Witt.*
Ada Emory. Yule, J. C. $1.50..........*Am. Bapt.*
Ada Hovey's idols. Newhall, M. $1.25...*Cong. Pub.*
Ada Leigh. Egan, P. 50c.................*De Witt.*
Ada library (The). 6 v. ill. 18°. '75. $4.50..*Nelson.*
Cont.: Little Ada's jewels, by F. Levien, 2 v. — Katie Summers, by Mrs. C. Hall, 2 v. — Roses without thorns, by E. F. Fleet, 2 v.
Adam, Alex. Latin grammar; rev. and enl. by B. A. Gould. 12°. $1.50....................*Butler.*
— Roman antiquities; with notes and indices, by J. Boyd. ('36.) 8th ed., with add. notes by L. L. Da Ponte. ill. 8°. shp., $2.50........*Claxton.*
Adam, C. G. D. Young ladies' vocal album: choruses, trios, etc., with vocal exercises by Rossini. obl. 8°. bds., $1.25........................*Ditson.*
Adam, *Rev.* J: Commentary on the Epistle of James. 8°. $5......................*Scribner, W. & A.*
Adam, S. First Baptist church in Providence not the oldest Bapt. church in Am. 18°. 30c...*So. Bapt.*
Adam, *Rev.* T: Private thoughts on religion; with sketch of life of A. 18°. 65c.........*Pres. Bd.*
Adam and the Adamite. McCausland, D. $2.50. *Scribner, W. & A.*
Adam and Christ. Wines, E. C. 30c......*Pres. Bd.*
Adam and his times. Lowrie, J. M. $1...*Pres. Bd.*
Adam Bede. *See* Eliot, George.
Adam Brown. Smith, H. 50c.............*Harper.*

Adams, *Mrs.* —. Bessie Grant's treasure. sq. 16°. 75c. *Fuller.*

Adams, Abigail. *See* Adams, J: *and* A.

Adams, C. B. *See* Gray, A., *and* Adams, C. B.;—Vermont geol. survey.

Adams, C. K. Democracy and monarchy in France. ('74.) New ed. 12°. '75. $2.50 .... *Holt.*

Adams, *Rev.* C: Earth (The) and its wonders. ill. 16°. $1.25 .... *Cin. Meth. Bk. Conc.*
— Life of Cromwell. 12°. '67. $1.25 .. *Meth. Bk. Conc.*
— Life of S: Johnson. 12°. '69. $1.25 .. *Meth. Bk. Conc.*
— Memoir of Washington Irving; with sel. from works and criticisms. 12°. '70. $1.25 .. *Meth. Bk. Conc.*
— Memorial of C: Wesley. 12°. '59. $1 .. *Meth. Bk. Conc.*
— Minister of Christ for the times. 16°. 70c. *Cin. Meth. Bk. Conc.*
— New Testament church-members. 12°. '51. 90c. *Meth. Bk. Conc.*
— Women of the Bible. 12°. '51. $1 .. *Meth. Bk. Conc.*
— Words that shook the world; or, Martin Luther his own biographer. 12°. '58. $1.25 .. *Meth. Bk. Conc.*

Adams, C: Fs. Address at Amherst Coll. before the Social Union, July 7, 1875. 8°. '75. pap., 25c. *Hurd & H.*
— Life of John Adams. *See* Adams, J: Works.
— Memoirs of John Quincy Adams, compr. portions of his diary, 1795–1848. v. 1–10. por. 8°. '74–'76. ea., $5 .... *Lippincott.*
— Memorial address on W. H. Seward. 8°. pap., 25c. *Appleton.*
— Struggle for neutrality in Am.: address, Dec. 13, 1870. 8°. '71. pap., 50c .... *Scribner.*
— *See also* Adams, J., Works;—Adams, J. *and* A., Familiar letters;—Adams, J. Q. *and* C. F., Life of J. Adams.

Adams, C: Fs., *jr.* The railroad problem: lecture. 8°. '75. pap., 15c .... *R. R. Gazette.*
— *and* H: Chapters of Erie, and other essays. 12°. '71. $2 .... *Osgood.*

Adams, Ctte. Ben Howard; or, truth and honesty. 18°. 45c. .... *Routledge.*
— Boys at home. 16°. $1.25 .... *Routledge.*
— Edgar Clifton; or, right and wrong. 16°. $1.25. *Routledge.*
— John Hartley, and how he got on in life. 16°. 75c. *Routledge.*
— Laura and Lucy: a tale for girls. 12°. $1.25. *Scribner, W. & A.*
— Mamma's little friend. 18°. 40c .... *Dutton.*
— Matilda Lonsdale. 16°. $1.25 .... *Routledge.*

Adams, Dan. Arithmetic. Rev. ed. 12°. '75. hf. bd., 75c.—Key. 12°. 75c .... *Collins & Bro.*
— Improved arithmetic. New ed. 12°. '70. hf. bd., 75c.—Key. 12°. 75c. .... *Collins & Bro.*

Adams, E. The Iowa band. 16°. $1.25 .. *Cong. Pub.*

Adams, Fs. Free school system of the U. S. 8°. $4.50. *Scribner, W. & A.*

Adams, Fs. Colburn. Siege of Washington; for little people. ill. sq. 12°. '67. $1.50 .... *Claxton.*
— The Von Toodleburgs; or, the memoirs of a very distinguished family. ill. 12°. '68. $1.75 .. *Claxton.*

Adams, *Mrs.* G. M. A ride through the Holy Land. ('74.) New ed. ill. 16°. '75. $1 .... *Hoyt.*

Adams, *Rev.* H. C. Balderscourt; or, holiday tales. 16°. $1.25 .... *Routledge.*
— Boy cavaliers (The); or, the siege of Clidesford. 16°. $1 .... *Routledge.*
— Bradford bridge; or, school-boy trials. 16°. $1.25. *Routledge.*
— Cherry stones (The); or, the force of conscience. 16°. 75c .... *Dutton; Routledge.*
— Chief (The) of the school; or, school-boy ambition. 16°. '73. 75c .... *Routledge.*
— Doctor's (The) birthday; or, the force of example. 16°. '72. 75c .... *Routledge.*

Adams, *Rev.* H. C., *continued.*
— Encombe stories (The); or, tales for Sunday reading. 16°. $1.75 .... *Scribner, W. & A.*
— Falcon family; or, Meta and Willie. 16°. $1.75. *Scribner, W. & A.*
— Falconhurst; or, birthday tales. 16°. $1. *Scribner, W. & A.*
— First (The) of June; or, school-boy rivalry. 18°. 60c. .... *McCauley.*
— *Same.* 16°. 75c. .... *Routledge.*
— Friend or foe: a tale of Sedgmoor. 16°. '70. $1. *Routledge.*
— Gannet Island; or, Willie's birthday. 16°. $1. *Scribner, W. & A.*
— Indian boy (The). 16°. 75c. .... *Routledge.*
— Judges (The) of Israel. 16°. $1 .. *Scribner, W. & A.*
— Lost rifle (The). 16°. '75. 75c.; $1.25 .. *Routledge.*
— School-boy stories (The) library. 3 v. ill. 16°. ea., $1.25 .... *Routledge.*

Cont.: Tales of Charlton school.—School-boy honor.—Walter's school-days.

— Stories for Sundays: tales ill. of Scripture. 16°. '74. $1.25. .... *Routledge.*
— Stories of the kings. 16°. $1 .... *Scribner, W. & A.*
— Stories of the prophets. 16°. $1 .. *Scribner, W. & A.*
— Sunday evenings at home: stories from hist. 2 v. ill. 12°. ea., $1.75. .... *Routledge.*
— *Same.* 5 v. ill. 16°. ea., 75c. .... *Routledge.*
— Tales of the civil wars. 16°. $1.25 ..... *Routledge.*
— Tales of Nethercourt. 16°. '75. $1.25 .. *Routledge.*
— Tales upon texts: stories ill. of Scripture. 12°. '70. $1.75 .... *Routledge.*
— Walter's friend; or, big boys and little boys. 16°. '72. 75c .... *Routledge.*
— White Brunswickers (The); or, reminiscences of school-boy life. 16°. '69. $1.50 ...... *Routledge.*
— Winborough boys (The); or, Ellerslie Park. 12°. '71. $1.75 .... *Routledge.*
— Woodleigh stories (The); or, tales for Sunday reading. 16°. $1.75 .... *Scribner, W. & A.*
— Wroxby College; or, the Luscombe prize. 12°. '73. $1.75 .... *Routledge.*

Adams, H. G. Cage and singing birds: how to catch, keep, breed and rear them. 16°. 50c ... *Routledge.*
— Language and poetry of flowers. ('53.) New ed. 12°. '70. $1.50; mor., $2.50 .... *Claxton.*

Adams, H: *See* Adams, C. F., *jr.*, *and* H.

Adams, J. B., *and* Durham, W. J. Real estate laws of Illinois; with decisions of Sup. Court and notes. 2 v. 8°. '74. shp., $12 ...... *Callaghan.*

Adams, J. S. New musical dict. 16°. $1.50; bds., $1.25 .... *Gordon.*

Adams, *Mrs.* J. S. Allegories of life. 4°. $1.25. *Lee & S.*

Adams, Jack. *See* Life and adventures of.

Adams, Ja. O. *See* New Hampshire, Board of Agri.

Adams, J: Works, with life, notes, etc., by C. F. Adams. 10 v. por. 8°. '50–'56. $30; hf. cf., $50. *Little, B. & Co.*
— *and* Abigail. Familiar letters during the revolution; ed., with memoir of Mrs. Adams, by C. F. Adams. por. cr. 8°. '75. $2 .... *Hurd & H.*

Adams, J: *jr.* Doctrine of equity: comment. on the law as administered by the Court of Chancery [Eng.]; with notes and ref. to Am. cases by J. R. Ludlow, etc. 6th Am. ed., ed. by G. Sharswood, jr. 8°. '73. $7.50 .. *T. & J. W. Johnson.*

Adams, J: Greenleaf. Gospel psalmist; for Universalists. 18°. '61. shp., $1.50;—with music. 8°. $1.50 .... *Universalist.*
— History of the apostles; for S.-schools. 16°. '39. per doz., pap., $1.25 .... *Universalist.*
— Memoir of Mrs. M. A. Adams. 18°. '65. 60c. *Universalist.*
— Sabbath-school melodist. 16°. '66. 35c. *Universalist.*
— Vestry harmonies: hymns and tunes for social worship. 12°. '68. per doz., $6 .... *Universalist.*

Adams, J: Greenleaf, *continued.*
— *and* Chapin, E. H. Hymns for Christian devotion [chiefly Universalist]. New ed. 18°. '70. $1.50–$5 .... *Universalist.*

Adams, J: Milton. *See* Maine, Supreme Court reports.

Adams, J: Quincy. Dermot Mac Morrogh; or, the conquest of Ireland: hist. tale of 12th cent. 3d ed. roy. 18°. '34. 20c.; 25c..... *I. N. Whiting.*
— Letters to W. Stone, E. Livingstone, etc., on nature of Masonic oaths, etc. 8°. pap., 50c. *E. A. Cook.*
— *and* C. F. Life of John Adams. 2 v. 16°. '71. $3; — in 1 v. 12°. $2 .... *Lippincott.*
— *See also* Davies, C., Metric system.

Adams, *Rev.* J: Quincy. Sanctification. ('62.) New ed. 18°. '63. 25c. .... *Hoyt.*
— (*ed.*) Experiences of the higher Christian life. 3d ed. 12°. '74. $1.25 .... *Tibbals.*

Adams, J: S. Five thousand musical terms: dict. of phrases, abbreviations, etc. New ed., rev., with treatise on playing the organ or piano by figures. 16°. '51. bds., 75c. .... *Ditson.*
— Psalms of life. 5th ed. 12°. '57. $1; bds., 80c. *Ditson.*

Adams, Moses (*pseud.*) *See* Bagby, G. W.

Adams, N. *See* New Hampshire, Law reports.

Adams, *Rev.* Neh. Cross (The) in the cell. 16°. $1. *Bost. Am. Tr.; Cong. Pub.*
— John Eliot. *See* Lives of the chief fathers of N. E.
— Under the mizzen mast. ('73.) New ed. 16°. '76. $1.50 .... *Hoyt.*

Adams, Rob. Rheumatic gout; or, chronic rheumatic arthritis of all the joints. 2d ed. 2 v., text, 8°; plates, f°. '73. $8.50 .... *Lindsay.*

Adams, S. F. "Nearer, my God, to thee." ill. 4°. $2. *Lee & S.*

Adams, S: W. Memoir of Rev. Nath. Kendrick. 12°. $1 .... *Am. Bapt.*

Adams, T. A. S. Enscotidion; or, shadow of death. [Poem.] 12°. '76. $1.25 .... *So. Meth.*

Adams, *Rev.* W. Treatise upon regeneration in baptism. 8°. $2.50 .... *Pott.*

Adams, W. B., *and* Parsons, P. M. Varieties of permanent way on railways. pl. 8°. (Lond.) '57. pap., $1 .... *Spon.*

Adams, W. H. Land of the Nile. ill. 16°. '71. $1.50. *Lothrop.*

Adams, W: Club foot: its causes, pathology and treatment. New ed., rev. and enl. ill. 8°. '73. $6. *Lindsay.*

Adams, *Rev.* W: (*of Oxford*). Distant hills (The). 18°. 60c. .... *Dutton.*
— Fall (The) of Crœsus: a story from Herodotus. 16°. 75c. .... *Pott.*
— Sacred allegories. ill. 16°. $1.25 .... *Pott.*
— *Same.* ill. 4°. mor., $4 .... *Lippincott.*
— Warnings of the holy week. 12°. '72. $1.50 .. *Pott.*

Adams, *Rev.* W: (*of N. Y.*) Conversations of Jesus Christ. 12°. '68. $1; $1.25 .... *Am. Tr.*
— In the world, not of the world. 18°. '67. 25c. *Am. Tr.*
— Mercy to babes. 18°. $1 .... *McCauley.*
— Missionary's (The) mother. 18°. '69. 20c. *Am. Tr.*
— Thanksgiving: memories of the day and helps to the habit. ('67.) New ed. 12°. '69. $2 ... *Scribner.*
— Three gardens (The), Eden, Gethsemane and Paradise; or, man's ruin and redemption and restoration. 12°. $2 .... *Scribner.*

Adams, W: H. Davenport. Beneath the surface: wonders of the sea. ill. 12°. '76. $1.25 ... *Nelson.*
— Buried cities of Campania. ill. 12°. '71. $1.50. *Lothrop.*
— — *See also* Wonder lib.
— Circle of the year. ill. 8°. '72. $2.50 ... *Lothrop.*
— Every-day objects. ill. 8°. '72. $2.50 ... *Lothrop.*
— Forest, jungle and prairie: scenes with the trapper and the hunter. ill. 8°. $2.50 .... *Nelson.*
— Golden book (The) of Eng. song. ill. cr. 8°. '74. $2.50 .... *Nelson.*

Adams, W: H. Davenport, *continued.*
— Queen of the Adriatic; or, Venice, past and present. ill. 12°. '72. $1.75 .... *Lothrop.*
— Records of noble lives: notable Eng. biographies. 12°. $1.50 .... *Nelson.*
— St. Paul: his life, his work, and writings. map. 12°. $1.50 .... *Nelson.*
— Sunshine of domestic life: sketches of womanly virtues, and stories of noble women. 12°. $1.50. *Nelson.*
— Temples, tombs and monuments of anc. Greece and Rome. ill. 12°. $1.50. *Lothrop; Nelson; Tibbals.*
— Wonders of lighthouses. 12°. $1.50 ...... *Tibbals.*

Adams, W: T. ["Oliver Optic."] Army and navy stories. 6 v. ill. 16°. ea., $1.50 ...... *Lee & S.*
Comprises Sailor boy ser. *and* Soldier boy ser.
— Boat-club series. 6 v. ill. 16°. ea., $1.25 .. *Lee & S.*
Cont.: The boat club. — All aboard. — Now or never. — Try again. — Poor and proud. — Little by little.
— Flora Lee story books. 6 v. ill. 24°. ea., 45c. *Lee & S.*
Cont.: Christmas gift. — Uncle Ben. — Birthday party. — The picnic party. — The gold thimble. — The do-somethings.
— Great western series. [To form 6 v.] v. 1. ill. 16°. $1.50 .... *Lee & S.*
Cont.: Going west; or, the perils of a poor boy.
— Household library. v. 1. ill. 12°. $1.75 ... *Lee & S.*
Cont.: In doors and out.
— Lake shore series. 6 v. ill. 16°. ea., $1.25. *Lee & S.*
Cont.: Through by daylight. — Lightning express. — On time. — Switch off. — Brake up. — Bear and forbear.
— Oliver Optic's almanac for our boys and girls. ill. 8°. '72. pap., 30c. .... *Lee & S.*
— Onward and upward series. 6 v. ill. 16°. ea., $1.25. *Lee & S.*
Cont.: Field and forest. — Plane and plank. — Desk and debit. — Cringle and cross-tree. — Bivouac and battle. — Sea and shore.
— Our standard-bearer: life of U. S. Grant. ill. 16°. $1.50 .... *Lee & S.*
— Riverdale stories. 12 v. ill. 24°. ea., 45c. .. *Lee & S.*
Comprises Flora Lee story books *and* Riverdale story books.
— Riverdale story-books. 6 v. ill. 24°. ea., 45c. *Lee & S.*
Cont.: Little merchant. — Young voyagers. — Dolly and I. — Proud and lazy. — Careless Kate. — Robinson Crusoe, jr.
— Sailor boy series. 3 v. ill. 16°. ea., $1.50 .. *Lee & S.*
Cont.: Sailor boy. — Yankee middy. — Brave Old Salt.
— Soldier boy series. 3 v. ill. 16°. ea., $1.50 .. *Lee & S.*
Cont.: Soldier boy. — Young lieutenant. — Fighting Joe.
— Spelling book for adv. classes. 12°. bds., 35c. *Ware.*
— Starry flag series. 6 v. ill. 16°. ea., $1.25. *Lee & S.*
Cont.: The starry flag; or, the young fisherman of Cape Ann. — Breaking away; or, the fortunes of a student. — Seek and find; or, the adventures of a smart boy. — Freaks of fortune; or, half round the world. — Make or break; or, the rich man's daughter. — Down the river; or, Buck Bradford and the tyrants.
— Way of the world. 12°. $1.50 .... *Lee & S.*
— Woodville stories. 6 v. ill. 16°. ea., $1.25. *Lee & S.*
Cont.: Rich and humble. — In school and out. — Watch and wait. — Work and win. — Hope and have. — Haste and waste.
— Yacht club series. 6 v. ill. 16°. ea., $1.50. *Lee & S.*
Cont.: Little Bobtail. — The yacht club. — Money maker. — The Coming Wave. — The Dorcas club. — Ocean born.
— Young America abroad. 1st ser. 6 v. ill. 16°. ea., $1.50 .... *Lee & S.*
Cont.: Outward bound. — Shamrock and thistle. — Red cross. — Dikes and ditches. — Palace and cottage. — Down the Rhine.
— *Same.* 2d ser. [To form 6 v.] v. 1–4. ill. 16°. ea., $1.50 .... *Lee & S.*
Cont.: Up the Baltic. — Northern lands. — Cross and crescent. — Sunny shores.
— (*ed.*) Our boys and girls series. 12 v. ill. 8°. ea., $1.50 .... *Lee & S.*
Cont.: Album. — Cabinet. — Companion. — Favorite. — Mirror. — Keepsake. — Museum. — Offering. — Repository. — Souvenir. — Storyteller. — Treasure.
— *See also* Calkins, N. A., *and* Adams, W. T., Universal speaker; — Great bonanza.

Adams-Reilly, A. *See* Shairp, J. C., Tait, P. G., *and* Adams-Reilly, A.

Addicks, *Mrs.* Barb. O'S. French elements: element. book for learning to speak French; from the Germ. of J. H. P. Seidenstücker; with table of the French sounds, etc. 12°. '74. 75c. *Collins & Bro.*

Addie (*pseud.*) Little boy's treasury of precious things. 18°. 60c. .... *Pres. Bd.*
— Select stories for little folks. 18°. 60c. ... *Pres. Bd.*
Addie and her turtle. 18°. 60c. .... *Whittaker.*
Addie Ansley; or, how to make others happy. ('60.) New ed. 18°. '75. 55c. .... *Hoyt.*
Addie's birthday; — brother Freddie; — country home; — new story book; — visitors. *See* Cousin Belle, Little Addie's lib.; Little keepsake lib.
Addie's party. *See* Cousin Belle, Little Addie's lib.; Library for the little folks.
Addington, Ste. *See* Jaudon, D., Watson, T., *and* Addington, S.
Addison, Alvin. Eveline Mandeville. 8°. pap., 25c. *U. P. James.*
Addison, C: G. History of the Knights Templars; adapted to the Am. system by R. Macoy. ill. 8°. '76. hf. mor., *$5 .... *Masonic.*
— Treatise on law of contracts; from Lond. ed. of L. W. Cave, with ref. to Am. decisions by J. A. Morgan. 3 v. 8°. '75. shp., $22.50 .. *Cockcroft.*
— Treatise on the law of torts: wrongs and their remedies. 4th Eng. ed., ed. by F. S. P. Wolferstan; with Am. notes by J. M. Dudley and E. Baylies. 2 v. 8°. '76. *net*, shp., $10 .... *Banks.*
— *Same;* with notes and ref. to Am. cases by H. G. Wood. 2 v. 8°. '75. shp., $15 ...... *Cockcroft.*
— *Same.* School ed. [abridg.] 12°. '74. $2.50; shp., $3 .... *Little, B. & Co.*
Addison, H: R. Locked in with a lady: farce. 16°. pap., 15c. .... *De Witt; French.*
— One hundred and seventeen Arundel street: farce. 16°. pap., 15c. .... *French.*
— Sophia's supper: farce. 16°. pap., 15c. .... *French.*
Addison, Jos. Works; with notes by G. W. Greene. 6 v. por. 12°. $9; shp., $12; hf. cf., $19.50. *Lippincott.*
Cont.: 1. Cato; Drummer; Rosamond; Poems. — 2. Remarks on Italy; Whig-Examiner; Present state of the war; Dialogues on medals; Of the Christian religion; Letters. — 3. The lover; Freeholder. — 4. Guardian; Tatler. — 5, 6. Spectator.
— Works; with notes by R. Hurd. 6 v. por. and ill. 12°. (Bohn.) ea., $1.25 ...... *Little, B. & Co.*
Cont.: 1. Poems; Dialogues on medals. — 2. Remarks on Italy; Tatler. — 3-5. Spectator. — 5. Guardian; Lover; Present state of the war; Trial and conviction of Count Tariff; Whig-Examiner. — 6. Freeholder; Of the Christian religion; The drummer; or, haunted house; Ancient and modern learning.
— *Same.* 6 v. por. and ill. 12°. (Bohn.) ea., $1.40. *Scribner, W. & A.*
— *Same.* 6 v. por. and ill. 12°. (Bohn.) ea., $1.50. *Lippincott.*
— Works; incl. Spectator. 3 v. 8°. $6; shp., $7.50; hf. mor., $12.75 .... *Harper.*
— Cato: tragedy. 16°. pap., 15c. .... *French.*
— *See also* Ovidius Naso, P.; — Spectator; — Tatler.
Address to a child, and other stories. 32°. '53. 30c. *Am. Tr.*
Addresses at the inaug. of Noah Porter, as pres. of Yale Coll., Oct. 11, 1871. 8°. '71. $1 .. *Scribner.*
Addresses to children. 32°. 25c. .... *Pres. Bd.*
Addrich im Moos. *See* Zschokke, H.
Adela Cathcart. MacDonald, G. $1.75 ...... *Loring.*
Adela Lincoln. *See* Carey, M. F.
Adelaide Lindsay. Marsh-Caldwell, A. 50c. .. *Harper.*
Adelaide Waldegrave. Smith, J. F. 75c. ... *Peterson.*
Adele. Kavanagh, J. $1.25 .... *Appleton.*
Adele. Samuels, S. B. C. 75c. .... *Lee & S.*
Adeler, Max (*pseud.*) *See* Clark, C: H.
Adeline de Chazal; or, first experience of the world after leaving school; tr. by Mother St. John. 12°. '74. $1.50 .... *Cunningham.*
Adelgitha. Lewis, M. G. 15c. .... *French.*
Adelmar the templar. *See* H., *Abbé.*
Aden Power. Owen, F. $1 .... *Burnham.*

Adhemar de Belcastel; tr. from the French. 12°. '75. $1.50 .... *Cath. Pub.*
Adirondack stories. 6 v. 18°. $3.38 ..... *W. Wood.*
Cont.: Hope on. — My first pennies. — David, the trapper. — Susie's flowers. — Hattie and Marcus. — Martha's home.
Adler, Adler. Adler's improved drawing copy-books. 8 nos. 4°. '71. ea., pap., 25c. ...... *Berendsohn.*
Adler, G: J. German-and-English and Eng.-and-Germ. dict. 8°. hf. mor., $6 .... *Appleton.*
— *Same;* [abridg.] 12°. $2.50 .... *Appleton.*
— Hand-book of Germ. literature. 12°. $1.50. *Appleton.*
— Progressive Germ. reader. 12°. $1.50 .... *Appleton.*
Adley, C: E. The port of Calcutta, with special ref. to the late cyclone. ill. 8°. pap., 80c. ..... *Spon.*
Admetus. Lazarus, E. $2 .... *Hurd & H.*
Admiral's daughter. Marsh-Caldwell, A. 50c. *Peterson.*
Admiralty and ecclesiastical reports. *See* England, Law reports.
Adolphus, J. L. *See* England, Common law reports.
Adolphus. 18°. 50c. .... *Cong. Pub.*
Adolphus; or, the good son. 18°. 15c. .... *Benziger.*
— *Same;* and other tales. 18°. '76. 50c. *Kelly, P. & Co.*
Adonis vanquished. Amcotts, V. 15c. .... *French.*
Adopted. Richmond, E. J. 60c. .... *Nat. Temp.*
Adopted child. ('73.) New ed. 16°. '75. $1.25 .. *Hoyt.*
Adopted child. Birch, S. 15c. .... *French.*
Adopted child. Jewsbury, G. E. $1 .... *Harper.*
Adopted heir. Pardoe, J. $1.75; $1.50 .... *Peterson.*
Adopted son. Tucker, C. 75c. .... *Carter.*
Adopted son of a princess. Jones, E. W. $1 .. *Tibbals.*
Adorning of good works. 18°. 30c. .... *Dutton.*
Adorno, *St.* Cath. Fieschi. *See* Catherine Fieschi Adorno, *St.*
Adrienne. Leslie, H. 15c. .... *De Witt; French.*
Adrienne the actress. Oxenford, J. 15c. ..... *French.*
Adrift in a boat. *See* Kingston, W. H. G.
Adrift in the world. Samuels, A. F. 50c. .... *Lee & S.*
Advance (The). Perkins, H. S. $1.25 .... *Brainard.*
Advance reader. post 8°. $1.25 .... *Nelson.*
Advent keepsake: Bible text for each day of the year. 16°. '69. 25c. .... *Sev. Day Adv.*
Adventure library. *See* Kingston, W. H. G.
Adventurer. *See* Chalmers, A., British essayists.
Adventures and misfortunes of a Saxon schoolmaster. 18°. 30c. .... *O'Shea.*
Adventures by sea and land: perils and hair-breadth escapes of travellers. ill. sm. 4°. $2 ... *Porter.*
Adventures in the Apache country. Browne, J. R. $2 .... *Harper.*
Adventures in Canada. Geikie, J. $1.25 ..... *Porter.*
Adventures in fairy land. Stoddard, R. H. $1.25. **Osgood.*
Adventures in the ice. *See* Enterprise and advent. lib.
Adventures in the land of the Behemoth. *See* Verne, Jules.
Adventures in Mexico and the Rocky Mountains. Ruxton, G. F. $1.50 .... *Harper.*
Adventures of an aide-de-camp. Grant, J. 75c. *Dick & F.*
Adventures of Arthur O'Leary. *See* Lever, C.
Adventures of an attorney in search of practice. *See* Stephen, *Sir* G.
Adventures of a Baltimore trader, etc. Standish, G. 30c. .... *Lippincott.*
Adventures of Baron Munchausen. *See* Raspe, R. E.
Adventures of Big-foot Wallace. Duval, J. C. $1.75. *Claxton.*
Adventures of Billy Bump. *See* Goodrich, S. G., Cottage lib.

Adventures of a brownie. *See* Craik, D. M.
Adventures of Caleb Williams. *See* Godwin, W.
Adventures of Captain Blake. Maxwell, W. H. 75c. *Dick & F.*
Adventures of Captain Farrago. Brackenridge, H. H. 75c. .... *Peterson.*
Adventures of Captain Hatteras. *See* Verne, Jules.
Adventures of Capt. Smith. *See* Young American's lib.
Adventures of a casket. *See* Catholic premium-book lib.
Adventures of Clarence Bolton. 8°. pap., 25c. *Dick & F.*
Adventures of Cortez. *See* Young American's lib.
Adventures of Daniel Boone. *See* Young American's lib.
Adventures of a day. 18°. 55c.......... *Am. S. S.*
Adventures of Dick Onslow among the red skins. Kingston, W. H. G. $1.50.......... *Tilton.*
Adventures of Don Quixote de la Mancha. *See* Cervantes.
Adventures of Elder Triptolemus Tub. *See* Rogers, G.
Adventures of a fly. Cooke, A. B. 50c..... *Dutton.*
Adventures of a German toy. 16°. 75c..... *Lee & S.*
Adventures of Gil Blas. *See* Lesage, A. R.
Adventures of Henry Hudson. *See* Young American's lib.
Adventures of hunters and travellers, and narratives of border warfare. ill. 12°. $1.25..... *T. Bliss.*
Adventures of a hymn; or, three days in the life of C. F. Gilbert. 18°. 40c.......... *Am. S. S.*
Adventures of Jamie and Jennie. Child, L. M. 75c. *Lothrop.*
Adventures of Johnny Ironsides. Girardin, J. $1.75. *Routledge.*
Adventures of Joshua Hawsepipe. Low, C. R. 75c. *Routledge.*
Adventures of Kwei, the Chinese girl. ('73.) New ed. 16°. '75. $1.25.......... *Hoyt.*
Adventures of Leo Rembrandt. Hoffman, F. 90c. *Ref. Ch. Pub.*
Adventures of a love-letter. Mathews, C. J. 15c. *French.*
Adventures of Margaret Catchpole. 8°. pap., 75c. *Dick & F.*
Adventures of Mark Willis. Cupples, A. J. 75c. *Nelson.*
Adventures of a marquis. *See* Dumas, A.
Adventures of Mick Costigan. Maxwell, W. H. 75c. *Dick & F.*
Adventures of a missionary; or, rivers of water in dry places. ill. 16°. $1.25.. *Cin. Meth. Bk. Conc.*
Adventures of Mr. Ledbury. *See* Smith, Albert.
Adventures of Mr. Verdant Green. *See* Bradley, E.
Adventures of Philip. *See* Thackeray, W. M.
Adventures of a Protestant in search of a religion. Iota. $1.50; $2 .... *Sadlier.*
Adventures of Pythagoras in India. *See* Voltaire.
Adventures of Reuben Davidger. Greenwood, J. $1.75.......... *Harper.*
Adventures of Robin Hood. New ed. ill. 16°. '75. $1.25.......... *Routledge.*
Adventures of Robinson Crusoe. *See* Defoe, D.
Adventures of Robinson Playfellow. ill. 12°. '72. $1.75.......... *Routledge.*
Adventures of Sydney Flint the coiner; by author of "Alice Harmon." 12°. $1.50; $2..... *Sadlier.*
Adventures of Telemaque. *See* Fenelon.
Adventures of three Englishmen, etc., in South Africa. *See* Verne, Jules.
Adventures of Tom King. 8°. pap., 25c. .. *Dick & F.*

Adventures of a travelled ant. Cooke, A. B. 50c. *Dutton.*
Adventures of a U. S. detective. Brooks, J. J. $2. *Souder.*
Adventures of a young naturalist. Biart, L. $1.75. *Harper.*
Adventures on the great hunting grounds of the world. Meunier, V. $1.25.......... *Scribner.*
Adversity. Manigault, G. $1.50 .... *Lippincott.*
Advertiser's handbook. *See* Pettengill, S. M.
Advice gratis. Dance, C. 15c. .... *Happy.*
Advice to husbands. Lancaster, C. S. 15c... *French.*
Advice to Irish girls in America. Cusack, M. F. $1. *McGee.*
Advice to a mother; — a wife. *See* Chavasse, P. H.
Advice to a young Christian. *See* Waterbury, J. B.
Advice to a young convert. Lee, L. M. $1.25. *So. Meth.*
Advice to young ladies. Arthur, T. S. $1.25. *J. E. Potter.*
Advice to young men. Arthur, T. S. $1.25. *J. E. Potter.*
Advice to young people series. *See* Arthur, T. S.
Æneids. *See* Virgilius.
Ænone: tale of slave life in Rome. 12°. '66. $2. (?) *Bradburn.*
Aerial world (The). Hartwig, G. $6 ..... *Appleton.*
Æschines. Orations on the crown against Ctesiphon [Gk.]; with notes by J. T. Champlin. 12°. $1.50.......... *Dennet.*
— *See also* Demosthenes.
Æschylus. [Tragedies: Gk.]; ed. by F. A. Paley, with index. 18°. 75c.......... *Harper.*
— *Eng.* Tragedies; lit. tr. by T. A. Buckley. 12°. (Bohn.) $1.25 .... *Little, B. & Co.*
— — *Same.* 12°. (Bohn.) $1.40 .. *Scribner, W. & A.*
— — *Same.* 12°. (Bohn.) $1.50.......... *Lippincott.*
— — *Same,* Appendix to: new readings from Hermann's ed., tr. by G. Burges. 12°. (Bohn.) $1.25. *Little, B. & Co.*
— — — *Same.* 12°. (Bohn.) $1.40 .. *Scribner, W. & A.*
— — — *Same.* 12°. (Bohn.) $1.50........ *Lippincott.*
— — *Same;* with appendix. 12°. $1.50 ..... *Harper.*
— *Eng.* Tragedies; tr. by R. Potter; with essay on Grecian drama. 18°. 75c. .... *Harper.*
— *Eng.* Tragedies: new metrical tr. with biog. essay and app. of rhymed choral odes, by E. H. Plumptre. cr. 8°. '73. $2.50.......... *Routledge.*
— *Eng.* Tragedies [condensed and explained] by R. S. Coplestone. (Anc. classics for Eng. readers.) 16°. '71. $1....... *Lippincott; Little, B. & Co.*
— Agamemnon [Gk.]; with notes and metrical table by C. C. Felton. 12°. $1.50....... *Dennet.*
— Eumenides [Gk.]; with Eng. notes and introd. by B. Drake. 8°. '53. $1.25.......... *Macmillan.*
— Prometheus [Gk.]; with notes by T. D. Woolsey. 12°. $1.25.......... *Hamersley.*
— Prometheus bound [Gk.]; with notes by J. Davies. 16°. (Weale.) 40c. .... *Allyn.*
— *Eng.* Prometheus bound; lit. tr. into Eng. verse by A. Webster. fp. 8°. '66. $1.50..... *Macmillan.*
— *Eng.* Prometheus chained; tr. for students by T. W. C. Edwards. 12°. *net,* 25c. .... *Peck.*
— Septem contra Thebas [Gk.]; with Eng. notes by A. Sachtleben. 12°. 90c. .... *Dennet.*
— *Same.* Seven against Thebes [Gk.]; with notes by J. Davies. 16°. (Weale.) 40c.......... *Allyn.*
Æsop. [Æsopus.] Fables. ill. 32°. 50c... *U. P. James.*
— *Same.* ill. 18°. 75c..... *Claxton; Lothrop; Nelson; Scribner, W. & A.*
— *Same.* ill. 12°. 75c.......... (?) *McLoughlin.*
— *Same.* ill. 16°. $1.25 .... *Porter.*
— *Same.* ill. 12°. $1.50 .... *World Pub.*
— *Same.* (People's ed.) ill. 12°. $1.......... *Wells.*
— *Same.* (Toy-book.) ill. 4°. $1; bds., 50c. *Routledge.*
— *Same.* ill. by E. Griset. 8°. $5 .... *Appleton.*

Æsop. [Æsopus.] *continued.*
— *Same.* ill. by E. Griset. cr. 4°. $3.50; $5..*Cassell.*
— *Same.* ill. by H. W. Herrick. 16°. '65. $1.50; $2. cr. 8°. $2; hf. cf., $4.50 ....*Hurd & H.*
— *Same.* pl. by H. L. Stephens. 4°. '68. $10. *Bouton.*
— *Same.* ill. by J. Tenniel. 12°. $1.25. *Collins & Bro.; Lippincott.*
— *Same.* 50 ill. by H. Weir. 16°. '74. 50c. chp. ed. 18°. '71. 45c....................*Routledge.*
— *Same.* 114 ill. by H. Weir. 12°. '68. $2; hf. cf. $3.50; cf., $5....................*Routledge.*
— *Same.* ill. by Wolf, etc. 16°. 75c. *Lippincott; Routledge.*
— *Same;* translated into human nature in 24 col. pl. by C. H. Bennett; with descript. text. cr. 4°. $2.40 ....*Scribner, W. & A.*
— *French.* ('64.) New ed., rev., with vocab. 16°. '74. 75c..................................*Holt.*
— Fables of Æsop and others. ill. 16°. $1.25. *Burnham.*
— *See also* Baldwin, E.; — child's edition; — Godolphin, M.; — Juvenile classic ser.

Æsop's little fable-book. ill. 16°. 25c......*Routledge.*
Æthiop. Dimond, W. 15c..................*French.*
Afar in the forest. Traill, C. P. $1..........*Nelson.*
Affair (An) of honour. Rede, W. L. 15c. ....*French.*
Affectionate address (An) to fathers; — to mothers. Baker, D. ea., 20c.................*Pres. Bd.*
Affectionate brothers. *See* Hofland, *Mrs.* B.
Affection's tribute. Naylor, R. S. $1.25....*Cen. Bk.*
Affen Religion (Die). Fick, C. J. H. 15c....*Barthel.*
Affleck, T: Hedging and hedge plants for the southwest. 16°. '71. $1.25; pap., 75c. *E. H. Cushing.*
Afflicted man's companion. *See* Willison, J.
Affliction. Stanford, C. 50c...............*Claxton.*
Affranchino, A. Mass in G; with Lat. text and piano or organ accomp. 8°. '75. pap., $1; bds., $1.25. *Pond.*
Afloat and ashore. *See* Cooper, J. F.
Afloat and ashore: nautical play. 16°. pap., 15c. *Happy.*
Afloat in the forest. Reid, M. $1.50 ....*Miller.*
Afoot and alone. Powers, S. *$2; $2.50; $3.50. *Col. Bk.*
Afraid of the dark. *See* Minnie's lib.; — Moss rose lib.
Afraja. Mügge, T. $1; $1.25; $1.50 ....*Porter.*
Africa and its explorers. 8°. *$3.50; shp., $4; hf. mor., $5..........................*Col. Bk.*
Africa unveiled. Rowley, H. $2..............*Pott.*
Africaine (L'). Arbuthnot, —. 15c........*French.*
Africaine (L'). *See* Meyerbeer, G.
Africaine (L'); or, the maid of Madagascar. 8°. pap., 25c..............................*De Witt.*
African adventure. Day, G. T. $1.50 .....*Lothrop.*
African Bible pictures. Officer, M. 35c. (?)*Luth. Pub.*
African box (The). White, C. 15c. ....*De Witt.*
African cruiser. Sadler, S. W. $1.25....*Routledge.*
African Crusoes. Lee, R. $1.50..........*Lee & S.*
African orphan boy (The), etc. 32°. '53. 30c. *Am. Tr.*
African preacher (The). White, W. S. 40c. *Pres. Bd.*
African trader (The). *See* Kingston, W. H. G.
Africaner; or, missionary trials. 18°. 25c...*Pres. Bd.*
Africa's mountain valley. Charlesworth, M. L. 60c. *Carter.*
After all. 18°. 18c.......................*Am. S. S.*
After all, not to create only. Whitman, W. 30c. *Roberts.*
After the ball. Perry, N. $1.50; $3; $4 ... *Osgood.*
After dark. *See* Collins, Wilkie.
After death. Randolph, P. B. $2.............*Colby.*
After the holidays. Ellis, *Miss* —. 75c......*Nelson.*

After life. Sewell, E. M. $2.............*Williams.*
After long years. Halifax, M. C. $1.75..*Macmillan.*
After many years. Ross, M. 30c.........*Am. News.*
After the party: comedy. 16°. pap., 15c. ...*French.*
After a shadow. *See* Arthur, T. S., Home stories.
After the storm. Arthur, T. S. $1 50 ..*J. E. Potter.*
After the truth. *See* Henry, S. M. I.
After the war. Reid, W. $2.50 ....*Wilstach.*
After years. Bradley, W. I. $1.50 ....*Hoyt.*
Aftermath. Longfellow, H. W. $1.50; $3; $4. *Osgood.*
Afternoon. Stork, T. $1.75...........*Lippincott.*
Afternoons with grandma. Carraud, Z. T. $1.25. *Cin. Meth. Bk. Conc.*
Afternoons with the saints. Anderdon, W. H. 60c.; 25c................................*Benziger.*
Afterthought (An). *See* Seneca, L. A.
Afterwards; or, Janet's true friend. 16°. $1.25. *Am. S. S.*
Against fate. Rayne, M. L. $1.50 ....*Keen.*
Against the stream. Charles, E. $1.75 ......*Dodd.*
Against tide. Ross, M. 30c. ....*Am. News.*
Against the world. Hadermann, J. R. $1.50; 75c. (?) *Shepard.*
Agamemnon (The). *See* Æschylus.
Agassiz, Alex. List of the echinoderms. 8°. '63. pap., 10c. ....*Mus. Comp. Zool.*
— North American acalephæ. ill. imp. 8°. '65. pap., $4 ....*Mus. Comp. Zool.*
— Preliminary report on the echini and starfishes dredged in deep water between Cuba and the Florida reef, by L. F. de Pourtalès. 8°. '69. pap., 40c...................*Mus. Comp. Zool.*
— Revision of the echini. 2 v. pl. 4°. '72–'74. pap., $40 ....*Mus. Comp. Zool.*
— *See also* Agassiz, E. C. *and* A.
— *and* Garman, S. W. (*ed.*) Exploration of Lake Titicaca. 4 v. 8°. '75–'76. pap. *Mus. Comp. Zool.*
Cont.: Fishes and reptiles, by W. S. Garman, 20c. — Notice of the palæozoic fossils, by O. A. Derby, 10c. — List of mammals and birds, by J. A. Allen, 10c. — Crustacea, by W. Faxon, 15c.
— *and* Pourtalès, L. F. de. Echini, crinoids and corals. ill. 4°. '74. pap., $3 ....*Mus. Comp. Zool.*
— — Recent corals from Tilibiche, Peru. ill. 8°. '76. pap., 15c. ....*Mus. Comp. Zool.*
Agassiz, *Mrs.* Eliz. C. *See* Agassiz, L. *and Mrs.* E. C.
— *and* Alex. Seaside studies in natural hist. ill. 8°. '65 $3 ....*Osgood.*
Agassiz, L: Centennial anniversary of A. v. Humboldt. 8°. '69. 50c.............*Bost. Soc. Nat. Hist.*
— Contributions to the natural hist. of the U. S. v. 1–4. 78 pl. 4°. '57–'62. $48.........*Little, B. & Co.*
Cont.: 1. Essay on classification; North Am. testudinata. — 2. Embryology of the turtle. — 3. Acalephs in general; Ctenophoræ. — 4. Discophoræ; Hydroidæ; Homologies of the radiata.
— Geological sketches. 2 v. 16°. '66–'76. ea., $1.50. *Osgood.*
— Methods of study in natural hist. 10th ed. ill. 16°. '63. $1.50..........................*Osgood.*
— Report upon the deep-sea dredging during the the 3d cruise of the U. S. steamer "Bibb." 8°. '69. pap., 15c. ....*Mus. Comp. Zool.*
— Structure of animal life: 6 lectures, Brooklyn, 1862. ('65.) New ed. ill. 8°. '74. $1.50...*Scribner.*
— *See also* Tribune popular science.
— *and Mrs.* E. C. A journey in Brazil. ill. 8°. '68. $5; hf. cf., $8.........................*Osgood.*
— *and* Gould, A. A. Comparative physiology. 12°. (Bohn.) $1.75...............*Little, B. & Co.*
— — Principles of zoology, pt. 1: Comparative physiology. New ed., rev. ill. 12°. $1.50..*Sheldon.*
Agassiz and spiritualism. Putnam, A. 25c. ..*Colby.*
Agate (*pseud.*) *See* Reid, Whitelaw.
Agate stories; by author of "Basket of flowers." 16°. $1.25...............................*Carter.*

Agatha; or, one thing I do; by author of "Early and latter rain." 18°. 65c. . . . . *Pres. Bd.*
Agatha's husband. *See* Craik, D. M.
Agathokles. *See* Zschokke, H.
Agathos. 18°. 60c. . . . . *Dutton.*
Age of chivalry; — of fables. *See* Bulfinch, T.
Age of reason. *See* Paine, Thomas.
Age we live in. Hoke, J. $1.20 . . . . *Un. B. Pub.*
Aged 40. Courtney, J. 15c. . . . . *French.*
Aggravating Sam: comic drama. 16°. pap., 15c. *French.*
Agincourt. *See* James, G. P. R.
Agnel, H. R. Book of chess: complete guide. ill. 12°. '57. $2 . . . . *Appleton.*
— Elementary tabular system of instruction in French. 8°. '62. $3.50 . . . . *Barnes.*
Agnes *of Rome, St.* Life. 18°. '56. 50c. *Cunningham.*
— *See also* Lives of the saints.
Agnes. Abbott, J. 90c. *Harper.*
Agnes. Arthur, T. S. 50c. . . . . *Peterson.*
Agnes. Oliphant, M. O. W. 75c. . . . . *Harper.*
Agnes Allen. 18°. 50c. . . . . *Whittaker.*
Agnes and her neighbors. Pratt, F. L. $1.50. *Lothrop.*
Agnes and Mattie. McKean, M. F. $1 . . . *Am. Bapt.*
Agnes Bernauer. 12°. pap., 15c. . . . . *Radde.*
Agnes Carelton. B., J. M. $1 . . . . (?) *Martien.*
Agnes De Vere. Buckstone, J. B. 15c. . . . . . *French.*
Agnes Evelyn. Reynolds, G. W. M. 75c. . . *Peterson.*
Agnes Fairfield; or, the triumph of faith. ('73.) New ed. 16°. '75. $1.15 . . . . *Hoyt.*
Agnes Graham. Dorsey, S. A. 75c. . . . . *Claxton.*
Agnes Grey. *See* Brontë, A.
Agnes Hilton. Hoffman, M. J. $1.50 . . . . *O'Shea.*
Agnes Hopetoun's schools and holidays. Oliphant, M. O. W. $1.50 . . . . *Macmillan.*
Agnes in search of truth. Brown, H. E. 80c. *Am. Tr.*
Agnes Lysle. Llewellyn, E. L. $1.25 . . . . *Am. Bapt.*
Agnes Morton's trial. *See* Janvier, *Mrs.* E. N.
Agnes of Braunsberg and Wilhelm, and other tales; tr. by Mrs. Sadlier. 18°. '63. 50c.; 75c. *Sadlier.*
Agnes of Sorrento. Stowe, H. B. $2 . . . . *Osgood.*
Agnes Sorel. James, G. P. R. 50c. . . . . *Harper.*
Agnes Stanhope. Remick, M. $1.50 . . . *Universalist.*
Agnes Thornton. 18°. 50c. . . . . *Cong. Pub.*
Agnes Wentworth. Palfrey, S. H. $1.50. *Lippincott.*
Agnes Wilbur. Trowbridge, C. M. 90c. . . *Garrigues.*
Agnew, C. R. Otitis. *See* Seguin, E. C., Series of Am. clin. lect.
Agnew, D. Hayes. Hand-book of practical anatomy. 2d ed., rev. ill. 12°. $2 . . . . *Lippincott.*
— Lacerations of the female perineum, and vesico-vaginal fistula: their history and treatment. ill. 8°. '73. $2 . . . . *Lindsay.*
Agnew, J: Holmes. A manual on the Christian Sabbath; with introd. by Rev. S. Miller. 18°. 50c. *Pres. Bd.*
Agnus dei (The): its origin and hist.; tr. by a father of the Soc. of Jesus. 32°. 20c.; 30c. . . . *O'Shea.*
Agreeable surprise. O'Keefe, J. 15c. . . . . . *French.*
Agreement (The) of science and revelation. Wythe, J. H. $1.75 . . . . *Lippincott.*
Aguilar, Grace. Works. 9 v. ill. 12°. ea., $1. *Appleton.*
Cont.: Days of Bruce, 2 v. — Home influence. — Home scenes and heart studies. — Mother's recompense. — Vale of Cedars. — Woman's friendship. — Women of Israel, 2 v.
— Home influence. 12°. $1 . . . . *Harper.*
— Josephine. 8°. pap., 50c. . . . . *Peterson.*
— Mother's recompense. 8°. pap., 75c. . . . . . . *Harper.*
— Padre (El) Clement. [Span.] ill. 16°. '75. $1. *Am. Tr.*

Ahn, F: Complete method of the German lang., by P. Henn. *See below* Germ. ser., ed. by Henn.
— First German reading book. 12°. 50c. . . . . . . *Witter.*
— French method; trans. and arranged by J. C. Oehlschläger. 12°. 75c. . . . . *Appleton.*
— [French series; ed.] by P. Henn. 9 v. 12°. '73–'75. *Steiger.*
Cont.: French primer, bds., 25c. — Practical and easy method of learning the Fr. lang., 1st course, bds., 40c. — Key, bds., 25c. — Same, 2d course, bds., 60c. — Key, bds., 25c. — Same, 1st and 2d course, in 1 v., hf. roan, $1. — First Fr. reader, with notes and vocab., or, with footnotes and vocab., ea., bds., 60c. — Key, 30c.
— German grammar. 12°. $1 . . . . *Appleton.*
— German handwriting, with notes by W. Grauert. 8°. '69. bds., 40c. . . . . *Steiger.*
— [German series; ed.] by W. Grauert. 7 v. 12°. '69–'74 . . . . *Steiger.*
Cont.: German primer, new ed., bds., 45c. — First reader, bds., 50c. — Key, bds., 30c. — Second reader, bds., 70c. — Key, bds., 35c. — First and second reader, in 1 v., hf. roan, $1.20. — Manual of conversation, $1.
— [German series; ed.] by P. Henn. 9 v. 12°. '73–'76. *Steiger.*
Cont.: First German book, bds., 25c. — Second, bds., 45c.; hf. roan, 60c. (for Key *see* note). — Third, bds., 45c.; hf. roan, 60c. — Key, bds., 25c. — Fourth, bds., 60c.; hf. roan, 80c. — Key, bds., 25c. — First German reader, with notes and vocab., or, with footnotes and vocab., ea., bds., 60c.; hf. roan, 80c. — Key, bds., 30c.
Note. The 1st and 2d German book together form: Rudiments of the German lang., first course ("new ed. of '73" — see also Ahn, F., Rudiments), bds., 65c.; hf. roan, 80c.; Key, bds., 25c. — The 3d and 4th book together form: Rudiments, etc., second course, bds., $1; hf. roan, $1.20. — Ahn-Henn's Rudiments, 1st and 2d course, together form: Ahn's complete method of the German lang., by P. Henn, hf. roan, $1.75.
— Handbook of German conversation. New ed., with add., etc., by C. Dagobert and W. Pfeiffer. 12°. 50c. . . . . *Witter.*
— Method of learning German. 1st and 2d course. 2 v. 8°. ea., hf. bd., 45c.; in 1 v., 80c. . . . . . . *Vering.*
— *Same;* with pronunc. by J. C. Oehlschläger. 1st and 2d course. 2 v. 8°. ea., hf. bd., 50c.; in 1 v., 90c. — Key, 60c. . . . . *Vering.*
— Method of learning the German lang.; rev. by Gust. Fischer. 1st and 2d course. 12°. '71–'74. ea., bds., 50c.; in 1 v., hf. roan, $1. — Key, bds., 30c. *Steiger.*
— New, practical and easy method of learning the German lang.; with pronunciation by J. C. Oehlschläger. Rev. ed. 3 v. 8°. '69 . . . . *Steiger.*
Cont.: First course: practical pt., bds., 60c. — Second course: theoretical pt., bds., 40c. — First and second course, bds., $1; hf. roan, $1.25.
— New, practical and easy method of learning the Spanish lang. 12°. $1. — Key, 25c. . . . . . . *Appleton.*
— New school dict. of the Eng. and Germ. lang. New ed. 16°. '70. 75c. . . . . *Witter.*
— Prakt. Lehrgang zur schnellen u. leichten Erlernung d. französ. Sprache; durchges. u. verb. v. J. C. Oehlschläger. 3 Ausg.; mit Anh.: kurze Theorie zu Ahn's französ. Lehrgang v. L. Soldan. 1. Cursus. 8°. hf. bd., 50c. . . . . *Vering.*
— Prakt. Lehrgang d. engl. Sprache, v. J. C. Oehlschläger. 1. u. 2. Cursus. 2 v. 8°. hf. bd., 1., 35c.; 2., 50c.; in 1 v., 75c. . . . . *Vering.*
— Rudiments of the German language. ('67.) New ed. 12°. '70. bds., 35c. *Steiger.*
Note. Called "old ed. of '70." — For Ahn-Henn's Rudiments, see above, German series, ed. by P. Henn.
— *See also* Pylodet, L.
Ahnfelts sånger. *See* Swenska Lutherska Tryckföneniagen.
Ahrens, J. B. A. Deutsches Gesangbuch. '72. 2d ed. 18°. $1.50; $3.50. . . . . *So. Meth.*
— [Germ. S.-school hymn-book.] Lob Gottes. sq. 16°. '73. *net,* 35c. *So. Meth.*
Aid to those who pray in private. Sprigg, D. F. 60c. *Dutton.*
Aida. *See* Verdi, G.
Aïdé, Hamilton. Nine days' wonder (A). 8°. $1.25; pap., 50c. . . . . *Estes.*
— Penruddocke. 8°. $1.25; pap., 75c. . . . . *Estes.*

Aide-de-camp (The). *See* Grant, James.

Aids to faith: theolog. essays [in] reply to the Oxford essays and reviews. 12°. $2.........*Appleton.*

Aids to family devotion. 12°. $2.50.........*Nelson.*

Aids to reflection. *See* Coleridge, S. T.

Aids to the study of German theology. cr. 8°. $2. *Scribner, W. & A.*

Aiken, A. W. [Tales.] 9 v. 8°. ea., pap., 20c. *Beadle.*
Cont.: California detective. — Injun Dick. — Kentuck, the sport. — Man from Texas. — Overland Kit. — Prairie Mazeppa. — Rocky Mountain Rob. — Winged whale. — Wolf demon.

Aiken, G. L. Uncle Tom's cabin: drama. 16°. pap., 15c..................................*French.*

Aiken, Ja. R. (*ed.*) Gems of prose and poetry. 16°. '76. $1.50..........................*Miller.*

Aikin, J: ["Uncle John."] Children's album of pretty pictures with stories. ill. sq. 16°. $1.50..*Cassell.*
— *Same.* ill. sq. 16°. $1.75...............*Lee & S.*
— Juvenile budget opened: sel. from writings of A., ed. by Mrs. S. J. Hale. 18°. 75c.........*Harper.*
— Juvenile budget reopened. 18°. 75c......*Harper.*
— *and* Barbauld, *Mrs.* A. L. Evenings at home; or, the juvenile budget opened. ill. 18°. 75c. *Lee & S.; Lippincott; Lothrop.*
— — *Same.* ill. 16°. $1...........*Scribner, W. & A.*
— — *Same.* (Household ser.) ill. 16°. $1.50; mor., $3..................................*Lee & S.*
— — *Same;* rev. by C. Hartley. ill. 16°. $1.25. *Hurd & H.*
— — *Same.* ill. 16°. $1. 12°. $1.25. (Presentation ed.) 12°. $1.75...................*Routledge.*
— — *Same;* in words of one syllable. ill. sq. 16°. $1.50 ....*Cassell.*
— — — *See also* Godolphin, M.

Aikin, Lucy. Memoirs of the court and times of Elizabeth. 2 v. in 1. 12°. (N. Y. and Lond.) '68. $2; hf. cf., $4 ....*Putnam.*
— *See also* Channing, W. E., *and* Aikin, L.

Aikman, Ja. Annals of the persecution in Scotland from the restoration to the revolution. 2 v. ill. 12°. $1.75...........................*Pres. Bd.*

Aikman, W: Altar in the house. sq. 24°. '76. pap., 10c...................................*Am. Tr.*
— Life at home; or, the family and its members. 12°. '70. $1.50; $2 .... *Wells.*

Aileen Ferrers. Morley, S. 50c............*Harper.*

Ailenroc. *See* Strykor, Cornelia.

Ailieford: a family history. 8°. pap., 50c...*Peterson.*

Aimard, Gst. [Tales.] 11 v. 8°. ea., pap., 75c. *Peterson.*
Cont.: Border rifles. — Gold seekers. — Indian chief. — Indian scout. — Pirates of the prairies. — Prairie flower. — Rebel chief. — Red track. — Tiger slayer. — Trail hunter. — Trapper's daughter.
— Freebooters (The). 8°. pap., 50c........*Peterson.*
— White scalper (The). 8°. pap., 50c.......*Peterson.*

Aimée. Giberne, A. $1.50 ....*Carter.*

Aims and obstacles. James, G. P. R. 50c. ..*Harper.*

Aimwell, Walter (*pseud.*) *See* Simonds, W.

Ainger, Alfr. Sermons preached in the Temple Church. 12°. '70. $1.50...................*Macmillan.*

Ainslie, Herb. (*pseud.*) *See* Maitland, E:

Ainslie, W. *See* Historical account of Brit. India.

Ainslie series; — stories. *See* Weeks, *Mrs.* H. C.

Ainsworth, Rob. English and Lat. dict.; ed. by C. Anthon. 18°. '76. $1.50............*Fortescue.*
— English and Lat. dict.; abridged by T. Morell. New ed., rev. by J. Carey. 8°. '76. shp., $3.50. *Fortescue.*

Ainsworth, W. F. (*ed.*) All round the world: record of voyages, travels and adventures. ill. and col. maps. 4°. '70. hf. mor., $13.50. *Putnam.*
— Earth delineated with pen and pencil: record of voyages, travels, and adventures. ill. demy 4°. '75. $10...............................*Routledge.*

Ainsworth, W. F. (*ed.*), *continued.*
— Wanderings in every clime; or, voyages, travels, and adventures all round the world. ill. 4°. '75. $10...............................*Routledge.*

Ainsworth, W: Harrison. Novels. 17 v. 16°. $12. *Routledge.*
Cont.: Windsor Castle. — Ovingdean Grange. — Lancashire witches. — Tower of London. — Flitch of bacon. — Miser's daughter. — Guy Fawkes. — Spendthrift. — Old St. Paul's. — Mervyn Clitheroe. — Star chamber. — Rookwood. — Crichton. — Auriol. — St. James. — Jack Sheppard. — James II.
— Auriol. ill. 8°. $3. (Railway lib.) 16°. bds., 50c. *Routledge.*
— Ballads, romantic, fantastical and humorous. ill. 16°. $1.50; mor., $3 ....*Lee & S.*
— *Same;* [incl.] The combat of the thirty. ill. 16°. '72. $1.75...............................*Routledge.*
— Boscobel. ill. 8°. $3. (Railway lib.) 16°. bds., 80c. ....*Routledge.*
— Constable of the tower. 8°. pap., 75c....*Dick & F.*
— Crichton. 12°. $1.50...................*Harper.*
— *Same.* ill. 8°. $3. (Railway lib.) 16°. bds., 50c. *Routledge.*
— Desperados of the new world. 8°. pap., 50c. *Peterson.*
— Flitch of bacon. ill. 8°. $3. (Railway lib.) 16°. bds., 50c. ....*Routledge.*
— Grace O'Malley, her life and adventures. 8°. pap., 50c. ....*Peterson.*
— Guy Fawkes. ill. 8°. $3. (Railway lib.) 16°. bds., 50c. ....*Routledge.*
— — *See also below* Life of Jack Sheppard; Pictorial life.
— James II. (Railway lib.) 16°. bds., 50c...*Routledge.*
— Lancashire witches. ill. 8°. $3. (Railway lib.) 16°. bds., 50c........................*Routledge.*
— Life of Arthur Spring. 8°. pap., 25c.....*Peterson.*
— Life of Henry Thomas, the western burglar and murderer. ill. 8°. pap., 25c. ....*Peterson.*
— Life of Jack Sheppard. ill. 8°. pap., 50c...*Peterson.*
— *Same.* ill. 8°. $3. (Railway lib.) 16°. bds., 50c. *Routledge.*
— *Same;* [also] Guy Fawkes. ill. 8°. $1.75..*Peterson.*
— Life of Mrs. Whipple and Jesse Strang, her paramour. 8°. pap., 25c,...............*Peterson.*
— Life of Ninon de L'Enclos; with her letters on love, courtship and marriage. 8°. pap., 25c. *Peterson.*
— Mervyn Clitheroe. ill. 8°. $3. (Railway lib.) 16°. bds., 50c.....................*Routledge.*
— Miser's daughter. 8°. $1.75; pap., $1...*Peterson.*
— *Same.* ill. 8°. $3. (Railway lib.) 16°. bds., 50c. *Routledge.*
— Mysteries of the court of Queen Anne. 8°. pap., 50c. ....*Peterson.*
— Mysteries of the court of the Stuarts. 8°. pap., 75c. ....*Peterson.*
— Old St. Paul's: tale of the plague and fire. ill. 8°. $3. (Railway lib.) 16°. bds., 50c...*Routledge.*
— *Same.* Pictorial Old St. Paul's. ill. 8°. pap., 75c. *Peterson.*
— Ovingdean Grange. ill. 8°. $3. (Railway lib.) 16°. bds., 50c..........................*Routledge.*
— Pictorial life and adventures of Davy Crockett. 8°. pap., 50c. ....*Peterson.*
— Pictorial life and adventures of Dick Turpin. 8°. pap., 50c. ....*Peterson.*
— Pictorial life and adventures of Guy Fawkes. 8°. pap., 75c. ....*Peterson.*
— — *See also above* Guy Fawkes; Life of Jack Sheppard.
— Pictorial old St. Paul's. *See above* Old.
— Rookwood. ill. 8°. $3. (Railway lib.) 16°. bds., 50c. ....*Routledge.*
— Ruth Garnet; or, the loves of the Earl of Rochester. 8°. pap., 50c.........................*De Witt.*
— St. James'. (Railway lib.) 16°. bds., 50c. *Routledge.*
— South sea bubble (The). ill. 8°. (Lond.) pap., 30c. ....*Am. News.*
— Spendthrift (The). 8°. pap., 50c. ......*Dick & F.*

Ainsworth, W: Harrison, *continued.*
— *Same.* ill. 8°. $3. (Railway lib.) 16°. bds., 50c. *Routledge.*
— Star chamber (The). ill. 8°. pap., 75c...*Peterson.*
— *Same.* ill. 8°. $3. (Railway lib.) 16°. bds., 50c. *Routledge.*
— Talbot Harland. ill. 8°. (Lond.) pap., 30c.*Am. News.*
— Tower hill. ill. 8°. (Lond.) pap., 30c...*Am. News.*
— Tower of London. ill. 8°. $2 50; pap.,$1.50.*Peterson.*
— *Same.* ill. 8°. $3. (Railway lib.) 16°. bds., 50c. *Routledge.*
— Windsor Castle. 8°. pap., 75c. ....*Peterson.*
— *Same.* ill. 8°. $3. (Railway lib.) 16°. bds., 50c. *Routledge.*
Airy, *Sir* G. B. Elementary treatise on partial differential equations; with diagrams. cr. 8°. '66. $2. *Macmillan.*
— On sound and atmospheric vibrations; with the mathematical elements of music. 2d ed., rev. and enl. cr. 8°. '71. $3.50.......*Macmillan.*
— Popular astronomy: lectures at Ipswich. 7th ed. 18°. $1.50........................*Macmillan.*
— Treatise on the algebraical and numerical theory of errors of observations and the combination of obs. 2d ed., rev. cr. 8°. '61. $2.50..*Macmillan.*
— Treatise on magnetism. cr. 8°. '71. $3.50.*Macmillan.*
Airy, Osmund. Treatise on geometrical optics. 12°. '70. $1.25........................*Macmillan.*
Aitken, Cora Kennedy. Legends and memories of Scotland. 16°. '74. $1.50 ....*Williams.*
Aitken, Ma. Carlyle (*ed.*) Scottish song. 18°. '74. $1.25 ....*Macmillan.*
Aitken, W: Outlines of the science and practice of medicine. 8°. $5 ....*Lippincott.*
— Science and practice of medicine. 6th ed., rev. 2 v. ill. 8°. $10........................*Lippincott.*
— *Same.* 3d Am. ed., rev. and enl. 2v. ill. and col. map. 8°. '72. $12; leath., $14.......*Lindsay.*
Ajax (The). *See* Sophocles.
A Kempis. *See* Thomas a *Kempis.*
Akenside, M: Poems. (Aldine ed.) 16°. 75c. *Lippincott.*
— *Same;* with memoir by A. Dyce. 18°. $1..*Osgood.*
— Pleasures of imagination. *See* Poems of pleasures.
Aker, Eliz. Poems. (Blue and gold ed.) 32°. '66. $1.25; hf. cf., $2.50; mor., $3. (Cabinet ed.) 16°. $1.50; hf.cf., $3; mor., $4 ......*Osgood.*
Alabama. Revised code; prep. by A. J. Walker. 8°. '67 ....*State.*
— Supreme Court reports. 70 v. 8°. shp., $400. *J. White.*

Cont.: 1820-'26, by H. Minor, 1 v.—1827-'31, by G. N. Stewart, 3 v.—1831-'34, by G. N. Stewart and B. F. Porter, 5 v.—1834-'39, by B. F. Porter, 9 v.
[New series.]
v. 1-11 (1840-'47), by the judges.—v. 12-15 (1847-'49), by J. J. Ormond.—v. 16-18 (1849-'51), by N. W. Cocke.—v. 19-21 (1851-'52), by J. W. Shepherd.—v. 22-24 (1853-'54), by the judges.—v. 25-41 (1854-'68), by J. W. Shepherd.—v. 42 (1868), by J. L. C. Danner.—v. 43-48 (1869-'72), by T. G. Jones.—v. 49-51 (1873-'74), by J. W. Shepherd.—v. 52 (1875), by T. G. Jones.

— *Same.* v. 30-49 ('58-'73). 20 v. 8°. ea., shp., $5. *Barrett.*

Cont.: v. 30-41 ('58-'68), by J. W. Shepherd.—v. 42 ('68), by J. L. C. Danner.—v. 43-48 ('69-'72), by T. G. Jones.—v. 49 ('73), by J. W. Shepherd.

— *Same.* v. 23 (1853); by the judges. [Reprint.] 8°. '70. shp., $15.......................*Gilbert.*
— *Same.* 1820-'39; condensed by W. R. Smith. [To form 10 v.] v. 1-5. 8°. '70. ea., shp., $6. *W. R. Smith.*

Comprising Minor (1 v.), Stewart (3 v.), Stewart and Porter (5 v.) and Porter (9 v.)

— — Digest. *See* Brickell, R. C.
Alabama: extravaganza. 16°. pap., 15c. ...*French.*
Alabama geological survey. First bienniel report on geol. of Ala.; by M. Tuomey. 8°. '50...*State.*
Alabama Med. Assoc. *See* Medical Assoc. of Ala.

Alabaster, H: The wheel of the law: Buddhism ill. from Siamese sources. 8°. $7..*Scribner, W. & A.*
Aladdin. [Toy-book.] ill. 4°. $1; 50c...*Routledge.*
Aladdin: burlesque. 16°. pap., 15c...*French; Happy.*
Aladdin: drama. 16°. pap., 15c.............*French.*
Aladdin: extravaganza. Keating, E. H. 15c...*French.*
Aladdin; or, the wonderful lamp. ill. by Darley. sm. 4°. $2.....................................*Porter.*
Aladdin and the wonderful lamp. f°. pap., 15c.; 20c. *J. E. Potter.*
— *See also* Arabian nights.
Alamance. [Fiction.] 8°. pap., 50c.......*Harper.*
Alamontade. *See* Zschokke, H.
Alarm to unconverted sinners. *See* Alleine, J.
Alarming sacrifice. Buckstone, J. B. 15c...*French.*
Alba (*pseud.*) *See* White, Alexina B.
Alban; or, the hist. of a young Puritan. Huntington, J. V. $2.50..............................*O'Shea.*
Albany Evening Journal almanac. [Annual.] 8°. pap., 25c..........................(?) *Weed.*
Albany Institute. Transactions. v. 1-6. 8°.(?)*Albany.*
Alberger, J: Antiquity of Christianity. 12°. '74. 75c.; pap., 35c..............................*Somerby.*
— Monks, popes and their political intrigues. 12°. '71. $1.50...............................*Somerby.*
Albert, *Prince Consort.* Golden precepts. 16°. $1.25. *Scribner, W. & A.*
Albert Lunel. Brougham, H. (*Lord.*) 75c...*Harper.*
Alberti, C: Perfect guide for the German accordeon without a master. 8°. '66. pap , 50c...*Ditson.*
Albertsen, Fk. The four-footed lovers. ill. 4°. $1.50. *Lee & S.*
Albertus Magnus, od. egyptische Geheimnisse. 12°. 75c.....................................*Radde.*
Albery, Ja. Apple blossoms: comedy. 12°. pap., 15c. *De Witt.*
— Tweedie's rights: comedy. 12°. pap., 15c...*De Witt.*
Alboin and Rosamond. Rodney, R. B. $1.25. *Lippincott.*
Albrechtsberger, J. G. Collected writings on thorough bass, harmony and composition; for self-instruction. roy. 8°. $5.........................*Peters.*
Albrizzi, Is. Teotochi (*Contessa*). *See* Canova, A.
Albro, J: Adams. Biblical and theological dict. 12°. $1.50 ....*Cong. Pub.*
— Life of T: Shepard. *See* Lives of the chief fathers of N. Eng.;—Shepard, T., Works.
Album: songs. Varley, N. $4 ......*G. D. Russell.*
Album comique: comic songs. 4°. $1.50..*Brainard.*
Album for children. Heaton, C. $1.75...*Routledge.*
Album library (The). 4 v. ill. 4°. $6.50....*Lee & S.*

Cont.: Children's album of pretty pictures, by Uncle John.—Children's Sunday album, by M. A. Mackarness.—Off to sea, by W. H. G. Kingston.—True Robinson Crusoes, by F. Denis and V. Chauvin.

Album (The) of language. Naphegyi, G. $20; $25; $30..................................*Lippincott.*
Alcaid. Kenney, J. 15c..................*French.*
Alcestis. *See* Euripides.
Alcestis. Talfourd, F. 15c................*French.*
Alcestis: a musical novel. (Leis. hour ser.) ('74.) New ed. 16°. '75. $1.25..................*Holt.*
Alchemy of happiness. Al-Ghazzali. $1.25..*Munsell.*
Alcock, *Sir* Rutherford. The capital of the tycoon: narrative of a three years' residence in Japan. maps and ill. 2 v. 12°. $3.50 ....*Harper.*
Alcock, T. Questions on Huxley's "Physiology." 18°. 50c. ....*Macmillan.*
Alcott, A. Bronson. Concord days. 16°. '72. $1.50. *Roberts.*
— Record of a school. New ed. 16°. '74. $1.50. *Roberts.*
— Tablets. 16°. '68. $1.50; $2.50..........*Roberts.*

Alcott, Louisa M. Aunt Jo's scrap-bag. 3 v. 16°. '71–'73. ea., $1 .... *Roberts.*
Cont.: My boys. — Shawl-straps. — Cupid and Chow-chow.
— Eight cousins; or, the aunt-hill. ill. 16°. '75. $1.50. *Roberts.*
— Hospital sketches, and camp and fireside stories. ill. 16°. '69. $1.50 .... *Roberts.*
— Kitty's class day at Harvard. sq. 16°. 75c.; pap., 50c. *Loring.*
— *Same;* [also] Aunt Kipp; [also] Psyche's art. ill. sq. 16°. '76. pap., 50c. .... *Loring.*
— Little men: life at Plumfield with Jo's boys. ill. 16°. '71. $1.50 .... *Roberts.*
— Little women; or, Meg, Jo, Beth and Amy. 2 v. ill. 16°. '68–'69. $3 .... *Roberts.*
— Moods. ill. 16°. $1.25 .... *Loring.*
— Morning glories; for children. 12°. $1.50.. *Carleton.*
— Old-fashioned girl (An). ill. 16°. '70. $1.50. *Roberts.*
— Silver pitchers, and other stories. ill. 16°. '76. $1.25 .... *Roberts.*
— Work: a story of experience. ill. 16°. '73. $1.75. *Roberts.*

Alcott, W: A. Lectures for the fireside: founded on the ten commandments. 12°. '59. $1.25; $2. *Darrow.*
— Tea and coffee: their physical, intellectual, and moral effects. ('48.) New ed. 16°. pap., 25c. *Wells.*
— Tobacco: its physical, intellectual, and moral effects. 16°. '48. pap., 25c. .... *Wells.*

Alcove (The). Abbott, J. 90c. .... *Harper.*

Alden, *Mrs.* Is. M. ["Pansy."] Bernie's white chicken and other stories. 16°. 75c. .... *West. Tr.*
— *Same;* [also] The diamond bracelet. 16°. '74. 75c. *Lothrop.*
— — *See also below* Pansy lib.; ser.
— Christmas time (A). 16°. '70. 25c.; pap., 15c. *Lothrop.*
— Cunning workmen. ill. 16°. '75. $1.25 ... *Lothrop.*
— Daisy and grandpa. *See below* Pansy pict. lib.
— Diamond bracelet. *See above* Bernie's; — *below* Pansy ser.
— Docia's journal. 18°. 60c. .... (?) *Martien.*
— *Same.* 16°. 75c. .... *Lothrop; West. Tr.*
— — *See also below* Pansy lib.; ser.
— Ester Ried. 12°. $1.25 .... *West. Tr.*
— *Same.* ill. 12°. '73. $1.50 .... *Lothrop.*
— — *See also below* Pansy lib.
— Ester Ried library. 5 v. 12°. $7.50 ...... *Lothrop.*
Cont.: Three people. — Ester Ried. — Julia Ried. — King's daughter. — Wise and otherwise.
— Four girls at Chautauqua. ill. 12°. '76. $1.50. *Lothrop.*
— Grandpa's darlings. ill. 16°. '75. $1.25 ... *Lothrop.*
— Helen Lester. 16°. 50c.; 75c. .... *West. Tr.*
— *Same;* [also] Nannie's experiment. ill. 16°. '74. 75c. .... *Lothrop.*
— — *See also below* Pansy lib.; ser.
— Household puzzles. 12°. $1.50.. *Lothrop; West. Tr.*
— Jessie Wells; or, how to save the lost. 12°. 75c. *Lothrop; West. Tr.*
— — *See also below* Pansy lib.; ser.
— Julia Ried: sequel to "Ester Ried." 12°. $1.50. *Lothrop; West. Tr.*
— — *See also above* Ester; — *below* Pansy lib.
— King's (The) daughter. 12°. $1.25 ...... *West. Tr.*
— *Same.* ill. 12°. '73. $1.50 .... *Lothrop.*
— — *See also above* Ester.
Little Minnie. *See below* Pansy pict. lib.
— Nannie's experiment, and other stories. 16°. 40c. *West. Tr.*
— — *See also above* Helen; — *below* Pansy ser.
— Pansy library. 4 v. 16°. $3 .... *West. Tr.*
Cont.: Jessie Wells. — Docia's journal. — Helen Lester. — Bernie's white chicken.
— Pansy library. ('67–'74.) New ed. 4 v. 16°. '75–'76. $6 .... *Hoyt.*
Cont.: Tip Lewis and his lamp. — Three people. — Ester Ried; or, asleep and awake. — Julia Ried.
— Pansy picture library. 4 v. ill. 4°. '76. ea., 75c.; bds., 60c. .... *Lothrop.*

Alden, *Mrs.* Is. M. ["Pansy."] *continued.*
Cont.: Daisy and grandpa. — Little Minnie. — Robbie and the stars. — Pictures from Bobby's life.
— Pansy series. 4 v. ill. 16°. $3 .... *Lothrop.*
Cont.: Jessie Wells. — Docia's journal. — Bernie's white chicken; [also] The Diamond bracelet. — Helen Lester; [also] Nannie's experiment.
— Pansy's picture book. ill. 4°. '76. $2; $2.25. *Lothrop.*
— Pictures from Bobby's life. *See above* Pansy pict. lib.
— Randolphs (The). ill. 12°. '76. $1.50 .. *Lothrop.*
— Robbie and the stars. *See above* Pansy pict. lib.
— Three people. 12°. $1.50 .... *West. Tr.*
— *Same.* ill. 12°. '72. $1.50 .... *Lothrop.*
— — *See also above* Ester; — *below* Pansy lib.
— Tip Lewis. *See above* Pansy lib.
— Wise and otherwise: sequel to "King's daughter." 12°. $1.50 .... *West. Tr.*
— *Same.* ill. 12°. '74. $1.50 .... *Lothrop.*
— — *See also above* Ester.
— *See also* Foster, *Mrs.* I. H., *and* Alden, *Mrs.* I. M., Dr. Deane's way; — How to teach the little folks.
— *and* Foster, *Mrs.* I. H. Modern prophets: temperance stories. ill. 12°. '74. $1.50 ..... *Lothrop.*

Alden, Jos. Alden ser. 4 v. ill. 24°. ea., 50c. *Lee & S.*
Cont.: The cardinal flower. — The lost lamb. — Henry Ashton. — The light-hearted girl.
— Alice Gordon; or, the uses of orphanage. ill. 18°. 75c. .... *Harper.*
— Anecdotes of the Puritans; [also] Old stone house. ('53.) New ed. ill. 18°. '57. 75c. ..... *Dodd.*
— Cardinal flower. *See above* Alden ser.
— Choice stories. sq. 16°. 75c. .... *Tibbals.*
— Christian ethics; or, the science of duty. 12°. '66. $1.25 .... *Ivison.*
— Citizen's manual: text-book on government. 16°. 50c. .... *Sheldon.*
— Days of boyhood. sq. 16°. 75c. .... *Tibbals.*
— Dying robin (The), and other tales. 18°. 75c. *Harper.*
— Elements of intellectual philos. 12°. $1.25. *Appleton.*
— Elizabeth Benton; or, religion in connection with fashionable life. 18°. 75c. .... *Harper.*
— Hand-book for Sunday school teachers. 16°. 75c. *Meth. Bk. Conc.*
— Henry Ashton. *See above* Alden ser.
— Introduction to the study of the Eng. lang.: grammar and rhetoric. 16°. 75c. ... *Potter, A. & Co.*
— Lawyer's (The) daughter. ill. 18°. 75c. .. *Harper.*
— Light-hearted girl. *See above* Alden ser.
— Little Dora. sq. 16°. 75c. .... *Tibbals.*
— Lost lamb. *See above* Alden ser.
— Naaman and Elisha; or, the nobleman's visit to the prophet. 18°. 35c. .... *Pres. Bd.*
— Natural speaker (The): sel. to aid in acquiring a simple business-like style of speaking. 12°. $1.25. *Appleton.*
— Old revolutionary soldier (The). sq. 16°. 75c. *Tibbals.*
— Our Father: considerations rel. to the Lord's prayer. 18°. 35c. .... *Pres. Bd.*
— Outlines of Christian evidences. 12°. '72. 25c. *Meth. Bk. Conc.*
— Outlines on teaching. 12°. '72. 25c... *Meth. Bk. Conc.*
— Rupert Caleb. sq. 16°. 75c. .... *Tibbals.*
— Science of government, in connection with Am. institutions. 12°. $1.50 .... *Sheldon.*
— Text-book of ethics; for union schools and Bible classes. 12°. '64. 60c. .... *Barnes.*
— Young schoolmistress (The). 18°. 75c. ... *Harper.*

Alden, Miriam. Bashie's service; or, where's a will, there's a way. ill. 16°. '72. $1.15 ..... *Crowell.*
— — *See also* Ollie lib.

Alden, T. J. F. *See* Pennsylvania, Sup. Court reports.

Alden series (The). 8 v. sq. 16°. ea., 75c... *Tibbals.*
Cont.: Choice stories, by J. Alden. — Rupert Cabel, by J. Alden. — Revolutionary tales, by J. Alden. — Little Clara, by Mrs. A. Bache. — Days of boyhood, by J. Alden. — Picture gallery, by Mrs. A. Bache. — Pebbles from the seashore, by Mrs. A. Bache. — Little Dora, by J. Alden.
— *See also* Alden, J.

Alderson, E. H. *See* England, Common law reports; Court of King's Bench reports.

Aldine edition of the British poets; ed. by Rev. J. Mitford, etc. 52 v. 16°. ea., 75c....... *Lippincott.*
Cont.: Goldsmith. — Burns, 3 v. — Gray. — Cowper, 3 v. — Falconer. — Shakespeare. — Pope, 3 v. — Akenside. — Milton, 3 v. Kirke White. — Surrey. — Young, 2 v. — Prior, 2 v. — Wyatt. — Dryden, 5 v. — Collins. — Beattie. — Church, 2 v. — Spenser, 5 v. — Thomson, 2 v. — Chaucer, 6 v. — Parnell. — Butler, 2 v. — Swift, 3 v.

Aldrich, J. The sacred lyre. 12°. '58. 75c... *Graves.*

Aldrich, M. Almy. History of the U. S. Marine Corps; from official reports and other doc. comp. by R. S. Collum. 8°. '75. $3..........(?) *Shepard.*

Aldrich, T: Bailey. Cloth of gold, and other poems. 16°. '74. $1.50; hf. cf., $3; mor., $4... *Osgood.*
— Marjorie Daw and other people. [Stories.] 16°. '73. $1.50; pap., $1...................... *Osgood.*
— Prudence Palfrey. [Fiction.] ill. 16°. '74. $1.50; pap., $1.............................. *Osgood.*
— Story of a bad boy. ill. 16°. '69. $1.50.... *Osgood.*

Alec Forbes of Howglen. Mac Donald, G. 75c. *Harper.*

Alec Tomlin; or, choose wisely. 16°. 50c. *Scribner, W. & A.*

Alex (*pseud.*) As it should be. 12°. $1.50.. *Lippincott.*
— As she would have it: the woman question. 12°. $1. *Lippincott.*

Alexander *the Great.* Life; rev. by T. O. Summers. 18°. '75. 50c....................... *So. Meth.*

Alexander, *Emperor.* Life. 18°. '65. 20c. *Am. Tr.*

Alexander *of Lycopolis.* Writings. *See* Methodius.

Alexander, —. Complete preceptor for the flute. 10th Am. ed. f°. bds., $2.50................ *Ditson.*
— Flute method. f°. bds., $2 .... *Willig.*

Alexander, *Mrs.* (*pseud.*) *See* Hector, *Mrs.* Annie F.

Alexander, Arch. Biographical sketches of the founder and principal alumni of the Log College. 12°. 90c..................................... *Pres. Bd.*
— Brief compend. of Bible truth. por. 12°. 70c. *Pres. Bd.*
— Canon (The) of the Old and New Test. ascertained; or, the Bible complete without the Apocrypha and unwritten traditions. 12°. $1.25 ..... *Pres. Bd.*
— Counsels from the aged to the young. 18°. 30c. *Pres. Bd.*
— Evidences of the authenticity, inspiration and authority of the Scriptures. por. 12°. $1... *Pres. Bd.*
— History of the patriarchs. 18°. 50c....... *Am. S. S.*
— Letters to the aged. 18°. 35c............. *Pres. Bd.*
— Outlines of moral science. ('52.) New ed. 12°. '76. $1.50 .... *Scribner.*
— Practical sermons; to be read in families and social meetings. por. 8°. $2............... *Pres. Bd.*
— Practical truths. ill. 12°. '57. 75c........ *Am. Tr.*
— Sinner guided to Christ. ill. 18°. '70. 25c... *Am. Tr.*
— Thoughts on relig. experience. 16°. $1.60. *Pres. Bd.*
— *German.* Gedanken über religiöse Erfahrung; übers. v. F. Steins. 12°. 80c.; $1 .... *Pres. Bd.*
— Universalism false and unscriptural: essay on the duration and intensity of future punishment. 18°. 35c.............................. *Pres. Bd.*
— Way (The) of salvation familiarly explained in a conversation between a father and his children. 32°. 20c.............................. *Pres. Bd.*

Alexander, C. F. Hymns for little children. 18°. 25c. *McCauley.*
— *Same.* 32°. '70. 25c.; pap., 12c. .... *Dutton.*
— Sunday book of poetry. 18°. 75c. 16°. $1.25. *Allyn.*
— *Same.* 18°. '65. $1.25................... *Macmillan.*

Alexander, C: Gertrude Morgan's adventures among the Indians of the far west. [*In* Eng. *or* Germ.] 8°. pap., 20c. .... *Barclay.*

Alexander, H: C. Life of J. A. Alexander. ('69.) New ed. por. cr. 8°. '75. $2.50.... *Scribner.*

Alexander, Ja. W. American mechanic and working man. 16°. $1.25.................(?) *Martien.*
— American Sunday-school (The) and its adjuncts. 18°. 80c.............................. *Am. S. S.*

Alexander, Ja. W., *continued.*
— Bring me up Samuel. 18°. '60. 20c..... *Randolph.*
— Broken crucible (The), and other tr. of German hymns. 16°. '61. 50c................. *Randolph.*
— Candy girl (The); or, Maria Cheeseman. 18°. '66. 55c............ *N. Y. Ref. Ch. Bd.; Pres. Com.*
— Carl, the young emigrant. 18°. 65c. .... *Am. S. S.*
— Charles Clifford; or, the children at River Bank. 18°. 70c.............................. *Am. S. S.*
— Consolation; in discourses on select topics. ('52.) 6th ed. 12°. '76. $2.......................... *Scribner.*
— Discourses on common topics of Christian faith and practice. ('58.) New ed. 12°. '64. $2.. *Scribner.*
— Faith: series of discourses. ('62.) New ed. 12°. '63. $2.................................. *Scribner.*
— Forty years' familiar letters: memoir of his life; ed. by J. Hall. ('60.) New [chp.] ed. por. 12°. '70. $2.50................................ *Scribner.*
— Good-better-best; or, the three ways of making a happy world. ill. 18°. '66. 80c. *N. Y. Ref. Ch. Bd.; Pres. Com.*
— Life of Archibald Alexander. por. 12°. $2.25. *Pres. Bd.; Scribner.*
— Merchant's (The) clerk. 18°. '56. 35c... *Randolph.*
— Patience. 18°. 25c. .... *Pres. Bd.*
— Plain words to a young communicant. 18°. '54. 40c. .... *Randolph.*
— Revival and its lessons. (cop. '58.) New ed. 18°. '61. 40c.................................. *Am. Tr.*
— Sacramental discourses. 12°. '60. $1.50. *Randolph.*
— Short stories for the little ones at home. 16°. 80c. *Am. S. S.*
— Thoughts on family worship. 12°. 80c... *Pres. Bd.*
— Thoughts on preaching: contributions to homiletics. 12°. $2.................................. *Scribner.*
— Uncle Austin and his nephews; or, the Scripture guide. ill. 18°. '66. 75c. .... *Am. S. S.; N. Y. Ref. Ch. Bd.; Pres. Com.*

Alexander, J: H: *See* Maryland geol. survey.

Alexander, J: H: Catena dominica: series of Sunday idyls. 16°. '67. $1.75 .... *Randolph.*
— Mountains of Palestine. 18°. '70. 70c. *N. Y. Ref. Ch. Bd.; Pres. Com.*
— Universal dict. of weights and measures, ancient and modern, reduced to the standards of the U. S. ('50.) New ed. 8° .'67. $3.50.. *Van Nostrand.*

Alexander, Jos. Addison. Acts of the apostles explained. 2 v. 12°. $4.............. *Pres. Bd.*
— *Same.* ('57.) New ed. 12°. '75. $4.. *Scribner.*
— Gospel accord. to Mark expl. 12°. $2... *Pres. Bd.*
— *Same.* ('58.) New ed. 12°. '70. $2. (Sunday-school ed.) 12°. '74. $1.25.......... *Scribner.*
— Gospel according to Matthew explained. 12°. $2. *Pres. Bd.*
— *Same.* ('60.) New ed. 12°. '70. $2. (Sunday-school ed.) 12°. '73. $1.25......... *Scribner.*
— Isaiah; tr. and explained. ('46–'47.) New ed., ed. by J. Eadie. 2 v. 8°. '65–'75. $6.50... *Scribner.*
— *Same*; abridged. 2 v. 12°. $4........ *Pres. Bd.*
— — *Same.* ('61.) New ed. 2 v. 12°. '69. $4. *Scribner.*
— Notes on New Test. literature and ecclesiast. hist. ('60.) New ed. 12°. '75. $2 ...... *Scribner.*
— Psalms; tr. and explained. 3 v. 12°. $6.. *Pres. Bd.*
— *Same.* ('50.) New [chp.] ed. 3 v. in 2. 12°. '73. $5...................................... *Scribner.*
— Sermons. ('60.) New ed. 2 v. in 1. por. 12°. '70. $2.50................................ *Scribner.*

Alexander, Jul. J. Collection of Brit. statutes in force in Md., according to Kilty's report; with notes and ref. 8°. '70. shp., $10.... *Cushings & B.*

Alexander, S: Davis. Princeton College during the 18th cent. 8°. '72. $2.50.......... *Randolph.*

Alexander, Ste. Harmonies of the solar system. 4°. '75. pap., $1...................... *Smith. Inst.*

Alexander, *Bp.* W: Leading ideas of the Gospels. [Sermons.] cr. 8°. '72. $1.75.... *Macmillan.*

Alexander, W: Lindsay. Ancient British church: inquiry into the hist. of Christianity in Britain previous to the estab. of the heptarchy; rev. by T. O. Summers. 18°. '57. 60c. .... *So. Meth.*
— Christ and Christianity: vindication of the divine authority of the Christian religion. 12°. '54. $1. *Meth. Bk. Conc.*
— Iona, the druid's isle, and its successive inhabitants; rev. by T. O. Summers. ('55.) 2d ed. 18°. '75. 60c. .... *So. Meth.*
Alexander: tragedy. 16°. pap., 15c. .... *French.*
Alexander library (The). 22 v. 18°. $10.75. *Am. S. S.*
Cont.: Amelia Finley. — The harvest. — Charles Clifford. — Letters to a very young lady. — Jane Scott. — The little story book. — Sunday school anniversary. — Jacob and Joseph. — Travels about home, 2 v. — The American Sunday school and its adjuncts. — Uncle Austin and his nephews. — Only son; or, Jonah Ross. — Carl, the young emigrant. — Letters to a younger brother. — Lame John. — Flower book. — Frank Harper. — Life of Absalom. — Hebrew customs. — A happy world. — Father's stories.
Alexis the runaway. Parker, R. A. $1 ...... *Lee & S.*
Alford, H: Eastertide sermons. 16°. $1.25 .. *Routledge.*
— Essays and addresses, chiefly on church subjects. demy 8°. $3 .... *Routledge.*
— Fireside homilies. 16°. '75. $1 .... *Randolph.*
— Genesis, and part of Exodus: rev. version, with ref. and comment. 8°. '72. $4 .... *Routledge.*
— Greek Testament; with crit. rev. text, digest of readings, ref., prolegomena and comment. 4 v. 8°. $30; shp., $36; hf. cf., $42 .... *Lee & S.*
— *Same.* v. 1: Four Gospels. 8°. $6; shp., $6.50; hf. mor., $8.25 .... *Harper.*
— How to study the New Testament. 3 v. 12°. ea., $1.75 .... *Routledge.*
Cont.: Gospels and Acts. — Epistles (1st sect.) — Epistles (2d sect.) and Revelations.
— Letters from abroad. [Italy.] cr. 8°. $2.50. *Routledge.*
— Life, journals and letters; ed. by his widow. ill. 8°. $5 .... *Lippincott.*
— Meditations in Advent: creation and providence. 16°. $1.25 .... *Routledge.*
— New Testament for Eng. readers: authorized version, with rev. Eng. text, ref., and comment. 4 v. 8°. $16; shp., $21; hf. cf., $26 .. *Lee & S.*
— New Testament: rev. of authorized version. cr. 8°. $2.50. fp. 8°. $2. 18°. $1 .... *Routledge.*
— Queen's (The) English: stray notes on speaking and spelling. 16°. $1.25 .... *Routledge.*
— Riviera (The): pen and pencil sketches from Cannes to Genoa. ill. 4°. $10 .... *Routledge.*
— Romanism in Rome. 18°. pap., 12c. .. *Bost. Am. Tr.*
— *Same.* 18°. '67. 40c. .. *N. Y. Ref. Ch. Bd.; Pres. Com.*
— State of the blessed dead. 18°. '75. 75c. .. *Randolph.*
— Week of prayer; abridg. from "Year of prayer." 32°. 50c. .... *Routledge.*
— Year of prayer: family prayers for the Christian year. cr. 8°. '67. $1.50. 18°. 75c. .... *Routledge.*
Alford, L. A. Great atonement (The). [Poem.] 16°. $1; $1.25 .... *J. E. Potter.*
— Masonic gem: collection of Masonic odes, poems, etc. 16°. 75c. .... *Masonic.*
Alfred *the Great.* Life; rev. by T. O. Summers. 18°. '57. 60c. .... *So. Meth.*
Alfred the Great. Knowles, J. S. 15c. ...... *French.*
Alfred and Herbert; or, who is a coward? 18°. 17c.; 22c. .... *Am. Bapt.*
Alfred and his mother. May, K. S. 60c. .. *H. A. Young.*
Alfred Raymond; or, a mother's influence. 18°. 40c. *Am. S. S.*
Alfred Warriner. Kingsbury, O. A. 75c. ... *Am. Tr.*
Algatchie (*pseud.*) Seen and unseen. [Fiction.] 12°. $1.50 .... *Carleton.*
Alger, Horatio, *jr.* Brave and bold ser. [To form 4 v.] v. 1–3. 16°. ea., $1.50 .... *Loring.*
Cont.: Brave and bold; or, the story of a factory boy. — Jack's ward; or, the boy guardian. — Shifting for himself.

Alger, Horatio, *jr.*, *continued.*
— Campaign ser. 3 v. 16°. ea., $1.25 ...... *Loring.*
Cont.: Frank's campaign. — Paul Prescott's charge. — Charlie Codman's cruise.
— Gran'ther Baldwin's thanksgiving, with other ballads and poems. 16°. $1.25 .... *Loring.*
— Helen Ford. 12°. $1.25 .... *Loring.*
— Luck and pluck ser. 4 v. 16°. ea., $1.50 .. *Loring.*
Cont.: Luck and pluck; or, John Oakley's inheritance. — Sink or swim; or, Harry Raymond's resolve. — Strong and steady; or, paddle your own canoe. — Strive and succeed; or, the progress of Walter Conrad.
— *Same.* 2d ser. 4 v. 16°. ea., $1.50 ..... *Loring.*
Cont.: Try and trust; or, the story of a bound boy. — Bound to rise; or, how Harry Walton rose in the world. — Risen from the ranks; or, Harry Walton's success. — Herbert Carter's legacy; or, the inventor's son.
— Ragged Dick ser. 6 v. 16°. ea., $1.25 ... *Loring.*
Cont.: Ragged Dick; or, street life in New York. — Fame and fortune; or, the progress of Richard Hunter. — Mark the match boy. — Rough and Ready; or, life among New York newsboys. — Ben the luggage boy; or, among the wharves. — Rufus and Rose; or, the fortunes of Rough and Ready.
— Tattered Tom ser. 4 v. 16°. ea., $1.25 ... *Loring.*
Cont.: Tattered Tom; or, the story of a street Arab. — Paul the peddler; or, the adventures of a young street-merchant. — Phil, the fiddler; or, the young street musician. — Slow and sure; or, from the sidewalk to the shop.
— *Same.* 2d ser. [To form 4 v.] v. 1–3. 16°. ea., $1.25 .... *Loring.*
Cont.: Julius; or, the street boy out west. — The young outlaw; or, adrift in the world. — Sam's chance and how he improved it.
— *and* Cheney, O. A. Seeking his fortune, and other dialogues. 16°. $1.25 .... *Loring.*
Alger, I: *See* Murray, Lindley.
Alger, Isr. *See* Bible [Whole]; Bible, New Test.
Alger, W: R. Critical hist. of the doctrine of a future life. roy. 8°. $3.50; hf. cf., $6.50 .. *Widdleton.*
— *Same;* with bibliog. of works rel. to nature, origin and destiny of the soul, by E. Abbot. 8°. $4.50; hf. cf., $7.50 .... *Widdleton.*
— Friendships of women. 16°. '67. $1.50; $2 .. *Roberts.*
— Poetry of the Orient. ('65.) New ed., enl. 16°. '74. $1.50 .... *Roberts.*
— Prayers offered in the Mass. House of Representatives, session of 1868. 16°. '68. $1.50 ...... *Roberts.*
— Solitudes of nature and of man; or, the loneliness of human life. 16°. '66. $1.50; $2 ...... *Roberts.*
Al-Ghazzali. The alchemy of happiness; tr. from the Turkish by H. A. Homes. 8°. '73. $1.25 .. *Munsell.*
Algy's lesson. De Morgan, S. E. 60c. .... *Cassell.*
Alhambra. *See* Irving, W.
Alhambra and the Kremlin. Prime, S. I. $3. *Randolph.*
Ali Baba: extravaganza. Keating, E. H. 15c. .. *French.*
Ali Baba; or, thirty-nine thieves: drama. Byron, H. J. 15c. .... *French.*
Ali Baba and the forty thieves. f°. pap., 15c.; 20c. *J. E. Potter.*
— *See also* Arabian nights.
Ali Bey, Mohamed. Memoir. 18°. 40c. .. *Am. S. S.*
— Memoir. 18°. '66. 45c. .... *Pres. Com.*
Ali Pacha. Payne, J. H. 15c. .... *French.*
Alice, *Aunt.* *See* Aunt Alice.
Alice, *Cousin* (*pseud.*) *See* Haven, *Mrs.* Alice B.
Alice. *See* Bulwer-Lytton.
Alice. *See* Yonge, C. M., "Star of hope" series.
Alice; or, the little sentinel. 18°. 25c. *Scribner, W. & A.*
Alice; or, the rose of the Black Forest. 18°. '67. 50c. *Cunningham.*
Alice and Adolphus. Gatty, M. 75c. .... *Carter.*
Alice and Bessie; or, growth in grace. 18°. 55c. *Am. S. S.*
Alice and her friends. Perkins, S. M. C. $1.50. *Universalist.*
Alice and her friends. Waller, F. 75c. .... *Dodd.*
Alice and her little school. 16°. 30c. .. *Ref. Ch. Pub.*

Alice and her mother. 18°. 22c. .... *Am. S. S.*
Alice and her pupil. ill. 24°. 25c. .... *Perkinpine.*
— *Same;* and other tales. 18°. 70c. .... *Pres. Bd.*
— *Same;* [also] A foolish fear. 18°. 35c. *Bost. Am. Tr.*
— *See also* Alice and Willie stories.
Alice and Willie stories. 6 v. ill. 18°. $2. *Bost. Am. Tr.*
Cont.: Alice and her pupil. — Betsey Bartlett. — My little servant-maids. — Rose and her trouble. — The three-penny omnibus. — Will Thornton.
Alice Arran. Smith, J. F. 25c. .... *Dick & F.*
Alice Barlow; or, principle is everything. 18°. 75c. *Pres. Bd.*
— *Same.* 18°. '66. 70c. . . *N. Y. Ref. Ch. Bd.; Pres. Com.*
Alice Benden. *See* Tonna, *Mrs.* C. E.
Alice Benson's trials. ill. 18°. '70. 75c. .... *Lothrop.*
Alice Blake; or, the thankful little girl. 18°. 22c. *Am. S. S.*
Alice Brand. Riddle, A. G. $1.50. . . *Appleton; Cobb.*
Alice Clifford and her day dreams. 18°. 60c. *Am. S. S.*
Alice Dunbar. Spottswood, L. 60c. ...... *Pres. Bd.*
Alice Fenton. *See* Guernsey, C. F.
Alice Field. Brigham, S. P. 35c. .... *Hoyt.*
Alice Franklin. *See* Howitt, Mary.
Alice Gordon. Alden, J. 75c. .... *Harper.*
Alice Grant. Richmond, E. J. $1.25. .... *Nat. Temp.*
Alice Gray: drama. 16°. pap., 15c. .... *French.*
Alice Harmon, and other tales; by an "exile of Erin." 16°. $1.25; $1.75 .... *Sadlier.*
Alice Herbert. *See* N., E. V.
Alice in the country. 18°. 50c. .... *Am. S. S.*
Alice Learmont. *See* Craik, D. M.
Alice Lee. *See* Discipline of.
Alice Lee's temptation. 24°. 25c. .... *Bost. Am. Tr.*
— *See also* Banner stories.
Alice Leigh's mission; [also] Little Gwen's story. ('71.) New ed. 16°. '76. $1.50 .... *Hoyt.*
— *See also* Books for the children's hour.
Alice Leighton. *See* Cupples, *Mrs.* A. J.
Alice Lorraine. Blackmore, R. D. 75c. .... *Harper.*
Alice Maitland's trial. 18°. '73. 40c. ...... *Am. Tr.*
Alice Murray. Hoffman, M. J. $2 .... *O'Shea.*
Alice the mystery: melodrama. 16°. pap., 15c. *French.*
Alice Neville. *See* Bowen, C. E.
Alice of Monmouth. Stedman, E. C. $1.50. . *Osgood.*
Alice Porter; by author of "High mountain apart." ill. 16°. $1.25 .... *N. Y. Ref. Ch. Bd.*
Alice Rosedale. Blake, C. L. 60c. .... *Pres. Bd.*
Alice Seymour. Grey, E. C. 25c. .... *Peterson.*
Alice Sherwin. M., C. J. $1.25; $1.75 ..... *Sadlier.*
Alice Stanley and other stories. ill. 12°. $1. . . *Nelson.*
Alice Sutherland. Bristol, M. C. $1.25 .... *Lothrop.*
Alice Thorne. *See* Ellerslie House lib.
Alice Thornton. 18°. 45c. .... *Cong. Pub.*
Alice Thorpe's promise; or, a New Year's day. 18°. 25c. .... *Scribner, W. & A.*
Alice Townsend's garden. *See* Dunning, *Mrs.* A. K.
Alice Tracy. Currier, S. $1.25 .... *Dutton.*
Alice Vale. Waisbrooker, L. $1.25 .... *Colby.*
Alice Wade. Scott, W. 25c. .... *De Witt.*
Alice Wade. *See* Bradley, *Mrs.* M. E.
Alice's adventures in wonderland. *See* Dodgson, C. L.
Alice's dream. *See* Whitaker, *Mrs.* M. A.
Alice's watch. *See* Yonge, C. M.
Alicia and her aunt. *See* Hofland, *Mrs.* B.
Alicia Warlock. Collins, W. $1.50; 75c. *W. F. Gill.*
Alick and his blind uncle. Blackburn, W. M. 50c. *Pres. Bd.*
Alide. Lazarus, E. $1.25 .... *Lippincott.*

Alig, M. Die sieben Zeitalter d. Kirche Jesu Christi. 8°. $2 .... *Benziger.*
Alighieri. *See* Dante Alighieri.
Aline. Stirling, E. 15c. .... *French.*
Alison, *Rev.* Arch. Essays on the nature and principles of taste; with corrections and improvements by A. Mills. 12°. $1.50 .... *Harper.*
Alison, *Sir* Arch. History of Europe, 1789-1852. 8 v. 8°. $16; shp., $20; hf. mor., $34. . *Harper.*
— *Same;* abridg. ('44.) 7th ed. 8°. '72. $2.50. *Barnes.*
— Military life of John, Duke of Marlborough. maps. 12°. $1.75 .... *Harper.*
— Miscellaneous essays. *See* Modern British essayists; — Wilson, J., Recreations of C. North.
Alive and merry: drama. 16°. pap., 15c. ... *French.*
All aboard. Adams, W. T. $1.25 .... *Lee & S.*
All about Jesus. Dickson, A. $2 .... *Carter.*
All at C: musical melodrama. 16°. pap., 15c. . . *French.*
All at Coventry. *See* Moncrieff, W. T.
All the children's lib. 6 v. ill. sq. 16°. ea., 75c. . . *Fuller.*
Cont.: A summer with the little Grays, by Miss Preston. — Faith and patience, by J. P. Walker. — Modesty and merit, by M. Eppendorff. — Noisy Herbert, etc., by Miss C. S. Whitmarsh. — The R. B. R.'s, by Miss Child. — Bessie Grant's treasure, by Mrs. Adams.
All for the best. Edgeworth, M. $1 .... *Miller.*
All for Christ. Carter, T. 75c. ..... *Meth. Bk. Conc.*
All for greed. Blaze de Bury. 38c. ..... *Littell & G.*
All for Jesus. *See* Faber, F. W.
All for love. Dupuy, E. A. $1.75 .... *Peterson.*
All for money. Chellis, M. D. $1.25 .... *Nat. Temp.*
All in the dark. Le Fanu, J. S. 50c. .... *Harper.*
All in der family: Dutch dramatic sketch. 16°. pap., 15c. .... *Happy.*
All in the wrong. *See* Hook, Theodore.
All in the wrong. Murphy, A. 15c. .... *French.*
All men's place. Whitefield, G. 50c. .... *Cassell.*
All round the world. Ainsworth, W. F. $13.50. *Putnam.*
All round the world; or, scenes and adventures in every land. ill. and map. 4°. $5; $6. . *U. S. Pub.*
All sorts of pop-guns. *See* Barrow, *Mrs.* F.
All that glitters is not gold. Morton, T. *and* J. M. 15c. .... *French.*
All the way across. Hall, J. 25c. .... *Am. S. S.*
All the world over. *See* Cook's all the world over.
All the world a stage. Brookes, G. 15c. ..... *French.*
Allan, J: Military operations in Me. *See* Kidder, F.
Allan, W. Strength of beams under transverse loads. ill. 18°. '75. bds., 50c. .... *Van Nostrand.*
— Theory of arches. ill. 18°. '74. bds., 50c. *Van Nostrand.*
Allan, W: *See* Hotchkiss, J., *and* Allan, W.
Allan Cameron. Martyn, S. T. 50c. .... *Am. Tr.*
Allan Haywood. Mathews, J. A. 75c. ...... *Carter.*
Allan Leslie; or, the young missionaries. 18°. 75c. *Dutton.*
Allan Phillips. Foster, *Mrs.* I. H. 90c. . . (?) *Martien.*
Allan's fault. Finley, M. F. $1 .... *Pres. Bd.*
Allatoona. Kilpatrick, J. 15c. .... *French.*
Allbutt, T. Clifford. On the use of the ophthalmoscope in diseases of the nervous system and of the kidneys; also in certain other general disorders. 8°. '71. $5 .... *Macmillan.*
Allcott, W: A. Life of Robert Morrison, the first Protestant missionary to China. 18°. '66. 50c. *Pres. Com.; N. Y. Ref. Ch. Bd.*
Alleghania. Pindar, C. L. $1.25 .... *Lippincott.*
Allegories of life. Adams, J. S. $1 .... *Lee & S.*
Allegro (L'). *See* Milton, J.
Alleine, Jos. Alarm to unconverted sinners. 18°. pap., 15c. .... *Bost. Am. Tr.*

Alleine, Jos., *continued.*
— *Same.* 18°. '34. 35c. .... *Am. Tr.*
— *Same.* 18°. 50c. .... *Pres. Bd.*
— *Same;* with biog. introd. by T. O. Summers. 18°. '57. 50c. .... *So. Meth.*
— *Same;* [also] Call to unconverted sinners, by R. Baxter. 18°. '36. 55c. .... *Meth. Bk. Conc.*
— — *Same;* ed. by T. O. Summers. 18°. '57. 65c. *So. Meth.*
— *German.* Weckstimme f. Sünder. 18°. '51. 50c. *Am. Tr.*
— Memoirs. 18°. 55c. .... *Am. S. S.*

Allen, A. B. Origin [etc.], of Berkshire swine. *See* American Berk. Assoc.

Allen, Ann H. The young lady's new oracle. 12°. '58. $1.25 .... *Mendenhall.*
— The young mother and nurse's oracle. 12°. '58. $1.25 .... *Mendenhall.*

Allen, C. W. History and mystery of common things; for schools. 12°. hf. roan, $1.50... *World Pub.*
— Stitch (A) in time; or, one thousand and one things worth knowing. ill. 12°. $1.50 .... *World Pub.*

Allen, C: Reprint of cases rel. to liability of telegraph companies; chronolog. arranged from the Eng., Irish and Am. reports, with notes and references. 8°. '73. shp., $10 .... *Hurd & H.*
— *See also* Massachusetts, Sup. Court reports.

Allen, Chester G. Song cabinet. [Sing. book.] 16°. '68. 45c.; 60c. .... *T. J. Hall.*
— *See also* Lowry, R., Sherwin, W. F., *and* Allen, C. G.; — Seward, T. F., Allen, C. G., *and* Mason, L.; — Webb, G. J., *and* Allen, C. G.
— *and* Seward, T. F. The vineyard of song; for singing schools, etc. obl. 4°. '74. bds., 75c. *Biglow.*
— *and* Sherwin, W: F. The victory: sacred and secular music. obl. 4°. '69. bds., $1.50... *Biglow.*
— — *and* Lowry, R. *See* Laurels and jewels.

Allen, D. H. Faith Cleveland; or, daily beauty. 18°. 75c. .... *Cong. Pub.*

Allen, *Mrs.* Eliz. Akers. ["Florence Percy."] Story of Thomas Fish. [Poem.] *See* Washburn, I., *jr.*, History of Livermore.

Allen, Ethan. Reason, the only oracle of man; or, a compendious system of natural religion. 12°. 50c. *Mendum.*

Allen, Fordyce A. Oral geography for junior and primary schools on Pestalozzian principles. 4°. '62. hf. bd., 50c. .... *Claxton.*
— Primary geography: object method of instruction. 4°. hf. bd., 63c. .... *Claxton; Lippincott.*
— *and* Shaw, B. F. Comprehensive geography, comb. mathematical, physical and political geog., with hist. facts. 4°. hf. bd., $1.75. *Claxton; Lippincott.*

Allen, F: B. Leaves from a summer sketch-book, White mountain and Adirondack scenery: photographs. 4°. '74. $6. .... *Estes.*

Allen, G: Life of Philidor, musician and chess-player; with essay on Philidor as a chess-author and chess-player, by Tassilo von Heydebrand and Der Lasa. ('63.) New ed. 12°. '65. $1.50.. *Holt.*

Allen, Harrison. Autopsy of Siamese twins. *See* College of Physicians of Philadelphia.
— Monograph of the bats of No. Am. 8°. '64. pap., 50c. .... *Smith. Inst.*
— Outlines of comparative anatomy and medical zoology. 2d ed. 8°. $2 .... *Lippincott.*

Allen, Ja. *See* Dilley, J. J., *and* Allen, J.

Allen, Ja. Adams. Medical examinations for life insurance. ('67.) 6th ed. 8°. '76. $2... *Spectator.*

Allen, Jerome. National system of map drawing; adapted to Monteith's and McNally's geographies. 8°. '69. pap., 25c. .... *Barnes.*
— *and* King, G. A. Object drawing books. ('70.) New ed. 3 nos. obl. 8°. '75. 1, 2, ea., 40c.; 3, 50c. — Manual, 25c. .... *Clark & M.*

Allen, Jl. Asaph. American bisons, living and extinct. ill. and map. 4°. '76. pap., $5.. *Mus. Comp. Zool.*
— Catalogue of the mammals of Mass. 8°. '69. pap., 75c. .... *Mus. Comp. Zool.*
— Foray of a colony of formica sanguinea upon a colony of black ants. 8°. '68. pap., 10c. ...... *Essex.*
— On the eared seals; with account of the habits of the northern fur seal, by C. Bryant. ill. 8°. '70. pap., $1 .... *Mus. Comp. Zool.*
— On the mammals and winter birds of east Florida. ill. 8°. '71. pap., $3.25 ..... *Mus. Comp. Zool.*
— Ornithological reconnaissance of Kan., Col., Wyoming and Utah. 8°. '72. pap., 50c. *Mus. Comp. Zool.*
— *See also* Agassiz, A., *and* Garman, S. W., Exploration of Lake Titicaca.

Allen, *Rev.* J: The daily monitor; with introd. by Rev. E. N. Kirk. 32°. 30c. ..... *Bost. Am. Tr.*

Allen, J: Barrow. First Latin exercise book. 12°. '75. $1.25 .... *Macmillan.*

Allen, J: Fisk. Victoria regia, or the great water lily of Am. ill. roy. f°. '54. $10 .... *Essex.*

Allen, Jos. Battles of the British navy. 2 v. ill. 12°. (Bohn.) ea., $1.75 .... *Little, B. & Co.*
— *Same.* 2 v. ill. 12°. (Bohn.) ea., $2. *Lippincott; Scribner, W. & A.*
— Life of Lord Nelson. ill. 16°. $1 .... *Routledge.*

Allen, *Rev.* Jos. Questions on Acts. 16°. 25c. *Un. S. S.*
— Questions on select portions of the four evangelists. 2 v. 16°. ea., 25c. .... *Un. S. S.*

Allen, Jos. H. Hebrew men and times from the patriarchs to the Messiah. 12°. '61. $1.50. (?) *Walker, W. & Co.*
— Latin lexicon, with tables of dates, etc. ('69.) 2d ed. 12°. '75. $1.25 .... *Ginn.*
— Latin primer. ('70.) 4th ed. 12°. '74. 1.25. *Ginn.*
— Manual of Lat. Grammar. ('68.) 8th ed. 12°. '75. $1.25 .... *Ginn.*
— *See also* Allen, W. F. *and* J. H.; — Goodwin, W. W., *and* Allen, J. H.
— *and* W. F. Latin reader, with notes and vocab. ('69.) 7th ed. 12°. '75. hf. leath., $2.50.. *Ginn.*
— — *and* Greenough, J. B. Shorter course of Lat. prose; with vocab. ('73.) 2d ed. 12°. '75. hf. leath., $2.50 .... *Ginn.*
— *and* Greenough, J. B. Latin composition: element. guide to writing in Lat. New ed. 12°. '76. $1.50. *Ginn.*
— — Latin grammar; founded on compar. grammar. ('72.) 4th ed. 12°. '75. hf. leath., $1.56.. *Ginn.*
— — Latin prose: course no. 1. 12°. '75. hf. leath., $2.50 .... *Ginn.*
— — Latin prose: course no. 2; with vocab. by R. F. Pennell. 12°. '75. hf. leath., $2.50..... *Ginn.*
— — Latin selections. 12°. '73. hf. leath., $1.56. *Ginn.*
— — Method of instruction in Lat. 2d ed. 12°. '75. $1.25 .... *Ginn.*

Allen, Lew. F. American cattle: their history, breeding and management. 12°. $2 .... *Taintor.*
— *Same.* ill. 12°. $2.50 .... *Judd.*
— Rural architecture. 12°. $1.50 .... *Judd.*

Allen, N. G. Devotions of the ages: collects, etc., ill. of the Christian year; with introd. by T. M. Clark. 16°. '66. $1.25.. *Claxton; Lippincott.*

Allen, N. H. German four-part songs for mixed voices; with Eng. words. 8°. '75. bds., $1.50. *Ditson.*
— *See also* Fischer, M. G., Fifteen sel. from works.

Allen, Pl. *See* Biddle, N., Hist. of exped. of Lewis and Clarke.

Allen, P: Lectures on aural catarrh; or, the commonest forms of deafness and their cure. ill. 12°. $2 .... *W. Wood.*

Allen, R. L. Domestic animals: hist. and descript. of the horse, mule, sheep, etc.; with directions for management, breeding, etc. 12°. $1 ..... *Judd.*

Allen, R. L., *continued.*
— New American farm book. 12°. $2.50 .... *Judd.*

Allen, R. W. An incentive to doing good. 24°. '59. 35c. .... *Meth. Bk. Conc.*

Allen, S. M. Ancient and modern theories of light, heat and color. 8°. '73. pap., 10c. ..... *Essex.*

Allen, T. Apparatus for obtaining borings by direct pressure. 8°. pap., 45c. .... *Am. Soc. of C. E.*
— Iron hulls for western river steamboats; [also] McAlpine's Foundations of the new Capitol at Albany, N. Y.; [also] Thurston's Determination of the mechanical equivalent of heat; [also] White's Erection of a bridge over the Danube, near Vienna; [also] Thacher's Tables of the strength of cast iron columns. 8°. '74. pap., 80c. .... *Am. Soc. of C. E.*

Allen, T F. (*ed.*) Encyclopedia of pure materia medica. [Hom.] [To form 10 v.] v. 1–3. 8°. '74. ea., $6; shp., $7; hf. mor., $7.50. *Boericke.*

Allen, T: Prentiss *and* W. F. Hand book of classical geog. 12°. 85c. .... *Ware.*

Allen, W. F. Gazetteer of railway stations in the United States and Canada. 12°. '74. $1.50; pap., $1 .... *Nat. R. W. Pub.*

Allen, W: B. Kentucky officers' guide and legal hand-book. 8°. '60. shp., $3 .... *Morton.*

Allen, W: Fs. Introduction to Lat. composition. ('70.) 5th ed. 12°. '74. $1.25 .... *Ginn.*
— *See also* Allen, J. H. *and* W. F.; — Allen, T. P. *and* W. F.
— *and* J. H. Latin lessons, to accompany the "Manual grammar"; with exercises in prosody. ('69.) 8th ed. 12°. '74. $1.25 .... *Ginn.*

Allen and Harry. Bell, C. D. 75c... *Scribner, W. & A.*

Allen house (The). Arthur, T. S. $1.25. *J. E. Potter.*

Allen Lucas. *See* Good boy's lib.

Allen White. *See* Sunshine and shadow lib.

Allerton homes. Lathrop, H. $1 ...... *J. A. Moore.*

All-hallow eve. Curtis, R. $2 .... *Cath. Pub.*

Alli. *See* Hoffmann, F.

Allibone, S: Austin. Critical dict. of Eng. literature and Brit. and Am. authors; with indexes. 3 v. roy. 8°. '58–'71. $22.50; shp., $25.50; hf. mor., $28.50; mor., $45 .... *Lippincott.*
— Dictionary of poet. quotations, British and American; with indices. 8°. $5; $6; hf. cf., $8; mor., $10. 4°. $10; mor., $18; $20 .... *Lippincott.*
— Divine origin of the Scriptures. 16°. 65c. *Am. S. S.*
— Prose quotations from Socrates to Macaulay; with indexes. 8°. $5; $5.50; shp., $6; hf. cf., $8; mor., $10 .... *Lippincott.*
— Union Bible companion. 12°. $1.25..... *Am. S. S.*

Allie Bird series. 3 v. 16°. $3 .... *Lothrop.*
Cont.: A little woman. — Grandma Crosby's household. — A girl's money.

Allie Moore's lesson. 18°. 25c. .... *Am. S. S.*

Allie Stuart. Grey, A. $1.50 .... *Nelson.*

Allies, T: W: The see of Peter, the rock of the church, the source of jurisdiction, and the centre of unity. 16°. '66. 75c. .... *Cath. Pub.*

Allingham, J: Till. Fortune's frolic: farce. 16°. pap., 15c. .... *French.*
— Mrs. Wiggins: farce. 16°. pap., 15c. ..... *French.*
— Weathercock: farce. 16°. pap., 15c. ..... *French.*

Allingham, W: Poems. (Blue and gold ed.) 32°. $1.50 .... **Osgood.*
— (*ed.*) Ballad book: selection of British ballads. 18°. '65. $1.25 .... *Macmillan.*
— *Same.* (Golden treas. ser.) 18°. 75c. 16°. $1.25. *Allyn.*

Allingham, W: Fistula, hæmorrhoids, painful ulcer, stricture, prolapsus and other diseases of the rectum: their diagnosis and treatment. 2d ed., rev. and enl. 8°. '73. $2 .... *Lindsay.*

Allinson, W: J. Poems. 12°. '73. $1.50 .. *Claxton.*

Allioli, J. F. v. *See* Bible [Whole], *Germ.*

Allis family (The); or, scenes of western life. 18°. 30c. .... *Am. S. S.*

Allongé, Auguste. Charcoal drawings; tr. by S. D. W.; with introd. by C. C. Perkins. sm. 4°. '76. $1 .... *Hurd & H.*

Allow me to apologise: farce. 16°. pap., 15c. *French.*

All's fair in love. Brougham, J. 15c. .... *French.*

All's for the best lib. *See* Arthur, T. S.

All's not gold that glitters. *See* Haven, *Mrs.* A. B.

All's well that ends well. *See* Shakespeare, W.

Allston, Jos. Blyth. Sumter. [Poem.] 12°. '74. 50c.; pap., 25c. .... *Turnbull.*

Allworth Abbey. Southworth, E. D. E. N. $1.75; $1.50 .... *Peterson.*

Allyn, Avery. Ritual of Freemasonry: key to the degrees in Masonry; and to the Phi Beta Kappa, Orange, and Odd Fellows' societies. ill. 12°. $5. *Dick & F.*

Allyn, R. *See* Lilienthall, M. E., *and* Allyn, R.

Ally's school-fellows. 18°. 35c. .... *Routledge.*
— *See also* Moss wreath lib.

Al-ma-kan-tur circle (The). 18°. pap., 25c. *Dick & F.*

Almar, G: [Plays.] 17 v. 16°. ea., pap., 15c. *French.*
Cont.: Battle of Sedgmoor. — Bull-fighter. — Cedar chest. — Charcoal burner. — Clerk of Clerkenwell. — Crossing the line: farce. — Don Quixote. — Earl of poverty. — Fire raiser. — Good-looking fellow: farce. — Knights of St. John. — Oliver Twist. — Pedlar's acre. — Robber of the Rhine. — Rover's bride. — Shadow. — Wife of seven husbands: melodrama.
— Gaspardo the gondolier. 16°. pap., 15c.... *Lee & S.*

Almeria. *See* Edgeworth, M.

Almost Christian (The) discovered. Mead, M. 55c. *Pres. Bd.*

Almost faultless: a novel of the present day. 8°. pap., 60c. .... *Appleton.*

Almost a nun. Wright, J. McN. $1 ...... *Pres. Bd.*

Almost a woman. Frost, S. A. $1.25 .... *Am. Tr.*

Almshouse boy. 18°. 50c. .... *Cong. Pub.*

Alone. Harland, M. $1.50 .... *Carleton.*

Alone: comedy. 16°. pap., 15c. .... *French.*

Alone in London. *See* Little folk lib.; — Smith, Hannah.

Alone in the world. ('71.) New ed. 16°. '74. $1.25. *Hoyt.*

Alone with Jesus. Lanphier, J. C. 85c.; $1 .. *Tibbals.*

Alonzo and John. 32°. 20c.; 15c. .... *Dutton.*

Alonzo and Melissa. *See* Jackson, D. J.

Alonzo the brave. Burnand, F. C. 15c. ..... *French.*

Aloysius Gonzaga, *St.* Life. 18°. 50c... *Cummiskey.*
— Life; ed. by E. H. Thompson. 12°. $1.50 .. *Sadlier.*

Alpers, W. *See* Ives, E., *jr.*, Alpers, W., *and* Timm, H. C.

Alpha (*pseud.*) *See* Phelps, *Miss* L. L.

Alphabet [ser. of toy-books]. 5 v. ill. 4°. ea., $1; 50c. .... *Routledge.*
Cont.: Alphabet of fairy tales — of flowers — of old friends — of pretty names — of trades.

Alphabet and easy words. [Toy-book.] ill. sq. 16°. bds., 25c. .... *Routledge.*

Alphabet of Scripture animals. Cook, H. N. 35c. *Am. Tr.*

Alphabet picture stories. 18°. 30c. ...... *Am. S. S.*

Alphabetical index to the New Test. 16°. 25c.; 40c.; 50c. .... *Am. S. S.*

Alphabetical reference list of books recorded in the "Publishers' Weekly," Jan. 18, 1872–Jan. 16, 1873. 8°. '73. *net*, pap., 25c. *Publishers' Weekly.*
— *Same;* Jan. 16, 1873–June 27, 1874. 8°. '74. *net*, pap., 25c. .... *Publishers' Weekly.*
Note. Previously included in "American catalogue" and "Trade circular annual"; subsequently incl. in "Publishers' trade-list annual."

Alphonso, *Bishop of St. Agatha.* Preparation for death; tr. from the Ital. by Rev. O. Shipley. sq. 12°. $1.50 .... *Lippincott.*

Alphonso. S., M. $1 .... *Cunningham.*

Alphonsus de Liguori, *St. See* Liguori, *St.*

Alpine cross. *See* Little Will.

Alpine glee singer (The). *See* Bradbury, W. B.

Alpine lyrics. *See* Heusser-Schweizer, M.

Alps and the Rhine. *See* Eddy, D. C., Percy family.

Alroy. Disraeli, B. 50c. .... *Appleton.*

Alsop, Reese F. Lessons for the Christian year; for S.-schools, Bible classes, etc. 2 pts. 24°. ea., pap., 10c.; bds., 18c. .... *Lent.*

Alsop, R: Charms (The) of fancy: poem, with notes and biog. sketch of author, ed. by T. Dwight. 12°. $1 .... *Appleton.*

Alsop, S: First lessons in algebra. 12°. '53. hf. bd., 70c. — Key. 12°. hf. bd., 70c. ...... *Fortescue.*

— Treatise on algebra. 3d ed., rev. and enl. 12°. '54. $1.50. — Key. 12°. hf. bd., 75c. ..... *Fortescue.*

— Treatise on surveying; [with] short treatise on logarithms, and a compendious system of plane trigonometry. 3d ed. ill. 8°. '57. $2.25. — Key. 8°. hf. roan, $1.25 .... *Fortescue.*

— *See also* Gummere, J.; — Vogdes, W., *and* Alsop, S.

Altar (The). Bartholomew, J. G. per doz., $3.50. *Universalist.*

Altar at home: prayers for the family and closet; ed. by Rev. H. A. Miles. ('55.) 16th ed. 16°. '73. 80c. .... *Am. Unit.*

— *Same.* 2d ser.: selections and prayers for domestic worship. ('62.) 6th ed. 16°. '72. 80c. *Am. Unit.*

Altar companion (The). [Cath. prayer book.] 32°. 50c.-$3 .... *O'Shea.*

Altar in the house. Aikman, W. 10c. ...... *Am. Tr.*

Altar incense. Macduff, J. R. $1 .... *Carter.*

Altar manual (The); ed. by a committee of clergy. 32°. '74. 50c. .... *Pott.*

Altar manual (The); or, instructions and devotions for confession and communion; from the "Delices des ames pieuses." ill. 24°. 75c.-$3.50. *Sadlier.*

Altars of Palestine. Headley, P. C. 25c.; 30c. *J. E. Potter.*

Alte Bauersfrau (Die). 32°. '65. 15c. ..... *Am. Tr.*

Alte Krieger (Der) u. s. Sohn. Nieritz, G. 25c. *Morwitz.*

Alte spanische Urkunde (Die). *See* Strubberg, F. A.

Altes in neuem Gewande. 18°. 35c. ...... *Ev. Assoc.*

Altes u. Neues. Bickel, P. W. 25c. ... *Germ. Bapt.*

Althaus, Jul. Treatise on medical electricity, and its use in treatment of paralysis, etc. 3d ed., rev. and enl. ill. 8°. '73. $6 .... *Lindsay.*

Althea. *See* Books of blessing.

Altisonant letters: letters to Squire Pedant for the benefit of the inquisitive young. ('55.) New ed. 12°. '73. 60c. .... *Pounsford.*

Alton Locke. *See* Kingsley, C.

Alton Park; or, conversations on religious and moral subjects. 12°. $1.25; $1.50 ...... *Cummiskey.*

Alvergnat, V. Modern class book of French pronunciation. ('72.) New ed. 12°. '74. $1.25. *Schoenhof.*

Alvira. O'Reilly, A. J. $1.50 .... *Sadlier.*

Alvord, B: Tangencies of circles and spheres. 4°. '56. pap., $1 .... *Smith. Inst.*

Always do right. 32°. 25c. .... *West. Tr.*

— *Same.* 18°. 50c. .... *Whittaker.*

Always happy. 16°. 75c. .... *Nelson.*

Always intended. Wigan, H. 15c. .. *French; Lee & S.*

Always tell the truth. *See* My own lib.

Alwyn. Moffat, J. C. $1.50 .... *Randolph.*

Alypius of Tagaste. Webb, J. B. $1.50 .. *Pres. Bd.*

Alzog, J: Manual of universal church hist.; tr. from 9th rev. and enl. Germ. ed., ed. and brought down to the present time by Rev. F. J. Pabisch. [To form 3 v.] v. 1-2. 8°. '74-'76. ea., $5 ... *Clarke.*

Cont.: v. 1. Early church hist. — v. 2. The middle ages.

Am I a child of God? 18°. 40c.; pap., 10c. .. *Am. S. S.*

Am I a Christian, and how can I know it? 32°. 40c. *Pres. Bd.*

Am I a sinner? 18°. 40c. *Am. S. S.; N. Y. Ref. Ch. Bd.; Pres. Com.*

Amadeus. Volmann, K. $1. .... *Scribner.*

Amaranth. [S.-school hymn book.] 18°. 70c. *Am. S. S.*

— *Same.* sq. 16°. '74. 20c.; — with notes. sq. 16°. '72. 40c. .... *So. Meth.*

Amateur actor (The). Venable, W. H. $1.50. *Wilson, H. & Co.*

Amateur casual (*pseud.*) *See* Greenwood, Ja.

Amateur drama series. *See* Baker, G: M.

Amateur guitarist. Worrall, H., *and* Hayden, W. L. $2.50 .... *Peters.*

Amateur mechanics' workshop: directions for manipulation of wood and metals; by author of "Lathe and its uses." 3d ed. ill. 8°. $3 .... *Baird.*

Amateur organist. Zundel, J. $2 .... *Ditson.*

Amateur painter (The): instruction in arts of painting, varnishing and gilding. 12°. pap., 25c. *Hurst.*

Amateur printer (The). ill. 12°. pap., 25c. ... *Hurst.*

Amateur series. 3 v. 12°. ea., $2 .... *Holt.*

Cont.: Moscheles' Recent music and musicians. — Chorley's Recent art and society. — Wagner's Art life and theories.

Amateur stage. nos. 1-47. 16°. ea., pap., 15c. *Happy.*

Amateur vagabond (*pseud.*) *See* P., A.

Amateur's first book for the guitar. obl. 8°. pap., 75c. *Peters.*

Amateur's first book for the pianoforte: elements of music and popular tunes. obl. 8°. pap., 75c. *Peters.*

Amateur's (The) guide to magic and mystery. sq. 18°. '74. pap., 25c. .... (?) *F. M. Reed.*

Amateur's song-book. 12°. bds., 50c. ...... *Ditson.*

Amateurs and actors. Peake, R. B. 15c. .... *French.*

Amaury. *See* Dumas, A.

Amazon (The). Dingelstedt, F. $1 .... *Putnam.*

Ambas Américas: contrastes. P., R. $2.50. *Appleton.*

Amber gods (The). Spofford, H. E. $1.75. * *Osgood.*

Amber witch. Wallace, W. V. $4.50; $6 .. *T. J. Hall.*

Ambition. Mayhew, T. 15c. .... *French.*

Ambitious youth's lib. 3 v. ill. 12°. $4.50 .. *Nelson.*

Cont.: Self-taught men. — The black prince. — Story of Mark Raffles, by W. Dalton.

Ambrose, I: Looking unto Jesus. 8°. $3. (?) *Martien.*

Ambrose Gwinnett. Jerrold, D. 15c. ...... *French.*

Amcotts, Vincent. Adonis vanquished: comedy. 16°. pap., 15c. .... *French.*

Amelia *See* Fielding, H.

Amelia; or, the triumph of piety; tr. by Mother St. John. 12°. '74. $1 .... *Cunningham.*

Amelia Finley; or, careless reading of the Bible reproved. 18°. 25c. *Am. S. S.; N. Y. Ref. Ch. Bd.; Pres. Com.*

Amelia Gale. 18°. 15c.; 20c. .... *Am. Bapt.*

America and her commentators. Tuckerman, H. T. $2.50. .... *Scribner.*

American Academy of Arts and Sciences. Memoirs. 4 v. 4°. 1785-1821. bds., $10. *Am. Acad. of A. & S.*

— *Same.* New ser. v. 1-9. 4°. '33-'73. pap., $10. *Am. Acad. of A. & S.*

— Proceedings, May, 1846-May, 1873. 8 v. 8°. '48-'73. pap., $5. .... *Am. Acad. of A. & S.*

— *Same.* New series. v. 1-3, May, 1873-'76. 3 v. 8°. '74-'76. pap., $5 .... *Am. Acad. of A. & S.*

American Academy of Dental Science. History of dental and oral science in America. roy. 8°. '76. $2.55 .... *Am. Acad. Dent. Sci.*

American adventure by land and sea. Sargent, E. 2 v. $1.50 .... *Harper.*

American angler's book. *See* Norris, T.

American annual cyclopædia. *See* Appleton's.

American Antiquarian Society. Archæologia Americana: transactions and collections of the Soc. 6 v. 8°. '20–'74. v. 1, 4, ea., $3.50; v. 2, $9; v. 3, 5, 6, ea., $4 .... *Am. Antiq.*

— By-laws; with resolutions of Congress and the General Court of Mass. 8°. '15. 50c... *Am. Antiq.*

— Catalogue of [its] library. 8°. '36. $1.50. *Am. Antiq.*

— Proceedings at [annual, semi-annual and special] meetings. 54 v. 8°. '43–'76. ea., 50c., 75c., *or* $1 .... *Am. Antiq.*

Contents of special nos.: Oct. 23, '43, Memorial address on W. Lincoln, by J. Davis. — Oct. 23, '49, Memoir of A. Gallatin, by E. E. Hale — Apr. 26, '54, Memoir of J. Davis, by T. Kinnicutt. — Oct. 22, '55, Catalogue of members. — Feb. 10, '59, Death of W. H. Prescott. — Apr. 25, '60, Notices of a visit to [Lond.] State Paper Office, and Notes on drawings by J. White, seen in the Brit. Museum. — Oct. 22, '60, Report upon the Am. coins and tokens in the cabinet of the Soc. — Oct. 21, '61, Essay on the time of making Michael Angelo's statues of Christ and Moses. — Apr. 30, '62, Remarks on the Huguenot settlements in N. E., by I. M Barton, and On the name California, by E. E. Hale. — Oct. 21, '62, Notice of I. Thomas. — Apr. 29, '63, Indications of ancient customs suggested by certain cranial forms, by D. Wilson. — Apr. 7, '64, Remarks on the Huguenots in N. E., and On a Latin inscription lately found at Castine. Me., by C. Folsom. — Oct. 21, '64, Notes on Roanoke Island and James River, by E. E. Hale, and On interesting localities in eastern Va., by C. Deane. — Jan. 17, '65, Death of Edward Everett. — Apr. 26, '65, Death of Lincoln, and On the medical dep't of the U. S. army during the civil war. — Oct. 21, '65, Death of Geo. Livermore, On early notices in Eng. literature of the discovery and first colonization of Am., and On Mexican civilization. — Mar. 16, '66, Death of Jared Sparks; Apr. 25, On the early paper currency of Mass. — Oct. 20, '66, On the mappe-monde of Cabot, 1544; Nov. 15, Death of W. Jenks. — Apr. 24, '67, On a letter from Mr. Bergenroth rel. to Eng. and Spain, by E. E. Hale, On Cabot's mappe-monde, by C. Deane, and Records of the Council for N. E., ed. by C. Deane. — Oct. 21, '67, On the ancient lake dwellings of Switzerland, Remarks of E. E. Hale, and Letter from J. H. Trumbull on the name Massachusetts. — Apr. 29, '68, Notice of Bp. Strachan, by D. Wilson, Catalogue of Indian relics, by W. A. Smith and S. Salisbury, jr., Prehistoric man and his associates, by J. R. Bartlett, Letter from W. Green resp. author of "Relation of Capt. Newport's discoveries in Va." — June 2, '68, Death of Levi Lincoln. — Apr. 28, '69, On prehistoric man, and On ancient tumuli in Georgia, by C. C. Jones, jr. — Oct. 21, '69, On the relations the antiquary holds to the science of archæology. — Apr. 27, '70, On the townships of N. E. — Oct. 21, '70, On town governments in N. E. — Apr. 26, '71, On prehistoric Am. occupation and civilization. — Oct. 21, '71, Letter from E. E. Salisbury on the original edition of "The Spectator," On the hist. of discovery in the Pacific, and On the value of magazine literature. — Apr. 23, '72, On town debts, by G. E. Ellis, On the hist. of discovery in the Pacific and its Am. shores, On the likelihood of an admixture of Japanese blood on our northwest coast, by H. Davis, and On cosmogony of Dante and Columbus, by E. E. Hale. — Oct. 21, '72, Star spangled banner and national songs, by S. Salisbury, — Apr. 30, '73, Prehistoric implements. — Oct. 23, '73, On the origin and early progress of Indian missions in N. E., and list of books in Indian language, Early maps in Munich, by E. E. Hale, On some of the connections by marriage of Columbus, by E C. Smyth, Memorandum as to the discovery of the bay of San Francisco, by J. T. Doyle, Memorial of Gov. Endicott, by S. Salisbury. — Mar. 14, '74, Death of C. Sumner; Apr. 29, On C. Mather's Medical manuscript, and The great awakening, by I. Smucker. — Oct. 21, '74, On the legal and political issues of the rebellion. — Apr. 28, '75, On the discoveries of H. Schliemann in the Troad. — Oct. 21, '75, On the Records of the Council for N. E., by C. Deane, and The criminal laws of Mass., by P. E. Aldrich.

— Semi-annual reports, May and October, 1839; with catalogue of members. 8°. '39. $1.. *Am. Antiq.*

American Association for the Advancement of Science. Memoirs, no. 1: Fossil butterflies, by S. H. Scudder. ill. 4°. '75. pap., $2; hf. mor., $3.50. *Am. Assoc. Adv. Sci.*

— Proceedings. v. 1–24. ill. 8°. '49–'76. ea., $1.50. *Am. Assoc. Adv. Sci.*

American Baptist year book. 12°. 50c... *Am. Bapt.*

American baron. De Mille, J. $1.50; $1.. *Harper.*

American Berkshire Assoc. American Berkshire record, v. 1: Pedigrees of Berkshire swine. roy. 8°. '76. $3 .... *Am. Berk.*

American Berkshire Assoc., *continued.*

— Premium essay on the origin, breeding and management of Berkshire swine; [by A. B. Allen]. 8°. '76. pap., 25c. .... *Am. Berk.*

American Bible Society. Reports, 1816–1871. [Reprint.] 4 v. 8°. ea., $3 .... *Am. Bib. Soc.*

American biog. series. *See* Hill, G.

American biography. v. 1–3. 4°. '72. ea., mor., $20. roy. 8°. ea., mor., $10 ...... *N. Y. and H. Pub.*

American book of genteel behavior: handbook of modern etiquette. 12°. pap., 25c. .... *Hurst.*

American boyhood. Biddle, H. P. $1.50.. *Lippincott.*

American boy's own book of sports and games. ill. 12°. $3; $4; hf. cf., $6 .... *Dick & F.*

American card player (The): directions for euchre, whist, bezique, etc. 16°. 75c.; bds., 50c. *Dick & F.*

American catalogue (The) of books for 1869: monthly lists of books pub. in the U. S. during 1869, with alphab. and classified index. 8°. '70. *net*, pap., $1 .... *Publishers' Weekly.*

— *See also* Alphabetical ref. list; — Annual Am. cat.

American chess player's (The) handbook. ill. 16°. '70. $1.25 .... *Porter.*

American Chesterfield (The): sel. from Chesterfield's letters, with extracts from other authors on politeness; by a member of the Phila. bar. ('27.) New ed. 18°. '72. 75c. .... *Claxton.*

American clinical lectures. *See* Seguin, E. C.

American college songster. Andrews, S. C. 90c.; 50c. *Sheehan & Co.*

American constitutions: Constitution of the U. S., and of the several states. 12°. $2 .... *Polock.*

American convent (The) as a school for Protestant children. 16°. '69. $1.25 .... *Whittaker.*

American cyclopædia. *See* Ripley, G., *and* Dana, C. A.

American Cyclops. Pasquino. $1.50.. *Kelly, P. & Co.*

American debater. McElligott, J. N. $1.50.. *Ivison.*

American dispensatory. King, J. $10..... *Wilstach.*

American ephemeris. *See* United States, *Bureau of Navigation.*

American Ethnological Soc. Transactions. v. 1–2. 8°. '45–'48. ea., pap., $4 .... *Am. Eth. Soc.*

American family (An) in Germany. Browne, J. R. $2 .... *Harper.*

American family (An) in Paris. ill. 16°. '69. $1.25. *Hurd & H.*

American family Robinson. Belisle, D. W. $1.25. *Porter.*

American farmer's new and universal handbook; [with] tables for the measurement of land, etc.; re-ed., with add., by J. W. O'Neill. ill. sm. 8°. $3; mor., $3.50 .... *Desilver.*

American fashionable letter writer. 32°. bds., 35c. *U. P. James.*

American fistiana: showing the progres of pugilism in the U. S., 1816–'73. 8°. pap., 50c..... *De Witt.*

American forest (The). Hawks, F. L. 75c... *Harper.*

American Geologists and Naturalists, Assoc. of. *See* Association.

American girl abroad. Trafton, A. $1.50.. *Lee & S.*

American Gun Club. *See* Verne, Jules.

American handbook of chemical and physical apparatus, etc. 8°. '72. $1.50 .... *Benjamin.*

American home cook-book. 16°. pap., 30c.; bds., 50c. *Dick & F.*

American horse doctor. *See* Secret art.

American housewife and kitchen directory. 16°. pap., 30c.; bds., 50c. .... *Dick & F.*

American Hoyle. *See* Dick, W. B.

American (An) in England. Mackenzie, A. S. 2 v. $2.50 .... *Harper.*

American (An) in Iceland. Kneeland, S. $2.50. *Lockwood, B. & Co.*

American Institute of Architects. Proceedings of 2-9 annual conventions, 1868-'75. 8 v. 4°. v. 2, pap., 50c.; v. 3-9, ea., pap., $1.. *Am. Inst. Arch.*

Cont.: [Besides the proceedings there are incl. in] v. 2. Address, by R. Upjohn. — 3. Address, by R. Upjohn, and Address on professional guilds, by E. L. Godkin. — 4. Addresses, by T. U. Walter and W. H. Furness. — 5. Address, by R. Upjohn, On terra cotta, by J. H. Sturgis, Effects of the fire in Chicago, by P. B. Wight, and Addresses by C. Eliot, etc. — 6. Address, by R. G. Hatfield, On cements and concrete, by N. H. Hutton, On mansard roofs, by A. C. Nash, and Address, by R. King. — 7. Address, by P. B. Wight, On mansard roofs, by A. J. Bloor, and Addresses, by Mayor Bond and E. A. Storrs. — 8. Addresses by H. A. Sims, S. Osgood, etc. — 9. Address, by H. Van Brunt.

v. I. is o. p.

American Institute of Mining Engineers. Transactions. v. 1-3. 8°. '71-'75. ea., pap., $5; hf. mor., $5.75.................... *Am. Inst. M. E.*

American Iron and Steel Association. The iron works of the U. S. 16°. '76. pap., $2.... *Am. Iron.*

American Joe Miller. ill. 8°. pap., 50c..... *Peterson.*

American Law Times reports; ed. by R. Cox. v. 1-6 (1868-'73); new ser., v. 1-2 (1874-'75). 8 v. 8°. ea., shp., $6...................... *Hurd & H.*

American leading cases. *See* Hare, J. I. C., *and* Wallace, J. W.

American leaves. Osgood, S. $1.75....... *Harper.*

American letter writer. 32°. 50c........... *Fisher.*

American mechanic and working man. Alexander, J. W. $1.25........................ (?) *Martien.*

American Medical Association. Code of medical ethics. 32°. 40c.................... *W. Wood.*

— *Same.* 8°. '75. 25c.; pap., 10c..... *Collins Print.*

— Transactions. v. 1-27. 8°. '48-'76. ea., $5. *Am. Med.*

American Methodism. Scudder, M. L. $3.50; $4. *Scranton.*

American notes. *See* Dickens, C.

American oratory: sel. from speeches of eminent Americans; comp. by a member of the Phila. bar. (cop. '36.) 8°. '72. $2.25; shp., $2.75.. *Claxton.*

American Oriental Soc. Journal. v. 1, no. 1; v. 2-9; v. 10, no. 1. 8°. '49-'72. v. 1, no. 1, pap., 50c.; v. 2-5, ea., $2.50; v. 6-9, ea., pap., $5; v. 10, no. 1, pap., $2.50.................... *Am. Orient.*

Nos. 2-4 of v. 1 are o. p.

American Otological Soc. Tranactions. [Annual.] 8°. ea., pap., $1.25................ *Jas. Campbell.*

American patriotism. Brown, L. $2......... *Mills.*

American Pharmaceutical Assoc. Proceedings, 1851-1876. 24 v. 8°. $48............ *Am. Pharm.*

1856 o. p.; none pub. for 1861.
Note. Include Minutes of the Convention of Pharmaceutists and Druggists, N. Y., 1851; and Minutes of National Pharmaceutical Convention, Phila., 1852.

American Philological Assoc. Transactions, 1869-'75. 6 v. 8°. '71-'76. ea., pap., $2.... *Am. Philol.*

American Philosophical Soc. Proceedings. 2 nos. 8°. no. 96, $2.50; 97, $1.50....... *Am. Philos. Soc.*

Nos. 1-95 are not for sale.

— Transactions. 20 v. [old ser., 6 v.; new ser., 14 v.] 4°. 1771-1876. ea., $5......... *Am. Philos. Soc.*

Pt. 2 of v. 6 (old ser.) is o. p.

American pioneers and patriots. *See* Abbott, J. S. C.

American pleader and lawyer's guide. Hening, W. W. 2 v. $10................ *J. W. Randolph.*

American pocket farrier and farmer's guide. *See* New.

American practical cookery book; by a practical housekeeper. ill. 12°. $1.75........... *J. E. Potter.*

American Public Health Assoc. Reports and papers [on public health] for 1873. v. 1. 8°. '75. $6.50. *Hurd & H.*

American religion. Weiss, J. $1.50....... *Roberts.*

American reports. *See* Thompson, I. G.

American rose culturist; with full directions for the treatment of the dahlia. ill. 12°. 30c.... *Judd.*

American rowing almanac and oarsman's pocket companion. ('73.) [Annual.] 12°. 50c........ *Judd.*

American school dialogues. ('67-'71.) New ed. nos. 1-2. 8°. '75. ea., pap., 40c.... *Schermerhorn.*

Cont.: American school dialogue book, no. 1., ed. by J. Richardson. — The gems of dialogues, ed. by L. S. Parsons.

American school melodist. Osgood, J. 50c... *Gordon.*

American school primer. 12°. bds., 11c. *Collins & Bro.*

American ser. [of readers, etc.] *See* New Am. ser.

American Social Science Assoc. Conference of boards of public charities, N. Y., May 20 and 22, 1874. 8°. '74. pap., 25c................. *Williams.*

— General meeting, Detroit, 1875; with const. and list of members. 8°. 15c.............. *Williams.*

— General meeting for 1874. 8°. pap., 20c. *Williams.*

— Handbook for immigrants to the U. S. maps. cr. 8°. '71. 50c......................... *Williams.*

— Health in schools: papers and reports of the Dept. of Health, Detroit, May, 1875. 8°. pap., 30c. *Williams.*

— Journal of social science; cont. trans. of the Assoc. 8 nos. 8°. pap. nos., 1-5., ea., $1.50; 6-8, ea., $1.............................. *Williams.*

— Officers and members for 1874. 8°. pap., 15c. *Williams.*

— Opening address of G. W. Curtis, N. Y., 1874; [also] The work of social science in the U. S., by F. B. Sanborn. 8°. '74. pap., 20c. *Williams.*

— Proceedings of the Conference of Charities, Detroit, May, 1875. 8°. pap., 50c. .... *Williams.*

American Soc. of Civil Engineers. Discussions at 7th annual convention. 5 nos. 8°. '75. pap. nos. 1, 3, ea., 40c.; 2, 45c.; 4, 65c.; 5, 90c. *Am. Soc. of C. E.*

Note. For other papers and discussions *see* names of individual authors.

American songster (The). 24°. 25c. *I. N. Whiting.*

American sphinx (The): enigmas, charades, problems, etc. sq. 18°. '74. pap., 25c. (?) *F. M. Reed.*

American state and American statesmen. Dix, W. G. $1.50................................ *Estes.*

American stud-book. v. 1, by J. H. Wallace; v. 2, comp. by S. D. and L. C. Bruce. 2 v. ill. 8°. '73. $20 .... *Turf, F. & F.*

American Sunday school hymn book. 32°. 20c.; 25c. .... *Am. S. S.*

American text book (The): cont. U. S. Constitution, Declaration of independence, and Washington's Farewell address. 24°. 25c....... *J. E. Potter.*

American text-book (The) for the million: hist. sketches of the U. S., the several states, descrip. of objects of interest, etc. 8°. '75. *$3; leath., $3.75....................... *Asher.*

American tour of Brown, Jones and Robinson. Toby. $5 .... *Appleton.*

American tune book; with course of instruction for singing schools, by L. Mason. obl. 8°. '69. bds., $1.50................................ *Ditson.*

American vocalist. Mansfield, D. H. $1.12. *Thompson.*

American wit and humor. ill. 8°. pap., 50c... *Harper.*

American woman (An) in China. Jeter, J. B. $1 25. *Lothrop.*

American woman (An) in Europe. Urbino, S. R. $1.50.............................. *Lee & S.*

American womanhood. Jackson, J. C. $1.25. *Austin.*

American wonderland. Bache, R. M. $1.50. *Claxton.*

American youth's library. 6 v. 18°. '72. $3.. *Claxton.*

Cont.: Grandfather's darling, by J. Hoffman. — Oh, I see you, by J. Hoffman. — The faithful watcher, thou shalt not steal. — Blind William, by G. Riedel. — Little things are the germs of greatness, by F. Hoffman; [also] Floating on the ice, by J. Hoffman. — The orphan, by C. v. Goehren.

Americanisms. De Vere, M. S. $3; $5.. *Scribner.*

Americans in Paris: comedy. 16°. pap., 15c. *French.*
America's advancement. Lester, C. E. $50... *Virtue.*
America's mission. Wadsworth, C. 25c. ..*Peterson.*
Americký besedník. *See* Jurka, A.
Americký Zpěvník. [Am. and Bohemian songs.] 32°. '76. $1.25 .... *Geringer.*
Amerikanische Bei-Spitz- u. Spottnamen. Mussehl, W. 25c. .... *Zickel.*
Amerikanische Jugendbibliothek. 15 v. 16°. ea., bds., 25c. .... *Morwitz.*
— *Same.* ea., 30c.; bds., 20c.; pap., 15c.....*Kohler.*
Amerikanische Mutter (Eine). Reynolds, L. $1; pap., 65c. .... *Zickel.*
Amerikanischer Kalender f. deutsche Lutheraner. ('70.) [Annual.] 4°. ea., pap., 10c...*Barthel.*
Amerikanisches Lesebuch. 3 v. 8° .... *Vering.*
Cont.: Erstes am. Lesebuch, v. A. Stamm, hf. bd., 35c. — Zweites, bearb. v. mehreren Lehrern, hf. leath., 50c. — Drittes, v. L. Soldan, hf. leath., $1.25.
Amerikanske Tolk (Den). [For Danes to learn English.] 18°. pap., 50c. .... *Radde.*
Ames, A. D. The poacher's doom: domestic drama. 16°. pap., 15c. .... *Ames.*
Ames, A. H. Missionary sermon, Baltimore Conference, Meth. Episc. Church, 1875. 12°. pap., 10c. .... *D. H. Carroll.*
Ames, Azel, *jr.* Sex in industry: a plea for the working girl. 16°. '75. $1 .... *Miller.*
Ames, Ma. Clemmer. *See* Clemmer, Ma.
Ames, S: *See* Angell, J. K., *and* Ames, S.; — Rhode Island, Sup. Court reports.
Ames' standard and minor dramas. 56 nos. 16°. ea., pap., 15c. .... *Ames.*
Amethyst (The). 18°. 50c.; pap., 25c....*Am. S. S.*
Amethyst (The). Tibbils, H. C. per. doz., $7.50. *Benham.*
Amherst, J. A. Invasion of Russia: spectacle. 16°. pap., 15c. .... *French.*
— Ireland as it is: drama. 16°. pap., 15c....*French.*
— Ireland as it was: drama. 16°. pap., 15c...*French.*
Ammianus Marcellinus. History of Rome from Constantine to Valens; tr. by C. D. Yonge. 12°. (Bohn.) $2.75 .... *Little, B. & Co.*
— *Same.* 12°. (Bohn.) $3. *Lippincott; Scribner, W. & A.*
Among the Alps. Richardson, M. K. $1.25..*Am. Tr.*
Among the Arabs. Naphegyi, G. $1.75..*Lippincott.*
Among the Arabs: adventures in the desert. ill. 12°. $1 .... *Nelson.*
Among the birds. Samuels, E. A. $1.25. *Lockwood, B. & Co.*
Among the breakers. Baker, G. M. 15c....*Lee & S.*
Among the brigands. Bowen, C. E. 75c.....*Nelson.*
Among the brigands. De Mille, J. $1.50...*Lee & S.*
Among the crags. Bates, L. 45c........... *Am. Tr.*
Among the hills. Whittier, J. G. $1.50; $4..*Osgood.*
Among the Isles of Shoals. Thaxter, C. $1.25. *Osgood.*
Among the lilies. Smith, C. A. $1.10 .... *Pres. Bd.*
Among the Maoris. Marryatt, E. $1.75. *Scribner, W. & A.*
Among the mountains. 16°. 25c........*Routledge.*
— *See also* Little folks series; — Willie Graham.
Among my books. Lowell, J. R. 2 v. ea., $2; $4; $5 .... *Osgood.*
Among my books. Reed, W. B. $1.50....... *Hale.*
Among our sailors. Jewell, J. G. $1.50.... *Harper.*
Among the stars. Smith, M. L. G. 65c...*Am. Bapt.*
Among the Tartar tents. Bowman, A. $1.75. *Scribner, W. & A.*
Among the trees. Bryant, W. C. $2.50; $5. *Putnam.*
Among the trees. Lorimer, M. $2.25; $5. *Hurd & H.*

Among the willows. Langille, J. H. 60c....*Am. Tr.*
Amoroso, king of little Britain. Planché, J. R. 15c. *French.*
Amorous corporations. Fourier, C. 25c. *D. Thomas.*
Amoroux, Jul. *See* Armengaud, J. E. *and* C., *and* Amoroux, J.
Amory, Rob. Physiological action of nitrous oxide on man and the lower animals: ill. by pulse tracings with the sphygmograph. 8°. '70. pap., 50c. *Jas. Campbell.*
— *See also* Clarke, E. H., *and* Amory, R.; — Medical jurisprudence.
— *and* Webber, S. G. Contributions to the physiol. study of veratrum, viride and veratria; with experiments on lower animals. 16°. '69. 75c.; pap., 50c. .... *Jas. Campbell.*
Amory, T: C. General Sullivan not a pensioner of Luzerne (minister of France at Phila., 1778–1783); with the report of the N. H. Hist. Soc., vindicating him from the charge made by Geo. Bancroft. 2d ed. 8°. '75. pap., 25c. .... *Williams.*
— Military services and public life of Gen. J. Sullivan of the Am. rev. army. por. 8°. '68. $2. *Williams.*
Amos, And. *See* Phillips, S. M., *and* Amos, A.
Amos, Sheldon. English code (An): its difficulties, and the modes of overcoming them. 8°. '73. $6. *Routledge.*
— Science of law. (Intern. sci. ser.) 12°. $1.75. *Appleton.*
Amos and his star. *See* Boyd, *Mrs.* E. E.
Amos Armfield; or, the leather-covered Bible. 18°. 45c. .... *Am. S. S.*
— *Same.* 32°. '47. 20c. .... *Am. Tr.*
Amphion. *See* Gould, J. E.
Ample apology (An). Roberts, G. 15c...... *French.*
Amulet (The). Conscience, H. $1; $1.25..*Murphy.*
Amy and the birds, and other stories; by author of "Summer at Walnut Ridge." ill. 18°. '75. 45c. *Meth. Bk. Conc.*
Amy and her brothers. Baker, S. S. 45c...*Am. Tr.*
Amy and her kitten. *See* Finley, M. F.
Amy and Ruth; or, trusting in Providence. 18°. 45c.; 55c. .... *Am. Bapt.*
Amy Annesley and Lettice Moden. 18°. 50c. *Whittaker.*
Amy books (The). 5 v. ill. 18°. '75. $1.50..*Dodd.*
Cont.: Amy Elliot. — Clara's trial. — A week in a tent. — A pair of shoes. — Madelaine's voyage.
Amy Carlton. Bowman, A. 75c.......... *Routledge.*
Amy Carr. Chesebro', C. 90c. .... *Dodd.*
Amy Cassonet. Tryon, G. W., *jr.* $5. ...... *Ditson.*
Amy Clifton; or, the golden cross. 18°. '71. 75c. *Dutton.*
Amy Douglass. 18°. 35c. .... *Cong. Pub.*
Amy Dudley's amusements. *See* Bertie and Amy books.
Amy Elliot. 18°. '75. 30c. .... *Dodd.*
Amy Garnett. Cox, W. N. $1.25 .... *Graves.*
Amy, the glass-blower's daughter. 18°. 35c. *Am. S. S.*
Amy Grant; or, the one motive. 18°. 75c...*Dutton.*
Amy Hall books. *See* Hildeburn, *Mrs.* M. J.
Amy Herbert. *See* Sewell, *Miss* E. M.
Amy Lawrence. Smith, J. F. 75c. .... *Dick & F.*
Amy Martin. Grosvenor, H. S. $1 .... *Hoyt.*
Amy Rivers. Dunning, A. K. 50c. .... *Pres. Bd.*
Amy Russell; or, lambs gathered. 18°. 45c...*Am. S. S.*
Amyrauld, Théophile. Reasons for leaving the Roman Catholic Church. [French.] 18°. 50c. *Am. Bapt.*
Amy's new home, and other stories. 18°. '64. 40c. *Am. Tr.*
— *Same.* 18°. 50c....*N. Y. Ref. Ch. Bd.; Pres. Com.*
— *Same.* 18°. 70c. .... *Pres. Bd.*
Amy's temptation. Sells, S. E. $1.25. *Cin. Meth. Bk. Conc.*

Anacreon. Odes; tr. by T. Moore. ill. obl. 16°. $5. *Scribner, W. & A.*

— *See also* Pindar.

Analytical Greek lexicon to New Test. sm. 4°. (Bagster.) hf. bd., $6.50 .... *Wiley.*

Anarchy of the ranters. *See* Barclay, R., Treatise on church government.

Anastasius. Hope, T. $1.50 .... *Harper.*

Anatolius *of Alexandria.* The Greek Catholic faith: a homily; tr. by Rev. N. Bjerring. sq. 24°. pap., 15c. .... *Dutton.*

Anatomical remembrancer (The); or, complete pocket anatomist; with corrections and add. by C. E. Isaacs. 18°. $1 .... *W. Wood.*

Anatomy of melancholy. *See* Burton, R.

Anchor (The). 18°. 30c. .... *Am. S. S.*

Anchor of hope. Wright, M. 50c. .... *Routledge.*

Anchor of the soul. *See* Arnot, W.

Anchored. Bates, L. 90c. .... *Am. Tr.*

Ancient alphabets: hand-book of manuscript, missal and ornamental alphabets [1–1600]. ill. obl. 8°. $1.50 .... *Spon.*

Ancient city. Coulanges, F. de. $2.50 .... *Lee & S.*

Ancient classics for Eng. readers. *See* Collins, W. L.

Ancient Egypt. *See* Land and sea.

Ancient faiths and modern. Inman, T. $5 .. *Bouton.*

Ancient harmony revived: sel. of church music from old and approved authors. 6th ed., rev. obl. 8°. '55. bds., $1.38 .... *Ditson.*

Ancient history from the monuments. 4 v. ill. 16°. ea., $1 .... *Scribner.*

Cont.: Egypt, by S. Birch. — Assyria, by G. Smith. — Babylonia, by G. Smith. — Persia, by W. Vaux.

Ancient Jerusalem; rev. by T. O. Summers. ('56.) 2d ed. 18°. '76. 50c. .... *So. Meth.*

Ancient lyre. Zeuner, C. $1.50 .... *Ditson.*

Ancient mariner. *See* Coleridge, S. T.

Ancient mysteries described. Hone, W. $1.50. *Scribner, W. & A.*

Ancient nation (The), a sign and a wonder; by author of "Knights of the frozen sea." ill. 12°. '75. $2 .... *Pott.*

Ancient plain song (The) of the church. Helmore, T. 50c. .... *W. H. Young.*

Ancient régime (The). *See* James, G. P. R.

Ancient régime (The). Taine, H. A. $2.50 ... *Holt.*

Ancient schoolmaster (The). Blackburn, W. M. 60c. *Pres. Bd.*

Ancient states and empires. *See* Lord, J.

Ancient testimony of the Society of Friends, commonly called Quakers, resp. some of their Christian doctrines and practices. 12°. '43. 12c.; pap., 10c. .... *Friends Bk. St.*

Ancient York Masons. *See* Freemasons.

Andachtsbüchlein. *See* Congregation of the Most Holy Redeemer.

Andenken an die erste hl. Communion. Hinssen, L. 90c. .... *Herder.*

Anderdon, W: H: Afternoons with the saints. 18°. 60c.; pap., 25c. .... *Benziger.*

— Antoine de Bonneval: tale of Paris in the days of St. Vincent de Paul. ill. 12°. '67. $1.50; $2. *Kelly, P. & Co.*

— The Catholic Crusoe: adventures of Owen Evans, navy surgeon's mate, set ashore on a desolate island in the Carribbean seas, A. D. 1739. ill. 12°. $1 .... *Benziger.*

— *Same.* 16°. $1.25; $1.75 .... *Sadlier.*

Andersen, Hs. Chr. Works. 10 v. ill. and por. cr. 8°. '69–'71. $16.50; hf. cf., $34.75 . *Hurd & H.*

Cont.: The improvisatore; or, life in Italy. — The two baronesses. — O. T.; or, life in Denmark. — Only a fiddler! — In Spain and Portugal. — A poet's bazaar. — Pictures of travel. — The story of my life. — Wonder stories told for children. — Stories and tales.

Andersen, Hs. Chr., *continued.*

— Bilderbuch ohne Bilder. With Eng. notes by L. Simonson. ('64.) New ed. 12°. '76. pap., 50c. .... *Holt.*

— Danish legends and fairy tales; tr. by C. Peachey. ill. 12°. (Bohn.) $1.75 .... *Little, B. & Co.*

— *Same.* ill. 12°. (Bohn.) $2. *Lippincott; Scribner, W. & A.*

— Eisjungfrau (Die) u. andere Geschichten. With Eng. notes by C. E. F. Krauss. ('66.) New ed. 12°. '76. pap., 50c. .... *Holt.*

— — *See also below* Fairy lib. for the young.

— Fairy library. 6 v. ill. 16°. ea., $1 .... *Miller.*

Cont.: Dream of little Tuk. — Little Ellie. — Little match-girl. — Shoes of fortune. — Story teller. — Ugly duck.

— Fairy library for the young. 15 v. ill. fp. 8°. $12. *Routledge.*

Cont.: Red shoes. — Little match-girl. — Tinder-box. — Marsh king's daughter. — The wild swans. — Old church-bell. — Poultry Meg's family. — Silver shilling. — The darning-needle. — Goloshes of fortune. — Everything in its right place. — Under the willow tree. — Ice maiden. — Put off is not done with. — Will o' the wisp.

— Fairy tales. ill. 12°. $1.50. (Chandos classics.) cr. 8°. $1; pap., 75c. .... *Scribner, W. & A.*

— *Same;* tr. by H. W. Dulcken. ill. 16°. $1.25; $1.50. *Routledge.*

— *Same;* tr. by Mrs. Paul. ill. 12°. $1.75. cr. 8°. $2.50 .... *Scribner, W. & A.*

— *Same;* tr. by Ward and Plesrier. ill. 4°. $7.50. *Scribner, W. & A.*

— Fairy world (The). ill. 12°. $1.50 .... *World Pub.*

— German fairy tales. ill. 12°. $1.50 .... *World Pub.*

— Improvisatore. 8°. pap., 50c. .... *Harper.*

— Only a fiddler! [also] O. T. 8° pap., 50c. *Harper.*

— Out of the heart, spoken to the little ones. ill. sq. 18°. $1.50 .... *Routledge.*

— Sand-hills of Jutland. ill. 16°. $1.50 .... *Lee & S.*

— Stories and tales. ill. sm. 4°. $2.50 .... *Routledge.*

— Stories for the household; ill. by A. W. Bayes. (Standard ed.) cr. 8°. $3; hf. cf., $5. *Routledge.*

— Tales. [French.] 12°. $2 .... *Routledge.*

— Tales for the young. ill. post 18°. 75c. *Scribner, W. & A.*

— What the moon saw, and other tales. ill. sm. 4°. $2.50 .... *Routledge.*

— Will-o'-the-wisps (The) are in town, and other stories. ill. sq. 16°. 75c. .... *Routledge.*

— Wonder book. ill. 12°. $1.50 .... *World Pub.*

— Wonderful library. 3 v. ill. 16°. ea., $1.50. *Miller.*

Cont.: Fairy tales. — Story book. — Wonderful tales.

Anderson, A. On faith. 18°. 40c. .. *U. P. Bd. of Pub.*

Anderson, C: New readings of old parables. 12°. '76. 75c. .... *Whittaker.*

Anderson, E. A. Northern ballads. 12°. $1. *Carleton.*

Anderson, *Mrs.* Eliza H. Following after Jesus: memorial of Susan Maria Underwood. por. 16°. $1 .... *Bost. Am. Tr.*

Anderson, G. H. Mass in F. 4°. $3.50 .... *Church.*

Anderson, G: W. Die Baptisten in d. Ver. St.; übers. u. bearb. v. P. W. Bickel. 16°. pap., 10c. .... *Germ. Bapt.*

— Way and walk: the way to Christ and the walk in Christ. 18°. 40c. .... *Am. Bapt.*

Anderson, J. Our Church; ed. by T. O. Summers. ('60.) 2d ed. 18°. '75. 65c. .... *So. Meth.*

Anderson, *Rev.* J. Identity of the church. 60c. (?) *Cumberland.*

Anderson, J. H. Great wizard of the north's handbook of natural magic. 12°. pap., 30c. *Dick & F.*

Anderson, Ja. Ancient constitutions of Freemasons. [Reprint of original ed., 1723.] 12°. hf. mor., $1. *Masonic; Redding.*

Anderson, Ja. Cloud and sunshine: drama. 16°. pap., 15c. .... *French.*

Anderson, Ja. Inaugural address before N. Y. Acad. of Med. 8°. '61. pap., 10c...*N. Y. Acad. Med.*
— Valedictory address before N. Y. Acad. of Med. 8°. '67. pap., 20c. ....*N. Y. Acad. Med.*

Anderson, *Rev.* J: Course of creation. [Geological.] ('53.) New ed. ill. 12°. '57. $1.50 .. *Wilstach.*

Anderson, *Dr.* J: Mandalay to Momien: narrative of two expeditions to west China, 1868, 1875, under Col. E. B. Sladen and Col. H. Browne. maps and ill. 8°. '76. $7.50 ....*Macmillan.*

Anderson, J: *C. E.* The strength of materials and structures. 12°. $1.50..............*Appleton.*

Anderson, J: J. Common school hist. of the U. S. ('68.) New ed. maps. 16°. '76. hf. roan, $1..............................*Clark & M.*
— Grammar school hist. of the U. S.; [also] U. S. Constitution, Declaration of independence and Washington's Farewell address. ('69.) New ed. por., maps, etc. 12°. '76. $1.20..*Clark & M.*
— Historical reader. ('71.) New ed. 12°. '76. $1.80. *Clark & M.*
— Introductory school hist. of the U. S. ('68.) New ed. maps. 16°. '76. 60c.........*Clark & M.*
— Junior class hist. of the U. S.; [also] Declaration of independence and U. S. Constitution. ('74.) New ed. maps. 16°. '76. $1......*Clark & M.*
— Manual of general hist.; with extracts from the works of celebrated authors. ('69.) New ed. maps. 12°. '76. $2..............*Clark & M.*
— Pictorial school hist. of the U. S.; [also] Declaration of ind. and U. S. Const. ('71.) New ed. por., maps, etc. 12°. '76. $1.65....*Clark & M.*
— School hist. of Eng. from invasion of Cæsar. ('74.) New ed. maps. 12°. '76. $1.60....*Clark & M.*
— United States reader. ('72.) New ed. maps. 12°. '76. $1.50......................*Clark & M.*
— *See also* Davenport, B., History of the U. S.

Anderson, Josephus. Bible Christian: a view of doctrinal, experimental and practical religion; ed. by T. O. Summers. ('55.) 8th ed. 18°. '75. 75c. ....*So. Meth.*

Anderson, *Mrs.* M. F. Baptists in Sweden. 16°. 80c. *Am. Bapt.*

Anderson, M'Call. Eczema: the pathology and treatment of the various eczematous affections or eruptions of the skin. 3d ed., rev. and enl. 8°. '75. $2.75........................*Lindsay.*
— On the treatment of diseases of the skin; with an analysis of 11,000 consecutive cases. cr. 8°. '72. $1.75..........................*Macmillan.*

Anderson, Ma. E. New songs for little people. ill. 16°. $1.50..............................*Lee & S.*
— Scenes in the Hawaiian Islands and California. ill. 16°. $1.15....................*Bost. Am. Tr.*

Anderson, Rasmus B. America not disc. by Columbus: hist. sketch of the disc. of Am. by the Norsemen in the 10th cent. 12°. '74. $1.....*Griggs.*
— Norse mythology; or, the religion of our forefathers: myths of the Eddas systematized and interpreted, with introd., vocab. and index. 2d ed. cr. 8°. '75. $2.50; $3; hf. cf., $5............*Griggs.*

Anderson, Rob. *See* Evolutions of batteries.

Anderson, *Rev.* Rob. Practical religion exemplified: passages from life of A. 12°. 75c. ..*McCauley.*

Anderson, Ruf. History of the missions of the Am. Board of Commissioners for Foreign Missions. 5 v. 12°. ea., $1.50 ....*Cong. Pub.*
Cont.: Sandwich Islands. — Missions to India. — Oriental missions, 2 v. — History of foreign missions.

Anderson, S. T. Essay on missions. 12°. '74. pap., 15c. ....*So. Meth.*

Anderson, W: Practical mercantile letter-writer. 12°. $1.25..............................*Appleton.*

Anderson, *Rev.* W: Model women. 12°. $1.75. *Nelson.*
— Treatise on regeneration. 2d ed. 12°. '71. $1.50. *Smith, E. & Co.*

Anderson, W: T. The Masonic token. ill. 12°. '75. $2.50 ....*Masonic.*

Andersson, C: J: Lake Ngami: explorations and discoveries during four years' wanderings in the wilds of southwestern Africa. ill. 12°. $1.75. *Harper; J. E. Potter.*
— Notes of travel in Africa. 12°. '75. $2..*Putnam.*
— Okavango River: narr. of travel, exploration and adventure. por., ill. and map. 8°. $3.25..*Harper.*

André, G: G. Draughtsman's handbook of plan and map drawing, incl. instructions for engineering, architectural and mechanical drawing. ill. cr. 4°. '74. $6..............................*Spon.*
— Practical treatise on coal mining. 12 pts. pl. roy. 4°. ea., pap., * $2 ....*Spon.*

André, *Maj.* J: The cow-chace: a poem, written at N. Y., 1780; with explan. notes by the editor. London: 1781. [Reprint.] 8°. '69. pap., 75c.; large pap., $1.50 ....*Clarke.*

André. Lord, W. W. $1................*Scribner.*

André Dunn. *See* Andrew Dunn.

Andrea Delfin. Heyse, P. 50c. ....*Burnham.*

Andreas Dunn. *See* Andrew Dunn.

Andreas Heimberger. Stern, A. 85c. ...*Luth. Pub.*

Andreas Hofer. Mundt, C. M. $1; $1.50; $3.50. *Appleton.*

Andrée de Taverney. *See* Dumas, A.

Andrés Dunn. *See* Andrew Dunn.

Andrew, *St.* *See* Lives of the saints.

Andrew, *Bp.* Ja. Osgood. Family government. ('48.) 10th ed. 18°. '75. 50c. ....*So. Meth.*
— — *See also* Young disciples lib.
— Miscellanies. 12°. '59. $1.............*So. Meth.*

Andrew, J: A. Address before the N. E. Historic-Geneal. Soc., Jan. 2, 1867; [with] proceed. at said meeting. 8°. '67. pap., 25c....*N. E. Hist. Gen.*

Andrew Douglass; by author of "Madeline." ('68.) New ed. 18°. '74. 75c. ....*Nat. Temp.*

Andrew Dunn. *Eng. ed. is o. p.*
— *German.* Andreas Dunn. 18°. '45. 25c. *Am. Tr.*
— *Portuguese.* Historia de André Dunn. 18°. '70. 20c. ....*Am. Tr.*
— *Spanish.* Andrés Dunn. 18°. 10c.....*Pres. Bd.*
— — Conversion de Andrés Dunn. 18°. '52. 15c. *Am. Tr.*

Andrewes, Lancelot. Devotions; tr. from the Greek. 12°. '65. $2. 18°. '73. 50c. ....*Pott.*
— Manual for the sick, with other devotions; ed. by Rev. H. P. Liddon. 32°. '70. 50c. ...*Dutton.*

Andrews, C. C. Campaign of Mobile, incl. the cooperation of Gen. Wilson's cavalry in Ala. maps and views. 8°. '67. $3.50 .... *Van Nostrand.*
— Hints to company officers on their military duties. 18°. '64. 60c................ *Van Nostrand.*

Andrews, E. B. *See* Ohio geol. survey.

Andrews, Emerson. Living life. 12°. $1.25; $1.50. *Earle.*
— Revival sermons. 12°. $1.25; $1.50.......*Earle.*
— Revival songs. 18°. 60c.; 80c............*Earle.*
— Travels in Bible lands. ill. 16°. 80c.; $1....*Earle.*
— Youth's picture sermons. ill. 16°. '71. 60c.; 80c. *Earle.*

Andrews, Ethan Allen. Exercises in Lat. etymology. 12°. '55. pap., 25c. ....*Crocker.*
— First Lat. book. ('46.) New ed. 12°. '48. 88c. *Crocker.*
— First lessons in Lat.: introd. to Andrews and Stoddard's "Lat. grammar." ('37.) New ed. 12°. '64. 75c...........................*Crocker.*
— Latin-English lexicon, founded on Germ.-Lat. lexicon of W. Freund; with add. and corrections. roy. 8°. shp., $6..........................*Harper.*
— **Latin** exercises. ('37.) New ed. 12°. '54. $1.25. *Crocker.*

Andrews, Ethan Allen, *continued.*
— — Key to same. ('38.) New ed. 12°. '41. $1. *Crocker.*
— Latin grammar: epitome of Andrews and Stoddard's "Lat. grammar." 12°. '69. $1.25.... *Crocker.*
— Latin lessons. New ed., rev. and enl. 12°. '64. 88c.............................. *Crocker.*
— Latin reader; with dict. and notes. ('37.) New ed. 12°. '49. $1.12.................... *Crocker.*
— Manual of Lat. gram.; prep. to study of complete gram. 12°. '59. 80c. .... *Crocker.*
— Questions on Andrews and Stoddard's "Lat. gram." ('36.) New ed. 18°. '55. pap., 15c... *Crocker.*
— Synopsis of Lat. grammar. ('51.) New ed. 12°. '57. pap., 25c.......................... *Crocker.*
— Viri Romæ; with dict. and notes. ('42.) New ed. 12°. '49. $1.25 .... *Crocker.*
— *and* Stoddard, S. Latin grammar. ('36.) New ed., rev. and enl. 12°. '57. $1.50....... *Crocker.*

Andrews, Fanny. A family secret. 8°. $1.50; pap., $1............................. *Lippincott.*

Andrews, H. P. Six steps to honor; or, great truths illustrated. sq. 16°. '56. $1... *Meth. Bk. Conc.*

Andrews, Isr. Ward. Manual of the U. S. Constitution, for Am. youth; with index and app. 12°. '74. $1.50. 8°. shp., $2..... *Wilson, H. & Co.*

Andrews, J: N. Works. 8 v. 16°. '65–'76. pap. *Sev. Day Adv.*

Cont.: The complete testimony of the fathers of the first 3 centuries conc. the Sabbath and first day of the week, 15c. — The date of the 70 weeks of Dan. IX. established: treatise on the commandment to restore and build Jerusalem, 10c. — The history of the Sabbath and first day of the week, $1.25. — The sanctuary and 2300 days, 10c. — Sermons on the Sabbath and law: outline hist. of the Sabbath for 6000 years, 25c. — The Sunday-seventh day examined: refutation of the teachings of Mede, Jennings, Akers, and Fuller, 10c. — The three messages of Revelation, 15c. — Two covenants, 10c.

Andrews, L. F. W. The two opinions; or, salvation and damnation. 12°. 75c. .... *Williamson.*

Andrews, Lorrin. Hawaiian dictionary. 8°. '67. $12. *Barnes.*

Andrews, R. R. Silverstone's wager: comedietta. 16°. pap., 15c. .... *Lee & S.*

Andrews, S. C. The American college songster. 12°. '76. 90c.; pap., 50c............. *Sheehan & Co.*

Andrews, S. J. Life of our Lord upon the earth; considered in the hist., chronol. and geog. relations. ('63.) 4th ed. post 8°. '71. $2.50. *Scribner.*

Andrews, Ste. Pearl. Basic outline of universology; with notices of alwato, the scientific universal lang. ill. roy. 8°. '71. $5........ *D. Thomas.*
— Primary synopsis of universology and alwato. 12°. '71. $1.50 .... *D. Thomas.*
— *and* Batchelor, G. New and comprehensive French instructor. 12°. $1.50.............. *Appleton.*
— — Practical [French] pronouncer and key. 12°. $1.25 .... *Appleton.*

Andrews, W. E. Easy and familiar instruction for the young. [Cath. reader and speller.] 18°. 25c. .... *Strong.*

Andromache. *See* Euripides.

Andromaque. *See* Racine, J.

Andy Blake. Boucicault, D. 15c.......... *French.*

Andy Hall. Davis, C. E. K. $1.15........... *Hoyt.*

Andy Luttrell. Denison, M. A. $1.50..... *Lothrop.*

Andy's lesson, and how he learned it. 18°. 45c. *Whittaker.*

Anecdotes: pithy sayings, sel. with a view to the tastes and habits of youth. 18°. 50c... *Am. S. S.*

Anecdotes for the family circle. ('46.) New ed. ill. 18°. '58. 80c. .... *Am. Tr.*

Anecdotes of the clergy of America. New ed. 12°. $1.50.............................. *Lippincott.*

Anecdotes of missionary worthies in the Moravian Church. 18°. 40c. .... *Am. S. S.*

Aner's return. Hoerman, A. S. $1.50 ...... *O'Shea.*

Anfang und Ende. Heyse, P. 40c............ *Holt.*

Anfangsgründe d. kathol. Religion f. Elementarschulen. 12°. hf. bd., 12c. .... *Vering.*

Ange (L') conducteur dans la dévotion Chrétienne. [Cath. prayer book.] 12°. *net*, 38c.–60c. *Benziger.*
— *Same.* 24°. 75c.–$2.50 .... *Strong.*

Angel (The) and the babe. *See* Stories of the good shepherd.

Angel (The) and the demon. Arthur, T. S. $1.25. *J. E. Potter.*

Angel children (The). Higgins, C. M. 80c... *Lee & S.*

Angel guide (The); for the Catholic child. [Prayer-book.] 32°. 40c.–$1.50 .... *Benziger.*

Angel in the cloud. Fuller, E. W. $1.25; $1.50.. *Hale.*

Angel (The) in the house. *See* Patmore, C.

Angel (The) of the attic. Morton, T. 15c... *French.*

Angel (The) of the household. Arthur, T. S. $1.50. *J. E. Potter.*

Angel (The) of the iceberg. Todd, J. $1.25.. *Bridgman.*

Angel of midnight. Barrière, T., *and* Plouvier, E. 15c.................................. *French.*

Angel or devil. Coyne, J. S. 15c........... *French.*

Angel over the left shoulder. *See* Todd, *Rev.* J.

Angel (The) over the right shoulder. Phelps, *Mrs.* E. S. 40c. .... *Draper.*

Angel visitor (The). Percival, F. E. $1.25. *J. E. Potter.*

Angel voices; or, words of counsel for overcoming the world. ill. 16°. $1.25. (Holiday ed.) sm. 4°. $3.50 .... **Osgood.*
— *Same.* 16°. '49. 75c. 12°. '63. $1.75..... *Randolph.*

Angel whispers. Eddy, D. C. $1.50......... *Locke.*

Angela. *See* Bischoff, J. E.

Angela. Marsh-Caldwell, A. $1.50......... *Harper.*

Angela Wildon. Reynolds, G. W. M. $1... *Dick & F.*

Angele Merici, *St.* Life. 12°. $1.......... *Sadlier.*

Angelic beings. Bell, C. D. $1.25.......... *Nelson.*

Angelic warfare. 32°. 15c.............. *Benziger.*

Angelic wisdom conc. the divine love, etc. *See* Swedenborg, E.

Angeline, the octoroon. 12°. pap., 20c....... *Hurst.*

Angell, G: T. Protection of animals. 8°. '74. pap., 10c. .... *Williams.*

Angell, H. Practical, plain and solid geometry. (Element. sci. ser.) ill. 16°. '71. 75c.... *Putnam.*

Angell, H. C. Treatise on diseases of the eye; with test pipes for determining exact state of vision. [Hom.] 4th ed., enl. ill. 8°. $3..... *Boericke.*

Angell, J. B. Progress in international law. 8°. '75. pap., 20c. .... *Williams.*

Angell, Ja. B. Manual of French literature. 12°. '57. $1.15............................ *Cowperthwait.*

Angell, J: Animal physiology. (Element. sci. ser.) ill. 16°. 75c.......................... *Putnam.*
— Magnetism and electricity. (Element. sci. ser.) ill. 16°. '75. 75c..................... *Putnam.*

Angell, Jos. K. Treatise on the law of carriers of goods and passengers. 4th ed., rev. and enl. by J. Lathrop. 8°. '68. shp., $6... *Little, B. & Co.*
— Treatise on the law of water-courses; with appendix. 6th ed., rev. and enl. by J. C. Perkins. 8°. '69. shp., $6........................ *Little, B. & Co.*
— Treatise on the limitations of actions at law and suits in equity and admirality; with app. 5th ed., rev. by J. W. May. 8°. '76. shp., $6.. *Little, B. & Co.*
— *and* Ames, S: Treatise on the law of private corporations aggregate; rev. and enl. by J. Lathrop. 10th ed. 8°. '75. shp., $6..... *Little, B. & Co.*
— *and* Durfee, T: Treatise on the law of highways. 2d ed., with notes and ref., by G. F. Choate. 8°. '68. shp., $5...................... *Little, B. & Co.*

Angell, Lew. *See* Association of Munic. and Sanit. Eng.

Angelo. Deslys, C. 50c. . . . . *Payot.*
Angelo. Hugo, V. 15c. . . . . *French.*
Angelo; or, the actress of Padua. A'Beckett, G. A. 15c. . . . . *French.*
Angel's (The) song. Guthrie, T. 75c. . . . . *Routledge.*
Angel's (The) song. Tayler, C. B. $1. . . . *Leighton.*
Angel's story: an allegory in verse. 18°. 18c. *Am. S. S.*
Angel's work; or, the choristers of St. Mark's. 18°. 40c. . . . . *Dutton.*
Angels (The). *See* Bright eye ser.
Angels' messages. Ward E. E. $1.50. . . . (?) *Sheffield.*
Angie, *Cousin*. *See* Cousin Angie.
Anguera, J. de. *See* De Anguera.
Angus, Jos. Bible hand-book. 8°. $3. — Questions on same. 18°. 30c. . . . . (?) *Martien.*
— Christ our life: in its origin, law and end. 12°. $1.25. . . . . *Am. Bapt.*
Angus Tarlton. Tucker, C. 35c. . . . *Carter; Dutton.*
Anicet-Bourgeois, Auguste. *See* Bourgeois.
Animal life all the world over. Dulcken, H. W. $4. *Routledge.*
Animal locomotion. Pettigrew, J. B. $1.75. *Appleton.*
Animal magnetism. Inchbald, E. 15c. . . . . . *French.*
Anmassungen (Die) des Papstes. 18°. '46. 25c. *Am. Tr.*
Ann, *St.* Life. *See* Mary, *Virgin*, Life.
Ann Ash; or, the foundling. 18°. 50c. . . . . *Claremont.*
— *Same.* 18°. 60c. . . . . *Dutton.*
Ann Ash; or, kindness rewarded. ('63.) 6th ed. 16°. '70. $1.25. . . . . *Perkinpine.*
Ann Lively, and other stories. 32°. '53. 30c. *Am. Tr.*
Ann Ray. 18°. 30c. . . . . *Am. S. S.*
Anna, *Cousin*. *See* Cousin Anna.
Anna; or, home life. 18°. 75c. . . . . *Carter.*
Anna Bailey. Judson, E. C. 25c.; 30c. . . *Am. Bapt.*
Anna Bolena. *See* Donizetti, G.
Anna Clayton. Dimmick, F. L. $1.50. . . . . *Pres. Bd.*
Anna Clayton. Moore, H. J. $1.25. . . . . *J. E. Potter.*
Anna, Countess of Stolberg. Wellmer, A. $1.50. *Routledge.*
Anna Cradock. *See* Jones, J. H.
Anna Fitzgerald; or, the three half-crowns. 18°. 25c. *Scribner, W. & A.*
Anna Hammer. Temme, J. D. H. 50c. . . . . *Harper.*
Anna Hand. *See* Finley, M. F.
Anna Lavater. Liethe, W. $1. . *Cin. Meth. Bk. Conc.*
Anna Lee; or, who are our best friends? 18°. 60c. *Cong. Pub.*
Anna the leech-vender. Glaubrecht, O. 50c. *Pres. Bd.*
Anna Maylie. Farman, E. $1.50. . . . . *Lothrop.*
Anna Maylie series. 4 v. 16°. $6. . . . . *Lothrop.*
Cont.: Anna Maylie. — Millie Lee. — Zina. — St. Augustine's ladder.
Anna Ross. *See* Kennedy, G.
Anna Shipton lib.; — series. *See* Shipton, A.
Annandale. Finley, M. F. 60c. . . . . *Pres. Bd.*
Annals of the Am. pulpit. *See* Sprague, W. B.
Annals of the Army of the Cumberland; by an officer. ill. and por. 8°. $3.50. . . . . *Lippincott.*
Annals of Christian martyrdom. 12°. '56. $1.25. *Meth. Bk. Conc.*
Annals of a fortress. Viollet-le-Duc. $5. . . . *Osgood.*
Annals of our time. *See* Irving, J.
Annals of the poor. *See* Richmond, L.
Annals of a quiet neighborhood. *See* Mac Donald, G.
Annals of Quodlibet. Kennedy, J. P. $1.75. *Lippincott.*
Annan, W: Defense of close communion; tested against the strictures of Drs. Pressley and Sproul. 12°. pap., 50c. . . . . *R. S. Davis (P.)*

Annan, W., *continued.*
— Difficulties of Armenian Methodism. 12°. $1.25. (?) *Martien.*
— Doctrine of close communion tested by Scripture and reason. 12°. '67. 75c. . . *R. S. Davis (P.)*
— High church Episcopacy; its origin, characteristics and fruits. 12°. '74. $1. . . . *R. S. Davis (P.)*
— Vindication of the letters on psalmody from the strictures of J. T. Pressley. 12°. '66. pap., 50c. . . . . *R. S. Davis (P.)*
Anna's vacation, and other stories. 18°. 50c. . . *O'Shea.*
Anne, *St.* *See* Lives of the saints.
Anne and Tilly. Denison, M. A. 60c. . . . (?) *Martien.*
Anne Austin. Denison, M. A. $1. . . . . . . *Am. Bapt.*
Anne Bell, and other stories. 18°. 35c. . . . . *Pres. Bd.*
Anne Blake. Marston, W. 15c. . . . . *French.*
Anne Boleyn. Boker, G. H. 15c. . . . . *French.*
Anne Dalton; or, how to be useful. ('63.) 7th ed. ill. 16°. '72. $1.25. . . . . *Perkinpine.*
Anne du Bourg. Schott, T. $1.10. . . . (?) *Luth. Pub.*
Anne Furness. Trollope, F. E. 75c. . . . . *Harper.*
Anne Hathaway. Falconer, E. 25c. . . . . *French.*
Anne Judge, spinster. Robinson, F. W. 50c. *De Witt.*
Anne Mason; or, the temple of shells. 12°. '71. $1.50. . . . . *Randolph.*
Anne of Geierstein. *See* Scott, *Sir* W.
Anne Severin. Craven, A. $1.50. . . . . *Cath. Pub.*
Anne's beach party; — new life; — Saturday afternoons. Denison, M. A. ea., 60c. . . (?) *Martien.*
Annesley, *Miss* M. Light in the valley: life and letters of Mrs. H. Bocking. 18°. 20c.; 25c. . . *Am. Bapt.*
— *Same.* 18°. '60. 40c. . . . . *Meth. Bk. Conc.*
Annesley library. 4 v. 12°. $5. . . . . *Nelson.*
Cont.: Christmas at Annesley, by M. E. Shipley. — The fairy spinner, by M. Hill. — Pollie and Jack, by A. Hepburn. — Turnaside Cottage, by M. S. Clarke.
Annetta. Hughes, M. S. $1.25. . *Cin. Meth. Bk. Conc.*
Annette. *See* Dumas, A. (*fils.*)
Annette. Walsingham, C. $1.75. . . . . *Claxton.*
Annie and the bears. *See* Baker, *Mrs.* H. N. W., Daisy Dale lib.
Annie and her cat. *See* Bright eye ser.
Annie and Pierre. M'Clellan, K. $1. . . . . *Whittaker.*
Annie Balfour, and her friends. Henderson, J. P. $1.25. . . . . *N. Y. Ref. Ch. Bd.; Pres. Com.*
Annie Foster: story for girls. 18°. 45c. . . *Am. S. S.*
Annie Grey. Olive. 35c. . . . . *Pres. Bd.*
Annie Lee: a story. 18°. 35c. . . . . *Pres. Bd.*
Annie Leighton. *See* New holiday lib.
Annie Leslie; or, the little orphan. 18°. 45c. *Pres. Bd.*
Annie Lincoln's lesson; or, a day in the life of a thankful child. 18°. 35c. . . . . *Pres. Bd.*
Annie Lyon; or, the secret of a happy home. ('61.) New ed. ill. 18°. '75. 45c. . . . . *Hoyt.*
Annie Maitland. Richmond, D. 50c. . . . . . *Rotuledge.*
Annie Marlowe. 18°. 50c. . . . . *Crowell.*
Annie Marlowe series. 6 v. ill. 18°. $3. . . . *Crowell.*
Cont.: Annie Marlowe. — Dorothy Siebel. — The lady artist. — Hans, the Swiss boy. — The rosette. — Little Syd.
Annie Morton, the timid Christian. 18°. 35c. *Cong. Pub.*
Annie Price. 18°. 50c. . . . . *Carter.*
Annie Reilly. McElgun, J. $1. . . . . *McGee.*
Annie Seldon. Dupuy, E. A. 25c. . . . . *U. P. James.*
Annie Sherwood; or, scenes at school. 18°. 55c. *Am. S. S.*
Annie Temple. Ingraham, J. H. 25c. . . . . *Beadle.*
Annie's gold cross and its mysterious motto; by author of "Nellie Grey." 16°. $1. . . . . *Pres. Bd.*
Annie's influence. Howard, M. 75c. . . . . . . *Pres. Bd.*
Annie's Prüfungen. Lexow, R. 75c.; 50c. . . *Steiger.*

Annihilation, not of the Bible. George, N. D. $1.50. *Cin. Meth. Bk. Conc.*

Annis Warleigh's fortunes. Parr, H. 75c...*Harper.*

Anniversary gems. Gracey, S. L. 60c...*Perkinpine.*

Anniversary speaker. Heston, N. 60c. *Cin. Meth. Bk. Conc.*

Annot and her pupil. 18°. 70c..........*Pres. Bd.*

Annual American catalogue: list of books pub. in U. S. and imported during 1871; with classified index. 8°. '72. *net*, pap., $1.......*Publishers' Weekly.*

— *See also* Alphabetical ref. list; — American catalogue.

Annual of phrenology and physiognomy. *See* Wells, S. R.

Annual of scientific discovery, 1850–'71. 21 v. por. 12°. ea., $2 *or* $3.........................*Mason.*

1850–'65, ed. by D. A. Wells; 1866–'69, ed. by S. Kneeland; 1870–'71, ed. by J. Trowbridge.

Annual record of homœop. literature [1870–'75]; ed. by C. G. Raue. 6 v. 8°. v. 1, $3.50; v. 2, $2.50; v. 3–6, ea., $3.....................*Boericke.*

Annual record of science and industry for 1871–'75; ed. by S. F. Baird and others. 5 v. 12°. ea., $2.................................*Harper.*

Annus Domini. Rossetti, C. G. $1.50......*Roberts.*

Anonymous kiss: vaudeville. 16°. pap., 15c. *Lee & S.*

Another glass. Morton, T. 15c..........*Lee & S.*

Another's burden. 18°. '75. 50c...........*Nelson.*

Ansart, Jos. The spirit of St. Vincent de Paul; tr. by the Sisters of Charity of Mt. St. Vincent. 12°. $2............................*O'Shea.*

Ansdale Hall. *See* Freeland, *Mrs.* C. J.

Ansiedler (Der) am Strande. *See* Hoffmann, F.

Ansted, D. T. Science of physical geog. 3d ed., enl. 12°. $3.........................*Lippincott.*

— World (The) we live in; first lessons in physical geog. 16°. 75c.................*Lippincott.*

Anstie, Fs. E. Neuralgia and diseases which resemble it. 12°. $2.50......................*Appleton.*

— Notes on epidemics, for the use of the public; ed. with Am. notes. 12°. $1..........*Lippincott.*

— On the uses of wines in health and disease. 12°. pap., 50c...........................*Redfield.*

— Stimulants and narcotics: their mutual relations, with researches on the action of alcohol, ether and chloroform. 8°. '65. $3.......*Lindsay.*

— *See also* Power, H., Holmes, T., Anstie, F. E., *and* Barnes, R.

Anstie, J. *See* England, Law reports.

Answers to ever-recurring questions. Davis, A. J. $1.50...........................*A. J. Davis.*

Answers to prayer; or, Dorothea Trudel. ('72.) New ed. 16°. '76. $1.25...................*Hoyt.*

Ante bellum. Cook, M. L. $2..........*Lippincott.*

Ante-Nicene Christian lib. *See* Roberts, *Rev.* A., *and* Donaldson, J.

Anteros. *See* Lawrence, G. A.

Anthem choir. *See* Ogden, W. A.

Anthem dulcimer (The). Woodbury, I. B. $1.34. *Huntington.*

Anthem offering (The). Hodges, D. F., Foster, G. W., *and* Tenney, J. H. $1............*Lee & S.*

Anthem thanksgiving (The). Woodbury, I. B. $1.50. *Huntington.*

Anthon, C: Classical dictionary. 8°. shp., $5. *Harper.*

— First Greek lessons. 12°. shp., $1.25.....*Harper.*

— Grammar of the Gk. lang. from the Germ. of Kühner; with sel. from Matthiæ Buttman, etc. 12°. shp., $1.50.................................*Harper.*

— Greek grammar. 12°. shp., $1.25.......*Harper.*

— Greek lessons, pt. 2: introd. to Gk. prose compos. 12°. shp., $1.25........................*Harper.*

— Greek prosody and metre. 12°. shp., $1.25..*Harper.*

— Greek reader, chiefly from Germ. of F. Jacobs; with Eng. notes, metrical index and lexicon. 12°. shp., $1.50...........................*Harper.*

Anthon, C: *continued.*

— Latin grammar, pt. 1: gram., with exercises in tr. and writing Lat. 12°. shp., $1.25.....*Harper.*

— Latin grammar, pt. 2: introd. to prose compos. 12°. shp., $1.25. — Key. hf. shp., 75c......*Harper.*

— Latin prosody and metre. 12°. shp., $1.25..*Harper.*

— Latin versification: exercises. 12°. shp., $1.25. — Key. hf. shp., 75c.....................*Harper.*

— Latin-Eng. and Eng.-Lat. dict.; chiefly from lexicons of Freund, Georges, and Kaltschmidt. sm. 4°. shp., $3.50..............................*Harper.*

— Manual of Gk. antiquities. 12°. shp., $1.50. *Harper.*

— Manual of Gk. literature. 12°. shp., $1.50..*Harper.*

— Manual of Roman antiquities. 12°. shp., $1.50. *Harper.*

— System of ancient and mediæval geog.; for schools. 8°. $3.................................*Harper.*

— *See also* Ainsworth, R., Eng. and Lat. dict.; — Jacobs, F., Greek reader; — Kühner, R., Greek gram.; — Smith, W., Classical dict.; — Zumpt, C. G., Lat. gram.; — and for classic text-books, *names* of authors.

Anthon, J: Law student: guide to the study of law. 8°. shp., $3.50....................*Appleton.*

Anthony, *Mrs.* A. S. The circus: a story for boys. 18°. 45c.......................*Bost. Am. Tr.*

— — *See also* Young hero stories.

Anthony, C. H. This, our life; with introd. by J. P. Newman. por. 12°. '76. $2........*Munsell.*

Anthony, H: B. Memorial addresses; delivered in the U. S. Senate. roy. 8°. '75. 50c....*Rider.*

Anthony's Christmas eve. 32°. 40c. *Scribner, W. & A.*

Anthropos, H. (*pseud.*) Schlaraffiade, od. treuer Bericht Meister Urians über s. Reiseins Schlaraffenland. [Verse.] 8°. '73. pap., 30c....*Pilger.*

Anthropos. Breed, W. P. 60c..........*Pres. Bd.*

Antichrist (Der) u. das Ende der Welt. Rohling, A. 40c....................................*Herder.*

Antidote to backsliding. 18°. '55. 40c. *Meth. Bk. Conc.*

Antidote to "Gates ajar." 12°. 25c......*Carleton.*

Antidote to the poison of popery. Janeway, J. J. 25c...........................*N. Y. Ref. Ch. Bd.*

Antignostikus. *See* Neander, J. A. W.

Antigone. *See* Sophocles.

Anti-mason's scrap-book: 24 cynosure tracts. 12°. pap., 20c...........................*E. A. Cook.*

Antiquary (The). *See* Scott, *Sir* W.

Antiquary (The). Terry, D. 15c.........*French.*

Antique poets. *See* British poets.

Antoine. Denison, C. W. $1.50.............*Hoyt.*

Antoine de Bonneval. Anderdon, W. H. $1.50; $2. *Kelly, P. & Co.*

Antoine, the dwarf; or, the death of the parricide. 8°. pap., 25c..........................*De Witt.*

Antoinette. Denison, M. A. $1.15..........*Hoyt.*

Anton, the fisherman. Hoffmann, F. 85c. (?) *Luth. Pub.*

Anton in Amerika. Solger, R. 2 v. $1.50; $1..*Steiger.*

Anton, the peasant boy. *See* Meadowside stories.

Antonia. Sand, G: $1.50................*Roberts.*

Antonina. *See* Collins, Wilkie.

Antoninus, Marcus Aurelius. Thoughts. 16°. $1.50. **Osgood.*

— *Same*; tr. by G. Long. 12°. (Bohn.) $1.25. *Little, B. & Co.*

— *Same.* 12°. (Bohn.) $1.40....*Scribner, W. & A.*

— *Same.* 12°. (Bohn.) $1.50..........*Lippincott.*

Antonio Bishallany. Whitehead, C. 45c...*Am. Tr.*

Antony and Cleopatra. *See* Shakespeare, W.

Antony and Cleopatra married and settled. Selby, C. 15c...............................*Happy.*

Antony Brade. Lowell, R. T. S. $1.75....*Roberts.*

Antony Waymouth. Kingston, W. H. G. $1.50..*Tilton.*

Anxious inquirer. *See* James, J. A.
Anyta. Calvert, G. H. $1.25 .... *Dutton.*
Anything for a change. Brooks, C. S. 15c. *De Witt; French.*
Anything for sport. Tuthill, L. C. 65c... *Perkinpine.*
Apartments. Brough, W. 15c. .... *French.*
Apgar E. A. *and* A. C. Geographical drawing-book. [Old ed.] obl. 4°. 94c. .... *Cowperthwait.*
— — *Same.* [New ed.] 4°. bds., 75c... *Cowperthwait.*
— — Hand-book to Warren's "Physical and outline charts." ('65.) New ed. 12°. '71. bds., 75c. *Cowperthwait.*
— — Plant analysis. 4°. '74. 80c. .... *Ivison.*
Apgar, E. H. *See* Sypher, J. R., *and* Apgar, E. H.
Apocalypse (The) revealed. *See* Swedenborg, E.
Apocrypha. See Bible.
Apocryphal New Testament: the Gospels, Epistles, etc., not incl. in the New Test. by its compilers. 12°. '75. $1.25 .... *Colby.*
— *Same.* 8°. $2 .... *De Witt.*
Apollos. Coxe, A. C. $1.50 .... *Lippincott.*
Apology for the Bible. *See* Watson, *Bp.* R.
Apostate. Sheil, R. L. 15c. .... *French.*
Apostles (The): Bible histories for children. 18°. 28c.; 35c. .... *Am. Bapt.*
Apostles of mediæval Europe. Maclear, G. F. $1.75. *Macmillan.*
Apostles of Palestine. Headley, P. C. 25c.; 30c. *J. E. Potter.*
Apostleship of prayer. Ramiere, H. $1.50.. *Murphy.*
Apostolic fisherman (The): a tale of the last century; by an aged relative. 18°. 22c....... *Am. S. S.*
— *Same.* 18°. '66. 25c. *N. Y. Ref. Ch. Bd.; Pres. Com.*
Appeal (An) to Baptist Christians; by a presbyter of the Prot. Episc. Church. 16°. pap., 12c... *Dutton.*
Appeal (An) to matter of fact and common sense. *See* Fletcher, J.
Appeal to the young. Foster, J. 20c. ...... *Am. Tr.*
Appeal to youth. White, J. 40c. .... *Sev. Day Adv.*
Appearance and principle. 18°. '73. 25c. *N. Y. Ref. Ch. Bd.; Pres. Com.*
Appearances. Simpson, J. P. 15c. .... *French.*
Appellate series reports. *See* England, Law reports.
Appelles and his contemporaries. Greenough, H. $1. *Burnham.*
Apple blossoms. Albery, J. 15c. .... *De Witt.*
Apple boys. *See* Baker, *Mrs.* H. N. W.
Apple gathering. *See* Abbott, J., Rollo story books.
Apple of life. Bulwer-Lytton, R. 25c. ...... *Osgood.*
Apple-pie order. *See* Bright eye ser.
Apple-pie picture book. ill. 16°. '73. 75c; bds., 50c. *Routledge.*
Apple tree (The), and its blossoms. 18°. 22c. *Am. S. S.*
Appleby *Brothers*. Illustrated hand-book of machinery and iron work. ill. 8°. '69. $4.50 .... *Spon.*
Appledore cook-book. Parloa, M. $1.25... *Graves.*
Appler, A: C. Life of the Younger brothers, James boys and Quantrell, the guerillas of the west. ill. 8°. '75. $1; pap., 50c. .... *Eureka.*
Apples of gold. Brookes, T. 70c. .... *Pres. Bd.*
Apples of gold. Fenelon, —. 15c. .... *Claxton.*
Apples of gold. *See* Laughing Kitty stories.
Apples of gold in pictures of silver. *See* Kruna.
Apples of gold in pictures of silver. Roberts, E. 35c.; 30c. .... *Ditson.*
Appleton, *Miss* Anna E. Stories for Eva. ('69.) 2d ed. ill. 16°. '70. 80c. .... *Am. Unit.*
Appleton, Jesse. Works; with memoir of his life and character. 2 v. in 1. 8°. '37. $3 ..... *Draper.*
Appleton, J: Rules of evidence stated and discussed. 8°. '60. $2.50 .... *T. & J. W. Johnson.*
— *See also* Law lib.; — Maine, Sup. Court reports.
Appleton, J: L. Englische Grammatik. 23d ed. 12°. hf. leath., $1.50 .... *Schäfer.*
Appleton, T. G. A Nile journal. ill. 12°. '76. $2.25. *Roberts.*
— A sheaf of papers. 16°. '74. $1.50 .... *Roberts.*
Appleton's American annual cyclopædia, and register of important events. ('61.) [Annual.] 8°. $5; shp., $6 .... *Appleton.*
Appleton's American cyclopædia. *See* Ripley, G., *and* Dana, C. A.
Appleton's cheap edition of the poets. 10 v. 16°. ea., pap., 50c. .... *Appleton.*
Cont.: Burns. — Byron. — Campbell. — Dante. — Dryden. — Milton. — Pope. — Scott. — Tasso. — Kirke White.
Appleton's cyclopædia of biog. *See* Hawks, F. L.
Appleton's cyclopædia of drawing. *See* Worthen, W. E.
Appleton's cyclop. of wit and humor. *See* Burton, W. E.
Appleton's dict. of mechanics. *See* Worthen, W. E.
Appleton's European guide-book. maps, plans and ill. 12°. $6; — in 2 v. mor., $6.50 ...... *Appleton.*
Appleton's general atlas of the world. 4°. hf. roan, $3. *Appleton.*
Appleton's hand atlas of modern geog.; in 31 maps. 4°. $2.50 .... *Appleton.*
Appleton's handbooks of Am. travel. 3 v. maps. 12°. ea., $2 .... *Appleton.*
Cont.: 1. Northern and eastern tour. — 2. Western tour. — 3. Southern tour.
Appleton's juvenile annual. ill. sm. 4°. $2.. *Appleton.*
Appleton's scientific series. *See* Worthen, W. E.
Application of photog. to illustrations of natural hist. ill. 8°. '71. pap., 25c. .... *Mus. Comp. Zool.*
Approaching crisis. Davis, A. J. $1.50.. *A. J. Davis.*
Appuleius, Lucius. Works: new tr. 12°. (Bohn.) $1.75. .... *Little, B. & Co.*
Cont.: Metamorphoses; or, golden ass; God of Socrates; The Florida; His defence; or, a discourse on magic; Metrical version of Cupid and Psyche; Mrs. Tighe's Psyche, a poem.
— *Same.* 12°. (Bohn.) $2. *Lippincott; Scribner, W. & A.*
April fool. Brough, W., *and* Halliday, A. 15c... *French.*
Apron strings. *See* Capron, M. J.
Apron-strings library. 5 v. 16°. $6 .... *Crowell.*
Cont.: Apron-strings, by M. J. Capron. — Tover tangle, by M. J. Capron. — Joanna, by M. P. Hazen. — Violet and Daisy. — Lucy, the light-bearer, by G. F. Sargent.
Aquinas. *See* Thomas Aquinas, *St.*
Arab (The) and his country. 18°. 60c. .... *Am. S. S.*
Arabella Stuart. *See* James, G. P. R.
Arabesques. Greenough, R. S. $2 .... *Roberts.*
Arabian days' entertainments. Hauff, W. $1.75. *Osgood.*
Arabian nights' entertainments; or, the thousand and one nights. ill. 8°. (Dick.) 50c.; pap., 25c. *Am. News.*
— *Same.* ill. 12°. $1.. *Lippincott; Porter; Routledge.*
— *Same.* ill. 12°. $1.25 .... *Miller.*
— *Same.* cr. 8°. $1.50 .... *Estes.*
— *Same.* ill. 12°. $1.50. *Carleton; Scribner, W. & A.; World. Pub.*
— *Same.* ('52.) New ed. ill. 12°. '74. $1.50. 18°. '71. 75c. .... *Claxton.*
— *Same.* ill. 12°. $1.50. 16°. $1.25 ...... *Eastman.*
— *Same.* ill. 8°. $2.50. ill. 12°. $1.50. 16°. $1.50. *Lee & S.*
— *Same.* (Chandos classics.) cr. 8°. $1; pap., 75c. *Scribner, W. & A.*
— *Same.* (Globe lib.) ill. cr. 8°. $1.75; hf. cf., $3.50; cf., $5. ill. 8°. '73. $2.50; $3.50... *Routledge.*
— *Same.* (Household ser.) ill. 16°. $1.50; mor., $3. *Lee & S.*
— *Same;* tr. by Forster. ill. 8°. $2.50; $4; hf. mor., $6. ill. 12°. $1.50 .... *Appleton.*

Arabian nights' entertainments, *continued.*
— — *Same;* rev., with introd., by G. M. Bussey. ill. 8°. $2.50; $3.50 .... *Miller.*
— *Same;* tr. and ed., with notes, by E. W. Lane. 2 v. ill. 12°. $3.50 .... *Harper.*
— — *Same.* 2 v. ill. cr. 8°. $6; $7.50; hf. cf., $11; mor., $13.50 .... *Miller.*
— *Same;* rev. and annotated by J. L. Mason. ill. cr. 4°. $5 .... *Cassell.*
— *Same;* arranged for youthful readers, by Mrs. Sugden. ill. 16°. '75. $1.25. ill. 12°. '75. $1.75. *Routledge.*
— *Same;* rev., with notes, by G. F. Townsend. ill. cr. 8°. $1.50; $2; hf. cf., $3.50 .... *Hurd & H.*
— — *Same.* ill. cr. 8°. $2.50. ill. 12°. $1.75. *Scribner, W. & A.*
— *Same.* 5 v. ill. 18°. ea., pap., 10c. ...... *Challen.*
Cont.: Aladdin, or, the wonderful lamp, etc. — Ali Baba and the forty thieves, etc. — Sinbad the sailor, etc. — Noureddin and the fair Persian. — The slave of love.
— *See also* Child's ed. of Arabian nights; — Library of celebrated books; — Treasure-box of wonder and entertainment.
Arabic reading lessons: extracts from the Koran, etc., analysed and tr., with elements of Arabic gram. post 8°. (Bagster.) $1.50; hf. bd., $1.75. *Wiley.*
Arabistan. Fogg, W. P. *$2.50; $3 .... *Dustin.*
Arabula, Sacred gospels of. *See* Davis, A. J.
Arator. Taylor, J. $2 .... *J. W. Randolph.*
Aratra pentelici. *See* Ruskin, J.
Arbell. Hooper, J. W. $1 .... *Routledge.*
Arbell's school days. Hooper, J. W. $1.25. *Nichols & H.*
Arblay, *Mme.* Fes. B. d'. Diary and letters; ed. by C. Barrett. New ed. 4 v. por. 8°. '76. $14. *Scribner, W. & A.*
— Evelina; or, the history of a young lady's introduction to the world. [Fiction.] 12°. $1 .. *Harper.*
Arbor (The) the boys built. *See* Witt, *Mme.* H. de.
Arbouville, Sophie de B. (*Comtesse*) d'. Three tales; tr. by M. B. Field. 12°. $1.50 .... *Harper.*
Cont.: Christine van Amberg; Resignation; Village doctor.
Arbuckle, Mat. Complete cornet method. 4°. '66. bds., $3 .... *Ditson.*
Arbuthnot, *Captain* —. L'Africaine: burlesque. 16°. pap., 15c. .... *French.*
Arcadia. *See* Sidney, *Sir* P.
Arcana cœlestia. *See* Swedenborg, E.
Arcana of nature. Tuttle, H. $1.25 .... *Colby.*
Archconfraternity (The) of the sacred heart. *See* Month of the sacred heart.
Archelaus, *Bp. of Cascar.* Works. *See* Thaumaturgus.
Archer, E. M. Christina North. [Fiction.] 8°. pap., 75c. .... *Appleton.*
— Under the limes. [Fiction.] cr. 8°. '74. $1.75. *Macmillan.*
Archer, G: W. ["Hesper Bendbow."] More than she could bear: story of the Gachupin war in Texas, 1812–13. 12°. '71. $1.50 ...... *Claxton.*
Archer, T: [Plays.] 4 v. 16°. ea., pap., 15c. .. *French.*
Cont.: Asmodeus, the little demon. — Inundation. — Marguerite's colours. — Three old men.
— Monseigneur: drama. 16°. pap., 15c. .... *Lee & S.*
Archibald, G. D. Union chant book: sel. from the Psalms, for congregations and Sabbath schools; arranged for chanting by D. H. Baldwin and S. W. Mason. 12°. '57. 60c.; bds., 50c. .. *Wilstach.*
Archibald Hamilton. Baärnhielm, E. W. $1.25. *Lothrop.*
Archibald Hughson. *See* Kingston, W. H. G.
Archibald Hughson, and other stories. 16°. $1.25. *Graves.*
Archie and his sisters; — and Nep. *See* Library for little lads and lasses.
Archie and Pussy series. *See* Hildeburn, *Mrs.* M. J.
Archie at the seaside, and other stories. 18°. 60c. *Am. S. S.*
Archie Blake. Eiloart, C. J. 75c. .... *Routledge.*
Archie Bruce. 18°. 60c. .... *Cong. Pub.*
— *See also* Dana Hill stories.
Archie Grey; or, do it heartily. 18°. 60c. .. *Whittaker.*
Archie Lee. *See* Sunbeam series.
Archie Lovell. Edwards, A. $1.75; $1 ...... *Sheldon.*
Archie Young. Bickerstaffe, M. B. 25c. *Scribner, W. & A.*
Archie's fourth of July. *See* Aunty Ray's little lib.
Archie's keys. Trowbridge, C. M. $1.25 .. (?) *Martien.*
Archie's old desk. Dodney, S. 50c. .. *H. A. Young.*
Archie's shadow. Peebles, M. L. $1.25 ...... *Nims.*
Architect of Cologne. Atkinson, M. E. $1 .. *Lothrop.*
Architects', builders' and carpenters' reference book. 4°. '72. $25 .... *J. A. Murphy.*
Architectural Association. *See* Sharpe, E.
Archy Hamilton. *See* Little Ben Hadden ser.
Arctander, J: W. Praktisk Haandbog for Skandinaver i Staten Minnesotas lovgivning. 12°. '76. hf. shp., $4 .... *J. B. West.*
Arctic adventures by sea and land. Sargent, E. $2. *Thompson.*
Arctic boat journey (An). Hayes, I. I. $2.50 .. *Osgood.*
Arctic Crusoe. St. John, P. B. $1.50; $1 .. *Lee & S.*
Arctic heroes. Mudge, Z. A. $1.25 .. *Meth. Bk. Conc.*
Arden, H. T. Belle of the barleymow: burlesque. 16°. pap., 15c. .... *French.*
— Princess Charming: extravaganza. 16°. pap., 15c. *French.*
Ardent spirits. 18°. '53. 35c. .... *Am. Tr.*
Are you a Christian? Winslow, H. 15c. .... *Am. Tr.*
Are you my wife? Ramsay, G. $2 .... *Cath. Pub.*
Area belle (The). Brough, W., *and* Halliday, A. 15c. *De Witt; French.*
Arena (The) and the throne. Townsend, L. T. $1.50. *Lee & S.*
Argyle, Anna. Olive Lacey. [Fiction.] 12°. $1.75. *Lippincott.*
Argyll, *Duke of.* [G. D. Campbell.] Iona. ill. 16°. $1.25. .... *Routledge.*
— Primeval man: examination of some recent speculations. cr. 8°. '69. $1.50 .... *Routledge.*
— Reign (The) of law. New ed., enl. cr. 8°. '67. $2. *Routledge.*
Ariadne Florentina. *See* Ruskin, J.
Arian, Cl. Helvetius; or, the true meaning of the system of nature; from the Fr. 12°. 20c. .. *Mendum.*
Arion. Willard, J. D. 5 bks. $4 .... *Ditson.*
Ariosto, Lodovico. Orlando Furioso; tr. by W. S. Rose. 2 v. ill. 12°. (Bohn.) ea., $1.75. *Little, B. & Co.*
— *Same.* 2 v. ill. 12°. (Bohn.) ea., $2. *Lippincott; Scribner, W. & A.*
Aristocracy; or, life among the upper ten. Nunes, J. A. 75c. .... *Peterson.*
Aristophanes. [Comedies explained, with extracts,] by W. L. Collins. 16°. '71. $1. *Lippincott; Little, B. & Co.*
— Comedies; tr., with notes, etc., by W. J. Hickie. 2 v. 12°. (Bohn.) ea., $1.75 .. *Little, B. & Co.*
Cont.: v. 1. Acharnians; Knights; Clouds; Wasps; Peace; Birds. — v. 2. Lysistrata; Thesmophoriazusæ; Frogs; Ecclesiazusæ; Plutus.
— *Same.* 2 v. 12°. (Bohn.) ea., $2. *Lippincott; Scribner, W. & A.*
— Acharnians (The) and Knights [Gk.]; ed. by W. C. Green. 12°. '71. $1.50 .... *Allyn.*
— Birds [Gk.]; with notes by C. C. Felton. New ed., rev. by W. W. Goodwin. ('61.) 5th ed. 16°. '72. $1.25 .... *Allyn.*

Aristophanes, *continued.*
— Clouds [Gk.]; with notes by C. C. Felton. New ed., rev. by W. W. Goodwin. ('61.) 8th ed. 16°. '73. $1.25 .... *Allyn.*

Aristophanes' apology. Browning, R. $1.50. *Osgood.*

Aristotle. [Aristoteles.] Works; lit. tr. 7 v. 12°. (Bohn.) v. 1-5, ea., $1.75; v. 6-7, ea., $1.25. *Little, B. & Co.*
Cont.: 1. Ethics, tr. by Brown.—2. Hist. of animals, tr. by R. Cresswell.—3. Metaphysics, tr. by J. H. McMahon.—4. Politics and economics, tr. by E. Walford.—5. Rhetoric and poetics, tr. by an Oxonian.—6-7. Organon, or logical treatises, tr. by O. F. Owen.
— *Same.* 7 v. 12°. (Bohn.) v. 1-5, ea., $2; v. 6-7, ea., $1.40 .... *Scribner, W. & A.*
— *Same.* 7 v. 12°. (Bohn.) v. 1-5, ea., $2; v. 6-7, ea., $1.75 .... *Lippincott.*
— On fallacies; or, the sophistici elenchi; with tr. and notes by E. Poste. 8°. '66. $3.... *Macmillan.*

Aristotle's book of fate and dict. of dreams. 16°. pap., 15c. .... *Dick & F.*

Arithmetic (The) of life. Sister Ruth. 45c... *Pres. Bd.*

Arizona. Compiled laws; incl. the Howell code and session laws, 1864-'71. 8°. '71. shp., $7.50. *Bancroft.*
— Statutes, 1864-'73. 7 v. 8°. hf. shp., $30. *Bancroft.*

Ark (The) of the Covenant. *See* Preston, T. S.

Ark of Elm Island. Kellogg, E. $1.25..... *Lee & S.*

Ark (The) of the people; with preface by Rev. P. E. Moriarty. 12°. '73. $2 .... *Cunningham.*

Arkansas. Digest of statutes in force 1846; with notes of Sup. Court decisions, by E. H. English. 8°. '48 .... *State.*
— Digest of statutes in force 1856; with notes of Sup. Court decisions, by J. Gould. 8°. '58.... *State.*
— Supreme Court reports, v. 1-27 (1837-'72). 27 v. 8°. '40-'73 .... *State.*
Cont.: v. 1-5 ('37-'44), by A. Pike.—v. 6-13 ('45-'53), by E. H. English.—v. 14-24 ('53-'67), by L. E. Barber.—v. 25-27 ('67-'72), by N. W. Cox.

Arkansas geological survey. Botanical and palæontological report of a geol. survey of A.; by L. Lesquereux. 8° .... *State.*
— First report of a geol. reconnaissance of the north. counties of A., in 1857-8; by D. D. Owen, W. Elderhorst and E. T. Cox. 8°. '58 .... *State.*
— Second report of a geol. recon. of the middle and south. counties of A., in 1859-'60: by D. D. Owen, R. Peter, L. Lesquereux and E. Cox. 8°. '60 .... *State.*

Arlington series (The). 4 v. 16°. $5.50... *Graves.*
Cont.: Ralph and Tib, by Mrs. A. S. Moffat.—Wheel of fortune, by Mrs. H. N. W. Baker.—Boys at Dr. Murray's, by G. Gaylord.—Deserted mill, by E. L. Llewellyn.

Arlot, —. Complete guide for coach painters; tr. by A. A. Fesquet; with app. ('71.) 3d ed. 12°. '73. $1.25 .... *Baird.*

Armadale. *See* Collins, Wilkie.

Armageddon. Baldwin, S. D. $2........ *So. Meth.*

Armand (*pseud.*) *See* Strubberg, F. A.

Armand. Ritchie, A. C. 15c. .... *French.*

Arme Gottfried (Der). Nieritz, G. 25c..... *Morwitz.*

Armengaud, J. E. *and* C., *and* Amoroux, J. Practical draughtsman's book of indust. design, and machinists' and engineer's drawing companion; tr. and enl. by W. Johnson. ('63.) 14th ed. wood-cuts and f°. pl. 4°. '75. $10...... *Baird.*

Armitage, W. E. (*ed.*) Hymns for Sunday schools. 32°. 15c. .... *Dutton.*

Armor, W: C. Lives of the governors of Penna.; with the incidental hist. of the state, 1609-1873. por. and ill. 12°. '74. *$3.50; shp., $4; hf. cf., $5.50 .... *T. H. Davis.*

Armstrong, E: *See* Historical Soc. of Penna.

Armstrong, Fs. C. Young commander. 16°. '73. bds., 80c. .... *Routledge.*

Armstrong, Fs. C., *continued.*
— Young middy. 12°. $1.50 .... *Tilton.*
— War hawk. 16°. '73. bds., 80c. .... *Routledge.*

Armstrong, Flo. C. The king in his beauty, and other hymns. ill. sq. 24°. '75. 75c....... *Randolph.*

Armstrong, G: D. Christian doct. of slavery. 12°. '57. $1 .... *Scribner.*
— Doctrine of baptism. 12°. $1.50 .... *Scribner.*
— Theology of Christian experience: an exposition of the "common faith" of the church of God. 12°. '58. $1.50 .... *Scribner.*

Armstrong, H. S. Trifles for the Christmas holidays. 12°. pap., 50c. .... *Lippincott.*

Armstrong, J. M. Voice of melody: collection of hymns. 16°. '60. 40c. .... *Ditson.*

Armstrong, *Gen.* J: Life of A. Wayne;—of R. Montgomery. *See* Sparks, J., Library of Am. biog.
— Treatise on agriculture; with notes by J. Buel and dissertation on the kitchen and fruit garden. 18°. hf. shp., 75c. .... *Harper.*

Armstrong, *Rev.* J: The pastor in his closet: help to the devotion of the clergy. 12°. 60c... *McCauley.*

Armstrong, Lebbeus. Masonry a work of darkness. 12°. pap., 20c. .... *E. A. Cook.*
— Temperance reformation: its history to 1851. ('53.) 2d ed., rev. and enl. por. 12°. $1.25..... *Wells.*

Armstrong, *Mrs.* M. F., *and* Ludlow, H. W. Hampton and its students. 8°. '74. $1.50... *Putnam.*

Armstrong, Rob. Chimneys for furnaces, fire places and steam boilers. 18°. '73. bds., 50c. *Van Nostrand.*
— Construction and management of steam boilers; with app. by R. Mallett. ill. 12°. 75c. .... *Baird.*

Army and navy stories. *See* Adams, W. T.

Army life: experiences and incidents, as given from the battle field at Fulton St. [N. Y.] prayer meeting. 18°. 50c. .... *N. Y. Ref. Ch. Bd.*

Armytage, Sydney (*ed.*) Beautiful pictures; with examples by Ward, Goodall, Paton, and others. 2 v. imp. 4°. ea., $10.50..... *Scribner, W. & A.*

Arnault, M. A., *and* Panckoucke, C. L. F. Life and campaigns of Napoleon Bonaparte; tr. from the French. ill. 12°. $1.25 .... *Porter.*

Arndt, Fs. Werth der Bibel. 18°. '70. 30c... *Am. Tr.*

Arndt, J: Wahres Christenthum. 2 v. 12°. '48. $1.10. *Am. Tr.*
— — Sechs Bücher vom "Wahren Christenthum," nebst dessen Paradiesgärtlein. 8°. leath., $3.50; mor., $5; chp. ed., $2.50 .... *Schäfer.*
— *Eng.* True Christianity. New Am. ed., rev. and enl., with introd. by C. F. Schäffer. 8°. '68. $4; $5; mor., $8 .... *Luth. Bk. St.*
— *Danish;* abridg. 18°. '61. 20c. .... *Am. Tr.*

Arne, T. A. Artaxerxes: opera. 16°. pap., 15c. *French.*

Arne. *See* Björnson, B.

Arnobius. The seven books Adversus; Gentes tr. by H. Bryce and H. Campbell. (Ante-Nicene Christ. lib.) 8°. $3 .... *Scribner, W. & A.*

Arnold, A. N. One woman's mission and how she fulfilled it: life of Mrs. H. E. Dickson, missionary to Greece. 16°. '71. $1.25...... *H. A. Young.*

Arnold, Ab. K. Notes on horses for cavalry service. ill. 18°. '69. 75c. .... *Van Nostrand.*

Arnold, Alb. N. Pre-requisites to communion: the Scripture term of admission to the Lord's table. 18°. pap., 15c. .... *Am. Bapt.*

Arnold, André. Dialogues, plays and speeches; for schools, social gatherings, etc. 16°. '76. pap., 30c. .... *Happy.*

Arnold, A: C. L. Rationale and ethics of Freemasonry; or, the Masonic institution a means of social and industrial progress. 12°. '72. $1.50... *Masonic.*

Arnold, A: C. L., *continued.*
— Signet of king Solomon; or, the Freemason's daughter. 12°. $1.25 .... *Redding.*
— *Same.* 12°. '72. $1.50 .... *Masonic.*
— *and* Samuels, E. A. The living world: descript. of the races of men, and species of animals, birds, etc. New ed. 24 pts. ill. sm. 4°. '74. ea., *50c. *S. Walker.*

Arnold, *Rev.* F. Farm on the mountains. ('71.) New ed. 16°. '74. $1.50 .... *Hoyt.*

Arnold, *Rev.* F: Turning points in life. 12°. $1.75. *Harper.*

Arnold, G: Poems; ed. with biog. sketch by W. Winter. por. 12°. '70. $2 .... *Osgood.*

Arnold, J: Glycerine oil: comic drama. 12°. pap., 15c. .... *De Witt.*
— Obeying orders: comic drama. 12°. pap., 15c. *De Witt.*

Arnold, Matt. Bible-reading for schools: prophecy of Israel's restoration (Isaiah, XL.–LXVI.) 3d ed. 18°. '72. 50c. .... *Macmillan.*
— Culture and anarchy: essay on political and social criticism. 2d ed. cr. 8°. '75. $2 ... *Macmillan.*
— Essay on Heine. 16°. '63. pap., 25c. .... *Holt.*
— Essays in criticism. 12°. $2 .... *Holt.*
— *Same.* New ed., enl. cr. 8°. '76. $3 ... *Macmillan.*
— French Eton (A); or, middle-class education and the state. fp. 8°. '64. $1 .... *Macmillan.*
— God and the Bible: review of objections to "Literature and dogma." 12°. $1.50 .... *Holt.*
— *Same.* cr. 8°. '75. $2 .... *Macmillan.*
— Higher schools and universities in Germany. cr. 8°. '74. $2 .... *Macmillan.*
— Isaiah XL.–LXVI., with the shorter prophecies allied to it; arranged and ed., with notes. cr. 8°. '75. $1.75 .... *Macmillan.*
— Literature and dogma: an essay towards a better appreciation of the Bible. 12°. $1.50 .... *Holt.*
— *Same.* 3d ed. cr. 8°. '74. $2.50 ..... *Macmillan.*
— New poems. 16°. $2 .... * *Osgood.*
— Poetical works. 2 v. fp. 8°. '59. ea., $1.75. *Macmillan.*
Cont.: Narrative and elegiac poems. — Dramatic and lyric poems.
— St. Paul and Protestantism; with essay on Puritanism and the Church of England. 3d ed. cr. 8°. '75. $1.75 .... *Macmillan.*

Arnold, S: Green. History of Rhode Island and Providence Plantations. 2d ed. 2 v. 8°. $6 .. *Appleton.*

Arnold, S. J. My aunt: comedy. 16°. pap., 15c. *French.*

Arnold, T. J. *See* Goethe, J. W. v., Faust.

Arnold, *Rev.* T: Christian life. 2 v. in 1. 12°. '76. $2 .... *Tibbals.*
— History of Rome. 8°. $3 .... *Appleton.*
— Introductory lectures on mod. hist. 12°. $1.50. *Appleton.*
— Life and correspondence. 2 v. in 1. 12°. $2 .. * *Osgood.*
— Life of Hannibal. 16°. 75c. .... *Hurd & H.*

Arnold, T: *A.M.* Manual of Eng. literature, hist. and crit.; with app. on Eng. metres. Am. ed., rev. 12°. '76. $2 .... *Ginn.*

Arnold, T: K. First and second Lat. book and pract. gram.; ed. by J. A. Spencer. 12°. $1.25. *Appleton.*
— First Greek book. 12°. $1.25 .... *Appleton.*
— Greek prose composition. 12°. $1.50 .... *Appleton.*
— Greek reading book; ed. by J. A. Spencer. 12°. $1.50 .... *Appleton.*
— Latin prose composition. 12°. $1.25 .... *Appleton.*
— Second Greek prose compos. 12°. $1.50 .. *Appleton.*
— *See also* Bojesen, E. F., *and* Arnold, T. K.; — Putz, W., *and* Arnold, T. K.; — Riddle, J. E., *and* Arnold, T. K.

Arnold, W. H. Free and easy: farce. 16°. pap., 15c. .... *French.*
— Woodman's hut: drama. 16°. pap., 15c. .. *French.*

Arnold and André. Calvert, G. H. $1.50 .. (?) *Lee & S.*

Arnold Lee. Bell, C. D. 75c. ..... *Scribner, W. & A.*

Arnot, M. Christ in the Psalms. 18°. 10c. *U. P. Bd. of Pub.*

Arnot, W: Anchor of the soul. sq. 24°. '74. 40c.; 60c.; chp. ed., 20c. .... *Am. Tr.*
— *Same.* cr. 8°. $1.75 .... *Nelson.*
— Church (The) in the house: lessons on Acts. 12°. $2.50 .... *Carter.*
— Laws from heaven for life on earth. 8°. $2.50. *Nelson.*
— Life of James Hamilton. 12°. $2.50 ...... *Carter.*
— Parables of our Lord. 8°. $2.50 .... *Nelson.*
— This present world. 16°. $1.25 .... *Carter.*

Arnott, H: Cancer: its varieties, their histology and diagnosis. pl. and ill. 8°. '72. $2.25 .. *Lindsay.*

Arnould, *Sir* Jos. Life of Thomas, Lord Denman. 2 v. 8°. $7; shp., $9 .... *Cockcroft.*
These form v. 5, 6 of Campbell's Lives of chief justices.
— *Same.* 2 v. 8°. $7; shp., $9; hf. cf., $12 .. *Estes.*
— — *See also* Campbell, J. (*Lord*), Lives of chief justices.

Arnoult, Émile. *See* Pinney, N., *and* Arnoult, É.

Around the manger. Parker, J. M. 40c. .... *Dutton.*

Around the moon. *See* Verne, Jules.

Around a spring. Droz, G. $1.25 .... *Holt.*

Around the tea table. Talmage, T. De Witt. *$3; $3.50; $5 .... *Cowperthwait.*

Around the world. Prime, E. D. G. $3 .... *Harper.*

Around the world in eighty days. *See* Verne, Jules.

Arrabiata (L'). *See* Heyse, P.

Arrah De Baugh. Kinnaman, F. C. 15c. ..... *Ames.*

Arrah-na-pogue. 8°. pap., 25c. .... *De Witt.*

Arrah Neil. *See* James, G. P. R.

Arrival of Dickens: Ethiop. drama. 16°. pap., 15c. *French.*

Arrom, C. B. de F. ["Fernan Caballero."] Elia; or, Spain fifty years ago. 12°. '73. $1.50. *Cath. Pub.*
— Familia de Alvareda. 12°. pap., $1 .... *Holt.*

Arrows from my quiver. Caughey, J. $2 ... *Palmer.*

Arrowsmith, Ja. Paper-hanger's companion. ('52.) 6th ed. 12°. '74. $1.25 .... *Baird.*

Arroyo de la Cuesta, Felipe. Grammar of the Mutsun lang., spoken at the mission of San Juan Bautista, Cal. 4°. '61. pap., $4 .... *Shea.*
— — *See also* Shea, J. G.
— Vocabulary of the Mutsun lang. of Alta California. *See* Shea, J. G., Library of Am. ling.

Ars, *Curé* d'. Life. 12°. $2 .... *O'Shea.*

Art and artifice. Brougham, J. 15c. .... *French.*

Art and artlessness. Baker, H. N. W. $1.50 .. *Lee & S.*

Art and etiquette of making love. 16°. pap., 30c.; bds., 50c. .... *Dick & F.*

Art foliage. Colling, J. K. $15 .... *Osgood.*

Art idea (The). Jarves, J. J. $1.75; $3.50 .. *Hurd & H.*

Art Maguire; or, the broken pledge. 18°. 75c.; $1.25. *Sadlier.*

Art of acting. 16°. pap., 15c. .... *French.*

Art of always rejoicing. Sarasa, A. A. de. 75c. *H. A. Young.*

Art of beauty. *See* Ovidius Naso, P.

Art of book canvassing; by an old hand. 16°. '75. pap., *25c. .... *N. Y. Bk. Conc.*

Art of confectionery. 12°. '64. $2.50 ...... *Tilton.*

Art of conversation. 12°. $1.50. .... *Carleton.*

Art of dining and of attaining high health. 16°. $1.50. *De Witt.*

Art of doing our best; as seen in the lives and stories of some thorough workers. ill. 16°. 75c. .. *Porter.*

Art of good living. Moncure, M. B. $1.25. *West, J. & Co.*

Art of hunting, trapping and fishing made easy; by an old hunter. 12°. pap., 25c. .... *Hurst.*

Art of letter-writing simplified. 18°. 10c. .. *Dick & F.*

Art of love. *See* Ovidius Naso, P.

Art of money making. Mills, J. D. *$2........*Intern.*

Art of pleasing. Hazard, W. P. 45c.........*Porter.*

Art of pleasing. Roy, G. 25c...............*Clarke.*

Art of printing. ('57.) 2d ed. 18°. '75. 50c...*So. Meth.*

Art of real pleasure. Blanchard, C. $1..*D. Thomas.*

Art of suffering. 16°. 50c.; 75c...........*Sadlier.*

Art of training animals. ill. 12°. $1; pap., 50c.*Haney.*

Art of ventriloquism. 12°. pap., 15c........*Hurst.*

Art, pictorial and industrial: essays on topics connected with ancient and modern art, with 25 ill. from orig. works, by the autotype process. 2d ser. 4°. '70. hf. mor., $8...............*Putnam.*

Art recreations: guide to ornamental work; by Mme. L. B. Urbino, H. Day and others. ('59.) New ed. 12°. '75. $3...................*Tilton.*

Art studies of home life: 24 photos. from paintings by great masters; with text, by G. W. Turner. demy 4°. $7.50......................*Cassell.*

Art thoughts. Jarves, J. J. $2.50; $4.50..*Hurd & H.*

Art tour to northern capitals of Europe. Atkinson, J. B. $3...........................*Macmillan.*

Art treasures of England. 34 pts. roy. 4°. '74. *$17; hf. mor., $25; mor., $30; $35. — f°. *$34; hf. mor., $50; mor., $65; $75. — India pap. proofs. f°. *$68; hf. mor., $90; mor., $100; $120. *Gebbie.*

Artaud de Montor, d'. Lives and times of the Roman pontiffs, from St. Peter to Pius IX.; tr. from the French. 2 v. 8°. $14–$25; — in 40 pts. 4°. ea., 25c............................*Sadlier.*

Artaxerxes. Arne, T. A. 15c.............*French.*

Artful dodge. Blanchard, E. L. 15c.......*French.*

Arthuis, A. Nervous and rheumatic affections, treated by static electricity; tr. by J. H. Etheridge. ill. 12°. '73. $2..........................*Keen.*

Arthur, Rob. Treatment and prevention of decay of the teeth. ill. 16°. $1.50..........*Lippincott.*

Arthur, Tim. Shay. Advice to young people. 6 v. 16°. $7.50......................*J. E. Potter.*

Cont.: Advice to young men. — Advice to young ladies. — Ten nights in a bar room and what I saw there. — The old man's bride; or, the lesson of the day. — The hand without the heart; or, the life trials of Jesse Loring. — Golden grains from life's harvest fields.

— Agnes; or, the possessed. 8°. pap., 50c...*Peterson.*

— All's for the best; or, the old peppermint man. sq. 18°. 60c........................*Nichols & H.*

— *Same.* ('50.) 10th ed. 16°. '76. 90c. ...*Miller.*

— All's for the best lib. 3 v. ill. 16°. $3.75..*Lippincott.*

Cont.: All's for the best. — The seen and unseen. — Stories of the household.

— Arthur's library for the household. ('51.) New ed. 12 v. ill. 16°. '73. $9; — in 6 v. 12°. $9..*Claxton.*

Cont.: Woman's trials. — Off-hand sketches, a little dashed with humor. — Stories for parents. — Lessons in life. — The two wives; or, lost and won. — Seed time and harvest. — The ways of Providence. — Home scenes and home influence. — Married life, its shadows and sunshine. — Words for the wise. — Stories for young housekeepers. — The tried and the tempted.

— Banker's (The) wife. 8°. pap., 50c......*Peterson.*

— Blind Nellie's boy. ('67.) 3d ed. ill. 16°. '72. $1. *Perkinpine.*

— Cast adrift. ill. 12°. '72. $2; $2.50; mor., $4. *J. M. Stoddart.*

— Cecilia Howard. 8°. pap., 50c..........*Peterson.*

— Danger; or, wounded in the house of a friend. ill. 12°. '75. $2; $2.50..............*J. M. Stoddart.*

— Debtor's daughter. 8°. pap., 50c.......*Peterson.*

— Divorced wife. 8°. pap., 50c............*Peterson.*

— Fireside-angel. ill. 18°. '69. 75c........*Lothrop.*

— Good time coming series. 6 v. 16°. $7.50. *J. E. Potter.*

Cont.: The good time coming. — The Allen house; or, twenty years ago and now. — What can a woman do? — The withered heart. — The angel and the demon. — The trials and confessions of a housekeeper.

— Home stories. 6 v. ill. 16°. $6..........*Sheldon.*

Arthur, Tim. Shay, *continued.*

Cont.: Hidden wings. — Sowing the wind. — Sunshine at home. — The peacemaker. — After a shadow. — Not anything for peace.

— Idle hands, and other stories. ill. sm. 4°. '71. $2. *Porter.*

— Insubordination. 8°. pap., 50c..........*Peterson.*

— Iron rule (The). 8°. pap., 50c..........*Peterson.*

— Lady (The) at home. 8°. pap., 50c......*Peterson.*

— Little gems from the "Children's hour." ill. sm. 4°. '75. $1.........................*J. M. Stoddart.*

— Lizzie Glenn; or, the trials of a seamstress. 12°. $1.75; pap., $1.50....................*Peterson.*

— Lost bride (The). 8°. pap., 50c.........*Peterson.*

— Love in a cottage. 8°. pap., 50c.........*Peterson.*

— Love in high life. 8°. pap., 50c.........*Peterson.*

— Lucy Sandford. 8°. pap., 50c...........*Peterson.*

— Mary Moreton. 8°. pap., 50c............*Peterson.*

— Orange blossoms, fresh and faded. ill. large 12°. '71. $2.50; $3; mor., $4.50....*J. M. Stoddart.*

— Orphan children. 8°. pap., 50c..........*Peterson.*

— Pitcher of cool water. ('70.) New ed. 18°. '75. 50c...............................*Nat. Temp.*

— Popular juvenile lib. 6 v. ill. 16°. $7.50. *Lippincott.*

Cont.: Who is greatest? — Peacemaker. — Lost children. — Poor wood cutter. — Wounded boy. — Lost boy.

— Pride and prudence. 8°. pap., 50c.......*Peterson.*

— Rainbow series. 6 v. 12°. $9........*J. E. Potter.*

Cont.: After the storm. — Light on shadowed paths. — Out in the world. — Our neighbors in the corner house. — Nothing but money. — What came afterwards.

— Receipts for putting up fruits and vegetables to keep. 12°. pap., 12c.........................*Peterson.*

— Six nights with the Washingtonians, and other temperance tales. ill., por., etc. roy. 8°. $3.50; roan., $4.50; mor., $6...............*Peterson.*

— Tales for rich and poor. 6 v. ill. 16°. '64. $4.50. *Collins & Bro.*

Cont.: Riches have wings. — Keeping up appearances. — Rising in the world. — Making haste to be rich. — Debtor and creditor. — Retiring from business.

— Temperance stories, and other tales. 3 v. ill. 12°. $5.25...........................*J. E. Potter.*

Cont.: Lights and shadows of real life. — Sketches of life and character. — Leaves from the book of human life.

— Three eras in a woman's life. 6 v. 16°. $9. *J. E. Potter.*

Cont.: The three eras in a woman's life; or, the maiden, the wife, and the mother. — Before and after marriage; or, sweethearts and wives, etc. — The martyr wife, etc. — Mary Ellis; or, the runaway match, etc. — The young lady at home. — Steps towards heaven; or, religion in common life.

— Three years in a man-trap. ill. 12°. '72. $2; $2.50; mor., $4.........................*J. M. Stoddart.*

— Tom Blinn's temperance society, and other stories. ('70.) New ed. 12°. '75. $1.25...*Nat. Temp.*

— Trial and triumph. 8°. pap., 50c........*Peterson.*

— Two brides (The). 8°. pap., 50c........*Peterson.*

— Two merchants (The). 8°. pap., 50c.....*Peterson.*

— Way to prosper, and other tales. 6 v. 16°. $9. *J. E. Potter.*

Cont.: The way to prosper, etc. — The angel of the household, etc. — True riches; or, wealth without wings, etc. — Heart histories and life pictures. — Home scenes: its lights and shadows as pictured by love and selfishness. — Sparing to spend; or, the Loftons and the Pinkertons.

— Woman to the rescue: a story of the "new [temperance] crusade." 12°. '74. $1.25..*J. M. Stoddart.*

— Wonderful story of Gentle Hand, and other stories. ill. sm. 4°. '72. $2............*J. M. Stoddart.*

— Year after marriage. 8°. pap., 50c.......*Peterson.*

— *See also* Carpenter, W. H., *and* Arthur, T. S.; — Smuggler's (The) daughter.

Arthur, W: Automatic or governor cut-off for steam-engines. 8°. pap., 45c.......*Am. Soc. of C. E.*

Arthur, *Rev.* W: Addresses in N. Y. 12°. '56. 70c. *Meth. Bk. Conc.*

— Duty of giving away a stated proportion of our income. 18°. '62. 20c...............*Meth. Bk. Conc.*

— *Same;* ed. by T. O. Summers. ('55.) 4th ed. 12°. '75. pap., 20c.......................*So. Meth.*

— Italy in transition: public scenes and private opinions in spring of 1860. 12°. $1.50.........*Harper.*

Arthur, *Rev.* W: *continued.*
— Successful merchant: life of S. Budgett. 16°. '52. $1 .... *Meth. Bk. Conc.*
— *Same.* ('58.) 3d ed. 18°. '75. 75c.... *So. Meth.*
— Tongue of fire; or, true power of Christianity. 12°. $1.25 .... *Harper.*
— *Same.* ('53.) 3d ed. 18°. '76. 75c...... *So. Meth.*
Arthur. Sue, E. 75c.......... *Harper.*
Arthur, and other stories. Bradley, M. E. 45c.; 50c. *Dutton.*
Arthur and Bessie in Europe. Hunt, S. K. 75c. *Cin. Meth. Bk. Conc.*
Arthur Arundel. Smith, H. 50c. .... *Harper.*
Arthur Blane. *See* Grant, James.
Arthur Bonnicastle. Holland, J. G. $1.75.. *Scribner.*
Arthur Brown. Kellogg, E. $1.25.......... *Lee & S.*
Arthur Conway. Milman, E. H. 50c. ...... *Harper.*
Arthur Ellerslie. *See* Wise, D.
Arthur Granville. 18°. 40c.......... *Dutton.*
Arthur Lee. ('72.) New ed. 16°. '75. $1.25... *Hoyt.*
Arthur Locke; or, not afraid to do right. 18°. 17c.; 22c.......... *Am. Bapt.*
Arthur Maitland's holidays. *See* New holiday lib.
Arthur Martin. Burdett, C. 75c. .... *Harper.*
Arthur Merton. Davis, C. E. K. $1.25.. *Garrigues.*
Arthur Mervyn. Brown, C. B. 2 v. ea., $1.. *Polock.*
Arthur Monteith. *See* Blackford, *Mrs.*, Scottish orphans.
Arthur Morland. 18°. 60c.......... (?) *Martien.*
Arthur O'Leary. *See* Lever, Charles.
Arthur Singleton; or, what lack I yet? by author of "Broken cisterns." 18°. 70c........ *Pres. Bd.*
Arthur Vandeleur. *See* Marsh, *Miss* C.
Arthur's aquarium. Parker, H. F. 75c... *Cong. Pub.*
Arthur's birthday party. 18°. 35c. ...... *Cong. Pub.*
Arthur's Seat. Hamilton, J. $1.50...... *Macmillan.*
Arthur's temptation. *See* Wise, D.
Arthur's triumph. *See* Wise, D.
Arthur's victory. Ward, A. E. $1.......... *Nelson.*
Arthur's visit to grandpa's. *See* Aunt Alice's lib.
Article 47. *See* Belot, A.
Articles of confederation. *See* United States.
Artist's (The) love. Southworth, E. D. E. N. $1.75; $1.50 .... *Peterson.*
Artist's (The) son. ('65.) New ed. ill. 16°. '73; $1.15 .... *Hoyt.*
Artists and Arabs. Blackburn, H. $1.50.. * *Osgood.*
Artists' children. Keene, S. F. $1.15.... *Cong. Pub.*
Artists' married life. Schefer, L. $1.25; 75c... *Miller.*
Arts and beauties of American women. 16°. '60. pap., 15c.......... *Hunter.*
Arts of intoxication. Crane, J. T. $1.25.. *Meth. Bk. Conc.*
Arts of life, and lessons from them. 18°. 60c... *Am. S. S.*
Arville, *Abbé* Menghi d'. *See* Menghi-d'Arville.
Arvine, K. Cyclopedia of moral and religious anecdotes; with introd. by G. B. Cheever. 8°. $5. *World Pub.*
Arwed Gyllenstierna. *See* Van der Velde, K. F.
As the hart pants. *See* Mendelssohn-Bartholdy, F.
As it is. Smith, W. R. $1.25.......... *W. R. Smith.*
As it should be. Alex. $1.50.......... *Lippincott.*
As like as two peas. Lille, H. 15c. .... *French.*
As pretty as seven. Bechstein, L. $3.. *Little, B. & Co.*
As she would have it. Alex. $1.......... *Lippincott.*
As a strong bird on pinions free. Whitman, Walt. 75c. *Somerby.*
As you like it. *See* Shakespeare, W.
Asa and his family; by author of "Ellen and her cousins." 18°. 70c. .... *Pres. Bd.*

Asaph. Mason, L. *and* W. $1.50.......... *Ditson.*
Asbury, *Bp.* Fs. Heart and church divisions, causes, evils and cures; extracted from works of Burroughs and Baxter. 18°. '49. 50c. *Meth. Bk. Conc.*
— *Same;* ed. by T. O. Summer. ('55.) 2d ed. 18°. '75. 60c.......... *So. Meth.*
— Journals. 3 v. 12°. '51. $5..... *Meth. Bk. Conc.*
Asbury twins (The). Clarke, R. S. $1.75.. *Lee & S.*
Ascanio. *See* Dumas, A.
Ascent of Mount Ararat. Parrott, F. $1... *Harper.*
Ascher, G. Modern pianist. f°. $1........ *Gordon.*
Asgill, J: The covenant of eternal life as revealed in the Scriptures; with introd. essay, memoir, notes, etc., by T. D. Gregg. 12°. '76. $1.50... *Ennis.*
Ash-Wednesday in the nursery. 18°. 40c... *Dutton.*
Ashcliffe Hall. Holt, E. S. $1.25.......... *Carter.*
Ashe, Jona. The Masonic manual: lectures on Freemasonry. New ed., with annotations and remarks by G. Oliver. 12°. '43. $3.75.. *Williams.*
Asher and Adams (*pub.*) Commercial, topog. and statist. atlas and gazetteer of the U. S., with maps of Canada, Europe and the world. f°. '76. hf. mor., $30. 2 v. $32.......... *Asher.*
— New map and guide of Central Park, with directions to places of interest in New York and vicinity: map with letter-press. 24°. '76. hf. bds., 25c. *Asher.*
— New topog. atlas and gazetteer of N. Y. [state]. maps. f°. '76. hf. mor., $12.......... *Asher.*
— Railroad atlas and pictorial album of Am. industry: maps with letter press. ill. f°. '76. hf. mor., $40 .... *Asher.*
— Series of commercial and topog. railroad maps and guides. 21 nos. maps. 12°. 80c.-$1.25.. *Asher.*
Cont.: New England states. — New York. — Pennsylvania and New Jersey. — Virginia, West Virginia, Delaware and Maryland. — North Carolina and South Carolina. — Alabama and Georgia. — Florida. — Mississippi and Louisiana. — Kentucky and Tennessee. — Arkansas and Indian territory. — Texas. — Ohio and Indiana. — Michigan. — Illinois. — Wisconsin. — Missouri. — Iowa. — Minnesota. — Kansas. — Nebraska. — California, Nevada and Oregon.
— *See also* American text-book; — History and resources of the Am. republic.
Ashes to ashes. Haweis, H. R. $1.75.... *Routledge.*
Asheton, Fes. A modern Cressida: a story of the day; [also] On the church steps, by S. C. Hallowell. 8°. 40c. .... *Lippincott.*
Ashfield farm; or, Ellen and Robert's first journey from home. ill. fp. 8°. 60c.......... *Cassell.*
Ashgrove farm; or, a place for every one. 18°. 45c. *Routledge.*
Ashgrove farm library. 5 v. 18°. $2.25.. *Routledge.*
Cont.: Ashgrove farm. — Ben Howard. — Annals of the poor. — Story of a mouse. — Stories for week-days and Sundays.
Ashgrove library. 4 v. 18°. $2.25..... (?) *Martien.*
Cont.: Master Charlie. — The schoolboy hero. — Frank Fielding. — The hospital boy.
Ashhurst, J: *jr.* Injuries of the spine: their pathology and treatment. 12°. $1.50........ *Lippincott.*
— The principles and practice of surgery. ill. 8°. $6.50; leath., $7.50 .... *Lea.*
Ashhurst, S: *See* Medical jurisprudence.
Ashland, Aria. The rebel scout: romance of the revolution. 8°. pap., 25c.......... *U. P. James.*
Ashleigh farm. *See* Sunbeam ser.
Ashley, J. M. A promptuary for preachers: Ascension day to Advent. 8°. '76. $6.......... *Pott.*
Ashley Priors; or, the beauty of holiness. 12°. $1.50. *Pott.*
Ashmead, J: W. *See* Pennsylvania, Reports.
Ashton, F: T. Theory and practice of the art of designing fancy cotton and woolen cloths from sample. ill. f°. (cop. '72.) '74. $10.. *Baird.*

Ashton, *Mrs.* S. G. Ashton series. 4 v. 18°. $2.50. *Tilton.*
Cont.: Sabbath talks on Psalms of David. — Sabbath talks about Jesus. — Frankie's book of Bible men. — Susan and Frankie.
— Fifty pictures and stories for little ones. 16°. $1. *Crowell.*
— Girlhood of celebrated women. ill. 12°. '76. $1.50. *World Pub.*
Ashton, T. J. On the diseases, injuries and malformations of the rectum and anus; with remarks on habitual constipation. 2d ed., from 4th Lond. ed., enl. ill. 8°. $3.25..................*Lea.*
Ashton cottage. 18°. 60c. ....*Carter.*
Ashton series. *See* Ashton, *Mrs.* S. G.
Ashwell, S: Practical treatise on the diseases peculiar to women. 3d Am. ed., rev. 8°. $3.50....*Lea.*
Ashworth, J: Strange tales from humble life. 2 v. 18°. ea., 60c. ....*U. P. Bd. of Pub.*
Ashworth, T. M. ["Ouno."] *See* Diekenga, I. E., *and* Ashworth, T. M.
Ask no questions: burletta. 16°. pap., 15c...*Happy.*
Askaros Kassis, the Copt. De Leon, E. $1.75. *Lippincott.*
Asked of God. *See* Shipton, A.
Asleep. Smith, F. I. B. $1.............. *Whittaker.*
Asleep in Jesus. Clark, W. B. 40c.....(?)*Martien.*
Asmodeus. Archer, T. 15c...............*French.*
Asmodeus' crutches. *See* Lesage, A. R.
Aspasia. Holland, C. $1.25............*Lippincott.*
Aspects of humanity, brokenly mirrored in the ever-swelling current of human speech. 12°. 75c. *Lippincott.*
Aspendale. Preston, H. W. $1.25.........*Roberts.*
Aspenridge. Thompson, J. C. $1.35.....*Pres. Bd.*
Aspirations of nature. Hecker, I. T. $1.50..*Cath. Pub.*
Assassins of Hebrew history. Headley, P. C. 25c.; 30c............................*J. E. Potter.*
Asser, J. Life of King Alfred. *See* Giles, J. A., Six old English chronicles.
Asses' ears. Fawcett, E. $1.75...........*Carleton.*
Assessor (Der) im Wandschrank. *See* Vierundzwanzig Stunden.
Association for the Improvement of Geometrical Teaching. Syllabus of plane geometry; corresponding to Euclid, bks. 1–6. 2nd ed. 12°. '76. pap., 50c...........................*Macmillan.*
Association of American Geologists and Naturalists. Transactions, 1st–3d meetings (1840–'42). ill. 8°. '43. $3; hf. mor., $4.50..*Am. Assoc. Adv. Sci.*
Association of Municipal and Sanitary Engineers and Surveyors. Proceedings, v. 1., 1873–4; ed. by L. Angell. 8°. '75. $4.25................*Spon.*
Asta-Buruaga, Francisco Solano. Diccionario jeográfico de Chile. 12°. '67. $3........*Appleton.*
Astoria. *See* Irving, W.
Astræa. Holmes, O. W. 75c..............*Osgood.*
Astrologer. 32°. 50c. ....*Fisher.*
At the back of the north wind. MacDonald, G. $2. *Routledge.*
At Capri. Bauer, K. $1.50; $1.25; 75c.......*Porter.*
At the councillor's. John, E. $1.75......*Lippincott.*
At her mercy. Payn, J. 50c. ....*Harper.*
At his gates. Oliphant, M. O. W. $1.50; $1..*Scribner.*
At home and abroad. Fuller, M. $1.50.....*Roberts.*
— *See also* Grandmother's lib.
At Jesus' feet: a prayer, promise and poem, for every day in the year. 12°. '71. $1.50..*Whittaker.*
At last. Harland, M. $1.50...............*Carleton.*
At last. *See* Kingsley, C.
At the lion's mouth. Chellis, M. D. $1.25..*Nat. Temp.*
At nightfall and midnight. Jacox, F. $3..*Randolph.*
At odds. Tautphœus, *Baroness* I. v. $1.75..*Lippincott.*
At our best. Ellis, S. $1.50...............*Lee & S.*
At school with an old dragoon. MacKenna, S. J. $2. *Routledge.*
At the sign of the Silver Flagon. Farjeon, B. L. 40c. *Harper.*
At the south pole. Kingston, W. H. G. $2..*Cassell.*
Atala. *See* Chateaubriand, F. A.
Atala. Waldron, W. W. 75c............*Whittaker.*
Atalanta. Talfourd, F. 15c...............*French.*
Atalanta in Calydon. Swinburne, A. C. $2..*Osgood.*
Atar Gull; or, the bridal eve. 8°. pap., 25c...*Dick & F.*
Atchi. Morton, J. M. 15c.........*De Witt; French.*
Athalie. Dorsey, S. A. 60c. ....*Claxton.*
Athalie. *See* Racine; — Mendelssohn-Bartholdy, F.
Athelings (The). Oliphant, M. O. W. 75c. *Harper.*
Athenæ Cantabrigienses. Cooper, C. H. *and* T. 2 v. ea., $6.............................*Macmillan.*
Athenæum (The). Burnap, W. C., *and* Wetmore, W. J. $1.25; $1..............*Schermerhorn.*
Athenæus. The Deipnosophists; or, the banquet of the learned; tr. by C. D. Yonge. 3 v. 12°. (Bohn.) ea., $1.75............*Little, B. & Co.*
— *Same.* 3 v. 12°. (Bohn.) ea., $2. *Lippincott; Scribner, W. & A.*
Athenagoras. Ed. by F. A. March; with notes by W. B. Owen. 12°. '76. $1.75...........*Harper.*
— *See also* Justin Martyr.
Athens: its grandeur and decay. ill. sq. 12°. '49. 75c. ....*Meth. Bk. Conc.*
Atherstone Priory. Comyn, L. N. $1.25; 75c...*Estes.*
Athletic sports and manly exercises; by J. H. Walsh, J. G. Wood and others. ill. 18°. $1..*Routledge.*
Athletic sports for boys. ill. 16°. $1; bds., 75c. *Dick & F.*
Atkins, E: Pure mathematics. (Adv. sci. ser.) 2 v. 12°. '74. ea., $1.50................*Putnam.*
Atkins, *Miss* M. A. Earl Whiting. 16°. $1.25. *Cong. Pub.*
— Earnest Brownley's trials and temptations. 18°. 75c. ....*Cong. Pub.*
— Ellis Amory. 18°. 75c. ....*Cong. Pub.*
— Motherless Maud. 16°. $1............*Cong. Pub.*
— Must; or, Ann Holbrook's girlhood. 16°. $1.25. *Cong. Pub.*
Atkinson, *Miss* —. Little Willie. ill. 32°. '64. 25c. *Am. Tr.*
Atkinson, E. *See* Ganot, A., Elementary treatise on physics.
Atkinson, H: G: *and* Martineau, H. Man's nature and development. 12°. $1.50.......*Mendum.*
Atkinson, J. Beavington. Art tour to northern capitals of Europe. cr. 8°. '73. $3....*Macmillan.*
Atkinson, J. J. Friction of air in mines. 18°. '74. bds., 50c.....................*Van Nostrand.*
— Practical treatise on the gases met with in coal-mines. 18°. '74. bds., 50c. .... *Van Nostrand.*
Atkinson, *Rev.* J: Class leader (The): his work and how to do it. 12°. '74. $1.50...*Meth. Bk. Conc.*
— Garden of sorrows; or, the ministry of tears. New ed., rev. 12°. '68. $1.50; $2. *Meth. Bk. Conc.*
— Living way: suggestions conc. the duties of the Christian life. 16°. 55c.....*Cin. Meth. Bk. Conc.*
— Memorial of Methodism in N. J. 2d ed. por. 12°. '60. $1.75.........................*Perkinpine.*
Atkinson, *Rev.* J: C. British birds' eggs and nests. ill. 16°. $1.25; bds., 50c............*Routledge.*
— Play hours and half holidays; or, further experiences of two school-boys. ill. 16°. $1.25. *Routledge.*
— Walks, talks, travels and exploits of two school-boys. ill. 16°. $1.25 ....*Routledge.*

Atkinson, Jos. M. The true path; or, the young man invited to the Saviour. [Lectures.] 12°. $1. *Pres. Bd.*

Atkinson, Ma: E. Architect of Cologne, and other poems. 12°. '73. $1 .... *Lothrop.*
— Hester's happy summer. 16°. '70. $1.25 .. *Lothrop.*
— Ivy leaves: religious poems. 12°. '72. $1. *Lippincott; Lothrop.*
— Rose and Millie. 16°. '72. $1.25 .... *Lothrop.*

Atkinson, T: Witlam. Oriental and western Siberia: seven years' explorations in Siberia, Mongolia, etc. ill. 12°. $1.75 .... *J. E. Potter.*
— *Same.* maps and ill. 8°. $3.50 .... *Harper.*
— Travels in the regions of the Amour, and the Russian acquisitions on the confines of India and China. map and ill. 8°. $3.50 .... *Harper.*

Atkinson, W: B. Hints in the obstetric procedure. 12°. '75. $1 .... *Collins Print.*
— Medical register and direct. of Philadelphia. 12°. '75. $2 .... *Collins Print.*

Atlantic almanac. 7 v. ill. 8°. '68–'74. ea., 50c. *Osgood.*

Atlantic glee book. Baker, B. F., *and* Southard, L. H. $1.35 .... *Gordon.*

Atlantic library. 6 v. ill. 16°. $6 .... *Appleton.*
Cont.: George Ready, by R. O'Lincoln. — Peter the Great. — Lances of Linwood, by C. M. Yonge. — Douglas farm, by M. E. Bradley. — Stories of an old maid, by E. de Girardin. — Sedgemoor, by Mrs. E. Manners.

Atlantic tales: stories from the "Atlantic monthly." sm. 4°. $3 .... **Osgood.*

Atlantic (The) to the Pacific. Lester, J. E. $1.50. (?) *Shepard.*

Atlas of political and classical geog.: maps, with letterpress and index. 8°. $2.50 .... *Putnam.*

Atlas of Scripture geog.: maps with questions. sm. 4°. '73. 75c. .... *Putnam.*

Atlee, Washington L. General and differential diagnosis of ovarian tumors, with special ref. to the operation of ovariotomy. ill. 8°. $5 .. *Lippincott.*

Atonement. Muskberry, W. 15c. .... *French.*

Atonement (The). *See* Park, E. A.

Atonement of Leam Dundas. Linton, E. L. $1.50; $1 .... *Lippincott.*

Atrocious criminal. Simpson, J. P. 15c. .... *French.*

Attaché (The). Haliburton, T. C. $1.25; 75c. *Dick & F.*

Atthill, Lombe. Clinical lectures on diseases peculiar to women. 2d ed., rev. and enl. ill. 8°. '73. $2.25 .... *Lindsay.*

Attic philosopher in Paris. Souvestre, E. 75c. *Appleton.*

Attic story. Morton, J. M. 15c. .... *French.*

Attila. James, G. P. R. $1.50 .... *Harper.*

Attorney (The). Irving, J. T. $1.50 ...... *De Witt.*

Attraction of the cross. Spring, G. $1.10; $1.50. *Am. Tr.*

Attractions (The) of heaven. Graves, H. A. 25c.; 40c.; $1 .... *Lothrop.*

Attractions of New Haven [Conn.]: guide to the city. maps and ill. 18°. 50c.; pap., 25c. .... *Tibbals.*

Attwell, H. (*ed.*) Book of golden thoughts. 18°. '71. $1.25 .... *Macmillan.*

Attwill, R: I. *See* Schofield, W. J., *and* Attwill, R. I.

Atwater, Clb. The Indians of the north-west; or, remarks made on a tour to Prairie du Chien, and thence to Washington City, in 1829. 12°. '31. 37½c. .... *I. N. Whiting.*

Atwater, *Rev.* E: E. History and significance of the sacred tabernacle of the Hebrews. ill. 8°. '75. $4 .... *Dodd.*

Atwater, J. J. Mother Goose in hieroglyphics. 12°. per doz., $5; pap., $2.50 .... *Thompson.*

Atwater, Lyman H. Manual of element. logic. 12°. $1.50 .... *Lippincott.*

Atwell, B. W. Principles of elocution and vocal culture. ('67.) 3d ed. 12°. '72. pap., 30c. *N. B. Williams.*

Atwood, A. The abiding comforter. 12°. '74. $1.25. *A. Wallace.*

Atwood, Dan. T. Country and suburban houses. [Architectural.] ill. 12°. $1.50 .... *Judd.*
— Modern American homesteads. [Architectural.] ill. 8°. '76. $3.50 .... *Bicknell.*

Au coin du feu. Souvestre, E. 75c. .. *G. R. Lockwood.*

Auber, D. F. E. Fra Diavolo; — Masaniello. *See* Ditson.

Auberlen, C: A: The divine revelation. 8°. $3. *Scribner, W. & A.*
— *See also* Foundations of our faith; — Lange, J. P., Commentary.

Aubigné, J. H. Merle d'. Council (The) and infallibility; tr. by N. Cyr, with introd. note. 18°. pap., 10c. .... *Bost. Am. Tr.*
— Discourses and essays; tr. by C. W. Baird. 12°. $1.50 .... *Harper.*
— History of the reformation in Europe in times of Luther and Calvin; tr. from the French. ('71.) 5th ed. roy. 8°. '73. *$5; shp., $6; hf. mor., $7.50 .... *Flint.*
— *Same.* 7 v. 12°. '76. $14 .... *Carter.*
— *Same;* [tr. and] ed. by M. L. Simons. maps and ill. roy. 8°. $5; shp., $6 .... *Porter.*
— History of the reformation in the 16th cent.; tr. ill. and por. 4°. $10 .... *Routledge; U. S. Pub.*
— *Same.* ill. and por. 4°. hf. mor., $12; $13.50; mor., $16 .... *Putnam.*
— *Same.* ill. and por. 4°. $10; hf. mor., $14; $16; cf., $15; mor., $18; $20 .... *Appleton.*
— *Same.* 5 v. 12°. '56. $6; — in 1 v. 8°. '75. $3. *Carter.*
— *Same.* ('44.) 2d ed. 5 v. 12°. '47. $5; hf. mor., $10. *Am. Tr.*
— *Germ.* Geschichte der Reformation. 5 v. 12°. '52–'57. $5 .... *Am. Tr.*
— *Ital.* Storia della riforma del secolo decimosesto. v. 1. 12°. '50. $1 .... *Am. Tr.*
— *Portug.* Historia da reforma. v. 1. 12°. '72. $1.25. *Am. Tr.*
— *Spanish.* Historia de la reformacion. 2 v. 12°. '49–'54. $2 .... *Am. Tr.*
— Oliver Cromwell; tr. from the French. 12°. $1.25. *Carter.*
— *Germ.* Oliver Cromwell. 18°. '70. 50c. ... *Am. Tr.*
— *See also* Labouchère, P. H., Illustrations of life of Luther.

Aubrey. Marsh-Caldwell, A. 75c. .... *Harper.*

Auchincloss, W. S. Application of the slide valve and link motion to stationary, locomotive, [etc.] engines, with new methods for proportioning the parts; with scale. ill. 8°. '75. $3 .. *Van Nostrand.*

Audin, J. M. V. ["Richard"], *and* Kaub, —. English and Germ. dialogues. New ed., rev. and enl.; with table of the new monies and measures. 18°. 75c. .... *Lippincott.*
— *and* Quétin, —. New familiar and progressive Eng. and Fr. dialogues; [with] table of monies and measures. New ed., rev. 18°. 75c. .. *Lippincott.*

Audsley, W. *and* G. Color in dress: a manual for ladies. 12°. '69. *50c. .... *Maclean.*

Audubon, *Miss* Hattie. The favorite fairy tales; in words of one syllable. ill. 12°. $1.50 .. *World Pub.*

Audubon, J: Ja. Birds of America; ill. by 500 col. pl. 8 v. imp. 8°. '70. hf. mor., $165; mor., $185. *G. R. Lockwood.*
— *Same.* 5 v., text, 4 v., imp. 8°.; pl., 1 v., f°. $250. *G. R. Lockwood.*
— Life and journals; compr. narratives of his expeditions in the Am. forests, etc. 12°. '67. $2.25; hf. cf., $4 .... *Putnam.*

Audubon, J: Ja., *continued.*
— *and* Bachman, J. Quadrupeds of No. Am.; ill. by 155 col. pl. 3 v. imp. 8°. '70. hf. mor., $60; mor., $65 . . . . . *G. R. Lockwood.*
— — *Same.* 5 v., text, 3 v., imp. 8°.; pl., 2 v., f°. $300. *G. R. Lockwood.*
Auer, Adelheid v. It is the fashion; tr. by Mrs. B. Elgard. 12°. $1.50 . . . . . *Lippincott.*
Auerbach, Brth. Black Forest village stories; tr. by C. Göpp. (Leis. hour ser.) ill. 16°. '75. $1.25. *Holt.*
— Dorfgeschichten. 3 v. ill. 12°. $3.50; pap., $2.50; hf. mor., $4 . . . . . *F. W. Thomas.*
— Edelweiss; tr. by E. Frothingham. (Leis. hour ser.) 16°. '69. $1.25 . . . . . *Holt.*
— German tales; tr. with introd. by C. C. Shackford. (Leis. hour ser.) 16°. '69. $1.25 . . . . . *Holt.*
— Good hour (The); or, evening holiday; tr. by H. W. Dulcken. ill. sm. 8°. '75. $3 . . . *Routledge.*
— Joseph in the snow. (Leis. hour ser.) ill. 16°. '76. $1.25 . . . . . *Holt.*
— Little barefoot (The): a tale of village life; tr. by E. B. Lee. (Leis. hour ser.) ill. 16°. '76. $1.25 . . . . . *Holt.*
— *Same;* tr. by H. W. Dulcken. ill. 4°. '72. $4. *Routledge.*
— On the heights; tr. by S. A. Stern. Library ed. ('67.) New ed. 12°. '75. $2. (Leis. hour ser.) 2 v. 16°. ea., $1.25 . . . . . *Holt.*
— Villa on the Rhine; tr. by J. Davis, with biog. sketch by B. Taylor. ('69.) New ed. (Leis. hour ser.) 2 v. 16°. '75. ea., $1.25. (Pocket ed.) 4 pts. pap., $1.25 . . . . . *Holt.*
— Waldfried; tr. by S. A. Stern. ('74.) New ed. 12°. '76. $2 . . . . . *Holt.*
Auersperg, Ant. Alex. (*Graf*) v. ["Anastatius Grün."] The last knight: a romance garland; tr. by J. O. Sargent. cr. 8°. '71. $2.50 . . . . . *Hurd & H.*
Auf dem Geierfels. Lexow, F. 75c.; 50c. . . . *Steiger.*
Auf der Universität. *See* Storm, T.
Aufgeregten (Die). *See* Goethe, J. W. v.
Aufrecht, L. The American Hebrew primer. 16°. bds., 15c . . . . . *Bloch.*
Aughey, J. H. Iron furnace; or, slavery and secession. 12°. $1.25 . . . . . (?) *Martien.*
Augier, Émile. Good for evil: drama. 16°. pap., 15c. *French.*
Augsburg confession (unaltered); [ed.] by C. H. Schott. 18°. pap., 15c . . . . . *Ludwig.*
— *German.* Augsburgische Confession (Die). 12°. bds., 20c . . . . . *Brumder.*
— *Swedish.* Oförändrade Augsburgiska bekännelsen (Den) jemte de tre äldsta symbola. 12°. 15c. *Engberg.*
— *See also* Krauth, C. P.; — Luther, M., Catechisms.
August and Elvie. Abbott, J. $1.50 . . . . . *Dodd.*
Augusta; [also] Christmas eve. 18°. 50c. . . . *O'Shea.*
Augustine, *St.* Works; ed., by Rev. M. Dods. 14 v. 8°. ea., $3 . . . . . *Scribner, W. & A.*
Cont.: City of God, 2 v. — Writings in connection with the Donatist controversy. — Anti-Pelagian works, 2 v. — On the Manichæan heresy. — Letters, 2 v. — On the trinity. — Harmony of the evangelists and Sermon on the mount. — Christian doctrine, The enchiridion, etc. — Lectures on St. John, 2 v. — Treatises in the Pelagian controversy.
— Confessions. 18°. '76. 50c . . . . . *Pott.*
— *Same.* 18°. 75c.; $1 . . . . . *Sadlier.*
— *Same;* ed. with introd. by W. G. T. Shedd. ('60.) New ed. 12°. '71. $1.50 . . . . . *Draper.*
— Life. 12°. $1.50 . . . . . *Sadlier.*
Augustine; or, the mysterious beggar; tr. by A. T. Sadlier. 18°. 50c.; 75c . . . . . *Sadlier.*
Augustinus, *St.* *See* Augustine, *St.*
Auld Scotch mither. Rankin, J. E. $1.25 . . *Lothrop.*
Aulnoy, Marie J. de B. (*Comtesse*) d'. Fairy tales; tr. by J. R. Planché. ill. post 8°. $2; $2.25; hf. cf., $3.50 . . . . . *Routledge.*

Aunt Agnes. ill. sq. 16°. 75c . . . . . *Nelson.*
Aunt Ailie. Bell, C. D. $1.75 . . . . *Scribner, W. & A.*
Aunt Alice (*pseud.*) First lessons in gentleness and truth. sq. 16°. 60c . . . . . *Bost. Am. Tr.*
Aunt Alice's lib. 10 v. 24°. '61. $2.50 . . . *Meth. Bk. Conc.*
Cont.: Lion and the lamb. — Miss Alice's story. — Little Frisky. — Getting rich. — My little sister. — Stick to it. — Hard things are good for folks. — Arthur's visit to grandpa's. — What made little Mollie so happy. — The little prayer.
Aunt Amy. *See* Wise, D.
Aunt Bertha's series. 4 v. 16°. $5 . . . . . *Graves.*
Cont.: Lillian's prayer. — Aunt Bertha's visit to the Elms. — Archibald Hughson. — Story of a lost child.
Aunt Bertha's visit to the Elms. 16°. $1.25 . . *Graves.*
Aunt Bessie's picture-book. ill. sq. 12°. '72. $1. *Routledge.*
Aunt Bessie's series of picture-books. 9 v. ill. sq. 12°. ea., $1 . . . . . *Routledge.*
Cont.: Aunt Bessie's picture-book. — Little Lily's picture-book. — Aunt Mary's Sunday picture-book. — Sunday reading for good children. — My first picture-book. — Cock Robin's picture-book. — Mother Hubbard's picture-book. — Pussy's picture-book. — Little Birdie's picture-book.
Aunt Betsy's rule. O'Brien, H. 75c . . . . . *Pres. Bd.*
Aunt Carrie (*pseud.*) *See* Smith, *Mrs.* Caroline L.
Aunt Carrie's budget. Myers, S. A. 60c . . . *Pres. Bd.*
Aunt Cecil (*pseud.*) Summer holidays at Hillside. 18°. '69. 40c . . . . . *Randolph.*
Aunt Cecil's Christmas story. 18°. 50c . . . *Whittaker.*
Aunt Celia's library. 12 v. 24°. $3 . . . . *Cong. Pub.*
Aunt Charity. 18°. 85c.; 90c . . . . . *Dutton.*
Aunt Charity's legacy; [also] Working for Jesus. 18°. 30c . . . . . *N. Y. Ref. Ch. Bd.*
Aunt Charlotte's maid. *See* Morton, J. M.
Aunt Clara; or, selfishness vs. Christianity. 16°. 30c. *West. Tr.*
Aunt Deborah's library. 6 v. ill. 18°. '71. $3.25. *Meth. Bk. Conc.*
Cont.: Stories from Aunt Deborah's drawer. — Lonely Lily. — Clarie's little charge. — Nellie Rodney's sorrows. — Frankie and his friends. — Little missionary.
Aunt Dinah's pledge. Chellis, M. D. $1.25. *Nat. Temp.*
Aunt Dinah's pledge: drama. 16°. pap., 15c . . . *French.*
Aunt Edith; or, love to God. 18°. 75c . . . . . *Carter.*
Aunt Effie's rhymes for children. 18°. 45c. *Routledge.*
Aunt Elinor's charge. *See* Boyd, E. E.
Aunt Elizabeth (*pseud.*) The old chest. ill. 18°. '56. 85c . . . . . *Dodd.*
Aunt Elizabeth. *See* Swallow stories.
Aunt Elsie's posts. Chaplin, J. D. 60c . . . *Bost. Am. Tr.*
Aunt Emma; by author of "Rose and Kate." 16°. 50c. *Routledge.*
Aunt Fanny (*pseud.*) *See* Barrow, *Mrs.* Fanny.
Aunt Fanny's home. Schenck, W. E. 70c . . . *Pres. Bd.*
Aunt Fanny's present: book of fairy tales. 18°. '72. 50c . . . . . *Cunningham.*
Aunt Friendly (*pseud.*) *See* Baker, Sarah.
Aunt Friendly's bound toy books. 4 nos. ill. imp. 16°. ea., $1 . . . . . *Scribner, W. & A.*
Aunt Friendly's everlasting toy books. 2 nos. ill. imp. 16°. ea., $1.50 . . . . . *Scribner, W. & A.*
Aunt Friendly's gift. ill. sm. 4°. $1.75. *Scribner, W. & A.*
Aunt Friendly's holiday album. ill. sm. 4°. $1.75. *Scribner, W. & A.*
Aunt Friendly's nursery keepsake. ill. sm. 4°. $1.75. *Scribner, W. & A.*
Aunt Friendly's nursery library. 4 v. col. ill. 16°. ea., $1 . . . . . *Lippincott.*
Cont.: Story book. — Gift book. — Nursery favorite. — Nursery picture book.
Aunt Friendly's series. [Toy books.] 6 nos. ill. sm. 4°. per gross, $30 . . . . . (?) *McLoughlin.*
Cont.: Cinderella. — Cock Robin. — House that Jack built. — Red Riding Hood. — Mother Hubbard. — Apple pie A B C.

Aunt Friendly's toy books. 12 nos. ill. 16°. $1.50; $3 .... *Scribner, W. & A.*

Aunt Gracie's lib. 10 v. 24°. '60. $2.50. *Meth. Bk. Conc.*
Cont.: Clara and her cousins. — Little boarding-school girls. — Our birthday trip. — Little Anna. — Mary, Anna and Nina. — Jennette; or, the great mistake. — Old Merritt. — Happy Christmas. — City of palms. — Stories about the Bible.

Aunt Harding's keepsake; or, the two Bibles. 18°. 30c. .... *Am. S. S.*

Aunt Harriet's tales about little words. McKeever, H. B. 75c. .... *Pres. Bd.*

Aunt Hattie (*pseud.*) *See* Babb, *Miss* Hattie.

Aunt Hattie (*pseud.*) *See* Baker, *Mrs.* H. N. W.

Aunt Hattie's lib. for boys and girls. *See* Baker, *Mrs.* H. N. W.

Aunt Hattie's stories. 10 v. 24°. $2.50. *Meth. Bk. Conc.*
Cont.: Henry Maynard's account book; or, what I owe papa and mamma. — Henry Maynard's "book of thanks"; or, what I owe God. — Henry Maynard trying to get out of debt. — The little captain; or, ruling one's own spirit. — Hattie Hale's likeness and what it taught her. — Cousin Robert's story. — Katie and the cup of cold water. — Work and no work. — Constance and Carle; or, faithful in that which is least. — Our looking-glasses.

Aunt Honor's keepsake. Sadlier, M. A. $1; $1.50. *Sadlier.*

Aunt Jane's hero. Prentiss, E. $1.50 ..... *Randolph.*

Aunt Jenny's American pets. *See* Hopley, C. C.

Aunt Jo's scrap-bag. *See* Alcott, L. M.

Aunt Judy's tales. Gatty, M. 75c. .... *Carter.*

Aunt Katie's talks at bed-time. Little, H. M. 40c. *Bost. Am. Tr.*

Aunt Kitty (*pseud.*) *See* McIntosh, *Miss* M. J.

Aunt Lizzie's stories. Bullard, A. 25c. ..... *Lee & S.*

Aunt Lois. Davis, C. E. K. $1.50 .... *Hoyt.*

Aunt Lottie (*pseud.*) Laughing Kittie and Purring Kittie, with other little folks at Robinwood. ill. 18°. 60c. .... *Bost. Am. Tr.*

— — *See also* Laughing Kittie stories.

Aunt Louisa (*pseud.*) *See* Valentine, *Mrs.* R.

Aunt Louisa (*pseud.*) Big picture books. 12 nos. ill. demy 4°. per gross, $60 .... (?) *McLoughlin.*
Cont.: Alphabet of country scenes. — Santa Claus, and his works. — Jack and the bean stalk. — Children in the wood. — World-wide fables. — Rip Van Winkle. — Puss-in-boots. — Robinson Crusoe. — Yankee Doodle. — My mother. — Cinderella. — Baby.

Aunt Lulu's series: nursery books, with primer. 6 nos. ill. 8°. per gross, $18 .... (?) *McLoughlin.*
Cont.: Pauline and the matches, etc. — Hop O' My Thumb, etc. — Robber kitten, etc. — Tom the thief, etc. — Little Bo-peep, etc. — Heedless Johnny, etc.

Aunt Maddy's diamonds. Myrtle, H. 45c... *Routledge.*

Aunt Madge's story. Clarke, R. S. 75c. ..... *Lee & S.*

Aunt Margaret. Abbott, J. 90c. .... *Harper.*

Aunt Margaret's story lib. 5 v. 18°. $2.25 .. *Routledge.*
Cont.: Aunt Margaret's visit. — Story of a penny. — Helen's fault. — The little Oxleys. — Visit to my birthplace.

Aunt Margaret's trouble. Trollope, F. E. 25c. *Peterson.*

Aunt Margaret's twelve stories. 18°. 50c... *Am. S. S.*

Aunt Margaret's visit. Sterne, G. M. 45c... *Routledge.*

Aunt Margery's maxims. *See* Poplar Dell lib.

Aunt Martha's cupboard. Kirby, M. *and* E. $1.25. *Nelson.*

Aunt Mary's illustrated reading-book. 12°. '73. 50c. *Routledge.*

Aunt Mary's stories. 6 v. sq. 18°. $2.50... *Sheldon.*
Cont.: The rose. — The tulip. — The lily. — The daisy. — The violet. — The jessamine.

Aunt Mary's story book. Salzmann, C. S. $1.25 .. *Miller.*

Aunt Mary's Sunday picture-book. ill. sq. 12°. '73. $1. *Routledge.*

Aunt Mattie's library. 4 v. 18°. '70. $3... *Graves.*
Cont.: Merry Christmas. — Fun and profit. — Sabbath schools. — Drifting goodward.

Aunt Matty. Rand, C. H. $1.50 .... *Lothrop.*

Aunt Mavor's picture-books for little readers. 97 v. ill. 8°. ea., 40c.; pap., 20 .... *Routledge.*

Aunt Mildred's legacy; by author of "Battles worth fighting." 16°. $1.25 .... *Carter.*

Aunt Patty's scrap bag. Hentz. C. L. $1.50; 75c. *Peterson.*

Aunt Peggy: memoir of Mrs. Ewing. 16°. 50c. (?) *Cumberland.*

Aunt Priscilla's story. *See* Leighton children.

Aunt Rebecca's charge. Whittlesey, *Mrs.* —. $1.25. *Hoyt.*

Aunt Ruth. Finley, M. F. 70c. .... *Pres. Bd.*

Aunt Ruth's Christmas present. 18°. 30c... *Am. S. S.*

Aunt Saidee's cow. Prichard, S. J. $1.25... *Carter.*

Aunt Sally; or, the cross the way to freedom. 16°. 50c. .... *West Tr.*

Aunt Sarah's sketches. 18°. 35c. .... *Cong. Pub.*

Aunt Sarah's stories. Woodruff, M. 30c... *Pres. Bd.*

Aunt Sue's lib. of picture books. 5 v. 18°. $2. *Am. S. S.*
Cont.: Book of one hundred pictures. — Second book. — Third book. — Fourth book. — Fifth book.

Aunt Susan (*pseud.*) *See* Prentiss, *Mrs.* Elizabeth.

Aunt Susie's library. 10 v. 32°. $2.25... *Cong. Pub.*

Aunt Winefred's legacy, and how it was doubly blessed. 18°. 55c. .... *Am. S. S.*

Aunt Winnie's stories. Brown, H. E. 35c. *Bost. Am. Tr.*

Aunt Zelpeth's baby; by author of "Adventures of a German toy." ill. 18°. $1 .... *Lee & S.*

Auntie's Christmas trees. 18°. 90c. .... *Dutton.*

Auntie's secret. Means, J. H. 90c. ..... *Cong. Pub.*

Aunty Chloe: Ethiop. drama. 16°. pap., 15c. *Happy.*

Aunty Lee lib. 6 v. ill. 18°. '72. $3. *Meth. Bk. Conc.*
Cont.: Traps to catch foxes. — Charity's birthday text. — Herbert's first year at Bramford. — Helen and her sisters. — On a candlestick. — Little Bessie and how she kept the wolf from the door.

Aunty May's children. 4 v. 18°. '64. $2.75. *Meth. Bk. Conc.*
Cont.: Ernest; or, no humbug. — Rachel; or, the city without walls. — Christie; or, where the tree fell. — Faith, the cripple.

Aunty Ray's little library. 10 v. 24°. '61. $2.50. *Meth. Bk. Conc.*
Cont.: Archie's Fourth of July. — Lottie and Jennie. — The fish-hooks. — Grace and her money-box. — Old Granny Tift. — Eva and the fairy tale. — Lucy and Belle. — Bessie and her lamb. — Winnie and his pets. — Frank and Joey.

Aurelian. Ware, W. $2 .... *Miller.*

Aurelius Gretianus (*Priest of the church of Arles*). Exiles of the Cebenna. 18°. 55c.; 60c... *Dutton.*

Aureola. Mackenzie, A. S. $1.50 .... *Claxton.*

Auriol. *See* Ainsworth, W. H.

Aurora Floyd. *See* Braddon, *Miss* M. E.

Aurora Floyd. Hazlewood, C. H. 15c. .... *French.*

Aurora Leigh. *See* Browning, E. B.

Aus dem Bagno. *See* Wartenburg, K.

Aus eiserner Zeit. *See* Hoffmann, F.

Aus der Gegenwart. *See* Gumpert, T. v.

Aus dem Leben eines Taugenichts. *See* Eichendorff, J. v.

Aus Liebe. Goldstein, M. 25c. .... *Steiger.*

Aus meinem Leben. *See* Goethe, J. W. v.

Aus Nacht zum Licht. *See* Baron, R.

Aus Wiskonsin. Krez, K. $1 .... *Steiger.*

Ausbund, d. i.: etliche schöne christliche Lieder, von den Schweizer Brüdern u. andern gedichtet. 8th Am. ed. 18°. leath., $2 .... *Baer.*

Ausgestossenen (Die). *See* Hartmann, M.

Auspicious day (The). Webster, A. $1.50. *Macmillan.*

Austen, Jane. Novels. New ed. 6 v. cr. 8°. (Lond.) '70–'72. $15; hf. cf., $25; cf., $35. *Little, B. & Co.*
Cont.: Emma; Sense and sensibility; Pride and prejudice; Mansfield Park; Northanger Abbey; Persuasion; Memoir; Lady Susan.

Austen, Jane, *continued.*
— Novels and tales. 5 v. 16°. '69. $4...*Routledge.*
Cont.: Pride and prejudice. — Sense and sensibility. — Mansfield Park. — Emma. — Northanger Abbey; [also] Persuasion.
— Emma. 12°. $1.25 ... *Porter.*
— Mansfield Park. 12°. $1.25 ... *Porter.*
— Pride and prejudice; [also] Northanger Abbey. 12°. $1.25 ... *Porter.*
— Sense and sensibility; [also] Persuasion. 12°. $1.25. *Porter.*
Austen, S. G. Divinity of our blessed Lord. 16°. '75. 50c. ... *Pott.*
Austerlitz. Haines, J. T. 15c ... *French.*
Austin, Arth. W. The woman and the queen, and other specimens of verse. 16°. '75. 75c.... *Williams.*
Austin, Cyril. Emmore; [also] Lotty's Christmas eve; [also] Men of Wycombe. 18°. '75. 50c.; 75c ... *Kelly, P. & Co.*
Austin, G: Lowell. Life of Franz Schubert. 16°. $1.25 ... (?) *Shepard.*
— Popular hist. of Massachusetts. por. 8°. *$3.50; shp., $4.50; hf. cf., $6.50 ... *Estes.*
Austin, *Mrs.* G: Lowell (*ed.*) Little people of God, and what the poets have said of them; [incl.] The child and the poets, by J. G. Whittier. sq. 12°. $2.50 ... (?) *Shepard.*
Austin, *Rev.* J. J. The golden age to come: dramatic poem. 12°. 75c. ... *Williamson*
Austin, Ja. G. Practical treatise on the preparation, [etc.], of calcareous and hydraulic limes and cements; with recipes for various purposes. 12°. $2 ... *Wiley.*
Austin, *Mrs.* Jane G. Cipher. [Fiction.] ill. 8°. $1.50; pap., $1 ... *Sheldon.*
— Fairy dreams. sq. 16°. $1.50 ... *Tilton.*
— Moonfolk: a true account of the home of the fairy tales. ill. 8°. '74. $2 ... *Putnam.*
— Shadow of Moloch Mountain. ill. 8°. $1.50; $1. *Sheldon.*
Austin, J: Devotions in the ancient way of offices; with pref. by Rev. R. F. Littledale. 8°. 75c. *Pott.*
Austin, J: Lectures on jurisprudence: the philosophy of positive law; abridg. by R. Campbell. 8°. '75. $3 ... *Holt.*
— *Same.* cr. 8°. (Lond.) '75. $5 ... *Little, B. & Co.*
— *Same.* 2 v. 8°. $7; shp., $9 ... *Cockcroft.*
Austin, Stella. Somebody. ill. 16°. '74. $1.. *Dutton.*
— Stumps. 18°. '55 ... *Am. S. S.*
— *Same.* ill. 16°. '64. $1 ... *Dutton.*
Austin Elliot. *See* Kingsley, Henry.
Australia and its settlements. ('56.) 3d ed. 18°. '75. 60c. ... *So. Meth.*
Australian Crusoes. *See* Rowcroft, Chas.
Australian views of Eng. Parkes, H. $1.25. *Macmillan.*
Australian wanderers. Lee, R. $1.50 ... *Lee & S.*
Auswanderer (Die). *See* Hoffmann, F.
Auswanderer (Die) nach Afrika. Nieritz, G. 25c. *Morwitz.*
Authority and free will. Scott, T. P. 25c. *Kelly, P. & Co.*
Author's (The) daughter. Howitt, M. 25c... *Harper.*
Autobiography of a London detective. Russell, W. H. C. 75c. ... *Dick & F.*
Autobiography of a lump of coal. *See* Carey, A.
Autobiography of a pioneer. Young, J. $1.75. *Meth. Bk. Conc.*
Autocrat of the breakfast table. *See* Holmes, O. W.
Autograph leaves of our country's authors. [Facsimiles.] 4°. '64. $6 ... *Cushings & B.*
Automaton-ear (The). McLandburgh, F. $1.50. *Jansen.*
Autumn at Karnford. Bell, C. D. 75c. *Scribner, W. & A.*
Autumn days and their teachings: sequel to "Country sights and sounds." 18°. 45c ... *Pres. Bd.*
Autumn dreams. Chiquita. $1.50 ... *Appleton.*
Autumn holidays. Boyd, A. K. H. $1.25..* *Osgood.*
Autumn leaf stories. J., E. M. 60c.... *J. A. Moore.*
Autumn leaves. *See* Morning glory lib.
Avalanche. Harris, A. 15c ... *French.*
Avard, Emma A. Letter to Santa Claus and how it was answered. ('74.) 2d ed. sq. 12°. '75. 50c.; 75c. ... *D. H. Carroll.*
Avare (L'). *See* Molière, J. B. P.
Ave Maria (The): book of [Cath.] prayers for servants and children of Mary. 32°. 50c.-$2.75; — with Epistles and Gospels. 24°. 70c.-$6... *T. Kelly.*
Aveling, T: Epitome of the new road-locomotive acts, for the use of owners and drivers. 18°. 20c... *Spon.*
Avenger. Lee, H. 15c ... *French.*
Avenger (The). *See* De Quincey, T.
Avenger (The) stayed. *See* Ragged scholars.
Avenging of the elect. Buck, D. D. 40c... *So. Bapt.*
Avery, A. S. How to draw: the right and the wrong way. ill. 4°. '71. pap., $1; — pt. 1., pap., 50c.; pt. 2., pap., 60c ... *Univ. Pub.*
Avery, Jane G. Boys and girls of Beech Hill. ill. 16°. '71. $1.25 ... *Crowell.*
— — *See also* Posie series.
— Bound Brook; or, Amy Rushton's mission. 16°. $1.50. *Cong. Pub.*
— Old distillery; or, Hope Archie. ('65.) New ed. ill. 16°. '76. $1.50 ... *Hoyt.*
— Tried and true; or, into the light. ('66.) New ed. ill. 16°. '73. $1.15 ... *Hoyt.*
Avery, M. A. The rebel general's loyal bride: a picture of scenes in the late civil war. ill. 12°. '73. *(?) ... (?) *Holland.*
— Shadowed perils. [Fiction.] 12°. '76. $1.25. *Authors.*
Avesta. Zend avesta: the religious book of the Parsees; tr. from the Germ. of Spiegel by A. H. Bleeck. 3 v. in 1. 8°. $10.50.. *Scribner, W. & A.*
Avillion. *See* Craik, D. M.
Avocat (L') Patelin. *See* Bruey, D. A. de.
Avonmore, *Lady*. *See* Yelverton, *Mrs.* T.
Avrillon, J: Baptiste. Guide for passing Advent holily; tr. and adapted to the Eng. church, ed. by E. B. Pusey. 16°. '72. $2 ... *Pott.*
— Guide for passing Lent holily; tr. and adapted to the Eng. church, ed. by E. B. Pusey. 16°. '72. $2. *Pott.*
Awake, thou sleeper. Clark, J. A. $1.25.... *Carter.*
Awakened sinner directed. Kimball, D. 45c. *Cong. Pub.*
Awaking: drama. 16°. pap., 15c ... *French.*
Away in the wilderness. Ballantyne, R. M. 75c. *Porter.*
Away in the wilderness. *See* Library of travel and adventure.
Away with melancholy. Morton, J. M. 15c... *French.*
Awdry, Frances. Story of a fellow soldier. [Account of Bp. Patteson's labors in Melanesia.] ill. fp. 8°. '75. $1.50 ... *Macmillan.*
Awful mystery (An). Fleming, M. A. 25c... *Beadle.*
Awkward arrival. Coyne, J. S. 15c. ... *French.*
Axon, W: E. The mechanic's friend: receipts and suggestions, rel. to aquaria, bronzing, cements, drawing, etc. ill. 12°. $1.50.... *Van Nostrand.*
Aydelott, B. P. Church's (The) duties in the temperance cause. 16°. 25c. ... *West. Tr.*
— Civil Sabbath (The). *See* Sabbath (The).
— Condition and prospects of the Prot. Episc. Church. 18°. '48. 50c. ... *Wilstach.*
— Drunkard (The) saved. 16°. pap., 25c... *West. Tr.*

Aydelott, B. P., *continued.*
— First sin: exposition of the questions connected with the fall of man. 16°. 60c. .... *West. Tr.*
— Great question (The): refutation of the skeptical philosophy. 12°. 75c. .... *West. Tr.*
— Thoughts for the thoughtful. 16°. 30c... *West. Tr.*
Ayesha. Leslie, E. $1.50 .... *Meth. Bk. Conc.*
Ayre, J: Treasury of Bible Knowledge: dict. of persons, places, events. 16°. '65. $2.50 .. *Randolph.*
— *Same.* maps and ill. 18°. $3; hf cf., $4 .. *Appleton.*
Ayton, R: Rendezvous: farce. 16°. pap., 15c. *French.*
Aytoun, W: Edmonstone. Book of ballads; — Firmilian. *See* Martin, T., *and* Aytoun, W. E.
— Lays of the Scottish cavaliers. 16°. $1.50; hf. cf., $3. *Widdleton.*
Aytoun. Read, E. T. 40c. .... *Lippincott.*
Azael the prodigal. Ball, E. 15c. .... *French.*
Azarian. Spofford, H. E. $1.50 .... *Osgood.*
Azile. Cross, J. T. H. $1.25 .... *So. Meth.*

B., C. Birthday book of proverbs: sentences, proverbs, [etc.], for every day. 32°. $1 ..... (?) *Shepard.*
B., C. C. (*pseud.*) *See* Benton, *Mrs.* C. C.
B., E. V. Ruth Ellis; or, finding her mission. 12°. $1.25 .... *Palmer.*
B., E. W. (*pseud.*) *See* Baärnhielm, E. W.
B., F. E. Lowly ways; or, the diary of a poor young lady. 16°. '71. $1 .... *Claxton.*
B., H. N. W. (*pseud.*) *See* Baker, *Mrs.* H. N. W.
B., J. Rays of light for dark hours; with introd. by R. R. Booth. 12°. '62. $1.50 .... *Randolph.*
B., J. M. Agnes Carelton. 16°. $1 ...... (?) *Martien.*
B., M. The little offices; tr. by the ladies of the Sacred Heart; [also] A devout method of hearing mass. 18°. '57. 50c. .... *Cunningham.*
B., M. A. A. Clouded in mystery. 12°. $1.50. *McKinney.*
B., M. E. (*pseud.*) *See* Bennett, M. E.
B., M. M. Persecutions in Scotland. 18°. '64. 20c. *Am. Tr.*
B., T. A. Trials and trust. 18°. 70c. .... *Pres. Bd.*
B. B. Williams, M., *and* Burnand, F. C. 15c. *French.*
B. O. W. C. stories. *See* De Mille, J.
Baärnhielm, E. W. Archibald Hamilton. ill. 16°. '69. $1.25 .... *Lothrop.*
Bab ballads. *See* Gilbert, W. S.
Babb, C. E. ["Uncle Jesse."] Sea shore (The): what Charley saw and did there. 16°. 40c... *West. Tr.*
— Talks about Jesus. 16°. 40c. .... *West. Tr.*
— Talks about the war. 16°. 40c. .... *West. Tr.*
Babb, *Miss* Hattie. ["Aunt Hattie."] Hard sum (The), and other stories. 12°. 70c. .... *West. Tr.*
— Little princess, and other stories. 18°. '74. 65c. *Meth. Bk. Conc.*
Babbage, C: Table of logarithms of the natural numbers. 8°. '72. $3 .... *Spon.*
Babbitt, Edn. Dwight. Babbittonian copy books. ('70.) New ed. 8 nos. obl. 12°. '76. ea., 15c. *Sherwood.*
— Babbittonian primary copy book for tracing. ('72.) New ed. obl. 12°. '76. 15c. .... *Sherwood.*
— Health guide: aiming at a higher science of life and the life forces. 16°. '74. $1 .... *Babbitt.*
— Vital magnetism, the life fountain: answer to Brown-Sequard's lectures on "nerve force." 16°. '75. bds., 25c. .... *Babbitt.*
Babble brook. *See* Maple grove stories.
Babbler (The). Sadlier, M. A. 25c. .... *Sadlier.*
Babcock, Emma S. Dutch tiles; or, loving words about the Saviour. 18°. 60c. .... *Pres. Bd.*
Babcock, Ruf. Memoir of J. M. Peck. 12°. $1.50. *Am. Bapt.*
Babcock, *Miss* Sa. A. Hidden treasure; or, the secret of success in life. 12°. '59. $1. *Meth. Bk. Conc.*

Babcock, *Miss* Sa. A., *continued.*
— Itinerant side; or, pictures of life in the itinerancy. ill. 12°. '57. $1 .... *Meth. Bk. Conc.*
Babe and the princess. 18°. 40c. *Cin. Meth. Bk. Conc.*
Babe (The) at the wedding. Power, P. B. 60c. *Carter.*
Babes in the balloon. ('70.) 4th ed. ill. 18°. '74. 50c. *Perkinpine.*
Babes in the basket. Baker, S. 60c. ...... *Randolph.*
Babes in the basket; or, Daph and her charge. ill. 4°. '73. $1.25. 16°. 75c. .... *Lothrop.*
Babes in the wood. 18°. 18c. .... *Am. S. S.*
Babes in the wood. f°. pap., 15c.; 20c. ill. 4°. 50c. *J. E. Potter.*
Babes in the wood. ill. 4°. $1; 50c. ...... *Routledge.*
Babes in the wood. Byron, H. J. 15c. .... *French.*
Babes in the wood. De Mille, J. $1.50; 75c. *W. F. Gill.*
Babes in the wood. Taylor, T. 15c. .... *Lee & S.*
Babolain. Droz, G. $1.25 .... *Holt.*
Babson, J: J. History of Gloucester [Mass.], Cape Ann, incl. Rockport. 8°. '60. $5 .... *Procter.*
— Notes and add. to "History of Gloucester," pt. 1: Early settlers. 8°. '76. $1; pap., 75c. .. *Perley.*
Baby. [Toy-book.] ill. 4°. $1; 50c. ...... *Routledge.*
Baby (The). Tonna, C. E. 35c. .... *Pres. Bd.*
Baby elephant. Stewart, J. C. 15c. .... *De Witt.*
Baby nightcaps. *See* Barrow, *Mrs.* F.
Baby's Christmas. Davis, K. $1; $1.25 ...... *Hoyt.*
Baby's (The) death. 32°. 20c.; 15c. .... *Dutton.*
Baby's first book. [Toy-book.] ill. 8°. per gross, $48 .... (?) *McLoughlin.*
Baby's (The) things. Abbott, E. 75c.; 35c.. *Randolph.*
Bacchæ. *See* Euripides.
Bacchus dethroned. Powell, F. $1 ..... *Nat. Temp.*
Bach, J: Sebastian. Magnificat in D. 8°. $1; pap., 75c. .... *Church.*
— Passion music; choruses according to St. Matthew. 8°. '69. bds., $1.25. .... *Ditson.*
— Twelve German chorals; with Eng. text. f°. pap., $1.25 .... *Ditson.*
Bache, Alex. D. Magnetic and meteorological observations at Girard College. pts. 1–12. 4°. '59–'65. pap., pts. 1–3, ea., 25c.; 4–6, $1; 7–9, $1; 10–12, 50c.; — in 1 v. 4°. '66. pap., $3 .... *Smith. Inst.*
— Magnetic survey of Pennsylvania. 4°. '63. pap., $1 .... *Smith. Inst.*
Bache, *Mrs.* Anna. Legends of fairy land. ('69.) 3d ed. 18°. '75. 75c. .... *Claxton.*
— Little Clara. sq. 16°. 75c. .... *Tibbals.*
— Pebbles from the sea-shore. sq. 16°. 75c... *Tibbals.*
— Picture gallery. sq. 16°. 75c. .... *Tibbals.*
— Sibyl's (The) cave; or, book of oracles. 32°. 25c.; pap., 10c. .... *U. P. James.*
Bache, Franklin. *See* Wood, G. B., *and* Bache, F.
Bache, R: Meade. American wonderland. 12°. '71. $1.50 .... *Claxton.*
— The young wrecker of the Florida reef; or, the adventures of Fred. Ransom. ill. 16°. $1.50 .. *Claxton.*
Bachelder, J: B. Bachelder's ill. tourist's guide of the U. S., incl. Gettysburg: what to see and how to see it. 12°. '73. $2 .... (?) *Bachelder.*
— Popular resorts [in the U. S.] and how to reach them. ill. 12°. '74. $1.50 ..... (?) *Bachelder.*
Note. A rev. ed. of above.
— *Same.* 3d ed., rev. ill. 12°. '75. $2 ... (?) *Bachelder.*
Bacheler, O. R. Hinduism and Christianity in Orissa. 24°. 50c. .... *Freewill.*
Bachelor Ben. *See* Giles, E. A.
Bachelor of the Albany. Savage, M. W. $1.50. *Harper.*
Bachelor of arts. Hardwicke, P. 15c. ...... *French.*
Bachelor of Salamanca. *See* Lesage, A. R.
Bachelor studies. Beldazzle. $1 .... *Carleton*

Bachelor's bed-room. Mathews, A. J. 15c...*French.*

Bachelor's buttons: drama. 16°. pap., 15c...*French.*

Bachman, J: Unity of the human race: refutation of the theory of Morton, Agassiz and Nott, on the characteristics of genera and species. 2d ed., ed. by T. O. Summers. ('56.) 3d ed. 12°. '76. pap., 20c. .... *So. Meth.*

— *See also* Andubon, J. J., Quadrupeds of N. Am.

Back court (The). Hosmer, M. 75c.....*Pres. Bd.*

Back-log studies. Warner, C. D. $2; $4; $5..*Osgood.*

Backbiting reproved. Tonna, C. E. 40c...*Pres. Bd.*

Backsheesh. Knox, T. W. *$3; $3.50. *A. D. Worthington.*

Backus, C: Scripture doctrine of regeneration. 18°. 40c........................ *Cong. Pub.*

Backus, I: Church history of New England. 12°. 90c........................ *Am. Bapt.*

— *Same.* 12°. $1........................ *So. Bapt.*

Backus, S. D. *See* Cleaveland, H. W. *and* W., *and* Backus, S. D.

Backwoodsman (The). Wraxhall, *Sir* C. F. L. $1.50........................ *Burnham.*

Bacon, A. M. Manual of gesture; with ill. figures. 12°. '73. $1.75........................ *Griggs.*

Bacon, A. O. Digest of Georgia reports (v. 1-40). 2 v. 8°. '72. shp., $10........................ *Burke.*

Bacon, *Mrs.* E. A. Memoir of Rev. Henry Bacon. por. 12°. '56. $1.25........................ *Universalist.*

Bacon, Fs. (*Lord*). Works; with life by B. Montagu. 3 v. 8°. $15; shp., $19.50; hf. cf., $22.50. *M. Murphy.*

Cont.: 1. Life; Essays; Meditations; Colours of good and evil; Miscellaneous tracts upon human philosophy; Apothegms; Ornamenta rationalia; Sentences; Notes for conversation; On death; Advancement of learning; New Atlantis; Wisdom of the ancients; Civil history; Biography; Miscellaneous tracts. — 2. Sylva sylvarum; Tracts rel. to Scotland, Ireland, Spain and England; Speeches; Charges; Papers rel. to Earl of Essex; Theological tracts; Miscellanies; Judicial charges.— 3. Letters; Law tracts; Great instauration, preface and pt. 2 (Novum organum); pt. 3 (Nat. hist., Of density and rarity, Of heavy and light, Of sympathy and antipathy of things: History of life and death); pts. 4, 5, Miscellaneous tracts; index.

— Works; ed. by J. Spedding, R. L. Ellis and D. D. Heath; with index. 15 v. por. cr. 8°. $33.75; hf. cf., $60........................ *Hurd & H.*

Cont.: v. 1-5. Philosophical works. — 6, 7. Literary and professional works. — 8-15. Letters and life, incl. occasional works and index.

— Bible thoughts. 12°. '70. $1........................ *Am. Tr.*

— Essays; or, counsels, civil and moral; with life and notes for students by J. R. Boyd. 12°. '67. $1.50........................ *Barnes.*

— *Same;* with annotations by Rev. R. Whately. (Student's Bacon.) cr. 8°. $2.50; hf. cf., $4.50; mor., $6........................ *Lee & S.*

— — *Same.* New ed., cont. pref., notes and index by F. F. Heard. 8°. $3.50; hf. cf., $6; mor., $9. *Lee & S.*

— *Same;* [also] Apophthegms, Wisdom of the ancients, New Atlantis, and Henry VII.; with introd. and notes. por. 12°. (Bohn.) $1.40..*Scribner, W. & A.*

— — *Same.* 12°. (Bohn.) $1.50........................ *Lippincott.*

— *Same;* [also] Colours of good and evil; with notes and glossarial index by W. A. Wright. 18°. '75. $1.25. cr. 8°. $2.50........................ *Macmillan.*

— *Same;* [also] Wisdom of the ancients; with biog. notice by A. Spiers, pref. by B. Montagu and notes. 9th ed., 16°. '76. $1; hf. cf., $2.25; cf., $2.75........................ *Little, B. & C.*

— *Same;* [also] Conduct of the understanding, by J. Locke. 18°. 75c........................ *Harper.*

— Novum organum; [also] Advancement of learning; with notes by J. Devey. 12°. (Bohn.) $1.75. *Little, B. & Co.*

— — *Same.* 12°. (Bohn.) $2. *Lippincott; Scribner, W. & A.*

— *See also* Hudson, H. N.

Bacon, G: B. Book of Psalms; arranged for responsive readings. 32°. 30c.; leath., 50c.; mor., $2.50. 16°. 70c.; mor., $3.50........................ *Taintor.*

— Sabbath question (The): sermons preached to the Valley church, Orange, N. J. 12°. '68. $1. *Scribner.*

— Siam, the land of the white elephant, as it was and is. map and ill. 12°. '73. $1.50........................ *Scribner.*

Bacon, Leon. Christian self-culture; or, counsels for the beginning, and progress of a Christian life. 16°. $1........................ *Bost. Am. Tr.*

— Genesis of the New England churches. ill. cr. 8°. $2.50........................ *Harper.*

Bacon, Leon. W. Book of worship: Psalms, hymns and spiritual songs. cr. 8°. $2.25; roan, $3; $4; mor., $5. 12°. $1.25; roan, $1.75; — without tunes. 18°. 60c.; $1.25. roan, $1.50..*Clark & M.*

— Church music. 16°. 50c........................ *Peck.*

— Congregational hymn and tune book. sq. 16. hf. roan, $1.25; roan, $1.50; $1.75; mor., $3.50....*Peck.*

— Vatican council. 12°. '72. 90c........................ *Am. Tr.*

— *See also* Hyacinthe, *Father.*

Bacon, Mat. New abridgment of the law; with add. and corrections by Sir H. Gwillim and C. E. Dodd; with notes and ref. to ed. of 1829, by B. Wilson; [also] notes and ref. to Am. law and decisions by J. Bouvier. 10 v. 8°. '60. $55. *T. & J. W. Johnson.*

Bacon, W: Parental training. 16°. 70c.....*Pres. Bd.*

Bad boy (The); or, the story of Edward Winthrop. 18°. 30c.; 40c........................ *Am. Bapt.*

Bad habits. 18°. 30c........................ *Dutton.*

Bad habits of good society. Baker, G. A., *jr.*. $1.50. *Patterson.*

Bad old ape. *See* Barrow, *Mrs.* F.

Bad temper (A): comedy. 16°. pap., 15c.....*Happy.*

Bad whiskey. Rickey, S., *and* Barney, *Master.* 15c. *De Witt.*

Baddeck, and that sort of thing. Warner, C. D. $1. *Osgood.*

Baddeley, T. Sure way to find out the true religion; in a conversation between a father and his son. 18°. 25c...*Kenedy; Noonan; Sadlier; Strong.*

Badeau, Ad. Military hist. of U. S. Grant, April, 1861 —April, 1865. v. 1. por. and maps. 8°. $4; hf. cf., $6.50........................ *Appleton.*

Badekuren. Putlitz, G. zu. 50c........................ *Holt.*

Badger, *Mrs.* C. M. Floral belles, from the greenhouse and garden: drawn and colored from nature. '66. New ed. f°. '67. mor., $30........................ *Scribner.*

Badois, C: Grammaire anglaise. 12°. $1.50. — Key, 50c........................ *Appleton.*

— *See also* Pinney, N., *and* Badois, C.

Bædeker, K. *See* Osgood's European guide books.

Baehler, Mt. Latin verbs; adapted to any grammar. 12°. '75. pap., 25c........................ *Dennis.*

Baer, *Mrs.* B: F. Irene; or, beach-broken billows. 12°. '74. $1.25........................ *Authors.*

Baer, Hm. Ceremonies of modern Judaism; with introd. by T. O. Summers. ('55.) 3d ed. 18°. '74. 75c........................ *So. Meth.*

Baffled. Goddard, J. 75c........................ *Harper.*

Bag of blessings. Power, P. B. 60c...*Carter; Dutton.*

Bagby, G: W. ["Moses Adams."] What I did with my fifty millions; ed. from the posthumous manuscript by C. Maurice. 16°. pap., 50c. *Lippincott.*

Bagehot, Wa. English constitution. New ed., rev. cr. 8°. '73. $2.25........................ *Little, B. & Co.*

— Lombard street: a description of the money market. ('73.) New ed. 12°. '76. $1.75......*Scribner.*

— Physics and politics: thoughts on the application of the principles of "natural selection" and "inheritance" to political society. (Intern. sci. ser.) 12°. $1.50........................ *Appleton.*

Bagg, I. N. (*ed.*) Account of the centennial celebration of West Springfield, Mass. [1774–1874], March 25, 1874; with hist. address of Rev. T. E. Vermilye, poem by Mrs. E. P. Champion, etc.; with app. of genealogies. 8°. $1....(?) *Morris.*

Bagioli, —. One hour daily studies. [Vocal exercises.] f°. $3.................... *Gordon.*

— Twelve solfeggi for two voices. f°. $3.... *Gordon.*

— Vocal method. f°. $3................. *Gordon.*

Bagley, D: T. *See* California, Supreme Court reports.

Bags of gold. Tucker, C. 50c.............. *Carter.*

Bagshaw, Fr. The threshold of the Catholic church: instructions for those entering her communion; with pref. by Mgr. Capel. 3d ed. 12°. '74. $1.50 .... *Cath. Pub.*

Bähr, B. Science of therapeutics, according to principles of homœopathy; tr. with add. from Kafka and others by C. J. Hempel. 2 v. roy. 8°. hf. mor., $10.............................. *Boericke.*

Bähr, C. W. F. On Kings. *See* Lange, J. P., Comment.

Baierische Hiesel (Der). 12°. pap., 15c...... *Radde.*

Baile, J. Wonders of electricity; tr. from the Fr.; ed., with additions, by J. W. Armstrong. ill. 12°. '72. $1.50...................... *Scribner.*

Bailey, Eb. First lessons in algebra. (cop. '59.) '62. 3d ed. 12°. '68. $1.25.—Key. 12°. $1. *Schermerhorn.*

Bailey, F. W. N. New tale of a tub: an adventure in verse. ill. 8°. 75c. .... *Wiley.*

Bailey, H. *See* South Carolina, Reports.

Bailey, H. J. Liturgy compared with the Bible. 16°. $2.25.............................. *Pott.*

Bailey, Jac. Whitman. Microscopic examination of soundings. 4°. '51. pap., $2....... *Smith. Inst.*

— Microscopic observations in S. Carolina, Georgia and Florida. 4°. '51. pap., $1........ *Smith. Inst.*

— New species of microscopic organisms. 4°. '54. pap., 50c....................... *Smith. Inst.*

Bailey, Ja. M. Life in Danbury. ill. 16°. $1.50..*Lee & S.*

Bailey, Ph. Ja. Festus: a poem. 32°. $1.25..*Morton.*

— *Same.* (Blue and gold ed.) 32°. $1.25.—(Household ed.) 16°. $1.75.—(Cabinet ed.) 16°. $1.50; hf. cf., $2.75; cf., $3.75.—(Red line ed.] ill. sm. 4°. $3.50; hf. cf., $5; cf., $7.—ill. 8°. $5; $6; hf. cf., $7.50; mor., $10............ *Miller.*

— *Same.* 12°. (Bohn.) $1.75....... *Little, B. & Co.*

— *Same.* 12°. (Bohn.) $2. *Lippincott; Scribner, W. & A.*

Bailey, Ruf. W. Daughters at school instructed in a series of letters. 12°. 80c........... *Pres. Bd.*

— Domestic duties; or, the family a nursery for earth and heaven. 18°. 50c............... *Pres. Bd.*

— English grammar. 10th ed. 12°. '54. hf. bd., 50c. *Claxton.*

— Primary English grammar. 18°. '55. hf. bd., 25c. *Claxton.*

Bailey, T. J. Defence of holy orders in the Church of England; with a photozincograph of a portion of the record of Abp. Parker's consecration; [also] Jurisdiction and mission. 16°. '71. $1.25..*Pott.*

Bailey, Una Lock. Dr. Plassid's patients. ill. 16°. '72. $1.25......................... *Lothrop.*

— *and* Pratt, F. L. Holiday tales. ill. 18°. 60c. *Bost. Am. Tr.*

— — — *See also* Pleasant grove ser.

Bailey, W. T. Richfield Springs and vicinity: historical, biog. and descriptive. 12°. '74. $1.50..*Barnes.*

Baillie, J: Life of Captain Bate. 18°. 75c..... *Carter.*

— Life studies; or, how to live: ill. in the biographies of Bunyan, Tersteegen, Montgomery, Perthes and Mrs. Winslow. 18°. 60c........... *Carter.*

— *Same.* 16°. $1........................ *Harper.*

Baillot, P., Rode, P., *and* Kreutzer, R. System for the violin. 4°. bds., $2.50................ *Pond.*

Baily, G. S. Manual of baptism. 16°. $1..*Am. Bapt.*

Baily, W: L. Our own birds of the U. S. New ed., rev. by E. D. Cope; [also] Trees, plants and flowers. ill. 12°. $1.25; $2.50...... *Lippincott.*

— Trees, plants and flowers: where and how they grow. ill. 12°. $1..................... *Lippincott.*

Bain, Alex. Brief English grammar. ('72.) New ed. 16°. '75. bds., 50c.—Key. 50c......... *Holt.*

— Emotions and the will. 8°. $5.......... *Appleton.*

— English compos. and rhetoric. 12°. $1.75..*Appleton.*

— Logic, deductive and inductive. New ed., rev. 12°. $2.............................. *Appleton.*

— Mental science: compend. of psychology and hist. of philosophy. 12°. $1.75............ *Appleton.*

— Mind and body: theories of their relations. (Intern. sci. ser.) 12°. $1.50............... *Appleton.*

— Moral science: compendium of ethics. 12°. $1.75. *Appleton.*

— Senses (The) and intellect. 3d ed. 8°. $5..*Appleton.*

Bain, J. W. God's songs, and the singer. 18°. 40c. *U. P. Bd. of Pub.*

— Secret orders. 18°. 40c.; pap., 20c. *U. P. Bd. of Pub.*

Bainbridge. W: Treatise on the law of mines and minerals. 1st Am. from 3d Lond. ed., by G. M. Dallas. 8°. '71. shp., $7.50..*J. Campbell & Son.*

Baine, A. C. Essay on the harmonious relations between divine faith and natural reason. 12°. '60. $1.50............................ *Murphy.*

Baird, A. J. The two prophets. 16°. 50c. (?) *Cumberland.*

Baird, C: W. History of Rye, Westchester Co., N. Y., 1660–1870, incl. Harrison and White Plains till 1788. ill. by A. Hosier. 8°. '71. $6..*Randolph.*

Baird, E. T. Songs of praise for Sabbath schools. New ed., rev. 12°. '67. bds., 35c....*Pres. Com.*

— *and* Converse, C: C. ["Karl Reden."] Voice of praise for Sabbath school, prayer meeting and family circle. obl. 16°. '72. bds., 35c.;—without music. 40c.; 20c.; bds., 25c........ *Pres. Com.*

Baird, H: Carey. Protection of home labor and home productions necessary to the prosperity of the Am. farmer. ('60.) 7th ed. 8°. '75. pap., 10c...*Baird.*

Baird, H: M. Life of Rev. Rob. Baird. 8°. '66. $2.25; $3........................... *Randolph.*

— Modern Greece: narrative of residence and travels, with observ. on its antiquities, literature, lang., politics and religion. ill. 12°. $1.50....*Harper.*

Baird, J. S. S. Classical manual: epitome of ancient geog., Gk. and Rom. mythol. 16°. 90c. *Sheldon.*

Baird, Rob. Impressions and experiences of the West Indies and N. Am. 12°. 75c............. *Lea.*

— Life of Eliza Astor Rumpff and Duchess de Broglie. ill. 18°. '49. 25c.................. *Am. Tr.*

— Religion in America: account of origin, present condition, etc., of the evangelical churches in the U. S.; with notices of the unevangelical denominations. 8°. $3...................... *Harper.*

Baird, Rob. H. The American cotton spinner and manager's and carder's guide. (cop. '51.) '63. 7th ed. 12°. '76. $1.50................ *Baird.*

Baird, S: J. Bible hist. of baptism. 8°. pap., 15c. *Pres. Com.*

— Church of Christ, its constitution and order: manual for families, S.-schools, etc. 18°. 30c...*Pres. Bd.*

— Collection of the acts, deliverances and testimonies of the supreme judicatory of the Presb. Church; with notes and documents. 8°. $4....*Pres. Bd.*

— History of the New School [Pres. Ch.] and of the question involved in the disruption of the Presbyterian Church in 1838. 12°. '68. $2...*Claxton.*

Baird, Spencer F. Catalogue of No. Am. mammals. 3 v. 4° and 8°. '57–'59. v. 1–2, ea., pap., 50c.; v. 3, pap., 25c..................... *Smith. Inst.*

— Herpetology. *See* Wilkes, C: United States explor. expedition.

— Mammals. *See* Gilliss, J. M.

Baird, Spencer F., *continued.*
— Mammals of No. Am.: descriptions based on collections in Smithsonian Institution. 87 col. pl. 8°. $15 .... *Lippincott.*
— Review of Am. birds in Smithsonian Museum. 8°. '66. pap., $2 .... *Smith. Inst.*
— Zoology. *See* Ives, J. C., Report on Colorado River.
— *See also* Annual record of sci. and ind.; — California geological survey.
— *and* Brewer, T. M., *and* Ridgway, R. History of N. Am. birds: land birds. 64 pl. and 593 woodcuts. 3 v. 4°. '75. $30; col. pl., $45; hf. mor., $65. *Little, B. & Co.*
— *and* Girard, C. Catalogue of serpents. 8°. '53. pap., $1 .... *Smith. Inst.*
— *and* Ridgway, R. New forms of Am. birds. 8°. '73. pap., 10c. .... *Essex.*

Baird, T. Spangler. Standard wages computing tables. obl. f°. '68. $5 .... *Baird.*

Baird, W. Duty and reward; or, the blessedness of doing good. 18°. '59. 30c. .... *Randolph.*

Baker, A. R. Question book on the topics in the Assembly's shorter catechism. 18°. '62. 20c.; bds., 15c. .... *Randolph.*
— Topics in Christ's Sermon on the mount; v. 1, for children; v. 2, for youth; v. 3, for adults. 18°. '62. ea., bds., 15c. .... *Graves.*

Baker, B. Long-span railway bridges; with formulæ and tables. 12°. '70. $2 .... *Baird.*
— *Same;* [with] similar tables, [etc.], rel. to short span railway bridges. 2d ed., rev. ill. 8°. '73. $2. *Spon.*
— On the strength of beams, columns and arches, with a view to ascertaining the practical strength of any given section of beam, [etc.], in cast iron, wrought iron, or steel. ill. cr. 8°. $3.50.. *Spon.*

Baker, B: F. Burning ship; with words by H. M. Ticknor. [Cantata.] obl. 4°. '58. bds., $1.. *Ditson.*
— Camillus. [Cantata.] 8°. $1.25; pap., $1.. *Gordon.*
— Choral harmony. [Church music.] obl. 8°. $1.75; bds., $1.38 .... *Gordon.*
— Elementary music book. 16°. '47. bds., 50c... *Ditson.*
— Formation and cultivation of the voice. f°. $2.50. *Gordon.*
— Modern instructions. [Piano method.] f°. $1.50. *Brainard.*
— School music book: songs, chants and hymns. obl. 16°. '54. bds., 50c. .... *Ditson.*
— Short anthems and sentences. [Church music.] obl. 8°. $2 .... *Gordon.*
— Storm king; with words by H. M. Ticknor. [Cantata.] 4°. '56. pap., 38c. .... *Ditson.*
— Sunbeam. [Sing. book.] obl. 8°. 75c... *Brainard.*
— Union glee book. obl. 8°. 85c. .... *Gordon.*
— *and* Fargo, J. F. Songs of the temple: hymn tunes, chants, etc. obl. 16°. $1.25 .... *Lee & S.*
— *and* Hodges, D. F. Jubilant voices: new hymn tunes, chants, etc.; with system of element. instruction. obl. 16°. $1.50 .... *Lee & S.*
— *and* Perkins, W. O. Union star: operatic choruses, glees, etc. obl. 8°. '61. bds., 85c. .... *Ditson.*
— *and* Southard, L. H. Atlantic glee book. obl. 8°. $1.35 .... *Gordon.*
— — Classical chorus book. obl. 4°. $1.50.... *Gordon.*
— — Method for the formation and cultivation of the voice. f°. '52. bds., $3.50 .... *Ditson.*
— — School chimes. [Singing book.] obl. 16°. 50c. *Gordon.*

Baker, C: R. Practical and scientific fruit culture. 8°. $4 .... *Lee & S.*

Baker, Dan. Affectionate address to fathers; — to mothers. 18°. ea., 20c. .... *Pres. Bd.*
— Baptism in a nutshell, for the masses. 16°. 25c. (?)*Martien.*
— Plain and Scriptural view of baptism. 18°. 40c. *Pres. Bd.*
— Revival sermons. 2 v. 12°. ea., $1.50.. (?)*Martien.*

Baker, De W. C. Brief hist. of Texas, with const. of the state; for schools. 12°. '73. $1.25.. *Barnes.*
— Texas scrap book (A). 8°. '75. $5; shp., $6... *Barnes.*

Baker, E. K. Complete drawing book; with rules for plane and object drawing. 10th ed. obl. 8°. '72. 25c. .... *M. Taylor.*
— Drawing models. 4 nos. 12°. '72. ea., 25c. *M. Taylor.*

Baker, Fs. A. Life and sermons; ed. by A. F. Hewit. 10th ed. 8°. '65. $2.50 .... *Cath. Pub.*

Baker, G: A., *jr.* Bad habits of good society. 24°. '76. $1.50 .... *Patterson.*
— Point-lace and diamonds: poems. ill. sm. 4°. '75. $1; $1.50; $3 .... *Patterson.*

Baker, G: E. Life of W. H. Seward, to 1860. por. 12°. $1.50 .... *Widdleton.*

Baker, G: M. [Plays.] 58 v. ea., pap., 15c... *Lee & S.*
Cont.: Among the breakers. — Boston dip (The): comedy. — Bread on the waters. — Capuletta; or, Romeo and Juliet restored. — Champion of her sex: farce. — Close shave: farce. — Coals of fire: farce. — Down by the sea. — Drop (A) too much: farce. — Duchess of Dublin: farce. — Enlisted for the war; or, the home guard. — Freedom of the press: farce. — Gentlemen of the jury: farce. — Great elixir: farce. — Greatest plague in life: farce. — Grecian bend: farce. — Humors of the strike: farce. — Hypochondriac: farce. — Last loaf. — Lightheart's pilgrimage: tableau. — Little brown jug. — Little more cider: farce. — Love of a bonnet: farce. — Man with the demijohn: farce. — Merry Christmas of the old woman who lived in her shoe: farce. — My brother's keeper. — My uncle the captain: farce. — Never say die: farce. — New brooms sweep clean: farce. — No cure no pay: farce. — One hundred years ago; or, our boys of 1776. — Once on a time. — Original idea. — Pedlar of Verynice. — Precious pickle: farce. — Public benefactor: farce. — Red chignon: farce. — Revolt of the bees: tableau. — Runaways: farce. — Santa Claus' frolics. — Sculptor's triumph: tableau. — Sea of troubles: farce. — Seeing the elephant: farce. — Seven ages: tableau. — Stand by the flag. — Sylvia's soldier. — Tempter. — Tender attachment: farce. — Thief of time: farce. — Thirty minutes for refreshments: farce. — Thorn among the roses: farce. — Too late for the train. — Tournament of Idylcourt: tableau. — Using the weed: farce. — Visions of freedom: tableau. — Wanted a male cook: farce. — War of the roses: tableau. — We're all teetotallers: farce.
— Amateur drama ser. 5 v. ill. 16°. ea., $1.50.. *Lee & S.*
Cont.: Amateur dramas. — The mimic stage. — The social stage. — The drawing-room stage. — The exhibition drama.
— Baker's (A) dozen: humorous dialogues. 16°. 75c.; hf. bd., 60c. .... *Lee & S.*
— Bonbons; or, the paint-king: drama. 16°. pap., 25c. *Lee & S.*
— Old man's (An) prayer. ill. sm. 4°. $1.50.. *Lee & S.*
— Running to waste: the story of a tomboy. ill. 16°. $1.50 .... *Lee & S.*
— Snow bound; or, Alonzo the brave and the fair Imogene: drama. 16°. pap., 25c. .... *Lee & S.*
— Temperance drama (The). [Plays.] 16°. 75c.; bds., 60c. .... *Lee & S.*
— (*ed.*) Ballads of beauty. ill. 4°. $3.50... *Lee & S.*
— Ballads of home. ill. 4°. $3.50 .... *Lee & S.*
— Reading club (The) and handy speaker: sel. for readings, etc. nos. 1–3. 16°. ea., 50c... *Lee & S.*

Baker, *Mrs.* H. N. W. ["Aunt Hattie"; "*Mrs.* Madeline Leslie."] Aunt Hattie's library for boys. 6 v. 18°. '67. $3 .... *H. A. Young.*
Cont.: Apple boys. — Chest of tools. — Factory boy. — Frankie's dog Tony. — Golden rule. — Lying Jim.
— *Same;* for girls. 6 v. 18°. '67. $3.. *H. A. Young.*
Cont.: Lilly's birthday. — The sheep and lambs. — Little Miss Fret. — Maggie and the mice. — The lost Kittie. — Ida's new shoes.
— Brookside series. 4 v. 16°. '65–'67. ea., $1.25. *H. A. Young.*
Cont.: Hole in the pocket. — Lost but found. — Stopping the leak. — Fashion and folly.
— Clarence's library. 6 v. 32°. '72. $1.50.. *H. A. Young.*
Cont.: Hide and seek. — Two rules. — Little Conscience. — Golden pennies. — Clarence's secret. — Stolen shilling.
— Corwin's nest series; or, stories of Bessie and Jamie. 6 v. 18°. '69. $4.50 .... *Graves.*
Cont.: Little Tot's lesson. — Birthday party. — Bessie and the squirrels. — Children at play. — Whistling Horace. — Jamie and his pony.
— Daisy Dale library. 6 v. 18°. '75. $2.40.. *Graves.*
Cont.: Little Daisy's letter. — Papa's present. — Ida and the beggar. — Annie and the bears. — The new society. — The twins.

Baker, *Mrs.* H. N. W., *continued.*
— Do good library (The). ('60–'63.) New ed. 5 v. ill. 18°. '74–'76. $2.75; ea., 55c. .... *Hoyt.*
Cont.: Virginia; or, the power of grace.—Bound boy.—Bound girl.—Prairie flower.—Little rag picker.
— Earning and spending; or, the two homes. 16°. '62. $1 .... *H. A. Young.*
— Gems for youth: no. 1. 6 v. 18°. '71. $3.60 .. *Graves.*
Cont.: Gem of uprightness—of self-denial—of perseverance—of temperance—of self-control—of generosity.
— *Same:* no. 2. 6 v. 18°. '72. $3.60 .... *Graves.*
Cont.: Gem of courtesy—of courage—of faithfulness—of neatness—of truthfulness—of earnestness.
— Georgy's menagerie. 6 v. ill. 18°. '64. $3.75 .. *Graves.*
Cont.: The lion.—The bear.—The deer.—The wolf.—The camel.—The elephant.
— Golden spring ser. 3 v. ill. 16°. '69. $3.75 .. *Graves.*
Cont.: Behind the curtain.—Helps and hindrances to the cross.—Breach of trust.
— Good hope ser. 4 v. 16°. '71. ea., $1 .. *H. A. Young.*
Cont.: Belle Clement's influence.—Sophie's letter book.—Lulu Reed's pupil.—Edith Withington.
— Happy home stories for boys. 6 v. ill. 18°. '71. $3. *H. A. Young.*
Cont.: Diligent Dick.—Lazy Robert.—Little Fritz.—Cousin Willie.—The new buggy.—Bertie and his sisters.
— *Same;* for girls. 6 v. ill. 18°. '71. $3 .. *H. A. Young.*
Cont.: Little Flyaway.—The spoiled picture.—Fleda's childhood.—The singing girl.—Molly and the wine glass.—The twins.
— Home life series. 4 v. 12°. ea., $1.50 .... *Lee & S.*
Cont.: Cora and the doctor.—Courtesies of wedded life.—Household angel in disguise.—Now and forever.
— Little Agnes' library for girls. 4 v. ill. 16°. ea., $1.50 .... *Lee & S.*
Cont: Little Agnes.—Trying to be useful.—I'll try.—Art and artlessness.
— Little favorite's lib. 12 v. 32°. '72. $3 .. *H. A. Young.*
Cont.: Hide and seek.—Two rules.—Little Conscience.—Clarence's secret.—Golden pennies.—Stolen shilling.—Jessie's holiday.—Little Annie.—Mary and Willie.—Marion's jewels.—Effie's Christmas.—Two sisters.
— Little Frankie series (The). 6 v. 16°. $2; ea., 35c. (?) *Shepard.*
Cont.: Little Frankie and his mother—at his plays—and his cousins—and his father—on a journey—at school.
— *Same.* 6 v. 16°. $2.70 .... *Nichols & H.*
— Little Maggie's library. 6 v. 32°. '68. $1.50. *H. A. Young.*
Cont.: Little Maggie.—The pet sparrow.—Susie's victory.—Six mince pies.—Ripe strawberries.—The silk apron.
— Little Willie's library. 6 v. 32°. '68. $1.50. *H. A. Young.*
Cont.: Charley's locket.—Young bird catchers.—The picture clock.—Will and the donkey.—The woolly bear.—Wilful Walter.
— Marion's library. 6 v. 32°. '72. $1.50 .. *H. A. Young.*
Cont.: Jessie's holiday.—Little Annie.—Mary and Willie.—Marion's jewels.—Effie's Christmas.—Two sisters.
— Minnie and her pets. 6 v. ill. 24°. ea., 75c. .. *Lee & S.*
Cont.: Minnie's pet parrot—pet cat—pet dog—pet pony—pet lamb—pet monkey.
— Myrtle branch (The); or, pictorial sketches for children and youth. ill. 16°. $1 .... *Graves.*
— Never give up; or, the newsboys. ill. 16°. '63. $1. *H. A. Young.*
— Pearl series; for boys. 6 v. 18°. '68. $3; $3.50. *Graves.*
Cont.: Pearl of love; or, Jessie's gift—of obedience; or, the soldier's son—of charity; or, the chain of seals—of patience; or, Maurice and Kitty Maynard—of penitence; or, Charlie's sad story—of hope; or, the story of Edgar.
— *Same;* for girls. 6 v. 18°. '69. $3; $3.50 .. *Graves.*
Cont.: Pearl of faith; or, the little housekeeper—of forgiveness; or, Ruth Stanley—of contentment; or, Floy and her nurse—of meekness; or, our little Belle—of diligence; or, the basket weavers—of peace; or, the little peace-maker.
— Play and study series for boys and girls. 4 v. ill. 16°. ea., $1.50 .... *Lee & S.*
Cont: The motherless children.—Play and study.—Howard and his teacher.—Jack the chimney sweeper.
— Robin nest stories. 6 v. sq. 16°. $2.70 .. *Nichols & H.*
— Robin Redbreast series. 6 v. 16°. $2; ea., 35c. (?) *Shepard.*

Baker, *Mrs.* H. N. W., *continued.*
Cont.: The robin's nest.—Little robins in the nest.—Little robins learning to fly.—Little robins in trouble.—Little robins' friends.—Little robins' love one to another.
— *Same.* 6 v. sq. 16°. $4.50 .... *Nichols & H.*
— Rosy dawn stories. 6 v. 18°. '69. $4.50. *H. A. Young.*
Cont.: The picnic party.—The water cress girl.—The little Indian.—The twin brothers.—The violet girls.—The two birthdays.
— Secret of success. ill. 16°. '65. $1 ... *H. A. Young.*
— Select library. ('62–'64.) New ed. 5 v. ill. 16°. '73–'75. $6 .... *Hoyt.*
Cont.: Every-day duties; or, the school-mates.—Light and shade.—White and black lies; or, truth better than falsehood.—Organ grinder; or, struggles after holiness.—Prize Bible.
— Silver lake series. 3 v. 16°. '68. ea., $1.25. *H. A. Young.*
Cont.: Truth and trust; or, Iron Mountain.—Hopes and fears; or, Broad Oaks.—Good for evil; or, Rose Cottage.
— Sunshine series. 6 v. 18°. '70. $3.90 ..... *Graves.*
Cont: Honeysuckle Cottage.—The little Florentine.—The load of chips.—Tony and his harp.—Timmy Top-boots.—Sophia and the gypsies.
— Sweet brier stories. 12 v. 32°. '68. $3 .. *H. A. Young.*
Cont.: Charley's locket.—Young bird catchers.—The picture clock.—Will and the donkey.—Woolly bear.—Wilful Walter.—Little Maggie.—The pet sparrow.—Susie's victory.—Six mince pies.—Ripe strawberries.—Silk apron.
— Tim series. ('61–'63.) New ed. 3 v. ill. 16°. '75. $3.75 .... *Hoyt.*
Cont.: Tim the scissors-grinder.—Sequel to *same.*—Tim's sister.
— Up the ladder; or, striving and thriving. 16°. '63. $1 .... *H. A. Young.*
— Wheel (The) of fortune; or, the dignity of labor. 16°. '66. $1.25 .... *Graves.*
— Woodbine series. 4 v. 16°. $5 .... *Graves.*
Cont.: Live and learn.—The governor's pardon; or, the bridge of sighs.—Paul Barton, the drunkard's son.—Walter and Frank; or, the Althrop farm.
— Woodlawn series. 6 v. ill. 18°. '68. $3.60. *H. A. Young.*
Cont.: Bertie's home.—Bertie and the plumbers—and the carpenters—and the masons—and the painters—and the gardeners.
— Worth and wealth; or, Jessie Dorr. ill. 16. '64. $1. *H. A. Young.*

Baker, J. M. Foreknowledge of God. 12°. 75c. *S. W. Bk. & Pub.*

Baker, J. S. Questions of the age. 18°. 30c.; pap., 15c. .... *So. Bapt.*

Baker, J: F. Supplement to Riddle's "Supplementary proceedings" [to 1876]; with notes and ref. 8°. '76. hf. shp., $2 .... *Ward & P.*
— Treatise on the [N. Y.] law of manufacturing corporations. 8°. '76. shp., $4.50 ..... *Ward & P.*

Baker, J: Gilb. *See* Hooker, *Sir* W. J., *and* Baker, J. G.

Baker, L. C. Secret service (The) in the late [civil] war. ill. 12°. $2 .... *J. E. Potter.*

Baker, *Mrs.* L. M. Friendless. 16°. 50c. .. *Williamson.*
— Louisa Murray. 16°. 50c. .... *Williamson.*

Baker, *Bp.* Osman Cleander. Guide in the administration of the discipline of the M. E. Church. Rev. ed. 12°. '55. $1.25 .... *Meth. Bk. Conc.*
— Last witness: dying sayings of Christians. 24°. 30c. *Cin. Meth. Bk. Conc.*

Baker, P. Devout communicant (The). 24°. 50c. *Cath. Pub.*
— Lenten monitor: moral reflections and devout aspirations. New ed. 24°. 60c. .... *Cath. Pub.*
— Sunday monitor. 18°. 50c. .... *Cath. Pub.*

Baker, *Mrs.* S. S. Amy and her brothers. 18°. '60. 45c. .... *Am. Tr.*
— Blue flag (The). 18°. '61. 60c. .... *Am. Tr.*
— *German.* Die blaue Flagge. 18°. '70. 50c. .. *Am. Tr.*
— Boy-patriot (The). 18°. '63. 50c. .... *Am. Tr.*
— Buster and baby Jim. 18°. '62. 40c. .... *Am. Tr.*
— Cheerily, cheerily. 18°. '62. 60c. .... *Am. Tr.*
— Chosen friends. 18°. '64. 25c. .... *Am. Tr.*
— Emily and Uncle Hanse. 18°. '61. 45c. ... *Am. Tr.*

Baker, *Mrs.* S. S., *continued.*
— Fisherman's (The) boy. 18°. '60. 40c. . . . *Am. Tr.*
— Hannah's path. 18°. '62. 40c. . . . *Am. Tr.*
— Kelly Nash. 18°. '63. 45c. . . . *Am. Tr*
— Lucy's pet. 32°. '61. 30c. . . . *Am. Tr.*
— New parasol. 32°. '61. 30c. . . . *Am. Tr.*
— Woodman's Nannette. 18°. '62. 40c. . . . *Am. Tr.*
— *Spanish.* Anita. 18°. '72. 30c. . . . *Am. Tr.*

Baker, *Sir* S: White. Albert N'yanza great basin of the Nile, and exploration of the Nile sources. 3d ed. maps and ill. cr. 8°. '74. $2.50. . *Macmillan.*
— *Same.* maps and ill. cr. 8°. $2.50; hf. cf., $4.50. *Lippincott.*
— Cast up by the sea; or, the adventures of Ned Grey. ill. 12°. $1.25. . . . *Harper; Lippincott.*
— Ismailïa: narrative of the expedition in central Africa for the suppression of the slave trade, organized by Ismail, Khedive of Egypt. maps, por. and ill 8°. $5. . . . *Harper.*
— *Same.* 2 v. 8°. '75. $15. . . . *Macmillan.*
— Library of travel and adventure. 3 v. ill. 12°. $3.75. . . . *Lippincott.*
Cont.: Eight years' wanderings in Ceylon. — The rifle and hound in Ceylon. — Cast up by the sea.
— Nile tributaries of Abyssinia, and the sword hunters of the Hamran Arabs. 4th ed. maps and ill. cr. 8°. '74. $2.50. . . . *Macmillan.*
— *Same.* maps and ill. cr. 8°. $2.50; hf. cf., $4.50. *Lippincott.*

Baker, Sa. ["Aunt Friendly."] Aunt Friendly's library. 6 v. 18°. '60–'65. ea., 40c. . . . *Randolph.*
Cont.: Bound out. — Hatty and Marcus. — Kate Darley. — The little musicians. — Orange seed. — Poor little Joe.
— Babes in the basket. 18°. '64. 60c. . . . *Randolph.*
— Barton Todd. 18°. '64. 60c. . . . *Randolph.*
— Boy friend. 18°. 60c. . . . (?) *Martien.*
— Christian effort: facts and incidents. 18°. '50. 55c. *Meth. Bk. Conc.*
— Coming to the light; or, the story of Fidgety Skeert. 18°. '64. 60c. . . . *Randolph.*
— Heart and hand. 18°. '58. $1.25. . . . *Randolph.*
— Mary Burns. 18°. '62. 60c. . . . *Randolph.*
— Meggie of the Pines. 18°. '63. 60c. . . . *Randolph.*
— Under the pear tree. 18°. '65. 60c. . . . *Randolph.*

Baker, T. Remarks on contagion. *See* Smith, S., Common nature of epidemics.

Baker, T: Mathematical theory of the steam-engine, with rules and examples; rev. by J. R. Young. 12°. 75c. . . . *Baird.*
— Mathematics: formulæ, rules and examples for candidates for the military, naval and civil service examinations, also for math. students and engineers. 12°. (Weale.) '62. 40c. . . . *Spon.*

Baker, Val. Clouds in the east: travels and adventures on the Perso-Turkoman frontier in 1874. maps and ill. 8°. '76. $6.75. . *Scribner, W. & A.*

Baker, W: E. S. The widow Seymour. [Fiction.] 12°. '76. $1.50. . . . *Wagenseller.*

Baker, W: G: Life and character. 12°. '59. $1.50. *Meth. Bk. Conc.*

Baker, W: M. ["G: F. Harrington."] Carter Quarterman. [Fiction.] ill. 8°. '76. pap., 75c. *Harper.*
— Inside: a chronicle of secession. ill. 8°. $1.75; pap., $1.25. . . . *Harper.*
— Life and labors of the Rev. Dan. Baker. 8°. $2. (?) *Martien; Pres. Bd.*
— Mose Evans: a simple statement of the singular facts in his case. [Fiction.] 16°. '74. $1.50. *Hurd & H.*
— New Timothy (The). [Fiction.] 12°. $1.50. . *Harper.*
— Oak-mot. sm. 12°. $1. . . . *Pres. Bd.*

Baker, W: S. American engravers and their works. sm. 4°. '75. $4. cr. 8°. $2. . . . *Gebbie.*
— Origin and antiquity of engraving. New ed., rev. heliot. ill. 8°. '75. $5. . . . *Osgood.*
— William Sharp, engraver; with descrip. catalogue of his works. cr. 8°. '75. $2. . . . *Gebbie.*

Baker's (The) boy; or, the results of industry. 18°. 15c. . . . *Benziger.*

Baker's (A) dozen. Baker, G. M. 75c.; 60c. . . *Lee & S.*

Bakewell, E. The new book of one syllable. sq. 16°. 50c. . . . *Routledge.*

Bakewell, J: Admonitory counsels to a Methodist. 18°. '42. 50c. . . . *Meth. Bk. Conc.*

Bakewell, *Mrs.* J: Mother's practical guide. 18°. '43. 60c. . . . *Meth. Bk. Conc.*

Bal-masque (The). Chicard, *Count.* 15c. . . . *French.*

Balance (The). Mayo, A. D. 60c. . . . *Universalist.*

Balance of comfort. Bernard, W. B. 15c. . . . *French.*

Balaustion's adventure. Browning, R. $1.50; $3; $4. . . . *Osgood.*

Balbirnie, J: Philosophy of the water-cure; with the confessions and observations of Sir E. L. Bulwer. 12°. pap., 50c. . . . *Wells.*

Balboa, Vasco Nunez de, Cortes, H., *and* Pizarro, F. Lives. 18°. 75c. . . . *Harper.*

Balch, D. M. Analysis of grapes. 8°. '65. pap., 10c. *Essex.*
— On the sodalite at Salem. 8°. '64. pap., 10c. *Essex.*

Balch, G: T. *See* Oarsman's manual.

Balch, T: Les Français en Amérique pendant la guerre de l' indépendance des Etats-Unis, 1777–1783. por. and map. 8°. pap., $3. . . . *Lippincott.*

Balch, W. S. Brief life of Christ, catechetically arranged in the order of a harmony of the Gospels. 16°. '30. per doz., pap., $1.25. . . . *Universalist.*

Bald-headed hist. of America. Small, G. G. 25c. *Collin & S.*

Baldauf, Jos., *and* Ulbricht, T. Progressive translator [from Eng. into German]. 8°. '75. bds., 40c. *Hoeger.*

Balderscourt. Adams, H. C. $1.25. . . . *Routledge.*

Baldwin, A. C. *See* Hyde, A., Baldwin, A. C., *and* Gage, W. L.; — Liberty or slavery.

Baldwin, *Mrs.* Anna E. The mechanical powers; or, six friendly giants. ill. 12°. '74. pap., 15c. (?) *Daily Advertiser.*

Baldwin, Aust. Table book and primary arithmetic. 18°. '48. 20c. . . . *G. R. Lockwood.*

Baldwin, D: A. The family pocket homœopathist. 32°. '65. 50c. . . . *Darrow.*

Baldwin, E. (*ed.*) Book of fables: sel. from Æsop and others. ill. 16°. '67. $1. . . . *Collins & Bro.*

Baldwin, G: C. Model prayer (The): lectures on the Lord's prayer. 16°. $1.50. . . . *Lee & S.*
— Representative men of the New Testament. 16°. $1. . . . *Am. Bapt.*
— Representative women, from Eve the wife of the first, to Mary the wife of the second Adam. 16°. $1. . . . *Am. Bapt.*

Baldwin, H: General view of the origin and nature of the Constitution and government of the U. S. 8°. $1.75. . . . *Kay.*
— *See also* United States, Circuit Court reports.

Baldwin, J: Is there a devil? with an inquiry into the origin of evil, and review of the popular notion of hell and heaven. ('65.) 7th ed. 12°. '73. pap., 25c. . . . *Colby.*

Baldwin, J: D. Ancient America; in notes on Am. archæology. ill. 12°. $2. . . . *Harper.*
— Pre-historic nations: inquiries conc. some of the great peoples and civilizations of antiquity, and their probable relation to a still older civilization of the Ethiopians or Cushites of Arabia. 12°. $1.75. . . . *Harper.*

Baldwin, J: Loraine. Laws of short whist; [also] Treatise on the game, by Ja. Clay. ('68.) New ed. 18°. '75. $1. . . . *Holt.*
— *Same.* 16°. (Lond.) $1.50. . . . *Little, B. & Co.*

Baldwin. Jos. G. The flush times of Alabama and Mississippi: humorous legal sketches. 12°. $1.75. *S. Whitney.*

Baldwin, S: D. Armageddon. New ed., rev. 12°. '54. $2 .... *So. Meth.*

— Life of Mrs. S. Norton. por. 12°. '60. $1.25. *So. Meth.*

Baldwin, Sim. E. Digest of cases decided in the Superior Court and Supreme Court of Errors of Conn., and in the U. S. courts for the dist. of Conn. roy. 8°. '71. shp., $8 .... *Little, B. & Co.*

Baldwin, T: Universal pronouncing gazetteer. 12°. '52. hf. roan, $1.50 .... *Claxton.*

— Vocabulary of geog. pronunciation. 12°. '51. hf. roan, 30c. .... *Claxton.*

— *See also* Thomas, J., *and* Baldwin, T.

Baldwin, T: Introduction to Irish farming. 18°. '74. 75c. .... *Macmillan.*

— Introduction to pract. farming. 18°. '75. 50c. *Macmillan.*

Baldwin, W: C: African hunting, from Natal to the Zambesi, incl. Lake Ngami, etc., 1852 to 1860. map and ill. 12°. $1.50 .... *Harper.*

Baldwinsville homicide (The). *See* Linsday, O.

Bale, J: Life and writings. *See* British reformers.

Balfe, Mich. W. The talisman. [Opera.] 4°. '74. $12. — Libretto. 8°. pap., 40c. .... *Pond.*

— *See also* Ditson.

Balfern, W. P. Glimpses of Jesus; or, Christ exalted in the affections of his people. 16°. 75c. *So. Bapt.*

— Lessons from Jesus. 16°. $1 .... *Sheldon.*

Balfour, *Mrs.* Clara L. Club night: a village record. sq. 16°. 50c. .... *Routledge.*

— Job Tufton's rest. ('70.) New ed. 12°. '74. $1.25. *Nat. Temp.*

— One by herself. ill. 12°. $1 .... *Nelson.*

— Scrub; or, the poor-house boy's first start in life. 18°. 50c. .... (?) *Martien.*

Balfour, F. M. *See* Foster, M., *and* Balfour, F. M.

Balfour, Fairfax. Perdita; or, fair and false. 8°. pap., 50c. .... *De Witt.*

Balfour, G. W. Clinical lectures on diseases of the heart and aorta. ill. 8°. '76. $5 .... *Lindsay.*

Balfour, J. H. Systematic and economic botany. (Adv. sci. ser.) ill. 12°. $1.50. (Element. sci. ser.) ill. 16°. '74. 75c. .... *Putnam.*

Note. Also pub. under title of Vegetable anatomy and physiology.

Balfour, Wa. Inquiry into the Scriptural import of the words, Sheol, Hades, Tartarus and Gehenna; tr. hell in Eng. versions; rev. with essays and notes by O. A. Skinner. 12°. '54. $1 .... *Universalist.*

Ball, E: ["E: Fitzball."] [Plays.] 26 v. 16°. ea., pap., 15c. .... *French.*

Cont.: Azael the prodigal: spectacle. — Children of the castle. — Devil's elixir: extravaganza. — Earthquake: extravaganza. — Esmeralda. — Father and son. — Floating beacon. — Flying Dutchman. — Fortunes of Nigel. — Haunted hulk. — Hofer. — Inchcape bell. — Innkeeper of Abbeville. — Joan of Arc: burlesque. — Jonathan Bradford: melodrama. — Kœuba. — Mary Glantonbury. — Miller of Derwent-water. — Momentous question. — Pierette: operetta. — Pilot. — Red Rover. — Robin Hood: spectacle. — Tom Cringle. — Wardock. — Kennilson. — Waverley.

— Daughter of the regiment: drama. 16°. pap., 15c. *Lee & S.*

— Miller of Derwent-water: drama. 16°. pap., 15c. *Ames.*

Ball, G. H. Christian baptism, the duty, the act, and the subjects. 24°. 25c. .... *Freewill.*

— Lessons for every Sunday. 32°. 18c. .... *Freewill.*

— Life work of the Saviour. [S.-school quest. book.] 18°. '70. 18c. .... *Lothrop.*

Ball, Rob. Stawell. Applied mechanics; with drawings and diagrams. 8°. $1 .... *Cassell.*

— Experimental mechanics. [Lectures.] 8°. '71. $6. *Macmillan.*

Ball, T. *See* Ireland, Chancery reports.

Ball and hoop; [also] Charles Gay; [also] Beauty. 18°. 30c. .... *Am. S. S.*

Ball-room companion. 32°. 20c. .... *Routledge.*

Ball-room companion. 48°. 25c. .... *Scribner, W. & A.*

Ball-room dancing without a master, and complete guide to the ball room. 12°. pap., 25c. .. *Hurst.*

Ball (The) we live on. Taylor, E. 40c. .... *So. Meth.*

Ballad of Lord Bateman. ill. 8°. pap., 25c. .. *Carleton.*

Ballad stories of the affections. Buchanan, R. $1.25. *Scribner, W. & A.*

Ballads for children. Sewell, M. $1 .... *Routledge.*

Ballads for little folk. Cary, A. *and* P. $1.50. *Hurd & H.*

Ballads, Scottish and English, from the old and new ballad writers. ill. 16°. $1.50 .... *Lee & S.*

Ballantyne, Randall H. Mabel Grant. 18°. 75c. .. *Carter.*

Ballantyne, Rob. M. Away in the wilderness; or, life among the red Indians and fur traders of N. A. ill. 16°. 75c. .... *Porter.*

— Black ivory: tale of adventure among the slavers of east Africa. ill. 12°. $1.75 .... *Nelson.*

— Chasing the sun; or, rambles in Norway. ill. 16°. 75c. .... *Porter.*

— Dog Crusoe (The): tale of the western prairies. ill. 16°. $1.25 .... *Porter.*

— Fast in the ice; or, adventures in the Polar regions. ill. 16°. 75c. .... *Porter.*

— Fighting the whales; or, doings and dangers on a fishing cruise. ill. 16°. 75c. .... *Porter.*

— Floating light of the Goodwin Sands. ('70.) 2d ed. ill. 12°. '75. $1.50 .... *Claxton.*

— Freaks on the fells; or, three months' rustication. ill. 16°. $1.25 .... *Porter.*

— *Same;* [also] Why I did not become a sailor. ill. 16°. $1.25 .... *Routledge.*

— Gascoyne, the sandal-wood trader: a tale of the Pacific. ill. 16°. $1.25 .... *Porter.*

— Gorilla hunters (The): a tale of the wilds of Africa. ill. 16°. $1.25 .... *Porter.*

— Jarwin and Cuffy. ill. 16°. $1 ... *Scribner, W. & A.*

— Library of adventure. 6 v. ill. 16°. $7.50 .. *Claxton.*

Cont.: Gorilla hunters. — Wild man of the west. — Shifting winds. — Three months' rustication. — Gascoyne, the sandal-wood trader. — Floating light of the Goodwin Sands.

— Library of sporting adventure. 3 v. ill. 12°. ea., $1.25 .... *Routledge.*

Cont.: The Red Eric. — Freaks on the fells. — The wild man of the west.

— Library of story. 3 v. 12°. $3.75 .... *Lippincott.*

Cont.: Fire brigade; or, fighting the flames. — Erling the bold: a tale of the Norse sea-kings. — Deep down: a tale of the Cornish mines.

— Life boat (The). 12°. $1.50 .... *Tilton.*

— Life in the Red Brigade: a story for boys. ill. 16°. '73. $1.25 .... *Routledge.*

— Ocean (The) and its wonders. ill. 12°. $1.25 .. *Nelson.*

— Pirate city (The). ill. 12°. $1.75 .... *Nelson.*

— Red Eric. ill. 12°. $1.25. .... *Lippincott.*

— Shifting winds. ill. 16°. $1.25 .... *Porter.*

— Silver lake (The). ill. 16°. $1 ... *Scribner, W. & A.*

— Wild man of the west: tale of the Rocky Mountains. ill. 16°. $1.25 .... *Porter; Routledge.*

— *See also* Great bonanza.

Ballantyne, T: Essays in mosaic. 16°. $1.25. *Scribner, W. & A.*

Ballantyne, W. Little kitten series. 10 v. ill. 18°. $4 .... *Nelson.*

Cont.: Three little kittens. — Me-a-ow; or, good advice to cats. — Robber kitten. — Chit-chat by a penitent cat. — Mister Fox. — Butterfly's ball. — Trip in a ship.

Ballard, *Rev.* A. Pleasant paths for little feet. 16°. '60. 65c. .... *Randolph.*

Ballard, Anna. Fifteen vocalises; to give execution and to equalize the voice. f°. '70. pap., 50c. *Ditson.*

Ballard, E: (*ed.*) Memorial of Topham celebration, Aug. 29, 1862, commemorative of the Topham colony on the peninsula of Sabino, Aug. 19 [o. s.], 1607. 8°. '63. $2.50 .... *Me. Hist. Soc.*

Ballard, *Mrs.* Jla. P. Building stones. ill. 16°. '71. $1.25 .... *Lothrop.*
— Grandmother's story. 12°. 50c. .... *West. Tr.*
— Hole in the bag. ('72.) New ed. 12°. '75. $1. *Nat. Temp.*
— Lift a little; or, the old quilt. 18°. 40c. .. *Bost. Am. Tr.*
— — *See also* Missing boat stories.
— Little gold keys (The). ill. 18°. 50c. .. *Bost. Am. Tr.*
— Little life. ill. 18°. '71. 50c. .... *Crowell.*
— Sabbath stories. 16°. 70c. .... *West. Tr.*
— Seven years from to-night. 16°. $1.25 .. *Cong. Pub.*

Ballestier, Jos. N. Annals of Chicago: a lecture. ('40.) New ed. 12°. '76. pap., 25c. .... *Fergus.*

Ballo in maschera. *See* Verdi, G.

Balloon (The). *See* Theodore Thinker's new stories.

Balloon travels of Robert Merry. Goodrich, S. G. $1.50 .... *Sheldon.*

Ballou, Adin. Primitive Christianity and its corruptions. 12°. '70. $1.50 .... *Universalist.*

Ballou, Hosea. Examination of the doct. of future retribution in connection with the moral nature of man, the principle of analogy, and the sacred Scriptures. 12°. '34. 75c. .... *Universalist.*
— Lecture sermons. 12°. '32. $1 .... *Universalist.*

Ballou, Hosea, *2d.* Ancient hist. of Universalism from time of the apostles to 5th general council; with app. tracing the doct. to the reformation; with notes by Rev. A. St. J. Chambré, and T. J. Sawyer. 12°. '71. $1 .... *Universalist.*
— Counsel and encouragement: discourses on the conduct of life. 12°. '65. $1 .... *Universalist.*

Ballou, M. M. Miralda: drama. 16°. pap., 15c. *French.*
— Treasury of thought: encyclopædia of quotations. 8°. '71. $5; hf. mor., $8 .... *Osgood.*

Balmès, Jacques Lucien. Criterion; or, how to detect error and arrive at truth. 12°. $1.50 ... *O'Shea.*
— Fundamental philosophy; tr. by Brownson. 2 v. 12°. $4; hf. mor., $6 .... *Sadlier.*
— Logic; tr. from the Spanish. 12°. $1 ...... *O'Shea.*
— Protestantism and Catholicity compared, in their effects on the civilization of Europe. 8°. '50. $3; $3.50 .... *Murphy.*

Baltimore. Rules for the conduct of business in the Supreme Bench and other courts of Baltimore city. 8°. '73. $2 .... *Murphy.*
— Acta et decreta Conc. Plen. Balt. II., Oct., 1866. 8°. '68. $3.50; $4.50; mor., $7 .... *Murphy.*
— Acta et decreta Conc. Prov. Balt. V. (1843), VI. (1846), VII. (1849), VIII. (1855), IX. (1858). 5 v. 8°. '44–'59. ea., pap., 40c. .... *Murphy.*
— Acta et decreta Conc. Prov. Balt. X., 1869. 8°. '70. pap., 50c. .... *Murphy.*
— Concilia Balt. ab. anno 1829 ad annum 1849–'52–'55–'58. 8°. mor., $6 .... *Murphy.*
— Concilium Plenarium tot. Am. Septent. Fœderatæ, 1852. 8°. '53. pap., 50c. .... *Murphy.*
— Decrees, with documents, etc., for theological seminaries; by order of Plenary Council. 8°. '68. $1.50 .... *Murphy.*
— Decrees with documents, etc., of Plenary Council; with Synodus diœcesana Baltimorensis septima, etc. 12°. '68. $2 .... *Murphy.*
— Decreta Conc. Plen. et Prov. Balt. 8°. '54. pap., 50c. .... *Murphy.*
— Form of exposition and benediction of the sacrament; by order of 9th Prov. Council. 25c. ... *Murphy.*
— Pastoral letter of the 2d Plen. Council, 1866. 8°. 40c. .... *Murphy.*
— Pastoral letter of 10th Prov. Council, May, 1869. 8°. 25c. .... *Murphy.*
— Pastoral letters of councils, etc., 1843–1860. 8°. ea., 25c. .... *Murphy.*
— Synodus diœcesana Balt., 1857–'63. 8°. ea., 40c. *Murphy.*
— Synodus diœcesana Balt. Septima, 1868. 8°. '68. 50c. *Murphy.*

Baltimore gun club. *See* Verne, Jules.

Baltimore trader. *See* Adventures.

Baltzell, I. The camp meeting singer. obl. 16°. '73. 10c. .... *E. S. German.*

Balzac, Honoré de. Droll stories, collected from the abbeys of Touraine; tr. from the French. ill. by Doré. 12°. $5 .... *Routledge.*

Bamber, E. F. *See* Rankine, W. J. M., *and* Bamber, E. F.

Bamboozling. Wilks, T. E. 15c. .... *French.*

Bamford, *Miss* M. Jessie Bower; or, Mrs. Schaffer's school. ('66.) New ed. ill. 16°. '75. $1.25 .. *Hoyt.*

Bampton lectures, 1858. Limits of religious thought; by Rev. H. L. Mansel. 12°. $1.50 .... *Pott.*
— *Same.* sm. 8°. $3.75 .... *Scribner, W. & A.*
— 1862. Critical history of free thought in reference to the Christian religion; by A. S. Farrar. 12°. '63. $2 .... *Appleton.*
— 1864. Progress of doctrine in the New Test.; by Rev. T. D. Bernard. 12°. $1.50 .. *Pott; Sheldon.*
— *Same.* 3d ed. cr. 8°. '73. $1.75 ...... *Macmillan.*
— 1865. Eight lectures on miracles; by J. B. Mozley. 12°. $2.50 .... *Pott; Scribner, W. & A.*
— 1866. Divinity of Jesus Christ; by H. P. Liddon. 12°. $2.50 .... *Pott; Scribner, W. & A.*
— 1867. Dogmatic faith (The): inquiry into the relation between revelation and dogma; by Rev. E. Garbett. 12°. $2 .... *Pott.*
— 1868. Administration of the Holy Spirit in the body of Christ; by Rev. G. Moberly. 12°. $2.25 .. *Pott.*
— *Same.* 12°. $3.75 .... *Scribner, W. & A.*
— 1869. Prophecy a preparation for Christ; by Rev. R. P. Smith. 12°. $1.75 ...... *Macmillan; Pott.*
— 1870. Christianity as taught by St. Paul; by Rev. W. J. Irons. 8°. $5 .... *Pott; Scribner, W. & A.*
— 1871. Dissent in its relation to the Church of England; by Rev. G. H. Curteis. cr. 8°. '74. $2.50. *Macmillan; Pott.*
— *Same.* 8°. $2.25 .... *Scribner, W. & A.*
— 1872. Permanence of Christianity; by Rev. J. R. T. Eaton. 8°. $4 .... *Pott.*
— *Same.* 8°. $6 .... *Scribner, W. & A.*
— 1873. Characteristics of Christian morality; by Rev. J. G. Smith. 8°. $2.50. *Pott; Scribner, W. & A.*
— 1874. Religion of the Christ: its historic and literary development, etc.; by Rev. S. Leathes. sm. 8°. $2 .... *Pott.*
— *Same.* 8°. $4 .... *Pott; Scribner, W. & A.*
— 1875. Doctrine of retribution; by W: Jackson. 8°. '76. $3 .... *Randolph.*

Bancroft, Aar. Life of Geo. Washington. ill. 12°. $1.25 .... *Porter.*

Bancroft, G: History of the U. S. 10 v. por., maps, etc. 8°. '34–'74. $25; shp., $35; hf. cf., $45; cf., $55 .... *Little, B. & Co.*
— *Same.* (Centenary ed.) 6 v. 12°. '76. ea., $2.25; shp., $3; hf. cf., $4 .... *Little, B. & Co.*
— Literary and hist. miscellanies. 8°. $3; hf. cf., $5.25 .... *Harper.*

Bancroft, H. H. Native races of the Pacific states of N. Am. 5 v. 8°. ea., *$5.50; shp., $6.50; hf. cf., $8; hf. mor., $8; mor., $10 .... *Appleton.*

Cont.: Wild tribes. — Civilized nations of Mexico and Central Am. — Mythology and languages of both savage and civilized nations. — Antiquities and architectural remains. — Aboriginal hist. and migration, with index.

Bancroft, Silas A. *See* Mason, W., *and* Bancroft, S. A.

Bancroft's tourist's guide to the Geysers, San Francisco, and around the bay (north). ('71.) 2d ed. 12°. '73. $1; bds., 75c. .... *Bancroft.*

Bancroft's tourist's guide to Yosemite, San Francisco and around the bay (south). ('71.) 2d ed. 12°. '73. $1; bds., 75c. .... *Bancroft.*

Band of hope review. [Annual.] 4°. bds., 50c. *Nelson.*

Band of hope speaker. M'Curdy, C. L. 60c. *Cin. Meth. Bk. Conc.*
Band of six. Berry, M. E. $1.25..........*Am. Tr.*
Bandages removed. Seiss, J. A. 10c...*Luth. Bk. St.*
Bandit: drama. 16°. pap., 15c..............*French.*
Bandit of the ocean; or, the female privateer. 8°. pap., 25c..............................*De Witt.*
Bandits of the Osage. Bennett, E. 25c. *U. P. James.*
Banditti of the prairie. Bonney, M. 75c...*Peterson.*
Banes, C: H. History of the Phila. Brigade: 69th, 71st, 72d and 106th Regiments, Penn. Vol. 12°. $2.................................*Lippincott.*
Bange Tage. *See* Hoffmann, F.
Bangs, Heman. Autobiography and journal; with introd. by Bp. Janes; ed. by his daughters. por. 12°. '74. $1.50........................*Tibbals.*
Bangs, Nat. History of the Meth. Episc. Church. 4 v. 12°. '38. $6....................*Meth. Bk. Conc.*
— Letters on sanctification. 18°. 60c. *Cin. Meth. Bk. Conc.*
— Life of Rev. F. Garrettson. 12°. '38. $1.*Meth. Bk. Conc.*
— Original church of Christ. 12°. '37. 75c. *Meth. Bk. Conc.*
— Responsibilities of the Meth. Episc. Church. 18°. 60c......................*Cin. Meth. Bk. Conc.*
Banim, J: Celt's paradise. [Poem.] 12°. $1..*Sadlier.*
— Damon and Pythias: play. 16°. pap., 15c...*French.*
— Peep o' day (The); or, Captain John Doe, the last of the guerillas: a tale of the Whiteboys. 8°. pap., 50c. ....(?)*Am. News.*
— Sergeant's wife: drama. 16°. pap., 15c....*French.*
— Smuggler (The). 12°. $1.50.............*Harper.*
— *and* Mich. Works. 10 v. 12°. '65. $15; hf. mor., $20; hf. cf., $25; ea., $1.50...........*Sadlier.*
Cont.: Peep o' day, by J.—The croppy, by M.—Mayor of Windgap *and* Canvassing, by J.—Bit o' writin', by J.—Boyne water, by J.—Denounced *and* The conformists, by J.—Peter of the castle *and* The Fetches, by J.—Father Connell, by J.—Ghost hunter, by M.—Life of J., by P. J. Murray.
Banim, Mich. *See* Banim, J. *and* M.
Banished count (The). Bovet, F. $2.50...*Clauder.*
Banished daughter (The), and other stories. ('63.) New ed. 16°. '75. $1..................*Hoyt.*
Banished son. Hentz, C. L. $1.75; $1.50...*Peterson.*
Bank director's (The) son. Lippard, G. 25c...*Peterson.*
Bank notes; [also] It's his way. 18°. 35c...*Pres. Bd.*
Banker's almanac and register for 1876; ed. by B. Homans, jr. 25th [ann.] ed. 8°. '76. $3. (?)*Homans.*
Banker's (The) daughter. Reynolds, G. W. M. $1.75; $1...............................*Peterson.*
Banker's (The) secret. Smith, J. F. 75c...*Dick & F.*
Banker's victim; or, the betrayed seamstress. 8°. pap., 25c. ....*De Witt.*
Banker's (The) wife. Arthur, T., S. 50c...*Peterson.*
Banker's (The) wife. Gore, C. G. 50c......*Harper.*
Bankers' (The) common place book: incl. Treatise on banking, by A. B. Johnson; Ten minutes' advice on keeping a bank, by J. W. Gilbert; Remarks on the law of bills of exchange, by Byles, etc. 12°. '70. $1.50...........................*Homans.*
Banknote (Die). *See* Hoffmann, F.
Banks, Natl. P. The bobbin boy: life of B. 12°. $1.50......................................*Tilton.*
Banks of the Hudson. Dibdin, T. 15c. .....*French.*
Bannan, B: *See* Daddow, S. H., *and* Bannan, B.
Banner boys. 4°. 25c....................*Am. Bapt.*
Banner stories. 12 v. ill. 24°. $2.50...*Bost. Am. Tr.*
Cont.: Alice Lee's temptation.—Disobedient chipmunk.—The dandelion.—The hedgehog.—Little Lucy Harris.—Little Queen Bess.—May queen.—Our birds' nest.—The returned father.—Something about eyes.—The ugly morsel.—Why not on Sunday?
Bannerman, Ja. Church (The) of Christ: nature, powers, ordinances, etc., of the Christian church. 2 v. 8°. $10.................*Scribner, W. & A.*
Bannerman, Ja., *continued.*
— On inspiration. 8°. $5..........*Scribner, W. & A.*
Bannister, H. M. *See* Illinois geol. survey.
Bannister, N. H. Putnam: drama. 16°. pap., 15c. *French.*
Bannon, B: Tables showing weight of round, square and flat bar iron, steel, etc., by measurement. (cop. '51.) '65. 4th ed. obl. 32°. '71. 63c. *Baird.*
Banquet (The). *See* Plato.
Banting, W: Letter on corpulence; addressed to the public. 18°. pap., 25c..............*Lippincott.*
Banvard, J: Private life of a king: memoirs of Prince of Wales, afterward George IV. of Eng. 12°. '75. $2.50................(?)*Lit. and Art Pub.*
Banvard, Jos. First explorers of No. Am.; with introd. by G. T. Day. ill. 16°. '74. $1.50..*Lothrop.*
— Great promises of the Bible. [Quest. books.] 3 pts. 18°. '71. ea., bds., 15c...........*H. A. Young.*
— Juvenile library. 8 v. 18°. $3.25......*Am. Bapt.*
Cont.: Young observers, 3 pts.—Wonders of the deep.—Heads and feet.—Curious habits of birds.—Sagacity of animals.—Wonderful stories.
— Life of Dan. Webster. New ed. ill. 16°. '75. $1.50. *Lothrop.*
— Old Grips and little Tid; or, acts of benevolence. ill. 16°. '71. 75c..........................*Ward.*
— Pictorial question book. 18°. bds., 15c...*Am. Bapt.*
— Pioneers of Maryland; with account of the old French war and various events in the early settlement of Am. 16°. '75. $1.25.................*Lothrop.*
— Plymouth and the pilgrims; or, incidents and adventures of the first settlers. ill. 16°. '74. $1.25. *Lothrop.*
— Practical question book. 18°. bds., 15c...*Am. Bapt.*
— Priscilla; or, trials for the truth. 16°. $1.50. *Am. Bapt.*
— Soldiers and patriots of the revolution. ill. 16°. '76. $1.25................................*Lothrop.*
— Southern explorers and colonists: account of early settlements of No. Car. and Va. ill. 16°. '74. $1.25................................*Lothrop.*
— Story truths. 4 v. ill. 18°. '61. $1.75.....*Am. Tr.*
— Topical question book. 18°. bds., 15c...*Am. Bapt.*
— Wonderful stories. 18°. 30c.; 40c. .....*Am. Bapt.*
— Wonders of the deep. 18°. 30c.; 40c. ..*Am. Bapt.*
— Young observers. 3 pts. 18°. ea., 30c.; 40c. *Am. Bapt.*
Bapteesement (The) o' th' bairn. *See* Leighton, R.
Baptism (The). 18°. 30c..................*Dutton.*
Baptism (The); or, the little inquirer. 18°. 28c.; 35c. *Am. Bapt.*
Baptism in a nutshell. Baker, D. 25c...(?)*Martien.*
Baptism in spirit and in fire. Challen, J. 10c...*Challen.*
Baptism of infants. 15c.............(?)*Cumberland.*
Baptismal balance. Brown, J. N. 10c....*Am. Bapt.*
Baptisms of the New Testament. Belcher, J. 55c.; 65c. *Am. Bapt.*
Baptist Church. Handbuch f. Gemeineglieder; übers. v. A. Henrick. 16°. 65c. ....*Germ. Bapt.*
— *See also* Seventh Day Baptists.
Baptist collection: "Plymouth collection" enl., and adapted to Baptist churches. 8°. '57. $2.50; $4.50; $6.50.........................*Barnes.*
Baptist facts vs. Methodist fiction. Dayton, A. C. 30c...............................*So. Bapt.*
Baptist family library. 20 v. 16°. $18....*Am. Bapt.*
Baptist harp. [Hymn and tune book.] 48°. 30c.-60c. 24°. 50c.-$1.50........................*Am. Bapt.*
Baptist hymn and tune book. 24°. 75c. 18°. 50c.; $1; shp., $1.25........................*So. Bapt.*
— *Same.* 12°. $1; mor., $4. 8°. $2.25; mor., $5. *Am. Bapt.*
Baptist hymn book. sq. 18°. 50c.—(Pocket ed.) 24°. 75c.-$5.—(Pew ed.) 18°. $1.25-$3.50.—(Pulpit ed.) 12°. $2-$4.........................*Am. Bapt.*

Baptist pamphlets. 2 v. 18°. hf. mor., $2.. *Am. Bapt.*

Baptist praise book (The) for congregational singing; by R. Fuller, E. M. Levey, S. D. Phelps and others. 8°. $2.50-$6.50. — Same: hymns only. sm. 4°. $1.75-$5. Chapel ed. sm. 4°. $1.25-$4.50 .... *Barnes.*

Baptist pretensions met and confuted. *See* Sedwick, B. F.

Baptist psalmody (The). *See* Manly, B. *and* B. *jr.*

Baptist Sunday-school quest. books on Acts and John. 4 v. 18°. ea., bds., 15c.......... *Am. Bapt.*

Baptist trophy. Softon, G. A. 75c. .... *So. Bapt.*

Baptista; by author of "Eildon Manor." ill. 16°. $1.75 .... *Scribner, W. & A.*

Baptists and the higher liberty. Carter, J. E. 25c.; 10c.......... *So. Bapt.*

Baptized child. Lee, H. W. 30c.; 10c...... *Dutton.*

Bar (The) of iron. *See* Tayler, C. B.

Barak Johnson: drama. 16°. pap., 15c...... *French.*

Barault, *L'abbé.* Elevation of the soul to God by means of spiritual considerations and affections; tr. from the French. 18°. 75c.......... *Strong.*

— *Same.* 18°. shp., 90c.......... *Cummiskey.*

Barba, J. Use of steel in construction: methods of working, applying and testing plates and bars; tr., with pref., by A. L. Holley. ill. 12°. '75. $1.50.......... *Van Nostrand.*

Barbadoes girl (The). *See* Hofland, *Mrs.* B.

Barbara. Edson, N. I. $1.50.......... *Lothrop.*

Barbara St. John. Chamberlain, P. B. $1.25. *Garrigues.*

Barbara's history. Edwards, A. B. 75c..... *Harper.*

Barbarossa (*pseud.*) *See* Scott, J:

Barbarossa. Bischoff, J. E. $2; $2.50.. *Cummiskey.*

Barbarossa. Brown, J. 15c.......... *French.*

Barbary doves (The); [also] Rowland Hill. 32°. 25c. *Pres. Bd.*

Barbauld, *Mrs.* Anna Letitia. Hymns in prose. ill. 32°. 25c.; 40c.......... *Scribner, W. & A.*

— *Same;* ill. by Coleman, Barnes, etc. sm. 4°. '68. $2; $2.50; mor., $5.......... *Hurd & H.*

— Lessons for children. 16°. 50c.......... *Routledge.*

— *Same;* with French tr. arranged according to Marcel's system, by I. de Veitelle. 16°. 75c... *Appleton.*

— *French;* with vocab. 16°. '45. 60c... *G. R. Lockwood.*

— Memoir, letters and sel. from poems and prose writings; by Mrs. G. A. Ellis. 2 v. por. 12°. '74. $5; hf. cf., $9.......... *Osgood.*

— Things by their right names and other stories, etc., in prose and verse; with sketch of life by Mrs. S. J. Hale. 18°. 75c.......... *Harper.*

— *See also* Aikin, J., *and* Barbauld, *Mrs.* A. L.

Barbe Bleue. *See* Ditson.

Barbee, W: J. Confirmation. 8°. pap., 10c... *Chase.*

— First principles of geology. 12°. '67. $1.75.. *Morton.*

Bärbele's Weihnachten. *See* Wildermuth, O.

Barber, A. L. The critical speller. 8°. '72. pap., 20c. *Barnes.*

Barber, E: C. The crack shot; or, young rifleman's complete guide. 12°. $1.75.......... *Woodward.*

Barber, Ja. The nation's defenders: account of the national homes for disabled volunteer soldiers. 2d ed., enl. 12°. '73. pap., 35c.......... *Dennis.*

Barber, J: Warner. Connecticut hist. collections. New ed. 8°. *net,* $2.25.......... *Peck.*

— Elements of general hist. 18°. *net,* 75c....... *Peck.*

— Heroes and heroic events in Am. hist. ill. 12°. $1.50. *World Pub.*

— Staff and scrip; or, help for the pilgrim in the journey of life. ill. 8°. '75. * $3.50; mor., $4.50. *Bradley & G.*

— *See also* Bible looking-glass; — Olney, J., *and* Barber, J. W.

Barber, Jos. American book of ready-made speeches. 16°. pap., 50c.; bds., 75c.......... *Dick & F.*

Barber, L. E. *See* Arkansas, Sup. Court reports.

Barber, M. A. S. Missionary tales for little listeners. 18°. 50c.......... *Pres. Bd.*

Barber, *Miss* Ma. Five years among the Indians. [*In* Eng. *or* Germ.] 8°. pap., 25c .... *Barclay.*

Barber and bravo: drama. 16°. pap., 15c.... *French.*

Barber baron. Raymond, —: 15c.......... *French.*

Barber of Seville. Beaumarchais, P. A. C. de. 15c. *French.*

Barber's chair (The). *See* Jerrold, D.

Barbier, J. *See* Carré, M., *and* Barbier, J.

Barbier (Il) di Seviglia. *See* Rossini, G.

Barbour, Lucian, *and* Howland, J. D. Indiana executor's manual. 8°. shp., $3.......... *Merrill.*

Barbour, Ol. L. Treatise on parties to actions at law and suits in equity. 8°. shp., $6.50.. *W. C. Little.*

— Treatise on the practice of the Court of Chancery, with precedents, notes and ref. 2d ed., rev. and enl. 3 v. 8°. '75. shp., $22.50.......... *Banks.*

— *See also* New York, Supreme Court reports; — Tiffany, J., *and* Barbour, O. L.

Barby's shuttle. Boyd, M. D. R. 75c... *J. A. Moore.*

Barca. *See* Calderon de la Barca, P.

Barcelo, Juan. *See* Pinney, N., *and* Barcelo, J.

Barchester Towers. *See* Trollope, A.

Barclay, Ant. Wilde's Summer rose; or, the lament of the captive: origin, etc., of R. H. Wilde's alleged plagiarism. 8°. '71. $1.50... *Ga. Hist.*

Barclay, D. R. *See* Missouri, Supreme Court reports.

Barclay, G: L. "Little Cuba"; or, circumstantial evidence. [Fiction.] [*In* Eng. *or* Germ.] 8°. pap., 25c. .... *Barclay.*

Barclay, Ja. B. My friend Thompson: drama. 16°. pap., 15c. .... *French.*

Barclay, Ja. T. The city of the great king; or, Jerusalem as it was, as it is, and as it is to be. ('57.) 7th ed. 8°. $5.......... *Challen.*

Barclay, J: Letters. 12°. shp., 75c... *Friends Bk. St.*

Barclay, Rob. Apology for the true Christian divinity: explanation and vindication of the principles and doctrines of the people called Quakers. 8°. $1.50. 12°. 50c. .... *Friends Bk. St.*

— Catechism (A) and confession of faith. 12°. 35c. *Friends Bk. St.*

— Treatise on church government, formerly called Anarchy of the ranters, etc.: a twofold apology for the church and people of God, called, in derision, Quakers. 12°. 35c. .... *Friends Bk. St.*

Barclay, Sidney (*pseud.*) *See* Post, L. M.

Barclays (The); or, trying to serve two masters. 18°. 60c. .... *Am. S. S.*

Bardeen, C. W. (*ed.*) Common school law for common school teachers. ('75.) 2d ed., rev. 16°. '76. 50c.......... *Bardeen.*

Bardell vs. Pickwick. *See* Dickens, C.

Bardour, the dangerous boy. 18°. 20c.; 25c. *Am. Bapt.*

Bards of the Bible. Gilfillan, G. $1.25..... *Harper.*

Bardsley, C: Wareing. Our English surnames: their sources and significations. 2d ed., rev. and enl. 12°. $3.......... *Routledge.*

— *Same.* cr. 8°. $3.60; hf. cf., $5.60.. *Scribner, W. & A.*

Barefaced impostor: farce. 16°. pap., 15c... *French.*

Baretti, J. J. *See* Neuman, H., *and* Baretti, J. J.

Barford mills. Winslow, M. E. $1...... *Nat. Temp.*

Barham, *Rev.* R: H. ["Thomas Ingoldsby."] Ingoldsby legends; or, mirth and marvel. 12°. $2. ill. 4°. $10.......... *Routledge.*

Barham, *Rev.* R: H., *continued.*
— *Same.* (Victoria ed.) 18°. $1.25. — (Popular ed.) 12°. $2.50. — Annotated ed., with etchings. 2 v. 8°. $12; hf. cf., $16; cf., $20; $22.50. *Scribner, W. & A.*
— *Same;* with memoir of author. 2 v. ill. cr. 8°. $3.50; hf. cf., $7. (Globe ed.) 1 v. 16°. $2.25.; hf. cf., $4 .... *Widdleton.*
— *See also* Stoddard, R. H., Bric-a-brac ser.
Baring, C: *See* Discourses on atonement.
Baring-Gould, Sabine. Curious myths of the middle ages. 16°. '68. $1.25 .... *Roberts.*
— *Same.* ill. 12°. hf. roxb., $2.50 .... *Lippincott.*
— Gabrielle André. [Fiction.] 8°. pap., 60c. *Appleton.*
— In exitu Israel: an historical novel. cr. 8°. '70. $1.50 .... *Macmillan.*
— Legends of Old Test. characters; from the Talmud and other sources. cr. 8°. '71. $2 .. *Macmillan.*
— Legends of the patriarchs and prophets, current at the east. cr. 8°. '72. $2 .... *Holt.*
— Lives of the saints. [To form 12 v.] v. 1–8. 12°. ea., $2.50 .... *Pott.*
— Some modern difficulties. 12°. '75. $2 .... *Pott.*
Barkeeper's manual. 12°. pap., 50c. .... *Haney.*
Barker, Fordyce. Puerperal disease: lectures at Bellevue Hospital. 8°. $5; shp., $6 .... *Appleton.*
— Sea-sickness. sm. 12°. 75c. .... *Appleton.*
Barker, G: F. College chemistry. 12°. '70. $1.75. *Morton.*
— Correlation of vital and physical forces. 12°. '75. pap., 25c. .... *Van Nostrand.*
Barker, Jos. Modern skepticism: a journey through the land of doubt and back again: a life story. 12°. '74. $1.75 .... *Smith, E. & Co.*
Barker, *Rev.* Jos. Jesus: a portrait. 12°. '74. $1. *Meth. Epis.*
Barker, Ma. A. (*Lady*). [Mrs. Frederic N. Broome.] Boys. ill. 12°. '74. $1.75 .... *Routledge.*
— Christmas cake in four quarters. [Juvenile.] ill. fp. 8°. '71. $1.50 .... *Macmillan.*
— First lessons in the principles of cooking. 18°. '74. 50c. .... *Macmillan.*
— Holiday stories for boys and girls. ill. 16°. '72. $1.50 .... *Routledge.*
— Ribbon stories. [Juvenile.] 2d ed. ill. fp. 8°. $1.50 .... *Macmillan.*
— Spring comedies: A wedding story; A stupid story; A Scotch story; A man's story. cr. 8°. '71. $1.50 .... *Macmillan.*
— Station life in New Zealand. 2d [chp.] ed. fp. 8°. '74. $1.50 .... *Macmillan.*
— Stories about. [Juvenile.] 3d ed. ill. fp. 8°. '71. $1.50 .... *Macmillan.*
— Sybil's book. [Juvenile.] ill. fp. 8°. '71. $1.50. *Macmillan.*
— Traveling about over old and new ground. ill. cr. 8°. '71. $2 .... *Routledge.*
Barker, *Mrs.* Sale. Lily's home. 16°. '75. 50c. *Routledge.*
— With a stout heart. ill. 16°. '74. $1.25 .. *Routledge.*
— (*ed.*) Little wide-awake for 1876. ill. sm. 4°. '75. $1.25; $2 .... *Routledge.*
Barker, Thdr. T. Vocal exercises; for baritone and bass. f°. '70. pap., $1.25 .... *Ditson.*
Barksdale, W. H. Pedobaptist concessions to Baptist principles. 18°. pap., 10c. .... *So. Bapt.*
Barley loaves; by author of "Christmas with the boys." 16°. $1.25 .... *Am. S. S.*
Barley wood. Parker, J. M. 75c. .... *Claremont.*
Barlow, *Mrs.* C. Y. Helen Mac Gregor; or, conquest and sacrifice. 16°. '65. $1.25 .... *Garrigues.*
— Stella Ashton; or, conquered faults. 18°. '68. 90c. *Garrigues.*
Barlow, E. H. *See* Sheldon, E. A., *and* Barlow, E. H.

Barlow, G: H. Manual of the practice of medicine; with add. by D. F. Condie. 8°. $2.50 .... *Lea.*
Barlow, J. W. Report of a reconnaissance of the basin of the Upper Yellowstone. *See* United States, *Corps of Eng.*
Barlow family. 18°. 50c.; 60c. .... *Am. Bapt.*
Barlow's tables of squares, cubes, square roots, cube roots, reciprocals of integer numbers to 10,000. 8°. '73. $2.50 .... *Spon.*
Barnaby Rudge. *See* Dickens, C.
Barnaby Rudge: drama. 16°. pap., 15c. .... *French.*
Barnard, C: Fs., *jr.* ["Jane Kingsford;" "*Mrs.* Maria Gilman."] Camilla, a tale of a violin: artist life of Camilla Urso. 18°. 75c.; pap., 50c. .. *Loring.*
— Charles Barnard's money and music: an art story. 12°. $1 .... (?) *Shepard.*
— Gardening for money: how it was done with flowers, strawberries, vegetables. 12°. $1.50 .... *Loring.*
— Soprano (The): a musical story. 12°. $1; pap., 60c. .... *Loring.*
— Tone masters (The). 3 v. ill. 16°. ea., $1.25. *Lee & S.*
Cont.: Mozart and Mendelssohn. — Handel and Haydn. — Bach and Beethoven.

Barnard, F: A. P. Metric system of weights and measures: address, Albany, August, 1871. 2d ed. 8°. '72. $3 .... *Van Nostrand.*
— Report on machinery and processes on indust. arts and apparatus of the exact sciences at the Paris Exposition, 1867. ill. 8°. '69. $5 .. *Van Nostrand.*
— *and* Guyot, A. (*ed.*) Johnson's new universal cyclopædia. [To form 4 v.] v. 1–2. maps, plans and eng. 8°. '74–'75. ea., *$10.75; hf. mor., $12.75; $15.75 .... (?) *A. J. Johnson.*
Barnard, G: Foliage and foreground drawing. ill. 16°. '75. $1.75 .... *Routledge.*
— Theory and practice of landscape painting in water-colors; with col. drawings and diagrams. roy. 8°. $9 .... *Routledge.*
Barnard, H: Military schools and courses of instruct. in science and art of war, in France, Prussia, Austria, Russia, Sweden, Switzerland, Sardinia, Eng. and the U. S. 8°. '62. $3.75 .... *Claxton.*
— Oral training lessons in nat. science and general knowledge; for teachers. 12°. '71. $1 .. *Barnes.*
Barnard, J: G. "C. S. A." (The), and battle of Bull Run: letter to an English friend. maps. 8°. '62. $2 .... *Van Nostrand.*
— Delta of the Mississippi. *See* Hamilton, S., Fabrication of béton blocks.
— Experiments on shield of casement at Fortress Monroe. 8°. pap., 50c. .... *Am. Soc. of C. E.*
— Notes on sea-coast defence: [compr.] sea-coast fortifications, the fifteen-inch gun, and casemate embrasure. pl. 8°. '61. $2 .... *Van Nostrand.*
— Peninsular campaign and its antecedents, as developed by the report of Gen. McClellan, and other documents. 8°. '64. $1. 12°. pap., 30c. *Van Nostrand.*
— Problems of rotary motion. 4°. '72. pap., $2. *Smith. Inst.*
— Report on defenses of Washington; — on fabrication of iron; — on North Sea Canal of Holland. *See* United States, *Corps of Eng.*
— Resistance of beams to flexure. *See* Chanute, O., Weight of rails.
— *and* Barry, W. F. Report of the engineer and artillery operations of the army of the Potomac. maps and plans. 8°. '64. $4 .... *Van Nostrand.*
Barnby, J. Eight four-part songs. 8°. pap., 50c. *Ditson.*
Barnby, Jos. Original tunes to popular hymns; for the voice, or piano or organ. 4°. $2 .. *Schirmer.*
Barnes, Alb. Apostolic church (The): inquiry into its organization and government, particularly with ref. to the claims of Episcopacy. 18°. 60c. *Pres. Bd.*
— Commentary on Acts. ('63.) 20th ed., rev. map. 12°. '70. $1.50 .... *Un. S. S.*

Barnes, Alb., *continued.*
— Lectures on the evidences of Christianity in the 19th century. 12°. $1.75 .... *Harper.*
— Life at threescore and ten. 18°. '71. 35c... *Am. Tr.*
— Notes, critical, explan. and pract., on the Psalms. 3 v. 12°. ea., $1.50 .... *Harper.*
— Notes on Daniel. 12°. $2 .... *World Pub.*
— Notes on Isaiah. 2 v. 12°. $4 .... *World Pub.*
— Notes on Job. 2 v. 12°. $4 .... *World Pub.*
— Notes on New Test. 11 v. maps and ill. 12°. ea., $1.50 .... *Harper.*
Cont.: Four Gospels, 2 v.—Acts.—Romans.—1st Corinthians.—2d Corinthians and Galatians.—Ephesians, Colossians and Philippians.—Thessalonians, Timothy, Titus and Philemon.—Hebrews.—James, Peter, John and Jude.—Revelations.
— — Questions on *same.* 7 v. 18°. ea., 30c... *Harper.*
Cont.: Matthew.—Mark and Luke.—John.—Acts.—Romans.—1st Corinthians.—Hebrews.
— Prayers for use of families; with essay and sel. of hymns. New ed., enl. por. roy. 12°. $1.75; $2.25; hf. cf., $2.50; $2.75; $3.50 .... *Desilver.*
— Thron (Der) der Sünde, od. d. Unterstützung d. Unmässigkeit v. Seiten d. Regierung. 12°. pap., 10c. .... *Ev. Assoc.*
Barnes, F: K. *See* Ship building.
Barnes, J: S. Submarine warfare, defensive and offensive, compr. hist. of invention of torpedo; [with] discussion of the offensive torpedo system. pl. and wood-cuts. 8°. '69. $5 ..... *Van Nostrand.*
Barnes, Josiah. Wonderful adventures by land and sea of the seven queer travellers who met at an inn. 12°. $1.75 .... *J. E. Potter.*
Barnes, Loring B. New congregational harp and chapel: hymns, tunes, etc. obl. 8°. '69. bds., $1.38 .... *Ditson.*
Barnes, Rob. Clinical exposition of the medical and surgical diseases of women. ill. 8°. $5; leath., $6 .... *Lea.*
— Obstetric operations; with add. by B. F. Dawson. ill. 8°. $4.50 .... *Appleton.*
— *See also* Power, H., Holmes, T., Anstie, F. E., *and* Barnes, R.
Barnes, Rob. Life and writings. *See* British reformers.
Barnes, W: Poems in the Dorset dialect. 16°. '64. $1 .... *H. H. Carter.*
— Rural poems. sq. 18°. '68. $1.25; ill., $2; mor., $5. *Roberts.*
Barnes, W: Settlement and early history [of Albany, N. Y.] sm. 8°. '71. pap., $1 .... *Munsell.*
Barnes, W: H. Body politic (The): a book for Americans. 12°. '66. $1.50 .... *Wilstach.*
— History of the 39th Congress of the U. S. por. 8°. $5 .... *Harper.*
Barnes' brief history of France. 12°. '75. $1.50. *Barnes.*
Barnes' brief history of the U. S.; for schools. 12°. '71. $1.50 .... *Barnes.*
Barnes' centenary hist. of the U. S. roy. 8°. '76. *$6; shp., $7.50; hf. cf., $9; mor., $12.—Serial ed., in 13 pts., ea., *50c.; in 1 v., *$7.50; shp., $9; hf. cf., $10.50; mor., $13.50 .... *Barnes.*
Barnet, Ja: Barnet's coast pilot for the lakes from Chicago to Lake Superior. ('59.) 7th ed. 8°. '74. bds., $2 .... *Barnet.*
— Martyrs and heroes of Illinois in the war of the rebellion: biog. sketches. por. 8°. $3; shp., $3.25. *Barnet.*
Barnett, J: Lillian Gervaise: drama. 16°. pap., 15c. *French.*
Barnett, Morris. [Plays.] 6 v. 16°. ea., pap., 15c. *French.*
Cont.: Bold dragoons: comic drama.—Married unmarried.—Monsieur Jacques: operetta.—Sarah, the Creole.—Serious family: comedy.—Yankee pedlar: farce.
Barnewall, R. V. *See* England, Common law reports; Court of King's Bench reports.

Barney, *Master.* *See* Rickey, S., *and* Barney, *Master.*
Barney the baron: farce. 16°. pap., 15c. .... *French.*
Barney's courtship. Macarthy, H. 15c..... *De Witt.*
Barnum, S: W. Romanism as it is: exposition of the Roman Cath. system. ('71.) New ed., enl. ill. 8°. '76. *$3.50; shp., $4; hf. mor., $5.. *Conn. Pub.*
Baron, R: Aus Nacht zum Licht. 16°. 25c... *Morwitz.*
— *Same.* 16°. 30c.; bds., 20c.; pap., 15c.... *Kohler.*
— Geschichte e. jungen Malers. 16°. '70. bds., 25c. *Steiger.*
— Schulmeister (Der) v. Tannenrode. 16°. '68. bds., 25c. .... *Steiger.*
— Was der Mensch säet, das wird er auch ernten. 16°. 25c. .... *Morwitz; Steiger.*
— *Same.* 16°. 30c.; bds., 20c.; pap., 15c.... *Kohler.*
Baron Munchausen. *See* Raspe, R. E.
Baron of Hertz. Labadye, F. de. $2 .... *O'Shea.*
Baronet's (The) bride; or, the husband's secret. 8°. pap., 25c. .... *De Witt.*
Baronet's (The) daughters. Grey, E. C. 50c. *Peterson.*
Baronin (Die). *See* Dedenroth, E. H. v.
Baron's (The) little daughter, and other tales in prose and verse; by author of "Hymns for little children"; ed. by W. Gresley. 16°. 60c. *McCauley.*
Barr, *Mrs.* Amelia E. Romances and realities: tales, sketches and papers. 12°. '75. $1.50.... *Ford.*
Barr, *Rev.* J. T. Merchant's daughter, and other narratives. 16°. 60c. .... *Cin. Meth. Bk. Conc.*
Barr, *Rev.* Ja. Pronouncing dict. of the Holy Bible: a concordance of subjects, and index to the Scriptures. ('68.) 2d ed. 12°. '75. $1..... *Virtue.*
Barr, J: Early relig. hist., [autobiog.]; with sketch of his character by a grandson. 18°. 35c. *Pres. Bd.*
Barr, *Rev.* J: Index to the Bible. 12°. $1.. *Meth. Bk. Conc.*
— Plain catechetical instruction for young communicants. 18°. 20c. .... *Pres. Bd.*
Barr, Rob. M. *See* Pennsylvania, Sup. Court reports.
Barrack-room. Bayly, T. H. 15c. .... *French.*
Barren fig tree (The). *See* Bunyan, J.
Barren honor. *See* Lawrence, Geo.
Barren honor. Wood, E. P. $1.25; 75c.... *Dick & F.*
Barrera, *Mme.* A. de. Memoirs of Rachel; by Mme. de B—. 12°. $1.50 .... *Harper.*
Barrett, Alfr. Boatman's daughter. ('55.) 4th ed. 18°. '75. 50c. .... *So. Meth.*
Barrett, B: F. Beauty for ashes; or, the old and new doctrine concerning infants after death. 12°. 50c. *Appleton.*
— Golden city (The). 12°. '73. $1.25 .... *Claxton.*
— Lectures on the new dispensation; to unfold and elucidate the leading doctrines of the New Church. 12°. $1.25 .... *Claxton.*
— Letters on the divine Trinity; addressed to H. W. Beecher. 4th ed., enl. 12°. '73. $1... *Claxton.*
— Letters on the future life; addressed to H. W. Beecher. 12°. '72. $1 .... *Claxton.*
— New view (The) of hell; showing its nature, whereabouts, duration, and how to escape it. 12°. '71. $1 .... *Claxton.*
— *See also* Swedenborg, E., Swedenborg lib.
Barrett, E: Dead reckoning; or, day's work. 8°. '63. $1.25 .... *Van Nostrand.*
— Gunnery instructions; simplified for the volunteer officers of the U. S. navy, with hints to executive and other officers. 12°. '63. $1.25.. *Van Nostrand.*
Barrett, Howard. Management of infancy and childhood. [Children's diseases.] 12°. '75. $2.50. *Routledge.*
Barrett, J. O. Immortelles of love. 12°. '73. $1; $1.50 .... *Colby.*
— Looking beyond. ('71.) 3d ed. 12°. '74. 75c. *Colby.*
— Social freedom: marriage as it is, and as it should be. ('73.) 2d ed. 12°. '75. 25c. .... *Colby.*

Barrett, J. O., *continued.*
— Spiritual pilgrim: biog. of J. M. Peebles. ('71.) 3d ed., rev. por. 12°. '74. $1.50........*Colby.*
— *See also* Peebles, J. M., *and* Barrett, J. O.
— *and* Peebles, J. M. The Gadarene; or, spirits in prison. 12°. '74. $1.25..................*Colby.*
Barrett, Jos. C. Old Abe, the live war eagle of Wisconsin. 12°. $1; pap., 50c...........*Atwood.*
Barrett, Jos. H. Illustrated life of Abraham Lincoln; with his messages, proclamations, letters, etc., and hist. of his administration. ('60.) 3d ed. 8°. '65. $3; shp., $3.50; hf. cf., $4.50... *Wilstach.*
— *Same;* tr. into German by J. L. C. Eggers. 8°. '65. $3; shp., $3.50; hf. cf., $4.50........ *Wilstach.*
Barrett, Ma. Our summer at Hillside farm. ill. 16°. $1..............................*Bost. Am. Tr.*
— — *See also* Prairie lib.
— Steps in the upward way: story of Fanny Bell. ill. 16°. $1.........................*Bost. Am. Tr.*
— William the Silent, and the Netherland war. maps and ill. 16°. '71. $1.50...............*Lothrop.*
Barrett, P. The deaf shoemaker. 18°. '59. 75c. *Dodd.*
Barrett, Selah H. Autobiography. 8°. '72. $1. *Freewill.*
— Memoirs of eminent preachers in the Freewill Baptist denomination. 8°. '74. $1........*Freewill.*
Barrett, W. A. Flowers and festivals: directions for floral decoration of churches. ill. 16°. $2..*Pott.*
— *See also* Stainer, J., *and* Barrett, W. A.
Barrett, Wa. (*pseud.*) *See* Scoville, Jos. A.
Barrière, Thdr., *and* Kock, H. de. Old house on the bridge of Notre Dame: drama. 16°. pap., 15c. *French.*
— *and* Plouvier, E. Angel of midnight: drama. 16°. pap., 15c. ....*French.*
Barriers burned away. Roe, E. P. $1.75.....*Dodd.*
Barring out. *See* Edgeworth, M.
Barrington, *Sir* Jonah. Personal sketches of his own times. ill. 12°. $1.75; hf. cf., $3.50.. *Widdleton.*
— *Same;* ed. by T. Young. 2 v. 8°. $6...*Routledge.*
— Rise and fall of the Irish nation. 12°. $1.50..*Sadlier.*
Barrington. *See* Lever, Charles.
Barroll, B: C. Maryland chancery practice; with rules of court, etc. 8°. '69. shp., $8..*Cushings & B.*
Barron, Alfr. Foot-notes; or, walking as a fine art; "by Q." 16°. '75. $1.50.............*Oneida.*
Barrow, *Mrs.* Fanny. ["Aunt Fanny."] Aunt Fanny's story book. *See* Continental lib.
— Good little hearts; or, stories about children who tried to be good and do good. 4 v. ill. 16°. '64. $2.50 ....*Hurd & H.*
— Little pet books. ('60.) 5th ed. 3 v. sq. 16°. '76. $2.50..................................*Allison.*
Cont.: Bad old ape. — Puss and John. — Mop and Frisk.
— Nightcap series. 6 v. ill. 18°. $5........*Appleton.*
Cont.: Nightcaps. — New nightcaps. — Baby nightcaps. — Little nightcaps. — Big nightcaps. — Fairy nightcaps.
— Pop-gun stories (The). 6 v. ill. 16°. $6..*Sheldon.*
Cont.: Pop-guns. — One big pop-gun. — All sorts of pop-guns. — Funny pop-guns. — Grasshopper pop-guns. — Post office pop-guns.
— Six mitten books (The). 6 v. ill. 16°. $5..*Appleton.*
Cont.: Mittens. — Little mittens. — More mittens. — The two story mittens. — New little mittens. — The orphan's home mittens.
— Story book for boys and girls. ill. 18°. 75c. *Appleton.*
— Take heed, and other stories. ill. 18°. '70. 75c. *Dutton.*
Barrow, *Sir* J: Memoir of the life of Peter the Great. 18°. 75c. ....*Harper.*
— Pitcairn's Island and its inhabitants; with account of the mutiny of the "Bounty." 18°. 75c...*Harper.*
— Voyages of discovery and research within the Arctic regions, 1811–'40. map. 12°. $1......*Harper.*
Barrows, E. P. Companion to the Bible. (cop. '67.) New ed. ill. 12°. '69. $1.75; hf. mor., $3..*Am. Tr.*

Barrows, E. P., *continued.*
— Sacred geography and antiquities. ill. 12°. '72. $2.25 ....*Am. Tr.*
— *See also* Bible [Whole]; Bible, New Test., *Germ.*
Barrows, *Mrs.* J. S. Little Gracie. ('64.) New ed. ill. 16°. '75. 45c.........................*Hoyt.*
Barrows, L. D. Home as it should be, with counsel for all. 18°. '74. 35c..........*Meth. Bk. Conc.*
— Rudiments of public speaking and debate. 12°. '61. $1.50..............................*Meth. Bk. Conc.*
— Scripture readings for devotion and study. 16°. '71. 20c. ....*N. E. Meth.*
Barrows, N. Sunday-school offices for the Christian year, with offertory, hymns, etc. 16°. 30c. *Dutton.*
Barrows, *Rev.* W. The church and her children. 12°. $1.50 ....*Cong. Pub.*
Barrows, W: The general; or, twelve nights in the hunters' camp. ill. 16°. '69. $1.25....*Lee & S.*
Barrows, *Mrs.* W: Pilgrim series for 1875. [S.-school quest. book.] 18°. bds., 15c........*Cong. Pub.*
Barry, Alfr. Atonement of Christ: lectures, 1871. 12°. $1 ....*Macmillan.*
Barry, C: A. How to draw. ill. 16°. '70. 50c.; pap., 25c. ....*Happy.*
Barry, J: S. Historical Sketch of Hanover, Mass. 8°. $2 ....*Burnham.*
Barry, *Mrs.* Martha E. The hard knot. *See* Golden sheaves lib.
Barry, Mich. Jos. Songs of Ireland. 12°. $1..*Noonan.*
Barry, P. Fruit-garden. 12°. $2.50............*Judd.*
Barry, S. Dutchman's ghost: farce. 16°. pap., 15c. *French.*
— Persecuted Dutchman: farce. 16°. pap., 15c. *French.*
Barry, T. A., *and* Patten, B. A. Men and memories of San Francisco, in the spring of '50. 8°. '73. $2 ....*Bancroft.*
Barry, W. F. *See* Barnard, J. G., *and* Barry, W. F.
Barry, W: History of Framingham, Mass., 1640–1847. 8°. '47. $2.50.............................*Burnham.*
Barry Lyndon. *See* Thackeray, W. M.
Barrymore, W: [Plays.] 4 v. 16°. ea., pap., 15c. *French.*
Cont.: El Hyder: spectacle. — Fatal snow storm. — Secret: farce. — Wallace, the hero of Scotland.
Barstow, *Mrs.* E. The young Christian merchant: memoir of G. W. Blake. 16°. 80c...*Bost. Am. Tr.*
Barstow, W: Sulphurets; with chapter on blow-pipe assay of minerals. 12°. '67. $1........*Roman.*
Bart Ridgeley. *See* Riddle, A. G.
Barth, C. History of the world. 12°. '47. $1. *Meth. Bk. Conc.*
Barth, Chr. Gottlieb. Alte Buchmann (Der). 18°. '51. 25c. .... *Am. Tr.*
— Altväter (Die). 18°. '51. 25c..............*Am. Tr.*
— Arme Heinrich (Der). 18°. '46. 25c......*Am. Tr.*
— *Eng.* Poor Henry; or, the pilgrim hut of Weisenstein. 18°. 50c. ....*Pres. Bd.*
— Benoni; or, the triumph of Christianity over Judaism; tr. from the German. 18°. 50c...*Pres. Bd.*
— Biblische Alterthümer. ill. 18°. '66. 70c...*Am. Tr.*
— Biblische Geschichten. 18°. '43. 50c.......*Am. Tr.*
— *Eng.* Bible stories for the young. 2 v. 18°. ea., 50c...............................*U. P. Bd. of Pub.*
— *Portug.* Historias da Biblia. ill. 18°. '69. 75c. *Am. Tr.*
— *Span.* Historias de la Biblia. ill. 18°. '59. 60c. *Am. Tr.*
— *Swed.* ill. 18°. '66. 60c.....................*Am. Tr.*
— Bild (Das) in Deinach. 18°. '53. 25c......*Am. Tr.*
— Expository and practical comment. on the books of Scripture arranged in chronol. order; tr. with introd. by Rev. J. J. Carruthers. 8°. $5; shp., $6; hf. mor., $6.50 ....*Hoyt, F. & D.*
— Felsenkind (Das). 18°. '52. 35c...........*Am. Tr.*

Barth, Chr. Gottlieb, *continued.*
— *Eng.* Child (The) of the rock. 18°. 65c. *Pres. Bd.*
— Huguenot galley-slaves (The); tr. from the German. 18°. 35c. . . . . *Pres. Bd.*
— Jerry Creed. [German.] 18°. '51. 25c. . . *Am. Tr.*
— Kirchengeschichte. ill. 18°. '50. 60c. . . . . . *Am. Tr.*
— Rabenfeder (Die). 18°. '51. 25c. . . . . *Am. Tr.*
— *Eng.* The raven's feather. 18°. 35c. . . . . . *Am. S. S.*
— Setma, das türkische Mädchen. 18°. '53. 25c. *Am. Tr.*
— *Eng.* Setma, the Turkish maiden. 18°. '76. 40c. *Am. S. S.*
— — *Same.* 18°. 50c. . . . . *Pres. Bd.*

Barth, H: Travels and disc. in north and central Africa: journal of an expedition in 1849–1855. 3 v. ill. 8°. $12; shp., $13.50; hf. cf., $18.75. . *Harper.*
— *Same:* in 1 v. ill. 12°. $1.75. . . . . *J. E. Potter.*

Barth, J. B. P., *and* Roger, Henri. Manual of auscultation and percussion; tr. from the French. 12°. '66. $1.25. . . . . *Lindsay.*

Barthe, E: History of the devotion to the Virgin Mary, etc. *See* Orsini, M., Life of Virgin Mary.
— Meditations on the litany of the Virgin Mary. 12°. '71. $1.50; $2 . . . . *Cunningham.*

Bartholdy, Fel. Mendelssohn. *See* Mendelssohn.

Bartholet Milon. Christopher, F. H. 40c. . . . . *Chase.*

Bartholomäusnacht in Paris. 18°. '75. 30c. . . *Am. Tr.*

Bartholomew, G. K. Latin gradual to accompany "Latin gram." 12°. '73. $1.15. . *Wilson, H. & Co.*
— Latin grammar. 12°. '73. $1.35. . *Wilson, H. & Co.*

Bartholomew, *Rev.* J. G. Altar (The): service book for S.-schools, with sel. of hymns and tunes. 16°. '62. per doz., bds., $3.50. . . . . *Universalist.*
— Comforter (The); or, the pastor's friend. 8°. '63. $1.50. . . . . *Universalist.*
— Sunday-school companion. 16°. '62. per doz., bds., $3 . . . . *Universalist.*

Bartholomew, J: Portable atlas of modern geography. imp. 8°. '73. $1. . . . . *Putnam.*
— Zell's descriptive hand atlas of the world. 26 pts. 4°. '73. ea., *50c.; — in 1 v. *$15; leath., $16; hf. mor., $16.50; $18; mor., $27.50. . *C. H. Davis.*
— *and* Weller, E: Collegiate atlas: modern and ancient maps, with index. imp. 8°. (Weale.) $3.75 . . . . *Allyn.*
— — Crown historical atlas: maps with text and index. sq. 16°. (Weale.) $1.25. . . . . *Allyn.*
— — Pocket class. atlas. sq. 16°. (Weale.) 75c. *Allyn.*
— — Pocket hist. atlas. sq. 16°. (Weale.) 75c. *Allyn.*
— — Student's atlas: modern and ancient maps, with index. imp. 8°. (Weale.) $3. . . . . *Allyn.*
— — Student's classical atlas: maps with descrip. text by L. Schmitz; and index. imp. 8°. (Weale.) $1.50 . . . . *Allyn.*

Bartholomew, W. N. Blank drawing book. obl. f°. 25c. . . . . *Potter, A. & Co.*
— Guide to drawing cards. 3 nos. obl. f°. 1, 2, 75c.; 3, 30c. . . . . *Potter, A. & Co.*
— Industrial drawing books. 10 nos. obl. f°. ea., 20c. *Potter, A. & Co.*

Cont.: 1-6. Free hand series. — 7-8. Geometric series. — 9. Model and object. — 10. Perspective.

— Primary school drawing cards. 3 nos. obl. f°. ea., 20c. . . . . *Potter, A. & Co.*
— Teacher's manual or guide to "Industrial drawing books." obl. f°. $2. . . . . *Potter, A. & Co.*

Bartholow, Roberts. Manual for enlisting and discharging soldiers; with special ref. to medical examin. of recruits, and detection of disqualifying and feigned diseases. 12°. '63. $1.25. . *Claxton.*
— Manual of hypodermic medication. 2d ed., rev. and enl. 12°. $1.50. *Lippincott.*
— Principle of physiol. antagonism. *See* Seguin, E. C., Series of Am. clin. lect.
— Spermatorrhœa: its causes, symptomatology, pathology, prognosis, diagnosis and treatment. 3d ed. 12°. $1 . . . . *W. Wood.*

Bartimeus of the Sandwich Islands. Bingham, H. 20c. *Am. Tr.*

Bartle, G: Scriptural doctrine of Hades. 16°. $1.50. *Lippincott.*

Bartlett, G. B. Parlor amusements for the young folks. New ed., rev. and enl. 16°. '74. 75c.; pap., 30c. . . . . *Happy.*

Bartlett, J: Familiar quotations. 7th ed., rev. and enl. 12°. '75. $3 . . . . *Little, B. & Co.*

Bartlett, J: Russell. Dictionary of Americanisms: glossary of words and phrases usually regarded as peculiar to the U. S. ('48.) 3d ed., rev. and enl. 8°. '59. $2.50. . . . . *Little, B. & Co.*
— Literature (The) of the rebellion: catalogue of books, etc., rel. to the civil war, with works on Am. slavery. 4°. '66. pap., $6; hf. mor., $8.50. . *Rider.*
— Memoirs of Rhode Island officers in service during the rebellion. por. 4°. '67. bds., $12.50. . *Rider.*

Bartlett, Levi. Genealogical and biog. sketches of the Bartlett family in Eng. and Am. 8°. '76. $2; pap., $1.50 . . . . *Bartlett.*

Bartlett, Ma. Belle. Minnie Carleton. ill. 18°. '61. 75c. . . . . *Dodd.*

Bartlett, R. Montgomery. Commercial and banking tables, embracing time, simple interest, unexpired time and interest account current, etc. ('51.) New ed. roy. 4°. '53. mor., $20. . . . . . *Wilstach.*

Bartlett, S: C. Future punishment. 16°. 75c. *Cong. Pub.*
— Life and death eternal: refutation of the doctrine of annihilation. 12°. $1.50. . . . . *Bost. Am. Tr.*

Bartlett, W. H., *and* Woodward, B. B. History of the U. S. ('56.) 8th ed. 3 v. roy. 8°. '72. hf. mor., $21 . . . . *Virtue.*

Bartlett, W: H. C. Elements of acoustics and optics. ('52.) 5th ed., rev. 8°. $3.50. . . . . *Barnes.*
— Elements of analytical mechanics. ('58.) 8th ed., rev. and enl. 8°. $5. . . . . *Barnes.*
— Elements of spherical astronomy. 3d ed., rev. 8°. $5. . . . . *Barnes.*
— Elements of synthetic mechanics. ('57.) 6th ed., rev. 8°. $5. . . . . *Barnes.*

Bartley, J. D. The school hymn and tune book. 18°. '75. 60c. . . . . *Barnes.*

Bartol, Cyrus A. Grains of gold: sel. from his writings. ('54.) 6th ed. 32°. '67. 60c. . . . . *Am. Unit.*
— Radical problems. 16°. '72. $2. . . . . *Roberts.*
— Rising faith (The). 16°. '74. $2. . . . . *Roberts.*

Bartoli, Dan. History of the life and institute of St. Ignatius Loyola; tr. from the Ital. by Mme. Calderon de la Barca. 2 v. sm 8°. $3. . . . *Strong.*
— *and* Maffei, J. P. Life of St. Francis Xavier; tr. from the Ital. 12°. '59. $2; $2.50. . . . *Murphy.*

Barton, C: History of a suit in equity. New ed., rev. and enl., with forms, by J. P. Holcombe; and app. 8°. '70. shp., $2.50. . . . . *Clarke.*

Barton, Jerome. Comic recitations and humorous dialogues. 16°. pap., 30c.; bds., 50c. . . . . *Dick & F.*
— *and* Spencer, A. J. One hundred and thirty comic dialogues and recitations; [compr.] Barton's Comic recitations and humorous dialogues, and Spencer's Comic speeches and dialogues. 16°. $1.50. . . . . *Dick & F.*

Barton, J: Graeff. Outline of the general principles of grammar; with exposition of chief idiomatic peculiarities of the Eng. lang. 16°. 60c. . . . . *Harper.*

Barton, Jlt. T. The five jewels of the Orient. [Masonic.] 16°. $2. *Masonic.*

Barton Todd. Baker, S. 60c. . . . . *Randolph.*

Bartram, Ra. C. Memoir. 24°. pap., 12c. *Friends Bk. St.*

Barwell, *Mrs.* —. Gilbert Harland; or, good in everything. ill. sq. 12°. 75c. . . . . *Meth. Bk. Conc.*

Basaroff, Y. The Russian orthodox church: treatise on her origin and life; tr. by Rev. N. Bjerring. 16°. pap., 40c. . . . . *Dutton.*

Basaroff, Y., *continued.*
— The sacrament of matrimony, according to the ritual of the orthodox Oriental Church; tr. by Rev. N. Bjerring. sq. 24°. 30c. . . . . *Dutton.*
Bascom, H: Bidleman. Works. ('59.) 3d ed. 4 v. 12°. '76. ea., $1.50 . . . . *So. Meth.*
Cont.: Sermons. — Lectures on infidelity, and various addresses. — Lectures and essays on moral and mental science, philosophy, natural theology, etc. — Sermons and sketches.
— Appeal of the southern commissioners. 8°. '46. pap., 50c. . . . . *So. Meth.*
— Cross of Christ; with sketch of author's illness and death, and Bp. Andrew's funeral discourse. 12°. '51. 80c. . . . . *So. Meth.*
— Life. 12°. '59. $1.50 . . . . *So. Meth.*
— Little iron wheel (The); with notes of application and ill. by J. R. Graves. 16°. 60c. . . . *So. Bapt.*
Bascom, J: Æsthetics; or, science of beauty. 12°. $1.75 . . . . *Potter, A. & Co.*
— Philosophy of Eng. literature: lectures before Lowell Institute, Boston. 12°. '75. $1.75 . . . . *Putnam.*
— Philosophy of religion. 12°. '76. $2 . . . . *Putnam.*
— Philosophy of rhetoric. 12°. $1.50 . . *Potter, A. & Co.*
— Political economy; for colleges. ('59.) New ed. 12°. '74. $1.50 . . . . *Draper.*
— Principles of psychology. 12°. '69. $1.75 . . *Putnam.*
— Science, philosophy and religion. 12°. '71. $1.75. *Putnam.*
Bash, *Mrs.* Isadore S. Brickey Sorrel; or, the twin cousins. 12°. 90c. . . . . *Un. B. Pub.*
Basham, W: R. Aids to the diagnosis of diseases of the kidneys. ill. 8°. '72. $2 . . . . *Lindsay.*
— On dropsy, and its connection with diseases of the kidneys, heart, lungs and liver. 3d ed. pl. 8°. '66. $5 . . . . *Lindsay.*
— Renal diseases: clinical guide to their diagnosis and treatment. ill. roy. 12°. $2 . . . . *Lea.*
Bashforth, F. General sheet table for facilitating calculation of earthworks. [Sheet.] 20c. . . . *Spon.*
— General table for facilitating the calculation of earthworks; with table of proportional parts. 8°. $1.50 . . . . *Spon.*
— Tables of remaining velocity, time of flight, and energy of various projectiles; from results of experiments with the Bashforth chronograph, 1865–'70. 8°. '71. pap., $1 . . . . *Spon.*
Bashful man. Moncrieff, W. T. 15c. . . . . *French.*
Bashfulness cured. 12°. pap., 20c. . . . . *Hurst.*
Bashie's service. *See* Alden, M.
Basia. *See* Joannes *Secundus.*
Basil *the Great.* *See* Chrysostom, *St.* J., *and* Basil.
Basil. *See* Collins, Wilkie.
Basil, and other tales. 18°. 70c. . . . . *Pres. Bd.*
Basil, the faithful boy. 32°. 20c.; 15c. . . . . *Dutton.*
Basil; or, honesty and industry. 18°. '66. 40c. *Am. Tr.*
— *Same.* ('66.) New ed. 18°. '72. 55c. . . . . *Hoyt.*
— *Same;* in German. 18°. '70. 35c. . . . . *Am Tr.*
Baskerville, Alfr. The poetry of Germany: sel., tr., with orig. text. 12°. $2; hf. mor., $2.25; mor., $4 . . . . *Kohler.*
— *Same.* 12°. $2.50; $3; hf. mor., $3.50 . . . *Schäfer.*
— Praktisches Lehrbuch d. engl. Sprache, umgearb. v. G. Fischer. 12°. '70. bds., 90c.; hf. roan, $1. *Steiger.*
Basket of barley loaves. 16°. $1 . . . . *Pres. Bd.*
Basket of chips for the little ones. Luola. 65c. *Pres. Bd.*
Basket of flowers. 32°. 25c. 16°. 50c. ill. 16°. $1. ill. 12°. $1.25 . . . . *Scribner, W. & A.*
Basket of flowers. St. A., J. H. 50c.; 75c. . . *Nelson.*
Bass, *Bp.* E: Life. 18°. 70c.; 90c. . . . . *Dutton.*
Bass, J. H. Complete Gk. and Eng. lexicon to the New Test. 12°. (Bohn.) 80c. *Scribner, W. & A.*
Bassett, Ja. Criminal pleadings and practice, with precedents of indictments. 8°. '69. shp., $4.50. *E. B. Myers.*
Bassini, Carlo. An analytical, physiolog. and pract. system for the cultivation of the voice; ed. by R. S. Willis. f°. '57. bds., $4; abridg., $3. — Same; for tenor voice. $4 . . . . *Ditson.*
— Education of the voice. obl. 8°. bds., $2. *Huntington.*
— New method for soprano and mezzo-soprano. 4°. bds., $3 . . . . *G. D. Russell.*
— Twenty melodic exercises in form of solfeggios for soprano and mezzo-soprano voices. 2 bks. 4°. '65. ea., $1.25; $2 . . . . *T. J. Hall.*
Bassnett, S. Outlines of a mechanical theory of storms. 12°. $2 . . . . *Appleton.*
Bastard (Der). Spindler, C. $1.25; $1; $1.50. *F. W. Thomas.*
Basté, Eug. Pierre ["Eugène Grangé"], *and* Montepin, X. A. de. Corsican brothers: drama. 16°. pap., 15c. . . . . *French.*
Bastian, H. Charlton. Beginnings of life: account of the nature, modes of origin, and transformation of lower organisms. 2 v. ill. 12°. $5 . . . . *Appleton.*
— Evolution and origin of life. cr. 8°. '74. $2. *Macmillan.*
— Modes of origin of lowest organisms; incl. discussion of the experiments of M. Pasteur, and reply to some statements by Huxley and Tyndall. cr. 8°. '71. $1.25 . . . . *Macmillan.*
— Paralysis from brain-disease in its common forms. 12°. $1.75 . . . . *Appleton.*
Bastiat, F: Essays on political economy. (Popular manuals.) 12°. '74. $1 . . . . *Putnam.*
— Sophisms of protection; with pref. by H. White. (Popular manuals.) 12°. '75. $1 . . . . *Putnam.*
Bataille (La) de dames. Scribe, E., *and* Legouvé, E. 40c. . . . . *Holt.*
Batchelder, J. P. Inaugural address before N. Y. Acad. of Med. 8°. '58. pap., 10c. *N. Y. Acad. Med.*
Batchelder, S: *jr.* Manual of the law of manufacturing corporations in Mass. 12°. '68. $2; shp., $2.50 . . . . *Little, B. & Co.*
Batchelor, G: *See* Andrews, S. P., *and* Batchelor, G.
Bate, J: A cyclopædia of illustrations of moral and relig. truths. 8°. $5 . . . . *Scribner, W. & A.*
Bateman, C: W. Questions on Kühner's "Elementary Greek grammar"; with modifications and notes by S. H. Taylor. 12°. '66. pap., 40c. . . . *Draper.*
Bateman, J. C. Ierne of Armorica: a tale of the time of Clovis. 12°. $1.50; $2 . . . . *Sadlier.*
Bateman, Josiah. Life of Henry Venn Elliott. 3d ed. por. cr. 8°. $2.50 . . . . *Macmillan.*
Bateman, Ma. Life and adventures. 8°. pap., 25c. *Peterson.*
Bateman, *Mrs.* S. F. Self: comedy. 16°. pap., 15c. *French.*
Bateman, W: O. The general commercial law as recognized in the jurisprudence of the U. S. 8°. '60. $5.50 . . . . *T. & J. W. Johnson.*
Bates, Clem. *See* Walker, J. B., *and* Bates, C.
Bates, Dan. M. *See* Delaware, Chancery Court reports.
Bates, D: Poetical works; ed. by S. Bates. 12°. '70. $1.50 . . . . *Claxton.*
Bates, E. T. *See* One hundred comic songs.
Bates, H. W. Illustrated travels: record of discovery, geog. and adventure. 6 v. ill. roy. 4°. ea., $7.50; $9 . . . . *Cassell.*
— Naturalist (The) on the river Amazon. ill. post. 8°. '74. $2.50 . . . . *Roberts.*
Bates, J. C. Report of the proceedings in the Probate Court of San Francisco on the will of Horace Hawes. 8°. '72. $4.50 . . . . *Bancroft.*
— *See also* Langdon, C. W.
Bates, *Miss* Lizzie. Among the crags. ill. 18°. '68. 45c. . . . . *Am. Tr.*
— Anchored. ill. 16°. '68. 90c. . . . . *Am. Tr.*

Bates, *Miss* Lizzie, *continued.*
— Beginning. ill. 16°. $1 .... *J. A. Moore.*
— Builders (The). ill. 16°. $1.25 .... *J. A. Moore.*
— Climbers (The). ill. 16°. '66. 90c .... *Am. Tr.*
— Dean Proctor. ill. 18°. '67. 25c .... *Am. Tr.*
— Had you been in his place. 16°. $1.25 .... *Carter.*
— How it was paid. 16°. $1.50 .... (?) *Martien.*
— Jonas Clare. ill. 16°. '70. 70c .... *Am. Tr.*
— Life of the Duchess Renée. 18°. '72. 60c... *Am. Tr.*
— Max Fleming. ill. 18°. '67. 30c .... *Am. Tr.*
— Netherclift: story of a merchant told by himself. ill. 16°. $1.25 .... *Bost. Am. Tr.*
— Paul Venner. ill. 16°. '67. $1.25 .... *Am. Tr.*
— Purpose. ill. 16°. '67. $1.25 .... *Am. Tr.*
— Scenes in Switzerland. ill. 18°. '68. 45c... *Am. Tr.*
— Seymours (The). ('71.) New ed. 12°. '75. $1. *Nat. Temp.*
— Stolen child (The). ill. 18°. '68. 50c. .... *Am. Tr.*
— Stories from the moorland. ill. 16°. '71. $1.25. *Lothrop.*
— Stories of the flowers. ill. 16°. '72. 80c... *Am. Tr.*
— Torch bearers. ill. 16°. '71. $1.25 .... *Lothrop.*
— True boy (The). ill. 18°. '67. 25c .... *Am. Tr.*
— Two ways of doing it. ill. 16°. $1 ..... *J. A. Moore.*
— Westbrooke; or, laying the foundations. ill. 18°. 75c .... *Bost. Am. Tr.*
— — *See also* Golden sheaves lib.
— Woman: her dignity and sphere. 18°. '70. 60c. *Am. Tr.*

Bates, L: A. The tide turning. *See* Hunt, S. K., The brook.

Bates, S: P. Battle of Gettysburg. por. and maps. 8°. '75. *$3 .... *T. H. Davis.*
— Lectures on mental and moral culture. 12°. '59. $1.50 .... *Barnes.*
— Martial deeds of Pennsylvania. maps, ill. and por. 8°. '75. *$6.75; hf. mor., $8.75; mor., $15. *T. H. Davis; Rutter.*
— Method of teachers' institutes, and the theory of education. 12°. '62. 75c .... *Barnes.*

Bates, S: W. *See* Smith, C., *and* Bates, S. W.

Bates, *Mrs.* Sa. B. Margie Hopkins; or, at home and in the army. ('66.) New ed. ill. 16°. '75. $1.15. *Hoyt.*

Bates, Stockton. Dream life, and other poems. 12°. '71. $1.50 .... *Claxton.*

Bates, W. G. *See* Celebration at Westfield, Mass.

Bates, W: Harmony of the divine attributes in the contrivance and accomplishment of man's redemption. 12°. $1 .... *Pres. Bd.*

Bathurst, D. *See* Adventurer (The).

Batkins, Jefferson Scattering (*pseud.*) *See* Jones, Jos. S.

Battey, T: C. Life and adventures of a Quaker among the Indians. ill. 12°. $1.50 .... *Lee & S.*

Battle, W: H. Digest of N. Carolina reports (1789–1866). 3 v. 8°. shp., $20 .... *Hale.*
— *See also* North Carolina, Reports.

Battle of Calvary. Chaffin, J. W. $1.25. *Cin. Meth. Bk. Conc.*

Battle of Dorking. *See* Chesney, G.

Battle of the frogs and mice. *See* Homer.

Battle of the giants. [Anti-Catholic.] 8°. '75. *$2.75. *Vent.*

Battle of Hexham. Coleman, G. 15c .... *French.*

Battle (The) of Lepanto. *See* Library of good example.

Battle of Sedgemoor. Almar, G. 15c .... *French.*

Battle of Waterloo: drama. 16°. pap., 15c... *French.*

Battle pieces and aspects of the war. Melville, H. $1.75 .... *Harper.*

Battlefields (The) of the revolution. Rhoads, T. Y. $1.75 .... *J. E. Potter.*

Battlefields (The) of Virginia. Hotchkiss, J., *and* Allan, W. $5 .... *Van Nostrand.*

Battles at home. Darling, M. G. $1.50.. (?) *Shepard.*

Battles lost and won. Merrill, G. E. $1.50.. *Lothrop.*

Battles of the British navy. Allen, J. 2 v. ea., $2. *Scribner, W. & A.*

Battles worth fighting. 18°. $1.25.. *Carter; Dutton.*

Battu, L. *See* Carré, M., *and* Battu, L.

Batzennoth (Die). 12°. pap., 20c .... *Radde.*

Baudrand, Barthélemy. The religious soul elevated to perfection, by the exercises of an interior life; tr. from the Fr. 18°. '60. 60c.... *Cunningham.*

Bauduy, Jerome K. Lectures on diseases of the nervous system. 8°. $4 .... *Lippincott.*

Bauer, Caro. ["Karl Detlef."] At Capri: a story of Italian life; tr. by MS. 12°. $1.50; pap., 75c. (Intern. ed.) $1.25 .... *Porter.*
— Clemence d'Orville; or, from the palace to the steppe; tr. from the German; [also] Clelia, by A. Wels; tr. from the German. 8°. '70. pap., 38c .... *Littell & G.*
— Must it be? tr. by MS. ill. 8°. $1.25; pap., 75c. *Lippincott.*
— Valentine the countess; tr. by MS. 12°. '74. $1.50; pap., 75c. (Intern. ed.) $1.25 .... *Porter.*

Bauer, L: Lectures on orthopædic surgery. 2d ed., rev. and enl. ill. 8°. $3.25 .... *W. Wood.*

Bauer (Der) und Soldat. 32°. '59. 25c...... *Am. Tr.*

Bauerman, H. Treatise on the metallurgy of iron. 1st Am. ed., rev. and enl.; with app. on the Martin process for making steel, from the report of A. S. Hewitt. ill. 12°. $2 .... *Baird.*

Baum, C. F. Choral-Vorspiele u. Zwischenspiele bei öffentl. Gottesdienst. pts. 1, 2. 8°. ea., pap., 35c. *Volkening.*
— Christliche Chorgesänge, mit Orgelbegleitung. pts. 1, 2. 8°. hf. bd., 25c .... *Volkening.*
— Festgesänge. pts. 1–4. 8°. ea., pap., 20c. *Volkening.*

Baum, J. Mass in G. 4°. pap., $1.50 .... *Peters.*

Baumbach, A. Melodica; or, the art of playing the piano made easy. obl. 8°. pap., 75c..... *Peters.*
— New collection of sacred music. obl. 4°. '71. $2.75; bds., $2.50 .... *Ditson.*
— Operatic gems. obl. 8°. $1.25; pap., $1... *Gordon.*
— Sacred quartettes: pieces for the opening and close of service. obl. 4°. '62. $2.75; bds., $2.50. *Ditson.*

Baumbach, J. Walten (Das) Gottes. [Tales.] 8°. 35c .... *Pilger.*
— Wege (Die) des Herrn sind wunderbar. [Tales.] 8°. '72. 30c .... *Pilger.*

Baumgarten, Mt. Apostolic history. 3 v. 8°. ea., $3. *Scribner, W. & A.*

Baur, W: Religious life in Germany, during the wars of independence: hist. and biog. sketches; tr. by Mrs. G. Sturge. 8°. $2.50 .... *Routledge.*

Bausman, B. Sinai and Zion. 12°. $2; $3. *Ref. Ch. Pub.*
— *Same;* in German. 12°. $2.50 .... *Ref. Ch. Pub.*

Bautain, M. Art of extempore speaking; ed. by a member of the N. Y. bar. ('59.) 6th ed. 12°. '74. $1.50 .... *Scribner.*

Baxley, Willis H. Spain: art remains and art realities, painters, priests and princes: notes of things seen and opinions formed during 3 years' residence and travels. 2 v. 12°. $5...... *Appleton.*

Baxter, J. H. Statistics, medical and anthropological. *See* United States, *Provost Marshal-General's Bureau.*

Baxter, Ja. Christian festival (The). [Music.] 8°. '74. pap., 40c.; bds., 60c .... *Crandall.*
— Euterpia (The): a library of music for church and Sabbath school, etc.; with a new school of instruction, for teachers, etc. ('72.) 4th ed. 8°. '75. bds., $1.25 .... *Crandall.*
— Technics for voice. ('71.) 2d ed. 8°. '72. bds., $1.25 .... *Crandall.*
— Thorough base. 8°. '74. bds., $1.25.... *Crandall.*

Baxter, M. Coming battle and appalling national convulsions. 8°. pap., 15c. .... (?) *Martien.*
— Coming wonders, expected between 1867 and 1875. ill. 12°. $1 .... *Lippincott*; (?) *Martien.*
— Louis Napoleon the destined monarch of the world. 12°. $1 .... (?) *Martien.*

Baxter, R: Select works; with life by Rev. L. Bacon. New ed. 2 v. 8°. *net*, $2.50 .... *Peck.*
— Call to the unconverted to turn and live. New ed., rev. 18°. pap., 15c. .... *Bost. Am. Tr.*
— *Same.* 18°. 30c.; pap., 15c. .... *Am. Tr.*
— *Same*; with introd. by T. Chalmers. 18°. 50c. *Pres. Bd.*
— *Same*; ed. by T. O. Summers. ('57.) 3d ed. 18°. '76. 40c. .... *So. Meth.*
— *Danish.* 18°. '48. 30c.; pap., 15c. .... *Am. Tr.*
— *Dutch.* 18°. '53. 30c. .... *Am. Tr.*
— *French.* La voix de Dieu. 18°. '40. 30c.; pap., 10c. .... *Am. Tr.*
— *Germ.* Zuruf an Unbekehrte. 18°. '42. 40c. *Am. Tr.*
— *Swedish.* 18°. '54. 30c. .... *Am. Tr.*
— *Welsh.* 18°. '47. 25c.; pap., 10c. .... *Am. Tr.*
— — *See also* Alleine, *Rev.* J., Alarm; — Young disciples' lib.
— Converse with God in desertion and solitude. 18°. 40c. .... *Pres. Bd.*
— Duties and responsibilities of the pastoral office: from "Reformed pastor." 18°. 50c. .... *Pres. Bd.*
— Reformed pastor; or, duty of personal labors for the souls of men. 12°. '50. 75c. .... *Am. Tr.*
— *Same.* 18°. 80c. .... *Cin. Meth. Bk. Conc.*
— *Germ.* Prediger des Evangel. 18°. '52. 70c. *Am. Tr.*
— — *See also above* Duties.
— Saints' (The) everlasting rest. 32°. 75c. ... *Nelson.*
— *Same.* ill. 18°. shp., 75c. .... *Polock.*
— *Same.* por. 12°. '70. $1.20 .... *Claxton.*
— *Same.* 12°. '28. $1.25. ill. 18°. '34. 70c. *Am. Tr.*
— *Same.* 16°. '74. $1.25 .... *Lothrop.*
— *Same.* 12°. '37. $1.50 .... *Meth. Bk. Conc.*
— *Same*; abridg. by W. M. Engles. 12°. $1 .. *Pres. Bd.*
— *Same*; abridg. by B. Fawcett. 18°. 60c. *Bost. Am. Tr.*; *Claxton.*
— *Danish.* 18°. '49. 65c. .... *Am. Tr.*
— *French.* Le repos éternel des saints. 18°. '40. 40c. *Am. Tr.*
— — *Same.* 18°. 25c. .... *Pres. Bd.*
— *German.* Ewige Ruhe der Heiligen. 18°. '43. 65c.; 70c.; 90c. .... *Am. Tr.*
— *Swedish.* 12°. '54. 70c. .... *Am. Tr.*
— *Welsh.* 12°. '47. $1 .... *Am. Tr.*
— *See also* Asbury, F., Heart and church divisions.
— *and* Bunyan, J: Leben. 18°. '66. 25c. .... *Am. Tr.*

Baxter, W: Life of Elder Walter Scott, with sketches of W. Hayden, A. Bentley, J. Henry, etc. por. 12°. $2 .... *Chase.*

Baxter, W: Pea Ridge and Prairie Grove; or, scenes and incidents of the war in Arkansas. 16°. '64. $1 .... *Cin. Meth. Bk. Conc.*

Bay, S. M. *See* Missouri, Supreme Court reports.

Bay leaves. Nash, G. $1.50 .... *Lockwood, B. & Co.*

Bay path (The). Holland, J. G. $2 .... *Scribner.*

Bayard, J. F. A., *and* Lemoine, G. La niaise de Saint Flour: comédie-vaudeville. 12°. '72. pap., 25c. *Holt.*

Bayard, S: On the Lord's supper. 18°. 50c. (?) *Martien.*

Bayard, S: J. Life of Gen. Geo. D. Bayard. 12°. '75. $1.75; hf. cf., $3.75 .... *Putnam.*

Bayard series. 19 v. 16°. ea., $1.25 .. *Scribner, W. & A.*

Cont.: Story of Chevalier Bayard.— St. Louis, King of France. — Cowley's Essays. — Laboullaye's Abdallah and the four-leaved shamrock. — Napoleon's table talk. — King and the commons. — Beckford's Vathek. — Words of Wellington. — Johnson's Rasselas. — Chesterfield's Letters. — Ballantyne's Essays in mosaic. — Browne's Religio-medici. — Coleridge's Christabel. — Hazlett's Round table. — Buchanan's Ballad stories of the affections. — Sterne's Story of my Uncle Toby. — Rochefoucauld's Maxims. — Xenophon's Memoirs of Socrates. — Prince Albert's Golden precepts.

Bayer, C. R. ["Robert Byr."] Sphinx (The); or, striving with destiny; tr. by A. A. Woodward. ill. 12°. '71. *$2 .... *Maclean.*
— Struggle (The) for existence; tr. by A. Forestier. 12°. $1.50 .... *McKinney.*

Bayle-Mouillard, Eliz. [Elizabeth Celnart.] The gentleman's and lady's book of politeness and propriety of deportment; tr. and enl., from the French. ('35.) 15th ed. 18°. '72. 75c. .. *Claxton.*

Bayles, R: M. Historical and descriptive sketches of Suffolk County [N. Y.]; with hist. outline of Long Island. 12°. '74. $2.25 .... *Munsell.*

Bayley, *Sir* E. *See* Moore, D., Marston, C. D., *and* Bayley, *Sir* E.

Bayley, G. W. R. Levees as a system of reclaiming low lands. 8°. '76. pap., 55c. ... *Am. Soc. C. E.*
— Toredo navalis; or, ship worm. *See* Coryell, M., Conflagration in the coal at Kidder Slope.

Bayley, Ja. R. Early hist. of the Cath. Church in the island of N. Y. 2d ed. 12°. '70. $1.50 .. *Cath. Pub.*
— Memoirs of Rev. S. W. G. Bruté, [incl.] his recollections of the French rev., and extracts from his journal. ill. 12°. '76. $1.50 .... *Cath. Pub.*

Bayley, P: Orestes in Argos: tragedy. 16°. pap., 15c. *French.*

Baylies, E. Questions and answers on law and practice. 8°. '73. $5 .... *Gould.*

Bayly, T: H. [Plays.] 9 v. 16°. ea., pap., 15c. *French.*

Cont.: Barrack-room: musical burletta. — Comfortable service: farce. — Forty and fifty: farce. — How do you manage? farce. — Perfection: comedy. — Spitalfields weaver. — Swiss cottage: operetta. — Tom Noddy's secret: farce. — You can't marry your grandmother.

Bayma, Jos. Elements of molecular mechanics. 8°. '66. $3.75 .... *Macmillan.*
— Love of religious perfection; tr. from the Lat. 18°. '65. 75c.; $1.25 .... *Murphy.*

Bayne, P: Christian life (The), social and individual. 12°. $1.75 .... *H. A. Young.*
— Essays in biography and criticism. 2 v. 12°. '58. $3.50 .... *H. A. Young.*
— Life and letters of Hugh Miller. 2 v. 12°. $3 .. *Carter.*
— *Same.* ill. and por. 2 v. 8°. '71. $15 .. *Routledge.*
— Testimony of Christ to Christianity. New ed. 16°. '76. 75c. .... *Tibbals.*

Baynes, H. S. Horæ Lucanæ: biog. of St. Luke. cr. 8°. $2.50 .... *Lippincott.*

Baynes, R. A. (*ed.*) Book of sacred poems. ill. 8°. $3.50; $5 .... *Cassell.*

Baynes, T: S. (*ed.*) Encyclopædia Britannica: a dict. of arts, sciences and general literature. 9th ed. [To form 21 v.] v. 1–4. ill. 4°. '75–'76. ea., $9; hf. mor., $11 .... *Little, B. & Co.*
— *Same.* Am. reprint. v. 1–3. imp. 8°. '75–'76. ea., $5; shp., $6; hf. mor., $7; hf. cf., $8; mor., $10. *J. M. Stoddart.*

Bazar book (The) of decorum: care of the person, manners, etiquette, etc. 16°. $1 .... *Harper.*

Bazar book of health. 16°. $1 .... *Harper.*

Bazar book of the household. 16°. $1 .... *Harper.*

Be thyself. Denton, W. 10c. .... *Denton.*

Beach, C: A. Pitzmaroon; or, the magic hammer: a fairy story. ill. 12°. '74. $1.25 .. *Whitney & A.*
— Waifs of the world; or, adventures afloat and ashore. ill. 16°. $1.75 .... *Scribner, W. & A.*

Beach, C: F. The Christian worker, a call to the laity. 16°. $1 .... *Lippincott.*
— The muzzled ox: thoughts on the support of the Gospel ministry. 18°. 25c.; pap., 10c. ... *Pres. Bd.*

Beach, E. T. P. Pelayo: an epic of the olden Moorish time. ill. 12°. $2; $2.50; mor., $4.50 .. *Appleton.*

Beach, Ha. Mar. Dolly's resolutions; or, letters from abroad. 12°. '72. $1.25 .... *Claxton.*

Beach, Lew. History of Cornwall [N. Y.]; incl. the features of a handbook. 8°. '73. $2 .. *Ruttenber.*

Beach, Wooster. The American practice condensed, or the family physician: the scientific system of medicine on vegetable principles. ('42.) New ed., rev. 8°. '74. shp., $4.50........ *Wilstach.*

— The family physician and home guide, for the treatment of disease on reform principles. ('42.) 2d ed. 8°. '66. mor., $6.............. *Wilstach.*

Beacon Hill library for boys; — for girls. ea., 6 v. 18°. $2.......................... *Cong. Pub.*

Beacon lights and beckonings. 18°. 50c... *Cong. Pub.*

Beaconsfield, *Earl of.* *See* Disraeli, B:

Beadle, J. H. Life in Utah; or, the mysteries and crimes of Mormonism. ill. 8°. '70. *$2.75; leath., $3.25.............................. *Nat. Pub.*

— Undeveloped west (The); or, five years in the territories. map and ill. 8°. '73. *$3.75.. *Nat. Pub.*

— Women's (The) war on whiskey: its hist., theory and prospects; with introd. by Dio Lewis. 16°. '74. 75c.; pap., 50c................. *Wilstach.*

Beadle's dime dialogues. 17 nos. 12°. ea., pap., 10c. *Beadle.*

Beadle's dime family handbooks. 5 nos. 12°. ea., pap., 10c. .... *Beadle.*

Cont.: Cook book. — Recipe book. — Family physician. — Housewife's manual. — Dressmaker.

Beadle's dime handbooks for young people. 8 nos. 12°. ea., pap., 10c..................... *Beadle.*

Cont.: Gents' letter-writer. — Book of etiquette. — Book of verses. — Book of dreams. — Fortune teller. — Ladies' letter-writer. — Lovers' casket. — Ball room companion.

Beadle's dime handbooks of games and pastimes. 9 nos. 12°. ea., pap., 10c.............. *Beadle.*

Cont.: One hundred games. — Chess. — Croquet. — Base-ball. — Cricket and football. — Swimming. — Yachting and rowing. — Riding and driving. — Pedestrianism.

Beadle's dime joke books. 3 nos. 16°. ea., pap., 10c. *Beadle.*

Beadle's dime lives of great Americans. 7 nos. 12°. ea., pap., 10c.......................... *Beadle.*

Cont.: Washington. — Paul Jones. — Anthony Wayne. — Ethan Allen. — Israel Putnam. — Lafayette. — Boone.

Beadle's dime melodist. 16°. pap., 10c....... *Beadle.*

Beadle's dime school melodist. 16°. pap., 10c. *Beadle.*

Beadle's dime song books. 34 nos. 16°. ea., pap., 10c. *Beadle.*

Beadle's dime speakers. 18 nos. 12°. ea., pap., 10c. *Beadle.*

Beadle's dramas and readings. 12°. pap., 20c. *Beadle.*

Beadle's illuminated dime pocket novels. 51 nos. 12°. ea., pap., 10c.......................... *Beadle.*

Beadle's standard dime novels. 362 nos. 12°. ea., pap., 10c. .... *Beadle.*

Beakley, J. *See* Hempel, C. J., *and* Beakley, J.

Beal, Nat. Stone Reed. Diamond leaves from the lives of the Dimond family; by an old, old bachelor. 12°. '72. $2.......................... *Beal.*

Beal, S: A catena of Buddhist scriptures from the Chinese. 8°. $7.50.......... *Scribner, W. & A.*

— The romantic legend of Sakya Buddha; from the Chinese Sanscrit. sm. 8°. $6.. *Scribner, W. & A.*

Beal, the pirate spy. 12°. pap., 20c. .... *Hurst.*

Beale, A. Simplicity and fascination: tale of the English yeomanry. 12°. $1.50............ *Loring.*

Beale, Lionel S. Bioplasm: contribution to the physiol. of life; or, an introd. to the study of physiol. and medicine. ill. 8°. '72. $3........ *Lindsay.*

— Disease germs, and treatment of diseases caused by them. 2d ed., enl. pl. 8°. '72. $5... *Lindsay.*

— How to work with the microscope. 4th ed. 400 ill. 8°. $7.50.......................... *Lindsay.*

— Kidney diseases, urinary deposits, and calculous disorders; incl. the symptoms, diagnosis, etc., of urinary diseases, with directions for the analysis of the urine. 3d ed. 70 pl. 8°. '69. $10.. *Lindsay.*

— Protoplasm; or, matter and life. 3d ed., enl. col. pl. 12°. '74. $4.50................. *Lindsay.*

Beale, Lionel S., *continued.*

— The use of the microscope in practical medicine. New ed. ill. 8°. $8.................. *Lindsay.*

Beamont, W. J. *See* Campion, W. M., *and* Beamont, W. J.

Bean, Ja. Christian minister's affectionate advice to a married couple; incl. letter from H: Venn; with sel. poems. 24°. '34. 60c.; 75c... *Bost. Am. Tr.*

Beans, E. W. Treatise on railway curves and the location of railroads. ill. 12°. '72. $1.50.. *Baird.*

Bear and forbear. Adams, W. T. $1.25.... *Lee & S.*

Bear-hunters. Buckstone, J. B. 15c......... *French.*

Bear-hunters of the Rocky Mountains. Bowman, A. $1.25...................... *Porter; Routledge.*

Beard, C. *See* Beard, J. R. *and* C.

Beard, G: M. Eating and drinking: food and diet in health and disease. 12°. '71. 75c...... *Putnam.*

— Our home physician: handy book of family medicine. ('69.) New ed. ill. 8°. '75. *$5; shp., $6.. *Treat.*

— Stimulants and narcotics, medically and morally considered. 12°. '71. 75c............... *Putnam.*

— *and* Rockwell, A. D. Treatise on the medical and surgical use of electricity. 2d ed., rev. and enl. ill. 8°. $6.25; leath., $7.25.......... *W. Wood.*

Beard, J. R. *and* C. Latin-English and Eng.-Lat. dict. cr. 8°. $1.75................... *Cassell.*

Beard, R: Lectures on theology. 3 v. 12°. v. 1, $2; v. 2, 3, ea., $3................. (?) *Cumberland.*

Beardmore, Natl. Manual of hydrology; cont. hydraulic and other tables, rivers, flow of water, wells, etc. pl. 8°. (Lond.) '62. $12.... *Spon.*

Beardsley, *Rev.* E. E. History of the Episcopal Church in Conn. 2 v. 8°. $8............. *Hurd & H.*

— Life and correspondence of Rev. Samuel Johnson. por. 8°. '73. $3.50............... *Hurd & H.*

Beardsley divorce case. 8°. pap., 25c....... *De Witt.*

Bearing the cross. Waterbury, J. B. 40c... *Cong. Pub.*

Bearing the cross; or, the divine master. 18°. 75c.; $1; mor., $2.50...................... *Dutton.*

Bearing our burdens. McLean, M. W. $1.25. *Cong. Pub.*

Bears of Augustusburg. Nieritz, G. $1.25... *O'Shea.*

Beaseley, S: Is he jealous? farce. 16°. pap., 15c. *French.*

Beasley, F. W. Papers from the Overlook House. [Fiction.] 12°. '66. $1.50.. *Claxton; Lippincott.*

Beasley, H: Book of prescriptions, English, French and American. 5th ed., rev. and enl. 16°. '72. $2.50 .... *Lindsay.*

— Druggist's (The) general receipt book and veterinary formulary. 7th ed. 8°. '71. $3.50.... *Lindsay.*

— Pocket formulary (The): synopsis of the British and foreign pharmacopœias. 9th ed., rev. 16°. '72. $2.50.............................. *Lindsay.*

Beasley, R. D. Elementary treatise on plane trigonometry; with examples. 3d ed., rev. and enl. cr. 8°. '73. $1.50................. *Macmillan.*

Beaten paths. Thompson, E. W. $1.50.... *Lee & S.*

Beatitudes (The). Webster, I. P. 30c. ..... *Ditson.*

Beatitudes (The) of the kingdom. Dykes, J. O. $1.25................................ *Carter.*

Beatrice. Kavanagh, J. $1.25............ *Appleton.*

Beatrice. Leland, O. S. 15c................ *French.*

Beatrice. *See* Noel, R.

Beatrice; or, the goldsmith's daughter. 8°. pap., 25c. *Dick & F.*

Beatrice Boville. La Rame, L. de. $1.50.. *Lippincott.*

Beatrice Cenci. Guerrazzi, F. D. $1.75 ... *Carleton.*

Beattie, Ja. Poems. (Aldine ed.) 16°. 75c. *Lippincott.*

— *Same;* with memoir by Rev. A. Dyce. por. 18°. $1. *Osgood.*

— — *See also* Gray, T., Poems; — Milton, J., Poetical works.

Beattie, Ja., *continued.*
— *and* Falconer, W: Poetical works; with lives, etc., by G. Gilfillan. 8°. cf., $4..........*Appleton.*
Beattie, R. H. What is faith? 18°. 40c....*Pres. Bd.*
Beattie, W: Life and letters of T: Campbell; with introd. letter by W. Irving. 2 v. 12°. $3..*Harper.*
Beatty, Ad. Essays on practical agriculture; including prize essays. 12°. '44. $1.25.....*Wilstach.*
Beatty, F. *See* Ireland, Chancery reports.
Beau Brummel. Jerrold, D. 15c............*French.*
Beau Tancred. Dumas, A. 50c...........*Routledge.*
Beauchamp, W: Eternal sonship of Christ. ('50.) 3d ed. 18°. '73. 50c.................*So. Meth.*
— Letters on itinerancy. ('55.) 2d ed. 18°. '75. 40c. *So. Meth.*
Beauchamp. James, G. P. R. 75c.........*Harper.*
Beauchampe. Simms, W. G. $1.75; 75c...*Widdleton.*
Beauchesne, A. de. Louis XVII., his life, his suffering, his death; the captivity of the royal family in the temple; tr. and ed. by W. Hazlitt; with autographs and plans. 2 v. 12°. $4...*Harper.*
Beauclercs (The). Clarke, C. 50c.........*Harper.*
Beauclerk, *Lady* Di. De Vere. True love. 12°. $1.25 ....*Lippincott.*
Beaudry, L: N. Historic records of the 5th N. Y. Cavalry in the late [civil] war. por. and ill. 12°. '74. $2.............................*Munsell.*
— Spiritual struggles of a Roman Catholic: autobiog. sketch. 12°. '75. $1.25.......*Meth. Bk. Conc.*
Beaufort, Emily A. *See* Strangford, *Vctss.*
Beauforts (The). 18°. '66. 50c.......*Cunningham.*
Beaumarchais, P. A. C. de. Barber of Seville: opera. 16°. pap., 15c.................*French.*
Beaumarchais. Brachvogel, A. E. $1.50; $1. *Appleton.*
Beaumont, Fs., *and* Fletcher, J. Dramatic and poet. works; ed. with introd. by G. Darley. por. and ill. 2 v. 8°. $10..................*Routledge.*
— — Popular selection from works; by Leigh Hunt. 12°. (Bohn.) $1.25............*Little, B. & Co.*
— — *Same.* 12°. (Bohn.) $1.40..*Scribner, W. & Co.*
— — Elder brother: comedy. 16°. pap., 15c. *French.*
— — Maid of the mill: opera. 16°. pap., 15c. *French.*
— — Rule a wife and have a wife. 16°. pap., 15c. *French.*
Beaumont, J. Law and practice of bills of sale, and bills of sale of ships, under the recent statutes. 8°. '60. $1.50...............*T. & J. W. Johnson.*
— — *See also* Law lib.
Beaumont, *Rev.* Jos. Memoir of Mrs. Mary Tatham. 12°. '39. 70c.................*Meth. Bk. Conc.*
— Sermons. *See* Wakeley, J. B., Wesleyan Demosthenes.
Beauseant (The). *See* Simons, J. W.
Beauties of the Bible. Sampson, E. $1.....*Harper.*
Beauties of the British dramatists. *See* Lippincott's pocket treasuries.
Beauties of Caledonia; or, gems of Scottish song. 4°. bds., $1.50..........................*Ditson.*
Beauties of Eng. hist.; — of Fr. hist. Frost, J. ea., 75c. ....*Harper.*
Beauties of faith; or, power of Mary's patronage: [Cath.] narratives and legends. 12°. $2..*O'Shea.*
Beauties of poetry and gems of art: poems, songs and ballads ill. by Eng. artists. fp. 4°. $2.50..*Cassell.*
Beauties of the sanctuary. Le Bon, H. 75c.; $1.25. *Kelly, P. & Co.*
Beauties of vocal melody. Dempster, W. R. $1. *Gordon.*
Beautiful birds in far-off lands. Kirby, M. *and* E. $2.50 ....*Nelson.*
Beautiful book (The) for little children. [Poems.] ill. sq. 16°. '74. 75c....................*Shorey.*

Beautiful books for boys and girls. 5 v. ill. sq. 8°. $3.50................................*Pres. Bd.*
Cont.: Little Red Cloak. — Jesus on earth. — Miss Muff and Little Hungry. — Ram-Krishna-Punt. — Hindoo life.
Beautiful cigar girl. Ingraham, J. H. 25c...*De Witt.*
Beautiful city (The). 18°. 30c. ....*Am. S. S.*
Beautiful fiend. Southworth, E. D. E. N. $1.75; $1.50 ....*Peterson.*
Beautiful forever. Hay, F. 15c....*De Witt; French.*
Beautiful French girl (The). 8°. pap., 50c. *Peterson.*
Beautiful Haidee. Byron, H. J. 15c.........*French.*
Beautiful half-breed (The); or, the border rovers. 8°. pap., 25c. ....*De Witt.*
Beautiful home. Charlesworth, M. L. 50c....*Carter.*
Beautiful nun (The). Judson, E. Z. C. 75c. *Peterson.*
Beautiful pictures. Armytage, S. 2 v. ea., $10.50. *Scribner, W. & A.*
Beautiful snow! Watson, J. W. $2; $3; $4..*Peterson.*
Beautiful thoughts [series]. *See* Ramage, C. T.
Beautiful villa. *See* Old pauper (The).
Beautiful widow (The). Shelley, P. B. $1.75; $1.50. *Peterson.*
Beautiful women: 16 photos. of female por. by Sir J. Reynolds and others. f°. $20.......*Routledge.*
Beauty. *See* Ball and hoop.
Beauty (The). Rosecrans, J. H., *and* Rheem, J. H. 75c................................*Crandall.*
Beauty: what it is and how to retain it; by a lady. ill. 48°. 25c..................*Scribner, W. & A.*
Beauty and the beast. ill. f°. pap., 15c.; 20c. *J. E. Potter.*
Beauty and the beast. [Toy book.] ill. 4°. $1; 50c. *Routledge.*
Beauty and the beast. Keating, E. H. 15c...*French.*
Beauty and the beast. Planché, J. R. 15c. ..*French.*
Beauty and the beast. Taylor, B. $1.50; $2..*Putnam.*
Beauty Benson. Strong, J. D. 25c. ....*Lothrop.*
Beauty for ashes. Barrett, B. F. 50c......*Appleton.*
Beauty is power. 12°. $1.50...............*Carleton.*
Beauty of the heart; or, the story of Margaret Craven. 18°. 60c..........................*Am. S. S.*
— *See also* Select lib. for girls.
Beauty (The) of holiness; or, the practical Christian's daily companion; by eds. of "Truths ill. by great authors." 16°. $1.50.........*Lippincott.*
Beauty of Immanuel. Halsey, Le R. J. 75c. *Pres. Bd.*
Beauty, or the beast. Oxenford, J. 15c......*French.*
Beauvoir, Rog. de. Safia; or, the magic of Count Cagliostro: a Venetian tale; tr. by B. F. Christian and E. Lies. 8°. pap., 50c.........*Harper.*
Beaux' strategem. Farquhar, G. 15c........*French.*
Beaven, Ja. Help to catechising. 18°. bds., 10c. *Dutton.*
Beaver, J. Christian songster. 24°. leath., 45c. *Un. B. Pub.*
Beazley, S: Boarding house: farce. 16°. pap., 15c. *French.*
— Lottery ticket: farce. 16°. pap., 15c.......*French.*
Beazley, S: *jr.* Knights of the cross: drama. 16°. pap., 15c...............................*French.*
Bebee. La Rame, L. de. $1.50..........*Lippincott.*
Beccaria, C. B. Essay on crimes and punishments; with comment. by Voltaire. 8°. $3..*W. C. Little.*
Becher, Mt. Hunting the slippers; or, painless dentistry: farce. 12°. pap., 15c...........*De Witt.*
— In the wrong house; or, No. 6 Duke street: farce. 12°. pap., 15c.......................*De Witt.*
— My uncle's suit; or, in possession: farce. 12°. pap., 15c.............................*De Witt.*
— The two T. J.'s: drama. 16°. pap., 15c.....*Ames.*

Bechstein, J: Mat. Chamber and cage birds: their management, habits, etc., and methods of taking them; tr. New ed., rev. by G. J. Barnesby. 12°. '72. $1.50 .... *Routledge.*
— *Same;* incl. Sweet's Warblers. ill. 12°. (Bohn.) $1.75; col. pl., $2.75 .... *Little, B. & Co.*
— *Same.* ill. 12°. (Bohn.) $2; col. pl., $3. *Lippincott; Scribner, W. & A.*
Bechstein, L: As pretty as seven, and other tales; tr. from the Germ. ill. 12°. (Lond.) $3. *Little, B. & Co.*
— Märchenbuch. ill. 18°. 75c.; $1 .... *Kohler.*
Bechuana girl; [also] Lessons from heathen lands; [also] Christ our intercessor. 18°. 25c. *Pres. Bd.*
Beck, —, *and* Lawton, —. Piano method. f°. $1. *Gordon.*
Beck, C: Latin syntax, chiefly from the Germ. of Zumpt. 12°. leath., $1 .... *Dennet.*
Beck, J: B. Essays on infant therapeutics; [also] Observations on Ergot; [also] Hist. of the origin of use of mercury in inflammatory complaints; with statistics of deaths from poisoning in N. Y., 1841–'43. 12°. $1 .... *W. Wood.*
Beck, Lew. C. Botany of the U. S. north of Virginia; with synopsis of the genera according to the Linnæan system, etc. 12°. $1.50 .... *Harper.*
— Manual of chemistry. ill. 12°. $1.25 .... *Lippincott.*
— *See also* New York geol. survey.
Beckel, J. C. Amateur melodeon school. 4°. $1.50. *Ditson.*
— Amateur's organ school: description for playing the instrument. 4°. '55. bds., $1.50 .... *Ditson.*
— Amateur's [piano] school. 4°. bds., $1.50 .. *Ditson.*
— Church manual: method for acquiring a knowledge of church music for the organ. 8°. '69. bds., $1 .... *Ditson.*
— Philadelphia anthem book, arranged in 4 pts., with organ accompaniment. obl. 8°. pap., 25c. *Ditson.*
— Psalter (The): sacred music, arranged in 3 and 4 pts., with organ accompaniment. obl. 8°. '46. bds., 40c. .... *Ditson.*
Becker, A. C. Dentition; according to the latest German authorities. [Hom.] 12°. 50c. .... *Boericke.*
— Diseases of the digestive organs and constipation, treated homœopathically. 2d Am. from 3d Lond. ed., with add. 12°. 50c. .... *Boericke.*
— Diseases of the eye, treated homœopathically; from the Germ. 12°. 50c. .... *Boericke.*
Becker, Bern. H. Scientific London. 12°. $1.75. *Appleton.*
Becker, W: A. Charicles: a tale ill. of private life among the ancient Greeks, with notes and excursuses; tr. from the Germ. by Rev. F. Metcalfe. 12°. $3 .... *Lippincott.*
— *Same.* 12°. $3; hf. cf., $5 .... *Appleton.*
— Gallus; or, Roman scenes of the times of Augustus, with notes and excursuses; tr. from the Germ. by Rev. F. Metcalfe. 12°. $3 .... *Lippincott.*
— *Same.* 12°. $3; hf. cf., $5 .... *Appleton.*
Beckett, *Sir* Edm. [*late* E. B. Denison.] Astronomy without mathematics; ed. with corr. and notes by P. E. Chase. 12°. '69. $1.50 .... *Putnam.*
— Rudimentary treatise on clocks, watches and bells. 6th ed., rev. and enl. ill. 12°. $1.75 .... *Baird.*
Beckett, W. H. New nonsense rhymes. ill. 8°. $1. *Carleton.*
Beckford, W. Vathek: an Arabian tale; with notes. 12°. $1.25; pap., 75c. .... *Miller.*
— *Same.* 16°. $1.25 .... *Scribner, W. & A.*
Beckmann, —, *and* Hertzog, —. Deutsches Lesebuch. 1. Stufe. 12°. 25c. .... *Kohler.*
Beckmann, J: History of inventions, discoveries and origins; tr. by W. Johnstone. 2 v. 12°. (Bohn.) ea., $1.25 .... *Little, B. & Co.*
— *Same.* 2 v. 12°. (Bohn.) ea., $1.40. *Scribner, W. & A.*
— *Same.* 2 v. 12°. (Bohn.) ea., $1.50 ...... *Lippincott.*

Beckoning series. *See* Cobden, P.
Beckwith, *Miss* Abbey. New question-book on the patriarchs, kings and prophets. 18°. '68. hf. bd. 15c. .... *Hoyt*
Beckwith, Arth. Composition of ancient and Rosendale cements. 8°. pap., 30c. .. *Am. Soc. of C. E*
— Observations on the materials and manufacture of terra-cotta, stone ware, fire-brick, porcelain and encaustic tiles. 8°. '72. pap., 60c. . *Van Nostrand*
Beckwith, E. L. Following the master. 16°. $1.10 *Pres. Bd*
Beckwith, L. F. Béton coignet. *See* Prosser, T. Application of new system of distillation.
Beckx, Pierre J: Month of Mary: scenes from the life of the Virgin, arranged for month of May; with prayers, etc. 32°. 38c. .... *O'Shea.*
— *Same.* 24°. 60c.; 75c. .... *Sadlier*
— *Same.* 32°. '65. 50c.–$2 .... *Murphy*
— *Same;* with introd. by Rev. F. W. Faber. 18°. '61. 50c.; 75c. .... *Kelly, P. & Co.*
Becky. *See* Boyd, *Mrs.* E. E.
Becon, T: Life and writings. *See* British reformers.
Bec's bed time. Hallowell, J. L. $1.25 ...... *Porter.*
Bed-time stories. *See* Moulton, L. C.
Beda *or* Bede *Venerabilis.* Ecclesiastical hist. of Eng.; also the Anglo-Saxon chronicle, [etc.], ed. by J. A. Giles. 12°. (Bohn.) $1.75 .. *Little, B. & Co.*
— *Same.* 12°. (Bohn.) $2. *Lippincott; Scribner, W. & A.*
Bede, Cuthbert (*pseud.*) *See* Bradley, E:
Bedell, Greg. T. Life and travels of St. Paul. 18°. 60c. .... *Am. S. S.*
— Life of Moses. 18°. 60c. .... *Am. S. S.*
— Pay thy vows: pastoral address subsequent to confirmation. 32°. 30c. .... *Whittaker.*
— Renunciation (The): essay on worldly amusements. 32°. 30c. .... *Whittaker.*
Bedell, W: Life, by his son; ed. by Rev. J. E. B. Mayor. fp. 8°. $1.75 .... *Macmillan.*
Bede's charity. Smith, H. $1.50 .... *Dodd.*
Bedford, C. R. Book of remembrance written before the Lord for them that fear him, and think upon his name. 12°. '71. $1.50 .... *Claxton.*
Bedford, Gunning S. Diseases of women and children. Rev. ed. 8°. $4; leath., $5 .... *W. Wood.*
— Principles and practice of obstetrics. 4th ed. ill. 8°. $5.50; shp., $6.50 .... *W. Wood.*
Bedfordshire tinker (The). Sargent, G. E. 35c. *Pres. Bd.*
Bee, T. *See* United States, Dist. Ct. reports.
Bee (The). 32°. 20c.; 15c. .... *Dutton.*
Bee (The). *See* Tonna, C. E., White lies.
Bee and the orange tree. Planché, J. R. 15c. .. *French.*
Bee hive. Millingen, J. V. 15c. .... *French.*
Bee hive series. 4 v. ill. 16°. $3 .... *Nelson.*
Cont.: The boy makes the man. — Wings and stings, by A. L. O. E. — Basket of flowers, by J. H. St. A. — Story of Reuben Inch.
Beebe, *Miss* Emma N. Happy light. 16°. $1.50. *Pres. Bd.*
— Ruth Hawthorne; or, led to the rock. 16°. $1.25. *Pres. Bd.*
Beebe, Marg. N. Margaret Chester. 16°. $1.25. *Cong. Pub.*
— — *See also* Mossy dell ser.
Beech, *Mrs.* Alice A. Queen Rhoda; or, the error of self-reliance in the Christian life. ('70.) New ed. ill. 16°. '74. $1.50 .... *Hoyt.*
Beech bluff. Warner, F. $1.50 .... *Cunningham.*
Beechcroft. Yonge, C. M. $1 .... *Appleton.*
Beechdale. Carlton, K. 40c. .... *Williamson.*
Beechenbrook. *See* Preston, *Mrs.* M. J.
Beecher, Alvah C. (*ed.*) Recitations and readings. 16°. pap., 30c.; bds., 50c. .... *Dick & F.*

Beecher, *Miss* Cath. E. Appeal to the people in behalf of their rights, as the authorized interpreters of the Bible. 12°. $1.50 .... *Harper.*
— Common sense applied to religion; or, the Bible and the people. 12°. $1.50 .... *Harper.*
— Domestic receipt-book: supplement to treatise on domestic economy. 12°. $1.50 .... *Harper.*
— Educational reminiscences and suggestions. 16°. '74. $1 .... *Ford.*
— Handy cook book. *See below* New housekeeper's manual.
— Housekeeper and health keeper: recipes for econom. and healthful cooking; also directions for securing health and happiness. ill. 12°. $1.50 ... *Harper.*
— Letters to the people on health and happiness. 16°. $1 .... *Harper.*
— Physiology and calisthenics in schools and families. ill. 16°. $1 .... *Harper.*
— Religious training of children in the family, the school and the church. 12°. $1.75 ...... *Harper.*
— Woman's profession as mother and educator; with views in opposition to woman suffrage. 12°. '71. *$1.25 .... *Maclean.*
— *and* Stowe, *Mrs.* H. B. New housekeeper's manual: rev. ed. of "The American woman's home"; [also] The handy cook book, by C. E. Beecher. ill. cr. 8°. '76. *$3 .... *Ford.*
— — Principles of domestic science; as applied to the duties and pleasures of home. ('70.) New ed. ill. 12°. '71. $1.50 .... *Ford.*

Beecher, *Rev.* C: Redeemer and redeemed: investigation of the atonement and of eternal judgment. 12°. $1.75 .... *Lee & S.*
— *See also* Beecher, L., Autobiography.

Beecher, *Rev.* E. *See* McDill, D., Blanchard, J., *and* Beecher, E.

Beecher, H: Ward. Aids to prayer. 24°. '64. 75c. *Randolph.*
— Lecture-room talks; from T. J. Ellinwood's reports. ('70.) New ed. por. 12°. '75. $1.75 ..... *Ford.*
— Lectures to young men. ('72.) New ed., enl. 12°. '76. $1.50 .... *Ford.*
— Life of Jesus, the Christ, v. 1: earlier scenes. ill. 8°. *$3.50. 4°. *$7.50 .... *Ford.*
— Life thoughts; gathered from extemp. discourses, by one of his congregation. 12°. $1.75 .... *Sheldon.*
— Morning and evening devotional exercises; ed. by L. Abbott. cr. 8°. $3 .... *Harper.*
— Norwood; or, village life in New England. [Fiction.] ('67.) New ed. ill. 12°. '75. $2 .. *Ford.*
— On war and emancipation. 8°. pap., 13c. *Peterson.*
— Overture (The) of angels: pictures of the angelic appearances attending the nativity of our Lord. ill. 12°. '69. $1.50 .... *Ford.*
— Pleasant talk about fruits, flowers and farming. New ed., enl. 12°. '73. $2 .... *Ford.*
— Plymouth collection of hymns and tunes for Christian congregations. 8°. '55. $2.50; $4.50; $6.50; — hymns only. 32°. $1.25; $2; $3. 18°. $1.75; $3; $4.50 .... *Barnes.*
— Prayers from Plymouth pulpit. 12°. $1.50 .. *Mason.*
— Sermons; sel. from published and unpublished discourses, rev. by author. 2 v. por. 8°. $5; hf. cf., $9.50 .... *Harper.*
— Sermons, 1869-'74; from phonog. reports by T. J. Ellinwood. 10 v. 8°. ea., $2.50 .... *Ford.*
— Star papers: experiences of art and nature. New ed., enl. 12°. '73. $1.75 .... *Ford.*
— Summer parish (A): sermons and morning services of prayer, at the Twin Mountain House, Aug., 1874. por. 12°. '74. $1.50 .... *Ford.*
— Yale [College] lectures on preaching. 3 v. 12°. '72-'74. v. 1, $1.25; 2, 3, ea., $1.50 .... *Ford.*
— *See also* Hall, J., Cuyler, T. L., *and* Beecher, H. W., Successful preaching; — Marshall, C. F., True hist. of Brooklyn scandal; — Tilton, T., *vs.* Beecher, H. W., Report of trial.

Beecher, *Mrs.* H: Ward. Motherly talks with young housekeepers: brief articles on topics of home interest, with receipts for cooking, etc. por. 12°. $2 .... *Ford.*

Beecher, Lyman. Autobiography, correspondence, etc.; ed. by C. Beecher. 2 v. por. 12°. $5; hf. cf., $8.50 .... *Harper.*
— Six sermons on intemperance. ('27.) New ed. 18°. '33. 25c.; pap., 10c. .... *Am. Tr.*

Beecher, T: K. Our seven churches. [Lectures.] 16°. '70. $1; $1.25; pap., 50c. .... *Ford.*

Beecher, Willis J. Farmer Tompkins. 16°. $1.25. *Pres. Bd.*

Beechnut. Abbott, J. 90c. .... *Harper.*

Beechwood. Springer, R. R. $1.50 ..... *Lippincott.*

Beer, J. W. The Jewish Passover and Lord's supper. 16°. '74. 75c. .... *Brumbaugh.*

Beers, N. P. System of progressive penmanship. 12 nos. 8°. '62. per doz., pap., $1.68 ..... *Barnes.*

Bees and hornets. Nickerson, S. D. $1.50 .. *Cong. Pub.*

Beethoven, L: van. Calm sea and happy voyage. 8°. 20c. .... *Gordon.*
— Engedi. [Oratorio.] 8°. $1; pap., 75c. ... *Gordon.*
— Fantasie: [words "Psalm of life" by H. W. Longfellow.] (op. 80.) 8°. '76. pap., 25c. .. *Church.*
— Letters, 1790-1826; with his letters to the Archduke Rudolph; tr. by Lady Wallace. por. and facsimiles. 2 v. in 1. 16°. $2 .... *Ditson.*
— Mass in C; with organ or piano accomp. by V. Novello. 8°. $1.12; pap., 80c.; bds., 90c. .... *Ditson.*
— Ninth symphony: vocal parts. 8°. 35c. .... *Church.*

Beethoven collection of sacred music. Ives, E., *jr.*, Alpers, W., *and* Timm, H. C. $2.25 ... *Ditson.*

Beetle, and other stories. 18°. 40c. .... *Dutton.*

Beeton, *Mrs.* Is. Book of household management. ill. demy 8°. $3.25 .... *Lindsay.*
— *Same.* ill. 12°. $3.50 .... *Appleton.*
— *Same.* ill. 12°. '61. (Lond.) hf. roxb., $3. *Am. News.*
— Every-day cookery and housekeeping book; with receipts. ill. 12°. hf. roan, $1.50 .... *Appleton.*

Beeton, S. O. Dictionary of biography. ill., por., etc. sm. 8°. hf. bd., $3.50 .... *Appleton.*
— Dictionary of geography. ill., maps, plans of cities, etc. sm. 8°. hf. bd., $3.50 .... *Appleton.*
— Dictionary of universal information. maps and ill. imp. 8°. hf. roan, $7 .... *Appleton.*

Beeton's boys' own library. 6 v. ill. 8°. ea., $2.50. *Scribner, W. & A.*
Cont.: Broderip's Zoological recreations. — Stories of the wars, 1574 to 1658. — Don Quixote. — Gulliver's travels. — Wild animals in freedom and captivity. — Greenwood's Wild sports of the world.

Beeton's pictorial speller. ill. 12°. (Lond.) 50c. *Am. News.*
— *Same.* ill. 18°. 75c.; 50c. .... *Nelson.*

Before and after marriage. Arthur, T. S. $1.50. *J. E. Potter.*

Before the table. Howson, J. S. $2.75 .. *Macmillan.*

Beggar of Cripplegate. Moncrieff, W. T. 15c. .. *French.*

Beggar (A) on horseback. Payn, J. 35c. ... *Harper.*

Beggar's (The) closet, and what it contained. ('60.) New ed. ill. 18°. '71. 60c. .... *Hoyt.*

Beggar's opera. Gay, J. 15c. .... *French.*

Beggar's petition. Pitt, G. D. 15c. .... *French.*

Beggar's (The) will, and other stories. 18°. 50c. *O'Shea.*

Beggars of Holland and grandees of Spain. Mears, J. W. $1.50 .... *Pres. Bd.*

Beginning. Bates, L. $1 .... *J. A. Moore.*

Beginning and the end. Dunning, A. K. 75c. *Pres. Bd.*

Beginning and the end: drama. 16°. pap., 15c. *French.*

Beginning and growth of the Christian life; or, the Sunday school teacher. ('55.) 4th ed. 16°. '67. 60c. .... *Am. Unit.*

Beginning (A) in German; by an old teacher. 2d ed., rev. 8°. '75. bds., 30c. . . . . *Hoeger.*

Beginning life. *See* Tulloch, J.

Beginnings (The) of life. Bastian, H. $5. . *Appleton.*

Begon, F. (*Comtesse*) de. [" *Mme.* de Stolz."] Blanche and Beryl; or, the two sides of life. ill. 16°. '73. $1.25. . . . . *Routledge.*

— Faculties of the soul, a dialogue; tr. by Mrs. J. Sadlier. 18°. pap., 25c. . . . . *Sadlier.*

— House on wheels; or, the stolen child; tr. by Miss E. F. Adams. ill. 12°. $1.25. . . . . *Lee & S.*

— *Same.* 12°. $1.25; pap., 50c. . . . *Scribner, W. & A.*

Beharrel, T. G. Biblical biography. 8°. $3. *Meth. Bk. Conc.*

Beharrlichkeit führt zum Ziel. *See* Hoffmann, F.

Behind the bars: retrospect of an insane asylum. 16°. $2. . . . . *Lee & S.*

Behind the curtain. *See* Baker, *Mrs.* H. N. W.

Behind the curtain: drama. 16°. pap., 15c. . . *French.*

Behind a mask: comedy. 16°. pap., 15c. . . . *French.*

Behind the scenes in Washington. Martin, E. W. $2.75. . . . . *Tibbals.*

Behind time. Webster, B., *jr.* 15c. . . . . *French.*

Behold the Lamb of God. Kirk, E. N. 50c. *Bost. Am. Tr.*

Behr, C: *See* Curtiss, N. P. B., *and* Behr, C.

Behr, H: G. Die Feier d. Weihnachtsabends. 32°. bds., 15c. . . . . *Ludwig.*

Beiden Veroneser (Die). *See* Shakespeare, W.

Beilstein, F. Manual of qualitative analysis. (Element. sci. ser.) ill. 12°. '74. 75c. . . . . *Putnam.*

Beineke, P. Chrysostomus. Thuet dies zu meinem Andenken: Erklärg. d. hl. Messe, u. andere Ceremonien, etc. 12°. $1.05. . . . . *Herder.*

Being of God. Squiers, M. P. $1.25. . . . . . *Darrow.*

Beitel, Calv. G. Digest of titles of corporations chartered by the legislature of Penna., 1700–1866. 8°. '67. shp., $5. — Same. 2d ed., rev. and enl. 8°. '74. $7.50 . . . . *J. Campbell & Son.*

Belcher, *Lady* Di. Some account of the mutineers of the "Bounty" and their descendants in Pitcairn's and Norfolk islands. ill. 12°. $1.50. . . . *Harper.*

Belcher, H: Short exercises in Lat. prose composition and examination papers in Lat. gram.; [with] a brief chapter on analysis of sentences. 18°. '75. 75c. — Key. 75c. . . . . *Macmillan.*

Belcher, Jos. Baptisms of the New Test. 18°. 55c.; 65c. . . . . *Am. Bapt.*

— Baptists martyr. 16°. $1.25. . . . . *Am. Bapt.*

— Bloom of youth. ill. 18°. '64. 40c. . . . . *Am. Tr.*

— Historical sketches of hymns, their writers and influence. 12°. '73. $1.50. . . . . *Munsell.*

— Life of Geo. Whitefield. ill. 12°. '57. $1.25. . *Am. Tr.*

— Married life. 32°. 50c. . . . . *Am. Bapt.*

— Pastor's jottings. ill. 12°. '64. $1. . . . . *Am. Tr.*

— Religious denominations in the U. S.: their hist., doctrines, government and statistics. ill. 8°. '54. shp., *$5. . . . . *J. E. Potter.*

— Sketches for the young. ill. 18°. '61. 40c. . . *Am. Tr.*

— Sketches from life: illustrations of the influence of Christianity; from the "American messenger." 3 v. ill. 12°. '57–'72. ea., $1.50. . . . . . . *Am. Tr.*

— William Carey: a biography. 16°. $1.25. . *Am. Bapt.*

Beldazzle (*pseud.*) Bachelor studies. 12°. $1. *Carleton.*

Belden, G: P. The white chief; or, twelve years among the wild Indians of the plains (1858–'70); ed. and rev. by J. S. Brisbin. ill. 12°. '70. *$2.50 . . . . *Vent.*

Belding, Pamelia. Infant class manual. 18°. 75c. *Meth. Bk. Conc.*

Belem, E. M. de. The Spanish phrase book, or key to Spanish conversation; with conjugations of auxiliary and regular verbs. 18°. 37c. . . *Appleton.*

Belem, E. M. de, *continued.*

— *Spanish.* Libro de frases inglesas y españolas. 18°. 37c. . . . . *Appleton.*

Belèze, Gu. *See* Pylodet, L.

Belfield, H. H. Graded examples. ('75.) New ed. 12°. '76. 20c.; with key, 45c. . . . . . . *Sherwood.*

— *See also* Kirk, A., *and* Belfield, H. H.

Belfrage, H: Sacramental addresses. 12°. $1.50. *Carter.*

Belfry voices. [Poetry.] sq. 12°. '69. $1. . *De Selding.*

Belial. [Fiction.] 8°. pap., 50c. . . . . *Harper.*

Beliefs (The) of the unbelievers. Frothingham, O. B. $1. . . . . *Putnam.*

Believer's daily remembrancer. Smith, J. $1. . *Carter.*

Believer's daily treasure: texts of Scripture for every day of the year. 64°. 40c. . . . . *Pres. Bd.*

Believer's refuge. Thompson, J. P. $1.50. . *Randolph.*

Believer's triumph. Smith, J. 75c. . . . . *Nelson.*

Believer's victory over Satan's devices. Parsons, W. L. $1.25. . . . . *Meth. Bk. Conc.*

Believing child (The); or, a brief sketch of Fanny Wilson. 18°. 30c. . . . . *Am. S. S.*

Believing tradesman (The). ('60.) New ed. ill. 18°. '73. 30c. . . . . *Hoyt.*

Belinda. *See* Edgeworth, Maria.

Belisle, D. W. American family Robinson; or, the adventures of a family lost in the great desert of the west. ill. 16°. $1.25 . . . . *Porter.*

— History of Independence Hall. ('58.) 3d ed. 12°. $2.50 . . . . *Challen.*

Belknap, D. P. Probate law and practice [in California, etc.] 3d ed., rev. 8°. '76. shp., $7.50. *Bancroft.*

Belknap, Jer. American biography; with add. and notes by F. M. Hubbard. 3 v. 18°. $2.25. *Harper.*

— Life; with sel. from correspondence and other writings, collected and arranged by his grand-daughter. 12°. $1.50. . . . . *Harper.*

Belknap, M. S. Water power of the falls of the Ohio River. *See* Thurston, R. H., Note on the resistance of materials.

Bell, Acton (*pseud.*) *See* Brontë, Anne.

Bell, Cath. D. [" Cousin Kate."] Allen and Harry; or, set about it at once. ill. 18°. 75c. *Scribner, W. & A.*

— Arnold Lee; or, rich and poor boys. ill. 18°. 75c. *Scribner, W. & A.*

— Aunt Ailie; or, patience and its reward. ill. 16°. $1.75. . . . . *Scribner, W. & A.*

— Autumn at Karnford. ill. 18°. 75c. *Scribner, W. & A.*

— Douglas family; or, friendship. ill. 18°. 75c. *Scribner, W. & A.*

— Ella and Marian; or, rest and unrest. ill. 16°. $1.75. . . . . *Scribner, W. & A.*

— Every Saturday. ill. 16°. $1. . . . *Scribner, W. & A.*

— Garden (The): an allegory. 18°. 25c. *Scribner, W. & A.*

— Georgie and Lizzie; or, self-denial. ill. 18°. 75c. *Scribner, W. & A.*

— Grahams (The); or, home life. ill. 16°. $1.75. *Scribner, W. & A.*

— Head (The) and the heart. ill. 18°. '67. 30c. *N. Y. Ref. Ch. Bd.; Pres. Com.*

— *Same.* ill. 18°. 35c. . . . . *Bost. Am. Tr.*

— — *See also* Head and heart ser.; — Moss rose stories; — *and below* Jane Thorn.

— Home sunshine; or, the Gordons. ill. 16°. $1.75. *Scribner, W. & A.*

— Hope Campbell; or, know thyself. 16°. '55. $1.25. *Randolph.*

— *Same.* ill. 16°. $1.75. . . . . *Scribner, W. & A.*

— Horace and May; or, unconscious influence. 16°. '56. $1.25 . . . . *Randolph.*

— *Same.* ill. 16°. $1.75. . . . . *Scribner, W. & A.*

Bell, Cath. D., *continued.*
— Jane Thorn; or, the head and the heart. 18°. 30c.; 35c. . . . . *Am. Bapt.*
— *Same.* ('61.) New ed. ill. 18°. '75. 40c. . . . *Hoyt.*
— — *See also above* Head and the heart.
— Jennie Carter; or, trust in God. ('61.) New ed. ill. 18°. '70. 40c. . . . . *Hoyt.*
— Jenny's trials. *See* Head (The) and heart ser.; — *and below* Trust in God.
— Kenneth and Hugh; or, self mastery. 16°. '57. $1.25 . . . . . *Randolph.*
— *Same.* ill. 16°. $1.75 . . . . . *Scribner, W. & A.*
— Lily Gordon, the young housekeeper. ill. 12°. $1.25. *Scribner, W. & A.*
— *Same.* 16°. '58. $1.25 . . . . . *Randolph.*
— Little Nellie; or, Patience Strong. 18°. 25c. *Scribner, W. & A.*
— Margaret Cecil; or, I can because I ought. ill. 16°. $1.75 . . . . . *Scribner, W. & A.*
— Mary Elliot; or, be ye kind one to another. ill. 16°. $1 . . . . . *Scribner, W. & A.*
— Ned the shepherd boy. *See* Head and heart ser.
— Rest and unrest; or, the story of a year. 16°. '58. $1.25 . . . . . *Randolph.*
— Rosa's wish, and how she attained it. ill. 16°. $1.75. *Scribner, W. & A.*
— Short stories. 2 sets, "A," "B." 32°. 30c. *Nelson.*
— Story of Ned. *See* Head and heart ser.
— Sydney Stuart; or, love seeketh not her own. ill. 12°. $1.25 . . . . . *Scribner, W. & A.*
— *Same.* 18°. '58. $1.25 . . . . . *Randolph.*
— Trust in God; or, Jenny's trials. 18°. '67. 30c. *N. Y. Ref. Ch. Bd.; Pres. Com.*
— *Same.* 18°. 35c. . . . . *Bost. Am. Tr.*
— — *See also* Head and heart ser.; — Moss rose stories; — *and above* Jenny's trials.
— Two ways (The). 18°. '67. 30c. *N. Y. Ref. Ch. Bd.; Pres. Com.*
— *Same.* 18°. 35c. . . . . *Bost. Am. Tr.*
— — *See also* Moss rose stories.
— Way (The) to be happy; or, Willie the gardener boy. 18°. '67. 30c. *N. Y. Ref. Ch. Bd.; Pres. Com.*
— *Same.* 18°. 35c. . . . . *Bost. Am. Tr.*
— *Same.* 18°. 45c. . . . . (?) *Martien.*
— — *See also* Head and heart ser.; — Moss rose stories.

Bell, *Sir* C: Expression, its anat. and philos.; with notes and ill. by the author, and the ed. of the "Phrenological journal." New ed., enl. 12°. '73. $1.25 . . . . . *Wells.*
— On the hand: its mechanism and vital endowments, as evincing design. (Bridgewater treatises.) 12°. $1 . . . . . *Harper.*
— *Same.* 7th ed., rev. 12°. (Bohn.) $1.75. *Little, B. & Co.*
— *Same.* 12°. (Bohn.) $2. *Lippincott; Scribner, W. & A.*

Bell, C: D. Angelic beings: their nature and ministry. 12°. $1.25 . . . . . *Nelson.*

Bell, C: H. Discourse before the N. E. Hist. Geneal. Soc., Mar. 18, 1871, [at] dedication of Society's house. 8°. '71. pap., 25c. . . . . *N. E. Hist. Gen.*

Bell, C: U. Index or summary digest to Mass. reports (v. 103–112, 115–117). 8°. '76. shp., $2.75 . . *Reed.*
— *See also* Massachusetts, Statutes and laws, etc.

Bell, Currer (*pseud.*) *See* Brontë, Charlotte.

Bell, E. M. Poems. 12°. $1.50 . . . . . *Lippincott.*

Bell, Ellis (*pseud.*) *See* Brontë, Emily.

Bell, G: A. *See* Bradbury, W. B., Bell, G. A., *and* Main, S.
— *and* Main, H. P. Book of praise for the Sunday school; with hymns and tunes. obl. 16°. '75. $1; bds., 50c. . . . . *Biglow.*
— — Christian songs for the Sunday school. obl. 16°. '72. 50c. . . . . *Biglow.*

Bell, Goodlow H. Progressive Bible lessons for Sabbath schools and families. 2 v. 16°. '72–'75. v. 1, 35c.; v. 2, 50c. . . . . *Sev. Day Adv.*

Bell, H: Glassford. Life of Mary, Queen of Scots. 2 v. 18°. $1.50 . . . . . *Harper.*
— *See also* Shakespeare, W.

Bell, I. Lowthian. Chemical phenomena of iron smelting. ill. 8°. $6 . . . . . *Baird.*

Bell, Ja. B. The homœopathic therapeutics of diarrhœa, dysentery, cholera, etc. 12°. $1.25; hf. mor., $2.25 . . . . . *Boericke.*

Bell, M. M. Eda Morton and her cousins; or, schoolroom days. ill. 16°. $1 . . . . . *Routledge.*
— Seven to seventeen; or, Veronica Gordon. ill. 16°. '75. $1.50 . . . . . *Dutton.*
— *Same.* ill. 16°. $1.75 . . . . . *Scribner, W. & A.*

Bell, *Mrs.* Mt. Julia Howard. 8°. pap., 50c. . . *Harper.*

Bell, Rob. Golden leaves, from the works of the poets and painters. 65 eng. 4°. $15 . . . . . *Routledge.*
— Life of George Canning. 12°. $1 . . . . . *Harper.*
— Temper: comedy. 16°. pap., 15c. . . . . *French.*

Bell, S: D. Practical forms for justices of the peace, sheriffs, etc., [in N. H.] 3d ed., enl. by S. N. Bell. 12°. '56. $2 . . . . . *Eastman.*

Bell, W. H. Quiddities of an Alaskan trip. ill. obl. 4°. $3.50 . . . . . *Lippincott.*

Bell, W: E. Carpentry made easy: science and art of framing. ('57.) 7th ed. ill. roy. 8°. $5 . . *Challen.*

Bell Brandon, and the withered fig tree. Myers, P. H. 50c. . . . . *Peterson.*

Bella. St. John, E. $1.50 . . . . . *Berry.*

Bella Trelawney. Smith, J. F. 75c. . . . . *Dick & F.*

Bellak, Ja. Analytical method for the pianoforte. 4°. bds., $1; pap., 75c. . . . . *Ditson.*
— Excelsior piano instructor. 4°. $2 . . . . . *Church.*
— Lee and Walker's juvenile piano instructor. obl. 16°. '52. pap., 60c. . . . . *Ditson.*
— Melodeon instructor. obl. roy. 8°. '57. pap., 50c. *Pond.*
— Method for the organ. f°. '76. bds., $1; pap., 75c. *Ditson.*
— Musical casket. f°. $1.25; bds., 75c. . . . . *Gordon.*
— Piano method. f°. pap., 75c.; bds., $1 . . . . *Gordon.*

Bellamy, E. Student's guide to surgical anatomy. ill. 12°. $2.25 . . . . . *Lea.*

Bellamy, *Mrs.* E. W. ["Kamba Thorpe."] Little Joanna. [Fiction.] 8°. pap., 60c. . . . *Appleton.*

Bellamy, Jos. Works. 2 v. 8°. $4 . . . . . *Cong. Pub.*
— True religion delineated; or, experimental religion. 8°. $2 . . . . . *Cong. Pub.*

Belle, *Cousin.* *See* Cousin Belle.

Belle; or, the promised blessing. 18°. 50c. *Claremont.*
— *Same.* 18°. 60c. . . . . *Dutton.*

Belle and Lily; or, the golden rule. ill. 16°. $1.25. *O'Shea.*

Belle Clement's influence. Baker, H. N. W. $1. *H. A. Young.*

Belle France (La). Parkes, B. R. $3 . . . . *Routledge.*

Belle Helene. *See* Ditson.

Belle Helene (La). [Fiction.] 8°. pap., 25c. *De Witt.*

Belle Lovell. Y., T. R. $1.25 . . . . . *Randolph.*

Belle of the barley mow. Arden, H. T. 15c. . . *French.*

Belle of the Bowery. 8°. pap., 25c. . . . . *Dick & F.*

Belle of the family. Grey, E. C. 50c. . . . . *Peterson.*

Belle of New York; or, a glimpse at high life in the great metropolis. 12°. $1.75 . . . . . *J. E. Potter.*

Belle of Washington. Lasselle, N. P. $1.75; $1.50. *Peterson.*

Belle poets (La). (Red line ed.) 6 v. ill. sq. 16°. $9; mor., $13.50; $21 . . . . . *Porter.*

Cont.: Burns' poems. — The moral and beautiful in the poems of Byron. — Griswold's Gems from the Am. poets. — Hood's poems. — The moral and beautiful from poems of Moore. — Dodd's Beauties of Shakespeare.

Belle Powers' locket. Mathews, J. H. $1 . . . . *Carter.*

Belle Rose. Achard, A. $1 . . . . . *Claxton.*

Bellehood and bondage. Stephens, A. S. $1.75; $1.50 .... *Peterson.*

Bellenger, H. *See* Witcomb, C., *and* Bellenger, H.

Belle's stratagem. Cowley, H. 15c. .... *French.*

Belles lettres letter-writer. 32°. pap., 10c. *U. P. James.*

Bellevue and Charity Hospital reports; ed. by W. A. Hammond. 8°. $4 .... *Appleton.*

Bellew, Fk. Art of amusing. ill. 12°. $1.50 .. *Carleton.*

Bellinger, C. B. *See* Oregon, Supreme Court reports.

Bellingham, H: Blue Beard repaired: burlesque. 16°. pap., 15c. .... *French.*

— *and* Best, —. Prince Camaralzaman: extravaganza. 16°. pap., 15c. .... *French.*

— — Princess Primrose: extravaganza. 16°. pap., 15c. *French.*

Bellini, Vincenzo. I Capuletti Montecchi; — Pirata (Il); — Puritani (I); — Sonnambula (La). *See* Ditson.

— Norma; with Italian and English words. [Opera.] 4°. bds., $1.50 .... *Ditson.*

— — *See also* Ditson.

Bellmonte, Clyde. May Earnest. *See* Pioneer lib.

Bello, Andrés. Compendio de la gramática castellana, por J. Márquez. 18°. 50c. .... *Appleton.*

Belloc, Bessie Parkes. Peoples of the world. ill. 16°. $2.50 .... *Cassell.*

Bellows, Alb. J. How not to be sick: sequel to "Philosophy of eating." cr. 8°. '68. $2 .. *Hurd & H.*

— Philosophy of eating. New ed., enl. cr. 8°. '70. $2. *Hurd & H.*

Bellows, C. F. R. Plane and spherical trigonometry. 8°. hf. leath., $1.50 .... *Sheldon.*

Bellows, H: W. Memorial address on Henry T. Tuckerman. por. 12°. '72. 75c. .... *Putnam.*

— Old world (The) in its new face: impressions of Europe in 1867–8. 2 v. 12°. $3.50 .... *Harper.*

— Re-statements of Christian doctrine. [Sermons.] ('59.) New ed. 12°. '70. $1 .... *Am. Unit.*

— *See also* Christianity and modern thought.

Bells (The). *See* Erckmann, E., *and* Chatrian, A.

Bells (The): drama. 16°. pap., 15c. .... *French.*

Belmont series (The). 5 v. ill. 16°. $6.25 .. *Graves.*

Cont.: Amy Garnett, by P. Curtiss. — Joe and the Howards, by Carl. — Day's motto. — Lynda Newton, by Mrs. L. J. H. Frost. — The myrtle branch, by Mrs. Leslie.

Beloe, C. H. Liverpool water works. 3d. ed. 8°. '75. pap., 60c. .... *Spon.*

— On the construction of catch-water reservoirs in mountain districts for the supply of towns, or for other purposes. ill. 8°. '72. $2 .... *Spon.*

Belohnte Treue; [also] Sakuntala; [also] Der Missionär in Afrika. 16°. 25c. .... *Morwitz.*

— *Same.* 16°. 30c.; bds., 20c.; pap., 15c. .... *Kohler.*

Belot, Adolphe. Article 47; tr. by J. Furbish. [Fiction.] 8°. $1.25; pap., 75c. .... *Lippincott.*

— L'article 47; or, breaking the ban: drama. 12°. pap., 15c. .... *De Witt.*

— A life chase: drama. 12°. pap., 15c. ...... *De Witt.*

— Men are what women make them; tr. by J. M. Furbish. 12°. $1.50 .... *McKinney.*

— Woman (The) of fire. 8°. '75. pap., 50c. *W. F. Gill.*

Beloved disciple. H., H. 50c. .... *Am. S. S.*

Beloved disciple. Kimball, J. W. 15c. .. *Bost. Am. Tr.*

Belphegor. Higgie, T., *and* Lacy, T. H. 15c. .. *French.*

Belphegor. Webb, C. 15c. .... *French.*

Belshazzar. Butterfield, J. A. $1.25; $1 .. *Ditson.*

Belshazzar's feast. Root, G. F. 50c. .... *Ditson.*

Belt, Rob. *See* England, Supplement to Vesey's Chancery reports.

Belton estate (The). *See* Trollope, Anthony.

Bement, C. N. Rabbit fancier (The). 12°. 30c. .. *Judd.*

Bement, C. N., *continued.*

— Treatise on the breeding, rearing, fattening and general management of domestic poultry. ill. 12°. $2 .... *Harper.*

Bemrose, W., *jr.* Fret-cutting and perforated carving. ill. 4°. $3 .... *Baird.*

— Manual of buhl-work and marquetry. col. ill. 4°. $3 .... *Baird.*

— Manual of wood-carving; with introd. by L. Jewitt. col. ill. 4°. $3 .... *Baird.*

Ben and Bertie series. 2 v. 18°. '74. ea., 90c. *Meth. Bk. Conc.*

Cont.: School life of Ben and Bertie. — Camp Tabor.

Ben Benson. Dawson, —. 25c. .... *Porter.*

Ben the boatswain. Wilks, T. E. 15c. ...... *French.*

Ben Boland's garden; or, home life. 16°. 90c. *Am. S. S.*

— *See also* Diamond lib.

Ben Bolt. Johnstone, J. B. 15c. .... *French.*

Ben Brace. *See* Chamier, F.; — Life and adventures of.

Ben Farrar's experience of the sunny side of the cross. 16°. $1.25 .... *Cong. Pub.*

— *See also* Island home lib.

Ben Holt's good name. 18°. 40c. .... *Am. S. S.*

— *Same.* 18°. '68. 40c. .... *Am. Tr.*

— *Same.* 18°. 60c. ...... *Bost. Am. Tr.;* (?) *Martien.*

— *Germ.* Ben Holt's guter name. 18°. '70. 35c. *Am. Tr.*

Ben Howard. Adams, C. 45c. .... *Routledge.*

Ben, the luggage boy. Alger, H., *jr.* $1.25 .. *Loring.*

Ben Ross: sequel to "Rosa Lane." 18°. 60c. *Am. S. S.*

Ben Sylvester's word. Yonge, C. M. 60c. *Appleton; Dutton.*

Benaiah. *See* Webb, *Mrs.* J. B.

Bench and bar. Bigelow, L. J. $2 .... *Harper.*

Bench and bar of Georgia. *See* Miller, S. F.

Bench and bar of N. Y. Proctor, L. B. $5.50; $6.50. *Ward & P.*

Bendan, D. Tirocinium; or, first lessons in Latin. 12°. 60c. .... *Ivison.*

Bendbow, Hesper (*pseud.*) *See* Archer, G: W.

Bendeman, E. (*ill.*) The frescoes of the ball room in the royal castle at Dresden: eng., with text by I. G. Droysen. obl. f°. bds., $8 ...... *Stroefer.*

Bender, C. Application of the theory of continuous girders to economy in bridge building; [also] Note on the resistance of materials as affected by flow and by rapidity of distortion, by R. H. Thurston. 8°. '76. $1.50 .... *Am. Soc. of C. E.*

— Sketch of improvements in suspension bridges. *See* McAlpine, W. J., Corrosion of iron.

Bender, C: E. Proportions of pins used in bridges. ill. 18°. '73. bds., 50c. .... *Van Nostrand.*

Bender, H: Englisch, f. Jedermann! od. Anweisg. d. Englische in kürzester Zeit zu lernen. sq. 16°. '73. pap., 25c. .... *Steiger.*

Bending willow. Fuller, J. G. $1.25 .... *Carter.*

Beneath the surface. Adams, W. H. D. $1.25 .. *Nelson.*

Beneath the wheels. Notley, *Mrs.* —. 50c. .. *Harper.*

Benedicite. Child, G. C. $2; $4 .... *Putnam.*

Benedict *of Sanfratello, St.,* (*the Moor*). Life; tr. by Mother St. John. 16°. '75. $1. *Cunningham; Sadlier.*

Benedict, D: General hist. of the Baptist denominations. 8°. $4 .... *So. Bapt.*

— Watery war; or, controversy between pedobaptists and Baptists. 18°. pap., 10c. .... *So. Bapt.*

Benedict, Erastus C. A run through Europe. 12°. '68. $2 .... *Barnes.*

— (*tr.*) Hymn of Hildebert; with tr. of other Lat. hymns. 16°. '68. $1.50 .... *Randolph.*

Benedict, Fk. Lee. [Novels.] 6 v. 8°. ea., $1.50; pap., $1 .... *Harper.*

Cont.: John Worthington's name. — Miss Dorothy's charge. — Miss Van Kortland. — Mr. Vaughan's heir. — My daughter Elinor. — St. Simon's niece.

Benedict, Fk. Lee, *continued.*
— *See also* Rougegorge and other stories.
Benedict, *Mrs.* Hester A. Vesta. [Poetry.] 16°. '72. $1.50 .... *Claxton.*
Benedict, J. Civil and criminal justice of N. Y. 5th ed., rev. and enl. 8°. shp., $7.50 .. *W. C. Little.*
Benedict, Jl. T. Algebra. 12°. $1.75 .... *Mason.*
Benedict, R. D. *See* United States, District Courts reports.
Benedict, Roswell Alphonzo. America. 18°. '76. pap., 50c. .... (?) *Mearns.*
Benedix, R. Eigensinn. *See* Wilhelmi, A., Einer muss heirathen.
— Weiberfeind (Der). *See* Elz, A., Er ist nicht eifersüchtig.
Benefit of Christ's death. *See* Paleario, A.
Benét, S. V. Electro-ballistic machines, and the Schultz chronoscope. 2d ed. ill. 4°. '71. $3. *Van Nostrand.*
— Treatise on milit. law and the practice of courts-martials. 6th ed., rev. and enl. 8°. '68. shp., $4.50 .... *Van Nostrand.*
Bengal tiger. Dance, C. 15c. .... *French.*
Bengel, J: Alb. Gnomon of the New Test.; tr. from the Lat. by C. T. Lewis and M. R. Vincent. ('60.) 7th ed. 2 v. 8°. '74. $9; shp., $12; hf. mor., $15 .... *Perkinpine.*
Benger, *Miss* Eliz. Ogilvey. Memoirs of Anne Boleyn. 7th Am. from 3d London ed.; with memoir of author by Miss Aiken. 12°. $1.75 .. *J. E. Potter.*
— Memoirs of Mary, Queen of Scots; with anecdotes of the court of Henry II. 2 v. in 1. por. 12°. $1.75 .... *J. E. Potter.*
Benham, Dan. Life and labors of Rev. J: Gambold. 12°. (Lond.) '65. $1 .... *Clauder.*
— Memoirs of James Hutton. por. 8°. (Lond.) '56. $2. *Clauder.*
— Origin and episcopate of the Bohemian Brethren. 12°. (Lond.) '68. $1.25 .... *Clauder.*
— Sketch of life of Jan Aug. Miertsching, interpreter of the Esquimaux lang. sq. 4°. pap., 50c. *Clauder.*
Benham, W. Companion to the lectionary: comment. on "Proper lessons." cr. 8°. '73. $2.50. *Macmillan.*
Benisch, A. *See* Bible, Pentateuch, *Hebrew.*
Benjamin, *Mrs.* E. Bedell. Brightside. 16°. '73. $1.25. *Carter.*
— Church in the wilderness: or, from Horeb to Canaan: a contin. of the national and relig. educ. of the Israelities. 16°. '72. hf. bd., 35c. ... *Randolph.*
— Eleven months in Horeb; questions on the national and religious education of the Israelites. 16°. '69. 20c. .... *Randolph.*
Benjamin, J. P. Treatise on the law of sale of personal property; with ref. to the Am. decisions and to the French code and civil law. 1st Am. from 2d Eng. ed.; ed. by J. C. Perkins. 8°. '73. shp., $7.50 .... *Hurd & H.; Morrison.*
Benjamin, L. A., *and* Woodbury, I. B. New York Normal School song book. obl. 16°. '63. bds., 45c. .... *Ditson.*
Benjamin, *Mrs.* M. G. The missionary sisters: memorial of Mrs. S. H. Everett and Mrs. H. M. Hamlin. ill. 12°. $1.25 .... *Bost. Am. Tr.*
Benjamin, Park. Wrinkles and recipes: suggestions, etc., for the mechanic, engineer, etc.; comp. from the "Scientific American." 3d ed. ill. 16°. '75. $1.50 .... *H. N. Munn.*
Benjamin; or, the pupil of the Christian Brothers. 18°. 50c.; 75c. .... *Sadlier.*
Benjamin, the temperance boy. 18°. 35c. .. *Cong. Pub.*
Benner, S: Benner's prophecies of future ups and downs in prices: what years to make money on pig-iron, hogs, corn and provisions. 16°. '75. $1. *Benner.*

Bennet, Ja. H: Treatment of pulmonary consumption by hygiene, climate and medicine. 8°. '72. $1.50. *Appleton.*
— Winter and spring on the shores of the Mediterranean; or, the Riviera, Mentone, Italy, etc., as winter climates. New ed., rev. ill. 12°. '70. $3.50 .... *Appleton.*
Bennett, C: H. *See* Æsop, Fables; — Chimes, rhymes and jingles.
Bennett, D. M. Discussion with Elder Shelton, on Noah's flood, etc. 16°. pap., 10c. .. *D. M. Bennett.*
— Hour with the devil. 16°. pap., 10c. *D. M. Bennett.*
— Thirty discussions, Bible stories, lectures and essays. 18°. '76. $1; pap., 75c. .... *D. M. Bennett.*
Bennett, Edm. H. Fire insurance cases; embracing all the reported cases in Gr. Brit. and Am.; with notes and ref. v. 1–4 (1729–1864). 4 v. 8°. '72–'76. ea., shp., $7.50 .... *Hurd & H.*
— *and* Heard, F. F. Selection of leading cases in criminal law; with notes. ('56–'57.) 2d ed. 2 v. 8°. '69. shp., $12 .... *Little, B. & Co.*
Bennett, Emerson. Bandits (The) of the Osage: a western romance. 8°. pap., 25c. .. *U. P. James.*
— Border rover (The). 12°. $1.75; pap., $1.50. *Peterson.*
— Bride of the wilderness. 12°. $1.75; pap., $1.50. *Peterson.*
— Clara Moreland. 12°. $1.75; pap., $1.50. *Peterson.*
— Ella Barnwell: hist. romance of border life. 8°. pap., 25c. .... *U. P. James.*
— Ellen Norbury. 12°. $1.75; pap., $1.50 .. *Peterson.*
— Fair rebel (The): tale of colonial times. 8°. pap., 25c. .... *U. P. James.*
— Female spy (The); or, treason in the camp: a story of the revolution. 8°. pap., 25c. .. *U. P. James.*
— Forest and prairie; or, life on the frontier. ill. 12°. $1.75 .... *J. E. Potter.*
— Forest rose (The): a tale of the frontier. 8°. pap., 25c. .... *U. P. James.*
— Heiress of Bellefonte; [also] Walde-Warren. 8°. pap., 75c. .... *Peterson.*
— Kate Clarendon. 12°. $1.75; pap., $1.50. *Peterson.*
— League of the Miami. 8°. pap., 25c. .. *U. P. James.*
— Leni Leoti: sequel to "Prairie flower." 8°. pap., 25c. .... *U. P. James.*
— Mike Fink, a legend of the Ohio. 8°. pap., 25c. *U. P. James.*
— Orphan's (The) trials. 12°. $1.75; pap., $1.50. *Peterson.*
— Outlaw's (The) daughter; or, adventures in the south. ('73.) 3d ed. 12°. '75. $1.50; pap., $1 .. *Claxton.*
— Phantom of the forest. 12°. $1.75 .... *J. E. Potter.*
— *Same.* ('67.) 2d ed. 12°. '74. $1.50; pap., $1. *Claxton.*
— Pioneer's daughter; [also] The unknown countess. 8°. pap., 75c. .... *Peterson.*
— Prairie flower (The); or, adventures in the far west. 8°. pap., 25c. .... *U. P. James.*
— Rosalie du Pont: sequel to "Female spy." 8°. pap., 25c. .... *U. P. James.*
— Traitor (The); or, the fate of ambition. 8°. pap., 75c. .... *U. P. James.*
— Unknown countess (The); or, crime and its results. 8°. pap., 25c. .... *U. P. James.*
— — *See also above* Pioneer's daughter.
— Villeta Linden; or, the artist's bride. 12°. '74. $1.50; pap., $1 .... *Claxton.*
— Viola. 12°. $1.75; pap., $1.50 .... *Peterson.*
Bennett, J: Letters to a young lady, on subjects calculated to improve the heart, etc. 10th ed. 18°. '68. 75c. .... *Claxton.*
Bennett, J: Hughes. Clinical lectures on the principles and practice of medicine. 5th Am. ed. ill. 8°. $6; leath., $7 .... *W. Wood.*
— Text-book of physiology: general, special and practical. ill. 12°. $3.50 .... *Lippincott.*

Bennett, *Mrs.* Marg. L. Early lessons about the Saviour. 18°. 12c. .... *Un. S. S.*
— Every Sunday. 18°. 12c. .... *Un. S. S.*
— Many teachers, but one lesson: a book for S.-schools and families. 16°. 60c. .... *Lee & S.*
— (*ed.*) Bible rule of life. sq. 16°. '73. 40c.; 50c. *Am. Unit.*
— Day unto day. ('71.) 8th ed. sq. 16°. '75. 75c.; $1 .... *Am. Unit.*

Bennett, *Mrs.* Ma. E. Queer people. ill. 16°. '72. $1.25 .... *Crowell.*
— Six boys: a mother's story as told by some extracts from her journal. ill. 16°. $1.25 .. *Bost. Am. Tr.*

Bennett, Natl. *See* California, Supreme Court reports.

Bennett, S. A. *See* Missouri, Supreme Court reports.

Bennett, T: Introduction to the art of singing. f°. pap., $2 .... *Ditson.*

Bennett, W. J. E. Catechism of devotion. 12°. '76. $2 .... *Pott.*
— The church's broken unity. 5 v. 12° .... *Pott.*
Cont.: Presbyterianism, Irvingism, $1.75. — Anabaptists, Independency, Quakers, $1.75. — Methodism, Swedenborgians, $1.75. — Romanism, 2 v., ea., $2.25.

Bennett, W: Sterndale. May queen; with words by H. F. Chorley. [Cantata.] 8°. $1.25; bds., $1.12; pap., $1 .... *Ditson.*
— — Choruses. 8°. pap., 65c. .... *Ditson.*
— Woman of Samaria. [Cantata.] 8°. $1.50; pap., $1; bds., $1.25 .... *Ditson.*

Bennie Goodhue. 18°. 60c. .... *Cong. Pub.*

Bennie Goodhue's library. 6 v. 18°. $3.60 .. *Cong. Pub.*
Cont.: Bennie Goodhue. — Lizzie doing good. — The two shawls. — Harry White's oath. — The silver spoon. — Loss and gain.

Benning, Howe (*pseud.*) *See* Henry, Ma. H.

Benn-Walsh, J: *See* Ormathwaite, *Lord.*

Benny. Mathews, J. H. 20c. .... *Am. Tr.*

Benny's birds. Robbins, S. S. 30c. .... *Hoyt.*

Benoni. Barth, C. G. 50c. .... *Pres. Bd.*

Benoni Blake, M.D. Maclellan, M. $1.75. *Routledge.*

Ben's boyhood. *See* Bowen, C. E.

Bensalem. Galbraith, T. 25c. .... *Galbraith.*

Benson, *Rev.* E. W. Boy life: its trial, its strength, its fulness. [Sermons, 1859–'73.] cr. 8°. '74. $2.50 .... *Macmillan.*

Benson, Egb. Vindication of the captors of Major André. N. Y., 1817. [Reprint.] 8°. $1.50; large pap., $3 .... *Sabin.*

Benson, H. C. Life among the Choctaw Indians. 12°. $1.75 .... *Cin. Meth. Bk. Conc.*

Benson, Jos. Commentary on the Old and New Test. 5 v. 8°. '39. shp., $20; cf., $25 .. *Meth. Bk. Conc.*
— Life of Rev. J. W. de La Fletchere; ed. by T. O. Summers. 18°. '57. $1 .... *So. Meth.*

Benson, L. Book of remarkable trials and notorious characters. ill. 12°. $3 .... *Routledge.*
— *Same.* ill. sm. 8°. $5 .... *Appleton.*

Benson, Lawr. Sluter. Geometry: elements of Euclid and Legendre simplified; with elements of plane and spherical trigonometry, etc. ('67.) 3d ed. 8°. '69. shp., $2 .... *Burnton.*
— My visit to the sun: crit. essays on physics, metaphysics and ethics. ('64.) 2d ed., rev. and enl. 8°. '74. $2.25 .... *Burnton.*
— Philosophic reviews. 8°. '74. $1.25 ..... *Burnton.*

Benson, R. M. Bible teachings: S. John VI. 12°. '76. $1.75 .... *Pott.*
— Redemption: some of the aspects of the works of Christ. [Lectures.] 16°. '61. $2 .... *Pott.*

Bentham, Jer. The rationale of judicial evidence; with notes by J. S. Mill. 4 v. 8°. '76. $20; shp., $24 .... *Cockcroft.*

Bentley, E. W. The classis of Orange: hist. discourse, Port Jervis, N. Y., 1875. 8°. pap., 25c. *N. Y. Ref. Ch. Bd.*

Bentley, R., *and* Trimen, H. Medicinal plants: descriptions, with figures, of the principal plants employed in medicine. [To form 36 pts.] pts. 1–10. ill. 8°. '76. ea., $2 .... *Lindsay.*

Bentley, Rensselaer. Pictorial definer. 12°. '52. hf. roan, 31c. .... *Claxton; Lippincott.*
— Pictorial primer. 12°. hf. bd., 19c. ..... *Thompson.*
— Pictorial spelling-book. 12°. hf. bd., 40c. .. *Sheldon.*

Bentley, *Rev.* W: Address [before] the Am. Antiq. Soc., King's Chapel, Boston, Oct. 23, 1816. 8°. '75. $1 .... *Am. Antiq.*

Bentley, W: W. *See* Perkins, H. S., *and* Bentley, W. W.; — Royal songs.

Bentley; or, the spoiled child. 18°. 60c. .. *Cong. Pub.*

Benton, *Mrs.* C. C. France and her people. 12°. $1.50 .... *Souder.*

Benton, J. G. Course of instruction in ordnance and gunnery; for U. S. Milit. Acad. 4th ed., rev. and enl. ill. 8°. '75. $5 .... *Van Nostrand.*

Benton, N. S. History of Herkimer Co. [N. Y.] por. and map. 8°. hf. shp., $3 .... *Munsell.*

Benton, R. A. *See* Harrison, H., *and* Benton, R. A.

Benton, T: Hart. Abridgment of the debates of Congress, 1789–1856. 16 v. 8°. ea., hf. mor., *$6. *Appleton.*
— Historical and legal examination of the Dred Scott case. 8°. $1.25; pap., 63c. .... *Appleton.*
— Thirty years' view: hist. of the working of the Am. government, 1820–1850. New ed., rev.; with index. 2 v. 8°. $6; shp., $8; hf. cf., $10; cf., $12 .... *Appleton.*

Beppo, the conscript. Trollope, T. A. $1.75; $1.50. *Peterson.*

Béranger, Pierre J: de. Dernières chansons de 1834 à 1851; avec une lettre et une preface de l'auteur. 18°. '58. pap., $1.50 .... *Payot.*
— Two hundred of his lyrical poems; done into Eng. verse by W: Young. 12°. $1.50 ...... *Appleton.*

Berard, A. B. Manual of Span. art and literature. ('66.) New ed. 12°. '70. 94c. ... *Cowperthwait.*
— School hist. of Eng. 12°. '61. $1.75 ...... *Barnes.*
— School hist. of the U. S. ('57.) New ed. 12°. '48. $1.20 .... *Cowperthwait.*

Berber (The). Mayo, W. S. $1.75 .... *Putnam.*

Berbiguier, A. T. Method for the flute; [also] Twenty-four studies in all the keys, by L. Drouet. f°. bds., $3 .... *Ditson.*

Berchman, J: Life. 12°. $1.50 .... *Sadlier.*

Berean question-book for 1874–6. 3 v. 18°. ea., 15c. *Meth. Bk. Conc.*

Bereaved mothers. 18°. 25c.; 30c. .... *Am. Bapt.*

Berg, Fz. Fibel; mit Schlüssel zum Uebersetzen in d. Engl., etc. 2 pts. 12°. '73–'74. pt. 1, 15c.; pt. 2, 20c. .... *Witter.*
— *See also* Robyn, H., *and* Berg, F.

Berg, Jos. F. Abaddon and Mahanaim; or, demons and guardian angels. 12°. '56. $1 .. *Perkinpine.*
— Answer to Bp. Hughes. 8°. pap., 13c. .... *Peterson.*
— Lecture on the Jesuits. 8°. pap., 13c. .... *Peterson.*
— Old paths: sketch of the order and discipline of the Ref. Dutch Church before the reformation. 16°. 75c.; pap., 50c. .... *N. Y. Ref. Ch. Bd.*
— Prophecy and the times; or, England and Armageddon: application of the predictions of Daniel and St. John to current events. 12°. '55. $1. *Perkinpine.*
— The stone and the image; or, the Am. republic the bane and ruin of despotism: exposition of the fifth kingdom of Daniel's prophecy. 12°. '56. $1. *Perkinpine.*
— *See also* Schweinitz, E. de, Berg, J. F., *and* Newton, R.

Bergen, Teunis G. The Bergen family, descendants of Hans Hansen Bergen, one of the early settlers of N. Y. and Brooklyn. por. and pl. 8°. '76. $6. *Munsell.*

Berger, E. (*pseud.*) *See* Sheppard, E. S.

Bergmann, A: Der Sprechunterricht im ersten Schuljahre. 12°. '75. 35c. .... *Witter.*

Bergstresser, P. Vain excuses answered. [Sermons.] 16°. '76. $1 .... (?) *Luth. Pub.*

Bériot, C: de. Violin school; [with] Eng. and French words. pt. 1: Mechanism of the elementary difficulties. (op. 102.) f°. pap., $4.75. *Schirmer.*

Berjeau, J. Ph. Homœopathic treatment of syphilis, gonorrhœa, spermatorrhœa and urinary diseases. New ed., rev. and enl. by J. H. P. Frost. 12°. $1.50 .... *Boericke.*

Berkeley, G: Principles of human knowledge; with prolegomena, and with ill. and annot. by C. P. Krauth. 8°. $3 .... *Lippincott.*

Berkeley men (The). *See* Lester, C. E.

Berkey, W: A. The money question: legal tender paper monetary system of the U. S. 8°. '76. $1.50; pap., $1 .... *Berkey.*

Berkley, Cora. The Hamiltons; or, sunshine in storm. 12°. 50c. .... *Strong.*

— The three Eleanors. 16°. $1 .... *Strong.*

Berlepsch, H. A. *See* Closs, G., *and* Fröhlicher, O., Rhododendron.

Berlin and Sans-souci. Mundt, C. M. $1.50; $1; $3.50 .... *Appleton.*

Berlin bei Nacht. Rasch, G. 40c. .... *F. W. Thomas.*

Berlin doll. *See* Life of a Berlin doll.

Berlioz, H. Treatise on modern instrumentation and orchestration. roy. 8°. $4.50 .... *Peters.*

Bernard, *St.* Life. 12°. '74. $1.50 .... *Cath. Pub.*

— Life. 12°. $1.50; $2 .... *Sadlier.*

Bernard *of Morlaix.* The heavenly land; tr. by S. W. Duffield. [Hymn.] 12°. '67. 75c. ... *Randolph.*

Bernard, Cl., *and* Robin, C: On the blood; from notes by W. F. Atlee. 12°. 75c. .... *Lippincott.*

Bernard, D: Light on Freemasonry. Rev. ed., with app. on the mysteries of Oddfellowship. 12°. $1.75 .... *Un. B. Pub.*

— Reminiscences of Morgan times. 12°. pap., 20c. *E. A. Cook.*

Bernard, F. Wonderful escapes; tr. and enl. by R. Whiteing. ill. 12°. '75. $1.25 .... *Scribner.*

Bernard, Mountague. Four lectures on subjects connected with diplomacy. 8°. '68. $3.50. *Macmillan.*

Bernard, T: D. Progress of doctrine in the New Test. *See* Bampton lectures.

Bernard, W: Bayle. [Plays.] 21 v. 16°. ea., pap., 15c. .... *French.*

Cont.: Balance of comfort: comedy. — Boarding school (The): farce. — Farmer's story. — Four sisters: farce. — His last legs: farce. — Irish attorney: farce. — Life's trial. — Lucille. — Man of two lives: romantic play. — Marie Ducange. — Middy ashore: farce. — Mummy: farce. — Nervous man: farce. — Old regimentals. — Passing cloud. — Platonic attachments: farce. — Practical man: farce. — St. Mary's eve. — Splendid investment: farce. — Storm in a tea cup: comedietta. — Tide of time: comedy.

— Boarding school: farce. 16°. pap., 15c. .... *Happy.*

— Life of Samuel Lover; with sel. from his unpub. papers and correspondence. por. 12°. $2 ... *Appleton.*

Bernard Ellis. 18°. 50c. .... *Whittaker.*

Bernard Lile. Clemens, J. $1.25 .... *Lippincott.*

Berneck, C. Gst. v. ["Bernd v. Guseck."] Deutschland's Ehre. [Fiction.] 8°. pap., 50c. *Morwitz.*

— Im Herzen v. Deutschland: hist. Roman. 8°. pap., 30c. .... *F. W. Thomas.*

Berners, J. First lessons on health. 3d ed. 18°. '74. 50c. .... *Macmillan.*

Berners, Juliana. Treatyse of fysshynge wyth an angle; from the "Boke of St. Albans," A. D., 1496. Am. ed., ed. by G. W. Van Siclen. sq. 16°. '75. $1.50 .... *Van Siclen.*

Bernese Oberland. *See* Walton, E.

Bernheim, G. D. History of the Germ. settlements and of the Luth. Church in North and South Carolina to [1850]. 12°. '72. $3 .. *Luth. Bk. St.*

Bernice, the farmer's daughter. Davis, C. E. K. $1.25 .... *Hoyt.*

Bernie's white chicken. *See* Alden, *Mrs.* I. M.

Bernstein, A. Popular books on natural science. ('69.) 2d ed. 8°. '72. $1; pap., 75c. *C. Schmidt.*

Bernthal. Mundt, C. M. 50c. .... *Harper.*

Berquin, Arnaud. Children's (The) friend. 16°. $1.25 .... *Nichols & H.*

— Child's (The) friend: selections from works of B. 18°. 75c. .... *Harper.*

Berquin's conversational French reader. ill. 16°. '55. 60c. .... *G. R. Lockwood.*

Berrie, E. Captain Smith: farce. 16°. pap., 15c. *Ames; French.*

Berriman, M. W. Militiaman's manual and swordplay without a master. 4th ed. 12°. '64. $1. *Van Nostrand.*

Berry, J. Analysis and parsing book; or, analysis and parsing in tabulated form. 5th ed. 12°. '71. 60c. .... *M. Taylor.*

Berry, *Mrs.* Martha E. Band of six. ill. 16°. '69. $1.25 .... *Am. Tr.*

— Carolina, the hotel-keeper's daughter. ill. 16°. '71. $1.25 .... *Lothrop.*

— Celesta stories. 3 v. ill. 16°. ea., $1 .... *Lee & S.*

Cont.: Celesta. — Crooked and straight. — The crook straightened.

— Cobbler's daughter. 16°. $1.50 .... *Cong. Pub.*

— Fanny Lightman's choice. ill. 18°. '68. 70c. *Am. Tr.*

— Hard Knot (The). ill. 18°. 75c. ...... *Bost. Am. Tr.*

— Lottie Lane. ill. 16°. '69. $1.25 .... *Am. Tr.*

— Marcia's faith. 16°. 75c. .... *Cong. Pub.*

— Mattie Carson. 16°. 75c. .... *Cong. Pub.*

— Sisters, and not sisters. ill. 16°. '66. 90c. .. *Am. Tr.*

Berry-pickers (The) of Wisconsin. 16°. 80c. .. *Pres. Bd.*

Bersier, *Mme.* Eug. Micheline; tr. by Mrs. C. Brock. ill. 12°. '75. $1.50 .... *Dutton.*

Bert Ashley. Howland, M. 60c. .... *West. Tr.*

Bertha. Bischoff, J. E. $2; $2.50 .... *Sadlier.*

Bertha. Pierson, H. W. 60c. .... *Dutton.*

Bertha; or, the consequences of a fault. *See* Catholic prem.-book lib.

Bertha Allston. Thompson, C. S. 30c. ..... *Am. Tr.*

Bertha, the beauty. Whittlesey, S. J. C. $1.50. *Claxton.*

Bertha Marchmont. *See* Cupples, *Mrs.* A. J.

Bertha Weisser's wish. Bissell, M. L. 75c. .. *Dutton.*

Bertha's engagement. Stephens, A. S. $1.75; $1.50. *Peterson.*

Bertha's journal. Harris, E. F. $1.50 ... *Cong. Pub.*

Bertha's rose; [also] Where Daisy's doll went. 18°. 30c. .... *N. Y. Ref. Ch. Bd.*

Bertha's trial. *See* Infant school lib.

Berthone, H: Stories of bird life. ill. 12°. 75c.; $1.50. *Nelson.*

Bertie and Amy books. 10 v. ill. 18°. '69. $5. *Meth. Bk. Conc.*

Cont.: Brother Bertie. — Brother Bertie and his aunt. — Brother Bertie's cure. — Talks with Amy Dudley. — Amy Dudley's amusements. — Eggs that were never peacocks. — Julius and his parrot. — Sybil and her live snowball. — Edwin and his pet squirrel. — More talks with Amy Dudley.

Bertie and the carpenters; — gardeners; — masons; — painters; — plumbers. *See* Baker, *Mrs.* H. N. W., Woodlawn ser.

Bertie and his best things. 18°. 45c. .... *Pres. Bd.*

Bertie and his friends; or, pilgrim life on the Battery. ill. 18°. 90c. *J. A. Moore.*

Bertie and his sisters. *See* Baker, *Mrs.* H. N. W.

Bertie Lee. 18°. 60c. . . . . *Carter.*

Bertie Page. *See* Finley, M. F.

Bertie Wade; or, do your own work. 18°. 20c.; 25c. *Am. Bapt.*

Bertie's birthday present; or, patience rewarded. ('69.) New ed. ill. 16°. '75. $1 . . . . *Hoyt.*

— *Same.* ill. 16°. '70. 70c. . . . . *Am. Tr.*

Bertie's fall. Miller, M. E. 45c. . . . . *Am. Tr.*

Bertie's home. *See* Baker, *Mrs.* H. N. W., Woodlawn series.

Bertie's library. 6 v. 32°. '70. $1.50. . *H. A. Young.*

Cont.: Little Bertie. — Willie's wish. — Curious Tom. — The two mottoes. — Little James. — Old Ben's stockings.

Bertie's telegraph. May, C. L. 75c. . . . *H. A. Young.*

Bertini, H: Piano instructor; with add. by W. C. Peters. [Eng., Fr. and Germ. text.] 4°. bds., $3; abridg., bds., $2.50. . . . . *Peters.*

— Piano method. 4°. $2; abridg., $1.50. . . *Brainard.*

— *Same.* f°. $3; abridg., $2.50. . . . . *Gordon.*

— Progressive and complete method for the piano-forte. 4°. bds., $2; abridg., $1.50. . . . . *Ditson; Pond.*

— *Same.* 4°. $2.50; abridg., $2. . . . . *Holmes.*

— Self-teaching catechism of music for the piano-forte. 12°. bds., 40c. . . . . *Ditson.*

Bertram. Maturin, C. R. 15c. . . . . *French.*

Bertram family (The). Charles, E. $1.50. . . . *Dodd.*

Bertram Noel. *See* Winter evening lib.

Bertram Raymond. Harcourt, H. $1.50. . . . *Claxton.*

Bertrams (The). *See* Trollope, Anthony.

Bertrand et Raton. *See* Scribe, A. E.

Berty's confession. Pratt, L. M. 50c. . . . . . . *Lothrop.*

Berty's visit. *See* Leighton children.

Berville, Guyard de. *See* Guyard de Berville.

Besant, W., *and* Rice, J. My little girl. 8°. pap., 75c. . . . . **Osgood.*

— — Ready-money Mortiboy. 8°. pap., 75c. . . **Osgood.*

— — With harp and crown. 8°. pap., 75c. . . **Osgood.*

Besant, Wa. French humorists; from the 12th to the 19th century. por. 8°. '74. $2.50. . . . . *Roberts.*

— Studies in early French poetry. cr. 8°. '68. $2.50. *Macmillan.*

Besieged city (The); [also] The heroes of Sweden, tr. and comp. by Mrs. Campbell Overend; rev. by A. G. Haygood. ('72.) 3d ed. 16°. '76. 75c. *So. Meth.*

Bessels, Emil. Physical observations. *See* United States, *Navy Dept.*

Besser, Rud. Christ the life of the world. cr. 8°. $3. *Scribner, W. & A.*

Bessere Leben (Das). 18°. 45c. . . . . *Ev. Assoc.*

Besset, *Mrs.* Jane M. Black princess (The): story for young persons. 16°. '72. 50c. . . . . . . *Routledge.*

— Memoirs of a doll; written by herself. 16°. 50c. *Routledge.*

Bessie, *Cousin.* *See* Cousin Bessie.

Bessie. Kavanagh, J. 75c. . . . . *Appleton.*

Bessie; or, the adopted daughter. 18°. 65c.; 75c. *Am. Bapt.*

Bessie and her grandfather. *See* Smith, *Mrs.* F. I. B.

Bessie and her lamb. *See* Aunty Ray's little lib.

Bessie and her little brothers. Jefferds, J. A. 50c. *Cong. Pub.*

Bessie and her Spanish friends; by author of "Faithful but not famous." 16°. '75. 90c. . . *Meth. Bk. Conc.*

Bessie and the squirrels. *See* Baker, *Mrs.* H. N. W., Corwin's nest series.

Bessie at Stony Lonesome. Connell, S. G. 90c. *Dutton.*

Bessie Baldwin's stories. *See* Ravenswood stories.

Bessie Bleak and the lost purse. 18°. '74. 50c. *Nelson.*

Bessie books. *See* Mathews, J. H.

Bessie Brown. Denison, M. A. $1. . . . . *Hoyt.*

Bessie Duncan; or, the first year out of school. 18°. 60c. . . . . *Am. S. S.*

— *See also* Child's lib.; — Select lib. for girls.

Bessie Fairfax. *See* Vicissitudes of Bessie Fairfax.

Bessie Gordon. 18°. 60c. . . . . *Cong. Pub.*

Bessie Gordon's lesson; or, the poor children in the basement. 18°. 25c. . . . . *Am. S. S.*

Bessie Grant's treasure. Adams, *Mrs.* —. 75c. *Fuller.*

Bessie Gray; or, the dull child. 18°. 40c. . . . . *Dutton.*

Bessie Grey; or, the value of little labors. 18°. 50c. *Pres. Bd.*

Bessie Hartwell. *See* Freeland, *Mrs.* C. J.

Bessie Haven. Dunning, A. K. 35c. . . . . . . *Pres. Bd.*

Bessie Kirkland. Miller, M. E. 60c. . . . . *Am. Tr.*

Bessie Lane's mistake. Hildeburn, M. J. 90c. *Pres. Bd.*

Bessie Lee and her little brother. 18°. 30c. *Am. S. S.*

Bessie Lovell; or, the power of a loving child. ill. 16°. $1.15. . . . . *Bost. Am. Tr.*

Bessie Melville. Cruse, M. A. $1. . . . . *Dutton.*

Bessie White. Hill, E. V. 60c. . . . . *Am. Tr.*

Bessie Wilmerton. Westcott, M. $1.75. . . . *Carleton.*

Bessie Wilson. 18°. 35c. . . . . *Cong. Pub.*

Bessie's light. *See* Kennedy, *Mrs.* M. G., Library for little children.

Bessie's new heart. *See* Pretty little lib.

Bessie's reward. *See* New Year lib.

Bessie's temptation. *See* New year lib.

Bessie's three teachers. *See* Pretty little lib.

Bessie's trials at boarding school. Perry, N. $1.25. *Lothrop.*

Bessie's visit. Trowbridge, C. M. 60c. . . . *Cong. Pub.*

Bessy Conway. Sadlier, M. A. 75c.; $1.25. . *Sadlier.*

Bessy Rane. Wood, E. P. $1.75; $1.50. . *Peterson.*

Best, —. *See* Bellingham, H., *and* Best, —.

Best, W. M. Principles of the law of evidence, with element. rules for conducting the examination of witnesses; ed. from J. A. Russell's 6th Lond. ed. by J. A. Morgan. 2 v. 8°. '75. shp., $15. . *Cockcroft.*

— *See also* England, Common law reports.

Best dowry, and other tales. 18°. 50c. . . . . *O'Shea.*

Best fellow in the world. *See* Wright, *Mrs.* J. McN.

Best friend (The). 18°. 18c. . . . . *Am. S. S.*

Best lesson (The), and the best time to learn it; by a Presbyterian minister. 18°. 40c. . . . . . *Pres. Bd.*

Best (The) of all good company. Jerrold, B. $2.50. (?) *Shepard.*

Best (The) of books and its history. Hanaford, J. H. $1. . . . . *Am. Bapt.*

Best (The) of everything; by author of "Enquire within upon everything." 12°. $1.25. . *Lippincott.*

Best (The) of husbands. Payn, J. 50c. . . . . *Harper.*

Best reading (The). Putnam, G. P. $1.50; $1. *Putnam.*

Best things (The). Newton, R. $1.25. . . . . . . *Carter.*

Best voyage (The): an allegory. 18°. 17c.; 22c. *Am. Bapt.*

Best way (The). Wigan, H. 15c. . . . . *French.*

Beste Erbtheil (Das). *See* Schmid, C. v.

Besten Sachen (Die). 18°. 45c. . . . . *Ev. Assoc.*

Beswick, S. Swedenborg rite, and the great Masonic leaders of the 18th century. 12°. '72. $1.50. *Masonic.*

Bet and Bounce. Dunning, *Mrs.* A. K. 35c. . . *Pres. Bd.*

Betham-Edwards, M. *See* Edwards, M. Betham.

Bethlehem. *See* Faber, F. W.

Bethlehem and her children. Lathrop, M. A. 30c. *Am. Tr.*

Bethune, G: W. Early lost, early saved: argument for the salvation of infants, with consolation for bereaved parents. 18°. 60c...*N. Y. Ref. Ch. Bd.*
— Expository lectures on the Heidelberg catechism. 2 v. cr. 8°. $4.50; hf. cf., $8.50.......*Sheldon.*
— Fruit of the Spirit. 18°. 60c.....*N. Y. Ref. Ch. Bd.*
— History of a penitent: a guide for the inquiring. 18°. 60c.......................*N. Y. Ref. Ch. Bd.*
— Memoirs of Mrs. Joanna Bethune; with extracts from writings. 12°. $1.50.............*Harper.*
— Thanksgiving and thank offerings. [Sermon.] 8°. 25c......................*N. Y. Ref. Ch. Bd.*
— (*ed.*) British female poets. [Selections.] ill. 12°. $1.50. 8°. $2; shp., $2.75........*World Pub.*
— *See also* Smitten household.

Bethune, *Mrs.* Joanna. Ten commandments, Lord's prayer, and other Scriptures analyzed and explained. 18°. pap., 10c......*N. Y. Ref. Ch. Bd.*
— *See also* Bethune, G. W.

Bethune, Mx. de. *See* Sully, *Duke of.*

Betrachtungen u. Seufzer e. Christenmenschen. Dilherr, J. M. $1.25.....................*Dette.*

Betrothal (The). *See* Patmore, C.

Betrothed (The). *See* Manzoni, A.

Betrothed (The). *See* Scott, *Sir* W.

Betsey and I are out. *See* Carleton, Will, Farm ballads; — Emerson, *Mrs.* N. S.

Betsey Bartlett. 24°. 25c...............*Perkinpine.*
— *Same*, and other tales. 18°. 35c.....*Bost. Am. Tr.*
— *See also* Alice and Willie stories.

Betsy Baker. Morton, J. M. 15c..........*French.*

Betsy Green. *See* History of Betsy Green.

Betsy Jane Ward, hur book of goaks. 12°. '66. $1.50. *Allison.*

Betsy Lee: a fo'c's'le yarn. [Poem.] fp. 8°. '73. 75c...............................*Macmillan.*

Better covenant (The). Goode, F. 75c....*Leighton.*

Better days for the working people. Blaikie, G. G. 75c.................................*Routledge.*

Better for worse. Braddon, M. E. 75c.....*Peterson.*

Better half (The). Williams, T. J. 15c. *Ames; French.*

Better home (The); [also] Elizabeth; [also] The sailor boy. 18°. 30c................*Am. S. S.*

Better land (The). Dodsworth, J. $1.25..*So. Meth.*

Better land (The). *See* Smith, *Rev.* J.

Better land (The). Thompson, A. C. $1.25. *Sheldon.*

Better life (The). Hammond, E. P. 75c......*Hoyt.*

Better part (The); or, scenes from real life. *See* Catholic prem.-book lib.

Better path stories. 4 v. ill. 16°. $4..........*Locke.*
Cont.: Little Josie. — Wayside flowers. — Hattie and Marcus. — Lake cottage.

Better self (The). Friswell, J. H. $1.75....*Porter.*

Better than diamonds; [also] The missionary prince. 18°. 30c.................................*Dutton.*

Better than gold. Strong, J. D. 30c......*Lothrop.*

Better than rubies. Campbell, E. F. R. $1.25. *Garrigues.*
— *See also* Short stories lib.

Better views of living. Child, A. B. $1......*Colby.*

Better way. Newton, A. E. 50c.; 25c. .. *Wood & H.*

Bettlerin (Die) v. Pont des Arts. *See* Hauff, W.

Betts, S: R. *See* United States, Admiralty cases.

Betty u. Toms. Nieritz, G. 25c...........*Steiger.*

Betty's bright idea. Stowe, H. B. 75c.; 30c...*Ford.*

Between the cliffs. Marshall, E. $1........*Carter.*

Between the crusts. Harrington, J. A. 25c. *Collin & S.*

Beulah. Evans, A. J. $1.75..............*Carleton.*

Beumer, Ph. J. Elementar Katechismus: d. deutsche Sprache, Rechnen, Geographie u. Naturkunde. 12°. hf. bd., 30c..................*Volkening.*

Bevan, J: Brief view of the doct. of the Christian relig. as professed by the Society of Friends. 12°. 35c. *Friends Bk. St.*

Bevan, Jos. Gurney. Memoirs of Isaac Penington. 12°. 62c.....................*Friends Bk. St.*

Beverly, R. History of Virginia, 1706-'20; with introd. by C. Campbell. pl. 8°. '55. $12..*J. W. Randolph.*

Beverly. Walworth, M. T. $1.75.........*Carleton.*

Beverly family (The). Chandler, J. R. 50c. *Cunningham.*

Beware of the dog; or, what is faith? 18°. 18c. *Am. S. S.*

Bewick, T: Select fables. [Reprint of Newcastle ed. of 1814.] ill. cr. 8°. $4............*Routledge.*

Bewitched closet (The). Lambla, H. L. 15c...*Ames.*

Beyer, Fd. Elementary instruction book for juvenile pupils; with Eng. and French words. [For piano.] (op. 101.) f°. bds., $3.............*Schirmer.*
— Preliminary school for the piano-forte, with Eng. and German text; [also] Czerny's Letters to young ladies. [With foreign *or* Am. fingering.] 4°. ea., $2.50; bds., $2...........*Ditson; Gordon.*
— Progressive method for the piano-forte; with Eng., Fr. and Germ. text. Am. fingering. 4°. '70. $2; bds., $1.50.........................*Ditson.*
— School for the piano-forte, for young students; tr. and adapted by G. F. Bristow. 4°. '51. $1.50; bds., $1.25................................*Pond.*
— *Same;* with Eng., Fr. and Germ. text. 4°. $2.50; bds., $2...............................*Peters.*

Beyond the breakers. Owen, R. D. $1.50; $1. *Lippincott.*

Beyond the Mississippi. Richardson, A. D. *$3.50; $4; $5; $8.........................*Am. Pub.*

Beyond the snow. Reed, P. F. $1.25....*Donnelley.*

Beza. [Théodore de Bèze.] Latin Testament. 12°. $1.25 ....*Appleton.*
— *See also* Bible, New Test., *Greek.*

Bhagavad-Gita (The); or, a discourse on divine matters between Krishna and Arjuna: a Sanskrit philos. poem; tr. with notes and introd. by J. C. Thompson. 12°. '74. $1.75..........*Rel. Phil.*

B'hoys of New York. Judson, E. Z. C. 75c. *Dick & F.*

Bianca. Maturin, E. $1.25...............*Harper.*

Bianca Cappello. Kinney, E. C. $1.50...*Hurd & H.*

Biarnois, A. French grammar. 12°. $1.25..*Sadlier.*

Biart, Lucien. Adventures of a young naturalist; ed. and adapted by P. Gillmore. ill. 12°. $1.75. *Harper.*

Bibb, G. M. *See* Kentucky, Court of Appeals reports.

Bibelforscher (Der): bibl. Fragebuch. 24°. 30c. *Ev. Assoc.*

Bible.

Note. The following entries (for obvious reasons) are limited as regards texts to those which, according to the publisher's record, present individual characteristics: for information concerning varieties of manufacture of the ordinary versions, Bagster eds., etc., *see* Prefatory note to this volume. Works *upon* the Bible (including commentaries with or without text) will be found in the general alphabet under names of authors or compilers,—only those in which the notes seem clearly subordinate to the text being placed here. In the second volume (subject-index) of the Catalogue all such works will be grouped under the subject Bible.

— [**Whole Bible.**] Annotated paragraph Bible; with notes, prefaces and ref. maps. roy. 8°. shp., $8; mor., $12; — in 3 v. shp., $10........*Sheldon.*
— Blank-paged Bible; with ref. to parallel and ill. passages. [Interleaved.] maps. 8°. mor., $9.50; $11 ....*Wiley.*
— Cassell's ill. family Bible; with notes, ref. and condensed concordance. ill. roy. 4°. $25; mor., $35 ....*Cassell.*
— Cheap family Bible; with pict. hist. of books of the Bible, comprehensive dict. of the Bible, Brown's Concordance, etc. ill. 4°. $5-$12..*J. E. Potter.*
— Child's Bible. *See* Child's.

Bible [Whole Bible], *continued.*

— Comprehensive family Bible; with marg. ref., notes, readings, etc., Blackwood's Comprehensive aids to the study of the Bible, Nevin's Improved pict. dict. of Bible, Krauth's Christ and his kingdom in shadows, Butler's Christian denominations, and Morris' Illustrated cities of the Bible. ill. and maps. 4°. *$10-$25 .... *J. E. Potter.*

— Comprehensive ref. Bible with Psalms in metre; with notes, tables, maps, diagrams, etc., by Sam. Davidson. 16°. $1.30-$3.50 ..... *U. P. Bd. of Pub.*

— Cottage Bible and family expositor; with notes by T. Williams, ref. and marg. readings of polyglot Bible, etc.; ed. by Wm. Patton. 2 v. maps and ill. roy. 8°. (cop. '68.) '76. $9 .... *Case.*

— Devotional family Bible; with reflections, marg. ref. and readings, by A. Fletcher. ('64.) 16th ed. ill. imp. 4°. '76. mor., $40 .... *Virtue.*

— Doré Bible; with 238 ill. by D. 2 v. sm. f°. $64; mor., $100; $125; $150 .... *Cassell.*

— English version of the polyglot Bible; with marg. readings, ref. and Psalms in metre. 24°. $1.50-$3.75. maps and ill. 18°. $1.75-$8.50 .. *Rutter.*

— Explanatory Bible; with marg. readings, ref., concordance and tables. ill. and maps. 4°. $8; $9; mor., $14 .... *Scranton.*

— Extra family Bible; with dict. of the Bible, Krauth's Christ and his kingdom in shadows, Blackwood's Comprehensive aids to study of Bible, Brown's Concordance, etc. ill. 4°. $10-$17. *J. E. Potter.*

— Family Bible, with notes, instructions, ref. and harmony, by J. Edwards and E. P. Barrows. maps and ill. 4°. '61. $6-$14. (Pocket ed.) 3 v. 18°. $3; shp., $5; — in 2 v. (Old Test.) 18°. '66. $2.25; shp., $3.50 .... *Am. Tr.*

— Family Bible; with ref., index of events, tables, etc. ill. 4°. $1.65; $1.75; —with Apocrypha, Brown's Concordance and Psalms in metre. ill. 4°. $2-$3.75 .... *Wilstach.*

— Family photograph Bible; [with] ref. and marg. readings of the polyglot Bible; with add. from Bagster's Comprehensive B. imp. 8°. '68. $5. *Case.*

— Family quarto Bible; [with ref. in centre column, Apocrypha, concordance, Psalms in metre, etc.] ill. 4°. $3.60-$10 .... *Lippincott.*

— [Family, quarto and pulpit Bibles; with tables of weights and measures, chronol. index, Scriptural quotations and Psalms in metre.] 4°. $3; — with Apocrypha and concordance. 4°. $3.50 .. *Hale.*

— Handy volume ed.; with marg. readings, ref. and introds. 13 v. 18°. $9-$40 ... *Scribner, W. & A.*

— Harper's illuminated and pict. Bible, incl. Apocrypha. ill. 4°. cf., $28; mor., $32; $35 .... *Harper.*

— Hieroglyphic Bible. *See* Hieroglyphic.

— Illustrated child's Bible. *See* Illustrated.

— Illustrated explan. Bible; with marg. ref., etc., Nevin's Improved pict. dict. of Bible, Erben's Pict. hist. of books of the Bible, Butler's Christian denominations, and Morris' Illustrated cities of the Bible. ill. and maps. 4°. *$8-$17 .. *J. E. Potter.*

— Illustrated pocket Bible for the young: pictures with questions, maps and index. 16°. (Bagster.) mor., $5 .... *Wiley.*

— — Concise answers to questions of *same*; for parents and teachers. fp. 8°. (Bagster.) $1.12 .... *Wiley.*

— Illustrated polyglot family Bible. [Eng. and Germ. ed.] ill. roy. 4°. '72. *$5-$24 .... *Maclean.*

— Literally tr. by J. E. Smith. roy. 8°. *$3 .. *Am. Pub.*

— New ill. Bible for the young; with hist. of each book, Gospels in harmony, biogs. of evangelists and apostles, notes, etc. ill. roy. 8°. '74. *$4.75; $5.50; mor., $7.50 .... *Am. Fam.; Maclean.*

— New ill. devotional and pract. polyglot Family Bible; with Apocrypha, concordance and Psalms in metre; also abridg. ed. of Smith's Dictionary of the Bible. ill. 4°. '72. *$10 .... *Nat. Pub.*

Bible [Whole Bible], *continued.*

— People's standard ed.; with concord., Psalms in metre, marg. ref. and readings, etc., treatise upon the literature, etc., of the B., and hist. of the sects, etc.; also a dict. of the Bible. ill. and por. 4°. '72. *$6.50-$20 .... *Ziegler.*

— Pictorial home Bible; incl. Apocrypha, concord. and marg. ref., with a cyclopedia, etc., by J. S. Vandersloot and M. L. Simons. ('71.) New ed. ill. 4°. '75. *$7.50-$18 .... *F. Scofield; So. Pub.*

— — *Same;* in German. ill. 4°. '71. *$8-$18. *Henry Bill; F. Scofield.*

— Pictorial household Bible; with marg. ref., notes and comments, and an ill. Bible dict. ill. and maps. 12°. '73. *(?) .... (?) *Holland.*

— Pocket Bible, with Psalms in metre. 32°. 75c.-$2.35. *U. P. Bd. of Pub.*

— Polyglot Bible. 32°. $1.25-$1.88 ...... *Thompson.*

— *Same.* roy. 8°. roan., $3.75; $4.50; mor., $6.50. *Sheldon.*

— *Same.* 18°. $1-$3.75; — with Psalms in metre. 18°. $1.05-$3.80 .... *Desilver.*

— Practical and devotional polyglot family Bible; with marg. readings, ref. and concord. ill. and maps. roy. 8°. leath., $7.50; $8; mor., $10 .. *Scranton.*

— Pronouncing Bible. imp. 4°. '68. $15-$50. roy. 8°. '59. $3.50-$8; — in 4 v. roy. 8°. $5.50; $6. *Meth. Bk. Conc.*

— Pronouncing Bible, with Psalms in meter; by I. Alger. 8°. $3.25-$4.50 ..... *U. P. Bd. of Pub.*

— Quarto family Bible; [with Apocrypha, concordance, index, etc.] ill. 4°. $5-$14 .... *Hale.*

— Reference Bible. [Pearl ed. with index on edge.] maps. roy. 24°. $1.80-$3.75 .... *Lippincott.*

— Reference Bible; [with] Psalms in metre. roy. 8°. $3.50-$7 .... *U. P. Bd. of Pub.*

— Reference family Bibles; ed. by A. Nevin, A. L. Rawson, T. H. Horne, etc. *See* Prefatory note.

— Royal family Bible; with notes and reflections by J. Brown, [and] add. notes by H. Cooke; enl. by J. L. Porter. Am. ed., ed. by W. Blackwood. ill. 4°. $15-$22 .... *J. E. Potter.*

— Royal pulpit Bible; with Brown's Concordance, Blackwood's Comprehensive aids to study of Bible; hist. of the translations, etc. ill. and maps. 4°. $16-$20 .... *J. E. Potter.*

— Self-interpreting Bible; with introd., marg. ref., ill., notes, etc., by J. Brown. New ed., with notes, etc., by H. Cooke. ill. f°. mor., $33.50. *Johnson & M.*

— Self-interpreting family Bible; with introd., marg. ref. and readings and notes by J. Brown; with add. notes by H. Cooke; enl. by J. L. Porter. Am. ed., ed. by W. Blackwood, [with] Krauth's Christ and his kingdom in shadows, Butler's Christian denominations of the world, Nevin's Improved pict. dict. of Bible, and Morris' Illustrated cities of the Bible. pl. and maps. 4°. *$16-$25 .... *J. E. Potter.*

— Student's treasury Bible; with ref. and variorum readings. roy. 18°. $1.25-$6 .... *Lippincott.*

— Teacher's polyglot Bible. 18°. $1.25-$6. *Lippincott.*

— Treasury Bible. [Interleaved with parallel passages from Canne, Brown, Blayney, Scott, etc.; with notes.] 18°. *net*, $7.50; mor., $10 ..... *Wiley.*

— With Apocrypha and concordance, Canne's marg. ref., index, table, etc. ill. 4°. *$6-$13. *Am. Pub.*

— With Apocrypha, concordance, Psalms in metre, tables, etc. 8°. $6-$15 .... *Kohler.*

— With concordance, Apocrypha, Bible index and chronology. 4°. '37. $6.50-$12 .. *Meth. Bk. Conc.*

— With concordance, marg. ref. and readings, dict. of the Bible, hist. of religious sects, etc. ill. 4°. '74. *$7.50-$20 .... *Henry Bill.*

— With marg. ref., various readings, notes, reflections, etc., by I. Cobbin. ill. 4°. '71. $9 .... *Case.*

Bible [Whole Bible], *continued.*
— With notes, introds., tables, indexes and maps; by G. D'Oyly and R. Mant. 3 v. 12°. '75. $10; hf. cf., $15 .... *Pott.*
— With notes, ref., etc., by T. Scott. 6 v. roy. 8°. shp., $18 .... *Crocker.*
— With the Psalms in metre. 32°. $1.12–$6.75 .. *Rutter.*
— *Same.* 24°. $1.30–$3 .... *U. P. Bd. of Pub.*
— Zell's new ill. family Bible; with comment. by J. Brown. 30 pts. ill. imp. 4°. ea., *50c.; — in 1 v. mor., $30 .... *C. H. Davis.*
— *Catholic version.* Catholic family Bible; with notes by R. Challoner. 44 pts. f°. ea., *25c. *Sadlier.*
— — Douay Bible; with annotations by R. Challoner. ill. imp. 4°. $8–$25. — chp. ed. roy. 4°. $5.50–$10. — imp. 8°. $4.50–$11 .... *T. Kelly.*
— — *Same;* [also] Hist. of the Cath. Bible, by I. F. Horstmann. ill. 4°. *$9–$22 ...... *J. E. Potter.*
— — Douay Bible; with notes by Haydock and Challoner, rev. under supervision of Card. Cullen. f°. $20–$60 .... *O'Shea.*
— — Douay Bible; with notes by F. P. Kenrick. 5 v. 8°. '62. $25–$75 .... *Kelly, P. & Co.*

Cont.: Job and the Prophets, $2.50. — Hist. books, $2.50; $4; shp., $4.50. — Pentateuch, $3.50; $4. — Psalms, Books of wisdom and Canticle of canticles, $3.50. — New Test., $3.50–$12.

— — Haydock's Catholic family Bible. ill. imp. 4°. $18–$75; — in 32 pts. ea., 50c. .... *T. Kelly.*
— — Sadlier's folio Bible; with Ward's Errata of the Protestant Bible. pl. f°. $18–$35 .... *Sadlier.*
— — Sadlier's new post quarto ed. of the Bible; tr. from the Lat. Vulgate and compared with the Heb., Gk., [etc.], eds.; rev. by R. Challoner. ill. 4°. $4–$9. — (Pocket ed.) 18°. $1.50–$7.50. — sm. 4°. $4–$15 .... *Sadlier.*

Note. Comprises the Douay version of Old Test. and Rheims version of New Test.

— — Tr. from Lat. Vulgate, compared with the Heb., Gk., [etc.], eds., by Challoner, with ref. and index; [with] Cath. dict. and concord. by J. O'Leary. 4°. $16–$22 .... *Sadlier.*
— — Tr. from the Lat. Vulgate, compared with the Heb., Gk., [etc.], eds., with notes by G. L. Haydock; text collated and annotations abridg. by F. C. Husenbeth. ('50.) 26th ed. ill. roy. 4°. '73. mor., $28 .... *Virtue.*

Note. Comprises Douay version of Old Test. and Rheims version of New Test.

— — *See also below under* German.
— *Hexaglot* Bible: the Septuagint, the Syriac [New Test.], the Vulgate, the authorized Eng. and Germ. versions, and most approved French version, arranged in parallel columns; ed. by E. R. De Levante and others. 6 v. 4°. '72. hf. mor., $60 .... *Tibbals.*
— *German.* Biblia ["Altenburger"]; mit [Luther's] Vorreden u. Randglossen, den Summarien des Vitus Dietrich [u.] Vorreden u. Schlussgebeten Francisci Vierlings. 3 v. 8°. '57–'64. v. 1, 2, ea., $2.50; v. 3, $2.25 .... *Barthel.*
— — *Same;* in 1 v. ('74.) 3d ed. sm. 8°. '76. $1. *Barthel.*
— — Die grosse allgemeine Volks-Bilder-Bibel. ill. 4°. $6–$12 .... *Kohler.*
— — Kleine Volks-Bilder-Bibel. ill. 8°. $3–$6 .. *Kohler.*
— — Mit Vorrede, Einleitgn, etc., v. W. J. Mann. [Luther's version.] 4°. $7–$25 .... *Kohler.*
— — [Pictorial Germ. family Bible (Luther's version); with ref. and notes by O. Delitsch, hist. of books of Bible, tables, Gospels in harmony, etc. Am. ed., ed. by C. P. Krauth.] ill. 4°. *$9–$22. *J. E. Potter.*
— — Taschen-Bibel. 16°. $1.50–$3 .... *Ev. Assoc.*
— — [*Catholic version;* tr. from Lat. Vulgate by J. F. v. Allioli, with annotations, etc.] ill. 4°. *$9–$20 .... *J. E. Potter.*
— — *See also above* Illust. polyg. fam. B.; Pictorial home B.

Bible [Whole Bible], *continued.*
— *Hebrew.* [Leeser's family Bible.] 4°. leath., $10; mor., $15; $20 .... *Frank.*
— — [Leeser's school Bible.] 18°. leath., $2; mor., $5 .... *Frank.*
— — Rec. A. Hahn. New ed., rev. by I. Leeser and J. Jaquett. 8°. hf mor., $3.50 ..... *Lippincott.*
— — Rev. and examined by M. L. Letteris. 8°. $2.50. *Wiley.*
— *Heb. and English.* Abridged school and family Bible; by J. L. Levinski. 3 v. 8°. $6 .... *Frank.*
— — *Same.* v. 1: Five books of Moses. 8°. $2 .. *Frank.*
— **Old Testament.** Vetus Testamentum (Græcum) ex versione Septuaginta; secundum exemplar Vat. Romae ed.; acc. potior varietas cod. Alex. New ed. 3 v. fp. 8°. '75. $9 .... *Macmillan.*
— **New Testament.** Annotated paragraph New Test. 8°. $2 50; shp., $3.25 .... *Sheldon.*
— — Collins' paragraph Test. cr. 8°. '59. $1.50. *Collins & Bro.*
— — Family New Test.; with notes, maps, etc. (Pocket ed.) 16°. '62. $1–$3.50 ...... *Am. Tr.*
— — Family New Test. and Psalms; with notes, maps, etc. 8°. '61. $1.75–$5 .... *Am. Tr.*
— — Literal tr. from the Syriac Peshito version of the New Test.; by Ja. Murdock. ('51.) New ed. 8°. '70. $2.50 .... *Carter.*
— — Polyglot New Test. 32°. 50c.; 60c... *Thompson.*
— — Polymicrian New Test.; with notes and ref. in centre column. maps. 32°. '63. 45c... *Draper.*
— — Pronouncing New Test. 24°. 20c.; 30c.; roan, 35c.; 40c. .... *Meth. Bk. Conc.*
— — Pronouncing Test.; by I. Alger. 12°. '22. hf. bd., 40c. .... *Crocker.*
— — Tr. from Gk. text of Tischendorf by G. R. Noyes. ('69.) 5th ed. 12°. '73. $1.50; large pap., $4. *Am. Unit.*
— — Tr. from Griesbach's text by S. Sharp. 16°. $1. *Routledge.*
— — With comment; ed. by E. Churton and W. B. Jones. 2 v. ill. 8°. $12; hf. cf., $16; cf., $18; mor., $20 .... *Appleton.*
— — With introd. and various readings by C. Tischendorf. 16°. '70. $1 .... *Pott.*
— — With notes or scholia by H. Crosby. 12°. '63. $1.50 .... *Scribner.*
— — With wood eng. from designs of Fra Angelico, Titian, Raphael, etc. 4°. mor., $50; $60; $70. *Appleton.*
— — [also] Following of Christ, by Thomas a Kempis. 24°. 75c.–$3 .... *O'Shea.*
— — *Catholic version.* Pictorial New Test. (Douay ed.) ill. imp. 8°. '69. $4; $5 ... *Kelly, P. & Co.*
— — — With notes by F. P. Kenrick. (Douay ed.) 8°. '62. $3.50–$12 .... *Kelly, P. & Co.*
— — *French.* Nouveau Test.; d'après la version rev. par J. F. Ostervald. 32°. 50c. .... *Appleton.*
— — *German.* Das Neue Test. mit Noten; v. J. Edwards u. E. P. Barrows. 12°. '70. $1.75; $2.25. *Am. Tr.*
— — *Greek.* Ad exempla R. Stephani accuratissime ed. cura P. Wilson. 12°. '70. $1.25 ... *Claxton.*
— — — E cod. Vaticano. 8°. $4; shp., $4.50; hf. mor., $5 .... *Appleton.*
— — — Ex cod. Vat. ed. A. Maius. 8°. $3 ... *Draper.*
— — — Griesbach's text, with readings of Mill and Scholz, [marg.] ref., introd. and chronol. tables. 12°. (Bohn.) $1.25; with lexicon, $1.75. *Little, B. & Co.*
— — — *Same.* 12°. (Bohn.) $1.40 .. *Scribner, W. & A.*
— — — *Same;* with lexicon. 12°. (Bohn.) $2. *Lippincott; Scribner, W. & A.*
— — — Polymicrian Gk. Test., ed. by W. Greenfield; rev. by J. P. Engles, with lexicon. 32°. $2. *T. Bliss; Lippincott.*
— — — Textus Stephanici, 1550; acc. variæ lectiones ed. Bezæ, [etc.], cur. F. H. Scrivener. fp. 8°. (Lond.) '73. $2 .... *Little, B. & Co.*

Bible [New Test.], *continued.*
— — — With Eng. Notes, by S. T. Bloomfield. 2 v. roy. 8°. $6 .... *Lippincott.*
— — *Greek and Eng.* Emphatic diaglot: Gk. text [of J. J. Griesbach] with interlin. Eng. tr.; with notes, ref. and app. by B. Wilson. sm. 12°. $4; $5 .... *Wells.*
— — *Greek and Latin.* By J. Leusden. cr. 8°. hf. roan, $1.75 .... *Lippincott.*
— [**Other parts.**]
— Acts. *See below* Gospels.
— Ecclesiastes. *See below* Job.
— Epistles. *See below* Gospels.
— Epistles and Gospels. *Catholic version.* 24°. 30c. *Sadlier.*

See also under names of compilers (and titles) of Cath. prayer books.

— Gospels. Anglo-Saxon version of the Gospels; ed. from the original MS. by B. Thorpe. post 8°. $3. *Lippincott.*
— — Apocryphal Gospels, Acts and Revelations; tr. by A. Walker. (Ante-Nicene Christ. lib.) 8°. $3 .... *Scribner, W. & A.*
— — Four Gospels; tr. from Gk. text of Tischendorf, with various readings, and with notes by N. S. Folsom. 12°. '69. $2.50 .... *Williams.*
— — Four Gospels; with 128 etchings after drawings by A. Bida. 2 v. f°. '73. $225 .... *Gebbie.*
— — *Same;* with 132 etchings by A. Bida. 4 v. f°. $140; — in 2 v. $200 .... *Cassell.*
— — Four Gospels in one: cont. every statement in Matthew, Mark, Luke and John in the words of the authorized version; by R. A. Campbell. ('71.) 2d ed., rev. 12°. '75. $1.50 .... *R. A. Campbell.*
— — Holy Gospels. ill. f°. $6 .... *Routledge.*
— — *Greek.* Four Gospels and Acts, in Gk.; with Eng. notes, maps, indexes, etc.; by J. A. Spencer; together with the Epistles and Apocalypse. 12°. $1.75; shp., $2.15 .... *Harper.*
— — *See also above* Epistles.
— Isaiah. Prophecies; tr. by F. J. Delitzsch. 16°. '72. 50c .... *Luth. Bk. St.*
— — Isaiah XL.–LXVI.; with the shorter prophecies allied to it; arranged and ed. with notes by M. Arnold. cr. 8°. '75. $1.75 .... *Macmillan.*
— Job. Book called Job, from the Heb., with foot notes, by O. S. Halsted. sm. 8°. '75. $1. *Halsted.*
— — Tr. by G. R. Noyes. 12°. $1 .... *Burnham.*
— — [also] Ecclesiastes and the Canticles; tr., with introds. and notes, by G. R. Noyes. New ed., rev. 12°. '67. $1.25 .... *Am. Unit.*
— — *Catholic version.* Historical books: Job and the prophets; with notes by F. P. Kenrick. (Douay ed.) 8°. '60. $2.50; $4; shp., $4.50. *Kelly, P. & Co.*
— John, Gospel of. *Greek.* [With interlinear tr., crit. annotation, notes, etc., by G. W. Heilig.] roy. 12°. hf. mor., $2.75 .... *Desilver.*
— — *Span.* Evangelio (El) segun San Juan. 18°. '70. 20c .... *Am. Tr.*
— — Gospel and Epistles. 64°. 40c .... *Pres. Bd.*
— Parables. *See* Parables.
— Pentateuch. Tr. into Eng. from the version of the LXX.; with notes on its omissions, etc., by H. Howard. 3 v. cr. 8°. '55–'57. v. 1, $3; v. 2, 3, ea., $3.50 .... *Macmillan.*
— — *Catholic version.* With notes by F. P. Kenrick. (Douay ed.) 8°. '60. $3.50; $4. *Kelly, P. & Co.*
— — *Hebrew.* Rödelheimed. 8°. $1 .... *Frank.*
— — — *Same;* with Germ. and Eng. trans. [In 1 *or* 5 v.] 8°. $1.75–$25 .... *Frank.*
— — — [also] Haphtorath: [sel. from prophecies]; with Eng. tr. by A. Benisch. 12°. $6; mor., $8; — in 2 v. hf. bd., $4.50; — in 5 v. ea., 50c... *Frank.*
— Prophets. *See above* Job.
— Proverbs. 64°. 25c .... *Pres. Bd.*

Bible, Proverbs, *continued.*
— — Book of proverbs, pt. 1: Hebrew text, King James' version, and a rev. vers. by T. J. Conant, with introd. and notes; pt. 2: the rev. vers., with introd. and notes. 4°. $4; — pt. 2, sep., $2.75 .... *Sheldon.*
— — Ill. by hist. parallels from drawings by J. Gilbert. sq. 12°. '69. $2.50; mor., $5 .... *Meth. Bk. Conc.*
— — *See also* Book of proverbs; — *and below* Psalms.
— Psalms of David, chron. arranged: amended version, with hist. introd. and notes, by four friends. 2d [chp.] ed., enl. cr. 8°. $2.25 .... *Macmillan.*
— — *Same;* with briefer notes. (Students' ed.) 18°. $1.25 .... *Macmillan.*
— — With introds. and notes by A. C. Jennings and W. H. Lowe. bks. 3 and 4. [Psalms 73–106.] cr. 8°. '75. $2.25 .... *Macmillan.*
— — One hundred and nineteenth Psalm. 18°. 40c. *Am. S. S.*
— — Twenty-third Psalm; with emblematic borders. ill. 4°. $2.50; mor., $5 .... *Hurd & H.*
— — [also] Proverbs; tr., with introd. and notes, by G. R. Noyes. New ed., rev. 12°. '67. $1.25. *Am. Unit.*
— — *Catholic version.* Psalms, Books of wisdom, and Canticle of canticles; with notes by F. P. Kenrick. (Douay ed.) 8°. '57. $3.50 ..... *Kelly, P. & Co.*
— — *Hebrew and Eng.* Hebrew-English Psalter; arranged in parallelism. ('61.) New ed. 16°. '71. $1.25 .... *Draper.*
— — *See also* Psalmist; — Psalms; — *and above* New Test.
— Revelations. *See above* Gospels.
— Song of songs. *See above* Job; Psalms.
Bible and the family. Fraser, D. $5 .. *Scribner, W. & A.*
Bible and gypsies in Spain. Borrow, G. $1.75 .. *Carter.*
Bible and modern thought. *See* Birks, T. R.
Bible and the school fund. Clark, R. W. 75c.; 40c. *Lee & S.*
Bible and science. Weiss, J. 10c. .... *Free Rel.*
Bible and slavery. Elliott, C. $1.25. *Cin. Meth. Bk. Conc.*
Bible and social reform. Tyler, R. H. $1.75 .. *Challen.*
Bible animals. Wood, J. G. *$4.75; $5.50; $6.75. *Bradley & G.*
Bible atlas. 4°. pap., 50c .... *Scribner, W. & A.*
Bible atlas and gazetteer. 4°. '62. $1.25 .... *Am. Tr.*
Bible baptism; or, the Scripture directory to baptism; by a layman. 18°. 25c.; pap., 10c.... *Pres. Bd.*
Bible Baptist (The). Hunt, T. P. 15c..... *Pres. Bd.*
Bible the best book. *See* Peter Thompson.
Bible biography illustrated; with introd. by H. W. Beecher, and dissertations on the evidences of divine revelation. ill. roy. 8°. *$4; leath., $4.50; mor., $7.50 .... *Lee & S.*
Bible blessings. Newton, R. $1.25 .... *Carter.*
Bible the book of the Lord. 18°. 30c...... *Pres. Bd.*
Bible boy (The) taken captive by the Indians. 18°. 22c .... *Am. S. S.*
Bible bulwarks. Newton, R. 40c.; 20c.... *Am. S. S.*
Bible Christian. Anderson, J. 75c........ *So. Meth.*
Bible Christian library. 6 v. 18°. $4.40..... *So. Meth.*

Cont.: Bible Christian, by J. Anderson. — Bible expositor. — Immersionists against the Bible, by N. H. Lee. — Watson's Apology *with* Refutation. — Opie on Lying. — Alleine's Alarm *and* Baxter's Call.

Bible-class lesson book. *See* New.
Bible-class lessons upon portions of the Old Test. 18°. bds., 20c. .... *Whittaker.*
Bible-class library. 25 v. 16°. $25 ...... *Am. Bapt.*
Bible cuts. *See* Holbein, H.
Bible dictionary. ill. 24°. 75c.; shp., $1. *S. W. Bk. & Pub.*
Bible doctrine of the soul. Ives, C. L. 50c.; 25c. *Judd & W.*

Bible educator; ed. by E. H. Plumptre and others. 4 v. ill. and maps. cr. 4°. ea., $3;—in 2 v. $10. *Cassell.*
— *Same.* 2 v. ill. and maps. 8°. '75. $10; hf. mor., $15 .... *Dutton.*
Bible emblems. Seelye, E. E. 80c.......... *Am. Tr.*
Bible expositor: confirmations of the truth of the Scriptures from observations of recent travelers, ill. manners, customs and places referred to in the Bible. ('55.) 4th ed. 18°. '76. 75c... *So. Meth.*
Bible for the young. *See* Crooke, G. A.
Bible from heaven: dissertation on the evidences of Christianity. 16°. '71. 20c...... *Sev. Day Adv.*
Bible gems. Kremer, R. E. $1; 60c..... *Lippincott.*
Bible gems. Marsh, E. F. 30c........... *West. Tr.*
— *See also* Bijou Bible text-books;—Diamond miniatures.
Bible gleanings. Cross, J. T. H. 40c...... *So. Meth.*
Bible history for the least and the lowest. 5 v. 18°. $3.50.......... *Am. S. S.*
Cont.: From the creation to the death of Abimelech.—From Jephthah's vow to the miracles of Elisha.—From Elisha to the close of the Old Test.—From the coming of Christ to the blessing of children.—From the story of the young ruler to the end of the New Testament.
Bible hours. Duncan, M. B. M. $1.25...... *Carter.*
Bible illustrations. *See* Newton, R:
Bible illustrée, ou récits de l'Ancien et du Nouveau Testament à l'usage de la jeunesse; trad. rev. par l'Abbé Bourquard. ill. 12°. 60c... *Benziger.*
Bible in the church. Westcott, B. F. $1.25. *Macmillan.*
Bible in the counting-house. Boardman, H. A. $1. *Lippincott.*
Bible in the family. Boardman, H. A. $1.. *Lippincott.*
Bible in India. Jacolliet, L. $2........... *Carleton.*
Bible in many tongues; rev. by T. O. Summers. ('55.) 3d ed. 18°. '75. 60c. .... *So. Meth.*
Bible in the public schools. ('69.) 2d ed. 24°. '70. pap., 25c. .... *Schermerhorn.*
— *See also* Minor, J. D.
Bible (The) is true; or, prophecy compared with history. 18°. 40c.......... *Am. S. S.*
Bible (The): its place and power in church and state. Gould, G. H. 10c. .... *H. E. Simmons.*
Bible jewels. Newton, R. $1.25........... *Carter.*
Bible (The), the Koran and the Talmud. Weil, G. $1.......... *Harper.*
Bible-lands. Van Lennep, H. J. $5; $6; $8.. *Harper.*
Bible lesson series. 3 v. 16°. $3........... *Lothrop.*
Cont.: Bible lessons.—Help for S.-school concerts.—The harvest and the reapers.
Bible lessons on Christian life and faith. 16°. 18c. *Un. S. S.*
Bible looking-glass, reflector, companion and guide to the truths of the Scriptures; by J. W. Barber and others. ill. 4°. *$3.75; mor., $6.. *Bradley & G.*
Bible lore. Gray, J. C. $1.25.......... *Dodd.*
Bible marvel-workers, Putnam, A. $1.25.... *Colby.*
Bible months. Groser, W. H. 75c........... *Nelson.*
Bible music. Jacox, F. $1.75 .... *Roberts.*
Bible natural history. 18°. 85c........... *Am. S. S.*
Bible not of man. Spring, G. 75c.......... *Am. Tr.*
Bible of every land: hist. of the Scriptures in every lang. in which tr. have been made. col. maps, tables, indexes, etc. 4°. (Bagster.) $4.50; hf. mor., $10.......... *Wiley.*
Bible of rational mind and religion. Vaiden, T. J. $3 .... *Mendum.*
Bible outlines. Newton, W. W. 10c..... *Whittaker.*
Bible picture book illustrating life of Christ. Tucker, C. $1.50.......... *Nelson.*
Bible picture story book. Tucker, C. $1.50.. *Nelson.*
Bible pictures. Ide, G. B. $2; $3......... *Lothrop.*
Bible pictures; [also] Morning ride; [also] Maria. 18°. 30c.......... *Am. S. S.*
Bible pictures and what they tell us. 12 bks. 18°. 50c.......... *Nelson.*
Bible places. Tristram, H. B. $1.50.......... *Pott.*
Bible portraits. Green, S. G. 50c....... *Perkinpine.*
Bible prayers. King, J. 25c.; 50c.......... *Am. Tr.*
Bible question fairly tested: Fenelon's Use of the Bible, with Fletcher's illustrations; Archbishop of Tours' Authority of the church to interpret the Scriptures; Höninghaus' Protestant evidences of Catholicity. 18°. '55. 75c........... *Murphy.*
Bible read with profit. Watson, T. 20c... *Pres. Bd.*
Bible reader (The). Fowle, W. B. $1..... *Barnes.*
Bible reader; or, Scripture reading made easy. 12°. 15c.......... *Am. S. S.*
Bible reader's help. 18°. 25c.......... *Nelson.*
Bible reader's help. maps. 18°. '67. 40c... *Am. Tr.*
Bible reading book. Hale, S. J. 75c........ *Claxton.*
Bible readings for every day. ('56.) 4th ed. 6 v. 18°. '76. $3.50.......... *So. Meth.*
Bible regained. Lee, S. $1.50.......... *Lee & S.*
Bible rhyme (The). Coxe, A. C. 50c.... *M. Taylor.*
Bible rhymes: sketches of Scripture hist. in verse. ill. 8°. 40c.......... *Pres. Bd.*
Bible rhymes on the Old and New Test. 18°. 25c.; 30c.......... *Am. Bapt.*
Bible rule of life. Bennett, M. L. 40c.; 50c. *Am. Unit.*
Bible rule of temperance. Duffield, G. 60c. *Nat. Temp.*
Bible sketches. *See* Green, S. G.
Bible sketches of the creation and fall. 18°. '66. 30c. *N. Y. Ref. Ch. Bd.; Pres. Com.*
Bible slaveholding not sinful. Ganse, H. D. 25c. *N. Y. Ref. Ch. Bd.*
Bible songs. $1.50–$4.......... (?) *Cumberland.*
Bible standard of duty. Gage, A. O. 15c... *Brown & G.*
Bible steps for little pilgrims. ill. sq. 8°. $2.50. *Scribner, W. & A.*
Bible stories. ill. sq. 12°. '71. bds., 50c... *Routledge.*
Bible stories. Gallaudet, T. H. 25c........ *Am. Tr.*
Bible stories. Stevenson, D. 40c.......... *So. Meth.*
— *See also* Barth, C. G.;—Juvenile picture books;—Library for little folks;—New.
Bible stories for boys and girls. 18°. 28c.; 35c. *Am. Bapt.*
Bible stories for children. ill. 16°. '74. 75c... *Lothrop.*
Bible stories for little children. Jones, M. 50c. *Nelson.*
Bible stories for the young in words of one syllable. ill. 12°. '76. $1.50.......... *World Pub.*
Bible stories for the young in words of the Scripture, according to the Douay version. ill. 4°. $15–$22. *T. Kelly.*
Bible stories for young children. 2 pts. 32°. ea., 30c. *Am. S. S.*
Bible stories in Bible lang. sq. 12°. $1.25.. *Appleton.*
Bible stories in short words. 18°. 45c...... *Pres. Bd.*
Bible story series; in words of one syllable. 5 v. ill. 16°. ea., $1.......... *World Pub.*
Cont.: Bunyan's Pilgrim's progress.—From the crib to the cross.—From the creation to Moses.—From Joshua to Daniel.—Children's Bible picture book.
Bible student's companion, Bible text-book and pocket concordance. maps. 12°. '76. $1.50; mor., $2.50. *Am. Tr.*
Bible studies. Caulkins, F. M. 6 pts. $3.. *Am. Tr.*
Bible teachings in nature. *See* Macmillan, H.
Bible text-book. maps and tables. 12°. '56. 75c.; mor., $1.50.......... *Am. Tr.*
Bible thoughts. Bacon, F. (*Lord*). $1..... *Am. Tr.*
Bible (The) true. Fly, E. M. $2.......... *Claxton.*

Bible (The) true. Plumer, W. S. 25c.....*Am. Tr.*
Bible vs. materialism. Roe, W. M. 50c......*Chase.*
Bible wines. Patton, W. 60c.; 30c......*Nat. Temp.*
Bible wonders. Newton, R. $1.25..........*Carter.*
Bible word book. Swinton, W. $1; 40c....*Harper.*
Bible work in Bible lands. Bird, J. $1.50..*Pres. Bd.*
Biblia e a sua leitura. 18°. '71. 35c........*Am. Tr.*
Biblia emprestada (A). 18°. '74. 25c.......*Am. Tr.*
Biblia prestada (La). 18°. '73. 30c........*Am. Tr.*
Biblical and theological dictionary. ill. 12°. $1.50. *Cong. Pub.*
Biblical atlas. *See* New.
Biblical geography: sketches of the countries and places mentioned in the Bible. map. 18°. 85c. *Am. S. S.*
Biblical reason why (The): hand-book for Biblical students, and guide to family Scripture readings. ill. 12°. $1.50......................*Dick & F.*
Biblical riddle school. Yeakel, R. 35c...*Ev. Assoc.*
Biblical standpoint. Wilbur, A. $1......*Williams.*
Biblical stories. *See* Hübner, J.
Biblische Geschichte. ill. 12°. 40c.; — mit Anhang der Evangelien. 12°. 50c...........*Benziger.*
Biblische Geschichte. Neumann, J. N. 40c. *Kreuzer.*
Biblische Geschichte. *See* Schmid, C. v.
Biblische Geschichten. *See* German Evang. Luth. Synod of Mo.
Biblische Historien. *See* Hübner, J.
Biblische Historien. Zahn, F. L. 60c.....*Steiger.*
Biblische Juwelen. 12°. '73. $1; $1.25..*Ev. Assoc.*
Biblische Räthselschule. 18°. 40c........*Ev. Assoc.*
Bickel, P. W. Altes und Neues. 12°. pap., 35c. *Germ. Bapt.*
— Gottes Walten auf dem Meere. [Selections.] 16°. 25c..........................*Germ. Bapt.*
— Der Psalter. 16°.(?)................*Germ. Bapt.*
— Samenkörner. 16°. 30c..............*Germ. Bapt.*
— Singvögelein (Das). 16°. 40c.........*Germ. Bapt.*
— *See also* Anderson, G. W., Die Baptisten in d. Ver. St.; — Cote, N., Taufe u. Taufkapellen; — Reid, W., Das Blut Jesu.
Bickerstaff, I: Hypocrite: comedy. 16°. pap., 15c. *French.*
— Love in a village: opera. 16°. pap., 15c....*French.*
— Romp: farce. 16°. pap., 15c.............*French.*
Bickerstaffe, Mona B. Archie Young. 32°. 25c. *Scribner, W. & A.*
Bickersteth, Ctte. Elizabeth u. Fanny Bickersteth. [Memoirs.] 12°. '71. $1; $1.25....*Ev. Assoc.*
Bickersteth, *Miss* E. Frances Leslie; or, the prayer divinely taught. 18°. 75c...........*Am. S. S.*
— *Same.* ill. 12°. $1.25....................*Nelson.*
Bickersteth, E: Christian hearer (The); abridg., ed., with add. matter by C. Colton. 12°. '38. 30c. *I. N. Whiting.*
— Devout communicant (The). 48°. '63. 50c.; mor., $2.................................*Dutton.*
— Help to the study of the Scriptures; abridg. New ed., enl. by C. Colton. 18°. '38. 25c...*I. N. Whiting.*
— *Same.* ('54.) 5th ed. 18°. '74. 75c. .....*So. Meth.*
— Questions ill. the Thirty-nine articles of the Church of Eng., with proof from Scripture and the primitive church. 12°. 50c.............*McCauley.*
— Treatise on the Lord's supper; adapted to the services of the Prot. Episc. Church, with introd., notes, etc., by G. T. Bedell. 18°. 50c. *Carter; Leighton.*
— Treatise on prayer. 12°. '56. 75c.........*Am. Tr.*
Bickersteth, E: H: Hades and heaven. 24°. $1..*Carter.*
— Master's (The) home call. 24°. 50c........*Carter.*
— Reef (The), and other parables. ill. 16°. $1.25. *Carter; Dutton.*

Bickersteth, E: H., *continued.*
— Rock (The) of ages; or, Scripture testimony to the one eternal godhead of the Father and of the Son and of the Holy Ghost. New ed., rev. 12°. $1.25................................*Pres. Bd.*
— *Same;* with introd. by F. D. Huntington. New ed. 12°. '61. $1.25......................*Dutton.*
— Shadowed home (The). 16°. $1.50........*Carter.*
— Spirit of life. 12°. $1.25.................*Carter.*
— Two brothers, and other poems. 12°. $2...*Carter.*
— Waters from the well-spring. 16°. $1......*Carter.*
— Yesterday, to-day and forever: poem in 12 books. 12°. '68. $2. chp. ed. 16°. $1.25......*Carter.*
Bickersteth, J: Lang. Memoir. 18°. 35c. *Am. S. S.*
Bickerton; or, the immigrant's daughter; by author of "Harry Layden." 12°. 60c.........*O'Shea.*
Bickham, W. D. Rosecrans' campaign with the 14th army corps, or the army of the Cumberland: narrative of personal observation. 12°. '63. $1.50; pap., $1..........................*Wilstach.*
Bickley, C: P. The mock marriage; or, the libertine's victim. 8°. pap., 25c.............*U. P. James.*
Bickmore, Alb. S. Travels in the East Indian archipelago. ill. 8°. $3.50; hf. cf., $6.....*Appleton.*
Bicknell, Amos J. Detail cottage and constructive architecture. ('73.) 4th ed. pl. 4°. '76. $10. *Bicknell.*
— Village builder; with supplement. ('72.) 3d ed. pl. 4°. '76. $12....................*Bicknell.*
— *Same:* supplement alone. ('71.) New ed. pl. 4°. '76. $5...........................*Bicknell.*
— Wooden and brick buildings, with details. 2 v. pl. 4°. '75. ea., hf. mor., $9..............*Bicknell.*
Bicknell, C: F. *See* Nevada, Supreme Court reports.
Bicknell, G: A. Practice of the Supreme and Circuit Courts of Indiana in civil cases. New ed. 8°. '71. shp., $6..........................*Clarke.*
— *Same;* in criminal cases. New ed. 8°. '71. shp., $6..................................*Clarke.*
Bicknell, T. W. Memorial of W. L. Noyes. *See* Noyes, W. L.
Bida, Alex. (*ill.*) *See* Bible, Gospels; — Christ in art.
Biddle, G. W., *and* McMurtrie, R. C. General index to Eng. common law reports (v. 1–83). 2d ed. [To form 3 v.] v. 1, 2. 8°. '62. $10. *T. & J. W. Johnson.*
Biddle, Hor. P. American boyhood. [Poetry.] 12°. $1.50............................*Lippincott.*
— Musical scale. 12°. '67. $1.50............*Ditson.*
Biddle, J: B. Materia medica for students. 7th ed., rev. and enl. 8°. '75. $4............*Lindsay.*
Biddle, N: History of the expedition of Capts. Lewis and Clarke across the Rocky Mts., etc.; [ed.] by P. Allen; rev. by A. M'Vickar. 2 v. ill. 18°. $1.50..................................*Harper.*
Biddle's architecture. Enl. ed., with 64 eng. by J. Haviland. 4°. hf. roan, $5.............*Polock.*
Biddy Malone; or, the bundle of silk. 18°. 45c. *Pres. Bd.*
Biddy Woodhull, the beautiful haymaker. 8°. pap., 25c..................................*Peterson.*
Bidpai. *See* Pilpay.
Bidwell, G: H. Printers' new hand-book: a treatise on the imposition of forms, with tables of signatures, etc. ('65.) 2d ed. 18°. '75. $1..*Bidwell.*
— The prompt computer; for book, newspaper and job printers in computing earnings of employés. 8°. '75. $2; hf. roan, $2.50..............*Bidwell.*
Bierbower, A. Principles of a system of philosophy. 12°. '70. $1.25..................*Meth. Bk. Conc.*
Bierce, M. H. ["Dod Grile."] Cobwebs from an empty skull. ill. sq. 12°. '73. $1.75..*Routledge.*
Bierly, W. R. Scientific speller. 4°. pap., 15c. *Keystone.*

Big banana (The): Dutch musical [dramatic] sketch. 16°. pap., 15c. . . . . *Happy.*

Big bear's (The) adventures and travels. Porter, W. T. $1.75; 75c. . . . . *Peterson.*

Big Bonanza (The). De Quille, D. *$3.50; $4; $5. *Am. Pub.*

Big brother (The). Eggleston, G. C. $1.50 . . *Putnam.*

Big Bruce and little Moss. *See* W., F.

Big dots and little dots. 18°. 75c. . . . . (?) *Martien.*

Big-foot Wallace. *See* Duval, J. C.

Big mistake (A). Leavitt, A. J. 15c. . . . . *De Witt.*

Big nightcaps. *See* Barrow, *Mrs.* F.

Big type stories. 6 v. ill. sq. 32°. $3.60 . . . . . . *Locke.*
Cont.: Birds and butterflies. — Learning with pleasure. — Susie and Rosie. — Child's play. — Pleasure and profit. — Pleasant stories.

Big type stories for little wide-awakes. 4 v. ill. 4°. $1 . . . . *Lothrop.*
Cont.: Madam Mob-cap. — Merry mice. — Tony. — Winket's valentine.

Bigelow, A. M. *and* L. S. Fruit for Sunday-school festivals. 16°. 40c. . . . . *Cin. Meth. Bk. Conc.*

Bigelow, H: J. On the mechanism of dislocation and fracture of the hip; with the reduction of the dislocation by the flexion method. ill. 8°. $2.50 . . *Lea.*

Bigelow, Jac. Brief expositions of rational medicine; [also] The paradise of doctors: a fable. 12°. 50c. . . . . *W. Wood.*

— Modern inquiries: classical, professional and miscellaneous. cr. 8°. '70. $2.50 . . . . *Little, B. & Co.*

— Nature in disease; ill. in various discourses and essays; with miscel. writings. 12°. $1.25 . . *W. Wood.*

— Useful arts (The) considered in connection with the applications of science. ill. 2 v. 12°. $3 . . *Harper.*

Bigelow, J: *See* Franklin, B., Life; — Hyacinthe, *Father,* The family.

Bigelow, L. G. Artistic photography. 12°. $5. *Benerman.*

Bigelow, L. J. Bench and bar: digest of the wit, humor, asperities and amenities of the law. New ed., enl. cr. 8°. $2 . . . . *Harper.*

Bigelow, L. S. *See* Bigelow, A. M. *and* L. S.

Bigelow, Melville M. Index of cases overruled, reversed, denied, limited, explained, etc., by the courts of Am., Eng. and Ireland. roy. 8°. '73. shp., $6 . . . . *Little, B. & Co.*

— Leading cases in the law of torts; sel. from the Am., Eng. and Irish courts, with notes. 8°. '75. shp., $6 . . . . *Little, B. & Co.*

— Reports of the life and accident insurance cases determined in the courts of Am., Eng. and Ireland, to March, 1875; with notes and ref. 4 v. 8°. '71–'75. ea., shp., $7.50 . . . . *Hurd & H.*

— Treatise on the law of estoppel and its application in practice. 2d ed. 8°. '76. shp., $6 . . *Little, B. & Co.*

— *See also* Redfield, I. F., *and* Bigelow, M. M.

Bigelow papers (The). Lowell, J. R. 2 v. ea., $1.50. *Osgood.*

Bigham, Rob. W. Vinny Leal's trip to the golden shore; ed. by A. G. Haygood. ('74.) 3d ed. 18°. '76. 50c. . . . . *So. Meth.*

Bigland, J: Natural history; with questions. ill. 12°. $1 . . . . *Lippincott.*

Biglow and Main's hymn evangel. *See* Hammond, E. P.

Biglow and Main's hymns of devotion; — songs of salvation. *See* Doane, W. H.

Bigot, Jacques. Relation de la mission Abnaquise de St. François de Sales. *See* Relation des affaires du Canada.

Bigsby, Bern. Elements of the Eng. language: introd. to the study of gram. and composition. 3d ed. 18°. '74. hf. bd., 50c. . . . . *Ginn.*

Bijou Bible text-books. 9 v. 48°. ea., 25c.; cf., 50c. *Scribner, W. & A.*

Bijou Bible text-books, *continued.*
Cont.: Rills from the river of life. — The dew of Hermon. — Daily gleanings. — Casket of pearls. — Bible gems. — Rays of light. — Echoes of heavenly music. — Redeemer's counsel. — Daily bread.

Bijou gift series (The). 4 v. 16°. $3 . . . . *Nelson.*
Cont.: The birds we see, by M. R. M. — With the birds, by M. R. M. — Humming birds, by M. and E. Kirby. — Wild flowers, by M. R. M.

Bilder aus der Geschichte Amerika's. ill. sm. 4°. '66. $1 . . . . *Am. Tr.*

Bilder a. d. häusl. Leben. *See* Zschokke, H.

Bilder-A B C- u. Lesebuch. 12°. 20c.; col., 30c. *Kohler.*

Bilderbuch für Kinder. 18°. '66. 30c. . . . . . . *Am. Tr.*

Bilderbuch (Ein) f. kleine Kinder, f. grosse drum nicht minder, etc. 8°. '66. pap., 30c. . . *Steiger.*

Bilderbuch ohne Bilder. *See* Andersen, H. C.

Bilious attack (A): farce. 16°. pap., 15c. . . . *French.*

Bill, Earl. Rules of practice of the U. S. courts for the northern dist. of Ohio. 12°. shp., $2 . . . . . *Cobb.*

Bill, Ledyard. A winter in Florida: obs. on the soil, climate and productions of our semi-tropical state. ('69.) 5th ed. ill. 12°. '71. $1.25 . . . . *Wood & H.*

Bill Arp's peace papers. ill. 12°. $1.50 . . . . . *Carleton.*

Bill Drock's investment. Chellis, M. D. $1.50. *H. A. Young.*

Bill Horton, the doomed highwayman. 8°. pap., 50c. *Peterson.*

Bill Riggs, jr. Wadsworth, O. A. 75c. . . . . . *Lothrop.*

Bill Riggs library. 4 v. 18°. $3 . . . . *Lothrop.*
Cont.: Bill Riggs, jr., by O. A. Wadsworth. — New year, by Mrs. D. M. Strong. — Fireside angel, by T. S. Arthur. — Pete Ogle.

Billing, Arch. Science of gems, jewels, coins and medals, ancient and modern. photos. 8°. $12.50. *Scribner, W. & A.*

Billing and cooing. Oxenford, J. 15c. . . . . . . *French.*

Billings, E. R. A book on tobacco: its history, varieties, culture, etc., and modes of use in different parts of the world. ill. 8°. *$3; $3.50; hf. cf., $4.50 . . . . *Am. Pub.*

Billings, Hammet. Tales of a monkey; or, the mischievous manœuvres of Dandy Jack. ill. sq. 16°. pap., 50c. . . . . *Locke.*

Billings, J: S. Bibliography of cholera; — Report on barracks and hospitals; — Report on hygiene of U.S. army. *See* United States, *Surgeon-General's Office.*

Billings, Josh. (*pseud.*) *See* Shaw, H: W.

Billingsley, A. S. From the flag to the cross: scenes and incidents of Christianity in the war. ill. 8°. '72. *$2.50; $3.50; mor., $5 . . . . . . *New World.*

Billow and the rock. Martineau, H. 50c. *Routledge.*

Billroth, Thdr. General surgical pathology and therapeutics; tr. by C. E. Hackley. New ed. woodcuts. 8°. $5; shp., $6 . . . . *Appleton.*

Billy Doo: farce. 16°. pap., 15c. . . . . *French.*

Billy Grimes' favorite. Nowell, H. P. H. $1 . . . *Lee & S.*

Billy Taylor. Buckstone, J. B. 15c. . . . . *French.*

Billy Vidkins. *See* Life of.

Billy's Christmas tree. Keene, S. F. 75c. . . . . . *Hoyt.*

Bilney, T: Life and writings. *See* British reformers.

Binding the sheaves. Robbins, S. S. $1.25 . . *Carter.*

Binfield, A. D. Eda May; or, the twin roses. 18°. 50c. . . . . *Nelson.*

Bingham, Anson. Law of descents. 8°. '70. shp., $6. *J. D. Parsons; Weed.*

— Law of executory contracts for the sale of real property. 8°. '72. shp., $7.50 . . . . *W. C. Little.*

— Law of real property. 8°. '68. shp., $6.50. *W. C. Little.*

— *See also* Colvin, A. J., *and* Bingham, A.

Bingham, Clb. The Columbian orator. ('10.) New ed. 12°. '71. $1 .... *Claxton.*
— Young American's speaker. ('56.) New ed. 12°. '74. 90c. .... *Claxton.*

Bingham, C: B. Surgical cases with illustrations. 8°. '76. pap., $2 50 .... *Williams.*

Bingham, Fk. Lester. Henry Granden; or, the unknown heir: drama. 16°. pap., 15c. .... *Ames.*

Bingham, *Mrs.* H. A. Mignonette. 16°. '68. $1.50. *Universalist.*

Bingham, Hiram. Bartimeus of the Sandwich Islands. 18°. '51. 20c. .... *Am. Tr.*

Bingham, J. Foote. The Christian marriage ceremony: its history, significance and curiosities; with notes and text of the Eng., Rom. and Gk. ceremonies. 12°. '71. $1 75 .... *Randolph.*

Bingham, Jos. Origines ecclesiasticæ: antiquities of the Christian church; with sermons and letters on the nature and necessity of absolution. 2 v. roy. 8°. '75. $11 .... *Pott; Scribner, W. & A.*

Bingham, L. M. The young quartermaster: life and death of Lieut. L. M. Bingham, of the 22d South Carolina Vol. 18°. 50c. .... *N. Y. Ref. Ch. Bd.*

Bingham, P. *See* England, Common law reports.

Bingham, Su. Eliz. Memoir. 18°. 35c. .... *Am. S. S.*

Bingham, W: Exercises for tr. into Latin: from [his] Lat. gram. 16°. pap., 25c. .... *Butler.*
— Grammar of the Eng. lang.; with exercises. 12°. 84c. .... *Butler.*
— Grammar of the Lat. lang.; with exercises and vocab. 12°. $1.50 .... *Butler.*
— Latin reader adapted to [his] Lat. gram.; with notes and vocab. 12°. $1.50 .... *Butler.*
— Latin series: element. manual of Lat. prose composition, with Eng.-Lat. vocab. by S. R. Winchell. 12°. $1 .... *Butler.*

Bingley, W: Natural history: anecdotes and descriptions of various beasts, birds, fishes, etc.; with add. from other authors. ill. 8°. '74. *$4.50; mor., $5.50 .... *Hubbard.*

Binkerd, A. D. The Mammoth Cave of Ky., and its denizens. 8°. '69. pap., 50c. .... *Clarke.*

Binks the bagman. Coyne, J. S. 15c. .... *French.*

Binnacle Jack; or, the cavern of death. 8°. pap., 25c. .... *De Witt.*

Binney, Amos. Theological compend. ('55.) 20th ed. 18°. '76. 50c. .... *So. Meth.*
— *and* Steele, Dan. Theological compend improved. 12°. '75. 90c. .... *Meth. Bk. Conc.*

Binney, Hor. Leaders of the old bar of Phila. 8°. '66. pap., $5 .... *J. Campbell & Son.*

Binney, T: From seventeen to thirty. 16°. '68. 90c. *Meth. Bk. Conc.*
— Sermons preached in the King's Weigh House Chapel, 1829–'69. New [chp.] ed. 12°. '69. $1.75. — 2d ser. 8°. '75. $4 .... *Macmillan.*

Binney, W: Greene. Bibliography of N. Am. conchology. 2 pts. 8°. '63–'64. pap., 1, $3; 2, $2. *Smith. Inst.*
— Catalogue of the terrestrial air-breathing mollusks of N. Am. ill. 8°. '73. pap., 50c. *Mus. Comp. Zool.*
— Land and fresh-water shells of N. Am. pts. 2, 3. 8°. '65. pap., pt. 2, $1.25; 3, $1 .... *Smith. Inst.*
— *and* Bland, T. *Same.* pt. 1. 8°. '69. pap., $2. *Smith. Inst.*
— — — *See also* Smithsonian Institution.

Binney the beaver. Guernsey, L. E. 50c. *H. A. Young.*

Binns, J: Treatise on the office of aldermen and justices of the peace in Penn., incl. forms of process and docket entries. 8th ed., rev. and enl. by F. C. Brightly. 8°. shp., $6 .... *Kay.*

Binns, W: Elementary treatise on orthographic projection: method of teaching mechan. and engineering drawing. 6th ed. ill. 8°. '74. $3.50 ... *Spon.*

Binns, W: *continued.*
— Second course of orthographic projection; with remarks on the teeth of wheels, projection of shadows, etc. pl. 8°. '69. $4.50 .... *Spon.*

Biographical encyc. of Ill. of the 19th century; — of Ohio; — of Penna. Robson, C. ea., $25 .. *Robson.*

Biographical series. (Cabinet ed.) 7 v. 16°. ea., 75c. *Hurd & H.*

Cont.: Carlyle's Robert Burns. — Macaulay's William Pitt. — Macaulay's Frederick the Great. — Liddell's Julius Cæsar. — Trollope's Columbus. — Bunsen's Martin Luther. — Arnold's Hannibal.

Biographical sketches. 1st ser. $1.25. — *Same.* New ser. $1.50 .... (?) *Cumberland.*

Biographical sketches and anecdotes for family reading. 18°. 60c. .... *Am. S. S.*

Biographical sketches and anecdotes of members of the Society of Friends. 12°. '70. $1.25; hf. cf., $1.75 .... *Friends Bk. St.*

Biographies of celebrated women. pl. 8°. mor., $20. *Cin. Meth. Bk. Conc.*

Biography of Satan. Graves, K. 60c. .... *Rel. Phil.*

Bion. Idylls. *See* Theocritus, Bion *and* Moschus.

Biot, J. B. Elementary treatise on analytical geometry; tr. by F. H. Smith. 8°. shp., $2.25 .... *Desilver.*

Birch, C: Bell. One hundred and eight Bible pictorial illustrations; with descriptions from Scripture. fp. 8°. (Bagster.) $5; hf. bd., $6.50 ... *Wiley.*

Birch, S. B. Constipated bowels: the various causes and the different means of cure. 3d ed. 12°. '68. $1 .... *Lindsay.*

Birch, S: Adopted child: musical drama. 16°. pap., 15c. .... *French.*

Birch, S: Egypt; from the earliest times to B.C. 300. (Anc. hist. from monuments.) ill. 16°. $1. *Scribner.*
— History of ancient pottery and porcelain, Egyptian, Assyrian, Greek, Roman and Etruscan. 200 ill. 8°. $21; cf., $27 .... *Scribner, W. & A.*
— Records of the past: Eng. tr. of the Assyrian and Egyptian monuments. v. 1, 2. cr. 8°. (Bagster.) ea., $1.50 .... *Wiley.*

Cont.: 1. Assyrian texts. — 2. Egyptian texts.

Bird, F. M. *See* Odenheimer, W. H., *and* Bird, F. M.

Bird, G: One hundred single and double chants; for 4 voices. 12°. bds., 50c.; — words. 10c. *Ditson.*

Bird, Hor. *See* Bird, J. *and* H.

Bird, I: Bible work in Bible lands. 12°. '72. $1.50. *Pres. Bd.*
— Jewish prisoner (The): life of Hermann Ollendorff, the converted Jew. 18°. 35c. .... *Bost. Am. Tr.*
— Martyr (The) of Lebanon; with introd. by Rev. J. Hawes. por. 16°. 80c. .... *Bost. Am. Tr.*

Bird, Jos. Protection against fire, and the best means of putting out fires. 12°. '73. $1.50 .. *Hurd & H.*

Bird, Jos. Vocal music reader. obl. 12°. '61. bds., 25c. .... *Ditson.*
— *and* Hor. Singing school companion: secular and sacred music, arranged for 4 voices. obl. 16°. '52. bds., $1 .... *Ditson.*

Bird, *Mrs.* M. A. Winifred's jewels. 12°. $1.50. *McKinney.*

Bird, Rob. Montgomery. Calavar, the knight of the conquest. ill. 12°. $1.75 .... *Widdleton.*
— Nick of the woods; or, the Jibbenainosay. ill. 12°. $1.75 .... *Widdleton.*

Bird (The) and the arrow, and other tales. 18°. 45c. *Pres. Bd.*

Bird (The) and the bell. Cranch, C. P. $2 .. *Osgood.*

Bird book (The); or, sketches and anecdotes of the bird creation. 18°. 50c. .... *Am. S. S.*

Bird (A) in the hand is worth two in the bush. Phillips, F. 15c. .... *French.*

Bird-nesting. *See* New Year Lib.

Birdie and his fairy friends. Canby, M. T. $1..*Claxton.*
Birdie's picture book. ill. 16°. '75. $1.50....*Nelson.*
Bird's nest. 6 bks. 32°. 50c. ....*Nelson.*
— *See also* Bright eye ser.
Bird's nest, and other stories. 18°. 45c. ...*Am. S. S.*
Birds (The). *See* Aristophanes.
Birds and butterflies. *See* Big type stories.
Birds and fishes. 16°. '75. 40c............*Lothrop.*
Birds and flowers. Howitt, M. $3.........*Nelson.*
Birds and their nests. Howitt, M. $2....*Routledge.*
Birds of Aristophanes. Planché, J. R. 15c...*French.*
Birds of a feather. Bradley, M. E. $1.....*Lee & S.*
Birds of a feather. Howitt, M. 40c. *Scribner, W. & A.*
Birds of prey. Braddon, M. E. 75c........*Harper.*
Birds of prey: drama. 16°. pap., 15c........*French.*
Birds (The) we see. M., M. K. 75c........*Nelson.*
Birkhof (Der). *See* Stöber, K.
Birks, T: R. Bible and modern thought. 12°. $1.75. *Cin. Meth. Bk. Conc.*
— — *See also* Inquiring Christian's lib.
— First principles of moral science. [Lectures.] cr. 8°. '73. $3........................*Macmillan.*
— Memoir of Rev. E. Bickersteth; with pref. by Rev. S. H. Tyng. 2 v. 12°. $3 ....*Harper.*
— Modern utilitarianism; or, the systems of Paley, Bentham and Mill, examined and compared. [Lectures.] cr. 8°. '74. $2.25.........*Macmillan.*
— Scripture doctrine of creation; with reference to religious nihilism and modern theories of development. 16°. '75. 75c..................*Pott.*
Birth and education. Schwartz, M. S. $1.50; $1. *Porter.*
Birth and triumph of love. ill. 12°. $1.....*Carleton.*
Birth of chemistry. Rodwell, G. F. $1..*Macmillan.*
Birthday book of proverbs. B., C. $1..(?)*Shepard.*
Birthday festival. *See* Kite story.
Birthday gift (A): letters to a young friend. 18°. 35c.................................*Am. S. S.*
Birthday motto-book (The); or, calendar of nature: reference book to natural history facts. [Interleaved.] 32°. 75c.; $1.75....*Scribner, W. & A.*
Birthday party. Adams, W. T. 45c.......*Lee & S.*
Birthday party. *See* Baker, *Mrs.* H. N. W., Corwin's nest ser.
Birthday party at the Hall. *See* Locust grove stories.
Birthday present(The). Bushe, M. C. $1.25..*Nelson.*
Birthday present (The). Clark, M. L. 75c...*Lothrop.*
Birthday present (The). Frost, S. A. 50c....*Am. Tr.*
Birthday present (The); by authors of "The parent's cabinet." ill. 16°. $1.75......*Scribner, W. & A.*
Birthday present (The). *See* Books about wonderful and curious things; — Minnie's lib.; — Moss rose ser.
Birthday stories. 6 v. 24°. $1.80..........*Lothrop.*
Cont.: My birthday. — Water cress girl. — Christmas tales. — Young fisherman. — Young Sapphira. — The two fawns.
Birthday stories for young people. 18°. 75c. *Scribner, W. & A.*
Birthday text library. 4 v. 32°. $3.........*Nelson.*
Cont.: Daily self examination. — Words in season. — Still waters. — Green pastures.
Birthplace of Podgers. Hollingshead, J. 15c. *De Witt; French.*
Birthright (The). Gore, C. G. 25c.........*Harper.*
Bisbee, Hm. Life of Seth Barnes. 12°. $1. *Williamson.*
Bischoff, Jos. E: ["Conrad de Bolanden."] Barbarossa: hist. tale of the 12th century; tr. from the Germ. 12°. $2; $2.50........*Cummiskey.*
— Bertha: hist. romance of the time of Henry IV. of Germany; tr. by S. B. A. Harper. 12°. $2; $2.50...............................*Sadlier.*
Bischoff, Jos. E: *continued.*
— New God (The): a narrative for the people; tr. from the Germ. 12°. '72. 75c.; pap., 25c. *Pustet.*
— Progressionists (The); [also] Angela; tr. from the Germ. 8°. '73. $1.50..............*Cath. Pub.*
Biscoe, Ellen L. Glimpses through. ill. 16°. '73. $1.50 ....*Lothrop.*
— Katharine's experience. ill. 16°. '71. $1.50..*Lothrop.*
— Winthorpes (The); or, personal effort: incidents in the hist. of a minister's family and parish. ill. 16°. $1.15...........................*Bost. Am. Tr.*
— Words and deeds; or, watching for opportunities. 16°. '72. $1.50......................*Crowell.*
— — *See also* Lettie Sterling ser.
Bishop, *Mrs.* G. M. The Christian seasons. 12°. $1.25. *U. S. Pub.*
Bishop, Jl. Prentiss. Commentaries on the criminal law. 5th ed. 2 v. 8°. '72. shp., $12. *Little, B. & Co.*
— Commentaries on criminal procedure; or, the law of pleading, evidence and practice in criminal cases. 2d ed., rev. and enl. 2 v. 8°. '72. shp., $12. *Little, B. & Co.*
— Commentaries on the law of marriage and divorce, of separations without divorce, and of the evidence of marriage in all issues. 5th ed. 2 v. 8°. '73. shp., $12......................*Little, B. & Co.*
— Commentaries on the law of married women, under the statutes of the several states and at common law and in equity. 2 v. 8°. '73–'75. shp., $12. *Little, B. & Co.*
— Commentaries on the law of statutory crimes. 8°. '73. shp., $6......................*Little, B. & Co.*
— First book of the law; explaining the nature, sources, books and practical applications of legal science, and methods of study and practice. 8°. '68. shp., $4......................*Little, B. & Co.*
Bishop, Nath. H. A thousand miles' walk across South America, over the pampas and the Andes. ill. 16°. $1.25.......................*Lee & S.*
Bishop (The) and the monk: lives of Pierpaolo Vergerio and John Craig. 18°. 50c.......*Pres. Bd.*
Bishop (The) and Nanette. Smith, F. I. B. $1.50. *Whittaker.*
Bishop's (The) little daughter. 18°. 90c.....*Dutton.*
Bispham, G: Tucker. Law of contracts in rem. 8°. pap., 30c...................................*Kay.*
— Principles of equity: treatise on the system of justice administered in the courts of chancery. 8°. shp., $6.50..............................*Kay.*
Bissell, A. H. *See* Minnesota, Statutes.
Bissell, Edn. Cone. Historic origin of the Bible. 8°. '73. $2.50.........................*Randolph.*
Bissell, Josiah H. *See* United States, Circuit and District Court reports.
Bissell, Ma. L. Bertha Weisser's wish. 16°. '63. 75c. *Dutton.*
— Ned Grant's quest. 16°. '68. $1..........*Dutton.*
— The Robinsons. ill. 16°. '72. $1.25......*Lothrop.*
Bissell, T. American musical class book. obl. 16°. '59. bds., 75c. ....*Ditson.*
— *See also* White, E. L., *and* Bissell, T.
Bisset, And. Practical treatise on the law of partnership, incl. the law rel. to joint-stock companies; with notes of Am. cases. 8°. shp., $2.50..*Kay.*
Bit (A) of fun. *See* Yonge, C. M., "Star of hope" ser.
Bit (A) of green; or, the story of lame William and his musk plant. 18°. 25c...........*Am. S. S.*
— *Same.* 18°. '66. 25c. *N. Y. Ref. Ch. Bd.; Pres. Com.*
Bit o' writin. *See* Banim, J. *and* M.
Bits of blarney. MacKenzie, R. S. $1.50; $2..*Sadlier.*
Bits of talk about home matters. Jackson, H. $1. *Roberts.*
Bits of travel. Jackson, H. $1.50..........*Roberts.*
Bitter dose (The), and other stories. 18°. 70c. *Pres. Bd.*

Bitter medicine (The). *See* Maple grove stories.

Bitter sweet. *See* Holland, J. G.

Bittere Leiden (Das) Jesu Christi. *See* Emmerich, A. K.

Bitzius, Alb. ["Jeremias Gotthelf."] Wealth and welfare. [Fiction.] cr. 8°. $2 ...... *Routledge.*

Bivouac (The). *See* Maxwell, W. H.

Bivouac and battle. Adams, W. T. $1.25 .. *Lee & S.*

Bivouac and battle-field. Noyes, G. F. $1.50. *Harper.*

Björnson, Björnstjerne. Arne; [also] The happy boy: tales of Norwegian country life. 4th ed. 12°. '72. $1.50 .... *Allyn.*

— Fisher maiden (The); tr. by M. E. Niles. ('69.) New ed. (Leis. hour ser.) 16°. '74. $1.25 .. *Holt.*

— Fishing girl (The); tr by A. Plesner and F. Richardson. 12°. '70. $1 .... *Cassell.*

— Love and life in Norway; tr. by A. Bethell and A. Plesner. 12°. '70. $1 .... *Cassell.*

Black, Ad. *and* C: General atlas of the world. Am. ed. 71 maps. f°. '76. hf. mor., $22.50. *Appleton; Little, B. & Co.*

— — *Same.* f°. '76. hf. mor., $25 .... *Lippincott.*

Black, C. C. *See* Heaton, *Mrs.* C., Life of da Vinci.

Black, C: *See* Black, Ad. *and* C:

Black, D. Campbell. Functional diseases of the renal, urinary and reprod. organs, with a general view of urinary pathology. 12°. '72. $2 50 ... *Lindsay.*

— Lectures on Bright's disease of the kidneys. ill. 8°. '76. $2 .... *Lindsay.*

Black, J. R. The ten laws of health; or, how disease is produced and can be prevented. 12°. $1.75. *Lippincott.*

Black, J. S. *See* United States, Supreme Court reports.

Black, Ja. B. *See* Indiana, Reports.

Black, *Mrs.* Sa. S. Rambling chats and chatty rambles. 16°. '72. $1 .... *Dutton.*

Black, W: Daughter of Heth. 8°. pap., 50c ... *Harper.*

— In silk attire. 8°. pap., 50c .... *Harper.*

— Kilmeny. 8°. pap., 50c .... *Harper.*

— Love or marriage? 8°. pap., 50c .... *Harper.*

— Maid of Killeena, and other tales. cr. 8°. '74. $1.75. *Macmillan.*

— *Same;* [also] The marriage of Moira Fergus, and other stories. 8°. pap., 50c .... *Harper.*

— Marriage of Moira Fergus. 8°. '75. pap., 25c. *W. F. Gill.*

— Monarch of Mincing Lane. ill. 8°. pap., 50c. *Harper.*

— Princess of Thule. New ed. cr. 8°. $1.75. *Macmillan.*

— *Same.* 8°. pap., 75c .... *Harper.*

— Strange adventures of a phaeton. New ed. cr. 8°. '73. $1.75 .... *Macmillan.*

— *Same.* 8°. pap., 75c .... *Harper.*

— Three feathers. ill. 8°. $1.50; pap., $1 ... *Harper.*

Black and white. Chaplin, J. D. 50c ... *Bost. Am. Tr.*

Black art (The); or, magic made easy. 64°. pap., 10c. *De Witt.*

Black art (The) fully exposed and laid bare. ill. sq. 18°. '74. pap., 25c .... (?) *F. M. Reed.*

Black band (The). Braddon, M. E. 50c .... *De Witt.*

Black baronet (The). Carleton, W. $1.50. *Noonan; Sadlier.*

Black Bess series. 2 v. 8°. ea., pap., 25c .... *De Witt.*
Cont.: Black Bess.—Edgeworth Bess.

Black brothers (The). 8°. pap., 25c .... *De Witt.*

Black chap (The) from Whitechapel. Williams, H. L., *jr.* 15c .... *De Witt.*

Black chemist (The). White, C. 15c .... *De Witt.*

Black cliff. Tucker, C. 50c .... *Carter.*

Black crook. [In English *or* German.] ill. 8°. '67. pap., 50c .... *Barclay.*

Black crook: burlesque. 16°. pap., 15c. *French; Happy.*

Black cruiser (The); or, the scourge of the seas. 8°. pap., 25c .... *De Witt.*

Black Danes. 18°. 50c .... *Dutton.*

Black diamonds. Dyer, S. $1.50 .... *Am. Bapt.*

Black doctor. Bourgeois, A., *and* Dumanoir, P. 15c. *French.*

Black domino. Wilks, T. E. 15c .... *French.*

Black dwarf (The). *See* Scott, *Sir* W.

Black eagle (The). 8°. pap., 25c .... *De Witt.*

Black-eyed beauty; or, one of the lost. 8°. pap., 25c .... *De Witt.*

Black-eyed Sukey. Cooper, F. F. 15c .... *French.*

Black-eyed Susan. Burnand, F. C. 15c. ... *French.*

Black-eyed Susan. Jerrold, D. 15c .... *French.*

Black-eyed William. White, C. 15c .... *De Witt.*

Black Forest village stories. Auerbach, B. $1.25. *Holt.*

Black gauntlet (The). Schoolcraft, M. H. $1.25. *Lippincott.*

Black horse (The) and carryall. M'Carty, J. H. $1.25. *Cin. Meth. Bk. Conc.*

Black ivory. Ballantyne, R. M. $1.75 ...... *Nelson.*

Black Jacob, a monument of grace. 18°. 35c. *Am. S. S.*

Black jokes. Turner, N. 10c .... *Dick & F.*

Black jokes for blue devils. 32°. pap., 25c ... *De Witt.*

Black Judy. 18°. '65. 40c .... *Randolph.*

Black mail: Ethiop. drama. 16°. pap., 15c. *French; Happy.*

Black Ole Bull: Ethiop. drama. 16°. pap., 15c. *French.*

Black panther (The). Wraxhall, *Sir* C. F. L. $1.25. *Burnham.*

Black Peter. *See* Konewka, P.

Black prince (The). ill. 12°. $1.50 .... *Nelson.*

Black princess (The). Besset, J. M. 50c. *Routledge.*

Black prophet. Carleton, W. $1.50 .... *Sadlier.*

Black ranger. Curtis, N. M. 25c .... *De Witt.*

Black robes. Nevin, R. P. $1.50 .... *Lippincott.*

Black sheep. Coyne, J. S. 15c .... *French.*

Black sheep. Simpson, J. P., *and* Yates, E. 15c. *De Witt; French.*

Black sheep. *See* Yates, Edmund.

Black ship (The). Charles, E. 75c ... *Carter; Dutton.*

Black shoemaker: Ethiop. drama. 16°. pap., 15c. *French; Happy.*

Black statue: Ethiop. drama. 16°. pap., 15c. *French; Happy.*

Black tulip (The). *See* Dumas, A.

Black valley, the railroad, and the country. Hanks, S. W. $1 .... *Cong. Pub.*

Black wit and darkey conversations. White, C. 10c. *Dick & F.*

Blackader, J. Life. 18°. 40c .... *Pres. Bd.*

Blackall, C. R. Nellie's work for Jesus. ('69.) 7th ed. 32°. '72. 40c. 18°. pap., 10c ...... *Blackall.*

— Our Sunday school work and how to do it. 18°. 20c.; pap., 10c .... *Am. Bapt.*

Blackberry girl (The). *See* Pretty little lib.

Blackburn, Colin. Treatise on the effect of the contract of sale on the legal rights of property and possession in goods, wares and merchandise. 8°. shp., $1.25 .... *Kay.*

— *See also* England, Common law reports.

Blackburn, H: Artists and Arabs. (Saunterer's ser.) ill. 18°. $1.50 .... * *Osgood.*

— Normandy picturesque. (Saunterer's ser.) ill. 18°. $1.50 .... * *Osgood.*

Blackburn, Hu. Elements of plane trigonometry. 12°. '71. 75c .... *Macmillan.*

Blackburn, J. S., *and* McDonald, W. N. Grammar school hist. of the U. S. ('71.) 5th ed. 12°. '76. $1.25 .... *Dulany.*

Blackburn, J. S., *and* McDonald, W. N., *continued.*
— — New school hist. of the U. S. ('70.) 9th ed. 12°. '76. $1.50 .... *Dulany.*
Blackburn, W: M. Admiral Coligny and the rise of the Huguenots. 2 v. 12°. $3 .... *Pres. Bd.*
— Alick and his blind uncle. 18°. 50c. ...... *Pres. Bd.*
— Ancient schoolmaster (The), and the greatest school of old times. 18°. 60c. .... *Pres. Bd.*
— Aonio Paleario and his friends; with a rev. ed. of "The benefits of Christ's death," [by A. Paleario]. 12°. $1.25 .... *Pres. Bd.*
— Cherry-bounce; or, wise management of human nature. 18°. 60c. .... *Pres. Bd.*
— College days of Calvin. 12°. 70c. .... *Pres. Bd.*
— Curious chapter (The), and how its prophecies were fulfilled by the young king Josiah. 18°. 65c. *Pres. Bd.*
— Early watermelons (The); or, Alick never afraid of the truth. 18°. 50c. .... *Pres. Bd.*
— Exiles of Madeira. 12°. 75c. .... *Pres. Bd.*
— Geneva's shield: story of the Swiss reformation. ill. 16°. '68. $1 .... *Dodd.*
— Holy child (The): or, early years of Jesus Christ. 18°. 70c. .... *Pres. Bd.*
— Judas the Maccabee and the Asmonean princes. 18°. 75c. .... *Pres. Bd.*
— My dog Rover, and some good that he did in the world. 18°. 50c. .... *Pres. Bd.*
— Nevers (The), a numerous family. 32°. '71. 25c. *Am. Tr.*
— *Same.* 18°. 45c. .... *Pres. Bd.*
— *Same.* ('68.) New ed. 18°. '75. 50c. .... *Hoyt.*
— Rebel prince (The): lessons from the career of the young man Absalom. 12°. $1 .... *Pres. Bd.*
— St. Patrick and the early church of Ireland. 16°. $1 .... *Pres. Bd.*
— Teddy, the bill-poster, and how he became Uncle Alick's right-hand man. 18°. 65c. ..... *Pres. Bd.*
— Theban legion (The). 16°. $1 .... *Pres. Bd.*
— Ulrich Zwingli, the patriotic reformer: a history. 12°. $1.50 .... *Pres. Bd.*
— Uncle Alick's Sabbath-school. 18°. 60c. ... *Pres. Bd.*
— Uncle Alick's series. 6 v. 18°. $3.40 .... *Pres. Bd.*
Cont.: Alick and his blind uncle. — Early watermelons. — Cherry bounce. — My dog Rover. — Uncle Alick's Sabbath school. — Teddy, the bill-poster.
— William Farel, and the story of the Swiss reform. 18°. $1.50 .... *Pres. Bd.*
— Young Calvin in Paris, and the little flock that he fed. 12°. 75c. .... *Pres. Bd.*
Blackburne, E: Life of Francis Blackburne, late lord chancellor of Ireland. 8°. '74. $4 .. *Macmillan.*
Blackest tragedy of all: Ethiop. drama. 16°. pap., 15c. .... *French.*
Blacket, W. S. The young men's Bible class. 18°. 75c. .... *Nelson.*
Blackfoot, the pirate. 8°. pap., 25c. .... *De Witt.*
Blackford, *Mrs.* —. Scottish orphans; [also] Arthur Monteith. New ed. 16°. $1 .... *Lippincott.*
Blackford, I: *See* Indiana, Reports.
Blackie, J: Stuart. Four phases of morals: Socrates, Aristotle, Christianity, utilitarianism. ('71.) New ed. 12°. '75. $1.50 .... *Scribner.*
— Greek and Eng. dialogues; for schools and colleges. 2d ed. 12°. '75. $1 .... *Macmillan.*
— Horæ Hellenicæ: essays and discussions on some important points of Gk. philology and antiquity. 8°. '74. $4 .... *Macmillan.*
— On self-culture, intellectual, physical, moral: a vade mecum for young men and students. ('74.) New ed. 16°. '75. $1 .... *Scribner.*
— Songs of religion and life. sq. 12°. '76. $1.50. *Scribner.*
Blacklock, M. Strickland. City sounds and rural echoes. 12°. '74. $1 .... (?) *Stevenson.*
Blackman, Emily C. History of Susquehanna Co., Penna. maps and ill. 8°. '73. $4; shp., $5. *Claxton.*
Blackman, G: C. *See* Tripler, C. S., *and* Blackman, G. C.
Blackman, O. Graded songs. 5 nos. 16°, 12° and 8°. ea., 10c. *to* 75c. .... *Church.*
— *See also* Whittemore, E. E., *and* Blackman, O.
Blackmore, R. D. Alice Lorraine: a tale of the South Downs. 8°. pap., 75c. .... *Harper.*
— Clara Vaughan. 12°. $1.75 .... *Lippincott.*
— Cradock Nowell. 8°. pap., 75c. .... *Harper.*
— Lorna Doone. 8°. pap., 75c. .... *Harper.*
— Maid of Sker. 8°. pap., 75c. .... *Harper.*
Blacksmith (The). Strong, J. D. 25c. .... *Lothrop.*
Blacksmith's (The) boy. *See* Brother Willie's lib.
Blacksmith's (The) revenge; or, how to get rid of disagreeable neighbors. 18°. '66. 25c. *N. Y. Ref. Ch. Bd.; Pres. Com.*
Blacksmith's (The) revenge; or, the power of kindness. 18°. 25c. .... *Am. S. S.*
Note. Same as above?
Blackstone, *Sir* W: Commentaries on the laws of England; with notes and life of author by G. Sharswood. 2 v. 8°. shp., $10 ...... *Lippincott.*
— *Same;* with life and notes by Christian, Chitty, Lee, etc., and ref. to Am. cases by a member of the N. Y. bar. 2 v. 8°. shp., $7.50 .... *Lippincott.*
— *Same;* with notes by Christian, Coleridge, Chitty and other Eng. editors; ed. by T. M. Cooley. ('70.) 2d ed. 2 v. 8°. '72. shp., $13 .. *Callaghan.*
— *Same;* with notes by J. F. Hargrave, G. Sweet, R. Couch and W. R. Welsley; with [Am.] notes by J. L. Wendell. 4 v. 8°. shp., $12 ...... *Harper.*
— *Same;* abridg. by R. M. Kerr. New ed. 12°. (Lond.) '73. $3 .... *Little, B. & Co.*
— *Same;* reduced to questions and answers, by J. C. Devereux; upon the plan of Kinne's Blackstone. 8°. shp., $3.50 .... *Baker, V. & Co.*
— — *See also* Dickson, F. S.
Blackwell, *Mrs.* Antoinette B. Island neighbors (The). [Fiction.] ill. 8°. pap., 75c. .. *Harper.*
— Physical basis of immortality. 12°. '76. $1.50. *Putnam.*
— Sexes throughout nature. 12°. '75. $1.25. *Putnam.*
— Studies in general science. 12°. '69. $1.75. *Putnam.*
Blackwell, Rob. S. Practical treatise on the power to sell land for the non-payment of taxes; embracing decisions of the federal courts and of the sup. judicial tribunals of the several states. 4th ed. 8°. '75. shp., $6 .... *Little, B. & Co.*
Blackwood, Stevenson A. Heavenly places: substance of addresses on Joshua. 16°. 75c. .. *Willard.*
— Triumph of faith: sequel to "Heavenly places." 16°. 75c. .... *Willard.*
Blackwood, W: (*ed.*) Complete Bible encyclopedia: a treasury of religious knowledge. ill. and por. 4°. *$20; $25; — in 3 v. ea., *$10; hf. mor., $12; — in 2 v. ea., mor., *$20 ...... *J. E. Potter.*
— *See also* Bible [Whole].
Blade and ear. Muzzey, A. B. $1.25; $1.50. *Lee & S.*
Blade-o'-grass. Farjeon, B. L. 35c. .... *Harper.*
Bladen, *Mrs.* Eliz. S. Water waif: a story of the revolution. 16°. '76. 75c. .... *Claxton.*
Blaikie, G. G. Better days for the working people. cr. 8°. bds., 75c. .... *Routledge.*
— Counsel and cheer for the battle of life. cr. 8°. bds., 75c. .... *Routledge.*
— For the work of the ministry: manual of homiletical and pastoral theology. 8°. $3 .... *Routledge.*
Blaikie, W: G. Bible history in connection with general hist. of the world. 12°. $1.50 ...... *Nelson.*
— Life and the true light; or, Bible and general history interlocked. maps. 12°. '69. $1.75 .... *Tibbals.*
— *See also* Guthrie, T., *and* Blaikie, W. G.
Blaine, D. P. Encyclopædia of rural sports. ill. 8°. $8; hf. mor., $12 .... *Lee & S.*

Blair, F. P., *jr.* Life. *See* Seymour, H., *and* Blair, F. P., *jr.*

Blair, Hu. Abridgment of "Lectures on rhetoric"; with quest. by a teacher of Phila. 16°. 63c. . . *Lippincott.*
— *Same.* 18°. '76. 65c. . . . . *Porter.*
— Advice to youth. *See* Practical morality.
— Lectures on rhetoric and belles-lettres; with quest. and anal. by A. Mills. 12°. '53. $1.50. *G. R. Lockwood.*
— *Same.* 8°. '73. $2.25; shp., $2.75 . . . . *Porter.*
— Sermons; with life by J. Finlayson. 8°. $2 . . *Harper.*
— Sermons on the death and ascension of Christ. *See* Fleetwood, J., Life of Christ.

Blair, *Rev.* J: Chronological tables; rev. and enl. by J. W. Rosse. 12°. (Bohn.) $3.50. *Little, B. & Co.*
— *Same.* 12°. (Bohn.) $4. *Lippincott; Scribner, W. & A.*

Blair, *Rev.* J: *See* Sermons and essays.

Blair, Rob. Poems. *See* Gray, T., Poems.

Blair, Wa. Latin pronunciation: inquiry into the proper sounds of the Lat. lang. during the classical period. 12°. '70. $1. . . . . *Barnes.*

Blaisdell, L. G. Musical echo. obl. 16°. 75c. *Gordon.*

Blake, *Lady* —. Lady of Lyndon. [Fiction.] 8°. $1 25; pap., 75c. . . . . *Estes.*
— Ruth Maxwell. [Fiction.] 8°. $1.25; pap., 75c. *Estes.*

Blake, *Mrs.* —. Cecile Ray: an autobiography. 16°. $1.25 . . . . *Routledge.*
— Orphan of Waterloo. 16°. 75c. . . . . *Routledge.*

Blake, C. D. *See* White, C. A., *and* Blake, C. D.

Blake, *Mrs.* Caro. L. Alice Rosedale; or, the power of a constant Christian life. 18°. 60c. . . *Pres. Bd.*
— Frank Eston; or, the joy of believing in Jesus. 18°. 50c. . . . . *Pres. Bd.*

Blake, E. Vale (*ed.*) Arctic experiences: Capt. G. E. Tyson's wonderful drift on the ice-floe, hist. of the "Polaris" expedition, cruise of the "Tigress" and rescue of the "Polaris" survivors; with a general Arctic chronology. map, por. and ill. 8°. '74. $4 . . . . *Harper.*

Blake, H: Nichols. Three years in the army of the Potomac. 12°. '65. $1.50 . . . . *Lee & S.*
— *See also* Montana, Supreme Court reports.

Blake, J. V. "Morning stars sang together": songs for Sunday schools. obl. 12°. '69. bds., 35c.; pap., 30c. . . . . *Ditson.*

Blake, Ja. Annals of Dorchester [Mass., 1628–1753]. 12°. '46. bds., 50c. . . . *D. Clapp; Dorch. Antiq.*

Blake, *Rev.* J: L. History of the Am. revolution. ill. and maps. 18°. 75c. . . . . *Harper.*
— Juvenile companion and fireside reader. 18°. 75c. *Harper.*
— Our world in a nutshell. ill. 12°. $1.50 . . *World Pub.*

Blake, Jona. History of Warwick, Mass., to 1854; brought down to the present time by others; with app. 12°. '73. $2 . . . . *Lockwood, B. & Co.*

Blake, L. H. Frank Sillaby. 16°. $1.25 . . . . *Cong. Pub.*
— *Same.* 16°. '74. $1.25 . . . . *H. A. Young.*

Blake, *Mrs.* Lillie Devereux. Fettered for life; or, lord and master: a story of to-day. 12°. $1.50; pap., $1 . . . . *Sheldon.*
— Forced vows. 8°. pap., 25c. . . . . *Beadle.*

Blake, M. Gethsemane and Calvary. 18°. 60c. *Cong. Pub.*

Blake, P. Carter. Sulphur in Iceland. 8°. '74. pap., 40c. . . . . *Spon.*

Blake, So. Jex. *See* Jex-Blake, S.

Blake, T: G. Lonely man of the ocean: drama. 16°. pap., 15c. . . . . *French.*
— Spanking legacy: farce. 16°. pap., 15c. . . . *French.*

Blake, W: Illustrations of Job reprod. in heliot.; with descrip. letter-press and sketch of B.'s life and works, by C. E. Norton. 4°. '74. $10 . . . *Osgood.*

Blake, W: *continued.*
— Poetical works; ed. with memoir by W. M. Rossetti. 16°. '74. $2.25 . . . . *Roberts.*
— Selections from poems. *See* Gilchrist, A., Life of B.

Blake, W: P. Precious metals (The); with chapter upon unification of gold and silver coinage. 8°. '69. $2.50 . . . . *Putnam.*
— Report on pottery, porcelain, tiles, terra-cotta, and brick [Vienna Exposition, 1873]. 8°. '75. $2. *Van Nostrand.*

Blakeman, E. D. Two hundred poetical riddles. sm. 12°. '75. pap., 20c. . . . . *D. M. Bennett.*

Blakes (The) and the Flanagans. Sadlier, M. A. $1.25; $1.75 . . . . *Sadlier.*

Blakey, Rob. Angling; or, how to angle, and where to go. ill. 16°. bds., 50c. . . . . *Routledge.*
— Shooting: manual of practical information. ill. 16°. bds., 50c. . . . . *Routledge.*

Blameless prince. Stedman, E. C. $1.50 . . . *Osgood.*

Blanc, C: Grammar of painting and engraving; tr. by K. N. Doggett, with the orig. ill. 4°. '73. $6.50; $7; hf. mor., $10; mor., $12. — (Popular ed.) '74. $4.50 . . . . *Hurd & H.*

Blanchard, Calv. Art of real pleasure. ill. 16°. '64. $1 . . . . *D. Thomas.*
— How to do it the best way. 16°. '67. pap., 25c. *D. Thomas.*
— Human nature unveiled. ill. 16°. '64. 75c. *D. Thomas.*
— Life of Thomas Paine. por. 12°. '60. $1. *D. Thomas.*
— Message to the "sovereign people" of the U. S.; exhibiting to their majesties the infernal treachery or worse inability of their religious counsellors, and of their political "servants." 12°. '60. pap., 25c. . . . . *D. Thomas.*
— New crisis (The); or, our deliverance from priestly fraud, political charlatanry and popular despotism. 12°. '57. pap., 15c. . . . . *D. Thomas.*
— Religio-political physics; or, the science and art of man's deliverance from ignorance-engendered mysticism and its resulting theo-moral quackery and governmental brigandage. 12°. '61. 50c.; pap., 25c. . . . . *D. Thomas.*
— Secret history of a votary of pleasure. ill. 16°. '66. $1 . . . . *D. Thomas.*
— Tell-tale (The); or, love secrets will out. 16°. '67. pap., 25c. . . . . *D. Thomas.*

Blanchard, Claude. Journal of B., commissary of the French auxiliary army sent to the U. S., 1780–1783; tr. by W. Duane, and ed. by T. Balch. sq. 12°. '75. $2.50 . . . . *Munsell.*

Blanchard, E. L. Artful dodge: farce. 16°. pap., 15c. . . . . *French.*
— Pork chops: extravaganza. 16°. pap., 15c. . . *French.*

Blanchard, Émile. Métamorphoses, mœurs et instinctes des insectes. *See* Duncan, P. M., Transformations of insects.

Blanchard, G: A., *and* Weeks, E. P. Laws of mines, minerals and water rights: select cases with notes. 8°. shp., $7.50 . . . . *S. Whitney.*

Blanchard, J. *See* Rice, N. L., *and* Blanchard, J.; — McDill, D., Blanchard, J., *and* Beecher, E.

Blanche; tr. from the French. 18°. '72. 40c. *Kenedy.*

Blanche and Agnes. Perring, *Mrs.* —. 45c. *Routledge.*

Blanche and Agnes lib. 5 v. 18°. $2.25 . . *Routledge.*
Cont.: Blanche and Agnes. — Story of a cat. — Minnie's legacy. — Neighbourly love. — Magdalene and Raphael.

Blanche and Beryl. Bégon, F. $1.25 . . . . *Routledge.*

Blanche Gamond, a heroine of faith. 18°. '70. 45c. *Am. Tr.*
— *Same.* ill. 16°. '69. 75c. . . . . *Hoyt.*

Blanche Gilroy. Hosmer, M. $1.50 . . . . . *Lippincott.*

Blanche Heriot. Smith, A. 15c. . . . . *French.*

Blanche Leslie. 32°. 60c. . . . . *Sadlier.*

Blanche of Brandywine. Lippard, G. $2; $1.50. *Peterson.*

Blanche of Brandywine: drama. 16°. pap., 15c. *French.*

Blanche Seymour; by author of "Erma's engagement." 8°. $1.25; pap., 75c. .... *Lippincott.*

Blanche's lesson, and other stories. ill. 18°. 70c. *Pres. Bd.*

Blanco, Francisco. Lecturas inglesas. 2 pts. 12°. '71. 1, 90c.; 2, $1.25; in 1 v., $1.75. *G. R. Lockwood.*

Bland, T. *See* Binney, W. G., *and* Bland, T.

Bland, Theodorick. *See* Maryland, Chancery reports.

Blandford, G. Fielding. Insanity and its treatment; with summary of the laws in the U. S. on the confinement of the insane, by I. Ray. 8°. $3.25..*Lea.*

Blanford, H. F. Physical geog. for Indian schools, and glossary of technical terms. 3d ed. 12°. '74. 75c. .... *Macmillan.*

Blanford, W. T. Geology and zoology of Abyssinia. col. ill. 8°. '70. $7 .... *Macmillan.*

Blanks and prizes. Smith, D. 15c......... *Lee & S.*

Blasius, W: Storms: their nature, classification and laws; with the means of predicting them, principally from their embodiments, the clouds. maps, pl., etc. cr. 8°. '75. $2.50............. *Porter.*

Blasted heath; or, the castle of the wolves. 8°. pap., 50c. .... *De Witt.*

Blatch, W: Historical confirmation of Scripture. 18°. '44. 35c....................... *Meth. Bk. Conc.*

Blatchford, S: *See* United States, Cases in prize; Circuit Court reports; Circuit Court rules; District Court reports; District Court rules.

Blatchley, J. S. *See* Littleton, H. A., *and* Blatchley, J. S.

Blätter a. d. Tagebuche d. armen Pfarrvikars v. Wiltshire. *See* Zschokke, H.

Blaue Wunder (Das). *See* Zschokke, H.

Blauen (Die) u. Gelben. Gerstäcker, F. 50c. *Morwitz.*

Blauvelt, *Mrs.* J. Remsen. The yoke and burden; or, the rewards of a well-spent life. 12°. '73. $1.50. *Ward.*

Blayney, B: *See* Bible [Whole].

Blaze de Bury, M. P. R. S. (*Baroness*). All for greed. 8°. '68. pap., 38c.................. *Littell & G.*

Blazing burgee (The): drama. 16°. pap., 15c. *French.*

Blazing star (The). Greene, W. B. $1.50.. *Williams.*

Bleak House. *See* Dickens, C.

Bleby, H: Romance without fiction; or, sketches from the portfolio of an old missionary. 12°. '74. $1.75 .... *Meth. Bk. Conc.*

Bledsoe, Alb. Taylor. Bishop Cummings movement (The). 16°. pap., 25c. .... *S. W. Bk. & Pub.*

— Infant baptism. 16°. pap., 25c.... *S. W. Bk. & Pub.*

— Philosophy of mathematics; with ref. to geometry and the infinitesimal method. 12°. $2..*Lippincott.*

— Theodicy; or, vindication of the divine glory, as manifested in the constitution and government of the moral world. New ed., rev. 8°. '53. hf. mor., $3.................... *Meth. Bk. Conc.*

Bleeding phantom (The). 8°. pap., 25c..... *De Witt.*

Bleek, F: Introduction to the New Test.; tr. by Rev. W. Urwick. 2 v. 8°. $6..... *Scribner, W. & A.*

— Introduction to the Old Test.; tr. by C. H. Venables. 2 v. cr. 8°. $9.............. *Scribner, W. & A.*

Bleek, W. H. J. On the origin of lang.; ed. with pref. by E. Häckell; tr. by T. Davidson. 8°. '69. pap., 50c.............................. *Schmidt.*

Bleeker, L. Order book of Capt. Leon. Bleeker, major of brigade in the early part of the expedition under James Clinton, against the Indian settlements of western N. Y. in 1779. 4°. '65. $3 .... *Sabin.*

Blending lights. Fraser, W. $2..*Am. Tr.; Carter.*

Blenkarn, J: Practical specifications of works in architecture, engineering, and in road making and sewering; [with] ser. of agreements and reports. 15 pl. 8°. $9.......................... *Baird.*

Blenkinsop, Ma. *See* Stokes, W. H., *and* Blenkinsop, M.

Blennerhasset papers (The). Safford, W. H. $3.50. *Wilstach.*

Blessings in disguise. Sheddan, S. S. 50c... *Pres. Bd.*

Blessings of an open Bible. Milner, V. W. $1.75. *J. E. Potter.*

Blessington, *Countess.* [Marg. Power Gardiner.] Country quarters. 12°. $1.75; pap., $1.50. *Peterson.*

— Ella Stratford; or, the orphan child. 8°. pap., 50c. *Peterson.*

Blessner, G. Flora sacra. [Church music.] ill. 8°. $1.75; bds., $1.38.................... *Gordon.*

Blighted being. Taylor, T. 15c............ *French.*

Blighted flower (The); tr. by Mrs. J. Sadlier. 16°. 50c.; 75c. .... *Sadlier.*

Blind Agnes. Caddell, C. M. 50c........... *Strong.*

Blind Alice. *See* New juvenile lib.

Blind Amos and his velvet principles. *See* Hood, E. P.

Blind Annie Lorimer; by author of "George Miller and his mother." 18°. 65c........... *Pres. Bd.*

Blind bargain. Reynolds, F. 15c........... *French.*

Blind Bartimeus. Hoge, W. J. 50c......... *Am. Tr.*

Blind basket-maker lib. *See* Charlesworth, M. L.

Blind beggar. 32°. 20c.; 15c............... *Dutton.*

Blind beggars (The). Offenbach, J. 40c..... *French.*

Blind Betsy. *See* Blind man and peddler.

Blind boy. Kenney, J. 15c................ *French.*

— *See also* French's serio-comic dramas.

Blind boy (The). *See* Flower transplanted (The).

Blind Cecilia. *See* History of Mary and Lucy Gutzlaff.

Blind Effie's trial. *See* New holiday lib.

Blind Ethan. Grosvenor, H. S. 30c. .... *Hoyt.*

Blind farmer (The) and his children. *See* Hofland, *Mrs.* B.

Blind Florette. Parker, H. F. $1.25.... *Cong. Pub.*

Blind girl (The), and other tales. Embury, E. C. 75c. .... *Harper.*

Blind girl of Wittenberg. *See* Wildenhahn, C. A.

Blind Graham. Perry, S. A. 90c........ *Cong. Pub.*

Blind grandfather, and other stories. 18°. 50c. *O'Shea.*

Blind Jakey. Dotey, C. 60c. .... *Lothrop.*

Blind Jessie; by author of "Diamonds re-set." ('66.) New ed. ill. 16°. '75. $1 .... *Hoyt.*

Blind John Netherway. ('67.) New ed. ill. 16°. '74. $1 .... *Hoyt.*

Blind Lilias; or, fellowship with God. 18°. 75c. *Carter; Dutton.*

Blind little Lucy. 18°. 25c. .... *Am. S. S.*

Blind man (The) and peddler; [also] Blind Betsy; or, comfort for the afflicted. 18°. 35c.... *Pres. Bd.*

Blind man's cottage. Provine, J. C. 50c. (?) *Cumberland.*

Blind man's holiday. 18°. 75c............... *Carter.*

Blind Nellie's boy. Arthur, T. S. $1.... *Perkinpine.*

Blind princess. Denison, M. A. $1........... *Hoyt.*

Blind Ruth; or, how may I do good? 18°. 35c. *Pres. Bd.*

Blind Tom. 18°. 90c. .... (?) *Martien.*

Blind William. *See* Riedel, G.

Blinde Knabe (Der). Nieritz, G. 25c....... *Steiger.*

Blinde Wilhelm (Der). *See* Riedel, G.

Blinden (Die). *See* Heyse, P.

Blindpits. Taylor, E. $1.75............... *Putnam.*

Blinks and Jinks: Ethiop. drama. 16°. pap., 15c. *French.*

Blinn, Leroy J. Practical workshop companion for tin, sheet-iron, and copper plate workers; with tables and ill. ('64.) 15th ed. 12°. '76. $2.50. *Baird.*

Bliss, *Mrs.* —. Practical cook book. ('50.) New ed. 12°. '75. $1.25 .... *Claxton.*

Bliss, Flo. ["Cousin Florrie."] Christ, or the world, which? 16°. '70. 90c. .... *Dutton.*

Bliss, Fk. C. Citizen's manual. 16°. '72. *$1. *F. C. Bliss.*

— Our country and government for 100 years. ill. 16°. '76. *$1; $1.25 .... *F. C. Bliss.*

— *See also* Hyde, A., Bliss, F. C., *and* Tyler, J.

Bliss, G: Treatise on the law of life insurance, with chapters on accident and guarantee insurance. 2d ed. 8°. shp., $6.50 .... *Baker, V. & Co.*

Bliss, Orville J. Three months in the Orient. 12°. '75. $1.25 .... *Griggs.*

Bliss, P. P. Charm (The). [S.-school music.] 16°. 35c. .... *Church.*

— Gospel songs. [S.-school music.] 12°. 50c.; bds., 35c.; mor., $1.50 .... *Church.*

— Joy (The). [Singing book.] 8°. 75c. .... *Church.*

— Song tree (The). [Collection of music.] 4°. $2.25; bds., $1.75 .... *Church.*

— Sunshine. [S.-school music.] sq. 16°. 35c. .. *Church.*

— *and* Sankey, Ira D. Gospel hymns and sacred songs. 12°. 35c. .... *Church.*

— — *Same.* 32°. '75. 10c.; — with music. 8°. '75. 25c.–$1.25 .... *Biglow.*

Bliss, W: R. Paradise in the Pacific: book of travel, adventure and facts in the Sandwich Islands. 16°. $1.25 .... *Sheldon.*

Blithedale romance (The). *See* Hawthorne, N.

Blithewood library. 3 v. 16°. $4.50 ... (?) *Martien.*
Cont.: Chubbs, jr. — The Langham revels. — Judge Branard's infantry.

Blitz, Antonio. Fifty years in the magic circle. por. and ill. 12°. '71. *$2 .... *Belknap.*

Blockade (The) of Phalsburg. Erckmann, E., *and* Chatrian, A. $1.25; 75c. .... *Scribner.*

Blockhaus (Das) in dem Berge. *See* Chesebro', *Miss* C.

Blodget, Lorim. Climatology of the U. S. and of the temperate latitudes of North America; with charts. roy. 8°. '57. $5 .. *Claxton; Lippincott.*

Blois, L: de. *See* Blosius, L: de.

Blondin (Der) v. Namur. *See* Zschokke, H.

Blood (The) and breath. Frobisher, J. E. 50c.; 25c. .... *Goodyear.*

Blood of the cross. Bonar, H. 40c. .... (?) *Martien.*

Blood of Jesus. *See* Reid, W.

Bloodgood, S. De Witt. The sexagenary; or, reminiscences of the Am. rev. of Schuyler, Burgoyne and Harriet Ackland. por. 8°. '66. $3. *Munsell.*

Bloody tenent (The) of persecution. Williams, R. $8; $10 .... *Tibbitts.*

Bloody tenent (The) yet more bloody. Williams, R. $8; $10 .... *Tibbitts.*

Bloom and brier. Falconer, W. $1.50 ..... *Claxton.*

Bloom of youth. Belcher, J. 40c. .... *Am. Tr.*

Bloomer, J. G. Commercial cryptograph: a telegraph code and double index-holocryptic cipher. 8°. $5 .... *Appleton.*

Bloomer costume. Stirling, E. 15c. .... *French.*

Bloomfield, Rob. Poems. ill. 16°. $1.75 .. *Routledge.*

— *Same.* (Household ser.) ill. 16°. $1.50; mor., $3. *Lee & S.*

— — *See also* British pocket classics.

— Farmer's boy, and other poems. 32°. 60c.; 90c.; mor., $1.50 .... *Porter.*

— *Same.* ill. 12°. '75. $1.25 .... *Putnam.*

Bloomfield, S. T. *See* Bible, New Test., *Greek.*

Bloomfield. Warren, E. $1.50 .... *Lothrop.*

Bloor, A. J. Paper on mansard roofs. *See* American Inst. of Arch.

Blosius, L: de. Oratory of the faithful soul; tr. by R. A. Coffin. 18°. 50c. .... *Cath. Pub.*

Bloss, C. A. Ancient history; ed. by J. I. Anderson. ('72.) New ed. ill., maps and chart. 12°. '76. $2 .... *Clark & M.*

Bloss, G: M. D. Historic and literary miscellany. 12°. '75. $2.50 .... *Clarke.*

Blossom of Churnington Green. Hoskins, F. R. 15c. *French.*

Blossoming of an aloe. Hoey, C. 50c. ...... *Harper.*

Blossoms and fruits. 18°. 40c. ... *U. P. Bd. of Pub.*

Blossoms in the desert. 18°. 17c.; 22c. .. *Am. Bapt.*

Blossoms of childhood. 18°. 50c. .... *Dutton.*

Blossoms of piety. 18°. 30c.; 40c. ...... *Am. Bapt.*

Blot, François René. In heaven we know our own; tr. from the French. 18°. 60c. ...... *Cath. Pub.*

Blot, Pierre. Handbook of practical cookery; for ladies and profess. cooks. 12°. $1.75 .. *Appleton.*

— How to cook the potato. *See* Compton, D. H., Cultivation of the potato.

Blot on the queen's head. Jenkins, E. 25c. (?) *Routledge.*

Blount, Marg. Clifford and the actress; or, the reigning favorite. 8°. pap., 50c. .... *Peterson.*

— Pride (The) of the downes. 8°. pap., 25c. .. *Beadle.*

Blount family (The). Brown, T. $1.50 .... *Lothrop.*

Blow (A) at the root of Antinomianism. Flavel, J. 25c. .... *Pres. Bd.*

Blow for blow. Byron, H. J. 15c. .. *De Witt; French.*

Bloxam, C. L. Chemistry, inorganic and organic. ill. 8°. $4; leath., $5 .... *Lea.*

— *Same.* ill. 8°. $4.50; leath., $5.50 ...... *Lindsay.*

— Laboratory teaching; or, progressive exercises in practical chemistry. 3d ed. ill. cr. 8°. $2. *Lindsay.*

— Metals: their properties and treatment. ill. 12°. $1.50 .... *Appleton.*

Blue and cherry. Leland, O. S. 15c. ...... *Lee & S.*

Blue and gold poets. 6 v. 32°. ea., $1.25 .. *Widdleton.*
Cont.: Poe. — Praed, 2 v. — Tupper, 2 v. — Tupper's Proverbial philosophy.

— *See also* Green and gold; — Miniature.

Blue and gold series. 27 v. 32°. ea., $1.25 .. *Osgood.*
Cont.: Mrs. Akers' Poems. — Emerson's Poems. — Emerson's Essays. — Holmes' Poems. — Longfellow's Poems, 2 v. — Longfellow's Prose works, 2 v. — Longfellow's Christus. — Lowell's Poems, 2 v. — Owen Meredith's Poems, 2 v. — Owen Meredith's New poems. — Owen Meredith's Lucile. — Miss Muloch's Poems. — Percival's Poems, 2 v. — Procter's Poems. — Saxe's Poems — Taylor's Poems. — Tennyson's Poems, 2 v. — Tennyson's Enoch Arden. — Whittier's Poems, 2 v.

Blue and red light. Pancoast, S. $2 .. *J. M. Stoddart.*

Blue band. Braddon, M. E. 50c. .... *De Witt.*

Blue Beard. Byron, H. J. 15c. .... *French.*

Blue Beard. Colman, G., *jr.* 15c. .... *French.*

Blue Beard. Heber, B. 15c. .... *French.*

Blue Beard. Keating, E. H. 15c. .... *French.*

Blue Beard. Planché, J. R., *and* Dance, C. 15c. *French.*

Blue Beard: juv. drama. 16°. pap., 40c. .... *French.*

Blue Beard; or, female curiosity: burlesque. 16°. pap., 15c. .... *Happy.*

Blue Beard repaired. Bellingham, H. 15c. .. *French.*

Blue Beard's keys. Thackeray, A. I. 75c. .. *Harper.*

Blue bell (The) of Red-Neap. Parr, L. $1 .. *Routledge.*

Blue bell series. 6 v. ill. sq. 16°. $4.50 ...... *Nelson.*
Cont.: Pretty tales. — Aunt Agnes. — Little Frank. — Sunday afternoons. — Pay your debts. — Watts' Songs.

Blue bird. *See* Our song birds.

Blue-book stories. Woods, H. F. 70c. .. *Bost. Am. Tr.*

Blue devils. Colman, G., *jr.* 15c. .... *French.*

Blue-eyed Jimmy. Monmouth, L. H. $1 .. *Lothrop.*

Blue-eyed witch. Egan, P. 50c. ....*De Witt.*

Blue flag. Baker, S. S. 60c...............*Am. Tr.*

Blue jacket series. 6 v. ill. 12°. ea., $1.50..*Lee & S.*
Cont.: Swiss Family Robinson. — Willis, the pilot — Prairie Crusoe. — Gulliver's travels. — Arctic Crusoe. — Young Crusoe.

Blue jackets. Stirling, E. 15c.............*French.*

Blue laws. *See* Connecticut, Code of 1650.

Blue ribbon. Tabor, E. 50c...............*Harper.*

Blue shawl. 16°. 75c. ....*Cong. Pub.*

Blue shawl series. 6 v. 16°. $5.50.......*Cong. Pub.*
Cont.: Blue shawl. — Faith Duncan, by J. E. Cutter. — Mother's ship. — Margaret and Bessie, by Mary L. Savage. — Rescued girl. — Marion's little sister, by Jennie M. Drinkwater.

Blue socks. Guernsey, L. E. 65c.........*Am. S. S.*

Blue umbrella. Hamilton, K. W. 70c.......*Pres. Bd.*

Blue violet. *See* Clark, *Mrs.* M. L.

Blue violet series. 12 v. 18°. $4.80........*Lothrop.*
Comprises Fair play ser. *and* May-flower ser.

Blueberrying. *See* Abbott, J., Rollo story books.

Blueskin baffled; or, the highwayman's traps. 8°. pap., 25c. ....*Dick & F.*

Blueskin series. 2 nos. 8°. ea., pap., 25c...*De Witt.*
Cont.: Blueskin. — Turpin in danger.

Bluff cragg. *See* Cupples, *Mrs.* A. J.

Blum, Jos. Das Leben des Papst Pius IX. 12°. '76. $1..............................*Benziger.*

Blumengarten (Der). [Tales.] 3 v. 24°. ea., 20c. *Ev. Assoc.*

Blumenkörbchen (Das). *See* Schmid, C. v.

Blumenstiel, A. The bankrupt law as it is, and the effect of the recent amendment; with the act of June 22, 1874. 8°. '74. pap., 25c... *Ward & P.*

Blumenstrauss (Ein) von Geschichten. 18°. 30c. *Ev. Assoc.*

Blunders in behavior corrected. 16°. 10c...*Dick & F.*

Blunders (The) of vice and folly. Hargreave, J. G. $2 ....*Routledge.*

Blunt, E. K. The Christ born: a Christmas story. 18°. 40c..........................*Lippincott.*

Blunt, H: History of the seven churches in Asia. 12°. 75c. ....*McCauley.*

— Parochial sermons. 12°. $1...........*McCauley.*

Blunt, J: H: Annotated Book of common prayer. imp. 8°. $12......................*Lippincott.*

— *Same.* 8°. '69. *net,* $10.................*Dutton.*

— *Same.* (Compendious ed.) sm. 8°. '76. $3.50. *Dutton; Pott.*

— Companion to the Old Test.: comment. on Scripture hist. to birth of our Lord. 12°. $1.50..*Lippincott.*

— Doctrine of the Church of England, 1536-1662. 8°. '68. $3.25...........................*Pott.*

— Household theology: handbook of religious instruction respecting the Bible, Prayer book, the Church, etc.; with an Am. introd. 16°. '72. $1.25..*Pott.*

— Key to Christian doct. and practice, founded on the Church catechism. 16°. $1........*Lippincott.*

— *Same.* 16°. '72. $1.25....................*Pott.*

— Key to the knowledge and use of the Book of common prayer. 16°. $1..................*Lippincott.*

— *Same.* 16°. '72. $1........................*Pott.*

— Key to the knowledge and use of the Holy Bible. 16°. $1 ....*Lippincott.*

— *Same.* 16°. '73. $1........................*Pott.*

— *Same;* [also] Key to the four Gospels, by J. P. Norris. 12°. $1.50..........................*Lippincott.*

— Key to the knowledge of Church hist. 2 v. 16°. ea., $1 ....*Lippincott; Pott.*

— Plain account of the English Bible. sq. 16°. '69. $1. *Dutton.*

— Reformation of the Church of Eng.: its hist., principles and results, [1514-1547]. 8°. '74. $4..*Pott.*

— (*ed.*) Dictionary of doctrinal and hist. theology. imp. 8°. $10.........................*Lippincott.*

— Dictionary of sects, heresies and schools of thought. imp. 8°. $10.........................*Lippincott.*

Blunt, J: Ja. Coincidences in Old and New Testament; with Paley's Horæ Paulinæ. 12°. $1.50. *Carter.*

— Sketch of the reformation in Eng. ill. 16°. $1.50. *Pott.*

Blut (Das) Jesu. *See* Reid, W.

Blüthen der neuen engl. u. amerik. Poesie. Nöroth, J. $1.25; 75c.........................*Schoenhof.*

Blüthen u. Früchte: Erzählungen f. d. Jugend. 8 v. 32°. ea., bds., 15c..................*Brumder.*

Blutige Schauplatz (Der). Braght, T. J. v. 4°. leath., $6 ....*Baer.*

Blydenburgh, J. W. Treatise on law of usury; with the statutes of the several states, digest of Am. decisions, and index to reported Eng. cases. 8°. shp., $3.50....................*Baker, V. & Co.*

Boaden, Caro. Fatality: drama. 16°. pap., 15c. *French.*

— First of April: farce. 16°. pap., 15c.......*French.*

Board and residence. Edwards, C. 15c......*French.*

Boarding house. Beazley, S. 15c...........*French.*

Boarding out; or, domestic life. Hale, S. J. 75c. *Harper.*

Boarding school. Bernard, W. B. 15c.*French; Happy.*

Boarding school days. *See* Gordon, C.

Boarding school girl. Tuthill, L. C. 65c...*Perkinpine.*

Boardman, A. Defence of phrenology. 12°. '47. $1.25 ....*Wells.*

Boardman, H: A. Bible (The) in the counting-house. 12°. $1..........................*Lippincott.*

— Bible (The) in the family. 12°. $1.....*Lippincott.*

— Christian ministry (The) not a priesthood. [Sermon.] 18°. 35c..........................*Pres. Bd.*

— Doctrine of election neither derogatory to God nor discouraging to man. 18°. 40c.......*Pres. Bd.*

— Great question (The): will you consider the subject of personal religion? 18°. '67. 65c. *Am. S. S.; N. Y. Ref. Ch. Bd.; Pres. Com.*

— Hymns of praise. 4th ed. 16°. roan, $1.25. *Lippincott.*

— Treatise on the Scripture doctrine of original sin; with notes. 18°. 40c...............*Pres. Bd.*

Boardman, *Mrs.* M. M. Boardman library (The). ('66-'67.) New ed. 4 v. ill. 16°. '70-'72. ea., $1.25 ....*Perkinpine.*
Cont.: Haps and mishaps of the Brown family. — The sister's triumph. — Nellie Gates and the little missionary. — The mother-in-law.

— Isaac Phelps, the widow's son; or, the rugged way made smooth. ('71.) New ed. 16°. '73. $1.25. *Hoyt.*

— Who shall publish the glad tidings? 16°. 75c. *Willard.*

— *Same.* 16°. '73. 85c......................*Hoyt.*

Boardman, W: E. Faith work under Dr. Cullis in Boston. 12°. $1 ....*Willard.*

— Gladness in Jesus. 16°. 75c.............*Willard.*

— He that overcometh; or, a conquering Gospel. 12°. $1.50.................................*Hoyt.*

— Higher Christian life (The). ('60.) New ed. 12°. '76. $1.50...........................*Hoyt.*

— In the power of the Spirit. 16°. $1...... *Willard.*

Boat (The) and the drowned officer. Tonna, C. E. 30c. *Pres. Bd.*

Boat-builder's (The) family. Mudge, Z. A. $1.25. *Lothrop.*

Boat-club series. *See* Adams, W. T.

Boat life in Egypt and Nubia. Prime, W. C. $2; $3.75. *Harper.*

Boatman's daughter. Barrett, A. 50c......*So. Meth.*

Bob, the bootblack. *See* Books about boys who fought and won.

Bob Brierly; or, the ticket-of-leave man. 8°. pap., 25c. *De Witt.*

Bob, the crossing-sweeper. *See* Sunshine and shadow lib.

Bob Saybrook; or, faithful unto death. 18°. 65c. *Cong. Pub.*

Bob, the shoe black. *See* Gem cluster.

Bob Tinker. Wyeth, M. E. C. 60c.........*Am. Tr.*

Bob Walker. Dunning, A. K. 35c........*Pres. Bd.*

Bobbin boy: life of N. P. Banks. 12°. $1.50..*Tilton.*

Bobby A 1: farce. 16°. pap., 15c..........*French.*

Bobby, the schoolmaster; or, our little canary bird. 18°. 25c..........................*Am. S. S.*

Bobby's teeth. *See* Swallow stories.

Bobin, I: Letters of B., private secretary of George Clarke, secretary of the province of N. Y., 1718–'30. sm. 8°. '72. $3..................*Munsell.*

Boccaccio, Gi. Decameron; tr. by W. K. Kelly. 12°. $1.40; hf. cf., $3................*Appleton.*
— — *Same.* 12°. (Bohn.) $1.25....*Little, B. & Co.*
— — *Same.* 12°. (Bohn.) $1.40..*Scribner, W. & A.*
— — *Same.* 12°. (Bohn.) $1.50........*Lippincott.*
— — *Same.* por. and ill. by L. Flameng. cr. 8°. '76. $3.75..................................*Gebbie.*
— *Same;* tr., with introd., by T. Wright. ill. 12°. $3. *Routledge; Scribner, W. & A.*
— Fables and tales. *See* Dryden, J.

Bôcher, F. Progressive French reader, with vocab. and notes. ('70.) New ed. 12°. '76. $1.50..*Holt.*

Bochsa, N. C: Instructions for the harp. f°. bds., $3.50 ....*Ditson.*

Bocock, J. A. God's word to inquirers; with introd. by Rev. W. S. White. 18°. 25c......*Pres. Bd.*

Bodemann, Th., *and* Kerl, Bru. Treatise on the assaying of lead, silver, copper, gold and mercury; tr. by W. A. Goodyear. 12°. $2.50...... *Wiley.*

Bodenhamer, W: Physical exploration of the rectum; with app. on the ligation of hæmorrhoidal tumors. ill. 8°. $1.25.......................... *W. Wood.*
— Practical observations on the ætiology, pathology, diagnosis and treatment of anal fissure. ill. 8°. $2.25.................................. *W. Wood.*
— Practical treatise on the ætiology, pathology and treatment of the congenital malformations of the rectum and anus. ill. 8°. $4......... *W. Wood.*

Body and mind. *See* Maudsley, H.

Body politic. Barnes, W. H. $1.50....... *Wilstach.*

Boehm, H: Reminiscences, historical and biographical, of sixty-four years in the ministry; ed. by Rev. J. B. Wakeley. New ed., rev. and enl. 12°. '65. $1.75..........................*Meth. Bk. Conc.*

Boenninghausen, C. Essay on the homœop. treatment of intermittent fever; tr. and ed. by C. J. Hempel. 8°. 50c.........................*Boericke.*
— Homœopathic therapeia of intermittent and other fevers; tr. and enl. by A. Korndörfer. 8°. $2.25. *Boericke.*
— The sides of the body and drug affinities: homœopathic exercises; tr. and ed. by J. C. Hempel. 12°. pap., 25c..........................*Boericke.*

Boero, Jos. Life of the blessed Mary Ann of Jesus de paredes y flores, called the Lily of Quito; tr. 16°. $1...............*Cunningham; Sadlier.*

Boethius, A. M. T. S. Consolation of philosophy: in Anglo-Saxon, with the A.-S. metres and Eng. tr. by S. Fox. 12°. (Bohn.) $1.75. *Little, B. & Co.*
— *Same.* 12°. (Bohn.) $2. *Lippincott; Scribner, W. & A.*

Bogardus, A. H. Field, cover and trap-shooting; ed. by C. J. Foster. ('74.) New ed. ill. 12°. '75. $2......................................*Ford.*

Bogart, W. H. Life of Daniel Boone, and the hunters of Kentucky, the pioneers of the west. ill. 12°. $1.50..................................*Lee & S.*

Bogatzky, C: H: v. Golden treasury for the children of God; tr. 32°. 75c.; mor., $1.50....*Nelson.*
— *Same.* 32°. '50. 60c.; 75c.; mor., $2....*Am. Tr.*
— *Same.* 24°. 75c..........................*Carter.*

Bogatzky, C: H: v., *continued.*
— *Same.* 16°. $1.25. 32°. 50c.; bds., 40c...*Routledge.*
— *Same;* tr. by C. W. Schäffer. 16°. $1; $1.25. (?)*Luth. Pub.*

Boggs, Ja. Resurrection of the redeemed; [also] Hades. 12°. $1.25....................*Lippincott.*

Boggs, *Mrs.* Mar. L. Elsie and Minnie; or, teachings for young Christians. 16°. $1.50....*Cong. Pub.*
— The Huntingdons. 16°. '63. $1.25..*H. A. Young.*

Bogue, D: La divina autoridad del Nuevo Testamento. 18°. '42. 45c.............................*Am. Tr.*
— Theological lectures; ed. by Rev. J. S. C. F. Frey. 8°. $2.50..............................*Harper.*
— Versuch über das göttliche Ansehn des N. Testaments. 18°. '42. 60c..........................*Am. Tr.*

Bogus Injun (The). White, C. 15c........*De Witt.*

Bohemian Brothers *or* Brethren. *See* Moravians.

Bohemian girl. *See* Balfe, M. W.

Bohemian girl: opera. 16°. pap., 15c.......*French.*

Bohemian martyrs: sketches of John Huss and Jerome of Prague. 18°. 40c............*Pres. Bd.*

Bohemians in the 15th century; tr. by Mrs. J. Sadlier. 16°. 60c.; $1.......................*Sadlier.*

Bohemians (The) of London. Whitty, E. M. $1.75; $1.50.................................*Peterson.*

Bohm, E. Die Sonntagsschule. [Evang.-luth.] 7 v. 16°. '71. bds.........................*Steiger.*

Cont.: Erster Cursus, 15c. — Zweiter, 20c. — Dritter, 18c. — Vierter, 20c. — Fünfter, 20c. — Sechster, sieb. u. achter, 20c. — Leitfaden f. Lehrer, 12c.

— (*ed.*) Katechismus [luth.] u. Sprüche, Lieder u. Gebete, sowie d. Perikopen d. Kirchenjahrs. 16°. '71. bds., 30c..........................*Steiger.*
— *See also* Zahn, F. L., Zweimal 25 bibl. Geschichten.

Böhmische Mägdekrieg (Der). *See* Van der Velde, K. F.

Böhmischen Amazonen (Die). *See* Van der Velde, K. F.

Bohn H: G. Papers on fishing tackle. *See* Walton, I., *and* Cotton, C., Complete angler.
— (*ed.*) Chronicles of the crusades. 12°. (Bohn.) $1.75..........................*Little, B. & Co.*

Cont.: Chronicle of Richard of Devizes, conc. deeds of Richard, 1189–'92; Geoffry de Vinsauf's Chronicle of Richard I., 1187–'92; De Joinville's Memoirs of Louis IX., 1226–'71.

— *Same.* 12°. (Bohn.) $2.......*Scribner, W. & A.*
— Guide to the knowledge of pottery and porcelain; with eng. list of marks and monograms. ill. 12°. (Bohn.) $1.75; col. ill., $3.75..*Little, B. & Co.*
— *Same.* ill. 12°. (Bohn.) $2; col. ill., $4.20. *Scribner, W. & A.*
— *Same.* ill. 12°. (Bohn.) $2.50; col. ill., $4.25. *Lippincott.*
— Handbook of games. 12°. (Bohn.) $1.75. *Little, B. & Co.*
— *Same.* 12°. (Bohn.) $2. *Lippincott; Scribner, W. & A.*
— Handbook of proverbs; compr. Ray's English proverbs, with add. [from] all lang.; with index. 12°. (Bohn.) $1.75..................*Little, B. & Co.*
— *Same.* 12°. (Bohn.) $2. *Lippincott; Scribner, W. & A.*
— *Same.* 12°. (Bohn.) hf. cf., $4........*Appleton.*
— Polyglot of foreign proverbs; with Eng. tr. and index. 12°. (Bohn.) $1.75......*Little, B. & Co.*
— *Same.* 12°. (Bohn.) $2. *Lippincott; Scribner, W. & A.*

Bohn libraries. *See* names of individual authors.

Bohne (Die). *See* Zschokke, H.

Boileau-Despreaux, N: Œuvres poétiques. 12°. (Paris.) $1.50...............*G. R. Lockwood.*

Boise, Ja. R. Exercises in Gk. prose compos. 12°. $1.50 ....*Appleton.*
— Exercises in Gk. syntax. ('74.) New ed. 12°. '75. hf. leath., $1.50..........................*Griggs.*

oise, Ja. R., *continued.*
- First lessons in Greek. ('70.) New ed., rev. 12°. '75. hf. leath., $1.25 .... *Griggs.*
- *and* Freeman, J: C. (*ed.*) Selections from Gk. authors; with notes and ref. ('72.) 3d ed. 12°. '75. $2.50 .... *Griggs.*

oissy, Teresa Gamba (*Marquise*) de [*formerly Contessa* Guiccioli]. My recollections of Lord Byron and those of eye-witnesses of his life; tr. by H. E. H. Jerningham. 12°. $1.75 .... *Harper.*

ojesen, E. F., *and* Arnold, T. K. Manual of Grecian and Roman antiquities. 12°. $2 .. *Appleton.*

oke of St. Albans. *See* Berners, J., Treatyse of fysshynge wyth an angle.

oker, G: H. Anne Boleyn: burlesque. 16°. pap., 15c .... *French.*
- Calaynos: tragedy. 16°. pap., 15c .... *French.*
- Königsmark, The legend of the hounds, and other poems. 12°. $1.75 .... *Lippincott.*
- Plays and poems. 3d ed. 2 v. 12°. $4 .. *Lippincott.*
- Poems of the war. 12°. $1.50 .... *Lippincott.*

okum, Hm. The Tennessee handbook and immigrant's guide. map. 12°. $1; pap., 50c .... *Lippincott.*

oland, J. M. High-churchism run mad; or, the fruits of close-communion. 12°. '76. pap., 10c. *So. Meth.*

olanden, Conr. de (*pseud.*) *See* Bischoff, Jos. E:

Bold as a lion. Strong, J. D. 30c .... *Lothrop.*

Bold dragoons. Barnett, M. 15c .... *French.*

Bold stroke for a husband. Cowley, H. 15c. *French.*

Bold stroke for a wife. Centlivre, S. 15c .... *French.*

Bolívar, Sim. Correspondencia general; con los manifiestos, mensages, exposiciones, etc., publicados por el heroe Colombiano, 1810-'30. v. 1, 2: Vida de Bolívar, por Felipe Larrazábal. 2 v. por. 8°. '71. $6 .... *Jenkins.*

Boller, A. P. Central Ave. bridge, Newark, N. J. *See* Thurston, R. H., Strength of materials.
- Practical notes on the construction of iron highway bridges. pl. 8°. '76. $2.50 .... *Wiley.*
- Wrought iron bridge, Bridgeport, Conn. 8°. pap., 85c .... *Am. Soc. of C. E.*

Bolles, Alb. S. Chapters on political economy. 12°. $1.50 .... *Appleton.*
- Conflict between labor and capital. 12°. $1.50. *Lippincott.*

Bolles, Ja. A. American church catholic (The). 12°. pap., 12c .... *Dutton.*
- Confirmation explained and defended. 16°. pap., 10c. *Dutton.*
- Holy matrimony. 12°. '70. $1 .... *Williams.*
- Rector's vade mecum: manual for pastoral use. 18°. '62. $1.25; mor., $3 .... *Dutton.*

Bolley, P. A. Manual of technical analysis; founded upon the "Handbuch" of Bolley, by B. H. Paul. 12°. (Bohn.) $1.75 .... *Little, B. & Co.*
- *Same.* 12°. (Bohn.) $2. *Lippincott; Scribner, W. & A.*

Bolling, R. Memoirs of the Bolling family (and Randolphs); tr. from the French by J. Robertson. por. sm. 4°. '68. pap., $15 .... *J. W. Randolph.*

Bolling, R. R. Bolling's guide to public officers. 8°. '72. shp., $2 .... *Bolling.*

Bolmar, A. Book of French verbs. 12°. $1. *Sheldon.*
- Colloquial phrases. 16°. 75c .... *Sheldon.*
- *See also* Fenelon, F. de S. de L., Adventures of Telemaque; — Levizac, J. P. V., French gram.

Bolster, W: W. Tax collector and form book. 8°. '71. shp., $4.50 .... *Dresser.*

Bölte, Amely. Madame de Stäel: an hist. novel; tr. by T. Johnston. 16°. '69. $1.50 ...... *Putnam.*

Bolton, C. Caught in a line: farce. 16°. pap., 15c. *French.*

Bolton, *Rev.* Ja. Favored colt. 18°. 40c ... *Whittaker.*

Bolton, *Rev.* Ja. J. The golden missionary penny, and other addresses. ill. 12°. $1.25 .... *Nelson.*

Bolton, Sa. Knowles. The present problem: story of the temperance movement. 12°. '74. $1. *Putnam.*

Boltwood, H. L. Grammar and how to teach it; for common and graded schools. ('71.) New ed. 12°. '76. 60c .... *Sherwood.*

Bolzius, J. M. *See* Reck, P. G. F. v., *and* Bolzius, J. M.

Bomard, C: A fatal passion. 12°. $1.75 .... *Carleton.*

Bombastes furioso. Rhodes, W. B. 15c .... *French.*

Bombaugh, C. C. (*ed.*) Book of blunders. 16°. $1. *Souder.*
— Gleanings for the curious from the harvest-fields of literature. 12°. $2; pap., $1.25 .... *Miller.*
— *Same.* ill. roy. 8°. '75. *$3.50; $4; $5. *Lloyd; A. D. Worthington.*
— Literature of kissing. 12°. $1.75; $2.50. *Lippincott.*

Bomberger, J. H. A. Infant baptism. 12°. 50c. *Ref. Ch. Pub.*

Bommer, G. Method of manure-making. 12°. 25c. *Judd.*

Bompas, H. *See* England, Law reports.

Bon Gaultier (*pseud.*) *See* Martin, T., *and* Aytoun, W. E.

Bona fide travellers. Brough, W. 15c .... *French.*

Bona mors: a pious association of the devout servants of Jesus Christ, dying on the cross, in order to obtain a good death. 24°. 25c .... *Cath. Pub.*

Bonaldi, F: Exercises for soprano; — for contralto. 4°. ea., 70c .... *Church.*
— Progressive vocal studies. f°. 70c .... *Gordon.*
— Six progressive studies for vocalization: soprano and contralto. f°. pap., 80c .... *Brainard; Ditson.*
— *Same.* 2 pts. 4°. ea., pap., 75c ..... *G. D. Russell.*

Bonaparte, C: Lucien. [*Prince of* Canino.] American ornithology. *See* Wilson, Alex.

Bonaparte, Nap. *See* Napoleon.

Bonar, A. R. Last days of Christian martyrs. 18°. 50c .... *U. P. Bd. of Pub.*

Bonar, And. A. Memoir and remains of Rev. R. M. McCheyne; with introd. by Rev. S. Miller. por. 12°. $1 .... *Pres. Bd.*
— Visitor's book of texts. 16°. $1.50 .... *Carter.*

Bonar, Horatius. Bible thoughts and themes. 5 v. 12°. ea., $2 .... *Carter.*

Cont.: Old Test. — Gospels. — Acts. — Lesser epistles. — Revelations.

— Blood of the cross. 24°. 40c .... (?) *Martien.*
— Christ (The) of God. 16°. $1.25 .... *Carter.*
— Earth's morning: thoughts on Genesis. 12°. $2. *Carter.*
— Eternal day. 18°. 75c .... *Carter.*
— Everlasting righteousness. 16°. $1.25 ...... *Carter.*
— Follow the Lamb. 18°. 40c .... *Carter.*
— God's way of holiness. 18°. 60c .... *Carter.*
— God's way of peace. 18°. 50c .... *Carter.*
— *Same.* 18°. '66. 50c. *N. Y. Ref. Ch. Bd.; Pres. Com.*
— *Same.* 18°. 55c .... *Pres. Bd.*
— *Portug.* O caminho da paz. 18°. '69. 25c. *Am. Tr.*
— Hymns of faith and hope. 3 v. 18°. $2.25. 16°. $3. *Carter.*
— Life of Rev. John Milne. 12°. $2 .... *Carter.*
— Looking to the cross. 24°. 40c .... (?) *Martien.*
— Morning of joy. 18°. 60c .... *Carter.*
— Night of weeping. 18°. 50c .... *Carter.*
— *Same.* 18°. '66. 50c. *N. Y. Ref. Ch. Bd.; Pres. Com.*
— Rent veil (The). 16°. $1.25 .... *Carter.*
— Song of the new creation. 16°. $1.25 ...... *Carter.*
— Word (The) of promise: handbook to the promise of Scripture. 16°. $1 .... *Bost. Am. Tr.*
— Words to the winners of souls. 18°. '67. 40c. *N. Y. Ref. Ch. Bd.; Pres. Com.*

Bonaventura, *St.* [John of Fidanza *or* Fidenza.] Life of Christ; [also] Devotion to the three hours; [also] Agony of our Lord on the cross; [also] Life of St. Joseph. 18°. '52. $1; $1.25...*Murphy.*
— *See also* Catholic anecdotes.
Bonawitz, J. H. Bride of Messina. [Opera.] f°. '74. $5...*Ditson.*
— — *See also* Ditson.
— Ostrolenka. [Opera.] f°. $5...*Ditson.*
— — *See also* Ditson.
Bonbons. Baker, G. M. 25c...*Lee & S.*
Boncœur, L. L'instructeur de l'enfance. ('64.) New ed. 12°. '70. 90c...*Holt.*
Bond, A. L. Child's natural hist.; in words of four letters. 16°. 50c...*Routledge.*
— Leaves from a Christmas bough. ill. sm. 4°. $3. *Routledge.*
Bond, Beverly W. Principles and facts of missions. 12°. '74. pap., 15c...*So. Meth.*
Bond, G. P. Account of the great comet of 1858. *See* Harvard Coll. Astron. Observ.
— Observations upon the great nebula of Orion. *See* Harvard Coll. Astron. Obser.
Bond, H: Genealogies of the families and descendants of the early settlers of Watertown, Mass., incl. Waltham and Weston; [with] early hist. of the town. ('55.) 2d ed., with memoir of author by H. G. Jones. ill., maps and notes. 2 v. in 1. 8°. '60. $6...*N. E. Hist. Gen.*
Bond, Hu. L. Opinion as to questions under the homestead act of Virginia in its relation to the bankruptcy act of March 2, 1867, and act amendatory thereof. 8°. '73. pap., 50c...*West, J. & Co.*
Bond, Lew. H. *See* United States, Circuit and District Court reports.
Bond, Rob. Golden maxims: a thought for every day in the year. 32°. 38c...*Appleton.*
Bond, T. E. Economy of Methodism ill. and defended. 8°. '52. $1.75...*Meth. Bk. Conc.*
Bond, W. C. History and description of Harv. Coll. Astron. Obs. *See* Harvard Coll. Astron. Observ.
— Observations of solar spots. *See* Harvard Coll. Astron. Observ.
— Observations on Saturn. *See* Harvard Coll. Astron. Observ.
Bondholders and bondmen. Van Evrie, J. H. 10c. *Van Evrie.*
Bone, J. H. A. Petroleum and petroleum wells; with guide book and descript. of oil regions of Penna., W. Va., Ky. and Ohio. 2d ed., rev. and enl. 18°. '65. 75c...*Claxton; Lippincott.*
Bone Squash: Ethiop. drama. 16°. pap., 15c. *French; Happy.*
Bones at a raffle: Ethiop. drama. 16°. pap., 15c. *Happy.*
Bonn, *Conference at.* Proceedings, Aug., 1875, between Old Catholics, Orientals, members of the Anglican and Am. churches and evangelicals from Europe and Am.; tr. by S. Buel, with pref. by R. J. Nevin. 12°. '76. $1...*Whittaker.*
Bonnechose, Émile de. History of France to [1871]; tr. cr. 8°. $2.50...*Routledge.*
Bonnefons, J: Pancharis. *See* Joannes *Secundus*, Basia.
Bonnell, J. M. First lessons in Eng. composition. 12°. '71. 80c...*Morton.*
— Manual of prose compos. 12°. '67. $1.50..*Morton.*
Bonner, J: Child's [histories]. 8 v. ill. 16°. ea., $1.25. *Harper.*

Cont.: Greece, 2 v. — Rebellion: v. 3 of United States. — Rome, 2 v. — United States, 3 v.

Bonner, T. D. Life and adventures of James P. Beckwourth, chief of the Crow Indians; written from his own dictation. ill. 12°. $1.50...*Harper.*
Bonney, *Mrs.* Cath. V. R. Legacy of hist. gleanings. 2 v. por., pl. and eng. 8°. '75. $10...*Munsell.*
Bonney, M. Banditti of the prairie. 8°. pap., 75c. *Peterson*
Bonney, S. W. Seaman's compass and chart. 32° '62. 25c...*Am. Tr*
Bonney, T. G. *See* Closs, G., Froelicher, O., *and* Roux, G.; — Walton, E.
Bonnie ærie. L., L. $1.50...*Lothrop*
Bonnie fish wife. Selby, C. 15c...*De Witt; French*
Bonnie Scotland. Lippincott, S. J. $1.50..**Osgood*
Bonnifield, M. S. *See* Nevada, Compiled laws; Statutes.
Bonnycastle, J: Introduction to algebra; rev. and enl. by J. Ryan, with problems by J. F. Jenkins 12°. '45. hf. roan, $1. — Key, $1. *Claxton; Lippincott*
— Introduction to mensuration and pract. geometry with treatise on gauging, and problems in mechanics by J. Ryan. 12°. '73. $1.25...*Porter*
— — Key to *same*, by B. Hallowell. New ed., rev. by J. Ryan. 12°. '34. $1...*Porter*
Bonomi, Jos. Nineveh and its palaces: disc. of Botta and Layard applied to elucidations of Holy Writ ill. 12°. (Bohn.) $1.75...*Little, B. & Co*
— *Same.* ill. 12°. (Bohn.) $2. *Lippincott; Scribner, W. & A*
Bonstetten, C: Vct. The man of the north and the man of the south; or, the influence of climate tr. from the French. 16°. '63. $1...*Christern*
Boodle, R. G. Deepening the spiritual life in our parishes. sq. 24°. 15c...*Pott*
Book (The): story of the mountains. *See* Meadow side stories.
Book about animals; — birds; — flowers. *See* Juvenile picture books.
Book about boys. *See* Moncrieff, A. R. H.
Book about dominies. Moncrieff, A. R. H. 75c. *Roberts*
Book (The) above all. Stockton, T. H. $1.50; $2. *Claxton.*
Book (The) and its story. R., L. N. $1.50..*Carter.*
Book (The) and the life. Vaughan, C. J. $1.25. *Macmillan.*
Book-case library. *See* Hofland, *Mrs.* B.
Book for a corner. Hunt, L. $2...*Lippincott.*
Book for the home. Upham, T. C. $1.50. *Bost. Am. Tr.*
Book-keeping made easy. 12°. pap., 25c...*Hurst.*
Book of alphabets; for painters and others. ill. obl. 8°. pap., 50c...*Haney.*
Book of anecdotes, and joker's knapsack. 12°. $1.75. *J. E. Potter.*
Book of animals. ill. 16°. '75. 40c...*Lothrop.*
Book of animals. ill. 4°. '73. $1.25...*Nelson.*
Book of animals; — birds. *See* Casket of juveniles.
Book of authors. Russell, W. C. $1.75; $3.75; $5. *Scribner, W. & A.*
Book of ballads. *See* Martin, T., *and* Aytoun, W. E.
Book of beauty: engravings and poems. 8°. $5. *H. Peterson.*
Book of beauty, vigor and elegance; with the art of dressing with taste. 12°. pap., 25c...*Hurst.*
Book of birds. ill. 16°. '75. 40c...*Lothrop.*
Book of blunders. Bombaugh, C. C. $1...*Souder.*
Book (The) of books. *See* Little Dot ser.
Book (The) of books: story of the Eng. Bible. 18°. 35c...*Am. S. S.*
Book of the church. *See* Southey, R.
Book of the colonies. ill. 12°. *net*, 80c...*Hamersley.*
Book of comic songs and recitations. 12°. pap., 20c. *Hurst.*
Book of common prayer. *See* Protestant Episc. Church; — Reformed Episc. Church.

Book of common prayer of the Reformed Episc. Church compared with that of the Prot. Episc. Church in the U. S. 8°. pap., 10c...*J. A. Moore.*

Book of costume; or, annals of fashion from the earliest period to the present time. ill. 8°. bds., $3. *French.*

Book of days. *See* Chambers, R.

Book of the east. Stoddard, R. H. $1.50; $3; $4. *Osgood.*

Book of English anecdotes. Hood, T., *the younger.* 50c. .... *Routledge.*

Book of epitaphs. 12°. $1.50 .... *Carleton.*

Book (A) of fair women. Fenn, G. M. $3.. *Cassell.*

Book of the farm. *See* Waring, G. E., *jr.*

Book of fireside games. 16°. pap., 30c.; bds., 50c. *Dick & F.*

Book of five hundred curious puzzles. ill. 16°. pap., 30c.; bds., 50c. .... *Dick & F.*

Book of five hundred riddles. ill. sq. 16°. pap., 25c. *Locke.*

Book (A) of funny beasts. Griset, E. 50c...*Appleton.*

Book of golden deeds. *See* Yonge, C. M.

Book of golden thoughts. Attwell, H. $1.25. *Macmillan.*

Book of good examples. ill. 12°. *net,* 80c. *Hamersley.*

Book of heroes and famous men. 16°. pap., 10c. *U. P. James.*

Book of the homilies; with the const. and canons of the Eng. and Am. churches. 8°. $3.90..*McCauley.*

Book of hours: offices for the seven canonical hours, litanies, etc. 12°. '65. mor., $1.....*Hurd & H.*

Book of household pets: instructions about the diseases, breeding, training and management of the canary, mocking-bird, etc. ill. 16°. 75c.; bds., 50c. .... *Dick & F.*

Book of humorous poetry: extracts from English and American poets. (Household ser.) ill. 16°. $1.50; mor., $3 .... *Lee & S.*

Book of humorous poetry: selections. 12°. $1.50; mor., $3.25; $3.75 .... *Appleton.*

Book of illustrious mechanics. ill. 12°. *net,* 80c. *Hamersley.*

Book of the Indians. ill. 12°. *net,* 80c....*Hamersley.*

Book of knowledge, and sure guide to rapid wealth. 12°. pap., 25c. .... *Hurst.*

Book of martyrs. *See* Foxe, J.

Book of natural history. ill. 16°. '75. 40c...*Lothrop.*

Book of nature. Byrn, M. L. $1 .... *Hurst.*

Book of nature. Good, J. M. *net,* $1.50..*Hamersley.*

Book of nature. Schoedler, F. $3 .... *Sheldon.*

Book of nature laid open. Hutton, W. 75c. *Harper.*

Book of nonsense. *See* Lear, E.

Book of nursery tales. ill. sm. 4°. $1.75. *Scribner, W. & A.*

Book of one hundred pictures. 18°. '65. 45c. *Meth. Bk. Conc.*

— *See also* Picture lib. for the little ones at home.

Book of one hundred and ninety stories and pieces. ill. 16°. $1 .... *Am. S. S.*

Book of one syllable. sq. 16°. 50c. .... *Routledge.*

Book of one thousand amusing tales and adventures. ill. 12°. $1.50 .... *Dick & F.*

Book of one thousand comical stories; or, endless repast of fun. ill. 12°. $1.50 .... *Dick & F.*

Book of Orm. Buchanan, R. $2 .... *Routledge.*

Book of parlor games. ill. 12°. $1.25 ...... *T. Bliss.*

Book of poetry. Engles, W. M. $2 .... *Pres. Bd.*

Book of praise. *See* Selborne, *Lord.*

Book of praise for the Sunday school. Bell, G. A., *and* Main, H. P. $1; 50c. .... *Biglow.*

Book of praise hymnal. *See* Selborne, *Lord.*

Book of praise: hymns and tunes for public and social worship; by W. T. Eustis, jr., E. P. Parker, M. M. Dunn, H. N. Dunning and L. L. Paine. 8°. '68. $2.13–$8.50; chp. ed., $1.60–$2. — Hymns only. 8°. $1.50–$5; chp. ed., $1–$1.30.... *Hamersley.*

Book of promises. Emmons, S. B. 60c. *Universalist.*

Book of proverbs. [Biblical.] 32°. '37. 15c...*Am. Tr.*

Book of ready-made speeches; with quotations, toasts and sentiments. 16°. bds., 50c...... *Routledge.*

Book (A) of remembrance. Bedford, C. R. $1.50. *Claxton.*

Book (The) of remembrance. Shields, C. W. 75c. *Pres. Bd.*

Book of riddles and five hundred home amusements. ill. 16°. pap., 30c.; bds., 50c......... *Dick & F.*

Book of roses. Parkman, F. $1.50 .... *Tilton.*

Book of sacred poems. Baynes, R. A. $3.50; $5. *Cassell.*

Book of Shakespeare gems: steel eng. [of] localities of Shakespeare's dramas. sm. 4°. $4...*Routledge.*

Book of snobs. *See* Thackeray, W. M.

Book of songs. Heine, H. $1.50 .... *Holt.*

Book of the sonnet. Hunt, L. 2 v. $3..... *Roberts.*

Book of table talk. Russell, W. C. $1.75; $3.50; $5 .... *Routledge.*

Book of theatrical anecdotes. Paul, H. 50c. *Routledge.*

Book of thought. Smithers, J. $1.25.... *Pounsford.*

Book of trades. *See* Picture puzzle toy books.

Book of two hundred pictures. 12°. $1.25..*Am. S. S.*

— *See also* New.

Book of useful knowledge. Cooley, A. J. $1.50. *Appleton.*

Book (A) of vagaries. Paulding, J. K. $2.50. *Scribner.*

Book of vespers. Osgood, S., *and* Farley, F. A. $1.25. *Miller.*

Book of wise and pithy sayings of good and great men of all ages. (Household ser.) ill. 16°. $1.50; mor., $3 .... *Lee & S.*

Book of wit and humor. (Household ser.) ill. 16°. $1.50; mor., $3 .... *Lee & S.*

Book of wonderful characters. Wilson, H., *and* Caulfield, J. $3 .... *Routledge.*

Book of wonders, mysteries and disclosures; [with] recipes for the manufacture of articles of everyday use; [also] Taxidermy, and traps and trapping. 16°. pap., 25c. .... *Happy.*

Book of worship. *See* Bacon, L. W.

Book of worship for the congregation and the home; principally from the Old and New Test. 16°. '52. 50c. .... *Lockwood, B. & Co.*

Book of worthies. Yonge, C. M. $1.25..*Macmillan.*

Book opened (The). *See* Nevin, A.

Book-stall boy of Batherton. Hodder, E. 75c. *Lothrop.*

Book (The) that will suit you. Smith, J. $1..*Dodd.*

Book the third: comedy. 16°. pap., 15c..... *French.*

Book 3, chapter 1. Pierron, E., *and* Laferriere, A. 15c. .... *French.*

Books about boys who fought and won. 4 v. ill. 18°. '71. $2.25 .... *Meth. Bk. Conc.*

Cont.: Josey, the runaway. — Irish Jem's three trials. — Bob, the bootblack. — Trial of obedience.

Books about wonderful and curious things. 4 v. 16°. '70. $3.50 .... *Meth. Bk. Conc.*

Cont.: Wonders in the air. — The wonders of fire and water. — The birthday present. — Elder Park garden.

Books and character of the New Test. 16°. 25c. *Un. S. S.*

Books and reading. Porter, N. $2; $4.50..*Scribner.*

Books for children. 32°. 15c. .... *Nelson.*

Books for the children's hour. 5 v. 18°. '72. $3.25. *Meth. Bk. Conc.*

Books for the children's hour, *continued.*
Cont.: The wood-carvers. — Alice Leigh's mission. — Real Robinson Crusoes. — Home tour with Aunt Bessie. — Little Grig and the tinker's letter.

Books for girls. *See* Craik, *Mrs.* D. M.

Books of blessing. 8 v. ill. 18°. '62. $4 .. *Meth. Bk. Conc.*
Cont.: The little black hen. — The two school-girls. — Martha's hymn. — Gertrude and her cat. — The prince in disguise. — The carpenter's house. — The rose in the desert. — Althea.

Books of nonsense. *See* Lear, E.

Books of the Vaudois. Todd, J. H. $2 .. *Macmillan.*

Boole, G: Investigation of the laws of thought on which are founded the theories of logic and probabilities. 8°. '54. $6 .... *Macmillan.*

— Treatise on the calculus of finite differences. 2d ed., ed. by J. F. Moulton. cr. 8°. '72. $4.50. *Macmillan.*

— Treatise on differential equations. 3d ed., ed. by I. Todhunter. cr. 8°. '72. $6 ...... *Macmillan.*

— — Supplement. cr. 8°. '65. $3.50 ..... *Macmillan.*

Boone, Dan. Life. ill. 12°. $1.25 .... *Lippincott.*

Booraem, H. Toler. *See* California, Supreme Court reports.

Boos, Mt. Leben. 18°. '50. 60c. .... *Am. Tr.*

Boot on the wrong foot. ill. fp. 8°. 50c. ..... *Cassell.*

Booth, Ab. Reign of grace. 12°. 75c. .... *Am. Bapt.*

Booth, Edn. *See* Hinton, H. L.; — Winter, W.

Booth, J. B. Pictorial hist. of the U. S.; with questions. 18°. 75c. .... *Sower.*

Booth, Ja. C. *See* Delaware geol. survey.

— *and* Morfit, C. Encyclopedia of chemistry. ('50.) 8th ed. ill. roy. 8°. '72. $5 .... *Baird.*

— — Improvements in chemical arts. 8°. '52. pap., 50c. *Smith. Inst.*

Booth, Junius Brutus. Booth memorials: passages, incidents and anecdotes in life of J. B. Booth (the elder) by his daughter. ill. 12°. '69. $1; pap., 50c. .... *Hinton.*

— Ugolino: tragedy. 16°. pap., 15c. .... *French.*

Booth, M. H. C. Wayside blossoms: poems. 18°. '65. $1 .... *Claxton.*

Booth, Ma. ["Carrie Carlton."] Inglenook. [Juvenile.] ('68.) 2d ed. 16°. '70. 75c. .. *Roman.*

Booth, Ma. L. New and complete clock and watch maker's manual; with app. on clock and watch making in Am. pl. 12°. $2 .... *Wiley.*

Booth, S: (*ed.*) Sunday hymns. 24°. '60. per 100, $37.50 .... *Goodenough.*

Booth, Wa. S. Justice's manual for Minnesota. ('65.) 4th ed. 12°. '75. $1 .... *Leonard.*

— Township manual for Minnesota: guide for officers in their duties under the statutes. ('73.) 3d ed. 12°. '76. 60c. .... *Leonard.*

Booth's Theatre portrait gallery; with descrip. of stage, and por. of actors. ill. roy. 8°. pap., 25c. *Hinton.*

Boots of the Swan. Selby, C. 15c. .... *French.*

Bordeaux wine and liquor dealers' guide: treatise on the manufacture of liquors; by a practical liquor manufacturer. 12°. $2.50 .... *Dick & F.*

Border beagles. Simms, W. G. $1.75; 75c. *Widdleton.*

Border marriage. Sorrell, W. J. 15c. ...... *French.*

Border reminiscences. Marcy, R. B. $2 ... *Harper.*

Border rifles (The). Aimard, G. 75c. ..... *Peterson.*

Border rover. Bennett, E. $1.75; $1.50 .. *Peterson.*

Border wars of the Am. revolution. Stone, W. L. 2 v. $1.50 .... *Harper.*

Borderland of science. Proctor, R. A. $4 .. *Lippincott.*

Borderlands of insanity. Wynter, A. $2 .. *Putnam.*

Bordese, L. Coronation; or, the crown of virtue. [Operetta.] 8°. pap., 50c. .... *Peters.*

— Mass in F, for 4 voices; with Lat. and Eng. words 8°. '69. $1; bds., 65c. .... *Ditson.*

— Mass in G minor. 4°. pap., $1.25 .... *Peters.*

Bordese, L., *continued.*

— Miracle of the roses. [Parlor operetta.] 8°. pap., $1.50 .... *Schirmer.*

Bordogni, Marco. Art of phrasing, respiration, accentuation and expression: ill. in 12 vocalises. 2 v. f°. pap., v. 1, $1.25; 2, $1.50 ...... *Ditson.*

— Thirty-six vocalises, for soprano or tenor voices; composed in a modern style. 3 v. f°. ea., pap., $3 .... *Ditson.*

— Twelve new vocalises; for mezzo-soprano. 2 nos. f°. ea., pap., $1.50 .... *Ditson.*

Borel, Eug. Cours de thèmes français. Progressive exercises for tr. Eng. into French. ('68.) New ed. 12°. '76. 75c. .... *Holt.*

— Grammaire française à l'usage des Anglais. Rev. by E. B. Coe. ('68.) New ed. 12°. '76. hf. roan, $1.75 .... *Holt.*

Borg, Selma, *and* Brown, M. A. (*ed.*) Northern lights: tales from the Swedish and Finnish. ill. 12°. '73. $1.50 .... *Porter.*

Borghese, *Princess.* *See* Talbot, G.

Borgo, —. Life of blessed John Berchmans; tr. from the Fr. 12°. '65. $1.50; $2 ..... *Cunningham.*

Borgo, C: Novena to the sacred heart of Jesus. *See* Month of the sacred heart.

Borlase, J. S. Daring deeds of adventure. ill. 12°. $1.25 .... *Scribner, W. & A.*

Born bad; or, the countess and the convict. 18°. pap., 25c. .... *De Witt.*

Born romp (A). Mumford, M. E. $1.50 .... *Souder.*

Born to good luck. Power, T. 15c. .... *French.*

Born with a silver spoon in his mouth. 18°. 35c. *Am. S. S.*

Börne, L: Sämmtliche Werke. 5 v. 12°. hf. mor., $9. *Kohler.*

— *Same.* 5 v. 12°. hf. mor., $9; $12; pap., $6. *Schäfer.*

— *Same;* neue wohlfeile Ausg. 25 nos. 12°. ea., pap., 15c. .... *Schäfer.*

— Briefe aus Paris. 2 v. 12°. $4; pap., $2.50. *Schäfer.*

— Menzel der Franzosenfresser. 16°. 75c. .... *Radde.*

— *Same.* 12°. $1.50; pap., $1 .... *Schäfer.*

Borrow, G: Bible and gypsies in Spain. 8°. $1.75. *Carter.*

— Lavengro: the scholar, the gipsy, the priest. 8°. pap., 75c. .... *Harper.*

— Romany Rye: sequel to "Lavengro." 8°. pap., 75c. *Harper.*

Borrowed feathers: drama. 16°. pap., 15c. .. *French.*

Borrowed half dollar. 18°. 17c.; 22c. ... *Am. Bapt.*

Borrowed plumes: farce. 16°. pap., 15c. .... *French.*

Borrowing. Bruce, E. M. 75c. .... *Universalist.*

Borys, G. She loved him madly. 12°. $1.75. *Carleton.*

Boscobel. *See* Ainsworth, W. H.

Böse Geist (Der) Lumpaci Vagabundus, od. das liederliche Kleeblatt. 12°. pap., 15c. *F. W. Thomas.*

— *See also* Lumpaci Vagabundus.

Bosom foes. Stuart, M. B. $1.50 .... *Carleton.*

Bosom friend (The). Grey, E. C. 50c. ..... *Harper.*

Bosses and their boys; or, the duties of masters and apprentices ill. and enforced. 18°. 50c. .. *Am. S. S.*

— *See also* Select lib. for boys.

Bossuet, Jacques Benigne. Exposition of the doct. of the Cath. church on matters of controv.; tr. 64°. pap., 20c.; — with notes. 18°. pap., 25c. *Cath. Pub.*

— *Same.* New ed., with notes by Rev. J. Fletcher. 18°. 60c. .... *Cath. Pub.*

— Histoire universelle. 12°. (Paris.) $1.50. *G. R. Lockwood.*

— History of the variations of the Prot. churches; tr. 2 v. 12°. $3; hf. mor., $5 .... *Sadlier.*

Bossuet and his contemporaries. Lear, S. $3.50 .. *Pott.*

Bost, Ami. History of the Moravians; tr. from the French, and abridg.; with app. 16°. (Lond.) '62. $1.25 .... *Clauder.*

Bostock, J. Sketch of hist. of medicine. *See* Good, J. M., Study of medicine.

Boston, T: Select works. 8°. $3 .... *Carter.*
— Crook in the lot. 18°. 45c. .... *U. P. Bd. of Pub.*
— *Same.* 18°. 50c. .... *Carter.*
— Human nature in its fourfold state. 18°. 75c. *Carter; U. P. Bd. of Pub.*
— *Same.* 12°. $1 .... *Pres. Bd.*

Boston, *Mass.* *See* Celebration of the cent. anniv.

Boston [Mass.] illustrated: artistic and pictorial descript. of B. and its surroundings. 16°. '72. $1; pap., 50c. .... *Osgood.*

Boston Academy's collection of choruses. obl. 4°. '36. bds., $2.50 .... *Ditson.*

Boston Academy's collection of church music. obl. 8°. '63. bds., $1.50 .... *Ditson.*

Boston anthem book. Mason, L. $2 .... *Ditson.*

Boston boy (The). Lewis, A. H. $1.25 ..... *Graves.*

Boston collection of music. *See* Mason, L., New carmina sacra.

Boston dip (The). Baker, G. M. 15c. ..... *Lee & S.*

Boston dip (The). Loring, F. W. 50c. ..... *Loring.*

Boston flute instruction book. obl. 8°. '45. pap., 60c. *Ditson.*

Boston glee book. Mason, L., *and* Webb, G. J. $1.50. *Ditson.*

Boston journal of natural history. *See* Boston Soc. of Nat. Hist.

Boston lectures, 1870–'72. Christianity and scepticism; by eminent divines of the U. S. 3 v. 12°. v. 1, 2, ea., $2; v. 3, $1.50 .... *Cong. Pub.*

Boston machinist (The). Fitzgerald, W. 75c. *Wiley.*

Boston musical treasure. Louis, J. 60c. .... *Ditson.*

Boston piano-forte instructor. *See* White, E. L.

Boston poets. 8 v. 8°. ea., shp., $4.50; mor., $10. *Mason.*

Cont.: Burns. — Byron. — Cowper. — Hemans. — Milton. — Moore. — Scott. — Shakespeare.

— *See also* Illustrated Boston poets.

Boston Society of Natural History. Boston journal of nat. hist., 1834–'63. 7 v. 8°. '37–'63. *Bost. Soc. Nat. Hist.*

Cont.: v. 2, $6.50; v. 6, $6; pt. 2 (v. 1), pts. 1, 2 (v. 2), ea., $2; pt. 3 (v. 1), pts. 2, 3, 4 (v. 4), pt. 2 (v. 6), pt. 3 (v. 7), ea., $1.50; pts. 3–4 (v. 2), $3; pt. 1 (v. 5), pt. 1, 3 (v. 6), pt. 2 (v. 7), ea., $1.75; pt. 4 (v. 6), pt. 4 (v. 7), ea., $1.25.
Note. v. 3; pts. 1, 4 (of v. 1); pt. 1. (of v. 4); pts. 2–4 (of v. 5); and pt. 1 (of v. 7) are o. p.

— Memoirs: new ser. of Boston jour. of nat. hist. v. 1 in 4 pts. 4°. '66–'69. ea., pap., $4; — pts. 1–4 of v. 2, ea., pap., $1 .... *Bost. Soc. Nat. Hist.*
— Proceedings. v. 2–4, 6–17. 15 v. 8°. '44–'76. v. 2–4, 6, 7, ea., $2.50; v. 8, $2.75; v. 9, $3.50; v. 10–17, ea., $4.50 .... *Bost. Soc. Nat. Hist.*

Boswell (*pseud.?*) Loves of Jonathan and Virginia. [Poetry.] 12°. pap., 50c. .... *Lippincott.*

Boswell, Ja: Life of Samuel Johnson. ill. 8°. $3.50. *Routledge.*
— *Same.* (Globe ed.) ill. cr. 8°. $1.75; hf. cf., $3.50; cf., $5 .... *Routledge.*
— *Same.* (Library ed.) 4 v. ill. cr. 8°. $5; — 4 v. in 2. $4.50; hf. cf., $8 .... *Routledge.*
— *Same;* with notes. por. 8°. $2.50 .... *Lee & S.*
— *Same;* with notes and biographical ill. by Malone. 8°. $2.25 .... *Barnes.*
— *Same;* incl. Tour to the Hebrides. 5 v. cr. 8°. hf. cf., $15 .... *Routledge.*
— — *Same.* New ed., with notes and add. by J. W. Croker. 2 v. por. 8°. $4; shp., $5. hf. cf., $8.50. *Harper.*

Boswell, Ja: *continued.*
— — *Same.* New ed., enl., with notes, by J. W. Croker and others. 4 v. 12°. '74. $6; shp., $8; hf. cf., $13 .... *Claxton.*
— — *Same;* ed. with add. and notes by J. W. Croker. 2d ed., rev. by J. Wright. 5 v. 12°. (Bohn.) $7.50 .... *Little, B. & Co.*
— — *Same.* 5 v. 12°. (Bohn.) $8 ... *Scribner, W. & A.*
— — *Same.* 5 v. 12°. (Bohn.) ea., $1.75 .. *Lippincott.*
— — *Same;* condensed by C. H. Jones. 12°. '76. $2.50 .... *Holt.*
— Tour to the Hebrides with Dr. Johnson. ill. cr. 8°. $1.50 .... *Routledge.*

Bosworth, J. S. *See* New York City, Superior Court reports.

Bosworth, Jos. Anglo-Saxon and Eng. dict. post 8°. $3.50 .... *Lippincott.*
— Gothic and Anglo-Saxon Gospels in parallel columns, with versions of Wycliffe and Tyndale. 2d ed. 8°. $6 .... *Scribner, W. & A.*

Both, C: Consumption in all its forms. ill. 8°. '73. $2 .... *A. Moore.*
— Small pox and vaccination; with a scientific exposition of vaccination. 12°. '72. 75c.; pap., 50c. *A. Moore.*

Both sides of the street. Walker, M. S. $1.60. *Hoyt.*

Bothwell. *See* Grant, James.

Botta, *Mrs.* Anne C. L. Handbook of universal literature. 12°. '60. $2.50 .... *Osgood.*

Botta, Vincenzo. Dante as philosopher, patriot and poet; with analysis of the "Divina commedia." ('65.) New ed. cr. 8°. '67. $2.50 .... *Scribner.*
— *See also* Roemer, J., Polyglot reader.

Bottle (The). Taylor, T. P. 15c. .... *French.*

Bottle (The); or, the first step to crime. 8°. pap., 25c. .... *De Witt.*

Bottle-nose Ben, the Indian hater. 12°. pap., 20c. *Hurst.*

Bottom of the sea. Sonrel, L. $1.25 ..... *Scribner.*

Botts, J: Minor. The great rebellion: its secret history, rise, progress and disastrous failure. 12°. $2.50 .... *Harper.*

Bouchée (Une) de pain. *See* Histoire d'une bouchée.

Boucher, Ph. El hombre y la Biblia. 18°. '74. 75c. *Am. Tr.*

Boucicault, Dion. [Plays.] 15 v. 16°. ea., pap., 15c. .... *French.*

Cont.: Andy Blake: comedy. — Colleen bawn. — Jessie Brown. — Knight of Arva. — Life of an actress. — London assurance: comedy. — Lover (A) by proxy: burletta. — Octoroon. — Old heads and young hearts. — Pauvrette. — Phantom. — Prima donna: comedy. — Queen of spades. — West-End; or, Irish heiress: comedy. — Willow copse.

— London assurance; with notes for tr. into French by P. W. Gengembre. 8°. '73. pap., 50c. *Holt.*
— Octoroon. 16°. pap., 15c. .... *Happy.*
— *and* Seymour, C. Wanted — a widow: farce. 16°. pap., 15c. .... *French.*

Boudoir cabal (The). Murray, G. 75c. .. *Brentano.*

Bought: play. 16°. pap., 15c. .... *French.*

Bought with a price. Tucker, C. 20c. ...... *Am. Tr.*

Bouley, H. Hydrophobia: means of avoiding its perils and preventing its spread; tr. by A. Liautard. 8°. pap., 35c. .... *Harper.*

Bound and how. Jewett, C. 10c. .... *Nat. Temp.*

Bound boy. Baker, H. N. W. 55c. .... *Hoyt.*

Bound Brook. Avery, J. G. $1.50 ..... *Cong. Pub.*

Bound by his vows. Buerstenbinder, E. $1.25. *Lippincott.*

Bound by a spell. Reback, H. 30c. ..... *Am. News.*

Bound down. Fitch, A. M. $1.50 .... *Lippincott.*

Bound girl. Baker, H. N. W. 55c. .... *Hoyt.*
— *See also* Bright gems for boys and girls; — Little girls' lib.

Bound out. *See* Baker, S.

Bound prentice to a waterman: drama. 16°. pap., 15c. *French.*

Bound to John Company. Braddon, M. E. 75c. *Harper.*

Bound to rise. Alger, H., *jr.* $1.50........*Loring.*

Bound to the wheel. Saunders, J. 75c......*Harper.*

Boundary tree (The); or, the spirit that heals differences. 18°. 35c....................*Am. S. S.*

Bouquet. Southard, L. H., *and* Pratt, G. W. 75c. *Gordon.*

Bouquet. Woodward, J. A. 15c...........*Lee & S.*

Bouquet (The): language and poetry of flowers. ill. sq. 16°. $1.50..........................*Locke.*

Bouquet library. 4 v. ill. 12°. $6.........*Nelson.*
Cont.: My school days in Paris, by M. S. Jeune. — Aunt Jenny's American pets, by C. C. Hopley. — Young governess. — Triumph of steam.

Bouquet series. 3 v. ill. sq. 16°. $4.50.......*Locke.*
Cont.: The bouquet. — Flora's dial. — Flora's cup.

Bourdaloue and Louis XIV. Bungener, L. F. $1.50. *Lothrop.*

Bourdeau, Dan. T. Comment le Sabbat a été changé. 16°. '75. 10c...................*Sev. Day Adv.*

— Refutation of 44 so-called objections against the anc. Sabbath. 16°. '76. pap., 15c. *Sev. Day Adv.*

— *Same;* in French. 16°. '75. pap., 15c. *Sev. Day Adv.*

Bourdillon, Fs. Earnest exhortations on the most important subjects. 12°. 60c.............*Nelson.*

— Lesser lights. 12°. '76. $1.25..............*Pott.*

— Odd five minutes (The). 12°. $1.25.........*Nelson.*

— Parables of our Lord explained and applied. 12°. '69. 90c.; $1.25.......................*Am. Tr.*

— *Same.* 12°. '68. $1.50...........*Meth. Bk. Conc.*

Bourdon, *Mme.* Mathilde F. [Tales.] 8 v. 18°. ea., 30c...................................*O'Shea.*
Cont.: Bread (The) of forgiveness. — Flowers from heaven. — Gabriel, a souvenir of the missions. — Jewess (The): tale of our own times. — Madame de Verceil. — Martha. — Patient mourner (The). — Two roads (The).

— Real life; tr. by Miss A. Newlin. 12°. '76. $1.50; $2............................*Kelly, P. & Co.*

— Science of happiness; or, the beatitudes in practice. 18°. $1..............................*O'Shea.*

Bourgeois, Anicet, *and* Dugué, F. Pirates of Savannah: drama. 16°. pap., 15c...........*French.*

— *and* Dumanoir, P. Black doctor: drama. 16°. pap., 15c...............................*French.*

— *and* Feval, P. Duke's daughter: drama. 16°. pap., 15c...................................*French.*

Bourgeois, X. The passions in their relations to health and disease; tr. by H. F. Damon. 16°. '73. $1.25. *Jas. Campbell.*

Bourgeois gentilhomme (Le). *See* Molière, J. B. P.

Bourguignon, H. On the cattle plague; or, contagious typhus in horned cattle. 12°. $1.25. *Lippincott.*

Bourke, Ulick I. Easy lessons, or self-instructions in Irish; with key. 12°. '73. $1.50.....*Haverty.*

Bourne, B: Franklin. The captive in Patagonia. ill. 16°. '74. $1.25..................*Lothrop.*

Bourne, C: The principles and practice of engineering, trigonometrical, subterraneous and marine surveying. 3d ed. pl. 8°. '67. $2.50...*Spon.*

Bourne, E: E. History of Wells and Kennebunk, to 1820. por. 8°. '75. $3.50........*Williams.*

Bourne, H. R. Fox. Famous London merchants. ill. 16°. $1.................................*Harper.*

Bourne, J: Catechism of the steam engine. ill. 16°. $1.75..................*Appleton; Lippincott.*

— Handbook of the steam engine: key to the "Catechism." ill. 16°. $1.75..*Appleton; Lippincott.*

— Recent improvements in the steam engine: supplement to the "Catechism." ill. 16°. $1.75..*Lippincott.*

— Treatise on the screw propeller, screw vessels and screw engines. New ed. wood cuts and eng. 4°. '67. $18; hf. mor., $24............*Wiley.*

Bourne, J: *continued.*

— Treatise on the steam engine in its various applications to mines, mills, steam navigation, etc.: 7th ed. of "Treatise on the steam engine," by the Artisan club. pl. and ill. 4°. $15.....*Appleton.*

Bourne, W: O. *See* Curtis, G. H., *and* Bourne, W. O.

Bourquard, A. H. L. Palmier céleste: recueil de prières et de pratiques pieuses d'après le "Céleste palmetum." 18°. *net,* 60c.–$2.40.....*Benziger.*

Boussingault, J. B. Rural economy in its rel. with chemistry, physics and meteorology; tr. with introd. and notes, by G. Law. 12°. $1.60..*Judd.*

Boutell, Ma. E. C. Picture natural hist.; ed. with introd. by Rev. C. Boutell. ill. 4°. $1.50..*Cassell.*

Bouverie, F. W. Nouveau théatre d'éducation. 16°. 75c..............................*Lippincott.*

Bouvet, Fs. Turks in Europe. *See* Gilson, A., Czar and the sultan.

Bouvier, Ha. M. Familiar astronomy; [also] Treatise on the globes, and astronomical dict. ill. 8°. $2.50.................................*Sower.*

— *Same;* abridg. 8°. $2......................*Sower.*

— Family save-all (The). 12°. $1.75.......*Peterson.*

— *Same.* (Reason why ser.) 12°. $1.25..*Lippincott.*

— National cook book. 12°. $1.75.........*Peterson.*

Bouvier, J: Institutes of Am. law. New ed., ed. by D. A. Gleason. 2 v. 8°. shp., $12..*Lippincott.*

— Law dictionary, adapted to the Const. and laws of the U. S., and of the states; with ref. to systems of foreign law. 14th ed., rev. and enl. 2 v. 8°. shp., $12...........................*Lippincott.*

Bovet, Fel. The banished count: life of Nicholas Louis Zinzendorf; tr. by Rev. J. Gill. 8°. (Lond.) '65. $2.50...................*Clauder.*

Bow, Rob. H: Economics of construction in rel. to framed structures; with diagrams and pl. 8°. '73. $2....................................*Spon.*

— Treatise on bracing; with its application to bridges and other structures of wood or iron. ill. 8°. $1.50..........................*Van Nostrand.*

Bow in the cloud. *See* Macduff, J. R.

Bow in the cloud. Stevens, W. B. *$3...*Hubbard.*

Bow of faith. Wright, M. 50c...........*Routledge.*

Bowden, J. E. Life and letters of F. W. Faber; with introd. by an American clergyman. por. 8°. '69. $2.50; $3; hf. cf., $3.50..............*Murphy.*

Bowditch, Natl. Ingersoll. Suffolk surnames. ('57.) 2d ed., enl. 8°. '58. $2..................*Williams.*

Bowditch, W: Ingersoll. Taxation of women in Massachusetts. New ed., rev. 8°. '75. pap., 20c. *Williams.*

Bowditch, *Rev.* W: R. Analysis, technical valuation, purification and use of coal gas. ill. 8°. '67. $4.50....................................*Spon.*

— *Same.* ill. 8°. $6.50.....................*Baird.*

Bowen, B. F. America discovered by the Welsh in 1170. 16°. $1.25..................*Lippincott.*

Bowen, *Mrs.* C. E. Alice Neville. ill. 18°. 50c...*Pott.*

— *Same;* [also] Riversdale. 16°. $1.25......*Carter.*

— Among the brigands. ill. 16°. 75c..........*Nelson.*

— Ben's boyhood; [also] Trusted and tried. ill. 16°. '73. 75c...........................*Lothrop.*

— Charlie Tyrrell. ill. 12°. 75c................*Pott.*

— Grandmamma's relics. ill. 16°. 75c........*Nelson.*

— Jack the conqueror; or, difficulties overcome. 18°. 75c..........................*Carter; Dutton.*

— *Same.* ill. sm. 4°. '71. $2.............*Routledge.*

— New stories on old subjects. ill. 12°. $1.50...*Pott.*

— Paul's penny. 18°. 50c....................*Carter.*

— Peter's pound. 18°. 35c...................*Carter.*

— *Same;* [also] Paul's penny. 18°. 75c......*Carter.*

— Potato roaster; [also] Boy guardian. 18°. 60c. *Carter.*

— Riversdale. ill. 16°. 50c.....................*Pott.*

— — *See also above* Alice Neville.

Bowen, Eli. Coal and coal oil, and the other minerals of the earth. 12°. $1.75........*Peterson.*

Bowen, Fs. American political economy. ('70.) New ed. cr. 8°. '75. $2.50................*Scribner.*

— History of the U. S. *See* Weber, G., Outlines of univ. hist.

— Lives of Baron Steuben and Sir W. Phips. *See* Sparks, J., Lib. of Am. biog.

— Principles of metaphys. and ethical sci. applied to the evidences of religion. 12°. $1.88..... *Ware.*

— Treatise on logic; or, the laws of pure thought. ('64.) 10th ed. 12°. '74. $2............*Allyn.*

Bowen, G: Daily meditations. 12°. $1.25..*Pres. Bd.*

— Love revealed. 12°. $1.50..............*Pres. Bd.*

Bowen, T. J. Yoruba grammar and dict. 4°. '58. pap., $4.........................*Smith. Inst.*

Bowen, W. H. Memoir of Geo. T. Day; with letters and sermons. 8°. '75. $1.50.........*Freewill.*

Bower, J: Public school singing-book. 24°. '60. hf. bd., 25c. ....*Fortescue.*

Bowers, P. P. Moss Rose. *See* Head and heart ser.

Bowes, G: S. Illustrative gatherings for preachers and teachers: anecdotes, facts, etc. ('63–'65.) New ed. 2 v. 12°. '75. ea., $1.75..*Perkinpine.*

— Scripture itself the illustrator. 16°. $1.50...*Carter.*

Bowled out. Craven, H. T. 15c...*French; Lee & S.*

Bowler, N. E. D. *See* Thompson, L. S., *and* Bowler, O. H. *and* N. E. D.

Bowler, O. H. *See* Thompson, L. S., and Bowler, O. H. *and* N. E. D.

Bowlers, —. *See* Thompson, M. M., *and* Bowlers, —.

Bowles, Emily. In the Camargue. [Fiction.] 12°. $1.25; pap., 75c......................*Loring.*

Bowles, S: Across the continent: a summer's journey to the Rocky Mountains, the Mormons and Pacific states with S. Colfax. cr. 8°. '65. $1.50; with map, $2......................*Hurd & H.*

— Our new west: records of travel between the Mississippi River and the Pacific Ocean. map, por. and ill. 8°. '69. *$3; leath., $3.50....*C. A. Nichols.*

— Pacific Railroad open: how to go, what to see. 16°. '69. 75c.; pap., 35c. ....*Osgood.*

Bowman, Anne. Among the Tartar tents; or, the lost fathers. ill. 16°. $1.75......*Scribner, W. & A.*

— Amy Carlton; or, first days at school. ill. 16°. 75c. *Routledge.*

— Bear hunters of the Rocky Mountains. ill. 16°. $1.25....................*Porter; Routledge.*

— Boy foresters (The): tale of the days of Robin Hood. ill. 16°. $1.25.....................*Routledge.*

— Boy pilgrims (The). ill. 16°. $1.25....*Routledge.*

— Boy voyagers (The). ill. 16°. $1.25....*Routledge.*

— Castaways (The): the adventures of a family in the wilds of Africa. ill. 16°. $1.25......*Routledge.*

— Clarissa; or, the Mervyn inheritance. ill. 16°. $1.25. *Routledge.*

— Doctor's (The) ward. *See* Young ladies' lib.

— Esperanza; or, the home of the wanderers. ill. 16°. $1.25................................*Routledge.*

— Forest library of adventure. 3 v. ill. 16°. $3.75. *Routledge.*

Cont.: Boy foresters. — Young exiles. — Bear hunters of the Rocky Mountains.

— Harry and his homes; or, the conquest of pride. ill. 16°. 75c...........................*Routledge.*

— How to make the best of it. ill. 16°. $1.25. *Routledge.*

— Hunter's library of adventure. 3 v. ill. 16°. $3.75. *Routledge.*

Cont.: Tom and the crocodiles. — Nile voyagers. — Esperanza; or, the home of the wanderers.

— Kangaroo hunters; or, adventures in the bush. ill. 16°. $1.25....................*Porter; Routledge.*

— Laura Temple: a tale for the young. 16°. 75c. *Routledge.*

Bowman, Anne, *continued.*

— More original double acrostics; with solutions to the 1st ser. 16°. 50c....................*Routledge.*

— New cookery book. ill. 12°. '68. hf. bd., $3. *Routledge.*

— Original double acrostics. 16°. 50c......*Routledge.*

— — *See also above* More.

— Rector's (The) daughter. ill. 16°. $1....*Routledge.*

— Sunshine and clouds in the morning of life. ill. 16°. $1..................................*Routledge.*

— Tom and the crocodiles. ill. 16°. $1.25..*Routledge.*

— Voyage library of adventure. 3 v. ill. 16°. $3.75. *Routledge.*

Cont.: Boy voyagers. — Castaways. — Young yachtsmen.

— Young exiles (The); or, the wild tribes of the north. ill. 16°. $1.25.......................*Routledge.*

— Young Nile voyagers. ill. 16°. $1.25....*Routledge.*

— Young yachtsmen; or, the wreck of the Gypsy. ill. 16°. $1.25...........................*Routledge.*

— (*ed.*) Poetry from the best authors. ill. 16°. $1. *Scribner, W. & A.*

Bowman, F. A. *See* Dana, C. A., *and* Bowman, F. A.

Bowman, Hetty. Christian daily life. 12°. $1.25. *Nelson.*

Bowman, J: E. Introduction to pract. chemistry, incl. analysis. 6th Am., from 6th Lond., ed., rev. ill. roy. 12°. $2.25.........................*Lea.*

— Practical handbook of medical chemistry; ed. by C. L. Bloxam. 6th Am., from 4th Eng., ed., rev. ill. roy. 12°. $2.25..........................*Lea.*

Bowne, B. P. Philosophy of Herbert Spencer. 12°. '74. $1.25...................*Meth. Bk. Conc.*

Bowring, J: Matins and vespers. (Blue and gold ed.) 32°. $1.50..................**Osgood.*

Bowyer, G: Commentaries on universal public law. 8°. '54. $3.................*T. & J. W. Johnson.*

— — *See also* Law lib.

Box, T: Practical hydraulics: rules and tables for engineers, etc. 12°. $2.50.............*Baird.*

— *Same.* 3d ed. pl. cr. 8°. '73. $2.50........*Spon.*

— Practical treatise on heat. pl. post 8°. $4.25. *Baird; Spon.*

— Practical treatise on mill-gearing, wheels, shafts, etc.; for engineers. pl. cr. 8°. '69. $2........*Spon.*

Box and Cox: drama. Morton, J. M. 15c....*French.*

Box and Cox: Ethiop. drama. Christy, E. B. 15c. *Happy.*

Box and Cox married. Coyne, J. S. 15c.....*French.*

Box of mischief. *See* French's comic dramas.

Boxer, Ja. Sacred dramas. 12°. $1.50.....*Lee & S.*

Boxing made easy; or, the complete manual of self-defense. ill. 12°. 15c...............*Dick & F.*

Boy adventurers (The); or, trial and trust. ill. post 18°. 75c......................*Scribner, W. & A.*

Boy (The) and the birds. 18°. 80c........*Am. S. S.*

Boy (The) and the constellations. Goddard, J. $1.25. *Scribner, W. & A.*

Boy (The) and the man. 18°. 50c........*Cong. Pub.*

Boy artist. ill. 16°. 50c......................*Nelson.*

Boy artist. Tucker, C. 60c. ....*Tibbals.*

Boy artist. *See* Maggie Fuller lib.

Boy artists. Foa, E. $1...................*Dutton.*

Boy at Bramley. Townsend, V. F. 75c.......*Loring.*

Boy cavaliers (The). Adams, H. C. $1..*Routledge.*

Boy farmers (The) of Elm Island. Kellogg, E. $1.25...............................*Lee & S.*

Boy foresters (The). Bowman, A. $1.25..*Routledge.*

Boy friend. Baker, S. 60c.............(?)*Martien.*

Boy guardian. *See* Bowen, C. E.

Boy hunters (The). Reid, M. $1.50........*Miller.*

Boy (The) in blue. Gildersleeve, C. H. $1.50. *Allison.*

Boy (The) in grey. Kingsley, H. $1.50..*Routledge.*

Boy inventor (The). Bulfinch, T. 75c. .... *Fuller.*
Boy Joe (The). *See* Dickens, C.
Boy joiner (The) and model maker. *See* Davidson, E. A.
Boy life. 18°. 70c. .... *Pres. Bd.*
Boy life. Benson, E. W. $2.50 .... *Macmillan.*
Boy (The) makes the man: example and encouragement for the young. ill. 18°. 75c. .... *Nelson.*
Boy martyrs. Tayleure, C. W. 15c. .... *French.*
Boy (The) not made to mind. *See* Bright gems for boys and girls; — Little boys' lib.
Boy patriot (The). Baker, S. S. 50c. ..... *Am. Tr.*
Boy pilgrims. Bowman, A. $1.25 .... *Routledge.*
Boy of Mt. Rhigi. Sedgwick, C. M. $1 .. *Perkinpine.*
Boy of spirit. ill. 18°. '68. 65c. .... *Perkinpine.*
Boy slaves (The). Reid, M. $1.50 .... *Miller.*
Boy tar (The). Reid, M. $1.50 .... *Miller.*
Boy (The) trained for the ministry. 18°. 70c.; 75c. *Dutton.*
Boy voyagers (The). Bowman, A. $1.25 .. *Routledge.*
Boy (The) who wondered. Gladstone, G. 75c. *Cassell.*
Boy (The) with an idea. *See* Eiloart, *Mrs.* C. J.
Boyce, A. P. Art of lettering, and sign painters' manual. ('71.) 3d ed. col. pl. obl. 4°. '75. $3.50 .... *Williams.*
— Modern ornamental and interior decorator: ill. of the arts of scroll, arabesque and ornamental painting. col. pl. obl. 4°. '74. $3.50 .. *Williams.*
Boyce, A: A. Manual of practice in the U. S. Circuit courts. 8°. shp., $6.50 .... *W. C. Little.*
Boyce, J. ["Pl. Peppergrass."] Mary Lee; or, the Yankee in Ireland. 12°. $1.50 .... *Noonan.*
— Shandy Maguire; or, tricks upon travellers: story of the north of Ireland. 12°. $1.50 ... *Noonan.*
— Spaewife (The); or, the queen's secret: tale of the days of Elizabeth. 12°. $2 .... *Noonan.*
Boyd, A. K. H. Autumn holidays. 16°. $1.25. **Osgood.*
— Counsel and comfort. 16°. $1.25 .... **Osgood.*
— Country parson's recreations. 2 v. 16°. $2.50. **Osgood.*
— Every-day philosopher. 16°. $1.25 .... **Osgood.*
— Graver thoughts. 2 v. 16°. $2.50 .... **Osgood.*
— Leisure hours. 16°. $1.25 .... **Osgood.*
Boyd, *Mrs.* E. E. Captain Charley, and his little right hand. ('69.) New ed. ill. 16°. '74. 75c. .. *Hoyt.*
— Farmer Burt's seed. ill. 18°. 80c. ..... *J. A. Moore.*
— Hearts of gold. 16°. '75. $1 .... *Meth. Epis.*
— Jack Bryson. ill. 18°. 80c. .... *J. A. Moore.*
— Lily's looking-glasses. ill. 18°. 45c. ... *J. A. Moore.*
— Little slate picker (The), and other stories. ill. 18°. 50c. .... *J. A. Moore.*
— Mary Morne and her friend; or, the two paths. ill. 18°. 75c. .... *J. A. Moore.*
— Our Guy; or, the elder brother. 16°. '75. $1 .. *Hoyt.*
— Paul Loring; or, mounting the ladder. ill. 18°. 80c. *J. A. Moore.*
— Prayer test lib. 4 v. ill. 18°. '75. $1.75 .. *Meth. Epis.*
Cont.: Children's prayer test. — Amos and his star. — Aunt Elinor's charge. — Becky.
— Stones and diamonds. 16°. $1.25 ...... (?) *Martien.*
— *Same.* 16°. '75. $1.25 .... *H. A. Young.*
— Together; or, life on the circuit. 16°. 90c. *Cin. Meth. Bk. Conc.*
— *and* Johnston, *Miss* E. M. The children's speaker and anniversary gem. 18°. 60c. ... *J. A. Moore.*
Boyd, Erskine. Driven from home. [Fiction.] ill. 8°. (Lond.) pap., 30c. .... *Am. News.*
Boyd, Ja. R. Child's book on the "Shorter catechism." 18°. 25c. .... *Pres. Bd.*
— Communion table (The). 18°. 50c. ...... *Pres. Bd.*
— Daily communion with God. 18°. '73. 30c.; 50c.; mor., $1.25 .... *Am. Tr.*
— Eclectic moral philosophy. 12°. $1.50 .... *Harper.*

Boyd, Ja. R., *continued.*
— Elements of Eng. compos. 12°. '60. $1.50 .. *Barne*
— Elements of logic; on the basis of lectures by W Barron. ('56.) 2d ed., enl. 12°. $1.25 .. *Barne*
— Elements of rhetoric and literary criticism. 12°. h roan, 75c. .... *Harpe*
— Life of Philip Doddridge. 12°. '60. 80c. .. *Am. T*
— Westminster shorter catechism, with analysis. 18 65c. .... *Pres. B.*
— *See also* Bacon, *Lord*, Essays; — Kane, *Lord*, El ments of crit.
— (*ed.*) Annotated poets. (Lib. ed.) 5 v. 12°. '50–'5 ea., $1.50. (School ed.) ea., hf. bd., $1.25. *Barne*
Cont.: Cowper's Task. — Milton's Paradise lost. — Pollok Course of time. — Thomson's Seasons. — Young's Nig thoughts.
Boyd, M: Reminiscences of fifty years. 12°. $1.75 *Appleto*
Boyd, *Mrs.* Ma. D. R. Barby's shuttle, and what wrought. ill. 18°. 75c. .... *J. A. Moor*
— Stepping stones over the brook. ill. 18°. 80c. *J. A. Moor*
— Three rules (The). ill. 16°. $1 .... *J. A. Moor*
Boyd, *Mrs.* Olivia A. Child-life in Oregon. ('66 New ed. ill. 18°. '72. 60c. .... *Hoy*
Boyd, Rob. Glad tidings, a book for inquirers; wi pref. by D. L. Moody. 16°. '76. 75c.; pap., 35 *Reve*
— My inquiry meeting; or, plain truths for anxio souls. ('75.) New ed. 32°. '76. 25c.; pap 15c. .... *Reve*
— Wonderful career of Moody and Sankey in Gt. Bri and Am. ill. and por. 12°. '75. $2. (?) *Goodspee*
— Young converts; or, beginners in Zion's ways; wi pref. by D. L. Moody. 16°. '72. $1 ..... *Revel*
Boydell, J: *and* Josiah. Shakespeare gallery: 98 pi tures ill. the dramatic works of S. imp. 4°. '7 $25; mor., $40 .... *Lippincott; Little, B. & C*
— *Same:* 100 heliot. ill. ('73.) 5th ed. 25 pts. ro 4°. '76. *$25; hf. mor., $33; mor., $45 .. *Gebbi*
Boyden, Alb. G. History and alumni record of th State Normal School, Bridgewater, Mass., t July, 1876. 8°. '76. pap., $1 .... *William*
Boyé, Mt. H. Treatise on pneumatics. ill. 8°. '5 $1.25 .... *Fortescu*
Boyer, Abel. French pronouncing dict.; with list words and phrases, etc.; rev. and enl. by T. Clark roy. 8°. hf. leath., $3 .... *Desilve*
Boyesen, Hjalmar H. Gunnar: a Norse romance (Saunterer's ser.) 18°. '74. $1.25 ..... *Osgoo*
— Norseman's (A) pilgrimage. sm. 12°. $1.50. *Sheldo*
Boyhood of great men. *See* Edgar, J. G.
Boyhood of great painters. 2 v. 16°. $1.20; $2. *Sadlie*
Boykin, S: Memoir of Howell Cobb. 12°. $3. *Lippincot*
Boyland, G: H. Six months under the red cross wit the French army. 12°. '73. $1.50 ...... *Clark*
Boyle, Esmeralda. Thistledown. [Poetry.] 12°. $1.50 *Lippincot*
Boyle, J: Battle fields of Ireland, 1688–1691: outlin hist. of the Jacobite war in Ireland. 12°. $1.50 *Coddington*
Boylston club: German and Eng. four-part songs. 8 '75. bds., $1.50 .... *Ditson*
Boyne water. *See* Banim, J. *and* M.
Boynton, C: B. History of the Am. navy during the re bellion. 2 v. maps, eng., etc. 8°. $8 .. *Appleton*
Boynton, E: C. History of West Point and its milit importance during the Am. rev.; and the origi and progress of the U. S. Milit. Acad. 2d ed maps and eng. 8°. '71. $3.50 ... *Van Nostrand*
Boynton, H. V. Sherman's historical raid: th "Memoirs" in the light of the record: a review based upon compilations from the files of th War Office. 8°. '75. $2 .... *Wilstach.*

Boynton, J. Practical sanctification. 12°. 75c. *Palmer.*

Boy's (A) adventures in the wilds of Africa. Howitt, W. $1.25 .... *Routledge.*

Boy's (A) adventures in the wilds of Australia. *See* Howitt, W.

Boy's (A) book. Sigourney, L. H. 60c. ..... *Carter.*

Boy's book about Indians. Tuttle, E. B. $1.50. *Lippincott.*

Boy's book of animals, birds and sports. ill. 12°. '76. $1.50 .... *World Pub.*

Boy's book of diversions. ill. sm. 4°. $1.50 .. *Morton.*

Boy's book of heroes. Peake, H. $1.25. *Scribner, W. & A.*

Boy's book of travel. *See* Winter evening lib.

Boy's country book. Miller, T. $2.50 .... *Routledge.*

Boy's good library. 6 v. 18°. $4 .... *Am. Bapt.*
Cont.: Boys in our school. — Joseph Murray. — Melzar. — Prince Alcohol. — Carroll Ashton. — Rodney Roverton, by G. B. Taylor.

Boy's heaven. Child, L. M. 75c. .... *Lothrop.*

Boy's home book of sports, games, exercises and pursuits; by writers of "Boy's own magazine." ill. 12°. $1.25 .... *Porter.*

Boy's (A) kingdom; or, four years in a cave; by author of "Under the lime trees." ill. 12°. '74. $1.75. *Nelson.*

Boy's own book: an encyclopedia of sports. ill. 12°. $1.50 .... *World Pub.*

Boy's own library. 4 v. 12°. $4 .... *Nelson.*
Cont.: Home amid the snow. — Afar in the forest. — Round the world. — Ruined cities of the east.

Boy's own toy maker. *See* Continental lib.

Boy's packet. 32°. 50c. .... *Nelson.*

Boy's picture gallery. 18°. pap., 10c. ...... *Am. S. S.*

Boy's pump book: how to make miniature pumps. 12°. '60. 25c. .... *Randolph.*

Boy's treasury of sports. ill. 16°. $1.50 .. *Clark & M.*

Boy's trip across the plains. Preston, L. 75c. *Roman.*

Boys. Barker, M. A. (*Lady*). $1.75 ...... *Routledge.*

Boys and birds. Dyer, S. $1.75 .... *Am. Bapt.*

Boys and boys. *See* Little folks ser.

— *Same;* [also] Kindness. ill. 18°. '72. 50c. *Lothrop.*

Boys and boys library. 6 v. ill. 18°. $1.80 .. *Lothrop.*
Cont.: Boys and boys. — Kindness. — Among the mountains. — Willie Graham. — Even grip. — The victory.

Boys and girls. Bramston, M. 50c. .... *Pott.*

Boys and girls at Donaldson. *See* Bradley, W. I.

Boys and girls in biology. Stevenson, S. H. $1.50. *Appleton.*

Boys and girls of Beech Hill. *See* Avery, J. G.

Boys at Chequasset. Whitney, A. D. T. $1 .. *Loring.*

Boys at Dr. Murray's. Bradley, W. I. $1.50 .. *Graves.*

Boys at Eaglewood. Guernsey, C. F. $1.50 .. *Am. S. S.*

Boys at home. Adams, C. $1.25 .... *Routledge.*

Boys at home. *See* Winter evening lib.

Boys at Sandover. Foster, C. F. $1.15 .. *Cong. Pub.*

Boys in blue. Hoge, A. H. *$3; $3.50 .... *Treat.*

Boys in our school. 18°. 70c.; 85c. ...... *Am. Bapt.*

Boys in the wood. 32°. 20c.; 15c. .... *Dutton.*

Boys of Beechwood. Eiloart, C. J. $1.25 .. *Routledge.*

Boys of the Bible. Williams, H. L. $1.50 .... *Allison.*

Boys of Ellenwood school. 18°. 40c. .... *Dutton.*

Boys of Grand Pré school. De Mille, J. $1.50. *Lee & S.*

Boys of Holy Writ and Bible narrative. ill. 16°. $1.75. *Scribner, W. & A.*

Boys of Wyoming valley. Wallace, S. S. T. 60c. *Pres. Bd.*

Boys who could not read. *See* Laurel ser.

Boys' and girls' illustrated gift-book. sq. 8°. $2. *Routledge.*

Boys' and girls' illustrated olio. ill. sq. 12°. '56. $1. *Meth. Bk. Conc.*

Boys' and girls' library. *See* Harper's.

Boys' book of trades, and the tools used in them. ill. sq. 8°. $2 .... *Routledge.*

Boys' keepsake. sq. 24°. 25c. .... *Am. S. S.*

Boys' own. 4°. bds., $1 .... (?) *H. D. Brown.*

Boys' own guide. Simonds, W. A. $1.25 .. *Cong. Pub.*

Boys' own library. *See* Beeton's.

Boys' own story book. ill. sq. 8°. '71. $2 .. *Routledge.*

Boys' picture-book of boats. ill. 4°. 35c. .. *Hurd & H.*

Boys' picture reading-book. ill. 16°. $1.25 .. *Routledge.*

Boys' story book. *See* Theodore Thinker.

Boys' treasury of sports and pastimes. 5 v. ill. 16°. $3.50 .... *Routledge.*
Cont.: Games and sports. — Games of skill and conjuring. — The young angler. — Athletic sports and recreations, by J. G. Wood. — Scientific amusement for young people.

Boys' treasury of sports and pastimes; by Rev. J. G. Wood, J. H. Pepper and others. ill. fp. 8°. $2.50 .... *Routledge.*

Boys' victory. ('68.) New ed. ill. 16°. '75. 85c. *Hoyt.*

Boys' words. 18°. 70c. .... *Am. S. S.*

Bozman, J: Leeds. History of Maryland, 1633–1860. roy. 8°. $5 .... *Murphy.*

Brace, C: Loring. Home life in Germany. 12°. $1.75. *Scribner.*

— Hungary in 1851; with an experience of the Austrian police. ill. and map. 12°. $1.75 ...... *Scribner.*

— Norse folk (The); or, a visit to the homes of Norway and Sweden. ill. 12°. $1.75 .... *Scribner.*

— Races (The) of the old world: manual of ethnology. ('63.) New ed. cr. 8°. '71. $2.50 .... *Scribner.*

— Short sermons for newsboys; with hist. of the formation of the Newsboys' Lodging-house. ill. 12°. '66. $1.50 .... *Scribner.*

Bracebridge Hall. *See* Irving, W.

Bracelet (Le). *See* Gaulle, *Mme.* de.

Bracelets (The). *See* Edgeworth, M.

Brachet, A: French grammar; adapted for Eng. schools by P. H. E. Brette and G. Masson. 12°. $1.25. *Lippincott.*

Brachvogel, A. E. Beaumarchais: hist. novel; tr. from the Germ. ill. 8°. $1.50; pap., $1 .... *Appleton.*

— Der Fels v. Erz. 2 v. 8°. pap., 50c. ...... *Morwitz.*

— Der fliegende Holländer. 2 v. 8°. ea., pap., 50c. *Morwitz.*

— Der Trödler. 12°. '65. pap., 40c. .... *Steiger.*

Brackenridge, H: M. History of the insurrection in western Pennsylvania, called the "whiskey insurrection" [1794]. 8°. '59. $1.75. *R. S. Davis (P.)*

— Recollection of persons and places in the west. New ed. 12°. $2 .... *Lippincott.*

Brackenridge, Hu. H. Adventures of Captain Farrago. ill. 12°. pap., 75c. .... *Peterson.*

— Major O'Regan's adventures. ill. 12°. pap., 75c. *Peterson.*

— Modern chivalry; or, the adventures of Captain Farrago and Teague O'Regan, his servant. 2 v. 12°. ea., $1.75 .... *Peterson.*

Brackenridge, W. D. Botany. *See* Wilkes, C: United States explor. expedition.

— Living plants and seeds. *See* Gilliss, J. M.

Brackett, Alb. G. History of the U. S. cavalry, [1789]–1863. ill. 12°. $2 .... *Harper.*

Brackett, Anna C. Education of American girls. 12°. '74. $1.75 .... *Putnam.*

— *See also* Eliot, I. M., *and* Brackett, A. C.

Brackett, G: E. Farm talk. 16°. $1; pap., 50c. *Lee & S.*

Bradbury, Osgood. Julia Mansfield; or, the fate of ambitious mothers. 8°. pap., 25c. ... *Dick & F.*

Bradbury, W: B. Alpine glee singer: 4 vocal parts. 8°. '50. bds., $1.50 ... *Ivison.*
— Anthem book. obl. 8°. '60. bds., $2 ... *Ditson.*
— Bradbury trio; [compr.] New golden chain, New golden shower and New golden censer. obl. 16°. '70. bds., $1 ... *Biglow.*
— Carol: music book of instruction and practice. 16°. '61. bds., 56c.; pap., 50c. ... *Ivison.*
— Eclectic tune book. 8°. $1.25 ... *Pres. Bd.*
— Esther, the beautiful queen; with words by C. M. Cady; rev. by R. W. Seager. [Cantata.] obl. 8°. '74. pap., 50c. — Libretto. 12c. ... *Ditson.*
— Flora's festival. obl. 12°. 35c. ... *Ivison.*
— Fresh laurels for the Sabbath school. [Singing book.] obl. 16°. '67. bds., 35c. ... *Biglow.*
— — *See also* Laurels and jewels.
— Golden hymns: sel. from "Bradbury trio." 32°. '66. bds., 15c.; pap., 10c. ... *Biglow.*
— Jubilee (The): collection of church music. New ed., enl. obl. 8°. '58. bds., $1.50 ... *Ditson.*
— Key-note (The): collection of church and singing school music. obl. 8°. '63. bds., $1.50 .. *Ditson.*
— Metropolitan glee book: collection of choruses and four-part songs. 8°. '52. bds., $1.50 ... *Ivison.*
— Musical gems; for school and home. 16°. '49. bds., 56c. ... *Ivison.*
— New chain; [also] New censer. obl. 16°. '70. bds., 65c. ... *Biglow.*
— *Same;* [also] New shower. obl. 16°. '66. bds., 65c. *Biglow.*
— New golden censer: a musical offering to the Sabbath schools. obl. 16°. '70. bds., 35c. ... *Biglow.*
— — *See also above* Bradbury trio; New chain.
— New golden chain of Sabbath school melodies. obl. 16°. '66. bds., 35c. ... *Biglow.*
— — *See also above* Bradbury trio; New chain.
— New golden shower. [Songs.] obl. 16°. '66. bds., 35c. ... *Biglow.*
— — *See also above* Bradbury trio; New chain.
— New shower; [also] New censer. obl. 16°. '70. bds., 65c. ... *Biglow.*
— — *See also above* New golden shower.
— New York glee and chorus book. obl. 8°. bds., $1.50. *Ditson.*
— Orio: Sunday school hymns from "Oriola." ('60.) New ed. 32°. '73. hf. bd., 25c. ... *Wilstach.*
— Oriola: hymn and tune book for S.-schools. ('62.) New ed., enl. sq. 16°. '73. hf. bd., 60c. *Wilstach.*
— Singing bird (The): collection of juvenile music, on a progressive plan. 8°. '52. bds., 56c. ... *Ivison.*
— Young shawm: collection of school music. obl. 12°. '55. bds., 60c. ... *Ditson.*
— — *See also* Shawm (The).
— *See also* Lowry, R., Sherwin, W. F., *and* Allen, C. G.; — Root, G. F., *and* Bradbury, W. B.; — Seward, T. F., Mason, L., *and* Bradbury, W. B.
— *and* Bell, G. A., *and* Main, S. The clariona: hymns and tunes for S.-schools. obl. 16°. '67. bds., 60c. *Biglow.*
— *and* Converse, C: C. Musical bouquet and institute choir. 12°. '56. bds., $1 ... *Ivison.*
— *and* Stearns, J. N. Temperance chimes. [Music book.] 12°. pap., 30c.; bds., 35c. ... *Nat. Temp.*

Bradbury, W. F. Eaton's elementary algebra. 12°. $1.25. — Key of answers to same. 25c. — Key of solutions to same. $1.25 ... *Thompson.*
— Elementary geometry. 12°. $1 ... *Thompson.*
— *Same;* [also] Elementary trigonometry. 12°. $1.50. — Key. $1 ... *Thompson.*
— Elementary trigonometry. 12°. $1 ... *Thompson.*
— Trigonometry and surveying. 8°. $1.75. — Key. $1. *Thompson.*

Bradbury trio (The). Bradbury, W. B. $1 .. *Biglow.*

Bradby, E. H. Sermons preached at Haileybury. 8°. '73. $4 ... *Macmillan.*

Braddon, *Miss* Ma. Eliz. [*Mrs.* J: Maxwell.] Aurora Floyd. 8°. $1; pap., 75c. ... *Peterson.*

Braddon, *Miss* Ma. Eliz., *continued.*
— *Same.* 8°. pap., 75c. ... *Harper.*
— Better for worse. 8°. pap., 75c. ... *Peterson.*
— Birds of prey. 8°. pap., 75c. ... *Harper.*
— Black band (The); or, the mysteries of midnight. 8°. pap., 50c. ... *De Witt.*
— Blue band (The); or, a story of woman's vengeance. 8°. pap., 50c. ... *De Witt.*
— Bound to John Company; or, the adventures and misadventures of Robert Ainsleigh. ill. 8°. pap., 75c. ... *Harper.*

Note. Same as "Robert Ainsleigh."

— Charlotte's inheritance: sequel to "Birds of prey." 8°. pap., 50c. ... *Harper.*
— Darrell Markham. 8° pap., 50c. ... *Dick & F.*
— Dead men's shoes. 8°. '76. pap., 75c. ... *Harper.*
— Dead-sea fruit. ill. 8°. pap., 50c. ... *Harper.*
— Diavola. 8°. pap., 50c. ... *Dick & F.*
— Doctor's (The) wife. 8°. pap., 50c. ... *Dick & F.*
— Dudley Carleon. 8°. pap., 25c. ... *Dick & F.*
— Eleanor's victory. 8°. pap., 75c. ... *Harper.*
— Factory girl (The); or, all is not gold that glitters. 8°. pap., 75c. ... *De Witt.*
— Fenton's quest. ill. 8°. pap., 50c. ... *Harper.*
— Henry Dunbar. 8°. pap., 50c. ... *Dick & F.*
— Hostages to fortune. ill. 8°. pap., 75c. ... *Harper.*
— John Marchmont's legacy. 8°. pap., 75c. ... *Harper.*
— Lady Audley's secret. 8°. pap., 50c. ... *Dick & F.*
— Lady Lisle (The). 8°. pap., 50c. ... *Dick & F.*
— Lady's (The) mile. 8°. pap., 50c. ... *Dick & F.*
— Lawyer's (The) secret. 8°. pap., 25c. ... *Peterson.*
— Leighton Grange; or, who killed Edith Woodville? 8°. pap., 25c. ... *De Witt.*
— Lost for love. ill. 8°. pap., 75c. ... *Harper.*
— Lovels (The) of Arden. ill. 8°. pap., 75c. ... *Harper.*
— My sister's confession. 8°. '76. pap., 50c. *W. F. Gill.*
— Octoroon (The); or, the lily of Louisiana. 8°. pap., 50c. ... *De Witt.*
— Only a clod. 8°. pap., 50c. ... *Dick & F.*
— Oscar Bertrand; or, the black band unmasked. 8°. pap., 50c. ... *De Witt.*
— Publicans and sinners; or, Lucius Davoren. 8°. pap., 75c. ... *Harper.*
— Robert Ainsleigh. 2 v. 12°. $3 ... *Lippincott.*

Note. Same as "Bound to John Company."

— Rupert Godwin. 8°. pap., 50c. ... *Dick & F.*
— Sir Jasper's tenant. 8°. pap., 50c. ... *Dick & F.*
— Strange world (A). 8°. pap., 75c. ... *Harper.*
— Strangers and pilgrims. ill. 8°. pap., 75c. ... *Harper.*
— Taken at the flood. 8°. pap., 75c. ... *Harper.*
— Three times dead. 8°. pap., 50c. ... *Dick & F.*
— To the bitter end. ill. 8°. pap., 50c. ... *Harper.*
— White phantom (The); or, the nameless child. 8°. pap., 75c. ... *De Witt.*
— *See also* Satchel ser.

Braden, C., *and* Hughey, G. W. Debate on the action, design and subjects of baptism, and the work of the Holy Spirit. 8°. $2 ... *Chase.*

Bradford, Alex. W. *See* New York City and County, Surrogate reports.

Bradford, Gam. Financial administration: address before Am. Soc. Sci. Assoc., May 19, 1874. 8°. '74. pap., 10c. ... *Williams.*
— Practical working of our government: address before Y. M. C. Union, Boston, March 15th, 1873. 8° pap., 15c. ... *Williams.*

Bradford, J: Life and writings. *See* British reformers.

Bradford, *Mrs.* Sa. H. Chosen people (The). 12°. '63. $1.25 ... *Randolph.*
— Lewie; or, the bended twig. 16°. $1.25 .. *Hurd & H.*
— Silver lake stories. 6 v. ill. 16°. '52. $3.60. *Hurd & H.*
— Story of Columbus. 16°. '64. $1 ... *Randolph.*
— Tales for little convalescents. ill. sm. 4°. '68. 50c. *Hurd & H.*

Bradford, W: *See* Morton, N., New England's memorial.

Bradford bridge. Adams, H. C. $1.25...*Routledge.*

Bradlaugh, C: Few words (A) about the devil, and other biog. sketches and essays. por. 12°. '74. $1.50...*Somerby.*

– Impeachment of the house of Brunswick. 12°. '74. $1.25; pap., 75c...*W. F. Gill.*

Bradley, C: Family and parish sermons. 8°. $2.50. *Appleton.*

– Repentance, false and true. 18°. 35c. *U.P.Bd. of Pub.*

Bradley, E: ["Cuthbert Bede."] Adventures of Mr. Verdant Green, an Oxford freshman. ill. 12°. $1.50...*Carleton; Scribner, W. & A.*

Bradley, F. A. Practical, plane and solid geometry. (Adv. sci. ser.) ill. 12°. $1.50...*Putnam.*

Bradley, Mar. G. (*ed.*) Golden gems. 12°. '73. $1.25...*Lothrop.*

Bradley, *Mrs.* Ma. E. Arthur, and other stories. 18°. 45c.; 50c...*Dutton.*

– Douglass farm. *See* Atlantic lib.

– Good girls' library. 10 v. ill. 18°. $6...*Sheldon.*
Cont.: Alice Wade and lame Isaac. — Mabel's new year, etc. — Emigrant's mother. — Pastor's household. — Child angel, etc. — Little Agnes. — Facts for girls. — Lois Mead. — Clementina's mirror. — Prisoner's child.

– Grace's visit; or, the wrong way to cure a fault. ill. 16°. '69. 80c...*Lothrop.*

– Holy days of the church. 18°. 50c...*Dutton.*

– Little fir-tree. 18°. 40c...*Dutton.*

– Story of a summer; or, what do ye more than others? ill. 18°. 60c...*Bost. Am. Tr.; Lothrop.*

– *and* Neely, *Miss* K. J. Proverb stories. 6 v. ill. 16°. ea., $1...*Lee & S.*
Cont.: Birds of a feather. — Fine feathers do not make fine birds. — Handsome is that handsome does. — A wrong confessed is half redressed. — One good turn deserves another. — Actions speak louder than words.

Bradley, S. M. Manual of comparative anatomy and physiology. 3d ed. ill. 8°. '75. $2.50..*Lindsay.*

Bradley, W. I. ["Glance Gaylord."] After years: sequel to "Culm rock." ('67.) New ed. ill. 16°. '75. $1.50...*Hoyt.*

– Boys at Dr. Murray's: a story of school life. 16°. '66. $1.50...*Graves.*

– Culm rock, the story of a year: what it brought and what it taught. ('67.) New ed. ill. 16°. '75. $1.50...*Hoyt.*

– Donald Deane. 16°. $1.50..*Cong. Pub.; H.A. Young.*

– Gay cottage: story for boys. ill. 18°. 50c.*Bost. Am. Tr.*

– – *See also* Gay cottage stories.

– Miss Patience Hathaway. ill. 16°. '68. $1.50. *H. A. Young.*

– Mr. Pendleton's cup. ill. 16°. '69. $1.25. *H. A. Young.*

– Rainford series. 4 v. ill. 16°. $6...*Graves.*
Cont.: Gilbert Starr and his lessons. — Gilbert's last summer at Rainford. — Will Rood's friendship. — Jack Arcombie.

– Uncle Downe's home. *See* Chip-basket stories.

– *Same;* [also] The boys and girls at Donaldson. ill. 18°. 50c...*Bost. Am. Tr.*

Bradshaw, *Mrs.* C. A. Henry Burney; or, a talk about angels. 18°. 50c...*Pres. Bd.*

Bradshaw, Wesley (*pseud.*) *See* Alexander, C:

Bradwell, Myra. Full report of examination of students for admission to the bar in Ill. Supreme Court, Jan. term, 1873. 8°. '73. $1; pap., 60c.; shp., $1.50...(?) *Chic. Leg. News.*

Brady, W. N. The kedge-anchor; or, young sailors' assistant: evolutions of modern seamanship, rigging, knotting, etc. 18th ed., rev. and enl. ill. 8°. $3.50...*Appleton.*

Braeme, C. M. Lord Lisle's daughter. ill. 8°. (Lond.) pap., 30c...*Am. News.*

Braganza (*pseud.*) *See* Bragg, H. A.

Braganzio, the brigand: amateur drama. 16°. pap., 15c. *French.*

Bragelonne. *See* Dumas, A.

Bragg, H. A. ["Braganza."] Tekel; or, Cora Glencoe. [Fiction.] 12°. $1.75...*Lippincott.*

Braght, Thieleon J. v. Der blutige Schauplatz, od. Märtyrer Spiegel. 4°. leath., $6...*Baer.*

Brahms, J: Triumphlied. [Cantata.] 8°. $1.50; pap., $1; bds., $1.25...*Church.*

Braid of cords. Tucker, C. 75c...*Carter.*

Brainard, G: W. New method for the piano; [also] Musical hints, by K. Merz. 4°. $3..*Brainard.*

Brainard's chorus gems: collection of choruses. 8°. bds., 75c...*Brainard.*

Brainard's melodic school for violin. 4°. $4; abridg., $3...*Brainard.*

Brainard's musical albums. [Songs with music.] 12 nos. 4°. ea., 50c...*Brainard.*

Brainards (The) at the Rocky Mountains. Slicer, A. E. H. $1...*Meth. Bk. Conc.*

Brainerd, D: Memoir. 18°. 45c...*Am. S. S.*

— The missionary in the wilderness; or, grace displayed among the heathen: extracts from diary of B. 18°. 40c...*Pres. Bd.*

Brainerd, Jehu. Elementary principles of plane and perspective drawing. 4°. '52. bds., 40c. *Wilstach.*

Brainerd, M. Life of Rev. Thomas Brainerd. por. cr. 8°. $2.50...*Lippincott.*

Brainerd, T: Life of John Brainerd. 8°. $2.50. *Pres. Bd.*

Braithwaite, J. Bevan. Memoirs of J. J. Gurney. 8°. $2.25...*Lippincott.*

Brake up. Adams, W. T. $1.25...*Lee & S.*

Brakespeare. *See* Lawrence, George.

Brame, C. M. Tales from the diary of a Sister of Mercy. 6th ed. 12°. '68. $1.50....*Cath. Pub.*

Bramleighs of Bishop's Folly. *See* Lever, C.

Bramley, H: R., *and* Stainer, J: Christmas carols, new and old. ill. 8°. bds., 1.50...*Ditson.*

— — *Same.* ill. 4°. '71. $4...*Routledge.*

Bramston, Ma. Boys and girls. ill. 16°. 50c...*Pott.*

— Country maidens. ill. 12°. $1.50...*Nelson.*

— Ralph and Bruno. cr. 8°. '75. $1.25...*Macmillan.*

Bramwell, W. Memoir of life and ministry. 18°. '36. 60c...*Meth. Bk. Conc.*

Branches of palm. L., L. $1.50...*Lothrop.*

Branches running over the wall; for S.-school teachers. 18°. 50c...*Nelson.*

Brand, J: Popular antiquities of England, Scotland and Ireland. New ed., enl. by Sir H. Ellis. 3 v. 12°. (Bohn.) ea., $1.75...*Little, B. & Co.*

— *Same.* 3 v. 12°. (Bohn.) ea., $2. *Lippincott; Scribner, W. & A.*

Brand of Dominick. Rule, W. H. $1.25. *Meth. Bk. Conc.*

Brand v. Hamburg. Nieritz, G. 25c...*Morwitz.*

Brand (Der) v. Moskau. Oertel, P. F. W. 25c. *Steiger.*

Brande, W. T. Dictionary of science, literature and art. ill. 8°. shp., $6...*Harper.*

— *and* Cox, G. W. Dictionary of science, literature and art. New ed., rev. 3 v. 8°. '72. $20; hf. mor., $30..*Little, B. & Co.; Scribner, W. & A.*

Brandegee, *Mrs.* S. K. The bugle call. 18°. '71. 40c.; pap., 25c...*Am. Tr.*

Brandes, K: Petrus in Rom u. Rom ohne Petrus. 12°. 75c...*Benziger.*

— Rome and the popes; tr. by Rev. W. I. Wiseman. 12°. $1.25...*Benziger.*

Brandis, Chr. A: *See* Bunsen, C. C. J., Brandis, C. A., *and* Loebell, J. W.

Brandon library (The). 4 v. 16°. $5.25...*Hoyt.*
Cont.: Miriam Brandon, by Mrs. J. F. Moore. — Charley Bartlett's adventure, by T. F. Gibbs. — Ned's search. — Mary Horton, by Mrs. H. S. Grosvenor.

Brandt, C. P. H. *See* Luther, M., Hochzeitsgeschenk.

Brandt, Csp. Life of James Arminius; tr. by J. Guthrie, with introd. by T. O. Summers. 12°. '56. $1.50...*So. Meth.*

Brandt, J. D. Gunnery catechism, as applied to the service of naval ordnance. New ed., rev. ill. 18°. '70. $1.50 .... *Van Nostrand.*

Brandt, Seb. Ye shyp of fooles; tr. by A. Barclay, preste. [Reprint of ed. of 1509.] With introd., notes and glossary. 112 wood eng. in fac-simile. 2 v. cr. 4°. $25; hf. mor., $35; hf. vellum, $40; mor., $50 .... *Appleton.*

Brann, H: A. Politico-historical essay on the popes, as the protectors of popular liberty. 8°. pap., 25c. .... *Sadlier.*

— Truth and error. 18°. $1 .... *Sadlier.*

Branston, T: F. Handbook of pract. receipts; with glossary of med. and chem. terms. 12°. '65. $1.50 .... *Lindsay.*

Brant, Jos. (*Mohawk Indian.*) Memoir. 12°. '72. 50c. .... *Munsell.*

Brantley, W: T. Union sermon. 8°. pap., 15c. *Peterson.*

Braun, C: A. Uræmic convulsions of pregnancy, parturition and childbed; tr., with notes by J. M. Duncan. 12°. $1 .... *W. Wood.*

Braune, K: On John, Ephesians, Philippians, etc. *See* Lange, J. P., Commentary.

Braune, W: Position of the uterus and fœtus at the end of pregnancy. col. lith. ill. imp. f°. '73. $16.50. (?) *Stechert.*

Braune Erika (Die). Jensen, W. 40c. .... *Holt.*

Braussi, Mathieu. ["Brother Philippe."] Children of the patriarchs; or, the 600,000 combatants conquering the promised land. 18°. 75c.; $1. *O'Shea.*

— Filial and fraternal piety; tr. by C. Farnville. 18°. 60c.; 90c. .... *O'Shea.*

— Meditations on the eucharist and sacred heart. 12°. $2 50 .... *Sadlier.*

— Meditations on our last end, on sin, and on the sacrament of penance. 12°. $1.50 .... *O'Shea.*

— Meditations on the passions of Jesus Christ. 12°. $1.50 .... *O'Shea.*

— Meditations on the Virgin. 12°. '73. $2; $3. *Kelly, P. & Co.*

— Particular examen (The): subjects for daily meditation. 12°. $2 .... *O'Shea.*

— Resumé of meditations. 12°. $2 .... *Sadlier.*

Braut (Die) v. Messina. *See* Schiller, J. F. v.

Brave and bold series. *See* Alger, H., *jr.*

Brave and gentle. *See* Children's prize stories.

Brave Bobby; [also] Peter and his pony. 16°. 50c. *Scribner, W. & A.*

Brave boy (A). 18°. '69. 25c. .... *Lothrop.*

Brave boy (The). 18°. 45c. .... *Routledge.*

Brave boy (The). 16°. '75. 50c. .... *Hoyt.*

Brave days of old. *See* Little Katie's little lib.

Brave heart (The). Hamilton, K. W. 75c. ... *Pres. Bd.*

Brave hearts. Raymond, R. W. $1.75 .... *Ford.*

Brave lady (A). *See* Craik, D. M.

Brave Leute. *See* Hoffmann, F.

Brave Lisette. Carless, L. M. 75c. .... *Cassell.*

Brave little Louis. *See* Witt, *Mme.* H. de.

Brave little tailor (The). Grimm, J. L. *and* W. $1 .... *Miller.*

Brave Max. *See* Wright, *Mrs.* J. McN.

Brave men's footsteps. *See* Doyle, C.

Brave Old Salt. Adams, W. T. $1.50 ...... *Lee & S.*

Bravo (The). *See* Cooper, J. F.

Bravo (The) of Perth; [also] Adventures of Baron Munchausen. 16°. pap., 10c. ...... *U. P. James.*

Brawnville papers. Tyler, M. C. $1.50 .... *Osgood.*

Bray, *Mrs.* R. M. Petite; or, the story of a child's life. ill. 16°. '73. $1.25 .... *Lothrop.*

— Story of a lost child. 16°. $1.25 .... *Graves.*

Brayton, W: *See* Vermont, Supreme Court reports.

Brazen gates. [Juvenile.] 12°. $1.50 ...... *Carleton*

Brazen serpent (The). *See* Jones, J. H.

Breach of promise. [Fiction.] 8°. pap., 50c. *Harper*

Breach of promise. Buckstone, J. B. 15c. .. *French*

Breach of promise. Robertson, T. W. 15c. .. *De Witt*

Breach of trust. *See* Baker, *Mrs.* H. N. W., Golden spring ser.

Bread-and-cheese and kisses. Farjeon, B. L. 35c. *Harper*

Bread and oranges. Warner, S. $1.25 ...... *Carter*

Bread from God. ill. sm. 4°. $1.50 .... *Am. S. S.*

Bread of forgiveness. Boudon, M. F. 30c. .. *O'Shea*

Bread of life. 18°. 40c.; pap., 10c. .... *Bost. Am. Tr.*

Bread on the waters. Baker, G. M. 15c. ... *Lee & S.*

Bread upon the waters. 18°. 60c. .... *Whittaker*

— *Same.* 18°. 75c. .... *Dutton*

Bread upon the waters; or, the sure recompense for deeds of mercy. 18°. 50c. .... *Am. S. S.*

Break up your fallow ground. Wilkinson, G. H. 20c. *Dutton*

Breakers ahead. McKeever, H. B. $1. . *J. A. Moore*

Breakfast, dinner and tea; viewed classically, poetically and practically. sq. 12°. $1.50 ... *Appleton*

Breakfast, luncheon and tea. Harland, M. $1.75. *Scribner*

Breaking away. Adams, W. T. $1.25 ..... *Lee & S.*

Breaking a butterfly. *See* Lawrence, George.

Breaking the rules. ill. 16°. 60c. .... *Tibbals*

Breaking the rules. 16°. $1.25 .... *H. A. Young*

Breaking the spell. Offenbach, J. $1 .... *Pond*

Breakwater series. *See* Townsend, V. F.

Breath of life. Catlin, G. 75c. .... *Wiley.*

Breathings of the better life. Larcom, L. $2.50; $3.75; $5 .... *Osgood.*

Breathings of the soul. Power, P. B. 20c. .. *Randolph.*

Breban, Ja. M. Interest tables. ('49.) 11th ed. demy 8°. '75. $4.50 .... *Claxton.*

Breck, J. Lloyd. Disciplines, instructive and devotional, to be used in preparation for baptism, confirmation and the communion. [Interleaved.] 8°. 75c.; roan, $1 .... *Dutton.*

Breck, Jos. New book of flowers. ill. 12°. $1.75 .. *Judd.*

Breckenridge, J: *See* Hughes, J., *and* Breckenridge, J.

Breckinridge, Rob. J. Knowledge of God objectively considered: pt. 1 of Theology considered as a science of positive truth, both inductive and deductive. ('57.) New ed. 8°. '69. $3 ... *Carter.*

— Knowledge of God subjectively considered: pt. 2 of Theology considered, etc. ('59.) New ed. 8°. '69. $3.50 .... *Carter.*

Bred in the bone. Payn, J. 50c. .... *Harper.*

Bree, J. J. van. St. Cecilia's day; tr. from the Dutch. [Cantata.] 8°. $1.25; pap., $1 .... *Ditson.*

Breech-loader (The). Gloan. $2 ...... *Woodward.*

Breed, D: R. More light. 24°. '75. 20c.; pap., 10c. *Am. Tr.*

Breed, W: P. Anthropos. 12°. 60c. ...... *Pres. Bd.*

— Bible lessons on Palestine. 18°. 20c. .... *Pres. Bd.*

— Christ liveth in me. 16°. 80c. .... *Pres. Bd.*

— Grapes from the great vine for young fruit-gatherers. 18°. 75c. .... *Pres. Bd.*

— Handbook for funerals. 16°. 50c. .... *Pres. Bd.*

— Jenny Geddes; or, Presbyterianism and its great conflict with despotism. 16°. $1.50 ..... *Pres. Bd.*

— Lessons in flying; for our home birds. 18°. 55c. *Pres. Bd.*

— Little priest (The). 18°. 75c. .... *Pres. Bd.*

— Man responsible for his belief. 18°. pap., 10c. *Pres. Bd.*

— Presbyterianism three hundred years ago. 16°. $1. *Pres. Bd.*

Breed, W: P., *continued.*
- Presbyterians and the revolution. 16°. 75c. *Pres. Bd.*
- Prisoners (The). 18°. 75c. .... *Pres. Bd.*
- Questions for 52 Bible lessons. 18°. 16c. *Am. S. S.*
- Sunny mount (The) and its peaks. 18°. 70c. *Pres. Bd.*
- Under the oak. 18°. 75c. .... *Pres. Bd.*
- (*ed.*) Home-songs for home-birds. sm. 12°. $1. *Pres. Bd.*

Breezie Langton. Smart, H. 75c. .... *Appleton.*

Brégy, F. A. Compendium of the gram. rules of the French lang. [To form 3 pts.] pts. 1, 2. 12°. '71–'73. pt. 1, 75c.; pt. 2, 50c. ..... *Eldredge.*
- *See also* Smith, L., Guide to Fr. conversation.

Bréhat, A. de. Jean Belin, the French Robinson Crusoe. ill. 18°. $1.25 .... *Loring.*

Brehm, Alfr. Edm. Cassell's book of birds; tr. by T. R. Jones; with eng. and 40 full-page col. pl. from designs by F. W. Keyl. 4 v. post 4°. ea., $3.50; $5;—in 2 v. hf. cf., $20 .... *Cassell.*

Breitmann, Hs. (*pseud.*) *See* Leland, C. G.

Bremen lectures on fundamental living religious questions; tr. by D. Heagle. 12°. $1.75 ... *Lothrop.*

Bremer, *Miss* Fredrika. Works; tr. by M. Howitt. 4 v. 12°. (Bohn.) ea., $1.25 ... *Little, B. & Co.*

Cont.: The neighbors, and other tales.—The president's daughter.—The home; [also] Strife and peace.—A diary; The H— family, etc.

— *Same.* 4 v. 12°. (Bohn.) ea., $1.40. *Scribner, W. & A.*
— *Same.* 4 v. 12°. (Bohn.) ea., $1.50 ..... *Lippincott.*
— Brothers and sisters. 8°. pap., 50c. .... *Harper.*
— Father (The) and daughter. 12°. $1.75; pap., $1.50. *Peterson.*
— Four sisters (The). 12°. $1.75; pap., $1.50 .. *Peterson.*
— H— family (The). 8°. pap., 50c. .... *Harper.*
— Home (The). 8°. pap., 50c. .... *Harper.*
— *Same.* 12°. $1.75; pap., $1.50 .... *Peterson.*
— Homes of the new world: impressions of America; tr. by M. Howitt. 2 v. 12°. $3 .... *Harper.*
— Life in the old world; or, two years in Switzerland and Italy. 2 v. 12°. $3.50 .... *Peterson.*
— Midnight sun (The). 8°. pap., 25c. .... *Harper.*
— Neighbors (The). 8°. pap., 50c. .... *Harper.*
— *Same.* 12°. $1.75; pap., $1.50 .... *Peterson.*
— New sketches of every day life. 8°. pap., 50c. *Harper.*
— Nina. 8°. pap., 50c. .... *Harper.*
— Parsonage of Mora. 8°. pap., 25c. .... *Harper.*
— President's (The) daughter. 8°. pap., 25c. *Harper.*

Brenda (*pseud.*) Froggy's little brother. 12°. $1.25. *Carter.*

Brenda library (The). 4 v. 16°. $5 .... *Hoyt.*

Cont.: Old sailor's story, by G. E. Sargent.—Faithful son, by G. E. Sargent.—Poor clerk.—Froggy's little brother.

Brend'amour (*ill.*) *See* Christ in art.

Brendecke, F: Das Bier als Nahrungs- u. Genussmittel. 8°. '76. pap., 10c. .... *Doerflinger.*

Brendle, D. F. The prodigal son. 16°. $1. *Ref. Ch. Pub.*

Breneman, Ab. A. *See* Caldwell, G. C., *and* Breneman, A. A.

Brentford parsonage. Robbins, S. S. $1.25 .. *Carter.*

Brents, T. W. Gospel plan of salvation. 12°. $2.50; shp., $3; $3.50 .... *Chase.*

Bresciani, Ant. Edmondo: sketch of Roman manners and customs; tr. from the Ital. 12°. $2. *Sadlier.*
— Mathilda of Canossa; [also] Yoland of Groningen; tr. by A. T. Sadlier. 12°. $2; $2.50 ... *Sadlier.*
— Life of the Egyptian Aloysius; or, the little angel of the Copts; tr. by Rev. A. F. Hewit. 18°. 75c.; $1 .... *O'Shea.*
— Lionello: a tale of secret societies. 12°. '60. $1.50; $2 .... *Kelly, P. & Co.*

Bresil, J. *See* Dennery, A. P., *and* Bresil, J.

Bressant. Hawthorne, J. $1.50 .... *Appleton.*

Bresse, J. A. C. Hydraulic motors, incl. all kinds of water wheels, etc.; tr. by F. A. Mahan. New ed., with Fr. measures tr. into Eng. feet and inches. 8°. $2.50 .... *Wiley.*

Brett, —. Pantomime Joe: from "Boys of England." ill. 8°. (Lond.) 75c. .... *Am. News.*

Brett, R. Churchman's guide to faith and piety: manual of instruction and devotions. 2 v. 18°. ea., $1;—in 1 v. $1.75 .... *Pott.*

Brette, P. H. E., *and* Masson, G. Children's own French book: sel. of stories in prose. 4th ed. sm. 8°. 75c. .... *Lippincott.*
— — First French reader. sm. 8°. $1 .... *Lippincott.*
— — Hachette's French readers, modern authors, v. 1: Edmond About, with notes, etc. 3d ed. sm. 8°. $1 .... *Lippincott.*

Breughel brothers (The). Ungern Sternberg, A. v. $2 .... *Osgood.*

Brevard, J. *See* South Carolina, Reports.

Brevia. Helps, *Sir* A. $1.50 .... *Roberts.*

Brewer, E. C. Dictionary of phrase and fable. demy 8°. $3.50 .... *Cassell.*
— *Same.* cr. 8°. $3.50; hf. cf., $6 .... *Claxton.*
— Guide to the scientific knowledge of things familiar. 16°. $1.25 .... *Miller.*

Brewer, J: M. *See* Maryland, Laws and rules of the Land Office.

Brewer, N. *See* Maryland, Court of Appeals reports.

Brewer, T: Mayo. North American oology. pt. 1. 4°. '57. pap., $5 .... *Smith. Inst.*
— *See also* Baird, S. F., Brewer, T. M., *and* Ridgway, R.

Brewer, W. Alabama: her history, resources, war record and public men, 1840–'72. 8°. '72. $3. *Barrett.*

Brewer's (The) family. Ellis, S. S. $1 ...... *Dodd.*

Brewster, Anne. Compensation; or, always a future. [Fiction.] 12°. $1.75 .... *Lippincott.*

Brewster, C: W. Rambles about Portsmouth. 2 ser.; with biog. sketch of author, by W. H. Y. Hackett. 2 v. 8°. '59–'69. ea., $2.50 ..... *Williams.*

Brewster, *Sir* D: Letters on natural magic; addressed to Sir W. Scott. ill. 18°. 75c. .. *Harper.*
— Life of Sir Isaac Newton. ill. 18°. 75c. ... *Harper.*
— Martyrs of science: lives of Galileo, Tycho Brahe, and Kepler. 18°. 75c. .... *Harper.*
— *Same.* por. 12°. '74. $2.25 .... *Routledge.*
— More worlds than one: the creed of the philosopher and the hope of the Christian. New ed. ill. 12°. '74. $2.25 .... *Routledge.*
— *See also* Euler, L.; —Thompson, J. B.

Brewster, F. C. Digest of Penna. Supreme Court cases (3d Wright–5th P. F. Smith); with tables of titles and cases. 8°. '69. shp., $4.50. *J. Campbell & Son.*
— Reports of equity, election and other cases determined principally in the courts of Phila. 4 v. 8°. shp., $24 .... *Kay.*

Brewster, G: New philosophy of matter, showing identity of imponderables and influence [of] electricity in producing chemical changes, etc. New ed., rev. and enl.; [also] Electricity as a curative agent, by A. H. Stevens. 12°. '73. *net,* *$3 .... *Claxton.*

Brewster, J. M. Life of William Burr. ('70.) 2d ed. 12°. '71. $1 .... *Freewill.*

Brewster, Marg. M. Little Ben, the motherless boy. 18°. '56. 50c. .... *Randolph.*
— Work; or, plenty to do, and how to do it. 24°. '58. $1 .... *Randolph.*

Breyfogle, W. L. Epitome of homœopathic medicines. 12°. $1.50;—interleaved. 18°. hf. mor., $3 .... *Boericke.*

Breymann, Hm. First French exercise book. 12°. '75. $1.75 .... *Macmillan.*
— French grammar, based on philol. principles. 12°. '74. $1.75 .... *Macmillan.*
— Second French exercise book. 12°. '75. $1.25. *Macmillan.*
Brian Boroihrne. Knowles, J. S. 15c. .... *French.*
Brian O'Linn: farce. 16°. pap., 15c. .... *French.*
Brian O'Lynn. Maxwell, W. H. 75c. .... *Peterson.*
Bric-a-brac hunter. Hall, H. B. $2.50 .. *Lippincott.*
Bric-a-brac series. *See* Stoddard, R. H.
Brice, Seward. Treatise on the doctrine of ultra vires: investigation of the principles which limit the capacities, powers and liabilities of corporations; with notes and ref. to Am. cases by A. Green. 8°. shp., $6.50 .... *Baker, V. & Co.*
Brick-dust. Pomeroy, M. M. $1.50 ...... *Carleton.*
Brickell, R. C. Digest of Alabama Sup. Court reports [1820-'70]. 2 v. 8°. '72-'74. shp., $25 .. *J. White.*
Brickey Sorrel. Bash, I. S. 90c. .... *Un. B. Pub.*
Bricktop (*pseud.*) *See* Small, G: G.
Brickwood, Edn. D. Boat racing; or, the arts of rowing and training. 12°. '76. $2.50. *Scribner, W. & A.*
Bridal. Knowles, J. S. 15c. .... *French.*
Bridal eve (The). Southworth, E. D. E. N. $1.75; $1.50 .... *Peterson.*
Bridal greetings. Wise, D. 50c.; $1 .. *Meth. Bk. Conc.*
Bridal keepsake. Coleman, *Miss* —. 50c. .. *Darrow.*
Bride and bridegroom. Dorr, J. C. R. $1.25. *Cin. Meth. Bk. Conc.*
Bride of Abydos. Byron, H. J. 15c. .... *French.*
Bride of Abydos. Dimond, W. 15c. .... *French.*
Bride of the broken vow. Gould, T. 75c. *W. H. Young.*
Bride of Lammermoor. Calcraft, J. W. 15c. .. *French.*
Bride of Lammermoor. *See* Scott, *Sir* W.
Bride of Llewellyn. Southworth, E. D. E. N. $1.75; $1.50 .... *Peterson.*
Bride (The) of love. Vernon, R. *$1.50 .. *Quak. City.*
Bride of Ludgate. Jerrold, D. 15c. .... *French.*
Bride of Messina. *See* Bonawitz, J. H.
Bride of Messina. *See* Schiller, J. F. v.
Bride of the wilderness. Bennett, E. $1.75; $1.50. *Peterson.*
Bride's (The) fate. Southworth, E. D. E. N. $1.75; $1.50 .... *Peterson.*
Bridge, Bewick. Algebra; with add. by the Christian Brothers. 12°. hf. bd., 45c. .... *Sadlier.*
— Treatise on the constitution, properties and analogies of the three conic sections. 8°. '31. *net*, 75c. *Peck.*
— Treatise on the elements of algebra. 52d Am., rev. from 7th Lond., ed. 12°. hf. roan, $1 .. *Desilver.*
Bridge, Christiana (*tr.*) *See* Demogeot, J., History of French literature.
Bridge of glass. Robinson, F. W. 50c. ...... *Harper.*
Bridge over the brook. 18°. 25c. .... *Am. S. S.*
Bridgeman, Eliza J. G. The daughters of China. 18°. 75c. .... *Carter.*
Bridgeman, H. *See* De Lolme, J. L., Wallace, R., *and* Bridgeman, H.
Bridgeman, I: V. [Plays.] 4 v. 16°. ea., pap., 15c. *French.*
Cont.: Good run for it: farce. — Matrimonial: farce. — Rifle and how to use it: farce. — Where's your wife? farce.
Bridgeman, J: I've eaten my friend: farce. 16°. pap., 15c. .... *French.*
Bridgeman, T: The American gardener's assistant. New ed., rev. and enl. by S. E. Todd. 12°. '66. $2 .... *Porter.*
Bridges, C: Memoir of Mary Jane Graham; abridg. 18°. 60c. .... *Pres. Bd.*
— On the Christian ministry. 8°. $2.50 ...... *Carter.*
Bridges, C: *continued.*
— On the Proverbs. 8°. $2.50 .... *Carter*
Bridges, J. Coal-pit; or, light in darkness; ed. by T. O. Summers. ('56.) 2d ed. 18°. '76. 40c. *So. Meth.*
Bridges, Mat. Ancient history. 12°. $1.25 .. *Sadlier.*
— Modern history. 12°. $1.50 .... *Sadlier.*
Bridges, Sallie. Marble Isle; [also] Legends of the round table, and other poems. 18°. $1.25. *Lippincott.*
Bridges, T. W. Gunner's pocket-book. cr. 32°. roan, 40c.; mor., 60c. .... *Spon.*
Bridget, *St.* (*The Mary of Erin.*) Life. 18°. 60c.; 90c. .... *O'Shea.*
— — *See also* Lives of the saints; — Mary of Egypt, *St*; — Patrick, *St.*
— Revelations. 18°. 60c. .... *Sadlier.*
Bridget Sullivan; or, the cup without a handle. 18°. 40c. .... *Pres. Bd.*
Bridgewater treatises on the power, wisdom and goodness of God as manifested in the creation. 11 v. 8°. (Bohn.) .... *Little, B. & Co.*
Cont.: 1. Bell's The hand as evincing design, $1.75.—2, 3. Kirby's Power, wisdom and goodness of God in the creation of animals, 2 v., ea., $1.75. — 4. Kidd's Adaptation of external nature to the physical condition of man, $1.25. — 5. Whewell's Astronomy and general physics with reference to natural theology, $1 25. — 6. Chalmer's Adaptation of external nature to the moral and intellectual constitution of man, $1.75. — 7. Prout's Chemistry, meteorology and digestion with reference to natural theology, $1.75. — 8, 9. Buckland's Geology and mineralogy with reference to natural theology, 2 v., $5.25. — 10, 11. Roget's Animal and vegetable physiology with reference to natural theology, 2 v., ea., $2.25.
— *Same.* 11 v. 8°. (Bohn.) v. 1-3, 6, 7, ea., $2; 4, 5, ea., $1.40; 8, 9, $6; 10, 11, ea., $2.40. *Scribner, W. & A.*
— *Same.* 11 v. 8°. (Bohn.) v. 1-3, 6, 7, ea., $2; 4, 5, ea., $1.50; 8, 9, $6; 10, 11, ea., $2.50. *Lippincott.*
Bridgman, E. G. Life of Rev. E. C. Bridgman. 12°. '64. $1.25 .... *Randolph.*
Brief biographies. *See* Higginson, T. W.
Brief biographies. Smiles, S. $1.50 .... *Osgood.*
Brief essays and brevities. Calvert, G. H. $1.50. *Lee & S.*
Brief history of England; with notes and questions. maps. 12°. 25c. .... *Nelson.*
Brief history of Scotland; with outlines of its geog. maps. 12°. 25c. .... *Nelson.*
Brief memoirs of the pious. 18°. 65c. .... *Pres. Bd.*
Brief portions for daily use. Smith, J. 25c. .. *Nelson.*
Brief relation of the state of New Eng. from the beginning of the plantation, to 1689: in a letter to a person of quality. London, 1689. [Reprint.] 4°. pap., 50c. .... *Sabin.*
Brief remarker on the ways of men. Sampson, E. $1.50 .... *Appleton.*
Brief state (A) of the province of Penna., in which the conduct of their assemblies is examined, and the cause of the encroachments of the French displayed, etc. [Reprint.] 8°. $1; large pap., $1.50 .... *Sabin.*
Brief thoughts on the things of God. Dalton, E. 50c. *Routledge.*
Briefe d. Herrn Inspectors Bräsig. *See* Reuter, F.
Briefs and papers: sketches of the bar and press; by two idle apprentices. 12°. $1.50 .... *Routledge.*
Brien, *Miss* H. O. A happy New Year. 16°. 30c. *Cong. Pub.*
Brierwood, Fk. Mabel Clifton. [Fiction.] 12°. '69. $1.50 .... *Claxton.*
Briery wood and other stories. *See* Home twilight stories.
Brigand (The). Hugo, V. 75c. .... *Peterson.*
Brigand (The). Planché, J. R. 15c. .... *French.*

Brigand (The) and his son. *See* French's serio-comic dramas.

Brigand (The); or, the mountain chief. 8°. pap., 50c. .... *Peterson.*

Brigands (The). 8°. pap., 25c. .... *De Witt.*

Brigands (The). James, G. P. R. 80c. ... *Routledge.*

Brigands (The) of Calabria: drama. 16°. pap., 15c. *Ames; French.*

Briggs, Chester. The Canaanite exterminated: treatise on present and entire sanctification. 12°. 60c. *Un. B. Pub.*

Briggs, G. W. Memoir of D. A. White. 8°. '64. pap., 30c. .... *Essex.*

Briggs, Milton. The western farmer and stock grower. 12°. '73. $1.25 .... *Day.*

Briggs, O. L. Golden censer: anthems, collects, prayers and thanksgivings; arranged by Rev. S. Fuller. 16°. '66. $1.25 .... *Dutton.*

Briggs, T: F. Banjo instructor. obl. 8°. '55. pap., 75c. .... *Ditson.*

Brigham, *Miss* S. P. Alice Field; or, the work of a young life. ('63.) New ed. ill. 18°. '72. 35c. *Hoyt.*

— Stolen gold piece (The), and other stories. ('63.) New ed. ill. 18°. '69. 40c. .... *Hoyt.*

Brigham, W: T. Cast catalogue of antique sculpture; with introd. to the study of ornaments. ill. 4°. $12 .... *Lee & S.*

Brigham, W: Tufts. Volcanic manifestations in New England. 4°. pap., 50c. .. *Bost. Soc. Nat. Hist.*

— — *See also* Lancaster, A.

Bright, *Mrs.* Amanda M. The three Bernices; or, Ansermo of the crag. 12°. '69. $1.75 .. *Claxton.*

Bright, J. M. Family practice. [Medical.] 8°. '57. shp., $5 .... *Morton.*

Bright, J. W. Cancer, its classification and remedies. 8°. $2 .... *Brinton.*

Bright, J: Speeches on questions of public policy. fp. 8°. '69. $1.50 .... *Macmillan.*

Bright, L: J. & Co. (*pub.*) New Orleans Price Current yearly report of the sugar and rice crops of Louisiana, 1875–6. 8°. '76. *$3 .... *Bright.*

Bright, Mta. A. ["Lyndon."] Margaret: a story of life in a prairie home. ('68.) New ed. 12°. '74. $1.50 .... *Scribner.*

— Oxley. ('73.) New ed. 12°. '74. $1.50 .. *Scribner.*

Bright days. Howitt, M. $1.25 .... *Lothrop.*

Bright eye library (The). 5 v. 18°. $3 ...... *Crowell.*

Cont.: Bessie and her grandfather, by Mrs. F. I. B. Smith. — Maggie, the fisherman's daughter. — Prying Polly. — Pierre and Annette. — Lottie Wilde's picnic, by Mrs. S. G. Knight.

Bright eye series (The). 20 v. 32°. $3 ...... *Nelson.*

Cont.: The little maid. — The dog at his master's grave. — Not beggars. — Little Gertrude. — Time about, fair play. — Wintergreen, the carpet-layer. — Thoughtful Alice. — Jessie's birthday. — Apple pie order. — Little Carl. — Susie's watch. — The casket. — Annie and her cat. — The little friends. — Jessie and her cousins. — Pauline. — The angels. — The peat-makers. — Charlie's prayers. — The bird's nest.

Bright gems for boys and girls. 12 v. 32°. '75. $3. *H. A. Young.*

Cont.: Sandy Duncan. — Tiny's musical box. — Ruth Dean's birthday. — Terence Moran. — Little trapper boy. — Boy not made to mind. — Marie's reward. — Poor Pat. — Word in season. — Waking up. — Bound girl. — Caught in her own trap.

Bright hope series (The). *See* Trowbridge, J. T.

Bright jewels for the Sunday school. Lowry, R., Sherwin, W. F., *and* Allen, C. G. 35c. .. *Biglow.*

Bright page library. 3 v. 16°. v. 1, 2, ea., 50c.; 3, 40c. .... (?) *Cumberland.*

Cont.: Aunt Peggy. — Carrie Holmes, by J. B. Logan. — Jewels.

Bright rays and reviving showers. 32°. 50c. .. *Nelson.*

Bright rays for dark days. 18°. 50c. .... *Nelson.*

— *Same.* ill. 16°. $1 .... *Cassell.*

Bright side (The) of New York. Richmond, J. F. *$3; $4 .... *Treat.*

Brightest and best. Lowry, R., *and* Doane, W. H. 35c.; 50c.; 75c. .... *Biglow.*

Brightie and her lamb. 18°. 90c. .... *Cong. Pub.*

Brightly, F: C. Collection of leading cases on the law of elections in the U. S.; with notes and ref. 8°. shp., $7.50 .... *Kay.*

— Digest of the decisions of the federal [U. S.] courts. 2 v. imp. 8°. shp., $16.50 .... *Kay.*

— Digest of the laws of the U. S., 1789–1869. 2 v. imp. 8°. shp., $16.50 .... *Kay.*

— Digest of N. Y. reports (1794–1875). 2 v. imp. 8°. *net*, shp., $20 .... *Banks.*

— Practical treatise on the law of costs in Penna.; with the fee-bill, decisions of the courts, and a view of the remedies for taking illegal fees. 8°. shp., $2.50 .... *Kay.*

— Reports of Penna. Supreme Court cases and of the Court of Nisi Prius at Phila.; with notes and ref. 8°. *net*, shp., $10 .... *Kay.*

— *See also* Pennsylvania, Constitution; — United States, Bankrupt law.

Brightside. Benjamin, E. B. $1.25 .... *Carter.*

Brightwell, *Miss* C. L. Above rubies; or, memorials of Christian gentlewomen. ill. 12°. $1.50. *Nelson.*

— *Same;* rev. by A. G. Haygood. ('72.) 3d ed. 16°. '76. 75c. .... *So. Meth.*

— Heroes of the laboratory and the workshop. ill. 16°. $1 .... *Routledge.*

— Lives of labor: incidents in the career of eminent naturalists and celebrated travellers. ill. 12°. $1.25 .... *Nelson.*

— Men of mark: short biographies. ill. 12°. $1.75. *Nelson.*

— My brother Harold. ill. 16°. 75c. .... *Nelson.*

— Palissy, the Huguenot potter. 12°. 90c. .. *Pres. Bd.*

— *Same.* ill. 12°. '59. $1.25 .... *Meth. Bk. Conc.*

Brill, Fs. Farm-gardening and seed-growing. 12°. $1. *Judd.*

Brilliant (The). Giffe, W. T. per. doz., $3.60. *Benham.*

Brilliant gems. Peters, J. L. $2.25; $1.75 .. *Peters.*

Brimley, G: Essays; ed. by W. G. Clark. por. fp. 8°. $1.25 .... *Macmillan.*

Brinckle, J. G. Poems. 12°. '71. $1.50 ... *Claxton.*

Brine, *Mrs.* M. D. What Robbie was good for. 18°. '76. 35c. .... *Am. Tr.*

Bring me up Samuel. Alexander, J. W. 20c. *Randolph.*

Bringing in sheaves. Earle, A. B. $1.50; $2 .. *Earle.*

Brinkerhoff, Jac. History of the true Reformed Dutch Church of the U. S. 12°. 75c. .. *N. Y. Ref. Ch. Bd.*

Brinkerhoff, Roeliff. The volunteer quartermaster: collection and codification of the laws, regulations, etc., gov. the quartermaster's dept. of the U. S. army, in force March 4, 1865. 12°. '65. $2.50 .... *Van Nostrand.*

Brinsmade, H. N. The well-watered plains; or, instructive lessons from the hist. of Lot. 18°. 35c. *Pres. Bd.*

Brinton, Dan. Garrison. Guide-book to Florida and the south. map. 16°. *$1 .... *Maclean.*

— Myths of the new world: treatise on the symbolism and mythology of the red race of Am. ('68.) New ed. 12°. '76. $2.50; large pap., $6 .. *Holt.*

— Religious sentiment (The): its source and aim. 12°. '76. $2.50 .... *Holt.*

— *See also* Steinwehr, A. v., *and* Brinton, D. G.

Brinton, W: Lectures on the diseases of the stomach; with introd. on its anat. and physiol. ill. 8°. $3.25 .... *Lea.*

Brisbane, W. D. Golden ready-reckoner, or lightning calculator. 18°. bds., 35c. ...... *Dick & F.*

Brisbane, W: H. Bible defended against objections of infidelity: examination of scientific, hist., chronol. and other Scripture difficulties. 12°. '55. 75c. . . . . *Perkinpine.*

— *See also* Higgins, S., *and* Brisbane, W. H.

Bristed, C: Astor. Five years in an Eng. university. 4th ed., rev. 12°. '72. $2.25 . . . . *Putnam.*

— Pieces of a broken-down critic. 8°. '58. $2.50 . . *Holt.*

Bristol, *Mrs.* Ma. C. Alice Sutherland. ill. 16°. '75. $1.25 . . . . *Lothrop.*

— Edna Harrington. ill. 16°. '71. $1.25 . . . . *Am. Tr.*

— Peter Midler. ill. 18°. '70. 40c. . . . . *Am. Tr.*

Bristol, *Mrs.* S. A. Clayton Allyn. ill. 18°. '65. 50c. *Am. Tr.*

Bristol Bill. 8°. pap., 25c. . . . . *De Witt.*

Bristol diamonds. Oxenford, J. 15c. . . . . . . *French.*

Bristow, F. L. The rainbow. [Music.] 8°. 50c. *Church.*

Bristow, F: Praise to God: choral and instrumental music. 8°. '69. $2.25 . . . . *Ditson.*

Bristow, G: F. *See* Nash, F. H., *and* Bristow, G. F.

Britain (Great). *See* England.

Britannicus. *See* Racine, J.

British Association. Reports of the committee on electrical standards; rev. by Sir W. Thomson, J. P. Joule, etc., with report to the Royal Society on units of electrical resistance, by F. Jenkin; ed. by F. Jenkin. pl. 8°. '73. $3.75 . . . . *Spon.*

British battles on land and sea. Grant, J. 3 v. ea., $5 . . . . *Cassell.*

British drama: collection of tragedies, comedies, operas and farces. 2 v. ill. 8°. shp., $6 . . *Polock.*

British dramatists. Works; with notes, biogs. and hist. introd., etc. ill. 8°. $2.50 . . . . *Lee & S.*

British essayists. *See* Chalmers, A.

British heroes in foreign wars. Grant, J. $2. Routledge.

British landscape painters, from Samuel Scott to David Cox; with essay and biog. notices. 16 steel eng. f°. '72. $10 . . . . *Routledge.*

British novelists. Masson, D. $1.25 . . . . *Lothrop.*

British pocket classics. 10 v. 32°. $8 . . . . *Lippincott.*

Cont.: Scott's Lay of the last minstrel; Scott's Lady of the lake. — Gay's Fables; Cowper's Task. — Pope's Essay on man; Locke's Essay on the human understanding. — Bloomfield's Poems; Poems of Gray and Collins. — Goldsmith's Poems; Falconer's Shipwreck. — St. Pierre's Paul and Virginia; Inchbald's Nature and art. — Johnson's Rasselas; Sterne's Sentimental journey. — Goldsmith's Vicar of Wakefield; Cottin's Elizabeth. — Coleridge's Poetical works; Thomson's Poetical works. — Walton's Angler.

British poets. 11 v. ill. roy. 8°. ea., mor., $10. *World Pub.*

Cont.: Burns. — Byron. — Campbell and Rogers. — Cowper. — Dryden. — Pope's Homer's Iliad and Odyssey. — Milton. — Moore. — Pope. — Shakespeare. — Scott.

Note. Formerly known as "Antique" poets.

British poets; ed. with notes. 130 v. 18°. ea., $1; hf. cf., $2.25 . . . . *Osgood.*

Cont.: Akenside. — Ballads, 8 v. — Beattie. — Butler, 2 v. — Burns, 3 v. — Byron, 10 v. — Campbell. — Chatterton, 2 v. — Churchill, 3 v. — Coleridge, 3 v. — Collins. — Cowper, 3 v. — Donne. — Dryden, 5 v. — Falconer. — Gay, 2 v. — Goldsmith. — Gray. — Herbert. — Herrick, 2 v. — Hood, 5 v. — Keats. — Marvell. — Milton, 3 v. — Montgomery, 5 v. — Moore, 6 v. — Parnell and Tickell. — Pope, 3 v. — Prior, 2 v. — Scott, 9 v. — Shakespeare. — Shelley, 4 v. — Skelton, 3 v. — Southey, 10 v. — Spenser, 5 v. — Surrey. — Swift, 3 v. — Thomson, 2 v. — Vaughan. — Watts. — White. — Wordsworth, 7 v. — Wyatt. — Young, 2 v.

— *See also* Routledge's British poets.

British poets; from Milton to Kirke White. 4 v. 12°. (Bohn.) $5 . . . . *Little, B. & Co.*

— *Same.* 4 v. 12°. (Bohn.) $5.60 . . *Scribner, W. & A.*

— *Same.* 4 v. 12°. (Bohn.) ea., $1.50 . . . *Lippincott.*

British reformers; from Wiclif to Foxe. [Lives.] New ed., rev. 12°. $1.50 . . . . *Nelson.*

British reformers. Lives and writings. 12 v. 12°. ea., $1.25 . . . . *Pres. Bd.*

Cont.: Wickliff to Bilney. — Tindal, Frith and Barnes. — Edward VI., Parr, Balnaves, etc. — Latimer. — Hooper. — Bradford. — Ridley and Philpot. — Cranmer, Rogers, Careless, etc. — Knox. — Becon. — Jewell. — Fox, Bale and Coverdale.

British school of sculpture; with essay and notices of artists. 20 steel eng. and wood cuts. f°. '72. $10 . . . . *Routledge.*

British slave (The). Howe, J. B. 15c. . . . . . *French.*

British wolf hunters (The). Miller, T. 50c. *Routledge.*

British workman (The). [Annual.] 4°. bds., 75c. *Nelson.*

Britt, J: Memoir of John Britt, the happy mute. 18°. 40c. . . . . *Am. S. S.*

Brittan, *Miss* Ht. G. Shoshie, the Hindoo Zenana teacher. 16°. '73. $1.25 . . . . *Whittaker.*

Britton, T: Allen. Treatise on the origin, progress, prevention and cure of dry rot in timber: remarks on the means of preserving wood from destruction by sea-worms, beetles, ants, etc. pl. and ill. cr. 8°. '75. $3 . . . . *Spon.*

Britts, Mattie Dyer. Edward Lee. 18°. 40c.; 50c. *Am. Bapt.*

Broad, broad ocean (The). Jones, W. $2.50. *Scribner, W. & A.*

Broad churchman (*pseud.*) *See* Warriner, E. A.

Broad grins. Coleman, G. $3 . . . . *Routledge.*

Broad grins of the laughing philosopher. 18°. pap., 10c. . . . . *Dick & F.*

Broad shadows on life's pathway. 18°. 75c. . . . *Carter.*

Broaddus, And. Dover selection of spiritual songs. ('28.) New ed. 32°. '75. shp., 60c. . . *Claxton.*

— Virginia sel. of psalms, hymns and spiritual songs. ('48.) New ed., enl. 32°. '75. shp., 75c. *Claxton.*

Broadus, J: A. Treatise on the preparation and delivery of sermons. ('70.) 6th ed. 12°. '75. $2. *Smith, E. & Co.*

Brobst, S. K. Prüfet die Geister: bibl. Untersuchungen. 24°. pap., 15c. . . . . *Brobst.*

— Sonntagsschul-Gebetbuch. 24°. 25c. . . . . *Brobst.*

— (*ed.*) Gesangbuch f. d. [luth.] Sonntagsschulen. 32°. 25c. . . . . *Kohler.*

Brock, *Mrs.* Carey. Carrying things to extremes. 18°. '71. pap., 20c. . . . . *Dutton.*

— Chapters on Bible classes. 16°. '71. $1 . . . . *Dutton.*

— Charity Helstone. 16°. $1.25 . . . . (?) *Martien.*

— Clear shining after rain. 12°. $1.25 . . . . *Pott.*

— Copsley annals; preserved in proverbs. 16°. '61. $1. *Dutton.*

— I must keep the chimes going. ill. 16°. '70. 75c. *Dutton.*

— Making the best of it. 18°. 50c. . . . . . (?) *Martien.*

— Margaret's secret and its success. 16°. $1.25. (?) *Martien.*

— More ways than one; or, the little missionary. 18°. 50c. . . . . (?) *Martien.*

— Penny wise and pound foolish. 16°. $1.25. (?) *Martien.*

— Rectory (The) and the manor. 16°. '72. $1.50. *Dutton.*

— Story of Reuben Inch; or, the power of perseverance. ill. 18°. 75c. . . . . *Nelson.*

— Sunday echoes in week-day hours. 6 v. 16°. '69–'76. $9; ea., $1.50 . . . . *Dutton.*

Cont.: Tales illustrative of the Collects — of the Church catechism — of the journeyings of the children of Israel — of Scripture characters — of the Epistles and Gospels — of the parables.

— Susie Grant; or, the lost property office. ill. 16°. '67. $1 . . . . *Dutton.*

— Wishing and choosing. 18°. 40c. . . . . *Dutton.*

— *Same.* 18°. 60c. . . . . (?) *Martien.*

— Working and waiting. 18°. 90c. . . . . . (?) *Martien.*

Brock, Sallie A. ["Virginia Madison."] Kenneth, my king. 12°. $1.75 . . . . *Carleton.*

Brock, W: Life of Gen. Sir H. Havelock. 18°. '62. 40c. . . . . *Am. Tr.*

— *Same.* 18°. 75c. . . . . *Carter.*

Brockenbrough, J. W. *See* United States, Circuit Court reports.

Brockenbrough, W. *See* Virginia, General Court reports.

rockett, Linus Pierpont. History and progress of education; by Philobiblius [*pseud.*]; with introd. by H. Barnard. 12°. '59. $1.50....... *Barnes.*
— Thorough business man (The): Walter Powell, of Melbourne and London, merchant, philanthropist and Christian; ed. and rewritten from Rev. B. Gregory's "Memoirs of Walter Powell, merchant." 12°. '72. $1.25........... *Routledge.*
— Year of battles. map and ill. 8°. '71. $2.50. (?) *Goodspeed.*

rocklesby, J: Amateur microscopist; or, views of the microscopic world. ill. sm. 4°. $1.75.. *W. Wood.*
— Common school astronomy. ill. 12°. hf. bd., 80c. *Sheldon.*
— Elements of astronomy. ill. 12°. $1.75.... *Sheldon.*
— Elements of phys. geog., with treatise on phys. phenomena of the U.S. ill. and maps. 4°. $1.88. *Butler.*
— Meteorology. 12°. $1.25................ *Sheldon.*

rockley moor. L., J. W. $1.50........ *Appleton.*

rockmann, J: H. Christian u. Ernst: eine Besprechung über d. Lehre d. Odd-Fellows oder sonderbaren Brüder auf Grundlage d. hl. Schrift. ('72.) 2d ed. sm. 8°. '76. pap., 50c. *Brockmann.*
— *English.* Oddfellowship: its doctrine and practice examined in the light of God's word, and judged by its own utterances. sm. 8°. '74. bds., 75c.; pap., 40c...................... *Brockmann.*

rockway, Z. R. Reformation of prisoners; read before Am. Soc. Sci. Assoc., May 22, 1874. 8°. pap., 10c........................... *Williams.*

roderip, W: J: Zoological recreations. ill. 8°. $2.50. *Scribner, W. & A.*
— — *See also* Beeton's boys' own lib.
— *See also* England, Common law reports.

rodhead, J: Romeyn. History of N.Y., 1609–1691. 2 v. 8°. ea., $3..................... *Harper.*

rodhurst, B. E. Deformities of the human body: system of orthopœdic surgery. ill. 8°. $3. *Lindsay.*

rodie, *Sir* B: Mind and matter; or, psycholog. inquiries. 12°. $1.25................ *W. Wood.*

roken arm (The). *See* Sylvan stories.

roken basket (The). *See* Finley, M. F.

roken bow (The). 18°. 50c............. *Nelson.*

roken bud. 16°. $1.25................. *Carter.*

roken chain. Tucker, C. 50c............ *Carter.*

roken chain (A): an episode of the French revolution. 18°. 15c..................... *Benziger.*

Broken chains. Buerstenbinder, E. $1.25; 75c... *Estes.*

Broken cisterns; or, the story of Jessie Worthington. 18°. 85c........................ *Am. S. S.*

Broken crucible. Alexander, J. W. 50c... *Randolph.*

Broken dreams. Gardner, C. E. $1.50.... *Carleton.*

Broken fetters. L., L. $1.50............ *Lothrop.*

Broken flowers. 32°. 20c.; 15c........... *Dutton.*

Broken fold. Dana, E. A. $1.50........ *Randolph.*

Broken fuchsia. Chapman, H. E. 50c... *Cong. Pub.*

Broken-hearted club. Coyne, J. S. 15c.... *De Witt.*

Broken hyacinth; or, Ellen and Sophia. 18°. 40c. *Am. S. S.*

Broken idols. McLean, M. W. $1.50.... *Cong. Pub.*

Broken lights. Cobbe, F. P. $1.75......... *Tilton.*

Broken pitcher. 32°. 20c.; 15c........... *Dutton.*

Broken pitcher; or, the ways of Providence. 16°. '66. $1.25............................ *Graves.*

Broken promise. Greene, L. L. 60c........ *Cassell.*

Broken rein. 16°. 90c.................. *Am. S. S.*

Broken resolutions. 18°. 40c........... *Cong. Pub.*

Broken rock. Kruna. 50c............. *Nat. Temp.*

Broken rock series. 6 v. 18°. $3........ *Nat. Temp.*
Cont.: Broken rock, by Kruna.—Frank Spencer's rule of life, by J. W. Kirton.—Come home, mother, by N. Brook.—Gertie's sacrifice, by Mrs. D. F. Gage.—The McAllisters, by Mrs. E. J. Richmond.—Pitcher of cool water, by T. S. Arthur.

Broken seal. Greene, S. D. $1; 50c..... *E. A. Cook.*

Broken sword. Dimond, W. 15c............ *French.*

Broken ties: drama. 16°. pap., 15c......... *French.*

Broken to harness. *See* Yates, Edmund.

Broken toys. Daly, J. 15c................ *French.*

Broken toys. Steele, A. C. $1.25; 75c....... *Estes.*

Broken vase; or, Annie Norton. 18°. 17c.; 22c. *Am. Bapt.*

Broken window, and other stories. 18°. 70c *Pres. Bd.*

Bromfield, Ma. E. Daddy Dick. 32°. 40c. *Scribner, W. & A.*
— Trot's letters to her doll. 12°. '75. $1.25.. *Nelson.*

Bronson, C. P. Elocution. ('45.) New ed. 8°. '73. $2.................................... *Morton.*

Bronson, *Mrs.* O. United States primer. 12°. '64. bds., 15c........................... *Am. Tr.*

Bronson, W. White. Memorial of Rev. Bird Wilson. 12°. $1.25........................ *Lippincott.*

Bronté, Anne. ["Acton Bell."] Agnes Grey. 8°. pap., 50c.......................... *Peterson.*
— — *See also* Bronté, E., Wuthering Heights.
— Poems. *See* Bronté, C., Professor.
— Tenant of Wildfell Hall. 16°. $1.25... *Lippincott.*
— *Same.* ill. 12°. $1.50.................... *Harper.*
— *Same.* (Ill. lib. ed.) 8°. $3.... *Scribner, W. & A.*
— — *See also* Bronté, C., E. *and* A.

Bronté, Ctte. [*Mrs.* Nichols; *pseud.*, "Currer Bell."] Jane Eyre. 16°. $1.25............ *Lippincott.*
— *Same.* 12°. '75. $1.25................ *Routledge.*
— *Same.* ill. 12°. $1.50. 8°. pap., 75c..... *Harper.*
— *Same.* (Ill. lib. ed.) cr. 8°. $3.. *Scribner, W. & A.*
— Professor (The). ill. 12°. $1.50.......... *Harper.*
— *Same;* and poems. (Ill. lib. ed.) cr. 8°. $3. *Scribner, W. & A.*
— *Same;* with poems by the three sisters. 16°. $1.25. *Lippincott.*
— Shirley. 16°. $1.25................... *Lippincott.*
— *Same.* ill. 12°. $1.50. 8°. pap., $1..... *Harper.*
— *Same.* (Ill. lib. ed.) cr. 8°. $3.. *Scribner, W. & A.*
— Villette. 16°. $1.25................... *Lippincott.*
— *Same.* ill. 12°. $1.50. 8°. pap., 75c....... *Harper.*
— *Same.* (Ill. lib. ed.) cr. 8°. $3.. *Scribner, W. & A.*
— *and* E. *and* A. Novels. 7 v. 16°. $8.75.. *Routledge.*
Cont.: Jane Eyre.—Professor.—Shirley.—Villette.—Wildfell Hall.—Wuthering Heights.—Life of C. Bronté, by Mrs. Gaskell.

Bronté, Emily. ["Ellis Bell."] Poems. *See* Bronté, C., Professor.
— Wuthering Heights. ill. 12°. $1.50....... *Harper.*
— *Same;* [also] Agnes Grey, by A. Bronté. 16°. $1.25.......................... *Lippincott.*
— — *Same.* (Ill. lib. ed.) 8°. $3.. *Scribner, W. & A.*
— — *See also* Bronté, C., E. *and* A.

Bronze series. 8 v. 4°. ea., 50c.; pap., 25c. *Nelson.*
Cont.: Pictures for the pets, with nursery rhymes.—Illustrated proverbs for the nursery.—The queen and princess of Dolly land.—New scenes of monkey life.—Lilly's picture book.—Little Red Riding Hood.—The cat's quadrille.—The robin.

Brook, J: French measures and Eng. equivalents. 18°. '73. roan, 40c.................... *Spon.*

Brook, Nelsie. Come home, mother. ('70.) New ed. 18°. '75. 50c................... *Nat. Temp.*

Brook (The). *See* Hunt, S. K.

Brook (The). Wright, W. B. $1.50...... *Scribner.*

Brook farm. 18°. 60c..................... *Carter.*

Brook Silverstone. *See* Marshall, E.

Brooke, *Mrs.* F. Rosina. [Operetta.] 16°. pap., 15c. *French.*

Brooke, H: The fool of quality; or, the history of Henry, Earl of Moreland; rev. with biog. pref. by Rev. C. Kingsley. [Fiction.] cr. 8°. '73. $1.75......................... *Macmillan.*

Brooke, J: T. The dance and dancing school. 18°. 50c............................... *Carter.*

Brooke, N. Charley Franklin; or, time unveils truth. 32°. 40c. .... *Scribner, W. & A.*

Brooke, Stopford A. Christ in modern life. [Sermons.] 12°. $2 .... *Appleton.*

— English literature. *See* Green, J. R., Literature primers.

— Sermons. 12°. $1.50 .... *Tibbals.*

— The theology of the Brit. poets. 12°. $2. *Appleton.*

Brooke, W: G. (*ed.*) Six judgments of the judicial committee of the privy council in ecclesiastical cases, 1850–'73; with hist. introd., notes and index. 12°. '74. $4.50 .... *Pott.*

Brookes, G: All the world a stage: farce. 16°. pap., 15c. .... *French.*

— Quash: farce. 16°. pap., 15c. .... *French.*

Brookes, Ja. H. How to be saved; or, the sinner directed to the Saviour. ('64.) New ed. 18°. '76. 50c.; pap., 20c. .... *McIntyre.*

— *Same;* in German. 18°. pap., 20c. .... *McIntyre.*

— May Christians dance? ('69.) New ed. 18°. '76. 60c.; pap., 25c. .... *McIntyre.*

Brookes, Sheridan. Calypso: burlesque. 16°. pap., 15c. .... *French.*

Brookes, T: Apples of gold; or, a word in season to young men and women. 18°. 70c. ... *Pres. Bd.*

— The mute Christian under the smarting rod; with sovereign antidotes. 18°. 55c. .... *Pres. Bd.*

Brookes of Bridlemere. Melville, G. J. W. $1.25. *Appleton.*

Brookfield, F. First book in composition. 12°. '55. hf. bd., 50c.; 55c. .... *Barnes.*

Brooks, Annie (*ed.*) A cluster of fruits from the tree of heavenly wisdom. [Stories.] 18°. 75c. *Pres. Bd.*

— The little girl's treasury of precious things. 18°. 50c. .... *Pres. Bd.*

Brooks, C: Shirley. Anything for a change: comedy. 16°. pap., 15c. .... *De Witt; French.*

— Creole: drama. 16°. pap., 15c. .... *French.*

— Gordian knot. [Fiction.] 8°. pap., 50c... *Harper.*

— Guardian angel: farce. 16°. pap., 15c..... *French.*

— Silver cord (The). [Fiction.] ill. 8°. $2; pap., $1.50 .... *Harper.*

— Sooner or later. [Fiction.] ill. 8°. $2; pap., $1.50. *Harper.*

— *See also* Oxenford, J., *and* Brooks, C. S.

Brooks, C: T. German lyrics. 16°. $1.25..* *Osgood.*

— *See also* Bund, L., Puck's nightly pranks; — Busch, W., Max and Maurice; — Goethe, J. W. v., Faust; — Kortum, C. A., The Jobsiad; — Schefer, L., Layman's breviary; The world priest; — Tall student (The).

Brooks, E: Methods of teaching mental arithmetic, and key to "Normal mental arithmetic." 16°. hf. bd., 38c. .... *Sower.*

— Methods of teaching written arith., and key to "Normal written arithmetic." 12°. hf. bd., $1.. *Sower.*

— Normal element. algebra. 12°. hf. bd., $1.25. — Key. $1.25 .... *Sower.*

— Normal element. arithmetic. 12°. hf. bd., 50c. — Key. hf. bd., 50c. .... *Sower.*

— Normal element. geometry, embracing brief treatise on mensuration and trigonometry. 12°. hf. roan, $1.25. — Key. hf. bd., $1.25 .... *Sower.*

— Normal higher arith. 12°. '76. hf. roan, $1.38.. *Sower.*

— Normal mental arithmetic. 16°. hf. bd., 38c. *Sower.*

— Normal primary arithmetic: mental and written exercises. 16°. hf. bd., 25c. .... *Sower.*

— Normal written arithmetic. 12°. hf. bd., 95c. *Sower.*

Brooks, Elbridge Gerry. Our new departure; or, the methods and work of the Universalist Church of Am. as it enters on its second century. 12°. '73. $1.75 .... *Universalist.*

— Universalism in life and doctrine. 12°. $1.25. *Williamson.*

Brooks, Erastus, *and* Hughes, *Abp.* J: Brooksiana: controversy between B. and H. [on taxation of church property]. 12°. $1 .... *Strong.*

— — Controversy [on taxation of church property]. 8°. pap., 25c. .... *De Witt.*

Brooks, F: Sermons; with introd. by Rev. Phillips Brooks. por. 12°. '75. $2 .... *Osgood.*

Brooks, Ja. A seven months' run, up, and down, and around the world: letters to the "N. Y. Evening Express." 12°. $1.75 .... *Appleton.*

Brooks, *Rev.* Ja. H. The way made plain. 16°. $1.25. *Am. S. S.*

Brooks, Ja. J. Adventures of a U. S. detective. ill. 12°. $2 .... *Souder.*

Brooks, Nat. Covington. First lessons in Greek. ('51.) New ed. 18°. '75. hf. roan, 75c. .... *Claxton.*

— First lessons in Latin. 18°. '51. 75c. ..... *Claxton.*

— *Same.* 18°. '67. 75c. .... *Barnes.*

— Harmonia evangelica: Gk. harmony of the four Gospels; with notes and lexicon. 18°. '71. hf. roan, 75c. .... *Claxton.*

— Manual of devotion: religious exercises for morning and evening. 16°. '52. 75c. .... *Barnes.*

— — *See also* Cleaveland, A. J., School harmonist.

— Sabbath-school manual: relig. exercises for morning and evening. 18°. '69. 75c.; hf. bd., 50c. *Claxton.*

— Scripture manual: religious exercises for morning and evening. 18°. '69. 75c. .... *Claxton.*

— Vitæ virorum illustrium Am., a Columbo ad Jacksonium; notis Anglicis ill. necnon vocum omnium interp. instructæ. 12°. '64. $1.50. *Barnes; Claxton.*

— *See also* L'Homond, C. F.; — Ross, J.; — and for classic text-books *names* of authors.

Brooks, T. B. Cost and methods of mining in Marquette iron region. 8°. pap., 50c. *Am. Soc. of C. E.*

— *See also* Pumpelly, R., Brooks, T. B., *and* Schmidt, A.

Brooks, W: K. The development of salpa. ill. 8°. '76. pap., 75c. .... *Mus. Comp. Zool.*

Brookside farmhouse from January to December. Finley, M. F. 70c. .... *Pres. Bd.*

Brookside series. 4 v. 12°. $4 .... *Nat. Temp.*
Cont.: The brook and the tide turning, by S. K. Hunt and L. Bates. — Paul Brewster and son, by H. A. Chapman. — Norman Brill's life work, by A. Eldridge. — Barford mills, by M. E. Winslow.

Brookside series. *See* Baker, *Mrs.* H. N. W.

Brook-Smith, J. *See* Smith, J. Brook.

Broom, Herb. Commentaries on the common law as introd. to its study. From 4th Lond. ed. 8°. '73. $6 .... *T. & J. W. Johnson.*

— — *See also* Law lib.

— Philosophy of law: notes of lectures delivered [1852–'75]. 12°. $1.50 .... *S. Whitney.*

— *Same.* 8°. '76. $2.50; shp., $3.... *Baker, V. & Co.*

— Selection of legal maxims, classified and ill. 7th Am., from 5th Lond., ed., enl. and rev.; with ref. to Am. cases. 8°. '74. $7.50.. *T. & J. W. Johnson.*

— *and* Hadley, E: A. Commentaries on the laws of England; with Am. notes by W. Wait. 2 v. 8°. '76. shp., $13 .... *J. D. Parsons.*

Broome, F: Napier. The stranger of Seriphos: dram. poem. fp. 8°. '69. $1.50 .... *Macmillan.*

Broome, *Mrs.* F: Napier. *See* Barker, Ma. A. (*Lady*).

Broome. *See* Flower garlands for little gleaners.

Brosamen v. d. Herrn Tische. Späth, A. 25c. *Kohler.*

Brose, A. Aufgaben zum Zifferrechnen. ('63–65.) 7th ed. 2 nos. 8°. '74. ea., 10c.; — Auflösung. 20c. .... *Barthel.*

Brother and sister. 32°. '53. 30c. .... *Am. Tr.*

Brother and sister. 18°. 75c. .... *Carter.*

Brother and sister. ill. 18°. '70. '75c. ...... *Lothrop.*

Brother and sister. Dimond, W. 15c. .... *French.*

Brother Ben. Morton, J. M. 15c... *French; Lee & S.*

Brother Bertie. ill. 12°. $1.25 .... *Nelson.*

Brother Bertie, *continued.*
— *See also* Bertie and Amy books.
Brother Bertie and his aunt. *See* Bertie and Amy books.
Brother Bertie's cure. *See* Bertie and Amy books.
Brother Bill and me. Suter, W. E. 15c. *French; Lee & S.*
Brother Philippe (*pseud.*) *See* Braussi, M.
Brother Reginald's golden secret; by author of "Hope on." 16°. 85c. . . . . *Tibbals.*
Brother Sam's conundrums. *See* Handbook of.
Brother soldiers. Robinson, M. S. 75c. . . . . *Tibbals.*
Brother Willie's library. 5 v. 18°. $3.75. . *Cong. Pub.*
Cont.: False imprisonment. — Philip Alderton's temptation. — Brother Willie. — Blacksmith's boy. — The skates, by Miss S. A. Flint.
Brotherhead, W: Centennial book of the signers [of the Dec. of ind.] (cop. '72.) New ed. ill. 4°. '76. hf. mor., $20; mor., $25. . . *J. M. Stoddart.*
Brotherhood of man. King, M. M. 25c. . . . . *Colby.*
Brotherly counsels to students. Jameson, F. J. 75c. *Macmillan.*
Brother's choice. Grosvenor, H. S. $1.15 . . . . *Hoyt.*
Brother's legacy. Pollard, M. M. 35c. *Cin. Meth. Bk. Conc.*
Brother's library. 4 v. ill. 16°. $4. . . . . *Routledge.*
Cont.: Humphrey Merton. — Talks about animals. — The young Muscovite. — The gypsey's secret.
Brother's prayer. 18°. 40c. . . . . *Cong. Pub.*
Brother's secret. Godwin, W. $1.75; $1.50. *Peterson.*
Brother's watchword. 18°. 75c. . . . . *Carter; Dutton.*
Brothers: a wayside lesson. 18°. 30c. . . . . *Dutton.*
Brothers and sisters. Bremer, F. 50c. . . . . *Harper.*
Brothers and sisters. Marshall, E. $1.25. . (?) *Martien.*
Brothers and sisters; or, grace illustrated in the conversion and happy death of I. M., Ab. and Almira Rowe; by their pastor. 32°. 20c. . . . . *Pres. Bd.*
Brothers bold (The). Griset, E. 50c. . . . . *Appleton.*
Brothers' bet. Carlen, E. F. 25c. . . . . *Harper.*
Brough, J: Take care of little Charley: farce. 16°. pap., 15c. . . . . *French.*
Brough, Rob. B. Burlesque dramas. 16°. pap., 40c. *French.*
Cont.: King Alfred and the cakes; William Tell; Orpheus and Eurydice.
— [Plays.] 8 v. 16°. ea., pap., 15c. . . . . *French.*
Cont: Crinoline: farce. — Doge of Duralto: extravaganza. — Kensington gardens: comedy. — King Alfred and the cakes: burlesque. — Masaniello: burlesque. — Medea: burlesque. — Moustache movement: farce. — Twelve labors of Hercules: comedy.
— *and* Edwards, S. Mephistopheles: extravaganza. 16°. pap., 15c. . . . . *French.*
Brough, W: [Plays.] 26 v. 16°. ea., pap., 15c. *French.*
Cont.: Apartments: farce. — Bona fide travellers: farce. — Caliph of Bagdad: extravaganza. — Comical countess: farce. — Conrad and Medora: pantomime. — Corsair: burlesque. — Dinorah under difficulties: extravaganza. — Endymion: extravaganza. — Ernani: burlesque. — Field of cloth of gold: extravaganza. — Gnome king: extravaganza. — Hercules and Omphale: extravaganza. — House out of window: farce. — How to make home happy. — Joan of Arc: burlesque. — Kind to a fault: comedy. — King Arthur: extravaganza. — Number one around the corner: farce. — Papillonetta: extravaganza. — Perdita: burlesque. — Perseus and Andromeda: extravaganza. — Phenomenon in smock frock: comic drama. — Prince Amabel: fairy extravaganza. — Rasselas: extravaganza. — Sylphide: extravaganza. — Trying it on: farce.
— Comical countess: farce. 16°. pap., 15c. . . *De Witt.*
— Kind to a fault: comedy. 16°. pap., 15c. . . *De Witt.*
— *and* Halliday, A. [Plays.] 13 v. 16°. ea., pap., 15c. . . . . *French.*
Cont.: Actor's retreat: extravaganza. — April fool: farce. — Area belle: farce. — Census: farce. — Colleen bawn settled: farce. — Doing Banting: farce. — Going to the dogs: farce. — Mudborough election: farce. — My heart's in the Highlands: farce. — Pretty horse-breaker: farce. — Shilling day at the great exhibition: farce. — Up stairs and down stairs: farce. — Valentine: farce.
— — Area belle (The): farce. 16°. pap., 15c. *De Witt.*

Brough, W: *continued.*
— — My heart's in the Highlands: farce. 16°. pap., 15c. . . . . *Ames.*
— — Pretty horse-breaker (The): farce. 16°. pap., 15c. . . . . *De Witt.*
Brougham, H: (*Lord*). Works. 11 v. cr. 8°. (Edinb.) '72. $19.25; hf. cf., $38.50. . . . . *Little, B. & Co.*
— Albert Lunel. [Fiction.] 8°. pap., 75c. . . *Harper.*
— Life and times: [autobiog.] 3 v. 12°. $6. . *Harper.*
— Old England worthies; ed. by B. and others. 15 pts. ill. and por. 4°. '72. ea., *50c. . . . . *S. Walker.*
— *and* Sedgwick, A., *and* Verplanck, G. C. Discourses on the objects and uses of science and literature; with prelim. observations on reading, by Bp. Potter. 18°. 75c. . . . . *Harper.*
Brougham, J: [Plays.] 28 v. 16°. ea., pap., 15c. *French.*
Cont.: All's fair in love: comedy. — Art and artifice. — Columbus: extravaganza. — David Copperfield. — Decided case: farce. — Demon lover: comedietta. — Dombey and son. — Flies in the web: comedy. — Franklin. — Game of life: comedy. — Game of love: comedy. — Gunmaker of Moscow: melodrama. — Irish emigrant. — Irish Yankee. — Jane Eyre. — Life in New York. — Love and murder: farce. — Metamora: burlesque. — Miller of New Jersey: spectacle. — Musard ball: extravaganza. — Neptune's defeat: burlesque. — Night and morning. — O'Flannigan and the fairies. — Playing with fire: comedy. — Po-ca-hontas: burlesque. — Red mask. — Romance and reality: comedy. — Shakespeare's dream: interlude.
— *and* Goodrich, F. B. Dark hour before dawn: play. 16°. pap., 15c. . . . . *French.*
Brought home. Smith, H. $1.25 . . . . *Dodd.*
Brought to the front. Kellogg, E. $1.25. . . *Lee & S.*
Broughton, Rhoda. Novels. 5 v. 12°. ea., $1.50. 8°. pap. . . . . *Appleton.*
Cont.: Good-bye, sweetheart, pap., 75c. — Red as a rose is she, pap., 60c. — Cometh up as a flower, pap., 60c. — Not wisely but too well, pap., 60c. — Nancy, pap., 75c.
— Good-bye, sweetheart. 12°. $1.50. . . . . *Lippincott.*
Brown, A. Morton. A wreath around the cross. 16°. $1 . . . . *Sheldon.*
Brown, Alex. Hopes crowned in death: memoir of B. ill. 18°. 50c. . . . . *N. Y. Ref. Ch. Bd.*
Brown, Arch. Law dictionary; with app. of legal maxims and abbr. by A. P. Sprague. 8°. '75. $4 . . . . *J. D. Parsons.*
Brown, Cath. Memoir. 18°. 45c. . . . . *Am. S. S.*
Brown, C: Brockden. Novels; with memoir of author. 6 v. 12°. ea., $1. . . . . *Polock.*
Cont.: Wieland. — Arthur Mervyn, 2 v. — Edgar Huntly. — Jane Talbot. — Ormund; [also] Clara Howard.
Brown, C: J. Divine glory of Christ. 12°. $1. *Nelson.*
— Word (The) of life. 12°. $1.50. . . . . *Carter.*
Brown, C: R. Government of Mich.: abstract of laws, duties of officers, etc. 4°. '74. $1. (?) *C. R. Brown.*
Brown, Crum. Chemistry. (Popular sci. man.) 18°. 40c. . . . . *Lippincott.*
Brown, *Rev.* D: Memoir. *See* Laborers in the east.
Brown, *Rev.* D: On the 2d advent. 12°. $1.75. *Carter.*
— *Same.* cr. 8°. $3.75. . . . . *Scribner, W. & A.*
Brown, *Rev.* D: Restoration of the Jews: hist., principles and bearings of the question. 12°. $2. *Routledge.*
Brown, *Rev.* D: Commentary on the four Gospels. 12°. $1. . . . . (?) *Martien.*
— *Same.* 8°. $4.25. . . . . *Pres. Bd.*
— *See also* Jamieson, R., Fausset, A. R., *and* Brown, D.
Brown, D: Pl. The forum; or, forty years' practice at the Phila. bar. 2 v. 8°. *net,* shp., $10. . . . *Kay.*
Brown, E: New scheme for the treatment of sewage matter, by utilizing it upon the waste land in the country. 8°. pap., 20c. . . . . *Spon.*
Brown, *Rev.* E: The Wadsworth memorial. 16°. $1.50. . . . . *J. A. Clark.*
Brown, Fs. H. Pupils' first primer in music, cont. new pronounc. vocab. of musical terms. 16°. '75. 33c.; 50c. . . . . *T. J. Hall.*
Brown, Fs. H: Medical register for Mass. 12°. '75. $2. . . . . *Lunt.*

Brown, G. W. *See* Norris, W. H., Brown, G. W., *and* Brune, F. W., *jr.*

Brown, G: The lady preacher: life and labors of Mrs. H. Reeves. por. 12°. '70. $1.25. (?) *Daughaday.*

Brown, Goold. First lines of Eng. grammar. New ed., rev. and enl. by H. Kiddle. 12°. hf. bd., 45c. .... *W. Wood.*

— Grammar of Eng. grammar. roy. 8°. leath., $6.25. *W. Wood.*

— Institutes of Eng. grammar. New ed., rev. and enl. by H. Kiddle. 12°. $1 .... *W. Wood.*

Brown, Harvey E. Report on quarantine on the s. and gulf coasts of the U. S. 8°. $1.25. *W. Wood.*

Brown, Helen. Leaf and flower pictures, and how to make them. ill. sq. 16°. '57. $1.75 ... *Randolph.*

Brown, *Mrs.* Helen E. Abroad; or, Lilian's new school. 16°. $1.25 .... *Bost. Am. Tr.*

— Agnes in search of truth. 16°. '72. 80c. .. *Am. Tr.*

— Aunt Winnie's stories. 24°. 35c. .... *Bost. Am. Tr.*

— Cup-bearer (The). ill. sq. 12°. $2.50 .. *Bost. Am. Tr.*

— Lillie; or, the little Christian's toilet. 16°. '74. $1. *Am. Tr.*

— Lonnie, our little lamb. 18°. 45c. ... *Bost. Am. Tr.*

— Medicine shelf (The). ill. 18°. 85c. .. *Bost. Am. Tr.*

— Mother (The) and her work. 16°. 60c. .. *Bost. Am. Tr.*

— Step by step; or, Tidy's way to freedom. ill. 18°. 50c. .... *Bost. Am. Tr.*

— Walter Lightfoot's pictures. ill. 18°. 60c. *Bost. Am. Tr.*

— Winter school (The); or, the boys' campaign against rum and tobacco. ill. 18°. 60c. ... *Bost. Am. Tr.*

Brown, H: Present and future prospects of Chicago: address before the Chicago Lyceum, Jan. 20, 1846; [also] Rise and progress of Chicago: address before the Centennial Library Association, Mar. 21, 1876, by J. A. Marshall; [also] "Chicago in 1836": strange early days, by H. Martineau. 12°. '76. 25c. .... *Fergus.*

Brown, *Rev.* H: Arminian inconsistencies and errors. 12°. $1.50 .... (?) *Martien.*

— Christian baptism tested by Scripture. 16°. '67. 50c. .... *N. Y. Ref. Ch. Bd.; Pres. Com.*

Brown, H: B. *See* United States, District and Circuit Court admiralty reports.

Brown, H: J. Voice from the pious dead of the medical profession: memoirs of physicians who have fallen asleep in Jesus. ('55.) 2d ed. 12°. '59. $1.50; $2 .... *Perkinpine.*

Brown, J. D. Collection laws: text-book for merchants and business men. 12°. shp., $2. *Lippincott.*

Brown, Ja. Baldwin. Buying and selling and getting gain. 16°. '72. pap., 40c. .... *Randolph.*

— Home life (The): in the light of its divine idea. 18°. 75c. .... *Appleton.*

— Idolatries old and new: their cause and cure. 12°. '69. $1.50 .... *Randolph.*

— Misread passages of Scripture. 2 v. 12°. '57. v. 1, 75c.; v. 2, $1 .... *Meth. Bk. Conc.*

— Our morals and manners. 18°. 75c. .... *Nelson.*

Compr. Buying and selling, *and* Young men and maidens.

— Young men and maidens: a pastoral for the times. 12°. '71. 75c. .... *Randolph.*

Brown, *Dr.* J: (*of Edinb.*) Marjorie Fleming. 16°. pap., 25c. .... *Osgood.*

— *Same.* 32°. '75. 35c.; pap., 10c. .... *Tompkins.*

— Plain words on health: lay sermons to working people. 16°. pap., 25c. .... *Routledge.*

— *Same.* 12°. 50c. .... *Carter.*

— Rab and his friends. 16°. pap., 25c. .... *Osgood.*

— *Same.* ill. 32°. '75. 50c.; pap., 10c.; leath., $2. *Tompkins.*

— *Same.* (Presentation ed.) ill. imp. 8°. $3. *Scribner, W. & A.*

— Spare hours. 2 v. por. and ill. 16°. '61–'66. ea., $1.50; hf. cf., $3 .... *Osgood.*

Brown, J: *D.D.* (*of Edinb.*) Discourses and sayings of our Lord. ('68.) New ed. 8°. '75. $3.50. *Carter.*

— On 1 Peter. 8°. '68. $3.50 .... *Carter.*

— On Romans. 8°. '57. $2 .... *Carter.*

Brown, *Rev.* J: (*of Haddington.*) Concordance to the Bible. 32°. 40c. .... *Clark & M.*

— *Same.* 32°. 50c. .... *Carter; Harper.*

— *Same.* 12°. 75c. .... *Sheldon.*

— — *See also* Pronouncing Bible dict.

— Dictionary of the Bible; with life of author. 8°. shp., $2.25 .... *Harper.*

— Explication of Assembly's catechism. 12°. $1. 18°. pap., 20c. .... *Carter.*

— *Same.* 12°. 90c. .... *U. P. Bd. of Pub.*

— *See also* Brown, W.; — Bible [Whole].

Brown, *Capt.* J: (*of Harper's Ferry.*) Life, trial and execution; with account of the attempted insurrection at Harper's Ferry. 8°. pap., 25c. *De Witt.*

Brown, J: (*of Langlin.*) Exclusive claims of Puseyite Episc. to the ministry indefensible; with article on the Anglican reform. 12°. $1 .... *Pres. Bd.*

Brown, *Rev.* J: (*of Leicester.*) Gospel ministry. 16°. 25c.; pap., 15c. .... *West. Tr.*

Brown, J: (*of Rothbury.*) Barbarossa: tragedy. 16°. pap., 15c. .... *French.*

Brown, *Rev.* J: Newton. Baptismal balance. 18°. pap., 10c. .... *Am. Bapt.*

— Baptist church manual. 18°. pap., 5c. .. *Am. Bapt.*

— *Same;* in Spanish. 18°. pap., 10c. ..... *Am. Bapt.*

— Life and times of Menno, the Dutch reformer. 18°. 30c. .... *Am. Bapt.*

— (*ed.*) Encyclopedia of relig. knowledge; with a missionary gazetteer; rev. by G. P. Tayler. ('58.) New ed. ill. roy. 8°. '75. shp., $6. *Claxton; So. Bapt.*

Brown, J: Porter. History of the dervishes; or, Oriental spiritualism. ill. cr. 8°. $3.50 .. *Lippincott.*

Brown, Leon. American patriotism; or, memoirs of common men: a monument to deceased soldiers of Polk Co., Iowa. 8°. $2 .... *Mills.*

— Rights of labor. 8°. '74. 50c. .... *Mills.*

Brown, Marie A. *See* Borg, S., *and* Brown, M. A.

Brown, Ma. R. Maggie and her friends. 18°. '68. 75c. .... *Randolph.*

Brown, Mat. Views and opinions. cr. 8°. $2. *Routledge.*

Brown, O. B. Carmina alterna: sel. of Psalms for responsive service; with introd. by Rev. E. E. Hale. 8°. bds., $1 .... *G. D. Russell.*

— *See also* Hill, S., *and* Brown, O. B.

Brown, R. C. L. The life of peace. 16°. '76. $1 .. *Pott.*

Brown, Rob. The races of mankind. 4 v. ill. cr. 4°. ea., $3.50 .... *Cassell.*

Brown, Ryland T. Manual of physiology and hygiene. ill. 12°. '72. $1.35 .... *Wilson, H. & Co.*

Brown, S: Gilman. Memoir of Rufus Choate. 2d ed. por. cr. 8°. '70. $2.50; hf. cf., $4. *Little, B. & Co.*

Brown, T. Allston. History of the Am. stage; with biog. sketches. por. cr. 8°. $3; hf. cf., $5. *Dick & F.*

Brown, Theron. ["Park Ludlow."] Blount family (The); or, a widow's toil, trust and triumph. ill. 16°. '73. $1.50 .... *Lothrop.*

— Nick Hardy; or, once in fun and twice in earnest: sequel to "Red shanty boys." 16°. '72. $1.50. *H. A. Young.*

— Red shanty boys; or, pictures of New Eng. school-life 30 years ago. 16°. '71. $1.50. *H. A. Young.*

— Walter Neal's example. ill. 16°. '76. $1.25 .. *Lothrop.*

Brown, T: Taxidermist's manual. 22d ed. ill. 16°. '72. $1 .... *Little, B. & Co.*

— *Same.* (Popular manuals.) 23d ed. ill. 16°. '75. $1.25 .... *Putnam.*

Brown, T: *C.E.* *See* Main, T. J., *and* Brown, T.

Brown, T: B. Thoughts suggested by the perusal of Gilfillan and other authors on the Sabbath. 16°. '70. pap., 15c. . . . . *Sev. Day Adv.*

Brown, Tom. Year at school. 16°. '74. 50c. *Routledge.*

Brown, W: Thoughts on paper currency and lending on interest, as affecting the prosperity of labor, commerce and manufactures. 16°. $1 . . *Lippincott.*

Brown, *Rev.* W: Summary of Scripture truth. 32°. '57. 25c. . . . . *Am. Tr.*

Brown, *Rev.* W: *M.D.* Memoir and select remains of Rev. J: Brown. 12°. 70c. . . . . *Pres. Bd.*

— Selection of passages of Scripture for young persons to commit to memory. 32°. 30c. . . . . *Pres. Bd.*

Brown, W: H. Historical sketch of the early movement in Illinois for the legalization of slavery. 12°. pap., 25c. . . . . *Fergus.*

Brown, W: Wells. The negro in the Am. rebellion: his heroism and his fidelity. 12°. *$2 . . *Lee & S.*

Brown and Arthur. Chalmers, A. M. 50c. *J. W. Randolph.*

Brown and Brahmins. Reece, R. 15c. . . . . . . *French.*

Brown Bessie. 32°. 40c. . . . . *Scribner, W. & A.*

Brown, Jones and Robinson. *See* American tour of.

Brown, Jones and Robinson. *See* Doyle, R.

Brown, Jones and Robinson. Trollope, A. 50c. *Harper.*

Brown Jones' and Jones Brown's adventures at Martha's Vineyard camp ground. Fowle, C. H. 15c. *Wheaton.*

Brown, the martyr: farce. 16°. pap., 15c. . . . *French.*

Brown pony. Strong, J. D. 25c. . . . . *Lothrop.*

Brown-stone front (A). Fulton, C. 75c. . . . *Hinton.*

Browne, Albert G., *jr.* *See* Massachusetts, Supreme Court reports.

Browne, Arth. Compendious view of the civil law and law of admiralty. 2 v. 8°. shp., $8. *Baker, V. & Co.*

— *Same.* 2 v. 8°. '40. $8 . . . . *T. & J. W. Johnson.*

Browne, *Miss* Augusta. Hamilton, the young artist; with essay on sculpture and painting by H. A. C. Browne. ('51.) New ed. 18°. '68. 75c. *Claxton.*

Browne, C. Symbolism and its connection with church art, architecture, etc. 16°. '65. pap., 75c. . . *Pott.*

Browne, Causten. Treatise on the construction of the statute of frauds in England and the U. S. 3d ed., rev. and enl. 8°. '70. shp., $6 . . *Little, B. & Co.*

Browne, C: F. ["Artemus Ward."] Complete writings with biog. ill. 12°. $2 . . . . *Carleton.*

— Sandwiches. 8°. 25c. . . . . *Carleton.*

Browne, Dan. Jay. American bird fancier: breeding, rearing, feeding, etc., of cage and house birds; with remarks on their diseases and remedies. ill. 12°. 30c. . . . . *Judd.*

— Trees of America, native and foreign, pictorially and botanically delineated, and scientifically and popularly described. ill. 8°. $5.50 . . . . *Harper.*

Browne, E: Har. Exposition of the Thirty-nine articles; ed., with notes, by Bp. J. Williams. New ed., rev. 8°. '70. $4 . . . . *Dutton.*

— *See also* Cook, F. C., Bible commentary.

Browne, Irving. Humorous phases of the law: v. 1 of Legal recreations. 12°. '76. $1.50. *Claxton; S. Whitney.*

Browne, J. E. A. Thoughts through the year: sonnets suggested by the Collects. 12°. $1 . . *Routledge.*

Browne, J. H. Balfour. Medical jurisprudence of insanity. 2d ed., enl.; with ref. to Scotch and Am. decisions, etc. 8°. '75. $5 . . . . *Lindsay.*

— *Same.* 8°. shp., $7.50 . . . . *S. Whitney.*

Browne, J: Ross. Adventures in the Apache country: a tour through Arizona and Sonora, with notes on the silver regions in Nev. ill. 12°. $2 . . *Harper.*

— American family (An) in Germany. ill. 12°. $2. *Harper.*

Browne, J: Ross, *continued.*

— Crusoe's island: a ramble in the footsteps of Alexander Selkirk; with sketches of adventure in California and Washoe. ill. 12°. $1.75 . . . . *Harper.*

— Land of Thor. ill. 12°. $2 . . . . *Harper.*

— Resources of the Pacific slope; with sketch of the settlement and exploration of Lower California. 8°. $3 . . . . *Appleton.*

— Yusef; or, the journey of the Frangi. ill. 12°. $1.75. *Harper.*

Browne, Junius Henri. Great metropolis (The): a mirror of N. Y. ill. 8°. *$3; shp., $3.50; hf. mor., $4.50 . . . . *Am. Pub.*

— Sights and sensations in Europe. ill. 8°. *$3; $3.50; hf. mor., $4.50 . . . . *Am. Pub.*

Browne, P: A. *See* Pennsylvania, Reports.

Browne, S. H. Claims of the Gospel ministry to a support; ed. by T. O. Summers. ('55.) 2d ed. 12°. '75. pap., 20c. . . . . *So. Meth.*

Browne, S. H. Manual of commerce: source, etc., of principal articles of commerce, [with] descript. of the means of facilitating commercial operations and an explan. of commercial terms; with index. 12°. '71. *$1.50; leath., $2 . . *C. A. Nichols.*

Browne, *Mrs.* Sara H. Life's changes. 18°. 60c. *Cong. Pub.*

— Maggie Manealy; or, the broken leg. 16°. 60c. *Cong. Pub.*

Browne, *Sir* T: Works; ed. by S. Wilkin. 3 v. 12°. (Bohn.) ea., $1.75 . . . . *Little, B. & Co.*

Cont.: 1. The vulgar errors.—2. Religio medici; Garden of Cyrus.—3. Urn-burial; Tracts; Correspondence.

— *Same.* 3 v. 12°. (Bohn.) ea., $2. *Lippincott; Scribner, W. & A.*

— Religio medici, and other papers. por. 16°. $2. **Osgood.*

— *Same;* [also] Urn-burial, etc. 16°. $1.25. *Scribner, W. & A.*

Browne, W: Hand. *See* Johnston, R. M., *and* Browne, W. H.

Browne, W: Hardcastle. Digest of statutes, decisions and cases throughout the U. S. upon divorce and alimony; with a brief of law and fact of all cases in divorce, decided in the Penna. Sup. Court, and with synopsis of Penna. laws and rules of practice. 8°. shp., $5.50 . . . . *Kay.*

— Treatise on the law of trade-marks and analogous subjects. 8°. '73. shp., $5.50 . . . *Little, B. & Co.*

— (*ed.*) Heart-throbs of eminent authors. 12°. '71. *$1.50; hf. mor., $2.50 . . . . *Maclean.*

Brownell, C: DeWolff. History of the Indian races of the west. continent. ill. 8°. *$3.50; leath., $4 . . . . *Am. Pub.*

Brownell, H. H. War lyrics. 16°. $1.50 . . **Osgood.*

Brownell, T: Church. Family prayer-book: Book of common prayer, and administration of the sacraments, etc., and ceremonies of the Prot. Episc. Ch.; with comment. ('46.) New ed. roy. 8°. '75. $3.50 . . . . *Claxton.*

Brownie Sanford. May, C. L. $1.25 . . *H. A. Young.*

Browning, E. *See* England, Law reports.

Browning, *Mrs.* Eliz. B. Poetical works. ill. 8°. $5; shp., $6; hf. cf., $7.50; mor., $10 . . . . . . *Miller.*

— *Same.* (Diamond ed.) 32°. $1.50; hf. cf., $3; cf., $3.75 . . . . *Miller.*

— *Same.* (Red line ed.) ill. sm. 4°. $4.50; hf. cf., $6; mor., $8 . . . . *Miller.*

— *Same.* 2 v. por. cr. 8°. $5; hf. cf., $9; mor., $12. *Miller.*

— *Same;* with memoir by T. Tilton. (Household ed.) 2 v. 12°. $4; hf. cf., $8; cf., $10 . . . . *Miller.*

— *Same;* with memoir by T. Tilton. (Handy-volume ed.) 4 v. por. sq. 16°. $5; hf. cf., $10; cf., $14 . . . . *Miller.*

— Aurora Leigh. (Diamond ed.) 32°. $1; hf. cf., $2.50; cf., $3.50 . . . . *Miller.*

Browning, *Mrs.* Eliz. B., *continued.*

— *Same.* (Blue and gold ed.) 32°. $1.25; hf. cf., $2.50; mor., $3.50 .... *Miller.*

— *Same.* (Cabinet ed.) 16°. $1.50; hf. cf., $2.75; mor., $3.75 .... *Miller.*

— *Same.* (Red line ed.) ill. sm. 4°. $3.50. *Miller; Osgood.*

— Essays on the Greek, Christian, and the English poets. (Blue and gold ed.) 32°. $1.25; hf. cf., $2.50; mor., $3.50. —(Cabinet ed.) 16°. $1.50; hf. cf., $2.75; mor., $3.75 .... *Miller.*

— Lady Geraldine's courtship. ill. 4°. $4; mor., $8. *Miller.*

— Last poems; with memoir by T. Tilton. (Blue and gold ed.) por. 32°. $1.25; hf. cf., $2.50; mor., $3.50. —(Cabinet ed.) por. 16°. $1.50; hf. cf., $2.75; mor., $3.75 .... *Miller.*

— Poems; with essay by H. T. Tuckerman. 3 v. por. 12°. $7.50; hf. cf., $13.50; mor., $18 ... *Miller.*

— Poems and essays; with memoir by T. Tilton. (Blue and gold ed.) 5 v. por. 32°. $6.25; hf. cf., $12.50; mor., $17.50 .... *Miller.*

— Poems of memory and hope. ill. 8°. $3.50; $6.50. *Miller.*

— The true Mary: Mrs. B's "Virgin Mary to the child Jesus," with comments and notes; ed. by Rev. W. A. Muhlenberg. 8°. 90c. .... *Whittaker.*

Browning, H. B. New theology; or, breviates of Christian doctrine. 16°. $1 .... *Lippincott.*

— Words in season: manual of instruction, comfort and devotion. 16°. 50c. .... *H. H. Carter.*

— *Same.* 16°. $1 .... *Lippincott.*

Browning, J. W. Unconditional perseverance. ('55.) 2d ed. 18°. '74. 60c. .... *So. Meth.*

Browning, Meshach. Forty-four years of a hunter's life. ill. 12°. $1.50 .... *Lippincott.*

Browning, Nellie. Good for evil, and other stories. 18°. 50c. .... *Pres. Bd.*

Browning, Rob. Complete works. 12 v. 16°. '55–'75. ea., $1.50 .... *Osgood.*

Cont.: Aristophanes' apology, incl. a transcript from Euripides: the last adventure of Balaustion. — Balaustion's adventure; incl. a transcript from Euripides [Alcestis], hf. cf., $3; mor., $4. — Dramatis personæ. — Fifine at the fair, etc. — Inn album. — Men and women. — Poems and dramas, 2 v. — Red cotton night-cap country; or, turf and towers. — The ring and the book, 2 v. — Sordello, Strafford, Christmas-eve and Easter-day.

— *Same.* 12 v. in 11. 16°. hf. cf., $34.50 .... *Osgood.*

— Lyrics of life. por. sm. 4°. 75c. .... *Osgood.*

— *See also* Companion poets.

Brownings (The). 16°. 75c. .... *Dodd.*

Brownlow, W. G. "Great iron wheel" examined. 12°. '58. $1 .... *So. Meth.*

Brownlows (The). *See* Oliphant, *Mrs.* M. O. W.

Brown-Sequard, E: Lectures on functional nervous affections. pt. 1. 8°. '73. $1.25 .... *Putnam.*

— Lectures on paralysis of the lower extremities. 8°. '72. $2.50 .... *Putnam.*

Brownson, Fs. I. Address [on] life and character of Rev. D: Elliott. 12°. '74. 90c. *R. S. Davis (P.)*

Brownson, Orestes A: American republic (The): its constitution, tendencies and destiny. 8°. $3; hf. cf., $5 .... *O'Shea.*

— Conversations on liberalism. 12°. $1 ...... *Sadlier.*

— Convert (The); or, leaves from my experience. 12°. $2 .... *Sadlier.*

— Essays. 12°. $2; hf. mor., $3; hf. cf., $3.50. *Sadlier.*

Brownson, S. M. Life of Demetrius Augustine Gallitzin, prince and priest. 8°. '73. $2.50. *Pustet.*

Brownson, Sa. A. Marion Elwood. 12°. $1.25; $1.75 .... *Sadlier.*

Bruce, Alex. B. Humiliation of Christ, in its physical, ethical and official aspects: 6th ser. of Cunningham lectures. 8°. '76. $6 .... *Scribner, W. & A.*

— Training of the twelve: expositions of passages in the Gospels, exhibiting the twelve disciples of Jesus under discipline for the apostleship. 8°. $5 .... *Scribner, W. & A.*

Bruce, C: Lame Felix. 16°. 80c. *Cin. Meth. Bk. Conc*

— *Same.* 16°. '75. $1 .... *H. A. Young*

Bruce, *Mrs.* E. M. Happy heart ser. for children. 6 v ill. 18°. '74. ea., 75c. .... *Universalis*

Cont.: A little light. — Borrowing. — Open doors. — Patie Johnny. — Merry Madge. — The May party.

Bruce, Edn. Forty-five opera choruses. obl. f°. '67 bds., $3 .... *Ditson*

— Operatic bouquet: quartettes, choruses, etc. 8°. '60 $2.50; bds., $2; pap., $1.50 .... *Ditson*

Bruce, Gainsford. *See* England, Law reports.

Bruce, G: B., *and* Emmett, D. D. Drummers' an fifers' guide. 4°. bds., $1.50 .... *Pond*

Bruce, L. C. *See* American stud-book; — Bruce, S. D *and* L. C.

Bruce, Rob. Life. 8°. pap., 75c. .... *Peterson*

Bruce, S. D. *See* American stud-book.

— *and* L. C. (*ed.*) American turf register, and racin calendar; with app. ('70.) [Annual.] 8°. $3 *Turf, F. & F*

Bruce, W: Commentary on Gospel of John; — o Matthew. 8°. ea., $2 .... *H. H. Carter*

— Sermons, expository and pract. 8°. 75c. *H. H. Carter*

Brucker, Jos. Gedanken über Welt u. Mensch. 8° '72. pap., 15c. .... *Doerflinger*

Bruckner, —. *See* Luthardt, C. E., Kalmis, —, *an* Bruckner, —.

Brückner, F. Amerikas Geographie u. Naturgeschichte ill. 8°. $4 .... *Witter*

Bruckner, W: H. *See* Chynoweth, J. B., *and* Bruckner, W. H.

Brudder Bones' book of stump speeches. Scott, J. F 30c.; 50c. .... *Dick & F*

Brüder Mathieu (Die). *See* Hartmann, M.

Brüderchen u. Schwesterchen. *See* Wildermuth, O.

Bruey: a little worker for Christ. 16°. $1.10 .. *Am. S. S*

Brueys, D: A: de. L'avocat Patelin. Ed. by G. Masson. [Text book.] 16°. 50c.; pap., 25c. *Lippincott*

Bruhns, C: (*ed.*) Life of Alex. v. Humboldt; comp by J. Lowenberg, R. Ave-Lallemant and A Dove; tr. by J. and C. Lassell. 2 v. por. 8° $10.50 .... *Lee & S*

Bruin. Reid, M. $1.50 .... *Miller*

Bruised and cured. Leavitt, A. J. 15c. ..... *De Witt*

Bruised reed (The): memoir of Rev. H: Mowes. 18° '43. 50c. .... *Am. S. S*

Bruised reed (The) and smoking flax. Sibbes, R. 75c *Pres. Bd*

Brull, A. Comparison of resisting properties of iro and steel. *See* Urbin, E., Practical guide fo puddling iron and steel.

Brune, F. W., *jr.* *See* Norris, W. H., Brown, G. W. *and* Brune, F. W., *jr.*

Bruni, B. New method for viola; with 25 studies. 4° '75. pap., $2 .... *Ditson*

Brunner, Alphonso A. Elementary and pronounc French reader; with vocab. 4th ed. 18°. '70 hf. bd., 60c. .... *Clarke*

— Gender of French verbs simplified. New ed., rev 18°. '64. bds., 25c. .... *Clarke*

Brunnow, F. Spherical astronomy; tr. from 2d Germ ed. by the author. ill. 8°. $6.50 .. *Van Nostrand*

Bruno. Abbott, J. 90c. .... *Harper*

Bruns, H: M. Latin grammar. 12°. '73. $1 .. *Morton*

Brunson, Alfr. Western pioneer: autobiog. 12°. $1.75 *Cin. Meth. Bk. Conc*

Brunton, Ma. Self-control. [Fiction.] 8°. pap., 75c *Harper*

Brunton, T. Lauder. Experimental investigation o the action of medicines: hand-book of pharmacology. ill. 8°. $1.25 .... *Lindsay*

— *See also* Hand-book for the physiol. laboratory.

rush, G: J. Manual of determinative mineralogy, with introd. on blow-pipe analysis. 8°. $3. *Wiley.*
- *See also* Dana, J. D.
rutė, S. W. G. Memoirs. *See* Bayley, J. R.
rutus. *See* Payne, J. H.
rutus. Voltaire, F. M. A. de. 15c.......... *French.*
ruyas, Ja. Radical words of the Mohawk lang. with their derivatives. 8°. '62. pap., $4....... *Shea.*
- — *See also* Shea, J. G.
ryan, Mich. Biographical and crit. dict. of painters and engravers. New ed., rev. and continued by G: Stanley. imp. 8°. $21.... *Scribner, W. & A.*
ryan, T: B. Praktische englische Grammatik. 12°. $1.25 .... *Appleton.*
ryan Maurice. Mitchell, W. $1.75. *Claxton; Lippincott.*
ryant, Arth. Forest trees for shelter, ornament and profit. 12°. $1.50............ *H. T. Williams.*
ryant, C: Account of the habits of the northern fur seal. *See* Allen, J. A., On the eared seals.
ryant, Dan. Live Injun; or, Jim Crow: dramatic sketch. 12°. pap., 15c................ *De Witt.*
ryant, E. E. *See* Spooner, J. C., *and* Bryant, E. E.
ryant, H. B., *and* Stratton, H. D. Business arithmetic for commercial colleges and business men. 8°. '72. $2.50......................... *Mason.*
- — Commercial arithmetic. (Counting-house ed.) 8°. $1.88.................................. *Mason.*
- — Commercial law for business men; rev. by A. Dean. 8°. $3.25; shp., $4 .... *Appleton.*
- — *and* Packard, S. S. Common school book-keeping. 12°. '61. $1.12.................. *Ivison.*
- — — Counting-house book-keeping. 8°. '63. $3.75. *Ivison.*
- — — High school book-keeping. 8°. '60. $2.50. *Ivison.*
- — — Interest tables. 4°. hf. roan, $5; $6. *Appleton.*
ryant, J. Pocket manual, or repertory of homœop. medicine. 3d ed. 18°. $3............ *Boericke.*
ryant, J. C. New commercial book-keeping. 8°. $2. *Bryant.*
- New counting-house book-keeping, with manufacturing and modern banking. 8°. $3.... *Bryant.*
- New elementary book-keeping. 8°. 80c..... *Bryant.*
ryant, J. D. Pauline Seward: a tale of real life. 2 v. in 1. 12°. '56. $2; $2.50........ *Murphy.*
ryant, T: Practice of surgery. ill. 8°. $6.25; leath., $7.25.................................. *Lea.*
ryant, W: Cullen. Among the trees. ill. sq. 8°. '74. $2.50; mor., $5................. *Putnam.*
- Letters from the east: notes of a visit to Egypt and Palestine. 12°. '69. $1.50; ill., $2.50.. *Putnam.*
- Letters from Spain and other countries. 12°. $1.25. *Appleton.*
- Letters of a traveller. por. 12°. '69. $2.. *Putnam.*
- Little people of the snow. ill. 4°. $5; mor., $9. *Appleton.*
- Orations and addresses. 12°. '73. $2..... *Putnam.*
- Poetical works. ill. 8°. mor., $12; $15.. *Appleton.*
- *Same.* (Blue and gold ed.) 18°. $1.50; cf., $3.50. *Appleton.*
- *Same.* (Red line ed.) ill. and por. sq. 12°. $3.50; hf. cf., $5; mor., $7...................... *Appleton.*
- *Same.* 3 v. 12°. $4.50; $6; hf. cf., $9; mor., $12 .... *Appleton.*
- Song of the sower. ill. 8°. $5; mor., $9.. *Appleton.*
- Story of the fountain. ill. 8°. $5; mor., $9. *Appleton.*
- Voices of nature. sm. 4°. '65. 75c. ...... *Osgood.*
- (*ed.*) Library of poetry and song: sel. from best poets. ill. 8°. *$5......................... *Ford.*
- Selections from the Am. poets. 18°. 75c... *Harper.*
- *See also* Companion poets; — Forest scenes; — Homer; — Laurel leaves; — Tales of Glauber Spa; — Winter poems.

Bryant, W: Cullen, *continued.*
— *and* Gay, S. H. Popular hist. of the U. S.; [with] sketch of pre-hist. period and age of the mound-builders. [To form 4 v.] v. 1. ill. 8°. '76. *$6; shp., $7.50; hf. mor., $8.50; mor., $10.50.. *Scribner.*
Bryant Gray. Thompson, J. P. 50c...... *Randolph.*
Bryce, Ja. Holy Roman empire. 5th ed.; with supplement. chapter on the new Germ. empire. cr. 8°. '75. $3..................... *Macmillan.*
— *See also* Library atlas of geog.
Bubbles and ballast: description of life in Paris during the days of the empire, etc.; by a lady. 12°. '71. $2...................... *Kelly, P. & Co.*
Buccaneer's daughter. Judson, E. Z. C. 25c. *Dick & F.*
Buccaneers (The). Thornbury, W. $1.75.. *Routledge.*
Buch der Lieder. *See* Heine, H.
Buch zum Todtlachen. 2 v. 12°. ea., 15c..... *Radde.*
Buchan, W: Domestic medicine: prevention and cure of diseases by regimen and simple medicines; with a family dispensatory. 59th Am. ed. 8°. '71. shp., $4............................. *Claxton.*
Buchanan, Cls. Memoir. 18°. 40c........ *Am. S. S.*
— — *See also* Laborers in the east.
Buchanan, G: Oration on evil of slavery. *See* Poole, W. F., Anti-slavery before 1800.
Buchanan, G: *See* George Buchanan.
Buchanan, Ja. On the doctrine of justification: outline of its hist. in the church and of its exposition from Scripture. 8°. $5... *Scribner, W. & A.*
Buchanan, Rob. Book of Orm: "Book of the visions seen by Orm, the Celt." cr. 8°. $2.. *Routledge.*
— Drama (The) of kings. 8°. '71. $5.... *Routledge.*
— Idyls and legends of Inverburn. cr. 8°. $1.75. *Routledge.*
— London poems. cr. 8°. $2............. *Routledge.*
— North coast, and other poems; ill. by Pinwell, etc. 4°. $10; mor., $15................. *Routledge.*
— Poems. 16°. '64. $1.50................. *Roberts.*
— Poetical and prose works. 3 v. 12°. '74. $2.25. *Osgood.*
— Saint Abe. 16°. $1.50................. **Osgood.*
— Undertones. 16°. $1.75................ *Routledge.*
— White rose and red: a love poem. 16°. $1.50. **Osgood.*
— (*ed.*) Ballad stories of the affections; from the Scandinavian. 16°. $1.25.......... *Scribner, W. & A.*
Buchanan, Rob. Culture of the grape, and wine making. ('52.) New ed. 12°. '65. 75c... *Wilstach.*
Buchanan, Robertson. Practical essays on mill work and other machinery, with examples of tools of modern invention, and supplement; ed. by T. Tredgold and G. Rennie. 3 v. 88 pl. roy. 8°. (Weale.) '41. $7...................... *Spon.*
Buchanan's administration on the eve of the rebellion. 8°. $1.50; pap., $1................ *Appleton.*
Buchheim, C. A. (*ed.*) Deutsche Lyrik. 18°. '75. $1.50.............................. *Macmillan.*
Büchlein (Das) v. Feldmarschall Blücher. Oertel, P. F. W. 25c......................... *Steiger.*
Büchner, Gottfr. Biblische Real- u. Verbal-Hand-Concordanz, durchges. u. verb. v. H. L. Heubner; mit Vorrede v. P. Schaff; u. Anh. v. Bibelstellen v. A. Späth. roy. 8°. hf. mor., $6; $6.50. *Kohler.*
— — Anhang, sep. roy. 8°. pap., 50c........ *Kohler.*
Buchner, J. Morbus Brightii; tr. by S. Lilienthal. [Hom.] 12°. $1.25................. *Boericke.*
Buchner, J. H. History of the mission of the Un. Breth. Church to the negroes in Jamaica, 1754–1854. 24°. (Lond.) '54. 50c........ *Clauder.*
Büchner, L: Kraft und Stoff: empirisch-naturphilosoph. Studien. 12°. '72. $1; pap., 75c. *Steiger.*
Buchsel, C: My ministerial experiences. cr. 8°. $1.50. *Routledge.*

Buck, A. H. *See* Manual of histology.

Buck, A. M. *See* Gardner, F., Gay, A. M., *and* Buck, A. M.

Buck, C: Religious experience. 12°. $1. *N. Y. Ref. Ch. Bd.*

— Theological dictionary. Am. ed., rev. and enl. by Rev. G. Bush; with app. cont. hist. of various denominations in the U. S. ill. roy. 8°. $3. 18°. $1.50 .... *Desilver.*

Buck, Dan. D. Avenging of the elect. 18°. 40c. *So. Bapt.*

— Harmony and exposition of our Lord's great prophecy. 8°. $2.25 .... *So. Bapt.*

— Resurrection destinies. 18°. '68. pap., 20c. *Darrow.*

— Walking in the light. 18°. 60c. *Cin. Meth. Bk. Conc.*

Buck, Dudley. Centennial meditation of Columbia: cantata. 8°. *net*, bds., 75c. .... *Schirmer.*

— Easter morning: cantata. f°. $1.50 .... *Brainard.*

— Forty-sixth psalm, "God is our refuge"; for chorus, solos and orchestra. 8°. '72. $1.25; bds., $1; pap., 80c. — Orchestral string parts. $5 .. *Ditson.*

— Hymn to music. 8°. pap., 40c. .... *Schirmer.*

— Legend of Don Munio: cantata. 8°. '74. $1.75; bds., $1.50 .... *Ditson.*

— — Choruses. 8°. '70. bds., $1 .... *Ditson.*

— New and complete dict. of musical terms. 16°. bds., 35c. .... *G. D. Russell.*

— Six songs for male voices. 8°. '72. pap., $2.50. *Ditson.*

Buck, Dudley, *jr.* Motet collection. 2 v. obl. 4°. '64–'71. ea., $2.75; bds., $2.50 .... *Ditson.*

— Selections from motets. obl. 4°. pap., 40c ... *Ditson.*

Buck, E: Ecclesiastical law. 12°. $1.50 .. *Cong. Pub.*

Buck, *Mrs.* L. A. How Tiptoe grew. ill. 16°. '75. $1. *Am. Tr.*

Buck, L. L. Erection of the Verrugas bridge; [also] Notes and suggestions on the Croton water works and supply for the future, by B. S. Church. 8°. '76. pap., 30c. .... *Am. Soc. of C. E.*

Buck, Ruth. How Charlie helped his mother. 18°. 75c. (?) *Martien; Whittaker.*

Buck, T. F. Western Texas, the Australia of America. 12°. '60. pap., 50c. .... *Mendenhall.*

Buck, W. C. Philosophy of religion. 12°. $1.50. *So. Bapt.*

Buckalew, C: R. Proportional representation, with app.; ed. by J. G. Freeze. 8°. '72. $3. *J. Campbell & Son.*

Bucke, C: Beauties, harmonies and sublimities of nature; ed. by Rev. W. P. Page. 18°. 75c. *Harper.*

— Ruins of ancient cities; with accounts of their rise, fall and present condition. 2 v. ill. 18°. $1.50. *Harper.*

Buckeye cookery and pract. housekeeping; comp. from orig. recipes. 12°. '76. $1.50; $1.75 .. *Buckeye.*

Buckingham, C. P. Elements of the differential and integral calculus; by a method, founded on the system of Newton, without infinitesimals or limits. 12°. '75. $2 .... *Griggs.*

Buckingham, Emma May. A self-made woman; or, Mary Idyl's trials and triumphs. 5th ed. 12°. '73. $1.50 .... *Wells.*

Buckingham, H: A. Harry Burnham. 8°. pap., 75c. *Dick & F.*

Buckingham, Leicester. [Plays.] 12 v. 16°. ea., pap., 15c. .... *French.*
Cont.: Don't lend your umbrella. — Faces in the fire: comedy. — Harlequin novelty: pantomime. — Little Red Riding Hood: extravaganza. — Love's martyr. — Lucrezia Borgia: burlesque. — Merry widow: comedy. — Silken fetters: comedy. — Silver lining: comedy. — Take that girl away. — Virginius: burlesque. — William Tell: burlesque.

— *and* Harris, A. Jeannette's wedding: operetta. 16°. pap., 15c. .... *French.*

Buckland, Anna Jane. Hill-side farm (The). ill. fp. 8°. 75c. .... *Cassell.*

Buckland, Anna Jane, *continued.*

— Love and duty; or, the happy life. ill. fp. 8°. 75c. *Cassel*

— Noble rivers, and stories concerning them. 16°. $ *Am. Bap*

Buckland, Fs. T. Curiosities of natural hist. 4 v. 16 $7.50 .... *Scribner, W. &*

— Log-book of a fisherman and zoologist. ill. cr. 8 $3 .... *Lippincot*

Buckland, W: Geology and mineralogy with ref. nat. theology: text and pl. (Bridgewater treat. 2 v. 12°. (Bohn.) $5.25 ..... *Little, B. & C*

— *Same.* 2 v. 12°. (Bohn.) $6. *Lippincott; Scribner, W. &*

Buckle, H: T: Essays; with biog. of author. po 12°. $1; hf. cf., $2.50 .... *Appleto*

— History of civilization in England; with index. 2 8°. $6; hf. cf., $10 .... *Appleto*

— History of civilization in Eng. and France, Spa and Scotland; with index. 3 v. cr. 8°. $6; h cf., $12; cf., $18 .... *Lee &*

— Miscellaneous and posthumous works; ed., wi biog. notice, by H. Taylor. 3 v. 8°. (Lond '72. $22.50 .. *Little, B. & Co.; Scribner, W. &*

Buckley, C. H. A. *See* Plato.

Buckley, F. Melodist: collection of vocal music. 24 40c. .... *Gordo*

Buckley, J. M. Appeal to persons of sense and r flection to begin a Christian life. 5th ed. 16 '75. pap., 15c. .... *Tibbal*

— Christians and the theatre. 12°. '75. 80c. *Meth. Bk. Con*

— Two weeks in the Yosemite valley. 12°. '72. pap 20c. .... *Meth. Bk. Con*

Buckley, Ja. Banjo guide. obl. 8°. '68. pap., 75c. *Ditso*

— New banjo book. 4°. bds., $1.50 .... *Ditso*

— New violin method. obl. 8°. '63. pap., 75c ... *Ditso*

Buckley, Mich. B. Sermons and lectures; with m moir by Rev. C. Davis. 12°. $1.50 ... *Noona*

Buckley, T. A. Dawnings of genius exemplified an exhibited in the early lives of distinguished me ill. 16°. $1.25 .... *Routledg*

— Famous cities lib. 3 v. ill. 16°. ea., $1.25 .. *Routledg*
Cont.: Great cities of the ancient world. — Great cities the middle ages. — Seven wonders of the world.

Buckman, B: E. Samuel J. Tilden unmasked. 8 '76. bds., $1 .... (?) *Buckma*

Buckmaster, J. Cookery: abridg. of lectures d livered in the National Training School for Cool ery, at the international exhibition; with recipe 12°. '74. $1 .... *Routledg*

Buckmaster, J. C. Elements of mechanical physic ('64.) 2d ed. ill. 12°. '75. $1.50 .... *Bair*

Buckner, H. F. Words of comfort. 18°. 50c. *Sheldo*

Buckner, W. P. Calculated tables of ranges for na and army guns; with method of finding distan of an object at sea. 8°. '65. $1.50 .. *VanNostran*

Bucknill, J: C: Mad folk of Shakespeare: psycho lectures. 2d ed. cr. 8°. '67. $2.50 .. *Macmilla*

— Unsoundness of mind in relation to criminal act 8°. '56. $1.50 .... *T. & J. W. Johnso*

— — *See also* Law lib.

— *and* Tuke, Dan. H. Manual of psycholog. med cine; cont. lunacy laws, nosology, œtiolog statistics, description, diagnosis, pathology an treatment of insanity. 3d ed., enl. pl. and ill. 8 '74. $8 .... *Lindsa*

Buckskin Mose; or, life from the lakes to the Pacific [by Curtis B. Hawley?] ill. 12°. $1.50 .. *Hinto*

Buckstone, J: B. [Plays.] 38 v. 16°. ea., pap., 15 *Frenc*
Cont.: Agnes De Vere. — Alarming sacrifice: farce. — Be hunters. — Billy Taylor: burletta. — Breach of promise: co edy. — Christening. — Dead shot: farce. — Dream at sea. Flowers of forest. — Good for nothing: comic drama. — Gre bushes. — Happiest day of life: farce. — Husband at sight: far

Buckstone, J: B., *continued.*
—Irish lion: farce.—Isabelle.—Jack Sheppard.—John Jones: farce.—King of the Alps.—Kiss (A) in the dark: farce.—Leap year: comedy.—Luke, the labourer.—Maid with milking pail.—Married life: comedy.—Mischief making: farce.—Nicholas Flam: comedy.—Open house: farce.—Pet of the petticoats: opera.—Popping the question: farce.—Presumptive evidence.—Rough diamond: farce.—Rural felicity: comedy.—Scholar: comedy.—Shocking events: farce.—Snakes in the grass: farce.—Snapping turtles: farce.—Two queens: comedy.—Victorine.—Wreck ashore.

— Christening (The): farce. 16°. pap., 15c...*Lee & S.*
— Damon and Pythias: farce. 16°. pap., 15c....*Lee & S.*
— Nicholas Flam: comedy. 16°. pap., 15c...*Lee & S.*
— Snapping turtles: dialogue. 12°. pap., 15c. *De Witt.*

Buckstone at home. Coyne, J. S. 15c.....*French.*
Buckstone's adventure. Lawrence, S. 15c...*French.*
Buckstone's ascent: burlesque. 16°. pap., 15c.*French.*
Buckstone's voyage: extravaganza. 16°. pap., 15c. *French.*
Bud and blossom. *See* Clark, *Mrs.* M. L.
Bud, blossom and fruit. Pike, J. $1.....*Cong. Pub.*
Bud of the Delaware; or, little Mamie. 18°. 17c.; 22c..............................*Am. Bapt.*
Bud of the Merrimac; or, little Mackie. 18°. 17c.; 22c..............................*Am. Bapt.*
Bud of promise. 18°. 20c.; 25c..........*Am. Bapt.*
— *Same.* 16°. 25c........................*West. Tr.*
— *Same.* 18°. '59. 35c....................*Am. Tr.*
Bud of Texas; or, little Jennie. 18°. 17c.; 22c. *Am. Bapt.*
Buddenbrock, J. v. (*ill.*) Jehovahblumen: chromoliths. with [Germ.] text. roy. 4°. $12..*Stroefer.*
Buddhaghosha. Parables; tr. from Burmese by H. T. Rogers; with Buddha's Dhamma pada or path of virtue, tr. from Pâli, by F. M. Müller. 8°. $6.25....................*Scribner, W. & A.*
Buddington, Zadel Barnes. Can the old love? [Fiction.] ill. 8°. $1.25; pap., 75c..........*Estes.*
Budington, W: Ives. Responsive worship: discourse, with notes and letters from Rev. G. B. Bacon, L. Bacon, R. S. Storrs, jr., and others. 16°. '73. 60c.;—with Psalter. 90c..............*Barnes.*
Buds and blossoms; rev. by T. O. Summers. ('55.) 2d ed. 2 v. 18°. '74. $1............*So. Meth.*
Buds and blossoms: or, stories for children. ill. 12°. $1.75......................*Scribner, W. & A.*
Buds and blossoms library. 10 v. 18°. $5.45. *So. Meth.*
Cont.: Buds and blossoms, 2 v.—World of waters, by F. Osborne, 2 v.—Fifty fine poems, ed. by T. O. Summers.—Fifty beautiful ballads, ed. by T. O. Summers.—John Nelson.—Johnny McKay.—Bereaved parents consoled, by Rev. J. Thornton.—Incidents in the life of a pastor.
Buds and flowers of childish life. ill. sq. 8°. $1.50. *Routledge.*
Buds for the bridal wreath. Tilden, W. P. $1.50. *Lee & S.*
Buds from memory's wreath. Crute, S. S. $1.50. *Claxton.*
Buds of grace, and other stories. ('63.) New ed. 16°. '76. 90c....................................*Hoyt.*
Buds of promise ser. 6 v. 32°. ea., 15c.; 20c. *Dutton.*
Cont.: Hidden beauty; Dew drop.—What the wind taught; Voice of the passion flower.—Sophie's dream; Lokka.—Jamie's wagon.—Kitty's pearls; Robert Spencer's revenge.—The conduct-book; Marbles.
Budsworth's songs. 32°. pap., 10c........*Peterson.*
Bué, Jul. Class-book of comparative idioms, French pt.: Exercices sur les formes idiomatiques comparées. sm. 8°. $1..................*Lippincott.*
— *and* Sandars, W. C. Class-book of comparative idioms: English pt. sm. 8°. $1....*Lippincott.*
Buedinger, M. (*ed.*) Way of faith: sel. from the Old Test.; tr. and ed. for Jewish schools and families. 8°. (Bagster.) $1.75 ....*Wiley.*
Buel, Jesse. Farmer's companion: essays on Am. husbandry, with tables; [also] Eulogy of Buel, by A. Dean. 12°. $1.50..............*Harper.*

Buel, Jesse, *continued.*
— Farmer's instructor: essays, practical directions and hints for the management of the farm and the garden. 2 v. 18°. $1.50..............*Harper.*
Buel, R: H. Safety valves. ill. 18°. '76. bds., 50c. *Van Nostrand.*
Buel, S: Eucharistic presence, eucharistic sacrifice, and eucharistic adoration: examination of "A theological defence for the Rev. James De Koven." 12°. '74. 75c.; pap., 50c... *Whittaker.*
— *See also* Long, J. H., *and* Buel, R. H.
Buell, J. S. Cider-maker's manual. 12°. $1.50. *Judd.*
Buffalo land. Webb, W. E. *$3.25; $3.75..*Maclean.*
Buffalo Society of Natural Sciences. Bulletin. v. 1–2. ill. 8°. '73–'76. v. 1, $3; v. 2, $4. *Buffalo Soc. Nat. Sci.*
Buffets. Doe, C. H. $1.25; 75c..............*Estes.*
Buffon, G: L: Leclerc. Natural hist. of man, the globe and quadrupeds; with add. by Cuvier and others. 8°. $2; shp., $2.75................*World Pub.*
Buffum, E: Gould. Sights and sensations in France, Germany and Switzerland: experiences of an Am. journalist in Europe. 12°. $1.50..*Harper.*
— Six months in the gold mines. 12°. 50c.......*Lea.*
Buford, *Lieut.* Harry T. *See* Velasquez, *Mme.* L. J.
Bugle blast. Rouse, E. S. S. $1.75; $1.50..*Challen.*
Bugle call. Brandegee, S. K. 40c.; 25c.....*Am. Tr.*
Bugle call. Root, G. F. 35c..............*Church.*
Bugle notes for the temperance army. Sherwin, W. F., *and* Stearns, J. N. 30c.; 35c....*Nat. Temp.*
Bugler's call book. 8°. pap., 25c............*Ditson.*
Buhl, L: Inflammation of the lungs, tuberculosis and consumption; tr. by M. D. Mann and S. B. St. John. 8°. '74. $1.50................*Putnam.*
Bühler, F. Mass no. 1, in E flat; arrang. by W. C. Peters. 4°. pap., $1.25................*Peters.*
— Mass no. 2, in E flat; arrang. by J. Molengraft. 4°. pap., $1.25..............................*Peters.*
— Mass no. 3, in F. 4°. pap., $1............*Peters.*
— Vespers no. 7; arrang. by W. Dressler. 4°. pap., $1.25......................................*Peters.*
Buhler, Hope. Sophie Danforth's school life; or, shod with peace. 16°. '71. $1.25...........*Dutton.*
Builders (The). 18°. '64. 30c............*Am. S. S.*
— *See also* Champney stories.
Builders (The). Bates, L. $1.25......*J. A. Moore.*
Builders of Babel. McCausland, D. $2.50. *Scribner, W. & A.*
Builders of the sea. *See* Land and sea.
Building in silence. Jacob, J. A. $2....*Macmillan.*
Building of a brain. Clarke, E. H. $1.25...*Osgood.*
Building of the ship. Longfellow, H. W. $3; $5.50. *Osgood.*
Building stones. Ballard, J. P. $1.25......*Lothrop.*
Buisson, B. Third French reader. sm. 8°. 75c. *Lippincott.*
Buist, K. A. Birds, their cages and their keep: manual of bird-keeping and bird-rearing. ill. cr. 8°. '74. $1.75..............................*Macmillan.*
Buist, Rob. American flower garden directory; with directions for care of plants in flower garden hothouse, etc., for every month in the year. 12°. $1.50.......................................*Judd.*
— Family kitchen-gardener. 12°. $1..........*Judd.*
Bulfinch, Mar. H. Frank Stirling's choice. 16°. '68. $1...*Dutton.*
— My angel, and other poems. 18°. 25c......*Dutton.*
— Ruth and Aunt Alice. 16°. '70. $1.......*Dutton.*
Bulfinch, Ste. Greenleaf. Communion thoughts. ('50.) 4th ed. 16°. '67. 75c..................*Am. Unit.*
— Harp and cross. ('57.) 4th ed. 16°. '67. 80c. *Am. Unit.*

Bulfinch, Ste. Greenleaf, *continued.*
— Manual of the evidences of Christianity. 12°. $1. *Lee & S.*
— Palestine and the Hebrew people. 16°. 25c...*Un.S.S.*
— Studies in the evidences of Christianity. 12°. $1.50. *Lee & S.*

Bulfinch, T: Age of chivalry; or, legends of King Arthur and the knights of the round table. ('58.) New ed. 12°. '76. $3........*Lee & S.; Tilton.*
— Age of fable; or, beauties of mythology. ('55.) New ed. 12°. '76. $3........*Lee & S.; Tilton.*
— Boy inventor (The); or, memoir of Matthew Edwards. ill. 16°. 75c..................*Fuller.*
— — *See also* Union ser.
— Legends of Charlemagne; or, romance of middle ages. ('62.) New ed. 12°. '76. $3..*Lee & S.; Tilton.*
— Oregon and Eldorado; or, the romance of the rivers. 12°. '66. $2.50........................*Tilton.*
— Poetry of the age of fable. 18°. '63. $2....*Tilton.*

Bulkeley, H. W. A word to parents; or, the obligations and limitations of parental authority. 18°. 35c..................................*Pres. Bd.*

Bulkley, L. D. Management of eczema. 8°. '75. bds., 50c..............................*Putnam.*

Bull, T: Hints to mothers for the management of health during the period of pregnancy, and in the lying-in room; with an exposure of popular errors. 12°. $1.......................*Wiley.*

Bull fighter. Almar, G. 15c................*French.*

Bull (A) in a china shop. Matthews, C. 15c. *Lee & S.*

Bullard, Asa. Children's book for Sabbath hours. ill. 4°. '73. *(?)..................(?)*Holland.*
— Cracked corn. 3 v. 16°. '73. *(?)....(?)*Holland.*
— Crumbs for little chickens. 18°. 60c....*Cong. Pub.*
— Sabbath school chestnuts. 18°. 60c....*Cong. Pub.*
— Sabbath school results. 18°. 75c.......*Cong. Pub.*
— Shady Dell stories. 6 v. ill. 32°. ea., 25c. *Lee & S.*
Cont.: My teacher's gem. — The scholar's welcome. — Going to school. — The good scholar. — The lighthouse. — Reward of merit.
— Sunnybank stories. 12 v. ill. 32°. ea., 25c...*Lee & S.*
Cont.: Uncle Henry's stories. — Dog stories. — Stories for Alice. — My teacher's gem. — The scholar's welcome. — Going to school. — Aunt Lizzie's stories. — Mother's stories. — Grandpa's stories. — The good scholar. — The lighthouse. — Reward of merit.
— [Teachers' books.] 6 v. ill. 32°. ea., 20c. *Thompson.*
Cont.: Teacher's gift — offering — present — reward — token — tribute.

Bullard, E. F. *See* Tiffany, J., *and* Bullard, E. F.

Bullions, P: Analysis, parsing and composition. 18°. 50c..................................*Sheldon.*
— Exercises in anal. and pars. 18°. bds., 25c. *Sheldon.*
— Exercises in Lat. composition. 12°. $1.50..*Sheldon.*
— Greek grammar. 12°. $1.75..............*Sheldon.*
— Greek lessons. 12°. $1....................*Sheldon.*
— Greek reader, with lexicon. 12°. $2.25...*Sheldon.*
— Latin-Eng. and Eng.-Lat. lexicon. 8°. shp., $5. *Sheldon.*
— Latin grammar. 12°. shp., $1.50........*Sheldon.*
— Latin reader. 12°. shp., $1.50...........*Sheldon.*
— Practical Eng. grammar. 12°. hf. leath., $1. *Sheldon.*
— Practical lesssons in Eng. gram. and composition. 12°. hf. bd., 45c.......................*Sheldon.*
— Principles of Eng. grammar. 12°. 90c.....*Sheldon.*
— School grammar: introd. to the "Pract. gram." 12°. hf. bd., 50c...........................*Sheldon.*
Note. For classic text-books ed. by B. *see* names of authors.
— *and* Kendrick, A. C. New Greek grammar. 12°. hf. leath., $2..............................*Sheldon.*
— *and* Morris, C. D'Urban. New Lat. grammar. 12°. $1.50.................................*Sheldon.*
— — New Lat. lessons. 12°. $1..............*Sheldon.*

Bullock, J: American cottage builder: a ser. of designs, plans and specifications. (cop. '54.) '66. 5th ed. ill. 8°. '73. $3.50..............*Baird.*
— (*ed.*) Rudiments of architecture and building. (cop. '54.) '65. 5th ed. 250 eng. 8°. '75. $3.50..*Baird.*

Bullock, W. H. Across Mexico in 1864–5. ill. cr. 8°. '65. $2.50..........................*Macmillan.*
— Polish experiences during the insurrection of 1863–4. cr. 8°. '64. $2.50..................*Macmillan.*

Bullock, W. T. Commentary on Ecclesiastes. *See* Cook, F. C., Bible commentary.

Bulls and bears of New York. Smith, M. H. *$2.75; $3.25..*Burr.*

Bulls and the Jonathans. Paulding, J. K. $2.50. *Scribner.*

Bulmer, *Miss* Agnes. Memoir of Mrs. Eliz. Mortimer. 18°. '36. 55c..................*Meth. Bk. Conc.*

Bülow, H. v. Annotations to the "Fifty select studies" [for the piano], by J. B. Cramer; tr. by A. R. Parsons. 8°. *net*, pap., 50c...*Schirmer.*

Bulwer, *Sir* H: Lytton. [Lord Dalling.] France, social, literary and political. 12°. $1.50......*Harper.*
— Life of Lord Palmerston, from his diary and papers. 2 v. cr. 8°. $5; hf. cf., $8.50.......*Lippincott.*

Bulwer-Lytton, *Sir* E: G: E. L. [*Lord* Lytton.] [Works.] 34 v...........................*Harper.*
Cont.: Alice; or, the mysteries, pap., 50c. — Athens, its rise and fall, $1.50. — Caxtonia: essays on life, literature, and manners, $1.75. — The Caxtons, $1.25; pap., 75c. — Coming race, $1; pap., 50c. — Devereux, pap., 50c. — The disowned, pap., 75c. — England and the English, $1.50. — Ernest Maltravers, pap., 50c. — Eugene Aram, pap., 50c. — Godolphin, $1.50; pap., 50c. — Harold, the last of the Saxon kings, pap., $1. — Kenelm Chillingly, $1.25; pap., 75c. — King Arthur: a poem, $1.75. — Last days of Pompeii, pap., 50c. — Last of the barons, pap., $1. — Leila; or, the siege of Granada, $1; pap., 50c. — Lost tales of Miletus, $1.50. — Lucretia; or, the children of night, pap., 75c. — Miscellaneous prose works, 2 v., $3.50. — My novel, $2.50; pap., $1.50. — Night and morning, pap., 75c. — The Parisians, $1.50; pap., $1. — Paul Clifford, pap., 50c. — Pausanias, the Spartan, 75c.; pap., 50c. — Pelham, pap., 75c. — The pilgrims of the Rhine, pap., 25c. — Rienzi, pap., 75c. — The rightful heir, pap., 15c. — A strange story, $1.25; pap., $1. — The student, $1.50. — What will he do with it? $2; pap., $1.50. — Zanoni, pap., 50c.
Note. The prices given without bindings are for cl. 12°; those in pap. are 8°.
— Novels. ill. 8°. $2; shp., $2.75.......*World Pub.*
— *Same.* 7 v. 8°. ea., pap., 50c.........*U. P. James.*
Cont.: Last days of Pompeii. — Eugene Aram. — Pelham. — Ernest Maltravers. — Alice. — Zanoni. — Godolphin.
— *Same.* 10 v. 8°. ea., pap., 25c............*De Witt.*
Cont.: Rienzi. — Pelham. — Paul Clifford. — Eugene Aram. — Disowned. — Falkland. — Pilgrims of the Rhine. — Last days of Pompeii. — The student. — Devereux.
— *Same.* (Globe ed.) 25 v. 16°. ea., $1.50; per set, $37; hf. cf., $74.50....................*Lippincott.*
Cont.: Caxtons. — My novel, 2 v. — What will he do with it? 2 v. — Devereux. — Last days of Pompeii. — Leila; Calderon; Pilgrims. — Rienzi. — Last of the barons. — Harold. — Eugene Aram. — Zanoni. — Pelham. — Disowned. — Paul Clifford. — Ernest Maltravers. — Godolphin. — Alice. — Night and morning. — Lucretia. — Strange story. — Kenelm Chillingly. — Parisians. — Pausanias.
— *Same.* (Knebworth ed.) 27 v. 12°. '75. $40. *Routledge.*
Cont.: Rienzi. — Paul Clifford. — Pelham. — Eugene Aram. — Last of the barons. — Last days of Pompeii. — Godolphin. — Pilgrims of the Rhine. — Night and morning. — Ernest Maltravers. — Alice. — Disowned. — Devereux. — Zanoni. — Leila. — Harold. — Lucretia. — Caxtons. — My novel, 2 v. — What will he do with it? — Strange story. — Kenelm Chillingly. — Coming race. — Falkland; Zicci. — Parisians, 2 v.
— *Same.* (Library ed.) 43 v. sm. 12°. hf. cf., $140; cf., $175..............................*Appleton.*
— *Same.* (Library ed.) 22 v. cr. 8°. $35; — in 20 v. hf. cf., $60. — (Standard ed.) 22 v. 16°. $22; hf. cf., $50...........................*Routledge.*
Cont.: Rienzi. — Paul Clifford. — Pelham. — Eugene Aram. — Last of the barons. — Last days of Pompeii. — Godolphin. — Pilgrims of the Rhine. — Night and morning. — Ernest Maltravers. — Alice. — Disowned. — Devereux. — Zanoni. — Leila. — Harold. — Lucretia. — Caxtons. — My novel, 2 v. — What will he do with it? — Strange story.
— *Same.* (Library ed.) 47 v. 12°. $58.50; hf. cf., $129.25..............................*Lippincott.*
Cont.: Caxtons, 2 v. — My novel, 4 v. — What will he do with it? 3 v. — Devereux, 2 v. — Last days of Pompeii, 2 v. — Rienzi, 2 v. — Leila; Calderon. — Last of the barons, 2 v. — Harold, 2 v. — Pilgrims of the Rhine. — Eugene Aram, 2 v. — Zanoni, 2 v. — Pelham, 2 v. — Disowned, 2 v. — Paul Clifford, 2 v. — Godolphin. — Ernest Maltravers, 2 v. — Alice, 2 v. — Night and morning, 2 v. — Lucretia, 2 v. — Strange story, 2 v. — Kenelm Chillingly, 2 v. — Parisians, 2 v. — Pausanias.

Bulwer-Lytton, *Sir* E: G: E. L., *continued.*
— *Same.* (Lord Lytton ed.) 25 v. 12°. ea., $1.50; per set, $37; shp., $49.50; hf.cf., $80..*Lippincott.*
Note. Contents same as in Globe ed.
— *Same.* (Railway lib.) 22 v. 16°. ea., bds., 80c. *Routledge.*
Note. Contents same as in Library ed. (of Routledge), except that What will he do with it? is bd. in 2 v., and Leila *and* Pilgrims of the Rhine are bd. together in 1 v.
— Coming race (The). (Puck ser.) 16°. 75c. *Hinton.*
— Courtier (The). 8°. pap., 25c. .... *Peterson.*
— Dramas. (Household ser.) ill. 16°. $1.50; mor., $3 .... *Lee & S.*
— Dramas and poems. por. 32°. '63. $1.25. (Diamond ed.) sq. 18°. '63. $1.50......... *Roberts.*
— Dramatic works. (Presentation poets.) ill. and por. 16°. $1.75 .... *Routledge.*
— Duchesse de la Vallière: drama. 16°. pap., 15c. *De Witt; French.*
— Falkland. 8°. pap., 25c. .... *Peterson.*
— Lady of Lyons: drama. 16°. pap., 15c. *Ames; De Witt; French.*
— *Same.* 8°. pap., 15c. .... *U. P. James.*
— *Same.* 16°. bds., 50c. (Acting ed.) 16°. '73. pap., 50c. .... *Routledge.*
— *Same;* adapted for school reading by H. L. Hinton, with notes and glossary. 12°. 50c...... *Hinton.*
— *Same;* with vocab. for tr. into Fr. by B. Maurice. 12°. $1.25 .... *Lippincott.*
— — *See also* Hinton, H. L.; Acting plays of Booth.
— Miscellaneous and dramatic writings. v. 1–5. 12°. ea., $1.50 .... *Routledge.*
— Money: comedy. 16°. pap., 15c. *De Witt; French.*
— *Same.* 16°. bds., 50c. (Acting ed.) 16°. '73. pap., 50c. .... *Routledge.*
— Not so bad as we seem: comedy. 16°. pap., 15c. *De Witt; French.*
— Oxonians (The): sequel to "The roué." 8°. pap., 50c. .... *Peterson.*
— Poems. (Household ser.) ill. 16°. $1.50; mor., $3 .... *Lee & S.*
— Poetical works. (Presentation poets.) ill. and por. 16°. $1.75 .... *Routledge.*
— Reynard the fox: eng. in phonic shorthand by E. B. Burns; with key. 12°. '76. 50c. ...... *Burns.*
— Richelieu: drama. 16°. pap., 15c. *Ames; De Witt; French.*
— *Same.* 16°. bds., 50c. (Acting ed.) 16°. '73. pap., 50c. .... *Routledge.*
— *Same.* (Booth's act. plays.) 8°. pap., 30c... *Hinton.*
— Rightful heir (The): drama. 12°. pap., 15c. *De Witt.*
— Roué (The); or, the hazards of women. 8°. pap., 50c. .... *Peterson.*
— Walpole; or, every man has his price: comedy. 12°. pap., 15c. .... *De Witt.*
— *See also* Horatius, Odes and epodes; — Schiller, J. F. v., Lay of the bell; Poems and ballads.

Bulwer-Lytton, E: Rob. [*Lord* Lytton; *pseud.,* "Owen Meredith."] Apple of life. sm. 4°. pap., 25c. *Osgood.*
— Fables in song. (Cabinet ed.) 16°. '74. $1.50; hf. cf., $3; mor., $4 .... *Osgood.*
— Lucile. (Red-line ed.) ill. sm. 4°. $3.50; hf. cf., $5; mor., $7. — (Blue and gold ed.) 32°. $1.25; hf. cf., $2.50; mor., $3. — (Cabinet ed.) 16°. $1.50; hf. cf., $3; mor., $4. — (Diamond ed.) 18°. $1; hf. cf., $2.25; mor., $3. — 8°. $5; mor., $10 .... *Osgood.*
— *Same;* and other poems. ill. 8°. '69. pap., 50c. *Osgood.*
— New poems, Chronicles and characters, etc. (Blue and gold ed.) 2 v. 32°. '68. $2.50; hf. cf., $5; mor., $6. — (Cabinet ed.) 2 v. 16°. $3; hf. cf., $6; mor., $8 .... *Osgood.*
— Poems. (Blue and gold ed.) 2 v. 32°. $2.50; hf. cf., $5; mor., $6. — (Cabinet ed.) 2 v. 16°. $3; hf. cf., $6; mor., $8. — ill. 12°. $2; hf. cf., $4; mor., $5 .... *Osgood.*
— Ring (The) of Amasis; from the papers of a Germ. physician. [Fiction.] 12°. $1.50..... *Harper.*

Bumble's courtship: dram. interlude. 16°. pap., 15c. *French.*

Bump, Orl. F. Bankrupt law (The) with amendments and decisions; also, the rules and forms as amended. 8°. shp., $7.50 ...... *Baker, V. & Co.*
— Treatise on conveyances made by debtors to defraud creditors; with ref. to all cases, Eng. and Am. 8°. '72. shp., $6.50 .... *Baker, V. & Co.*
— *See also* United States, Annotated internal revenue laws.

Bumstead, Freeman J. Pathology and treatment of venereal diseases. 3d ed., rev. and enl. ill. 8°. $5; leath., $6 .... *Lea.*

Bumstead, J: On the wing: a book for sportsmen. ill. 16°. '69. $1.50 .... *Happy.*

Bumstead, Josiah F. My first school book; for reading and spelling. 16°. '41. bds., 25c...... *Marvin.*
— Spelling and thinking combined. 16°. '41. bds., 25c. *Marvin.*

Bunbury, *Miss* Selina. Fanny the flower girl; or, honesty rewarded. 18°. 35c.......... *Pres. Bd.*
— *Same.* 18°. 50c. .... *Carter.*
— *Same;* [also] Infant's prayer; ed. by T. O. Summers. ('53.) 3d ed. 18°. '75. 40c.... *So. Meth.*
— Glory, glory, glory. 18°. 35c. .... *Carter.*
— Visit to the catacombs, or first Christian cemeteries at Rome; and a midnight visit to Mount Vesuvius; ed. by T. O. Summers. ('55.) 4th ed. 18°. '74. 40c. .... *So. Meth.*
— Visit to my birthplace. 18°. 45c. .... *Routledge.*

Bunce, O. Love in '76: comedietta. 16°. pap., 15c. *French.*

Bunce, Ol. B. Romance of the revolution: stories of the days of '76. ill. 12°. '70. $1.25..... *Porter.*

Bunch of cherries. *See* Kirton, J. W.

Bunch of grapes. 18°. 50c. .... (?)*Martien.*

Bund, L: Puck's nightly pranks; tr. by C. T. Brooks, with Konewka's silh. ill. 4°. '70. pap., 50c. *Roberts.*

Bundle of sticks. Kirby, M. *and* E. 75c... *Routledge.*

Bungay, G: W. De Witt's common school vocalist. 32°. bds., 15c. .... *De Witt.*
— Off hand takings: crayon sketches of the noticeable men of our age. ill. 12°. $2........ *De Witt.*
— Temperance anecdotes. ('70.) New ed. 12°. '75. $1 .... *Nat. Temp.*

Bungener, L. L: Fél. Historical ser.; tr. from the Fr. 4 v. 12°. '74. ea., $1.50 .... *Lothrop.*
Cont.: Bourdaloue and Louis XIV. — Louis XV. and his times. — Rabaut and Bridaine. — The tower of constancy.
— History of the Council of Trent; [tr. by D. D. Scott]; ed. from 2d. Lond. ed. by J. M'Clintock. 12°. '55. $1.50 .... *Harper.*
— Life, labors and writings of John Calvin. 8°. $4.25. *Scribner, W. & A.*
— Rome and the council in the 19th century; tr. from the Fr. cr. 8°. $2.50........ *Scribner, W. & A.*
— Was der Weihnachtsbaum sagt; [tr. from the Fr.] 32°. bds., 15c. .... *Ludwig.*

Bunker, Anson. Life, confession and terrible doom of Anson Bunker, the murderer of Benjamin Nathan and fourteen other persons. [In Eng. *or* Germ.] 8°. pap., 25c. .... *Barclay.*

Bunker Hill memorial; with poem by O. W. Holmes. 8°. '75. pap., 25c. .... *Osgood.*

Bunkley, Jose. M. Testimony of an escaped novice from the sisterhood of St. Joseph, Emmettsburg, Maryland. 12°. $1.50 .... *Harper.*

Bunn, Alfr. My neighbour's wife: farce. 16°. pap., 15c. .... *French.*
— *See also* Dibdin, T., *and* Bunn, A.

Bunner, E. History of Louisiana. 18°. 75c... *Harper.*

Bunnett, *Miss* F. E. The hidden power. 16°. $1.25. (?)*Martien.*

Bunsen, Chr. C: J. (*Baron*) v. God in hist.; or, the progress of man's faith in the moral order of the world; tr. by S. Winkworth, with pref. by A. P. Stanley. 3 v. 8°. $21........*Scribner, W. & A.*
— Life of Martin Luther; tr. 16°. 75c.....*Hurd & H.*
— Signs of the times: letters to E. M. Arndt on the dangers to relig. liberty in the present state of the world; tr. by S. Winkworth. 12°. $1.50..*Harper.*
— *and* Brandis, C. A., *and* Loebell, J. W. Life and letters of B. G. Niebuhr; with essays on his character and influence. 12°. $1.50.......*Harper.*

Bunsen, Fes. Memoir of C. C. J. Bunsen: in letters and from recollections. 2 v. por. and ill. cr. 8°. $7.50; hf. cf., $10.50...............*Lippincott.*

Bunte Blätter. Memmler, L. 25c...........*Steiger.*

Bunting, J. Sermons. 2 v. 8°. '37. shp., $6. *Meth. Bk. Conc.*

Bunting, T: Percival. Life of Jabez Bunting; with notices of contemporary persons and events. v. 1. por. 12°. $1.50......................*Harper.*

Buntline, Ned (*pseud.*) *See* Judson, E. Z. C.

Bunyan, J: Works. ill. 4°. hf. mor., $20; mor., $25. *Appleton.*
— *Same.* 11 v. 12°. $12......*Am. Bapt.; So. Bapt.*
— *Same;* with introd. by J. P. Gulliver. ill. roy. 8°. '71. *$4.75; shp., $5.75..........*Bradley & G.*
— *Same;* with sel. notes, and essay by W. Landels. 30 pts. 4°. '72. ea., *30c............*S. Walker.*
— Allegorical works. 3 v. 12°. $3.50......*Am. Bapt.*
— Autobiography. fp. 8°. (Bagster.) 50c.......*Wiley.*
— Barren fig tree (The). 18°. 50c.........*Am. Bapt.*
— Grace abounding to the chief of sinners: [autobiog.] 18°. '56. $1...........................*Dodd.*
— Heavenly footman. 18°. 35c............*Am. Bapt.*
— Holy war. 24°. '70. 30c.................*Lothrop.*
— *Same.* ill. 18°. 85c......................*Am. S. S.*
— *Same.* 12°. $1.25.....................*Am. Bapt.*
— *Same.* ill. 8°. $2......................*Pres. Bd.*
— *Same;* with life of B. ill. 12°. $1.50; $2.50. *Sheldon.*
— *Same;* with notes by G. Burder. ill. 18°. '70. 75c. *Claxton.*
— *Same;* with annotations by R. Maguire, and life by W. Brock. ill. imp. 8°. $3.50; $5.....*Cassell.*
— Life. ill. 18°. 85c.....................*Am. S. S.*
— Minor works. por. 18°. 75c..............*Sower.*
— Pilgrim's progress. ill. 16°. pap., 30c. *Huntington.*
— *Same.* 16°. 50c..........................*Nelson.*
— *Same.* 18°. 60c. — ill. 32°. 75c. — ill. 12°. 75c.; $1.25; $1.75. — 8°. $1.75; col. ill., $2..*Nelson.*
— *Same.* ill. 18°. '49. 70c.; $1.25; mor., $3. — 12°. '30. $1.50; $2.25; mor., $4; $5.......*Am. Tr.*
— *Same.* ill. 18°. 75c......................*Sower.*
— *Same.* ill. 16°. 75c....................*Hurd & H.*
— *Same.* ill. 18°. 75c. ill. 12°. $1; $2.50..*Lippincott.*
— *Same.* 18°. 85c........................*Am. S. S.*
— *Same.* ill. 18°. 90c................*Bost. Am. Tr.*
— *Same.* ill. 12°. $1.......................*Appleton.*
— *Same.* 18°. '37. $1. 12°. $2.50...*Meth. Bk. Conc.*
— *Same.* 18°. '64. $1.25.................*Macmillan.*
— *Same.* 16°. $1.25........................*Pres. Bd.*
— *Same.* col. ill. 16°. '70. $1.25..........*Dutton.*
— *Same.* 12°. $1.25..*Am. Bapt.; Am. S. S.; So. Bapt.*
— *Same.* ill. 12°. $1.25; mor., $4...........*Porter.*
— *Same.* ill. 12°. $1.50......................*Lee & S.*
— *Same.* ill. 12°. $1.50; $2.50.............*Sheldon.*
— *Same.* 8°. $1.75.........................*Am. S. S.*
— *Same.* ill. 4°. $2. — ill. 12°. $1.25. — ill. 18°. 75c. *Carter.*
— *Same.* col. ill. 8°. $2.50...............*Am. S. S.*
— *Same.* ill. roy. 8°. $3.50..................*Lee & S.*
— *Same.* ill. 4°. '69. $3.50; mor., $7.50. — 18°. '72. 75c. — 12°. '72. $1..................*Lothrop.*
— *Same.* ill. 8°. cf., $9......................*Claxton.*
— *Same.* 2 v. 12°. ea., pap., 10c............*Challen.*
— *Same.* 8°. (Bagster.) $1.12. fp. 8°. $1.50..*Wiley.*
— *Same.* (Cottage lib.) ill. 16°. pap., 50c. *Huntington.*

Bunyan, J: *continued.*
— *Same;* ill. by Stothard. (Golden treas. ser.) 18° 75c.; $1.25..........................*Allyn*
— *Same.* (Household ser.) ill. and por. 16°. $1.50 mor., $3.............................*Lee & S*
— *Same.* (Large type ed.) ill. 16°. $1; $1.25. 12° $1.50....................................*Estes*
— *Same.* (Red line ed.) sq. 4°. '71. $3; hf. cf., $5 cf., $6..........................*H. A. Young*
— *Same.* [Fac-simile of 1st ed.] 12°. '75. $3. ill. 8° $3.25.....................*Scribner, W. & A*
— *Same;* with life. ill. 12°. $1.50.......*World Pub*
— *Same;* with life, notes, etc. roy. 32°. 50c.; bds. 40c...................................*Routledge*
— *Same;* [with] life, introd. and notes. por. and ill 12°. '64. $1.50.................*Collins & Bro*
— *Same;* with memoir by J. Allen. col. ill. 12°. '70 $1. (Presentation ed.) ill. 12°. $1.75..*Routledge*
— *Same;* with memoir by G. Cheever and index. (New pict. family ed.) ill. 8°. *$3; $4..*J. E. Potter.*
— *Same;* with memoir by G. B. Cheever and index. ill. and por. cr. 8°. '63. $5; mor., $9..*Scribner.*
— *Same;* with introd. essay, by W. Landels. (Family ed.) col. pl. and ill. 4°. $15.......*Routledge.*
— *Same;* with notes by R. Maguire. ill. imp. 8°. $3.50; $5...........................*Cassell.*
— *Same;* with memoir and notes, by G. Offor. ill. cr. 8°. $1.25. ill. 4°. $3.50–$10...........*Routledge.*
— *Same;* with memoir by T. Scott. por. 18°. '74. 75c. 12°. $1.50......................*Claxton.*
— *Same;* with notes by T. Scott, and life by J. Conder. ill. 8°. $2.50........................*Pres. Bd.*
— *Same;* with life by R. Southey. ill. 12°. $1.50. *Harper.*
— *Same;* with biog. introd. by T. O. Summers. ('54.) 20th ed. ill. 18°. '76. $1.............*So. Meth.*
— *Danish.* 18°. '52. 65c......................*Am. Tr.*
— *Dutch.* pt. 1. 18°. '51. 35c...............*Am. Tr.*
— *French.* Le pélérinage du Chrétien. ill. 18°. '40. 40c.....................................*Am. Tr.*
— — *Same.* 18°. 25c.......................*Pres. Bd.*
— *Germ.* Die Pilgerreise. ill. 18°. '42. 70c.; 90c. *Am. Tr.*
— *Ital.* Il pellegrinaggio del Christiano. ill. 18°. '58. 70c.....................................*Am. Tr.*
— *Span.* El viador. ill. 18°. '52. 40c.......*Am. Tr.*
— *Swedish.* 18°. '54. 40c....................*Am. Tr.*
— *Welsh.* 12°. '45. 70c......................*Am. Tr.*
— *Same;* [incl.] the 3d pt.: The travels of the ungodly; [or], the life and death of Mr. Badman; ed. by R. Philip. ('68.) 2d ed. med. 8°. '72. $3.50......................................*Virtue.*
— *Same;* [also] Life of Bunyan by himself; or, grace abounding to the chief of sinners. ill. 12°. $1.75. *J. E. Potter.*
— — Child's pilgrim's progress. 18°. 50c. *Carter; Cong. Pub.*
— — *Same.* 2 v. 32°. 60c...................*Pres. Bd.*
— — Pictorial scenes from Pilgrim's progress; by C. R. Conder. col. ill. 4°. $5..........*Claxton.*
— — Pilgerreise. [Extract from Pilgrim's progress.] 24°. 20c...........................*Ev. Assoc.*
— — Pilgrim's progress in verse. fp. 8°. (Bagster.) 50c..*Wiley.*
— — Pilgrim's progress in verse, by E. P. Dyer. 12°. *$2..*Lee & S.*
— — Pilgrim's progress in words of one syllable, by S. P. Day. ill. roy. 16°. $1.50.............*Cassell.*
— — — *See also* Godolphin, M.; — Walker, *Mrs.* E. A.
— — *See also* Cabinet lib. of Household reading.
— Practical works. 8 v. 12°. $9; ea., $1.25..*Am. Bapt.*
Cont.: Experimental works. — Doctrinal works. — Directing works. — Devotional works. — Consoling works. — Awakening works. — Inviting works. — Searching works.
— Riches of B.; sel. by Jeremiah Chaplin. 12°. '51. 40c...*Am. Tr.*
— Sinner's progress. 12°. $1.25........*Am. Bapt.*
— *See also* Baxter, R., *and* Bunyan, J.

unyon, C. J. Treatise upon the law of life assurance, constitution of assurance companies, etc. 8°. '54. $3 ..... *T. & J. W. Johnson.*
— *See also* Law lib.

urbury, *Mrs.* E. J. Florence Sackville; or, self-dependence. 8°. pap., 75c. ..... *Harper.*

urch, J: C. *See* California, Civil code.

urch divorce case. 8°. pap., 25c. ..... *De Witt.*

urckett, *Miss* Flo. ["Edith Lee."] Wildmoor. [Fiction.] 12°. $2 ..... *Lippincott.*

ürcklin, A. Toni u. Madlein. 12°. '65. pap., 45c. *Steiger.*

urdell, J: Teeth: their structure, disease and treatment. ill. 12°. '47. pap., 25c. ..... *Wells.*

urden bearing; or, the story of Jenny Ellis. ill. 18°. 60c. ..... *Am. S. S.*

urden of human sin as borne by Christ. Thrupp, J. F. $1.25 ..... *Macmillan.*

urder, G: Fifty-two village sermons. 8°. '57. $1.50. *Am. Tr.*
- Sermons to the aged. 12°. '30. pap., 15c. ..*Am. Tr.*
- Village sermons: 101 discourses on the principal doctrines of the Gospel; with prayers. ('31.) New ed. 8°. '68. shp., $2 ..... *Claxton.*

urder, H: F. Pleasures of religion. 18°. 60c. *Pres. Bd.*

urdett, C: Arthur Martin; or, the mother's trials. 18°. 75c. ..... *Harper.*
- Life of Kit Carson. ill. 12°. '62. $1.75 .. *J. E. Potter.*
- Margaret Moncrieffe, the beautiful spy: a story of army and high life in New York in 1776. ill. 12°. $1.75 ..... *J. E. Potter.*
- Mary Grover; or, the trusting wife. 18°. 75c. *Harper.*

urditt, B. A. [Preceptors.] 4 v. obl. 8°. '50. ea., pap., 50c. ..... *Ditson.*

Cont.: Preceptor for the bugle — for the cornopean — for the post horn — for the sax horn.

- *See also* Keach, O. W.

urdocks and daisies. 18°. '75. 25c. ..... *Am. Tr.*

urdon-Sanderson, J. *See* Handbook for the physiol. laboratory.

ureau of Medicine and Surgery. *See* United States.

ureau of Navigation. *See* United States.

ürger, Gf. A: Gedichte. 12°. 75c.; pap., 50c.; hf. mor., $1 ..... *F. W. Thomas.*
- *Eng.* Ballads; [with] outline ill. by M. Retzsch. obl. f°. '72. $5; mor., $9 ..... *Roberts.*
- Lenore: ballad, tr. by H. D. Wireman. 12°. $1.50. *Kohler.*

ürger-General (Der). *See* Goethe, J. W. v.

urges, Arn. American kennel and sporting field: hist. of the origin of dogs; also, instructions on breeding, etc., with stud list of imported dogs in the U. S. ill. sq. 8°. '76. $4 ..... *Ford.*

urges, *Sir* Ja. B. Riches: play. 16°. pap., 15c. *French.*

urgess, *Rev.* Alex. Memoir of life of Rev. Geo. Burgess. demy 8°. '69. $3 ..... *Claxton.*
- Sunday-school questions on the ecclesiastical year. 16°. '59. hf. bd., 15c. ..... *Dutton.*

urgess, E. L. Elementary gymnastics. ill. 48°. 25c. *Scribner, W. & A.*

urgess, G: American metrical Psalter; or, the Psalter in Eng. metre. 18°. $1 ..... *Huntington.*
- Catechism on the Church catechism. 18°. bds., 25c. *Whittaker.*
- Last journal; with introd. by Bp. A. Lee. 12°. '63. 75c.; pap., 50c. ..... *Dutton.*
- List of persons admitted to the order of deacons in the Prot. Episc. Church in the U. S., 1785–1857; with index by Rev. W. S. Bartlett. 12°. '74. pap., $1 ..... *Williams.*
- Poems. 12°. $1.50 ..... *Brown & G.*
- Sermons on the Christian life. 12°. $1.25. *McCauley.*
- *See also* Hymns for church and home.

Burgess, J. Tom. Harry Hope's holidays: what he saw, what he did, and what he learnt during a year's rambles in country places. ill. 16°. '71. $1.25 ..... *Routledge.*

Burgess, Lucy M. Child's guide to spiritualism. 12°. '74. 25c. ..... *Colby.*

Burgess, O. A., *and* Underwood, B. F. Debate: The Christian religion as set forth in the New Test. is true in fact and of divine origin; [also] The Bible is erroneous in many of its teachings regarding science and morals, and is of human origin. 12°. '76. $1; pap., 60c. .. *D. M. Bennett.*

Burgh, N. P. Indicator diagram (The) practically considered. 2d ed. ill. cr. 8°. '75. $2.50 .... *Spon.*
— Link-motion and expansion-gear. 90 pl. and 229 ill. sm. 4°. '72. hf. mor., $15 ..... *Spon.*
— Modern compound engines: supplement to "Modern marine engineering." 18 pl. 4°. '73. $7.50. *Spon.*
— Modern marine engineering, applied to paddle and screw propulsion. 36 pl. and 259 ill. 4°. '72. $17. *Spon.*
— Pocket-book of rules for proportions of modern engines and boilers; with app. 4th ed. roy. 32°. '72. roan, $1.50 ..... *Baird; Spon.*
— Practical ill. of land and marine engines. 20 pl. f°. '64. $15 ..... *Spon.*
— *Same.* f°. $21 ..... *Baird.*
— Practical treatise on boilers and boiler making. 1163 ill. and 50 pl. 4°. '73. hf. mor., $30 ..... *Spon.*
— Practical treatise on condensation of steam. ill. roy. 8°. '71. $10 ..... *Spon.*
— Practical treatise on modern screw propulsion. 52 pl. and 103 ill. 4°. '69. hf. mor., $15.50 ..... *Spon.*
— Principles that govern the future development of the marine boiler engine and screw propeller. pl. imp. 8°. '68. pap., 75c. ..... *Spon.*
— Slide-valve (The) practically considered. ill. 12°. '67. $2 ..... *Baird.*
— *Same.* 3d ed. ill. cr. 8°. '75. $2 ..... *Spon.*

Burghley, *Lord.* [W: Cecil.] Ten precepts to his son. *See* Practical morality.

Burgmuller, F. Elementary method for the piano. f°. $2.50 ..... *Gordon.*
— Elementary theoretical and practical instructor for the piano-forte. 4°. bds., $2 ..... *Ditson.*
— Instructor for the piano-forte; [also] Czerny's Letters on the art of playing the piano-forte. 4°. $2.50; bds., $2 ..... *Ditson.*

Burgomaster's (The) family. Walrée, E. C. W. van. $1.50; $1.25 ..... *Scribner.*

Burgon, J: W. England and Rome: three letters to a pervert. 16°. '66. $1.25 ..... *Dutton.*
— Ninety short sermons for family readings. 2 ser. 4 v. 16°. '67. $6 ..... *Pott.*
— Treatise on the pastoral office. 8°. '64. $4. *Macmillan.*

Burgoyne, *Gen.* —. Lord of the manor: opera. 16°. pap., 15c. ..... *French.*

Buried alive. *See* Dumas, A.

Buried Bible, and other stories. 18°. 50c. ... *Carter.*

Buried cities. Tarbox, I. N. 75c. ..... *Cong. Pub.*

Buried cities of Campania. Adams, W. H. D. $1.50. *Lothrop.*

Buried in the snow. Hoffmann, F. 80c. (?) *Luth. Pub.*

Burke, C. Rip Van Winkle: drama. 16°. pap., 15c. *French.*

Burke, Edm. Works. 12 v. cr. 8°. (Lond.) $30; hf. cf., $48; large pap., $60. — New ed. '71. $18; hf. cf., $36 ..... *Little, B. & Co.*
— *Same*; with memoir. 3 v. por. 8°. $6; shp., $7.50; hf. cf., $12.75 ..... *Harper.*
— *Same*; and speeches. 8 v. 12°. (Bohn.) ea., $1.40. *Scribner, W. & A.*
— — *Same.* 8 v. 12°. (Bohn.) ea., $1.50 .. *Lippincott.*

Burke, Edm., *continued.*
— Philosophical inquiry into the origin of our ideas of the sublime and beautiful; with introd. discourse on taste; adapted to popular use by A. Mills. 12°. $1.50 .... *Harper.*
— Speeches. *See* Chatham, *Earl of*, Burke, E., *and* Erskine, T.; —*and above* Works.
— *See also* Hudson, H. N.

Burke, Ja. *See* Lingard, J., History of Eng.

Burke, O. J. Abbey of Ross. 16°. 50c.; 75c... *Sadlier.*

Burke, P: Ulric. American practical arithmetic. 12°. bds., 60c. .... *Sadlier.*
— American primary arith. 16°. bds., 25c.... *Sadlier.*
— Practical key to arithmetic. 16°. bds., $1.25.. *Sadlier.*

Burke, T: N. English misrule in Ireland: lectures in reply to Froude, with review of the so-called "bull" of Adrian IV., by Rev. P. H. Moran, and "Analysis of the rebellion of 1841," by M. Corey. por. 12°. '73. pap., 50c. .... (?) *Lynch.*
— Final answer to Froude's lecture [1872], entitled, "Mr. Froude's last words"; [also] lecture by Wendell Phillips [1872], entitled, "Review of Froude"; with sketch of Burke. 12°. '73. pap., 10c. .... *O'Brien.*
— Ireland and the Irish: lectures on Irish hist. and biog.; with Wendell Phillips' panegyric on O'Connell, "Treaty of Limerick," etc. por. 12°. '73. $1 .... (?) *Lynch.*
— Ireland's case stated in reply to Mr. Froude. 12°. '73. $1 .... *Haverty.*
— Ireland's Catholicity and what saved it. 24°. pap., 10c. .... *Coddington.*
— Lecture on O'Connell. ill. 8°. pap., 25c... *Sadlier.*
— Lectures and sermons. 2 v. por. 8°. '73–'74. ea., $2; $3; hf. mor., $5; mor., $7.50 ..... *Haverty.*
— O'Connell centenary. ill. 8°. pap., 25c.... *Sadlier.*
— St. Dominick and the Dominicans. 24°. pap., 10c. *Coddington.*
— Sermons and lectures on moral and hist. subjects. por. 12°. '73. $1 .... (?) *Lynch.*

Burke, Ulick Ralph. Handbook of sewage utilization. cr. 8°. '72. $1.50 .... *Spon.*

Burkhardt, C. B. Fairy tales and legends of many nations. ill. 16°. $1.50; $2 .... *Miller.*

Burkitt, W: Expository notes; with practical asseverations on the New Testament. 2 v. 8°. leath., $6 .... *Clark & M.*
— Plain words about infant baptism. 2d ed., with new notes. 18°. pap., 15c. .... *Claremont.*

Bürkner, H. Grosse Bilder-Fibel. 12°. pap., 10c.; col. ill., 25c. .... *Kohler.*

Burlamaqui, J. J. Principles of natural and politic law. 8°. shp., $3.50 .... *W. C. Little.*

Burleigh (*pseud.*) *See* Smith, Mat. H.

Burleigh, Jos. Bartlett. American primary school reader. 2 v. 18°. bds., no. 1, 10c.; 2, 15c.... *Lippincott.*
— Constitution of the U. S., with index; [also] Washington's Farewell address, and a synopsis, parallel, etc., of the national and state governments. 12°. '71. 75c. .... *Claxton.*
— Legislative guide. 12°. '68. $1.75 .... *Claxton.*
— Thinker (The): ser. of school readers. 4 nos. '71. hf. bd. .... *Claxton.*

Cont.: 1, 2, 18°, ea., 30c. — 3, 12°, 40c. — 4, 12°, $1.

Burleigh, W: H. Poems; with a memoir by C. Burleigh. por. cr. 8°. '71. $2.25 ...... *Hurd & H.*
— Rum fiend, and other poems. 12°. 20c... *Nat. Temp.*

Burley's United States Centennial [Exposition] gazet. and guide. ill. 8°. '76. $2; $2.50; $3.. *Burley.*

Burlinson, H., *and* Simpson, W. H. Iron ship-builder's, engineer's and iron merchant's guide and assistant; cont. calculated weights of upwards of 150,000 different sizes of iron plates. roy. 4°. (Lond.) '65. hf. mor., $12 .... *Spon.*

Burman slave girl. 18°. '54. 35c. .... *Am. Tr.*

Burman village in Siam. 18°. 17c.; 22c... *Am. Bapt.*

Burmese war: drama. 16°. pap., 15c. .... *French.*

Burn, And. Life. por. 18°. 55c. .... *Pres. Bd.*

Burn, Rob. Rome and the campagna: hist. and topog. descript. of the site, buildings, etc., of ancient Rome. eng., maps and plans. 4°. $25.. *Macmillan.*

Burn, Rob. Scott. Hints for farmers, and useful information for agricultural students. 16°. bds., 50c. *Routledge.*
— Illustrated archit., engineering and mechanical drawing book. ill. 12°. $1 .... *Judd.*
— Illustrated book of ornamental drawing and archit. design. ill. 12°. $1 .... *Judd.*
— Illustrated drawing book for schools, students and artizans. ill. 12°. $1 .... *Judd.*

Burnand, Fs. C. [Plays.] 32 v. 16°. ea., pap., 15c. *French.*

Cont.: Acis and Galatea: burlesque. — Alonzo the brave; or, Faust and Imogene: burlesque. — Black-eyed Susan: burlesque. — Cox and Box: musical farce. — Cupid and Psyche: extravaganza. — Deal boatman. — Deerfoot: farce. — Dido: burlesque. — Evil genius: comedy. — Fair Rosamond: burlesque. — Helen: burlesque. — Humbug: comedy. — In for a holiday: farce. — Ixion: extravaganza. — King of the merrows: extravaganza. — Lord Lovel and Lady Nancy Bell: burlesque. — Madame Beliott's ball. — Mary Turner: burlesque. — Paris: burlesque. — Patient Penelope: burlesque. — Pirithoüs, the son of Ixion: extravaganza. — Poll and Partner Joe. — Robin Hood: extravaganza. — Romance under difficulties: farce. — Rumplestilskin: extravaganza. — Snowdrop: extravaganza. — Ulysses: burlesque. — Venus and Adonis: extravaganza. — Villikins and his Dinah: Ethiop. drama. — White cat: burlesque. — White fawn: extravaganza. — Windsor Castle: burlesque.

— Deerfoot: farce. 12°. pap., 15c. .... *De Witt.*
— Happy-Thought Hall. ill. sq. 16°. '72. $2.. *Roberts.*
— Happy thoughts. 16°. '68. $1 .... *Roberts.*
— In for a holiday: farce. 12°. pap., 15c. ... *De Witt.*
— More happy thoughts. 16°. '71. $1 .... *Roberts.*
— My health. 16°. '72. $1 .... *Roberts.*
— My time and what I've done with it. [Fiction.] cr. 8°. '74. $1.75; pap., $1 .... *Macmillan.*
— New history of Sandford and Merton. ill. 16°. '72. $1.75 .... *Roberts.*
— Out of town. 16°. '72. $1.25 .... *Roberts.*
— Poll and partner Joe; or, the pride of Putney: drama. 12°. pap., 15c. .... *De Witt.*
— To Buddlecombe and back. ill. sq. 16°. '76. 50c. *Roberts.*
— *See also* Williams, M., *and* Burnand, F. C.
— *and* Williams, M. Easy shaving: farce. 16°. pap., 15c. .... *De Witt; French.*

Burnap, U. C. *See* Hymns of the church.
— *and* Flint, Ja. Anthems of the church. obl. 4°. $2.75; bds., $2.50 .... *Brainard.*
— *and* Wetmore, W. J. Athenæum: part songs for ladies' voices. ('72.) 3d ed. 8°. '76. $1.25; bds., $1 .... *Schermerhorn.*
— — Polytechnic: music for schools, etc. ('72.) 3d ed. 8°. '74. $1.75; bds., $1 .... *Schermerhorn.*

Burnet, D: Staats. Christian Sunday school library. 40 v. 32°. $12 .... *Chase.*
— Pastorate (The). 8°. pap., 10c. .... *Chase.*
— Poverty (The) of Jesus the wealth of the saints. 8°. pap., 10c. .... *Chase.*

Burnet, Gilb. On the Thirty-nine articles; ed. by Page. 8°. $2.50 .... *Appleton.*

Burnet, J: Hints on compos. sm. 4°. $3.50. *Benerman.*

Burnett, Adelaide. Margaret Claire. 16°. 75c. *Cong. Pub.*

Burnett, H. The path which led a Protestant lawyer to the Catholic Church. 8°. $2 ...... *Benziger.*

Burney, F. *See* Arblay, *Mme.* Fes. B. d'.

Burnham, B. F. *See* United States, Digest.

Burnham, C. G. Primary arith. 12°. 30c... *Appleton.*

Burnham, G: P. American counterfeits: how detected and how avoided. ill. and por. 12°. '75. *(?) (?) *Holland.*
— Hundred thousand dollars in gold: how to make it. ill. 12°. '75. *(?) .... (?) *Holland.*

Burnham, G: P., *continued.*
— Practical treatise on selecting, housing and breeding fowls, and raising poultry and eggs for market. ill. 12°. $2 .... *Lee & S.*
Burnham, S: *See* Marshall, L., Proctor, J. C., *and* Burnham, S.
Burnham, S: *jr.* Uncle Paul's stories for boys and girls. ill. sm. 4°. $1 .... *Bost. Am. Tr.*
— Victor's stories for boys and girls. ill. sm. 4°. $1. *Bost. Am. Tr.*
Burning ship. *See* Baker, B. F.
Burning village. *See* Casket of juveniles.
Burnouf, J. L. Elementos de gramática latina; tr. del frances por J. V. González. 12°. 90c... *Appleton.*
Burns, Dawson. Bases of the temperance reform. 12°. '73. $1 .... *Nat. Temp.*
— *See also* Lees, F. R., *and* Burns, Dawson.
Burns, E. A. Principles of Eng. grammar defined and ill. ('59.) New ed. 12°. '75. $1.. *Pounsford.*
Burns, Eliza B. Anglo-American alphabet: rev. spelling. 8°. pap., 10c .... *Burns.*
— Burns' phonetic shorthand; on basis of I. Pitman's "Phonography." ('73.) 3d ed. 12°. '76. $1. *Burns.*
— Little dictionary; or, phonog. word and phrase lists. 12°. '76. 25c .... *Burns.*
— Reading lessons in steno-phonog. 12°. '76. 50c. *Burns.*
— Reynard the fox, by Bulwer; eng. in phonic shorthand by B.; with key. 12°. '76. 50c.... *Burns.*
— Second reader in steno-phonog. 12°. '76. 50c. *Burns.*
Burns, G: C. American woolen manufacturer. 8°. '72. $6.50 .... *Freeman.*
Burns, Islay. Life of W. C. Burns. 12°. $2.50.. *Carter.*
Burns, Jabez. Cyclopædia of sermons. 8°. $2.50. *Appleton.*
— Mothers of the wise and good. 16°. $1.25.. *Tibbals.*
— *See also* Cook's letters from the sea.
Burns, Ja. D. Celestial city (The): glimpses within its gates. 12°. 50c .... *Bost. Am. Tr.*
— Evening hymn (The). 32°. 50c .... *Nelson.*
— Heavenly Jerusalem; or, glimpses within the gates. 18°. 50c .... *Nelson.*
Burns, R. S. Building construction: stone, brick and slate work. (Element. sci. ser.) 2 v. ill. 16°. '74. ea., 75c .... *Putnam.*
— Building construction: timber and iron work. 2 v. ill. 16°. '74. ea., 75c. (Adv. sci. ser.) ill. 12°. $1.50 .... *Putnam.*
Burns, Rob. Works; with glossary. 8°. $2; $2.50. *U. P. James.*
— *Same;* with life and notes. ill. and por. 8°. $2.50. *Lee & S.*
— *Same.* (Globe ed.) ill. 16°. $1.25; hf. cf., $3.25; mor., $4. chp. ed. 16°. pap., 60c.... *Appleton.*
— *Same;* with memoir. (Globe ed.) por. and ill. 12°. $1.50; hf. cf., $3.50; mor., $5.. *Lippincott.*
— *Same;* with life, ed. by R. Chambers. 4 v. 12°. $6; hf. cf., $13 .... *Harper.*
— *Same;* with life by A. Cunningham. ill. 8°. $3; mor., $7; $7.50 .... *Lippincott.*
— — *Same.* ill. roy. 8°. mor., $15 .... *Appleton.*
— — *Same.* (Boston ed.) 8°. shp., $3.50; mor., $10. *Appleton; Lee & S.*
— *Same;* with memoir and notes, by Rev. G. Gilfillan. 2 v. 8°. hf. cf., $7; cf., $9 .... *Appleton.*
— *Same;* incl. correspondence, etc.; with memoir by W. Gunnyon, and notes. por. and ill. roy. 8°. '71. $2.50; shp., $3; mor., $7 .... *Claxton.*
— *Same;* cont. letters, poems and life by Lockhart. ill. 8°. $2; shp., $2.75 .... *World Pub.*
— *Same;* with life, and crit. on his writings; [also] Some observations on the character and condition of the Scottish peasantry, by J. Currie; with add. poems and songs, and glossary. (Globe ed.) 4 v. in 1. 16°. '71. $1.25; pap., 50c... *Claxton.*
— Poems. 12°. $1.50 .... *Locke.*
— *Same.* (Aldine ed.) 3 v. 16°. ea., 75c... *Lippincott.*

Burns, Rob., *continued.*
— *Same.* (Blue and gold ed.) 18°. $1.25. *Nichols & H.*
— *Same.* (Boston ed.) 8°. shp., $4.50; mor., $10. *Mason.*
— *Same.* (Cabinet ed.) 16°. $1.50..... *Nichols & H.*
— *Same.* (Diamond ed.) 16°. $1; hf. cf., $2.25; mor., $3 .... *Osgood.*
— *Same.* (Red-line ed.) por. and ill. sm. 4°. $3.50; hf. cf., $5; mor., $7 .... *Osgood.*
— *Same.* (Scribner's popular poets.) ill. 12°. $1.50. *Scribner, W. & A.*
— *Same;* with memoir. 3 v. por. 18°. $3.... *Osgood.*
— *Same;* ed. by R. A. Willmott. ill. 16°. $1.50. *Lee & S.*
— — *Same.* (British poets.) ill. 12°. $2.25; hf. cf., $3.50; mor., $5 .... *Routledge.*
— Poems and songs. ill. 4°. $6; mor., $12.. *Appleton.*
— *Same.* (Diamond ed.) 16°. $1; hf. cf., $2.50; mor., $3.25 .... *Lippincott.*
— Poems, songs and letters; ed., with gloss. index and memoir, by A. Smith. (Globe ed.) 12°. '70. $1.50 .... *Macmillan.*
— Poetical works. 8°. $3 .... *Desilver.*
— *Same.* ill. 8°. shp., $4.50; mor., $10...... *Mason.*
— *Same.* (Chandos classics.) cr. 8°. $1; pap., 75c. *Scribner, W. & A.*
— *Same.* (Red-line ed.) por. and ill. sm. 4°. $4 50; hf. cf., $6; mor., $8 .... *Miller.*
— *Same;* with life and correspondence. ill. 8°. (Dick.) 50c.; pap., 25c .... *Am. News.*
— *Same;* with memoir. (Blue and gold ed.) 2 v. por. 32°. $2.50; hf. cf., $5; mor., $7.. *Miller.*
— *Same;* with notes, glossary and life. (Cabinet ed.) 16°. $1.50. — (Blue and gold ed.) 18°. $1.25. *Nichols & H.*
— *Same;* with notes, memoir, etc. (Chandos poets.) por. and ill. cr. 8°. $3.75; cf., $7.50; mor., $8. *Scribner, W. & A.*
— *Same;* with memoir. (Household ed.) 2 v. 16°. $2.50; hf. cf., $5; mor., $7.50 .... *Miller.*
— *Same;* with notices by A. Cunningham, and glossary. 32°. 60c.; 90c.; mor., $1.50. — (Red line ed.) sq. 16°. $1.50; mor., $2.25; $3.50..... *Porter.*
— *Same;* with life, notes and correspondence by A. Cunningham. ill. 12°. $1.50....... *World Pub.*
— *Same;* with glossary and life by J. Currie. 32°. 75c .... *U. P. James.*
— *Same;* ed., with memoir, by A. Smith. 2 v. 18°. '65. $2.50 .... *Macmillan.*
— *Same;* ed by R. A. Willmott. (Household ser.) ill. 16°. $1.50; mor., $3 .... *Lee & S.*
— — *Same.* (Presentation poets.) ill. 12°. $1.75; ivorine, $3; mor., $3.50 .... *Routledge.*
— *Same;* incl. pieces not in Currie's ed., [with] life of the author and glossary. 2 v. in 1. 18°. '71. 75c .... *Claxton.*
— *Same;* [also] Poetical works of Sir W. Scott. por. and ill. 8°. '72. $3.50 .... *Routledge.*
— Cotter's Saturday night. ill. 4°. $4; mor., $8. *Porter.*
— Tam O'Shanter. ill. roy. 4°. $5; mor., $8. *Widdleton.*
— *See also* Burnsiana; — Hudson, H. N.
Burnsiana: the [Robert] Burns calendar; compr. events in his history, names associated with him, bibliog., etc. por. 4°. bds., $3.75. *Scribner, W. & A.*
Burnt overcoat. 18°. 40c. .... *Dutton.*
Burr, Aar. Private journal of B. during four years' residence in Europe, with sel. from correspondence; ed. by M. L. Davis. 2 v. 8°. $4.. *Harper.*
— Trial for high treason, in the U. S. Circuit Court, 1807. 8°. '70. shp., $3.50 .... *Morrison.*
— — *See also* Causes célèbres.
Burr, Enoch F. About spiritualism. 18°. '72. 20c. *Am. Tr.*
— Ad fidem; or, parish evidences of the Bible. ('71.) 4th ed., enl. 12°. '76. $2... *Lockwood, B. & Co.*

Burr, Enoch F., *continued.*
— Ecce cœlum; or, parish astronomy. ('67.) 16th ed. 12°. $1.25....................*Lockwood, B. & Co.*
— Facts in aid of faith. 18°. '72. 25c........*Am. Tr.*
— Pater mundi; or, modern science testifying to the Heavenly Father. 2 v. 12°. '69–'73. ea., $1.75. *Lockwood, B. & Co.*

Cont.: Father of the world. — Pater mundi; or, the doctrine of evolution.

— Sunday afternoons; for little people. 16°. '74. 75c. *Meth. Bk. Conc.*
— Thy voyage; or, a song of the sea, and other poems. sq. 8°. '74. $3.50..............*Meth. Bk. Conc.*
— Toward the strait gate; or, parish Christianity for the unconverted. ('75.) 12°. $2.50. *Lockwood, B. & Co.*
— Work in the vineyard: a plea for Christian work. 12°. '76. $2........................*Crowell.*

Burr, Fearing, *jr.* Field (The) and garden vegetables of Am. ('63.) New ed. cr. 8°. '65. $3...*Tilton.*
— Garden vegetables, and how to cultivate them. 12°. '65. $2.50..........................*Tilton.*

Burr, W. H. *See* Walworth, C. A., *and* Burr, W. H.

Burr cliff. *See* Trowbridge, J. T., Brighthope ser.

Burrage, H: S. Brown University in the civil war: a memorial. 4°. '68. $4.50..............*Rider.*

Burrall, F: A. Asiatic cholera. 12°. $1.50. *W. Wood.*

Burrell, A. B. Reminiscences of George La Bar, the centenarian of Monroe Co., Pa., and incidents in the early settlement of the Penn. side of the river valley from Easton to Bushkill. por. demy 8°. '70. $1....................*Claxton.*

Burrill, Alex. M. Law dict. and glossary. 2 v. roy. 8°. shp., $10..................*Baker, V. & Co.*
— Treatise of the nature, principles and rules of circumst. evidence. 8°. shp., $6.50. *Baker, V. & Co.*
— Treatise on voluntary assignments for the benefit of creditors; with the statutory provisions and decisions of the courts in the several states, and forms. 8°. shp., $7.50.........*Baker, V. & Co.*

Burris, F. H. The Trinity; with introd. by J. Haven. 12°. '74. $1.50.......................*Griggs.*

Burritt, Elihu. Prayers and devotional meditations; from the Psalms. 12°. '71. 75c.; $1. *Randolph.*
— Sanskrit handbook for the fireside. 8°. $2. *Brown & G.*
— Ten-minute talks; with autobiog. 12°. $2.25. *Lee & S.*

Burritt, Elij. Hinsdale. Celestial atlas. 4°. $1.25. *Sheldon.*
— Geography of the heavens. New ed., rev. and enl. by H. Mattison. ill. 12°. $1.25........*Sheldon.*

Burroughs, Jer. *See* Asbury, F., Heart and church divisions.

Burroughs, J: Notes on Whitman. ('67.) 2d ed. 12°. '71. $1.........................*Somerby.*
— Wake-Robin. 16°. '71. $1.50.........*Hurd & H.*
— Winter sunshine. 16°. '75. $1.50......*Hurd & H.*

Burrowes, G: On the song of Solomon. 12°. $2. (?)*Martien.*

Burrowes, J. F. Companion to "Thorough bass primer." 12°. bds., 60c..................*Ditson.*
— Guide to practice. *See* Jousse, J., Catechism of music; — Lenhart, —, Elements of music.
— Piano-forte primer. 12°. 30c...*Brainard; Church.*
— *Same.* New ed., rev. and enl. by L. H. Southard. 12°. '74. 45c.; bds., 30c...............*Ditson.*
— — *See also* Jousse, J., Catechism of music.
— *Same;* [also] Guide to practice, by S. Jackson. 8°. *net*, pap., 50c. ....*Schirmer.*
— — *Same.* 16°. 45c.; bds., 30c. ....*Gordon.*
— — *Same.* 16°. '50. 45c.; bds., 30c.........*Pond.*
— *Same;* with Czerny's Letters; ed. by W. C. Peters. 12°. 60c.; bds., 50c.....................*Peters.*
— — *Same.* New ed., rev. and enl. by Geo. A. Russell. 12°. '75. 50c.; bds., 30c.........*Holmes.*

Burrowes, J. F., *continued.*
— Thorough bass primer. 16°. 60c.; bds., 50c. *Gordon.*
— *Same.* 12°. '74. bds., 60c.................*Ditson.*
— *Same;* [also] Companion to thorough bass; ed. by W. C. Peters. 12°. bds., 75c...........*Peters.*

Burrows, Montagu. Worthies of All Souls [Oxford]: four centuries of Eng. hist., ill. from the college archives. 8°. '74. $5..............*Macmillan.*

Bürstenbinder, E. ["Ernst Werner."] Bound by his vows; or, at the altar; tr. by J. S. L. 16°. $1.25..............................*Lippincott.*
— Broken chains; tr. by F. A. Shaw. 8°. '74. $1.25; pap., 75c....................................*Estes.*
— Good luck; tr. 8°. '74. $1.25; pap., 75c....*Estes.*
— Hero (A) of the pen; tr. 8°. '75. $1.50; pap., 75c. *W. F. Gill.*

Burt, N. C. Far east (The): letters from Egypt, Palestine and other lands of the Orient. ill. and maps. 12°. '69. $1.75...................*Clarke.*
— Hours among the Gospels; or, wayside truths from the life of our Lord. 12°. '65. $1.50. *Claxton; Lippincott.*
— Land (The) and its story; or, the sacred hist. geog. of Palestine. map, charts and ill. 8°. *$3.50; hf. mor., $5.......................*Appleton.*
— Pastor's (A) selection of hymns and tunes for the church and family. 12°. $1........*Lippincott.*

Burt, W. A. Key to solar compass, and surveyor's companion. 2d ed. 16°. '75. $2.50. *Van Nostrand.*

Burt, W. H. Characteristic materia medica. [Hom.] 12°. $3; interleaved, hf. mor., $5.....*Boericke.*
— Therapeutics of tuberculosis, or pulmonary consumption. [Hom.] 8°. '76. $2..........*Boericke.*

Burton, *Mrs.* Bella F. A year in the country; or, Keilei's missionary work. ill. 16°. '71. $1.25. *Lothrop.*

Burton, *Mrs.* H: S. Don Quixote de la Mancha: comedy. 12°. '76. pap., 25c.............*Carmany.*

Burton, *Mrs.* Jennie D. Maddest marriage (The) ever was. 8°. pap., 25c....................*Beadle.*
— Strangely wed. 8°. pap., 25c. ....*Beadle.*

Burton, J: Hill. The history of Scotland from Agricola's invasion to [1748]; with index. 8 v. 12°. $25; hf. cf., $41; hf. mor., $55..*Scribner, W. & A.*

Burton, R: F. City (The) of the saints, and across the Rocky Mts. to California. maps and ill. 8°. $3.50...................................*Harper.*
— Lake regions (The) of central Africa: a picture of exploration. maps and ill. 8°. $3.50..*Harper.*
— Vikram and the vampire; or, tales of Hindu deviltry. ill. 12°. $2.50 ....*Appleton.*

Burton, Rob. Anatomy of melancholy. 8°. '75. $2.75; shp., $3.50..............................*Claxton.*
— *Same.* ill. 8°. hf. cf., $6..............*Appleton.*
— *Same.* 3 v. cr. 8°. $5.25; hf. cf., $10.50. *Widdleton.*

Burton, *Mrs.* W. Dinzey. The little Oxleys: their sayings and doings. 16°. 45c...........*Routledge.*

Burton, Warren. Culture of the observing faculties in the family and the school. 16°. 75c....*Harper.*

Burton, W: Evans. Ellen Wareham: drama. 16°. pap., 15c...................................*French.*
— Yankee among the mermaids. ill. 12°. pap., 75c. *Peterson.*
— (*ed.*) Cyclopædia of wit and humor of Am., Ireland, Scot. and Eng. 600 ill. and 24 por. imp. 8°. *$7; hf. mor., $9....................*Appleton.*

Burtons of Burton Hall. Greene, L. L. $1. *Scribner, W. & A.*

Burtt, And. Elementary grammar. ('59.) New ed. 12°. '71. 80c................................*English.*
— Practical grammar. ('68.) New ed. 12°. '71. $1. *English.*
— Primary grammar. 12°. '71. 50c.......*English.*

Bury, M. P. R. S. Blaze de. *See* Blaze de Bury.

usbee, P. *See* North Carolina, Equity reports; Law reports.

uscapié (El). *See* Cervantes, Exemplary novels.

usch, W: Buzz a buzz; or, the bees; tr. by H. Watkins. ill. 8°. '73. $1.50................*Holt.*
- Hurdy gurdy: woodcuts, with stories in rhyme. 8°. bds., $1; $1.25........................*Stroefer.*
- Jack Huckaback, the scapegrace raven: in picture and rhyme. 8°. bds., 75c.; $1.......*Stroefer.*
- Max and Maurice: a juvenile history; tr. by C. T. Brooks. ill. 12°. '70. $1.25...........*Roberts.*
- *See also* Illustrated flying sheets.

usey, S: C. Immigration: its evils and consequences. 12°. 50c.; pap., 25c...................*De Witt.*

ush, *Mrs.* Annie Forbes. Memoirs of the queens of France. 2 v. in 1. 12°. $1.75....*J. E. Potter.*

ush, Belle. Voices of the morning. [Poetry.] 18°. $1.25.............................*Lippincott.*

ush, C: P. Five years in China; or, the factory boy made a missionary: life of Rev. W. Aitchison. 16°. 80c...........................*Pres. Bd.*
- Work for all, and ways of working. 12°. 50c. *Pres. Bd.*

ush, G: Commentaries. 4 v. 12°. '41–'58. $4; ea., $1.50..........................*H. A. Young.*

Cont.: Exodus.—Leviticus.—Numbers.—Joshua and Judges.

- Illustrations of the Scriptures. ('36.) New ed. ill. roy. 8°. '69. $3......................*Claxton.*
- Life of Mohammed. 18°. 75c...........*Harper.*

ush, R: J. Reindeer, dogs and snow-shoes: journal of Siberian travel and explorations in 1865–'67. ill. cr. 8°. $3.........................*Harper.*

ush, W. P. D. *See* Kentucky, Reports.

ush boys (The). Reid, M. $1.50...........*Miller.*

ushe, M. C. Birthday present. ill. 12°. $1.25. *Nelson.*

ushnell, Hor. Character (The) of Jesus; forbidding his possible classification with men. ('60.) New ed. 16°. '67. $1....................*Scribner.*
- Christ and his salvation: sermons. 12°. $2..*Scribner.*
- Christian nurture. New ed., rev. and enl. 12°. '76. $2.............................*Scribner.*

Note. An enl. ed. of Views of Christian nurture.

- Forgiveness and law, grounded in principles interpreted by human analogies. ('74.) New ed. 12°. '76. $1.75..........................*Scribner.*
- God in Christ. 12°. *net*, $1.25.........*Hamersley.*
- God's thoughts fit bread for children: sermon. 16°. '69. 50c.; pap., 20c.........*Lockwood, B. & Co.*
- Moral uses of dark things. 12°. '76. $2..*Scribner.*
- Nature and the supernatural, as together constituting the one system of God. ('58.) New ed. 12°. '76. $2.25.............................*Scribner.*
- Sermons for the new life. ('58.) 7th ed. 12°. '76. $2 .... *Scribner.*
- Sermons on living subjects. ('72.) New ed. 12°. '76. $2.............................*Scribner.*
- Vicarious sacrifice (The) grounded on principles of universal obligations. ('65.) New ed. 12°. '76. $2.25 ....*Scribner.*
- Women's suffrage: the reform against nature. 12°. $1.50 ....*Scribner.*
- Work and play; or, literary varieties. 12°. '76. $2. *Scribner.*

ushnell, W: H. Biographical sketches of the early settlers of Chicago. 2 v. 12°. ea., pap., 25c. *Fergus.*

ushranger of Van Dieman's land. Rowcroft, C. 50c. *Harper.*

ushrangers (The). Thomes, W. H. $1.50. *Lee & S.*

ussey, G. Moir. Fables; with dissertation on hist. of fable. ill. 8°. $2.50; hf. cf., $5....*Appleton.*

ussieres, Thdr. de (*Baron*). The conversion of Marie Alphonse Ratisbonne. 18°. 50c.........*Strong.*

uster and Baby Jim. Baker, S. S. 40c....*Am. Tr.*

Buswell, H. F., *and* Walcott, C. H. Practice and pleading in personal actions in Mass.; with notes, decisions and forms. 8°. '75. shp., $5.75..*Reed.*

Busy bee library (The). 10 v. ill. 16°. $4...*Nelson.*

Cont.: Who was the first paper maker? —Who was the first architect? —Who were the first builders? —Who were the first weavers? —Who were the first miners?

Note. Sold only in double sets of 5 v. ea.

Busy bees. 16°. $1.25.......................*Carter.*

Busy hands and patient hearts; or, blind boy of Dresden and his friends. 18°. '73. 65c.....*Meth. Epis.*

Busybody. Centlivre, S. 15c..............*French.*

But once: a temperance story. 16°. $1.25. (?)*Martien.*

Butler, Alban. Annunciation (The) of the blessed Virgin. 24°. pap., 10c.............*Coddington.*
— Lives of the fathers, martyrs and other saints. 2 v. pl. roy. 8°. '50. $7; $8.50; —in 4 v. roy. 8°. $8; $12; shp., $12.50; $18; mor., $22..*Murphy.*
— *Same.* 4 v. 4°. $8–$20; —in 12 v. $15–$30; —in 2 v. 57 pl. 4°. $25–$38; —in 57 pts. ea., pap., 25c. *Sadlier.*
— *Same;* ed. by Rev. F. C. Husenbeth. ('58.) 10th ed. 2 v. pl. roy. 8°. '74. $15..............*Virtue.*
— [Lives of the saints.] 5 v. 24°. ea., pap., 10c. *Coddington.*

Cont.: Life of St. Bridget—of St. John the Baptist—of St. Joseph—of St. Margaret—of St. Patrick.

— Movable feasts (The), fasts and other annual observances of the Catholic Church. 12°. $1.25. *Strong.*

Butler, B. C. Lakes George and Champlain, from their first disc. to 1759. maps. 12°. '68. $1.50. (?) *Weed.*

Butler, B: F. American Cyclops, hero of New Orleans and spoiler of silver spoons: a poem, by Pasquino [*pseud.*]; with etchings. 4°. '67. $1.50. *Kelly, P. & Co.*
— Life and public services of Gen. Butler, the hero of New Orleans. 12°. pap., 25c. ....*Peterson.*

Butler, C: Musical text book. obl. 16°. 25c. *Gordon.*
— Seminary bell. [School sing. bk.] obl. 12°. 75c. *Gordon.*
— Silver bell. [School sing. bk.] obl. 16°. 50c. *Gordon.*
— *and* Southard, L. H. School bell. [Sing. bk.] obl. 16°. 50c. ....*Gordon.*

Butler, C: M. On the Apocalypse. 12°. $1.50. *Carter.*

Butler, Clem. M. Christian denominations. *See* Bible [Whole].
— Ecclesiastical history. 2 v. 8°. '68–'72. ea., $3.50. *Claxton.*

Cont.: 1. From 1st to 13th cent.—2. From 13th to close of 18th cent.

— Flock (The) fed: instructions preparatory to confirmation. 18°. '61. 40c. ....*Randolph.*
— Inner Rome: political, religious and social. 12°. '66. $1.75................*Claxton; Lippincott.*
— St. Paul in Rome. 12°. '65. $1.75. *Claxton; Lippincott.*

Butler, *Mrs.* Clifford. Year with the Everards. ill. 16°. '73. $1.25..........................*Dutton.*

Butler, Fs. Breeding, training, diseases, etc., of dogs; with easy method of instructing [them] in a variety of performances. ill. 8°. $2....*Holmes.*
— *Same.* ill. 16°. '70. $1.50...............*Holmes.*
— Dogs: poetically described, and ill. with 31 eng. of different breeds. 18°. '60. pap., 50c. ..*Holmes.*
— Poetical sketches. 1st ser. 16°. '70. 75c...*Holmes.*
— Spanish teacher and colloquial phrasebook. 18°. 60c.................................*Appleton.*
— *Spanish.* Maestro (El) de inglés y de español ó libro de frases familiares. 18°. 60c. ..*Appleton.*

Butler, G: Family prayers. cr. 8°. $2...*Macmillan.*
— Sermons preached in Cheltenham College. cr. 8°. $2.50...........................*Macmillan.*

Butler, H. D. Family aquarium: how to fit-up, stock and maintain marine and fresh water aquaria. 12°. 75c..........................*Dick & F.*

Butler, H. Montagu. Sermons preached in Harrow School. 2 v. cr. 8°. '69. ea., $2.50..*Macmillan.*

Butler, J. J. Commentary on the four Gospels. ill. 12°. '71. $2..........*Lothrop.*
— Commentary on the Gospels and the Epistles. 2 v. 12°. '71. $2..........*Freewill.*
— Theology. 8°. '64. $1.60..........*Freewill.*

Butler, *Rev.* Ja. Catechism. pap., 10c.......*Dooley.*
— *Same;* [also] Scriptural catechism; rev. and enl. by Milner. 18°. '75. 10c..........*Kenedy.*
— — *Same.* 32°. 10c..........*Noonan.*
— — *Same;* with prayers at mass. 18°. 25c...*Sadlier.*

Butler, Jessee H. Home: poems. por. 12°. '75. $1.50; $2..........*Colby.*

Butler, J: S. Critical discussion of the systems of rifling and projectiles, with suggestions for their improvement. 36 pl. 4°. '75. $7.50....*Van Nostrand.*

Butler, Jos. Works. 8°. $2.50..........*Carter.*
— Analogy of religion, natural and revealed, to the const. and course of nature. 8°. $1.50..*Carter.*
— *Same.* 12°. $1.50..........*Cin. Meth. Bk. Conc.*
— *Same;* with pref. by S. Halifax. 18°. hf. roan, 75c. *Harper.*
— *Same;* with pref. and index by Rev. E. Steere. (Student's ed.) 16°. '70. $1.25..........*Pott.*
— *Same;* with introd., notes and index by H. Malcolm. 12°. $1.25..........*Lippincott.*
— *Same;* with life of author, ed. by Rev. Jos. Cummings. 12°. '75. $1.75........*Meth. Bk. Conc.*
— *Same;* with an [incomplete] analysis by Rob. Emory, completed and ed. with life, notes and index by G. R. Crooks. 12°. $1.50..........*Harper.*
— *Same;* with analysis by W. C. E. Hobart and notes; also Crauford's questions for examination; ed. by C. E. West. 18°. $1..........*Harper.*
— *Same;* and sermons, with notes. 12°. (Bohn.) $1.25. *Little, B. & Co.*
— — *Same.* por. 12°. (Bohn.) $1.40. *Scribner, W. & A.*
— — *Same.* 12°. (Bohn.) $1.50..........*Lippincott.*
— Ethical discourses; [also] some remains, hitherto unpub., prepared as a text-book in moral philosophy, with a syllabus by Dr. Whewell; ed. by J. C. Passmore. 12°. hf. mor., $1.75....*Desilver.*
— Sermons. 8°. $1.75..........*Carter.*

Butler, Marian. Frank's victory, and other tales. 18°. 70c..........*Pres. Bd.*
— Martyr's daughter, and other tales. 18°. 70c. *Pres. Bd.*
— Susie's mistake, and other stories. 18°. 65c. *Pres. Bd.*

Butler, Marie Radcliff. Grandma's patience; or, Mrs. James' Christmas gift. ill. 32°. 40c......*Chase.*
— Riverside; or, winning a soul. ill. 12°. 75c...*Chase.*

Butler, Noble. American spelling-book. 16°. '71. bds., 20c..........*Morton.*
— Common school speaker. 16°. '56. $1.....*Morton.*
— First book in spelling and reading. 16°. '68. bds., 20c..........*Morton.*
— Introductory grammar. 16°. '71. bds., 20c. *Morton.*
— [New school readers.] 5 v. ill. '69–'75....*Morton.*

Cont.: New first school reader, 16°, bds., 20c. — second, 16°, bds., 40c. — third, 16°, bds., 55c. — fourth, 12°, bds., 65c. — fifth, 12°, $1.25.

— Practical and crit. grammar. 12°. '74. $1..*Morton.*
— Practical grammar. 12°. '46. bds., 85c...*Morton.*
— *and* Goodrich, S. G. [Readers.] 6 v. '57–'58. *Morton.*

Cont.: First reader, 16°, bds., 20c. — Second, 16°, bds., 40c. — Third, 16°, bds., 55c. — Fourth, 12°, bds., 85c. — Fifth, 12°, $1.40. — Sixth, 12°, $1.85.

Butler, R: *See* Glengall, *Lord.*

Butler, S: Hudibras. (Chandos classics.) cr. 8°. $1; pap., 75c..........*Scribner, W. & A.*
— *Same.* (Scribner's pop. poets.) ill. 12°. $1.50. *Scribner, W. & A.*
— *Same;* with life of author, annotations and index. 18°. 75c..........*U. P. James.*
— *Same;* with notes and life of author. ill. 32°. '72. $1.25..........*Roberts.*

Butler, S: *continued.*
— *Same;* with notes by Nash. (Globe ed.) por. 12 $1.25; hf. cf., $3.25; mor., $4.......*Appleto*
— *Same;* with variorum notes, biog. and index; ed. b H. G. Bohn. ill. 12°. (Bohn.) $1.75; — in 2 por. 12°. ea., $1.75..........*Little, B. & C*
— *Same.* ill. 12°. (Bohn.) $2; — in 2 v. por. 12°. $ *Scribner, W. &*
— *Same.* 2 v. por. 12°. (Bohn.) ea., $2..*Lippincot*
— Poems. (Aldine ed.) 2 v. 16°. ea., 75c. *Lippincot*
— *Same;* with life and notes by J. Mitford. 2 v. po 18°. $2..........*Osgoo*
— Poetical works; with life and notes by G. Gilfilla 8°. mor., $6; hf. cf., $5.50; cf., $7..*Appleto*

Butler, T. A. Poems. 12°. $1.50..........*Sadlie*

Butler, T. B. Philosophy of the weather, and a guid to its changes. 12°. $1.25..........*Appleto*

Butler, W. F. Ventilation of buildings. ill. 8°. '7 pap., 40c..........*Spo*
— *Same.* ill. 18°. '73. bds., 50c......*Van Nostran*

Butler, *Rev.* W: Land of the Veda: personal remini cences of India. map and ill. 8°. '71. $4..*Este*
— *Same.* map and ill. 4°. '71. $4; hf. cf., $6; mor $8..........*Meth. Bk. Con*

Butler, W: Allen. Poems. 16°. '71. $2.....*Osgoo*

Butler, W: Archer. History of ancient philosophy; e by W. H. Thompson. 8°. $5.......*Macmilla*
— Sermons, doctrinal and practical; ed., with memo of author, by T. Woodward. 8th [chp.] ed. po 8°. '73. $2.50. — 2d ser.; ed. by J. A. Jeremi 6th [chp.] ed. 8°. '73. $2.50.......*Macmilla*

Butler, W: F. The wild north land: story of a wint journey with dogs across northern No. Am. ma and ill. cr. 8°. $1.75..........*Porte*

Butler's new Am. ser. [of readers, etc.] *See* Ne American ser.

Butler's pict. hist. of the U. S. *See* Stewart, J. A.

Butt, Bce. May. Miss Molly. (Leis. hour ser.) 16 '76. $1.25..........*Hol*

Buttercups and daisies. ill. sq. 8°. '75. $1.50. *Routledg*

Butterfield, C. W. Historical account of the exped tion against Sandusky in 1782. por. 8°. '7 $3.50..........*Clark*

Butterfield, Dan. Camp and outpost duty for infantr 18°. 60c..........*Harpe*

Butterfield, J. A. Belshazzar; with libretto by C. F Blackall. [Cantata.] 8°. '73. bds., $1.25; pap $1..........*Ditso*

Butterfield, J: W. Digest of decisions in office of th 2d comptroller of the [U. S.] treasury. 3d e 8°. '69. shp., $5..........*Morriso*

Butterflies (The) of No. Am.: col. pl. with descrip letter-press. 1st ser. 4°. hf. mor., $30. — 2d se pts. 1–5. ea., $2.50..........*Hurd & I*

Butterfly hunters. Conant, H. S. $1.50....*Osgoo*

Butterfly's ball. *See* Ballantyne, W.

Butterfly's flights. Robbins, S. S. 3 v. $2.25..*Carte*

Butterworth, H. Monthly Sunday school concert 16°. '75. 75c..........*H. A. Young*
— Sunday school concert book. 18°. '73. 60c. *H. A. Young*

Butterworth, Hzk. Story of the hymns. ill. sq. 12 '75. $2; $2.50..........*Am. T*

Butterworth, J: Concordance of the Holy Scripture 8°. shp., $1.75..........*Crocke*
— *Same.* New ed., enl. by A. Clarke. ill. roy. 8 '69. $1.75..........*Claxton*

Buttman, Alex. Grammar of the Greek New. Test.; t by H. Thayer. ('73.) New ed. 8°. '76. $2.7 *Drape*

Buttman, Ph. Greek grammar for high-schools an universities; rev. and enl. by A. Buttman; t from 18th Germ. ed. by E. Robinson. 8°. shp. $2.50..........*Harpe*

Butts, I: Protection and free trade; with memoir. por. 12°. '75. $1.25 ... *Putnam.*

Butts, I: R. Merchant's and shipmaster's manual, and shipbuilder's and sailmaker's assistant. ('65.) 5th ed. 12°. '73. shp., $2.50 ... *Williams.*

— New business man's assistant and ready reckoner; with tables. 12°. '52. pap., 50c. ... *Williams.*

— Tinman's manual, and builder's and mechanic's handbook. ('60.) 5th ed. 12°. '73. $1.20 .. *Williams.*

Butts, *Mrs.* M. F. Three girls. 16°. $1.25. *Cong. Pub.*

Buxton, H. J. W. Waterside mission sermons. 2d ser. 12°. '75. $2 ... *Pott.*

Buy an orange, sir? 18°. 50c. ... (?) *Martien.*

— *See also* Sunshine and shadow lib.

Buy your own cherries. *See* Kirton, J. W.

Buy your own goose. Kirton, J. W. 25c. .. *Am. S. S.*

Buying and selling and getting gain. Brown, J. B. 40c. ... *Randolph.*

Buzz a buzz. Busch, W. $1.50 ... *Holt.*

Buzzard, T: Clinical aspects of syphilitic nervous affections. 12°. '74. $1.75 ... *Lindsay.*

By and by. Maitland, E. $1.75 ... *Putnam.*

By and by, and other stories. 18°. 70c. ... *Pres. Bd.*

By his own might. Hillern, W. v. $1.75 .. *Lippincott.*

By the sea. Currier, S. $1.25 ... *Dutton.*

By sea and by land. Merewether, H. A. $2.50. *Macmillan.*

By the sea side: a tale for children; by a Sister of Mercy. 18°. 50c. ... *O'Shea.*

By still waters. Mayo, I. F. $1.75 ... *Dodd.*

By-ways of Europe. Taylor, B. $1.50; $2. *Putnam.*

Bye-path meadow. Hood, E. P. $1.50 ... *Lothrop.*

Byer, —. Selling out ye pope: a satire. 16°. '73. pap., 25c. ... *Hinton.*

Byerly, Ste. Spelling book. 12°. per doz., $1.25. *Polock.*

Byerly, T: *and* Robertson, Ja. Craigie. ["Sholto *and* Reuben Percy."] The Percy anecdotes; with introd. by J. Timbs. (Chandos lib.) 3 v. 12°. ea., $1.75.; hf. cf., $3.75; cf., $5 .. *Scribner, W. & A.*

Byfield, Natl. Account of the late revolution in New Eng. London, 1689. [Reprint.] 4°. pap., $1; large pap., $1.50 ... *Sabin.*

Byford, W: Heath. Chronic inflammation and displacement of the unimpregnated uterus. New ed., rev. and enl. ill. 8°. '71. $3 ... *Lindsay.*

— Philosophy of domestic life. 16°. $1; pap., 50c. *Lee & S.*

— Practice of medicine and surgery; applied to the diseases and accidents incident to women. 2d ed., rev. and enl. 8°. '67. $5; shp., $6 ... *Lindsay.*

— Treatise on the theory and practice of obstetrics. ill. 8°. $4.50 ... *W. Wood.*

Byles, *Sir* J: Barn. Sophisms of free trade and popular political economy examined. ('72.) 5th ed. 12°. '73. $1.25; pap., 75c. ... *Baird.*

— Treatise on the law of bills of exchange, promissory notes, etc. 6th Am., from 11th Lond., ed., ed. by M. B. Byles; with Am. notes by G. Sharswood. 8°. '74. $6.50 ... *T. & J. W. Johnson.*

— — *See also* Banker's commonplace book.

Byr, Rob. (*pseud.*) *See* Bayer, C. R.

Byrd, Ann. Narratives, pious meditations and relig. exercises. 2d ed. 18°. '76. 40c. .. *Friends Bk. Assoc.*

Byrd, W: History of the dividing line between Virginia and North Carolina; Journey to the land of Eden; Progress to the mines, etc., 1692–1739: ed. by T. H. Wynne. 2 v. sm. 4°. '66. pap., $10 ... *J. W. Randolph.*

Byrn, M. Lafayette. Artist's and tradesman's companion. [Varnishing, painting, etc.] ill. 12°. '53. $1 ... *Claxton.*

Byrn, M. Lafayette, *continued.*

— Book of nature: exposition of the science of life and sexual physiology. 12°. $1 ... *Hurst.*

— Complete practical brewer: instructions in the art of brewing beer, ale, etc. ('52.) 8th ed. ill. 12°. '76. $1.25 ... *Baird.*

— Complete practical distiller; with directions from the French of Th. Fling. (cop. '53.) '70. 2d ed. 12°. '74. $1.50 ... *Baird.*

— Life and adventures of an Arkansaw doctor, by David Rattlehead [*pseud.*] ill. 12°. 50c. .. *U. P. James.*

— Mystery of medicine explained; a family physician and household companion. 12°. $2.50 .. *Hurst.*

— Travels; or, the recollections of a backwoodsman, by David Rattlehead [*pseud.*] ill. 12°. 50c. *U. P. James.*

Byrne, Janet. Patsy's first glimpse of heaven. ill. fp. 8°. 50c. ... *Cassell.*

— Picture teaching for young and old. ill. 4°. $1.50. *Cassell.*

— Scraps of knowledge for the little ones. ill. fp. 4°. $1.50 ... *Cassell.*

Byrne, Miles. The Irish abroad and at home. 12°. '60. $1.50 ... *Haverty.*

Byrne, Ol. Apprentice (The): first book for mechanics, machinists and engineers. 12°. $1.50 ... *Fisher.*

— Essential elements of pract. mechanics, based on the principle of work. 2d ed. ill. 8°. '72. $2.50. *Spon.*

— General method of solving equations of all degrees; particularly to equations of the 2d, 3d and 4th degrees. 8°. '68. pap., 40c. ... *Spon.*

— Handbook for the artisan, mechanic and engineer. (cop. '53.) '70. 2d ed. ill. 8°. '74. $5 .. *Baird.*

— Mechanics: their principles and practical applications. ill. 12°. $1 ... *De Witt.*

— Pocket book for railroad- and civil-engineers. (cop. '55.) '64. 4th ed. 18°. '72. $1.75 ... *Baird.*

— Pocket companion for machinists, mechanics, inventors and engineers. ill. 12°. $2 ... *De Witt.*

— Practical metal-workers' assistant. New ed., rev.; with app. by J. Percy and A. A. Fesquet. ('51, cop. '64.) 8th ed. ill. 8°. '74. $7 ... *Baird.*

— Practical model calculator. ('51.) 3d ed. 8°. '72. $4.50 ... *Baird.*

— Young dual arithmetician; or, dual arithmetic; [with] tables of ascending and descending dual logarithms, dual numbers and corresponding natural numbers. 2d ed. 12°. (Lond.) '71. $1.25 .. *Spon.*

Byrne, Ste. Irish emigration to the United States: what it has been, and what it is. 2d ed. 12°. '74. $1.25 ... *Cath. Pub.*

Byrne, *Mrs.* W. P. Cosas de España; ill. of Spain and the Spaniards as they are. 2 v. ill. 8°. $7.50. *Routledge.*

Byrnes of Glengoulah. Nolan, A. $1.50 ... *O'Shea.*

Byron, G: G. N. (*Lord*). Works. ill. 8°. (Dick.) $1; pap., 50c. ... *Am. News.*

— *Same.* ill. 8°. $3; mor., $7; $7.50 ... *Lippincott.*

— *Same.* (Boston ed.) ill. 8°. shp., $3.50; mor., $10. *Lee & S.*

— *Same;* with life by H. L. Bulwer, and index. ill. 8°. $2; shp., $2.75 ... *World Pub.*

— *Same;* with life by J. W. Lake, and suppressed poems. 8°. '72. $2.25; $2.75; $3; mor., $5.50. roy. 8°. mor., $8 ... *Claxton.*

— *Same;* ed., with life, by T. Moore. 4 v. por. cr. 8°. $9; hf. cf., $16 ... *Widdleton.*

— — *Same.* 4 v. por. and ill. 12°. $10; shp., $12; hf. cf., $16 ... *Lippincott.*

— Poems. 12°. $1.50 ... *Locke.*

— *Same.* (Blue and gold ed.) 18°. $1.25. *Nichols & H.*

— *Same.* (Boston ed.) 8°. shp., $4.50; mor., $10. *Mason.*

— *Same.* (Cabinet ed.) 16°. $1.50 ... *Nichols & H.*

— *Same.* (Chandos classics.) cr. 8°. $1; pap., 75c. *Scribner, W. & A.*

Byron, G: G. N. (*Lord*), *continued.*
— *Same.* (Scribner's pop. poets.) ill. 12°. $1.50. *Scribner, W. & A.*
— *Same.* 10 v. por. 18°. $10 .... *Osgood.*
— *Same;* ed. by Rev. R. A. Willmott. ill. 16°. $1.50. ill. 8°. $2.50 .... *Lee & S.*
— — *Same.* (British poets.) ill. 12°. $2.25; hf. cf., $3.50; mor., $5 .... *Routledge.*
— — *Same.* (Household ser.) ill. 16°. $1.50; mor., $3 .... *Lee & S.*
— — *Same.* (Presentation poets.) ill. 12°. $1.75; ivorine, $3; mor., $3.50 .... *Routledge.*
— Poetical works. ill. 12°. $1.50 .... *World Pub.*
— *Same.* ill. 8°. shp., $4.50; mor., $10 .... *Mason.*
— *Same.* ill. and por. 8°. mor., $10; $15. chp. ed. por. and ill. 8°. shp., $3.50 .... *Appleton.*
— *Same.* 6 v. por. 8°. (Murray.) mor., $54; cf., $42 .... *Appleton.*
— *Same.* (Globe ed.) 16°. '70. $1.25; $1.75; pap., 50c.; mor., $4 .... *Claxton.*
— *Same.* (Globe ed.) por. 12°. $1.50; hf. cf., $3.50; mor., $5 .... *Lippincott.*
— *Same.* (Pocket vol. ed.) 8 v. 16°. (Lond.) '73. $8.50 .... *Little, B. & Co.*
— *Same;* with memoir. (Cabinet ed.) 16°. $1.50. (Blue and gold ed.) 18°. $1.25 ... *Nichols & H.*
— *Same;* with notes. (Chandos poets.) por. and ill. cr. 8°. $3.75; cf., $7.50; mor., $8. *Scribner, W. & A.*
— *Same;* with notes and memoir. ill. 8°. $3.75. *Porter.*
— *Same;* with notes and life by T. Moore. ill. 4°. '67. hf. mor., $13.50; mor., $15; $16. *Johnson & M.*
— *Same;* with notes by T. Moore, Lord Jeffrey, Scott, Heber and others. ('47.) 8th ed. ill. roy. 8°. '75. hf. mor., $8; mor., $10 .... *Virtue.*
— *Same;* with memoir by W. B. Scott. (Red-line ed.) ill. sq. 8°. '74. $4 .... *Routledge.*
— Childe Harold's pilgrimage. 18°. $1.25 .... *Nelson.*
— *Same.* 16°. $1.25 .... *Osgood.*
— Don Juan. (Emerald ser.) 24°. '74. 75c.; bds., 50c.; pap., 25c.; — in 2 v. $1 .... *Routledge.*
— Manfred: tragedy. 16°. pap., 15c .... *French.*
— Moral and beautiful in [his] poems; ed. by W. Colton. 32°. 60c.; 90c.; mor., $1.50. — (Red line ed.) sq. 16°. $1.50; mor., $3.50 ... *Porter.*
— Sardanapalus: tragedy. 16°. pap., 15c .... *French.*
— Songs. ill. sq. 16°. $1.25 .... *Routledge.*
— Werner: tragedy. 16°. pap., 15c .... *French.*
— *See also* Two visions.

Byron and Moore gallery: illustrations, with descrip. letter-press in prose and verse, and biogs. of authors. ill. 4°. '71. hf. mor., $13.50; $14; mor., $15; $16 .... *Johnson & M.*

Byron gallery: portraits of principal female characters in Byron's poems; with text. roy. 8°. $7.50; mor., $10 .... *Appleton.*

Byron, H: Ja. [Plays.] 42 v. 16°. ea., pap., 15c. *French.*
Cont.: Ali Baba; or, the 39 thieves: extravaganza. — Babes in the wood: burlesque. — Beautiful Haidee: extravaganza. — Blow for blow. — Blue Beard: farce. — Bride of Abydos: burlesque. — Camaralzaman: extravaganza. — Cinderella: burlesque. — Corsican brothers: burlesque. — Cyril's success: comedy. — Eighteen hundred and sixty-three: burlesque. — Esmeralda: burlesque. — Fra Diavolo: burlesque. — Freischutz (Der): burlesque. — Garibaldi "excursionists": farce. — George de Barnwell: burlesque. — "Grin" bushes: burlesque. — £100,000: comedy. — Ill-treated Il Trovatore: burlesque. — Ivanhoe: burlesque. — Jack the giant-killer: extravaganza. — Lady Belle Belle: extravaganza. — Lady of Lyons: travestie. — Little Don Giovanni: burlesque. — Lord Bateman: burlesque. — Lucia di Lammermoor: burlesque. — Lucretia Borgia: burlesque. — Maid and magpie: burlesque. — Mazourka: burlesque. — Miss Eily O'Connor: burlesque. — Motto, I am "all there": burlesque. — Nymph of Lurleyburg: burlesque. — Old story: comedy. — Orpheus and Eurydice: extravaganza. — Pan: extravaganza. — Pandora's box: extravaganza. — Pilgrim of love: fairy romance. — Robert Macaire: burlesque. — Robinson Crusoe: burlesque. — Somnambula (La): burlesque. — Timothy to the rescue: farce. — War to the knife: comedy.

Byron, H: Ja., *continued.*
— [Plays.] 9 v. 12°. ea., pap., 15c .... *De Witt.*
Cont.: Blow for blow. — Cyril's success: comedy. — Dearer than life. — Lancashire lass (The); or, tempted, tried and true: melodrama. — Not such a fool as he looks. — £100,000: comedy. — Timothy to the rescue: farce. — War to the knife: comedy. — William Tell with a vengeance: burlesque.
— Sensation dramas. no. 1. 16°. pap., 40c ... *French.*
— *See also* Talfourd, F., *and* Byron, H. J.

C., A. W. Sybil's way. ill. 16°. '70. $1.25 .. *Lothrop.*
C., C. S. (*pseud.*) *See* Calverley, C. S.
C., J. F. (*pseud.*) *See* Clarke, J. F.
C., L. (*pseud.*) *See* Clarke, L.
C., M. A. L. Little Patie, the child who loved the Saviour. ill. 24°. 30c .... *Bost. Am. Tr.*
C., S. Not a minute to spare. 16°. 30c ..... *West Tr.*
— *Same.* 18°. 40c .... *Dutton.*
— *Same.* 18°. 45c .... *Pres. Bd.*
C., S. T. Little doorkeeper; or, patience and peace. 18°. 90c .... (?) *Martien.*
— Waggie and Wattie. 18°. 75c .... (?) *Martien.*
C., W. A. Mick Tracy, the Irish Scripture reader. 16°. $1.50 .... *Am. Bapt.*
C. E. K. D. library. *See* Davis, *Mrs.* C. E. K.
C. S. A. (The), and the battle of Bull Run. Barnard, J. G. $2 .... *Van Nostrand.*
Ça ira. Trammell, W. D. $1.50 .... *U. S. Pub.*
Caballero, Fernan (*pseud.*) *See* Arrom, C. B. de F.
Cabell, J. C. *See* Jefferson, T., *and* Cabell, J. C.
Cabin and parlor. Randolph, J. T. $1.75; $1.50. *Peterson.*
Cabin and plantation songs, as sung by the Hampton students, with music; ed. by T. P. Fenner. 8°. '76. pap., 40c .... *Putnam.*
Cabin boy. Stirling, E. 15c .... *French; Happy.*
Cabin boy; or, the fruits of S.-school instruction. 18°. 17c.; 22c .... *Am. Bapt.*
Cabin by the wayside. Campbell, *Lady.* 50c. *Routledge.*
Cabin in the brush. Wright, J. McN. 80c. *J. A. Moore.*
Cabin on the prairie. Pearson, C. H. $1.25. *Lee & S.*
Cabinet. Dibdin, T. 15c .... *French.*
Cabinet edition of the poets. 4 v. ill. 16°. ea., $1.50; hf. cf., $3 .... *Lippincott.*
Cont.: Cowper. — Wordsworth. — Crabbe. — Campbell and Coleridge.
Cabinet editions of the poets. 23 v. 16°. ea., $1.50. *Osgood.*
Cont.: Mrs. Akers' Poems. — Holmes' Poems. — Longfellow's Poems, 2 v. — Longfellow's Prose works, 2 v. — Longfellow's Christus. — Lowell's Poems, 2 v. — Owen Meredith's Poems, 2 v. — Owen Meredith's New poems, 2 v. — Owen Meredith's Lucile. — Owen Meredith's Fables in song. — Miss Muloch's Poems. — A. A. Procter's Poems. — Saxe's Poems. — Taylor's Poems. — Tennyson's Poems, 2 v. — Whittier's Poems, 2 v.
Cabinet library. *See* Goodrich, S. G.
Cabinet library of household reading. 3 v. ill. 12°. $3.75 .... *Lippincott.*
Cont.: Bunyan's Pilgrim's progress. — Villages of the Bible. — Pilgrimage to Rome.
Cabinet maker's album of furniture: collection of designs. ill. obl. roy. 8°. '68. $5 .... *Baird.*
Cabinet question. Planché, J. R. 15c .... *French.*
Cabinet series of the poets. (World ed.) 12 v. ill. 16°. ea., $1.12; $1.35 .... *World Pub.*
Cont.: Sigourney and Norton. — Scott and Coleridge. — Scott's Lady of the lake, and Howitt. — Milton. — Hemans and Wordsworth. — Goldsmith and Southey. — Pollok and Montgomery. — Young and Campbell. — Cowper and Rogers. — Moore's Lalla Rookh, and Thomson. — Tupper. — Pope and Sterne.
Cabman 93. Williams, T. J. 15c .... *De Witt.*
Cabot, L: Immature state of the odonata. ill. imp. 8°. '71. pap., $1 .... *Mus. Comp. Zool.*
Cachet. Hamilton, M. J. R. $1.75 .... *Carleton.*
Caddell, Cecilia Ma. Blind Agnes; or, the little bride of the blessed sacrament. 18°. 50c ..... *Strong.*

Caddell, Cecilia Ma., *continued.*
— Nellie Netterville; or, one of the transplanted: tale of the times of Cromwell in Ireland. 4th ed. 12°. '68. $1.50 .... *Cath. Pub.*
— Wild times: tale of the days of Queen Elizabeth. 2d ed. 12°. '73. $1.50 .... *Cath. Pub.*
Caddy's three dresses. Hosmer, M. $1.50. (?) *Martien.*
Cady, C. M. Minnehaha glee-book. obl. 8°. bds., $1.50. *Peters.*
Cady, D. R. Carrie and Susie; or, silent influence. 18°. 45c .... *Cong. Pub.*
Cæcilia. Cooney, Ma. 40c .... *Sadlier.*
Cæcilia (The). Lasar, S. $1 .... *Ditson.*
Cæsar, Caius Jul. Commentaries on the Gallic war [Lat.]; with dict. and notes, ed. by E. A. Andrews. ('45.) New ed. 12°. '73. $1.50 .. *Crocker.*
— *Same;* with vocab. and notes, by W. Bingham. 12°. $1.50 .... *Butler.*
— *Same;* with notes, lexicon, etc., by N. C. Brooks. ('59.) New ed. maps, plans, etc. 12°. '69. hf. roan, $1.50 .... *Claxton.*
— *Same;* ed. by P. Bullions. 12°. $1.50 .... *Sheldon.*
— *Same;* ed. with vocab. by J. H. Hanson. 8°. $1.75. *Potter, A. & Co.*
— *Same;* ed. by A. Harkness. 12°. $1.50 .. *Appleton.*
— *Same;* ed by F. P. Leverett; with Eng. notes. 12°. 94c .... *R. S. Davis (B.)*
— *Same;* ed. by G. Long. 18°. 75c .... *Harper.*
— *Same;* ed. by L. Schmitz and C. G. Zumpt. roy. 18°. 60c.; hf. bd., 70c .... *Lea.*
— *Same;* notes by J. A. Spencer. 12°. $1.50. *Appleton.*
— *Same;* with notes, lexicon, index, etc., by G. Stuart. ('67.) 11th ed. 16°. '75. $1.25 .... *Eldredge.*
— *Same;* 4 bks.; ed. with introd. and notes, by J. H. Allen and J. B. Greenough. ('74.) 2d ed. map. 12°. '75; $1.25; with vocab., $1.50 ...... *Ginn.*
— *Same;* to end of his 2d expedition into Britain; with a Lat. ordo and Eng. notes, by C. Wiley. ('73.) New ed. 12°. '76. hf. roan, $1.25 .... *Holt.*
— *Same;* with Gk. paraphase of 1st bk., and with Eng. notes, plans, sieges, etc., and indexes, by C. Anthon. 12°. shp., $1.50 .... *Harper.*
— *Eng.* Commentaries; with anal. and interl. tr. of first 5 bks. New ed., with interl. tr. of the 6th and 7th bks., by T. Clarke. roy. 12°. $2.25 ... *Desilver.*
— *Eng.;* with the Supplementary books attributed to Hertius; incl. the Alexandrian, African and Spanish wars; lit. tr., with notes and index. 12°. $1.50 .... *Harper.*
— — *Same.* 12°. (Bohn.) $1.75 ..... *Little, B. & Co.*
— — *Same.* 12°. (Bohn.) $2. *Lippincott; Scribner, W. & A.*
— *Eng.;* tr. by W. Duncan. 2 v. 18°. $1.50 .. *Harper.*
— *Eng.;* [condensed and explained] by A. Trollope. 16°. (Edinb.) '71. $1 .. *Lippincott; Little, B. & Co.*
— Life. 18°. '46. 40c .... *Meth. Bk. Conc.*
Cæsar and God. Krauth, C. P. 10c .... *Luth. Bk. St.*
Cæsar Borgia. [Fiction.] 16°. bds., 80c ... *Routledge.*
Cæsar, the watch dog: drama. 16°. pap., 15c. *French.*
Cæsars (The). *See* De Quincey, T.
Caged lion. *See* Yonge, C. M.
Cagnotte (La). Labiche, E., *and* Delacour, A. 40c. *Holt.*
Cain, W: A practical theory of voussoir arches. ill. 18°. '74. bds., 50c .... *Van Nostrand.*
Cain and Abel to the tabernacle. *See* Davis, *Mrs.* C. E. K., Child lib.
Cain and Patsy: story of slave life. 24°. 30c. *Bost. Am. Tr.*
Caird, Ja. Prairie farming in Am., with notes by the way on Canada and the United States. 12°. 50c.; pap., 25c .... *Appleton.*
Caird, J: Religion in common life. ('56.) 2d ed. 18°. '75. 35c.; pap., 20c .... *So. Meth.*
— — *See also* Village lib.
— Sermons. 12°. $1.50 .... *Carter.*

Cairn, J: Romanism and rationalism, as opposed to pure Christianity. 16°. 75c .... *Routledge.*
Cairnes, J: E. Essays on political economy. 8°. '73. $3.50 .... *Macmillan.*
— Logical method of political economy. New ed. 8°. '75. $2.50 .... *Macmillan.*
— Political essays. 8°. '73. $3.50 .... *Macmillan.*
— Some leading principles of political economy newly expounded. cr. 8°. $2.50 .... *Harper.*
— *Same.* 8°. '75. $5 .... *Macmillan.*
Caius Gracchus. Knowles, J. S. 15c .... *French.*
Cakes and ale at Woodbine. Coffin, R. B. $1.50. *Hurd & H.*
Calabrella, *Baroness* de (*ed.*) Evenings at Haddon Hall; ill. by G. Cattermole. 12°. (Bohn.) $1.75. *Little, B. & Co.*
— *Same.* 12°. (Bohn.) $2. *Lippincott; Scribner, W. & A.*
— *See also* Orsay, *Count* d', *and* Calabrella.
Calamities and quarrels of authors. *See* Disraeli, I:
Calavar. Bird, R. M. $1.75 .... *Widdleton.*
Calaynos. Boker, G. H. 15c .... *French.*
Calcraft, J. W. Bride of Lammermoor: drama. 16°. pap., 15c. .... *French.*
Calder, F: Life of Episcopius. 12°. '37. $1.20. *Meth. Bk. Conc.*
Calderon. *See* Bulwer-Lytton, *Sir* E. G. E. L.
Calderon de la Barca. *See* Vega Carpio, F. L. da.
Calderon's life a dream. *See* Trench, R. C.
Calderwood, H: Hand-book of moral philos. 2d ed. cr. 8°. '74. $2 .... *Macmillan.*
— On teaching: its ends and means. 12°. '75. $1.25. *Putnam.*
— Philosophy of the infinite: treatise on man's knowledge of the infinite being, in answer to Sir W. Hamilton and Dr. Mansel. chp. ed., rev. 8°. '72. $3.50 .... *Macmillan.*
Calderwood, W: Life of Mrs. Lizzie G. Calderwood. 18°. '61. 25c .... *Am. Tr.*
Calderwood secret. Johnson, V. W. 50c ... *Harper.*
Caldor, M. T. Accelerate: charade in opera. 16°. pap., 15c .... *Lee & S.*
— College Ned: parlor opera. 16°. pap., 15c ... *Lee & S.*
— Conjuration: charade in opera. 16°. pap., 15c. *Lee & S.*
— Diamonds and toads: operatissimo. 16°. pap., 15c. *Lee & S.*
— Social charades and parlor operas. 16°. 75c.; bds., 60c .... *Lee & S.*
Caldwell, *Mrs.* Anne M. *See* Marsh-Caldwell, *Mrs.* A.
Caldwell, Augustine. Caldwell records: John and Sarah (Dillingham) Caldwell, Ipswich, Mass., and their descendants. 8°. '73. pap., $1.25. *Lunt.*
Caldwell, C. Thoughts on the original unity of the human race. 12°. pap., 75c ...... *U. P. James.*
Caldwell, D. Parochial lectures on the first fifty Psalms. 8°. $2 .... (?) *Martien.*
Caldwell, G. C. Agricultural qualitative and quantitative chemical analysis. 12°. $2 .... *Judd.*
— *and* Breneman, Ab. A. Manual of introd. chem. practice. 12°. '75. $1.50 .... *Finch.*
Caldwell, Ja. Staneford. Treatise of the law of arbitration; with precedents. 8°. '53. *net*, shp., $5. *Ward & P.*
Caldwell, M. P. Practical arith. 24°. bds., 75c. *Burke.*
Caldwell, Merritt. Christianity tested by eminent men: sketches of Christian biog. 16°. '51. 60c. *Meth. Bk. Conc.*
— Manual of elocution. 12°. hf. roan, 95c ... *Lippincott.*
Caldwell, S. L., *and* Gordon, A. J. Service of song for Baptist churches. sq. 8°. $2; mor., $3; $5. — 18°. $1.25–$4. — (Centennial ed.) $1.25–$4.50. — 32°. 60c.–$3 .... *Sheldon.*
Caleb in the country; — in town. *See* Abbott, J., Jonas books.

Caleb Krinkle. Coffin, C. C. $2 .... *Lee & S.*

Caleb White, and other stories. ('63.) New ed. 16°. '74. $1 .... *Hoyt.*

Caleb Williams. *See* Adventures of.

Calendar of the Prayer book. *See* Protestant Episcopal Church.

Calhoun, J. C. Works. 6 v. 8°. $15; shp., $20; hf. cf., $33; cf., $38 .... *Appleton.*
Cont.: 1. On government. — 2. Reports and letters. — 3, 4. Speeches. — 5, 6. Reports and letters.

Caliban: the missing link. Wilson, D. $2 .. *Macmillan.*

California. Civil practice act, incl. amend. to 1868, with notes, ref. and forms; by C. H. Parker. 8°. '68. shp., $7.50 .... *Bancroft.*

— Code of civil procedure, annotated. 2 v. in 1. 8°. $5. *S. Whitney.*

— *Same;* adopted 1872, and amended, with ref. and notes by W. Olney. 18°. shp., $3 .. *S. Whitney.*

— *Same;* amended in '73–4, and '75–6, with ref. and app.; comp. by A. Hart. 18°. $3 .. *S. Whitney.*

— *Same;* amended to 1875–6; annotated by C. Haymond and J. C. Burch. 2 v. in 1. 8°. shp., $5. *Bancroft.*

— — Amendments to code, 1873–4; with annotations by R. Desty. 8°. '74. $5. — Same. '75–'76. 8°. shp., $3 .... *Bancroft.*

— General laws, 1850–'64; with notes of decisions and prior statutes, by T. H. Hittell. 2 v. in 1. roy. 8°. shp, $7 .... *S. Whitney.*

— — Supplement to general laws, 1864–'71; with ref. to repealed acts, special legislation, etc., by C. H. Parker. roy. 8°. shp., $3 .... *S. Whitney.*

— Insurance laws; comp. by J. Hasbrouck. 8°. shp., $5 .... *S. Whitney.*

— Law of private corporations. *See* Proffatt, J.

— Mechanic's lien law, as amended 1874; with remarks and forms. 8°. '74. pap., 75c .... *Bancroft.*

— Mining laws. *See* Congdon, H. B.

— Statutes, 1869–'72. 2 v. 8°. ea., $3 ... *S. Whitney.*

— *Same*, 1850–'76. 21 v. 8°. shp., $66. — Same, 1875–'76. shp., $3.50 .... *Bancroft.*

— Supreme Court reports, 1850–'76. 50 v. 8°. ea., shp., $5 .... *Bancroft.*
Cont.: 1 ('50–'51), by N. Bennett. — 2–4 ('52–'54), by H. P. Hepburn. — 5 ('55), by W. G. Morris. — 6–8 ('56–'57), by H. T. Booraem. — 9–12 ('58–'59), by H. Lee. — 13–15 ('59–'60), by J. B. Herman. — 16–19 ('60–'62), by D. T. Bagley. — 20–22 ('62–'63), by C. J. Hillyer. — 23–32 ('63–'67), by C. A. Tuttle. — 33–37 ('67–'69), by J. E. Hale. — 38 ('69), by T. Robinson. — 39–40 ('70–'71), by R. A. Thompson. — 41–50 ('71–'75), by C. A. Tuttle.
Note. v. 1–32 reprinted with annotations, 1870–'76.

— *Same*, 1850–'75. 50 v. 8°. shp., $250 .. *S. Whitney.*

— — Digest. *See* Desty, R.; — Parker, C. H.

— — Table of cases cited in reports. *See* Desty, R.

California Academy of Sciences. Memoirs. v. 1, 2. 4°. *Cal. Acad. Sci.*
Cont.: Pacific coast mosses, by Lesquereux, $1. — Natural system of volcanic rocks, by Richthofen, $1.50.

— Proceedings. v. 1, 3–6. pl. 8°. pap., v. 1, 3, 4, ea., $2.50; v. 5 (pt. 1), $1; v. 5 (pt. 2), $1.50; v. 5 (pt. 3), v. 6, ea., $2 .... *Cal. Acad. Sci.*

California and Oregon. Johnson, T. T. $1.25. *Claxton.*

California and the Yosemite Valley: views with descrip. letter-press. obl. 24°. 75c .... *Nelson.*

California detective. Aiken, A. W. 20c ..... *Beadle.*

California geological survey. Barometric hypsometry; by J. D. Whitney. roy. 8°. '74. $1.50; pap., $1. *Little, B. & Co.*

— Geographical catalogue of the mollusca found west of the Rocky Mts. between lat. 33° and 49° n.; by J. G. Cooper. 4°. '67. pap., 50c. ..... *Payot.*

— Geology, v. 1: Report of progress and synopsis of the field work, 1860–'64. ill. roy. 8°. '65. $5. *Little, B. & Co.; Payot.*

— Mining statistics, no. 1: Tabular statement of the quartz mines and mills between the Merced and Stanislaus rivers in 1865; by A. Remond. 4°. pap., 50c. .... *Payot.*

California geological survey, *continued.*

— Ornithology, v. 1: Land birds of Cal. and adjacent states and territories; based on manuscript and collections of J. G. Cooper, and ed. by S. F. Baird. ill. 4°. $10 .... *Little, B. & Co.; Payot.*

— Palæontology. 2 v. pl. roy. 8°. '64–'69. $10. *Little, B. & Co.; Payot.*
Cont.: 1. Descriptions and figures of the cretaceous and triassic fossils, by W. M. Gabb; [and] of the jurassic and carboniferous fossils, by F. B. Meek. — 2. Remainder of the cretaceous and whole of the tertiary palæont., by W. M. Gabb.

— Yosemite guide-book; by J. D. Whitney. maps and ill. 8°. $3; pocket form, $1 .... *Payot.*

— *Same.* 8°. '70. $3. 18°. '74. $1.50 .. *Little, B. & Co.*

California State Medical Society. Transactions, 1870–'75. 6 v. 8°. ea., pap., $1 .... *Cal. Med.*

Caliph of Bagdad. Brough, W. 15c .... *French.*

Calista. Newman, J. H. $1.25; $1.75 ...... *Sadlier.*

Calkins, Alonzo. Opium and the opium appetite; with notices of alcoholic beverages, cannabis indica, tobacco, etc. 12°. $1.75 .... *Lippincott.*

Calkins, N. A. Manual to accompany Prang's "Natural history series." 8°. '73. pap., 50c ... *Prang.*

— Primary object lessons. 12°. $1.50 .... *Harper.*

— *See also* Kiddle, H., Harrison, T. F., *and* Calkins, N. A.

— *and* Adams, W. T. Universal speaker. 12°. $1.50. *Thompson.*

Call, D. *See* United States, Circuit Court reports.

Call at no. 1–7. Triplet, J. 15c .... *French.*

Call of the hour. Guest, W. 40c.; 25c ..... *Lothrop.*

Call to Christians. Law, W. $1; 75c ..... *Am. Bapt.*

Call to prayer. *See* Ryle, J. C.

Call to the unconverted. *See* Baxter, R:

Callamura. Pleasants, J. $1.75 .... *Claxton.*

Callcott, J. W. Musical grammar. 16°. $1 .. *Ditson.*

Called to account. Thomas, A. 50c .... *Harper.*

Callender, J: Historical discourse on the civil and religious affairs of the colony of Rhode Island; with memoir, notes, etc., by R. Elton. roy. 8°. (Boston.) '43. $2.50 .... *Rider.*

Callery, J. M. *See* Yvan, M., *and* Callery, J. M.

Calligraphische Musterhefte f. deutsche Schrift. nos. 1–9. 4°. per doz., 90c .... *Barthel.*

Callimachus Cyrenæus. *See* Hesiodus, Callimachus Cyrenæus *and* Theognis.

Callingham, Ja. Sign writing and glass embossing. ('71.) 2d ed. 12°. '73. $1.50 .... *Baird.*

Callirhoe. Sand, M. $1.75 .... *Claxton.*

Calls to the Saviour; [cont.] Hall's Come to Jesus, Ryle's Call to prayer, Hall's Quench not the spirit, *and* Ryle's Only one way of salvation. 18°. 50c .... *Pres. Com.*

— *See also* Hall, N., *and* Ryle, J. C.

Calm sea and happy voyage. Beethoven, L. v. 20c. *Gordon.*

Calmet, Augustin. Dictionary of the Bible; rev. and enl. by E. Robinson. maps and ill. roy. 8°. '32. shp., $5.50; — abridg. 18°. '33. shp., $1. *Crocker.*

Calvary songs. Robinson, C. S., *and* Perkins, T. E. 35c .... *Am. S. S.*

Calverley, C. S. Fly-leaves. [Poetry.] (Leis. hour ser.) ('72.) New ed., enl. 16°. '75. $1.25 .. *Holt.*

Calvert, F. Crace. *See* Crace-Calvert, F.

Calvert, G: H: Anyta, and other poems. 16°. '68. $1.25 .... *Dutton.*

— Arnold and André: hist. drama. New ed. 16°. '76. $1.50 .... (?) *Lee & S.*

— Brief essays and brevities. 12°. $1.50 .... *Lee & S.*

— Essays æsthetical. 12°. $1.50 .... *Lee & S.*

— First years in Europe. 12°. $1.75 .... *Lee & S.*

— Gentleman (The). 16°. '66. $1.25 .... *Dutton.*

— Life and works of Goethe: essay. 12°. $1.50. *Lee & S.*

alvert, G: H: *continued.*
Maid (The) of Orleans: hist. tragedy. 16°. '74. $1.50 .... *Putnam.*
Nation's (A) birth, and other national poems. 12°. '76. $1.50 .... (?)*Lee & S.*
See also Joubert, Jos., Thoughts.
alvert, J. Vazeeri Rupi, the silver country of the Vazeers, in Kulu. map and col. pl. 8°. '73. $6.. *Spon.*
alvin, J: Institutio Christianæ religionis; cur. A. Tholuck. 2 v. 8°. $7 .... *Scribner, W. & A.*
Eng. Institutes of the Christian religion; tr. by J. Allen. 2 v. 8°. $4 .... *Pres. Bd.*
— *Same;* tr. by H. Beveridge. 2 v. 8°. $7. *Scribner, W. & A.*
Same; tr. into French. 2 v. 8°. $2 ..... *Pres. Bd.*
Letters; ed. by J. Bonnet. 4 v. 8°. $2.. *Pres. Bd.*
Necessity of reforming the church, with remarks on paternal admonition; tr. by H. Beveridge. 18°. 60c. .... *Pres. Bd.*
See also Luther, M., *and* Calvin, J.
alvinism as it is. Foster, R. S. $1.25. *Cin. Meth. Bk. Conc.*
alvoer, C. Vom Beichten. 8°. '76. 15c... *Barthel.*
alypso. Brookes, S. 15c. .... *French.*
amacho, Sim. *See* Roemer, J., Polyglot reader.
amaralzaman. Byron, H. J. 15c. .... *French.*
ambridge, Ada. Hymns on the holy communion. 24°. '66. 50c. .... *Randolph.*
ambridge, R. O. *See* World (The).
ambridge characteristics in the 17th cent. Mullinger, J. B. $1.50 .... *Macmillan.*
ambridge Lent sermons: sermons preached during Lent, 1864, in Great St. Mary's church, Cambridge [Eng.] cr. 8°. '64. $2.50 .... *Macmillan.*
ambridge [Mass.] platform of [Cong.] Church discipline, 1648; [also] Confession of faith, 1680; [also] Platform of ecclesiast. government, by N. Emmons. 12°. 50c. .... *Cong. Pub.*
ambridge Senate-House. Problems and riders, with solutions. 6 v. 8°. '48–'64 .... *Macmillan.*
Cont.: 1. Problems, by Ferrers and Jackson, '48–51, $6.—2. Riders, by Jameson, '48–'51, $3.—3. Problems and riders, by Walton and MacKenzie, '54, $4.—4. Problems and riders, by Campion and Walton, '57, $3.50.—5. Problems and riders, by Watson and Routh, '60, $3.—6. Problems and riders, by Walton and Wilkinson, '64, $4.
amden, C: When I was young. ill. 12°. '72. $1.25. *Routledge.*
ameos. Landor, W. S. $2 .... *Osgood.*
ameos from Eng. hist. *See* Yonge, C. M.
ameron, *Mrs.* —. Farmer's daughter. 18°. 50c. *Carter.*
ameron, D. *See* North Carolina, Reports.
ameron, Reb. Salted with fire. [Fiction.] 12°. $1. *Hale.*
ameron Hall. Cruse, M. A. $1.75 .... *Claxton.*
ameron Masten. 18°. 40c. .... *Dutton.*
ameron pride. Holmes, M. J. $1.50 ..... *Carleton.*
ameron's bells. 18°. 60c. .... *Whittaker.*
amilla. Barnard, C. F., *jr.* 75c.; 50c. .... *Loring.*
amilla's husband. Phillips, W. 15c. .... *French.*
amille: drama. Dumas, A. 15c. .... *French.*
amille: Ethiop. drama. 16°. pap., 15c. ..... *Happy.*
amille. [Fiction.] *See* Dumas, A. (*fils*).
amillus. Baker, B. F. $1.25; $1 .... *Gordon.*
ammann, H: J. Exposition of the Church catechism. 16°. '63. 35c.; hf. bd., 15c. .... *Dutton.*
amors. Feuillet, O. $1.75; $1.50 .... *Peterson.*
amp, D: N. Key and questions to physical and political outline maps. obl. 12°. '70. $1.. *Andrews.*
amp, G. Sidney. Democracy. 18°. 75c. ... *Harper.*
amp: farce. 16°. pap., 15c. .... *French.*
amp at the Olympic. Planché, J. R. 15c... *French.*

Camp life in Florida. Hallock, C. $1.50 ..... *Forest.*
Camp meeting chorister. 24°. 50c. .... *Sower.*
Camp meeting singer. Baltzell, I. 10c. *E. S. German.*
Camp Tabor. 18°. 90c. .... *Meth. Bk. Conc.*
Campaginator (*pseud.*) Priesthood and clergy unknown to Christianity. 12°. '57. 75c... *Claxton.*
Campagnoli, B. Violin method. f°. $6 ..... *Ditson.*
Note. A portion is also published as Book 1, f°, bds., $2.
Campaign series. *See* Alger, H., *jr.*
Campaigning on the Oxus. MacGahan, J. A. $3.50. *Harper.*
Campan, *Mme.* J. L. H. G. Memoirs of the court of Marie Antoinette. 12°. $1.75 ..... *J. E. Potter.*
Campanella. Mercier, J. $1.25... *Scribner, W. & A.*
Campaner Thal. Richter, J. P. $1 25 .... *Holt.*
Campbell, *Lady.* Cabin by the wayside: a tale for the young. ill. 16°. '72. 50c. .... *Routledge.*
— Story of an apple. ill. 16°. 50c. .... *Routledge.*
Campbell, A. J. (*ed.*) American pract. encyc., or home book of useful knowledge. ('66.) 20th ed. roy. 8°. '76. $3.50; leath., $4.50.. *A. J. Campbell.*
— True friend (A): reflections on life, character and conduct; cont. the best thoughts of the best authors. ('72.) 12th ed. roy. 8°. '76. $2.75–$6.50 .... *A. J. Campbell.*
Campbell, *Rev.* A. J. Power of Christ to save. 18°. 75c. .... *Carter.*
Campbell, A. L. V. Rule Britannia: farce. 16°. pap., 15c. .... *French.*
— Tom Bowling: drama. 16°. pap., 15c. ..... *French.*
Campbell, Alex. Works. 6 v. 12°. $7.50 .... *Chase.*
Cont.: The Christian system.—Debate with Owen.—Lectures on the Pentateuch.—Debate with Purcell.—Christian baptism.—Memoirs of Thos. Campbell.
— Christian baptism, with its antecedents and consequents. 12°. $1 .... *Chase.*
— Christian Baptist; rev. by D. S. Burnet. 7 v. in 1. 8°. $2.50; $3 .... *Chase.*
— Christian system (The), in ref. to the union of Christians and a restoration of primitive Christianity. 12°. $1.50. .... *Chase.*
— Familiar lectures on the Pentateuch; also short extracts from his sermons, [with] sketch of life; ed. by W. T. Moore. por. 12°. $1.50 ...... *Chase.*
— Life and death: refutation of materialism and modern Sadduceeism. 24°. pap., 10c. .... *Chase.*
— Living oracles: New Test., tr. from the Gk. by G. Campbell, J. MacKnight and P. Doddridge; with pref. emendations and app. 32°. 40c. .... *Chase.*
— Memoirs of T. Campbell; with brief memoir of Mrs. Jane Campbell. 12°. $1.25 .... *Chase.*
— Popular lectures and addresses. ('63.) 3d ed. por. 8°. $3 .... *Challen.*
— *See also* Owen, R., *and* Campbell, A.
— *and* Purcell, J. B. Debate on the Roman Cath. relig., Cincinnati, O. 12°. $1.50 .... *Benziger; Chase.*
Campbell, C. D. N. Sermons. cr. 8°. '72. $1.50. *Hurd & H.*
Campbell, C: History of colony and ancient dominion of Va. 8°. $2.50 .... *Claxton; Lippincott.*
— Some materials for a memoir of J. D. Burk, with sketch of life of J. J. Burk. 8°. '68. $1.50. *Munsell.*
Campbell, *Miss* Emma. Green pastures. ill. 18°. '66. 50c. .... *Am. Tr.*
— Paul Preston; or, who is the hero? ('64.) New ed. ill. 16°. '75. $1.15 .... *Hoyt.*
Campbell, Emma F. R. Better than rubies; or, Mabel's treasure. 16°. '69. $1.25 ..... *Garrigues.*
— Toward the mark; or, Grace Allen's aim: sequel to "Better than rubies." 16°. '75. $1.25. *Garrigues.*
Campbell, Gbr. New element. course in the Germ. lang. 12°. $1.25 .... *Potter, A. & Co.*
Campbell, G: Philosophy of rhetoric. 12°. $1.50. *Harper.*

Campbell, G: Douglas. *See* Argyll, *Duke* of.

Campbell, H. F. Excito-secretory system. 8°. $1.50. *Lippincott.*

Campbell, Ht. Self-devotion; or, the history of Catharine Randolph. [Fiction.] 8°. pap., 50c. *Harper.*

Campbell, J. F. My circular notes: extracts from journals, letters, etc., while travelling westwards round the world, July 6, 1874, to July 6, 1875. 2 v. ill. cr. 8°. '76. $7.50........*Macmillan.*

Campbell, J. M. *See* United States, Circuit Court decisions.

Campbell, Ja. V. Outlines of the polit. hist. of Michigan. 8°. '76. $4.50.........(?) *Schober.*

Campbell, J: (*ed.*) Pamphlets issued during the habeas corpus controversy of 1862. 8°. '65. shp., $7.50....................*J. Campbell & Son.*

Campbell, J: (*Lord*). Index to Lives of the lord chancellors and chief justices of Eng. 8°. '76. $3.50; shp., $4.50; hf. cf., $6............*Cockcroft.*

— Lives of the chief justices of Eng. 4 v. cr. 8°. (Lond.) '74. $8; hf. cf., $14...*Little, B. & Co.*

— *Same.* 4 v. ill. and por. 8°. $14; shp., $18; hf. cf., $24. — 4 v. 12°. $8................*Estes.*

— *Same;* continued by Sir J. Arnold [v. 5, 6]. 6 v. 8°. $21; shp., $27; hf. cf., $36......*Cockcroft.*

Note. v. 5, 6, form Life of Thomas, Lord Denham.

— Lives of the lord chancellors and keepers of the great seal of Eng. 10 v. cr. 8°. (Lond.) $20; hf. cf., $35; cf., $45...........*Little, B. & Co.*

— *Same.* 10 v. 12°. hf. cf., $35..........*Appleton.*

— *Same;* ed. by J. A. Mallory. 10 v. ill. 8°. $35; shp., $45; hf. cf., $60.......*Cockcroft; Estes.*

— Lives of Lords Kenyon, Ellenborough and Tenterden. cr. 8°. $2; shp., $2.25; hf. mor., $2.50...*Lea.*

Note. Same as v. 3 of Chief justices.

— On Shakespeare's legal acquirements. 12°. $1. *Appleton.*

Campbell, *Rev.* J: Voyages to and from Cape of Good Hope. 18°. 65c...................*Pres. Bd.*

— Walks of usefulness in London and its environs. 18°. 50c............................*Pres. Bd.*

Campbell, J: G. E. H. D. S. *See* Lorne, *Marquis of.*

Campbell, J: H. Legal Gazette reports: cases in the Phila. courts, Supreme Court of Nisi prius, and in the judicial districts of Penna., 1869–'71. 8°. '72. shp., $6..............*J. Campbell & Son.*

Campbell, J: McLeod. Christ the bread of life: an attempt to give a profitable direction to the present occupation of thought with Romanism. 2d ed., enl. cr. 8°. '69. $1.50......*Macmillan.*

— Nature of the atonement, and its relation to remission of sins and eternal life. 3d ed., enl. cr. 8°. '73. $2.50....................*Macmillan.*

— Reminiscences and reflections, [rel.] to early ministry in parish of Row, 1825–'31; with introd. by Donald Campbell. cr. 8°. '73. $2.50......*Macmillan.*

— Responsibility for the gift of eternal life: sermons, 1829–'31. cr. 8°. '73. $2.........*Macmillan.*

— Thoughts on revelation, with special ref. to the present time. 12°. '74. $1.25........*Claxton.*

— *Same.* 2d ed. cr. 8°. '74. $2.......*Macmillan.*

Campbell, Loomis J. Concise school hist. of the U. S.; based on Seavey's Goodrich's "History." maps and ill. 16°. hf. roan, $1.18............*Ware.*

— *Same;* tr. into Germ. by G. Fischer. 16°. hf. roan, $1.25.............................*Ware.*

— *See also* Hillard, G. S., *and* Campbell, L. J.; — Soule, R., *and* Campbell, L. J.; — Worcester, J. E.

— *and* Root, O., *jr.* Columbian speaker: sel. for declamation. 16°. 75c..................*Lee & S.*

Campbell, M. Forest oracle: drama. 16°. pap., 15c..............................*French.*

Campbell, *Mrs.* N. W. Why am I a Presbyterian? 18°. 75c......................(?) *Martien.*

— Why should I be a pastor? 18°. 40c...(?) *Martien.*

Campbell, *Mrs.* N. W., *continued.*

— Why should I be a ruling elder? 18°. 40c. (?) *Martie*

Campbell, Rob. Allen. Atlas of Missouri. ('72.) Ne ed. roy. f°. '76. $12.50.......*R. A. Campbe*

— Universal interest and equation table. 12°. '76. $ *R. A. Campbe*

— (*ed.*) Gazetteer of Missouri: descript., hist., geo and statistics. maps and ill. roy. 8°. '74. $ $12.50..........................*R. A. Campbe*

— *See also* Bible, Gospels.

Campbell, S. M. Across the desert. 12°. $1.50. *Pres. B*

Campbell, T: Poems. 12°. $1.50...........*Lock*

— *Same.* (Blue and gold ed.) 18°. $1.25. *Nichols & I*

— *Same.* (Scribner's pop. poets.) ill. 12°. $1.50. *Scribner, W. &*

— *Same;* with biog. sketch by Rev. W. A. Hill. po 18°. $1.............................*Osgoo*

— *Same;* ed. by Rev. R. A. Willmott, with biog. et (British poets.) ill. 12°. $2.25; hf. cf., $3.5 mor., $5..........................*Routledg*

— *Same;* [also] Poems, by S. T. Coleridge. (Cabin ed.) ill. 16°. $1.50; hf. cf., $3.....*Lippincot*

— — *See also* Rogers, S.; — Young, E.

— Poetical works. ill. 16°. $1.50...........*Lee &*

— *Same.* ill. 12°. '76. $1.50............*World Pu*

— *Same.* (Blue and gold ed.) 18°. $1.25. *Nichols & I*

— *Same.* (Chandos classics.) cr. 8°. $1; pap., 75c. *Scribner, W. &*

— *Same.* (Globe ed.) ill. 16°. $1.25; hf. cf., $3.25 mor., $4; chp. ed., pap., 60c..........*Appleto*

— *Same.* (Household ser.) ill. 16°. $1.50; mor., $ *Lee &*

— *Same;* with memoir by W. E. Aytoun. (Househo ed.) 16°. $1.25; hf. cf., $2.50; mor., $3.7 (Red line ed.) por. sm. 4°. $3.50; hf. cf., $5 mor., $7..............................*Mille*

— *Same;* with life by E. Sargent. por. 12°. '7 $1.50; $2; hf. cf., $3.50; mor., $5....*Putnam*

— *Same;* ed. by Rev. R. A. Willmott. (Presentatio poets.) ill. 12°. $1.75..............*Routledge*

— *Same;* [also] Poetical works of S. T. Coleridge with memoirs. 16°. $1.50; hf. cf., $3. *Lippincot*

— Cyclopedia of Eng. poetry, with biog. and crit. notices and essay on Eng. poetry. ill. 8°. $3; mor., $7 $7.50.................................*Lippincot*

— Gertrude of Wyoming. ill. 12°. $2.50; cf., $4.50 mor., $5......................*Appleton*

— Life of Petrarch. *See* Petrarch.

— Pleasures of hope. ill. 12°. '75. $1.25....*Putnam*

— *Same.* ill. 12°. $2.50; mor., $5.........*Appleton*

— — *See also* Poems of pleasures.

— *See also* Stone, W. L., History of Wyoming; — Shakespeare, W.

Campbell, Wa. The old forest ranger; or, wild sport in India. ill. 12°. $2...............*Routledge*

Campbell & Co. (*pub.*) Commercial law register. 8° shp., $6.........................*Campbell & Co*

Campbellism exposed. Phillips, W. 70c. *Cin. Meth. Bk. Conc*

Campbellism exposed. Williams, A. P. $1.50. *So. Bapt*

Camp-fires of Napoleon. ill. 8°. $2.50.......*T. Bliss*

Camp-fires of the revolution. Watson, H. C. $2. *Miller*

Campin, Fs. On the construction of iron roofs. ill and pl. 8°. '68. $2...........*Van Nostrand*

— Practical treatise on mechanical engineering. pl and ill. 8°. '63. $6...................*Baird*

— Practice of hand turning in wood, ivory, shell etc.; with instructions for turning in metal 2d ed. ill. cr. 8°. '68. $2.................*Spon*

— *Same.* ill. 12°. $3.............................*Baird*

Camping out series. *See* Stephens, C. A.

Campion, —. Problems and rider. *See* Cambridge Senate House.

Campion, J: T: Michael Dwyer; or, the insurgent captain of the Wicklow Mountains; and reminiscences of '98. ('75.) New ed. 16°. '76. $1. *Kenedy.*

Campion, W. M., *and* Beamont, W. J. Prayer book; with hist. ill. and notes. 12°. '75. $2....... *Pott.*

Campion Court. Worboise, E. J. $1.75.. *Routledge.*

Camus, C. E. Treatise on the teeth of wheels; tr. from the Fr. 3d ed., rev. and enl.; with details of the present practice of millwrights, engine makers and other machinists, by I. Hawkins. pl. 8°. '68. $2........................ *Spon.*

Can the old love? Buddington, Z. B. $1.25; 75c. *Estes.*

Can you forgive her? *See* Trollope, Anthony.

Canaanite exterminated. Briggs, C. 60c. *Un. B. Pub.*

Canadian Crusoe. Traill, C. P. $1.25.. *Nichols & H.*

Canarienvogel (Der) u. d. Johanniskäferchen. *See* Schmid, C. v.

Canary bird. ill. sq. 12°. '71. bds., 50c... *Routledge.*

Canary birds: manual of information for bird-keepers. 12°. 75c.; pap., 50c.................. *Judd.*

Canby, Marg. T. Birdie and his fairy friends. 16°. '73. $1.............................. *Claxton.*

Cancelled will (The). Dupuy, E. A. $1.75. *Peterson.*

Candide. *See* Voltaire, F. M. A. de.

Candle (A) lighted by the Lord: a life story for young and old. 16°. '76. $1.25............... *Hoyt.*

Candler, H. Help to arithmetic. 16°. '68. $1. *Macmillan.*

Candlish, Rob. S. Sermons. 12°. $2....... *Carter.*

Candy elephant (The). Dolliver, C. G. 75c... *Roman.*

Candy girl. *See* Alexander, J. W.

Canino, *Prince of.* *See* Bonaparte, C. L.

Canne, J: *See* Bible [Whole].

Cannibal islands (The); or, Fiji and its people. 18°. 75c................................. *Pres. Bd.*

Cannon, C: Ja. Lessons for young learners. 2 v. 18°. v. 1, 13c.; v. 2, 25c.................... *Strong.*

— Practical spelling book. 18°. 25c.......... *Strong.*

— Ravellings from the web of life. 12°. $1.50; $2. *Sadlier.*

Canoe and the saddle. Winthrop, T. $1.25..... *Holt.*

Canoe travelling. Powell, W. B. $3.. *Scribner, W. & A.*

Canonbury House. Reynolds, G. W. M. 50c. *De Witt.*

Canova, Antonio. Works in sculpture and modelling; with descriptions of the Countess Albrizzi, memoir by Cicognara and 150 pl. by H. Moses. 4°. $12.60. *Scribner, W. & A.*

Canright, Dudley M. History of the doctrine of the immortality of the soul; with app. by Dan. T. Taylor. 16°. '71. 25c......... *Sev. Day Adv.*

— Ministration of angels, and the origin, hist. and destiny of Satan. 16°. '75. 20c... *Sev. Day Adv.*

— Morality of the Sabbath. 16°. '75. pap., 15c. *Sev. Day Adv.*

— Two laws (The) as set forth in the Old and New Test. 16°. '76. pap., 15c....... *Sev. Day Adv.*

Cantab. *See* Robertson, T. W.

Cantara. *See* Nash, F. H., *and* Bristow, G. F.

Cantarium Romanum: [Katholisches] Choralgesangbuch. Schulausgabe. 12°. 50c. — Same: f. Orgel u. den Sängerchor in 4- stimmigem Satze. obl. 4°. $1.50........................ *Benziger.*

Cantata Catholica. Hellebusch, B. H. F. $2.50. *Benziger.*

Cantate (The). Werner, A. 2 nos. ea., $2.25.. *Ditson.*

Cantate Domino. Steiner, L. H., *and* Schwing, H. $2.................................... *Ditson.*

Canterbury, Ira. *See* Simpson, H., *and* Canterbury, I.

Canterbury bells (The). 16°. '60. $1.50.. *Randolph.*

Canterbury tales. *See* Chaucer, G.

Cantica ecclesiastica. Webb, G. J. $2...... *Ditson.*

Cantica laudis. Mason, L., *and* Webb, G. J. $1.50. *Ditson.*

Cantica sacra; or, hymns for the children of the Cath. church. 24°. pap., 15c.; bds., 25c. *Noonan.*

Canticle of canticles. *See* Bible, Psalms.

Cantus divinus. Rosewig, A. H. $2.75..... *Ditson.*

Cantus ecclesiæ. Darley, W. H. W., *and* Standbridge, J. C. B. $1.50........................ *Ditson.*

Canvassing. *See* Banim, J. *and* M.

Canzonetta (The). Fitzhugh, E. J. $1...... *Pond.*

Cap-makers (The); by author of "Blind Annie Lorimer." 18°. 60c..................... *Pres. Bd.*

Cape and the Kaffirs. Ward, H. 80c.. *Scribner, W. & A.*

Capecelatro, Alph. La mere de Dieu. Tr. from the Ital. 18°. '64. 50c............... *Cunningham.*

Capel, T: J. Reply to Gladstone's political expostulation. 8°. pap., 30c.................. *Appleton.*

— *See also* Gladstone, W. E., Vatican decrees.

Capen, Nahum. History of democracy; or, political progress. ill. roy. 8°. *$5; shp., $6; hf. mor., $7; mor., $9......................... *Am. Pub.*

Capers, W: Autobiography. *See* Wightman, W. M.

— Short sermons and true tales; with notice of author by T. O. Summers. ('55.) 2d ed. 18°. '74. 40c. *So. Meth.*

— — *See also* Village lib.

Capers. Small, G. G. 25c............... *Collin & S.*

Capital match. Morton, J. M. 15c... *Ames; French.*

Capitola. Hazelwood, C. H. 15c........... *French.*

Caprice (Un). *See* Musset, A. de.

Capron, Carrie. Helen Lincoln; or, the power of principle. 12°. $1.50................. *Harper.*

Capron, Ma. J. ["Archie Fell."] Apron strings, and which way they were pulled. ill. 16°. 71. $1.25. *Crowell.*

— — *See also* Apron-strings lib.

— Charity Hurlburt. ('70.) New ed. ill. 16°. '75. $1.50.................................. *Hoyt.*

— Earthen vessels. ('67.) New ed. ill. 16°. '73. $1.50.................................. *Hoyt.*

— Mrs. Thorne's guests; or, salt with savor and without. ill. 16°. '71. $1.50.................. *Lothrop.*

— Tover tangle, and the way it was straightened out. 16°. '72. $1.25........................ *Crowell.*

— — *See also* Apron-strings lib.

— Worth while. 16°. $1.50.............. *Cong. Pub.*

Capron, S. M. School lyrics: collection of sacred hymns. 32°. 40c...................... *Harper.*

Capsadell, Lou. Her waiting heart. [Fiction.] 12°. '75. $1.25 .... *Authors.*

— Women's secrets; or, how to be beautiful; tr. and ed. from the Persian and French. 12°. '76. 75c.; pap., 25c................................ *Authors.*

Captain Blake. *See* Maxwell, W: H.

Captain Blood and the beagles. 8°. pap., 25c. *Peterson.*

Captain Blood, and the hangman's daughter. 8°. pap., 25c................................. *Peterson.*

Captain Brand. Wise, H. A. $2; $1.50.... *Harper.*

Captain Carleton. *See* Defoe, D.

Captain Charley. Boyd, E. E. 75c........... *Hoyt.*

Captain Charlotte. Stirling, E. 15c......... *French.*

Captain Christie's granddaughter. *See* Lamb, R. B.

Captain Farrago. *See* Adventures of.

Captain Hatteras. *See* Verne, Jules.

Captain Hawkes; or, the life of a highwayman. 8°. pap., 25c.......................... *Dick & F.*

Captain Heron; or, the highwayman of Epping Forest. 8°. pap., 25c......................... *Dick & F.*

Captain John. Porter, A. E. $1.50.......... *Hoyt.*

Captain Kyd. Ingraham, J. H. 50c........ *De Witt.*

Captain Kyd. Jones, J. S. 15c............. *French.*

Captain McLeane. 8°. pap., 25c. . . . . *De Witt.*
Captain of the guard. *See* Grant, Ja.
Captain of the watch. Planché, J. R. 15c. . . *French.*
Captain O'Sullivan. *See* Maxwell, W: H.
Captain Paul. *See* Dumas, A.
Captain Rougemont. *See* Catholic premium-book lib.
Captain Russell's watchword. Grosvenor, H. S. $1.25. *Hoyt.*
Captain Singleton. *See* Defoe, D.
Captain Smith. Berrie, E. 15c. . . . . *Ames; French.*
Captain Waltham. Scudder, J. $1.10. *N. Y. Ref. Ch. Bd.; Pres. Bd.*
Captain Wolf, and other sketches of animal biog.; by the author of "Under the lime trees." ill. 12°. $2 . . . . *Appleton.*
Captain 's not a-miss. Wilks, T. E. 15c. . . . . *French.*
Captain's story. Townsend, M. A. 30c. . . *Lippincott.*
Captive boy (The) in Terra del Fuego. *See* Winifred Leigh lib.
Captive children. 18°. 30c. . . . . *Dutton.*
Captive in Patagonia. Bourne, B. F. $1.25 . . *Lothrop.*
Captive of Nootka Sound. *See* Goodrich, S. G., Peter Parley's little lib.
Captives (The). Leslie, E. $1 . . . . *Nelson.*
Captives (The). *See* Plautus, T. M.
Captives of Abb's Valley: a legend of frontier life. 18°. 50c. . . . . *Pres. Bd.*
Captivity of Judah. *See* Mortimer, *Mrs.* M.
Capture and escape. Larimer, S. L. $1.50 . . *Claxton.*
Captured scout (The) of the army of the James. Trumbull, H. C. 65c. . . . . . *Lockwood, B. & Co.*
Capuletta. Baker, G. M. 15c. . . . . *Lee & S.*
Capuletti (I) e Montecchi. *See* Bellini, V.
Carafas of Maddaloni. *See* Reumont, A. v.
Carboy, J: (*pseud.*) *See* Harrington, J: A.
Carcassi, Matteo. Guitar method. New ed., rev. by J. Holland. 4°. $3; abridg., $2 . . . . *Brainard.*
— New and improved method for the guitar. f°. '53. bds., $3; abridg., $2 . . . . *Ditson.*
Card-drawing. *See* Griffin, G.
Carden, Allen D. (*ed.*) The Missouri harmony: collection of psalms, hymns, tunes and anthems; rev., enl. and corr. by C. Warren. ('36.) 3d ed. 8°. '58. hf. bd., 75c. . . . . *Wilstach.*
Cardinal flower (The). Alden, J. 50c. . . . . . *Lee & S.*
Cardiphonia. Newton, J. $1.20 . . . . *Pres. Bd.*
Care cast upon the Lord. Hall, J. 35c.; 60c. *Randolph.*
Career of the Christ-idea in hist. Tuttle, H. $1.50. *Colby.*
Careless, J: Life and writings. *See* British reformers.
Careless girl reformed. 18°. 60c. . . . . *Cong. Pub.*
Careless Kate. Adams, W. T. 45c. . . . . *Lee & S.*
Careless Susan. ill. sq. 16°. pap., 20c. . . . . *Am. S. S.*
Cares and comforts. Finley, M. F. 65c. . . . *Pres. Bd.*
Carey, Annie. Autobiography of a lump of coal, a grain of salt, a drop of water, a piece of old iron, a bit of flint. 16°. $1 . . . . *Cassell.*
— *Same.* ill. 4°. $1.25 . . . . *Lee & S.*
— History of a book. ill. fp. 4°. $1.50 . . . . . . *Cassell.*
— Threads of knowledge drawn from a cambric handkerchief, a Brussels carpet, a print dress, a kid glove, a sheet of paper. ill. 16°. $1 . . . . *Cassell.*
Carey, C: Stokes. Commonplace book of epigrams. 12°. $2 . . . . *Appleton.*
Carey, H: Chrononotonthologos: tragedy. 16°. pap., 15c. . . . . *French.*
Carey, H: C: Financial crises: their causes and effects. ('63.) 3d ed. 8°. '72. pap., 25c. . . . . *Baird.*
— Harmony of interests: agricultural, manufacturing and commercial. (cop. '52.) '65. 3d ed. 8°. '72. $1.50 . . . . *Baird.*
Carey, H: C: *continued.*
— Letters on international copyright. 8°. '67. pap., 50c. . . . . *Baird.*
— Letters to the president on the foreign and domestic policy of the Union. 8°. pap., 75c. . . . . . *Polock.*
— Manual of social science; a condensation of [his] "Principles of social science," by K. McKean. ('64.) 8th ed. 12°. '74. $2.25 . . . . *Baird.*
— Miscellaneous papers on the national finances, the currency, and other economic subjects. por. 8°. '75. $2.50 . . . . *Baird.*
— Past, present and future. (cop. '47.) '59. New ed. 8°. '72. $2.50 . . . . *Baird.*
— Principles of social science. 3 v. 8°. $10 . . *Lippincott.*
— Reconstruction, industrial, financial, and political: letters to H: Wilson. 8°. '67. 50c. . . . . . *Baird.*
— Resources of the Union: lecture. 8°. pap., 50c. *Baird.*
— Review of the farmer's question. 8°. '70. 25c. *Baird.*
— Review of the report [on the revenue] of D. A. Wells. 8°. '69. pap., 50c. . . . . *Baird.*
— Slave-trade (The), domestic and foreign: why it exists, and how it may be extinguished. ('53.) '59. 4th ed. 8°. '72. $2 . . . . *Baird.*
— Unity of law: as exhibited in the relations of physical, social, mental and moral science. ('72.) 3d ed. 8°. '73. $3.50 . . . . *Baird.*
— Wealth: of what does it consist? 8°. '70. pap., 25c. *Baird.*
Carey, J: *See* Protestant Episc. Church, Book of common prayer.
Carey, M. F. Adela Lincoln. *See* Fuller, M. V., Fashionable dissipation.
Carey, Rosa N. Wooed and married. [Fiction.] 12°. $1.75 . . . . *Lippincott.*
Carey, *Mrs.* Stanley. Gerald Marsdale; or, the outquarters of St. Andrew's Priory. 16°. $1.25; $1.75 . . . . *Sadlier.*
Cargill, T: Strains upon bridge girders and roof trusses, incl. the Warren, lattice, trellis [etc.], forms of girders, the curved roof, and simple and compound trusses. ill. 8°. '73. $5 . . . . *Spon.*
Carhart, —. Melodeon instructor. obl. 8°. '55. bds., $1.50 . . . . *Ditson.*
Caricature hist. of the Georges. *See* Wright, T.
Caring for God's sparrows. 18°. 35c. . . . . . . *Pres. Bd.*
Carion, C: Stellwag v. *See* Stellwag von Carion, C:
Carl (*pseud.*) *See* Newhall, C. S.
Carl and Jocko. Abbott, J. 90c. . . . . *Harper.*
Carl Bartlett. Erickson, D. S. $1.25 . . . *H. A. Young.*
Carl, the young emigrant. Alexander, J. W. 65c. *Am. S. S.*
Carlén, *Miss* Emilie Flygare. Brothers' (The) bet; or, within six weeks. 8°. pap., 25c. . . . . . *Harper.*
— Ivar; or, the Skjuts-boy. 8°. pap., 50c. . . *Harper.*
— John. 8°. pap., 25c. . . . . *Dick & F.*
— Lover's (A) stratagem; or, the two suitors. 8°. pap., 50c. . . . . *Harper.*
— Marie Louise. 8°. pap., 25c. . . . . *Dick & F.*
— Twelve months of matrimony. 8°. pap., 50c. *Peterson.*
— Woman's life. 8°. pap., 75c. . . . . *Dick & F.*
Carless, *Miss* L. M. Brave Lisette. ill. fp. 8°. '70. 75c. . . . . *Cassell.*
Carleton (*pseud.*) *See* Coffin, C. C.
Carleton, G: W. Our artist in Cuba. ill. 16°. $1.50. *Carleton.*
— Our artist in Peru. ill. 16°. $1.50 . . . . . . *Carleton.*
Carleton, Hiram. Treatise on the meaning of the derivatives of the Gk. root ΒΑΦ. 24°. '75. 30c. *Williams.*
Carleton, J: W: ["Craven."] Recreations in shooting. ill. 12°. (Bohn.) $1.75 . . . . *Little, B. & Co.*
— *Same.* ill. 12°. (Bohn.) $2. *Lippincott; Scribner, W. & A.*

Carleton, Will. Betsey and I are out. *See* Emerson, *Mrs.* N. S.; — *and below* Farm ballads.

— Farm ballads. ill. sq. 8°. $2; $2.50 ...... *Harper.*
Note. Includes "Betsey and I are out," the authorship of which is disputed by Mrs. N. S. Emerson.

— Farm legends. ill. sq. 8°. $2; $2.50 ...... *Harper.*

Carleton, W: Works. 10 v. 12°. $15; hf. mor., $20; hf. cf., $25 ...... *Sadlier.*
Cont.: Willy Reilly. — Jane Sinclair. — Poor scholar, etc. — Emigrants of Adharrah. — Black prophet. — Evil eye. — Tithe proctor. — Fardorougha, the miser. — Valentine M'Clutchy; [also] Life of C., by J. Savage. — Black baronet.

— Novels and tales. 5 v. 16°. $3.75 ...... *Routledge.*
Cont.: Fardorougha. — Tithe proctor. — Clarionet. — Emigrants. — Jane Sinclair; [also] Neal Malone.

— Black baronet; or, the chronicles of Ballytrain. 12°. $1.50 ...... *Noonan; Sadlier.*

— Black prophet: tale of the Irish famine. 12°. $1.50. *Sadlier.*

— Evil eye; or, the black spectre. 12°. $1.50 .. *Noonan.*

— Fardorougha, the miser; or, the convicts of Lisnamona. 8°. '68. bds., 50c. ...... *Haverty.*

— Redmond, Count O'Hanlon, the Irish rapparee. 16°. 60c.; $1 ...... *Sadlier.*

— Traits and stories of the Irish peasantry. 16°. $1.25; $1.75 ...... *Sadlier.*

— *Same.* ill. 12°. $3; hf. cf., $5 .... *Scribner, W. & A.*

— *Same.* 2 v. ill. 8°. hf. cf., $12 ...... *Appleton.*

— Tuber Derg. 18°. 75c.; $1.25 ...... *Sadlier.*

— Valentine M'Clutchy, the Irish agent; or, chronicles of Castle Cumber property. 8°. $1.50 .. *Sadlier.*

— Willy Reilly and his dear Coleen bawn. 8°. pap., 50c. ...... *De Witt.*

— *Same.* ill. 12°. pap., 50c. ...... *Kenedy.*

— *Same.* 12°. $1.50 ...... *Noonan; Sadlier.*

Carlier, A: Marriage in the U. S.; tr. by B. J. Jeffries. 16°. '67. $1 ...... *Holt.*

Carlile, R: Gospel of Jesus Christ. 12°. pap., 10c. *Mendum.*

Carlino. Ruffini, G. 35c. ...... *Lippincott.*

Carll, J. F. *See* Pennsylvania geol. survey.

Carll, M. M. Child's book of nat. hist., ill. the animal, vegetable and mineral kingdoms; with applications to the arts. 16°. '60. hf. bd., 50c. *Barnes.*

Carl's home. Cornell, S. B. $1.25 ...... *Hoyt.*

Carlton, Carrie (*pseud.*) *See* Booth, Ma.

Carlton, Kate. Beechdale. 16°. 40c. ... *Williamson.*

Carlton, S. P., *and* Moore, W. D. Destiny of man. 12°. $1.25 ...... *Williamson.*

Carlyle, G. The light of all ages. 12°. '73. $1.75. *Routledge.*

Carlyle, T: Works. (Library ed.) 34 v. por., maps, etc. demy 8°. $127.50; ea., hf. cf., $5.75; cf., $7.50 ...... *Scribner, W. & A.*
Cont.: Sartor resartus: life and opinions of Herr Teufelsdrockh, $3.75. — French rev., 3 v., ea., $4.50. — Life of Schiller and examination of his writings, $3.75. — Critical and misc. essays, 6 v., ea., $4.50. — On heroes, hero-worship and the heroic in hist., $3.75. — Past and present, $4.50. — Cromwell's letters and speeches, 5 v., ea., $4.50. — Latter-day pamphlets, $4.50. — Life of J. Sterling, $4.50. — Hist. of Frederick II., 10 v., ea., $4.50. — German translations, 3 v., ea., $4.50. — Index to works, $3.

— Works. (Chp. ed.) 38 v. 16°. (Lond.) '71–'74. ea., 80c. ...... *Little, B. & Co.*
Cont.: Miscellaneous essays, 7 v. — French revolution, 3 v. — Frederick the Great, 10 v. — Cromwell's letters, etc., 5 v. — Sartor resartus. — John Sterling. — Life of Schiller. — Past and present. — Heroes and hero worship. — Latter-day pamphlets. — Translations (Wilhelm Meister, etc.), 5 v. — General index. — Choice of books.

— Works. (People's ed.) 38 v. 16°. ea., 90c.; hf. cf., $2.50. — 18 v. $35 ...... *Scribner, W. & A.*
Cont.: Sartor resartus. — French revolution, 3 v. — Life of Schiller. — Critical and miscellaneous essays, 7 v. — Heroes and hero worship. — Past and present. — Cromwell's letters, etc., 5 v. — Latter-day pamphlets. — Life of Sterling. — Frederick the Great, 10 v. — On the choice of books. — Wilhelm Meister, 3 v. — Translations, 2 v. — General index.

— — *Same.* 37 v. 16°. ea., 90c. — 18 v. hf. cf., $60. *Lippincott.*

Carlyle, T: *continued.*
Note. Contents the same as in ed. of S., W. & A. with the omission of On the choice of books.

— Critical and miscellaneous essays. 8°. $2.50; shp., $3.50; hf. cf., $5 ...... *Appleton.*

— *Same.* 4 v. por. 8°. $9; hf. cf., $16 .. *Hurd & H.*

— — *See also* Modern Brit. essayists.

— Early kings of Norway; [also] An essay on the portraits of John Knox. 12°. $1.50 ...... *Harper.*

— German romance: specimens of its chief authors, with biog. and crit. notices. 2 v. in 1. 12°. '41. $1.25 ...... *Burnham.*

— History of Frederick the Great. maps, por., plans, etc. 6 v. 12°. $12; shp., $14.40; hf. cf., $22.50 ...... *Harper.*

— History of the French revolution. 2 v. 12°. $3.50; shp., $4.30; hf. cf., $7 ...... *Harper.*

— Latter-day pamphlets. ('55.) New ed. 12°. '60. $1. *Draper.*

— Letters and speeches of Oliver Cromwell, incl. supplement to 1st ed.; with elucidations. 2 v. 12°. $3.50; shp., $4.30; hf. cf., $7 ...... *Harper.*

— Life of Robert Burns. 16°. 75c. ...... *Hurd & H.*

— On heroes, hero-worship and the heroic in history. 12°. 75c. ...... *Wiley.*

— Past and present; [also] Chartism; [also] Sartor resartus. 12°. $1.75; shp., $2.15; hf. cf., $3.50 ...... *Harper.*

— Sartor resartus: life and opinions of Herr Teufelsdrockh. 12°. 75c. ...... *Miller.*

— *See also* Mill, J. S., Froude, J. A., *and* Carlyle, T.

Carlyon's year. Payn, J. 25c. ...... *Harper.*

Carmen's inheritance. *See* Fisher, F. C.

Carmina alterna. Brown, O. B. $1 .. *G. D. Russell.*

Carmina cœli. Nason, E. $1.50 ...... *Hoyt.*

Carmina collegensia. Waite, H. R. $3; $4 .. *Ditson.*

Carmina concordiæ. Weed, T. $1.75 ...... *Pond.*

Carmina meloda. Johnson, J. C. 45c. ...... *Ditson.*

Carmina Princetonia. Marquand, F. A., Markoe, F. H., *and* Henderson, W. J. $1.50 ...... *Dennis.*

Carmina sacra. *See* Mason, L.

Carmina Yalensia. Garretson, F. V. D. $1.75; $2.25. *Taintor.*

Carnes, *Capt.* (*pseud.*) *See* Cummings, M. J.

Carnival of Venice. *See* Ditson.

Carnochan, J: Murray. Ætiology, pathology and treatment of congenital dislocations of the head of the femur. ill. 8°. $2 ...... *W. Wood.*

Carol. Bradbury, W. B. 56c.; 50c. ...... *Ivison.*

Carolina. Berry, M. E. $1.25 ...... *Lothrop.*

Caroline Amelia Eliz. (*Queen consort of* George IV.) Trial. *See* Causes célèbres.

Caroline. Abbott, J. 90c. ...... *Harper.*

Caroline; or, self-conquest. 18°. '67. 50c. *Cunningham.*

Caroline Jones; or, outward and inward adorning. 16°. 40c. ...... *West. Tr.*

Caroline Morin. Lawrence, W. H. 20c. .... *Am. Tr.*

Caroline of Brunswick. Reynolds, G. W. M. $1.75; $1 ...... *Peterson.*

Caroline Tracy; or, the milliner's apprentice. 8°. pap., 25c. ...... *Dick & F.*

Caroline Westerley. Phelps, L. 75c. ...... *Harper.*

Carové, F. W. Das Märchen ohne Ende. With Eng. notes. ('64.) New ed. 12°. '72. pap., 25c. *Holt.*

— *Eng.* The story without an end; tr. by S. Austin, with pref. and key to emblems by A. B. Alcott. ill. 18°. 50c. ...... *Miller.*

Carpenter, Cyrus C. Iowa surveyor's manual, with diagrams and index. 8°. '70. $1.50 ...... *Mills.*

Carpenter, G. T., *and* Hughes, J: Destiny of the wicked. [Debate.] 12°. '75. $1.50 .... *Cen. Bk.*

Carpenter, Ja. *See* Nasmyth, J., *and* Carpenter, J.

Carpenter, Jos. E. Comic reciter. 16°. bds., 50c. *Routledge.*
— Devout songster. 32°. 25c. .... *Routledge.*
— Penny readings in prose and verse. 10 v. 16°. ea., 50c. .... *Scribner, W. & A.*
— Popular readings, in prose and verse. 5 v. ea., $2; per set, hf. cf., $20; cf., $25.. *Scribner, W. & A.*
— Popular reciter. 16°. bds., 50c. .... *Routledge.*
— Sacred songster. 32°. 25c. .... *Routledge.*
Note. Compr. Comic reciter, *and* Popular reciter.
— Songs of grace. 32°. 25c. .... *Routledge.*
— Songs of the righteous. 32°. 25c. .... *Routledge.*
— Standard reciter. 16°. $1.25 .... *Routledge.*

Carpenter, P. P. American mollusca. 8°. '73. pap., $1 .... *Smith. Inst.*
— *See also* Lea, I., *and* Carpenter, P. P.

Carpenter, Ste. H. English of the 14th century; ill. by notes on Chaucer's "Prologue" and "Knight's tale." 2d ed. 12°. '73. $1.75. .... *Ginn.*
— Introduction to the study of Anglo-Saxon. 12°. '75. $1.25 .... *Ginn.*

Carpenter, T: Scholar's spelling assistant. 12°. 20c. *Sadlier.*
— Speller. 18°. 25c. .... *Strong.*

Carpenter, W: D. Animal physiology. 12°. (Bohn.) $2.25 .... *Little, B. & Co.*
— *Same.* 12°. (Bohn.) $2.40 ..... *Scribner, W. & A.*
— *Same.* 12°. (Bohn.) $2.50 .... *Lippincott.*
— Mechanical philosophy, horology and astronomy, 12°. (Bohn.) $1.75 .... *Little, B. & Co.*
— *Same.* 12°. (Bohn.) $2. *Lippincott; Scribner, W. & A.*
— Microscope (The) and its revelations. 5th Lond. ed., rev. and enl. ill. fp. 8°. '75. $5.50.. *Lindsay.*
— *Same.* 5th ed., rev. and enl. pl. and ill. 12°. (Lond.) '75. $6 .... *Little, B. & Co.*
— On the use of alcoholic liquors in health and disease; with pref. by D. F. Condie. 12°. 60c. ..... *Lea.*
— Physiology of temperance and total abstinence. 12°. (Bohn.) $1; bds., 60c. ...... *Scribner, W. & A.*
— Principles of comparative physiology. ill. 8°. $5. *Lea.*
— Principles of human physiology. New Am. from 4th Lond. ed.; ed. with add. by F. G. Smith. ill. 8°. $5.50; leath., $6.50 .... *Lea.*
— *Same.* 8th ed., rev. and enl.; ed. by H. Power. ill. 8°. '76. $5.50 .... *Lindsay.*
— Principles of mental physiology. 12°. $3. *Appleton.*
— Unconscious action of the brain, and epidemic delusions. cr. 8°. '74. pap., 25c. .... *Estes.*
— Vegetable physiology and systematic botany. New ed., rev. by E. Lankester. ill. 12°. (Bohn.) $2.25. *Little, B. & Co.*
— *Same.* ill. 12°. (Bohn.) $2.40.. *Scribner, W. & A.*
— *Same.* ill. 12°. (Bohn.) $2.50 .... *Lippincott.*
— Zoology. New ed., rev. by W. S. Dallas. 2 v. ill. 12°. (Bohn.) ea., $2.25 .... *Little, B. & Co.*
— *Same.* 2 v. ill. 12°. (Bohn.) ea., $2.40. *Scribner, W. & A.*
— *Same.* 2 v. ill. 12°. (Bohn.) ea., $2.50.. *Lippincott.*

Carpenter, W: H. Regicide's (The) daughter: a tale of the two worlds. 18°. '51. 60c. ..... *Claxton.*
— *and* Arthur, T. S. (*ed.*) Cabinet histories of the states. New ed. 12 v. 16°. '68. $9.. *Claxton.*
Cont.: Virginia. — New York. — Massachusetts. — Georgia. — Connecticut. — Pennsylvania. — New Jersey. — Kentucky. — Ohio. — Tennessee. — Vermont. — Illinois.

Carpenter of Rouen. Jones, J. S. 15c. .... *French.*

Carpenter's house. *See* Books of blessing.

Carpentry and joinery. ill. 16°. $1.25. *Scribner, W. & A.*

Carr, B. Easy chant mass in D. 4°. pap., 30c... *Peters.*
— Easy mass in C minor. 4°. pap., 50c. ...... *Peters.*

Carr, Ez. S. The patrons of husbandry on the Pacific coast. 8°. '75. $3.75 .... *Bancroft.*

Carr, G. P. River of life, and other poems. 12°. '71. 75c. .... *Turnbull.*

Carraud, *Mme.* Zulma Touranger. Les goûters de la grandmère. *See* Ségur, *Comtesse* E. de, Les petites filles modèles.
— *Eng.* Afternoons with grandma; tr. by Mrs. M. Kinmont. ill. 16°. '73. $1.25.. *Cin. Meth. Bk. Conc.*
— Tresor de contes élémentaires. With vocab. 12°. 75c. .... *Schoenhof.*

Carré, Michel. Faust and Marguerite; tr. by T. W. Robertson: drama. 12°. pap., 15c. .... *De Witt.*
— *and* Barbier, J. Jeanette's wedding day; tr. from the Fr.: musical farce. 16°. pap., 15c... *French.*
— *and* Battu, L. Love by lantern light; tr. from the Fr.: operetta. 16°. pap., 15c. .... *French.*

Carrel, Armand. History of the counter-revolution, for the re-estab. of popery, under Charles II. and James II.; [also] History of reign of James II., by C. J. Fox; [also] Memoir of reign of James II., by Lord Lonsdale. por. 12°. (Bohn.) $1.25. *Little, B. & Co.*
— *Same.* por. 12°. (Bohn.) $1.40.. *Scribner, W. & A.*
— *Same.* por. 12°. (Bohn.) $1.50 ...... *Lippincott.*

Carreño, Juan de la C. *See* Ollendorff, H. G.

Carreño, Manuel Antonio. Manual de urbanidad y buenas maneras. 18°. $1.50 .... *Appleton.*
— *Same:* compendio, para las escuelas. 18°. 50c. *Appleton.*

Carriage painters' (The) companion. col. ill. sm. 4°. '71. 75c. .... *Masury.*

Carriage painters' manual. ill. 12°. $1 .... *Judd.*

Carrie, *Aunt* (*pseud.*) *See* Smith, *Mrs.* C. L.

Carrie, *Cousin.* *See* Cousin Carrie.

Carrie Allison. Davis, C. E. K. 50c. .... *Hoyt.*

Carrie and Susie. Cady, D. R. 45c. ..... *Cong. Pub.*

Carrie Hamilton. Denison, M. A. $1 .... *Am. Bapt.*

Carrie Harrington. Moos, H. M. 50c. .... *Bloch.*

Carrie Holmes. Logan, J. B. 50c... (?) *Cumberland.*

Carrie Prince. *See* Mudge, Z. A., Pure gold ser.; Rustic lib.

Carrie Trueman. Dunning, A. K. 45c. .... *Pres. Bd.*

Carrie Williams. *See* Sisters' lib.

Carrie Williams and her scholars. ('72.) New ed. 16°. '76. $1.25 .... *Hoyt.*
— *See also* Loving heart and helping hand lib.

Carrie's hard lesson. *See* Dunning, *Mrs.* A. K.

Carrie's peaches. *See* Hildeburn, *Mrs.* M. J.

Carrie's Sabbath. 18°. 35c. .... *Cong. Pub.*

Carrington, F. A. *See* England, Common law reports.

Carroll, A. Sketches and collections. 12°. $1.25. *Cin. Meth. Bk. Conc.*

Carroll, Alfr. L. Hygiene in schools and colleges. *See* Lincoln, D. F., Report on school hygiene.

Carroll, J. Halsted. Memorial of Gerard Hallock. 8°. '66. pap., 25c. .... *N. Y. Ref. Ch. Bd.*

Carroll, Lew. (*pseud.*) *See* Dodgson, C: Lutwidge.

Carroll, M. How Marjory helped. ill. 16°. $1.50. *Lee & S.*

Carroll Ashton. 18°. 50c.; 60c. .... *Am. Bapt.*

Carrollton debate. *See* Graves, J. R., *and* Ditzler, J.

Carruthers, Rob. Life of Alex. Pope; incl. many of his letters. ill. 12°. (Bohn.) $1.75. *Little, B. & Co.*
— *Same.* ill. 12°. (Bohn.) $2. *Lippincott; Scribner, W. & A.*
— *See also* Chambers, R.

Carry your parcel, sir? Onley, M. 75c. ...... *Nelson.*

Carrying things to extremes. Brock, C. 20c... *Dutton.*

Carryl, Jos. Seed thoughts: sel. from "Exposition of Job"; with introd. by Rev. J. E. Rockwell. 16°. '69. 75c. .... *Pres. Bd.*

Carry's confession. Robinson, F. W. 75c... *Harper.*

Carry's rose. *See* Cupples, *Mrs.* A. J.

Carson, Alex. Baptism: its mode and subjects. 8°. $1.75 .... *Am. Bapt.*
— *Same.* 8°. $2 .... *So. Bapt.*
Carson, E. T. Freemasonry 33 degrees; or, monitor of the ancient and accepted rite. 12°. '60. $1. *Pounsford.*
Carson, J. G. Secret societies: argument against fellowshiping Freemasons in the Christian church. 12°. pap., 10c. .... *E. A. Cook.*
Carson, Jos. History of the medical dept. of the Univ. of Penna.; with sketches of deceased professors, 8°. '69. $2 .... *Lindsay.*
Carson family. 18°. 28c.; 35c. .... *Am. Bapt.*
Carswell, E: John Swig: poem. 12°. 15c. *Nat. Temp.*
Carte de visite. Williams, M., *and* Burnand, F. C. 15c. *French.*
Cartee, Corn. S. Elements of physical and polit. geog. ill. 12°. hf. roan, $1.25 .... *Ware.*
— Questions adapted to text of the New Test. 2 pts. 16°. ea., 18c. .... *Un. S. S.*
— School atlas of physical geography. 8°. hf. roan, $2.25 .... *Ware.*
Carter, *Mrs.* —. ["Elsie Gorham."] Rainy day in the nursery. ill. 16°. 75c. .... *Lee & S.*
Carter, *Mrs.* Ann Augusta. Great rosy diamond (The). ill. 16°. 80c. .... *Lee & S.*
— Stories in prose and verse. 16°. '67. 50c. *H. H. Carter.*
Carter, H: (*ed.*) Rounds, canons and catches; by ancient and modern composers. 12°. 50c... *Ditson.*
Carter, Hor. *See* Indiana, Reports.
Carter, J. E. Baptists and the higher liberty. 18°. 25c.; pap., 10c. .... *So. Bapt.*
Carter, J: Pym. Elements of general hist. ill. 12°. '71. $1.50 .... *Univ. Pub.*
Carter, R. Brudenell. Practical treatise on diseases of the eye. ill. 8°. '75. $6 .... *Macmillan.*
— *Same;* ed., with test-types and add., by J. Green. ill. 8°. '76. $3.75 .... *Lea.*
Carter, T. J. P. King's College chapel [Cambridge, Eng.]: notes on its hist. and present condition. photos. 8°. '67. $2.25 .... *Macmillan.*
Carter, T: All for Christ. 16°. '75. 75c. *Meth. Bk. Conc.*
— French mission life. 16°. '56. 60c... *Meth. Bk. Conc.*
— History of the great reformation. 12°. '60. $1.50. *Meth. Bk. Conc.*
Carter, T: T. A book of private prayer. 32°. '74. 50c. .... *Pott.*
— Devout Christian's (The) help to meditation on the life of Christ. 2 v. 12°. '70. $3 .... *Pott.*
— Doctrine of confession in the Church of Eng. 8°. '69. $2 .... *Pott.*
— Doctrine of the priesthood in the Church of Eng. 8°. '63. $1.50 .... *Pott.*
— Footsteps of the Holy Child: lessons on the incarnation. 16°. '67. $1.75 .... *Pott.*
— Path of holiness: a first book of prayers for children. 18°. '73. 75c. .... *Pott.*
— Repentance: manual of prayer and instruction. 18°. '75. 75c. .... *Pott.*
— Spiritual instructions on the eucharist. 8°. '75. $1.75 .... *Pott.*
— Star (The) of childhood: first book of prayers and instruction for children. ill. 16°. $1.. *Lippincott.*
— *Same.* 16°. '72. $1.25 .... *Pott.*
— Treasury of devotion: manual of prayer for general use. 18°. '70. 90c.; mor., $2.50 ...... *Dutton.*
— *Same.* 18°. '74. 90c. .... *Pott.*
— Way (The) of life: book of prayers and instructions for the young. 18°. '71. 75c. .... *Pott.*
— (*tr.*) Meditations on the hidden life of our Lord; from the Fr. v. 1–3. 16°. '75 .... *Pott.*
Cont.: The hidden life, $1.50. — Public life of our Lord, 2 v., ea., $2.25.
Carter, W: Port wine *vs.* jealousy: dramatic sketch. 12°. pap., 15c. .... *De Witt.*

Carter Quarterman. Baker, W. M. 75c..... *Harper.*
Carter's cheap Sunday school library. 2 nos. ea., 50 v. 18°. ea. set, *net*, $20 .... *Carter.*
Cartoon portraits. Waddy, F. $7.50..... *Routledge.*
Cartouche. Waldron, W. R. 15c. .... *French.*
Cartwright, P: Autobiography; ed. by W. P. Strickland. 12°. '56. $1.75 .... *Meth. Bk. Conc.*
— Fifty years a presiding elder; ed. by Rev. W. S. Hooper. 12°. $1.50 .... *Cin. Meth. Bk. Conc.*
Carulli, Ferdinando. Complete method for the guitar. f°. bds., $4; abridg., $2.25 .... *Ditson.*
Carved cartoon (The). Clare, A. $1.50 .... *Pott.*
Carvosso, W: Life. 18°. '37. 75c... *Meth. Bk. Conc.*
— Memoir: autobiog., ed. by his son. ('55.) 8th ed. 18°. '75. 80c. .... *So. Meth.*
Cary, Alice. Ballads, lyrics and hymns. ill. cr. 8°. '65. $2.25–$6 .... *Hurd & H.*
— Clovernook children. 16°. $1.50 .... **Osgood.*
— Lover's (A) diary. ill. 16°. $3 .... **Osgood.*
— Pictures of country life. cr. 8°. '59. $2.. *Hurd & H.*
— Snow-berries. ill. 16°. $1.50 .... **Osgood.*
— *See also* Cary, P. *and* A.; — Rougegorge.
— *and* Phœbe. Ballads for little folk; ed. by M. Clemmer. ill. sm. 4°. '73. $1.50 .... *Hurd & H.*
— — Last poems; ed. by M. Clemmer. cr. 8°. '73. $2; $2.50; hf. cf., $4; mor., $6 .... *Hurd & H.*
— — Writings: poems, with Mrs. Ames' [i.e., Clemmer's] memorial. 4 v. cr. 8°. $7.75; hf. cf., $16; cf., $24 .... *Hurd & H.*
— — *See also* Clemmer, Ma.
Cary, H. F. (*tr.*) *See* Dante Alighieri, Divine comedy.
Cary, M. R. Isabel's difficulties; or, light on the daily path. ill. 16°. '71. $1.50 .... *Dutton.*
Cary, Phœbe. Poems of faith, hope and love. por. cr. 8°. '67. $1.50–$6 .... *Hurd & H.*
— *See also* Cary, A. *and* P.
— *and* Alice. Josephine gallery. por. 4°. $5; mor., $10 .... *Lippincott.*
Carynthia. Winstanley, E. 30c. .... *Am. News.*
Casa (La) en el desierto. *See* Reid, Mayne.
Casaubon, I: Anglican Catholicity vindicated against Roman innovations; with introd., prep. by W. R. Whittingham and H. Harrison; [also] Confession of faith of James I. sq. 12°. '75. $1 25; pap., 75c. .... *Turnbull*
Casco Bay: drama. 16°. pap., 15c. .... *French.*
Case, C. C. *See* McGranahan, J., *and* Case, C. C.
Casella. *See* Finley, M. F.
Casey, Jos. *See* Pennsylvania, Supreme Court reports.
Casey, Silas. United States infantry tactics; for instruction, etc., of the soldier, company, etc. 3 v. pl. 24°. '65. $2.50 .... *Van Nostrand.*
Cash boy's trust. Payne, A. M. $1 .... *Carter.*
Casimir Maremma. Helps, *Sir* A. $2..... *Roberts.*
Cask of gold. 8°. pap., 25c. .... *De Witt.*
Casket (The). 6 v. ill. 32°. 50c. .... *Nelson.*
Casket (The). *See* Bright eye ser.
Casket (The): selections. 16°. 50c...(?) *Cumberland.*
Casket hymns. Hull, A. 20c. .... *Ditson.*
Casket library. *See* Mudge, Z. A.
Casket of gems. *See* Dunning, *Mrs.* A. K.
Casket of gems. *See* May, A., Sunny nook stories.
Casket of gems. [Poet. sel.] 16°. $1.50..... *Lee & S.*
Casket of jewels. 18°. 35c.; 45c. .... *Am. Bapt.*
Casket of juveniles. 6 v. sq. 32°. $2.70..... *Mason.*
Cont.: Emily's and Clara's trip to Niagara Falls. — Leonard Barton. — Book of animals. — Book of birds. — Burning village. — May-day ramble.
Casket of pearls. *See* Bijou Bible text-books.
Casket of S.-school melodies. Hull, A. 45c. *Ditson.*

Caspari, E. Homœopathic domestic physician; tr. from the Germ., ed. by F. Hartmann; [also] Treatise on anatomy and physiology, by W. P. Esrey; with add. and pref. by C. Hering. ill. 8°. $1 .... *Boericke.*

Caspari, K: H: Erzählungen. 3 v. 16°. ea., 25c. *Morwitz.*

Cont.: Geschichten a. d. Spessart. — Der Schulmeister u. s. Sohn. — Strassburg auf der Schanz.

— Frank's friend; or, the rampart of Strasburg; tr. from the Germ. 18°. 35c........(?)*Luth. Pub.*

— Geistliches u. Weltliches zu e. volksthüml. Auslegg. d. Kleinen Katechismus Lutheri. 8°. hf. bd., $1.50 .... *Volkening.*

— The schoolmaster and his son; tr. from the Germ. ill. 16°. $1....................(?)*Luth. Pub.*

— *See also* Luther, M., Kleiner Katechismus.

Caspar's adventures. ill. sq. 16°. 50c....*Perkinpine.*

Caspers, A. The footsteps of Christ; tr. by A. E. Rodham. 12°. $3.75............*Scribner, W. & A.*

Cassagnac, Adolphe Granier de. History of the working and burgher classes; tr. by B. E. Green. demi 8°. '71. $2.50.................*Claxton.*

Cassard, Andres. Cincuenta años. 8°. '74. $3. *G. R. Lockwood.*

— Manual de masonería. 2 v. 8°. '66. $7. *G. R. Lockwood.*

— Obras masónicas. 10 v. 8°..............*Appleton.*

Cont.: Manual de la masonería, 2 v., $7. — Catecismos de los tres grados simbólicos, 3 pts., per doz., assorted, $7.50; pap., $6. — El espejo masónico, 4 v., $15. — Manual de la estrella del oriente para los vice-patronos, $2.50; sin diploma, $1.50.

Note. v. 4 of "El espejo masónico," sep., $5.

Cassel, P. Judges and Ruth. *See* Lange, J. P., Commentary.

Cassell's Bible dict. 600 ill. imp. 8°. '69. $10..*Cassell.*

Cassell's biographical dict.; ed. by T. T. Shore. por. imp. 4°. '70. $12.......................*Cassell.*

Cassell's book of birds. *See* Brehm, A. E.

Cassell's children's treasuries. 7 v. roy. 16°. ea., 50c. *Cassell.*

Cont.: The children's joy. — Pretty pictures and pleasant stories. — Our picture book. — Tales for the little ones. — My Sunday book of pictures. — Sunday garland of pictures and stories. — Sunday readings for little folks.

Cassell's draw. copies. 5 ser. obl. 8°. ea., $3.50. *Cassell.*

Note. Each ser. can also be had in 12 pts., ea., 25c.

Cassell's free-hand draw. book. obl. 8°. $1.50..*Cassell.*

Cassell's graduated copy books. 12 bks. 4°. ea., 10c. *Cassell.*

Cassell's illustrated history of the war between France and Germany. 2 v. ill. and plans. cr. 4°. $10; hf. cf., $18.........................*Cassell.*

Cassell's "new code" readers. 9 v. fp. 8°....*Cassell.*

Cont.: Boy's, *or* Girl's elementary, ea., 15c.; 20c. — Boy's, *or* Girl's first, ea., 20c.; 25c. — Boy's and girl's second, 25c.; 35c. — Boy's and girl's third, 30c.; 40c. — Boy's and girl's fourth, 40c.; 45c. — Boy's and girl's fifth, 45c.; 50c. — Boy's and girl's sixth, 50c.; 60c.

Cassell's new popular educator: encyclopædia of elementary, advanced and technical education. 6 v. cr. 4°. ea., $2.50; — in 3 v. hf. cf., $25..*Cassell.*

Cassell's popular natural hist. 4 v. ill. and col. pl. cr. 4°. $18; — in 2 v. hf. mor., $25.....*Cassell.*

Cassell's popular recreator: guide to in-door and outdoor amusement. 2 v. ill. cr. 4°. ea., $3. — 2 v. in 1. $5..............................*Cassell.*

Cassell's practical geometrical, mechanical and ornamental drawing book. obl. 8°. $1.25...*Cassell.*

Cassell's technical educator: an encyclopædia of technical education. 4 v. col. designs and ill. cr. 4°. ea., $3; — in 2 v. hf. cf., $18...........*Cassell.*

Cassell's technical manuals; with drawings and diagrams. 16 v. post 8°. ea., $1–$2......*Cassell.*

Cont.: Ball's Applied mechanics. — Davidson's Drawing for bricklayers. — Davidson's Building construction. — Davidson's Drawing for cabinet-makers. — Davidson's Drawing for carpenters and joiners. — Church's Colour. — Davidson's Gothic

Cassell's technical manuals, *continued.*

stone work. — Davidson's Linear drawing. — Davidson's Linear drawing and projection. — Davidson's Drawing for machinists and engineers. — Davidson's Drawing for metal-plate workers. — Davidson's Model drawing. — Davidson's Orthographical and isometrical projection. — Davidson's Practical perspective. — Davidson's Drawing for stonemasons. — Ryan's Systematic drawing and shading.

Cassels, S: J. Christ and antichrist: Jesus of Nazareth proved to be the Messiah, and the papacy proved to be the antichrist predicted in the Scriptures. 12°. 90c..........................*Pres. Bd.*

Casserly, P. S. Latin prosody. 16°. hf. roan, 63c. *Lippincott.*

Cassidy, J. *See* Keach, O. W., Burditt, B. A., *and* Cassidy, J.

Cassilda. *See* Catholic premium-book lib.

Cassin, J: Mammalogy and ornithology of the U. S. exploring expedition under Com. Wilkes. 4°, with f° atlas of 50 col. eng. $50....*Lippincott.*

— *See also* Gilliss, J. M.; — Wilkes, C.

Cassy. Smith, H. $1........................*Dodd.*

Cast adrift. Arthur, T. S. $2; $2.50; $4. *J. M. Stoddart.*

Cast away in the cold. Hayes, I. I. $1.50..*Osgood.*

Cast — king of Granada. Eotis. 15c........*French.*

Cast out. Eldridge, A. $1.35..............*Pres. Bd.*

Cast up by the sea. *See* Baker, *Sir* S. W.

Cast upon the world. Newton, C. E. 15c....*De Witt.*

Castaways (The). Bowman, A. $1.25..*Routledge.*

Castaways (The). Reid, M. $1.25........*Sheldon.*

Caste. Jolly, E. 50c......................*Harper.*

Caste. Robertson, T. W. 15c..............*De Witt.*

Castelar, Emilio. Life of Lord Byron, and other sketches; tr. by Mrs. A. Arnold. 12°. $1.50. *Harper.*

— Old Rome and new Italy; tr. by Mrs. A. Arnold. 12°. $1.75.............................*Harper.*

Castilian days. Hay, J. $2; $4; $5......*Osgood.*

Castilian martyrs: narrative of two Spanish maidens and their brother. ill. 18°. '66. 45c. *N. Y. Ref. Ch. Bd.; Pres. Com.*

Casting down imaginations. Thompson, A. R. 10c. *N. Y. Ref. Ch. Bd.*

Castle, Jos. Triumph of truth. *See* Caughey, Ja.

Castle and the cottage. Perrin, *Mrs.* —. 50c. *Routledge.*

Castle Avon. Marsh-Caldwell, A. 50c......*Harper.*

Castle builders. Yonge, C. M. $1.........*Appleton.*

Castle Daly. Keary, A. $1.50; $1.25; $1...*Porter.*

Castle Dangerous. *See* Scott, *Sir* W.

Castle Nowhere. Woolson, C. F. $2.......*Osgood.*

Castle of Andalusia. O'Keefe, J. 15c......*French.*

Castle of Ehrenstein. *See* James, G. P. R.

Castle of Otranto. *See* Walpole, H.

Castle of Rousillon; tr. by Mrs. J. Sadlier. 16°. 75c.; $1.25.....................................*Sadlier.*

Castle of Sorrento: opera. 16°. pap., 15c...*French.*

Castle on the rock. 18°. 40c................*Dutton.*

Castle Rackrent. *See* Edgeworth, Maria.

Castle Richmond. *See* Trollope, A.

Castle spectre. Lewis, M. G. 15c..........*French.*

Castle Wafer. Wood, E. P. $1.25; 75c...*Dick & F.*

Castlemon, Harry (*pseud.*) *See* Fosdick, C. A.

Castle's heir. Wood, E. P. $1.75; $1.50..*Peterson.*

Castles in the air. Coffin, R. B. $1.50...*Hurd & H.*

Castleton, D. R. (*pseud.*) Salem: tale of the 17th century. 12°. $1.25.........................*Harper.*

Caswell, A. Meteorological observations, Providence, R. I. 4°. '60. pap., $2............*Smith. Inst.*

Cat and the rat. *See* Prairie books.

Catacombs of Rome. 16°. $1...........*Am. S. S.*

Catafego, Jos. Arabic dictionary. 8°. (Lond.) $20. *Wiley.*

Catalogue of books for a pastor's library. ('55.) New ed. '72. pap., 10c. . . . . *Draper.*

Cataract of the Ganges. Moncrieff, W. T. 15c. *French.*

Catastrophe of the hall: silh. ill. by P. Konewka. 4°. '71. bds., 50c. . . . . *Porter.*

Catch him who can. Hook, T. 15c. . . . . *French.*

Catch a weazel. Morton, J. M. 15c. . . . . *French.*

Catching an heiress. Selby, C. 15c. . . . . *French.*

Catching a mermaid. Coyne, J. S. 15c. . . . . *French.*

Cate, *Miss* E. J. A year with the Franklins; or, to suffer and be strong. 18°. 75c. . . . . *Harper.*

Catechetical assistant [on the "Shorter catechism"]. 32°. 15c. . . . . *Pres. Bd.*

Catechism for beginners. 2 nos. 18°. 1, pap., 4c.; 2, bds., 20c. . . . . *Whittaker.*

Catechism of the apostleship of prayer. 18°. '74. 40c.; pap., 25c. . . . . *Murphy.*

Catechism of the [Catholic] diocese of Boston; with short prayers at mass. 32°. 10c. . . . . *Noonan.*

Catechism of the Christian doctrine. [Catholic.] 32°. 10c. . . . . *Noonan.*

— *Same.* 18c. . . . . *Dooley.*

— *Same.* 18°. 20c.; pap., 10c. . . . . *Hoffmann.*

— *Same;* arranged for Catholic schools by a priest. ('70.) 5th ed., rev. and enl. 18°. '76. 20c.; pap., 10c. *Hoffmann.*

— *Span.* Catecismo de la doctrina Cristiano. 18°. 15c. . . . . *Strong.*

Catechism of Christian doctrine for instruction of youth in the Moravian Church. 16°. '75. pap., 15c. . . . . *Clauder.*

Catechism of the devotion of the sacred heart of Jesus. 18°. '74. 40c.; pap., 25c. . . . . *Murphy.*

Catechism of the distinctive doctrines of the evangelical Protestant and the Roman Catholic churches. 16°. bds., 10c. . . . . *Ludwig.*

Catechism of ecclesiastical hist.; by a friend of youth. sq. 16°. '67. 30c. . . . . *Murphy.*

Catechism of geography; for schools. 16°. hf. bd., 25c. . . . . *Sadlier.*

Catechism (The) of perseverance. Gaume, J. J. 75c. . . . . *Noonan.*

Catechism of sacred hist., abridg. for schools; tr. from the French. 16°. '59. 20c. . . . . *Kelly, P. & Co.*

Catechism of Scripture hist.; comp. by the Sisters of Mercy in Ireland; rev. by M. J. Kerney. 18°. '54. 75c. . . . . *Murphy.*

Catechism on baptism: answers to 145 pædobaptist questions. 12°. pap., 10c. . . . . *Am. Bapt.*

Catechism on the Collects. 18°. 20c. . . . . *Dutton.*

Catecismo rapaldi (El). 24°. 12c. . . . . *Strong.*

Catena dominica. Alexander, J. H. $1.75 . . *Randolph.*

Cates, J. M. D. Marriage and married life. 12°. $1.25. *So. Bapt.*

Cates, W. L. R. Dictionary of general biog.; with index and supplement. 8°. $8; hf. mor., $12. *Scribner, W. & A.*

— *See also* Woodward, B. B., *and* Cates, W. L. R.

Catharine *of Sienna, St.* Life. 12°. $1.50 . . *Sadlier.*

Catharine Fieschi Adorno, *St.* Life and doctrine; tr. from the Ital. 2d ed. 12°. '74. $2 . . *Cath. Pub.*

— *See also* Lives of the saints.

Catharine Gray. 18°. 35c. . . . . *Am. S. S.*

Catharine Volmar. Reynolds, G. W. M. 50c. *De Witt.*

Cathcart, G. R. Literary reader. 12°. '74. $1.60. *Ivison.*

— Youth's speaker. ill. 12°. '71. 75c. . . . . *Ivison.*

Cathedral (The). Lowell, J. R. $1.25 . . . . *Osgood.*

Catherine. *See* Thackeray, W. M.

Catherine Blum. Dumas, A. 50c. . . . . *Routledge.*

Catherine Hamilton: tale for little girls. 18°. 60c. *Cath. Pub.*

Catherine Howard. Dumas, A. 15c. . . . . *French.*

Catherine Howard. Suter, W. D. 15c. . . . . *De Witt.*

Catherine Lewis. 18°. 60c. . . . . *Dutton.*

Catherine's lovers. *See* Erckmann, E., *and* Chatrian, A.

Catholic anecdotes; tr. from the Fr. by Mrs. J. Sadlier. 3 v. 12°. v. 1, 75c.; v. 2, 3, ea., $1; — 3 v. in 1. $2.50; $3.50 . . . . *Sadlier.*

Catholic anecdotes, parables and tales; by Père Bonaventure and others. 18°. $1 . . . . *O'Shea.*

Catholic bride (The); tr. by C. C. Pise. sq. 16°. '48. 60c.; 80c. . . . . *Murphy.*

Catholic choir. Peters, W. C. 2 v. ea., $3.50 . . *Peters.*

Catholic choralist. 32°. 30c.; pap., 15c. . . . . *Strong.*

Catholic Christian instructed. 12°. 50c. . . *Cath. Pub.*

— *Same.* 16°. 40c.; pap., 25c. . . . . *Sadlier.*

Catholic Church. Councils. *See* Baltimore.

— Epistles and Gospels for the Sundays and principal festivals. 32°. 30c. . . . . *Benziger; Noonan.*

Note. These are also contained in many Catholic prayer books, which will be found in the general alphabet under names of compilers or titles.

— Exposition and benediction of the blessed sacrament. Ordo in oratione quadraginta horarum. New ed., rev. 8°. '75. 50c. . . . . *Murphy.*

— Form of consecration of a bishop according to the Lat. rite; with explan. by F. P. Kenrick. 18°. '68. 25c. . . . . *Murphy.*

— Form of ordination of a priest; comp. by a priest of the mission. 24°. '74. 25c. . . . . *Fox.*

— General catechism; prepared by order of National Council. 18°. 25c. . . . . *Sadlier.*

— Mass book; cont. Office for holy mass, with the Epistles and Gospels for all the Sundays and holy days. 18°. 50c.–$5 . . . . *Sadlier.*

Note. Masses and vespers are also included in many Catholic prayer books, for which see (in general alphabet) names of compilers and titles, and also names of musical composers.

— Missal (The) for the laity: the Roman missal tr. into Eng. 18°. $1.50–$35 . . . . *Cummiskey.*

— Office of the dead, according to the Roman ritual and missal; with Gregorian chants in modern notation. 12°. $1.25 . . . . *Cummiskey.*

— Official documents connected with the definition of the dogma of the immaculate conception of the Virgin Mary. [In Lat. and Eng.] 8°. '55. $2.50. *Murphy.*

— Ordo divini officii recitandi missæque celebrandæ a clero provinciarum S. Ludovidi Milwauchiensis et S. Fidei, juxta rubricas breviarii ac missalis Romani, pro 1876. 24°. 75c. . . . . *Herder.*

— Rituale Romanum; ordered by 10th Provincial Council of Baltimore. demy 8°. '73. $3.50–$6. *Murphy.*

— — Excerpta ex Rituali Romano pro administratione sacramentorum. 48°. '74. 25c. . . . . *Fox.*

— — *Same.* ('60.) 5th ed. 32°. '76. $1; mor., $2. *Kelly, P. & Co.*

— Rituale Romanum, Pauli v. jussu ed., et a Benedicto xiv. auct. et castig.; cum coll. benedictionum et instructionum; cum supplem. rit. Rom. pro prov. Am. Septentrion. Fœd. 8°. '72. roan, $3 . . . . *Pustet.*

— Ritus et preces ad missam celebrandum in usum præcique corum qui sacris initiantur. 32°. '57. 50c.–$2 . . . . *Murphy.*

— *See also* Ceremonial.

Catholic Crusoe (The). *See* Anderdon, W. H.

Catholic guide (The) in public and private devotions; with Epistles and Gospels for the Sundays and holidays of the year. 24°. $1.50–$8 . . *Benziger.*

Catholic harmonist. Peters, W. C. $1.50 . . . . *Peters.*

Catholic harp. Peters, W. C. $1.25 . . . . *Peters.*

Catholic hymn book. 32°. 30c.; 15c........*Strong.*

Catholic hymns and canticles; with music by Rev. A. Young. 12°. $1....................*Cath. Pub.*

— *See also* Hymn books.

Catholic legends. 12°. $1; $1.50..........*Sadlier.*

Catholic manual for children. [Prayer book.] 64°. '62. 20c.-$1..........................*Murphy.*

— *See also* Child's Catholic manual.

Catholic offering (The). Walsh, W. $1.50..*Strong.*

Catholic prayer book (The): manual of devotions for the faithful. 18°. $1-$30...........*Benziger.*

Catholic premium-book library. 1st ser. 10 v. 8°. ea., 50c.; per set, hf. mor., $8.50....*Benziger.*

Cont.: Bertha. — Captain Rougemont. — Cassilda. — Episodes of the Commune. — The adventures of a casket. — The better part. — The fisherman's daughter. — The great-grandmother's secret. — The priest of Auvrigny. — The village steeple.

— *Same.* 2d ser. 5 v. 12°. ea., 35c.......*Benziger.*

Cont.: Life of our Lord. — Life of the Virgin. — Life of St. Patrick. — The holy isle. — Diary of a confessor.

— *Same.* 3d ser. 6 v. 18°. ea., 15c.......*Benziger.*

Cont.: Adolphus. — A broken chain. — Nicholas. — Nina and Pippo. — The baker's boy. — The last days of the papal army.

Catholic priest (The). Müller, M. 50c.....*Kreuzer.*

Catholic pulpit (The): sermons. 8°. '51. $3.50; $4. *Murphy.*

Catholic reform. Hyacinthe, *Father.* $2..*Macmillan.*

Catholic vocalist. Rocholl, H. T. 5 nos. ea., 50c. *Ditson.*

Catholic youth's hymn book. *See* Christian Brothers.

Catholic youth's lib. 4 ser. 18°. ser. 1, 2, ea., 12 v., $6; $9; ser. 3, 4, ea., 6 v., $3; $4.50..*Sadlier.*

Catholicity and pantheism. Concilio, J. de. $2. *Sadlier.*

Catholic's pocket companion. [Prayer book.] 48°. 25c.-60c............................ *T. Kelly.*

— *Same.* 48°. 25c.-85c.........................*Strong.*

Catholic's (The) pocket manual; or, guide to salvation. 48°. 25c.-$1.25.................*Sadlier.*

Catholic's (The) pocket manual of devotion. 48°. 25c.-75c..........................*Benziger.*

Catholic's vade mecum: pocket manual of prayers for daily use. 24°. 65c.-$25. *Cummiskey; Kelly, P. & Co.*

— *See also* Vade mecum.

Catlett, Ja. M. *See* Warder, T. B., *and* Catlett, J. M.

Catlin, G: The breath of life; or, mal-respiration and its effects upon the enjoyments and life of man. ill. 8°. 75c.............................. *Wiley.*

Catlin, Jac. Compendium of the system of divine truth. 12°. $1.25.................*Cong. Pub.*

Cato. *See* Addison, Jos.

Caton, J: Dean. Last of the Illinois, and a sketch of the Pottawatomies; [also] Origin of the prairies. 12°. '76. pap., 25c.....................*Fergus.*

— Summer (A) in Norway, with notes on [its] industries, etc. ill. 8°. '75. $2.50...........*Jansen.*

Cat's tea party. [Toy-book.] ill. 4°. $1; 50c. *Routledge.*

Catskill fairies (The). Johnson, V. W. $3..*Harper.*

Catskill Mountain guide; with maps. ill. 8°. '76. pap., 25c.............................. *Van Loan.*

Catspaw. Jerrold, D. 15c. ....*French.*

Cattermole, G. (*ill.*) Evenings at Haddon Hall. *See* Calabrella, *Baroness* de.

Catullus, Quintus (*or* Caius) Valerius, *and* Tibullus, A. Poems; [also] Vigil of Venus; lit. tr. by W. K. Kelly, with metrical versions of Lamb, Grainger and others. 12°. (Bohn.) $1.75..*Little, B. & Co.*

— — *Same.* 12°. (Bohn.) $2. *Lippincott; Scribner, W. & A.*

Caughey, Ja. Arrows from my quiver. 8°. $2..*Palmer.*

— Earnest Christianity. 8°. $1.50............*Palmer.*

— Glimpses of life in soul-saving. 8°. $2....*Palmer.*

— Light in the dark. 8°. $1.50..............*Palmer.*

— Revival miscellanies. 8°. $1.50............*Palmer.*

Caughey, Ja., *continued.*

— Showers of blessings. 8°. $1.50...........*Palmer.*

— Triumph of truth, and continental letters and sketches; with introd. by Jos. Castle. ('57.) 4th ed. 12°. '58. $1.75..........................*Perkinpine.*

Caught by the cuff. Hay, F. 15c...*De Witt; French.*

Caught by the ears. Selby, C. 15c..........*French.*

Caught in her own trap. *See* Bright gems for boys and girls; — Little girls' lib.

Caught in his own toils: musical farce. 16°. pap., 15c. *Happy.*

Caught in his own trap: farce. 16°. pap., 15c. *French.*

Caught in a line. Bolton, C. 15c............*French.*

Caulfield, J. *See* Wilson, H., *and* Caulfield, J.

Caulkins, *Miss* Fes. M. Bible studies. 6 pts. ill. 18°. '60. $3................................*Am. Tr.*

— Children of the Bible. 32°. 25c...*U. P. Bd. of Pub.*

— *Same.* ill. 18°. '42. 25c.................*Am. Tr.*

— Child's hymn book. ill. 32°. '47. 25c......*Am. Tr.*

— Eve and her daughters. ill. sq. 18°. '61. 30c. *Am. Tr.*

— Tract primer. ill. 18°. '48. 35c.; pap., 20c.; bds., 25c. *Am. Tr.*

— *French.* Premier livre pour les enfants. ill. 18°. '52. 35c..................................*Am. Tr.*

— *German.* Erstes Lesebuch für Kinder. ill. 18°. '52. 35c.......................................*Am. Tr.*

— *Portuguese.* Cartilha com estampas. ill. 18°. '53. 30c. ....*Am. Tr.*

— *Spanish.* Cartilla para los niños. ill. 18°. '52. 35c. *Am. Tr.*

Caunter, Hobart. India. *See* Romance of hist.

— New Test. pictures. ill. 18°. 75c. *Scribner, W. & A.*

— Old Test. pictures. ill. 18°. 75c. *Scribner, W. & A.*

Cause and cure of panics. Skinner, B. 15c. *Mendum.*

Causeries avec les enfants. Sauveur, L. $1.25..*Holt.*

Causeries avec mes élèves. Sauveur, L. $1.50..*Holt.*

Causes and cure of skepticism. 32°. 25c...*Pres. Bd.*

Causes célèbres. 5 v. 8°. '74. $17.50; shp., $22.50. *Cockcroft.*

Cont.: v. 1-3, Trial of Queen Caroline. — v. 4, 5, Trial of Aaron Burr.

Causey building. *See* Abbott, J., Rollo story books.

Cautions for doubters. *See* Titcomb, J. H.

Cauwet, Pierre. Poésies. 8°. '67. pap., $2..*Payot.*

Cavalcaselle, G. B. *See* Crowe, J. A., *and* Cavalcaselle, G. B.

Cavalier. James, G. P. R. $1.75; $1.50..*Peterson.*

Cavalier: drama. 16°. pap., 15c.............*French.*

Cavalier and his lady. Newcastle, *Duke and Duchess of.* $1.25...........................*Macmillan.*

Cavaliers and Roundheads. Edgar, J. G. $1.75. *Scribner, W. & A.*

Cavaliers of fortune. *See* Grant, Ja.

Cavé, *Mme.* E. Methode Cavé, pour apprendre à dessiner juste de mémoire, d'après les principes d'Albert Dürer et de Leonardo da Vinci. 8 ser. f°. ea., pap., $2.25.....................*Putnam.*

— *Eng.* Cavé method of learning to draw from memory. 12°. '68. $1......................*Putnam.*

— Method of teaching colors. 12°. '68. $1..*Putnam.*

Cave, Ht. Stories of Christ the Lord. sq. 12°. '68. 90c...........................*Meth. Bk. Conc.*

Cave-hunting. Dawkins, W. B. $7.....*Macmillan.*

Cave in the hills; or, Cæcilius Viriathus. 18°. 40c.; 45c. ....*Dutton.*

Cave of Machpelah. Challen, J. $1.50.....*Challen.*

Cavendish (*pseud.*) *See* Jones, H:

Cavendish, Clara. Woman of the world: drama. 16°. pap., 15c...............................*French.*

Cavendish, Marg. *See* Newcastle, *Duchess of.*

Cavendish, T: *See* Drake, *Sir* F., Cavendish, T., *and* Dampier, W.

Cavendish, W: *See* Newcastle, *Duke of.*

Caverly, A. M. History of Pittsford, Vermont. 8°. '72. $3 ... *Tuttle.*

Caverly, Rob. B. Heroism of Hannah Duston, together with the Indian wars of New Eng. ill. 12°. * $1.50; hf. mor., $2 ... *Russell.*

Caverly family. *See* H., H. H.

Cavis, C. H. V. Eastman's map of the mountain and lake region of New Hampshire. (Pocket ed.) 18°. 40c. ... *Eastman.*

Cawdray, Rob. Treasury of similes. *See* Spencer, J., Things new and old.

Caxton, Laura (*pseud.*) *See* Comins, Lizzie B.

Caxtoniana. *See* Bulwer-Lytton, *Sir* E. G. E. L.

Caxtons (The). *See* Bulwer-Lytton, *Sir* E. G. E. L.

Cazeaux, P. Theoretical and practical treatise on midwifery, incl. diseases of pregnancy and parturition; tr. by S. Tarnier. ill. roy. 8°. '74. $6.50; leath., $7.50 ... *Lindsay.*

Cazelles, E. Outline of the evolution philosophy; tr. by O. B. Frothingham; with app. by E. L. Youmans. 12°. $1 ... *Appleton.*

Cazenave, P. L. Alphée, *and* Schedel, H. E. Manual of diseases of the skin; tr. with notes and add. by T. H. Burgess. 2d Am. ed., with notes by H. D. Bulkley. 8°. $2 ... *W. Wood.*

Cazin, Achille. Phenomena and laws of heat; tr. and ed. by E. Rich. ill. 12°. '74. $1.25 ... *Scribner.*

Cecil, *Aunt.* *See* Aunt Cecil.

Cecil, E. Life of Lafayette; for young persons. ill. 16°. $1.25 ... *O'Shea.*

— Life of Washington; for young persons. ill. 16°. $1.25 ... *O'Shea.*

Cecil, R: A friendly visit to the house of mourning. 32°. 25c. ... *Pres. Bd.*

— Remains. *See* Pratt, J.

— Truth of Scripture. 32°. '46. 15c. ... *Am. Tr.*

— *and* Flavel, *Rev.* J: Gift for mourners. ill. 32°. '34. 25c. ... *Am. Tr.*

Cecil, W: *See* Burghley, *Lord.*

Cecil Castlemon's gage. La Rame, L. de. $1.50. *Claxton; Lippincott.*

Cecil Dreeme. Winthrop, T. $1.25 ... *Holt.*

Cecile Ray. Blake, *Mrs.* —. $1.25 ... *Routledge.*

Cecilia, *St.* Life. *See* Mary *of Egypt, St.*

Cecilia Howard. Arthur, T. S. 50c. ... *Peterson.*

Cecilian glee book. White, E. L., *and* Johnson, A. N. $1.35 ... *Gordon.*

Cecil's autumn adventures; by author of "Cecil's summer at Elm Terrace." 16°. 80c. ... *Am. S. S.*

Cecil's books of natural hist. Peabody, S. H. 3 v. $3.75 ... *Claxton.*

Cecil's summer at Elm Terrace. ill. 18°. 55c. *Am. S. S.*

Cecil's tryst. Payn, J. 50c. ... *Harper.*

Cedar brook series. *See* M., *Mrs.* A. S.

Cedar chest. Almar, G. 15c. ... *French.*

Cedar Christian. Cuyler, T. L. 90c. ... *Carter.*

Celebrated children of all ages and nations. Masson, M. $1.25 ... *Routledge.*

Celebration (The) at Westfield, Mass., on the 200th anniversary of [its] incorporation, Oct. 6, 1869; with hist. address of W. G. Bates, and other speeches and poems, and app. [of] hist. documents. 8°. (Westfield.) '70. $1.25 .. (?) *Morris.*

Celebration of the centennial anniversary of the evacuation of Boston, March 17th, 1776; [with] Chronicle of the siege of Boston, by G. E. Ellis. ill. and maps. 8°. '76. $3 ... *Williams.*

Celebration of the 200th anniversary of the settlement of Hadley, Mass., June 8, 1859; with hist. address by Rev. F. D. Huntington, poem, by E. C. Porter, etc. 8°. (Northampton.) '59. $1.50; pap., 75c. ... (?) *Morris.*

Celebrities of the past and present. Maceuen, M. $1.50 ... *Porter.*

Celesta stories. *See* Berry, *Mrs.* M. E.

Celestial city. Burns, J. D. 50c. ... *Bost. Am. Tr.*

Celestial dawn. Evans, W. F. 75c. ... *H. H. Carter.*

Celestial scenery. Dick, T. 75c. ... *Harper.*

Celestine Darscott. *See* History of.

Celia; or, the force of example. 18°. 40c. ... *Am. S. S.*

Celio. Foster, G. G. 50c. ... *De Witt.*

Cellini, Benvenuto. Memoirs; tr. by T. Roscoe. 12°. (Bohn.) $1.25 ... *Little, B. & Co.*

— *Same.* 12°. (Bohn.) $1.40 ... *Scribner, W. & A.*

— *Same.* 12°. (Bohn.) $1.50 ... *Lippincott.*

Celnart, Eliz. *See* Bayle-Mouillard, Eliz.

Celt's paradise. Banim, J. $1 ... *Sadlier.*

Censer (The new). *See* Bradbury, W. B.

Census. Brough, W., *and* Halliday, A. 15c. ... *French.*

Centenary addresses, delivered before the General Convention of the New Jerusalem, Cincinnati, 1857. 8°. $1.25 ... *New Ch.*

Centenary memorial of the planting and growth of Presbyterianism in West Penn., etc.: hist. discourses. ill. 8°. '76. $2.50 ... *W. W. Waters.*

Centenary singer. *See* Methodist Episc. Church.

Centennial and other poems. Harrington, K. $1.75. *Lippincott.*

Centennial chimes: marches, quicksteps, polkas, etc. 4°. bds., $1 ... *Church.*

Centennial city (The). *See* Syckelmoore, W.

Centennial collection of national songs of the principal countries. 8°. '76. 60c.; bds., 50c.; pap., 40c. ... *Ditson.*

Centennial commissioner (A) in Europe. Forney, J. W. $2 ... *Lippincott.*

Centennial grand cheap library. 2 nos. ill. 16°. no. 1, 50 v., $26; no. 2, 50 v., $28 ... *Am. S. S.*

Centennial guide and purchasers' directory of Phila. map. 16°. '76. 25c. ... *Sibole.*

Centennial meditation of Columbia. Buck, D. *net,* 75c. ... *Schirmer.*

Centennial old folks' collection. obl. 8°. '75. bds., 50c.; pap., 40c. ... *Ditson.*

Centennial orations commemorative of the opening events of the Am. rev., with other proceedings; [ed. by A. H. Hoyt and J. W. Dean]. por. 8°. '75. $2; pap., $1.50 ... *N. E. Hist. Gen.*

Centennial poets. 3 v. ill. 8°. ea., pap., $1 .. *Osgood.*
Cont.: Whittier. — Tennyson. — Longfellow.

Centennial portfolio. Westcott, T. $4.50; $3.50; $7; $10; $20 ... *T. Hunter.*

Centennial records of the women of Wisconsin. ill. 8°. $2 ... *Atwood.*

Centennial school singer (The). Curtis, G. H., *and* Bourne, W. O. 40c. ... *Biglow.*

Centennial universal history. ill. and por. 8°. '76. * $3; leath., $3.75 ... *Ziegler.*

Centennial verse. 12°. $1.25 ... *Cath. Pub.*

Centennial view of our country. McCabe, J. D. * $4; $5 ... *Hubbard.*

Centennial wealth (The) of the world. Gerard, S., *jr.* 50c. ... *Vose.*

Centlivre, *Mrs.* Susannah. Bold stroke for a wife: comedy. 16°. pap., 15c. ... *French.*

— Busybody: comedy. 16°. pap., 15c. ... *French.*

— Wonder: comedy. 16°. pap., 15c. ... *French.*

Central Pacific Railway: 12 views, with descript. letter-press. obl. 24°. 75c. ... *Nelson.*

Century after (A). Stoddard, R. H. $9; $11; $13.50. *Allen.*

Century (A) of anecdote. Timbs, J. $1.75; $3.75; $5. *Scribner, W. & A.*

Century (A) of Gospel work. Noble, W. F. P. *$3.50; $4.25; $5.50 .... *Watts.*

Century (A) of gossip. Nash, W. G. $1.50 .... *Keen.*

Century (The) of independence: documents and statistics connected with the polit. hist. of Am., with record of the principal events, etc. [In Eng. *or* Germ.] ill. 12°. '76. *$2 .... *Un. Bk. Conc.*

Century (The) of queens; with sketches of some princes of literature and art. ill. 4°. $6; mor., $12 .... *Miller.*

Ceremonial for the reception and profession of the Sisters of Mercy. 8°. '70. *net,* 75c. *Kelly, P. & Co.*

Ceremonial for the use of the Catholic churches in the U. S. 4th ed. 12°. $2.50 .... *Noonan.*

— *Same;* orig. pub. by order of the 1st Council of Baltimore; rev. by Rev. T. A. Becker. ('65.) New ed., rev. 8°. '76. *net,* $2.50 .... *Kelly, P. & Co.*

Cerise. *See* Melville, G. J. W.

Certain inducements to well minded people, who are here straitened in their estates or otherwise. [Reprint.] 4°. 50c.; large pap., $1 ..... *Sabin.*

Certain sermons or homilies appointed to be read in churches in the time of Queen Elizabeth. 12°. $1.75 .... *Pott.*

Cervantes Saavedra, Miguel. El ingenioso hidalgo Don Quijote de la Mancha, segun el texto correg. y anot. por el Sr. Ochoa. 12°. $1.50 .. *Appleton.*

— *Same.* Nueva ed. clásica, con notas. (Lib. ed.) 2 v. 12°. $2.50. (School ed.) 12°. $1.50. *Lee & S.*

— *Eng.* Don Quixote de la Mancha. 12°. $1. *Lippincott.*

— *Same.* cr. 8°. $1; pap., 75c ...... *Scribner, W. & A.*

— *Same.* ill. 12°. $1.50. *Carleton; Lee & S.; Scribner, W. & A.*

— *Same.* 8°. $1.75; pap., $1 .... *Peterson.*

— *Same.* 2 v. in 1. ill. 8°. $2; shp., $2.75. *World Pub.*

— *Same.* ill. 8°. $2.50 .... *Scribner, W. & A.*

— *Same.* ill. 8°. $3.50; hf. cf., $6; cf., $7. — ill. 12°. $1.50 .... *Appleton.*

— *Same.* 2 v. ill. cr. 8°. $2.50; $3; shp., $3.20; hf. mor., $3.70 .... *Lea.*

— *Same.* (Chandos lib.) 12°. $1.75: hf. cf., $3.75; cf., $5. — cr. 8°. $1; pap., 75c. *Scribner, W. & A.*

— *Same.* (Household ser.) ill. 16°. $1.50; mor., $3. *Lee & S.*

— *Same;* tr. by C. Jarvis. ill. 12°. $1; hf. cf., $3. *Porter.*

— — *Same.* (Globe lib.) ill. cr. 8°. $1.75; hf. cf., $3.50; cf., $5. — (Presentation poets.) ill. 12°. $1.75 .... *Routledge.*

— *Same;* tr. by P. A. Motteux; with notes and essay on life and writings by J. G. Lockhart. 4 v. 12°. '70. $5; hf. cf., $10; cf., $12 ... *Little, B. & Co.*

— *Same;* ed. by J. W. Clarke, with biog. notice by T. T. Shore; ill. by Doré. roy. 4°. $15; mor., $20; $25 .... *Cassell.*

— — *See also* Beeton's boy's own lib.

— Don Quixote, for boys. ill. 16°. $1.25 ... *Routledge.*

— Exemplary novels; [also] El buscapié, the serpent; [also] La tia fingida, the pretended aunt; tr. by W. Kelly. 12°. (Bohn.) $1.25 .. *Little, B. & Co.*

— *Same.* 12°. (Bohn.) $1.40 .... *Scribner, W. & A.*

— *Same.* 12°. (Bohn.) $1.50 .... *Lippincott.*

— Galatea, a pastoral romance; tr. by G. W. J. Gyll. 12°. (Bohn.) $1.25 .... *Little, B. & Co.*

— *Same.* 12°. (Bohn.) $1.40 .... *Scribner, W. & A.*

— *Same.* 12°. (Bohn.) $1.50 .... *Lippincott.*

Cesarine Dietrich. Sand, G. $1.25; 75c ...... *Estes.*

Cezinski, Mar. Helen Egerton; or, for conscience' sake. 16°. $1.50 .... *Am. Bapt.*

Chadbourne, P. A. Instinct: its office in the animal kingdom and its relation to the higher powers in man. 12°. '72. $1.75 .... *Putnam.*

— Lectures on natural history: its relations to intellect, taste, wealth and religion. 12°. '60. 75c. *Barnes.*

Chadbourne, P. A., *continued.*

— Natural theology; or, nature and the Bible from the same author: lecture before the Lowell Institute, Boston. 12°. '67. $1.50 .... *Putnam.*

Chadwick, H: American cricket manual; [also] La crosse. 12°. 75c. 32°. bds., 50c ...... *De Witt.*

— De Witt's base-ball guide. [Annual.] 64°. pap., 10c. *De Witt.*

— De Witt's base-ball umpire's guide. 64°. 50c *De Witt.*

— Guide to curling and skating. 16°. pap., 10c. *Beadle.*

Chadwick, *Mrs.* J. Home cookery. 12°. '52. hf. bd., 50c .... *Nichols & H.*

Chaff, Gumbo (*pseud.*) *See* Howe, Elias.

Chaffer, W: Collector's handbook of marks and monograms on pottery and porcelain of the renaissance and modern periods. 12°. $3 .. *Scribner, W. & A.*

— Marks and monograms on pottery and porcelain. ill. roy. 8°. $21 .... *Scribner, W. & A.*

Chaffin, J. W. Battle of Calvary; or, Universalism and cognate theories against Jesus of Nazareth. 16°. $1.25 .... *Cin. Meth. Bk. Conc.*

Chaillé, Stanford E. Origin and progress of med. jurisprudence, 1776–1876. 8°. '76. pap., 30c. *Brentano.*

Chailly, N: C: Practical treatise on midwifery; tr. and ed. by G. S. Bedford. ill. 8°. shp., $3 .. *Harper.*

Chain (The new). *See* Bradbury, W. B.

Chain of events: drama. 16°. pap., 15c. ..... *French.*

Chain of guilt. Taylor, T. P. 15c .... *French.*

Chain of sacred wonders. Latta, S. A. $3.50. *Pounsford.*

Chain-bearer (The). *See* Cooper, J. F.

Chairman and speaker's guide. 16°. 10c ... *Dick & F.*

Chaldee paradigms: consisting of the gram. introd. to the "Analytical Heb. and Chal. lexicon." 4°. (Bagster.) $1.25 .... *Wiley.*

Chaldee reading lessons. fp. 8°. (Bagster.) $1.50; hf. bd., $1.75 .... *Wiley.*

Chalkley, T: Journal. 12°. $1; cf., $1.50. *Friends Bk. St.*

Challen, Ja. Baptism in spirit and in fire. 18°. '59. pap., 10c .... *Challen.*

— Cave of Machpelah, and other poems. 12°. '56. $1.50 .... *Challen.*

— Christian morals. 18°. '59. 50c.; pap., 20c. *Challen.*

— Frank Elliot; or, wells in the desert. 12°. $1. *Challen.*

— Gospel (The) and its elements. 18°. '56. 50c.; pap., 20c .... *Challen.*

— Igdrasil; or, the tree of existence. 12°. '58. $1.50. *Challen.*

— Island of the giant fairies. 12°. '68. pap., 10c. *Challen.*

— Juvenile library. 33 v. 18°. '58. ea., pap., 10c.; bds., 40c .... *Challen.*

— Koinonia; or, the weekly contribution. 32°. 40c. *Chase.*

— *Same.* ('60.) 2d ed. 18°. 50c .... *Challen.*

— Question book on Acts. 24°. pap., 10c.; bds., 15c. *Challen.*

— Question book on Matthew. 24°. '60. pap., 10c.; bds., 15c .... *Challen.*

Challenge dance: Ethiop. drama. 16°. pap., 15c. *French; Happy.*

Challice, *Mrs.* A. E. Illustrious women of France, 1790–1873. por. post 8°. $3 .. *Scribner, W. & A.*

Challis, F. My wife's husband: farce. 16°. pap., 15c. *French.*

Challoner, N. B. New guide di musica. 4°. pap., $1. *Ditson.*

— Piano preceptor. f°. pap., $1 .... *Willig.*

— *Same.* f°. $1.50 .... *Brainard.*

Challoner, *Bp.* R: Bible history. 18°. 50c ... *Strong.*

— Catholic Christian (The) instructed in the ceremonies, etc., of the Church. 24°. 25c. 32°. pap., 20c .... *Cath. Pub.*

— *Same.* 16°. 25c.; pap., 20c .... *O'Shea.*

halloner, *Bp.* R: *continued.*
Same. 12°. '59. 40c.; 50c.; pap., 25c. *Kelly, P. & Co.*
Considerations upon Christian truths and Christian duties. roy. 12°. $2 .... *Cummiskey.*
Life of St. Mary of Egypt. 24°. pap., 10c. *Coddington.*
Lives of the fathers of the deserts. 12°. $1.25; $1.75 .... *Sadlier.*
Think well on't: reflections on the great truths of the Christian religion for every day of the month. 32°. 30c. .... *Cath. Pub.; O'Shea.*
Same. 32°. '75. 40c. .... *Kenedy.*
Same. 32°. '51. 30c.-60c. .... *Murphy.*
Same. 32°. $1 .... *Sadlier.*
See Bible [Whole], *Cath.*

halmers, Alex. (*ed.*) British essayists; with pref., historical and biographical. 38 v. 16°. '56-'66. $47.50; $57; hf. cf., $95; cf., $114. — 12°. bds., $95 .... *Little, B. & Co.*

Cont.: Tatler, 4 v. — Spectator, 8 v. — Guardian, 3 v. — Rambler, 3 v. — Adventurer, 3 v. — World, 3 v. — Connoisseur, 2 v. — Idler, 1 v. — Mirror, 2 v. — Lounger, 2 v. — Observer, 3 v. — Looker-on, 3 v. — Index, 1 v.

halmers, *Mrs.* Anna Meade. Brown and Arthur: an episode arranged from "Tom Brown's school days." 18°. '61. 50c. .... *J. W. Randolph.*

halmers, Ja. The channel railway, connecting England and France. 2d ed. pl. 8°. '67. $2 .. *Spon.*

halmers, T: Astronomical and commercial discourses. 12°. $1.50 .... *Carter.*
- Correspondence; ed. by Rev. W. Hanna. 12°. $1.50; hf. cf., $3.25 .... *Harper.*
- Life. 18°. 90c. .... *Cong. Pub.*
- Life and writings; ed. by Rev. W. Hanna. 4 v. 12°. $6; hf. cf., $13 .... *Harper.*
- On Romans. 8°. $2.50 .... *Carter.*
- Posthumous works; ed. by Rev. W. Hanna. 9 v. 12°. $13.50; hf. cf., $29.25 .... *Harper.*

Cont.: Daily Scripture readings, 3 v. — Institutes of theology, 2 v. — Prelections on Butler's Analogy, Paley's Evidences of Christianity, and Hill's Lectures on divinity; with introd. lectures and addresses. — Sabbath Scripture readings, 2 v. — Sermons, 1798-1847.

- Power (The), wisdom and goodness of God, as manifested in the adaptation of external nature to the moral and intellectual constitution of man. 12°. $1.50; hf. cf., $3.25 .... *Harper.*
- *Same.* 12°. (Bohn.) $1.75 ...... *Little, B. & Co.*
- *Same.* 12°. (Bohn.) $2. *Lippincott; Scribner, W. & A.*
- Sermons. 2 v. in 1. 8°. $3 .... *Carter.*
- Treatise on polit. economy in connection with the moral state and moral prospects of society. 2d Am. ed. roy. 12°. '42. $1 ...... *I. N. Whiting.*
- *See also* Discourses on atonement.

halybæus, H. M. Historical developments of speculative philos., from Kant to Hegel; with introd. by Sir W. Hamilton. 12°. '54. $1.50 .. *Draper.*

hamber of peace, and other religious poems. 24°. '74. $1.50 .... *Randolph.*

hamberlain, C: *jr.* Put to the test. [Fiction.] 16°. $1.50 .... *Hinton.*

hamberlain, P. B. Barbara St. John. 16°. '69. $1.25 .... *Garrigues.*

hamberlayne, Isr. Great specific against despair of pardon. 12°. pap., 12c.; 20c. *Cin. Meth. Bk. Conc.*
- Saving faith: its rationale. 12°. '71. $1.25. *Meth. Bk. Conc.*

hamberlin, D. B. Natural system of Eng. grammar: introductory course. 12°. '71. bds., 45c. *Scribner.*

hamberlin, E. M. Sovereigns of industry. 16°. $1.25. *Lee & S.*

hambers, A. See Shakespeare, W.

hambers, Rob. Book of days: miscellany of popular antiquities. 2 v. ill. roy. 8°. $8; shp., $9.50; hf. cf., $12 .... *Lippincott.*
– Cyclopedia of Eng. literature. 2 v. ill. 8°. '75. ea., $2; shp., $2.75 .... *World Pub.*

Chambers, Rob., *continued.*
— *Same.* 3d ed., rev. by Rob. Carruthers. 2 v. large 8°. $7.50 .... *R. Worthington.*
— — *Same.* 2 v. roy. 8°. '76. $8; shp., $9.50; hf. cf., $12 .... *Lippincott.*
— Life of Sir W. Scott. 12°. hf. roxb., $1.25. *Lippincott.*
— *Same;* [also] Abbotsford notanda, by Rob. Carruthers; ed. by W. Chambers. 12°. hf. roxb., $1.25 .... *Lippincott.*
— Manual of English literature. 12°. roan, $1.75. *Lippincott.*
— Selections from [Chambers'] Repository. ill. 12°. 50c. .... *Lippincott.*
— *See also* Chambers, W. *and* R.
— *and* W: Miscellany of useful and entertaining tracts. 10 v. por. and ill. 12°. $10; hf. cf., $27.50 .... *Lippincott.*
— — Papers for the people. 6 v. 12°. $9 .. *Lippincott.*

Chambers, T: K. Lectures, chiefly clinical: illustrative of a restorative system of medicine. 8°. '65. $6 .... *Lindsay.*
— Manual of diet and regimen in health and sickness. 8°. $2.75 .... *Lea.*
— Restorative medicine: an Harveian annual oration, with two sequels. sm. 12°. $1 .... *Lea.*

Chambers, Talbot W. Hours of prayer in the [Fulton St., N.Y.,] noon prayer meeting. 16°. $1. *N. Y. Ref. Ch. Bd.*
— Memoir of Theodore Frelinghuysen. por. 12°. $1.50. *Harper.*
— On the minor prophets. *See* Lange, J. P., Commentary.

Chambers, W: Historical and miscellaneous questions, with answers. 16°. roan, $2.25 .. *Lippincott.*
— Historical questions, with answers. ill. 16°. roan, $1.25 .... *Lippincott.*
— Memoir of Rob. Chambers, with autobiographic reminiscences of W: Chambers. 3d ed. 12°. '72. $1.50 .... *Scribner.*
— *Same.* 12°. hf. roxb., $1.50 .... *Lippincott.*
— Miscellaneous questions, with answers. 16°. roan, $1.25 .... *Lippincott.*
— *See also* Chambers, R. *and* W.
— *and* Rob. Encyclopedia: dictionary of universal knowledge for the people. 10 v. ill. and maps. roy. 8°. $25 .... *R. Worthington.*
— — *Same.* 10 v. maps and ill. 8°. (Lond.) $30; hf. cf., $50 .... *Little, B. & Co.*
— — *Same.* 10 v. ill. and maps. roy. 8°. $40-$85. — 80 pts. 8°. ea., pap., 45c. — (Globe ed.) 5 v. ill. 8°. $23.20; shp., $31.25; hf. mor., $37.50. — 58 pts. 8°. ea., 40c. .... *Lippincott.*
— — Etymological dict. 12°. '76. $1.25. *R. Worthington.*
— — *Same;* ed. by J. Donald. post 8°. $2 .. *Lippincott.*
— — Happy hour library. 3 v. ill. 16°. $4.50 .. *Miller.*

Cont.: Every day book. — Leisure hour book. — The parlor book.

— — Home books and miscellany. 6 v. ill. 16°. $9. *Miller.*

Cont.: Every day book. — Leisure hour book. — Parlor book. — Summer day book. — Winter evening book. — Young folks' companion.

— — Information for the people. 2 v. maps and ill. roy. 8°. *4.50; $5 .... *J. E. Potter.*
— — *Same.* 5th ed., rev. by A. Findlater. 2 v. roy. 8°. $8; shp., $9.50; hf. cf., $12 .... *Lippincott.*
— — Library of instructive amusement. 3 v. ill. 16°. $4.50 .... *Miller.*

Cont.: Summer day book. — Winter evening book. — Young folks' companion.

— — Miscellany. 10 v. 12°. $10 .... *R. Worthington.*
— — Scientific course. 5 v. 12°. .... *Barnes.*

Cont.: Introduction to the sciences, 50c. — Treasury of knowledge, $1.25. — Page's Elements of geology, $1.25. — Hamilton's Vegetable and animal physiology, $1.25. — Reese's Elements of zoology, $1.50.

— — *Same.* Introduction to the sciences; ed. by D. M. Reese. 12°. '49. 50c. .... *Barnes.*

Chambers, W: and Rob., *continued.*
— — *Same.* Treasury of knowledge; ed. by D. M. Reese. 12°. '49. $1.25 .... *Barnes.*
Chambliss, J. E. Life and labors of David Livingstone. ill. 8°. '75. *$3; leath., $4; hf. mor., $5. *Hubbard.*
Chamier, F. Novels. 4 v. 12°. $5 ...... *Routledge.*
Cont.: Ben Brace. — Tom Bowling. — Jack Adams. — Life of a sailor.
— Ben Brace. 16°. bds., 80c. .... *Routledge.*
— Jack Adams. 16°. bds., 80c. .... *Routledge.*
— Tom Bowling. 16°. bds., 80c. .... *Routledge.*
Chamisso, Adelbert v. Peter Schlemihl; tr. by Sir J. Bowring. ill. cr. 8°. '74. $2 .... *Denham.*
Champagne: comedy. 16°. pap., 15c. .... *French.*
Champagne Charlie; or, the sports of New York. 8°. pap., 25c. .... *De Witt.*
Champagne country (The). *See* Tomes, R.
Champion, *Mrs.* E. P. *See* Bagg, I. N.
Champion of her sex. Baker, G. M. 15c. .. *Lee & S.*
Champion school for the flute; — piano; — violin. Lazare, C. ea., 60c. .... *G. D. Russell.*
Champion stories. *See* DeWitt's champion stories.
Champlin, H: L. American firemen: essays, lurid leaves, sketches, sparks. 16°. '75. $1 .. *Champlin.*
Champlin, Ja. Tift. First principles of ethics. 12°. $1.50 .... *Potter, A. & Co.*
— Intellectual philosophy. 12°. $1.50 .. *Potter, A. & Co.*
— Lessons on polit. economy. 12°. '68. $1.25 .. *Barnes.*
— Practical grammar of the English language. 12°. 50c. .... *Appleton.*
— Short and comprehensive Greek grammar. 12°. $1.25 .... *Appleton.*
Champney, Basil. Quiet corner of England; [with] etchings by A. Dawson. imp. 8°. '75. $5 .. *Bouton.*
Champney, H. N. Textual commentary on the Psalms. 16°. (Bagster.) $1.25 .... *Wiley.*
Champney stories (The). 5 v. 18°. $1.75 .. *Am. S. S.*
Cont.: White dress, etc. — Poor prisoner, etc. — Shipwreck, etc. — Builders, etc. — Journey, etc.
Chance acquaintance (A). Howells, W. D. $1.25; $2 .... *Osgood.*
Chance child (A). *See* Mayo, I. F.
Chance for himself. Trowbridge, J. T. $1.25 .. *Porter.*
Chance medley of light matter. Grattan, T. C. 50c. *Harper.*
Chancery appeal cases. *See* England, Law reports.
Chances and changes. Jourdan, B. A. $2 .. *Routledge.*
Chances and changes. *See* Happy child's lib.
Chandler, J: Horæ sacræ. 32°. 50c.; roan, 75c.; mor., $2.25 .... *Dutton.*
Chandler, Jos. R. Beverly family (The). 18°. '70. 50c. .... *Cunningham.*
— Grammar of the English language. 12°. hf. roan, 60c. .... *Desilver.*
Chandler, W. E. *See* New Hampshire, Law reports; Supreme Court reports.
Chandler, Z. M. Grammar and analysis. 12°. 60c. *Wilson, H. & Co.*
Chandos. La Rame, L. de. $1.50 .... *Lippincott.*
Chandos classics. 40 v. cr. 8°. ea., $1; pap., 75c. *Scribner, W. & A.*
Cont.: Andersen's Fairy tales. — Arabian nights. — Burns' Poetical works. — Butler's Hudibras — Byron's Poems. — Campbell's Poetical works. — Coleridge's Poetical works. — E. Cook's Poems. — Cowper's Poems. — Dante, tr. by Cary. — Cervantes' Don Quixote. — Combe's Dr. Syntax's three tours. — German literature, as exemplified by the works of Tieck, Hoffmann, Richter, Pichler and Zschokke. — Gibbon and Ockley's Fall of the Saracens. — Grimm's Fairy tales. — Hallam's Constitutional history, and De Lolme's Constitution of Eng. — Hemans' Poetical works. — Hood's Poetical works. — Johnson's Lives of the poets. — Keats' Poetical works. — Roberts' Legendary ballads of England and Scotland. — Lockhart's Spanish ballads, and Southey's Chronicle of the Cid. — Milton's Poetical works. — Moore's Poetical works. — Pope's Homer's Iliad. — Pope's Homer's Odyssey. — Russell's Representative actors. —

Chandos classics, *continued.*
Defoe's Robinson Crusoe. — Neale's Romance of history: England. — Ritchie's Romance of hist.: France. — Trueba's Romance of hist.: Spain. — Macfarlane's Romance of hist.: Italy. — Caunter's Romance of hist.: India. — Scott's Poetical works. — Scott's Essays on chivalry, romance and the drama. — Scott's Lives of the novelists and dramatists. — Shakespeare's Complete works. — Shelley's Poetical works. — Swiss family Robinson. — Wordsworth's Poetical works.
Chandos juveniles. 7 v. cr. 8°. ea., $1; pap., 75c. *Scribner, W. & A.*
Cont.: Andersen's fairy tales. — Arabian nights. — Don Quixote. — Eastern tales. — Grimm's Fairy tales. — Robinson Crusoe. — Swiss family Robinson.
Chandos library. 27 v. ill. 12°. ea., $1.75; hf. cf., $3.75; cf., $5 .... *Scribner, W. & A.*
Cont.: R. and S. Percy's Percy anecdotes, 3 v. — Southey's Book of the church. — Pepys' Diary and correspondence. — Timbs' Abbeys, castles and ancients halls of England and Wales, 3 v. — Johnson's Lives of the poets. — Russell's Book of authors. — Evelyn's Diary and correspondence. — Gibbon's life, etc. — Gibbon's Decline and fall of the Roman empire, 3 v. — Russell's Representative actors. — Jewitt's William Hutton and the Hutton family. — Timbs' Century of anecdote. — Timbs' Romance of London, 2 v. — Daniel's Merrie England in the olden time. — Morley's Bartholomew Fair. — Scott's Essays on chivalry, romance and the drama. — Pope's Homer's Iliad and Odyssey. — Scott's Lives of celebrated novelists and dramatists. — Lockhart's Spanish ballads, and Southey's Chronicle of the Cid. — Cervantes' Don Quixote.
Chandos poets. 19 v. ill. and por. cr. 8°. ea., $3.75; cf., $7.50; mor., $8 ... *Scribner, W. & A.*
Cont.: Cowper. — Milton. — Wordsworth. — The spirit of praise. — Christian lyrics. — Moore. — E. Cook. — Roberts' Legendary ballads of Eng. and Scot. — Scott. — The poets of the nineteenth century. — Shakespeare's Plays and poems. — Hemans. — Byron. — Burns. — Montgomery. — Hood. — Coleridge. — Shelley. — Iliad and Odyssey, tr. by Pope.
Chaney, G: L. F. Grant and Co.; or, partnerships. ill. 16°. '74. $1.50 .... *Roberts.*
Chaney, *Mrs.* G: L. "William Henry" dramatized [from the "William Henry" books of Mrs. A. M. Diaz]. 16°. '74. pap., 25c. .... *Osgood.*
Chaney, H: A. Digest of Michigan reports: supplement to Cooley's Digest of 1872. 12°. '76. shp., $5; interleaved, $6 .... *Richmond.*
— Notary public guide and manual; with forms. 12°. 75c. .... *Richmond.*
Chang-Ching-Fou. Martin, W. 15c. .... *French.*
Change of base. *See* Curtis, A. W. *and* D. S.
Change of system. Paul, H. 15c. .... *French.*
Changed brides (The). Southworth, E. D. E. N. $1.75; $1.50 .... *Peterson.*
Changed cross (The). Hobart, C. 75c. .. *Randolph.*
— *Same;* and other poems [*anon*]. ('62.) New ed., enl. 24°. '72. $1.50 .... *Randolph.*
— *Same;* [also] Margaret Brown [*anon*]. ill. sm. 4°. '69. $1; pap., 50c. .... *Randolph.*
— *Same;* [also] The shadow of the rock [*anon*]. ('69.) 2d ed. 24°. '72. $3 .... *Randolph.*
Changing base. Everett, W. $1.25 .... *Lee & S.*
Changing the crosses and winning the crown. Ideen, M. A. $1 .... *Lippincott.*
Channing, Barb. H. Sunny skies; or, adventures in Italy. ill. 16°. '69. $1.25 .... *Lothrop.*
Channing, E. T. Life of W. Ellery. *See* Sparks, J., Lib. of Am. biog.
Channing, W: Ellery. Works. 8°. $1.75 .. *Routledge.*
— *Same.* ('41.) 24th ed. 6 v. bd. in 3. 12°. '74. $3.
— Same. ('74.) 4th ed. 8°. '75. $1 .. *Am. Unit.*
— Perfect life (The): discourses, ed. by W. H. Channing. 12°. '72. $1.50 .... *Roberts.*
— Thoughts; sel. from [his] writings. ('56.) 14th ed. 32°. '71. 60c. .... *Am. Unit.*
— *and* Aikin, Lucy. Correspondence; ed. by A. L. Le Breton. 12°. '74. $2 .... *Roberts.*
Channing, W: Ellery (*the younger*). Thoreau, the poet naturalist; with memorial verse. 16°. '73. $2 .... *Roberts.*
— Wanderer (The): colloquial poem. 16°. '71. $1.25; pap., 75c.; hf. cf., $3; mor., $4 .... *Osgood.*

Channing, W: H: Memoir of W. E. Channing; with extracts from correspondence and manuscripts. 2 v. cr. 8°. $3.50 .... *Routledge.*
— *Same.* ('48.) 10th ed. 3 v. por. 12°. '74. $2.50. *Am. Unit.*
— Religions of China. 8°. pap., 25c. .... *Free Rel.*
Channings (The). Wood, E. P. $1.75; $1.50. *Peterson.*
Chantry library (The). 4 v. 16°. $6 .... *Hoyt.*
Cont.: Chantry's boy, by Mrs. M. A. Denison. — Which wins. — Tom Carter. — John Dane.
Chantry's boy. Denison, M. A. $1.50 .... *Hoyt.*
Chants chrétiens. [Hymn book.] 18°. 40c. *Pres. Bd.*
Chants évangéliques. [Hymns.] 12°. '57. 30c. *Am. Tr.*
Chanute, O. Elements of cost of railroad freight traffic. *See* Thurston, R. H., Strength of materials of machine construction.
— Weight of rails and breaking of iron rails; [also] Failure of dam on Mill River, by J. B. Francis, T. G. Ellis and W. E. Worthen; Barnard's Resistance of beams to flexure; Smith's Draw spans and their turn-tables; Collingwood's Foundations, Brooklyn anchorage, East River bridge. 8°. '74. pap., 70c. .... *Am. Soc. of C. E.*
— *See also* Rapid transit and terminal freight facilities.
— *and* Morison, G: Kansas City bridge; with account of the regimen of the Missouri River. pl. 4°. '70. $6 .... *Van Nostrand.*
Chaos is come again. Morton, J. M. 15c. ... *French.*
Chapel (The): collection of tunes in all metres. obl. 8°. '66. bds., 40c.; pap., 33c. .... *Ditson.*
Chapel companion (The). [Cath. prayer book.] 32°. '51. 38c.–$1.50 .... *Murphy.*
Chapel gems. Root, G. F. 35c.; 30c. .... *Church.*
Chapel hymn book. Hubbell, G. A. 50c. .... *Tibbals.*
Chapel hymns. *See* Congregational churches in Conn.
Chapel melodies. Vail, S. J., *and* Lowry, R. 50c.; 40c. .... *Biglow.*
Chapel window. 18°. 60c. .... *Dutton.*
Chapin, Edn. Hubbell. Crown of thorns: a token for the sorrowing. 16°. '60. $1.25 ... *Universalist.*
— Discourses on the beatitudes. 12°. '53. 75c. *Universalist.*
— Discourses on the Lord's prayer. 12°. '50. $1; $1.25. *Universalist.*
— Duties of young men. 32°. '55. 60c. ... *Universalist.*
— Duties of young women. 32°. '63. 75c. *Universalist.*
— Hours of communion. 32°. '44. 60c. ... *Universalist.*
— Humanity in the city: discourses. 12°. $1.25 .. *De Witt.*
— Moral aspects of city life. 12°. $1 .... *Williamson.*
— Providence and life: sermons. 12°. $1.50. *Williamson.*
— True manliness. 12°. $1 .... *Williamson.*
— *See also* Adams, J. G., *and* Chapin, E. H.
Chapin, *Mrs.* Sallie F. Fitz-Hugh St. Clair, the So. Carolina rebel boy; or, it is no crime to be born a gentleman. ('72.) 3d ed. 12°. '73. $1.50 .. *Claxton.*
Chapin, W: Memoir of Mrs. Susan Howard. 18°. '37. 35c. .... *Meth. Bk. Conc.*
Chaplain with the children. P., B. K. $1.25 .. *Palmer.*
Chaplet (The). Cooper, G., *and* Millard, H. 50c. *G. D. Russell.*
Chaplet of flowers: texts for every day. 64°. '49. 15c.; 20c.; 50c. .... *Am. Tr.*
Chaplet of pearls. *See* Yonge, C. M.
Chaplin, *Mrs.* A. C. Christ's cadets. 16°. $1.50. *Am. Bapt.*
Chaplin, J. D. *See* Chaplin, J. *and* J. D.
Chaplin, *Mrs.* Jane Dunbar. Aunt Elsie's posts. ill. 18°. 60c. .... *Bost. Am. Tr.*
— Black and white; or, the heart, not the face. ill. 18°. 50c. .... *Bost. Am. Tr.*
— Firelight stories. ill. 18°. 40c. ...... *Bost. Am. Tr.*
— Gems of the bog: tale of the Irish peasantry. ill. 16°. $1.25 .... *Bost. Am. Tr.*

Chaplin, *Mrs.* Jane Dunbar, *continued.*
— Little Happy-heart; or, love and labor. ill. 18°. 75c. *Bost. Am. Tr.*
— — *See also* Mother's pearl ser.
— Maple hill; or, Aunt Lucy's stories. ill. 18°. 45c. *Bost. Am. Tr.*
— Mother West's neighbors. 16°. '76. 90c. *Bost. Am. Tr.*
— Out of the wilderness. 16°. '69. $1.50; $1.25. *H. A. Young.*
— Songs for my children. ill. 18°. 55c. .. *Bost. Am. Tr.*
— Transplanted shamrock (The); or, the way to win an Irish heart. ill. 18°. 50c. ..... *Bost. Am. Tr.*
— Two granddaughters. ill. 18°. 75c. .. *Bost. Am. Tr.*
— — *See also* Mother's pearl ser.
— Wee Meggie Forsythe, and the muckle wisdom. ill. 16°. $1.50 .... *Bost. Am. Tr.*
Chaplin, Jer. Evening of life. 12°. '58. $1.50. *H. A. Young.*
— Hand of Jesus. 18°. '68. $1.50 .... *Graves.*
— Life of Benj. Franklin. ill. 16°. '76. $1.50 .. *Lothrop.*
— Life of Henry Dunster. 16°. '72. $1.50 ... *Osgood.*
— Memorial hour; or, the Lord's supper in its relation to doctrine and life. 16°. '74. $1.25 .. *Lothrop.*
— *and* J. D. Life of Charles Sumner; with introd. by W. Claflin. ill. 16°. '74. $1.50 ...... *Lothrop.*
Chapman, A. W. Flora of the southern U. S. 8°. '60. $3.60 .... *Ivison.*
Chapman, E. N. Hysterology: treatise, descriptive and clinical, on the diseases and displacements of the uterus. ill. 8°. $4.50 .... *W. Wood.*
Chapman, G. *See* Homer.
Chapman, G: T. Sermons upon the ministry, worship and doctrines of the Prot. Episc. Church. New ed. 12°. '62. $1.75 .... *Dutton.*
Chapman, *Miss* Helen E. Broken fuchsia. 18°. 50c. *Cong. Pub.*
— Paul Brewster and son. 12°. '75. $1 ... *Nat. Temp.*
— Paul Winslow; or, blessings in disguise. 18°. 45c. *Pres. Bd.*
— Pine cottage. 16°. 60c. .... *Cong. Pub.*
— Traveller's inn. 16°. 75c. .... *Cong. Pub.*
Chapman, H: C. Evolution of life. pl. 8°. $2.75. *Lippincott.*
Chapman, *Miss* J. E. C. (*ed.*) Easter hymns. sq. 18°. '76. $1.25 .... *Lockwood, B. & Co.*
Chapman, J. G. American drawing book. ('47.) New ed., rev. 4°. '70. $6 .... *Barnes.*
— Elementary drawing book. 4°. '71. hf. bd., $1.50. *Barnes.*
Chapman, J. L. Baptism, with ref. to its import, modes, etc., and the duty of parents to baptize children. ('53.) 3d ed. 12°. '75. $1.50. *So. Meth.*
— Defense of the government of the Meth. Episc. Church. 12°. '55. pap., 10c. .... *So. Meth.*
— Tracts for the times on infant baptism; with quest. on mode of baptism. 12°. '54. 75c. .. *So. Meth.*
Chapman, J: Diarrhœa and cholera: their origin, proximate cause, and cure through the agency of the nervous system by means of ice. 16°. pap., 25c. 8°. $3.75 .... *Lippincott.*
Chapman, Ma. S. Edith's Testament. 16°. 75c. *Cong. Pub.*
— The Swiss children. ill. 18°. '64. 40c. .... *Am. Tr.*
Chapman, R. Treatise on rope-making. Rev. ed. 12°. '68. $1 .... *Spon.*
Chapman, T. J. *See* Dickens, C., Schools and schoolmasters.
Chapman, W. C. Vaccination as a preventive of small pox. 8°. '76. pap., 50c. .... *Brown & F.*
Chappel, Alonzo (*ill.*) *See* Duyckinck, E. A.
Chappelsmith, J. Tornado in Indiana. 4°. '55. pap., 25c. .... *Smith. Inst.*
Chapsal, G. P. *See* Noel, F. J., *and* G. P.

Chaptal, J. A. C. [*Comte de* Chanteloup.] Chemistry applied to agriculture; with a chapter on the organization, etc., of plants, by Sir H. Davy, essay on lime as a manure, by M. Puvis, and observations to the same by Renwick; tr. and ed. by W. P. Page. 18°. hf. shp., 75c.....*Harper*.
Chapter of accidents. Lee, S. 15c..........*French*.
Chapters for children. Mogridge, G. 50c...*So. Meth*.
Chapters from the Bible of the ages. Stebbins, G. B. $1.50; $2..............................*Colby*.
Chapters of Erie. Adams, C. F., *jr.*, *and* H. $2. *Osgood*.
Chapters on animals. Hamerton, P. G. $2..*Roberts*.
Chapters on the "Shorter catechism." 16°. $1.25. (?) *Martien*.
Chapters on wives. Ellis, S. S. $1.50......*Harper*.
Character and characteristic man. Whipple, E. P. $1.50..............................*Osgood*.
Character of the gentleman. *See* Lieber, F.
Character sketches. *See* Macleod, N.
Characters, scenes and incidents of the reformation; rev. by T. O. Summers. ('55.) 2d ed. 18°. '75. $1..............................*So. Meth*.
Charades and responses. sq. 12°. $1.25..*Lippincott*.
Charcoal burner. Almar, G. 15c..........*French*.
Charcoal sketches. Neal, J. C. $2.50; 75c. *Peterson*.
Chard, T: S. Across the sea, and other poems. sq. 16°. '74. (cop. '76.) $1..................*Jansen*.
Chardenal, C. A. First French course. 3d ed. 12°. '74. 75c..............................*Sever*.
— French exercises; for advanced pupils. 12°. '76. $1.50..............................*Sever*.
— French primer; for junior classes. 12°. '74. 50c. *Sever*.
— Second French course, and reader. 2d ed. 12°. '74. $1.25..............................*Sever*.
Chardon, G. Memoirs of a guardian angel; tr. from the French. 2d ed. 18°. '70. $1.50...*Murphy*.
Charette. 12°. $1.50....................*Carleton*.
Charicles. Becker, W. A. $3; $5. *Appleton; Lippincott*.
Charity: play. 16°. pap., 15c..............*Happy*.
Charity; or, Nettie's victories. 18°. 40c....*Dutton*.
Charity Barnes, the cobbler's daughter; or, what perseverance will accomplish. 18°. 55c...*Am. S.S*.
Charity chapters. Tappan, *Miss* —. 60c...*Cong. Pub*.
Charity Helstone. Brock, C. $1.25....(?) *Martien*.
Charity Hospital reports. *See* Bellevue.
Charity Hurlburt. Capron, M. J. $1.50.......*Hoyt*.
Charity stories. 8 v. ill. 18°. '74. $3.25....*Am. Tr*.
Charity superior to knowledge. Winans, W. 20c. *So. Meth*.
Charity's birthday text. 32°. '71. 25c.......*Am. Tr*.
— *See also* Aunty Lee lib.
Charlemagne. Life and times; rev. by T. O. Summers. ('55.) 3d ed. 18°. '75. 50c..........*So. Meth*.
Charlemont. Simms, W. G. $1.75; 75c... *Widdleton*.
Charles, *St*. *See* Lives of the saints.
Charles, A. *See* England, Law reports.
Charles, *Mrs*. E. H. Hawthorn blossoms. [Poetry.] 12°. $1.50..........................*Lippincott*.
Charles, *Mrs*. Eliz. Against the stream, the story of a heroic age in England. 12°. '73. $1.75..*Dodd*.
— Bertram family (The). 12°. '75. $1.50.....*Dodd*.
— Black ship (The), with other allegories and parables. 18°. 75c....................*Carter; Dutton*.
— Chronicles of the Schönberg-Cotta family; by two of themselves. 16°. '63. $1..............*Dodd*.
— Conquering and to conquer. 12°. '75. $1.25..*Dodd*.
— Diary of Kitty Trevylyan: story of the times of Whitfield and the Wesleys. 16°. '64. $1.....*Dodd*.
— *Same*. 12°. $1.75..........................*Nelson*.

Charles, *Mrs*. Eliz., *continued*.
— Draytons (The) and the Davenants: story of the civil wars. 16°. '66. $1......................*Dodd*.
— Early dawn (The); or, sketches of Christian life in Eng. in the olden time. 16°. '64. $1....*Dodd*.
— *Same*. 12°. $1.75..........................*Nelson*.
— Mary, the handmaid of the Lord. 18°. '65. $1..*Dodd*.
— On both sides of the sea: story of the commonwealth and restoration: sequel to "Draytons and the Davenants." 16°. '67. $1..............*Dodd*.
— Shining light. 18°. 60c..................*Pres. Bd*.
— Song (The) without words: leaves from a very old book, dedicated to children. 16°. '65. $1..*Dodd*.
— Tales of Christian life. 5 v. 16°. ea., $1...*Carter*.
Cont.: Cripple of Antioch. — Martyrs of Spain. — Two vocations. — Tales and sketches. — Wanderings in Bible lands.
— Victory (The) of the vanquished: story of the 1st century. 16°. '70. $1..................*Dodd*.
— Voice of Christian life in song. 16°. $1....*Carter*.
— Wanderings over Bible lands and seas; rev. by A. G. Haygood. 12°. '73. $1.50...........*So. Meth*.
— Winifred Bertram, and the world she lived in. 16°. '65. $1..............................*Dodd*.
— Women (The) of the Gospels; [also] The three wakings, and other poems. 18°. '66. $1..*Dodd*.
— *See also* Luther, M., Watchwords for the warfare of life.
Charles, R. The cabinet-maker: collection of designs for cabinet-makers. pl. f°. '68. hf. bd., $5. *Spon*.
Charles, the cheerful giver. *See* Witt, *Mme*. H. de.
Charles II. Payne, J. H. 15c..............*French*.
Charles XII. Planché, J. R. 15c............*French*.
Charles and Frederick. Donnollon, J. P. 50c. *Cunningham*.
Charles Atwell. 18°. '60. 30c..............*Am. Tr*.
Charles Auchester. *See* Sheppard, E. S.
Charles Barnard's money and music. Barnard, C. F., *jr*. $1..........................(?) *Shepard*.
Charles Clifford. Alexander, J. W. 70c...*Am. S. S*.
Charles Elliott; or, the sixth commandment. 18°. 30c.; 40c..............................*Am. Bapt*.
Charles Gay. *See* Ball and hoop.
Charles Hamilton. Good child's lib.
Charles Linn. *See* Good boy's lib.
Charles Marshall; or, the lost bride. [In Eng. or Germ.] 8°. pap., 20c...................*Barclay*.
Charles Morton. ill. 24°. 25c...........*Perkinpine*.
Charles Norwood. Trowbridge, C. M. $1.25. (?) *Martien*.
Charles O'Malley. *See* Lever, C:
Charles Ransford; or, life on a cruiser. 8°. pap., 25c. *Peterson*.
Charles Roussell. 18°. 60c................*Carter*.
Charles Tyrrel. James, G. P. R. $1.50....*Harper*.
Charles Vavasseur. Smith, J. F. 75c.....*Dick & F*.
Charlesworth, Mar. L. Africa's mountain valley. 18°. 60c..............................*Carter*.
— Beautiful home. 18°. 50c..................*Carter*.
— Blind basket-maker library: sequel to "Ministering children." 4 v. 16°. '67. $4...*Meth. Bk. Conc*.
Cont.: Nurse Brame. — The blind basket-maker and his little daughter. — Charley and Edith. — Little Sue and her friends.
— Cottage and its visitor. 18°. 75c..........*Carter*.
— England's yeomen. 12°. $1.50.............*Carter*.
— Last command (The). 24°. 30c.............*Carter*.
— Letters on affliction. 8°. '70. 50c.........*Dutton*.
— Ministering children. ill. 12°. '57. $1.50. *Meth. Bk. Conc*.
— *Same*. ('58.) New ed. 12°. '74. $1.50; — in 2 v. 18°. $1.50..............................*Carter*.
— — Sequel. ('67.) New ed. 12°. '76. $1.50; — in 2 v. 18°. $1.50..............................*Carter*.
— *Same*; and sequel. 2 v. 4°. $3..............*Carter*.
— *Same*; and sequel. 4 v. ill. 18°. ea., 75c. *N. Y. Ref. Ch. Bd.; Pres. Com*.

Charlesworth, Mar. L., *continued.*
— Ministering children [lib.] 4 v. ill. 18°. $2.25. *Bost. Am. Tr.*
Cont.: Herbert; or, true charity, 75c.—Patience; or, the sunshine of the heart, 50c.—Rose; or, the little comforter, 60c.—Ruth and little Jane, 40c.
— Ministry of life. ill. 12°. $1.25. *Appleton; Meth. Bk. Conc.*
— Oliver of the mill. 16°. '76. $1.50........*Carter.*
— Sunday afternoons in the nursery. sq. 16°. 75c. *Carter.*
Charlevoix, Pierre F. X. de. History and general description of New France; tr., with notes, by J. G. Shea. ('66.) New ed. 6 v. 8°. '72. $45; pap., $40........*Shea.*
— Life of Catherine Teaghokuita. *See* Montreuil, A. de, Life of St. Zita.
Charley Adams. Goodale, E. 60c.............*Hoyt.*
Charley and Edith. *See* Charlesworth, M. L.
Charley and Georgy; or, the children at Gibraltar; by author of "Helen's fault." 18°. 45c...*Routledge.*
Charley and Georgy lib. 5 v. 18°. $2.25..*Routledge.*
Cont.: Charley and Georgy.—Story of a dog.—Brave boy.—Village school.—Keeper's travels in search of his master.
Charley Bartlett's adventures. Gibbs, T. F. $1.25. *Hoyt.*
Charley Dean's task. 18°. 45c...........*Cong. Pub.*
Charley Franklin. Brooke, N. 40c. *Scribner, W. & A.*
Charley Hope's Testament. ill. 18°. '72. 75c. *Lothrop.*
Charley Hunter; or, the fate of a forger. 8°. pap., 25c. *Dick & F.*
Charley Laurel. *See* Kingston, W. H. G.
Charley Roberts ser. *See* Thurston, L. M.
Charley Watson; or, the drunkard's little son. 16°. $1. (?) *Martien.*
Charley Wheeler's reward. Chellis, M. D. $1.25..*Hoyt.*
Charley's locket. *See* Baker, *Mrs.* H. N. W.
Charlie; or, the bad habit. 18°. 45c.......*Am. S. S.*
Charlie; or, a mother's influence. 18°. 40c. *Pres. Bd.*
Charlie and the blind man. H., E. M. 50c. *Cong. Pub.*
Charlie and Lucy. *See* Library of pleasant stories.
Charlie Ashley. *See* Walker, J. G.
Charlie Barton; or, the mission garden. 32°. 25c. *Pres. Bd.*
Charlie Bell. Kellogg, E. $1.25...........*Lee & S.*
Charlie Burton. 18°. 40c...............*Cong. Pub.*
Charlie But, and other stories. 18°. 60c....*Am. S. S.*
Charlie Codman's cruise. Alger, H., *jr.* $1.25..*Loring.*
Charlie Evans. Dunning, A. K. 45c.......*Pres. Bd.*
Charlie Grant; or, how to do right. 18°. 40c. *Pres. Bd.*
Charlie Hope. 18°. 25c...................*Dutton.*
Charlie Hubert; or, consecrated gifts. 16°. '57. 60c. *Randolph.*
Charlie Kempsey's farm. 18°. 30c.........*Am. S. S.*
Charlie Scott. ill. 16°. '67. 60c............*Am. Tr.*
Charlie Scott; or, there's time enough. ('66.) New ed. ill. 16°. '74. 75c....................*Hoyt.*
Charlie Seymour. Sinclair, C. 50c..........*Carter.*
Charlie Smeaton. ('63.) New ed. 16°. '74. 90c. *Hoyt.*
Charlie Tyrrell. Bowen, C. E. 75c...........*Pott.*
Charlie's calico rooster. May, C. L. 75c. *H. A. Young.*
Charlie's friend. 12 bks. 18°. 50c. ....*Nelson.*
Charlie's lessons about animals; [also] The story of little Flora. ill. fp. 8°. 60c...........*Cassell.*
Charlie's prayers. *See* Bright eye ser.
Charlie's sled. 32°. 25c.................. *West. Tr.*
Charlotte. ill. 32°. '54. 30c................*Am. Tr.*
Charlotte Ackerman. Müller, O. $1.50; $1.25; $1. *Porter.*
Charlotte and her enemy. ill. 18°. '73. 45c. *N. Y. Ref. Ch. Bd.; Pres. Com.*
— *Same.* 18°. 50c........................*Cong. Pub.*
— *See also* Library for happy hours.

Charlotte and Lucy Temple. *See* Rowson, *Mrs.* S.
Charlotte Elizabeth stories. *See* Tonna, *Mrs.* C. E.
Charlotte Elmore. 18°. 35c.; 40c........*Am. Bapt.*
Charlotte Emma. Smith, W. H. 20c.......*Am. Tr.*
Charlotte, the Hindoo orphan. *See* Laurel ser.
Charlotte Temple. *See* Rowson, *Mrs.* S.
Charlotte's home. 18°. 45c............(?) *Martien.*
Charlotte's inheritance. Braddon, M. E. 50c. *Harper.*
Charlton School. *See* Tales of.
Charm (The). ill. 16°. 80c................*Lee & S.*
Charm (The). Bliss, P. P. 35c............*Church.*
Charm (The), and other picture stories for young people. ill. 4°. 75c....................*Am. S. S.*
Charming pair. Williams, T. J. 15c. *De Witt; French.*
Charming widow. Macquoid, K. S. $1.75..*Carleton.*
Charming woman. Wigan, H. 15c. ....*French.*
Charms: drama. 16°. pap., 15c.............*French.*
Charms and counter-charms. McIntosh, M. J. $1.25. *Appleton.*
Charms (The) of fancy. Alsop, R. $1 ....*Appleton.*
Charnock, Ste. Discourses on Christ crucified. 18°. 60c...............................*Pres. Bd.*
— Discourses on regeneration: abridg. 12°. 90c. *Pres. Bd.*
— Discourses upon the existence and attributes of God. ('68.) New ed. 8°. '74. $3............*Carter.*
Chart of life. Porter, J. $1.........*Meth. Bk. Conc.*
Charter of American liberties: Declaration of Independence, U. S. Constitution, Washington's farewell address, etc. 32°. 40c. ....*Thompson.*
Charteris. Meline, M. M. $1.50........*Lippincott.*
Chartism. *See* Carlyle, T.
Chase, A. W. Recipes; or, information for everybody. ('67.) New ed., rev., and enl. 12°. '76. $1.25; mor., $2..................*R. A. Beal.*
— *Same;* tr. into Germ. by C. F. Spring. 12°. $1.25. *R. A. Beal.*
Chase, F. S. Gathered sketches from early hist. of N. H. and Vt. 12°. 75c.................*Claremont.*
Chase, G: B. Lowndes of S. Carolina: hist. and geneal. memoir. 8°. '76. $1.25.; bds., $1... *Williams.*
Chase, G: Wingate. Digest of Masonic laws. 12°. $2. *Redding.*
— Masonic harp: Masonic odes, hymns, etc. 16°. '68. 75c.....................................*Ditson.*
— *Same;* [also] Masonic monitor: monitorial prayers, etc. 16°. '59. $1.....................*Ditson.*
Chase, H: S. Familiar lectures about the teeth. 16°. $1 .... *Gray.*
Chase, Hor. New Hampshire probate directory: laws rel. to courts of probate, with forms. 2d ed., enl. 12°. '54. $1.50..................*Eastman.*
Chase, Irah. Constitution of the holy apostles; incl. the canons. 8°. $2.50...............*Appleton.*
— Infant baptism, an invention of men. 12°. 90c. *Am. Bapt.*
Chase, Jackson H. Council monitor: text book of cryptic Masonry. 32°. $1............*Redding.*
— *Same.* 16°. '75. $1.......................*Masonic.*
— Manual of royal arch Masonry. 16°. '75. $1..*Masonic.*
— Royal arch companion. 32°. $1.........*Redding.*
Chase, Ma. Granger. Laura Clifford; or, emulation. 18°. 90c.................................*Dutton.*
— Two Christmas days. 18°. 60c............*Dutton.*
— Worth and riches. 18°. 75c..............*Dutton.*
Chase, Philander. Life. 18°. 50c..........*Dutton.*
Chase, Salmon P. (*ed.*) Statutes of Ohio and the North-western territory, 1788–1833; with ordinance of 1787, constitutions of Ohio and the U. S., etc., [with] sketch of the hist. of Ohio, ref., notes and indexes. 8°. '33. $2.......*I. N. Whiting.*
— *See also* United States, Circuit Court decisions.

Chase, T: *See* Juvenal, Selections from satires.
— *and* Stuart, G., *and* Crowell, E. P. (*ed.*) Classical series. v. 1–13. 16°.................*Eldredge.*
Cont.: Cæsar's Commentaries, $1.25. — First 6 bks. of Virgil's Æneid, $1.25. — Virgil's Æneid, $1.50. — Virgil's Eclogues, Georgics and Moretum, $1.25. — Cicero's Select orations, $1.50. — Sallust's Catiline and Jugurthine war, $1.25. — Cornelius Nepos, $1.25. — Horace's Odes, satires and epistles, $1.50. — Cicero's De senectute et de amicitia, $1.25. — Cicero's De officiis, $1.50. — Cicero's Tusculan disputations, $1.25. — Terence's Andria and Adelphœ, $1.25. — Tacitus, $1.25. — Juvenal, $1.25.
Chase, Warren. Gist of spiritualism: lectures. ('65.) 3d ed. 12°. '73. 50c.....................*Colby.*
— Life line of the lone one: an autobiography. ('57.) 3d ed. 12°. '60. $1.....................*Colby.*
Chasing the sun. Ballantyne, R. M. 75c.....*Porter.*
Chaste as ice, pure as snow. Despard, M. C. $1.50; $1.25; 75c..............................*Porter.*
Chastel, Ste. The charity of the primitive churches; tr. by G. A. Matile. 12°. $1.25.....*Lippincott.*
Chastelard. Swinburne, A. C. $1............*Holt.*
Chat in the play-room; [also] Life at a farm house. 16°. 50c..........................*Scribner, W. & A.*
Chateau Lescure; or, the last marquis; [by Jas. B. Kirker?] 18°. 50c.......................*Strong.*
Chateau Morville; or, life in Touraine; tr. from the French by E. R. 12°. '72. $1.50......*Claxton.*
Chateaubriand, F. A. (*Vicomte*) de. Atala. [French.] 12°. $2..............................*Routledge.*
— *Same;* [also] René. [French.] 12°. $1. *G. R. Lockwood.*
— *Eng.* Atala; tr. by J. S. Harry; ill. by G. Doré. cr. f°. $10; mor., $20...............*Cassell.*
— Genius of Christianity; or, the spirit and beauty of the Christian religion; tr., with pref., biog. notice and notes by Rev. C. I. White. por. demi 8°. '56. $2.50; $3............................*Murphy.*
— — Spirit and beauty of the Christian relig.: sel. from "Genius of Christianity"; tr. with introd. by Mrs. E. B. Stork. 12°. $1; $1.25....(?)*Luth. Pub.*
— Martyrs (Les), ou le triomphe de la religion chrétienne. 12°. $2.....................*Routledge.*
— *Same.* 12°. $1.50.................*G. R. Lockwood.*
— *Eng.* Martyrs (The). 12°. $1.50; $2; hf. mor., $3.50...................................*Sadlier.*
— Natchez (Les). 12°. $1.50.......*G. R. Lockwood.*
Chatelaine, *Mme.* de. Bridal etiquette. 16°. 10c. *Dick & F.*
— Child's own book of fairy tales. ill. 12°. $1.50. *World Pub.*
— Sir Wilfred's seven flights: fairy tale. ill. 16°. $1. *Routledge.*
— Truly noble: a tale. ill. 16°. $1..........*Cassell.*
Chatham, *Earl of* [W: Pitt], Burke, Edm., *and* Erskine, T: Celebrated speeches; [also] argument of Sir J. Mackintosh in the case of Peltier; sel. by a member of the Phila. bar. ('34.) New ed. 8°. '75. $2.25; shp., $2.75............*Claxton.*
Chatrian, Alex. *See* Erckmann, E., *and* Chatrian, A.
Chats for small chatterers. ill. 16°. $1.......*Cassell.*
Chats with the little ones. *See* Sauveur, L.
Chatsworth. Ward, R. P. 50c............*Harper.*
Chatterbox. [Annual.] ill. sq. 8°. $2.50; bds., $1.50. *Appleton.*
Chatterbox. [Annual.] ill. 4°. (Lond.) $2.50; bds., $1.50.........................*Am. News.*
Chatterbox junior: a centennial present for very young America. ill. 4°. '76. $1.15..*World Pub.*
Chatterton, T: Poems; with life, hist. of the Rowley controversy, etc. 2 v. por. 18°. $2....*Osgood.*
Chaucer, Geof. Works. por. and ill. roy. 8°. $4.50. *Routledge.*
— Canterbury tales; with notes and glossary by T. Tyrwhitt. (Globe ed.) 16°. $1.25; hf. cf., $3.25; mor., $4..............................*Appleton.*

Chaucer, Geof., *continued.*
— — *Same.* (Presentation poets.) ill. 12°. $1.75; $3. *Routledge*
— *Same;* ed. by R. A. Willmott, with biog. and crit notice. (British poets.) ill. 12°. $2.25; hf. cf. $3.50; mor., $5..................*Routledge*
— *Same;* and other poems; [also] Faerie queen, and other poems, by E. Spenser; with notes, glossary and memoir. (Globe ed.) ill. 16°. $1.25; hf cf., $3.25; mor., $4.................*Appleton*
— — *Same.* ill. 8°. hf. roxb., $2.50. *Appleton; Lee & S*
— Fables and tales. *See* Dryden, J.
— Poems. 12°. $1.50.........................*Locke*
— *Same.* (Aldine ed.) 6 v. 16°. ea., 75c. *Lippincott*
— Poetical works; with notes and glossary by T. Tyrwhitt. por. roy. 8°. $4.50..........*Routledge*
— *Same.* (Household ser.) ill. 16°. $1.50; mor., $3. *Lee & S*
— Reprints from the Canterbury tales, and Legends of goode women; for students. 12°. 75c.; pap. 35c...................................*Sheehan*
— *and* Crabbe, G. Poetical works. ill. 8°. '74. $2.50 *Routledge*
Chaumière Indienne (La). *See* Saint Pierre, J. H. B. de.
Chaumonot, P. J. M. La vie du R. P. Pierre Chaumonot, S. J., écrite par lui même, l'an 1688. 8°. '58. pap., $3........................*Shea*
Chauncey Judd. Warren, I. P. $1.50.....*Crowell.*
Chauveau, A. Comparative anatomy of the domesticated animals. 2d ed., rev. and enl. with coöperation of S. Arloing; tr. and ed. by Ja. Fleming ill. 8°. $6..............................*Appleton.*
Chauvenet, W: Elements of geom. 12°. $2..*Lippincott.*
— Manual of spherical and practical astronomy. 2 v. ill. 8°. $7...........................*Lippincott.*
— New method of correcting lunar distances, and of finding the error and rate of a chronometer, by equal altitudes. 8°. '68. $2.... *Van Nostrand.*
— Plane and spherical trigonom. 8°. $1.75..*Lippincott.*
— Treatise on the method of least squares; or, the application of the theory of probabilities in the combination of observations. 8°. $1.75.*Lippincott.*
Chauvin, V. *See* Denis, F., *and* Chauvin, V.
Chavasse, Pye H: Advice and counsel to a mother on the management of her children. 2 v. in 1. 12°. $2.................................*Lippincott.*
— *Same.* 16°. '62. $1.....................*D. Thomas.*
— Advice to a wife on the management of her own health; and on the treatment of the complaints incidental to pregnancy, labor and suckling. 12°. $1.50..................................*Lippincott.*
— Aphorisms of the mental culture and training of a child. 16°. '73. $1.50..........................*Lindsay.*
— Counsel to a mother: continuation of "Advice to a mother." 16°. $1.......................*Lippincott.*
— Physical training of children; with prelim. dissertation by F. H. Getchell. pl. 8°. '71. *$3; leath., $3.50.................................*New World.*
— Woman as a wife and mother. ill. 12°. $2.50..*Souder.*
Chavette, E. (*pseud.*) *See* Vachette, E.
Chawner, Rob. Diseases of the horse and how to treat them. 12°. '74. $1.25.................*Porter.*
Chazournes, R. de. Little month of St. Joseph: prayers and meditations for March. 32°. '68. 25c.; 40c.........................*Kelly, P. & Co.*
Cheap, *Mrs.* —. First day of the week. 18°. '59. 40c. *So. Meth.*
— Last day of the week. 18°. '59. 40c......*So. Meth.*
— Lessons from nature. ('56.) 3d ed. 18°. '75. 60c. *So. Meth.*
— Week completed. 18°. '59. 40c.........*So. Meth.*
Cheap excursion. Stirling, E. 15c...........*French.*
Cheap library. 50 v. 18°. *net*, $13.50.......*Am. Tr.*
Cheap Sunday school lib. 100 v. 18°. $18..*Pres. Bd.*

Checkmate. Halliday, A. 15c.....*De Witt; French.*
Checkmate. *See* Le Fanu, J. S.
Checks to Antinomianism. *See* Fletcher, J. W.
Cheerful chapters. *See* Mogridge, G.
Cheerful heart (The); or, a silver lining to every cloud. ill. 16°. 50c.........................*Lee & S.*
Cheerful voices. Emerson, L. O. 50c. ......*Ditson.*
Cheerily, cheerily. Baker, S. S. 60c.......*Am. Tr.*
Cheering words for the Master's workers. sq. 18°. '71. $1.50...........................*Randolph.*
Cheery chime of Garth. Prosser, *Mrs.* —. 75c. *Nelson.*
Cheeseman, Lew. Difference between old and new school Presbyterians; with introd. by J. C. Lord. 12°. '48. $1.50.....................*Darrow.*
Cheetham, S: *See* Smith, W., *and* Cheetham, S.
Cheever, D: W. Two cases of œsophagotomy for the removal of foreign bodies. 2d ed., enl. 8°. '68. 75c. ....*Jas. Campbell.*
Cheever, G: Barrell. Bible in the common schools. 16°. $1.25.............................*Carter.*
— Defense of capital punishment. 12°. 50c.... *Wiley.*
— Hill Difficulty, and other miscellanies. 12°. $1.. *Wiley.*
— Journal of the pilgrims at Plymouth in 1620. 12°. $1. *Wiley.*
— Lectures on Bunyan. 12°. $2..............*Carter.*
— Lectures on Cowper. 12°. $1.50...........*Carter.*
— Wanderings of a pilgrim in the Alps. 12°. $1.. *Wiley.*
— Wanderings of the river of the water of life. 12°. $1 ....*Wiley.*
— Waymarks of the pilgrimage; or, teaching by trials. 18°. 50c........................*Bost. Am. Tr.*
— (*ed.*) Poets of America: [selections] with notes. ill. 12°. $1.50.......................*World Pub.*
— Prose writers of America. ill. 12°. $1.50.. *World Pub.*
— *See also* Pictorial life.
— *and* Sweetser, J. E. Christian melodies: hymns and tunes for social and private worship. 2d ed. 12°. '51. $1.............................*Barnes.*
Cheever, H. T. Autobiography of Capt. Obadiah Congar, for 50 years mariner from the port of N. Y. 18°. $1.............................*Harper.*
— Island world of the Pacific. 12°. $1.50.... *Harper.*
— Life in the Sandwich Islands; or, the heart of the Pacific as it was and is. 12°. '51. $1.50..*Barnes.*
— Whale (The) and his captors; or, the whaleman's adventures and the whale's biography, as gathered on the homeward cruise of the "Commodore Preble." ill. 18°. $1.................*Harper.*
Cheever, N. W. Michigan probate law. 8°. '76. shp., $5.50......................*Richmond.*
Cheever, W: M. Practical evangelism; or, Bible Christianity enforced. 12°. 60c..... *Cong. Pub.*
Chellis, *Miss* Ma. D. All for money. 12°. '75. $1.25. *Nat. Temp.*
— Charley Wheeler's reward. ('68.) New ed. ill. 16°. '75. $1.25..............................*Hoyt.*
— Chellis library. ('68–'72.) New ed. 4 v. 12°. '74–'76. $5; ea., $1.25..................*Nat. Temp.*
Cont.: Aunt Dinah's pledge. — Temperance doctor. — Out of the fire. — At the lion's mouth.
— Deacon Sims' prayers. 16°. $1.50. *Cong. Pub.; H. A. Young.*
— Effie Wingate's work. 16°. '68. $1.50.. *H. A. Young.*
— Father Merrill. ill. 16°. '72. $1.50.......*Crowell.*
— — *See also* Father Merrill ser.
— Good work. 16°. '73. $1.50.............*Lothrop.*
— Jimmy's shoes; or, starlight. ('67.) New ed. ill. 16°. '73. $1.25.............................*Hoyt.*
— Molly's Bible. 16°. '69. $1.50....... *H. A. Young.*
— Mystery of the lodge. 12°. '74. $1.50.... *Lothrop.*
— Old mill (The). 16°. $1.50........... *Cong. Pub.*
— Old Sunapee. ('67.) New ed. ill. 16°. '74. $1.50.. *Hoyt.*
— Old times. ('72.) New ed. 12°. '75. $1.25.. *Nat. Temp.*
— Standard ed. of temp. tales. 4 v. 16°. '69–'71. $6; ea., $1.50........................*H. A. Young.*

Chellis, *Miss* Ma. D., *continued.*
Cont.: Bill Drock's investment. — Old doctor's son. — Mark Dunning's enemy. — Hermit of Holcombe.
— Things common and uncommon. 16°. $1.50. *Cong. Pub.*
— Two boys saved; or, a plain woman. 16°. $1.25. *Cong. Pub.*
— Wealth and wine. ('74.) New ed. 12°. '75. $1.25. *Nat. Temp.*
Chellis library. *See* Chellis, Ma. D.
Cheltnam, C: Smith. [Plays.] 12 v. 16°. ea., pap., 15c.....................................*French.*
Cont.: Christmas eve in a watch house: farce. — Deborah (Leah). — Dinner for nothing: farce. — Edendale. — Fairy's father: farce. — Lesson in love: comedy. — Lucky escape. — Mrs. Green's snug little business: farce. — More precious than gold: comedy. — Shadow of crime. — Slowtop's engagement: farce. — Ticket-of-leave-man's wife.
— Deborah (Leah); or, the Jewish maiden's wrong: drama. 12°. pap., 15c. ....*De Witt.*
Chemical history of the six days of creation. Phin, J. 75c.....................................*Indust.*
Chemistry of a candle. Faraday, M. $1... *Harper.*
Chemistry of common life. Johnston, J. F. W. $3. *Appleton.*
Chemnitz, M. Examen Concilii Tridentini, d. h.: Prüfung des Concils von Trient; a. d. Lat. v. 1. 8°. hf. leath., $1.50................ *Volkening.*
— *and* Leyser, P., *and* Gerhard, J. Perikopen: echt evangel. Auslegung d. Sonn- u. Festtags Evangelien d. Kirchenjahrs, übers. u. ausgezogen; hrsg. v. d. monatl. Predigerconf. zu Fort Wayne, Ind. 7 v. 8°. '58–'76. $10.50........*Barthel.*
Cheney, *Mrs.* Ednah D. Child of the tide. 16°. $1.50. *Lee & S.*
— Faithful to the light, and other tales. ('70.) 2d ed. ill. 16°. '72. 80c.....................*Am. Unit.*
— Patience: games for the fireside. 24°. 75c... *Lee & S.*
— Sally Williams, the mountain girl. ill. 12°. $1.50. *Lee & S.*
— Social games. 24°. $1..................*Lee & S.*
Cheney, O. A. *See* Alger, H., *jr.*, *and* Cheney, O. A.
Cherbuliez, Vct. Count Kostia; tr. by O. D. Ashley. (Leis. hour ser.) 16°. '73. $1.25........ *Holt.*
— Joseph Noirel's revenge; tr. by W. F. West. (Leis. hour ser.) 16°. '72. $1.25...............*Holt.*
— Miss Rovel; tr. by F. A. Shaw. 8°. '75. $1.25; pap., 50c. ....*Estes.*
— Prosper; tr. by C. Benson. (Leis. hour ser.) 16°. '74. $1.25................................*Holt.*
— Romance of an honest woman; tr. ('74.) New ed. 12°. '75. $1.50..................... *W. F. Gill.*
Cherry, A. Soldier's daughter: comedy. 16°. pap., 15c....................................*French.*
— Travelers: opera. 16°. pap., 15c.........*French.*
Cherry, P. P. Grave Creek mound, its stone and hist. with its vindication. 16°. pap., 10c. *J. A. Clark.*
Cherry and Fair Star: pantomime. 16°. pap., 15c. *French*
Cherry and Violet. Manning, A. $1.........*Dodd.*
Cherry bounce. Blackburn, W. M. 60c... *Pres. Bd.*
Cherry bounce. Raymond, R. J. 15c....... *French.*
Cherry, the missionary; or, the church in the wilderness. 16°. 90c.........................*Am. S. S.*
— *See also* Diamond lib.
Cherry orchard (The); or, the disobliging boy, and how he was cured. ill. cr. 4°. pap., 20c.; 25c. *J. E. Potter.*
Cherry ripe series. 12 v. sm. 8°. ea., 12½c. *Nelson.*
Cont.: Ripe cherries. — Country scenes — New book of pictures. — Busy farm. — The swan. — Little verses for good boys and girls. — Pictures from best book. — Giant killer. — Our Lily. — Pretty Rose. — Buttercups from daisies. — Little Red Riding Hood.
Cherry, the singer. Samuels, S. B. C. $1. *Lockwood, B. & Co.*
Cherry stones. Adams, H. C. 75c. *Dutton; Routledge.*

Cherub (The). Johnson, J. C. 35c.; 30c.... *Ditson.*

Cherubini, L. Treatise on counterpoint and fugue; tr. by Mrs. Cowden Clarke; musical part supervised by J. Pittman. 8°. $2.50.. *Ditson; Peters.*

Cherubino and Seraphina. Wildermuth, O. $1.25. *Cin. Meth. Bk. Conc.*

Chéry, M. Month of the holy rosary: devotions for October. 18°. 60c.................... *O'Shea.*

Chesbrough, E. S. Plan and progress of the Detroit River tunnel. 8°. pap., 30c... *Am. Soc. of C. E.*

— — *See also* Steele, J. D., Tests of bridge irons.

Chesebro', *Miss* Caro. Amy Carr; or, the fortune teller. ill. 16°. '63. 90c.......................... *Dodd.*

— Foe (The) in the household. [Fiction.] 8°. '71. $1.25; pap., 75c.......................... *Estes.*

— Glen cabin (The). ill. 18°. '65. 60c...... *Am. Tr.*

— *German.* Blockhaus (Das) in dem Berge. ill. 18°. '71. 50c.............................. *Am. Tr.*

Chesebrough, A. S. Home work; or, parochial Christianization. 16°. $1. 18°. pap., 40c. *Bost. Am. Tr.*

Cheshire Pastoral Association. Christian hymns for public and private worship; comp. by a committee. 16°. $1.50.................... *Fuller.*

Chesney, C. C. Essays in military biog. 12°. '74. $2.50.................................. *Holt.*

Chesney, G: Battle of Dorking; the fall of England, 1875–1925: reminiscences of a volunteer. 12°. 50c.; pap., 25c............... *Porter; Putnam.*

— Dilemma. [Fiction.] 8°. '76. pap., 75c... *Harper.*

Chess congress of 1862. *See* Lowenthal, J.

Chest of tools. *See* Baker, *Mrs.* H. N. W.

Chester, J: Derwent; or, recollections of young life in the country. 12°. '72. $1.50..... *Randolph.*

Chester, S. Electro science as a part of the education of civil engineers. 8°. pap., 30c. *Am. Soc. of C.E.*

— Nitro glycerine: its manufacture and use. 8°. pap., 45c.......................... *Am. Soc. of C.E.*

Chester, *Miss* Sa. E. Lady Linnet. ill. 18°. '71. 25c. *Am. Tr.*

— Nine Saturdays. 18°. '68. 60c......... *Randolph.*

— Ollie and the boys. ill. 16°. '72. $1.25.... *Crowell.*

— — *See also* Ollie lib.

— Our three boys. ill. 16°. '75. $1.25...... *Am. Tr.*

— Proud little Dody. ill. 12°. '75. $1.25.... *Am. Tr.*

— Roly and Poly story books. 3 v. in 1. ill. 16°. '68. $1.50.............................. *Randolph.*

— Sir Genevieve. 16°. '69. $1.25.......... *Randolph.*

— Swallow stories. 12 v. ill. 32°. '73. $2... *Am. Tr.*

— Thanksgiving. ill. 32°. '74. 25c.......... *Am. Tr.*

Chester, Florence. *See* Mudge, Z. A., Pure gold ser.; Rustic lib.

Chesterfield, *Lord.* [Ph. Dormer Stanhope.] Works, incl. Letters to his son. 12°. $1.25; hf. cf., $3. *Lippincott.*

— *Same;* with memoir. 8°. $2.50; hf. cf., $4.75. *Harper.*

— Letters, sentences and maxims. 16°. $1.25. *Scribner, W. & A.*

— *Same;* sel. from his works by A. Howard. sq. 18°. $1.25................................ *Porter.*

— Letters to his son. 2 v. por. sm. 8°. $5; hf. cf., $10.............................. *Appleton.*

— *See also* American Chesterfield; — Practical morality.

Chesterfield Thinskin: farce. 16°. pap., 15c. *French.*

Chesterfield's letter-writer and complete book of etiquette. 16°. bds., 35c............. *Dick & F.*

Chesterman, Edn. (*ed.*) "You ask! — I'll tell!" condensed encyclopedia of all things of every day life. 12°. '73. *$2.25; hf. mor., $3..... *Flint.*

Chevalier, Mich. On the probable fall in the value of gold; tr. by R. Cobden. 8°. '59. $1.25.. *Appleton.*

Chevalier d'Harmental (The). *See* Dumas, A.

Chevalier de Maison Rouge. *See* Dumas, A.

Chevalier de St. George. Robertson, T. W. 15c. *De Witt; French.*

Chevallier, E. *See* Lenormant, F., *and* Chevallier, E.

Cheves, L. *See* South Carolina, Chancery reports; Reports.

Chevreul, Mich. Eug. Laws of contrast of color, and their application to the fine arts; tr. from the Fr. ill. 16°. $2.......................... *Routledge.*

— Principles of harmony and contrast of colors, and their applic. to the arts; tr. by C. Martel. 12°. (Bohn.) $1.75; col. pl., $2.75.. *Little, B. & Co.*

— *Same.* 12°. (Bohn.) $2; col. pl., $3. *Lippincott; Scribner, W. & A.*

Note. Another tr. of Laws of contrast.

— — *See also* Painter, gilder and varnisher's companion.

Chew Alley. Davis, C. E. K. $1.50.......... *Hoyt.*

Cheyne, C. H. *See* Jones, C. A., *and* Cheyne, C. H.

Cheyne, C. H. H. Earth's motion of rotation; including the theory of precession and nutation. cr. 8°. '67. $1.50.......................... *Macmillan.*

— Elementary treatise on the planetary theory; with problems. 2d ed. cr. 8°. '70. $2.50.. *Macmillan.*

Cheyne, T. K. Book of Isaiah chronol. arranged: an amended version, with hist. and crit. introd. and notes. cr. 8°. '70. $2.25............ *Macmillan.*

— Notes and criticisms on the Hebrew text of Isaiah. 8°. '70. pap., $1.......................... *Macmillan.*

Chicago. Rules of practice of the courts of record in Chicago; embracing the U. S. Circuit and District Courts, Ill. Supreme Court, etc. 8°. '73. shp., $1.50.......................... *E. B. Myers.*

Chicago illustrated almanac for 1874. 12°. pap., 25c. (?) *O. L. Fox.*

Chicard, *Count.* Bal masque. 16°. pap., 15c. *French.*

Chichester, Darwin. Hannah's vow; or, hallowed motherhood. sq. 18°. $1........ *Bost. Am. Tr.*

Chicot. Dumas, A. 50c.................. *Routledge.*

Chief end of man. Hall, J. 40c.......... *Pres. Bd.*

Chief of the school. Adams, H. C. 75c... *Routledge.*

Chief's daughter. Tucker, C. 75c.......... *Carter.*

Chignonens historia, eller hwarifrån kommer allt fruntimmers-löshår. 12°. pap., 10c..... *Engberg.*

Child, *Miss* —. The R. B. R.'s, my little neighbors. ill. sq. 16°. 75c.......................... *Fuller.*

Child, A. B. A B C of life. ('69.) 5th ed. 12°. '74. pap., 25c.......................... *Colby.*

— Better views of living; or, life according to the doctrine, "whatever is, is right." ('68.) 3d ed. 12°. '74. $1.............................. *Colby.*

— Christ and the people. ('66.) 4th ed. 12°. '73. $1.25.................................. *Colby.*

— Soul affinity. ('70.) 6th ed. 12°. '74. pap., 20c... *Colby.*

— Unhappy marriages. 12°. '68. pap., 15c..... *Colby.*

— Whatever is, is right. ('64.) 5th ed. 12°. '74. $1...................................... *Colby.*

Child, Fs. J. (*ed.*) Ballads, English and Scottish. 8 v. 18°. $8.............................. *Osgood.*

Child, G. Chaplin. Benedicite: illustrations of power, wisdom and goodness of God; with introd. by H: G. Weston. 12°. '67. $2; hf. cf., $4.. *Putnam.*

Child, *Mrs.* Lydia Mar. Children of Mount Ida, and other stories. 12°. '71. $1.25...... (?) *Francis.*

— Freedmen's (The) book. 16°. '65. $1.25.. *Osgood.*

— Looking towards sunset. ill. 4°. '64. $3; hf. cf., $5; mor., $6.50.......................... *Osgood.*

— Married women: biographies of good wives. 12°. '71. $1.25.......................... (?) *Francis.*

— Progress of religious ideas through successive ages. ('55.) New ed. 3 v. cr. 8°. '76. $6.75; hf. cf., $13.50.................................. *Miller.*

— Romance of the republic. 4th ed. 16°. '67. $2. *Osgood.*

— Stories. 5 v. ill. 18°. '69–'70. ea., 75c... *Lothrop.*

Cont.: Boy's heaven. — Jamie and Jennie. — Making something. — Good little Mitty. — The Christ child.

— (*ed.*) Rainbows for children. ill. 16°. $1.50.. *Osgood.*

Child (The). Dupanloup, F. A. P. $1.50...*Noonan.*
Child (The) and the poets. *See* Whittier, J. G.
Child angel (The). *See* Bradley, *Mrs.* M. E., Good girls' lib.
Child angel (The). *See* Denison, *Mrs.* M. A.
Child (The) assisted in giving the heart to God. Kimball, D. 35c........................*Cong. Pub.*
Child at home. *See* Abbott, J. S. C.
Child captives (The). Hosmer, M. 75c....*Pres. Bd.*
Child Christian matured. 18°. 65c.; 75c...*Am. Bapt.*
Child Jesus. *See* Davis, *Mrs.* C. E. K.
Child land: picture pages for the little ones. ill. 4°. '75. $1.50..............................*Nelson.*
Child library. *See* Davis, *Mrs.* C. E. K.
Child-life. Richenau, R. $1.75...........*Routledge.*
Child-life. Whittier, J. G. $3; $5; $6.....*Osgood.*
Child-life in Egypt. 16°. $1.10............*Am. S. S.*
Child-life in Europe. Watson, E. H. $1.50..*W.F. Gill.*
Child-life in India. *See* Silver penny ser.
Child-life in Italy. Watson, E. H. $1.50..*W.F. Gill.*
Child-life in many lands. Strong, J. D. $1..*Lothrop.*
Child-life in New England. Hall, S. L. $1..*Cong. Pub.*
Child-life in Oregon. Boyd, O. A. 60c........*Hoyt.*
Child-life in pictures: 24 heliot. pl. from Correggio, Copley, Reynolds, etc. 4°. '75. $10...*Osgood.*
Child-life in prose. Whittier, J. G. $3; $5; $6. *Osgood.*
Child-life series. 5 v. 16°. $5.............*Lothrop.*
Cont.: Child life, by J. D. Strong. — Little Lilly's travels. — Old friends. — Haps and mishaps. — Neighborly love.
Child martyr (The) and early Christians in Rome. ('70.) New ed. ill. 16°. '72. $1.15.......*Hoyt.*
Child-nature; by authors of "Poems written for a child." ill. sq. 16°. $1.50...........*Routledge.*
Child of the church. 18°. 40c...............*Dutton.*
Child of faith. 18°. 40c.......................*Dutton.*
Child of the island glen. Kellogg, E. $1.25..*Lee & S.*
Child of Jesus. 18°. 30c.; 40c...........*Am. Bapt.*
Child of Mary. *See* Sisters of Notre Dame.
Child of nature. Inchbald, E. 15c..........*French.*
Child of prayer: a father's memorial to D. A. Tyng. 32°. '66. 50c.......................*Randolph.*
Child of Providence; or, Arthur Montrose. 18°. 45c.; 55c. ....*Am. Bapt.*
Child of the regiment: comedy. 16°. pap., 15c. *French.*
Child of the rock. Barth, C. G. 65c.......*Pres. Bd.*
Child of the tide. Cheney, E. D. $1.50.....*Lee & S.*
Child of Waterloo. Reynolds, G. W. M. 75c. *Peterson.*
Child of the wreck. Planché, J. R. 15c......*French.*
Child (The) one hundred years old; by author of "Learn to say no." 18°. 50c.........*Pres. Bd.*
Child pictures from Dickens. ill. 16°. $1.50..*Dutton.*
Child Samuel (The). Goulburn, E. M. $1.25..*Pott.*
Child stealer: drama. 16°. pap., 15c........*French.*
Child-wife (The). *See* Dickens, C.
Child-world; by authors of "Poems written for a child." ill. sq. 16°. $1.50...................*Routledge.*
Child world. Dodge, M. A. 2 v. ea., $1.50..*W.F. Gill.*
Childe, E: Lee. Life and campaigns of Gen. Lee; tr. by G. Litting. por. 8°. '75. $3.....*Routledge.*
Childe, J: New England's Jonas cast up at London. Lond., 1647. [Reprint.] 4°. pap., 50c...*Sabin.*
Childe Harold's pilgrimage. *See* Byron, *Lord.*
Childhood. Crafts, W. F. $1.50..........*Lee & S.*
Childhood; or, little Alice. sq. 16°. '55. 60c. *Meth. Bk. Conc.*
Childhood of religions. Clodd, E. $1.25..*Appleton.*
Childhood of the world. *See* Clodd, E.
Childhood songs. Larcom, L. $2.25; $5..*Osgood.*
Children and Jesus. Hammond, E. P. 45c.; 55c. *Am. Bapt.*
Children and the lion. Wilberforce, W. $1.25. *Meth. Bk. Conc.*
Children at play. *See* Baker, *Mrs.* H. N. W., Corwin's nest ser.
Children brought to Christ. Dayton, A. C. 25c.; 10c....................................*So. Bapt.*
Children called to Jesus. 18°. 25c.; pap., 10c. *So. Bapt.*
Children in the boat. 32°. 20c.; 15c.......*Dutton.*
Children in heaven. Schenck, W. E. $1.75..*Pres. Bd.*
Children in paradise. Wines, F. H. $1..(?) *Martien.*
Children in the wood. Morton, T. 15c.....*French.*
Children in the wood. Stoddard, R. H. 25c. *Hurd & H.*
Children invited to Christ. ill. 18°. '49. 25c. *Am. Tr.*
Children led to the Saviour. Waterbury, J. B. 20c. *Am. Tr.*
Children of the abbey. *See* Roche, R. M.
Children of Abraham; or, sketches of Jewish converts. 18°. 50c......................*Pres. Bd.*
Children of Amity Court. Thurston, L. M. $1. *Lee & S.*
Children of Blackberry Hollow. 6 v. ill. 18°. $1.80. *Am. S. S.*
Cont.: Red shoes. — White frock. — Tom Lane's cent. — The little brown house. — Little lights. — New bonnet.
Children of the Bible. 18°. 40c. *Pres. Com.; Pres. Bd.*
Children of the Bible. *See* Caulkins, F. M.
Children of the big house. *See* Harland stories.
Children of blessing. Richmond, D. $1.25..*Routledge.*
Children of the castle. Ball, E. 15c........*French.*
Children of the church. O'Reilly, E. R. 50c...*Pott.*
Children of the church, and sealing ordinances. 18°. 45c....................................*Pres. Bd.*
Children of Cloverly. *See* Smith, Hannah.
Children of the covenant. *See* Witherspoon, T. D.
Children of the east. Jessup, H. A. 90c. *Cong. Pub.*
Children of elfland. Paul, H. B. 75c. *Scribner, W. & A.*
Children of the great king. ill. 16°. $1.25..*Crowell.*
— *See also* Maude Grenville lib.; — Posie ser.
Children of Jerusalem. Johnson, J. C. 30c. *Ditson.*
Children of Lake Huron; or, the cousins at Cloverly. 16°. '66. $1.25.................*Meth. Bk. Conc.*
Children of the lighthouse. 18°. 90c. ...(?) *Martien.*
Children (The) of long ago; by author of "Words for women." ill. 18°. 70c............*Am. S. S.*
Children of many lands. Strong, J. D. 60c. *Bost. Am. Tr.*
Children of Mary: lives of pupils of La Maison des Oiseaux, Paris. 16°. '74. $1.25; $1.75. *Kelly, P. & Co.*
Children of Mount Ida. Child, L. M. $1.25..(?) *Francis.*
Children of the New Forest. *See* Marryat, F.
Children of the New Testament. Stork, T. 75c.; $1. (?) *Luth. Pub.*
Children of Oakford Farm. 18°. 75c..... *Whittaker.*
Children of the olden time. Mackarness, M. A. $1.25 ....*Scribner, W. & A.*
Children of the parsonage; by author of "Sunny days." ill. 16°. '72. $1..............*Dutton.*
Children of the patriarchs. Braussi, M. 75c.; $1. *O'Shea.*
Children of the pear garden. Hervey, E. L. $1. *Scribner, W. & A.*
Children of Stantoun Corbet ser. *See* Guernsey, L. E.
Children of the state. Hill, F. $1.50....*Macmillan.*
Children of the sun. ill. post 18°. 75c. *Scribner, W. & A.*
Children of the valley; or, the ghost of the ruins. 18°. '65. 50c...................*Cunningham.*
Children on the plains. 18°. 60c............*Carter.*

Children with the poets. McKeever, H. B. $1.50; $2; $2.25; $4.50 .... *Claxton.*
Children with wings. 18°. 17c.; 22c...... *Am. Bapt.*
Children's album of pretty pictures. *See* Aikin, J.
Children's band. Plunkett, I. 50c. *Dutton; Scribner, W. & A.*
Children's Bible picture-book. ill. 4°. $1.50.. *Harper.*
Children's Bible picture-book; in words of one syllable. ill. 16°. $1 .... *World Pub.*
Children's Bible story-book. Neally, A. R. $1.50. *Dutton.*
Children's book for Sabbath hours. Bullard, A. *(?) (?) *Holland.*
Children's book of prayer and praise; for S.-schools. 32°. 20c. .... *Dutton.*
Children's bread. *See* Schieffelin, S. B.
Children's cave, and other stories. 18°. 17c.; 22c. *Am. Bapt.*
Children's chip-basket. *See* Hathaway, H. N.
Children's choir. Evans, J. M. 18c...... *Am. Bapt.*
Children's church. Latimer, F. 60c...... *Pres. Bd.*
Children's church. *See* Newton, R. H.
Children's daily text-book. 32°. 20c........ *Nelson.*
Children's emblem annual. ill. 16°. '71. 35c.; pap., 15c. .... *Tibbals.*
Children's friend. [Annual.] 4°. bds., 75c... *Nelson.*
Children's friend. Berquin, A. $1.25.. *Nichols & H.*
Children's garden. 16°. 50c...... *Scribner, W. & A.*
Children's garland. *See* Patmore, C.
Children's gift. Walton, E. L. *net*, 50c. *Friends Bk. Assoc.*
Children's harp; or, select poetry for the young. 16°. 50c........ *Scribner, W. & A.*
Children's hearts and hands. 16°. 80c..... *Am. S. S.*
Children's holidays. *See* Continental lib.
Children's hosanna. Collins, C., *jr.* 50c.; 37c.; 25c. *J. E. Potter.*
Children's hour. S., E. W., *and* M., S. W. $1.25. *Claxton; Lippincott.*
Children's hour library. 5 v. 16°. $3.75... *Lothrop.*
Cont.: Songs for little folks. — Bible stories. — Stories of birds. — Stories of animals. — Picture lessons.
Children's hymnal; with music. ill. cr. 8°. $1.50; — without music. 35c.; pap., 25c..... *Huntington.*
Children's island. Genlis, *Comtesse* de. 25c. *Scribner, W. & A.*
Children's joy. ill. roy. 16°. 50c........ *Cassell.*
Children's library. 3 v. ill. 24°. $1.50... *Routledge.*
Children's library. 64 v. ill. 32°. hf. bd., $6.. *Am. Tr.*
Children's library: ser. A. 239 v. 24°. ea., 12c.-20c.; per set, hf. roan, $30.68........ *Meth. Bk. Conc.*
— *Same:* ser. B. 252 v. 18°. ea., 15c.; per set, hf. roan, $37.80........ *Meth. Bk. Conc.*
Children's Methodist speaker. 16°. '66. 50c.. *Tibbals.*
Children's offerings to heathen idols. 18°. 18c. *Am. S. S.*
Children's packets. 5 ser. 32°. ea., 20c... *Pres. Bd.*
Children's party; or, a day at Upland. 16°. 60c. *Am. S. S.*
Children's pastime: pictures and stories for the little ones. ill. sm. 4°. '75. $1.75........ *Nelson.*
Children's picture-book. Warren, J. S. 40c. *Bost. Am. Tr.*
Children's picture-book of quadrupeds and other mammalia. ill. 4°. $1.50........ *Harper.*
Children's picture-book of sagacity of animals. ill. 4°. $1.50........ *Harper; Routledge.*
Children's picture-books of birds. ill. 4°. $1.50.. *Harper.*
Children's picture fable-book. ill. 4°. $1.50. *Harper; Routledge.*
Children's picture story-book. Pratt, L. M. $1.50. *Lothrop.*
Children's pleasure book. ill. 4°. bds., 60c... *Claxton.*
Children's poetry-book. ill. 18°. $1.50.... *Routledge.*
Children's post office at Maple grove. *See* Maple grove stories.
Children's praise. *See* Converse, C. C., *and* Schenck, W. E.
Children's prayer test. *See* Boyd, *Mrs.* E. E.
Children's prize. ill. 4°. (Lond.) bds., 75c. *Am. News.*
Children's prize stories. 6 v. ill. 64°. $1.50.. *Locke.*
Cont.: Love one another. — Brave and gentle. — The fireman's dog. — Little Jack. — Stories for good boys. — Stories for good girls.
Children's progressive lyceum. Davis, A. J. 60c. *A. J. Davis.*
Children's providence. *See* Maple grove stories.
Children's sayings. *See* Hadley, C.
Children's services: book of pictorial family worship. ill. sm. 4°. $2.50........ *Routledge.*
Children's speaker. Boyd, E. E., *and* Johnston, E. M. 60c. .... *J. A. Moore.*
Children's Sunday album. *See* Mackarness, M. A.
Children's tabernacle. Tucker, C. 75c...... *Carter.*
Children's treasure. ill. 4°. $1.25; bds., 75c. *Lee & S.*
Children's treasury. [Annual.] 4°. bds., 50c. *Nelson.*
Children's treasury. *See* Tucker, *Mrs.* C.
Children's treasury of Eng. song. Palgrave, F. T. $1.25 .... *Macmillan.*
Children's trials. Linden, A. $1.25........ *O'Shea.*
Children's trials; or, common errors in the conduct of life, and their consequences. 18°. 55c. *Am. S. S.*
Children's victories; or, Ossie and Maria. 16°. $1.25. *Am. S. S.*
Child's best teacher. [Verse.] 18°. 22c... *Am. S. S.*
Child's Bible. ill. 96°. pap., 15c........ *U. P. James.*
Child's Bible: consecutive arrangement of portions of Scripture in the wording of the authorized version. ill. demy 4°. $12; hf. mor., $15; leath., $16; mor., $18 .... *Cassell.*
— *See also* Illustrated child's Bible.
Child's book. Sigourney, L. H. 50c......... *Carter.*
Child's book of animals. ill. 4°. 25c........ *Am. S. S.*
Child's book of ballads. 18°. 60c. 16°. 80c. *Am. S. S.*
Child's book of common things. Hooker, W. *net*, 30c. *Peck.*
Child's book of divinity. Macduff, J. R. 35c.... *Carter.*
Child's book of favorite stories. col. ill. 4°. $1.50.. *Wiley.*
Child's book of nature. *See* Hooker, W.
Child's book of religion. Frothingham, O. B. $1. *Putnam.*
Child's book of song and praise: music, with pianoforte accomp. ill. imp. 8°. $3.50....... *Cassell.*
Child's book of trades. ill. sq. 12°. '71. bds., 50c. *Routledge.*
Child's book on the creed. 18°. 40c....... *Whittaker.*
Child's book on repentance. Gallaudet, T. H. 40c. *Am. Tr.*
Child's book on the Sabbath. Hooker, H. 40c. *Am. Tr.*
Child's book on the soul. Gallaudet, T. H. 40c. *Am. Tr.*
Child's budget. ill. 18°. 70c........ *Pres. Bd.*
Child's Bunyan. *See* Bunyan, J.
Child's cabinet library. 50 v. 32°. $4.50.. *Am. S. S.*
Child's cabinet of things both rare and useful. sq. 16°. 50c........ *Pres. Bd.*
Child's catechism of Scripture history. 4 v. 18°. ea., 20c. *Pres. Bd.*
Cont.: Genesis to Numbers. — Deuteronomy, Joshua and Judges. — From the accession of David to the death of Jehosaphat. — From Jehosaphat to end of Old Testament.
Child's Catholic manual: abridg. of the Christian doctrine, [with] prayers, etc. 32°. 45c.-$2.50.. *O'Shea.*
Child's Catholic manual: prayer book for children. 32°. 45c.-$2.50........ *O'Shea.*
— *See also* Catholic manual.

Child's Catholic piety. [Prayer book.] 48°. 30c.-85c. *T. Kelly; Strong.*
Child's Christmas carol; by a lady of Phila. 18°. pap., 10c. .... *McCauley.*
Child's Christmas sheaf from the Bible fields. Abbott, E. A. $1 .... *Bost. Am. Tr.*
Child's colored gift-book. ill. sq. 12°. $1.75 .. *Routledge.*
Child's colored Scripture-book. ill. sq. 12°. $1.75. *Routledge.*
Child's commandment and child's promise. 32°. 25c. *Am. S. S.*
Child's country book. Miller, T. $1.50 ... *Routledge.*
Child's country story-book. Miller, T. $1.50. *Routledge.*
Child's daily [Cath.] prayer book. 48°. '69. 25c.-$2. *Kelly, P. & Co.*
Child's daily food: texts of Scripture with questions. 32°. 25c. .... *Bost. Am. Tr.*
Child's delight. Howitt, M. $1.50 .... *Miller.*
Child's delight. Valentine, R. $1.50 .. (?) *McLoughlin.*
Child's dream of a star. *See* Dickens, C.
Child's duty. *See* Picture page lib.
Child's edition of Arabian nights, Robinson Crusoe, Æsop's fables and Gulliver's travels. ill. 12°. $1.50 .... *World Pub.*
Child's effort; [also] Tongue bridle. 32°. 20c.; 15c. *Dutton.*
Child's famous picture-book. ill. 4°. $1.50. *Scribner, W. & A.*
Child's finger-post; or, help for the heedless. ill. post 18°. 75c. .... *Scribner, W. & A.*
Child's first history of Am.; by author of "Little Dora." ill. sq. 18°. 50c. .... *Appleton.*
Child's first lesson-book. ill. sq. 12°. '71. $1.25. *Routledge.*
Child's friend. Berquin, A. de. 75c. .... *Harper.*
Child's guide through the Bible; or, a help to understand the Bible. 18°. 40c. .... *Am. S. S.*
Child's guide to heaven. Hammond, E. P. 35c ... *Hoyt.*
Child's home library. 50 v. 32°. $5 .... *Am. S. S.*
Child's hymn book. Caulkins, F. M. 25c ... *Am. Tr.*
Child's illustrated poetry-book. 18°. 45c ... *Routledge.*
Child's illustrated Scripture quest. book on the Gospels. 16°. 20c. .... *Dutton.*
Child's influence. Lockyer, L. $1 .... *Dutton.*
Child's lesson-book on the Bible. 18°. per doz., $2.40. *Meth. Bk. Conc.*
Child's lesson-book on the New Test. 18°. per doz., $1.80 .... *Meth. Bk. Conc.*
Child's lesson-book on the Old Test. 18°. per doz., $2.16 .... *Meth. Bk. Conc.*
Child's library. 27 v. 32°. $6 .... *Cong. Pub.*
Child's library. 6 v. 32°. $1.90 .... *Am. S. S.*
Cont.: Little herdsman. — How to do right. — Parley, the porter. — Master key. — Unknown path. — Bessie Duncan.
Child's mission. Wallace, S. S. T. 35c .... *Pres. Bd.*
Child's Noah's ark. *See* Pearl ser.
Child's own book of fairy tales. ill. sq. 16°. $2 .. *Miller.*
Child's own book of fairy tales. Chatelaine, *Mme.* de. $1.50 .... *World Pub.*
Child's own book of pictures. sm. 4°. '73. $1 .. *Nelson.*
Child's own library. 3 v. ill. sq. 16°. $5.50 .. *Miller.*
Cont.: Child's own book. — Child's treasury of fairy tales. — Edgeworth's Parent's assistant.
Child's own treasury of fairy tales. ill. 4°. $1.75 .. *Miller.*
Child's picture-book. *See* Pretty picture ser.
Child's picture-book of animals. ill. obl. 4°. $4.50. *Routledge.*
Comprising Child's picture-book of wild animals *and* Child's picture-book of domestic animals.
Child's picture-book of domestic animals. ill. obl. 4°. $2.50 .... *Routledge.*
Child's picture-book of wild animals. ill. obl. 4°. $2.50. *Routledge.*
Child's picture scrap-book. ill. f°. bds., $2; col. ill., $4.50 .... *Routledge.*
Child's picture story-book. ill. sm. 4°. $2 .. *Routledge.*
Child's pictures. ill. 18°. '70. 30c. .... *Am. Tr.*
Child's pilgrim's progress. *See* Bunyan, J.
Child's play. *See* Big type stories.
Child's poetical keepsake. ill. sq. 16°. 75c ... *Pres. Bd.*
Child's popular fairy tales. Dulcken, H. W. $3. *Scribner, W. & A.*
Child's prayer. *See* J. H. and his nurse.
Child's prayer and hymn book; for Catholic schools. 32°. '51. 30c.-$1 .... *Murphy.*
Child's primer. [French.] 16°. 30c. ...... *Pres. Bd.*
Child's Sabbath day book. sq. 16°. '54. 45c. *Meth. Bk. Conc.*
Child's scrap-book. 18°. 40c. .... *Pres. Bd.*
Child's Scripture question book. ill. 32°. '53. bds., 16c. *Am. S. S.*
— *Same.* ill. 24°. '67. 16c. .... *Pres. Com.*
Child's speaker. Northend, C. 60c. .... *Barnes.*
Child's story-book. Cousin Martha *and* Mary. 40c. *Pres. Bd.*
Child's treasure. Guernsey, L. E. 90c. .. *Whittaker.*
Child's treasury. 24 v. 18°. 25c. .... *Nelson.*
Child's treasury. Collins, R. 60c. .... *Claxton.*
Child's treasury of fairy tales. sq. 16°. $1.75 .. *Miller.*
Child's true Christian religion. 12°. 50c.; 75c. *New Ch.*
Child's warfare. Hewer, M. E. 90c. ...... (?) *Martien.*
Child's wreath of home poems. ill. 16°. 75c .... *Locke.*
Childs, T. S. The heritage of peace; or, Christ all in all. sq. 24°. '68. 75c.; $1.25 ...... *Randolph.*
Chillingworth, W: Religion of Protestants a safe way to salvation; or, answer to "Charity maintained." 12°. (Bohn.) $1.25 .. *Little, B. & Co.*
— *Same.* 12°. (Bohn.) $1.40 .... *Scribner, W. & A.*
— *Same.* 12°. (Bohn.) $1.50 .... *Lippincott.*
Chilperic. Ronger, F. $1 .... *Pond.*
Chimasia. Orthos. $1 .... *Lippincott.*
Chime (The). Taylor, V. C. $1.50 .... *Ditson.*
Chimes and rhymes for youthful times. ill. sq. 8°. '71. $1.50 .... *Routledge.*
Chimes for childhood. ill. 12°. $1.50 ...... *Lee & S.*
Chimes for childhood. Estes, D. 60c.; 75c .. *Estes.*
Chimes, rhymes and jingles; ed. and ill. by C. H. Bennett, etc. sq. 16°. 60c.; 90c.; pap., 30c. *Miller.*
Chiming bells. Jarvis, C. H. 45c. .... *Sower.*
Chimney-corner. Craven, H. T. 15c ...... *French.*
Chimney-corner. Stowe, H. B. $1.75 .... *Osgood.*
China, pictorial, etc. *See* Corner, Jla.
China and crockery trade reference book. 4°. '70. $25. *J. A. Murphy.*
China cup (The). *See* Maggie Fuller lib.
China cup (The); or, Ellen's trial. 18°. 50c. *Pres. Bd.*
Chinaman (The) in California; by author of "Rich and poor." 18°. 55c. .... *Pres. Bd.*
Chincapin Charlie. Eyster, N. $1.25 .... *Meth. Epis.*
Chinese bride: a story of real life. 18°. 45c.; 55c. *Am. Bapt.*
Chinese classics. *See* Legge, J.
Chinese coast. 18°. '53. 35c. .... *Am. Tr.*
Chinese mother (The). Tandy, W. 50c. *Kelly, P. & Co.; Sadlier.*
Chinese problem (The). Townsend, L. T. 75c.; 50c. (?) *Lee & S.*
Chinks of Clannyford. Hamilton, K. W. $1.40. *Pres. Bd.*
Chip and Kitty. *See* Leighton children.

Chip-basket stories. 5 v. ill. 18°. $2.50. *Bost. Am. Tr.*
Cont.: Children's chip-basket, by H. N. Hathaway. — Mattie's missionary box. — Polly Grey's jewels. — Uncle Downe's home, by Glance Gaylord. — Walks and talks, by Uncle Walter.

Chipman, D. *See* Vermont, Supreme Court reports.

Chipman, Natl. *See* Vermont, Supreme Court reports.

Chipman, R. Manning. Chipman lineage, particularly as in Essex Co., Mass. 8°. '72. 50c......*Essex.*

Chips for the chimney corner. Munsell, F. 60c. *Munsell.*

Chips from a German workshop. *See* Müller, F. M.

Chips from Uncle Sam's jack-knife. ill. 8°. pap., 25c. *Dick & F.*

Chiquita (*pseud.*) Autumn dreams. [Poems.] 12°. $1.50 .... *Appleton.*

Chitchat by a penitent cat. *See* Ballantyne, W.

Chittenden, G:, B. (*ed.*) Meteorological observations in Colorada. *See* United States, *Geog. and Geol. Survey.*

Chittenden, L. E. Capture of Ticonderoga. 8°. $1.50. *Vt. Hist.*

— *Same.* 8°. '72. $2 .... *Tuttle.*

Chittenden, L. S. *See* Shuey, W. J., Hanley, W., *and* Chittenden, L. S.

Chitty, Jos. Treatise on bills of exchange, promissory notes, etc., with ref. to law of Scotland, France and Am. 13th Am. ed., ed. by J. C. Perkins, from 9th Lond. ed., rev. and enl. by J. H. Chitty and J. W. Hulme. 8°. shp., $8 .... *Merriam.*

— Treatise on pleading and parties to actions. 7th Eng. ed., rev. and enl. by H. Greening. 16th Am. ed., with notes and ref. by J. C. Perkins. 2 v. 8°. '76. $16 .... *Merriam.*

Chitty, Jos., *jr.* Practical treatise on the law of contracts not under seal, and upon the usual defences to actions thereon. 11th Am., from 9th Eng., ed., enl. by J. C. Perkins. 2 v. 8°. '74 shp., $15. *Hurd & H*

— *See also* England, Common law reports.

Chitty, Thompson, *and* Temple, L. Treatise on the law of carriers of goods and passengers; with statutes and forms; with Am. notes by D. W. Sellers. 8°. '57. $4 .... *T. & J. W. Johnson.*

Chiushingura; or, the loyal league: romance of Japanese life; tr. from the Japanese by F. V. Dickins, with introd. by H. Atkinson; ill. by Japanese artists. obl. 8°. '76. $3 ..... *Putnam.*

Chivalry and the crusades. James, G. P. R. 75c. *Harper.*

Chloe. Collier, M. A. 20c .... *Am. Tr.*

Chloe Lankton; or, light beyond the clouds. 18°. 70c. *Am. S. S.*

Choice (The). McGranahan, J., *and* Case, C. C. 75c. .... *Church.*

Choice consolation for the suffering children of God. 16°. '60. $1.25 .... *Dutton.*

Choice dialogues for Sunday school concerts. 2 v. 18°. '75. ea., 60c. .... *Garrigues.*

Choice library. 24 v. ill. 16°. $12 .... *Lothrop.*

Choice library. 3 v. 12°. $3.75 .... *Nelson.*
Cont.: Birthday present, by M. C. Bushe. — Stars in a stormy night, by E. L. M. — Grey house on the hill, by Mrs. Greene.

Choice library. 5 v. 16°. $5 .... *Graves.*
Cont.: Choice stories for boys. — Choice stories for girls. — Choice stories for young folks. — How to be a lady. — How to be a man.

Choice lib. for boys and girls. 60 v. 18°. $30 .. *Am. S. S.*

Choice little library. 6 v. ill. 32°. '74. $2 .... *Hoyt.*
Cont.: Emma Herbert. — Ned Grahame. — Ivan. — Fairest rose. — Eddie and May. — Little Kit.

Choice medley (The); or, "here a little and there a little." 18°. 40c .... *Am. S. S.*

Choice memorials. 18°. 75c. .... *Cong. Pub.*

Choice notes on the four Gospels, drawn from old and new sources. 4 v. cr. 8°. '68–'69. v. 1, 2, ea., $1.50; v. 3, 4, ea., $1.75 .... *Macmillan.*
Cont.: Matthew. — Mark. — Luke. — John.

Choice of a state of life. Rossignoli, C. G. 90c.; $1.25 .... *Murphy.*

Choice poems: sel. Eng. poems and lyrics. (Household ser.) ill. 16°. $1.50; mor., $3 .... *Lee & S.*

Choice poems and lyrics; sel. from the best authors. 16°. $1.75 .... *Routledge.*

Choice poems for children. ill. 18°. 55c... *Am. S. S.*

Choice poetry. ill. sq. 16°. 75c .... *Nelson.*

Choice readings. Diehl, A. T. $1.50 ...... *Claxton.*

Choice series of classic Eng. poems. 13 v. ill. 12°. '75. ea., $1.25 .... *Putnam.*
Cont.: Gray's Elegy. — Goldsmith's Deserted village. — Keats' Eve of St. Agnes. — Coleridge's Ancient mariner. — Bloomfield's Farmer's boy. — Campbell's Pleasures of hope. — Wordsworth's Pastoral poems. — Milton's L'allegro. — Tennyson's May queen. — Shakespeare's Songs and sonnets. — Rogers' Pleasures of memory. — Poetry of nature. — Elizabethan poets.

Choice stories. Alden, J. 75c .... *Tibbals.*

Choice stories for boys; — for girls; — for young folks. *See* Choice lib.

Choice stories for young readers. ill. 24°. 60c. *Hoyt, F. & D.*

Choir and congregation. Root, G. F. $2; $1.50. *Church.*

Choir manual: prayers used by the Sisters of Mercy. New ed. 16°. '75. *net*, 75c..... *Kelly, P. & Co.*

Choisy. Story, J. P. $1.25; 75c. .... *Estes.*

Choked life. Potter, H. C. 10c .... *Dutton.*

Cholula; or, the young Mexican. ill. 18°. 80c. *J. A. Moore.*

Chomet, Antoine Jos. (*called* Hector). Influence of music on health and life; tr. by L. A. Flint. sq. 16°. '75. $1.25 .... *Putnam.*

Choosing a bride. *See* Lacy's home plays for ladies.

Chopin, F: Collection of mazurkas and waltzes arranged for the piano-forte; with biog. and review of works by F. Liszt. 4°. $5 .... *Ditson.*

— *See also* Schumann, R., *and* Chopin, F.

Chops of the channel. Hay, F. 15c. *De Witt; French.*

Choral classics: cantatas and choruses with solos. 13 nos. 4°. ea., pap., 10c.–50c .... *Ditson.*

Choral friend. Zundel, J. $1.25 .... *Barnes.*

Choral harmony. Baker, B. F. $1.75; $1.38. *Gordon.*

Choral selections. 2 nos. 8°. ea., pap., 40c. *Ditson.*

Choral tribute. Emerson, L. O. $1.50 ...... *Ditson.*

Choralist: choruses, anthems, trios, etc.; with piano accomp. 23 nos. 4°. ea., pap., 15c. .... *Ditson.*

Choralists' companion. [Music.] 8°. $1.50. *Church.*

Chorister (The). *See* Perkins, W. O.

Chorley, H. F. Recent art and society as described in autobiography [of C.]; by C. H. Jones. 12°. '74. $2 .... *Holt.*

— *See also* Bennett, W. S., May queen; — Lapointe, S., Faerie gold for young and old; — Stoddard, R. H., Bric-a-Brac ser.

Chorlton, W: Grape-grower's guide. 12°. 75c. *Judd.*

Chorsånger för kyrkan, skolan och hemmet. $2; — in 6 nos. ea., 35c. .... *Engberg.*

Chorus choir. Tourjée, E. $2 .... *Ditson.*

Chorus gems: sel. choruses for musical societies. roy. 8°. 75c. .... *Brainard.*

Chorus wreath: sacred and secular choruses. 8°. '64. bds., $1.50 .... *Ditson.*

Chosen friends. Baker, S. S. 25c .... *Am. Tr.*

Chosen people. Bradford, S. H. $1.25 ... *Randolph.*

Chosen people. Yonge, C. M. 50c. .... *Pott.*

Choules, J: Overton. *See* Young Americans abroad.

Chouquet, Gst. Easy conversations in French. 16°. '54. 75c. .... *G. R. Lockwood.*

— First lessons in French. Enl. ed. 16°. '74. 75c. *G. R. Lockwood.*

— First readings in French. Enl. ed., with vocab. 16°. $1 .... *G. R. Lockwood.*

houquet, Gst., *continued.*
- French conversations and dialogues. 18°. 75c. *Appleton.*
- Young ladies' guide to French composition. 12°. $1.25 .... *Appleton.*
hris and Otho. Smith, J. P. $1.75 ...... *Carleton.*
hris Johnson: drama. 16°. pap., 15c....... *Happy.*
hrist. *See* Jesus Christ.
hrist all in all to believers. Henry, P. 75c. *Pres. Bd.*
hrist alone. Smith, J. 10c.............. *Pres. Bd.*
hrist and adornments. Platt, S. H. 40c... *West. Tr.*
hrist and antichrist. Cassels, S. J. 90c... *Pres. Bd.*
hrist and the Bible. Muhlenberg, W. A. 60c. *Randolph.*
hrist and the church. Preston, T. 50c... *Cath. Pub.*
hrist and the controversies of Christendom. Dale, R. W. 75c........ *Whittaker.*
hrist and his church. Hepworth, G. H. 25c. *Appleton.*
hrist and his salvation. Bushnell, H. $2.. *Scribner.*
hrist and the lawyer. *See* Harbaugh, H.
hrist and other masters. Hardwick, C. $3. *Macmillan.*
hrist and the people. Child, A. B. $1.25.... *Colby.*
hrist and the sea. Spaulding, J. 25c...... *Am. Tr.*
hrist and the twelve. Holland, J. G. *$3.50; $4; $5; $8........ *C. A. Nichols.*
hrist and the world. Huntington, F. D. 75c.; 25c. *Dutton.*
hrist at the door. Ward, S. H. $1...... *Randolph.*
hrist bearer. Hunt, H. C. 40c. .... *Dutton.*
hrist born (The). Blunt, E. K. 40c.... *Lippincott.*
hrist, the bread of life. Campbell, J. McL. $1.50. *Macmillan.*
hrist child. Child, L. M. 75c........... *Lothrop.*
hrist child. Ford, T. 30c................ *Dutton.*
hrist crucified. Charnock, S. 60c....... *Pres. Bd.*
hrist ever with you. Winslow, O. 40c. *N. Y. Ref. Ch. Bd.*
hrist in art: story of the words and acts of Jesus as related [by] the evangelists, in one narrative; with pl. by Brend 'amour of Düsseldorf, after designs of A. Bida. 4°. *$5.50................ *Ford.*
hrist in the cellars and garrets. 18°. pap., 15c. *Bost. Am. Tr.*
hrist in the desert. Parsons, H. M. 50c... *Pres. Bd.*
hrist in a German home. Goodwin, A. H. 90c. *Am. Tr.*
hrist in literature: treasury of readings in prose and verse ill. of the acts and words of Jesus; with the four Gospels, arranged in one narrative, for reference. ill. 8°. *$3.50................ *Ford.*
hrist in modern life. Brooke, S. A. $2.. *Appleton.*
hrist in the Psalms. Arnot, M. 10c. *U. P. Bd. of Pub.*
hrist in song. Schaff, P. $2.50; $3..... *Randolph.*
hrist in the soul. Upham, T. C. $1.25.... *Crowell.*
hrist in the will, the heart, and the life. Muzzey, A. B. $1.25........ *Am. Unit.*
hrist knocking at the door of sinners' hearts. Flavel, J. 90c........ *Am. Tr.*
hrist knocking at men's hearts. Gossner, J. 15c. *Am. Tr.*
hrist, the life of the world. Besser, R. $3. *Scribner, W. & A.*
hrist, the light of the world. Vaughan, C. J. $1.50. *Routledge.*
hrist liveth in me. Breed, W. P. 80c..... *Pres. Bd.*
hrist (The) of the apostle's creed. Scott, W. A. $3. *Randolph.*
hrist (The) of God. Bonar, H. $1.25...... *Carter.*
hrist (The) of God. Davidson, R. 35c... *Pres. Bd.*
hrist (The) of the Gospels and the Christ of modern criticism. Tulloch, J. $1 .... *Macmillan.*
hrist (The) of history. Young, J. $1.25... *Carter.*

Christ (The) of Paul. Reber, G. $2...... *Somerby.*
Christ on the cross. Stevenson, J. $2.25.... *Wiley.*
Christ, or the world, which? Bliss, F. 90c... *Dutton.*
Christ, our example. Fry, C. $1.25.. *Bost. Am. Tr.*
Christ, our intercessor. *See* Bechuana girl.
Christ, our life. Angus, J. $1.25........ *Am. Bapt.*
Christ, our sanctification. Clark, D. 10c. *Friends Pub. H.*
Christ satisfying the instincts of humanity. Vaughan, C. J. $1.25........ *Macmillan.*
Christ, the spirit. Hitchcock, E. A. $3....... *Miller.*
Christ was born on Christmas-day. *See* Christmas carol.
Christ, the wonderful. [S.-school quest. book.] 18°. '65. hf. bd., 15c........ *Hoyt.*
Christabel. *See* Coleridge, S. T.
Christabel Hope. Mercier, J. $1.25.. *Scribner, W. & A.*
Christbaum (Der). Schmid, C. v. 20c.... *Morwitz.*
Christening (The). *See* Buckstone, J. B.
Christian, L. H. Faith and works: teaching of Paul and James on justification perfectly harmonious. 18°. 50c........ *Pres. Bd.*
Christian Elliott; or, Mrs. Danver's prize. 18°. 60c. *Am. S. S.*
Christian Melville; by author of "Matthew Paxton." 16°. '72. $1........ *Routledge.*
Christian und Ernst. Brockmann, J. H. 50c. *Brockmann.*
Christian altar (The). Wyatt, W. E. 50c. *Appleton.*
Christian ambassador (The). Varley, H. $1.. *Willard.*
Christian (The) and his cross. *See* Monod, T.
Christian (The) armed against the seductions of the world. 32°. 50c........ *Sadlier.*
Christian armor (The); with ill. selections in prose and poetry. ill. sq. 12°. $2...... *Bost. Am. Tr.*
Christian art and symbolism. Tyrwhitt, R. St. J. $2........ *Roberts.*
Christian assurance. Miller, E. 35c.; 40c. *Meth. Epis.*
Christian ballads. *See* Coxe, A. C.
Christian Baptist. Campbell, A. $2.50; $3.. *Chase.*
Christian belief and life. Peabody, A. P. $1.50. *Roberts.*
Christian believing and living. Huntington, F. D. $1.75 .... *Dutton.*
Christian benevolence. Greenwald, E. 10c. *Luth. Bk. St.*
Christian book (The) of concord. *See* Evangelical Luth. Ch.
Christian Brothers. Catholic youth's hymn book. 4°. pap., 15c.; — with music. 4°. 60c.; $1.. *O'Shea.*
— [Readers.] 3 v........ *Sadlier.*
Cont.: First reader, 16°, 12½c. — Second, 16°, 25c. — Third, 12°, 60c.
— [Readers.] 4 v. .... *Strong.*
Cont.: First reader, 18°, 13c. — Second, 18°, 25c. — Third, 12°, 63c. — Fourth, 12°, 88c.
— [Spellers and readers.] 5 v........ *O'Shea.*
Cont.: Guide to spelling, 12°, 25c. — Manual of orthography, 12°, 40c. — First book of reading lessons, 18°, 12c. — Second, 18°, 25c. — Third, 18°, 63c.
Christian calling. Davies, J. L. $1.75.. *Macmillan.*
Christian (A) companion for the chamber of sickness; by a minister. 18°. 60c........ *Pres. Bd.*
Christian companionship for retired hours. 16°. $1.50. *Routledge.*
Christian conquests. Tucker, C. 75c. ...... *Carter.*
Christian consistency. Mannering, E. 60c. *Pres. Bd.*
Christian consolations. Peabody, A. P. $1.. *Am. Unit.*
Christian (The) contemplated. Jay, W. 60c. *Carter.*
Christian doctrine of sin. Müller, J. 2 v. ea., $3. *Scribner, W. & A.*
Christian effort. Baker, S. 55c..... *Meth. Bk. Conc.*

Christian exertion explained and enforced. 18°. '45. 40c. .... *Meth. Bk. Conc.*
— *Same.* 18°. 50c. .... *Am. S. S.*
Christian festival. Baxter, J. 40c.; 60c... *Crandall.*
Christian friend (The). Ritchie, A. 40c... *West. Tr.*
Christian gift (The). Ward, F. DeW. 60c. *Darrow.*
Christian giving. Seiss, J. A. 10c.... *Luth. Bk. St.*
Christian graces. [Cantata.] obl. 24°.. pap., 10c. *Gordon.*
Christian graces. Thompson, J. P. $1..... *Sheldon.*
Christian guide to heaven: spiritual exercises for Catholics. 32°. 45c.-$30.......... *Cummiskey.*
Christian hearer (The). Bickersteth, E. 30c. *I. N. Whiting.*
Christian hero (The); or, Robert Annan. ('72.) New ed. 16°. '74. 90c................. *Hoyt.*
Christian home (The). Collier, J. A. $1.. *Pres. Bd.*
Christian home life. ill. 12°. '65. $1.10..... *Am. Tr.*
— *Same.* 12°. 90c. .... *Bost. Am. Tr.*
Christian household (The). Weaver, G. S. 75c. *Wells.*
Christian households. *See* Phelps, *Mrs.* A. L.
Christian hymnal. 12°. $1-$3.75. — Supplement. 12°. 10c.............................. *Chase.*
Christian hymnal (The). *See* Sewall, F.
Christian hymn-book; comp. by A. Campbell, etc., enl. and rev. by a committee. 48°. 50c.-$2. — 24°. 75c.-$4. — 12°. $2-$4.50 .... *Chase.*
Christian hymns. *See* Cheshire Pastoral Association.
Christian (The) in the world. Faunce, D. W. $1.50. *Roberts.*
Christian instructed (The); [also] Stations of Jerusalem; tr. by Mrs. J. Sadlier. 32°. 40c. *Sadlier.*
Christian instructor. Hopkins, J. $1...... *Barnes.*
Christian laborer (The), the Christian hero. 18°. '53. 30c...................... *Meth. Bk. Conc.*
Christian lawyer (The): life and character of W. G. Baker. 12°. $1.50........... *Meth. Bk. Conc.*
Christian life (The). Bayne, P. $1.75.. *H. A. Young.*
Christian life. *See* Hooker, H.
Christian life (The), manifold and one. Westcott, B. F. $1........................... *Macmillan.*
Christian lyrics, from modern authors. ill. cr. 8°. $3.75; cf., $7.50; mor., $8.... *Scribner, W. & A.*
Christian melodies. Cheever, G. B., *and* Sweetser, J. E. $1................................ *Barnes.*
Christian ministry (The) not a priesthood. Boardman, H. A. 35c.................... *Pres. Bd.*
Christian mirror (The). Jeter, J. B. 65c... *Sheldon.*
Christian nurture. Bushnell, H. $2....... *Scribner.*
Christian painter (A) of the 19th century: life of Hippolyte Flandrine. 12°. '75. $2.50........ *Pott.*
Christian paradoxes. Crawford, N. M. $1.50.. *So. Bapt.*
Christian pastorate. Kidder, D. P. $1.75. *Cin. Meth. Bk. Conc.*
Christian patriot (The). Robbins, G. $1.. *Putnam & D.*
Christian perfection. Fletcher, J. 40c. *Meth. Bk. Conc.*
Christian philosopher. Dick, T. 55c. *Meth. Bk. Conc.*
Christian physician (The). Richards, W. 20c. *Am. Tr.*
Christian pilgrim (The). 18°. 40c......... *Am. S. S.*
Christian polymathist. Cory, N. E. $2..... *Cen. Bk.*
Christian praise: hymns and tunes for Presbyterian churches. 8°. $1.34. — Baptist ed. 8°. $1.34. *Huntington.*
Christian profession (The). *See* Claybaugh, J.
Christian progress. *See* James, J. A.
Christian psalmist (The new). *See* Leonard, S. W.
Christian purity. Foster, R. S. $1.75.. *Meth. Bk. Conc.*
Christian queen (The). 18°. '55. 35c....... *Am. Tr.*
Christian remembrancer. L., H. L. 90c..... *Nelson.*

Christian rule of marriage. Malcolm, H. 75c. *Lippincot*
Christian Sabbath vindicated. Ignotus. $1.50. *Claxton*
Christian sacraments. Stone, J. S. $3... *Randolph*
Christian sanctity. Woodford, J. R. $1.. *Macmillan*
Christian school books. 6 v. 12°... *N. Y. Ref. Ch. Bd*
Cont.: A B C book, 15c. — Primer, 20c. — First reader, 35c — Second, 65c. — Third, 90c. — Appendix to Third reader Treasures for the memory and heart, 15c.
Christian seasons. Bishop, G. M. $1.25.. *U. S. Pub*
Christian singers of Germany. *See* Winkworth, C.
Christian soldier (The). Senour, F. 10c... *Pres. Bd*
Christian soldier (The): life of R. E. Lee. 18°. '7[?] $1 .... *Claxton*
Christian soldiers (The); or, the triumphs of grace i the army. 18°. 60c.................. *Pres. Bd*
Christian songs for the Sunday school. Bell, G. A. *and* Main, S. 50c..................... *Biglow*
Christian songster. Beaver, J. 45c. .... *Un. B. Pub*
Christian spiritual conversation on saving faith; [also Confession of faith of the Mennonites; with app 18°. leath., 75c............................. *Baer*
Christian steward (The); by a layman. 16°. 25c. pap., 15c. .... *West. Tr*
Christian student. Otheman, E. 55c. *Meth. Bk. Conc*
Christian Sunday school hymn-book; sel. by a com and re-ed. by J. W. M'Garvey and W. Baxter 32°. hf. bd., 15c........................ *Chase*
Christian teacher (The). 18°. 75c........ *Cong. Pub*
Christian theism. Thompson, R. A. $1.50.. *Harper*
Christian trumpet. Pellegrino, G. R. $1.50.. *Noonan*
Christian truth and modern opinion: sermons preache in N. Y. by clergymen of the Prot. Episc. Church 12°. '74. $1.25.................... *Whittaker*
Christian union. 18°. 40c. .... *Am. Bap*
Christian unity and its recovery. Davenport, J. S $1.25................................. *Appleton*
Christian use of money. Wyckoff, J. F. 20c. *Am. Tr*
Christian way. Smith, B. per doz., $3.. *Universalist*
Christian year (The). 18°. 50c.; mor., $1... *Nelson*
Christian year (The). Horn, E. T. $1.. *Luth. Bk. St*
Christian year. *See* Keble, J.
Christiana and her children: pt. 2 of Cottage lecture on the Pilgrim's progress. ill. 18°. $1. *Am. S. S*
Christiana Hatherly's childhood. ill. 18°. 70c. *Am. S. S*
Christianity and discipline. *See* Monad, T.
Christianity and law. *See* Palmer, B. M.
Christianity and modern infidelity. Morgan, R. W $1.50; 60c........................ *Claremont*
Christianity and modern thought; by Rev. H. W Bellows and others. ('72.) 3d ed. 12°. '7[?] $1.25 .... *Am. Uni*
Christianity and positivism. McCosh, J. $1.75. *Carter*
Christianity and scepticism. *See* Boston lectures.
Christianity and science. Peabody, A. P. $1.75. *Carter*
Christianity and statesmanship. Hague, W. $1.50 *Lothrop*
Christianity before the time of Christ. Craven, M. B 25c...................................... *Colby*
Christianity from God. Tobey, A. $1.. *Bost. Am. Tr*
Christianity in earnest. Steele, A. 60c.... *So. Meth*
Christianity in the kitchen. Mann, M. $1.25. **Osgood*
Christianity makes heroes. Reed, A. 40c. *West. Tr*
Christianity no finality. Denton, W. 10c... *Denton*
Christianity, the science of manhood. *See* Savage M. J.
Christian's daily guide. [Cath. prayer book.] 32° 40c.-$5 .... *O'Shea*

Christian's daily treasury. Temple, E. $1.50. *So. Bapt.*
Christian's gift. Clark, R. W. $1.25...*J. E. Potter.*
Christian's great interest. Guthrie, W. 60c. *Pres. Bd.*
Christian's guide to heaven: manual of spiritual exercises for Catholics. 32°. '51. 45c.-$9..*Murphy.*
— *Same;* with Epistles and Gospels. 32°. '64. 45c.-$15..........*Kelly, P. & Co.*
— *Same;* with the evening office of the Church in Latin and English. 32°. 35c.-$1.25.......*Benziger.*
Christian's mirror. Tucker, C. 75c. *Carter; Dutton.*
Christian's mistake. *See* Craik, D. M.
Christian's panoply. Tucker, C. 75c........*Carter.*
Christian's pattern. *See* Thomas *a Kempis.*
Christian's pocket book. 32°. 40c........*Am. Bapt.*
Christian's portion. Sibbes, R. 25c........*Pres. Bd.*
Christian's (The) secret of a happy life. Smith, H. W. $1..........*Willard.*
Christian's treasury. [Cath. prayer book.] ill. 24°. 60c.-$5..........*O'Shea.*
Christians and the theatre. Buckley, J. M. 80c. *Meth. Bk. Conc.*
Christie, Albany. Martyrdom of St. Cecily: drama. 18°. 25c..........*Sadlier.*
Christie, H. R. *and* T. H. R. Favorite songs. [Hymn book.] 8°. bds., 60c..........*R. W. Carroll.*
Christie, J. R. Elementary test questions in pure and mixed mathematics. cr. 8°. '66. $3..*Macmillan.*
Christie, T. H. R. *See* Christie, H. R. *and* T. H. R.
Christie, W. D. Life of the first Earl of Shaftesbury, 1621-1683. 2 v. por. cr. 8°. '71. $8..*Macmillan.*
Christie. *See* Aunty May's children; — Glen Elder lib.
Christie; or, the way home. 2 v. 16°. $2.50; — 2 v. in 1. $2.25..........*Am. S. S.*
Christie Elwood. 16°. $1..........*Carter.*
Christie Johnson. *See* Reade, C.
Christie's faith. Robinson, F. W. $1.75....*Harper.*
Christie's old organ; or, "Home, sweet home." 16°. '76. 50c..........*Carter.*
Christina North. Archer, E. M. 75c......*Appleton.*
Christine. Curtis, L. J. $1.50..........*De Witt.*
Christine, and other poems. Miles, G. H. $2. *Cath. Pub.*
Christine Thornton. Jackson, E. A. 75c....*Dutton.*
Christine und ihr Hof. *See* Van der Velde, K. F.
Christine Van Amberg. *See* Arbouville, S. de B.
Christison, Rob. Dispensatory or commentary on the pharmacopœias of Gt. Brit. and the U. S.; with supplement by R. E. Griffith. ill. 8°. $4..*Lea.*
Christliche Soldaten-Geschichten. 18°. '65. 40c. *Am. Tr.*
Christlicher Familien-Kalender. ill. 8°. pap., 15c. *Ev. Assoc.*
Christliches Gemüths-Gespräch; in Frag u. Antwort f. d. Jugend, etc. 32°. 45c..........*Baer.*
Christlieb, Thdr. Bekämpfung des Unglaubens. 18°. '74. 40c..........*Am. Tr.*
— *Eng.* Best methods of counteracting modern infidelity; tr. from the Germ. 12°. 75c....*Harper.*
— Modern doubt and Christian belief; tr. from the Germ. 8°. '74. $3; hf. mor., $5.....*Am. Tr.*
— *Same;* tr. by H. U. Weitbrecht and others, and ed. by T. L. Kingsbury. 8°. '75. $3......*Scribner.*
Christmas. ill. 16°. 75c..........(?) *Luth. Pub.*
Christmas angel (The). Raymond, R. W. 35c.; 20c..........*Randolph.*
Christmas at Annesley. Shipley, M. E. $1.25..*Nelson.*
Christmas at the Beeches. *See* Hopkins, *Miss* I. T.
Christmas at Cedar Hill. Guernsey, L. E. $1. *Whittaker.*
Christmas at Fern Lodge. 18°. 45c...... *Whittaker.*
Christmas at sea. 18°. 45c.......... *Whittaker.*
Christmas at Sunberry Dale. *See* Sunberry Dale lib.
Christmas boxes. Mayhew, A., *and* Edwards, S. 15c..........*French.*
Christmas cake in four quarters. Barker, M. A. (*Lady*). $1.50..........*Macmillan.*
Christmas carol. *See* Dickens, C.
Christmas carol: drama. 16°. pap., 15c.....*French.*
Christmas carol, "Christ was born on Christmas day:" ill. by J. A. Hows. 4°. mor., $5....*Hurd & H.*
Christmas carol: ill. after designs from MSS. of 13th and 14th centuries. 4°. (Lond.) '73. $25. *Little, B. & Co.*
Christmas carols, old and new: collection of Germ. and Eng. Christmas carols. 12°. '69. pap., 38c..........*Ditson.*
Christmas carols; with music. [Toy book.] ill. 8°. per gross, pap., $54..........(?) *McLoughlin.*
Christmas charities. 32°. 20c.; 15c.........*Dutton.*
Christmas chimes. Dressler, W. 20c. ......*Peters.*
Christmas day. 18°. 20c.; 25c..........*Dutton.*
Christmas earnings: story of the crisis of 1857. 18°. 45c..........*Dutton.*
Christmas eve. 18°. 35c..........*Pres. Bd.*
Christmas eve. 18°. 40c..........*Dutton.*
Christmas eve. *See* Augusta.
Christmas eve and Christmas day. Hale, E. E. $1.50..........*Roberts.*
Christmas eve, and other stories. 18°. 45c. *Whittaker.*
Christmas eve in a watch house. Cheltnam, C. S. 15c..........*French.*
Christmas fairies. Ford, T. $1.25........*Claxton.*
Christmas festival. Leonard, W. A. 75c...*Somerby.*
Christmas gambol. *See* Lacy's home plays for ladies.
Christmas gift. Adams, W. T. 45c.......*Lee & S.*
Christmas gift, and other stories. ill. 18°. 60c. *Am. S. S.*
Christmas gifts from the infant Jesus: devotional gems. 48°. per 100, *net,* $7.50; $10..........*Murphy.*
Christmas guest (The). Southworth, E. D. E. N. $1.75; $1.50..........*Peterson.*
Christmas hamper (The). Lemon, M. 50c. *Routledge.*
Christmas holidays. Strickland, J. 50c...*Routledge.*
Christmas holidays; or, a visit at home. 18°. 22c. *Am. S. S.*
Christmas holidays at Cedar Grove. Seymour, M. A. $1..........*Dutton.*
Christmas holly. Harland, M. $2; $4.50..*Sheldon.*
Christmas holydays (The) in Rome. Kip, W. I. $1.50..........*Dutton.*
Christmas in England. *See* Irving, W.
Christmas is coming. Morehead, L. M. 75c. *Lippincott.*
Christmas journey. Hall, T. O. $1..... *Whittaker.*
Christmas library. 3 v. 16°. $2.75.........*Dutton.*
Cont.: Rambling chats and chatty rambles, by J. O. Y. — Lizzie's secret, by A. A. Maguire. — A child's influence, by Lisa Lockyer.
Christmas morning. Pratt, L. M. 50c. ....*Lothrop.*
Christmas mummers (The). Yonge, C. M. $1.50. *Pott.*
Christmas nights' entertainments. Palafox, J. de. 75c. *Kenedy.*
Christmas pantomime: extravaganza. 16°. pap., 15c. *French.*
Christmas poems and pictures: carols, songs and descript. poems, rel. to festival of Christmas. ill. 4°. '66. $2.50; mor., $5..........*Hurd & H.*
Christmas scenes in New York. 18°. 45c. *Whittaker.*
Christmas secret (The). 18°. 30c..........*Dutton.*
Christmas stocking. Johnson, V. W. $1.50. (?) *O'Kane.*
Christmas stories. ill. sq. 16°. 50c......*Perkinpine.*
Christmas stories about Santa Claus. Snow, S. P., *and* Floy, H. 25c..........*Meth. Bk. Conc.*

Christmas story (A). *See* New Year lib.
Christmas tales. ill. 24°. '69. 30c. . . . . *Lothrop.*
Christmas tapers. Jackson, E. A. 75c. . . . . . *Dutton.*
Christmas tide. Murray, T. B. 40c. . . . . *Dutton.*
Christmas time. *See* Alden, *Mrs.* I. M.
Christmas tree. *See* Gerty and May books.
Christmas tree: drama. 12°. '70. pap., 25c. *Kelly, P. & Co.*
Christmas vigils; or, Kitty Clarke's dream. 18°. 50c. *Dutton.*
Christmas visit (The). Pratt, L. M. 75c. . . . *Lothrop.*
Christmas week at grandmother Cheeryheart's. Washburn, M. L. $1 . . . . *Cong. Pub.*
Christmas with the boys; by author of "Ruth Allerton." 16°. 85c. . . . . *Am. S. S.*
Christmas with the girls; by author of "Christmas with the boys." 16°. $1 . . . . *Am. S. S.*
Christoph Columbus. Nieritz, G. 25c. . . . . *Morwitz.*
Christopher, *Mrs.* Fanny H. Bartholet Milon: sequel to "Duke Christopher." 32°. 40c. . . . . . *Chase.*
— Duke Christopher: a story of the reformation. 32°. 40c. . . . . *Chase.*
Christopher, Hiram. The remedial system; or, man and his Redeemer. 8°. '76. $3 . . *Tr. P. & P. Co.*
Christopher Tadpole. *See* Smith, Albert.
Christophers, S. W. Epworth singers and other poets of Methodism. 12°. '75. $3 . . . . *Randolph.*
— Hymn writers and their hymns. 2d ed. 12°. '67. $1.75 . . . . *Randolph.*
Christ's cadets. Chaplin, A. C. $1.50 . . . . . *Am. Bapt.*
Christ's lambs in heathen lands. 16°. 50c. . . *West. Tr.*
Christ's infant kingdom. Tucker, J. F. 50c. *Cong. Pub.*
Christtags-Gesprache des Jugendfreundes. 8°. pap., 10c. . . . . *Brobst.*
Christtags-Harfe. Mattes, H. L. 10c. . . . . . . *Brobst.*
Christus. *See* Longfellow, H. W.
Christus consolator. Macleod, A. $1.75 . . *Randolph.*
Christus consolator. Thompson, A. C. $1 . . *Am. Tr.*
Christus redemptor. Southgate, H. $3.50 . . . *Cassell.*
Christy, E. Byron. Box and Cox: Ethiop. drama. 16°. pap., 15c. . . . . *Happy.*
Christy and White's complete Ethiopian melodies. 32°. $1 . . . . *Peterson.*
Christy and Wood's [song books]. 5 v. 32°. ea., pap., 10c. . . . . *Peterson.*
Cont.: Ethiopian song book. — Melodeon song book. — New song book. — Plantation melodies. — Serenader's song book.
Christy's grandson. Mathews, J. A. 75c. . . . . *Carter.*
Chronicle of the Cid. *See* Southey, R.
Chronicles of Carlingford. *See* Oliphant, *Mrs.* M. O. W.
Chronicles of Clovernook. Jerrold, D. 25c. . . *Harper.*
Chronicles of Cosynook. Hall, S. C. $1.50 . . *Nelson.*
Chronicles of the crusades. *See* Bohn, H. G.
Chronicles of four little Christmas stockings. 18°. 55c. *Pres. Bd.*
Chronicles of Gotham. White, R. G. 25c. . . *Carleton.*
Chronicles of an old manor house. Sargeant, G. E. $1.50 . . . . *Pres. Bd.*
Chronicles of the Schönberg-Cotta family. Charles, E. $1 . . . . *Dodd.*
Chronicles of Sunset Mountain. 16°. $1.50 . . *Lothrop.*
Chronicles of the tombs. *See* Pettigrew, T. J.
Chronological [Biblical and ecclesiastical] school atlas: maps, with letter press. 4°. (Bagster.) $3.25; hf. bd., $4.50 . . . . *Wiley.*
Chrononhotonthologos. Carey, H. 15c. . . . *French.*
Chrysostom, *St.* Picture of the religion of his age. 16°. '76. 75c. . . . . *Pott.*
— *and* Basil *the Great.* The divine liturgies. 16°. pap., 50c. . . . . *Dutton.*
Chrystabelle. Falconer, E. 15c. . . . . *French.*
Chubbs, jr.: book for boys. 16°. $1.50 . . (?) *Martien.*
Chubbuck, Emily. *See* Good boy's lib.
Church, A. J. (*ed.*) Horæ Tennysonianæ: [Lat. version of sel. from Tennyson]; by J. Conington, Seeley, Hessey, T. E. Kebbel, etc. 12°. '70. $1.75 . . . . *Macmillan.*
Church, Alb. E. Elements of analytical geometry. ('51.) 3d ed. 8°. $2.50 . . . . *Barnes.*
— Elements of descriptive geometry; with its application to shades, shadows and perspective. 2 v. 8°. '64. $4 . . . . *Barnes.*
— Elements of the differential and integral calculus. 8°. '61. $2.50 . . . . *Barnes.*
Church, Arth. H. Colour; with col. pl. and diagrams. post 8°. $1.25 . . . . *Cassell.*
Church, B. S. Notes on the Croton water works. *See* Buck, L. L., Erection of the Verrugas bridge.
Church, Ella Rodman. Golden days. [Stories.] 16°. '72. $1.25 . . . . *Dutton.*
Church, J: A. Notes of a metallurgical journey in Europe. ill. 8°. '73. $2 . . . . *Van Nostrand.*
Church, Pharcellus. Seed truths; or, Bible views of the mind, morals and relig. 12°. $1.75 . . *Sheldon.*
Church, R: W: Beginning of the middle ages: hist. of Engl. in its connection with that of Europe in the 9th century. 16°. $1 . . . . *Estes.*
— Civilization before and after Christianity. 12°. '72. pap., 50c. . . . . *Macmillan.*
— On some influences of Christianity upon national character: lectures, 1873. cr. 8°. '73. $1.50. *Macmillan.*
— Sacred poetry of early religions: lectures. 18°. '74. 50c. . . . . *Macmillan.*
— Saint Anselm. cr. 8°. '70. $1.75 . . . . . . *Macmillan.*
— Sermons preached before the Univ. of Oxford. 2d ed. cr. 8°. '69. $1.50 . . . . *Macmillan.*
Church, *Mrs.* Ross. *See* Marryat, Florence.
Church (The) and her children. Barrons, W. $1.50. *Cong. Pub.*
Church (The) and her enemies. Plumer, W. S. 40c. *Am. Bapt.*
Church and home. Leach, G. $2.75; $2.50 . . *Ditson.*
Church and state in the United States. Thompson, J. $1.50 . . . . *Osgood.*
Church and the world. Preston, T. S. 20c. *Coddington.*
Church architecture: 20 churches of moderate cost exemplified in elevations, plans, etc., by Upjohn, Renwick, etc. 4°. $6 . . . . *Woodward.*
Church bell. Perkins, W. O. *and* H. S. $1.25. *G. D. Russell.*
Church calendar. 18°. 35c.; 50c. . . . . *Dutton.*
Church choir. Münscher, J. $1.75; $1.60 . . . *Ditson.*
Church chorister. Gilbert, W. B. $1 . . . . *Dutton.*
Church congress. *See* Church of England.
Church decoration: manual of ornamentation; ed. by a practical illuminator. ill. 12°. '75. $1.75. *Dutton.*
Church defence: report of a conference on the present dangers of the church; by author of "My clerical friends." 18°. '73. 60c. . . . . *Cath. Pub.*
Church doctrinal class book. *See* New.
Church doctrine proved by the Bible. 16°. 50c. *Pott.*
Church floral decorations: hints by a lady; with introd. by Rev. W. Gresley. ill. 16°. $1.25; col. ill., $1.75 . . . . *Pott.*
Church glorious (The). Knox, J. 25c. *N. Y. Ref. Ch. Bd.*
Church harmonies: hymn and tune book for congregations. 8°. '73. $1.50; mor., $5 . . *Universalist.*
Church history stories. *See* Leslie, Emma.
Church in earnest. James, J. A. 75c. . . . . *Sheldon.*

Church in the house. Arnot, W. $2.50....... *Carter.*
Church in the wilderness. Benjamin, E. B. 35c. *Randolph.*
Church levies and priestcraft versus true religion. Hamilton, D. H. 10c.......... *D. H. Hamilton.*
Church life, its ground and obligations; by author of "Ecclesia Dei." cr. 8°. $1.50...... *Routledge.*
Church melodies. Hastings, T. *and* T. S. $1.35. *Randolph.*
Church melodist. White, E. L. $1.50...... *Ditson.*
Church member's (The) book: admonitions and instruction. 16°. 25c................. *Freewill.*
Church member's guide. James, J. A. 60c... *Sheldon.*
Church (The) of all ages. Irons, W. J. $3.75.. *Pott.*
Church of England. Church congress, Leeds, Eng., 1872: authorized report. 8°. '73. $3; pap., $2.50 .... *Dutton.*
— *Same.* Bath, Eng., 1873. 8°. '74. $3..... *Dutton.*
— *Same.* Stoke-upon-Trent, Eng., 1875. 8°. '76. $3.50. *Pott.*
— First Book of common prayer of Edward VI.; also Ordinal of 1549, with Order of the communion, 1548. 16°. '70. $3...................... *Pott.*
— Liber precum publicarum Ecclesiæ Anglicanæ. Tr. by Profs. Bright and Medd. 16°. '69. $3.. *Pott.*
— *See also* Protestant Episc. Church; — Reformed Episc. Church.
Church of the first days; — of the Gentiles; — of Jerusalem; — of the world. *See* Vaughan, C. J.
Church (The) of the first three centuries. Lamson, A. $3................................ *Fuller.*
Church (The) of the future. Moore, W. T. 10c. *Chase.*
Church of the New Jerusalem. *See* New Church.
Church porch (The). *See* Huntington, W. R.
Church primer: first lessons for little ones. 18°. 35c.; 40c. .... *Dutton.*
Church psalmist: psalms and hymns for evang. Christians. 12°. $1.75–$4. 18°. $1.25–$3.50; — with Conf. of faith and Catechism. $1.35; $1.40; $1.60. 32°. 75c.–$2.50.............. *Pres. Bd.*
Church singer. [Hymn book.] 4°. $1.25. *Meth. Bk. Conc.*
Church song. *See* Seiss, J. A., *and* Engelman, C. P.
Church welcome. *See* Perkins, W. O.
Churchill, C: Poems. (Aldine ed.) 2 v. 16°. ea., 75c. *Lippincott.*
— *Same;* with memoir. 3 v. por. 18°. $3... *Osgood.*
Churchill, *Mrs.* E. K. Overcoming. ill. 16°. '70. $1.25 .... *Lothrop.*
Churchill, Fleetwood. On puerperal fever and other diseases peculiar to women. 8°. $2.50.... *Lea.*
— On the theory and practice of midwifery. New Am., from 4th Lond., ed., rev. and enl.; with notes and add. by D. F. Condie. ill. 8°. $4; leath., $5.. *Lea.*
Churchill, Fk. Taking by storm: drama. 16°. pap., 15c. .... *French.*
Churchill, J: *See* Marlborough, *Duke of.*
Churchman, J: Journal. 12°. 75c... *Friends Bk. St.*
Church's floral kalendar. roy. 4°. $10... *Routledge.*
Churton, E: *See* Bible, New Test.
Churton, H: (*pseud.*) *See* Tourjee, A. W.
Chwolson, D. The Semitic nation; tr. from the Russian by E. M. Epstein. 16°. 50c............ *Bloch.*
Chy-Loo and his teachers; by author of "Story of a Chinese boy." 18°. 35c............ *Am. S. S.*
Chynoweth, Ja. Bennett, *and* Bruckner, W: H. American manures, and farmers' and planters' guide. 12°. $1.50...................... *Judd.*
Cibber, Colley. Love makes a man: comedy. 16°. pap., 15c............................ *French.*
— She would and she would not: comedy. 16°. pap., 15c.................................. *French.*
— *See also* Van Brugh, J., *and* Cibber, C.

Cicely Brown's trials. Prosser, *Mrs.*—. $1.. *Lothrop.*
Cicely's choice. O'Reilly, R. $1........... *Dutton.*
Cicero, Mcs. Tullius. Academica: text rev. and explained by J. S. Reid. 12°. '74. $1.50. *Macmillan.*
— *Eng.* Academics, De finibus, and Tusculan questions; tr. by C. D. Yonge; with sketch of Gk. philosophy. 12°. (Bohn.) $1.75.. *Little, B. & Co.*
— *Same.* 12°. (Bohn.) $2. *Lippincott; Scribner, W. & A.*
— Cato major; sive, de senectute. [Lat.] With introd. and notes by J. H. Allen and J. B. Greenough. 2d ed. 12°. '73. 75c..................... *Ginn.*
— *Same;* [also] Lælius; sive, de amicitia. With notes, etc., by E. P. Crowell and H. B. Richardson. 16°. '73. hf. leath., $1.25........... *Eldredge.*
— — *Same;* [also] Brutus. With notes by W. B. Smith. 16°. (Weale.) 80c..................... *Allyn.*
— — *Same;* [also] Epistolæ selectæ; rec. G. Long. 18°. 75c................................ *Harper.*
— — *Same;* [also] Paradoxa; [also] Somnium Scipionis; [also] Life of Atticus, by Cornelius Nepos; with Eng. notes by C. Anthon. 12°. shp., $1.50. *Harper.*
— De officiis. [Lat.] With notes, etc., by E. P. Crowell. ('71.) 3d ed. 16°. '75. hf. leath., $1.50. *Eldredge.*
— *Same;* notes by Thatcher. 12°. $1.25... *Appleton.*
— *Same.* De officiis libri 3. With analysis and Eng. comment., ed. by H. A. Holden; rev. and enl. by C. Anthon. 12°. shp., $1.50 .... *Harper.*
— *Same.* De officiis libri tres; [also] Cato major; [also] Lælius; cum [Ang.] notis. 18°. '69. 60c. *Claxton.*
— *Eng.* Offices, Old age, Friendship, Scipio's dream, Paradoxes, etc.; lit. tr. by C. R. Edmonds. 12°. (Bohn.) $1.25................ *Little, B. & Co.*
— — *Same.* 12°. (Bohn.) $1.40.... *Scribner, W. & A.*
— — *Same.* 12°. (Bohn.) $1.50 .... *Lippincott.*
— — *Same.* 12°. $1.50.................... *Harper.*
— De oratore. [Lat.] With notes by J. L. Kingsley. ('39.) New ed. 12°. '76. $1....... *Clark & M.*
— *Eng.* Oratory and orators; tr. and ed. by J. S. Watson. 12°. $1.50...................... *Harper.*
— — *Same:* 12°. (Bohn.) $1.75.... *Little, B. & Co.*
— — *Same.* 12°. (Bohn.) $2. *Lippincott; Scribner, W. & A.*
— *Same.* Three dialogues on the orator; tr. by W. Guthrie; rev. with notes. 18°. 75c.... *Harper.*
— On the nature of the gods, Divination, Fate, Laws, A republic, etc.; tr. by C. D. Yonge and F. Barham. 12°. (Bohn.) $1.75...... *Little, B. & Co.*
— — *Same.* 12°. (Bohn.) $2. *Lippincott; Scribner, W. & A.*
— Oratio pro Cluentio. [Lat.] With notes by A. Stickney. ('60.) 4th ed. 16°. '73. $1.. *Allyn.*
— Orations [Lat.]; ed. by C. Folsom, with Eng. notes. 12°. $1.25...................... *R. S. Davis (B.)*
— *Eng.* Orations; lit. tr. by C. D. Yonge. 12°. $1.50. *Harper.*
— — *Same.* 4 v. 12°. (Bohn.) ea., $1.75. *Little, B. & Co.*
Cont.: v. 1. Orations against Verres, etc. — v. 2. Catiline, Archias, Agrarian law, Rabirius, Muræna, Sylla, etc. — v. 3. Orations for his house, Plancius, Sextius, Cælius, Milo, Lagarius, etc. — v. 4. Miscellaneous orations, and rhetorical works; with index.
— — *Same.* 4 v. 12°. (Bohn.) ea., $2. *Lippincott; Scribner, W. & A.*
— *Same;* tr. by Duncan; [also] The offices, tr. by Cockman; [also] Cato and Lælius, tr. by Melmoth. 3 v. por. 18°. $2.25 .... *Harper.*
— Orationes selectæ 14; rec. R. Klotz, ed. altera emend. 16°. '76. 75c.; pap., 50c............. *Harper.*
— — Select orations [Lat.]; with Eng. notes and indexes by C. Anthon. 12°. shp., $1.50....... *Harper.*
— *Same;* ed. by P. Bullions. 12°. $1.50.... *Sheldon.*
— *Same;* with notes by A. Harkness. 12°. '73. $1.50. *Appleton.*
— *Same;* with notes by Johnson. 12°. $1.50.. *Appleton.*

Cicero, Mcs. Tullius, *continued.*
— *Same;* with notes, lexicon, life of Cicero, etc., by G. Stuart. ('69.) 9th ed. 16°. '75. hf. mor., $1.50 .... *Eldredge.*
— *Same;* with Lat. ordo, and Eng. notes, by C. Wiley. ('73.) New ed. 12°. '74. hf. roan, $1.50.. *Holt.*
— *Same;* chronolog. arranged; with life, introds. and index. ('73.) 2d ed. 12°. hf. mor., $1.75; — without notes. $1 .... *Ginn.*
— Orationes et epistolæ selectæ. Ed. with vocab. by J. H. Hanson. 8°. $1.75 ..... *Potter, A. & Co.*
— Orations against Catiline; with notes and introd., tr. from K. Halm; with add. by A. S. Wilkins. 12°. '71. $1.25 .... *Macmillan.*
— — Four orations against Catiline; with interlinear tr. by W. Underwood; and the seven remaining orations with interlinear tr. by T. Clark. 12°. hf. mor., $2.25 .... *Desilver.*
— Second Philippic oration; with introd. and notes, tr. from Karl Halm; ed. with corrections and add. by J. E. B. Mayor. 3d ed. 12°. '67. $1.25. *Macmillan.*
— Tusculan disputations [Lat.]; with Eng. notes, by C. Anthon. 12°. shp., $1.50 .... *Harper.*
— *Same.* Bk. 1: The dream of Scipio, and extracts from On old age and On friendship; with notes by T. Chase. 16°. '73. hf. mor., $1.25.. *Eldredge.*
— — *See also above* Cato major; De officiis.
— [Writings; outlined and explained] by W. L. Collins. 16°. $1 .... *Lippincott; Little, B. & Co.*
— *See also* Gardner, F., Gay, A. M., *and* Buck, A. M.
— *and* Quintilian. Ars oratoria: sel. from C. and Q. on oratory; with notes by M. Kellogg. 12°. '72. $1.25 .... *Ivison.*
Cicognara, Lp. (*Comte*) de. *See* Canova, A., Works on sculpture.
Cid (Le). *See* Corneille, P.
Cincinnati, *Ohio.* Superior Court reports, 1855–60; by W. Disney. 2 v. 8°. '67–'71. shp., $12. *Clarke.*
— — Select cases decided in general and special terms, 1870–'73; by C. P. Taft, B. Storer, jr., and P. R. Taft. 2 v. 8°. shp., $12 .... *Clarke.*
Cincinnati [Ohio] Board of Education. Bible in the public schools. *See* Minor, J. D.
Cincinnati music reader. 2 nos. 16°. ea., 15c.; — in 1 v. 25c. .... *Church.*
Cincinnati selections for chanting. sq. 8°. '75. pap., 15c. .... *Church.*
Cincuenta años. Cassard, A. $3... *G. R. Lockwood.*
Cinderella. [Toy-book.] ill. 4°. $1; 50c. *Routledge.*
Cinderella. Byron, H. J. 15c. .... *French.*
Cinderella. *See* Cruikshank, G.
Cinderella. *See* Ditson.
Cinderella. Keating, E. H. 15c. .... *French.*
Cinderella. Lacy, R. 15c. .... *French.*
Cinderella and the little glass slipper. f°. pap., 15c.; 20c.; 30c. .... *J. E. Potter.*
Cineas. Villefranche, J. M. $1.50 .... *Cunningham.*
Cinna. *See* Corneille, P.
Cinnamon-Isle boy. Hutchings, E. C. 50c. *Am. Tr.*
Cinq-Mars. *See* Vigny, A. de.
Ciocci, Rafaelle. Iniquities and barbarities practised at Rome in 19th cent. 12°. pap., 25c. *Peterson.*
Cipher. Austin, J. G. $1.50; $1 .... *Sheldon.*
Ciprina. Reynolds, G. W. M. 50c. .... *Peterson.*
Circassian boy. Lermontoff, M. $1.50 ..... *Osgood.
Circe. White, B. 50c. .... *Harper.*
Circle of blessing. Gatty, M. 50c... *Carter; Dutton.*
Circle of human life. Tholuck, F. A. G. 75c. *Carter.*
Circle of the year. Adams, W. H. D. $2.50.. *Lothrop.*
Circling year (The): ill. from the "Leisure hour" and the "Sunday at home." 4°. $3 ...... *Appleton.*
Circuit rider (The). Eggleston, E. $1.75 ...... *Ford*
Circumstances alter cases. Hoppin, W. J. 15c. *French*
Circus (Der). [Tale.] 18°. 30c. .... *Ev. Assoc*
Circus (The). *See* Anthony, *Mrs.* A. S.
Circus girl (The) and Sunday-school scholar. 18° 55c. .... *Am. S. S*
Circus life and circus celebrities. Frost, T. $2. *Routledge*
Cirillo, Vincenzo. Forty vocal exercises; arranged to develope the voice and render it flexible; with Eng. and Ital. text. f°. '72. pap., $3... *Ditson.*
— Twenty exercises; arranged to give precision and celerity in the execution of chromatic scales and trills. f°. '74. bds., $4 .... *Ditson.*
Cist, C: Sketches and statistics of Cincinnati in 1851 12°. '51. $1.50 .... *Wilstach*
Citateur. *See* Pigault-Le Brun, C. A. G.
Cities of Palestine: views with letter-press. obl. 24° 50c.; 75c. .... *Nelson*
Cities of refuge. Macduff, J. R. 50c. .... *Carter*
Citizen. Murphy, A. 15c. .... *French*
Citizen of Prague; tr. by M. Howitt. [Fiction.] 8°. pap., $1 .... *Harper.*
Citoyenne Jacqueline. Keddie, H. $2... *Routledge*
City (The) and ragged schools. Guthrie, T. $1.50 *Carter*
City cousins: sequel to "Annie Sherwood." 18°. 75c *Am. S. S.*
— *See also* Pioneer lib.
City of God. *See* Augustine, *St.*
City of God and the church makers. Abbey, R. $1.50. *Hurd & H.*
City of the great King. Barclay, J. T. $5.. *Challen.*
City of Nocross. *See* Tucker, *Mrs.* C.
City of palms. *See* Aunt Gracie's lib.
City of the saints. Burton, R. F. $3.50 .... *Harper*
City of sin. Remington, E. F. $1.25. *Meth. Bk. Conc.*
City of Toronto: views with descript. letter press. obl. 24°. 75c. .... *Nelson.*
City out of sight. Dougherty, L. C. 30c.; 10c. *So. Bapt.*
City poems. Smith, A. $1 .... *Osgood.
City scenes. *See* Juvenile picture books.
City sights for country eyes. ill. 4°. 65c. .. *Am. S. S*
City sounds and rural echoes. Blacklock, M. S. $1. (?) *Stevenson.*
City sparrows, and who feeds them. 16°. $1.25. *Dutton; Hoyt.*
City (A) without walls: story of a boy's conflicts and victory. 18°. 50c. .... *Nelson.*
Civilization. Wilkins, J. H. 15c. .... *French.*
Clack, *Mrs.* L: General Lee and Santa Claus. ill. sm. 4°. '67. 80c. .... *Eyrich.*
Clackitts of Inglebrook Hall. Prosser, *Mrs.* —. 75c.; 50c. .... *Randolph.*
Claggett, T: J: Life. 18°. 45c.; 50c. .... *Dutton.*
Claiborne, J. F. H. Life and correspondence of J. A. Quitman. 2 v. 12°. $3.50 .... *Harper.*
— Life and times of Sam Dale, the Mississippi partisan. ill. 12°. $1.50 .... *Harper.*
Claiborne. *See* Taylor, G. B., Oakland stories.
Claims of spiritualism, embracing the experience of an investigator; by a medical man. ('71.) 2d ed. 12°. '73. pap., 25c. .... *Colby.*
Clairville, L: François Nicolaie. Les petites misères de la vie humaine: vaudeville. ('66.) New ed. 12°. '76. pap., 25c .... *Holt.*
— *See also* Dennery, A. P., *and* Clairville, L. F. N.
Clandestine marriage. Colman, G., *and* Garrick, D. 15c. .... *French.*
Clandestine marriage. Dupuy, E. A. $1.75. *Peterson.*

Clap, Rog. Memoirs. [Reprint.] ('44.) New ed. 12°. '54. bds., 50c....*D. Clapp; Dorch. Antiq.*

Clapp, Eb. Clapp memorial: sketches and genealogy. 8°. '76. $4........................*D. Clapp.*

— History of Dorchester. *See* Dorchester Antiq. and Hist. Soc.

Clapp, N. B. Institute melodies. [School sing. book.] obl. 16°. 50c........................*Gordon.*

Clapp, W. W., *jr.* Fiammina (La): play. 16°. pap., 15c...............................*French.*

— History of the Boston stage, 1749–1853. 12°. '53. $1.25............................*Burnham.*

— My husband's mirror: comedietta. 16°. pap., 15c. *French.*

Clara (*pseud.*) Poems. 8°. $3........*Lippincott.*

Clara. Hackländer, F. W. $1.50...........*Harper.*

Clara and her cousins. *See* Aunt Gracie's lib.

Clara Augusta (*pseud.*) Poems. 12°. $1.50. *Lippincott.*

Clara C.; or, usefulness attainable by all. *See* Lost found.

Clara Claiborne. 18°. 25c.; 30c..........*Am. Bapt.*

Clara De Monthely. *See* Malan, C.

Clara Douglas; or, the unrequited love of a mother. 18°. 45c..........................*Am. S. S.*

Clara Dwight in the home of her adoption. Hulen, S. E. 75c. ....*Cong. Pub.*

Clara Howard. *See* Brown, C. B.

Clara Lake's dream. Wood, E. P. 25c. ...*Peterson.*

Clara Moreland. Bennett, E. $1.75; $1.50..*Peterson.*

Clara Stanley. 18°. 75c.....................*Carter.*

Clara Vaughan. Blackmore, R. D. $1.75..*Lippincott.*

Clara's childhood. 18°. 40c..............*Am. S. S.*

Clara's garden. 18°. 40c. ....*Dutton.*

Clara's little library. *See* Witt, *Mme.* H. de.

Clara's trial. ill. 18°. '75. 30c................*Dodd.*

Clare, Aust. The carved cartoon: a picture of the past. ill. 12°. $1.50.....................*Pott.*

Clare, Isr. South. Centennial history: hist. of all nations, with full hist. of the U. S. to [1876]. por. and ill. 8°. '66. *$3; leath., $3.75...*McCurdy.*

Clare, Ma. Fes. *See* Cusack, M. F.

Clare Maitland. 18°. 50c.; 75c............*Sadlier.*

Clarel: a pilgrimage in the Holy Land. Melville, H. 2 v. $3..........................*Putnam.*

Claremont library. 10 v. 18°. $5.60......*So. Meth.*
Cont.: Claremont tales. — Heavenly world, by J. Edmondson. — Heart and church divisions, by F. Asbury. — Home, by D. Hay. — Letters to parents, by G. E. Sargent. — Lessons from nature, by Mrs. Cheap. — Frank Netherton. — Alleine's Alarm. — Devout exercises of the heart, by Mrs. E. Rowe. — Hidden life exemplified, by Cummings.

Claremont tales. *See* Tucker, *Mrs.* C.

Clarence; or, self-will and principle. McConaughy, J. E. 60c. ....*Perkinpine.*

Clarence and Hallie books. *See* Kennedy, *Mrs.* M. G.

Clarence's library; — secret. *See* Baker, *Mrs.* H. N. W.

Clari. Payne, J. H. 15c....................*French.*

Claribel. Guernsey, L. E. 55c..........*Am. S. S.*

Claridge, C. J., *and* Souter, R., *jr.* Fast coach: farce. 16°. pap., 15c.................*French.*

Clarie's little charge. 18°. 50c.............*Carter.*

— *Same.* ill. 16°. '75. 75c....................*Dodd.*

— *See also* Aunt Deborah's lib.

Clarion (The). Marshall, L. 50c.....*G. D. Russell.*

Clariona (The). Bradbury, W. B., Bell, G. A., *and* Main, S. 60c. ....*Biglow.*

Clarionet (The). *See* Carleton, W:

Clarissa. Bowman, A. $1.25............*Routledge.*

Clarissa Harlowe. Lacy, T. H., *and* Courtney, J. 15c. *French.*

Clarissa Harlowe. *See* Richardson, S:

Clark, *Dr.* —. New illustrated marriage guide. ill. $1. *Un. Pub. Co.*

Clark, Alex. School-day dialogues. 11th ed., rev. and enl. 12°. '74. $1.50..........(?) *Daughaday.*

Clark, Alex. Starting out: a story of the Ohio hills. ill. 12°. '75. $1.25................*Lippincott.*

Clark, Alex. Work for Christianity; or, the Gospel in the trades; with introd. by W. C. Bryant. 12°. '74. $1.50..........................*Claxton.*

Clark, Alvan. Elements of astronomy. New ed. 12°. '76. 30c....................*G. R. Lockwood.*

Clark, Annie E. Poems. 18°. $1.......*Lippincott.*

Clark, B. F. Mirthfulness and its exciters. 12°. '70. $1.50................................*Lee & S.*

Clark, C: *See* England, House of Lords reports.

Clark, C: Heber. ["Max Adeler."] Out of the hurly-burly; or, life in an odd corner. ill. 12°. '74. *$2.50; $3; mor., $4.................*Maclean.*

Clark, Davis Wasgatt. Death-bed scenes. 12°. '59. $1.75........................*Meth. Bk. Conc.*

— Fireside reading. 5 v. 16°. $6..*Cin. Meth. Bk. Conc.*
Cont.: Historical sketches. — True tales for the spare hour. — Travels and adventure. — Anecdotes of animals. — Anecdotes of birds and fishes.

— Life and times of Bp. Hedding. 12°. '55. $2.25. *Meth. Bk. Conc.*

— Man all immortal. 12°. '64. $1.75. *Cin. Meth. Bk. Conc.*

— — *See also* Inquiring Christian's lib.

— Mental discipline. 18°. '50. 75c...*Meth. Bk. Conc.*

— Sermons. 12°. '68. $2.......*Cin. Meth. Bk. Conc.*

— (*ed.*) Methodist Episcopal Church: collection of sermons. 12°. $1.75......*Cin. Meth. Bk. Conc.*

Clark, Dougan. Christ, our sanctification. 32°. '75. pap., 10c.....................*Friends Pub. H.*

Clark, E. C. Early Roman law: the regal period. cr. 8°. '72. $2...................*Macmillan.*

Clark, Edm. Bible lessons for S.-school concerts and anniversaries. 16°. '74. $1..........*Lothrop.*

— Gathered sheaves; for S.-school concerts and Bible services. 16°. '75. $1..................*Hoyt.*

— Pearls reset: exercises for the S.-school concert. 18°. '74. 75c........................*Graves.*

Clark, E: L. Israel in Egypt; or, Egypt's place among the ancient monarchies. ill. 8°. '73. $5. *Meth. Bk. Conc.*

Clark, F. Le Gros, *and* Wagstaffe, W. W. Outlines of surgery and surgical pathology, incl. diagnosis and treatment of obscure and urgent cases, etc. 2d ed., rev. and enl. 8°. '72. $3......*Lindsay.*

Clark, Fk. E. Our vacations and how to enjoy them. 16°. '74. $1............................*Estes.*

Clark, G: Rogers. Sketches of his campaign in the Illinois in 1778–9; with introd. by H. Pirtle and app. por. 8°. '69. $2; — imp. 8°. large pap., $4. *Clarke.*

Clark, G: W. [Works.] 4 v. 12°. ea., $1.50..*Am. Bapt.*
Cont.: Harmonies of the Gospels. — Notes on Matthew — Mark — Luke.

— Mighty worker. *See* International Sunday school commentary.

Clark, H: Ja. Mind in nature; or, the origin of life and the mode of development in animals. ill. 8°. '65. $3.50..........................*Appleton.*

Clark, Hu. Introduction to heraldry. 18th ed., rev. and enl. by J. R. Planché. ill. 12°. (Bohn.) $1.75; col. ill., $5.50..........*Little, B. & Co.*

— *Same.* ill. 12°. (Bohn.) $2; col. ill., $6. *Lippincott; Scribner, W. & A.*

Clark, Ja. G. Ray's differential and integral calculus. 8°. '75. shp., $2.25........... *Wilson, H. & Co.*

Clark, J: Elements of drawing; ed. by D. M. Reese. 12°. '49. $1; $1.15....................*Barnes.*

Clark, J: A. Awake, thou sleeper. 12°. $1.25..*Carter.*
— Gathered fragments. 12°. $1.50..........*Carter.*
— Pastor's testimony. 12°. $1.25..........*Carter.*
— Walk about Zion. 12°. $1.25..........*Carter.*
— Withered branch revived. ill. 18°. '48. 25c. *Am. Tr.*
— Young disciple: memoir of Anzonetta R. Peters. 12°. $1.50..........*Carter.*
— *Same.* 18°. '49. 45c..........*Am. Tr.*

Clark, J: A. *See* Pennsylvania, Cases decided by the federal and state courts.

Clark, Jos. S. Historical sketch of Cong. churches in Mass., 1620–1858. 12°. $1.25......*Cong. Pub.*

Clark, Latimer. Experimental investigations of the laws which govern the propagation of the electric current in long submarine telegraph cables. pl. sm. f°. (Lond.) '61. bds., $1..........*Spon.*
— *and* Sabine, Rob. Electrical tables and formulæ for the use of telegraph inspectors and operators. ill. cr. 8°. '76. $5..........*Spon.*

Clark, Lew. Theoretical navigation and nautical astronomy. ill. 8°. '72. $3..... *Van Nostrand.*

Clark, Martha. Victims of amusements. 8°. pap., 50c. *Peterson.*

Clark, Ma. Senior. Lost legends of the nursery songs. ill. 12°. $2..........*Routledge.*
— Turnaside cottage. ill. 12°. $1.25..........*Nelson.*

Clark, N. G. Outline of the elements of the Eng. language. ('63.) New ed. 12°. '72. $1.25. *Scribner.*

Clark, Ruf. W. Bible (The) and the school fund. 16°. 75c.; pap., 40c..........*Lee & S.*
— Christian's (The) gift. 16°. $1.25......*J. E. Potter.*
— Great duties taught in the Bible. 18°. bds., 15c. *Cong. Pub.*
— Great truths of the Bible. 18°. bds., 15c. *Cong. Pub.*
— Heaven and its Scriptural emblems. ill. 12°. $1.75. *J. E. Potter.*
— Heroes of the Bible. 18°. bds., 15c.....*Cong. Pub.*
— National series of S.-school lessons for 1873. 18°. bds., 15c..........*Cong. Pub.*
— Notes on the International S.-school lessons for 1876. 12°. '75. $1..........*Dodd.*
— Standard question-book on Isaiah. 18°. '59. hf. bd., 15c..........*Hoyt.*
— Work of God in Gt. Brit. under Moody and Sankey, 1873–'75; with biog. sketches. New ed., cont. discourses by Moody. 12°. '75. $1.50..*Harper.*

Clark, S. W. Analysis of the English language. 12°. '51. hf. bd., 60c..........*Barnes.*
— Easy lessons in language; with diagrams and ill. 18°. '74. hf. bd., 35c..........*Barnes.*
— English grammar for beginners; with diagrams and ill. 18°. '72. hf. bd., 60c..........*Barnes.*
— First lessons in English grammar. 18°. '56. hf. bd., 45c..........*Barnes.*
— Normal grammar; with diagrams. 12°. '70. $1. — Key, $1..........*Barnes.*
— Practical grammar; with diagrams. ('64.) 40th ed., rev. 12°. $1. — Key, 75c..........*Barnes.*

Clark, S: Bible atlas of maps and plans; with notes and index by G. Grove. 4°. '68. $5......*Pott.*
— *See also* Cook, F. C., Bible commentary.

Clark, Sereno Dickenson. Faithful steward (The). 18°. 40c..........*Cong. Pub.*
— Utility and glory of God's immutable purposes. 18°. 75c..........*Cong. Pub.*

Clark, T. *and* T. (*pub.*) Foreign theological library. 81 v. 8°. ea., $3..........*Scribner, W. & A.*

Cont.: Auberlin's Divine revelation. — Baumgarten's Apostolic hist., 3 v. — Bleek's Introd. to the New Test., 2 v. — Codet's Comment. on St. Luke, 2 v. — Delitzsch's Biblical comment. on Hebrews, 2 v. — Delitzsch's Biblical comment. on Isaiah, 2 v. — Delitzsch's Biblical comment. on Job, 2 v. — Delitzsch's Biblical comment. on Psalms, 3 v. — Delitzsch's Solomonic writings, 3 v. — Delitzsch's Comment. on Proverbs, v. 1. — Dorner's Doctrine of person of Christ, 5 v. — Ebrard's Comment. on St. John. — Ebrard's Gospel hist. — Harless' System of Christian ethics. — Hengstenberg's Christology of the Old Test., 4 v. — Hengstenberg's Comment. on Ecclesiastes. — Hengstenberg's

Clark, T. *and* T., *continued.*

Comment. on Ezekiel. — Hengstenberg's Comment. on John, 2 v. — Hengstenberg's Hist. of the Kingdom of God under the Old Test., 2 v. — Hengstenberg's Comment. on Psalms, 3 v. — Keil's Biblical comment. on Chronicles. — Keil's Biblical comment. on Daniel. — Keil's Introd. to the Old Test., 2 v. — Keil's Biblical comment. on Kings. — Keil's Comment. on Jeremiah, 2 v. — Keil and Delitzsch's Comment. on Joshua, Judges and Ruth. — Keil and Delitzsch's Comment. on minor prophets, 2 v. — Keil and Delitzsch's Comment. on Pentateuch, 3 v. — Keil and Delitzsch's Comment. on Samuel. — Keil and Delitzsch's Comment. on Ezra, Nehemiah and Esther. — Kurtz' Hist. of the old covenant, 3 v. — Martensen's Christian dogmatics. — Martensen's Christian ethics. — Müller's Christian doctrine of sin, 2 v. — Oehler's Theology of the Old Test., v. 1. — Schmid's Biblical theology of the New Test. — Steir's On the words of the Lord Jesus, 8 v. — Steir's On the words of the Apostles. — Steir's On the words of the risen Saviour. — Tholuck's Comment. on John. — Tholuck's Comment. on Sermon on the Mount. — Ullmann's Reformers before the reformation, 2 v. — Winer's Confessions of Christendom.

Clark, T: Practical and progressive Latin grammar. roy. 12°. $1.50..........*Desilver.*

Clark, *Bp.* T: March. Dew of youth: lectures to young men and women. 12°. $1.25...*Lee & S.*
Note. A rev. ed. of Lectures on discipline and culture.
— Primary truths of religion. 12°. $1.....*Appleton.*

Clark, W. B. Asleep in Jesus; for bereaved parents. 18°. 40c..........(?)*Martien.*

Clark, W. D. Select London lectures. 12°. $1.75. *Cin. Meth. Bk. Conc.*

Clark, W. G. Four sermons preached in Trinity College, Cambridge. fp. 8°. '60. 75c...*Macmillan.*

Clark, W. R. The comforter. 16°. '76. 75c....*Pott.*

Clark, W: M.. Model dialogues. 12°. '74. $1.50. (?)*Daughaday.*

Clark, W: Tierney. Account of the suspension bridge across the Danube, uniting Pesth with Buda. pl. roy. 8°. (Weale.) '53. $5..........*Spon.*

Clarke, A. Traveler's prayer. 24°. 25c. *Cin. Meth. Bk. Conc.*

Clarke, Ad. Christian theology: sel. from his works. 12°. '37. $1.25..........*Meth. Bk. Conc.*
— *Same;* with life of C. by S. Dunn; rev. by T. O. Summers. ('56.) 2d ed. 12°. '74. $1.25..*So. Meth.*
— Commentaries on the New Test. por. roy. 8°. shp., $5..........*Desilver.*
— *Same.* 2 v. roy. 8°. shp., $10.........*Pounsford.*
— Commentary on the Old and New Test. 4 v. por. and maps. roy. 8°. shp., $20..........*Pounsford.*
— *Same.* 6 v. imp. 8°. '37. shp., $24; cf., $30; mor., $45..........*Meth. Bk. Conc.*
— Life; ed. by Rev. J. B. B. Clarke. 12°. '37. $1.50. *Meth. Bk. Conc.*
— Memoirs of Mrs. Mary Cooper. 18°. '37. 50c. *Meth. Bk. Conc.*
— Memoirs of the Wesley family. 12°. '46. $1.75. *Meth. Bk. Conc.*
— Nature and design of the eucharist. 18°. 35c. *Cin. Meth. Bk. Conc.*
— Succession of sacred literature. 12°. '39. $1.25. *Meth. Bk. Conc.*
— *and* Coke, T: Preacher's manual; incl. Clavis Biblica and Letter to a Meth. preacher. 12°. '37. $1..........*Meth. Bk. Conc.*
— — *Same.* ('54.) 3d ed. 18°. '76. 75c...*So. Meth.*

Clarke, B: Across the sea: some thoughts on the voyage of life. ill. 12°. $1..........*Nelson.*
— First heroes of the cross. ill. 12°. $1.50...*Nelson.*
— *Same.* ('73.) 2d ed. 16°. '76. 75c......*So. Meth.*
— From tent to palace; or, the story of Joseph. ill. 12°. $1.50..........*Nelson.*
— Land of the pigtail. ill. 12°. $1.50..........*Nelson.*
— Pounceford Hall: a story of school life. ill. 12°. $1.50..........*Nelson.*

Clarke, C: The Beauclercs, father and son. [Fiction.] 8°. pap., 50c..........*Harper.*

Clarke, C: Cowden. *See* Shakespeare, W.
— *and Mrs.* Ma. C. Many happy returns of the day. ill. 12°. $1.75..........*Routledge.*

Clarke, C: L. *See* New York, Chancery reports.

Clarke, *Mrs.* D. W. C. Lizzie Maitland. 16°. $1. *Strong.*

Clarke, Dorus. Revision of the Eng. version of the Bible. 18°. 50c. .... *Bost. Am. Tr.*

Clarke, E: H. Building (The) of a brain. 16°. '74. $1.25 .... *Osgood.*

— Sex in education; or, a fair chance for girls. 16°. '73. $1.25 .... *Osgood.*

— *and* Amory, Rob. Physiological and therapeutical action and value of the bromide of potassium and the bromide of ammonium. 16°. '72. $1.50. *Jas. Campbell.*

Clarke, Fk. Wigglesworth. Specific gravity tables. 8°. '73. pap., $1 .... *Smith. Inst.*

— — Supplement. 8°. '76. pap., 50c. .... *Smith. Inst.*

— Specific heat tables. pt. 2. 8°. '76. pap., 50c. *Smith. Inst.*

— Tables: expansion by heat. 8°. '76. pap., 50c. *Smith. Inst.*

— Weights, measures and money of all nations. 12°. hf. bd., $1.50 .... *Appleton.*

Clarke, G: Voyage to America, 1703; with introd. and notes by E. B. O'Callaghan. sm. 8°. '67. bds., $4 .... *Munsell.*

Clarke, G: S. Practical geometry and engineering drawing; [with] rules for shading, shade-lining, etc. pl. demy 4°. '75. $7.25 .... *Spon.*

Clarke, G: W. Christ crucified. 18°. '48. 60c. *Meth. Bk. Conc.*

Clarke, *Mrs.* H: Steele. Marble preacher. ill. 16°. '73. $1.50 .... *Lothrop.*

— Their children. ill. 16°. '75. $1.50 .... *Lothrop.*

Clarke, Hovey K. *See* Michigan, Supreme Court reports.

Clarke, Hu. A. Improved school for the parlor organ. 4°. '75. bds., $2.50 .... *Ditson.*

— New method for the piano. 4°. '73. bds., $3.75. *Ditson.*

Clarke, J. B. B. Life of A. Clarke. *See* Clarke, Ad.

Clarke, J. G. Reduction of ruling or maximum grades; [also] Operation of the gunpowder pile driver, by S. R. Probasco; [also] Pneumatic foundations, by W. S. Smith. 8°. '74. pap., 50c. *Am. Soc. of C. E.*

Clarke, Ja. Catechism of the rudiments of music; for assistance of teachers of the piano-forte. New ed., rev. and enl. 12°. '67. bds., 38c. *Ditson.*

Clarke, Ja. Freeman. Christian doctrine of the forgiveness of sin. ('67.) 3d ed. 16°. '74. 50c. *Am. Unit.*

— Christian doctrine of prayer. ('54.) 7th ed. 16°. '74. 75c. .... *Am. Unit.*

— Common sense in religion. 12°. '73. $2 ... *Osgood.*

— Hour (The) which cometh. 12°. $1.50 .... *Lee & S.*

— Orthodoxy: its truth and errors. ('66.) 11th ed. 12°. '74. $1.25 .... *Am. Unit.*

— Steps of belief; or, rational Christianity maintained against atheism, free religion and Romanism. ('70.) 5th ed. 16°. '74. $1 .... *Am. Unit.*

— Ten great religions: essays. 8th ed. 12°. '71. $3; hf. cf., $5.50 .... *Osgood.*

— *and* Lilian. Exotics; by J. F. C. and L. C. [*pseud.*] (Saunterers' ser.) 2d ed. 18°. '75. $1.25 .. *Osgood.*

Clarke, Lilian. *See* Clarke, J. F. *and* L.

Clarke, Marcus. His natural life. [Fiction.] 8°. pap., 75c. .... *Harper.*

Clarke, *Mrs.* Ma. Cowden. Concordance to Shakespeare. New ed., rev. roy. 8°. (Lond.) '75. $9; hf. cf., $12.50; cf., $15 ..... *Little, B. & Co.*

— Girlhood of Shakespeare's heroines; in a series of tales. 2 v. ill. 12°. '71. ea., $2 ...... *Putnam.*

— Iron cousin (The); or, mutual influence. 16°. bds., 80c. .... *Routledge.*

— *Same.* 12°. $1.50 .... *Appleton.*

— Rambling story (A). 16°. '75. $1.50 ..... *Roberts.*

— Trust (The) and the remittance: two love stories in metred prose. 16°. '74. $1.25 .... *Roberts.*

Clarke, *Mrs.* Ma. Cowden, *continued.*

— Yarns of an old mariner. ill. 16°. $1.50 ... *Lee & S.*

— *See also* Clarke, C. C. *and Mrs.* M. C.; — Shakespeare, W.

Clarke, Ma. Latham. ["Mada."] Birthday present. ill. 18°. '69. 75c. .... *Lothrop.*

— Bud and Blossom; [also] Blue Violet. ill. 16°. '72. 50c. .... *Lothrop.*

— Daisy's mission. ill. 24°. '70. 30c. .... *Lothrop.*

— Kitty's tableaux. ill. 24°. '70. 30c. .... *Lothrop.*

— Little Blossom. ill. 24°. '70. 30c. .... *Lothrop.*

— Little white-mice boy. ill. 24°. '70. 30c. .. *Lothrop.*

— May flower series. 6 v. ill. 24°. $1.80 ... *Lothrop.*
Cont.: Daisy's mission. — Little white-mice boy. — Bud and Blossom. — Kitty's tableaux. — Little Blossom. — Blue Violet.

— Old, old story (The): question book for children. 18°. 15c. .... *Lothrop.*

— Precious words: quest. book. 18°. '72. 15c. *Lothrop.*

— Rainy day at school. ill. 18°. '69. 75c. ... *Lothrop.*

— Story of Jesus: quest. book. 32°. 15c. .... *Freewill.*

— Wonderful works of Jesus: question book. 32°. 15c. .... *Freewill.*

— *Same.* 18°. '71. 15c. .... *Lothrop.*

Clarke, N. H. B. O'Neal the Great: drama. 16°. pap., 15c. .... *French.*

— Pirate of the isles: drama. 16°. pap., 15c. .. *French.*

Clarke, Reb. So. ["Sophie May."] Asbury twins (The). ill. 12°. $1.75 .... *Lee & S.*

— Doctor's (The) daughter. ill. 12°. $1.50 .. *Lee & S.*

— Dotty Dimple stories. 6 v. ill. 24°. ea., 75c. ... *Lee & S.*
Cont.: Dotty Dimple at her grandmother's — at home — out West — at play — at school. — Dotty Dimple's Flyaway.

— Little Prudy stories. 6 v. ill. 24°. ea., 75c. .. *Lee & S.*
Cont.: Little Prudy. — Little Prudy's sister Susy. — Little Prudy's Captain Horace. — Little Prudy's cousin Grace. — Little Prudy's story book. — Little Prudy's Dotty Dimple.

— Little Prudy's Flyaway ser. 6 v. ill. 24°. ea., 75c. *Lee & S.*
Cont.: Little folks astray. — Prudy keeping house. — Aunt Madge's story. — Little grandmother. — Little grandfather. — Miss Thistledown.

— Our Helen. ill. 12°. $1.75 .... *Lee & S.*

Clarke, R: H. Lives of deceased bishops of the Catholic church in the U. S. 2 v. por. imp. 8°. $8; hf. mor., $12; mor., $20 .... *O'Shea.*

Clarke, S. M. S. Scenes and sketches of English history. ill. 12°. $1.50 .... *Nelson.*

Clarke, S: Scripture promises. 32°. 38c. .. *Appleton.*

— *Same.* 32°. '41. 40c.; 50c. .... *Am. Tr.*

— *Same.* 32°. 50c. .... *Carter.*

— *Same.* 32°. '57. 50c.; 75c. .... *Perkinpine.*

Clarke, T: Curtis. Accidents to railway structures. 8°. pap., 55c. .... *Am. Soc. of C. E.*

— Description of the iron railway bridge across the Mississippi River at Quincy, Ill.; with plans. 4°. '69. $7.50 .... *Van Nostrand.*

— Education of civil engineers. *See* Forshey, C. G., Levees of the Mississippi River; — Whipple, S., Upright arched bridges.

— Notes on the crushing strength of Am. iron. *See* Steele, J. D., Tests of bridge irons.

— Tests and testing machines. *See* Ellis, T. G., Descriptions of hydraulic experiments.

— *See also* Griffen, J., *and* Clarke, T. C.

Clarke, W. Fairlie. Treatise on diseases of the tongue. ill. 8°. '73. $5 .... *Lindsay.*

Clarke, W. P. *See* Iowa, Supreme Court reports.

Clarke, W: H. [Dollar music instructors.] 3 v. 4°. '71-'73. ea., bds., $1 .... *Ditson.*
Cont.: Dollar instructor for the piano-forte — for the reed organ — for the violin.

— Home recreations: songs and instrumental pieces. obl. 8°. bds., $1.50 .... *G. D. Russell.*

— New method for reed organs. 4°. '69. bds., $2.50. *Ditson.*

Clarner, F. Amerikanisches Gartenbuch: Gemüse- Obst- u. Weinbau, Blumenzucht, etc. 6th ed. ill. 8°. $1.50 .... *Schäfer.*

Clarus u. Maria. Nieritz, G. 25c. . . . . *Morwitz.*
Clary, Fes. A. The color-bearer. 18°. '64. 40c. *Am. Tr.*
Class and desk. *See* Gray, W. C.
Class of five. 18°. 65c.; 75c. . . . . *Am. Bapt.*
Classic tales. 12°. (Bohn.) $1.25 . . *Little, B. & Co.*
— *Same.* 12°. (Bohn.) $1.40 . . . . . *Scribner, W. & A.*
— *Same.* 12°. (Bohn.) $1.50 . . . . *Lippincott.*
Classical chorus book. Baker, B. F., *and* Southard, L. H. $1.50 . . . . *Gordon.*
Classical library. *See* Harper's.
Classmates (The); or, the college revival; by a Presbyterian minister. 18°. 60c. . . . . . *Pres. Bd.*
Clater, Fs. Every man his own cattle doctor; rev. by G. Armatage. ill. 8°. hf. bd., $6 . . *Scribner, W. & A.*
— *See also* Farmer's barn book.
Claude, J: Essay on the composition of a sermon. 18°. '48. 55c. . . . . *Meth. Bk. Conc.*
Claude and the countess. 8°. pap., 25c. . . . . . *De Witt.*
Claude captured. 8°. pap., 25c. . . . . *De Witt.*
Claude, the colporteur. 16°. $1.25 . . . . *Carter.*
Claude Duval and his companions. 8°. pap., 25c. *Dick & F.*
Claude Duval, the dashing highwayman. 8°. pap., 25c. *Dick & F.*
Claude Duval ser. 28 nos. 8°. ea., pap., 25c. *De Witt.*
Cont.: Gentleman Jack. — Jack and his bride. — Dare-devil Dick. — Grace Manning. — Renegade gypsy. — Highwayman's stratagem. — Ride for life. — Claude's last bullet. — Black Bess. — Claude in his dungeon. — Struggle for life. — Claude in the convent. — Claude and the abbess. — Duval and the duchess. — Claude to the rescue. — Death to the traitor. — Duval in Newgate. — Highwayman's bride. — Rosa Bell, the prince's victim. — Duval in a duel. — Lucy Thornton. — Claude captured. — Cask of gold. — Moonlight Jack. — Duval denounced — Claude in the cave. — Luke, the lurker. — Duval at bay.
Claude in the cathedral. 8°. pap., 25c. . . . . . *De Witt.*
Claude in the cave. 8°. pap., 25c. . . . . *De Witt.*
Claude in the convent. 8°. pap., 25c. . . . . *De Witt.*
Claude in his dungeon. 8°. pap., 25c. . . . . *De Witt.*
Claude Melnotte as a detective. Pinkerton, A. $1.50. *Keen.*
Claude to the rescue. 8°. pap., 25c. . . . . *De Witt.*
Claude's last bullet. 8°. pap., 25c. . . . . *De Witt.*
Claudia. Douglas, A. M. $1.50 . . . . *Lee & S.*
Claudia. *See* Tucker, *Mrs.* C.
Claudine v. Villa Bella. *See* Goethe, J. W. v.
Claudius, Mt. Das Häuschen am See, od. wo die Noth am grössten, ist Gottes Hülfe am nächsten. 16°. '67. bds., 25c. *Steiger.*
— *Eng.* Cottage by the lake. ill. 16°. 75c. (?)*Luth. Pub.*
Clauson-Thue, W. The A B C universal commercial electric telegraphic code; for use of merchants, ship-owners, brokers, etc. 8°. '74. $4.25 . . *Spon.*
Clauss, C. *See* Gems of the Dresden gallery.
Claverings (The). *See* Trollope, A.
Clavers, *Mrs.* Ma. (*pseud.*) *See* Kirkland, *Mrs.* C. M.
Clavigo. *See* Goethe, J. W. v.
Claxton, Rob. Bethell. Questions on the Gospels. ('68.) New ed. 18°. '74. hf. bd., 25c. *Claxton.*
Clay, C: Complete handbook of obstetric surgery; or, short rules of practice. 1st Am. from 3d. Lond. ed. ill. 12°. '74. $2.25 . . . . *Lindsay.*
Clay, H: Life. ill. 16°. $1.25 . . . . *Lee & S.*
— Life and speeches. 2 v. por. and ill. 8°. $4.50 . . *Sower.*
— Life, correspondence and speeches; ed. by C. Colton. 6 v. 8°. $18; shp., $20; hf. cf., $25 . . . . *O'Shea.*
— Principal speeches; with life. 8°. pap., 25c. *U. P. James.*
— Speeches. *See* Mallory, D:
Clay, Ja. Treatise on whist. *See* Baldwin, J. L., Laws of short whist.
Clay, Wa. Lowe. Power of the keys, and other sermons preached in Coventry. fp. 8°. '64. $1. *Macmillan.*
Clay, Wa. Lowe, *continued.*
— The prison chaplain: memoir of C., with sel. fro[m] his reports and correspondence, and sketch [of] prison discipline in Eng. 8°. $4 . . . . *Macmillan*
— (*ed.*) Essays on church policy. 8°. $2.50 . . *Macmillan*
Claybaugh, Jos. Christian profession (The): letter[s] on [its] nature, etc. 18°. 60c. . . *U. P. Bd. of Pu[b.]*
— *Same.* 12°. '55. 75c. . . . . *Wilstach*
— Essay on relations of baptized youth to the church. *See* Ritchie, A., Sacramental catechism.
Clayton, Ellen Creathorne. Queens of song: memoir[s] of female vocalists; with chronol. list of opera[s] performed in Europe. por. 8°. $3; hf. mor. $4.75 . . . . *Harper*
Clayton, J: A letter to the Royal Society, May 1[2], 1688, giving an account of several observables i[n] Virginia. [Reprint.] 4°. pap., 50c. . . . . *Sabin*
Clayton Allyn. Bristol, S. A. 50c. . . . . *Am. Tr*
Clayton rangers; or, the Quaker partisans. ill. 12° $1.25 . . . . *Lippincott*
Clean your boots, sir? *See* Erickson, D. S.; — Go ahead lib.
Clear case. A'Beckett, G. A. 15c. . . . . *French*
Clear shining after rain. Brock, C. $1.25 . . . . . *Pott*
Cleaveland, And. J. School harmonist: accompaniment to Brooks' "Manual of devotions fo[r] schools." 16°. '59. 75c. . . . . *Barnes*
Cleaveland, C. H. Pronouncing medical lexicon ('55.) New ed. 18°. '57. $1 . . . . *Wilstach*
— *Same.* New ed., rev. 24°. '76. $1.25; $1.50. *Lindsay*
Cleaveland, *Mrs.* E. H. J. No sects in heaven, and othe[r] poems. ('68.) New ed. sq. 24°. '69. $1.25. *Clark & M*
Cleaveland, H: W. *and* W: *and* Backus, S. D. Cottage and farm archit. 100 eng. 8°. $4 . . *Appleton*
Cleaveland, J: Banking system of N. Y. [state] with notes and ref. to adjudged cases; incl. account of the N. Y. Clearing House and the national bank act. 8°. shp., $5.50 . . *Baker, V. & Co*
Cleaveland, P. Meteorological observations, Brunswick, Me., 1807–'59. 4°. '67. pap., $1. *Smith. Inst*
Cleaveland, W: *See* Cleaveland, H: W. *and* W: *and* Backus, S. D.
Cleft stick (The). Oxenford, J. 15c. *French; Lee & S*
Clefts of the rock. Macduff, J. R. $1.50 . . . . *Carter*
Cleland, J. Animal physiology. (Adv. sci. ser.) ill 12°. '74. $1.50 . . . . *Putnam*
Clelia. *See* Wels, A.
Clem and Joyce. Smith, F. I. B. 75c. . . . . . . *Lothrop*
Clemence d'Orville. *See* Bauer, K.
Clemency Franklin. Keary, A. $1.25 . . . *Macmillan*
Clemens *Alexandrinus.* *See* Clement *of Alexandria*
Clemens *Romanus.* *See* Clement I.
Clemens, Jer. Bernard Lile: hist. romance. 12°. $1.25 . . . . *Lippincott.*
— Mustang Gray: romance. 12°. $1.25 . . . *Lippincott.*
— Rivals (The): tale of the times of Burr and Hamilton. 12°. '59. $1.25 . . . . . *Claxton; Lippincott*
— Tobias Wilson: tale of the great rebellion. 12°. '65. $1.75 . . . . *Claxton; Lippincott.*
Clemens, S: L. ["M: Twain."] Autobiography and first romance. 16°. '71. 75c.; pap., 40c. *Sheldon*
— Innocents abroad; or, the new pilgrim's progress. ill. 8°. *$3.50–$8 . . . . *Am. Pub.*
— Roughing it. ill. 8°. *$3.50–$8 . . . . *Am. Pub.*
— Sketches new and old. ill. f°. *$3–$6 . . . . *Am. Pub.*
— *See also* Lotos leaves.
— *and* Warner, C: D. Gilded age: a tale of to-day. ill. 8°. *$3.50–$8 . . . . *Am. Pub.*
Clement *of Alexandria.* [Clemens *Alexandrinus.*] Writings; tr. by W. Wilson. (Ante-Nicene Christ. lib.) 2 v. 8°. ea., $3 . . *Scribner, W. & A.*
Cont.: 1. Exhortation to the heathen; The instructor; Miscellanies; or, Stromata. — 2. Miscellanies, *contin.*

Clement I. [Clemens *Romanus*.] Clementine homilies; [also] Apostolical constitutions. (Ante-Nicene Christ. lib.) 8°. $3...*Scribner, W. & A.*
— Clementine recognitions. *See* Tatian *and* Theophilus, Writings.
Clement, —. *See* Dennery, A. P., *and* Clement, —.
Clement, Clara Erskine. Handbook of legendary and mythological art. ill. cr. 8°. '71. $3.25; hf. mor., $5; mor., $7.................*Hurd & H.*
— Painters, sculptors, architects, engravers, and their works; with monograms and ill. cr. 8°. '73. $3.25; hf. mor., $5; mor., $7.......*Hurd & H.*
Clément, Fél. Biographies des musiciens célèbres. ('73.) New ed. 12°. '76. $1.50.....*Schoenhof.*
Clement, J. Noble deeds of Am. women; with introd. by Mrs. L. H. Sigourney. ill. 12°. $1.50. *Lee & S.*
Clement, J. A. Baptist pretensions to antiquity. ('60.) 2d ed. 18°. '75. $1..................*So. Meth.*
Clement; or, true stories about conscience. 18°. 22c. *Am. S. S.*
Clementi, M. Preludes and exercises; [for the piano]. f°. $1.75........................*Brainard.*
Clementina's mirror. *See* Bradley, *Mrs.* M. E., Good girl's lib.
Clement's trial and victory; or, sowing and reaping; by author of "Little Lisette." ill. 12°. $1.50. *Pott.*
Clemmer, Ma. [*formerly Mrs.* Ma. C. Ames]. Eirene; or, a woman's right. [Fiction.] 8°. '70. $1.25; pap., 75c...........................*Putnam.*
— His two wives. 12°. '74. $1.75........*Hurd & H.*
— Memorial of A. and P. Cary, with their later poems. por. cr. 8°. '72. $2–$6.............*Hurd & H.*
— Outlines of men, women and things. 16°. '73. $1.50. *Hurd & H.*
— Ten years in Washington: life and scenes at the national capital as a woman sees them. ill. roy. 8°. *$3; $3.50.........*Lloyd; A. D. Worthington.*
Clergyman's (The) orphan; [also] The infidel reclaimed; [also] Jane Clark, the orphan; by a clergyman. ill. 18°. 75c..............*Harper.*
Clergyman's self-examination concerning the Apostles' creed. fp. 8°. '64. 75c. ....*Macmillan.*
Clergyman's widow and her young family. Hofland, B. 50c.................................*Porter.*
Clerical adventures. *See* Hood, E. P., World of anecdote lib.
Clerk of Clerkenwell. Almar, G. 15c.......*French.*
Clerk (The) of works. Hoskins, G. G. 60c. ..*Spon.*
Cléry, J. B. Faithful servant. ill. 16°. 50c....*Pott.*
Cleve Hall. *See* Sewell, E. M.
Cleveland, Cecilia. Story of a summer: journal leaves from Chappaqua. 12°. '74. $1.50....*Carleton.*
Cleveland, C: Dexter. Compendium of Am. literature. 12°. '59. $2.50......................*Barnes.*
— Compendium of English literature. 12°. '48. $2.50. *Barnes.*
— Compendium of Grecian antiquities. 12°. hf. roan, 95c.............................*Lippincott.*
— Concordance to Milton's poetical works. 12°. $1.25. *Keystone.*
— *Same.* 16°. $3.................*Scribner, W. & A.*
— — *See also* Milton, J.
— English literature of the 19th century. 12°. '66. $2.50...............................*Barnes.*
— Hymns. 18°. 75c......................*Keystone.*
— (*ed.*) Lyra sacra Americana: gems from Am. sacred poetry, with notes, biog. sketches and indices. 2 v. 18°. '68. $3.......................*Scribner.*
Cleveland, H. A. (*ed.*) Golden sheaves from the fields of ancient and modern literature. ill. 8°. *$2.50.............................*McCurdy.*
Cleveland, H. W. S. Hints to riflemen. ill. 12°. $1.50. *Appleton.*
Cleveland, H. W. S., *continued.*
— Landscape architecture, as applied to the wants of the west; with essay on forest planting on the great plains. 16°. '73. $1.............*Jansen.*
Cleveland, H: R. Life of H. Hudson. *See* Sparks, J., Lib. of Am. biog.
Cleveland, R: J. Narrative of voyage and commercial enterprises. 2 v. in 1. 12°. $1..*Burnham.*
Clevelands (The). *See* Sheldon, *Mrs.* E. M.
Clevenger, S. R. Treatise on government surveying. ill. 16°. '74. mor., $2.50....... *Van Nostrand.*
Clever Jack; or, the adventures of a donkey, written by himself. ill. 16°. $1............*Lippincott.*
Clever little Madge. *See* Herd boy ser.
Clever stories. Sherwood, M. M. 75c........*Carter.*
Clever stories of many nations. Saxe, J. G. $3.50. *Osgood.*
Clever woman of the family. *See* Yonge, C. M.
Cliff climbers (The). Reid, M. $1.50........*Miller.*
Cliff hut; or, the fortunes of a fisherman's family. 18°. 45c................................*Pres. Bd.*
Cliff hut series. 4 v. 18°. $1.85...........*Pres. Bd.*
Cont.: Cliff hut.—Bird and arrow.—Wild roses.—China cup.
Clifford, —. Atoms. *See* Hunt, R., Coal as a reservoir of power.
Clifford, Fk. S. A romance of perfume lands; or, the search for Captain Jacob Cole; with facts about perfumes and toilet articles. ill. 12°. '75. $2.50; pap., 50c..........................*Clifford.*
Clifford, Nath. *See* United States, Circuit Court reports.
Clifford and the actress. Blount, M. 50c...*Peterson.*
Clifford and the actress. Reynolds, G. W. M. 50c. *Peterson.*
Clifford Castle: tale of the English reformation. 12°. $1.50...............................*Nelson.*
Clifford conquers. 8°. pap., 25c. ....*De Witt.*
Clifford household. Moore, J. T. $1.........*Dodd.*
Clifford in danger. 8°. pap., 25c............*De Witt.*
Clifford troupe. Westmoreland, M. J. $1.75. *Carleton.*
Clifton, Arth. Instructions for the piano-forte; with popular airs. f°. pap., $1.....*Ditson; Willig.*
— Piano method. f°. $1...................*Gordon.*
— Piano-forte preceptor. 4°. 60c. ....*Ditson.*
Clifton, M. Delano. Der two subprises: Dutch farce. 16°. pap., 15c. ....*Ames.*
— In the wrong box: Ethiop. drama. 16°. pap., 15c. *Ames.*
— Schnapps: Dutch farce. 16°. pap., 15c......*Ames.*
Clifton, W. C. Vocal instructor. f°. pap., $1..*Ditson.*
Clifton Grey. Egan, P. 25c. ....*De Witt.*
Clifton Rice. Robbins, S. S. 90c. ......(?)*Martien.*
Clifton tracts (The). *See* St. Vincent de Paul.
Climbers (The). Bates, L. 90c............*Am. Tr.*
Climbing and sliding. Pike, M. H. $1.25. *Lockwood, B. & Co.*
Climbing the glacier. 18°. '65. 40c.......*Randolph.*
Climbing the mountain. Grosvenor, H. S. $1.15. *Hoyt.*
Climbing poems. Rankin, S. B. $1.25....*Turnbull.*
Climbing the rope. Nowell, H. P. H. $1...*Lee & S.*
Cline, A. J. Henry Courtland; or, what a farmer can do. 12°. $1.75.....................*Lippincott.*
Clinton, G: W., *and* Wait, W: Digest of N. Y. reports (1794–1872). 8 v. 8°. shp., $48...*Gould.*
Clinton, *Sir* H: Narrative, rel. to his conduct during his commands in No. Am.; with extracts from his correspondence. (Lond., 1783.) New ed. f°. '65. pap., $10.—4°. pap., $5.—8°. pap., $2.50......................*J. Campbell & Son.*

Clinton, *Sir* H: *continued.*
— Observations on some parts of the answer of Cornwallis to Sir H: Clinton's "Narrative;" with extracts of letters, etc. (Lond., 1783.) New ed. f°. '66. pap., $10. — 4°. pap., $5. — 8°. pap., $2.50 .... *J. Campbell & Son.*
Clinton. Simonds, W. $1.25 .... *Miller.*
Clique of gold. Gaboriau, E. $1.25; 75c..... *Estes.*
Clives of Burcot. *See* Smith, Hannah.
Clock of the passion. *See* Liguori, *St.*
Clock on the stairs. Hazlewood, C. H. 15c... *French.*
Clock (The) struck one. Watson, S. $1.50.. *Rel. Phil.*
Clock (The) struck three. Watson, S. $1.50. *Rel. Phil.*
Clockmaker (The). *See* Haliburton, T. C.
Clockmaker's hat. Girardin, D. de. 15c.... *French.*
Clodd, E: Childhood of religions. 12°. $1.25.. *Appleton.*
— Childhood of the world. 16°. 75c. ....(?) *Shepard.*
— *Same.* 12°. '73. 75c.; pap., 50c........ *Somerby.*
— *Same.* 2d ed. 12°. '74. 75c. — School ed. 18°. '74. 50c. .... *Macmillan.*
Cloister and the hearth. *See* Reade, C.
Cloister legends. 16°. $1; $1.50.......... *Sadlier.*
Clok, H: Diseases of sheep, with their remedies. ('68.) New ed. 12°. '69. $1.25; pap., 75c. *Claxton.*
Clos pommier (Le). *See* Achard, A.
Close shave (A). Baker, G. M. 15c. ...... *Lee & S.*
Closer walk (The). Darling, H. 65c...... *Pres. Bd.*
Closet companion (The): manual of prayer, with introd. by Rev. A. Barnes. 18°. 70c... *Pres. Bd.*
Closet lib. of devotion. 4v. sq.18°. '74. $6. *H. A. Young.*
Cont.: Waiting at the cross, by D. C. Eddy. — Leaves gathered, by Mrs. J. H. Thomas. — Words and mind of Jesus, by J. R. Macduff. — Thoughts that cluster, by Mrs. J. H. Thomas.

Closing scene (The). Neale, E. $1.50...... *Sower.*
Closing scenes. 18°. 55c.; 65c.......... *Am. Bapt.*
Closing scenes in the life of Jesus. Headley, P. C. 25c.; 30c.......... *J. E. Potter.*
Closs, G., *and* Fröhlicher, O. (*ill.*) Rhododendron (Swiss Alps): photos., with [Germ.] text by H. A. Berlepsch. roy. 4°. $24.......... *Stroefer.*
— — *and* Roux, G. (*ill.*) Lake and mountain scenery of the Swiss Alps: photos. and woodcuts, with text by T. G. Bonney. roy. 4°. $30....... *Stroefer.*
Cloth of gold. Aldrich, T. B. $1.50; $3; $4. *Osgood.*
Clotilde. Pontmartin, A. de. $1.75... *J. M. Stoddart.*
Cloud, D. C. Monopolies and the people. 8°. '73. $2.50; shp., $3.......... *Day.*
Cloud and the sunbeam. Dunning, A. K. 45c. *Pres. Bd.*
— *See also* Sunbeam ser.
Cloud and sunshine. Anderson, J. 15c...... *French.*
Cloud pictures. Underwood, F. H. $1.50.. *Lee & S.*
Cloud with the silver lining. *See* Mackarness, *Mrs.* M. A.
Clouded gem (The): allegory by author of "Valley of stains." 18°. 25c.; pap., 10c...... *Am. S. S.*
Clouded happiness. Orsay, *Countess* d'. 50c. *Harper.*
Clouded in mystery. B., M. A. A. $1.50.. *McKinney.*
Clouds. Marsden, F. 15c.......... *De Witt.*
Clouds (The). *See* Aristophanes.
Clouds after rain; or, the afflictions of Bertha Melville; by author of "Early dawn." 18°. 75c. *Pres. Bd.*
Clouds and sunbeams. 18°. 50c.......... *Cong. Pub.*
Clouds and sunshine. Finley, M. F. 70c... *Pres. Bd.*
Clouds and sunshine. *See* Tucker, *Mrs.* C.
Clouds in the east. Baker, V. $6.75.. *Scribner, W. & A.*
Clough, Arth. Hu. Poems; with memoir. (Blue and gold ed.) 32°. $1.50.......... **Osgood.*
— *Same.* 3d ed., with new memoir. fp. 8°. '74. $2. *Macmillan.*

Clough, Arth. Hu., *continued.*
— *Same;* and prose remains, ed. by his wife; with sel. from his letters and a memoir. 2 v. cr. 8°. '69. $6.......... *Macmillan.*
Clover glen. 18°. '64. 40c.......... *Randolph.*
Cloverly. Higham, M. R. $1.25.......... *Randolph.*
Cloverly series. *See* Smith, Hannah.
Clovernook children. Cary, A. $1.50..... **Osgood.*
Club-book (The). James, G. P. R. $1.50.. *Harper.*
Club night. Balfour, C. L. 50c. .... *Routledge.*
Clunes, G. C. Story of Pauline: an autobiography. New ed. cr. 8°. '71. $1.75....... *Macmillan.*
Cluster. *See* Mercer's cluster.
Cluster (The). Martin, S. W., Towne, T. M., *and* Stillman, J. M. $1.50.......... *Peters.*
Cluster of fruits from the tree of heavenly wisdom. Brooks, A. 75c.......... *Pres. Bd.*
Clyde, Alton. Under foot. [Fiction.] ill. 8°. pap., 50c. .... *Harper.*
Clyde Wardleigh's promise. Nauman, M. D. $1.50. *Claxton.*
Clyffards of Clyffe: a love story. 12°. $1.75; pap., $1.50.......... *Peterson.*
Clymer, Meredith. Legitimate influence of epilepsy upon criminal responsibility. 8°. pap., 25c. *Campbell & Co.*
Coach-makers' illustrated hand-book. ('72.) New ed. 8°. '75. $3.......... *I. D. Ware.*
Coaina. Dorsey, A. H. $1.......... *O'Shea.*
Coal-heaver's revenge. Stout, G. L. 15c... *De Witt.*
Coal-pit. Bridges, J. 40c.......... *So. Meth.*
Coals of fire. Baker, G. M. 15c. .... *Lee & S.*
Coast Survey. *See* United States.
Coates, H: T. The comprehensive speaker. cr. 8°. '71. hf. bd., $1.50.......... *Porter.*
Coates, *Mrs.* W. H. Our Willie; or, home-teaching. ('66.) 2d ed. 18°. '68. 60c........ *Perkinpine.*
Cobb, J. F. The great czar. ill. 16°. 50c...... *Pott.*
— Stories of success. ill. 12°. $1.50.......... *Pott.*
Cobb, Ja. First floor: farce. 16°. pap., 15c. *French.*
— Haunted tower: opera. 16°. pap., 15c..... *French.*
— Paul and Virginia: opera. 16°. pap., 15c. *French.*
Cobb, Lyman. Miniature lexicon of the Eng. language. 48°. $1; $1.50.......... *Harper.*
Cobb, *Miss* Ma. L. Poetical dramas; for home and public exhibitions. 16°. 75c.; hf. bd., 60c. *Lee & S.*
Cobb, Sophie Dickinson. Hillsboro' farms. 12°. $1.50. *Lee & S.*
Cobb, Sylvanus. Autobiography; with memoir by S. Cobb, jr. por. 12°. '67. $1.50.. *Universalist.*
— Compend of Christian divinity. 12°. '45. $1.50. *Universalist.*
Cobb, Sylvanus, *jr.* The iron cross. 8°. pap., 25c. *Peterson.*
Cobb, T: R. R. Historical sketch of slavery. 8°. '58. $1.50.......... *T. & J. W. Johnson.*
— Inquiry into the law of negro slavery in the U. S.; [with] Historical sketch of slavery. 8°. '58. $5. *T. & J. W. Johnson.*
Cobbe, Fes. Power. Broken lights. 12°. '64. $1.75. *Tilton.*
— Hopes of the human race, hereafter and here. 12°. '76. $1.50.......... *Miller.*
— Religious demands of the age: preface to Theodore Parker's works. 16°. pap., 25c. .... *Fuller.*
— Religious duty. 12°. $1.75.......... *Lee & S.*
— Studies, new and old, of ethical and social subjects. cr. 8°. $3.......... *Lee & S.*
Cobbet, T: Practical treatise on prayer. 12°. $1.25. *Cong. Pub.*
Cobbett, W: American gardener. 12°. 75c..... *Judd.*

Cobbett, W: *continued.*
— History of the "Protestant" reformation in Eng. and Ireland. 12°. '51. 75c. .... *Murphy.*
— *Same.* 18°. $1.25 .... *Sadlier.*
— Legacies to parsons. 18°. 60c. .... *Sadlier.*
— Life of Andrew Jackson. 18°. 75c. .... *Harper.*
— *See also* Fessing, Jos., Die versuchte Ausrottung der kathol. Religion in England.

Cobbin, Ingram. Book of popery: description of the origin, progress, doctrines, etc., of the papal church. 18°. 60c. .... *Pres. Bd.*
— Child's commentator on the Bible; with introd. by L. P. Brockett. 8°. '73. $3.50..(?) *Goodspeed.*
— *Same.* 4 v. 18°. $3 .... *Cong. Pub.*
— Cobbin's commentary on the Bible for young and old; ed. by E. J. Goodspeed. ill. and map. 8°. '76. $4 .... (?) *Goodspeed.*
— Illustrated New Testament; with notes. ill. 8°. '71. $2.50 .... (?) *Goodspeed.*
— Pictorial Bible and commentator for young people. New ed., rev. and enl. by J. S. Vandersloot. 4°. '75. *$3.50; $4.25 .... *F. Scofield.*
— Youth's Bible and commentator: the Scriptures written in a simple manner for the young. ill. sq. 12°. $2.50 .... *Routledge.*
— *See also* Bible [Whole].

Cobbler (The) and his rose. 18°. 75c...(?) *Martien.*

Cobbler of Preston. Johnson, C. 15c. .... *French.*

Cobbler's daughter. Berry, M. E. $1.50..*Cong. Pub.*

Cobbold, T. Spencer. Worms: lectures on practical helminthology. post 8°. '72. $2 .... *Lindsay.*

Cobden, Halsted E. C. Daily communings with God; sel. chiefly from writings of Archb. Leighton. 18°. '60. 75c. .... *Whittaker.*

Cobden, Pl. Beckoning series. [To form 6 v.] v. 1–5. ill. 16°. ea., $1.25 .... *Lee & S.*
Cont.: Who will win? — Going on a mission. — The turning wheel. — Good luck. — Take a peep.

Cobden, R: Political writings. 2 v. 8°. $6..*Appleton.*

Cobden Club essays. System of land tenure in various countries; ed. by J. W. Probyn. 16°. $1.75. *Cassell.*
— 2d ser., 1871–'72. demy 8°. $7.50 .... *Cassell.*
— 1875. Local government and taxation; ed. by J. W. Probyn. demy 8°. $7.50 .... *Cassell.*

Cobwebs from an empty skull. Bierce, M. H. $1.75. *Routledge.*

Cobwebs to catch flies. ill. 32°. 25c.; 40c. *Scribner, W. & A.*

Cochran, Wesley. The life of human souls. 16°. '68. $1 .... *Perkinpine.*

Cock, Micajah R. American poultry book. ill. 18°. 60c. .... *Harper.*

Cock, T: Inaugural address before N. Y. Acad. of Med. 8°. '52. pap., 10c. .... *N. Y. Acad. Med.*

Cock (The) and the jewel. *See* Stories about animals ser.

Cock Robin's picture-book. ill. sq. 12°. '74. $1. *Routledge.*

Cock-sparrow. [Toy-book.] ill. 4°. $1; 50c. *Routledge.*

Cockburn, H: T: (*Lord*). Life of Lord Jeffrey, with sel. from his correspondence. demy 8°. '68. $1.25 .... *Claxton.*

Cockburn, Ja. Review of the causes of the late disorders in the meeting of Friends, in Phila. 8°. *net*, 50c. .... *Friends Bk. Assoc.*

Cockburn, S. Medical reform: examination into nature of prevailing system of medicine, and exposition of its evils, with allopathic revelations. [Hom.] 18°. 50c. .... *Boericke.*

Cocke, N. W. *See* Alabama, Supreme Court reports.

Cocke, W: Archer. Comparison of the common and civil law systems in the jurisprudence of the U. S. 8°. shp., $3.50 .... *Baker, V. & Co.*

Cocke, W: Archer, *continued.*
— Constitutional history of the United States. v. 1. 8°. $2.50 .... *Lippincott.*

Cocker, B: F. Christianity and Greek philosophy. cr. 8°. $2.75 .... *Harper.*
— Lectures on the truth of the Christian religion. 12°. '73. $1.50 .... *Arnold.*
— Theistic conception of the world: an essay in opposition to certain tendencies of modern thought. cr. 8°. $2.50 .... *Harper.*

Cockneys in California. Coyne, J. S. 15c...*French.*

Cockton, H: Novels. 7 v. 8°. ea., pap., 75c. *Peterson.*
Cont.: Fatal marriage. — Love match. — Percy Effingham. — The prince; or, George St. George Julian. — The steward. — Sylvester Sound, the somnambulist. — Valentine Vox, the ventriloquist.
— Select novels. 3 v. 16°. ea., hf. roxb., $1.25; bds., 80c. .... *Routledge.*
Cont.: Valentine Vox. — George Julian. — Stanley Thorne.
— Love match (The). 8°. pap., 50c. .... *U. P. James.*
— Valentine Vox, the ventriloquist. 8°. $2..*Peterson.*
— *Same.* ill. 8°. $3. 12°. $1.25; bds., $1..*Routledge.*

Coco, the monkey. Dumont, M. 75c. .... *Claxton.*

Cocoanut basket. 18°. 45c.; 55c. .... *Am. Bapt.*

Codman, J: Mormon country (The): a summer with the Latter-day saints. ill. and map. 12°. '74. $1.50 .... *U. S. Pub.*
— Ten months in Brazil; with notes on the Paraguayan war. ('72.) 3d ed. 12°. '76. $1.50 .... *Miller.*

Coe, B: H. Cartones de dibujo para las escuelas. 10 nos. 18°. ea., 35c. .... *Appleton.*
— Copy book, with instructions. 8°. 37½c. .... *Wiley.*
— Cottages: introd. to landscape drawing. 4 nos. 8°. ea., 20c. .... *Wiley.*
— Drawing for little folks; or, first lessons for the nursery. 8°. 20c. .... *Wiley.*
— Drawing-cards. 10 pts. obl. 8°. ea., 25c...*Appleton.*
— Easy lessons in landscape. 4 nos. 8°. ea., 20c. *Wiley.*
— First studies in drawing. 3 nos. 8°. ea., 20c. *Wiley.*
— Heads, animals and figures, adapted to pencil drawing. 3 nos. 8°. ea., 20c. .... *Wiley.*
— New draw. lessons. 4 pts. obl. 8°. ea., 25c. *Appleton.*
— Progressive drawing book. 4°. $3.50 .... *Wiley.*
— *and* Schell, F. P. Elementary drawing. 3 pts. 18°. ea., 25c.; — in 1 v. 80c. .... *Appleton.*
— — Pen and ink drawings. obl. 18°. 25c. .... *Ivison.*

Coe, Spencer W. Madison Square Church collection: sacred quartettes. ('67.) New ed. 4°. '76. $2.75. *Pond.*

Cœlebs in search of a wife. More, H. $1.25. *Lippincott.*

Cofer, Mt. H. Supplemental digest of Kentucky Court of Appeals reports (14th Ben Monroe to 2d Duvall). 8°. '67. shp., $6.50 .... *Clarke.*

Coffee planter of Ceylon. Sabonadière, W. $3..*Spon.*

Coffee-pot Sam. ('68.) New ed. ill. 16°. '71. 80c. *Hoyt.*

Coffey, C. Devil to pay: opera. 16°. pap., 15c. *French.*

Coffin, C: C. ["Carleton."] Caleb Krinkle. 12°. $2. *Lee & S.*
— Following the flag. ill. 16°. $1.50 .... **Osgood.*
— Four years of fighting. ill. 8°. $3.50; shp., $4.50. **Osgood.*
— Great Boston fire. ill. 12°. 75c.; pap., 25c. (?) *Shepard.*
— My days and nights on the battlefield. ill. 16°. $1.50. **Osgood.*
— Our new way round the world. ill. and maps. cr. 8°. $2.50 .... **Osgood.*
— Seat of empire. ill. and maps. 16°. $1.50..**Osgood.*
— Winning his way. ill. 16°. $1.25 .... **Osgood.*

Coffin, J. H. C. Navigation and nautical astronomy. 5th ed. ill. 12°. '75. $3.50 .... *Van Nostrand.*

Coffin, Ja. H: Elements of conic sections and analyt. geometry. New ed. 8°. '74. $1.50..*Collins & Bro.*
— Orbit, etc., of meteoric fire ball, July 20, 1860. 4°. '69. pap., $1 .... *Smith. Inst.*

Coffin, Ja. H: *continued.*
— Psychrometrical tables. 8°. '56. pap., 25c. *Smith. Inst.*
— Solar and lunar eclipses ill. and explained, with method of calc. them. 8°. '45. $1.88. *Collins & Bro.*
— Winds of the northern hemisphere. 4°. '53. pap., $3. *Smith. Inst.*

Coffin, Levi. Reminiscences of C., reputed pres't of the underground railroad. 12°. '76. $2. *West. Tr.*

Coffin, Rob. B. ["Barry Gray."] Works. 5 v. cr. 8°. '65–'71. ea., $1.50 .... *Hurd & H.*
Cont.: My married life at Hillside. — Matrimonial infelicities. — Out of town. — Cakes and ale at Woodbine. — Castles in the air.

Coghlan, W. E. St. George's key. ill. 16°. $1. *Scribner, W. & A.*

Cogswell, Fs. Key to the Putnam arithmetical drill and review cards. 12°. bds., 50c........ *Ware.*
— *See also* Walton, G. A., *and* Cogswell, F.

Cogswell, W. B. Use of surface condenser with blast furnace boilers. 8°. pap., 50c...*Am. Soc. of C. E.*

Cogswell, W: Assistant to family religion; or, manual of theology and devotions. 12°. $1.... *Crocker.*
— Theological class book; for Bible classes and S.-schools. 18°. '31. 40c........ *Crocker.*

Cohen, D. S. ["Daisy Shortcut"], *and* Sommer, H. B. ["Arry O'Pagus".] Our show, one hundred years a republic: humorous account of the International Exposition. ('75.) New ed. ill. 8°. '76. $1; pap., 50c........ *Claxton.*

Cohen, J. I., *and* Lee, J. F. Digest of Md. reports (v. 9–20). 8°. '66. shp., $12.... *Cushings & B.*

Cohen, J. Solis. Croup; in its relation to tracheotomy. 8°. '74. $1........ *Lindsay.*
— Diseases of the throat; embracing affections of the pharynx, œsophagus, larynx, trachea and nasal passages. ill. 8°. $5........ *W. Wood.*
— Inhalation: its therapeutics and practice. New ed., enl. ill. 12°. '76. $2.75........ *Lindsay.*

Cohn, Morris M. Essay on religion, from a historical and philosophical standpoint. 16°. 50c...*Bloch.*

Coin book (The): compr. hist. of coinage, a synopsis of the mint laws, dict. of coins, list of works on coinage, etc. ill. 8°. $2.50........ *Lippincott.*

Coit, T: W. Exclusiveness: lecture, 1855. 3d ed. 8°. pap., 25c........ *W. H. Young.*
— Lectures on early hist. of Christianity in England; with sermons on several occasions. 12°. '60. $1.75........ *W. H. Young.*
— Necessity of preaching doctrine: sermons, 1860. 8°. pap., 25c........ *W. H. Young.*
— Sameness of words no hindrance to devotion: sermon. 3d ed. 12°. pap., 10c........ *W. H. Young.*

Coke, *Sir* E: Exact abridgment in Eng. of [his] 11 books of reports by Sir T. Ireland; and of the 12th and 13th books by J. A. Dunlap. 8°. $3. *T. & J. W. Johnson.*

Coke, T. *See* Clarke, A., *and* Coke, T.

Colange, L. (*ed.*) People's encyclopedia. ill. 12°. '75. shp., $10; hf. mor., $11...... *C. H. Davis.*
— The picturesque world; or, scenes in many lands; ill. by Doré and others. [To form 2 v.; 48 pts.] pts. 1–16. 4°. ea., *50c........ *Estes.*
— Zell's popular encyclopedia. New ed., rev. 64 pts. maps and ill. 4°. '75. ea., *50c.; — in 2 v., *$37–$49; — in 3 v., $39.50–$54.50; — in 4 v., ea., 16 pts., $42–$62; — in 5 v., $55–$75..*C. H. Davis.*

Colbert, El. Fixed stars. ('72.) New ed. 8°. '75. 60c........ *Sherwood.*

Colburn, Dana P. Arithmetic and its applications. ('55.) New ed. 12°. '70. $1.15... *Cowperthwait.*
— Child's arithmetic. ('59.) New ed. 16°. '70. bds., 25c........ *Cowperthwait.*
— Common school arithmetic. ('58.) New ed. 12°. '70. bds., 85c........ *Cowperthwait.*
— Intellectual arithmetic. ('59.) New ed. 16°. '70. bds., 32c........ *Cowperthwait.*

Colburn, Jer. Bibliography of the local history of Mass. 8°. '71. $6........ *Lunt.*

Colburn, Warren. First lessons: intellectual arithmetic, upon the inductive method of instruction; with introds. by W. Colburn, jr., and G. B. Emerson. 18°. 40c........ *Lee & S.*
— Intellectual arithmetic upon the inductive method of instruction. ('49.) New ed. 16°. '63. hf. bd., 40c........ *Hurd & H.*
— Sequel to arithmetic. 12°. '26. $1...*Nichols & H.*

Colburn, Zerah. Gas-works of London. cr. 8°. '65. bds., 75c........ *Spon.*
— Locomotive engine (The). (cop. '51.) '53. 2d ed. ill. 12°. '75. $1.25........ *Baird.*
— Locomotive engineering and the mechanism of railways; with 64 eng. and 240 wood-cuts. 20 pts. f°. $15; — in 2 v. $16; hf. mor., $20... *Wiley.*
— Steam boiler explosions. 18°. '73. bds., 50c. *Van Nostrand.*

Colby, J. H. Treatise upon New York criminal law and practice; with precedents. 2 v. 8°. shp., $15. *W. C. Little.*

Colby, J: Autobiography. 12°. '28. 75c..... *Freewill.*

Cole, Chester C. *See* Iowa, Supreme Court reports.

Cole, D: Offerings to the Lord: the Old and the New Testament aspects compared. 8°. pap., 10c. *N. Y. Ref. Ch. Bd.*

Cole, Ja. R. Primary writing grammar; or, syllabus of language lessons; for intermediate schools. ('73.) 2d ed., rev. obl. 12°. '74. pap., 25c. *Cushing, T. & Co.*

Cole, S. W. American fruit book. 18°. 75c..... *Judd.*
— American veterinarian. 18°. 75c........ *Judd.*

Cole, W. H. Institute reader and normal class-book. 12°. '70. $1.15........ *Wilson, H. & Co.*

Coleen bawn (The). *See* Carleton, W: Willy Reilly; — Colleen bawn.

Coleman, *Miss* —. Bridal keepsake. 32°. '56. 50c. *Darrow.*

Coleman, *Mrs.* Chapman. Life of John J. Crittenden, with sel. from his correspondence and speeches. por. 8°. $4; shp., $5........ *Lippincott.*

Coleman, G: Broad grins; with life of author by G. B. Buckstone. 12°. $3........ *Routledge.*

Coleman, H. S. First mass in F. 4°. pap., $2..*Peters.*
— Mass; for 4 voices with accomp. for organ. ('56.) New ed. 4°. '76. bds., $2.50........ *Pond.*

Coleman, Ja. Freeman. The knightly heart, and other poems. cr. 8°. '73. $2........ *Estes.*

Coleman, Lyman. Genealogy of the Lyman family in Gt. Brit. and Am.: ancestors and descendants of Richard Lyman from High Ongar in England, 1631. por. and pl. 8°. '72. hf. shp., $5..*Munsell.*

Coleman, *Rev.* Lyman. Ancient Christianity exemplified. 8°. $2........ *Lippincott.*
— Historical text book and atlas of biblical geography; with maps. 8°. $2........ *Claxton; Pres. Bd.*
— Manual on prelacy and ritualism: the apostolical and primitive church, popular in its government, and simple in its worship; with introd. essay by A. Neander. 12°. $1........ *Lippincott.*

Coleman, W. S. British butterflies. ill. 16°. $1.25. *Routledge.*
— Our woodlands, heaths and hedges. ill. 16°. $1.25; bds., 50c........ *Routledge.*

Coleridge, Christabel. Giftie, the changeling. 32°. 25c........ *Scribner, W. & A.*

Coleridge, S: Taylor. Complete works, with introd. essay; ed. by Rev. W. G. T. Shedd. 7 v. por. 12°. $12; hf. cf., $26........ *Harper.*
Cont.: Aids to reflection; Statesman's manual. — The friend. — Biographia literaria. — Lectures on Shakespeare and other dramatists. — Literary remains. — Second lay sermon and table talk. — Poetical and dram. works.
— Poems. 12°. $1.50........ *Locke.*
— *Same.* (Blue and gold ed.) 18°. $1.25. *Nichols & H.*

Coleridge, S: Taylor, *continued.*
— *Same.* (Scribner's pop. poets.) ill. 12°. $1.50. *Scribner, W. & A.*
— *Same;* with memoir. 3 v. por. 18°. $3.... *Osgood.*
— *Same;* ed. by D. and S. Coleridge. 12°. $2; mor., $5 .... *Appleton.*
— — *See also* Campbell, T., *and* Coleridge, S. T.; — Scott, *Sir* W.
— Poetical works. por. and ill. 16°. $1.50..*Lee & S.*
— *Same.* (Chandos classics.) cr. 8°. $1; pap., 75c. *Scribner, W. & A.*
— *Same.* (Chandos poets.) por. and ill. cr. 8°. $3.75; cf., $7.50; mor., $8.......... *Scribner, W. & A.*
— *Same.* (Household ser.) ill. and por. 16°. $1.50; mor., $3............................*Lee & S.*
— *Same;* ed. with memoir by W. B. Scott. (Presentation poets.) ill. 12°. $1.75; $3...... *Routledge.*
— — *See also* British pocket classics; — Campbell, T.
— *Same;* and dramatic works. (Blue and gold ed.) 18°. $1.25......................*Nichols & H.*
— *Same;* and misc. works. 8°. leath., $3...*Desilver.*
— *Same;* [also] Poetical works of Shelley and Keats. 8°. $3............................*Desilver.*
— Aids to reflection. 12°. '72. $1.50........*Tibbals.*
— *Same.* New ed., rev.; with index, etc., by T. Fenby. 16°. '73. $1.50...................*Routledge.*
— Biographia literaria, and two lay sermons. 12°. (Bohn.) $1.25................*Little, B. & Co.*
— *Same.* 12°. (Bohn.) $1.40......*Scribner, W. & A.*
— *Same.* 12°. (Bohn.) $1.50..........*Lippincott.*
— *Same;* ed. by H. N. Coleridge [and by his widow]. 2 v. 12°. '72. $5.......................*Holt.*
— Christabel, and other poems. 16°. $1.25. *Scribner, W. & A.*
— Friend: essays on morals, politics and religion. 12°. (Bohn.) $1.25.............*Little, B. & Co.*
— *Same.* 12°. (Bohn.) $1.40.....*Scribner, W. & A.*
— *Same.* 12°. (Bohn.) $1.50..........*Lippincott.*
— Rime of the ancient mariner. ill. 12°. '75. $1.25. *Putnam.*
— *Same;* with 20 ill. by J. N. Paton. f°. '75. $2.50. *Tompkins.*
— Shakespeare, Ben Jonson, Beaumont and Fletcher: notes and lectures. 16°. '74. $2....*Routledge.*
— Table talk. 12°. '74. 75c.; pap., 50c...*Routledge.*
— *See also* Hudson, H. N., Pamphlet sections.

Coleridge, Sara H. Memoir and letters; ed. by her daughter. por. cr. 8°. $2.50..........*Harper.*
— Phantasmion: fairy romance. 12°. '74. $2..*Roberts.*

Coles, Ab. The evangel: in verse. ill. 12°. $6; mor., $10............................*Appleton.*
— The microcosm: a poem, "know thyself." ill. 12°. $2.25....................................*Appleton.*
— (*ed.*) Latin hymns with original translations. 4 v. photos. cr. 8°.........................*Appleton.*
Cont.: Dies iræ, 13 orig. translations, $2.50; mor., $4.50. — Stabat mater dolorosa, $1.50; mor., $3.50. — Stabat mater speciosa, $1.50; mor., $3.50. — Old gems in new settings, $2.50; mor., $4.50.
— *Same;* in 1 v. photos. cr. 8°. $4.50; mor., $7. — chp. ed. $2.50; mor., $4.50.........*Appleton.*

Coles, G: Concordance of the Scriptures. 18°. '47. $1.50 ....*Meth. Bk. Conc.*
— Heroines of Methodism. 12°. '57. $1.25. *Meth. Bk. Conc.*
— Questions on Proverbs. 18°. per doz., $1.80. *Meth. Bk. Conc.*

Coles, Ja. Oakley. Manual of dental mechanics. ill. demy 8°. '73. $2.50 ....*Lindsay.*
— On deformities of the mouth congenital and acquired; with their mechanical treatment. ill. 8°. '70. $2.50......................................*Lindsay.*

Coles, Miriam. *See* Harris, Miriam C.

Coleson, *Miss* Annie. True narrative of her captivity among the Sioux Indians. [In Eng. *or* Germ.] 8°. pap., 25c.........................*Barclay.*

Colesworthy, D. C. School is out. cr. 8°. '76. $2.50. *Barry.*

Colesworthy, D. C., *continued.*
— The year. [Poems.] 16°. $1.50.........*Lee & S.*

Colfax, Schuyler. Education of the heart: necessity of proper moral culture for human happiness. 12°. pap., 10c...............................*Wells.*
— Example and effort. 12°. pap., 15c.....*Nat. Temp.*
— *See also* Grant, U. S., *and* Colfax, S.

Colladay, W. R. Genealogical and chronol. table of the sovereigns of Eng. 16°. '63. 50c. *Randolph.*

Collection of hymns and tunes for social and domestic worship. ('74.) 4th ed. 8°. '75. $2; bds., $1.50. *So. Meth.*

Collection of hymns for public, social and domestic worship. ('47.) New ed. 12°. '66. $1.75–$10. — 18°. $1.25–$7. — 24°. 80c.–$5.75. — 72°. 50c.–$5. *So. Meth.*

Collections of casts: subjects selected for the Girls' High and Normal School, Boston; mode and cost of procuring them, with add. list of subjects. 12°. '71. pap., 15c.................. *Williams.*

Colleen bawn. Boucicault, D. 15c..........*French.*

Colleen bawn. *See* Carleton, W: Willy Reilly; — Griffin, G.

Colleen bawn settled. Brough, W., *and* Halliday, A. 15c. .... *French.*

College atlas; with maps, index of places, and table of mountain heights. roy. 8°. $3..*Scribner, W. & A.*

College glee book. Stevens, C. W. $1.50; $2..*Gordon.*

College hymn and tune book. Perkins, H. S. 30c. *Peters.*

College library (The). *See* Farrar, F. W.

College (The), the market, and the court. Dall, C. H. $2.50....................................*Lee & S.*

College Ned. Caldor, M. F. 15c...........*Lee & S.*

College of Physicians of Philadelphia. Transactions, 3d ser. v. 1: Report of an autopsy on the bodies of the Siamese twins, Chang and Eng, with other papers; by Harrison Allen. ill. 8°. '75. $2.50. *Lindsay; Phila. Coll. Phy.*

College prayer book (The); comp. by a father of Soc. Jesu. 24°. $1–$3......................*O'Shea.*

College scrapes. 8°. pap., 15c..................*Haney.*

College series of French plays; with Eng. notes by F. Bôcher. ('64–'67.) New ed. 2 v. 12°. '76. ea., $1.75....................................*Holt.*

College stories; by eleven sophomores. sq. 12°. '74. $1.50....................................*Roberts.*

Collegians (The). *See* Griffin, G.

Collegiate atlas: modern geography with maps. imp. 8°. '73. $4..............................*Putnam.*

Collens, T. Wharton. The Eden of labor; or, the Christian Utopia. 12°. '76. $1.25; pap., $1. *Baird.*

Collet, Pierre. Life of St. Vincent de Paul. 12°. '54. $1.25; $1.50..........................*Murphy.*

Colley, Ja. Life of Alice Dunbar, known as the "female Jack Sheppard." [In Eng. *or* Germ.] 8°. pap., 25c...............................*Barclay.*

Collier, D: Einleitung zum richtigen Verstande d. hl. Schrift. 12°. '45. $1.25............*Ev. Assoc.*

Collier, J. *See* Spencer, H., Descriptive sociology.

Collier, J: Payne. Bibliographical and critical account of the rarest books in the Eng. language. 4 v. cr. 8°. '66. $12......................*Scribner.*

Collier, Jos. Avery. Christian home (The); or, religion in the family. 12°. $1...........*Pres. Bd.*
— Dawn of heaven. 12°. $1.50 ....*Carter.*
— Little crowns: how to win them. 18°. 75c...*Carter.*
— Pleasant paths for little feet. ill. 18°. '64. 60c. *Am. Tr.*
— The right way: on peace. 18°. '56. 45c...*Am. Tr.*
— Young men of the Bible. ill. 18°. '63. 60c. *Am. Tr.*

Collier, Ma. A. Chloe. 18°. '65. 20c.......*Am. Tr.*
— Memoir of T. F. Buxton; [incl.] sketch of emancipation in the West Indies, and of the Niger expedition for the suppression of the slave trade. 16°. 75c.......................... *Bost. Am. Tr.*
Collier, R. P. Treatise on the law relating to mines. 8°. '53. $1.50............*T. & J. W. Johnson.*
— — *See also* Law lib.
Collier, Rob. Laird. Every-day subjects in Sunday sermons. ('69.) 2d ed. 16°. '71. $1.....*Am. Unit.*
Collier, W. F. History of the British empire. 12°. $1. *Nelson.*
— *Same;* advanced class book. 12°. $1.75...*Nelson.*
— *Same;* senior class book. 12°. $1.25......*Nelson.*
— History of England, with sketch of the Indian and colonial empire. 8°. $3.50............*Nelson.*
— History of Eng. literature. 12°. $1.75.....*Nelson.*
— Outlines of general hist. 12°. $1.50.......*Nelson.*
— *See also* International atlas; — Library atlas of geog.; — Student's atlas of hist. geog.
Collier, W: Fs. Great events of history. 12°. $1.25. *Nelson.*
— *Same.* Am. ed., ed. by O. R. Willis. ('72.) 3d ed. 12°. '75. $1.50..................*Schermerhorn.*
Collier boy (The). *See* Smith, Hannah.
Collier (Le) de perles. Mazères, E. 30c. .....*Holt.*
Collier's (The) tale. 18°. 35c..............*Carter.*
Colling, Ja. Kellaway. Art foliage, for sculpture and decoration; with analysis of geom. form, etc. 72 pl. 4°. '74. $15...................... *Osgood.*
— Examples of Eng. mediæval foliage: pl., woodcuts and col. decoration, with descript. letter-press. 4°. '75. $15.......................... *Osgood.*
Collingwood, F. Caissons of the East River [N. Y.] bridge. 8°. pap., 50c........*Am. Soc. of C. E.*
— Foundations, Brooklyn anchorage, East River bridge. *See* Chanute, O., Weight of rails.
— Further notes on the caissons of the East River bridge. 8°. pap., 40c........*Am. Soc. of C. E.*
— Power of water to transport sand in sluices. *See* Craven, A. W., Address to Am. Soc. of Civ. Engineers.
— Submarine blasting. *See* Steele, J. D., Construction of the Falls skew-bridge.
Collins, *Mrs.* A. M. Great western cook book. 12°. '51. 75c.............................*Barnes.*
Collins, Barnabas V. Sermon delivered in the Ref. Prot. Dutch Ch. of Ponds, N. J., Nov. 21, 1852: a review of seven years' ministry. 8°. pap., 25c. *N. Y. Ref. Ch. Bd.*
Collins, C., *jr.* The children's hosanna. [S.-school hymn book.] obl. 4°. 50c.; bds., 37c.; pap., 25c.............................*J. E. Potter.*
Collins, C: Allston. Cruise upon wheels: chronicle of some autumn wanderings among the deserted post-roads of France. 12°. bds., $1..*Routledge.*
Collins, Eliz. Journal. 18°. 40c....*Friends Bk. St.*
Collins, J. My first drawing book; for slate exercises. sm. 4°. '70. bds., 40c.........*Keystone.*
Collins, J. Churton. Sir Joshua Reynolds as a portrait painter; with por. of beauties of the court of George III. f°. hf. mor., $45....*Macmillan.*
Collins, J. H. Elements of mineralogy. (Element. sci. ser.) ill. 16°. '74. 75c..............*Putnam.*
— Principles of metal mining. (Element. sci. ser.) ill. 16°. '75. 75c..........................*Putnam.*
Collins, Ja. E. Private book of useful alloys, and memoranda for goldsmiths, jewellers, etc. 18°. '72. 75c. .... *Van Nostrand.*
Collins, *Miss* Jennie. Nature's aristocracy; or, battles and wounds in time of peace; ed. by R. H. Conwell. 12°. $1.50.....................*Lee & S.*
Collins, Lew. Historical sketches of Kentucky. ill. 8°. '47. $5........................*R. H. Collins.*

Collins, Lew., *continued.*
— History of Kentucky; brought down to 1874 by R. H. Collins. 2 v. por., map and ill. 8°. '74. $10; $12; hf. mor., $13.........*R. H. Collins.*
Collins, Mortimer. Marquis and merchant. 8°. pap. 50c..................................*Appleton.*
— The Summerfield imbroglio. sq. 16°. '76. pap., 25c..................................*Loring.*
— Two plunges for a pearl. 8°. pap., 75c...*Appleton.*
— Vivian romance. 8°. pap., 50c...........*Harper.*
Collins, Reb. Child's treasury. ill. 18°. '68. 60c. *Claxton.*
— Parents' gift; or, reading book for little children. ill. 18°. '68. 60c.......................*Claxton.*
— Pious remembrancer. 2d ed. 64°. '70. 15c. *Claxton.*
— Treasured gems: sel. in prose and verse. 12°. '74. 75c. ....*Collins & Bro.*
Collins, R: H. History of Ky. *See* Collins, L.
Collins, Ste. Autobiography. 12°. $1...*Lippincott.*
Collins, T: *and* Watts, J. Half-hours with some ancient and modern celebrated free thinkers. [Selections.] 12°. 75c.................*Mendum.*
Collins, Wilkie. Novels and tales. 9 v. 16°. $13.50. *Routledge.*

Cont.: After dark. — Antonina. — Armadale. — Basil. — Dead secret. — Hide and seek. — No name. — Queen of hearts. — Woman in white.

— *Same.* (Library ed.) 15 v. ill. and por. 12°. ea., $1.50....................................*Harper.*

Cont.: Armadale. — Basil. — Hide and seek. — Man and wife. — No name. — Poor Miss Finch. — The dead secret. — The moonstone. — The new Magdalen. — The woman in white. — Antonina. — After dark, and other stories. — Queen of hearts. — My miscellanies. — The law and the lady.

— After dark. 8°. 75c.......................*Peterson.*
— Alicia Warlock. 8°. '75. $1.50; pap., 75c. *W. F. Gill.*
— Antonina; or, the fall of Rome: a romance of the 5th century. 8°. pap., 50c..............*Harper.*
— Armadale. ill. 8°. pap., $1..............*Harper.*
— Basil; or, the crossed path. 12°. $1.50. 8°. pap., 75c. ....*Peterson.*
— Dead alive (The). 16°. '74. $1; pap., 50c. (?) *Shepard.*
— Dead secret. 12°. $1.50. 8°. pap., 50c...*Peterson.*
— Frozen deep (The). 12°. '74. $1.50; pap., 75c. *W. F. Gill.*
— Hide and seek. 8°. pap., 75c...........*Peterson.*
— Law (The) and the lady. 8°. pap., 75c....*Harper.*
— Mad Monkton, and other stories. 8°. pap., 50c. *Peterson.*
— Man and wife. ill. 8°. pap., $1...........*Harper.*
— Miss or Mrs. 8°. pap., 50c...............*Peterson.*
— Moonstone. ill. 8°. pap., $1..............*Harper.*
— New Magdalen. 8°. pap., 50c.............*Harper.*
— No name. [Fiction.] ill. 8°. pap., $1.....*Harper.*
— No name: drama. 12°. pap., 15c. ....*De Witt.*
— Poor Miss Finch. ill. 8°. pap., $1.........*Harper.*
— *Same.* 8°. pap., 50c.......................*De Witt.*
— Queen of hearts. 12°. $1.50..............*Harper.*
— Queen's revenge. 8°. pap., 75c...........*Peterson.*
— Sights afoot. 8°. pap., 50c.............*Peterson.*
— Sister Rose. 8°. pap., 25c...............*Peterson.*
— Stolen mask. 8°. pap., 25c..............*Peterson.*
— Woman in white. ill. 8°. pap., $1........*Harper.*
— Yellow mask. 8°. pap., 25c. ....*Peterson.*
— *See also* Dickens, C., *and* Collins, W.; — Satchel ser.
Collins, W: Ballads, songs and poems. ('75.) 2d ed. ill. 16°. '76. $1............................*Kenedy.*
— Poems. (Aldine ed.) 16°. 75c........*Lippincott.*
— *Same;* with memoir by A. Dyce, and essay on the genius and poems of C. by Sir E. Brydges. por. 18°. $1....................................*Osgood.*
— — *See also* British pocket classics; — Gray, T.; — Milton, J.
— *Same;* [also] Poems of Gray and Goldsmith; ed. with notes by E. Sargent. 12°. $1.50; hf. cf., $3.50 ....*Putnam.*
Collins, W: Lucas (*ed.*) Ancient classics [outlined and explained] for Eng. readers. 20 v. 16°. (Edinb.) '71–'74. ea., $1; — in 10 v. $20. *Little, B. & Co.*

Collins, W: Lucas (*ed.*), *continued.*
Cont.: Homer's Iliad, by W. L. Collins. — Homer's Odyssey, by W. L. Collins. — Herodotus, by G. C. Swayne. — Cæsar's Commentaries, by A. Trollope. — Virgil, by W. L. Collins. — Horace, by T. Martin. — Æschylus, by R. S. Coplestone. — Xenophon, by Sir A. Grant. — Cicero, by W. L. Collins. — Sophocles, by C. W. Collins. — Pliny's letters, by A. Church and W. J. Brodribb. — Euripides, by W. B. Donne. — Juvenal, by E. Walford. — Aristophanes, by W. L. Collins. — Hesiod and Theognis, by J. Davis. — Plautus and Terence, by W. L. Collins. — Tacitus, by W. B. Donne. — Lucian, by W. L Collins. — Plato, by C. W. Collins. — Greek anthology, by Lord Neaves.

— *Same.* 20 v. 16°. ea., $1; — in 10 v. $15; hf. cf., $25 .... *Lippincott.*

— *Same.* 20 v. 16°. ea., $1.25; — in 10 v. hf. cf., $25. *Scribner, W. & A.*

— (*ed.*) New series of ancient classics. v. 1–2. 16°. ea., $1 .... *Lippincott.*
Cont.: Livy. — Ovid.

Collis, Lauriston. Mystery of Holly Tavern: a story of nine travellers. 8°. pap., 40c.... *Lippincott.*

Colloquia crucis. Greenwell, D. $1.25... *Routledge.*

Colloquies of Edward Osborne. *See* Manning, A.

Collord, G: W. Latin accidence and primary lesson book. 12°. shp., $1.50 .... *Harper.*

Collot, Alex. G. Dramatic French reader. 12°. $1.50. *Appleton.*

— New and improved standard French and Eng. and Eng. and French dictionary. Rev. ed. 8°. hf. mor., $4 .... *Schäfer.*

— Progressive French anecdotes and questions; [with] Collot's French dialogues and phrases. 18°. '73. $1 .... *C. H. Davis.*

— Progressive French dialogues and phrases. 18°. '73. $1 .... *C. H. Davis.*

— Progressive French grammar and exercises. 18°. '44. $1 .... *C. H. Davis.*

— — Key. 18°. '44. 65c. .... *C. H. Davis.*

— Progressive interlinear French reader. 18°. '44. $1. *C. H. Davis.*

— Progressive pronouncing French reader. 18°. '73. $1. *C. H. Davis.*

Collott, P. Doctrinal and spiritual catechism; tr. by Mrs. Sadlier. 16°. 63c. .... *Sadlier.*

Collyer, Rob. Works. 3 v. por. 12°. ea., $1.50. *Lee & S.*
Cont.: The life that now is. — Nature and life. — A man in earnest.

Colman, G: Battle of Hexham: drama. 16°. pap., 15c. *French.*

— Jealous wife: comedy. 16°. pap., 15c..... *French.*

— *See also* Connoisseur (The).

— *and* Garrick, D. Clandestine marriage: comedy. 16°. pap., 15c. .... *French.*

Colman, G: *jr.* [Plays.] 13 v. 16°. ea., pap., 15c. *French.*
Cont.: Blue Beard. — Blue devils. — Heir at law: comedy. — Inkle and Yarico. — Iron chest. — John Bull. — Love laughs at locksmiths: farce. — Mountaineers. — Poor gentleman: comedy. — Review: mus. farce. — Surrender of Calais. — Who wants a guinea? comedy. — X. Y. Z.: farce.

Colman, Ja., *and* Wheelock, E: Willard. Lives. 18°. 35c.; 45c. .... *Am. Bapt.*

Colman, Jla. Boys' and girls' illustrated bird-book. col. ill. sq. 12°. '57. $1 .... *Meth. Bk. Conc.*

Colomb, *Capt.* —. Davenport Done; or, an April fool: comedietta. 16°. pap., 15c....... *French.*

Colomba. *See* Merimée, P.

Colonel Dacre. Jolly, E. 50c. .... *Harper.*

Colonel Jack. *See* Defoe, D.

Col. Thorpe's scenes in Arkansaw. Thorpe, J. B. $1.75 .... *Peterson.*

Color-bearer (The). Clary, F. A. 40c..... *Am. Tr.*

Colorado. Supreme Court reports, v. 1 (1864–'72); by M. Hallett. 8°. '72. shp., $7.50.. *Bancroft.*

— *Same:* v. 1, 2 (1864–'75); by M. Hallett. 2 v. 8°. shp., $15 .... *S. Whitney.*

Colored album for children. Heaton, C. $1.75. *Routledge.*

Colored illustrated primer. *See* New colored.

Colored picture-book for the little ones. sq. 12°. bds., 50c. .... *Routledge.*

Colossians. *See* Bible.

Colter, *Mrs.* J. J. One quiet life. ill. 16°. '76. $1.50. *Lothrop.*

— Robbie Meredith. ill. 16°. '76. $1....... *Lothrop.*

Coltman, F. J. *See* England, Exchequer reports.

Colton, C. W. Common school geog. maps and ill. 4°. $2; — without maps. hf. bd., $1.75.. *Sheldon.*

— New introd. geog. ill. sq. 8°. hf. bd., 90c.... *Sheldon.*

— Outlines of physical geog.; rev. and enl. by A. J. Robinson; with an article on phys. geog. by C. C. Morgan. maps. 4°. hf. bd., $1.50.... *Sheldon.*

— *and* Fitch, G: W. American school quarto geog. 4°. $2; with atlas, $3 .... *Sheldon.*

— — Introductory geog. sq. 8°. hf. bd., 80c... *Sheldon.*

— — Modern school geography. sm. 4°. hf. bd., $1.15. *Sheldon.*

— — Primer of geography. 12°. hf. bd., 50c. *Sheldon.*

Colton, Clb. C. Lacon; or, many things in few words: addressed to those who think. (Globe ed.) 16°. '49. $1.25; hf. cf., $2.75 .... *Porter.*

— *Same.* 12°. hf. cf., $2.50; cf., $3....... *Appleton.*

Colton, Calv. Last seven years of the life of Henry Clay. 8°. '56. shp., $2.25 .... *Barnes.*

— — *See also* Clay, H: Life.

— Public economy of the U. S. 8°. '48. $2.25.. *Barnes.*

Colton, Chauncey. The Christian hearer. *See* Bickersteth, E.

Colton, T. G. Jewish heroes. 18°. 80c... *Cong. Pub.*

— The Jewish persecutor. 18°. 75c....... *Cong. Pub.*

Columba, *St.* Life. *See* Patrick, *St.*, Life.

Columbia. Mietzka, G. A. 38c. .... *Gordon.*

Columbian glee book. Woodbury, I. B. $1.50. *Thompson.*

Columbian orator. Bingham, C. $1....... *Claxton.*

Columbian spelling book. 12°. 45c......... *O'Shea.*

Columbus, Christopher. Life and voyages; with introd. by one of the Dominican Fathers. 12°. $1. *O'Shea.*

— *and* Vespucius, A. Lives. ill. 18°. 75c... *Harper.*

Columbus. Brougham, J. 15c. .... *French.*

Colville family (The). *See* Smedley, F. E.

Colvin, And. J., *and* Bingham, A. Rents, covenants and conditions. 8°. shp., $3...... *W. C. Little.*

Colwell, Ste. Ways and means of payment: analysis of the credit system. 8°. $2.50..... *Lippincott.*

Comala. Gade, N. W. $1.25 .... *Ditson.*

Combat of the people. Wise, I. M. 50c....... *Bloch.*

Combat of the thirty. *See* Ainsworth, W. H.

Combe, And. Physiology of digestion; with relation to principles of dietetics. ill. 18°. pap., 50c. *Wells.*

— *Same.* ill. 18°. 75c. .... *Harper.*

— Principles of physiology. ill. 18°. 75c.... *Harper.*

— *Same;* with notes and observations by O. S. Fowler. ill. 8°. '42. $1.50 .... *Wells.*

— Treatise on the physiological and moral management of infancy. 18°. 75c. .... *Harper.*

— *Same;* with notes by J. Bell. 12°. $1.25... *Wells.*

— *Same;* ed. by Sir. J. Clark. 12°. $1.50.. *Appleton.*

Combe, G: Capital punishment; or, the proper treatment of criminals. 12°. pap., 10c....... *Wells.*

— Constitution of man in relation to external objects. 18°. $1 .... *Harper.*

— *Same.* 18°. '71. 75c. 12°. $1.25 .... *Claxton.*

— *Same.* 16°. $1.50 .... *Osgood.*

— *Same.* ill. and por. 12°. $1.50 .... *Wells.*

— Lectures on phrenology; with notes, etc., by A. Boardman. 12°. '39. $1.50 .... *Wells.*

Combe, G: *continued.*
— Moral philosophy; or, the duties of man considered in his individual, social and domestic capacities. 18°. 75c. . . . . *Harper.*
— *Same.* 12°. $1.50 . . . . . *Wells.*
— System of phrenology. ill. 12°. $1.50 . . . . *Harper.*
Combe, W: Three tours of Dr. Syntax; in search of 1, the picturesque; 2, consolation; 3, a wife. (Chandos classics.) cr. 8°. $1; pap., 75c. *Scribner, W. & A.*
— *Same.* (Scribner's pop. poets.) ill. 12°. $1.50. *Scribner, W. & A.*
— *Same.* ill. 12°. '71. $1.75 . . . . . *Putnam.*
— *Same.* col. ill. by T. Rowlandson. 3 v. 8°. hf. cf., $20; cf., $27.50. — chp. ed. in 1 v. col. ill. sm. 8°. $4; hf. cf., $5.50; cf., $6.50 . . . . . *Appleton.*
— Tour of Dr. Syntax in search of the picturesque. col. ill. 8°. $3 . . . . . *Miller.*
Combination fortune-teller and dictionary of dreams. ill. 16°. $1.25 . . . . . *Dick & F.*
Come home, mother. 18°. 60c. . . . . *Cong. Pub.*
Come home, mother. Brook, N. 50c. . . . . *Nat. Temp.*
Come, let us sing. Mendelssohn-Bartholdy, F. 40c.; 50c. . . . . *Ditson.*
Come to Jesus. *See* Hall, Newman.
Comedy and tragedy. Fournier, M. R. 15c. *French.*
Comedy of the convocation in the Eng. church; ed. by Archd. Chasuble. 10th ed. 8°. '68. $1 . . *Cath. Pub.*
Comedy of errors. *See* Shakespeare, W.
Comedy of errors: burlesque. 16°. pap., 15c. *French.*
Comedy of errors: Ethiop. drama. 16°. pap., 15c. *Happy.*
Comedy of terrors. De Mille, J. $1.25; 75c. . . *Estes.*
Comenius, J: Amos. The school of infancy; with life of author by D. Benham. 8°. (Lond.) '58. $1.25 . . . . . *Clauder.*
Comer, G: N. Navigation simplified: manual of instruction in navigation as practised at sea; with tables and examples. 8°. $2.50 . . . . . *Harper.*
Comerford, M. Pleadings of the sacred heart of Jesus; from the Fr. 18°. '74. 60c. . . . . *Cath. Pub.*
Cometh up as a flower. Broughton, R. $1.50; 60c. *Appleton.*
Comfort, *Mrs.* A. M. *See* Comfort, G. F. *and Mrs.* A. M.
Comfort, G: F. [German series.] 7 v. 12° . . *Harper.*
Cont.: First book in G., $1. — First G. reader, 80c. — G. course, $2. — G. primer, 75c. — G. reader, $2. — Manual of G. conversation, $1.50. — Teacher's companion to "G. course," 75c.
Note. The "German course" is also issued in 4 pts.: pt. 1, 90c.; pts. 2-4 in 1 v., $1.50.
— *and Mrs.* A. M. Woman's education. 12°. '74. $1. *Durston.*
Comfort, Lucy Randall. Folks and fairies: stories for little children. ill. 4°. $1 . . . . . *Harper.*
Comfort for afflicted youth; in letters from a father to his children. 18°. 25c. . . . . *Pres. Bd.*
Comfort for the heavy-laden. Cowper, W. 30c. *Pres. Bd.*
Comfort for hours of sorrow. 16°. 75c. . . . . *Dutton.*
Comfort Strong. Robbins, S. S. $1.25 . . . . *Carter.*
Comfort ye, comfort ye. Macduff, J. R. $1.50 . . *Carter.*
Comfortable lodgings. Peake, R. B. 15c. . . *French.*
Comfortable service. Bayly, T. H. 15c. . . . *French.*
Comforted; by author of "Talks with a child on the beatitudes." 12°. 75c. . . . . *Lippincott.*
Comforter (The). Bartholomew, J. G. $1.50. *Universalist.*
Comforter (The). Clark, W. R. 75c. . . . . *Pott.*
Comforting promises from the Bible. 32°. 35c. *Am. S. S.*
Comic and sentimental songster. 32°. 50c.; pap., 25c. *Noonan.*
Comic Blackstone. A'Becket, G. A. $1.50. *Lippincott.*
Comic centennial hist. of the United States. Hopkins, L. $1.50 . . . . . *Carleton.*
Comic English grammar. ill. 16°. 25c. . . . . *Dick & F.*
Comic hist. of Eng.; — of Rome. *See* A'Becket, G. A.
Comic history of the United States. Sherwood, J. D. $2.50 . . . . . *Osgood.*
Comic hodge podge. ill. 4°. pap., 25c. . . . . *De Witt.*
Comic miseries of human life. ill. 12°. $1.50 . . *De Witt.*
Comic reciter (The). 5 pts. 16°. ea., pap., 15c.; — in 1 v. 16°. $1 . . . . . *French.*
Comic songster. *See* New.
Comic wandering Jew. ill. 8°. pap., 25c. . . *Dick & F.*
Comical adventures of David Dufficks. ill. 8°. pap., 25c. . . . . . *Dick & F.*
Comical countess. Brough, W. 15c. *De Witt; French.*
Comical doings of a funny man. Dodge, O. E. 15c. *Happy.*
Comical medicine-man. Small, G. G. 25c. . . *Collin & S.*
Comines, Philippe de. Memoirs; cont. hist. of Louis XI. and Charles VIII., and of Charles the Bold; [also] Chronicle of Jean de Troyes; ed. by A. R. Scoble. 2 v. 12°. (Bohn.) ea., $1.25 . . . . *Little, B. & Co.*
— *Same.* 2 v. 12°. (Bohn.) ea. $1.40. *Scribner, W. & A.*
— *Same.* 2 v. 12°. (Bohn.) ea., $1.50 . . *Lippincott.*
Coming battle and appalling national convulsions. Baxter, M. 15c. . . . . (?) *Martien.*
Coming earthquake. Taylor, D. T. 80c. . . *Hastings.*
Coming man (The). Smith, J. 2 v. $5 . . *Routledge.*
Coming (The) of Christ in his kingdom. Orvis, W. B. $1.50 . . . . . *Tibbals.*
Coming race (The). *See* Bulwer-Lytton, *Sir* E. G. E. L.
Coming to Christ. Green, W. S. 75c. . . . . *Lippincott.*
Coming to confirmation. Newton, W. W. 15c. *Williams.*
Coming to Jesus. *See* Kennedy, *Mrs.* M. G., Clarence and Hallie books.
Coming to the King. Hinsdale, G. W. $1 . . *Randolph.*
Coming to the light. Baker, S. 60c. . . . . *Randolph.*
Coming to the light. Newbury, F. E. $1.50 . . *Lothrop.*
Coming Wave. Adams, W. T. $1.50 . . . . . *Lee & S.*
Coming wonders expected between 1867 and 1875. *See* Baxter, M.
Comings, B. N. Class-book of physiology. pl. and ill. 12°. $1.75 . . . . . *Appleton.*
— Companion class-book. 12°. 60c. . . . . *Appleton.*
— *See also* Comstock, J. L., *and* Comings, B. N.
Comins, Lizzie B. ["Laura Caxton."] Hartwell farm (The). ill. 12°. $1.50 . . . . . *Loring.*
— Marion Berkley. ill. 12°. $1.50 . . . . . *Loring.*
Comly, I: *See* Comly, J. *and* I.
Comly, J: Journal of life and religious labors. 8°. '53. *net*, shp., $2 . . . . . *Friends Bk. Assoc.*
— Reader and book of knowledge. 12°. hf. roan, 48c. *Lippincott.*
— Spelling book. 12°. bds., 20c. . . *Lippincott; Porter.*
— *and* I: (*ed.*) Friends' miscellany: essays and fragments, biographical, religious, etc. 11 v. 12°. '34. *net*, shp., $11 . . . . *Friends Bk. Assoc.*
Commander of Malta. *See* Sue, E.
Commandment with promise. 18°. 60c. . . . . *Carter.*
— *Same;* rev. by T. O. Summers. 18°. '55. 70c. *So. Meth.*
Comment on parle français à Paris. Guide for learning to speak French. 12°. $1.50 . . . . *Appleton.*
Commentary (The) wholly Biblical; with tables, indexes, etc. 2 v. chart and maps. 4°. $19.50; hf. mor., $26; mor., $35; — in 3 v. 4°. $20; hf. mor., $33; mor., $40 . . . . . *Wiley.*
Commercial letter-writer. 16°. bds., 50c. . . *Routledge.*

Commission of Fish and Fisheries. *See* United States.
Commissioner (The). James, G. P. R. $1..*Harper.*
Commodianus. *See* Tertullian.
Commodore Rollingpin's log. 12°. $1.50..*Carleton.*
Common Bench reports. *See* England, Common law reports; Law reports.
Common evil (The). White, O. W. 10c...*J. A. Clark.*
Common law reports. *See* England, Common law reports.
Common Pleas reports. *See* England, Law reports.
Common prayer (Book of). *See* Protestant Episc. Ch.; — Reformed Episc. Ch.
Common school primer. 16°. '66. bds., 20c...*Morton.*
Common sense. Newby, C. J. 50c........*Peterson.*
Common sense. *See* Paine, T:
Common sense applied to religion. Beecher, C. E. $1.50...............................*Harper.*
Common sense cook book. 12°. pap., 25c....*Haney.*
Common sense in the household. Harland, M. $1.75. *Scribner.*
Common sense in the kitchen. Frost, S. A. $1.75. *Souder.*
Common sense in the kitchen. Henderson, W. C. $1.50..............................*World Pub.*
Common sense in religion. Clarke, J. F. $2..*Osgood.*
Common sense theology. Hamilton, D. H. $1.50. *D. H. Hamilton.*
Common sense thoughts on the Bible. Denton, W. 10c. ....*Denton.*
Common sense view of King David and his times. Mason, H. H. $1.50....................*Colby.*
Common sights in town and country. ill. 4°. 65c.*Am. S. S.*
Commonplace. Rossetti, C. G. $1.50......*Roberts.*
Commonplace book. Southey, R. 2 v. $3; $7.50. *Harper.*
Commonplace book of the Bible. Locke, J. $1.25. *Am. Tr.*
Commonplace book (A) of epigrams. Carey, C. S. $2 ....*Appleton.*
Commuck, T: Indian melodies; harmonized by T. Hastings. [Hymn book.] 4°. 50c. *Meth. Bk. Conc.*
Communicant's companion: prayers and meditations on the communion and communion office. 32°. '68. 25c...................................*Pott.*
Communicant's (The) spiritual companion. Haweis, T. 50c. ....*Leighton.*
Communings in the sanctuary. Richardson, R. $1. *Tr. P. & P. Co.*
Communion thoughts. Bulfinch, S. G. 75c. *Am. Unit.*
Communion wine and Bible temperance. Thayer, W. M. 50c.; 20c.......................*Nat. Temp.*
Comödie (Die) der Irrungen. *See* Shakespeare, W.
Companion for the afflicted. Walker, T. H. $1.10. *Meth. Bk. Conc.*
Companion for the Sunday school teacher; by a teacher. 16°. '69. 45c..........................*Claxton.*
Companion of the sanctuary. [Cath. prayer book.] 48°. 30c.–$15...........................*Noonan.*
— *Same;* with the Epistles and Gospels. 32°. 38c.–$18. *Noonan.*
Companion poets: selections. 2 v. ill. and por. sm. 4°. '65. ea., $2; hf. cf., $2.25; mor., $3.50; — in 6 v. ea., 75c.; per set, $4.50...........*Osgood.*
Cont.: 1. Longfellow; Tennyson; Browning.—2. Holmes; Whittier; Bryant.
Companion series. 3 v. 18°. $1.80........*Lothrop.*
Cont.: Story of a child's companion. — Larry Connor's charge. — Mark Woodford's promise.
Companion series. 3 v. ill. 12°. $3.75; $6..*T. Bliss.*
Cont.: Young lady's mentor. — Young lady's companion. — Young lady's delight.
Companion to the Bible. Barrows, E. P. $1.75; $3. *Am. Tr.*

Companions of my solitude. Helps, *Sir* A. $1.50. *Roberts.*
Companions of St. Paul. Howson, J. S. $1.75. *Routledge.*
Compendium of the faith of the Baptists. 18°. pap., 10c...................................*Sheldon.*
Compensation; or, always a future. Brewster, A. $1.75 ....*Lippincott.*
Complete angler. *See* Walton, I., *and* Cotton, C.
Complete dictionary of the language of flowers. 16°. '75. pap., 25c..........................*Happy.*
Complete duty of man. Venn, H. 80c......*Am. Tr.*
Complete florist; or, flower gardener. 12°. pap., 25c. *Peterson.*
Complete fortune-teller and dream book. 12°. pap., 20c. *Hurst.*
Complete guide to the game of bézique. ill. 48°. 25c. *Scribner, W. & A.*
Complete handbook of etiquette for ladies and gentlemen. 16°. 75c. ....*Miller.*
Complete kitchen and fruit gardener. 12°. pap., 25c. *Peterson.*
Complete letter-writer. 16°. bds., 50c.....*Routledge.*
Complete letter-writer for ladies and gentlemen. 12°. pap., 25c. ....*Hurst.*
Complete letter-writer for ladies and gentlemen. 16°. 75c. ....*Porter.*
Complete ready reckoner in dollars and cents; [with] forms of notes, receipts, etc. ('70.) New ed. 18°. '71. 25c..........................*Claxton.*
Complete summary of history. 12°. '68. 60c. *Barnes.*
Complete Sunday school manual. [Catholic catechism, prayers, etc.] 24°. 30c..............*Noonan.*
Complete triumph of moral good over evil. cr. 8°. $2.25 ....*Lippincott.*
Comprehensive commentary on the Bible: text with Scott's marg. ref., Henry's comment. condensed, etc. (Bapt. ed.) 6 v. roy. 8°. $20..*So. Bapt.*
Comprehensive dict. of Bible. *See* Bible [Whole].
Comprehensive series of geographies for Cath. schools. 3 v. sm. 4°. '76. no. 1, 50c.; no. 2, $1; no. 3, $1.80 ....*O'Shea.*
Compton, D. H. Cultivation of the potato; [also] How to cook the potato, by Prof. Blot. ill. 12°. 25c. ....*Judd.*
Comstock, And., *and* Lawrence, P. Elocution and model speaker. ill. 12°. $2..........*Peterson.*
Comstock, G. F. *See* New York, Court of Appeals reports.
Comstock, J: Lee. Elements of botany. 12°. $2. *Sheldon.*
— Elements of chemistry. 12°. shp., $1.75..*Sheldon.*
— Elements of geology. 12°. $1.75 ....*Sheldon.*
— Elements of mineralogy. 12°. shp., $1.25..*Sheldon.*
— Outlines of physiology, comparative and human. 12°. shp., $1.50 ....*Sheldon.*
— System of natural philosophy. 12°. shp., $1.75. *Sheldon.*
— Young botanist. 18°. 60c...............*Sheldon.*
— *and* Comings, B. N. Principles of physiology; with essay on the preservation of health. ill. 4°. $2.25; col. ill., $3............................*W. Wood.*
Comstock, Sa. D. Memoir. 18°. 55c.; 65c. *Am. Bapt.*
Comstock, W: Rum: drama. 12°. '76. pap., 15c. *De Witt.*
Comte, Auguste. Philosophy of mathematics; tr. by W. M. Gillespie from "Cours de philosophie positive." 8°. $1.50.....................*Harper.*
— Philosophy of the science: an exposition of the "Cours," etc., by G. H. Lewes. 12°. (Bohn.) $1.75............................*Little, B. & Co.*
— *Same.* 12°. (Bohn.) $2. *Lippincott; Scribner, W. & A.*
Comus. *See* Milton, J.

Comyn, L. N. Atherstone Priory. [Fiction.] 16°. $1.25; pap., 75c. .... *Estes.*
— Elena: an Italian tale. 8°. $1.25; pap., 75c. *Estes.*
Con Cregan. *See* Lever, C:
Con O'Regan. Sadlier, M. A. $1; $1.50.... *Sadlier.*
Conant, E: Drill book for schools. 12°. '73. 60c. *Tuttle.*
Conant, *Mrs.* Helen S. Butterfly hunters. ill. sq. 16°. $1.50 .... * *Osgood.*
Conant, *Mrs.* J. H. Biography of Mrs. C., the world's medium of the 19th century. ('72.) 2d ed. por. 12°. '73. $1.50; $2 .... *Colby.*
— Spirit invocations: prayers and praises publicly offered through the vocal organs of Mrs. C.; comp. by A. Putnam. 16°. '76. $1.25 .... *Colby.*
— *See also* Putnam, A.
Conant, T. C. *See* Abbott, L., *and* Conant, T. C.
Conant, T: J. Book of Proverbs: pt. 1., Hebrew text, King James' version, and a rev. version with introd. and notes; pt. 2., the revised version with introd. and notes. 4°. $4; — pt. 2, sep., $2.75. *Sheldon.*
— Meaning and use of baptizein, philologically and historically investigated. 8°. $1.... *Am. Bib. Un.*
— On Psalms. *See* Lange, J. P., Commentary.
Conant farm. 16°. $1.25 .... *Carter.*
Conaro, L: Discourses and letters on a sober and temperate life; with biog. of author by P. Maroncelli, and notes and app. by J. Burdell. 16°. '42. pap., 25c. .... *Wells.*
Concealed treasure (The). *See* Dupuy, E. A., Annie Seldon.
Concert (The). Pratt, L. M. 50c......... *Lothrop.*
Concert programme. 18°. '74. 40c.......... *Am. Tr.*
Concertina without a master. obl. 8°. '57. pap., 75c. *Ditson.*
Concilio, J. de. Catholicity and pantheism. 12°. $2. *Sadlier.*
Concilium Baltimorense Provinciale. *See* Baltimore.
Concilium Plenarium Baltimorensis. *See* Baltimore.
Concise glossary of architecture. ill. 16°. $3.75. *Scribner, W. & A.*
Concise view of the doctrines of the Cumberland Presbyterian Church. 20c.......... (?) *Cumberland.*
Concone, Jos. Duets. *See* Panseron, H., A B C.
— Exercises for the voice. f°. pap., $1.50.... *Ditson.*
— *Same.* (op. 11.) 4°. $1.25 .... *Church.*
— *Same.* (op. 11.) f°. $1.50............ *Brainard.*
— *Same.* (op. 9.) bk. 1. 4°. $1.25 .... *Church.*
— Exercises in singing. 4°. pap., $1.25.. *G. D. Russell.*
— Fifteen vocalises; for soprano or mezzo-soprano. (op.12.) 2 bks. 4°. ea., pap., $1.25.. *G.D.Russell.*
— *Same.* 2 bks. f°. ea., $1.50... *Brainard; Ditson.*
— Fifty lessons for middle register of voice. (op. 9.) 2 bks. f°. ea., $2; — in 4 pts. f°. ea., $1.25. *Brainard.*
— *Same.* 4°. pap., $2; — in 2 bks. ea., $1. *G.D.Russell.*
— *Same.* f°. $3.50. — Same: in 2 bks. ea., bds., $2; pl. ed., ea., pap., $2. — Same: bk. 1 in 2 pts. ea., pap., $1.25. — Same; for bass voice. 2 pts. ea., pap., $2.50............................ *Ditson.*
— Forty lessons; for bass or baritone. 2 bks. f°. ea., pap., $3.............................. *Ditson.*
— Forty lessons; for contralto. 2 bks. f°. ea., pap., $3 .... *Ditson.*
— Lessons in vocalization. 12°. bds., 40c..... *Ditson.*
— *Same.* f°. 40c.......................... *Gordon.*
— Mass in E flat. 4°. pap., $1.25............ *Peters.*
— Mass in F; for 2 or 4 voices. 8°. $1; pap., 65c. *Gordon.*
— Mass in F for four voices; adapted by T. Bissell. 8°. '69. $1; pap., 65c.................. *Ditson.*
— Twenty-five lessons in singing. (op. 10.) 2 bks. 4°. ea., pap., $1.50..................... *G. D. Russell.*
— Twenty-five melodic vocalizations. (op. 10.) 2 bks. f°. ea., $1.50....................... *Brainard.*

Concone, Jos., *continued.*
— *Same.* 2 bks. f°. ea., pap., $1.50; — in 1 v. $2.50. *Ditson.*
— Vocal studies. 5 nos. f°. ea., 50c.–$3.50.. *Gordon.*
Concord days. Alcott, A. B. $1.50........ *Roberts.*
Concordance to Old and New Test., to the Apocrypha, and Psalter contained in Book of common prayer. roy. 8°. $5 .... *Pott.*
Concordia. *See* Engelke, L.
Concordia. Grobe, C. 60c................ *Ditson.*
Concordia. Taylor, V. C. 50c............. *Ditson.*
Conde, José Antonio. Dominion of the Arabs in Spain; tr. by Mrs. Foster. 3 v. 12°. (Bohn.) ea., $1.25..................... *Little, B. & Co.*
— *Same.* 3 v. 12°. (Bohn.) ea., $1.40. *Scribner, W. & A.*
— *Same.* 3 v. 12°. (Bohn.) ea., $1.50... *Lippincott.*
Condensed classics. *See* Johnson, R.
Condensed novels. Harte, B. $1.50....... *Osgood.*
Conder, Cl. Reignier. *See* Bunyan, J: Pictorial scenes from "Pilgrim's progress."
Conder, Eust. R. Sleepy forest, and other stories for children. ill. sq. 12°. '73. $1.75.... *Routledge.*
Conder, F. R. Child's history of Jerusalem. ill. 12°. '74. $1.75.......................... *Routledge.*
Condie, D. Fs. Practical treatise on the diseases of children. 6th ed., rev. and enl. 8°. $5.25; leath., $6.25.............................. *Lea.*
Condorcet, A. N. C. (*Marquis*) de. Observations on the 31st bk. of Montesquieu's "Spirit of laws." *See* Destutt de Tracy, A. L. C.
Conduct book (The); [also] Marbles. 32°. 20c.; 15c. .... *Dutton.*
Conduct of life. Emerson, R. W. $1.50... *Osgood.*
Cone, Ma. Two years in California. map and ill. 12°. '76. $1.75....................... *Griggs.*
Cone, Spencer H. Life. por. 12°. $1.50... *Sheldon.*
Cones, And., *and* Johns, Wa. R. Petrolia: brief hist. of the Penn. petroleum region, its development, growth, resources, etc., 1859–'69. 12°. *$3. *Appleton.*
Coney and Andy. *See* Cousin Anna's lib.
Confectioner's handbook. 16°. pap., 25c.... *Happy.*
Confederate chieftains (The). Sadlier, M. A. $2; $2.50.................................. *Sadlier.*
Confederate flag (The) on the ocean. Peck, W. H. 25c. .... *Van Evrie.*
Confederate States of America. Army regulations. 12°. '63. bds., $2............. *J. W. Randolph.*
— Provisional government, Feb. 8, 1861, to Feb. 18, 1862; with the constitutions, treaties with the Indians, etc. 8°. '64. $10.... *J. W. Randolph.*
— Statutes at large (complete). 5 v. 8°. '62–'64. pap., $50.......................... *J. W. Randolph.*
Confederate view of the treatment of prisoners. 8°. $1.25; hf. cf., $1.50; hf. mor., $1.75... *Ellyson.*
Confederated republic of Israel. Thomson, E. 12c. *Cin. Meth. Bk. Conc.*
Confession. Simms, W. G. $1.75; 75c... *Widdleton.*
Confessions of an apostate. Sadlier, M. A. 75c.; $1.25................................ *Sadlier.*
Confessions (The) of Christendom. Winer, G. B. $3..................... *Scribner, W. & A.*
Confessions of a convert from baptism in water to baptism with water. 18°. 50c........ *Pres. Bd.*
Confessions of a decanter. •18°. 45c.; 55c. *Am. Bapt.*
Confessions of an English opium eater. *See* De Quincey, T.
Confessions of a minister. Leonhardt, J. 50c. *H. Peterson.*
Confessions of a pretty woman. Pardoe, J. 75c. *Peterson.*

nfessors of Connaught. Meaney, M. L. $1. *Cunningham.*

nfidential advice to a lover. 12°. pap., 20c. *Hurst.*

nfidential reference-book and commercial ratings, embracing the book, stationery and paper trades, *etc.* ('71.) New ed. 4°. '76. $30..*J. A. Murphy.*

Note. Previous editions were pub. under title of Booksellers nd stationers' reference book.

nflict of studies. Todhunter, I. $3.50..*Macmillan.*

nflicts and triumphs series. 5 v. 16°. $5..*Am. Bapt.*

Cont.: Harry's conversion, by H. C. Fish.—Harry's conicts, by H. C. Fish.—Roger Bernard, by G. B. Taylor.—oe Witless.—Coster Grew, by G. B. Taylor.

nformists (The). *See* Banim, J. *and* M.

nfounded foreigners. Reynolds, F. 15c...*French.*

nfucius. *See* Legge, J.

ngar, Ob. *See* Cheever, H. T.

ngdon, C: T. Tribune essays: articles contributed to "The N. Y. Tribune," 1857–'63; with introd. by H. Greeley. 12°. $2..............*Redfield.*

ngdon, H. B. Mining laws and forms: statutes of California and Nevada, with [those] of Mexico; with forms. 3d ed. 8°. '64. $3......*Bancroft.*

ngdon, Ja. A. Cavalry compendium: instructions for non-commissioned officers and privates. 18°. '64. $1..................*Claxton; Lippincott.*

ngo. Abbott, J. 90c.....................*Harper.*

ngo's kraal. *See* Jejana.

ngregation (The). Mansfield, L. W. 75c. *Randolph.*

ngregation of the Most Holy Redeemer. Andachtsbüchlein f. d. Erzbruderschaft d. heiligsten u. unbefleckten Herzens Mariä zur Bekehrung d. Sünder. 32°. 25c.................*Kreuzer.*

Besuchungen d. allerh. Sakramentes d. Altares. 18°. 50c.–$1.25.....................*Kreuzer.*

Heilige Familie (Die), Jesus, Maria u. Joseph. 18°. 60c...............................*Kreuzer.*

Trost der armen Seelen. 18°. 75c.–$2....*Kreuzer.*

Worte d. Heiles. 32°. 40c.–$1.50........*Kreuzer.*

See also Mission book.

ngregational Church. Platform. *See* Cambridge.

ngregational churches in Connecticut. Chapel hymns for Christian use and worship; prep. by the Gen. Assoc. 24°. shp., 60c.; roan, 75c.—32°. shp., 60c.; roan, 75c.; mor., $1.50...*Peck.*

Psalms and hymns; prep. by the Gen. Assoc. 12°. $1.50–$4. 18°. $1.20–$3. 32°. 75c.–$2.50..*Peck.*

ngregational harp (The new). *See* Barnes, L. B.

ngressional Temperance Society. Temperance in the Am. Congress: addresses at 1st meeting, House of Representatives, 1867. 12°. '67. pap., 25c...................................*Wells.*

ngreve, J: High hopes and pleadings for a broader view of Christianity: sermons. cr. 8°. '75. $2.50............................*Macmillan.*

ngreve, W: Love for love: comedy. 16°. pap., 15c....................................*French.*

See also Ovidius Naso, P.;—Wycherly, W., Congreve, W., Vanbrugh, *Sir* J., *and* Farquhar, G.

ningsby. Disraeli, B. 60c.............*Appleton.*

nington, J: Horæ Tennysonianæ. *See* Church, A. J.

See also Virgil.

njugal lesson. Danvers, H. 15c. ....*French.*

njuration. Caldor, M. T. 15c...........*Lee & S.*

nklin, C: H. Treatise on the powers and duties of justices of the peace in Iowa. 2d ed., rev. and adapted to code of 1873, etc.; with ref. by C. H. Conklin and J. B. Bissell. 8°. '74. shp., $7.50. *Mills.*

nkling, Alfr. Jurisdiction, law and practice of the U. S. courts in admiralty and maritime causes; with forms. 2 v. 8°. shp., $15.... *W. C. Little.*

Conkling, Alfr., *continued.*

— Treatise on the organization, jurisdiction and practice of the U. S. courts, with rules and forms. 5th ed., rev. and enl. 8°. shp., $8.50.. *W. C. Little.*

Connecticut. Code of 1650: compilation of the earliest laws and orders of the General Court; [also] The constitutional compact adopted by Windsor, Hartford and Wethersfield in 1638–9; with extracts from the laws of New Haven colony called blue laws. 12°. pap., 35c............*U. P. James.*

— Digest of cases in the Superior Court and Supreme Court of Errors. *See* Baldwin, S. E.

— Digest of laws. *See* Swift, Z.

— Joint stock laws. 12°. $2..................*Peck.*

— Supreme Court of Errors reports, 1802–'13; by T. Day. 5 v. 8°. $25.........*T. & J. W. Johnson.*

— *Same.* v. 1–38 (1814–'71). 8°...........*State.*

Cont.: v. 1–21 ('14–'52), by T: Day.—v. 22–24 ('52–'56), by W. N. Matteson.—v. 25–38 ('56–'71), by J: Hooker.

— *Same.* v. 39–41 ('72–'74); by J: Hooker. 3 v. 8°. ea., shp., $5..........................(?) *Case.*

Connecticut Academy of Arts and Sciences. Transactions. v. 1, 2, 3 (pt. 1). 8°. '66–'76. pap., v. 1 (pt. 1), $2.50; v. 1 (pt. 2), v. 3 (pt. 1), ea., $3.50; v. 2 (2 pts.), ea., $3..*Conn. Acad. of A. & S.*

Connecticut (The) by daylight, from New York to the White Mountains. 16°. pap., 25c. (?) *G. Watson.*

Connecticut civil officer: power and duties of justices of the peace, constables [and] selectmen; with forms. 8°. shp., $2.75.............*Hamersley.*

Connecticut geological survey. Report on geol. of C.; by J. G. Percival. 8°. '42...........*State.*

— Report on geol. survey of C.; by C. U. Shepard. 8°. '37....................................*State.*

Connecticut Medical Society. Transactions, 1867–'76. 10 v. 8°. v. 1, 3–8, ea., pap., 50c.; v. 2, 9, 10, ea., pap., 75c.......................*Conn. Med.*

Connell, *Miss* Emily. Swords and shields. ill. 16°. $1 ....*J. A. Moore.*

Connell, *Miss* Sa. G. Bessie at Stony Lonesome; or, Charlie's mission. 18°. 90c............*Dutton.*

— Eleanor's lessons. ill. 16°. $1........*J. A. Moore.*

— Margarethe and Waldemar. 18°. 90c......*Dutton.*

Connelly, Emma M. Under the surface. [Fiction.] 12°. $1.50........................*Lippincott.*

Conner, P. S. P. Memoir of Sir W: Penn. sq. 8°. '76. $1.50..........................*Munsell.*

Connoisseur, *Mme.* —. Complete fortune-teller and dream book. 16°. pap., 10c.......*U. P. James.*

— *Same;* [also] The oraculum; or, Napoleon's book of fate. 16°. pap., 25c..........*U. P. James.*

Connoisseur (The). *See* Chalmers, A., British essayists.

Connor, G. C. One hundred songs of praise. 16°. per doz., pap., $1.50; bds., $1.80.......*Burke.*

Conolly, J. *See* Cyclopædia of practical medicine.

Conover, O. M. *See* Wisconsin, Reports.

Conquered heart (The); by author of "Hemlock ridge." ('67.) New ed. ill. 18°. '70. 60c. *Hoyt.*

Conquering and to conquer. Charles, E. $1.25..*Dodd.*

Conquering game: drama. 16°. pap., 15c...*French.*

Conqueror (The). Flint, S. A. 75c..... *Cong. Pub.*

Conquest and self-conquest. McIntosh, M. J. 75c. *Harper.*

Conquest of Ireland. *See* Adams, J. Q.

Conquest of the sea. Siebe, H. $2......*Routledge.*

Conquests of the seven hills. Laing, C. H. B. $1.25. *Porter.*

Conrad, Jul. Die Schicksals-Braut, od. die Geheimnisse d. Kaisers. [Napoleon III.] 8°. $1.50; pap., $1........................*F. W. Thomas.*

Conrad, Rob. T. Jack Cade: tragedy. 16°. pap., 15c. *French.*

Conrad, T: K. Thoughts on prayer. 16°. '74. $1. *Randolph.*

Conrad, Tim. Abbott. Check list of the invertebrate fossils of No. Am. 8°. '66. pap., 25c. *Smith. Inst.*

— Fossil shells. *See* Gilliss, J. M.

— Fossils of the tertiary formation of the U. S. 49 pl. 8°. '38. $5 .... *Acad. of Nat. Sci.*

— Monograph of the urionidæ of No. Am. 60 pl. 8°. '40. $8 .... *Acad. of Nat. Sci.*

Conrad and Gertrude. 18°. '67. 50c... *Cunningham.*

Conrad and Medora. Brough, W. 15c....... *French.*

Conrad, the squirrel. *See* Life and times of.

Conscience, Hendrik. Short tales. 12 v. 12°. '56-'75. ea., $1; $1.25 .... *Murphy.*

Cont.: The poor gentleman.—Happiness of being rich.—The miser.—Count Hugo of Craenhove.—Curse of the village.—Village innkeeper.—Conscript and blind Rosa.—Ricketicketack and wooden Clara.—Fisherman's daughter.—The amulet.—Ludovic and Gertrude.—Young doctor.

— Fashion; or, Siska Von Roosemael. ill. 18°. 50c. *Strong.*

— Flemish life; in four stories. ill. 12°. $1.50. *World Pub.*

— Lion of Flanders. 12°. '60. $1.25.. *Kelly, P. & Co.*

— Little Frank; or, a painter's progress; [also] What a mother can endure. ill. 18°. 50c....... *Strong.*

— Merchant of Antwerp; tr. by R. Lyle. 12°. '72. $1.50; $2 .... *Kelly, P. & Co.*

Conscience. Dorsey, A. H. $1 .... *Strong.*

Conscience. Follen, E. L. 50c............ *Lee & S.*

Conscience. Maurice, F. D. $1.75..... *Macmillan.*

Conscript (The). *See* Dumas, A.

Conscript (The). Erckmann, E., *and* Chatrian, A. $1.25; 75c. .... *Scribner.*

Conscript and blind Rosa. Conscience, H. $1; $1.25. *Murphy.*

Conscrit (Le) de 1813. Erckmann, E., *and* Chatrian, A. $1.25 .... *Holt.*

Consecrated property: essay. 16°. '55. 50c. *Meth. Bk. Conc.*

Consecrated talents. 18°. 60c............. *Dutton.*

Consecrated talents; or, the life of Mrs. Mary W. Mason; with introd. by Bp. Janes. 12°. '70. $1.50 .... *Meth. Bk. Conc.*

Consecutive questions on John; — Luke; — Mark. 18°. ea., per doz., $1.80 .... *Meth. Bk. Conc.*

Consecutive questions on Matthew. 18°. per doz., $2.16 .... *Meth. Bk. Conc.*

Consecutive union question book: Matthew-John. 4 v. 24°. ea., 16c.................... *Am. S. S.*

Consideration for others. Marshall, E. 50c... *Carter.*

Considerations for days of adversity. 32°. 20c. *Pres. Bd.*

Considerations for young men. Waterbury, J. B. 35c. .... *Am. Tr.*

Considerations of the uses and abuses of S.-school libraries. 32°. 15c.................. *Am. S. S.*

Consolatio. *See* Kennaway, C. E.

Consolation for the afflicted and those that mourn; tr. from the French by Miss A. T. Sadlier. 32°. 50c.-$2.50 .... *Sadlier.*

Consolation for those who mourn. Ryan, P. J. 50c. *Ryan.*

Consolation in conflict, sickness and sorrow. Means, J. C. 75c...................... *Bost. Am. Tr.*

Consolation of philosophy. *See* Boethius, A. M. T. S.

Consolations in travel. Davy, *Sir* H. $1.50.. *Roberts.*

Conspirator's victim. Judson, E. Z. C. 75c. *Dick & F.*

Conspirators (The). Dumas, A. 50c.... *Routledge.*

Constable, A. *See* Stoddard, R. H., Bric-a-brac ser.

Constable, C. Arched beams. 8°. pap., 90c. *Am. Soc. of C. E.*

Constable, C., *continued.*

— Retaining walls; [also] Croes' Flow of west bra of Croton River; [also] Form, weight, manu ture and life of rails, by A. Welch, M. N. F ney, O. Chanute and I. M. St. John; [al Welch's Memoir of rails. 8°. '74. pap., $1 *Am. Soc. of C.*

Constable, H: Duration and nature of future pun ment. 8°. 25c. .... *Judd &*

Constable of France. *See* Grant, James.

Constable of the tower. Ainsworth, W. H. 75c. *Dick &*

Constance and Carle. *See* Aunt Hattie's stories.

Constance and Marion; or, the cousins. 18°. 60c.; $1 .... *Kelly, P. &*

Constance Aylmer. P., H. F. $1.50...... *Scrib*

Constance Herbert. Jewsbury, G. E. 50c... *Har*

Constance Lindsay. H., C. G. 50c. .... *Har*

Constance Sherwood. Fullerton, *Lady* G. $2. *Cath. I*

Constancia's household: story of the Spanish refo ation. ill. 12°. $1.50 .... *Nels*

Constant watchfulness. *See* Revellers (The).

Constantius, *Patriarch of Constantinople.* Mem of the patriarchs of Antioch. *See* Neale, J. History of the Holy Eastern Church.

Constellation collection of anthems. obl. 8°. b $1.50 .... *Dits*

Constitution (The). *See* United States.

Constitutional amendment (The); or, the Sund the Sabbath, the change and the restitution: cussion between W. H. Littlejohn and the edi of the "Christian statesman." 16°. '73. $1; p 40c.; — pt. 1, sep., pap., 10c...... *Sev. Day A*

Constitutions of the several states and the U. S.; cluding Declaration of independence and Artic of confederation. 8°. $2.50........... *Bar*

Construction of mill dams; compr. building of r and reservoir embankments and head ga etc. ill. 8°. '74. $2.50 .... *Le*

Construction of the Victoria bridge, in Canada, Ja. Hodges. 2 v. pl. and wood-eng. imp and roy. f°. (Lond.) '60. hf. mor., $30.. *Sp*

Consuelo. *See* Sand, G.

Contarini Fleming. Disraeli, B. 50c...... *Apple*

Contemplations on the mercy of God. Etheric J. W. 50c................ *Cin. Meth. Bk. C*

Contemporary art: 30 etchings and chromo.-li with explan. text. f°. $15; mor., $25.. *Lippinc*

Contented Jim. *See* Finley, M. F.

Contentment better than wealth. *See* Haven, A. B., Home ser.

Contest and armor. Abercrombie, J. 50c.... *Car*

Continental concert tunes; for old folks' concerts. 40c. .... *Chu*

Continental harmony: collection of psalm tunes, obl. 8°. '57. bds., $1.50 .... *Dits*

Continental library. 4 v. 16°. $6........... *Mas*

Cont.: Autobiog. of Benjamin Franklin.—Life of E Allen.—Lives of Mary and Martha Washington.— stories of the days of Washington.

Continental library. 6 v. ill. 12°. $4.50... *Applet*

Cont.: William Tell.—Boy's own toy-maker.—A Fanny's story-book.—Good in everything.—Children's days.—Winter evening recreations.

Continentalist (The). *See* Hamilton, A.

Contos para os meninos. 32°. '69. 40c....... *Am.*

Contraband Christmas. Root, N. W. T. 75c. *Dutt*

Contradictions. Dunning, A. K. $1.50... *Loth*

Contrast. 18°. 30c.; 35c. .... *Am. Bo*

Contrast. *See* Dunning, *Mrs.* A. K.

Contrast. *See* Edgeworth, M.

ntrast. Hull, M. $1.50 .... *Colby.*

ntrast: story for boys. 18°. 45c........ *Am. S. S.*

ntrast between the righteous and the wicked, in Bible language. 32°. pap., 10c.......... *Hoyt.*

ntrasts: dedicated to the rate-payers of London. 12°. '73. $1.75 .... *Routledge.*

ntributions to thought. Wheildon, W. W. $1.50. *Wheildon.*

nvalescent (The). Willis, N. P. $1.75 .. *Scribner.*

nvenient food. Summers, T. O. 35c..... *So. Meth.*

nvent (The). McCrindell, R. 75c........ *Carter.*

nvent life; or, should Protestant children be educated in Roman Catholic schools? a story. 16°. '76. $1.25 .... *Whittaker.*

nvent life unveiled. O'Gorman, E. *$1.50. *Conn. Pub.*

nvention chorus book: collection of anthems, choruses, etc. obl. 8°. '60. pap., 60c... *Ditson.*

nvention of Pharmaceutists and Druggists. Minutes. *See* American Pharmac. Assoc.

nvention of 1787. *See* United States.

nversations for the young. Watson, R. $1.25. *Meth. Bk. Conc.*

nversations of a Cath. missionary with Americans. Perrodin, J. C. $1.25; 50c......... *Hoffmann.*

nversations of a father with his children. ill. 12°. $1 .... *Pres. Bd.*

nversations of James Northcote. *See* Hazlett, W.

nversations on religious subjects. Janney, S. M. *net*, 50c. .... *Friends Bk. Assoc.*

nversations with Theodore and his sister. Stockly, H. E. *net*, 40c. .... *Friends Bk. Assoc.*

nverse, C: C. ["Karl Reden."] Silver wings: collection of S.-school music. obl. 12°. bds., 35c.; pap., 30c........................ *Ditson.*

Spring holiday: a cantata; with libretto by C. M. Cady. obl. 16°. '55. bds., 75c......... *Ditson.*

Zion hymn and tune book. obl. 16°. pap., 25c.; bds., 30c.......................... *Brainard.*

See also Baird, E. T., *and* Converse, C. C.; — Bradbury, W. B., *and* Converse, C. C.

and Goodenough, S. J. Anthem book of the Meth. Episc. Church. obl. 8°. $1..... *Meth. Bk. Conc.*

and Schenck, W. E. Children's praise: S.-school hymns and tunes. sq. 16°. 30c.; pap., 25c., 20c. *Pres. Bd.*

nverse, Fk. B. Banjo (The) and how to play it. 16°. bds., 50c...................... *Dick & F.*

Banjo instructor. obl. 8°. 75c............ *Gordon.*

Banjoist (The): rudiments, exercises and collection of music. 8°. '72. bds., $1............. *Pond.*

Complete banjo instructor, without a master. 16°. bds., 50c........................... *Dick & F.*

onverse with God. Baxter, R. 40c. ..... *Pres. Bd.*

onversion de Andrés Dunn. *See* Andrew Dunn.

onversion of Capt. W. E. Sees. 30c. (?)*Luth. Pub.*

onversion of Paul Darst. Lucas, D. R. $1.25. *Cen. Bk.*

onversion of St. Paul. Geer, G. J. 75c.; $1.. *Wells.*

onversion of a skeptic. Gaddis, M. P. 75c. *Cin. Meth. Bk. Conc.*

onvert (The). Brownson, O. A. $2...... *Sadlier.*

onvert of Massachusetts. 18°. 55c......... *Dutton.*

onvert of Saint Paul. Dumas, A. 25c... *U. P. James.*

onverted collier. 18°. '66. 40c.; 50c. *Meth. Bk. Conc.*

onverted infidel. Scarlett, J. 60c. *Meth. Bk. Conc.*

onverted Unitarian: memoir of E— E—. 18°. 50c. *Pres. Bd.*

onvict (The). *See* James, G. P. R.

onvict once. Stephens, J. B. $1.50 ... *Macmillan.*

onvict's family; by author of "Annie Lorimer." 18°. 70c............................ *Pres. Bd.*

Convict's son and the two farmers. ('65.) 6th ed. ill. 16°. '72. $1.25................ *Perkinpine.*

Conway, H. J. Hiram Hireout: farce. 16°. pap., 15c. *French.*

— Our Jemimy: farce. 16°. pap., 15c. ...... *French.*

Conway, J: D. Complete poems; or, hours of idleness. 16°. '75. $1................... *Conway.*

Conway, M. D. Earthward pilgrimage (The). 12°. $1.75 .... *Holt.*

— Sacred anthology: book of ethnical Scriptures. ('74.) New ed. 8°. '75. $4.................. *Holt.*

Conwell, Russell H. History of the great fire in Boston. map and ill. 12°. *$1.50........ *Russell.*

— Why and how? why the Chinese emigrate, and the means they adopt for the purpose of getting to Am. ill. 16°. $1.50................. *Lee & S.*

— Woman and the law. 16°. '76. 75c.....(?)*Russell.*

Conybeare, W: J: On infidelity. 12°. $1... *Wiley.*

— *and* Howson, J. S. Life and epistles of St. Paul. New ed. ill. 12°. '73. $3........... *Randolph.*

— — *Same.* 8°. $4.50................. (?)*Scranton.*

— — *Same;* with introd. by L. Bacon. ill. and maps. 8°. $4.50; leath., $5; hf. mor., $6.. *Scranton.*

— — *Same;* with introd. by J. McCosh. ill. and maps. 8°. *3.50; shp., $4.................. *Col. Bk.*

— — *Same.* ('54.) New ed. 2 v. maps and ill. 8°. '75. $5; hf. cf., $9; mor., $12; — in 1 v. $3; shp., $4.50; hf. cf., $5.50; mor., $8... *Scribner.*

Conyngham, D. P. Lives of the Irish saints and martyrs; with introd. by T. S. Preston. 4°. $2.50; $3.50; — pl. 4°. $10–$22; — in 35 pts. 4°. ea., 25c. .... *Sadlier.*

— O'Donnells of Glen Cottage. 12°. $1.50; $2.. *Sadlier.*

Cook, Eben. Sot weed factor; or, a voyage to Maryland: a satyr. Lond., 1708. [Reprint.] 4°. pap., $1.25 .... *Shea.*

Cook, Eliza. Poems. 12°. $1.50.............. *Locke.*

— *Same.* New ed., enl. ill. 12°. '69. $1.50; mor., $4. *Claxton.*

— *Same.* (Chandos classics.) cr. 8°. $1; pap., 75c. *Scribner, W. & A.*

— *Same.* (Chandos poets.) ill. cr. 8°. $3.75; cf., $7.50; mor., $8.............. *Scribner, W. & A.*

— *Same.* (Household ser.) ill. and por. 16°. $1.50; mor., $3.......................... *Lee & S.*

— *Same.* (Presentation poets.) ill. 12°. $1.75. *Routledge.*

— *Same.* (Scribner's pop. poets.) ill. 12°. $1.50. *Scribner, W. & A.*

— *Same;* ed. by R. A. Willmott, with biog., etc. (British poets.) ill. 12°. $2.25; hf. cf., $3.50; mor., $5. *Routledge.*

Cook, F. C. Commentary on Job. *See below* Bible commentary.

— Exodus; with explan. and crit. commentary. roy. 8°. '74. $1.50.......................... *Scribner.*

— — *See also below* Bible commentary.

— Leviticus, Numbers and Deuteronomy; with explan. and crit. comment. roy. 8°. '74. $2.50.. *Scribner.*

— (*ed.*) Bible commentary. v. 1–6. roy. 8°. '71–'75. ea., $5.............................. *Scribner.*

Cont.: v. 1. Genesis, by E. H. Browne; Exodus, by F. C. Cook and S. Clark; Leviticus, by S. Clark; Numbers and Deuteronomy, by T. E. Espin. — v. 2. Joshua, by T. E. Espin; Judges, Ruth and Samuel, by Lord A. Hervey; First Kings, by G. Rawlinson. — v. 3. Second Kings, Chronicles, Ezra, Nehemiah and Esther, by G. Rawlinson. — v. 4. Job, by F. C. Cook; Psalms, by G. H. S. Johnson, F. C. Cook and C. I. Elliot; Proverbs, by E. H. Plumptre; Ecclesiastes, by W. T. Bullock; Song of Solomon, by T. Kingsbury. — v. 5. Isaiah, by W. Kay; Jeremiah and Lamentations, by R. Payne Smith. — v. 6. Ezekiel, Daniel and the minor prophets.

Note. Also known as Speaker's commentary.

— *See also* Johnson, G. H. S., Cook, F. C., *and* Elliot, C. I.

Cook, G: H. *See* New Jersey geol. survey.

Cook, *Mrs.* Ht. N. Alphabet of Scripture animals. 18°. '42. 35c.......................... *Am. Tr.*

Cook, *Mrs.* Ht. N., *continued.*
— *Germ.* Biblische Naturgeschichte für Kinder. 18°. '45. 35c. ... *Am. Tr.*
— Trees, fruits and flowers of the Bible. 18°. '48. 35c. *Am. Tr.*
Cook, J. Magnetism and electricity. (Pop. sci. man.) 18°. 40c. ... *Lippincott.*
Cook, Ja. Voyages. *See* Kippis, A.
Cook, *Mrs.* Ma. Louise. ["Ma. Lennox."] Ante bellum. [Fiction.] 12°. $2 ... *Lippincott.*
Cook, N. F. Satan in society. ('70.) New ed. 12°. '75. *$2 ... *Vent.*
Cook, Robley D. New York highway laws: manual of public highways and private roads; with forms. 8°. '70. $3.50 ... *Weed.*
— *Same.* 8°. '75. $3.50 ... *J. D. Parsons.*
— *See also* New York, Supreme Court reports.
Cook, S. W. Out in the streets: temperance drama. 16°. pap., 15c. ... *Ames.*
Cook, T. J. Union: music for the church and songs for the fireside. obl. 8°. bds., 80c. *Huntington.*
— *and* Perkins, T. E. Book of Sabbath anthems. obl. 8°. bds., 80c. ... *Huntington.*
— — New olive branch. obl. 8°. bds., $1.50. *Huntington.*
— — *and* Hastings, T. Oriental glee and anthem book. obl. 8°. bds., 80c. ... *Huntington.*
Cook, T: Handbook for northern Italy. 4th ed. 12°. '75. $2 ... *Cook.*
— Handbook to Florence. 12°. '74. bds., 50c. ... *Cook.*
— Handbook to Venice. 12°. '74. bds., 50c. ... *Cook.*
— Letters from the sea and from foreign lands, descriptive of a tour round the world. 4th ed. 8°. '75. pap., 50c. ... *Cook.*
— Tourist's handbook for Holland, Belgium and the Rhine. 4th ed. 12°. '74. $1 ... *Cook.*
— Tourist's handbook for southern Italy. 4th ed. 12°. '75. $2 ... *Cook.*
— Tourist's handbook to Switzerland, via Paris. 4th ed. 12°. '74. $1 ... *Cook.*
— Up the Nile by steam. ('75.) 5th ed. map. 8°. '76. pap., 25c. ... *Cook.*
Cook, T: and Son (*pub.*) Cook's continental time-table and tourist's handbook. 12th ed. 12°. '76. pap., 50c. ... *Cook.*
Cook, Son and Co. (*pub.*) American guide to Europe. 8°. '75. $6 ... *N. Y. & H. Pub.*
— *See also* Cook's.
Cooke, A. P. A text-book of naval ordnance and gunnery. 400 ill. 8°. $12.50 ... *Wiley.*
Cooke, Anna B. Adventures of a fly, and other stories. 18°. 50c. ... *Dutton.*
— Adventures of a travelled ant, and other stories. 18°. 50c. ... *Dutton.*
— Queen (A). 18°. 75c. ... *Dutton.*
Cooke, H. A. *See* Stowe (Phineas) and Bethel work.
Cooke, H: *See* Bible [Whole].
Cooke, J: Esten. Doctor Vandyke. ill. 8°. $1.25; pap., 75c. ... *Appleton.*
— Fairfax. 12°. $1.50 ... *Carleton.*
— Hammer and rapier. 12°. $1.50 ... *Carleton.*
— Heir of Gaymount. pap., 50c. ... *Van Evrie.*
— Henry St. John, gentleman: a tale of 1774-'75. 12°. $1.50 ... *Harper.*
— Her majesty the queen: hist. romance. 12°. $1.50. *Lippincott.*
— Hilt to hilt. 12°. $1.50 ... *Carleton.*
— Justin Harley: a romance of old Virginia. ('74.) New ed. ill. 12°. '76. $1.75 ... *Claxton.*
— Leather stocking and silk; or, hunter John Myers and his times: a story of the valley of Virginia. 12°. $1.50 ... *Harper.*
— Life of Gen. R. E. Lee. por., maps and wood-eng. 8°. *$5; shp., $6; hf. mor., $7 ... *Appleton.*

Cooke, J: Esten, *continued.*
— Mohun; or, the last days of Lee and his paladin final memoirs of a staff officer serving in Vi ginia; from the MSS. of Col. Surrey [*pseud.*] Eagles nest. ill. 12°. '69. $2.25 ... *Huntingto*
— Out of the foam. 12°. $1.50 ... *Carleto*
— Pretty Mrs. Gaston, and other stories. ill. 1 $1.50 ... *Jud*
— Stonewall Jackson: a milit. biog. por. and ma 8°. $2.50; shp., $3.50. — chp. ed. $2 .. *Appleto*
— Surrey of Eagle's nest; or, the memoirs of a sta officer serving in Virginia; ed. from MS. Col. Surrey [*pseud.*] ill. 12°. $2.25 .. *Huntingto*
— Wearing of the gray: sketches, etc., of the ci war. ill. 8°. '67. *$4; shp., $5 ... *Trea*
Cooke, Josiah P., *jr.* Chemical problems and rea tions. 12°. $1 ... *Butle*
— Elements of chemical physics. ('60.) 2d ed. '73. $5 ... *Ally*
— First principles of chemical philosophy. ('71.) ed. 12°. '75. $3.50 ... *Ally*
— New chemistry (The). (Intern. sci. ser.) 12°. $ *Appleto*
Cooke, M. C. Fungi: their nature and uses; ed. M. J. Berkeley. 12°. $1.50 ... *Appleto*
— Handbook of British fungi, with descript. of all t species and ill. of the genera. 2 v. cr. 8°. '7 $12 ... *Macmilla*
— Manual of botanic terms; incl. the recent terat logical terms. 16°. $1.50 ... *Putnar*
Cooke, Parsons. Divine law of beneficence. 1 '50. 25c.; pap., 10c. ... *Am. T*
— *Germ.* Geordnete Liebesthätigkeit. 18°. '51. 35 *Am. T*
Cooke, Philip St. G: Cavalry tactics. ill. 12°. '7 $1 ... *Van Nostran*
— *Same.* 2 v. 18°. '61. $1.50; — in 1 v. $1 .. *Claxto*
— Handy-book for U. S. cavalry. 18°. '61. pap., 30 *Claxto*
Cooke, T. Shades of the heroes; for 5 voice [Music.] 8°. 25c. ... *Gordo*
— Vocal method. f°. bds., $3. *Ditson; Gordon; Willi*
Cooke, W. H. Church-teaching for the children the church. 18°. '74. 25c. ... *Po*
Cooking Club library. 4 v. 16°. $5 ... *Lothro*
Cont.: The Cooking Club, by E. Farman. — Bessie's tria by N. Perry. — The Wentworths, by S. C. Pindar. — Virgini by W. H. G. Kingston.
Cooking Club (The) of Tu-whit Hollow. Farman, $1.25 ... *Lothro*
Cookman, Alfr. Stayed on God. ('72.) 3d ed. 1 '73. 50c. ... *Tibba*
Cookman, G: G. Speeches. 18°. '40. 35c. *Meth. Bk. Con*
— *Same;* with biog. introd. by T. O. Summers. ('57 2d ed. 18°. '75. 40c. ... *So. Met*
— — *See also* Young disciples lib.
Cook's all the world over. Hodder, E. 2 v. e $1.75 ... *Coo*
Cook's programmes of personally conducted Palesti tours with extensions to Egypt, the Nile, etc for season of 1875-6. 8°. pap., 25c. ... *Coo*
Cook's tourists' handbook for the Black Forest. 8°. '76. shp., $1 ... *Coo*
Cook's tourists' handbook for Egypt, the Nile and t Desert. cr. 8°. '76. $2 ... *Coo*
Cook's tourists' handbook for Palestine and Syri cr. 8°. '76. $2.50 ... *Coo*
— *See also* Cook, Son and Co.
Cook's own book; with directions for carving; by Boston housekeeper. ill. 12°. $1.75 ... *Mille*
Cool as a cucumber. Jerrold, B. 15c. ... *Frenc*
Cooley, Arn. Ja. Book of useful knowledge; co 6000 receipts. ill. 8°. hf. bd., $1.50 ... *Appleto*
— Complete practical treatise on perfumery. 1 '74. $1.50 ... *Bair*

Cooley, Arn. Ja., *continued.*
— Cyclopædia of pract. receipts. 5th ed., rev. and enl. by R. V. Tuson. ill. roy. 8°. '72. $10..*Lindsay.*
— Handbook of compound medicines; or, the prescriber's and dispenser's vade-mecum. 12°. $1.25 ....*Lippincott.*
— Handbook of perfumes, cosmetics and other toilet articles. 12°. $1.50..........*Lippincott.*
— Handbook of the toilet in ancient and modern times. 12°. $1.50..........*Lippincott.*

Cooley, Edg. A. Digest of Michigan [misc.] reports (1836–'70). 8°. '72. $5; $7 ....*Richmond.*

Cooley, Le Roy C. Easy experiments in physical science. ('70.) New ed. ill. 12°. '76. 75c. *Scribner.*
— Elements of chemistry. ('73.) New ed. ill. 12°. '76. $1..........*Scribner.*
— Natural philosophy. ('71.) New ed. ill. 12°. '76. $1..........*Scribner.*
— Text-book of chemistry. ('69.) New ed. ill. 12°. '76. $1.25..........*Scribner.*
— Text-book on natural philosophy. ('68.) New ed. ill. 12°. '76. $1.50..........*Scribner.*

Cooley, T: M. Law of taxation. 8°. '76. shp., $7.50 ....*Callaghan.*
— Treatise on the const. limitations upon legislative power in the several states. 3d ed., enl. 8°. '74. shp., $6..........*Little, B. & Co.*
— *See also* Michigan, Supreme Court reports.

Coolidge, G: A. (*ed.*) Brochure of Bunker Hill. ill. obl. 16°. '75. pap., 50c..........*Osgood.*

Coolidge, R. H. Statistical report on sickness and mortality in U. S. army. *See* United States, *Surgeon-General's Office.*

Coolidge, Su. (*pseud.*) *See* Woolsey, Sa. C.

Coolie (The). Jenkins, E. $1.25; 50c. ..*Routledge.*

Coomes, Oll. Idaho Tom. 8°. pap., 20c....*Beadle.*

Coon hunt: Ethiop. drama. 16°. pap., 15c...*Happy.*

Cooney, Myron A. Cæcilia: drama. 18°. 40c. *Sadlier.*

Cooney in de hollow: Ethiop. drama. 16°. pap., 15c. *Happy.*

Coons, A. New song. 16°. '76. 55c.; bds., 45c.; 50c. —Miniature ed. 35c.; bds., 25c.; 30c. *Gordon.*

Cooper, A. R. Cultivation of art, and its relations to religious puritanism and money-getting. 12°. '74. 50c.; pap., 25c. ....*Somerby.*

Cooper, B. B. Lectures on the principles and practice of surgery. 8°. $2..........*Lea.*

Cooper, C: H: *and* T. Athenæ Cantabrigienses. [Biography.] 2 v. 8°. '58. ea., $6..*Macmillan.*
Cont.: v. 1. 1500–1585.—v. 2. 1586–1609.

Cooper, Fk. (*pseud.*) *See* Simms, W: Gilmore.

Cooper, F: Fox. Black-eyed Sukey: burlesque. 16°. pap., 15c..........*French.*
— Hercules: farce. 16°. pap., 15c..........*French.*

Cooper, G: Maud Irving; or, the little orphan. [Operetta.] 12°. bds., 75c.; pap., 60c...*Peters.*
— *and* Millard, H. The chaplet: collection of hymns and songs. 8°. bds., 55c..........*G. D. Russell.*

Cooper, J. A. Counsels to S.-school teachers. 18°. 75c..........*Nelson.*

Cooper, J. W. Game fowls: their origin and hist., with descript. of the breeds, strains and crosses. ill. 12°. $5..........*Judd.*

Cooper, Ja. Fenimore. Works. (Household ed.) 32 v. 16°. ea., $1.25; per set, $40; hf. cf., $80. *Hurd & H.*
Cont.: Precaution.—Spy.—Pioneers.—Pilot.—Lionel Lincoln.—Last of the Mohicans.—Red Rover.—Homeward bound.—Home as found.—Pathfinder.—Mercedes of Castile.—Deerslayer.—Two admirals.—Wing-and-wing.—Wyandotte.—Afloat and ashore.—Prairie.—Wept of Wish-ton-wish.—Water-witch.—Bravo.—Heidenmauer.—Headsman.—Monikins.—Miles Wallingford.—Red skins.—Chain-bearer.—Satanstoe.—The crater.—Jack Tier.—Sea lions.—Oak openings.—Ways of the hour.

Cooper, Ja. Fenimore, *continued.*
— *Same.* (New lib. ed.) 32 v. 12°. ea., $1.50. *Appleton.*
Cont.: Spy.—Pilot.—Red Rover.—Deerslayer.—Pathfinder.—Last of the Mohicans.—Pioneers.—Prairie.—Lionel Lincoln.—Wept of Wish-ton-wish.—Water-witch.—The bravo.—Mercedes of Castile.—Two admirals.—Afloat and ashore.—Miles Wallingford.—Wing-and-wing.—Oak openings.—Satanstoe.—Chain-bearer.—Red skins.—The crater.—Homeward bound.—Home as found.—Heidenmauer.—Headsman.—Jack Tier.—Sea lions.—Wyandotte.—The Monikins.—Precaution.—Ways of the hour.
— *Same.* (New octavo ed.) v. 1–11. ill. 8°. ea., $1.25; pap., 75c..........*Appleton.*
Cont.: Spy.—Pilot.—Red Rover.—Deerslayer.—Pathfinder.—Last of the Mohicans.—Pioneers.—Prairie.—Water-witch.—Two admirals.—Wing-and-wing.
— *Same.* (Riverside ed.) 32 v. ill. cr. 8°. $72; hf. cf., $128..........*Hurd & H.*
Note. Contents the same as in Household ed.
— Select works. (Popular ed.) 10 v. cr. 8°. ea., pap., 75c. ....*Hurd & H.*
Cont.: Deerslayer.—Pioneers.—Last of the Mohicans.—Prairie.—Pathfinder.—Spy.—Pilot.—Two admirals.—Wing-and-wing.—Afloat and ashore.
— Leather-stocking tales. 5 v. 12°. $7.50; hf. cf., $17.50;—in 1 v. ill. 4°. $4; shp., $5; hf. mor., $5 ....*Appleton.*
Cont.: Deerslayer.—Pathfinder. - Mohicans.—Pioneers.—Prairie.
— *Same.* (Household ed.) 5 v. 16°. $6.25; hf. cf., $12.50.—(Riverside ed.) 5 v. cr. 8°. $11.25; hf. cf., $20..........*Hurd & H.*
Cont.: Deerslayer.—Pioneers.—Last of the Mohicans.—Prairie.—Pathfinder.
— Naval history. New ed., contin. to 1860. 8°. $3.75. *Mason.*
— Sea tales. 5 v. 12°. $7.50; hf. cf., $17.50;—in 1 v. ill. 8°. $4; shp., $5; hf. mor., $6.50..*Appleton.*
Cont.: Pilot.—Red Rover.—Water-witch.—Wing-and-wing.—Two admirals.
— *Same.* (Household ed.) 10 v. 16°. $12.50; hf. cf., $25..........*Hurd & H.*
Cont.: Pilot.—Red Rover.—Jack Tier.—Two admirals.—Wing-and-wing.—Sea lions.—Water-witch.—Afloat and ashore.—Miles Wallingford.—The crater.
— Stories of adventure, sel. from works. ('62.) New ed. 3 v. ill. 16°. '68. ea., $1.25...*Hurd & H.*
Cont.: Stories of the prairie.—Stories of the sea.—Stories of the woods.

Cooper, Ja. G. *See* California geological survey.

Cooper, Rob. Autobiography. 12°. pap., 15c. *Mendum.*
— Infidel's or inquirer's text-book: lectures on the Bible. 12°. '58. $1..........*Mendum.*
— Lectures on the soul. 12°. 75c..........*Mendum.*

Cooper, S: Dictionary of practical surgery; with notes and add., and supplement. index by D. M. Reese. 8°. shp., $4..........*Harper.*
— *Same;* brought down to the present time by S. A. Lane and others. 2 v. 8°. '61–'62. $15..*Lindsay.*
— First lines of the theory and practice of surgery; with notes and add. by W. Parker. 2 v. 8°. $5. *W. Wood.*

Cooper, Su. Fenimore. Rural hours. ('68.) 2d ed. 12°. '76. $2..........*Putnam.*

Cooper, T. Notes on the erection of the Illinois and St. Louis bridge. *See* Whipple, S., Upright arched bridges.

Cooper, Thompson. New biographical dictionary. cr. 8°. '74. $5..........*Macmillan.*
— *See also* Cooper, C. H. *and* T.

Cooper, W. F. *See* Tennessee, Chancery reports.

Cooper Gent, and other sketches from "The country parson's visits to his poor." 18°. 60c. *Am. S. S.*

Coopers (The). Haven, A. B. $1.25......*Appleton.*

Coopers: Ethiop. drama. 16°. pap., 15c. *French; Happy.*

Cope, E. M. Introduction to Aristotle's Rhetoric; with analysis, notes and app. 8°. '67. $4.50. *Macmillan.*

Cope, E: Drinker. Batrachia: bulletin of National Museum, no. 1. 8°. '75. pap., 25c..... *Smith. Inst.*
— — *See also* United States, *National Mus.*
— On the hypothesis of evolution, physical and metaphysical. 12°. '70. pap., 25c.... *Van Nostrand.*
— Vertebrata of the cretaceous formations of the west. *See* United States, *Geol. Survey of the Ter.*
Copeman, E: Cerebral affections of infancy. 12°. $2. *Lippincott.*
Copland, Ja. Dictionary of practical medicine; with prescriptions, classification of diseases, and formulæ; ed. with notes and add. by C. A. Lee. 3 v. roy. 8°. shp., $21.................. *Harper.*
Copley, F: S. Plain and ornamental alphabets. maps and ill. 12°. $3.................. *Woodward.*
Copley, Josiah. Thoughts of favored hours, upon Bible incidents, etc. 18°. 50c....... *Lippincott.*
Copp, H: N. *See* United States, Mining acts.
Coppée, H: Elements of logic. 12°. $1.25.. *Butler.*
— Elements of rhetoric. 12°. $1.60.......... *Butler.*
— English literature as an interpreter of Eng. hist. ('72.) New ed. 12°. '75. $2.25....... *Claxton.*
— Field manual for battalion drill; tr. from Fr. authorities. 18°. '61. 63c....... *Claxton; Lippincott.*
— Field manual of courts-martial. 18°. $1.. *Lippincott.*
— Field manual of evolutions of the line; tr. from Fr. authorities. 18°. '61. 63c. *Claxton; Lippincott.*
— Select academic speaker. 6th ed. 12°. $2.40.. *Butler.*
— (*ed.*) Gallery of Eng. and Am. poets; with introd. essay. 20 pts. 200 eng. 4°. '73. ea., 50c.; — in 1 v. $13.50–$20............. *J. M. Stoddart.*
— *Same.* 20 pts. por. and ill. 4°. '73. ea., 50c. *S. Walker.*
— Gallery of Eng. and Am. women famous in song; with introd. 24 pts. 100 eng. 4°. '75. ea., 50c.; — in 1 v. hf. mor., $17.50; mor., $22.50. *J. M. Stoddart.*
Copsley annals. Brock, C. $1............. *Dutton.*
Copsley annals library. 4 v. 16°. $4....... *Dutton.*
Cont.: Copsley annals, by C. Brock.—Susie Grant, by C. Brock.—I must keep the chimes going, by C. Brock.—Ned, Nellie and Amy, by M. H. Seymour.
Copy. Thompson, H. M. $2............... *Dutton.*
Coquette (The). Foster, H. $1.75; $1.50.. *Peterson.*
Coquette (The). Reynolds, F. M. 75c.... *Peterson.*
Cora and the doctor. Baker, H. N. W. $1.50.. *Lee & S.*
Cora and Hattie. Sanford, D. P. 15c.; 20c... *Dutton.*
Cora and her cousins. Sanford, D. P. 15c.; 20c. *Dutton.*
Cora and the little ones. Sanford, D. P. 15c.; 20c. *Dutton.*
Cora Belmont; or, the sincere lover. 12°. $1.75; pap., $1.50........................ *Peterson.*
Cora O'Kane; or, the doom of the rebel guard. 8°. 25c.............................. *Claremont.*
Coralie and Rosalie. 18°. 55c.; 60c......... *Dutton.*
Corbesier, A. J. Principles of squad instruction for the broadsword. 16°. $1.50........ *Lippincott.*
Corbet, J: Self-employment in secret: an inquiry into the state of the soul. 18°. 25c....... *Pres. Bd.*
Corbet, Rob. St. J: The holiday camp; or, three days' picnic. ill. 16°. $1.25.............. *Routledge.*
— Ralph Luttrell's fortunes. ill. 16°. $1.75. *Scribner, W. & A.*
Corbett, A. The poultry yard and market: treatise on gallinoculture. 12°. '76. 50c. .... *Judd.*
Corbett, W: Advice to young men on the duties of life. 18°. 75c........................ *Sower.*
— Thirteen sermons. 18°. 75c................ *Sower.*
Corbin, *Mrs.* Caro. F. His marriage vow. [Fiction.] 12°. $1.50......................... *Lee & S.*
Cord and creese. De Mille, J. $1.25; 75c... *Harper.*
Corderoz, E: Father Reeves, the Methodist class-reader. [Biog.] 18°. '53. 35c. *Meth. Bk. Conc.*
Corderoz, E: *continued.*
— *Same;* with introd. by T. O. Summers. ('56.) 3d ed. 18°. '75. 50c.................. *So. Meth.*
— — *See also* Young disciples lib.
Cordery, B. Meriton. French revolution, and the wars that came of it, 1787–1815. 16°. $1..... *Estes.*
— *and* Phillpotts, J. S. King and commonwealth: hist. of Charles I. and the great rebellion. maps and plans. cr. 8°. '76. $1.75........... *Coates.*
Cords of love. Waterbury, J. R. 50c.... *Cong. Pub.*
Corfield, W. H. Lectures on water supply, sewerage, and sewage utilization. f°. (Chatham, Eng.) '74. pap., $1............................ *Spon.*
— Sewerage and sewage utilization. 18°. '75. bds., 50c. .... *Van Nostrand.*
— Water and water supply. 18°. '75. bds., 50c. *Van Nostrand.*
Corinne. *See* Stael-Holstein.
Coriolanus. *See* Shakespeare, W.
Corkhill, G: B. Rules of practice in Iowa courts. 8°. shp., $2.50; interleaved, $3.50........... *Mills.*
Corkran, J. F. History of the French National Constituent Assembly, 1848. 12°. $1.50... *Harper.*
Cormenin, L: M. de la H. Orators of France; tr. by G. H. Colton. ill. 12°. $1.25....... *Lippincott.*
Corneille, Pierre. Œuvres. 2 v. 12°. $3. *G. R. Lockwood.*
— *Same.* 12°. $2......................... *Routledge.*
— Cid (Le). Ed. by J. Bué. [Text book.] 16°. 50c.; pap., 25c. .... *Lippincott.*
— *Same.* Ed. with notes for students by E. S. Joynes. ('70.) New ed. 12°. '76. pap., 50c........ *Holt.*
— Cinna. [Fr.] Ed. by H. Tarver. [Text book.] 16°. 50c.; pap., 25c................ *Lippincott.*
— Horace. [Fr.] Ed. by P. H. E. Brette. [Text book.] 16°. 50c.; pap., 25c................ *Lippincott.*
— Polyeucte. [Fr.] Ed. by G. Masson. [Text book.] 16°. 50c.; pap., 25c................ *Lippincott.*
— Théatre. 12°. $1.50.............. *G. R. Lockwood.*
Cornelia; or, the deaf mute. 18°. 35c....... *Dutton.*
Cornelia's visit to Roseville; by author of "Kitty Dennison." 18°. 55c.................. *Pres. Bd.*
Cornelio; or, the false vocation. 18°. pap., 12c. *O'Shea.*
— *Same;* [also] Valentine. 18°. 30c........ *O'Shea.*
Cornelison, I. A. Jennie McClintock: a memoir. 18°. 60c.............................. *Pres. Bd.*
Cornelius, *Mrs.* Ma. H. Cook book; or, young housekeeper's friend. 12°. $1.50; interleaved, $2.25. *Thompson.*
Cornelius Nepos. *See* Nepos.
Cornelius O'Dowd. *See* Lever, C:
Cornell, J. H. Introit Psalms for Sundays and holy days, as prescribed by the first prayer book of King Edward VI. sm. 4°. '71. $1......... *Pott.*
— Primer of modern tonality: introd. to study of harmony. 12°. *net,* $1................. *Schirmer.*
— Tune book for the Hymnal; with indexes. 8°. '72. 75c.; $1.............................. *Pott.*
Cornell, S. S. First steps in geography. ill. 4°. 45c. *Appleton.*
— Grammar-school geog. 4°. $1.50.—New ed., rev. 31 maps. 4°. $1.75................... *Appleton.*
— High-school geog. and atlas. 2 v.: text, 12°, $1; atlas, 4°, $2....................... *Appleton.*
— Intermediate geography. 4°. $1.25.—New ed., rev. $1.50 .... *Appleton.*
— Physical geography. 4°. $1.60.......... *Appleton.*
— Primary geography. ill. sm. 4°. 90c..... *Appleton.*
— Clave de los mapas mudos de Cornell, para uso del maestro. 12°. 60c. .... *Appleton.*
— *See also* Veitelle, I. de, Novísima geografía elemental.
Cornell, Sa. B. Carl's home. ('67.) New ed. ill. 16°. '70. $1.25........................... *Hoyt.*

Cornell, W: Mason. Handy home book of 500 medical recipes and family receipts. sq. 12°. '75. 75c. *W. F. Gill.*
— History of Pennsylvania. por. and ill. 8°. '76. *$3.50; hf. mor., $4.25; shp., $4.50..*Quak. City.*
— Horace Greeley: his life and public services. 12°. $1.50....*Lee & S.*
— Robert Raikes, the founder of S.-schools. ('60.) New ed. ill. 16°. '71. 30c....*Hoyt.*
— *See also* Sumner, C: Memoir and eulogies.
Cornell, W: N. C. How to enjoy life; or, physical and mental hygiene. 12°. '58. $1.50..*Challen.*
Cornell University. The University guide: account of the buildings, museums and collections. 16°. '75. 25c.; pap., 10c....*Finch.*
Corner, Jla. China, pictorial, descriptive and hist.; with account of Ava and the Burmese, Siam and Anam. ill. 12°. (Bohn.) $1.75..*Little, B. & Co.*
— *Same.* 12°. (Bohn.) $2. *Lippincott; Scribner, W. & A.*
— Sabbath day readings; or, children's own Sabbath book. ill. sq. 16°. $1.25....*Pres. Bd.*
Corner cupboard; cont. domestic information, etc. 12°. hf. roxb., $1.25....*Lippincott.*
Corner cupboard; or, facts for everybody. ill. 12°. $1.50....*Dick & F.*
Corner cupboard series. 3 v. ill. 12°. $3.75..*Nelson.*
Cont.: Aunt Martha's corner cupboard. — Little snowdrop. — Trot's letters to her doll, by M. E. Bromfield.
Corner houses. 32°. '71. 25c....*Am. Tr.*
Corner houses; or, kindness wins, and other stories. ('68.) New ed. ill. 16°. '76. $1.15....*Hoyt.*
— *See also* New holiday lib.
Corner stall. Wright, J. McN. $1.15....*Hoyt.*
Corner stone (The). Abbott, J. $1.75....*Harper.*
Cornet (The); or, the earth in its varied phases, etc. 12°. $2.25....*Hale.*
Cornhill to Cairo. *See* Thackeray, W. M.
Cornish, O. W. Foiled: drama. 12°. pap., 15c. *De Witt.*
Cornish, W. F. Treatise on purchase deeds of freehold estates, etc. New ed., ed. by G. Horsey. 8°. '56. $1.50....*T. & J. W. Johnson.*
— — *See also* Law lib.
Cornwall, Barry (*pseud.*) *See* Procter, B. W.
Cornwall, C. M. Free, yet forging their own chains. 12°. '76. $1.50....*Dodd.*
Cornwall, *Mrs.* Su. Peyton. The Finland family; or, fancies taken for facts: tale of the past for the present. ill. 16°. '52. $1....*Dodd.*
Cornwallis, C: (*Marquis*). Answer to the "Narrative" of Sir H: Clinton. Lond., 1783. [Reprint.] f°. '66. pap., $10. — 4°. pap., $5. — 8°. pap., $2.50. *J. Campbell & Son.*
Cornwallis, Kinahan. Pilgrims of fashion. [Fiction.] 12°. $1....*Harper.*
Coronation. Bordese, L. 50c....*Peters.*
Coronation (The). Seward, T. F., Allen, C. G., *and* Mason, L. $1.50....*Biglow.*
Coroner's inquisition. Hall, A. O. 15c....*French.*
Coronet (The new). *See* Root, G. F.
Corporal's wedding: drama. 16°. pap., 15c. *French.*
Corps of Engineers. *See* United States.
Corsair. Brough, W. 15c....*French.*
Corsair (The). *See* Sand, G.
Corse de Leon. James, G. P. R. $1.50....*Harper.*
Corsican brothers. Baste, E. P., *and* Montepin, X. A. de. 15c....*French.*
Corsican brothers. Byron, H. J. 15c....*French.*
Corsican brothers. *See* Dumas, A.
Corsican twins: Ethiop drama. 16°. pap., 15c. *French; Happy.*

Corson, *Mme.* Caroline. New French instructor. 12°. '74. $1.25....*Andrus.*
— Soirées littéraires: causeries de salon. ('64.) New ed. 16°. '76. 75c....*Holt.*
Corson, Hiram. Elocutionary manual. roy. 12°. $1.50. *Desilver.*
— Handbook of Anglo-Saxon and early English; with notes, glossary and gram. synopses. ('71.) New ed. 12°. '76. $3....*Holt.*
— Syllabus of a course of lectures on the Eng. language and literature. 8°. '76. 50c.; interleaved, $1. *Finch.*
Corson, J: W. On the treatment of pleurisy; with cases showing the value of combinations of croton oil, ether and iodine, as counter-irritants in other diseases. 16°. 50c....*W. Wood.*
Cortes, Hernando. *See* Balboa, V. N. de, Cortes, H., *and* Pizarro, F.
Corthell, E. L. Levees of the Mississippi. *See* Rapid transit and terminal freight facilities.
Cortley Hall. Tucker, C. 75c....*Carter.*
Corvin, O. Secret letter writer: system of cypher writing. 18°. $1....*Radde.*
— *German.* Geheimschreiber. 18°. $1....*Radde.*
Corwin's nest ser. *See* Baker, *Mrs.* H. N. W.
Cory, I: Preston. Ancient fragments of the Phœnician, Chaldæan, Egyptian and other writers; with inquiry into the philos. and trinity of the ancients. New ed., enl. with notes and introd. by E. R. Hodges. 8°. $3.75....*Scribner, W. & A.*
Cory, N. E. (*ed.*) The Christian polymathist: essays on pastoral work, Scriptural exegesis, etc. 12°. '76. $2....*Cen. Bk.*
Coryell, M. Coal trade and labor question. 8°. pap., 30c....*Am. Soc. of C. E.*
— Conflagration in the coal at Kidder Slope; [also] Bayley's Toredo navalis; or, ship worm; Van Buren's Improvement of water front, N. Y. City; Whipple's Utica lift draw-bridge. 8°. '74. pap., 90c....*Am. Soc. of C. E.*
— Production of traffic, etc. *See* Thurston, R. H., Note on the resistance of materials.
Coryton, J: Treatise on the law of letters patent in Gt. Brit. and Ireland; with statutes, rules, etc. 8°. '55. $3....*T. & J. W. Johnson.*
— — *See also* Law lib.
Cosas de España. Byrne, W. P. 2 v. $7.50..*Routledge.*
Cosin, J: Collection of private devotions. 18°. '67. 50c....*Pott.*
Cosmic God (The). *See* Wise, I. M.
Cosmo's visit. 18°. 60c....*Carter.*
Cosmos. *See* Humboldt, A. v.
Cost of religion. Barker, J. 10c....*Mendum.*
Cost of a secret. Crow, *Mrs.* —. 30c....*Am. News.*
Costa, Mich. Eli; with words by W. Bartholomew. [Oratorio.] 8°. $2; pap., $1.60; bds., $1.75. *Ditson.*
— *Same.* Choruses. 8°. bds., $1.25....*Ditson.*
— Naaman; with words by W. Bartholomew. [Oratorio.] 8°. $2; pap., $1.60. bds., $1.75..*Ditson.*
— *Same.* Choruses. 8°. bds., $1.25....*Ditson.*
Coster Grew. Taylor, G. B. $1....*Am. Bapt.*
Costumes of America. ill. 16°. pap., 10c. *U. P. James.*
Costumes of Europe. ill. 16°. pap., 10c. *U. P. James.*
Cosy nook series. 3 v. 12°. $4.50....*Nelson.*
Cont.: Chronicles of Cosy nook, by S. C. Hall. — Ship of ice, by S. W. Sadler. — Country maidens, by M. Bramston.
Cote, C. H. O. Memoir. 18°. 50c....*Am. Bapt.*
Cote, Wolfred Nelson. Baptism and baptisteries. ill. 18°. 60c....*Am. Bapt.*
— *Germ.* Taufe u. Taufkapellen; bearb. v. P. W. Bickel. 16°. 55c....*Germ. Bapt.*
Cotel, P: Catechism of vows. 18°. '68. *net*, 50c. *Kelly, P. & Co.*

Cothran, G. W. *See* New York, Revised statutes.

Cotta, Bernh. v. Treatise on ore deposits; tr. from 2d Germ. ed. by F. Prime, jr., and rev. by author. ill. 8°. '70. $4 .... *Van Nostrand.*

Cottage (The) and its visitor. Charlesworth, M. L. 75c. .... *Carter.*

Cottage and parlor library. 12 v. 16°. $10.75; $16.75. —2d ser. 10 v. $10.75; $16.25 .... *Sadlier.*

Cottage boy (The); or, the hist. of Peter Thompson. 18°. 22c. .... *Am. S. S.*

Cottage by the lake. Claudius, M. 75c. (?) *Luth. Pub.*

Cottage by the stream. Tucker, C. 35c. .... *Carter.*

Cottage door (The). *See* Laurel ser.

Cottage evening tales. 18°. '65. 50c. .... *Cunningham.*

Cottage fireside. Duncan, H. 60c. .... *Carter.*

Cottage girl (The); or, account of Ann Edwards. 18°. 22c. .... *Am. S. S.*

Cottage lectures; or, "Pilgrim's progress" practically explained. ill. 18°. $1 .... *Am. S. S.*

Cottage lib. 5 v. ill. 16°. ea., pap., 30c. .... *Huntington.*
Cont.: Home ballads. — Hood's song of the shirt. — "Under green leaves." — Favorite English poems. — Bunyan's Pilgrim's progress.

Cottage library. *See* Goodrich, S. G.

Cottage on the cliff. Ward, C. G. 50c. .... *De Witt.*

Cottage on the rock. Shipton, A. 75c.; 25c. .... *Hoyt.*

Cottage on the shore; or, little Gwen's story. 18°. 75c. *Whittaker.*

Cottage piety exemplified. Taylor, R. $1.25. *Lippincott.*

Cottager's wife. 18°. '60. 30c. .... *Am. Tr.*

Cottagers of Glenburnie. *See* Hamilton, E.

Cottagers of Glencarran. *See* Katie Johnstone's lib.

Cottagers of the plain. 18°. 30c. .... *Am. S. S.*

Cotterill, —. Family prayers. 18°. 60c. .... *McCauley.*

Cotter's Saturday night. *See* Burns, Rob.

Cottin, *Mme.* So. Ristaud. Elizabeth, ou les exilés de Sibérie. With vocab. 12°. $1 .... *Lockwood.*
— *Eng.* Elizabeth; or, the exiles of Siberia. 32°. 38c. *Appleton.*
— — *See also* British pocket classics; — Johnson, S: Rasselas; — Saint Pierre, J. H. B. de, Paul and Virginia.

Cotton, C: *See* Walton, I., *and* Cotton, C:

Cotton, C: P. Manual of railway engineering, for the field and the office. 2d ed., rev. and enl. 8°. '74. $3 .... *Spon.*

Cotton, *Bp.* G: E: Lynch. Expository sermons on the Epistles for the Sundays of the Christian year. 2 v. cr. 8°. '64. $5 .... *Macmillan.*
— Sermons and addresses delivered in Marlborough College during six years. cr. 8°. '58. $2.50. *Macmillan.*
— Sermons chiefly connected with public events of 1854. fp. 8°. $1 .... *Macmillan.*
— Sermons preached to English congregations in India. cr. 8°. '67. $2.50 .... *Macmillan.*

Cotton, J: Answer to Roger Williams, ed. by Rev. J. L. Drinan; [also] Queries of highest consideration [by R. Williams]; ed. by R. A. Guild. [Reprint. by Narragansett Club: v. 2.] sm. 4°. '67. $8; — 4°. $10 .... *Tibbitts.*

Cotton. W., S. 50c. .... *Pott.*

Cottrell, C. C., *and* Littell, E. D. Ships and sailors, ancient and modern: progress of naval art with hist. ill. 12°. $1.50 .... *Appleton.*

Coues, Elliott. Birds of the northwest. *See* United States, *Geog. and Geol. Survey.*
— Field ornithology: instruction on collecting, preparing and preserving birds; [also] A check list of No. Am. birds. 8°. '74. $2.50 .. *Estes; Nat. Agcy.*
— — Check list alone. 8°. '74. pap., 75c. .. *Nat. Agcy.*

Coues, Elliott, *continued.*
— Key to No. Am. birds. pl. and ill. imp. 8°. '72. $7. *Estes; Nat. Agcy.*
— List of the birds of New Eng., with notes. 8°. '68. pap., 75c. .... *Essex.*
— Myology of the ornithorhynchus. ill. 8°. '71. pap., 50c. .... *Essex.*
— Ornithology. *See* United States, *National Mus.*
— Osteology and myology of didelphys Virginiana; with app. on the brain, by J. Wyman. 4°. pap., $2.50 .... *Bost. Soc. Nat. Hist.*
— Report upon mammals; — Synopsis of reptiles and batrachians of Arizona. *See* United States, *Corps of Eng.*
— *See also* Kidder, J. L., *and* Coues, E.

Coulanges, Fustel de. The ancient city: study on the religion, laws and institutions of Greece and Rome; tr. by W. Small. cr. 8°. $2.50 .. *Lee & S.*

Coule, —. *See* Williams, W., *and* Coule, —.

Coulin, Fk. The son of man: discourses on the humanity of Jesus Christ; tr. from the Fr. 12°. $1.75 .... *Claxton.*

Coulson, J. G. A. [Novels.] 4 v. 8°. ea., $1.25; pap., 75c. .... *Hale.*
Cont.: Flesh and spirit. — Harwood. — Lacy diamonds. — The odd trump.

Coultas, Harland. Animals and their young. ill. sm. 4°. '74. $2 .... *Routledge.*

Coulter, J: M. Synopsis of the flora of Colorado. *See* United States, *Geog. and Geol. Survey.*

Coulyng castle. Giberne, A. $1.50 .... *Carter.*

Council of the Orient: instructor for members of the council. [Masonic.] 32°. $2 .... *Redding.*

Council of Trent. Catechism; tr. by Rev. J. Donovan. 8°. $2 .... *Cath. Pub.*

Counsel and cheer for the battle of life. Blaikie, G. G. 75c. .... *Routledge.*

Counsel and comfort. Boyd, A. K. H. $1.25 .. **Osgood.*

Counsel and comfort for daily life. sq. 24°. '72. $1. *Whittaker.*

Counsel and encouragement. Ballou, H. (2d.) $1. *Universalist.*

Counsel to a mother. Chavasse, P. H. $1 .. *Lippincott.*

Counsels and knowledge from the words of truth. Whitfield, F. 50c. .... *Leighton.*

Counsels for young students. Vaughan, C. J. 75c. *Macmillan.*

Counsels of the aged to the young. Alexander, A. 30c. *Pres. Bd.*

Counsels of an invalid. Wilson, G. $1 .. *Macmillan.*

Counsels on holiness of life. Granada, L. de. $1.50. *Dutton.*

Counsels to Christians. 16°. 40c. .... *West. Tr.*

Counsels to converts. George, A. C. $1.25. *Cin. Meth. Bk. Conc.*

Counsels to converts. Parsons, J. U. 15c. .. *Am. Tr.*

Count and the secretary. *See* French's comic dramas.

Count Christoval. Reynolds, G. W. M. $1.75; $1. *Peterson.*

Conut Hugo of Craenhove. Conscience, H. $1; $1.25. *Murphy.*

Count Julien. Simms, W. G. 75c. .... *Dick & F.*

Count Kostia. Cherbuliez, V. $1.25 .... *Holt.*

Count Leslie; or, the triumphs of filial piety. 18°. '66. 50c. .... *Cunningham.*

Count Mirabeau. Mundt, T. $1.50; $1 .. *Appleton.*

Count Monte Leone; or, the spy in society: legend of the carbonari of France and Italy. 8°. pap., 50c. *U. P. James.*

Count of Monte Cristo. *See* Dumas, A.

Count of Moret. *See* Dumas, A.

Count of Morian. Dumas, A. 75c. .... *Dick & F.*

Count Raymond. Tonna, C. E. 90c. .... *Dodd.*

Count Robert of Paris. *See* Scott, *Sir* W.
Count Ulrich. Kingston, W. H. G. 50c.; 60c. *Am. Bapt.*
Count Ulrich of Lindburg. *See* Popular lib. of hist.
Counter attraction. Tilbury, W. H. 15c.... *French.*
Counterfeit coin. Ross, M. 30c........ *Am. News.*
Counterparts. Sheppard, E. S. $1.25; 75c. *Burnham; Estes.*
Countess and the page. Reynolds, G. W. M. 75c. *Peterson.*
Countess de Charny. *See* Dumas, A.
Countess Gisela. *See* John, E.
Countess Kate. Yonge, C. M. $1......... *Loring.*
Countess of Arnheim. Reynolds, G. W. M. 75c. *Dick & F.*
Countess of Glosswood: a Cath. tale. 12°. '70. $1.25; $1.75.................. *Kelly, P. & Co.*
Countess of Lascelles. Reynolds, G. W. M. 75c. *Peterson.*
Countess of Monte Cristo. 8°. $1.75; pap., $1. *Peterson.*
Countess of Rodolstadt. *See* Sand, G.
Country book for the field, forest and fireside. Howitt, W. $1.25.......................... *Routledge.*
Country children in town. 18°. 40c....... *Am. S. S.*
Country cousins (The). *See* Picture (The).
Country girl. Garrick, D. 15c............. *French.*
Country life. Cousin Mary. 80c........... *Lee & S.*
Country life: sel. from the poets. ill. sm. 4°. '72. $2.50. *Routledge.*
— *Same.* ill. sm. 4°. '74. $2.50........... *Putnam.*
Country living and country thinking. Dodge, M. A. $1.50................................ *Estes.*
Country maidens. Bramston, M. $1.50..... *Nelson.*
Country merchant. *See* Life and adventures of.
Country neighborhood. Dupuy, E. A. 50c... *Harper.*
Country of the dwarfs. Du Chaillu, P. B. $1.50. *Harper.*
Country parson (*pseud.*) *See* Boyd, A. K. H.
Country parson's recreations. Boyd, A. K. H. 2 v. $2.50.............................. * *Osgood.*
Country picture-book. ill. sm. 4°. 35c.... *Hurd & H.*
Country quarters. Blessington, *Countess of.* $1.75; $1.50............................ *Peterson.*
Country scenes. *See* Juvenile picture books.
Country school house (The); or, stories of every-day life among boys and girls. 18°. 35c... *Am. S. S.*
Country sights and sounds, for little eyes and ears; by author of "Five gifts." 18°. 45c... *Pres. Bd.*
Country sights for city eyes. ill. 4°. 65c... *Am. S. S.*
Country squire. Dance, C. 15c............. *French.*
Country stories. *See* Larned, A., Home story ser.
Country strolls. Mogridge, G. 60c........ *So. Meth.*
Country tales. Mogridge, G. 50c......... *So. Meth.*
Country year-book. Howitt, W. $1.50..... *Harper.*
County family (A). Payn, J. 50c...... *Littell & G.*
Coupon bonds. Trowbridge, J. T. $3..... * *Osgood.*
Couppey, J. H. Twenty five studies [for the piano]: "L'agilité." f°. $3; — in 6 bks. ea., 60c. *Brainard.*
Courbon, F. Familiar instructions on mental prayer; tr. from the French, and ed. by W. T. Gordon. 16°. '70. 75c..................... *Cath. Pub.*
Courcillon, Eug. de. Le curé manqué; or, social and religious customs in France. 12°. $1.25.. *Harper.*
Courcy, H: de. The Catholic church in the U. S.; tr. and concl. by J. G. Shea. sm. 8°. $2.25.. *Strong.*
Courier of Lyons. Stirling, E. 15c........ *French.*
Course of creation. Anderson, J. $1.50... *Wilstach.*
Course of faith. James, J. A. $1.25........ *Carter.*
Course of painting in neutral tint; with 24 pl. from designs by R. P. Leitch. obl. 4°. $2.50.. *Cassell.*
Course of sepia painting; with 24 pl. from designs by R. P. Leitch. obl. 4°. $2.50.......... *Cassell.*
Course of time. *See* Pollok, R.
Court and camp of David. Headley, P. C. $2.50; $1.50.................................. *Hoyt.*
Court and city: comedy. 16°. pap., 15c..... *French.*
Court beauties. Planché, J. R. 15c......... *French.*
Court cards. Simpson, J. P. 15c........... *French.*
Court of Claims. *See* United States.
Court of lions: burlesque. 16°. pap., 15c... *French.*
Court of love. *See* Ovidius Naso, P.
Court of Oberon. Hardwicke, *Countess of.* 15c. *French.*
Courtenay, E: H. Treatise on the differential and integral calculus. 8°. '55. $3........... *Barnes.*
Courteney, E: S. C. Dictionary of abbreviations. 16°. 10c............................... *Dick & F.*
Courtesies of wedded life. Baker, H. N. W. $1.50. *Lee & S.*
Courtier. *See* Bulwer-Lytton, *Sir* E. G. E. L.
Courtin' (The). Lowell, J. R. $3; $7...... *Osgood.*
Courting and farming. Smith, J. P. $1.75.. *Carleton.*
Courtland children. 18°. 40c. .... *Dutton.*
Courtney, *Mrs.* E. S. Twice tried; or, the three influences. ('69.) 2d ed. ill. 18°. '75. 75c. *Claxton.*
Courtney, J: [Plays.] 7 v. 16°. ea., pap., 15c... *French.*
Cont.: Aged 40: comedy. — Double-faced people: comedy. — Eustache Baudin. — Old Joe and young Joe. — Soldier's progress. — Time tries all. — A wicked wife.
— The two polts: farce. 12°. pap., 15c....... *De Witt.*
— *See also* Lacy, T. H., *and* Courtney, J.
Courts.
See under names of countries, states, cities, etc., for specific names of courts.
Courts and corners. Hosmer, M. 90c.... *Cong. Pub.*
Courtship and adventures of Captain Sly-Boots. 8°. pap., 25c.......................... *Dick & F.*
Courtship and adventures of Jonathan Homebred. ill. 12°. $1.50 .... *Dick & F.*
Courtship and marriage. Hentz, C. L. $1.75; $1.50. *Peterson.*
Courtship and matrimony. Morris, R. $1.75; $1.50. *Peterson.*
Courtship made easy. 18°. 10c........... *Dick & F.*
Courtship of Chevalier Sly-Fox Wykoff. ill. obl. 8°. 25c................................ *Dick & F.*
Courtship of Miles Standish. Longfellow, H. W. 50c. *Osgood.*
Cousin, Vct. Course of the hist. of modern philosophy; tr. by O. W. Wright. 2 v. 8°. '52. $4.. *Appleton.*
— Elements of psychology; tr. by C. S. Henry. 12°. '56. $1.75.............................. *Ivison.*
— Lectures on the true, the beautiful, and the good; tr. by O. W. Wright. 8°. '54. $2.... *Appleton.*
— Youth of Mme. de Longueville; tr. by F. W. Ricord. 12°. '54. $1.25......................... *Appleton.*
Cousin Alice (*pseud.*) *See* Haven, *Mrs.* Alice B.
Cousin Alice. ill. 18°. '74. 60c......... (?) *Martien.*
Cousin Amy, and other stories. 18°. 70c... *Pres. Bd.*
Cousin Angie (*pseud.*) Worth, not wealth; and other tales. ill. 16°. 80c.................. *Lee & S.*
Cousin Anna (*pseud.*) Singing Will; or, evil thoughts resisted. ill. 18°. '71. 35c. *N. Y. Ref. Ch. Bd.; Pres. Com.*
Cousin Anna's lib. 8 v. 18°. '61. $2.50.. *Meth. Bk. Conc.*
Cont.: Tom, the oyster boy. — My first Sunday-school. — Willie and Clara. — Sunday evenings readings. — Coney and Andy. — Freddy's fifth birthday. — Two boys side by side. — Harry Perry.
Cousin Annie; or, heart and hand. ill. 18°. 75c. *Scribner, W. & A.*

Cousin Belle (*pseud.*) Library for the little folks. 6 v. 32°. '70. $1.50 .... *Graves.*
Cont.: Laura's garden. — Addie's brother Freddie. — Magic lantern. — Lost child. — Working for papa. — Sail on the river.
— Little Addie's library. 12 v. 32°. '70. $3 .. *Graves.*
Compr.: Library for the Little folks *and* Little keepsake library.
— Little keepsake library. 6 v. 32°. '70. $1.50 .. *Graves.*
Cont.: Addie's country home. — Addie's birthday. — Working for mamma. — Addie's visitors. — Addie's new story-book. — Addie's party.

Cousin Bessie. 16°. 75c. .... *Dodd.*

Cousin Bessie series. 6 v. 16°. '63-'65. ea., 75c. *Dodd.*
Cont.: Cousin Bessie. — Alice and her friends. — The Brownings. — Toil and trust. — Tom Burton. — The Grahams.

Cousin Carrie (*pseud.*) Keep a good heart: story for the merry Christmas time. ill. 12°. $1 .. *Appleton.*
— Sun rays from fair and cloudy skies. ill. 12°. $1. *Appleton.*

Cousin Clara. G., M. H. 40c. .... *Am. S. S.*

Cousin Clara. Wise, D. $1.25 .... *H. A. Young.*

Cousin Clara's library. 5 v. 18°. $3.75 .. *Cong. Pub.*
Cont.: Ellis Amory, by M. S. Atkins. — Elsie Bailey, by S. Flint. — Clara Dwight, by S. E. Hulen. — Earnest Brownley. — Young teacher, by S. E. Hulen.

Cousin Deborah's story. *See* Guernsey, L. E.

Cousin Fannie: comedy. 16°. pap., 15c. .... *French.*

Cousin Ellen's stories. Sanford, D. P. 50c. .. *Dutton.*

Cousin Florence: comedietta. 16°. pap., 15c. *Happy.*

Cousin Florrie (*pseud.*) *See* Bliss, Flo.

Cousin from India. Craik, G. M. 90c. .... *Harper.*

Cousin Geoffrey. *See* Hook, Thdr.

Cousin George (*pseud.*) Grandma's story about St. Bartholomew's eve. 18°. 35c. .... *Pres. Bd.*

Cousin Guy. *See* Taylor, G. B., Oakland stories.

Cousin Harry. Gray, E. C. $1.75; $1.50 .. *Peterson.*

Cousin Joe. 18°. 40c. .... *Am. S. S.*

Cousin Joe's visit: Ethiop. drama. 16°. pap., 15c. *French.*

Cousin John's library. 4 v. 16°. $6 .... *Hoyt.*
Cont.: Stolen from home, by M. A. Denison. — Susan Osgood's prize. — Rescued, by J. F. Moore. — Antoine, by C. W. Denison.

Cousin Kate (*pseud.*) *See* Bell, Cath. D.

Cousin Lambkin: farce. 16°. pap., 15c. .... *French.*

Cousin Martha *and* Mary (*pseud.*) Child's story book. 18°. 40c. .... *Pres. Bd.*

Cousin Mary (*pseud.*) Country life, and other stories. ill. 16°. 80c. .... *Lee & S.*

Cousin Mary (*pseud.*) Little Italian boy. ill. 18°. 25c. .... *Pres. Bd.*
— Pictorial second book. 18°. 50c. .... *Pres. Bd.*
— *See also* Cousin Martha.

Cousin Maude. Holmes, M. J. $1.50 .... *Carleton.*

Cousin Nellie. *See* Wise, D.

Cousin Nellie's library. 10 v. 32°. $2.25 .. *Cong. Pub.*

Cousin Peter: drama. 16°. pap., 15c. .... *French.*

Cousin Phillis. Gaskell, E. C. 25c. .... *Harper.*

Cousin Regulus. Franklin, J. 83c. .... *Thompson.*

Cousin Robert's story. *See* Aunt Hattie's stories.

Cousin Sue (*pseud.*) Wild roses: a story for little readers. 18°. 45c. .... *Pres. Bd.*

Cousin Tom. Roberts, G. 15c. ... *French; Lee & S.*

Cousin Virginia (*pseud.*) *See* Johnson, V. W.

Cousin William (*pseud.*) Facts and fancies: a book of sketches and counsels for young people. 18°. 75c. .... *Nelson.*

Cousin William. *See* Hook, T.

Cousin Willie. *See* Baker, *Mrs.* H. N. W., Happy home stories for boys.

Cousin Zilpha (*pseud.*) Link, and other stories. ill. 16°. 60c. .... *Bost. Am. Tr.*
— Sunny dell. ill. 16°. '71. 60c. .... *Lothrop.*
— Twilight stories. ill. 18°. 40c. .... *Bost. Am. Tr.*

Cousins (The). 18°. 35c. .... *Cong. Pub.*

Cousins (The). McIntosh, M. J. 75c. .... *Harper.*

Coutan, A. Choix de poésies. [Text book.] 12°. $1.50. *Appleton.*

Covel, Ja., *jr.* Bible dictionary. maps and ill. 18°. '38. $1 .... *Meth. Bk. Conc.*
— Questions on Acts. 18°. per doz., $1.80. *Meth. Bk. Conc.*

Covell, L. T. Digest of English grammar. 12°. 90c. *Appleton.*

Covenant of grace. Rankin, J. 40c. .. *U. P. Bd. of Pub.*

Coventry, T., *and* Hughes, S. Digested index to the Eng. common law reports, from Henry 3d to George 3d; with table of titles and cases. 2 v. 8°. shp., $10 .... *Kay.*

Coverdale, Miles. Life and writings. *See* British reformers.

Coveted bonnet (The). *See* Leighton children.

Cow chace (The). André, J. 75c.; $1.50 ... *Clarke.*

Cowan, Fk. Curious facts in the history of insects. 12°. $2.25 .... *Lippincott.*

Cowan, J: Science of a new life. ill. 8°. (cop. '69.) '74. *$3; leath., $3.50; hf. mor., $4 .. (?) *Cowan.*
— *Germ.* Die Wissenschaft eines neuen Lebens. Nach der 20. eng. Aufl. deutsch v. H. Beverung. por. 8°. '72. $3; shp., $3.50; hf. mor., $4 .. (?) *Cowan.*
— Self-help in the attainment of perfection of character and success in life; with phrenol. and physiol. chart. sq. 12°. '70. $1 .... (?) *Cowan.*

Coward (The). Morford, H. $1.75; $1.50 .. *Peterson.*

Cowdery, Jabez F. Law encyclopedia; with forms. 3d ed., rev. 8°. '75. shp., $7.50 .... *Bancroft.*

Cowdery, M. F. Elementary moral lessons. ('56.) New ed. 12°. '69. 94c. .... *Cowperthwait.*

Cowell, Herb. *See* England, Law reports.

Cowen, P. H. Digest of the criminal laws of the U. S. 8°. shp., $7.50 .... *W. C. Little.*

Cowles, H: Critical, explanatory and pract. notes on the Old and New Test. 9 v. 12°. .... *Appleton.*
Cont.: Minor prophets, $2. — Ezekiel and Daniel, $2.25. — Isaiah, $2.25. — Jeremiah and his lamentations, $2. — Proverbs, Ecclesiastes and Song of Solomon, $2. — Revelations, $1.50. — Psalms, $2.25. — Pentateuch, $2. — Hebrew history, death of Moses to close of the Scripture narrative, $2.

Cowley, Ab. Essays. 16°. $1.25 .. *Scribner, W. & A.*
— *Same;* with life and notes. ill. 18°. '68. $1.25. *Roberts.*

Cowley, Alex. Copy-books: revised system. 12 nos. ea., pap., 15c. .... *English.*

Cowley, *Mrs.* Ha. Belle's stratagem: comedy. 16°. pap., 15c. .... *French.*
— Bold stroke for a husband: comedy. 16°. pap., 15c. *French.*

Cowper, W: Works; with memoir. por. 8°. (Dick.) 50c.; pap., 25c. .... *Am. News.*
— Complete works; with biog. by H. F. Cary. ill. 8°. shp., $2.75. 12°. $1.50 .... *World Pub.*
— *Same:* his life, letters and poems with private correspondence; ed. by T. S. Grimshawe. ill. 8°. shp., $4.50; mor., $10 .... *Mason.*
— *Same;* ed. with memoir by R. Southey. 8 v. 12°. (Bohn.) ea., $1.25 .... *Little, B. & Co.*
Cont.: Memoir and correspondence, 4 v. — Poetical works, 2 v. — Homer's Iliad and Odyssey, tr., 2 v.
— *Same.* 8 v. 12°. (Bohn.) ea., $1.40. *Scribner, W. & A.*
— *Same.* 8 v. 12°. (Bohn.) ea., $1.50 .. *Lippincott.*
— Poems. 12°. $1.50 .... *Locke.*
— *Same.* (Aldine ed.) 3 v. 16°. ea., 75c. *Lippincott.*
— *Same.* (Blue and gold ed.) 18°. $1.25 .. *Nichols & H.*
— *Same.* (Boston ed.) 8°. shp., $4.50; mor., $10. *Mason.*
— *Same.* (Cabinet ed.) 16°. $1.50 .... *Nichols & H.*
— *Same.* (Cabinet ed.) ill. 16°. $1.50; hf. cf., $3. *Lippincott.*
— *Same.* (Chandos classics.) cr. 8°. $1; pap., 75c. *Scribner, W. & A.*

Cowper, W: *continued.*
— *Same.* (Scribner's pop. poets.) ill. 12°. $1.50. *Scribner, W. & A.*
— *Same;* with memoir by J. Newton. 3 v. por. 18°. $3 .... *Osgood.*
— *Same;* ed. by R. A. Willmott; with biog., etc. (British poets.) ill. 12°. $2.25; hf. cf., $3.50; mor., $5 .... *Routledge.*
— *Same;* [also] Poems by S. Rogers. ill. 16°. $1.12; $1.35. — 32°. 85c.; $1.12 .... *World Pub.*
— Poetical works; with memoir and critical notice of writings. ill. 16°. $1.50; hf. cf., $3. *Lippincott.*
— *Same.* (Household ser.) ill. 16°. $1.50; mor., $3. *Lee & S.*
— *Same;* ed. with notes. (Chandos poets.) ill. cr. 8°. $3.75; cf., $7.50; mor., $8 ... *Scribner, W. & A.*
— *Same;* with life. (Globe ed.) ill. 16°. $1.25; hf. cf., $3.25; mor., $4 .... *Appleton.*
— *Same;* ed. with notes and biographical introd. by W. Benham. (Globe ed.) 12°. '70. $1.50. *Macmillan.*
— *Same;* ed by R. A. Willmott. (Presentation poets.) ill. 12°. $1.75; ivorine, $3; mor., $3.50. *Routledge.*
— Task. (School ed.) 18°. hf. bd., 38c. *Clark & M.; Nichols & H.*
— *Same;* [also] Table-talk, and other poems; with notes, etc., by J. R. Boyd. (Lib. ed.) 12°. '53. $1.50. (School ed.) $1.25 .... *Barnes.*
— — *See also* British pocket classics.
— *See also* Homer.
— *and* Thomson, Ja. Works; incl. letters and poems never before published in this country; with memoir of T. 8°. '73. $2.25; $2.75; shp., $2.50; mor., $5 .... *Claxton.*

Cowper, *Rev.* W: Comfort for the heavy-laden; with notice of author. 18°. 30c. .... *Pres. Bd.*

Cowperthwait, A. C. Insanity in its medico-legal relations. 8°. '76. $1 .... *J. M. Stoddart.*

Cox, E. T. Art of garnishing churches at Christmas and other festivals. ill. 8°. $1.75 .... *Pott.*

Cox, E: Companion to the sea medicine-chest, and compendium of domestic medicine; rev. and enl. by R. Davis. 12°. 75c. .... *W. Wood.*

Cox, E: T. *See* Arkansas geol. survey; — Indiana geol. survey.

Cox, E: W. Spiritualism answered by science. 12°. '72. 50c. .... *Hinton.*

Cox, G. V. Recollections of Oxford. cr. 8°. '70. $2.50 .... *Macmillan.*

Cox, G: W. Crusades. (Epochs of hist.) 16°. $1. *Estes.*
— *Same.* (Epochs of hist.) ('74.) New ed. maps. 16°. '75. $1 .... *Scribner.*
— General hist. of Greece, to death of Alexander the Great; with a sketch of subsequent hist. maps and plans. 12°. '76. $2 .... *Harper.*
— Manual of mythology. ('68.) New ed. ill. 16°. '75. $1 .... *Holt.*
— Tales of ancient Greece; with notes and table of pronunciation. 12°. (Lond.) '72. $2.75. *Little, B. & Co.*
— *See also* Brande, W. T., *and* Cox, G. W.
— *and* Sankey, C: (*ed.*) Epochs of ancient hist.: Greece and Rome. [To form 4 v.] v. 1. 16°. ea., $1. *Estes; Scribner.*
Cont.: Greeks and the Persians, by G. W. Cox.

Cox, I. Arts of writing, reading and speaking; for self improvement. 12°. $1.50 .... *Carleton.*

Cox, N. W. *See* Arkansas, Sup. Court reports.

Cox, Palmer. Squibs; or, everyday life illustrated. ill. 12°. *$2; $2.50; hf. mor., $4 ...... *Am. Pub.*

Cox, Rowland. American trade mark cases to 1871; with Eng. cases and the U. S. act in rel. to the registration of trade marks, etc. [To form 2 v.] v. 1. 8°. '71. shp., $8 .... *Clarke.*

Cox, Rowland, *continued.*
— *See also* American Law Times reports.

Cox, S: Day with Christ. 16°. '71. $1 ...... *Dutton.*
— Expositor's note book: brief essays on obscure or misread Scriptures. 12°. '73. $2.50 .. *Smith, E. & Co.*
— Pilgrim psalms: exposition of the songs of degrees. 8°. '75. $5 .... *Routledge.*
— Resurrection: expository essays. cr. 8°. $2. *Routledge.*

Cox, S: H. Interviews, memorable and useful. 12°. $1.50 .... *Harper.*

Cox, S: Sullivan. Search for winter sunbeams. ill. 12°. $3 .... *Appleton.*
— Why we laugh. 12°. '76. $1.50 .... *Harper.*

Cox, *Mrs.* W. N. ["Percy Curtiss."] Amy Garnett, the alms home girl. ill. 16°. '70. $1.25 .. *Graves.*
— Profile House (The). 16°. $1.50 .... *Graves.*
— Richard Peters; or, could he forgive him? 16°. '74. $1.25 .... *Graves.*
— Sloppy Dingle. 16°. $1.50 .... *Graves.*

Cox and Box. Burnand, F. C. 15c. .... *French.*

Coxe, Arth. Cleveland. Apollos; or, the way of God: plea for the religion of Scripture. 12°. $1.50. *Lippincott.*
— Bible rhyme (The). 12°. '73. 50c. ...... *M. Taylor.*
— Christian ballads. 18°. 90c.; $1.50; cf., $3. *McCauley.*
— *Same;* ill. by J. A. Hows. 8°. $3.50; mor., $7; $8. *Appleton.*
— Covenant prayers. 12°. '75. $1.25; $2 .. *M. Taylor.*
— Criterion (The). 12°. '66. 75c. .... *M. Taylor.*
— *Same.* 12°. $1 .... *Lippincott.*
— Hallowe'en, a romaunt; with lays, meditative and devotional. 18°. '69. 75c. .... *Lippincott.*
— Impressions of England. 12°. $1.25 ... *Lippincott.*
— Moral reforms suggested in a pastoral letter. 12°. $1 .... *Lippincott.*
— Office (An) of devotion for parochial and S.-schools. 12°. '73. 50c. .... *M. Taylor.*
— Thoughts on the services. 18°. 80c. ...... *Dutton.*
— *Same.* 18°. 80c.; $1.13; mor., $3. — 12°. $1.75; mor., $4 .... *Lippincott.*

Coxe, Marg. Claims of the country on Am. females. 2 v. 12°. '42. $1.25; $1.50 ...... *I. N. Whiting.*
— Life of John Wycliffe; with app. 18°. '40. 40c.; 50c. .... *I. N. Whiting.*
— Woman: her station providentially appointed, and the duties assigned to woman in her station. 2 v. in 1. 12°. '48. $1.25 .... *I. N. Whiting.*
— Young ladies' companion and token of affection: series of letters. 12°. '39. $1; $1.50 .. *I. N. Whiting.*

Coxe, R: S. *See* New Jersey, Supreme Court reports.

Coxe, W: History of the house of Austria, 1218–1848. 4 v. 12°. hf. cf., $12 .... *Appleton.*
— *Same.* 4 v. 12°. (Bohn.) ea., $1.25 .. *Little, B. & Co.*
— *Same.* 4 v. 12°. (Bohn.) ea., $1.40 .. *Scribner, W. & A.*
— *Same.* 4 v. 12°. (Bohn.) ea., $1.50 ... *Lippincott.*
— Memoirs of John, Duke of Marlborough. 3 v. 12°. hf. cf., $9 .... *Appleton.*
— *Same.* 3 v. 12°. (Bohn.) ea., $1.25 .. *Little, B. & Co.*
— *Same.* 3 v. 12°. (Bohn.) ea., $1.40. — Atlas of plans to same. 4°. $4.20 ...... *Scribner, W. & A.*
— *Same.* 3 v. 12°. (Bohn.) ea., $1.50. — Atlas of plans to same. $4.25 .... *Lippincott.*

Coyne, J. D. *See* Coyne, J. S. *and* J. D.

Coyne, Jos. Stirling. [Plays.] 38 v. 16°. ea., pap., 15c. .... *French.*
Cont.: Angel or devil. — Awkward arrival: comedy. — Binks, the bagman: farce. — Black sheep. — Box and Cox married: farce. — Buckstone at home: extravaganza. — Catching a mermaid: extravaganza. — Cockneys in California: farce. — Did you ever send your wife to Camberwell? farce. — Duck hunting: farce. — Duel in the dark: farce. — Everybody's friend: comedy. — Fraud and its victims. — Hope of the family: comedy. — Leo the terrible: burlesque. — Little rebel: farce. — My wife's daughter: comedy. — Nothing venture, nothing win. — Old chateau. — Our clerks: farce. — Pas de fascination: farce. — Pets of the parterre: comedietta. — Philosopher's stone: extravaganza. — Prince Dorus: extravaganza. — Samuel in search of himself: farce. — Secret agent: comedy. — Sir Roger de Coverly. — Terrible secret: farce. — That affair at Finchley: farce. — To

Coyne, Jos. Stirling, *continued.*
parents and guardians: comic drama. — Trumpeter's daughter: farce. — Unprotected female: farce. — Urgent private affairs: farce. — Vicar of Wakefield. — Wanted, 1000 milliners: farce. — Water witches: farce. — What'll they say at Brampton? comedietta. — Woman in red.

— Broken-hearted club: comedietta. 12°. pap., 15c. *De Witt.*
— Everybody's friend: comedy. 12°. pap., 15c. *De Witt.*
— Little rebel (The): farce. 12°. pap., 15c. *De Witt.*
— Pippins and pies. 16°. bds., 50c. *Routledge.*
— Widow hunt (A): comedy. 12°. pap., 15c. *De Witt.*
— Woman in red: drama. 12°. pap., 15c. *De Witt.*
— *and* J. D. Home wreck: drama. 16°. pap., 15c. *French.*

Cozy couple. Lawrence, S. 15c. *French.*

Cozy house stories. 5 v. 18°. $3. *Bost. Am. Tr.*
Cont.: Christmas at the Beeches, by I. T. Hopkins. — Cozy house tales, by I. T. Hopkins. — Lucy's fair, by M. L. Johnson. — Walter Lightfoot's pictures, by H. E. Brown. — Winnie and her grandfather, by S. P. Martyn.

Cozy house tales. *See* Hopkins, *Miss* I. T.

Cozzens, F: S. Works. 3 v. 12°. ea., $1.50. *Hurd & H.*
Cont.: Sparrowgrass papers; or, living in the country. — Sayings of Dr. Bushwacker. — Acadia, or a month among the Blue-Noses.

— Sparrowgrass papers; or, living in the country. 12°. $1.75. *Lippincott.*

Cozzens, S: Woodworth. Marvellous country (The); or, three years in Arizona and New Mexico, the Apaches' home. ill. 8°. $3.50; shp., $4.50; hf. mor., $6. *Lee & S.*

Crabb, G: English synonyms. 8°. $2; shp., $2.50. *Harper.*
— To learn and to know; or, the world's book of knowledge. ill. 12°. $1.50. *World Pub.*

Crabbe, G: Poems. (Blue and gold ed.) 18°. $1.25. *Nichols & H.*
— *Same.* (Cabinet ed.) ill. 16°. $1.50; hf. cf., $3. *Lippincott.*
— — *See also* Chaucer, G., *and* Crabbe, G.

Crabbe, W. H. *See* United States, District Court reports.

Crabtre, A. D. The funny side of physic; or, the mysteries of medicine. ill. 8°. *$3; leath., $3.50. *Burr.*

Crace-Calvert, F. Dyeing and calico printing; with account of recent improvements in use of aniline colors; ed. by J. Stenhouse and C. E. Groves. ill. 8°. '76. $8. *Wiley.*

Crack shot (The). Barber, E. C. $1.75. *Woodward.*

Cracked corn. Bullard, A. 3 v. *(?) (?)*Holland.*

Crackers for Christmas. Knatchbull-Hugessen, E. H. $1.75. *Macmillan.*

Cracraft, J. W. The old paths: essential and important truths of the Gospel. 12°. '70. $1.50. *Clarke.*

Cracroft, E: Essays, political and miscellaneous. 2 v. 12°. $5. *Lippincott.*

Cradle lands. Herbert, M. E. (*Lady*). $2. *Cath. Pub.*

Cradle of liberty. Glover, S. F. 15c. *French.*

Cradock Nowell. Blackmore, R. D. 75c. *Harper.*

Crafts, J. M. A short course in qualitative analysis; with the new notation. 2d ed. 12°. $1.50. *Wiley.*

Crafts, W: A. History of the U. S., and biog. of signers of Declaration of independence. New ed. 32 pts. ill. 4°. '75. ea., *50c. *S. Walker.*
— Pioneers in the settlement of America, 1510–1849. 24 pts. ill. 4°. '76. ea., *50c. *S. Walker.*

Crafts, *Mrs.* W: F. Open letters to primary teachers, with hints for intermediate class teachers; with an app. 12°. '76. $1. *Meth. Bk. Conc.*
— *and* Merrill, *Miss* J. B. Songs for little folks. sq. 18°. '75. 60c.; bds., 35c. *Biglow.*

Crafts, *Rev.* W: F. Childhood: the text-book of the age. ill. 12°. $1.50. *Lee & S.*

Crafts, *Rev.* W: F., *continued.*
— Ideal Sunday school (An); or, the Sunday school as it is and as it should be. 18°. '76. 75c.; pap., 30c. *Hoyt.*
— Through the eye to the heart; or, eye-teaching in the S.-school. 12°. '73. $1.50. *Meth. Bk. Conc.*
— Trophies of song. 16°. '75. $1.25. *Lothrop.*
— (*ed.*) Historic hymns; with responsive exercises. '74. 10c. *Lothrop.*

Cragfont; by a young lady of Georgia. 8°. '67. pap., 50c. *Eyrich.*

Cragin, *Miss* Ma. A. Kate Jameson. 16°. $1.25. *Cong. Pub.*
— My brother Willie. 16°. 75c. *Cong. Pub.*
— Old Bright. 16°. 45c. *Cong. Pub.*
— Work to do; or, Josiah Warren's reward. 16°. $1.25. *Cong. Pub.*

Craig, A. R. Modern palmistry; or, the book of the hand; with some account of the gipsies. ill. 12°. $1.75. *Redfield.*

Craig, B. F. Weights and measures: account of the decimal system, with tables of conversion. sq. 32°. '68. 50c. *Van Nostrand.*

Craig, J. Duncan. Scriptural coincidences. 12°. (Bagster.) $1.25. *Wiley.*

Craig, J: Universal English dictionary. 2 v. 8°. hf. roan, $15. *Routledge.*

Craig-Knox, Isa. *See* Knox, I. C.

Craigallen castle. Gore, C. G. 50c. *Dick & F.*

Craighill, W: P. Army officer's pocket companion; partly tr. from the French of M. de. Rouvre. 18°. '63. roan, $2. *Van Nostrand.*

Craik, D: The practical American millwright. ('70.) 3d ed. wood-eng. 8°. '74. $5. *Baird.*

Craik, *Mrs.* Dinah Mar. [*formerly Miss* Muloch]. Novels. 5 v. 16°. $6.25. *Routledge.*
Cont.: Olive. — Two marriages. — Agatha's husband. — Head of the family. — The Ogilvies.

— Adventures of a brownie, as told to my child. ill. sq. 16°. 90c. *Harper.*
— Agatha's husband. ill. 12°. $1.50. 8°. pap., 50c. *Harper.*
— Alice Learmont; or, a mother's love. ill. 16°. 50c. *Lee & S.*
— Avillion, and other tales. 8°. pap., $1.25. *Harper.*
— Best popular fairy stories; sel. and rendered anew. ill. 12°. $1.50. *Harper.*
— Brave lady (A). ill. 8°. $1.50; pap., $1. 12°. $1.50. *Harper.*
— Christian's mistake. 12°. $1.50. *Harper.*
— *Same.* ('75.) 3d ed. 12°. '76. 50c.; bds., 35c. *Donnelley.*
— Fair France: impressions of a traveler. 12°. $1.50. *Harper.*
— Fairy book. 18°. '68. $1.25. *Macmillan.*
— Hannah. 12°. $1.50. 8°. pap., 50c. *Harper.*
— Head of the family. ill. 12°. $1.50. 8°. pap., 75c. *Harper.*
— Hero (A). ill. 16°. 50c. *Routledge.*
— *Same;* and other tales. 12°. $1.25. *Harper.*
— Is it true? tales, curious and wonderful. ill. 16°. 90c. *Harper.*
— John Halifax, gentleman. 12°. $1.50. 8°. pap., 75c. *Harper.*
— Life for a life. 12°. $1.50. 8°. pap., 50c. *Harper.*
— Little lame prince. ill. sq. 16°. $1. *Harper.*
— Little Sunshine's holiday: a picture from life. ill. 16°. 90c. *Harper.*
— Mistress and maid. 12°. $1.50. 8°. pap., 50c. *Harper.*
— My mother and I. ill. 12°. $1.50. 8°. pap., 50c. *Harper.*
— Noble life (A). 12°. $1.50. *Harper.*
— Nothing new. 8°. pap., 50c. *Harper.*
— Ogilvies. ill. 12°. $1.50. 8°. pap., 50c. *Harper.*
— Olive. ill. 12°. $1.50. 8°. pap., 50c. *Harper.*
— Our year: a child's book, in prose and verse. ill. 16°. $1. *Harper; Macmillan.*

Craik, *Mrs.* Dinah Mar., *continued.*
— Poems. (Blue and gold ed.) 32°. $1.25; hf. mor., $2.50; mor., $3.—(Cabinet ed.) 16°. $1.50; hf. cf., $3; mor., $4 .... *Osgood.*
— Sermons out of church. 12°. $1.50 .... *Harper.*
— Songs of our youth; set to music. sq. 4°. $2.50. *Harper.*
— Studies from life. 12°. $1.50 .... *Harper.*
— Twenty years ago; from the journal of a girl in her teens. ill. 16°. 90c. .... *Harper.*
— Two marriages (The). 12°. $1.50 .... *Harper.*
— Unkind word (The), and other stories. 12°. $1.50. *Harper.*
— Woman's (The) kingdom. ill. 8°. $1.50; pap., $1. 12°. $1.50 .... *Harper.*
— Woman's (A) thoughts about women. 12°. $1.75; pap., $1.50 .... *Peterson.*
— (*ed.*) Books for girls. 6 v. ill. 16°. ea., 90c. *Harper.*

Cont.: Little Sunshine's holiday, by D. M. Craik. — Cousin from India, by G. M. Craik. — Twenty years ago, by D. M. Craik. — Is it true? by D. M. Craik. — An only sister, by Mme. P. DeWitt. — Miss Moore, by G. M. Craik.

Craik, G: L. Compendious hist. of Eng. literature, and of the Eng. lang. ('61.) New ed. 2 v. 8°. '75. $5; hf. cf., $12 .... *Scribner.*
— English of Shakespeare; ill. in a philol. commentary on "Julius Cæsar;" ed. by W. J. Rolfe. 16°. $1.75 .... *Ginn.*
— Pursuit of knowledge under difficulties, its pleasures and rewards; ill. by memoirs of eminent men. 2 v. 18°. $1.50 .... *Harper.*
— *Same;* with notes and preface by F. Wayland. 2 v. 12°. $3 .... *Harper.*
— *Same.* 12°. (Bohn.) $1.75 .... *Little, B. & Co.*
— *Same.* 12°. (Bohn.) $2. *Lippincott; Scribner, W. & A.*

Craik, Georgiana M. Cousin from India. ill. 16°. 90c. *Harper.*
— Faith Unwin's ordeal. 16°. '69. $1.25 .... *Holt.*
— Mildred. 8°. pap., 50c. .... *Harper.*
— Miss Moore. ill. 16°. 90c. .... *Harper.*
— Sylvia's choice. 8°. pap., 50c. .... *Harper.*

Craik, H: Brief reply to "Essays and reviews." 8°. (Bagster.) pap., 15c. .... *Wiley.*
— Characteristics of the languages of Asia and Europe. cr. 8°. (Bagster.) pap., 50c. .... *Wiley.*
— Hebrew language (The): hist. and characteristics. 8°. (Bagster.) $1.50 .... *Wiley.*
— Improved renderings of the New Test. cr. 8°. (Bagster.) 50c. .... *Wiley.*
— Principia Hebraica: principles of the Heb. grammar. f°. (Bagster.) $4.50 .... *Wiley.*
— Revision of our Eng. Bible. 8°. (Bagster.) pap., 25c. .... *Wiley.*

Craik, Ja. The divine life and new birth; with supplement on the incarnation. ('65.) New ed. 12°. '76. $1.25 .... *Morton.*

Crakett, W: Tyronis thesaurus; or, Entick's Lat.-Eng. dict., with index of the preterperfects and supines of verbs; rev. and enl. by M. G. Sarjant. sq. 12°. '75. hf. roan, $1.50 .... *Cushings & B.*

Cramer, J. A. The patron's pocket companion. 18°. '75. 60c.; mor., $1 .... *R. W. Carroll.*

Cramer, J. B. Celebrated instructions for the pianoforte. 4°. bds., $2 .... *Ditson.*
— Piano method. f°. bds., $2. *Brainard; Gordon; Willig.*

Cramoisy memoirs on the French colonies in North America. *See* Shea, J. G.

Cramond. Murray, W. H. 15c. .... *French.*

Cramp, J. M. Baptist history, to close of 18th century. 12°. $2.25 .... *Am. Bapt.; So. Bapt.*

Crampton, G. E. E. Silver sands; or, Pennie's romance. ill. 16°. '72. $1.50 .... *Lothrop.*

Cranch, Cp. Pearse. Bird (The) and the bell; with other poems. 16°. '75. $2 .... *Osgood.*

Cranch, Cp. Pearse, *continued.*
— Kobboltozo: sequel to "Last of the Huggermuggers." ill. 4°. $1.25 .... *Lee & S.*
— Last of the Huggermuggers. ill. 4°. $1.25 .. *Lee & S.*
— Satan: a libretto poem. 2d ed. sq. 18°. '73. 75c. *Roberts.*
— *See also* Virgil.

Cranch, W: *See* United States, Supreme Court reports; Circuit Court reports.

Crandall, Lucy S. The fairy glass. ill. sq. 12°. '71. $1.25 .... *Claxton.*

Crane, A. M. *See* Seemuller, *Mrs.* A. M.

Crane, J. Townley. Arts of intoxication: the aim and the results. 16°. '70. $1.25 ... *Meth. Bk. Conc.*
— Essay on dancing. 18°. '49. 35c. ... *Meth. Bk. Conc.*
— Holiness the birthright of all God's children. New ed., rev. and enl. 16°. '74. $1 .. *Meth. Bk. Conc.*
— Methodism and its methods. 12°. '75. $1.50. *Meth. Bk. Conc.*
— Popular amusements. 16°. $1 .. *Cin. Meth. Bk. Conc.*
— Right way: lectures on the Decalogue. 12°. '53. $1. *Meth. Bk. Conc.*

Crane, Wa. New toy book. ill. 4°. '73. $2.50. *Routledge.*
— Picture-book; ill. nursery rhymes and stories. 4°. '72. $2.50 .... *Routledge.*

Cranford. *See* Gaskell, *Mrs.* E. C.

Cranmer, T: Life and writings. *See* British reformers.

Crapsey, E: Nether side of New York; or, the crime, poverty and vice of the great metropolis. 8°. $1.75; pap., $1 .... *Sheldon.*

Crary, C: New York law and practice in special proceedings. 2 v. 8°. shp., $15 ...... *W. C. Little.*

Crasset, J. Meditations for every day in the year; tr. by Mrs. A. H. Dorsey, with introd. by C. Walworth. 12°. $1.80 .... *O'Shea.*

Crater (The). *See* Cooper, J. F.

Craven (*pseud.*) *See* Carleton, J: W:

Craven, A. W. Address to American Society of Civil Engineers, June 15, 1870; [also] McAlpine's Engineers in courts of law; Lowthorp's Cast iron for compressive members of iron bridges; Whipple's Truss bridge building; Steele's Compressed air as a motor for subterranean railways; Collingwood's Power of water to transport sand in sluices. 8°. pap., 65c. .... *Am. Soc. of C. E.*
— Large water mains: Croton aqueduct department: causes of failure. 8°. pap., 75c. *Am. Soc. of C. E.*

Craven, *Mme.* A: Anne Severin; tr. from the Fr. 2d ed. 12°. '69. $1.50 .... *Cath. Pub.*
— Fleurange; tr. from the Fr. 5th ed. 8°. '72. $1.50. *Cath. Pub.*
— *Same;* tr. by M. M. R. (Leis. hour ser.) ('73.) New ed. 16°. '75. $1.25 .... *Holt.*
— Jettatrice; tr. from the Fr. 8°. '75. $1.25; pap., 75c. *Estes.*
— Sister's (A) story; tr. by E. Bowles. 5th ed. 8°. '70. $2.70 .... *Cath. Pub.*
— Veil (The) withdrawn; tr. from the Fr. 2d ed. 8°. '75. $1.50 .... *Cath. Pub.*

Craven, H. T. [Plays.] 9 v. 16°. ea., pap., 15c. *French.*

Cont.: Bowled out: farce. — Chimney corner. — Done brown: farce. — Meg's diversion. — Milky white: serio-comic drama. — Miriam's crime. — My preserver: comedy. — One tree hill. — Post boy. — Unlucky Friday.

— Bowled out: farce. 16°. pap., 15c. .... *Lee & S.*
— Milky white: drama. 12°. pap., 15c. .... *De Witt.*
— Miriam's crime: drama. 12°. pap., 15c. ... *De Witt.*
— Post-boy (The): drama. 12°. pap., 15c. .. *De Witt.*

Craven, J. T. Child's first music book: introd. to art of playing the piano-forte. 4°. pap., 75c. *Ditson.*

Craven, M. B. Biblical chronology. 2d ed. 8°. '76. pap., 10c. .... *Colby.*
— Christianity before the time of Christ. 2d ed. 12°. '76. pap., 25c .... *Colby.*

Craven, M. B., *continued.*
— Criticism on the apostle Paul in defense of women's rights. ('72.) 3d ed. 12°. '75. pap., 25c... *Colby.*
— Criticism on the theological idea of deity. ('72.) 2d ed. 12°. '74. $1.50.................. *Colby.*
— Triumph of criticism: crit. work on the Bible and our theol. idea of deity, as received from its authors. ('69.) 6th ed. 12°. pap., 25c..... *Colby.*
Crawford, A. J. Life, trial and confession of Mrs. Fortmeyer. [In Eng. *or* Germ.] 8°. pap., 25c. *Barclay.*
Crawford, Alex. W: *See* Lindsay, A. W. C. (*Lord*).
Crawford, *Mrs.* Alice Arn. A few thoughts for a few friends. sq. 12°. '75. $2.............. *Jansen.*
Crawford, *Mrs.* M. J. E. Songs of early and later years. 16°. '71. $1.25.............. *Claxton.*
Crawford, N. M. Christian paradoxes. 12°. $1.50. *So. Bapt.*
Crawford, T. J. Mysteries of Christianity. (Baird lecture for 1874.) 12°. $3.75.. *Scribner, W. & A.*
— On the atonement. 8°. $4.50.... *Scribner, W. & A.*
— On the fatherhood of God. 8°. $4.50. *Scribner, W. & A.*
Crawford, W: Dying thoughts; or, meditations on death and heaven. 18°. 70c.......... *Pres. Bd.*
Crawley, *Capt.* (*pseud.*) *See* Pardon, G. F.
Crayon, Geof. (*pseud.*) *See* Irving, W.
Crayon, Porte (*pseud.*) *See* Strother, D: H.
Crayon miscellany; — reader. *See* Irving, W.
Craythorns of Stony Hollow. Hildeburn, M. J. $1.15. *Pres. Bd.*
Crazy Jane. Somerset, C. A. 15c........... *French.*
Creagh, W: H. Scripture catechism. 18°. per doz., $1.80.......................... *Meth. Bk. Conc.*
Cream of fun. Hood, T. 50c....... *Scribner, W. & A.*
Cream of tenors: Ethiop. drama. 16°. pap., 15c. *Happy.*
Creasy, *Sir* E: Shepherd. Fifteen decisive battles (The) of the world; from Marathon to Waterloo. 12°. $1.50......................... *Harper.*
— Rise and progress of the Eng. constitution. 12°. $1.50..... .... *Appleton.*
Creath, Jac., *jr.* Autobiography; ed. by P. Donan. 12°. $1.25............................ *Chase.*
Creation (The). *See* Haydn, J.
Creation (The); or, a morning walk with Anna. [Verse.] 18°. 30c.................. *Am. S. S.*
Creator and creation. *See* Hickok, L. P.
Creator and creation. Young, J. $2...... *Routledge.*
Creator (The) and the creature. *See* Faber, F. W.
Creatures of impulse: fairy [dram.] tale. 16°. pap., 15c.............................. *French.*
Credo. Townsend, L. T. $1.50........... *Lee & S.*
Creed and customs. Russell, G. B. $2.. *Ref. Ch. Pub.*
Creed of all men. *See* Abbey, R.
Creery, W. R. Catechism of U. S. history, with questions on Constitution of U. S. ill. 12°. '69. 50c. *Kelly, P. & Co.*
— Grammar school spelling book. 12°. '69. 60c.; hf. roan, 75c...................... *Kelly, P. & Co.*
— Illustrated primary school spelling book; with exercises in element. arithmetic. ('68.) New ed., rev. 12°. '71. 35c. — Key to exercises. 12°. '69. 50c...................... *Kelly, P. & Co.*
— *See also* Newell, M. A., *and* Creery, W. R.
Creigh, Alfr. History of the knights templar of Penna. 2 v. 12°. ea., $2.50............... *Lippincott.*
Creighton, Mandell. Age of Elizabeth. (Epochs of hist.) maps and tables. 16°. $1.. *Estes; Scribner.*
— Rome. *See* Green, J. R., History primers.
— (*ed.*) Epochs of Eng. hist. [To form 8 v.] v. 1. maps. 16°. 50c...................... *Estes.*
Cont.: Early Eng. to the conquest, by F. Y. Powell.

Cremation. Leavitt, A. J. 15c............. *De Wi*
Cremer, Hm. Biblico-theological lexicon of New Test ment. Greek. 8°. $7....... *Scribner, W. &*
Cremony, J: C. Life among the Apaches. 12°. '6 $2.................................. *Carman*
Creole. Brooks, C. S. 15c................ *Frenc*
Creole (Der). *See* Zschokke, H.
Creole ball: Ethiop. drama. 16°. pap., 15c... *Happ*
Creole wife (The); or, love and mystery. 8°. pa 25c.................................. *De Wi*
Crescent and the cross. Martyn, S. T. 90c. *Am. T*
Cressou, E. T. Report upon hynioptera. *See* Unit States, *Corps of Eng.*
Creswell, C. *See* England, Common law reports.
Crew of the Dolphin. Smith, H. $1.25....... *Dod*
Creyton, Pl. (*pseud.*) *See* Trowbridge, J. T.
Crichton, And. History of Arabia, ancient and moder 2 v. map and ill. 18°. $1.50.......... *Harp*
— *and* Wharton, H. Scandinavia, ancient and moder hist. of Denmark, Sweden and Norway. m and ill. 18°. $1.50..................... *Harp*
Crichton. *See* Ainsworth, W: H.
Cricket on the hearth. Smith, A. 15c ...... *Frenc*
Cricket's (The) friends. Johnson, V. W. $1. *Lockwood, B. & C*
Cridge, *Mrs.* Anne Denton. Man's rights. 12°. pa 15c.................................. *Dento*
Crime and the family. Nash, S. $1.25...... *Clar*
Crimeless criminal: farce. 16°. pap., 15c.... *Fren*
Criminal (The). 8°. pap., 25c.............. *De W*
Criminals of America. Farley, P. $3..... *U. S. P*
Crimson scarf (The). Legouix, J. E. $1..... *Pon*
Crimson star (The). Wright, S. A. $1.50... *Sicke*
Cringle and cross-tree. Adams, W. T. $1.25.. *Lee &*
Crinoline. Brough, R. B. 15c.............. *Fren*
Cripple (The); [also] The mountain in the plain, J. Hamilton; [also] To a boy anxious about soul, by R. M. McCheyne. 18°. 25c... *Pres. B*
Cripple Dan. 18°. 75c..................... *Cart*
Cripple of Antioch. Charles, E. $1.......... *Cart*
Cripple of Rothenstein. 18°. 30c. .... *Dutto*
Crippled William. 18°. 60c............. *Cong. P*
Cris Fairlie's boyhood. Eiloart, C. J. $2.50. *Scribner, W. &*
Crisenoy, Jul. de. Our naval school and naval o cers: condition of the French navy prior to t Franco-German war; tr. by R. W. Meade. 1 '73. 75c........................ *Van Nostran*
Crisman, E. B. Anniversary sermon. pap., 10c. (?) *Cumberlan*
— Origin and doctrines of the Cumberland Presbyteri Church. 75c.................. (?) *Cumberlan*
Crispin, *Mrs.* L. H. Piety and pride. ('60.) New ill. 16°. '73. $1......................... *Ho*
Crispino e la comare. *See* Ditson.
Critchfield, L. J. *See* Ohio, Supreme Court repor
Criterion (The). *See* Coxe, A. C.
Critic. Sheridan, R. B. B. 15c.............. *Fren*
Critical and social essays; reprinted from the N. "Nation." 16°. '67. $1.50............. *H*
Criticus (*pseud.*) *See* Orme, W.
Crittenden, S. W. Elementary treatise on book-ke ing by single and double entry; for comm schools. 12°. '52. hf. bd., 90c. — Key. hf. b 50c.................................. *Fortesc*
— Inductive and practical treatise on book-keeping single and double entry. (Counting house e roy. 8°. '70. $2.75. — Key [incl. Key to "H school ed."] hf. bd., $1............ *Fortesc*
— *Same.* (High school ed.) roy. 8°. '70. $1.50.. *Fortesc*

Crittenden, S. W., *continued.*
— Treatise on single entry book-keeping. 12°. '54. 50c. — Key. 12°. 25c. . . . . *Fortescue.*
Crittenden, *Rev.* S. W. Sacraments of the church. 16°. 85c. . . . . *Pres. Bd.*
Crivelli, D. Instructions and exercises in art of singing. f°. pap., $1.50 . . . . . . *Ditson; Gordon.*
Croaking Kate. Power, P. B. 30c. . . . . . *Am. S. S.*
Crochet worker (The). Fry, S. M. 45c. *N. Y. Ref. Ch. Bd.; Pres. Com.*
Crock of gold. Tupper, M. F. 75c. . . . . . *Peterson.*
Crock of gold: drama. 16°. pap., 15c. . . . . . *French.*
Crocker, Uriel H. Notes on common forms: a book of Mass. law. 2d ed., rev. and enl. 8°. '72. shp., $5 . . . . . . *Little, B. & Co.*
Crockett, D: Life: [autobiog.] ill. 12°. '65. $1.75. *J. E. Potter.*
Croes, J. J. R. Flow of west branch of Croton River. *See* Constable, C., Retaining walls.
— Memoir of the construction of a masonry dam; [also] Compound and non-compound engines, steam jackets, etc., by C. E. Emery. 8°. '75. pap., $1.30 . . . . . . *Am. Soc. of C. E.*
Croes, *Bp.* J: Life. 18°. 70c.; 75c. . . . . . *Dutton.*
Croff, G. B. Progressive American architecture. pl. 4°. '75. $10 . . . . . . *Bicknell.*
Croffut, W. A. *See* Draper, L. C., *and* Croffut, W. A.
Crofton boys (The). Martineau, H. 50c. *Routledge.*
— *See also* Happy child's lib.
Crofton cousins. Marshall, E. 40c. *Scribner, W. & A.*
Crofutt, G: A. Trans-continental tourist from New York to San Francisco. ill. 4°. $1.50 . . *Carleton.*
Croker, J. C. *See* Legends and fairy tales of Ireland.
Croll, Ja. Climate and time in their geological relations: a theory of secular changes of the earth's climate. 12°. $2.50 . . . . . . *Appleton.*
Croly, G: Life of George IV.; with anecdotes of distinguished persons. 18°. 75c. . . . . . *Harper.*
— Salathiel: story of the past, the present, and the future. 12°. $1.50; pap., 75c. . . . . *U. P. James.*
— *Same.* 8°. pap., 75c. . . . . . *Peterson.*
— *Same.* 16°. bds., 80c.; hf. roxb., $1.25 . . *Routledge.*
Croly, *Mrs.* Jennie C. ["Jennie June."] American cookery book. ('66.) 15th ed. 12°. '76. $1.50. *Am. News.*
— For better or worse: a book for all men and some women. 12°. $1.50 . . . . . . *Lee & S.*
— Talks on women's topics. 12°. $1.75 . . . . . *Lee & S.*
Crombie, F. *See* Roberts, A., Donaldson, J., *and* Crombie, F.
Crompton, C. *See* England, Exchequer reports.
Cromwell, Ol. Letters and speeches. *See* Carlyle, T.
Cromwell, *Mrs.* R. N. The three gifts. ill. 18°. '72. 40c. . . . . . *Am. Tr.*
Crook in the lot. *See* Boston, T:
Crook (The) straightened. Berry, E. M. $1 . . *Lee & S.*
Crooke, G: A. (*ed.*) The Bible for the young: precepts and narratives from the Scriptures presented in simple language; from the writings of I. Cobbin, M. Henry, etc. ill. 12°. '75. *$3; $3.50; mor., $4 . . . . . . *Lloyd; So. Pub.; Watts.*
Crooked and straight. Berry, E. M. $1 . . . . *Lee & S.*
Crooked (The) made straight, and other stories. 18°. 70c. . . . . . *Pres. Bd.*
Crooked places. Mayo, I. F. $1.75 . . . . . . *Dodd.*
Crooked sixpence (The). ill. cr. 16°. 25c. . . *Cassell.*
Crooks, G: R. Life and letters of Rev. J. M'Clintock. 12°. '76. $1.75 . . . . . . *Meth. Bk. Conc.*
— *See also* McClintock, J., *and* Crooks, G. R.
— *and* Schem, Alex. J. Latin-English school lexicon; on the basis of the Lat.-Germ. lexicon of C. F. Ingerslev. ('58.) New ed. 8°. '73. hf. roan, $3.50. *Claxton.*

Croppy (The). *See* Banim, J. *and* M.
Croquet; or, social prayer illustrated. ill. 18°. 25c. *N. Y. Ref. Ch. Bd.*
Croquet as played by the Newport Croquet Club; by one of the members. 16°. '65. 50c.; pap., 25c. *Sheldon.*
Croquet as played by the Phila. Croquet Club. 18°. '73. pap., 20c. . . . . . *Claxton.*
Crosby, Alpheus. Compendious Greek grammar. 12°. $1.50 . . . . . . *Potter, A. & Co.*
— First lessons in geometry. 18°. 50c. . . . . *Appleton.*
— Greek grammar. 12°. $2 . . . . . . *Potter, A. & Co.*
— Greek lessons. 12°. $1 . . . . . . *Potter, A. & Co.*
— Greek tables. 12°. 75c. . . . . . *Potter, A. & Co.*
— Outline of sentential analysis, and other grammatical sketches. 12°. '71. pap., 10c. . . *Potter, A. & Co.*
Crosby, Alpheus B. Eulogy on Nathan Lord, late Pres't of Dartmouth Coll. 8°. pap., 25c. *Hardy.*
Crosby, *Miss* F. J. *See* Root, G. F., Pilgrim fathers.
Crosby, Fk. Everybody's lawyer and book of forms; rev. by S. J. Vandersloot. ('59.) New ed. 12°. '76. shp., $2; $2.25 . . . . . . *J. E. Potter.*
— Life and public services of A. Lincoln; with his speeches, messages, etc. por. 12°. $1.75. *J. E. Potter.*
— *Germ.* Leben u. Thaten Abraham Lincoln's; a. d. Engl. v. C. T. Eben. 12°. $1.75 . . *J. E. Potter.*
Crosby, G: S. The mystery; or, platonic love. ill. 12°. $1.75 . . . . . . *Lippincott.*
Crosby, Howard. Bible manual; with maps. 16°. '69. 35c. . . . . . *Univ. Pub.*
— Expository notes on Joshua. 12°. $1 . . . . . *Carter.*
— Healthy Christian (The). 18°. '71. 50c.; pap., 25c. *Am. Tr.*
— Social hints for young Christians. 16°. 50c. *Crowell.*
— Thoughts on the Decalogue. 16°. 90c. . . . *Pres. Bd.*
— *See also* Bible, New Test.; — Pictorial life; — and for classic text-books *names* of authors.
Crosby, Nath. First half century of Dartmouth College. 8° pap., 25c. . . . . . *Hardy.*
Crosby, Sylvester S. Early coins of Am. and the laws governing their issue; [with] descript. of the Washington pieces, Anglo-Am. tokens, etc. 12 pts. ill. 4°. '73. ea., $1; — in 1 v. hf. mor., $15 . . . . . . *Crosby.*
Crosby, W. Economy of railroad curvature. *See* Jordan, G., Foundations under water.
Crosby, W. E. *See* Sudlow, *Miss* P. W., *and* Crosby, W. E.
Croserio, C. Homœopathic manual of obstetrics; tr. by M. Cote. ('53.) New ed. 12°. '66. 75c. *Wilstach.*
Cross, B. G. Piano method. f°. $3 . . . . . . *Gordon.*
Cross, J. A year in Europe. 12°. '59. $2 . . *So. Meth.*
Cross, *Mrs.* J. T. H. [Works]; ed. by T. O. Summers. ('53–'58.) New ed. 4 v. 18°. '70–'75. ea., 40c. *So. Meth.*

Cont.: Bible gleanings. — Drift-wood. — Heart-blossoms. — Wayside flowerets.

— Azile; ed. by T. O. Summers. ('68.) 2d ed. 12°. '75. $1.25 . . . . . . *So. Meth.*
Cross, Jer. L. Masonic chart. New ed., rev. by W. M. Cunningham. ill. 12°. $1.75 . . . . . . *Moss.*
— Masonic text-book; rev. by W. M. Cunningham. ill. 24°. roan, $1.50 . . . . . . *Moss; Redding.*
— Templars' chart, with tactics and drill; rev. by W. M. Cunningham, to correspond with the regulations of the grand encampment of the U. S. ill. 12°. $1.75 . . . . . . *Moss.*
— True Masonic chart; or, hieroglyphic monitor. por. 12°. $1.50 . . . . . . *Masonic.*
Cross, Jona. Five years in the Alleghanies. ill. 18°. '63. 50c. . . . . . *Am. Tr.*
— Gospel workers. 18°. '64. 25c. . . . . . *Am. Tr.*
— Illustrations of the "Shorter catechism" for children and youth. 2 v. 18°. $1.50 . . . . . . *Pres. Bd.*

Cross, Jona., *continued.*
— Pilgrim boy. ill. 18°. '57. 40c. . . . . *Am. Tr.*
— Ten commandments illustrated. ill. 18°. '62. 40c. *Am. Tr.*
Cross, Jos. Headlands of faith: dissertations on cardinal truths of Christianity; ed. by T. O. Summers. ('56.) 2d ed. 12°. '75. $1.50 . . *So. Meth.*
— Hebrew missionary: essays on book of Jonah; ed. by T. O. Summers. ('55.) 2d ed. 18°. '75. 65c. *So. Meth.*
Cross, M. H. Grand mass in G. 4°. $2.50 . . *Ditson.*
— Missa solemnis; for male voices. 8°. $1 . . . *Ditson.*
Cross and crescent. Adams, W. T. $1.50 . . *Lee & S.*
Cross and crown. McCabe, J. D. *$3.75; $6 . . *Jones.*
Cross and crown series. 3 v. sm. 4°. ea., $1.25; $1.50; mor., $4.50 . . . . *Lee & S.*
Cont.: Life's quiet hours. — Life's morning. — Life's evening.
Cross and shamrock. Quigley, H. $1.50 . . . *Noonan.*
Cross-bearer: a vision. 12°. $1; $1.50 . . *Bost. Am. Tr.*
Cross in the cell. *See* Adams, N.
Cross lady (The). 18°. 15c.; 20c. . . . . *Am. Bapt.*
Cross of Berny; or, Irene's lovers; by Mme. D. de Girardin, T. Gautier, J. Sandeau and J. Méry. [Fiction.] 12°. '73. $1.50; pap., $1 (Intern. ed.) $1.25 . . . . *Porter.*
Cross of Christ. Bascom, H. B. 80c. . . . . . *So. Meth.*
Cross of Jesus. *See* Thompson, D.
Cross of St. John. *See* French's serio-comic dramas.
Cross-purposes. De Leon, T. C. $1.25 . . *Lippincott.*
Cross (The) the way to freedom. 16°. 50c. . . *West. Tr.*
Cross way willow: the effects of good fun. 18°. 17c.; 22c. . . . . *Am. Bapt.*
Crossing the Atlantic. Hoppin, A. $5 . . . . . *Osgood.*
Crossing the line. Almar, G. 15c. . . . . *French.*
Crossing the river. Marsh, C. 60c. . . . . *Carter.*
Crossing-sweeper (The). *See* Mathews, J. A., Golden ladder ser.
Crossland, *Mrs.* Newton. Herbert Freeth's prosperity. 12°. $1.75 . . . . *Lippincott.*
— Hildred. 16°. $1.25 . . . . *Routledge.*
— Island of the rainbow: fairy tale, and other fancies. ill. 16°. 50c. . . . . *Routledge.*
Croswell, H. Manual of family prayers. 12°. '56. 50c. . . . . *Pott.*
Croswell, W: Poems, sacred and secular; ed., with memoir, by A. C. Coxe. por. 16°. $1.25. *Osgood.*
Crotch, G. R. Check list of the coleoptera of Am., north of Mexico. 8°. '73. pap., 50c. . . *Nat. Agcy.*
Crouch, Jla. Three successful girls. 12°. '71. $1.50. *Hurd & H.*
Crounse, L. *See* Nebraska, Supreme Court reports.
Crow, *Mrs.* —. Cost of a secret. ill. 8°. (Lond.) pap., 30c. . . . . *Am. News.*
— Lestelle. ill. 8°. (Lond.) pap., 30c. . . . . *Am. News.*
— Rose (The) and shamrock. ill. 8°. (Lond.) pap., 30c. . . . . *Am. News.*
— Two pearls. ill. 8°. (Lond.) pap., 30c. *Am. News.*
— Yellow diamond (The). ill. 8°. (Lond.) pap., 30c. *Am. News.*
Crowding the season: comedy. 16°. pap., 15c. *French.*
Crowe, *Mrs.* Cath. Linny Lockwood. 16°. bds., 80c. *Routledge.*
— Night side of nature; or, ghosts and ghost seers. 16°. $1; bds., 80c. . . . . *Routledge.*
— *Same.* 12°. $1.50 . . . . *Widdleton.*
— Story of Arthur Hunter and his first shilling. ill. fp. 8°. 75c. . . . . *Cassell.*
Crowe, Eyre Evans. History of France. 3 v. 12°. $2.25 . . . . *Harper.*
Crowe, J. A., *and* Cavalcaselle, G. B. Early Flemish painters: notices of their lives and work. 2d ed. ill. cr. 8°. (Lond.) '72. $4.50 . . *Little, B. & Co.*

Crowell, E. P. *See* Chase, T., Stuart, G., *and* Crowell, E. P.
Crowell, J: Republics; or, popular government a[n] appointment of God. 16°. $1 . . . . *Pres. Bd.*
Crowell, Ma. Reed. Vials of wrath. 8°. pap., 25c. *Beadle.*
Crowell, W: Church-member's handbook: guide t[o] doctrines and practice of Baptist churches. 18°. 50c. . . . . *Sheldon.*
— Church-member's manual. 12°. $1.25 . . . *Am. Bapt.*
Crowen, *Mrs.* T. J. American lady's cookery book. 12°. $2 . . . . *Dick & F.*
Crowest, F. Great tone poets: memoirs of the greate[r] musical composers. cr. 8°. $2.50 . . *Scribner, W. & A.*
Crowfield, Cp. (*pseud.*) *See* Stowe, *Mrs.* Ht. B.
Crown (The). Dowling, L. H. 35c. *Church; Dowling.*
Crown cases. *See* England, Crown cases.
Crown diamonds. *See* Ditson.
Crown diamonds: opera. 16°. pap., 15c. . . . . *French.*
Crown from the spear. Hamilton, C. V. $1.25; 75c. *Estes.*
Crown Inn (The). Reichel, W. C. $3 . . . . . *Clauder.*
Crown jewel library. 12 v. 18°. $4.80 . . . . . *Lothrop.*
Comprises School *and* Birthday stories.
Crown jewels. 24°. '69. 30c. . . . . *Lothrop.*
Crown king (The). Stewart, N. C., *and* North, J. M. 75c. . . . . *Brainard.*
Crown of glory. Straub, S. W. 35c. . . . . *Jansen.*
Crown of glory; or, faithful unto death: Scottish story. 12°. '75. $1.25 . . . . *Nelson.*
Crown of Jesus: Catholic manual. [Prayers an[d] hymns.] 18°. $1.50–$3.50 . . . . *Strong.*
— *See also* Little crown of Jesus.
Crown of life. Ogden, W. A. 35c. . . *W. W. Whitney.*
Crown of Mary; or, the rosary; by a Dominica[n] father. [Cath. prayer book.] 18°. 25c.; pap. 15c. . . . . *O'Shea.*
Crown of success. Tucker, C. 75c. . . . . *Carter.*
Crown of thorns. Chapin, E. H. $1.25 . . *Universalist.*
Crown of wild olives. Ruskin, J. $1; $1.50 . . *Wiley.*
Crown prince. Wilks, T. E. 15c. . . . . *French.*
Crown without the conflict. Lundie, R. H. 25c. *Carter.*
Crowned in palm-land. Nassau, R. H. $1.75. *Lippincott.*
Crowning testimony. Palmer, P. 25c. . . . . *Palmer.*
Crowquill, Alfr. (*pseud.*) *See* Forrester, Alfr. H.
Croxall, S. *See* Æsop.
Crucifix of Baden, and other stories. 8°. '76. $1.50. *Cath. Pub.*
Cruden, Alex. Complete concordance to the Bible. 8°. $2.75 . . . . *So. Bapt.*
— *Same.* 8°. $2.75; shp., $3.50. *Appleton; Lippincott.*
— *Same.* 8°. $2.75; shp., $3.50; hf. mor., $4.50 . . *Dodd.*
— *Same.* 8°. $3.50 . . . . *Pres. Bd.*
— *Same.* 4°. (Bagster.) $2.50. — 8°. $2. — fp. 8°. $1.75. — 32°. $1.12 . . . . *Wiley.*
— *Same;* ed. by C. S. Carey. (Globe ed.) 12°. $1.75; hf. cf., $3.50; cf., $5. — 8°. $3.50 . . . . *Routledge.*
— *Same;* ed. by J. Eadie. 12°. $1.50 . . *Scribner, W. & A.*
— — *Same.* 12°. $1.75; shp., $2; hf. cf., $3.50. — (Pocket ed.) 32°. hf. mor., $1.50 . . . *Lippincott.*
— *Same;* ed. by W. Youngman. por. 8°. $3.75. *Scribner, W. & A.*
— *Same;* abridg. 8°. $1.50 . . . . *So. Bapt.*
— *Same;* condensed. 12°. '71. $2; shp., $2.50; mor., $4.50 . . . . *Lothrop.*
— *Same;* condensed by J. Eadie. 8°. '55. $1.50; shp., $2; hf. mor., $3 . . . . *Am. Tr.*
— — *Same;* with introd. by D. King. 8°. '75. $1.50; shp., $2 . . . . *Dodd.*
— — *See also* Hitchcock, R. D., Analysis of the Bible.
— Concordance to the New Testament. fp. 8°. (Bagster.) $1. — 32°. 63c. . . . . *Wiley.*

Cruel as the grave. Southworth, E. D. E. N. $1.75; $1.50 .... *Peterson.*

Cruel brother, and other stories. 18°. 30c... *Whittaker.*

Cruel kindness: play. 16°. pap., 15c. .... *French.*

Cruel to be kind. Williams, T. J., *and* Harris, A. 15c. .... *French.*

Cruikshank, A. *See* Cruikshank, J. *and* A., *and* Fish, F. H.

Cruikshank, G: (*ill.*) Fairy library. 4 v. ill. sq. 16°. ea., pap., 50c. .... *Routledge.*
Cont.: Jack and the bean-stalk. — Hop-o'-my-thumb. — Cinderella. — Puss-in-boots.

— My sketch-book. obl. f°. hf. bd., $6; India pap., $12 .... *Sabin.*

— Three courses and a dessert: a series of tales with 50 ill. 12°. (Bohn.) $1.75 ..... *Little, B. & Co.*

— *Same.* 12°. (Bohn.) $2. *Lippincott; Scribner, W. & A.*

Cruikshank, J. *and* A., *and* Fish, Fs. H: Sabbath school gems of music and poetry. New ed., rev. obl. 8°. '50. 50c. .... *Barnes.*

Cruikshank, Ja. Exercises in analysis, parsing and composition. 12°. '69. 50c. .... *Sheldon.*

Cruise of the Betsey. Miller, H. $1.50 ..... *Carter.*

Cruise of the Casco. Kellogg, E. $1.25 .... *Lee & S.*

Cruise of the Dashaway. Nowell, H. P. H. $1. *Lee & S.*

Cruise of the Frolic. *See* Kingston, W. H. G.

Cruise upon wheels. Collins, C. A. $1 ..... *Routledge.*

Cruising in the last war. Peterson, C. J. 15c. *Peterson.*

Crum, C. C. Lectures on the beatitudes. 12°. '48. $1. *Meth. Bk. Conc.*

Crumbling path: a vision of life. 18°. 25c... *Am. S. S.*

Crumbs for little chickens. Bullard, A. 60c. *Cong. Pub.*

Crumbs from the bread of life. Green, S. G. 50c. *Perkinpine.*

Crumbs from the Master's table. Mason, W. 15c.; 20c. .... *Am. Tr.*

Crumbs swept up. Talmage, T. de W. $2; $3; $4.50. *Souder.*

Crump, A. Practical treatise on banking, currency and the exchanges. 12°. $3 ...... *Scribner, W. & A.*

— Theory of stock exchange speculation. 2d ed. 8°. $5.25 .... *Scribner, W. & A.*

Crump, W: H. The world in a pocket book; or, universal popular statistics. 12°. $1.75 .. *J. E. Potter.*

Crumrine, Boyd. *See* Pittsburgh [Penn.] reports.

Crusade of the children. 18°. 40c. .... *Am. S. S.*

Crusade of the children in the 13th cent. Gray, G. Z. $1; $1.75 .... *Hurd & H.*

Crusade of the period. Mitchel, J. $1.25 .. (?) *Lynch.*

Crusader's library. 10 v. 18°. $6.35 ...... *So. Meth.*
Cont.: Crusaders. — Glimpse of the dark ages. — Leila Ada, the Jewish convert, by O. W. T. Heighway. — Ancient Brit. church, by W. L. Alexander. — Iona, by W. L. Alexander. — Modern Judaism. — Palm tribes. — Greek and Eastern churches. — Hebrew missionary, by J. Cross. — St. Peter's chain, by C. D. Oliver.

Crusades; rev. by T. O. Summers. ('55.) 2d ed. 18°. '75. 60c. .... *So. Meth.*

Cruse, M. A. Bessie Melville: sequel to "The little Episcopalian." 18°. $1 .... *Dutton.*

— Cameron Hall: a story of the civil war. 12°. '66. $1.75 .... *Claxton.*

— Little Episcopalian (The). 18°. 90c. .... *Dutton.*

Crushed flowers (The), and other stories. 18°. 35c. *Bost. Am. Tr.*

— *See also* Uncle Reuben ser.

Crusoe library. 3 v. ill. 12°. $4.50 .... *Nelson.*
Cont.: Robinson Crusoe. — Swiss Family Robinson. — Sandford and Merton.

Crusoe library. 6 v. ill. 12°. ea., $1.50 .... *Lee & S.*
Cont.: Robinson Crusoe. — Arabian nights. — Arctic Crusoe. — Young Crusoe. — Prairie Crusoe. — Willis, the pilot.

Crusoe's island. Browne, J. R. $1.75 ...... *Harper.*

Crust (The) and the cake. Mayo, I. F. $1.75 .. *Dodd.*

Crutch (The). 18°. 40c. .... *Dutton.*

Crute, *Mrs.* Sallie Spotswood. Buds from memory's wreath. [Poetry.] 16°. '72. $1.50 .... *Claxton.*

Cruveilhier, J. Anatomy of the human body; ed. by G. S. Pattison. ill. 8°. shp., $4 .... *Harper.*

Cryptogram (The). De Mille, J. $2; $1.50 .. *Harper.*

Crystal (The). Pease, F. H. $1.50 ...... *Brainard.*

Crystal fountain series. 5 v. 18°. $2.80 .. *Nat. Temp.*
Cont.: Model landlord, by M. A. Holt. — John Bentley's mistake, by M. A. Holt. — Adopted, by E. J. Richmond. — Fatal dower, by E. J. Richmond. — Work and reward, by M. A. Holt.

Crystal gems. *See* Diamond miniatures.

Crystal spring (The new). *See* Whiting, S. K.

Crystals. Mitchell, A. M. 70c. .... *Pres. Bd.*

Cuadros infantiles. 18°. '70. 30c. .... *Am. Tr.*

Cubitt, G: Columbus; or, the discovery of America; ed. by T. O. Summers. ('56.) 2d ed. 18°. '75. 50c. .... *So. Meth.*

— Life of Martin Luther. 12°. '46. $1 .. *Meth. Bk. Conc.*

Cubitt, J. Newark dyke bridge. *See* Roebling, J., Niagara Falls and international suspension bridge.

Cudjo's cave. Trowbridge, J. T. $2 .... *Tilton.*

Cudlip, *Mrs.* Pender. *See* Thomas, *Miss* Annie.

Cuentos de la tia Luisa. *See* Aunt Louisa.

Cuentos morales para niños formales. 12 v. ill. 8°. $1.50 .... *Appleton.*

Cuentos para los niños. 32°. '68. 30c. ..... *Am. Tr.*

Cues from all quarters. Jacox, F. $1.50 .... *Roberts.*

Cuestiones sobre el evangelio de San Mateo. 18°. '67. 30c. .... *Am. Tr.*

Cull, A. Winter evening's entertainment; with words by S. Dyer. [Cantata.] 8°. '66. bds., $1 .. *Ditson.*

Cullen, W: Practical treatise on the construction of horizontal and vertical water-wheels. 2d ed., rev. and enl. 11 pl. sm. 4°. '71. $5 ..... *Spon.*

Cullerier, A. Atlas of venereal diseases; tr. and ed. by F. J. Bumstead. 26 col. pl. 4°. $17; — in 5 pts. ea., $3 .... *Lea.*

Cullis, C. (*ed.*) Faith hymns. 32°. 25c.; 15c. *Willard.*

Cullum G: W. Systems of military bridges, in use by the U. S., the European powers, and in British India. 2d ed. pl. 8°. '69. $3.50 .. *Van Nostrand.*

Culm rock. Bradley, W. I. $1.50 .... *Hoyt.*

Culprit fay (The). *See* Drake, J. R.; — Ensign, J. L.

Culture and anarchy. Arnold, M. $2 .... *Macmillan.*

Culture and the Gospel. McCall, S. 75c.; $1; 60c. *Randolph.*

Culture (The) demanded by modern life. Youmans, E. L. $2 .... *Appleton.*

Culture of pleasure. 12°. $2 .... *Carter.*

Culver, Newell. Methodism forty years ago and now. 12°. '73. $1.25 .... *Meth. Bk. Conc.*

Culver, R: American guitarist. 8°. '51. pap., 60c. *Ditson.*

— Guitar instructor. 8°. '46. bds., $1.50 ..... *Ditson.*

— Practical reader. 12°. '55. $1 .... *Lippincott.*

— Questional reader and union speaker. 12°. $1. *Lippincott.*

Culver, S. Fruit preserver's manual. 18°. pap., 15c. *Darrow.*

Culverwell, Rob. J. Diseases of winter: consumption, coughs, colds, etc.; their remedial and avertive treatment. 8°. pap., 25c. .... *U. P. James.*

— Guide to health and long life. 8°. pap., 25c. *U. P. James.*

— How to be happy: laws of life, health and happiness. 8°. pap., 25c. .... *U. P. James.*

Cumberers (The), and other tales; rev. by A. G. Haygood. ('73.) 2d ed. 16°. '76. 75c. .... *So. Meth.*

Cumberland, R: Jew: comedy. 16°. pap., 15c. *French.*

— West Indian: comedy. 16°. pap., 15c. .... *French.*

— Wheel of fortune: comedy. 16°. pap., 15c. *French.*

— *See also* Observer (The).

Cumberstone contest (The); by author of "The best cheer." ill. 16°. '73. $1.25 .... *Dodd.*
Cumming, J: God in history and in science. 12°. '51. 75c. .... *Meth. Bk. Conc.*
— Is Christianity from God? 18°. 75c....... *Pres. Bd.*
— Romanism as it is: an oration. 18°. pap., 10c. *Pres. Bd.*
Cumming, R. Gordon. Five years of a hunter's life in south Africa. 2 v. ill. 12°. $3........ *Harper.*
— Wild men and wild beasts: scenes in camp and jungle. ill. 12°. '75. $1.50 .... *Scribner.*
Cummings, A. W. Life and death of Mrs. F. A. Cummings. ('59.) 2d ed. por. 18°. '76. 75c. *So. Meth.*
Cummings, J. W. Italian legends and sketches. 12°. $1 .... *Strong.*
— Spiritual progress. 12°. $1.50 .... *O'Shea.*
Cummings, M. F., *and* Miller, C. C. Architectural details. ('65.) 5th ed. ill. 4°. '76. $10.. *Bicknell.*
Cummings, M. J. ["Captain Carnes."] Little Toss. ill. 16°. '72. $1.25 .... *Lothrop.*
— Uncle Anthony. ill. 16°. '73. $1.25...... *Lothrop.*
Cummings, M. S. Mabel Vaughan. 12°. '47. $1.75. *Nichols & H.*
Cummings, S: The western pilot; cont. charts of the Ohio and of the Mississippi, with directions for navigating, etc. 8°. hf. bd., 75c.... *U. P. James.*
Cummings, T. J. *See* Duffy, T., *and* Cummings, T. J.
Cummins, J: *See* Idaho, Supreme Court reports.
Cummins, Mar. S. El Fureidis. 16°. '60. $1.75. *Osgood.*
— The lamplighter. 16°. '54. $1.75......... *Osgood.*
Cummiskey, Eug. (*ed.*) Sunday school prayer and hymn book. [Catholic.] ill. 32°. 40c.–$3. *Cummiskey.*
Cummiskey's juvenile lib. *See* Florie's ser.
Cundiff, B. A. Theological catechism. 18°. '72. hf. bd., 20c. .... *So. Meth.*
Cunnabel, J. S. Accordion: airs arranged as progressive lessons for the accordion. 2d ed., rev. and enl. obl. 8°. '50. pap., 50c. .... *Ditson.*
Cunning workmen. Alden, I. M. $1.25.... *Lothrop.*
Cunning workmen series. 4 v. 16°. $5.... *Lothrop.*
Cont.: Cunning workmen, by Pansy. — Grandpa's darling, by Pansy. — Mrs. Deane's way, by F. Huntington. — Dr. Deane's way, by Pansy and F. Huntington.
Cunningham, Allan. Lives of eminent painters and sculptors. 5 v. por. 18°. $3.75...... *Harper.*
— Lord Roldan. [Fiction.] 12°. $1.50..... *Harper.*
Cunningham, D: Tables for facilitating the calculation of earthworks in the construction of railways, roads, canals, etc. roy. 8°. $4.25.. *Spon.*
Cunningham, E: Seven autumn leaves from fairy land; with etchings. sq. 16°. '73. $1.50.. *Williams.*
Cunningham, *Mrs.* V. Madelaine: drama. 16°. pap., 15c. .... *French.*
Cunningham, W: Discussions on church principles. 8°. $5 .... *Scribner, W. & A.*
— Historical theology: review of the principal doctrinal discussions in the Christian church since the apostolic age. 2 v. 8°. $10...... *Scribner, W. & A.*
— Reformers (The) and theology of the reformation. 8°. $5 .... *Scribner, W. & A.*
— Selection of sermons, 1828–1860. 8°. $5. *Scribner, W. & A.*
Cunningham, W: M. Manual of the ancient and accepted Scottish rite; with rev. constitution. [Masonic.] 12°. $2......... *Moss; Redding.*
— Masonic funeral service and order of exercises for a sorrow-lodge. 12°. 25c.; pap., 15c....... *Moss.*
Cunnington, W: H. History of the Polaris expedition. *See* Sargent, E., Wonders of the Arctic world.
Cunnyngham, W. G. E. Thoughts on missions: the principles, facts and obligations of Christian missions. 12°. '74. pap., 15c........ *So. Meth.*

Cuore, L. B. Italian conversation grammar on Otto's system. ('64.) New ed. 12°. '76. hf. roan $1.75. — Key. 75c. .... *Holt*
Cup (The) and the cross. *See* Dale, J. W.
Cup-bearer (The). Brown, H. E. $2.50.. *Bost. Am. Tr*
Cup of tea. *See* Nuitter, C., *and* Derley, J.
Cupboard love. *See* Hay, F.
Cupid and Chow-chow. Alcott, L. M. $1... *Roberts*
Cupid and Psyche. Burnand, F. C. 15c..... *French*
Cupid in waiting: comedy. 16°. pap., 15c. .. *French*
Cupid's eye-glass. Picton, T. 15c.......... *De Witt*
Cupid's yokes. Heywood, E. H. 15c. ..... *Mendum*
Cupper, R. A. Universal stair-builder; [with] plans 4°. $3.50 .... *Woodward*
— *Same;* with plans and pl. 4°. '51. $7.50... *Baird*
Cupples, *Mrs.* Ann Jane. Adventures of Mark Willis ill. 16°. 75c. .... *Nelson*
— Alice Leighton; — Bertha Marchmont; — Bluff cragg — Carry's rose. *See* Merry heart lib.
— Driven to sea; or, the adventures of Norrie Seaton 16°. $1.50 .... (?) *Shepard*
— — *See also* Standard sea tales.
— Fanny Sylvester. *See* Merry heart lib.
— Grandpapa's keepsakes. ill. 18°. 75c....... *Nelson*
— *Same.* 16°. 85c. .... *Tibbals*
— Hugh Wellwood's success. *See* Merry heart lib.
— Might and right books. 12 v. ill. 16°. $1.80.. *Nelson*
Cont.: Wisdom of forethought. — Might and right. — Folly of flattery. — Wisdom of experience. — Self-reliance. — Justice and judgment. — Time for everything. — Folly of revenge. — Theory and practice. — Vanity and ambition. — Truth and honesty. — Selfishness and kindness.
— My pretty scrap book. *See* Peep show ser.
— Sights at a peep show; or, pretty pictures and pleasing stories. 18°. '75. 50c......... *Nelson*
— — *See also* Peep show ser.
— Singular creatures; or, Tappy's chicks. ill. 16° $1.50 .... *Lee & S.*
— Story of Dollikins. ill. 32°. $1; $1.50.... *Nelson.*
— Story of our doll. 12°. 90c. .... *Nelson.*
— Tappy's chicks, and other links between nature and human nature. ill. cr. 8°. '72. $2... *Routledge.*
— — *See also above* Singular creatures.
— Vea and her cousins. *See* Merry heart lib.
— Walks and talks with grandpapa. ill. 18°. '75. 50c. .... *Nelson*
— — *See also* Peep show ser.
Cupples, G: Deserted ship: adventures in the early life of Cupples Howe, mariner. ill. 16°. $1.50. (?) *Shepard.*
— — *See also* Standard sea tales.
— Green hand (The): a "short yarn." 8°. pap., 75c. *Harper.*
— *Same.* 16°. bds., 80c. .... *Routledge.*
Cupples, *Mrs.* G: *See* Cupples, *Mrs.* Ann Jane.
Curate and the rector: a domestic story. 12°. $1.75 *Routledge.*
Curate in charge. Oliphant, M. O. W. 50c... *Harper.*
Curate of Ellerton. ('67.) New ed. ill. 16°. '70. 80c. *Hoyt.*
Curate of Linwood. 18°. 60c. .... *Whittaker.*
Curate's discipline. Eiloart, C. J. 50c....... *Harper.*
Curate's home. Giberne, A. $1.25.......... *Carter.*
Cure, E. Capel. Seven words of Christ on the cross sermons. fp. 8°. '68. $1.25 .... *Macmillan*
Cure for coquettes: comedy. 16°. pap., 15c. *Happy.*
Cure for the fidgets. Williams, T. J. 15c.... *French.*
Cure for the heart-ache. Morton, T. 15c. ... *French.*
Cure for love. Parry, T. 15c. .... *French.*
Cure for thought-taking. MacDonald, G. 50c.; 10c *Crowell.*
Curé manqué (Le). Courcillon, E. de. $1.25.. *Harper.*
Curfew. Tobin, J. 15c. .... *French.*
Curfew chimes. Macduff, J. R. 75c. .... *Carter.*

Curiosities of animal life. 12°. '50. 75c. *Meth. Bk. Conc.*

Curiosities of Christian missions. 18°. 30c.; 40c. *Am. Bapt.*

Curiosities of human nature. *See* Goodrich, S. G.

Curiosities of the law reporters. Heard, F. F. $2. *Lee & S.*

Curiosity; or, the young footman. 18°. 20c.; 25c. *Am. Bapt.*

Curious case: drama. 16°. pap., 15c. .... *French.*

Curious chapter. Blackburn, W. M. 65c... *Pres. Bd.*

Curious eyes (The). 18°. 25c. .... *Am. S. S.*

Curious facts for little people about animals. ill. 16°. $1 .... *Cin. Meth. Bk. Conc.*

Curious myths of the middle ages. *See* Gould, S. B.

Curious Tom. *See* Bertie's lib.; — Moss rose ser.

Curley, Edn. A. Nebraska: its advantages, resources and drawbacks. maps and ill. 8°. '75. $4. *Am. News.*

Curling, H: Love at first sight. 8°. pap., 50c. *Peterson.*

Curnock, N. Life of John Wesley; rev. by T. O. Summers. ('55.) 2d ed. 18°. '75. 40c... *So. Meth.*

Curo, *Mlle.* —. La jeune savante. *See* Souvestre, E.

Curr, Jos. Familiar instructions in the faith and morality of the Cath. church. 18°. 40c... *Cummiskey.*

Curran, J: Philpot. Speeches, while at the bar; with memoir and introd. notes; ed. by J. A. L. Whittier. 2d ed. por. 8°. '72. $3.50; shp., $4; hf. cf., $5 .... *Callaghan.*

— *See also* Sheil, R. L., *and* Curran, J. P.

Curran, W: H: Life of J. Philpot Curran; with notes and add. by R. S. Mackenzie. 12°. $1.75; hf. cf., $3.50 .... *Widdleton.*

Currents and counter-currents in medical science. Holmes, O. W. $1.75 .... *Osgood.*

Currer Lyle. Reeder, L. $1.75; $1.50..... *Peterson.*

Currie, Gilb. E. United States insurance almanac and statistical register. [Annual.] 8°. '76. $2.. *Currie.*

Currie, Ja. Observations on the Scottish peasantry. *See* Burns, R., Works.

Currier, Amos N. Tables of Latin suffixes. 12°. '73. 50c. .... *Eldredge.*

Currier, Sophronia. Alice Tracy; or, faint yet pursuing. 16°. '70. $1.25 .... *Dutton.*

— By the sea. 12°. '71. $1.25 .... *Dutton.*

Curry, Dan. Life story of Bp. W. D. Clark. 12°. '73. $1.50 .... *Meth. Bk. Conc.*

Curse of Clifton. Southworth, E. D. E. N. $1.75; $1.50 .... *Peterson.*

Curse of gold. Stephens, A. S. $1.75; $1.50.. *Peterson.*

Curse of immortality. Evans, A. E. $2.25.. *Macmillan.*

Curse of mammon. Reynoldson, T. H. 15c... *French.*

Curse of the village. Conscience, H. $1; $1.25. *Murphy.*

Curteis, Arth. M. The Roman empire, A. D. 395–800. 12°. $1.50 .... *Lippincott.*

Curteis, G: Herb. Dissent in relation to Church of England. *See* Bampton lectures.

Curteis, W. C. *See* England, Ecclesiastical reports.

Curtis, A. W. *and* D. S. The spirit of seventy-six; or, the coming woman; [also] A change of base; [also] Dr. Mondschein: dramas. 16th ed. 16°. '74. $1; $1.75; pap., 75c....... *Little, B. & Co.*

Curtis, B. R. Digest of U. S. Supreme Court decisions, to 1855. 8°. '64. shp., $5.50... *Little, B. & Co.*

— *See also* United States, Circuit Court reports; Sup. Court decisions.

Curtis, D. S. *See* Curtis, A. W. *and* D. S.

Curtis, G: H: Little singer. 16°. '57. 60c... *Barnes.*

— Musical monitor: vocal method for schools. ('70.) New ed. obl. roy. 8°. '76. bds., $1...... *Pond.*

Curtis, G: H: *continued.*

— School vocalist: musical manual for academies, etc. 12°. '56. $1 .... *Barnes.*

— *and* Bourne, W: O. Centennial school singer. obl. 16°. '76. bds., 40c. .... *Biglow.*

— *and* Nash, Fs. H: Grammar school vocalist: choruses, glees, etc. 8°. '60. bds., $1 .... *Ditson.*

Curtis, G: Ticknor. American conveyancer (The): legal forms and instruments in use throughout the U. S. 2d ed., rev. and enl. by M. H. Durgin. cr. 8°. '71. shp., $2 .... *Little, B. & Co.*

— Equity precedents: supplement to Story's "Treatise on equity pleadings." 4th ed. 8°. '69. shp., $6. *Little, B. & Co.*

— History of the origin, formation and adoption of the Constitution of the U. S. 2 v. 8°. $6; shp., $8; hf. cf., $10.50 .... *Harper.*

— Life of Dan. Webster. 2 v. por. and wood-cuts. 8°. *10; shp., $12; hf. mor., $14. — 2 v. sm. 8°. *$6; hf. mor., $12 .... *Appleton.*

— Treatise on the law of patents in the U. S. 4th ed. 8°. '73. shp., $6 .... *Little, B. & Co.*

— *See also* Massachusetts, Supreme Court reports; — United States, Digest.

Curtis, G: W: Howadji in Syria. 12°. $1.50.. *Harper.*

— Lotus-eating: a summer book. ill. 12°. $1.50.. *Harper.*

— Nile notes of a Howadji. 12°. $1.50...... *Harper.*

— Potiphar papers. ill. 12°. $1.50.......... *Harper.*

— Prue and I. 12°. $1.50 .... *Harper.*

— Trumps. [Fiction.] ill. 12°. $2 .... *Harper.*

— *See also* American Soc. Sci. Assoc.

Curtis, J. T., *and* Lillie, J. Epitome of homœop. practice. 18°. 75c. .... *Boericke.*

Curtis, Laura J. Christine; or, woman's trials and triumphs. 12°. $1.50 .... *De Witt.*

Curtis, M. A. *See* North Carolina geol. and nat. hist. survey.

Curtis, Newton M. Black ranger; or, the maid and the marksman. 8°. pap., 25c. .... *De Witt.*

Curtis, Rob. All-hallow eve; or, the test of futurity, and other stories. 2d ed. 8°. '71. $2.. *Cath. Pub.*

Curtis, T. F. Progress of Baptist principles in the last hundred years. 16°. '74. $1.50 .... *Lothrop.*

Curtiss, N. P. B. Piano method. f°. $2.50.. *Gordon.*

— Progressive method for the Spanish guitar. f°. '50. bds., $3 .... *Ditson.*

— *and* Behr, C: New method for the zither: German and English music. 4°. '75. bds., $1.50.. *Ditson.*

Curtiss, Percy (*pseud.*) *See* Cox, *Mrs.* W. N.

Curtius, Ern. History of Greece; tr. by A. W. Ward; rev. after latest Germ. ed. by W. A. Packard. ('70–'74.) 5 v. cr. 8°. '76. ea., $2.50; hf. cf., $4.50 .... *Scribner.*

Curtius, G: Grammar of the Greek language; tr. from the Germ., and ed. by W. Smith. 12°. $2. *Harper.*

— — Appendix to same. *See* Sewell, J. B.

Curtius Rufus, Quintus. De gestis Alexandri Magni; rec. L. Schmitz et C. G. Zumpt. roy. 18°. '52. 80c.; hf. bd., 90c. .... *Lea.*

— *Same;* ed. and ill. with Eng. notes by Prof. Crosby. 12°. $1.50 .... *Appleton.*

— *See also* Gardner, F., Gay, A. M., *and* Buck, A. M.

Curwen, H: History of booksellers. ill. and por. 12°. $3 .... *Routledge; Scribner, W. & A.*

Curwen, Maskell E. Manual upon the preparation of abstracts of title to real property; with ref. to statutes of Penn., Ohio, Ky., etc. 12°. '67. $1.50; shp., $1.75 .... *Clarke.*

— *See also* Ohio, Public statutes.

Curzon, Rob. Ancient monasteries of the east. 12°. '54. shp., $1.50 .... *Barnes.*

— Armenia: a year at Erzeroom and on the frontiers of Russia, Turkey and Persia. map and ill. 12°. $1.25 .... *Harper.*

Cusack, Ma. Fes. (*religious name* Ma. Fes. Clare). ["Nun of Kenmare."] Advice to Irish girls in Am. 12°. $1........................*McGee.*
— Daily steps to heaven. 12°. $1.50; $2....*Sadlier.*
— History of Ireland. 8°. $4; hf. mor., $5; hf. cf., $6; mor., $8........................*Sadlier.*
— Hornehurst rectory. cr. 12°. $2.50; $3....*Sadlier.*
— Life of Daniel O'Connell. 8°. *$3.50; hf. mor., $5; hf. cf., $6........................*Sadlier.*
— *Same.* 35 pl. 4°. *$10; hf. mor., $15; mor., $17; $18; $20; — in 35 pts. 4°. ea., *25c....*Sadlier.*
— Life of Father Matthew. 16°. $1........*Sadlier.*
— St. Patrick's manual. 18°. $1–$50........*Sadlier.*

Cush going to mill. *See* Todd, J.

Cushing, Clb. Treaty of Washington: its negotiation, execution, and the discussions relating thereto. cr. 8°. $2........................*Harper.*

Cushing, Luther Stearns. Elements of the law and practice of legislative assemblies in the U. S. 2d ed. 8°. '66. shp., $6.......*Little, B. & Co.*
— Introduction to the study of the Roman law. 12°. '54. $1........................*Little, B. & Co.*
— Rules of proceedings in deliberative assemblies. 16°. 65c........................*Thompson.*

Cushion and corner library. *See* Greene, *Mrs.* L. L.

Cushions and corners. *See* Greene, *Mrs.* L. L.

Cushman, H: Wyles. Historical and biog. genealogy of the descendants of Robert Cushman, 1617–1855. 8°. '55. $6....................*N. E. Hist. Gen.*

Cushman, J: F. *See* Mississippi, High Court of Errors and Appeals reports.

Cushman, R. W. Grace and apostleship, ill. in the life of Judson. 8°. 40c....................*Am. Bapt.*
— Pure Christianity (A) the world's only hope. 18°. 75c. *Sheldon.*

Custer, *Mrs.* E. S. Ella Ross. ill. 16°. '67. 70c. *Am. Tr.*

Custer, G. A. My life on the plains. ill. 8°. $2. *Sheldon.*

Customs and manners of the Bedouin Arabs. 18°. 50c. *Am. S. S.*

Cut off with a shilling. Smith, S. T. 15c. *De Witt; French.*

Cuthbertson, Fs. Euclidian geometry. 12°. '74. $1.75........................*Macmillan.*

Cutler, Helen R. Jottings from life; or, passages from the diary of an itinerant's wife. 16°. $1. *Cin. Meth. Bk. Conc.*

Cutler, H: Ste. Canticles of the Church for morning and evening prayers; pointed and arranged for chanting. 16°. '66. 50c.; pap., 25c.........*Dutton.*
— Masonic harmonia: collection of music, orig. and selected. 12°. '70. 75c................*Macoy.*
— *Same.* 12°. '62. $1........................*Masonic.*
— Trinity anthems. ('65.) New ed. 4°. '76. $3..*Pond.*
— Trinity psalter; with introd. by Rev. M. Dix. 16°. '58. $1........................*Dutton.*

Cutler, S: Name (The) above every name; or, devotional meditations; with a text for every day. 12°. '74. $1; $1.50; $2..............*Lothrop.*
— Work of the Spirit: meditations on the nature and work of the Holy Ghost. 12°. $1..*Bost. Am. Tr.*

Cutter, Calv. Anatomy, physiology and hygiene. ill. 12°. hf. roan, $1.70................*Lippincott.*
— First book on anatomy, physiology and hygiene. ill. 12°. hf. roan, 80c................*Lippincott.*
— New analytic anatomy, physiology and hygiene, human and comparative. ill. 12°. hf. roan, $1.70. *Lippincott.*
— New first book on anatomy, physiology and hygiene, human and comparative. ill. 12°. hf. roan, 90c. *Lippincott.*
— Questions, diagrams and illustrations, for unific and synthetic review of analytical anatomy. ill. 12°. pap., 15c........................*Lippincott.*
— Second book on analytic anatomy, physiology, etc. ill. 12°. hf. roan, $1.50..............*Lippincott.*

Cutter, Eph. Contribution to the treatment of the versions and flexions of the unimpregnated uterus. ('71.) New ed. ill. 16°. '76. $1.50..*Jas. Campbell.*
— Thyrotomy for the removal of laryngeal growths: modified. ill. 8°. '71. pap., 50c...*Jas. Campbell.*

Cutter, *Mrs.* Eunice P. Human and comparative anatomy, physiology and hygiene; for schools. ill. 12°. '52. hf. bd., 50c...*Claxton; Lippincott.*

Cutter, J. E. Faith Duncan; or, dare to do right. 16°. 90c........................*Cong. Pub.*

Cutts, J. Madison. Brief treatise upon constitutional and party questions, as received from the late S. A. Douglas. 12°. $1.25............*Appleton.*

Cuyler, G: W. *See* Wells, D. A., Dodge, E., *and* Cuyler, G. W.

Cuyler, T. L. Cedar Christian, and other practical papers and personal sketches. ('64.) New ed. 16°. '73. 90c........................*Carter.*
— Empty crib (The): memorial of little Georgie. ('68.) New ed. 24°. '73. $1....................*Carter.*
— Heart-life. 18°. '71. 50c.; 75c.; mor., $1.50. *Am. Tr.*
— Stray arrows. ('51.) New ed. 18°. '72. 60c. *Carter.*
— Thought hives. ('72.) New ed. por. 12°. '74. $1.75. *Carter.*
— *See also* Hall, J., Cuyler, T. L., *and* Beecher, H. W.

Cvriasvm urbis (The new). *See* Wood, S.

Cyclopædia of education. *See* Kiddle, H., *and* Schem, A. J.

Cyclopædia of practical medicine; by R. Dunglison, J. Forbes, A. Tweedie and J. Conolly. 4 v. roy. 8°. $11; leath., $15........................*Lea.*

Cyclopædic science simplified. *See* Pepper, J. H.

Cyclopedia of female poets. ill. 8°. $3; mor., $7; $7.50........................*Lippincott.*

Cyclopedia of things worth knowing. roy. 8°. '74. *$3.75; shp., $4.50....................*Intern.*

Cyclops. *See* Euripides.

Cymberline. *See* Shakespeare, W.

Cymon and Iphigenia. Planché, J. R. 15c...*French.*

Cynic: play. 16°. pap., 15c................*French.*

Cypress wreath (The). *See* Griswold, R. W.

Cyprianus, Thascius Cæcius, *St.* Writings; tr. by R. E. Wallis. (Ante-Nicene Christ. lib.) 2 v. 8°. ea., $3..................*Scribner, W. & A.*

Cyril Ashley. *See* Tucker, *Mrs.* C.

Cyrilla. Tautphoeus, J. M. (*Baroness*) v. $1.75; 75c........................*Peterson.*

Cyrilla Maude's first love. Wood, E. P. 25c. *Peterson.*

Cyril's success. Byron, H. J. 15c...*De Witt; French.*

Cyrus *the Great.* Life; rev. by T. O. Summers. ('55.) 2d ed. 18°. '75. 50c................*So. Meth.*

Cythara (The). Woodbury, I. B. $1.50..*Huntington.*

Czar (The) and the sultan. Gilson, A. 75c. *Harper.*

Czarina (The). Hofland, B. 50c...........*Harper.*

Czerny, C: Letters to young ladies on the art of playing the piano. 12°. 60c.......*Ditson; Gordon.*
— — *See also* Beyer, F., Preliminary school for the piano-forte; — Burgmuller, F., Instructor for the piano forte; — Burrowes, J. F., Piano forte primer; — Lenhart, —, Elements of music.
— Piano-forte method. 4°. bds., $3.75.......*Ditson.*
— Theoretical and practical school for the piano-forte; abridg. by E. L. White. 4°. bds., $2...*Ditson.*

D., A. C. Sylvia and Janet; or, too quickly judged. ill. 16°. $1.75..............*Scribner, W. & A.*

Dabb, A. N. Practical designs for country school houses. 4°. hf. bd., $5....................*Keystone.*

Dablon, Cl. Relation de ce qui s'est passé de plus remarquable aux missions des Pères de la Compagnie de Jésus en la Nouvelle France, les années 1672–'73. 8°. '61. pap., $3..............*Shea.*
— *Same*: 1673–'79. 8°. '60. pap., $4..........*Shea.*

Dabney, Rob. L. Defence of Virginia and the south. 12°. $1.50 .... *Hale.*
— Lectures on sacred rhetoric. 12°. '70. $1.50. *N. Y. Ref. Ch. Bd.; Pres. Com.*
— Life of Gen. T. J. (Stonewall) Jackson. 8°. $3; hf. cf., $4 .... *Hale.*
— *Same.* 8°. '66. $4; hf. cf., $6 .... *Eyrich.*
— Sensualistic philosophy of the 19th century. cr. 8°. '75. $2 .... *Randolph.*
Da Costa, C. A. Lessons in vocal music. f°. '55. pap., $1 .... *Ditson.*
Da Costa, D. A. Atlantic coast guide; with account of summer resorts. maps. 16°. '72. $1 .. *Dutton.*
Da Costa, J. M. Medical diagnosis, with special ref. to pract. medicine. ill. 8°. $6; shp., $7. *Lippincott.*
— Toner lecture, 3: the heart. 8°. '74. pap., 25c. *Smith. Inst.*
— *See also* Pennsylvania Hospital reports.
Dadd, G: H. American cattle doctor. 12°. $1.50. ill. 8°. $2.50 .... *Judd.*
— American reformed horse book: breeding, rearing and management on reformed system of practice. ill. 8°. $2.50 .... *Judd.*
— Modern horse doctor. ill. 12°. $1.50 .... *Judd.*
Daddow, S. H., *and* Bannan, B: Coal, iron and oil; or, the practical Am. miner. maps and ill. 8°. $7.50; hf. mor., $9 .... *Lippincott.*
Daddy Dacre's school. Hall, S. C. 50c. .. *Routledge.*
Daddy Dick. Bromfield, M. E. 40c. .. *Scribner, W. & A.*
Daddy Gray. Halliday, A. 15c. ... *De Witt; French.*
Daddy Hardacre: drama. 16°. pap., 15c .... *French.*
Dadmun, J: W. Masonic choir: collection of hymns and tunes, arrang. for male voices by O. B. Brown. 8°. 75c. .... *G. D. Russell.*
Dafforne, Ja. *See* Landseer, *Sir* E.; — Leslie, C. R.; — Maclise, D.; — Mulready, W.; — Stanfield, C.
Daffy Down Dilly and her friends; by authors of "The fairy egg." 18°. 60c. .... *Loring.*
Dagg, J: Leadley. Elements of moral science. 12°. $1.50 .... *Burke.*
— Evidences of Christianity. 12°. $1.50 ...... *Burke.*
— Manual of theology. 2 v. 8°. v. 1, $1.50; v. 2, $2. *Am. Bapt.*
Cont.: Treatise on church order. — Treatise on Christian doctrine.
— *Same;* in 1 v. 8°. $4.50 ...... *Sheldon; So. Bapt.*
Daguerreotypes. White, C. 15c. .... *De Witt.*
Dahlgren, J: A. Memoir of Ulric Dahlgren. por. 12°. $1.75 .... *Lippincott.*
Dailey, D: Life of Rev. T: Smith. 18°. '48. 50c. *Meth. Bk. Conc.*
Daillé, J: Exposition of the Epistle of St. Paul to the Colossians; tr. by F. S., rev. by J. Sherman. 8°. $2.50 .... *Pres. Bd.*
— Exposition of the Epistle of St. Paul to the Philippians; tr. by J. Sherman. 8°. $2 .... *Pres. Bd.*
— Treatise on the right use of the fathers in the decision of controversies in religion; with pref. by G. Jekyll. 12°. $1 .... *Pres. Bd.*
Daily Bible readings. 32°. 75c.; mor., $2.25 .. *Am. Bapt.*
Daily bread. *See* Bijou Bible text-books.
Daily bread: daily text-book. 32°. 20c. ...... *Nelson.*
Daily bread: sel. for every day. 18°. 65c. .. *Pres. Bd.*
Daily bread, and other stories; by E. E. Hale and others. ('70.) 3d ed. ill. 16°. '71. 80c. ...... *Am. Unit.*
Daily bread for every household. Sewall, F. $1. *Randolph.*
Daily comfort. *See* Daily food ser.
Daily commentary. 8°. $2.50 .... *Carter.*
Daily communion with God. Boyd, J. R. 30c.; 50c.; $1.25 .... *Am. Tr.*
Daily companion: pocket manual of [Cath.] prayer. ('68.) 10th ed. 48°. '75. 25c.–$4.50 .. *Kenedy.*

Daily counsellor. Sigourney, L. H. $1.50 .. *Brown & G.*
Daily devotion for the household: prayers with hymns and passages of Scripture. 24 pl. roy. 4°. $15. *Cassell.*
Daily devotions for Catholics. [Prayer book.] 64°. 30c.–$2 .... *Strong.*
— *Same.* 32°. '73. 50c.–$6 .... *Cunningham.*
Daily duty. Tweedie, W. K. 50c. .... *Nelson.*
Daily exercise. [Cath. prayer book.] 48°. 18c.; 40c. .... *Benziger.*
— *Same.* 48°. '51. 20c.–$1 .... *Murphy.*
— *Same.* 64°. 25c.–$2 .... *Noonan.*
— *Same.* 48°. '70. 25c.–$3 .... *Cunningham.*
Daily food. 64°. '71. 15c.; 20c. ...... *H. A. Young.*
— *See also* Daily food ser.; — Diamond miniatures.
Daily food for Christians: texts for every day. 64°. '32. 15c.–$1.50 .... *Am. Tr.*
— *French.* Pain quotidien pour les chrétiens. 64°. '51. 20c. .... *Am. Tr.*
— *Portuguese.* O pão quotidiano. 32°. '74. 30c. *Am. Tr.*
Daily food series. 6 v. 64°. $1.80 .... *Locke.*
Cont.: Daily food. — Good counsel. — Daily comfort. — Devout sayings. — One thousand meditations. — Daily food.
Daily gleanings. *See* Bijou Bible text-books.
Daily governess. Hall, S. C. $1.25 .. *Scribner, W. & A.*
Daily light on the daily path. 32°. '75. 60c; 90c.; mor., $1.75 .... *Am. Tr.*
Daily light on the daily path. [Devotional texts.] 2 v. 16°. (Bagster.) ea., $1.12; mor., $3. — 32°. ea., 75c.; mor., $2.25 .... *Wiley.*
Daily manna. Stow, B. 25c.; 40c.; $1 .... *Lothrop.*
— *See also* Maná diario.
Daily manna library. 6 v. 24°. $1.50. 16°. $2.40; $4.50 .... *Lothrop.*
Cont.: Daily manna. — Marriage ring. — Young communicant. — Lyric gems. — Active Christian. — Family circle.
Daily meditations; or, good thoughts for priest and people; tr. by T. Noethen, with introd. by Abp. Spalding. 12°. '66. $2; $2.50 .... *Murphy.*
Daily monitor. Allen, J. 30c. .... *Bost. Am. Tr.*
Daily monitor: texts. 72°. '40. 20c.; 30c. *Meth. Bk. Conc.*
Daily News [Lond.] correspondence of the war between Germany and France, 1870–1; with notes, etc. maps. cr. 8°. '71. $2.50 ...... *Macmillan.*
Daily offerings of prayer and praise. f°. '74. pap., $1. *Randolph.*
Daily piety. [Cath. prayer book.] 32°. 30c.–$2. *T. Kelly; Strong.*
Daily portion. Hawker, R. $1.50 .... *Routledge.*
Daily praise and prayer. Shippen, R. R. $1; $1.25. *Am. Unit.*
Daily prayers: manual of Cath. devotion; with Epistles and Gospels. 18°. $1–$50 .... *Sadlier.*
— *Same;* without Epistles and Gospels. 18°. 75c.–$40. *Sadlier.*
Daily prayers [Hebrew]; with Eng. notes. 12°. 40c.; leath., 65c. .... *Frank.*
Daily prayers for communicants. 32°. '71. 40c. .. *Pott.*
Daily prayers for the Lord's hidden ones. 12°. 60c. *Bost. Am. Tr.*
Daily readings. Fry, C. 90c. .... *Pres. Bd.*
Daily readings for holy seasons; by W. P. Walsh, W. Harrison, J. Scholefield and J. Richardson. 12°. $2.50 .... *Nelson.*
Daily remembrancer (The) on peace and war. Hemmenway, J. 75c. .... *Peace.*
Daily Scriptural watchword. Johnson, J. *net,* 75c. *Friends Bk. Assoc.*
Daily Scripture expositor. 32°. '32. 30c. .... *Am. Tr.*
Daily self-examination: verses and questions for each evening of the year. 32°. interleaved, 75c. *Nelson.*
Daily service (The): book of offices for daily use. 16°. '74. $2.50 .... *Hurd & H.*

Daily steps to heaven. Cusack, M. F. $1.50; $2. *Sadlier.*
Daily steps towards heaven. 32°. 60c.; roan, 80c.; mor., $2.50 .... *Dutton.*
Daily texts. 64°. '31. 15c.; 20c. .... *Am. Tr.*
Daily thanks and praise: text-book. 32°. 20c. *Nelson.*
Daily thoughts. Talmage, T. De W. $2 ..... *Dodd.*
Daily thoughts for a child. *See* Geldart, *Mrs.* T.
Daily walk with God in his own ordinances. Porter, S. 60c. .... *Darrow.*
Daily walks with wise men. Head, N. $1.75 .. *Harper.*
Daily watchwords. M., M. A. S. $1.50 ..... *Nelson.*
Dainty Maurice. Ray, R. 45c. .... *J. A. Moore.*
Dairyman (The). 18°. '60. 30c. .... *Am. Tr.*
Dairyman's daughter. *See* Richmond, L.
Dairyman's daughter library. 10 v. 18°. $4.40. *So. Meth.*
Cont.: Dairyman's daughter, by L. Richmond. — Boatman's daughter, by A. Barrett. — Talks pleasant, by T. O. Summers. — Rambles among mountains, by N. T. Langridge. — Youthful Christianity, by S. Martin. — The little book of knowledge. — Seasons, months and days, by T. O. Summers. — First day of the week, by Mrs. Cheap. — Last day of the week, by Mrs. Cheap. — Week completed, by Mrs. Cheap.
Daisy. Warner, S. $2 .... *Lippincott.*
Daisy; or, the fairy spectacles. ill. 16°. 80c. *Lee & S.*
Daisy; or, the lost lamb. 32°. 25c. .... *Am. S. S.*
Daisy and grandpa. *See* Alden, *Mrs.* I. M.
Daisy and her friends. ill. post 18°. 75c. *Scribner, W. & A.*
Daisy books. 3 v. ill. 18°. '70. $1.50 .. *Meth. Bk. Conc.*
Cont.: Daisy's home. — Daisy's visit to Henwood. — Daisy's cousin.
Daisy Brentwell. Widdermer, I. $1.75 .... *Putnam.*
Daisy Bright. ('69.) New ed. ill. 16°. '75. 75c. *Hoyt.*
Daisy Burns. Kavanagh, J. $1.25 .... *Appleton.*
Daisy chain (The). Yonge, C. M. $1.75. *Appleton; Macmillan.*
Daisy Dale library. *See* Baker, *Mrs.* H. N. W.
Daisy Dare and Baby Power. Jeffrey, R. V. $2.50; $3; $5.50 .... *Claxton.*
Daisy Deane. Davis, C. E. K. $1 .... *Hoyt.*
Daisy Delafield. *See* Hildeburn, *Mrs.* M. J.
Daisy library. 10 v. ill. 32°. '72. $2.25 .... *Am. Tr.*
Daisy Maynard's four promises. 16°. 75c. .... *Carter.*
Daisy Nichol. Hardy, *Lady* D. 50c. .... *Harper.*
Daisy Seymour. F., L. A. $1.25 .... *Lothrop.*
Daisy Ward's work. MacLain, M. W. $1.25 .. *Loring.*
Daisydingle Sunday-school (The). 18°. 35c. *Am. S. S.*
Daisy's companions. O'Reilly, R. $1 ...... *Dutton.*
Daisy's companions; by author of "Grandmama's nest." 18°. '70. 60c. .... *Am. S. S.*
Daisy's cousin; — home; — visit to Henwood. *See* Daisy books.
Daisy's mission. Clark, M. L. 30c. .... *Lothrop.*
Daisy's work. Mathews, J. H. 60c. .... *Carter.*
Dalby, R. M. Sacred melodeon: revival hymns. ('55.) New ed. 32°. '69. 40c. .... *Pounsford.*
Dalby, W. B. Lectures on the diseases and injuries of the ear. ill. 12°. '73. $1.50 .... *Lindsay.*
Dale, Fanny. *See* Golden rule for boys and girls; — Household words for boys and girls.
Dale, Fel. He's a lunatic: farce. 16°. pap., 15c. *De Witt; French.*
— Six months ago: comedietta. 16°. pap., 15c. *De Witt; French.*
— *See also* Simpson, J. P., *and* Dale, F.
Dale, H. *See* Xenophon.
Dale, Ja. W. Cup (The) and the cross; or, the baptism of Calvary. 8°. 75c. .... *Pres. Bd.*
— *Same.* 8°. '72. 75c.; pap., 50c. .... *Rutter.*

Dale, Ja. W., *continued.*
— Inquiry into the meaning of ΒΑΠΤΙΖΩ, as determined by the usage of classical Greek writers. 8°. $3.50 .... *Pres. Bd.; Rutter.*
— Inquiry into the usage of ΒΑΠΤΙΖΩ, and the nature of Christic and patristic baptism, as exhibited in the Scriptures and patristic writings. 8°. $5. *Pres. Bd.; Rutter.*
— Inquiry into the usage of ΒΑΠΤΙΖΩ, and the nature of Johannic baptism, as exhibited in the Scriptures. 8°. $4 .... *Pres. Bd.; Rutter.*
— Inquiry into the usage of ΒΑΠΤΙΖΩ, and the nature of Judaic baptism, as shown by Jewish and patristic writings. 8°. $3.50 .... *Pres. Bd.; Rutter.*
Dale, R. W. Atonement (The). (Cong. union lectures, 1875.) 12°. $2 .... *Barnes.*
— Christ and the controversies of Christendom; with introd. by L. W. Bancroft. 12°. '74. 75c. *Whittaker.*
— Jewish temple (The) and the Christian church: discourses on the Epistle to the Hebrews. 12°. $2. *Tibbals.*
— Week-day sermons. cr. 8°. $1.75 ...... *Routledge.*
Dalgairns, J: Bern. Devotion to the heart of Jesus; with an introd. to the hist. of Jansenism. 18°. '59. 75c. .... *Kelly, P. & Co.*
— The holy communion: its philosophy, theology and practice. 12°. '68. $2 .... *Cath. Pub.*
Dalgleish, Wa. Scott. Grammatical analysis with progressive exercises; with pref. by A. H. Dundon. ('65.) New ed. 12°. '74. 60c. .. *Scribner.*
Dall, *Mrs.* Caro. H. College, the market, and the court; or, woman's relation to education, employment and citizenship. cr. 8°. $2.50 .... *Lee & S.*
— Egypt's place in history: a presentation. 8°. pap., $1.50 .... *Lee & S.*
— Historical pictures retouched. pt. 1: Studies, pictures and fancies. 16°. $1.50 .... *Lee & S.*
— Life of Dr. Marie Zakrzewska: a practical ill. of woman's right to labor. 16°. $1 .... *Lee & S.*
— Patty Gray's journey to the Cotton Islands. 3 v. 16°. ea., $1.25 .... *Lee & S.*
Cont.: From Boston to Baltimore. — From Baltimore to Washington. — On the way.
— Sunshine: lectures on health. 16°. pap., 37c. *Lee & S.*
Dall, W: H. Alaska and its resources. ill. and map. 8°. $7.50; cf., $10.50; $12 .... *Lee & S.*
— Revision of the craniidæ and discinidæ. ill. 8°. '71. pap., 85c. .... *Mus. Comp. Zool.*
Dallas, Alex. Ja. *See* United States, Supreme and Circuit Court reports.
Dallas, G. M. Life and writings of Alex. Ja. Dallas. 8°. $5 .... *Lippincott.*
— Series of letters from London, 1856–1860; ed. by Julia Dallas. 2 v. in 1. 8°. $5 .... *Lippincott.*
Dallas Galbraith. Davis, R. H. $1.50; $1 .. *Lippincott.*
Dalling, *Lord.* *See* Bulwer, *Sir* H. L.
Dalrymple, E. A. *See* Maryland Hist. Soc.
Dalrymple, J. S. Lurline: opera. 16°. pap., 15c. *French.*
— Naiad queen: spectacle. 16°. pap., 15c. ... *French.*
Dalton, E: Brief thoughts on the things of God and the soul; in words of one syllable. 18°. 50c. *Routledge.*
Dalton, J: C. Anniversary discourse before N. Y. Acad. of Med. 8°. '73. pap., 25c. *N. Y. Acad. Med.*
— Treatise on human physiology. ill. 8°. $5.50; leath., $6.50 .... *Lea.*
— Treatise on physiology and hygiene. ill. 18°. hf. leath., $1.50 .... *Harper.*
Dalton, T. Arithmetical examples progressively arranged; with exercises and examination papers. New ed., enl. 18°. '73. $1 .... *Macmillan.*
— Rules and examples in algebra. pt. 1. 18°. '74. $1. *Macmillan.*

Dalton, *Rev.* W. Commentary on the New Test.; ed. and continued by Rev. W. Dalton. 4th ed. 2 v. roy. 8°. $12 .... *Claxton.*

Dalton, W: Lost among the wild men: incidents in the life of an old salt. ill. 12°. $1.50 .. *Routledge.*

— The powder monkey; or, adventures of two boy negroes in Madagascar. ill. 12°. '74. $2 .. *Routledge.*

— The story of Mark Raffles. ill. 12°. $1.50 .. *Nelson.*

— The tiger prince; or, adventures in the wilds of Abyssinia. ill. 16°. $1.25 ... *Lippincott; Roberts.*

— White elephant; [also] War tiger. ill. 12°. $1.50. *World Pub.*

— Wolf boy. *See* Rowcroft, C., Australian Crusoes.

Daltons (The). *See* Lever, C:

Daly, Augustin. Griffith Gaunt: drama. 16°. pap., 15c. *French.*

— Under the gaslight: drama. 16°. pap., 15c... *French.*

Daly, C. P. *See* New York, Common Pleas reports.

Daly, J: Broken toys: drama. 16°. pap., 15c. *French.*

— Times: drama. 16°. pap., 15c .... *French.*

Dalzel, And. Collectanea Græca minora. With notes. 6th Am. ed. 12°. '45. hf. roan, $1.13 .. *Claxton.*

Dame blanche (La). *See* Ditson.

Dame Dingle's series. [Toy books.] 6 nos. ill. 8°. per gross, $30 .... (?) *McLoughlin.*
Cont.: Wandering Bunny. — Spoilt Piggy-wiggy. — Cat's party. — Rich Mrs. Duck. — Dog's dinner party. — King Gobble's feast.

Dame Dolores. Taylor, *Miss* —. 50c... *Kelly, P. & Co.*

Dame Durden. *See* Dickens, C.

Dame Nature and her three daughters. Saintine, X. B. $1.25 .... *Hurd & H.*

Dammast, *Mrs.* Jeanie Selina. High and low; or, help each other. ill. 18°. 75c .... *Nelson.*

— Holiday pictures. ill. 18°. '73. 50c .... *Am. Tr.*

Damon, Howard F. Neuroses (The) of the skin: their pathology and treatment. 8°. $2 .... *Lippincott.*

— Photographs of the diseases of the skin; with letter-press. 4°. '69. hf. mor., $12 .... *Jas. Campbell.*

— The structural lesions of the skin: their pathology and treatment. ill. 8°. $3 .... *Lippincott.*

Damon and Pythias. Banim, J. 15c .... *French.*

Damon and Pythias. Buckstone, J. B. 15c... *Lee & S.*

Damon and Pythias. White, C. 15c .... *De Witt.*

Damoreau, *Mme.* Cinti. Method of singing. f°. '68. $5; — in 3 pts. pts. 1, 2, bds., $2.50; pt. 3, bds., $2 .... *Ditson.*

Dampier, W: *See* Drake, *Sir* F., Cavendish, T., *and* Dampier, W

Damrosch, Lp. Ruth and Naomi: words and music. 8°. $1.25; bds., $1 .... *G. D. Russell.*

— Saint Cecilia: anthems, motettes, etc., for church services, etc. 8°. '75. $1.50; bds., $1.25 .. *Pond.*

Dana, A. H. Inductive inquiries in physiology, ethics and ethnology. 12°. '73. $1.25 .... *Barnes.*

Dana, C: A. Life of U. S. Grant. 8°. '66. *$2.50; leath., $3; hf. cf., $4 .... *C. A. Nichols.*

— (*ed.*) Household book of poetry. ill. 8°. $5; hf. cf., $8; mor., $10 .... *Appleton.*

— *See also* Ripley, G: *and* Dana, C: A.

— *and* Bowman, F. A. (*ed.*) Household book of songs; for four voices. 4°. pap., $1.50; hf. roan, $2.50. *Appleton.*

Dana, Eliza A. The broken fold: poems of memory and consolation. 16°. '68. $1.50 ... *Randolph.*

Dana, J. J. Humpy Dumpy. 12°. '74. $1.25. *Nat. Temp.*

— Mrs. Marsh's help. ill. 16°. '73. $1.25 ... *Crowell.*

— — *See also* Ollie lib.

Dana, Ja. Dwight. Corals and coral islands. maps and ill. 8°. '72. $4 .... *Dodd.*

— Crustacea; — Geology; — Zoophytes. *See* Wilkes, C: United States explor. expedition.

Dana, Ja. Dwight, *continued.*

— Descriptive mineralogy. 5th ed., rev. and enl.; aided by G. J. Brush. ill. 8°. $10 .... *Wiley.*

— — Appendix to 1875. 8°. $1 .... *Wiley.*

— Geological story briefly told. ill. 12°. '75. $1.50. *Ivison.*

— Manual of geology; with chart and ill. 8°. '74. $5; hf. mor., $6 .... *Ivison.*

— Manual of mineralogy, incl. observ. on mines, reduction of ores, and the application of the sciences to the arts. ill. 12°. *net*, $1.75 .... *Peck.*

— On the structure and classification of zoophytes. 4°. $4 .... *Lea.*

— Text-book of geology; for schools and academies. New ed., rev. ill. 12°. '74. $2 .... *Ivison.*

Dana, Jos. Liber primus; or, first book of Lat. exercises; with Colloquies from Erasmus, and vocab. by C. K. Dillaway. 12°. '32. shp., $1 .. *Claxton.*

Dana, Malcolm McG. Norwich memorial: annals of Norwich, New London Co., Conn., in the great rebellion. sq. 8°. '73. *$3.50 ..... *T. H. Davis.*

Dana, *Mrs.* Ma. S. B. *See* Shindler, *Mrs.* M. S. B. D.

Dana, R: H., *jr.* To Cuba and back: a vacation voyage. 16°. '59. $1.25 .... *Osgood.*

— Two years before the mast. 16°. '69. $1.50 .. *Osgood.*

Dana, S: L. Muck manual: soils, manures, composts, etc., and especially use of muck, the great natural fertilizer of the country. 12°. $1.25 ...... *Judd.*

Dana Hill stories. 6 v. 18°. $3.60 .... *Cong. Pub.*
Cont.: Hedgerow-side lessons. — Little Jennie. — Come home. — Crippled William. — Archie Bruce. — Jessie Wright.

Dance, C: [Plays.] 15 v. 16°. ea., pap., 15c. *French.*
Cont.: Bengal tiger: farce. — Country squire: comedy. — Delicate ground: comic drama. — Dream of the future: comedy. — Kill or cure: farce. — Marriage a lottery: comedy. — Match in the dark: comedietta. — Morning call: comedietta. — Naval engagements: farce. — Pleasant dreams: farce. — Stock exchange. — Two b'hoys: burletta. — Victor vanquished: comedy. — Who speaks first? farce. — Wonderful woman.

— Advice gratis: farce. 16°. pap., 15c .... *Happy.*

— *See also* Planché, J. R., *and* Dance, C.

Dance, G: Petticoat government: farce. 16°. pap., 15c .... *French.*

— *See also* Planché, J. R., *and* Dance, G.

Dance album (The): explanations of modern dances, with music. 18°. '72. 50c .... *Routledge.*

Dance and the martyr. Monod, A. 25c ..... *Am. Tr.*

Dance of death. *See* Holbein, H.

Dance of modern society. Wilkinson, W. C. 50c.; 25c .... *Mason.*

Dancer's guide and ball room companion. sq. 18°. '74. pap., 25c .... (?) *F. M. Reed.*

Dancing barber: farce. 16°. pap., 15c .... *Happy.*

Dancing feather (The). 8°. pap., 25c ...... *Dick & F.*

Dancing mad: Ethiop. drama. 16°. pap., 15c. *Happy.*

Dancing, religion and revelry. Garnett, T. E. 40c. *So. Bapt.*

Dandelion, and other stories. ill. 24°. 25c. *Bost. Am. Tr.*

— *See also* Banner stories.

Dandelion's dodges. *See* Williams, T. J.

Danesbury House. Wood, E. P. $1.25 .... *Harper.*

Danger. Arthur, T. S. $2; $2.50 .... *J. M. Stoddart.*

Danger ahead. 16°. '18. 50c .... *Hoyt.*

Danger of rejecting the atonement. Winslow, O. 20c. *Randolph.*

Dangerous game. Yates, E. $1.50; 75c... *W. F. Gill.*

Dangerous guest; by author of "Gilbert Rugge." 8°. pap., 50c .... *Harper.*

Dangers and duties of the mercantile profession. Hillard, G. S. 25c .... *Osgood.*

Dangers of dining out. *See* Happy child's lib.

Daniel. *See* Bible.

Daniel. Leben. 24°. 25c. 18°. 50c.; 75c. *Ev. Assoc.*

Daniel, C: Life of blessed Margaret Mary, a religious of the visitation of St. Mary; and the hist. of origin of devotion to the sacred heart of Jesus; tr. by author of "Happy hours of childhood." 8°. $2.50; $3 .... *O'Shea.*

Daniel, G: Disagreeable surprise: farce. 16°. pap., 15c .... *French.*

— Doctor Bolus: farce. 16°. pap., 15c .... *French.*

— Merrie England in the olden time. (Chandos lib.) 12°. $1.75; hf. cf., $3.75; cf., $5 .. *Scribner, W. & A.*

Daniel, J: W. Law and practice of attachment under Virginia code and under new code of West Virginia. 8°. '69. shp., $4.50 .... *West, J. & Co.*

— On negotiable instruments. 2 v. 8°. shp., $13. *Baker, V. & Co.*

Daniel, *Mrs.* Mackenzie. The heiress in the family. 12°. $1.75; pap., $1.50 .... *Peterson.*

Daniel; or, the captivity and restoration. Root, G. F., *and* Bradbury, W. B. 60c .... *Ditson.*

Daniel Dennison. Hofland, B. 50c .... *Harper.*

Daniel Deronda. *See* Eliot, George.

Daniel in the lion's den. *See* Three dramas.

Daniel Quorm and his religious notions. Pearce, M. G. $1 .... *Meth. Bk. Conc.*

Daniel Tracey's store in Covington. 16°. $1.25. *Am. S. S.*

Daniel, the uncompromising young man. Payne, C. H. 20c .... *Meth. Bk. Conc.*

Daniell, E. R. Pleading and practice of the High Court of Chancery. 4th Eng. ed., rev. by T. E. Headlam. 4th Am. ed., rev. and enl.; with notes and forms by J. C. Perkins. 3 v. 8°. '71. shp., $18 .... *Little, B. & Co.*

Daniell, J: F. Chemical philosophy. *See* Renwick, J., Familiar ill. of natural philosophy.

Daniell, Olive C. Dedham receipts. ('71.) 3d ed. 16°. '72. pap., 25c .... *Williams.*

Daniell, W. H. The voice, and how to use it. 16°. $1. * *Osgood.*

Daniels, E. *See* Wisconsin geol. survey.

Daniels, W. H. D. L. Moody and his work. ill. 12°. '76. *$2; $2.50; hf. mor., $3.50 ..... *Am. Pub.*

Danish legends and fairy tales. *See* Andersen, H. C.

Dankers, Jasp., *and* Sluyter, P: Journal of a voyage to New York, and a tour in several of the American colonies in 1679–'80; tr. and ed. by H. C. Murphy. ill. 8°. '67. $6 ...... *L. I. Hist.*

Danks, H. P. Anthem services: quartette or chorus choirs. obl. 4°. $2.75; bds., $2.50 ..... *Ditson.*

— Our favorite: duets, trios, etc. 12°. bds., 60c. *G. D. Russell.*

— Pauline; or, the belle of Saratoga: operetta. 4°. bds., $2 .... *Peters.*

— Sacred selections for church and home. obl. 4°. $2.75; bds, $2.50 .... *Peters.*

Danner, J. L. C. *See* Alabama, Supreme Court reports.

Dante Alighieri. Complete works. (School ed.) 12°. $1.50 .... *Lee & S.*

— La divina commedia. 12°. $1.50 .. *G. R. Lockwood.*

— *Eng.* Divine comedy; tr. [in verse] by H. W. Longfellow. 3 v. 8°. '67. $13.50; hf. cf., $27; mor., $35.—chp. ed. 3 v. 12°. '70. $6; hf. cf., $12; mor., $15;—in 1 v. 12°. '71. $3; hf. cf., $5.50; mor., $7 .... *Osgood.*
Cont.: Inferno.—Purgatorio.—Paradiso.

— *Same;* tr. [in verse] by I. C. Wright; with eng. after Flaxman. 12°. (Bohn.) $1.75. *Little, B. & Co.*

— *Same.* 12°. (Bohn.) $2 .. *Lippincott; Scribner, W. & A.*

— — Vision of hell, purgatory and paradise; tr. [in verse] by H. F. Cary. (Chandos classics.) cr. 8°. $1; pap., 75c .... *Scribner, W. & A.*

— — *Same.* (Scribner's pop. poets.) ill. 12°. $1.50. *Scribner, W. & A.*

Dante Alighieri, *continued.*

— — *Same.* 12°. (Bohn.) $2.75 .... *Little, B. & Co.*

— — *Same.* 12°. (Bohn.) $3. *Lippincott; Scribner, W. & A.*

— Inferno (The): lit. prose tr., with text of orig. collated from best ed. and notes, by J. C. Carlyle. 18°. $1.50 .... *Harper.*

— *Same;* tr. [in verse] by H. F. Cary, ill. by Doré; with notes, life of Dante, and chronology. cr. f°. $25; mor., $40; $60 .... *Cassell.*

— — Hell (The); tr. into lit. blank verse by W. M. Rossetti. fp. 8°. '65. $1.50 .... *Macmillan.*

— Purgatory and paradise; tr. [in verse] by H. F. Cary, ill. by Doré; with notes. cr. f°. $25; mor., $40; $60 .... *Cassell.*

— *French.* Le purgatoire et le paradis; ill. par G. Doré. f°. $50; mor., $80 .... *Appleton.*

— New life; tr. by C. E. Norton. 8°. '67. $4.50; hf. cf., $9; mor., $12.50 .... *Osgood.*

— Poems; tr. by H. F. Cary. (Globe ed.) ill. 16°. $1.25; hf. cf., $3.25; mor., $4.—chp. ed., pap., 60c .... *Appleton.*

Danvers, H. Conjugal lesson: farce. 16°. pap., 15c. *French.*

— Fascinating individual: farce. 16°. pap., 15c. *French.*

D'Anvers, N. Elementary history of art: introd. to ancient and modern architecture, sculpture, painting and music. ill. cr. 8°. $4; hf. cf., $6. *Scribner, W. & A.*

— Robert's holidays. 12°. $1.25; pap., 50c. *Scribner, W. & A.*

Danzig ist über. *See* Vierundzwanzig Stunden.

Darby, J: Botany of the southern states. 12°. '55. $2. *Barnes.*

— Text book of chemistry, theoretical and practical. 12°. '61. $1.75 .... *Barnes.*

Darby, J: (*pseud.*) *See* Garretson, Ja. E.

Dare-devil Dick; or, the curse of gold. 12°. pap., 20c. *Hurst.*

— *Same.* 8°. pap., 25c .... *De Witt.*

Dare Fairfax. Gott, A. A. $1 .... *Hale.*

Dare to do right series. *See* Mathews, Jla. A.

Darien. Warburton, E. 50c .... *Harper.*

Daring deeds of adventure. Borlase, J. S. $1.25. *Scribner, W. & A.*

Daring deeds of good and bad women. 8°. pap., 25c. *Dick & F.*

Daring deeds of the revolution. Watson, H. C. $1.25. *Lee & S.*

Daring to do right library. 4 v. 18°. $2.75 .. *Am. Bapt.*
Cont.: Herbert Graham.—Willie and Lillie.—Henry Hilliard.—Teddy's dream.

Dark cloud. Rose, G. 15c .... *French.*

Dark deeds. [Fiction.] 8°. pap., 50c .... *De Witt.*

Dark deeds: burlesque. 16°. pap., 15c ...... *Happy.*

Dark hour before dawn. Brougham, J., *and* Goodrich, F. B. 15c .... *French.*

Dark mountains. Monro, E. 60c .... *Dutton.*

Dark night (The); or, the fear of man bringeth a snare. 18°. 50c .... *Am. S. S.*

Dark night's (A) work. Gaskell, E. C. 50c ... *Harper.*

Dark noight's (A) business: Irish [dram.] sketch. 16°. pap., 15c .... *Happy.*

Dark river. Monro, E. 60c .... *Dutton.*

Dark scenes of history. James, G. P. R. $1.50 .. *Harper.*

Dark secret (The). Fleming, M. A. 25c ..... *Beadle.*

Dark shades of city life. 8°. pap., 25c ...... *Peterson.*

Dark valley (The). *See* Library of good example.

Darkey drama. 5 nos. 16°. ea., pap., 40c .... *French.*

Darkey plays: collection of Ethiop. dramas. 6 nos. 16°. ea., pap., 30c .... *Happy.*

Darkey tragedian: Ethiop. drama. 16°. pap., 15c. *Happy.*

Darkey's dream: Ethiop. drama. 16°. pap., 15c. *Happy.*
Darkey's (The) stratagem. White, C. 15c...*De Witt.*
Darkness and daylight. Holmes, M. J. $1.50..*Carleton.*
Darkness to light. ill. 18°. '71. 60c........*Lothrop.*
Darley, Fel. O. C. (*ill.*) Sketches abroad with pen and pencil. 2d ed. 4°. '68. $2.50; $3; hf. cf., $5. *Hurd & H.*
— Thirty outline compositions from Judd's "Margaret." imp. f°. $15; hf. mor., $20; mor., $25..*Widdleton.*
— *See also* War pictures.
Darley, W. H. W., *and* Standbridge, J. C. B. Cantus ecclesiæ; or, the sacred chorister: psalm and hymn tunes, etc.; with instruction in vocal music by L. Meignen. 8th ed., rev. obl. 8°. '44. bds., $1.50........................*Ditson.*
— — Chants; for four voices, with organ or piano accompaniment. 8°. '40. bds., $1........*Ditson.*
Darling, H: The closer walk; or, the believer's sanctification. 16°. 65c..................*Pres. Bd.*
Darling, *Miss* Ma. G. Battles at home. ill. 16°. $1.50. (?)*Shepard.*
— In the world: sequel to "Battles at home." ill. 16°. $1.50........................(?)*Shepard.*
Darlington, J: *See* Phillips, J. A., *and* Darlington, J.
Darlington, W: American weeds and useful plants; rev. with add. by G. Thurber. 12°. $1.75..*Judd.*
— Flora cestrica; or, herborizing companion; cont. all the plants of the middle states, their Linnæan arrangement, glossary of botanical terms, etc. 3d ed. 12°. '53. $2.25...............*Lindsay.*
Darning-needle (The). *See* Andersen, H. C.
Darnley. *See* James, G. P. R.
Darras, J. E. General hist. of the Cath. Church; with introd. and notes by M. J. Spalding. 4 v. ill. 8°. $12–$32......................*O'Shea.*
Darrell Markham. Braddon, M. E. 50c. ..*Dick & F.*
Darryll Gap. Townsend, V. F. $1.50.....*Lee & S.*
Dart, P. C. Freight computations. 8°. '68. hf. mor., $2.50...........................*Appleton.*
Dartnell, G. E. Ella's locket and what it brought her. ill. 18°. $1........................*Nelson.*
Darton, Marg. E. The earth and its inhabitants. 12°. $1.50.......................... *Routledge.*
Darusmont, Fes. Wright. Biography and notes of D. 12°. pap., 10c. ....*Mendum.*
Darwin, C: Rob. Descent of man, and selection in relation to sex. ill. 12°. $3..........*Appleton.*
— Emotional expressions of man and the lower animals. 12°. $3.50; hf. cf., $6........*Appleton.*
— Journal of researches into the nat. hist. and geol. of countries visited during the voyage of the Beagle. 12°. $2; hf. cf., $4.50...............*Appleton.*
— *Same.* 2 v. 12°. $2..................*Harper.*
— Movements and habits of climbing plants. 12°. $1.25...........................*Appleton.*
— Origin of species by means of natural selection. New ed., rev. and enl., with index. 12°. $2; hf. cf., $4.50.......................*Appleton.*
— Variation of animals and plants under domestication; with pref. by A. Gray. 2 v. ill. 12°. $6; hf. cf., $11 ....*Appleton.*
Darwinism and deity. *See* Force, M. F.
Daryl, Sidney. Told in the twilight; or, short stories for long evenings. ill. sq. 12°. $1.25... *Claxton.*
— With the tide; or, a life's voyage. ill. 12°. $1.25. *Scribner, W. & A.*
— *Same.* sq. 12°. $1.50...................*Claxton.*
Dasent, G. Webbe. Lady Sweetapple; or, three to one. [Fiction.] ill. 8°. pap., 75c.....*Appleton.*
Dash, *La comtesse* (*pseud.*) *See* Saint-Mars, N. C. de C.
Dash and the ducklings. [Toy-book.] ill. 4°. $1; 50c...............................*Routledge.*
Dashiell, T. G. A pastor's recollections. 12°. $1.25. *Appleton.*
Dashington. 8°. pap., 25c................*De Witt.*
Dashmore, Fk. Fair Minthe; or, the curious origin of mint julep. 12°. '76. 75c.; pap., 25c...*Authors.*
Dashwood Priory. May, E. J. $1.25....*Routledge.*
Dassler, C. F. W. Digest of Kansas reports. 8°. '74. shp., $7.50..........................*Gilbert.*
Dat same old coon: Ethiop. drama. 16°. pap., 15c. *Happy.*
Date book of Scottish history. 18°. 20c......*Nelson.*
D'Aubigné, J. H. Merle. *See* Aubigné.
Daudet, Alph. The new Don Quixote; or, the wonderful adventures of Tartarin of Tarascon. 12°. '75. $1.......................... *W. F. Gill.*
Daugherty, H. H. Law of sheriffs. 8°. shp., $3. *Merrill.*
Daughter. Knowles, J. S. 15c. ....*French.*
Daughter at home. 18°. 80c. 16°. $1.10..*Am. S. S.*
Daughter at school. Todd, J. $1.50....*Bridgman.*
Daughter of affliction: memoir of Miss Mary Rankin. por. 12°. $1.25.................*Un. B. Pub.*
Daughter of Bohemia. Fisher, F. C. $1.50; $1. *Appleton.*
Daughter of an Egyptian King. Ebers, G. $1.75. *Lippincott.*
Daughter of an empress. Mundt, C. M. $1.50; $1; hf. cf., $3.50.........................*Appleton.*
Daughter of a genius. Hofland, B. 50c. ....*Porter.*
Daughter (A) of Heth. Black, W. 50c.....*Harper.*
Daughter of night. Fullom, S. W. 50c.....*Harper.*
Daughter of the regiment. Ball, E. 15c....*Lee & S.*
Daughter of the regiment: opera. 16°. pap., 15c. *French.*
Daughter of Tyrconnell. Sadlier, M. A. 50c.; 75c. *Sadlier.*
Daughter to marry. Planché, J. R. 15c.....*French.*
Daughter's own book; or, practical hints from a father to his daughter. 18°. '69. 60c....*Claxton.*
Daughters at school instructed. Bailey, R. W. 80c. *Pres. Bd.*
Daughters of China. Bridgeman, E. J. G. 75c. *Carter.*
Daughters of the cross. Martyn, S. T. 80c. *Am. Tr.*
Daughters of the prairie. *See* Eggleston, *Mrs.* N. H.
Davault's mills. Jones, C. H. $1.75....*Lippincott.*
Daveis, E: H. *See* United States, District Court reports.
Davenant, *Sir* W: Love and honor: drama. 16°. pap., 15c. ....*French.*
Davenport, Bishop. History of the U. S. ('67.) New ed., rev. by J. J. Anderson. ill. sq. 16°. '76. 90c. ....*Claxton.*
Davenport, F: S. *See* Wilder, S., *and* Davenport, F. S.
Davenport, J: S. Christian unity and its recovery. 12°. $1.25.........................*Appleton.*
Davenport, R: Alfr. History of the Bastile and its captives. ill. sm. 8°. $2.50....*Scribner, W. & A.*
— Perilous adventures: remarkable instances of courage, perseverance and suffering. 18°. 75c. *Harper.*
Davenport brothers, the world-renowned spiritual mediums: their biog. and adventures in Europe and Am. 12°. '69. $1.50..............*Colby.*
Davenport Done. Colomb, *Capt.* —. 15c...*French.*
Davenport Dunn. *See* Lever, C:
Davenport [Iowa] Academy of Natural Sciences. Proceedings, 1867–'76. ill. cr. 8°. '76. $3.50; pap., $2.50.......................*Dav. Acad. Nat. Sci.*
David, Fd. Violin school; ed. by B. Listemann. 2 pts. 4°. pt. 1, bds., $2.50; pt. 2, pap., $3....*Ditson.*
— *Same;* [with] Eng. and Germ. words. f°. pap., pt. 1, $4; pt. 2, $5;—in 1 v. bds, $9..*Schirmer.*

David, J: M. A spiritual retreat of eight days; ed. with add. and introd. by M. J. Spalding. sm. 12°. '69. $1.25; $1.50 .... *Murphy.*
David. *See* Bible, Psalms; — Psalms.
David. Kingsley, C. $1 .... *Macmillan.*
David. *See* Neukomm, S.
David Copperfield. Brougham, J. 15c. ..... *French.*
David Copperfield. *See* Dickens, C:
David Dufficks. *See* Comical adventures.
David Elginbrod. MacDonald, G. $1.75 .... *Loring.*
David Garrick. Robertson, T. W. 15c. .... *De Witt.*
David Hewson; [also] Magdalen. 18°. 60c. *Whittaker.*
David, the king. Knox, C. E. $2 .... *Randolph.*
David, king of Israel. *See* Krummacher, F. W.
David, king of Israel. Taylor, W. M. $2 .. *Harper.*
David Lloyd's last will. Smith, H. 75c. ...... *Dodd.*
David, the trapper. *See* Adirondack stories.
David Watson; or, the pirate cutter. Midshipman Easy. 25c. .... *Dick & F.*
David Woodburn. Frost, J. $1.25 .... *Hoyt.*
Davidson, And. Bruce. Introductory Hebrew grammar. 8°. $3 .... *Scribner, W. & A.*
Davidson, B: Analytical Hebrew lexicon. 4°. (Bagster.) $11 .... *Wiley.*
— Bagster's analyt. Heb. and Chaldee lexicon; with alphabet. arrangement of every word in the Old Test., etc. sm. 4°. *net*, hf. bd., $11 ..... *Wiley.*
— Concordance of the Heb. and Chaldee Scriptures. sm. 4°. (Bagster.) $26 .... *Wiley.*
Davidson, E. Life. 18°. '53. 35c. .... *Am. Tr.*
Davidson, Ellis A. Animal kingdom: element. text book in zoology. New ed., rev. ill. 12°. '71. 75c. .... *Cassell.*
— Boy-joiner (The) and model-maker: directions for making articles of use and ornament, tools, models, etc. ill. fp. 4°. $2.50 .. *Am. News; Cassell.*
— Elements of building construction, and archit. drawing. ill. post 8°. $1 .... *Cassell.*
— Gothic stonework. ill. post 8°. $1.50 ..... *Cassell.*
— Linear drawing and practical geometry. ill. post 8°. $1 .... *Cassell.*
— Linear drawing and projection. ill. post 8°. $1.75. *Cassell.*
— [Mechanical drawing books.] 6 v. post 8°. ea., $1.50 .... *Cassell.*
Cont.: Drawing for bricklayers — for cabinet makers — for carpenters and joiners — for machinists and engineers — for metal-plate workers — for stone masons.
— Model drawing. ill. post 8°. $1.50 .... *Cassell.*
— Orthographical and isometrical projection. ill. post 8°. $1 .... *Cassell.*
— Our bodies: element. text-book in human physiology. ill. fp. 8°. 50c. .... *Cassell.*
— Practical manual of house painting, graining, marbling and sign-writing. col. ill. and wood-eng. 12°. $3 .... *Baird.*
— Practical perspective. ill. post 8°. $1.50 ... *Cassell.*
Davidson, G: Coast pilot of California, etc. *See* United States, *Coast Survey.*
Davidson, Ja. Wood. School history of South Carolina. 16°. hf. bd., 90c. .... *Duffie.*
Davidson, Lucretia Mar. Poems; ed. by M. O. Davidson. por. and ill. cr. 8°. $2.50; $3; mor., $7.50. *Hurd & H.*
Davidson, Rob. Christ (The) of God; or, the relation of Christ to Christianity. 18°. 35c. *Pres. Bd.*
— Relation of baptized children to the church. 18°. 45c. *Pres. Bd.*
Davidson, S: Revision of the Heb. text of the Old Test. 8°. (Bagster.) $4.50 .... *Wiley.*
— *See also* Bible [Whole].
Davidson, W: Sermons on the parables; with essay on his character as a preacher, pastor and orator, etc; ed. by D. McDill. 12°. '76. $2 .. *West. Tr.*

Davie Armstrong. 18°. 60c. .... *Cong. Pub.*
Davies, C: Arithmetic for academies and schools. ["Old school arithmetic."] 16°. '50. hf. bd., 75c.; 80c.; 90c. — Key. 16°. hf. bd., 75c. *Barnes.*
— Differential and integral calculus on basis of continuous quantity and consecutive differences. 8°. '73. shp., $2; $2.13; $2.25 .... *Barnes.*
— Elementary algebra. 12°. '52. $1.25; $1.35; $1.45. — Key. 12°. $1.25 .... *Barnes.*
— Elements of algebra on the basis of Bourdon. New ed., rev. 8°. '73. shp., $2.25; $2.38; $2 50. — Key. 8°. '73. $2.25 .... *Barnes.*
— Elements of analyt. geometry. New ed., rev. 8°. '73. shp., $2; $2.13; $2.25 .... *Barnes.*
— *Same;* and of the differential and integral calculus. 8°. '73. shp., $2.50; $2.63; $2.75 ..... *Barnes.*
— Elements of descript. geometry, with application to spherical trigonometry, etc. 8°. '34. $2.75; $2.88; $3 .... *Barnes.*
— Elements of geom. and trigonom.; from works of Legendre. 8°. '62. $2.25; $2.38; $2.50 .. *Barnes.*
— Elements of geometry and trigonometry, with applications in mensuration. 12°. '51. $1.40; $1.50; $1.60 .... *Barnes.*
— Elements of surveying and levelling, with descript. of instruments and tables. 8°. '70. shp., $2.50; $2.63; $2.75 .... *Barnes.*
— Elements of written arithmetic. 16°. '63. hf. bd., 50c.; 60c.; 70c. .... *Barnes.*
— Examination of the demonstrations of Davies' Legendre, showing how the polygon becomes the circle by the methods of Newton. 12°. '73. pap., 10c. .... *Barnes.*
— First lessons in arithmetic. 16°. '52. hf. bd., 40c.; 48c.; 56c. .... *Barnes.*
— Grammar of arithmetic: analysis of the language of figures and science of numbers. 16°. '50. hf. bd., 50c.; 60c.; 70c. .... *Barnes.*
— Intellectual arithmetic. 16°. '62. hf. bd., 40c.; 48c.; 56c. .... *Barnes.*
— Mathematical dict., and cyclop. of mathematical science. 8°. '55. $4; $4.25; $4.50 .... *Barnes.*
— Mathematical tables: logarithms, sines and tangents, traverse tables, etc. 8°. $1; $1.13; $1.25. *Barnes.*
— Metric system, with ref. to its introd. into the U. S.; [incl.] reports of J. Q. Adams and lecture of Sir J. Herschel. 12°. '70. $1.50; $1.60; $1.70. *Barnes.*
— Nature and utility of mathematics, with best methods of instruction explained and ill. 12°. '73. $1.50; $1.60; $1.70 .... *Barnes.*
— New element. algebra. 12°. '59. $1.25; $1.35; $1.45. — Key. 12°. '59. $1.25 .... *Barnes.*
— Outlines of mathematical science. 12°. '67. $1; $1.10; $1.20 .... *Barnes.*
— Practical arithmetic. 12°. '62. hf. bd., 90c.; $1; $1.10. — Key. 12°. '63. 90c. .... *Barnes.*
— Practical mathematics with drawing and mensuration, applied to the mechanic arts. 12°. '52. $1.50; $1.60; $1.70 .... *Barnes.*
— Primary arithmetic. 16°. '62. hf. bd., 25c.; 32c.; 40c. *Barnes.*
— School arithmetic, analyt. and pract. 16°. '52. hf. bd., 80c.; 90c. — Key. 16°. '56. hf. bd., 80c. .. *Barnes.*
— Selected propositions in geometrical construction and applications of algebra to geom.: key to app. of Davies' Legendre. 8°. '75. $1 .... *Barnes.*
— Treatise on shades, shadows and linear perspective. 8°. '70. $3.75; $3.88; $4 .... *Barnes.*
— University algebra. 12°. '64. $1.50; $1.60; $1.70. — Key. 12°. '59. $1.50 .... *Barnes.*
— University arithmetic. 12°. '63. $1.40; $1.50; $1.60. — Key. 12°. '64. $1.40 .... *Barnes.*
Davies, E. D. Art of ventriloquism. 18°. pap., 25c. *Fisher.*
Davies, G. S. Gaudentius: story of the Colosseum. 16°. $1.25 .... *Pott.*

Davies, G: C. Songs of the Church: psalms and hymns of the Prot. Episc. Church. 12°. $1..*Pounsford.*

Davies, J: Llewelyn. Baptism, confirmation and the Lord's supper, as interpreted by their outward signs: addresses. fp. 8°. '63. 50c...*Macmillan.*

— Christian calling: sermons. fp. 8°. '75. $1.75. *Macmillan.*

— Epistles of St. Paul to the Ephesians, the Colossians, and Philemon; with introds., notes and essay on the traces of foreign elements in the theology of these epistles. 8°. '66. $2..*Macmillan.*

— Gospel (The) and modern life: sermons, with pref. on a recent phase of deism. New ed. fp. 8°. '75. $1.75........................*Macmillan.*

— Sermons on the manifestation of the Son of God; with pref. to laymen on the present position of the clergy of the Church of England, and app. on the testimony of Scripture and the Church as to the possibility of pardon in the future state. fp. 8°. '64. $1.75........................*Macmillan.*

— Theology and morality: essays on questions of belief and practice; with introd. by H. C. Potter. 12°. '73. $2........................*Whittaker.*

— Warnings against superstition: sermons. fp. 8°. '74. $1........................*Macmillan.*

— Work of Christ; or, the world reconciled to God; with a pref. on the atonement controversy. fp. 8°. '63. $1.75........................*Macmillan.*

Davies, R: Life. 12°. 62c..........*Friends Bk. St.*

Davies, S: Sermons on important subjects. ('67.) New ed. 3 v. 12°. '76. $3.75..........*Carter.*

— Sermons; with funeral sermon by S. Finley, and memoirs by T. Gibbons, T. Bostwick and W. B. Sprague. 3 v. 8°. $7.50............*Pres. Bd.*

Davies, Thdr. Losing to win. [Fiction.] 12°. $1.50; pap., $1........................*Sheldon.*

Davies, T: Preparation and mounting of microscopic objects. 12°. $1.25........*Putnam; W. Wood.*

Davies, T: A. Genesis disclosed. 12°. $1.50..*Carleton.*

— How to make money, and how to keep it. 12°. $1.50........................*Carleton.*

Davillier, Ch. (*Baron*). Spain, historical, social, typographical and descriptive; with 300 eng. by G. Doré. imp. 4°. $18..........*Scribner, W. & A.*

Davis, A. J. *See* Gottheil, G., *and* Davis, A. J.

Davis, And. Jackson. Answers to ever-recurring questions from the people: sequel to "Penetralia." 12°. '62. $1.50............*A. J. Davis.*

— Approaching crisis; or, truth versus theology. 12°. '51. $1.50........................*A. J. Davis.*

— Arabula; or, the divine guest. 12°. '67. $1.50 *A. J. Davis.*

— Children's progressive lyceum: recitations, hymns and songs. 12°. '64. 60c...........*A. J. Davis.*

— Death and the after-life. 12°. '65. 75c.; pap., 50c. *A. J. Davis.*

— Diakka (The), and their earthly victims: explanation of much that is false and repulsive in spiritualism. 12°. '73. 50c.; pap., 25c..........*A. J. Davis.*

— Events in the life of a seer: sequel to "Magic staff." 12°. '68. $1.50........................*A. J. Davis.*

— Fountain (The); with jets of new meanings. 12°. '70. $1........................*A. J. Davis.*

— Free thoughts concerning religion. 12°. '72. 75c.; pap., 50c........................*A. J. Davis.*

— Genesis and ethics of conjugal love. 12°. '74. 75c.; pap., 50c........................*A. J. Davis.*

— Great harmonia (The): a philos. revelation of the natural, spiritual and celestial universe. 5 v. 12°. '50–'59. ea., $1.50..............*A. J. Davis.*

Cont.: The physician. — The teacher. — The seer. — The reformer. — The thinker.

— Harbinger of health: med. prescriptions for the mind and body. 12°. '61. $1.50........*A. J. Davis.*

— Harmonial man; or, thoughts for the age. 12°. '72. 75c.; pap., 50c........................*A. J. Davis.*

Davis, And. Jackson, *continued.*

— History and philosophy of evil. 12°. '71. 75c.; pap., 50c........................*A. J. Davis.*

— Inner life (The); or, spirit mysteries explained. 12°. '53. $1.50........................*A. J. Davis.*

— Magic staff: autobiog. 12°. '57. $1.75..*A. J. Davis.*

— Penetralia; cont. harmonial answers. ('56.) New ed. 12°. '76. $1.75..............*A. J. Davis.*

— Philosophy of special providences. 12°. '72. 50c.; pap., 30c........................*A. J. Davis.*

— Philosophy of spiritual intercourse. 12°. '51. $1.25. *A. J. Davis.*

— Principles of nature: her divine revelations, and a voice to mankind. 8°. '47. $3.50....*A. J. Davis.*

— Sacred gospels of Arabula. 12°. '72. 60c. *A. J. Davis.*

— Stellar key to the summerland. 12°. '67. 75c.; pap., 50c........................*A. J. Davis.*

— Tale of a physician; or, the seeds and fruits of crime: story of the life and trials of Sophia Aragoni. 12°. '69. $1........................*A. J. Davis.*

— Temple (The): diseases of the brain and nerves. 12°. '71. $1.50; pap., $1..........*A. J. Davis.*

Davis, C. A. The dance and the dancing school. 15c. (?) *Cumberland.*

Davis, *Mrs.* Caro. E. K. [*formerly Miss* C. E. Kelly]. Andy Hall; or, the mission scholar in the army. ('63.) New ed. ill. 16°. '75. $1.15......*Hoyt.*

— Arthur Merton; or, sinning and sorrowing. 16°. '65. $1.25........................*Garrigues.*

— Baby's Christmas. ('63.) New ed. ill. sq. 16°. '76. $1; $1.25........................*Hoyt.*

— Bernice, the farmer's daughter. ('63.) New ed. ill. 16°. '76. $1.25........................*Hoyt.*

— C. E. K. D. library. ('71–'73.) New ed. 4 v. 16°. '75–'76. $6........................*Hoyt.*

Cont.: Granny Bright's blanket. — Chew Alley; or, how to make sunshine. — Aunt Lois; or, happiness to others. — Heart's delight.

— Carrie Allison; or, in the vineyard. ('61.) New ed. ill. 18°. '75. 50c........................*Hoyt.*

— Child library (The). ('70.) New ed. 4 v. ill. 18°. '76. $3.25; ea., 80c........................*Hoyt.*

Cont.: Cain and Abel to the tabernacle. — The child Jesus. — Tabernacle to Jonah. — The parables.

— Christmas story. ('68.) New ed. ill. 16°. '71. 85c. *Hoyt.*

— Daisy Deane. ('61.) New ed. ill. 16°. '73. $1..*Hoyt.*

— Faithful in least. ('71.) New ed. 16°. '74. $1.50. *Hoyt.*

— Friday Lowe, and sequel. 2 v. 16°. '68–'70. ea., $1.25........................*Garrigues.*

— Gerty Harding's mission. ('67.) New ed. ill. 16°. '75. $1.15........................*Hoyt.*

— Gold bracelets; or, Florence Archer's temptation. ('66.) New ed. ill. 16°. '72. $1.15.......*Hoyt.*

— Grace Hale. ('60.) New ed. ill. 18°. '70. 60c. *Hoyt.*

— Home vineyard: sketches of mission work. 18°. '66. 80c........................*Garrigues.*

— Into the highways. ('70.) New ed. ill. 16°. '74. $1.50........................*Hoyt.*

— John Brett's household. 18°. '69. 90c...*Garrigues.*

— Johnny's captain. ('64.) New ed. ill. 18°. '69. 55c. *Hoyt.*

— Life of Alice Haven. ('61.) New ed. ill. 18°. '75. 45c........................*Hoyt.*

— Little apple blossom. ('63.) New ed. ill. 16°. '75. 50c........................*Hoyt.*

— Little conqueror ser. ('65.) New ed. 4 v. ill. 18°. '76. $2........................*Hoyt.*

Cont.: Little conqueror; or, the children's comfort-bags. — Frankie's little meeting. — Frankie's little friend. — Frankie's work.

— Little Maidie. 3 pts. ill. 16°. ea., 75c.; — in 1 v. $1.75........................*Hoyt.*

— Little sermon talks. ('65.) New ed. ill. 16°. '69. 65c........................*Hoyt.*

— Little Three Year Old. 16°. '73. 75c.; $1.25. *Lothrop.*

— Mary's patience bank. ('66.) New ed. ill. 16°. '71. $1.15........................*Hoyt.*

Davis, *Mrs.* Caro. E. K., *continued.*
— Matty Frost. ('61.) New ed. ill. 18°. '75. 55c. *Hoyt.*
— Miss Wealthy's hope. ill. 16°. '74. $1.50..*Lothrop.*
— No cross, no crown. ('70.) New ed. ill. 16°. '75. 80c. ....*Hoyt.*
— Old barracks; or, seeking the light. ('65.) New ed. ill. 16°. '71. $1.25....................*Hoyt.*
— Papa's boy. ill. 16°. '75. 75c. ....*Lothrop.*
— Papa's little soldiers. ('62.) New ed. ill. 18°. '72. 45c. ....*Hoyt.*
— Penny Rust's Christmas. ('71.) New ed. 16°. '74. $1.15 ....*Hoyt.*
— Ruth Chenery. ('67.) New ed. ill. 16°. '74. $1.25. *Hoyt.*
— Squire's daughter. ('69.) New ed. ill. 16°. '73. $1.25 ....*Hoyt.*
— Sunny path. ('71.) New ed. 16°. '76. $1.50..*Hoyt.*
— Two books. ('71.) New ed. 16°. '73. $1.15..*Hoyt.*
— Upward path. ('68.) New ed. ill. 16°. '76. $1.25. *Hoyt.*
— Yachtville boys. ('69.) New ed. ill. 16°. '73. 75c. *Hoyt.*

Davis, C: H. Law of deposit of flood tide. 4°. '52. pap., 75c............................*Smith. Inst.*
— Narrative of north pole expedition. *See* United States, *Navy Dept.*

Davis, C: H. S. History of Wallingford, Conn., 1690–[1870]; incl. Meriden, one of its parishes, until 1806, and Cheshire, incorporated in 1780. por. and pl. 8°. $6........................*Munsell.*

Davis, Edn. A. Digest of Indiana Supreme Court decisions; with table of cases and index. 2 v. 8°. '75. *net*, shp., $12....................*Clarke.*

Davis, H: G. Conservative surgery. ill. 8°. $3. *Appleton.*

Davis, H: Winter. Speeches and addresses in the U. S. Congress, and on public occasions; with life by J. A. J. Creswell. por. 8°. $4.....*Harper.*

Davis, J. A. G. Treatise on criminal law. 8°. '38. hf. shp., $10..................*J. W. Randolph.*

Davis, Jefferson, *and* Jackson, T. J. ["Stonewall" Jackson.] Lives and public services. ill. 12°. $1.75............................*J. E. Potter.*

Davis, J: Elementary astronomy. 12°. $2..*Keystone.*

Davis, J: F. History of China. 2 v. map and ill. 18°. $1.50..........................*Harper.*

Davis, L. A. Gospel life of Jesus. 16°. '76. $1.25. *Lothrop.*

Davis, L. D. Life in the itinerancy. 12°. '57. $1.50. *Meth. Bk. Conc.*
— Life in the laity. 16°. 75c.....*Cin. Meth. Bk. Conc.*

Davis, Mat. L. Memoirs of Aaron Burr; with sel. from correspondence. 2 v. por. 8°. $4..*Harper.*
— — *See also* Burr, A., Private journal.

Davis, Minnie S. Marion Lester; or, the mother's mistake. 16°. '63. $1...........*Universalist.*

Davis, Nath. Carthage and her remains: excavations and researches on the site of [C.] maps and ill. 8°. $4; hf. cf., $6.25................*Harper.*

Davis, Nath. Smith. Clinical lectures on various diseases; ed. by F. H. Davis. 2d ed., enl. roy. 12°. $1.75..............................*Lea.*
— History of the Am. Med. Assoc., to Jan., 1855. por. 8°. $1..............................*Brinton.*

Davis, R. C. Reminiscences of a voyage around the world. 16°. '69. $1..............*R. A. Beal.*

Davis, R. T. Pauperism in N. Y. City; read at annual meeting of the Am. Soc. Sci. Assoc., 1874. 8°. '74. pap., 10c.....................*Williams.*

Davis, *Mrs.* Reb. Harding. Dallas Galbraith. 8°. $1.50; pap., $1..................*Lippincott.*
— John Andross. ill. 12°. $1.50..............*Judd.*
— Kitty's choice: a story of Berrytown. 8°. pap., 40c. *Lippincott.*
— Waiting for the verdict. ill. 8°. $1.75.....*Sheldon.*

Davis, *Mrs.* S. M. Life and times of Sir Philip Sidney. ('58.) New ed. pl. 12°. '75. $1.50....*Ford.*

Davis, *Mrs.* T. E. ["Mollie E. Moore."] Poems. ('67.) 3d ed. 12°. '72. $2; $2.50; mor., $5. *E. H. Cushing.*

Davis, T: Poems and essays; with introd. by J. Mitchell. New ed. por. 12°. '55. $1.50..*Haverty.*

Davis, W. S. Acoustics: light and heat. (Adv. sci. ser.) ill. 12°. $1.50.....................*Putnam.*
— Elements of geology. (Element. sci. ser.) ill. 16°. '73. 75c..................................*Putnam.*

Davis, W. W. H. El Gringo; or, New Mexico and her people. 12°. $1.50................*Harper.*

Davis, Wa. B., *and* Durrie, D. S. History of Missouri, to 1876. ill. and por. 8°. '76. $5; leath., $6.25.....................*Clarke; A. J. Hall.*

Davis, W: M. Nimrod of the sea; or, the American whaleman. ill. 12°. $2..............*Harper.*

Davis, Z. A. The Freemason's monitor. ('53.) New ed., rev. and enl. por. 12°. '76. $1.75..*Claxton.*

Davis, the pirate; or, the freebooter of the Pacific. 8°. pap., 50c...........................*Peterson.*

Davy, H: Paper on Milford Haven and its new pier works. 8°. pap., 40c..................*Spon.*

Davy, *Sir* Hum. Consolations in travel; or, the last days of a philosopher. 16°. '70. $1.50..*Roberts.*
— Salmonia; or, days of fly-fishing. 16°. '70. $1.50. *Roberts.*

Davy's jacket. Ward, H. L. H. 75c........*Lothrop.*

Davy's motto; or, deeds speak louder than words. ill. 16°. '69. $1.25...........................*Graves.*

Davy's school-days; or, deeds speak louder than words. 16°. $1.25.........................*Cong. Pub.*

Note. Same as above?

Dawes, *Mrs.* S. E. Eddie Gray. 32°. '63. 25c. *Am. Tr.*
— Hattie May. ill. 18°. '68. 60c............*Am. Tr.*
— Hours with mamma: Bible stories. ill. 16°. '65. $1. *Am. Tr.*
— Lindenwood. ill. 16°. '68. $1.25..........*Am. Tr.*
— Pictures and stories for little ones. ill. 16°. '73. 70c. *Am. Tr.*
— Rose and her pets; in words of one syllable. sq. 18°. '69. 60c.............................*Am. Tr.*
— Star of Bethlehem: a sacred poem. sq. 16°. $1.25. *Locke.*
— Stories about Nellie. 6 v. ill. 18°. '73. $2.50..*Hoyt.*
— Wayside flowers; or, Daisy's little friends. ill. 16°. $1 ....*Locke.*

Dawkins, W. Boyd. Cave-hunting: researches on the evidence of caves resp. the early inhabitants of Europe. ill. 8°. '74. $7............*Macmillan.*

Dawn library. 10 v. 18°. $5.70..........*So. Meth.*

Cont.: Dawn of modern civilization. — Successful men of modern times. — Memoir of Casson. — Methodism; or, Christianity in earnest. — Australia. — Trial of the witnesses, by T. Sherlock. — Thomas Spencer, by T. Raffles. — Richard Williams, by J. Hamilton. — Switzerland. — Methodism in Charlestown, by Rev. F. A. Mood.

Dawn of heaven. Collier, J. A. $1.50.......*Carter.*

Dawn of light. Leslie, M. E. 65c.........*Pres. Bd.*

Dawn of modern civilization: sketches of social condition of Europe, 12th–16th cent.; rev. by T. O. Summers. ('56.) 2d ed. 18°. '75. 60c...*So. Meth.*

Dawnay, Arch. D. Treatise upon railway signals and accidents. ill. 8°. '74. pap., $1..........*Spon.*

Dawnings of genius. *See* Young American's lib.

Dawnings of genius exemplified and exhibited. Buckley, T. A. $1.25..........................*Routledge.*

Dawson, —. [Stories.] 4 v. 32°. ea., 25c...*Porter.*

Cont.: Ben Benson. — Discontented Tom. — Edith Locke. — Eva Bruen.

Dawson, Alfr. *See* Champney, B., Quiet corner of England.

Dawson, B: F. *See* Barnes, R., Obstetric operations.

Dawson, C: C. Collection of family records, with biog. sketches, etc., of families of name of Dawson. por. 8°. '74. $6........... *Munsell.*

Dawson, G: Pleasures of angling. ill. 12°. $1.50. *Sheldon.*

— *See also* Hardwich, T. F.

Dawson, H: B. *See* Fœderalist (The).

Dawson, J: W: Acadian geology: the geological structure, organic remains and mineral resources of Nova Scotia, New Brunswick and Prince Edward Island. 2d ed., rev. and enl.; with geol. maps and ill. 8°. '68. $7........ *Macmillan.*

— Nature and the Bible: lectures, Dec., '74, before Union Theol. Sem., N. Y. 12°. '75. $1.75.. *Carter.*

— Story of the earth and man. ill. 12°. $1.50.. *Harper.*

Day, Alb. Methomania: treatise on alcoholic poisoning. 16°. '67. 60c.; pap., 40c.... *Jas. Campbell.*

Day, Alfr. Analysis and index to Dialogues of Plato. *See* Plato.

Day, B: H. American ready reckoner. 16°. 75c.; bds., 50c.; leath., $1..................... *Dick & F.*

— Book-keeping without a master. sm. 4°. 50c. *Dick & F.*

Day, C: H. Fun in black; or, sketches of minstrel life. 32°. pap., 25c.................. *De Witt.*

— Kate Vaugh; or, spiders' webs and flies. ('66.) 5th ed. 16°. '70. pap., 15c........... *Hunter.*

Day, *Rev.* G. T. African adventure and adventurers. ill. 16°. '73. $1.50.................. *Lothrop.*

Day, G: T. Life of Martin Cheney. 8°. '53. $1.. *Freewill.*

— *See also* Bowen, W. H.

Day, H: A lawyer abroad: what to see and how to see. 12°. '74. $2......................... *Carter.*

Day, H: *See* Art recreations.

Day, H: G: Properties of conic sections proved geometrically. cr. 8°. '68. $1.25... *Macmillan.*

Day, H: N. American speller. ('68.) New ed. 12°. '76. bds., 25c...................... *Scribner.*

— Art of discourse: system of rhetoric. ('67.) 7th ed. 12°. '76. $1.50...................... *Scribner.*

— Art of elocution. ('59.) New ed., rev. 12°. '67. $1.50.............................. *Wilstach.*

— Art of English composition. ('67.) 8th ed. 12°. '76. $1.50.............................. *Scribner.*

— Elements of logic. ('67.) New ed. 12°. '76. $1.50. *Scribner.*

— Elements of psychology. 12°. '76. $1.50.. *Putnam.*

— Elements of rhetoric. 4th ed. 12°. '50. $1.50. *Barnes.*

— Introduction to the study of Eng. literature. ('68.) New ed. 12°. '76. $2.25.............. *Scribner.*

— Logical praxis. New ed. 12°. '75. $1.... *Putnam.*

— Principles of æsthetics. ('72.) New ed. ill. 12°. '76. $2.25.......................... *Putnam.*

Note. First pub. under title of Science of æsthetics.

— Rhetorical praxis: principles of rhetoric, exemplified and applied in exercises for systematic practice. ('60.) 2d ed., rev. 12°. '76. $1.25... *Wilstach.*

— Science of ethics. 12°. '76. $1.50........ *Putnam.*

— Young composer (The): guide to Eng. composition. ('70.) New ed. 12°. '76. $1........ *Scribner.*

— *See also* Hamilton, W.

Day, Hor. The opium habit; with suggestions as to its remedy. 12°. $1.75................ *Harper.*

Day, Jer. Elements of algebra; abridg. by I. B. Thomson. 12°. $1.—Key. $1....... *T. Bliss.*

— *Same.* 12°. *net*, 85c.—Key. *net*, 85c........ *Peck.*

— Large algebra. New ed., rev. and enl. by the author and A. D. Stanley. 8°. $2....... *T. Bliss.*

— *Same.* 8°. *net*, $1.75.—Key. *net*, $1.50...... *Peck.*

— The principles of plain trigonometry, mensuration, navigation and surveying. 8°. *net*, $2.50.. *Peck.*

Day, *Rev.* Lál Behári. Govinda Sámanta; or, the history of a Bengal raijat. [Fiction.] cr. 8°. '74. $1.75.............................. *Macmillan.*

Day, S: P. Pilgrim's progress in words of one syllable. *See* Bunyan, J.

— The rare romance of Reynard the fox, the crafty courtier, with the shifts of his son Reynardine; in words of one syllable. ill. roy. 16°. $1.50.. *Cassell.*

Day, T: History of Sandford and Merton. 18°. hf. bd., 75c.................................. *Harper.*

— *Same.* ill. 18°. '72. 75c.................. *Lothrop.*

— *Same.* 16°. 75c......................... *Routledge.*

— *Same.* ill. 16°. $1....... *Miller; Scribner, W. & A.*

— *Same.* ill. sq. 16°. '63. $1.25............. *Roberts.*

— *Same.* ill. 12°. $1.25; $1.50.............. *Nelson.*

— *Same.* ill. 12°. $1.50................. *World Pub.*

— *Same.* ill. 12°. (Bohn.) 80c...... *Scribner, W. & A.*

— *Same.* (Globe ed.) col. ill. 16°. $1.25; hf. cf., $3. *Lippincott.*

— *Same;* rev. by C. Hartley. ill. 16°. $1.25.. *Hurd & H.*

— — *Same.* ill. 16°. $1.50................... *Lee & S.*

— — *Same* (Household ser.) ill. 16°. $1.50; mor., $3.................................... *Lee & S.*

— — *Same.* (Presentation ed.) ill. 12°. $1.75; $1.25. 16°. $1............................ *Routledge.*

— *Same;* in words of one syllable, by M. Godolphin. ill. sq. 16°. $1.25........................ *Miller.*

— — *Same.* col. ill. roy. 16°. $1.50......... *Cassell.*

— *French.* Tr. par Berquin. [Text book.] 12°. hf. bd., $1............................ *Fortescue.*

— *See also* Crusoe lib.; — Juvenile classic ser.; — Treasure-box of amusement and instruction.

Day, T: *See* Connecticut, Supreme Court of Errors reports.

Day, W. G. *See* Sewall, F., *and* Day, W. G.

Day (A). *See* Adventures of.

Day after the fair. Somerset, C. A. 15c..... *French.*

Day after the holidays. Moncrieff, A. R. H. $1.50. *Appleton.*

Day after to-morrow. Prosser, *Mrs.* —. $1.50.. *Hoyt.*

Day after the wedding. Kemble, C. 15c...... *French.*

Daybreak; or, truth struggling. 18°. 75c..... *Carter.*

Daybreak in Britain. Tucker, C. 35c....... *Carter.*

Day-breaking, if not the sun-rising, etc. *See* Eliot, J:

Day by day: private prayers. 32°. '67. 25c.; mor., 50c.................................. *Randolph.*

Day (A) by the fire. Hunt, L. $1.50....... *Roberts.*

Day dawn: texts for every day. 128°. '75. 15c.; mor., 35c................................... *Am. Tr.*

Day dawn (The), and the rain. Ker, J. $2... *Carter.*

Day dreams. 18°. '54. 60c................ *Am. S. S.*

Day dreams. 12°. '74. $1.50.............. *Turnbull.*

Day dreams. Nunes, H. H. 75c......... *Lippincott.*

Day-hours of the Church of England, according to the Prayer book and the authorized tr. of the Bible. New ed. 12°. '72. 90c.................. *Pott.*

Day in Capernaum. ill. 16°. $1.25.....(?) *Luth. Pub.*

Day in Paris. Selby, C. 15c............... *French.*

Day of adventures. 18°. 50c............. *Cong. Pub.*

Day of reckoning. Planché, J. R. 15c....... *French.*

Day of rest: Sunday reading, with stories and sketches. ill. f°. '74. bds., $1.75.............. *Routledge.*

Day of small things. 18°. 35c............ *Cong. Pub.*

Day-school singer. Phillips, P. 50c. *Wilson, H. & Co.*

Day-spring. Martin, M. 40c.............. *So. Meth.*

Day-spring (The); or, union collection of songs for the sanctuary. obl. 8°. bds., $1.24.. *Huntington.*

Day-spring library. 10 v. 18°. $4.10...... *So. Meth.*

Cont.: Day-spring, by M. Martin.—Heart-blossoms, by J. T. H. Cross.—Convenient food.—Abyssinian boy.—Fanny, the flower-girl, by S. Bunbury.—Bible gleanings, by J. T. H. Cross.—Driftwood, by J. T. H. Cross.—Lectures to children.—Bible stories, by D. Stevenson.—Laura Eugenia Ellis.

Day star. *See* Giberne, A.

Day star series. 4 v. 12°. $5 .... *Nelson.*
Cont.: Day star, by A. Giberne.—Brother Bertie.—The Warringtons abroad.—Little Rosy's pet.

Day thoughts. Shaw, R. T. $1.50 .... *Lippincott.*

Day unto day. Bennett, M. L. $1 .... *Am. Unit.*

Day well spent. Hereford, J. 15c. .... *Ames.*

Day well spent. Oxenford, J. 15c. .... *French.*

Day with Christ. Cox, S. $1 .... *Dutton.*

Day with the haymakers. 18°. 35c. .... *Pres. Bd.*

Day's fishing. Morton, J. M. 15c. .... *French.*

Day's pleasure. Howells, W. D. 50c. ...... *Osgood.*

Day's ride. *See* Lever, C:

Day's work. Pilon, M. R. 35c. .... *Authors.*

Days at Millgate; or, lame Johnnie's holiday. 18°. 40c. *Am. S. S.*

Days at Muirhead. 18°. 75c. .... *Carter.*

Days at Seadown. 16°. $1 .... *Am. Bapt.*

Days in north India. Macleod, N. $1.50 .. *Lippincott.*

Days near Rome. Hare, A. J. C. $3.50; in 2 v., $5. *Porter.*

Days of boyhood. Alden, J. 75c. .... *Tibbals.*

Days of Bruce. Aguilar, G. 2 v. $2 ...... *Appleton.*

Days of chivalry. L'Epine, E. $5 .... *Cassell.*

Days of my life. Oliphant, M. O. W. $1.50 .. *Harper.*

Days of old: stories from old English history; by author of "Ruth and her friends." 18°. 75c. *Carter; Dutton; Macmillan.*

Days of shoddy. Morford, H. $1.75; $1.50 .. *Peterson.*

Days of yore. Keddie, H. $2 .... *Routledge.*

Dayton, A. C. Baptist facts vs. Methodist fiction. 18°. 30c. .... *So. Bapt.*

— Baptist question book. 2 v. 18°. ea., 25c. .. *So. Bapt.*

— Children brought to Christ. 18°. 25c.; pap., 10c. *So. Bapt.*

— Infidel's daughter. 12°. $1.50 .. *Am. Bapt.; So. Bapt.*

— Pædobaptist and Campbellite immersion: review of arguments of Waller, Fuller, Wayland, Broaddus and others. 12°. 60c. .... *So. Bapt.*

— Theodosia Ernest; or, the heroine of faith. 12°. $1.50 .... *Am. Bapt.*

— *Same.* ill. 12°. $1.50; $2.25 .... *So. Bapt.*

— — v. 2: Ten days' travel in search of the church. 12°. $1.50; $2.25 .... *So. Bapt.*

Dayton, *Miss* Laura H. Grace Warren. 18°. 40c. *So. Bapt.*

De *or* D'.
Note. For names (not English or American) beginning with de or d' look for initial letter of name following this prefix.

De imitatione Christi. *See* Thomas *a Kempis.*

De profundis. Gilbert, W. $2. .... *Routledge.*

Deacon, E. E. *See* England, Common law reports.

Deacon Gibbs' enemy. Dunning, A. K. $1.25. *Pres. Bd.*

Deacon Sims' prayers. Chellis, M. D. $1.50. *Cong. Pub.; H. A. Young.*

Dead alive. *See* Collins, Wilkie.

Dead alive: Ethiop. drama. 16°. pap., 15c. .... *French.*

Dead guest. *See* Zschokke, H.

Dead heart. Phillips, W. 15c. .... *French.*

Dead letter. Victor, M. V. F. 25c. .... *Beadle.*

Dead marquise. Kip, L. $1.50 .... *Putnam.*

Dead men's shoes. Braddon, M. E. 75c. .... *Harper.*

Dead men's shoes. Haderman, J. R. $2 .. *Lippincott.*

Dead monkey. *See* Sunbeam lib.

Dead reckoning. Barrett, E. $1.25 .. *Van Nostrand.*

Dead-sea fruit. Braddon, M. E. 50c. ...... *Harper.*

Dead secret. *See* Collins, Wilkie.

Dead shot. Buckstone, J. B. 15c. .... *French.*

Dead shot. *See* Marksman.

Dead sin, and other stories. Mayo, I. F. $1.75 .. *Dodd.*

Dead witness: drama. 16°. pap., 15c. .... *French.*

Deady, Mat. P. *See* Oregon, Organic and general laws;—United States, Circuit and Dist. Court reports.

Deaf and dumb. Holcroft, T. 15c. .... *French.*

Deaf as a post. Poole, J. 15c. .... *French.*

Deaf—in a horn: Ethiop. drama. 16°. pap., 15c. *French; Happy.*

Deaf shoemaker. Barrett, P. 75c. .... *Dodd.*

Deal boatman. Burnand, F. C. 15c. .... *French.*

Dealings of God, man and the devil. Dow, L. $3. *Pounsford.*

Dealings with the fairies. Mac Donald, G. $1.25. *Routledge.*

Dean, Alb. F. Interest and equation exponents. 7th ed. 4°. '76. hf. leath., $5 .... *L. L. & M. King.*

Dean, Amos. History of civilization. 7 v. por. 8°. '68–'69. $21 .... *Munsell.*

Dean, J: Gray substance of the medulla oblongata. 4°. '64. pap., $2.50 .... *Smith. Inst.*

Dean, J: Ward. Brief memoir of Giles Firmin, one of the ejected ministers of 1662. 8°. '66. pap., 25c. *N. E. Hist. Gen.*

— Sketch of life of John H. Sheppard. por. 8°. '73. pap., 50c. .... *N. E. Hist. Gen.*

— Story of the embarkation of Cromwell and his friends for New Eng. [*anon.*] 8°. '66. pap., 25c. *N. E. Hist. Gen.*

Dean, Philotus. Elementary arithmetic. ('68.) New ed. 16°. '74. 50c. .... *English.*

— High school arithmetic. 12°. '74. $1.35 .. *English.*

— Intellectual arithmetic. ('61.) New ed. 16°. '74. 45c.—Key. 55c. .... *English.*

— Intermediate arithmetic. ('65.) New ed. 12°. '74. 80c.—Key. $1 .... *English.*

— Primary arithmetic. ('60.) New ed. 16°. '74. 25c. *English.*

— Public school arithmetic. ('59.) New ed. 12°. '74. 80c.—Key. 75c. .... *English.*

Dean, Theodosia. Life. 16°. $1 .... *Am. Bapt.*

Deane, H: C. Principles of conveyancing: epitome of the law of corporeal hereditaments and conveyancing; with notes by a member of the Boston bar. 8°. '75. shp., $4 .... *Little, B. & Co.*

Deane, J. F. *See* Vermont, Reports.

Deane, Milly. Marjory. [Fiction.] cr. 8°. $1.50. *Macmillan.*

De Anguera, J. Complete method for guitar. f°. $3. *Gordon.*

Dean's (The) English. Moon, G. W. $1.25 .. *Routledge.*

Dear feast of Lent. Harris, M. C. $1.25 .... *Dutton.*

Dear Lady Disdain. McCarthy, J. $1.75; $1 .. *Sheldon.*

Dearborn, A. Flute preceptor. obl. 8°. $3. *Brainard.*

Dearborn, N. S. American text book of letters; with diagram of the capital script alphabet. obl. 4°. $2 .... *Lee & S.*

— Scrolls, monograms, ornaments, cuts, etc. obl. 4°. hf. mor., $2.50 .... *Lee & S.*

Dearborn, W: L. Making brick masonry impervious to water. 8°. pap., 30c. ...... *Am. Soc. of C. E.*

Dearer than life. Byron, H. J. 15c. .... *De Witt.*

Dearest mamma. Gordon, W. 15c. *De Witt; French.*

Dearsly, H: R. Criminal process: view of the whole proceedings taken in criminal prosecutions. 8°. '54. $1.50 .... *T. & J. W. Johnson.*

— — *See also* Law lib.

Death and the after-life. Davis, A. J. 75c.; 50c. *A. J. Davis.*

Death and life. Ware, M. E. $1.25 ...... *Lippincott.*

Death-bed scenes. Clark, D. W. $1.75 .. *Meth. Bk. Conc.*

Death-bed triumphs of eminent Christians. 12°. 70c. *Pres. Bd.*

Death, the devil, and the doctor on the war. Silsbee, S. 50c. .... *Wilstach.*

eath of Marlowe. Horne, R. H. 15c. .... *French.*
eath of Wallenstein. *See* Schiller, J. F. v.
eath to the traitor. 8°. pap., 25c. .... *De Witt.*
eath token: drama. 16°. pap., 15c. .... *French.*
ebar, J. H. Diss. West Virginia handbook and immigrant's guide. map. 8°. $1; pap., 75c. *Gibbens.*
ebatable land (The) between this world and the next. Owen, R. D. $2 .... *Carleton.*
ebate (The) between the church and science; or, the ancient Hebraic idea of the six days of creation; with essay on the literary character of Tayler Lewis. 12°. '60. $1.50 .... *Draper.*
ebbil (De) and de maiden: Ethiop. drama. 16°. pap., 15c. .... *Happy.*
ebbil and Dr. Faustum: Ethiop. drama. 16°. pap., 15c. .... *Happy.*
ebby's friends. 18°. 75c. .... *Cong. Pub.*
e Belem, E. M. *See* Belem, E. M. de.
ebenham's vow. Edwards, A. B. 75c. .... *Harper.*
ebit and credit. Freytag, G. $1.50 .... *Harper.*
e Bonay, J: Raphalina; or, the female Tichborne. 8°. '73. pap., 25c. .... (?) *H. L. Williams.*
eborah (Leah). Cheltnam, C. S. 15c. *De Witt; French.*
eborah's diary. Manning, A. 17c. ..... *Littell & G.*
eborah's drawer. O'Reilly, R. $1 .... *Dutton.*
ebt: farcical comedy. 16°. pap., 15c. ...... *French.*
ebtor and creditor. Arthur, T. S. 75c. *Collins & Bro.*
ebtor's daughter. Arthur, T. S. 50c. ..... *Peterson.*
ecalogne, John Mary. Life. 18°. '64. 50c.; $1. *Kelly, P. & Co.*
ecameron. *See* Boccaccio, G.
e Camp, M. T. Personation: interlude. 16°. pap., 15c. .... *French.*
ecided case (A). Brougham, J. 15c. ..... *French.*
ecision. Hofland, B. $1 .... *Nelson.*
ecision (The). *See* Kennedy, Grace.
eclaration of independence. *See* United States.
eclaration of independence: farce. 16°. pap., 15c. *French.*
eclaration of the state of the colonie and affaires in Virginia; by his maiestie's Counseil for Virginia, 1620. London. [Reprint.] 4°. pap., 75c. *Sabin.*
Declension and revival. Winslow, C. $1 .... *Carter.*
De Colange, L. *See* Colange, L.
De Colyar, H: A. Treatise on the law of guaranties and principal and surety; with notes to Am. cases by J. A. Morgan. 8°. shp., $6. *Baker, V. & Co.*
De Costa, B: F. Hudson's sailing directions. 8°. '69. $1.50 .... *Munsell*
— Lake George: its scenes and characteristics; with sketches of Schroon Lake, the lakes of the Adirondacks, and Lake Luzerne. ill. 16°. '68. $1.50 .... *Randolph.*
— Northmen in Maine: examination of views of J. G. Kohl. 8°. '70. $1.50 .... *Munsell.*
— Rector of Roxburgh; or, a story for our own times. 16°. '71. $1.25 .... *Dutton.*
— Scenes in the Isle of Mount Desert, coast of Maine. 16°. '68. $1.50;—with photos. 4°. $4 .. *Randolph.*
Decourcelle, A., *and* Thiboust, L. I dine with my mother: farce. 16°. pap., 15c. .... *French.*
Decree of divorce: musical [dram.] sketch. 16°. pap., 15c. .... *Happy.*
Dedenroth, E. H. v. Baronin (Die); [also] Mit eiserner Hand. 8°. pap., 50c. .... *Morwitz.*
— Gespenst (Das). *See* Strubberg, F. A., Die alte spanische Urkunde.
Deeds not words: drama. 16°. pap., 15c. .... *French.*
Deeds of dreadful note: farce. 16°. pap., 15c. *Happy.*

Deems, C: F. Home altar (The): appeal in behalf of family worship, with prayers and hymns, etc. 18°. '67. $1.25 .... *Hurd & H.*
— Jesus. ill. 8°. $4–$10 .... *U. S. Pub.*
— What now? 16°. '69. 40c. .... *Am. Tr.*
Deems, Ja. M. Solfeggi: element. and progressive method of vocal music. 8°. '71. bds., 75c. *Ditson.*
Deep, deep sea. Planché, J. R., *and* Dance, C. 15c. *French.*
Deep down. Ballantyne, R. M. $1.25 .... *Lippincott.*
Deep waters. *See* Drury, A. H.
Deepdale end. 16°. 90c. .... *Cong. Pub.*
Deepening the spiritual life. Boodle, R. G. 15c. .. *Pott.*
Deerfoot. Burnand, F. C. 15c. .... *De Witt; French.*
Deering, Ma. S. Illustrated guide book for Portland [Me.] and vicinity, by "our young woman about town"; with hist. of Portland by W. Willis. ill. and maps. 18°. '73. bds., 50c. .. *Loring, S & H.*
Deerings of Medbury. Townsend, V. F. $1.25 .. *Loring.*
Deerslayer (The). *See* Cooper, J. F.
Deerstalkers. Herbert, H. W. 75c. .... *Peterson.*
Defence of Guenevere. Morris, W. $2 .... *Roberts.*
Defence of Virginia and the south. Dabney, R. L. $1.50 .... *Hale.*
Defense of church principles: lectures by clergymen of the Church of Eng. 16°. pap., 50c. .... *Pott.*
Defense of Jesus. St. Martin, M. $1. *Cin. Meth. Bk. Conc.*
Defense of our fathers. Emory, J. $1 .. *Meth. Bk. Conc.*
Defoe, Dan. Works; with life. 8°. $2.50. *Appleton; Lee & S.*
— *Same*; ed. by Wa. Scott. 7 v. 12°. (Bohn.) ea., $1.25 .... *Little, B. & Co.*
Cont.: 1. Life and adventures of Captain Singleton; Col. Jack.—2. Memoirs of a cavalier; Capt. Carleton; Dickory Cronke, etc.—3. Moll Flanders; History of the devil.—4. Roxana; Mother Ross.—5. The great plague; Fire of London; Storm, etc.—6. Duncan Campbell; Voyage round the world, etc.—7. Robinson Crusoe.

— *Same.* 7 v. 12°. (Bohn.) ea., $1.40. *Scribner, W. & A.*
— *Same.* 7 v. 12°. (Bohn.) ea., $1.50 ... *Lippincott.*
— Robinson Crusoe. 8°. pap., 10c. .... *Beadle.*
— *Same.* 32°. 25c. .... *Porter.*
— *Same.* 12°. pap., 25c. .... *Lippincott.*
— *Same.* 18°. 35c. .... *Routledge.*
— *Same.* ill. 16°. 50c.; pap., 20c. .... *U. P. James.*
— *Same.* 18°. 75c. .... *Claxton; Lippincott.*
— *Same.* sq. 8°. '72. 75c. .... *Tuttle.*
— *Same.* sq. 18°. $1 .... *Nichols & H.*
— *Same.* ill. 16°. $1 .... *Routledge; Scribner, W. & A.*
— *Same.* ill. 12°. $1 .... *Lippincott.*
— *Same.* ill. cr. 8°. $1; pap., 75c. .. *Scribner, W. & A.*
— *Same.* 16°. $1.25 .... *Eastman.*
— *Same.* ill. 12°. $1.25 .... *Miller; Scribner, W. & A.*
— *Same.* ill. 16°. $1.50; col. ill., $1.50 .... *Lee & S.*
— *Same.* ill. 12°. $1.50 .... *Carleton; Eastman; Lee & S.; Nelson; Routledge; Scribner, W. & A.*
— *Same.* ill. cr. 8°. '68. $1.50; $2; hf. cf., $3.50. *Hurd & H.*
— *Same.* ill. 16°. $1.75 .... *Scribner, W. & A.*
— *Same.* ill. 12°. $1.75 .... *Scribner, W. & A.*
— *Same.* ill. cr. 8°. $2.50 .... *Scribner, W. & A.*
— *Same.* ill. roy. 8°. $3.50 .... *Cassell; Lee & S.*
— *Same.* ill. and por. 4°. $3.50; hf. cf., $5; cf., $9; mor., $12.—ill. 8°. $3.50 .... *Routledge.*
— *Same.* ill. 8°. cf., $7 .... *Scribner, W. & A.*
— *Same.* 12°. (Bohn.) $1.25; ill., $1.75. *Little, B. & Co.*
— *Same.* 12°. (Bohn.) $1.75; ill., $2 ... *Lippincott.*
— *Same.* ill. 12°. (Bohn.) $2 ...... *Scribner, W. & A.*
— *Same.* (Chandos classics.) ill. cr. 8°. $1; pap., 75c. *Scribner, W. & A.*
— *Same.* (Globe ed.) ill. 16°. $1; hf. cf., $3. *Lippincott.*
— *Same.* (Holiday ed.) ill. 8°. $3 .... *Locke.*

Defoe, Dan., *continued.*
— *Same.* (Household ed.) ill. 8°. $1.50 ..... *Nelson.*
— *Same.* (National ed.) ill. 32°. 50c.; 75c.; pap., 25c. *Scribner, W. & A.*
— *Same.* (Presentation poets.) ill. 12°. $1.75. *Routledge.*
— *Same.* (World-wide lib.) 12°. pap., 25c. *Routledge.*
— *Same;* with memoir of D. (Grandville ed.) ill. cr. 8°. $2; hf. cf., $4 ..... *Routledge.*
— *Same;* with biog. sketch. ill. 12°. $1.50. *Estes; Harper; Locke; World Pub.*
— *Same;* with memoir, and essay on his writings. 12°. $1 ..... *Porter.*
— *Same;* with memoir, and essay on his writings. ill. 8°. $2; hf. cf., $4.50. 12°. $1.50 ..... *Appleton.*
— *Same;* with autobiog. and life of A. Selkirk. ill. 8°. '72. *$2.50; $3; hf. mor., $5 ..... *Hubbard.*
— *Same;* ed. by J. W. Clark. 18°. '66. $1.25. *Macmillan.*
— *Same;* ed. with introd. by H. Kingsley. (Globe ed.) 12°. '68. $1.50 ..... *Macmillan.*
— *Same;* ed. by Peter Parley. ('35.) New ed. ill. sq. 16°. '75. $1 ..... *Clark & M.*
— — *See also* Gibert, *Mme.* M., Second Fr. reader; — Godolphin, M.; — Treasure-box of wonder and entertainment.
— *French.* 12°. $2 ..... *Routledge.*
— *German.* Neu erzählt v. O. L. Heubner. ill. 18°. 50c.; 75c ..... *Kohler.*
— History of the devil. 12°. $1.50 ..... *Sower.*
— Religious courtship; or, marriage on Christian principles. 12°. $1 ..... *Pounsford.*

De Fontaine, F. G. Cyclopedia of the best thoughts of Dickens. 8°. $5; mor., $10 ..... *Hale.*
— Gleanings from a Confederate army note-book; by "Personne" [*pseud.*] 12°. $1 ..... *Duffie.*

De Fontaine, *Mrs.* F. G. Wisdom teeth for little people. sm. 4°. bds., 60c ..... *Hale.*

De Forest, J: W. European acquaintance: sketches of people in Europe. 12°. $1.50 ..... *Harper.*
— History of the Indians of Connecticut, to 1850. 8°. *net*, $2.60 ..... *Hamersley.*
— *Same.* por., map and pl. 8°. '71. $2.50 .. *Munsell.*
— Kate Beaumont. ill. 8°. '71. $1.25; pap., 75c. *Estes.*
— Miss Ravenel's conversion from secession to loyalty. 12°. $1.50 ..... *Harper.*
— Overland. $1.75; pap., $1 ..... *Sheldon.*
— Playing the mischief. 8°. pap., 75c. ..... *Harper.*
— The Wetherel affair. 8°. $1.75; pap., $1 .. *Sheldon.*

Deformed (The). Marsh-Caldwell, A. 25c. *Peterson.*

De Garmo, W: B. The dance of society: crit. analysis of quadrilles, round dances, and other relative matter. 8°. '75. $1.50 ..... *Pond.*

De Gerando, Jos. M. *See* Gerando, J. M. de.

De Gex, J. P. *See* England, Chancery reports.

Deghuée, Jos. Aufgaben u. Anleitg. zum schriftl. Rechnen: deutsch u. engl. 3 pts. 8°. '66. bds., $1.80; pt. 1, 80c.; pt. 2, $1 ..... *Steiger.*
— Geographie f. Schulen. 12°. '68. bds., 80c. *Steiger.*

De Graff, Sim. The geometrical stair-builder's guide. ill. 4°. (cop. '54.) '72. $5 ..... *Baird.*

De Granada, Lew. *See* Granada, Lewis de.

De Groot, Susan. Memoir. 18°. 30c. .... *Am. S. S.*

Deharbe, Jos. Katechismus. (Old issue.) 3 v. no. 1, 12°, 33c.; 2, 12°, 25c.; 3, 16°, 12c. .... *Benziger.*
— *Same.* New ed. 12°. 30c ..... *Benziger.*
— *Same.* 12°. '75. hf. roan, 25c. ..... *Herder.*
— *Eng.* Full catechism of the Catholic religion; tr. by J. Fander. 4th ed. 16°. '75. 75c. *Cath. Pub.*
— Kleiner kathol. Katechismus. 16°. '75. hf. roan, 10c. ..... *Herder.*
— *Same.* 12°. bds., 15c ..... *Benziger; Hoffmann.*
— *Same.* 12°. hf. bd., 18c ..... *Vering.*
— *Same:* Auszug d. katholischen Katechismus, od. Lehrbegriffs. 12°. hf. bd., 15c ..... *Hoffmann.*
— *Eng.* Little Catholic catechism for beginners; tr. by T. Noethen. 32°. 10c ..... *Noonan.*

De Hart, W: Observations on military laws and courts-martial. 8°. shp., $4 ..... *Appleton.*

Dehon, Thdr. Life. 18°. 45c.; 50c ..... *Dutton.*

Deipnosophists (The). *See* Athenæus.

De Kay, Ja. E. *See* New York geol. survey.

De Koninck, L. L., *and* Dietz, E. Practical manual of chemical analysis and assaying, as applied to the manufacture of iron; ed. with notes by R. Mallet. Am. ed., with notes by A. A. Fesquet. 12°. '73. $2.50 ..... *Baird.*

Del Dunstan's childhood; by author of "Waiting for the morning." 16°. $1.10 ..... *Am. S. S.*

De la Beche, *Sir* H: T: Geological observer. ill. 8°. $4 ..... *Lea.*

Delacour, A. *See* Labiche, E., *and* Delacour, A.

Delafield, E. Biographical sketch of J. Kearny Rodgers. 8°. '52. pap., 25c ..... *N. Y. Acad. Med.*

Delafield, Fs. Some forms of dyspepsia. *See* Seguin, E. C., Am. clin. lect.
— Treatise on post-mortem examinations and morbid anatomy. 8°. $3.50 ..... *W. Wood.*

Delafield, H., *and others* vs. Parish, T., *and others.* Parish will case in the Court of Appeals [N. Y.]; statement and opinion of the court. 8°. shp. $7.50 ..... *Baker, V. & Co.*

Delaforce. Tucker, C. 75c. ..... *Dutton.*

Delamer, E. S. The flower garden: culture in the open ground of bulbous, tuberous, fibrous-rooted and shrubby flowers. 16°. bds., 50c ..... *Routledge.*
— The kitchen-garden; or, the culture in the open ground of roots, vegetables, herbs and fruits. 16°. bds., 50c. ..... *Routledge.*

Delamotte, Ph. H. Beginner's drawing book. cr. 8°. '69. pap., 75c ..... *Macmillan.*

Delaplaine. Walworth, M. T. $1.75 ..... *Carleton.*

De la Rame, L. *See* La Rame, L. de.

Delavan, E: C. Consideration of the temperance argument and history. ('65.) New ed. 12°. '69. $1.50 ..... *Nat. Temp.*

Delavigne, C. Louis XI.; tr. from the Fr.: drama. 16°. pap., 15c. ..... *French.*
— Monastery of St. Just; tr. by J. Oxenford: drama. 16°. pap., 15c ..... *French.*

Delaware. Court of Chancery reports, 1814–'33; by D. M. Bates. 8°. '76. *net*, shp., $8. *T. & J. W. Johnson.*
— Superior Court, Court of Errors and Appeals, and criminal courts reports, v. 6–9 (1855–'74); by J. W. Houston. 4 v. 8°. '66–'75. shp., $10. *James & W.*

Note. v. 1–5 (1832–'55), by S. M. Harrington, are o.p.

Delaware Dick; or, the chase of the Wasp. 8°. pap., 25c ..... *De Witt.*

Delaware geological survey. Memoir of a geol. survey of D.; by J. C. Booth. 8°. '41 ..... *State.*

Deléon, *L'abbé.* Under the ban: tr. of "Le maudit." [Fiction.] 8°. $1.75; pap., $1.25 ..... *Harper.*

De Leon, Edn. Askaros Kassis, the Copt: romance of modern Egypt. 12°. $1.75 ..... *Lippincott.*

De Leon, T. C. Cross-purposes: Christmas experience in seven stages. ill. 16°. $1.25 *Lippincott.*
— "South songs," from the lays of later days. 16°. '66. $1.75 ..... *Eyrich.*

De Levante, E: R. *See* Bible [Whole], *Hexaglot.*

Delicate attentions: drama. 16°. pap., 15c... *French.*

Delicate ground. Dance, C. 15c. ..... *French.*

Délices des ames pieuses. *See* Altar manual.

De Liefde, Jac. Golden cap. 16°. $1.25 .... *Carter.*
— Great Dutch admirals (The). ill. 12°. $2 .. *Routledge.*
— Signet ring, and other gems. New ed. 16°. '75. $1.25 ..... *Lothrop.*

De Liefde, J: A Dutchman's difficulties with the Eng. language. 24°. pap., 25c. . . . . *Routledge.*
— The postman's bag: a story for boys and girls. ill. 12°. $1.50. . . . . *Routledge.*
De Liefde, J: B. Galama; or, the beggars. 8°. $1.25; pap., 75c. . . . . *Scribner.*
— The romance of charity; abridg. from "Charities of Europe." ill. cr. 8°. $2.50. . . . . *Routledge.*
— Walter's escape; or, the capture of Breda. ill. 12°. $1.25. . . . . *Scribner, W. & A.*
Delille, C. J. Condensed French instruction. ('67.) New ed. 16°. '71. 60c. . . . . *Holt.*
Delinquent. Reynolds, F. 15c. . . . . *French.*
Delisser, G: P. Horseman's guide. 16°. $1; bds., 75c. . . . . *Dick & F.*
Delitsch, Otto. *See* Bible [Whole], *Germ.*
Delitzsch, Fz. Jul. Biblical commentaries; tr. from the Germ. 10 v. 8°. ea., $3. . *Scribner, W. & A.*
Cont.: Hebrews, 2 v. — Isaiah, 2 v. — Job, 2 v. — Psalms, 3 v. — Proverbs, v. 1.
— Biblical psychology. 8°. $6. . . . . *Scribner, W. & A.*
— Solomonic writings. 3 v. 8°. ea., $3. . *Scribner, W. & A.*
— *See also* Bible, Isaiah; — Keil, K. F., *and* Delitzsch, F. J.
Delizie del cristiano, ossia esercizj di pietà ricavati dai migliori autori. 24°. *net*, 35c.; 44c. . . *Benziger.*
Dell, W: The doctrine of baptisms reduced from its ancient and modern corruptions, and restored to its primitive soundness and integrity, etc. 16°. *net*, pap., 10c. . . . . *Friends Bk. Assoc.*
Della Balcom. 16°. $1.25. . . . . *Cong. Pub.*
Del Mar, Em. La guia para la conversacion en español é inglés, por F. J. Vingut. 12°. $1. *G. R. Lockwood.*
— Spanish and English conversations. 12°. '54. $1.25. *G. R. Lockwood.*
De Lolme, J: Lew. Constitution of England; ed., with notes, by J. Macgregor. 12°. (Bohn.) $1.25. . . . . *Little, B. & Co.*
— *Same.* 12°. (Bohn.) $1.40. . . . . . *Scribner, W. & A.*
— *Same.* 12°. (Bohn.) $1.50 . . . . *Lippincott.*
— — *See also* Hallam, H., Constitutional history.
— Lessons in French. 8°. 50c.; pap., 25c. . . . *Cassell.*
— *and* Wallace, R., *and* Bridgeman, H. French-English and Eng.-French dict. cr. 8°. $1.75. . . . *Cassell.*
De l'Orme. James, G. P. R. $1.50. . . . . *Harper.*
Deluge (The) in the light of modern science. Denton, W. 10c. . . . . *Denton.*
Delusion: drama. 16°. pap., 15c. . . . . *French.*
Demarest, D: D. History and characteristics of the Ref. Prot. Dutch Church. ill. 12°. $1; mor., $2.50 . . . . *N. Y. Ref. Ch. Bd.*
— The manly independent thinker. 8°. pap., 25c. *N. Y. Ref. Ch. Bd.*
Demarest, G. L. Atlantic primary arithmetic: simple numbers. ('71.) 3d ed. 18°. '75. hf. bd., 50c. . . . . *Ginn.*
— Psalms, hymns and spiritual songs. 16°. per doz., $4 . . . . *Williamson.*
— Songs of joy; for Universalist Sunday-schools. [Hymn book.] 18°. '70. 40c. . . . . *Universalist.*
— Year (A) of worship; for S.-schools and homes. [Service book.] 18°. '73. 45c. . . . *Universalist.*
Demcker, Rob. A course of systematic and progressive drawing: in 6 pts. and teacher's guide. 8°. $2.25. . . . . *Krebs.*
De Mille, Ja. American baron (The). ill. 8°. $1.50; pap., $1. . . . . *Harper.*
— B. O. W. C. stories. 6 v. ill. 16°. ea., $1.50. . *Lee & S.*
Cont.: The B. O. W. C. — Boys of Grand Pré School. — Lost in the fog. — Fire in the woods. — Picked up adrift. — Treasure of the seas.
— Babes in the wood. 8°. '74. $1.50; pap., 75c. *W. F. Gill.*
— Comedy (A) of terrors. 8°. $1.25; pap., 75c. *Estes.*

De Mille, Ja., *continued.*
— Cord and creese; or, the Brandon mystery. ill. 8°. $1.25; pap., 75c. . . . . *Harper.*
— Cryptogram (The). ill. 8°. $2; pap., $1.50. . *Harper.*
— Dodge Club (The); or, Italy in 1859. ill. 8°. $1.25; pap., 75c. . . . . *Harper.*
— Lady of the ice. ill. 8°. $1.25; pap., 75c. . . *Appleton.*
— Lily and the cross: a tale of Acadia. ill. 16°. $1.50. *Lee & S.*
— Living link (The). ill. 8°. $1.50; pap., $1. . *Harper.*
— Open question. ill. 8°. $1.50; pap., $1. . *Appleton.*
— The Young Dodge Club. [To form 3 v.] v. 1, 2. ill. 16°. ea., $1.50. . . . . *Lee & S.*
Cont.: Among the brigands. — The seven hills.
Demi-monde. Dumas, A. 75c.; 50c. . . . . *Lippincott.*
Deming, H: C. Life of U. S. Grant. por. 8°. '68. $2.50; leath., $3.50. . . . . *Scranton.*
Democracy and monarchy in France. Adams, C. K. $2.50. . . . . *Holt.*
Democracy in America. *See* Tocqueville, A. C. H. C. de.
Democratic vistas. Whitman, W. $1. . . . *Whitman.*
Demogeot, J. History of French literature; adapted from the Fr. by C. Bridge. 12°. $1.50. . *Lippincott.*
Demoiselle (La) de Saint-Cyr. *See* Drohojowska, *Comtesse.*
De Molay Encampment. *See* Freemasons.
Demon lover. Brougham, J. 15c. . . . . *French.*
De Monte, —. Mass in C; arrang. by W. C. Peters. 4°. pap., $1. . . . . *Peters.*
De Morgan, S. E. Algy's lesson. ill. fp. 8°. 60c. *Cassell.*
Demosthenes. Orations; tr., with notes, etc., by C. R. Kennedy. 2 v. 12°. $3. . . . . *Harper.*
Cont.: Olynthiac, etc. — On the crown; On the embassy.
— — *Same.* 5 v. 12°. (Bohn.) v. 1, $1.25; v. 2–5, ea., $1.75. . . . . *Little, B. & Co.*
Cont.: v. 1. The Olynthiac, Philippic, and other public orations. — v. 2. On the crown and the embassy. — v. 3. Against Leptines, Midias, Androtion and Aristocrates. — v. 4. Private and other orations. — v. 5. Miscellaneous orations.
— — *Same.* 5 v. 12°. (Bohn.) v. 1, $1.40; v. 2–5, ea., $2. . . . . *Scribner, W. & A.*
— — *Same.* 5 v. 12°. (Bohn.) v. 1, $1.75; v. 2–5, ea., $2. . . . . *Lippincott.*
— *Same;* tr. by T. Leland. 2 v. 18°. $1.50. . *Harper.*
— Olynthiacs [Gk.]; ed. by W. S. Tyler. 12°. 90c. *Allyn.*
— *Same;* [also] Philippics; ed. by W. S. Tyler. ('75.) 2d ed. 12°. '76. $1.50. . . . . *Allyn.*
— Oration on the crown [Gk.]; with notes by J. T. Champlin. 12°. $1.50. . . . . *Dennet.*
— *Same;* ed. by A. Holmes. New ed., rev. by W. S. Tyler. ('73.) 3d ed. 12°. '76. $1.50. . . *Allyn.*
— *Same.* De corona; [also] Æschines against Ctesiphon: Gk. text with Eng. notes by B. Drake. 12°. '72. $1.50. . . . . *Macmillan.*
— — *Same;* with notes by M. L. D'Ooge. 12°. '75. $1.75. *Griggs.*
— *Eng.* On the crown; tr., with notes, by T. Leland. 12°. (Bohn.) $1. . . . . *Little, B. & Co.*
— — *Same.* 12°. (Bohn.) $1.20. . . . *Scribner, W. & A.*
— — *Same.* 12°. (Bohn.) $1.25. . . . . *Lippincott.*
— Philippics [Gk.]; ed. by W. S. Tyler. 12°. $1. *Allyn.*
— *Same.* 1st–3d Philippics; with introds. and notes, ed. by Smead. 12°. hf. bd., $1.50. . . *Appleton.*
— Select popular orations [Gk.]; with notes by J. T. Champlin. 12°. $1.50. . . . . *Dennet.*
Dempster, C. Iseulte. [Fiction.] 8°. pap., 50c. *Harper.*
Dempster, J: Lectures and addresses. 12°. $1.75. *Cin. Meth. Bk. Conc.*
Dempster, W. R. Beauties of vocal melody. f°. $1. *Gordon.*
Denaux, Prosper, *and* Legouvé, E. Louise de Lignerolles: drama. 16°. pap., 15c. . . . . . . *French.*

Dendy, Wa. Cooper. Philosophy of mystery. 12°. $1. *Harper.*

Dene hollow. Wood, E. P. $1.75; $1.50..*Peterson.*

Dengler, Adf. Index to the maps on record in the Register's Office in N.Y. City. 8°. $2..*Ward & P.*

Denier, Tony. Parlor pantomimes. 10 pts. 16°. ea., pap., 25c..........*French.*

— Parlor tableaux. 12°. pap., 25c....*French; Happy.*

— Shadow pantomimes; or, harlequin in the shade. 12°. pap., 25c..........*French; Happy.*

— (*ed.*) Amateur's guide to home or drawing-room theatricals. 12°. '66. pap., 25c..........*Happy.*

Dening, *Mrs.* H. She spake of him. 16°. $1.25. *Carter.*

Denio, H. *See* New York, Supreme Court and Court of Errors reports.

Denis, F., *and* Chauvin, V. True Robinson Crusoes; tr. and abridg. by C. Russell. 16°. $1.50. *Cassell; Lee & S.*

Denis Downe. Thomas, A. 50c..........*Harper.*

Denis Duval. *See* Thackeray, W. M.

Denison, C: Wheeler. Antoine; by an ex-consul. ('74.) New ed. 16°. '75. $1.50..........*Hoyt.*

— The tanner boy: life of U. S. Grant. ill. 16°. '64. $1.25..........*Roberts.*

Denison, E. B. *See* Beckett, *Sir* Edmund.

Denison, F: Sabbath institution traced and defended in its hist. and changes. 18°. 30c....*Am. Bapt.*

— Sabres and spurs: First R. I. Cavalry. 12°. '76. $2. *Freeman.*

— Supper institution. 18°. 60c..........*Am. Bapt.*

Denison, J: L. (*ed.*) Illustrated history of the new world. [Germ. and Eng. eds.] ill. and por. 12°. '73. *$4.75; $5.75; mor., $6.25.....*Henry Bill.*

Denison, *Mrs.* Ma. Andrews. ["Clara Vance."] Andy Luttrell. ill. 16°. '69. $1.50..........*Lothrop.*

— Anne Austin; or, piety and pride in contrast. 16°. $1..........*Am. Bapt.*

— Antoinette: the original of the "Child angel." ('60.) New ed. ill. 16°. '75. $1.15..........*Hoyt.*

— Bessie Brown, the soldier's daughter. ('66.) New ed. ill. 16°. '75. $1..........*Hoyt.*

— Blind princess. ('66.) New ed. ill. 16°. '75. $1. *Hoyt.*

— Carrie Hamilton; or, the beauty of true religion. 16°. $1..........*Am. Bapt.*

— Chantry's boy. ('72.) New ed. 16°. '74. $1.50..*Hoyt.*

— Child angel (The). 32°. '73. 20c......*Randolph.*

— *Same.* ('61.) New ed. ill. 18°. '71. 30c.....*Hoyt.*

— — *See also above* Antoinette.

— Denison series. 3 v. 16°. ea., $1.50...(?)*Martien.*
Cont.: A noble sister. — Hannah's triumph. — Off the track.

— Home pictures. 12°. $1.50..........*Harper.*

— Idaline: the mission of a short life. 16°. $1. *Am. Bapt.*

— Jenny Boardman; or, life in Campsie. 16°. $1.50. *Am. Bapt.*

— John Dane; or, the trials of artist life. ('74.) New ed. 16°. '76. $1.50..........*Hoyt.*

— Kept from idols. ('70.) New ed. ill. 16°. '74. $1.50. *Hoyt.*

— Led to the light. 16°. $1.25..........(?)*Martien.*

— Lieut. Messenger. ('63.) New ed. ill. 16°. '69. 60c. *Hoyt.*

— Little folks at Redbow. 16°. '75. $1.50..*H. A. Young.*

— Lover's trials. 12°. $1.75; pap., $1.50...*Peterson.*

— Nellie Walters. 18°. 75c..........(?)*Martien.*

— Opposite the jail. ('60.) New ed. ill. 16°. '75. $1.25. *Hoyt.*

— Out of prison. ill. 16°. '64. $1.50...*H. A. Young.*

— Saturday afternoon ser. 5 v. 18°. $3; ea., 60c. (?)*Martien.*
Cont.: Anne's Saturday afternoons. — Anne's new life. — Anne's beach party. — Anne and Tilly. — Orphan Anne.

— Stolen from home. ('73.) New ed. 16°. '75. $1.50. *Hoyt.*

— Strawberry Hill. ill. 16° '70. $1.50.....*Lothrop.*

Denison, *Mrs.* Ma. Andrews, *continued.*

— Sunshine cottage. 16°. '75. 75c..........*Hoyt.*

— The Talbury girls. ill. 16°. '71. $1.50....*Lothrop.*

— Victor Norman, rector; or, Bessie's husband. 12°. $1.50..........*Lippincott.*

— Young sergeant (The); or, the triumphant soldier. ('61.) New ed. ill. 18°. '70. 45c..........*Hoyt.*

Denison, Ste. C: *See* England, Crown cases.

Denkmäler für Kinder. [Tales.] 24°. 25c...*Ev. Assoc.*

Denman, J. S. Student's speaker. 18°. hf. bd., 50c. *Sheldon.*

— Student's spelling-book. 16°. hf. bd., 15c. *Sheldon.*

Dennan, *Mrs.* M. A. Stella; or, the pathway heavenward. ('62.) New ed. ill. 18°. '75. 50c..*Hoyt.*

Dennery, A. P. *See* Dumanoir, P. F. P., *and* Dennery, A. P.

— *and* Bresil, J. Jocrisse, the juggler: drama. 16°. pap., 15c..........*French.*

— *and* Clairville, L. F. N. My wife's diary: farce. 16°. pap., 15c..........*French.*

— *and* Clement, —. Noémie; tr. by T. W. Robertson: drama. 16°. pap., 15c.......*De Witt; French.*

— *and* Dugué, Fd. Sea of ice: drama. 16°. pap., 15c..........*French.*

Denny, Eb. Military journal; with memoir. 8°. '59. $2.25..........*R. S. Davis (P.)*

— — *See also* Historical Soc. of Penn.

Denounced. *See* Banim, J. *and* M.

Densel, Ma. Goldy books. 3 v. ill. 18°. '72. $2..*Dutton.*
Cont.: Goldy and Goldy's friends. — Three little Tylers. — Tel. Tyler at school.

— Lloyd Dalan. ill. 16°. '73. $1.25..........*Dutton.*

Densmore, Jl. Economic science; or, the law of balance in the sphere of wealth; with introd. by L. Waisbrooker. 12°. '75. pap., 25c. ...*Colby.*

Denton, Eliz. M. F. *See* Denton, W. *and* E. M. F.

Denton, J. Bailey. Sanitary works and sewage utilization. 8°. pap., 40c..........*Spon.*

— Sewage farming; with remarks on the position of sewer authorities in rel. to lands to which sewage is applied. 8°. pap., 40c..........*Spon.*

— The sewage question: treatment and utilization of sewage. 8°. '71. pap., 80c..........*Spon.*

— The storage of water. 8°. '74. pap., 40c.....*Spon.*

Denton, *Rev.* W: Commentary on Acts. 2 v. 8°. '74–'76. v. 1, $5.50; v. 2, $4.50..........*Pott.*

— Commentary on the Epistles for the Sundays and other holy days. 2 v. 8°. '75. $11.......*Pott.*

— Commentary on the Gospels for the Sundays and other holy days. 3 v. 8°. '75. $16.50....*Pott.*

— Commentary on the Lord's prayer. 12°. '65. $1. *Meth. Bk. Conc.*

— *Same.* 16°. '64. $1.25..........*Pott.*

— Grace (The) of the ministry, considered as a divine gift of uninterrupted transmission and two-fold character. 8°. '72. $7.50..........*Pott.*

Denton, *Prof.* W: Irreconcilable records; or, Genesis and geology. 12°. 50c..........*Denton.*

— Our planet, its past and future; or, lectures on geology. ('68.) 7th ed. 12°. '75. $1.50...*Denton.*

— Radical discourses. 12°. '72. ea., pap., 10c...*Denton.*
Cont.: The deluge in the light of modern science. — Common sense thoughts on the Bible. — What is right. — Christianity no finality. — Be thyself. — The God proposed for our national constitution. — Who are Christians? — Sermons from Shakespeare's text. — Man's true savior. — Is spiritualism true? 15c.

— Radical rhymes. 12°. '71. $1.25..........*Denton.*

— *and* E. M. F. The soul of things; or, psychometric researches and discoveries. 3 v. 12°. '63–'73. $5; v. 1, 3, ea., $1.50; v. 2, $2..........*Denton.*

Denutry, C: House (The) in Balfour Street. 12°. $1.50..........(?)*O'Kane.*

Deportirten (Die). Nieritz, G. 25c.......*Morwitz.*

Depping, Gu. Wonders of bodily strength and skill in all ages and all countries; tr. and enl. by C. Russell. ill. 12°. '73. $1.25..........*Scribner.*

Depths of the sea. Thomson, C. W. $9..*Macmillan.*

De Puy, H: W. Life of Ethan Allen. 16°. $1.50..*Mason.*

De Puy, W. H. Threescore years and beyond; or, experiences of the aged. ill. 8°. '71. $3.50; mor., $7.50 .... *Meth. Bk. Conc.*

De Quille, Dan. The Big Bonanza: account of the discovery, development, etc., of the Comstock silver lode; with introduction by Mark Twain. ill. 8°. '76. *$3.50; $4; hf. mor., $5..*Am. Pub.*

De Quincey, T: Works. 21 v. 16°. ea., $1.25. **Osgood.*

Cont.: Confessions of an Eng. opium eater. — Biog. essays. — Miscellaneous essays. — Narrative and miscellaneous papers, 2 v. — Essays on the poets. — Literary reminiscences, 2 v. — The Cæsars. — Hist. and critical essays, 2 v. — Autobiog. sketches. — Essays on philosophical writers, etc. — Letters to a young man, etc. — Note-book of an Eng. opium eater. — Theolog. essays, etc., 2 v. — Memorials, etc., 2 v. — Logic of political economy, etc. — The avenger, etc.

— *Same.* (Lib. ed.) 11 v. 12°. ea., $1.50..**Osgood.*

Cont.: Confessions of an opium eater; Autobiog. sketches. — Note book; Miscellaneous essays. — Literary reminiscences. — Narrative papers. — Hist. essays. — Philosophical writers. — Theolog. essays. — Memorials. — Biog. essays; Essays on the poets. — The Cæsars; The avenger. — Letters to a young man; Logic of political economy.

— *Same.* (Riverside ed.) 12 v. cr. 8°. ea., $1.75; per set, $21; hf. cf., $42 .... *Hurd & H.*

Cont.: Confessions of an English opium eater. — Autobiographic sketches. — Literary reminiscences. — Literary criticism. — The eighteenth century in literature and scholarship. — Essays in ancient history and antiquities. — Essays on Christianity, paganism and superstition. — Essays in philosophy. — Politics and political economy. — Romances and extravaganzas. — Narrative and miscellaneous papers. — Biographical and historical essays.

Note. From the same plates as the two editions above, but rearranged. Those editions are now superseded by this.

— *Same.* 16 v. 12°. ea., $1.50 .... (?) *Shepard.*

— Beauties sel. from his writings. 16°. $1.50..**Osgood.*

— Opium eater. 12°. pap., 25c .... *Lippincott.*

— *Same;* [also] Notes from the pocket book of a late opium eater. 12°. pap., 25c .... *Routledge.*

Derby, Alex. Ida Goldwin. [Fiction.] 12°. '76. pap., 75c .... *De Witt.*

Derby, E: (*Earl of*). [E: Stanley.] *See* Homer, Iliad.

Derby, Ellen. Elton Wheatley, the stammerer; or, like other folks. ill. 18°. 40c.....*Bost. Am. Tr.*

— — *See also* Missing boat stories.

Derby, G: H. ["J: Phœnix."] Phœnixiana; or, sketches and burlesques. ill. 12°. $1.25; pap., 50c .... *Appleton.*

— Squibob papers. 12°. $1.50 .... *Carleton.*

Derby, Orville A. *See* Agassiz, A., *and* Garman, S. W., Exploration of Lake Titicaca.

Derby, Perley. Hutchinson family. 8°. '70. $2..*Essex.*

Derleth, Alois. Mass no. 1, in E flat. 4°. pap., $1.50. *Peters.*

— Mass no. 2, in F. 4°. pap., $1.25 .... *Peters.*

Derley, J. *See* Nuitter, C., *and* Derley, J.

Dermot MacMorrogh. *See* Adams, J: Q.

De Rohan. Sue, E. 50c .... *Harper.*

Derrick, Fs. (*pseud.*) *See* Notley, *Mrs.* —.

Derrière les haies. Witt, H. G. de. $1...*Lippincott.*

Derry, J. T. History of the U. S.; for schools. ill. 12°. $1.50 .... *Lippincott.*

Derwent. Chester, J. $1.50 .... *Randolph.*

De Sanctis, L. Rome, Christian and papal: sketches of its religious monuments and ecclesiastical hierarchy; with notices of the Jesuits and the inquisition. 12°. $1.50 .... *Harper.*

Desaussure, H. W. *See* South Carolina, Chancery reports.

Descartes, René. Discourse on the method of rightly conducting the reason and seeking truth in the sciences; tr. 12°. $2.25......*Scribner, W. & A.*

Descent of man. Darwin, C. R. $3......*Appleton.*

Deschanel, A. P. Elementary treatise on natural philosophy; tr. and ed. by J. D. Everett. 4 pts. ill. 8°. ea., $1.75 .... *Appleton.*

Cont.: Mechanics, hydrostatics and pneumatics. — Heat. — Electricity and magnetism. — Sound and light.

— *Same;* with problems and index. 8°. $6.50. *Appleton.*

Description (A) of Georgia, by a gentleman who has resided there upwards of seven years, and was one of the first settlers. London, 1741. [Reprint.] 4°. pap., 25c .... *Sabin.*

Description of the New York Central Park; with plans and ill. sm. 4°. $8; mor., $10.....*Huntington.*

Description of the province of New Albion. Printed, 1648. [Reprint.] 4°. pap., 50c .... *Sabin.*

Desdemonum: Ethiop. drama. 16°. pap., 15c..*Happy.*

Desert. Summers, T. O. 40c .... *So. Meth.*

Desert deserted; or, last days of Brigham Young: farce. 16°. pap., 15c .... *French.*

Desert home (The). Reid, M. $1.50 .... *Miller.*

Desert island (The). 16°. 45c .... *Cummiskey.*

Desert of the exodus. Palmer, E. H. $3....*Harper.*

Desert pathway. Robertson, W. $1.50 .... *Carter.*

Desert world. Mangin, A. $6; $8.50; $12..*Nelson.*

Deserted family. Trowbridge, J. T. $1.25. *J. E. Potter.*

Deserted heroine. 18°. '68. 20c .... *Am. Tr.*

Deserted mill. Llewellyn, E. L. $1.25 .... *Graves.*

Deserted ship. Cupples, G. $1.50 .... (?) *Shepard.*

Deserted ship. Howe, C. $1.25 .... *Routledge.*

Deserted village. *See* Goldsmith, O.

Deserted wife. Southworth, E. D. E. N. $1.75; $1.50 .... *Peterson.*

Deserter (The). 32°. '54. 30c .... *Am. Tr.*

Deserter (The). Tonna, C. E. 90c .... *Dodd.*

Deserters: Ethiop. drama. 16°. pap., 15c....*French.*

Des Essarts, Alfr. Stanislas Langlois. The sheaf; tr. by C. Farville. 18°. 90c.; $1.20....*O'Shea.*

Deshon, G: Guide to Catholic young women. 12°. $1 .... *Cath. Pub.*

Designs and instructions for decorating pottery in imitation of Greek, Roman, Egyptian and other styles of vases. 12°. '76. pap., 50c.....*Tilton.*

Desk and debit. Adams, W. T. $1.25......*Lee & S.*

Deslonde, *Mrs.* M. D. The miller of Silcott mill. 12°. $1.75 .... *Carleton.*

Deslys, C: Angelo, the Milanese vespers; or, the avengers of Italy. 8°. '64. pap., 50c....*Payot.*

Despard, M. Old New York. *See* Greatorex, E.

Despard, *Mrs.* M. C. Chaste as ice, pure as snow. [Fiction.] 12°. $1.50; pap., 75c. (Intern. ed.) 12°. $1.25 .... *Porter.*

Desperados of the new world. Ainsworth, W. H. 50c .... *Peterson.*

Desperate game. Morton, J. M. 15c...*Ames; French.*

Desperate remedies. Hardy, T. $1.25 .... *Holt.*

Dessar, J. H. First elements of the Hebrew grammar. 16°. bds., 15c .... *Bloch.*

— Grosse deutsche Sprach- u. Rechtschreibschule. 2d ed. 12°. '72. 75c .... *Witter.*

— Kleine deutsche Sprach- u. Rechtschreibschule. 2d ed. 12°. '72. 35c .... *Witter.*

Dessert book (The); by a Boston lady. 12°. '71. $1.50 .... *Tilton.*

De Stael. *See* Stael.

Destiny. *See* Ferrier, Ma.

Destiny. Flynn, D. F. $1.50; $2....*Kelly, P. & Co.*

Destiny of the wicked. Carpenter, G. T., *and* Hughes, J. $1.50 .... *Cen. Bk.*

Destiny of the wicked. Smith, U. 15c. *Sev. Day Adv.*

Destroyer of the second republic. Hugo, V. $1.50. *Sheldon.*

Destruction of Jerusalem. 18°. 65c.......*Am. S. S.*

Destruction of Jerusalem an irresistible proof of the divine origin of Christianity. 18°. 35c. *Pres. Bd.*

Destutt de Tracy, A. L. C. Commentary and review of Montesquieu's Spirit of laws; [also] Observations on the 31st book by A. N. C. Condorcet; with two letters of Helvetius on the same. 8°. '11. $1.25. *T. & J. W. Johnson.*

Desty, Rob. Alphabetical table of cases cited in California reports, and of California cases cited in reports of sister states. 8°. shp., $5..*S. Whitney.*

— *Same.* 8°. '74. shp., $7.50.............*Bancroft.*

— Digest of California Supreme Court decisions (v. 34–46). 8°. shp., $6.50...............*S. Whitney.*

— *Same.* 8°. '75. shp., $7.50.............*Bancroft.*

— Federal procedure: manual of practice in U. S. courts. 18°. shp., $3.............*S. Whitney.*

Desultory man. James, G. P. R. $1.50....*Harper.*

Detective (The) and the somnambulist. Pinkerton, A. $1.50..............................*Keen.*

Detectives' club. ill. 8°. pap., 25c..........*Haney.*

De Teissier, G. F. House of prayer: exposition of the order for morning and evening prayer in the Church of Eng. 18°. '66. $1......*Macmillan.*

Dethroned heiress. Dupuy, E. A. $1.75..*Peterson.*

Detlef, K: (*pseud.*) *See* Bauer, Karoline.

De Tocqueville. *See* Tocqueville.

Dettingen, G. F. H. Te Deum. [Music.] 8°. $1; pap., 50c.; bds., 75c..................*Church.*

Deucalion. Ruskin, J. $1..............(?) *Wiley.*

Deuel, Caro. R. Scripture lessons. 18°. 40c.; pap., 20c.........................*Meth. Bk. Conc.*

Deus homo. Parsons, T. $2.50..........*Lippincott.*

Deus semper. Thompson, G. W. $2.......*Claxton.*

Deutsch, Em. Literary remains; with brief memoir. 8°. '74. $4................................*Holt.*

Deutsch, Sol. Hebrew grammar with Heb.-Eng. and Eng.-Heb. exercises and Hebrew chrestomathy. ('68.) 2d ed., enl. 8°. '72. $2.50........*Holt.*

— Key to the Pentateuch, explanatory of the text and the gram. forms. [To form 3 pts.] pt. 1: Genesis. 8°. '71. $1.50.............................*Holt.*

Deutsch-amerikanische Bibliothek: erste Reihe. 10 v. 12°. '72. ea., 75c.; pap., 50c....*Steiger.*

Deutsch-amerikanische Dolmetscher (Der). 16°. pap., 12c.........................*Benziger.*

Deutsch-amerikanisches Hand-Lexicon d. allgem. Wissens. 2 v. 8°. '75. $10.50; hf. mor., $12. *Zickel.*

Deutsch evangelisch-lutherisch. *See* German Evangelical Lutheran.

Deutsch, Französisch u. Englisch. *See* Hartmann, M.

Deutsche Bilderbogen: illustrations with [Germ.] text. v. 1–8. f°. ea., bds., $1.25; col. ill., ea., bds., $2.............................*Stroefer.*

Deutsche Freiheits-Sänger (Der). 12°. pap., 15c. *F. W. Thomas.*

Deutsche Kinderfreund (Der). Wilmsen, F. P. 75c. *Radde.*

Deutsche Lyrik. Buchheim, C. A. $1.50..*Macmillan.*

Deutsche Selbstarzt (Der), in allen Fällen v. syphil. od. vener. Krankheiten. 12°. 50c.......*Radde.*

Deutsche Sprachlehre f. Schulen der Ver. Staaten. (Old issue.) 12°. 33c..................*Benziger.*

Deutsche (Der) unter den Kalmücken. 18°. '71. 25c. *Am. Tr.*

Deutsche Volks-Lieder, od. Männerchöre u. Quartette mit deutschem u. engl. Text. 32°. pap., 15c. *Kohler.*

Deutsche Volksmärchen. Hoffmann, F. 25c. *Steiger.*

Deutschen Flüchtlinge (Die). 12°. 35c.; pap., 15c. *Benziger.*

Deutscher (Ein). Ruppius, O. 75c.; 50c....*Zickel.*

Deutscher Wald und Hain. *See* Fischbach, J.

Deutsches Lesebuch f. Sonntags-schulen: 1. Stufe. 12°. 15c..............................*Kohler.*

Deutschland's Ehre. Berneck, C. G. v. 50c. *Morwitz.*

Deux-Ponts, Gu. (*Comte*) de. My campaigns in America: journal, 1780–'81; tr. with introd. and notes by S. A. Green. 8°. '68. $3...........*Lunt.*

De Vane. Hilliard, H. W. $2.............*Eyrich.*

De Vere, Aubrey. Infant bridal, and other poems. fp. 8°. $1.50...........................*Macmillan.*

— Irish odes, and other poems. 12°. '68. $2..*Cath. Pub.*

— May carols, and hymns and poems. 16°. '65. $1.25. *Cath. Pub.*

De Vere, Mx. Schele. Americanisms. ('71.) New ed. cr. 8°. '72. $3; hf. cf., $5............*Scribner.*

— First French reader. 12°. '67. 75c.....*Univ. Pub.*

— Grammar of the French language. 12°. '67. $1.75. *Univ. Pub.*

— Grammar of the Span. lang., with a hist. of the lang. and exercises. 12°. $1.50...........*Appleton.*

— Great empress [Agrippina 2d.] por. 12°. $1.75. *Lippincott.*

— Introduction to the study of French. 12°. '69. 75c. *Univ. Pub.*

— Modern magic. 12°. '72. $2.............*Putnam.*

— Romance of Am. history: early annals. 12°. '72. $1.50..............................*Putnam.*

— Stray leaves from the book of nature. New ed. ill. 12°. '72. $1.50....................*Putnam.*

— Studies in English; or, glimpses into the inner life of our language. ('66.) New ed. cr. 8°. '72. $2.50; hf. cf., $4.50................*Scribner.*

— Wonders of the deep. 3d ed. ill. 12°. '69. $1.50; $2..................................*Putnam.*

De Vere. Ward, R. P. $1.50.............*Harper.*

Devereux, J. C. *See* Blackstone, *Sir* W.; — United States, Court of Claims reports.

Devereux, T. P. *See* North Carolina, Equity reports; Law reports.

Devereux. *See* Bulwer-Lytton, *Sir* E. G. E. L.

Devey, Jos. Logic; or, the science of inference. 12°. (Bohn.) $1.75................*Little, B. & Co.*

— *Same.* 12°. (Bohn.) $2. *Lippincott; Scribner, W. & A.*

Devil (The): does he exist? tr. by Mrs. J. Sadlier. 32°. $1; 60c.; pap., 25c..............*Sadlier.*

Devil (The) and Dr. Faustus. Rede, L. 15c. *French.*

Devil (The) in history. Read, H. $3; $3.50; $4..*Treat.*

Devil (The) to pay. Coffey, C. 15c..........*French.*

Devil (The) upon two sticks. *See* Lesage, A. R.

Devilish good joke. Higgie, T. 15c........*French.*

Devil's chain. Jenkins, E. 75c.; 50c........*Harper.*

Devil's ducat. Jerrold, D. 15c.............*French.*

Devil's elixir. Ball, E. 15c................*French.*

Devil's mount. Higgie, T. 15c.............*French.*

Devil's pulpit. Taylor, R. $2...............*Mendum.*

Devil's ring: extravaganza. 16°. pap., 15c...*French.*

De Vinne, Dan. Irish primitive church. 12°. $1.50. *Hart; Tibbals.*

De Vinne, Theo. L. Invention of printing. cr. 8°. '76. $6....................................*Hart.*

Devoted bride. Tucker, St. G. $1.75; $1.50..*Peterson.*

Devotedness to Christ. Pierce, G. F. 20c. *So. Meth.*

Devotion to St. Joseph. [Prayer book.] 16°. $1; $1.25...............................*Sadlier.*

Devotional chimes. Hull, A. 75c...........*Ditson.*

Devotional hour library. 3 v. 16°. $3.....*Lothrop.*
Cont.: Memorial hour.— Baxter's Saints' rest.—Gethsemane.

Devotional hymn and tune book; with supplement. sq. 16°. 75c.; —fine ed. $2.75 .... *Am. Bapt.*

Devotional hymn book. 24°. 50c.; 70c. .. *Am. Bapt.*

Devotional hymns. 32°. '63. 35c. .... *Randolph.*

Devotional library. 4 v. 24°. $3.50 ...... *Randolph.*
Cont.: Go and tell Jesus; [also] Wait on the Lord. — Hymns from the land of Luther. — None like Christ; [also] My time's in God's hand. — Spiritual songs and devotional hymns.

Devotional melodies. Safford, O. P. 40c. *Universalist.*

Devotional poetry for the children. Johnson, J. *net,* 20c. .... *Friends Bk. Assoc.*

Devotional series. 5 v. 18°. $3.75; $6.25 .. *Lothrop.*
Cont.: Morning and night watches, by J. R. Macduff. — Rule and exercise of holy living, by J. Taylor. — Mind and words of Jesus; [also] Faithful promiser, by J. R. Macduff. — Imitation of Christ, by Thomas a Kempis. — Rule and exercise of holy dying, by J. Taylor.

Devotions for Advent and Christmas. 18°. pap., 15c. *Dutton.*

Devotions for the forty hours: exposition of the sacrament. 24°. 40c. .... *Sadlier.*
— *See also* Gilbert, D.

Devotions of the ages. Allen, N. G. $1.25. *Claxton; Lippincott.*

Devout communicant. Baker, P. 50c. ..... *Cath. Pub.*

Devout communicant. Bickersteth, E. 50c.; $2. *Dutton.*

Devout exercises of the heart. *See* Rowe, *Mrs.* E.

Devout life (The). *See* François de Sales, *St.*

Devout manual. [Cath. prayer book.] 18°. 75c.–$3. 32°. 35c.–$12 .... *T. Kelly; Strong.*

Devout sayings. *See* Daily food ser.

Devout songster. Carpenter, J. E. 25c. .. *Routledge.*

Devout women of Israel. Headley, P. C. 25c.; 30c. *J. E. Potter.*

Dew, T: Digest of ancient and modern history. 8°. $2.50 .... *Appleton.*

Dew drop. *See* Hidden beauty; —Nursery lib.

Dew drops: daily texts. 128°. '31. 15c.; mor., 35c. *Am. Tr.*
— *Germ.* Thautropfen. 128°. '69. 15c. .... *Am. Tr.*

Dew drops and sunshine. Newman, J. P. $1.50. *Meth. Bk. Conc.*

Dew for the drooping flower. 18°. 25c.; 30c. *Am. Bapt.*

Dew of Hermon. *See* Bijou Bible text-books.

Dew of youth. Clark, T. M. $1.25 .... *Lee & S.*

Dewall, — van. A great lady: a romance. ill. 8°. $1.25; pap., 75c. .... *Lippincott.*

Dewees, W. P. On the physical and medical treatment of children. 8°. $2.80 .... *Lea.*
— Treatise on the diseases of females. ill. 8°. $3 .. *Lea.*

Dewey, D. M. Dewey's large series col. fruit plate book. no. 1. 40 pl. roy. 8°. $10. — no. 2. 60 pl. $15 .... *Dewey.*
— Dewey's local agents' [fruit] plate book. 8°. $3.50. *Dewey.*
— Dewey's pocket series col. fruit plate book. no. 1. 45 pl. 8°. $10. — no. 2. 65 pl. $15. — no. 3. 100 pl. $25 .... *Dewey.*
— Dewey's tree agents' private guide. 8°. $1; pap., 25c. *Dewey.*
— Fruits, flowers and oriental trees of Am.; for nurserymen. col. pl. roy. 8°. '76. $15 .... *Dewey.*

Dewey, Ma. E. Life and letters of Catharine M. Sedgwick. por. 12°. $2 .... *Harper.*

Dewey, Orville. Works. ('47.) 20th ed. 3 v. 12°. '76. $4.50; hf. cf., $10.50 .... *Miller.*
— Problem of human destiny; or, the end of Providence in the world and man. 8°. $2.50 .... *Miller.*
— Sermons on the two great commandments. 12°. '76. $1.50 .... *Miller.*

De Witt, E. L. *See* Ohio, Supreme Court reports.

De Witt, Jennie. Kate Weston; or, the will to do. ill. 12°. $1.50 .... *De Witt.*

De Witt, J: Scripture doctrine of regeneration defended: sermon. 8°. pap., 25c. *N. Y. Ref. Ch. Bd.*
— Sure foundation and how to build upon it. 12°. 85c. *N. Y. Ref. Ch. Bd.*

DeWitt, T: Discourse in the North Ref. Dutch Ch., N. Y., Aug., 1856. ill. 8°. $1.50 .. *N. Y. Ref. Ch. Bd.*
— The tabernacle of God with men: discourse. ill. 8°. pap., 25c. .... *N. Y. Ref. Ch. Bd.*

De Witt's champion stories. 32 nos. 32°. ea., pap., 10c. *De Witt.*

De Witt's complete Am. farrier and horse doctor. 12°. 75c. 32°. bds., 50c. .... *De Witt.*

DeWitt's Connecticut cook book and housekeeper's assistant. 12°. 75c. 32°. bds., 50c. .... *De Witt.*

De Witt's forget-me-not song books. 4 nos. 64°. ea., 50c. .... *De Witt.*

De Witt's musical album ser. 10 nos. 4°. ea., pap., 50c. .... *De Witt.*

De Witt's perfect orator. 12°. 75c. 32°. bds., 50c. *De Witt.*

De Witt's song and joke books. 216 nos. 32°. ea., pap., 10c. .... *De Witt.*

De Witt's ten cent joke books. 3 nos. 64°. ea., pap., 10c. .... *De Witt.*

De Witt's ten cent romances. 115 nos. 32°. ea., pap., 10c. .... *De Witt.*

De Witt's ten cent songsters. 12 nos. 64°. ea., pap., 10c. .... *De Witt.*

De Witt's twenty five cent song books. 14 nos. 32°. ea., pap., 25c. .... *De Witt.*

De Wolf, D. F. Instructive speller. 16°. '62. 25c. *Wilson, H. & Co.*

Dexter, H: Martyn. As to Roger Williams. 12°. $2 .... *Cong. Pub.*
— Congregationalism, what it is, whence it is, etc. ('65.) 4th ed., rev. and enl. 12°. '76. $2; pap. $1.25 .... *Lockwood, B. & Co.*
— Verdict of reason upon the question of the future punishment of the impenitent; with index. 16°. '65. $1 .... *Lockwood, B. & Co.*

Diadem of school songs. Tillinghast, W. 60c *Schermerhorn.*

Diakka (The). Davis, A. J. 50c.; 25c. *A. J. Davis.*

Diakkaism. Gardner, A. 10c. .... *Colby.*

Diálogos de un clérigo español. 18°. '65. 30c. *Am. Tr.*

Dialogue between Christ, a youth and the devil; or, the danger and refuge of the soul. 18°. 22c. *Am. S. S.*

Dialogues between two chimneys of Madrid. *See* Lesage, A. R.

Dialogues of devils on the many vices which abound in the civil and relig. world. 18°. 75c. .. *Sower.*

Diamante (El) del catolico. [Prayer book.] 24°. 75c.–$4 .... *Strong.*

Diamantring (Der). *See* Schmid, C. v.

Diamond arrow. Moncrieff, W. T. 15c. .... *French.*

Diamond bracelet. 32°. '59. 30c. .... *Am. Tr.*

Diamond bracelet. *See* Alden, *Mrs.* I. N.

Diamond bracelet. Wood, E. P. 25c. ..... *Peterson.*

Diamond brooch. 18°. 50c. .... *Carter.*

Diamond cross series. *See* McKeever, *Miss* H. B.

Diamond cut diamond. Murray, W. H. 15c. *French; Lee & S.*

Diamond cut diamond. Thomas, J. R. $1 ... *Peters.*

Diamond cut diamond. Trollope, T. A. $1.25 .. *Harper.*

Diamond editions. 11 v. 18°. ea., $1 .... *Osgood.*
Cont.: Burns. — Harte. — Longfellow. — Longfellow's Christus. — Lowell. — Owen Meredith's Lucile. — Procter. — Saxe. — Scott. — Tennyson. — Whittier.

Diamond hymns. Riggs, A. L. 15c.; 12c. .. *Church.*

Diamond in the cage. Rockwell, J. E. $1.15 .. *Pres. Bd.*

Diamond leaves. Beal, N. S. R. $2 .... *Beal.*

Diamond library. 5 v. 16°. $5.25.......*Am. S. S.*
Cont.: Story of a diamond. — Ben Boland's garden. — Cherry, the missionary. — Twin roses. — Theresa's journal.

Diamond manual. [Cath. prayer book.] 48°. 25c.–$6.................................*O'Shea.*
— *See also* Gahan, W.

Diamond miniatures. 12 v. 64°. $3.........*Locke.*
Cont.: Daily food. — Sacred gift. — The offering. — Gift of piety. — Crystal gems. — The seasons. — Bible gems. — Golden vase. — Bible gems. — Friendship's jewel. — The wedding ring. — Floral wreath.

Diamond on the hearth. James, M. 50c...*Appleton.*
Diamond rose. Keddie, H. $2..........*Routledge.*
Diamonds and rubies. Waring, S. M. 40c...*Dutton.*
Diamonds and toads. Caldor, M. T. 15c...*Lee & S.*
Diamonds reset. Dunning, A. K. $1.....*Pres. Bd.*
Diamonds, unpolished and polished. Richmond, J. F. $1.25........................*Meth. Bk. Conc.*
Diana Carew. Forrester, *Mrs.* —. $1.50..*Lippincott.*
Diana De Poitiers. Dumas, A. $1........*Dick & F.*
Diana of Meridor. *See* Dumas, A.
Diana, the sorceress. 8°. pap., 25c..........*De Witt.*
Diapason (The). Root, G. F. $1.50.......*Ditson.*
Diary (A). *See* Bremer, *Miss* F.
Diary: daily texts. interleaved, 64°. '31. 20c.; 25c. *Am. Tr.*
Diary (A) in the east. Russell, W. H. $5..*Routledge.*
Diary of a besieged resident in Paris. *See* Labouchère, H.
Diary of a confessor, and other tales. 12°. 35c. *Benziger.*
Diary of a detective police officer. Russell, W. H. C. 75c...............................*Dick & F.*
Diary of an ennuyée. Jameson, A. $1.50...*Osgood.*
Diary of Kitty Trevylyan. *See* Charles, *Mrs.* E.
Diary of a medical student. *See* Warren, S:
Diary of an old doctor. Maitland, J. A. $1.75; $1.50. *Peterson.*
Diary of a pawnbroker; or, the three golden balls. ill. 8°. pap., 50c.........................*Peterson.*
Diary of a late physician. *See* Warren, S:
Diary of a refugee; by a lady of Virginia. 12°. $2..*Hale.*
Diary of a Samaritan; by a member of the Howard Assoc. of New Orleans. 12°. $1.50....*Harper.*
Diary of the sun. ('69.) New ed. ill. 16°. '73. 50c. *Hoyt.*
Diavola. Braddon, M. E. 50c............*Dick & F.*
Diaz, *Mrs.* Abbey M. Domestic problem (A): work and culture in the household. 16°. '75. $1; pap., 50c.................................*Osgood.*
— King's (The) lily and rose-bud: a fairy story. ill. 16°. '68. $1.50.......................*Osgood.*
— Lucy Maria. ill. 16°. '73. $1.50..........*Osgood.*
— School-master's (The) trunk: papers on home life in Tweenit. ill. 16°. '74. $1; pap., 50c. *Osgood.*
— Story-book for the young folks. ill. 16°. '75. $1.50. *Osgood.*
— William Henry and his friends. ill. 16°. '71. $1.50. *Osgood.*
— William Henry letters (The). ill. 16°. '70. $1.50. *Osgood.*
— — *See also* Chaney, *Mrs.* G. L.
Dibble, Sheldon. Thoughts on missions. 18°. '48. 40c. *Am. Tr.*
Dibdin, C: Great devil: drama. 16°. pap., 15c. *French.*
— Quaker: operetta. 16°. pap., 15c..........*French.*
— Sea songs; ed., with memoir, by T. Dibdin. 12°. (Bohn.) $1.
Lippincott; Little, B. & Co.; Scribner, W. & A.
— Waterman: opera. 16°. pap., 15c..........*French.*
— Wild man: drama. 16°. pap., 15c.... ....*French.*
Dibdin, C: *jr.* My spouse and I: farce. 16°. pap., 15c.....................................*French.*
Dibdin, Hor. Taming a truant: comedy. 16°. pap., 15c......................................*French.*
Dibdin, T: [Plays.] 19 v. 16°. ea., pap., 15c...*French.*
Cont.: Banks of the Hudson. — Cabinet: opera. — Don Giovanni: extravaganza. — English fleet: opera. — Fate of Calais. — Five miles off: comedy. — Heart of Midlothian. — Humphrey Clinker: farce. — Jew (The) and the doctor: farce. — Lady of the lake. — Man (The) and the marquis: farce. — Mother Goose: pantomime. — Of age to-morrow: farce. — Paul Jones. — Ruffian boy. — St. David's day: farce. — Suil Dhuv, the coiner. — Two Gregories: farce. — Valentine and Orson.

— *and* Bunn, A. Kenilworth: drama. 16°. pap., 15c. *French.*
Dibdin, T: Frognall. Bibliomania; or, book madness: a bibliographical romance. ill. demy 18°. hf. roxb., $8.40.................*Scribner, W. & A.*
Dicey, A. V. Treatise on the rules for the sel. of parties to action; ed. by J. H. Truman. 8°. '76. shp., $7.50.....................................*Cockcroft.*
Dick, J: Lectures on Acts. 8°. $2.25.......*Carter.*
— Lectures on theology. 2 v. in 1. 8°. $3....*Carter.*
— *Same;* with biog. introd. by an Am. ed. imp. 8°. shp., $3.50...........................*Pounsford.*
— *Same.* por. imp. 8°. $4.................*So. Bapt.*
Dick, T: Works. 2 v. ill. roy. 8°. shp., $6.50. *Pounsford.*
— *Same.* 10 v. in 5. 12°. '74. $10; shp., $12.50; hf. cf., $18.75..............................*Claxton.*
Cont.: Philosophy of a future state. — Christian philosopher; or, the connection of science and philosophy with religion. — Philosophy of religion. — On the improvement of society. — On the mental illumination and moral improvement of mankind. — On the sin and the evils of covetousness. — Celestial scenery. — Sidereal heavens. — Practical astronomer. — Solar system; with reflections in ref. to the wonders therein displayed.

— Celestial scenery; or, the wonders of the planetary system displayed. ill. 18°. 75c.........*Harper.*
— Christian philosopher; abridged. 18°. '38. 55c. *Meth. Bk. Conc.*
— Improvement of society by the general diffusion of knowledge. 18°. '38. 55c.......*Meth. Bk. Conc.*
— *Same.* 18°. 75c...........................*Harper.*
— Philosophy of the future state. 18°. 75c....*Sower.*
— Philosophy of religion. 18°. '38. 55c. *Meth. Bk. Conc.*
— Practical astronomer: ill. of light and colors, descript. of telescopes, etc. ill. 12°. $1..*Harper.*
— Sidereal heavens, and other subjects connected with astronomy. ill. 18°. 75c.............*Harper.*
Dick, W: Brisbane. ["Josh. Jed. Jinks"; "Leger D. Mayne"; "Trumps."] American Hoyle: gentleman's handbook of games. ill. 12°. $2..*Dick & F.*
— Encyclopedia of practical receipts and processes. roy. 8°. $5; shp., $6; hf. cf., $7.50...*Dick & F.*
— Uncle Josh's trunk full of fun. ill. 8°. pap., 15c. *Dick & F.*
Dick and the angel. Howitt, M. 25c.; 50c. *Lothrop.*
Dick and Daisy ser. *See* Samuels, A. F.
Dick and Fitzgerald's song-books. 71 nos. 16°. ea., pap., 10c.............................*Dick & F.*
Dick and his donkey. 18°. 40c...*Am. S.S.; Pres. Bd.*
Dick and his friend Fidus. 18°. 90c.....(?)*Martien.*
Dick and his mother. 32°. 20c.; 15c........*Dutton.*
Dick Barford. *See* Little Katie's little lib.
Dick Boldhero. *See* Goodrich, S. G., Cottage lib.
Dick Bolter; or, getting on in life. 18°. 60c. *Am. S.S.*
Dick Clinton. *See* Life and adventures of.
Dick Cutler; or, the intemperate father. 18°. 40c. *Cong. Pub.*
Dick Duncan. *See* Wise, D., Glen Morris' stories.
Dick Fly-by-night. 8°. pap., 25c............*De Witt.*
Dick Fraser. Lamb, J. 60c............(?)*Martien.*
Dick Lightheart series. *See* Hemyng, B.
Dick Markham. Smith, J. F. 75c........*Dick & F.*
Dick Mason. Dunning, A. K. 45c........*Pres. Bd.*
Dick Mason and Harry Slack. *See* Locust Grove stories.

Dick Massey. Russell, T. O'N. $1........*Kenedy.*

Dick Onslow. *See* Adventures of.

Dick Parker. *See* Life of.

Dick Rodney. *See* Grant, Ja.

Dick Tarleton. Smith, J. F. 25c........*Dick & F.*

Dick Traverse abroad ser. *See* Samuels, A. F.

Dick Turpin. Ainsworth, W. H. 50c.....*Peterson.*

Dick Turpin and Tom King. Suter, W. E. 15c. *French.*

Dick Wortley. Parker, J. M. 18°. 50c.....*Dutton.*

Dickens, C: Works. 15 v. 12°. ea., $1.50; per set, hf. cf., $60........................*Carleton.*
Cont.: Barnaby Rudge; Edwin Drood.—Bleak House.—Child's England; Miscellanies.—Christmas books; Tale of two cities.—David Copperfield.—Dombey and son.—Great expectations; Pictures of Italy and America.—Little Dorrit.—Martin Chuzzlewit.—Nicholas Nickleby.—Old curiosity shop; Miscellanies.—Oliver Twist; Uncommercial traveller.—Our mutual friend.—Pickwick, and catalogue.—Sketches by Boz; Hard times.

— *Same.* 18 v. ill. 8°. ea., $1.75; per set, $31.50; shp., $40; hf. cf., $48; $54; $60.....*Peterson.*
Cont.: American notes; Picnic papers.—Barnaby Rudge.—Bleak House.—Christmas stories.—David Copperfield.—Dickens' new stories.—Dombey and son.—Great expectations.—Lamplighter's story.—Little Dorrit.—Martin Chuzzlewit.—Nicholas Nickleby.—Old curiosity shop.—Oliver Twist.—Our mutual friend.—Pickwick papers.—Sketches by Boz.—Tale of two cities.

— *Same.* 34 v. ill. 12°. ea., $1.50; per set, $50; shp., $68; hf. cf., $100..............*Peterson.*
Cont.: American notes; Uncommercial traveller.—Barnaby Rudge, 2 v.—Bleak House, 2 v.—Christmas stories, 2 v.—David Copperfield, 2 v.—Dickens' new stories.—Dombey and son, 2 v.—Great expectations.—Holly-tree Inn, etc.—Hunted down, etc.—Little Dorrit, 2 v.—Martin Chuzzlewit, 2 v.—Mystery of Edwin Drood; Master Humphrey's clock.—Nicholas Nickleby, 2 v.—Old curiosity shop, 2 v.—Oliver Twist, 2 v.—Our mutual friend, 2 v.—Pickwick papers, 2 v.—Sketches by Boz, 2 v.—Tale of two cities, 2 v.

— *Same.* 35 v. 8°. pap................*Peterson.*
Cont.: Barnaby Rudge, 50c.—Bleak House, 50c.—Christmas stories, 50c.—David Copperfield, 50c.—Dickens' new stories, 25c.—Doctor Marigold's prescriptions, 25c.—Dombey and son, 50c.—Great expectations, 50c.—Hard times, 25c.—Haunted house, 25c.—Holly-tree Inn, etc., 25c.—House to let, 25c.—Hunted down, etc., 50c.—Lazy tour of two idle apprentices [by Collins and D.], 25c.—Life of Joseph Grimaldi, 50c.—Little Dorrit, 50c.—Martin Chuzzlewit, 50c.—Message from the sea, 25c.—Mrs. Lirriper's legacy, 25c.—Mrs. Lirriper's lodgings, 25c.—Mugby Junction, 25c.—Mystery of Edwin Drood, 25c.—Nicholas Nickleby, 50c.—No thoroughfare, 25c.—Old curiosity shop, 50c.—Oliver Twist, 50c.—Our mutual friend, 50c.—Perils of English prisoners, 25c.—Pickwick papers, 50c.—Picnic papers, 50c.—Sketches by Boz, 50c.—Somebody's luggage, 25c.—Tale of two cities, 25c.—Tom Tiddler's ground, 25c.—Uncommercial traveller, 25c.

— *Same.* 30 v. ill. post 8°. (Lond.) $60; hf. cf., $112.50; cf., $150............*Little, B. & Co.*
Cont.: Barnaby Rudge; Hard times, 2 v.—Bleak House, 2 v.—Child's history of England.—Christmas books.—Christmas stories.—David Copperfield, 2 v.—Dombey and son, 2 v.—Great expectations.—Little Dorrit, 2 v.—Martin Chuzzlewit, 2 v.—Mystery of Edwin Drood.—Nicholas Nickleby, 2 v.—Old curiosity shop, 2 v.—Oliver Twist.—Our mutual friend, 2 v.—Pickwick papers, 2 v.—Pictures from Italy; American notes.—Sketches by Boz.—Tale of two cities.—Uncommercial traveller.

— *Same;* ill. by Nast. (Am. ed.) v. 1–7. 8°. '72–'76. ea., hf. mor., *$5; mor., $9;—in pts. ea., *25c.........................*N. Y. Bk. Conc.*

— *Same.* (Author's ed.) 14 v. ill. 16°. ea., $1; hf. cf., $2.75............................*Porter.*
Cont.: Barnaby Rudge; Hard times.—Bleak House.—Christmas books; Uncommercial traveller.—David Copperfield.—Dombey and son.—Little Dorrit.—Martin Chuzzlewit.—Mystery of Edwin Drood; Uncollected pieces; Sketches.—Nicholas Nickleby.—Old curiosity shop; Reprinted papers.—Oliver Twist; Italy; American notes.—Our mutual friend.—Pickwick papers.—Tale of two cities; Great expectations.

— *Same.* (Charles Dickens ed.) 16 v. ill. 12°. $25; hf. cf., $50; cf., $60...............*Lippincott.*
Cont.: American notes; Uncommercial traveller.—Barnaby Rudge.—Bleak House.—David Copperfield.—Dombey and son.—Hard times; Great expectations.—Little Dorrit.—Martin Chuzzlewit.—Mystery of Edwin Drood; History of Eng.—Nicholas Nickleby.—Old curiosity shop.—Oliver Twist.—Our mutual friend.—Pickwick papers.—Sketches; Christmas books.—Tale of two cities.

Dickens, C: *continued.*

— *Same.* (Cheap pop. ed.) 19 v. 8°. pap...*Appleton.*
Cont.: American notes, 15c.—Barnaby Rudge, 30c.—Bleak House, 35c.—Christmas stories, 25c.—David Copperfield, 35c.—Dombey and son, 35c.—Great expectations, 25c.—Hard times, and add. Christmas stories, 25c.—Little Dorrit, 35c.—Martin Chuzzlewit, 35c.—Mystery of Edwin Drood, 20c.—Nicholas Nickleby, 35c.—Old curiosity shop, 30c.—Oliver Twist, 25c.—Our mutual friend, 35c.—Pickwick papers, 35c.—Sketches, 25c.—Tale of two cities, 20c.—Uncommercial traveller, 35c.

— *Same.* (English ed.) v. 1–6. sm. 4°. ea., hf. mor., *$5; mor., $7;—in pts. ea., *30c. *N. Y. Bk. Conc.*

— *Same.* (Globe ed.) 15 v. ill. 12°. ea., $1.25; per set, $18.50; hf. cf., $45............*Hurd & H.*
Cont.: Barnaby Rudge; Sketches, pt. 2.—Bleak House.—Christmas stories; American notes; Pictures from Italy.—David Copperfield.—Dombey and son.—Little Dorrit.—Martin Chuzzlewit.—Mystery of Edwin Drood.—Nicholas Nickleby.—Old curiosity shop; Sketches, pt. 1.—Oliver Twist; Great expectations.—Our mutual friend.—Pickwick papers.—Tale of two cities; Hard times.—Uncommercial traveller; Master Humphrey's clock.

— *Same.* (Handy vol. ed.) 14 v. ill. 12°. ea., 75c.; per set, $10.50.....................*Appleton.*
Cont.: Barnaby Rudge; Edwin Drood.—Bleak House.—David Copperfield.—Dombey and son.—Great expectations; Sketches by Boz.—Little Dorrit.—Martin Chuzzlewit.—Nicholas Nickleby.—Old curiosity shop; American notes.—Oliver Twist; Christmas stories.—Our mutual friend.—Pickwick.—Tale of two cities; Hard times, etc.—Uncommercial traveller, etc.

— *Same.* (Harper's household ed.) 13 v. ill. 8°..*Harper.*
Cont.: Barnaby Rudge.—Bleak House.—Christmas stories.—David Copperfield.—Dombey and son.—Little Dorrit.—Martin Chuzzlewit.—Nicholas Nickleby.—Our mutual friend.—Pickwick papers, *ea.*, $1.50; pap., $1.—Old curiosity shop, $1.25; pap., 75c.—Oliver Twist, $1; pap., 50c.—Tale of two cities, $1; pap., 50c.

— *Same.* (Household ed.) 9 v. pl. and ill. sm. 4°. ea., *$5.....................*N. Y. Bk. Conc.*

— *Same.* (Household ed.) 56 v. ill. 16°. $84; hf. cf., $168..........................*Hurd & H.*
Cont.: American notes; Pictures from Italy, 2 v.—Barnaby Rudge, 3 v.—Bleak House, 4 v.—Christmas stories, 3 v.—David Copperfield, 4 v.—Dombey and son, 4 v.—Great expectations, 2 v.—Hard times, 2 v.—Little Dorrit, 4 v.—Martin Chuzzlewit, 4 v.—Master Humphrey's clock.—Mystery of Edwin Drood.—Nicholas Nickleby, 4 v.—Old curiosity shop, 3 v.—Oliver Twist, 2 v.—Our mutual friend, 4 v.—Pickwick papers, 4 v.—Sketches, 2 v.—Tale of two cities, 2 v.—Uncommercial traveller.

— *Same.* (Large pap. ed.) 56 v. ill. 8°. ea., *$5. *Hurd & H.*
Note. Contents the same as in Household ed.

— *Same.* (New household ed.) [To form 19 v.] v. 1–11. 8°.........................*Appleton.*
Cont.: Barnaby Rudge.—Bleak House.—David Copperfield.—Little Dorrit.—Martin Chuzzlewit.—Nicholas Nickleby.—Our mutual friend.—Pickwick papers, *ea.*, $1.75; pap., $1.25.—Great expectations.—Oliver Twist.—Tale of two cities, *ea.*, $1.25; pap., 75c.

— *Same;* with introds. by E. P. Whipple. (New ill. lib. ed.) 29 v. ill. cr. 8°. ea., $2: per set, $58; hf. cf., $116.......................*Hurd & H.*
Cont.: Barnaby Rudge; Hard times, 2 v.—Bleak House, 2 v.—Child's history of England, etc.—Christmas books.—David Copperfield, 2 v.—Dombey and son, 2 v.—Great expectations.—Little Dorrit, 2 v.—Martin Chuzzlewit, 2 v.—Mystery of Edwin Drood; Master Humphrey's clock, etc.—Nicholas Nickleby, 2 v.—Old curiosity shop, 2 v.—Oliver Twist.—Our mutual friend, 2 v.—Pickwick papers, 2 v.—Pictures from Italy; American notes.—Sketches by Boz.—Tale of two cities.—Uncommercial traveller.

— *Same.* (New national ed.) 7 v. por. and ill. 8°. $20; shp., $25; hf. cf., $30.........*Peterson.*

— *Same.* (People's ed.) 40 pts. ill. roy. 8°. '73. ea., *50c.;—in 7 v. ea., shp., *$5; hf. cf., $6..*Gebbie.*

— *Same.* (People's ed.) 22 v. ill. 12°. ea., $1.50; per set, $34–$66....................*Peterson.*
Cont.: American notes; Uncommercial traveller.—Barnaby Rudge.—Bleak House.—Christmas stories.—David Copperfield.—Dickens' new stories.—Dombey and son.—Great expectations.—Holly-tree Inn, etc.—Hunted down, etc.—John Jasper's secret [by H. Morford].—Life and writings.—Little Dorrit.—Martin Chuzzlewit.—Mystery of Edwin Drood; Master Humphrey's clock.—Nicholas Nickleby.—Old curiosity shop.—Oliver Twist.—Our mutual friend.—Pickwick papers.—Sketches by Boz.—Tale of two cities.

— *Same.* (Popular lib. ed.) 6 v. ill. and por. sm. 8°. $10.50; shp., $15; hf. cf., $21........*Appleton.*

Dickens, C: *continued.*
— *Same.* (Riverside ed.) 28 v. ill. cr. 8°. ea., $1.75; per set, $49; hf. cf., $98............*Hurd & H.*
Cont.: American notes; Pictures from Italy. — Barnaby Rudge; Sketches (pt. 2), 2 v. — Bleak House, 2 v. — Christmas stories. — David Copperfield, 2 v. — Dombey and son, 2 v. — Great expectations. — Hard times. — Little Dorrit, 2 v. — Martin Chuzzlewit, 2 v. — Master Humphrey's clock. — Nicholas Nickleby, 2 v. — Old curiosity shop; Sketches (pt. 1), 2 v. — Oliver Twist. — Our mutual friend, 2 v. — Pickwick papers, 2 v. — Tale of two cities. — Uncommercial traveller; Mystery of Edwin Drood.
— *Same.* (Standard ed.) 30 v. ill. 8°. ea., $3..*Lippincott.*
Cont.: American notes; Pictures from Italy. — Barnaby Rudge; Hard times, 2 v. — Bleak House, 2 v. — Child's history of England. — Christmas books. — Christmas stories. — David Copperfield, 2 v. — Dombey and son, 2 v. — Great expectations. — Little Dorrit, 2 v. — Martin Chuzzlewit, 2 v. — Mystery of Edwin Drood. — Nicholas Nickleby, 2 v. — Old curiosity shop, 2 v. — Oliver Twist. — Our mutual friend, 2 v. — Pickwick papers, 2 v. — Sketches by Boz. — Tale of two cities. — Uncommercial traveller.
— Bardell vs. Pickwick: drama. 12°. pap., 15c. *De Witt.*
— Bleak House. 2 v. ill. 12°. $3...........*Harper.*
— Child's dream of a star. (Red-line ed.) ill. 12°. '70. $3; mor., $7....................*Osgood.*
— Child's history of England. ill. 12°. $1.....*Porter.*
— *Same.* ill. 12°. $1.25...................*Carleton.*
— *Same.* ill. 16°. '71. $1.50.................*Osgood.*
— *Same.* ill. post 8°. (Lond.) '73. $2..*Little, B. & Co.*
— *Same.* 2 v. 16°. $1.50; — in 1 v. $1.25..*Harper.*
— Christmas books. ill. 8°. mor., $10.......*Osgood.*
— *Same;* ill. by Darley and Phiz. cr. 8°. $2.50; mor., $6..............................*Hurd & H.*
— Christmas carol; ill. by S. Eytinge, jr. 8°. '68. $5; mor., $9. (Vest pocket ed.) ill. 32°. '76. 50c. *Osgood.*
— Goblins (The) who stole the sexton. ill. fp. 4°. per gross, $15....................(?)*McLoughlin.*
— Great expectations. ill. 12°. $1.75....*J. E. Potter.*
— Hard times. 12°. $1.25. 8°. pap., 50c....*Harper.*
— Holiday stories. 8°. pap., 75c...........*Peterson.*
— Memoir of A. A. Procter. *See* Procter, A. A.
— Memoirs of Joseph Grimaldi. ill. 12°. $1.50. (Railway lib.) 16°. bds., $1............*Routledge.*
— Mrs. Lirriper's legacy. 8°. pap., 10c......*Harper.*
— Mystery of Edwin Drood. ill. 8°. pap., 25c. *Harper.*
— *Same;* [also] Pt. 2, by the spirit pen of D. through a medium, T. P. James. 12°. '73. $2; pap., $1.......................*N. Y. News.*
— — *Same.* ('73.) New ed. 8°. '75. $2; pap., $1. *T. P. James.*
— Somebody's luggage. 8°. pap., 25c........*Peterson.*
— Child pictures from Dickens. ill. 16°. $1.50..*Dutton.*
— Cyclopedia of best thoughts of D.; ed. by F. G. De Fontaine. 8°. $5; mor., $10........*Hale.*
— Dialogues from D.; by W. E. Fette. 2 v. ill. 16°. ea., $1.50............................*Lee & S.*
— Little folks: juv. sel. from works. 12 v. ill. 16°. $10. — 6 v. (2 v. in 1.) $9..........*Clark & M.*
Cont.: Child-wife. — Little Nell. — Smike. — Little Paul. — Boy Joe; Sam Weller. — Oliver Twist; Jew Fagin. — Florence Dombey. — Dolly Varden. — Sissy Jupe. — Tiny Tim; Dot; Fairy cricket. — Dame Durden. — Two daughters.
— Readings. 16°. $1.50...................**Osgood.*
— Schools and schoolmasters; from works of D. by T. J. Chapman. 12°. '71. $1.25..........*Barnes.*
— Speeches. *See* Taylor, T.
— Speeches, letters and sayings; with life by G. A. Sala and Dean Stanley's sermon. por. 8°. $1; pap., 50c.......................................*Harper.*
— Uncollected pieces. *See* Mackenzie, R. S.
— *and* Collins, W. Christmas stories; Two idle apprentices; No thoroughfare. ill. 12°. '75. $1.50. *W. F. Gill.*
— — — *See also above* Works, 35 v. (Lazy tour of).
— — No thoroughfare: drama. 12°. pap., 15c. *De Witt.*
Dickens dictionary. *See* Pierce, G. A.
Dickerman, C. W., *and* Flint, C. L. (*ed.*) How to make the farm pay; or, the farmer's book of practical information. ill. 8°. '69. *$3.75; leath., $4.50; — in German. *3.75........*McCurdy; Zeigler.*

Dickerman, Nath. W. Memoir of Gorham D. Abbott. ('30.) New ed. 18°. '36. 40c..........*Am. Tr.*
Dickeson, M. W. American numismatical manual of the currency and money of the aborigines; and colonial, state, and U. S. coins. 20 pl. 4°. $10. *Lippincott.*
Dickey, J: Questions on the "Shorter catechism"; with table of definitions. 18°. 10c.....*Pres. Bd.*
Dickins, F: V. (*tr.*) *See* Chiushingura.
Dickinson, Anna E. A paying investment. 16°. '76. $1......................................*Osgood.*
— What answer? a story of to-day. 16°. '68. $1.50. *Osgood.*
Dickinson, Jona. Familiar letters to a gentleman upon a variety of seasonable and important subjects in religion. 12°. $1....................*Pres. Bd.*
— Scripture doctrine conc. eternal election, original sin, grace in conversion, justification by faith and the saints' perseverance. 18°. 60c.......*Pres. Bd.*
Dickinson, Peard. Memoirs. 18°. '53. 40c. *Meth. Bk. Conc.*
Dickinson, R: W. Resurrection of Jesus Christ hist. and logically viewed. sm. 12°. 75c...*Pres. Bd.*
Dickory Cronke. *See* Defoe, D.
Dick's English classics. 13 v. 8°..........*Am. News.*
Cont.: Shakespeare, $1.25; pap., 60c. — Byron, $1; pap., 50c. — Scott's poems, 50c.; pap., 25c. — Goldsmith, 80c.; pap., 40c. — Burns, 50c.; pap., 25c. — Arabian nights, 50c.; pap., 25c. — Milton, 50c.; pap., 25c. — Cowper, 50c.; pap., 25c. — Wordsworth, 50c.; pap., 25c. — Moore, 50c.; pap., 25c. — Thomson, 50c.; pap., 25c. — Hemans, 80c.; pap., 40c. — Pope, $1; pap., 50c.
Dick's robins. Seamer, F. 50c...........*Nelson.*
Dick's strength. ill. 16°. '75. 60c..........*Lothrop.*
Dickson, A. E. Temptation in the desert. 18°. '72. 40c.......................................*Am. Tr.*
Dickson, A. F. Short sermons for plain readers and hearers. 12°. 70c..................*Pres. Bd.*
— *Same.* 2d ser.: Old words newly spoken. 12°. $1. *Pres. Bd.*
Dickson, Alex. All about Jesus. 12°. '75. $2. *Carter.*
Dickson, F: S. Analysis of Blackstone's Commentaries. ('73.) 2d ed. 4°. hf. shp., $4........... *Welsh.*
— Analysis of Kent's Commentaries. 8°. '75. shp., $5. *Welsh.*
Dickson, I. A. R. Working for Jesus. 18°. '73. 25c. *Am. Tr.*
Dickson, J. Thompson. Science and practice of medicine in rel. to the mind. ill. 8°. $3.50..*Appleton.*
Dickson, S: H: Studies in pathology and therapeutics. 12°. $1.50............................*W. Wood.*
Dickson, Wa. B., *and* Mowbray, B. On poultry; ed. by Mrs. Loudon. 12°. (Bohn.) $1.75. *Little, B. & Co.*
— — *Same.* 12°. (Bohn.) $2. *Lippincott; Scribner, W. & A.*
Dictation spelling book. 12°. 30c..........*O'Shea.*
Dictionary of the Bible. 24°. *75c.; shp., $1; mor., $1.25; $1.50..........................*Quak. City.*
Dictionary of correspondences, representatives and significatives derived from the word of God. 8°. $1.50.............................*H. H. Carter.*
Dictionary of daily wants. 12°. $3.75...*Lippincott.*
Dictionary of Lat. quotations, incl. proverbs, maxims, etc., and collection of Greek quotations; with Eng. tr. 12°. hf. cf., $4............*Appleton.*
— *Same.* 12°. (Bohn.) $1.75; with index verborum. $2.25.............................*Little, B. & Co.*
— *Same:* 12°. (Bohn.) $2; with index verborum. $2.40; — index alone. 40c.....*Scribner, W. & A.*
— *Same.* 12°. (Bohn.) $2; with index verborum. $2.50.......................................*Lippincott.*
Dictionary of love. 12°. $1.50..........*Dick & F.*
Dictionary of medical and surgical knowledge. 12°. hf. roxb., $3..........................*Lippincott.*

Dictionary of popular quotations in daily use. 16°. pap., 15c. . . . . *Happy.*

Dictionary of quotations. *See* New.

Dictionary of quotations, from the Gk., Lat. and modern languages; tr. by author of "Live and learn." cr. 8°. $2. . . . . *Lippincott.*

Dictionary of Scripture nat. hist. 18°. 90c. . . *Am. S. S.*

Dictionary of select and popular quotations in daily use. ('31.) 6th Am. ed., rev. and enl. 12°. '73. $1.50. . . . . *Claxton.*

Dictionary of useful knowledge. 12°. hf. roxb., $3. *Lippincott.*

Did I dream it? Wooler, J. P. 15c. . . *Ames; French.*

Did she do right? Finley, M. F. 50c. . . . . . *Souder.*

Did you ever send your wife to Camberwell? Coyne, J. S. 15c. . . . . *French.*

Didley Dumps, the newsboy. 18°. 90c. . . (?) *Martien.*

Dido. Burnand, F. C. 15c. . . . . *French.*

Didron, Adolphe Nap. History of Christian art; or, Christian iconography; tr. from the French. v. 1. ill. 12°. (Bohn.) $1.75. . . . . . *Little, B. & Co.*

— *Same.* v. 1. ill. 12°. (Bohn.) $2. *Lippincott; Scribner, W. & A.*

Didymus, Ioannes. Sigillologia: account of the great or broad seal of the Confederate States of Am. 8°. '73. pap., 25c. . . . . (?) *Kewand.*

Diedrichs, J: Theory of strains: calculation and construction of bridges, roofs, and cranes, with application of trigonom. notes, etc. pl. and diagrams. 8°. '71. $5. . . . . . *Van Nostrand.*

Diegesis (The). Taylor, R. $2. . . . . *Mendum.*

Diehl, *Mrs.* Anna T. (*formerly Mrs.* Randall). Choice readings. ('73.) 3d ed. 12°. '75. hf. roan, $1.50. *Claxton.*

— Reading and elocution. 12°. '69. $1.40. . . . *Ivison.*

Diekenga, I. E., *and* Ashworth, T. M. ["Ouno."] Tom Chips. [Fiction.] 12°. $1.50. *Lippincott.*

Dielman, H: A short, complete and easy mass. f°. '54. bds., $1.50. . . . . *Willig.*

Dies irae. *See* Coles, Ab.

Dies piscatoriæ. *See* Norris, T., American angler's book.

Dieterich, J: Conr. Institutiones catecheticae: Auslegung d. Katechismus Luthers in Frage u. Antwort: a. d. Lat. v. F. W. A. Notz. 8°. '76. hf. mor., $2. . . . . *Dette.*

— *See* Luther, Mt., Katechismus.

Dietz, E. *See* De Koninck, L. L., *and* Dietz, E.

Dieulafait, L: Diamonds and precious stones: a popular account of gems; tr. by F. Sanford. ('73.) New ed. ill. 12°. '74. $2. . . . . *Scribner.*

Dieulafoy, Georges. Treatise on the pneumatic aspiration of morbid fluids: a medico-chirurgical method of diagnosis and treatment of cysts and abscesses of the liver, strangulated hernia, etc. cr. 8°. $4. . . . . *Lippincott.*

Differences. Mayer, N. 50c. . . . . *Bloch.*

Digby Heathcote. Kingston, W. H. G. $1.50. *Routledge.*

Digging a grave with a wine-glass. ('71.) New ed. 16°. '75. $1.25. . . . . *Hoyt.*

Dike, S. F. Doctrine of the Lord in the primitive Christian church. 16°. 50c. . . . . *H. H. Carter.*

Dikes and ditches. Adams, W. T. $1.50. . . *Lee & S.*

Dilemma (The). Chesney, G. 75c. . . . . *Harper.*

Dilherr, J: Mich. Betrachtungen u. Seufzer e. Christenmenschen. Tr. by J. A. F. W. Müller. 16°. '74. $1.25. . . . . *Dette.*

Diligent Dick. *See* Baker, *Mrs.* H. N. W., Happy home stories for boys.

Dilke, *Sir* C: Wentworth. Fall of Prince Florestan of Monaco; by himself. 8°. $1.75. . . . *Macmillan.*

Dilke, *Sir* C: Wentworth, *continued.*

— Greater Britain: a record of travel in English-speaking countries, 1866–'67. maps and ill. 12°. $1. . . . . *Harper.*

— *Same.* ill. cr. 8°. $1.50. . . . . *Lippincott.*

— *Same.* 6th [chp.] ed. cr. 8°. $3. . . . . . *Macmillan.*

Dilley, J. J. Sleeping hare: comedy. 16°. pap., 15c. *French.*

— *and* Allen, J. The living statue; or, chiselling: farce. 12°. pap., 15c. . . . . *De Witt.*

Dillnberger, Emil. Handy book of the treatment of women's and children's diseases according to the Vienna Medical School; tr. by P. Nicol. 12°. '71. $1.75. . . . . *Lindsay.*

Dillon, J: F. Treatise on the law of municipal corporations. ('72.) 2d ed., rev. and enl. 2 v. 8°. shp., $15. . . . . *Cockcroft.*

— *See also* United States, Circuit Court reports.

Dilthey, K: Novellen und Erzählungen. 3 v. 12°. '72. ea., 75c.; pap., 50c. . . . . *Steiger.*

Cont.: 1. Die schönsten Tage e. Tänzerin; Mein Onkel Fischer in Baltimore. — 2. New York in alter Zeit; Gefahren e. Sängerfestes. — 3. Henriette Sontag.

Dilworth, J: Pictorial description of the tabernacle in the wilderness. 24°. pap., 10c. . . . . . *Nelson.*

Dimitri Roudine. Turgénieff, I. $1.25. . . . . . . *Holt.*

Dimmick, F. M. Anna Clayton; or, the inquirer after truth. 12°. $1.50. . . . . *Pres. Bd.*

Dimock, Su. Memoir. 8°. '75. $1.25. . . . . *Roberts.*

Dimond, W: [Plays.] 9 v. 16°. ea., pap., 15c. . . *French.*

Cont.: Æthiop. — Bride of Abydos. — Broken sword. — Brother and sister: operatic drama. — Foundling of the forest. — Hunter of the Alps. — Lady and the devil. — Stage struck: farce. — Young hussar.

— Hunter of the Alps: drama. 16°. pap., 15c. . . *Ames.*

Dingelstedt, Fz. The Amazon; tr. by J. M. Hart. New ed. 16°. '72. $1. . . . . *Putnam.*

Dinks (*pseud.*) *See* Herbert, H. W.

Dinner for nothing. Cheltnam, C. S. 15c. . . . *French.*

Dinner question (The). Selby, C. 50c. . . *Routledge.*

Dinner-table etiquette, with carving. ill. 48°. 25c. *Scribner, W. & A.*

Dinners and housekeeping. 16°. 20c. . . . . *Routledge.*

Dinorah. *See* Meyerbeer, G.

Dinorah under difficulties. Brough, W. 15c. . . *French.*

Dinwidddie, Rob. Letters. *See* Goodman, A. T.

Diogenes Laertius. Lives and opinions of the ancient philosophers; tr., with notes, by C. D. Yonge. 12°. (Bohn.) $1.75. . . . . *Little, B. & Co.*

— *Same.* 12°. (Bohn.) $2. *Lippincott; Scribner, W. & A.*

Diogenes; extravaganza. 16°. pap., 15c. . . . . *French.*

Dion and the sibyls. Keon, M. G. $1.50. . *Cath. Pub.*

Dionysius *of Alexandria.* *See* Thaumaturgus, G.

Dircks, H: Inventors and inventions. por. cr. 8°. '67. $1.50. . . . . *Spon.*

— Patent law considered as affecting the interests of the million. 8°. $1.50. . . . . *Spon.*

— Perpetuum mobile; or, search for self-motive power, during 17th–19th centuries. 2 v. ill. and por. cr. 8°. '61–'71. ea., $4. . . . . *Spon.*

— Scientific studies; or, practical in contrast with chimerical pursuits: in 2 lectures, Life of Edward Somerset, Marquis of Worcester, inventor of the steam engine, [and] Chimeras of science, astrology, alchemy, etc. ill. cr. 8°. '69. $1. . *Spon.*

Directions to inquiring souls. McIlvaine, J. H. 25c. *Carter.*

Directory of the carriage and wagon manufacturers of the U. S. and Canada. 16°. '76. $5. (Pocket ed.) 32°. $5. . . . . *I. D. Ware.*

Directory of the nurserymen, florists and seedsmen of the U. S. ('75.) [Biennial.] 8°. *$10. *D. W. Scott.*

Dirks, Servais. Life of St. Anthony of Padua; tr. from the Fr. 12°. $1.50; $2.......... *O'Shea.*
Disagreeable surprise. Daniel, G. 15c...... *French.*
Disappointed ambition. 16°. 75c.; $1.25... *Sadlier.*
Discarded daughter. Southworth, E. D. E. N. $1.75; $1.50.............................. *Peterson.*
Discarded queen. Reynolds, G. W. M. 75c. *Peterson.*
Discarded wife. Dupuy, E. A. $1.75..... *Peterson.*
Discipline. *See* Methodist Episc. Church.
Discipline of Alice Lee. 16°. '59. $1.. *Meth. Bk. Conc.*
Discipline of life. Phelps, L. $1.75......... *Barnes.*
Discipline of life. Ponsonby, *Lady* E. 50c... *Harper.*
Discipline of sorrow. Eliot, W. G. 50c... *Am. Unit.*
Discontent. Gardner, H. C. $1.25.. *Meth. Bk. Conc.*
Discontented bird. *See* New Year library.
Discontented boy; or, the gifts of God remembered. 18°. 35c............................ *Am. S. S.*
Discontented little girl. Hildeburn, M. J. 30c. *Pres. Bd.*
Discontented Tom. Dawson, —. 25c....... *Porter.*
Discourses on atonement; by C: Baring, T: Chalmers, W: A. Butler, Rob. Hall and J: Maclaurin. 18°. '59. 40c.............................. *Am. Tr.*
Discreet princess. Planché, J. R. 15c....... *French.*
Disestablishment and disendowment. Freeman, E. A. $1.............................. *Macmillan.*
Disinthralled. Dutcher, G. M. *$1.50; $2; $3. *Col. Bk.*
Dismal castle brightened. Hosmer, M. $1.15. *Cong. Pub.*
Disney, W: *See* Cincinnati, Superior Court reports.
Disobedient chipmunk. 24°. 25c..... *Bost. Am. Tr.*
— *See also* Banner stories.
Disosway, E. Fables for little folks. ill. 16°. '71. 85c. *Lent.*
Disosway, E. T. South Meadows: a tale of long ago. 12°. '74. $1.50............................ *Porter.*
Disowned (The). *See* Bulwer-Lytton, *Sir* E. G. E. L.
Disraeli, B: [*Earl of Beaconsfield.*] Novels and tales. 9 v. 8°. pap. .... *Appleton.*
Cont.: Alroy, 50c. — Coningsby, 60c. — Contarini Fleming, 50c. — Henrietta Temple, 50c. — Lothair, $1. — Tancred, 50c. — Venetia, 50c. — Vivian Grey, 60c. — Young duke, 50c.

— *Same.* 6 v. sm. 8°. hf. cf., $20........ *Appleton.*
— Lothair. 12°. $2...................... *Appleton.*
— Miriam Alroy. 8°. pap., 50c............ *Peterson.*
— The young duke. 12°. $1.50............. *Harper.*
Disraeli, I: Complete works; ed. by B. Disraeli. 9 v. cr. 8°. $15; hf. cf., $30... *Putnam; Widdleton.*
Cont.: Curiosities of literature, 4 v. — Amenities of literature, 2 v. — Calamities of authors, 2 v. — Literary characters.

— Amenities of literature: sketches and characters of Eng. literature. 2 v. 12°. $2.50...... *Harper.*
— Curiosities of literature. por. cr. 8°. $1.75; hf. cf., $3.50; cf., $5.......................... *Routledge.*
— *Same;* [also] The literary character; [also] Curiosities of Am. literature by R. W. Griswold. 8°. $2; shp., $2.75 .... *World Pub.*
Distant cousins: talks with Amy and Georgie about far-off cousins; by author of "What makes me grow?" ill. 16°. '74. $1.50. .... *Dutton.*
Distant hills (The). Adams, W. 60c....... *Dutton.*
Distillers' and brewers' reference book. 4°. '70. $25. *J. A. Murphy.*
Distin, J. Tutor for the sax horn and cornet-a-piston or cornopean. 8°. pap., 75c............ *Ditson.*
Distinctive principles of the Presb. Church in the U. S. called the South. Church. 12°. 25c... *Pres. Com.*
Distinguished Christians. 12°. 75c....... *Am. Bapt.*
District of Columbia. Supreme Court reports, 1873–'74; by A. MacArthur. 8°. '75.... *U. S. Govt.*
— *See also* United States.

Disturnell, J: Sailing on the great lakes and rivers of America. 16°. $3................ *Disturnell.*
— (*ed.*) New York as it was and as it is, incl. Brooklyn and vicinity. maps and ill. sm. 16°. '76. $3. *Disturnell.*
— United States register, or blue book for 1876. 8°. '76. $1.50.......................... *Disturnell.*
Ditson, G. L. Federati of Italy: a romance of Caucasian captivity. 12°. '71. $1.50........ *Colby.*
Ditson and Co.'s standard opera librettos; with Eng. and Ital. words and music. 74 nos. 8°. '60. ea., pap., 25c.............................. *Ditson.*
Cont.: Aïda. — Anna Bolena. — Belle Hélène. — Barbe Bleue. — Bohemian girl. — Carnival of Venice. — Cinderella. — Crispino e la comare. — Crown diamonds. — Der Freischütz. — Dinorah. — Don Bucefalo. — Don Carlos. — Don Giovanni. — Don Pasquale. — Ernani. — Etoile du nord. — Faust. — Fra Diavolo. — Fleur de thé. — Fille de Mme. Angot. — Fidelio. — Geneviève de Brabant. — Giroflé-Girofla. — Grande duchesse. — Gustavus III. — I Capuletti e Montecchi. — I Lombardi. — I Martiri. — I Puritani. Il barbiere di Siviglia. — Il flauto magico. — Il giuramento. — Il pirata. — Trovatore. — Ione. — L'Africaine. — Dame blanche. — L'elisire d' amore. — La favorita. — La fille du régiment. — La gazza ladra. — La Juive. — La sonnambula. — La traviata. — Le prophète. — Les Huguenots. — Linda di Chamounix. — Lohengrin. — Lucia di Lammermoor. — Lucrezia Borgia. — Luisa Miller. — Maria di Rohan. — Maritana. — Marriage of Figaro. — Martha. — Masked ball. — Masaniello. — Mignon. — Norma. — L'ombra. — Orpheus. — Otello. — Perichole. — Poliuto. — Rigoletto. — Robert le diable. — Romeo and Juliet. — Rose of Castile. — Sappho. — Semiramide. — Vêpres Siciliennes. — William Tell. — Zampa.

— *Same.* chp. ed. 63 nos. 8°. ea., pap., 15c.; — in 2 v. $5 .... *Ditson.*
Cont.: Aïda. — Anna Bolena. — L'Africaine. — Bohemian girl. — Ballo in maschera. — Barber of Seville. — Belle Hélène. — Barbe Bleue. — Bride of Messina. — Crown diamonds. — Crispino e la comare. — Daughter of the regiment. — Der Freischütz. — Dinorah. — Don Giovanni. — Doctor of Alcantara. — Dame blanche. — Ernani. — Favorita. — Fidelio. — Faust. — Fille de Mme. Angot. — Fra Diavolo. — Gazza ladra. — Geneviève de Brabant. — Grande duchesse. — Hamlet. — Huguenots. — Ivanhoe. — The Jewess. — Lohengrin. — Lucrezia Borgia. — Lucia di Lammermoor. — Linda di Chamounix. — Martha. — Maritana. — Marriage of Figaro. — Merry wives of Windsor. — Mignon. — Masaniello. — Magic flute. — Mirella. — Norma. — Orpheus. — Ostrolenka. — Postillon du Lonjumeau. — Princesse de Trebizonde. — Perichole. — Poliuto. — Rose of Castile. — Robert the devil. — Rigoletto. — Ruy Blas. — Satanella. — Son and stranger. — Stradella. — Sonnambula. — Traviata. — Trovatore. — Tannhäuser. — Two Cadis. — William Tell. — Zampa.

Ditzler, Jac. *See* Graves, J. R., *and* Ditzler, J.; — Wilkes, L. B., *and* Ditzler, J.
Divided money. *See* Laurel ser.
Divina commedia. *See* Dante.
Divine and moral songs. *See* Watts, I:
Divine aspects of human society. Huntington, F. D. $2.25 .... *Carter.*
Divine comedy. *See* Dante.
Divine human (The) in the Scriptures. Lewis, T. $1.50 .... *Carter.*
Divine law of beneficence. Cooke, P. 25c.; 10c. *Am. Tr.*
Divine law of birth. Horton, W. R. 30c... *H. H. Carter.*
Divine life and new birth. Craik, J. $1.25.. *Morton.*
Divine pictures of the Christian centuries. Simons, E. D. $1.25........................ *W. H. Young.*
Divine pilot (The); tr. from the French. 18°. 75c.; $1; mor., $2.50......................... *Dutton.*
Divine promises ill. with passages of Scripture. 32°. (Bagster.) roan, 63c.................. *Wiley.*
Divine protection during the Irish rebellion in 1798: narrative of the preservation of the family of J. and E. Goff. 24°. 15c....... *Friends Bk. St.*
Divine revelation. Auberlen, C. A. $3.. *Scribner, W. & A.*
Divine teacher (The): sayings of Christ. 12°. '75. $1. *Whittaker.*
Divine tragedy (The). *See* Longfellow, H. W.
Diving bell (The). *See* Woodworth, F. C.
Divinity of Christ: examination of Liddon's Bampton lectures. 12°. '72. $1.75............... *Roberts.*
Divorce appeals cases. *See* England, Law reports.

Divorce reports. *See* England, Law reports.
Divorced wife. Arthur, T. S. 50c........*Peterson.*
Dix, J: A. Speeches and addresses. 2 v. por. 8°. $7........................*Appleton.*
Dix, Morgan. Guide for candidates for adult baptism. 18°. pap., 15c........................*Dutton.*
– Lectures on the pantheistic idea of an impersonal substance-deity as contrasted with the Christian faith conc. God. 12°. $1...........*Hurd & H.*
– Lectures on the two estates: of the wedded in the Lord, and of the single for the kingdom of heaven's sake. 12°. '72. $1.25; pap., 50c........*Pott.*
– Manual for the young people of the Church; with prayers and hymns. 32°. 20c............*Pott.*
– Manual of Christian life. 16°. 40c.......*McCauley.*
– Manual of instruction for confirmation classes; [also] A catechism on confirmation, by Rev. J. De Koven. 18°. '67. bds., 10c..............*Pott.*
– Thoughts on the lost unity of the Christian world, and on the steps necessary to secure its recovery: sermon. 8°. pap., 25c..............*Appleton.*
Dix, W: Giles. American state and American statesmen. 12°. '75. $1.50..................*Estes.*
Dixie: Ethiop. drama. 16°. pap., 15c........*Happy.*
Dixon, E: H. Backbone: — photographed from the scalpel. por. 12°. $1.50..............*De Witt.*
– Diseases of the sexual system. 12°. $1.50..*De Witt.*
– Woman and her diseases from the cradle to the grave. 12°. $1.75................*J. E. Potter.*
Dixon, Ja. Guide to the study of diseases of the eye; with test types and ill. 3d ed., rev. 12°. '66. $2.50.............................*Lindsay.*
Dixon, *Rev.* Ja. Methodism in its economy, origin, etc. 18°. '43. 65c..................*Meth. Bk. Conc.*
Dixon, T: Practical mill-wright's and engineer's ready reckoner: tables for finding diameter and power of cog-wheels, etc. 4th ed. 12°. '70. $1.25..*Spon.*
Dixon, W: Hepworth. Free Russia. ill. cr. 8°. $2. *Harper.*
– Her majesty's tower: an historical study. cr. 8°. $2. *Lippincott.*
– Holy Land (The): a record of travel. ill. cr. 8°. $2...............................*Lippincott.*
– New America: record of travel in the U. S. ill. cr. 8°. $2........................*Lippincott.*
– Spiritual wives. por. cr. 8°. $2.......*Lippincott.*
Dixon and his copyists. Noyes, J. H. 25c...*Oneida.*
Do-good library. *See* Baker, *Mrs.* H. N. W.
Do-good library. *See* Finley, M. F.
Do-somethings (The). Adams, W. T. 45c. *Lee & S.*
D'ye know me now? farce. 16°. pap., 15c....*French.*
– *See also* French's comic dramas.
Do you speak English, French, German, Italian, Portuguese, [or] Spanish? pocket manuals for students. 7 v. 18°. ea., bds., 60c...........*Holt.*
Do your best. 18°. 40c......................*Dutton.*
Do your duty. 16°. 25c..................*Routledge.*
Doane, G. H. Manual of instructions and prayers for persons seeking the true religion. 18°. 75c. *Strong.*
Doane, G: Washington. Songs by the way; ed. by W. C. Doane. por. 8°. '75. $2..........*Munsell.*
Doane, N. Infant baptism briefly considered. 16°. '75. 75c.......................*Meth. Bk. Conc.*
Doane, W: Croswell. Questions on the Collects, Epistles and Gospels of the Church's year; and their connection. 18°. 35c..........*McCauley.*
Doane, W: Howard. Hymns of devotion; comp. from "Songs of devotion." 32°. '73. bds., 20c. *Biglow.*
– Hymns of salvation; comp. from "Songs of salvation." 32°. '72. bds., 20c.............*Biglow.*
– Little sunbeam: choruses, quartettes, etc., for S.-schools. 16°. '67. bds., 25c...*Church; Ditson.*
– Silver spray. [S.-school music.] 12°. 40c. *Church.*

Doane, W: Howard, *continued.*
— Songs of devotion for Christian associations. 12°. '70. 75c.; $1.25; bds., 50c............*Biglow.*
— *See also* Lowry, R., *and* Doane, W. H.
Dobbs, C. E. The hero of truth. 18°. 30c.; pap., 15c.............................*So. Bapt.*
Dobell, Hor. Winter cough: catarrh, bronchitis, emphysema, asthma. 3d ed., enl. col. pl. 8°. '75. $3.50..............................*Lindsay.*
Dobney, H. H. Free churches: "a tract for my own congregation." 8°. '72. $1..........*Routledge.*
Dobson, G: C. New system for the banjo. 8°. '72. bds., $1............................*Ditson.*
Docharty, Gerardus Beekman. Elements of analyt. geometry, and of differential and integral calculus. 12°. shp., $1.75................*Harper.*
— Elements of plane and solid geometry, with the elements of plane and spherical trigonometry. 12°. shp., $1.75.........................*Harper.*
— Institutes of algebra. 12°. shp., $1.50....*Harper.*
— Practical and commercial arithmetic. 12°. shp., $1.50..............................*Harper.*
Docia's journal. *See* Alden, *Mrs.* I. M.
Dock (The) and the scaffold. *See* Speeches from the dock.
Dockham, C. Augustine (*ed.*) Dockham's Am. report and directory of the cotton, woolen, silk, jute and linen manufacture and dry goods trade. ('68.) [Biennial.] 8°. $6............*Dockham.*
— Dockham's boot, shoe and leather report and directory. ('70.) [Biennial.] 8°. $5......*Dockham.*
Doctor (The). Southey, R. $1.25..........*Harper.*
Doctor and student. Saint Germain, C. $3..*Clarke.*
Doctor Antonio. Ruffini, G. $1.75........*Carleton.*
Dr. Austin's guest. Gilbert, W. $2.......*Routledge.*
Dr. Basilius. *See* Dumas, A.
Dr. Blackburn, the yellow fever fiend. 12°. pap., 20c. *Hurst.*
Doctor Bolus. Daniel, G. 15c............*French.*
Dr. Deane's way. Foster, I. H., *and* Alden, I. M. $1.25.............................*Lothrop.*
Doctor Dilworth. Oxenford, J. 15c.......*French.*
Doctor Dunbar. Hogg, M. H. 75c..........*Nelson.*
Dr. Grant and the mountain Nestorians. Laurie, T. $1.50.............................*Lothrop.*
Dr. Howell's family. Goodwin, H. R. $1.50..*Lee & S.*
Dr. Jacob. Edwards, M. B. $1..............*Roberts.*
Doctor Jenner. Nieritz, G. 25c............*Steiger.*
Dr. Johns. Mitchell, D. G. $3.50........*Scribner.*
Dr. Kendall's children and their cousins. 16°. $1.10. *Am. S.S.*
Doctor Leslie's boys. Hildeburn, M. J. 70c. *Pres. Bd.*
Doctor Marigold's prescriptions. *See* Dickens, C:
Dr. Mondschein. *See* Curtis, A. W. *and* D. S.
Doctor of Alcantara. *See* Eichberg, J.
Dr. Oldham's talk at Greystones. Henry, C. S. $1.50. *Dutton.*
Dr. Ox. Verne, J. $3; $1................**Osgood.*
Dr. Plassid's patients. Bailey, U. L. $1.25..*Lothrop.*
Dr. Savory's tongs. ill. fp. 8°. 75c...........*Cassell.*
Dr. Syntax's three tours. *See* Combe, W.
Doctor Thorne. *See* Trollope, A.
Dr. Vandyke. Cooke, J. E. $1.25; 75c....*Appleton.*
Dr. Wainwright's patient. Yates, E. 50c. ...*Harper.*
Doctor's apple. ('70.) 4th ed. ill. 18°. '74. 50c. *Perkinpine.*
Doctor's birthday. Adams, H. C. 75c. ...*Routledge.*
Doctor's daughter. Clarke, A. S. $1.50....*Lee & S.*
Doctor's dilemma. Smith, H. 75c.........*Appleton.*
Doctor's little daughter. Meteyard, E. $2..*Routledge.*

Doctor's visit. *See* Violet stories.

Doctor's ward. *See* Bowman, A.

Doctor's ward. Richmond, D. $1.25........*Routledge.*

Doctor's wife. Braddon, M. E. 50c........*Dick & F.*

Doctrinal library. 10 v. 18°. $4.75.......*So. Meth.*
Cont.: Summers On holiness. — Wesley On Christian perfection. — Eternal sonship, by Rev. W. Beauchamp. — Divine Providence, by Rev. D. Kinnear. — Essay on apostasy, by W. J. Parks. — Kinnear On holiness. — Fletcher On Christian perfection. — Beauchamp's Letters. — Church and ministry, by Rev. R. Abbey. — Proselytism and proselyters, by Rev. G. W. Langhorne.

Doctrine of hell, ventilated. Walworth, C. A., *and* Burr, W. H. 60c...................*Cath. Pub.*

Doctrines of Scripture. 16°. 25c. ....*Un. S. S.*

Documentary history of Ohio canals; from the first measures taken for their construction to 1831–2. 8°. '32. $1.50..................*I. N. Whiting.*

Doda's birthday library. 4 v. ill. 16°. ea., $1...*Pott.*
Cont.: Doda's birthday, by E. J. Ellis. — Eldergowan, by R. Mulholland. — Markhams of Ollerton, by E. Glaister. — Tom, by H. R. Russell.

Dodd, G: Dictionary of manufactures, mining, machinery and the industrial arts. 12°. '74. $2.50. *Routledge.*

Dodd, H: Ph. (*ed.*) The epigrammatists: sel. from epigrammatic lectures of ancient, mediæval and modern times; with notes, etc. 12°. (Bohn.) $2.25.........................*Little, B. & Co.*
— *Same.* 12°. (Bohn.) $2.40......*Scribner, W. & A.*
— *Same.* 12°. (Bohn.) $2.50............*Lippincott.*

Dodd, Phelps. Tar and feather outrage; [also] The cruel murder of C. G. Kelsey. [In Eng. *or* Germ.] 8°. pap., 25c...................*Barclay.*

Dodd, W: Beauties of Shakespeare: selections. 32°. 60c.; 90c.; mor., $1.50. — sq. 16°. $1.50; mor., $2.25; $3.50..............................*Porter.*
— *Same.* (Household ser.) ill. 16°. $1.50; mor., $3. *Lee & S.*
— *Same.* ill. 12°. $1.75; ivorine, $3......*Routledge.*
— Discourses to young men; ill. by anecdotes. 18°. '71. 75c..............................*Claxton.*

Dodd family abroad. *See* Lever, C:

Doddridge, Ph. Evidences of Christianity. *See* Fleetwood, J., Life of Christ.
— Family expositor on New Testament. 8°. $5..*Carter.*
— Family religion recommended. 18°. 45c. *Cong. Pub.*
— Life of Col. Ja. Gardiner. por. 18°. 60c. *Pres. Bd.*
— On regeneration. 16°. $1. 18°. 80c....*Am. Bapt.*
— Rise and progress of religion in the soul. 18°. '28. 70c...............................*Am. Tr.*
— *Same.* 18°. 75c.........................*Sower.*
— *Same.* por. 12°. 90c....................*Pres. Bd.*
— *Same.* 12°. '75. $1.......................*Claxton.*
— *Danish.* 18°. '50. 65c....................*Am. Tr.*
— *Germ.* Anfang und Fortgang wahrer Gottseligkeit. 12°. '44. 70c...........................*Am. Tr.*
— Scripture lessons in verse. sq. 16°. 40c...*Pres. Bd.*
— Thoughts on sacramental occasions. 18°. 40c. (?) *Martien.*

Dodds, Ja. Thomas Chalmers: biog. study. 12°. '73. $1.25.................................*So. Meth.*
— *Same.* 12°. '70. $1.50........... *Meth. Bk. Conc.*

Döderlein, Chr. Alb. Handbook of Latin synonymes; tr. by H. H. Arnold, with introd. by S. H. Taylor. ('58.) New ed., rev. 16°. '75. $1.25...*Draper.*

Dödes, J. J. Manual of hermeneutics for the writings of the New Test.; tr. by G. W. Stegman, jr. cr. 8°. $1.50....................*Scribner, W. & A.*

Dodge, Alice A. Jerry and his friends; or, the way to heaven. ill. 18°. 75c...........*Bost. Am. Tr.*
— — *See also* Honor bright lib.
— Kate Woodman; or, the heart revealed. ill. 16°. 80c. *Bost. Am. Tr.*
— Pleasant grove. ill. 18°. 60c........*Bost. Am. Tr.*
— — *See also* Pleasant grove ser.
— Progress: sequel to "Jerry and his friends." ill. 18°. 75c..............................*Bost. Am. Tr.*

Dodge, Alice A., *continued.*
— — *See also* Honor bright lib.
— Rebe's common sense. ill. 16°. $1.15..*Bost. Am. Tr*
— The way to the cross. ill. 18°. 85c..*Bost. Am. Tr*

Dodge, *Rev.* E. Evidences of Christianity. 12°. $1.50 *Sheldon*

Dodge, Edn. *See* Wells, D. A., Dodge, E., *and* Cuyler, G. W.

Dodge, J. R. West Virginia: its farms and forests mines and oil wells. 12°. $1.50.....*Lippincott*

Dodge, Ma. Abigail. ["Gail Hamilton."] Works. 8 v 16°. ea., $1.50.............................*Estes*
Cont.: Country living and country thinking. — Gala days. — Stumbling-blocks. — A new atmosphere. — Skirmishes and sketches. — Summer rest. — Wool gathering. — Woman's wrongs

— Child world. 2 pts. ill. sq. 16°. '72–'73. ea., $1.50 *W. F. Gill*
— Little folk life. 16°. 90c................*Harper*
— Nursery noonings. 16°. $1.25............*Harper*
— Sermons to the clergy. 12°. '75. $2.... *W. F. Gill*
— Twelve miles from a lemon: social and domestic sketches. 12°. $1.50.................*Harper*
— Woman's worth and worthlessness: complement to "A new atmosphere." 12°. $1.50.....*Harper*
— *and* Stoddard, *Mrs.* R. H. Little folk life series. 3 v ill. sq. 16°. ea., $1.................*W. F. Gill*

Dodge, Ma. E. *See* Dodge, Ma. M.

Dodge, *Mrs.* Ma. Mapes. Few friends (A), and how they amused themselves: tale in nine chapters. 12°. '69. $1.25.........................*Lippincott.*
— Hans Brinker; or, the silver skates: story of life in Holland. ('63.) New ed. 12°. '76. $1.50. — ill. ed. ('75.) New ed. '76. $3...............*Scribner*
— Rhymes and jingles. ('74.) New ed. ill. sm. 4°. '76. $3; $1.50...........................*Scribner.*
— Theophilus and others. 12°. '76. $1.50..(?) *Scribner*
Note. Mrs. Dodge's first books were pub. under name of Ma. E. Dodge.

Dodge, N. S. A grandfather's stories about Am. hist. ill. 16°. $1.25. School ed. sm. 4°. $1..*Lee & S.*

Dodge, Ossian E. Comical doings of a funny man ill. 8°. pap., 15c.........................*Happy.*
— Ossian's harp: songs, comic and sentimental. 12°. '64. pap., 25c.........................*Ditson*

Dodge, R: Irving. The Black Hills: description of the routes, scenery, soil, etc. map and ill. 12°. '76 $2......................................*Miller.*

Dodge Club (The). De Mille, J. $1.25; 75c. *Harper*

Dodge (A) for a dinner: farce. 16°. pap., 15c. *French.*

Dodgson, C: L. ["Lew. Carroll."] Alice's adventures in wonderland. New ed. ill. 12°. '69. $1.50..............................*Macmillan.*
— *Same.* ill. 12°. $1.25; $1.50; $2........*Lee & S.*
— *French.* 12°. $2......................*Macmillan.*
— *Germ.* 12°. $2.........................*Macmillan.*
— *Ital.* 12°. $2..........................*Macmillan.*
— Elementary treatise on determinants. 4°. '67. $3.50. *Macmillan.*
— Through the looking-glass, and what Alice found there. ill. 12°. $2.......*Lee & S.; Macmillan.*

Dodney, Sa. Archie's old desk. 18°. '75. 50c. *H. A. Young.*

Dods, J: Bovee. Philosophy of electrical psychology. 12°. '50. $1.25.............................*Wells.*
— Six lectures on the philosophy of mesmerism. 12°. '73. pap., 50c. ....*Wells.*
— Spirit manifestations examined and explained. 12°. $1......................................*De Witt.*

Dodsley, Rob. Economy of human life; by an ancient Brahmin. [*anon.*] 18°. 60c. ......*Lippincott.*
— Miller of Mansfield: [dram.] entertainment. 16°. pap., 15c...............................*French.*

Dodsworth, Jer. Better land; or, the Christian emigrant's guide to heaven; rev. by T. O. Summers. ('55.) 3d ed. 12°. '75. $1.25........*So. Meth.*

Dodworth, Allan. Brass band school: instruction with music. 4°. bds., $2 .... *Peters.*

Dodworth, H. B. Cornet instructor. f°. $4.. *Gordon.*

— Rudimental instructor for baritone. 12°. 75c. *Gordon.*

— Rudimental instructor for B flat bass. 12°. 75c. — Same; for E flat bass. 12°. 75c....... *Gordon.*

— Rudimental instructor for E flat cornet. 12°. 75c. — Same; for B flat cornet. 12°. 75c... *Gordon.*

— Rudimental instructor for E flat tenor. 12°. 75c. — Same; for B flat tenor. 12°. 75c..... *Gordon.*

Doe, C: H. Buffets. [Fiction.] 8°. '75. $1.25; pap., 75c. .... *Estes.*

Doe, Wa. P. (*ed.*) Eminent authors on effective revival preaching. 12°. '76. *$1.25 .... *Doe.*

Does he love me? comedy. 16°. pap., 15c.... *French.*

Does protection protect? Grosvenor, W. M. $2.50. *Appleton.*

Doesticks, Q. K. Philander P. B. (*pseud.*) *See* Thomson, Mortimer.

Doesticks' letters. Thomson, M. $1.75; $1.50. *Peterson.*

Dog (The). 18°. 35c.; 40c................. *Dutton.*

Dog at his master's grave. *See* Bright eye ser.

Dog Crusoe. Ballantyne, R. M. $1.25........ *Porter.*

Dog fiend. *See* Marryat, F:

Dog in the manger. *See* Stories about animals.

Dog life: narratives exhibiting instinct, intelligence, etc. ill. sm. 4°. '74. $1.75........... *Nelson.*

Dog of Montargis: drama. 16°. pap., 15c.... *French.*

Dog stories. Bullard, A. 25c. .... *Lee & S.*

Doge of Duralto. Brough, R. B. 15c. ...... *French.*

Dog's dinner party. [Toy-book.] ill. 4°. $1; 50c. *Routledge.*

Dogs and their doings. *See* Morris, F. O.

Doheny, Mich. History of the Am. revolution. 12°. $1 .... *Noonan.*

Doigts (Les) de fée. Scribe, E., *and* Legouvé, E. 40c.................................. *Holt.*

Doing and dreaming. Mayo, I. F. $1.25...... *Dodd.*

Doing and suffering. 18°. 75c............ *Am. S. S.*

Doing Banting. Brough, W., *and* Halliday, A. 15c. *French.*

Doing for the best. Lacy, R. 15c... *De Witt; French.*

Doing the han'som'. Harris, A. 15c......... *French.*

Doing his best. Trowbridge, J. T. $1.25..... *Porter.*

Doing my uncle. Lacy, R. 15c. .... *French.*

Doings in Maryland; or, Matilda Douglas. 12°. $1.75. *Lippincott.*

Doings of the Bodley family in town and country. Scudder, H. E. $2 .... *Hurd & H.*

Doisy, Louisa. Helen May; or, unto her life's end. 16°. '69. $1 .... *Whittaker.*

Dolby, W: (*ed.*) History of Ireland from the invasion by Henry II. ('51.) 19th ed. eng. roy. 8°. '74. hf. mor., $10 .... *Virtue.*

Doll, C. L. Pupil's introd. to study of the piano. f°. pap., $1.25 .... *Schirmer.*

Doll world library. *See* O'Reilly, *Mrs.* Rob.

Dollars and cents. Hollenius, L. J. 15c.... *De Witt.*

Dollars and cents. Warner, A. B. $1.75. *Claxton; Lippincott.*

Döllinger, J. J. I. v. Fables resp. the popes of the middle ages, tr. by A. Plummer; with essay on the prophetic spirit and the prophecies of the Christian era, tr., with introd. and notes by H. B. Smith. 12°. $2.25 .... *Dodd.*

— Lectures on the reunion of the churches; tr. by H. N. Oxenham. 12°. '72. $1.50.......... *Dodd.*

Dolliver, Clara G. Candy elephant (The), and other stories. ('69.) 2d ed. ill. 16°. '70. 75c. *Roman.*

— No baby in the house, and other stories. ('68.) 2d ed. 16°. '70. 75c.................... *Roman.*

Dolliver romance (The). *See* Hawthorne, N.

Doll's club series. *See* Johnson, V. W.

Dolly: opera. 16°. pap., 15c. .... *French.*

Dolly and I. Adams, W. T. 45c........... *Lee & S.*

Dolly Varden. *See* Dickens, C.

Dolly's Christmas chickens. 18°. 50c........ *Carter.*

Dolly's resolutions. Beach, H. M. $1.25.... *Claxton.*

Dolores. Forrester, *Mrs.* —. $1.75..... *Lippincott.*

Dombey and son. Brougham, J. 15c. ...... *French.*

Dombey and son. *See* Dickens, C.

Domestic affection. *See* Hemans, *Mrs.* F. D.

Domestic concert collection. Johnson, A. N. 35c. *Church.*

Domestic economist: receipts. 12°. pap., 25c. *Fisher.*

Domestic economy. Lemon, M. 15c........ *French.*

Domestic felicity. Lambla, H. L. 15c........ *Ames.*

Domestic hearthstone: amateur drama. 16°. pap., 15c. *French.*

Domestic portraiture. Richmond, L. $1.25.. *Carter.*

Domestic problem (A). Diaz, A. M. $1; 50c. *Osgood.*

Domestic tales. *See* Happy child's lib.

Dominic, *St.* Life; [with] hist. sketch of the Dominican Order, [and] introd. by Rev. J. S. Alemany. 12°. $1.50; $2 .... *O'Shea.*

Dominic. Hoffmann, F. $1.10....... (?) *Luth. Pub.*

Dominican artist (A). *See* Lear, *Mrs.* S.

Dominican manual. [Cath. prayer book.] 4°. 50c.–$3 .... *O'Shea.*

— *See also* St. Dominic's manual.

Dominique. Murray, W. H. 15c. .... *French.*

Domus Dei. Donnelly, E. C. $1.50... *Cunningham.*

Don Bernardo's daughter; or, love, war and adventure. 8°. pap., 25c....................... *Dick & F.*

Don Bucefalo. *See* Ditson.

Don Cæsar de Bazan. Dumanoir, P. F. P., *and* Dennery, A. P. 15c.................. *French.*

Don Carlos. *See* Ditson.

Don Carlos. *See* Schiller, J. F. v.

Don Cato: Ethiop. drama. 16°. pap., 15c.... *Happy*

Don Giovanni. Dibdin, T. 15c............. *French.*

Don Giovanni. *See* Mozart, W. A.

Don Juan. 12°. pap., 15c................... *Radde.*

Don Juan. *See* Byron, *Lord.*

Don Munio. *See* Buck, D.

Don Paddy De Bazan: farce. 16°. pap., 15c. *French.*

Don Pasaquale: opera. 16°. pap., 15c....... *French.*

Don Pasquale. *See* Donizetti, G.

Don Quixote. Almar, G. 15c. .... *French.*

Don Quixote de la Mancha. Burton, H. S. 50c. *Carmany.*

Don Quixote de la Mancha. *See* Cervantes.

Donald, Ja. Chambers' etymological dictionary. 12°. $2 .... *Lippincott.*

Donald Deane. Bradley, W. I. $1.50. *Cong. Pub.; H. A. Young.*

Donald Fraser; by author of "Bertie Lee." 16°. $1. *Carter.*

Donald's hamper. 18°. 30c.; 35c. .... *Am. Bapt.*

— *Same.* 18°. 50c...................... (?) *Martien.*

Donaldson, Ja. Apostolical fathers: crit. account of their genuine writings and of their doctrines. cr. 8°. '74. $3 .... *Macmillan.*

— *See also* Roberts, A., *and* Donaldson, J.; — Roberts, A., Donaldson, J., *and* Crombie, F.

Donaldson, J: W: Theatre of the Greeks: hist. of Gk. drama. ill. 12°. (Bohn.) $1.75.. *Little, B. & Co.*

— *Same.* ill. 12°. (Bohn.) $2. *Lippincott; Scribner, W. & A.*

Donaldson, Paschal. Odd-fellows' pocket companion; rev. and enl. by I. D. Williamson. ('62.) New ed. ill. 18°. '76. $1.50. — Same; in German. 18°. $1.50 . . . . *R. W. Carroll.*
— Odd-fellows' pocket text book and manual. 32°. $1.50 . . . . *Moss.*
— Odd-fellows' text book and manual. New ed., rev. by G. Bertram. ill. 12°. $2 . . . . *Moss.*
Donaldson, S., *jr.* Little orator, and other tales. sq. 16°. '64. 30c.; pap., 20c. . . . . *Murphy.*
Mother of Washington, and other tales. sq. 16°. '64. 30c.; pap., 20c. . . . . *Murphy.*
— Visit to ancient Rome. sq. 16°. '64. 30c.; pap., 20c. . . . . *Murphy.*
Donaldson, W: New formulas for loads and deflections of solid beams and girders. 8°. '72. $1.50. *Spon.*
— Switches and crossings: formulæ for ascertaining angles of crossings, lengths of switches, etc. pl. 8°. '71. $4.25 . . . . *Spon.*
— Tables for plate-layers; compiled from "Switches and crossings." pl. 12°. '71. $1.75 . . . . *Spon.*
— Treatise on art of constructing oblique arches with spiral courses. pl. 8°. '67. $1.50 . . . . *Spon.*
Donat Clare; or, the manuscript man. ('68.) New ed. ill. 16°. '74. $1.25 . . . . *Hoyt.*
Donauweibchen (Das). 12°. pap., 15c. *Radde; F. W. Thomas.*
Donbavand, R. Wild Ireland; or, recollections of some days and nights with Father Michael. 8°. pap., 35c. . . . . *Lippincott.*
Doncaster, J: Friendly hints to youth. 24°. '41. 30c. *Meth. Bk. Conc.*
Done brown. Craven, H. T. 15c. . . . . *French.*
Done on both sides. Morton, J. M. 15c. *French; Lee & S.*
Donelan, J. P. My trip to France. 12°. $1 . . *Strong.*
Donizetti, Gaetano. Anna Bolena; Don Pasquale; La favorita; Linda di Chamounix; Maria di Rohan. *See* Ditson.
— Lucia di Lammermoor; with Ital. and Eng. words. [Opera.] 4°. bds., $1.50 . . . . *Ditson.*
— — *See also* Ditson.
— Lucrezia Borgia; with Ital. and Eng. words. [Opera.] 4°. bds., $1.50 . . . . *Ditson.*
— — *See also* Ditson.
Donkersley, R: Facts about wives and mothers. 12°. '65. $1.25 . . . . *Meth. Bk. Conc.*
— The full envelope; or, gleanings for youthful readers. 16°. '74. $1 . . . . *Meth. Bk. Conc.*
Donkey boy. 18°. 30c. . . . . *Dutton.*
— *Same.* 18°. 60c. . . . . *Cong. Pub.*
Donlevy, Alice. Handbook of illumination. ill. obl. 4°. '67. $2 . . . . *Randolph.*
Donne, Al. Mothers and infants, nurses and nursing; tr. from the Fr. ill. 12°. $1.25 . . . . *Burnham.*
Donne, J: Poems; with memoir by I. Walton. por. 18°. $1 . . . . *Osgood.*
Donnegan, Ja. New Greek and Eng. lexicon, on the plan of Schneider; from 2d Lond. ed., rev. and enl. by R. B. Patton. 8°. shp., $6 . . . . *Butler.*
Donnel, —. Thoughts. 75c. . . . . (?) *Cumberland.*
Donnelly, Eleanor C. Domus Dei: religious and memorial poems. 8°. '75. $1.50 . . *Cunningham.*
Donnollon, J: P. Charles and Frederick. 18°. '66. 50c. *Cunningham.*
Don't and do. 18°. 25c. . . . . *Am. S. S.*
Don't forget your opera glasses. Woolf, B. E. 15c. *French.*
Don't judge by appearances. Morton, J. M. 15c. *French; Lee & S.*
Don't lend your umbrella. Buckingham, L. 15c. *French.*
Don't say so, you may be mistaken: story for hard times and all times. ('64.) 6th ed. ill. 16°. '70. $1.25 . . . . *Perkinpine.*
— *See also* Sunshine and shadow lib.
Don't touch it. *See* Sylvan stories.
Don't wait; or, the story of Maggie. 18°. '66. 60c. *Randolph.*
Dooley, E. J. Maria immaculata: music for the Cath. Church. 8°. '76. $2.50; bds., $2.25 . . . *Ditson.*
Doolittle, Just. Social life of the Chinese; with account of their religious, governmental, educational and business customs and opinions. ill. cr. 8°. $4 . . . . *Harper.*
— Vocabulary and handbook of the Chinese lang.; romanized in the Mandarin dialect. 2 v. 8°. '72. ea., $10 . . . . *Randolph.*
Doolittle, T. Sandford. Sermon delivered in the First Ref. Dutch Church of Schenectady, N. Y., Dec. 7, 1865. 8°. pap., 25c. . . . . *N. Y. Ref. Ch. Bd.*
Doomed. Reback, H. 30c. . . . . *Am. News.*
Doomed chief. Thompson, D. P. $1.75 . . *J. E. Potter.*
Doomed city; or, the land lying waste. 32°. 25c. *Pres. Bd.*
Doomed ship; or, wreck of Arctic regions. 8°. pap., 50c. . . . . *Peterson.*
Door of escape. Reeves, M. 75c. . . . . (?) *Martien.*
Door without a knocker. Prosser, *Mrs.* —. $1.50. *Nelson.*
Door without a knocker; from "Sunday at home." ('68.) New ed. ill. 16°. '74. $1.15 . . . . *Hoyt.*
Doors outward. Robbins, S. S. $1.25 . . . . *Carter.*
Dora. Kavanagh, J. $1.50; $1 . . . . *Appleton.*
Dora. Reade, C. 15c. . . . . *Lee & S.*
Dora and Charley. 32°. 15c. . . . . *Dutton.*
Dora and her papa. Meteyard, E. $1.75 . . *Routledge.*
Dora Darling, the daughter of the regiment. 12°. '64. $1.50 . . . . *Tilton.*
Dora Deane. Holmes, M. J. $1.50 . . . . *Carleton.*
Dora Felton's visit. 18°. '74. 40c. . . . . *Am. Tr.*
Dora Hamilton; or, sunshine and shadow. ill. 18°. '64. 60c. . . . . *Am. Tr.*
— *Same.* ill. 18°. 75c. . . . . *Bost. Am. Tr.*
— *Same.* 16°. '65. 90c. . . . . *Meth. Bk. Conc.*
Doran, J: Works. 9 v. cr. 8°. $15; hf. cf., $30. *Widdleton.*
Cont.: Annals of the stage, 2 v. — Table traits and something on them. — Habits and men. — Queens of England of the house of Hanover, 2 v. — Knights and their days. — Monarchs retired from business, 2 v.

Dora's device. Reece, R. 15c. . . . . *French.*
Dora's mistake. Martyn, S. T. 90c. . . . . *Am. Tr.*
Dora's motto. Mathews, J. H. $1 . . . . *Carter.*
Dora's stewardship. 18°. 40c. . . . . *Am. S. S.*
Dorcas: a model female portrait; from writings of Cox and Jay. 18°. 35c. . . . . *Pres. Bd.*
Dorcas Club. Adams, W. T. $1.50 . . . . *Lee & S.*
Dorchester Antiquarian and Historical Society. Collections. 3 nos. 12°. '44–'50. ea., bds., 50c. *Dorch. Antiq.*
Cont.: 1. Memoirs of R. Clap. — 2. Annals of town of Dorchester, by J. Blake. — 3. Journal of R. Mather; [also] His life and death.

— History of Dorchester; by a committee of the Soc. [chiefly by E. Clapp]. 8°. '59. $5. *E. Clapp; Dorch. Antiq.*
Dörchläuchting. Reuter, F. $1; 75c. . . . . *Steiger.*
Dore, Alfr. *See* Lowenburg, J., Lallemant, R. A., *and* Dore, A.
Doré, Gst. Legend of the wandering Jew: 12 designs, with explan. introd. f°. $6.50; $8 . . . . *Cassell.*
— *See also* Bible [Whole]; — Cervantes; — Chateaubriand; — Dante; — Davillier, C.; — Fairy tales told again; — La Fontaine; — L'Epine, E., Days of chivalry; — Milton, J; — Raspe, R. E.; — Tennyson, A.
Doré gallery (The): 250 eng. sel. from Doré's works; with memoirs of Doré, crit. essay, and letter press by Edm. Ollier. sm. f°. $60; — in 2 v. $65; mor., $70; $80 . . . . *Cassell.*

Doré; by a stroller in Europe. 12°. $1.50... *Harper.*
Dorfgeschichten. Auerbach, B. 3 v. $3.50; $2.50; $4... *F. W. Thomas.*
Doring, H. Life of Beethoven. *See* Moschelles, I., Life of B.
Dörner, H: The German-English guide: grammar of Eng. for Germans. pt. 1. 8°. 60c... *Krebs.*
Dorner, I: A: Doctrine of the person of Christ; tr. from the Germ. 5 v. 8°. ea., $3. *Scribner, W. & A.*
— History of Protestant theology, particularly in Germany; tr. by G. Robson and S. Taylor. 2 v. 8°. $10... *Scribner, W. & A.*
Dorney, H: Contemplations and letters. 12°. '58. $1. *Draper.*
Dornröschen. Schletterer, H. M. *net,* $1.50. *Schirmer.*
Dornrosen: Erstlingsblüthen deutscher Lyrik in Amerika. 16°. '71. $1... *Steiger.*
Dorothea Trudel; or, the prayer of faith. 16°. 75c. *Willard.*
Dorothy Fox. Parr, L. $1.25; 75c... *Lippincott.*
Dorothy Siebel. ill. 18°. 50c... *Crowell.*
— *See also* Annie Marlowe ser.
Dorothy's ladder; by author of "Burden bearing." 16°. $1... *Am. S. S.*
Dorothy's story-book. *See* Silver barrel lib.
Dorr, B. Recognition of friends in another world. 32°. 40c... *McCauley.*
Dorr, C. A. Music for the church service: responses, chants, etc., for congregational and choir use. 4°. '59. 75c... *Dutton.*
Dorr, *Mrs.* Jla. C. R. Bride and bridegroom; or, letters to a young married couple. 16°. $1.25. *Cin. Meth. Bk. Conc.*
— Expiation. [Fiction.] 12°. $1.50... *Lippincott.*
— Poems. 12°. $1.50... *Lippincott.*
— Sybil Huntington. [Fiction.] 12°. $1.75.. *Lippincott.*
Dorsey, *Mrs.* Anna H. Coaina, the rose of the Algonquins. 12°. $1... *O'Shea.*
— Conscience; or, the trials of May Brook. 18°. $1. *Strong.*
— Flemmings (The); or, truth triumphant. 12°. $2. *O'Shea.*
— Nora Brady's vow; [also] Mona, the vestal. 12°. $1.75... *Lippincott.*
— Old gray rosary. 12°. $1... *O'Shea.*
— Oriental pearl. sq. 16°. '51. 60c.; 80c.... *Murphy.*
— Student of Blenheim Forest; or, the trials of a convert. 12°. '67. $1.50; $1.75... *Murphy.*
Dorsey, Clem. *See* Maryland, Statutory testamentary law.
Dorsey, J. M. History of Moses, Aaron, Joshua and others, deduced from a review of the Bible; also remarks on the morals of the Old and New Test., and some of the ancient philosophers. 12°. 75c... *Mendum.*
Dorsey, Sa. Anne. ["Filia."] Agnes Graham. 8°. '69. pap., 75c... *Claxton.*
— Athalie; or, a southern villeggiatura: a winter tale. 8°. '71. pap., 60c... *Claxton.*
Dort. Articles of the synod of Dort; tr. from the Lat. with notes by T. Scott. 12°. 85c.... *Pres. Bd.*
Dos Passos, J. R. Hints for legislative reform. 8°. pap., 25c... *Campbell & Co.*
Dossey, W: Dossey's choice: psalms and hymns and spiritual songs. 18°. shp., 75c... *Desilver.*
Dot. *See* Dickens, C.
Dot books. *See* Frost, S. A.
Dot mad tog: Dutch drama. 16°. pap., 15c... *Happy.*
Dot madrimonial adverdisement: Dutch drama. 16°. pap., 15c... *Happy.*
Dot quied lotgings: Dutch drama. 16°. pap., 15c. *Happy.*

Doten, *Miss* Lizzie. My affinity, and other stories. 12°. '69. $1.50... *Colby.*
— Poems from the inner life. ('63.) 11th ed. 12°. '75. $1.50; $2... *Colby.*
— Poems of progress. ('71.) 3d ed. ill. 12°. '73. $1.50; $2... *Colby.*
Dotey, Clara. Blind Jakey. ill. 18°. '71. 60c. *Lothrop.*
Dot's travels. *See* Dot books.
Dotty Dimple books. *See* Clarke, R. S.
Doty, Duane. Smith's interest tables. 12°. '75. $1. *E. B. Smith.*
— Williams and Packard's gems of penmanship. obl. 4°. $5... *Appleton.*
Douai, Adolph. Bilderfibel u. erstes deutsches Lesebuch. 12°. '66. bds., 30c... *Steiger.*
— Complete and practical German grammar. 12°. $2. *Potter, A. & Co.*
— Kindergarten: manual for introd. of Fröbel's system of primary educ. ill. 12°. '71. $1.. *Steiger.*
— Rational phonetic primer. 2d ed. 12°. '74. bds., 20c... *Steiger.*
— Rational readers. 3 nos. 12°. '73–'74. bds... *Steiger.*
Cont.: First reader, 30c. — Second, 50c. — Third, 80c.
— Reform of the common Eng. branches of instruction: introd. to the "Rational readers." 12°. '72. bds., 30c... *Steiger.*
Douay catechism. 18°. pap., 18c.; hf. bd., 25c. *Strong.*
— *See also* Catechism.
Double-bedded room. Morton, J. M. 15c.... *French.*
Double dummy. Harrington, N. H., *and* Yates, E. 15c... *French.*
Double-faced people. Courtney, J. 15c.... *French.*
Double fault. Yateman, M. R. 90c.... *Cong. Pub.*
Double play. Everett, W. $1.25... *Lee & S.*
Double story. *See* Mac Donald, G.
Double triumph. O'Reilly, A. J. 40c... *Sadlier.*
Double wedding. Warfield, C. A. $1.75.. *Peterson.*
Double witness of the Church. Kip, W. I. $1.50. *McCauley.*
Doubleday, Abner. Reminiscences of Forts Sumter and Moultrie, S. C., 1860–'61. 12°. $1.. *Harper.*
Doublet, Vct. Elements of logic; tr. from the Fr. 18°. 60c... *O'Shea.*
— Logic for young ladies; tr. 18°. 60c... *O'Shea.*
Doubly false. Stephens, A. S. $1.75; $1.50.. *Peterson.*
Doubtful victory. Oxenford, J. 15c. *French; Lee & S.*
Doubts of infidels. *See* Pigault-Le Brun, C. A. G.
Doubts removed. Malan, C. 10c... *Revell.*
Doudney, Sa. Faith Harrowby; or, the smuggler's cave. ill. 12°. $1... *Nelson.*
— Great Salterns (The). 16°. '76. $1.25... *Hoyt.*
— Marion's three crowns. ill. 16°. 50c... *Nelson.*
— Oliver's oath. ill. 12°. '75. $1... *Nelson.*
— Pilot's daughter: story of the Eng. sea-coast. ill. 12°. '76. $1... (?)*Nelson.*
— Under grey walls. ill. 12°. $1... *Nelson.*
Dougherty, *Mrs.* Lizzie C. City out of sight. 18°. 30c.; pap., 10c... *So. Bapt.*
Doughty, J: Manual of New Church doctrine. 8°. bds., 50c... *Lippincott.*
Doughty, *Mrs.* S. P. Life of Swedenborg; for children. 18°. '56. 50c... *H. H. Carter.*
— Little stories for little folks. 16°. '65. 50c. *H. H. Carter.*
— Mountains and mole-hills. 16°. '70. 50c. *H. H. Carter.*
— Playing Santa Claus. 16°. '65. 50c... *H. H. Carter.*
— Stories and rhymes for boys and girls. 16°. '69. 50c... *H. H. Carter.*
— Trifles. 18°. '68. 30c... *H. H. Carter.*
— Truths for children. 16°. '67. 50c.... *H. H. Carter.*
— Willie Benton, and other tales. 16°. '70. 50c. *H. H. Carter.*

Douglas, *Miss* Amanda M. Claudia. 12°. $1.50. *Lee & S.*
— Drifted asunder; or, the tide of fate. 12°. '75. $1.50. *W. F. Gill.*
— Home nook; or, the crown of duty. 12°. $1.50. *Lee & S.*
— In trust; or, Dr. Bertrand's household. 12°. $1.50. *Lee & S.*
— Kathie's stories for young people. 6 v. ill. 16°. ea., $1 .... *Lee & S.*
Cont.: In the ranks. — Kathie's three wishes. — Kathie's Aunt Ruth. — Kathie's summer at Cedarwood. — Kathie's soldiers. — Kathie's harvest days.
— Lucia: her problem. 12°. $1.50 .... *Sheldon.*
— Seven daughters. ill. 16°. $1.50 .... *Lee & S.*
— Stephen Dane. 12°. $1.50 .... *Lee & S.*
— Sydnie Adriance; or, trying the world. 12°. $1.50. *Lee & S.*
— There's no place like home. ill. 12°. '74. $1.50. *W. F. Gill.*
— With fate against him. 12°. $1.50 .... *Sheldon.*
Douglas, J. S. Homœopathic treatment of intermittent fevers. 18°. 38c. .... *Boericke.*
— Practical homœopathy for the people. ('56.) 13th ed. 12°. '75. $1 .... *Douglas.*
Douglas, Marion (*pseud.*) *See* Greene, Annie D.
Douglas, S. *See* England, Common law reports.
Douglas, Silas H., *and* Prescott, A. B. Qualitative chemical analysis. 8°. '74. $3 ...... *Fiske & D.*
Douglas. Home, J. 15c. .... *French.*
Douglas. Rede, W. L. 15c. .... *French.*
Douglas family. Bell, C. D. 75c. ... *Scribner, W. & A.*
Douglas ser. of Christian Gk. and Lat. writers. *See* March, F. A.
Douglass, Elson. Social life; or, philosophy of society. ill. 8°. *$2.50 .... *McCurdy.*
Douglass, J: T. Wooing under difficulties: farce. 16°. pap., 15c. .... *Ames.*
Dove, H. W. Circulation of the waters on the face of the earth. cr. 8°. '74. pap., 25c. .... *Estes.*
Dove, J: Virginia text book; cont. hist. of Masonic grand lodges, constitution, digest of laws, etc. 3d ed. pl. 12°. '66. $2 .... *J. W. Randolph.*
— Virginia text book of royal arch Masonry. pl. 12°. '53. $2 .... *J. W. Randolph.*
— *See also* Freemasons, Grand Lodge of Va.
Dove (The). 18°. 40c. .... *Dutton.*
Dove (The). *See* Our song birds.
Dove (The). Scott, J. W. 40c.; 25c. ...... *Claxton.*
Dove, and other stories. *See* Dove ser.
Dove in the eagle's nest. *See* Yonge, C. M.
Dove of the tabernacle. Kinane, C. H. 75c.; $1. *Haverty.*
Dove series. 6 v. ill. 18°. $4.80 .... *Sheldon.*
Cont.: Dove, and other stories. — Great things done by little people. — Little facts for little people. — Little animals described for little people. — True stories for little people. — Little Lilla; or, the way to be happy.
Dover, *Lord.* [G. J. W. A. Ellis.] Life of Frederick II. of Prussia. 2 v. 18°. $1.50 .... *Harper.*
Dover selection of spiritual songs. Broaddus, A. 60c. *Claxton.*
Dove's nest. *See* Llewellyn, E. L.
Dove's nest lib. *See* Llewellyn, E. L.
Doves in a cage. Jerrold, D. 15c. .... *French.*
Dow, *jr.* (*pseud.*) *See* Paige, Elbridge Gerry.
Dow, Howard M. Masonic Orpheus: songs, hymns, etc.; arranged for male voices. obl. 4°. '70. $3; bds., $2.50 .... *Ditson.*
Dow, J. M. New question-book on prayer. 2 pts. 18°. '68. ea., hf. bd., 15c. .... *Hoyt.*
Dow, Lorenzo. Dealings of God, man and the devil, as exemplified in the life of L. Dow; with his writings. ('58.) New ed. 8°. '75. shp., $3. *Pounsford; Stevens.*

Dowager. Mathews, C. J. 15c. .... *French.*
Dower house. Thomas, A. 50c. .... *Harper.*
Dowling, A. *See* England, Common law reports.
Dowling, C: Hutton. Practical formulæ and rules for finding the strain and breaking weight of wrought-iron bridges; with tables. ill. 8°. '62. 40c. *Spon.*
Dowling, J: History of Romanism; with chronol. table, indexes and glossary. ('53.) 2d ed., rev. and enl. ill. imp. 8°. '71. $5 .... *E. Walker.*
— Judson memorial. 18°. 75c. .... *Sheldon.*
— Power of illustration: an element of success in preaching and teaching. 18°. 40c. .... *Sheldon.*
— The prayer-meeting hymn book. 32°. '75. 30c.; bds., 25c. .... *Ward.*
Dowling, L. H. The crown: book of S.-school songs. obl. 16°. '71. bds., 35c. ..... *Church; Dowling.*
— The palm of victory: book of S.-school songs. obl. 16°. '74. bds., 20c. .... *Dowling.*
Dowling, M. G. Othello: travestie. 16°. pap., 15c. *French.*
Down by the sea. Baker, G. M. 15c. ...... *Lee & S.*
Down by the waves. Harks, S. W. 60c. .. *Cong. Pub.*
Down in a balloon: drama. 16°. pap., 15c. .. *French.*
Down in a mine; or, buried alive; by author of "Story of a pocket Bible." ill. 18°. 60c. *Am. Tr.; Bost. Am. Tr.; N. Y. Ref. Ch. Bd.; Pres. Com.*
— *See also* Winter school stories.
Down in a saloon. Walker, M. S. $1.50 ...... *Hoyt.*
Down the Rhine. Adams, W. T. $1.50 .... *Lee & S.*
Down the river. Adams, W. T. $1.25 .... *Lee & S.*
Down the river; or, practical lessons under the code duello. ill. 12°. $1.50 .... *Hale.*
Down the steps. 16°. $1.25 .... *Carter.*
Downes, J: Occultations in 1853. 4°. '53. pap., 30c. *Smith. Inst.*
Downing, And. Jackson. Cottage residences: designs, with list of trees, shrubs, etc., by H. W. Sargent and C. Downing; with new designs in rural architecture, by G. E. Harney. 4°. $6 ... *Wiley.*
— Fruits and fruit-trees of America. 2d ed., rev. and enl. by C. Downing. ill. 8°. '76. $5 .... *Wiley.*
— Fruits of America. 2 v. pl. 8°. $35 ...... *Dewey.*
— Hints to persons about building in the country; [also] Hints to young architects, to facilitate their practical operations, by G. Wightwick. ill. 8°. $2 .... *Wiley.*
— Rural essays on horticulture, landscape gardening, etc.; ed., with memoir, by G. W. Curtis. 8°. '54. $3.50 .... *World Pub.*
— Selected fruits: from "Fruits and fruit-trees of America"; with new varieties, etc., by C. Downing. ill. 12°. $2.50 .... *Wiley.*
— Treatise on theory and practice of landscape gardening, adapted to No. Am.; with supplement by H. W. Sargent. ill. 8°. $6.50 .... *Judd.*
Downing, C: Encyclopedia of fruits; or, fruit and fruit-trees of Am.; with app. cont. new varieties to 1876. 2 v. ill. 8°. ea., $2.50 .... *Wiley.*
Downing, *Maj.* Jack (*pseud.*) *See* Smith, Seba.
Downing, Josh. W. Remains, with memoir; ed. by E. H. Downing. 12°. '41. 90c. *Meth. Bk. Conc.*
Downing, *Mrs.* S. E. C. Songs in the valley of Achor. 24°. '74. 60c.; 75c. .... *Randolph.*
Downs, *Mrs.* Eliz. Harry Maitland; or, the tyrant father. ('71.) New ed. 16°. '75. $1.50 .. *Hoyt.*
— Nettie Loring. ('73.) New ed. 12°. '75. $1.25. *Nat. Temp.*
Downward and upward; by author of "The climbers." 12°. '71. $1.50 .... *Claxton*
Dowson, J. Emerson *and* Alfr. Tramways: their construction and working. cr. 8°. '75. $1.50. *Spon*
Doyle, *Rev.* —. Douay catechism: abridg. of "Christian doctrine." 18°. pap., 10c. ..... *Cummiskey.*

Doyle, C. Brave men's footsteps. ill. 16°. $1.25. *Routledge.*
— *See also* Plucky fellows lib.
Doyle, *Sir* Fs. Hastings. Lectures on poetry. cr. 8°. $1.25 .... *Macmillan.*
Doyle, J. Life. 18°. 75c.; $1.25 .... *Sadlier.*
Doyle, J. A. History of the U. S.; with maps, ill. of acquisition of territory and increase of population, by F. A. Walker. 16°. '76. $1.40 .. *Holt.*
Doyle, J. E. P. Plymouth Church and its pastor; or, Henry Ward Beecher and his accusers. por. 12°. '74. *$2.50 .... (?) *Park Pub.*
Doyle, Mt. Farmer's manual: a treasury of information. ill. 12°. bds., 50c. .... *Routledge.*
— Field and garden plants. 16°. bds., 50c. .. *Routledge.*
— Small farms: a practical treatise. 16°. bds., 50c. *Routledge.*
— (*ed.*) Illustrated book of domestic poultry. col. ill. 8°. $4.50 .... *Porter.*
Doyle, R: Foreign tour of Brown, Jones and Robinson: hist. of what they saw and did in Belgium, Germany, Switzerland and Italy. ill. 4°. $5. *Appleton.*
— Laughable adventures of Brown, Jones and Robinson: where they went, and how they went, what they did, and how they did it. ill. obl. 8°. pap., 30c. .... *Dick & F.*
D'Oyly, G. *See* Bible [Whole].
Draft (The). White, C. 15c. .... *De Witt.*
Dragon, the faithful shepherd dog. *See* Witt, *Mme.* H. de.
Draiper, Edm. S. Six hundred easy, profitable and pleasant ways to make money: recipes for making articles in constant demand and of ready sale. sq. 16°. $1; pap., 50c. .... *Harper.*
Drake, B: Life of Black Hawk; with sketches of Keokuk, the Sac and Fox Indians, and the Black Hawk war. 12°. '49. 50c. .... *I. N. Whiting.*
— *See also* Todd, C. S., *and* Drake, B.
Drake, C: D. Treatise on the law of suits by attachment in the U. S. 4th ed. 8°. '73. shp., $6. *Little, B. & Co.*
Drake, Dan. Pioneer life in Kentucky: letters addressed to his children; ed., with notes and biog. sketch, by C. D. Drake. por. 8°. '70. $3; large pap., $6 .... *Clarke.*
— Systematic treatise on the principal diseases of the interior valley of No. Am. 8°. '54. shp., $5. *Claxton.*
Drake, *Sir* Fs., Cavendish, T: *and* Dampier, W: Lives and voyages; incl. introd. view of the earlier discoveries in the South seas, and hist. of the buccaneers. 18°. 75c. .... *Harper.*
Drake, Fs. S. Dictionary of Am. biography; [with] supplement. 8°. '72. $6; shp., $7; hf. cf., $8.50; cf., $10; mor., $12 .... *Osgood.*
— List of members of the Mass. Society of the Cincinnati; incl. roll of orig. members, with biog. 8°. '72. $2; pap., $1.50 .... *Williams.*
— Memorials of the Society of the Cincinnati of Mass. ill. 8°. '73. $13 .... *Williams.*
Drake, Jos. Rodman. The culprit fay. sm. 4°. '75. 50c.; pap., 25c. .... *Tompkins.*
— *Same.* ill. 12°. $2 .... *Carleton.*
— *Same:* cantata by J. L. Ensign. 8°. '72. bds., $1. *Ditson.*
Drake, R: Revelations of a slave smuggler: autobiog., with pref. by H. B. West. ill. 8°. pap., 25c. *De Witt.*
Drake, S. B. Exhibition book; for Sabbath and day schools. 8°. '63. pap., 10c. .... *Darrow.*
Drake, S: Adams. Historic fields and mansions of Middlesex [Co., Mass.] ill. 8°. '74. $5. **Osgood.*
— Nooks and corners of the New Eng. coast. ill. sq. 8°. $3.50 .... *Harper.*
Drake, S: Adams, *continued.*
— Old landmarks and historic personages of Boston. ill. 12°. $3 .... **Osgood.*
— (*ed.*) Bunker Hill: the story told in letters from the battle-field by British officers engaged. 8°. '75. $1 .... *Nichols & H.*
Drake, S: G. Aboriginal races of No. Am.; with add. by J. W. O'Neill. roy. 8°. $4; shp., $4.50; hf. cf., $6 .... *Desilver.*
— History of the French and Indian war. por. and eng. sq. 8°. '70. $4 .... *Munsell.*
Dram-drinker (The). 18°. 18c. .... *Am. S. S.*
Drama in Pokerville. Field, J. M. 75c. .... *Peterson.*
Drama of drunkenness. ill. 18°. 50c. .... *Am. S. S.*
Drama of kings. Buchanan, R. $5 .... *Routledge.*
Dramatic reciter (The). 16°. pap., 40c. .... *French.*
Dramatic school speaker. 32°. '76. pap., 10c. *De Witt.*
Dramatic speaker (The). 12°. pap., 15c. .... *De Witt.*
Dramatic stories. Phelps, L. H. $1 .... *Griggs.*
Dramatis personæ. Browning, R. $1.50 .... *Osgood.*
Dramatist. Reynolds, F. 15c. .... *French.*
Draper, Alonzo. Fife without a master. obl. 8°. '57. pap., 60c. .... *Ditson.*
Draper, Ella E. Our best: practical receipts. 16°. '76. pap., 30c. .... *Williams.*
Draper, G. Holy Spirit's work; or, the still small voice to the listening soul. 18°. '72. 60c. .... *Tibbals.*
Draper, H: Construction of a silvered glass telescope. 4°. '64. pap., $1 .... *Smith. Inst.*
— Text-book on chemistry. 12°. $1.50 .... *Harper.*
Draper, J: C. Text-book on anatomy, physiology and hygiene. ill. 8°. $3.75; shp., $4.25 .... *Harper.*
— Year book of nature and popular science. 12°. '73. $2 .... *Scribner.*
Draper, J: W: Anniversary discourse before N. Y. Acad. of Med. 8°. '63. pap., 25c. *N. Y. Acad. Med.*
— History of the Am. civil war. 3 v. 8°. '67–'70. $10.50; shp., $12; hf. cf., $17.25 .... *Harper.*
— History of the conflict between religion and science. (Intern. sci. ser.) 12°. $1.75 .... *Appleton.*
— History of the intellectual development of Europe. 8°. '63. $5; shp., $5.50; hf. cf., $7.25 .. *Harper.*
— *Same.* New ed., rev. 2 v. 12°. '76. $3; hf. cf., $6.50 .... *Harper.*
— Human physiology, statical and dynamical. ill. 8°. $5; shp., $5.50; hf. cf., $7.25 .... *Harper.*
— Text-book on natural philosophy. ill. 12°. shp., $1.50 .... *Harper.*
— Text-book on physiology; abridg. from "Human physiology." ill. 12°. $1.50 .... *Harper.*
— Thoughts on the future civil policy of Am. cr. 8°. '65. $2.50; hf. mor., $4.75 .... *Harper.*
Draper, Lyman C., *and* Croffut, W. A. Helping hand for town and country: information conc. house, garden, field, apiary, etc. ill. roy. 8°. '69. *$4.25; shp., $5 .... *Wilstach.*
Draper, W. H. Nature of the gouty vice. *See* Seguin, E. C., Am. clin. lect.
Drapery question. Selby, C. 15c. .... *French.*
Draughts and backgammon. 48°. 25c. *Scribner, W. & A.*
Drawing for young children. sq. 8°. $1 .. (?) *Francis.*
Drawing-room magic. ill. 12°. pap., 30c. .... *Happy.*
Drawing-room, 2d floor and attics. Morton, J. M. 15c. .... *French.*
Drawing room stage. Baker, G. M. $1.50 .. *Lee & S.*
Drayton: story of Am. life. 12°. $1.50 .... *Harper.*
Drayton Hall series. *See* Mathews, J. A.
Draytons and the Davenants. Charles, E. $1 .. *Dodd.*
Dreadfully alarming: farce. 16°. pap., 15c. .. *French.*
Dream at sea. Buckstone, J. B. 15c. .... *French.*
Dream book and fortune teller. *See* New.
Dream children. Scudder, H. E. $1 .... *Hurd & H.*

Dream chintz (The). *See* Mackarness, *Mrs.* M. A.
Dream life. Bates, S. $1.50 .... *Claxton.*
Dream life. Mitchell, D. G. $1.75; $4; $3 .. *Scribner.*
Dream numbers. Trollope, T. A. $1.75; $1.50. *Peterson.*
Dream of the future. Dance, C. 15c. .... *French.*
Dream of heaven. ('60.) New ed. ill. 18°. '75. 40c. *Hoyt.*
Dream of little Tuk. Andersen, H. C. $1 .... *Miller.*
Dream spectre. Wilks, T. E. 15c. .... *French.*
Dreamer's handbook and fortune teller. 16°. pap., 15c. *Happy.*
Dreaming and doing, and other stories. ('61.) New ed. ill. 18°. '75. 30c. .... *Hoyt.*
Dreams. Robertson, T. W. 15c. .... *De Witt.*
Dreams of delusion. Simpson, J. P. 15c. ... *French.*
Dreamthorpe. Smith, A. $1.50 .... *Routledge.*
Drebing, Gst. L. Das gemeine Recht d. Ver. Staaten, nebst d. Statuten d. einzelnen Staaten u. d. Bankerottgesetze. 8°. '65. $2.25; pap., $1.50. *Steiger.*
Dred. *See* Stowe, *Mrs.* H. B.
Dred. Suter, W. E. 15c. .... *French.*
Dred Scott case. *See* Benton, T. H.
Drei Jahre von Dreissigen. *See* Rellstab, L.
Drei Katharinen. *See* Gumpert, T. v.
Drei Müllerstöchter (Die). 12°. pap., 15c. .... *Radde.*
Drei Spiegelbilder unserer Zeit. 12°. 75c. .. *Benziger.*
Dreifaltige Schnur (Eine). 32°. '46. 25c. ... *Am. Tr.*
Dreissig Geschichten f. d. Jugend. 18°. 35c. . *Ev. Assoc.*
Dreizler, C. B. Schwäbische Dorfpredigten. 12°. '70. pap., 15c. .... *Steiger.*
Dreka, L: Dictionary blotter. sm. 4°. '74. 75c. .. *Dreka.*
Drelincourt, —. Les enseignements de l'église romaine. 18°. '46. 30c.; pap., 10c. ..... *Am. Tr.*
Dresden gallery: 50 examples of the old masters, reprod. in photog.; with letter press. f°. '75. $20. *Routledge.*
Dresden gallery: photos., with comments by J. Hübner. f°. pap., $6. — Same; with Germ. text. 2 ser. f°. ea., $36. 8°. $10 .... *Stroefer.*
— *See also* Gems of the Dresden gallery.
Dresdener Kreutz-Katechismus. 16°. bds., 40c. *Ludwig.*
Dress and care of the feet. ill. 12°. '71. $1 .... *Wells.*
Dress reform. Woolson, A. G. $1.50 .... *Roberts.*
Dresser, Cp. Principles of decorative design; with col. pl., designs and diagrams. cr. 4°. $3.50 .. *Cassell.*
— Studies in design, for manufacturers, architects, designers, etc.: 60 orig. designs, with letter press and chapters on principles of designing. f°. $27.50 .... *Cassell.*
Dresser, Hor. E. *See* United States, Tariff and internal revenue law.
Dressler, R. New and complete instructions for the flute. f°. bds., $3 .... *Ditson.*
Dressler, W: Christmas chimes: hymns, carols, etc. obl. 8°. pap., 20c. .... *Peters.*
— Easter bells: hymns, carols, etc. obl. 8°. pap., 20c. *Peters.*
— Fairy echoes. cr. 8°. bds., 60c. .... *Peters.*
— Musical chimes. obl. 8°. bds., $1 .... *Peters.*
— Ne plus ultra glee and chorus-book; with piano accomp. obl. 8°. bds., $1.50 .... *Peters.*
— Peters' Catholic melodist. 4°. bds., $1.50 ... *Peters.*
— Sacred selections. obl. roy. 8°. bds., $1.50 .. *Peters.*
— Sänger-Fest. [For male voices.] obl. 8°. bds., $1.50 .... *Peters.*
— Temperance echoes. 12°. bds., 75c. .... *Peters.*
— Young pianist. 4°. $2.25; bds., $1.75 ..... *Peters.*
Drew, B: Pens and types; or, hints and helps to all who write, print and read. 16°. $1.50; 75c.; hf. bd., 60c. .... *Lee & S.*
Drew, *Mrs.* C: Lenny's search. 16°. $1.50 .. *Cong. Pub.*
Drew, S: Life and missionary labors of T: Coke. 12° '37. $1 .... *Meth. Bk. Con.*
— Original essay on the immateriality and immortality of the soul. 18°. 75c. .... *Sower.*
Drew, W. A. Practical book-keeping. ('73.) New ed. 8°. '76. $1.50 .... *Sherwood.*
Drew, W. H. Geometrical treatise on conic sections. 4th ed. cr. 8°. '75. $1.75. — Solution to same. cr. 8°. '68. $1.75 .... *Macmillan.*
Drew, W: H. Freemason's handbook. 32°. '75. 75c. $1 .... *Masonic.*
— *German.* 32°. '75. 75c. .... *Masonic.*
Drewry, C: S. On injunctions. *See* Law lib.; — Locke, J., Law and practice of foreign attachment.
Drewry, G: Overend. Commonsense management of the stomach. 16°. '75. $1 .... *Dodd.*
Dried flowers. 18°. 40c. .... *Cong. Pub.*
Drift of medical philosophy. Gorton, D. A. 75c.; 60c. *Lippincott.*
Drift-wood. Cross, J. T. H. 40c. .... *So. Meth.*
Drifted asunder. Douglas, A. M. $1.50 .. *W. F. Gill.*
Drifted snow flakes. Thomas, J. H. 2 v. ea., $1.50. *H. A. Young.*
Drifting anchor. Winton, N. W. $1.25 .... *Lothrop.*
Drifting anchor series. 5 v. 16°. $5 .... *Lothrop.*

Cont.: Drifting anchor. — Percy Raydon. — George Clifford's loss and gain. — Cicely Brown's trials. — How and why.

Drifting and steering. Peebles, M. L. $1.25 .. *Nims.*
Drifting boat (The); or, Joe Fenton's revenge. 18°. 60c. .... *Am. S. S.*
Drifting goodward. Aunt Mattie. 18°. 75c. .. *Graves.*
Dring, T: *See* Greene, A. G.
Drinking fountain. *See* Two watches.
Drinking-fountain stories. ('70.) New ed. ill. 12°. '73. $1 .... *Nat. Temp.*
Drinkwater, *Mrs.* Jennie M. Fred and Jeanie. 16°. $1.25 .... *Carter.*
— Marion's little sister and the hard things she found to do. 16°. $1 .... *Cong. Pub.*
— Not bread alone. 16°. $1.25 .... *Carter.*
— Only Ned. 16°. $1.25 .... *Carter.*
— Penny saved and penny earned. 16°. 65c. *Cong. Pub.*
Drisler, H: *See* Smith, W., *and* Drisler, H.
Driven from home. Boyd, E. 30c. ...... *Am. News.*
Driven from the path. Smart, C. $1.75 ... *Appleton.*
Driven to sea. *See* Cupples, *Mrs.* A. J.
Drobisch, —. Mass no. 1, in C; arrang. by W. C. Peters. 4°. pap., $1.25 .... *Peters.*
— Mass no. 2, in F. 4°. pap., $1.25 .... *Peters.*
Drohojowska, A. J. F. A. S. de L. (*Comtesse*). La demoiselle du Saint-Cyr. *See* Souvestre, E., Le testament de Madame Patural.
Droll dialogues and laughable recitations. Martine, A. 30c.; 50c. .... *Dick & F.*
Droll stories. Balzac, H. de. $5 .... *Routledge.*
Drop of water. *See* Edgeworth, M.
Drop (A) too much. Baker, G. M. 15c. .... *Lee & S.*
Dropped from the clouds. *See* Verne, Jules.
Drops from the brook by the way: text and prayer for every day. sq. 18°. $1.25 ...... *Bost. Am. Tr.*
Drops from the well-spring. 18°. 75c. .... *Cong. Pub.*
Drops of truth. Jeanie. 75c. .... *Pres. Bd.*
Drops of water. Wheeler, E. 75c. ...... *Nat. Temp.*
Drops of water from many fountains. Eldredge, M. $1 .... *Palmer.*
Drouet, L. Twenty-four studies in all the keys. *See* Berbiguier, A. T., Method for the flute.
Drown, Dan. A: Idyls of Strawberry Bank. [Poems.] ill. 12°. '73. $2; $2.50 .... *Williams.*
Droysen, I. G. *See* Bendeman, E.

roz, Gst. Around a spring; tr. by MS. ('71.) New ed., rev. (Leis. hour ser.) 16°. '76. $1.25.. *Holt.*
- Babolain; tr. by MS. (Leis. hour ser.) ('73.) New ed. 16°. '76. $1.25 .... *Holt.*
ruids (The): pictures of Britain at the time of Christ. 18°. 45c. .... *Am. S. S.*
ruitt, Rob. Principles and practice of modern surgery. ill. 8°. $4; leath., $5 .... *Lea.*
- Surgeon's vade-mecum: manual of mod. surgery. 10th ed., rev. and enl. ill. demy 8°. '70. $5.. *Lindsay.*
rummer (The). *See* Addison, Jos.
rummer boy. ill. 12°. 90c. .... *Nelson.*
rummer boy. Trowbridge, J. T. $1.50.... *Tilton.*
rummer boy series. 5 v. 12°. $4.50 .... *Nelson.*
Cont.: Drummer boy. — Joseph Pilmore. — Besieged city. — Orphans of Glenulva. — Master Peter.
rummer boys. 18°. 30c. .... *Dutton.*
rummer's assistant; or, the art of drumming. 8°. pap., 50c. .... *Ditson.*
rummond, *Mrs.* —. Emily Vernon. 18°. 75c. *Carter.*
rummond, D: T: K. On the parables: parabolic teaching of Christ; or, the engravings of the New Test. ('55.) New ed. 12°. '72. $1.75. *Carter.*
rummond, Ja. Forest flower (The): memorial of Dan. McKillican. 18°. 30c. .... *Pres. Bd.*
- Mary searching for Jesus. 18°. 20c...... *Pres. Bd.*
runkard (The); or, the fallen saved. Smith, W. H. 15c. .... *French.*
runkard saved. Aydelott, B. P. 25c..... *West. Tr.*
runkard's children: drama. 16°. pap., 15c. *French.*
runkard's doom. Pitt, G. D. 15c. .... *French.*
runkard's warning: drama. 16°. pap., 15c. *French.*
rury, Anna H. Deep waters. 8°. '63. pap., 25c. *Burnham.*
- *Same.* 8°. $1.25; pap., 75c. .... *Estes.*
- Eastbury. 12°. $1.50 .... *Harper.*
- Misrepresentation. 8°. pap., $1 .... *Harper.*
rury, M. S. Secrecy vs. the family, state and church. 12°. pap., 10c. .... *E. A. Cook.*
rusie's own story. Giberne, A. $1.50 .... *Pott.*
ry goods dealers' reference book. 4°. '70. $50. *J. A. Murphy.*
ryburgh Abbey. *See* Swain, C.
ryden, J: Works. por. and ill. roy. 8°. $4.50. *Routledge.*
- *Same;* with life by J. Mitford. 2 v. 8°. $4; shp., $5; hf. cf., $8.50 .... *Harper.*
- Poems. 12°. $1.50 .... *Locke.*
- *Same.* (Aldine ed.) 5 v. 16°. ea., 75c. *Lippincott.*
- *Same;* with life and notes by J. Mitford. 5 v. por. 18°. $5 .... *Osgood.*
- *Same;* ed. by R. A. Willmott, with biog. and crit. notice. (British poets.) ill. 12°. $2.25; hf. cf., $3.50; mor., $5 .... *Routledge.*
- Poetical works. ill. 12°. $1.50 .... *World Pub.*
- *Same.* (Globe ed.) 16°. $1.25; hf. cf., $3.25; mor., $4; chp. ed., pap., 60c. .... *Appleton.*
- *Same.* (Household ser.) ill. and por. 16°. $1.50; mor., $3 .... *Lee & S.*
- *Same.* (Presentation poets.) ill. 16°. $1.75. *Routledge.*
- *Same;* ed. with memoir, rev. text and notes by W. D. Christie. (Globe ed.) 12°. '70. $1.50. *Macmillan.*
- *Same;* with notes by J. Warton and others. por. roy. 8°. $4.50 .... *Routledge.*
- Fables and tales from Boccaccio and Chaucer; with memoir of life and writings of D. ('55.) New ed. 32°. 60c. .... *D. Thomas.*
- *See also* Ovidius Naso, P.; — Plutarch; — Virgil.
rysdale, J., *and* Hayward, J. W. Health and comfort in house building; or, ventilation with warm air by self-acting suction power. pl. 8°. '72. $3 .... *Spon.*

Du sollst nicht stehlen. *See* Hoffmann, J.
Duane, J. C. Manual for engineer troops. pl. and ill. 12°. '64. hf. mor., $2.50 ..... *Van Nostrand.*
Duane, R. B. Memorial of Nathan B. Crocker. 4°. '66. $1.50 .... *Rider.*
Duane, W: J. Biographical memoir. 8°. '68. pap., 40c. .... *Claxton.*
Duben, Gst. v. Treatise on microscopical diagnosis; tr., with add., by L. Bauer. ill. 8°. $1... *Wiley.*
Dublin, an hist. sketch; ed. by T. O. Summers. ('58.) 2d ed. 18°. '59. 50c. .... *So. Meth.*
Du Bois, A. J. Elements of graphical statics, and their application to framed structures, etc., cranes, bridges, etc.: text and plates. 2 v. 8°. $5 .... *Wiley.*
— New method of graphical statics. ill. 8°. '75. $2. *Van Nostrand.*
Du Boisgobey, Fortuné. The golden tress; tr. from the Fr. 12°. '75. $1.50 .... *Claxton.*
Dubourg, A. W. *See* Taylor, T., *and* Dubourg, A.W.
Du Breuil, Alph. Scientific and profitable culture of fruit trees; tr., with introd. by G. Glenny. ill. 16°. $2 .... *Routledge.*
— Thomery system of grape culture. 12°. 50c. *Woodward.*
— Vineyard culture improved and cheapened; tr. by E. and C. Parker; with notes and adaptations to Am. culture by J. A. Warder. ill. 12°. '67. $2 .... *Clarke.*
Ducat, Arth. C. Practice of fire underwriting. ('62.) 7th ed. 8°. '76. $1.50 .... *Hine.*
Ducatel, Jul. *See* Maryland geol. survey.
Du Chaillu, Pl. B. Country of the dwarfs. ill. 12°. $1.50 .... *Harper.*
— Explorations and adventures in equatorial Africa. ill. 8°. $5 .... *Harper.*
— Journey to Ashango land, and further penetration into equatorial Africa. ill. 8°. $5 ...... *Harper.*
— Lost in the jungle. ill. 12°. $1.50 .... *Harper.*
— My Apingi kingdom; with life in the great Sahara, and sketches of the chase. ill. 12°. $1.50.. *Harper.*
— Stories of the gorilla country. ill. 12°. $1.50.. *Harper.*
— Wild life under the equator. ill. 12°. $1.50.. *Harper.*
Duchenne, G. B. Localized electrization and its application to pathology and therapeutics; tr. by H. Tibbits. ill. 8°. $3 .... *Lindsay.*
Duchess of Dublin. Baker, G. M. 15c. .... *Lee & S.*
Duchess of Malfi. Webster, J. 15c. .... *French.*
Duchess of Mansfeldt. *See* Lacy's home plays for ladies.
Duchess or nothing. Gordon, W. 15c. .... *French.*
Duchesse de la Vallière. *See* Bulwer-Lytton, *Sir* E. G. E. L.
Duck hunting. Coyne, J. S. 15c. .... *French.*
Du Cygne, Mt. Ars rhetorica. 2d ed. 18°. '66. 75c. *Murphy.*
Dudevant, *Mme.* A. L. A. D. *See* Sand, G: (*pseud.*)
Dudevant, J. F. M. A. *See* Sand, Maurice (*pseud.*)
Dudleigh, Agnes. Madge, Kate and Dick; or, ripening lives. 16°. $1 .... *Pres. Bd.*
Dudley, C. W. *See* South Carolina, Chancery reports.
Dudley, J. L. Tides and tendencies of religious thought. 12°. '73. $1.50 .... *Claxton.*
Dudley, Ma. Abridged memoir; with accounts of her daughters, Hannah and Charlotte Dudley. 18°. 50c.; $1 .... *Friends Bk. St.*
Dudley, T. M., *jr.* Sunday school lessons for the church year. 12°. '73. pap., 20c.; bds., 25c. *Turnbull.*
Dudley, T: Letter to the Countess of Lincoln, March, 1631. Washington, 1838. [Reprint.] 4°. pap., 25c. .... *Sabin.*
Dudley Carleon. Braddon, M. E. 25c..... *Dick & F.*

Duehrmig, G. Hosanna of the little ones: hymns for Cath. schools. obl. sm. 4°. 50c. ..... *Benziger.*

Duel. Peake, R. B. 15c. ..... *French.*

Duel between France and Germany. Sumner, C. 50c. *Lee & S.*

Duel in the dark. Coyne, J. S. 15c. ..... *French.*

Duel in the snow: drama. 16°. pap., 15c. ..... *French.*

Duenna. Sheridan, R. B. 15c. ..... *French.*

Duer, J. Law and practice of marine insurance. 2 v. 8°. shp., $13 ..... *Baker, V. & Co.*

— *See also* New York City, Superior Court reports.

Duer, W: Alex. Lectures on the constitutional jurisprudence of the U. S. 18°. 75c. ..... *Harper.*

— Life of Wm. Alexander. *See* New Jersey Hist. Soc.

Duff, Alex. Jesuits (The): their origin and order, morality and practices, suppression and restoration. 18°. pap., 10c. ..... *Pres. Bd.*

— Life and happy death of Charlotte Green. 18°. 30c. *Am. S. S.*

Duff, P. Book-keeping by single and double entry. 8°. $3.75 ..... *Harper.*

Duffet, F. Extracts from French literature. 12°. '76. $1 ..... *Wilson, H. & Co.*

— Progressive and practical method for the study of French. 2 pts. 12°. '73–'74. ea., $1.—Key. 75c. *Wilson, H. & Co.*

Duffey, *Mrs.* E. B. No sex in education; or, an equal chance for both boys and girls: review of E. H. Clarke's "Sex in education." 16°. '74. $1. *J. M. Stoddart.*

— Our behavior: manual of etiquette and dress. 12°. '76. $2 ..... *J. M. Stoddart.*

— Relations of the sexes. 2d ed. 12°. '76. $2.. *Wood & H.*

— What women should know: a woman's book about women. 12°. '73. $2 ..... *J. M. Stoddart.*

Duffey, J: B. Lives and portraits of the presidents; [with U. S. Const.] 12°. '76. pap., 25c. *Arthur.*

Duffield, G: Bible rule of temperance. 18°. '68. 60c. *Nat. Temp.*

Duffield, S: W. Warp and woof: a book of verse. 16°. '70. $1.25 ..... *Randolph.*

Duffield, W: W. School of the brigade, and evolutions of the line. 18°. '62. $1.. *Claxton; Lippincott.*

Duffy, T: *and* Cummings, T. J. Remarkable trials of all countries. 8°. '73. $3.50; shp., $4.50. *Ward & P.*

Dufour, G. H. Principles of strategy and grand tactics; tr. by W. P. Craighill. ill. 12°. '64. $3. *Van Nostrand.*

Dufton, W: Practical billiards; cont. many new theories of the game. ill. 8°. $6 ..... *Routledge.*

Duganne, A: J. H. History of government. 12°. $1.50. *De Witt.*

— Mysteries of three cities, Boston, N. Y. and Phila. 8°. pap., 75c. ..... *Peterson.*

— Rose Warrington. 8°. pap., 25c. ..... *Peterson.*

— War in Europe [in 1859]: its remote and recent causes, with the Vienna treaties of 1814 and 1815. maps. 8°. pap., 25c. ..... *De Witt.*

— Woman's vows and Masons' oaths: drama. 12°. pap., 15c. ..... *De Witt.*

Du Gue, B. French-English and Eng-Fr. dictionary. 18°. $1.50 ..... *Routledge.*

Dugué, F. *See* Bourgeois, A., *and* Dugué, F.; — Dennery, A. P., *and* Dugué, F.

Du Hamel, J. Pleasonton. Protestant gems of the Prayer book. ('69.) 2d ed. 16°. '70. 50c.; $1. *Claxton.*

Duhring, Jla. Gentlefolks and others. 12°. $2. *Lippincott.*

— Philosophers and fools. cr. 8°. $2 ..... *Lippincott.*

Duhring, L: A. Atlas of skin diseases: pl. with descript. text. [To form 10 pts.] pt. 1. 4°. '76. $2.50 ..... *Lippincott.*

Du Huys, C: The Percheron horse; tr. from the Fr. ill. 12°. $1 ..... *Judd.*

Duke, R. T. W. *See* Smith, F. H., *and* Duke, R. T. W.

Duke and cousin. Grey, E. C. 50c. ..... *Peterson.*

Duke (The) and the scholar. Kington-Oliphant, T. L. $2 ..... *Macmillan.*

Duke Christopher. Christopher, F. H. 40c. ... *Chase.*

Duke Ernest. Hervey, R. $2 ..... *Macmillan.*

Duke of Marchmont. Reynolds, G. W. M. 75c. *Peterson.*

Duke of Monmouth. Griffin, G. $1.50 ..... *Sadlier.*

Duke's daughter. Bourgeois, A., *and* Feval, P. 15c. *French.*

Duke's motto; or, the little Parisian. 8°. pap., 25c. *De Witt.*

Dukesborough tales. Johnston, R. M. $1.50. *Turnbull.*

Dulce domum. Perry, F. $2.50 ..... *Routledge.*

Dulcie's lonesome night. 18°. 30c. ..... *Am. S. S.*

Dulcken, H. W. Animal life all the world over; with remarks on the trees and plants of various regions. ill. obl. 4°. $4 ..... *Routledge.*

— Children's Bible history. ill. sq. 16°. '71. $1.50. *Routledge.*

— Child's popular fairy tales. ill. cr. 8°. $3. *Scribner, W. & A.*

— Golden harp: hymns, rhymes and songs, for the young. sq. 12°. $1.75 ..... *Routledge.*

— Handy history of Eng. for the young. ill. sq. 16°. '71. $1.50 ..... *Routledge.*

— Happy day stories for the young. ill. 4°. '74. $2. *Routledge.*

— Natural history: pictures of the animal creation drawn from nature. 2 v. ill. f°. ea., $2.50. *Nelson.*
Cont.: Domestic animals. — Wild animals.

— Old friends and new friends. ill. sm. 4°. $1.75. *Scribner, W. & A.*

— One by one: child's book of tales and fables. sq. 12°. $1.75 ..... *Routledge.*

— Rhyme and reason: picture-book of verses for little folks. sq. 12°. $1.75 ..... *Routledge.*

Dulles, J: W. The soldier's friend: a devotional manual. 32°. 10c. ..... *Pres. Bd.*

Dumanoir, P. *See* Bourgeois, A., *and* Dumanoir, P.

— *and* Dennery, A. P. Don Cæsar de Bazan; tr. by G. A. A'Beckett and Mark Lemon: drama. 16°. pap., 15c. ..... *French.*

Dumas, Alex. Novels. 18 v. in 10. 16°. $15.. *Routledge.*
Cont.: Count of Monte Cristo. — Three musketeers; [also] Twenty years after. — Vicomte de Bragelonne, 2 v. — Memoirs of a physician. — Queen's necklace; [also] Countess de Charny. — Nanon; [also] Two Dianas. — Taking the Bastile. — Dr. Basilius; [also] The conspirators. — Ascanio; [also] Chicot, the jester.

— *Same.* (Railway lib.) 31 v. 16°. bds... *Routledge.*
Cont.: Vicomte de Bragelonne, 2 v., $2. — Count of Monte Cristo, $1. — Memoirs of a physician, $1. — Taking the Bastile, $1. — The half brothers, 80c. — Marguerite de Valois, 80c. — Ascanio. — Beau Tancred. — Black Tulip. — Captain Paul. — Catherine Blum. — Chevalier de Maison Rouge. — Chicot. — The conspirators. — Countess de Charny. — Dr. Basilius. — Forty-five guardsmen. — Ingenue. — Isabel of Bavaria. — Nanon. — Page of the Duke of Savoy. — Pauline. — The queen's necklace. — Regent's daughter. — The Russian gypsy. — The three musketeers. — Twenty years after. — Twin captains. — Two Dianas. — Watchmaker, *ea.*, 50c.

— Adventures of a marquis. 8°. $1.75; pap., $1. *Peterson.*

— Amaury. 8°. pap., 50c. ..... *Harper.*

— Andrée de Taverney. 8°. $1.75; pap., $1.. *Peterson.*
Note. Tr. of part of "La Comtesse de Charny."

— Ascanio; or, the sculptor's apprentices: hist. romance of the 16th century. 8°. pap., 75c. ..... *Harper.*

— Black tulip (The). 8°. pap., 50c. ..... *Peterson.*

— Buried alive. 8°. pap., 25c. ..... *Peterson.*
Note. Same as "Pauline."

— Catherine Howard: play. 16°. pap., 15c... *French.*

— Chevalier (The). 8°. $1.75; pap., $1 .... *Peterson.*

— Chevalier d'Harmental; or, love and conspiracy. 8°. pap., 50c. ..... *Harper.*

Dumas, Alex., *continued.*
— Chevalier (Der) v. Maison Rouge. 12°. 75c.; pap., 50c. .... *F. W. Thomas.*
— Chevalier of Maison Rouge: drama. 16°. pap., 15c. *French.*
— Conscript (The); or, the days of the first Napoleon. 8°. $1.75; pap., $1 .... *Peterson.*
— Convert (The) of St. Paul: a tale of Greece and Rome. 8°. pap., 25c. .... *U. P. James.*
Note. Tr. of "Acté."
— Corsican brothers. 8°. pap., 50c. .... *Peterson.*
— Count of Monte Cristo. 16°. $1.50 .... *Routledge.*
— *Same.* ill. 8°. $1.75; pap., $1.50 .... *Peterson.*
— *Same.* ill. 8°. $3; hf. cf., $5 .... *Routledge.*
— *Germ.* Der Graf von Monte Christo. 8°. $2; pap., $1.50; hf. mor., $2.25 .... *F. W. Thomas.*
— — *See also* Herr (Der) der Welt.
— Count of Moret. 8°. pap., 50c. .... *Peterson.*
— Count of Morian. 8°. pap., 75c. .... *Dick & F.*
Note. Same as "Count of Moret"?
— Countess of Charny; or, the fall of the French monarchy. 8°. $1.75; pap., $1 .... *Peterson.*
— Diana De Poitiers. 2 v. in 1. 8°. pap., $1 .. *Dick & F.*
Note. Same as "Two Dianas."
— Diana of Meridor. 8°. $1.75; pap., $1 ... *Peterson.*
— Edmond Dantes: sequel to "Monte Cristo." 8°. $1.75; pap., 75c. .... *Peterson.*
— Fallen angel (The). 8°. pap., 75c. .... *Peterson.*
— Felina de Chambure. 8°. pap., 75c. .... *Peterson.*
— Forty-five guardsmen (The). 8°. $1.75; pap., $1. *Peterson.*
— George; or, the planter of the Isle of France. 8°. pap., 50c. .... *Peterson.*
— Half brothers (The). 16°. $1 .... *Routledge.*
Note. Same as "The iron hand."
— Horrors of Paris. 8°. pap., 75c. .... *Peterson.*
Note. Tr. of part of "Les Mohicans de Paris."
— Iron hand (The). 8°. $1.75; pap., $1 .... *Peterson.*
Note. Same as "The half brothers."
— Iron mask (The): contin. of "Three guardsmen." 8°. $1.75; pap., $1 .... *Peterson.*
Note. Tr. of part of "Le Vicomte de Bragelonne."
— Isabel of Bavaria, queen of France; or, mysteries of the court of Charles v. 8°. pap., 75c. .. *Peterson.*
— Ladies of St. Cyr: comedy. 16°. pap., 15c. .. *French.*
— Louisa; or, adventures of a French milliner. 8°. pap., 50c. .... *U. P. James.*
Note. Credited to Dumas by this publisher.
— Louise la Vallière. 8°. $1.75; pap., $1 .. *Peterson.*
Note. Tr. of part of "Le Vicomte de Bragelonne."
— Love and liberty; or, French revolution of 1792–'93. 12°. $1.75; pap., $1.50 .... *Peterson.*
— Madame de Chamblay. 8°. pap., 50c. .... *Peterson.*
— Man with five wives. 8°. pap., 75c. .... *Peterson.*
— Marguerite de Valois. 8°. pap., 75c. .... *Dick & F.*
— *Same.* 16°. $1 .... *Routledge.*
— Marriage verdict (The). 8°. pap., 75c. .. *Peterson.*
Note. Tr. of "Sylvandire."
— Masaniello; or, the fishermen's league. 8°. pap., 25c. *De Witt.*
Note. The page headings read — "or, the fisherman of Naples."
— Memoirs of a physician. 16°. $1.50 .... *Routledge.*
— *Same.* ill. 8°. $1.75; pap., $1 .... *Peterson.*
— Mohicans of Paris. 8°. pap., 75c. .... *Peterson.*
— Napoleon [Fr.] With notes by Fasquelle; for schools. 12°. '55. $1.25 .... *Ivison.*
— Otec La Ruine; přel. G. Reišl. [Bohemian.] 16°. '75. 90c. .... *Geringer.*
— Paul Jones; or, the son of the sea. 8°. pap., 25c. *Dick & F.*
Note. Same as "Captain Paul."
— Polish spy (The): tale of the French rev.; tr. by H. L. Williams, jr. 8°. pap., 50c. ..... *De Witt.*
— Queen's necklace. 8°. $1.75; pap., $1 ... *Peterson.*
— Rosa Woodville, the jailor's daughter. 8°. pap., 75c. *Dick & F.*

Dumas, Alex., *continued.*
— Six years later; or, taking of the Bastile. 8°. $1.75; pap., $1 .... *Peterson.*
Note. Same as "Taking the Bastile."
— Sketches in France. 8°. pap., 75c. .... *Peterson.*
— Taking the Bastile; or, six years later. 12°. $1.25. *Routledge.*
Note. Same as "Six years later."
— Tales of Algeria; or, life among the Arabs; tr. by R. M. Bache. ill. 12°. '68. $1.75 .... *Claxton.*
— Three guardsmen; or, the three mousquetaires. 8°. $1.75; pap., 75c. .... *Peterson.*
Note. Same as "Three musketeers."
— Three musketeers; [also] Twenty years after. 16°. $1.50 .... *Routledge.*
— Three strong men. 8°. pap., 25c. .... *De Witt.*
— Twenty years after: sequel to "Three guardsmen." 8°. $1.75; pap., 75c. .... *Peterson.*
— Twin lieutenants. 8°. pap., 75c. .... *Peterson.*
Note. Same as "Twin captains."
— Vicomte Bragelonne, the son of Athos: continuation of "Twenty years after." 8°. $1.75; pap., 75c. *Peterson.*
— *Same.* 2 v. 16°. $2.50 .... *Routledge.*
— Wedding dress (The); tr. by F. Robinson. 8°. pap., 25c. .... *De Witt.*
— Woman's love. 8°. pap., 25c. .... *Dick & F.*
— Young chevalier (The). 8°. pap., 75c. .. *Dick & F.*

Dumas, Alex. (*fils*). Annette; or, the lady of the pearls. 8°. pap., 75c. .... *Peterson.*
— Camille; or, the fate of a coquette. 8°. pap., 25c. *De Witt.*
— *Same.* 12°. $1.75; pap., $1.50 .... *Peterson.*
— Camille: drama. 16°. pap., 15c. .... *French.*
— Demi-monde (The): a satire on society; tr. by Mrs. E. G. Squier. 12°. 75c.; pap., 50c. *Lippincott.*
— Man-woman; or, the temple, the hearth, the street; tr. and ed. by G. Vandenhoff, with memoir of D. 12°. $1 .... *Lippincott.*

Dumb boy (The). 18°. 22c. .... *Am. S. S.*

Dumb boy of Fribourg; tr. by Miss A. T. Sadlier. 18°. 50c.; 75c. .... *Sadlier.*

Dumb maid of Genoa. Farrell, J. 15c. ..... *French.*

Dumb man of Manchester. Rayner, B. F. 15c. *French.*

Dumb Savoyard: melodrama. 16°. pap., 15c. *French.*

Dumb traitor. Wilmer, M. E. $1.25 .... *Nat. Temp.*

Dümling, Hm. Arithmetisches Exampelbuch. ('72.) 5th ed. nos. 1–3. cr. 8°. '75. ea., 20c. — Auflösungen. nos. 1–3. cr. 8°. ea., 15c. .... *Barthel.*
— *Same;* no. 4: Die bürgerl. Rechnungsarten. 8°. '76. 50c. .... *Barthel.*
— Illustrirtes Thierleben f. Schule u. Haus; mit besonderer Berücksichtigung d. nordamerik. Thiere: Säugethiere. 8°. $2.50 ..... *Brumder.*

Dumont, Fk. Over the plains songster. [In Eng. *or* Germ.] 12°. pap., 20c. .... *Barclay.*

Dumont, *Mme.* Melaine. Coco, the monkey; tr. by L. Harnard. ill. 18°. '70. 75c. .... *Claxton.*
— Velvet-coat, the cat; tr. by L. Harnard. ill. 18°. '69. 75c. .... *Claxton.*

Dun (The). *See* Edgeworth, M.

Dunallan. *See* Kennedy, G.

Dunbar, C: F. Extract from laws of U. S. rel. to currency and finance. 12°. '76. pap., 75c. .. *Sever.*

Dunbar, E: E. Romance of the age; or, the discovery of gold in California. ill. 12°. $1.25 .. *Appleton.*

Duncan, *Rev.* —. Pastor's manual. 18°. 50c. *Cong. Pub.*

Duncan, Alex. The examiner, or teacher's aid. ('63.) New ed. 12°. '65. 50c. .... *Wilson, H. & Co.*

Duncan, And. Practical surveyor's guide. ('54.) 7th ed. ill. 12°. '74. $1.25 .... *Baird.*

Duncan, D. *See* Spencer, H., Descriptive sociology.

Duncan, H: Cottage fireside. 18°. 60c. ..... *Carter.*
— Sacred philos. of the seasons. 2 v. 12°. $3 .. *Carter.*

Duncan, H: *continued.*
— *Same;* ed. by F. W. P. Greenwood. 4 v. 12°. $6. *Harper.*

Duncan, J. Matthews. Fecundity, fertility, sterility and allied topics. 8°. $6 .... *W. Wood.*
— On the mortality of child-bed and maternity hospitals. 8°. $2.50 .... *W. Wood.*
— Practical treatise on perimetritis and parametritis. 12°. $2.50 .... *W. Wood.*
— Researches in obstetrics. 8°. $6. .... *W. Wood.*

Duncan, *Mrs.* M. G. L. Memoir of G: A. Lundie. 18°. 75c .... *Carter.*
— Memoir of Mary L. Duncan. 16°. $1. *Bost. Am. Tr.; Carter.*
— *Same.* 16°. 70c .... *West. Tr.*

Duncan, Malcolm C. Masonic ritual and monitor: guide to the three symbolic degrees of the ancient York rite, etc. 16°. $2.50; leath., $3 .. *Dick & F.*
— *Germ.* Rituale der Freimaurerei. 16°. $2 .. *Dick & F.*

Duncan, Ma. B. M. Bible hours. 16°. '67. $1.25 .. *Carter.*

Duncan, P. Mt. Transformations of insects: adapted from Blanchard's "Métamorphoses, mœurs et instinctes des insectes." ill. demy 8°. $3.50 .. *Cassell.*
— *Same.* ill. 8°. $7.50 .... *Claxton.*

Duncan, R. S. History of Sunday schools. 12°. '76. $1; mor., $2 .... *So. Bapt.*

Duncan, S: A: American system of patents; read before the Am. Soc. Sci. Assoc., Boston, 1870. 8°. pap., 15c .... *Williams.*

Duncan, W: C. Life, character, etc., of John the Baptist; based upon "Johannes der Täufer," v. L. v. Rhoden. 12°. 75c .... *Sheldon.*
— Tears of Jesus of Nazareth. 12°. 75c ..... *Sheldon.*

Duncan Campbell. *See* Defoe, D.

Dundas, *Hon. Mrs.* —. Wrecked not lost. ill. 16°. 75c .... *Nelson.*
— *Same.* ill. 16°. '74. $1 .... *Lothrop.*

Dunducketty's picnic. Williams, T. J. 15c. *Lee & S.*

Dungan, D. R. Modern revivalism. 24°. '76. pap., 15c. .... *Cen. Bk.*
— On the rock; or, truth stranger than fiction. 12°. '76. $1.50 .... *Cen. Bk.*
— Our plea and our mission; or, is there sufficient reason for our existence as a separate religious body? 32°. '76. pap., 10c. .... *Cen. Bk.*
— Prohibition vs. license. 16°. '70. pap., 15c. *Cen. Bk.*

D'Unger, Rob. Life of Cordelia Thomson. [In Eng. *or* Germ.] 8°. pap., 20c .... *Barclay.*

Dunglison, Robley. History of medicine to [1800]; ed. by R. J. Dunglison. 12°. '72. $2.50 .. *Lindsay.*
— Human physiology. 2 v. ill. 8°. $7 .... *Lea.*
— Medical lexicon: dict. of med. science. New ed., rev. and enl. roy. 8°. '73. $6.50; leath., $7.50 .. *Lea.*
— New remedies, with formulæ for their preparation and administration. 8°. $4 .... *Lea.*
— *See also* Cyclopædia of practical medicine.

Dunham, S: Astley. History of Spain and Portugal. 5 v. 12°. $3.75 .... *Harper.*

Dunlap, Ja. D. Book of forms for practice in courts of Penna. and of the U. S. 8°. shp., $6 .. *Kay.*

Dunlap, *Miss* Jla. *See* Hosmer, *Miss* M., *and* Dunlap, *Miss* J.

Dunlap, M. E. Abridgment of element. law. 8°. '76. $3.50; shp., $4 .... *Soule.*

Dunlap, T: Wiley's Am. iron trade manual of the United States. 4°. $7.50 .... *Wiley.*

Dunlap, W: History of State of New York. 2 v. 18°. $1.50 .... *Harper.*

Dunlevy, A. H. History of the Miami Assoc., 1797–1836. 16°. $1 .... *Stevens.*

Dunlop, Ja. Digest of the general laws of the U. S.; with ref. to acts repealed, and notes of decisions of the Supreme Court, 1789–1856. roy. 8°. shp., $6.25 .... *Claxton; Lippincott.*

Dunlop, Ja., *continued.*
— New digest of Acts of Assembly of Penn., chronol. arranged; with notes and ref. 4th ed., brought down to 1853. 8°. $5 ...... *T. & J. W. Johnson.*

Dunn, Lew. R. Holiness to the Lord. 12°. '74. $1. *Meth. Bk. Conc.*
— Mission of the Spirit. 12°. '71. $1.25 .. *Meth. Bk. Conc.*

Dunn, M. M. *See* Book of praise.

Dunn, Sara. Heiress of the mount. ill. 8°. pap., 30c. *Am. News.*

Dunning, *Mrs.* A. K. ["Nellie Grahame."] Amy Rivers; or, the girl who did not know how to live. 18°. 50c .... *Pres. Bd.*
— Beginning (The) and the end. 18°. 75c ... *Pres. Bd.*
— Bessie Haven; or, the girl who wanted to shine. 18°. 35c .... *Pres. Bd.*
— Bet and Bounce. 18°. 35c .... *Pres. Bd.*
— Bob Walker; or, the boy who couldn't get up in the morning. 18°. 35c .... *Pres. Bd.*
— Carrie Trueman; or, the girl who disobeyed her parents. 18°. 45c .... *Pres. Bd.*
— Charlie Evans; or, the boy who could not keep his temper. 18°. 45c .... *Pres. Bd.*
— Cloud (The) and the sunbeam. 18°. 45c. *Pres. Bd.*
— Contradictions; or, high life at Edgerton. ill. 16°. '69. $1.50 .... *Lothrop.*
— Deacon Gibbs' enemy. 16°. $1.25 .... *Pres. Bd.*
— Diamonds reset. 12°. $1 .... *Pres. Bd.*
— Dick Mason; or, the boy who trusted in himself. 18°. 45c .... *Pres. Bd.*
— Emily Sherwood; or, the girl who had a disagreeable temper. 18°. 30c .... *Pres. Bd.*
— Evil tongue (The). 18°. 70c .... *Pres. Bd.*
— First glass of wine. ('66.) New ed. ill. 18°. '76. 50c. .... *Hoyt.*
— Fred Wilson's sled. 18°. 35c .... *Pres. Bd.*
— Grace and Polly. 18°. 35c .... *Pres. Bd.*
— Grace Avery's influence. ill. 16°. '73. $1.50 .. *Lothrop.*
— Grace Mansfield's experiment. 18°. '68. 90c. *Garrigues.*
— Harry Edwards; or, the boy who told lies. 18°. 35c. *Pres. Bd.*
— Hatty Winthrop; or, the little girl who could not guard her tongue. 18°. 45c .... *Pres. Bd.*
— Jack Myers; or, the boy who stole a penny. 18°. 35c .... *Pres. Bd.*
— Lilian Gordon; or, the little girl who was not afraid to die. 18°. 50c .... *Pres. Bd.*
— Little Annie's first thoughts about God. 18°. 40c. *Pres. Bd.*
— Little Robbie. ill. sq. 18°. '67. 50c .... *Am. Tr.*
— Little thing (A). 18°. 35c .... *Pres. Bd.*
— Mary Grey's perplexities. 16°. $1.25 ... *Cong. Pub.*
— Mary Raymond. 18°. 30c .... *Pres. Bd.*
— Mary's new friends. 18°. 35c .... *Pres. Bd.*
— Mat Warner; or, the boy who wanted his own way. 18°. 45c .... *Pres. Bd.*
— Minister's wife; or, life in a country parish. 16°. $1 .... *Am. S. S.*
— Minna Croswell; or, the girl who was afraid of being laughed at. 18°. 50c .... *Pres. Bd.*
— Mr. Wallingford's mistake. 16°. $1 ..... *Pres. Bd.*
— Mrs. Latimer's meetings. 18°. 35c .... *Pres. Bd.*
— Ned Turner; or, the boy who said "wait a minute." 18°. 50c .... *Pres. Bd.*
— Only a child. 18°. 35c .... *Pres. Bd.*
— Only a penny. 18°. 50c .... *Pres. Bd.*
— Only this once. 18°. 35c .... *Pres. Bd.*
— Our Father. ill. 18°. '69. 25c .... *Am. Tr.*
— Ralph Waring's money. 16°. $1.25 ...... *Am. S. S.*
— Rebella; or, the shining way. 18°. 50c ... *Pres. Bd.*
— Ruth Cummings; or, the girl who could not deny herself. 18°. 45c .... *Pres. Bd.*
— Stepmother's recompense; or, Mrs. Ellerton's trials and rewards. 12°. $1 .... *Pres. Bd.*
— Stories for the little ones. 10 v. 18°. $3.50 .. *Pres. Bd.*
Cont.: Home missionary. — Contrast. — Lion's den. — Golden rule. — Stray lambs. — Watchful eye. — Carrie's hard lesson. — Alice Townsend's garden. — Shining light. — Casket of gems.

Dunning, *Mrs.* A. K., *continued.*
— Story of four lives. ill. 16°. '71. $1.50......*Lothrop.*
— Three homes (The); or, three ways of spending the Sabbath. 18°. 65c....................*Pres. Bd.*
— Tim Harrison; or, the boy that couldn't say no. 18°. 45c....................................*Pres. Bd.*
— Trifles. ill. 16°. '71. $1.25..............*Lothrop.*
— Whispers from dreamland. 18°. 50c.....*Pres. Bd.*
Dunning, H. N. *See* Book of praise.
Dunraven, *Earl of.* The great divide: travels in the upper Yellowstone in summer of 1874. ill. 8°. '76. $5......................*Scribner, W. & A.*
Dunton, S. *See* Payson, J. W., Dunton, S., *and* Scribner, W. M.
Duntonian system of rapid writing. 10 nos. 4°. per doz., $1.80..........................*Lee & S.*
Dupanloup, Fel. A. P. Child (The); tr. by Kate Anderson. 12°. $1.50................*Noonan.*
— Future œcumenical council: letter to the clergy of his diocese. 8°. '63. pap., 25c...*Kelly, P. & Co.*
— On Freemasons. 32°. 60c.; pap., 25c......*Sadlier.*
Duparcq, N: E: de la B. *See* La Barré Duparcq.
Dupin, A. M. J. Trial of Jesus. 18°. '68. 25c. *Am. Tr.*
Duplais, Pierre. Treatise on the manufacture and distillation of alcoholic liquors; tr. and ed. by M. McKennie; with the U. S. regulations for assessment of taxes on distilled spirits. pl. and wood eng. 8°. '71. $10....................*Baird.*
Duplessis, Georges. Wonders of engraving; tr. from the Fr. ill. 12°. '76. $1.50..........*Scribner.*
Duppa, R: Life and works of Michael Angelo; [also] Life and works of Raffaello, by A. C. Quatremère de Quincy. ill. 12°. (Bohn.) $1.75..*Little, B. & Co.*
— — *Same.* ill. 12°. (Bohn.) $2. *Lippincott; Scribner, W. & A.*
Dupré, A: *See* Thudichum, J. L. W., *and* Dupré, A.
Du Pui, Ja. Exposition of the prophecies of the Apocalypse. ('73.) 2d ed., rev. and enl. 12°. '74. $1.25..............................*Claxton.*
Dupuy, Eliza A. [Novels.] 14 v. 12°. ea., $1.75. *Peterson.*

Cont.: All for love. — Cancelled will. — Clandestine marriage. — Dethroned heiress. — Discarded wife. — Gipsy's warning. — The hidden sin. — Michael Rudolph. — Mysterious guest. — New way to win a fortune. — Planter's daughter. — Was he guilty? or, how he did it. — Who shall be victor? — Why did he marry her?

— Annie Seldon; or, the concealed treasure. 8°. pap., 25c..............................*U. P. James.*
— Country neighborhood (The). 8°. pap., 50c. *Harper.*
— Emma Walton; or, trials and triumphs. 8°. pap., 50c..............................*U. P. James.*
— Huguenot exiles (The); or, the times of Louis XIV. 12°. $1.25..............................*Harper.*
Dupuy, Starke. Hymns; ed. by J. M. Peck. 16°. '43. 70c..............................*Morton.*
Durand, E. Dulcimer without a master. obl. 8°. '67. pap., 75c..............................*Ditson.*
Durang, C. Terpsichore; or, ball-room guide. ill. 32°. 75c..............................*Fisher.*
Durbin, J. P. Observations in the east, chiefly in Egypt, Palestine, Syria and Asia Minor. 2 v. 12°. $3; hf. cf., $6.50..............*Harper.*
— Observations in Europe, principally in France and Gt. Brit. 2 v. ill. 12°. $3; hf. cf., $6.50..*Harper.*
Dürer, Albr. Little passion. *See* Prime, W. C.
Durfee, Calv. Biographical annals of Williams Coll.; with introd. by S. I. Prime. 8°. *$5...*Lee & S.*
Durfee, T: *See* Angell, J. K., *and* Durfee, T.
Durham, W. J. *See* Adams, J. B., *and* Durham, W. J.
Durivage, Ol. F. Fellow (The) that looks like me: Ethiop. interlude. 12°. pap., 15c.......*De Witt.*
— Lady of the lions: burlesque. 16°. pap., 15c. *French.*

Durkee, Silas. Contributions to dermatology, eczema, impetigo, scabies, ecthyma, rupia, lupus. 8°. '70. pap., $1.50................*Jas. Campbell.*
— Gonorrhœa and syphilis. 5th ed., rev. and enl. por. and ill. 8°. '67. $5............*Lindsay.*
Durnton Abbey. Trollope, T. A. 50c......*Harper.*
Durrie, Dan. Steele. Bibliographia genealogica Americana: alphabetical index to Am. genealogies. 8°. '68. $3....................*Munsell.*
— Genealogy of the Holt family in the U. S. 8°. '64. hf. shp., $5..............................*Munsell.*
— History of Madison, Wis., incl. the four lake country, to 1874; with notes on Dane Co. and its towns. 8°. '74. $3......................(?)*Atwood.*
— *See also* Davis, W. B., *and* Durrie, D. S.
Duryea, A. Standing orders of the 7th Reg't, Nat'l Guards [N. Y.] 16°. '61. 50c...*Van Nostrand.*
Duryea, Jos. T. Presbyterian hymnal. 8°. $2–$5. sq. 12°. $1.50–$4.— Same; without tunes. $1.25–$3. sq. 18°. 75c.–$2.50..............*Pres. Bd.*
Dussauce, H. General treatise on the manufacture of soap; from notes of Larmé, Fontelle, Malapayre, etc., with add. ill. 8°. '69. $10..*Baird.*
— General treatise on the manufacture of vinegar. 8°. '71. $5..............................*Baird.*
— Practical guide for the perfumer; from notes of Debay, Lunel, etc. 12°. '68. $5........*Baird.*
— Practical treatise on the fabrication of matches, gun cotton, and fulminating powder. 12°. '64. $3. *Baird.*
— Treatise on the arts of tanning, currying and leather dressing; from notes of Sallerou, Grouvelle, etc. ('65.) New ed. 212 ill. 8°. '67. $25..*Baird.*
Dutch governor: drama. 16°. pap., 15c. .....*French.*
Dutch Reformed Church. *See* Reformed Church in Am.
Dutch tiles. Babcock, E. S. 60c..........*Pres. Bd.*
Dutcher, Addison P. Pulmonary tuberculosis: its pathology, nature, symptoms, diagnosis, etc. cr. 8°. $3..............................*Lippincott.*
Dutcher, G: M. Disinthralled: a story of my life. ill. 12°. *$1.50; $2; hf. mor., $3......*Col. Bk.*
Dutcher, J. C. The old home by the river. ill. 16°. '74. $1.25..............................*Tibbals.*
Dutcher, Salem. Minority, or proportional representation: its nature, aims, history, etc. roy. 8°. '72. $1.50..............................*U. S. Pub.*
Dutchman in Ireland: comic [dram.] sketch. 16°. pap., 15c. ....*Happy.*
Dutchman's (A) difficulties with the Eng. language. De Liefde, J. 25c..................*Routledge.*
Dutchman's fireside. Paulding, J. K. $2.50..*Scribner.*
Dutchman's ghost. Barry, S. 15c..........*French.*
Dutchman's ghost. Tooley, L. 15c. ....*De Witt.*
Duties and difficulties. 18°. 90c.........(?)*Martien.*
Duties of a Christian towards God. 12°. $1; hf. roan, 63c. [*See also* Duty of] ....*O'Shea.*
Duties of young men. 18°. 75c.; $1.......*Sadlier.*
Duties of young men; — of young women. *See* Chapin, E. H.
Dutton, Amy. Streets and lakes of a city: reminiscences of Amy Dutton; with pref. by the Bp. of Salisbury. fp. 8°. $1.25..........*Macmillan.*
Duty and reward. Baird, W. 30c. ....*Randolph.*
Duty contemplated as duety. Munson, M. A. 20c. *Williams.*
Duty of a Christian towards God. La Salle, J. B. de. 63c. ....*Sadlier.*
Duty of personal effort in the S.-school cause. 24°. '56. 18c..............................*Meth. Bk. Conc.*
Duty is safety. Sherwood, M. M. 35c.......*Carter.*
Duval, J: C. Adventures of Big-foot Wallace, the Texas ranger and hunter. ('70.) 3d ed. por. and ill. 12°. '73. $1.75...............*Claxton.*

Duval, T. H. *See* Texas, Supreme Court reports.
Duval and the duchess. 8°. pap., 25c. ...... *De Witt.*
Duval at bay. 8°. pap., 25c. ...... *De Witt.*
Duval denounced. 8°. pap., 25c. ...... *De Witt.*
Duval in a duel. 8°. pap., 25c. ...... *De Witt.*
Duval in Newgate. 8°. pap., 25c. ...... *De Witt.*
Duvall, Alvin. *See* Kentucky, Reports.
Duvernoy, J. B. Ecole primaire. [For the piano.] (op. 176.) f°. $1.50 ...... *Gordon.*
— Elementary lessons for the piano: Am. fingering. 2 bks. f°. ea., 75c. — Foreign fingering. 2 bks. ea., 75c. ...... *Gordon.*
Duveyrier, Anne H. Jos. (*Baron*) de. ["Mélesville."] *See* Scribe, E., *and* Duveyrier, A. H. J.
Duy, Alb. W. Memoir. 18°. 60c. ...... *Am. S. S.*
Duyckinck, Evert A: History of the world. 4 v. ill. and por. 8°. '73. hf. mor., $30; $32; mor., $38; $40 ...... *Johnson & M.*
— Lives and portraits of the presidents of the U. S., [1789–1872]: ill. by A. Chappel. 4°. $5; hf. mor., $7.50; mor., $1 ...... *Johnson & M.*
— *Span.* Version castellana por I. G. Grediaga. 4°. $5; hf. mor., $7.50; mor., $10 .... *Johnson & M.*
— National hist. of the war for the union; with ill. and por. by Chappel and Nast. 4 v. roy. 8°. '68. hf. mor., $25; $27; mor., $33; $35 .. *Johnson & M.*
— National portrait gallery of eminent Americans; from paintings by A. Chappel, with biog. and hist. narratives. ('62.) New ed. 2 v. 4°. '64. hf. mor., $27; $28; mor., $30; $32 .. *Johnson & M.*
— New gallery of portraits of eminent men and women of Europe and Am.; with biog. 2 v. 4°. '73. hf. mor., $27; $28; mor., $30; $32 .. *Johnson & M.*
— *and* G: L. Cyclopedia of Am. literature; ed. to date by M. L. Simons. 52 pts. por. and ill. 8°. '75. ea., *50c.; — in 2 v. leath., *$33; hf. mor., $35.50; $37; mor., $43 ...... *C. H. Davis.*
Duyckinck, G: L. Life of Jeremy Taylor. 18°. 60c.; 75c. ...... *Dutton.*
— Life of Bp. Ken. 18°. 90c.; $1 ...... *Dutton.*
— Life of Latimer. 18°. 90c. ...... *Dutton.*
— *See also* Duyckinck, E. A. *and* G. L.; — Shakespeare, W.
Dva Sirotci [Two orphans]; přel. F. B. Zdrubek. 8°. '76. 25c. ...... *Geringer.*
Dwarf and her story. 18°. 40c. ...... *Whittaker.*
Dwarf's mirror. Wildermuth, O. $1.25. *Cin. Meth. Bk. Conc.*
Dwarris, *Sir* Fortunatus. Statutes, their rules of construction, and the boundaries of legislation and of judicial interpretation; with Am. notes and add. by P. Potter. 8°. '71. shp., $7.50 .. *Gould.*
Dwellers (The) in Five Sisters' Court. Scudder, H. E. $1.25; $1.50 ...... *Hurd & H.*
Dwight, B: W. Higher Christian education. 4th ed. 12°. '59. $1.50 ...... *Barnes.*
— History of descendants of J: Strong of Northampton, Mass. 2 v. por. 8°. '71. hf. shp., $15. *Munsell.*
— Lives of the signers of the Declaration of independence. 12°. '51. $1.50 ...... *Barnes.*
— Modern philology. ('64.) New ed. 2 v. 8°. '70. $6 ...... *Scribner.*
Dwight, Ma. Ann. Grecian and Roman mythology; with introd. by T. Lewis. ill. 8°. '49. $2.50. — abridg. school ed. 12°. '49. $1.25 ..... *Barnes.*
— Introduction to the study of art. 12°. $1.25 .. *Appleton.*
Dwight, Thdr. History of Conn. 18°. 75c. .. *Harper.*
Dwight, Thdr. W: On charitable uses: argument in the Rose will case, with [other] cases. 2 v. 8°. shp., $20 ...... *Baker, V. & Co.*
Dwight, T: *jr.* Description of the balænoptera musculus in the possession of the Bost. Soc. of Nat. Hist. ill. 4°. pap., $1.25 .. *Bost. Soc. Nat. Hist.*
Dwight, Tim. Theology explained and defended: sermons, with life of author. 4 v. por. 8°. $8; shp., $10 ...... *Harper.*
Dwight, Wilder. Life and letters. por. 8°. '68. $2. *Osgood.*
Dwyer, C. P. Immigrant builder; or, practical hints to handy men. ill. demy 8°. '72. $1.50 .. *Claxton.*
Dwyer, Fs. On seats and saddles, bits and bitting. ill. 12°. $2 ...... *Lippincott.*
Dyer, C. C. J. Sunny days abroad; or, the old world seen with young eyes. ('71.) New ed. 12°. '76. $1.25 ...... *Whittaker.*
Dyer, D: History of the Albany Penitentiary [1849–'57]. pl. and por. 8°. '67. bds., $1 .... *Munsell.*
Dyer, E. P. *See* Bunyan, J., Pilgrim's progress in verse.
Dyer, F. J. The old man of the cliff; or, a summer's vacation. ('74.) New ed. 16°. '75. 90c. .. *Hoyt.*
Dyer, S: Anthems. New ed. obl. 8°. '34. bds., $2. *Ditson.*
Dyer, S: O. The quartette: glees, with piano accomp. 7 v. 16°. '76. ea., pap., $1; — in 5 v. $5 .. *Pond.*
Dyer, Sidney F. Psalmist. 16°. '51. 60c. .... *Morton.*
Dyer, Sydney. Black diamonds; or, the curiosities of coal. 16°. $1.50 ...... *Am. Bapt.*
— Boys and birds; or, Miss Truat's mission. 16°. $1.75. *Am. Bapt.*
— Great wonders in little things. 16°. $2 .. *Am. Bapt.*
Dyer, T: H: Pompeii: its history, etc. New ed., rev. and brought down to 1874. wood-cuts, map and plan. 12°. (Bohn.) $2.75 ...... *Little, B. & Co.*
— *Same.* ill. 12°. (Bohn.) $3. *Lippincott; Scribner, W. & A.*
— History of Rome. maps and ill. 8°. $5. *R. Worthington.*
— Life of John Calvin. por. 12°. $1.50 ...... *Harper.*
Dyer and color-maker's companion. ('50.) 8th ed. 12°. '76. $1.25 ...... *Baird.*
Dying for love. Morton, J. M. 15c. ...... *French.*
Dying Irish girl. *See* Little Nelly.
Dying legacy to the people of his charge. Murray, N. 75c. ...... *Harper.*
Dying robin. Alden, J. 75c. ...... *Harper.*
Dying Saviour. *See* Hall, M.
Dying Saviour, and the gipsy girl. *See* Sibree, M.
Dying sheep. *See* Peter Thompson.
Dying thoughts. Crawford, W. 70c. ...... *Pres. Bd.*
Dykes, J. Oswald. Beatitudes of the kingdom. 16°. $1.25 ...... *Carter.*
— Laws of the kingdom. 16°. $1.25 ...... *Carter.*
— On the written word. cr. 8°. $1.25 ...... *Routledge.*
— Relations of the kingdom. 16°. $1.25 ..... *Carter.*
Dymond, Jona. Essays on the principles of morality. 12°. '76. $1.25 ...... *Collins & Bro.*
— *Same;* with pref., etc., by G. Bush. 8°. $1.50 .. *Harper.*
— On war. 12°. 30c. ...... *Peace.*
Dynevor Terrace. Yonge, C. M. $1.75. *Appleton; Macmillan.*
Dyrbington Court. 18°. $1.25; $1.75 ...... *Sadlier.*

E., A. L. O. (*pseud.*) *See* Tucker, *Mrs.* Ctte.
E., B. E. A hundred years ago: a centennial poem. sm. 4°. '76. 75c. ...... *Lothrop.*
E., S. Further queries upon the present state of the New-English affairs. [Reprint.] 4°. 50c.; large pap., $1 ...... *Sabin.*
E—, E. Memoir. 18°. 50c. ...... *Pres. Bd.*
Each for himself. *See* Gerstäcker, F:
Eadie, J: Analytical concordance to the Scriptures. 8°. $3 ...... *Sheldon.*
— Biblical encyclopedia. maps and ill. 8°. $4. *Routledge.*
— Commentary on the Gk. text of the Epistle to the Galatians. 8°. $5 ...... *Scribner, W. & A.*

Eadie, J: *continued.*
— Divine love. 12°. '76. $1.50 .... *Tibbals.*
— Lectures on the Bible to the young. 18°. 40c. *U. P. Bd. of Pub.*
— Life of John Kitto; rev. by A. G. Haygood. 12°. '72. $1.50 .... *So. Meth.*
Eads, Ja. B. Discussion on upright arched bridges. 2 v. 8°. '74–'75. pt. 1, pap., $1.20; pt. 2, pap., 40c .... *Am. Soc. of C. E.*
— — *See also* Hamilton, S., Fabrication of béton blocks; — Thurston, R. H., Efficiency of furnaces burning wet fuel.
— On the means of averting bridge accidents. *See* Hamilton, S., Fabrication of béton blocks.
Eagle and dove: a story of France during the empire, the war and the commune. 12°. $2 .... *O'Shea.*
Eagle crag. Mathews, J. A. 75c .... *Carter.*
Eagle Hill: sel. in prose and verse. 18°. 60c. *Am. S. S.*
Eagle's nest. Ruskin, J. $1.50 .... *Wiley.*
Eagleston, J. H. Early California voyages. 8°. '74. pap., 10c .... *Essex.*
Eames, Jane A. Sarah Barry's home. 18°. 70c. *Dutton.*
Earl, H: H. Fall River [Mass.]: its rise and progress, 1803–'76. ('73.) 4th ed., rev. and enl. 32°. '76. 50c.; pap., 20c .... *B. Earl.*
Earl of poverty. Almar, G. 15c .... *French.*
Earl Whiting. Atkins, M. A. $1.25 ...... *Cong. Pub.*
Earl Whiting. Erickson, D. S. $1.25 ... *H. A. Young.*
Earle, —. Sermon to the eldership. 15c. (?) *Cumberland.*
Earle, A. B. Bringing in sheaves. 12°. $1.50; $2. *Earle.*
— Rest (The) of faith. 24°. pap., 50c.; 75c.; leath., $1 .... *Earle.*
— Revival hymns and tunes. 24°. 30c.; bds., 10c. *Earle.*
Earle, J. C. Manual of the lives of the popes, St. Peter to Pius IX. 12°. '67. $1.50; $2 .. *Murphy.*
Earle, J: Microcosmography; or, a piece of the world discovered: essays and characters, with notes and app. by P. Bliss. 16°. '67. $1 .... *Munsell.*
Earl's daughter. Sewell, E. M. $1 .... *Appleton.*
Earl's Dene. Francillon, R. E. 50c .... *Harper.*
Earl's secret. Pardoe, J. $1.75; $1.50 ...... *Peterson.*
Early, Jubal A. Campaigns of Gen. Lee. 8°. '72. pap., 30c .... *Murphy.*
— Memoir of the last year of the war for independence in the Confederate States. 8°. '66. pap., $1. *Eyrich; J. W. Randolph.*
Early American spirit. Storrs, R. S. $1; 60c. *Randolph.*
Early and latter rain; or, the convict's daughter. 18°. 70c .... *Pres. Bd.*
Early choice (The). *See* Tweedie, W. K.
Early crowned: memoir of M. E. North. 16°. '66. $1.25 .... *Meth. Bk. Conc.*
Early dawn (The). Charles, E. $1 .... *Dodd.*
Early dawn; or, the conversion of Annie Herbert. 18°. 50c .... *Pres. Bd.*
Early genius, and remarkable records of its achievements; by author of "Success in life." 12°. $1.50 .... *Nelson.*
Early flowers: hymns, with organ or piano accomp. 8°. '72. pap., 40c .... *Ditson.*
Early friends of Jesus. Headley, P. C. 25c.; 30c. *J. E. Potter.*
Early friendships. *See* Happy child's lib.
Early lessons. *See* Edgeworth, M.
Early lessons about the Saviour. Bennett, M. L. 12c. *Un. S. S.*
Early lost, early saved. Bethune, G. W. 60c. *N. Y. Ref. Ch. Bd.*
Early man in Europe. Rau, C. $2.50 ..... *Harper.*
Early morn (The). Foster, J. 25c ..... *J. E. Potter.*
Early piety; or, recollections of Harriet B—. ('55.) 2d ed. 16°. '57. 25c .... *Am. Unit.*
Early piety exemplified. *See* Mather, N.
Early records of city and county of Albany and Rensselaerswyck [N. Y.], 1656–'75; tr. from the Dutch, with notes, by Jona. Pearson. roy. 8°. '69. hf. mor., $10 .... *Munsell.*
Early religious education. Eliot, W. G. 50c. *Am. Unit.*
Early (The) saved. Lape, T. 53c.; 50c.; 15c. *Tibbals.*
Early Saxons (The); or, the character and influence of the Saxon race. 18°. 50c .... *Am. S. S.*
Early social life of man. Lum, D. D. 25c .... *Colby.*
Early travels in Palestine. *See* Wright, T:
Early watermelons. Blackburn, W. M. 50c. *Pres. Bd.*
Early witnesses. Thompson, J. P. 75c .... *Randolph.*
Earnest, Elsie (*pseud.*) *See* Scruggs, *Mrs.* M. V.
Earnest boy (The). *See* Locust grove stories.
Earnest Brownley's trials and temptations. 75c. *Cong. Pub.*
— *See also* Cousin Clara's lib.
Earnest Christian's library. 4 v. 16°. '65. $5. *Meth. Bk. Conc.*

Cont.: Plain words on Christian living, by C. J. Vaughan. — Cross of Jesus, by D. Thompson. — Sure words of promise. — Soul gatherer, by author of "Way home."

Earnest communicant. Oxenden, A. 35c.; 75c. *Randolph.*
Earnest exhortations. Bourdillon, F. 60c .... *Nelson.*
Earnest hours. Plumer, W. S. $1.25. *N. Y. Ref. Ch. Bd.; Pres. Com.*
Earnest life. 18°. 45c .... *Cong. Pub.*
Earnest men. *See* Tweedie, W. K.
Earnest minister. Wallace, A. $1.50 .... *A. Wallace.*
Earnest ministry. James, J. A. 90c .... *Pres. Bd.*
Earnest search for truth. Lowry, S. A. 50c. *Pres. Bd.*
Earnest student. Macleod, N. $1.50 .. *R. Worthington.*
Earnest thoughts for every day. 32°. 60c. *Whittaker.*
Earnest words for earnest men. Vaughan, C. J. $1.25. *Routledge.*
Earnest words on true success in life. Palmer, R. $1.50 .... *Barnes.*
Earnestness. Tayler, C. B. $1 .... *Leighton.*
Earning and spending. Baker, H. N. W. $1. *H. A. Young.*
Earnshaw, S. Partial differential equations: essay towards a new method of integrating them. cr. 8°. '71. $2.50 .... *Macmillan.*
Ears of the spiritual harvest; or, narratives of the Christian life. 12°. 75c .... *Pres. Bd.*
Earth and its treasures. Mangin, A. $1.25 .. *Nelson.*
Earth and its wonders. Adams, C. $1.25. *Cin. Meth. Bk. Conc.*
Earth and man. Guyot, A. $1.75 .... *Scribner.*
Earth and sea. Figuier, L. $6; $8.50 .... *Nelson.*
Earth delineated with pen and pencil. *See* Ainsworth, W. F.
Earth, a great magnet. Mayer, A. M. 50c.; 25c. *Van Nostrand.*
Earth, plants and man. Schouw, J. F. $2. *Scribner, W. & A.*
Earth we live on. 16°. 50c .... *Scribner, W. & A.*
Earthen vessels. Capron, M. J. $1.50 .... *Hoyt.*
Earthly paradise. *See* Morris, W.
Earthly trials. Stebbins, J. E. *$3; $3.50 .... *Fitch.*
Earthquake. Ball, E. 15c .... *French.*
Earthquakes and volcanoes. *See* Wonder lib.
Earth's morning. Bonar, H. $2 .... *Carter.*
Earths in the universe. *See* Swedenborg, E.
Earthward pilgrimage. Conway, M. D. $1.75 .. *Holt.*

Eassie, W: Healthy houses: history, defects, and remedies of drainage, etc. ill. 12°. $1....*Appleton.*
— Sanitary arrangements for dwellings. ill. 8°. '74. $2.25 ....*Putnam.*
East, E. Hyde. *See* England, Court of King's Bench reports.
East, J: My Saviour. 18°. 75c....*Carter.*
East, T. The moral wreck. ill. 16°. '74. 75c...*Nelson.*
East and west poems. Harte, B. $1.50; $3; $4. *Osgood.*
East Lynne. Wood, E. P. $1.25; 75c....*Dick & F.*
East Lynne: drama. 16°. pap., 15c. *French; Lee & S.*
Eastbury. Drury, A. H. $1.50....*Harper.*
Easter bells. Dressler, W. 20c....*Peters.*
Easter day. M'Clellan, K. 50c....*Whittaker.*
Easter eggs. *See* Schmid, C. v.
Easter garlands; or, Isle of Wight. 18°. 75c. *Dutton.*
Easter holidays at Cedar Grove. Seymour, M. A. 75c. *Dutton.*
Easter in heaven. Weninger, F. X. $1; $1.50..*Sadlier.*
Easter lilies. sq. 16°. '76. pap., 75c....*Randolph.*
Easter morning. Buck, D. $1.50....*Brainard.*
Easter walk. *See* Harbaugh, H.
Eastern fairy legends. ill. 12°. $1.25....*Lippincott.*
Eastern life. Martineau, H. $3....*Roberts.*
Eastern manners and customs. ill. 18°. '71. 50c. *Lothrop.*
Eastern manners and customs: 12 views with letter-press. obl. 24°. 50c.; 75c....*Nelson.*
Eastern side. Feudge, F. R. $1.50....*Am. Bapt.*
Eastern tales. Valentine, R. $1; $1.50; $1.75; 75c....*Scribner, W. & Co.*
Eastern traveler. MacGregor, J. 30c....*Pres. Bd.*
Eastlake, C: L. Hints on household taste, in furniture, upholstery, etc.; ed. by C. C. Perkins. pl. and ill. 12°. '72. $3.50; hf. cf., $5; mor., $7....*Osgood.*
Eastman, E. C. Writing book. 2 nos. 4°. 1, per doz., 80c.; 2, per doz., 70c....*Eastman.*
Eastman, G: W. *See* Fulton, L. S., *and* Eastman, G. W.
Eastman, Jla. A. Kitty Kent's troubles. ill. 16°. '73. $1.50....*Lothrop.*
— Romneys of Ridgemont. ill. 16°. '71. $1.50. *Lothrop.*
— School days of Beulah Romney. ill. 16°. '72. $1.50. *Lothrop.*
— Striking for the right. ill. 16°. '72. $1.75..*Lothrop.*
— Young Rick. pt. 2. ill. 16°. '76. $1....*Lothrop.*
— *Same:* complete. ill. 16°. '76. $1.50....*Lothrop.*
Eastman, Ph. *See* Maine, Digest.
Eastman, S: C. White Mountains guide. maps. 12°. $1....*Eastman.*
Eastman, Sophie E. Finding his footprints. ill. 16°. 75c....*Bost. Am. Tr.*
Eastman's eastern coast guide. [New Eng.] maps. 12°. $1.50....*Eastman.*
Eastman's map of the mountain and lake region of New Hampshire; by C. H. V. Cavis. (Pocket ed.) 18°. 40c....*Eastman.*
Eastman's pocket railroad and township map of New Eng. 18°. 75c....*Eastman.*
Easton, Alex. Practical treatise on street or horse-power railways. pl. 8°. '59. $2....*Baird.*
Eastwood, B: Complete cranberry manual. 12°. 75c. *Judd.*
Eastwood, Fs. (*pseud.*) *See* Knevels, *Mrs.* D. C.
Eastwood, J., *and* Wright, W. A. The Bible word book: glossary of old Eng. Bible words. 2d ed. 16°. '74. $1.50....*Tibbals.*
Easy, *Midshipman* (*pseud.*) *See* Midshipman Easy.
Easy book for little children. ill. sq. 16°. '73. 75c. *Nichols & H.; Shorey.*
Easy lessons. sq. 18°. '56. 40c....*Am. Tr.*
Easy poems. *See* Good child's lib.
Easy reading for little folks. 16°. '75. 40c...*Lothrop.*
Easy rhymes and simple poems. 16°. 50c. *Scribner, W. & A.*
Easy shaving. Burnand, F. C., *and* Williams, M. 15c....*De Witt; French.*
Easy spelling and reading. [Toy book.] ill. sq. 16°. bds., 25c....*Routledge.*
Eating for strength. Holbrook, M. L. $1..*Wood & H.*
Eaton, Ctte. A. Rome in the 19th century. 2 v. ill. 12°. (Bohn.) ea., $1.75....*Little, B. & Co.*
— *Same.* 2 v. ill. 12°. (Bohn.) ea., $2. *Lippincott; Scribner, W. & A.*
Eaton, D. C. Botany. *See* United States, *Corps of Eng.*
Eaton, E. K. Cornet instructor. obl. 8°. 75c. *Gordon.*
— New method for cornet. 4°. '70. bds., $1.50..*Ditson.*
Eaton, E. O. Amateur brass band book. f°. $3. *Brainard.*
Eaton, H. M. Itinerant's wife: her qualifications, etc. 18°. '51. 30c....*Meth. Bk. Conc.*
Eaton, J. R. T. Permanence of Christianity. *See* Bampton lectures.
Eaton, Ja. S. Common school arithmetic. 12°. 95c. — Answers. 25c. — Solutions. 95c...*Thompson.*
— Elements of arith. 16°. hf. bd., 45c....*Thompson.*
— Grammar school arith. 12°. $1.10....*Thompson.*
— High school arith. 12°. $1.25. — Answers. 25c. — Solutions. $1.25....*Thompson.*
— Intellectual arithmetic. 16°. hf. bd., 42c. *Thompson.*
— Primary arithmetic. 16°. 26c....*Thompson.*
— Questions on principles of arithmetic. 12°. pap., 15c. *Thompson.*
Eaton, Lilley. Genealogical hist. of Reading, Mass., incl. Wakefield, Reading, and North Reading, with chronol. and hist. sketches, 1639–1874. ill. 8°. '74. $3....*Eaton; Lockwood, B. & Co.*
Eaton, T. E. The angels. 18°. 55c....*Am. Bapt.*
Eaton, W: H. *See* McLean, A., *and* Eaton, W. H.
Ebb-tide. Fisher, F. C. $1.50; $1....*Appleton.*
Ebenezer Venture. La Bree, L. 15c....*French.*
Eberle, J: Treatise on the diseases and physical educ. of children. ('33.) 4th ed., enl. by T. D. Mitchell. 8°. shp., $3.50....*Claxton; Lippincott.*
Ebers, G: The daughter of an Egyptian King: hist. romance; tr. by H. Reed. 12°. $1.75..*Lippincott.*
Ebon and gold. McIlvain, C. L. $1.50....*Carleton.*
Ebrard, J. H. A. Commentary on St. John. 8°. $3. *Scribner, W. & A.*
— The Gospel history. 8°. $3....*Scribner, W. & A.*
Ebsworth, Jos. Rival valets: farce. 16°. pap., 15c. *French.*
Eby, B: Kurtzgefasste Kirchen-Geschichte u. Glaubenslehre der taufgesinnten Christen u. Menno-niten. 32°. leath., 40c....*Baer.*
Ecarte. Richardson, J. 50c....*De Witt.*
Ecce cœlum. Burr, E. F. $1.25..*Lockwood, B. & Co.*
Ecce Deus. Parker, J. $1.50....*Roberts.*
Ecce Deus homo; or, the work and kingdom of the Christ of Scripture. 12°. '68. $1.50..*Lippincott.*
Ecce ecclesia. Abbey, R. $1.75....*So. Meth.*
Ecce femina. Peck, E. $1.50....*Carleton.*
Ecce femina. White, C. $1.50....*Lee & S.*
Ecce homo. Gladstone, W. E. $1.50; 75c. *Routledge.*
Ecce homo. Seeley, J. R. $1.50....*Roberts.*
Ecce unitas. Ralston, T. N. 80c....*Meth. Bk. Conc.*
Ecclesiastes. *See* Bible.
Ecclesiastical reports. *See* England, Ecclesiastical reports; Law reports.

Ecclesiazusæ. *See* Aristophanes.
Echeverria, Gonzalez. On epilepsy: anatomo-patholog. and clinical notes. ill. 8°. $5.. *W. Wood.*
Echo (The). *See* Hager, J. M.
Echo (The): Sabbath school singing book. sq. 16°. '69. 60c.; pap., 30c.; bds., 35c.............*Am. Tr.*
Echo band: Ethiop. drama. 16°. pap., 15c...*French.*
Echo bank. Ervie. 85c................*Nat. Temp.*
Echo (L') de Paris. Worman, J. H. $1.25..*Barnes.*
Echoes from home. ill. 12°. $1.50..........*Lee & S.*
Echoes from the south. Pollard, E. A. *$1.25..*Treat.*
Echoes of the foot hills. Harte, B. $1.50; $3; $4. *Osgood.*
Echoes of heavenly music. *See* Bijou Bible text-books.
Eckel, *Mrs.* Lizzie St. J: Maria Monk's daughter: autobiog. ill. and por. cr. 8°. '74. $1.75..*U. S. Pub.*
Ecker, Alex. Convolutions of the brain; tr. by R. T. Edes. 8°. $1.25...................*Appleton.*
Eckermann, J: P: *See* Goethe, J. W. v., Conversations.
Eckstein, C. F. Practical treatise on chimneys; with remarks on stoves, consumption of smoke and coal, etc. post 8°. (Weale.) '52. 75c....*Spon.*
Eclectic historical atlas. *See* Thalheimer, M. E.
Eclectic Sunday school library. 2 v. 12°. ea., 60c. *Meth. Bk. Conc.*
Cont.: Lesson compend, by J. H. Vincent and J. L. Hurlbut.—Historical ill. of the Old Test., by G. Rawlinson.
Eclectic tune book. Bradbury, W. B. $1.25..*Pres. Bd.*
Eclipsing the son. Hartopp, W. W. 15c.....*French.*
Economy of health. Johnson, J. 75c.......*Harper.*
Economy of human life. Dodsley, R. 60c. *Lippincott.*
Eda May. Binfield, A. D. 50c..............*Nelson.*
Eda Morton and her cousins. Bell, M. M. $1..*Routledge.*
Eda Morton library. 4 v. ill. 16°. $4.....*Routledge.*
Cont.: Eda Morton.—Rector's daughter.—Arbell.—Medwins of Wykeham.
Eddie and May. *See* Choice little lib.
Eddie Ellerslie. *See* Tucker, *Mrs.* C.
Eddie Ellerslie series. 4 v. 16°. $6........*Graves.*
Cont.: Eddie Ellerslie.—Home stories.—The foundling.—School life.
Eddie Gray. Dawes, S. E. 25c............*Am. Tr.*
Eddy, A. D. Samuel Howell: memoir. 18°. 25c. *Am. S. S.*
Eddy, Dan. C. Angel whispers: echoes of spirit voices. 12°. $1.50....................*Locke.*
— New question book on Acts. 18°. '63. bds., 15c. *Graves.*
— Percy family. 5 v. ill. 16°. '59-'60. $5..*Graves.*
Cont.: Visit to Ireland.—England and Scotland.—Paris to Amsterdam.—Baltic to Vesuvius.—Alps and the Rhine.
— Walter's tour in the east. 6 v. ill. 16°. $6..*Sheldon.*
Cont.: Walter in Egypt—in Athens—in Jerusalem—in Damascus—in Samaria—in Constantinople.
— Young man's friend. 12°. '65. $1.50.......*Graves.*
— Young woman's friend. 16°. $1.50........*Graves.*
— (*ed.*) Waiting at the cross: collection of prose and poetry. 18°. '69. $1.50.........*H. A. Young.*
Eddy, H: I. Analytic geometry, plane. ('74.) New ed. 12°. '75. $1.75............*Cowperthwait.*
— *Same:* plane and solid. 12°. $2.50..*Cowperthwait.*
Eddy, Z. *See* Hitchcock, R. D., Eddy, Z., *and* Schaff, P.; —Hymns of the church.
Eddy's tickets. Sanford, D. P. 15c.; 20c....*Dutton.*
Eddystone elf. Pitt, G. D. 15c............*French.*
Ede, G: Management of steel. 12°. $1.50..*Appleton.*
Edelweiss. Auerbach, B. $1.25...............*Holt.*
Eden, C: H. Australia's heroes. 12°. '76. $2.50..*Pott.*
— Fortunes of the Fletchers. ill. 12°. $1.25..*Pott.*
— Inherited task. ill. 16°. 50c....................*Pott.*
— Twin brothers of Everdale. ill. 18°. $1....*Nelson.*
Eden, R. C. History of the 37th Wisconsin Vol. Inf. 12°. 50c.............................*Atwood.*
Eden, R. H. *See* England, High Court of Chancery reports.
Eden in England. Tucker, C. $1.25; 75c.....*Carter.*
Eden of labor. Collens, T. W. $1.25; $1....*Baird.*
Edendale. Cheltnam, C. S. 15c.............*French.*
Edersheim, Alfr. Temple (The): its ministry and services as they were at the time of Jesus Christ. 8°. $1.75................................*Nelson.*
— True to the end: a story of Scottish life. ill. 12°. '74. $1.25..........................*Routledge.*
— What is her name? 18°. 55c............*Am. S. S.*
— *Same.* 12°. '74. $1.........................*Nelson.*
Edgar, J. H., *and* Pritchard, G. S. Note-book on practical, solid, or descriptive geometry; cont. problems with help for solution. 3d ed., enl. 12°. '71. $1.25....................*Macmillan.*
Edgar, J: G. Boyhood of great men. ill. 16°. $1.20. *Harper.*
— Cavaliers and Roundheads; or, stories of the great civil war. ill. 16°. $1.75.....*Scribner, W. & A.*
— Famous men lib. 3 v. ill. 16°. ea., $1.25..*Routledge.*
Cont.: Boyhood of great men.—Foot-prints of famous men.—History for boys.
— Foot-prints of famous men. ill. 16°. $1.20..*Harper.*
— Great men and gallant deeds. ill. 16°. $1.50..*Lee & S.*
— History for boys; or, annals of the nations of modern Europe. ill. 16°. $1.20...........*Harper.*
— Sea kings and naval heroes. ill. 16°. $1.20..*Harper.*
— *Same.* ill. 16°. $1.75...........*Scribner, W. & A.*
— Wars of the roses. ill. 16°. $1.20........*Harper.*
— *Same.* ill. 12°. $1.25...........*Scribner, W. & A.*
Edgar, S: Variations of popery. ('54.) 5th ed. 8°. '76. $2.50...........................*So. Meth.*
Edgar Clifton. Adams, C. $1.25.........*Routledge.*
— *See also* Winter evening lib.
Edgar Huntly. Brown, C. B. $1............*Polock.*
Edgar Montrose. Reynolds, G. W. M. 50c...*Peterson.*
Edgar's struggle: story of temptation. ill. 16°. 45c. *Duffie.*
Edgarton, Warren P. New York speaker; with introd. on declamation by W. Russell. 12°. $1.75..*Sheldon.*
— Western orator. 12°. hf. roan., $1.75...*Lippincott.*
Edged tools. Robbins, S. S. $1.25..........*Carter.*
Edger, H: Religious positivism: exposition of the system of worship, propounded by A. Comte. 12°. '74. pap., 50c..................*Somerby.*
Edgerton, A. J. Railroad laws of Minnesota. 8°. '72. shp., $6...............................*Combs.*
Edgeworth, Mar. Novels. 4 v. 16°. $3..*Routledge.*
Cont.: Manœuvring; Madame de Fleury; The dun.—Ennui; Emilie de Coulanges.—Absentee.—Vivian; Almeria.
— *Same.* 10 v. ill. 12°. ea., $1.50..........*Harper.*
Cont.: 1. Castle Rackrent; Essay on Irish bulls; Essay on self-justification; Forrester; Prussian vase; Good aunt.—2. Angelina; Good French governess; Madamoiselle Panache; The knapsack; Lame Jervis; The will; Out of debt, out of danger; Limerick gloves; The lottery; Rosanna.—3. Murad the unlucky; Manufacturers; Ennui; The contrast; The grateful negro; Tomorrow; The dun.—4. Manœuvring; Almeria; Vivian.—5. The absentee; Madame de Fleury; Emily de Coulanges; Modern Griselda.—6. Belinda.—7. Leonora; Letters on female education; Patronage.—8. Patronage; Comic dramas.—9. Harrington; Thoughts on bores; Ormond.—10. Helen.
— Novels and tales. 10 v. ill. 12°. hf. cf., $30; cf., $35. *Appleton.*
— *Same.* 10 v. ill. 16°. $15............*Routledge.*
Cont.: Moral tales.—Popular tales.—Belinda.—Castle Rackrent.—Irish bulls.—Fashionable life.—Patronage, 2 v.—Harrington.—Helen.
— Barring out; —Contrast; —Drop of water; —Simple Susan; —Waste not, want not. *See* Present for my darling lib.
— Bracelets (The); or, amiability and industry rewarded. ill. 4°. 50c.............*J. E. Potter.*
— Early lessons, etc.; ed. by Mrs. Valentine. ill. cr. 8°. $2.50.....................*Scribner, W. & A.*
— Edgeworth lib. 4 v. ill. 16°. ea., $1.25..*Routledge.*
Cont.: Popular tales.—Parent's assistant.—Moral tales.—Early lessons.

Edgeworth, Mar., *continued.*
— Edgeworth library. 5 v. 12°. $7.50..*Kelly, P. & Co.*
Cont.: Frank, 2 v. — Harry and Lucy, 2 v. — Rosamond.
— Frank. 16°. 50c....................*Routledge.*
— *Same.* 2 v. ill. 18°. $1.50..............*Harper.*
— Harry and Lucy. 16°. 50c..............*Routledge.*
— *Same.* 2 v. ill. 12°. $3..................*Harper.*
— — *See also* Harry and Lucy lib.
— Lazy Lawrence; or, idleness and industry contrasted. ill. 4°. 50c....................*J. E. Potter.*
— Moral and popular tales. ill. 12°. $2.50. *Lippincott; Scribner, W. & A.*
— Moral tales. 2 v. 18°. $1.50..............*Harper.*
— Moral tales and novels. New ed. 10 v. ill. fp. 8°. (Lond.) '70. $15; hf. cf., $30; cf., $40. *Little, B. & Co.*
— My favorite's library. 8 v. 32°. $2.....*Routledge.*
Cont.: Bracelets. — False key. — Mimic. — Orphans. — Forgive and forget. — Little merchants. — Lazy Lawrence. — Purple jar.
— Parent's assistant. ill. 16°. $1.25......*Hurd & H.*
— *Same.* ill. 12°. $1.50....................*Harper.*
— *Same.* ill. sq. 16°. '76. $1.75..............*Miller.*
— Popular library. 3 v. ill. 16°. $3.75........*Miller.*
Cont.: All for the best, etc. — Moral tales. — Popular tales.
— Popular tales. 2 v. ill. 18°. $1.50.......*Harper.*
— Rosamond. 16°. 50c.................*Routledge.*
— *Same.* ill. 12°. $1.50....................*Harper.*
— — *See also* Harry and Lucy lib.
— Tales of fashionable life. 4 v. 16°. $3..*Routledge.*
— Ungrateful negro (The). *See* Good child's lib.
— Waste not, want not; or, two strings to your bow. ill. 4°. 50c....................*J. E. Potter.*
— *See also* Edgeworth, R. L. *and* M.
Edgeworth, R: L. *and* M. Treatise on practical education. ill. 12°. $1.50................*Harper.*
Edgeworth Bess. *See* Black Bess ser.
Edina. Wood, E. P. $1; 75c.............*Peterson.*
Edith and her ayah. *See* Tucker, *Mrs.* C.
Edith Hinton. M., E. 75c..................*Nelson.*
Edith Leigh's prayer book. M'Clellan, K. 90c. *Whittaker.*
Edith Locke. Dawson, —. 25c. ....*Porter.*
Edith Lyle. Holmes, M. J. $1.50.........*Carleton.*
Edith Prescot. Marshall, E. $1.25........*Lothrop.*
Edith Somers. Gurley, E. S. 90c...........*Am. Tr.*
Edith Vaughan's victory. Pierson, H. W. 90c. (?) *Martien.*
Edith Vernon's life work. 12°. '65. $1.25. *Meth. Bk. Conc.*
Edith Withington. Baker, H. N. W. $1..*H. A. Young.*
Edith's last Lent. G., E. W. 30c...........*Dutton.*
Edith's ministry. McKeever, H. B. $1.50..*J. A. Moore.*
Edith's mistake. Stabler, J. L. $1.25....*Lippincott.*
Edith's Testament. Chapman, M. S. 75c...*Cong. Pub.*
Edith's two account-books; by author of "Annie Lincoln's lesson." 18°. 70c.............*Pres. Bd.*
Editor's troubles. Harrigan, E. 15c........*De Witt.*
Edma and Marguerite. Wolliez, *Mme.* 60c...*O'Shea.*
Edmands, B. F. *See* Stow, B., *and* Smith, S. F., Psalmist.
Edmond Dantes. *See* Dumas, A.
Edmond Darley series. 12 v. ill. 18°. $2.40..*Nelson.*
Cont.: Edmond Darley. — Kind action. — Hidden talent. — Uncle Dick. — Tim Leeson. — Lost rabbit.
Note. Sold only in double sets of 6 v. ea.
Edmondo. Bresciani, A. $2..............*Sadlier.*
Edmonds, J: W. *See* New York, Reports of sel. cases; Revised statutes.
Edmonson, Jona. Concise system of self-government. 18°. 50c...............*Cin. Meth. Bk. Conc.*
— Scripture views of heaven. 18°. '41. 55c. *Meth. Bk. Conc.*

Edmonson, Jona., *continued.*
— *Same;* ed. by T. O. Summers. ('54.) 4th ed. 18°. '76. 60c..........................*So. Meth.*
— Short sermons; with introd. by J. P. Durbin. por. 8°. $3...............................*Sower.*
Edmunds, J. A. Medical use of alcohol. ('74.) New ed. 12°. '75. 60c.; pap., 25c.......*Nat. Temp.*
Edna Browning. Holmes, M. J. $1.50....*Carleton.*
Edna Harrington. Bristol, M. C. $1.25.....*Am. Tr.*
Edna Willis; or, the promise fulfilled. 18°. 60c. (?) *Martien.*
Edson, *Miss* Eliz. M. Plain questions on the Collects, Epistles and Gospels of the Christian year. 18°. hf. bd., 25c.........................*Dutton.*
Edson, N. I. Barbara. ill. 16°. '75. $1.50..*Lothrop.*
— Silent Tom. ill. 16°. '72. $1.75..........*Lothrop.*
Eduard, der Hirtenknabe. 18°. 30c........*Ev. Assoc.*
Education. Morton, T. 15c...............*French.*
Education in Japan: letters by prominent Americans to A. Mori. 12°. $1.50.............*Appleton.*
Education of the heart. Colfax, S. 10c....... *Wells.*
Educator (The). Phelps, L. $1.50........*Barnes.*
Edward vi. *of Eng.* Life and writings. *See* British reformers.
Edward and Miriam: tale of Iceland. 18°. 60c. *Am. S. S.*
Edward Clifford. 18°. 75c................*Carter.*
Edward Hall. 18°. 50c.; 60c............*Am. Bapt.*
Edward Howard. 18°. 55c................*Dutton.*
Edward Lee. Britts, M. D. 40c.; 50c...*Am. Bapt.*
Edward Morton; or, the way to do good. 18°. 17c.; 22c.................................*Am. Bapt.*
Edward Osborne. Manning, A. 25c.....*Tompkins.*
Edward Rivers; or, the boy that was not spoiled. 18°. 40c. ....*Cong. Pub.*
Edward Trueman. 18°. 40c...............*Dutton.*
Edwardes, Conway. Board and residence: farce. 16°. pap., 15c..............................*French.*
— Linda of Chamouni: burlesque. 16°. pap., 15c. *French.*
— Only somebody; or, dreadfully alarming: farce. 12°. pap., 15c..............................*De Witt.*
Edward's prize; or, the premium. 18°. 25c. *Scribner, W. & A.*
Edwards, Amelia B. Barbara's history. 8°. pap., 75c. *Harper.*
— Debenham's vow. ill. 8°. pap., 75c.......*Harper.*
— Half a million of money. 8°. pap., 75c....*Harper.*
— *Same.* 12°. $1.25; bds., $1............*Routledge.*
— Hand and glove. 8°. pap., 50c.............*Harper.*
— History of France 16°. bds., 50c.........*Routledge.*
— In the days of my youth. 12°. $1.50; pap., 75c. (Intern. ed.) $1.25.......................*Porter.*
— Ladder of life. 16°. pap., 40c..........*Routledge.*
— *Same.* 8°. pap., 50c......................*Harper.*
— *Same.* (Railway lib.) 16°. bds., 50c...*Routledge.*
— Miss Carew. 8°. pap., 50c..................*Harper.*
— My brother's wife. 8°. pap., 50c..........*Harper.*
— Outlines of Eng. hist.; with questions. Am. ed. brought down to 1868. 16°. bds., 30c.... *Ware.*
— Summary of history of England for schools. 18°. bds., 20c...........................*Routledge.*
— Summary of history of France. 16°. bds., 50c. *Routledge.*
Edwards, *Mrs.* Annie. Archie Lovell. 8°. $1.75; pap., $1...............................*Sheldon.*
— Estelle. 12°. $1.50; pap., $1..............*Sheldon.*
— Leah, a woman of fashion. 8°. $1.75; pap., $1. *Sheldon.*
— Miss Forrester. 8°. $1.75; pap., $1......*Sheldon.*
— Ordeal for wives. 12°. $1.50; pap., $1...*Sheldon.*
— Ought we to visit her? 8°. $1.75; pap., $1..*Sheldon.*
— Philip Earnscliff. 8°. $1.75; pap., $1....*Sheldon.*
— Point of honor. 8°. pap., 50c..............*Harper.*

Edwards, *Mrs.* Annie, *continued.*
— *Same.* 12°. $1.50; pap., $1............ *Sheldon.*
— Steven Lawrence, yeoman. 8°. $1.75; pap., $1. *Sheldon.*
— Susan Fielding. 8°. $1.75; pap., $1...... *Sheldon.*
— Vagabond heroine. 12°. $1.25; pap., 75c. *Sheldon.*

Edwards, Bela Bates. Writings; with memoir by E. A. Park. ('53.) New ed. 2 v. 12°. '58. $3. *Draper.*

Edwards, Bruce. Rachel Noble's experience. ('67.) New ed. 18°. '75. 90c............ *Nat. Temp.*

Edwards, *Mrs.* C. M. My sister Margaret. ill. 12°. '59. $1.25 .... *Meth. Bk. Conc.*
— Rainbow side. ill. 12°.' 58. $1.25..*Meth. Bk. Conc.*

Edwards, C: Juryman's guide. 8°. shp., $2. *Baker, V. & Co.*
— On referees. 8°. shp., $7.50.......... *W. C. Little.*
— Treatise on the stamp act of July 1, 1862, and amendatory statutes to March, 1863; with authorities, cases and expositions. 2d ed., rev. and enl. 8°. shp., $4........... *Baker, V. & Co.*
— *See also* New York, Chancery reports.

Edwards, E: Free town libraries: their formation, management and hist. in Britain, France, Germany and America; with notices of book-collectors, etc. 8°. $4.................. *Wiley.*
— Lives of the founders of the British Museum, 1570–1870. 8°. '70. $8; large pap., $16.... *Bouton.*

Edwards, H. Sutherland. Life of Rossini. por. 12°. $1.75 .... *Ditson.*

Edwards, I. Essay on brokers and factors or commission merchants; incl. comment. on the factor's act. 12°. '70. $2.................. *Weed.*

Edwards, J. K. The marriage guide. 18°. '60. pap., 25c.............................. *Hunter.*

Edwards, J: C. *See* Missouri, Supreme Court reports.

Edwards, J: D. Carpenter's manual. 12°. pap., 50c. *Haney.*

Edwards, J: Ellis. Life of J. W. Childs. ('52.) 2d ed. 12°. '57. $1..................... *So. Meth.*
— Random sketches of European travel in 1856. 12°. '57. $1.50........................... *Harper.*
— Revival tracts. ('58.) 5th ed. 18°. '70. pap., 20c. *So. Meth.*

Edwards, Jona. Works. 2 v. por. 8°. $5..*Cong. Pub.*
— *Same.* 4 v. 8°. '69. $12................. *Carter.*
— History of the work of redemption. 12°. $1..*Pres. Bd.*
— *Same.* 18°. '38. 70c.................... *Am. Tr.*
— *Fr.* Histoire de la rédemption. 12°. pap., 25c. *Am. Tr.*
— *Welsh.* 12°. '49. 70c.................... *Am. Tr.*
— Life. 18°. 50c.......................... *Am. S. S.*
— Life of D: Brainerd; abridg. ill. 18°. '33. 70c. *Am. Tr.*
— *Germ.* Leben von David Brainerd. ill. 18°. '53. 60c.................................. *Am. Tr.*
— On revivals. 12°. '45. 80c............... *Am. Tr.*
— On the will. 8°. $1.50.................. *Carter.*
— Resolutions. *See* Willison, J., Christian's Scripture directory.
— Treatise on relig. affections. ill. 18°. '36. 60c. *Am. Tr.*
— Work of the Holy Spirit in the human heart; abridg. by J. Wesley. 18°. 40c.... *Cin. Meth. Bk. Conc.*
— *Same.* ('55.) 3d ed. 18°. '73. 50c...... *So. Meth.*

Edwards, Jona. (*the younger*). Christian love; with pref. by T. Edwards. 16°. $1.25..... *Pres. Bd.*

Edwards, Just. Sabbath manual. 18°. '45. 45c. *Am. Tr.*
— *Dutch.* pts. 1 and 3. 18°. '53. 30c....... *Am. Tr.*
— *French.* Le manuel du sabbat. pt. 1. 18°. '46. pap., 8c.............................. *Am. Tr.*
— *Germ.* Gründe für die Sonntagsfeier. 18°. '45. 35c.; pap., 15c.............................. *Am. Tr.*
— *Span.* El manual del domingo. pt. 1. 18°. '47. pap., 5c.............................. *Am. Tr.*
— Temperance manual. 18°. '47. 25c.; pap., 10c. *Am. Tr.*
— *French.* Manuel sur la tempérance. 18°. '49. pap., 10c.................................. *Am. Tr.*

Edwards, Just., *continued.*
— *Germ.* Handbuch der Mässigkeit. 18°. '48. 30c. *Am. Tr.*
— *Spain.* Manual de temperancia. 18°. '49. pap., 8c. *Am. Tr.*
— *See also* Bible [Whole]; New Test

Edwards, M. A. Philip in Palestine. [Juvenile.] 16°. $1.25 .... (?) *Martien.*

Edwards, *Miss* Mta. Betham. Dr. Jacob. 16°. '68. $1 .... *Roberts.*
— Holiday letters from Athens, Cairo and Weimar. 12°. '73. $2...................... *Routledge.*
— Kitty. 8°. pap., 50c..................... *Harper.*
— Little Bird Red and little Bird Blue. ill. sq. 12°. '66. 60c.......................... *Hurd & H.*
— The Sylvestres; or, the outcasts. ill. 8°. $1.25; pap., 75c.......................... *Lippincott.*

Edwards, Monroe. Life. 8°. pap., 50c..... *Peterson.*

Edwards, P: On baptism: candid reasons for renouncing the principles of anti-pædobaptism; also a short method with the Baptists. 18°. 60c. *Pres. Bd.*

Edwards, R: *See* Warren, M. E., *and* Edwards, R.
— *and* Webb, J. R. Analytical readers. 9 v. '66–'71. bds...................... *Sherwood; Taintor.*
Cont.: Analyt. first reader, 18°, 28c. — *Same,* in Leigh's phonic type, 16°, 30c. — Analyt. second, 16°, 45c. — *Same,* in Leigh's phonic type, 16°, 50c. — Analyt. third, 16°, 75c. — Analyt. fourth, 12°, 90c. — Analyt. fifth, 12°, $1.25. — Analyt. sixth, 12°, $1.50. — Analyt. intermediate, 12°, 80c.

Edwards, Sutherland. *See* Brough, R. B., *and* Edwards, S.; — Mayhew, A., *and* Edwards, S.

Edwards, T: *See* England, High Court of Admiralty reports.

Edwards, Tryon. Jewels for the household: sel. of thought and anecdote for family reading. 16°. '72. *$2.............................. *Case.*
— Sketches for the fireside: anecdotes for the family. ill. 12°. '67. *$2.50.................. *Case.*

Edwin and his pet squirrel. *See* Bertie and Amy books.

Edwin Brothertoft. Winthrop, T. $1.25...... *Holt.*

Edwin Drood (Mystery of). *See* Dickens, C.

Edwin of Deira. Smith, A. $1......... *Macmillan.*

Eells, Ja. Memorial of S: Eells. cr. 8°. '73. $1.75. *Cobb.*

Effective ministry (An). Van Vechten, J. 25c. *N. Y. Ref. Ch. Bd.*

Effie Gray. Perry, C. T. 50c. .... *H. H. Carter.*

Effie Maurice; or, what do I love best? 18°. 30c.; 40c.................................. *Am. Bapt.*

Effie Morison. Martyn, S. T. 45c. .... *Am. Tr.*

Effie Wingate's work. Chellis, M. D. $1.50. *H. A. Young.*

Effie's Christmas. *See* Baker, *Mrs.* H. N. W.

Effie's friends. Pratt, L. M. 50c.......... *Lothrop.*

Effie's trial, and other stories. 18°. 70c. ... *Pres. Bd.*

Egan, Pierce. [Novels.] 16 v. 8°. pap.... *De Witt.*
Cont.: Ada Leigh, 50c. — Blue-eyed witch, 50c. — Clifton Grey, 25c. — Ever my queen, 50c. — Flower of the flock, 50c. — Lady Blanche, 50c. — Lillian's fate, 25c. — Lionel Jocelyn, 50c. — London apprentice and the goldsmith's daughter, 25c. — Love me, leave me not, 50c. — Mark Jarrett's daisy, $1. — My love Kate, 50c. — Myra; or, the cruise of the Seabird, 25c. — The poor boy; or, the betrayer baffled, 50c. — Snake in the grass, 50c. — The veiled lady, 25c.

— *Same.* 8 v. 8°. pap................... *Dick & F.*
Cont.: Fair Lilias, $1.50. — Fair Rosamond, 75c. — Hagar Lot, 75c. — Imogene; or, the marble heart, $1.50. — The poor girl, 75c. — Quinten Matsys, 75c. — The scarlet flower, 75c. — Such is life, 75c.
— Lady Maude, the wonder of Kingswood Chase. 8°. $1.75; pap., $1.50.................. *Peterson.*

Egar, J. H. Three-fold grace of the Trinity. 12°. $1.50 .... *Lippincott.*

Egbert, Ja. Introduction to spelling. 18°. hf. bd., 28c.............................. *W. Wood.*

Eggleston, E: Circuit rider. [Fiction.] ('74.) New ed. ill. 12°. '76. $1.75............... *Ford.*

Eggleston, E: *continued.*
— Counsel for teachers: tracts. 24°. '72. 30c.; 50c. *Adams, B. & L.*
— End of the world. [Fiction.] ill. 12°. $1.50..*Judd.*
— Hoosier school-master. [Fiction.] ill. 12°. $1.25. *Judd.*
— Mr. Blake's walking-stick: Christmas story. 16°. '70. 50c. .... *Adams, B. & L.*
— Mystery of Metropolisville. [Fiction.] ill. 12°. $1.50 .... *Judd.*
— Schoolmaster's stories for boys and girls. ill. 12°. '75. $1.50 .... (?) *Shepard.*
— Sunday-school conventions and institutes; with suggestions on county and township organization. 18°. '71. pap., 20c. .... *Adams, B. & L.*
— Sunday-school manual: guide to S.-school work. 16°. '72. 75c.; pap., 30c. ...... *Adams, B. & L.*
Eggleston, G: Cary. Big brother (The): story of Indian war. ill. 8°. $1.50 .... *Putnam.*
— How to educate yourself. 12°. '72. 75c...*Putnam.*
— How to make a living. 12°. '75. 75c.....*Putnam.*
— Man of honor. [Fiction.] ill. 12°. $1.25.....*Judd.*
— Rebel's recollections. 16°. '74. $1.50...*Hurd & H.*
Eggleston, *Mrs.* N. H. Daughters of the prairie. ill. 16°. $1 .... *Bost. Am. Tr.*
— — *See also* Prairie lib.
— Maggie; or, light of the prairie home. 18°. 50c. *Cong. Pub.*
Eggs that were never peacocks. *See* Lee, F., *and* Locke, U.
Eglantine. Tabor, E. 50c. .... *Harper.*
Egle, W: H. History of Pennsylvania. 8°. '76. $5.50; leath., $6; hf. mor., $7 .... *Peale.*
Egleston, T. Catalogue of minerals. 8°. '63. pap., 50c. .... *Smith. Inst.*
— Lectures on mineralogy, School of Mines, Columbia Coll. pl. 8°. '72. $4.50....... *Van Nostrand.*
Egliseau, S. S. Gleanings from real life. 18°. 60c. *Pres. Bd.*
— Lizzie Ferguson; or, the Sabbath-school scholar. 18°. 60c. .... *Pres. Bd.*
— Lucy Dunlevy. sq. 16°. 50c. .... *Pres. Bd.*
— Sketches for you. sq. 16°. 70c. .... *Pres. Bd.*
Egloffstein, F. W. v. Contributions to geol. and physical geog. of Mexico. 8°. '64. $4.....*Appleton.*
Egmont. *See* Goethe, J. W. v.
Egypt, and other poems. Tyler, M. A. $1..*Lippincott.*
Egypt 3300 years ago. *See* Illustrated lib. of wonders.
Egypt Ennis. Etheridge, K. 50c. .... *Authors.*
Egyptian (The). Wilkins, J. H. 15c. ......*French.*
Egyptian dream book and fortune-teller. ill. 16°. bds., 35c. .... *Dick & F.*
Egyptian sepulchres and Syrian shrines. Strangford, *Vctss.* $2.50 .... *Macmillan.*
Egyptian sketch book. Leland, C. G. $1.75..*Hurd & H.*
Egypt's place in hist. Dall, C. H. $1.50....*Lee & S.*
Eh? what is it? Stewart, J. C. 15c. .... *De Witt.*
Ehefabrikanten (Die). *See* Winterfeld, A. v.
Ehlert, L: Letters on music to a lady; tr. by F. R. Ritter. 12°. '70. $1.50 .... *Ditson.*
Ehre (Die) des Herzens. *See* Vacano, E. M.
Ehre Vater u. Mutter. *See* Hoffmann, F.
Eia Popeia: deutsche Kinderheimath. ill. 8°. 50c. *Kohler.*
Eichbaum, G. R. Selection of stone for masonry. 8°. pap., 25c. .... *Am. Soc. of C. E.*
Eichberg, Jul. Doctor of Alcantara; with libretto by B. E. Wolf. [Opera bouffe.] f°. '62. $3.50.— Choruses. f°. pap., $1 .... *Ditson.*
— — *See also* Ditson.
— Two Cadis. [Comic opera.] 4°. '68. bds., $1.50. *Ditson.*
— — *See also* Ditson.
— *See also* National music course.

Eichendorff, Jos. v. Aus dem Leben eines Taugenichts. ('64.) New ed. 12°. '76. pap., 75c. *Holt.*
— *Same;* tr. into Eng. by C. G. Leland. 12°. $1.50. *Holt.*
Eichorn, C: Practical German grammar. 12°. $1.50. *Appleton.*
Eigensinn. *See* Benedix, R.
Eigensinn u. Busse. *See* Hoffmann, F.
Eight cousins. Alcott, L. M. $1.50 .... *Roberts.*
Eight months on duty. M., R. de. $1.75..*Routledge.*
Eight weeks' work in San Francisco. Hammond, E. P. 20c. .... *Bancroft.*
Eight years old; or, the two birthdays. 18°. 35c.; 45c. *Am. Bapt.*
Eight years' wanderings in Ceylon. *See* Baker, *Sir* S. W.
Eighteen centuries of beginnings of church hist. Yonge, C. M. $2 .... *Pott.*
Eighteen Christian centuries. White, J. $2..*Appleton.*
Eighteen hundred and sixty-three. Byron, H. J. 15c. *French.*
Eighteen hundred and thirteen. Stolle, F. $1; 75c.; $1.25 .... *F. W. Thomas.*
Eighteen hundred and twelve. Rellstab, L. $2; $1.50; $2.25 .... *F. W. Thomas.*
Eighteen presidents. Taylor, W. A. $1; 50c. *W. A. Taylor.*
Eighty years ashore and afloat; or, adventures of Uncle Jethro. 12°. $1.50 .... *Graves.*
Eildon Manor: tale for girls. ill. 12°. $1.25. *Scribner, W. & A.*
Eiloart, *Mrs.* C. J. Archie Blake: a sea-side story. ill. 16°. 75c. .... *Routledge.*
— Boy with an idea. ill. 16°. $1.75..*Scribner, W. & A.*
— *Same.* ill. sm. 8°. '74. $1.75 .... *Putnam.*
— Boys of Beechwood. ill. 16°. $1.25.....*Routledge.*
— Cris Fairlie's boyhood: a tale of an old town. cr. 8°. $2.50 .... *Scribner, W. & A.*
— Curate's discipline. 8°. pap., 50c. .... *Harper.*
— Ernie Elton at home. ill. 16°. 75c. ......*Routledge.*
— Ernie Elton at home and at school. ill. 16°. $1.25. *Routledge.*
— Ernie Elton at school, and what came of his going there. ill. 16°. 75c. .... *Routledge.*
— Ernie Elton, the lazy boy. ill. 16°. 75c...*Routledge.*
— From thistles — grapes? 8°. pap., 50c.....*Harper.*
— Johnny Jordan and his dog. ill. 16°. $1.25. *Routledge.*
— Love (The) that lived. 8°. pap., 50c. ......*Harper.*
— Tom Dunstone's troubles. ill. 16°. $1.25..*Routledge.*
— Woman's wrong. 12°. $1.75; pap., $1.50..*Peterson.*
— Young squire. ill. cr. 8°. $2.50..*Scribner, W. & A.*
Eily O'Conner: drama. Wilks, T. E. 15c.....*French.*
Eily O'Connor: burlesque. 16°. pap., 15c....*French.*
Einer muss heirathen. *See* Wilhelmi, A.
Einfache Gedanken über geheime Gesellschaften. 12°. 36c. .... *Un. B. Pub.*
Einsamen (Die). Heyse, P. 40c. .... *Holt.*
Einstein, Morris. Origin and development of relig. ideas and beliefs. 12°. $1 .... *Mendum.*
Eirene. Clemmer, M. $1.25; 75c. .... *Putnam.*
Eiserne Maske (Die); [also] Zampa. 16°. 25c. *Morwitz.*
Eisjungfrau (Die). *See* Andersen, H. C.
Ekkoes from Kentucky. Locke, D. R. $1.50..*Lee & S.*
El Fureidis. Cummins, M. S. $1.75 .... *Osgood.*
El Gringo. Davis, W. W. H. $1.50 .... *Harper.*
El Hyder. Barrymore, W. 15c. .... *French.*
El Khuds, the holy. Turner, W. M. $5; $8..*Challen.*
Elam, C: On cerebria and other diseases of the brain. 8°. '72. $2.50 .... *Lindsay.*
— Physician's (A) problems. 16°. $1.75....* *Osgood.*
— *Same.* cr. 8°. '69. $1.75. .... *Macmillan.*
Elbert's return. Wise, D. $1.25 .... *Perkinpine.*

Elder, W: Enchanted beauty, and other tales and sketches. 16°. $1.25 .... *J. E. Potter.*
— Questions of the day, economic and social. 8°. '71. $3 .... *Baird.*
Elder brother. Beaumont, F., *and* Fletcher, J. 15c. *French.*
Elder brother. Sadlier, M. A. 25c .... *Sadlier.*
Elder Park; or, scenes in our garden. ('67.) New ed. 16°. '73. 90c .... *Hoyt.*
— *See also* Books about wonderful and curious things.
Elder Park series. 5 v. ill. 16°. $4.50 .... *Hoyt.*
Cont.: Elder park. — Buds of grace. — Charley Smeaton. — Philip Oakover. — Little Bessie.

Eldergowan. Mulholland, R. $1 .... *Pott.*
Elderhorst, W: Manual of qualitative blowpipe anal. and determinative mineral.; ed. by H. B. Nason and C. F. Chandler. 6th ed., rev. and enl. ill. 12°. '73. $2.50 .... *Porter.*
— *See also* Arkansas geol. survey.
Elderkin, J: Slow horses made fast and fast horses made faster. 12°. '71. 50c .... *Haney.*
— Turf and trotting horse of Am. *See* Walsh, J. H., Every horse owner's cyclop.
Eldest child (The). 18°. 18c .... *Am. S. S.*
Eldorado. Taylor, B. $1.50; $2 .... *Putnam.*
Eldredge, Mira. Drops of water from many fountains. 12°. $1 .... *Palmer.*
Eldridge, Abby (*pseud.*) Cast out. 16°. $1.35. *Pres. Bd.*
— Christmas story, and other tales. 18°. 75c. *Pres. Bd.*
— Ella Graham; or, great effects from small causes. 18°. 50c .... *Pres. Bd.*
— Kate Stanley; or, the power of perseverance. 18°. 65c .... *Pres. Bd.*
— Love's labor; or, the seed and its blossoms. 18°. 75c .... *Pres. Bd.*
— Lucy Clifton. 18°. 75c .... *Pres. Bd.*
— Norman Brill's life-work. 12°. '75. $1 .. *Nat. Temp.*
— Walter and Alice; or, the mother's prayer answered. 18°. 60c .... *Pres. Bd.*
Eldridge, J: Gas-fitter's guide. 2d ed. ill. post 8°. (Lond.) '72. pap., 40c. .... *Spon.*
— Pump-fitter's guide. ill. 12°. (Lond.) '72. pap., 40c. .... *Spon.*
Eleanor: an autobiography. 16°. $1.10 .... *Am. S. S.*
Eleanor Willoughby's self. ('71.) New ed. ill. 16°. '75. $1.25 .... *Hoyt.*
Eleanor's lessons. Connell, S. G. $1 ... *J. A. Moore.*
Eleanor's stories. 18°. 60c .... *Cong. Pub.*
Eleanor's three birthdays. McKeever, H. B. $1. *Porter.*
Eleanor's victory. Braddon, M. E. 75c ..... *Harper.*
Eleanor's visit. Mathews, J. H. $1.25 ...... *Carter.*
Elect lady (The). Vanzandt, A. B. 60c ... *Pres. Bd.*
Election day. 18°. 35c .... *Am. S. S.*
Election times. 16°. 40c .... *West. Tr.*
Elective affinities. *See* Goethe, J. W. v.
Electra. *See* Euripides.
Electra: extravaganza. 16°. pap., 15c ...... *French.*
Elegant narratives. ill. 12°. '50. $1.10 ..... *Am. Tr.*
Elegy in a country churchyard. *See* Gray, T:
Elementary German grammar. 18°. 30c ..... *Radde.*
Elementary German primer. 18°. 15c ...... *Radde.*
Elementary Scripture quest. books. 3 v. 24°. ea., 16c .... *Am. S. S.*
Elementary spelling-book. 16°. bds., 23c ..... *Ware.*
Elena. Comyn, L. N. $1.25; 75c .... *Estes.*
Eleonore. Ingersleben, *Frau* v. $1.50 ... *Lippincott.*
Elephant (Der). Winterfeld, A. v. 50c ..... *Morwitz.*
Elephant and gingerbread nuts. 32°. 20c.; 15c. *Dutton.*

Elephant Club (History and records of). Thomson, M. $1.75; $1.50 .... *Peterson.*
Elephant of Siam: extravag. 16°. pap., 15c ... *French.*
Elephant on ice: Ethiop. drama. 16°. pap., 15c. *Happy.*
Elephant's carpet bag of fun. ill. 8°. pap., 15c. *Happy.*
Eleven days at Moravia. Hazard, T. R. 10c ... *Colby.*
Eleven months in Horeb. Benjamin, E. B. 20c. *Randolph.*
Eleven sophomores. *See* College stories.
Elfen (Die). *See* Tieck, L.
Elfie Grafton. 18°. 45c .... *Cong. Pub.*
Elfred. Abbott, J. 90c .... *Harper.*
Elfreda. Leslie, E. $1.50 .... *Meth. Bk. Conc.*
Elgas, J. Mat. [Readers]; arranged accord. to Germ. ser. of J. Schätz. 3 v. 8°. '75-'76 ...... *Pustet.*
Cont.: First reader, 25c. — Second reader, 50c. — Progressive third reader, 75c.

Eli. *See* Costa, M.
Eli Perkins (at large). Landon, M. D. $1.25 .. *Ford.*
Elia. Arron, C. B. de F. $1.50 .... *Cath. Pub*
Elia; — Eliana. *See* Lamb, C:
Eligible situation (An): farce. 16°. pap., 15c. *Happy.*
Elijah. *See* Mendelssohn Bartholdy, F.
Elijah, the prophet. Taylor, W. M. $1.50 .. *Harper.*
Elijah, the Tishbite. *See* Krummacher, F. W.
Elim. Huntington, F. D. $1.50; $4; $5 .... *Dutton.*
Elinor Johnston. 18°. '68. 50c .... *Cunningham.*
Elinor Preston. Sadlier, M. A. 75c.; $1.25 .. *Sadlier.*
Eliot, C: W., *and* Storer, F: H. Compendious manual of qualit. chem. anal.; rev. by W. R. Nichols. New ed., rev. ill. 12°. '74. $1.50 .. *Van Nostrand.*
— — Manual of inorganic chemistry. ill. 8°. '66. $2.75. *Ivison.*
— — *Same;* abridg. by W. R. Nichols. 12°. '72. $1.50. *Ivison.*
Eliot, George (*pseud.*) [*Mrs.* M. E. Lewes, *formerly Miss* Evans.] Novels. (Household ed.) 5 v. 16°. ea., $1 .... * *Osgood.*
Cont.: Adam Bede. — Romola. — Mill on the Floss. — Felix Holt. — Silas Marner; Scenes of clerical life.
— *Same.* (Lib. ed.) 2 v. ill. 12° $3.50 ... * *Osgood.*
— *Same.* 7 v. ill. cr. 8°. (Lond.) hf. cf., $22.50. *Little, B. & Co.*
Cont.: Adam Bede. — Mill on the Floss. — Silas Marner. — Scenes of clerical life. — Felix Holt. — Romola. — Middlemarch.
— Adam Bede. ill. 12°. $1.50; hf. cf., $2.25 .. *Harper.*
— Daniel Deronda. 8°. '76. pap., $1.50. 2 v. 12°. $3 .... *Harper.*
— Felix Holt. ill. 12°. $1.50; hf. cf., $2.25. 8°. pap., 75c .... *Harper.*
— How Lisa loved the king. 16°. '69. 50c .... *Osgood.*
— Legend of Jubal, and other poems. 16°. '74. $1.50; hf. cf., $3; mor., $4 .... *Osgood.*
— Middlemarch. 8°. $2; pap., $1.50. 2 v. 12°. $3; hf. cf., $7 .... *Harper.*
— *Same.* 4 v. 16°. $3.50. 2 v. 12°. $3.50 .. *Lippincott.*
— Mill on the Floss. ill. 12°. $1.50; hf. cf., $2.25. 8°. pap., 75c .... *Harper.*
— Romola. ill. 12°. $1.50; hf. cf., $2.25. 8°. $2; pap., $1.50 .... *Harper.*
— Scenes of clerical life. 8°. pap., 75c ..... *Harper.*
— *Same;* [also] Silas Marner. ill. 12°. $1.50; hf. cf., $2.25 .... *Harper.*
— Silas Marner. 12°. $1 .... *Harper.*
— Spanish gypsy (The). 16°. '68. $1.50; hf. cf., $3; mor., $4 .... *Osgood.*
— Wit and wisdom of E. sq. 18°. '73. $1.25 .. *Roberts.*
— *See also* Feuerbach, L., Essence of Christianity; — Strauss, D. F., Life of Jesus.
Eliot, Ida M., *and* Brackett, Anna C. (*ed.*) Poetry for home and school. sq. 16°. '76. $1.25 .. *Putnam.*
Eliot, J: The day-breaking if not the sun-rising of the Gospel with the Indians in New Eng. Lond., 1647. [Reprint.] 4°. '65. $1; large pap., $2 .. *Sabin.*

Eliot, S: History of liberty: period of the anc. Romans and early Christians. 4 v. cr. 8°. $6... *Miller.*
— History of the U. S., 1492-1872. 12°. $1.88.. *Ware.*
Eliot, W: G. Discipline of sorrow. ('55.) 7th ed. 16°. '68. 50c. .... *Am. Unit.*
— Doctrines of Christianity. ('52.) 20th ed. 12°. '75. 50c. .... *Am. Unit.*
— Early religious education. ('55.) New ed. 16°. '71. 50c. .... *Am. Unit.*
— Lectures to young men. ('53.) 10th ed. 16°. '73. 60c. .... *Am. Unit.*
— Lectures to young women. ('53.) 9th ed. 16°. '69. 60c. .... *Am. Unit.*
Elisabeth: Geschichte a. d. Zeit der Kreuzzüge. 12°. 35c.; pap., 15c. .... *Benziger.*
Elisama; or, the captivity and restoration of the Jews, 606-408 B. C. 18°. 75c. .... *Am. S. S.*
Elisha. ill. 32°. '54. 30c. .... *Am. Tr.*
Elisire (L') d' amore. *See* Ditson.
Elixir of love. Reynoldson, T. H. 15c. ...... *French.*
Eliza Cunningham. ill. 18°. '40. 25c. .... *Am. Tr.*
Eliza Metcalf's basket. Leslie, E. $1 .... *Nelson.*
Elizabeth, *St.* Life. 12°. $1.50; $2 .... *Sadlier.*
— *See also* Lives of the saints.
Elizabeth, *St.* (*Matron of Israel.*) Life. 18°. '76. 50c. *Kelly, P. & Co.*
— *See also* Three Elizabeths.
Elizabeth, *St.* (*Queen of Hungary.*) St. Elizabeth, the queen saint of Hungary. 18°. '76. 50c. *Kelly, P. & Co.*
— *See also* Three Elizabeths.
Elizabeth, *St.* (*Queen of Portugal.*) St. Elizabeth, the lily of Portugal; or, the queen saint. 18°. '76. 60c. .... *Kelly, P. & Co.*
— *See also* Three Elizabeths.
Elizabeth, *Aunt.* *See* Aunt Elizabeth (*pseud.*)
Elizabeth. *See* Better home (The).
Elizabeth; or, the exiles of Siberia. *See* Cottin, S. R.
Elizabeth and beggar boys. ill. 16°. 50c. .... *Nelson.*
Elizabeth Benton. Alden, J. 75c. .... *Harper.*
Elizabeth Fry; or, the Christian philanthropist. 18°. 85c. .... *Am. S. S.*
Elizabethan poets. [Selections.] ill. 12°. '75. $1.25. *Putnam.*
Eliza's basket. Leslie, E. $1 .... *Nelson.*
Ella. Simonds, W. $1.25 .... *Miller.*
Ella and her grandfather. 18°. 28c.; 35c... *Am. Bapt.*
Ella and Maggie. 18°. 45c. .... *Pres. Bd.*
Ella and Marian. Bell, C. D. $1.75.. *Scribner, W. & A.*
Ella Barnwell. Bennett, E. 25c. .... *U. P. James.*
Ella Clinton. Finley, M. F. 60c. .... *Pres. Bd.*
Ella Dalton. 18°. 65c. .... *Pres. Bd.*
Ella Graham. Eldridge, A. 50c. .... *Pres. Bd.*
Ella Rosenberg. Kenney, J. 15c. .... *French.*
Ella Ross. Custer, E. S. 70c. .... *Am. Tr.*
Ella Stratford. Blessington, *Countess.* 50c. *Peterson.*
Ella's battles. Feudge, F. R. $1 .... *Am. Bapt.*
Ella's birds. 32°. 20c.; 15c. .... *Dutton.*
Ella's locket. Dartnell, G. E. $1 .... *Nelson.*
Ella's troubles. 32°. 20c.; 15c. .... *Dutton.*
Ellen, the teacher. Hofland, B. 50c. .... *Porter.*
Ellen; or, the disinterested girl. 18°. 22c... *Am. S. S.*
Ellen; or, submission in affliction. 18°. 30c... *Pres. Bd.*
Ellen and Frank. Perring, *Mrs.* —. 45c... *Routledge.*
Ellen and her cousins. 18°. 70c. .... *Pres. Bd.*
Ellen Carrol. G., M. H. 40c. .... *Am. S. S.*
Ellen Grant. 8°. pap., 25c. .... *Dick & F.*
Ellen Grey; or, the power of conscience. 18°. 35c. *Am. S. S.*
Ellen Hart; or, the little servant girl. 18°. 35c. *Am. S. S*
Ellen Herbert; or, family changes. 18°. 75c. *Harper*
Ellen Leslie. *See* New juvenile lib.
Ellen Linn. Abbott, J. 90c. .... *Harper*
Ellen Manning; or, trials and their uses. 18°. 40c. *So. Bapt*
Ellen Mason; or, prejudice vanquished. 18°. 28c. 35c. .... *Am. Bapt*
Ellen Meyrick. 18°. 35c.; 40c. .... *Dutton*
Ellen Middleton. Fullerton, *Lady* G. $1.50; $2. *Murphy*
Ellen Monroe. Reynolds, G. W. M. $1.50.. *Dick & F*
Ellen Montgomery's book-shelf. Warner, S. *and* A. B 5 v. $5 .... *Carter*
Ellen Mordaunt; or, the fruits of true religion. 18° 75c. .... *Am. S. S*
Ellen Murray. Flint, S. A. 65c. .... *Cong. Pub*
Ellen Norbury. Bennett, E. $1.75; $1.50.. *Peterson*
Ellen Percy. Reynolds, G. W. M. 75c. .... *Peterson*
Ellen Sinclair; or, the earnest inquirer. 32°. 15c. *Am. S. S*
— *Same.* 18°. 25c. .... *Pres. Bd*
Ellen Stanley. ill. 18°. '68. 65c. .... *Perkinpine*
Ellen Story. Fawcett, E. $1.25; 75c. .... *Hale*
Ellen Strong's victory. *See* Gem cluster.
Ellen Vincent, and the blank sheet. ('65.) New ed ill. 16°. '75. 75c. .... *Hoyt*
Ellen Wareham. Burton, W. E. 15c. .... *French*
Ellen Wareham. Pickering, E. 38c. ...... *Peterson*
Ellena. Radcliffe, A. 50c. .... *U. P. James*
Ellen's idol. *See* Phelps, E. S.
Ellen's May-day; or, where there is a will there is a way. ill. 24°. '69. 30c. .... *Lothrop.*
Ellerslie House. Leslie, E. $1 .... *Am. Bapt.*
Ellerslie House lib. 4 v. 16°. '69. $4.75.. *Meth. Bk. Conc*
Cont.: Ellerslie House.— Alice Thorne.— Kate and her cousins.— Wreck of the Osprey.
Ellery, Ma. T. Impulse and principle. 16°. $1.50 *Cong. Pub.*
Ellet, C: *jr.* On inundations of the delta of the Mississippi and other rivers. pl. and tables. roy. 8°. $3.25 .... *Lippincott.*
— Physical geog. of the U. S. 4°. '50. pap., $2. *Smith. Inst.*
Ellet, E. Mountain-top tract in Va. *See* Roebling, J., Niagara Falls.
Ellett, *Mrs.* Eliz. F. Domestic hist. of the Am. rev ill. 12°. $1.25 .... *Lippincott.*
— Love in a maze. 8°. pap., 25c. .... *Beadle*
— Pioneer women of the west. 12°. $1.25 .... *Porter.*
— Queens of Am. society. ill. roy. 8°. '67. $3.75; $4.50; mor., $6 .... *Porter.*
— *Same.* roy. 8°. '76. $5 .... *N. Y. & H. Pub.*
— Rambles about the country. 18°. 75c. .... *Harper.*
— Scripture gift book. 12°. *net*, 75c. .... *Hamersley.*
— Women artists in all ages and countries. 12°. $1.50. *Harper.*
— (*ed.*) New cyclopædia of domestic economy, and practical housekeeper. ill. 8°. '72. *$3.30; $4.25; $5.25 .... *Henry Bill.*
Ellicott, C. J. Commentaries. ('60-'65.) New ed. 5 v. 8°. '72. $10; — in 2 v. $8 .... *Draper.*
Cont.: Galatians, with introd. by C. E. Stowe, $1.50.— Ephesians, $1.50.— Thessalonians, $1.50.— Pastoral Epistles, $2.— Philippians, Colossians and Philemon, $2.
— Historical lect. on Christ. *See* Hulsean lectures.
— *See also* Lightfoot, J. B., Trench, R. C., *and* Ellicott, C. J.
Ellie; or, nothing perfect here. W., K. M. $1.50. (?) *Martien.*
Ellie and Archie. 16°. '75. 50c. .... *Hoyt.*
Ellie Laura. O'Leary, J. 40c. .... *Sadlier.*
Ellie Randolph. Neely, K. 75c. .... *Carter; Dutton.*

Ellie's scrap-book. 18°. 65c. . . . . *Pres. Bd.*

Elliot, —. *See* Griggs, —, *and* Elliot, —.

Elliot, C. I. *See* Johnson, G. H. S., Cook, F. C., *and* Elliot, C. I.

Elliot, C: S. Songs of Yale. 4th ed., rev. and enl. by E. P. Howe. 12°. '76. $1 . . . . . . *H. G. Phillips.*

Elliot, Fes. Italians (The). [Fiction.] 12°. $1.50. *Appleton.*

— Romance of old court-life in France. ill. 8°. $2; pap., $1.50 . . . . *Appleton.*

Elliot, G: H. European light-house systems. ill. 8°. '75. $5 . . . . *Van Nostrand.*

Elliot, G: T. Obstetric clinic. 8°. $4.50 . . *Appleton.*

Elliot, Jona. (*ed.*) Debates in the state conventions on the adoption of the federal Constitution. 5 v. 8°. $12.50; shp., $15 . . . . *Lippincott.*

Elliot, S: H. Emily Maria. ill. 18°. '46. 25c. *Am. Tr.*

Elliott, Alfr. In-doors: games and pastimes for the parlor. ill. 12°. $1.50 . . . . *Nelson.*

Elliott, C: Bible and slavery. 12°. $1.25. *Cin. Meth. Bk. Conc.*

— Delineation of Romanism. 2 v. 8°. '41. $6. *Meth. Bk. Conc.*

— Life of Bp. Roberts. 12°. '56. $1 . . . *Meth. Bk. Conc.*

— Sabbath (The). sm. 12° 65c. . . . . *Pres. Bd.*

— Sinfulness of Am. slavery. 2 v. 12°. $2.50. *Cin. Meth. Bk. Conc.*

Elliott, C: Wyllys. Book of Am. interiors: 22 full-page heliotypes, and [other] ill.; with letter-press, and essays on the dining-room and library. 4°. '75. $10 . . . . *Osgood.*

— New England history, 986–1776. 2 v. por. 8°. $6. *Scribner.*

— Remarkable characters and memorable places of the Holy Land. ill. 8°. *$4 – $5.50 . . . . *Burr.*

Elliott, *Miss* Ctte. Hymns for a week, morning and evening; with pref. by Bp. Stevens. 32°. '65. 30c. . . . . *Dutton.*

— Leaves from her unpublished journals, letters and poems. 12°. $2 . . . . *Nelson.*

— Poems; with memoir by her sister. 12°. $2 . . *Nelson.*

— *Same.* por. 12°. '74. $2 . . . . *Randolph.*

Elliott, Dan. Giraud. *See* Wolf, Jos., Life and habits of wild animals.

Elliott, F. R. Handbook for fruit growers. ill. 12°. $1; pap., 60c. . . . . *Dewey.*

— Handbook of landscape gardening. ill. 8°. '76. $1.50. *Dewey.*

— Lawn and shade trees. ill. 12°. $1.50 . . *Woodward.*

— Western fruit-grower's guide. 12°. $1.50 . . . . *Judd.*

Elliott, J. W. Mother Goose set to music. ill. 8°. $1; per gross, pap., $54 . . . . (?) *McLoughlin.*

— National nursery rhymes and nursery songs set to music. ill. 4°. $2.50; bds., $1.50 . . . *Routledge.*

Elliott, *Mrs.* Sa. A. Housewife: receipts in cookery and suggestions for housekeepers. 12°. hf. roan, $1.50 . . . . *Hurd & H.*

Elliott, W. L. Manual for cavalry: routine of duty in quarters, in camp, and on the march. 18°. '64. pap., 25c. . . . . *Claxton; Lippincott.*

Ellis, *Miss* —. After the holidays. ill. 16°. 75c. *Nelson.*

Ellis, *Mrs.* —. Complete cook. New ed., with Miss Leslie's 75 receipts. ill. 12°. $1.25 . . . . . *Miller.*

Ellis, Alex. J. Practical hints on the quantitative pronunc. of Latin. 12°. '74. $1.75 . . . . *Macmillan.*

Ellis, B: Medical formulary: prescriptions from physicians of Am. and Europe. 12th ed., rev. by A. H. Smith. 8°. $3 . . . . *Lea.*

Ellis, Calv. Capillary bronchitis of adults. *See* Seguin, E. C., Ser. of Am. clin. lect.

Ellis, Dan. Thrilling adventures. [Autobiog.] ill. 12°. $2.50 . . . . *Harper.*

Ellis, E. J. Doda's birthday. ill. 16°. $1 . . . . . . *Pott.*

Ellis, E: Practical manual of the diseases of children. 2d ed., rev. 12°. '73. $2.75 . . . . *Lindsay.*

Ellis, F. *See* England, Common law reports.

Ellis, G: Specimens of early Eng. metrical romances; rev. by J. O. Halliwell. 12°. (Bohn.) $1.75. *Little, B. & Co.*

— *Same.* 12°. (Bohn.) $2. *Lippincott; Scribner, W. & A.*

Ellis, G: E: Half-century of the Unitarian controversy. 8°. '57. $1.50 . . . . *Am. Unit.*

— History of the battle of Bunker's [Breed's] Hill, June 17, 1775. map. 8°. '75. 75c.; pap., 25c. ill. 18°. 75c. . . . . *Lockwood, B. & Co.*

— Memoir of Sir Benjamin Thompson, Count Rumford; with notices of his daughter. 8°. '71. $5. *Am. Acad. of A. & S.*

— *See also* Celebration.

Ellis, G: J. W. A. *See* Dover, *Lord.*

Ellis, *Mrs.* Grace A. *See* Barbauld, *Mrs.* A. L., Memoir.

Ellis, J: Avoidable causes of disease, insanity and deformity. 12°. $2 . . . . *Boericke.*

— Family homœopathy. 12°. $1.50 . . . . *Boericke.*

Ellis, Laura E. Memoir. 18°. '58. 35c. . . . . *So. Meth.*

Ellis, *Mrs.* Sa. S. Brewer's (The) family. ill. 16°. '66. $1 . . . . *Dodd.*

— Chapters on wives. 12°. $1.50 . . . . *Harper.*

— Hearts and homes; or, social distinctions. 8°. $2. *Appleton.*

— Home; or, the iron rule. 12°. $1.50 . . . . . . *Harper.*

— Look to the end; or, the Bennetts abroad. 8°. pap., 50c. . . . . *Harper.*

— Mothers of great men. ill. 12°. $3 . . . . . . *Routledge.*

— Temper and temperament; or, varieties of character. 18°. 75c. . . . . *Harper.*

Ellis, Sumner. At our best, and other essays. 16°. $1.50 . . . . *Lee & S.*

Ellis, T. F. *See* England, Common law reports.

Ellis, T. G. Aneroid barometer in estimating altitudes. 8°. pap., 80c. . . . . *Am. Soc. of C. E.*

— Description of hydraulic experiments with large apertures at Holyoke, Mass., 1874; [also] Tests and testing machines, strength of steel wire, by T. C. Clarke. 8°. '76. pap., $2.10. *Am. Soc. of C. E.*

— Experimental strains upon a bowstring trussed girder. 8°. pap., 40c. . . . . *Am. Soc. of C. E.*

— Failure of dam on Mill River. *See* Chanute, O., Weight of rails.

— Formation of bars at mouths of rivers. *See* Jordan, G., Foundations under water.

— Mexican method of making hard lime floors. 8°. pap., 30c. . . . . *Am. Soc. of C. E.*

Ellis, W: Three visits to Madagascar, 1853, '54, '56. map and ill. 12°. $1.75 . . . . *J. E. Potter.*

— *Same.* map, wood-cuts and photos. 8°. $3.50; hf. cf., $5.75 . . . . *Harper.*

Ellis Amory. Atkins, M. A. 75c. . . . . *Cong. Pub.*

Ellmore, A. Which is the true church? 24°. '73. pap., 15c. . . . . *Cen. Bk.*

Elloie (*pseud.*) *See* Stith, *Miss* Z.

Ellsworth, *Mrs.* —. [" *Mrs.* L. L. Worth."] Smith's saloon; or, the Grays and the Grants. ill. 16°. '71. $1.25 . . . . *Crowell.*

Ellsworth, E. E. Zouave drill and biography: manual of arms, sword and sabre. 12°. 50c.; pap., 25c. *Peterson.*

Ellsworth, H. W. Book-keeping and business manual, single and double entry. obl. 4°. $1.50; — in 2 pts. ea., 90c. . . . . *Taintor.*

— Steps of book-keeping, single and double entry: short course. sq. 8°. 75c . . . . *Taintor.*

— Tracing copy books: primary ser. 3 nos. sm. obl. 12°. ea., per doz., $1.20 . . . . *Taintor.*

— *Same*: intermediate ser. 4 nos. sm. obl. 12°. ea., per doz., $1.20 . . . . *Taintor.*

Ellsworth, H. W., *continued.*
— *Same:* grammar ser. 8 nos. and exercise drill book. obl. 12°. ea., per doz., $1.80 .... *Taintor.*
Ellsworth stories. 18°. 30c.; 40c.......... *Am. Bapt.*
Ellwood, T: Journal. 12°. 75c...... *Friends Bk. St.*
Elm Grove cottage. Lathrop, H. $1.25........ *Hoyt.*
Elm Grove series. 5 v. ill. 16°. $6.25......... *Hoyt.*
Cont.: Eleanor Willoughby. — Mary Bruce. — Grace Martin. — Hattie Powers, by Miss A. E. Thomas. — Elm Grove cottage, by Mrs. H. Lathrop.
Elm Island stories. *See* Kellogg, E:
Elmendorf, Ant. Valedictory sermon, North Ref. Dutch Church, Brooklyn, N. Y., April 30, 1865. 8°. pap., 25c. .... *N. Y. Ref. Ch. Bd.*
Elmendorf, Joachim. *See* Porter, E. S., *and* Elmendorf, J.
Elmer, Alb. D. *See* Elmer, W. *and* A. D.
Elmer, L. Q. C. Reminiscences of N. J., with biog. sketches of the governors, and reminiscences of the bench and bar. 8°. '72. $3.50...... *Dennis.*
— — *See also* New Jersey Hist. Soc.
— *See also* New Jersey, Digest of laws.
Elmer, W: *and* A. D. Physician's handbook. [Annual.] 18°. $1.50; $1.75................... *Townsend.*
Elmer's morning glory. *See* Morning glory lib.
Elmira [N. Y.] Farmers' Club. Report of discussions, 1874. 12°. $1.25. — Same, 1875. 12°. $1.25; pap., $1 .... *Elmira.*
Elmira's ambitions. Guernsey, C. F. $1.25.. *Am. S. S.*
Elms homestead. Johnson, M. O. $1.... *Lippincott.*
Elmsgrove; or, the Sunday-school boys contrasted. 18°. 40c.............................. *Am. S. S.*
Elmwood, Rose. Madelin e.ill. 18°. '64. 30c. *Am. Tr.*
Elmwood. L., K. $1.25........... *Kelly, P. & Co.*
Elmwood. Whiting, H. C. $1.25....... *Cong. Pub.*
Elocution made easy, and the reciter's companion. 12°. pap., 20c. .... *Hurst.*
Elocutionist's annual. 3 nos. 16°. '73–'75. ea., 75c., (?) *Daughaday.*
Elopements in high life. Sulivan, R. 15c... *French.*
Eloquence a virtue. Theremin, F. $1..... *Draper.*
Elsässische Lebensbilder. 18°. '71. 50c.... *Am. Tr.*
Elsie. M., A. C. $1.75................ *Macmillan.*
Elsie, the blind flower girl. 18°. 50c......... *Dutton.*
Elsie and Gatty. *See* My holiday books.
Elsie and Jemmy. 18°. 40c................. *Dutton.*
Elsie and Minnie. Boggs, M. L. $1.50.... *Cong. Pub.*
Elsie Bailey. Flint, S. A. 75c........... *Cong. Pub.*
Elsie Dinsmore. Finley, M. F. $1.50........ *Dodd.*
Elsie Earnest (*pseud.*) *See* Scruggs, *Mrs.* M. V.
Elsie Lee. Grey, M. 45c................. *Pres. Bd.*
Elsie Lee. Mallary, M. J. $1.25.......... *Am. Bapt.*
Elsie Lee. *See* New holiday lib.
Elsie Magoon. Gage, F. D. $1.50...... *Lippincott.*
Elsie Venner. Holmes, O. W. $2.......... *Osgood.*
Elsie Wood; [also] Forgiven. ill. 18°. '72. 50c. *Lothrop.*
— *See also* Little folks ser.
Elsie Wood lib. 6 v. ill. 24°. $1.80........ *Lothrop.*
Cont.: Elsie Wood. — Forgiven. — Light in the window. — Naomi's home. — Neddie and Maggie. — The prize.
Elsie's choice; by author of "May's garden." ill. 12°. $1.50 .... *Nelson.*
Elsie's dowry. Leslie, E. $1............... *Nelson.*
Elsie's expedition. Weatherley, F. E. $1.25. *Scribner, W. & A.*
Elsie's girlhood. Finley, M. F. $1.50........ *Dodd.*
Elsie's holidays at Roselands. Finley, M. F. $1.50. *Dodd.*
Elsie's married life. 8°. pap., 75c......... *Peterson.*
Elsie's Santa Claus. Mathews, J. H. $1.25.. *Carter.*

Elsie's womanhood. Finley, M. F. ill. 16°. '75. $1.5[illegible] *Dodd*
Elster's folly. Wood, E. P. $1.75; $1.50.. *Peterson*
Elton, C. A. Specimens of the Gk. and Roman classi[cal] poets; tr. into Eng. verse, with biog. and cri[tical] notices. 3 v. cr. 8°. $6.......... *Lippincott.*
Elton Wheatley. *See* Derby, E.
Elverly series. 4 v. 16°. $5.......... *H. A. Young*
Cont.: Stones and diamonds, by Mrs. E. E. Boyd. — Scho[ol] girls of Elverly. — Spirit in prison, by C. F. Guernsey. — Lam[p] Felix, by G. Bruce.
Elves (The). Tieck, L. 50c.............. *Harper*
Elwell, E: H. Portland [Me.] and vicinity. ill. 8[°] '76. $1.50; $2............... *Loring, S. & B*
Elwell, J: J. Malpractice and med. evidence; compr[ising] elements of med. jurisprudence. 3d ed., rev. an[d] enl. 8°. shp., $7.50.. *Baker, V. & Co.; Ingham*
Elwes, Alfr. French and English dictionary. 8[°] (Lond.) $1.50......................... *Wiley*
— Italian, French and English dictionary. fp. 8[°] (Lond.) $3.......................... *Wiley*
— Paul Blake. *See* Hazen, J. A., Five years befor[e] the mast.
— Spanish and English dictionary. 12°. (Lond.) $2 *Wiley*
— Swift and sure; or, the career of two brothers. il[l.] 12°. $1.50........................... *Nelson*
Elwood, Ja. L. Grain tables. ('64.) New ed. 12[°] '76. $1.25........................ *Darrow*
Ely, Ez. Styles, *and* Thomas, A. C. Discussion o[n] universal salvation. 16°. 65c...... *Williamson*
Elz, A. Er ist nicht eifersüchtig; [also] Der Weiber feind, v. R. Benedix; [also] Im Wartesalon erste[r] Klasse, v. H. Müller. ('70.) New ed. 12[°] '75. pap., 50c......................... *Holt*
Elze, K: F: Essays on Shakespeare; tr. from the Germ. 8°. '74. $4...................... *Macmillan*
— Lord Byron: biog., with essay on his place in literature; tr. 8°. '72. $6.50...... *Scribner, W. & A*
Emancipation of faith. Schedel, H. E. $4... *Appleton*
Emanuel, Harry. Diamonds and precious stones their hist., value and characteristics, with tests o[f] identification and table of present value. ill. 8[°] '73. $2.75.......................... *Putnam*
Ember hours. Heygate, W. E. $1.25 .... *Pott*
Emblems from Eden. *See* Hamilton, J.
Embury, *Mrs.* E. C. Blind girl (The), and other tales 18°. 75c............................ *Harper*
— Pictures of early life; or, sketches of youth. 18[°] 75c. .... *Harper*
Emden, W. S. Head of the family: comedietta. 16[°] pap., 15c. .... *French*
— Love's labyrinth: comedietta. 16°. pap., 15c. *French*
Emerald (The). ill. 16°. $1........... (?) *Luth. Pub*
Emerald (The). [S.-school hymn book.] sq. 16[°] '72. 40c.......................... *So. Meth*
Emerald (The); or, book of Irish melodies. 16[°] bds., 50c.......................... *Dick & F*
Emerald (The); or, wearing-of-the-green songster. 18[°] 40c.; pap., 20c. .... *Sadlier*
Emerald ser. 3 v. 24°. ea., 50c.; pap., 25c. *Routledge*
Cont.: Moore's Irish melodies. — Moore's Lalla Rookh. — Byron's Don Juan.
Emergencies, and how to treat them. Howe, J. W $3 .... *Appleton*
Emerson, F: National arithmetic. 3 pts. 16°. 1 15c.; 2, 50c.; 3, 95c.; — Key to pts. 2–3, 50c. *Mason*
Emerson, G. R. London, and how the great cit[y] grew. 12°. $1.25................. *Routledge*
Emerson, G: B. Report on the trees and shrubs o[f] Mass. 2d ed. 2 v. 148 pl. 8°. '75. $12; — with 36 col. pl., $20............ *Little, B. & Co*
— *See also* Potter, A., *and* Emerson, G. B.

merson, G: B., *continued*.
- *and* Flint, C: L. Manual of agriculture for the school, the farm, etc. 12°. $1.50....... *Ware*.

merson, Irving. Song land; for schools, etc. obl. 12°. bds., 50c. .... *Brown & G.*
- Song tablet. obl. 12°. bds., 50c....... *Brown & G.*

merson, Jos. Biblical outline: view of Scripture hist., doctrines and duties. maps. 16°. '33. pap., 25c.......................... *Crocker*.
- Evangelical primer. 18°. '44. pap., 12c... *Crocker*.
- *See also* Marsh, J:

merson, L. O. Chants and responses. obl. 8°. '73. bds., $1.......................... *Ditson*.
- Cheerful voices: songs, duets, etc., for juv. classes. obl. 12°. '72. bds., 50c............... *Ditson*.
- Choral tribute: church music for choirs, etc. obl. 8°. '69. bds., $1.50................... *Ditson*.
- Chorus book: oratorio and opera choruses, glees, etc. 8°. '76. bds., $1.25.............. *Ditson*.
- Collection of music adapted to the Prot. Episc. Church. obl. 8°. '73. bds., 75c......... *Ditson*.
- Encore (The): collection of secular and sacred music. obl. 8°. '76. bds., 75c. .... *Ditson*.
- Golden harp: hymn-tunes and choruses. obl. 12°. '58. bds., 35c.; pap., 30c.............. *Ditson*.
- Golden wreath: melodies for schools. obl. 12°. '57. bds., 50c. .... *Ditson*.
- Greeting: glees, quartettes and choruses. obl. 8°. '67. bds., $1.50...................... *Ditson*.
- Harp of Judah: collection of sacred music. obl. 8°. '63. bds., $1.50...................... *Ditson*.
- Jubilate (The): collection of sacred music. obl. 8°. '66. bds., $1.50...................... *Ditson*.
- Merry chimes: songs, duets, etc., for juv. classes. obl. 16°. '65. bds., 50c............... *Ditson*.
- National chorus book: oratorios and opera choruses. 8°. '71. bds., $1.50.................. *Ditson*.
- Salutation (The): collection of sacred music. obl. 8°. '76. bds., $1.38.................. *Ditson*.
- Singing school: collection of music with course of element. study. obl. 8°. '71. bds., 75c... *Ditson*.
- *See also* Palmer, H. R., *and* Emerson, L. O.
- *and* Mathews, W. S. B. Emerson method for reed organs: progressive lessons. obl. 4°. '72. bds., $2.50.............................. *Ditson*.
- *and* Morey, J. H. Sabbath guest: anthems, sentences, etc. obl. 8°. '70. bds., $1.50.. *Ditson*.
- *and* Palmer, H. R. Standard (The): collection of sacred and secular music. obl. 8°. '72. bds., $1.50 .... *Ditson*.
- *and* Starkweather, L. B. Glad tidings: hymns and music, for S.-schools. obl. 12°. '69. bds., 35c.; pap., 30c............................ *Ditson*.
- *and* Tilden, W. S. American school music reader. 3 bks. 16°. '73–'74. bds., 1, 35c.; 2, 50c.; 3, with app., 50c. .... *Ditson*.
- — High school choir: studies and recreations for adv. sing. classes. obl. 8°. '75. bds., $1.... *Ditson*.
- — Hour of singing. obl. 12°. '71. bds., $1.. *Ditson*.

merson, N. A. Arithmetic. 3 pts. 12°. hf. roan, 1, 15c.; 2, 50c.; 3, 95c. — Key to pts. 2, 3. 12°. 50c. .... *Lippincott*.

merson, *Mrs.* N. S. Betsey and I are out. [Poem.] 12°. $1.50........................ *Carleton*.

Note. Mrs. Emerson disputes the authorship of this with Will Carleton, under whose name it was first published, and to whom it is generally attributed.

- — *See also* Carleton, Will, Farm ballads.
- Little folks' letters. 12°. $1.50.......... *Carleton*.

merson, Ralph Waldo. Works. 10 v. 16°. '46–'75. ea., $1.50; per set, hf. cf., $30; cf., $40.. *Osgood*.

Cont.: Conduct of life. — English traits. — Essays, 2 v. — Letters and social aims. — May-day and other pieces. — Miscellanies. — Poems. — Representative men. — Society and solitude.

- *Same*. (Little classic ed.) [To form 9 v.] v. 1–4. 18°. '76. ea., $1.50.................. *Osgood*.

Cont.: Conduct of life. — Essays, 1st ser. — Miscellanies. — Society and solitude.

Emerson, Ralph Waldo, *continued*.
— Culture, behavior, beauty. [Essays.] (Vest-pock. ser.) 32°. '75. 50c.................... *Osgood*.
— Essays. (Blue and gold ed.) 32°. '65. $1.25; hf. cf., $2.50; mor., $3................ *Osgood*.
— Letters and social aims. 12°. hf. cf., $3... *Osgood*.
— Poems. (Blue and gold ed.) 32°. $1.25; hf. cf., $2.50; mor., $3....................... *Osgood*.
— Power, wealth, illusions. [Essays.] (Vest-pock. ser.) 32°. '75. 50c................. *Osgood*.
— Prose works. ('69.) 8th ed. 2 v. 12°. $5; hf. cf., $9; mor., $12.......................... *Osgood*.
— Society and solitude. 12°. hf. cf., $3...... *Osgood*.
— (*ed.*) Parnassus: collection of poetry, with pref. essay. 8°. '74. $4; hf. cf., $7.50; mor., $10. *Osgood*.
— *See also* Winter poems.

Emerson, W. R. Putkins, heir to castles in the air: comic drama. 16°. pap., 15c.......... *Lee & S.*

Emerson, W: A. Practical instruction in wood engraving; [with] hist. of the art. ill. 16°. '76. pap., 50c. .... *C. J. Batcheller*.

Emery, C. E. Compound engines, etc. *See* Croes, J. J. R., Memoir of construction, etc.

Emery, *Miss* E. B. Queens. [Fiction.] 16°. '63. $1.50 .... *Estes*.

Emery, G: F. *See* United States, Dist. Court reports.

Emery, M. Pilgrimage of grace: tale of the days of Henry VIII.; from the Fr. 12°. $2..... *O'Shea*.

Emery, S. E. Uncle Rod's pet. 16°. 75c..... *Dutton*.

Emery, *Miss* Sa. A. Three generations. [Fiction.] 8°. $1.50; pap., $1...................... *Lee & S.*

Emigrant children; or, learning to follow Jesus. ill. 16°. '72. $1.25....................... *Lothrop*.

Emigrant squire. Myers, P. H. 50c....... *Peterson*.

Emigrant's lost son. Wall, G. H. 50c.... *Routledge*.

Emigrant's mother. *See* Bradley, *Mrs.* M. E., Good girl's lib.

Emigrant's quest. 18°. 40c................ *Dutton*.

Emigrant's son. ('66.) New ed. ill. 18°. '74. 40c. *Hoyt*.

Emigrant's story. Trowbridge, J. T. $1.50; $3; $4. *Osgood*.

Emigrants (The). *See* Carleton, W:

Emilia Galotti. *See* Lessing, G. E.

Emilia Wyndham. Marsh-Caldwell, A. 75c... *Harper*.

Emilie, the peace-maker. *See* Geldart, *Mrs.* T.

Emilie de Coulanges. *See* Edgeworth, M.

Emily, the waiting-maid. 18°. 40c........ *Cong. Pub.*

Emily; or, the lessons of a summer. 18°. 35c. *Cong. Pub.*

Emily and Clara's trip to Niagara Falls. *See* Casket of juveniles.

Emily and her cousin. 18°. 60c.; 70c..... *Am. Bapt.*

Emily and Uncle Hanse. Baker, S. S. 45c... *Am. Tr.*

Emily Ashton. Lee, M. E. $1.10........... *Am. Tr.*

Emily Chester. Seemuller, A. M. $2...... **Osgood*.

Emily Douglas. 16°. '69. $1.25.......... *Randolph*.

Emily Gray and her kind aunt. 18°. 50c.... *Pres. Bd.*

Emily Herbert. *See* New juvenile lib.

Emily Maria. Elliot, S. H. 25c........... *Am. Tr.*

Emily Milman. *See* Katie Johnstone's lib.; — Sister's lib.

Emily Sherwood. Dunning, A. K. 30c..... *Pres. Bd.*

Emily Somerville; [also] Little boy of Bethlehem. 32°. 25c.......................... *Pres. Bd.*

Emily Tappan; or, first impressions of God. 18°. 50c. *Cong. Pub.*

Emily Vernon. Drummond, *Mrs.* —. 75c.... *Carter*.

Emily's bracelet; or, the wedding present. ('69.) New ed. ill. 16°. '74. 75c..................... *Hoyt*.

Emily's choice. *See* N., E. V.

Eminent orators of France. ill. 12°. $1.25..*Lippincott.*
Eminent women of the age; by J. Parton, H. Greeley, T. W. Higginson and others. ill. 8°. '68. *$3.50; $4; mor., $6.50..........*Betts.*
Emma (*pseud.*) Out at sea; or, from Boston to Ceylon. 18°. 55c..........*Pres. Bd.*
Emma. Abbott, J. 90c..........*Harper.*
Emma. *See* Austen, Jane.
Emma, the child that Jesus called. 18°. 40c...*Dutton.*
Emma Allen; or, the Lord's prayer in daily life. 18°. 50c..........*Pres. Bd.*
Emma Alston; or, the new life. 18°. 60c...*Am. S. S.*
— *Same.* 16°. 90c..........*Am. Bapt.*
Emma and her nurse. 18°. 40c..........*Am. S. S.*
Emma and Maria; or, the mother's legacy. 18°. 20c.; 25c..........*Am. Bapt.*
Emma De Lissau. 12°. 90c..........*McCauley.*
Emma Gray; or, humble ways of doing good. 18°. 60c..........*Cong. Pub.*
Emma Herbert; or, be ye perfect. 18°. 60c...*Pres. Bd.*
— *See also* Choice little lib.
Emma Marble and her cousin. 18°. 90c...(?) *Martien.*
Emma Parker; or, scenes in the homes of the city poor; by author of "Witnessing for Jesus." 16°. '72. $1.50..........*Randolph.*
Emma von Finkenstein. *See* Schmid, C. v.
Emma Walton. Dupuy, E. A. 50c..... *U. P. James.*
Emma Welford. *See* Gem cluster.
Emma Wilfred. 18°. 90c..........*Cong. Pub.*
Emmanuel Dannan. 18°. 40c..........*Dutton.*
Emma's pilgrimage. Wildermuth, O. $1.25. *Cin. Meth. Bk. Conc.*
Emma's visit. 18°. 20c..........*Cong. Pub.*
Emmerich, Anna Kath. Das bittere Leiden Jesu Christi. 12°. $1.25..........*Benziger.*
— *Eng.* Sufferings of Jesus; tr. by a Sister of Mercy. 18°. 60c..........*O'Shea.*
Emmet, T: Addis. Vesico-vaginal fistulæ, from parturition and other causes; with cases of recto-vaginal fistula. ill. 8°. $2.75.......... *W. Wood.*
Emmett, Dan. D. Hard times: extravaganza. 12°. pap., 15c..........*De Witt.*
— *See also* Bruce, G. B., *and* Emmett, D. D.
Emmons, Eb. American geology: principles of the science; with biog. of author. 3 v. maps and pl. 8°. '55. hf. shp., $5..........*Munsell.*
— Manual of geol. ('60.) 2d ed. ill. 12°. $1.25..*Barnes.*
— *See also* New York geol. survey; — North Carolina geol. and nat. hist. survey.
Emmons, Natl. Platform of ecclesiast. government. *See* Cambridge [Mass.] platform.
— Works. 6 v. por. 8°. ea., $4..........*Cong. Pub.*
Emmons, S. Bulfinch. Bible dictionary; with brief compend. of hist. [of Christ] and his apostles and evangelists. 18°. '41. 65c...*Universalist.*
— Book of promises; or, the Universalist's pocket companion. 32°. '40. 60c..........*Universalist.*
— The spirit land. 16°. $1.25..........*J. E. Potter.*
Emmore. *See* Austin, C.
Emory, *Bp.* J: Defense of our fathers. 8°. '38. $1. *Meth. Bk. Conc.*
— Episcopal controversy and defense. 8°. $1.20. *Meth. Bk. Conc.*
— Episcopal controversy reviewed. 8°. '38. 90c. *Meth. Bk. Conc.*
— Life and works. 8°. $3 ....*Cin. Meth. Bk. Conc.*
Emory, Rob. History of discipline of the Meth. Episc. Church; rev. to 1864. 12°. $1.50..*Meth. Bk. Conc.*
— Life of Bp. Emory. 8°. '41. $1.75 ..*Meth. Bk. Conc.*
Emotional expressions of man. Darwin, C. R. $3.50; $6 ....*Appleton.*
Empire city (The). Lippard, G. 75c.......*Peterson.*
Empire of the mother over the character and destiny of the race. Wright, H. C. 75c.; 50c......*Colby.*
Employment seeker's guide. 12°. pap., 25c...*Haney.*
Empress Eugenie's boudoir. Reynolds, G. W. M. 50c. *De Witt.*
Empress Josephine. Mundt, C. M. $1.50; $1; $3.50. *Appleton.*
Empress of the isles; or, the lake bravo: romance of Canad. struggle in 1837. 8°. pap., 25c. *U. P. James.*
Empty cage. ill. 32°. '60. 30c..........*Am. Tr.*
Empty crib. Cuyler, T. L. $1..........*Carter.*
Empty heart. Harland, M. $1.50..........*Carleton.*
En avant, messieurs. Mathias, G. H. D. $1..*Claxton.*
Enault, L: Woman of honor; tr. by Mrs. C. P. Tutt. 8°. pap., 75c..........*Peterson.*
Note. Formerly pub. under title of "Pupil of the legion of honor."
Enchanted beauty. Elder, W. $1.25...*J. E. Potter.*
Enchanted keys, and other Oriental tales; with introd. by Miss Pardoe. ill. 12°. '59. $1.50; $2. *Kelly, P. & Co.*
Note. Formerly pub. under titles of "One thousand and one days," and of "Hassan Abdallah."
Enchanted plants. Montolieu, J. I. P. 35c. *U. P. James.*
Enchanted princess. Nauman, M. D. $1...*Claxton.*
Enchanted wood: extravaganza. 16°. pap., 15c. *French.*
Enchanting and enchanted. Hackländer, F. W. $1.25. *Lippincott.*
Enchanting fairy lib. 5 v. ill. 12°. $6.25..*Lippincott.*
Cont.: Princess and goblin. — Enchanting and enchanted. — Seaside and fireside fairies. — Eastern fairy legends. — Eva's adventures; The merman.
Enchantress (The). *See* Hager, J. M.
Enchiridion. *See* Luther, M.
Encombe stories. Adams, H. C. $1.75. *Scribner, W. & A.*
Encore (The). Emerson, L. O. 75c..........*Ditson.*
Encouragements to faith. Kimball, J. W. 75c. *Willard.*
Encyclopædia Britannica. *See* Baynes, T. S.
Encyclopedia of chemistry. [To form 40 pts.] pts. 1–6. ill. 8°. ea., pap., 50c..........*Lippincott.*
Encyclopedia of popular songs. 18°. $1.25..*Dick & F.*
End of controversy controverted. Hopkins, J. 2 v. $2..........*Claremont.*
End of religious controversy. *See* Milner, J:
End of the tether: drama. 16°. pap., 15c....*French.*
End of the world. Eggleston, E. $1.50.......*Judd.*
Ende, H: Mississippi und Rhein: Centennial Phantasie. 8°. '76. 75c.; pap., 30c.; 50c. *Doerflinger.*
Ende gut, Alles gut. *See* Shakespeare, W.
Endicott, C. M. Account of Leslie's retreat. 8°. '56. pap., 25c..........*Essex.*
— Account of the piracy of the ship "Friendship," of Salem, in 1831. 8°. '58. pap., 15c.......*Essex.*
— History of Salem and Danvers aqueduct. 8°. '60. pap., 15c..........*Essex.*
Endless amusement: riddles, charades, etc. ill. 12°. pap., 30c..........*Happy.*
Endless misery examined and refuted. Williamson, J. D. 75c..........*Williamson.*
Endlich, J: Liturgische Gesänge zum luther. Hauptgottesdienste. obl. 4°. pap., 25c. *Brobst; Kohler.*
Endymion. Brough, W. 15c..........*French.*
Enfants, louez le Seigneur! [Cath. prayer book.] 48°. *net*, 15c.; 21c..........*Benziger.*
Engedi. Beethoven, L. van. $1; 75c.......*Gordon.*
Engel, C: Musical instruments. ill. cr. 8°. '75. $1. *Scribner, W. & A.*
Engelbrecht, J. C. Materia musica; or, materials for the pianist. 12°. '68. 75c..........*Ditson.*

Engelhardt, F: J. American rowing almanac. 24°. '74. 50c. . . . . *Turf, F. & F.*

Engelke, Lp. Concordia: Sammlg. vierstimmiger Männerchöre mit deutschem u. engl. Text. nos. 1-6. obl. 4°. ea., pap., 50c.; — eingelne Stimmlefte. ea., pap., 25c. . . . . *Schäfer.*

Engelman, C: P. *See* Seiss, J. A., *and* Engelman, C. P.

Engelmann, G. Botany. *See* Ives, J. C., Report on Colorado River.

Engelmann, H: *See* Illinois geol. survey.

Engine room (The): who should be in it, and what they should do; also, applic. of indicator to marine engines; by an old hand. ill. 8°. $1.50. . . . *Spon.*

Engineer (The). Abbott, J. 90c. . . . . *Harper.*

England. Acts of Parliament. *See below* Law reports.

— Chancery reports; ed., with notes and ref. to Am. law and subsequent Eng. decisions, by J. C. Perkins. 23 v. 8°. shp., $92. . . . . . . *Little, B. & Co.*

Cont.: Macnaghten and Gordon, 3 v. ('49-'51), $12. — De Gex, Macnaghten and Gordon, 8 v. ('51-'57), $32. — De Gex and Jones, 4 v. ('57-'59), $16. — De Gex, Fisher and Jones, 4 v. ('59-'62), $16. — De Gex, Jones and Smith, 4 v. ('62-'65), $16.

— *Same.* 1815-'22; by H. Maddock. 6 v. in 3. 8°. '29. $15. . . . . *Kay; T. & J. W. Johnson.*

— — Supplement to Vesey's Chancery reports, during time of Lord Chancellor Hardwicke; by R. Belt. 8°. shp., $4.50. . . . . *Kay.*

— Common law reports: reprint of cases decided in the Courts of King's and Queen's Bench (1819-'65); Court of Common Bench (1813-'65); Court of Nisi Prius (1814-'49). 118 v. 8°. $515; ea., $4 -$5. . . . . *T. & J. W. Johnson.*

Cont.: 1. 1813-'16, by W. P. Taunton (v. 5, 6). — 2. 1816-'17, by W. P. Taunton (v. 7); 1814-'16, by T. Starkie (v. 1). — 3. 1815-'17, by F. L. Holt; 1820-'22, by T. Starkie (v. 2, 3). — 4. 1813-'16, by C. Marshall (v. 1, 2); 1817-'19, by J. B. Moore (v. 1, 2, 3); 1817-'19, by W. P. Taunton (v. 8). — 5. 1819-'20, by R. V. Barnewall and E. H. Alderson (v. 3); 1819-'20, by W. J. Broderip and P. Bingham (v. 1); 1818-'19, by N. Gow. — 6. 1820-'21, by R. V. Barnewall and E. H. Alderson (v. 4); 1820-'21, by W. J. Broderip and P. Bingham (v. 2). — 7. 1821-'22, by R. V. Barnewall and E. H. Alderson (v. 5); 1821-'22, by W. J. Broderip and P. Bingham (v. 3). — 8. 1822-'23, by R. V. Barnewall and C. Creswell (v. 1); 1822-'24, by P. Bingham (v. 1). — 9. 1823-'24, by R. V. Barnewall and C. Creswell (v. 2); 1824-'25, by P. Bingham (v. 2). — 10. 1824-'25, by R. V. Barnewall and C. Creswell (v. 3, 4). — 11. 1825, by P. Bingham (v. 3); 1825-'26, by R. V. Barnewall and C. Creswell (v. 5). — 12. 1825-'27, by F. A. Carrington and J. Payne (v. 1, 2). — 13. 1826-'28, by P. Bingham (v. 4); 1826-'27, by R. V. Barnewall and C. Creswell (v. 6). — 14. 1827, by R. V. Barnewall and C. Creswell (v. 7); 1827-'29, by F. A. Carrington and J. Payne (v. 3). — 15. 1828, by R. V. Barnewall and C. Creswell (v. 8); 1828-'29, by P. Bingham (v. 5). — 16. 1822-'26, by A. Dowling and A. Ryland (v. 1-8); 1822-'23, by A. Dowling and A. Ryland (v. 1); 1819-'21, by J. B. Moore (v. 4, 5). — 17. 1829, by R. V. Barnewall and C. Creswell (v. 9); 1837-'38, by J. Manning and A. Ryland (v. 1, 2); 1821-'25, by J. B. Moore (v. 6-10); 1827-'29, by J. B. Moore and J. Payne (v. 1, 2). — 18. 1819, by J. Chitty, jr. (v. 1, 2). — 19. 1829-'30, by P. Bingham (v. 6); 1829-'31, by F. A. Carrington and J. Payne (v. 4). — 20. 1830-'31, by R. V. Barnewall and J. L. Adolphus (v. 1); 1830-'31, by P. Bingham (v. 7). — 21. 1829-'30, by R. V. Barnewall and C. Creswell (v. 10); 1831-'32, by P. Bingham (v. 8); 1823-'26, by E. Ryan and W. Moody. — 22. 1831, by R. V. Barnewall and J. L. Adolphus (v. 2); 1826-'27, by A. Dowling and A. Ryland (v. 1-8); 1827-'30, by W. Moody and B. H. Malkin; 1825-'27, by J. B. Moore (v. 11, 12). — 23. 1832, by R. V. Barnewall and J. L. Adolphus (v. 3); 1832-'33, by P. Bingham (v. 9). — 24. 1832-'33, by R. V. Barnewall and J. L. Adolphus (v. 4); 1831-'33, by F. A. Carrington and J. Payne (v. 5). — 25. 1833-'34, by P. Bingham (v. 10); 1833-'35, by F. A. Carrington and J. Payne (v. 6). — 26. 1781-'85, by S. Douglas (v. 3, 4). — 27. 1833-'34, by R. V. Barnewall and J. L. Adolphus (v. 5); 1834-'35, by P. Bingham (New cases, v. 1). — 28. 1834, by J. L. Adolphus and T. F. Ellis (v. 1); 1831-'33, by J. B. Moore and J. Scott (v. 1, 2); 1832-'34, by S. Nevile and W. M. Manning (v. 1, 2, 3). — 29. 1834-'35, by J. L. Adolphus and T. F. Ellis (v. 2); 1835-'36, by P. Bingham (New cases, v. 2). — 30. 1835-'36, by J. L. Adolphus and T. F. Ellis (v. 3); 1833-'34, by J. B. Moore and J. Scott (v. 3, 4); 1834-'35, by S. Nevile and W. M. Manning (v. 4); 1835-'36, by J. Scott (v. 2). — 31. 1835-'36, by J. L. Adolphus and T. F. Ellis (v. 4, 5). — 32. 1836-'37, by P. Bingham (New cases, v. 3); 1835-'37, by F. A. Carrington and J. Payne (v. 7). — 33. 1837, by J. L. Adolphus and T. F. Ellis (v. 6); 1837-'38, by P. Bingham (New cases, v. 4). — 34. 1837-'38, by J. L. Adolphus and T. F. Ellis (v. 7); 1837-'39, by F. A. Carrington and J. Payne (v. 8). — 35. 1838, by J. L. Adolphus and T. F. Ellis (v. 8); 1838-'39, by P. Bingham (New cases, v. 5). — 36. 1839, by J. L. Adolphus and T. F. Ellis (v. 9); 1835-'36, by S. Nevile and W. M. Manning (v. 5, 6); 1836-'37, by S. Nevile and T. E. Perry (v. 1); 1836-'37, by J. Scott (v. 3, 4). — 37. 1839, by J. L. Adolphus and T. F. Ellis (v. 10); 1839-'40, by P. Bingham (New cases, v. 6). — 38. 1839-'41, by F. A. Carrington and J. Payne (v. 9); 1835-'36, by E. E. Deacon. — 39. 1839-'40, by J. L. Adolphus and T. F. Ellis (v. 11); 1840, by J. Manning and T. C. Granger (v. 1). — 40. 1840-'41, by J. L. Adolphus and T. F. Ellis (v. 12); 1840-'41, by J. Manning and T. C. Granger (v. 2). — 41. 1841, by J. L. Adolphus and T. F. Ellis (New ser., v. 1); 1840-'42, by F. A. Carrington and J. R. Marshman. — 42. 1841-'42, by J. L. Adolphus and T. F. Ellis (New ser., v. 2); 1841-'42, by J. Manning and T. C. Granger (v. 3). — 43. 1842-'43, by J. L. Adolphus and T. F. Ellis (New ser., v. 3); 1842, by J. Manning and T. C. Granger (v. 4). — 44. 1843, by J. Manning and T. C. Granger (v. 5). — 45. 1843, by J. L. Adolphus and T. F. Ellis (New ser., v. 4). — 46. 1843-'44, by J. Manning and T. C. Granger (v. 6). — 47. 1844, by F. A. Carrington and A. V. Kirwan (v. 1). — 48. 1843-'44, by J. L. Adolphus and T. F. Ellis (New ser., v. 5). — 49. 1844, by J. Manning and T. C. Granger (v. 7). — 50. 1845, Common Bench (v. 1). — 51. 1844-'45, by J. L. Adolphus and T. F. Ellis (New ser., v. 6). — 52. 1845-'46, Common Bench (v. 2). — 53. 1845, by J. L. Adolphus and T. F. Ellis (New ser., v. 7). — 54. 1846-'47, Common Bench (v. 3). — 55. 1846, by J. L. Adolphus and T. F. Ellis (New ser., v. 8). — 56. 1847, Common Bench (v. 4). — 57. 1847-'48, Common Bench (v. 5). — 58. 1846-'47, by J. L. Adolphus and T. F. Ellis (New ser., v. 9). — 59. 1847, by J. L. Adolphus and T. F. Ellis (New ser., v. 10). — 60. 1848, Common Bench (v. 6). — 61. 1844-'49, by F. A. Carrington and A. V. Kirwan (v. 2). — 62. 1849, Common Bench (v. 7). — 63. 1847-'48, by J. L. Adolphus and T. F. Ellis (New ser., v. 11). — 64. 1848, by J. L. Adolphus and T. F. Ellis (New ser., v. 12). — 65. 1849, Common Bench (v. 8). — 66. 1848-'49, by J. L. Adolphus and T. F. Ellis (New ser., v. 13). — 67. 1850, Common Bench (v. 9). — 68. 1849, by J. L. Adolphus and T. F. Ellis (New ser., v. 14). — 69. 1850, by J. L. Adolphus and T. F. Ellis (New ser., v. 15). — 70. 1851, Common Bench (v. 10). — 71. 1851, by J. L. Adolphus and T. F. Ellis (v. 16). — 72. 1852-'53, by T. F. Ellis and C. Blackburn (v. 1). — 73. 1852, Common Bench (v. 11). — 74. 1853, Common Bench (v. 12). — 75. 1853, by T. F. Ellis and C. Blackburn (v. 2). — 76. 1853, Common Bench (v. 13). — 77. 1854, by T. F. Ellis and C. Blackburn (v. 3). — 78. 1854, Common Bench (v. 14). — 79. 1852, by J. L. Adolphus and T. F. Ellis (New ser., v. 17). — 80. 1854, Common Bench (v. 15). — 81. 1856, Common Bench (v. 16). — 82. 1854-'55, by T. F. Ellis and C. Blackburn (v. 4). — 83. 1852, by J. L. Adolphus and T. F. Ellis (New ser., v. 18). — 84. 1856, Common Bench (v. 17). — 85. 1856, by T. F. Ellis and C. Blackburn (v. 5). — 86. 1856, Common Bench (v. 18). — 87. 1856-'57, Common Bench (New ser., v. 1). — 88. 1856, by T. F. Ellis and C. Blackburn (v. 6). — 89. 1857, Common Bench (New ser., v. 2). — 90. 1857, by T. F. Ellis and C. Blackburn (v. 7). — 91. 1857-'58, Common Bench (New ser., v. 3). — 92. 1857-'58, by T. F. Ellis and C. Blackburn (v. 8). — 93. 1858, Common Bench (New ser., v. 4). — 94. 1859, Common Bench (New ser., v. 5). — 95. 1859, Common Bench (New ser., v. 6). — 96. 1858-'59, by T. F. Ellis, C. Blackburn and F. Ellis. — 97. 1860, Common Bench (New ser., v. 7). — 98. 1860, Common Bench (New ser., v. 8). — 99. 1860-'61, Common Bench (New ser., v. 9). — 100. 1861, Common Bench (New ser., v. 10). — 101. 1861, by W. M. Best and G. J. P. Smith (v. 1). — 102. 1858-'59, by T. F. Ellis and F. Ellis (v. 1). — 103. 1861-'62, Common Bench (New ser., v. 11). — 104. 1862, Common Bench (New ser., v. 12). — 105. 1859-'60, by T. F. Ellis and F. Ellis (v. 2). — 106. 1862-'63, Common Bench (New ser., v. 13). — 107. 1860, by T. F. Ellis and F. Ellis (v. 3). — 108. 1863, Common Bench (New ser., v. 14). — 109. 1863, Common Bench (New ser., v. 15). — 110. 1862, by W. M. Best and G. J. P. Smith (v. 2). — 111. 1864, Common Bench (New ser., v. 16). — 112. 1864, Common Bench (New ser., v. 17). — 113. 1862-'63, by W. M. Best and G. J. P. Smith (v. 3). — 114. 1864-'65, Common Bench (New ser., v. 18). — 115. 1865, Common Bench (New ser., v. 19). — 116. 1863-'64, by W. M. Best and G. J. P. Smith (v. 4). — 117. 1864, by W. M. Best and G. J. P. Smith (v. 5). — 118. 1865, by W. M. Best and G. J. P. Smith (v. 6).

Note. The nos. in ( ) are the v. of the original ed.

— — *See also below* Law reports.

— — Index. *See* Biddle, G. W., *and* McMurtrie, R. C.; — Coventry, T., *and* Hughes, S.

— Court of King's Bench reports; by E. H. East, ed. with notes and ref. by G. M. Wharton. 16 v. in 8. 8°. '45. $30. . . . . *T. & J. W. Johnson.*

— *Same.* 58 Geo. III. — 60 Geo. III.; by R. V. Barnewall and E. H. Alderson. 2 v. in 1. 8°. shp., $6. — 2 v. 8°. shp., $7. . . . . *Baker, V. & Co.*

— Crown cases; reserved for the consideration of, and decided by, the twelve judges of Eng., 1799-1852. v. 4-6. 3 v. 8°. ea., $4. . . . *T. & J. W. Johnson.*

Cont.: 1 (1799-1824), by W. O. Russell and E. Ryan. — 2, 4 (1824-'44), by W. Moody. — 3 (1822-'40), by R. Jebb. — 5, 6 (1844-'52), by S. C. Denison.

Note. v. 1-3 are o. p.

— *Same.* 1837-'44; by W. Moody. v. 2. 8°. $4. *T. & J. W. Johnson.*

England, *continued.*
— *Same.* 1844–'52; by S. C. Denison; with notes to Am. decisions by G. Sharswood. 2 v. 8°. '53. $8.......... *T. & J. W. Johnson.*
— Digest of British statutes. *See* Roberts, S.
— Ecclesiastical reports, 1809–'44. v. 4–7. 4 v. 8°. $18.......... *T. & J. W. Johnson.*

Cont.: 4, by S. Haggard.—5, by S. Haggard and G. Lee.—6, by G. Lee and W. C. Curteis.—7, by W. C. Curteis.

— Exchequer reports, 1825–'65; with Am. notes by J. I. C. Hare, H. B. Wallace, H. Wharton and J. Parsons. 47 v. 8°. ea., $4..... *T. & J. W. Johnson.*

Cont.: 1825, by T. McCleland and E. Younge.—1826–'30, by E. Younge and J. Jervis, 3 v.—1830–'33, by C. Crompton and J. Jervis, 2 v.—1833–'34, by C. Crompton and R. Meeson, 2 v.—1834–'36, by C. Crompton, R. Meeson and H. Roscoe, 2 v.—1836–'47, by R. Meeson and W. N. Welsby, 16 v.—1847–'56, by W. N. Welsby, E. T. Hurlstone and J. Gordon, 11 v.—1856–'61, by E. T. Hurlstone and J. P. Norman, 7 v.—1862–'65, by E. T. Hurlstone and F. J. Coltman, 3 v.

— — *See also below* Law reports.
— — Digest. *See* Fish, A. I.
— High Court of Admiralty reports; commencing with the judgments of Sir W. Scott, Easter term, 1808; by T. Edwards. 8°. '15. $3.. *T. & J. W. Johnson.*
— — Digest. *See* Pritchard, W. T.
— High Court of Chancery select reports, 1724–1733. 2d ed., with notes and ref. by S. Macnaghten. 8°. '51. $2.50.......... *T. & J. W. Johnson.*
— *Same.* 1757–1766; arranged from the orig. MSS. of Lord Chancellor Northington, with notes and ref. by R. H. Eden. 2 v. in 1. 8°. shp., $5.50... *Kay.*
— House of Lords reports of cases upon appeals and writs of error, 1831–'46; by C. Clark and W. Finnelly; ed. with notes and ref. to Am. law by J. C. Perkins. 12 v. 8°. '31–'46. $60. *Little, B. & Co.*
— *Same.* 1847–'66. 11 v. 8°. '66. shp., $55. *Little, B. & Co.*
— — Digest. *See* Harrison, R. T.
— Law reports: decisions of the Eng. courts [with statutes], 1865–'75. [In contin. of Common law reports and Exchequer reports.] 1. Common law series. 39 v. 8°. ea., $5.. *T. & J. W. Johnson.*

Cont.: Queen's Bench reports, 10 v. (1865–'75, by W. Mills and H. Holroyd; Bail Court, by Arthur Wilson, 10 v.)—Common Pleas reports, 10 v. (1865–'70, by J. Scott and H. Bompas, 5 v.; 1870–'75, by J. Scott and E. Lumbey, 5 v.)—Exchequer reports, 10 v. (1865–'74, by J. Anstie and A. Charles, 9 v.; 1874–'75, by J. Anstie, A. Charles, A. P. Stone and J. M. Moorsom, 1 v.)—Admiralty and ecclesiastical reports, 4 v. (1865–'69, by E. Browning, 2 v.; 1869–'75, by Gainsford Bruce, 2 v.)—Probate, divorce and matrimonial reports, 3 v. (1865–'69, by T. H. Tristram, R. Searle and J. G. Middleton, 1 v.; 1869–'75, by R. Searle and J. G. Middleton, 2 v.)—Crown cases reserved reports, 20 v.

— *Same.* 2. Equity series. 30 v. 8°. ea., $5. *T. & J. W. Johnson.*

Cont.: Chancery appeal cases, including bankruptcy and lunacy cases, 10 v.—Equity cases before the Master of the Rolls and the Vice Chancellors, 2 v.

— *Same.* 3. Appellate series. 15 v. 8°. $115. *T. & J. W. Johnson.*

Cont.: Eng. and Irish appeals (House of Lords cases), 7 v. (1866–'70, by C. Clark, 4 v.; 1870–'75, 3 v.)—Privy Council appeals, 6 v. (1865–'71, by E. F. Moore, 3 v.; 1871–'73, 1 v.; 1873–'74, by W. MacPherson, 1 v.; 1874–'75, by Herbert Cowell, 1 v.)—Scotch and divorce appeals, 2 v.

— *Same.* 4. Public general statutes, with list of local and private acts, 1865–'75. 10 v. 8°. $110. *T. & J. W. Johnson.*
— — *See also above* Common law reports; Exchequer reports.
— Reports. *See* Moak, N. C.
England and Rome. Burgon, J. W. $1.25.. *Dutton.*
England and Scotland. *See* Eddy, D. C., Percy family.
England two hundred years ago. Gillett, E. H. $1.50. *Pres. Bd.*
England's antiphon. MacDonald, G. $1.75. *Lippincott; Macmillan.*
England's daybreak: narr. of the reformation; with pref. by E. H. Bickersteth. 16°. '70. $1.50. *Dutton.*
England's yeomen. Charlesworth, M. L. $1.50... *Carter.*
Engles, Jos. P. *See* Bible, New Test., *Greek.*
— *and* Wallace, J. A. Catechism of Scripture history. [Germ.] 4 pts. 18°. ea., 10c.......... *Pres. Bd.*
Engles, W: M. Bible dictionary. 12°. $1.25.. *Pres. Bd.*
— Evening's entertainment; or, a country visit. ill. sq. 16°. 75c.......... *Pres. Bd.*
— Rills from the fountain of wisdom: Book of proverbs arranged and illustrated. 12°. 75c.... *Pres. Bd.*
— Sailor's companion: book of devotions for seamen. 12°. 80c.......... *Pres. Bd.*
— Sick-room devotions. 32°. 30c.......... *Pres. Bd.*
— Soldier's pocket-book. 32°. 10c.......... *Pres. Bd.*
— *Same;* in Germ. 32°. 10c.......... *Pres. Bd.*
— World (The) and its influences. 18°. 50c... *Pres. Bd.*
— (*ed.*) Book of poetry. 12°. $2.......... *Pres. Bd.*
— Records of the Presb. Church in the U. S. [Minutes of the presbyteries and synods of Phila. and N. Y., 1706–1788.] 8°. $2.75.......... *Pres. Bd.*
English, E. H. *See* Arkansas, Digest of statutes; Sup. court reports.
English, T. D. Mormons: drama. 16°. pap., 15c. *French.*
English, W. B. Rosina Meadows: drama. 16°. pap., 15c.......... *French.*
English Alice. ill. 16°. '75. 90c...... *Meth. Bk. Conc.*
English boy. *See* Seaboy's grave.
English Catholic's vade mecum: manual of devotions. 32°. '74. 50c.; roan, 75c.......... *Pott.*
English channel (The). *See* Abbott, Jac, Florence stories.
English classics. *See* Miniature Eng. classics.
English fleet. Dibdin, T. 15c.......... *French.*
English gipsy songs, in Rommany; with metrical Eng. tr. by C. G. Leland, E. H. Palmer and J. Tuckey. 12°. $2.......... *Lippincott.*
English governess. Leonowens, A. H. $1.50.. *Coates.*
English governess. McCrindell, R. 90c... *McCauley.*
English Harry. *See* Mudge, Z. A., Casket lib.; Pure gold ser.
English hearts and hands. Marsh, C. $1.25.. *Carter.*
English humorists. *See* Thackeray, W. M.
English lessons for Eng. people. *See* Abbott, E. A., *and* Seeley, J. R.
English Mary. *See* Pretty little lib.
English men of science. Galton, F. $1.... *Appleton.*
English misrule in Ireland. Burke, T. N. 50c. (?) *Lynch.*
English Nellie; or, glimpses of beggar-life. 18°. 90c. *Cong. Pub.*
English orphans. Holmes, M. J. $1.50.... *Carleton.*
English past and present. *See* Trench, R. C.
English poets: photog. portraits, with biog. and crit. notices. 4°. $10; mor., $15.......... *Appleton.*
English portraits. Sainte-Beuve, C. A. $2.... *Holt.*
English pulpit. 8°. $2.25.......... *Carter.*
English radical leaders. Hinton, R. J. $1.50.. *Putnam.*
English statesmen. Higginson, T. W. $1.50.. *Putnam.*
English traits. Emerson, R. W. $1.50...... *Osgood.*
English travelers and Italian brigands. Moens, W. J. C. $1.75.......... *Harper.*
English universities and the Eng. poor. Rowsell, T. J. $1.......... *Macmillan.*
English versus American bridges. 8°. '74. pap., 25c. *R. R. Gazette.*
English visit of Keshub Chunder Sen; ed. by S. D. Collet. 12°. '71. $3.......... *Routledge.*
Englishman's Greek concordance of the New Test.; with indexes, Gk.-Eng. and Eng.-Gk. 8°. $5; shp., $5.50; hf. cf., $7.25.......... *Harper.*
— *Same.* roy. 8°. (Bagster.) $10.......... *Wiley.*
Englishman's Hebrew and Chaldee concordance of the Old Test.; with indexes, etc. 2 v. 8°. (Bagster.) $25.......... *Wiley.*

Englishman's house is his castle. Morton, J. M. 15c. *French.*

Enigmas of life. Greg, W. R. $2............*Holt.*

Enlisted for life. Feudge, F. R. $1........*Am. Tr.*

Enlisted for the war. Baker, G. M. 15c.....*Lee & S.*

Ennemoser, Jos. History of magic; tr. by W. Howitt, with app. 2 v. 12°. (Bohn.) ea., $1.75. *Little, B. & Co.*

— *Same.* 2 v. 12°. (Bohn.) ea., $2. *Lippincott; Scribner, W. & A.*

Ennis, Jac. Origin of the stars and the causes of their motions and light. 12°. $2...........*Appleton.*

Ennisfellen. Samuels, S. B. C. 75c........*Lee & S.*

Ennui. *See* Edgeworth, M.

Enoch Arden. *See* Tennyson, A.

Enoch Crosby: tale of the revolution. ill. 16°. pap., 25c...........................*U. P. James.*

Enoch Roden's training. ill. 16°. 80c...*Bost. Am. Tr.*

— *See also* Maude Grenville lib.

Enscotidion. Adams, T. A. S. $1.25......*So. Meth.*

Ensign, J. L. Culprit fay: cantata, [with] words from Drake's poem. 8°. '72. bds., $1.......*Ditson.*

Enterprise and adventure lib. 3 v. ill. 16°. $3.75. *Routledge.*

Cont.: Adventures in the ice. — Women of worth. — Famous London merchants.

Enterprise beyond the seas. Fyfe, J. H. $1.50..*Nelson.*

Enterprise lib. *See* Fyfe, J. H.

Entertaining knowledge by popular authors: hist., geog. and nat. hist. ill. 8°. $2......*Routledge.*

Entertaining library. 6 v. 16°. $7......*Am. Bapt.*

Cont.: Jennie Boardman. — Stale bread. — Mick Tracy. — Odd gentleman. — Representative men. — Representative women.

Entertaining library. 4 v. ill. 12°. $5..*Lippincott.*

Cont.: Vicar of Wakefield, by O. Goldsmith. — Ranald Bannerman's boyhood, by G. MacDonald. — Our own birds, etc., by W. L. Baily. — Romance of nat. hist.

Entertaining naturalist. *See* Loudon, *Mrs.* J. W.

Enthoffer, J. Manual of topography, and text-book of topog. drawing. 2 v. text, 8°; atlas, 4°. $15. *Appleton.*

Entire devotion. Palmer, P. 40c..........*Palmer.*

Entranced (The). Lippard, G. 25c.......*Peterson.*

Entrances and exits. Winstanley, E. 60c...*Am. News.*

Envious boy; or, the writing prize. 18°. 17c.; 22c. *Am. Bapt.*

Environs and neighborhood of Jerusalem: 72 views, with letter-press. obl. 24°. 50c.; 75c...*Nelson.*

Eolian songster. 16°. pap., 35c.........*U. P. James.*

Eoline. Hentz, C. L. $1.75; $1.50........*Peterson.*

Eothen. Kinglake, A. W. $1.50............*Mason.*

Eotis (*pseud.*) Cast — king of Granada: drama. 16°. pap., 15c...........................*French.*

Epicurean (The). Moore, T. $1.25.........*Miller.*

Epidemic delusions. Marvin, F. R. 50c. ..*Somerby.*

Epigrams and literary follies. *See* Lippincott's pocket treasuries.

Episcopacy and slavery. Peck, G. 35c. *Cin. Meth. Bk. Conc.*

Episcopal Church. *See* Protestant Episc. Ch.; — Reformed Episc. Ch.

Episcopal common praise: chants, Psalms in metre and hymns; with music. 8°. '69. $2.50; $4.50; $6.50...........................*Barnes.*

Episcopal invitation: "Should I not become an Episcopalian?" answered by a Presbyterian. 18°. 25c...........................*Pres. Bd.*

Episode of the Russian campaign. 18°. 30c.; pap., 15c...........................*O'Shea.*

Episodes and lyric pieces. Weeks, R. K. $1.50..*Holt.*

Episodes in an obscure life. *See* Row, R:

Episodes of the Commune. *See* Catholic premium-book lib.

Epistles. *See* Bible.

Epistles and Gospels for Sundays and festivals. 32°. '69. 25c...................*Kelly, P. & Co.*

Note. See also under names of compilers (and titles) of prayer books.

Epithalamium. *See* Spenser, E.

Epitome de analogía y sintáxis segun la gramatica castellana. 24°. pap., 12½c.........*Appleton.*

Epitome of spiritualism and spirit-magnetism; by author of "Vital magnetic cure." 12°. '76. 60c.; pap., 35c.......................*Colby.*

Epochs of anc. hist. *See* Cox, G. W., *and* Sankey, C.

Epochs of Eng. hist. *See* Creighton, M.

Epochs of hist. *See* Morris, E. E.

Eppendorff, Max. Modesty and merit. ill. sq. 16°. 75c...............................*Fuller.*

Epworth singers. Christophers, S. W. $3..*Randolph.*

Equality: hist. of Lithconia. 18°. pap., 15c...*Mendum.*

Equatorial needle (The). Ross, W. A. 20c...*Spon.*

Er ist nicht eifersüchtig. *See* Elz, A.

Erasmus, Desiderius. In praise of folly; with life of Erasmus and his epistle to More; ill. by Holbein. 8°. hf. mor., $5.50...........*Scribner, W. & A.*

Erbaulisches u. unpartheiisches kleines Handbüchlein. 18°. hf. bd., 25c......................*Baer.*

Erben, Wash. B. Pictorial hist. of books of Bible. *See* Bible [Whole].

Erbschaft (Die). *See* Zschokke, H.

Erckmann, Emile, *and* Chatrian, Alex. Bells (The); tr. from the Fr. [Fiction.] 16°. 75c...*Hinton.*

— — Bells (The); or the Polish Jew; tr. from the Fr.: drama. 12°. pap., 15c...............*De Witt.*

— — Blockade of Phalsburg: episode of the end of the empire; tr. from the Fr. por. and ill. 16°. '71. $1.25; bds., 75c...................*Scribner.*

— — Conscrit (Le) de 1813. With Eng. notes by F. Bôcher. ('67.) New ed. 12°. '76. $1.25..*Holt.*

— — *Eng.* The conscript: story of the French war of 1813. ill. 16°. '69. $1.25; bds., 75c...*Scribner.*

— — Forest house; [also] Catherine's lovers; tr. from the Fr. 16°. '71. $1.50..............*Roberts.*

— — Invasion of France in 1814: the night march of the Russian army past Phalsburg; tr. from the Fr. ill. 16°. '71. $1.25; bds., 75c....*Scribner.*

— — Madame Therese; or, the volunteers of '92; tr. from the Fr. ('68.) New ed. ill. 16°. '69. $1.25; bds., 75c...................*Scribner.*

— — Miller's (A) story of the war; or, the plebiscite; by one of the 7,500,000 who voted yes; tr. from the Fr. ill. 16°. '72. $1.25; bds., 75c...*Scribner.*

— — Waterloo: sequel to "Conscript of 1813;" tr. ill. 16°. '69. $1.25; bds., 75c.......*Scribner.*

Erechtheus. Swinburne, A. C. $2.80. *Scribner, W. & A.*

Erfahrungen eines jungen Predigers. 18°. '63. 25c. *Am. Tr.*

Erfindung (Die) des Porcellans. Nieritz, G. 25c. *Morwitz.*

Eric. Farrar, F. W. $1.75........*Dutton; Mason.*

Eric. Samuels, S. B. C. 75c.............*Lee & S.*

Erich. *See* Hoffmann, F.

Erichsen, J: Eric. Concussion of the spine, nervous shock, and other obscure injuries of the nervous system, in their clinical and medico-legal aspects. 12°. $2.25........................*W. Wood.*

— Science and art of surgery; rev. from 6th Eng. ed. enl. 2 v. ill. 8°. $9; leath., $11.........*Lea.*

Erickson, D. S. Carl Bartlett; or, what can I do? 16°. '69. $1.25................*H. A. Young.*

— Clean your boots, sir? or, Robert Rightheart. 18°. '70. 50c........................*H. A. Young.*

Erickson, D. S., *continued.*
— *Same;* [also] Horace Welford. 16°. $1.25. *H. A. Young.*
— Earl Whiting. 16°. '70. $1.25 .... *H. A. Young.*
— Good measure. ill. 16°. '69. $1.50 ... *H. A. Young.*
— Wadsworth boys. ill. 16°. '72. $1.50 ..... *Lothrop.*
Erin-go-bragh songster. ('74.) 2d ed. 18°. '75. 25c. *Kenedy.*
Erinnerungen aus Deutschland's trübster Zeit. Münch, F. 50c. ..... *Witter.*
Erlenkötter, G. [Lesebücher.] 5 v. 8°.... *Schäfer.*
Cont.: Erstes Lesebüchlein, 10c. — Erstes Lesebüch. d. Elementarschule, 15c. — Zweites Leseb., 40c. — Drittes Leseb., 50c. — Leseb. f. Realschulen (no. 4), 62c.
— Liederbuch f. Schule u. Haus. sm. obl. 4°. 50c. *Schäfer.*
— Mensch u. Natur: Lehrb. gemeinnütziger Kenntnisse. 8°. 90c ..... *Schäfer.*
— Rechenbuch f. deutsche Elementarschulen in Am. 2 pts. 8°. ea., 35c.; — Antwortenheft. 8°. ea., 20c. ..... *Schäfer.*
— Rechenfibel. 4th ed. 8°. 15c. ..... *Schäfer.*
— Zeichnen Vorlagen. 4°. 15c. ..... *Schäfer.*
Erling the bold. Ballantyne, R. M. $1.25 .. *Lippincott.*
Erma's engagement; by author of "Blanche Seymour." 8°. $1.25; pap., 75c. ...... *Lippincott.*
Ermina: pt. 2d of "Juliana Oakley." 18°. 40c. *Am. S. S.*
Erminie. Fleming, M. A. 25c. ..... *Beadle.*
Erna, the forest princess. Nieritz, G. 60c... *Darrow.*
Ernani. Brough, W. 15c. ..... *French.*
Ernani. *See* Verdi, G.
Ernest. 18°. '64. 60c. ..... *Randolph.*
Ernest. *See* Aunty May's children.
Ernest Linwood. Hentz, C. L. $1.75; $1.50 .. *Peterson.*
Ernest Maltravers. *See* Bulwer-Lytton, *Sir* E. G. E. L.
Ernest Maltravers. Medina, L. 15c. ..... *French.*
Ernestine. Robertson, W. 15c. ..... *French.*
Erni, Henri. Mineralogy simplified. *See* Kobell, F. v.
Ernie Elton. Eiloart, C. J. 75c. ..... *Routledge.*
Ernie Elton at home. Eiloart, C. J. 75c... *Routledge.*
Ernie Elton at home and at school. Eiloart, C. J. $1.25. *Routledge.*
Ernie Elton at school. Eiloart, C. J. 75c... *Routledge.*
Ernscliff Hall; or, two days spent with a great aunt: drama. 12°. '73. pap., 25c. .... *Kelly, P. & Co.*
— *Same.* 16°. '74. 20c. ..... *Cath. Pub.*
Ernst, H: Accountant and book-keeper's manual of commercial calculations reduced to their utmost simplicity. 8°. $1.50 ..... *Harper.*
Ernst, O. H. Manual of pract. milit. engineering. woodcuts and lith. pl. 12°. '73. $5 .. *Van Nostrand.*
Ernsthafte Christenpflicht (Die). [Prayers.] 18°. leath., 60c. ..... *Baer.*
Eroberung (Die) v. Mexico. *See* Van der Velde, K. F.
Errand boy (The); or, your time is your employer's. ('63.) 9th ed. ill. 16°. '72. $1.25 .. *Perkinpine.*
Errata of the Protestant Bible. *See* Ward, T.
Errett, I: Fellowship. 8°. pap., 10c. ..... *Chase.*
— First principles; or, the elements of the Gospel analyzed and discussed. 24°. pap., 15c. .... *Chase.*
— Plan of salvation. 8°. pap., 10c. ..... *Chase.*
— Talks to Bereans: 23 sermons, designed as a help for Christians. 12°. $1 ..... *Chase.*
— True basis of Christian union. 12°. pap., 10c... *Chase.*
— Walks about Jerusalem: search after the landmarks of primitive Christianity. 12°. $1 .... *Chase.*
Erring, yet noble. Reed, I. G. $1.50; $1 .... *Loring.*
Errors of the Bible. Wright, H. C. 60c.; 35c... *Colby.*
Errors of Socinianism. Hare, E. 80c... *Meth. Bk. Conc.*
Ersilia. Poynter, E. F. $1.25 ..... *Holt.*
Erskine, E. *See* Fisher, J., *and* Erskine, E.
Erskine, Ralph. Gospel sonnets. 18°. 75c... *Carter.*
Erskine, T: Remarks on the internal evidence for the truth of revealed religion. ('53.) New ed. 16°. '71. 75c. ..... *Draper.*
Erskine, T: (*Lord*). Speeches, while at the bar; with memoir and notes; ed. by J. L. High. ('70.) 2d ed. 4 v. 8°. '76. $12–$18 .... *Callaghan.*
— *Same;* with memoir by E: Walford. 2 v. 8°. $7. *Scribner, W. & A.*
— — *Same.* 2 v. por. 8°. $7.50 ..... *Estes.*
— — *See also* Chatham, *Earl of*, Burke, E., *and* Erskine, T.
Erskine, *Mrs.* T: Wyncote. (Leis. hour ser.) 16°. '75. $1.25 ..... *Holt.*
Erste Blatt (Das) der Bibel. Gaussen, L. 60c.; 80c. *Ev. Assoc.*
Ersten Lilien (Die). 24°. 20c. ..... *Ev. Assoc.*
Erstes Lesebuch f. Sonntagschulen. 12°. '76. bds., 30c. ..... *Ev. Assoc.*
Ervie (*pseud.*) Echo bank. ('67.) New ed. 18°. '75. 85c. ..... *Nat. Temp.*
Erwin u. Elmira. *See* Goethe, J. W. v.
Erzählungen f. d. Jugend. 18°. '53. 35c.... *Am. Tr.*
Erzählungen im Nebel. *See* Zschokke, H.
Erzstufen. *See* Van der Velde, K. F.
Es ist sehr möglich. *See* Zschokke, H.
Escape of the dove. *See* Jude Cain.
Eschenburg, J: J. Classical antiquities: pts. 1–3 of Manual of class. lit.; tr. ill. 8°. $2.25 .. *Fortescue.*
— Manual of classical literature; tr. by Prof. Fiske. 8°. '43. $4.50 ..... *Fortescue.*
Eshelman, M. M. True vital piety; or, non-conformity to the world. 16°. '74. 75c. ...... *Brumbaugh.*
Esmarch, F: Resection in gunshot injuries. *See* Stromeyer, L., Gunshot fractures.
Esmeralda. Ball, E. 15c. ..... *French.*
Esmeralda. Byron, H. J. 15c. ..... *French.*
Esmeralda. Smith, A. 15c. ..... *French.*
Esperanza. Bowman, A. $1.25 ..... *Routledge.*
Espin, T. E. Commentary on Joshua; — on Numbers and Deuteronomy. *See* Cook, F. C., Bible commentary.
Espousals (The). *See* Patmore, C.
Espy, Josiah. Memorandums of a tour in Ohio, Ky. and Indiana Territory in 1805; [also] Two western campaigns in the war of 1812–'13, by S. Williams; [also] The Leatherwood God: account of the appearance and pretensions of J. C. Dilks in eastern Ohio, 1828, by R. H. Taneywell. 8°. '70. $2.50; large pap., $5 ..... *Clarke.*
Esrey, W. P. Treatise on anatomy and physiology. [Hom.] ill. 8°. 75c. ..... *Boericke.*
— — *See also* Caspari, E., Homœopathic dom. physician.
Essay on man. *See* Pope, A.
Essays æsthetical. Calvert, G. H. $1.50 .... *Lee & S.*
Essays and colors of good and evil. *See* Bacon, Fs.
Essays in mosaic. Ballantyne, T. $1.25. *Scribner, W. & A.*
Essays of Elia. *See* Lamb, C.
Essays of an optimist. Kaye, W. $1.50 .. *Lippincott.*
Essays on Eng. writers; for improvement of students in Eng. literature. 16°. $3 .... *Scribner, W. & A.*
Essays on social subjects. 16°. $1.75 .... **Osgood.*
Essence of religion. Feuerbach, L. 75c... *Somerby.*
Essex County [Mass.] Natural History Society. Journal, 1836–'52. 8°. $1; pap., 50c. .... *Essex.*
Note. This Society was afterwards merged into the Essex Institute.
Essex Institute. Bulletin. v. 1–7. 8°. '69–'75. ea., $1. *Essex.*
Note. Issued in continuation of Proceedings.

Essex Institute, *continued.*
— Historical collections. v. 1–8. sm. 4°. '59–'66. ea., $3. — Same. v. 9–13. 8°. '68–'76. ea., $3 .. *Essex.*
Note. v. 1, 5 and 10 are ill.; v. 1–8 form 1st ser., v. 9 — the 2d ser.
— Historical notice, with const., by-laws and lists of officers and members. 8°. '66. pap., 25c... *Essex.*
— Naturalists' directory, 1867–8; ed. by F. W. Perkins. 8°. pap., $1; bd. and interleaved, $2..... *Essex.*
— Proceedings and communications. 6 v. 8°. '48–'68. $24; — in nos., pap., $18................ *Essex.*
Cont.: v. 1, '48–'56, $2. — v. 2, '56–'58, ill., $2. — v. 3, '58–'63, $2. — v. 4, '64–'65, ill., $5. — v. 5, '66–'67, ill., $6. — v. 6, '68–'71, ill., $3.
Note. v. 4, 5 contain also the "Naturalists' directory." After v. 6 suc. by the Bulletin.

Essie Garnet; or, hearing not heeding; by author of "Broken rein." 18°. 50c............ *Am. S. S.*

Essie's journey. Henry, M. H. 75c...... *Cong. Pub.*

Estee, Morris M. Pleadings, practice and forms; in actions, both legal and equitable. 3 v. 8°. '70. shp., $22.50........................ *Bancroft.*

Estelle. Edwards, A. $1.50; $1........... *Sheldon.*

Estelle; or, the conspirator of the isles. 8°. pap., 25c. *De Witt.*

Estelle Russell. *See* Marie Celeste, *Sister.*

Estelle's stories about dogs. ill. 16°. 50c.... *Lee & S.*

Ester Ried. *See* Alden, *Mrs.* I. M.

Estes, Dana (*ed.*) Chimes for childhood. ill. 16°. '68. 60c.; 75c................................ *Estes.*
— Half-hour recreations in popular science. 12 pts. cr. 8°. '74. ea., pap., 25c.; — in 1 v., $2.50 .. *Estes.*
Cont.: Strange discoveries resp. the aurora and recent solar researches, by R. A. Proctor. — Cranial affinities of man and the ape, by R. Virchow. — Spectrum analysis explained. — Spectrum analysis discoveries. — Nebulæ meteoric showers and comets. — Unconscious action of the brain, and epidemic delusions, by W. B. Carpenter. — Geology of the stars, by A. Winchell. — On yeast, by T. H. Huxley. — The stone age past and present, by E. B. Tylor. — Origin of metalliferous deposits, by T. S. Hunt. — Coal as a reservoir of power, by R. Hunt; [also] Atoms, by — Clifford. — Circulation of the waters on the face of the earth, by H. W. Dove.
— *Same.* 2d ser. [To form 12 pts.] pts. 1–4. cr. 8°. ea., pap., 25c. .... *Estes.*
Cont.: Transmission of sound by the atmosphere, by J. Tyndall. — Gigantic cuttle fish, by W. S. Kent. — Glacial epoch of our globe, by A. Braun. — Sun and the earth, by B. Stewart. — Brain and mind, by B. G. Wilder. — Ice age in Great Britain, by A. Geikie.
— Spectrum analysis discoveries; from works of Schellen, Young, Roscoe, Lockyer, Huggins and others. cr. 8°. '74. pap., 25c.................... *Estes.*
— Spectrum analysis explained; abridg. from works of Schellen, Roscoe, Huggins, Lockyer, Young and others. ill. 12°. $1.50.................. *Estes.*

Estes, H. C. Christian doctrine of the soul: essay. 16°. '73. $1.............. *Lockwood, B. & Co.*

Esther. Bradbury, W. B. 50c. — Libretto, 12c. *Ditson.*

Esther. *See* Racine, J.

Esther and her times. Lowrie, J. M. $1... *Pres. Bd.*

Esther de Medina. Reynolds, G. W. M. $1.50. *Dick & F.*

Esther Hudson; or, the dead bride: sequel to "White hand." 8°. pap., 25c.................. *De Witt.*

Esther Maxwell's mistake. Janvier, E. N. $1. *Nat. Temp.*

Esther Parsons. Tucker, C. 50c........... *Carter.*

Esther Stanhope; or, the crowning delight. 18°. 25c. *Scribner, W. & A.*

Esther West. Knox, I. C. $2............... *Cassell.*

Esther's regret. *See* Leslie, E.

Estrella de Belen. 16 nos. 4°. 75c.; pap., 35c... *Am. Tr.*

Estvan, Mathilde. Harry Delaware; or, an American in Germany. 8°. '72. $1............ *Putnam.*

Etchings from the National Gallery; with notes by R. N. Wornum. 18 pl. f°. '76. $10...... *Bouton.*

Eternal day. Bonar, H. 75c................ *Carter.*

Eternal sonship of Christ. Beauchamp, W. 50c. *So. Meth.*

Ethan Hale; or, light at last; by author of "Christie; or, the way home." 18°. 35c......... *Am. S. S.*

Ethel Linton. W., E. A. $1.25.. *Cin. Meth. Bk. Conc.*

Ethel Mildmay's follies; by author of "Petite's romance." 8°. $1.25; pap., 75c........... *Estes.*

Ethel Ripon. *See* Sargent, G. E.

Ethel Seymour. ill. 18°. '74. 40c.......... *Am. Tr.*

Ethel Trevor. Reynolds, G. W. M. 50c..... *De Witt.*

Ethel's gift. Reed, R. P. 20c............... *Am. Tr.*

Ethel's pearls. Washington, N. 80c. .... *Am. Tr.*

Ethel's story; or, the advantages of cheerfulness. ('63.) 7th ed. ill. 18°. '71. 63c........... *Perkinpine.*

Ethel's trials. *See* Guernsey, L. E.

Ethelwerd, F. *See* Giles, J. A., Six old Eng. chronicles.

Ethelyn's mistake. Holmes, M. J. $1.50.. *Carleton.*

Etheridge, J. W. Contemplations on mercy of God. 18°. 50c.................. *Cin. Meth. Bk. Conc.*
— Life of Ad. Clarke. 12°. '59. $1.75.; hf. cf., $2.25 .... *Meth. Bk. Conc.*
— *Same;* rev. by T. O. Summers. 12°. '59. $2. *So. Meth.*

Etheridge, Kelsic. Egypt Ennis; or, prisons without walls. ('75.) 2d ed. 8°. '76. pap., 50c. *Authors.*
— Nine little busters. sm. 4°. '76. 75c.; pap., 25c. *Authors.*
— Slippers and gown. 12°. '75. $1.25...... *Authors.*

Ethics of the dust. Ruskin, J. $1.25; $1.75... *Wiley.*

Ethiopian comicalities. Fox, C. 10c....... *Dick & F.*

Ethnographic atlas: maps with explanations. 4°. (Bagster.) $3.25...................... *Wiley.*

Etiquette and usages of society. 18°. 10c... *Dick & F.*

Etiquette for gentlemen. 32°. 20c........ *Routledge.*
— *Same.* ill. 48°. 25c.............. *Scribner, W. & A.*

Etiquette for ladies. 32°. 20c........... *Routledge.*
— *Same.* ill. 48°. 25c. .... *Scribner, W. & A.*

Etiquette letter-writer for ladies and gentlemen. 16°. bds., 50c.......................... *Lippincott.*

Etiquette of the ball-room; or, the dancer's companion. 16°. pap., 25c.................... *Ditson.*

Etiquette of courtship and matrimony. 32°. 20c. *Routledge.*
— *Same.* ill. 48°. 25c............ *Scribner, W. & A.*

Etiquette of the toilet, [for] ladies and gentlemen. ill. 48°. 25c................. *Scribner, W. & A.*

Etoile du nord. *See* Meyerbeer, G.

Eton boy. Morton, E. 15c................. *French.*

Etruscan researches. Taylor, I. $4..... *Macmillan.*

Etting, Fk. M. History of Independence Hall. heliot. ill. sq. 4°. '76. $5.................... *Osgood.*

Ettrick Shepherd (The). *See* Hogg, J.

Etty, W: Pictures by E.; with letterpress by a critic. f°. '74. $10......................... *Routledge.*

Etymological vocab. of words in the Gk. New Test. fp. 8°. (Bagster.) $1.25; hf. bd., $1.50.. *Wiley.*

Eucharistic year: meditations before and after communion for every day which has a special Epistle and Gospel in the Book of common prayer. 18°. 50c. .... *Pott.*

Eucharistica. Walsh, W. $1............. *Strong.*

Eucharistica: meditations and prayers on the eucharist from the old divines; with introd. by Bishop Wilberforce. 32°. '67. 50c............. *Pott.*

Euclid. [Eucleides.] Elements of geometry: first 6 books, with supplement by J. Playfair. New ed., rev. 8°. hf. roan, $1.75............ *Lippincott.*
— *Same;* [also] 11th and 12th bks. from text of Robt. Simson; with corrections, etc., by R. Wallace. 8°. 75c.............................. *Cassell.*

Eugene, the little rag-picker. *See* Little Blue Mantle lib.

Eugene Aram. *See* Bulwer-Lytton, *Sir* E. G. E. L.

Eugene Aram. Moncrieff, W. T. 15c.......*French.*

Eugene Cooper. Perkins, S. M. $1.15.......*Hoyt.*

Eugenie, *Sister.* *See* Sister Eugenie.

Eulenspiegel (Der). 12°. pap., 20c..........*Radde.*
— *See also* Wiederstandene.

Euler, Leon. Letters on nat. philos. addressed to a German princess, tr. by Hunter; with notes and life by Sir D. Brewster, and add. notes by J. Griscom. 2 v. ill. 18°. $1.50.........*Harper.*

Eumenides. *See* Æschylus.

Eunice Somers. Gale, N. $1..........*Cong. Pub.*

Eunice Somers. Sanford, D. P. $1.........*Dutton.*

Eureka. *See* Ralston, T: N.

Euripides. Ex rec. F. A. Paley; acc. verb. et nom. index. 3 v. 18°. '61. $2.25..........*Harper.*
— Tragedies; lit. tr., with notes, by T. A. Buckley. 2 v. 12°. $3......................*Harper.*

Cont.: 1. Hecuba; Orestes; Phœnissæ; Medea; Hippolytus; Alcestis; Bacchæ; Heraclidæ; Iphigenia in Aulide; Iphigenia in Tauris. — 2. Hercules furens; Troades; Ion; Andromache; Suppliants; Helen; Electra; Cyclops; Rhesus.

— — *Same.* 2 v. 12°. (Bohn.) ea., $1.75. *Little, B. & Co.*
— — *Same.* 2 v. 12°. (Bohn.) ea., $2. *Lippincott; Scribner, W. & A.*
— *Same;* tr. by R. Potter. 3 v. por. 18°. $2.25. *Harper.*
— — [Tragedies, condensed and explained] by W. B. Donne. (Anc. classics for Eng. readers.) 16°. '72. $1............*Lippincott; Little, B. & Co.*
— Alcestis [Gk.]; with notes by J. Milner. 16°. (Weale.) 40c..........................*Allyn.*
— *Same;* with notes by T. D. Woolsey. 12°. $1.25. *Hamersley.*
— Hecuba and Medea [Gk.]; with notes by W. B. Smith. 16°. (Weale.) 60c............*Allyn.*
— Iphigenie in Aulis. *See* Schiller, J. F. v.
— Medea; tr. into Eng. verse by A. Webster. fp. 8°. '68. $1.50......................*Macmillan.*
— *See also* Browning, R., Aristophanes' apology; Balaustion's adventure.

Europäische Geheimnisse. 18°. 75c.........*Radde.*

Europäische Minen u. Gegenminen. *See* Meding, G.

Europe for $2 a day. Sweetser, M. F. 25c...*Osgood.*

Europe viewed through Am. spectacles. Fulton, C. C. $1.75; $1.25.....................*Lippincott.*

European acquaintance. De Forest, J. W. $1.50. *Harper.*

Eurydice: burlesque. 16°. pap., 15c........*French.*

Eusebius *Cæsariensis.* Ecclesiastical history; tr. from the Germ. by C. F. Crusé. 8°. $2.50..*Lippincott.*
— *Same.* 12°. (Bohn.) $1.75.......*Little, B. & Co.*
— *Same.* 12°. (Bohn.) $2. *Lippincott; Scribner, W. & A.*
— *Same:* first book and selections; ed. by F. A. March, with introd. by A. Ballard and notes by W. B. Owen. 12°. $1.75.....................*Harper.*
— *Germ.* Kirchengeschichte; übers. v. F. A. Stroth. 8°. hf. leath., $2.25...............*Volkening.*
— — *See also* Greek ecclesiastical historians.

Eustace and his family. 32°. 40c...*Scribner, W. & A.*

Eustace diamonds. *See* Trollope, Anthony.

Eustace Quentin. Reynolds, G. W. M. $1.75; $1. *Peterson.*

Eustache: drama. 16°. pap., 15c...........*French.*

Eustache Baudin. Courtney, J. 15c........*French.*

Eustachius. *See* Schmid, C. v.

Eustis, W: T., *jr.* Service of praise. [Hymns and tunes.] 8°. '75. $1.50...............*Scribner.*
— *See also* Book of praise.

Eutaw. Simms, W. G. $1.75; 75c.......*Widdleton.*

Euterpia (The). Baxter, J. $1.25........*Crandall.*

Euthanasy. Mountford, W. $2............*Osgood.*

Eutropius. *See* Justin, Nepos, C., *and* Eutropius.

Eva; or, the Swedish Sunday school. ('63.) New ed. ill. 16°. '75. $1.........................*Hoyt.*

Eva and Bertie. ill. 18°. '72. 50c...........*Am. Tr.*

Eva and the fairy tale. *See* Aunty Ray's little lib.

Eva Bruen. Dawson, —. 25c..............*Porter.*

Eva May. 8°. pap., 25c...................*Dick & F.*

Eva Merton. Finley, M. F. 70c. ....*Pres. Bd.*

Eva St. Clair. James, G. P. R. 50c.......*Peterson.*

Evadne. Sheil, R. L. 15c...................*French.*

Evagrius *Scholasticus.* *See* Greek ecclesiastical historians; — Theodoretus.

Evaline: a Catholic tale. 12°. $1.25.........*O'Shea.*

Evan Harrington. Meredith, G. $1.50......*Harper.*

Evangel (The). Coles, A. $6; $10......*Appleton.*

Evangel Wiseman. Ford, S. R. $1.50...*Am. Bapt.*

Evangelical Alliance Conference. History, essays, orations, etc., of 6th Gen. Conf., N. Y., 1873; ed. by P. Schaff and S. I. Prime. por. 8°. $6; shp., $7; hf. cf., $8.50..................*Harper.*

Evangelical Association. Doctrines and discipline. 32°. 30c.; 50c. — Germ. and Eng. ed. 50c.; 75c. *Ev. Assoc.*
— *Germ.* Glaubenslehre und Kirchenordnung der Evangel. Gemeinschaft. 32°. 30c....*Ev. Assoc.*
— Hymn book. 24°. $1.25–$2.75. 12°. $1.50–$2.75. *Ev. Assoc.*

Evangelical economy developed. Potter, T. $1.50. *Wilstach.*

Evangelical Lutheran Church. Christian book of concord; or, symbolical books of the Evang. Luth. Church; tr. from the Germ. and ed. by S. Henkel. 8°. '52. leath., $2.50. — Same. 2d ed., rev. 8°. '54. leath., $3.50..............*Henkel.*
— *See also* Lutheran church.

Evangelical Lutheran Synod of No. Am. Book of worship. 24°. $1–$5. — (Pulpit ed.) 12°. $2–$4. *Duffie.*

Evangeline. *See* Longfellow, H. W.

Evangelisch *or* Evangelisch-lutheranisch. *See* German Evangelical Lutheran.

Evangelisch-lutherischer Gebets-Schatz: Sammlung v. Gebeten Luthers u. anderer; nebst e. Hausgesangbüchlein. ('64.) 12th ed. 8°. '75. $1.60; $3.50..................................*Barthel.*
— *Same:* Der kleine Gebets-Schatz: Auszug, nebst neuen Anhängen. ('70.) 5th ed. 16°. '76. 30c. *Barthel.*

Evangelisch-lutherisches Perikopenbuch. 4°. '76. $1.50; $2.............................*Barthel.*
— *See also* Kirchen-Agende f. ev. luth. Gemeinden.

Evangelische Kinder Harfe für christliche Schulen. 18°. 30c. ....*Pres. Bd.*

Evangelisches Concordienbuch: symbolische Glaubensschriften d. evang.-luth. Kirche. 12°. $125. *Ludwig.*

Evangelisches Gesangbuch u. Viole. 12°. leath., $1.35–$3.25..........................*Ev. Assoc.*
— *Same.* 24°. leath., $1–$2.75...........*Ev. Assoc.*

Evangelist's library. 2 v. 16°.................*Pott.*

Cont.: Catechism, $1.50. — Parochial missions, $1.25.

Evangelists in the church. Headley, P. C. $1.75..*Hoyt.*

Evans, A. Eubule. Curse of immortality. [Poem.] cr. 8°. '73. $2.25.....................*Macmillan.*

Evans, Alb. S. A la California: sketches of life in the Golden State; with introd. by W. H. L. Barnes. ('73.) 3d ed. ill. 8°. '74. $3.50.....*Bancroft.*
— Our sister republic — Mexico. ill. 8°. *$3.; shp., $3.50; hf. mor., $4.50....................*Col. Bk.*

Evans, *Miss* Augusta J. [*now Mrs.* Wilson]. [Novels.] 6 v. 12°. . . . *Carleton.*

Cont.: Beulah, $1.75. — Inez, $1.75. — Infelice, $2. — Macaria, $1.75. — St. Elmo, $2. — Vashti, $2.

Evans, C. A. Southern Methodist hymn and tune book. 12°. bds., 75c. . . . *Burke.*

Evans, C: Biographical sketch of William Penn. 12°. pap., 15c. . . . *Friends Bk. St.*

— Friends in the 17th century. 8°. $2; hf. mor., $2.75. *Friends Bk. St.*

Evans, C: P. Evils of intemperance: essays. 32°. pap., 10c. . . . *Chase.*

Evans, D. M. Landmarks of truth; or, harmony of the Bible with reason and science. ill. 8°. *$3; $3.50; $4.00; mor., $5. . . . *Quak. City.*

Evans, E. *See* Washington territory, Sup. Ct. reports.

Evans, *Mrs.* E. E. Abuse of maternity, through its rejection, and through its unwise acceptance. 12°. $1. . . . *Lippincott.*

Evans, E. P. Abriss der deutschen Literaturgeschichte. ('69.) New ed. 12°. '73. $1.50. . . . *Holt.*

— Progressive Germ. reader, with notes and vocab.; with ref. to Otto's Grammar. ('69.) New ed. 12°. '76. hf. roan, $1.50. . . . *Holt.*

Evans, E. W. Primary elements of plane and solid geometry. 12°. '62. 75c. . . . *Wilson, H. & Co.*

Evans, Hu. Davey. Essay on the episcopate of the Prot. Episc. Ch. in the U. S. 12°. 63c. . . . *McCauley.*

— Treatise on the Christian doct. of marriage. cr. 8°. '70. $1.50. . . . *Hurd & H.*

— Treatise on proceeding in common law courts of Maryland. 2d ed., rev. and enl. 8°. '67. shp., $8. . . . *Cushings & B.*

Evans, J: Ancient stone implement weapons, and armaments of Gt. Brit. ill. 8°. $5; hf. cf., $10. *Appleton.*

Evans, J: M. Children's choir. [S.-school music.] sq. 16°. 18c. . . . *Am. Bapt.*

Evans, Marian. *See* Eliot, George (*pseud.*)

Evans, Owen (Adventures of). *See* Anderdon, W: H., Catholic Crusoe.

Evans, Rob. W. Rectory of Valehead. 18°. $1. . *Dutton.*

Evans, T: Concise account of the Society of Friends. 12°. 40c. . . . *Friends Bk. St.*

— Examples of youthful piety. 12°. 62c. *Friends Bk. St.*

— Exposition of the faith of the Society of Friends. 12°. 75c. . . . *Friends Bk. St.*

— *See also* Evans, W. *and* T.

Evans, W. F. Celestial dawn (The); or, the connection of earth and heaven. 8°. 75c. . . *H. H. Carter.*

— Mental cure; ill. influence of mind on body, in health and disease, and psychol. method of treatment. ('69.) 4th ed. 12°. '75. $1.50. . . . *Colby.*

— Mental medicine: treatise on med. psychology. 16°. '72. 75c. . . . *H. H. Carter.*

— *Same.* ('72.) 3d ed. 12°. '74. $1.25. . . . *Colby.*

— New age (The) and its messenger. 16°. '64. 38c. *H. H. Carter.*

— Soul and body; or, the spiritual science of health and disease. 12°. '76. $1. . . *H. H. Carter; Colby.*

Evans, W: Journal of life and relig. services. 8°. $2.50; shp., $2.75; hf. mor., $3. . *Friends Bk. St.*

— *and* T: (*ed.*) Piety promoted: dying sayings of many of the people called Quakers. 4 v. 12°. $4. . . . *Friends Bk. St.*

Evarts, W: M. Eulogy on S. P. Chase. 8°. pap., 25c. . . . *Hardy.*

Eva's adventures in shadow-land. *See* Nauman, M. D.

Eva's engagement ring. Wilmer, M. E. 90c. *Nat. Temp.*

Eve, Pl. F. Collection of remarkable cases in surgery. 8°. shp., $5. . . . *Lippincott.*

Eve and her daughters. Caulkins, F. M. 30c. . . *Am. Tr.*

Eve of St. Agnes. *See* Keats, J.

Eveleen Wilson. Pilgrim, J. 15c. . . . *French.*

Eveleen Wilson; or, trials of an orphan girl. 8°. pap., 50c. . . . *Peterson.*

Eveleth, S: F. School house architecture: designs, plans, etc. 4°. $6. . . . *Woodward.*

Evelina. Arblay, F. B. d'. $1. . . . *Harper.*

Eveline Mandeville. Addison, A. 25c. . . *U. P. James.*

Evelyn, J: Diary and correspondence. 4 v. ill. 12°. hf. cf., $14; cf., $18; — in 1 v. sm. 8°. $1.75; hf. cf., $3.50. . . . *Appleton.*

— *Same;* ed. by W. Bray. 4 v. por. 12°. (Bohn.) ea., $1.75. . . . *Little, B. & Co.*

— — *Same.* 4 v. por. 12°. (Bohn.) ea., $2. *Lippincott; Scribner, W. & A.*

— — *Same.* (Chandos lib.) 12°. $1.75; hf. cf., $3.75; cf., $5. . . . *Scribner, W. & A.*

— Memoirs, ill. of life and writings, [incl.] diary and sel. of his letters; ed. by W. Bray. 12°. '69. $2.50; hf. cf., $4.50. . . . *Putnam.*

Evelyn Grey; or, flowers thrive in the sunshine. 18°. 30c.; 40c. . . . *Am. Bapt.*

— *Same.* 18°. 85c. . . . *Am. S. S.*

Evelyn Hope, and the game of life. 18°. 40c. *Cong. Pub.*

Evelyn Marston. Marsh-Caldwell, A. 50c. . . *Harper.*

Evelyn Willis at school. 18°. 50c. . . . *Cong. Pub.*

Evelyn's story. Worboise, E. J. $1.75. . . . *Routledge.*

Even grip. *See* Little folks ser.; — Victory.

Evening amusements for every one. Planche, F. d'A. $1.50. . . . *Porter.*

Evening by evening. Spurgeon, C. H. $1.75. *Sheldon; So. Bapt.*

Evening hour ser. 4 v. 16°. $5.50. . . . *H. A. Young.*

Cont.: Frank Sillaby. — Jeanie Darley. — rapper's son. — African trader.

Evening hours with my children. 4°. $1. . . . *Carter.*

Evening hymn. Burns, J. D. 50c. . . . *Nelson.*

Evening hymn. *See* Keble, J.

Evening incense. Macduff, J. R. 25c. . . . *McCauley.*

Evening of life. Chaplin, J. $1.50. . . . *H. A. Young.*

Evening portion. Hawker, R. 75c. . . . *Routledge.*

Evening rest. L., L. $1.50. . . . *Lothrop.*

Evening rest ser. 3 v. 16°. $4.50. . . . *Lothrop.*

Cont.: Evening rest. — Branches of palm. — Broken fetters.

Evening thoughts: daily text-book. 32°. 20c. *Nelson.*

Evening visit. 18°. 35c. . . . *Pres. Bd.*

Evening walk; or, the rainbow. 18°. 22c. . . *Am. S. S.*

Evening's entertainment. Engles, W. M. 75c. *Pres. Bd.*

Evening's entertainment: compr. Glass of water, by E. Scribe; Robinson Crusoe, [also] Cantab, by T. W. Robertson: dramas. 16°. pap., 40c. . . *French.*

Evenings at Donaldson Manor. McIntosh, M. J. $1. *Appleton.*

Evenings at Haddon Hall. *See* Calabrella, *Baroness* de.

Evenings at home. *See* Aikin, J., *and* Barbauld, *Mrs.* A. L.; — Godolphin, Ma.; — Juvenile classic ser.; — Treasure-box of amusement and instruction.

Evenings at the microscope. *See* Gosse, P. H.

Evenings at the tea-table: short stories. ill. sq. 16°. '71. $1.50. . . . *Routledge.*

Evenings in the South of France. Guizot, E. C. P. 55c. . . . *Am. S. S.*

Evenings with Jesus. Jay, W. $1.75. . . *J. E. Potter.*

Evenings with the old story-tellers. ill. 12°. $1.50. *World Pub.*

Evenings with the sacred poets. Saunders, F. $3.50; $1.75. . . . *Randolph.*

Events in the life of Miss Dollikins. Marks, E. M. 50c. . . . *Nelson.*

Events in the life of a seer. Davis, A. J. $1.50. *A. J. Davis.*

Events of the century. 8°. '76. $2....*U. S. C. Pub.*

Ever my queen. Egan, P. 50c. ....*De Witt.*

Everard, J. N. *See* Joannes *Secundus.*

Everest, C. Music teacher: element. instruction in vocal music. obl. 16°. '67. bds., 50c...*Ditson.*

— Piano-forte instructor. 4°. '62. bds., $1.50..*Ditson.*

— Sabbath (The): psalm and hymn tunes. obl. 8°. '73. bds., $1.50......................*Ditson.*

— Singing teacher: element. instruct. in vocal music. 2 v. obl. 16°. '71. bds., pt. 1, 25c.; 2, 20c...*Ditson.*

— Vocal instructor. f°. '61. pap., $1.50.....*Ditson.*

Everest, C: W. Harebell. 32°. *net*, 19c...*Hamersley.*

— The primrose. 32°. *net*, 19c..........*Hamersley.*

— The poets of Connecticut; with biog. sketches. 12°. '43. $1.75............................*Barnes.*

Everett, A. B. *and* B. H. The sceptre: church music. obl. 4°. '71. bds., $1...............*Biglow.*

Everett, A. H. Life of J. Warren. *See* Sparks, J., Lib. of Am. biog.

Everett, B: H. *See* Everett, A. B. *and* B. H.

Everett, C: Carroll. Science of thought: a system of logic. 12°. '69. $2..............*Nichols & H.*

Everett, E: Dorchester in 1630, 1776 and 1855: oration. 8°. '55. 75c..................*D. Clapp.*

— Importance of pract. educ. and useful knowledge: selection from orations and discourses of E. 12°. $1.50..........................*Harper.*

— Life of Geo. Washington. por. 12°. $1.50. hf. cf., $3.50...............................*Sheldon.*

— Life of J. Stark. *See* Sparks, J., Lib. of Am. biog.

— Orations and speeches. 8th ed. [To form 4 v.] v. 1, 2. 8°. $12–$24............*Little, B. & Co.*

Everett, G: H. *and* Su. Health fragments; or, steps toward a true life. ('74.) New ed. ill. 8°. '76. $2. *Somerby.*

Everett, J. Life of Samuel Hick. ('59.) 3d ed. 18°. '75. 75c............................*So. Meth.*

— Village blacksmith. *See* Village lib.

— Wall's End miner: life of W. Crister. 18°. '38. 50c. *Meth. Bk. Conc.*

Everett, Su. *See* Everett, G. H. *and* S.

Everett, W: Royal Club ser. 2 v. ill. 16°. ea., $1.25. *Lee & S.*

Cont.: Changing base; or, what Edward Rice learned. — Double play; or, how Joe Hardy chose his friends.

Evergreen. ill. 32°. 50c...................*Nelson.*

Evergreen. Hoffmann, E. A. 35c.–75c....*Ev. Assoc.*

Evergreen lib. 5 v. 18°. $4............*Am. Bapt.*

Cont.: Ocean sketches, by Mrs. M. B. Ingalls. — Wilmot family. — Holiday afternoons. — Leonette. — Grace and Rosabelle.

Evergreen stories. 10 v. 64°. $2.25...... *W. Wood.*

Compr. Sylvan stories *and* Golden stories.

Everhart, Ja. Bowen. Fox chase (The): a poem. ill. 12°. '73. $1..........................*Porter.*

— Poems. 12°. $1.25....................*Lippincott.*

Everlasting fortune-teller and dream book; [also] Napoleon's oraculum. 12°. pap., 30c....*Dick & F.*

Everlasting righteousness. Bonar, H. $1.25..*Carter.*

Everlasting Victoria primer. ill. demy 8°. 50c. *Scribner, W. & A.*

Evers, H: Nautical astronomy. (Element. sci. ser.) ill. 16°. '75. 75c. — (Adv. sci. ser.) 12°. $1.50. *Putnam.*

— Navigation. (Element. sci. ser.) ill. 16°. '74. 75c. — (Adv. sci. ser.) ill. 12°. '75. $1.50..*Putnam.*

— Steam and the steam engine: land, marine and locomotive. 16°. (Lond.) '73. $1.25..*Little, B. & Co.*

— *Same.* (Element. sci. ser.) 2 v. ill. 16°. '73. $1.50; — in 1 v. (Adv. sci. ser.) ill. 12°. $1.50. *Putnam.*

Evers, K: Octave study; [for the piano]. f°. 60c. *Brainard.*

Everts, W. W. Book of worship; for parish, family and public use. 12°. $1.50..........*Sheldon.*

— House of God: eng. of 13 churches, with plans and descript. 12°. '72. $1.50.............*Am. Tr.*

— Pastor's handbook: sel. of Scripture. 18°. 75c. *Sheldon*

— Sanctuary (The). 18°. 60c..............*Sheldon.*

— Scripture text-book and treasury. 12°. $1.25.*Sheldon.*

Every boy his own manufacturer. 5 pts. ill. 8°. '73. ea., pap., 25c...........................*Happy.*

Every day. Pike, M. H. $1.25..*Lockwood, B. & Co.*

Every day blunders in speaking. Routledge, E. 20c. *Routledge.*

Every day book. *See* Chambers, W. *and* R., Happy hour lib.

Every day book of hist. Munsell, J. $2.50..*Munsell.*

Every day cookery and housekeeping book. Beeton, I. $1.50..............................*Appleton.*

Every day doctor. Hosmer, G. H. $3.50..*Appleton.*

Every day duties. Baker, H. N. W. $1.25....*Hoyt.*

Every day duty. *See* Good boy's lib.

Every day errors of speech. Meredith, L. P. 75c. *Lippincott.*

Every day facts for every-day life. 12°. '75. $1.50. *Dodd.*

Every day faults: narratives. 18°. 50c.....*Pres. Bd.*

Every day lessons. Perkins, E. M. 60c. *Bost. Am. Tr.*

Every day made holy; or, truth for all times. 32°. interleaved, 75c. ....*Nelson.*

Every day manuals. *See* Smith, Ja.

Every day Margaret. Washburn, M. L. $1.25. *Cong. Pub.*

Every day objects. Adams, W. H. D. $2.50..*Lothrop.*

Every day philosopher. Boyd, A. K. H. $1.25. **Osgood.*

Every day religion. Talmage, T. DeW. $2..*Harper.*

Every day subjects in Sunday sermons. Collier, R. L. $1..................................*Am. Unit.*

Every day wonders ill.; or, facts in physiol. which all should know. 18°. 60c...............*Am. S. S.*

Every day's need: recipes by ladies of the Business Woman's Union. sq. 16°. '76. 60c. *Bus. Wom. Un.*

Every horse owner's cyclopædia. 12°. $3.75...*Judd.*

Every inch a king. Gardner, C. E. $1.50. *Meth. Bk. Conc.*

Every lady her own dressmaker, dyer, etc. sq. 18°. '74. pap., 20c..................(?)*F. M. Reed.*

Every lady her own shoemaker: complete self-instructor in making gaiters and shoes. 18°. 50c...*De Witt.*

Every little boy's book: cyclopedia of in and out door games. ill. 16°. $1.25...............*Routledge.*

Every little helps. 18°. 35c...............*Pres. Bd.*

Every man his own cattle doctor. Clater, F. $6. *Scribner, W. & A.*

Every man his own lawyer. *See* Wells, J. G.

Every man in his humor. Jonson, B. 15c....*French.*

Every man in his place. ill. 16°. '72. 75c...*Lothrop.*

Every one has his fault: comedy. 16°. pap., 15c. *French.*

Every Sabbath. O'Kane, T. C. 35c.........*Church.*

Every Saturday. Bell, C. D. $1...*Scribner, W. & A.*

Every Sunday. Bennett, M. L. 12c........*Un. S. S.*

Every Sunday. Norton, J. N. $2....... *Whittaker.*

Every thing in Christ. Rogers, E. P. 60c.; $1. *N. Y. Ref. Ch. Bd.*

Every thing in its right place. *See* Anderson, H. C.

Every woman her own flower-gardener. Johnson, S. O. $1; 50c.......................*H. T. Williams.*

Everybody's boy. ill. cr. 16°. 25c...........*Cassell.*

Everybody's friend. Coyne, J. S. 15c. *De Witt; French.*

Everybody's friend. Shaw, H. W. *$3.50; $4; $5. *Am. Pub.*

Everybody's friend; or, the universal handbook. 12°. '65. pap., 25c. ... *Happy.*

Everybody's husband. Ryan, R. 15c. ... *French.*

Everybody's lawyer. Crosby, F. $2; $2.25. *J. E. Potter.*

Everybody's providence. Reed, R. P. $1.75. *Cong. Pub.*

Everybody's song book. Tucker, W. G., *and* Purday, C. H. $1 ... *Routledge.*

Evidences for heaven. Head, T. 35c. ... *Pres. Bd.*

Evidences of Christianity; by C. Leslie, W. Soame, S. Jenyns and others. 18°. 70c. ... *Am. Tr.*

Evil eye. Carleton, W. $1.50 ... *Noonan; Sadlier.*

Evil eye. Peake, R. B. 15c. ... *French.*

Evil genius. Burnand, F. C. 15c. ... *French.*

Evil tongue. Dunning, A. K. 70c. ... *Pres. Bd.*

Evilela; or, the maid of Midian: Jewish tragedy. 12°. pap., 10c. ... *Mendum.*

Evolution and progress. Gill, W. I. $1.50 .. *Authors.*

Evolutions of field batteries of artillery; tr. from the Fr. and arranged by R. Anderson. pl. 24°. '60. $1 ... *Van Nostrand.*

See also Instructions for field artillery.

Ewald, A. H. Bijou dict. of the Eng. lang. 48°. 50c.; mor., $1 ... *Scribner, W. & A.*

Ewald, G: H: Antiquities of Israel; tr. by H. S. Solly. 8°. '76. $5 ... *Lockwood, B. & Co.*

Ewald, H. F. Story of Waldemar Krone's youth; tr. from the Danish. 12°. $1.25; pap., 75c. *Claxton; Lippincott.*

Ewbank, T: Descriptive account of hydraulic and other machines for raising water; with obs. on mechanic arts, incl. steam engine. ('63.) New ed., enl. ill. 8°. '76. $6 ... *Scribner.*

— Indian remains. *See* Gilliss, J. M.

— Life in Brazil: journal of visit to land of the cocoa and the palm. ill. 8°. $3; hf. cf., $5.25 .. *Harper.*

Ewell, Ja. Medical companion; or, family physician. 11th ed., rev. and enl. ill. 8°. shp., $5 .. *Desilver.*

Ewell, M. D. Leading cases on disabilities incident to infancy coverture, idiocy, etc.; with notes. 8°. '76. shp., $6 ... *Little, B. & Co.*

Ewige Jude (Der). 18°. pap., 10c. ... *Radde.*

Ewing, Alex. Present day papers on prominent questions on theology. 5 ser. 12°. '74. ea., $3. *Routledge.*

— Revelation considered as light: discourses. 8°. '73. $3 ... *Routledge.*

Ewing, Barb. Memoir. 18° 45c. ... *Am. S. S.*

Ewing, Finis. Historical memoirs. $1.50. (?) *Cumberland.*

— Lectures. 75c. ... (?) *Cumberland.*

Ewing, Juliana Horatia. Six to sixteen. ill. 16°. '75. $1.50 ... *Roberts.*

Ewing, T: *and* Woodford, S. L. Joint discussions on the finance question. 8°. '76. pap., 30c. .. *J. V. Lee.*

Examination of H. P. Liddon's Bampton lectures on the divinity of Christ; by a clergyman of the Church of Eng. 12°. '72. $1.75 ... *Am. Unit.*

Example and effort. Colfax, S. 15c. ... *Nat. Temp.*

Example better than precept. 32°. 40c. *Scribner, W. & A.*

Examples for youth: conversations on the lives of Christians. 32°. 25c. ... *Pres. Bd.*

Examples of mod. architecture, ecclesiastic and domestic: views of churches, chapels, schools, etc., erected from designs of G. G. Scott, G. E. Street, etc. 4°. '73. $15 ... *Osgood.*

Examples of youthful piety. Evans, T. 62c. *Friends Bk. St.*

Excellent woman as described in Proverbs; with introd. by W. B. Sprague. ill. 16°. '75. $1.50. 8°. $2.50 ... *Lothrop.*

Excelsior: essays on politeness, education and means of obtaining success in life: pt. 1 for young gentlemen, by T. E. Howard; pt. 2 for young ladies, by a lady. 12°. '71. $1.50; $2 .. *Kelly, P. & Co.*

Excelsior glee and chorus book. 8°. '65. bds., $1. *Ditson*

Excelsior toy books. 43 nos. cr. 8°. ea., 25c.; 50c. *Scribner, W. & A.*

Exchange no robbery. Hook, T. 15c. ... *French.*

Excise trials. White, C. 15c. ... *De Witt.*

Excursions in field and forest. Thoreau, H. D. $1.50. *Osgood.*

Exercices de piété à l'usage du vrai chrétien. 32°. *net*, 20c.; 26c. ... *Benziger.*

Exercices de piété pour le soulagement des âmes du purgatoire. 18°. *net*, 30c.; 41c. ... *Benziger.*

Exercise of faith. Mahan, M. 50c. ... *McCauley.*

Exeter Hall. *See* McDonnell, W.

Exile. Reynolds, F. 15c. ... *French.*

Exile of Erin. *See* Alice Harmon.

Exile of Tadmore; tr. by Mrs. J. Sadlier. 18°. 50c.; 75c. ... *Sadlier.*

Exiles in Babylon. *See* Tucker, *Mrs.* C.

Exiles of the Cebenna. Aurelius Gretianus. 55c.; 60c. *Dutton.*

Exiles of Lucerna. Macduff, J. R. 75c. ... *Dutton.*

Exiles of Madeira. Blackburn, W. M. 75c. *Pres. Bd.*

Exotics. Clarke, J. F. *and* L. $1.25 ... *Osgood.*

Expanse of heaven. Proctor, R. A. $2 ... *Appleton.*

Expedition of Humphrey Clinker. *See* Smollett, T.

Experience of life. *See* Sewell, E. M.

Experience of several Methodist preachers. 12°. 90c. *Cin. Meth. Bk. Conc.*

Experience teaches. *See* Short stories lib.

Experiences of a church plate. 18°. 35c. .. *Am. S. S.*

Experiences of a diplomatist. Ward, J. $3.50. *Macmillan.*

Experiences of a French detective. Russell, W. H. C. 75c. ... *Dick & F.*

Experiences of the higher Christian life. Adams, J. Q. $1.25 ... *Tibbals.*

Experiences of Richard Taylor. Johnstone, J. 25c. *Littell & G.*

Expiated; by author of "Six months hence." [Fiction.] 8°. $1.25; pap., 75c. ... *Estes.*

Expiation. Dorr, J. C. R. $1.50 ... *Lippincott.*

Expiation. Kehoe, J. 40c. ... *Murphy.*

Explanations of the [Prot. Episc.] Church service. 18°. $1 ... *Dutton.*

Explanatory question book. *See* New.

Exposition and benediction of the blessed sacrament. *See* Catholic Church.

Exposition of the grange. Geeslin, A. W. 25c. *E. A. Cook.*

Exposition of the new birth. Rowe, J. F. 10c. *Chase.*

Exposition of social freedom: monogamic marriage the highest devel. of sexual equality; by author of "Vital magnetic cure." 12°. '75. pap., 25c. *Colby.*

Exposition of the Sons of Malta. 8°. pap., 13c. *Peterson.*

Exposition of vulgar and common errors. *See* Small books on great subjects.

Expressman and the detective. Pinkerton, A. $1.50. *Keen.*

Extract from a MS. collection of annals rel. to Va.; from the "Virginia Gazette," April 21, 1774. Wash., 1838. [Reprint.] 4°. pap., 25c. .. *Sabin.*

Extract of fun: a cordial for young and old. ill. 8°. pap., 50c. . . . . . *Scribner, W. & A.*
Extracts from the diary of a country pastor. Gardner, H. C. $1 . . . . . *Cin. Meth. Bk. Conc.*
Extraordinary and mirth provoking adventures of Oscar Shanghai. ill. obl. 8°. 25c. . . . . *Dick & F.*
Extrasitzungen des Herrn Diabolus. Freimund, E. 20c. . . . . *Brobst.*
Extremes. Falconer, E. 15c. . . . . *French.*
Eye doctor. 18°. 35c. . . . . *Am. S. S.*
Eyebright, Daisy (*pseud.*) *See* Johnson, *Mrs.* S. O.
Eyes and ears. 18°. 25c.; pap., 10c. . . . . *Dutton.*
Eyes for every thing. *See* Little Alice's lib.
Eyre, *Sir* Ja. The stomach and its difficulties. 6th ed. 16°. 75c. . . . . *Lippincott.*
Eyster, Nellie. Sunny hour lib. 4 v. 16°. '74. ea., $1.25 . . . . . *Meth. Epis.*
Cont.: Sunny hours. — Chincapin Charley. — On the wing. — Tom Harding.
Ezekiel. MacAndrews, B. $1.50 . . . . . *Nelson.*

F., E. E. *See* Flagg, E. E.
F., H. H. Lame Bessie; or, simple faith. 16°. '75. $1. *Lothrop.*
F., L. A. Daisy Seymour. ill. 16°. '71. $1.25 . . *Lothrop.*
— Helen Freeman; or, the right path. ill. 18°. 80c. *J. A. Moore.*
F., M. E. The invalid's work. 18°. 50c. . . . *Pres. Bd.*
F. Grant & Co. Chaney, G. L. $1.50 . . . . . *Roberts.*
F. O. B. grain tables; showing cost in sterling (free on board) of wheat and Indian corn; with tables. 32°. '73. $1 . . . . . (?) *Held.*
Faber, Arth. Sermons at a new school. cr. 8°. '73. $2 . . . . . *Macmillan.*
Faber, F: W: Bethlehem. 16°. 45c. . . . . *Cummiskey.*
— Hymns; sel. by R. P. Smith. 12°. '74. $1.75. *Routledge.*
— *Same.* 16°. $1.50 . . . . . *Willard.*
— Hymns; with sketch of life. ill. 16°. '75. $2; mor., $4.50 . . . . . *Dutton.*
— Life and works. 9 v. 12°. '54–'69. ea., $1.50; $2; per set, $13.50; $18; hf. cf., $27 . . . . . *Murphy.*
Cont.: Life and letters, by J. E. Bowden. — All for Jesus; or, the easy ways of divine love. — Blessed sacrament; or, works and ways of God. — Growth in holiness; or, the progress of the spiritual life. — Creator and the creature; or, the wonders of the divine love. — Foot of the cross; or, the sorrows of Mary. — Bethlehem. — Spiritual conference. — The precious blood; or, the price of our salvation.
— Tales of the angels; or, Ethel's book. sq. 16°. '60. 60c.; 80c. . . . . . *Murphy.*
Faber, G: Stanley. Difficulties of infidelity; [also] Modern infidelity considered, by Rob. Hall; with catalogue of books on evidences of revealed religion. 12°. $1.50 . . . . . *Tibbals.*
Fabiola. Wiseman, N. $1.50; $2 . . . . . *Sadlier.*
Fable for critics. Lowell, J. R. 75c. . . . . *Osgood.*
Fables and legends of many countries. Saxe, J. G. $1.50 . . . . . *Osgood.*
Fables for little folks. Disosway, E. 85c. . . . . *Lent.*
Fables for the young folks. Prosser, *Mrs.* —. 75c. *Bost. Am. Tr.*
Fables in pictures. Speckter, O. 50c. . . . . *Porter.*
Fables in song. *See* Bulwer-Lytton, E. R.
Fables in verse. ill. sq. 16°. 50c. . . . . *Perkinpine.*
Fables of infidelity. *See* Patterson, R.
Fabre, Fd. Abbé Tigrane; or, who shall be pope? tr. by L. W. Bacon. 12°. '75. $1.50 . . . . . *Ford.*
Fabrics: a story of to-day; by author of "Finished, or not." 16°. '71. $1.50 . . . . . *Randolph.*
— *Same.* ill. 16°. '73. $1.50 . . . . . *Lothrop.*
Fabulous histories. Trimmer, S. 50c. . . . . *Routledge.*
Faces in the fire. Buckingham, L. 15c. . . . . *French.*

Fackler, D. Parks. Agents' monetary, life and valu tion tables; with explanations. [Life insurance ('68.) 2d ed. 8°. '70. $1.50 . . . . . *Hin*
Facta non verba: comparison between good works [o ladies in Rom. Cath. convents in Eng. and tl unfettered efforts of their Prot. sisters; by a thor of "Contrasts." 12°. '74. $1.75 . . *Routledg*
Factory boy. *See* Baker, *Mrs.* H. N. W.
Factory boy; or, Providence illustrated. 18°. '5 45c.; 50c. . . . . *Am. Bap*
Factory girl. Braddon, M. E. 75c. . . . . *De Wi*
Factory girl. *See* Gem cluster.
Factory girls. ('60.) New ed. ill. 18°. '76. 75c. . . *Hoy*
Factory lad: drama. 16°. pap., 15c. . . . . *Frenc*
Facts (The); or, at whose door does the sin (?) li Train, G. F. 25c. . . . . *De Wi*
Facts about wives and mothers. Donkersley, R. $1.2 *Meth. Bk. Con*
Facts and fallacies. Taylor, J. 40c. . . . . *Spo*
Facts and fancies. Cousin William. 75c. . . . . *Nelso*
Facts and fancies for school-day reading. Sedgwic C. A. 75c. . . . . *Putnan*
Facts for boys. *See* Good boy's lib.
Facts for girls. *See* Bradley, *Mrs.* M. E.
Facts in aid of faith. Burr, E. F. 25c. . . . . *Am. T*
Facts in mesmerism. Townshend, C. H. $1.25. *Harpe*
Facts of consciousness. Greene, W. B. 25c. . . *Lee &*
Faculties of the soul. Bégon, F. 25c. . . . . *Sadlie*
Faded hope. Sigourney, L. H. 75c. . . . . *Carte*
Fadette (*pseud.*) *See* Rodney, *Mrs.* M. R. L.
Fading flowers: on death of children. sq. 12°. '5 $1.50 . . . . . *Tilto*
Faerie gold for young and old. Lapointe, S. $1. *Routledg*
Faerie queene. *See* Spenser, E.
Fagot of stories. Power, P. B. 60c. . . . . *Carte*
Fagots for the fireside. Goodrich, S. G. $1.50. *Appleto*
Fahnestock, W: Baker. Statuvolism; or, artificial son nambulism, called mesmerism or animal magne ism. ('69.) 3d ed. 12°. '71. $1.50 . . *Rel. Ph*
Faint heart did win fair lady: comedy. 16°. pap., 15 *Frenc*
Faint heart never won fair lady. Planché, J. R. 15 *Frencl*
Fair, Laura D. Trial for the murder of A. P. Cri tenden. 8°. pap., 75c. . . . . *Bancrof*
Fair encounter: comedy. 16°. pap., 15c. . . . . *Frenc*
Fair exchange. Williams, M. 15c. . . . . *Frencl*
Fair France. *See* Craik, D. M.
Fair god. Wallace, L. $2; $4 . . . . . *Osgoo*
Fair Lilias. Egan, P. $1.50 . . . . . *Dick &*
Fair maid of Perth. Milner, H. M. 15c. . . . . *Frencl*
Fair maid of Perth. *See* Scott, *Sir* W.
Fair Minthe. Dashmore, F. 75c.; 25c. . . . . *Author*
Fair one with the golden locks. [Toy-book.] ill. 4 $1; 50c. . . . . *Routledg*
Fair one with golden locks. Planché, J. R. 15c. *Frencl*
Fair penitent. Rowe, N. 15c. . . . . *Frenc*
Fair play. Southworth, E. D. E. N. $1.75; $1.50. *Peterso*
Fair play. Strong, J. D. 30c. . . . . *Lothro*
Fair play series. 6 v. ill. 24°. $1.50 . . . . . *Lothro*
Cont.: Wintergreen girl. — Kitty Collins. — Susie's watch. Fair play, and other stories. — Better than gold. — Bold as a lio
Fair pretender. Simpson, J. P. 15c. . . . . *Frenc*
Fair Puritan. Herbert, H. W. $1.50 . . . . . *Lippincot*
Fair Quakeress; or, the perjured lawyer. 8°. pap 25c. . . . . *De Wi*

Fair rebel. Bennett, E. 25c. . . . . *U. P. James.*
Fair Rosamond. Burnand, F. C. 15c. . . . . *French.*
Fair Rosamond. Egan, P. 75c. . . . . *Dick & F.*
Fair Rosamond's bower. Longbridge, F. 15c. . . *French.*
Fair Saxon (A). McCarthy, J. $1.50; $1. . *Sheldon.*
Fair to see. Lockhart, L. W. M. 75c. . . . . . *Harper.*
Fairbain, Rob. B. What is the meaning of the oblation in the prayer of consecration in the eucharistic service? 8°. '74. pap., 20c. . . . . *Whittaker.*
Fairbairn, Pat. Ezekiel and his book of prophecy. 8°. $5. . . . . *Scribner, W. & A.*
— Hermeneutical manual; or, introd. to the exegetical study of New Test. 8°. $5. . . *Scribner, W. & A.*
— Pastoral epistles (The): Greek text and translation, with introd., notes and dissertations. cr. 8°. $3.75. . . . . *Scribner, W. & A.*
— Prophecy viewed in respect to its distinctive nature, special function, and proper interpretation. 8°. $3 . . . . *Meth. Bk. Conc.*
— *Same.* 8°. $5. . . . . *Scribner, W. & A.*
— Revelation of law in Scripture. 8°. '69. $2.50. . *Carter.*
— *Same.* 8°. $5 . . . . *Scribner, W. & A.*
— Typology of Scripture. 5th ed., enl. 2 v. 8°. $10. *Scribner, W. & A.*
Fairbairn, W: Cast and wrought iron for building. 8°. $2 . . . . *Wiley.*
— Principles of mechanism and machinery of transmission. ('67.) 9th ed. ill. 12°. '76. $2.50. . *Baird.*
Fairbanks, G: R. History of Florida, 1512–1842. 12°. '71. $2.50. . . . . *C. Drew; Lippincott.*
— The Spaniards in Florida. 2d ed., rev. and enl. 12°. '68. pap., $1. . . . . *C. Drew.*
Note. First pub. in N. Y. (1855) under title of "History and antiquities of St. Augustine."
Fairbanks, Lorenzo. New lightning calculator: short methods of arith. computations for business men, etc. 12°. '68. pap., 50c. . . . . *Claxton.*
— Practical business arith. 12°. '71. $1.50. . *Univ. Pub.*
— Science and practice of book-keeping by double and single entry. 8°. $4. . . . . *Sower.*
Fairchild, Ashbel G. Great supper (The): illustration and defence of leading doctrines of grace. 18°. 50c. . . . . *Pres. Bd.*
— *Same;* tr. into Germ. by F. Steins. 18°. 20c. *Pres. Bd.*
— Scripture baptism, its mode and subject. 18°. 55c. *Pres. Bd.*
Fairchild, J. M. Moral philosophy; or, the science of obligation. 12°. $1.50. . . . . *Sheldon.*
Fairchild, Ja. H. Doctrine of sanctification at Oberlin, Ohio. 8°. pap., 15c. . . . . *Goodrich.*
— Needed phases of Christianity. 12°. '75. pap., 25c. (?) *Pratt & B.*
Fairchild family. *See* Sherwood, *Mrs.* M. M.
Fairchilds (The). *See* Guernsey, L. E.
Faire gospeller (The). Manning, A. $1. . . . . . *Dodd.*
Faire-mount. Peterson, H. $1. . . . . *Claxton.*
Fairer than a fairy. Grant, J. 80c. . . . . *Routledge.*
Fairest rose. *See* Choice little lib.
Fairfax. Cooke, J. E. $1.50. . . . . *Carleton.*
Fairfield, Fs. Gerry The clubs of New York. 12°. '73. $2.25. . . . . *Hinton.*
— Ten years with spiritual mediums. 12°. '75. $1.25. *Appleton.*
Fairfield, *Miss* Genevieve Genevra. Irene: tale of southern life; [also] Hathaway Strange. ill. 8°. pap., 35c. . . . . *Lippincott.*
— Genevra; or, the history of a portrait. 8°. pap., 75c. *Peterson.*
Fairfield, J. *See* Maine, Supreme Court reports.
Fairholt, F: W: Dictionary of terms in art. ill. cr. 8°. $2.50. . . . . *Routledge.*
— Tobacco, its history and associations. ill. cr. 8°. '59. $2. . . . . *Spon.*
— *Same.* ill. cr. 8°. $2.40. . . . . *Scribner, W. & A.*

Fairie queene. *See* Spenser, E.
Fairlamb, J. Remington. Treasured tokens. [Opera.] 4°. '73. $10. — Libretto. 8°. pap., 40c. . . *Pond.*
Fairy bells; and what they tolled us. Lander, S. W. $1.25. . . . . *Lockwood, B. & Co.*
Fairy book. ill. 16°. $1.50. . . . . *Harper.*
Fairy book. Craik, D. M. $1.25. . . . . *Macmillan.*
Fairy bridal. Hewitt, J. H. 50c. . . . . *Ditson.*
Fairy cricket. *See* Dickens, C:
Fairy dreams. Austin, J. G. $1.50. . . . . *Tilton.*
Fairy echoes. Dressler, W. 60c. . . . . *Peters.*
Fairy egg, and what it contained. Weston, H. H. $1.25. *Loring.*
Fairy family. Maclaren, A. $1.75. . . . . . . *Macmillan.*
Fairy folk ser.; by authors of "Fairy egg." 3 v. ill. 18°. ea., 60c. . . . . *Loring.*
Cont.: Daffy Down Dilly and her friends. — The history of A B C. — The wonderful bag and what was in it.
Fairy freaks: fairy play. 16°. pap., 15c. . . . . *Happy.*
Fairy Frisket. *See* Tucker, *Mrs.* C.
Fairy gifts. Knox, K. $1. *Pott.*
Fairy glass. Crandall, L. S. $1.25. . . . . *Claxton.*
Fairy grotto. Stratton, G. W. 80c.; 90c. . . *Stratton.*
Fairy legends. Valentine, R. $1.50. . (?) *McLoughlin.*
Fairy library. 3 v. ill. 16°. $3.75. . . . . *Routledge.*
Cont.: Andersen's Fairy tales. — Grimm's Home stories. — Old tales for the young.
Fairy library. *See* Cruikshank, G.
Fairy mythology. *See* Keightley, T.
Fairy nightcaps. *See* Barrow, *Mrs.* F.
Fairy spinner. Hill, M. $1.25. . . . . *Nelson.*
Fairy stories. ill. 12°. $1. . . . . *Nelson.*
Fairy stories. *See* Grandmother's lib.
Fairy stories with a purpose. ill. 18°. 75c. . . . . *Nelson.*
Fairy tales. *See* Parr, H.
Fairy tales from gold lands. Newman, M. W. 2 v. ea., 75c. . . . . *Roman.*
Fairy tales of all nations. Laboulaye, E. $2; $2.50, *Harper.*
Fairy tales told again; by author of "Little red shoes;" ill. by G. Doré. 2d ed. imp. 8°. $2.50. . *Cassell.*
Fairy tree. Moody, S. $1.50. . . . . *Nelson.*
Fairy world. Andersen, H. C. $1.50. . . . *World Pub.*
Fairyland; or, the riddle and the key. Paxton, A. 15c. . . . . *French.*
Fairy's father. Cheltnam, C. S. 15c. . . . . *French.*
Fairy's well. 18°. pap., 12c. . . . . *O'Shea.*
Faith: poem. Leavitt, J. M. 40c. . . *Cin. Meth. Bk. Conc.*
Faith and falsehood: drama. 16°. pap., 15c. . . *French.*
Faith and free thought: 2d course of lectures on modern skepticism, Christian Evidence Soc. 12°. '73. $2.50. . . . . *Randolph.*
Faith and its effects. Palmer, P. 75c. . . . . *Palmer.*
Faith and mod. thought. Welch, R. B. $1.50. . *Putnam.*
Faith and patience. Paget, F. E. $2.50. . . . . *Pott.*
Faith and patience. Walker, J. P. 75c. . . . . . . *Fuller.*
Faith and patience. Winthrop, S. $1. . . . . *Randolph.*
Faith and works. Christian, L. H. 50c. . . . . *Pres. Bd.*
Faith explained. Walker, C. 25c. . . . . *Am. Tr.*
Faith hymns. Cullis, C. 15c.; 25c. . . . . *Willard.*
Faith in Hungary; by author of "From dawn to dark in Italy." 16°. 85c. . . . . *Pres. Bd.*
Faith of Abraham and of Christ. Ward, H. D. $1.50. *Claxton.*
Faith of our fathers. *See* Gibbons, J.
Faith, the cripple. *See* Aunty May's children.
Faith Cleveland. Allen, D. H. 75c. . . . . . *Cong. Pub.*
Faith Duncan. Cutter, J. E. 90c. . . . . *Cong. Pub.*

Faith Gartney's girlhood. Whitney, A. D. T. $1.75. *Loring.*
Faith Harrowby. Doudney, S. $1 .... *Nelson.*
Faith Unwin's ordeal. Craik, G. M. $1.25 ..... *Holt.*
Faith White's letter book. Whiting, M. H. $1.50; $2. *Hoyt.*
Faithful, Emily. A reed shaken with the wind. [Fiction.] 12°. '73. $1.50 .... *Adams, V. & Co.*
Faithful and effective ministry. Kluge, E. T. 15c. *Clauder.*
Faithful and true. Robbins, S. S. $1.25 ..... *Carter.*
Faithful Bridget. ill. 18°. '66. 35c. *N. Y. Ref. Ch. Bd.; Pres. Com.*
Faithful, but not famous. ill. 16°. '73. $1.25 .. *Lothrop.*
— *See also* Hartz boys' lib.
Faithful, but not famous: hist. tale; by author of "Soldier Fritz." 16°. 90c. .... *Am. S. S.*
Faithful dog. *See* Home lib.
Faithful Ellen. ill. 18°. '57. 25c. .... *Am. Tr.*
Faithful forever. Patmore, C. $1.25 .... *Osgood.*
Faithful friends. 32°. 20c.; 15c. .... *Dutton.*
Faithful in least. Davis, C. E. K. $1.50 .... *Hoyt.*
Faithful in little. 16°. $1 .... *Carter; Dutton.*
Faithful Lina. *See* Meadowside stories.
Faithful ministry. Holmes, G. M. $1.50 .... *Lothrop.*
Faithful mother's reward: conversion and death of J. P. B. 18°. 75c. .... *Pres. Bd.*
Faithful nurse; or, the story of Mary Grey. 18°. 60c. *Am. S. S.*
Faithful promiser. *See* Macduff, J. R.
Faithful Rover. 18°. 50c. .... *Carter.*
Faithful Ruth: story of Bethlehem. 18°. 40c. *Am. S. S.*
Faithful Ruth; or, trust in God. ('60.) New ed. 16°. '76. $1 .... *Hoyt.*
Faithful servant (A). Cléry, J. B. 50c. .... *Pott.*
Faithful shepherd. Todd, J. 75c. *Bridgman; Cong. Pub.*
Faithful sister. 18°. 50c. .... *Carter.*
Faithful son. Sargent, G. E. $1.25 .... *Hoyt.*
Faithful steward. Clark, S. D. 40c. ..... *Cong. Pub.*
Faithful to the light. Cheney, E. D. 80c. .. *Am. Unit.*
Faithful unto death. ill. 16°. $1.25 .... (?) *Luth. Pub.*
Faithful watcher. *See* American youth's lib.
Faithless guardian. Van Namee, J. W. $1.50 .. *Colby.*
Faith's battles and victories. *See* Grasty, J. S.
Faith's work perfected; or, Franke's orphan house at Halle; ed. and tr. by W. L. Gage. 16°. '67. 75c. *Randolph.*
Falcon family. Adams, H. C. $1.75 .. *Scribner, W. & A.*
Falconer, Edm. [Plays.] 7 v. 16°. ea., pap., 15c. *French.*

Cont.: Chrystabelle: extravaganza. — Extremes; or, men of the day: comedy. — Family secret: comedy. — Husband for an hour. — Next of kin. — Peep o' day. — Too much for good nature: farce.

— Anne Hathaway: a ballad. 16°. pap., 25c. .. *French.*
— Peep o' day; or, savourneen dheelish: drama. 12°. pap., 15c. .... *De Witt.*
Falconer, W: Poems. (Aldine ed.) 16°. 75c. *Lippincott.*
— *Same;* with memoir by J. Mitford. 18°. $1 .. *Osgood.*
— — *See also* Beattie, Ja., *and* Falconer, W:
— Bloom and brier; or, as I saw it long ago. 12°. '70. $1.50 .... *Claxton.*
— The shipwreck. *See* British pocket classics.
Falconhurst. Adams, H. C. $1 .... *Scribner, W. & A.*
Falkenberg: tale of the Rhine. 8°. pap., 75c. .. *Harper.*
Falkland. *See* Bulwer-Lytton, *Sir* E. G. E. L.
Fall of Algiers. Payne, J. H. 15c. .... *French.*
Fall of Jerusalem. *See* Hallock, M. A.
Fall of man. Farrar, F. W. $1.50 ...... *Macmillan.*
Fall of man. White, R. G. 50c. .... *Carleton*
Fall of Prince Florestan. Dilke, *Sir* C: W. $1.75. *Macmillan*
Fallais Ingles? or, do you speak English? for Portuguese students. 18°. '65. bds., 60c. .... *Holt*
Fallais Portuguez? or, do you speak Portuguese? 18° '65. bds., 60c. .... *Holt*
Fallen (The). Kenyon, J. B. $1.50 .... *Curtiss & C*
Fallen angel. *See* Dumas, A.
Fallen pride. Southworth, E. D. E. N. $1.75; $1.50 *Peterson*
Fallet, C. Les princes de l'art, architectes, sculpteurs, peintres et graveurs. ('69.) New ed. 12° '76. $1.50 .... *Holt*
Falling in harness: memoir of Rev. J. W. Barton. 18° 35c.; pap., 10c. .... *Am. S. S*
Falloux, Alfr. F: P. (*Comte*) de. Life and letters of Mme. Swetchine; tr. by H. W. Preston. 16° '67. $1.50 .... *Roberts*
Fallows, S: Constitutions of the U. S. and of Wisconsin; for schools. 12°. '71. 50c. ..... *Atwood*
Falls of the Clyde. Soane, G. 15c. .... *French*
False alarms. Kenney, J. 15c. .... *French*
False and constant. Lunn, J. 15c. .... *French*
False brand (The); or, honesty is the best policy. 18° 30c. .... *Am. S. S*
False colors. Thomas, A. 50c. .... *Harper*
False friendship. 18°. 70c. .... *Pres. Bd*
False heir. James, G. P. R. 50c. .... *Harper*
False imprisonment. 18°. 75c. .... *Cong. Pu*
False key. Edgeworth, M. 25c. .... *Routledge*
False pride; or, two ways to matrimony. 12°. $1.75 pap., $1.50 .... *Peterson*
False shame. *See* Little door-keeper's lib.
Falsehood and truth. Tonna, C. E. 90c. ..... *Dodd*
Falsely accused. Tucker, C. 50c. .... *Carter*
Falsely accused. *See* Plot (The).
Fame and fortune. Alger, H., *jr.* $1.25 ..... *Loring*
Familia de Alvareda. Arrom, C. B. de F. $1 .. *Holt*
Familiar discourses to the young; by a Catholic priest. 12°. '73. 75c. .... *Cath. Pub*
Familiar hymns and spiritual songs. 3d ed. 24°. 35c *Cen. Bk*
Familiar hymns for the Meth. Episc. Church. 24° '64. 15c. .... *Meth. Bk. Conc*
Familiar lessons for Sunday schools. ('66.) New ed 18°. '72. 50c. .... *Lockwood, B. & Co*
Familiar letters from Europe. Felton, C. C. $1.50. *Estes*
Familiar letters to you, a young convert, from your pastor. 12°. 60c. .... *Pres. Bd*
Familiar quotations. (Household ser.) ill. 16°. $1.50 mor., $3 .... *Lee & S*
Familiar quotations: extracts and aphorisms from the best authors. 12°. $1.75 .... *Routledge*
Familiar talks to boys. Hall, J. $1 .... *Dodd*
Familiar words: an index verborum, or quotation handbook. 16°. $3 .... *Scribner, W. & A*
Familie Besson-Völker (Die). Schmidt-Weissenfels, E. 40c. .... *F. W. Thomas*
Familie Labeo (Die). 12°. '72. $1; $1.25 .. *Ev. Assoc*
Familien-Gebete. 12°. 50c. .... *Kohler*
Family (The); tr. by Mrs. J. Sadlier. 32°. 60c.; pap. 25c. .... *Sadlier*
Family (The): discourses. Hyacinthe, *Father.* $1.50 *Putnam*
Family aquarium. Butler, H. D. 75c. ...... *Dick & F*
Family at Heatherdale. Mackay, *Mrs.*—. 75c. .. *Carter*
Family circle. Graves, H. A. 25c.; 40c.; $1 .. *Lothrop*
Family doctor. Walker, M. S. $1.50 .... *Hoyt*

Family doctor: dict. of domestic med. and surgery for family use; by a dispensary surgeon. ill. cr. 8°. $1.75 .... *Routledge.*
Family doom. Southworth, E. D. E. N. $1.75; $1.50. *Peterson.*
Family failing. Oxenford, J. 15c. .... *French.*
Family health almanac. 16°. pap., 10c. .. *Sev. Day Adv.*
Family instructor. Sears, R. *$3.50; $4.50. *J. E. Potter.*
Family instructor; or, a manual of the duties of domestic life; by a parent. 18°. 75c. .... *Harper.*
Family jars. Lunn, J. 15c. .... *French.*
Family kitchen-garden. Buist, R. $1 .... *Judd.*
Family monitor. James, J. A. 75c. .. *U. P. Bd. of Pub.*
Family pictures: farce. 16°. pap., 15c. ...... *French.*
Family pride; by author of "Pique." 12°. $1.75; pap., $1.50 .... *Peterson.*
Family pride: comedy. 16°. pap., 15c. ...... *Happy.*
Family save-all (The). *See* Bouvier, H. M.
Family scenes. Headley, P. C. 25c.; 30c. .. *J. E. Potter.*
Family scrap-book; or, hints on domestic duties. 18°. 60c. .... *Am. S. S.*
Family secret. Andrews, F. $1.50; $1 .. *Lippincott.*
Family secret. Falconer, E. 15c. .... *French.*
Family secrets; by author of "Family pride." 12°. $1.75; pap., $1.50 .... *Peterson.*
Family secrets revealed. 18°. 22c. .... *Am. S. S.*
Family singing book. Weber, F. 75c. .... (?)*Andrè.*
Family theatricals. Smith, C. W. 50c. .... *Routledge.*
Family tree. Fonblanque, A., *jr.* $1.25; 75c. .. *Estes.*
Family worship: prayers for morning and evening, by 180 clergymen of Scotland. 8°. $2.50 ... *Carter.*
Famous Americans. 4 v. 12°. $6 .... *Lothrop.*
Cont.: Life of B. Franklin, by J. Chaplin. — Life of C. Sumner, by J. and J. D. Chaplin. — Life of A. Lawrence, by W. R. Lawrence. — Life of D. Webster, by J. Banvard.
Famous Americans of recent times. Parton, J. $3. *Osgood.*
Famous boys and famous men. ill. 12°. $1.50. *World Pub.*
Famous boys lib. 3 v. ill. 16°. $3.75 .... *Routledge.*
Cont.: Dawnings of genius, by T. A. Buckley. — Heroines of domestic life. — Celebrated children of all nations.
Famous cases of circumstantial evidence; with introd. on theory of presumptive proof by S. M. Phillips. 2d ed. 8°. $3; shp., $4.50 .... *Estes.*
Famous cities lib. 10 v. 18°. $5 .... *So. Meth.*
Cont.: Ancient Jerusalem. — Modern Jerusalem. — London in modern times. — London in the olden time. — Tyre. — Old Edinburgh. — Modern Edinburgh. — Paris, ancient and modern. — Venice. — Dublin.
— *See also* Buckley, T. A.
Famous fairy tales for little folks. ill. sq. 16°. $1. *Miller.*
Famous islands and memorable voyages. ill. 16°. '73. $1 .... *Lothrop.*
Famous jingles. [Toy-book.] ill. 8°. $1. (?)*McLoughlin.*
Famous London merchants. Bourne, H. R. F. $1. *Harper.*
— *See also* Enterprise and adventure lib.
Famous men library. *See* Edgar, J. G.
Famous men of ancient times. *See* Goodrich, S. G.
Famous men of modern times. *See* Goodrich, S. G.
Famous painters and paintings. Shedd, J. A. $5; $8. *Osgood.*
Famous persons and places. Willis, N. P. $1.75. *Scribner.*
Fanchon, the cricket. Sand, G. $1.50; $1 .. *Peterson.*
Fanchon, the cricket. Waldauer, A. 15c. ... *French.*
Fan Fan, the tulip. Suter, W. E. 15c. ...... *French.*
Fanfan stories. Smith, F. I. B. 85c. .. *Bost. Am. Tr.*
Fankwei. Wood, W. M. $1.50 .... *Harper.*
Fannie and Robbie. Hale, A. G. 75c. ...... *Dutton.*
Fannie's rule. *See* Hildeburn, *Mrs.* M. J.
Fanning, D: Narrative; giving an account of his adventures in No. Car., 1775–1783; with introd. and notes. [Reprint.] 8°. $3 .... *Sabin.*
Fanning, T. True method of searching the Scriptures. 24°. pap., 15c. .... *Chase.*
Fanny, *Aunt* (*pseud.*) *See* Barrow, *Mrs.* Fanny.
Fanny. Lamb, M. J. 60c. .... *Lothrop.*
Fanny, the flower girl. *See* Bunbury, S.
Fanny Aiken. 18°. 75c. .... *Carter.*
Fanny and her aunt. 18°. 35c. .... *Cong. Pub.*
Fanny and her brothers; or, a visit to the sea shore. 32°. 35c. .... *Am. S. S.*
— *See also* Library for little folks.
Fanny and her mamma. sq. 18°. 75c. .... *Carter.*
Fanny and her mother; or, easy reading lessons. 18°. 80c. .... *Am. S. S.*
Fanny Ashley. *See* Little Dot ser.
Fanny Fern lib. *See* Parton, *Mrs.* S. P.
Fanny Graham; or, a peep at the heart. 18°. 30c. *Am. S. S.*
Fanny Hunter in Kansas and Missouri. *See* Western adventures.
Fanny Lightman's choice. Berry, M. E. 70c. *Am. Tr.*
Fanny Lynn; or, a lamb of the flock. 18°. 20c.; 25c. *Am. Bapt.*
Fanny Mansfield; or, the adopted sister. 18°. 60c. *Am. S. S.*
Fanny Percy's knight errant. Graham, M. $1. *Nat. Temp.*
Fanny Raymond. 18°. 35c.; 45c. .... *Am. Bapt.*
Fanny Sylvester. *See* Cupples, *Mrs.* A. J.
Fanny's Bible text; by author of "Faithful, but not famous." ill. 18°. 50c. .... *Nelson.*
— *Same.* ill. 16°. '73. 75c. .... *Lothrop.*
Fanny's birthday gift. Mathews, J. H. $1.25 .. *Carter.*
Fanny's return. *See* Patty Parsons.
Fanshawe. *See* Hawthorne, N.
Fantastic stories. Leander, R. $1.75 ..... *Routledge.*
Far above rubies. Riddell, J. H. $1.50; $1 .. *Claxton.*
Far away. Hildeburn, M. J. 50c. .... *Pres. Bd.*
Far east (The). Burt, N. C. $1.75 .... *Clarke.*
Far from the madding crowd. Hardy, T. $1.25 .. *Holt.*
Far off. 18°. 75c. .... *Carter.*
Farabeuf, L. H. Ligation of arteries; tr. by J. D. Jackson. 12°. $1.75 .... *Lippincott.*
Faraday, Mich. Chemistry of a candle: lectures on the chem. hist. of a candle, also lecture on platinum; ed. by W. Crookes. ill. 16°. $1 .. *Harper.*
— *Same.* New ed. ill. 12°. '74. $2 ...... *Routledge.*
— Physical forces: lectures on the various forces of matter and their relations to each other; ed. by W. Crookes. ill. 16°. $1 .... *Harper.*
— *Same.* ill. 12°. '74. $2 .... *Routledge.*
Fardorougha. *See* Carleton, W:
Fargo, J. F. *See* Baker, B. F., *and* Fargo, J. F.
Faris *al Shidiac.* Arabic grammar. fp. 8°. (Lond.) $2.50 .... *Wiley.*
Farjeon, B. L. Novels. 3 v. 12°. hf. roxb., $3.75. *Routledge.*
Cont.: Joshua Marvel. — London's heart. — Grif.
— *Same.* 11 v. ill. 8°. pap. .... *Harper.*
Cont.: At the sign of the Silver Flagon, 40c. — Blade-o'-grass, 35c. — Bread-and-cheese and kisses: a Christmas story, 35c. — Golden grain: sequel to "Blade-o'-grass," 35c. — Grif: story of Australian life, 40c. — Island pearl (An), 35c. — Jessie Trim, 50c. — Joshua Marvel, 40c. — King of No-land, 25c. — London's heart, $1. — Love's victory, 25c.
— Christmas stories. 8°. $2 .... *Harper.*
— Grif. 8°. pap., 25c. .... *De Witt.*
— *Same.* 8°. 90c. .... *Harper.*

Farjeon, B. L., *continued.*
— Joshua Marvel. 8°. 90c. .... *Harper.*
— London's heart. ill. 8°. $1.50 .... *Harper.*

Farley, F: A. Unitarianism defined: Scripture doct. of the Father, Son and Holy Ghost. ('60.) New ed. 12°. '73. 60c. .... *Am. Unit.*
— *See also* Osgood, S., *and* Farley, F. A.

Farley, Ph. Criminals of America: tales of lives of thieves. por. 8°. '76. $3 .... *U. S. Pub.*

Farm ballads;—legends. Carleton, W. ea., $2; $2.50. *Harper.*

Farm of Muiceron; [also] Madame Agnes; tr. from the French. 2d ed. 8°. '74. $1.50 ..... *Cath. Pub.*

Farm on the mountains. Arnold, F. $1.50 ..... *Hoyt.*

Farm talk. Brackett, G. E. $1; 50c. .... *Lee & S.*

Farm-yard A B C. sq. 12°. '71. bds., 50c. .. *Routledge.*

Farman, Ella. Anna Maylie. 16°. '73. $1.50 .. *Lothrop.*
— Cooking Club of Tu-whit Hollow. ill. 16°. '76. $1.25. *Lothrop.*
— Girl's (A) money. ill. 16°. '74. $1 .... *Lothrop.*
— Grandma Crosby's household. ill. 16°. '73. $1. *Lothrop.*
— Little woman (A). ill. 16°. '73. $1 .... *Lothrop.*
— Mrs. Hurd's niece. ill. 16°. '76. $1.50 .... *Lothrop.*
— White hand (A). ill. 16°. '75. $1.50 .... *Lothrop.*
— *See also* Stories by Mrs. L. C. Moulton, etc.; — Two fortune-seekers.

Farmer, H: Mass in B flat; with Lat. and Eng. words. 8°. '59. $1.12–80c. .... *Ditson; Gordon.*

Farmer. O'Keefe, J. 15c. .... *French.*

Farmer and family. Knill, R. 25c. .... *Am. Tr.*

Farmer boy. Thayer, W. M. $1.50 .. *Lockwood, B. & Co.*

Farmer Burt's seed. Boyd, E. E. 80c. .. *J. A. Moore.*

Farmer Goodwin's rule. 18°. 30c. .... *Am. S. S.*
— *Same.* 18°. '66. 30c. .. *N. Y. Ref. Ch. Bd.; Pres. Com.*

Farmer Tompkins. Beecher, W. J. $1.25 .. *Pres. Bd.*

Farmer's barn book; by Clater, Youatt, Skinner and Mills: diseases of oxen, sheep, swine, etc. ('50.) New ed. 12°. '69. $1.50 .... *Claxton.*

Farmer's boy. *See* Bloomfield, R.

Farmer's daughter. Cameron, *Mrs.* —. 50c. .. *Carter.*

Farmer's daughter. *See* Happy child's lib.

Farmer's instructor. Buel, J. $1.50 .... *Harper.*

Farmer's lib. 4 v. ill. 12°. $8 .... *Porter.*

Cont.: Horse in the stable and the field, by Stonehenge. — American gardener's assistant, by T. Bridgeman. — Book of the farm, by G. E. Waring, jr. — Trotting horse of America, by H. Woodruff.

Farmer's story. Bernard, W. B. 15c. .... *French.*

Farmer's vacation. Waring, G. E., *jr.* $5 ...... *Osgood.*

Farmers and planters' reference book. 4°. '69. $50. *J. A. Murphy.*

Farming for boys. Morris, E. $1.50 .... * *Osgood.*

Farming for fun. Small, G. G. 25c. ...... *Collin & S.*

Farnham, *Mrs.* E. W. Life in the prairie land. 12°. $1 .... *Harper.*

Farnham, J. T. Early days of California. ill. 12°. $1.75 .... *J. E. Potter.*

Farquhar, G: Beaux' stratagem: comedy. 16°. pap., 15c. .... *French.*
— Inconstant: comedy. 16°. pap., 15c. .... *French.*
— Recruiting officer: comedy. 16°. pap., 15c. .. *French.*
— *See also* Wycherly, W., Congreve, W., Vanbrugh, *Sir* J., *and* Farquhar, G.

Farquharson, Martha (*pseud.*) *See* Finley, Martha F.

Farr, E: Ancient history. 4 v. 12°. '56. shp., $4.50. *Wilstach.*

Farrand, Ht. S. Little hands. 16°. 75c. .. *Cong. Pub.*

Farrand, S. A. *See* Felter, S. A., *and* Farrand, S. A.

Farrar, Ad. Storey. Critical hist. of free thought in ref. to Christian religion. 12°. $2 .... *Appleton.*
— — *See also* Bampton lectures.

Farrar, Ad. Storey, *continued.*
— Science in theology: sermons. 12°. '60. $1. *Smith, E. & Co.*

Farrar, C. S. The war: its causes and consequences. 12°. '64. $1.25 .... *Eyrich.*

Farrar, Eliza Ware. Recollections of seventy years. 16°. $1.50 .... * *Osgood.*

Farrar, F: W: College lib. 3 v. 12°. $5; ea., $1.75. *Dutton.*

Cont.: Eric; or, little by little. — St. Winifred's; or, the world of school. — Julian Home.

— Fall of man, and other sermons. 2d [chp.] ed. fp. 8°. '71. $1.50 .... *Macmillan.*
— Life of Christ; with notes, app., index, etc. 2 v. 8°. '74. $6; — in 1 v. without notes and app. 8°. '75. $2.50 .... *Cassell; Dutton.*
— *Same;* with Am. app. giving tr. of non-Eng. matter. 2d Am. ed., with introd. by T. Lewis. roy. 8°. '75. $4.50–$7.50 .... *Wendell.*
— Seekers after God: lives of Seneca, Epictetus and Marcus Aurelius. ill. 12°. $1.75 .... *Lippincott.*
— *Same.* (Sunday lib.) cr. 8°. '68. $1.75 .. *Macmillan.*
— Silence and the voices of God, with other sermons 12°. '74. $1 .... *Dutton.*
— *Same.* New ed. cr. 8°. '75. $1.25 .... *Macmillan.*
— Witness of hist. to Christ. *See* Hulsean lectures.

Farrar, Tim. Manual of the U. S. Const. 3d ed., rev 8°. '72. $3.50 .... *Little, B. & Co.*

Farrar, W. H. Arithmetical problems. 12°. hf. roan 75c. — Key. 12°. 75c. .... *Ware.*

Farrell, J: Dumb maid of Genoa: melo-drama. 16° pap., 15c. .... *French.*

Farren, G. Bill in chancery. 8°. '66. $3 .. *E. B. Myers.*

Farther disc. of the present state of the Indians in New Eng. conc. the progress of the Gospel among them. Lond., 1661. [Reprint.] 4°. $2; large pap., $3 .... *Sabin.*
— *See also* Strength out of weakness.

Fascinating individual. Danvers, H. 15c. .... *French.*

Fashion. Ritchie, A. C. M. 15c. .... *French.*

Fashion. Wall, H. 25c. .... *West, J. & Co.*

Fashion; or, Siska von Roosemael. Conscience, H. 50c. .... *Strong.*

Fashion and famine. Stephens, A. S. $1.75; $1.50 *Peterson.*

Fashion and feeling: comedy. 16°. pap., 15c. .. *French.*

Fashion and folly. Baker, H. N. W. $1.25 .. *H. A. Young.*

Fashionable dissipation. *See* Fuller, M. V.

Fashionable letter writer. 16°. bds., 60c. .... *Miller.*

Fashionable life. *See* Edgeworth, Maria.

Fasquelle, L: Colloquial reader: narratives in Fr. for tr.; with conversational exercises, ref. and vocab. 12°. '53. $1.25 .... *Ivison.*
— Course of Fr. for beginners. 12°. '58. 90c. .. *Ivison.*
— Esprit de la conversation française: manual of Fr. conversation. 12°. '57. $1.25 .... *Ivison.*
— Lessons in French; rev. by Prof. de Lolme. 2 pts 8°. ea., $1.25; in 1 v., $2. — Key. 75c. .. *Cassell.*
— New method of learning French, analytic and synthetic. 12°. '60. $1.88. — Key. $1.25 .. *Ivison.*

Fast coach. Claridge, C. J., *and* Souter, R., *jr.* 15c *French.*

Fast family: comedy. 16°. pap., 15c. .... *Happy.*

Fast friends. Trowbridge, J. T. $1.25 .... *Porter.*

Fast in the ice. Ballantyne, R. M. 75c. ...... *Porter.*

Fast in the ice. *See* Library of travel.

Fast life in London and Paris. 8°. pap., 25c. .. *De Witt.*

Fast life on the modern highway. Taylor, J. $1.50 $1 .... *Harper.*

Fast or feast: pastoral idyl. sm. 4°. '76. $1 .. *Lee & S.*

Fast train: farce. 16°. pap., 15c. .... *French.*

Fastre, J. A. M. Acts of the early martyrs. 4 v. 12°. '71–'76. ea., $1.50 .... *Cunningham.*

Fatal blow; or, the effects of anger. 18°. 17c.; 22c. *Am. Bapt.*

Fatal boots. *See* Thackeray, W. M.

Fatal brand: drama. 16°. pap., 15c. .... *French.*

Fatal dower. Richmond, E. J. 60c. ..... *Nat. Temp.*

Fatal dowry. Massinger, P. 15c. .... *French.*

Fatal fall. 18°. 18c. .... *Am. S. S.*

Fatal glass: drama. 16°. pap., 15c. .... *French.*

Fatal ladder; or, Harry Linford. 18°. 40c. .. *Am. S. S.*

Fatal marriage. Southworth, E. D. E. N. $1.75; $1.50 .... *Peterson.*

Fatal marriages. Cockton, H. 75c. .... *Peterson.*

Fatal passion. Bomard, C. $1.75 .... *Carleton.*

Fatal secret. Glenwood, I. $2 .... *J. E. Potter.*

Fatal snow storm. Barrymore, W. 15c. ..... *French.*

Fatal tree. 8°. pap., 25c. .... *De Witt.*

Fatality. Boaden, C. 15c. .... *French.*

Fate (The). James, G. P. R. 50c. .... *Harper.*

Fate and fortunes of O'Neils and O'Donnells. 12°. $2. *Sadlier.*

Fate of Calais. Dibdin, T. 15c. .... *French.*

Fate of Marvin. Hogg, T. E. $2 .... *E. H. Cushing.*

Fated to be free. Ingelow, J. $1.75 .... *Roberts.*

Father and daughter. *See* Bremer, F.

Father and son. Ball, E. 15c. .... *French.*

Father Brighthopes. *See* Trowbridge, J. T.

Father Clement. *See* Kennedy, Grace.

Father Connell. *See* Banim, J. *and* M.

Father Darcy. Marsh-Caldwell, A. 75c. .... *Harper.*

Father De Lisle; or, Tyborne and its victims in the days of Queen Elizabeth; by author of "Eastern hospitals and English nurses." [Fiction.] 16°. 60c.; $1 .... *Sadlier.*

Father Fitzroy; or, the martyr of a secret: tale of the Irish famine. 12°. $1.50 .... *O'Shea.*

Father Gabrielle's fairy. Peckham, M. C. 80c. *Am. Unit.*

Father Jerome's library for little folks. 12 v. 32°. $3.60; pap., $2.40 .... *Sadlier.*

Father Kemp's old folks' concert music. obl. 8°. '74. bds., 50c.; pap., 40c. .... *Ditson.*

Father Laval. McSherry, J. 60c.; 80c. ... *Murphy.*

Father Merrill. *See* Chellis, M. D.

Father Merrill series. 3 v. 16°. $4.50 ..... *Crowell.*
Cont.: Father Merrill, by M. D. Chellis. — Jack Masters, by L. A. Mills. — Two families, by A. Shaw.

Father Miller. Hoffmann, F. 75c. ..... *Ref. Ch. Pub.*

Father Muller; or, the good heart. ('72.) New ed. 16°. '75. $1.25 .... *Hoyt.*

Father Oswald. 18°. '51. $1; $1.25 .... *Murphy.*

Father Prout (*pseud.*) *See* Mahoney, F.

Father Prout's reliques. *See* Mahoney, F.

Father Roach. *See* Lover, S.

Father Rowland: a No. Am. tale. 18°. 60c. .. *Cath. Pub.*

Father Sheehy. Sadlier, M. A. 50c.; 75c. .. *Sadlier.*

Father Tom and the pope. *See* Murray, J. F.

Fatherhood of God. Crawford, T. J. $4.50. *Scribner, W. & A.*

Fatherland ser.; tr. from the German. 1st ser. 6 v. ill. 16°. $4.85 .... (?)*Luth. Pub.*
Cont.: Cottage by the lake, 75c. — In the midst of the North Sea, 75c. — Anton, the fisherman, 85c. — René, the little Savoyard, 85c. — Fritz; or, filial obedience, 65c. — Geyer Walty, $1.

— *Same.* 2d ser. 6 v. ill. 16°. $5.10 .. (?)*Luth. Pub.*
Cont.: Under the earth, 70c. — Olaf Thorlaksen, $1. — Treasure of the Inca, 85c. — Buried in the snow, 80c. — Dominic, $1.10. — Seppeli, the Swiss boy, 65c.

— *Same.* 3d ser. 5 v. ill. 16°. $4.70 .. (?)*Luth. Pub.*
Cont.: Greek slave: or, filial love, $1.10. — Leonhard, the runaway, 50c. — Little Madelon; or, maternal love, $1. — Gottlieb Frey, $1.10. — Schoolmaster and his son, $1.

Fatherland ser., *continued.*

— *Same.* 4th ser. 5 v. ill. 16°. $5.35 .. (?)*Luth. Pub.*
Cont.: Iron age of Germany, $1.10. — Wolfgang, prince of Anhalt, $1.25. — Little cloister ruin, 70c. — Iron head, $1.15. — Three kings, $1.15.

— *Same.* 5th ser. 5 v. ill. 16°. $5.10 .. (?)*Luth. Pub.*
Cont.: Valley mill, $1. — Hop blossoms, 85c. — Faithful unto death, $1.25. — The emerald, $1. — Self-will, $1.

— *Same.* 6th ser. 4 v. ill. 16°. $4.60 .. (?)*Luth. Pub.*
Cont.: Knight and peasant, $1. — Gustavus Vasa, $1.20. — Day in Capernaum, $1.25. — Hans Egede, $1.15.

— *Same.* 7th ser. 6 v. ill. 16°. $5 .... (?)*Luth. Pub.*
Cont.: Salzburger exodus, 85c. — Anne du Bourg, $1.10. — Rich man and the poor man, 65c. — Herdsman of Dambach, 80c. — Three bank notes, 85c. — Christmas, 75c.

— *Same.* 8th ser. v. 1: Blind girl of Wittenberg. ill. 16°. $1.50 .... (?)*Luth. Pub.*

Father's care. *See* Mother's last words.

Father's coming home. 16°. '64. $1 .. *Meth. Bk. Conc.*

Father's letters to his children. 18°. 35c. ... *Am. S. S.*

Father's letters to his daughter. West, R. A. 35c. *Am. Tr.*

Father's letters to his son. 18°. 35c. .... *Am. S. S.*

Father's promise. 18°. 17c.; 22c. .... *Am. Bapt.*

Father's stories. 18°. 18c. .... *Am. S. S.*

Father's story of Charley Ross. Ross, C. K. $2. *J. E. Potter.*

Father's tales of the French revolution. 18°. '66. 50c. *Cunningham.*

Fathers and sons. *See* Hook, Thdr.

Fathers and sons. Turgénieff, I. $1.25 .... *Holt.*

Fathers of the Congregation of the Most Holy Redeemer. *See* Mission book.

Faugh-a-ballagh song-book (The). ('73.) 3d ed. 18°. '76. 25c. .... *Kenedy.*

Fault-finding. *See* Gardner, *Mrs.* H. C.

Faunce, D. W. Christian (The) in the world. 16°. '74. $1.50 .... *Roberts.*

— Words and acts of the apostles. 18°. '71. bds., 15c. *Graves.*

— Words and works of Jesus. 18°. '69. bds., 15c. *Graves.*

Faurot, Randal. Pilgrim's progress, from the City of Destruction to the celestial City of Refuge, from a Gospel stand-point. 12°. $1 .... *Chase.*

Fausset, A. R., *and* Smith, B. M. Commentary on the poetical books of the Scriptures. 12°. $1.50. (?)*Martien.*

— *See also* Jamieson, R., Fausset, A. B., *and* Brown, D.

Faust. *See* Goethe, J. W. v.

Faust. *See* Gounod, C. F.

Faust: burlesque. 16°. pap., 15c. .... *French.*

Faust, a romance of the secret tribunals. Reynolds, G. W. M. 50c. .... *De Witt.*

Faust and Marguerite. Carre, M. 15c. *De Witt; French.*

Faust's death. Moelling, C. E. 75c. ...... *Lippincott.*

Faust's Leben, Thaten, etc. 12°. pap., 15c. .. *Radde.*

Faustus. Soane, G. 15c. .... *French.*

Fauvel-Gouraud, Fs. Phreno-mnemotechnic dict.: philos. classification of homophonic words of the Eng. lang. 8°. $2 .... *Wiley.*

— Phreno-mnemotechny; or, the art of memory: lectures. 8°. $2 .... *Wiley.*

Favored colt. Bolton, J. 40c. .... *Whittaker.*

Favorita (La). *See* Donizetti, G.

Favorite (The). Giffe, W. T. per doz., $7.50 .. *Benham.*

Favorite animals. ill. 16°. 25c. .... *Routledge.*

Favorite authors: companion-book of prose and poetry. ill. sm. 4°. '60. $3; mor., $6 .... *Osgood.*

Favorite colored picture book. [Toy-book.] ill. roy. 8°. $1 .... (?)*McLoughlin.*

Favorite Eng. poems; by Milton, Gray, Dryden, etc. (Cottage lib.) ill. 16°. pap., 30c. .. *Huntington.*

Favorite fairy tales. Audubon, H. $1.50.. *World Pub.*
Favorite fairy tales for little folks. ill. sq. 16°. $1. *Miller.*
Favorite narratives for the Christian household. 12°. $1 .... *Nelson.*
Favorite picture book for the nursery. ill. roy. 4°. $1.10 .... *Nelson.*
Favorite poems by gifted bards. 2d ed. ill. fp. 4°. $2.50 .... *Cassell.*
Favorite prescriptions of living practitioners. Green, H. $2.50 .... *Wiley.*
Favorite series. [Toy-books.] 6 nos. ill. 8°. per gross, $24 .... (?) *McLoughlin.*
Cont.: When the cat's away the mice will play. — Favorite animals and birds. — Lost on the sea shore. — Rhymes and jingles. — Mary's new doll. — Baby's birthday.
Favorite songs. Christie, H. R. *and* T. H. R. 60c. *R. W. Carroll.*
Favorite tales. 5 v. 12°. $5 .... *Nelson.*
Cont.: The playfellow, by Mrs. Hofland. — Way of the world, by Mrs. Hofland. — Nellie Nowlan. — Fairy stories. — Scenes of the olden times.
Fawcett, Edg. Asses' ears. 12°. $1.75 ... *Carleton.*
— Ellen Story: a novel of society. 8°. '76. $1.25; pap., 75c. .... *Hale.*
— Purple and fine linen. 12°. $1.75 .... *Carleton.*
Fawcett, H: Economic position of the British labourer. fp. 8°. '65. $1.50 .... *Macmillan.*
— Manual of political economy. 4th ed., rev. and enl. cr. 8°. '74. $3.50 .... *Macmillan.*
— Pauperism: its causes and remedies. cr. 8°. '71. $2.25 .... *Macmillan.*
— Speeches on some current political questions. 8°. '73. $3.50 .... *Macmillan.*
— *and Mrs.* M. G. Essays and lectures on political and social subjects. 8°. '72. $3.50 ..... *Macmillan.*
Fawcett, *Mrs.* Millicent G. Political economy for beginners; with questions. 18°. '70. $1.. *Macmillan.*
— Tales in polit. economy. fp. 8°. '74. $1.. *Macmillan.*
— *See also* Fawcett, H. *and Mrs.* M. G.
Faxon, W: *See* Agassiz, A., *and* Garman, S. W.
Faxon's ill. handbook of summer travel. Sears, E. S. $1 .... *Faxon.*
Fay, Clara C. Boston receipts: 200 common-sense receipts for economical and healthful cooking. [Interleaved.] 16°. '76. pap., 50c... *Williams.*
Fay, F. R. On Joshua; — Romans. *See* Lange, J. P., Commentary.
Fay, Jos. D. Digest of statutes of N. Y. 3 v. roy. 8°. '74. shp., $25.50 .... *Cockcroft.*
— Guide to changes in the statute law of N. Y., 1858–'73. 8°. '73. shp., $2 .... *Baker, V. & Co.*
Fay, Thdr. S. First steps in geography. 12°. hf. bd., $1 .... *Putnam.*
— Great outline of geog. 3d ed., enl.; with col. atlas. 2 v. f°. '69. $2.75 .... *Putnam.*
Fayoum (The). Lenoir, P. $2.50 .... *Routledge.*
Fazio. Milman, H. H. 15c. .... *French.*
Fear and love. 18°. 30c. .... *Am. S. S.*
Fear not; [also] Rest in Christ. 32°. 25c... *Pres. Bd.*
Fearful tragedy in Seven Dials. Selby, C. 15c. *De Witt; French.*
Fears for democracy. Ingersoll, C. $1.75; $1.25. *Lippincott.*
Feast: Ethiop. drama. 16°. pap., 15c. *French; Happy.*
Feasts of sacrifice and remembrance: origin and teaching of the Lord's supper; with introd. pref. by Bp. of Ripon. 32°. 75c. .... *Nelson.*
Feathered arrow. *See* Gerstäcker, F:
Feathered tribes of the British islands. Mudie, R. 2 v. ea., $3 .... *Lippincott.*
Feathers for arrows. Spurgeon, C. H. $1.25.. *Sheldon.*
Featherstonhaugh, G. W. *See* United States, *Corps of Eng.*
Feats on the fiord. *See* Martineau, H.
Fechner, W: Systematical Germ. copy books: new ser. 7 nos. obl. 8°. '76. per doz., pap., $1.80.. *Steiger.*
Federalist (The): essays on the Const. by Hamilton, Jay and Madison; reprint from orig. text, ed. by H. B. Dawson. ('64.) New ed. 8°. '74. $3; $2.50 .... *Scribner.*
— *Same;* [also] Continentalist, and other papers, by Hamilton; ed. by J. C. Hamilton. 8°. $3.50; shp., $4.25 .... *Lippincott.*
Federati of Italy. Ditson, G. L. $1.50 .... *Colby.*
Feier (Die) d. Weihnachtsabends. Behr, H. G. 15c. *Ludwig.*
Feiling, C. A. *See* Tales from the German.
Feldner, E: Kleine deutsche Sprachlehre f. deutsch-am. Schulen. 12°. '55. bds., 30c...... *Steiger.*
Feldweibel (Der). *See* Zschokke, H.
Felice, G. de. How and why; or, search the Scriptures; tr. from the Fr. ill. 16°. '72. $1.. *Lothrop.*
— La voix du colporteur biblique. 18°. '47. 30c.; pap., 10c. .... *Am. Tr.*
Felina de Chambure. *See* Dumas, A.
Feline, Adr. Manual of French pronunc., with extracts from the Fr. classics, written in phonetic characters. New ed., enl. by W. Watson. 16°. $1.25 .... *Lee & S.*
Felix Holt. *See* Eliot, G:
Felix Kent. Hoffman, M. J. $2 .... *O'Shea.*
Fell, Archie (*pseud.*) *See* Capron, M. J.
Fell, Wa. W. On guaranty and surety. 8°. shp., $6.50. *W. C. Little.*
Felon's bond. Suter, W. E. 15c. .... *French.*
Fellow that looks like me. Durivage, O. F. 15c. *De Witt.*
Fellowes, D. Fourth school reader. 18°. '57. 25c. *Claxton.*
Fellows, A. N. First steps in Eng. grammar. 16°. 25c. .... *Taintor.*
Fellowship (The). Errett, I. 10c. .... *Chase.*
Fellowship: letters to my sister mourners. 16°. '68. 50c. .... *Pott.*
— *Same.* fp. 8°. '68. $1 .... *Macmillan.*
— *Same.* 16°. '68. $1.25 .... *Randolph.*
Fells of Swarthmore Hall. Webb, M. $1.25.. *Lippincott.*
Fels, Gsell. Venice; with photogs. and designs by T. Choulant, F. Eibner, E. Kirchner, etc.; Eng. tr. by J. Gostwick. roy. 4°. $20 .... *Stroefer.*
Fels (Der) v. Erz. Brachvogel, A. E. 2 v. ea., 50c. *Morwitz.*
Felter, S. A. [Arithmetics.] ('62–'72.) New ed. 10 v. '76 .... *Scribner.*
Cont.: First lessons in numbers, 16°, bds., 25c. — Grammar school arith., 12°, bds., 95c. — Intellectual arith., 16°, bds., 45c. — Intermediate arith., 12°, 75c. — *Same;* without answers, 80c. — New pract. arith., prep. by S. H. Peabody, 12°, $1. — *Same;* without answers, $1. — Primary arith., 16°, bds., 35c. — *Same;* without answers, 35c. — Teacher's manual of arith., 16°, bds., 25c.
— *and* Farrand, S. A. New intermediate arith. ('75.) New ed. 12°. '76. 80c. .... *Scribner.*
Felton, Corn. Conway. Familiar letters from Europe. 16°. $1.50 .... *Estes.*
— Greek reader. 12°. *net,* $1.75 .... *Hamersley.*
— Lectures on Greece, ancient and modern. 8°. '67. $5 .... *Osgood.*
— Life of W. Eaton. *See* Sparks, J., Library of Am. biog.
— Selections from Gk. historians; with notes. ('52.) 18th ed. 12°. '72. $2 .... *Allyn.*
— Selections from modern Gk. writers; with notes. 2d ed. 12°. '57. $1.25 .... *Allyn.*
Female Bluebeard. Sue, E. 50c. .... *Peterson.*
Female depravity; or, the house of death. 8°. pap., 25c. .... *De Witt.*
Female detective. Hazlewood, C. H. 15c. .. *De Witt.*

Female life in N. Y. ill. 8°. pap., 50c......*Peterson.*
Female Massaroni. Somerset, C. A. 15c.....*French.*
Female minister. [Fiction.] 8°. pap., 50c...*Harper.*
Female spy. Bennett, E. 25c..........*U. P. James.*
Feminine soul. Strutt, E. 50c.; 25c...*H. H. Carter.*
Femmes (Les) qui pleurent. Siraudin, P., *and* Thiboust, L. 25c..........*Holt.*
Femmes savantes (Les). *See* Molière, J. B. P.
Fenelon, —. Apples of gold. 64°. 15c.....*Claxton.*
Fénelon, François de S. de la M. Aventures (Les) de Télémaque, fils d'Ulysse. 12°. $1.50. *G. R. Lockwood.*
— *Same.* 12°. $2..........*Routledge.*
— *Same;* ed. by A. Bolmar. 12°. $1.25. —Key. 12°. $1..........*Sheldon.*
— *Same;* ed. by Le Brun. 12°. $1.25......*Appleton.*
— — *Same.* 12°. hf. roan, $1.40.........*Lippincott.*
— *Same;* ed. by Surenne. 18°. 75c........*Appleton.*
— *Same;* with notes by Fasquelle. 12°. '50. $1.25. *Ivison.*
— *Eng.* Adventures of Telemachus; tr. by Dr. Hawkesworth. ill. 8°. $2; hf. cf., $4..*Appleton.*
— — *Same;* with life of F. by Lamartine, and biog. notices, etc.; ed. by O. W. Wight. cr. 8°. $2.25; hf. cf., $4..........*Hurd & H.*
— Christian counsel and spirit. letters; tr. 18°. $1..*Dodd.*
— Christian counsels; sel. from [his] devotional works; tr. by A. M. James. 16°. '70. $1.25....*Dutton.*
— Lives of anc. philosophers; tr., with notes and life of author, by J. Cormack. 18°. 75c......*Harper.*
— On the education of a daughter. sq. 16°. '51. 60c.; 80c..........*Murphy.*
— Selections from writings; with introd. by T. S. Preston, and sketch of life by J. G. R. Hassard. 12°. $1.25; $1.75..........*O'Shea.*
— Spiritual progress; or, instruct. in divine life of the soul; incl. Christian counsel and spiritual letters, and Mme. Guyon's Short and easy meth. of prayer; ed. by J. W. Metcalf. 12°. '53. $1.50......*Dodd.*
— Use of the Bible. *See* Bible question fairly tested.
Fenian chief; or, martyr of '65. 8°. pap., 25c...*De Witt.*
Fenian spy: Ethiop. drama. 16°. pap., 15c. *French; Happy.*
Fenn, G: Manville. Book (A) of fair women: eng., with poems. fp. 4°. $3..........*Cassell.*
— Hollowdell Grange; or, holiday hours in a country home. ill. 16°. $1.25..........*Routledge.*
— Original penny readings: short sketches. 3d ed. 2 v. fp. 8°. $2.50..........*Routledge.*
— "Ship ahoy!" a yarn in thirty-six cable lengths. ill. 8°. pap., 40c..........*Harper.*
— Treasure hunters. 8°. pap., 40c..........*Harper.*
— World of wit and humor: sketches and poems. ill. 8°. *$3.50; $4; shp., $4.50; hf. mor., $6; mor., $10..........*Am. Pub.*
Fenner, C. S. Vision: its optical defects, and the adaptation of spectacles. ill. 8°. '75. $3.50..*Lindsay.*
Fenollosa, Manuel. The piano-forte: instruction book. 4°. bds., $2.50..........*Ditson.*
Fenton's quest. Braddon, M. E. 50c.......*Harper.*
Fentons (The). Spottswood, L. A. $1.25..*Meth. Epis.*
Fenwick, S: Morbid states of the stomach and duodenum, and their rel. to diseases of other organs. pl. 8°. '68. $5..........*Lindsay.*
— Student's guide to medical diagnosis. 3d Eng. ed., rev. and enl. ill. roy. 12°. $2.25..........*Lea.*
Fergus Morton. *See* Macduff, J. R.
Ferguson, A. History of the progress and termination of the Rom. republic. 12°. 75c........*Harper.*
Ferguson, S: Hibernian nights' entertainments. 12°. '60. $1.75..........*Haverty.*
Fergusson, Ja. History of architecture in all countries. 2d ed. v. 1, 2. ill. 8°. (Lond.) '75. hf. mor., $24..........*Little, B. & Co.*

Fergusson, Ja., *continued.*
— *Same.* New ed., rev. 4 v. '76. ill. 8°. hf. roxb. *Scribner, W. & A.*
Cont.: v. 1-2, Ancient architecture, $24.—v. 3, Indian and eastern architecture, $17.—v. 4, Modern architecture, $12.
— History of the modern styles of archit. 2d ed. eng. 8°. (Lond.) '73. hf. mor., $12.50..*Little, B. & Co.*
— Rude stone monuments in all countries: their age and uses. 234 ill. 8°. (Lond.) '72. hf. mor., $8.50. *Little, B. & Co.*
— *Same.* 200 ill. 8°. $9..........*Scribner, W. & A.*
Fern, Fanny (*pseud.*) *See* Parton, *Mrs.* S. P.
Fern bank series for girls. 5 v. 18°. $3...*Randolph.*
Cont.: Coming to the light.—Meggie of the Pines.—Babes in the basket.—Mary Burns.—Under the pear tree.
Fern Glen. *See* Holt, M. H.
Fern Glen ser. 4 v. 16°. $5..........*Lothrop.*
Cont.: Fern Glen.—Little Toss.—Uncle Anthony.—Petite.
Fern paradise. Heath, F. G. $3....*Scribner, W. & A.*
Fernald, Woodbury M. First causes of character: view at foundations as operative before birth from hered. and spirit. sources. 16°. $1.50...*Lee & S.*
— True Christian life and how to attain it: essays. 12°. '74. $1.50..........*Lockwood, B. & Co.*
Fernande. Sardou, V. 15c..........*De Witt.*
Fernandez, B: Dias. Series of letters on the evidences of Christianity. 16°. 50c..........*Bloch.*
Fernando. *See* Schmid, C. v.
Ferncliffe. J., S. $1.50..........*Cunningham.*
Fernrohr (Das): e. Allegorie. 18°. 30c...*Ev. Assoc.*
Fern's Hollow. *See* Smith, Hannah.
Fernside lib. ('63.) 6th ed. 6 v. ill. 16°. '70. $7.50. *Perkinpine.*
Cont.: Ann Ash.—Anne Dalton.—Convict's sons.—Don't say so.—Errand boy.—Two firesides.
Fernwood; or, Hettie's birthday visit. 16°. 85c. *Am. S. S.*
Fernyhurst Court: an everyday story; by author of "Stony edge." ill. 8°. pap., 60c....*Lippincott.*
Ferree, Abby M. L. Spirituelle: directions in development. ('68.) 4th ed. 12°. '73. pap., 25c...*Colby.*
Ferrel, W: Converging series, ratio of diameter, and circumf. of circles. 4°. '71. pap., 50c. *Smith. Inst.*
Ferrero, E: Art of dancing; or, etiquette of the ball-room. 16°. pap., 50c.; bds., 75c.....*Dick & F.*
Ferrers, N. M. Treatise on trilinear co-ordinates, the method of reciprocal polars, and the theory of projections. 3d ed. cr. 8°. '76. $2.50..*Macmillan.*
— *See also* Cambridge Senate-House.
Ferrette, Jul. The Damascus ritual: an Arabic liturgy extracted partly from the Common prayer book. 16°. (Bagster.) 75c..........*Wiley.*
Ferrier, *Miss* Ma. Novels. 3 v. 12°. ea., pap., 25c. *Lippincott.*
Cont.: Destiny.—Inheritance.—Marriage.
— *Same.* 3 v. 16°. hf. roxb., $3.75.......*Routledge.*
— Marriage. 8°. pap., 50c..........*Harper.*
Ferris, I: Discourse commemorative of services and character of Rev. J. C. Guldin, March 29, 1863. 8°. pap., 25c..........*N. Y. Ref. Ch. Bd.*
— Memorial discourse; or, fifty years' ministry in the Ref. Ch. of Am., Feb. 26, 1871. 8°. pap., 25c. *N. Y. Ref. Ch. Bd.*
Ferrotypers' guide. 18°. pap., 75c......*Benerman.*
Ferry, Gbr. Vagabond life in Mexico. 12°. $1.50. *Harper.*
Ferryman of the Tiber. La Grange, A. K. de. $1.25. *O'Shea.*
Ferryman's child. 18°. 80c..........*Cong. Pub.*
— *See also* Sea-side stories.
Ferryman's family. Leslie, E. 75c..........*Nelson.*
Fertige Rechner (Der). 24°. 20c.........*Benziger.*

Fervent chrétien; ou, recueil de prières à l'usage des fidèles de toutes les conditions. 18°. *net*, 70c.; roan, 75c.; $1 .... *Benziger*.

Fervent prayer. Oxenden, A. 50c....... *Hammond*.

Fessenden, B. L. G. Modern school for the violin. 4°. '56. bds., $2.50 .... *Ditson*.

Fessing, Jos. Die versuchte Ausrottung der kathol. Religion in Engl. unter Heinrich VIII. u. seinen Nachfolgern, Wm. Cobbett nacherzählt. 12°. pap., 20c .... *Herder*.

Fessler, Jos. True and false infallibility. 2d ed. 16°. pap., 50c .... *Cath. Pub*.

— *See also* Vaughan, H., *and* Ullathorne, W. B., Reply in Gladstone controversy.

Festival chimes. Martin, S. W. $1.50...... *Peters*.

Festival glee book. Root, G. F., *and* Bradbury, W. B. $2.25 .... *Ditson*.

Festival of Ashtaroth. Middleton, A. C. 15c. *Mendum*.

Festus. *See* Bailey, P. J.

Fetches. *See* Banim, J. *and* M.

Fetich in theology. Miller, J. $1.25......... *Dodd*.

Fetis, Fs. Ja. Music explained to the world: how to understand music and enjoy its performance; tr. for the Bost. Acad. of Mass. 8°. bds., $1.50. *Ditson*.

Fetridge, W. Pembroke. Harper's handbook for travellers in Europe and the east. [Annual.] 3 v. maps and plans. 12°. ea., leath., $3; — in 1 v. leath., $7 .... *Harper*.

— Harper's phrase-book: handbook of travel-talk for travellers and schools. sq. 4°. $1.50... *Harper*.

— Rise and fall of the Paris commune in 1871. map and por. 12°. $2 .... *Harper*.

Fette, W. Eliot. *See* Dickens, C., Dialogues.

Fetter, G. W. Philadelphia speller. 12°. '76. bds., 40c. .... *Eldredge*.

Fetter Lane to Gravesend: Ethiop. farce. 16°. pap., 15c .... *Ames*.

Fettered. *See* Phillips, W.

Fettered for life. Blake, L. D. $1.50; $1.. *Sheldon*.

Feudal times. White, J. 15c............... *French*.

Feudge, *Mrs*. Fanny R. Eastern side; or, missionary life in Siam. 16°. $1.50 .... *Am. Bapt*.

— Ella's battles. 16°. $1 .... *Am. Bapt*.

— Enlisted for life. ill. 16°. '71. $1 .... *Am. Tr*.

Feuerbach, A. R. German criminal trials; tr. by Lady Duff Gordon. 12°. $1 .... *Harper*.

Feuerbach, L: Essence of Christianity; tr. by Geo. Eliot [Mrs. Lewes]. 12°. '75. $3.... *Somerby*.

— Essence of religion, God the image of man: man's dependence upon nature the last and only source of relig. 12°. '73. 75c .... *Somerby*.

Feuersbrunst (Die). *See* Schmid, C. v.

Feuillet, Octave. Camors: a love story; tr. from the Fr. 12°. $1.75; pap., $1.50 .... *Peterson*.

— Honour before wealth: drama; tr. from the Fr. 16°. pap., 15c .... *French*.

— Led astray; tr. from the Fr. 12°. $1.75.. *Carleton*.

— Marriage in high life; tr. by C. Logan. [Fiction.] 12°. '76. $1.50; pap., 75c. — (Intern. ed.) $1.25. *Porter*.

— Roman d'un jeune homme pauvre. [Fiction.] ('65.) New ed. 12°. '76. $1.25 .... *Holt*.

— *Eng*. Romance of a poor young man. 12°. $1.50. *Miller*.

— Roman d'un jeune homme pauvre. [Comedy.] With Eng. notes by F. Bôcher. ('66.) New ed. 12°. '76. pap., 40c .... *Holt*.

— Story of Sibylle; tr. from the Fr. [Fiction.] 8°. '71. $1.25; pap., 75c .... *Estes*.

— Village (Le): scènes provinciales. With vocab. ('65.) New ed. 12°. '72. pap., 25c .... *Holt*.

Feval, P. *See* Bourgeois, A. *and* Feval, P.

Few days in Athens. Wright, F. 75c....... *Mendum*.

Few friends and how they amused themselves. Dodge, M. M. $1.25 .... *Lippincott*.

Few leisure hours. 18°. 40c............. *Cong. Pub*.

Few thoughts for a few friends. Crawford, A. A. $2. *Jansen*.

Few words about the devil. Bradlaugh, C. $1.50. *Somerby*.

Few words of advice to ladies on travelling. S., H. M. L. 50c .... *Cook*.

Fewsmith, J. The prayer-meeting. 32°. 20c.; pap., 10c .... *Pres. Bd*.

Fewsmith, W: *and* Singer, Edg. A. Elementary grammar of Eng. 12°. hf. bd., 45c.......... *Sower*.

— — Grammar of the Eng. lang. 12°. hf. bd., 65c. *Sower*.

Ffirth, J: Life of Rev. B: Abbott. 18°. '39. 55c. *Meth. Bk. Conc*.

Fiammina (La). Clapp, W. W. 15c........ *French*.

Fibel [Alte] nach der Buchstabirmethode. ('55.) 30th ed. 8°. '75. 20c .... *Barthel*.

Fibel (Neue) nach der Schreib-Lese-Methode. ('70.) 12th ed. 8°. '76. 20c .... *Barthel*.

— *See also* Neue.

Fichte, J. G. Science of knowledge, theoretically and practically considered; tr. by A. E. Kröger. 12°. $2 .... *Lippincott*.

— Science of rights; tr. by A. E. Kröger. 12°. $2. *Lippincott*.

Fick, C. J. H. Affen Religion (Die). [Dialogue in verse.] 16°. '72. 15c .... *Barthel*.

— Geheimniss (Das) der Bosheit im römischen Pabstthum. 2d ed., enl. 8°. '74. 75c...... *Barthel*.

— Lutherbuch (Das), od. Leben u. Thaten d. Martin Luther. ('50.) 15th ed. 8°. '75. 30c... *Barthel*.

Fickle girl. 18°. 40c .... *Dutton*.

Ficklin, Jos. Algebraic problems. 12°. '74. $1.25. — Key. $1 .... *Ivison*.

— Complete algebra. (Robinson's shorter course.) 12°. '74. $2. — Key. $1 .... *Ivison*.

Fiddling Freddy. Floyd, C. $1........... *Randolph*.

Fidelio. *See* Beethoven, L. van; — Ditson.

Fidelity rewarded; or, little George. ('72.) New ed. 16°. '76. $1 .... *Hoyt*.

Fido and Frank. *See* Llewellyn, E. L., Dove's nest lib.

Fieber, F: Treatment of nerv. diseases with electricity; tr. by G. M. Schweig. 12°. '74. 75c... *Putnam*.

Field, Chester. Scripture ill. by facts, incidents and anecdotes; with introd. by Rev J. Todd. 18°. 75c .... *Harper*.

Field, D: Dudley. Centennial address; with hist. sketches of Middletown and its parishes; also of Cromwell, Portland, Chatham and Middle Haddam, Conn. 12°. '53. $3.......... *J. W. Bliss*.

— Outlines of an international code. 2d ed., rev. and enl. 8°. shp., $7.50........... *Baker, V. & Co*.

Field, F. E. Green-houses and green-house plants; with introd. by W. C. Bryant. ill. 12°. '70. 75c. *Putnam*.

Field, G: Rudiments of colors and coloring; rev. by R. Mallett. ill. cr. 8°. $2.......... *Routledge*.

Field, G: W. Treatise on Iowa county and township officers; with forms. 2d ed., rev. 8°. '76. shp., $5 .... *Mills*.

— Treatise on the law of damages. 8°. '76. *net*, shp., $6.50 .... *Mills*.

Field, H: M. History of the Atlantic telegraph. ill. 12°. '66. $1.25 .... *Scribner*.

— The Irish confederates, and the rebellion of 1798. por. and map. 12°. $1.50 .... *Harper*.

Field, *Mrs*. H: M. Home sketches in France. por. 12°. '75. $1.50 .... *Putnam*.

Field, Hor. Glitter and gold. cr. 8°. $2.. *Lippincott*.

— Heroism. 12°. $1.50 .... *Lippincott*.

Field, Hor., *continued.*
— Home (A) for the homeless; or, union with God. 12°. $3.75 .... *Lippincott.*

Field, J. M. Drama in Pokerville. ill. 12°. pap., 75c. *Peterson.*

Field, Kate. Hap hazard: travel and character sketches in America and Europe. (Saunterer's ser.) 18°. '73. $1.25 .... *Osgood.*
Pen photographs of C. Dickens and his readings. ill. 12°. '71. $1.50 .... *Osgood.*
— Planchette's diary. 12°. '68. pap., 50c... *Redfield.*
— Ten days in Spain. (Saunterer's ser.) ill. 18°. '74. $1.25 .... *Osgood.*

Field, M. Rural architecture. ill. and plans. 8°. $2. *Carleton.*

Field, Maunsell B. Memories of many men and of some women. 12°. $2 .... *Harper.*

Field, R: S. Provincial courts of N. J. *See* New Jersey Hist. Soc.

Field, T: W. Battle of Long Island; with preceding events and subsequent Am. retreat; with authentic doc. maps and eng. 8°. '69. $4.. *L. I. Hist.*
— Essay towards an Indian bibliography: catalogue of books rel. to Am. Indians in library of F.; with bibl. and hist. notes, etc. 8°. '73. $5.. *Scribner.*
— Pear culture. 12°. $1.25 .... *Judd.*

Field, Wa. Stones of the temple; or, lessons from the fabric and furniture of the church. ill. 12°. $2.50. *Appleton.*

Field and fold. Sidney, E. 50c. .... *So. Meth.*

Field and forest. Adams, W. T. $1.25 ..... *Lee & S.*

Field, cover and trap-shooting. Bogardus, A. H. $2. *Ford.*

Field, dungeon and escape. Richardson, A. D. *$3; $3.50; $5 .... *Am. Pub.*

Field flowers. Swift, J. M. $1.50.......... *Claxton.*

Field jewels for little gatherers: stories by Mrs. M. A. Mackarness, Rev. H. C. Adams, W. H. G. Kingston and others. 12 v. 12°. $3...... *Routledge.*

Field of cloth of gold. Brough, W. 15c..... *French.*

Field of forty footsteps: drama. 16°. pap., 15c. *French.*

Field of ice. Verne, J. $1.50.......... *Routledge.*

Fielding, H: Works; with essay on his life and genius by A. Murphy; ed. by J. P. Brown. New ed. 10 v. por. 8°. (Lond.) '72. $30; hf. cf., $50. *Little, B. & Co.*
— Novels; with memoir by Sir W. Scott. ill. 8°. $2; shp., $2.75........................ *World Pub.*
— History of Amelia. 16°. bds., 80c....... *Routledge.*
— *Same.* 12°. $1.50........................ *Harper.*
— History of Tom Jones, a foundling. 16°. bds., $1. 12°. pap., 50c..................... *Routledge.*
— *Same.* 2 v. ill. 12°. (Bohn.) $2.50.. *Little, B. & Co.*
— *Same.* 2 v. ill. 12°. (Bohn.) $2.80. *Scribner, W. & A.*
— *Same.* 2 v. ill. 12°. (Bohn.) $3....... *Lippincott.*
— *Same;* with memoir. ill. 12°. $1.25; bds., $1. *Routledge.*
— *Same;* with memoir of author by T. Roscoe. 2 v. 12°. $2.75 .... *Harper.*
— Joseph Andrews. 16°. bds., 80c. .... *Routledge.*
— Miser: comedy. 16°. pap., 15c. .... *French.*
— Tom Thumb: burlesque opera. 16°. pap., 15c. *French.*
— Writings and life. 8°. $2.50... *Appleton; Lee & S.*
— *and* Smollett, Tob. Selected works. 6 v. 12°. $9; hf. cf., $18.—16°. hf. roxb., $8 ..... *Routledge.*
Cont.: Tom Jones, by F.—Joseph Andrews, by F.—Amelia, by F.—Peregrine Pickle, by S.—Roderick Random, by S.—Humphrey Clinker, by S.

Fields, Ja. T: Barry Cornwall and his friends. (Vest pock. ser.) por. 32°. '76. 50c. .... *Osgood.*
— Hawthorne. (Vest pock. ser.) por. and ill. 32°. '75. 50c. .... *Osgood.*
— Yesterdays with authors. 12°. '72. $2; hf. cf., $4. *Osgood.*

Fields, W: (*ed.*) The scrap-book: tales and anecdotes. ('51.) 5th ed., rev. and enl. 8°. '74. $2. *Claxton.*

Fiera (La). Nota, A. 75c.................. *Holt.*

Fieschi Adorno, *St.* Cath. *See* Catharine Fieschi.

Fiesko. *See* Schiller, J. F. v.

Fifine at the fair. Browning, R. $1.50...... *Osgood.*

Fifteen days. Putnam, M. L. $1.50........ *Osgood.*

Fifteen decisive battles of the world. Creasy, E. S. $1.50 .... *Harper.*

Fifteen minutes around N. Y. 8°. pap., 25c... *De Witt.*

Fifteen years. Robinson, T. A. L. v. J. $1.50.. *Appleton.*

Fifteen years of a drunkard's life: melo-drama. 16°. pap., 15c........................ *French.*

Fifteen years of prayer in the Fulton St. meeting. *See* Prime, S. I.

Fifteen years' labor lost: drama. 16°. pap., 15c... *French.*

Fifth wheel: comedy. 12°. pap., 15c........ *De Witt.*

Fifty Catholic tracts on various subjects. 3d ed. 12°. '73. $1.25........................ *Cath. Pub*

Fifty fine poems. Summers, T. O. 60c. ... *So. Meth.*

Fifty pictures and stories for little ones. Ashton, S. G. $1 .... *Crowell.*

Fifty reasons why the Rom. Cath. religion ought to be preferred to all others. 16°. 25c........ *Strong.*

Fifty two village sermons. Burder, G. $1.50.. *Am. Tr.*

Fifty volume lib.; for Sunday schools. 50 v. 18°. $15. *Randolph.*
— *See also* New.

Fifty years ago. Willard, C. A. $1.50.... *Randolph.*

Fifty years in the magic circle. Blitz, A. *$2.. *Belknap.*

Fifty years in a Maryland kitchen. Howard, B. C. $1.50 .... *Turnbull.*

Fifty years in N. Y. Matthews, J. M. 25c. *N. Y. Ref. Ch. Bd.*

Fifty years a presiding elder. Cartwright, P. $1.50. *Cin. Meth. Bk. Conc.*

Fifty years' hist. of the temp. cause. Stebbins, J. E. *$2.50; $2.75 .... *Fitch.*

Figaro in London. A'Beckett, G. A. 15c.... *French.*

Fight at Dame Europa's school, shewing how the Germ. boy thrashed the French boy, and how the Eng. boy looked on. 12°. pap., 10c......... *Lee & S.*
— *Same.* 16°. '71. pap., 15c................ *Eyrich.*

Fighting the battle. Samuels, A. F. 50c.... *Lee & S.*

Fighting by proxy. Kenney, J. 15c......... *French.*

Fighting fire. Fowler, W. W. *$3; $3.50... *Dustin.*

Fighting for the union: Ethiop. drama. 16°. pap., 15c. *French; Happy.*

Fighting Joe. Adams, W. T. $1.50....... *Lee & S.*

Fighting their way. Proctor, —. $1.50.. *World Pub.*

Fighting the whales. Ballantyne, R. M. 75c... *Porter.*
— *See also* Library of travel and adventure.

Fights for the championship of Eng. 8°. pap., 50c. *De Witt.*

Figuier, L: Birds and reptiles: account of their various orders, with descrip. of habits, etc.; tr. from the Fr. wood-eng. 8°. $5 .... *Appleton.*
— *Same;* ed. by P. Gillmore. ill. cr. 8°. $3.50. *Appleton; Cassell.*
— Earth and sea; tr. from the Fr. ill. imp. 8°. '71. $6; hf. cf., $8.50...................... *Nelson.*
— Human race (The); tr. from the Fr. wood-eng. 8°. $6 .... *Appleton.*
— *Same;* rev. by R. Wilson. 242 ill. cr. 8°. $3.50. *Cassell.*
— Insect world: account of the orders of insects, with descrip. of habits, etc.; tr. from the Fr. wood-eng. 12°. $3.50; hf. cf., $5; cf., $6... *Appleton.*
— *Same.* 3d ed., rev. by P. M. Duncan. 570 ill. cr. 8°. $3.50...... .... *Cassell.*

Figuier, L: *continued.*
— Mammalia: their various orders and habits ill. by typical species; tr. from the Fr. wood-eng. 8°. $5; hf. cf., $7; cf., $8 .... *Appleton.*
— *Same;* adapted by E. P. Wright. 260 eng. 8°. $3.50 .... *Cassell.*
— Ocean world; tr. from the Fr. 3d ed., rev. by E. P. Wright. ill. cr. 8°. $3.50 .... *Appleton; Cassell.*
— Primitive man: theories of the descent of man; tr. from the Fr. ill. 8°. '71. $3.50 ...... *Putnam.*
— *Same.* wood-cuts. 8°. $4 .... *Appleton.*
— Tomorrow (The) of death; or, the future life according to science; tr. by S. R. Crocker. 16°. '72. $1.75 .... *Roberts.*
— Vegetable world; with glossary of botanical terms; tr. from the Fr. New ed., rev. ill. cr. 8°. $3.50. *Appleton; Cassell.*
— World before the deluge; tr. from the Fr. 4th ed., rev.; ed. by H. W. Bristow. ill. cr. 8°. $3.50. *Appleton; Cassell.*

Filbert tree (The). 16°. 75c. .... *Cong. Pub.*
File No. 113. Gaboriau, E. $1.25; 75c. ...... *Estes.*
Filia (*pseud.*) *See* Dorsey, S. A.
Filial love and other stories. 18°. 50c. ...... *O'Shea.*
Filiola: drama. 12°. '73. pap., 25c. .. *Kelly, P. & Co.*
Fille de Mme. Angot. *See* Ditson.
Fille du régiment. *See* Ditson.
Filling up the chinks. *See* Greene, *Mrs.* L. L.
Fillmore, A: D. Little minstrel: songs and music. ('67.) New ed. 16°. '75. bds., 35c. *R. W. Carroll.*
— New violet: music and hymns. ('67.) New ed. 16°. '75. bds., 35c. .... *R. W. Carroll.*
— Nightingale; or, Sunday school singer. ('50.) New ed. sm. 8°. '71. hf. bd., 60c. ...... *Pounsford.*
— Temperance musician: temperance music, for 1, 2, 3, or 4 voices. ('50.) New ed. 32°. '66. hf. bd., 40c. .... *Pounsford.*
— *See also* Leonard, S. W., *and* Fillmore, A. D.
— *and* C. L. The polyphonic; or, juvenile choralist. ('63.) New ed. 16°. '76. bds., 35c. .. *R. W. Carroll.*
— *and* Ja. H. New harp of Zion: church music, with course of instruction for schools. ('66.) New ed. 8°. '76. bds., $1.25 .... *R. W. Carroll.*
Fillmore, C. L. *See* Fillmore, A. D. *and* C. L.
Fillmore, Ja. H. Hours of song: book of rudiments and coll. of new music, sacred and secular. ('75.) 2d ed. 8°. '76. bds., 50c. .... *Fillmore.*
— Joyful notes. 8°. '75. bds., 50c. .... *Fillmore.*
— Songs for the wee ones. ill. obl. 16°. '76. bds., 25c. *Chase; Fillmore.*
— Songs of glory. ('74.) New ed. obl. 16°. '76. bds., 35c. .... *Chase; Fillmore.*
— *See also* Fillmore, A. D. *and* J. H.
Final perseverance of the saints. 15c. .. (?) *Cumberland.*
Financial crises. Carey, H. C. 25c. .... *Baird.*
Financial review. [Annual.] 4°. '76. $1.50 .. *Dana.*
Fincke, B. On high potensies, clinical cases and observations. [Hom.] 8°. $1.25 .... *Boericke.*
Findel, J. G. History of Freemasonry; rev., with pref., by D. M. Lyon. 8°. $5 .... *Lippincott.*
— *Same.* 8°. $6 .... *Redding.*
Finding his footprints. Eastman, S. E. 75c. *Bost. Am. Tr.*
Finding shelter; or, little Nan. ('72.) New ed. 16°. '74. $1 .... *Hoyt.*
Finding the truth. Henry, S. M. I. $1.25. *Cin. Meth. Bk. Conc.*
Findlater, A. Popular science manuals. 3 v. 18°. ea., 40c. .... *Lippincott.*
Cont.: Astronomy. — Chemistry. — Language.
Findling (Der). Nieritz, G. 25c. .... *Steiger.*
Fine feathers do not make fine birds. Bradley, M. E. $1 .... *Lee & S.*
Fine pictures. *See* Little Alice's lib.

Finette. Laboulaye, E. $1 .... *Tilton.*
Finette. *See* Yonge, C. M., Star of hope ser.
Finger-post of public business: mode of forming and conducting societies, etc. 12°. $1.50. *Dick & F.*
Finished or not; by author of "Fabrics." ill. 12°. '73. $1.50 .... *Lothrop.*
Fink, Alb. Cost of railroad transportation, r.r. accounts and gov. regulation of r.r. tariffs. 8°. '75. pap., 50c. .... *R. R. Gazette.*
Fink, W. W. Hades: poem. 12°. pap., 40c. *Lippincott.*
Finker, Ma. Agnes. Grapes and thorns. 4th ed. 8°. '72. $2 .... *Cath. Pub.*
— Winged word (A), and other stories. 3d ed. 8°. '73. $1.50 .... *Cath. Pub.*
Finland family. Cornwall, S. P. $1 .... *Dodd.*
Finlason, W. Selection of leading cases on pleading and parties to actions; with notes [on] principles of pleading. 8°. shp., $1.50 .... *Kay.*
Finley, I: J., *and* Putnam, Ruf. Pioneer record and reminiscences of early settlers and settlement of Ross Co., Ohio. 8°. '71. $2.50 .... *Clarke.*
Finley, Ja. Bradey. Autobiography. 12°. $1.75. *Cin. Meth. Bk. Conc.*
— Life among the Indians. 12°. $1.75. *Cin. Meth. Bk. Conc.*
— Memorials of prison life. 12°. '49. $1.25. *Meth. Bk. Conc.*
— Sketches of western Methodism. 12°. $1.75. *Cin. Meth. Bk. Conc.*
Finley, Martha F. ["Martha Farquharson."] Allan's fault. 16°. $1 .... *Pres. Bd.*
— Annandale: a story of the times of the covenanters. 18°. 60c. .... *Pres. Bd.*
— Aunt Ruth; or, persecuted, not forsaken. 18°. 70c. *Pres. Bd.*
— Brookside farmhouse from Jan. to Dec. 16°. 70c. *Pres. Bd.*
— Cares and comforts. 18°. 65c. .... *Pres. Bd.*
— Casella; or, the children of the valleys. 16°. $1.25. *Lippincott.*
— — *See also* Stapleton lib.
— Clouds and sunshine; or, the faith-brightened pathway. 18°. 70c. .... *Pres. Bd.*
— Did she do right? ill. 8°. pap., 50c. .... *Souder.*
— Do-good lib. 9 v. 18°. $3.25 .... *Pres. Bd.*
Cont.: Anna Hand, the meddlesome girl. — Grandma Foster's sunbeam. — Little Patience. — Little helper. — Little Dick Positive. — Loitering Linus. — Maud's two homes. — Milly, the little girl who tried to help others. — Stupid Sally.
— Ella Clinton; or, by their fruits ye shall know them. 18°. 60c. .... *Pres. Bd.*
— Elsie books. v. 1–4. ill. 16°. '67–'75. ea., $1.50. *Dodd.*
Cont.: Elsie Dinsmore. — Elsie's girlhood. — Elsie's holidays at Roselands. — Elsie's womanhood.
— Eva Merton; or, the blue morocco shoes. 18°. 70c. *Pres. Bd.*
— Honest Jim ser. 6 v. 18°. $2.10 .... *Pres. Bd.*
Cont.: Honest Jim. — Contented Jim. — How Jim did it. — Twin babies. — Noll, the beggar boy. — Noll in the country.
— Hugo and Franz. 18°. 75c. .... *Pres. Bd.*
— Lame Letty; or, bear ye one another's burdens. 18°. 60c. .... *Pres. Bd.*
— Little books for little readers. 6 v. 32°. $1.50. *Pres. Bd.*
Cont.: White dress. — Broken basket. — Jamie by the lake. — Bertie Page. — Amy and her kitten. — Jane Hart.
— Little Joe Carter, the cripple; or, learning to forgive. 18°. 50c. .... *Pres. Bd.*
— Marion Harvie: tale of persecution in 17th cent. ill. 18°. 65c. .... *Pres. Bd.*
— Mysie's work, and how she did it. 18°. 75c. .. *Pres. Bd.*
— Nursery tales for her little friends. 18°. 40c. *Pres. Bd.*
— Old-fashioned boy. ill. 16°. $1.50 .... *Souder.*
— Peddler of La Grave. 18°. 55c. .... *Pres. Bd.*
— Robert and Daisy; or, "thou shalt not covet." 18°. 45c. .... *Pres. Bd.*
— Rufus the unready. 16°. $1.25 .... *Pres. Bd.*

Finley, Martha F., *continued.*
— Shannons (The); or, from darkness to light. 16°. $1.25 .... *Pres. Bd.*
— Try: better do it than wish it done. 18°. 70c. *Pres. Bd.*
— Wanted — a pedigree. ill. 12°. $2 .... *Souder.*
— Week in Lilly's life. 18°. 60c .... *Pres. Bd.*
— Willie Elton, the little boy who loved Jesus. 18°. 45c. *Pres. Bd.*

Finley, S: *See* Sermons and essays.

Finnelly, W. *See* England, House of Lords reports.

Finnette: or, a doll's fortune. 18°. 25c. *Scribner, W. & A.*

Finney, C: G. Autobiography. 12°. '76. $2. *Barnes; Goodrich.*
— *Same.* 8°. '76. *$3; shp., $4; hf. cf., $6 .. *Barnes.*
— Gospel themes: sermons; ed. by H. Cowles. 12°. '76. $1.50 .... *Goodrich.*
— Masonry: [its] unchristian character. 12°. $1. *West. Tr.*
— Revival lectures. 12°. $1.75 .... *Goodrich.*

Finney, S. J. The Bible: is it of divine origin, authority and influence? ('59.) 4th ed. 12°. '73. 60c.; pap., 35c .... *Colby.*

Finotti, Jos. M. Bibliographia Cath. Americana: list of works by Cath. authors and pub. in U. S., 1784–[1825]. 8°. '72. $5 .... *Cath. Pub.*

Fior d'Aliza. Lamartine, A. de. $1.25 .... *Hurd & H.*

Fire brigade. Ballantyne, R. M. $1.25 .. *Lippincott.*

Fire eater. Selby, C. 15c .... *French.*

Fire fighters. McConaughy, J. E. $1.25 .. *Nat. Temp.*

Fire in the woods. De Mille, J. $1.50 ...... *Lee & S.*

Fire of London. Fullerton, *Lady* G. $1; $1.50. *Kelly, P. & Co.*

Fire raiser. Almar, G. 15c .... *French.*

Firelight stories. Chaplin, J. D. 40c ... *Bost. Am. Tr.*

Fireman. Johnson, S. D. 15c .... *French.*

Fireman's dog. *See* Children's prize stories.

Fires in theatres. Shaw, E. M. 40c .... *Spon.*

Fireside (The). Muzzey, A. B. $1.25 .. *Nichols & H.*

Fireside amusements: anagrams, enigmas, charades, etc. ill. 8°. pap., 30c .... *Happy.*

Fireside angel. Arthur, T. S. 75c .... *Lothrop.*

Fireside chats. *See* Hodder, E.

Fireside diplomacy: comedietta. 16°. pap., 15c. *Happy.*

Fireside echoes: ballads with choruses. 4°. $2.25; bds., $1.75 .... *Peters.*

Fireside fairies. *See* Fireside lib.

Fireside friend. Phelps, L. $1.50 .... *Harper.*

Fireside homilies. Alford, H. $1 .... *Randolph.*

Fireside lib. 5 v. 12°. $5 .... *Nelson.*
Cont.: Katie Johnson's cross. — Old and new home. — Sowing the good seed. — Jessie Grey. — Alice Herbert.

Fireside lib. 5 v. 16°. $6.50 .... *Hoyt.*
Cont.: Alice Leigh's mission. — Aunt Rebecca's charge, by Mrs. Whittlesey. — Little Christie. — Carry Williams. — A lost piece of silver.

Fireside lib. 8 v. ill. 16°. $7 .... *Appleton.*
Cont.: Richard the fearless. — A year with Maggie and Emma. — Legends of the flowers. — Keep a good heart. — Mary Lee — Midsummer fays. — Fireside fairies. — Leisure moments improved.

Fireside lib. *See* Harper's.

Fireside magician. Preston, P. 30c.; 50c ... *Dick & F.*

Fireside pictures. ill. 18°. '66. 30c .... *Am. Tr.*

Fireside reading. *See* Clark, D. W.

Fireside saints. *See* Jerrold, D.

Fireside science. Nichols, J. R. $1.50 ... *Hurd & H.*

Fireside stories. 18°. 40c .... *Cong. Pub.*

Fireside stories. 6 v. 18°. $1.50 .... *Lothrop.*
Cont.: My pets. — The plot. — Falsely accused. — Robie Grey. — A brave boy. — Little Gretchen.

Fireside stories. *See* Larned, A., Home story ser.

Fireside stories lib. *See* Howitt, W:

Fireside tales. Howitt, M. 75c .... *Roberts.*

Fireside travels. Lowell, J. R. $1.50 ...... *Osgood.*

Fireworks (The). *See* Witt, *Mme.* H. de.

Firmilian. *See* Martin, T., *and* Aytoun, W. E., Book of ballads.

First affections. Simpson, J. P. 15c .... *French.*

First and last journey. 18°. 60c ..... *Carter; Dutton.*

First and true love. Sand, G. 75c .... *Peterson.*

First bereavement. *See* Macduff, J. R.

First book of spelling and reading lessons. 16°. 18c. *Benziger.*

First causes of character. Fernald, W. M. $1.50. *Lee & S.*

First Christmas for our dear little ones. Mulholland, R. $1.50 .... *Pustet.*

First commandment. 18°. 22c .... *Am. S. S.*

First day of the week. 18°. 35c .... *Am. S. S.*

First day of the week. Cheap, *Mrs.* —. 40c. *So. Meth.*

First false step. Reynolds, G. W. M. 50c ... *De Witt.*

First fam'lies of the Sierras. Miller, J. $1.50 .. *Jansen.*

First flight from the nest; or, Nellie's six months in Boston. 18°. 40c .... *Am. S. S.*

First floor. Cobb, J. 15c .... *French.*

First footsteps in the way of knowledge. ill. sq. 18°. '56. 50c .... *Am. Tr.*

First friendship. Jackson, H. 50c .... *Harper.*

First glass of wine. Dunning, A. K. 50c ...... *Hoyt.*

First groves of Palestine. Headley, P. C. 25c.; 30c. *J. E. Potter.*

First heroes of the cross. *See* Clarke, B.

First Hindoo convert. 18°. 30c.; 40c ..... *Am. Bapt.*

First impressions. *See* Happy child's lib.

First kings of Palestine. Headley, P. C. 25c.; 30c. *J. E. Potter.*

First Lent lilies. 18°. 25c.; pap., 10c .... *Dutton.*

First lessons. [Danish.] 12°. '67. pap., 10c ... *Am. Tr.*

First lessons in business; by author of "Guide to the unprotected." 18°. '75. 50c .... *Macmillan.*

First lessons in gentleness and truth. Aunt Alice. 60c. *Bost. Am. Tr.*

First lessons in hist. of U. S., for common schools; by a practical teacher. 12°. hf. roan, 84c. *Ware.*

First lessons in reading. *See* Little learner's toys.

First lessons in spelling and reading. sq. 18°. per doz., $1.80 .... *Meth. Bk. Conc.*

First lessons on the Gospels. 18°. bds., 15c. *Am. Bapt.*

First love. Scribe, E. 15c .... *De Witt.*

First love. Sue, E. 50c .... *Peterson.*

First love. Suter, W. E. 15c .... *French.*

First love and last love. *See* Grant, Ja.

First night: drama. 16°. pap., 15c .... *French.*

First of April. Boaden, C. 15c .... *French.*

First of June. 18°. 60c .... *Dutton.*

First of June. *See* Adams, H. C.

First of the Maccabees. Wise, I. M. 50c ..... *Bloch.*

First of May: farce. 16°. pap., 15c .... *French.*

First patch. ('70.) 4th ed. ill. 18°. '74. 50c. *Perkinpine.*

First planting of Christianity. *See* Neander, J. A. W.

First prophets of Palestine. Headley, P. C. 25c.; 30c. *J. E. Potter.*

First question-book. 2 v. 18°. ea., bds., 15c. *Cong. Pub.*

First Sabbath excursion and its consequences. 18°. 35c. *Pres. Bd.*

First Scripture question book. 18°. bds., 15c. *Am. Bapt.*

First sin. Aydelott, B. P. 60c .... *West. Tr.*

First steps in the open path. Leonard, C. H. 10c. *Universalist.*

First steps in thorough bass; by a teacher of music. 12°. '54. bds., 75c .... *Ditson.*

First Sunday-school reader. ill. 12°. 25c...*Am. Bapt.*

First temptation, and other tales. 18°. 70c...*Pres. Bd.*

First thoughts; or, beginning to think. ill. 12°. 50c. *Appleton.*

First three kings of Israel. *See* Tuck, R.

First twenty years of my life. 18°. 75c.....*Am. S. S.*

First years in Europe. Calvert, G. H. $1.75..*Lee & S.*

Fischbach, Gst. Belagerung u. Bombardement v. Strassburg [1870]. 8°., pap., 40c. *F. W. Thomas.*

Fischbach, J. (*ill.*) Deutscher Wald und Hain. Photos.; with [Germ.] text by H. Masius. obl. 4°. $15....*Stroefer.*

Fischer, Gst. Latin Grammar. pt. 1. 12°. (cop. '66.) '72. $1.75....*Schermerhorn.*

— *See also* Ahn, F., Method of learning Germ.; — Baskerville, A., Prakt. Lehrb. d. engl. Sprache.

Fischer, M. G. Fifteen sel. from works of F. for organ; arr. by N. H. Allen. f°. pap., $2.50....*Ditson.*

Fischerin (Die). *See* Goethe, J. W. v.

Fischerknabe (Der). 18°. 30c....*Ev. Assoc.*

Fish, A. I. Digest of Eng. Exchequer reports, from McCleland and Younge to v. 9 of Exchequer reports. 8°. $5....*T. & J. W. Johnson.*

Fish, Dan. W. Arithmetical problems. 12°. '74. $1. — Key. $1....*Ivison.*

— Complete arith. (Robinson's shorter course.) 2 pts. ill. 12°. '74. ea., 80c.; — in 1 v. $1.40. — Key. $1....*Ivison.*

— First book in arith. (Robinson's shorter course.) ill. 12°. '74. 50c....*Ivison.*

— Robinson's junior class arith. ill. 16°. '74. bds., 80c. *Ivison.*

Fish, E. J. Ecclesiology: inquiry as to fundament. idea and const. of the New Test. church; with suppl. on ordination. 12°. '75. $2....*Authors.*

Fish, Fs. H. *See* Cruikshank, J. *and* A., *and* Fish, F. H.

Fish, H: C. Adult's catechism on evidences and doctrines of Christianity. 18°. hf. bd., 20c...*Sheldon.*

— Agent's manual of life insurance. sq. 8°. $2. — sm. 8°. $1.50. — 12°. $1. — (Pocket ed.) 16°. $1.50. *Wynkoop.*

— *Same;* abridg. sq. 16°. 75c....*Wynkoop.*

— *Same;* tr. into Germ. sq. 16°. $1.50....*Wynkoop.*

— Bible lands illustrated: handbook of Bible lands and Christian antiquities. ill. and maps. 8°. '76. *$3.50; $4; hf. mor., $5; mor., $8..*Am. Pub.*

— Child's catechism. 18°. pap., 10c....*Sheldon.*

— Harry's conflicts. 16°. $1....*Am. Bapt.*

— Harry's conversion. 16°. $1....*Am. Bapt.*

— Heaven in song: gems of poetry on the better land. 4°. $6; mor., $10. 12°. $2.50....*Sheldon.*

— Primitive piety revived: aggressive power of the Christian church. 12°. $1.25....*Cong. Pub.*

— Youth's catechism on the life and sayings of Jesus. v. 1, 2. 18°. ea., hf. bd., 20c....*Sheldon.*

— (*ed.*) History and repository of pulpit eloquence. 2 v. in 1. por. 8°. '56. $5....*Dodd.*

— Pulpit eloquence of 19th cent.: sup. to History and repository of pulpit eloquence; with biog. and descrip. sketches, [and] introd. essay by E. A. Park. 8°. '57. $4....*Dodd.*

Fish out of water. Lunn, J. 15c....*French.*

Fishbourne, E. Gardiner. Current fallacies in naval archit. 2 ser. pl. 8°. '71–'72. ea., pap., 40c. *Spon.*

— Loss of H. M. S. "Captain"; ill. a new principle of naval arch. pl. 8°. '70. pap., 60c....*Spon.*

— Our ironclads and merchant ships. pl. 8°. '74. $4.25. *Spon.*

Fisher, D: Music hath charms: comedy. 16°. pap., 15c....*French.*

Fisher, E. T. Easy French reading. ('68.) New ed. 16°. '76. $1....*Holt.*

Fisher, Eb., *and* Walden, J. H. Christian doctrine of salvation: debate on "All men will be finally saved." 12°. '69. pap., 30c....*Universalist.*

Fisher, E: Marrow of modern divinity; with notes by T. Boston. 12°. $1.50....*Pres. Bd.*

Fisher, F. *See* England, Chancery reports.

Fisher, Fes. C. ["Chr. Reid."] Novels. 8 v. ill. 8°. *Appleton.*

Cont.: Carmen's inheritance, $1.25; pap., 75c. — Daughter of Bohemia, $1.50; pap., $1. — Ebb-tide, $1.50; pap., $1. — Hearts and hands, pap., 50c. — Mabel Lee, $1.50; pap., $1. — Morton House, $1.50; pap., $1. — Nina's atonement, etc., $1.50; pap., $1. — Valerie Aylmer, $1.50; pap., $1.

— Carmen's inheritance. ill. 8°. '73. pap., 75c. *Claxton; Maclean.*

Fisher, G: P. Life of Benjamin Silliman. 2 v. por. and ill. cr. 8°. '66. $5....*Scribner.*

— Reformation (The). ('73.) New ed. 8°. '76. $3. *Scribner.*

— Supernatural origin of Christianity; with special ref. to theories of Renan, Strauss, etc. ('65.) New ed., enl. 8°. '75. $3....*Scribner.*

Fisher, Ja., *and* Erskine, E. Assembly's shorter catechism explained. 12°. shp., $1..*U. P. Bd. of Pub.*

Fisher, Jona. Fisher's catechism: Assembly's shorter catechism expl. [in] question and answer. 12°. $1.35....*Pres. Bd.*

Fisher, R. A. Digest of reported cases rel. to criminal law, criminal information and extradition; founded on Harrison's "Analytical digest." New ed., rev. by A. Hart. 8°. '72. shp., $7.50..*S. Whitney.*

— Digest of reported Eng. cases rel. to patents, trade marks and copyrights; founded on Harrison's "Analytical digest"; ed. and brought down to present time, with index, table of cases, etc., by H. Hooper. 8°. '72. shp., $4....*Clarke.*

Fisher, S: R. Exercises on the Heidelberg catechism. 16°. 50c....*Ref. Ch. Pub.*

— Family assistant: book of prayer. 12°. $1.25. *Ref. Ch. Pub.*

— Heidelberg catechism simplified: introd. to the "Exercises on Heid. catechism." 24°. 18c.; pap., 12c....*Ref. Ch. Pub.*

Fisher, S: S. Reports of cases upon letters patent for inventions in U. S. Circuit Courts. New ed. 6 v. 8°. '70–'74. ea., *net*, shp., $25....*Clarke.*

Fisher, S: W. Three great temptations of young men; with lectures to business and professional men. ('52.) New ed. 12°. '60. $1.25....*Wilstach.*

Fisher, Sidney G: Trial of the Constitution. 8°. $2. *Lippincott.*

Fisher, T. W. Plain talk about insanity. 8°. '72. $1.50. *A. Moore.*

Fisher, W. W. Caleo. Poetical works. 12°. '76. $1.50; $2....*Claxton.*

Fisher, W: The petrel; or, love on the ocean. 8°. pap., 75c....*Peterson.*

Fisher, W: H. Collection of reports of cases [on] letters patent for inventions in U. S. Supreme and Circuit Courts, 1850–['73]. v. 1. 8°. '73. shp., $15....*Clarke.*

Fisher, W: R: Law of mortgage as applied to redemption, foreclosure and sale in equity of encumbered property; with law of the priority of encumbrancers. 8°. '57. $4....*T. & J. W. Johnson.*

— *See also* Law lib.

Fisher Bill. ('65.) New ed. ill. 18°. '75. 45c...*Hoyt.*

Fisher boy. *See* Kingston, W. H. G.

Fisher boy. Mudge, Z. A. 50c....*Bost. Am. Tr.*

Fisher boy lib. 3 v. 16°. $3....*Lothrop.*

Cont.: Fisher boy. — Peter, the ship boy. — Ralph and Dick.

Fisher boy's secret. *See* Library for little lads and lasses.

Fisher boys of Pleasant Cove. Kellogg, E. $1.25. *Lee & S.*

Fisher life. Kingston, W. H. G. $1....*Cong. Pub.*

Fisher maiden. Björnson, B. $1.25....*Holt.*

Fisherman's boat; or, lessons of kindness. 18°. 45c.; 55c....*Am. Bapt.*

Fisherman's boy. Baker, S. S. 40c. . . . . *Am. Tr.*
Fisherman's children. 18°. 80c. . . . . *Cong. Pub.*
— *See also* Sea-side stories; — Variety lib.
Fisherman's daughter. Conscience, H. $1; $1.25. *Murphy.*
Fisherman's daughter. Mudge, Z. A. 50c. *Bost. Am. Tr.*
Fisherman's daughter. *See* Catholic prem.-book lib.
Fisherman's daughter, and other stories. ('68.) New ed. ill. 16°. '73. 85c. . . . . *Hoyt.*
Fisherman's luck. White, C. 15c. . . . . *De Witt.*
Fishermen of Gamp's Island. *See* Variety lib.
Fishermen's ballads. Proctor *Brothers.* 50c. *Proctor.*
Fishermen's children; by author of "Hope on." ill. 18°. 75c. . . . . *Nelson.*
Fisher's comic books. 12 nos. ill. 12°. ea., pap., 25c. *Fisher.*
Fisher's fifty cent handbooks. 6 nos. 18°. ea., bds., 50c. . . . . *Fisher.*
Fisher's fifty cent song books. 14 nos. 32°. ea., 50c. *Fisher.*
Fisher's one dollar song books. 4 nos. 18°. ea., $1. *Fisher.*
Fisher's song books. 95 nos. 18°. ea., pap., 10c. *Fisher.*
Fisher's ten cent handbooks. 20 nos. 32°. ea., pap., 10c. . . . . *Fisher.*
Fisher's ten cent joke books. 8 nos. 32°. ea., pap., 10c. . . . . *Fisher.*
Fisher's ten cent song books. 49 nos. 32°. ea., pap., 10c. — 10 nos. 18°. ea., pap., 10c. . . . . . *Fisher.*
Fisher's twenty-five cent handbooks. 11 nos. 32°. ea., bds., 25c. . . . . *Fisher.*
Fisher's twenty-five cent song books. 9 nos. 18°. ea., pap., 25c. . . . . *Fisher.*
Fisher's River: North Carolina scenes and characters; by "Skitt, who was rais'd thar." ill. 12°. $1.50. *Harper.*
Fishers of Derby Haven. 16°. $1 . . . . *Am. Bapt.*
— *See also* Lyntonville lib.
Fishhooks (The). *See* Aunty Ray's little lib.
Fishing girl. Björnson, B. $1 . . . . *Cassell.*
Fishing in Am. waters. Scott, G. C. $3.50 . . *Harper.*
Fishing smack. 32°. 40c. . . . . *Scribner, W. & A.*
Fishing tourist. Hallock, C. $2 . . . . *Harper.*
Fisk, B. F. Greek exercises. 12°. 94c. *R. S. Davis (B.)*
— Greek grammar. 12°. $1.25 . . . . *R. S. Davis (B.)*
Fisk, H. C. Handbook of revivals. 12°. $1.50 . . *Earle.*
Fisk, Ja. Life. *See* Stokes, E. S., Life and trial.
Fisk, Wilbur. Calvinistic controversy; with sermon on predestination and election. 12°. '37. $1. *Meth. Bk. Conc.*
Fiske, D. T. Life of Fidelia Fiske. 12°. $1.75. *Cong. Pub.*
Fiske, Fidelia. Recollections of Mary Lyon; with sel. from her instructions to the pupils of Mount Holyoke Seminary. 12°. $1.50 . . . . . . *Bost. Am. Tr.*
Fiske, J: Myths and myth-makers: old tales and superstitions interpreted by compar. mythology. 12°. '72. $2 . . . . *Osgood.*
— Outlines of cosmic philosophy; based on doctr. of evolution, with criticisms on the positive philos. 2 v. 8°. '74. $6 . . . . *Osgood.*
— Tobacco and alcohol: 1, It does pay to smoke; 2, The coming man will drink wine. ('68.) New ed. 16°. '69. $1 . . . . *Holt.*
— Unseen world, and other essays. 12°. '76. $2 . . *Osgood.*
Fiske, Nat. W. Classical antiquities. 8°. '43. hf. roan, $2.25 . . . . *Fortescue.*

Note. Forms first 3 pts. of "Manual of class. literature."

— Supplemental vol. of plates, ill. "Manual of classical literature." 8°. '43. hf. mor., $1.50 . . *Fortescue.*
Fiske, Ol. Address to the members of the Am. Antiq. Soc.; with laws, etc., of the Soc., acts and resolves of Congress, and of several states rel. to the Soc. 8°. '19. $1 . . . . *Am. Antiq.*
Fiske, W: O. Mass in D: score and parts. f°. pap., $3 . . . . *Schirmer.*
— Offertorium: music for the Cath. Church. obl. 4°. '72. $2.75; bds., $2.50 . . . . *Ditson.*
— Vespers in C; with Lat. and Eng. words. f°. pap., $1.25 . . . . *Ditson.*
— Vespers in C; with magnificat. f°. $1.25 . . *Gordon.*
Fit of the blues. Robillard, V. 40c. . . . . *French.*
Fitch, Anna M. Bound down; or, life and its possibilities. 12°. $1.50 . . . . *Lippincott.*
Fitch, Eleazer T. Sermons preached in Yale Coll. 8°. '71. $2 . . . . *Judd & W.*
Fitch, G: W. Mapping plates; or, lines of latitude and longitude. 4°. 60c. . . . . *Sheldon.*
— *See also* Colton, C. W., *and* Fitch, G. W.
Fitch, J. G. Art of questioning. 16°. '67. 15c. *Meth. Bk. Conc.*
— Art of securing attention. 16°. '67. 15c. *Meth. Bk. Conc.*
— Art of teaching in a Sunday school. 18°. 50c. *Nelson.*
Fittig, Rud. Outlines of organic chemistry. *See* Wöhler, F.
Fitts, J. H. History of Thomas' Farmers' almanac. 8°. '74. pap., 20c. . . . . *Essex.*
Fitz, Asa. Exercise song book: songs and rounds with physical exercises. 12°. '58. bds., 25c. . . *Ditson.*
— Gymnastic song book: songs with exercises, marches, etc. 12°. pap., 12c. . . . . *Thompson.*
— School-exhibition book. 12°. 45c. . . . *Potter, A. & Co.*
— School service book: hymns, chants, Scripture readings, etc. 12°. pap., 15c. . . . . *Thompson.*
Fitz, Ellen E. Manual to terrestrial globe. 12°. '76. hf. bd., $1 . . . . *Ginn.*
Fitz, J. W. *and* J. Southern and western apple and peach culturist; and treatise on insects and their extermination. pl. 8°. '72. $2.50 . . *J. W. Randolph.*
Fitzallan, the catechist. 18°. 35c. . . . . *U. P. Bd. of Pub.*
Fitzball, E: (*pseud.*) *See* Ball, E:
Fitzboodle papers. *See* Thackeray, W. M.
Fitzgerald, P. A. Exhibition speaker. ill. 12°. $1.25. *Sheldon.*
Fitzgerald, Percy. Loves of famous men. 16°. 75c.; pap., 50c. . . . . *J. M. Stoddart.*
— Romance of the Eng. stage. 12°. $2 . . . *Lippincott.*
— *See also* Paul, H., Timbs, J., *and* Fitzgerald, P.
Fitzgerald, R. A. Wickets in the west: tour of the all-England eleven in America. 12°. '73. $2.50. *Routledge.*
Fitzgerald, W. The Boston machinist: school for the apprentice and adv. machinist. 18°. 75c. . . *Wiley.*
Fitzgibbon, W: The mine of wealth: secrets for the million. [In Eng. and Germ.] 8°. pap., 50c. *Barclay.*
Fitzhugh, E: J. Canzonetta: vocal music for schools, etc. ('65.) New ed. obl. roy. 8°. '76. bds., $1 . . *Pond.*
Fitz-Hugh St. Clair. Chapin, S. F. $1.50 . . *Claxton.*
Fitzmaurice, *Lord* Edm. Life of William, Earl of Shelburne, afterwards first Marquess of Lansdowne; with extracts from his papers and correspondence. v. 1, 2. 8°. ea., $4 . . . *Macmillan.*
Fitzroy, *Lady* C: Little Mary's first going to church. 18°. 70c.; 75c. . . . . *Dutton.*
Fitzsmyth of Fitzsmyth Hall. Morton, J. M. 15c. *French.*
Fivas, A. de. Classic Fr. reader. 12°. $1.50 . . *Appleton.*
— Elementary Fr. reader. 16°. 75c. . . . . *Appleton.*
— New grammar of Fr. grammars. 12°. $1.25. *Appleton.*
Five acres too much. Roosevelt, R. B. $1.50 . . *Harper.*

Five black arts: hist. and process of printing, gas light, pottery, glass and iron. ill. 12°. $2.25.. *Widdleton.*
Five blue eggs. 18°. 25c.......... *Am. S. S.*
Five days' entertainments at Wentworth Grange. Palgrave, F. T. $2.......... *Macmillan.*
Five gateways of knowledge. Wilson, G. 75c. *Macmillan.*
Five gifts; [also] Harry's honest pennies; by author of "Johnny Wright." 18°. 35c.......... *Pres. Bd.*
Five happy children. Sanford, D. P. $1..... *Dutton.*
Five happy weeks. Sangster, M. E. 50c..... *Am. Tr.*
Five hundred employments adapted to a woman. Penny, V. $1.75.......... *J. E. Potter.*
Five hundred French phrases. 16°. 10c.... *Dick & F.*
Five hundred mistakes corrected; in speaking, pronounc. and writing the Eng. lang. 12°. 60c... *Moss.*
— *Same.* 12°. 80c.......... *Miller.*
Five hundred pounds reward; by a barrister. [Fiction.] 8°. pap., 50c.......... *Harper.*
Five in one: farce. 16°. pap., 15c.......... *French.*
Five jewels of the Orient. Barton, J. T. $2.. *Masonic.*
Five little pigs. [Toy-book.] ill. 4°. $1; 50c. *Routledge.*
Five miles off. Dibdin, T. 15c.......... *French.*
Five-minute chats with young women. Lewis, D. $1.50.......... *Harper.*
Five pearls of beauty lib. 5 v. 16°. $5... *Am. Bapt.*

Cont.: Ellerslie House, by E. Leslie. — Maude Maynard. — Days at Seadown. — The Harleys, by H. C. Fish. — Morning gleam.

Five thousand musical terms. Adams, J. S. 75c. *Ditson.*
Five thousand a year. Wood, E. P. 25c.... *Peterson.*
Five weeks in a balloon. *See* Verne, Jules.
Five years among the Indians. Barber, M. 25c. *Barclay.*
Five years before the mast. *See* Hazen, J. A.
Five years in the Alleghanies. Cross, J. 50c... *Am. Tr.*
Five years in China. Bush, C. P. 80c...... *Pres. Bd.*
Five years in an English university. Bristed, C. A. $2.25.......... *Putnam.*
Five years of a hunter's life. Cumming, R. G. 2 v. $3.......... *Harper.*
Five years of prayer. Prime, S. I. $1.50.... *Harper.*
Fjellstedt, P. Apokryfiska böckerna med förklaring. 8°. 35c.; 75c.; pap., 15c.......... *Engberg.*
Flag of distress. Reid, M. $1.75; $1.50...... *Miller.*
Flag of truce. Warner, S. $1.25.......... *Carter.*
Flag of truce *See* Maple grove stories.
Flagg, Eliz. E. Little people whom the Lord loved. ill. 16°. '71. $1.25.......... *Crowell.*
— — *See also* Posie ser.
Flagg, Willard C. Farmers' movement in the western states; read before Am. Soc. Sci. Assoc., May 20, 1874. 8°. pap., 10c.......... *Williams.*
Flagg, W: J. Good investment (A): story of the upper Ohio. ill. 8°. pap., 50c.......... *Harper.*
— Handbook of the sulphur-cure, as applicable to the vine disease in Am., and diseases of apple and other fruit trees. 12°. pap., 50c....... *Harper.*
— Three seasons in European vineyards. 12°. $1.50. *Harper.*
Flagg, Wilson. Birds and seasons of New Eng. 12 heliot. ill. 8°. '75. $4; hf. cf., $7..... *Osgood.*
— Woods and by-ways of New Eng. 22 heliot. ill. 8°. '72. $4; hf. cf., $7.......... *Osgood.*
Flaherty, W. E. Annals of England: epitome of Eng. hist. 8°. hf. bd., $6.......... *Scribner, W. & A.*
Flameng, Lp. (*ill.*) *See* Boccaccio, Decameron; — Margaret d'Angoulême, Heptameron.
Flaminia, and other stories. 8°. '76. $1.50.. *Cath. Pub.*
Flammarion, Camille. Atmosphere (The); tr. from the French, ed. by J. Glaisher. ill. 8°. $6; hf. cf., $8.25.......... *Harper.*
— Stories of infinity; tr. by S. R. Crocker. 16°. '73. $1.50.......... *Roberts.*
— Wonders of the heavens; tr. by Mrs. N. Lockyer. ill. 12°. '74. $1.25.......... *Scribner.*
Flanders, H: Exposition of U. S. Const. 12°. '73. $1.75.......... *Claxton.*
— Lives and times of chief justices of U. S. Supreme Court. 2 v. 8°. '55. $7.50.. *Claxton; Lippincott.*
— *Same.* New ed., rev. 2 v. 8°. '75. $7; shp., $9. *Cockcroft.*
— Treatise on law of fire insurance. ('71.) 2d ed. roy. 8°. '74. shp., $7.50.......... *Claxton.*
— Treatise on law of shipping; with special ref. to Am. practice. 8°. '53. $4.50.... *T. & J. W. Johnson.*
Flandrine, Hip. Life of F.: a Christian painter of the 19th cent. 12°. '75. $2.50.......... *Pott.*
Flashes of light from the spirit land. Putnam, A. $1.50.......... *Colby.*
Flatbootmann (Der). Gerstäcker, F. 40c... *Steiger.*
Flauto (Il) magico. *See* Ditson.
Flavel, J: Blow (A) at the root of Antinomianism. 32°. 25c.......... *Pres. Bd.*
— Christ knocking at the door of sinners' hearts. 12°. '50. 90c.......... *Am. Tr.*
— Explanation of the Shorter catechism. 12°. 40c. *U. P. Bd. of Pub.*
— *Same.* 18°. 60c.......... *Carter.*
— Fountain of life; or, display of Christ in his essential and mediatorial glory. 12°. '40. 90c. *Am. Tr.*
— Jesus Christ's alluring love. 18°. '67. 50c... *Am. Tr.*
— Method of grace. 12°. '45. 90c.......... *Am. Tr.*
— Mystery of providence. 18°. 60c. .... *Pres. Bd.*
— *See also* Cecil, R: *and* Flavel, J:
Flavia. Leslie, E. $1.50.......... *Meth. Bk. Conc.*
Flavius Josephus. *See* Josephus, Flavius.
Flaxman, J: Lectures on sculpture. ill. 12°. (Bohn.) $2.25.......... *Little, B. & Co.*
— *Same.* ill. 12°. (Bohn.) $2.40.. *Scribner, W. & A.*
— *Same.* ill. 12°. (Bohn.) $2.50.......... *Lippincott.*
Fleda's childhood. *See* Baker, *Mrs.* H. N. W., Happy home stories for girls.
Fleet, Esther Faithful. Roses without thorns. 2 v. ill. 18°. '75. $1.50.......... *Nelson.*
Fleeta (*pseud.*) *See* Hamilton, *Miss* K. W.
Fleetwood, J: Life of Christ and his apostles. ill. 12°. $1.50..... *Lee & S.; Routledge; World Pub.*
— *Same.* ill. 12°. $1.75.......... *J. E. Potter.*
— *Same.* 30 pts. ill. 4°. '72. ea., *50c.... *S. Walker.*
— *Same;* with introd. by G. B. Cheever. 8°. $2; shp., $2.75.......... *World Pub.*
— *Same;* with introd. by Prof. Segur. ill. 12°. $1.50. *Lee & S.*
— *Same;* with hist. of the Jews. New ed., with notes by Rev. J. N. Brown. ill. 8°. *$3.75; mor., $5.75.......... *Bradley & G.*
— *Same;* with hist. of the Jews and essay on the truth of the Bible; rev. and enl. by J. Belcher. ill. 8°. *$3; $4.......... *J. E. Potter.*
— *Same;* [with] contin. of hist. of Jews to present time, by Rev. W. Patton. ill. 12°. '72. *$3.. *Case.*
— *Same;* [also] Meditation on love of Christ and the Christian laid forth, by J. Hale; [also] The golden grove, [and] The worthy communicant, by J. Taylor; with introd. by Rev. H. Stebbing. ('68.) 9th ed. eng. 4°. '76. hf. mor., $14.. *Virtue.*
— *Same;* [also] Evidences of Christianity, by P. Doddridge; [also] The golden grove, by J. Taylor; [also] Meditations upon the Lord's prayer, by Sir M. Hale; [also] Sermons on death and ascension of Christ, by H. Blair; with introd. by J. A. Spencer. ill. 4°. '68. hf. mor., $19.50; mor., $21.50; $22.50.......... *Johnson & M.*
— — *See also* Hayes, A. P., Light in the east.

Fleischhacker, J: C. Catechism of the Prot. Episc. Church in Germ. and Eng. 18°. '73. bds., 20c. *Whittaker.*

Fleischmann, K. Die Waldlilie. 16°. 25c. *Germ. Bapt.*

Fleming, A. Church polity: its spiritual grounds and congreg. superstructure. 16°. $1... *Cong. Pub.*

— Church polity of the Pilgrims, the polity of the New Test. 32°. 35c.................. *Cong. Pub.*

Fleming, C., *and* Tibbins, J. French and Eng., and Eng. and French dict.; with tables of verbs by P. W. Gengembre; ed. by J. Dobson. 8°. shp., $6; — abridg. 12°. $2................ *Butler.*

Fleming, G: Animal plagues: their hist., nature and prevention. 8°. $4............... *Lippincott.*

— Manual of veterinary sanitary science and police. 2 v. ill. 8°. $9.............. *Scribner, W. & A.*

— Practical horse-shoeing. ill. 12°. 75c..... *Appleton.*

— — *See also* Mayhew, E., Illustrated horse doctor.

Fleming, Howard. Narrow gauge railways in Am.: statistics and directory of narrow gauge railways in N. Am. 8°. '76. $1.50............ *Fleming.*

Fleming, May Agnes. [Novels.] 5 v. 8°. ea., pap., 25c.................................. *Beadle.*

Cont.: Awful mystery. — Dark secret. — Erminie. — Twin sisters. — Victoria.

— *Same.* 6 v. 12°. ea., $1.75............. *Carleton.*

Cont.: Guy Earlscourt's wife. — Mad marriage. — Norine's revenge; Sir Noel's heir. — One night's mystery. — Terrible secret. — Wonderful woman.

Fleming, Rob. Fulfilling of the Scriptures; for confirming believers and convincing unbelievers. 18°. 75c.......................... *Pres. Bd.*

Fleming, W: Vocabulary of philos.; with add. by C. P. Krauth. sm. 8°. $2.50.......... *Sheldon.*

Flemming, D. Lambden. Life and death; or, the creeping shadow: art of preserving health. 8°. '76. *$2.50; $3; $4..................... (?) *Gootee.*

Flemmings. Dorsey, A. H. $2............ *O'Shea.*

Flentje, L: Familien Weine, od. Anleitung Wein zu bereiten aus Johannisbeeren, Stachelbeeren, Erdbeeren, etc., insbesondere aus unreifen u. wilden Trauben. 12°. '64. pap., 75c... *Steiger.*

— Haus-Rezepte. 8°. '72. $1.50........... *Steiger.*

— Materialismus (Der) d. Lebens gegen d. todten "Kraft u. Stoff"-Materialismus. 8°. '74. pap., 40c. .... *Steiger.*

Flesh and spirit. Coulson, J. G. A. $1.25; 75c. *Hale.*

Fletcher, Alex. Guide to family devotion: hymn and portion of Scripture, etc., for morning and evening of every day. ('56.) 5th ed. eng. roy. 4°. '73. hf. mor., $16.................... *Virtue.*

— Lectures to children. 2 v. ill. 18°. ea., 45c. *Am. Tr.*

— Scripture nat. hist. 2 v. ill. roy. 16°. '68. $9.. *Virtue.*

— *See also* Bible [Whole].

Fletcher, Banister. Arbitrations: text-book for surveyors in tabulated form. cr. 8°. '75. $2.. *Spon.*

— Compensations: text-book for surveyors in tabulated form. cr. 8°. '75. $2.................. *Spon.*

— Dilapidations: text-book for architects and surveyors in tabulated form: who are liable for dilapidation, and extent of liability of lessors, lessees, etc. cr. 8°. '72. $2................... *Spon.*

Fletcher, E. B. On man immortal. 16°. $1.25.. *Bailey.*

Fletcher, *Mrs.* Eliza Dawson. Autobiography; with letters and other family memorials. por. 8°. '75. $2.50................................ *Roberts.*

Fletcher, *Rev.* J. Christian perfection. 24°. '38. 40c. *Meth. Bk. Conc.*

— *Same;* ed. by T. O. Summers. ('54.) 5th ed. 18°. '75. 40c.............................. *So. Meth.*

— *Same;* rev. by S. D. Akin. 12°. '58. $1.50.. *So. Meth.*

Fletcher, J. P. Notes from Nineveh, and travels in Mesopotamia, Assyria and Syria. 12°. 75c. *Lea.*

Fletcher, Ja. History of Poland. 18°. 75c. *Harper.*

Fletcher, J: *See* Beaumont, F., *and* Fletcher, J.

Fletcher, J: W: Works. 4 v. 8°. '37. shp., $12; cf., $14........................ *Meth. Bk. Conc.*

— Address to seekers of salvation. 18°. '36. 15c. *Meth. Bk. Conc.*

— Appeal to matter of fact and common sense; or, a rational demonstration of man's corrupt and lost estate. 18°. 55c........... *Cin. Meth. Bk. Conc.*

— *Same;* with introd. by D. Edwards. 18°. 50c. *Un. B. Pub.*

— *Same;* ed. by T. O. Summers. ('57.) 3d ed. 18°. '75. 60c.............................. *So. Meth.*

— *Same;* [also] Address. 18°. '37. 55c. *Meth. Bk. Conc.*

— *Germ.* Berufung auf Thatsachen: d. verderbte u. verlorene Stand der Menschen. 16°. '39. 60c. *Ev. Assoc.*

— Beauties; from "Checks to Antinomianism;" ed. by T. Spicer. 12°. $1......... *Cin. Meth. Bk. Conc.*

— Checks to Antinomianism. 2 v. 8°. '37. $6. *Meth. Bk. Conc.*

— Letters. 12°. '49. $1.25......... *Meth. Bk. Conc.*

Fletcher, Jos. Reflections on the spirit of relig. controversy. 12°. 60c................ *Cath. Pub.*

Fletcher, Jose. Prayers and meditations for the holy communion; with pref. by Bp. Ellicott. New ed. 32°. '70. 50c. .... *Dutton.*

Fletcher, L. J. Doctrinal series. 5 v. 16°. '63–'64. *Universalist.*

Cont.: 1. Infant school, per doz., pap., $1.25. — 2. First impressions, per doz., pap., $1.25. — 3. Key to the young heart, per doz., bds., $2.50. — 4. Guide to salvation, per doz., bds., $3. — 6. Universalism: its doctrines and their foundation, per doz., bds., $3.

Note. No. 5 not issued.

— Manual and harp; for S.-schools. 16°. '61. per doz., bds., $4.50 .... *Universalist.*

Fletcher, Mta. Practical ethics for schools and families; with chart. 12°. '75. $1... *Barnes; Mills.*

Fletcher, W: B. Cholera: its characteristics, hist., etc. map and ill. 8°. '66. pap., $1.... *Clarke.*

Fleur de thé. *See* Ditson.

Fleurange. *See* Craven, A.

Fleurs de la piété chrétienne: recueil de prières. 24°. *net,* 77c.; $1.05; $2.10............. *Benziger.*

Fleury, *l'Abbé* —. Der Feldzug d. Revolution in Italien gegen Rom. 12°. 75c............. *Benziger.*

Fleury, Cl. Manners of the anc. Israelites; tr. from the Fr.; enl. by A. Clarke. 18°. '37. 65c. *Meth. Bk. Conc.*

— Short historical catechism; tr. from the Fr. 18°. pap., 10c......................... *Cummiskey.*

Fleury, Lamé. *See* Lamé Fleury.

Fliegende Holländer (Der). Brachvogel, A. E. 2 v. ea., 50c............................ *Morwitz.*

Flies in the webb. Brougham, J. 15c....... *French.*

Flint, Aust. Clinical reports on continued fever; with remarks on management, identity of typhus and typhoid fever, etc. 8°. '55. $2....... *Lindsay.*

— Compendium of percussion and auscultation, and of physical diagnosis of diseases affecting lungs and heart. 18°. 50c.................... *W. Wood.*

— Essays on conservative medicine and kindred topics. roy. 12°. $1.38 .... *Lea.*

— Phthisis: its morbid anatomy, etiology, symptomatic events and complications, etc. 8°. $3.50.. *Lea.*

— Practical treatise on diagnosis, pathology and treatment of diseases of the heart. 2d ed., rev. and enl. pl. 8°. $4 .... *Lea.*

— Practical treatise on physical exploration of chest, and diagnosis of diseases affecting the respiratory organs. 2d ed., rev. 8°. $4.50............ *Lea.*

— Treatise on principles and practice of medicine. 4th ed., rev. and enl. 8°. '66. $6; leath., $7.. *Lea.*

— Valedictory address; [also] Inaugural address by S. S. Purple, before N. Y. Acad. of Med. 8°. '75. pap., 15c................ *N. Y. Acad. Med.*

Flint, Aust., *continued.*
— (*ed.*) Contributions rel. to the causation and prevention of disease, and to camp diseases, with report of the diseases, etc., among the prisoners at Andersonville, Ga. (Report of the U. S. Sanitary Commission.) 8°. '67. $6.50 .... *Hurd & H.*
— *See also* Seguin, E. C., Series of Am. clin. lect.

Flint, Aust., *jr.* Manual of chem. examinations of the urine. 3d ed. 16°. '72. $1 .... *Appleton.*
— Physiological effects of severe and protracted muscular exercise; with special ref. to influence upon the excretion of nitrogen. 8°. '71. $2 .. *Appleton.*
— Physiology of man. 5 v. 8°. ea., $4.50; shp., $5.50. *Appleton.*

Cont.: 1. Introduction: the blood; circulation; respiration. — 2. Alimentation; digestion; absorption; lymph and chyle. — 3. Secretion; excretion; ductless glands; nutrition; animal heat; movements; voice and speech. — 4. Nervous system. — 5. Special senses; generation; index.

— Recherches expérimentales sur une nouvelle fonction du foie. 8°. '68. 75c. .... *Appleton.*
— Text-book of human physiology. pl. and ill. imp. 8°. '75. $6; shp., $7 .... *Appleton.*

Flint, C: L. Grasses and forage plants. ('59.) New ed. ill. 12°. '74. $2.50 .... *W. F. Gill; Tilton.*
— Milch cows and dairy farming. ('58.) New ed. ill. 12°. '74. $2.50 .... *W. F. Gill; Tilton.*
— *See also* Dickerman, C. W., *and* Flint, C. L.; — Emerson, G. B., *and* Flint, C. L.; — New England Agri. Soc.

Flint, H: M. Life and public services of Stephen A. Douglas; with his speeches and reports. por. 12°. $1.75 .... *J. E. Potter.*
— Railroads of the U. S.: their hist. and statistics, with synopsis of the U. S. railroad laws. 12°. $1.75 .... *J. E. Potter.*

Flint, Ja. *See* Burnap, U. C., *and* Flint, J.

Flint, Ja. H. From nation to nation. 16°. $1.25. *Am. Bapt.*

Flint, Rob. Philosophy of hist. in France and Germany. 8°. $6 .... *Scribner, W. & A.*

Flint, *Miss* Sa. A. ["F. S. A."] Conqueror (The). 18°. 75c. .... *Cong. Pub.*
— Ellen Murray; or, one that everybody loved. 18°. 65c. .... *Cong. Pub.*
— Elsie Bailey; or, one that loved everybody. 18°. 75c. *Cong. Pub.*
— Great success. 16°. $1.50 .... *Cong. Pub.*
— Hid treasures. 16°. $1.50 .... *Cong. Pub.*
— Hope Douglass. 16°. $1.25 .... *Cong. Pub.*
— Making honey; or, Frances Stuart. 16°. $1.25. *Cong. Pub.*
— More victories: sequel to "Conqueror." 18°. 75c. *Cong. Pub.*
— Pleasant reading. 16°. 45c. .... *Cong. Pub.*
— Ruth Edwards' victory. 18°. 75c. .... *Cong. Pub.*
— Silver lining. 16°. $1.25 .... *Cong. Pub.*
— Skates. 18°. 75c. .... *Cong. Pub.*
— The soldier's ring. 18°. 50c. .... *Cong. Pub.*

Flint, Tim. Biographical memoir of Daniel Boone; with incidents in the early annals of the country. 12°. 45c. .... *I. N. Whiting.*
— *Same.* ill. 12°. $1.25; $1.50 .... *U. P. James.*

Flirt (The). Grey, E. C. 75c. .... *Peterson.*

Flirtations in America; or, high life in N. Y. 8°. pap., 75c. .... *Peterson.*

Flirtations in fashionable life. Sinclair, C. $1.75; $1.50 .... *Peterson.*

Flitch of bacon. *See* Ainsworth, W: H.

Floating beacon. Ball, E. 15c. .... *French.*

Floating city. *See* Verne, Jules.

Floating light of the Goodwin Sands. Ballantyne, R. M. $1.25; $1.50 .... *Claxton.*

Floating on the ice. *See* Hoffmann, J.

Flock fed. Butler, C. M. 40c. .... *Randolph.*

Flood, Ja. M. *See* Summerbell, N., *and* Flood, J. M.

Flood, T. L. One hundred ministers: lights and shadow[s] of ministerial life. 16°. '74. $1.50 ...... *Este[s]*

Flood and field. *See* Maxwell, W: H.

Flood, field and forest. Rooper, G. $2 .... *Routledg[e]*

Floods (The). 18°. 17c.; 22c. .... *Am. Bap[t.]*

Flora. *See* Tucker, *Mrs.* Ctte.

Flora cestrica. Darlington, W. $2.25 ...... *Lindsa[y]*

Flora Lee story books. *See* Adams, W. T.

Flora Lyndsay. Moodie, S. $1.25 .... *De Wit[t]*

Flora Morris' choice. Hildeburn, M. J. $1.25 .. *Pres. B[d.]*

Flora Mortimer. *See* Good child's lib.

Flora sacra. Blessner, G. $1.75; $1.38 .... *Gordo[n]*

Flora Selwyn; or, how to behave: story for girls. il[l.] fp. 8°. 60c. .... *Cassel[l]*

Floral belles. Badger, C. M. $30 .... *Scribne[r]*

Floral offering: language and poetry of flowers. il[l.] 12°. $1.50; $2.25; mor., $3 .... *T. Blis[s]*

Floral wreath. *See* Diamond miniatures.

Flora's cup. ill. sq. 16°. $1.50 .... *Lock*
— *See also* Bouquet ser.

Flora's dial: poetic sentiment of flowers. sq. 16°. $1.5[0] *Lock[e]*
— *See also* Bouquet ser.

Flora's festival. Bradbury, W. B. 35c. .... *Iviso[n]*

Flora's pocket dict. of lang. and sentiment of flower[s] 32°. '70. 45c. .... *Porte[r]*

Florence *of Worcester.* Chronicle, with the two co[n]tinuations: annals of Eng. history to Edward [I.] 12°. (Bohn.) $1.75 .... *Little, B. & C[o.]*
— *Same.* 12°. (Bohn.) $2. *Lippincott; Scribner, W. & A[.]*

Florence; or, the orphan ward. Wood, H. J. 50c. *Routledg[e]*

Florence and Eddie; or, perseverance rewarded. 18[°.] 25c. .... *Am. S. S[.]*

Florence and John. *See* Abbott, Jac.

Florence Arnot. *See* New juvenile lib.

Florence Baldwin's pic-nic. Wise, D. $1.25. *Perkinpin[e]*

Florence Dombey. *See* Dickens, C:

Florence Egerton. 18°. 75c. .... *Carte[r]*

Florence Erwin's three homes. 16°. $1.25 .. *Nichols & H[.]*

Florence McCarthy. Morgan, *Lady* S. O. $1.50; $[2.] *Sadlie[r]*

Florence O'Neill. Stewart, A. M. $1.50; $2. *Kelly, P. & C[o.]*

Florence rewarded. Wise, D. $1.25 .... *Perkinpin[e]*

Florence Sackville. Burbury, E. J. 75c. ..... *Harpe[r]*

Florence stories. *See* Abbott, Jac.

Florence's return. *See* Abbott, Jac.

Florette. *See* Zschokke, H.

Florian, J. P. C. de. Guillelmo Tell, y Andrés Hofer tr., con la vida del autor. 12°. $1.50 .. *Appleto[n]*
— History of the Moors in Spain; tr. from the Fr. with account of rise and decline of Mohammeda[n] empire, etc. 18°. 75c. .... *Harpe[r]*

Florida. Code of procedure. '70 .... *Stat[e]*
— Supreme Court reports. 13 v. 8° .... *Stat[e]*

Cont.: 1846–'47, by J. Branch. — '48–'49, by J. T. Archer an[d] D. P. Hogue. — '50–'52, by D. P. Hogue, 2 v. — '53–'59, by M. [D.] Papy, 4 v. — '59–'67, by J. B. Galbraith, 3 v. — '67–'69, by J. [B.] Galbraith and A. R. Meek. — '69–'71, by J. B. C. Drew.

— — Index. *See* Galbraith, J: B.

Florida Land Agency [Jacksonville, Fla.] Florida its soil, climate, health, productions, resource[s] and advantages; with sketch of its hist. 8°. pap. 25c. .... *William[s]*

Florie's ser. 12 v. 16°. $5.40; ea., 45c. ... *Cummiskey*

Cont.: Great Tenabraka. — Miss Touchall. — Young raider[s.] — Old beggar. — George, the little chimney sweep. — Lost chil[d.] — Desert island. — Bethlehem. — Pat, the little emigrant. — Idl[e]ness. — Negligence. — Little gardeners.

Florrie, *Cousin* (*pseud.*) *See* Bliss, Florence.

Florus, Lucius Annæus. *See* Sallust, Florus, L. A., *and* Velleius.

Floss Silverthorn. Giberne, A. $1.25.......*Carter.*

Flossy Lee. Wynne, F. 80c.............*J. A. Moore.*

Flossy Lee at the mountains. Wynne, F. 80c. *J. A. Moore.*

Flotow, F. v. Martha; or, the fair at Richmond; with Ital., Germ. and Eng. words. [Opera.] 8°. '60. pap., $1; bds., $1.50..................*Ditson.*

— — *See also* Ditson.

Flounced robe, and what it cost. McKeever, H. B. 85c....................................*Hoyt.*

Flour and grist mills reference book. 4°. '68. $50. *J. A. Murphy.*

Flower, W: H: Diagrams of the nerves of the human body; ed. with add. by W. W. Keen. 2d Am. ed. roy. 4°. $2........................*Hamilton.*

— Introduction to the osteology of the mammalia. ill. 12°. '70. $2.......................*Macmillan.*

Flower basket. Sawyer, T. J. 50c...... *Williamson.*

Flower book: descr. various flowers, and deriving lessons therefrom. 18°. 25c.............*Am. S. S.*

Flower by the prison. ill. 16°. '71. $1.25...*Lothrop.*

Flower-de-luce. Longfellow, H. W. $2.50..*Osgood.*

Flower festival. Johnson, J. C. 45c.........*Ditson.*

Flower, fruit and thorn pieces. Richter, J. P. 2 v. $2.50....................................*Holt.*

Flower garden. [Cath. prayer book.] 32°. '60. 50c.–$6..............................*Cunningham.*

— *See also* Little flower garden.

Flower garden. Tonna, C. E. 90c...........*Dodd.*

Flower garlands for little gleaners. 12 v. 12°. $3. *Routledge.*

Cont.: Sunday evenings at home, 8 v.—Snow drop, etc.—Heartsease; Lily of the valley.—Broome, etc.—Wild rose and poppies.

Flower gathered. ill. 18°. '53. 35c..........*Am. Tr.*

Flower girl. 18°. 60c...................*Cong. Pub.*

Flower of faith. Pickney, W. 20c........*McCauley.*

Flower of the family ser. *See* Prentiss, *Mrs.* E.

Flower of the flock. Egan, P. 50c.........*De Witt.*

Flower of the forest; or, the discarded daughter. 8°. pap., 25c.............................*De Witt.*

Flower of innocence. *See* Tonna, *Mrs.* C. E., Charlotte Elizabeth stories.

Flower people. Mann, M. $1.50..........** Osgood.*

Flower pictures. *See* Grandmother's lib.

Flower queen. *See* Root, G. F.

Flower transplanted; [also] The blind boy; [also] Little George. 32°. 20c..............*Pres. Bd.*

Flowerets. *See* Mathews, J. H.

Flowers and fossils. Stayman, J. K. $2....*Claxton.*

Flowers and gardens: notes on plant beauty. cr. 8°. '72. $2.50...............................*Routledge.*

Flowers by the wayside. 18°. 60c.........*Am. S. S.*

Flowers for the altar. Reynolds, M. W. $7.50. *Lippincott.*

Flowers for busy bees to light on. ill. 4°. 75c.; $1. *Am. S. S.*

Flowers from the garden of the visitation: lives of several religious of the order; tr. from the Fr. 16°. '75. $1.25; $1.75...............*Kelly, P. & Co.*

Flowers from heaven. Bourdon, M. F. 30c...*O'Shea.*

Flowers in the grass. Llewellyn, E. L. 75c...*Pres. Bd.*

Flowers of Christian wisdom. 32°. 75c......*Sadlier.*

Flowers of devotion. [Cath. prayer book.] 48°. '69. 30c.–$10.......................*Kelly, P. & Co.*

Flowers of elocution. Hentz, C. L. $1.50..*Desilver.*

Flowers of fable. ill. 18°. $1..............*Harper.*

Flowers of forest. 18°. 35c.............. *Whittaker.*

Flowers of forest. Buckstone, J. B. 15c....*French.*

Flowers of forest. *See* Sherwood, *Mrs.* M. M.

Flowers of history. *See* Matthew *of Westminster.*

Flowers of paradise. [Cath. prayer book.] 24°. 50c.–$15. 32°. 45c.–$12...................*O'Shea.*

Flowers of piety. [Cath. prayer book.] 32°. 30c.–$1.40..............................*Benziger.*

— *Same.* 32°. 35c.–$14. 48°. 30c.–$12....*T. Kelly.*

— *Same.* 32°. 35c.–$14. 48°. $1–$12.......*Strong.*

— *See also* Little flowers.

Flowers that never fade: stories in prose and verse. ill. 16°. 75c.............................*Fuller.*

— *See also* Union ser.

Flowers, their language, poetry and sentiment. (Red line ed.) col. ill. sq. 24°. '70. $1.50....*Porter.*

Floy, H: *See* Snow, S. P., *and* Floy, H:

Floy, Ja. Works. 2 v. 12°. ea., $1.75..*Meth. Bk. Conc.*

Cont.: Sermons, reviews and essays—Old Test. characters delin. and ill.

Floy Lindsley. Hopkins, I. T. $1.25........*Am. Tr.*

Floyd, Cornelia. ["Neil Forrest."] Fiddling Freddy. 16°. '71. $1.......................*Randolph.*

— Honest and earnest. 16°. '73. $1......*Randolph.*

— Jack and Rosy. 16°. '70. $1...........*Randolph.*

— Mice at play: a story for the whole family. ill. sq. 16°. '75. $1.50.......................*Roberts.*

Flüchtling (Der) im Jura. *See* Zschokke, H.

Flückiger, F: A., *and* Hanbury, Dan. Pharmacographia: hist. of principal drugs of vegetable origin in Gt. Brit. and Brit. India. 8°. hf. bd., $9. *Macmillan.*

Flush times of Alabama. Baldwin, J. G. $1.75. *S. Whitney.*

Flute made easy. obl. 8°. '54. pap., 75c.....*Ditson.*

Fly, Elij. M. The Bible true: cosmogony of Moses compared with facts of science. ('70.) New ed. 12°. '71. $2.........................*Claxton.*

Fly and the web. Troughton, A. C. 15c.....*French.*

Fly-leaves. Calverley, C. S. $1.25...........*Holt.*

Flying arrow; or, pirate's revenge. 8°. pap., 25c. *De Witt.*

Flying artillerist. 8°. pap., 50c...........*Peterson.*

Flying Dutchman. 8°. pap., 50c...........*Peterson.*

Flying Dutchman. Ball, E. 15c............*French.*

Flying Yankee. Jones, J. 50c............*Peterson.*

Flynn, Dan. F. Destiny; or, the priest's blessing. 12°. '70. $1.50; $2..................*Kelly, P. & Co.*

Foa, *Mme.* Eugénie. Boy artists; or, sketches of childhood of Michael Angelo, Mozart, Haydn, Watteau and Sebastian Gomez; tr. from the Fr. ill. 16°. '59. $1.......................*Dutton.*

— Contes biographiques. With vocab. ('65.) New ed. 12°. '76. $1..............................*Holt.*

— Le petit Robinson de Paris. With vocab. ('64.) New ed. 12°. '76. 90c..................*Holt.*

Foden, Ja. Boiler-maker's and iron ship-builder's companion. fp. 8°. $2..................*Spon.*

Foe in the household. Chesebro', C. $1.25; 75c...*Estes.*

Fœderalist. *See* Federalist.

Foes of faith. Vaughan, C. J. $1........*Macmillan.*

Fogg, G. G. *See* New Hampshire, Law reports.

Fogg, W. P. Arabistan; or, the land of the "Arabian nights;" with introd. by B. Taylor. ill. 8°. '75. *$2.50; $3............................*Dustin.*

Foggy night at Offord. Wood, E. P. 25c...*Peterson.*

Foiled. Cornish, O. W. 15c..............*De Witt.*

Fold of the good shepherd. 18°. 60c.........*Dutton.*

Folgen des Leichtsinns. *See* Hoffmann, F.

Folger, I: H. Handbook of Nantucket [Mass.]: hist. sketch, with notes. [*anon.*] ('74.) New ed. map. 18°. '75. pap., 25c.....(?) *Island Review.*

Folk songs. Palmer, J. W. $15; $18 ....*Scribner.*
Folks and fairies. Comfort, L. R. $1 ......*Harper.*
Folle-Farine. La Rame, L. de. $1.50....*Lippincott.*
Follen, C: German reader; with add. by G. A. Schmidt. ('58.) New ed., rev. 12°. '70. hf. roan, $1.50. *Holt.*
Follen, *Mrs.* Eliza Lee. Little songs. sq. 18°. 60c. *Nichols & H.*
— New songs. ill. sm. 4°. 75c. ....*Lee & S.*
— Twilight stories. 12 v. ill. 4°. ea., 50c.....*Lee & S.*

Cont.: Travellers' stories. — True stories about dogs. — Made-up stories. — Peddler of dust sticks. — When I was a girl. — Who speaks next? — Talkative wig. — What animals do and say. — Two festivals. — Conscience. — Piccolissima. — Little songs.

— Well-spent hour: story for girls. ill. 16°. $1.25. *Fuller.*
Follies of free thought. Monser, J. W. 20c...*Cen. Bk.*
Follies of a night. Planché, J. R. 15c.......*French.*
Follow Jesus. *See* Hall, Newman.
Follow the lamb. Bonar, H. 40c ....*Carter.*
Follow the leader: drama. 16°. pap., 15c....*French.*
Follow thou me. Huntington, W. R. 20c....*Dutton.*
Following after Jesus. Anderson, E. H. $1. *Bost. Am. Tr.*
Following the drum. 12°. pap., 50c.......*Peterson.*
Following the flag. Coffin, C. C. $1.50....**Osgood.*
Following fully. *See* Shipton, A.
Following the leader. ill. 18°. 75c. ...*Bost. Am. Tr.*
Following the master. Beckwith, E. L. $1.10. *Pres. Bd.*
Following of Christ. *See* Thomas *a Kempis.*
Following on to know; or, old days at Hetherington. ill. 16°. '71. 80c................*Am. Tr.*
— *Same.* ('72.) New ed. 16°. '75. $1.25....*Hoyt.*
— *Same.* ill. 16°. '74. $1.25..............*Dutton.*
Folly as it flies. Reynolds, F. 15c..........*French.*
Folly of flattery. *See* Cupples, *Mrs.* A. J.
Folly of procrastination; or, the story of Charles and Edward Martin. 18°. 30c............*Am. S. S.*
Folly of revenge. *See* Cupples, *Mrs.* A. J.
Folsom, A. P. *and* M. T. Help for Sunday school concerts: poems. 16°. '75. $1.......*Lothrop.*
Folsom, E. G. Logic of accounts: exposition of theory and practice of double entry book-keeping. 12°. '72. $2............................*Barnes.*
Folsom, M. T. *See* Folsom, A. P. *and* M. T.
Folsom, Natl. S. *See* Bible, Gospels.
Fonblanque, Albany, *jr.* Family tree (A). 8°. '76. $1.25; pap., 75c. ....*Estes.*
— Tangled skein (A). 8°. pap., 75c.......*Burnham.*
— *Same.* 8°. $1.25; pap., 75c...............*Estes.*
Fonblanque, E: Barrington de. Political and military episodes in latter half of 18th cent.; from life and correspondence of John Burgoyne. por., ill. and maps. 8°. '76. $5.........*Macmillan.*
Fonssagrives, J. B. Mother's work with sick children; tr. and ed. by F. P. Foster. 12°. '72. $1.25 ....*Putnam.*
Fontainbleau. O'Keefe, J. 15c.............*French.*
Fontaine, E: How the world was peopled: lectures. 12°. $2..............................*Appleton.*
Fontaine, F. G. de. *See* De Fontaine.
Fontaine, Felix. Golden wheel dream book and fortune teller. ill. 16°. bds., 35c.........*Dick & F.*
Fontaine, Ja. Memoirs of a Huguenot family; tr. by Ann Maury; with tr. of Edict of Nantes. New ed. 12°. '72. $1.75..........................*Putnam.*
Fontaine, J: de la. *See* La Fontaine, J. de.
Fontana, G. B. Elementary gram. of Italian. 12°. $1.50 ....*Appleton.*

Fonthill recreations. Sleeper, M. G. 3 v. $3.75. *Tibbal.*
Fonvielle, W. de. Thunder and lightning; tr. and e[d.] by T. L. Phipson. ill. 12°. '75. $1.25..*Scribne[r.]*
Food for husks; by author of "Lascine." 12°. $1.5[0.] *Sadlie[r.]*
Food for lambs. 18°. per doz., $1.44..*Meth. Bk. Con[c.]*
— *Same.* 32°. '64. 35c......................*Am. T[r.]*
Food for the soul. Smith, J. 25c............*Nelso[n.]*
Fool of quality. Brooke, H. $1.75.......*Macmilla[n.]*
Foolish fear. *See* Alice and her pupils.
Foolish son, and deed of release. 32°. 15c...*Dutto[n.]*
Fool's revenge. *See* Taylor, T.
Foot of the cross. *See* Faber, F. W.
Foot of the cross. Winslow, O. 75c.........*Carte[r.]*
Foote, A. L. R. Aspects of Christianity. 16°. 65c. *Cin. Meth. Bk. Con[c.]*
Foote, E: B. Plain home talk and med. common sens[e] [In Eng. or Germ.] ill. 12°. '70. $3.25..*Murra[y.]*
— Science in story; or, Sammy Tubbs, the boy docto[r,] and Sponsie, the troublesome monkey. 5 v. il[l.] 16°. '74. $7.50; $5; — in 1 v. $2....*Murra[y.]*
Foote, H: S. Bench and bar of the south and sout[h]west. 8°. '76. $2.........................*Soul[e.]*
— War of the rebellion; or, Scylla and Charybdi[s.] 12°. $2.50...........................*Harpe[r.]*
Foote, H: Wilder. King's Chapel and evacuation [of] Boston: discourse, King's Chapel, March 1[2,] 1876. 8°. 20c.......................*William[s.]*
— The wisdom from above: sermon, King's Chape[l,] Jan. 3, 1875, [on] death of Rev. Ja. Walke[r.] 8°. pap., 30c. ....*William[s.]*
Foote, J: Ophthalmic memoranda resp. [most com]mon] diseases of the eye. 18°. 50c....*W. Woo[d.]*
— Practitioner's pharmacopœia and universal formulary prescriptions sel. from eminent Brit. and foreig[n] med. authorities; with add. by B. W. McCready 12°. $2.............................*W. Woo[d.]*
Foote, S: Liar: comedy. 16°. pap., 15c. *De Witt; French*
— Mayor of Garratt: farce. 16°. pap., 15c...*French*
Foote, W: C. Pocket concordance to the Bible. 12[°.] '75. 75c.; mor., $1.50..................*Am. T[r.]*
Foote, W: H: The Huguenots, or reformed Frenc[h] church. 8°. $2...*N. Y. Ref. Ch. Bd.; Pres. Com*
— Sketches of Virginia, historical and biographical. 8[°.] '53. $2..................*Claxton; Lippincot[t.]*
Footfalls on the boundary of another world. Owen, R. D. $1.75 ....*Lippincot[t.]*
Foot-notes. Barron, A. $1.50.............*Oneida*
Footprints of the Creator. Miller, H. $1.50..*Carter*
Footprints of famous men. *See* Edgar, J. G.
Footprints of an itinerant. Gaddis, M. P. $1.75. *Cin. Meth. Bk. Conc*
Footprints of a letter-carrier. Rees, J. $2.25. *Lippincott*
Footprints of life. Harvey, P. $1.25........ *Wells*
Footprints of popery; or, places where martyrs hav[e] suffered. 18°. 60c....................*Pres. Bd*
Footprints of sorrow. Reid, J. $2..........*Carter*
Footprints on life's pathway. Smith, F. M. $1. *Routledge*
Footsteps in the light. 18°. 60c...........*Pres. Bd*
Footsteps of Christ. Caspers, A. $3.75. *Scribner, W. & A*
Footsteps of the Holy Child. Carter, T. T. $1.75..*Pott*
Footsteps of the Messiah. Leask, W. $1.50. (?) *Martien*
Footsteps of St. Paul. Macduff, J. R. $1.50..*Carter*
For better for worse; or, Hattie and Nellie. 16°. '71 $1.25 ....*Cong. Pub.; Graves*
For better or worse. Croly, J. C. $1.50.....*Lee & S*

For better or worse: comedy. 16°. pap., 15c...*French.*

For the colony in Virginea Britannia: lavves diuine, morall and martiall, etc. London, 1612. [Reprint.] 4°. pap., 75c...*Sabin.*

For conscience' sake; by author of "Alice Lee's discipline." ill. 16°. '72. 90c...*Dodd.*

For earth or heaven. 16°. $1.25...(?)*Martien.*

For England, ho! Pocock, I. 15c...*French.*

For a good child. [Toy-book.] ill. 4°. $1.75. *Routledge.*

For her sake. Robinson, F. W. 75c...*Harper.*

For the king. Gibbon, C. 50c...*Harper.*

For the king's dues. Macdonell, A. $1.75..*Macmillan.*

For lack of gold. Gibbon, C. 50c...*Harper.*

For liberty's sake. Marsh, J. B. $2...*Routledge.*

For love and life. Oliphant, M. O. W. 75c...*Harper.*

For want of a nail. ill. sq. 12°. '71. bds., 50c. *Routledge.*

For a woman's sake. Phillips, W. 30c....*Am. News.*

For a woman's sake. Wackenhusen, H. $1.50; 75c. *W. F. Gill.*

Forayers. Simms, W. G. $1.75; 75c.... *Widdleton.*

Forbes, A. P. Explanation of the thirty-nine articles; with an epistle to Dr. Pusey. 12°. '71. $5..*Pott.*

— Memoriale vitæ sacerdotalis; or, solemn warnings of the great shepherd, Jesus Christ, to the clergy of his holy church. 16°. '73. $1.50...*Pott.*

— Remains of Rev. A. W. Haddan. 8°. '76. $6..*Pott.*

— Short explanation of the Nicene creed, for persons beginning study of theology. 12°. '52. $3..*Pott.*

Forbes, E. C. Bible lessons on Scripture hist. 16°. hf. bd., 20c...*N. Y. Ref. Ch. Bd.*

Forbes, G: Transit of Venus. 12°. '74. $1..*Macmillan.*

Forbes, Granville. Village sermons; by a Northamptonshire rector; with pref. on inspiration of Scripture. cr. 8°. '63. $2...*Macmillan.*

— Voice of God in the Psalms: sermons. cr. 8°. '66. $2...*Macmillan.*

Forbes, J. H. ["Arthur Locker."] On a coral reef: story of a runaway trip to sea. roy. 16°. $1.50. *Cassell.*

Forbes, *Rev.* J: Analytical comment. on Epistle to the Romans. 8°. $5...*Scribner, W. & A.*

Forbes, *Sir* J: Homœopathy, allopathy and young physic. *See* Henderson, W., Inquiry into homœop. pract. of med.

— *See also* Cyclopædia of pract. med.

Forbes, R. B. Life boats, projectiles, and other means for saving life. 8°. '72. $1...*Lunt.*

Forbes, W: Sectorian system of hand-railing. pl. f°. '76. $3...*J. W. Randolph.*

Forbidden ground. *See* Tucker, *Mrs.* C.

Force, M. F. Prehistoric man; Darwinism and deity; The mound builders. [Essays.] 8°. '73. pap., 75c...*Clarke.*

Force, P: Auroral phenomena in north latitudes. 4°. '56. pap., $1.25...*Smith. Inst.*

Force and nature. Winslow, C. F. $4. *Lippincott; Macmillan.*

Force of truth. *See* Scott, T.

Forced vows. Blake, L. D. 25c...*Beadle.*

Forces of nature. Guillemin, A. $12.50..*Macmillan.*

Ford, Corydon L. Questions on anatomy; for use of students. 8°. '73. pap., $1...*Fiske & D.*

— Questions on structure and development of human teeth. 8°. '75. pap., 50c...*Fiske & D.*

Ford, J: *See* Massinger, P., *and* Ford, J.

Ford, S. H. Origin of Baptists. 18°. 60c...*So. Bapt.*

—Servetus, hero martyr of 16th cent. 16°. 40c. *So. Bapt.*

Ford, S. V. R. Sunday-school teaching. 12°. 10c. *Meth. Bk. Conc.*

Ford, Sallie Rochester. Evangel Wiseman; or, the mother's question. 12°. $1.50...*Am. Bapt.*

— Grace Truman; or, love and principle. por. 12°. $1.50...*Sheldon.*

— Mary Bunyan, the dreamer's blind daughter: a tale of relig. persecution. ill. 12°. $1.50....*Sheldon.*

Ford, *Mrs.* Theodosia. Christ child. 18°. 30c...*Dutton.*

— Christmas fairies. ill. 16°. '71. $1.25...*Claxton.*

— Magic mirror: Christmas story. 18°. 20c...*Claremont.*

Fordyce, Ja. On honor as a principle. *See* Practical morality.

Fore and aft. Phelps, W. D. $1.50...*Nichols & H.*

Forecastle Tom. Shindler, M. S. B. D. 75c...*Harper.*

Foregleams and foreshadows of immortality. Sears, E. H. $1.75...*Claxton.*

Foregone conclusion. Howells, W. D. $2..*Osgood.*

Foreign tour of Brown, Jones and Robinson. *See* Doyle, R.

Foreigner in far Cathay. Medhurst, W. H. $1.50. *Scribner.*

Foreknowledge of God. Baker, J. M. 75c. *S. W. Bk. & Pub.*

Forest and frontier lib. of travel and adventure. 6 v. ill. 12°. $7.50...*T. Bliss.*

Cont.: Heroes and hunters of the west.—Adventures of hunters and travellers.—Voyage and venture.—Thrilling stories of forest and frontier.—Romance of travel.—Home made happy.

Forest and prairie life. Bennett, E. $1.75..*J. E. Potter.*

Forest boy. *See* Mudge, Z. A.

Forest choir. Root, G. F. 60c...*Church.*

Forest crossing. ill. 18°. '75. 50c...*Nelson.*

Forest-days. *See* James, G. P. R.

Forest exiles. Reid, M. $1.50...*Miller.*

Forest flower. Drummond, J. 30c...*Pres. Bd.*

Forest glen series. *See* Kellogg, E.

Forest home; or, Una and Pietro. 18°. 40c. *Am. S. S.*

Forest house. *See* Erckmann, E., *and* Chatrian, A.

Forest, jungle and prairie. Adams, W. H. D. $2.50. *Nelson.*

Forest keeper. Holl, H. 15c...*French.*

Forest lib. of adventure. *See* Bowman, Anne.

Forest life and trees. Springer, J. S. $1.50..*Harper.*

Forest minstrel. *See* Hogg, J.

Forest oracle. Campbell, M. 15c...*French.*

Forest pictures in the Adirondacks. Hows, J. A. $3. *Hurd & H.*

Forest rose. Bennett, E. 25c...*U. P. James.*

Forest rose. Woodworth, S. 15c...*French.*

Forest scenes; by W. C. Bryant, H. W. Longfellow, Fitz-Greene Halleck and A. B. Street; ill. by J. A. Hows. 4°. '64. $6.50; mor., $10..*Hurd & H.*

Forest tragedy. Lippincott, S. J. $1.25...**Osgood.*

Forest voices. Putlitz, G. H. G. v. $2.50...*Munsell.*

Forester, Fanny (*pseud.*) *See* Judson, *Mrs.* E. C.

Forester, Fk. (*pseud.*) *See* Herbert, H: W:

Forester, T. Norway and its scenery: comprising Price's journal, with add., and a road book. ill. 12°. (Bohn.) $2..*Lippincott; Scribner, W. & A.*

Foresti, F. Italian reader. 12°. $1.50....*Appleton.*

Forestville lib. 4 v. 16°. $5...*Hoyt.*

Cont.: My little corner.—Our forest home.—Jessie's work.—The adopted child.

Forge on the heath. *See* Sister's lib.

Forger's daughter. Russell, M. $1.75...*J. E. Potter.*

Forgery (The). *See* James, G. P. R.

Forget me not. 18°. 30c.; 40c...*Am. Bapt.*

Forget me not. 24°. $1.50...*Locke.*

Forget-me-not songster. 18°. 40c.; pap., 20c...*Sadlier.*

— *See also* New Negro; — New popular.

Forgive and forget. Edgeworth, M. 25c...*Routledge.*

Forgiven. *See* Elsie Wood; — Little folks ser.
Forgiven at last. Hadermann, J. R. $1.75.. *Lippincott.*
Forgiveness; or, the story of Margaret Lisle. 16°. 90c. *Am. S. S.*
Forgiveness and law. Bushnell, H. $1.75.. *Scribner.*
Forgiving kiss. Loth, M. $1.75.......... *Carleton.*
Forgotten by the world: memoirs of an Englishwoman; by author of "Hester Kirton." cr. 8°. $1.75; $1. *Routledge.*
Forlorn hope. *See* Yates, E.
Forney, J: W. Anecdotes of public men. 12°. $2. *Harper.*
— Centennial commissioner (A) in Europe, 1874–'76. 12°. $2.......................... *Lippincott.*
— Letters from Europe. por. 12°. $1.75.... *Peterson.*
Forney, M. N. Catechism of the locomotive. ill. 12°. '75. $2.50...................... *R. R. Gazette.*
— Form, weight, [etc.,] of rails. *See* Constable, C., Retaining walls.
— *See also* Rapid transit.
Forrest, G: Handbook of gymnastics. roy. 32°. bds., 20c.............................. *Routledge.*
— *See also* Walsh, J. H., *and* Forrest, G.
Forrest, Ma. Women of the south distinguished in literature. ill. 8°. '66. $3.50........ *Univ. Pub.*
Forrest, Neil (*pseud.*) *See* Floyd, Cornelia.
Forrest divorce case. 8°. pap., 50c.......... *De Witt.*
Forrest Mills. Thurston, L. M. 80c....... *Am. Unit.*
Forrester, *Mrs.* —. Diana Carew; or, for a woman's sake. 12°. $1.50.................. *Lippincott.*
— Dolores. 12°. $1.75.................. *Lippincott.*
— My hero: a love story. 12°. $1.75; pap., $1.50. *Peterson.*
Forrester, Alfr. H: ["Alfr. Crowquill."] The pictorial grammar. ill. 12°. 50c.... *Scribner, W. & A.*
Forrester, Fs. (*pseud.*) *See* Wise, Dan.
Forry, S: Statistical report on sickness and mortality in U. S. army. *See* United States, *Surgeon-General's Office.*
Fors clavigera. Ruskin, J. 2 pts. ea., $1.... *Wiley.*
Forsaken daughter: a love story. 12°. $1.75; pap., $1.50............................ *Peterson.*
Forshey, C. G. Levees of the Mississippi River; [also] Fox's Proportions of the heads of eye-bars; [also] Whipple and Herschel's Upright arched bridges; [also] Clarke's Education of civil engineers; [also] Thurston's Efficiency of furnaces burning wet fuel. 8°. '74. pap., 70c. *Am. Soc. of C. E.*
Forster, E. (*tr.*) *See* Arabian nights' entertainments.
Förster, Erwin. *See* Schiller gallery.
Forster, J: Life and times of Oliver Goldsmith. New ed. 2 v. ill. 8°. (Lond.) '71. $7.50; hf. cf., $11.50......................... *Little, B. & Co.*
— Life of Charles Dickens. 3 v. por. and fac-similes. 12°. $6; hf. cf., $12. — (Eng. ed.) 3 v. ill. 8°. $16.50.......................... *Lippincott.*
— Life of Jonathan Swift. [To form 3 v.] v. 1: 1667–1711. por. cr. 8°. $2.50............... *Harper.*
— Life of W. S. Landor. por. cr. 8°. $3... *Eastman.*
— — *See also* Landor, W. S.
— Statesmen of the commonwealth of Eng.; with treatise on popular progress in Eng. hist.; ed. by J. O. Choules. por. 8°. $2.25; shp., $2.75; hf. cf., $4.50.............................. *Harper.*
Forster, T: Gale. Unity of God. *See* Hardinge, E., Two Bibles of 19th cent.
— What is spiritualism? address, Music Hall, Boston. ('67.) 5th ed. 8°. '73. pap., 25c......... *Colby.*
Försterling, O. (*ill.*) Die schöne Müllerin. Woodcuts, with [Germ.] poems by W. Müller. roy. 4°. $10. *Stroefer.*
Forsthaus (Das). *See* Temme, J. D. H.

Forsyth, Ja. Book of designs for headstones, mur[al] and other monuments; with introd. by C. Boute[ll]. 4°. '71. $5.............................. *Bair[d]*
Forsyth, J: Memoir of Alex. Proudfit; with se[l.] from diary and correspondence, and recollection[s] by his son. por. 12°. $1.25........... *Harpe[r]*
Forsyth, W: History of lawyers. 8°. '75. $3.50; shp., $4.50....................... *Cockcrof[t]*
— History of trial by jury; ed. by J. A. Morgan. 8[°.] '75. $3 50; shp., $4.50............ *Cockcrof[t]*
— Hortensius: hist. essay on office and duties of an ad[vocate]. 2d ed. ill. 8°. (Lond.) '74. hf. roxb. $5......................... *Little, B. & C[o.]*
— Life of Cicero. 3d ed. ill. 8°. (Lond.) '69. h[f.] roxb., $3.50.................. *Little, B. & C[o.]*
— *Same.* ('69.) New ed. 2 v. ill. cr. 8°. '71. $5; h[f.] cf., $9. — New [chp.] ed. 2 v. in 1. $2.50; h[f.] cf., $4.50.......................... *Scribne[r]*
— Novels and novelists of 18th cent.; in ill. of manner[s] and morals of the age. 12°. $1.50... *Appleto[n]*
Fort, G: F. Early hist. and antiquities of Freemasonry as connected with anc. Norse guilds and Orient[al] and mediæval building fraternities. cr. 8°. '7[5]. $3.50...................... *Sample; Soude[r]*
Fortescue, *Sir* J: De laudibus legum Angliæ; tr. b[y] F. Gregor, with notes by A. Amos, and life [of] author by T. Fortescue, Lord Clermont. 8°. '7[4]. $3................................ *Clark*
Fortescue. Knowles, J. S. $1............ *Harpe[r]*
Fortnum, C. D. E. Majolica. ill. cr. 8°. '75. $1. *Scribner, W. & A.*
Fortunatus Wünschhütlein. 12°. pap., 15c... *Radd[e]*
Fortune hunter. Ritchie, A. C. 50c....... *Peterso[n]*
Fortune seeker. Southworth, E. D. E. N. $1.75; $1.50............................. *Peterson*
Fortune teller. *See* Tonna, *Mrs.* C. E.
Fortune teller and dream book. Gabriel. 20c... *Hurs[t]*
Fortune telling made easy; or, the dreamer's su[re] guide. 12°. pap., 25c.................. *Hurs[t]*
Fortune Wildred, the foundling. 8°. pap., 25c... *De Wit[t]*
Fortune's frolic. Allingham, J. T. 15c..... *Frenc[h]*
Fortune's frolic. *See* French's comic dramas.
Fortunes and misfortunes of Harry Racket Scapegrac[e]. Smedley, F. E. $1.75; 75c.......... *Peterso[n]*
Fortunes of the Fletchers. Eden, C. H. $1.25.. *Pot[t]*
Fortunes of Glencore. *See* Lever, C:
Fortunes of Nigel. Ball, E. 15c........... *Frenc[h]*
Fortunes of Nigel. *See* Scott, *Sir* W.
Fortunes of Torloch O'Brien: tale of the wars [of] King James. 16°. bds., 80c.; — ill. 8°. $3. *Routledg[e]*
Fortunio. Planché, J. R. 15c.............. *Frenc[h]*
Forty acres; or, dancing the old year out and the ne[w] year in. ('65.) New ed. ill. 16°. '73. $1.15. *Hoy[t]*
Forty and fifty. Bayly, T. H. 15c.......... *Frenc[h]*
Forty-five guardsmen. *See* Dumas, A.
Forty-five Players' Congress. *See* O'Hara, P.
Forty-four years of a hunter's life. Browning, M[.] $1.50.............................. *Lippincot[t]*
Forty hours devotion. [Cath. prayer book.] New ed. rev. 24°. 20c.; pap., 15c............ *Noona[n]*
Forty thieves: drama. 16°. pap., 15c........ *Frenc[h]*
Forty winks. Roberts, G. 15c.............. *Frenc[h]*
Forty years in the Turkish empire. Prime, E. D. G[.] $2.50.............................. *Carte[r]*
Forty years' experience in Sunday schools. Tyng, S[.] H. $1............................ *Sheldo[n]*
Forty years' fight with the drink demon. Jewett, C[.] $1.50............................ *Nat. Tem[p.]*
Forum (The). Brown, D. P. 2 v. *net*, $10.... *Kay*
Forum Romanum. Gilbert, *Sir* J. $4..... *Morrison*

orward the flag. Robinson, M. S. 75c.... *Tibbals.*

orwood, W. S. Historical and descrip. narrative of the Mammoth Cave, Ky.; with sci. details of the eyeless fishes. ill. 12°. pap., $1.25...*Lippincott.*

osbery, T. V. Hymns and poems for the sick and suffering. 16°. '70. $1.25 ....*Dutton.*

oscari. Mitford, M. R. 15c...............*French.*

osdick, C: A. ["Harry Castlemon."] Frank and Archie ser. 3 v. ill. 16°. '64-'65. ea., $1.25. *Porter.*

Cont.: Frank, the young naturalist. — Frank in the woods. — Frank on the prairie.

- Go-ahead ser. 3 v. ill. 16°. '68-'70. ea., $1.50..*Porter.*

Cont.: Tom Newcombe. — Go-ahead. — No moss.

- Gunboat ser. 6 v. ill. 16°. '64-'68. ea., $1.25..*Porter.*

Cont.: Frank, the young naturalist. — Frank on a gunboat. — Frank in the woods. — Frank before Vicksburg. — Frank on the lower Mississippi. — Frank on the prairie.

- Rocky mountain ser. 3 v. ill. 16°. '68-'71. ea., $1.25.............................*Porter.*

Cont.: Frank among the rancheros. — Frank at Don Carlos' rancho. — Frank in the mountains.

- Snowed up; or, the sportsman's club in the mountain. ill 16°. $1.25..................*Porter.*

- Sportsman's club ser. 3 v. ill. 16°. '73-'74. ea., $1.25.............................*Porter.*

Cont.: The sportsman's club in the saddle — afloat — among the trappers.

oss, E: Biographia juridica: biog. of judges of Eng., 1016-1870. 8°. (Lond.) '70. hf. cf., $9. *Little, B. & Co.*

oster, Balt. Lectures and essays on clin. medicine. New ed., rev. and enl. ill. 8°. '74. $3.50..*Lindsay.*

oster, Birket (*ill.*) Beauties of Eng. landscape: sel. from the poets, with wood-eng. 4°. '73. $6; mor., $20........................*Routledge.*

- Gift books. 7 v. ill. sm. 4°. ea., $2.50; mor., $5. *Appleton.*

Cont.: Campbell's Gertrude of Wyoming. — Campbell's Pleasures of hope. — Gray's Elegy. — Keats' Eve of St. Agnes. — Milton's L'Allegro. — Poetry of nature. — Tennyson's May queen.

- Pictures of Eng. landscapes: 30 eng. by Dalziel brothers. 4°. $10; mor., $15......*Routledge.*

oster, C. F. Boys at Sandover. 16°. $1.15..*Cong. Pub.*

oster, C: Story of the Bible from Genesis to Revelation, in simple language for the young. ('73.) New ed. ill. roy. 12°. '74. *$2.75; $3.25; mor., $5............................*Betts.*

oster, Elon (*ed.*) Cyclopædia of poetry. 8°. '72. $5; shp., $6; hf. mor., $7; mor., $10..*Palmer.*

- Cyclopædia of prose. ill. 8°. '70. $5; shp., $6; hf. mor., $7; mor., $10 ....*Palmer.*

oster, Emilie. Haven children; or, frolics at the funny old house on Funny Street. ill. sq. 16°. '75. $1.50............................*Dutton.*

oster, G. G. Celio; or, New York above ground and under ground. 8°. pap., 50c..........*De Witt.*

- New York by gaslight. 8°. pap., 25c. .....*De Witt.*

- New York naked; or, the mysteries of the town. 8°. pap., 50c. ....*De Witt.*

oster, G. W. *See* Hodges, D. F., Foster, G. W., *and* Tenney, J. H.; — Hodges, D. F., *and* Foster, G. W.

oster, *Mrs.* Ha. The coquette; or, the life and letters of Eliza Wharton. 12°. $1.75; pap., $1.50. *Peterson.*

oster, *Mrs.* I. H. ["Faye Huntington."] Allan Phillips. 18°. 90c...................(?)*Martien.*

- Fred Roberts' start in life. 18°. '75. 60c. *H. A. Young.*

- In earnest; or, Edith Palmer's motto. ill. 16°. 90c. *J. A. Moore.*

- Kitty Farnham's letters. ill. 18°. 75c...*J. A. Moore.*

- Louise's mistake. 18°. '75. 50c. .....*H. A. Young.*

- Mr. McKenzie's answer. 12°. '75. $1.25..*Nat. Temp.*

- Mrs. Deane's way. ill. 16°. '75. $1.25 ...*Lothrop.*

- Those boys. ill. 16°. '74. $1.50 ....*Lothrop.*

Foster, *Mrs.* I. H., *continued.*

— Through patience. ill. 18°. 80c. ......*J. A. Moore.*

— *See also* Alden, *Mrs.* I. M., *and* Foster, *Mrs.* I. H.

— *and* Alden, *Mrs.* I. M. Dr. Deane's way, and other stories. ill. 16°. '75. $1.25 ....*Lothrop.*

Foster, J. K. Strong consolation; or, the penitent sinner encouraged. 32°. 20c. ....*Pres. Bd.*

Foster, J: Appeal to the young. 18°. '38. 20c. *Am. Tr.*

— Critical essays; ed. by J. E. Ryland. 2 v. 12°. (Bohn.) ea., $1.25.............*Little, B. & Co.*

— *Same.* 2 v. 12°. (Bohn.) ea., $1.40..*Scribner, W. & A.*

— *Same.* 2 v. 12°. (Bohn.) ea., $1.50.......*Lippincott.*

— Early morn: address to the young on importance of religion. 32°. 25c................*J. E. Potter.*

— Essays; in a series of letters; ed. by T. O. Summers. ('55.) 2d ed. 18°. '66. 75c...........*So. Meth.*

— Essays on decision of character. 12°. $1.25..*Carter.*

— *Same.* 12°. (Bohn.) $1.25........*Little, B. & Co.*

— *Same.* 12°. (Bohn.) $1.40......*Scribner, W. & A.*

— *Same.* 12°. (Bohn.) $1.50...........*Lippincott.*

— Essays on evils of popular ignorance. 12°. $1.25. *Carter.*

— *Same.* 12°. (Bohn.) $1.25 ....*Little, B. & Co.*

— *Same.* 12°. (Bohn.) $1.40.....*Scribner, W. & A.*

— *Same.* 12°. (Bohn.) $1.50 ....*Lippincott.*

— Fosteriana: thoughts, reflections and criticisms of F., sel. and ed. by H. G. Bohn. 12°. (Bohn.) $1.75..........................*Little, B. & Co.*

— *Same.* 12°. (Bohn.) $2. *Lippincott; Scribner, W. & A.*

— Improvement of time. 12°. $1.25..........*Carter.*

— Lectures at Broadmead Chapel; ed. by J. E. Ryland. 2 v. 12°. (Bohn.) ea., $1.25....*Little, B. & Co.*

— *Same.* 2 v. 12°. (Bohn.) ea., $1.40. *Scribner, W. & A.*

— *Same.* 2 v. 12°. (Bohn.) ea., $1.50..*Lippincott.*

— Lectures on Christian morals; with introd. by T. O. Summers. ('55.) 2d ed. 18°. '75. 75c. *So. Meth.*

— Life and correspondence. 2 v. 12°. (Bohn.) ea., $1.25.........................*Little, B. & Co.*

— *Same.* 2 v. 12°. (Bohn.) ea., $1.40..*Scribner, W. & A.*

— *Same.* 2 v. 12°. (Bohn.) ea., $1.50 ......*Lippincott.*

Foster, J: Gray. Submarine blasting in Boston Harbor, Mass.: removal of Tower and Corwin rocks. 7 pl. 4°. '69. $3.50............*Van Nostrand.*

Foster, J: Wells. Address before the Am. Assoc. for the Adv. of Sci., Aug., 1870. 8°. pap., 25c. *Am. Assoc. Adv. Sci.*

— Pre-historic races of the U. S. ('73.) 3d ed. ill. cr. 8°. '74. $3.50; hf. cf., $6; cf., $7.50..*Griggs.*

Foster, J: W: *and* Whitney, J. D. Report on geol. and topog. of the Lake Superior land district, Mich. 2 v. and atlas. 8°. '50-'51..........*U. S. Govt.*

Foster, J: Y. New Jersey and the rebellion. maps and por. 8°. '68. $3.50; shp., $4.50; hf. cf., $5; mor., $6.............................*Dennis.*

Foster, Lem. The Sabbath, man's heavenly birthright. 16°. pap., 10c....................*West. Tr.*

Foster, M. Physiology. (Sci. primer.) 18°. 50c. *Appleton.*

— *and* Balfour, F. M. Elements of embryology. pt. 1. cr. 8°. '74. $2.25..................*Macmillan.*

Foster, Mich. *See* Handbook for physiolog. laboratory.

Foster, R. S. Calvinism as it is. 12°. $1.25. *Cin. Meth. Bk. Conc.*

— Christian purity; or, the heritage of faith. ('51.) New ed. 12°. '69. $1.75........*Meth. Bk. Conc.*

Foster, S. Conant. Anniversary address before N. Y. Acad. of Med. 8°. '62. pap., 25c...*N. Y. Acad. Med.*

Foster, *Miss* S. R. *See* Hanna, *Mrs.* S. R.

Foster, Sa. H. The Portsmouth [N. H.] guide book: survey of the city and neighborhood, with notices of buildings, etc. sq. 16°. '76. 75c.....*Foster.*

— Watchwords for little soldiers; or, stories on Bible texts. ('68.) 2d ed. ill. 16°. '70. 80c. *Am. Unit.*

Foster, Ste. C. Gentle Annie melodist: melodies (words and music) by W. V. Wallace and others. ('58.) New ed. 2 v. 32°. '68. ea., 35c.; pap., 30c. .... *Ditson; Pond.*

Foster, Vere. Graded system of drawing. 28 nos. sm. 4°. ea., 15c. .... *Scribner.*

Foster, W. First principles of chemistry; ill. by experiments. 12°. shp., $1.25 .... *Harper.*

Foster, W. L. *See* New Hampshire, Law reports.

Foster-brother (The). Hunt, L. 50c. ..... *Harper.*

Foster brothers; or, pleasing better than teasing; by author of "Jamie's mittens." 16°. $1 .. *Lee & S.*

Fosteriana. *See* Foster, John.

Fothergill, J. Milner. Digitalis: mode of action and use, ill. effect of remedial agents over diseased conditions of the heart. 12°. '71. $1.25 .. *Lindsay.*

— Heart (The) and its diseases, and their treatment. ill. 8°. '72. $5 .... *Lindsay.*

— Maintenance of health. 12°. '75. $2. 8°. $5 .. *Putnam.*

Fothergill, Jessie. Healey: a romance. 8°. pap., 50c. *Harper.*

Foul play. *See* Reade, C:

Found afloat. *See* Hazlewood ser.

Found dead. Payn, J. 50c. .... *Harper.*

Found in a four-wheeler. Williams, T. J. 15c. .. *French.*

Foundations. Porter, R. $1 .... *Randolph.*

Foundations of history. Schieffelin, S. B. 80c. *N. Y. Ref. Ch. Bd.*

Foundations of our faith; by C. A. Auberlen, W. F. Gess and others. cr. 8°. $2.50 ...... *Routledge.*

Founded on facts. Wooler, J. P. 15c. .. *De Witt; French.*

Foundling. 18°. 70c. .... *Pres. Bd.*

Foundling, and other stories. 16°. $1.50 .... *Graves.*

Foundling of Fivecot. *See* Gem cluster.

Foundling of the forest. Dimond, W. 15c. .. *French.*

Foundling of Sebastopol. Tandy, W. 40c. .. *Sadlier.*

Fountain (The). 18°. 22c. .... *Am. S. S.*

Fountain (The). Davis, A. J. $1 ...... *A. J. Davis.*

Fountain Kloof (The); or, missionary life in South Africa. 16°. $1.50 .... *Pres. Bd.*

Fountain of beauty. Kingdom, J. M. 15c. .. *French.*

Fountain of life. Flavel, J. 90c. .... *Am. Tr.*

Fountain of living waters. Irving, T. 60c. .. *Randolph.*

Fountain of youth. *See* Müller, F. P.

Fouqué, F. H. K. *See* La Motte Fouqué.

Four-and-twenty fairy tales. Planché, J. R. $2; $2.25; $3.50 .... *Routledge.*

Four and what they did. Weeks, H. C. $1.25. *Hurd & H.*

Four catechisms: Watts' Historical cat. on the Old Test.; On the New Test.; Short cat. for young children; Shorter cat., with analyses, etc. 18°. pap., 12c. .... *Pres. Bd.*

Four civilizations of the world. Wikoff, H. $1.50. *Lippincott.*

Four cousins: drama. 16°. pap., 15c. .... *French.*

Four-footed lovers. Albertsen, F. $1.50 .. *Lee & S.*

Four Georges. *See* Thackeray, W. M.

Four girls at Chautauqua. Alden, I. M. $1.50 .. *Lothrop.*

Four gold pieces. Gouraud, J. $1.25; 50c. *Scribner, W. & A.*

Four Gospels and the one Christ. Johnson, G. B. 75c. *Nelson.*

Four little people; or, Bob, Trot, Jamie and Lina; by author of "Cecil at Elm Terrace." 18°. 50c. *Am. S. S.*

Four little pitchers. May, C. L. 75c. ... *H. A. Young.*

Four phases of morals. Blackie, J. S. $1.50 .. *Scribner.*

Four pillars of temperance. Kirton, J. W. 75c. *Nat. Temp.*

Four pistareens (The); or, honesty the best policy. 18°. 22c. .... *Am. S. S.*

Four principal gates of hell. *See* Liguori, *St.*

Four quarters of the world. Goodrich, S. G. $1.50. *Desilver.*

Four seasons. ill. 32°. '53. 30c. .... *Am. Tr.*

Four seasons. La Motte Fouqué. $1.25 .. *Routledge.*

Four sisters. Bernard, W. B. 15c. .... *French.*

Four sisters. Bremer, F. $1.75; $1.50 .... *Peterson.*

Four sisters. Richmond, D. $1.25 ...... *Routledge.*

Four steps: a short journey to Jesus. 18°. 17c.; 22c. *Am. Bapt.*

Four thousand miles of African travel. Southworth, A. S. $2.50 .... *Baker, P. & Co.*

Four years among the Spanish-Americans. Hassaurek, F. $1.75 .... *Hurd & H.*

Four years in Ashantee. Ramseyer, F. A., *and* Kühne, J. $1.75 .... *Carter.*

Four years in the old world. Palmer, P. $3.50. *Palmer.*

Four years in the saddle. Gilmor, H. $2 .... *Harper.*

Four years of fighting. Coffin, C. C. $3.50; $4.50. **Osgood.*

Four years on board the whale ship. 12°. $1.25. *Lippincott.*

Fourberies de Scapin. *See* Molière, J. B. P.

Fourcy, Lefebvre de. Elements of trigonometry; tr. by F. H. Smith; with tables of logarithms, etc., by E. Loomis. 8°. '67. $2.50 .... *Kelly, P. & Co.*

Fourier, C: The amorous corporations; tr. by C. Blanchard. 16°. '67. pap., 25c. ...... *D. Thomas.*

Fournier, M. R. Comedy and tragedy: comedy. 16°. pap., 15c. .... *French.*

Fourteen months in American Bastiles. Howard, F. K. 50c. .... *Kelly, P. & Co.*

Fourteen pet goslings. Frank. 75c. .... *Tilton.*

Fourteen picture lessons on the Lord's prayer. 4°. pap., 50c.; bds., 75c. .... *Am. Bapt.*

Fourteen weeks ser. *See* Steele, J. D.

Fourth commandment. ill. 32°. '53. 30c. .... *Am. Tr.*

Fourth Gospel the heart of Christ. Sears, E. H. $2.50. *Lockwood, B. & Co.*

Fourth watch. *See* Warner, A. B.

Fowle, C: H. Brown Jones' and Jones Brown's adventures at Martha's Vineyard camp ground. 8°. pap., 15c. .... *Wheaton.*

Fowle, E. (*ed.*) Plain preaching for a year. 3 v. 16°. '75. $6 .... *Pott.*

Fowle, W: B. Bible reader: sel. from Scriptures for schools and families. 12°. '66. $1 .... *Barnes.*

— Common school speller. 12°. 25c. ...... *Claremont.*

— False orthography: compan. to National ser. of spellers and readers. 12°. '66. hf. bd., 50c. .. *Barnes.*

— Familiar dialogues, and popular discussions for schools. 12°. 75c. .... *Claremont.*

— Free speaker: pieces for declamation. 12°. '59. $1.25 .... *Nichols & H.*

— Hundred dialogues. 12°. '54. $1.25 .. *Nichols & H.*

— Parlor dramas. 12°. '56. $1.25 ...... *Nichols & H.*

— Principles of linear and perspective drawing. 12°. hf. bd., 60c. .... *Barnes.*

— Teacher's institute (The); or, familiar hints to young teachers. 12°. '66. $1.25 .... *Barnes.*

Fowler, Abijah *and* Josiah. Arithmetic; or, youth's assistant. 16°. hf. bd., 50c. .... *Duffie.*

— — The federal instructor; or, youth's assistant. [Arithmetic.] 18°. 50c. .... *Moss.*

Fowler, C. H. Fallacies of Colenso reviewed. 16°. 75c. .... *Cin. Meth. Bk. Conc.*

Fowler, J. H. New Test. miracles and modern miracles. ('54.) 3d ed. 8°. '73. pap., 60c. .. *Colby.*

Fowler, Josiah. *See* Fowler, A. *and* J.

'owler, L. N. Marriage: its hist. and ceremonies; with phrenol. and physiol. exposition of functions and qualifications for happy marriages. 12°. '46. $1.25 .... *Wells.*
– *See* Fowler, O. S. *and* L. N., *and* Kirkham, S.
'owler, Laura T. Manual of oral instruction for graded schools. 4°. '67. 75c........ *Bancroft.*
'owler, O. S. Amativeness; or, evils and remedies of excessive and perverted sexuality: sup. to "Love and parentage." ('47.) 40th ed. 12°. pap., 25c........ *Wells.*
– Creative and sexual science; or, manhood, womanhood and their interrelations, etc. ('70.) New ed. ill. roy. 8°. '75. *$3.75; leath., $4.50.. *Nat. Pub.*
– Education and self-improvement: compr. Physiology, animal and mental; Self-culture and perfection of character; Memory and intellectual improvement. ill. 12°. '45. $3.50........ *Wells.*
– Hereditary descent: its laws and facts applied to human improvement. 12°. '45. $1.25... *Wells.*
– Home (A) for all; or, the gravel wall and octagon mode of building. 12°. '53. $1.25...... *Wells.*
– Human science; or, phrenology: its principles, proofs, etc., as applied to health, intellect, etc. ill. roy. 8°. '73. *$3.75; leath., $4.50.. *Nat. Pub.*
– Love and parentage. ('46.) 40th ed. ill. 12°. $1. pap., 50c........ *Wells.*
– Maternity. 12°. '48. $1.25........ *Wells.*
– Matrimony: phrenol. and physiol. applied to sel. of congenial companions for life. ('44.) 34th ed., rev. 8°. pap., 50c........ *Wells.*
– Memory and intellectual improvement, applied to self-education and juvenile instruction. ('45.) 25th ed., rev. 12°. $1.25........ *Wells.*
– Physiology, animal and mental; applied to preservation and restoration of health of body and power of mind. 12°. '47. $1.25........ *Wells.*
– Self-culture and perfection of character; incl. management of youth. 12°. '46. $1.25...... *Wells.*
– *and* L. N., *and* Kirkham, S: Phrenology proved, illustrated and applied. 12°. '36. $1.50.. *Wells.*
'owler, S. P. Account of Rev. Samuel Parris and of his connection with the witchcraft delusion of 1692. 8°. '57. pap., 15c........ *Essex.*
'owler, W: Chauncey. Conditions of success in geneal. investigations, ill. in character of Nath. Chauncey. 8°. '66. pap., 25c... *N. E. Hist. Gen.*
– Elementary Eng. grammar for common schools. 16°. hf. leath., 75c........ *Harper.*
– English lang. in its elements and forms; with hist. of its origin and development. New ed., rev. and enl. 8°. $2.50; shp., $3........ *Harper.*
– *Same;* abridg.; with March's Method of philol. study of the Eng. lang. 12°. shp., $1.75.... *Harper.*
– Essays, historical, literary, educational. 8°. '76. $1.50 .... (?) *Case.*
– Sectional controversy passages in political history of U. S. ('62.) New ed. 8°. '68. $2... *Scribner.*
'owler, W: Worthington. Fighting fire: the great fires of hist. ill. 8°. '73. *$3; leath., $3.50. *Dustin.*
– Ten years in Wall st.; or, revelations of inside life and experience on 'change. ill. and por. 8°. '70. *$3; leath., $3.50; $4........ *Dustin.*
– Woman on the Am. frontier. ill. 8°. $2.75; $3.50. *Scranton.*
'ownes, G: Manual of element. chemistry, theoretical and practical. New Am., from 10th Lond. ed., rev.; ed. by R. Bridges. ill. roy. 12°. $2.75; leath., $3.25........ *Lea.*
'ox, C. D. Proportions of the heads of eye-bars. *See* Forshey, C. G., Levees of Mississippi River.
'ox, C: Digest of law of partnership, as presented in reports of Eng. and Am. decisions. 8°. '72. shp., $6.50........ *Ward & P.*
'ox, C: Ethiopian comicalities. 18°. pap., 10c. *Dick & F.*

Fox, C: *See* Parker, R. G., *and* Fox, C.
Fox, C: Ja. History of reign of James II. *See* Carrel, A., Hist. of counter-revolution.
Fox, George. Journal of life and travels. 8°. $1.75. *Friends Bk. St.*
— *Germ.* 12°. 60c........ *Friends Bk. St.*
Fox, H. J. (*ed.*) Sabbath psalter: public and family worship. 12°. '65. 60c........ *Meth. Bk. Conc.*
Fox, H: R: V. *See* Holland, *Lord.*
Fox, H: Watson. Memoir. 18°. 75c........ *Am. S. S.*
— Memoir of C. C. Hoffman, missionary at Cape Palmas. map and ill. 12°. '68. $2.50.... *Randolph.*
Fox, J: Acts and monuments of the church: [Book of martyrs]. 8°. $5........ *Carter.*
— Book of martyrs. ill. 32°. 69. 25c. ...... *Lothrop.*
— *Same.* 12°. '70. $1.25........ *Claxton.*
— *Same.* New ed., rev. with notes and app. by Rev. B. Moore. ill. cr. 4°. $5; $6........ *Cassell.*
— *Same;* with pref. by Rev. S. Waldegrave. ill. 18°. 60c........ *Claxton.*
— *Same;* abridg. from Milner's ed. by T. A. Buckley. 12°. 75c........ *Routledge.*
— The English martyrology; abridg. by Charlotte Elizabeth [Tonna]. 2 v. ill. 12°. $2..... *Pres. Bd.*
— Life and writings. *See* British reformers.
Fox, Jos. Natural history: diseases and structure of the human teeth. ill. 8°. $4........ *Lindsay.*
Fox, T: B. (*ed.*) Memoir of Ja. P. Walker; with sel. from his writings. por. 12°. '69. $1.50.. *Am. Unit.*
Fox, T: Lew. Account of early hist. of Freemasonry in Eng.; with ill. of [its] principles and precepts. 16°. (Lond.) '72. $1........ *Williams.*
Fox, Tilbury. Atlas of skin diseases: chromo-lith. pl. with descrip. text and notes. [To form 18 pts.] pts. 1–10. roy. 4°. ea., $2........ *Lindsay.*
— Skin diseases: their description, pathology, diagnosis and treatment. 2d Am., from 3d Lond. ed., rev. and enl. by M. H. Henry. ill. 8°. $5.. *W. Wood.*
Fox, Wilson. Diseases of the stomach. 3d ed., rev. and enl. 8°. '72. $3........ *Macmillan.*

Note. First pub. under title of Diagnosis and treatment of the varieties of dyspepsia.

— *Same.* ill. 8°. $2........ *Lea.*
— On the artificial production of tubercle in the lower animals. ill. 4°. '68. $2........ *Macmillan.*
— On the treatment of hyperpyrexia, as ill. in acute, articular rheumatism, by means of the internal application of cold. 8°. '71. $1.25.. *Macmillan.*
Fox and the crow. *See* Stories about animals ser.
Fox chase. Everhart, J. B. $1........ *Porter.*
Fox hunter. *See* Malan, C.
Fox hunting. Stephens, C. A. $1.25........ *Porter.*
Foxton, E. (*pseud.*) *See* Palfrey, S. H.
Foye, Ja. C. Tables for determination and classification of minerals found in the U. S. 16°. '75. 75c........ *Jansen.*
Fra Diavolo. [Germ.] 12°. pap., 15c........ *Radde.*
Fra Diavolo: opera. 16°. pap., 15c........ *French.*
Fra Diavolo: opera. *See* Auber, D. F. E.
Fra Diavolo: travestie. Byron, H. J. 15c.... *French.*
Fradenburgh, J. N. Lineage of language. 8°. '76. $3. *Authors.*
Fragments for the young. 18°. 40c...... *Whittaker.*
Fragments for young people. 72°. '40. 15c. *Meth. Bk. Conc.*
Fragments of science for unscientific people. Tyndall, J. $2........ *Appleton.*
Fragrance from crushed flowers. 18°. 45c. *Bost. Am. Tr.*
Family Parsonage. *See* Trollope, A.
Francatelli, C: E. Cookery book. 16°. 20c... *Routledge.*
— Modern cook: guide to the culinary art in all its branches. ill. roy. 8°. $5........ *Peterson.*

France and her people. Benton, C. C. $1.50..*Souder.*

Frances, Marg. Rose Carleton's reward. ill. 12°. $1. *Chase.*

Frances Egerton; or, indolence rebuked. 18°. 20c.; 25c. .... *Am. Bapt.*

Frances Hildyard. Wood, E. P. 25c....... *Peterson.*

Frances Leslie. Bickersteth, E. 75c....... *Am. S. S.*

Frances Leslie. *See* Glen Elder books.

Frances Meadows; or, traits of character. 16°. 50c. *Scribner, W. & A.*

Frances Morton; or, the light of West Morelands; by author of "Mark Barnett." ('64.) New ed. ill. 16°. '75. $1.15........ *Hoyt.*

Francesca da Rimini. Pellico, S. 75c......... *Holt.*

Francesco *d'Assisi, St.* Life; [also] Sketch of the Franciscan order; by a religious of the Order of Poor Clares, with add. by Pamfilo da Magliano. 8°. $2.50........ *O'Shea.*

Francillon, R. E. Earl's Dene. 8°. pap., 50c... *Harper.*

— Zelda's fortune. ill. 8°. $1.25; pap., 75c.... *Estes.*

Francis *of Assisi.* *See* Francesco *d'Assisi.*

Francis *of Rome, St.* Life. 16°. $1; $1.50..*Sadlier.*

Francis *of Sales.* *See* François de Sales.

Francis, *Miss* —. Charade dramas. 16°. pap., 40c. *French.*

Francis, Convers. Life of J. Eliot. *See* Sparks, J., Library of Am. biog.

Francis, F: Fish culture, and mod. system of breeding fish in inland waters. post 8°. $3 ..... *Routledge.*

Francis, G. H. Orators of the age. 12°. $1..*Harper.*

Francis, J. Annals, anecdotes and legends of life assurance. Am. ed., rev. 12°. $2..... *Wynkoop.*

Francis, J. B. Darcy's experiments on flow of water through pipes. 8°. pap., 40c...*Am. Soc. of C. E.*

— Durability of cast iron water-mains. *See* McAlpine, W. J., Corrosion of iron.

— Experiments in deflection of continuous beams. 8°. pap., 25c. .... *Am. Soc. of C. E.*

— Failure of dam on Mill River. *See* Chanute, O., Weight of rails.

— Lowell hydraulics: experiments on flow of water over weirs, and in open canals of uniform rectangular section, Lowell, Mass. 3d ed., rev. and enl. 23 copper pl. 4°. '71. $15.. *Van Nostrand.*

— Provincetown dyke. 8°. pap., 40c...*Am. Soc. of C. E.*

Francis, J: Wakefield. Anniversary discourse, N. Y. Acad. of Med. 8°. '47. pap., 25c. *N. Y. Acad. Med.*

— Inaugural address before N. Y. Acad. of Med. 8°. '48. pap., 10c........ *N. Y. Acad. Med.*

— Old New York: reminiscences of the past sixty years; with memoir of author by H. T. Tuckerman. por. sm. 8°. $2.25; hf. cf., $4; large pap., $10........ *Widdleton.*

Francis, S: W. Report of V. Mott's surgical cliniques in the Univ. of N. Y., 1859–'60. por. 16°. $1.50. *W. Wood.*

Francis Leslie. Bickersteth, E. $1.25...... *Nelson.*

Francis Lucas. 18°. 45c. .... *Dutton.*

Francke, A: Hm. Memoir. 18°. 60c. ..... *Am. S. S.*

Francke, H. Outlines of a new theory of disease, applied to hydropathy; tr. by R. Blakie. 12°. $1.50.. *Wiley.*

Franco, J: Jos. Simon Peter and Simon Magus: a legend; tr. 12°. '71. $1.50 ..... *Cunningham.*

— Tigranes; tr. from the Ital. [Fiction.] 12°. '74. $1.50........ *Cunningham.*

Franco, Secondo. Devotion to sacred heart of Jesus; tr. from the Ital. 18°. '70. $1; $1.50.... *Murphy.*

François *de Sales, St.* Golden sayings; tr. 32°. pap., 10c........ *Pott.*

— Introduction to the devout life; tr. 18°. '75. $1..*Pott.*

— *Same.* 18°. '71. $1.25........ *Lothrop.*

— *Same;* [with] life. 18°. 75c. .... *Cath. Pub.*

— *Same;* [with] life. 24°. 60c. 18°. 75c...*O'Shea.*

François *de Sales, St., continued.*

— Life. 16°. $1; $1.50........ *Sadlier.*

— Practical piety; collected from his letters and discourses; tr. sm. 12°. '69. $1; $1.50..*Murphy.*

— Spirit; tr. 12°. '72. $3........ *Pott.*

— *Same;* ed. by J. P. Camus, Bp. of Belley; tr. by a priest of the diocese of Boston. 12°. $2..*O'Shea.*

— Spiritual director of devout and religious; tr. 18°. 50c. *Cath. Pub.*

— Spiritual letters; tr. 32°. '76. 50c. .... *Pott.*

— *Same;* sel. and tr. by Mrs. S. Lear. 12°. '71. $2.50. *Pott.*

— Treatise on the love of God; tr. 12°. $1.75..*O'Shea.*

— True spiritual conferences; tr. 12°. $1.50..*Sadlier.*

Franconia stories. *See* Abbott, Jac.

Franctireurs (Die). *See* Gerstäcker, F.

Frank (*pseud.*) Fourteen pet goslings. sq. 16°. '58. 75c. .... *Tilton.*

Frank. *See* Edgeworth, M.

Frank; or, what can one boy do? 18°. 45c...*Cong. Pub.*

Frank, the fisher boy; or, perils on land and sea. ill. 8°. (Lond.) 50c........ *Am. News.*

Frank, the young naturalist. Fosdick, C. A. $1.25. *Porter.*

Frank among the rancheros. Fosdick, C. A. $1.25. *Porter.*

Frank and Amy's visit to Palestine. Robbins, *Mrs.* —. 75c........ *Cong. Pub.*

Frank and Archie series. *See* Fosdick, C. A.

Frank and Joey. *See* Aunty Ray's little lib.

Frank and Rufus. Trowbridge, C. M. 90c. (?) *Martien.*

Frank at Don Carlos' rancho. Fosdick, C. A. $1.25. *Porter.*

Frank Austin's diamond. Mathews, J. A. 75c..*Carter.*

Frank before Vicksburg. Fosdick, C. A. $1.25..*Porter.*

Frank Burton's dream. *See* Golden chain lib.

Frank Earnest; or, going into the Master's vineyard. 18°. 40c........ *Dutton.*

Frank Elliot. Challen, J. $1........ *Challen.*

Frank Elston; or, patience in well doing. ill. 18°. '66. 75c. .... *N. Y. Ref. Ch. Bd.; Pres. Com.*

Frank Eston. Blake, C. L. 50c. .... *Pres. Bd.*

Frank Evans, the doubter. 18°. 30c....... *Cong. Pub.*

Frank Fairlegh. *See* Smedley, F. E.

Frank Fielding. Veitch, A. 60c......... (?) *Martien.*

Frank Forest. Stone, D. 75c........ *Dodd.*

Frank Forester's [sporting books]. *See* Herbert, H. W.

Frank Fox Phipps, Esq.: farce. 16°. pap., 15c. *French.*

Frank gone to the war. *See* M., *Mrs.* A. S.

Frank Gordon. Goulding, F. R. 75c. ...(?) *Martien.*

Frank Grover, the blacksmith's boy. 18°. 80c. *Cong. Pub.*

Frank Harley. 18°. 25c.; 30c........ *Am. Bapt.*

Frank Harper; or, the country boy in town. 18°. 55c. *Am. S. S.*

Frank Harrison. 18°. 50c. .... *Carter.*

Frank Harvey in Paris. Hildeburn, M. J. 70c. *Pres. Bd.*

Frank Herbert; or, the young student. 18°. 40c. *Cong. Pub.*

Frank Hilton. *See* Grant, Ja.

Frank in the mountains; — in the woods. Fosdick, C. A. ea., $1.25........ *Porter.*

Frank Irving; or, the wayward son. 18°. 60c.; 70c. *Am. Bapt.*

Frank Leslie's comic almanac for 1874. ill. 12°. '73. pap., 15c. .... (?) *Leslie.*

Frank Leslie's illustrated almanac for 1873. sm. 4°. '73. pap., 50c........ (?) *Leslie.*

Frank Manly. Trowbridge, J. T. $1.50.. *W. F. Gill.*

Frank Martin; or, a schoolboy's trials and triumphs. ill. 18°. 75c........ *Nelson.*

Frank May, the minister's son. Porter, A. E. $1.25. *Cong. Pub.*

Frank Merton's conquest. ill. 18°. '74. 40c...*Am. Tr.*

Frank Mildmay. *See* Marryat, F:

Frank Nelson, the runaway boy. Hanaford, P. A. $1.25 .... *H. A. Young.*

Frank Netherton; or, the talisman. 18°. 60c. *Am. S. S.; Carter.*

— *Same.* ('60.) 3d ed. 18°. '73. 65c.....*So. Meth.*

— *Same.* ill. 18°. 70c. *N. Y. Ref. Ch. Bd.; Pres. Com.; Pres. Bd.*

Frank Oldfield. *See* Wilson, T. P.

Frank on a gunboat. Fosdick, C. A. $1.25..*Porter.*

Frank on the lower Mississippi. Fosdick, C. A. $1.25. *Porter.*

Frank on the prairie. Fosdick, C. A. $1.25..*Porter.*

Frank Randolph. 18°. 35c........ *Cong. Pub.*

Frank Rivers. Ingraham, J. H. 25c. .... *De Witt.*

Frank Sillaby. *See* Blake, L. H.

Frank Spencer's rule of life. Kirton, J. W. 50c. *Nat. Temp.*

Frank Starr's Am. novels. 201 nos. 8°. ea., pap., 10c. *Starr.*

Frank Stirling's choice. Bulfinch, M. H. $1..*Dutton.*

Frank Talbot. Grosvenor, H. S. 40c. .... *Hoyt.*

Frank Warrington. Harris, M. C. $1.50...*Carleton.*

Frank Wentworth: story of Hawthorn Hall. ('70.) New ed. ill. 16°. '74. $1.15.......... *Hoyt.*

Frank Wildman's adventures. *See* Gerstäcker, F.

Franke, A. H. Lebensregeln. 18°. '50. 25c...*Am. Tr.*

Franke, W. B. Monumental designs. pl. f°. '75. $9. *Bicknell.*

Frankenstein. Milner, H. M. 15c......... *French.*

Frankenstein. Shelley, M. W. $1; 60c. ....*Allyn.*

Frankie and his friends. *See* Aunt Deborah's lib.

Frankie's book of Bible men. *See* Ashton, *Mrs.* S. G., Ashton ser.

Frankie's dog Tony. *See* Baker, *Mrs.* H. N. W.

Frankie's little friend. Davis, C. E. K. 50c....*Hoyt.*

Frankie's little meeting. Davis, C. E. K. 50c...*Hoyt.*

Frankie's work. Davis, C. E. K. 50c......... *Hoyt.*

Frankland, E. How to teach chemistry: lectures. ill. 12°. '75. $1.25................ *Lindsay.*

Franklin, B: Autobiography and essays. 18°. '71. 75c. *Claxton.*

— *Same.* ill. 16°. $1.50.................. *Mason.*

— *Same;* with letters and misc. writings. 2 v. 18°. $1.50..................... *Harper.*

— *Same;* ed. by J. Bigelow. 3 v. cr. 8°. $7.50; shp., $9; hf. cf., $13.50............ *Lippincott.*

— *Same;* with sketch of public services by H. H. Weld. ill. 8°. $4; shp., $4.50; hf. cf., $6.25..*Harper.*

— Life. ill. 16°. $1.25.................. *Lee & S.*

— Printer boy: life of F. 16°. '60. $1.50...... *Tilton.*

— Way to wealth. *See* Practical morality.

Franklin, B: Christian experience; or, sincerity seeking the way to heaven. 32°. pap., 10c..... *Chase.*

— The union movement: dialogue ill. duty and practicability of Christian union upon the Bible and the Bible alone. 24°. pap., 10c.............. *Chase.*

Franklin, J: (*ill.*) *See* Parables of our Lord.

Franklin, Jose. Martin stories. 6 v. ill. 16°. $5; ea., 83c..................... *Thompson.*

Cont.: Martin. — Cousin Regulus. — Martin and Nelly. — Martin and the miller. — Martin on the mountain. — Trouting; or, gipsying in the woods.

— Nelly stories. 6 v. ill. 16°. $5; ea., 83c... *Thompson.*

Cont.: Nelly and her friends. — Nelly's first school days. — Nelly and her boat. — Nelly's visit. — Little Bessie. — Zelma.

Franklin. Brougham, J. 15c............... *French.*

Franklin globe manual. sm. 4°. bds., 56c..... *Nims.*

Franklin Institute Journal. 101 v. 8°. '26–'76. ea., $1.50.................. *Franklin Inst.*

Franklin ser. of readers. *See* Hillard, G. S., *and* Campbell, L. J.; — Hillard, G. S., *and* Sprague, H. B.

Frank's campaign. Alger, H., *jr.* $1.25.... *Loring.*

Frank's friend. Caspari, K. H. 35c....(?) *Luth. Pub.*

Frank's pet rooster. *See* Picture stories for little folks.

Frank's search for sea-shells. Parker, H. F. $1.15. *Bost. Am. Tr.*

Frank's Sieg. 18°. 30c.................. *Ev. Assoc.*

Frank's victory. Butler, M. 70c........... *Pres. Bd.*

Frank's victory. *See* Gay cottage stories; — New holiday lib.

— *Same;* [also] The Nevers. ill. 18°. 50c. *Bost. Am. Tr.*

Franz, Agnes. Bertrand du Guesclin; tr. from the Germ. [Biography.] 18°. 50c......... *O'Shea.*

Franz, Rob. Thirty-five songs. 8°. *net,* pap., $2.25. *Schirmer.*

Franz, the little street singer. 18°. 40c....... *Dutton.*

Fraser, Don. The Bible and the family. 8°. $5. *Scribner, W. & A.*

— Synoptical lectures on the books of Bible. 3 v. 12°. $6 .... *Carter.*

Cont.: 1. Genesis; Song of songs. — 2. Isaiah; Acts. — 3. Romans; Revelations.

Fraser, J. Baillie. Historical and descrip. account of Persia; incl. descrip. of Afghanistan and Beloochistan. 18°. 75c.................... *Harper.*

— History of Mesopotamia and Assyria. 18°. 75c. *Harper.*

Fraser, J: Humorous chap-books of Scotland. v. 1, 2. 8°. '73–'74. ea., $1.25............. *Hinton.*

Fraser, Rob. W. Moriah; or, sketches of the sacred rites of anc. Israel. 12°. $1.......... *Pres. Bd.*

Fraser, W: Blending lights. 12°. $2........ *Carter.*

— *Same.* 12°. '75. $2....................... *Am. Tr.*

Fraser miscellanies. *See* Thackeray, W. M.

Fraser-Tytler, C. C. *See* Tytler, C. C. F.

Fraud and its victims. Coyne, J. S. 15c..... *French.*

Fräulein Mina. Norris, M. H. $1.25..*Meth. Bk. Conc.*

Frazer, J: American form book and legal guide. 12°. hf. shp., $1.25................... *U. P. James.*

Frazier family; or, home politeness. 18°. 20c.; 25c. *Am. Bapt.*

Freaks of fortune. Adams, W. T. $1.25...*Lee & S.*

Freaks on the fells. *See* Ballantyne, R. M.

Fred and the gorillas. Miller, T. $1.25...*Routledge.*

Fred and his relations. *See* Gem cluster.

Fred and Jeanie. Drinkwater, J. M. $1.25..*Carter.*

Fred Arden. Smith, J. F. 75c........... *Dick & F.*

Fred Brenning. Redford, A. H. 75c. ...... *So. Meth.*

Fred Brenning lib. 10 v. ill. 16°. $7.50....*So. Meth.*

Cont.: Fred Brenning, by A. H. Redford. — First heroes of the cross, by B. Clarke. — Papers for thoughtful girls, by S. Tytler. — Stepping stones. — Clouded intellect, by J. Ingelow. — "Above rubies." — Tossed on the waves, by E. Hodder. — Besieged city, by Mrs. C. Overend. — The cumberers. — The junior clerk, by E. Hodder.

Fred Douglas and his mule. Small, G. G. 25c. *Collin & S.*

Fred Franks. Tucker, C. 50c. .... *Dutton.*

Fred Graham. Smith, J. F. 75c.......... *Dick & F.*

Fred Kenny. *See* Little Dot ser.

Fred Lawrence. Teller, M. E. 75c.......... *Dodd.*

Fred, Maria and me. Prentiss, E. $1.50...*Scribner.*

Fred Markham in Russia. Kingston, W. H. G. 75c. *Harper.*

Fred Mortimer. 18°. '64. 60c........... *Randolph.*

Fred Roberts' start in life. Foster, I. H. 60c. *H. A. Young.*

Fred Vernon. Smith, J. F. $1........... *Dick & F.*

Fred Wilder. Trowbridge, C. M. $1..... *Cong. Pub.*

Fred Wilson's sled. Dunning, A. K. 35c...*Pres. Bd.*

Freddie fighting his way. 18°. 50c.......... *Carter.*

Freddy, the runaway; or, the lost one found. 18°. 40c. .... *Am. S. S.*

Freddy's fifth birthday. *See* Cousin Anna's lib.

Frederick Gordon. Hamilton, K. W. 60c... *Pres. Bd.*

Frederick the Great. Maddox, F. M. 15c... *French.*

Frederick the Great and his court. Mundt, C. M. $1.50; $1; $3.50 .... *Appleton.*

Frederick the Great and his family. Mundt, C. M. $1.50; $1; $3.50 .... *Appleton.*

Frederick Latimer. McKeever, H. B. $1.25.. *Am. Bapt.*

Frederick of Prussia. Selby, C. 15c........ *French.*

Frederick Stanly; or, the fatal falsehood. 18°. 40c. *Cong. Pub.*

Fredericks, A. (*ill.*) *See* Shakespeare, W., Midsummer-night's dream.

Frederico und Alfonso. 12°. 35c.; pap., 15c. *Benziger.*

Fredet, P. Ancient history; from the flood to the Roman empire. 12°. '51. $1.50........ *Murphy.*

— Modern history. ('51.) 32d ed., contin. to 1867. 12°. '67. $1.50 .... *Murphy.*

Fred's fresh start, and what he did by moral courage. ('70.) New ed. ill. 16°. '75. 90c.......... *Hoyt.*

Fred's hard fight. Howard, M. $1.25..... *Nat. Temp.*

Fred's scrap book. *See* Dot books.

Free and easy. Arnold, W. H. 15c. .... *French.*

Free communionist: essays. 24°. '41. 75c... *Freewill.*

Free hand drawing: guide to ornamental, figure and landscape draw.; by an art student. ill. 18°. bds., 50c............ *Van Nostrand.*

Free lance (A) in the field of life and letters. Wilkinson, W. C. $1.50 .... *Mason.*

Free negroism. Van Evrie, J. H. 10c.... *Van Evrie.*

Free public libraries: suggestions on their foundation and administration, with sel. list of books. New ed., rev. 12°. '71. pap., 25c......... *Williams.*

Free Religious Association. Proceedings, 1867-'76. 10 v. 8°. ea., pap., 35c............ *Free Rel.*

Free Russia. Dixon, W. H. $2............ *Harper.*

Free, yet forging their own chains. Cornwall, C. M. $1.50............ *Dodd.*

Freebooter's prize. 12°. pap., 20c.... ...... *Hurst.*

Freebooters. Aimard, G. 50c............ *Peterson.*

Freedboy in Alabama. Mitchell, A. M. 65c. *Pres. Bd.*

Freedley, Edn. T. Legal adviser; or, how to diminish losses, avoid lawsuits, etc. 12°. $1; shp., $1.25 .... *Lippincott.*

— *Same.* 12°. $1.75 .... *J. E. Potter.*

— Opportunities for industry, and safe investment of capital; or, a thousand chances to make money. 12°. $1............ *Lippincott.*

— Practical treat. on business. 12°. $1.25.. *Lippincott.*

Freedmen's book. Child, L. M. $1.25 ..... *Osgood.*

Freedom and fellowship in religion; with introd. by O. B. Frothingham. 16°. '75. $2 ..... *Roberts.*

Freedom of the press. Baker, G. M. 15c... *Lee & S.*

Freedom of the will. Hazard, R. G. $2... *Appleton.*

Freeholder. *See* Addison, Jos.

Freeland, *Mrs.* Carrie J. ["C. J. G."] Ansdale Hall; or, stand by your colors. ill. 18°. 60c. *Bost. Am. Tr.*

— — *See also* Pleasant grove ser.

— Bessie Hartwell; or, charity. ill. 16°. '73. $1.25. *Crowell.*

— — *See also* Ollie lib.

— Good fight of faith. 12°. '76. $1.50 ...... *Crowell.*

— Ruth Derwent: a story of duty and love. ill. 16°. $1.15............ *Bost. Am. Tr.*

Freeman, Ab. C. Cotenancy and partition: law of co-ownership as independent of partnership rel. between the co-owners. 8°. shp., $7.50. *S. Whitney.*

Freeman, Ab. C., *continued.*

— Treatise on law of executions in civil cases, and of proceedings in aid and restraint thereof. 8°. shp., $7.50............ *S. Whitney.*

— Treatise on law of judgments. 2d ed., rev. and enl. 8°. '74. shp., $7.50 .... *Bancroft.*

Freeman E: A. Comparative politics; [also] Unity of history: lectures. 8°. '74. $3... *Macmillan.*

— Disestablishment and disendowment: what are they? cr. 8°. '74. $1 .... *Macmillan.*

— Europe. *See* Green, J. R., History primers.

— Growth of the English constitution. 2d ed. cr. 8°. '72. $2 .... *Macmillan.*

— Historical essays. 2d ser. 8°. '73. $2.50.. *Macmillan.*

— History of cathedral church of Wells, as ill. hist. of cathedral churches of old foundation. 12°. '70. $1.25 .... *Macmillan.*

— History of federal government, from foundation of Achaian League to disruption of the U. S., v. 1: General introd.: history of Greek federations. 8°. '63. $6............ *Macmillan.*

— History of Norman conquest of England, its causes and results. Rev. Am. ed. [To form 5 v.] v. 1-4. maps and plans. 8°. '75. $16.. *Macmillan.*

— Old English history. 2d ed., rev. col. maps. 12°. '75. $2............ *Macmillan.*

— Unity of history. [Rede lecture, Cambridge, 1872.] cr. 8°. '72. $1 .... *Macmillan.*

— (*ed.*) Historical course. v. 1-6. 16°........... *Holt.*

Cont.: Freeman's General sketch of hist, $1.25. — Thompson's Hist. of England, $1. — Macarthur's Hist. of Scotland, $1. — Hunt's Hist. of Italy, $1. — Sime's Hist. of Germany, $1. — Doyle's Hist. of U. S., $1.40.

Freeman, H. C. *See* Illinois geol. survey.

Freeman, J. D. *See* Mississippi, Chancery reports.

Freeman, Ja. M. Handbook of Bible manners and customs. ill. 12°. '74. $2.50... *Meth. Bk. Conc.*

— Use of illustrations in Sunday-school teaching. 12°. 15c. .... *Meth. Bk. Conc.*

Freeman, J: C. *See* Boise, J. R., *and* Freeman, J. C.

Freeman, Norm. L. *See* Illinois, Sup. Court reports.

Freeman, P. Principles of the divine service: true manner of understanding and using the order for morning and evening prayer, and for the administration of communion in the English Church. 2 v. 8°. '72. $6............ *Pott.*

Freemasonry exposed. Small, G. G. 25c... *Collin & S.*

Freemasons. Early hist. and trans. of Grand Lodge of N. Y., 1781-1815. [To form 10 pts.] pts. 1-4. 8°. '76. ea., 50c............ *Sickels.*

— Funeral service for lodges. 24°. pap., 10c... *Parson.*

— Grand Encampment for Mass. and R. I. Proceedings. [Annual.] 8°. pap., $2....... *Freeman.*

— Grand Lodge of Ancient York Masons of Va. Proceedings, 1778-1822; [with] introd. [on] origin and progress of Masonry in Va., 1773-'78, by J: Dove. 12°. '74. $4.50.......... *West, J. & Co.*

— — *Same.* pl: 8°. '74. $4.......... *J. W. Randolph.*

— Masonic code of state of N. Y. 32°. 50c... *Redding.*

— Review of the 3d annual convention of District Grand Lodge, No. 7, New Orleans, Jan. 17-21, 1875. 8°. '76. pap., 50c............ *Waldo.*

— *See also* Knights Templar; — Memoir of pilgrimage; Pittsburgh conv.; — Syracuse conv.

Freewill Baptists. Minutes of the Gen. Conf. of Freewill Baptist Conv. 16°. '59. $1...... *Freewill.*

— Psalmody; comp. by order of Gen. Conf. ('53.) New ed. 18°. '76. $1; $2........... *Freewill.*

— Treatise on [their] faith and usages; by authority of Gen. Conf. ('30.) 6th ed. 24°. 25c... *Freewill.*

Frehse, F. Wörterbuch zu F. Reuter's Werken. 12°. '70. 50c............ *Steiger.*

Freie Seele (Eine). Nieritz, G. 25c. ...... *Morwitz.*

Freigeist (Der). *See* Lessing, G. E.

Freiheit, Autorität u. Kirche. Ketteler, W. E. 50c. *Benziger.*

Freiherr v. d. Trenck, od. ein verfehltes Leben. 12°. '74. pap., 35c. . . . . *Zickel.*

Freihof (Der) v. Aarau. *See* Zschokke, H.

Freiligrath, Fd. v. Gedichte. 2 v. 12°. '60. $3; pap., $2. . . . . *Zickel.*

Freimund, El. (*pseud.*) Extrasitzungen des Herrn Diabolus mit seinen Gesellen u. Lehrlingen gehalten im 19ten Jarh. in seiner Hauptstadt Teuflingen. [Satire.] 12°. pap., 20c. . . . . *Brobst.*

Freischütz (Der). 12°. pap., 15c. . . . . *Radde.*

Freischütz (Der). Byron, H. J. 15c. . . . . *French.*

Freischütz (Der). *See* Ditson.

Freligh, Mt. Homœopathic pocket companion; abridg. from "Homœopathic practice of medicine." ('56.) 7th ed. 18°. '67. $1;—in Spanish. $1.25. . *Hurlburt.*

— Homœopathic pract. of med. ('55.) 13th ed., rev. and enl. 8°. '73. $3.50; shp., $4. . . . *Hurlburt.*

Fremy, E. *See* Pelouze, J., *and* Fremy, E.

French, B. F. Historical collections of Louisiana and Florida. 8°. '75. $4. . . . . *Mason.*

— History of iron trade, 1621–1857. 8°. $2. . . . *Wiley.*

French, B: B. Currency rates of French exchange giving the equivalent of 100 dollars currency in francs, etc. 18°. '75. $3. . . . . *Clayton.*

— *See also* New Hampshire, Law reports.

French, H. F. Farm drainage. ill. 12°. $1.50. . *Judd.*

French, J: H. [Arithmetics.] 4 v. hf. leath. . . *Harper.*
Cont.: Common-school arith., 12°, $1. — Element. arith., 16°, 50c. — First lessons in numbers, 16°, 40c. — Mental arith., 16°, 50c.

— Vermont school report. 8°. '74. $1.50. . . . . *Tuttle.*

French, *Mrs.* L. Virg. My roses: the romance of a June day. 12°. '71. $1.50. . . . . *Claxton.*

French, Sydney, *and* Sorrell, W. J. Friend in need: comedy. 16°. pap., 15c. . . . . *French.*

French, W. R. Scriptural ser. 5 v. 16°. '58–'65. per doz. . . . . *Universalist.*
Cont.: 1. Little moralist, pap., 60c. — 2. Gospel precepts, pap., $1. — 3. Gospel lessons, pap., $1.25. — 4. Gospel doctrines, bds., $2.50. — 5. Sabbath school assistant, bds., $3.

French artists of the present day; with biog. notes by René Menard. pl. f°. '76. $10. . . . . *Bouton.*

French (The) at home. Rhodes, A. $1.25. . . . *Dodd.*

French Bessie. 18°. 50c. . . . . *Carter.*

French children at home. Peyrac, *Mme.* de. 90c.

French country family (A). *See* Witt, H. G. de.

French detective (Experiences of a). Russell, W. H. C. 75c. . . . . *Dick & F.*

French domestic cookery. ill. 16°. $1.50. . . . *Harper.*

French Eton (A). Arnold, M. $1. . . . . *Macmillan.*

French exhibition. Hay, F. 15c. . . . . *French.*

French fairy tales. Segur, *Comtesse.* $1.50. . . *Porter.*

French flower (The). *See* Abbott, Jac., Harlie stories.

French fortune-teller. Sue, E. 75c. . . . . *Dick & F.*

French home life. 12°. $1.50. . . . . *Appleton.*

French horn instructor. f°. pap., $1. . . . . *Ditson.*

French love songs. *See* Swinburne, A. C.

French Onondaga dict.; from a MS. of 17th cent.; ed. by J. G. Shea. 8°. '60. pap., $4. . . . . *Shea.*

French-polisher's manual, by a French-polisher. roy. 32°. (Perth.) '62. pap., 20c. . . . . *Spon.*

French political leaders. King, E. $1.50. . . *Putnam.*

French prisoner in Russia; tr. by P. S. 2d ed. 8°. '74. $1.50. . . . . *Cath. Pub.*

French pronounc. handbook for travelers who have no knowledge of Fr. 24°. '72. 50c. . . . . *Routledge.*

French Protestant (The); or, Louis Michaud. 18°. 55c. . . . . *Am. S. S.*

French Protestants; or, revocation of the Edict of Nantes, and its consequences to Prot. churches of France and Italy. 18°. 55c. . . . . *Pres. Bd.*

French spy. Haines, J. T. 15c. . . . . *French.*

French's amateur operas. 6 nos. 16°. ea., pap., 40c. *French.*

French's comic dramas; for college, camp and cabin. 5 pts. 16°. ea., pap., 40c. . . . . *French.*
Cont.: 1. Spanking legacy; Furnished apartments; Spectre bridegroom; Martyr to science; Illustrious stranger. — 2. Smoked miser; Sleeping draughts; Cherry bounce; All at Coventry. — 3. Make your wills; Review; Fortune's frolic; D'ye know me now. — 4. Pison; Box of mischief; Jack of all trades; Sudden arrival. — 5. Look before you leap; Settling the verdict; Count and the secretary.

French's juv. plays. 5 nos. 16°. ea., pap., 40c. . . *French.*
Cont.: King Alfred and the cakes. — Blue Beard. — Jack and the bean stalk. — Old Poz. — Organ grinder.

French's serio-comic dramas. 2 pts. 16°. ea., pap., 40c. . . . . *French.*
Cont.: 1. Joseph in Egypt; Harvest storm; Cross of St. John; Blind boy. — 2. Test of truth; Two brothers; Grandfather's story; Brigand and his son.

French's standard and minor drama. 80 v. 16°. ea., $1.25; — in 640 nos. ea., pap., 15c. . . . . *French.*
Note. Specific entries under author and title.

French's standard Eng. operas. 9 nos. 16°. ea., pap., 15c. . . . . *French.*

Freneau, Ph. Poems rel. to Am. rev.; with notes and memoir by E. A. Duyckinck. por. and facsimile. sm. 8°. $1.75; hf. cf., $3.50. . *Widdleton.*

Frere, J: Hookham. Works; with memoir by Sir B. Frere. 2d ed., enl. 3 v. ill. and por. cr. 8°. '74. $7.50; hf. cf., $13; large pap., $12. . *Denham.*

Frere, M. Old Deccan days; or, Hindoo fairy legends in southern India. ill. 12°. $1.25. . . . *Lippincott.*

Fresenius, C. R. Manual of qualitative chemical analysis; tr. into the new system, and newly ed. by S. W. Johnson. 8°. '74. $3. — New ed. 8°. '75. $4.50. . . . . *Wiley.*

— System of instruction in quantitative chem. analysis; ed., with add., by S. W. Johnson; with chem. notation and nomenclature. 8°. $6. . . . . *Wiley.*

Fresenius, J: Ph. Evangelien u. Epistel Predigten. 2 v. 8°. '74. hf. mor., $5.75; ea., $3. . . . *Dette.*

Fresh gleanings. Mitchell, D. G. $1.75. . . . *Scribner.*

Fresh laurels. *See* Bradbury, W. B.

Fresh leaves from the book, and its story. R., L. N. $2 . . . . . *Carter.*

Freshet (The). *See* Abbott, Jac., Rollo story books.

Fretful girl. 18°. 40c. . . . . *Am. S. S.*

Fretful Lillie. *See* Wise, D.

Freut Euch des Lebens! Taschenliederbuch f. d. deutsche Volk. 16°. '64. 60c.; bds., 40c. . . *Steiger.*

Frey, H: Histology and histo-chemistry of man: elements of composition and structure of the human body; tr. from 4th Germ. ed. by A. E. J. Barker. ill. 8°. $5; shp., $6. . . . . *Appleton.*

— The microscope and microscopic technology; tr. and ed. by G. R. Cutter. ill. 8°. $6. . . . . *W. Wood.*

Frey, J. S. C. F. Messiahship of Jesus. 12°. 90c. *Am. Bapt.*

— Scripture types. 2 v. 12°. $1.50. . . . . *Am. Bapt.*

Freytag, Gst. Debit and credit; tr. by L. C. C., with pref. by C. C. J. Bunsen. 12°. $1.50. . *Harper.*

— Ingo; tr. by Mrs. Malcolm. (Leis. hour ser.) 16°. '73. $1.25. . . . . *Holt.*

— Ingraban; tr. by Mrs. Malcolm. (Leis. hour ser.) 16°. '73. $1.25. . . . . *Holt.*

— Lost manuscript; tr. by Mrs. Malcolm. 8°. pap., 75c. *Appleton.*

Friarswood post-office. Yonge, C. M. 60c. . . *Appleton.*

Frick, J. Physical technics: instructions for making experiments in physics and the construct. of phys. apparatus with limited means; tr. by J. D. Easter. ill. 8°. '61. $3. . . . . *Claxton; Lippincott.*

Friday Lowe. *See* Davis, *Mrs.* C. E. K.

Fridolin, od. der Gang nach d. Eisenhammer. 12°. pap., 15c. . . . . *Radde; F. W. Thomas.*

Friedheim, J: Instructions for playing the double or contra bass. f°. pap., $3 .... *Ditson.*
Friedrich, F: The lost despatch; tr. by L. A. Williams. 8°. '71. $1.25; pap., 50c. .... *Estes.*
— Nemesis. *See* Hiltl, G: Die Schlossdiebe.
— Des Sohnes Heimkehr. *See* Winterfeld, A. v., Die Ehefabrikanten.
Friedrich, O: Der amerikan. Pastetenbäcker. 16°. pap., 15c. .... *Morwitz.*
Friend. *See* Coleridge, S. T.
Friend from Leatherhead: farce. 16°. pap., 15c.. *French.*
Friend in need. French, S., *and* Sorrell, W. J. 15c. *French.*
Friend in need. Tucker, C. 50c. .... *Nelson.*
Friend in need. *See* Mother's return.
Friend of chastity; by a friend of virtue. 24°. '46. 25c. .... *Freewill.*
Friend or foe. Adams, H. C. $1 .... *Routledge.*
Friend Waggles. Morton, J. M. 15c. .... *French.*
Friendless. Baker, L. M. 50c. .... *Williamson.*
Friendly, *Aunt* (*pseud.*) *See* Baker, S.
Friendly advice to parents on management and education of children. 18°. 55c. .... *Am. S. S.*
Friendly counsels to Christians. 16°. 40c... *West. Tr.*
Friendly counsels to a little child. 32°. 40c... *Am. S. S.*
Friendly crook to guide young lambs. 4°. 75c... *Am. S. S.*
Friendly fairies; or, once upon a time. ill. 12°. $1.50. (?) *Shepard.*
Friendly fairies ser. 2 v. 12°. ea., $1.50.. (?) *Shepard.*
Cont.: Friendly fairies.—Twins of St. Marcel, by Mrs. A. S. Orr.
Friendly hands and kindly words: stories. ill. 16°. 75c. *Porter.*
Friendly hints to youth. Doncaster, J. 30c. *Meth. Bk. Conc.*
Friendly talks on union. Summers, T. O. 10c. *So. Meth.*
Friendly visit to the house of mourning. Cecil, R. 25c. *Pres. Bd.*
Friendly words with fellow pilgrims. *See* Kimball, J. W.
Friends (The). 18°. 40c. .... *Dutton.*
Friends (Society of). Christian advices; issued by Phila. Yearly Meeting to its members. 12°. '59. 30c. .... *Friends Bk. St.*
— Devotional poems for First Day schools; adopted by Gen. Conf. 32°. *net*, 25c. .... *Friends Bk. Assoc.*
— Rules of discipline of Phila. Yearly Meeting. 12°. 50c. *Friends Bk. St.*
— *See also* Ancient testimony; — Tract Association of Friends.
Friends and acquaintances. Row, R. $1.75.. *Routledge.*
Friends in council. *See* Helps, *Sir* A.
Friends in need. Guernsey, C. F. $1.50.. (?) *Martien.*
Friends of freedom. 18°. 30c. .... *Dutton.*
Friends or foes. Wigan, H. 15c. .... *French.*
Friends' almanac. 12°. *net*, pap., 10c. *Friends Bk. Assoc.*
Friends' library. 14 v. roy. 8°. '34–'50. ea., shp., 50c.–$2.50 .... *Friends Bk. St.*
Friends' miscellany. Comly, J. *and* I. 11 v. *net*, $11. *Friends Bk. Assoc.*
Friends' pocket almanac. 48°. *net*, pap., 10c. *Friends Bk. Assoc.*
Friendship of books. Maurice, F. D. $2.50. *Macmillan.*
Friendship's jewel. *See* Diamond miniatures.
Friendship's offering. 24°. $1.50 .... *Locke.*
Friendship's token. 24°. $1.50 .... *Locke.*
Friendships of the Bible. ill. 12°. '54. 85c. *Meth. Bk. Conc.*
Friendships of women. Alger, W. R. $1.50; $2. *Roberts.*

Fries, R. Gretchen; or, the day-laborer's daughter. ill. 16°. '73. 80c. .... *Am. Tr.*
— *Germ.* Die Tochter des Taglöhners. ill. 18°. '72. 35c. .... *Am. Tr.*
— The uhlan's wife. ill. 18°. '74. 50c. .... *Am. Tr.*
— *Germ.* Die Frau des Ulanen. 18°. '73. 50c. *Am. Tr.*
Fries, Wulf, *and* Suck, A: Violoncello school. 4°. bds., $3 .... *G. D. Russell.*
Frieze, H: S. Notes on 10th and 12th books of Quintilian. 12°. $1.50 .... *Appleton.*
Frings, C: Die Behandlung d. amerik. Weine, der Krankheiten derselben u. deren Heilung. 12°. '69. pap., 50c. .... *Witter.*
Frisbie, Barnes. History of Middletown, Vt. 8°. '70. $1 .... *Tuttle.*
Frisk and his flock. Sanford, D. P. $2.25... *Dutton.*
Friskie, the pony. *See* Abbott, Jac., Harlie stories.
Friswell, J. Hain. About in the world. 16°. $3. *Scribner, W. & A.*
— Better self: essays for home life. cr. 8°. $1.75. *Porter.*
— Man's (A) thoughts. 16°. $3 .... *Scribner, W. & A.*
— Other people's windows. 16°. $3.. *Scribner, W. & A.*
— The silent hour. 16°. $3 .... *Scribner, W. & A.*
Frith, J: Life and writings. *See* British reformers.
Frithiof's saga. *See* Tegnér, E.
Fritschel, G. Die Zinsfrage: 12 Thesen üb. d. Ausleihen v. Geld auf Interessen. 8°. pap., 20c. *Brobst.*
Fritz; or, experience teacheth wisdom. ill. post 18°. 75c. .... *Scribner, W. & A.*
Fritz; or, filial obedience. Hoffmann, F. 65c. (?) *Luth. Pub.*
Fritz Harold. 18°. 60c. .... *Carter.*
Fritz Hazell. *See* Sargent, L. M.
Frobisher, Jos. E. The blood and breath: system of exercise for the lungs and limbs. ill. 12°. '76. 50c.; pap., 25c. .... *Goodyear.*
— Selected readings. ('74.) 2d ed. 12°. '75. 75c.; $1; pap., 30c. .... *Schermerhorn.*
— Voice and action: treatise on culture of the voice, etc., with readings and recitations. 12°. '67. $1.25. *Goodyear; Ivison.*
Frog prince. [Toy-book.] ill. 4°. $1; 50c... *Routledge.*
Frog prince: fairy play. 16°. pap., 15c. ..... *Happy.*
Froggy's little brother. Brenda. $1.25 ...... *Carter.*
Froggy's little brother; or, the honest street sweeper. ill. 16°. '75. $1.25 .... *Hoyt.*
Frogs (The). *See* Aristophanes.
Fröhliche Botschaft, od. Glauben u. Liebe. 18°. 40c. *Ev. Assoc.*
Froissart, J: Chronicles of England, France, Spain and the adjoining countries. 2 v. ill. roy. 8°. hf. roxb., $12. — (Illum. ed.) 2 v. roy. 8°. hf. mor., $12; — with notes and ill. (Globe ed.) cr. 8°. '75. $1.75–$5 .... *Routledge.*
— *See also* Joinville, J. de, *and* Froissart, J.
Frolich, L. (*ill.*) Picture-book. sm. 4°. '68. $2. *Roberts.*
Frölicher, O. (*ill.*) *See* Closs, G., Frölicher, O., *and* Roux, G.
From atheism to Christianity. Porter, G. P. 60c. *Meth. Bk. Conc.*
From the clouds to the mountains. *See* Verne, Jules.
From the creation to Moses: stories from Old Test., in words of one syllable. ill. 16°. $1... *World Pub.*
From the crib to the cross. Walker, E. A. $1. *World Pub.*
From Dan to Beersheba. Newman, J. P. $1.75. *Harper.*
From dawn to dark in Italy: tale of the reformation in 16th cent. 16°. $1.50 .... *Pres. Bd.*
— *Same.* ill. 12°. $1.75 .... *Bost. Am. Tr.*
— *Same.* ill. sm. 8°. $1.75 .... *Nelson.*

From the earth to the moon. *See* Verne, Jules.
From everglade to cañon. Rodenbough, T. F. $7.50. *Van Nostrand.*
From the flag to the cross. Billingsley, A. S. *$2.50; $3.50; $5 .... *New World.*
From four to fourteen. Tompkins, J. H. $1.25..*Am. Tr.*
From heaven to New York. Reed, I. G. 50c...*Murray.*
From the Hub to the Hudson. Gladden, W. 75c. *E. D. Merriam.*
From jest to earnest. Roe, E. P. $1.75 ......*Dodd.*
From Joshua to Daniel: 2d ser. of Bible stories from the Old Test., in words of one syllable. ill. 16°. $1 .... *World Pub.*
From Liverpool to St. Louis. Hall, N. $1.75. *Routledge.*
From my youth up. Harland, M. $1.50...*Carleton.*
From nation to nation. Flint, J. H. $1.25..*Am. Bapt.*
From night to light. ill. 16°. '72. $1.25 ....*Lothrop.*
From nowhere to the North Pole. Hood, T. $3. *Routledge.*
From the oak to the olive. Howe, J. W. $2..*Lee & S.*
From the plow to the pulpit: autobiography. 16°. '74. 60c. .... *Carter.*
From seventeen to thirty. Binney, T. 90c. *Meth. Bk. Conc.*
From shore to shore. Hanaford, P. A. *$1.50..*Russell.*
From tent to palace. Clarke, B. $1.50......*Nelson.*
From thistles—grapes? Eiloart, J. C. 50c...*Harper.*
From village to court. Morton, J. M. 15c....*French.*
Froment, Mathilde. *See* Bourdon, M. F.
Frondes agrestes. *See* Ruskin, J:
Fronmüller, G. F. C. On Peter and Jude. *See* Lange, J. P.
Frontier ser. 5 v. ill. 16°. ea., $1.25......*Lee & S.*

Cont.: Twelve nights in the hunters' camp.—One thousand miles' walk across South America.—The cabin on the prairie.—Planting the wilderness.—The young pioneers of the north-west.

Frost, C: C. *See* Tuckerman, E., *and* Frost, C. C.
Frost, G: Life of Geo. Washington. ill. 8°. $4. *Desilver.*
Frost, H: W. *See* United States, Digest.
Frost, *Mrs.* J. David Woodburn, the mountain missionary. ('65.) New ed. ill. 16°. '72. $1.25. *Hoyt.*
Frost, J: American speaker: treatise on elocution, and selections. por. 12°. hf. roan, $1.50...*Desilver.*
— Beauties of Eng. hist. 18°. 75c. .... *Harper.*
— Beauties of Fr. hist. 18°. 75c. .... *Harper.*
— Class book of nature. 16°. *net*, 60c.....*Hamersley.*
— Cyclopedia of eminent Christians. ill. 8°. $2; shp., $2.75 .... *World Pub.*
— History of Mexico and the Mexican war. ill. and maps. 8°. $4 .... *Desilver.*
— History of the U. S. for common schools. ill. 18°. hf. roan, 83c. .... *Desilver.*
— *Same;* for schools and academies. ill. 12°. hf. roan, $1.75 .... *Desilver.*
— Our flag on the ocean; or, naval battles and naval commanders. ill. 12°. $1.50........ *World Pub.*
— Pictorial hist. of U. S., from disc. by Northmen in 10th cent. 2 v. in 1. ill. 12°. '53. *$5....*Case.*
— Pictorial world: anc. hist. to death of Constantine, hist. of middle ages to disc. of Am., and mod. hist. 3 v. ill. roy. 8°. mor., $9;—in 1 v., $6..*Desilver.*
— Pioneer mothers of the west. 12°. $1.50..*Lee & S.*
— Thrilling adventures among the Indians. ill. 12°. $1.75 .... *J. E. Potter.*
— *Germ.* Interessante Abenteuer unter d. Indianern. ill. 8°. $2 .... *Kohler.*
— Wild scenes of a hunter's life; or, the hunting and hunters of all nations. ill. 12°. $1.50..*Lee & S.*
Frost, *Mrs.* L. J. H. Lynda Newton; or, life's discipline. ill. 16°. '71. $1.50 .... *Graves.*

Frost, Percival. Elementary treatise on curve tracing. 8°. '72. $6 .... *Macmillan.*
— First three sections of Newton's Principia; with notes and problems. 8°. '63. $3.50..*Macmillan.*
— *and* Wolstenholme, *Rev.* J. Solid geometry. New ed., rev. and enl. v. 1. 8°. '75. $8..*Macmillan.*
Frost, *Miss* S. Annie. Almost a woman. ill. 16°. '76. $1.25 .... *Am. Tr.*
— Amateur theatricals and fairy-tale dramas. 16°. pap., 30c.; bds., 50c. .... *Dick & F.*
— Art of dressing well. 16°. pap., 30c.; bds., 50c. *Dick & F.*
— Birthday present. ill. 18°. '75. 50c........*Am. Tr.*
— Book of tableaux and shadow pantomimes. 16°. pap., 30c.; bds., 50c. .... *Dick & F.*
— Common sense in the kitchen. 12°. $1.75..*Souder.*
— Dialogues for young folks. 16°. pap., 30c.; bds., 50c. *Dick & F.*
— Dot books. 4 v. 128°. '74. 75c. .... *Am. Tr.*
— Grandpapa's home. ill. 18°. '75. 75c......*Am. Tr.*
— Humorous and exhibition dialogues. 16°. pap., 30c.; bds., 50c. .... *Dick & F.*
— Laws and by-laws of American society: treatise on etiquette. 16°. pap., 30c.; bds., 50c...*Dick & F.*
— Little folks' picture book. ill. 18°. '75. 30c...*Am. Tr.*
— New book of dialogues. 16°. pap., 30c.; bds., 50c. *Dick & F.*
— Original letter writer; with table of synonyms. 16°. bds., 50c. .... *Dick & F.*
— Original letter writer; [also] Laws and by-laws of Am. society. 16°. $1.50 .... *Dick & F.*
— Parlor stage: drawing-room proverbs, charades and tableaux vivant. 16°. $1.50......... *Dick & F.*
— Prize medal. ill. 18°. '75. 50c. .... *Am. Tr.*
— Robbie's light. ill. 18°. '73. 30c. .... *Am. Tr.*
— School and exhibition dialogues: compr. Humorous exhibition dialogues; [also] Dialogues for young folks. 16°. $1.50 .... *Dick & F.*
— Sunshine for rainy days. ill. sm. 4°. '73. $1..*Am. Tr.*
— Very little tales. 4 v. ill. 64°. '73. 80c....*Am. Tr.*
— Week's (A) holiday. ill. 18°. '72. 75c.....*Am. Tr.*
Frost, T: Circus life and circus celebrities. 12°. '75. $2 .... *Routledge.*
— Half-hours with early explorers. ill. fp. 4°. $2.50. *Cassell.*
— The old showman and the old London fairs. 12°. '75. $2 .... *Routledge.*
Frothingham, Oct. Brooks. Beliefs of the unbelievers, and other discourses. 12°. '76. $1....*Putnam.*
— Child's book of religion for S.-schools and homes. New ed. 16°. '76. $1 .... *Putnam.*
— Life of Theodore Parker. por. 8°. '74. $3; hf. cf., $5.50 .... *Osgood.*
— Religion of humanity. ('73.) New ed. 12°. '75. $1.50 .... *Putnam.*
— Safest creed, and 12 other discourses of reason. 12°. '74. $1.50 .... *Somerby.*
— Stories from the lips of the teacher; retold by a disciple. New ed. ill. 16°. '76. $1.......*Putnam.*
— Stories of the patriarchs. 16°. '76. $1....*Putnam.*
— Transcendentalism in New England: a history. por. 8°. '76. $2.50 .... *Putnam.*
Frothingham, R: Battle of Bunker Hill. ill. 16°. '75. 75c.; pap., 60c. .... *Little, B. & Co.*
— History of siege of Boston, and of battles of Lexington, Concord and Bunker Hill; also account of Bunker Hill monument. 4th ed. maps and pl. 8°. '73. $3.50 .... *Little, B. & Co.*
— Life and times of Joseph Warren. 8°. '65. $3.50. *Little, B. & Co.*
— Rise of the republic of the U. S. 2d ed. 8°. '73. $3.50 .... *Little, B. & Co.*
Frou-Frou. Meilhac, H., *and* Halévy, L. 15c...*French.*
Froude, Ja. Ant. Calvinism: address, St. Andrews, Mar. 17, 1871. 12°. '71. 75c. .... *Scribner.*
— English (The) in Ireland in 18th cent. ('73.) New ed. 3 v. cr. 8°. '75. $2.50 .... *Scribner.*

Froude, Ja. Ant., *continued.*
— History of Eng., from fall of Wolsey to defeat of Span. armada. 12 v. cr. 8°. $27; hf. cf., $48; cf., $63 .... *Lee & S.*
— *Same.* (Lib. ed.) 12 v. cr. 8°. '65–'71. ea., $3; per set, hf. cf., $50. — (Pop. ed.) 12 v. 12°. ea., $1.25; per set, $15. — (Chelsea ed.) 12 v. 12°. hf. roan, $21 .... *Scribner.*
— Short studies on great subjects. 2 ser. (Lib. ed.) cr. 8°. '70–'71. ea., $2.50; hf. cf., $4.50. — (Pop. ed) 12°. ea., $1.50; hf. cf., $3. — (Chelsea ed.) '76. hf. roan, $4 .... *Scribner.*
— *See also* Mill, J. S., Froude, J. A., *and* Carlyle, T.

Frozen deep (The). Collins, W. $1.50; 75c... *W. F. Gill.*

Frozen ears. 12°. 60c .... *Cong. Pub.*

Frozen north. *See* Land and sea.

Frozen zone and its explorers. *See* Hyde, A., Baldwin, A. C., *and* Gage, W. L.

Frühlings-Kuren. Meinecke, C. 20c .... *Steiger.*

Fruit for Sunday-school festivals. Bigelow, A. M. *and* L. S. 40c .... *Cin. Meth. Bk. Conc.*

Fruit gathering; or, one summer's work and its reward. 18°. 50c .... *Am. S. S.*

Fruit of the spirit. Bethune, G. W. 60c. *N. Y. Ref. Ch. Bd.*

Fruits and flowers. Walker, W. 63c. .... *Lippincott.*

Fruits of early piety; or, memorials of a young disciple. 18°. 25c. .... *Am. S. S.*

Fruits of the wine cup: drama. 16°. pap., 15c... *French.*

Fry, B: St. Ja. Property consecrated. *See* Systematic beneficence.

Fry, Caro. Christ our example; with autobiog. 16°. $1.25 .... *Bost. Am. Tr.*
— Daily readings: passages of Scripture sel. for social reading; with applications. 12°. 90c... *Pres. Bd.*

Fry, Clara W. T. Little Splendid's vacation. ('68.) 2d ed. ill. 16°. '75. 80c. .... *Am. Unit.*

Fry, Edward. Treatise on specific performance of contracts, incl. those of public companies. 8°. '58. $3 .... *T. & J. W. Johnson.*
— *Same.* 2d ed.; with notes and ref. by W. S. Schuyler. 8°. shp., $7.50 .... *W. C. Little.*
— — *See also* Law Library.

Fry, Jac. Sin of adultery: sermon. 12°. pap., 10c. *Luth. Bk. St.*

Fry, *Mrs.* Sa. M. Crochet worker; or, path of truth. ill. 18°. '66. 45c... *N. Y. Ref. Ch. Bd.; Pres. Com.*
— — *See also below* Jenny.
— Hannah Lee; or, rest for the weary. ill. 18°. '61. 60c. *Am. Tr.*
— *Same.* ill. 18°. '66. 65c. *N. Y. Ref. Ch. Bd.; Pres. Com.; Pres. Bd.*
— *Same.* ('60.) New ed. ill. 18°. '75. 75c..... *Hoyt.*
— *Germ.* Hanna Lee. ill. 18°. '71. 60c..... *Am. Tr.*
— Jenny, the crochet-worker; or, the path of truth. 18°. 55c. .... *Pres. Bd.*
— — *See also* Crochet-worker.
— Little orange seller; or, the story of Patty White. 32°. 40c. .... *Am. S. S.*
— *Same.* 18°. '66. 40c... *N. Y. Ref. Ch. Bd.; Pres. Com.*
— Little water-cress sellers. 18°. 25c....... *Am. S. S.*
— *Same.* 18°. '66. 40c. *N. Y. Ref. Ch. Bd.; Pres. Com.*
— Lost key (The). 18°. 55c. .... *Am. S. S.*
— *Same.* 18°. '73. 55c... *N. Y. Ref. Ch. Bd.; Pres. Com.*
— *Same.* ill. 18°. 70c. .... *Pres. Bd.*
— Margaret Craven; or, beauty of the heart. ill. 18°. '67. 60c .... *N. Y. Ref. Ch. Bd.; Pres. Com.*
— Matty Gregg; or, the woman that did what she could. ill. 18°. 50c .... *Am. S. S.*
— *Same.* 18°. '66. 60c. *N. Y. Ref. Ch. Bd.; Pres. Com.*
— Poor Nelly; or, the golden mushroom. ill. 18°. '66. 70c .... *N. Y. Ref. Ch. Bd.; Pres. Com.*
— Young envelope makers. ill. 18°. '66. 60c. *N. Y. Ref. Ch. Bd.; Pres. Com.*

Fry, *Mrs.* Sa. M., *continued.*
— Young hop-pickers; or, the safety of acting uprightly. 18°. '60. 30c .... *Am. Tr.*
— *Same.* 18°. 35c.; 45c .... *Am. Bapt.*
— *Same.* 18°. 40c .... *Am. S. S.*
— *Same.* 18°. '66. 40c. *N. Y. Ref. Ch. Bd.; Pres. Com.*
— *Same.* ('60.) New ed. ill. 18°. '69. 45c. ... *Hoyt.*

Fry, W. H. Stabat mater; with Lat. and Eng. words. [Oratorio.] f°. '55. $4 .... *Ditson.*

Fry, W: H. Complete treatise on artificial fish-breeding. 12°. $1.25 .... *Appleton.*

Fryer, W: J., *jr.* Architectural iron work: organization and mechan. and financ. management of a foundry and shops. ill. 8°. '76. $3.50... *Wiley.*

Fuchs, C. W. C. Practical guide to determination of minerals by the blowpipe; tr. and ed. by T. W. Danby. 8°. '74. $2.50 .... *Claxton.*

Fuchs, R. Mass in C. 4°. pap., $1.25....... *Peters.*

Fuchsia (The): memoir of Elizabeth E— by her S.-school teacher. 18°. 35c .... *Am. S. S.*

Fugitive verses. Townsend, A. W. $1.... *Turnbull.*

Führer (Der) v. Cincinnati: Wegweiser durch die Stadt u. ihre Umgebg. ill. and map. 8°. '75. $1.50. *Burgheim.*

Fülborn, E: German instructor. 12°. '52. hf. roan, $1.25 .... *Lippincott.*

Fulfilling of Scriptures. Fleming, R. 75c... *Pres. Bd.*

Full envelope. Donkersley, R. $1... *Meth. Bk. Conc.*

Full proof of the ministry. Norton, J. N. 75c. *Claremont.*

Fuller, And. Works. 3 v. 8°. $9.. *Am. Bapt.; So. Bapt.*
— Principal works; with memoir by A. G. Fuller. 12°. (Bohn.) $1.25 .... *Little, B. & Co.*
— *Same.* 12°. (Bohn.) $1.40 ...... *Scribner, W. & A.*
— *Same.* 12°. (Bohn.) $1.50 .... *Lippincott.*
— Gospel worthy of all acceptation: duty of sinners to believe in Jesus Christ. 18°. 40c.... *Cong. Pub.*
— Remains. 12°. $1.25 .... *Am. Bapt.*

Fuller, And. S. Forest tree culturist. ill. 12°. $1.50. *Woodward.*
— Grape culturist. 12°. $1.50 .... *Judd.*
— Small fruit culturist. ill. 12°. $1.50 .... *Judd.*
— Strawberry culturist. ill. 12°. pap., 20c...... *Judd.*

Fuller, Dan. Political class-book of Pennsylvania; compr. exposition of Const. of state, and of some features of the political institutions, etc. 12°. '53. hf. bd., 60c. .... *Fortescue.*

Fuller, Edn. W. Angel (The) in the cloud: poem. 12°. $1.25; $1.50 .... *Hale.*
— Sea gift. [Fiction.] 12°. $1.50 .... *Hale.*

Fuller, Erasmus Q. Appeal to the records in vindication of policy and proceedings of the Meth. Episc. Ch. in relation to the south. 12°. '76. $1.50. *Cin. Meth. Bk. Conc.*
— The two Sabbaths. 16°. 60c.... *Cin. Meth. Bk. Conc.*

Fuller, H: W: On diseases of the lungs and air-passages. 8°. $3.50 .... *Lea.*

Fuller, Hiram. Transformation scenes in the U. S. 12°. $1.50 .... *Carleton.*

Fuller, Jane G. Bending willow. 16°. $1.25.. *Carter.*
— Lucy Lee; or, all things for Christ. ill. 16°. '68. 90c .... *Dodd.*
— Uncle John's flower gatherers: companion for the woods and fields. ill. 16°. '69. $1.25.... *Dodd.*

Fuller, J: E. Complete and perpetual calendar, from 1724 O. S., to 1900 N. S. 16°. 75c .... *Lee & S.*

Fuller, Lydia. Mistaken; or, the seeming and the real. 12°. $1.50 .... *Lippincott.*

Fuller, Marg. Works. 6 v. 12°. '74. $9... *Roberts.*
Cont.: Memoirs, 2 v. — Woman in the 19th cent. — Life within and life without. — At home and abroad. — Art, literature and the drama.

Fuller, Metta Vcta. Fashionable dissipation; [also] Adela Lincoln, by M. F. Carey. 2 v. in 1. 16°. $1.25 .... *J. E. Potter.*

Fuller, R: Sermons. 12°. $1.50 .... *Sheldon.*
— *See also* Baptist praise book.
Fuller, S: Loutron; or, water baptism. 12°. pap., 20c. *Claremont.*
Fuller, T: Good thoughts in bad times, and other papers. 16°. $1.50 .... *Dutton.*
Fullerton, *Lady* Georgiana. Constance Sherwood: autobiog. of the 16th cent. 2d ed. ill. 8°. '72. $2. *Cath. Pub.*
— Ellen Middleton. 12°. '57. $1.50; $2 .... *Murphy.*
— Fire of London; or, Rosemary. 16°. '75. $1; $1.50. *Kelly, P. & Co.*
— — *See also below* Rosemary.
— Germaine cousin, the shepherdess of Pibrac: drama. 18°. 25c. .... *Sadlier.*
— Grantley Manor. 12°. '57. $1.50; $2 .... *Murphy.*
— Lady-bird. 12°. '57. $1.50; $2 .... *Murphy.*
— Life of St. Francis of Rome. 16°. $1; $1.50. *Sadlier.*
Mrs. Gerald's niece. 8°. pap., 60c. .... *Appleton.*
— *Same.* 8°. $1.50; $2 .... *Sadlier.*
— Portrait in my uncle's dining-room, and other tales. 8°. '70. pap., 38c. .... *Littell & G.*
— — *See also below* Straw-cutter's daughter.
— Reparation: story of reign of Louis XIV., and other tales. 18°. '75. 50c.; 75c. .... *Kelly, P. & Co.*
— Rose Le Blanc. 16°. $1; $1.50 .... *Sadlier.*
— Rosemary: tale of fire in London. 12°. $1 .. *O'Shea.*
— — *See also above* Fire of London.
— Seven stories. 16°. '74. $1.50; $2 .. *Kelly, P. & Co.*
— Stormy life. ill. 8°. $1.50; pap., $1 ..... *Appleton.*
— *Same.* 8°. $1.50; $2 .... *Sadlier.*
— Straw-cutter's daughter. 12°. $1 .... *O'Shea.*
— *Same;* [also] Portrait in my uncle's dining-room. 16°. $1; $1.50 .... *Sadlier.*
— Tales of truth and trust; or, six short stories. 12°. $1 .... *O'Shea.*
— Too strange not to be true. ill. 8°. $1.50; pap., $1. *Appleton.*
— *Same.* 8°. $1.50; $2 .... *Sadlier.*
— Trouvaille; or, the soldier's adopted child. 18°. '75. 50c.; 75c. .... *Kelly, P. & Co.*
— Two cottages (The). 18°. '72. 50c. .... *Kenedy.*
— Which is which? or, the fire in London: drama. 18°. 25c. .... *Sadlier.*
Fullom, S. W. Daughter of night. 8°. pap., 50c. *Harper.*
Fulton, Chandos. A brown-stone front. [Fiction.] 16°. '73. 75c. .... *Hinton.*
Fulton, C: Carroll. Europe viewed through Am. spectacles. 8°. '74. $1.75; pap., $1.25 .. *Lippincott.*
Fulton, *Rev.* J. Index canonum. 8°. '72. $4 ... *Pott.*
Fulton, *Rev.* J. D. Memoir of Timothy Gilbert. por. 12°. $1.50 .... *Lee & S.*
— Woman as God made her: discourses. 16°. $1; pap., 50c.; — with por. $1.50 .... *Lee & S.*
— Woman vs. ballot: a tract for the times. 16°. pap., 15c. .... *Lee & S.*
Fulton, Ja. Alex. Peach culture. ill. 12°. $1.50 .. *Judd.*
Fulton, Just. D. Show your colors: story of Boston life. ill. 16°. '75. $1 .... *Ward.*
Fulton, Levi S., *and* Eastman, G: W. Practical system of book-keeping by single and double entry. ('51.) New ed., rev. 16°. '76. $1.13 ..... *Nims.*
Fulton, Rob. *See* Illustrated book of pigeons.
Fulton street [N. Y.] hymn-book, for union prayer-meetings, etc. 24°. 30c. ...... *N. Y. Ref. Ch. Bd.*
Fun and flirtation forfeits. ill. 48°. 25c. *Scribner, W. & A.*
Fun and profit. Aunt Mattie. 75c. .... *Graves.*
Fun and work. 18°. 50c. .... *Carter.*
Fun better than physic. Hall, W. W. *$1.50. *D. E. Fisk.*
Fun everlasting. 8°. pap., 15c. .... *Haney.*
Fun for all; or, chips from the elephant's trunk. ill. 8°. pap., 15c. .... *Happy.*

Fun for the million: comic anecdotes and stories. ill. sq. 12°. pap., 50c. .... *Appleton.*
Fun in black. Day, C. H. 25c. .... *De Witt.*
Fun-jottings. Willis, N. P. $1.75 .... *Scribner.*
Funck, H: Restitution od. Erklärung einiger Hauptpunkte des Gesetzes, wie es durch Christum erfüllet ist, etc. 12°. leath., $1.50 .... *Baer.*
Fünf hundert tausend Thaler. Pittawall, E. $2.25; $1.75; $2.50 .... *F. W. Thomas.*
Fünfzig Passions-Betrachtungen. 18°. '51. 60c. *Am. Tr.*
Funken, P. Eug. Gedichte. 12°. $1.50 .... *Benziger.*
Funny animals. ill. f°. $1.50; $2 ...... *J. E. Potter.*
Funny book about the Ashantees. Griset, E. 50c. *Appleton.*
Funny philosophers. Yellott, G. $1.50 .. *Lippincott.*
Funny picture books. *See* Griset, E.
Funny pop-guns. *See* Barrow, *Mrs.* F.
Funny side of physic. Crabtre, A. D. *$3: $3.50. *Burr.*
Fur country (The). *See* Verne, Jules.
Furber, Dan. L. *See* Phelps, A., Park, E. A., *and* Furber, D. L.
Furber, G: C. The twelve months' volunteer; or, journal of a campaign in Mexico. ill. and map. 8°. $3 .... *U. P. James.*
Furchtloss u. treu. *See* Hoffmann, F.
Furman, C: E. Home scenes, and other poems. 16°. '73. 80c.; $1 .... *Darrow.*
Furman, Gbr. Antiquities of Long Island, with bibliog. by H. Onderdonk, jr. 12°. '75. $3 .. *Bouton.*
Furneaux, C: Free hand drawing set. obl. 8°. 25c.; with instruments, $1.25 .... *Potter, A. & Co.*
Furness, *Mrs.* Hor. H. Concordance to Shakespeare's poems. 8°. $4 .... *Lippincott.*
Furness, W. H. Unconscious truth of the four Gospels. 12°. $1.25 .... *Lippincott.*
Furnished apartments: interlude. 16°. pap., 15c. *French.*
— *See also* French's comic dramas.
Furniss, J. Tracts for spiritual reading; for first communions, retreats, missions, etc. ('71.) 8th ed. 18°. '76. $1 .... *Kenedy.*
Furniture and cabinet makers' trade reference book. 4°. '71. $25 .... *J. A. Murphy.*
Fürst, Jul. Hebrew and Chaldee lexicon to Old Test.; tr. by S. Davidson. roy. 8°. hf. bd., $9 .. *Wiley.*
— *Same.* 4th ed., enl. 8°. '66. hf. bd., $9 ..... *Holt.*
Fürstenblick (Der). *See* Zschokke, H.
Further manifestation of the progress of the Gospel among the Indians in New England. Lond., 1659. [Reprint.] 4°. '65. $1; large pap., $1.50 .. *Sabin.*
Fusang. Leland, C. G. $1.75 .... *Bouton.*
Fyfe, J. Hamilton. Enterprise lib. 3 v. ill. 12°. ea., $1.50 .... *Nelson.*
Cont.: Merchant enterprise. — Enterprise beyond the seas. — Triumphs of invention and discovery.

Fyffe, C. A. Greece. *See* Green, J. R., History primers.

G., A. Willie and Lucy abroad. ill. sq. 16°. 75c. *Nelson.*
— Willie and Lucy at home. ill. sq. 16°. 50c. .. *Nelson.*
— Willie and Lucy at the seaside. ill. sq. 16°. 75c. *Nelson.*
G., B. C. Mrs. Gordon's household; or, one way of doing good. 16°. 50c. .... *Scribner, W. & A.*
G., C. *See* Round the table.
G., C. J. (*pseud.*) *See* Freeland, *Mrs.* Carrie J.
G., E. A. Notes on Portugal. 16°. '76. $1; pap., 75c. (?) *Phila. Cath.*
G., E. W. Edith's last Lent. 18°. 30c. ...... *Dutton.*

G., F. F. Little Nan; or, a living remembrance. ill. 16°. '75. 75c. .... *Dodd.*

— *Same;* [also] Neddie's care; or, suffer the little children, by Minn. ill. 18°. '70. 75c. .. *Dutton.*

— Polly and Winnie. ill. 16°. '75. 75c. .... *Dodd.*

G., H. B. *See* Goodwin, *Mrs.* H. B.

G., L. Jessie Grey; or, the discipline of life: Canadian tale. ill. 12°. $1 .... *Nelson.*

G., L. The photograph: comedy. 18°. pap., 25c. *Coddington.*

G., M. E. The old nursery rhymes; or, the merrie heart. ill. roy. 16°. $1.50 .... *Cassell.*

G., M. H. Cousin Clara: sequel to "Ellen Carrol." 18°. '34. 40c. .... *Am. S. S.*

— Ellen Carrol; or, Christian charity. 18°. '34. 40c. *Am. S. S.*

Gabb, W. M. *See* California geological survey.

Gabled house (The); or, self sacrifice; by author of "The climbers." 12°. '69. $1.50 ..... *Claxton.*

Gaboon stories. Preston, I. S. 80c. .... *Am. Tr.*

Gaboriau, Emile. Clique of gold; tr. from the Fr. 8°. '74. $1.25; pap., 75c. .... *Estes.*

— File, no. 113; tr. from the Fr. 8°. '75. $1.25; pap., 75c. .... *Estes.*

— Herr Lecoq; [tr.] 8°. pap., 50c. .... *Morwitz.*

— Mystery of Orcival; tr. from the Fr. 8°. '71. $1.25; pap., 75c. .... *Estes.*

— Other people's money; tr. from the Fr. 8°. '74. $1.25; pap., 75c. .... *Estes.*

— Widow Lerouge; tr. from the Fr. 8°. '73. $1.25; pap., 75c. .... *Estes.*

— Within an inch of his life; tr. from the Fr. 8°. '74. $1.25; pap., 75c. .... *Estes.*

Gabriel (*pseud.*) The fortune teller and dream book. 12°. pap., 20c. .... *Hurst.*

Gabriel. Bourdon, M. F. 30c. .... *O'Shea.*

Gabriel. Howitt, M. $1 .... *Collins & Bro.*

Gabriel Conroy. Harte, B. *$3–$7 .... *Am. Pub.*

Gabriele, das Weib des Spielers. *See* Pitawall, C.

Gabrielle. Sue, E. 75c. .... *Dick & F.*

Gabrielle André. Baring-Gould, S. 60c. .. *Appleton.*

Gabrielle de Belle Isle: play. 16°. pap., 15c. .. *Happy.*

Gadarene (The). Barrett, J. O., *and* Peebles, J. M. $1.25 .... *Colby.*

Gaddis, M. P. Conversion of a skeptic. 16°. 75c. *Cin. Meth. Bk. Conc.*

— Footprints of an itinerant. 12°. $1.75. *Cin. Meth. Bk. Conc.*

— Recollections of Rev. G. W. Walker. 12°. $1.75. *Cin. Meth. Bk. Conc.*

— Sacred hour. 16°. $1 .... *Cin. Meth. Bk. Conc.*

Gade, Niels W. Comala: dram. poem after Ossian; set to music by N. W. Gade; tr. by J. C. D. Parker. 8°. '75. bds., $1.25 .... *Ditson.*

— Spring's message [Frühlings-Botschaft]: an ode for four voices. 8°. pap., 20c. .... *Peters.*

— *Same.* 8°. 35c. .... *Church.*

Gadsden, Cp. Edwards. Life. 18°. 45c.; 50c. .. *Dutton.*

Gaffer Grey's legacy. *See* Lacy's home plays for ladies.

Gaffney's tavern. Hildeburn, M. J. $1.10 .. *Pres. Bd.*

Gage, Annie O. Bible standard of duty: quest. book of pract. religion; with introd. by Rev. W. L. Gage. 16°. bds., 15c. .... *Brown & G.*

Gage, *Mrs.* Fes. Dana. Elsie Magoon; or, the old still-house: temperance tale. 12°. $1.50 .. *Lippincott.*

— Gertie's sacrifice; or, glimpses at two lives. ('68.) New ed. 18°. '74. 50c. .... *Nat. Temp.*

— Poems. 12°. $1.75 .... *Lippincott.*

— Steps upward. 12°. $1.50 .... *Lippincott.*

Gage, *Mrs.* W. L. Helen on her travels, what she saw and did in Europe. 16°. '52. $1 .... *Hurd & H.*

Gage, W: Leon. Favorite hymns in their original forms; selected and verified. 18°. $1.25 ...... *Barnes.*

Gage, W: Leon., *continued.*

— Home of God's people. ill. 8°. '74. *$3; leath. $3.50; $4; mor., $6 .... *Dustin*

— Life of Carl Ritter. 12°. '67. $2 .... *Scribner*

— Modern hist. atlas. sm. 8°. hf. mor., $3.50 .. *Appleton*

— Studies in Bible lands. ill. 8°. $2; $2.50. *Bost. Am. Tr*

— *See also* Hyde, A., Baldwin, A. C., *and* Gage, W. L

Gahan, W: Catholic piety: prayers, etc. 24°. $2.75 $12. — chp. ed. 24°. 50c.–$1.25 .... *Strong*

— *Same.* 12°. 65c.–$3 .... *Cummiskey*

— *Same;* with Gospels and Epistles. 32°. '75. 50c.– $7 .... *Cunningham*

— Compendious abstract of hist. of church of Christ with contin. by J. G. Shea. 16°. $1.25 .. *Cath. Pub*

— Diamond manual of Catholic piety. [Prayer book. 48°. '75. 25c.–$5 .... *Cunningham*

— Sermons; ed. by Rev. Ja. O'Leary. cr. 8°. $3 mor., $5 .... *Sadlier*

Gairdner, Ja. Houses of Lancaster and York; wit the conquest and loss of France. maps. 16° $1 .... *Estes*

— *Same.* maps. 16°. '75. $1 .... *Scribner*

Gala days. Dodge, M. A. $1.50 .... *Estes*

Galama. De Liefde, J. B. $1.25; 75c. ...... *Scribner*

Galatea. *See* Cervantes.

Galaxy of wit and wisdom; or, fun for the million [Selections.] ill. 16°. $1 .... *Miller*

Galbraith, J. A., *and* Haughton, S. [Text-books. 13 v. 16° .... *Cassell*

Cont.: Algebra, pt. 1, $1.50. — *Same*, complete, $3. — Arith metic, $1.50 — Astronomy, $2. — Euclid, 2 v., ea., $1. — Hydro statics, $1.50. — Mathematical tables, $1.50. — Mechanics, $1.50 — Optics, $1.50. — Plane trigonometry, $1. — Steam engine, $1.50 — Tides and tidal currents, $1.25.

Galbraith, J: B. Index to decisions of Supreme Cour of Florida, v. 1–11 (1846–'66). 8° .... *State*

— *See also* Florida, Sup. Court reports.

Galbraith, T: Bensalem; or, the new economy: dia logue for indust. classes on the financial question 12°. '74. pap., 25c. .... *Galbraith*

Gale, E. C. Hints on dress. 12°. '72. 75c. .. *Putnam*

Gale, *Mrs.* N. Eunice Somers; or, talks about th angels. 16°. $1 .... *Cong. Pub*

Gale, *Rev.* Nahum. Conversion through personal effort 18°. 50c. .... *Cong. Pub*

— Pilgrims' first year in New England. 16°. $1.25. *Cong. Pub*

— Prophet of the highest; or, mission of John the Bap tist. ill. 16°. $1 .... *Bost. Am. Tr*

— Uncle Charles; or, labors more abundant. 16°. $1 *Cong. Pub*

Gale Breezeley. Johnstone, J. B. 15c. .... *French*

Galilei, Galileo. Private life of Galileo; comp. princi pally from his correspondence and that of hi eldest daughter, Sister Maria Celeste. por. cr 8°. '70. $1.50 .... *Macmillan*

— *Same.* 12°. '70. $1.50 .... *Lockwood, B. & Co*

Gallant Tom; or, perils of the ocean. 8°. pap., 50c *Peterson*

Gallaudet, T: H. Adam to Jacob. ill. 18°. '38. 40c *Am. Tr*

— Bible stories. ill. 18°. '34. 25c. .... *Am. Tr*

— Child's book on repentance. ill. 18°. '34. 40c. *Am. Tr*

— Child's book on the soul. ('36.) New ed. ill. 18° '52. 40c. .... *Am. Tr*

— David to Rehoboam. ill. 18°. '43. 60c. .... *Am. Tr*

— History of Jonah. ill. 18°. '33. 40c. .... *Am. Tr*

— History of Joseph. ill. 18°. '34. 40c. .... *Am. Tr*

— Life of Josiah. ill. 18°. '37. 25c. .... *Am. Tr*

— Scripture biography. 11 v. ill. 18°. '56. $5 .. *Am. Tr*

— Youth's book of natural theology. ill. 18°. (cop. '32.) '34. 45c. .... *Am. Tr*

— *and* Hooker, H. Family and school dict. sm. 4°. 75c *Sheldon*

— — Practical spelling book. 12°. *net*, 20c. .. *Hamersley*

Gallerie deutscher Dichter. Photo-por. after C. Jäger and others, and woodcuts after F. Wanderer; with [Germ.] text by O. Roquette. roy. 4°. mor., $18 .... *Stroefer.*

Gallerie deutscher Tondichter. Photo-por. after C. Jäger, and woodcuts; with [Germ.] text by E. Hanslick. roy. 4°. mor., $18 .... *Stroefer.*

Gallery of Eng. and Am. poets. *See* Coppée, H.

Gallery of Eng. and Am. women famous in song. 24 pts. 4°. '74. ea., *50c .... *S. Walker.*

— *See also* Coppée, H.

Gallery of great composers: Bach, Handel, Glück, etc. heliot. ill. 4°. '73. $10 .... *Osgood.*

Gallery of landscape painters: ill. of Am. scenery from paintings by W. H. Beard, G. S. Brown, Casilear, Colman, De Haas, Gignoux, etc. 24 eng. 4°. '71. $18–$30 .... *Putnam.*

Gallery of pictures; cont. Our British portrait-painters, and Stanfield gallery. imp. 4°. mor., $25. *Lippincott.*

Gallison, J. *See* United States, Circuit Court reports.

Gallitzin, D. A. Letters to a Protestant friend on the Scriptures. 2d ed. 18°. 60c .... *Cath. Pub.*

Galloping Dick. *See* Life of.

Galloping Gus; [also] Purse and pistol. 8°. pap., 50c. *Peterson.*

Galloway, Jos. D. Gas fitters and plumbers' guide. ill. 12°. '75. $1; pap., 75c .... *Baird.*

Galloway, Rob. Manual of qualitative analysis. ill. roy. 12°. $2.50 .... *Lea.*

Gallus. *See* Becker, W. A.

Gallus Jake: Ethiop. drama. 16°. pap., 15c ... *Happy.*

Galon, Alice. The wrecked heart. [In Eng. or Germ.] 8°. pap., 25c .... *Barclay.*

Galt, J: Life of Byron. 18°. 75c .... *Harper.*

Galton, Douglas. Address on general principles which should be observed in construction of hospitals, Leeds, 1869. cr. 8°. '69. $1.25 ..... *Macmillan.*

Galton, Fs. English men of science: their nature and nurture. 12°. $1 .... *Appleton.*

— Hereditary genius: inquiry into its laws and consequences. 12°. $2 .... *Appleton.*

— Meteorographica; or, methods of mapping the weather. ill. 4°. '63. pap., $3 .... *Macmillan.*

Gambler's fate. Milner, H. M. 15c .... *French.*

Gambler's league; or, the trials of a country maid. 8°. pap., 25c .... *De Witt.*

Gambler's wife. Grey, E. C. 50c .... *Harper.*

Game of billiards: temperance [dram.] sketch. 16°. pap., 15c .... *Happy.*

Game of cards; tr. by L. J. Hollenius. 12°. pap., 15c. *De Witt.*

Game of cricket. ill. 16°. pap., 15c .... *Happy.*

Game of life. Brougham, J. 15c .... *French.*

Game of love. Brougham, J. 15c .... *French.*

Game of modern ombre: its rules and regulations, according to Hobah. 16°. '74. 75c ..... *Williams.*

Game of romps. Morton, J. M. 15c .... *French.*

Game of speculation. Lawrence, S. 15c .... *French.*

Game of whist. 16°. pap., 15c .... *Dick & F.*

Gamekeeper's daughter. *See* Little Dot ser.

Games and sports. ill. 16°. 75c .... *Routledge.*

— *See also* Boy's treasury of sports.

Games of skill and conjuring. ill. 16°. 75c ... *Routledge.*

— *See also* Boy's treasury of sports.

Gamester (The). Moore, E. 15c .... *French.*

Gammer Grethel. *See* Grimm, J. L. *and* W. C.

Ganem. Talfourd, F. 15c .... *French.*

Gannet Island. Adams, H. C. $1. *Scribner, W. & A.*

Gannett, H. Lists of elevations in U. S., etc.; — Meteorol. obs. in Utah, etc. *See* United States, *Geog. and geol. survey.*

Gannett, W: C. Ezra Stiles Gannett: a memoir. 8°. '75. $3 .... *Roberts.*

Gano (*pseud.*) Grandpapa's Carlie; or, the young soldier. ill. 18°. 60c .... *Bost. Am. Tr.*

— *See also* Laughing Kitty stories.

Ganot, Adolphe. Elementary treatise on physics, experimental and applied; tr. and ed. by E. Atkinson. ill. 12°. $5 .... *W. Wood.*

— Natural philos. for general readers and young persons; tr. by E. Atkinson. ill. 12°. $3 ..... *Appleton.*

— Popular physics; ed. by W. G. Peck. 12°. '75. $1.75. *Barnes.*

Gans, D. Epistle lessons for the church year. 16°. 50c .... *Ref. Ch. Pub.*

— Gospel lessons for the church year. 16°. 50c. *Ref. Ch. Pub.*

Ganse, H. D. Bible slaveholding not sinful: reply to "Slaveholding not sinful," by S. B. Howe. 8°. pap., 25c .... *N. Y. Ref. Ch. Bd.*

Gant, F: J. Diseases of the bladder, prostate gland and urethra; incl. practical view of urinary diseases, deposits and calculi. 4th ed., rev. and enl. ill. 12°. '76. $4; $3.50 .... *Lindsay.*

Gantillon, H. E. Diseases of the womb: uterine catarrh frequently the cause of sterility: new treatment. 8°. '71. pap., 50c .... *Jas. Campbell.*

Gaol cradle: who rocks it? 12°. '73. $1.50 .. *Routledge.*

Garbett, E. Preliminaries to good building. *See* Roebling, J., Niagara Falls and intern. susp. bridge.

Garbett, *Rev.* E: Dogmatic faith. *See* Bampton lectures.

— God's word written. 12°. '68. $1 .... *Am. Tr.*

— *Same.* 12°. $1.50 .... *Bost. Am. Tr.*

Garbett, R. Catholic choir-book. obl. 4°. $2.50. *Noonan; Sadlier.*

— Morning and evening service of the Catholic Church. obl. 4°. bds., $2.25 .... *Ditson.*

Garcia, Manuel. New treatise on art of singing. f°. $5 .... *Ditson.*

Gardell, *Mrs.* J. S. H. Conversations on Italy in Eng. and French. 12°. hf. roan, $1.25 ... *Lippincott.*

Garden (The). Bell, C. D. 25c ..... *Scribner, W. & A.*

Garden (The). *See* Goodrich, S. G., Peter Parley's little lib.

Garden lesson. *See* Maple Grove stories.

Garden of Cyrus. *See* Browne, *Sir* T.

Garden of Eden. Yeager, G. 75c .... *Lippincott.*

Garden of the Lord. Mercein, I. 20c ... *Meth. Bk. Conc.*

Garden of roses. *See* Thomas *a Kempis.*

Garden of sorrows. Atkinson, J. $1.50; $2. *Meth. Bk. Conc.*

Garden of the soul: manual of [Cath.] spiritual exercises and instruct. for Christians who aspire to perfection. 32°. 45c.–$13 .... *Benziger.*

— *Same.* 18°. 75c.–$25 .... *Sadlier.*

— *Same.* 18°. $1–$16 .... *Sadlier.*

Garden of spices. Rutherford, S. $2; $2.50. *Cin. Meth. Bk. Conc.*

Garden prayer. Kingsbury, H. 15c.; 50c ... *Am. Tr.*

Gardening by myself. Warner, A. B. $1.25; 50c. *Randolph.*

Gardening for money. Barnard, C. F., *jr.* $1.50. *Loring.*

Gardening for pleasure. Henderson, P. $1.50 .. *Judd.*

Gardening for profit. Henderson, P. $1.50 ... *Judd.*

Gardenshire, J. B. *See* Missouri, Sup. Court reports.

Gardiner, C. Leben. 18°. '46. 25c. .... *Am. Tr.*

Gardiner, F: Diatessaron: life of our Lord in words of the Gospels. 16°. '71. $1 .... *Draper.*

Gardiner, F: *continued.*
— Harmony of the four Gospels in Eng., according to auth. version; corrected by best crit. eds. of original. ('71.) New ed. 8°. '73. $2..*Draper.*
— Harmony of the four Gospels in Gk., according to text of Tischendorf; with collation of textus receptus, and of texts of Griesbach, Lachmann and Tregelles; with tables, notes, etc. ('71.) New ed. 8°. '73. $2..................*Draper.*
— On Leviticus. *See* Lange, J. P., Commentary.
— Principles of textual criticism; with list of Gk. uncials, and table [of] parts of text of New Test. in each. 8°. '76. 75c.; pap., 50c..........(?)*Draper.*
Gardiner, Ja. Life. 18°. 60c..............*Am. S. S.*
Gardiner, Marg. Power. *See* Blessington, *Countess of.*
Gardiner, S: Rawson. The first two Stuarts, and the Puritan revolution, 1603–1660. maps. 16°. '76. $1..............................*Scribner.*
— The thirty years' war, 1618–1648. 16°. $1...*Estes.*
— *Same.* ('74.) New ed. 16°. '75. $1....*Scribner.*
Gardiner, W: Music of nature: attempt to prove that what is passionate and pleasing in singing, etc., is derived from sounds of the animated world; with illustrations. 8°. $5.............*Ditson.*
Gardner, A. Diakkaism; or, clairvoyant travels in Hades. 12°. '75. pap., 10c. ....*Colby.*
Gardner, A: K. Conjugal sins against the laws of life and health, and their effects upon the father, mother and child. 12°. '74. $1.50; pap., $1. *Lee & S.*
— Our children: handbook for instruction of parents and guardians. 12°. $2..............*Carleton.*
Gardner, Celia E. Broken dreams. [Poetry.] 12°. $1.50..................................*Carleton.*
— Every inch a king. 12°. '76. $1.50..*Meth. Bk. Conc.*
— Rich Medway's two loves. 12°. $1.75....*Carleton.*
— Stolen waters. [Poetry.] 12°. $1.50....*Carleton.*
— Tested. [Fiction.] 12°. $1.75 ....*Carleton.*
Gardner, D. P. Farmer's dictionary: vocab. of technical terms, and compendium of pract. farming. ill. 12°. shp., $2.50...................*Harper.*
— New medical dict.; with formulas of the principal pharmacopœias and articles on treatment of disease. 8°. shp., $3..................*Harper.*
Gardner, Dan. Institutes of international law, public and private, as settled by U. S. Supreme Court and by our republic; with ref. to decisions. 8°. shp., $5.50....................*Baker, V. & Co.*
Gardner, E: C. Homes and how to make them. ill. sq. 12°. '74. $2.....................*Osgood.*
— Illustrated homes; describing real homes and real people. ill. sq. 12°. '75. $2...........*Osgood.*
Gardner, F. B. Carriage painter's illustrated manual. 16°. '71. $1.......................... *Wells.*
— How to paint: complete compendium of the art. 16°. '72. $1.............................. *Wells.*
Gardner, Fs. Dictionary of the Lat. language. 8°. '43. shp., $3.25 ....*Claxton; Lippincott.*
— *and* Gay, A. M., *and* Buck, A. M. (*ed.*) Selections from the Latin classic authors; with notes and vocab. 2 v. 16°. 1, $1.25; 2, $1.50...*Lee & S.*
Cont.: Pt. 1, Phædrus, Justin and Nepos. — Pt. 2, Quintus Curtius, Ovid, Cicero De senectute and De amicitia.

Gardner, *Mrs.* H. C. Discontent, and other stories. 12°. '74. $1.25................*Meth. Bk. Conc.*
— Extracts from the diary of a country pastor. 16°. $1. *Cin. Meth. Bk. Conc.*
— Fault-finding; [also] Madeline Hascall's letters. 12°. $1.25....................*Cin. Meth. Bk. Conc.*
— Glimpses of our lake region in 1863, and other papers. 12°. '74. $1.50........*Meth. Bk. Conc.*
— King's (A) daughter, and other stories. 16°. '71. $1.25 ....*Meth. Bk. Conc.*
— Mehetabel: story of the revolution. ill. 16°. '75. $1.25 ....*Meth. Bk. Conc.*
— Rosamond Dayton. 16°. $1.25..*Cin. Meth. Bk. Conc.*

Gardner, *Mrs.* H. C., *continued.*
— *Same.* 12°. $1.50..........................*Lee & S*
— Rosedale: story of self-denial. 12°. $1.75. *Cin. Meth. Bk. Conc*
Gardner, J: Longevity: means of prolonging life afte middle age. 12°. '75. $1.50.........*W. F. Gill*
Gardner, W. W. Church communion, as practised b the Baptists, expl. and defended. 12°. $1. *So. Bapt.; Stevens*
— Missiles of truth. 12°. $1..............*So. Bapt*
Gareschè, F. P. Science and religion, the moder controversy: lecture. 8°. pap., 15c...*Benziger*
Gareth and Lynette. *See* Tennyson, A.
Garibaldi, Giu. Garibaldi, his boyhood and youth from T. Dwight's tr. of Autobiog. 12°. '59 pap., $1.50..............................*Barnes*
— Rule of the monk; or, Rome in the 19th cent [Fiction.] 8°. pap., 50c..............*Harper.*
Garibaldi "excursionists." Byron, H. J. 15c...*French*
Garland, Hu. A. Life of John Randolph. 2 v. in 1 por. 8°. $2........................*Appleton*
Garland (The). 32°. 50c..................*Nelson*
Garland of flowers; or, treasures of piety. 12°. $2.50 *Sadlier.*
Garland of poetry and prose. ill. 4°. '72. $4.50..*Lothrop*
Garland of poetry for the young. Kirkland, C. M. $2.25..................................*Scribner*
Garland of prayer. [Cath. prayer book.] 32°. $2.50–$20......................................*Sadlier.*
— *Same.* 16°. $2–$40.........................*Benziger*
Garland of the year. [Selections.] ill. sm. 4°. $2.50; mor., $5 ....*Estes*
Garman, S. W. *See* Agassiz, A., *and* Garman, S. W.
Garnal, M. Results of obs. with transit instrument, etc. *See* United States, *Naval Observatory.*
Garnelle; or, the rover's oath. 8°. pap., 25c...*Dick & F.*
Garnered fruits. 18°. 50c.; 60c..........*Am. Bapt*
Garnered sheaves. Holland, J. G. $4; $6; $7.50. *Scribner.*
Garnered sheaves. Richardson, A. D. *$2.50; $4. *Col. Bk.*
Garnett, R: Idylls and epigrams; chiefly from the Greek anthology. fp. 8°. '69. 75c...*Macmillan.*
Garnett, *Mrs.* T. E. Dancing, religion and revelry. 18°. 40c...........................*So. Bapt.*
Garrard, Kenner (*pseud.*) *See* Nolan, L. E.
Garret, Augusta Brown. Precious stones of the heavenly foundations. 12°. $1.50......*Sheldon.*
Garretson, F. V. D. Carmina Yalensia: Am. college songs, with music and piano-forte accomp. 8°. $1.75; $2.25...............................*Taintor.*
Garretson, Ja. E. ["J: Darby."] Odd hours of a physician. 12°. $1.50...............*Lippincott.*
— System of oral surgery: diseases and surgery of mouth, jaws, and associate parts. pl. and woodcuts. 8°. $10; shp., $11...........*Lippincott.*
— Thinkers and thinking. 16°. $1.50.....*Lippincott.*
— Two thousand years after; or, a talk in a cemetery. 12°. '75. $1.........................*Claxton.*
Garrett, Alex. C: Historical continuity: sketches on the Church. 18°. '75. pap., 20c....*Whittaker.*
Garrett, E: *and* Ruth (*pseud.*) *See* Mayo, Isabella F.
Garrett, Phin. (*ed.*) Excelsior dialogues; for adv. speakers. 12°. '67. $1.25..............*Garrett.*
— One hundred choice selections. nos. 1–12. 16°. '66–'76. ea., 75c.; pap., 30c..............*Garrett.*
— *Same;* in 3 v. 16°. ea., $2; $2.50.........*Garrett.*
Note. Pub. under title of Speaker's garland.
Garrick, D: Country girl: comedy. 16°. pap., 15c. *French.*
— Irish widow: farce. 16°. pap., 15c.........*French.*
— Katharine and Petruchio: drama. 16°. pap., 15c. *French.*
— *See also* Colman, G., *and* Garrick, D.

Garrick fever. Planché, J. R. 15c...*De Witt; French.*

Garrod, Alfr. Baring. Essentials of materia medica and therapeutics. 8°. $4.............*W. Wood.*

Garstang Grange. Trollope, T. A. $1.75; $1.50. *Peterson.*

Gärtner, C: Violin school for the pupils of his National Conserv. of Music. 4°. '70. $1.50..(?)*André.*

Gasc, Fd. E. A. French dictionary. 24°. $1.25. *Lippincott.*

— *See also* Translator (The).

Gascoyne. *See* Ballantyne, R. M.

Gasfitters and plumbers' reference book. ('71.) New ed. 4°. '75. $30................*J. A. Murphy.*

Gaskell, *Mrs.* Eliz. C. Novels and tales. 7 v. ill. 12°. ea., $1.75; per set, hf. cf., $25; half roxb., $27.50......................*Scribner, W. & A.*

Cont.: Cranford.—Lizzie Leigh; Dark night's work, etc.—Mary Barton; Cousin Phillis, etc.—North and south.—Ruth; Gray woman, etc.—Sylvia's lovers.—Wives and daughters.

— *Same.* 8 v............................*Harper.*

Cont.: Cousin Phillis, pap., 25c.—Cranford, $1.25.—Dark night's work, pap., 50c.—Mary Barton, pap., 50c.—My Lady Ludlow, pap., 25c.—North and south, pap., 50c.—Right at last, etc., $1.50.—Sylvia's lovers, pap., 75c.

Note. The prices given without bindings are for cl. 12°; those in pap. are 8°.

— Gray woman (The). 8°. pap., 25c.......*Peterson.*

— Life of Charlotte Bronté. 12°. $1.50....*Appleton.*

— *Same.* 12°. $3................*Scribner, W. & A.*

— — *See also* Bronté, C., E. *and* A.

— Moorland cottage. 18°. 75c.............*Harper.*

— Wives and daughters. 8°. $1.50; pap., $1..*Harper.*

Gaskell, J: New elements from old subjects, presented as the basis for a science of mind; [also] the philosophy of numeration, the philosophy of government, the philosophy of definitions, as applications of the aforesaid elements. 8°. '74. $2.50..............................*Claxton.*

Gaspar. Richardson, W. C. 50c...........*Searcy.*

Gaspardo, the gondolier. Almar, G. 15c....*Lee & S.*

Gasparin, Agénor Étienne (*Comte*) de. Happiness: discourses at Geneva; tr. by M. L. Booth. 16°. 75c............................*Bost. Am. Tr.*

Gasparin, Valérie Boissier (*Comtesse*) de. Human sadness; tr. sm. 8°. $1.50.........*Routledge.*

— *Same;* tr. by M. L. Booth. 16°. 75c...*Bost. Am. Tr.*

— Near and heavenly horizons; tr. 12°. $1.50..*Carter.*

— *Same.* cr. 8°. $1.50...................*Routledge.*

Gasparini, J. Attributes of Christ. 12°. $1.50..*O'Shea.*

Gate of heaven. [Cath. prayer book.] 32°. 38c.–$50. *Sadlier.*

Gate of paradise: dream of Easter-eve. 18°. '75. pap., 20c..................................*Dutton.*

Gate of pearl. Giles, C. $1................*New Ch.*

Gate of prayer. Summers, T. O. 50c.....*So. Meth.*

Gate of the temple. Newton, W. W. 40c...*Whittaker.*

Gates ajar. *See* Phelps, E. S.

Gates of praise. Macduff, J. R. $1.........*Carter.*

Gates of prayer. Macduff, J. R. $1.........*Carter.*

Gates wide open. Wood, G. $1.50.........*Lee & S.*

Gath to the Cedars. Kent, S. H. $2.50. *Scribner, W. & A.*

Gathered blossoms. 18°. 70c.............*Pres. Bd.*

Gathered flowerets. Summers, T. O. 50c...*So. Meth.*

Gathered flowers: songs and choruses for the pianoforte. 4°. '73. $2; $2.50; bds., $1.50..*Ditson.*

Gathered fragments. Clark, J. A. $1.50....*Carter.*

Gathered gems: tales and pencillings in prose and poetry. 12°. $1.25...................*Nelson.*

Gathered lambs. Hammond, E. P. 70c....*West. Tr.*

Gathered leaves of S.-school song. Neilson, W. H., *jr.* 30c............................*Biglow.*

Gathered lilies. 32°. 25c.................*West. Tr.*

Gathered pearls. 18°. 50c.; 60c.........*Am. Bapt.*

Gathered sheaves. Clark, E. $1.............*Hoyt.*

Gattina, Fd. Petrucelli della. Popery exposed; tr. 12°. $1.75; pap., $1.50...................*Peterson.*

— Rome and the papacy; tr. 12°. $1.75; pap., $1.50. *Peterson.*

Gatty, *Mrs.* M. Alice and Adolphus. 18°. 65c. *Carter.*

Compr. Worlds not realized; Proverbs illustrated.

— Aunt Judy's tales. 18°. 75c...............*Carter.*

— Circle of blessing. 18°. 50c.......*Carter; Dutton.*

— Imperfect instruments. 18°. '76. pap., 15c. *Randolph.*

— Motes in the sunbeam. 18°. 50c...........*Carter.*

— Parables from nature. 18°. 75c............*Carter.*

Compr. Motes in the sunbeam; Circle of blessing.

— Proverbs illustrated. 18°. 50c.............*Carter.*

— Worlds not realized. 18°. 50c.............*Carter.*

Gaudentius, *Rev.* —. Voice of Jesus suffering to the minds and hearts of Christians. 12°. $2..*O'Shea.*

Gaudentius. Davies, G. S. $1.25............*Pott.*

Gaulle, *Mme.* — de. Le bracelet. *See* M., M. de, La petite maman.

Gaultier, Bon (*pseud.*) *See* Martin, T., *and* Aytoun, W. E., Book of ballads.

Gaume, J: Jos. Catechism of perseverance: hist., doctr., moral and liturgical exposition of the Cath. religion; tr. by F. B. Jamison. New ed., rev. and enl. 18°. 75c................*Noonan.*

— Christian cemetery in the 19th cent.; or, the last war-cry of the Communists; tr. by R. Brennan; with pref. by T. S. Preston. 12°. $1.50...*Benziger.*

— Sign of the cross in the 19th cent.; tr. by a daughter of St. Joseph. 12°. '73. $1.50...*Cunningham.*

Gauss, C: F. Theoria motus: theory of motions of heavenly bodies about the sun in conic sections; with app. by C: H: Davis. 4°. '57. $5..*Little, B. & Co.*

Gaussen, L. Canon of the Script. examined in light of hist.; tr. by E. N. Kirk. 12°. $1.50..*Bost. Am. Tr.*

— Erste Blatt (Das) der Bibel. [Tr.] 18°. 60c.; 80c. *Ev. Assoc.*

— Jonah, the prophet: lessons on his life; tr. from the Fr. ill. 16°. '67. 60c...........*Bost. Am. Tr.*

— Origin and inspirations of the Bible; tr. 12°. $1.75. *Cin. Meth. Bk. Conc.*

— World's birthday; tr. ill. 12°. $1.25......*Nelson.*

Gaut Gurley. Thompson, D. P. $1.75...*J. E. Potter.*

Gautier, Théophile. Constantinople; tr. by R. H. Gould. Am. ed., rev. 12°. '75. $2......*Holt.*

— Winter (A) in Russia; tr. by M. M. Ripley. ('74.) New ed. 12°. '75. $2.......................*Holt.*

— *See also* Cross of Berny.

Gautrelet, François Xavier. The Christian nurse and her mission in the sick room; tr. by Rev. J. M. Neale. 16°. 75c..........................*Pott.*

Gavin, J. *See* Indiana, Statutes.

Gavroche, the gamin of Paris. *See* Hugo, V.

Gay, A. M. *See* Gardner, F., Gay, A. M., *and* Buck, A. M.

Gay, *Mlle.* Delphine. *See* Girardin, *Mme.* D. de.

Gay, H. Acis and Galatea: opera. 16°. pap., 15c. *French.*

Gay, J: Beggar's opera: comic opera. 16°. pap., 15c. *French.*

— Fables; ed. by Rev. O. F. Owen. ill. cr. 8°. $2.50. *Scribner, W. & A.*

— — *See also* British pocket classics.

— Poems; with memoir by S. Johnson. 2 v. por. 18°. $2......................................*Osgood.*

Gay, M. A. H. A pastor's story, and other pieces. 2d ed. 12°. '73. $1.50................*Turnbull.*

Gay, Sydney Howard. *See* Bryant, W. C., *and* Gay, S. H.

Gay boys of old Yale. 8°. '69. pap., 25c.....*Hunter.*

Gay cottage. *See* Bradley, W. I.

Gay cottage stories. 5 v. 18°. $2.50...*Bost. Am. Tr.*
Cont.: Frank's victory.—Gay cottage, by W. I. Bradley.—Nellie Newton.—Our Charlie, by Mrs. A. S. Southworth.—Rabbit snares, by Mrs. H. N. Marvin.

Gay life in New York; or, fast men and war widows. 8°. pap., 25c. .... *De Witt.*

Gay old man (A) am I: musical monologue. 16°. pap., 15c. .... *Happy.*

Gayarre, C: History of Louisiana. 3 v. 8°. ea., $4. *Widdleton.*
Cont.: French domination.—Span. domination.—Am. domination.

— Philip II. of Spain; with introd. letter by G. Bancroft. por. 8°. $2.50; hf. cf., $4 .... *Widdleton.*

— Romance of the history of Louisiana: lectures. 12°. $1 .... *Appleton.*

— *See also* Louisiana, Reports.

Gayler, C: Love of a prince: drama. 16°. pap., 15c. *French.*

— Out of the streets. 12°. $1.50 .... *De Witt.*

— Son of a night: drama. 16°. pap., 15c..... *French.*

Gaylord, Glance (*pseud.*) *See* Bradley, W. I.

Gaylord, Willis, *and* Tucker, Luther. American husbandry: essays, etc., designed for its improvement. 2 v. 18°. hf. shp., $1.50 .... *Harper.*

Gayworthys (The). Whitney, A. D. T. $2..*Loring.*

Gazza ladra (La). *See* Rossini, G.

Gazzam, A. W. American and Eng. digest and rules of practice in U. S. courts in bankruptcy. 2 v. 8°. shp., $15 .... *W. C. Little.*

— Treatise on the bankrupt law for business men. 4th ed., rev. and enl. 8°. shp., $6.50..*W. C. Little.*

Gebetbüchlein f. die Schuljugend. 8th ed. 32°. bds., 10c. .... *Herder.*

Geburtstag der Reformation, und ein Tag aus Dr. Martin Luther's Leben. 18°. '76. 40c...*Am. Tr.*

Gedanken über Welt u. Mensch. *See* Brucker, J.

Geduldige Helena (Die). 12°. pap., 15c.....*Radde.*

Geer, G: Jarvis. Conversion of St. Paul: discourses. 12°. '71. 75c.; $1 .... *Wells.*

Geeslin, A. W. (*ed.*) Exposition of the grange. ('75.) 3d ed. ill. 12°. '76. pap., 25c........ *E. A. Cook.*

Gefahren e. Sängerfestes. *See* Dilthey, K.

Gefangene (Der) v. Chillon. *See* Hartmann, M.

Geheimnissvolle Pedlar (Der). Leonhart, R. 75c. *Zickel.*

Gehörnte Siegfried. *See* Geschichte v. d.

Geib, W. Tuning the piano-forte. 12°. '69. pap., 35c. *Ditson.*

Geibel, E. *See* Stilke, H., Das Jahr in Blüthen.

Geiger, Hm. Lydia: tale of 2d cent. 12°. '67. $1.50. *Cummiskey.*

Geier-wally. Hillern, W. v. $1.25....... *Appleton.*

Geikie, Arch. Geology. (Pop. sci. man.) 18°. 40c. *Lippincott.*

— *Same.* (Sci. primer.) 18°. 50c.......... *Appleton.*

— Physical geog. (Sci. primer.) 18°. 50c...*Appleton.*

— *See also* Wilson, G., *and* Geikie, A.

Geikie, Ja. Great ice age, and its rel. to antiquity of man. maps and ill. 12°. $2.50....... *Appleton.*

Geikie, J: C. Adventures in Canada; or, life in the woods. ill. 16°. $1.25 .... *Porter.*

— — *See also below* Life in the woods.

— Life: book for young men. 3d ed. cr. 8°. $1.75. *Routledge.*

— *Same;* with introd. by Rev. S. H. Tyng, jr. 12°. '73. $1.50 .... *Whittaker.*

— Life in the woods: story of the Canadian bush. 12°. '73. $2 .... *Routledge.*

— — *See also above* Adventures.

— Light from beyond to cheer the Christian pilgrim. 16°. '72. $1 .... *Routledge.*

Geistliche Viole (Die). [Hymns.] 24°. leath., 40c.; 50c.; 75c. .... *Ev. Assoc.*

— *See also* Evangelisches Gesangbuch.

Geistliche Volkslied (Das): Sammlg. (vierstimmig) f. aussergottesdienstl. Kreise. 8°. hf. bd., 50c. *Volkening.*

Geistliches Gebetkämmerlein. Stohlmann, J. F. C. 25c. .... *Radde.*

Geldard, Ja. Handbook of cotton manufacture: guide to machine building, spinning and weaving. ill. 12°. $2.50 .... *Wiley.*

Geldart, *Mrs.* T: Daily thoughts for a child. 16°. 50c. .... *Routledge.*

— Emilie, the peacemaker. 16°. 50c....... *Routledge.*

— Geldart ser. 6 v. ill. 18°. $3.60 .... *Sheldon.*
Cont.: Daily thoughts for a child.—Truth is everything.—Sunday morning thoughts.—Emilie, the peacemaker.—Sunday evening thoughts.—Stories of Scotland.

— Glimpses of our island home. ill. 16°. 75c. *Routledge.*

— History of England. ill. 16°. $1.......... *Sheldon.*

— Mary Leigh; or, purpose in life. ill. 16°. $1. *Scribner, W. & A.*

— May Dundas; or, the force of example. 16°. 75c. *Routledge.*

— Truth is everything. 16°. 50c.......... *Routledge.*

Geldfürst (Ein). Hammer, R. 50c.......... *Zickel.*

Gelobt sei Jesus Christus: Gebetbuch f. Katholiken. 32°. leath., 50c.; 65c.; 85c.......... *Benziger.*

Gelobt sei Jesus Christus: e. [Kathol.] Gebetbuch herausg. v. d. Versamml. d. Allerhl. Erlösers. 24°. '45. 60c.–$2.50 .... *Murphy.*

Gem (The). [S.-school hymn book.] sq. 16°. '73. 40c. .... *So. Meth.*

Gem (The): songs for primary and grammar schools. 32°. '71. 20c. .... *Kelly, P. & Co.*

Gem (The): songs, marches, etc., arranged as duets for flutes. 7 nos. 8°. ea., pap., 30c....*Ditson.*

Gem cluster. 12 v. ill. 18°. '73. $4.50...... *Nelson.*
Cont.: Bob, the shoe-black.—Factory girl.—Giant conquered.—Myra's pink dress.—Fred and his relations.—Marion Grey.—Ellen Strong's victory.—Esther's regret, by Emma Leslie.—Emma Welford.—Foundling of Fivecot.—Jeannie Barker, by Mrs. Seamer.—Plague of the village.

Gem library (The). 5 v. 16°. $2.50..(?) *Cumberland.*
Cont.: The two prophets, by A. J. Baird.—Tall man of Winton, by "Over Forty."—Casket.—Great teacher, by A. Templeton.—The blind man's cottage, by J. C. Provine.

Gem of courage; — courtesy; — earnestness; — faithfulness; — generosity; — neatness; — perseverance; — self-control; — self-denial; — temperance; — truthfulness; — uprightness. *See* Baker, *Mrs.* H. N. W.

Gem of the lake. Wright, S. A. 50c........ *Sickels.*

Gemeinschaftliche Lieder-Sammlung. [Hymns.] 32°. leath., 60c. .... *Baer.*

Gemma. Trollope, T. A. $1.75; $1.50...*Peterson.*

Gems. Spurgeon, C. H. $1.50 .... *Sheldon.*

Gems for the bridal ring. Rankin, J. E. $1..*Cong. Pub.*

Gems for the prayer-meeting. 32°. '64. 15c.; bds., 10c. .... *Am. Tr.*

Gems for Sabbath schools. 18°. 60c....... *Cong. Pub.*

Gems for youth. *See* Baker, *Mrs.* H. N. W.

Gems from Am. poets. *See* Griswold, R. W.

Gems from the coral island. *See* Gill, W.

Gems from sacred mines: texts and hymns. [Interleaved.] 12°. '69. $1.75 .... *Randolph.*

Gems from Shakespeare: pl. by Rob. Smirke; with descript. text. sm. 4°. $4.......... *Lippincott.*

Gems of Am. poets. ill. 32°. 38c.— (Blue and gold ed.) 18°. 75c. .... *Appleton.*

Gems of the bog. Chaplin, J. D. $1.25..*Bost. Am. Tr*

Gems of devotion: prayers for Catholics. 48°. '45 30c.–$6 .... *Murphy*

Gems of the Dresden gallery: eng., with Eng., French and Germ. texts by C. Clauss. f°. $25..*Stroefer*

Gems of Eng. song; with piano-forte accomp. 4°. '75 $3; $4; bds., $2.50 .... *Ditson*

Gems of German lyrics. Wireman, H. D. $1.50; $2.50. *Claxton.*

Gems of German song; with piano-forte accomp. 4°. '65. $3; $4; bds., $2.50.............. *Ditson.*

Gems of India. Humphrey, E. J. $1.25.. *Meth. Bk. Conc.*

Gems of paradise. [Cath. prayer book.] 24°. $1.50 –$30. — 48°. 31c.–$15. — 64°. 25c.–$10.. *Sadlier.*

— *Same;* with the Epistles and Gospels. (Red line ed.) ill. 24°. $1.50–$75.................... *Sadlier.*

Gems of praise combined. Sweney, J. R. 25c.; 20c. *Meth. Epis.*

Gems of prayer. [Cath. prayer book.] ('69.) 6th ed. 64°. '74. 20c.–$1.75.................. *Kenedy.*

Gems of prose and poetry. Aiken, J. R. $1.50.. *Miller.*

Gems of sacred poetry. 64°. '31. 20c.; 25c... *Am. Tr.*

Gems of sacred song; with piano-forte accomp. 4°. '66. $3; $4; bds., $2.50............... *Ditson.*

Gems of Scottish song. 4°. '66. $3–$2.50.... *Ditson.*

Gems of thought. Hall, H. 50c........... *Pres. Bd.*

Gems that sparkle. 18°. 35c.; 45c........ *Am. Bapt.*

General (The). Barrows, W. $1.25........ *Lee & S.*

General assembly. *See* Presbyterian Church.

General Assoc. of Connecticut. *See* Congregational churches in Conn.

General catechism of the Christian doctrine. [Catholic.] ('53.) New ed. 32°. '76. per 100, $2.75; — with app. by the Christian Brothers. ('70.) 18th ed. 24°. '76. 15c................ *Kenedy.*

General Frankie. Lynn, E. 60c.......... *Randolph.*

General illumination. 18°. 20c.; 25c...... *Am. Bapt.*

General Lee and Santa Claus. Clack, L. 80c... *Eyrich.*

Generali, P. Mass in G; arrang. by W. Dressler. 4°. pap., $2.50........................... *Peters.*

— Vespers, no. 4; arrang. by W. Dressler. 4°. pap., $1.25.............................. *Peters.*

Generalship; or, how I managed my husband. Roy, G. $1; 50c.......................... *Clarke.*

Generous enemy, and other stories. 18°. 50c... *O'Shea.*

Genesis disclosed. Davies, T. A. $1.50... *Carleton.*

Genesis of New England churches. Bacon, L. $2.50. *Harper.*

Genesis of species. Mivart, St. G. $1.75; $4.. *Appleton.*

Geneste, Mx. Parallel histories of Judah and Israel; with explanatory notes. 2 v. roy. 8°. (Bagster.) $10................................. *Wiley.*

Geneva. *See* United States, Argument at G.

Geneva's shield. Blackburn, W. M. $1...... *Dodd.*

Geneviève. *See* Lamartine, A. de.

Geneviève. Stratton, G. W. 70c.; 80c.... *Stratton.*

Geneviève de Brabant. *See* Ditson.

Geneviève de Brabant. Schmid, C. v. 60c. *Cath. Pub.*

Genevra. Fairfield, G. G. 75c. .... *Peterson.*

Gengembre, P. W. Practical French reader. 8°. '68. $1.50 .... *Holt.*

Genial showman. Hingston, E. P. 75c...... *Harper.*

Genius of Christianity. Chateaubriand, F. A. (*Vicomte*) de. $2.50; $3................. *Murphy.*

Genius of the Gospel. Thomas, D. $4.50. *Smith, E. & Co.*

Genlis, S. F. D. de St. A. (*Comtesse*) de. Children's island; tr. 18°. 25c......... *Scribner, W. & A.*

— Siége (Le) de la Rochelle. 12°. $1.50. *G. R. Lockwood.*

Genovefa. *See* Heilige Genovefa; — Schmid, C. v.

Genoveva. *See* Geschichte v. d. hl. Pfalzgräfin.

Genoveva. *See* Trench, R. C.

Gentianella. Randolph, *Mrs.* —. $1.50; 75c.; $1.25. *Porter.*

Gentile nations (The). *See* Smith, G.

Gentle, F. A. *See* Gibbs, W., *and* Gentle, F. A.

Gentle Annie melodist. *See* Foster, S. C.

Gentle Gracie. 18°. '64. 40c............. *Randolph.*

Gentle Hand. *See* Arthur, T. S.

Gentle John, the happy young villager. 32°. 25c. *Pres. Bd.*

Gentle life (The): essays in aid of formation of character. 2 v. 16°. ea., $3...... *Scribner, W. & A.*

Gentle life ser. 13 v. 16°. ea., $3.. *Scribner, W. & A.*

Cont.: About in the world, by J. H. Friswell. — Concordance to Milton's poems, by D. Cleveland. — Familiar words: index verborum. — Imitation of Christ, by T. *a Kempis.* — Essays on English writers. — Montaigne's essays. — A man's thoughts, by J. H. Friswell. — Other people's windows, by J. H. Friswell. — Silent hour, by J. H. Friswell. — Varia: readings from rare books. — Sidney's Arcadia, ed. by Friswell. — Gentle life, 2 v.

Gentle skeptic. *See* Walworth, C.

Gentlefolks and others. Duhring, J. $2.. *Lippincott.*

Gentleman (The). Calvert, G. H. $1.25... *Dutton.*

Gentleman from Ireland. O'Brien, F. J. 15c... *French.*

Gentleman George; or, the advantages of reading. 18°. 25c..................... *Scribner, W. & A.*

Gentleman in black. Gilbert, W. S. 15c.... *French.*

Gentleman Jack. 8°. pap., 25c............ *De Witt.*

Gentleman of the old school. *See* James, G. P. R.

Gentleman's daughter. 8°. pap., 25c...... *Dick & F.*

Gentleman's glee book. Mason, L. $1.50... *Ditson.*

Gentleman's letter writer. 18°. 60c......... *Miller.*

Gentleman's letter writer. 16°. 20c...... *Routledge.*

Gentleman's letter writer. 16°. 35c......... *Porter.*

Gentleman's manual of etiquette, and guide to polite society. 16°. 75c...................... *Miller.*

Gentlemen of the jury. Baker, G. M. 15c... *Lee & S.*

Gentlemen's art of dressing with economy; by a lounger at the clubs. 16°. '76. bds., 50c. *Scribner, W. & A.*

Gentlemen's companion lib. 4 v. 16°. $2.85.. *Miller.*

Cont.: Handbook of etiquette. — Gentleman's book of etiquette. — Gentleman's letter writer. — Young husband's book.

Gentlemen's handbook of etiquette and manual of politeness. 12°. $1.50............... *Lee & S.*

Gentry, T: G. Life histories of birds of eastern Pennsylvania. v. 1. 12°. '76. $2....... *Nat. Agcy.*

Geoffrey de Vinsauf. Chronicle of Richard I. *See* Bohn, H. G., Chronicles of the crusades.

Geoffrey *of Monmouth.* British history. *See* Giles, J. A., Six old English chronicles.

Geoffrey, the Lollard. Knevels, D. C. $1.25.. *Dodd.*

Geoffrey Moncton. Moodie, S. $1.25...... *De Witt.*

Geoffrey's birthday. 32°. 20c.; 15c......... *Dutton.*

Geoffry Hamlyn (Recollections of). *See* Kingsley, H.

Geographical and geol. survey of the territories. *See* United States.

Geological stories. Taylor, J. E. $1.75.... *Putnam.*

Geological story briefly told. Dana, J. D. $1.50. *Ivison.*

Geological surveys. *See* names of various states and United States.

Geology and revelation. *See* Molloy, Gerald.

Geology and scripture. Smith, J. P. $2. *Scribner, W. & A.*

Geology of the stars. Winchell, A. 25c....... *Estes.*

Geometrical Teaching (Assoc. for Improvement of). *See* Association.

Geometry and faith. Hill, T. $1.......... *Putnam.*

Geordie's tryst. ill. 18°. '74. 50c.......... *Nelson.*

George, *Cousin.* *See* Cousin George.

George, A. C. Counsels to converts. 12°. $1.25. *Cin. Meth. Bk. Conc.*

— Satisfactory portion. 18°. 60c... *Cin. Meth. Bk. Conc.*

— Short sermons on consecration and kindred themes. 12°. '73. $1.25................ *Meth. Bk. Conc.*

George, H. H. On secret societies. 12°. pap., 10c. *E. A. Cook.*

George, Hereford B. Genealogical tables illustrative of modern history. 2d ed., rev. and enl. 4°. '75. $6 .... *Macmillan.*

George, Ja. Z. Digest of Mississippi Supreme Court and High Court of Errors and Appeals reports. roy. 8°. '72. $25 .... *T. & J. W. Johnson.*

— *See also* Mississippi, Reports.

George, N. D. Annihilation not of the Bible. 12°. $1.50 .... *Cin. Meth. Bk. Conc.*

— Universalism not of the Bible. 12°. '73. $1.75. *Meth. Bk. Conc.*

George, *Uncle* (*pseud.*) *See* Tarbox, I. N.

George; or, the planter of the Isle of France. *See* Dumas, A.

George, the little chimney sweep. 16°. 45c. *Cummiskey.*

George Barnwell. Lillo, G. 15c .... *French.*

George Buchanan, the king's jester: his witty sayings and laughable exploits. [In Eng. or Germ.] 12°. pap., 20c .... *Barclay.*

George Canterbury's will. Wood, E. P. $1.75; $1.50. *Peterson.*

George Clifford's loss and gain; by author of "Stories and pictures from church history." ill. 16°. '71. $1 .... *Lothrop.*

George de Barnwell. Byron, H. J. 15c .... *French.*

George Geith. Riddell, J. H. $2 .... *Burnham.*

George Howard; or, the weak made strong. 18°. 35c. *Am. S. S.*

George Julian. *See* Cockton, H:

George Lee. Hildeburn, M. J. 60c .... *Pres. Bd.*

George Miller and his mother. 18°. 75c .... *Pres. Bd.*

George Morton and his sister. Trowbridge, C. M. $1.25 .... (?) *Martien.*

George Perley's lesson. *See* Mudge, Z. A., Casket lib.; Pure gold ser.

George Ready. *See* Atlantic lib.

George Rowland, the servant boy. ('61.) New ed. ill. 18°. '71. 50c .... *Dutton; Hoyt.*

George Seton. 8°. pap., 25c .... *Dick & F.*

George Somerville; or, the boy who would be a minister. 18°. 40c .... *Am. S. S.*

George Washington Brown. Vox. 25c .... *Am. News.*

George Wayland, the little medicine carrier. ill. 18°. '67. 40c .... *Am. Tr.*

— *Same.* 18°. 50c .... (?) *Martien.*

— *Same.* 18°. 70c .... *Pres. Bd.*

George Wilson and his friend. 18°. 35c .... *Am. S. S.*

Georgia. Annotated code; by D. Irvin, G. N. Lester and W. B. Hill. 8°. '73. shp., $10; — in 2 v., interleaved, shp., $12 .... *Burke.*

— Annotated penal code; by Hopkins. 8°. shp., $7. *Burke.*

— Superior courts reports for the east. dist., 1805–'11; by T. U. P. Charlton. 8°. '27 .... *State.*

— *Same.* 1811–'37; by R. M. Charlton. 8°. '38 .. *State.*

— Superior courts of law and chancery reports, 1830–'33; by G. M. Dudley. 8°. '37 .... *State.*

— Superior courts decisions, 1842–3. 8°. '43–'44 .. *State.*

— Supreme Court reports, v. 1–29 ('46–'60). 29 v. 8°. .... *State.*

Cont.: 1–3 ('46–47), by J. M. Kelly. — 4–5 ('48), by J. M. Kelly and T. R. R. Cobb. — 6–20 ('49–'56), by T. R. R. Cobb. — 21–29 ('57–'60), by B. Y. Martin.

— *Same.* v. 30–55 ('61–'76). 26 v. 8°. ea., shp., $7. *Burke.*

Cont.: 30–33 ('60–'63), by G. N. Lester. — 34–36 ('64–'66), by L. E. Bleckley. — 37–55 ('67–'76), by N. J. Hammond and H: Jackson.

— — Digest. *See* Bacon, A. O.; — Harris, N. E.

— — *See also* Jackson, H:

Georgia Historical Society. Collections. v. 2, 3. 8°. '42–'73. ea., $3. pt. 1, v. 3. 8°. '48. pap., $1 .. *Ga. Hist.*

Note. v. 1 is o p.

Georgia scenes. ill. 12°. $1.50 .... *Harper.*

Georgics. *See* Virgil.

Georgie. *See* Abbott, Jac., Rollo story books.

Georgie and Lizzie. Bell, C. D. 75c ... *Scribner, W. & A.*

Georgie's present. *See* Golden chain lib.

Georgy's menagerie. *See* Baker, *Mrs.* H. N. W.

Gerald Fitzgerald. Lever, C. 50c .... *Harper.*

Gerald Marsdale. Carey, S. $1.25; $1.75 .. *Sadlier.*

Geraldine: tale of conscience. 12°. $2 ...... *O'Shea.*

Gerando, Jos. Marie (*Baron*) de. Self-education; tr. by E. P. Peabody. 12°. '60. $3 ..... *Burnham.*

Gerard, C: B. Descendants of Ralph Chapman. sm. 4°. '76. $2.25 .... *Black.*

Gerard, G: Cabinet des fées; or, recreative readings; for students in Fr. 12°. $1.50 .... *Appleton.*

Gerard, Ja. W., *jr.* City water rights: treatise on title of N. Y. City and others, to streets, wharves, piers, etc. 8°. '73. shp., $5 .... *Baker, V. & Co.*

— Old stadthuys of New Amsterdam; read before the N. Y. Hist. Soc., June 15, 1875. 8°. '75. pap., $1 .... *Patterson.*

— Old streets of N. Y. 8°. '74. pap., $1 .. *Patterson.*

— Titles to real estate in N. Y. [State]; for conveyancers and students at law. 2d ed. 8°. '73. shp., $6.50 .... *Baker, V. & Co.*

Gerard, Ste., *jr.* Centennial wealth of the world: names of the richest men in the world. 8°. '76. pap., 50c. .... *Vose.*

Gerbet, Olympe-Philippe. Lily of Israel; or, life of Virgin Mary; [also] Veneration of Virgin Mary. ('73.) 3d ed. ill. 16°. '76. 75c.; $1 .... *Kenedy.*

Gerda. Schwartz, M. S. $1.50; $1; $1.25 .. *Porter.*

Gere, J. Government of children. 18°. '51. 35c. *Meth. Bk. Conc.*

Geretteten Diebe (Die). ill. 32°. '61. 25c ... *Am. Tr.*

Gerhard, F: (*ed.*) Der Geschäftsmann in Amerika: ein Handbuch f. alle die vorwärts wollen. 8th ed. 2 v. 8°. '76. $4.75 .... *Zickel.*

Gerhard, J. *See* Chemnitz, M., Leyser, P., *and* Gerhard, J.

Gerhard, W. W. Diagnosis, pathology and treatment of diseases of the chest. ('59.) 4th ed., rev. and enl. 8°. shp., $4 .... *Claxton; Lippincott.*

Gerhardt, Pl. Spiritual songs; tr. by J. Kelly. 16°. $2.50 .... *Routledge.*

Gerhart, E. V. Philosophy and logic. 12°. $1.25. *Ref. Ch. Pub.*

Geringer, Aug. (*ed.*) Čes.-Americká domácí Bibliotéka. [Bohemian-Am. family lib.] 6 v. 16°. *Geringer.*

Cont.: Quadroona, $1. — Vyhnancůvsyn, $3.40. — Phil. Foghorn, 30c. — Vídeňský kat, 2 v., $5. — Otec La Ruine, 90c.

Gerlach, O: v. Commentary on the Pentateuch. 8°. $3. *Scribner, W. & A.*

Germaine cousin. Fullerton, *Lady* G. 25c ... *Sadlier.*

German and Eng. interpreter. 12°. 75c ...... *Kohler.*

German Baptist. *See* Baptist.

German classics for Am. students. *See* Hart, J. M.

German echo. Worman, J. H. $1.25 .... *Barnes.*

German emigrant. Tooley, L. 15c .... *De Witt.*

German-English and Eng.-Germ. pronounc. dict. cr. 8°. $1.75 .... *Cassell.*

German Evangelical Assoc. *See* Evangelical Assoc.

German Evangelical Lutheran Church. Gesangbuch. f. d. ev. luth. Kirche in d. Ver. Staaten. 32°. 75c.–$2.50 .... *Kohler.*

— *Same.* 12°. $1.50–$3.50 .... *Kohler.*

— Ordnung des Gottesdienstes an Sonn-u. Festtagen; a. d. Kirchenbuch. d. Allgem. Kirchenversamml. 8°. 25c.; pap., 15c .... *Brobst.*

— Sonntagschulbuch f. evangel. Gemeinen. sq. 16°. '76. 60c.; bds., 45c .... *Brobst; Kohler.*

German Evangelical Lutheran Church, *continued.*
— *Pennsylvania Synod.* Liturgie u. Agende. 12°. $1.25; leath., $1.50; mor., $3 .... *Kohler.*
— *Synod of Iowa.* Bericht üb. die auf Anlass d. Schrift Pastor Klindworth's "Die traurigen Zustände in d. Iowa Synode" veranstaltete Untersuchg. 8°. '76. pap., 50c.... *Germ. Ev. Luth. Syn. of Iowa.*
— — Hauptstücke des kleinen Katechismus Luthers. [With prayers, etc.] 12°. '74. bds., 10c. *Germ. Ev. Luth. Syn. of Iowa.*
— *Synod of Mo., O. and other states.* Biblische Geschichten f. Oberklassen. ('70.) 3d ed. 8°. '74. 65c. .... *Barthel.*
— — Die Synodalberichte 1-10 (1847-'60). 2d ed. 8°. '76. $2.50 .... *Barthel.*
— — Synodalhandbuch; zusammengestellt v. C. A. T. Selle. 16°. '73. 40c. .... *Barthel.*
— *Synod of the West.* Evangelische Agende. ('57.) 2d ed. roy. 8°. '75. $2; $3. *Germ. Ev. Syn. of the West.*
— — Evangelisches Gesangbuch. 8°. '67. $1.25-$2.50. 12°. 90c.-$3 .... *Germ. Ev. Syn. of the West.*
— — Kleine evang. Agende. 12°. '75. $1. *Germ. Ev. Syn. of the West.*
— — Kleiner evang. Katechismus. 12°. '67. 15c. *Germ. Ev. Syn. of the West.*
— — Schüler (Der) im Westen. [Readers.] 3 v. 16°. '69-'72 .... *Germ. Ev. Syn. of the West.*
Cont.: Lese-Fibel, bds., 20c. — Erstes Lesebuch, bds., 35c. — Zweites Lesebuch, bds., 50c.

— *Synod of Wisconsin and other states.* Evangelisch-lutherisches Gesangbuch. 8°. leath., 80c.; $1.85; mor., $2.10. — 18°. leath., $1.20; $2.25; mor., $2.50 .... *Brumder.*

German Evangelical Lutheran Congregation, U. A. C., of St. Louis, Mo. Die Wucherfrage: Protokoll d. Verhandlungen d. deutsch ev.-luth. Gemeinde U. A. C. zu St. Louis, Mo. 8°. '69. 30c. *Barthel.*
German fairy tales. *See* Grimm, J. L. *and* W. C.
German literature; as exemplified by works of Tieck, Hoffman, Richter, Pichler and Zschokke. cr. 8°. $1; pap., 75c. .... *Scribner, W. & A.*
German lyrics. Brooks, C. T. $1.25 ...... * *Osgood.*
German political leaders. Tuttle, H. $1.50.. *Putnam.*
German popular tales. *See* Grimm, J. L. *and* W. C.
German romance. *See* Carlyle, T.
German tales. Auerbach, B. $1.25 .... *Holt.*
Gerok, C. On Acts. *See* Lange, J. P.
Gerok, K: Drei Lieder. [With music by C. Wonnberger.] obl. 4°. pap., 25c. .... *Brobst.*
Gerolstein. *See* Sue, E.
Gersoni, H: Sketches of Jewish life. 16°. 75c... *Bloch.*
Gerstäcker, F: Novels and tales; tr. from the Germ. 4 v. 16°. hf. roxb., $5 .... *Routledge.*
Cont.: Two convicts. — Feathered arrow. — Each for himself. — A wife to order.

— Blauen (Die) u. Gelben. 8°. pap., 50c... *Morwitz.*
— Flatbootmann (Der). 12°. '65. pap., 40c... *Steiger.*
— Franctireurs (Die). *See* Pitawall, C., Gabriele.
— Frank Wildman's adventures on land and water; tr. ill. 16°. $1 .... *Routledge.*
— *Same.* 16°. $1.25 .... *Nichols & H.*
— *Same.* ill. 12°. $1.25 .... *Lippincott.*
— How a bride was won; or, a chase across the Pampas; tr. ill. 8°. $1.50; pap., $1 .... *Appleton.*
— Im Eckfenster. 8°. pap., 50c. .... *Morwitz.*
— Loch (Das) in der Hose. 12°. '66. pap., 25c. *Steiger.*
— Narrative of a journey round the world; tr. 12°. $1.50 .... *Harper.*
— Two convicts (The); tr. 16°. bds., 80c... *Routledge.*
— Verschleierte Dame (Die). 12°. '73. pap., 20c. *Zickel.*
— Wild sports in the far west; tr. ill. 16°. $1.. *Routledge.*
— *Same.* 16°. $1.25 .... *Nichols & H.*
— *Same.* 12°. $1.25 .... *Lippincott.*
— Young gold-diggers; tr. ill. 16°. 75c.... *Routledge.*

Gerstäcker, F: *continued.*
— Young whaler; or, the adventures of Charles Holberg; tr. ill. 16°. $1 .... *Routledge.*
Gertie's sacrifice. Gage, F. D. 50c...... *Nat. Temp.*
Gertrude. *See* Sewell, E. M.
Gertrude, the peace-maker. 18°. 25c.; 30c... *Am. Bapt.*
Gertrude and her cat. *See* Books of blessing.
Gertrude of Wyoming. *See* Campbell, T:
Gertrude Terry. Graham, M. $1.35 ...... *Pres. Bd.*
Gertrude's cherries. Jerrold, D. 15c. .... *French.*
Gertrude's money box. Lemon, H. 15c. *De Witt; French.*
Gerty and May. Selous, H. C. $1 .... *Lee & S.*
Gerty and May books. 4 v. 18°. '67. $1.25. *Meth. Bk. Conc.*
Cont.: Joy House and its treasures. — Pleasant picnic. — Little Billy. — Christmas tree.

Gerty Harding's mission. Davis, C. E. K. $1.15.. *Hoyt.*
Gerty's Christmas. *See* Sunbeam ser.
Gerum, Henri. Motettes. [Music.] 4°. $1. — Voice parts. 50c. .... *Church.*
Gerusalemme liberata. *See* Tasso, T.
Gervase Castonel. Wood, E. P. $1.25; 25c... *Dick & F.*
Gervase Skinner. *See* Hook, Thdr.
Gervinus, G: Gf. Introduction to hist. of 19th cent.; tr. 12°. (Bohn.) 40c. .... *Scribner, W. & A.*
— *Same.* 12°. (Bohn.) 75c. .... *Lippincott.*
— Shakespeare commentaries; tr. by F. E. Bunnett; with pref. by F. J. Furnivall. 8°. $5.25. *Scribner, W. & A.*
Gesandschaftsreise (Die) nach China. *See* Van der Velde, K. F.
Gesangbuch f. d. Sonntag-Schulen d. ev.-luth. u. deutsch ref. Kirchen in d. Ver. St. 32°. 25c. *Brobst.*
Gesänge für Sonntag-Schulen. sq. 16°. '67. 30c.; pap., 25c. .... *Am. Tr.*
Geschenkbuch zum hl. Christfest. 24°. 25c. *Ev. Assoc.*
Geschichte (Die) des Johann. 24°. 25c... *Ev. Assoc.*
Geschichte e. jungen Malers. Baron, R. 25c... *Steiger.*
Geschichte e. verlorenen Börse, od. Hannchen u. ihre Freunde. 18°. 45c. .... *Ev. Assoc.*
Geschichte v. d. gehörnten Siegfried. 12°. pap., 15c. *Radde; F. W. Thomas.*
Geschichte v. d. hl. Pfalzgräfin Genoveva. 12°. pap., 15c. .... *F. W. Thomas.*
— *See also* Genoveva.
Geschichten aus dem Spessart. Caspari, K. H. 25c. *Morwitz.*
Geschichten des Pfarrers Siebentisch. Stöber, K. 25c. *Morwitz.*
Gesenius, F: H: W: Hebrew and Chaldee lexicon; tr. and ed. with add. and cor. by S. P. Tregelles. sm. 4°. (Bagster.) hf. bd., $7 .... *Wiley.*
— Hebrew and Eng. lexicon of Old Test., incl. the Biblical Chaldee; tr. by E. Robinson. ('36-'44.) New ed. 8°. '49-'54. hf. mor., $7.50... *Crocker.*
— Hebrew grammar; ed. by Rödiger; tr. by Conant; with index. 8°. $3 .... *Appleton.*
— *Same;* tr. with add. and Hebrew chrestomathy by M. Stuart. 8°. '46. $1.25 .... *Draper.*
— *Same;* with Heb. reading book. sm. 4°. (Bagster.) $3.25. — Same; with J. Lloyd's Analysis of first eleven chapters of Genesis. $4.50 .... *Wiley.*
— Hebrew lexicon; [ed.] by S. P. Tregelles. 4°. (Bagster.) hf. bd., $7 .... *Wiley.*
— — Index. *See* Potter, J. L.
Gespenst (Das). *See* Dedenroth, E. H. v.
Gess, W. F. *See* Foundations of our faith.
Gesta Romanorum; or, entertaining moral stories; with obs. and notes by Rev. C. Swan. New ed., with introd. by T. Wright. 2 v. 12°. '72. large pap., $10 .... *Bouton.*

Gesunde Speise f. d. Jugend. [Tales.] 18°. 45c. *Ev. Assoc.*

Get thee behind me, Satan. Logan, O. $1.50. *Adams, V. & Co.*

Getchell, F. H. Maternal management of infancy. 18°. 75c. . . . . *Lippincott.*

Gethsemane. Nebelin, C. E. $1.25 . . . . *Lothrop.*

Getreue Seelenhirte (Der). *See* Haas, N.

Getting on in the world. Mathews, W. $2; $2.50; $3.50; $5 . . . . *Griggs.*

Getting rich. *See* Aunt Alice's lib.

Getting square on the call boy. White, C. 15c. . . *De Witt.*

Getting to Paris. Williams, F. S. $1.75 . . . . *Lee & S.*

Getze, J. A. School for the parlor organ, melodeon and harmonium. f°. '69. bds., $2.50 . . *Ditson.*

— Tara's harp: songs and glees for youth. obl. 16°. '58. bds., 50c. . . . . *Ditson.*

— Young organist: instructor for the organ. f°. '59. bds., $2.50 . . . . *Ditson.*

— Zion's harp. obl. 12°. '60. bds., 60c. . . . . *Ditson.*

— *See also* Jarvis, C., *and* Getze, J. A.

Geyelin, G: Kennedy. Poultry breeding in a commercial point of view, as carried out by the National Poultry Co. (limited), Bromley, Kent; with pref. by Charles L. Flint. ill. 12°. $1.25 . . . . *Judd.*

Geyer, And. (*ed.*) Stationer's price book for use of the wholesale and retail trade, and for commercial travellers. nar. 12°. (cop. '74.) '76. leath., $2.50 . . . . *H. Lockwood.*

Geyer Wälty. *See* Hoffmann, F.

G'hals of New York. Judson, E. Z. C. 50c. . . *De Witt.*

Ghiberti, Lorenzo. Gates of the Baptistery at Florence: 34 photog. prints with descriptive text. [18 x 42 in.] '74. $30 . . . . *Y. S. of F. Arts.*

Ghost (The): comedy. 12°. '68. 50c. . . *Kelly, P. & Co.*

Ghost (The): Ethiop. drama. White, C. 15c. . . *De Witt.*

Ghost hunter. *See* Banim, J. *and* M.

Ghost in a pawnshop. Mackey, —. 15c. . . . *De Witt.*

Ghost of Bone Squash: Ethiop. drama. 16°. pap., 15c. . . . . *Happy.*

Ghost-seer (The). *See* Schiller, J. F. v.

Ghost stories. ill. 8°. pap., 25c. . . . . *Peterson.*

Giacometti, Paolo. Marie Antoinette: drama. 16°. pap., 15c. . . . . *French.*

Giant cities of Bashan. *See* Porter, J. L.

Giant conquered. *See* Gem cluster.

Giant judge. Scott, W. A. $1 . . . . *Pres. Bd.*

Giant killer. *See* Tucker, *Mrs.* C.

Giant land; or, the wonderful adventures of King Pippin. ill. 8°. (Lond.) 75c. . . . . *Am. News.*

Giants and wonderful things. Newton, R. $1.25. *Carter.*

Gibb, *Miss* —. Morag: tale of Highland life. 16°. $1.25 . . . . *Carter.*

— *Same.* 12°. '73. $1.25 . . . . *Meth. Bk. Conc.*

Gibbon, C: [Novels.] 4 v. 8°. ea., pap., 50c. *Harper.*

Cont.: For the king. — For lack of gold. — In honor bound. — Robin Gray.

Gibbon, E: History of the decline and fall of the Roman empire. (Chandos lib.) 3 v. 12°. ea., $1.75; hf. cf., $3.75; cf., $5 . . . . *Scribner, W. & A.*

— *Same;* with notes by F. Guizot. 2 v. imp. 8°. shp., $7 . . . . *Pounsford.*

— — *Same.* ('49.) 4th ed. 2 v. maps and eng. roy. 8°. '70. hf. mor., $16 . . . . *Virtue.*

— *Same;* with notes by H. H. Milman, and index. (Crown ed.) 6 v. por. 12°. '75. $6; $7.50; shp., $9; hf. cf, $18 . . . . *Claxton.*

— — *Same.* (Standard ed.) 6 v. por. 12°. $6; shp., $9; hf. cf., $18 . . . . *Porter.*

— — *Same.* (Standard ed.) 6 v. ill. 12°. $9; shp., $12; hf. cf., $19.50 . . . . *Appleton.*

Gibbon, E: *continued.*

— — *Same.* 6 v. 12°. $9; shp., $12; hf. cf., $19.50. *Lippincott.*

— *Same;* with notes, by H. H. Milman and F. Guizot, and index. 6 v. 12°. $6; shp., $8.40; hf. cf., $16.50 . . . . *Harper.*

— — *Same;* with add. notes, by W: Smith. 8 v. por. and maps. 8°. (Lond.) '62. $22.50; hf. cf., $40; cf., $48 . . . . *Little, B. & Co.*

— *Same;* with notes, incl. those of Guizot, Wenck, Niebuhr, etc., with index; ed. by an English Churchman. 7 v. 12°. (Bohn.) ea., $1.25. *Little, B. & Co.*

— — *Same.* 7 v. 12°. (Bohn.) ea., $1.40. *Scribner, W. & A.*

— — *Same.* 7 v. 12°. (Bohn.) ea., $1.50 . . *Lippincott.*

— Life, correspondence, etc.; with index. (Chandos lib.) 12°. $1.75; hf. cf., $3.75; cf., $5. *Scribner, W. & A.*

Gibbons, *Rev.* Ja. Faith of our fathers: exposition and vindication of the church founded by Christ. roy. 18°. pap., 50c. . . . . *Murphy.*

Gibbons, Ja. S. Banks of New York: their dealers, the Clearing House and the panic of 1857. ('58.) 10th ed. ill. 12°. '73. $2.50 . . *Appleton; Homans.*

— Public debt of the U. S.: its organization, its liquidation, administration of the Treasury, etc. 12°. '67. $2 . . . . *Scribner.*

Gibbs, G: Alphabetical vocab. of the Clallam and Lummi; — of the Chinook lang. *See* Shea, J. G., Lib. of Am. ling.

— Dictionary of the Chinook jargon, or trade language of Oregon. 8°. '63. pap., $2 . . . . *Shea.*

— *Same.* 8°. '63. pap., 50c. . . . . *Smith. Inst.*

— — *See also* Shea, J. G., Lib. of Am. ling.

— Instructions for ethnology and philology. 8°. '63. pap., 25c. . . . . *Smith. Inst.*

Gibbs, G: C. *See* Michigan, Sup. Court reports.

Gibbs, J. W. Latin analyst. 12°. '58. *net*, 50c. . . *Peck.*

— Philological studies. 12°. *net*, 75c . . . . *Peck.*

— Teutonic etymology. 16°. '60. *net*, 50c. . . . *Peck.*

Gibbs, Jos. Cotton cultivation in its various details. pl. cr. 8°. '62. $3 . . . . *Spon.*

Gibbs, T: F. Charley Bartlett's adventures. ('74.) New ed. 16°. '75. $1.25 . . . . *Hoyt.*

Gibbs, W., *and* Genth, F. A. Ammonia cobalt bases. 4°. '56. pap., $1 . . . . *Smith. Inst.*

Giberne, Agnes. Aimée: tale of James II. 16°. $1.50. *Carter.*

— Coulyng Castle. 16°. $1.50 . . . . *Carter.*

— Curate's home. 16°. $1.25 . . . . *Carter.*

— Day star; or, Gospel stories. 16°. $1.25 . . . *Carter.*

— *Same.* ill. 12°. $1.25 . . . . *Nelson.*

— Drusie's own story. 12°. $1.50 . . . . *Pott.*

— Floss Silverthorn. 16°. $1.25 . . . . *Carter.*

— Lost (The) found. ill. 16°. '76. 60c. . . . *Lothrop.*

— Mists of the valley. ill. 16°. '73. $1 . . . . *Dodd.*

— Not forsaken; or, the old home in the city. ('73.) New ed. 16°. '75. $1.25 . . . . *Hoyt.*

Gibert, *Mme.* M. Elementary French reader. 12°. '75. 40c. . . . . *Witter.*

— French pronounc. gram. for young students; with vocab. ('67.) New ed. 12°. '76. 90c. . . . *Holt.*

— Second French reader: Robinson Crusoe, abridg., with key. 12°. '71. 75c. . . . . *Witter.*

Gibraltar gallery. Abbott, J. 90c. . . . . *Harper.*

Gibson, R: H. The American dyer: treatise on coloring of wool, cotton, yarn and cloth. 8°. '73. $10 . . . . *Baird; Freeman.*

Gibson, S. Manual of sign, carriage and decorative painting. 12°. pap., 50c. . . . . *Haney.*

Gibson, W: Institutes and practice of surgery. 8th ed., rev. 2 v. ill. 8°. leath., $6.50 . . . . *Lea.*

Gideon. *See* Life of.

Gideon's rock. Saunders, K. $1 . . . . *Lippincott.*

Gieseler, J: C. L. Text-book of church hist.; tr. from 4th rev. Germ. ed. by S. Davidson and J. W. Hull. New Am. ed., rev. and ed. by H. B. Smith. [To form 5 v.] v. 1–4. 8°. ea., $2.25; shp., $2.75 .... *Harper.*

Giffe, W. T. Brilliant (The): cluster of song brilliants for Sunday schools. ('74.) 3d ed. obl. 16°. per doz., $3.60 .... *Benham.*

— Favorite (The); for sing. school conventions, etc. ('75.) 7th ed. obl. 12°. per doz., $7.50 .. *Benham.*

Gifford, E. H. Glory of God in man: sermons. fp. 8°. '65. $1 .... *Macmillan.*

— Voices of the prophets: lectures. cr. 8°. $2.50. *Scribner, W. & A.*

Gift, Theo. (*pseud.*) *See* Havers, *Miss* Dora.

Gift book for the million. Heisler, D. Y. $1. *Ref. Ch. Pub.*

Gift for mourners. Cecil, R., *and* Flavel, J. 25c. *Am. Tr.*

Gift for my Sunday school scholars; or, S.-school teaching carried into daily life. 18°. 40c... *Am. S. S.*

Gift for a pet. *See* Pearl ser.

Gift for the Well-spring children. 18°. 75c... *Cong. Pub.*

Gift for you: selections of prose and poetry. 12°. $1.50 *Locke.*

Gift for young ladies. Vernon, E. *net*, 19c... *Hamersley.*

Gift for young men. Hawes, J. *net*, 28c... *Hamersley.*

Gift lib. 3 v. 18°. $2 .... *Dutton.*

Cont.: Take heed, by Aunt Fanny.—Mark, the fisher boy, by Mrs. D. P. Sanford.—Little Nan, by F. F. G.; Neddie's care, by Minn.

Gift lib. 5 v. ill. 18°. $2 .... *Hoyt.*

Cont.: Little Gracie, by Mrs. J. S. Barrows.—Annie Lyon.—Dream of heaven.—Three Christmas days, by Mrs. E. H. Morse.—Emigrant's son.

Gift of Jesus. Reid, William. 40c. .... *Hoyt.*

Gift of the knees; or, the ministry of prayer the ministry of power. 16°. $1.25 .... *Bost. Am. Tr.*

Gift of love. 24°. $1.50 .... *Locke.*

Gift of piety. *See* Diamond miniatures.

Gift of power. Platt, S. H. $1.25. *Hope; Meth. Bk. Conc.*

Gift of remembrance. 24°. $1.50 .... *Locke.*

Giftie, the changeling. Coleridge, C. 25c. *Scribner, W. & A.*

Gifts for little ones. *See* Nursery lib.

Gihan, A. L. (*ed.*) Medical essays. *See* United States, *Bureau of Med. and Surg.*

Gihon, Ja. L. Freemasonry: its origin and spread in the old world, its introd. into Am., with descript. of new temple at Phila. ill. 16°. $1 .... *Souder.*

Gil Blas. *See* Lesage, A. R.

Gil Blas. Macfarren, G. 15c. .... *French.*

Gilbart, Ja. W. History and principles of banking. ('60.) 2d ed. 8°. '76. shp., $5 .... *Baird.*

— Practical treatise on banking. 4th Am. ed. 8°. '75. shp., $5 .... *Homans.*

— Principles and practice of banking. 8°. $8. *Scribner, W. & A.*

— Ten minutes advice on keeping a bank. *See* Banker's common-place book.

Gilbert, Clayton H. Rescued: temperance drama. 16°. pap., 15c. .... *Ames.*

Gilbert, D. Love of Jesus; or, visits to the blessed sacrament for every day in the month; [also] Devotion of the forty hours; with introd. by an Am. clergyman. 32°. '71. 50c.; 75c. ...... *Murphy.*

Gilbert, Fk. Relations of railroads to the people, as set forth in the U. S. Const. and decisions of Ill., etc.; with introd. by J. M. Palmer and app. 8°. '73. shp., $3.50 .... *Callaghan.*

Gilbert, G. K. Report on geol. of Nev., Utah, etc. *See* United States, *Corps of Eng.*

Gilbert, *Sir* Jeffrey. Forum Romanum: history and practice of the High Court of Chancery. Am. ed., ed. by S. Tyler. 8°. '74. $4 .... *Morrison.*

Gilbert, *Sir* J: (ill.) *See* Shakespeare, W.;—Bible, Proverbs.

Gilbert, T., *and* Prass, F. Writing reader; compr. in different hand-writings sel. from standard authors. 8°. '58. hf. roan, $1.25 .... *D. Thomas.*

Gilbert, Wa. B. Church chorister: a manual for training singing boys. 18°. '70. $1 .... *Dutton.*

— Church music: services and anthems. 25 pts. 8°. '74. ea., pap., 15c.–50c.;—in 1 v. 8°. $6 .. *Dutton.*

— *See also* Protestant Episc. Ch., Revised hymnal.

Gilbert, W: De profundis: tale of the social deposits. cr. 8°. $2 .... *Routledge.*

— Dr. Austin's guest. cr. 8°. $2 .... *Routledge.*

— Magic mirror: a round of tales for old and young. ill. 12°. $2 .... *Routledge.*

— Struggle in Ferrara. ill. 8°. $1.50; pap., $1. *Lippincott.*

— Washerwoman's foundling. ill. sq. 16°. 75c. *Routledge.*

— Wizard of the mountain. 2 v. 8°. $5 ... *Routledge.*

Gilbert, W: S. "Bab" ballads; or, much sound and little sense. ill. 12°. $1.75 .... *Porter.*

— *Same.* 2 ser. ill. sm. 4°. ea., $3 .... *Routledge.*

— Gentleman in black: musical [dram.] legend. 16°. pap., 15c. .... *French.*

— Old score: comedy. 16°. pap., 15c. .... *French.*

— Original plays. 12°. '76. $1.75 .... *Scribner.*

— Princess (The): allegory. 16°. pap., 15c... *French.*

— *See also* Sullivan, A., *and* Gilbert, W. S.

Gilbert Gresham: an autobiog. 18°. 75c... *Am. S. S.*

Gilbert Gurney. *See* Hook, Thdr.

Gilbert Harland. Barwell, *Mrs.*—. 75c. *Meth. Bk. Conc.*

Gilbert Rugge. Jackson, H. $1 .... *Harper.*

Gilbert Starr and his lessons. *See* Bradley, W. I.

Gilbert's last summer at Rainford. *See* Bradley, W. I.

Gilbert's shadow. *See* Greene, *Mrs.* L. L.

Gilchrist, Alex. Life of William Blake (Pictor Ignotus); with sel. from his poems and other writings; with fac-simile ill. from his work. 2 v. 8°. '63. $10 .... *Macmillan.*

Gildas Badonicus *the Wise.* Chronicle. *See* Giles, J. A., Six old Eng. chronicles.

Gilded age. *See* Clemens, S. L., *and* Warner, C. D.

Gilded youth: drama. 16°. pap., 15c. ...... *French.*

Gilder, R: Watson. The new day: a poem in songs and sonnets. ('75.) New ed. ill. 12°. '76. $1.50. *Scribner.*

Gilderoy. Murray, W. H. 15c. .... *French.*

Gilderoy, the freebooter. 8°. pap., 25c. ...... *De Witt.*

Gilder's manual. 12°. pap., 50c. .... *Haney.*

Gildersleeve, Basil L. Latin exercise book. ('71.) New ed. 12°. '73. $1 .... *Univ. Pub.*

— Latin grammar. ('71.) New ed., rev. 12°. '72. $1.50 .... *Univ. Pub.*

— Latin primer. 12°. '75. 90c. .... *Univ. Pub.*

— Latin reader. 12°. '75. $1 .... *Univ. Pub.*

Gildersleeve, *Mrs.* C. H. The boy in blue: story of the late war. 12°. '66. $1.50 .... *Allison.*

Gilead. Smith, J. H. $1.50 .... *Scribner.*

Giles, Alfr. E. Sabbath question considered by a layman. 12°. '74. pap., 10c. .... *Colby.*

Giles, Chauncey. Gate of pearl. sq. 18°. $1 .. *New Ch.*

— Lectures on the incarnation, atonement and mediation of Christ. 12°. 75c.; pap., 40c... *Lippincott.*

— Lectures on nature of the Spirit; and of man as a spiritual being. 12°. $1.25; pap., 60c. *Lippincott.*

— Magic shoes (The). sq. 16°. $1 .... *New Ch.*

— Magic spectacles (The). sq. 18°. $1 ...... *New Ch.*

— Wonderful pocket (The). sq. 16°. $1 .... *New Ch.*

Giles, *Miss* Ella A. Bachelor Ben. 12°. $1.50..*Atwood.*
— *Same.* 2d ed. 12°. '75. $1.50............*Jansen.*
— Out from the shadows. 12°. $1.50..........*Atwood.*
— *Same.* ('75.) 2d ed. 12°. '76. $1.50......*Jansen.*

Giles, H: Human life in Shakespeare. 12°. $2..*Lee & S.*
— Lectures. 12°. $2–$3....................*Sadlier.*

Giles, J. A. (*ed.*) Six old Eng. chronicles; with notes. 12°. (Bohn.) $1.75............*Little, B. & Co.*

Cont.: Life of King Alfred, by J. Asser; Chronicle, by F. Ethelwerd; British hist., by Geoffrey of Monmouth; Chronicle, by St. Gildas the wise; Hist. of the Britons, by A. Nennius; Ancient state of Britain, by Richard of Cirencester.

— *Same.* 12°. (Bohn.) $2. *Lippincott; Scribner, W. & A.*

Giles Oldham. Tucker, C. 75c.............*Carter.*

Giles's minority. O'Reilly, R. $1...........*Dutton.*

Gilfillan, G: Bards of the Bible. 12°. $1.25..*Harper.*
— Life of Walter Scott. 12°. $1.25..........*Nelson.*
— Martyrs and heroes of the covenant. 16°. $1..*Carter.*

Gilfillan, Ja. Sabbath viewed in the light of reason, revelation and history. 12°. '63. $1.25..*Am. Tr.*

Gill, J: Infant baptism a part and pillar of popery; rev. and ed. by G. B. Ide. 18°. 35c...*Am. Bapt.*

Gill, Ma. Harvey. Hours with the youngest; or, a year in the infant school. 2 v. 16°. '64–'66. ea., $1.25..........................*Randolph.*
— Text and hymns for the youngest. 18°. '64. 15c. *Randolph.*

Gill, R. W. *See* Maryland, Court of Appeals reports.

Gill, Thdr. Catalogue of fishes. 8°. '75. pap., 25c. *Smith. Inst.*
— Families of mollusks. 8°. '71. pap., 25c...*Smith. Inst.*
— List of families of fishes. 8°. '72. pap., 25c. *Smith. Inst.*
— List of families of mammals. 8°. '72. pap., 25c. *Smith. Inst.*
— Primary subdivisions of the cetaceans. 8°. '71. 25c. *Essex.*
— Prodrome of a monograph of finnipedes. 8°. '66. 25c.................................*Essex.*

Gill, T: H. A golden chain of praise. [Hymns.] 12°. '69. $2.25........................*Randolph.*

Gill, *Rev.* W: Gems from the coral islands: East. Polynesia. ill. 12°. $1.25. — Same: West. Polynesia. ill. 12°. $1.10......................*Pres. Bd.*

Gill, W: F. Home recreations. ill. 16°. '74. $1.50. *W. F. Gill.*
— The martyred church. ill. sm. 4°. '73. $2..*W. F. Gill.*

Gill, *Rev.* W: I. Analytical processes; or, the primary principle of philosophy. (Intern. prize ser.) 12°. '76. $2..............................*Authors.*
— Evolution and progress: exposition and defence, with review of leading opponents. ('74.) 3d ed. 12°. '75. $1.50..........................*Authors.*

Gillespie, W: System of progressive penmanship. 6 nos. 4°. '60. per doz., $1.50..........*Murphy.*

Gillespie, W: M. Manual of the principles and practice of roadmaking; ed. by C. Staley. ('71.) 10th ed., enl. 12°. $2.50.............*Barnes.*
— Practical treatise on surveying. ill. 8°. $3..*Appleton.*
— Treatise on levelling, topography and higher surveying; ed. by Cady Staley. 8°. $2.50..*Appleton.*

Gillet, J. H. *See* Rolfe, W. J., *and* Gillet, J. H.

Gillett, E. H. Ancient cities and empires: their prophetic doom read in the light of hist. and modern research. 12°. $1.25................*Pres. Bd.*
— Commemorative discourse: sermon on character and labors of Rev. Jeremiah S. Lord, April 18, 1869. 8°. pap., 25c..............*N. Y. Ref. Ch. Bd.*
— England two hundred years ago. 16°. $1.50..*Pres. Bd.*
— God in human thought; or, natural theology traced in literature; with Eng. bibliog. from Spenser to Butler. 2 v. 8°. '74. $5............*Scribner.*
— History of the Presb. Church in United States. 2 v. 12°. $5............................*Pres. Bd.*

Gillett, E. H., *continued.*
— Life and times of John Huss; or, the Bohemian reform. of 15th cent. 2 v. 8°. '61. $7..*Randolph.*
— Life lessons in the school of Christian duty. 12°. $1.10................................*Pres. Bd.*
— Moral system (The); with hist. and crit. introd., with special reference to Butler's "Analogy." 12°. '74. $1.25.......................*Scribner.*
— What then? or, the soul's to-morrow. 32°. 25c.; pap., 15c...................................*Pres. Bd.*
— *See also* Pictorial life.

Gillett, Ransom H. Federal government (The): its offices and their duties. 8°. shp., $5. — 12°. $2. *Potter, A. & Co.*
— Life and times of Silas Wright. 2 v. ill. 8°. '74. $10; $12..............................*Argus.*

Gillies, J: Life and sermons of George Whitefield; ed. by C. E. Stowe. por. and ill. 8°. $4. — 12°. $1.50....................................*Sower.*

Gillies, R. P. *See* Stoddard, R. H., Bric-a-brac ser.

Gilliland, W. History of the Champlain valley: account of settlement of Willsborough [Essex Co., N. Y.]; with memoir and notes by W. C. Watson. 8°. '63. hf. cf., $3.50...........*Munsell.*

Gilliss, J. R. Tunnels of the Pacific R. R. 8°. pap., $1........................*Am. Soc. of C. E.*

Gilliss, Ja. Melville. Eclipse of the sun, Sept. 7, 1858. 4°. '59. pap., 50c..........*Smith. Inst.*
— United States naval astronomical expedition to the south. hemisphere, 1849–'52. v. 1–3, 6. 4°. '55–'56..................................*U. S. Govt.*

Cont.: 1. Chili, its geog., climate, etc. — 2. The Andes and pampas, by A. MacRae; Minerals, by J. L. Smith; Indian remains, by T. Ewbank; Mammals, by S. F. Baird; Birds, by J. Cassin; Reptiles, fishes and crustacea, by C. Girard; Shells, by A. A. Gould; Dried plants, by A. Gray; Living plants and seeds, by W. D. Brackenridge; Fossil mammals, by J. Wyman; Fossil shells, by T. A. Conrad. — 3. Observations to determine the solar parallax, by J. M. Gilliss. — 6. Magnetical and meteorol. obs., by J. M. Gilliss.

— *Same.* 2 v. ill. 4° $9................*Lippincott.*

Gillmore, Parker. ["Ubique."] Gun, rod and saddle. 12°. $1............................*Woodward.*
— Prairie and forest: description of the game of N. Am., with personal adventures in their pursuit. ill. 12°. $1.50........................*Harper.*
— *See also* Biart, L., Adventures of a young naturalist.

Gillmore, Q. A. Coignet-béton and other artificial stone. pl. 8°. '71. $2.50.......*Van Nostrand.*
— — *See also* United States, *Corps of Eng.*
— Official report of operations against defences of Charleston harbor, 1863. pl., views, maps, etc. 8°. '65. $10; hf. mor., $12.....*Van Nostrand.*
— *Same.* Supplementary report. ill., maps and views. 8°. '68. $5...................*Van Nostrand.*
— Practical treatise on construction of roads, streets and pavements. 12°. '76. $2....*Van Nostrand.*
— Practical treatise on limes and hydraulic cements, and mortars; cont. reports of experiments in N. Y. city, 1858–'61. 5th ed., rev. and enl. ill. 8°. '74. $4.........................*Van Nostrand.*
— — *See also* United States, *Corps of Eng.*
— Report on strength of the building stones in the U. S., etc. 8°. '76. $1.50.............*Van Nostrand.*
— Siege and reduction of Fort Pulaski, Georgia, March–April, 1862. maps and views. 8°. '62. $2.50. *Van Nostrand.*
— — *See also* United States, *Corps of Eng.*

Gilman, Arth. First steps in Eng. literature. 7th ed. 16°. '74. $1...........................*Hurd & H.*
— First steps in general hist. maps and charts. 2d ed. 16°. '74. $1.25.....................*Hurd & H.*
— Line of John Gilman, of Exeter, N. H.; with account of other Gilmans in Eng. and Am. por. sq. 8°. '69. $5..................................*Munsell.*
— Seven historic ages: talks about kings, queens and barbarians. ill. 16°. '73. $1........*Hurd & H.*

Gilman, B. F. Pencillings by the seashore. 16°. $1.25. *Cong. Pub.*

Gilman, C. *See* Illinois, Supreme Court reports.

Gilman, *Mrs.* Caro. Poetic fate book: oracles from the poets. 16°. 75c.; hf. bd., 60c....... *Lee & S.*

— Recollections of a southern matron and a New Eng. bride. 12°. $1.75................. *J. E. Potter.*

— Young fortune-teller: oracles for youth. 16°. 75c.; hf. bd., 60c........................ *Lee & S.*

— *and* Jervey, *Mrs.* C. H. Stories and poems. ill. 4°. $1.75.......................... *Lee & S.*

Gilman, *Mrs.* Mar. (*pseud.*) *See* Barnard, C. F., *jr.*

Gilmer, F. W. *See* Virginia, Court of Appeals reports.

Gilmor, Harry. Four years in the saddle. 12°. $2. *Harper.*

Gilmore, J. H. New Sunday school speaker. 18°. '71. 60c. .... *H. A. Young.*

— Outlines of art of expression. 2d ed. 12°. '76. $1.25............................ *Ginn.*

Gilmore, *Rev.* J: Storm warriors: life-boat work on the Goodwin Sands. cr. 8°. '73. $1.75.. *Macmillan.*

Gilmore, J: R. ["Edm. Kirke."] Life of Jesus, accord. to his orig. biographers. 16°. $1.50.. *Lee & S.*

— On the border. 12°. $1.75.............. *Lee & S.*

Gilmore, P. S. History of the National Peace Jubilee, and musical festival in Boston, June, 1869. ill. 8°. *$5.............................. *Lee & S.*

Gilmour, R: Bible hist.; for Cath. schools. map and ill. 12°. 60c.; 30c................. *Benziger.*

— Catholic national readers. 4 v. 12°...... *Benziger.*
Cont.: First reader, 25c.—Second, 40c.—Third, 75c.—Fourth, $1.

— *See also* Protestantism or Catholicism.

Gilpin, Bern. Life. 18°. 35c. .... *Am. S. S.*

Gilpin, H. D. *See* United States, Dist. Ct. reports.

Gilpin, W: Grain, pastoral and gold regions of N. Am. 8°. $2.50 .... *Sower.*

— Mission of the No. Am. people, geog., social and political; with charts. 8°. $4.50.... *Lippincott.*

Gilray, Ja. Works; with story of his life and times, and descrip. of his engravings; ed. by T. Wright. pl. and wood-eng. 4°. $12.60; mor., $28. *Scribner, W. & A.*

Gilson, Adr. Czar and sultan; or, Nicholas and Abdul Medjid, their private lives and public actions; [also] The Turks in Europe, their rise and decadence, by F. Bouvet. 16°. 75c.... *Harper.*

Gingerbread. [Toy-book.] ill. 4°. $1; 50c... *Routledge.*

Ginx's baby. *See* Jenkins, E.

Giorg, Kara. Poesien des Urwalds. 12°. $1.. *Benziger.*

Giorza, P. Mass in F: vocal music with organ accomp. 8°. *net*, pap., $3.................. *Schirmer.*

Giovanni in London. Moncrieff, W. T. 15c... *French.*

Gipsies (The); or, friends in need. 18°. 25c.; 30c. *Am. Bapt.*

Gipsy (The). *See* James, G. P. R.

Gipsy chief. Reynolds, G. W. M. $1.75; $1. *Peterson.*

Gipsy farmer. Johnstone, J. B. 15c........ *French.*

Gipsy Fred. Hoffmann, F. $1.25 ...... (?) *Martien.*

Gipsy Fred ser. 4 v. 16°. $5 .... (?) *Martien.*
Cont.: Gipsy Fred.—Archie's keys.—Subtle spell.—Oakville dove's nest.

Gipsy girl. *See* Hall, M.

Gipsy in New York. Pollard, J. 90c... *Meth. Bk. Conc.*

Gipsy Jack. Moncrieff, W. T. 15c........ *French.*

Gipsy Jem; or, Willie's revenge. 18°. 50c. (?) *Martien.*

Gipsy's adventures. Pollard, J. 90c... *Meth. Bk. Conc.*

Gipsy's daughter. Grey, E. C. 50c........ *Peterson.*

Gipsy's early days. Pollard, J. 90c... *Meth. Bk. Conc.*

Gipsy's prophecy. Southworth, E. D. E. N. $1.75; $1.50.............................. *Peterson.*

Gipsy's quest. Pollard, J. 90c...... *Meth. Bk. Conc.*

Gipsy's travels. Pollard, J. 90c. .... *Meth. Bk. Conc.*

Gipsy's warning. Dupuy, E. A. $1.75 .... *Peterson.*

Giraffe hunters (The). Reid, M. $1.50 ..... *Miller.*

Giralda. Welstead, H. 15c................ *French.*

Giraldus de Barri *Cambrensis.* Historical works; ed. by T. Wright, with index. 12°. (Bohn.) $1.75. *Little, B. & Co.*

— *Same.* 12°. (Bohn.) $2. *Lippincott; Scribner, W. & A.*

Girard, C: Fresh-water fishes of N. Am. 4°. '51. pap., $1.50............................ *Smith. Inst.*

— Herpetology of the U. S. exploring expedition, 1838–'42, under Com. Wilkes; with col. pl. 2 v.: text, 4°; pl., f°. $30........... *Claxton; Lippincott.*

— — *See also* Wilkes, C: U. S. explor. expedition.

— Reptiles, fishes and crustacea. *See* Gilliss, J. M.

— *See also* Baird, S. F., *and* Girard, C.

Girard, Pl. E. Book of French verbs: new system of conjugation. 12°. '70. pap., 50c. ..... *Claxton.*

— Complete Fr. class-book. 12°. '70. $1.75.. *Claxton.*

— French grammar; with exercises and conversational lessons. 12°. '70. hf. roan, 90c. ...... *Claxton.*

— Progressive French reader. 12°. '70. hf. roan, $1. *Claxton.*

— Treatise on French pronunciation. 12°. '70. pap., 25c.................................. *Claxton.*

Girardin, *Mme.* Delphine de [*formerly Mlle.* Gay]. Clockmaker's hat: farce; tr. 16°. pap., 15c. *French.*

— Joie (La) fait peur: comédie. With Eng. notes by F. Bôcher. ('64.) New ed. 12°. '76. pap., 30c. *Holt.*

— Marguerite; or, the two loves; tr. by J. L. Starr. 8°. pap., 25c....................... *Appleton.*

— *See also* Cross of Berny.

Girardin, J. Adventures of Johnny Ironsides; tr. from the Fr. ill. 12°. '75. $1.75 .... *Routledge.*

Girardin, Saint-M: Lectures on dramatic literature. 12°. $1.25........................... *Appleton.*

Giraud, G. *See* Goldoni, C., Giraud, G., *and* Nata, A.

Girax, E. Appendix to Marx's "Musical composition." 12°. $1............................. *Gordon.*

Girding on the armor. Robbins, S. S. $1.25.. *Carter.*

Girl at the wheel: extravaganza. 16°. pap., 15c. *French.*

Girl he married. *See* Grant, Ja.

Girl of the family. Mackarness, M. A. $1.25.. *Routledge.*

Girl of the gibbet. 8°. pap., 25c............ *De Witt.*

Girl of the period. Linton, E. L. 10c....... *Redfield.*

Girlhood and womanhood. Keddie, H. $2.. *Routledge.*

Girlhood of celebrated women. Ashton, S. G. $1.50. *World Pub.*

Girlhood of Shakespeare's heroines. Clarke, M. C. 2 v. ea., $2.......................... *Putnam.*

Girlhood ser. 6 v. ill. 12°. ea., $1.50 ...... *Lee & S.*
Cont.: An American girl abroad, by A. Trafton.—Doctor's daughter, by S. May.—Sally Williams, by Mrs. E. D. Cheney.—Only girls, by V. F. Townsend.—Lottie Eames.—Rhoda Thornton's girlhood, by Mrs. M. E. Pratt.

Girl's adventures. *See* Yonge, C. M.

Girl's book. Sigourney, L. H. 60c.......... *Carter.*

Girl's money. Farman, E. $1............. *Lothrop.*

Girl's romance. Robinson, F. W. 50c...... *Harper.*

Girls of the period: burlesque. 16°. pap., 15c... *Happy.*

Girls' birthday-book: tales, essays and narratives. ill. 12°. $1.75 .... *Routledge.*

Girls' choice lib. 6 v. 18°. $3............ *Am. Bapt.*
Cont.: Cocoanut basket.—Nellie Newton.—Mary Howson.—Twin sisters.—Nothing to do.—Mary Mansfield, by G. E. Merrill.

Girls' packet. 32°. 25c..................... *Nelson.*

Girls' story book. *See* Theodore Thinker.

Giroflé-Girofla. *See* Ditson.

Gisippus. *See* Griffin, Ger.

Gist of spiritualism. Chase, W. 50c.......... *Colby.*

Gitanilla. Wilson, J. C. 15c.............. *French.*

Giuramento (Il). *See* Ditson.

Giuseppe's home. Mathews, J. A. $1.10.... *Carter.*

Giuseppo Balsamo. 12°. pap., 15c........... *Radde.*

Give a dog a bad name. Lawrence, S. 15c. *French; Lee & S.*

Give it up! no, never; or, the history of John Brook "who would never give in." 18°. 18c... *Am. S. S.*

Give me my wife. Suter, W. E. 15c... *Ames; French.*

Give us a pull. *See* Harland stories.

Giving to Jesus. *See* Kennedy, *Mrs.* M. G.

Glad tidings. Boyd, R. 75c.; 35c........... *Revell.*

Glad tidings. Emerson, L. O., *and* Starkweather, L. B. 35c.; 30c.......................... *Ditson.*

Glad tidings. Ingham, H. A. 50c.......... *Darrow.*

Glad tidings. Moody, D. L. $2; $1......... *Treat.*

Glad tidings. Simmons, H. E. 50c. .... *Am. Tr.*

Glad tidings. Tweedie, W. K. $1.25....... *Lothrop.*

Gladden, Wash. From the Hub to the Hudson (Hoosac Tunnel route); with sketches of nature, hist. and industry in n. w. Mass. ('69.) 2d ed. 16°. '70. 75c.................. *E. D. Merriam.*

— Plain thoughts on art of living. 16°. $1.50..* *Osgood.*

— Workingmen and their employers. cr. 8°. '76. $1.75. *Lockwood, B. & Co.*

Gladiators (The). Melville, G. J. W. 60c... *Appleton.*

Gladness in Jesus. Boardman, W. E. 75c... *Willard.*

Gladstone, *Mrs.* G: Boy who wondered; or, Jack and Minnchen. ill. fp. 8°. 75c............. *Cassell.*

— Sailing orders. ill. 16°. '73. 75c........... *Lothrop.*

— Stick to the raft. ill. 16°. '75. 60c........ *Lothrop.*

— Tom Gillies: the knots he tied and untied. 16°. $1.25................ *Cong. Pub.; H. A. Young.*

— *Same.* ill. 16°. '74. 75c.................. *Dutton.*

— Uncle Max, the soldier of the cross: a German tale. ill. 18°. '74. 50c....................... *Nelson.*

— *Same.* ill. 16°. '73. 75c.................. *Lothrop.*

— *Same.* ('73.) New ed. 16°. '75. $1........ *Hoyt.*

Gladstone, J. H. Life of M. Faraday. 16°. 90c. *Harper.*

— *Same.* por. cr. 8°. '73. $1.50........ *Macmillan.*

Gladstone, W: Ewart. Ecce homo. 12°. $1.50; pap., 75c.......................... *Routledge.*

— Homeric synchronism: enquiry into time and place of Homer. post 8°. '76. $2........... *Harper.*

— Italy and her church; with introd. by H. M. Thompson. 8°. '75. pap., 40c.............. *Brentano.*

— Juventus mundi: gods and men of the heroic age. 2d ed. map. cr. 8°. '70. $2.50..... *Macmillan.*

— *Same.* cr. 8°. '69. $2.50; hf. cf., $4.. *Little, B. & Co.*

— Rome and the newest fashions in religion; [compr.] The Vatican decrees, Vaticanism, Speeches of Pius IX. 8°. $1.75.................. *Harper.*

— Speeches of Pius IX. 8°. '75. $1.75...... *Harper.*

— Vatican decrees in their bearing on civil allegiance; with replies of Abp. Manning, Lord Acton and Mons. Capel. 8°. pap., 25c.......... *Appleton.*

— *Same;* [also] History of the Vatican council, by Rev. P. Schaff. 8°. '75. $1; pap., 60c... *Harper.*

— Vaticanism: answer to "Reproofs and replies." 8°. '75. pap., 40c....................... *Harper.*

— *and* Schaff, Ph. El papa y el poder civil; tr. 12°. '76. $1.50............................ *Am. Tr.*

Gladwyn, Gilb. On papa's lap; or, talks with my children. ill. 16°. 60c........... *Bost. Am. Tr.*

Glaister, Eliz. Markhams of Ollerton. ill. 16°. $1.. *Pott.*

Glance at New York: drama. 16°. pap., 15c... *French.*

Glance at philosophy. Goodrich, S. G. $1.. *Thompson.*

Glance at the sciences. Goodrich, S. G. $1.. *Thompson.*

Glance backward at missionary life in north India. Warren, J. 80c..................... *Pres. Bd.*

Glandon, Auguste. Young Brahmin's story. ill. 12°. $1.50 .... *Nelson.*

Glanmore; or, the bandits of Saratoga: romance of the revolution. 8°. pap., 25c...... *U. P. James.*

Glänzende Bahnen. *See* Silberstein, A:

Glass cable. Wilmer, M. E. $1.25...... *Nat. Temp.*

Glass cable ser. 4 v. 12°. $5............ *Nat. Temp.*
Cont.: Glass cable, by M. E. Wilmer. — Fire fighters, by J. E. McConaughy. — Dumb traitor, by M. E. Wilmer. — Nettie Loring, by G. S. Downs.

Glass of water. *See* Scribe, E.

Glass of water. Suter, W. E. 15c.......... *French.*

Glaubensklee, Thdr. G. Eclectic reader: sel. from Germ. authors. 12°. '57. 90c.......... *Ivison.*

— Synthetic gram. of German. 12°. '57. $1... *Ivison.*

Glauber Spa. *See* Tales of.

Gläubige Kaufmann (Der). 18°. 25c...... *Ev. Assoc.*

Glaubrecht, O: Anna, the leech-vender; tr. by Mrs. Clarke. 18°. 50c. .... *Pres. Bd.*

— Schreckensjahre. 16°. 25c............. *Morwitz.*

— Stumme (Die) v. Portici; [also] Johann v. Leyden, v. N. Hürte. 16°. 25c.............. *Morwitz.*

— Zigeuner (Der). 16°. 25c.............. *Morwitz.*

Glaucia. Leslie, E. $1.50 .... *Meth. Bk. Conc.*

Glaucus. *See* Kingsley, C.

Gleaners (The). 18°. '59. 40c........... *Randolph.*

Gleanings. Lunt, W. P. $1.50............... *Lunt.*

Gleanings among the sheaves. Spurgeon, C. H. $1.25. *Sheldon.*

Gleanings for the curious. *See* Bombaugh, C. C.

Gleanings for the drawing-room; in prose and verse. ill. 4°. '74. $3.......................... *Routledge.*

Gleanings from a Confederate army note-book. De Fontaine, F. G. $1 .... *Duffie.*

Gleanings from Gospel story. 18°. 55c..... *Am. S. S.*

Gleanings from memory; or, stories of my childhood; by a mother. 18°. 40c.............. *Am. S. S.*

Gleanings from real life. Egliseau, S. S. 60c. *Pres. Bd.*

Gleanings from science. Rich, A. B. 45c... *Cong. Pub.*

Gleanings from Scripture. Whitfield, F. 50c. *Leighton.*

Gleason, *Mrs.* R. B. Talks to my patients: handbook for the maid, wife and mother. 5th ed. 12°. '70. $1.50.................................. *Wood & H.*

Glee hive. Mason, L., *and* Webb, G. J. 75c... *Ditson.*

Gleichnisse (Die) des Herrn. ill. 8°. bds., 20c.; col., 30c............................... *Kohler.*

Gleig, G. R. History of the Bible. 2 v. map. 18°. $1.50................................ *Harper.*

— True story (A) of the battle of Waterloo. 12°. $1.50. *Harper.*

Glen cabin. *See* Chesebro', *Miss* C.

Glen Elder; or, the orphans: tale of Scottish life. ('68.) New ed. ill. 16°. '75. $1.15..... *Hoyt.*

Glen Elder books. 5 v. 16°. '68. $6.. *Meth. Bk. Conc.*
Cont.: Orphans of Glen Elder. — Frances Leslie. — Lyceum boys. — Harleys of Chelsea Place. — Rosa Lindesay.

Glen Elder lib.; by author of "Christie." 7 v. 16°. $6.65.............................. *Am. S. S.*
Cont.: Orphans of Glen Elder. — Christie; or, the way home, 2 v. — Little house in the hollow. — Shenac's work at home. — Story of little Gabriel. — Stephen Grattan's faith.

Glen Morris' stories. *See* Wise, Dan.

Glenarvon; or, holidays at the cottage. ill. 18°. '60. 85c................................. *Dodd.*

Glencoe parsonage. Porter, A. E. $1...... *Lothrop.*

Glencore and his fortunes. Lever, C. 50c... *Harper.*

Glendale ser. 4 v. 16°. $5........... *H. A. Young.*
Cont.: Tom Gillies, by Mrs. Geo. Gladstone.— Huntingdons, by M. L. Hayward. — Earl Whiting, by D. S. Erickson. — Clean your boots.

Glendenning, And. Tonnage table of ships and steamers according to builder's measurement. 12°. (Port-Glasgow.) 50c. .... *Spon.*

Glengall, *Lord.* [R: Butler.] Irish tutor: farce. 16°. pap., 15c.......................... *French.*

Glenn, S. F. *See* Louisiana, Reports.
Glennair. Hazlett, H. $1.50 .... *Claxton.*
Glennie, J. S. Stuart. *See* Stuart-Glennie, J. S.
Glenwood, Ida. Fatal secret. 12°. $2 .. *J. E. Potter.*
Gliddon, G: R. Ancient Egypt. 8°. pap., 25c. *Peterson.*
— *See also* Nott, J. C., *and* Gliddon, G. R.
Glimpse at the art of Japan. Jarves, J. J. $2.50; $3 .... *Hurd & H.*
Glimpse of the world. *See* Sewell, E. M.
Glimpses of animated nature. O'Neill, J. W. $3.50; $3.75; $4 .... *Desilver.*
Glimpses of the dark ages; rev. by T. O. Summers. ('56.) 2d ed. 18°. '76. 65c. .... *So. Meth.*
Glimpses of heaven; or, light beyond Jordan. 18°. 55c. .... *Am. S. S.*
Glimpses of history. Towle, G. M. $1.50 .. *Lee & S.*
Glimpses of Jesus. Balfern, W. P. 75c. .. *So. Bapt.*
Glimpses of life in Africa. Scott, A. M. 25c. *Am. Tr.*
Glimpses of life in soul-saving. Caughey, J. $2. *Palmer.*
Glimpses of our island home. Geldart, T. 75c. *Routledge.*
Glimpses of our lake region. Gardner, H. C. $1.50. *Meth. Bk. Conc.*
Glimpses of the past. *See* Tonna, *Mrs.* C. E.
Glimpses of photog. Himes, C. F. $1.25 .. *Benerman.*
Glimpses of pleasant homes; by author of "Life of Mother McCauley." 3d ed. ill. 12°. '69. $1.50. *Cath. Pub.*
Glimpses of Spain. Wallis, S. T. $1.50; $3.25 .. *Harper.*
Glimpses of the spirit land. Lloyd, S. H. $1.50. *Widdleton.*
Glimpses of the supernatural: facts, records and traditions. 12°. $2 .... *Carleton.*
Glimpses of west Africa. Whiton, S. J. 85c. *Bost. Am. Tr.*
Glimpses through. Biscoe, E. L. $1.50 .... *Lothrop.*
Glin Gath: drama. 16°. pap., 15c. .... *French.*
Glitter. A'Beckett, G. A. 15c. .... *French.*
Glitter and gold. Field, H. $2 .... *Lippincott.*
Gloag, Paton J. Commentary on Acts. 2 v. 8°. $10. *Scribner, W. & A.*
— Introduction to the Pauline Epistles. 8°. $6. *Scribner, W. & A.*
— Primeval world. cr. 8°. $1.50 ... *Scribner, W. & A.*
Gloam (*pseud.*) The breech-loader. ill. 12°. $2. *Woodward.*
Globe lib. 10 v. 18°. $3.70 .... *So. Meth.*
Cont.: The sea. — The mountain. — The river. — The valley. — The desert. — Prairie. — Ball we live on. — The coal pit, by J. Bridges. — Volcanoes. — Visit to the catacombs, by S. Bunbury.
— *See also* Routledge's.
Gloria Patri: prayers, chants and responses. 12°. '66. per doz., $12; $15 .... *Universalist.*
Glories of the Cath. Church. *See* New.
Glories of the sacred heart. *See* Manning, H. E.
Glory (The). Root, G. F. $1.50 .... *Church.*
Glory and sorrow; [also] Selim, the pasha of Salonique; tr. by P. S. ill. 16°. '75. $1 .. *Cath. Pub.*
Glory, glory, glory. Bunbury, Selina. 35c. .. *Carter.*
Glory of America. Thomas, R. $1.50 .... *Sower.*
Glory of God in man. Gifford, E. H. $1 .. *Macmillan.*
Glory of Israel. Tonna, C. E. 40c. .... *Am. S. S.*
Glory of New York. Rogers, E. P. 25c. .. *U. S. Pub.*
Glory of the Redeemer. Winslow, O. $1.50 .. *Carter.*
Glorying in the cross of Christ. McLaurin, J. 35c. *Randolph.*
Glover, Anna. Glover memorials and genealogies. 8°. '67. $3 .... *D. Clapp.*
Glover, H. Palomita; or, the veiled songstress: operetta. 4°. bds., $2 .... *Peters.*
Glover, Ma. Baker. Science and health. 12°. '75. $2.50 .... *Chr. Sci.*
Glover, S. F. Cradle of liberty: drama. 16°. pap., 15c. *French.*
Gluck, C. W. v. Orpheus. [Vocal music.] 8°. 35c. *Church.*
Gluge, Gli. Atlas of patholog. histology; tr., with notes and add., by J. Leidy. ill. imp. 4°. $4 .... *Lea.*
Glycerine oil. Arnold, J. 15c. .... *De Witt.*
Glyndon, Howard (*pseud.*) *See* Searing, *Mrs.* L. C.
Gnome king. Brough, W. 15c. .... *French.*
Go ahead. Fosdick, C. A. $1.50 .... *Porter.*
Go ahead! [or,] Jack the cabin boy. ill. 18°. 60c. *Crowell.*
— *See also* Go ahead lib.
Go ahead lib. 4 v. ill. 16°. $2 .... *Routledge.*
Cont.: Go ahead. — Little Jack. — Clean your boots, sir? — Little standard bearer.
Go ahead lib. 5 v. 18°. $3 .... *Crowell.*
Cont.: Go ahead. — Little standard bearer. — Big Bruce and Little Moss, by F. W. — Mend your nets. — Hand of the diligent.
Go ahead ser. *See* Fosdick, C. A.
Go and tell Jesus. *See* Come to Jesus; — Winslow, O.
Go, or die. Kelley, D. C. 20c. .... *So. Meth.*
Go-to-bed Tom. Morton, T. 15c. .... *French.*
Go to Putney. Lemon, H. 15c. .... *De Witt; French.*
Goadby, H: Text-book of vegetable and animal physiology. ill. 8°. $3 .... *Appleton.*
Goaks and tears. Lewis, C. B. 50c. .... (?) *Shepard.*
Goat-land: story of country life; by author of "Life of a bear." ill. 4°. '75. $1.75 .... *Nelson.*
Gobineau, Jos. Arth. (*Comte*) de. Typhaines Abbey: tale of the 12th cent.; tr. by C. D. Meigs. 2d ed. 12°. '69. $1.50; pap., $1 .... *Claxton.*
Gobinet, C: Instruction of youth in Christian piety; [from] the Scriptures and holy fathers; tr. by J. A. Turbique. 12°. $1.50 .... *Noonan.*
Goblins (The). *See* Grimm, J. L. *and* W. C.
Goblins who stole the sexton. Dickens, C. per gross, $15 .... (?) *McLoughlin.*
Gobright, L. A. Jack and Jill. 4°. '72. pap., 50c. *Claxton.*
— Recollections of men and things at Washington during the third of a century. ('69.) 2d ed. 12°. '71. $1.75 .... *Claxton.*
God and the Bible. *See* Arnold, M.
God and man. Lacordaire, J. B. H. $2. *Scribner, W. & A.*
God the father, and man the image of God. King, M. M. 25c. .... *Colby.*
God in Christ. Bushnell, H. *net*, $1.25 .. *Hamersley.*
God in history. Bunsen, C. C. J. (*Baron*) v. 3 v. $21. *Scribner, W. & A.*
God in history and in science. Cumming, J. 75c. *Meth. Bk. Conc.*
God in human thought. Gillett, E. H. 2 v. $5 .. *Scribner.*
God in Old Test. history. Marvin, E. M. 25c. *S. W. Bk. & Pub.*
God is love. 16°. $1.25 .... *Carter.*
God is our refuge. *See* Buck, Dudley.
God-man. *See* Townsend, L. T.
God our father; by author of "Happiness of heaven." 3d ed., rev. 18°. '73. $1; $1.50 ..... *Murphy.*
God our refuge and strength. Smith, J. 10c. .. *Pres. Bd.*
God (The) proposed for our national Constitution. Denton, W. 10c. .... *Denton.*
God sovereign and man free. Rice, N. L. 65c. *Pres. Bd.*
God with us. Hovey, A. $1.50 .... *H. A. Young.*
Goddard, Jla. Baffled; or, Michael Brand's wrong. ill. 8°. pap., 75c. .... *Harper.*

Goddard, Jla., *continued.*
— Boy (The) and the constellations. ill. 12°. $1.25. *Scribner, W. & A.*
Goddard, Pl. B., *and* Parker, Jos. E. Anatomy, physiology and pathology of the human teeth; with methods of treatment and of making and setting artificial teeth. ill. 4°. $3.75 .... *W. Wood.*
Goddard, W: Giles. Political and misc. writings; ed. by F. W. Goddard. 2 v. roy. 8°. '70. $6..*Rider.*
Godet, F. Commentary on St. Luke. 2 v. 8°. ea., $3 .... *Scribner, W. & A.*
Godfray, Hu. Elementary treatise on the lunar theory; with sketch of problem to time of Newton. 2d. ed., rev. cr. 8°. $2.25 .... *Macmillan.*
— Treatise on astronomy. 8°. '74. $4.50..*Macmillan.*
Godfrey, B: Diseases of hair: affections of the hair system. 12°. '72. $1.50 .... *Lindsay.*
Godkin, E. L. On professional guilds. *See* American Inst. of Arch.
Godkin, Ja. The land-war in Ireland: a hist. for the times. 8°. '70. $2.50 .... *Macmillan.*
Godolphin, Ma. One-syllable books. 4 v. ill. sq. 12°. ea., $1.25 .... *Appleton.*
Cont.: Robinson Crusoe. — Swiss family Robinson. — Evenings at home. — Pilgrim's progress.

— *Same.* 4 v. ill. sq. 12°. ea., $1.50 ...... *Routledge.*
— Æsop's fables in words of one syllable. ill. sq. 16°. $1.25 .... *Miller.*
— *Same.* col. ill. roy. 16°. $1.50 .... *Cassell.*
— History of Sandford and Merton in words of one syllable. ill. sq. 16°. $1.25 .... *Miller.*
— *Same.* col. ill. roy. 16°. $1.50 .... *Cassell.*
— Robinson Crusoe in words of one syllable. ill. 4°. per gross, $60 .... (?) *McLoughlin.*
— *Same.* ill. fp. 4°. $1 .... (?) *McLoughlin.*
— Sunday book of one syllable. ill. sq. 16°. 50c. *Routledge.*
Godolphin. *See* Bulwer-Lytton, *Sir* E. G. E. L.
God's dealings with the Chicago Foundling's Home. Shipman, G. M. 30c. .... *Revell.*
God's furnace; by one tried in the fire. 12°. '69. 75c. *Randolph.*
God's glory in the heavens. Leitch, W. $2.25. *Routledge.*
God's little boy that went home. *See* Maple grove stories.
God's new world. Wesley, J. 50c. .... *Cassell.*
God's ownership of the sea. Swain, L. 25c... *Draper.*
God's rescues. Williams, W. R. 75c..... *Randolph.*
God's rule for Christian giving. Speer, W. 75c. *Pres. Bd.*
God's songs, and the singer. Bain, J. W. 40c. *U. P. Bd. of Pub.*
God's thoughts fit bread for children. Bushnell, H. 50c.; 20c. .... *Lockwood, B. & Co.*
God's way. Holt, M. A. 90c. .... *Meth. Bk. Conc.*
God's way of holiness; — of peace. *See* Bonar, H.
God's word for inquirers. Irwin, J. C. 10c... *Am. Tr.*
God's word through preaching. Hall, J. $1.50. *Cin. Meth. Bk. Conc.; Dodd.*
God's word to inquirers. Bocock, J. A. 25c... *Pres. Bd.*
God's word written. *See* Garbett, E.
Gods (The). *See* Ingersoll, R. G.
Godwin, Parke. Cyclopædia of biography. New ed., with supplement, by G. Sheppard. 8°. $3.50; hf. cf., $5.50 .... *Putnam.*
— History of France, to 1789. v. 1, Ancient Gaul. 8°. $3; hf. cf., $5.25 .... *Harper.*
— Out of the past: essays. 12°. '72. $2.... *Putnam.*
Godwin, S. P. Heart-breathings; or, the soul's desire expressed in earnestness. 18°. '68. 75c. *Claxton; Lippincott.*
Godwin, W: Adventures of Caleb Williams; or, things as they are. [Fiction.] 8°. pap., 50c... *U. P. James.*

Godwin, W: *continued.*
— *Same.* 16°. $1; pap., 37c. .... *Harper*
— Brother's secret. 12°. $1.75; pap., $1.50..*Peterson*
— Lives of the necromancers. 16°. 80c. *Scribner, W. & A*
Goethe, J: Wolfg. v. Werke. 32 v. 12°. ea., pap. 10c.-50c. .... *F. W. Thomas*
Cont.: Aus meinem Leben, 50c. — Benvenuto Cellini, 40c. — Wilhelm Meisters Lehrjahre, 40c. — Wilhelm Meisters Wanderjahre, 35c. — Faust, 30c. — Die Wahlverwandtschaften, 15c — Leiden d. jungen Werther. — Die Laune d. Verliebten. — Di Mitschuldigen. — Iphigenie auf Tauris. — Torquato Tasso. — Die natürliche Tochter. — Egmont. — Clavigo. — Stella. — De Gross-Cophta. — Der Bürger-General. — Die Aufgeregten. — Der Triumph d. Empfindsamkeit. — Die Vögel. — Erwin u Elmire. — Claudine v. Villa Bella. — Jery u. Bätely. — Lila — Die Fischerin. — Scherz, List u. Rache. — Hermann u Dorothea. — Achilleïs. — Reineke Fuchs. — Mahomet. — Tancred. — Götz v. Berlichingen, *ea.*, 10c.

— Sämmtliche Werke. 6 v. 8°. $8; pap., $6; hf mor., $10 .... *F. W. Thomas*
— *Eng.* Works. 6 v. 12°. hf. cf., $18; cf., $21.50. *Appleton*
— — *Same.* 7 v. 12°. $10.50; hf. cf., $21; tree cf. $28 .... *Lippincott*
— — *Same.* 7 v. 12°. (Bohn.) ea., $1.25. *Little, B. & Co*
Cont.: 1-2. Autobiography, and Travels in Italy, France and Switzerland; with por. — 3. Faust, Iphigenia, Torquato Tasso Egmont, etc., tr. by Miss Swannwick; and Götz von Berlichingen, tr. by Sir W. Scott. — 4. Novels and tales. — 5. Wilhelm Meister's apprenticeship. — 6. Conversations with Eckermann and Soret; tr. by J. Oxenford. — 7. Poems and ballads, incl Hermann and Dorothea; tr. by E. A. Bowring.

— — *Same.* 7 v. 12°. (Bohn). ea., $1.40. *Scribner, W. & A.*
— Poems; tr. by E. A. Bowring. New ed., rev., incl. Hermann and Dorothea. 12°. $1.75..*Lippincott.*
— Poems and ballads; tr. by W. E. Aytoun, and T. Martin. 16°. '72. $1.50 .... *Holt.*
— Conversations with Eckermann and F. Soret; tr. by J. Oxenford. 16°. $1.50 .... *Lippincott.*
— Correspondence with a child. 12°. $1.75..*Osgood.*
— Egmont: Trauerspiel; mit Anmerkgn. zum Uebers. ins Eng. v. W. Steffen. ('66.) New ed. 12°. '76. pap., 50c. .... *Holt.*
— Elective affinities; tr. (Leis. hour ser.) 16°. '72. $1.25 .... *Holt.*
— Faust: Tragödie, erster Theil. With Eng. notes. ('66.) New ed. 12°. '76. pap., 75c...... *Holt.*
— *Same;* ill. by A. Liezen-Mayer in 50 cartoons, cont. 13 eng. by Bankel and others; [with] Eng. tr. by T. J. Arnold. f°. $40; mor., $60.... *Stroefer.*
— *Eng.* Faust. 16°. pap., 15c. .... *French.*
— — *Same:* metrical tr. by Rev. C. T. Brooks. 16°. $1.25 .... *Osgood.*
— — *Same:* prose tr. by A. Hayward. 16°. $1.25. *Osgood.*
— — *Same;* [with] silh. ill. by P. Konewka. 4°. '70. $3; mor., $8 .... *Roberts.*
— — *Same;* tr. in verse by B. Taylor. 2 v. imp. 8°. '70. $9; hf. cf., $18; mor., $25. — (Kennett ed.) 2 v. 16°. $4.50; hf. cf., $9; mor., $12..*Osgood.*
— — — *Same.* ill. by E. Seibertz, A. Liezen-Mayer and L. Hofman. f°. $30; mor., $45..*Stroefer.*
— Hermann und Dorothea. Ed., with notes and glossary, by J. M. Hart. 12°. '75. $1.... *Putnam.*
— *Same;* with Eng. notes by E. C. F. Krauss. ('66.) New ed. 12°. '76. pap., 40c. .... *Holt.*
— *Eng.* Hermann and Dorothea; tr. by H. Dale; with photos. from orig. of W. Kaulbach and L. Hofman. roy. 4°. $15; mor., $20. 8°. $10. — Same; in Germ. roy. 4°. $15. 8°. $10 .... *Stroefer.*
— — *Same;* tr. by E. Frothingham. ill. 8°. '70. $2; mor., $5. 16°. $1 .... *Roberts.*
— Iphigenie auf Tauris: Schauspiel. With Eng. notes by E. C. F. Krauss. ('66.) New ed. 12°. '76. pap., 40c. .... *Holt.*
— Reynard the fox; tr. by T. Arnold; [with] eng. and wood-cuts after designs by W. Kaulbach. roy. 4°. $18; $20 .... *Stroefer.*
— Roman elegies; tr. into Eng. verse in the orig. metre by L. Noa. sm. 4°. '76. 60c. .... *Schoenhof.*

Goethe, J: Wolfg. v., *continued.*
— Wilhelm Meister; tr. by T. Carlyle. 2 v. por. 12°. $3.50 .... *Osgood.*
— Female characters of G. *See* Kaulbach, W.
— *See also* Gottschall, R., Gedankenharmonie; — Masterpieces of foreign literature.
Goethe and Schiller. Mundt, C. M. $1.50; $1; $3.50. *Appleton.*
Goff, *Mrs.* H. N. K. Was it an inheritance? or, Nannie Grant. 12°. '76. $1.50 .... *Claxton.*
Goff, Milton B. Complete arithmetic. 12°. '76. $1.10. *English.*
— First book in arith. 16°. '76. bds., 40c.... *English.*
Goffine, Leon. Devout instructions on the Epistles and Gospels; tr. by Rev. T. Noethen, with explan. of Christian faith and duty and of church ceremonies. 12°. $2.25 .... *Strong.*
— Explanation of the Epistles and Gospels for the Sundays and festivals throughout the year; tr. by Rev. G. M. Pilz. ill. 8°. '76. $2....... *Pustet.*
Goggeshall, W: T. Oakshaw; or, the victims of avarice: tale of intrigue. 12°. 75c.... *U. P. James.*
Göhren, Caro. v. The orphan. *See* American youth's lib.
Going for the cup. White, C. 15c. .... *De Witt.*
Going home. Warde, M. M. $2........ *Cummiskey.*
Going home. Winslow, O. 20c........... *Randolph.*
Going on a mission. Cobden, P. $1.25...... *Lee & S.*
Going to the bad. Taylor, T. 15c........... *French.*
Going to the Centennial. Small, G. G. 25c. *Collin & S.*
Going to Cobham. Hazelwood, C. H. 15c.... *French.*
Going to the Derby. Morton, J. M. 15c..... *French.*
Going to the dogs. Brough, W., *and* Halliday, A. 15c. *French.*
Going to Jericho. Swift, J. F. $1.50........ *Roman.*
Going to the mill. 18°. 35c.; 45c......... *Am. Bapt.*
Going to school. Bullard, A. 25c.......... *Lee & S.*
Going west. Adams, W. T. $1.50.......... *Lee & S.*
Gold. Reade, C. 15c. .... *French.*
Gold and diadem. Lowry, R., *and* Doane, W. H. 65c. .... *Biglow.*
Gold and dross. Mayo, I. F. $1.75........... *Dodd.*
Gold and free banks. Pilon, M. R. $1 ..... *Authors.*
Gold and the Gospel. 12°. '54. 75c... *Meth. Bk. Conc.*
Gold and name. Schwartz, M. S. $1.50; $1.. *Porter.*
Gold bought too dear. 18°. 25c.; 30c..... *Am. Bapt.*
Gold bracelet. ill. 24°. 25c............. *Perkinpine.*
— *Same.* ill. 18°. '60. 40c................. *Am. Tr.*
Gold bracelets. Davis, C. E. K. $1.15 .... *Hoyt.*
Gold brick. Stephens, A. S. $1.75; $1.50.. *Peterson.*
Gold digger: what he lost and what he failed to realize. ('60.) New ed. ill. 18°. '71. 45c........ *Hoyt.*
Gold dollar. Trowbridge, C. M. 60c..... (?) *Martien.*
Gold-dust. Pomeroy, M. M. $1.50....... *Carleton.*
Gold Elsie. John, E. $1.50 .... *Lippincott.*
Gold filings. Thornton, J. 70c. .... *Pres. Bd.*
Gold-foil hammered from popular proverbs. Holland, J. G. $1.75 .... *Scribner.*
Gold, frankincense and myrrh. Reed, E. $1.. *Claxton.*
Gold-hunters in Europe. Thomes, W. H. $1.50. *Lee & S.*
Gold-hunters' adventures. Thomes, W. H. $1.50. *Lee & S.*
Gold-hunters' lib. *See* Thomes, W. H.
Gold key: dram. story; tr. from the Fr. 16°. $1. *Lippincott.*
Gold seekers. Aimard, G. 75c........... *Peterson.*
Gold seekers and bread winners. 16°. 50c. *Scribner, W. & A.*
Gold thimble. Adams, W. T. 45c.......... *Lee & S.*

Gold thread. *See* Macleod, N.
Gold worshipers (The); or, the days we live in: a future hist. novel. 8°. pap., 50c....... *Harper.*
Goldammer, H. Die Einordnung d. Kindergartens in d. Schulwesen d. Gemeinde; nach H. Goldammer f. amerik. Verhältnisse v. H. Reffelt. 12°. '74. pap., 15c. .... *Steiger.*
Golden age to come. Austin, J. J. 75c... *Williamson.*
Golden apples. Woods, E. $1.............. *Carter.*
Golden apples and silver pictures. 18°. 17c.; 22c. *Am. Bapt.*
Golden ass (The). *See* Appuleius, L.
Golden bird. Grimm, J. L. *and* W. C. $1.. *Miller.*
Golden book of the confraternities. [Cath. prayer book.] 24°. 60c.; roan, $1............ *Strong.*
Golden book of Eng. song. Adams, W. H. D. $2. *Nelson.*
Golden branch. Planché, J. R. 15c......... *French.*
Golden calf. Jerrold, D. 15c............... *French.*
Golden cap. De Liefde, J. $1.25........... *Carter.*
Golden censer. Briggs, O. L. $1.25......... *Dutton.*
Golden censer. Harbaugh, H. $1; $1.25; $1.75; $2.50 .... *Ref. Ch. Pub.*
Golden censer. Hart, J. S. 85c........... *Pres. Bd.*
Golden censer. Summers, T. O. 75c.; $1.25; $3. *So. Meth.*
Golden censer (The new). *See* Bradbury, W. B.
Golden chain. Marsh, C. 90c............... *Carter.*
Golden chain lib. 5 v. ill. 16°. $2.50..... *Routledge.*
Cont.: Links in a golden chain. — Frank Burton's dream. — Made for it. — Life of Luther. — Georgie's present.

Golden chain (The new). *See* Bradbury, W. B.
Golden chain of praise. Gill, T. H. $2.25.. *Randolph.*
Golden chain of S.-school melodies. *See* New Golden.
Golden chord: piano-forte pieces. 4°. $3; $4; bds., $2.50 .... *Brainard.*
Golden circle: piano-forte music. 4°. $3; $4; bds., $2.50 .... *Brainard.*
Golden city. Barrett, B. F. $1.25......... *Claxton.*
Golden city, and the way to get there. 18°. 17c.; 22c. *Am. Bapt.*
Golden crown. Merrill, H. T. 10c .... *Church.*
Golden crowns ser. Reade, C. $1.25....... *Cassell.*
Golden dawn. Newman, M. W. 75c......... *Roman.*
Golden day lib. 3 v. 16°. $3.75............ *Dutton.*
Cont.: Golden days, by E. R. Church. — Sophie Danforth's school life, by H. Buhler. — Ottalie's stories for the little folks, by Mme. O. Wildermuth.

Golden days. Church, E. R. $1.25......... *Dutton.*
Golden eagle. Howe, J. B. 15c............. *French.*
Golden earrings: autobiog.; from the French. 18°. 45c.; 55c. .... *Am. Bapt.*
Golden farmer. Webster, B. 15c........... *French.*
Golden fence, and other tales. 16°. $1... *Lippincott.*
Golden fleece. Planché, J. R. 15c.......... *French.*
Golden fleece. *See* Tucker, *Mrs.* C.
Golden fountain. Wilson, J. H. $1.50...... *Nelson.*
Golden fruit. Wright, J. McN. $1.50 .... *Hoyt.*
Golden fruit. Zabriskie, F. N. 50c....... *Randolph.*
Golden gate. Hunt, H. G. B. 75c. .... *Cassell.*
Golden gate. Shaw, K. 35c. .... *Church.*
Golden gems. Bradley, M. G. $1.25 ...... *Lothrop.*
Golden gleanings. 18°. 35c.; 45c......... *Am. Bapt.*
Golden grain. Farjeon, B. L. 35c. .... *Harper.*
Golden grain lib. ('70.) 4th ed. 6 v. ill. 18°. '74. $3 .... *Perkinpine.*
Cont.: Snowed in. — Nate's gold ring. — First patch. — Doctor's apple. — Pigeon's bronze boots. — Two tough knots.

Golden grains. Kiehl, E. M. $1.50...... *Lippincott.*

Golden grains from life's harvest-field. Arthur, T. S. $1.25 .... *J. E. Potter.*

Golden grove. *See* Taylor, J.

Golden guide to London. ill. and map. cr. 8°. '75. $1.50 .... *Scribner, W. & A.*

Golden hair. Wraxhall, *Sir* L. $1.50 ..... *Lee & S.*

Golden haired Gertrude. Tilton, T. $1; 75c. *Tibbals.*

Golden harp. Dulcken, H. W. $1.75 .... *Routledge.*

Golden harp. Emerson, L. O. 35c.; 30c. ... *Ditson.*

Golden harp album. Heaton, C. $1.75 ... *Routledge.*

Golden heart. Wright, J. McN. $1.50 .... *Hoyt.*

Golden hills. Walshe, E. H. $1.40 ...... *Pres. Bd.*

Golden hour ill. lib. 4 v. ill. 16°. $5 ..... *Routledge.*
Cont.: Lillian's golden hours. — Through life and for life. — Village idol. — Girl of the family.

Golden hour ser. 4 v. ill. sq. 16°. $3 ...... *Lothrop.*
Cont.: Christmas visit. — Queer carriage. — Somebody's darlings. — Our Bertie.

Golden hours. Prentiss, E. $1.50 .... *Randolph.*

Golden hymns. Bradbury, W. B. 15c.; 10c. *Biglow.*

Golden island. Pearce, C. E. 50c. ...... *Am. News.*

Golden key. Shryock, D. 25c. .... *Church.*

Golden ladder. Smith, M. J. P. 25c. ...... *Am. Tr.*

Golden ladder. Wright, S. A. $2.50 .... *Sickels.*

Golden ladder ser. *See* Mathews, J. A.

Golden leaves. Bell, R. $15 .... *Routledge.*

Golden leaves. Hays, W. S. 2 v. ea., $2.25; $1.75. *Peters.*

Golden leaves from Brit. and Am. dram. poets. *See* Hows, J. W. S.

Golden leaves from late Eng. poets. Stoddard, R. H. $1.50 .... *Randolph.*

Golden leaves ser. 4 v. 12°. ea., $2.50; $3; mor., $5 .... *Huntington.*
Cont.: Golden leaves from Am. poets. — Golden leaves from Brit. poets. — Golden leaves from dram. poets. — Golden leaves from later Eng. poets.

Golden legend. *See* Longfellow, H. W.

Golden lib. *See* Wright, *Mrs.* J. McN.

Golden life. Wright, J. McN. $1.50 .... *Hoyt.*

Golden light ser. 3 v. ill. 4°. per doz., pap., $1.50. *Sheldon.*

Golden light stories. 3 v. 16°. $3.75 .... (?) *Martien.*
Cont.: Led to the light. — Malcolm's cottage and Malcolm's friend. — George Morton and his sister.

Golden lines. ill. 16°. '73. $1.50 .... *Lothrop.*

Golden links; or, thoughts for the hours. ('68.) 2d ed. 16°. '69. $1.25 .... *Claxton.*

Golden Lion of Granpere. Trollope, A. $1.25; 75c. *Harper.*

Golden lives. Yapp, A. $2 .... *Routledge.*

Golden lyre. Taylor, V. C. $1.50 .... *Ditson.*

Golden manual (The). [Cath. prayer book.] 18°. $1.25–$60 .... *Sadlier.*

Golden maxims. Bond, R. 38c. .... *Appleton.*

Golden maxims for every day. 24°. '46. 30c. *Meth. Bk. Conc.*

Golden memories of an earnest life. Whiting, R. A. $1.50 .... *Colby.*

Golden mill: tale of filial piety; tr. from the Germ. ill. 12°. $1 .... *Nelson.*

Golden missionary penny. Bolton, J. J. $1.25 .. *Nelson.*

Golden motto. 16°. $1.25 .... *H. A. Young.*

Golden motto ser. 4 v. 16°. $5 .... *H. A. Young.*
Cont.: Golden motto. — True friendships. — Young adventurer. — Runaway, by P. A. Hanaford.

Golden mushroom; by author of "Watercress sellers." ('60.) New ed. ill. 18°. '75. 65c. .... *Hoyt.*

Golden pennies. *See* Baker, *Mrs.* H. N. W.

Golden picture book. ill. 4°. '76. $2 .... *Nelson.*

Golden precepts. Albert, *Prince Consort.* $1.25. *Scribner, W. & A.*

Golden ray ser. 4 v. 16°. $5.50 .... *Cong. Pub.*
Cont.: Impulse and principle, by M. T. Ellery. — Station master's daughter, by Miss S. D. Nickerson. — Mary Grey's perplexities, by Mrs. A. K. Dunning. — Broken idols, by Mrs. M. W. McLain.

Golden ready reckoner. Brisbane, W. D. 35c. *Dick & F.*

Golden red-line gift books. 6 v. 24°. $7.50; ea., $1.50 .... *Locke.*
Cont.: Language of flowers. — Forget-me-not. — Friendship's token. — Friendship's offering. — Gift of love. — Gift of remembrance.

Golden ringlet lib. 5 v. 18°. $3 .... *Am. Bapt.*
Cont.: Golden ringlets. — Little Meg's children. — Little peat cutters, by E. Marshall. — Count Ulrich, by W. H. G. Kingston. — Louis Michaud.

Golden ringlets. 18°. 45c.; 55c. .... *Am. Bapt.*

Golden robin. Perkins, W. O. 50c. .... *Ditson.*

Golden rule. 18°. 60c. .... *Cong. Pub.*

Golden rule. *See* Baker, *Mrs.* H. N. W., Aunt Hattie's lib. for boys.

Golden rule. *See* Dunning, A. K.

Golden rule. Mackarness, M. A. $1.25 .. *Routledge.*

Golden rule. Müller, M. $2 .... *Kreuzer.*

Golden rule. Straub, S. W. 35c. .... *Church.*

Golden rule and its fruits. Goodwin, M. F. 35c. *Bost. Am. Tr.*

Golden rule and other stories. 18°. 70c. ... *Pres. Bd.*

Golden rule for boys and girls; ed. by F. Dale. ill. 18°. '59. 63c. .... *Perkinpine.*

Golden rule ill. lib. 4 v. ill. 16°. $5 ...... *Routledge.*
Cont.: Golden rule, by Mrs. M. A. Mackarness — Children of blessing. — Influence, by Mrs. M. A. Mackarness. — Four sisters.

Golden sands from the ocean of life; by author of "Emma Allen." 18°. 60c. .... *Pres. Bd.*

Golden sayings for the young. ill. roy. 4°. $1.75. *Nelson.*

Golden secret. 16°. 60c. .... *Cong. Pub.*

Golden secret. *See* Snow-drop ser.

Golden secret; by author of "Hope on." ill. 18°. 75c. *Nelson.*

Golden secret lib. 4 v. ill. 16°. $3 .... *Nelson.*
Cont.: Golden secret. — King Jack of the Haylands. — Susy's flowers. — Lessons from the life of Christ.

Golden sheaves. Cleveland, H. A. *$2.50 .. *McCurdy.*

Golden sheaves lib. 4 v. 18°. $3 ..... *Bost. Am. Tr.*
Cont.: Grace's visit. — Hard knot, by Mrs. M. E. Berry. — Little sheaves for little gleaners, by C. Pearl. — Westbrooke, by Miss L. Bates.

Golden shower (The new). *See* Bradbury, W. B.

Golden songs and ballads; comp. by author of "Annie's gold cross." 18°. 75c. .... *Pres. Bd.*

Golden sorrow. Hoey, C. 50c. .... *Harper.*

Golden spring ser. *See* Baker, *Mrs.* H. N. W.

Golden state. *See* McClellan, R. G.

Golden stories. 5 v. 64°. $1.12 .... *W. Wood.*
Cont.: White kitten. — Tent in the garden. — Willie Wilson, the newsboy. — Loving words and loving deeds. — Watermelon.

Golden sunbeams. Hodges, D. F., *and* Tenney, J. H. 30c.; 35c. .... *Lee & S.*

Golden sunset. Macduff, J. R. 35c. .... *Carter.*

Golden thorns. ill. 16°. '76. $1 .... *Carter.*
— *See also* Vinegar Hill stories.

Golden thread ser. 6 v. 16°. $6 .... *Randolph.*
Cont.: Fiddling Freddy, by N. Forrest. — Honest and earnest, by N. Forrest. — Jack and Rosy, by N. Forrest. — Henry and Bessie, by Mrs. E. Prentiss. — Little threads, by Mrs. E. Prentiss. — Peterchen and Gretchen, by Mrs. E. Prentiss.

— *See also* Prentiss, *Mrs.* E.

Golden threads. Knight, H. C. $2; $3 .... *Am. Tr.*

Golden treasures of poetry, romance and art. ill. sm. 4°. '75. $3 .... *W. F. Gill.*

Golden treasury: select. of prayers chiefly from works of St. Alphonsus Liguori. 48°. 30c.–$2 .. *Noonan.*

— *Same.* 32°. 75c. — $2.50 .... *O'Shea.*

Golden treasury for the children of God. *See* Bogatzky, C. H. v.

Golden treasury of piano lyrics. f°. '69. $4..*L. Meyer.*

Golden treasury of songs and lyrical poems. *See* Palgrave, F. T.

Golden treasury of thought. Taylor, T. $3. *Routledge; Scribner, W. & A.*

Golden treasury psalter. (Student's ed.) 18°. '70. $1.25 .... *Macmillan.*

Note. Same as the Psalms chronologically arranged by four friends, but with briefer notes.

Golden treasury ser. 8 v. 18°. ea., 75c. 16°. ea., $1.25. *Allyn.*

Cont.: Golden treasury of songs and lyrics, by F. T. Palgrave. — Children's garland, by C. Patmore. — Book of praise, by Roundell Palmer. — Pilgrim's progress, by J. Bunyan. — Book of golden deeds, by Miss Yonge. — Jest book, by M. Lemon. — Ballad book, by W. Allingham. — Sunday school book of poetry, by Miss Alexander.

Golden tress. Du Boisgobey, F. $1.50..... *Claxton.*

Golden truth ser. *See* Means, *Mrs.* C. A.

Golden truths. *See* Means, *Mrs.* C. A.

Golden truths. Norton, J. N. $2....... *Whittaker.*

Golden vase. *See* Diamond miniatures.

Golden vine; or, Henry Sherwood. 18°. 17c.; 22c. *Am. Bapt.*

Golden wheel dream book. Fontaine, F. 35c. *Dick & F.*

Golden work. Wright, J. McN. $1.50........ *Hoyt.*

Golden wreath. Emerson, L. O. 50c........ *Ditson.*

Goldene Aepfel in silbernen Schalen. 18°. 35c. *Ev. Assoc.*

Goldene Schlüssel (Der). *See* Hartmann, M.

Goldey Mew. *See* Infant school lib.

Goldkörner. Oertel, P. F. W. $1.50; $2..*Ev. Assoc.*

Goldmacherdorf (Das). *See* Zschokke, H.

Goldmaker's village. *See* Happy child's lib.

Goldne Ring (Der) meiner Mutter. 32°. '64. 15c.; pap., 5c.............................. *Am. Tr.*

Goldoni, C., Giraud, G., *and* Nata, A. Select Ital. comedies. 12°. 75c.................. *Appleton.*

Goldsbury, J: English grammar. 12°. 25c. — Sequel. 12°. 25c....................... *Dennet.*

Goldsmid, *Sir* F: J: Telegraph and travel: narrative of formation and development of tel. communication between England and India. maps and ill. 8°. '74. $8......................... *Macmillan.*

Goldsmith, Christabel (*pseud.*) *See* Smith, Julie P.

Goldsmith, Ol. Works; with memoir. ill. and por. 8°. (Dick.) 80c.; pap., 40c........ *Am. News.*

— *Same;* with account of life and writings. (Globe ed.) cr. 8°. $1.75–$5.............. *Routledge.*

— *Same;* ed. by P. Cunningham. 4 v. ill. 8°. (Lond.) '54. $12; hf. cf., $18; cf., $28..*Little, B. & Co.*

— Miscellaneous works. 8°. $2.50.......... *Lee & S.*

— *Same;* with biog. introd. by Prof. Masson. (Globe ed.) 12°. '69. $1.50............... *Macmillan.*

— *Same;* incl. pieces now first collected, with notes by J. Prior. 4 v. ill. 12°. '74. $6; shp., $8; hf. cf., $13 .... *Claxton.*

— Poems. ill. 16°. *net,* $1.................... *Sadlier.*

— *Same.* 12°. $1.50......................... *Locke.*

— *Same.* (School ed.) 16°. hf. bd., 25c.... *Sadlier.*

— *Same;* with life by Macauley and anecdotes collected by Rev. J. Mitford. por. 18°. $1....... *Osgood.*

— *Same;* [also] Poems, by R. Southey. ill. 16°. $1.12; $1.35. 32°. 85c.; $1.12.... *World Pub.*

— — *See also* British pocket classics; — Collins, W:

— *Same;* [also] Vicar of Wakefield. 16°. $1; $1.50. *Sadlier.*

— Poems, plays and essays; with Aiken's memoirs, and introd. by H. T. Tuckerman. (Blue and gold ed.) 18°. $1.25. — (Cabinet ed.) 16°. $1.50. *Nichols & H.*

— Select poems; ed. with notes by W. J. Rolfe. ill. sm. 4°. 90c.......................... *Harper.*

Goldsmith, Ol., *continued.*

— — *See also below* Vicar of Wakefield.

— Poetical works. ill. 4°. $9; mor., $12..*Routledge.*

— *Same;* ed. with life by Rev. J. Mitford. (Aldine ed.) 16°. 75c........................... *Lippincott.*

— *Same.* (Etching club ed.) por. and ill. sm. 4°. $3.50; cf., $8...................... *Lee & S.*

— *Same;* with memoir and notes, ed. by B. Corney. ill. 8°. $3; $3.75; mor., $7.50........... *Harper.*

— Deserted village. ill. 12°. '75. $1.25..... *Putnam.*

— *Same.* ill. 12°. '65. $2.50................ *Tilton.*

— Essays. 32°. 38c....................... *Appleton.*

— Gems: [compr.] The traveller, The deserted village; [also] The hermit; with notes and sketch of G. ill. 12°. '73. $1.......................... *Wells.*

— Good natured man: comedy. 16°. pap., 15c...*French.*

— History of the earth and animated nature. New ed., rev. ill. 8°. '74. $4; in 2 v., shp., $5..*Claxton.*

— — Natural history. ill. 12°. hf. roan, 88c...*Polock.*

Note. Same as Animated nature.

— History of England to death of George II.; with contin. by J. Frost. ill. demy 8°. $2.50..*Desilver.*

— *Same;* ed. by W. Pinnock; with contin. and questions by W. C. Taylor. ill. 12°. $1.75..*Desilver.*

— History of Greece; abridg. by author; ed. by H. W. Herbert. 18°. 75c................... *Harper.*

— *Same;* ed. by W. Pinnock; rev. and enl. by W. C. Taylor. ill. 12°. hf. roan, $1.75......*Desilver.*

— History of Rome; abridg. by author; ed. by H. W. Herbert. 18°. 75c................... *Harper.*

— *Same;* ed. by W. Pinnock; with introd., etc., by W. C. Taylor. ill. 12°. hf. roan, $1.75....*Desilver.*

— *Same;* for schools; [ed.] by W. Grimshaw. ('26.) New ed., rev. 12°. hf. bd., 95c........ *Claxton.*

— She stoops to conquer: comedy. 16°. pap., 15c. *French.*

— Traveller (The); with etchings by Birket Foster. 4°. $4............................ *Routledge.*

— — *See also above* Gems.

— *Same;* [also] Deserted village; with notes by J. W. Hales. 12°. '74. pap., 20c......... *Macmillan.*

— Vicar of Wakefield. 18°. 75c.... *Harper; Nelson.*

— *Same.* ill. 12°. $1; hf. cf., $2.50. 32°. 38c. *Appleton.*

— *Same.* New ed. 12°. '74. $1; ill., $1.25..*Putnam.*

— *Same.* (Entertaining lib.) 12°. $1.25. large cr. 8°. pap., 25c........................... *Lippincott.*

— *Same;* with memoir by Rev. R. A. Willmott. 16°. '75. 75c.; 90c. — (World-wide lib.) 12°. pap., 25c.................................. *Routledge.*

— *Same;* arranged as a guide for the construction of Fr. sentences. 12°. hf. roan, $1.50..*Lippincott.*

— *Same;* [also] Select poems and comedies; with introd., notes, and life of G. by J. F. Waller. eng. imp. 8°. $3.50; $5 .... *Cassell.*

— *Same;* [also] Paul and Virginia, by J. H. B. de Saint Pierre. ill. 12°. $1.................... *Porter.*

— *Same;* [also] Rasselas, by S. Johnson. 2 v. in 1. 12°. $1........................... *Lippincott.*

— — *See also* British pocket classics; — *and above* Poems.

— *French.* Le vicaire de Wakefield. 12°. $1.25. *G. R. Lockwood.*

— *and* Johnson, S., Shenstone, W., *and* Smollet, T. Poetical works; with biogs. and notes. (Household ser.) ill. 16°. $1.50; mor., $3.... *Lee & S.*

— — — — Poems; ed. by Rev. R. A. Willmott. (Presentation poets.) ill. 12°. $1.75; $3..*Routledge.*

Goldstein, Max. Aus Liebe: Dramolet. 12°. '75. pap., 25c............................ *Steiger.*

Goldsuche (Der). *See* Hoffmann, F.

Goldy and Goldy's friends. Densel, M. 75c...*Dutton.*

Goldy books. *See* Densel, M.

Goloshes of fortune. *See* Andersen, H. C.

Gone before. Southgate, H. $1.50...... *Lippincott.*

Gonzaga, *St.* Aloysius. *See* Aloysius Gonzaga, *St.*

Good, J: Mason. Book of nature. roy. 8°. *net,* $1.50. *Hamersley.*

Good, J: Mason, *continued.*
— Study of medicine; rev. by S. Cooper; with notes by A. S. Doane; [also] Sketch of hist. of medicine, by J. Bostock. 2 v. 8°. shp, $6.. *Harper.*
Good and great men. ill. 12°. $1.50..... *World Pub.*
Good angels. ill. 18°. '75. 20c.............. *Am. Tr.*
Good beginnings and happy endings. *See* Yonge, C. M.
Good behavior: first class reader for district schools. 16°. '76. hf. bd., 25c................. *Cheney.*
Good — better — best. *See* Alexander, J. W.
Good boy's book. *See* Juvenile picture books.
Good boy's lib.; by Emily Chubbuck, Mrs. Judson and others. 10 v. ill. 18°. $6............ *Sheldon.*
Cont.: Great secret. — Facts for boys. — Allen Lucas. — Swiss basket maker, etc. — My friend's family. — London apprentice. — Little Granite. — Every day duty. — Martyrs of Vilvorde. — Charles Lynn.
Good bye stories for little children. McKeever, H. B. 70c.............................. *Pres. Bd.*
Good bye, sweetheart! *See* Broughton, R.
Good cheer. Straub, S. W. 60c............ *Jansen.*
Good child's album. [Toy-book.] ill. 4°. $1.75. *Routledge.*
Good child's ill. instruction book. ill. 4°. $1; $1.25. *J. E. Potter.*
Good child's lib. 8 v. 32°. $2.......... *Routledge.*
Cont.: Little Henry, by Mrs. M. M. Sherwood. — Charles Hamilton. — Flora Mortimer. — Easy poems. — Ungrateful negro, by M. Edgeworth. — Young cottager, by L. Richmond. — Tale of the universe. — Learning better, etc.
Good company for every day in the year. ('65.) 6th ed. pl. sm. 4°. $3; mor., $6......... *Osgood.*
Good cook. ill. 12°. $1.75 .... *Fisher.*
Good counsel. *See* Daily food ser.
Good counsel stories. 6 v. 18°. $4.75..(?) *Martien.*
Cont.: Dick and his friend Fidus. — Two councils. — Howard Ashley. — Nettie Wallace. — Harry's mistakes. — How Charley helped his mother.
Good daughters. *See* Meadowside stories.
Good English. Gould, E. S. $1.25 ...... *Widdleton.*
Good fellow. Walcot, C. M. 15c. .... *French.*
Good fight. King, A. $1.25............... *Lothrop.*
Good fight. *See* Peebles, *Mrs.* M. L.
Good fight of faith. Freeland, C. J. $1.50.. *Crowell.*
Good for evil. 16°. '74. 50c............... *Nelson.*
Good for evil. Angier, E. 15c............. *French.*
Good for evil. Baker, H. N. W. $1.25.. *H. A. Young.*
Good for evil. Browning, N. 50c.......... *Pres. Bd.*
Good for evil. Tucker, C. 75c............. *Carter.*
Good for nothing. Buckstone, J. B. 15c..... *French.*
Good for nothing. Melville, G. J. W. 60c. *Appleton.*
Good Friday. *See* Harbaugh, H.
Good friends: stories for the young. 32°. 25c. *West. Tr.*
Good genius that turned everything into gold. Mayhew, H. *and* A. 75c.................. *Harper.*
Good girl's book. *See* Juvenile picture books.
Good girl's lib. *See* Bradley, *Mrs.* M. E.
Good grandmother. ill. 16°. 50c............ *Nelson.*
Good grandmother and her offspring. Hofland, B. 50c. *Porter.*
Good grandson; or, the way to spend pocket money. ('63.) 7th ed. ill. 18°. '71. 63c.... *Perkinpine.*
Good habits and good manners. 32°. 40c. *Scribner, W. & A.*
Good hope series. *See* Baker, *Mrs.* H. N. W.
Good hour. Auerbach, B. $3........... *Routledge.*
Good in everything. *See* Continental lib.
Good Indian missionary: memoir of Rev. J. Eliot. 18°. 22c........................... *Am. S. S.*
Good investment. Flagg, W. J. 50c........ *Harper.*
Good little hearts. Barrow, F. 4 v. $2.50.. *Hurd & H.*
Good little Mitty. Child, L. M. 75c....... *Lothrop.*
Good little wife: comedy. 16°. pap., 15c..... *French*
Good looking fellow. Almar, G. 15c........ *French*
Good Louise. *See* Wright, *Mrs.* J. McN.
Good luck. Bürstenbinder, E. $1.25; 75c.... *Estes*
Good luck. Cobden, P. $1.25............. *Lee & S*
Good manners: handbook of etiquette and the usage of good society. sq. 24°. '70. $1.50.... *Porter*
Good man's legacy. Osgood, S. 10c.......... *Wells*
Good match. Perrier, A. $1.50.............. *Ford*
Good measure. Erickson, D. S. $1.50.. *H. A. Young*
Good morals and gentle manners. Gow, A. M. $1.25 *Wilson, H. & Co*
Good natured man. Goldsmith, O. 15c...... *French*
Good news. McIntosh, R. M. 35c.; 30c..... *Ditson*
Good news of God. Kingsley, C. $1.25.. *Macmillan*
Good night and good morning. ill. 4°. $1; $1.50. *Am. S. S*
Good night, Senor Pantaloon: comic operetta. 16° pap., 15c............................. *French*
Good night's rest: Ethiop. drama. White, C. 15c. *De Witt*
Good night's rest: farce. 16°. pap., 15c...... *French*
Good old stories. [Toy-book.] ill. 4°. $1.50. (?) *McLoughlin.*
Good report. Haven, A. B. $1.25........ *Appleton*
Good run for it. Bridgeman, I. V. 15c...... *French.*
Good scholar. Bullard, A. 25c............ *Lee & S*
Good seeds. 32°. 20c.; 15c................. *Dutton*
Good selections. ('72–'74.) New ed. nos. 1–2. 12°. '75. ea., 75c.; $1; pap., 30c.... *Schermerhorn.*
Cont.: Good selections in prose and poetry, ed. by W. M Jelliffe. — Selected readings, ed. by J. E. Frobisher.
Good sense. Holbach, *Baron* P. T. d'. $1.. *Mendum.*
Good shepherd. sq. 12°. '57. 40c.... *Meth. Bk. Conc.*
Good shepherd. Heygate, W. E. $1.......... *Pott.*
Good shepherd. *See* Juvenile picture books.
Good society. Grey, E. C. 75c............ *Peterson.*
Good soldier. Taylor, A. A. E. 10c....... *Pres. Bd.*
Good steward. Junkin, D. X. 60c........ *Pres. Bd.*
Good stories. 30 v. 18°. $7.50............ *Lothrop.*
Good stories. 4 v. ill. 24°. ea., 50c........ **Osgood.*
Good stories for the little ones; by a teacher of infants. ill. 18°. 50c........................ *Pres. Bd.*
Good stories for our boys. 4 v. ill. 12°. ea., 75c... *Pott.*
Cont.: Marshal Vavasour, by S. W. Sadler. — Michael Penguyne, by W. H. G. Kingston. — Charlie Tyrrell, by C. E. Bowen. — Charlie Ashley, by J. G. Walker.
Good teacher. Henderson, T. S. 90c..... *Am. Bapt.*
Good things. 16°. $1.25................ *Cong. Pub.*
Good things for Cath. readers: misc. of Cath. biog., hist., travels, etc. ill. 12°. '74. $2.. *Cath. Pub.*
Good thoughts in bad times. *See* Fuller, T.
Good time coming. Arthur, T. S. $1.25.. *J. E. Potter.*
Good voices. *See* Abbott, E. A.
Good way. *See* Tomlinson, D. G.
Good woman in the wood. Planché, J. R. 15c. *French.*
Good work. Chellis, M. D. $1.50......... *Lothrop.*
Good work ser. 4 v. 16°. $6............. *Lothrop.*
Cont.: Good work, by M. D. Chellis. — Finished or not. — Mystery of the lodge. — Fabrics.
Goodale, *Miss* E. Charley Adams, the morning laborer. ('60.) New ed. ill. 18°. '72. 60c........ *Hoyt.*
— Where is the harm? ('64.) New ed. ill. 16°. '72. 80c. .... *Hoyt.*
Goodale, G: L. Wild flowers of America; with ill. by I. Sprague. pt. 1. 4°. $5.......... *Hurd & H.*
Goode, Fs. The better covenant; with pref. by Rev. J. H. Fowles. 8°. '68. 75c. .... *Leighton.*
Goodé, G. Brown. Catalogue of the fishes of the Bermudas. (Bull. of Nat. Museum, no. 5.) 8°. '76. pap., 25c........................ *Smith. Inst.*

Goodé, G. Brown, *continued.*
— — *See also* United States, *National Mus.*
— Classification of animal resources, etc. (Bull. of Nat. Museum, no. 6.) 8°. '76. pap., 25c. *Smith. Inst.*
Goode, W. H. Outposts of Zion. 12°. $1.75. *Cin. Meth. Bk. Conc.*
Goode, W: Divine rule of faith and practice. 2 v. in 1. 12°. $2 .... *McCauley.*
Goodell, A. C., *jr.* Centennial address, Oct. 5, 1874. 8°. 30c. .... *Essex.*
Goodeve, T. M. Elements of mechanism. ill. 12°. $1.50 .... *Appleton.*
Goodfellow, *Mrs.* —. Cookery as it should be. 12°. $1.75 .... *Peterson.*
Goodison, J: Drawing from objects: manual for teachers and pupils of common schools. sm. 4°. '66. 60c. .... *Ivison.*
Goodly cedars. 18°. '55. 60c. .... *Randolph.*
Goodman, Alfr. T. (*ed.*) Journal of Capt. Wm. Trent from Logstown to Pickawillany, in 1752; with letters of Gov. Robert Dinwiddie, hist. notice of the Miami Confederacy of Indians, etc. 8°. '71. $2.50 .... *Clarke.*
Goodman, Marg. Sisterhoods in the Church of Eng.; with notices of some charitable sisterhoods in the Romish church. 12°. '63. $2.50 .... *Pott.*
Goodrich, A. B. Sunday school service and tune book. sq. 18°. 20c. .... *Dutton.*
— *See also* Protestant Episc. Ch., Revised hymnal.
Goodrich, Aar. History of the character and achievements of the so-called Christopher Columbus; with app. ill. 8°. $3.50 .... *Appleton.*
Goodrich, *Rev.* C: A. Bible geog. 18°. 50c. .. *Carter.*
— Bible history of prayer. ('47.) New ed. 12°. '61. $1.25 .... *Draper.*
— Child's hist. of U. S. ('31.) New ed. sm. 4°. '48. 56c. .... *Cowperthwait.*
— History of U. S.; [also] U. S. Const. and Declaration of independence. New ed., rev. col. maps and ill. 12°. hf. roan, $1.35 .... *Ware.*
— *Same;* for schools, rev. and brought down to present time by W. H. Seavey. maps and ill. 12°. hf. roan, $1.56 .... *Ware.*
Goodrich, *Rev.* Chauncey A. Greek grammar. 16°. *net*, $1.20 .... *Hamersley.*
— Lessons in Gk. parsing. 18°. '42. *net*, 50c. ... *Peck.*
— Lessons in Lat. parsing. 18°. *net*, 50c. ..... *Peck.*
— Select British eloquence; with biog. sketches and notes. 8°. $4; shp., $4.50; hf. cf., $6.25 .. *Harper.*
Goodrich, Fk. B. ["Dick Tinto."] Court of Napoleon; or, society under the first empire; with por. of its beauties, etc. New ed. imp. 8°. $5; mor., $10 .... *Lippincott.*
— Ocean's story; or, triumphs of 30 centuries: descript. of maritime adventures, discoveries, etc., and of the rise and progress of ship-building and ocean navigation; with account of adventures beneath the sea, by E. Howland ill. 8°. '73. *$3; $4; hf. mor., $4.50 .... *Hubbard.*
— World famous women. ill. roy. 8°. '70. $6; mor., $9 .... *Rutter.*
— *See also* Brougham, J., *and* Goodrich, F. B.
— *and* Warden, F. L. Romance after marriage: comedy. 16°. pap., 15c. .... *French.*
Goodrich, S: G. ["Peter Parley."] American child's pict. hist. of U. S. ill. 16°. pap., 84c. .. *Butler.*
— Ancient history. 8°. $2 .... *Morton.*
— Balloon travels of Robert Merry and his young friends over various countries in Europe. ill. 12°. $1.50 .... *Sheldon.*
— Biographical lib. 6 v. ill. 12°. ea., $1.50 ... *Locke.*
Cont.: Famous men of modern times. — Famous men of ancient times. — Famous American Indians. — Lives of benefactors. — Lives of celebrated women. — Curiosities of human nature.
— Cabinet lib. 20 v. ill. 12°. $18 .... *Thompson.*
Comprises Youth's lib. of biog.; — of hist.; — of literature and science.

Goodrich, S: G., *continued.*
— Cottage lib. 12 v. 18°. $7.20 .... *Sheldon.*
Cont.: Make the best of it. — Right is might. — Persevere and prosper. — Tales of the sea and land. — What to do and how to do it. — Home in the sea. — Wit bought. — Truth finder. — Tale of the Revolution. — Dick Boldhero. — Take care of no. 1. — Adventures of Billy Bump.
— Four quarters of the globe. ill. 16°. $1.50 .. *Desilver.*
— Géographie élémentaire. ill. 8°. pap., $1 .... *Butler.*
— Histoire des États-Unis. 12°. $1.75 .... *Butler.*
— Historietas morales para la infancia. [Tr. from Eng. into Span.] ill. 12°. $1.50 .... *Appleton.*
— Merry stories; or, fact, fancy and fiction. ill. 12°. $2 .... *Miller.*
— Modern history. 8°. $2 .... *Morton.*
— One thousand and one lives: their beginning and ending. ill. 12°. $1.50 .... *World Pub.*
— Parley's book of quadrupeds. ill. 16°. '64. $1. *Collins & Bro.*
— Parley's [1st–3d bks.] of hist. comb. with geog. 3 v. maps and ill. sm. 4°. ea., hf. roan, $1.25 .. *Ware.*
Cont.: 1. West. hemisphere. — 2. Mod. hist. of Europe, Asia and Africa. — 3. Anc. hist.
— Parley's tales about animals. ill. 12°. $1.25 .. *Morton.*
— Peter Parley's book of fables. ill. 16°. pap., 25c. *U. P. James.*
— Peter Parley's common school hist. of the world. ill. 12°. $1.75 .... *Butler.*
— Peter Parley's juveniles. 13 v. ill. 16°. ea., 50c. *Desilver.*
Cont.: Bible stories. — Book of anecdotes. — Juvenile tales. — Tales about Africa — about America — about anc. and mod. Greece — about anc. Rome — about Asia — about Europe — about the islands in the Pacific — about the sun, moon and stars — of the sea. — Winter evening tales.
— Peter Parley's little lib. of true stories. ('34.) New ed. 8 v. ill. 16°. '69. $6 .... *Claxton.*
Cont.: Adventures of Capt. James Riley. — Captive of Nootka Sound. — The ship. — La Perouse. — The farm. — Alexander Selkirk. — The mine. — The garden.
— Peter Parley's own story. 16°. $1.25 .... *Sheldon.*
— Peter Parley's universal history. ('37.) New ed., rev. ill. and maps. 12°. '74. $1.56 .... *Ivison.*
— *Span.;* aument. con la historia de España y de la América española; por L. T. Mantilla. maps and ill. 12°. '74. $1.50 .... *Ivison.*
— Petite histoire universelle. 12°. $1.75 ..... *Butler.*
— Pictorial hist. of anc. Rome; with sketches of the hist. of modern Italy. 12°. $1.75 .... *Butler.*
— Pictorial hist. of England. 12°. $1.75 ..... *Butler.*
— Pictorial hist. of France. 12°. $1.75 .... *Butler.*
— Pictorial hist. of Greece, ancient and modern. 12°. $1.75 .... *Butler.*
— Pictorial hist. of the U. S.; with notices of other portions of Am. ill. 16°. $1.75 .... *Butler.*
— Pictorial nat. history. 12°. $1.75 .... *Butler.*
— Popular stories. 3 v. ill. 12°. $4.50 .... *Appleton.*
Cont.: Fagots for the fireside. — Parley's present. — Wanderers.
— Thousand and one stories of fact and fancy, wit and humor, rhyme, reason, etc. ill. 12°. $2 .. *Miller.*
— Youth's lib. of biog. 6 v. ill. 16°. ea., $1. *Thompson.*
Cont.: Famous men of modern times. — Lives of benefactors. — Lives of famous American Indians. — Famous men of ancient times. — Lives of celebrated women. — Curiosities of human nature.
— Youth's lib. of hist. 7 v. ill. 16°. $7 .. *Thompson.*
Cont.: Lights and shadows of Am. hist. — of European hist. — of African hist. — of Asiatic hist. — History of the Am. Indians. — Manners and customs of Am. Indians. — Manners and customs of nations.
— Youth's lib. of literature and science. 7 v. ill. 16°. $7 .... *Thompson.*
Cont.: A glance at the sciences. — Anecdotes of the animal kingdom. — Literature, ancient and modern. — Wonders of geology. — Glance at philos. — Enterprise, industry and art of man. — World and its inhabitants.
— *See also* Butler, N., *and* Goodrich, S. G.; — Defoe, Dan., Robinson Crusoe.
Note. For titles of the spurious "Peter Parley" books (not by Goodrich) *see under* Parley.

Goodspeed, Edg. J. Full hist. of the wonderful career of Moody and Sankey in Gt. Brit. and Am.; [also] Mr. Moody's sermons, Mr. Sankey's songs, etc. por. and ill. 12°. '76. $2...(?) *Goodspeed.*
— History of the great fires in Chicago and the west; with hist. of the rise and progress of Chicago; [also] a record of the great fires of the past. ill. and maps. 8°. '71. $2.50 ......(?) *Goodspeed.*
— *and* Hicks, E. W. Life of Jesus; for young people. 4°. '74. $3...................(?) *Goodspeed.*

Goodwin, *Miss* A. H. Christ in a German home. 16°. '72. 90c............................*Am. Tr.*

Goodwin, Dan. R. Southern slavery in its present aspects. 12°. '64. $1.50............*Claxton.*

Goodwin, E: Lily White: romance. 12°. pap., $1. *Lippincott.*

Goodwin, Elij. Family companion: book of sermons. 12°. $1.50............................*Chase.*

Goodwin, *Mrs.* H. B. *See* Talcott, *Mrs.* H. B.

Goodwin, H: M. Discourses on Christ and humanity, with a review, hist. and crit., of doctrines of Christ's person. 12°. $2..............*Harper.*

Goodwin, Lavina S. The little helper. ill. 16°. 50c. *Lee & S.*

Goodwin, *Mrs.* M. F. The golden rule and its fruits. ill. 18°. 35c....................*Bost. Am. Tr.*

Goodwin, Natl. Descendants of Thomas Olcott, one of the first settlers of Hartford, Conn. New ed., rev. and enl. by H. S. Olcott. 8°. '74. hf. shp., $2.................................*Munsell.*

Goodwin, T. A. Mode of man's immortality; or, the when, where, and how of the future life. 12°. '74. $1.25..............................*Ford.*

Goodwin, T: Latin and Eng. dict. (Lond.) fp. 8°. $2.....................................*Wiley.*
— Latin-Eng. and Eng.-Lat. dictionary. 2 pts. 16°. (Weale.) pt. 1, 80c.; pt. 2, 60c..........*Allyn.*

Goodwin, T: Return of prayers. 32°. 35c...*Pres. Bd.*

Goodwin, W: W. Greek grammar. ('70.) 5th ed. 12°. '75. hf. mor., $1.56................*Ginn.*
— Greek moods and tenses. ('60.) 6th ed. 12°. '75. $1.75....................................*Ginn.*
— *and* Allen, J. H. Greek reader; with maps, notes, references, etc. ('71.) 4th ed. 12°. '76. hf. mor., $2.................................*Ginn.*

Goody Two-Shoes. [Toy-book.] ill. 4°. $1; 50c. *Routledge.*

Goody Two-Shoes picture-book (The). demy 4°. '74. $2.50...............................*Routledge.*

Goose with the golden eggs. Mayhew, A., *and* Edwards, S. 15c................*De Witt; French.*

Göpp, C. Leitfaden d. parlamentareschen Geschäfts-Ordnung f. Deutsch-Amerikaner. 32°. '71. bds., 25c.; 30c..................................*Steiger.*

Gordian knot. Brooks, C. S. 50c..........*Harper.*

Gordon, A. *See* England, Chancery reports.

Gordon, A. J. Congregational worship. 12°. '75. $1. *H. A. Young.*
— In Christ; or, the believer's union with his Lord. 12°. '72. $1.50..................*H. A. Young.*
— New vestry hymn and tune book. 12°. '72. $1. *H. A. Young.*
— *See also* Caldwell, S. L., *and* Gordon, A. J.

Gordon, C. A. Family Sabbath day miscellany. ill. 12°. $1.50..............................*Sower.*

Gordon, Clar. ["Vieux Moustache."] An old boy's stories. 2 v. ill. 16°. '72. ea., $1.25..*Hurd & H.*
Cont.: Boarding school days. — Our fresh and salt tutors.

Gordon, Eliz. (*Duchess of*). Memoirs. 16°. $1.25. *Carter.*

Gordon, G: The pinetum: synopsis of all the coniferous plants at present known; with descript., hist. and synonyms, and add. index of popular names by H. G. Bohn. 2d ed., enl. 8°. (Lond.) $9 ....*Putnam.*

Gordon, G: H. History of the 2d Mass. Reg. of Inf. 8°. '75. $2.........................*Williams.*

Gordon, *Miss* Helen. Questions on life of our Saviour: infant ser. 18°. 20c. — primary ser., 30c. — advanced ser., 30c..........................*Dutton.*

Gordon, J. *See* England, Exchequer reports.

Gordon, J. E. H. Elementary book on heat. cr. 8°. '75. 75c..............................*Macmillan.*

Gordon, Lucie (*Lady*) Duff. Last letters from Egypt; [also] Letters from the Cape; with memoir by Mrs. Ross. por. cr. 8°. '75. $2....*Macmillan.*

Gordon, *Mrs.* Ma. Memoir of John Wilson (Christopher North). ill. and por. cr 8°. $1.75; hf. cf., $3.50..............................*Widdleton.*

Gordon, S. T. Piano-forte without a master. obl. 8°. 50c......................................*Gordon.*
— Reed organ and melodeon without a master. obl. 8°. 50c. ....*Gordon.*

Gordon, Wa. [Plays.] 7 v. 16°. ea., pap., 15c. *French.*
Cont.: Dearest mamma: comedietta. — Duchess or nothing: farce. — Home for a holiday: farce. — My wife's relations: comedietta. — Odd lot: farce. — Old Trusty. — Through fire and water: comic drama.
— Dearest mamma: comedietta. 16°. pap., 15c. *De Witt.*
— My wife's relations: comedietta. 16°. pap., 15c. *Ames.*

Gordon, W: R. Child's Scripture guide. 18°. 40c. *N. Y. Ref. Ch. Bd.*
— Church of God and her sacraments. 16°. 75c. *N. Y. Ref. Ch. Bd.*
— Life of Henry Ostrander; with sel. sermons. 12°. $2...........................*N. Y. Ref. Ch. Bd.*
— Supreme Godhead of Christ. 12°. 65c. *N. Y. Ref. Ch. Bd.*

Gordon Lodge. White, M. A. $1.50; $2. *Kelly, P. & Co.*

Gordon Warren. 12°. pap., 25c.............*Radde.*

Gore, *Mrs.* Cath. G. Novels. 6 v. 8°. pap. . *Harper.*
Cont.: Banker's wife, 50c. — Birthright, 25c. — Queen of Denmark, 50c. — Peers and parvenus, 50c. — Self, 75c. — Story of a royal favorite, 50c.
— Abednego, the money-lender: a romance. 8°. pap., 25c. ....*U. P. James.*
— *Same.* 8°. pap., 50c.....................*Peterson.*
— Craigallen Castle. 8°. pap., 50c..........*Dick & F.*
— King O'Neill: drama. 16°. pap., 15c.......*French.*
— Maid of Croissey: drama. 16°. pap., 15c...*French.*
— Progress and prejudice. 12°. $1.........*De Witt.*

Gorham, Elsie (*pseud.*) *See* Carter, *Mrs.* —.

Gorilla hunters. Ballantyne, R. M. $1.25. *Claxton; Porter.*

Gorling, A., Meyer, E., *and* Waltman, A. Art treasures of Germany: pictures from galleries of Dresden, Cassell, Brunswick, etc.; with por. and notices. 30 pts. 4°. ea., *50c; — in German. 60 pts. ea., *60c..........................*S. Walker.*

Gorton, D. A. Drift of medical philosophy: essay. 12°. 75c.; pap., 60c.......................*Lippincott.*
— Essay on principles of mental hygiene. 12°. $1.75. *Lippincott.*

Gorton, S: Letter to Natl. Morton. Warwick, 1669. [Reprint.] 4°. pap., 25c...................*Sabin.*
— Simplicitie's defence against seven-headed policy. London, 1646. [Reprint.] 4°. pap., $1.50..*Sabin.*
— *Same;* ed. by W. R. Staples. roy. 8°. (Providence.) '35. $2.50..............................*Rider.*

Goschen, G: J. Reports and speeches on local taxation. 8°. '72. $3.......................*Macmillan.*

Gospel among the animals. Osgood, S. 25c.; 10c. *Wells.*

Gospel among the Bechuanas, and other tribes of s. Africa. 18°. 75c...................*Am. S. S.*

Gospel among the Caffres: story of Rev. Moffat and his labors in Africa. ill. 16°. $1.....*Bost. Am. Tr.*

Gospel among the Dakotahs. Riggs, S. R. $1.50. *Cong. Pub.*

Gospel and its fruits. Wilson, J. H. $1.25...*Carter.*

Gospel and mod. life. Davies, J. L. $1.75.. *Macmillan.*
Gospel for the poor. Mason, J. M. 20c.....*Am. Tr.*
Gospel fountain. Wood, J. 75c............*Pres. Bd.*
Gospel fruits: essay in opposition to caste. 16°. 50c. *West Tr.*
Gospel hymns and sacred songs. *See* Bliss, P. P., *and* Sankey, I. D.
Gospel in Enoch. Tucker, H. H. $1.25..*Lippincott.*
Gospel in the riviera. Wright, J. McN. 90c. *Un. B. Pub.*
Gospel its own advocate. Griffin, G. $1.25..*Appleton.*
Gospel life of Jesus. Davis, L. A. $1.25..*Lothrop.*
Gospel liturgy: prayer book for churches, congregations and families. 18°. shp., 75c.; mor., $4. *Universalist.*
Gospel ministry. Brown, J. 25c.; 15c..... *West. Tr.*
Gospel ministry. White, W. S. 65c.......*Pres. Bd.*
Gospel mystery of sanctification. Marshall, W. 60c. *U. P. Bd. of Pub.*
Gospel of Jesus Christ. Carlile, R. 10c....*Mendum.*
Gospel of the kingdom. Ward, H. D. $2.50..*Claxton.*
Gospel of the kingdom, according to holy men of old; by author of "Samson, a myth-story of the sun." 2 v. 12°. '75–'76. ea., pap., 50c.........*Colby.*
Gospel of the Pentateuch. Kingsley, C. $1.25. *Macmillan.*
Gospel of the resurrection. Westcott, B. F. $2. *Macmillan.*
Gospel psalmist. Adams, J. G. $1.50..*Universalist.*
Gospel singer. Phillips, P. 35c.............*Ditson.*
Gospel songs. Bliss, P. P. 50c.; 35c.; $1.50..*Church.*
Gospel sonnets. Erskine, R. 75c............*Carter.*
Gospel sunbeams. 18°. '68. 45c.; 75c.......*Am. Tr.*
Gospel themes. Finney, C. C. $1.50 .....*Goodrich.*
Gospel treasury. Mimpriss, R. $1.75; $7.50..*Dodd.*
Gospel trumpet. Shaw, K. 15c.............*Church.*
Gospel workers. Cross, J. 25c. ....*Am. Tr.*
Gospel worthy of all acceptation. Fuller, A. 40c. *Cong. Pub.*
Gospels. *See* Bible.
Gospels for Sundays and festivals during the year. 32°. '60. pap., 19c..............*Cunningham.*
Gospels in the 2d cent. Sanday, W. $3.75..*Macmillan.*
Goss, C. C. American Methodism: statistical hist. of the 1st century. 12°. $1...*Cin. Meth. Bk. Conc.*
Goss, Warren Lee. The soldier's story of his captivity at Andersonville, Belle Isle and other rebel prisons. New ed. ill. 12°. *$2.50.....*Lee & S.*
Gosse, Ph. H. Evenings at the microscope: researches among the minuter organs and forms of animal life. 12°. $1.50......................*Appleton.*
— *Same.* ill. 8°. '74. $2......................*Pott.*
— History of the Jews, from Christian era to dawn of reformation. 16°. '74. $1...............*Pott.*
— Life in its lower and higher forms. 12°. $1.50..*Carter.*
— Romance of natural hist. ill. 12°. $1.25..*Lippincott.*
— Wonders of the great deep. ill. 12°. *$2; $2.75; mor., $3.50........................*Quak. City.*
— Year at the shore. col. ill. cr. 8°. $4.50..*Routledge.*
Gossip, G. H. D. Chess-players' manual. 8°. '74. $3.50. *Routledge.*
Gossip. Harris, A., *and* Williams, T. J. 15c...*French.*
Gossner, J: Anklopfen (Das) des Heilandes. 18°. '50. 25c...............................*Am. Tr.*
— *Dutch.* 18°. '54. 15c....................*Am. Tr.*
— Uralte katholische Glaube (Der). 18°. '49. 25c. *Am. Tr.*
— *Span.* El catolicismo primitivo. 18°. '52. 20c. *Am. Tr.*
— Schatzkästchen. 12°. '56. 90c............*Am. Tr.*
— *Same.* sm. 8°. $1–$4.....................*Kohler.*
— Tag (Der) des Herrn. 18°. '50. 25c.......*Am. Tr.*
— Weg (Der) zur Seligkeit. 18°. '54. 25c....*Am. Tr.*

Gostwick, Jos. English poets: essays, with twelve por. by C. Jäger. 8°. '75. $10.......*Stroefer.*
— *See also* Jäger, C.; — Krämer, P.
— *and* Harrison, Rob. Outlines of Germ. literature. ('73.) New ed. 12°. '74. $2.50...........*Holt.*
Gother, J: Papist misrepresented and represented; or, a two-fold character of popery. 18°. '63. per 100, $10.................................*Fox.*
— *Same.* 16°. 25c..........................*Strong.*
— *See also* Manual of controversy.
Gothic album for cabinet-makers: coll. of designs. ill. obl. roy. 8°. '68. $3...............*Baird.*
Gott, Ada Augusta. Dare Fairfax. 12°. $1....*Hale.*
Gott, H: Wizard of the moor: melodrama. 16°. pap., 15c...................................*French.*
Gottes Walten auf dem Meere. Bickel, P. W. 25c. *Germ. Bapt.*
Gottfried der junge Einsiedler. Schmid, C. v. 20c. *Morwitz.*
Gottheil, G., *and* Davis, A. J. Temple Emanu-el: hymn-book for schools. 16°. '75. bds., 25c. *Pond.*
Gotthelf, Jer. (*pseud.*) *See* Bitzius, Alb.
Gotthold, J. Newton. The vow of the Ornani: drama. 16°. pap., 15c..........................*Ames.*
— When women weep: comedietta. 16°. pap., 15c. *Ames.*
Gotthold's emblems. *See* Scriver, C.
Gottlieb Frey. ill. 16°. $1.10. ....(?)*Luth. Pub.*
Gottschall, R. Gedankenharmonie v. Goethe u. Schiller. 12°. '72. $1.25; pap., 75c.........*Zickel.*
Götz v. Berlichingen. *See* Goethe, J. W. v.
Gough, J: B. Autobiography and personal recollections. 8°. '70. *$3.25; leath., $3.75; hf. cf., $4.50 ....*C. A. Nichols.*
Goulburn, E. M. Acts of the deacons: lectures. 12°. '67. $2...............................*Pott.*
— Child Samuel. 16°. '76. $1.25..............*Pott.*
— Farewell counsels of a pastor to his flock. 16°. '65. $1...*Pott.*
— Gospel of the childhood. 16°. '73. $1.25.....*Pott.*
— Holy catholic church: its divine ideal, ministry and institutions. 12°. '73. $1.50.............*Pott.*
— Idle word (The): relig. essays upon the gift of speech. 16°. '67. 75c. ....*Pott.*
— *Same.* 12°. 75c.......................*Appleton.*
— Introduction to devot. study of the Scriptures. 16°. '67. $1....................................*Pott.*
— *Same.* 12°. $1.........................*Appleton.*
— Manual of confirmation; with introd. note and an appeal, by H. C. Potter. 16°. pap., 15c...*Dutton.*
— Office of the holy communion in the Book of common prayer: lectures. 12°. $1......*Appleton.*
— *Same.* 12°. '75. $1.75......................*Pott.*
— Popular objections to Book of common prayer considered. 16°. '68. $1..................*Pott.*
— Principles of the cathedral system vindicated, and enforced upon members of cathedral foundations. 12°. '70. $2..............................*Pott.*
— Pursuit of holiness: sequel to "Thoughts on personal religion." 12°. 75c...........*Appleton.*
— *Same.* 16°. '76. 75c.; pap., 25c............*Pott.*
— Sermons on various occasions. 12°. $1...*Appleton.*
— Short devotional forms. 32°. '76. 60c.........*Pott.*
— Thoughts on personal religion. 16°. '76. $1..*Pott.*
— *Same;* with pref. by G. Houghton. 12°. $1...*Appleton.*
— (*ed.*) Family prayers. 12°. '68. $1.50. 18°. 50c...*Pott.*
Gould, A: A. Mollusca and shells. *See* Wilkes, C: U. S. explor. expedition.
— Shells. *See* Gilliss, J. M.
— *See also* Agassiz, L., *and* Gould, A. A.
Gould, B: Apthorp. Latin grammar. *See* Adam, A.
Gould, B: A., *jr.* Address before Am. Assoc. for Adv. of Sci., 1869. 8°. pap., 25c. *Am. Assoc. Adv. Sci.*
— Ancestry of Zacheus Gould of Topsfield. 8°. '72. $1. *Essex.*

Gould, B: A., *jr.*, *continued.*
— Military and anthrop. statistics of Am. soldiers. (Report of U. S. Sanitary Com.) 8°. '69. $6.50. *Hurd & H.*
— On the transatlantic longitude. 4°. '69. pap., $1. *Smith. Inst.*
Gould, E: S. Good English; or, popular errors in philology. 12°. $1.25 .... *Widdleton.*
Gould, Edn. Swedenborg and modern biblical criticism. 16°. '70. 62c. .... *H. H. Carter.*
Gould, G. H. The Bible: its place and power in church and state. 24°. pap., 10c. *H. E. Simmons.*
Gould, Ja. Principles of pleading in civil actions. 4th ed., with notes by G. Gould. 8°. '73. shp., $5. *Gould.*
Gould, Ja. L. *See* Sheville, J., *and* Gould, J. L.
Gould, *Miss* Jeanie T. Marjorie's quest. ill. 12°. '72. $1.50 .... *Osgood.*
Gould, J: Humming birds. *See* Jardine, *Sir* W., Naturalist's lib.
Gould, J: E. Amphion: four, five and six part songs for male voices; with words by H. A. Clarke. 5 bks. 16°. '68. $5. — Vocal pts., $4; ea., $1.25. *Ditson.*
— *See also* White, E. L., *and* Gould, J. E.
Gould, Josiah. *See* Arkansas, Digest of statutes.
Gould, Lucius D. American stair-builder's guide. ill. 8°. '75. $3 .... *Bicknell.*
— Carpenters and builders' assistant. pl. 8°. '74. $3. *Bicknell.*
Gould, S. Baring. *See* Baring-Gould, S.
Gould, T: R. The tragedian: essay on the histrionic genius of J. B. Booth. por. 12°. $1.75 .. *Hurd & H.*
Gould, Tracy. The bride of the broken vow: poem. sm. 32°. '74. pap., 75c. .... *W. H. Young.*
Goulding, F. R. Frank Gordon; or, when I was a little boy. 18°. 75c. .... (?) *Martien.*
— Marooner's Island; or, Dr. Gordon in search of his children. ('68.) 7th ed. 16°. '75. $1.50 .. *Claxton.*
— Woodruff stories. 3 v. ill. 16°. '70. $1.50 .. *Claxton.*
Cont.: Sapelo; or, child life on the tidewater. — Nacoochie; or, boy life on the mountains. — Saloquah; or, boy life among the Indians.
— Young Marooners on the Florida coast; or, Robert and Harold. ill. 16°. $1.50 .... *Claxton.*
Gouley, J. W. S. Diseases of the urinary organs; incl. stricture of the urethra, affections of the prostate and stone in the bladder. ill. 8°. $3.75 .. *W. Wood.*
Goullon, H. Scrofulous affections and the advantages of their treatment by homœop.; tr. by E. Tietze. 8°. $2 .... *Boericke.*
Gounod, C: F. Choral music: collection of compositions and arrangements. 8°. pap., 50c. .. *Ditson.*
— Faust: lyric dramas; adapted to Eng. and Ital. words. 4°. '64. bds., $1.50 .... *Ditson.*
— — *See also* Ditson.
— Messe solennelle: (St. Cecilia); ed. with piano forte accomp. by J. Barnby. 8°. '70. $1.12; bds., $1; pap., 80c. .... *Ditson.*
— Romeo and Juliet; — Sappho. *See* Ditson.
Gouraud, Fs. Fauvel. *See* Fauvel-Gouraud, Fs.
Gouraud, *Mme.* Julie. Four gold pieces; tr. 12°. $1.25; pap., 50c. .... *Scribner, W. & A.*
— Little boy's (A) story; tr. by H. Glyndon. ill. 16°. $1.50 .... *Hurd & H.*
— Two children of St. Domingo; tr. 12°. $1.25; pap., 50c. .... *Scribner, W. & A.*
Gournay, P. F. de. First steps in French. 16°. '66. 60c. .... *Kelly, P. & Co.*
Goûters (Les) de la grand'mère. *See* Carraud, Z. T.
Gouttes de rosée. Pylodet, L. 75c. .... *Holt.*
Gove, Ma. S. Lectures to women on anat. and physiol.; with app. on water cure. 12°. $1 ...... *Harper.*
Governess. *See* Sherwood, *Mrs.* M. M.
Governess and her pupil, and other stories. 18°. 70c. *Pres. Bd.*
Government and communion practised by the Congregational Churches in the U. S., represented by elders and managers in a national council at Boston, 1865. 16°. 50c. .... *Cong. Pub.*
Governor (*pseud.*) *See* Morford, H:
Governor's pardon. Baker, H. N. W. $1.25 .. *Graves.*
Governor's wife. Mildenhall, T. 15c. ...... *French.*
Govinda Sámanta. Day, L. B. $1.75 ... *Macmillan.*
Gow, Alex. M. Good morals and gentle manners. 12°. '73. $1.25 .... *Wilson, H. & Co.*
Gow, N. *See* England, Common law reports.
Gowan, W: Bibliotheca Americana. 5 v. in 1. 8°. '75. $5 .... *Munsell.*
Gowrie. *See* James, G. P. R.
Goyder, T: *and* D: G. Spiritual reflections for every day; with morning and evening prayers. 3 v. cr. 8°. $2.50 .... *H. H. Carter.*
Gozzi, *Conte* Carlo. Turandot. *See* Schiller, J. F. v.
Grabowski, Stanislaus (*Graf*). Schön Käthchen v. Heilbronn. 8°. $2; pap., $1.50 .. *F. W. Thomas.*
Grace, Pierce C. Outlines of history. 18°. 50c. *Strong.*
Grace Abbott; or, the Sunday tea party. 18°. '63. 30c. .... *Am. Tr.*
— *Same.* 18°. '67. 40c. .. *N. Y. Ref. Ch. Bd.; Pres. Com.*
— *Same.* 18°. 50c. .... *Pres. Bd.*
Grace abounding to the chief of sinners. *See* Bunyan, J.
Grace and apostleship. Cushman, R. W. 40c. *Am. Bapt.*
Grace and Clara, and other tales. 18°. 70c. .. *Pres. Bd.*
— *See also* New juvenile lib.
Grace and glory. Wood, J. 75c. .... *Pres. Bd.*
Grace and her money-box. *See* Aunty Ray's little lib.
Grace and Polly. Dunning, A. K. 35c. .... *Pres. Bd.*
Grace and Rosabelle. 18°. 60c.; 70c. .... *Am. Bapt.*
Grace and truth under twelve different aspects. Mackay, W. P. $1; 50c. *Gospel; Randolph; Revell.*
Grace Avery's influence. Dunning, A. K. $1.50. *Lothrop.*
Grace Barclay's diary. Post, L. M. $1.50 .. *Randolph.*
Grace Braman. 18°. 50c. .... *Cong. Pub.*
Grace Church [N. Y.] collection of sacred music; with organ accomp. by W. A. King. obl. f°. '52. $2.25 .... *Ditson.*
Grace Courtney. *See* Henry, M. H.
Grace culture. Hunt, E. M. $1.20 .... *Pres. Bd.*
Grace Darling. Stirling, E. 15c. .... *French; Happy.*
Grace Dermott; or, help for the afflicted. 18°. 75c. *Pres. Bd.*
Grace Dermott; or, how to lighten heavy burdens. 18°. 60c. .... *Am. S. S.*
Note. Same as above?
Grace Dudley. Peterson, C. J. 50c. .... *Peterson.*
Grace for grace. James, W. $1.50 .... *Dodd.*
Grace Hale. Davis, C. E. K. 60c. .... *Hoyt.*
Grace Hall. *See* Silvertone lib.
Grace Harland; or, Christ's path to happiness; by author of "Little watchman." 18°. 75c. *Pres. Bd.*
Grace Harriet. Lord, C. 25c. .... *Am. Tr.*
Grace Houghton's story. 18°. 75c. .... *Dutton.*
Grace Huntley. Holl, H. 15c. .... *French.*
Grace Huntly. Hall, A. M. $1.25 ... *Scribner, W. & A.*
Grace Irving's friends; — vacation. *See* Keene, S. F.
Grace Kennedy stories. *See* Kennedy, G.
Grace Lee. Kavanagh, J. $1.25 .... *Appleton.*
Grace Maitland; or, the childhood of Jesus. 18°. 28c.; 35c. .... *Am. Bapt.*
Grace Manning. 8°. pap., 25c. .... *De Witt.*

Grace Mansfield's experiment. Dunning, A. K. 90c. *Garrigues.*
Grace Martin. ('72.) New ed. 16°. '73. $1.25.. *Hoyt.*
Grace Milford. 18°. 60c. .... *Dutton.*
Grace Morton. Meaney, M. L. $1.... *Cunningham.*
Grace of charity. 18°. 50c.................. *Nelson.*
Grace of Christ. Plumer, W. S. $1.40 .... *Pres. Bd.*
Grace of the ministry. Denton, W. $7.50 .... *Pott.*
Grace O'Gara, the little mountain guide; or, how to be happy; by author of "Johnny McKay." ill. 18°. '66. 75c. ...*N. Y. Ref. Ch. Bd.; Pres. Com.*
Grace O'Malley. Ainsworth, W. H. 50c...*Peterson.*
Grace O'Malley. Maxwell, W. H. 50c..... *Peterson.*
Grace Raymond; or, the evil and cure of passionate temper. 18°. 40c.................. *Am. S. S.*
Grace Roche's legacy. 18°. 50c.........(?) *Martien.*
Grace Tilden. 16°. $1.25............... *Cong. Pub.*
Grace triumphant: memoir of John Fleming. 18°. 35c. *Am. S. S.*
Grace Truman. Ford, S. R. $1.50 .... *Sheldon.*
Grace Warren. Dayton, L. H. 40c........ *So. Bapt.*
Grace Welden; or, the beautiful bonnet girl. 8°. pap., 25c.............................. *Dick & F.*
Grace Wilard. 8°. pap., 25c. .... *De Witt.*
Grace Willoughby. Maxwell, W. H. 50c... *U. P. James.*
Grace's rose. *See* New Year lib.
Grace's visit. ill. 18°. 75c............. *Bost. Am. Tr.*
— *Same.* ill. 16°. '67. 80c................. *Am. Tr.*
— *See also* Golden sheaves lib.; — Lyntonville lib.
Grace's visit. Bradley, M. E. 80c. .... *Lothrop.*
Graces of Mary: devotions for May. 24°. 60c.; 75c. *Sadlier.*
Gracey, S. L. Anniversary gems; for S.-school celebrations. ('69.) 3d ed. 18°. '74. 60c. *Perkinpine.*
Gracie, the child emancipator. *See* Shaw, *Miss* C. E.
Gracie Goodwin. *See* Mudge, Z. A.
Gracie's lib. 3 v. 16°. $3.75..........(?) *Martien.*
Cont.: Gracie's mission. — Charity Helstone. — Margaret's secret.
Gracie's mission. Pierson, H. W. $1.25..(?) *Martien.*
Graciosa and Percinet. Planché, J. R. 15c...*French.*
Graded readers. *See* New.
Graduated Sunday-school text-books. 3 nos. 18°. ea., per doz., $2.40................ *Meth. Bk. Conc.*
Cont.: Lessons in Bible hist. (Old Test.) — Lessons in New Test. hist. — Bible morality.
Græca minora; with Eng. notes and lexicon. 12°. hf. roan, $1.13..................... *Lippincott.*
Graeter, Fs. (*ed.*) Hydriatics; or, manual of the water cure; especially as practised by Vincent Priesnitz in Graefenberg. 18°. 50c........ *Boericke.*
Graf Hugo v. Craenhove. 12°. 35c.; pap., 15c. *Benziger.*
Graf von Monte-Christo. *See* Dumas, A.
Graff, A. Elementary Germ. grammar; with exercises. 8°. '75. hf. mor., $1.25.............. *Schmidt.*
Graffiti d' Italia. Story, W. W. $3.75. *Scribner, W. & A.*
Gräfin Julia. *See* Schmid, C. v.
Grafted trees; or, the two natures. 18°. '64. 40c. *Randolph.*
Grafton, H: D. Treatise on the camp and march; [also on] construction of field-works and milit. bridges; with app. of artillery ranges, etc. 12°. '63. 75c....................... *Van Nostrand.*
Grafton family (The). Sargent, G. E. $1...*Nelson.*
Graglia, C. *or* G. A. Italian dictionary. 16°. $1.75. *G. R. Lockwood.*
— Italian-Eng. and Eng.-Ital. dict. 18°. $1..*Routledge.*
Graham, And. J. Biographical sketch. [Phonographic.] 12°. 25c.; 50c............. *Graham.*
— Brief longhand. 12°. 63c............... *Graham.*

Graham, And. J., *continued.*
— Easy spelling and reading ser. 3 v. 12°... *Graham.*
Cont.: Phonetic spelling book, 14c. — First phonetic read. bk., 19c. — Second phonetic read. bk., 58c.
— First standard-phonog. reader; eng. in corresponding style and ill. with notes and ref. 12°. $1.58. — Key. 58c.......................... *Graham.*
— Handbook of standard or Am. phonography. 12°. $2............ *Appleton; Lee & S.; Lippincott.*
— *Same.* 12°. $2.20...................... *Graham.*
— Little teacher. [Phonography.] 12°. 75c.; pap., 50c. .... *Graham.*
— Phonographic odds and ends. 12°. 75c.... *Graham.*
— Second standard-phonog. reader; eng. in report. style; with key and notes. 12°. $1.87.. *Graham.*
— Standard phonog. dict. 12°. $5; mor., $7.. *Graham.*
— Synopsis of Eng. grammar. 12°. 75c..... *Graham.*
— Synopsis of standard phonog. 12°. 55c... *Graham.*
Graham, Austyn. Will she have him? [Fiction.] ill. 8°. (Lond.) pap., 30c.............. *Am. News.*
Graham, D. M. Life of Clement Phinney. 12°. 75c. *Freewill.*
Graham, Ennis. Not without thorns. [Fiction.] 8°. $1.25; pap., 75c....................... *Estes.*
— Tell me a story. [Juvenile.] fp. 8°. '75. $1.50. *Macmillan.*
Graham, G: F. English synonymes; ed. by Prof. Reed. 12°. $1.50.................. *Appleton.*
Graham, Grace (*pseud.*) *See* Titterington, *Mrs.* S. B.
Graham, Ma. Fanny Percy's knight errant. 12°. '76. $1 .... *Nat. Temp.*
— Gertrude Terry. 16°. $1 35............ *Pres. Bd.*
— Grandfather's last work. 18°. 40c....... *Am. S. S.*
— The whole armor, thereby saved from temptation. ('70.) New ed. ill. 16°. '74. $1.25...... *Hoyt.*
Graham, Ma. Jane. Test of truth; with introd. by Rev. G. W. Samson. 18°. 40c........... *Am. Bapt.*
— Works; or, truth and grace; with memoir. por. 16°. $1.10............................ *Am. S. S.*
Graham, Sylvester. Chastity: lectures to young men, with appendix by R. T. Trall. 12°. '36. pap., 50c.................................. *Wells.*
— Lectures on the science of human life; with index and biog. sketch of author. 12°. '43. $3.. *Wells.*
— Philosophy of sacred hist. considered in relation to human aliment and the wines of Scripture. 12°. '54. $3.50............................ *Wells.*
Graham-Taverner, *Mrs.* F. *See* Taverner, *Mrs.* F. G.
Grahame, Edith. Terrenia. 18°. 50c....... *Pres. Bd.*
Grahame, Nellie (*pseud.*) *See* Dunning, *Mrs.* A. K.
Grahams (The). 16°. 75c.................. *Dodd.*
Grahams (The). Bell, C. D. $1.75..*Scribner, W. & A.*
Grain in the husk. 18°. 40c................ *Dutton.*
Graindorge, F: T: (*pseud.*) *See* Taine, H. A.
Grains for the grangers. Smith, S. $1.75..*J. E. Potter.*
Grains of gold. ill. 18°. 70c.............. *Pres. Bd.*
Grains of gold. Bartol, C. A. 60c........ *Am. Unit.*
Graley, A. A. *See* Kingsbury, H., *and* Graley, A. A.
Gramática de la Academia española. 12°. '53. $1. *G. R. Lockwood.*
Gramm, C. E. Erstes Rechnenbuch. 12°. 20c...*Kohler.*
— Facitbuch. 12°. 10c..................... *Kohler.*
— Kleine Elementarschüler (Der). 12°. 25c...*Kohler.*
Grammar made easy. 12°. pap., 20c. .... *Hurst.*
Grammar school chorus; [incl.] Wilhelm's Method of teaching vocal music, [and] Selections by J. B. Sharland. 8°. '60. bds., 80c........... *Ditson.*
Grammar school hymn book. 16°. 50c. *Potter, A. & Co.*
Grammar school trio. Heath, W. F. 10c...*Brainard.*
Grammont, Philibert (*Comte*) de. *See* Hamilton, *Count* A.
Granada, Luis de. Counsels on holiness of life; tr. from the Span.; ed. by Rev. O. Shipley. 16°. '71. $1.50 .... *Dutton.*

Granada, Luis de, *continued.*
— Memorial of a Christian life; tr.; rev. by Rev. F. A. L'Estrange. 18°. 75c. . . . . *Cath. Pub.*
— *Same.* New ed., rev.; with pref. by one of the Dominican Fathers of N.Y. 16°. 75c. . . *Benziger.*
Grand, P. M. Compendio de aritmética elemental. 12°. 25c. . . . . *Appleton.*
Grand Army of the Republic. Ritual; with signs of recognition, pass words, grip, etc.; [also] Ritual of the Machinists and Blacksmiths' Union. 12°. pap., 25c. . . . . *E. A. Cook.*
Grand cheap lib.; for the school and home. no. 1. 50 v. ill. 16°. $26. — Same. no. 2. 50 v. ill. large 16°. $28. . . . . *Am. S. S.*
Grand defect (The); or, Helen and her cousin Julia. 18°. 40c. . . . . *Am. S. S.*
Grand Lodge. *See* Freemasons.
Grande duchesse. *See* Ditson.
Grandeur des Romains. Montesquieu, C. de S. de. $1.50. . . . . *G. R. Lockwood.*
Grandfather (The). Pickering, E. 50c. . . . . *Harper.*
Grandfather Gregory. Mogridge, G. 40c. . . *So. Meth.*
Grandfather Merrie; or, the command and the promise. 18°. 50c. . . . . *Am. S. S.*
— *See also* Select lib. for boys.
Grandfather Milly's luck. Samuels, A. F. 50c. *Lee & S.*
Grandfather Percy (*pseud.*) Homes of the birds; or, nests and their builders. ill. 18°. 50c. . . *Nelson.*
Grandfather Whitehead. Lemon, M. 15c. . . *French.*
Grandfather's Bible. 16°. 80c. . . . . *Cong. Pub.*
Grandfather's chair. *See* Hawthorne, N.
Grandfather's darling. *See* Hoffmann, J.
Grandfather's faith. Mathews, J. A. $1.10. . *Carter.*
Grandfather's last work. Graham, M. 40c. . . *Am. S. S.*
Grandfather's Nell. 16°. $1.25. . . . . *Carter.*
Grandfather's pocket-book. Johnson, V. W. $1. *Lockwood, B. & Co.*
Grandfather's stories. ill. cr. 4°. $1.50; $2. *J. E. Potter.*
Grandfather's stories about Am. hist. Dodge, N. $1.25; $1. . . . . *Lee & S.*
Grandfather's story. 16°. 75c. . . . . *Claremont.*
Grandfather's story. *See* French's serio-comic dramas.
Grandfather's visit. *See* Home lib.
Grandma Berry's secret. Sanford, D. P. 20c.; 15c. *Dutton.*
Grandma Crosby's household. Farman, E. $1. . *Lothrop.*
Grandma Foster's sunbeam. *See* Finley, M. F.
Grandma Gray. *See* Robin Ranger's lib.
Grandma Merritt's stories. 16°. 90c. . . . . . *Am. S. S.*
Grandmama Wise; or, visits to Rose Cottage. 18°. 75c. . . . . *Pres. Bd.*
Grandmamma Gilbert. Mogridge, G. 40c. . . *So. Meth.*
Grandmamma's pocket ser. 7 v. 18°. $2.50. . *Pres. Bd.*
Cont.: Persevering Dick. — Our little fruit gatherers. — Caring for God's sparrows. — Kitty's knitting needles. — Every little helps. — Will and the way. — Seaside rambles.
Grandmamma's relics. Bowen, C. E. 75c. . . *Nelson.*
Grandmamma's Sunshine. 18°. 75c. . . . . *Carter.*
Grandmamma's trunkful of stories. Parker, C. E. R. 50c. . . . . *Am. Tr.*
Grandma's patience. Butler, M. R. 40c. . . . . . *Chase.*
Grandma's story about St. Bartholomew's Eve. Cousin George. 35c. . . . . *Pres. Bd.*
Grandma's strong box. May, C. L. 75c. *H. A. Young.*
Grandma's wardrobe. Marshall, E. 75c. (?) *Martien.*
Grandmother; or, when I was a child. 18°. 25c. *Am. S. S.*
Grandmother and granddaughter. *See* Storme, T.
Grandmother Brown's school days. Guernsey, L. E. $1.50. . . . . *Am. S. S.*
Grandmother Hope (*pseud.*) *See* Knight, *Mrs.* S. G.
Grandmother True; or, when I was a little girl. ('60.) New ed. ill. 18°. '71. 50c. . . . . *Hoyt.*
Grandmother's curiosity cabinet; tr. by A. B. Cooke. ill. 16°. '69. $1. *Dutton.*
Grandmother's lib. 6 v. ill. 16°. $4.50. . *Appleton.*
Cont.: Nutcracker and mouse king. — Pleasure and profit. — Fairy stories. — At home and abroad. — Flower pictures. — The pet bird.
Grandmother's money. Robinson, F. W. 50c. *De Witt.*
Grandmother's parable. 18°. 30c. . . . . *Pres. Bd.*
Grandmother's stories for her children. Moore, S. *net*, 15c.; 10c. . . . . *Friends Bk. Assoc.*
Grandmother's story. Ballard, J. P. 50c. . . *West. Tr.*
Grandmother's story. *See* New Year lib.
Grandpapa's adventure. *See* Prairie books.
Grandpapa's Carlie. *See* Gano.
Grandpapa's home. Frost, S. A. 75c. . . . . . . *Am. Tr.*
Grandpapa's keepsakes. *See* Cupples, *Mrs.* A. J.
Grandpapa's talks. Scudder, J. 2 v. 60c. *N. Y. Ref. Ch. Bd.*
Grandpa's darlings. Alden, I. M. $1.25. . . . *Lothrop.*
Grandpa's house. Weeks, H. C. $1.25. . . . *Hurd & H.*
Grandpa's pleasant companions. *See* Herd boy ser.
Grandpa's stories. Bullard, A. 25c. . . . . *Lee & S.*
Grangé, Eug. (*pseud.*) *See* Basté, E. P.
Grange (The) illustrated. Wells, J. G. $2. . *J. G. Wells.*
Grange lib. 4 v. 12°. $4. . . . . *Nelson.*
Cont.: Hayslop Grange, by E. Leslie. — Eliza's basket, by E. Leslie. — Arthur's victory, by A. E. Ward. — Captives, by E. Leslie.
Granger, M. M. *See* Ohio, Sup. Court reports.
Granger, T. C. *See* England, Common law reports.
Granny Bright's blanket. Davis, C. E. K. $1.50. . *Hoyt.*
Granny's spectacles. Mackarness, M. A. 60c. . . *Cassell.*
Grant, B: *See* Pennsylvania, Sup. Court reports.
Grant, Duncan. Duty of children to love and seek Christ. 32°. 30c. *Pres. Bd.*
Grant, E. B. Beet root sugar, and the cultivation of the beet. 16°. $1.25 . . . . *Lee & S.*
Grant, Eliz. Holiday rambles; or, peeps into the book of nature. ill. 16°. 50c. . . . . *Routledge.*
Grant, Ja. Novels and tales. 27 v. 16°. ea., $1; per set, hf. roxb., $40. . . . . *Routledge.*
Cont.: Aide-de-camp. — Arthur Blane. — Bothwell. — Captain of the guard. — Cavaliers of fortune. — Constable of France. — First love and last love. — Frank Hilton. — Girl he married. — Harry Ogilvie. — Highlanders of Glen Ora. — Jane Seton. — King's own borderers. — Lady Wedderburn's wish. — Legends of the black watch. — Letty Hyde's lovers. — Lucy Arden. — Mary of Lorraine. — Oliver Ellis. — Only an ensign. — Phantom regiment. — Philip Rollo. — Romance of war. — Scottish cavalier. — Second to none. — White cockade. — Yellow frigate.
— *Same.* (Railway lib.) 34 v. 16°. ea., bds., 80c. *Routledge.*
Cont.: Aide-de-camp. — Arthur Blane. — Bothwell. — Captain of the guard. — Cavaliers of fortune. — Constable of France. — Dick Rodney. — Fairer than a fairy. — First love and last love. — Frank Hilton. — Girl he married. — Harry Ogilvie. — Highlanders of Glen Ora. — Jack Manly. — Jane Seton. — King's own borderers. — Lady Wedderburn's wish. — Legends of the black watch. — Letty Hyde's lovers. — Lucy Arden. — Mary of Lorraine. — Oliver Ellis. — Only an ensign. — Phantom regiment. — Philip Rollo. — The queen's cadet. — Rob Roy. — Romance of war. — Secret despatch. — Scottish cavalier. — Second to none. — Under the red dragon. — White cockade. — Yellow frigate.
— Adventures of an aide-de-camp. 8°. pap., 75c. *Dick & F.*
— British battles on land and sea. 3 v. ill. cr. 4°. ea., $5. . . . . *Cassell.*
— British heroes in foreign wars; or, the cavaliers of fortune. col. ill. 12°. '73. $2. . . . . . . *Routledge.*
— Dick Rodney; or, adventures of an Eton boy. 16°. $1.25. . . . . *Nichols & H.*
— *Same.* ill. 12°. $1.25. . . . . *Lippincott.*
— Frank Hilton. 8°. pap., 75c. . . . . *Dick & F.*
— Harry Ogilvie. 8°. pap., 75c. . . . . *Dick & F.*

Grant, Ja., *continued.*
— Philip Rollo. 8°. pap., 75c. .... *Dick & F.*
— Rob Roy; [also] Romance of adventure. 12°. $1.50. *World Pub.*
— Rob Roy lib. of adventure. 3 v. ill. 16°. ea., $1.25. *Routledge.*
Cont.: Rob Roy's adventures. — Jack Manly. — Dick Rodney; or, the adventures of an Eton boy.
— Yellow frigate. 8°. pap., 75c. .... *Dick & F.*
Grant, Ja. Law of banking. 8°. '57. $3.50. *T. & J. W. Johnson.*
— — *See also* Law lib.
— Treatise on the law of corporations. *See* Law lib.
Grant, J: Experiments on the strength of cement, chiefly in ref. to the Portland cement. pl. 8°. '75. $4.25 .... *Spon.*
Grant, T: Meditations of Sisters of Mercy before renewal of vows. 12°. '75. *net*, 75c. *Kelly, P. & Co.*
Grant, U. S., *and* Colfax, Schuyler. Lives. por. and ill. 12°. $1; pap., 75c. .... *Peterson.*
— *and* Wilson, H: Lives. por. and ill. 12°. $1; pap., 75c. .... *Peterson.*
Gran'ther Baldwin's thanksgiving. Alger, H., *jr.* $1.25. *Loring.*
Grantley Manor. Fullerton, *Lady* G. $1.50; $2. *Murphy.*
Granville De Vigne. La Rame, L. de. $1.50. *Lippincott.*
Granville valley. Abbott, J. $1.50.......... *Dodd.*
Grape, J: T. *See* Sanders, H., *and* Grape, J. T.
Grapel, W: Sources of the Roman civil law: an introd. to the Institutes of Justinian. 8°. '57. $1.50. *T. & J. W. Johnson.*
— — *See also* Law lib.
Grapes and thorns. Fincker, M. A. $2 .. *Cath. Pub.*
Grapes from the great vine. Breed, W. P. 75c. *Pres. Bd.*
Grapes of Eshcol. Macduff, J. R. $1 .... *Carter.*
Grasshopper pop-guns. *See* Barrow, *Mrs.* F.
Grassi, Gius. *See* James, W., *and* Grassi, G.
Grasty, J: S. Faith's battles and victories; or, thoughts for troublous times. 16°. '69. $1. *N. Y. Ref. Ch. Bd.; Pres. Com.; Randolph.*
— Memoirs of Rev. S. B. McPheeters. 12°. $1.50. *S. W. Bk. & Pub.*
Grateful Irish boy; or, twenty-five cents. 18°. 45c. *Am. S. S.*
Grateful orphan; or, our Katie. ill. 18°. '72. 40c. *N. Y. Ref. Ch. Bd.; Pres. Com.*
Gratitude and probity. *See* Simple stories lib.
Grattan, P. R. *See* Virginia, Court of Appeals and General Court reports.
Grattan, T. C. Chance medley of light matter. 8°. pap., 50c. .... *Harper.*
— History of the Netherlands to 1830. 12°. $1 .. *Harper.*
Grätz, H. History of the Jews from downfall of Jewish state to conclusion of Talmud; tr. by Rev. J. K. Gutheim. 8°. '73. *$3.......... *Am. Jew.*
— Influence of Judaism on the Prot. reformation; tr. by Rev. S. Tuska. 16°. 50c. .... *Bloch.*
Grauert, E. J. New method of learning Portuguese. 12°. $2 .... *Appleton.*
Grauert, W. [Deutsche Lesebücher.] 3 v. 12°. '67-'71. *Steiger.*
Cont.: Zweites d. Lesebuch, bds., 65c. — Drittes, bds., 75c. — Viertes, hf. roan, $1.
— — *See also* Douai, A., Bilderfibel.
— Lehrbuch d. englischen Sprache. 2 pts. 12°. '68. ea., bds., 40c.; in 1 v., 70c. .... *Steiger.*
— Leitfaden d. Weltgeschichte. ('67.) 3d ed., rev. 12°. '76. bds., 70c. .... *Steiger.*
— Manual of the Germ. lang. 2 pts. 12°. '69. ea., bds., 40c.; in 1 v., bds., 70c.; hf. roan, 90c. .. *Steiger.*
— *See also* Ahn, F., German handwriting; Germ. ser.
Gravel pit and its lessons. 18°. 17c.; 22c... *Am. Bapt.*

Gravenhurst. Smith, W. $4 ..... *Scribner, W. & A.*
Graver thoughts. Boyd, A. K. H. 2 v. $2.50 .. * *Osgood.*
Graves, *Mrs.* A. C. Child's catechism in rhyme. 18°. 20c. .... *So. Bapt.*
— Seclusaval; or, the arts of Romanism. 12°. $1.50. *Am. Bapt.*
— *Same.* 12°. $2; mor., $3 .... *So. Bapt.*
Graves, *Mrs.* A. J. Woman in Am.: examination into moral and intellectual condition of Am. female society. 18°. 75c. .... *Harper.*
Graves, H. A. (*ed.*) Attractions of heaven. 24°. '74. 25c.; 40c. 16°. $1 .... *Lothrop.*
— Family circle (The): its affections and pleasures. 24°. '74. 25c.; 40c. 16°. $1 .... *Lothrop.*
Graves, J. R. Middle life. [Exposé of spiritualism and Swedenborgianism.] 18°. 75c. ... *So. Bapt.*
— New Baptist psalmist; with music. 18°. $1-$2.50; — without music. 18°. 85c.-$2.25 ... *So. Bapt.*
— Spiritualism. 18°. pap., 15c. .... *So. Bapt.*
— The trilemma, death by three horns: is the baptism of the Romish church valid? New ed., enl. 18°. 60c. .... *So. Bapt.*
— *and* Ditzler, Jac. The great Carrollton debate: Methodists *vs.* Baptists. roy. 8°. '76. $3.50; shp., $4; mor., $7 .... *So. Bapt.*
— — *Same.* 6 v. roy. 8°. .... *So. Bapt.*
Cont.: 1. Immersion, $2; shp., $2.50. — 2. Infant baptism, $1. — 3. Church of Christ, $1. — 4. Lord's supper, 50c. — 5. Believer's baptism, 50c. — 6. Final perseverance of saints, 50c.
Graves, Kersey. Biography of Satan: hist. exposition of the devil and his fiery dominions. ('65.) 7th ed. 12°. '72. pap., 60c. .... *Rel. Phil.*
— World's sixteen crucified saviors; or, christianity before Christ. ('75.) 4th ed. 12°. '76. $2 .. *Colby.*
Gravier, J. Lettre sur les affaires de la Louisiane. *See* Relation des affaires du Canada.
Gray, Agnes. Lady Willacy's protegèes. ill. 12°. $1.50. *Nelson.*
Gray, Alonzo. Elements of natural philosophy. ill. 12°. shp., $1.50 .... *Harper.*
— *and* Adams, C. B. Elements of geol. ill. 12°. shp., $1.50 .... *Harper.*
Gray, Amy. Lily of the valley, and other poems. 12°. '68. $1.50 .... *Kelly, P. & Co.*
Gray, Asa. Botany. *See* Ives, J. C., Report on Colorado River; — Wilkes, C: U. S. explor. expedition.
— Dried plants. *See* Gilliss, J. W.
— Field, forest and garden botany. 8°. '68. $2 .. *Ivison.*
— How plants behave, how they move, climb, etc. 4°. '72. 75c. .... *Ivison.*
— How plants grow: introd. to structural botany. sm. 4°. '58. $1.12 .... *Ivison.*
— Lessons in botany and vegetable physiology; with dict. of botan. terms. ill. 8°. '57. $1.30 .. *Ivison.*
— Manual of botany; arranged according to natural system. 8th ed. pl. 8°. '68. $2.25; — bound with "Lessons." $3 .... *Ivison.*
— School and field book of botany; compr. "Lessons in botany" and "Field, forest and garden botany." ill. 8°. '57. $2.50 .... *Ivison.*
— Structural and systematic botany. ill. 8°. '57. $3.50. *Ivison.*
Gray, Barry (*pseud.*) *See* Coffin, Rob. B.
Gray, D: Poems; with introd. by Lord Houghton, and memoirs. 16°. '64. $1.50 .... *Roberts.*
— Poetical works; ed. by H. G. Bell. New ed., enl. fp. 8°. '74. $2.25 .... *Macmillan.*
Gray, G: Zabriskie. Crusade of the children in the 13th cent. 16°. '70. $1. 12°. $1.75 .. *Hurd & H.*
— Scriptural doctrine of recognition in the world to come. 18°. '75. 60c.; $1 .... *Whittaker.*
Gray, H: Anatomy, descriptive and surgical; with drawings by H. V. Carter, and dissections by G. and Carter. ill. imp. 8°. $6; leath., $7 .. *Lea.*
Gray, Hester. Kitty Barton: simple story for children. ill. 32°. 60c. .... *Lee & S.*

Gray, Hor., *jr.* *See* Massachusetts, Supreme Court reports.

Gray, *Rev.* Horatio. Memoirs of Rev. B. C. Cutler. 12°. '64. $3 .... *Randolph.*

Gray, Ja. Comper. Bible lore: chapters on the rare MSS., various translations, and notable characteristics of the Bible. 12°. '72. $1.25 ...... *Dodd.*

— Biblical museum: commentary. 5 v. 12°. '72-'75. ea., $1.50 .... *Randolph.*
Cont.: Matthew and Mark. — Luke and John. — Acts and Romans. — Corinthians to Philemon. — Hebrews to Revelation.

— Class (The) and desk: manual for S.-school teachers. 4 v. 12°. ea., $1.25 .... *Nelson.*
Cont.: Genesis to Esther. — Job to Malachi. — Gospels. — Epistles.

— Stones of Palestine: lecture on ruins of the Holy Land. 12°. 10c. .... *Meth. Bk. Conc.*

— Topics for [S.-school] teachers. 2 v. ill. and maps. 12°. '69. $3 .... *Meth. Bk. Conc.*

Gray, J: F., *and* Hempel, C. J. Homœopathic examiner. 2 v. 8°. hf. mor., $5 .... *Boericke.*

Gray, L: M. Ada and Gerty. ill. 16°. '75. $1.25. *Am. Tr.*

Gray, Rob. Life; ed. by Rev. C. Gray. 2 v. por. 8°. '75. $12 .... *Dutton.*

Gray, Robertson (*pseud.*) *See* Raymond, R. W.

Gray, T: Poems. (Aldine ed.) 16°. 75c. .. *Lippincott.*

— *Same;* with memoir by Rev. J. Mitford. por. 18°. $1 .... *Osgood.*

— *Same;* incl. poet. works of Beattie, Blair, Collins, Thomson and Kirke White. ill. 8°. $2.50; $3.50. *Routledge.*

— — *See also* British pocket classics; — Collins, W:

— Poetical works. ill. sq. 16°. '71. $1.25 .... *Putnam.*

— *Same.* ill. 16°. '75. $1.50 .... *Routledge.*

— *Same.* (Household ed.) 16°. $1.25; hf. cf., $2.50; cf., $3.75 .... *Miller.*

— *Same.* (Red line ed.) ill. sm. 4°. $3.50; hf. cf., $5; cf., $7 .... *Miller.*

— *Same;* with memoir by Rev. J. Mitford. (Blue and gold ed.) por. 32°. $1.25; hf. cf., $2.50; cf., $3.50 .... *Miller.*

— — *See also* Milton, J:

— Select poems; ed. with notes by W. J. Rolfe. ill. sq. 16°. '76. 90c. .... *Harper.*

— Elegy in a country churchyard. ill. 12°. '75. $1.25. *Putnam.*

— *Same.* ill. 12°. $2.50; mor., $5 .... *Appleton.*

— *Same,* and other poems. ill. 8°. $1.50; $2 .. *Carter.*

Gray, W: C. Life of Lincoln. 16°. '67. 90c. .. *West. Tr.*

Gray-nook ser. 4 v. 16°. $5.25 .... *Randolph.*
Cont.: Belle Lovel. — Canterbury bells. — Emily Douglas. — Heart and hand.

Gray woman of Scharfenstein, and other stories. 18°. 50c. .... *O'Shea.*

Graydon, W. Forms of conveyancing, and of practice in courts of Common Pleas, Quarter Sessions, Oyer and Terminer, and Supreme and Orphans' Courts in Penn. 4th ed., enl. with notes and ref. by R. E. Wright. 8°. shp., $4.50 .... *Kay.*

Grayson, E. Standish, the Puritan: tale of the Am. revolution. 12°. $1.50 .... *Harper.*

Grayson, W. S. True theory of Christianity. 16°. $1.25 .... *Appleton.*

Grayson, W: J. James Louis Petigru: biog. sketch. por. 12°. $1.50 .... *Harper.*

Graziani, Nazareno. Sketches of life and times of Pius IX. 12°. '76. $1 .... *Fox.*

Graziella. *See* Lamartine, A. de.

Great aim of the S.-school teacher. 32°. 35c. .. *Am. S. S.*

Great army: sketches of life and character in a Thames-side district; by the river-side visitor. 12°. '75. $2.50 .... *Routledge.*

Great arrival: Ethiop. drama. 16°. pap., 15c. *French; Happy.*

Great atonement. Alford, L. A. $1; $1.25 .. *J. E. Potter.*

Great awakening. Tracy, J. $1.25 ...... *Cong. Pub.*

Great battle year. Robinson, M. S. 75c. .... *Tibbals.*

Great biography. Hamilton, J. $1.25 .... *Carter.*

Great bonanza: narrative of adventure and discovery; by Oliver Optic, R. M. Ballantyne, C. E. Bishop and others. ill. roy. 4°. $2 .... *Lee & S.*

Great Britain. *See* England.

Great Brooklyn romance. *See* Tilton, T., *vs.* Beecher, H. W.

Great car hook tragedy; with life, trial and execution of William Foster. [In Eng. or Germ.] 8°. pap., 25c. .... *Barclay.*

Great change. Redford, G. 60c. .... *Am. S. S.*

Great Chicago fire. [In Eng. or Germ.] 8°. pap., 25c. .... *Barclay.*

Great Chinese wizard's handbook of magic. 12°. pap., 20c. .... *Hurst.*

Great Christians of France. *See* Guizot, F. P. G.

Great comforter. Smith, J. 10c. .... *Pres. Bd.*

Great commission. Harris, J. $1.50. *Sheldon; So. Meth.*

Great concern of salvation. Halyburton, T. 50c. *Pres. Bd.*

Great conflict. Loomis, H. $1 ...... *Meth. Bk. Conc.*

Great controversy between God and man. Hastings, H. L. $1 .... *Hastings.*

Great conversers. Mathews, W. $1.75 ...... *Griggs.*

Great czar. Cobb, J. F. 50c. .... *Pott.*

Great day; tr. by Mrs. J. Sadlier. 18°. 50c.; 75c. *Sadlier.*

Great devil. Dibdin, C. 15c. .... *French.*

Great divide. Dunraven, *Earl of.* $5 .. *Scribner, W. & A.*

Great Dutch admirals. De Liefde, J. $2 .. *Routledge.*

Great duties taught in the Bible. Clark, R. W. 15c. *Cong. Pub.*

Great elixir. Baker, G. M. 15c. .... *Lee & S.*

Great elm. Abbott, J. 90c. .... *Harper.*

Great empress. De Vere, M. S. $1.75 ... *Lippincott.*

Great events of history. *See* Collier, W. F.

Great expectations. *See* Dickens, C.

Great fortunes, and how they were made. McCabe, J. D. *$3.50; $4.50; $7 .... *Maclean.*

Great grandmother's secret. *See* Catholic premium-book lib.

Great gun trick. Le Ros, C. 15c. .... *French.*

Great harmonia. *See* Davis, A. J.

Great Hoggarty diamond. *See* Thackeray, W. M.

Great ice age. Geikie, J. $2.50 .... *Appleton.*

Great illustrated Egyptian dream book. 12°. 50c. *Radde.*

Great iron wheel examined. Brownlow, W. G. $1. *So. Meth.*

Great journey. sq. 12°. '54. 60c. ..... *Meth. Bk. Conc.*

Great journey. *See* Macduff, J. R. 50c. ...... *Carter.*

Great lady. Dewall, — van. $1.25; 75c. .. *Lippincott.*

Great lessons from little things. Taylor, J. $1.50. *Cassell.*

Great men and gallant deeds. Edgar, J. G. $1.50. *Lee & S.*

Great men of God. Noble, W. F. P. *$3.75; $5.50. *St. L. B. & B. Pub.*

Great metropolis. Browne, J. H. *$3; $3.50; $4.50. *Am. Pub.*

Great mysteries and little plagues. Neal, J. 75c. *Roberts.*

Great New York trunk mystery; or, murder of Alice A. Bowlsby. [In Eng. or Germ.] 8°. pap., 25c. .... *Barclay.*

Great pilot. Newton, R. $1.25 .... *Carter.*

Great possessions; by author of "Poke and her sisters." 16°. $1.10 .... *Am. S. S.*

Great problem. Leifchild, J. R. $2.25.....*Putnam.*

Great promises of the Bible. Banvard, J. 3 pts. ea., 15c............................*H. A. Young.*

Great question. Aydelott, B. P. 75c.......*West. Tr.*

Great question. *See* Boardman, H. A.

Great question. *See* Wright, L.

Great question: essay. 16°. '56. 50c...*Meth. Bk. Conc.*

Great Redeemer. 18°. 15c.........*N. Y. Ref. Ch. Bd.*

Great reform. *See* Stevens, A.

Great reformer. Tucker, C. 50c..........*Pres. Bd.*

Great revival of 1800. Speer, W. 70c.....*Pres. Bd.*

Great revival of Norwalk, Ohio. 12°. '75. pap., 50c. *Ingham.*

Great rosy diamond. Carter, A. A. 80c.....*Lee & S.*

Great Russian bear: comedietta. 16°. pap., 15c. *French.*

Great Salterns. Doudney, S. $1.25...........*Hoyt.*

Great secret. *See* Good boy's lib.

Great south. King, E. *$6; $7; $8; $10..*Am. Pub.*

Great specific against despair of pardon. Chamberlayne, I. 12c.; 20c.........*Cin. Meth. Bk. Conc.*

Great success. *See* Flint, S. A.

Great supper. Fairchild, A. G. 50c.......*Pres. Bd.*

Great supper not Calvinistic. Lee, L. M. 75c. *So. Meth.*

Great teacher. Templeton, A. 50c...(?) *Cumberland.*

Great Tenabraka. 16°. 45c.............*Cummiskey.*

Great things done by little people. 18°. 45c...*Am. S. S.*
— *See also* Dove ser.; — Maggie Fuller lib.

Great tone poets. Crowest, F. $2.50..*Scribner, W. & A.*

Great truths. 18°. 35c.............*U. P. Bd. of Pub.*

Great truths by great authors: quotations, maxims, aphorisms, etc. ('53.) New ed. demy 8°. '75. $2–$4.50 ....*Claxton.*

Great truths in simple words. *See* Mortimer, *Mrs.* M.

Great truths of the Bible. Clark, R. W. 15c. *Cong. Pub.*

Great Udderzook mystery: trial of Wm. E. Udderzook for murder of M. S. Goss. [In Eng. or Germ.] 8°. pap., 25c................*Barclay.*

Great western cook book. Collins, A. M. 75c. *Barnes.*

Great western series. *See* Adams, W. T.

Great wizard of the north's handbook of natural magic. Anderson, J. H. 30c................*Dick & F.*

Great wonders in little things. Dyer, S. $2..*Am. Bapt.*

Greater Britain. *See* Dilke, *Sir* C. W.

Greatest plague in life. Baker, G. M. 15c...*Lee & S.*

Greatest plague of life. *See* Mayhew, H. *and* A.

Greatest plague of life; or, adventures of a lady in search of a good servant; by one who has been "worried to death." 8°. pap., 50c.....*Peterson.*

Greatorex, Eliza. Homes of Ober-Ammergau: 20 etchings in heliotype from the orig. pen and ink drawings; with notes from a diary. sm. 4°. '74. $12.............................*Putnam.*
— Old New York, from the Battery to Bloomingdale: etchings reprod. by H. Thatcher from orig. drawings, with descript. by M. Despard. 10 pts. '75. hf. mor., $30; India pap. proofs, $50...*Putnam.*
— Summer etchings in Colorado; with 21 ill. drawn and etched by author; and introd. by Grace Greenwood. 4°. '74. $3; mor., $6........*Putnam.*

Greatorex, H. W. Greatorex collection of psalm and hymn tunes, etc. obl. 8°. '51. $1.75; bds., $1.50 ....*Ditson.*

Grecian bend. Baker, G. M. 15c.........*Lee & S.*

Grecian daughter. Murphy, A. 15c.........*French.*

Greedy giant; or, end of covetousness. ill. cr. 4°. pap., 20c.; 25c....................*J. E. Potter.*

Greek and Eastern churches (The): their hist., faith and worship; rev. by T. O. Summers. ('55.) 2d ed. 18°. '74. 50c...................*So. Meth.*

Greek anthology as sel. for Westminster, [etc.]; tr. by G. Burges [with] metrical versions by Bland, etc. 12°. (Bohn.) $1.75.......*Little, B. & Co.*
— *Same.* 12°. (Bohn.) $2. *Lippincott; Scribner, W. & A.*

Greek ecclesiastical historians (The): [histories] of Eusebius, Sozomen, Evagrius and Theodoret. 6 v. 8°. (Bagster.) $12...............*Wiley.*

Greek maid at the court of the Emperor Nero. [Juvenile.] 16°. $1..................(?) *Martien.*

Greek slave; or, filial love. (Fatherland ser.) ill. 16°. $1.10..........................(?) *Luth. Pub.*

Greek student's manual. [Aid to study of N. Test.] fp. 8°. (Bagster.) $4.25; hf. bd., $4.75.. *Wiley.*

Greeks of to-day. Tuckerman, C. K. $1.50..*Putnam.*

Greeley, Hor. Essays [on] political economy [and in favor of] protection. 16°. $1.50.......*Porter.*
— Memorial of. 8°. '73. $1; pap., 50c...*N. Y. Tribune.*
— Recollections of a busy life; [also] Literature as a vocation, Poets and poetry, etc.; [and] discussion with R. D. Owen on the law of divorce. 8°. '68. shp., $3. — New ed., with memoir of [his] last years and death. 8°. '73. $3..*N. Y. Tribune.*
— What I know of farming. 12°. $1.50....*Carleton.*
— *See also* Eminent women of the age.

Greeley or Grant? Sumner, C. 25c.........*Lee & S.*

Green, Ashbel. Lectures on Shorter catechism of the Presb. Church. 2 v. 12°. $2.25......*Pres. Bd.*

Green, Ben E. Irrepressible conflict between labor and capital. 8°. '71. pap., 30c........*Claxton.*

Green, C. E. *See* New Jersey, Court of Chancery reports.

Green, D: *See* Mason, L., *and* Green, D.

Green, Duff. How to pay off the national debt, regulate the value of money, and maintain stability in the values of property and of labor. 12°. '71. $1.50..............................*Claxton.*

Green, G: Mathematical papers; ed. by N. M. Ferrers. 8°. '71. $6................*Macmillan.*

Green, H. W. *See* New Jersey, Court of Chancery reports; Statutes.

Green, H: Shakespeare and the emblem writers: exposition of their similarities of thought and expression. wood-cuts. roy. 8°. '69. $10; large pap., $16.............................*Bouton.*

Green, Hor. Favorite prescriptions of living practitioners; with toxicol. table. 8°. $2.50.. *Wiley.*
— Observations on the pathology of croup; with treatment by topical medications. 8°. $1.25.. *Wiley.*
— On the surgical treatment of polypi of the larynx, and œdema of the glottis. 8°. $1.25..... *Wiley.*
— Practical treatise on pulmonary tuberculosis. col. pl. 8°. $5.............................. *Wiley.*
— Treatise on diseases of the air passages. 4th ed., rev. and enl. 8°. $3.................... *Wiley.*

Green, J. H. Gambler's (The) life. 12°. $1.75; pap., $1.50............................*Peterson.*
— Gambling exposed. 12°. $1.75; pap., $1.50..*Peterson.*
— One hundred tricks with cards. 16°. pap., 30c.; bds., 50c...........................*Dick & F.*
— Reformed gambler. 12°. $1.75; pap., $1.50..*Peterson.*
— Secret band of brothers. 12°. $1.75; pap., $1.50. *Peterson.*

Green, J. S. *See* New Jersey, Sup. Court reports.

Green, J: R: Short history of the Eng. people; with chronol. and geneal. tables and maps. cr. 8°. '75. $3.50.........................*Macmillan.*
— *Same.* 8°. $1.75..........................*Harper.*
— Stray studies from England and Italy. sq. cr. 8°. '76. $3.75 ....*Macmillan.*
— *Same.* post 8°. '76. $1.75; $2..........*Harper.*
— (*ed.*) History primers. v. 1–3. 32°. ea., 50c. *Appleton; Macmillan.*

Cont.: Rome, by M. Creighton. — Greece, by C. A. Fyffe. — Europe, by E. A. Freeman.

Green, J: R: *continued.*
— Literature primers. v. 1, 2. 24°. ea., 50c. *Appleton; Macmillan.*
Cont.: Grammar, by R. Morris.—Eng. literature, by S. A. Brooke.

Green, N. St. J: Criminal law reports. 2 v. 8°. '74–'75. ea., shp., $7.50 .... *Hurd & H.*

Green, S. W. Doctrines: lectures to children. 18°. 50c. .... *Nelson.*

Green, S: Introd. to Bible study. *See* Pioneer lib.

Green, S: G. Bible portraits: addresses to children. 18°. '69. 50c. .... *Perkinpine.*
— Bible sketches and their teachings. 2 v. 18°. ea., 50c. .... *U.P.Bd. of Pub.*
— *Same.* 3 v. ill. 16°. ea., $1 .... *Bost. Am. Tr.*
— Crumbs from the bread of life: lectures for children [on] evangelical doctr. 18°. '69. 50c. .. *Perkinpine.*
— Handbook to Gk. grammar of New Test. cr. 8°. (Lond.) $3 .... *Wiley.*
— Rays from the sun: lectures on the Bible for children and their teachers. 18°. '69. 50c. .. *Perkinpine.*
— Sabbaths with my class; with introd. on Bible class teaching. 18°. '59. 40c. .... *So. Meth.*

Green, Sanford M. Law practice. ('60.) 2d ed. [To form 2 v.] v. 1. 8°. '76. shp., $6.50 .. *Richmond.*

Green, T. H: Pathology and morbid anatomy. 2d Am. ed., enl. ill. 8°. '76. $2.75 .... *Lea.*

Green, T. S. Critical notes on [Gk.] New Test. cr. 8°. (Bagster.) $3 .... *Wiley.*
— Developed criticism of [Gk.] New Test. 8°. (Bagster.) $3 .... *Wiley.*
— Grammar of the New Test. dialect. cr. 8°. (Bagster.) $3; hf. bd., $3.50 .... *Wiley.*
— Greek-English lexicon to New Test. 18°. hf. mor., $1.50 .... *Wiley.*
— Pocket Gk.-Eng. lexicon to the New Test. fp. 8°. (Bagster.) hf. bd., $1.50 .... *Wiley.*

Green, W: Memoir. 18°. 18c. .... *Am. S. S.*

Green, W: H: Argument of the book of Job unfolded. ('73.) New ed. 12°. '74. $1.75 .... *Carter.*
— Elementary Heb. gram. 12°. (Lond.) $1.25 .. *Wiley.*
— Grammar of the Heb. lang. 8°. $3.50 ...... *Wiley.*
— Pentateuch vindicated from aspersions of Bp. Colenso. 12°. $1.25 .... *Wiley.*
— *See also* Preparing to teach.

Green, W: S. Coming to Christ: poems. 12°. 75c. *Lippincott.*

Green and gold, and blue and gold eds. of the standard poets. 24 v. 32°. ea., $1.25 .... *Miller.*
Cont.: Browning's poems, 5 v.—Browning's Aurora Leigh.—Browning's last poems.—Burns, 2 v.—Bailey's Festus.—Campbell.—Gray.—Hood, 3 v.—Keble's Christian year.—Keats.—Macaulay's Lays of ancient Rome.—Scott, 3 v.—Shelley, 3 v.

Green bushes. Buckstone, J. B. 15c. .... *French.*

Green eyed monster. Planché, J. R. 15c. .... *French.*

Green gate. Wichert, E. $1.75 .... *Lippincott.*

Green hand. *See* Cupples, G.

Green Hollow. Ide, G. B. 70c.; 85c. ..... *Am. Bapt.*

Green house, and who lived in it. Sanford, D. P. 20c.; 15c. .... *Dutton.*

Green Island: tale for youth. 16°. '76. 60c.; $1. *Kelly, P. & Co.*

Green-leaf stories. 4 v. 32°. ea., 15c.; 20c. .. *Dutton.*
Cont.: Willie's lesson.—Willie and the scythe.—Ella's troubles.—What Minnie found to do.

Green man. Jones, R. 15c. .... *French.*

Green Mountain boy. Jones, J. S. 15c. ...... *French.*

Green Mountain boys; — ser. *See* Thompson, D. P.

Green Mountain stories. *See* Robbins, S. S.

Green pastures. [Interleaved.] 32°. 75c. .... *Nelson.*

Green pastures. Campbell, E. 50c. .... *Am. Tr.*

Green pastures. Smith, J. 40c. .... *Pres. Bd.*

Green velvet dress. 18°. 20c.; 25c. ...... *Am. Bapt.*

Greene, Alb. G. Old Grimes. ill. 4°. '67. $1.50 .. *Rider.*
— Recollections of the Jersey prison ship; from MS. of Thomas Dring, one of the prisoners. 4°. (Providence.) '29. $5 .... *Rider.*

Greene, Annie D. ["Marion Douglas."] Picture-poems for young folks. ill. 16°. '71. $1.50. *Osgood.*

Greene, C: E. Graphical method for analysis of bridge trusses, extended to continuous girders and draw spans. pl. 8°. '75. $2 .... *Van Nostrand.*

Greene, C: S. Thrilling stories of the great rebellion; [incl.] account of death of Lincoln, and capture of the assassins, etc. ill. 12°. $1.75 .. *J. E. Potter.*

Greene, G. *See* Iowa, Sup. Court reports.

Greene, G. S., *jr.* Resistance of bricks to a crushing force. 8°. pap., 25c. .... *Am. Soc. of C. E.*

Greene, G: Wash. Class-book of botany. 4°. $2. *Appleton.*
— German element in war of Am. independence. 12°. '75. $1.50 .... *Hurd & H.*
— Historical view of the Am. revolution. 4th ed. cr. 8°. '72. $1.50 .... *Hurd & H.*
— History of the middle ages. 12°. $1.50 ... *Appleton.*
— Life of Nathanael Greene. 3 v. 8°. '67–'71. $12. *Hurd & H.; Putnam.*
— Primary botany. ill. 4°. $1.25 .... *Appleton.*

Greene, *Mrs.* L. L. Broken promise. fp. 8°. 60c. *Cassell.*
— Burtons of Burton Hall. ill. 16°. $1 .. *Scribner, W. & A.*
— Cushion and corner lib. 4 v. 16°. '65–'70. $4.25. *Dutton.*
Cont.: Cushions and corners; or, holidays at old orchard, $1.—School-boy baronet, $1.25.—Winter and summer at Burton Hall, $1.—Filling up the chinks, $1.

— Cushions and corners. ill. 16°. $1 .. *Scribner, W. & A.*
— Filling up the chinks. ill. 12°. $1.25. *Scribner, W. & A.*
— Gilbert's shadow; or, the magic beads. ill. 16°. '75. $1.50 .... *Dutton.*
— *Same.* 16°. $1.75 .... *Scribner, W. & A.*
— Grey house on the hill. ill. 12°. $1.25 ..... *Nelson.*
— Little castle maiden. ill. 16°. $1 .. *Scribner, W. & A.*
— School boy baronet. ill. 16°. $1.75 .. *Scribner, W. & A.*
— Star in the dust heap. ill. 16°. '76. $1.75. *Scribner, W. & A.*

Greene, *Mrs.* R. J. *See* Greene, *Mrs.* L. L.

Greene, Reuben. The problem of health and how to solve it. 12°. '76. $1.50 .... *Jas. Campbell.*

Greene, Rob., *and* Peele, G: Dramatic and poet. works; with memoirs and notes by A. Dyce. por. and ill. roy. 8°. $6 .... *Routledge.*

Greene, S: D. Broken seal: reminiscences of abduction and murder of W: Morgan. ('73.) 6th ed. 12°. '75. $1; pap., 50c. .... *E. A. Cook.*

Greene, S: S. Analysis of the Eng. lang. [Old ser.] ('46.) New ed. 16°. '69. bds., 80c. .. *Cowperthwait.*
— *Same.* New ser. ('74.) New ed. 16°. '76. $1.20. *Cowperthwait.*
— Elements of Eng. grammar. [Old ser.] ('53.) New ed. 16°. '72. bds., 80c. ... *Cowperthwait.*
— First lessons in Eng. grammar. [Old ser.] ('48.) New ed. 16°. '70. bds., 56c. .... *Cowperthwait.*
— Introduction to Eng. grammar. New ser. ('68.) New ed. 16°. '75. bds., 56c. .... *Cowperthwait.*
— New Eng. grammar. New ser. ('67.) New ed. 16°. '75. $1.05 .... *Cowperthwait.*

Greene, W: Batchelder. Blazing star; with app. [on] Jewish Kabbala; also tract on philos. of Herbert Spencer, and one on New Eng. transcendentalism. 12°. '72. $1.50 .... *Williams.*
— Facts of consciousness, and philos. of Herbert Spencer. 12°. pap., 25c. .... *Lee & S.*
— Theory of the calculus. 8°. $2; pap., 50c. .. *Lee & S.*
— Transcendentalism. 12°. pap., 25c. .... *Lee & S.*

Greener, W. W. Choke-bore guns, and how to load for all kinds of game. ill. cr. 8°. $3.50 .. *Cassell.*

Greener, W. W., *continued.*
— Modern breech-loaders, sporting and military. ill. cr. 8°. $2.50 .... *Cassell.*
Greenfield, W: Greek lexicon to New Test. fp. 8°. (Bagster.) $1.12; hf. bd., $1.50. 32°. $1.. *Wiley.*
— *See also* Bible, New Test., *Greek.*
Greenhow, E: Headlam. Chronic bronchitis, especially as connected with gout, emphysema, and diseases of the heart. 12°. '69. $2...... *Lindsay.*
— Lectures on Addison's disease. ill. 8°. '76. $3.50. *Lindsay.*
Greenleaf, B: Common school arith. 12°. 94c.; $1.04. —Key. 94c.......... *R. S. Davis (B.)*
— Elements of geom.; with applic. to mensuration. 12°. $1.38. —Key. 62c.......... *R. S. Davis (B.)*
— Elements of geom. and trigon.; with applic. and tables. 12°. $1.87. —Key. 75c... *R. S. Davis (B.)*
— Elements of plane and spherical trigon.; with tables. 12°. 94c. .... *R. S. Davis (B.)*
— Key to Treatise on algebra. 12°. $1.38. *R. S. Davis (B.)*
Note. The Treatise is o. p.
— National arithmetic. 12°. $1.38. —Key. $1.25. *R. S. Davis (B.)*
— New element. algebra. 12°. $1.38. —Key. $1.38. *R. S. Davis (B.)*
— New element. arith. 16°. 45c..... *R. S. Davis (B.)*
— New element. geom. 12°. $1...... *R. S. Davis (B.)*
— New higher algebra. 12°. $1.87. —Key. $1.87. *R. S. Davis (B.)*
— New intellectual arithmetic. 16°. 42c. —Key. 37c. *R. S. Davis (B.)*
— New practical arithmetic. 12°. 94c. $1.04. —Key. 94c. .... *R. S. Davis (B.)*
— New primary arith. ill. 16°. 25c... *R. S. Davis (B.)*
— Primary arith. [Old ed.] 16°. 37c... *R. S. Davis (B.)*
Greenleaf, C: R. Manual for medical officers of U. S. army. 12°. '64. $1.25.... *Claxton; Lippincott.*
Greenleaf, Jona. Thoughts on prayer: its duty, form, subjects, etc. 12°. 60c. .... *Pres. Bd.*
Greenleaf, Sim. Collection of cases, overruled, denied, doubted, or limited in their application, from Am. and Eng. reports; rev. and enl. by J. Townshend. 4th ed. 8°. shp., $4.... *Baker, V. & Co.*
— Examination of testimony of the four evangelists by [legal] rules of evidence; with account of trial of Jesus; with varying versions of most ancient MSS. as compared with the King James Bible, by C. Tischendorf. roy. 8°. '74. $5; shp., $6. *Cockcroft.*
— Treatise on law of evidence. New ed., enl. by I. F. Redfield. 3 v. 8°. '66. shp., $18.. *Little, B. & Co.*
— *See also* Maine, Reports.
Greenough, A. J. (*pseud.*) *See* Avery, Jane G.
Greenough, H: Appelles and his contemporaries. [Fiction.] 16°. '59. $1.......... *Burnham.*
Greenough, Ja. B. Queen of hearts: dramatic fantasia. ('75.) 2d ed. 16°. '76. 50c....... *Sever.*
— *See also* Allen, J. H., *and* Greenough, J. B.; — Allen, J. H. *and* W. F., *and* Greenough, J. B.
Greenough, *Mrs.* Jeannie. Plain talk. 16°. 75c. *Cong. Pub.*
Greenough, *Mrs.* R: S. *See* Greenough, *Mrs.* Sa. D.
Greenough, *Mrs.* Sa. D. Arabesques: Monare, Apollyona, Domitia, Ombra: four stories of the supernatural. sq. 16°. '71. $2 .... *Roberts.*
— In extremis: story of a broken law. sq. 16°. '72. $1.50 .... *Roberts.*
— Treason at home. 12°. $1.75; pap., $1.50.. *Peterson.*
Greenough, W. A. American railway manual and supply directory. 8°. '73. $4..... *Greenough.*
— United States iron, hardware, and metal trades directory. 8°. '75. $6.......... *Greenough.*
Greenough, W: W. Free lending libraries; read before the Am. Soc. Sci. Assoc., N. Y., May 22, 1874. 8°. '74. pap., 10c.......... *Williams.*

Greenwald, Em. Baptism of children. 12°. 25c. *Luth. Bk. St.*
— Christian benevolence: sermon. 12°. pap., 10c. *Luth. Bk. St.*
— Lutheran reformation: discourses. 12°. '68. $1.25. *Luth. Bk. St.*
— Meditations for Passion week. 12°. '73. 75c.; $1; $1.25.......... *Luth. Bk. St.*
— Questions on the Epistles for the church year. 32°. 20c. .... *Baer.*
— Questions on the Gospels for the church year. 2 v. 32°. ea., 20c. .... *Baer.*
— Sprinkling the true mode of baptism. 12°. '76. 35c. *Luth. Bk. St.*
— True church (The): its way of justification, and its holy communion: discourses. 12°. '76. 75c. *Luth. Bk. St.*
— Young Christian's manual of devotion. 16°. '73. 50c.......... *Luth. Bk. St.*
Greenwell, Dora. Colloquia crucis. 16°. '72. $1.25. *Routledge.*
— Essays. cr. 8°. $2.......... *Routledge.*
— Patience of hope; with introd. by J. G. Whittier. 16°. $1.......... *Dutton.*
— *Same.* 16°. $1.25.......... *Routledge.*
— Poems. cr. 8°. $2.......... *Routledge.*
— Present heaven (A). 16°. $1.......... *Dutton.*
— Stories that might be true, and other poems. 16°. $1.25.......... *Routledge.*
— Two friends. 16°. $1.......... *Dutton.*
Greenwood, F. Margaret Denzil's history. 8°. pap., 75c. .... *Harper.*
Greenwood, Fs. W. P. Collection of psalms and hymns. 18°. roan, $1.88.......... *Ware.*
— Lives of the twelve apostles; [also] Life of John the Baptist. ('35; reprint. '68.) 2d ed. 16°. '74. 60c.......... *Am. Unit.*
— Sermons of consolation. 16°. '63. $1... *Am. Unit.*
— Sermons to children. ('40.) New ed. 16°. '68. 60c. *Am. Unit.*
Greenwood, Grace (*pseud.*) *See* Lippincott, Sa. J.
Greenwood, J. G. Elements of Greek grammar. 4th ed. 12°. '74. $1.75.......... *Macmillan.*
Greenwood, Ja. ["Amateur casual."] Adventures of Reuben Davidger, seventeen years and four months captive among the Dyaks of Borneo. ill. 8°. $1.75.......... *Harper.*
— In strange company: experiences of a roving correspondent. 12°. '74. $1.75.......... *Routledge.*
— Legends of savage life. ill. 4°. '74. $2... *Putnam.*
— Low life deeps: account of the strange fish to be found there. ill. 12°. $3..... *Scribner, W. & A.*
— Peter's adventures. ill. 4°. bds., $1.50.. *Routledge.*
— Seven curses of London. 8°. pap., 25c.... *Harper.*
— *Same.* 12°. $1.50.......... * *Osgood.*
— True history of a little ragamuffin. 8°. pap., 50c. *Harper.*
— Wild sports of the world. ill. cr. 8°. $2.50. *Harper; Scribner, W. & A.*
— — *See also* Beeton's boys own lib.
— Wilds of London. ill. cr. 8°. '75. $3... *Routledge.*
Greenwood, W. H. Metallurgy. (Adv. sci. ser.) 2 pts. 12°. '75. ea., $1.50.......... *Putnam.*
Greenwood leaves. *See* Lippincott, S. J.
Greer, F. H: Guide to Florida and California. roy. 8°. '75. 50c.......... *N. Y. & H. Pub.*
— Men of mark. 4°. '72. $6; mor., $25. *N. Y. & H. Pub.*
— Universal biography. [To form 3 v.] v. 1, 2. 4°. '72. ea., mor., $15.......... *N. Y. & H. Pub.*
Greeting. Emerson, L. O. $1.50.......... *Ditson.*
Greg, W. R. Enigmas of life. 12°. $2....... *Holt.*
— Literary and social judgments. 12°. $2...... *Holt.*
— Rocks ahead. 12°. $2.......... * *Osgood.*
Gregg, J: Mick Healy, the Irish peasant. ('55.) 2d ed. 18°. '75. 40c.......... *So. Meth.*

Gregg, *Rev.* J: C. Life in the army; in departments of Virginia and the gulf, incl. obs. in New Orleans; with acc. of life and experience in ministry. ('66.) 2d ed. ill. 12°. '68. $1.25......... *Perkinpine.*

Gregg, S. Infant church-membership. 16°. $1. *Cin. Meth. Bk. Conc.*

Gregg, T: Fruit culture for the million. ill. 12°. '57. 75c.................................... *Wells.*

Gregg, Tresham D. Methodization of the Hebrew verbs. 8°. (Bagster.) $1.12.......... *Wiley.*

Gregor, Chr. Choralbuch, enth. alle zu dem Gesangbuch d. evang. Brüder-Gemeinen v. J. 1778 gehörigen Melodien. obl. 8°. '59. hf. bd., $1.75. *Clauder.*

— *See also* Lonas, H.; — Kästner, C. A.; — Kunz, H.; — Nitschke, A.

Gregory, B: The thorough business man: memorials of Walter Powell, merchant, Melbourne and London. por. 12°. '71. $2......... *Routledge.*

Gregory, D. S. Christian ethics; or, the science of the life of human duty. 12°. '75. $1.50.. *Eldredge.*

Gregory, G: Church history. New ed., rev. and enl. by M. Ruter. 8°. '39. $2.50.... *Meth. Bk. Conc.*

Gregory, G: Lectures on eruptive fevers; with notes and tables by H. D. Bulkley. ill. 8°. $3.. *W. Wood.*

Gregory, H. D. Index to Mitchell's New school atlas. 8°. pap., 80c........................... *Butler.*

— *See also* Mitchell, S. A.

Gregory, J. G. State of the church and the world at the final outbreak of evil and revelation of antichrist. 12°. $1.25................. (?) *Martien.*

Gregory, J. M. *See* Hovey, A., *and* Gregory, J. M.

Gregory, Ja. J. H. Cabbages: how to grow them. 12°. 30c. .... *Judd.*

— Onion raising: what kinds to raise, and way to raise them. 12°. 30c.......................... *Judd.*

— Squashes: how to grow them. 12°. pap., 30c... *Judd.*

Gregory, Olinthus Gilb. Evidences, doctrines and duties of the Christian religion. 12°. (Bohn.) $1.25............................ *Little, B. & Co.*

— *Same.* 12°. (Bohn.) $1.40..... *Scribner, W. & A.*

— *Same.* 12°. (Bohn.) $1.50.......... *Lippincott.*

— Mathematics for practical men; adapted to surveyors, architects, mechanics and civil engineers. ('50.) 5th ed. pl. 8°. '68. $3................ *Baird.*

Gregory, W: Handbook of inorganic chemistry; [also] Physics of chemistry, by J. M. Sanders. ('56.) 4th ed. 8°. $2.50....................... *Barnes.*

— Handbook of organic chemistry; ed. by J. M. Sanders. ('56.) 4th ed. 8°. $2.50......... *Barnes.*

Gregory Gold. Strong, J. D. 25c.......... *Lothrop.*

Gregory Gold ser. 6 v. ill. 24°. $1.50...... *Lothrop.*

Cont.: Gregory Gold. — Minna's proud heart. — Beauty Benson. — The blacksmith. — Truthful Jenny. — Wilful waste.

Greith, C: Choral mass in F. 4°. pap., $1.... *Peters.*

Grenville, G: N. T. *See* Nugent, *Lord.*

Gretchen; or, the chapel of Winkelried. 18°. pap., 12c.................................... *O'Shea.*

— *See also* Henrietta.

Gretchen; or, the day-laborer's daughter. Fries, R. 80c.................................... *Am. Tr.*

Gretchen's troubles. [Juvenile.] 18°. 75c. (?) *Martien.*

Greuber, C. S. Catechism on the church militant, the church expectant, and the church triumphant. 18°. '75. pap., 50c.......................... *Pott.*

Greville, C: C. F. Journal of reigns of George IV. and William IV.; ed. by H. Reeve. 2 v. 12°. $4. *Appleton.*

— *See also* Stoddard, R. H., Bric-a-brac ser.

Greville, R. K. *See* Historical and descript. account of Brit. India.

Grey, Annie. Allie Stuart. ill. 12°. $1.50.... *Nelson.*

Grey, C: Early years of the Prince Consort [Albert]; comp. under direction of Queen Victoria. por. 12°. $2; $1; pap., 25c................ *Harper.*

Grey, *Mrs.* E. C. [Novels.] 18 v. 8°. pap... *Peterson.*

Cont.: Alice Seymour, 25c. — The flirt, 75c. — Good society, 75c. — Hyacinthe, 25c. — The lion-hearted, 75c. — Mary Seaham, 75c. — Passion and principle, 75c. — Baronet's daughters. — Belle of the family. — Duke and cousin. — Gipsy's daughter. — Lena Cameron. — The little wife. — Manœuvring mother. — Marriage in high life. — Old dower house. — Sybil Lennard. — Young prima donna, *ea.*, 50c.

— Bosom friend. 8°. pap., 50c.............. *Harper.*

— Cousin Harry. 12°. $1.75. pap., $1.50... *Peterson.*

— Gambler's wife. 8°. pap., 50c............. *Harper.*

— Little beauty. 12°. $1.75; pap., $1.50 ... *Peterson.*

— Young husband. 8°. pap., 50c............ *Harper.*

Grey, Georgia. Virgilia: story of Rome under Nero. 16°. $1.15............................. *Pres. Bd.*

Grey, Heraclitus. Playing trades. ill. roy. 16°. $1.50. *Cassell.*

Grey, Ma. Elsie Lee; or, impatience cured. 18°. 45c. *Pres. Bd.*

Grey, *Mrs.* Theresa. Journal of a visit to Egypt, Constantinople, etc. 12°. $1.50............ *Harper.*

Grey house on the hill. Greene, L. L. $1.25.. *Nelson.*

Grey mare. Leland, H. P. $1.50........... *Claxton.*

Grey mare: comedietta. 16°. pap., 15c...... *Happy.*

Grey woman. Gaskell, E. C. 25c.......... *Peterson.*

Greycliff. *See* Hamilton, K. W.

Greystone Lodge. 18°. 50c................ *Carter.*

Grieb, Chr. F. Dictionary of the Eng. and German lang., with sup. by J. C. Oehlschläger. 2 v. 8°. leath., $12; — in 32 nos., ea., pap., 25c..... *Kohler; Schäfer.*

Grier, J. B. Studies in the English of Bunyan. 12°. $1.25 .... *Lippincott.*

Griesbach, J. J. *See* Bible, New Test., *Greek; Greek and Eng.*

Griesinger, Thdr. Leben u. Treiben in New York: ernste u. humor. Skizzen. 5th ed. 12°. '76. 50c.; pap., 25c......................... *Zickel.*

— New York vor zwanzig Jahren, od. die alte Brauerei: Criminalroman. 12°. '73. $1.50. pap., $1.. *Zickel.*

Grif. *See* Farjeon, B. L.

Griffen, J., *and* Clarke, T. C. Loads and strains of bridges. 8°. pap., 50c........ *Am. Soc. of C. E.*

Griffin, Edm. D. Park Street [Boston] lectures. 12°. $1.25 .... *Cong. Pub.*

Griffin, G: Gospel (The) its own advocate. 12°. $1.25. *Appleton.*

Griffin, Ger. Works. 10 v. 12°. $15; $20; $25; ea., $1.50.................................. *Sadlier.*

Cont.: 1. The collegians: tale of Garryowen. — 2. Tales of the Munster festivals: Card-drawer; The half-sir; Suil Dhuv, the coiner. — 3. Holland tide, etc. — 4. The rivals; Tracy's ambition. — 5. Talis qualis; or, tales of the jury room. — 6. Duke of Monmouth. — 7. Tales of the five senses; Night at sea. — 8. Poetical works; Tragedy of Gisippus. — 9. The invasion. — 10. Life; by his brother.

— Novels. 3 v. 16°. $2.25............... *Routledge.*

Cont.: Colleen bawn. — Rivals. — Munster festivals.

— Colleen bawn. 12°. pap., 25c........... *Routledge.*

Note. Same as "Collegians."

— Collegians. 8°. pap., 50c............. *U. P. James.*

— Gisippus: tragedy. 16°. pap., 15c......... *French.*

— Tales of the five senses. 16°. 75c.; $1.25.. *Sadlier.*

Griffin, Gilderay Welles. Memoir of Col. C. S. Todd. 8°. '72. $1.50........................ *Claxton.*

— My Danish days; with a glance at the hist., traditions and literature of the old northern country. ('70.) 2d ed. 12°. '75. $1.50......... *Claxton.*

— Studies in literature. 12°. '70. $1....... *Turnbull.*

— *Same.* ('70.) 2d ed. 12°. '71. $1.75...... *Claxton.*

Griffith, Allen Ayrault. Lessons in eloc., and drill book in vocal physiol. 12°. '72. $1.50.. *Adams, B. & L.*

Griffith, Cecil. Victory Deane. 12°. $1.25.. *Loring.*

Griffith, Rob. E. Universal formulary: methods of preparing and administering officinal and other medicines. 3d ed., rev. and enl. by J. M. Maisch. 8°. $4.50; leath., $5.50 .... *Lea.*

Griffith, *Mrs.* T. H. Year with Gerty West. 16°. $1.25. *Am. Bapt.*

Griffith Gaunt. Daly, A. 15c. .... *French.*

Griffith Gaunt. *See* Reade, C:

Griffiths, J: W. Progressive ship builder. ('75.) New ed. 2 v. ill. 4°. '76. $12 .... *Griffiths.*

Griffiths, W. Handsel. Lessons in the art of prescribing. 18°. '75. $1.25 .... *Macmillan.*

Grigg, —, *and* Elliot, —. Common school readers. 4 v. 12°. bds., no. 1, 13c.; 2, 25c.; 3, 45c.; 4, 75c. *Lippincott.*

Grigg, J: Southern and western songster. ('26.) New ed., enl. 18°. '69. 75c. .... *Claxton.*

Grigsby, H. B. Discourse on life and character of L. W. Tazewell. 8°. '60. $2 .... *J. W. Randolph.*

— Discourse on Virginia convention of 1776. 8°. '55. $3 .... *J. W. Randolph.*

Grile, Dod (*pseud.*) *See* Bierce, M. H.

Grim old age: comedy. 16°. pap., 15c. .... *French.*

Grimes, J. Stanley. Mysteries of head and the heart expl. ill. 12°. '75. $2 .... *Keen.*

Grimke, F: Considerations upon nature and tendency of free institutions. 8°. '48. $2.50 .... *Clarke.*

— *Same.* 2d ed., rev. and enl. 8°. '56. $2.75. *Claxton; Lippincott.*

Grimkie. *See* Abbott, Jac., Florence stories.

Grimm, Hm. Das Kind; [also] Der Landschaftsmaler. 12°. '64. pap., 35c. .... *Steiger.*

— Life of Michael Angelo; tr. by F. E. Bunnett. 2 v. cr. 8°. '72–'75. $5–$10 .... *Little, B. & Co.*

— Venus (Die) von Milo; [also] Rafael und Michel Angelo. ('66.) New ed. 12°. '75. pap., 75c. *Holt.*

Grimm, Jac. L: *and* W: C: Brave little tailor, and other fairy tales; tr. 16°. $1 .... *Miller.*

— — Fairy tales; tr. ill. 12°. $1.50; $1.75. *Scribner, W. & A.*

— — *Same.* (Chandos classics.) cr. 8°. $1; pap., 75c. *Scribner, W. & A.*

— — Gammer Grethel; or, Germ. fairy tales and popular stories; tr. by E. Taylor. ill. 12°. (Bohn.) $1.25 .... *Little, B. & Co.*

— — *Same.* 12°. (Bohn.) $1.40 ... *Scribner, W. & A.*

— — *Same.* 12°. (Bohn.) $1.50 .... *Lippincott.*

— — German fairy tales; tr. 16°. $1.50 .... *Miller.*

— — German popular stories, tr.; ill. after designs of G. Cruikshank, ed. by E. Taylor, with introd. by J. Ruskin. 12°. (Lond.) $3 .. *Little, B. & Co.*

— — German popular tales and household stories; tr. ill. 12°. $2.50 .... *Porter.*

— — Goblins (The); tr. ill. sm. 4°. $1.50 ... **Osgood.*

— — Golden bird, and other stories; tr. 16°. $1 .. *Miller.*

— — Home fairy tales; tr. 16°. $1.50 .... *Miller.*

— — Home stories; tr. ill. 16°. $1.25 ..... *Routledge.*

— — Household stories; tr. ill. cr. 8°. $2.50; hf. cf., $4.50 .... *Routledge.*

— — Kinder- u. Hausmärchen. 18°. $1; $1.25; bds., 75c.; leath., $1.60 .... *Radde.*

— — King of the swans and other fairy tales; tr. 16°. $1 .... *Miller.*

— — Popular tales and household stories, tr.; ill. by E. H. Wehnert. 12°. $2.50 .... *Appleton.*

— — Stray leaves from fairy land; tr. ill. 12°. $1.25. *T. Bliss.*

— — Tales and stories: new tr. ill. cr. 8°. $2.50. *Scribner, W. & A.*

— — Three brothers and other stories; tr. 16°. $1. *Miller.*

Grimm, W: C: *See* Grimm, J. L. *and* W. C.

Grimshaw, W: Etymological dict. of the Eng. lang. 12°. '48. shp., 80c. .... *Claxton.*

— Handy dictionary. 16°. hf. roan, 90c. .. *Lippincott.*

Grimshaw, W: *continued.*

— History of England. 12°. hf. roan, 95c. — Questions and key. pap., 15c. .... *Lippincott.*

— History of France to death of Louis XVI. 12°. '29. hf. roan, 95c. — Questions and key. pap., 15c. *Claxton; Lippincott.*

— History of Greece. 12°. hf. roan, 95c. — Questions and key. pap., 15c. .... *Lippincott.*

— History of Napoleon. 12°. hf. roan, 95c. — Questions and key. pap., 15c. .... *Lippincott.*

— History of Rome. 12°. hf. roan, 95c. — Questions and key. pap., 15c. .... *Lippincott.*

— History of South America. 12°. hf. roan, 95c. — Questions and key. pap., 15c. .... *Lippincott.*

— History of the U. S. to 1848. 12°. hf. roan, 95c. — Questions and key. pap., 15c. *Claxton; Lippincott.*

— Pictorial history of the U. S., with questions. 12°. hf. roan, $1.13. — Questions and key. pap., 15c. *Lippincott.*

Grimshaw, Bagshaw and Bradshaw. Morton, J. M. 15c. .... *French.*

Grimshawe, T. S. *See* Cowper, W:

Grin bushes. Byron, H. J. 15c. .... *French.*

Grindon, Leo H. Life: its nature, varieties and phenomena. 12°. $2.25 .... *Lippincott.*

— Little things of nature considered in ref. to divine benevolence. 8°. 50c. .... *H. H. Carter.*

— *Same.* 16°. '64. $1 .... *Lockwood, B. & Co.*

— Phenomena of plant life. 12°. 50c. ... *H. H. Carter.*

— *Same.* 16°. '64. $1 .... *Lockwood, B. & Co.*

— Sex in nature. 16°. '64. $1.25 .. *Lockwood, B. & Co.*

— Sexuality of nature. 12°. 75c. .... *H. H. Carter.*

Note. Same as above?

— Trees of old England. 8°. 75c. ...... *H. H. Carter.*

Gringo, Harry (*pseud.*) *See* Wise, H. A.

Griscom, J: H. Animal mechanism and physiology. ill. 18°. 75c. .... *Harper.*

— Anniversary discourse before N. Y. Acad. of Med. 8°. '54. pap., 25c. .... *N. Y. Acad. Med.*

— First lessons in human physiology. 16°. '45. 60c. *G. R. Lockwood.*

— On use of tobacco. 32°. '68. pap., 25c. ... *Putnam.*

Griseldis u. Markgraf Walther. 12°. pap., 15c. *Radde.*

Griset, Ern. (*ill.*) Comical pictures; with rhymes by Tom Hood. 4°. bds., $2 .... *Routledge.*

— Funny picture books. 4 pts. col. ill. 4°. ea., 50c. *Appleton.*

Cont.: Three youthful mariners. — Funny book about the Ashantees. — Brothers bold, and their marvellous adventures in central Africa. — Book of funny beasts.

Grist, —. On mission. 40c.; $1.50 .... *Dooley.*

Grist to the mill. Planché, J. R. 15c. .... *French.*

Griswold, Alex. Viets. Life. 18°. 50c. ..... *Dutton.*

— Prayers; adapted to occasions for which provision is not made in Book of common prayer. 12°. '60. $1.25 .... *Dutton.*

Griswold, H. *See* Ohio, Sup. Court reports.

Griswold, J. Fire underwriters' text-book. 8°. '72. shp., $7.50 .... *Hine.*

Griswold, Ruf. Wilmot. Curiosities of Am. literature. *See* Disraeli, I: Curiosities of lit.

— Female poets of Am. New ed., rev. and enl. by R. H. Stoddard. por. roy. 8°. $5–$10 ..... *Miller.*

— Gems from the Am. poets; with biog. notices. 32°. 60c.; 90c.; mor., $1.50. — (Red line ed.) sq. 16°. $1.50; mor., $2.25; $3.50 .... *Porter.*

— Poets and poetry of Am. New ed., rev. and enl. by R. H. Stoddard. por. roy. 8°. $5–$10 .. *Miller.*

— Poets and poetry of England in 19th cent. New ed., rev. and enl. by R. H. Stoddard. ill. 8°. $5–$10. *Miller.*

— Prose writers of Am. New ed., rev.; with essay on present intellectual condition of the country. por. imp. 8°. '70. $5–$10 .... *Porter.*

Griswold, Ruf. Wilmot, *continued.*
— Republican court; or, American society in the days of Washington. New ed., rev. and enl. por. imp. 8°. mor., $15. — (chp. ed.) 8°. $5; $6; mor., $7.50 .... *Appleton.*
— (*ed.*) Voices of comfort; [also] The cypress wreath. 24°. '74. 25c.; 40c. 16°. $1 .... *Lothrop.*
Griswold, *Mrs.* Ste. M. A woman's pilgrimage to the Holy Land; or, pleasant days abroad: notes of a tour through Europe and the east. ill. 8°. *$2.50; $2.75 .... *Burr.*
Griswold, W. Railroad-engineer's pocket companion for the field. (cop. '54.) '66. 3d ed. 12°. '71. $1.75 .... *Baird.*
Griswold, Wayne. Kansas: her resources and developments; or, the Kansas pilot. ill. 8°. '71. pap., 50c. .... *Clarke.*
Grizzly Jake. 32°. '76. pap., 10c. .... *De Witt.*
Grobe, C: Concordia: vocal music, with element. exercises. obl. 16°. '61. bds., 60c. .... *Ditson.*
— New method for piano. 4°. $3; bds., $2.50.. *Ditson.*
Grocer's boy. *See* Katie Johnstone's lib.
Grocer's shop. 32°. 20c.; 15c. .... *Dutton.*
Grocers' reference book. 4°. '73. $50.. *J. A. Murphy.*
Grocott, J. C. Index to familiar quotations. 12°. $3. *Routledge.*
Groesbeck, J: Book-keeping. 8°. $2..(?) *Crittenden.*
— Crittenden commercial arithmetic (The) and business manual. ('69.) 11th ed. 12°. '75. $1.50.— Key. 16°. $1 .... *Eldredge.*
— Practical book-keeping, single and double entry. 8°. '75. hf. leath., $2. — (College ed.) 8°. '75. hf. leath., $2 .... *Eldredge.*
Gron, *Abbé* F. Exposition of the Lord's prayer; tr. 64°. 30c. .... *Cath. Pub.*
— Portraiture of true devotion; tr. 32°. 30c. *Cath. Pub.*
Gröning, J. *See* Korfmacher, W. H.
Gropings after truth. Huntington, J. 75c... *Cath. Pub.*
Groschel, —. Practical piano method: foreign fingering. f°. $2 .... *Gordon.*
Groser, W. H. Bible months; or, the seasons in Palestine as ill. of Scripture. 18°. 75c..... *Nelson.*
— Illustrative teaching. 18°. '61. 30c..... *Randolph.*
— Instruments (The): what to teach; or, the intellectual part of a teacher's preparation for his Sabbath duties. 18°. '69. pap., 10c. .... *Perkinpine.*
— Joshua and his successors: introd. to Joshua, Judges, Ruth and Samuel I.; with notes. 2 v. 18°. ea., 90c. .... *Nelson.*
— Men worth imitating: sketches of noble men. ill. 12°. $1 .... *Nelson.*
— Our work: lectures on the principle and practice of S.-school teaching. 18°. 75c. .... *Nelson.*
— Ready for work; or, hints on the preparation of Bible lessons. 18°. 50c. .... *Nelson.*
— Teacher's (The) model and the model teacher. 16°. '70. 75c. .... *Randolph.*
— What is a child? 16°. '67. 15c..... *Meth. Bk. Conc.*
Grosh, A. B. Mentor in the granges and homes of Patrons of Husbandry. por. and ill. 12°. '76. *$2 .... *Clark & M.*
— Odd-fellow's improved manual. por. and eng. 32°. $1.50. 12°. $2; mor., $3.25; — in German. 32°. $1.50 .... *Clark & M.*
Gross, Eug. L. Digest of Illinois criminal laws. 8°. '68. shp., $4.50 .... *Gross.*
— *See also* Illinois, Statutes.
— *and* W. L. Index to Illinois laws (1818–'69). roy. 8°. shp., $3 .... *Gross.*
Gross, H. Comparative materia medica; ed. by C. Hering. [Hom.] roy. 8°. hf. mor., $10.. *Boericke.*
Gross, J. B. Doctrine of the Lord's Supper, as set forth in book of concord, crit. examined and its fallacy demonstrated. 12°. $1.25... *Lippincott.*
Gross, Magnus. Die amerikanische Krisis: Vorträge. 12°. '74. pap., 25c. .... *Steiger.*
— Languages and popular education: addresses. 12°. '71. pap., 30c. .... *Steiger.*
Gross, S: D. American medical biog. of 19th cent. por. 8°. '61. $3.50 .... *Lindsay.*
— Manual of military surgery. ('61.) 2d ed. ill. 18°. '62. 63c. .... *Claxton; Lippincott.*
— Practical treatise on foreign bodies in the air-passages. ill. 8°. $2.75 .... *Lea.*
— System of surgery: pathological, diagnostic, therapeutic and operative. 5th ed., rev. 2 v. eng. imp. 8°. leath., $15 .... *Lea.*
Gross, W: L. *See* Gross, E. L. *and* W. L.; — Illinois, Digest of statutes.
Gross Busekow. Winterfeld, A. v. 50c.... *Morwitz.*
Gross-Cophta (Der). *See* Goethe, J. W. v.
Grosse amerikanische Dollmetscher (Der). 12°. 75c. *Kohler.*
Grosse amerikanische Dollmetscher (Der). [F. Deutsche um englisch zu lernen.] 18°. 40c.; pap., 30c.; mit Wörterbuch, bds., 50c. .... *Radde.*
Grosse Dame (Die). Wonliarliarski, W. A. v. 25c. *Steiger.*
Grosse Frage (Die) beantwortet. 32°. '65. 15c.; pap., 5c. .... *Am. Tr.*
Grosse unfehlbare Traumdeuter (Der). 12°. 35c. *Radde.*
Grosses illustr. egyptisches Traumbuch. 12°. 50c. *Radde.*
Grossmutter (Die). Nieritz, G. 25c. ...... *Morwitz.*
Grossvater's Liebling. *See* Hoffmann, J.
Grosvenor, *Mrs.* —. Life's lessons. 18°. 75c. *Cong. Pub.*
Grosvenor, *Mrs.* H. S. Amy Martin. ('60.) New ed. ill. 16°. '76. $1 .... *Hoyt.*
— Blind Ethan. ('60.) New ed. ill. 18°. '70. 30c... *Hoyt.*
— Frank Talbot; or, unstable as water. ('61.) New ed. ill. 18°. '69. 40c. .... *Hoyt.*
— Grosvenor ser. ('60–'68.) New ed. 4 v. ill. 16°. '74–'76. $5 .... *Hoyt.*
Cont.: Old red house. — Climbing the mountain; or, how I rose in the world. — Brother's choice. — Capt. Russell's watchword.
— Leaving home. ('60.) New ed. ill. 16°. '69. 35c. *Hoyt.*
— Little Jerry, the ragged urchin, and under what teachings he was reclaimed from the streets. ('60.) New ed. ill. 16°. '69. 35c. .... *Hoyt.*
— May Horton; or, life at Aunt Upton's. ('60.) New ed. 16°. '75. $1.25 .... *Hoyt.*
— Simon Martin; or, the first glass. ('60.) New ed. 16°. '76. $1 .... *Hoyt.*
— Why the mill was stopped; or, overcoming evil with good. ('61.) New ed. ill. 18°. '75. 50c... *Hoyt.*
Grosvenor, W. M. Does protection protect? examination of effect of different forms of tariff upon Am. industry. 8°. $2.50 .... *Appleton.*
Grote, G: Aristotle; ed. by A. Bain and G. C. Robertson. 2 v. 8°. (Lond.) '72. hf. cf., $15; cf., $18 .... *Little, B. & Co.*
— History of Greece. 12 v. 12°. $18; shp., $22.80; hf. cf., $39 .... *Harper.*
— *Same.* New ed., with index. 10 v. por., maps and plans. 8°. (Lond.) '72. $40; hf. cf., $60. — Same. 12 v. post 8°. (Lond.) '69. $21; hf. cf., $39; cf., $51 .... *Little, B. & Co.*
— Minor works; with crit. remarks on his intellectual character, writings and speeches; by A. Bain. por. 8°. (Lond.) '73. $5.50.... *Little, B. & Co.*
— Persian wars: chapters 36 and 38–41 of "History of Greece." 12°. hf. bd., $1.50 .... *Harper.*
Grotius, Hg. De veritate religionis Christianæ. 12°. $1 .... *Dennet.*
Grotto nymph. Thaxter, A. W. 15c. .... *French.*
Grou, N: J: Hidden life of the soul; from the writings of Grou by Mrs. S. Lear. 12°. '75. $2.50. — 16°. $1.25. — 48°. 50c. .... *Pott.*

Ground and object of hope for mankind. Maurice, F. D. 75c. . . . . . *Lee & S.*
Grounded staff. Maguire, R. 50c. . . . . . *Cassell.*
Grounds of the Catholic doctrine. 18°. 25c. . . *Noonan.*
Grounds of the Cath. doct.: reason why a Cath. cannot conform to the Prot. religion. 16°. 25c. . . *Strong.*
— *Same.* 32°. 20c. . . . . . *Cath. Pub.*
Grounds of a holy life. Turford, H. 20c. *Friends Bk. Assoc.*
Grout, Lew. Zulu-land; or, life among the Zulu Kaffirs of Natal and Zulu-land, south Africa. map and ill. 12°. $1.50. . . . . . *Pres. Bd.*
Grove, G: *See* Smith, W: *and* Grove, G:
Grove, S. J. Greek and Eng. dictionary. 8°. shp., $2.50 . . . . . . *Lippincott.*
Grover, J. W. Estimates and diagrams of railway bridges for turnpikes, etc. 22d ed. 37 col. pl. f°. '70. $12.50 . . . . . . *Spon.*
— Examples of station buildings, and their cost, as executed on several railways: app. to "Estimates and diagrams of railway bridges," etc. 13 pl. f°. $4.25 . . . . . . *Spon.*
— Iron and timber railway superstructures and general works; with earthwork tables and outlines of a specification and requirements. pl. f°. '74. $17. . . . . . *Spon.*
Groves of Blarney. Hall, A. M. 15c. . . . . . *French.*
Growing like Jesus. *See* Kennedy, *Mrs.* M. G.
Growth in holiness. *See* Faber, F. W.
Grubb, Sa. L. A brief account of life and religious labors. 12°. 20c. . . . . . *Friends Bk. St.*
Gruhler, J. Der Lebenslauf eines Dollars v. ihm selbst erzählt. 8°. '76. bds., 20c. . . . . . *Pilger.*
— *See also* Wackernagel, W., *and* Gruhler, J.
Grumbler (The). *See* Pickering, E.
Grumbling Tommy and contented Harry. 18°. 25c. *Am. S. S.*
Grün, Anast. (*pseud.*) *See* Auersperg, A. A. (*Graf*) v.
Grund, J. W. Twelve études [for the piano]; with notes by R. Schumann. (Op. 24.) f°. $2.50; in 2 bks., ea., $1.50. . . . . . *Brainard.*
Gründe gegen die Lehre d. Universalisten. 12°. '63. pap., 8c. . . . . . *Am. Tr.*
Gründung (Die) v. Maryland. *See* Zschokke, H.
Grüner, M. L. Manufacture of steel; tr. by L. Smith; with app. on the Bessemer process in the U. S. ill. 8°. '72. $3.50. . . . . . *Van Nostrand.*
— Studies of blast furnace phenomena; tr., with app., by L. D. B. Gordon. 8°. '74. $2.50. . . . *Baird.*
Guarded by a fear. Sheridan, M. B. 35c. . . *Authors.*
Guarded jewels. 18°. 55c.; 65c. . . . . . *Am. Bapt.*
Guardian. *See* Addison, Jos.; — Chalmers, A.; — Tatler.
Guardian angel. Brooks, C. S. 15c. . . . . . *French.*
Guardian angel. Holmes, O. W. $2. . . . . . *Osgood.*
Guays, J. F. E. Le B. des. *See* Le Boys des Guays.
Gubernatis, Angelo de. Zoological mythology: legends of animals. 2 v. 8°. '72. $8. . . . . . *Macmillan.*
Guckgucksuhr (Die). Nieritz, G. 25c. . . . *Morwitz.*
Guendaline. *See* Library of good example.
Guénon, François. Treatise on milch cows. ill. 8°. 75c. . . . . . *Judd.*
Guenot, C. Vengeance of a Jew. 12°. $1.50; $2. *Cummiskey.*
Guéranger, Prosper. Life of St. Cecilia; tr. from the Fr. 12°. $1.50 . . . . . . *Cunningham; Sadlier.*
Guerike, H. E. F. Church history; tr. by W. G. T. Shedd. ('57.) New ed. 8°. '72. $3. . *Draper.*
Note. Includes first 6 centuries.
— *Same.* 8°. $5. . . . . . *Scribner, W. & A.*
— Church history: mediæval church to A. D. 1073. 8°. '70. $1.50. . . . . . *Draper.*
Guerilla chief. 8°. pap., 75c. . . . . . *Peterson.*
Guérin, Eugénie de. Journal; tr. cr. 8°. $2. . *Routledge.*
— *Same;* ed. by G. S. Trébutien. 10th ed. 12°. '66. $2 . . . . . . *Cath. Pub.*
— Letters; tr. cr. 8°. $2. . . . . . *Routledge.*
— *Same;* ed by G. S. Trébutien. 6th ed. 12°. '66. $2. *Cath. Pub.*
Guérin, Georges Maur. de. Journal; with essay by M. Arnold, and memoir by Sainte Beuve; tr. by E. T. Fisher. 12°. '63. $1.25. . . . . . *Holt.*
Guernsey, Clara F. Boys of Eaglewood; or, life at school. 16°. $1.50. . . . . . *Am. S. S.*
— Elmira's ambitions; or, Miss Ross and her career. 16°. $1.25. . . . . . *Am. S. S.*
— Friends in need. 16°. $1.50. . . . . . (?) *Martien.*
— Ice raft. 16°. $1.25. . . . . . (?) *Martien.*
— Mallory girls; or, the wrong and the right way. 16°. $1.50. . . . . . *Am. S. S.*
— Mere piece of mischief; or, Amiel's troubles. 18°. 90c. . . . . . (?) *Martien.*
— Merman and the figure head: Christmas story. ill. 16°. $1. . . . . . *Lippincott.*
— — *See also* Enchanting fairy lib.
— New boy. 16°. $1.25. . . . . . (?) *Martien.*
— Oliver's prisoner. 16°. $1. . . . . . (?) *Martien.*
— Plaid pincushion. 18°. '71. 45c. . . . . . *Whittaker.*
— Red crosses. 16°. 90c. . . . . . (?) *Martien.*
— Silver lib. 3 v. 16°. $3. . . . . . *Am. S. S.*
Cont.: Silver cup, $1.10. — Silver rifle, $1. — Alice Fenton; or, alone in London, 90c.
— Spirit in prison. 16°. '75. $1.25 . . . . *H. A. Young.*
— Tutor and teamster: sequel to "Friends in need." 16°. $1.50 . . . . . . (?) *Martien.*
Guernsey, E. Gentleman's handbook of homœopathy. 12°. $1. . . . . . *Boericke.*
— Homœopathic domestic practice. 9th ed., rev. and enl. 8°. hf. mor., $2.50. . . . . . *Boericke.*
Guernsey, Eg. History of the U. S. New ed., rev. 12°. $1.75. . . . . . *Moss.*
Guernsey, H. N. Application of principles and pract. of homœop. to obstetrics, and disorders peculiar to women and children. 2d ed., rev. and enl. ill. 8°. hf. mor., $9. . . . . . *Boericke.*
Guernsey, Lucy Ellen. Binney, the beaver. 18°. '75. 50c. . . . . . *H. A. Young.*
— Blue socks; or, count the cost. 18°. 65c. . . *Am. S. S.*
— Children of Stantoun Corbet ser. 3 v. 18°. $2. *Am. S. S.*
Cont.: Cousin Deborah's story; or, the great plague, 60c. — Mabel; or, the bitter root, $1. — Lady Lucy's secret; or, the gold thimble, 60c.
— Child's treasure. 18°. '70. 90c. . . . . . *Whittaker.*
— Christmas at Cedar Hill. 16°. '69. $1. . *Whittaker.*
— Claribel; or, rest at last. 18°. 55c. . . . . . *Am. S. S.*
— Grandmother Brown's school-days; or, education as it was 70 years since. 16°. $1.50 . . . . *Am. S. S.*
— Heiress of McGregor. 16°. $1.50. . . . . . *Am. S. S.*
— Irish Amy; or, the child on the street and on the farm. 16°. $1.10. 18°. 80c. . . . . . *Am. S. S.*
— Jenny and the birds. 18°. 75c. . . . . . *Am. S. S.*
— Jenny and the insects. 16°. $1.10. . . . . *Am. S. S.*
— Lady Betty's governess; or, the Corbet chronicles. 12°. '73. $1.50. . . . . . *Whittaker.*
— Lady Rosamond's book: pt. 2 of the Stantoun-Corbet chronicles. 12°. '74. $1.50 . . . . . . *Whittaker.*
— Langham revels; or, the fair dame of Staunton. 16°. $1.50 . . . . . . (?) *Martien.*
— Milly; or, the hidden cross. 12°. $1. . . . . *Loring.*
— Nelly's lib. 5 v. 16°. $4.90. . . . . . *Am. S. S.*
Cont.: Nelly; or, the best inheritance, 90c. — Ethel's trials in becoming a missionary, $1.25. — Mabel; or, the bitter root, $1. — On the mountain; or, lost and found, 90c. — Fairchilds; or, do what you can, 90c.
— Orphan nieces; or, duty and inclination. 16°. '56. $1.25. . . . . . *Randolph.*
— Our Tabby and her travels. 16°. '58. $1. . *Randolph.*
— Percy's holidays. 18°. 40c. . . . . . *Am. S. S.*
— Red plant. 18°. 40c. . . . . . *Am. S. S.*

Guernsey, Lucy Ellen, *continued.*
— Rhoda's education; or, too much of a good thing. 16°. $1.25 .... *Am. S. S.*
— School girl's treasury. 18°. '69. 90c.... *Whittaker.*
— Straight forward; or, walking in the light. ('60.) New ed. ill. 16°. '72. $1.25 .... *Hoyt.*
— Sunday-school exhibition and its consequences. 16°. 85c. .... *Am. S. S.*
— Tame turtle; or, Geordie McGregor's trouble. 16°. 85c. .... *Am. S. S.*
— Upward and onward; or, history of Rob Merritt. 18°. '55. 85c. .... *Randolph.*
— Winifred; or, after many days. 12°. '69. $1.50. *Whittaker.*

Guernsey, R. S. Juries and physicians on questions of insanity. 8°. pap., 25c. .... *Campbell & Co.*
— Key to Story's "Equity jurisprudence;" for universities, colleges and law schools. 8°. '76. shp., $4 .... *Ward & P.*
— Living authors at the New York bar. 8°. $1.50; pap., $1 .... *Campbell & Co.*
— On municipal law and its relations to const. of man. 8°. pap., 25c. .... *Campbell & Co.*
— Supplement to mechanics' lien law, rel. to N. Y. City. 8°. pap., 25c. .... *Campbell & Co.*

Guerrazzi, F. D. Beatrice Cenci; tr. [Fiction.] 12°. $1.75 .... *Carleton.*
— Manfred; tr. [Fiction.] 12°. $1.75 .... *Carleton.*

Guersant, P. On surgical diseases of children; tr. by R. J. Dunglison. 8°. $2.50 .... *Lea.*

Guesses at truth. *See* Hare, A. W. *and* J. C.

Guest, W: Call of the hour. 12°. '70. 40c.; pap., 25c. .... *Lothrop.*
— Young man setting out in life. 18°. '68. 35c.; pap., 20c. .... *Am. Tr.*

Guettier, A. Metallic alloys: guide to chem. and phys. properties, preparation, composition and uses; tr. by A. A. Fesquet. ('71.) 12°. '72. $3.. *Baird.*

Guhl, E., *and* Koner, W. Life of the Greeks and Romans, described from ancient monuments; tr. by F. Hüffer. ill. large 8°. $6 .... *Appleton.*

Guiccioli, *Contessa.* *See* Boissy, Teresa Gamba.

Guide for little foot steps. 64°. 15c.; 20c... *Am. S. S.*

Guide to acquaintance with God. Sherman, J. 30c. *Pres. Bd.*

Guide to authorship. 12°. pap., 50c. .... *Haney.*

Guide to the chapter; cont. the degrees of mark master, past master, etc. [Masonic.] 12°. $1.50 .... *Redding.*

Guide to Florida. *See* Rambler.

Guide to heaven: manual of Cath. devotions. ill. 32°. 60c.-$2.75; — with Epistles and Gospels. 24°. 80c.-$6 .... *T. Kelly.*

Guide to Honiton lace-making. ill. 12°. pap., 50c. *Symonds.*

Guide to the island of Mackinac and its vicinity. map. 16°. '75. $1 .... *Disturnell.*

Guide to knowledge of life. Mann, R. J. $1.50. (?) *Francis.*

Guide to needlework. ill. 12°. '76. pap., 50c. *Symonds.*

Guide to the Saviour. 18°. 55c. .... *Am. S. S.*

Guide to the Saviour. Sutton, A. 50c..... *Freewill.*

Guide to the stage. White, C. 15c. .... *De Witt.*

Guide to the unprotected in every day matters rel. to property and income; by a banker's daughter. 4th ed., rev. fp. 8°. '67. $1.25 .... *Macmillan.*

Guide to wealth. Smead, W. 75c. .... *Mendenhall.*

Guide to West Point and the U. S. Milit. Acad. maps and ill. 18°. '67. $1 .... *Van Nostrand.*

Guide to young disciples. Pike, J. G. 70c... *Am. Tr.*

Guiding star. John, D. C. 35c. .... *Ditson.*

Guido. *See* Van der Velde, K. F.

Guido and Lita. Lorne, *Marquis of.* $1.50.. *Macmillan.*

Guido, od. das Gespenst d. Ahnfrau. 12°. pap., 15c. *Radde.*

Guignard, Augustin. Mass for soprano, alto, tenor and bass. f°. pap., $1 .... *Ditson.*

Guigon, A. B. Index to Virginia reports from 1st to 11th Grattan. 8°. '59. hf. shp., $5.. *J. W. Randolph.*

Guila (*pseud.*) Invalid's cook-book. 16°. 20c. *Routledge.*

Guilbert, *Bp. of London.* Virginia's cure: advisive narrative conc. Virginia, disc. true ground of that churches unhappiness, etc. 1662. [Reprint.] 4°. pap., 50c. .... *Sabin.*

Guild, *Mrs.* C. S. Hymns and rhymes; for home and school. sq. 18°. 75c. .... *Nichols & H.*

Guild, Curtis. Over the ocean; or, sights and scenes in foreign lands. cr. 8°. $2.50 .... *Lee & S.*

Guild, E. E. Pro and con of supernatural religion. 18°. '76. 75c.; pap., 40c. .... *D. M. Bennett.*
— Universalists' book of reference: facts, arguments and scripture texts pro and con, on the great controversy between Limitarians and Universalists. 12°. '53. $1 .... *Universalist.*

Guild Court. Mac Donald, G. 50c. .... *Harper.*

Guilford Street stories. 3 v. 18°. '74. $1.25. *Meth. Bk. Conc.*
Cont.: Jeanie Nesbit. — Malcolm Dykes. — Very disobliging.

Guillaume, L. Interior architecture. pl. f°. '75. $3. *Bicknell.*

Guillemin, Amédée. Forces of nature: introd. to study of phys. phenomena; tr. by Mrs. N. Lockyer, and ed., with add., by J. N. Lockyer. col. pl. and woodcuts. roy. 8°. $12.50; hf. cf., $16; hf. mor., $18 .... *Scribner, W. & A.*
— *Same.* 2d ed. col. plates and woodcuts. roy. 8°. '73. $12.50 .... *Macmillan.*
— Heavens (The): ill. handbook of popular astronomy, tr.; ed. by J. N. Lockyer. 4th ed., rev. by R. A. Proctor. ill. 8°. $4.50; hf. cf., $7; hf. mor., $8; cf., $9 .... *Scribner, W. & A.*
— Sun (The); tr. by T. L. Phipson. ill. 12°. '72. $1.25 .... *Scribner.*
— *Same.* ill. 12°. $1.50 .... *Lippincott.*
— Wonders of the moon; tr. by M. G. Mead; ed. with add. by M. Mitchell. ill. 12°. '72. $1.50.. *Scribner.*

Guilt and innocence. Schwartz, M. S. $1.50; $1. *Porter.*

Guitar without a master. obl. 8°. '61. pap., 75c. *Ditson.*

Guitéras, Eusebio. Método práctico elemental para aprender frances. 12°. 75c. .... *Appleton.*

Guizot, *Mme.* Elis. Ctte. P. Evenings in the south of France; tr. 18°. 55c. .... *Am. S. S.*
— Moral tales; tr. by Mrs. L. Burke. ill. 16°. $1.25. *Routledge.*
— Popular tales; tr. by Mrs. L. Burke. ill. 16°. $1.25. *O'Shea.*
— Young student; or, Ralph and Victor; tr. ill. 12°. $1 .... *Appleton.*

Guizot, François P. G. Corneille and his times; tr. 12°. $1.50 .... *Harper.*
— Essay on character and influence of Washington in the rev.; tr. 12°. 75c. .... *Miller.*
— Great Christians of France: Saint Louis and Calvin; tr. 12°. $1.75 .... *Lippincott; Macmillan.*
— History of civilization [475–1789]. 4 v. 12°. $6; hf. cf., $12 .... *Appleton.*
— *Same;* with notes by Prof. Henry. 12°. hf. bd., $1.50 .... *Appleton.*
— *Same;* tr. by W. Hazlitt. 3 v. 12°. (Bohn.) ea., $1.25 .... *Little, B. & Co.*
— — *Same.* 3 v. 12°. (Bohn.) ea., $1.40. *Scribner, W. & A.*
— — *Same.* 3 v. 12°. (Bohn.) ea., $1.50.. *Lippincott.*
— History of Eng. rev. of 1640; tr. by W. Hazlitt. 12°. (Bohn.) $1.25 .... *Little, B. & Co.*
— — *Same.* 12°. (Bohn.) $1.40 .... *Scribner, W. & A.*
— — *Same.* 12°. (Bohn.) $1.50 .... *Lippincott.*

Guizot, François P. G., *continued.*
— History of the origin of representative government in Europe; tr. by A. R. Scoble. 12°. (Bohn.) $1.25 .... *Little, B. & Co.*
— — *Same.* 12°. (Bohn.) $1.40 ... *Scribner, W. & A.*
— — *Same.* 12°. (Bohn.) $1.50 .... *Lippincott.*
— Love in marriage: hist. study: [Lady Rachel Russell]; tr. 16°. '64. 85c. .... *Meth. Bk. Conc.*
— Meditations on actual state of Christianity; tr. 12°. '67. $1.75 .... *Meth. Bk. Conc.*
— *Same.* ('66.) New ed. 12°. '70. $1.75 .. *Scribner.*
— Meditations on essence of Christianity; tr. 12°. '65. $1.75 .... *Meth. Bk. Conc.*
— *Same.* ('64.) New ed. 12°. '70. $1.75 .. *Scribner.*
— Memoir of M. de Barante; tr. by D. M. Craik. cr. 8°. '67. $2 .... *Macmillan.*
— Monk and his contemporaries; tr. by A. R. Scoble. 12°. (Bohn.) $1.25 .... *Little, B. & Co.*
— — *Same.* 12°. (Bohn.) $1.40 ... *Scribner, W. & A.*
— — *Same.* 12°. (Bohn.) $1.50 .... *Lippincott.*
— Popular history of France; tr. by R. Black. 55 pts. pap., *$27.50. — 6 v. roy. 8°. *$33; shp., $39; hf. cf., $45; tr. cf., $60 .... *Estes.*
— Shakespeare and his times; tr. 12°. $1.50 .. *Harper.*
Guizot, *Mlle.* H. *See* Witt, *Mme.* H. G. de.
Gulf stream. Myers, S. A. 70c. .... *Pres. Bd.*
Gulistan; or, rose garden. Sadi. $2.50 .... * *Osgood.*
Gulliver's travels. *See* Swift, J.
Gully, Ja. Manby. The water-cure in chronic diseases. 12°. '50. $1.50 .... *Wells.*
— *See also* Wilson, J., *and* Gully, J. M.
Gummere, J: Elementary treatise on astronomy; [with] lunar, etc., tables. 6th ed.; rev. by E. O. Kendall. 8°. '54. shp., $3 .... *Fortescue.*
— Treatise on surveying; with system of plane trigonom. 17th ed., rev. and enl. by G. H. Holliday. 8°. $2. — Key, by S: Alsop. 8°. $1.25 .. *Porter.*
Gummere, S: R. Scholar's progressive etymolog. spelling book. 12°. '76. hf. bd., 35c. — Same: pt. 1 only. 18°. '76. hf. bd., 20c. .... *Fortescue.*
Gumpach, Js. v. Roman census: explan. of Luke ii., 1–5. 8°. (Bagster.) pap., 35c. .... *Wiley.*
Gumpert, Thekla v. Der Heckpfennig; [also] Drei Katharinen; [also] Aus der Gegenwart. 16°. 25c. .... *Morwitz; Steiger.*
— *Same.* 16°. 30c.; bds., 20c.; pap., 15c. ... *Kohler.*
Gun, rod and saddle. Gillmore, P. $1 .... *Woodward.*
Gun, rod and saddle. Mast, I. $1.25 ..... *Meth. Epis.*
Gunboat ser. *See* Fosdick, C. A.
Gunderode; tr. from the German. 12°. '60. $1.50. *Burnham.*
Gundlach, W. Liederbuch f. Schul u. Volksgesang in Worten u. Weisen: e. Samml. zwei u. dreistimmiger Lieder. 2d ed. 8°. '75. bds., 75c. *Schmidt.*
Gunmaker of Moscow. Brougham, J. 15c. .. *French.*
Gunn, J: C. Domestic medicine and poor man's friend. ('50.) New ed., enl. 8°. '76. $5.50 .. *Clark & M.*
— New family physician, or home-book of health; with treatise on anatomy, physiol., etc. ('57.) 5th ed. roy. 8°. '76. *$8 .... *Wilstach.*
Gunnar. Boyesen, H. H. $1.25 .... *Osgood.*
Gunning, W. D. Is it the despair of science? or, science applied to spiritualism, not in the manner of Dr. Hammond. ('70.) 2d ed. 12°. '73. pap., 15c. .... *Colby.*
Gunnison, E. Norman. One summer's dream: idyl of the vineyard, and other poems. 12°. '75. $1.50; $1.75; $2; mor., $3.50 .... *Hiram Young.*
Gunnison, J. W. History of the Mormons of Salt Lake. ('52.) New ed. 12°. '68. 75c. .. *Claxton.*
Gunther, F. A. New manual of homœop. veterinary med.; tr. with add. 12°. '71. $1.25. *O. Clapp.*
Günther, M. Populäre Symbolik: luth. Wegweiser zur Prüfg. d. amerik. Kirchen u. relig. Gesellschaften. 8°. hf. leath., $1.75 ..... *Volkening.*
Gurley, *Mrs.* E. S. Edith Somers. ill. 16°. '71. 90c. *Am. Tr.*
Gurley, W: Life. 12°. $1 ..... *Cin. Meth. Bk. Conc.*
Gurney, Jos. J: Essay on habitual exercise of love to God. 18°. '42. 45c. .... *Am. Tr.*
— Letter of redemption. 12°. pap., 15c. .. *Lippincott.*
Gurney, T. E. American school for the melodeon, seraphine, etc. 8°. '53. bds., $1.50 .... *Ditson.*
Gurney married. *See* Hook, Thdr.
Gus Howard. Smith, J. F. 75c. .... *Dick & F.*
Gus Williams' "Jakey Woolfenstein" songster. 32°. '76. pap., 10c. .... *De Witt.*
Guseck, Bernd v. (*pseud.*) *See* Berneck, C. Gustav v.
Gustav Adolf. Topelius, Z. $1.50 .... *Porter.*
Gustave. *See* Taylor, G. B.
Gustavus Adolphus. Life. 3d ed. ill. 12°. 75c.; mor., $2.50 .... (?) *Luth. Pub.*
— Leben. 18°. '63. 30c. .... *Am. Tr.*
Gustavus III. *See* Ditson.
Gustavus Vasa. Nieritz, G. $1.20 .... (?) *Luth. Pub.*
Gute Fridolin (Der) u. d. böse Dieterich. *See* Schmid, C. v.
Gute Same (Der): kathol. Gebetbuch herausg. v. d. Versamml. d. allerhl. Erlösers. ill. 32°. '50. 45c.–$2 .... *Murphy.*
Gute Worte, od. goldene Aepfel in silbernen Schalen. 18°. 30c. .... *Ev. Assoc.*
Guter Rath für Krieger im Felde. 32°. '62. 15c.; pap., 5c. .... *Am. Tr.*
Guthrie, F: Magnetism and electricity. (Adv. sci. ser.) 12°. '76. $1.50 .... *Putnam.*
Guthrie, T: Works. ('56–'74.) New ed. 11 v. 12°. '73–'76. $16 .... *Carter.*

Cont.: Autobiog. and life, 2 v., $4. — Christ and the saint's inheritance. — The city, its sins and sorrows; Ragged schools. — Gospel in Ezekiel. — Man and the Gospel; Our Father's business. — On the parables. — Out of harness. — Speaking to the heart. — Studies of character from the Old Test. — Way to life, *ea.*, $1.50.

— Angels' song. 18°. 75c. .... *Routledge.*
— Our Father's business. cr. 8°. $1.50 .... *Routledge.*
— Out of harness. cr. 8°. $2 .... *Routledge.*
— Speaking to the heart. cr. 8°. $1.50 .... *Routledge.*
— Studies of character from the Old Test. 2 ser. cr. 8°. ea., $1.75 .... *Routledge.*
— *See also* McLeod, N., *and* Guthrie, T.
— *and* Blaikie, W. G. Saving knowledge; addressed to young men. cr. 8°. $1.75 .... *Routledge.*
Guthrie, W: Christian's great interest; or, trial of a saving interest in Christ, and the way to attain it. 18°. 60c. .... *Pres. Bd.*
Gutta percha Willie. Mac Donald, G. $1.25 .. *Hoyt.*
Gutterson, A. C. Months and seasons. [Music.] 8°. 20c. .... *Church.*
Gutzkow, K: Das Urbild des Tartüffe: Lustspiel. 12°. 25c. .... *Radde.*
Gutzlaff, Ma. History of. 18°. 22c. .... *Am. S. S.*
Guy, Ja. Elements of astronomy; [also] New treatise on use of the globes; abridg. by T. Keith. ill. roy. 18°. hf. roan, $1.25 .... *Desilver.*
Guy Beauchamp's victory. ill. 18°. 50c. ..... *Nelson.*
Guy Carlton. *See* Wise, D.
Guy Dalesford. Tucker, *Mrs.* C. 75c. .... *Carter.*
Guy Deverell. Le Fanu, J. S. 50c. .... *Harper.*
Guy Earlscourt's wife. Fleming, M. A. $1.75 .. *Carleton.*
Guy Faux. Macfarren, G. 15c. .... *French.*
Guy Fawkes. *See* Ainsworth, W: H.
Guy Fawkes: drama. 16°. pap., 15c. .... *French.*
Guy Livingstone. *See* Lawrence, G: A.

Guy Mannering. *See* Scott, *Sir* W.

Guy Mannering. Terry, D. 15c. .... *French.*

Guy Rivers. Simms, W. G. $1.75; 75c... *Widdleton.*

Guyard de Berville, —. Story of Chevalier Bayard. 16°. $1.25 .... *Scribner, W. & A.*

Guyer, G. P. Wonderful life of Ella Cameron, maid, wife and widow of a day. [In Eng. or Germ.] 8°. pap., 20c. .... *Barclay.*

Guyon, *Mme.* J. M. B. de la Mothe. Letters; tr. and ed. by Mrs. P. L. Upham. 12°. $1 .... *Palmer.*

— Short and easy method of prayer. *See* Fenelon, F. de S. de la M., Spiritual progress.

Guyot, Arn. Common school geog. ('66.) New ed. 4°. '76. $2 .... *Scribner.*

— *Same.* Teachers' ed.; with teachers' guide. ('66.) New ed. 4°. '76. $2.50 .... *Scribner.*

— Earth (The) and man: lectures on compar. phys. geog.; tr. by C. C. Felton. ('49.) New ed. maps. 12°. '75. $1.75 .... *Scribner.*

— Elementary geog. ('68.) New ed. maps and ill. 4°. '76. 75c. .... *Scribner.*

— Grammar-school geog. ('74.) New ed. maps and ill. 4°. '76. $2 .... *Scribner.*

— Intermediate geography. ('67.) New ed. 4°. '76. $1.50 .... *Scribner.*

— Introduction to the study of geography. ('66.) New ed. maps and ill. 4°. '76. $1 .... *Scribner.*

— New intermediate geog. ('75.) New ed. 4°. '76. $1.50 .... *Scribner.*

— Physical geog. ('73.) New ed. maps, ill., etc. 4°. '76. $2.25 .... *Scribner.*

— Tables, meteorological and physical. 8°. '59. pap., $3 .... *Smith. Inst.*

— *See also* Barnard, F. A. P., *and* Guyot, A.; — Hewitt, E. C. A.

Guy's life lesson. Keene, *Mrs.* S. F. $1.50 .... *Hoyt.*

Gwendoline's harvest. Payn, J. 25c. ..... *Harper.*

Gwilt, Jos. Encyclopædia of architecture. 5th ed., rev. and enl. by W. Papworth. 8°. 1,600 ill. $20; hf. mor., $26 .... *Lee & S.*

Gwynne, A. Practical treatise on law of sheriff and coroner; with forms and ref. to statutes of Ohio, Indiana and Kentucky. 8°. '49. shp., $3 ... *Clarke.*

Gwynne, Talbot. School for fathers: old Eng. story. 12°. $1.25 .... *Harper.*

Gwynneth Vaughan. Lemon, M. 15c. ..... *French.*

Gymnastic song book. Fitz, A. 12c. .... *Thompson.*

Gypsy Bess. 8°. pap., 25c. .... *De Witt.*

Gypsy Breynton. Phelps, E. S. $1 .... *Dodd.*

Gypsy's cousin Joy. Phelps, E. S. $1 .... *Dodd.*

Gypsy's secret. *See* Brother's lib.

Gypsy's sowing and reaping. Phelps, E. S. $1 .. *Dodd.*

Gypsy's year at the Golden Crescent. Phelps, E. S. $1 .... *Dodd.*

H., *Abbé.* Adelmar, the templar: tale of the crusaders; tr. from the Fr. 18°. '72. 40c. .... *Kenedy.*

— — *See also* Kenedy's juvenile lib.

H., *Mrs.* —. Three years in field hospitals. 12°. $1.50. *Lippincott.*

H., C. G. Constance Lindsay; or, the progress of error. [Fiction.] 8°. pap., 50c. .... *Harper.*

H., E. *See* Huntington, E.

H., E. M. Charlie and the blind man. 18°. 50c. *Cong. Pub.*

H., H. *See* Jackson, *Mrs.* H.

H., H. *or* T. Beloved disciple: life of Apostle John. 18°. '35. 50c. .... *Am. S. S.*

H., H. H. Caverly family; or, Mrs. Linden's teachings. 18°. 75c. .... *Claremont; Dutton.*

H., H. L. *See* Henry, H. L.

H., Hd. *See* Hinton, Howard.

H., L. C. *See* Hill, L. C.

H., M. G. Poverty: its cause and cure. 12°. 10c. *Somerby.*

H., M. R. Rownie. ill. 16°. 90c. .... *Pott.*

H—, *Marquis de.* *See* Harcourt, *Marquis* de.

H— family. *See* Bremer, *Miss* F.

Haas, J. C. Liederkranz f. christl. Schulen. 2 pts. 8°. ea., 15c.; in 1 v., 25c. .... *Schäfer.*

— Schulgeographie v. Amerika. 8°. 25c. .... *Schäfer.*

— Schulharmonie. obl. 8°. 30c. .... *Kohler.*

— Siona: vierstimmige Gesänge f. kirchliche Singchöre. 2 v. 8°. ea., bds., 75c.; in 1 v., $1.50 .. *Schäfer.*

Haas, N: Der getreue Seelenhirte. 8°. '68. hf. mor., $2.50 .... *Dette; Volkening.*

Habberton, J: Helen's babies; by their latest victim. [*anon.*] sq. 16°. '76. $1; pap., 50c. ... *Loring.*

— (*ed.*) Select British essayists, [v. 1]: Spectator (selected papers), by Addison and Steele; with introd. essay and biog. sketches. sq. 12°. '76. $1.25 .... *Putnam.*

Habermann, J. Christliche Morgen-u. Abend-Gebete. 32°. 25c.; 30c. .... *Kohler.*

— *Eng.* Morning and evening prayers. 32°. 25c.; 30c. *Kohler.*

— *Eng. and German.* 32°. 50c.; 60c. .... *Kohler.*

Habermeister. Schmid, H. $1.25 .... *Holt.*

Habersham, A. W. My last cruise: visits to the Malay and Loo-Choo Islands, coasts of China, Formosa, etc. ill. 8°. $2.50 .... *Lippincott.*

Habershon, S. O. Diseases of the liver: their pathology and treatment. (Lettsonian lectures, 1872.) 12°. $1.50 .... *Lindsay.*

Habit and intelligence. Murphy, J. J. 2 v. $5. *Macmillan.*

Habitations of man in all ages. Viollet-le-Duc, E. E. $5 .... *Osgood.*

Habits of birds. 18°. 30c.; 40c. .... *Am. Bapt.*

Habits of good society. 12°. $1.50 .... *Carleton.*

Habits of good society. 16°. $1.50 ...... *Lippincott.*

Habitual drinking. Softon, G. A. 50c. .... *So. Bapt.*

Habla vd. español? or, do you speak Spanish? manual of Span. and Eng. conversation. ('65.) New ed. 8°. '76. bds., 60c. .... *Holt.*

Habla vd. ingles? or, do you speak English? for Span. students. 18°. '72. bds., 60c. .... *Holt.*

Hachette's French readers. *See* Brette, P. H., *and* Masson, G.

Häckel, Ern. History of creation: exposition of doctrine of evolution; tr. from the Germ.; rev. by E. R. Lancaster. 2 v. 8°. $5 .... *Appleton.*

Hackett, Horatio Balche. Christian memorials of the war; with hist. notes. 12°. $1.50 .. *H. A. Young.*

— Commentary on Acts. 8°. '58. $3 .... *Un. S. S.*

— Illustrations of Scripture; suggested by a tour through the Holy Land. New ed., rev. and enl. ill. 12°. '60. $1.50 .... *H. A. Young.*

— *See also* Smith, W: Bible dictionary.

Hackländer, F: W: Clara; or, slave life in Europe; [tr.] with pref. by Sir A. Alison. 12°. $1.50. *Harper.*

— Enchanting and enchanted; tr. ill. 12°. $1.25. *Lippincott.*

— Kainszeichen (Die). 2 v. 8°. ea., pap., 50c. .. *Morwitz.*

— Letzte Bombardier (Der). 8°. pap., 50c. .. *Morwitz.*

Hackley, C: W. Elementary course of geometry. 12°. shp., $1.50 .... *Harper.*

— Treatise on algebra. 8°. shp., $2; $1.50 .. *Harper.*

— Treatise on trigonometry, plane and spherical; with application. 4th ed. 8°. '50. $2.50 .... *Barnes.*

Hackwood, R. H. *See* Kennedy, A., *and* Hackwood, R. H.

Had you been in his place. Bates, L. $1.25 .. *Carter.*

Hadassah and the court of king Ahasuerus. Jones, J. H. 45c. .... *Pres. Bd.*

Hadassah, the Jewish orphan. 18°. 50c....*Am. S. S.*
Haddan, A. W. Apostolical succession in the Church of Eng. 8°. '70. $2....................*Pott.*
Haddon Hall. *See* Calabrella, *Baroness* de.
Hadermann, *Miss* Jeanette R. Against the world. 12°. $1.50; pap., 75c..................(?) *Shepard.*
— Dead men's shoes. 12°. $2...........*Lippincott.*
— Forgiven at last. 12°. $1.75..........*Lippincott.*
— Heavy yokes: romance of southern life. 8°. '76. $1.50; pap., 75c...................*W. F. Gill.*
Hades. *See* Boggs, J.
Hades. Fink, W. W. 40c..............*Lippincott.*
Hades and heaven. Bickersteth, E. H. $1...*Carter.*
Hadley, A. *See* New Hampshire, Law reports.
Hadley, Caro. Children's sayings; or, early life at home. ill. post 18°. 75c.....*Scribner, W. & A.*
— *Same.* ill. sq. 12°. $1...................*Sheldon.*
— Stories of the apostles: their lives and writings. ill. post 18°. 75c.................*Scribner, W. & A.*
— Stories of old: Bible narratives. ill. 16°. $1.75. — post 18°. 75c................*Scribner, W. & A.*
— *Same.* 3 v. 12°. $3.75................*Sheldon.*
Hadley, E. A. *See* Broom, H., *and* Hadley, E. A.
Hadley, Hiram. Lessons in lang.: introd. to study of Eng. gram. ('70.) 10th ed. 12°. '75. bds., 60c.; — in 2 pts. 12°. '76. 1, 50c.; 2, 45c.....*Hadley.*
— *See also* Lee, M. P., *and* Hadley, H.
Hadley, Ja. Brief history of the Eng. language. roy. 4°. '64. pap., 25c..................*Merriam.*
Note. From Webster's Dictionary.
— Elements of Gk. gram. 12°. hf. bd., $1.50..*Appleton.*
— Essays, philological and critical; with introd. by W. D. Whitney. 8°. '73. $5...............*Holt.*
— Greek verbs. 12°. pap., 30c...........*Appleton.*
— New Gk. grammar. 12°. $2.............*Appleton.*
— Roman law, its history and system of private law: 12 lectures. 12°. $1.50................*Appleton.*
Hadley, *Mass.* *See* Celebration.
Haeseler, C. H. Across the Atlantic. 12°. $2..*Peterson.*
Hagan, J. M. *See* West Virginia, Sup. Court reports.
Hagar, D. B. Common school arith. ('71.) New ed. 12°. '76. bds., $1. — Key. ('74.) New ed. 12°. '76. $1..................*Cowperthwait.*
— Dictation problems and reviews in arith. ('74.) New ed. 12°. '76. bds., 50c.........*Cowperthwait.*
— Elementary algebra. ('73.) New ed. 12°. $1.25. — Key. ('74.) New ed. 12°. '75. $1.25. *Cowperthwait.*
— Elementary arith. ('71.) New ed. 12°. '75. bds., 50c. ....*Cowperthwait.*
— Primary lessons in numbers. ('71.) New ed. 16°. '75. bds., 30c...................*Cowperthwait.*
Hagar Lot. Egan, P. 75c.................*Dick & F.*
Hagarene. Lawrence, G. A. 75c.........*Harper.*
Hagen, Hm. A. Monograph of the No. Am. astacidæ. ill. imp. 8°. '71. pap., $4....*Mus. Comp. Zool.*
— On some insect deformities. ill. 4°. '76. pap., 75c. *Mus. Comp. Zool.*
— Report upon neuroptera. *See* United States, *Corps of Eng.*
Hagenbach, K. R. History of Christian doctrine; tr. and ed. by H. B. Smith. 2 v. 8°. $6..*Sheldon.*
— History of the church in 18th–19th centuries; tr. with add. by J. F. Hurst. 2 v. 8°.' 69. $6..*Scribner.*
Hager, Alb. D. *See* Vermont geol. survey.
Hager, J. M. The echo: collection of musical gems; [also] The enchantress: [operetta]. roy. 8°. '60. hf. bd., 75c......................*Barnes.*
Haggard, S. *See* England, Ecclesiastical reports.
Hagner, C: V. Early hist. of falls of Schuylkill, Manayunk, etc. demy 8°. '69. $1.25......*Claxton.*
Hagner, Phebe. Catechism on morn. and eve. service of Book of common prayer. 16°. 20c...*Dutton.*

Hague, Ja. D. Mining industry. *See* United States, *Corps of Eng.*
Hague, W: Christianity and statesmanship, with kindred topics. New ed., rev. and enl. 16°. '74. $1.50................................*Lothrop.*
— Home life. 16°. 90c..................*Am. Bapt.*
— Question books. 6 v. 18°. ea., bds., 15c...*Am. Bapt.*
Cont.: Acts, 2 v. — John, 2 v. — Matthew, 2 v.
Hahn, A: Greek Testament; with notes by Robinson. 12°. $2..........................*Appleton.*
— *See also* Bible [Whole], *Hebrew.*
Hahn, Edm. Die Sclaverei der Liebe. 8°. pap., 50c. *Morwitz.*
Hahnemann, S. Lesser writings; coll. and tr. by R. E. Dudgeon; with pref. and notes by E. E. Marcy. [Hom.] por. 8°. hf. mor., $4..*Boericke.*
— Organon of art of healing; tr. by C. Wesselhöft. [Hom.] 8°. $2.......... ....*Boericke.*
Haid, Leo. Major John André: hist. drama. 12°. pap., 50c...........................*Murphy.*
Hailmann, W: N. Elementary German reader; with Germ. and Eng. notes. 12°. '72. bds., 50c. *Knœfel.*
— Erziehungs-Grundsätze f. Schule u. Haus. [Kindergarten]. 8°. '75. pap., 25c.....*Doerflinger.*
— Kindergarten culture: sketch of Fröbel's system of early educ. adapted to Am. institutions. ill. 12°. '73. 75c.....................*Wilson, H. & Co.*
— Literary German reader. 12°. '70. $1.25..*Knœfel.*
— System of object teaching; with introd. by N. McElligott. 12°. '66. $1................*Ivison.*
— Twelve lectures on history of pedagogy. ill. 12°. '74. 75c............................*Wilson, H. & Co.*
Haines, Elij. M. Compilation of Ill. laws rel. to township organization and management of county affairs; with forms and notes. New ed., embr. laws to 1875. 8°. pap., $2; bds., $2.50; shp., $3............................*E. B. Myers.*
— Treatise on justices of the peace in Illinois. 6th ed., rev. 8°. '73. shp., $6............*E. B. Myers.*
Haines, J: T: [Plays.] 9 v. 16°. ea., pap., 15c...*French.*
Cont.: Austerlitz. — French spy. — Idiot witness: melodrama. — My poll and partner Joe: naut. drama. — Ocean of life. — Richard Plantagenet. — Ruth. — Wizard of the wave: naut. drama. — Yew tree ruins.
Hajji Baba. *See* Life and adventures of.
Haldane, Alex. Memoirs of R. and J. A. Haldane. 8°. $2.50...............................*Carter.*
Haldane, Rob. Inspiration of the Scriptures. 12°. 40c...............................*Cong. Pub.*
— On Romans. 8°. $3...... ....*Carter.*
Haldeman, S: S. Affixes in their origin and application; exhibiting etymol. structure of Eng. words. New ed., rev. 12°. $2..................*Butler.*
— Analytical orthography: investigation of sounds of the voice and their alphabetical notation. (Trevelyan prize essay.) 4°. $1.75; pap., $1.50. *Lippincott.*
— Elements of Lat. pronunciation. 12°. 63c. *Lippincott.*
— Monograph of the fresh water univalve mollusca of the U. S., 1840–'44; with contin. to 1871 by G. W. Tryon, jr. 2 v. col. pl. 8°. $40; — col. ed., $25; — plain ed., $18.........*Acad. of Nat. Sci.*
— Pennsylvania Dutch: dialect of south Germ. with an infusion of Eng. 12°. $1.25......*Ref. Ch. Pub.*
Hale, Anne G. Fannie and Robbie: a year book for children of the Church. 16°. '65. 75c...*Dutton.*
Hale, B: Illustrations of the Prayer book. 18°. 50c. *Dutton.*
Hale, *Mrs.* C. L. Woodland lays. 12°. $2...*Lippincott.*
Hale, E. M. Lectures on diseases of the heart. [Hom.] 8°. $2...............................*Boericke.*
— Materia medica and special therapeutics of the new remedies. [Hom.] 4th ed., rev. and enl. 2 v. 8°. hf. mor., v. 1, $5; v. 2, $6........*Boericke.*
Cont.: 1. Symptomatology. — 2. Special therapeutics.
Hale, E: Fall of the Stuarts, and western Europe, 1678 to 1697. 16°. $1.........*Estes; Scribner.*

Hale, E: Everett. ["Col. F: Ingham."] Christmas eve and Christmas day: ten Christmas stories. 16°. '72. $1.50 ... *Roberts.*
— His level best, and other stories. 16°. $1.50 .. *Osgood.*
— How to do it. 16°. $1.25 ... *Osgood.*
— If, yes, and perhaps. 16°. $1.50 ... *Osgood.*
— In his name. sq. 18°. '74. $1.25 ... *Roberts.*
— Ingham papers. 16°. $1.50 ... *Osgood.*
— One hundred years ago: how the war began. 8°. '75. pap., 25c. ... *Lockwood, B. & Co.*
— Our new crusade: temperance story. sq. 18°. '75. $1.25; pap., 75c. ... *Roberts.*
— Scenes from Christian history. 16°. 42c... *Un. S. S.*
— Summer vacation (A). 16°. '74. pap., 50c... *Roberts.*
— Ten times one is ten. 16°. '70. 88c. ... *Roberts.*
— Ups and downs: an every day novel. 16°. '73. $1.50. *Roberts.*
— Workingmen's homes. ill. 16°. $1.25; pap., 75c. *Osgood.*
— *See also* Daily bread; — Six of one by half a dozen of the other; — Tales for travellers.

Hale, G: S. *See* United States, Digest.

Hale, H. Ethnography and philology. *See* Wilkes, C: U. S. explor. expedition.

Hale, J. E. *See* California, Sup. Court reports.

Hale, Jos. Meditation on the love of Christ. *See* Fleetwood, J., Life of Christ.

Hale, Lucretia P. Lord's supper and its observance. 16°. '65. $1.50 ... *Am. Unit.*
— Service of sorrow. 16°. '66. $1.75 ... *Am. Unit.*
— Struggle for life; or, Board Court and Langdale; with introd. by E. E. Hale. 4th ed. 12°. '68. $1.50 ... *Williams.*
— (*ed.*) Seven stormy Sundays. ('58.) 5th ed. 16°. '68. $1 ... *Am. Unit.*
— *See also* Six of one by a half a dozen of the other.

Hale, Ma. P. Leaves from Sunday-school and mission fields. 16°. 75c. ... *Bost. Am. Tr.*

Hale, *Sir* Mat. History of the pleas of the crown; with notes by S. Emlyn. Am. ed.; with notes and ref. by W. A. Stokes and E. Ingersoll. 2 v. 8°. shp., $13 ... *Kay.*
— Meditations upon the Lord's prayer. *See* Fleetwood, J., Life of Christ.

Hale, Salma. History of the U. S. to 1817. 2 v. 18°. $1.50 ... *Harper.*

Hale, *Mrs.* Sa. J. Bible reading book: portions of Old and New Test., forming a connected narrative of God's dealings with man and man's duties to God. ('54.) New ed. 12°. '76. 75c. ... *Claxton.*
— Boarding out; or, domestic life. 18°. 75c... *Harper.*
— Dictionary of poet. quotations. ('49.) New ed. ill. 8°. '76. $2.25–$7.50 ... *Claxton.*
— Juveniles. 10 nos. ill. 16°. per gross, $24. (?) *McLoughlin.*
Cont.: Short tales in short words. — Gift to young friends. — Spring flowers. — Uncle Buncle's stories. — Good little boy's book. — Countries of Europe. — Good little girl's book. — Happy changes. — Three baskets. — Wise boys.
— Keeping house and house keeping: story of domestic life. 18°. 75c. ... *Harper.*
— Liberia; or, Mr. Peyton's experiments. 12°. $1.25. *Harper.*
— Manners; or, happy homes and good society all the year round. 12°. '68. $1.50 ... *Tilton.*
— New cook-book. 12°. $1.75 ... *Peterson.*
— Receipts for the million; cont. 4545 receipts. 12°. $1.75 ... *Peterson.*
— Woman's record: biog. sketches with selections; with por. and eng. by B. J. Lossing. New ed., enl. 8°. $5–$10 ... *Harper.*

Hales, J. W. (*ed.*) Longer English poems; with notes, philological and explanatory, and introd. on the teaching of English. 12°. '75. $1.75. *Macmillan.*

Halévy, Ludovic. *See* Meilhac, H., *and* Halévy, L.

Haley, J: W. Examination of alleged discrepancies of the Bible; with introd. by A. Hovey. ('74.) 3d ed. cr. 8°. '76. $2.25 ... *Draper; Estes.*

Half brothers. *See* Dumas, A.

Half caste: drama. 16°. pap., 15c. ... *French.*

Half century of Unitarian controversy. Ellis, G. E. $1.50 ... *Am. Unit.*

Half crown (The) and his philosophy. [Juvenile.] 16°. $1 ... (?) *Martien.*

Half crown ser. 5 v. 16°. $5 ... (?) *Martien.*
Cont.: Half crown and his philosophy. — Charley Ashley. — Sunshine Bill. — Blind Amos and his velvet principles. — Story of a week.

Half a dozen boys; by author of "Ruth Allerton." sq. 24°. 35c. ... *Am. S. S.*

Half a dozen girls; by author of "Ruth Allerton." sq. 24°. 35c. ... *Am. S. S.*

Half hour lectures on art. Scott, W. B. $3. *Scribner, W. & A.*

Half hour readings for Sunday afternoons. Milner, T. $1.25 ... *Nelson.*

Half hour recreations in popular science. *See* Estes, D.

Half hours among the animals. ill. 4°. '75. $1.75. *Nelson.*

Half hours in the deep: nature and wealth of the sea. ill. 16°. '75. $1.50 ... *Dodd.*

Half hours in the far east, among the people and wonders of India. ill. 16°. '75. $1.50 ... *Dodd.*

Half hours in the far north: life amid snow and ice. ill. 16°. '75. $1.50 ... *Dodd.*

Half hours in the Temple Church. Vaughan, C. J. $1.25 ... *Routledge.*

Half hours in the tiny world: wonders of insect life. ill. 16°. '75. $1.50 ... *Dodd.*

Half hours with the best authors. *See* Knight, C.

Half hours with the best French authors; tr. ill. 8°. $2.50 ... *Nelson.*
— *Same.* ill. 12°. $3.50. roy. 8°. mor., $10 .. *Appleton.*

Half hours with the best letter-writers. Knight, C. $3. *Routledge.*

Half hours with early explorers. Frost, T. $2.50. *Cassell.*

Half hours with insects. Packard, A. S., *jr.* 12 pts. ea., 25c. ... *Estes.*

Half hours with Irish authors: selections from Griffin, Carleton, Lever and Lover. ill. 12°. $1.50 .. *McGee.*

Half hours with old Humphrey. Mogridge, G. $1. *Meth. Bk. Conc.*

Half hours with the poets. sq. 8°. $6; $7.50 .. *Miller.*

Half hours with the sacred poets. ill. 12°. $1.50. *Routledge.*

Half hours with some ancient and modern celebrated freethinkers. Collins, T., *and* Watts, J. 75c. *Mendum.*

Half hours with the stars. *See* Proctor, R. A.

Half hours with the telescope. Proctor, R. A. $1.25. *Putnam.*

Half a million of money. *See* Edwards, A. B.

Half sir (The). *See* Griffin, Ger.

Half tints: table d'hôte and drawing-room. 12°. 75c. *Appleton.*

Half truths and the truth. Manning, J. $2 ... *Lee & S.*

Halfway. Starr, M. 75c. ... *Pres. Bd.*

Haliburton, T: Chandler. ["Sam Slick."] Novels and tales. 3 v. 12°. hf. roxb., $3.75 ... *Routledge.*
Cont.: Sam Slick in Eng. — Clockmaker. — Letter bag of the Great Western.
— Attaché (The); or, Sam Slick in England. 12°. $1.25; pap., 75c. ... *Dick & F.*
— Clockmaker (The); or, the sayings and doings of Samuel Slick of Slickville. (Cabinet ed.) ill. 16°. '71. $1.25; $1.75; hf. roxb., $3; mor., $4.50 ... *Hurd & H.*
— — *See also below* Sam Slick.

Haliburton, T: Chandler, *continued.*
— Old judge; or, life in a colony. 8°. pap., 75c...*Dick & F.*
— Rule and misrule of the English in America. 12°. $1.25...*Harper.*
— Sam Slick, the clockmaker. ill. 12°. $1.75; pap., $1.50...*Peterson.*
— — *See also above* Clockmaker.
— Sam Slick in search of a wife. 12°. $1.25; pap., 75c...*Dick & F.*
— Sam Slick's nature and human nature. 12°. $1.25; pap., 75c...*Dick & F.*
— Sam Slick's sayings and doings. 12°. $1.25; pap., 75c...*Dick & F.*
— Yankee stories. 12°. $1.75; pap., $1.50..*Peterson.*
— Yankee yarns and Yankee letters. 12°. pap., 75c. *Peterson.*
Halifax, M. C. After long years. [Fiction.] cr. 8°. $1.75...*Macmillan.*
Hall, *Miss* —. Jewish history told for children. 16°. 50c...*Fuller.*
Hall, *Miss* A. Manual of morals. 18°. '49. 65c. *Thompson.*
Hall, Ab. Oakey. Coroner's inquisition: farce. 16°. pap., 15c...*French.*
— Old Whitey's Christmas trot: Christmas tale. ill. sq. 4°. $1...*Harper.*
Hall, Alex. Universalism. 12°. '46. shp., $1.50.. *Wilstach.*
— *Same.* ('55.) New ed. 12°. '74. $1.50..*Pounsford.*
Hall, *Mrs.* Anna Mar. Animal sagacity. ill. sm. 4°. $2...*Routledge.*
— Chronicles of Cosynook. ill. 12°. $1.50...*Nelson.*
— Daddy Dacre's school. ill. 16°. 50c.....*Routledge.*
— Daily governess. ill. 12°. $1.25..*Scribner, W. & A.*
— Grace Huntly. ill. 12°. $1.25....*Scribner, W. & A.*
— Groves of Blarney: drama. 16°. pap., 15c...*French.*
— Kate Kemp, and the swan's egg. ill. 16°. $1. *Perkinpine.*
— Lucky penny, and other tales. 16°. $1..*Routledge.*
— Merchant's daughter. ill. 12°. $1.25. *Scribner, W. & A.*
— Midsummer eve: fairy tale of love. 8°. pap., 50c. *Harper.*
— Sketches of Irish character. ill. 12°. $3..*Routledge.*
— *Same.* ill. 8°. $3; hf. cf., $5.50........*Appleton.*
— Tales of woman's trials. 8°. pap., 75c.....*Harper.*
— White boy (The): a story of Ireland in 1822. 8°. pap., 50c...*Harper.*
Hall, B. M. Life of Rev. John Clark. 12°. '56. $1.25. *Meth. Bk. Conc.*
Hall, B: F. Methodism: source and secret of its power. 32°. '70. pap., 15c... *Tr. P. & P. Co.*
Hall, B: F. *See* Opinions of attorneys general.
Hall, *Mrs.* C: Katie Summers. 2 v. ill. 18°. '75. $1.50. *Nelson.*
Hall, C: F. Arctic researches and life among the Esquimaux: narrative of expedition in search of Franklin in 1860–'62. New ed. maps and ill. 8°. $5; hf. cf., $7.25...*Harper.*
Hall, C: H. Notes on the Gospels. 2 v. 12°. '71. $3. *Hurd & H.*
— Spina Christi; or, musings in holy week. 32°. '75. $1...*Dutton.*
— True Protestant ritualism: review of "Law of ritualism." 16°. '67. $1.50..*Claxton; Lippincott.*
— *and* Whiteley, S. B. (*ed.*) Hymnal according to use of Prot. Episc. Church in U. S. 32°. '72. 60c.; $1; $2.25; — with tunes. 12°. $1.25; — with tunes and chants. 12°. $1.50; $3; $5..*Barnes.*
Hall, C: W. Twice taken: tale of the maritime British provinces. 16°. $1.75...*Lee & S.*
Hall, Clara Oakey. Sweet bells jangled: dramatic love tale. 8°. '76. pap., 50c.........(?)*Am. News.*
Hall, Dan. *See* New Hampshire, Superior Court reports.
Hall, E: B. Memoir of Mrs. Mary L. Ware. ('52.) 13th ed. por. 12°. '74. $1..........*Am. Unit.*
— Sermons, 1832–'66; with memoir. 16°. $1.25..*Lee & S.*
Hall, Edn. Exposition of law of baptism as it regards the mode and the subjects. 16°. 75c...*Pres. Bd.*
Shorter catechism of the Westminster Assembly; with anal. and Scripture proofs. 18°. 20c...*Pres. Bd.*

Hall, Eug. J. Poems of the farm and fireside. ('74.) 3d ed. ill. 8°. '75. $1.75; $2.25......*Jansen.*
Hall, Everard. Index to Virginia reports, with notes; from Washington to 3d Leigh. 2 v. 8°. '25–'35. shp., $3...*J. W. Randolph.*
Hall, Fitzedward. Modern English. 16°. '73. $2.50. *Scribner.*
— Recent exemplifications of false philology. 12°. '72. $1.25...*Scribner.*
Hall, F: Life of Maximilian I.: with sketch of Empress Carlota. ill. and por. 12°. $2.........*Miller.*
Hall, Harrison (*ed.*) Gems of thought: moral and religious reflections from Matthew Henry and others. 32°. 50c...*Pres. Bd.*
Hall, Herb. Byng. Bric-a-brac hunter; or, chapters on chinamania. ill. 12°. $2.50.....*Lippincott.*
Hall, Hiland. Early history of Vermont to 1791. 8°. '68. $4...*Vt. Hist.*
Hall, J. P. *See* New York City, Superior Court reports.
Hall, Ja. Legends of the west; ill. of habits, etc., of pioneers of the west. 12°. '74. $2.....*Clarke.*
— Romance of Western hist.: sketches of hist., life and manners in the west. 12°. '71. $2.....*Clarke.*
Hall, Ja. *See* New York geol. survey; — Wisconsin geol. survey.
Hall, *Rev.* J: (*of N. Y.*) All the way across. 18°. 25c. *Am. S. S.*
— Care cast upon the Lord. 24°. '71. 35c.; 60c. *Randolph.*
— Chief end of man: exposition of first answer to the Shorter catechism. 18°. 40c.........*Pres. Bd.*
— Familiar talks to boys. 12°. $1............*Dodd.*
— God's word through preaching. (Lyman Beecher lectures, Yale Coll.) 12°. '75. $1.50. *Cin. Meth. Bk. Conc.; Dodd.*
— How to study an Intern. S.-school lesson. 16°. pap., 10c...*Am. S. S.*
— Minor characters of the Bible. 18°. 35c...*Pres. Bd.*
— Only rule of faith: exposition of second answer of the Shorter catechism. 18°. 35c......*Pres. Bd.*
— Papers for home reading. por. 12°. '71. $1.75..*Dodd.*
— Preaching: manner and matter. 12°. '74. 20c. *Meth. Bk. Conc.*
— Questions of the day. 12°. '73. $1.75......*Dodd.*
— Sabbath-school theology; or, conversations with a class. 18°. 40c...*Pres. Bd.*
— Sower and the seed. 18°. 50c...........*Pres. Bd.*
— Thoughts for the old year and the new. 32°. '74. 35c.; pap., 15c...*Randolph.*
— Why weepest thou? 32°. '74. 30c.; pap., 15c. *Randolph.*
— (*ed.*) Family prayers; for four weeks. 12°. '68. $1; $1.50...*Randolph.*
— *See also* Preparing to teach.
— *and* Cuyler, T. L., *and* Beecher, H. W. Successful preaching. 18°. '71. 25c.............*Am. Tr.*
— *and* Stuart, G: H. American evangelists, D. L. Moody and Ira D. Sankey, in Great Britain and Ireland. por. 12°. $1.50...*Dodd.*
Hall, *Rev.* J: (*of Trenton*). History of Presb. Ch. of Trenton, N. J. 8°. '60. $1.50......*Randolph.*
Hall, J: C: Analytical synop. of nat. hist. of man. *See* Pickering, C., History of races of man.
Hall, J: K. Masonic prayers. 4°. '70. $1.25.. *Williams.*
— Master key to treasures of the royal arch. [Masonic.] 24°. '66. 75c...*Williams.*
— Master workman and Masonic monitor: guides to the masters of lodges in the lectures and work of Freemasonry. 16°. '69. 75c........ *Williams.*
Hall, J: Vine. Autobiography; ed. by N. Hall. ill. 12°. '65. 60c...*Am. Tr.*
— Der Sünderfreund. 18°. '75. 30c.........*Am. Tr.*
Hall, Jos. Pious meditations and devout breathings. 18°. 60c...*Pres. Bd.*
Hall, Lyman W. Elementary outline of mental philosophy. 12°. '50. 45c............*I. N. Whiting.*

Hall, Marie. The dying Saviour; [also] The gipsey girl, and other stories; from the studio. 12°. '74. $1.25 .... *Randolph.*

Hall, Ma. L. Our world, no. 1: first lessons in geog. 10th ed., rev. maps. sm. 4°. hf. bd., 94c... *Ginn.*
— Our world, no. 2: 2d ser. of lessons in geog. ('72.) 3d ed. ill. and maps. 4°. '74. hf. bd., $2.. *Ginn.*

Hall, *Mrs.* Mat. Queens of England before the Norman conquest. cr. 8°. $2 25; $2.50; hf. mor., $3.. *Lea.*
— Royal princesses of England, from reign of George I. por. 12°. $2 .... *Routledge.*

Hall, Newman. Closing scenes of life of W: Gordon; [also] memoir of J. D. Godman, by T. Sewall. 12°. 80c. .... *Pres. Bd.*
— — *See also* Triumphing over death.
— Come to Jesus. 18°. '51. 20c. 32°. '63. 15c... *Am. Tr.*
— *Same.* 32°. 25c. .... *Pres. Bd.*
— *Same.* 18°. '67. 25c... *N. Y. Ref. Ch. Bd.; Pres. Com.*
— — *See also below* Calls to the Saviour.
— *Same;* [also] Go tell Jesus, by O. Winslow. 2 v. in 1. 16°. 40c. .... *West. Tr.*
— *Danish.* 18°. '69. 20c. .... *Am. Tr.*
— *Germ.* Komm zu Jesus. 18°. '58. 25c.; pap., 10c. *Am. Tr.*
— *Span.* Acudid á Jesus. 18°. '69. 20c.; pap., 8c. *Am. Tr.*
— *Swedish.* 18°. '57. 20c. .... *Am. Tr.*
— Follow Jesus. 18°. '68. 25c.; pap., 10c... *Am. Tr.*
— *Same.* 18°. 35c. .... *Carter.*
— From Liverpool to St. Louis: impressions of America. cr. 8°. $1.75 .... *Routledge.*
— It is I; or, the voice of Jesus in the storm. 18°. '53. 20c. .... *Am. Tr.*
— *Same.* 32°. 25c. .... *Pres. Bd.*
— Now. 18°. 35c. .... *Carter.*
— Parting word. 16°. 60c. .... *Sheldon.*
— Quench not the spirit. 18°. '67. 25c. *N. Y. Ref. Ch. Bd.; Pres. Com.*
— *Same.* 18°. 35c. .... *Carter.*
— — *See also below* Calls to the Saviour.
— Reasonableness and efficacy of prayer. 18°. '74. 75c. .... *Lockwood, B. & Co.*
— Scriptural claims of total abstinence. 12°. pap., 15c. *Nat. Temp.*
— Sermons; with hist. of Surrey Chapel and its institutions. por. 12°. $1.75 .... *Sheldon.*
— Triumphing over death: closing scenes of life of William Gordon. 16°. $1.25.. *Cin. Meth. Bk. Conc.*
— — *See also above* Closing scenes.
— Warning cry from Niagara. 18°. 30c..... *Pres. Bd.*
— *and* Ryle, *Rev.* J. C. Calls to the Saviour; compr. Hall's Come to Jesus, [and] Quench not the spirit; [also] Ryle's Call to prayer. 18°. 60c. *Bost. Am. Tr.*

Hall, Rob. Miscellaneous works and remains; with memoir by Dr. Gregory, and essay on his character by J. Foster. 12°. (Bohn.) $1.25. *Little, B. & Co.*
— — *Same.* 12°. (Bohn.) $1.40... *Scribner, W. & A.*
— — *Same.* 12°. (Bohn.) $1.50 .... *Lippincott.*
— *Same;* ed. by O. Gregory and J. Belcher. 4 v. por. 8°. $8; shp., $10 .... *Harper.*
— — *Same.* 6 v. 16°. $7.50 .... *Routledge.*
— Help to Zion's travellers. 18°. 90c...... *Am. Bapt.*
— Modern infidelity. 18°. 30c. .... *Am. Bapt.*
— — *See also* Faber, G. S.

Hall, Ruf. Journal of life, religious exercises and travels. 12°. *net*, shp., 35c... *Friends Bk. Assoc.*

Hall, S: Carter. *See* Jewitt, L., *and* Hall, S. C.

Hall, *Mrs.* S: Carter. *See* Hall, *Mrs.* Anna Mar.

Hall, S: R. Alphabet of geology; or, first lessons in geology. ill. 16°. 90c. .... *Sheldon.*

Hall, Sara Lord. Child-life in New England. 16°. $1. *Cong. Pub.*

Hall, Thph. D. *See* Smith, W., *and* Hall, T. D.

Hall, Theresa Oakey. Christmas journey, and other stories. 16°. '72. $1 .... *Whittaker.*

Hall, Theresa Oakey, *continued.*
— Her mother's Fancy. 12°. '75. $1.50..(?) *Shepard.*
— Nuts for Christmas cracking. ill. sq. 8°. '74. $2. *Whittaker.*

Hall, W: W. Works. 6 v. 12°. '70–'75. ea., hf. roan, $1.50 .... *Hurd & H.*
Cont.: How to live long; or, health maxims, physical, mental and moral. — Health by good living. — Sleep; or, the hygiene of the night. — Health and disease as affected by constipation. — Bronchitis and kindred diseases. — Coughs and colds.
— Bronchitis and kindred diseases. 12°. $1.50. *Widdleton.*
— Consumption. 12°. $1.50 .... *Widdleton.*
— Fun better than physic; or, everybody's life preserver. 12°. *$1.50 .... *D. E. Fisk.*
— Guide-board to health, peace and competence. ill. roy. 8°. *$4–$7 .... *D. E. Fisk.*
— Health and disease. 12°. '66. $1.50.... *Widdleton.*
— Health at home; or, Hall's family doctor. ill. 8°. '72. *$4; leath., $5; hf. mor., $6 .... *Betts.*
— Sleep. 12°. '66. $1.50 .... *Widdleton.*

Hall (The) and the hovel; or, the unequal yoke. 18°. 35c. .... *Am. S. S.*

Hallam, H: Works. New ed. 10 v. post 8°. (Lond.) '60–'66. ea., $1.75; per set, hf. cf., $35. *Little, B. & Co.; Widdleton.*
Cont.: Const. hist. of Eng., 3 v. — Introd. to literature of Europe, 4 v. — View of state of Europe during middle ages.
— Constitutional hist. of Eng., accession of Henry VII. to death of George II. 8°. $2; shp., $2.50.. *Harper.*
— *Same.* (School ed.); ed. by W. Smith. 12°. $2. *Harper.*
— *Same;* [also] Constitution of Eng., by J. L. De Lolme. (Chandos classics.) cr. 8°. $1; pap., 75c. .... *Scribner, W. & A.*
— Introduction to the literature of Europe, in 15th–17th centuries. 2 v. 8°. $4; shp., $5...... *Harper.*
— View of the state of Europe during the middle ages. 8°. $2; shp., $2.50 .... *Harper.*
— *Same.* (School ed.); ed. by W. Smith. 12°. $2. *Harper.*

Hallam, Rob. A. Lectures on Moses. 12°. '66. $1.25. *Dutton.*
— Sermons. 12°. $1.25 .... *McCauley.*

Halleck, Fitz-Greene. Complete poet. works; ed. by J. G. Wilson. 12°. $2.50–$6. — 18°. $1–$3; — large-pap. ed., ill., $10; mor., $15 .... *Appleton.*
— Life and letters; ed. by J. G. Wilson. ill. 12°. '69. $2.50; hf. cf., $4.50; mor., $6; large pap. ed., ill., $10; mor., $15 .... *Appleton.*
— Selections from British poets. 2 v. 18°. $1.50.. *Harper.*
— *See also* Forest scenes.

Halleck, H: W. Bitumen. *See* United States, *Corps of Eng.*
— Treatise on international law and the laws of war. 8°. '66. $2.50 .... *Claxton; Lippincott.*

Hallett, A. R. *See* Perkins, W. O., *and* Hallett, A. R.

Hallett, Mos. *See* Colorado, Sup. Court reports.

Hallett, W: T. Builders' contract. 12°. 10c.... *Judd.*
— Builder's specifications. 2d ed. roy. 8°. '74. pap., $1.75. .... *Bicknell.*
— Specifications; [with] form of contract in use in N. Y. City. New ed., rev. and enl. 12°. $1.75.. *Judd.*

Halliday, And. [Plays.] 4 v. 16°. ea., pap., 15c. *French.*
Cont.: Checkmate: comedy. — Daddy Gray. — Loving cup. — Romeo and Juliet: burlesque.
— Check-mate: comedy. 16°. pap., 15c...... *De Witt.*
— Daddy Gray: drama. 16°. pap., 15c....... *De Witt.*
— *See also* Brough, W., *and* Halliday, A.

Halliday, S. B. Little street-sweeper; or, life among the poor. ('59.) New ed. ill. 12°. '75. $1.25.. *Ford.*
— Winning souls: sketches and incidents during forty years of pastoral work. 12°. '73. $1.... *Ford.*

Halliwell, Ja. Orchard. Nursery rhymes of England. ill. 12°. $1; pap., 50c. .... *Scribner, W. & A.*

Hallock, C: Camp life in Florida: handbook for sportsmen and settlers. 12°. '75. $1.50.. *Forest.*
— Fishing tourist: angler's guide and reference book. ill. cr. 8°. $2 .... *Harper.*

Hallock, *Mrs.* M. A. Beasts and birds. 4 pts. ill. 4°. '70. ea., bds., 30c.; in 1 v., $1.50; $2..*Am. Tr.*
— Child's hist. of Solomon. ill. sq. 18°. '69. 50c. *Am. Tr.*
— Child's life of Daniel. ill. sq. 18° '70. 50c...*Am. Tr.*
— Fall of Jerusalem. ill. 18°. '70. 50c. *Am. Tr.; Lothrop.*

Hallock, W: A. Leben des Harlan Page. ill. 18°. '45. 50c....*Am. Tr.*
— The venerable Mayhews and the aboriginal Indians of Martha's Vineyard. 18°. '74. 50c....*Am. Tr.*

Hallowed songs. (Harmonized ed.) sq. 18°. 75c. — (Melody ed.) sq. 18°. 40c. — (Hymn ed.) sq. 18°. 25c....*Meth. Bk. Conc.*

Halloween. Coxe, A. C. 75c....*Lippincott.*

Hallowell, B: Geometrical anal. 8°. $2.50..*Lippincott.*
— Key to Bonnycastle's Mensuration. New ed., rev. by J. Ryan. 12°. '34. $1....*Porter.*
— Memoirs of Margaret Brown. 16°. *net*, 50c. *Friends Bk. Assoc.*

Hallowell, *Mrs.* J. L. Bec's bedtime, and other stories. ill. 12°. '73. $1.25....*Porter.*

Hallowell, Sa. C. On the church steps. *See* Asheton, F., A modern Cressida.

Halpine, C: G. ["Miles O'Reilly."] Poetical works; with biog. sketch and notes; ed. by R. B. Roosevelt. por. cr. 8°. '69. $2.50....*Harper.*

Halpine, *Miss* M. G. Prayer of faith. 16°. 45c. *Cong. Pub.*

Halsey, C. S. Bible chart of genealogy and chronology, to A. D. 100. 4°. '73. $1.25....*Ginn.*
— Genealogical and chronological chart of rulers of England, Scotland, France, Germany and Spain. 2d ed. 4°. $1.50....*Ginn.*

Halsey, Le Roy J. Beauty of Immanuel: his name shall be called wonderful. 12°. 75c....*Pres. Bd.*
— Life pictures from the Bible: ill. of Scrip. character. 12°. $1.65....*Pres. Bd.*
— Memoir of Rev. L. W. Green; with sel. from his sermons. por. cr. 8°. '71. $2....*Scribner.*

Halsted, G. B. *See* New Jersey, Court of Chancery, etc., reports.

Halsted, J. R. Digest of law of evidence. 2d ed. 2 v. 8°. shp., $8....*Baker, V. & Co.*

Halsted, Ol. S. Theology of the Bible, itself the teacher and its own interpreter: five versions of Old Test. and four of the New compared with the originals. 8°. '66. $3....*Halsted.*
— *See also* Bible, Job.

Halsted, W. Digested index of New Jersey Superior Courts decisions. 2 v. 8°. '43....*State.*
— *See also* New Jersey, Supreme Court reports.

Halvei, the unknown. Wilks, T. E. 15c....*French.*

Halves. Payn, J. 50c....*Harper.*

Haly, W: W. *See* Troubat, F. J., *and* Haly, W. W.

Halyburton, T: Great concern of salvation. 18°. 50c. *Pres. Bd.*

Hambleton, J: The three last things; or, death, judgment and eternity. 18°. 40c....*Pres. Bd.*

Hamersly, Lew. R. Records of living officers of the U. S. navy and marine corps; with hist. of naval operations, 1861–5. 8°. $5; shp., $6..*Lippincott.*

Hamerton, Eugenie. Mirror of truth, and other marvellous histories. ill. 16°. '74. $2....*Roberts.*

Hamerton, Ph. Gilb. Chapters on animals; with etchings. sq. 12°. '74. $2....*Roberts.*
— Etching and etchers; with etchings. 8°. '76. $7.50. *Roberts.*
— Examples of modern etchings: 20 etchings. f°. '76. $10....*Bouton.*
— Harry Blount. [Juvenile.] 16°. '75. $1.50..*Roberts.*
— Intellectual life (The). sq. 12°. '73. $2...*Roberts.*
— Painter's (A) camp. 16°. '67. $1.50. sq. 12°. $2. *Roberts.*
— Round my house: notes of rural life in France in peace and war. sq. 12°. '76. $2....*Roberts.*

Hamerton, Ph. Gilb., *continued.*
— Sylvan year: leaves from note-book of Raoul Dubois; with etchings. 8°. '75. $6....*Roberts.*
— *Same;* [also] The unknown river, an etcher's voyage of discovery. por. sq. 12°. '76. $2..*Roberts.*
— Thoughts about art. ('71.) New ed., rev. sq. 12°. '73. $2....*Roberts.*
— Unknown river; with etchings. 8°. '71. $6; mor., $9....*Roberts.*

Hamill, S. S. Science of elocution. 12°. '72. $1.75. *Meth. Bk. Conc.*

Hamilton, *Miss.* —. Little Buttercup and Jenny Wren. 16°. '75. 75c.; $1; pap., 50c....*Gospel.*

Hamilton, Alex. *See* Federalist; — Hamilton, J. C.

Hamilton, Alex. V. Household cyclop. of pract. receipts and daily wants. ill. 12°. '73. *(?)..(?)*Holland.*

Hamilton, Alfr. May I believe? or, the warrant of faith. 18°. 50c....*Pres. Bd.*
— Only believe; or, the sure way of peace. 18°. 30c. *Pres. Bd.*

Hamilton, Allan McL. Clinical electro-therapeutics, medical and surgical. 8°. $2....*Appleton.*

Hamilton, *Count* Anthony. Fairy tales and romances; tr. by M. Lewis, H. T. Ryde and C. Kenney. 12°. (Bohn.) $1.25....*Little, B. & Co.*
— *Same.* 12°. (Bohn.) $1.40....*Scribner, W. & A.*
— *Same.* 12°. (Bohn.) $1.50....*Lippincott.*
— Memoirs of Count Grammont; with sketch of Hamilton and notes. por. 8°. $6..*Scribner, W. & A.*
— Memoirs of court of Charles II., by Count Grammont; with add. as ed. by Sir W. Scott. 12°. (Bohn.) $1.25....*Little, B. & Co.*
— *Same.* 12°. (Bohn.) $1.40....*Scribner, W. & A.*
— *Same.* 12°. (Bohn.) $1.50....*Lippincott.*

Hamilton, C. K., *jr.* Perfect method for the zither. obl. 8°. pap., 75c....*Peters.*

Hamilton, *Mrs.* Celia V. Crown from the spear. 8°. '72. $1.25; pap., 75c....*Estes.*
— Ropes of sand. 8°. '73. $1.25; pap., 75c....*Estes.*
— Woven of many threads. 8°. '71. $1.25; pap., 50c. *Estes.*

Hamilton, *Rev.* D. H. Autology: inductive system of ment. sci., whose centre is the will, and whose completion is the personality. 8°. $5....*Lee & S.*

Hamilton, D. Howland. Church levees and priestcraft versus true religion. [Poem.] 12°. pap., 10c....*D. H. Hamilton.*
— Common sense theology; or, naked truths in rough shod rhymes. 8°. $1.50....*D. H. Hamilton.*
— Key to self-improvement and happiness. [Poem.] 12°. pap., 10c....*D. H. Hamilton.*
— My soul's religious history. [Poem.] 12°. pap., 10c. *D. H. Hamilton.*
— What shall we believe? [Poem.] 12°. pap., 10c. *D. H. Hamilton.*

Hamilton, E: The sanctus: collection of sacred music. obl. 8°. '57. bds., $1.38....*Ditson.*
— Voice of praise: collection of music. obl. 8°. '62. bds., $1.38....*Ditson.*

Hamilton, *Miss* Eliz. Cottagers of Glenburnie: tale for the farmer's ingle-nook. 2 v. ill. 18°. $1.25. *Perkinpine.*
— — Sequel. *See* My favorite lib.

Hamilton, Fk. H. Practical treatise on fractures and dislocations. 5th ed., rev. ill. 8°. $5.75; leath., $6.75....*Lea.*
— Principles and practice of surgery. ill. 8°. $7; leath., $8....*W. Wood.*
— (*ed.*) Contributions rel. to surgery of the [Civil] war; in its hygienic and practical aspects. (Report of U. S. San. Com.) 2 v. 8°. $13....*Hurd & H.*

Hamilton, Gail (*pseud.*) *See* Dodge, Ma. A.

Hamilton, G: Elements of vegetable and animal physiology. 12°. '49. $1.25....*Barnes.*

Hamilton, H: R. Greek-Eng. and Eng.-Greek dictionary. 2 pts. 16°. (Weale.) ea., 80c....*Allyn.*

Hamilton, *Rev.* J. Mountain in the plain. *See* Cripple.

Hamilton, J. A. Complete preceptor. *See* Violoncello without a master.
— Harmony and thorough base; with key. 16°. 60c. *Gordon.*
— Key to harmony and thorough base. 16°. 40c. *Gordon.*
— Musical dictionary of Ital., French, etc., and other musical terms; with add. from works of Busby, Czerny and others. 16°. '54. 75c. *Ditson; Gordon.*
— Preceptor for violoncello. 8°. pap., 75c. . . . . *Ditson.*
— Violoncello instructor. obl. 8°. 75c. . . . . . *Gordon.*

Hamilton, *Rev.* J. W. Memorial of Jesse Lee and the old elm: eighty-fifth anniversary of sermon under the old elm, 1875. 12°. '75. 75c.; pap., 50c. . . . . *N. E. Meth.*

Hamilton, Ja. Select works. 4 v. 16°. $5. . *Carter.*
— Emblems from Eden. 18°. 50c. . . . . *Carter.*
— *Same.* 18°. 60c. . . . . *Am. S. S.*
— Great biography. 16°. $1.25 . . . . *Carter.*
— Happy home. 18°. 75c. . . . . *Carter.*
— Harp on the willows. 18°. 50c. . . . . *Carter.*
— Lake of Galilee. 18°. 50c. . . . . *Carter.*
— Lamp and lantern; or, light for the tent and the traveler. 18°. 50c. . . . . *Carter.*
— *Same.* 18°. '66. 55c. . . *N. Y. Ref. Ch. Bd.; Pres. Com.*
— Life in earnest. 18°. 50c. . . . . *Carter.*
— *Same.* 16°. 50c. . . . . *West. Tr.*
— Life of Lady Colquhoun. 16°. $1 . . . . *Carter.*
— Life of Richard Williams. 16°. $1 . . . . *Carter.*
— *Same.* ('56.) 2d ed. 18°. '75. 75c. . . . . . *So. Meth.*
— Moses, the man of God. 16°. $1.50 . . . . . . *Carter.*
— Mount of Olives. 18°. 50c. . . . . *Carter.*
— *Same.* 18°. '66. 50c. . . *N. Y. Ref. Ch. Bd.; Pres. Com.*
— Pearl of parables. 16°. $1.25 . . . . *Carter.*
— Royal preacher. 16°. $1.25 . . . . *Carter.*
— Sermons and lectures. 12°. $2.50 . . . . *Carter.*

Hamilton, Ja. A. Reminiscences; or, men and events during the last three-quarters of a century. 8°. '69. $5 . . . . *Scribner.*

Hamilton, J: Arthur's seat; or, the church of the banned. [Fiction.] cr. 8°. '69. $1.50. . *Macmillan.*
— Thoughts on the principles of truth, and the causes and effect of error. cr. 8°. '56. $1.75. . *Macmillan.*

Hamilton, J: C. History of the U. S. as traced in writings of Alex. Hamilton and his contemporaries. 7 v. 8°. $22.50 . . . . *Lippincott.*

Hamilton, *Miss* Kate W. ["Fleeta."] Blue umbrella. 18°. 70c. . . . . *Pres. Bd.*
— Brave heart. 18°. 75c. . . . . *Pres. Bd.*
— Chinks of Clannyford. 16°. $1.40 . . . . . . *Pres. Bd.*
— Frederick Gordon; or, principle and interest. 18°. 60c. . . . . *Pres. Bd.*
— Greycliff; [also] Vashti Lethby's heritage. 16°. $1.30 . . . . *Pres. Bd.*
— Norah Neill; or, the way by which he led thee. 18°. 60c. . . . . *Pres. Bd.*
— Old brown house; or, mother's birth-day. 18°. 50c. *Pres. Bd.*
— Shadow of the rock. 18°. 50c. . . . . *Pres. Bd.*

Hamilton, M. Our games: story for children. ill. 18°. $1 . . . . *Nelson.*

Hamilton, *Mrs.* M. J. R. Cachet. 12°. $1.75. . *Carleton.*

Hamilton, N. E. S. A. German, French and Eng. dictionary. 12°. (Lond.) $1.60 . . . . *Wiley.*

Hamilton, R: Winter. Sermons; with life by Bp. Simpson. 12°. $1.75 . . . . *Meth. Bk. Conc.*

Hamilton, Rob. S. Social science: review of progress of thought in social philos. 12°. '73. $2. *Hinton.*

Hamilton, Schuyler. Fabrication of béton blocks by manual labor; [also] Barnard's Delta of the Mississippi, considered in relation to an open river mouth; [also] On the means of averting bridge accidents, by James B. Eads, etc.; [also] On form, weight, manufacture and life of rails, by A. Welch; [also] Statistics of the cost and work of pumping engines, by G. P. Low, jr., etc.;

Hamilton, Schuyler, *continued.*
[also] Railway signals, by J. D. Steele; [also] On upright arched bridges, by S. H. Shreve and J. B. Eads. 8°. '75. pap., $1.50. *Am. Soc. of C. E.*

Hamilton, T: Youth and manhood of Cyril Thornton. [Fiction.] 12°. $1.50 . . . . *Harper.*

Hamilton, W. G. (*ed.*) Useful information for railway men. 6th ed., enl. 32°. '74. $2. . *Van Nostrand.*

Hamilton, *Sir* W: Discussions on philosophy and literature, educ. and university reform; with introd. by Rev. R. Turnbull. 8°. $3 . . . . *Harper.*
— Lectures, embracing the metaphysical and logical courses; ed. by H. L. Mansell and J. Veitch. 2 v. roy. 8°. ea., $3.50 . . . . *Sheldon.*
— Logic; reduced and prepared for colleges and schools by H. N. Day. ('63.) New ed., rev. 12°. '66. $1.25 . . . . *Wilstach.*
— Metaphysics; arranged and abridg. for colleges and students by F. Bowen. ('61.) 14th ed. 12°. '76. $2 . . . . *Allyn.*
— Outlines of philosophy; for schools and colleges, by J: C. Murray; with introd. by J. McCosh. 12°. $1.50 . . . . *Sheldon.*
— Philosophy; arranged and ed. by O. W. Wight. 8°. $2 . . . . *Appleton.*

Hamilton, the young artist. Browne, A. 75c. *Claxton.*

Hamiltons (The). Berkley, C. 50c. . . . . *Strong.*

Hamlet. Poole, J. 15c. . . . . *French.*

Hamlet. *See* Shakespeare, W:

Hamlet. *See* Ditson.

Hamlet (The). Warton, T. $3 . . . . *Routledge.*

Hamlet, the dainty: Ethiop. drama. 16°. pap., 15c. *French; Happy.*

Hamley, E: Bruce. Lady Lee's widowhood. [Fiction.] 8°. pap., 50c. . . . . *Harper.*
— Our poor relations. 18°. '73. $1.25 . . . . . . *Tilton.*

Hamlin, H: [Question books.] 4 v. 18°. '59–'61. hf. bd. . . . . *Hoyt.*
Cont.: Child's ill. Script. quest. book, 18c.—Explanatory quest. book, 17c.—New quest. book on Acts, 15c.—Script. quest. book on New Test., 15c.

Hamline, Leonidas Lent. Works. 2 v. 12°. ea., $2. *Cin. Meth. Bk. Conc.*
— Life and letters. 12°. '66. $2.25 . . . *Meth. Bk. Conc.*

Hamline, *Mrs.* Melinda. Memoir of Mrs. Angeline B. Sears. 18°. 60c. . . . . *Cin. Meth. Bk. Conc.*

Hammer, Rud. Ein Geldfürst: Roman. 12°. '76. pap., 50c. . . . . *Zickel.*

Hammer and anvil. Spielhagen, F. $1.50 . . . . *Holt.*

Hammer and rapier. Cooke, J. E. $1.50. . *Carleton.*

Hammersly, Lew. B. Records of living officers of the U. S. navy and marine corps. New ed., rev. 8°. '70. $5 . . . . *Van Nostrand.*

Hammond, C. *See* Ohio, Sup. Court reports.

Hammond, E: Payson. Better life (The), and how to find it. ('69.) New ed. ill. 16°. '76. 75c. . . *Hoyt.*
— Children and Jesus. 18°. 45c.; 55c. . . . . *Am. Bapt.*
— Child's guide to heaven. ('63.) New ed. ill. 18°. '75. 35c. . . . . *Hoyt.*
— Eight weeks' work in San Francisco. 16°. '75. pap., 20c. . . . . *Bancroft.*
— Gathered lambs. 12°. 70c. . . . . *West. Tr.*
— Hymn evangel; comp. by Biglow and Main from "Song evangel." 18°. '75. pap., 15c.; bds., 20c. . . . . *Biglow.*
— Jesus, the lamb of God. ('72.) New ed. 16°. '75. 85c. . . . . *Hoyt.*
— Jesus the way; or, the child's guide to heaven. 18°. 50c. . . . . *Nelson.*
— Little ones in the fold. ('63.) New ed. ill. 16°. '74. 75c. . . . . *Hoyt.*
— New praises of Jesus: hymns and tunes. obl. 16°. '69. bds., 25c. . . . . *Biglow.*
— Revival melodist. sq. 18°. '63. pap., 15c. . . . *Hoyt.*

Hammond, E: Payson, *continued.*
— Song evangel. [Sing. book.] ('73.) New ed. obl. 16°. '75. 35c.; bds., 30c. . . . . *Biglow.*
Hammond, H. L. New stories from an old book. ill. 18°. 70c. . . . . *Bost. Am. Tr.*
Hammond, J. Pinkney. Army chaplain's manual. 12°. '63. $1.25 . . . . *Claxton; Lippincott.*
Hammond, J: Leah and Rachel; or, the two fruitfull sisters, Virginia and Mary-land. Lond., 1656. [Reprint.] 4°. pap., 75c. . . . . *Sabin.*
Hammond, M. M. Biography. 18°. '62. 40c. . . *Am. Tr.*
— *Same.* 12°. $1.25 . . . . *Carter.*
Hammond, Nat. J. *See* Georgia, Sup. Court reports.
Hammond, S. H. Hunting adventures in the northern wilds: a tramp in the Chateaugay woods. ill. 12°. $1.75 . . . . *J. E. Potter.*
— Wild northern scenes; or, sporting adventures with the rifle and the rod. ill. 12°. $1.75 . . *J. E. Potter.*
Hammond, W. G. Legal education in the northwest; read before the Am. Soc. Sci. Assoc. 8°. '75. pap., 10c. . . . . *Williams.*
Hammond, W. P. *See* Potter, S. A., *and* Hammond, W. P.
Hammond, W: A. Clinical lectures on diseases of the nervous system; with notes by T. M. B. Cross. 8°. $3.50 . . . . *Appleton.*
— Lectures on venereal diseases. 8°. '64. $3. *Claxton; Lippincott.*
— On insanity in its medico-legal relations: opinion rel. to testamentary capacity of J. C. Johnson, of Chowan Co., N. C. 8°. $1.50 . . *Baker, V. & Co.*
— Physiological essays. 8°. $2 . . . . *Lippincott.*
— Physiological memoirs. 8°. '63. $2 . . . . *Claxton.*
— Robert Severne: his friends and his enemies. 12°. $1.75 . . . . *Lippincott.*
— Sleep and its derangements. 12°. $1.75 . . *Lippincott.*
— Spiritualism and allied causes of nervous derangement. 2d ed. 8°. '76. $2.25 . . . . *Putnam.*
— Treatise on diseases of the nervous system. New ed. ill. large 8°. $6; shp., $7 . . . . *Appleton.*
— (*ed.*) Military, medical and surgical essays; prepared for U. S. Sanitary Commission. 8°. $5. *Lippincott.*
— *See also* Bellevue and Charity Hospital reports.
Hammond's library: Jesus and the children. 5 v. 18°. $2.50 . . . . *Am. Bapt.*
Cont.: Children and Jesus, by E. P. Hammond. — Jesus and the little ones. — Jesus the way, by E. P. Hammond. — Jesus' lambs. — Golden gleanings.
Hampton, W. Life and character of Gen. Lee. 8°. '71. 30c. . . . . *Murphy.*
Hampton and its students. Armstrong, M. F., *and* Ludlow, H. W. $1.50 . . . . *Putnam.*
Hampton students. *See* Cabin and plantation songs.
Hamton, Ja. Narrative of life and religious exercises. 12°. *net*, bds., 35c. . . . . *Friends Bk. Assoc.*
Hanaford, *Mrs.* Jos. H. Best of books and its history. 16°. $1 . . . . *Am. Bapt.*
Hanaford, L. B. H., *and* Payson, J. W. Book-keeping by single-entry. 8°. 75c. — Same; by double and single-entry. 8°. $1.50. — Key. 12°. 45c. *Potter, A. & Co.*
Hanaford, *Mrs.* Phebe A. Frank Nelson; or, the runaway boy. 16°. '65. $1.25 . . . . *H. A. Young.*
— From shore to shore, and other poems. por. 12°. *$1.50 . . . . *Russell.*
— Soldier's daughter. ill. 16°. '66. $1.50 . . *Universalist.*
— Women of the century. por. 8°. *$2.50; hf. mor., $3 . . . . *Russell.*
— *and* Miles, *Miss* E. E. (*ed.*) Our home beyond the tide. [Poetry.] 16°. $1.50 . . . . *Locke.*
Hanbury, Dan. *See* Flückiger, F. A., *and* Hanbury, D.
Hance, E: H. Physician's med. compound and pharmac. formulæ. 16°. $1. 12°. $1.50 . . *Lippincott.*
Hancock, H. J. B. Archery. ill. 48°. 25c. *Scribner, W. & A.*
Hancock, H: Operative surgery of the foot and ankle. ill. 8°. '73. $6 . . . . *Lindsay.*
Hancock, J: Constitution and government of the U. S.; with questions and answers. 3d ed., rev. 18°. '67. 50c. . . . . *Claxton.*
Hancock, Sallie J. Rayon d'amour. [Poetry.] por. 12°. $2 . . . . *Lippincott.*
Hancock, W: John Smith: farce. 16°. pap., 15c. *Ames; French.*
— Margate sands: farce. 16°. pap., 15c. . . . . *French.*
— Stolen — 20*l.* reward: farce. 16°. pap., 15c. . . . *French.*
— *and* Moore, A. Mr. Scroggins: farce. 16°. pap., 15c. . . . . *De Witt; French.*
Hand, S. *See* New York, Court of Appeals reports.
Hand and glove. Edwards, A. B. 50c. . . . . *Harper.*
Hand of the diligent; or, Joseph Martin. 18°. 60c. *Crowell; (?) Martien.*
— *See also* Go ahead lib.
Hand of Ethelberta. Hardy, T. $1.25 . . . . *Holt.*
Hand of Jesus. Chaplin, J. $1.50 . . . . *Graves.*
Hand shadow stories. sq. 12°. per doz., pap., $1.88. *Thompson.*
Hand without the heart. Arthur, T. S. $1.25. *J. E. Potter.*
Handbook for home improvement; compr. How to write, How to talk, How to behave, How to do business. 12°. '57. $2.25 . . . . *Wells.*
Handbook for the physiol. laboratory; by E. Klein, J. Burdon-Sanderson, M. Foster and T. L. Brunton; ed. by J. Burdon-Sanderson: 350 figures, with letter-press explan. 8°. '73. $6; leath., $7; in 2 v., $7 . . . . *Lindsay.*
Handbook for the sick; with pref. by Rev. W. B. Mackenzie. 8°. '70. 75c. . . . . *Dutton.*
Handbook for visitors to Oxford; with wood-cuts by Jewitt and steel pl. by Le Keux. New ed. 8°. '76. $6 . . . . *Scribner, W. & A.*
Handbook of alphabets: illuminated initial letters, MS., missal and ornamental alphabets, etc. obl. 8°. (Lond.) $5 . . . . *Spon.*
Handbook of Anglo-Saxon derivations. 12°. $1.25. *Appleton.*
Handbook of Anglo-Saxon root-words. 12°. $1. *Appleton.*
Handbook of Brother Sam's conundrums. roy. 32°. bds., 20c. . . . . *Routledge.*
Handbook of business. 12°. pap., 25c. . . . . *Hurst.*
Handbook of carvings. 32°. 20c. . . . . *Routledge.*
Handbook of domestic medicine. 12°. (Bohn.) $1.75. *Little, B. & Co.*
— *Same.* 12°. (Bohn.) $2 . . *Lippincott; Scribner, W. & A.*
Handbook of dominoes. 18°. pap., 15c. . . . . *Haney.*
Handbook of elocution and oratory. 12°. pap., 30c. *Happy.*
Handbook of the engrafted words of the Eng. lang. 12°. $1.50 . . . . *Appleton.*
Handbook of etiquette. *See* Lady's companion lib.
Handbook of fishing. roy. 32°. bds., 25c. . . *Routledge.*
Handbook of five hundred riddles. roy. 32°. bds., 25c. *Routledge.*
Handbook of good manners, and guide to politeness. 12°. pap., 20c. . . . . *Hurst.*
Handbook of the Oneida Community; cont. sketch of its present condition, internal economy and leading principles. 8°. pap., 25c. . . . . *Oneida.*
Handbook of out-door games. 16°. pap., 15c. . . *Happy.*
Handbook of practical receipts; by an American gentleman and lady. 18°. '60. 50c. . . . . *Barnes.*
Handbook of quoits and bowls. roy. 32°. bds., 25c. *Routledge.*
Handbook of rowing and sailing. roy. 32°. bds., 20c. *Routledge.*
Handbook of swimming. roy. 32°. bds., 25c. *Routledge.*

Handbook of ventriloquism. 18°. pap., 15c...*Haney.*
Handbook on oil painting; chiefly comp. from Bouvier's manual, with sel. from Merriwell, De Montalbert and others, with vocab. by an American artist. 12°. $2 .... *Wiley.*
Handcuffs; or, the deserter. ('61.) New ed. ill. 32°. '64. 25c..*Hoyt.*
Handel, G: F. Israel in Egypt; with organ or piano accomp. by V. Novello. [Oratorio.] 8°. $1.25; pap., 80c.; bds., $1.....................*Ditson.*
— — Choruses. 8°. bds., 65c..................*Ditson.*
— Joshua; with organ or piano accomp. by V. Novello. [Oratorio.] 8°. $1.25; pap., 80c.; bds., $1 ....*Ditson.*
— — Choruses. 8°. pap., 50c..................*Ditson.*
— Judas Maccabæus; with organ or piano accomp. by V. Novello. [Oratorio.] 8°. $1.25; pap., 80c.; bds., $1...................................*Ditson.*
— — Choruses. 8°. bds., 65c..................*Ditson.*
— Messiah. [Oratorio.] f°. $1.75 ....*Gordon.*
— *Same;* with organ or piano accomp. by V. Novello. 8°. $1.25; pap., 80c.; bds., $1 ....*Ditson.*
— — Choruses. 8°. bds., 65c. ....*Ditson.*
— — *Same.* 8°. bds., 75c. ....*Gordon.*
— Samson; with organ or piano accomp. by V. Novello. [Oratorio.] 8°. $1.25; bds., $1; pap., 80c. *Ditson.*
— — Choruses. 8°. bds., 65c. ....*Ditson.*
Handel and Haydn. Barnard, C. F., *jr.* $1.25..*Lee & S.*
Handie. Abbott, J. 90c.......................*Harper.*
Hands not hearts. Wilkinson, J. W. 50c....*Harper.*
Handsome husband. Planché, J. R. 15c....*French.*
Handsome is that handsome does. Bradley, M. E. $1...*Lee & S.*
Handsome Jack. 8°. pap., 25c.............*De Witt.*
Handsome Jack ser. 9 nos. 8°. ea., pap., 25c...*De Witt.*
Cont.: Handsome Jack.—Jenny Diver.—Roger O'Donnell.—Tyburn tree.—Dick Fly-by-night.—Captain McLeane.—Gypsy Bess.—Jack Rann.—Sixteen-string Jack.
Handsome Lawrence. *See* Sand, G.
Handwriting of God in Egypt, Sinai and the Holy Land. Randall, D. A. $3.50; $4. (?) *Goodspeed; Randall.*
Handy, I: W. K. United States bonds; or, duress by federal authority: journal during imprisonment of fifteen months at Fort Delaware. ill. 8°. '74. $4; shp., $5; hf. cf., $6..................*Turnbull.*
Handy, J. H. *See* Cincinnati, Superior Court reports.
Handy, R. D. *See* Cincinnati, Superior Court reports.
Handy, Wash. R. Text-book of anatomy, and guide to dissections. ill. 8°. '54. $4 ....*Lindsay.*
Handy Andy. *See* Lover, S:
Handy Andy. Montgomery, H. W. 15c. ....*French.*
Handy Andy: Ethiop. drama. 16°. pap., 15c...*Ames.*
Handy book for the U. S. soldier on coming into service. 18°. '61. pap., 25c............*Claxton.*
Handy book of ill. and suggestions for floral decorators. 16°. pap., 50c.................................*Pott.*
Handy royal atlas: 46 maps with index. imp. 4°. hf. mor., $26.25 ....*Scribner, W. & A.*
Handy volume poets. 10 v. 32°. $15.......*Porter.*
Cont.: Griswold's Gems from the Am. poets.—Burns.—Hood.—Shelley.—Selections from Byron.—Selections from Moore.—Dodd's Beauties of Shakespeare.—Bloomfield's Farmer boy, etc.—Scott's Lady of the lake.—Hogg's Mountain bard and Forest minstrel.
Handy volume ser. 8 v. 16°...............*Roberts.*
Cont.: Burnand's Happy thoughts, $1.—Edwards' Dr. Jacob, $1.—Sargent's Planchette, $1.25.—French's Realities of Irish life, $1.—Barnes' Poems of rural life, $1.25.—Visit to my discontented cousin, $1.—Burnand's More happy thoughts, $1.—Burnand's My health, $1.
Handyside, H: Treatise on improved method for overcoming steep gradients on railways. 8°. '74. pap., 40c. ....*Spon.*
Hanes, J: L. Digest of criminal decisions cont. in U. S. and state reports; with table of cases cited. 8°. '56. *net*, shp., $7.50............*Ward & P.*
Hanging of the crane. *See* Longfellow, H. W.
Hangman of Newgate; or, the highwayman's adventure. 8°. pap., 25c...........................*Dick & F.*
Hank, J. F. American violinist. f°. $1.50..*Gordon.*
Hankey, *Miss* —. Old, old story. ill. sq. 18°. '70. 50c.; pap., 25c...............................*Am. Tr.*
Hanks, Stedman W. Black valley: the railroad and the country, with account of introd. of water: allegory. ill. 16°. $1..................*Cong. Pub.*
— Light on the ocean. 18°. 75c...........*Cong. Pub.*
— Mutineers of the "Bounty;" or, influences of the Bible at Pitcairn's Island. 18°. 65c...*Cong. Pub.*
— Sailor boys; or, light on the sea. 16°. 75c. *Cong. Pub.*
Hanley, W: Harps. [Sing. book.] 24°. shp., 35c. *Un. B. Pub.*
— *See also* Shuey, W. J., Hanley, W., *and* Chittenden, L. S.
Hanlon, J: Life, trial and execution of John Hanlon, murderer of little Mary Mohrman. [In Eng. or Germ.] 8°. '70. pap., 25c............*Barclay.*
Hanna, J. S. Ready reckoner, and log. table and form book. 16°. hf. bd., 60c............*Lippincott.*
Hanna, Sa. R. Bible history. 12°. '59. $1.25..*Barnes.*
Hanna, T. A. T. Kings and apostles. *See* International S.-school comment.
Hanna, W: Life of Christ. ('70.) New ed. 3 v. 12°. '76. $4.50 ....*Carter.*
— *Same.* ill. 8°. '71. $3.50-$7 ....*Am. Tr.*
— Resurrection of the dead. 12°. $1.25......*Carter.*
— Wars of the Huguenots. 16°. $1.25.......*Carter.*
— *See also* Chalmers, T.
Hanna Lee. *See* Fry, S. M.
Hannah, J: Letter on theology. 48°. 30c. *Cin. Meth. Bk. Conc.*
— Wrestling Jacob. 24°. '43. 30c.....*Meth. Bk. Conc.*
— *and* Jobson, Fs. J. Sermons. 12°. '57. 55c. *Cin. Meth. Bk. Conc.*
Hannah. *See* Craik, D. M.
Hannah. Moos, H. M. $2.50; $1............*Bloch.*
Hannah and Alice. 18°. 30c...............*Dutton.*
Hannah Lee. *See* Fry, S. M.
Hannah Maria (*pseud.*) *See* Beach, H. M.
Hannah Thurston. Taylor, B. $1.50; $2....*Putnam.*
Hannah's lesson. McConaughy, J. E. 60c. *Perkinpine.*
Hannah's path. Baker, S. S. 40c..........*Am. Tr.*
Hannah's triumphs. Denison, M. A. $1.50. (?) *Martien.*
Hannah's vow. Chichester, D. $1....*Bost. Am. Tr.*
Hannahs (The). Philip, R. 60c............*Carter.*
Hannay, D: Ned Allen; or, the past age. [Fiction.] 8°. pap., 50c. ....*Harper.*
Hannay, Ja. Singleton Fontenoy, R. N. [Fiction.] 8°. pap., 50c. ....*Harper.*
— *Same.* 16°. bds., 80c.....................*Routledge.*
— Studies on Thackeray. 16°. $1.25......*Routledge.*
Hanne Nüte un de lütte Pudel. Reuter, F. $1; 75c. *Steiger.*
Hannibal. Nichol, J. $2.50............*Macmillan.*
Hanover, M. D. Practical treatise on law of horses. 2d ed., rev. and enl. 8°. '75. shp., $4..*Clarke.*
Hans. *See* Hoffmann, F.
Hans, som kom till folkhögskolan. 15c......*Engberg.*
Hans, the stranger. Toliver, E. $1.50...*J. E. Potter.*
Hans, the Swiss boy. 18°. 50c..............*Crowell.*
— *See also* Annie Marlowe ser.
Hans Breitmann about town; — as an Uhlan; — in church; — in Europe. *See* Leland, C. G.
Hans Breitmann's ballads; — party. *See* Leland, C. G.
Hans Brinker. Dodge, M. M. $1.50; $3..*Scribner.*

Hans Dampf in allen Gassen. *See* Zschokke, H.

Hans Egede. ill. 16°. $1.15..........(?)*Luth. Pub.*

Hans von Stein: drama. 16°. pap., 15c......*French.*

Hanschmann, A. B. Das System d. Kindergartens nach Fröbel. 12°. '74. pap., 15c.......*Steiger.*

Hanslick, E. *See* Gallerie deutscher Tondichter.

Hanson, G: A. Old Kent: notes ill. of most ancient records of Kent Co., Maryland. 8°. '76. $4; $5.50. 4°. $15; hf. mor., $20.....*Des Forges.*

Hanson, J. H. Preparatory Latin prose book; with vocab. $3....................*Potter, A. & Co.*

— *and* Rolfe, W. J. Handbook of Latin poetry. 8°. $3..............................*Potter, A. & Co.*

Hanson, J: Wesley. Aiōn — aiōnios, the Greek word tr. everlasting, eternal, in the Bible, shown to denote limited duration. 8°. '76. 75c...*N. W. Univ.*

— Historical sketches of 6th Regt., Mass. Vol., in 1861–'64. ill. 12°. *$2.50..............*Lee & S.*

— History of Gardiner, Pittston and West Gardiner, etc., 1602–1852. 12°. $1...................*Burnham.*

— (*ed.*) Witnesses to the truth: passage from disting. authors, developing the great truth of universal salvation. 16°. '54. 75c..........*Universalist.*

Hap hazard. Field, K. $1.25..............*Osgood.*

Haphtorath. *See* Bible, Pentateuch, *Hebrew.*

Happiest day of life. Buckstone, J. B. 15c...*French.*

Happiest man alive: comedy. 16°. pap., 15c...*French.*

Happiness: its nature and sources described, and mistakes conc. it corrected. 32°. 35c.....*Am. S. S.*

Happiness of being able to read. 32°. 20c.; 15c. *Dutton.*

Happiness of being rich. Conscience, H. $1; $1.25. *Murphy.*

Happiness of the blessed. Mant, R. $1.50..*Dutton.*

Happiness of heaven; by a father of the Society of Jesus. 3d ed., rev. 18°. '71. $1; $1.50..*Murphy.*

Happy boy. *See* Björnson, B.

Happy change. 18°. 30c..................*Am. S. S.*

Happy Charlie. 18°. 50c..................*Carter.*

Happy child-life. ill. sq. 12°. '75. $1.50..*Routledge.*

Happy children. ill. 4°. 25c...............*Am. Bapt.*

Happy child's lib. 18 v. 16°. $9..........*Appleton.*
Cont.: Crofton boys. — Dangers of dining out. — Domestic tales. — Early friendships. — Farmer's daughter. — First impressions. — Looking-glass for the mind. — Minister's family. — Peasant and prince. — Poplar grove. — Somerville Hall. — Tired of house-keeping. — Twin sisters. — Chances and changes. — Goldmaker's village. — Never too late. — Ocean work. — Rural tales.

Happy child's picture of animals and birds. ill. 4°. 45c. *Porter.*

Happy choice. Kimball, D. 40c.........*Cong. Pub.*

Happy Christmas. *See* Aunt Gracie's lib.

Happy couple. White, C. 15c..............*De Witt.*

Happy day lib. 6 v. ill. 18°. '68. $4....*Perkinpine.*
Cont.: Ellen Stanley. — Happy days. — Mary Leeson. — Keeper's travels. — Hurrah for New England. — When are we happiest?

Happy day stories for the young. Dulcken, H. W. $2. *Routledge.*

Happy days. ill. 18°. '68. 65c...........*Perkinpine.*

Happy days at Fern Bank. Marshall, E. $1. (?)*Martien.*

Happy days of childhood; or, pleasures of the country. ill. cr. 4°. pap., 20c.; 25c..........*J. E. Potter.*

Happy dispatch: Japanese opera bouffe. 16°. pap., 15c. *Happy.*

Happy family. *See* Prairie books.

Happy fireside. Martyn, S. T. 50c........*Am. Tr.*

Happy half hours. *See* Little folk lib.

Happy half hours: readings for the hearth and home. ill. sm. 4°. $1.50............*Nelson; Routledge.*

Happy heart ser. for children. *See* Bruce, *Mrs.* E. M.

Happy hearts. *See* Maple grove stories.

Happy holidays at Woodleigh House; or, Aunt Elsie and her guests. ill. 12°. $1.25..........*Nelson.*

Happy home. Hamilton, J. 75c. ....*Carter.*

Happy home. Murray, N. 75c.............*Harper.*

Happy home. *See* Missing boat stories.

Happy home; or, story of Annie Lyon. ill. 18°. 40c. *Bost. Am. Tr.*

Happy home stories. *See* Baker, *Mrs.* H. N. W.

Happy hour. Sharland, J. B. 25c..........*Ditson.*

Happy hour; or, holiday fancies and every-day facts. ill. 4°. $3..........................*Appleton.*

Happy hour lib. *See* Chambers, W. *and* R.

Happy hours. Kingsbury, H., *and* Graley, A. A. 75c.; 50c............................*Taintor.*

Happy hours at home. 18°. 90c..........*Cong. Pub.*

Happy hours at Wynford. *See* Silver barrel lib.

Happy hours of childhood: tales for little ones; by a member of the Order of Mercy. ill. sq. 16°. 60c.; 90c...............................*O'Shea.*

Happy land. 18°. 25c.; 30c...............*Dutton.*

Happy land. 18°. 35c......................*Carter.*

Happy land. *See* Library of pleasant stories.

Happy land: burlesque. 16°. pap., 15c......*French.*

Happy land; or, Willie the orphan; by author of "Lonely Lily." ill. 16°. '75. 75c.......*Dodd.*

Happy lib. 5 v. ill. 18°. $2.75...............*Hoyt.*
Cont.: Miles Lawson. — Mackerel Will. — Robert Walton. — Rose Darling. — Pleasant surprises.

Happy lib. 5 v. 16°. $3.75................*Nelson.*
Cont.: Always happy. — Holiday tales, by F. Melford. — Grandmamma's relics, by C. E. Bowen. — Among the brigands, by C. E. Bowen. — Wrecked not lost, by Mrs. Dundas.

Happy light. Beebe, E. N. $1.50........*Pres. Bd.*

Happy man. Lover, S. 15c................*French.*

Happy New-Year. ill. 32°. '53. 30c.........*Am. Tr.*

Happy New Year. Brien, H. O. 30c.....*Cong. Pub.*

Happy pair (A). Smith, S. T. 15c...*De Witt; French.*

Happy recovery. *See* Simple stories lib.

Happy resolve. 18°. '66. 35c. *N. Y. Ref. Ch. Bd.; Pres. Com.*

Happy songs for the Sunday school. Hoffmann, E. A. 50c.; 35c.; 25c......................*Ev. Assoc.*

Happy thought hall. Burnand, F. C. $2....*Roberts.*

Happy thoughts. Burnand, F. C. $1.......*Roberts.*

— *See also* More happy thoughts.

Happy village. *See* Sister's lib.

Happy voices: Sabbath school sing. book. sq. 18°. '65. 60c.; pap., 30c.; bds., 35c.........*Am. Tr.*

Happy voices; [also] Echo. sq. 18°. '71. $1; bds., 60c...............................*Am. Tr.*

Happy world; or, good, better, best. 18°. 80c. 16°. $1.10...........................*Am. S. S.*

Haps and mishaps. Lippincott, S. J. $1.75..*Osgood.*

Haps and mishaps of the Brown family. Boardman, M. M. $1.25....................*Perkinpine.*

Haps and mishaps of childhood. ill. 16°. '70. $1. *Lothrop.*

Haraszthy, A. Grape culture, wines and wine making. 12°. $5..................................*Judd.*

— *Same.* ill. 8°. $5 ....*Harper.*

Harbaugh, H: Child's catechism. 24°. hf. bd., 18c.; pap., 12c..........................*Ref. Ch. Pub.*

— Christological theology. 16°. 30c.....*Ref. Ch. Pub.*

— Fathers of the German reformed church in Europe and Am. 4 v. 12°. $6...........*Ref. Ch. Pub.*

— Future life. 12°. $4; $4.75..........*Ref. Ch. Pub.*

— Golden censer. 24°. $1; $1.25; $1.75; mor., $2.50. *Ref. Ch. Pub.*

— Good Friday; [also] Easter walk; [also] Christ and the lawyer. 16°. 40c.............*Ref. Ch. Pub.*

— Harfe. [Penna. Germ. poems.] 8°. $1.25. *Ref. Ch. Pub.*

Harbaugh, H: *continued.*
— Heaven. 12°. $1.25 .... *Ref. Ch. Pub.*
— Heavenly home; or, employments and enjoyments of saints in heaven. 12°. $1.50 ...... *Ref. Ch. Pub.*
— Heavenly recognition. 12°. $1.25 .... *Ref. Ch. Pub.*
— Life of Rev. Mich. Schlatter. 12°. $1.50 .. *Ref. Ch. Pub.*
— True glory of woman. 12°. $1.25 ..... *Ref. Ch. Pub.*
— Union with the church. 16°. 50c ...... *Ref. Ch. Pub.*
— Youth in earnest: life of T. D. Fisher. 16°. 90c. *Ref. Ch. Pub.*
Harbert, *Mrs.* Lizzie B. Out of her sphere. demy 8°. '71. $1.50 .... *Mills.*
Harbinger of health. Davis, A. J. $1.50 .. *A. J. Davis.*
Harbison, M. Elements of zoology. (Element. sci. ser.) ill. 16°. '75. 75c .... *Putnam.*
Harbour bar: tale of Scottish life. cr. 8°. $1.75. *Macmillan.*
Harcourt, *Marquis* de. [C. L. S. de Choiseul-Praslin.] Memoir of Duchess of Orleans; with biog. souvenirs and original letters; tr. by G. H. D. Schubert. 12°. $1.25 .... *Porter.*
Harcourt, Helen. Bertram Raymond; or, the cruise of the Dolphin. 12°. '72. $1.50 ...... *Claxton.*
Harcourt, *Sir* W: G: V. Letters on some questions of international law; by Historicus (*pseud.*); reprinted from the "Times," with add. 8°. '63. $3 .... *Macmillan.*
— — Additional letters. 8°. pap., $1 ..... *Macmillan.*
Hard case. Picton, T. 15c .... *De Witt.*
Hard cash. Heywood, E. H. 15c .... *Mendum.*
Hard cash. *See* Reade, C:
Hard knot. *See* Berry, *Mrs.* M. E.
Hard master. McConaughy, E. 85c ...... *Nat. Temp.*
Hard problem. Mead, M. E. $1.25 .... *Am. Tr.*
Hard struggle. Marston, W. 15c .... *French.*
Hard sum. Babb, H. 70c .... *West. Tr.*
Hard text. 32°. 25c .... *West. Tr.*
Hard things are good for folks. *See* Aunt Alice's lib.
Hard times. *See* Dickens, C:
Hard times. Emmett, D. D. 15c .... *De Witt.*
Hard words made easy. 16°. 10c .... *Dick & F.*
Hardin, M. D. *See* Kentucky, Court of Appeals reports.
Harding, Stanley. Amateur trapper and trap-maker's guide. ill. 16°. pap., 50c.; bds., 75c ... *Dick & F.*
Harding, W. A. Alphabetical outlines in Germ. text, old Eng., plain and ornamental print. 4°. pap., 50c .... *Fortescue.*
Harding, W. E. Athlete's guide. 18°. 50c ... *Dick & F.*
Hardinge, Emma. Two Bibles of the 19th century; [also] The unity of God, by T. G. Forster: lectures. ('70.) 2d ed. 8°. '73. 20c ...... *Colby.*
Hardingham, G. G. M. Practical aëronautics. pl. 8°. '71. pap., 60c .... *Spon.*
Hardscrabble. Richardson, J. 25c .... *De Witt.*
Hardscrabble of Elm Island. Kellogg, E. $1.25. *Lee & S.*
Hardter, J. Die Elemente d. Zeichnens: Vorlagen. obl. 8°. '65. pap., 25c .... *Steiger.*
— Erstes Lesebuch. New ed. 12°. '70. bds., 18c. *Steiger.*
— Kleines lutherisches Schul-Gesangbüchlein. 24°. '62. bds., 18c. .... *Steiger.*
— Zweites Lese-u. Lehrbuch. New ed. 12°. '72. bds., 30c. .... *Steiger.*
Hardware and house furnishing trade reference book. 4°. '71. $25 .... *J. A. Murphy.*
Hardwich, T. F. Manual of photog. chemistry. 8th ed., rev. by G. Dawson. ill. 12°. '73. $2 .. *Lindsay.*
Hardwick, C: Christ and other masters: enquiry into some of the parallelisms and contrasts between Christianity and religious systems of the ancient world. New ed., rev., with pref. memoir by Rev. F. Procter. cr. 8°. '73. $3 .... *Macmillan.*

Hardwick, C: *continued.*
— History of the articles of religion. 8°. $2 .. *McCauley.*
— History of the Christian church, [575–1517]. 3d ed., ed. by W. Stubbs. maps. cr. 8°. '72. $3. *Macmillan.*
— History of the Christian church during the reformation. 3d ed., rev. by W. Stubbs. cr. 8°. '73. $3. *Macmillan.*
— Twenty sermons for town congregations. cr. 8°. '53. $1.75 .... *Macmillan.*
Hardwicke, *Countess of.* Court of Oberon: fairy dram. scene. 16°. pap., 15c .... *French.*
Hardwicke, P. Bachelor of arts: comic drama. 16°. pap., 15c .... *French.*
Hardy, *Uncle.* *See* Uncle Hardy (*pseud.*)
Hardy, *Lady* Duffus. Daisy Nichol. [Fiction.] 8°. pap., 50c .... *Harper.*
Hardy, F. [Hand books.] 5 v. ill. 48°. ea., 25c. *Scribner, W. & A.*
Cont.: A B C of billiards — of chess — of magic. — Cribbage and dominoes. — Ventriloquism made easy.
Hardy, T: Desperate remedies. (Leis. hour ser.) 16°. '74. $1.25 .... *Holt.*
— Far from the madding crowd. (Leis. hour ser.) ('74.) New ed. 16°. '76. $1.25 .... *Holt.*
— Hand of Ethelberta. (Leis. hour ser.) 16°. '76. $1.25 .... *Holt.*
— Pair of blue eyes. (Leis. hour ser.) ('73.) New ed. 16°. '76. $1.25 .... *Holt.*
— Under the greenwood tree. (Leis. hour ser.) ('73.) New ed. 16°. '75. $1.25 .... *Holt.*
Hardy and Hunter. Ward, F. M. $1.25 .. *Routledge.*
Hare, A: J. C. Cities of northern and central Italy. 3 v. ill. 12°. '76. $6 .... (?) *Routledge.*
— Days near Rome. ill. 12°. $3.50; in 2 v., $5 .. *Porter.*
— Memorials of a quiet life. por. 12°. '72. $3; in 2 v., $5 .... *Randolph.*
— *Same;* with introd. by Bp. Huntington. 2 v. 12°. '72. $5–$12; 2 v. in 1, $3 .... *Routledge.*
— Records of a quiet life. 16°. '73. $2 ...... *Roberts.*
— Walks in Rome. 2d Am. ed. cr. 8°. '71. $3.50. *Routledge.*
— Wanderings in Spain. ill. 12°. '73. $3 .. *Routledge.*
— *Same.* ill. cr. 8°. '73. $3 .... *Dodd.*
Hare, A: W. Alton sermons. 12°. '74. $2.50 .. *Randolph.*
— *Same.* 12°. '74. $3.50 .... *Routledge.*
— *and* J. C. Guesses at truth; by two brothers. New ed. 18°. '71. $1.25 .... *Macmillan.*
— — *Same.* 12°. $1.75 .... *Dutton.*
Hare, E: Errors of Socinianism. 12°. '37. 80c. *Meth. Bk. Conc.*
— On justification. 18°. '41. 60c ..... *Meth. Bk. Conc.*
Hare, *Mrs.* Emily. Little Blossom's reward. ill. 16°. 80c .... *Lee & S.*
Hare, J. I. Clark, *and* Wallace, H. B. American leading cases: sel. decisions of Am. courts, with especial ref. to merc. law; with notes. 5th ed., rev. and enl. 2 v. 8°. '72. $15 .... *T. & J. W. Johnson.*
Hare, Jos. T. Life and adventures. 8°. pap., 50c. *Peterson.*
Hare, Jul. C: Victory of faith. 3d ed., ed. by E. H. Plumptre; with introd. notices by Prof. Maurice and Dean Stanley. cr. 8°. '74. $2.25 .. *Macmillan.*
— *See also* Hare, A. W. *and* J. C.
Hare, Rob. Explosiveness of nitre. 4°. '50. pap., 50c. *Smith. Inst.*
Hare, T: Treatise on disc. of evidence by bill and answer in equity. 2d Am. ed.; with notes and ref. to Am. decisions by R. S. Rowley. 8°. shp., $3.50 .... *Baker, V. & Co.*
— *See also* Sterne, S., On representative government.
Harebell (The). Everest, C. W. *net*, 19c ... *Hamersley.*
Harem life in Egypt and Constantinople. 12°. $1.75; pap., $1.50 .... *Peterson.*
Harfe (Die). Harbaugh, H. $1.25 ..... *Ref. Ch. Pub.*

Harfe (Die). Schaaf, J. nos. 1–4. ea., 25c.; in 1 v., $1 .... *Schäfer.*

Hargrave, T. L. *See* North Carolina, Reports.

Hargreave, J: G. Blunders of vice and folly, and their self-acting chastisements. cr. 8°. $2.. *Routledge.*

Hargreaves, W: Our wasted resources. ('75.) New ed. 12°. '76. $1.25.......... *Nat. Temp.*

Harker family. Thompson, E. $1.25.... *Nat. Temp.*

Harkey, Sim. W. Justification by faith as taught by Lutherans. 12°. '75. $1.25; $1.50..(?) *Luth. Pub.*

Harkness, Alb. Elementary Lat. grammar. 12°. $1.25. *Appleton.*

— First Gk. book; with reader. 12°. $1.50.. *Appleton.*

— First Lat. book. 12°. $1.50 .... *Appleton.*

— Introduction to Lat. prose composition. 12°. $1.50. *Appleton.*

— Introductory Lat. book. 12°. $1.25...... *Appleton.*

— Latin reader. 12°. $1.25.......... *Appleton.*

— New Lat. grammar. 12°. $1.50.......... *Appleton.*

— Second Lat. book and reader. 12°. $1.25.. *Appleton.*

Harkness, W: Magnetic observations on the Monadnock. 4°. '72. pap., $2.......... *Smith. Inst.*

Harks, S. W. Down by the waves. 32°. 60c. *Cong. Pub.*

Harlan, Ja. *See* Monroe, B., *and* Harlan, J.

Harland, Marion (*pseud.*) [*Mrs.* Ma. V. H. Terhune.] [Novels.] 16 v. 12°. ea., $1.50...... *Carleton.*
Cont.: Alone. — At last. — Empty heart. — From my youth up. — Helen Gardner. — Hidden path. — Husbands and homes. — Jessamine. — Miriam. — Moss side. — My little love. — Nemesis. — Phemie's temptation. — Ruby's husband. — Sunnybank. — True as steel.

— Breakfast, luncheon and tea. [Cook-book.] ('75.) New ed. 12°. '76. $1.75. — (Kitchen ed.) 12°. $1.75 .... *Scribner.*

— Christmas holly. ill. 4°. $2; mor., $4.50.. *Sheldon.*

— Common sense in the household: manual of practical housewifery. ('71.) New ed. 12°. '76. $1.75. — (Kitchen ed.) $1.75.......... *Scribner.*

Harland stories. 5 v. 24°. $1.75.......... *Am. Bapt.*
Cont.: Harry's experiment. — Our baby. — Sunset cottage. — Give us a pull. — Children of the big house.

Harlequin Little Red Riding Hood: juvenile pantomime. 16°. pap., 15c.......... *Happy.*

Harlequin novelty. Buckingham, L. 15c.... *French.*

Harlequin pantomimes. 6 v. 16°. ea., pap., 15c. *French.*
Cont.: Harlequin Aladdin. — H. Alfred the Great. — H. Blue Beard. — H. Cherry. — H. Hogarth. — H. O'Donoghue.

Harless, Théophile C. A. System of Christian ethics; tr. 8°. $3.......... *Scribner, W. & A.*

Harley, A. J. The young Crusoe; or, adventures of a shipwrecked boy. ill. 16°. $1.50...... *Lee & S.*

Harley, G: The urine and its derangements; with the applic. of physiol. chemistry to diagnosis and treatment of constitutional as well as local diseases. ill. 8°. $2.75.......... *Lindsay.*

Harleys (The). 16°. $1 .... *Am. Bapt.*

Harleys of Chelsea Place. *See* Glen Elder books.

Harlie stories. *See* Abbott, Jac.

Harlie's letter. *See* Abbott, Jac.

Harman, H: M. Journey to Egypt and the Holy Land, in 1869–1870. cr. 8°. $1.75....... *Lippincott.*

Harmistoun, J. Magic circle. [Piano music.] 4°. $2.25; bds., $1.75.......... *Peters.*

Harmonia evangelica. Brooks, N. C. 75c... *Claxton.*

Harmonia sacra. White E. L., *and* Gould, J. E. $1.50. *Ditson.*

Harmonial man. Davis, A. J. 75c.; 50c... *A. J. Davis.*

Harmonies of nature. Hartwig, G. $10; $12. *Appleton.*

Harmonist. [Hymn book.] 8°. '37. $1.25. *Meth. Bk. Conc.*

Harmony of divine dispensations. *See* Smith, G.

Harmony of the Gospels. *See* Primary Bible questions.

Harmony of interests. Carey, H. C. $1.50.. *Baird.*

Harmony of prophecy. Keith, A. $1.50.... *Harper.*

Harmony of the spheres. Romberg, A. 50c... *Gordon.*

Harms, L: Foreign mission work. 30c...(?) *Luth. Pub.*

Harness, W. *See* Stoddard, R. H., Bric-a-brac ser.

Harney, G: E. Barns, outbuildings and fences; with plans, designs, ill., etc. roy. 4°. $6.. *Woodward.*

Harold; by author of "Jennie Graham." 18°. 75c. *Pres. Bd.*

Harold. *See* Bulwer-Lytton, *Sir* E. G. E. L.

Harold. *See* Tennyson, A.

Harold Hawk. Selby, C. 15c.......... *French.*

Harold Tracy. Smith, J. F. 75c.......... *Dick & F.*

Harp (The). Mason, L. *and* T. B. $1.25.. *Wilstach.*

Harp and cross. Bulfinch, S. G. 80c...... *Am. Unit.*

Harp of Erin songster. 18°. 40c.; pap., 20c... *Sadlier.*

Harp of Judah. Emerson, L. O. $1.50...... *Ditson.*

Harp of praise. Marshall, L. $1.25.......... *Pond.*

Harp of a thousand strings; or, laughter for a lifetime. ill. 12°. $1.50.......... *Dick & F.*

Harp of Zion (The new). *See* Fillmore, A. D. *and* J. H.

Harp on the willows. Hamilton, J. 50c....... *Carter.*

Harpel, Osc. H: Harpel's typograph, or book of specimens. 8°. '70. $5–$10.......... *Harpel.*

— Rustic pictures and random rhymes. 16°. '76. $2. *Harpel.*

— (*ed.*) Poets and poetry of printerdom. ill. 8°. '75. $10.......... *Harpel.*

— *See also* Draiper, E. S.

Harper, L. *See* Mississippi agric. and geol. survey.

Harper, Ma. J. Practical compos.; with models and exercises. ('69.) New ed. 12°. '71. $1.. *Scribner.*

Harper, W. *See* South Carolina, Reports.

Harper's boys' and girls' lib. 32 v. ill. 18°. ea., 75c. *Harper.*
Cont.: Lives of the apostles and early martyrs. — Swiss family Robinson, 2 v. — Sunday evenings, 3 v. — Mrs. Hofland's Son of a genius. — Thatcher's Indian traits, 2 v. — Thatcher's Tales of the Am. revolution. — Miss Eliza Robins' Tales from Am. hist., 3 v. — Mrs. Hofland's Young Crusoe; or, the shipwrecked boy. — Perils of the sea. — Lives of distinguished females. — Mrs. Phelps' Caroline Westerley. — Mrs. Hughs' Ornaments discovered. — Clergyman's orphan; Infidel reclaimed. — Uncle Philip's Natural hist. — Uncle Philip's Evidences of Christianity. — Uncle Philip's History of Virginia. — Uncle Philip's American forest. — Uncle Philip's History of N. Y., 2 v. — Uncle Philip's Whale fishery and the Polar seas, 2 v. — Uncle Philip's History of the lost colonies of Greenland. — Uncle Philip's History of Mass., 2 v. — Uncle Philip's History of New Hampshire, 2 v.

Harper's classical library: translations. 37 v. 18°. ea., 75c. .... *Harper.*
Cont.: Xenophon, 2 v. — Demosthenes, 2 v. — Sallust. — Cæsar, 2 v. — Cicero, 3 v. — Virgil, 2 v. — Æschylus. — Sophocles. — Euripides, 3 v. — Ovid, 2 v. — Horace and Phædrus, 2 v. — Cicero on the orator. — Thucydides, 2 v. — Livy, 5 v. — Herodotus, 3 v. — Homer, 3 v. — Juvenal and Persius. — Pindar and Anacreon.

Harper's fireside library. 9 v. 18°. ea., 75c... *Harper.*
Cont.: Alden's Alice Gordon. — Alden's Lawyer's daughter. Alden's Young schoolmistress. — Burdett's Arthur Martin. — Alden's Dying robin. — Ellen Herbert. — Mayhew's Good genius that turned everything into gold. — William, the cottager. — Mayhew's Magic of kindness.

Harper's Greek and Lat. texts. 16 v. 18°. ea., 75c. *Harper.*
Cont.: Cæsar. — Virgilius. — Horatius. — Cicero. — Sallust. — Lucretius. — Æschylus. — Sophocles. — Euripides, 3 v. — Herodotus, 2 v. — Thucydides, 2 v. — Xenophon.

Harper's handbook for travellers. *See* Fetridge, W. P.

Harper's lib. of sel. novels.
Note. Entered specifically under authors and titles.

Harper's new class. lib.: lit. translations. 25 v. 12°. ea., $1.50.......... *Harper.*
Cont.: Cæsar. — Virgil. — Sallust. — Horace. — Cicero's Orations. — Cicero's Oratory and orators. — Cicero's Offices, etc. — Tacitus, 2 v. — Terence. — Juvenal. — Xenophon. — Homer's Iliad and Odyssey, 2 v. — Herodotus. — Demosthenes, 2 v. — Thucydides. — Æschylus. — Sophocles. — Euripides, 2 v. — Livy, bks. 1-30, 2 v. — Plato.

Harper's phrase-book. Fetridge, W. P. $1.50.. *Harper.*

Harper's pictorial hist. of the great rebellion in the U. S. 2 v. maps, plans, por., etc. 4°. $12.. *Harper.*

Harper's school geog. maps and ill. 4°. '76. hf. bd., $1.80 ... *Harper.*

Harper's school history. ill. and maps. sq. 12°. $3; — in 3 pts., ea., $1.25 ... *Harper.*

Harper's story books. *See* Abbott, Jac.

Harper's symmetrical penmanship, with marginal drawing-lessons. [To form 10 nos.] nos. 1–6. obl. 12°. per doz., $2 ... *Harper.*

Harper's United States readers. *See* Willson, M.

Harps. Hanley, W. 35c. ... *Un. B. Pub.*

Harps. Vonneida, S. 40c.; 75c. ... *Un. B. Pub.*

Harrie Lee. *See* Wood, *Mrs.* M. F.

Harriet and Helen. 16°. 40c. ... *West. Tr.*

Harriet and her scholars. 18°. 40c. ... *Am. S. S.*

Harriet Fisher; or, the missionary at home. 18°. 40c. *Am. S. S.*

Harrigan, E: Editor's troubles: Ethiop. farce. 12°. pap., 15c. ... *De Witt.*

— Porter's troubles: Ethiop. dram. sketch. 12°. pap., 15c. ... *De Witt.*

Harrington, C: Summering in Colorado. 12°. '74. $1; pap., 50c. ill. 12°. $1.50; $2 ... *Richards.*

Harrington, E. Burke. *See* Michigan, Court of Chancery reports.

Harrington, G: F. (*pseud.*) *See* Baker, W: M.

Harrington, J: A. [" J: Carboy."] Between the crusts. ill. 8°. '75. pap., 25c. ... *Collin & S.*

— Strange woman. ill. 8°. '76. pap., 25c. ... *Collin & S.*

Harrington, Kate. Centennial and other poems. 12°. $1.75 ... *Lippincott.*

Harrington, M: W. Analysis of plants; with blanks. (School ed.) 4°. '76. 75c. — (University ed.) 4°. '76. 90c. ... *Sheehan.*

Harrington, N. H. *See* Yates, E., *and* Harrington, N. H.

— *and* Yates, E. Double dummy: farce. 16°. pap., 15c. ... *French.*

— — If the cap fits: comedietta. 16°. pap., 15c. ... *French.*

— — Your likeness, one shilling: farce. 16°. pap., 15c. ... *French.*

Harrington, R: Pedlar boy; or, the old mill ruin: drama. 16°. pap., 15c. ... *French.*

Harrington, S. M. *See* Delaware, Reports.

Harrington. *See* Edgeworth, M.

Harris, Arth. [Plays.] 8 v. 16°. ea., pap., 15c. *French.*

Cont.: Avalanche. — Doing the han'som': farce. — Little treasure: comedy. — My son Diana: farce. — Ruthven. — Tom Trasher: farce. — Too much of a good thing. — Very serious affair: farce.

— *See also* Buckingham, L., *and* Harris, A.; — Williams, T. J., *and* Harris, A.

— *and* Williams, T. J. Gossip: comedy. 16°. pap., 15c. ... *French.*

— — Ruth Oakley: drama. 16°. pap., 15c. ... *French.*

Harris, Chapin A. Dictionary of med. terminology, dental surgery, and collateral sciences. 3d ed., rev. and enl. by F. J. S. Gorgas. roy. 8°. $6.50; leath., $7.50 ... *Lindsay.*

— Principles and pract. of dentistry. 10th ed., rev. and enl. by P. H. Austen. ill. roy. 8°. '71. $6.50; leath., $7.50 ... *Lindsay.*

Harris, Cornwallis. Wild sports and adventures in Africa. 8°. $1.75; pap., $1.50 ... *Peterson.*

Harris, E: D. Genealogical record of Daniel Pond and descendants. 8°. '73. $2.50 ... *Lunt.*

Harris, Emily F. Bertha's journal. 16°. $1.50. *Cong. Pub.*

Harris, G. E. *See* Mississippi, Reports.

Harris, G: Civilization considered as a science. 12°. $1.50 ... *Appleton.*

Harris, G: Collyer. Sermons; with memoir by C. M. Yonge. por. fp. 8°. '75. $1.75 ... *Macmillan.*

Harris, G: W. Sut Lovingood: yarns spun by "a nat'ral born durn'd fool;" warped and wove for public wear by H. ill. 12°. $1.50 ... *Dick & F.*

Harris, G: W. *See* Pennsylvania, Supreme Court reports.

Harris, J: Active Christian (The); from writings of H. 24°. '74. 25c.; 40c. 16°. $1 ... *Lothrop.*

— Christian liberality expl. and enforced; ed. by T. O. Summers. 12°. '58. 20c. ... *So. Meth.*

— Great commission; or, the Christian church constituted and charged to convey the Gospel to the world; with introd. by T. O. Summers. 12°. '59. $1.50 ... *Sheldon; So. Meth.*

— Mammon; or, covetousness the sin of the Christian church. 18°. 40c. ... *U. P. Bd. of Pub.*

— *Same.* 18°. '39. 50c. ... *Meth. Bk. Conc.*

— *Same.* ('56.) 3d ed. 18°. '76. 50c. ... *So. Meth.*

— Witnessing church; ed. by T. O. Summers. 12°. '58. pap., 10c. ... *So. Meth.*

— *Same.* 24°. '40. 30c. ... *Meth. Bk. Conc.*

Harris, Jos. Treatise on the pig. ill. 12°. $1.50 ... *Judd.*

Harris, Ma. Trial for murder of A. J. Burroughs, before Supreme Court of Dist. of Col., 1865; [by] J. O. Clephane. 8°. '65. pap., 75c. ... *Morrison.*

Harris, *Mrs.* Miriam [*formerly Miss* Coles]. [Novels.] 6 v. 12°. ea., $1 50 ... *Carleton.*

Cont.: Frank Warrington. — A perfect Adonis. — Richard Vandermarck. — Rutledge. — St. Philip's. — Sutherlands.

— Dear feast of Lent: devotional readings. 16°. '74. $1.25 ... *Dutton.*

— Louie's last term at St. Mary's. [Juvenile.] 12°. $1.50 ... *Carleton.*

— Rosary for Lent; or, devotional readings, original and compiled. New ed. 16°. '70. $1.50 ... *Dutton.*

— Round hearts; for children. 12°. $1.50 ... *Carleton.*

Harris, N. E. Digest of Georgia reports (v. 41–50). 8°. '76. shp., $7 ... *Burke.*

Harris, N: Complete system of practical book-keeping. 8°. $1.65 ... *Clark & M.*

Harris, S: Kingdom of Christ on earth: lectures, Andover Theol. Sem. 8°. '74. $1.75 ... *Draper.*

— Zaccheus; or, Scripture plan of benevolence. 18°. '50. 25c. ... *Am. Tr.*

Harris, Thad. W: Entomological correspondence; ed. by S. H. Scudder. por. and ill. 8°. '69. $5. *Bost. Soc. Nat. Hist.*

— Insects injurious to vegetation. New ed., rev. and enl., by C. L. Flint. ill. 8°. $4; $6.50 ... *Judd.*

— Remarks on scarabæus goliatus and other African beetles allied to it. 8°. '38. pap., 10c. ... *Essex.*

Harris, T: *See* Maryland, Court of Appeals reports; Important cases.

Harrison, B: *See* Indiana, Reports.

Harrison, F: Religion of inhumanity: a criticism. 12°. '74. pap., 20c. ... *Somerby.*

Harrison, Gbr. Life of John Howard Payne. por. roy. 8°. '75. $6 ... *Munsell.*

Harrison, Gessner. Exposition of laws of Lat. grammar. 12°. shp., $1.50 ... *Harper.*

— Treatise on Gk. prepositions. 8°. $3.25 ... *Lippincott.*

Harrison, H., *and* Benton, R. A. Vocabularies to Morris' Latin grammar. 12°. 75c. ... *Huntington.*

Harrison, H: W: Battle-fields and naval exploits of the U. S. from Lexington to Mexico. ill. 8°. $2. *T. Bliss.*

Harrison, J. *See* New Jersey, Sup. Court reports.

Harrison, Jennie. Little Boots. ill. 16°. '74. $1.25. *Dodd.*

— Morning glory stories. 18°. '65. 75c. ... *Randolph.*

— Old back room. ill. 16°. '73. $1.25 ... *Dodd.*

— On the ferry-boat. 16°. 60c. ... *Hurd & H.*

— The right way, and how Agnes Turner walked in it. 18°. '68. 40c. ... *Randolph.*

Harrison, J: P. Elements of materia medica and therapeutics. 2 v. 8°. '44. shp., $5.50 ... *Wilstach.*

Harrison, Mat. Rise, progress and present structure of the Eng. lang. 2d ed. 12°. $1.50..*Fortescue.*

Harrison, R. T. Digest of cases in the House of Lords and courts of common law and bankruptcy (1756–1851). 7 v. 8°. *net*, shp., $21; — v. 6, 7, ea., *net*, shp., $4.50 .... *Kay.*

Harrison, Rob. *See* Gostwick, J., *and* Harrison, R.

Harrison, Rob., *M. D.* The Dublin dissector; or, manual of anatomy. 3d ed., enl. by R. Watts. roy. 12°. leath., $2 .... *W. Wood.*

Harrison, T: F. *See* Kiddle, H., Harrison, T. F., *and* Calkins, N. A.

Harrison, W. *See* Daily readings for holy seasons.

Harrison, W. B. Mechanic's tool book. ill. 12°. '72. $1.50 .... *Van Nostrand.*

Harrison, W. P. Theophilus Walton; or, the majesty of truth: a reply to "Theodosia Earnest." 12°. $1.50 .... *So. Meth.*

Harrison, Wa. Pickett's men: fragment of war history. por. 12°. '70. $2 .... *Van Nostrand.*

Harrison, Wilmot. Special performances: farce. 16°. pap., 15c. .... *De Witt; French.*

Harry. Lamb, M. J. 60c. .... *Lothrop.*

Harry, the boy that did not own himself. ill. 18°. 35c. *Bost. Am. Tr.*

Harry, the sailor-boy. ill. 18°. '63. 40c. .... *Am. Tr.*

Harry, the shrimper. *See* Sylvan stories.

Harry, the whaler. ill. 18°. '63. 45c. .... *Am. Tr.*

Harry and Archie. 18°. 40c. .... *Dutton.*

Same: sequel. 18°. 40c. .... *Dutton.*

Harry and Dolly lib. 6 v. 18°. $3 .... *Carter.*

Cont.: Harry and his pony. — Dolly's Christmas chickens. — Faithful Rover. — Maggie and the sparrows. — Cosmo's visit. — Fun and work.

Harry and his dog Fidele; by author of "Madeline; or, the lost bracelet." 18°. 35c. ...... *Pres. Bd.*

Harry and his homes. Bowman, A. 75c. .. *Routledge.*

Harry and his homes. Richmond, D. 75c. .. *Routledge.*

Harry and his pony. 18°. 50c. .... *Carter.*

Harry and Lucy. *See* Edgeworth, Mar.

Harry and Lucy lib. 5 v. ill. 16°. $2.50 .. *Routledge.*

Cont.: Harry and Lucy, by M. Edgeworth. — Castle and cottage. — Rosamond, by M. Edgeworth. — Story of an apple. — Young naturalist, by Mrs. J. W. Loudon.

Harry and Phil. ill. 18°. '73. 50c. *N. Y. Ref. Ch. Bd.; Pres. Com.*

— *See also* Library for happy hours.

Harry and Willie; by author of "Creation." 18°. 22c. *Am. S. S.*

Harry Ashton. Smith, J. F. 75c. .... *Dick & F.*

Harry Blake's trouble. ill. 18°. '69. 40c. .... *Am. Tr.*

Harry Blount. Hamerton, P. G. $1.50 ..... *Roberts.*

Harry Budd; or, hist. of an orphan boy. sq. 16°. '55. 90c. .... *Meth. Bk. Conc.*

Harry Burnham. Buckingham, H. A. 75c. .. *Dick & F.*

Harry Coverdale. *See* Smedley, F. E.

Harry Dangerfield. Tucker, C. 50c. .. *Carter; Dutton.*

Harry Delaware. Estvan, M. $1 .... *Putnam.*

Harry Edwards. Dunning, A. K. 35c. ..... *Pres. Bd.*

Harry Harpoon; or, the whaleman's yarn. 8°. pap., 25c. .... *De Witt.*

Harry Harson. Irving, J. T. $1.50 .... *De Witt.*

Harry Heathcote of Gangoil. Trollope, A. 25c. *Harper.*

Harry Helm; or, the cruise of the Bloodhound. 8°. pap., 50c. .... *Peterson.*

Harry Hope's holidays. Burgess, J. T. $1.25. *Routledge.*

Harry Huntley's self denial. *See* Hildred's great work.

Harry Lane, and other stories; in verse. sq. 12°. '68. $1 .... *Meth. Bk. Conc.*

Harry Lawley. Leslie, E. $1 .... *Nelson.*

Harry Lawton. ill. 12°. $1.50 .... *Nelson.*

Harry Lee; or, hope for the poor. ill. 12°. $1.50. *Harper.*

Harry Lorrequer. *See* Lever, C:

Harry Maitland. Downs, E. $1.50 .... *Hoyt.*

Harry Ogilvie. *See* Grant, Ja.

Harry Perry. *See* Cousin Anna's lib.

Harry Racket Scapegrace (Fortunes and misfortunes of). Smedley, F. E. $1.75; 75c. ..... *Peterson.*

Harry Seymour, the little boy whose feet would run home. 18°. 25c. .... *Am. S. S.*

Harry Somers. 32°. 40c. .... *Scribner, W. & A.*

Harry Tempest; or, the pirate's protege. 8°. pap., 50c. .... *Peterson.*

Harry Weston's battles. *See* Sunberry Dale lib.

Harry White's oath. 18°. 60c. .... *Cong. Pub.*

Harry Williams and his shipmates. 18°. 30c.; pap., 12c. .... *Dutton.*

Harry Wilson, the news-boy. 18°. 40c. .... *Am. S. S.*

Harry's battles, and how he fought them. 18°. 60c. (?) *Martien.*

Harry's conflicts. Fish, H. C. $1 .... *Am. Bapt.*

Harry's conversion. Fish, H. C. $1 ...... *Am. Bapt.*

Harry's escape. *See* Little Alice's lib.

Harry's experiment. *See* Harland stories.

Harry's honest pennies. *See* Five gifts.

Harry's ladder to learning. ill. sq. 8°. 75c. .. *Harper.*

Harry's mistakes. Parrott, M. A. 75c. .. (?) *Martien.*

Harry's perplexity and what came of it. ill. 18°. 50c. *Nelson.*

Harry's snow shoes. *See* Yonge, C. M.

Harry's summer in Ashcroft. ill. 4°. 75c. .... *Harper.*

Harry's vacation. Richards, W. C. $1.25 .. *Appleton.*

Harsha, D: A. Life of John Bunyan; with notices of some of his contemporaries and specimens of his style. 12°. $1.50 .... *Lippincott.*

— Life of Philip Doddridge; with notices of some of his contemporaries and specimens of his style. 12°. $1.50 .... *Lippincott.*

— Lives of Rev. J. Hervey and Rev. G. Whitfield. 8°. '66. $1.50 .... *Munsell.*

— Most eminent orators and statesmen of anc. and mod. times. ill. 8°. '54. $2.75 .... *Porter.*

— Wanderings of a pilgrim. 64°. 40c. .... *Pres. Bd.*

— (*ed.*) Devotional thoughts; from Bp. Hall to Wm. Jay. por. 12°. (cop. '66.) '69. $1.50; $1.75. *Am. Tr.*

Harsha, J. W. Song of the redeemed, salvation to God and to the lamb. por. 12°. $1.75 .. *Lippincott.*

Hart, Alb. *See* California, Civil code.

Hart, G: The violin: its famous makers and their imitators. ill. 8°. '76. $4 .... *Bouton.*

Hart, Ger. (*pseud.*) *See* Irving, T. J.

Hart, H. Martyn. Manual of chemistry; for advanced students. cr. 8°. $1.50 .... *Cassell.*

Hart, Ja. Morgan. German universities. 12°. '74. $1.75. *Putnam.*

— (*ed.*) German classics for Am. students; with notes and glossary. 2 v. .... *Putnam.*

Cont.: 1. Goethe's Hermann and Dorothea, 12°, $1. — 2. Schiller's Die Piccolomini, 16°, $1.25.

Hart, J: S. Class book of poetry. ('44.) New ed. 12°. '76. hf. leath., $1.50 .... *Eldredge.*

— Class book of prose. 12°. '76. $1.50 .... *Eldredge.*

— Composition and rhetoric. ('70.) New ed. 12°. '76. hf. leath., $1.50 .... *Eldredge.*

— Constitution of the U. S. ('74.) 3d ed. 12°. '75. 60c. .... *Eldredge.*

— English grammar. ('62.) New ed. 12°. '76. bds., 56c. .... *Eldredge.*

— English grammar and analysis. ('74.) 3d ed. 12°. '75. hf. leath., 90c. .... *Eldredge.*

Hart, J: S., *continued.*
— Epitome of Greek and Roman mythology; with notes and vocab. 12°. '53. 65c............. *Claxton.*
— Essay upon, and selections from, writings of Edmund Spenser; with memoir of life. ill. 12°. $2; $2.50; hf. leath., $3.25; cf., $4........... *C. H. Davis.*
— First lessons in composition. ('59.) New ed. 12°. '75. 90c.; bds., 60c................ *Eldredge.*
— Golden censer: thoughts on the Lord's prayer. sm. 12°. 85c.............................. *Pres. Bd.*
— In the school-room; or, chapters in the philos. of educ. ('68.) 5th ed. 12°. '76. $1.25.. *Eldredge.*
— Language lessons for beginners. 16°. '74. 30c. *Eldredge.*
— Manual of Am. literature. ('72.) 3d ed. 12°. '75. hf. leath.. $2.50.................... *Eldredge.*
— Manual of Eng. literature. ('72.) 6th ed. 12°. '75. hf. leath., $2.50..................... *Eldredge.*
— Mistakes of educated men. 18°. '62. 50c... *Garrigues.*
— Removing mountains. 16°. $1.25.......... *Carter.*
— Short course in literature, English and American. ('73.) 5th ed. 12°. '76. hf. leath., $1.50.. *Eldredge.*
— Sunday-school idea. 16°. '70. $1.50... *Garrigues.*
— Thoughts on S.-schools. 12°. 85c....... *Pres. Bd.*

Hart, Jos. C. Miriam Coffin; or, the whale-fishermen. [Reprint.] 12°. '72. $2............. *Coleman.*

Hart and water brooks. Macduff, J. R. $1.... *Carter.*

Harte, Bret. Condensed novels. [Burlesques.] ill. 16°. '71. $1.50........................... *Osgood.*
— East and west poems. 16°. '71. $1.50; hf. cf., $3; mor., $4............................. *Osgood.*
— Echoes of the foot hills: poems. 16°. '74. $1.50; hf. cf., $3; mor., $4.................. *Osgood.*
— Gabriel Conroy. [Fiction.] ill. 8°. '76. *$3–$7. *Am. Pub.*
— Heathen Chinee: poem. ill. 16°. '71. pap., 25c. *Osgood.*
— Luck of Roaring Camp, and other sketches. 16°. '70. $1.50; hf. cf., $3; — ill. by S. Eytinge, jr. 4°. '71. $8................................ *Osgood.*
— Mrs. Skagg's husband, and other sketches. 16°. '72. $1.50; hf. cf., $3......................... *Osgood.*
— Mliss: an idyl of Red Mountain. [Fiction.] 8°. pap., 50c.................................. *De Witt.*
— Poems. (Diamond ed.) 18°. '73. $1; hf. cf., $2.25; mor. $3. — (Red-line ed.) ill. sm. 4°. '71. $3.50; hf. cf., $5; mor., $7. — 16°. '70. $1.50; hf. cf., $3; mor., $4............................ *Osgood.*
— Tales of the Argonauts, and other stories. 16°. '75. $1.50....................................... *Osgood.*

Hartford bridge. Pearce, W. 15c........... *French.*

Hartford in the olden time. Stuart, I. W. $4.50. *J. W. Bliss.*

Hartley, Cecil B. Hunting sports in the west. ill. 12°. $1.75............................ *J. E. Potter.*
— Life of Daniel Boone; added his autobiography. ill. 16°. '65. $1.75................... *J. E. Potter.*
— Life of Empress Josephine. 12°. $1.25.... *Porter.*
— Life of Francis Marion; with sketches of other [rev.] patriots. ill. 12°. $1.75............ *J. E. Potter.*
— Lives of the three Mrs. Judsons, the female missionaries. por. 12°. $1.75............ *J. E. Potter.*

Hartley, F. J. Pictorial teaching and Bible illustration. 18°. '69. pap., 10c.......... *Perkinpine.*

Hartley, Flo. Gentlemen's book of etiquette and fashion. 12°. $1.50........................ *Locke.*
— Ladies' book of etiquette and fashion. 12°. $1.50. *Locke.*
— Ladies' handbook of fancy and ornamental work. ill. 4°. $2............................ *J. E. Potter.*

Hartley, I. S. Vedder lectures on modern infidelity, 1874. 12°. $1.25............... *N. Y. Ref. Ch. Bd.*

Hartley, O. C. *See* Texas, Sup. Court reports.

Hartley, R. K. *See* Texas, Sup. Court reports.

Hartley, Wa. Noel. Air and its rel. to life: lectures, 1874. 12°. $1.50...................... *Appleton.*

Hartman, W: D., *and* Mechener, Ez. Conchologi cestrica: the molluscous animals and their shell of Chester Co., Pa. ill. 12°. '74. $1.. *Claxton*

Hartmann, J: L: Evangelischer Glaubensgrund. 32° '73. 15c.; 20c.; 30c..................... *Dette*

Hartmann, Moritz. Ausgestossenen (Die); [also Rostet nicht; [also] Deutsch, Französich u. Eng lisch. 12°. '65. pap., 25c............. *Steiger*
— Gefangene (Der) v. Chillon. 12°. '65. pap., 35c. *Steiger*
— Goldene Schlüssel (Der); [also] Die Brüder Mathieu 12°. '65. pap., 25c.................... *Steiger*
— Last days of a king: hist. romance; tr. by M. E Niles. 12°. '67. $1.25; pap., 75c. *Claxton; Lippincott*

Hartmann, W: Der Männerchor: Sammlg. d. neues ten deutschen Compositionen f. vierstimmiger Männergesang. nos. 1–9. large 8°. ea., pap. 25c.; in 1 v., $1.50.................. *Schäfer*

Hartopp, W. W. Eclipsing the son: comic drama 16°. pap., 15c.......................... *French*

Hartshorne, H: Cholera: its nature, prevention and treatment. 16°. '60. pap., 25c...... *Lippincott*
— Conspectus of the medical sciences: handbooks on anatomy, physiology, etc. 2d ed., rev. ill. roy 12°. $4.25; leath., $5...................... *Lea*
— Essentials of the principles and practice of medicine ill. roy. 12°. $2.63; hf. bd., $2.88......... *Lea.*
— Family adviser and guide to the medicine chest handbook of domestic med. New ed., rev. and enl. 18°. 75c....................... *Lippincott.*
— Glycerin and its uses. 18°. 60c........ *Lippincott.*
— Handbook of anatomy and physiology. 2d ed., rev. ill. roy. 12°. $1.75........................ *Lea.*

Hartt, C: F: Geology and physical geography of Brazil. map and ill. 8°. '70. $5; hf. cf., $8.. *Osgood.*

Hartwell, Ma. A woman in armor. 12°. $1.50.. *Carleton.*

Hartwell farm. Comins, L. B. $1.50....... *Loring.*

Hartwick Seminary [Otsego Co., N. Y.] Memorial of the semi-centennial anniversary, Aug. 21, 1866. por. and ill. 8°. '67. $3....... *Munsell.*

Hartwig, G: Aerial world: popular account of the phenomena and life of the atmosphere. pl., map and ill. 8°. $6......................... *Appleton.*
— Harmonies of nature; or, the unity of creation. ill. 8°. hf. cf., $10; cf., $12.............. *Appleton.*
— Polar and tropical worlds; ed. by A. H. Guernsey. 2 v. in 1. ill. 8°. '72. *$4.25; leath., $4.75; hf. cf., $6.......................... *C. A. Nichols.*
— Sea and its living wonders. ill. 8°. '73. $6.. *Dodd.*
— Tropical world. ill. 8°. '73. $3............. *Dodd.*

Hartz boys. Hoffmann, F. $1.25.......... *Lothrop.*

Hartz boys lib. 4 v. 16°. $5.............. *Lothrop.*
Cont.: Hartz boys. — Mark Churchill. — Night to light. — Faithful but not famous.

Hartzel, Jonas. Baptismal controversy: its exceeding sinfulness. 12°. '76. $1.50........... *Cen. Bk.*
— Church discipline. 12°. '75. pap., 10c..... *Cen. Bk.*
— Divinity of Christ and the duality of man. 12°. '74. 75c.................................. *Cen. Bk.*

Harvard Advocate. Verses. *See* Verses from.

Harvard College. Museum of Compar. Zoology. *See* Museum of Comp. Zool.

Harvard College Astron. Observatory. Annals. v. 1, 2 (ea. in 2 pts.), 3–7. 4°. '56–'71. v. 1 (per pt.), 2 (pt. 2), 4, 6, 7, ea., $5; v. 2 (pt. 1), 5, ea., $10; v. 3, $20........................ *Harv. Coll. Ob.*
Cont.: v. 1, pt. 1, Hist. and description of the Obs., by W. C. Bond. — v. 1, pt. 2, Zone catalogue of 5500 stars. — v. 2, pt. 1, Observations on Saturn, by W. C. Bond. — v. 2, pt. 2, Zone catalogue of 4484 stars. — v. 3, Account of the great comet of 1858, by G. P. Bond. — v. 4, Catalogue of standard polar and clock stars, by T. H. Safford. — v. 5, Observations upon the great nebula of Orion, by G. P. Bond; ed. by T. H. Safford. — v. 6, Zone catalogue of 6100 stars. — v. 7, Observations of solar spots, 1747–1749, by W. C. Bond and C. H. F. Peters.

Harvard examination papers; coll. and arr. by R. F. Leighton. ('73.) 2d ed. 12°. '74. $1.56.. *Ginn.*

Harvest: texts of Scripture ref. to harvest season. 18°. 25c. . . . . *Am. S. S.*

Harvest and the reaper. Van Cott, M. N. $1.50; $2. *Tibbals.*

Harvest and the reapers. Newcombe, H. $1 . . *Lothrop.*

Harvest of flowers. *See* Weiss, J.

Harvest queen. *See* Lacy's home plays for ladies.

Harvest storm. Hazelwood, C. H. 15c. . . . . *French.*

— *See also* French's serio-comic dramas.

Harvest work of the Holy Spirit. Headley, P. C. $1.25 . . . . . *Hoyt.*

Harvestings. Kittredge, C. B. 75c. . . . . *Cong. Pub.*

Harvey, C. The synagogue. *See* Herbert, G., Poetical works.

Harvey, E. American trotting horse. *See* Walsh, J. H., Every horse owner's cyclopedia.

Harvey, Ph. Footprints of life; or, faith and nature reconciled. [Poetry.] 12°. '68. $1.25 . . *Wells.*

Harvey, T: W. Elementary grammar. 12°. '69. 45c. *Wilson, H. & Co.*

— First lessons in Eng. language. ill. 12°. '75. 30c. *Wilson, H. & Co.*

— Graded-school primary speller. 16°. '75. 20c. *Wilson, H. & Co.*

— Graded-school readers. 75 . . . . . *Wilson, H. & Co.*
Cont.: First, 16°, 20c. — Second, 16°, 45c. — Third, 16°, 60c. — Fourth, 12°, 90c. — Fifth, 12°, $1.15.

— Practical grammar of Eng. language. 12°. '68. 85c. *Wilson, H. & Co.*

Harvey, W: H. Marine algæ of No. Am. 3 pts. 4°. '52–'58. pap. 1, $6; 2, $10; 3, $6; — in 1 v., pap., $20 . . . . . *Smith. Inst.*

Harvey boys. 18°. 50c. . . . . *Am. S. S.*

Harveys (The). *See* Kingsley, H:

Harwood, A. A. Law and practice of U. S. naval courts-martial. 8°. '67. shp., $4 . . *Van Nostrand.*

Harwood, Annie. King's daughters: words on work to educated women. 12°. '69. 80c. . . . . *Randolph.*

Harwood, E. Acting proverbs; or, drawing room theatricals. 16°. bds., 50c. . . . . *Routledge.*

Harwood. Coulson, J. G. A. $1.25; 75c. . . . . *Hale.*

Hasbrouck, J. *See* California, Insurance laws.

Hase, K: A: History of the Christian church; tr. by E. Blumenthal and C. P. Wing. 8°. '55. $3.50. *Appleton.*

Hasheesh eater (The): passages from the life of a Pythagorean. 12°. $1.50 . . . . . *Harper.*

Haskell, B. D. Tekel: examination and refutation of materialistic or dead-sleeping theology. 16°. '75. pap., 25c. . . . . (?) *Woodward & P.*

Haskell, E. F. Housekeeper's encyclopædia: useful information in cooking and house keeping. sm. 8°. $1.75 . . . . . *Appleton.*

Haskell, T. H. New Gloucester [Me.] centennial [Sept. 7, 1874]: hist. address, remarks, record of the Falmouth Convention, 1774, etc. 8°. $1.25. *Hoyt, F. & D.*

Haskins, C. H. The galvanometer and its uses: manual for electricians and students. ill. 16°. '73. $2 . . . . . *Van Nostrand.*

Haskins, *Rev.* D. G. What is confirmation, or the laying on of hands? 16°. 12c. . . . . *Dutton.*

Haskins, D: Greene. French and English first book: rudiments of Fr. and Eng. gram. combined. 12°. '58. $1 . . . . . *Barnes.*

Haskins, S. M. Explanations and instructions in catechetical form on rite of confirmation and communion. 16°. pap., 12c. . . . . *Dutton.*

— Treatise on early confirmation, and communion. 16°. pap., 12c. . . . . *Dutton.*

— *Same.* 12°. 35c. . . . . *Appleton.*

Haslett, C: Mechanics', machinists' and engineers' pract. book of reference; ed. by C. W. Hackley. 16°. leath., $2.50 . . . . . *Huntington.*

Hassall, Arth. H. Illustrations of the microscopic anat. of the human body; with add. by H. Van Arsdale. ill. 8°. hf. mor., $6 . . . . . *W. Wood.*

Hassan, Abdallah. *See* Enchanted keys.

Hassard, Annie. Floral decorations for the dwelling house: guide to home arrang. of plants and flowers. Am. ed., rev. ill. 12°. '76. $1.50 . . . *Macmillan.*

Hassard, J. R. G. Life, correspondence and writings of Abp. Hughes. 8°. $3; mor., $6 . . . . *Appleton.*

Hassaurek, F. Four years among the Spanish-Americans. cr. 8°. '68. $1.75 . . . . . *Hurd & H.*

Hasta, O. S. v. Luther-Lied: e. Epos im Volkston. 12°. $1 . . . . . *Brumder.*

Haste and waste. Adams, W. T. $1.25 . . . . *Lee & S.*

Haste to the rescue. *See* W—, *Mrs.* C:

Hastings, Anna. The Russel family. ill. 18°. '56. 75c. . . . . *Dodd.*

Hastings, Hor. L. Great controversy between God and man: its origin, progress and end. ('58.) 6th ed. 12°. '70. $1 . . . . . *Hastings.*

— Reasons for my hope; or, the tokens of speedy redemption. ('60.) 8th ed. 12°. pap., 25c. *Hastings.*

— Signs of the times; or, a glance at Christendom as it is. ('52.) 5th ed. 12°. '70. $1 . . . . *Hastings.*

— Social hymns: original and selected. ('65.) 6th ed. 32°. '70. pap., 10c. . . . . *Hastings.*

— Thessalonica; or, the model church: primitive Christianity. ('61.) 6th ed. 12°. '70. $1 . . *Hastings.*

Hastings, T: Church music: musical compositions for devot. use in choirs, congregations, etc. obl. 8°. '60. bds., $1.50 . . . . . *Ditson.*

— Dissertation on musical taste. 12°. '53. $1.75. *Ditson.*

— History of forty choirs. 12°. '53. $1.75 . . . . *Ditson.*

— Introits. 8°. '66. bds., $1 . . . . . *Randolph.*

— Mother's (The) hymn book. 32°. '60. 35c. *Randolph.*

— Presbyterian juvenile psalmodist. [Tune book.] sq. 18°. 45c. . . . . *Pres. Bd.*

— Presbyterian psalmodist. [Tune book.] 8°. $1.25 –$1.75 . . . . . *Pres. Bd.*

— Sabbath-school songs. 12°. 40c. . . . . *Ditson.*

— Sacred praise: appeal to Christian worshippers in behalf of a neglected duty. [Treatise on music.] 18°. '56. 60c. . . . . *Barnes.*

— Selah: psalm and hymn tunes, etc. roy. 8°. '56. hf. bd., $1.50 . . . . . *Barnes.*

— *See also* Cook, T. J., Perkins, T. E., *and* Hastings, T.; — Shawm (The).

— *and* T. S. Church melodies: psalms and hymns, with music for congregations. 12°. '58. hf. roan, $1.35. *Randolph.*

Hastings, T: S. Memoirs of Lottie. ill. 18°. '63. 40c. *Am. Tr.*

— *See also* Hastings, T. *and* T. S.

Hasty conclusion: burletta. 16°. pap., 15c. . . *Happy.*

Haswell, C: H. Book-keeping by double entry expl. and ill. in a complete record of merc. and financial transactions. 8°. hf. mor., $3.50 . . *Appleton.*

— Engineers' and mechanics' pocket-book: cont. weights and measures, rules of arith., etc. 12°. (Pocket-book form.) $3 . . . . . *Harper.*

— Mensuration; for tuition and reference; with tables. 12°. $1.25 . . . . . *Harper.*

— Tables: areas and circumferences of circles, circumferences of angled hoops, cutting of boiler-plates, covering of solids, and weights of various metals, etc.; with notes. 12°. $1. — (Pocket-book form.) $1.25 . . . . . *Harper.*

Haswell, J. M. *See* Napoleon III., the man of his time.

Hatch, Alice J. Under the cedars; or, what the years brought. 12°. $1.50 . . . . . *Lee & S.*

Hatch, W: Stanley. Chapter of the hist. of the war of 1812 in the northwest; with a descript. and biog. sketch of the Indian chief Tecumseh. 18°. '72. shp., $1.25 . . . . . *Clarke.*

Hatfield, Edn. F. Chapel hymn book; abridg. from "Church hymn book." 16°. '73. $1.25..*Ivison.*
— Church hymn book. 16°. $1.50-$4.75......*Ivison.*
— *Same;* with tunes and psalter. 8°. $2.50; $4.50; mor., $7..............................*Ivison*
— Psalter, or, Book of psalms, complete; with sel. from the prophecies, arranged for responsive worship. 12°. 90c.-$4.50..............*Ivison.*
Hatfield, R. G. American house carpenter; with principles of pract. geometry. New ed., rev. and enl. pl. 8°. $3.50..........................*Wiley.*
— Experimental tests on building stones. 8°. pap., 35c. *Am. Soc. of C. E.*
— Fire-proof floors: table [of] distances from centres at which rolled iron beams should be placed, and weight of metal. 4°. pap., 30c...*Am. Inst. Arch.*
Hathaway, Ht. N. Children's chip-basket. *See* Chip-basket stories.
Hathaway Strange. *See* Fairfield, G. G.
Hattie and Marcus; or, first steps in the better path. 16°. $1..............................*Locke.*
— *See also* Adirondack stories; — Better path stories.
Hattie Hale's likeness. *See* Aunt Hattie's stories.
Hattie May. Dawes, S. E. 60c. ....*Am. Tr.*
Hattie Powers. Thomas, A. E. $1.25 ....*Hoyt.*
Hattie Preston. 18°. 60c................*Cong. Pub.*
Hatty and Marcus. *See* Baker, S.
Hatty Winthrop. Dunning, A. K. 45c.....*Pres. Bd.*
Hauff, W: Werke. 9 v. 12°. ea., pap., 10c.-25c. *F. W. Thomas.*
Cont.: Märchen, 25c. — Lichtenstein, 25c. — Der Mann im Monde, 15c. — Mittheilungen a. d. Memoiren d. Satans, 15c. — Jud Süss. — Bettlerin vom Pont des Arts. — Othello. — Phantasien im Bremer Rathskeller. — Die letzten Ritter von Marienburg. — Gedichte, *ea.*, 10c.
— Sämmtliche Werke. 8°. $2.50; pap., $2; hf. mor., $2.75..........................*F. W. Thomas.*
— Arabian days' entertainments; tr. by H. P. Curtis. ill. 12°. $1.75.......................*Osgood.*
— Die Bettlerin vom Pont des Arts; [also] Jud Süss. 18°. 75c...................................*Radde.*
Haughton, S. Manual of natural philos. ill. cr. 8°. $1.50..............................*Cassell.*
— Three kingdoms of nature. ill. cr. 8°. $2.50. *Cassell.*
— *See also* Galbraith, J. A., *and* Haughton, S.
Haunted castle; or, the abducted niece. 8°. pap., 25c. *De Witt.*
Haunted homestead. Southworth, E. D. E. N. $1.75; $1.50..................................*Peterson.*
Haunted house. *See* Dickens, C:
Haunted house: Ethiop. dram. 16°. pap., 15c. *French; Happy.*
Haunted house; or, the evils of strong drink. 18°. 40c..................................*Am. S. S.*
Haunted hulk. Ball, E. 15c. ....*French.*
Haunted inn. Peake, R. B. 15c. ....*French.*
Haunted mill. Wooler, J. P. 15c...........*French.*
Haunted rooms. Tucker, C. $1.25; 75c.....*Carter.*
Haunted tower. Cobb, J. 15c...............*French.*
Haunted tower. Wood, E. P. 50c.........*Peterson.*
Haunts of the wild flowers. Pratt, A. $1.25; 80c. *Routledge.*
Haupt, A. Theory of counterpoint, fugue and double counterpoint; tr. by H. C. Eddy. 8°. *net*, $1.50. *Schirmer.*
Haupt, Hm. Military bridges; with suggestions of new expedients, incl. designs for trestle and truss-bridges for milit. railroads. 69 lith. eng. 8°. '64. $6.50...................*Van Nostrand.*
— Theory of bridge construct. ill. 8°. $3.50..*Appleton.*
Häuschen (Das) am See. Claudius, M. 25c...*Steiger.*
Hauser, *Mrs.* I. L. The Orient and its people. 12°. '76. $1.75..........................*Hauser.*

Häusser, L: Period of the reformation, 1517-1648. 12°. '74. $2.50.........................*Carter.*
Haussonville, *Countess* d'. Life of Robert Emmet; tr. by J. P. Leonard. 12°. '60. bds., 75c...*Haverty.*
Have you seen it? ill. 4°. 65c.............*Am. S. S.*
Haven, *Mrs.* Alice B. ["Cousin Alice."] Coopers (The); or, getting under way: a tale of real life. 12°. $1.25..........................*Appleton.*
— Good report: morning and evening lessons for Lent. 12°. $1.25.............................*Appleton.*
— Home ser. of juv. books. 8 v. ill. 12°. $10..*Appleton.*
Cont.: No such word as fail. — Out of debt out of danger. — Contentment better than wealth. — Nothing venture, nothing have. — Place for everything. — Patient waiting no loss. — All's not gold that glitters. — Where there's a will, there's a way.
— Home stories. 12°. $1.25................*Appleton.*
— Loss and gain; or, Margaret's home. 12°. $1.25. *Appleton.*
— Memoir of. por. 12°. '65. $1.25........*Appleton.*
— Sunday at Oatlands. 18°. 50c.............*Dutton.*
Haven, Erastus Otis. Pillars of truth: sermons on the decalogue. 12°. '66. $1.25....*Meth. Bk. Conc.*
— Rhetoric; for schools, colleges and private study. 12°. $1.50............................*Harper.*
— Young man advised: illustrations and confirmations of some of the hist. facts of the Bible. 12°. '55. $1.25.......................*Meth. Bk. Conc.*
— *See also* Warren, W. F., Newhall, F. H., *and* Haven, E. O.
Haven, Gilb. Our next-door neighbor: recent sketches of Mexico. maps and ill. cr. 8°. $3.50..*Harper.*
— Pilgrim's wallet; or, scraps of travel gathered in England, France and Germany. 16°. '65. $1.75. *Hurd & H.*
— Sermons, lectures and speeches on slavery and its war. cr. 8°. $3.......................*Lee & S.*
— *and* Russell, T: Father Taylor, the sailor preacher. por. 12°. *$1.50; hf. mor., $2.........*Russell.*
Haven, Jos. History of anc. and mod. philosophy. 12°. $2..............................*Sheldon.*
— Mental philosophy. roy. 12°. $2.........*Sheldon.*
— Moral philosophy; incl. theoretical and practical ethics. roy. 12°. $1.75..............*Sheldon.*
Haven, Marion (*pseud.*) *See* Hazen, Ma. P.
Haven, S: Studies in philosophy and theology. 12°. '69. $2................................*Draper.*
Haven (The) and prize. Marsh, C. 18°. 35c...*Carter.*
Haven children. Foster, E. $1.50..........*Dutton.*
Haverfield, T. T. Old oak farm, and what became of its Sunday work. ill. 16°. 60c..........*Tibbals.*
— *Same.* ill. 18°. 75c.........................*Nelson.*
— *Same.* ('70.) New ed. 16°. '75. $1.......*Hoyt.*
Havergal, Fes. Ridley. Little pillows; or, good-night thoughts for the little ones. 32°. '75. 35c...*Dutton.*
— Ministry of song: book of sacred poetry. ('72.) 2d ed. 24°. '73. $1.50-$3.50...............*Lent.*
— Morning bells; or, waking thoughts for the little ones. 16°. '75. 35c...........................*Dutton.*
— Our work and our blessings; or, under the surface. 24°. '76. $1.........................*Randolph.*
Havergal, W. H. History of the Old-hundredth psalm tune, with specimens; with pref. note by Rev. J. M. Wainwright. 16°. '54. $1.50.......*Ditson.*
Havers, Dora. ["Theo. Gift."] Jack's sister; or, true to her trust. [Fiction.] 8°. pap., 75c...*Harper.*
— Pretty Miss Bellew. (Leis. hour ser.) 16°. '75. $1.25..................................*Holt.*
Haverty, Mt. Illustrated national hist. of Ireland. ill. 4°. $7.50-$20; — in 36 pts., ea., 25c...*T. Kelly.*
Havet, Alfr. French manual; [for] acquiring convers. knowledge of Fr. 12°. $1.25........*Appleton.*
Haviland, J: *See* Biddle's architecture.
Hawarden, E: Charity and truth; or, Catholics not uncharitable in saying that none are saved out of the Cath. Church. 12°. '60. $1.25..*Cunningham.*

Haweis, Hu. Reg. Ashes to ashes: a cremation prelude. 12°. '75. $1.75 .... *Routledge.*
— Music and morals. ill. 12°. $1.75 .... *Harper.*
— *Same.* 2d ed. 12°. '71. $3 .... *Routledge.*
— Pet; or, pastimes and penalties. ill. 12°. $1.50. *Harper.*

Haweis, T: Communicant's spiritual companion: preparation for the Lord's supper; with introd. by Rev. E. W. Appleton. 16°. '61. 50c... *Leighton.*

Hawes, Granville P. Law rel. to general voluntary assignments for benefit of creditors, as provided for in the N. Y. statute of 1860, as amended; with notes. 8°. shp., $2 .... *Baker, V. & Co.*

Hawes, Hor. *See* Bates, C. J., Report of proceedings on will of H.

Hawes, J. H. Manual of U. S. surveying: system employed in subdividing public lands of U. S. cr. 8°. $3 .... *Lippincott.*

Hawes, Jl. Gift for young men. 32°. *net*, 28c. *Hamersley.*
— Lectures to young men on the formation of character. 12°. $1.25 .... *Cong. Pub.*
— Letters on Universalism. 18°. '52. 25c.... *Am. Tr.*

Hawes, Ste. New Testament text book: hist. tabular view of the Gospels, tables of the parables, discourses and miracles of Christ, etc. maps. 16°. 75c. .... *Lee & S.*

Hawker, Rob. Daily portion; [compr.] "Morning portion" and "Evening portion." 16°. $1.50. *Routledge.*
— Evening portion. 16°. 75c. .... *Routledge.*
— Morning portion. 16°. 75c. .... *Routledge.*
— Zion's pilgrim; or, the way to the heavenly Canaan familiarly illustrated. 18°. 45c. ...... *Pres. Bd.*

Hawkins, F. V. Concise treatise on construction of wills; with Am. notes and ref. by J. Sword. 8°. $5 .... *T. & J. W. Johnson.*

Hawkins, J. *See* Louisiana, Reports.

Hawkins, Jac. Evangelical catechism; for S.-school and family circle of any Christian denomination. 2 nos. 16°. ea., per doz., pap., 75c. ...... *Duffie.*

Hawks, Fs. Lister. ["Uncle Philip."] American forest (The): conversations with the children about the trees of Am. ill. 18°. 75c. .. *Harper.*
— English lang.: element. instruction. ill. 16°. '67. bds., 25c. .... *Pott.*
— Evidences of Christianity: convers. about truth of the Christian rel. 18°. 75c. .... *Harper.*
— Greenland: convers. with the children about the lost colonies of Greenland. ill. 18°. 75c... *Harper.*
— History of North Carolina. 2 v. 8°. $5; shp., $6; hf. cf., $7 .... *Hale.*
— Household prayers for four weeks; with add. prayers for special occasions, by Rev. J. E. Riddle. New ed., rev. and enl. 12°. '72. $1 .... *Pott.*
— Massachusetts: convers. with the children about hist. of Mass. 2 v. ill. 18°. $1.50 ...... *Harper.*
— Narrative of the expedition under Com. M. C. Perry to the China seas and Japan in 1852-4. 3 v. 4°. '56 .... *U. S. Govt.*
Cont.: Narrative of the expedition. — Reports on agriculture, botany, zool., etc. — Obs. on the zodiacal light, by G. Jones.
— *Same;* in 1 v. ill. 8°. shp., $5; hf. cf., $9. — 4°. $9; hf. cf., $10 .... *Appleton.*
— Natural history: convers. with the children about tools and trades among inferior animals. ill. 18°. 75c. .... *Harper.*
— New Hampshire: convers. with the children about hist. of N. H. 2 v. ill. 18°. $1.50.... *Harper.*
— New York: convers. with the children about hist. of N. Y. 2 v. ill. 18°. $1.50 .... *Harper.*
— Virginia: convers. with the children about hist. of Va. ill. 18°. 75c. .... *Harper.*
— Whale fishery: convers. about the whale fisheries and Polar seas. 2 v. 18°. $1.50 ...... *Harper.*
— (*ed.*) Cyclopædia of biography, foreign and American. ill. roy. 8°. $5-$8 .... *Appleton.*
— *See also* North Carolina, Reports.

Hawkshaw, J. Denby Dale viaduct; — Paddock viaduct. *See* Roebling, J., Niagara Falls and intern. susp. bridge.

Hawley, B. Manual of Methodism: doctrines, general rules, usages. 12°. '68. $1 .... *Meth. Bk. Conc.*

Hawley, Curtis B. *See* Buckskin Mose.

Hawley, T: P. *See* Nevada, Sup. Court reports.

Hawn, F. *See* Kansas geol. survey.

Haws, Jl. Counsels to young men. *See* Pioneer lib.
— Lectures to young men on formation of character; with introd. by J. McCoy. 18°. 35c... *Un. B. Pub.*

Hawthorn blossoms. Charles, E. H. $1.50.. *Lippincott.*

Hawthorndean. Thompson, C. M. $1.50. *Cunningham.*

Hawthorne, Emily. *See* Charles, *Mrs.* E. H.

Hawthorne, Julian. Bressant. [Fiction.] 12°. $1.50. *Appleton.*
— Idolatry. [Fiction.] 12°. '74. $2 .... *Osgood.*
— Saxon studies. [Essays.] 12°. '75. $2 ... *Osgood.*

Hawthorne, Natl. Works. 23 v. 16°. '50-'76. ea., $1.50; hf. cf., $3; per set, cf., $85 ...... *Osgood.*
Cont.: American note books, 2 v. — Blithedale romance. — Dolliver romance, etc. — English note books, 2 v. — Fanshawe, etc. — French and Italian note books, 2 v. — House of the seven gables. — Marble faun, 2 v. — Mosses from an old manse, 2 v. — Our old home. — Scarlet letter. — Septimius Felton. — Snow image, etc. — Tanglewood tales. — True stories from history and biography. — Twice told tales, 2 v. — Wonder book.
— *Same.* (Little classic ed.) 23 v. ill. 18°. '75-'76. ea., $1.25 .... *Osgood.*
Contents same as above.
— *Same.* (Ill. lib. ed.) 11 v. 12°. ea., $2; hf. cf., $4 .... *Osgood.*
Cont.: Twice-told tales. — Mosses from an old manse. — Scarlet letter; Blithedale romance. — House of the seven gables; Snow image. — Marble faun. — Eng. note-books. — Am. note-books. — French and Ital. note-books. — Our old home; Septimius Felton. — Wonder book; Grandfather's chair. — Tanglewood tales; Biographical sketches.
— Snow-image: childish miracle. ill. sm. 4°. '66. $1. *Hurd & H.*
— Twice-told tales. ill. 12°. $1.50 .... *World Pub.*

Hawthorne, *Mrs.* So. Notes in England and Italy. 3d ed. 12°. '69. $2; hf. cf., $4. — ill. 12°. '74. $5 .... *Putnam.*

Hay, D: Home; or, the way to make home happy; with introd. by Rev. A. Barrett; rev. by T. O. Summers. ('58.) 9th ed. 18°. '76. 50c... *So. Meth.*

Hay, E: History of the Irish rebellion of 1798. 12°. $1 .... *Noonan.*

Hay, Elzey (*pseud.*) *See* Andrews, Fanny.

Hay, F: [Farces.] 9 v. 16°. ea., pap., 15c... *French.*
Cont.: Beautiful forever. — Caught by the cuff. — Chops of the channel. — Cupboard love. — French exhibition. — Lame excuse. — Our domestic. — Photographic fix. — Suit of tweeds.
— *Same.* 8 v. 12°. ea., pap., 15c. .... *De Witt.*
Cont.: Beautiful forever. — Caught by the cuff. — Chops of the channel. — Cupboard love. — Lame excuse. — Our domestics. — Photographic fix. — Lodgers and dodgers.

Hay, G: Abridgment of the Christian doctrine. 32°. 30c. .... *Cath. Pub.*
— Scripture doctrine of miracles displayed. 16°. $1. *Strong.*
— Sincere Christian instructed in the faith of Christ, from the written word of God. 12°. $1.50.. *Noonan.*
— *Same.* 8°. $2 .... *Cummiskey.*

Hay, J: Castilian days. ('71.) 8th ed. 12°. $2; hf. cf., $4; mor., $5 .... *Osgood.*
— Jim Bludso; [also] Little Breeches. [Poems.] ('71.) 8th ed. ill. 16°. pap., 25c. .... *Osgood.*
— Pike county ballads, and other poems. ('71.) 7th ed. 16°. $1.50; hf. cf., $3 .... *Osgood.*
— *See also* Lotos leaves.

Hay, Ma. Cecil. Hidden perils. 8°. '76. pap., 75c. *Harper.*
— Old Myddelton's money. 8°. pap., 50c.... *Harper.*
— Squire's legacy. 8°. '76. pap., 75c. .... *Harper.*
— Victor and vanquished. 8°. pap., 50c. ..... *Harper.*

Hay fever. Hoppin, A. $3 .... *Osgood.*

Hayden, Amos Sutton. Christian hymn and tune book. sq. 8°. $1.50; mor., $3.50 .... *Church.*

— Early hist. of the disciples in the Western Reserve, Ohio; with biog. of principal agents in their relig. movement. 12°. *$2 .... *Chase.*

— Hymnist: heart hymns and home melodies, with tunes. 18°. hf. bd., 25c. .... *Chase.*

— Sacred melodeon: church music on a new system of notation. ('49.) New ed. 8°. '76. hf. bd., $1.25. *Wilstach.*

Hayden, Fd. Vandeveer. *See* Meek, F. B., *and* Hayden, F. V.; — United States, *Corps of Eng.; Geol. Survey of the Ter.*

Hayden, Sidney. Washington and his Masonic compeers. ill. 12°. '75. $2.50 .. *Masonic; Redding.*

Hayden, T: Diseases of the heart and aorta. 2 v. ill. 8°. '75. $8 .... *Lindsay.*

Hayden, *Rev.* W. B. Lectures on the Apocalypse. 8°. 50c. .... *H. H. Carter.*

— Light on the last things. 12°. $1.25 .... *Lippincott.*

— Ten chapters on marriage. 8°. 50c. .. *H. H. Carter.*

Hayden, W. L. *See* Worrall, H., *and* Hayden, W. L.

Hayden, W: New and improved method for the guitar. f°. '70. bds., $3 .... *Ditson.*

Haydn, Jos. Creation (The); with organ or piano accomp., ed. by V. Novello. [Oratorio.] 8°. $1.25; pap., 80c.; bds., $1 .... *Ditson.*

— — Choruses. 8°. bds., 65c. .... *Ditson.*

— First mass in B flat; with Lat. words and organ accomp., ed. by V. Novello. obl. roy. 8°. bds., $1; pap., 80c. .... *Peters.*

— *Same;* with piano or organ accomp. by V. Novello; with Lat. and Eng. text. 8°. '64. $1.12; pap., 80c. .... *Ditson.*

— Second mass in C; with Lat. words and organ accomp., ed by V. Novello. obl. roy. 8°. bds., $1; pap., 80c. .... *Peters.*

— *Same;* with organ or piano accomp. by V. Novello; with Lat. and Eng. text. 8°. '64. $1.12; pap., 80c. .... *Ditson.*

— Third mass in D; with Lat. words and organ accomp., ed. by V. Novello. obl. roy. 8°. bds., $1; pap., 80c. .... *Peters.*

— *Same;* with organ or piano accomp. by V. Novello; with Lat. and Eng. text. 8°. $1.12; pap., 80c.: bds., $1 .... *Ditson; Gordon.*

— Fourth mass in B flat; with organ or piano accomp. by V. Novello; with Lat. and Eng. text. 8°. '64. $1.12; pap., 80c. .... *Ditson.*

— Sixth mass in B flat; with organ or piano accomp. by V. Novello; with Lat. and Eng. text. 8°. '65. $1.25; pap., $1 .... *Ditson.*

— Seventh mass in G; with Lat. words and organ accomp., ed. by V. Novello. obl. roy. 8°. bds., 80c.; pap., 65c. .... *Peters.*

— *Same;* with organ or piano accomp. by V. Novello; with Lat. and Eng. text. 8°. $1; pap., 65c. .. *Ditson.*

— Eighth mass in B flat; with organ or piano accomp. by V. Novello; with Lat. and Eng. text. 8°. $1; pap., 65c. .... *Ditson.*

— Sixteenth mass in B flat; with Lat. words and organ accomp., ed. by V. Novello. obl. roy. 8°. bds., $1.12; pap., 90c. .... *Peters.*

— *Same;* with organ or piano accomp. by V. Novello; with Eng. and Lat. text. 8°. $1.25; pap., $1. *Ditson.*

— Seasons. [Oratorio.] 4°. $3; bds., $2.25; — in 4 pts. obl. 4°. ea., 50c. .... *Gordon.*

— *Same;* ed. by V. Novello. 8°. $1.75; bds., $1.50; pap., $1.25 .... *Ditson.*

— — Choruses. obl. 4°. bds., $1 .... *Ditson.*

— Spring; from "The seasons." 8°. pap., 50c. .. *Ditson.*

Haydn, Jos. Dictionary of dates; ed. by B. Vincent; rev. for Am. readers. 8°. $5; shp., $6 .. *Harper.*

— *Same;* with Am. supplement, by G. P. Putnam. 14th ed. 8°. '74. $9; hf. mor., $12 ... *Putnam.*

Haydock, G. L. *See* Bible [Whole], *Cath.*

Haydon, B: Rob. Autobiography and journals; ed. by T. Taylor. 2 v. 12°. $3 .... *Harper.*

Hayes, Arth. P. Light in the east; [incl.] Life of Christ, by J. Fleetwood; with lives of the patriarchs and prophets, etc. ill. 8°. *$4; roan, $4.75; mor., $6.50 .... *Nat. Pub.*

Hayes, E: (*ed.*) Ballads of Ireland; with notes, historical and biog. 2 v. ill. 12°. $4 ...... *Sadlier.*

Hayes, I: I. Arctic boat journey in the autumn of 1854. ill. 12°. '60. $2.50 .... *Osgood.*

— Cast away in the cold. ill. sq. 16°. $1.50 .. **Osgood.*

— Land of desolation: narrative of obs. and adventure in Greenland. ill. 12°. $1.75 .... *Harper.*

— Open Polar sea: voyage of disc. in the "United States." chart, ill. and por. 8°. '66. $3.75; hf. cf., $6. — post 8°. $2.50 .... *Hurd & H.*

— Physical observations in the Arctic seas. 4°. '67. pap., $5 .... *Smith. Inst.*

Hayes, J: L. United States industrial directory. 8°. '76. $5 .... *N. A. of Wool Man.*

— *See also* United States textile manufacturers' directory.

Haygood, Atticus G. Our children. 12°. $1.50. *S. W. Bk. & Pub.*

— Prize essay on missions. ('74.) 10th ed. 12°. '76. pap., 20c. .... *So. Meth.*

— (*ed.*) Our keepsake. ('71.) 4th ed. ill. roy. 8°. '75. pap., $1 .... *So. Meth.*

Haymakers. Root, G. F. $1 .... *Ditson.*

Haymakers; [also] Rude boys reformed; [also] Choctaw girl. 18°. 30c. .... *Am. S. S.*

Haymarket spring meeting: extravaganza. 16°. pap., 15c. .... *French.*

Haymond, Creed. *See* California, Civil code.

Hayne, Pl. H. Legends and lyrics. [Poetry.] 12°. $1.50 .... *Lippincott.*

— Mountain of the lovers; with poems of nature and tradition. 12°. $1.50 .... *Hale.*

Hayne, Rob. Y. *See* Webster, D., *and* Hayne, R. Y.

Haynes, C: *and* J. E. Star of hope: Sabbath school songs. obl. 8°. bds., 35c. .... *Peters.*

Haynes, D. C. Baptist denomination. 12°. '75. $1.50. (?) *H. D. Brown.*

Haynes, Eliz. K. Life. 18°. 30c.; 40c. .. *Am. Bapt.*

Haynes, Freeman Oliver. Outlines of equity. [Lectures.] 8°. '58. $2.50 ...... *T. & J. W. Johnson.*

— — *See also* Law lib.

Haynes, Gid. Pictures from prison life: hist. sketch of the Mass. state prison. ill. 12°. $1.50 .. *Lee & S.*

Haynes, J. E. *See* Haynes, C. *and* J. E.

Hays, W: S. Golden leaves: songs and choruses. 2 v. 4°. ea., $2.25; bds., $1.75 .... *Peters.*

Hayslop Grange. Leslie, E. $1 .... *Nelson.*

Hayter, A. U. Church music: psalm and hymn tunes, etc. obl. f°. '63. $2.75; bds., $2.50 .... *Ditson.*

— Collection of cathedral chants. obl. 8°. '43. bds., $1; — words, 10c. .... *Ditson.*

Hayter, C: Perspective and drawing. ill. 8°. (Bagster.) $2.25 .... *Wiley.*

Hayward, C., *jr.* Life of S. Cabot. *See* Sparks, J., Library of Am. biog.

Hayward, J. W. *See* Drysdale, J., *and* Hayward, J. W.

Hayward, Mar. L. Huntingdons. 16°. $1.25. *H. A. Young.*

— Velma Lee. 18°. 75c. .... *Cong. Pub.*

Hayward, S: *See* Pike, S., *and* Hayward, S:

Haywood, *Miss* Ctte. E. Sunset Hill. 16°. $1.50. *Cong. Pub.*

— — *See also* Island home lib.

Haywood, J: *See* North Carolina, Law reports; — Tennessee, Sup. Court of Errors and Appeals reports.

[H]azael; or, know thyself. 18°. 40c........Am. S. S.

[H]azard, Rowland G. Two letters on causation and freedom in willing, addressed to J. S. Mill. 12°. $2........................Appleton; Lee & S.

— *Germ.* Zwei Briefe über Verursachung und Freiheit im Wollen, gerichtet an J. S. Mill; mit Anhang über d. Existenz d. Stoffes und unsere Begriffe d. unendlichen Raumes; a. d. Eng. 8°. '75. $2.50 .... *Westermann.*

[H]azard, S: Santo Domingo, past and present; with a glance at Hayti. maps and ill. cr. 8°. $3.50. *Harper.*

[H]azard, T: R. Blasphemy: who are the blasphemers? the "orthodox" Christians, or "spiritualists"? ('71.) 3d ed. 16°. '74. pap., 10c.......*Colby.*

— Eleven days at Moravia. ('71.) 2d ed. 16°. '74. pap., 10c..............................*Colby.*

— Mediums and mediumship. ('71.) 2d ed. 16°. '74. pap., 10c..............................*Colby.*

— (*ed.*) Spiritual communion tracts. 16°. '76. ea., pap., 10c..............................*Colby.*

[H]azard, Willis P. Art of pleasing: Am. ladies' and gentlemen's book of etiquette. 32°. 45c...*Porter.*

— The Jersey, Alderney and Guernsey cow: their history, nature and management. ill. 8°. '72. $1.50..................................*Porter.*

[H]azardous ground: drama. 16°. pap., 15c...*French.*

[H]azel, Harry (*pseud.*) *See* Jones, Justin.

[H]azel blossoms. Whittier, J. G. $1.50–$4..*Osgood.*

[H]azel farm. ('68.) New ed. ill. 18°. '75. 50c...*Hoyt.*

[H]azel Glen. 18°. 40c....................*Pres. Bd.*

[H]azeltine, Miron J. Brevity and brilliancy in chess. 12°. '66. $1........................*Appleton.*

— (*ed.*) Clipper chess problem tournament. 18°. $1. *De Witt.*

[H]azelton, Mabel (*pseud.*) *See* Rand, C. H.

[H]azelwood lib. 6 v. ill. 18°. $3 ....*Hoyt.*
Cont.: Robin. — George Rowland. — John Lennard. — Little Apple Blossom. — Hazel farm. — Nevers.

[H]azelwood lib. 8 v. 18°. $4.75........*Am. Bapt.*
Cont.: Horace Hazelwood. — One of our soldiers. — Patty Grant. — Confessions of a decanter. — Edward Lee, by M. D. Britts. — Henry Wilson. — Jeweled chain. — Willie and Lucy.

[H]azelwood ser. 4 v. ill. 16°. $6.....*Hoyt, F. & D.*
Cont.: Horace Hazelwood, etc. — Miss Matty, etc. — White roe of Glenmere, etc. — Found afloat, etc.

[H]azen, E: Euphonic spelling book and reader. 16°. bds., 19c. ....*Lippincott.*

— New speller and definer. 16°. hf. roan, 38c...*Lippincott.*

— Popular technology; or, professions and trades. 2 v. ill. 18°. $1.50 ....*Harper.*

— Speller and definer. 18°. bds., 25c...*Porter; Sheldon.*

[H]azen, Jac. A. Five years before the mast; [also] Paul Blake, by Alfred Elwes. ill. 12°. $1.50. *World Pub.*

[H]azen, Ma. Last sheaf. 16°. $1.25......*Cong. Pub.*

[H]azen, Ma. H. Tom Carroll; or, his place in the world. 16°. $1.25 ....*Cong. Pub.*

[H]azen, Ma. P. ["Mabel;" "Marion Haven."] Joanna; or, learning to follow Jesus. ill. 16°. '71. $1.25. *Crowell.*

— — *See also* Apron-strings lib.

— Mission school in Mill Village. ill. 16°. $1.15. *Bost. Am. Tr.*

— Mother's ship, and the cargo it brought. 16°. $1. *Cong. Pub.*

[H]azen, W. B. Our barren lands: interior of the U. S. west of the one-hundredth meridian, and east of the Sierra Nevada. 8°. '75. pap., 50c...*Clarke.*

— School and army in Germany and France; with diary of siege life at Versailles. 12°. $2.50....*Harper.*

[H]azlett, Helen. ["M. H. Tatem."] Glennair; or, life in Scotland. 12°. '69. $1.50......*Claxton.*

— Heights of Eidelberg. New ed. 12°. '70. $1.50. *Claxton.*

Hazlewood, Colin H. [Plays.] 14 v. 16°. ea., pap., 15c...................................*French.*
Cont.: Aurora Floyd. — Capitola. — Clock on the stairs. — Going to Cobham: farce. — Harvest storm. — Hop pickers and gipsies. — Jenny Foster. — Jessie Vere. — Lady Audley's secret. — Lizzie Lyle. — Marble bride. — Mother's dying child. — Poul a dhoil. — Return of the wanderer.

— Female detective: drama. 16°. pap., 15c...*De Witt.*

Hazlitt, W: Works. 5 v. 12°. '76. $7.50–$16.25. *Claxton.*

— Lectures on dram. literature of age of Elizabeth; [also] Characters of Shakespeare's plays. 12°. (Bohn.) $1.25.................*Little, B. & Co.*

— — *Same.* 12°. (Bohn.) $1.40...*Scribner, W. & A.*

— — *Same.* 12°. (Bohn.) $1.50........*Lippincott.*

— Lectures on the Eng. comic writers; [also] Lectures on the Eng. poets. 12°. (Bohn.) $1.25. *Little, B. & Co.*

— — *Same.* 12°. (Bohn.) $1.40...*Scribner, W. & A.*

— — *Same.* 12°. (Bohn.) $1.50........*Lippincott.*

— Life of Napoleon. 3 v. ill. 12°. $4.50–$13.50. *Lippincott.*

— Plain speaker: opinions on books, men and things. 12°. (Bohn.) $1.75............*Little, B. & Co.*

— *Same.* 12°. (Bohn.) $2..*Lippincott; Scribner, W. & A.*

— Round table: essays on literature, men and manners. 16°. $1.25..................*Scribner, W. & A.*

— *Same;* [also] Conversations of James Northcote; [also] Characteristics. 12°. (Bohn.) $1.75. *Little, B. & Co.*

— — — *Same.* 12°. (Bohn.) $2. *Lippincott; Scribner, W. & A.*

— Sketches and essays; [also] Winterslow. 12°. (Bohn.) $1.25................*Little, B. & Co.*

— — *Same.* 12°. (Bohn.) $1.40...*Scribner, W. & A.*

— Table talk: essays on men and manners. 12°. (Bohn.) $1.25................*Little, B. & Co.*

— *Same.* 12°. (Bohn.) $1.40......*Scribner, W. & A.*

— *Same.* 12°. (Bohn.) $1.50...........*Lippincott.*

— *See also* Shakespeare, W.; — Stoddard, R. H., Bric-a-brac ser.

He cometh not, she said. Thomas, A. 50c...*Harper.*

He's a lunatic. Dale, F. 15c.......*De Witt; French.*

He's overhead. 18°. 30c....................*Am. S. S.*

He knew he was right. *See* Trollope, Ant.

He lies like truth. Kimpton, F. 15c..........*French.*

He that overcometh. Boardman, W. E. $1.50..*Hoyt.*

He would be a gentleman. *See* Lover, S:

Head, *Sir* F. B. Life of Bruce, the African traveler. 18°. 75c..............................*Harper.*

Head, G: E. New system of fortifications. ill. 4°. '69. pap., $1........................ *Van Nostrand.*

Head, J. W. *See* Tennessee, Sup. Court reports.

Head, Ja. H. Home pastimes, or tableaux vivants. 12°. '60. $2...........................*Tilton.*

— Jewels from the quarry of the mind. 12°. $2.50. *H. A. Young.*

Head, Nelson (*ed.*) Daily walks with wise men; relig. exercises for every day. 12°. $1.75....*Harper.*

Head, *Mrs.* Thomasen. Evidences for heaven. 18°. 35c...................................*Pres. Bd.*

Head and heart. *See* Bell, C. D.; — Head and heart ser.

Head and heart enlisted against popery, under the banner of truth. 18°. '66. 60c. *N. Y. Ref. Ch. Bd.; Pres. Com.*

Head and heart ser. 12 v. 18°. $3..........*Nelson.*
Cont.: Head and heart, by C. D. Bell. — Ned, the shepherd boy, by C. D. Bell. — Way to be happy, by C. D. Bell. — Jenny's trials, by C. D. Bell. — Kitty's knitting needles. — Stories on the Lord's prayer. — Love thy neighbor. — Trust in God. — Wisdom's ways. — We love Him. — Moss rose, by P. B. Bowers. — Story of Ned, by C. D. Bell.

Head of the family. *See* Craik, D. M.

Head of the family. Emden, W. S. 15c.....*French.*

Headland, F. W. Action of medicines in the system. 6th Am. ed., rev. and enl. 8°. '74. $3..*Lindsay.*

Headlands of faith. Cross, J. $1.50...... *So. Meth.*
Headley, Jl. T. Adirondack; or, life in the woods. New ed., with map of Verplanck Colvin's survey of 1873. 12°. '75. $2............ *Scribner.*
— Chaplains and clergy of the revolution. ('61.) New ed. 12°. '76. $2............ *Scribner.*
— Farragut and our naval commanders. ('67.) New ed. ill. and por. 8°. '68. *$3.50; shp., $4.50; hf. cf., $5.50............ *Treat.*
— Grant, Sherman and their generals. [Eng. and Germ. ed.] ('65.) New ed. ill., maps and por. 8°. '67. *$3.50; shp., $4.50; hf. cf., $5.50....... *Treat.*
— Great rebellion. ill. roy. 8°. $5; — in 2 v., ea.,*$3.50; $4; hf. mor., $5............ *Am. Pub.*
— Great riots of N. Y. ill. cr. 8°. '73. $2..... *Treat.*
— Illustrated life of Washington; with an account of Mount Vernon, by B. J. Lossing. ill. roy. 8°. *$3.50; leath., $4............ *C. A. Nichols.*
— Imperial guard of Napoleon. 12°. $1.75.. *Scribner.*
— Letters from Italy, the Alps and the Rhine. 12°. $1.75............ *Scribner.*
— Life and times of Grant. ill. 8°. '68. *$2.50.. *Treat.*
— Life of Gen. H. Havelock. 12°. $1.75... *Scribner.*
— Life of Oliver Cromwell. 12°. $1.75..... *Scribner.*
— Lives of Winfield Scott and Andrew Jackson. 12°. $1.75............ *Scribner.*
— Miscellanies. 12°. $1.50............ *Scribner.*
— Napoleon and his marshals. ('65.) New ed. 2 v. in 1. por. 12°. '76. $2.50............ *Scribner.*
— Sacred heroes and martyrs. ('70.) New ed. ill. 8°. '72. *$3.50; $4; mor., $6............ *Treat.*
— Sacred mountains, characters and scenes in the Holy Land. ('65.) New ed. ill. 8°. '75. $2.. *Scribner.*
— Second war with England. 2 v. 12°. $3.50.. *Scribner.*
— Sketches and rambles. 12°. $1.50....... *Scribner.*
— Washington and his generals. ('58.) New ed. 2 v. in 1. por. 12°. '75. $2.50............ *Scribner.*
Headley, Phin. Camp. [Works.] 25 v. ill. 4°. ea., 25c.; 30c............ *J. E. Potter.*
Cont.: Altas of Palestine. — Apostles of Palestine. — Assassins of Hebrew hist. — Closing scenes in life of Jesus. — Devout women of Israel. — Early friends of Jesus. — Early life of Jesus. — Family scenes and sacrifices in Palestine. — First groves of Palestine. — First kings of Palestine. — First prophets of Palestine. — Jesus and the common people. — Jesus and his beloved disciple. — Labors of Jesus. — Magicians of Palestine. — Mordecai and Esther. — Palestine after the Messiah's advent. — Palestine under pagan kings. — Patriarchs of Palestine. — Prophet heroes of Palestine. — Spies and traitors of Hebrew hist. — Tent and town; or, human habitations of Palestine. — Traitors and assassins after Christ's advent. — Travels and ministry of Jesus. — Youth's illuminated Bible hist.
— Court and camp of David. ('68.) New ed. ill. roy. 8°. '76. $2.50. — (S.-school ed.) ('70.) New ed. ill. 16°. '76. $1.50............ *Hoyt.*
— Evangelists in the church, A. D. 35–1875. 12°. '75. $1.75............ *Hoyt.*
— Harvest work of the Holy Spirit ill. in labors of Rev. E. P. Hammond in Gt. Brit. and Am. ('62.) New ed. 16°. '75. $1.25............ *Hoyt.*
— Heroines of the Bible; or, the women of sacred history. 18°. '67. hf. bd., 15c............ *Hoyt.*
— Historical lib. 6 v. ill. 12°. ea., $1.50.... *Lee & S.*
Cont.: Island of fire. — Life of Empress Josephine. — Life of Napoleon. — Life of Mary, Queen of Scots. — Life of Lafayette. — Women of the Bible.
Heads and feet. 18°. 30c.; 40c............ *Am. Bapt.*
Heads and hearts. Robinson, F. W. 50c.... *De Witt.*
Heads and tails. Lippincott, S. J. $2......... *Ford.*
Heads or tails. Simpson, J. P. 15c......... *French.*
Headship of Christ. Miller, H. $1.50...... *Carter.*
Headsman. *See* Cooper, J. F.
Heady, Morrison. Seen and heard: poems or the like. 12°. '69. $1.50............ *Turnbull.*
Healey. Fothergill, J. 50c............ *Harper.*
Healing beams. 18°. pap., 10c............ *Dutton.*
Healing waters of Israel. Macduff, J. R. $1.25.. *Carter.*
Health and education. *See* Kingsley, C.
Health and its conditions. Hinton, J. $1.25.. *Putnam.*
Health at home. Hall, W. W. *$4; $5; $6.. *Betts.*
Health by good living. Hall, W. W. $1.50.. *Hurd & H.*
Health catechism. Trall, R. T. 10c.......... *Wells.*
Health, disease and remedy. Moore, G. 75c... *Harper.*
Health for household lib. 3 v. 12°. $5.25.. *Lippincott.*
Cont.: Advice to a wife, by P. H. Chavasse. — Advice and counsel to a mother, by P. H. Chavasse. — Ten laws of health, by J. R. Black.
Health fragments. Everett, G. H. *and* S. $2. *Somerby; Wood & H.*
Health hints: how to acquire bodily symmetry, health, vigor and beauty. 8°. '73. 50c...... (?) *Cowan.*
Health trip to the tropics. Willis, N. P. $1.75. *Scribner.*
Healthy Christian. Crosby, H. 50c.; 25c... *Am. Tr.*
Healthy houses. Eassie, W. $1.......... *Appleton.*
Healy, Ma. Lakeville; or, substance and shadow. [Fiction.] ill. 8°. $1.50; pap., $1.... *Appleton.*
— Summer's (A) romance: a novelette. 16°. '72. $1.50. *Roberts.*
Healy, T. W. *See* Nevada, Laws; Statutes.
Hear my prayer. Mendelssohn-Bartholdy, F. 40c. *Ditson.*
Heard, Franklin Fiske. Curiosities of the law reporters. 12°. $2............ *Lee & S.*
— *See also* Bennett, E. H., *and* Heard, F. F.; — Storer, H. R., *and* Heard, F. F.
Heard, I: V. D. History of the Sioux war and massacres of 1862–'63. ill. 12°. $1.75..... *Harper.*
Heard, J. B. Tripartite nature of man: spirit, soul and body. 3d ed. cr. 8°. $3.. *Scribner, W. & A.*
Hearn, C: W. The practical printer. 16°. $2.50. *Benerman.*
Hearn, J. A. Reflections on the passion of our Lord, in verse. 12°. '64. 75c......... *Kelly, P. & Co.*
Heart. *See* Tupper, M. F.
Heart and church divisions. *See* Asbury, F.
Heart and hand. Baker, S. $1.25....... *Randolph.*
Heart and its inmates. ill. 16°. '72. 90c......... *Hoyt.*
Heart and voice: hymn and tune book, for cong. sing. in Meth. Epis. Church. 8°. $2..... *Lippincott.*
Heart-blossoms for my little daughter. Cross, J. T. H. 40c............ *So. Meth.*
Heart breathings. Godwin, S. P. 75c. *Claxton; Lippincott.*
Heart echoes. Lewis, M. $1.25.......... *Turnbull.*
Heart echoes. Manville, H. A. $1; $1.25.... *Wells.*
Heart histories and life pictures. Arthur, T. S. $1.50. *J. E. Potter.*
Heart hungry. Westmoreland, M. J. $1.75.. *Carleton.*
Heart-life. Cuyler, T. L. 50c.; 75c.; $1.50.. *Am. Tr.*
Heart life in song. Marr, F. H. $1....... *Turnbull.*
Heart of Africa. Schweinfurth, G. 2 v. $8.. *Harper.*
Heart of the continent. Ludlow, F. H. $2.50; $3.75. *Hurd & H.*
Heart of Mid-Lothian. Dibdin, T. 15c....... *French.*
Heart of Mid-Lothian. *See* Scott, *Sir* W.
Heart strains of Christmas-tide: hymns, carols, etc. sm. 4°. '74. 50c............ *Tompkins.*
Heart-throbs of eminent authors. Browne, W. H. *$1.50; $2.50............ *Maclean.*
Heart to heart: hymns by author of "The old, old story." 18°. '72. 35c.; pap., 20c.... *Randolph.*
Heart treasure. Heywood, O. $1........ *Am. Bapt.*
Hearth and home. [Songs.] 4°. $2.25; bds., $1.75. *Peters.*
Hearthstone. Osgood, S. $1.50............ *Dutton.*
Hearthstone sketches. 18°. 45c......... *Cong. Pub.*
Heart's delight. Davis, C. E. K. $1.50....... *Hoyt.*
Hearts and faces. *See* Trowbridge, J. T.
Hearts and hands. Fisher, F. C. 50c...... *Appleton.*
Hearts and homes. Ellis, S. S. $2......... *Appleton.*

Hearts and voices. Sanders, H., *and* Grape, J. T. 10c. . . . . . *D. H. Carroll.*
Hearts of gold. Boyd, E. E. $1 . . . . . . *Meth. Epis.*
Heartsease. Yonge, C. M. $1.75 . . *Appleton; Macmillan.*
Heartsease. *See* Flower garlands for little gleaners.
Heartsease for the weary and worn. 18°. 50c. . . *Am. S. S.*
Heat as a mode of motion. Tyndall, J. $2 . . *Appleton.*
Heat as a source of power. Trowbridge, W. P. $3.50. *Wiley.*
Heath, Cp. Course of operative surgery; with pl. drawn by M. Léveillé. [To form 5 pts.] pts. 1, 2. imp. 4°. ea., $2.50 . . . . . . *Lindsay.*
— Injuries and diseases of the jaws. 2d ed., rev. ill. 8°. '72. $5 . . . . . . *Lindsay.*
— Manual of minor surgery and bandaging; with formulæ. ill. 16°. '76. $2 . . . . . . *Lindsay.*
— Practical anatomy: manual of dissections. New ed., ed. with add. by W. W. Keen. ill. roy. 12°. $3.50; leath., $4 . . . . . . *Lea.*
Heath, F. G. Fern paradise: a plea for the culture of ferns. 12°. $3 . . . . . . *Scribner, W. & A.*
Heath, R. B. *See* Patton, J. M., *and* Heath, R. B.; — Virginia, Special Court of Appeals reports.
Heath, S. *See* Maine, Sup. Court reports.
Heath, W. F. Grammar school trio: collection of three-part songs. 12°. pap., 10c. . . . . *Brainard.*
Heathen books and Christian tracts. 18°. 18c. . . *Am. S. S.*
Heathen Chinee. Harte, B. 25c. . . . . . *Osgood.*
Heathen sacrifices; [also] The Hindoo girl; [also] Little George. 18°. 25c. . . . . . *Pres. Bd.*
Heathens of the heath. McDonnell, W. $1.50. *D. M. Bennett; Mendum.*
Heaton, *Mrs.* C: [Juveniles.] 5 v. ill. sq. 12°. '70–'75. ea., $1.75 . . . . . . *Routledge.*
Cont.: Album for children. — Colored alb. for children. — Golden harp alb. — Nursery alb. — Sunday alb. for children.
— History of Albrecht Dürer of Nuernberg; with a tr. of his letters and journals, and account of his works. lith. and autotype ill. roy. 8°. $12 . . *Macmillan.*
— Life of Leonardo da Vinci; with essay on his scientific and literary works by C. C. Black, and account of his more important paintings and drawings. ill. roy. 8°. $12 . . . . . . *Macmillan.*
Heaton, W: Story of Robin Hood. ill. roy. 16°. $1.50. *Cassell.*
Heaven. Harbaugh, H. $1.25 . . . . . . *Ref. Ch. Pub.*
Heaven and hell. *See* Swedenborg, E.
Heaven and its Scripture emblems. Clark, R. W. $1.75 . . . . . . *J. E. Potter.*
Heaven and its wonders. *See* Swedenborg, E.
Heaven anticipated. McLeod, N. 35c. . . . . *Am. Tr.*
Heaven in song. Fish, H. C. $2.50; $6; $10 . . *Sheldon.*
Heaven opened. Winslow, O. $2 . . . . . . *Carter.*
Heaven our home. 16°. '63. $1.25 . . . . . . *Roberts.*
Heaven ser. 3 v. 16°. '63–'65. ea., $1.25 . . *Roberts.*
Cont.: Heaven our home. — Meet for heaven. — Life in heaven.
Heavenly birth. Logan, J. B. 25c. . . (?) *Cumberland.*
Heavenly dews. Llewellyn, E. V. C. $1.25 . . *Turnbull.*
Heavenly Father. Naville, E. $1.75 . . . . . . *Lee & S.*
Heavenly footman. *See* Bunyan, J.
Heavenly home. Harbaugh, H. $1.50 . . *Ref. Ch. Pub.*
Heavenly hymns for heavy hearts. 12°. 85c. . . *Pres. Bd.*
Heavenly Jerusalem. Burns, J. D. 50c. . . . . *Nelson.*
Heavenly land. Bernard *of Morlaix.* 75c. . . *Randolph.*
Heavenly life. Newton, A. L. $1.75 . . . . . . *Carter.*
Heavenly manna: texts for every day. 64°. '33. 15c.; 20c. . . . . . *Am. Tr.*
Heavenly places. Blackwood, S. A. 75c. . . *Willard.*
Heavenly recognition. Harbaugh, H. $1.25. *Ref. Ch. Pub.*
Heavenly watchwords. J., L. B. 55c. . . . . *Pres. Bd.*
Heavens and the earth. Milner, T. $1.25 . . . . *Nelson.*
Heavenward. Reimensnyder, J. B. 50c. . . *Luth. Bk. St.*
Heavenward: hymns and poems of consolation. post 8°. '67. $2.50; $3 . . . . . . *Randolph.*
Heavenward bound. Wadsworth, O. A. 90c. . . *Pres. Bd.*
Heavenward earthward. McKeever, H. B. $1.25. *Garrigues.*
Heavenward led. Jones, C. $1.25 . . . . . . *Porter.*
Heavenward paths for little feet; by author of "At Jesus' feet." 18°. '71. 90c. . . . . . *Dutton.*
Heavy yokes. Haderman, J. R. $1.50; 75c. *W. F. Gill.*
Heavysege, C: Saul: dram. poem. 16°. $2 . . * *Osgood.*
Hebberd, S. S. Secret of Christianity. 12°. $1.50. *Lee & S.*
Heber, B. Blue Beard: drama. 16°. pap., 15c. *French.*
Heber, Reg. Life. 18°. 45c.; 50c. . . . . . *Dutton.*
— Poetical works. (Handy vol. ed.) sq. 16°. $1.25; hf. cf., $2.50; mor., $3.50 . . . . . . *Miller.*
Hebraist's vade mecum: verbal index to Heb. and Chaldee Scriptures. demy 8°. (Bagster.) $6. *Wiley.*
Hebrew. *See* Jewish.
Hebrew characteristics; [compr.] Extracts from Jewish moralists, from Zung's Zur Geschichte und Literatur; Jewish marriages in post biblical times, by J. Perles; Interment of the dead in post bibl. Judaism, by J. Perles. 8°. '75. *$3 . . *Am. Jew.*
Hebrew customs; or, the missionary's return; by author of "Jane Scott's only son." 18°. 35c. *Am. S. S.*
— *Same.* 18°. '66. 40c. . . *N. Y. Ref. Ch. Bd.; Pres. Com.*
Hebrew-English Psalter. *See* Bible, Psalms.
Hebrew grammar, systematical and practical, with a chrestomathy; by S. Mannheimer, I. Mayer, S. Deutsch, J. H. Dessar and R. Felsenthal; with notes by I. Mayer. 16°. 50c. . . . . . *Bloch.*
Hebrew heroes. Tucker, C. 75c. . . . . . *Carter.*
Hebrew lawgiver. Lowrie, J. M. 2 v. $2.50 . . *Pres. Bd.*
Hebrew missionary. Cross, J. 65c. . . . . . *So. Meth.*
Hebrew prayers. *See* Daily prayers.
Hebrew student's manual. fp. 8°. (Bagster.) $4.25; hf. bd., $4.75 . . . . . . *Wiley.*
Hecht, Sim. Elementary exercises in Heb. grammar; with Eng. and Germ. notes. 16°. 35c. . . . *Bloch.*
— Jewish hymns for S.-schools and families. [In Eng. or Germ.] 12°. 35c. . . . . . *Frank.*
Hecker, F: Reden u. Vorlesungen. 12°. '72. pap., 50c. . . . . . *Witter.*
Hecker, I. T. Aspirations of nature. 4th ed., rev. 12°. $1.50 . . . . . . *Cath. Pub.*
— Questions of the soul. 12°. $1.50 . . . . . . *Cath. Pub.*
Hecker, J: Scientific basis of education: letters to Dept. of Public Instruction in N. Y. City. 2d ed. 8°. '66. $2.50 . . . . . . *Barnes.*
Heckpfennig (Der). *See* Gumpert, T. v.
Hector, *Mrs.* Annie F. ["*Mrs.* Alexander."] Her dearest foe. (Leis. hour ser.) 16°. '76. $1.25 . . *Holt.*
— Ralph Wilton's weird. (Leis. hour ser.) ('75.) New ed. 16°. '76. $1.25 . . . . . . *Holt.*
— Which shall it be? (Leis. hour ser.) ('74.) New ed. 16°. '76. $1.25 . . . . . . *Holt.*
— Wooing o't. (Leis. hour ser.) ('73.) New ed. 16°. '76. $1.25 . . . . . . *Holt.*
Hector O'Halloran. *See* Maxwell, W: H.
Hecuba. *See* Euripides.
Hedding, Elij. Special salvation. 18°. pap., 15c. *Meth. Bk. Conc.*
Hedge, F: H. German prepositions. 16°. '75. pap., 25c. . . . . . *Sever.*
— Primeval world of Hebrew tradition. 16°. '69. $1.50. *Roberts.*

Hedge, F: H., *continued.*
— Prose writers of Germany; with introd., biog. notices and tr. por. imp. 8°. '70. $5–$10.....*Porter.*
— Reason in religion. 16°. '75. $1.50.......*Roberts.*
Hedge, Levi. Logic. 12°. 75c..............*Mason.*
Hedge of thorns. 18°. 35c................*Am. S. S.*
Hedged in. Phelps, E. S. $1.50...........*Osgood.*
Hedgehog, and other stories. 24°. 25c...*Bost. Am. Tr.*
— *See also* Banner stories.
Hedgehog letters. *See* Jerrold, D.
Hedgerow-side lessons. 18°. 60c.........*Cong. Pub.*
Hedges, I: A. "Sorgo," the sugar of the north; or, the cultivation of sugar cane. ill. 12°. '62. 60c.; pap., 40c.........................*Pounsford.*
Hedges, *Mrs.* Ma. J. The white rose. ('74.) New ed. 12°. '75. $1.25...................*Nat. Temp.*
— Working and winning. ill. 16°. '72. 90c...*Am. Tr.*
Hedley, *Bp.* —. Spirit of faith; or, what must I do to believe? 18°. '75. 60c..............*Cath. Pub.*
Hedwig, *Queen of Poland. See* Sobieski, *and* Hedwig.
Hedwig: an hist. legend. 18°. 50c..........*O'Shea.*
Heenan, J. C. *See* Sayers, T., *and* Heenan, J. C.
Heerbrand, Jac. Kurzes Handbuch der christl. Glaubens- u. Sittenlehre. pts. 1-3. 8°. ea., pap., 30c. *Volkening.*
Heeren, A. H. L. School manual of anc. geog. 12°. 80c...............................*Putnam.*
Hefele, C: Jos. History of the Christian councils. v. 1, to 325; tr. and ed. by W. R. Clark. 8°. $6. *Pott; Scribner, W. & A.*
— *Same.* v. 2, 326–429; tr. and ed. by H. N. Oxenham. 8°. $6...........*Pott; Scribner, W. & A.*
Hegel, G: W. F. Lectures on philos. of hist.; tr. by J. Sibree. 12°. (Bohn.) $1.75..*Little, B. & Co.*
— *Same.* 12°. (Bohn.) $2. *Lippincott; Scribner, W. & A.*
Heidelberg. *See* James, G. P. R.
Heidelberg catechism. 24°. hf. bd., 15c. *Ref. Ch. Pub.*
— *Same.* 8°. 75c. 18°. per doz., $1.80. *N. Y. Ref. Ch. Bd.*
— *Same;* [also] Const. of Ref. Ch. in the U. S. 32°. 25c.; 40c.; hf. bd., 20c...........*Ref. Ch. Pub.*
— Triglott catechism of the Heid. catechism in Germ., Lat. and Eng.; with hist. introd. 4°. '63. $3.50. *Ref. Ch. Pub.; Scribner.*
— *Germ.* Heidelberger Katechismus. 18°. 20c. *N. Y. Ref. Ch. Bd.*
— *Same;* v. P. Schaff. 18°. 20c.; — mit Anmerkgn. 30c.; 40c.............................*Kohler.*
— *Same;* [also, Const. of Ref. Ch. in the U. S.] 32°. 40c..........................*Ref. Ch. Pub.*
— *See also* Palatinate catechism.
Heidenfeld, Thdr. E. [Phonetic readers.] 3 v. 8°. '75. bds.............................*Schmidt.*
Cont.: Phonetic primer and first reader, 30c. — Phon. second reader, 40c. — Phon. third reader, 80c.
Heidenmauer. *See* Cooper, J. F.
Heidner, F. W. Practical course of Germ. grammar and conversation. 12°. bds., 75c.......*Enderis.*
— *Same;* with read. exercises. 12°. bds., $1..*Enderis.*
— The school translator: easy Eng. and Germ. pieces, with vocab. 8°. bds., 35c. ....*Enderis.*
Heighway, O. W. T. Leila Ada, the Jewish convert. ('55.) 3d ed. 18°. '75. 75c...........*So. Meth.*
— *Same.* por. 12°. 80c....................*Pres. Bd.*
— *Same.* 12°. $1...........................*Wiley.*
— Leila Ada's relatives. 12°. $1............*Wiley.*
Heights of Eidelberg. Hazlett, H. $1.50...*Claxton.*
Heilig, G: W: *See* Bible, John.
Heilige Elisabeth (Die) v. Ungarn. 12°. 75c. *Benziger.*
Heilige Familie (Die). *See* Congregation of the Most Holy Redeemer.
Heilige Genovefa (Die). 12°. pap., 15c......*Radde.*
— *See also* Genovefa.

Heilige Kreuzweg (Der) Jesu Christi. 24°. pap., 10c. *Hoffmann.*
Heilsfülle (Die). Orwig, W. W. $1.50...*Ev. Assoc.*
Heilung (Die) der Eroberungssucht. *See* Van der Velde, K. F.
Heimath und Fremde: Romane u. Erzählungen. v. 1–43. 8°. ea., pap., 50c..............*Morwitz.*
Heimathsgrüsse aus Amerika: Sammlg. v. Gedichten Deutscher in Am. 16°. '70. bds., 40c...*Steiger.*
Heimkehr vom Himmel zur Erde. Schmidt, F. 40c. *F. W. Thomas.*
Hein, Jul. *See* United States, Const., *Germ.*
Heine, H: Werke. 6 v. 12°. ea., $2.......*Schäfer.*
Cont.: Buch der Lieder.—Reisebilder.—Romanzero; Wintermärchen. — Der Salon. — Vermischte Schriften, 2 v.
— Sämmtliche Werke. 7 v. 12°. $12–$10. *Kohler; Schäfer.*
— *Same:* wohlfeile Ausgabe. 7 v. $10; pap., $6; — in 40 nos. ea., pap., 15c.................*Schäfer.*
— Poems; tr. by E. A. Bowring. 12°. (Bohn.) $1.75. *Little, B. & Co.*
— *Same.* 12°. (Bohn.) $2..*Lippincott; Scribner, W. & A.*
— Book of songs; tr. by C. G. Leland. ('64.) New ed. 16°. '74. $1.50......................*Holt.*
— Immortellen; hrsg. v. A. Strodtmann. 12°. '72. $1.25; pap., 75c.......................*Zickel.*
— Letzte Gedichte u. Gedanken. 12°. '71. $1.25; pap., 75c...................................*Zickel.*
— Pearls from Heine; tr. by Furness, Bowring, Leland, Baskerville and others. ill. 4°. '75. 50c...*Holt.*
— Prose miscellanies; tr. by S. L. Fleischman. 12°. $1.50 ....*Lippincott.*
— Reisebilder. 12°. $1.50–$1.75.......*F. W. Thomas.*
— *Eng.* Pictures of travel; tr. by C. G. Leland. por. $1.50; hf. mor., $2...................*Kohler.*
— — *Same.* por. 12°. $1.50; mor., $3......*Schäfer.*
— Scintillations from prose works of H.; tr. by S. A. Stern; with biog. and crit. sketch. (Leis. hour ser.) ('73.) New ed. 16°. '74. $1.25..*Holt.*
Heinrich, der Matrosenknabe. 18°. 30c. ..*Ev. Assoc.*
Heinrich v. Eichenfels. *See* Schmid, C. v.
Heir at law. Colman, G., *jr.* 15c. ....*French.*
Heir at law; or, the victim of crime: sequel to "Maud, the maniac." 8°. pap., 25c............*De Witt.*
Heir expectant; by author of "Raymond's heroine." 8°. pap., 50c.........................*Harper.*
Heir of Gaymount. Cooke, J. E. 50c..... *Van Evrie.*
Heir of Malreward; or, restored; by author of "Son and heir." 8°. $1.50; pap., $1.....*Lippincott.*
Heir of Redclyffe. Yonge, C. M. $1.75. *Appleton; Macmillan.*
Heir of Wast-Wayland. Howitt, M. $1.50..*Harper.*
Heir to Ashley. Wood, E. P. $1.25; 75c...*Dick & F.*
Heiress. Stephens, A. S. $1.75; $1.50....*Peterson.*
Heiress in the family. Daniel, M. $1.75; $1.50. *Peterson.*
Heiress of Haughton. Marsh-Caldwell, A. 50c. *Harper.*
Heiress of Kilorgan. Sadlier, M. A. $1.25; $1.75. *Sadlier.*
Heiress of McGregor. Guernsey, L. E. $1.50..*Am. S. S.*
Heiress of the mount. Dunn, S. 30c......*Am. News.*
Heiress of Sweetwater: a love story. 12°. $1.75; pap., $1.50.........................*Peterson.*
Heirs of Derwentwater. Robinson, F. W. 50c...*De Witt.*
Heirs of the kingdom. Smith, M. S. 50c...*So. Meth.*
Heisch, P. I. Memoirs of J. G. Lavater. 18°. (Bagster.) $1.25 ....*Wiley.*
Heiskell, J. B. *See* Tennessee, Sup. Court reports.
Heisler, D. Y. Gift book for the million; or, life pictures of "The prodigal son." 12°. $1..*Ref. Ch. Bd.*
Heiss, M. The four Gospels, examined and vindicated on Catholic principles. 8°. '63. $1.20; pap., 80c...............................*Hoffmann.*

Held u. Kaiser. Meding, G. 2 v. ea., 50c... *Morwitz.*
Helen, *St.* *See* Lives of the saints.
Helen. Burnand, F. C. 15c............... *French.*
Helen. *See* Edgeworth, Mar.
Helen. *See* Euripides.
Helen and Arthur. Hentz, C. L. $1.75; $1.50.. *Peterson.*
Helen and her cousins; or, two months at Ashfield rectory. 18°. '72. 60c............... *Dutton.*
Helen and her sisters. *See* Aunty Lee lib.
Helen Arnold; or, the district school. 16°. 90c. *Am. S. S.*
Helen De Vere. Smith, J. F. 75c........ *Dick & F.*
Helen Egerton. Cezinski, M. $1.50...... *Am. Bapt.*
Helen Erskine. Robinson, M. H. $1.50.. *Lippincott.*
Helen Ethinger. Whittlesey, E. L. $1.50 .. *Claxton.*
Helen Ford. Alger, H., *jr.* $1.25.......... *Loring.*
Helen Freeman. F., L. A. 80c......... *J. A. Moore.*
Helen Gardner. Harland, M. $1.50....... *Carleton.*
Helen Harlow's vow. Waisbrooker, L. $1.25.. *Colby.*
Helen Heath. 18°. 40c. .... *Cong. Pub.*
Helen Lester. *See* Alden, *Mrs.* I. M.
Helen Lincoln. Capron, C. $1.50.......... *Harper.*
Helen MacGregor. Barlow, C. Y. $1.25.. *Garrigues.*
Helen Maurice; or, the daughter at home. 18°. '64. 60c. .... *Am. Tr.*
— *Same.* 18°. '66. 65c... *N. Y. Ref. Ch. Bd.; Pres. Com.*
— *Same.* 16°. $1........................ *Am. Bapt.*
Helen May. Doisy, L. $1.............. *Whittaker.*
Helen Mordaunt. Webb, J. B. $1.25..... *Routledge.*
Helen Morton's trial. 18°. 60c............. *Dutton.*
Helen Mulgrave; or, Jesuit executorship. 12°. $1.25. *De Witt.*
Helen of the glen. Pollok, R. 35c... *N. Y. Ref. Ch. Bd.*
Helen on her travels. Gage, W. L. $1.... *Hurd & H.*
Helen Spencer; or, home duties. 18°. 50c... *Cong. Pub.*
Helena Bertram. Richmond, D. $1...... *Routledge.*
Helena Butler. 18°. '66. 50c.......... *Cunningham.*
Helena's cloud with the silver lining; by author of "How Marjorie watched." 16°. '74. 90c. *Meth. Bk. Conc.*
Helena's household: tale of Rome in 1st century. ('67.) New ed. 12°. '76. $2................. *Carter.*
Helene; or, the children of love. 8°. pap., 25c. *Dick & F.*
Helen's adventures. 18°. 30c.; 40c....... *Am. Bapt.*
Helen's babies. Habberton, J. $1; 50c..... *Loring.*
Helen's fault. Marsh-Caldwell, A. 45c. .. *Routledge.*
Helen's lesson. T., E. C. 75c............. *Pres. Bd.*
Helen's music box. 18°. 30c................ *Dutton.*
Helen's portfolio: a lesson on faith. 18°. 17c.; 22c. *Am. Bapt.*
Helen's school days. 18°. 35c............ *Am. S. S.*
Helen's victory; by author of "Soldier Fritz." ill. 18°. '74. 50c................................ *Nelson.*
— *Same.* 16°. '75. 75c.................... *Lothrop.*
Helfenstein, Ja. Comparative grammar of the Teutonic languages: being [also] a hist. grammar of the Eng. lang. 8°. '70. $5........ *Macmillan.*
Helffenstein, Jac. The Saviour we need; with introd. by Rev. H. D. Ganse. 18°. 65c...... *Pres. Bd.*
— Why delay? 18°. 50c................... *Pres. Bd.*
Heliodorus *Emesenus*, Longus *and* Tatius, Achilles. Greek romances; tr. by R. Smith. 12°. (Bohn.) $1.75........................... *Little, B. & Co.*
— — — *Same.* 12°. (Bohn.) $2. *Lippincott; Scribner, W. & A.*
Hellebusch, B. H. F. Cantata Catholica: masses, vespers, litanies, hymns, etc., for the Cath. Church. obl. 4°. '76. hf. bd., $2.50.......... *Benziger.*
— Katholisches Gesang- u. Gebetbuch. 12°. $1. *Benziger.*

Hellebusch, B. H. F., *continued.*
— Requiem mass. 4°. 25c.................. *Church.*
— Vollständige Gesangschule. 12°. 50c.... *Benziger.*
Hellenbroek, A. Specimen of divine truths; for instruction of youth; tr. from the Dutch. 18°. per doz., $1.80.................. *N. Y. Ref. Ch. Bd.*
Hellwag, W. Tracé et profil en long du chemin de fer du Gothard; avec devis approximatif suivi d'un rapport sur les causes du surcroît des frais de construction des lignes tessinoises de plaine; tr. de l'allemand par E. Lauber. 2 v. f°. '76. pap., $12.................................... *Spon.*
Helm, Alfr. *See* Nevada, Sup. Court reports.
Helm, Ja. I. Life of Martha T. Sharp. ('48.) New ed. ill. 18°. '53. 35c.................. *Am. Tr.*
Helm, cross and sword. Lorraine, A. M. $1.75. *Cin. Meth. Bk. Conc.*
Helm Lodge; or, the object of life. 16°. 90c... *Am. S. S.*
Helme, Eliz. St. Clair of the Isles. 12°. pap., 25c. *Lippincott.*
Helmholtz, H. Mechanism of the ossicles of the ear and membrana tympani; tr. by A. H. Buck and N. Smith. ill. 8°. $1.25.............. *W. Wood.*
— Popular lectures on scientific subjects; tr. by E. Atkinson; with introd. by Prof. Tyndall. 12°. $2. *Appleton.*
Helmore, *Rev.* T: Ancient plain song of the church. sm. 4°. bds., 50c................. *W. H. Young.*
Helmuth, W. T. Surgery and its adaptation to homœop. practice. ill. 8°. shp., $3.50...... *Boericke.*
— System of surgery. 571 eng. 8°. '73. $10; shp., $11.50................................ (?) *Carle.*
Help by the way: a daily monitor. 32°. 50c... *Nelson.*
Help for Sunday school concerts. Folsom, A. P. *and* M. T. $1.............................. *Lothrop.*
Help heavenward. Winslow, O. 75c......... *Carter.*
Help of Christians. *See* Sisters of Mercy.
Help to the Acts of the apostles; adapted to lesson system of reading and teaching the Scriptures. 18°. 80c. .... *Am. S. S.*
Help to the Gospels. 18°. 70c............. *Am. S. S.*
Help to reading of the Bible. *See* Nicholls, B. E.
Help to a worthy reception of the Lord's supper; [also] Rules and instructions for a devout behavior in public worship. 18°. pap., 18c. — Rules, sep., pap., 10c.............................. *Dutton.*
Help to Zion's travellers. Hall, R. 90c.... *Am. Bapt.*
Helpful Nellie, and other stories. ill. fp. 8°. 50c. *Cassell.*
Helpful thoughts for young men. Woolsey, T. D. $1.25 .... *Lothrop.*
Helping hand. Somerset, P. 25c.......... *Barclay.*
Helping hand. Taylor, T. 15c. .... *French.*
Helping hand for town and country. Draper, L. C., *and* Croffut, W. A. *$4.25; $5...... *Wilstach.*
Helping hand series. *See* Nowell, H. P. H.
Helping mamma. *See* Swallow stories.
Helpless Christie; or, Earnest's Bible verses. 18°. 45c. *Am. S. S.*
Helps, *Sir* Arth. Brassey's life and labors. por. and maps. 8°. '74. $2.50................ *Roberts.*
— Brevia: short essays and aphorisms. 16°. '70. $1.50. *Roberts.*
— Casimir Maremma. 16°. '70. $2........ *Roberts.*
— Companions of my solitude. 16°. '70. $1.50.. *Roberts.*
— Conversations on war and general culture. 12°. '70. $1.50 .... *Roberts.*
— Essays written in the intervals of business. 16°. '70. $1.50 .... *Roberts.*
— Friends in council. 2 v. 12°. $4; hf. cf., $8. — (Household ed.) 4 v. 12°. $5; hf. cf., $10; mor., $15 .... *Miller.*
— Ivan DeBiron; or, the Russian court in middle of last cent. [Fiction.] cr. 8°. '74. $2.25... *Roberts.*

Helps, *Sir* Arth., *continued.*
— Life of Hernando Cortes. 2 v. in 1. maps. 12°. '71. $2 .... *Putnam.*
— Oulita, the serf: tragedy. 18°. '74. $1.75 .. *Routledge.*
— Realmah. [Fiction.] 16°. '69. $2 ...... *Roberts.*
— *Same.* New [chp.] ed. cr. 8°. '69. $3 .. *Macmillan.*
— Social pressure. 12°. '75. $2.25 .... *Roberts.*
— Some talk about animals and their masters. 12°. '73. $1.75 .... *Routledge.*
— Spanish conquest in Am., and its rel. to hist. of slavery, and government of colonies. 4 v. large 12°. ea., $1.50 .... *Harper.*
— Thoughts upon government. 8°. '72. $2.25 .. *Roberts.*
Helps and hindrances to the cross. *See* Baker, *Mrs.* H. N. W.
Helps at the mercy seat. [Prayers.] sq. 24°. $1.50. *Hoyt, F. & D.*
Helps for every hour: texts. 48°. '46. 15c. *Meth. Bk. Conc.*
— *Same.* 18°. 22c.; 40c.; 50c. .... *Am. S. S.*
Helps for the quiet hour. 4 v. 24°. $7 .... *Randolph.*
Cont.: Hymns of the church on earth. — Ore from precious mines. — Pearls of thought. — Shadow of the rock.

Helps over hard places. *See* Peebles, *Mrs.* M. L.
Helps to every day holiness. Rose, A. C. 50c. *Palmer.*
Helps to a life of prayer. Manning, J. $1.25 ... *Lee & S.*
Helps to prayer. Kidder, D. P. $3.50 .. *Meth. Bk. Conc.*
Helps to the pulpit: sketches and skeletons of sermons. 12°. $2 .... *Sheldon.*
Helvétius, C. A. Two letters on Montesquieu's Spirit of laws. *See* Destutt de Tracy, A. L. C.
Helvetius. Arian, C. 20c. .... *Mendum.*
Hem of his garment. Sewall, F. $1.50 .. *Lippincott.*
Hem-stitched handkerchief. *See* Leighton children.
Hemans, *Mrs.* Felicia Dorothea. Poetical works. cr. 8°. $1.50. — ill. 8°. $3–$7.50 ...... *Lippincott.*
— *Same.* ('35.) New ed. 8°. '76. $2.25; $2.75; mor., $5. — roy. 8°. mor., $7.50 .... *Claxton.*
— *Same.* (Chandos classics.) cr. 8°. $1; pap., 75c. *Scribner, W. & A.*
— *Same.* (Globe ed.) 2 v. ill. 16°. $2.50; hf. cf., $6.50; mor., $8 .... *Appleton.*
— *Same.* (Household ser.) ill. and por. 16°. $1.50; mor., $3 .... *Lee & S.*
— *Same.* (Presentation poets.) ill. 16°. $1.75; $3; mor., $3.50 .... *Routledge.*
— *Same;* with life. por. 8°. (Dick.) 80c.; pap., 40c. *Am. News.*
— *Same;* with memoir, notes, etc. (Chandos poets.) por. and ill. cr. 8°. $3.75; cf., $7.50; mor., $8 .... *Scribner, W. & A.*
— *Same;* ed. by Mrs. Sigourney. ill. 8°. shp., $4.50; mor., $10 .... *Mason.*
— — *Same.* 8°. shp., $3.50; mor., $10 ... *Appleton.*
— — *Same.* (Boston ed.) 8°. $2.50; shp., $3.50; mor., $10 .... *Lee & S.*
— *Same;* with essay by H. T. Tuckerman. ill. 12°. $1.50 .... *World Pub.*
— Poems. 12°. $1.50 .... *Locke.*
— *Same.* (Blue and gold ed.) 18°. $1.25 .. *Nichols & H.*
— *Same.* (Boston ed.) 8°. shp., $4.50; mor., $10. *Mason.*
— *Same.* (Cabinet ed.) 16°. $1.50 ..... *Nichols & H.*
— *Same.* (Scribner's pop. poets.) ill. 12°. $1.50. *Scribner, W. & A.*
— *Same;* with essay by H. T. Tuckerman; ed. by R. W. Griswold. ill. roy. 24°. 75c. ... *Lippincott.*
— *Same;* ed. by Rev. R. A. Willmott; with biog., etc. (British poets.) ill. 12°. $2.25; hf. cf., $3.50; mor., $5 .... *Routledge.*
— *Same;* [also] Poems by W. Wordsworth. ill. 16°. $1.12; $1.35. — 32°. 85c.; $1.12 .... *World Pub.*
— Domestic affection. ill. 32°. 38c. .... *Appleton.*
— Songs of the affections: sel. from works. 32°. 35c.; pap., 10c. .... *U. P. James.*

Hemenway, Abby Mar. Poets and poetry of Vermont. 8°. $1.50 .... *Tuttle.*
— (*ed.*) Historical gazetteer of Vermont. 3 v. 8°. $18; ea., hf. mor., $7 .... *Claremont.*
Hemlands-sånger. *See* Swenska Lutherska Tryckföreningen.
Hemlock Ridge; or, only Dan White's son. ('60.) New ed. ill. 18°. '69. 55c. .... *Hoyt.*
Hemlock swamp. *See* Whittlesey, E. L.
Hemmed in. Stewart, J. C. 15c. .... *De Witt.*
Hemmenway, J: (*ed.*) Daily remembrancer on peace and war. 32°. '75. 75c. .... *Peace.*
Hemmerlein, H. Progressive organ pieces. f°. '67. pap., $1.75 .... *Ditson.*
Hemming, G. W. Elementary treatise on differential and integral calculus. 2d ed. 8°. $3 .. *Macmillan.*
Hempel, C: Jul. Complete repertory of the homœop. materia medica. 8°. hf. mor., $6 ..... *Boericke.*
— Homœopathic domestic physician. 18°. 50c. *Boericke.*
— *French.* 18°. 75c. .... *Boericke.*
— *Germ.* 18°. 75c. .... *Boericke.*
— New and comprehensive system of materia medica and therapeutics; arranged upon a physiol.-patholog. basis. [Hom.] 2d ed., rev. and enl. 2 v. roy. 8°. hf. mor., $12 .... *Boericke.*
— Organon of specific homœop.; or, an inductive exposition of the principles of the hom. healing art. 8°. hf. mor., $1 .... *Boericke.*
— Science of homœopathy: crit. and synthet. index of doct. of the hom. school. 8°. $1.75 ... *Boericke.*
— *See also* Gray, J. F., *and* Hempel, C. J.; — Schiller, J. F. v.
— *and* Beakley, J. Homœopathic theory and practice; with hom. treatment of surg. diseases. 4th ed. 8°. hf. mor., $3.50 .... *Boericke.*
Hemsley, W. B. Handbook of hardy trees, shrubs and herbaceous plants; based on the French work of Decaisne and Naudin; with introd. by E. S. Rand, jr. ill. 8°. '73. $7.50 .... *Estes.*
Hemyng, Bracebridge. Dick Lightheart ser. 3 v. 8°. ea., $1.50; bds., 75c. .... *Am. News.*
Cont.: Scapegrace of the school; or, adventures of Dick Lightheart. — Scapegrace at sea; or, adventures of D. L. after leaving school. — Scapegrace of London; or, concluding adventures of D. L. ashore.
— Jack Harkaway after school days, afloat and ashore. ill. 8°. $1.50; bds., 75c. .... *Am. News.*
— Jack Harkaway among the brigands. ill. 8°. $1.50; bds., 75c. .... *Am. News.*
— Jack Harkaway and his son's adventures around the world. ill. 8°. 75c. .... *Am. News.*
— Jack Harkaway at Oxford. ill. 8°. $1.50; bds., 75c. *Am. News.*
— Jack Harkaway's school-days. ill. 8°. $1; bds., 50c. *Am. News.*
Hen and chickens. 32°. 20c.; 15c. .... *Dutton.*
Henck, J: B. Field-book for railway engineers. 12°. $2.50 .... *Appleton.*
Henderson, Eb. Commentaries on the minor prophets; with biog. sketch of author by E. P. Barrows. ('59.) New ed. 8°. '68. $3.50 .... *Draper.*
— Commentary on Ezekiel; tr. from orig. Heb. 8°. '70. $2 .... *Draper.*
— Commentary on Jeremiah and Lamentations; tr. from orig. Heb. 8°. '68. $2.50 .... *Draper.*
— Syriac lexicon to New Test. post 8°. (Bagster.) $1.25; hf. bd., $1.75 .... *Wiley.*
Henderson, Ja. Life. 16°. 75c. .... *Carter.*
Henderson, J: Handbook of grasses of Gt. Brit. and Am. 12°. $1.50 .... *Judd.*
Henderson, Jla. Putnam. ["Theta."] Annie Balfour and her friends; or, influence and how to use it. 16°. '70. $1.25 .. *N. Y. Ref. Ch. Bd.; Pres. Com.*
— Miss Mary and her scholars; or, the Lord's prayer illustrated and explained. ill. 16°. '71. 75c. *N. Y. Ref. Ch. Bd.; Pres. Com.*

Henderson, N. P. Test words in Eng. orthography. ('69.) New ed. 18°. '76. bds., 25c...*Clark & M.*

Henderson, P: Gardening for pleasure. ill. 12°. $1.50. *Judd.*

— Gardening for profit. ill. 12°. $1.50.........*Judd.*

— Practical floriculture. ill. 12°. $1.50........*Judd.*

Henderson, T. S. The good teacher: manual for S.-school teachers. 16°. 90c...........*Am. Bapt.*

Henderson, T: Comprehensive grammar of the Eng. lang. 12°. hf. bd., 25c.............*Lippincott.*

Henderson, W. Inquiry into the homœop. practice of medicine; [also] Homœopathy, allopathy and young physic, by J. Forbes; [also] Letter to J. Forbes, by W. Henderson. 8°. $1....*Boericke.*

Henderson, W. C. Common-sense in the kitchen; or, healthy cooking and family receipt book. ill. 12°. $1.50........................*World Pub.*

Henderson, W. J. *See* Marquand, F. A., Markoe, F. H., *and* Henderson, W. J.

Hendryx, Warren B. The teacher, the class and the book: series of 52 Sunday school lessons. 18°. 75c.; hf. bd., 50c.......................*Chase.*

Heness, Thdr. Der Leitfaden; or, guide for the instruction in German without gram. and dict. ('75.) New ed. 12°. '76. $1.50...........*Schoenhoff.*

Hengstenberg, Ern. W: Works; tr. from the Germ. 14 v. 8°. ea., $3............*Scribner, W. & A.*

Cont.: Christology of the Old Test., 4 v. — Comment. on Ecclesiastes — on Ezekiel — on Psalms, 3 v. — on Gospel of John, 2 v. — Dissertations on the genuineness of Daniel and the integrity of Zechariah. — History of the kingdom of God under the Old Test., 2 v.

— Commentary on Ecclesiastes, with other treatises; tr. by D. W. Simon. 8°. '60. $3..*Smith, E. & Co.*

Hening, W: Waller. American pleader and lawyer's guide. 2 v. 8°. '11-'26. shp., $10..*J. W. Randolph.*

— Virginia justice. 8°. '25. shp., $2..*J. W. Randolph.*

— *See also* Virginia, Court of Appeals and Court of Chancery reports; Statutes.

Henkel, D: Answer to Joseph Moore, the Methodist; with a few fragments on doct. of justification. 12°. '25. 75c.........................*Henkel.*

— Treatise on person and incarnation of Christ, in which some arguments of the Unitarians are examined. 12°. '30. 65c.........................*Henkel.*

Henkeldukaten. *See* Hoffmann, F.

Henkle, M. M. Analysis of principles of church government, particularly of Meth. Episc. Ch. 18°. '57. 65c..............................*So. Meth.*

— Platform of Methodism. 12°. '55. $1.50..*So. Meth.*

Henkle, W. D. Test spelling-book. 16°. '72. 35c. *Wilson, H. & Co.*

— *See also* Stoddard, J. F., *and* Henkle, W. D.

Henn, P. *See* Ahn, F., French ser.; German ser.

Hennen, W: D. Digest of Louisiana reports [Superior Court of Orleans, Court of Errors and Appeals and Supreme Court of L.]; from 1st Martin to 15th Louisiana annual. 2 v. 8°. '61. shp., $16.................................*Hurd & H.*

Hennequin, Alfr. Treatise on the French verbs. 12°. '74. 90c..............................*Ivison.*

Hennessy, W. J. (*ill.*) *See* Winter, W., Booth in twelve dram. characters.

Henning, C: Practical instruction for the violin; with Germ. and Eng. text. 3 v. f°. '69. pap., v. 1, 3, ea., $2.50; 2, $1.50.................*Ditson.*

Henninges, R. E. Spring. [Cantata.] obl. 8°. 40c. *Brainard.*

Henny Penny. [Toy-book.] ill. 4°. $1; 50c. *Routledge.*

Henny Penny picture-book. demy 4°. '72. $2.50. *Routledge.*

Henri and the wolves. 18°. 17c.; 22c.....*Am. Bapt.*

Henrich, A. Wem haben wir unsere Religionsfreiheit zu verdanken? pap., 15c.....*Germ. Bapt.*

Henrich's struggles. 18°. 35c...........*Cong. Pub.*

Henrici, Olaus. Skeleton structures, especially in their applic. to building of steel and iron bridges. pl. and diagrams. 8°. '67. $1.50..*Van Nostrand.*

Henrietta. 18°. pap., 12c.................*O'Shea.*

Henrietta: drama. 16°. pap., 15c..........*French.*

Henrietta; [also] Gretchen. 18°. 30c.......*O'Shea.*

Henrietta and the ayah. 18°. 35c........*Routledge.*

— *See also* Moss wreath lib.

Henrietta Temple. Disraeli, B. 50c.......*Appleton.*

Henriette Sontag. Dilthey, K. 75c.; 50c....*Steiger.*

Henry, *St.* *See* Lives of the saints.

Henry *of Huntingdon.* Chronicle of the hist. of Eng. [to 1485]; tr. and ed. by T. Forester. 12°. (Bohn.) $1.75.................*Little, B. & Co.*

— *Same.* 12°. (Bohn.) $2..*Lippincott; Scribner, W. & A.*

Henry, Clb. Sprague. About men and things: papers from my study-table drawer. 12°. '73. $1.50. — New ed. 12°. '76. pap., 75c.......*Whittaker.*

— Considerations on some of the elements and conditions of social welfare and human progress. 12°. $1.25............................*Appleton.*

— Dr. Oldham's talk at Greystones. New ed. 12°. '72. $1.50..................................*Dutton.*

— Epitome of hist. of philos. 2 v. 18°. $1.50..*Harper.*

— Household liturgy; or, order of daily prayer for families. 18°. '73. 50c................*Whittaker.*

Henry, Guy V. Military record of civilian appointments in U. S. army. 2 v. 8°. '73. $10. *Van Nostrand.*

Henry, H. A. Class book for Jewish youth; [incl.] abridg. hist. of the Bible. 12°. 65c.....*Frank.*

Henry, H. L. Little Ada; or, the three New Years. ill. 18°. '71. $1.....................*Claxton.*

Henry, J. T. Early and later hist. of petroleum; with facts in regard to its development in west. Penn., etc. 8°. '73. $4.50; shp., $5......(?)*Rodgers.*

Henry, Ja. Sketches of Moravian life and character. pl. 12°. $1.75........................*Lippincott.*

Henry, L: (*pseud.*) *See* Lewis, A. H.

Henry, Ma. H. ["Howe Benning."] Essie's journey, and what she found in it. 16°. 75c...*Cong. Pub.*

— Grace Courtney; or, seeking the shepherd. ill. 16°. '71. $1.15...........................*Crowell.*

— — *See also* Posie ser.

— Nix's offerings. ill. 16°. '73. $1.50.......*Crowell.*

— — *See also* Lettie Sterling ser.

Henry, Mat. Bible manual: sel. of Scripture, with classification of text by Rev. W. W. Everts. 12°. $2.............................*Sheldon.*

— Commentary on Old and New Test. New ed., with add. notes, crit., hist. and geog.; with life of author. 3 v. ill. demy 4°. $30.........*Cassell.*

— *Same.* 5 v. 4°. '76. shp., $25.—9 v. 8°. $27..*Carter.*

— Commentary on the Psalms. 12°. (Bohn.) $1.50. *Little, B. & Co.*

— *Same.* 12°. (Bohn.) $1.80......*Scribner, W. & A.*

— *Same.* 12°. (Bohn.) $2..............*Lippincott.*

— Communicant's companion. 18°. 60c.......*Carter.*

— *Same;* with introd. by Rev. J. Brown. por. 12°. 90c..................................*Pres. Bd.*

— Memoirs of Mrs. A. Hutton and Mrs. E. Radford. *See* Williams, *Sir* J. B., Memoirs of Mrs. S. Savage.

— Method for prayer. 18°. 65c...........*Pres. Bd.*

— On meekness. 18°. '36. 40c..............*Am. Tr.*

— *See also* Comprehensive comment. on the Bible; — Hall, H., Gems of thought.

Henry, Ph. Christ all in all to believers. 18°. 75c. *Pres. Bd.*

Henry, *Mrs.* Sarepta M. I. After the truth. 3 pts. 12°. ea., $1.25............*Cin. Meth. Bk. Conc.*

Cont.: Finding. — Teaching. — Using.

— Victoria, with other poems. 16°. $1. *Cin. Meth. Bk. Conc.*

Henry, T: Charlton. Letters to an anxious inquirer; with biog. sketch. por. 18°. 65c......*Pres. Bd.*

Henry IV., V., VI., VIII. *See* Shakespeare, W.

Henry VIII. Mundt, C. M. $1.50; pap., $1; hf. cf., $3.50 ....*Appleton.*

Henry and Bessie. Prentiss, E. $1......*Randolph.*

Henry and the bird's nest. 18°. 18c........*Am. S. S.*

Henry and his bearer. Sherwood, M. M. 30c...*Am. S. S.*

Henry Arden. Martel, C. $1..........*Perkinpine.*

Henry Ashton. Alden, J. 50c. ....*Lee & S.*

Henry Burney. Bradshaw, C. A. 50c.....*Pres. Bd.*

Henry Burton; or, the reward of patience. ill. post 18°. 75c....................*Scribner, W. & A.*

Henry Courtland. Cline, A. J. $1.75....*Lippincott.*

Henry Curran. 18°. 20c.; 25c...........*Am. Bapt.*

Henry Day learning to obey Bible commands. Phelps, P. H. 90c. ....*Thompson.*

Henry Day's story books. Phelps, P. H. 90c. *Thompson.*

Henry De La Tour. Smith, J. F. 75c. ....*Dick & F.*

Henry Dunbar. Braddon, M. E. 50c. .....*Dick & F.*

Henry Dunbar. Taylor, T. 15c....*De Witt; French.*

Henry Esmond. *See* Thackeray, W. M.

Henry Granden. Bingham, F. L. 15c........*Ames.*

Henry Hilliard; or, the three college friends. 18°. 65c.; 75c...............................*Am. Bapt.*

Henry Langdon. Hopkins, L. P. 55c.........*Hoyt.*

Henry Masterton. James, G. P. R. $1.50..*Harper.*

Henry Maynard trying to get out of debt. *See* Aunt Hattie's stories.

Henry Maynard's account book; — book of thanks. *See* Aunt Hattie's stories.

Henry Minturn; or, my dark days. ('60.) New ed. ill. 18°. '74. 55c. ....*Hoyt.*

Henry Morgan. Horsburgh, M. 50c....(?)*Martien.*

Henry Morris; or, living for an object. 18°. 60c. *Am. S. S.*

Henry of Eichenfels. 18°. 35c.; 40c........*Dutton.*
— *See also* Yonge, C. M., "Star of hope" ser.

Henry of Guise. James, G. P. R. $1.50....*Harper.*

Henry Powers, banker. Kimball, R. B. $1.75..*Carleton.*

Henry Roberts. Weston, M. D. 40c......*Cong. Pub.*

Henry St. John. Cooke, J. E. $1.50.......*Harper.*

Henry Smeaton. James, G. P. R. 50c. ....*Harper.*

Henry Willard; or, value of right principles; by author of "Edward Clifford." ill. 18°. '58. 85c...*Dodd.*

Henry Wilson; or, the society Bible. 18°. 35c.; 45c. *Am. Bapt.*

Henry Wilson's voyage; or, only in fun. 18°. 55c. *Am. S. S.*

Henry Wood; or, the first step in the downward road. 18°. 50c.................................*Am. S. S.*

Henry's birthday; or, beginning to be a missionary. sq. 12°. '55. 60c. ....*Meth. Bk. Conc.*

Hensel, Octavia. Life and letters of L. M. Gottschalk. 12°. '70. $1.50............................*Ditson.*

Henshaw, H. W. Report upon ornithol. coll. *See* United States, *Corps of Eng.*

Henshaw, J: P. K. Life. 18°. 55c.; 60c...*Dutton.*

Henshaw, Marshall. Analysis of the Greek verb. obl. 4°. $1.50..................*Potter, A. & Co.*

Henslow, G: Theory of evolution of living things, and the application of the principles of evolution to religion. cr. 8°. '73. $2.50......*Macmillan.*

Hentz, Caro. Lee. [Novels.] 13 v. 12°....*Peterson.*

Cont.: Aunt Patty's scrap bag, $1.50; pap., 75c. — Banished son. — Courtship and marriage. — Eoline; or, Magnolia Vale. — Ernest Linwood. — Helen and Arthur. — Linda. — Lost daughter. — Love after marriage. — Marcus Warland. — Planter's northern bride. — Rena; or, the snow bird. — Robert Graham, *ea.*, $1.75; pap., $1.50.

— Flowers of elocution. 12°. $1.50.........*Desilver.*

Hentz, N: Marcellus. Spiders of the U. S.; ed. by E. Burgess, with notes by J. H. Emerton. ill. 8° '75. $3.50; pap., $3.......*Bost. Soc. Nat. Hist*

Henze, Adph. Schönschreib-Hefte, nach d. deutschen Preis National Handschrift. 9 nos. obl. 8°. ea. pap., 10c...................................*Siemon*

— *Same.* 9 nos. obl. 8°. '74. per doz., pap., 90c...*Steiger*

— *Same;* in Eng. script. 6 nos. obl. 8°. '74. per doz. pap., 90c. ....*Steiger*

Heop, D. P. Report of reconnoissance of basin of Upper Yellowstone. *See* United States, *Corp of Eng.*

Hepburn, A. D. Manual of Eng. rhetoric. 12°. '75 $1.25 ....*Wilson, H. & Co*

Hepburn, Alice. Pollie and Jack. ill. 12°. $1.25. *Nelson*

Hepburn, H. P. *See* California, Sup. Court reports.

Hepburn, Ja. Curtis. Japanese-Eng. and Eng.-Jap dict. 16°. '74. $3..................*Randolph*

Heptameron. *See* Margaret d'Angoulême.

Hepworth, *Mrs.* G. H. ["Una Savin."] Little gentleman in green: Am. fairy story. 18°. 75c...*Loring*

Hepworth, *Rev.* G: H. Christ and his church: sermons. 8°. pap., 25c................*Appleton*

— Rocks and shoals: lectures to young men. 16°. '70 60c. ....*Am. Unit*

Her dearest foe. Hector, A. F. $1.25.........*Holt*

Her face was her fortune. Robinson, F. W. 50c. *Harper.*

Her lord and master. Marryat, F. 50c......*Harper*

Her majesty the queen. Cooke, J. E. $1.50..*Lippincott.*

Her majesty's tower. Dixon, W. H. $2..*Lippincott.*

Her mother's Fancy. Hall, T. O. $1...... *Whittaker.*

Her waiting heart. Capsadell, L. $1.25....*Authors.*

Heraclidæ. *See* Euripides.

Herald picture books. *See* Sheeleigh, M.

Herbert, G: Works in prose and verse; ed. by R. A. Willmott. ill. 16°. $1.75...........*Routledge.*

— Poetical works. (Globe ed.) 16°. $1.25; hf. cf., $3.25; mor., $4......................*Appleton.*

— *Same;* [also] The synagogue, by C. Harvey; with introd. by J. Nicol, and text ed. by C. C. Clarke. 16°. '72. $1.50......................*Putnam.*

— Poems. ill. sm. 4°. '70. $4.50; mor., $8..*Dutton.*

— *Same;* with memoir by R. A. Willmott. por. 18°. $1...*Osgood.*

— — *Same.* (British poets.) ill. 12°. $2.25; hf. cf., $3.50; mor., $5.......................*Routledge.*

— — *Same.* (Household ser.) ill. 16°. $1.50; mor., $3..*Lee & S.*

— Life. 18°. 85c.; 90c.......................*Dutton.*

Herbert, G: Rob. C: [*Earl of Pembroke*], *and* Kingsley, G. H. South sea bubbles; by the earl and the doctor. 12°. $1.50..............*Appleton.*

Herbert, H: W: ["Dinks"; "Fk. Forester."] Deer stalkers. ill. 12°. pap., 75c..........*Peterson.*

— Fair Puritan (The): hist. romance of New Eng. in the days of witchcraft. 12°. $1.50..*Lippincott.*

— Fish and fishing of the U. S. and Brit. provinces of N. Am. 12th ed. ill. post 8°. $3.50..*Woodward.*

— Frank Forester's Am. game in its seasons. ill. 12°. $3 ....*Woodward.*

— Frank Forester's complete manual for young sportsmen, of fowling, fishing and field sports. post 8°. $3 ....*Woodward.*

— Frank Forester's field sports of the U. S. and Brit. provinces of N. Am. 14th ed., rev. ill. post 8°. $6 ....*Woodward.*

— Frank Forester's sporting scenes and characters. 2 v. ill. 12°. $4.......................*Peterson.*

— Hints to horse-keepers. 12°. $1.75.........*Judd.*

— Horse and horsemanship of the U. S. and Brit. provinces of N. Am. New ed., enl. by S. D. and B. G. Bruce. 2 v. ill. roy. 8°. $10...... *Woodward.*

— My shooting box. ill. 12°. pap., 75c......*Peterson.*

Herbert, H: W: *continued.*
— Quorndon hounds. ill. 12°. pap., 75c..... *Peterson.*
— The Roman traitor. 12°. $1.75; pap., $1.50.. *Peterson.*
— Warwick woodlands. ill. 12°. pap., 75c... *Peterson.*
— *and* Mayhew, E., *and* Hutchinson, W. N. The dog: instructions [on his] breeding, rearing, breaking, kennelling, etc. ill. post 8°. $3.... *Woodward.*
Herbert, Lucian. Das Testament Peter des Grossen. [Fiction.] 8°. pap., 50c.............. *Morwitz.*
Herbert, Ma. Eliz. (*Lady*). Cradle lands: Egypt, Syria, Palestine, Jerusalem, etc. 4th ed. ill. 12°. '69. $2.......................... *Cath. Pub.*
— Impressions of Spain. 3d ed. ill. 12°. '69. $2. *Cath. Pub.*
— Love. 16°. 75c.; $1.25.................. *Sadlier.*
— Three phases of Christian love: the mother, the maiden and the religious. 5th ed. 12°. '66. $1.50.................................. *Cath. Pub.*
Herbert, Sa. A. F. ["Herb. Newbury."] May Bell. ill. 16°. '69. $1.50.................. *Lothrop.*
— Trust; or, Eaton parsonage. 18°. '66. 60c... *Randolph.*
— Weakness and strength; or, out of the deep. 18°. '67. 70c.......................... *Pres. Bd.*
Herbert. *See* Charlesworth, *Mrs.* M. L.
Herbert. Samuels, S. B. C. 75c.......... *Lee & S.*
Herbert Atherton. 18°. 75c. .... *Dutton.*
Herbert Carter's legacy. Alger, H., *jr.* $1.50.. *Loring.*
Herbert Freeth's prosperity. Crossland, N. $1.75. *Lippincott.*
Herbert Graham; or, a day's temptation. 18°. 60c.; 75c. .... *Am. Bapt.*
Herbert Percy. 18°. 60c. .... *Carter.*
Herbert's first year at Bramford. *See* Aunty Lee lib.
Herbert's keys; or, honesty in little things. ill. 16°. 60c. .... *Tibbals.*
— *Same.* ill. 18°. 75c. .... *Nelson.*
Hercules. Cooper, F. F. 15c.............. *French.*
Hercules and Omphale. Brough, W. 15c.... *French.*
Hercules furens. *See* Euripides.
Herd boy. *See* Herd boy ser.
Herd boy ser. 8 v. ill. 18°. '75. $2 .... *Nelson.*
Cont.: Herd boy. — Uncle Dick's story. — My comical puss. — Jack Tar at sea. — Grandpa's pleasant companions. — Clever little Madge. — Watching crabs. — Nice secret.

Herdsman of Dambach. Körber, P. 80c. (?) *Luth. Pub.*
Here and there. sq. 12°. '54. pap., 30c... *Meth. Bk. Conc.*
Here a little and there a little. *See* Mortimer, *Mrs.* M.
Here, there and everywhere. Kingston, W. H. G. $1.50 .... *World Pub.*
Hereafter (The). Hull, D. W. 75c.; 50c. ... *Colby.*
Hereditary genius. Galton, F. $2........ *Appleton.*
Hereford, J: A day well spent: farce. 16°. pap., 15c. .... *Ames.*
Heretic (The). Lajétchnikoff, —. 50c...... *Harper.*
Hereward the wake. Kingsley, C. $1.75.. *Macmillan.*
Hering, Const. Analytical therapeutics; tr. [Hom.] v. 1. roy. 8°. $4; hf. mor., $5....... *Boericke.*
— Homœopathic domestic physician; rev. and enl. from the Germ. 8°. hf. mor., $2.50....... *Boericke.*
— Materia medica, tr.; with patholog. index. [Hom.] v. 1. 8°. hf. mor., $5................ *Boericke.*
— Treatment of typhoid fevers; tr., with add. [Hom.] 4°. pap., 60c...................... *Boericke.*
Note. A portion of Analytical therapeutics.

Hering, Jeanie. Little pickles. ill. fp. 8°. 50c... *Cassell.*
Heritage of peace. Childs, T. S. 75c.; $1.25. *Randolph.*
Herman, H: M. On law of estoppel. 8°. shp., $7.50. *W. C. Little.*
— Treatise on law of executions. roy. 8°. '75. shp., $7.50 .... *Cockcroft.*

Herman, J: B. *See* California, Sup. Court reports.
Hermann. Palfrey, S. H. $1.50; in 2 v., $3.50. *Lee & S.*
Hermann Agha. Palgrave, W. G. $1.25 ...... *Holt.*
Hermann and Dorothea. *See* Goethe, J. W. v.
Hermit. *See* Goldsmith, O.
Hermit. Parnell, T. $1.25............... *Am. S.S.*
Hermit of the Chesapeake. Price, G. R. 25c... *Barclay.*
Hermit of Holcombe. Chellis, M. D. $1.50. *H. A. Young.*
Hermit of the rock. Sadlier, M. A. $1.25; $1.75. *Sadlier.*
Hermit of Stentorpe; or, the star in the dark house. 32°. 25c..................... *Scribner, W. & A.*
Hermits (The). Kingsley, C. $1.75. *Lippincott; Macmillan.*
Hermon. McIntosh, R. M. $1.34...... *Huntington.*
Hernani. Hugo, V. 15c.................... *French.*
Herndon, *Mrs.* Ma. E. Oswyn Dudley; or, the bandits of Italy. 8°. pap., 50c........ *U. P. James.*
Herne, Peregrine. Perils and pleasures of a hunter's life; or, the romance of hunting. ill. 12°. $1.75. *J. E. Potter.*
Hero (A). *See* Craik, D. M.
Hero and martyr. *See* Reade, C:
Hero Carthew. Parr, L. $1.25 .... *Holt.*
Hero girl. Putnam, E. T. H. $1.75..... *J. E. Potter.*
Hero of Brittany. *See* Popular lib. of hist.
Hero of the pen. Bürstenbinder, E. $1.50; 75c. *W. F. Gill.*
Hero of truth. Dobbs, C. E. 30c.; 15c. ... *So. Bapt.*
Hero without courage. *See* Home twilight stories.
Herodotus. [Gk.] Recensuit J. W. Blakesley. 2 v. 18°. $1.50.......................... *Harper.*
— *Same;* with notes by Prof. Johnson. 12°. $1.50. *Appleton.*
— *Same:* text of Schweighæuser; with notes by C. S. Wheeler. 2 v. map. 12°. $2......... *Dennet.*
— *Eng.;* tr. by W. Beloe. 3 v. 18°. $2.25.. *Harper.*
— *Same;* lit. tr. by H. Cary. 12°. $1.50..... *Harper.*
— — *Same.* 12°. (Bohn.) $1.75..... *Little, B. & Co.*
— — *Same.* 12°. (Bohn.) $2. *Lippincott; Scribner, W. & A.*
— History: new version with notes and app. by G. Rawlinson, assisted by Sir H. C. Rawlinson and Sir J. G. Wilkinson. 4 v. maps and ill. 8°. $24......................... *Scribner, W. & A.*
— [Outlined and expl.] by G. C. Swayne. (Anc. classics for Eng. readers.) 16°. $1. *Lippincott; Little, B. & Co.*
— *See also* Homer.
— *and* Thucydides. Selections; with notes by R. H. Mather. ('72.) 4th ed. 16°. '75. $1.... *Allyn.*
Heroes (The). Kingsley, C. $1.50...... *Macmillan.*
Heroes and hero worship. *See* Carlyle, T:
Heroes and heroic events in Am. hist. Barber, J. W. $1.50 .... *World Pub.*
Heroes and hunters of the west: sketches of Boone, Kenton, Brady, etc. ill. 12°. $1.25.... *T. Bliss.*
Heroes and judges. *See* Johnson, F.
Heroes for the truth. Tweedie, W. K. 70c... *Pres. Bd.*
Heroes of the Arctic. Whymper, F. $1.50.... *Pott.*
Heroes of Asgard. Keary, A. *and* E. $1.50.. *Macmillan.*
Heroes of the Bible. Clark, R. W. 15c... *Cong. Pub.*
Heroes of the desert. Manning, A. $1.50... *Nelson.*
Heroes of Heb. hist. Wilberforce, S. $2.... *Carter.*
Heroes of Methodism. Wakeley, J. B. $1.75. *Meth. Bk. Conc.*
Heroes of the seven hills. Laing, C. H. B. $1.25. *Porter.*
Heroes of Sweden. *See* Besieged city.
Heroes of the workshop. ill. 16°. $1..... *Routledge.*

Heroes' lib. 10 v. 18°. $5.35 .... *So. Meth.*
Cont.: Alexander the Great. — Alfred the Great. — Cyrus. — Leo x. — Charlemagne. — Columbus, by G. Cubitt. — Mohammed. — Wycliffe. — Lives of eminent Anglo-Saxons, 2 v.

Heroic life; or, pictures of heroes. ill. 16°. $1.25. *Lippincott.*

Heroic wife. Kingston, W. H. G. 75c .... *Pott.*

Heroic women of France; tr. from the French. 12°. pap., 25c .... *U. P. James.*

Heroic women of history. Watson, H. C. $1.75. *J. E. Potter.*

Heroine of the Confederacy. O'Connor, F. J. $2. *Eyrich.*

Heroine of a week. 18°. 50c .... *Am. S. S.*

Heroine of the White Nile. Wells, W. $1. *Meth. Bk. Conc.*

Heroines in obscurity. Keddie, H. $2.... *Routledge.*

Heroines of the Bible. Headley, P. C. 15c.... *Hoyt.*

Heroines of charity. 16°. $1; $1.50 .... *Sadlier.*

Heroines of domestic life. Owen, O. F. $1.25. *Routledge.*

Heroines of early Methodism. Martin, M. *and Miss* —. 50c. .... *So. Meth.*

Heroines of Eng. poetry. por. 4°. $5; mor., $10. *Lippincott.*

Heroines of hist. Jenkins, J. S. *$3; $3.50; $6.. *Betts.*

Heroines of hist. *See* Owen, *Mrs.* O. F.

Heroines of Methodism. Coles, G. $1.25. *Meth. Bk. Conc.*

Heroism. Field, H. $1.50 .... *Lippincott.*

Heroism and adventure. ill. 16°. $1.75. *Scribner, W. & A.*

Heroism of boyhood. *See* Maude Grenville lib.

Herold, L. J. F. Zampa. *See* Ditson.

Herr Lecoq. Gaboriau, E. 50c .... *Morwitz.*

Herr (Der), der Welt: Fortsetzg. d. Romans "Der Graf v. Monte Christo." 8°. $1.50; pap., $1.25; hf. mor., $1.75 .... *F. W. Thomas.*

Herranz y Quiroz, Diego Narciso. Elementos de gramática castellana. New ed., rev. and enl. 32°. 30c .... *Appleton.*

Herrick, Har. Birds of Grand Menan. 8°. '73. pap., 15c .... *Essex.*

Herrick, Rob. Poems; with memoir. 2 v. por. 18°. $2 .... *Osgood.*

Herrick, W: A. Powers, duties and liabilities of town and parish officers in Mass. cr. 8°. '70. $2.50; shp., $3 .... *Little, B. & Co.*

Herring, Jeanie. Honor and glory: a book for boys. ill. 16°. '75. 50c .... *Routledge.*

Herrmann, —. Handbook of magic. 16°. pap., 30c. *Dick & F.*

Herrmanns, K. Handfibel. 32d ed. 8°. 25c... *Schäfer.*

Herrn Quints Verlobung. *See* Zschokke, H.

Herrnhuter Familie (Die). *See* Zschokke, H.

Herron, S. P. Thoughts on life and character. 12°. $1.50 .... *Lippincott.*

Herschel, Clem. Continuous, revolving drawbridges: principles of construc. and calculation of strains. ill. 8°. '75. $1.50.. *Am. Soc. of C. E.; Little, B. & Co.*
— On waves of translation that emanate from a submerged orifice; with exam. of proposed Baie Verte canal. 8°. '75. pap., 40c. .... *Am. Soc. of C. E.*
— Upright arched bridges. *See* Forshey, C. G., Levees of the Mississippi.

Herschel, *Sir* J: F: W: Familiar lectures on scientific subjects. ill. cr. 8°. $2.50.... *Routledge.*
— Outlines of astron. pl. and ill. 12°. $2.50 .. *Sheldon.*
— *Same.* pl. and ill. 8°. $4 .... *Appleton.*
— Preliminary discourse on study of nat. philos. 12°. $1.50 .... *Harper.*
— *See also* Davies, C., Metric system.

Hersey, C. Hist. of Worcester, Mass. *See* Lincoln, W.

Herttell, T: Intemperate drinking: exposé of [its] causes, and means by which it may be obviated New ed. 12°. '67. pap., 15c. .... *Mendum.*
— Right of married women to hold property. New ed 12°. '67. pap., 20c .... *Mendum*

Hertz, H: King René's daughter: lyric drama; tr 16°. pap., 15c .... *French*
— *Same;* tr. by T. Martin. ('66.) New ed. 16°. '75 $1.25 .... *Holt*

Hertzog, —. *See* Beckmann, —, *and* Hertzog, —.

Hertzog, J. B. Dialoge zur Unterhaltung in Schule u Haus. 4th ed. 8°. 25c .... *Schäfer*

Hervé (*pseud.*) *See* Ronger, Florimond.

Hervey, Arth. C: (*Lord*). Commentary on Judges Ruth and Samuel. *See* Cook, F. C., Bible com ment.
— Genealogies of Christ, as contained in Gospels o Matthew and Luke, reconciled with each other and shown to be in harmony with the true chro nology of the times. 8°. $3 .... *Macmillan*

Hervey, *Mrs.* Eleanor Louisa. Children of the pea garden. ill. 16°. $1 .... *Scribner, W. & A*
— New stories and old legends. ill. fp. 8°. 75c... *Cassell*
— The rock light; or, duty our watchword. ill. 16° $1 .... *Scribner, W. & A*

Hervey, G: W. Principles of courtesy. 12°. $1.50 *Harper*
— Rhetoric of conversation; or, bridles and spurs fo management of tongue. 12°. $1.50.... *Harper*
— System of Christian rhetoric for preachers and othe speakers. 8°. $3.50 .... *Harper*

Hervey, Ja. Life; [also] Life of Rev. A. M. Toplady 18°. 60c .... *Pres. Bd*
— Meditations. 12°. $1.50. 18°. 75c. ...... *Carter*
— Meditations and contemplations. 2 v. in 1. 16°. 75c *U. P. James*

Hervey, Rosamond. Aarbergs (The). [Fiction.] cr 8°. $1.75 .... *Macmillan*
— Duke Ernest, a tragedy; and other poems. fp. 8° '66. $2 .... *Macmillan*

Hervey, T: K. Poems. 32°. $1.50 ...... *Osgood*

Hervey, *Mrs.* T: K. *See* Hervey, *Mrs.* E. L.

Herz, H: Complete method for piano. 4°. bds., $5. *Peters*

Herz Jesu Missionsbuch. Weninger, F. X. $1; $1.65 *Benziger*

Herz (Das) d. Menschen: e. Tempel Gottes od. e Werkstätte d. Satans. 12°. 20c .... *Radde*

Herz vergessen (Das). Putlitz, G. zu. 40c..... *Holt*

Herzberg, R. Sewing machine: its hist., constructio and application; tr. by U. Green. ill. roy. 8° '64. bds., $3 .... *Spon*

Herzberg, W: Jewish family papers; or, letters of missionary; tr. by Rev. F. de S. Mendes. 8° '75. *$3 .... *Am. Jew*

Herzog Ernst. 12°. pap., 15c. .... *Radde*

Herzog Max. *See* Pfeufer, K. v.

Hesekiel, G: Life of Bismarck, with notices of hi ancestry; tr. and ed., with notes and app., by K R. H. Mackenzie. ill. 8°. $3 .... *Harper*

Heshusius, Tilemann. Wer Gewalt, Fug u. Rech habe, Prediger zu berufen. 8°. pap., 15c. *Volkening*
— Zehn Predigten v. d. Rechtfertigung d. Sünders vo Gott. 8°. '76. $1 .... *Dette*

Hesiodus, Callimachus Cyrenæus *and* Theognis Works; lit. tr. with notes by J. Banks. 12° (Bohn.) $1.75 .... *Little, B. & Co*
— — — *Same.* 12°. (Bohn.) $2. *Lippincott; Scribner, W. & A*
— *and* Theognis. [Writings, outlined and expl.] b J. Davies. (Anc. classics for Eng. readers.) 16° $1 .... *Lippincott; Little, B. & Co*

Hesperus. Richter, J. P. 2 v. $2.50 .... *Holt*

Hess, C: Normal piano instructor. 6 pts. 4°. 1–3, ea., $2; 4–6, ea., $2.50 .... *Church.*

Hessey, J. A. Moral difficulties connected with the Bible. (Boyle lectures, 1871–'73.) 3 v. 16°. '72–'73. 1, 75c.; 2, 3, ea., $1.25 .... *Pott.*

Hester Howard's temptation. Warfield, C. A. $1.75. *Peterson.*

Hester Kirton. Macquoid, K. $1 .... *Lippincott.*

Hester Morley's promise. Smith, H. $1.75 .... *Dodd.*

Hester Power's girlhood. Sheppard, E. $1 .. *Loring.*

Hester Strong's life-work. Southworth, S. A. $1.50. *Lee & S.*

Hester's fortune. Plunkett, I. $1.25 .. *Scribner, W. & A.*

Hester's happy summer. Atkinson, M. E. $1.25. *Lothrop.*

Heston, Newton. Anniversary speaker; or, young folks on the S.-school platform. ('57.) 11th ed. 18°. '75. 60c. .... *Perkinpine.*

— *Same.* 2d ser. ('65.) 6th ed. 18°. '72. 60c. *Cin. Meth. Bk. Conc.; Perkinpine.*

Heth, H: System of target practice. 18°. '62. 75c. *Van Nostrand.*

Hetherington, W. M. Apologetics of the Christian faith. 8°. $5 .... *Scribner, W. & A.*

— History of the church of Scotland, to 1843. ('44.) New ed. 8°. '70. $2.50 .... *Carter.*

— History of the Westminster Assembly. 12°. $1.25. *Carter.*

Hetty. Keary, M. 50c. .... *Scribner, W. & A.*

Hetty. Kingsley, H. 25c. .... *Harper.*

Hetty Baker; or, proud and humble. 18°. 25c. *Am. S. S.*

Hetty Homer. Warner, F. 50c. ...... *Cunningham.*

Hetty Porter. *See* Winifred Leigh lib.

Hetty's hopes. Robbins, S. S. $1.50 .... *Hoyt.*

Hetty's tongue, and other stories. 18°. 70c. .. *Pres. Bd.*

Heubner, H. L. *See* Büchner, G., Bibl. Real- u. Verbal-Hand-Concordanz.

Heures petites; ou, exercices de piété. [Cath. prayer book.] 32°. *net*, 14c. 48°. *net*, 12c. .. *Benziger.*

Heurtly, C. A. Instruction for adult candidates for holy baptism. 16°. 25c. .... *Pott.*

Heusser-Schweizer, Meta. Alpine lyrics: sel. of poems; tr. by H. L. L. 18°. '75. 75c. .. *Nelson.*

— *Same.* sq. 18°. '75. 90c. .... *Randolph.*

Hewer, M. E. Child's warfare; or, the conquest of self. 18°. 90c. .... (?) *Martien.*

Hewit, A. F. King's highway; or, the Cath. Ch. the only way of salvation as revealed in the Scriptures. 12°. '74. $1.50 .... *Cath. Pub.*

— Life of a modern martyr, Bp. Borie. 18°. 50c. *O'Shea.*

— Light in darkness: treatise on the obscure night of the soul. 16°. '74. 75c. .... *Cath. Pub.*

— Problems of the age; with studies in St. Augustine on kindred subjects. 12°. '68. $2 ... *Cath. Pub.*

Hewitt, E. C. Key to Guyot's maps. ('74.) New ed. 12°. '76. 75c. .... *Scribner.*

Hewitt, Graily. Diagnosis, pathology and treatment of diseases of women; incl. diagnosis of pregnancy. 3d ed., rev. and enl. ill. 8°. '74. $5; leath., $6 .... *Lindsay.*

Hewitt, J. O. M. Our Bible: 3 lectures at Unity Church, Oak Park. ill. 12°. '75. $1.25 .. *Jansen.*

Hewitt, J: Hill. Fairy bridal. [Cantata.] obl. 8°. pap., 50c. .... *Ditson.*

— Musical enthusiast: parlor operetta. obl. 8°. '72. pap., 50c. .... *Ditson.*

— Revellers: a cantata. obl. 4°. '74. bds., 30c. *Biglow.*

— — *See also* Lowry, R., *and* Doane, W. H.

Hewson, Addinell. Earth as a topical application in surgery. ill. 8°. '72. $2.50 .... *Lindsay.*

Hewson, W: Principles and practice of embanking lands from river floods, as applied to the levees of the Mississippi. 8°. '70. $2 .. *Van Nostrand.*

Hey, W. Fünfzig Fabeln. 12°. 50c. .... *Kohler.*

Heydenreich, L. W. Elementary Germ. reader; with vocab. 12°. $1 .... *Appleton.*

Heygate, W. E. Ember hours. 16°. '74. $1.25 .. *Pott.*

— Eucharist: its types, etc. 16°. '74. $1.75 .... *Pott.*

— Good shepherd: meditations for the clergy upon example and teaching of Christ. 18°. '60. $1 .. *Pott.*

— Manual: book of devotions. 32°. '75. 50c.; roan, 75c. .... *Pott.*

Heyl, Lew. Digest of U. S. statutes rel. to revenue, commerce, navigation and the currency. roy. 8°. '66. shp., $7.50 .... *Little, B. & Co.*

— United States duties on imports. New ed., rev. and enl. 8°. '75. $3 .... *Morrison.*

Heyse, Pl. Andrea Delfin; tr. 16°. '64. pap., 50c. *Burnham.*

— Anfang und Ende: Novelle. ('66.) New ed. 12°. '75. pap., 40c. .... *Holt.*

— Einsamen (Die): Novelle. ('68.) New ed. 12°. '76. pap., 40c. .... *Holt.*

— *Eng.* Solitaries (The); tr. 16°. '69. pap., 25c. *Claxton.*

— La Rabbiata; [also] Das Mädchen v. Treppi; [also] Die Blinden. 12°. '64. pap., 25c. .... *Steiger.*

— Maiden of Treppi; or, love's victory; tr. by A. W. Hinton. 16°. '74. 75c. .... *Hinton.*

Heythuysen, F. van. Equity draftsman: forms of pleading in suits in equity; rev. and enl. by E. Hughes. 4th Am. ed., with notes and ref. to Am. cases by a member of the Phila. bar. 8°. shp., $6.50 .... *Kay.*

Heywood, J. C. How will it end? a romance. 12°. $1.50; pap., 75c. .... *Lippincott.*

Heywood, Ol. Heart treasure; or, the furniture of a holy soul; rev. by G. B. Ide. 16°. $1 .. *Am. Bapt.*

Hiatus. Outis. $3 .... *Macmillan.*

Hiawatha. *See* Longfellow, H: W.

Hi-a-wa-tha. Walcot, C. M. 15c. .... *French.*

Hiawatha, the story of the Iroquois sage; [in prose and verse]. 16°. '73. 85c. .... *Randolph.*

Hibbard, F. G. Geography and hist. of Palestine. 12°. '57. $1.75 .... *Meth. Bk. Conc.*

— On baptism: its subjects, mode, obligation, import and relative order. 12°. '41. $1.75 .. *Meth. Bk. Conc.*

— Psalms chronol. arranged; with hist. introd. 8°. '56. $3.50; hf. mor., $4.50 ..... *Meth. Bk. Conc.*

Hibbard, R. G. Declamation for the million. ('64.) New ed. 16°. '75. 30c. .... *Sherwood.*

Hibberd, Shirley. Clever dogs, horses, etc.; with anecdotes of other animals. ill. sm. 4°. $2. *Routledge.*

Hibernia collection. O'Flanagan, P. 50c. .... *Ditson.*

Hibernian nights' entertainments. Ferguson, S. $1.75. *Haverty.*

Hick, El. Journal of life and relig. labors. [Autobiog.] 5th ed. 8°. *net*, shp., $1.25 .. *Friends Bk. Assoc.*

— Letters; with obs. on slavery of the Africans, their descendants and use of the produce of their labor. 8°. *net*, $1 .... *Friends Bk. Assoc.*

Hick, J: Experiments on the friction of the leather collars in hydraulic presses. pl. 8°. '67. pap., 40c. .... *Spon.*

Hickling, W: (*pseud.*) *See* De Costa, B. F.

Hickok, Laurens Perseus. Creator and creation; or, the knowledge in the reason of God and his work. 8°. '72. $2.25 .... *Ivison.*

— *Same.* 8°. $2.75 .... *Lee & S.*

— Humanity immortal; or, man tried, fallen and redeemed. 8°. '72. $2.25 .... *Ivison.*

— *Same.* 8°. $2.75 .... *Lee & S.*

— Logic of reason, universal and eternal. 8°. '74. $2. *Ivison; Lee & S.*

Hickok, Laurens Perseus, *continued.*
— Mental science; or, the human mind as given in consciousness. 12°. '54. $1.60............*Ivison.*
— Moral science. 12°. '53. $1.60............*Ivison.*
— Rational cosmology; or, the eternal principles, and necessary laws of the universe. 8°. $2..*Appleton.*
— Rational psychology; or, subjective idea and objective law of all intelligence. 8°. '61. $2.50..*Ivison.*
Hicks, Alb. W. Life, trial, confession and execution. 8°. pap., 50c.........................*De Witt.*
Hicks, E. W. *See* Goodspeed, E. J., *and* Hicks, E. W.
Hicks, Smith. Little confectioner: recipes and processes for making the more popular forms of confectionery. 24°. '76. 60c. ....*N. Y. News.*
Hid in a cave; [also] The selfish little girl. ill. fp. 8°. 60c.....................................*Cassell.*
Hid treasures. Flint, S. A. $1.50........*Cong. Pub.*
Hidden angels; by author of "The hospital boy." 16°. $1.25 ....(?)*Martien.*
Hidden beauty; [also] Dew drop. 32°. 20c.; 15c. *Dutton.*
Hidden depths. 12°. $1.50 ....*Claxton.*
Hidden foe, and other stories. 16°. 40c..... *West. Tr.*
Hidden hand. Jones, R. 15c...............*Lee & S.*
Hidden hand. Taylor, T. 15c......*De Witt; French.*
Hidden home; tr. from the Fr. 16°. $1.25.(?)*Martien.*
Hidden life. MacDonald, G. $1.50 ....*Scribner.*
Hidden life of the soul. *See* Grou, N. J.
Hidden path. Harland, M. $1.50 ....*Carleton.*
Hidden perils. Hay, M. C. 75c............*Harper.*
Hidden power. Bunnett, F. E. $1.25...(?)*Martien.*
Hidden saints: life of Sœur Marie, the workwoman of Liege; by author of "Wild times." 12°. $1.25; $1.75..................................*Sadlier.*
Hidden sin. [Fiction.] ill. 8°. $1.50; pap., $1..*Harper.*
Hidden sin. Dupuy, E. A. $1.75.........*Peterson.*
Hidden talent. *See* Edmond Darley ser.
Hidden treasure. Babcock, S. A. $1..*Meth. Bk. Conc.*
Hidden treasure. Young, L. 35c..........*Pres. Bd.*
Hidden treasure lib. 3 v. 16°. $3.75....(?)*Martien.*
Cont.: Hidden angels. — Hidden power. — Hidden home.
Hidden wings. *See* Arthur, T. S.
Hide and seek. *See* Baker, *Mrs.* H. N. W.
Hide and seek. *See* Collins, W.
Hide and seek. Lunn, J. 15c...............*French.*
Hiding place. Macfarlane, J. $1.50....(?)*Martien.*
Hieroglyphic Bible for the young. sq. 16°. 40c.; pap., 25c. ....*Miller.*
Hieroglyphic geog. of the U. S., pt. 1: New Eng. states and N. Y. ill. 4°. '74. $2.50....*Dutton.*
Higgie, T: [Plays.] 4 v. 16°. ea., pap., 15c...*French.*
Cont.: Devilish good joke: farce. — Devil's mount. — House dog: farce. — Wilful murder: farce.
— *and* Lacy, T. H. Belphegor: drama. 16°. pap., 15c.....................................*French.*
Higgins, Alvin S. Mishaps of Mr. Ezekiel Pelter. ill. 12°. '74. $1.50.........................*Griggs.*
Higgins, Ctte. M. The angel children; or, stories from cloud-land. ill. 16°. 80c..............*Lee & S.*
Higgins, Godf. Anacalypsis: attempt to draw aside the veil of the Saitic Isis. [To form 3 v.] v. 1. 8°. '76. $5...............................*Bouton.*
Higgins, H. M. Parlor lute. [Sing. book.] obl. 8°. pap., 50c. ....*Peters.*
— Patriotic glee book. obl. 8°. bds., $1.50....*Peters.*
Higgins, S. B. Ophidians: zoölog. arrangements of different genera. 12°. $2............*Boericke.*
Higgins, Sol., *and* Brisbane, W: H. Remarkable providences ill. the divine government; with essay on providence by Rev. J. Castle. ('58.) 6th ed. 12°. '64. $1.75...........................*Perkinpine.*
Higgins, W. Mullinger. The earth: its physical condition and most remarkable phenomena. ill. 18°. 75c. ....*Harper.*
Higginson, T: Wentworth. English statesmen. *See below* Brief.
— Sympathy of religions. 12°. pap., 10c....*Free Rel.*
— Young folks' hist. of the U. S. ill. sq. 16°. $1.50 — Questions. 16°. $1.50.............*Lee & S.*
— (*ed.*) Brief biographies of contemporary statesmen 4 v. sq. 16°. '75–'76. ea., $1.50.......*Putnam.*
Cont.: 1. English statesmen, by T. W. Higginson. — 2. English radical leaders, by R. J. Hinton. — 3. French leaders, by E King. — 4. German political leaders, by H. Tuttle.
— *See also* Longfellow, S: *and* Higginson, T. W.
High, Ja. L. Treatise on law of extraordinary legal remedies. 8°. '74. shp., $7.50.....*Callaghan.*
— Treatise on law of injunctions in Eng. and Am. 8°. '73. shp., $7.50....................*Callaghan.*
— Treatise on the law of receivers in Gt. Brit. and Am. 8°. '76. shp., $7.50...............*Callaghan.*
High and low. ill. 16°. 60c.................*Tibbals.*
High and low. Dammast, J. S. 75c.........*Nelson.*
High art. Roberts, L. A. *$1.50........*D. E. Fisk.*
High C. Rosenfeld, S. 15c................*De Witt.*
High churchism run mad. Boland, J. M. 10c. *So. Meth.*
High days and holidays in old England and New England. 4 v. ill. 16°. '70. $3....*Meth. Bk. Conc.*
High hopes. Congreve, J. $2.50.........*Macmillan.*
High Jack, the heeler. Leavitt, A. J. 15c...*De Witt.*
High life below stairs. Townley, J. 15c.....*French.*
High life in N. Y. Slick, J. $1.75; $1.50..*Peterson.*
High life in Washington. Lasselle, N. P. $1.75; $1.50. *Peterson.*
High, low, Jack and game. Planché, J. R., *and* Dance, C. 15c......................*French.*
High mills. Saunders, K. $1.25; 75c....*Lippincott.*
High mountain apart; or, the desert place of delight. ill. 18°. 40c...................*N. Y. Ref. Ch. Bd.*
High priest of Israel. Rhind, W. G. $7.50... *Wiley.*
High school choralist: sel. of choruses and four-part songs. 8°. '66. bds., $1..............*Ditson.*
High school hymn book. 16°. 65c....*Potter, A. & Co*
Higham, Ma. R. Cloverly: a story. 12°. '76. $1.25. *Randolph.*
Higher Christian education. Dwight, B. W. $1.50. *Barnes.*
Higher law. Maitland, E. $1.75..........*Putnam.*
Higher rock; or, guide to young people in moral and relig. duty. 12°. $1.25...............*Am. S. S.*
Highest price for left-off clothes: Ethiop. drama. 16°. pap., 15c. ....*French; Happy.*
Highland Agnes; or, the triumph of faith in humble life. 18°. 35c.........................*Am. S. S.*
Highland glen. *See* Wrench, M.
Highland parish. Macleod, N. $1.25.......*Carter.*
Highland pastor: sequel to "George Somerville." 18°. 60c. ....*Am. S. S.*
Highland reel. O'Keefe, J. 15c............*French.*
Highland widow. *See* Scott, *Sir* W.
Highlanders of Glen Ora. *See* Grant, Ja.
Highlands of Scotland. *See* Maxwell, W: H.
Highwayman: farce. 16°. pap., 15c........*French.*
Highwayman's bride. 8°. pap., 25c........*De Witt.*
Highwayman's doom. 8°. pap., 25c........*De Witt.*
Highwayman's holiday. Suter, W. E. 15c...*French.*
Highwayman's ride to York. 8°. pap., 25c...*Dick & F.*
Highwayman's stratagem. 8°. pap., 25c....*De Witt.*
Highwaymen's avenger; or, escape of sixteen-stringed Jack. 8°. pap., 25c...............*Peterson.*
Highways and byways. Webster, B. 15c...*French.*

Highways and hedges; or, following the master. 16°. $1.50 .... *Cong. Pub.*

Higinbotham, Jose. M. "Una and her paupers:" memorials of A. E. Jones; with introd. by F. Nightingale. 12°. '72. $2..*Randolph; Routledge.*

Hilda. *See* Hoffmann, F.

Hilda: sequel to "Ethel's story on patience." ('63.) 7th ed. ill. 18°. '71. 63c. .... *Perkinpine.*

Hilda; or, the golden age; by author of "Faithful but not famous." ill. 18°. 50c. .... *Nelson.*

Hildebrandt, H. Catarrh of the female sexual organs; tr., with add. of homœop. treatment, by S. Lilienthal. 8°. pap., 30c. .... *Boericke.*

Hildebrant, G. C. Winter in Spitzbergen: tale of the northland. ill. 16°. '52. $1 .... *Dodd.*

Hildeburn, *Mrs.* Ma. J. Amy Hall books. 6 v. 18°. $2.10 .... *Pres. Bd.*

Cont.: Amy Hall; or, pleasing one's self. — Carrie's peaches; or, forgive your enemies. — Daisy Delafield; or, the lost lamb. — Fannie's rule; or, better than gold. — Miss Clare's party; or, the pattern child. — Three cents; or, Lettie's way of doing good.

— Archie and Pussy ser. 6 v. 18°. $2.10...*Pres. Bd.*

Cont.: Archie and Pussy. — Little Mischief. — New sled. — Mrs. Lee and her boy Bertie. — Uncle Hugh's house. — Polly and her friends.

— Bessie Lane's mistake; or, wealth is not happiness. 16°. 90c. .... *Pres. Bd.*

— Craythorns of Stony Hollow. 16°. $1.15..*Pres. Bd.*

— Discontented little girl. 18°. 30c. .... *Pres. Bd.*

— Dr. Leslie's boys. 18°. 70c. .... *Pres. Bd.*

— Far away; or, life at Tanna and Samoa. 18°. 50c. *Pres. Bd.*

— Flora Morris' choice; or, "be not conformed to the world." 16°. $1.25 .... *Pres. Bd.*

— Frank Harvey in Paris, and how he spent his Sundays. 18°. 70c. .... *Pres. Bd.*

— Gaffney's tavern. 16°. $1.10 .... *Pres. Bd.*

— George Lee; or, making the best of trials. 18°. 60c. *Pres. Bd.*

— Lessons for the little ones. [S.-school quest. bk.] 18°. 20c. .... *Pres. Bd.*

— Money; or, the Ainsworths. 18°. 60c....*Pres. Bd.*

— Only in fun; or, the teasing boy. 18°. 50c...*Pres. Bd.*

Hildred. Crossland, N. $1.25 .... *Routledge.*

Hildred's great work; [also] Harry Huntley's self-denial. 18°. '75. 60c. .... *H. A. Young.*

Hildreth, E. E. Lessons from daily life. 12°. $1. *Lippincott.*

Hildreth, R: History of the U. S. to 1821. 6 v. 8°. '49–'52. $18; shp., $21; hf. cf., $31.50..*Harper.*

— Theory of politics: inquiry into foundations of governments and causes and progress of polit. revolutions. 12°. $1.50 .... *Harper.*

Hildreth, S: Prescott. Early history of the northwest. 16°. $1 .... *Cin. Meth. Bk. Conc.*

— Sketches of pioneer history. 12°. '50. $1. *Meth. Bk. Conc.*

— *and* Wood, J. Meteorological obs. at Marietta, O. 4°. '67. pap., $1 .... *Smith. Inst.*

Hildyard, Fs. Treatise on principles of law of marine insurance. 8°. shp., $2.50 .... *Kay.*

Hiles, J: Short voluntaries for the organ. 9 nos. 8°. ea., pap., 50c. .... *Ditson.*

Hilgard, Eug. W. Geology of lower Louisiana. 4°. '72. pap., $2 .... *Smith. Inst.*

— *See also* Lousiana geol. survey; — Mississippi agric. and geol. survey.

Hill, A. F. John Smith's funny adventures on a crutch; or, the remarkable peregrinations of a one-legged soldier after the war. ill. 12°. $1.75..*J. E. Potter.*

— Our boys: scenes of army and camp life [in the Civil war]. por. and ill. 12°. $1.75.....*J. E. Potter.*

— Secrets of the sanctum: an inside view of an editor's life. 12°. '71. $1.50 .... *Claxton.*

— The white rocks; or, the robbers of the Monongahela. 12°. $1.75 .... *J. E. Potter.*

Hill, *Mrs.* A. P. New cookery book, and family domestic receipts. 12°. $2 .... *Carleton.*

Hill, Adams S. General rules for punctuation and for the use of capital letters. ('74.) New ed., rev. 16°. '76. pap., 25c. .... *Sever.*

Hill, *Mrs.* Anne. Progressive lessons in painting of flowers and fruit. col. ill. 4°. $1.50..*Fortescue.*

Hill, Berkeley. On syphilis and local contagious disorders. 8°. $3.25 .... *Lea.*

Hill, Britton A. Absolute money: system of national finance under a co-operative government. 8°. '75. $1: pap., 50c. .... *Gray.*

— Liberty and law under federative government. 16°. '73. $1.50 .... *Gray.*

— Specie resumption and national bankruptcy, identical and indivisible: final appeal for repeal of "specie resumption act." 8°. '76. pap., 25c. ..... *Gray.*

Hill, Dan. Harvey. Algebra for schools. 8°. hf. roan, $2 .... *Lippincott.*

— Commentary on Sermon on the mount. 12°. $1.25. (?) *Martien.*

— Crucifixion of Christ. 12°. $1.25......(?)*Martien.*

— Elements of algebra. 8°. '57. $2 .... *Claxton.*

Hill, *Mrs.* E. V. Bessie White. ill. 18°. '72. 60c...*Am. Tr.*

Hill, E: Judson. Chancery jurisdiction and practice in Ill.; with forms. ('73.) 3d ed., rev. and enl. 2 v. 8°. '76. shp., $10 .... *E. B. Myers.*

— Common law jurisdiction and practice in Ill. 2 v. 8°. '72. shp., $10 .... *E. B. Myers.*

— Compendium of Ill. highway statutes and decisions; with forms, precedents, notes and ref. 12°. '73. bds., $1.50; shp., $2 .... *E. B. Myers.*

— Municipal officer of Ill. 12°. '73. shp., $3..*E. B. Myers.*

— Probate jurisdiction and practice in Ill. ('73.) 2d ed., rev. 8°. '75. shp., $5 .... *E. B. Myers.*

Hill, F. H. Political portraits: characters of some of our public men. [*anon.*] 12°. $1.50..*Lippincott.*

Hill, Flo. Children of the state: the training of juvenile paupers. 12°. '68. $1.50 .... *Macmillan.*

— *See also* Hill, R. *and* F.

Hill, F: S. Shoemaker of Toulouse: drama. 16°. pap., 15c. .... *French.*

— Six degrees of crime: drama. 16°. pap., 15c...*French.*

Hill, G: Lectures on divinity. 8°. '72. $3.50..*Carter.*

Hill, G: Canning. ["Lew. Myrtle."]. American biog. ser. ('57–'64.) New ed. 5 v. ill. 16°. '74. $5; ea., $1 .... *Claxton.*

Cont.: Capt. John Smith. — Israel Putnam. — Benedict Arnold. — Daniel Boone, the pioneer. — Benjamin Franklin.

— Our parish; or, pen paintings of village life. 12°. $1.75 .... *J. E. Potter.*

Hill, Georgiana. Cook's own book. 16°. 20c. *Routledge.*

— [Receipt books.] 13 v. 16°. ea., 20c....*Routledge.*

Cont.: How to cook apples in a hundred different ways — eggs — fish — game — onions — puddings — rabbits — salads — soups — vegetables — make cakes — make pickles — preserve fruit.

Hill, H. Poacher's sons. ill. 16°. 50c. .... *Nelson.*

Hill, H. B. Lecture-notes on qualitative analysis. 16°. '75. 75c. .... *Putnam.*

Hill, Hamilton Andrews. Exemption of church property from taxation; read before Am. Statistical Assoc., May 5, 1876. 8°. pap., 25c... *Williams.*

Hill, J: W. Manual of the law of fixtures. 2d ed. 8°. hf. shp., $2 .... *Baker, V. & Co.*

Hill, Junius W., *and* Trowbridge, J. C. One hundred and ten select pieces for church or cabinet organ. 4°. $6; — in 8 pts., ea., pap., $1... *G. D. Russell.*

Hill, L. C. Laure: the history of a blighted life. ('69.) 2d ed. 12°. '72. $1.50 .... *Claxton.*

Hill, L. L. *See* Somers, G. G., Williams, W. R., *and* Hill, L. L.

Hill, Miranda. Fairy spinner. ill. 12°. $1.25..*Nelson.*

Hill, N: *jr.* *See* New York, Supreme Court and Court of Errors reports.

Hill, Rosamond *and* Flo. What we saw in Australia. cr. 8°. '75. $3 .... *Macmillan.*

Hill, S., *and* Brown, O. B. Tuner's manual. [Piano forte.] 16°. 60c .... *Gordon.*

Hill, T: First lessons in geometry: facts before reasoning. 18°. bds., 45c .... *Ware.*

— Geometry and faith. sq. 16°. '75. $1 .... *Putnam.*

— Map of solar eclipse, Mar. 15, 1858. 8°. '58. pap., 15c .... *Smith. Inst.*

— Second book in geometry: reasoning upon facts. 12°. hf. roan, 75c .... *Ware.*

— True order of studies. 12°. '76. $1.25 .... *Putnam.*

Hill, U. C. Practical violin school: synopsis of violin playing. f°. '55. bds., $2.50 .... *Ditson.*

Hill, W. B. *See* Georgia, Annotated code.

Hill, W. H. Elements of philosophy; compr. logic and general principles of metaphysics. 12°. '73. $1.50 .... *Murphy.*

Hill, W. R. *See* South Carolina, Reports.

Hill, W. W. Twyman Hogue; or, early piety illustrated: biog. sketch; with introd. by L. W. Green. 18°. 65c .... *Pres. Bd.*

Hill, Wa. N. Notes on certain explosive agents. 8°. '75. pap., $1 .... *Allyn.*

Hill Difficulty. Cheever, G. B. $1 .... *Wiley.*

Hill farm. Temple, C. 60c .... *Lothrop.*

Hillard, G: Stillman. Dangers and duties of the mercantile profession. 8°. '66. pap., 25c ... *Osgood.*

— First (primary) reader. [Old ser.] 12°. 25c ... *Taintor.*

— Life and campaigns of G. B. McClellan. 12°. '64. $1.25 .... *Claxton; Lippincott.*

— Life of Capt. J: Smith. *See* Sparks, J., Lib. of Am. biog.

— New ser. of readers. 9 v. 12°. hf. bd ... *Taintor; Ware.*

Cont.: Primer, or first reader, 24c. — Second reader, 35c. — Third, 56c. — Fourth, 70c. — Intermediate, 75c. — Fifth, $1.25. — Sixth, $1.50. — Primer (Leigh's type), 30c. — Second reader (Leigh's type), 50c.

— Political duties of the educated classes. 8°. pap., 35c .... *Osgood.*

— Six months in Italy. 16°. '53. $2 .... *Osgood.*

— *and* Campbell, L. J. Franklin ser. of readers. 9 v. 12°. hf. bd .... *Taintor; Ware.*

Cont.: — Franklin primer, or first reader, 25c. — Second reader, 40c. — Third, 60c. — Fourth, 80c. — Intermediate, 80c. — Fifth, $1.25. — Sixth reader and speaker, $1.50. — Primer (Leigh's type), 30c. — Second reader (Leigh's type), 50c.

Hillebrand, L. Sparring: theory and art of self-defense. ill. 18°. 50c .... *Fisher.*

Hiller, Fd. Memoir of Mendelssohn; tr. 12°. $1.50. *Church.*

— Mendelssohn: letters and recollections; tr. by M. E. v. Glehn; ed. by G. Grove. por. cr. 8°. $2.25. *Macmillan.*

Hiller, O. Prescott. Notes on the Psalms; with new tr. from the Heb. v. 1. 8°. $1.75 .... *H. H. Carter.*

— Sermons on the ten commandments. 16°. '68. 50c. *H. H. Carter.*

— Who was Swedenborg? 18°. '68. 25c. *H. H. Carter.*

— *Same.* 16°. pap., 25c .... *Lippincott.*

Hillern, Wilhelmine v. By his own might; tr. by MS. 12°. $1.75 .... *Lippincott.*

— Geier-wally: tale of the Tyrol; tr. 8°. $1.25. *Appleton.*

— Only a girl; or, a physician for the soul; tr. by Mrs. A. L. Wister. 12°. $2 .... *Lippincott.*

— Twofold life (A); tr. by MS. 12°. $1.75 .. *Lippincott.*

Hilles, M. W. The pocket anatomist. 32°. '67. $1. — (Pocket form.) $1.25 .... *Lindsay.*

Hillgrove, T: Ball-room guide and complete dancing master. ill. 16°. $1; bds., 75c .... *Dick & F.*

Hilliard, Fs. Elements of law. 2d ed., rev. and enl. 8°. shp., $3.50 .... *Baker, V. & Co.*

— Law of contracts. 2 v. 8°. shp., $11 .... *Kay.*

Hilliard, Fs., *continued.*

— Law of injunctions. 3d ed., rev. 8°. shp., $6.50 .. *Kay.*

— Law of new trials and other rehearings; incl. writs of error, appeals, etc. 2d ed., rev. 8°. shp., $6.50 .... *Kay.*

— Law of vendors and purchasers of real property. 2d ed. 8°. '68. shp., $6 .... *Little, B. & Co.*

— Practical and element. treatise on law of sales of personal property. New ed., rev. and enl. 8°. '69. $7.50 .... *T & J. W. Johnson.*

— Treatise on law of bankruptcy and insolvency. ('63.) 3d ed. 8°. '72. shp., $5.50 .. *Claxton; Lippincott.*

— Treatise on law of mortgages of real and personal property. 4th ed., enl. 2 v. 8°. '72. shp., $12. *Little, B. & Co.*

— Treatise on law of taxation. 8°. '75. shp., $6. *Little, B. & Co.*

— Treatise on remedies for torts or private wrongs. 2d ed. 8°. '73. shp., $6 .... *Little, B. & Co.*

— Treatise on torts; law rel. to wrongs upon real and personal property, upon the person, character and all absolute and rel. rights. 4th ed., rev. and enl. 2 v. 8°. '74. shp., $12 .... *Little, B. & Co.*

Hilliard, H: Wash. De Vane: story of plebeians and patricians. 2 v. in 1. 12°. '65. $2 .... *Eyrich.*

— Speeches and addresses. 8°. $2.50 .... *Harper.*

Hillier, T: Clinical treatise on diseases of children. 8°. '68. $3 .... *Lindsay.*

— Handbook of skin diseases. 2d ed. ill. roy. 12°. $2.25 .... *Lea.*

Hillman, Jos. Revivalist: revival hymns and tunes; harmonized by Rev. L. Hartsough. ('72.) New ed. 16°. '76. 75c .... *Nims.*

Hillmantel, L: *See* Wernli, J., *and* Hillmantel, L.

Hills, O. A. Popular amusements. 16°. pap., 10c. *West. Tr.*

Hills of the Shatemuc. Warner, S. $1.75 .. *Lippincott.*

Hillsboro' farms. Cobb, S. D. $1.50 .... *Lee & S.*

Hillside, A. M. Familiar compend of geology for the school and family. 16°. 94c .... *Sower.*

Hillside cottage. Martyn, S. T. 75c .... *Cong. Pub.*

Hillside farm. Buckland, A. J. 75c .... *Cassell.*

Hillside farm; or, home influences illustrated. ('60.) New ed. ill. 18°. '70. 60c .... *Hoyt.*

Hillyars and Burtons. *See* Kingsley, H:

Hillyer, Curtis J. *See* California, Sup. Court reports.

Hilt to hilt. Cooke, J. E. $1.50 .... *Carleton.*

Hiltl, G: Die Schlossdiebe; [also] Nemesis, v. F. Friedrich. 8°. pap., 50c .... *Morwitz.*

— Um Thron u. Leben. 8°. pap., 50c .... *Morwitz.*

Hilton, H: *See* New York, Common Pleas reports.

Himes, C. F. Glimpses of photography. sm. 4°. $1.25 .... *Benerman.*

Himlo Himlini. 12°. pap., 15c .... *Radde.*

Himmlische Vergnügen (Das) in Gott. Schmolke, B. $2–$6 .... *Kohler.*

Himmlisches Palmgärtlein. 32°. 30c.; leath., 50c.; 85c .... *Benziger.*

Himnos cristianos. 8°. '67. 12c .... *Am. Tr.*

Hind, Helen Mar. (*ill.*) Silhouettes and songs, ill. of the months; ed. by E. E. Hale, [with] sel. from Spenser's Faerie Queen, and poems by Whittier, Lowell, Holmes, etc. obl. f°. '75. $3; mor., $7; $10 .... *Lockwood, B. & Co.*

Hind, J: Russell. Introduction to astronomy; with vocab. 12°. (Bohn.) $1.25 .... *Little, B. & Co.*

— *Same.* 12°. (Bohn.) $1.40 .... *Scribner, W. & A.*

— *Same.* 12°. (Bohn.) $1.50 .... *Lippincott.*

Hindley, C: Ready-made speeches. 16°. bds., 50c. *Routledge.*

— Tavern anecdotes and sayings: incl. origin of signs, and reminiscences [of] taverns, coffee-houses, clubs, etc. ill. 12°. '75. $2 .... *Routledge.*

Hindmarch, W. M. Treatise on law of patents and practice of obtaining letters patent; with acts of Congress, decisions of the courts and forms. 8°. shp., $2.50 .... *Kay.*

Hindmarsh, Rob. Vindication of Swedenborg against the slanders and misrepresentations of J. G. Pike and others; abridg. 12°. pap., 25c. .... *New Ch.*

Hindoo fortune-teller and oracle of destiny. 16°. pap., 15c. .... *Dick & F.*

Hindoo tales. Jacob, P. W. $2 .... *Routledge.*

Hindrances to the prosperity of Sunday-schools. 18°. 40c. .... *Am. S. S.*

Hinds, J: Farriery and stud book: treatise on diseases and accidents of the horse; with add. by T. M. Smith, and sup. by J. S. Skinner. ('48.) New ed. 12°. '68. shp., $1.25 .... *Claxton.*

— *See also* New Am. pocket farrier.

Hine, C. C. Fire insurance: book of instructions for agents. ('65.) 5th ed. sq. 8°. '72. $2.50 .. *Hine.*

— Fire insurance: forms of policies, endorsements, certificates, etc., for agents. ('66.) New ed. sq. 8°. '70. $1 .... *Hine.*

— Insurance blue book. ('74.) [Annual.] 4°. $1.50; $2 .... *Hine.*

— Insurance statutes of the U. S. and Canada. 8°. '76. shp., $12 .... *Hine.*

— Letters to [a fire insurance] agent from the patriarch. 8°. '76. $1.50 .... *Hine.*

Hiner, R. Kentucky conference pulpit. 12°. '74. $2. *So. Meth.*

Hinkley, E. O., *and* Mayer, L. Law of attachment in Maryland. 8°. '69. shp., $4 .. *Cushings & B.*

Hinman, Royal R. Catalogue of the first Puritan settlers of Conn. New ed., enl. por. 8°. '46. $4; hf. cf., $5 .... *Munsell.*

Hinrichs, Gst. Contributions to molecular science. ('68–'69.) New ed. 4 pts. in 1 v. 8°. '74. pap., 50c. .... *Day.*

— Elements of chemistry and mineralogy. pl. large 12°. '71. $1.50 .... *Day.*

— Principles of chemistry. 8°. '74. $2.50 ...... *Day.*

— Principles of pure crystallography. 8°. '71. pap., 50c. .... *Day.*

Hinsdale, B. A. Genuineness and authenticity of the Gospels. 12°. $1.25 .... *Chase.*

— History of a great mind (J: Stuart Mill). 8°. pap., 10c. .... *Chase.*

Hinsdale, Grace Webster. Coming to the king, and thinking aloud: daily devotions for children. 24°. '65. $1 .... *Randolph.*

Hinssen, L. Andenken an die erste hl. Communion. 16°. 90c. .... *Herder.*

Hinton, H: L. (*ed.*) Acting plays of Edwin Booth. 14 nos. 8°. ea., pap., 30c. .... *Hinton.*

Cont.: Richard III. — Macbeth. — Merchant of Venice. — Fool's revenge. — Romeo and Juliet. — Brutus. — Lady of Lyons. — Othello. — Much ado about nothing. — Richelieu. — Merchant of Venice (acts 1-4). — Cibber's Richard III. — Hamlet. — Julius Cæsar.

— *Same.* v. 1. 8°. $1.75 .... *Hinton.*

Cont.: Richard III.; Macbeth; Merchant of Venice; Romeo and Juliet; Othello; Fool's revenge; Brutus; Lady of Lyons.

— Standard drama; for school reading; with foot notes and glossary. 6 v. 12°. ea., 50c. ...... *Hinton.*

Cont.: Merchant of Venice. — Romeo and Juliet. — Lady of Lyons. — Othello. — Macbeth. — Richard III.

Hinton, Howard. My comrades. ill. 12°. '74. $1.50. *Hinton.*

Hinton, I: Taylor. History of baptism. 12°. 90c. *Am. Bapt.*

Hinton, Ja. Health and its conditions. 2d Am. ed. 12°. '71. $1.25 .... *Putnam.*

— Man and his dwelling-place: essay toward the interpretation of nature. 12°. $1.75 ...... *Appleton.*

— Mystery of pain: book for the sorrowful. sm. 12°. $1 .... *Appleton.*

Hinton, Ja., *continued.*

— Physiology for practical use; with introd. by E. L. Youmans. 12°. $2.25 .... *Appleton.*

Hinton, R: J. English radical leaders. (Brief biographies.) 16°. '76. $1.50 .... *Putnam.*

Hints about business: manual of business laws, customs and methods. 16°. 75c. ...... *Hoyt, F. & D.*

Hints and thoughts for Christians. Todd, J. 80c. *Am. Tr.*

Hints for farmers. Burn, R. S. 50c. ..... *Routledge.*

Hints for legislative reform. Dos Passos, J. R. 25c. *Campbell & Co.*

Hints for living. Kingsbury, O. A. $1.25 .. *Lothrop.*

Hints for the table; or, economy of good living; with a few words on wine. 16°. bds., 50c. .. *Routledge.*

Hints for teachers. Stabler, L. C. *net*, 40c. *Friends Bk. Assoc.*

Hints on Bible marking. *See* Menzies, S.

Hints on composition. Burnet, J. $3.50 .. *Benerman.*

Hints on decoration of churches at Christmas and Easter. 18°. 75c.; pap., 50c. .... *Dutton.*

Hints on dress. Gale, E. C. 75c. .... *Putnam.*

Hints on house painting. 12°. 40c. .... *Masury.*

Hints on household taste. Eastlake, C. L. $3.50; $5; $7 .... *Osgood.*

Hints to the charitable. 18°. 40c. .... *Am. S. S.*

Hints to Christians. Skinner, T. H. 10c. .. *Randolph.*

Hints to converts. Scott, A. P. 25c. .... *D. H. Carroll.*

Hippolytus, *Bp.* Refutation of all heresies; tr. by Rev. J. H. MacMahon; with fragments from his commentaries on various books of Scripture; tr. by S. D. F. Salmond. (Ante-Nicene Christ. lib.) 8°. $3 .... *Scribner, W. & A.*

Hippotheatron. White, C. 15c. .... *De Witt.*

Hiram Hireout. Conway, H. J. 15c. .... *French.*

Hirell. Saunders, J. 50c. .... *Harper.*

Hirlanda. 12°. pap., 15c. .... *Radde.*

Hirschfelder, J. O. Pocket manual of percussion and auscultation; tr. from the Germ. sq. 16°. '73. 75c. .... *Bancroft.*

Hirtius, Aulus. *See* Cæsar.

His excellency. Mathews, C. 15c. .... *French.*

His first brief: comedietta. 16°. pap., 15c. ... *Happy.*

His first champagne. Rede, W. L. 15c. ..... *French.*

His first peccadillo: farce. 16°. pap., 15c. ... *French.*

His jewels. 16°. $1.25 .... *Cong. Pub.*

His last legs. Bernard, W. B. 15c. .... *French.*

His last victory. Phillips, W. 15c. .... *French.*

His level best. Hale, E. E. $1.50 .... *Osgood.*

His marriage vow. Corbin, C. F. $1.50 ..... *Lee & S.*

His natural life. Clarke, M. 75c. .... *Harper.*

His own enemy: farce. 16°. pap., 15c. *De Witt; French.*

His two wives. Clemmer, M. $1.75 ...... *Hurd & H.*

His young wife. Smith, J. P. $1.75 .... *Carleton.*

Hiscox, E: T. Baptist church directory: guide to doctrines, discipline, etc., of Baptist churches. 16°. 90c. .... *Sheldon.*

— Baptist short method: difference between Baptists and others, etc. 18°. 65c. .. *Am. Bapt.; So. Bapt.*

— Manual of Bible readings; with eccles. formulas. 16°. 60c. .... *Am. Bapt.*

— Star book: manual for Baptist church-members. 18°. '73. 15c. .... *Ward.*

— Star book on Christian baptism. 18°. '76. 15c. .. *Ward.*

Hislop, Alex. Proverbs of Scotland; with notes and glossary. 16°. $1.50 .... *Robertson.*

Histoire de la mère Michel et de son chat. La Bedollière, E. de. 75c. .... *Holt.*

Histoire d'une bouchée de pain. *See* Macé, J.

Histoires intéressantes. v. 1, 2. 18°. '54. ea., 50c. *Am. Tr.*

Historia de André Dunn. *See* Andrew Dunn.

Historia de Gil Blas. *See* Lesage, A. R.

Historia de José: extratada de las sagradas escrituras. 18°. 10c. .... *Pres. Bd.*

Historic devices, badges and war cries. Palliser, B. $9 .... *Scribner, W. & A.*

Historic doubts about Napoleon. 18°. 50c. .. *Carter.*

Historic hymns. *See* Crafts, W. F.

Historic progress and Am. democracy. Motley, J. L. 50c. .... *Scribner.*

Historic tales for youth. Lee, M. E. 75c .... *Harper.*

Historical account of circumnavigation of the globe, and of progress of disc. in Pacific Ocean, from Magellan to death of Cook. ill. 18°. 75c... *Harper.*

Historical account of Washington Monument in Richmond, Va.; with biog. sketches. 16°. '69. pap., 50c. .... *J. W. Randolph.*

Historical and descriptive account of British India; by H. Murray, J. Wilson, R. K. Greville, W. Ainslie, W. Rhind, R. Jameson, A. R. Wallace, and C. Dalrymple. 3 v. ill. 18°. $2.25 .. *Harper.*

Historical atlas; with index. 12°. $1.25. *Scribner, W. & A.*

Historical collections of the Mahoning valley [Ohio]. 8°. $2.50 .... *Cobb.*

Historical companion. Webb, A. C. pt. 1, 60c.; 2, 75c. .... *Eldredge.*

Historical continuity. Garrett, A. C. 20c... *Whittaker.*

Historical gleanings. *See* Rogers, J. E. T.

Historical Jesus (The) of Nazareth. Schlesinger, M. $1 .... *Somerby.*

Historical pictures retouched. *See* Dall, *Mrs.* C. H.

Historical question book. 18°. bds., 15c... *Am. Bapt.*

Historical reason why of English history. 12°. $1.25. *Lippincott.*

Historical Society of Pennsylvania. Memoirs. v. 1, 5–11. 8°. '56–'74. ea., $3.50 .... *Penn. Hist.*

Cont.: 1. Ed. by E. Armstrong. — 5. Braddock's expedition against Fort Du Quesne, ed. by W. Sargent. — 6. Contributions to Am. hist. — 7. Record of the court at Upland, Pa., 1676–1681; A military journal kept by Maj. E. Denny, 1781–1795. — 8. Minutes of the Committee of Defence of Phila., 1814–'15. — 9, 10. Correspondence between Wm. Penn and Jas. Logan, and others, 1700–1750, ed. by E. Armstrong. — 11. History of New Sweden, or the settlements on the Delaware, by I. Acrelius; tr. by W. M. Reynolds.

Note. v. 1 pub. 1826, reprint. 1864.

Historical tales for young Am. Protestants. sq. 16°. '57. 90c .... *Meth. Bk. Conc.*

Historical tales for young Protestants. ill. 18°. '62. 60c. .... *Am. Tr.*

— *Same.* ill. 12°. 80c .... *Pres. Bd.*

— *Same.* 16°. 85c .... *Am. S. S.*

Historicals for young folks. Noque, O. $1.25 .. *Lothrop.*

Historicus (*pseud.*) *See* Harcourt, *Sir* W: G. V.

History and descript. of the Cincinnati and Covington bridge. 18°. '67. pap., 15c .... *Mendenhall.*

History and descrip. of the Tyler Davidson Fountain, donated to Cincinnati by Henry Probasco; with dedicatory exercises, etc. ill. and por. 18°. '72. pap., 40c .... *Clarke.*

History and mystery of common things. Allen, C. W. $1.50 .... *World Pub.*

History and philos. of marriage; or, polygamy and monogamy compared; by a Christian philanthropist. New ed., rev. 16°. '69. $1.25 .. *Jas. Campbell.*

History and records of the Elephant Club. Thomson, M. $1.75; $1.50 .... *Peterson.*

History and resources of the Am. republic at the first centennial of her independence. maps and ill. 8°. '76. $4; leath., $5 .... *Asher.*

History of A B C. 18°. 60c .... *Loring.*

History of Amelia. *See* Fielding, H:

History of the [anti-Masonic] National Christian Assoc. 12°. pap., 25c .... *E. A. Cook.*

History of Betsy Green, a Sunday scholar. 18°. 25c. *Am. S. S.*

History of the Bible for Cath. schools; tr. by Theo. Nöthen. 8th ed. 12°. '72. 35c .... *Zickel.*

History of birds. ill. sq. 16°. 50c .... *Perkinpine.*

History of a book. Carey, A. $1.50 .... *Cassell.*

History of the Capitol [Richmond, Va.] disaster. 8°. '70. pap., 25c .... *Ellyson.*

History of Celestine Darscott, the blind woman of Paturages. 32°. 30c .... *Pres. Bd.*

History of Christianity to time of Constantine; with introd. by Rev. F. D. Huntington. ill. 16°. 60c. *Bost. Am. Tr.*

History of the Covenanters in Scotland. Sime, W. 2 v. $1.40 .... *Pres. Bd.*

History of the cross. Ward, H. D. $1 ..... *Claxton.*

History of the crusades. *See* Popular lib. of hist.

History of the Delaware and Iroquois Indians. 18°. 55c. .... *Am. S. S.*

History of destruction of Jerusalem and desolation of Palestine; with account of Jewish nation to its final dispersion. map and ill. 8°. '69. $2.75; shp., $3.25 .... *Wilstach.*

History of the devil. *See* Defoe, D.

History of the devil. Paden, I. 10c... *D. M. Bennett.*

History of England for the young; comp. by Sisters of Holy Child Jesus. 12°. '65. $1 .. *Cunningham.*

History of European morals. Lecky, W. E. H. $6; $10 .... *Appleton.*

History of forty choirs. Hastings, T. $1.75 .. *Ditson.*

History of the Freewill Baptists, 1780–1830; with introd. by I. D. Stewart. 8°. '61. $1 ... *Freewill.*

History of the Fr. rev. *See* Young American's lib.

History of God's church. Pond, E. $4.50; $5; $6. *Scranton.*

History of Great Britain, [1603–1837]; with notes and questions. 12°. 75c .... *Nelson.*

History of a great mind. Hinsdale, B. A. 10c. *Chase.*

History of Henry Esmond. *See* Thackeray, W. M.

History of Henry Milner. *See* Sherwood, *Mrs.* M. M.

History of Huguenots. 18°. 75c .... *Am. S. S.*

History of Irish martyrs. cr. 12°. $2; $2.50 .. *Sadlier.*

History of Irish saints. cr. 12°. $2.50; $3.50 .. *Sadlier.*

History of the Italian war of 1859. [Germ.] 8°. pap., 25c. .... *De Witt.*

History of Jericho. ill. sq. 18°. '61. 30c ..... *Am. Tr.*

History of Joseph. [Toy-book.] ill. sq. 12°. '71. bds., 50c. — 4°. $1; 50c .... *Routledge.*

History of Joseph. Winslow, O. $1.25 ..... *Carter.*

History of little Tom Thumb. ill. f°. 15c.; 20c. *J. E. Potter.*

History of a lost purse; or, Jessie and her friends. ill. 16°. 75c .... *Bost. Am. Tr.*

History of Lucy Neville. 18°. 18c .... *Am. S. S.*

History of Madagascar, embr. progress of the Christian mission in that island. 18°. 80c .... *Am. S. S.*

History of Mary and Lucy Gutzlaff; [also] Blind Cecilia. 18°. 25c. .... *Pres. Bd.*

History of Maryland; with brief biog. of statesmen, philanthropists, theologians, etc. ill. 12°. hf. bds., 60c .... *Butler.*

History of Micah, the Ephraimite, and his house of gods. 18°. 50c. .... *Am. S. S.*

History of Minna and her lamb and her doves. 18°. 35c. .... *Pres. Bd.*

History of the Moravian missions among the Indians in No. Am. 12°. (Lond.) '38. 90c ...... *Clauder.*

History of Moses, the lawgiver. [Toy-book.] ill. sq. 12°. '71. bds., 50c. — 4°. $1; 50c... *Routledge.*

History of a mouthful of bread. *See* Macé, J.

History of my friends. Achard, E. $1.50..*Putnam.*

History of my pets. Lippincott, S. J. $1..**Osgood.*

History of origin, endowments and claims of the widows' fund of the Ref. Dutch Ch. 12°. pap., 10c. ....*N. Y. Ref. Ch. Bd.*

History of the Orissa mission. 18°. 60c....*Am. S. S.*

History of orphan asylum in Phila. 18°. 30c...*Am. S. S.*

History of Orrin Pierce. 18°. 30c.........*Am. S. S.*

History of Pendennis. *See* Thackeray, W. M.

History of a penitent. Bethune, G. W. 60c. *N. Y. Ref. Ch. Bd.*

History of a pocket Prayer-book. 18°. 90c...*Dutton.*

History of the Prayer book; by author of "One year." 18°. 75c. ....*Pott.*

History of Prince Perrypets. Knatchbull-Hugessen, L. $1.50........................*Macmillan.*

History of Rasselas. *See* Johnson, S:

History of the robins. *See* Trimmer, *Mrs.* S. K.

History of Salem witchcraft: review of C. W. Upham's work; with notes. 12°. '72. $1... *Wells.*

History of Sandford and Merton. *See* Day, T:

History of the Sandwich Islands. 18°. 65c...*Am. S. S.*

History of Susan Elmaker; or, an answer to the question, "If a man die shall he live again?" 18°. 55c...............................*Am. S. S.*

History of Susan Gray. Sherwood, M. M. 45c. *Routledge.*

History of Switzerland, B. C. 110–A. D. 1830. 12°. 75c. *Harper.*

History of Thomas and Joseph. 18°. 22c...*Am. S. S.*

History of Thomas Brown: reasons for observing the Sabbath. [In rhyme.] 18°. 18c. ....*Am. S. S.*

History of a threepenny bit. ('69.) New ed. 18°. '73. 75c...........................*Nat. Temp.*

History of Tom Jones. *See* Fielding, H.

History of Tom Thumb. [Toy-book.] ill. 4°. $1; 50c..............................*Routledge.*

History of two lives. Sanford, L. E. 50c...*Nat. Temp.*

History of the U. S.: pict. description. 8°. $2..*Lee & S.*

History of the war in La Vendée. 12°. $1.25; $1.75. *Sadlier.*

History of William and Mary College [Va.], 1660–1874. 8°. '74. pap., 50c.......*J. W. Randolph.*

History primers. *See* Green, J. R.

Histrionic speaker. 12°. pap., 15c. ....*De Witt.*

Hit him, he has no friends. Yates, E., *and* Harrington, N. H. 15c...................*French; Lee & S.*

Hit or miss. Pocock, I. 15c...............*French.*

Hitchcock, C: H. *See* Hitchcock, E. *and* C. H.—New Hampshire geol. survey;—Vermont geol. survey.

Hitchcock, E: Autobiography; or, reminiscences of Amherst Coll. pl., map and por. 12°. '63. $1.75. *Bridgman.*

— Dyspepsia forestalled and resisted: lectures on diet, regimen and employment. ('30.) New ed. 12°. '31. $1.........................*Bridgman.*

— History of a zoological temperance convention. 16°. 75c. ....*Nat. Temp.*

— Illustrations of surface geology. 4°. '57. pap., $4. *Smith. Inst.*

— Life and labors of Ma. Lyon. ill. 12°. '58. $1..*Am. Tr.*

— Memoir of Ma. Lyon, founder of Mt. Holyoke Sem. ('51.) New ed. ill. 12°. '76. $1.25..*Bridgman.*

— *See also* Massachusetts geol. survey;—Vermont geol. survey.

— *and* C: H. Elementary and popular treatise on geology. ill. 12°. '60. $1.60...........*Ivison.*

— *and* E: *jr.* Anatomy and physiology. ill. 12°. '60. $1.60..................................*Ivison.*

Hitchcock, E: *jr.* *See* Hitchcock, E: *and* E: *jr.*;—Vermont geol. survey.

Hitchcock, Ethan Allen. Christ the spirit: attempt to state the primitive views of Christianity. 2 v. 12°. $3..............................*Miller.*

Hitchcock, I. Irvine. Book-keeping: journal and ledger. 4°. '25. $1.—Key. 75c...*Nichols & H.*

Hitchcock, Roswell Dwight. Analysis of the Bible: Old and New Test. arranged [by] subjects on the basis of M. Talbot; with indexes, tables, etc., by N. West, [also] Cruden's concordance; rev. by J. Eadie. ill. and map. 8°. '70. *$6.75; hf. mor., $8.75........................(?)*A. J. Johnson.*

— Life and character of Rev. E. Robinson. 16°. '63. 50c...................................*Randolph.*

— *and* Eddy, Z., *and* Schaff, P. Hymns and songs for social and Sabbath worship. 4°. '75. $1.20; $1.25; mor., $4.50; $6.............*Randolph.*

— — — Hymns and songs of praise; for public and social worship. 8°. '74. $2.25–$7.50; without tunes, $1.75–$6.50.................*Randolph.*

Hitchman, W. Consumption: its nature, prevention and homœop. treatment; with ill. of homœop. practice. 12°. 75c. ....*Boericke.*

Hitherto. Whitney, A. D. T. $2..........*Loring.*

Hittell, J: S. Brief history of culture. 12°. $1.50. *Appleton.*

— Resources of California. ('63.) 6th ed., rev. 12°. '74. $1.75; pap., $1.25..............*Roman.*

Hittell, Thdr. H. *See* California, General laws;—Nevada, Sup. Court reports.

Hive (The) and its wonders. 18°. 45c......*Am. S. S.*

Hoadly, B. Suspicious husband: comedy. 16°. pap., 15c....................................*French.*

Hoadly, E. S. *See* Mason, W., *and* Hoadly, E. S.

Hoadly, L. Ives. Guide to the new convert: a preparation to profess religion. 18°. 40c..*Cong. Pub.*

Hoare, G. T. (*ed.*) True stories of brave deeds. ill. 12°. $1.25...................*Scribner, W. & A.*

Hoare, Prince. [Farces.] 4 v. 16°. ea., pap., 15c. *French.*

Cont.: Lock and key.—My grandmother.—No song, no supper.—Spoiled child.

Hoaryhead and M'Donner. Abbott, J. $1.75..*Harper.*

Hobart, *Mrs.* C: Changed cross. ill. 24°. '74. 75c. *Randolph.*

— *See also* Changed cross.

Hobart, J: H: Catechism. 18°. bds., 10c...*Dutton.*

— Companion for the festivals and fasts of the Prot. Episc. Ch.; sel. and altered from Nelson's Companion; with forms of devotion. 23d ed. 12°. '71. $1.50..............................*Dutton.*

— Companion to the Prayer book. 12°. pap., 10c...*Dutton.*

— Life. 18°. 60c...........................*Dutton.*

— Office of devotion, and short office of devotion; with sel. of hymns and carols. 18°. pap., 10c...*Dutton.*

Hobart, W. C. E. *See* Butler, J., Analogy.

Hobbs, A. I. Philosophy of getting religion. 8°. pap., 10c. ....*Chase.*

Hobbs, J. H. Architectural designs for country and suburban residences. ill. 8°. $3....*Lippincott.*

Hoblyn, R: D. Dictionary of terms used in medicine and the collateral sciences. New ed., rev. and enl. by I. Hays. roy. 12°. $1.50; leath., $2..*Lea.*

Höchst wunderbaren Schicksale (Die) u. Abenteuer d. Knopfmacher-Gesellen Pechmann aus Leipzig. ill. 12°. pap., 15c...........*F. W. Thomas.*

Hochzeitsgeschenk. *See* Luther, M.

Hodder, Edn. ["Old Merry."] Book-stall boy of Batherton. ill. 16°. '73. 75c.........*Lothrop.*

— Cook's all the world over. 2 v. 12°. ea., $1.75..*Cook.*

— Fireside chats with youngsters. sq. 12°. $1.25. *Claxton.*

— *Same.* ill. 16°. $1.75.............*Scribner, W. & A.*

— Junior clerk. ('71.) 2d ed. 16°. '74. 75c...*So. Meth.*

— — *See also* Silver beach lib.

Hodder, Edn., *continued.*
— Old Merry's travels on the continent. ill. 16°. $1. *Scribner, W. & A.*
— *Same.* ill. 16°. $1.25 .... *Lippincott.*
— On holy ground: travels in Palestine. 12°. '74. $1.50. *Meth. Bk. Conc.*
— Tossed on the waves: story of young life. ('72.) 3d ed. 16°. '76. 75c. .... *So. Meth.*

Hodder, G. *See* Stoddard, R. H. Bric-a-brac ser.

Hodgdon, N. C. Denominational offering; from the literature of Universalism. 12°. '70. $1.50. *Universalist.*

Hodge, Arch. A. Atonement. 12°. $1.50 .. *Pres. Bd.*
— Commentary on Conf. of faith. 12°. $1.50 .. *Pres. Bd.*
— Outlines of theology. ('60.) New ed. 12°. '75. $2. *Carter.*
— *Same.* 8°. $2 .... *Pres. Bd.*
— Questions on theol. adapted to lectures of H. on dialectics, etc. 12°. '67. *net*, $1 ... *R. S. Davis (P.)*

Hodge, C. Commentaries. 4 v. 12°. ea., $1.75. *Pres. Bd.*

Cont.: On Ephesians. — On Romans. — On 1 Corinthians. — On 2 Corinthians.

— *Same.* ('56–'59.) New ed. 4 v. 12°. '72–'74. ea., $1.75 .... *Carter.*
— Commentary on Romans. 8°. $4; — abridg. ed. 12°. $1.75 .... (?) *Martien.*
— Constitutional hist. of the Presb. Ch. in the U. S. 2 v. in 1. 8°. $3 .... *Pres. Bd.*
— Essays and reviews. 8°. $3 .... *Carter.*
— Questions on Romans; for Bible classes, etc. 18°. 30c. .... *Pres. Bd.*
— Systematic theology. 3 v. and index. 8°. '71–'72. v. 1, 2, ea., $4.50; 3, $5; index, $1; per set, $15; $12; — in 3 v., hf. cf., $22.50 .... *Scribner.*
— Way of life. 16°. mor., $4. — 12°. $1.25; $1.50. — ill. 18°. 85c. .... *Am. S. S.*
— What is Darwinism? 12°. '74. $1.50 .... *Scribner.*
— What is Presbyterianism? 18°. 35c. ..... *Pres. Bd.*

Hodge, H: Linear perspective. 4°. bds., 75c. *Putnam.*

Hodge, Hu: Lenox. Fœticide; or, criminal abortion. 4th ed. 24°. '72. 50c.; pap., 30c. ..... *Lindsay.*
— Note-book for cases of ovarian tumors, and other abdominal enlargements. 12°. '76. 50c. .. *Lindsay.*
— On diseases peculiar to women; incl. displacements of the uterus. ill. 8°. $4.50 .... *Lea.*
— Principles and practice of obstetrics. lith. pl. and wood-cuts. 4°. $14 .... *Lea.*

Hodges, D. F. Living waters: collection of sacred songs. 16°. '75. bds., 30c.; pap., 25c. .. *Ditson.*
— Sacred crown: hymn tunes, anthems, etc. obl. 16°. $1.50 .... *Lee & S.*
— *See also* Baker, B. F., *and* Hodges, D. F.
— *and* Foster, G. W. Morning star: music for choirs, singing schools, etc. obl. 16°. $1.50 .. *Lee & S.*
— — *and* Tenney, J. H. Anthem offering. [Music.] obl. 16°. $1 .... *Lee & S.*
— *and* Tenney, J. H. Golden sunbeams: music for the S.-school and home circle. obl. 4°. pap., 30c.; bds., 35c. .... *Lee & S.*

Hodges, E: Trinity collection of church music; with add. by S. P. Tuckerman. obl. 4°. '64. $2.75: bds., $2.50 .... *Ditson.*

Hodges, F. H. Evening service in C. [Church music.] 4°. $1.25 .... *Gordon.*

Hodges, J. S. B. Book of common praise. 16°. 25c. *Huntington.*

Hodges, Ja. Construction of the great Victoria Bridge, in Canada. 2 v. pl. and ill. imp. 4°. and roy. f°. (Weale.) '60. hf. mor., $30 .. *Spon.*

Hodges, R: M. Practical dissections. roy. 12°. hf. bd., $2 .... *Lea.*

Hodges, W: Baptism, tested by Scripture and history. 12°. '73. $2 .... *Dutton.*

Hodgson, F. Ecclesiastical polity of Methodism. 18°. 35c. .... *Cin. Meth. Bk. Conc.*

Hodgson, F., *continued.*
— System of new divinity examined. 12°. '39. 85c. *Meth. Bk. Conc.*

Hodgson, Fs. Mythology for Latin versification. New ed., rev. by F. C. Hodgson. 12°. '71. $1.25. *Macmillan.*

Hodgson, W: Historical memoirs of the Society of Friends. 2d ed. 12°. '67. $1.75 ... *Lippincott.*
— Reformers and martyrs. 12°. $2 ...... *Lippincott.*

Hoerman, A. S. Aner's return; or, the migrations of a soul: allegorical tale; tr. by I. A. Bergrath. 12°. $1.50 .... *O'Shea.*

Hoey, *Mrs.* Cashel. Blossoming of an aloe. 8°. pap., 50c. .... *Harper.*
— Golden sorrow (A). 8°. pap., 50c. .... *Harper.*
— House of cards. 8°. '69. pap., 75c. .... *Littell & G.*

Hofacker, L: Das Heil in Christus. 18°. '52. 50c. *Am. Tr.*
— Predigten. 8°. $2.50–$7 .... *Kohler.*

Höfer, E: The old countess; tr. from the Germ. 12°. $1 .... *Lippincott.*

Hofer. Ball, E. 15c. .... *French.*

Hoffert, H. Guide to the sewage question for 1876. 8°. '76. pap., 40c. .... *Spon.*

Hoffman, C: Fenno. Catechisings on the Collects. 18°. 45c. .... *Dutton.*
— Lays of the Hudson. ill. 32°. 38c. .... *Appleton.*
— Poems; collected and ed. by E. F. Hoffman. por. 16°. '75. $1.75 .... *Porter.*

Hoffman, D: Legal outlines: lectures. 8°. shp., $4. *Baker, V. & Co.*

Hoffman, *Rev.* Eug. A: Eucharistic week. 32°. '70. 50c. .... *Dutton.*
— Weekly eucharist. 18°. pap., 12c. .... *Dutton.*

Hoffman, Ma. J. Agnes Hilton; or, practical views of Catholicity: tale of trials and triumphs. 12°. $1.50 .... *O'Shea.*
— Alice Murray. 12°. $2 .... *O'Shea.*
— Felix Kent; or, the new neighbors. 12°. $2 .. *O'Shea.*
— Orphan sisters. 12°. $1.50; $2 .... *Sadlier.*

Hoffman, Murray. Ecclesiastical law in N. Y. [State]. 8°. '68. $2.50; shp., $3 .... *Pott.*
— Law and practice as to references, and powers and duties of referees; with notes and forms. 8°. '75. shp., $6.50 .... *Ward & P.*
— Provisional remedies of the [N. Y.] code of procedure. 8°. shp., $5 .... *Baker, V. & Co.*
— Ritual law of the church; with its application to communion and baptismal offices. 8°. '72. $4; shp., $4.50 .... *Pott.*
— Treatise on the practice of the Court of Chancery; with forms. 3 v. 8°. shp., $20. — v. 3 [forms], sep., $5 .... *Baker, V. & Co.*
— *See also* New York, Chancery reports.

Hoffman, Ogden. *See* United States, Dist. Court reports.

Hoffmann, Elisha A. Evergreen: S.-school music book. ('73.) 6th ed. obl. 16°. '75. 35c.; 50c., 75c. .... *Ev. Assoc.*
— Happy songs for the S.-school, the social meeting and the home circle. 12°. '76. 50c.; bds., 35c.; pap., 25c. .... *Ev. Assoc.*
— *See also* Tenney, J. N., *and* Hoffmann, E. A.; — Yeokel, R., *and* Hoffmann, E. A.

Hoffmann, Ern. Thdr. Nutcracker and mouseking: a legend; tr. cr. 8°. '75. 75c. .. *Lockwood, B. & Co.*

Hoffmann, Fz. Erzählungen. v. 1–52. 18°. ea., 20c.; 30c.; pap., 15c.; — 2 v. in 1, ea., 50c.; — 4 v. in 1, ea., 75c. .... *Kohler.*

Cont.: 1. Geyer Wälty. — 2. Liebet eure Feinde. — 3. Prüfungen. — 4. Oheim und Neffe. — 5. Die Macht des Gewissens. — 6. Der Ansiedler am Strande. — 7. René. — 8. Der Schein trügt. — 9. Jeder ist seines Glückes Schmied. — 10. Reue versöhnt. — 11. Willy. — 12. Der Goldsucher. — 13. Weihnachten. — 14. Mutterlieb. — 15. Furchtlos und treu. — 16. Die Strandfischer. — 17. Brave Leute. — 18. Die Waisen. — 19. Treue gewinnt. — 20. Wilhelm Tell. — 21. Im Schnee begraben. — 22.

Hoffmann, Fz., *continued.*
Hüte dich vor dem ersten Fehltritt. — 23. Loango. — 24. Die Banknote. — 25. Der Vogelhändler. — 26. Beharrlichkeit führt zum Ziel. — 27. Eigensinn und Busse. — 28. Nur Kleinigkeiten. — 29. In demselben Hause. — 30. Wie die Saat so die Erndte. — 31. Nemesis. — 32. Der Pachthof. — 33. Der Tugenden Vergeltung. — 34. Die Lebensversicherung. — 35. Der Schatz des Inka. — 36. Ehre Vater und Mutter. — 37. Ein Wort, ein Mann. — 38. Folgen des Leichtsinns. — 39. Das treue Blut. — 40. Aus eiserner Zeit. — 41. Nur immer brav. — 42. Bange Tage. — 43. Untreue schlägt den eigenen Herrn. — 44. Moschele. — 45. Die Auswanderer. — 46. Hilda, oder Gott lenkt. — 47. Das Pfarrhaus. — 48. Lebenskämpfe. — 49. Erich, oder der Segen des Herrn macht reich. — 50. Robert, oder hoch im Norden. — 51. Alli, od. selig sind die Barmherzigen. — 52. Hans, od. ein Bibelblatt.
— Erzählungen. 4 v. 16°. ea., 25c. .... *Morwitz.*
Cont.: Neger u. Weisse, etc. — Der Widerspenstige. — Kleines ist die Wiege des Grossen, etc. — Die Henkeldukaten, etc.
— *Same.* 4 v. 16°. ea., 30c.; bds., 20c.; pap., 15c. *Kohler.*
— Adventures of Leo Rembrandt; tr. by L. H. Steiner. ill. 16°. 90c. .... *Ref. Ch. Pub.*
— Anton, the fisherman; tr. (Fatherland ser.) ill. 16°. 85c. .... (?) *Luth. Pub.*
— Buried in the snow; tr. (Fatherland ser.) ill. 16°. 80c. .... (?) *Luth. Pub.*
— Deutsche Volksmärchen. 16°. '64. bds., 25c. .. *Steiger.*
— Dominic; tr. (Fatherland ser.) ill. 16°. $1.10. (?) *Luth. Pub.*
— Father Miller; tr. by L. H. Steiner. ill. 16°. 75c. *Ref. Ch. Pub.*
— Fritz; or, filial obedience; tr. (Fatherland ser.) ill. 16°. 65c. .... (?) *Luth. Pub.*
— Geyer Wälty; or, fidelity rewarded; tr. (Fatherland ser.) ill. 16°. $1 .... (?) *Luth. Pub.*
— Gipsy Fred; tr. 16°. $1.25 .... (?) *Martien.*
— Hartz boys; tr. ill. 16°. '72. $1.25 ...... *Lothrop.*
— Little things are the germs of greatness. *See* American youth's lib.
— Mozart's early days; tr. by Mrs. C. A. Smith. ('73.) New ed. 16°. '74. $1 .... *Hoyt.*
— Old school master; tr. by L. H. Steiner. ill. 16°. 90c. .... *Ref. Ch. Bd.*
— René, the little Savoyard; tr. (Fatherland ser.) ill. 16°. 85c. .... (?) *Luth. Pub.*
— Sagen u. Märchen. 16°. '68. bds., 25c. ... *Steiger.*
— Sagen vom Rübezahl. 16°. '68. bds., 25c. .. *Steiger.*
— Three bank-notes; tr. by R. H. Shively. (Fatherland ser.) 16°. '75. 85c. .... (?) *Luth. Pub.*
— Treasure of the Inca; tr. (Fatherland ser.) ill. 16°. 85c. .... (?) *Luth. Pub.*
— Under the earth; tr. (Fatherland ser.) ill. 16°. 70c. .... (?) *Luth. Pub.*

Hoffmann, F: Manual of chem. analysis as applied to exam. of med. chemicals. 8°. $3 .... *Appleton.*
— (*ed.*) Popular health almanac for 1876. 12°. '75. pap., 10c. .... *Steiger.*

Hoffmann, H: Kindergarten toys and how to use them. ill. 12°. '74. pap., 20c. .... *Steiger.*

Hoffmann, H: Der Struwelpeter. ill. 8°. bds., 25c. *Radde.*
— *Same.* ill. 4°. bds., 75c. .... *Witter.*

Hoffmann, Jul. Erzählungen. 4 v. 16°. ea., 25c. *Morwitz.*
Cont.: Ich sehe dich schon. — Du sollst nicht stehlen. — Grossvaters Liebling. — Der schwarze Sam.
— *Same.* 4 v. 16°. ea., 30c.; bds., 20c.; pap., 15c. *Kohler.*
— Floating on the ice; — Grandfather's darling; — Oh, I see you. *See* American youth's lib.

Hofland, *Mrs.* Barb. [Tales.] 12 v. ill. 18°. ea., 50c. *Porter.*
Cont.: Affectionate brothers. — Alicia and her aunt. — Barbadoes girl. — Blind farmer and his children. — Clergyman's widow. — Daughter of a genius. — Ellen, the teacher. — Good grandmother and her offspring. — Merchant's widow. — Officer's widow. — Sisters. — Son of a genius.
— Affectionate brothers. ill. 16°. 50c. .... *Nelson.*
— Alicia and her aunt; or, think before you speak. ill. 16°. 50c. .... *Nelson.*
— Barbadoes girl. 12°. pap., 25c. .... *U. P. James.*
— Blind farmer. ill. 16°. 50c. .... *Nelson.*

Hofland, *Mrs.* Barb., *continued.*
— Book-case lib. 4 v. ill. 12°. $4 .... *Nelson.*
Cont.: Humility. — Integrity. — Decision. — Reflection.
— Czarina (The): romance of court of Russia. 8°. pap., 50c. .... *Harper.*
— Daniel Dennison and the Cumberland statesman. 8°. pap., 50c. .... *Harper.*
— Playfellow (The). ill. 12°. $1 .... *Nelson.*
— Son of a genius. ill. 18°. 75c. .... *Barnes; Harper.*
— Stolen boy. 18°. pap., 25c. .... *U. P. James.*
— Unloved one: a domestic story. 8°. '44. pap., 50c. *Harper.*
— Way of the world. ill. 12°. $1 .... *Nelson.*
— Young Crusoe; or, the shipwrecked boy. ill. 18°. 75c. .... *Harper.*
— *Same.* ill. 12°. $1 .... *Nelson.*

Hofland, T: Cp. British angler's manual; enl. by E. Jesse. 12°. (Bohn.) $2.75 ...... *Little, B. & Co.*
— *Same.* 12°. (Bohn.) $3 .. *Lippincott; Scribner, W. & A.*

Hofman, L. (*ill.*) *See* Goethe, J. W. v., Faust; Hermann u. Dorothea.

Hofmann, C: Practical treatise on manufacture of paper. ill. and pl. 4°. '73. $15 .... *Baird.*

Hofmann, D. C. G. Institutiones theologiae exegeticae. New ed. 12°. '76. $1.50 .... *Barthel.*

Hofsten, H. Lena; or, the Stark family; tr. by C. Larsen. 16°. '76. $1 .... *Cin. Meth. Bk. Conc.*

Hogarth, J. *See* Hogarth, W:

Hogarth, W: Works; with life and anec. descrip. of the pictures; with fac simile-eng. from orig. reduced by J. Ireland and J. Nichols. 3 v. 12°. $9 .... *Routledge.*
— Works: 148 eng. by Cooke and Davenport, with descrip. and comments by Rev. J. Trusler; anecdotes by J. Hogarth, Ireland, etc. 2 v. 4°. $20; hf. mor., $28; mor., $33. — New [chp.] ed. 4°. $15; hf. mor., $20; mor., $27.50 ... *Miller.*

Hoge, *Mrs.* A. H. The boys in blue; or, heroes of the rank and file. ('67.) New ed. ill. 8°. '68. *$3; $3.50 .... *Treat.*

Hoge, W: J. Blind Bartimeus; or, the story of a sightless sinner and his great physician. ('58.) New ed. 18°. '61. 50c. .... *Am. Tr.*

Hogg, C: Pullar. Tables for setting out railway curves: cards arrang. with explanations and examples. '72. $2 .... *Spon.*

Hogg, Jabez. Elements of experimental and natural philosophy. 12°. (Bohn.) $1.75 .. *Little, B. & Co.*
— *Same.* 12°. (Bohn.) $2 .. *Lippincott; Scribner, W. & A.*
— The microscope. ill. and pl. 12°. $3.50; hf. cf., $5.50 .... *Routledge.*

Hogg, Ja. ["Ettrick Shepherd."] Loves and adventures. ill. 12°. $1.50 .... *World Pub.*
— Mountain bard; [also] Forest minstrel: legendary ballads and songs. ill. 32°. 60c.; 90c; mor., $1.50 .... *Porter.*
— *See also* Noctes ambrosianæ.

Hogg, M. H. Doctor Dunbar. ill. 16°. '74. 75c. .. *Nelson.*

Hogg, T: E. Fate of Marvin, and other poems. 12°. '73. $2 .... *E. H. Cushing.*

Hogue, D. P. *See* Florida, Sup. Court reports.

Hohensteins (The). Spielhagen, F. $2 ...... *Holt.*

Hohmann, Chr. H: Practical course of instruction in singing; tr. from the Germ. 4 v. 12°. '58. bds., pt. 1, 30c.; 2, 20c.; 3, 4, 40c.; 2, 3 and 4, 45c. .... *Ditson.*

Hoke, Jac. Age we live in: its dangers and duties. 12°. $1.20 .... *Un. B. Pub.*
— Holiness; or, the higher Christian life. 12°. 75c. *Un. B. Pub.*

Holbach, Pl. T. (*Baron*) d'. Good sense; tr. 12°. $1 .... *Mendum.*
— Letters to Eugenia; or, a preservative against religious prejudice; tr. by A. C. Middleton. 12°. $1. *Mendum.*

Holbach, Pl. T. (*Baron*) d', *continued.*
— System of nature; or, laws of the moral and physical world; tr. by H. D. Robinson. 2 v. in 1. 8°. $2 .... *Mendum.*
Holbeach, H: Holidays at Limewood. ill. 16°. 50c. *Routledge.*
— Shoemaker's village. cr. 8°. '71. $1.75 .. *Routledge.*
— Student in life and philosophy: narrative and discussion. 2 v. post 8°. $7 .... *Routledge.*
Holbein, Hs. (*ill.*) Dance of death, and Bible cuts: 150 eng. in fac-simile; with introd. and descriptions by F. Douce and T. F. Dibdin. 2 v. in 1. 12°. (Bohn.) $2.75 .... *Little, B. & Co.*
— *Same.* 12°. (Bohn.) $3. *Lippincott; Scribner, W. & A.*
Holbrook, Alfr. Complete English grammar. 12°. 90c. .... *Stevens.*
— Normal methods of teaching. 4th ed. 12°. '76. $1.50. *Barnes.*
— Normal singer. sm. 4°. '63. 30c. .... *Stevens.*
— School management. 8°. '70. $1.50 .... *Stevens.*
— Training lessons in grammar. 12°. '72. 60c... *Stevens.*
— Writing speller. sm. 4°. '70. pap., 15c.... *Stevens.*
Holbrook, J. C. Prairie breaking; or, scenes in the life of a western pastor. ('63.) New ed. ill. 18°. '69. 45c. .... *Hoyt.*
Holbrook, J. H. Ten years among the mail-bags; or, notes from the diary of a special agent of the Post-Office Dept. ill. cr. 8°. '74. *$2.50. *Cowperthwait.*
Holbrook, Jos. P. Quartet and chorus choir. 4°. '70. $3; hf. bd., $2.50 .... *Barnes.*
Holbrook, M. L. "Eating for strength." 4th ed. 12°. '74. $1 .... *Wood & H.*
— Parturition without pain: directions for avoiding most of the pains and dangers of child-bearing. 16°. '70. $1 .... *Wood & H.*
Holbrook, N. M. Arithmetic. ('49.) New ed. 12°. '74. hf. bd., 31c. .... *Bailey.*
Holcombe, Ja. P. Introduction to equity jurisprudence, on basis of Story's commentaries; with notes and ref. to Eng. and Am. cases. 8°. '46. shp., $3 .... *Clarke.*
— Law of debtor and creditor in the U. S. and Canada. 8°. shp., $4 .... *Appleton.*
— Literature in letters. 12°. $2; hf. cf., $4.50. *Appleton.*
Holcombe, W: H. Directions for treatment of dengue and yellow fever. *See* Shipman, G. E., Homœopathic family guide.
— How I became a homœopath. 8°. pap., 15c... *Boericke.*
— In both worlds. 16°. $1.25 .... *Lippincott.*
— Other life (The). 12°. $1.50 .... *Lippincott.*
— Our children in heaven. 16°. $1.25 .... *Lippincott.*
— Our future life: [phonograpic]; with key. 12°. '76. 25c. .... *Burns.*
— Sexes (The), here and hereafter. 12°. $1.50. *Lippincott.*
— Southern voices. [Poetry.] 12°. $1.50 .. *Lippincott.*
— What is homœopathy? 8°. pap., 15c..... *Boericke.*
— Yellow fever and its homœop. treatment. 12°. pap., 38c. .... *Boericke.*
Holcombes (The). Magill, M. T. $1.50 .. *Lippincott.*
Holcroft, T: Deaf and dumb: drama. 16°. pap., 15c. .... *French.*
— Road to ruin: comedy. 16°. pap., 15c..... *French.*
Hold him, please. *See* Prairie books.
Hold your tongue. Planché, J. R. 15c....... *French.*
Holden, C. F. Book on birds. ('72.) 2d ed. 16°. '76. 40c.; pap., 25c. .... *Holden.*
Holden, E. S. Notes on the bastion system of fortification: its defects and their remedies. 8°. '72. pap., 50c. .... *Van Nostrand.*
Holden, Edg. The sphygmograph: its physiol. and pathol. indications. ill. 8°. '74. $3 ...... *Lindsay.*
Holden, Luther. Human osteology: descript. of the bones, with delineations of the attachments of the muscles, etc. ill. 8°. $6 .... *Lindsay.*
— Manual of the dissection of the human body; with notes and add. by E. Mason. ill. 8°. '68. $5. *De Witt; Lindsay.*
Holden, W. A. History of Queensbury, N. Y.; with account of aborigines of north. N. Y. por. and pl. 8°. '74. $5 .... *Munsell.*
Holden with the cords. Woodruff, J. L. M. $2 .. *Dutton.*
Holdich, Jos. Life of A. H. Hurd. 18°. '41. 55c. *Meth. Bk. Conc.*
— Life of Rev. Wilbur Fisk. 8°. $2.50 ...... *Harper.*
— Questions on hist. parts of the Old Test. 2 v. 18°. per doz., ea., $1.80 .... *Meth. Bk. Conc.*
Holdsworth, W. A. Law of bills of exchange, promissory notes, cheques, etc. 16°. '74. bds., 50c. *Routledge.*
Hole, C: Brief biog. dict; with add. and corr. by W. A. Wheeler. 16°. $1.50 .... *Hurd & H.*
Hole in the bag. Ballard, J. P. $1 ...... *Nat. Temp.*
Hole in the bag ser. 4 v. 12°. $4 .... *Nat. Temp.*
Cont.: Hole in the bag, by J. P. Ballard. — Jewelled serpent, by E. J. Richmond. — Time will tell, by Mrs. Wilson. — Zoa Rodman, by E. J. Richmond.
Hole in the pocket. Baker, H. N. W. $1.25. *H. A. Young.*
Holiday (The). 18°. 25c. .... *Am. S. S.*
Holiday afternoons. 18°. 70c.; 85c....... *Am. Bapt.*
Holiday album for boys; — for girls. ill. 16°. '74. ea., $1 .... *Lothrop.*
Holiday book. *See* Theodore Thinker.
Holiday camp. Corbet, R. St. J. $1.25 .. *Routledge.*
Holiday chaplet. *See* Tucker, *Mrs.* C.
Holiday fun. *See* Picture puzzle toy books.
Holiday guest: stories, tricks, tableaux, etc. ill. 4°. pap., 10c. .... *Happy.*
Holiday hours improved. 18°. 65c. .... *Am. S. S.*
Holiday house. Sinclair, C. 75c. .... *Carter.*
Holiday letters from Athens, Cairo and Weimar. Edwards, M. B. $2 .... *Routledge.*
Holiday lib. 4 v. ill. 16°. ea., 50c. .... *Pott.*
Cont.: Robin the bold. — Month at Brighton, by M. E. Shipley. — Boys and girls, by M. Bramston. — Riversdale, by C. E. Bowen.
Holiday library. *See* Seymour, M. A.
— *See also* New.
Holiday pictures. Dammast, J. S. 50c..... *Am. Tr.*
Holiday rambles. Grant, E. 50c. .... *Routledge.*
Holiday scrap-book. ill. 4°. pap., 25c..... *Am. S. S.*
Holiday ser. 3 v. 4°. ea., 50c.; pap., 25c... *Nelson.*
Cont.: Three little kittens. — Good friends, Lilly, Carrie and Floss. — Four-footed friends and favorites.
Holiday stories. *See* Dickens, C:
Holiday stories. *See* Larned, A.
Holiday stories for boys and girls. Barker, M. A. (*Lady*). $1.50 .... *Routledge.*
Holiday tales. *See* Bailey, U. L., *and* Pratt, F. L.
Holiday tales. Milford, F. 75c. .... *Nelson.*
Holiday wreath. ill. 4°. 90c.; $1.50 ...... *Am. Bapt.*
Holidays and the reasons why they are observed. 18°. 45c. .... *Pres. Bd.*
Holidays at Chestnut Hill. ill. sq. 16°. 80c... *Lee & S.*
Holidays at Limewood. Holbeach, H. 50c... *Routledge.*
Holidays at Llandudno. ill. fp. 8°. 60c...... *Cassell.*
Holidays at Wilton. ill. 16°. 25c. .... *Routledge.*
Holidays on high lands. Macmillan, H. $2 .. *Macmillan.*
Holiness. Hoke, J. 75c. .... *Un. B. Pub.*
Holiness (The) acceptable to God. Morgan, J. 75c. *Goodrich.*
Holiness as set forth in the Scriptures. Smith, H. W. 20c.; 15c. .... *Willard.*

Holiness the birthright of all God's children. Crane, J. T. $1 .... *Meth. Bk. Conc.*

Holiness through faith. S., R. P. 50c.; 75c. *Randolph.*

Holiness to the Lord. Dunn, L. R. $1 .. *Meth. Bk. Conc.*

Holl, H: Forest keeper: drama. 16°. pap., 15c. *French.*

— Grace Huntley: drama. 16°. pap., 15c. .... *French.*

Holland, *Lord.* [H: R: V. Fox.] Foreign reminiscences; ed. by his son. 12°. '51. $1.25 .. *Harper.*

Holland, C. Aspasia: an autobiography. 12°. $1.25. *Lippincott.*

Holland, H. *See* Schnorr, J., Nibelungen-Saga.

Holland, *Sir* H: Medical notes and reflections. 8°. $3.50 .... *Lea.*

— Recollections of past life: reminisc. of men, manners and things. 12°. $2 .... *Appleton.*

Holland, H: W. *See* Bennett, E. H., *and* Holland, H. W.

Holland, J. Simon. Office and cabin companion for engineers and officers of steam vessels. 2d ed. 12°. (Lond.) '64. $1.25 .... *Spon.*

Holland, J: Memoir of Rev. John Summerfield. ill. 12°. '50. 75c. .... *Am. Tr.*

Holland, Josiah Gilb. ["Tim. Titcomb."] Works. ('57–'75.) New ed. 13 v. 12°. '74–'76. $22. *Scribner.*

Cont.: Arthur Bonnicastle: story of Am. life, ill., $1.75. — Bay path: tale of New Eng. colonial life, $2. — Bitter-sweet: poem, $1.50; $2.50. — Goldfoil hammered from popular proverbs, $1.75. — Kathrina: poem, $1.50; $2.50. — Lessons in life: essays, $1.75. — Letters to the Joneses: essays, $1.75. — Marble prophecy, and other poems, ill., $1.50; $2. — Miss Gilbert's career: Am. story, $2. — Mistress of the manse: poem, $1.50. — Plain talks on familiar subjects: lectures, $1.75. — Sevenoaks: story of to-day, ill., $1.75. — Titcomb's letters to young people, $1.50; $2.50; mor., $4.

— Select works. (Brightwood ed.) 6 v. 16°. $9. *Scribner.*

Cont.: Bitter-sweet, $1.50. — Kathrina, $1.50. — Lessons in life, $1.75. — Goldfoil, $1.75. — Titcomb's letters to young people, $1.50. — Plain talks, $1.75.

— Bitter-sweet; with drawings by E. J. Whitney. ('68.) New ed. sm. 4°. '69. $9; mor., $12 .. *Scribner.*

— Garnered sheaves: complete poet. works. (Red line ed.) sq. 12°. '74. $4–$7.50 .... *Scribner.*

— History of west. Mass.; [with] account of its scientific aspects and leading interests and separate histories of its one hundred towns. 2 v. map. 8°. $4.50 .... (?) *Morris.*

— Kathrina; with drawings by W. J. Hennessy and C. C. Griswold. ('68.) New ed. sm. 4°. '69. $9; mor., $12 .... *Scribner.*

— Life of Lincoln. [In Eng. or Germ.] 8°. '65. *$3; $3.50; hf. cf., $4 .... *C. A. Nichols.*

— (*ed.*) Christ and the twelve: scenes and events in life of our Saviour and his apostles, as painted by the poets. ill. 8°. *$3.50; $4; hf. mor., $5; mor., $8 .... *C. A. Nichols.*

Holland, Just. Comprehensive method for the guitar. 4°. bds., $3.25 .... *Peters.*

— Modern method for the guitar. 4°. $2.50 .. *Brainard.*

Holland, Saba (*Lady*). Memoir of Sydney Smith; with sel. from his letters; ed. by Mrs. Austin. 2 v. 12°. $3; hf. cf., $6.50 .... *Harper.*

Holland tide. *See* Griffin, Ger.

Hollands (The). Townsend, V. F. $1.25 .. *Loring.*

Hollatz, D: Evangeliche Gnadenordnung. 18°. '46. 40c. *Am. Tr.*

— *Danish.* 18°. '51. 30c. .... *Am. Tr.*

Hollen, J. C. Original lists of persons of quality. cr. 4°. '74. hf. mor., $10; large pap., $17.50 .. *Bouton.*

Hollenius, L. J. Dollars and cents: comedy. 12°. pap., 15c. .... *De Witt.*

Holley, Alex. L. American and European railway practice in economical generation of steam. 77 lith. pl. f°. '67. $12 .... *Van Nostrand.*

— Treatise on ordnance and armor; with 493 eng. and 147 tables. 8°. '65. $10; $12 .. *Van Nostrand.*

Holley, Marietta. My opinions and Betsey Bobbet's; by Josiah Allen's wife. ill. 12°. *2.50; $3; hf. mor., $4 .... *Am. Pub.*

Holley, O. L. Life of Franklin. ill. and por. 12°. $1.75 .... *J. E. Potter.*

Hollick, F: Anatomy and physiology; with a dissected plate of the human figure. f°. $2 .... *Peterson.*

— Diseases of woman: their causes and cure familiarly expl. ill. 18°. $1 .... *Am. News.*

— Family physician. 32°. pap., 25c. .... *Peterson.*

— Male generative organs, in health and disease, from infancy to old age. ill. 18°. $1 .... *Am. News.*

— Marriage guide; or, natural history of generation. ill. 18°. $1 .... *Am. News.*

— Matron's manual of midwifery, and diseases of women during pregnancy and childbirth. ill. 18°. $1 .... *Am. News.*

— Nerves (The), and the nervous. ill. 18°. $1. *Am. News.*

— Popular treatise on venereal diseases. ill. 18°. $1. *Am. News.*

Holliday, F. C. Bible handbook, theologically arranged. 12°. $1.50 ...... *Cin. Meth. Bk. Conc.*

— Indiana Methodism. 8°. $3; $3.50. *Cin. Meth. Bk. Conc.*

Hollingshead, J: Birth-place of Podgers: farce. 16°. pap., 15c. .... *De Witt; French.*

Hollister, Gid. Hiram. History of Connecticut. 2 v. 8°. '57. $5 .... *Brown & G.*

— Thomas à Becket, a tragedy; and other poems. 16°. $1.75 .... *Lee & S.*

Hollister, J. C. Questions on Sunday evening lessons. 2 v. 18°. ea., 25c. .... *Dutton.*

— Sunday-school service and tune book. 18°. 40c. *Dutton.*

Holloway, H: C. Mental geometry: generalization of geom. demonstrations in planes, solids and spherics. 12°. '64. $1.50 .. *Claxton; Lippincott.*

Holloway, Laura Carter.• In the home of the presidents. por. and ill. cr. 8°. '75. $3.50 .. *U. S. Pub.*

Hollowdell Grange. Fenn, G. M. $1.25 .. *Routledge.*

Holly, H. H. Designs for country seats, country churches, city buildings, railway stations, etc. 8°. '63. $5 .... *Appleton.*

Holly, H. W. Art of saw-filing. 18°. '64. 75c. .. *Wiley.*

— Carpenters and joiners' handbook. 18°. '64. 75c. *Wiley.*

Holly and mistletoe; from the German. ill. 16°. $1.25. *O'Shea.*

Holly books. *See* Miller, *Mrs.* M. E.

Holly boy. S., A. G. 25c. .... *Am. Tr.*

Holly Bush Hall. Suter, W. E. 15c. .... *French.*

Holly cross. Seymour, M. A. 25c. .... *Dutton.*

Holly-tree inn. *See* Dickens, C.

Hollywood series. *See* Wise, D.

Holm, Saxe (*pseud.*) Stories. ('73.) New ed. 12°. '76. $1.50; $1.75 .... *Scribner.*

Holman, W: Fertilizers ventilated: chemical manures. 8°. '76. pap., 25c. .... (?) *J. W. Randolph.*

Holme, J: Stanford (*ed.*) Light at evening time: book of support and comfort for the aged. por. 4°. $2.50–$8 .... *Harper.*

Holmes, Alice. Very little dialogues for very little folks. 16°. pap., 30c.; bds., 50c. .... *Dick & F.*

Holmes, Arth. Parties and their principles: manual of historical and political intelligence. 12°. $1.50. *Appleton.*

Holmes, E: Life of Mozart, incl. his correspondence. 12°. $1 .... *Harper.*

Holmes, G: F. Elementary spelling book. 16°. '66. hf. bd., 18c. .... *Univ. Pub.*

— English grammar. ('67.) New ed. 12°. '71. 90c. *Univ. Pub.*

— First lessons in Eng. grammar. ill. 16°. '73. hf. bd., 50c. .... *Univ. Pub.*

Holmes, G: F., *continued.*
— Pictorial primer. 16°. '67. pap., 10c... *Univ. Pub.*
— [Readers.] 6 v. 12°. '70–'72......... *Univ. Pub.*
Cont.: First, bds., 20c.—Second, hf. bd., 35c.—Third, hf. bd., 50c.—Fourth, hf. bd., 75c.—Fifth, $1.25.—Sixth, $1.50.
— School history of the U. S., to 1870; with U. S. Constitution and Declaration of independence. maps and ill. 12°. '70. $1.50........... *Univ. Pub.*

Holmes, H. *See* Virginia, General Court reports.

Holmes, *Rev.* J: Historical sketches of the missions of the United Brethren, to 1817. 2d ed., rev. 8°. (Lond.) '27. $1..................... *Clauder.*
— History of the Church of the United Brethren. 2 v. 8°. (Lond.) '30. $5................. *Clauder.*

Holmes, *Rev.* J: Milton. A faithful ministry; ed. by G. B. Bacon. 16°. '74. $1.50......... *Lothrop.*

Holmes, *Mrs.* Ma. J. [Novels.] 17 v. 12°. ea., $1.50. *Carleton.*
Cont.: Cameron pride.—Cousin Maude.—Darkness and daylight.—Dora Deane.—Edith Lyle.—Edna Browning.—English orphans.—Ethelyn's mistake.—Homestead on the hillside.—Hugh Worthington.—'Lena Rivers.—Marian Grey.—Meadow brook.—Millbank.—Rose Mather.—Tempest and sunshine.—West Lawn.

Holmes, Mead. Soldier of the Cumberland: memoir of Mead Holmes, jr.; with introd. by J. S. Hart. por. 16°. $1..................... *Bost. Am. Tr.*

Holmes, Natl. Authorship of Shakespeare. 3d ed., rev. and enl. cr. 8°. '76. $2.50..... *Hurd & H.*

Holmes, Ol. Wendell. Astræa: the balance of illusions. 16°. '50. 75c......................... *Osgood.*
— Autocrat of the breakfast table. 18°. $1.50; hf. cf., $2.50; mor., $3..................... *Osgood.*
— Border lines in some provinces of medical science. 16°. '62. $1.............................. *Osgood.*
— Breakfast table ser. 3 v. 12°. '58–'72. ea., $2; per set, hf. cf., $12; mor., $15......... *Osgood.*
Cont.: Autocrat.—Professor at the breakfast table.—Poet at the breakfast table.
— Currents and counter-currents in medical science; with other essays. 16°. '61. $1.75..... *Osgood.*
— Elsie Venner: romance of destiny. ('61.) 12th ed. 16°. $2.............................. *Osgood.*
— Guardian angel. 16°. '67. $2............. *Osgood.*
— Humorous poems. por. sm. 4°. '65. 75c... *Osgood.*
— Mechanism in thought and morals. 16°. '71. $1. *Osgood.*
— Poems. por. 16°. $1.50.—(Blue and gold ed.) por. 32°. '62. $1.25; hf. cf., $2.50; mor., $3.—(Cabinet ed.) por. 16°. '62. $1.50; hf. cf., $3; mor., $4....................... *Osgood.*
— Songs in many keys. 16°. '61. $1.50...... *Osgood.*
— Songs of many seasons. 16°. '74. $2; hf. cf., $3.50; mor., $4.50............................ *Osgood.*
— Soundings from the "Atlantic." 16°. '63. $1.75. *Osgood.*
— *See also* Bunker Hill memorial;—Companion poets;—Laurel leaves.

Holmes, Tim. Surgery: its principles and practice. ill. 8°. '76. $6; leath., $7................ *Lea.*
— (*ed.*) System of surgery, theoretical and practical, in treatises by various authors. 5 v. ill. 8°. $45; hf. mor., $50...................... *W. Wood.*
— *See also* Power, H., Holmes, T., Anstie, F. E., *and* Barnes, R.

Holmes, W. C. Instructions for management of gas works. 8°. '74. $1.50................ *Spon.*

Holroyd, H. *See* England, Law reports.

Holst, H. v. Political and const. hist. of the U. S.; tr. by J. J. Lalor and A. B. Mason. [To form 3 v.] v. 1. 8°. '76. $3.50–$5........... *Callaghan.*

Holt, Emily Sa. Ashcliffe Hall. 16°. $1.25.. *Carter.*
— Imogene. 12°. $1.50.................... *Carter.*
— Isoult Barry. 16°. $1.50 .... *Carter.*
— Mistress Margery: tale of the Lollards. 18°. 75c. *Am. S. S.*
— *Same.* 16°. $1.... .... *Claxton.*
— Robin Tremayne. 12°. $1.50............. *Carter.*

Holt, Emily Sa., *continued.*
— Verena. 12°. $1.50 .... *Carter.*
— Well in the desert. 16°. $1.25 .... *Carter.*
— White rose of Langley. 12°. $1.50 .... *Carter.*

Holt, F. L. *See* England, Common law reports.

Holt, H. E. *See* National music course.

Holt, J. S. Abraham Page, Esq. [Fiction.] 12°. $1.50 .... *Lippincott.*
— What I know about Ben Eccles. 12°. $1.50.. *Lippincott.*

Holt, *Mrs.* M. A. God's way; or, gaining the better life. ill. 16°. '75. 90c.......... *Meth. Bk. Conc.*
— John Bentley's mistake. ('73.) New ed. 18°. '75. 50c.................................... *Nat. Temp.*
— Model landlord. ('74.) New ed. 18°. '75. 60c. *Nat. Temp.*
— Work and reward. ('73.) New ed. 18°. '74. 50c. *Nat. Temp.*

Holt, M. H. Fern Glen; or, Lilian's prayer. ill. 16°. '73. $1.25........ *Cong. Pub.; Graves; Lothrop.*
— *Same.* 16°. '72. $1.50............... *H. A. Young.*
— Lilian Grey. ill. 16°. '75. $1.25......... *Lothrop.*

Holton, I. F. New Granada: twenty months in the Andes. ill., maps and index. 8°. $3; hf. cf., $5.25 .... *Harper.*

Holy angels. 12°. '75. $2.75 .... *Pott.*
Holy child. Blackburn, W. M. 70c........ *Pres. Bd.*
Holy child of Nazareth. 18°. 30c............ *Dutton.*
Holy day stories; tr. by R. H. Shively. ill. 16°. 50c. *Ref. Ch. Pub.*
Holy days of the Church. Bradley, M. E. 50c... *Dutton.*
Holy dying. *See* Taylor, Jer.
Holy grail. *See* Tennyson, A.
Holy house of Loretto. Kenrick, P. R. $1.25. *Cummiskey.*
Holy isle; or, lives of the most notable Irish saints. 12°. 35c. .... *Benziger.*
Holy Land. *See* Juvenile picture books.
Holy life. Hopkins, E. H. 75c............... *Revell.*
Holy life. *See* Turford, H.
Holy living. *See* Taylor, Jer.
Holy Spirit resisted. Kimball, D. 40c.... *Cong. Pub.*
Holy types. Seiss, J. A. $1.50...... *Smith, E. & Co.*
Holy war. *See* Bunyan, J:
Holy way of the cross. [Cath. prayer book.] 32°. 15c.; pap., 10c. .... *Murphy; Sadlier.*
— *See also* Liguori, *St.* A. M. de.
Holy week. Maugin, C. $1.25............. *Murphy.*
Holy well. *See* Little Lottie ser.
Holy word in its own defence. *See* Silver, A.

Holyoake, Aust., *and* Watts, C: (*ed.*) Secularists' manual of songs and ceremonies; for marriages, funerals, etc. 12°. '71. 50c.......... *Somerby.*

Holyoake, G: Jac. History of cooperation in Eng.: its literature and its advocates. 12°. $2.. *Lippincott.*
— Logic of death; or, why should the atheist fear to die? 12°. pap., 10c. .... *Somerby; Mendum.*
— Logic of life; deduced from principle of freethought. 12°. 10c. .... *Somerby.*
— *See also* Paine, T:

Homans, I: Smith. Banker's almanac and register. ('51.) [Annual.] 8°. $3........... *Homans.*
— Commercial laws of the states: summary. 8°. '70. $3...................................... *Homans.*
— *See also* Wedgwood, W: B., *and* Homans, I: S.
— *and* I: S., *jr.* (*ed.*) Cyclopedia of commerce and commercial navigation. roy. 8°. $7.50; shp., $8;—in 2 v., shp., $10............... *Harper.*

Homans, I: S., *jr.* *See* Homans, I. S. *and* I. S., *jr.*

Homburg, C. Paris in Blut u. Feuer. [Paris Commune.] 8°. pap., 50c........... *F. W. Thomas.*

Home, Dan. Douglas. Incidents in my life. 12°. '74. $1.50................................ *Somerby.*

Home, H: *See* Kames, *Lord.*
Home, J: Douglas: tragedy. 16°. pap., 15c...*French.*
Home. *See* Bremer, *Miss* F.
Home. Butler, J. H. $1.50; $2............*Colby.*
Home. Ellis, S. S. $1.50..................*Harper.*
Home. Robertson, T. W. 15c.............*De Witt.*
Home. Sedgwick, C. M. $1...............*Miller.*
Home. Stockton, F. R. *and* M. E. 75c. ...*Putnam.*
Home. Tweedie, W. K. *$2.25; $3.25..*Henry Bill.*
Home; or, the unlost paradise. Palmer, R. $1.25. *Randolph.*
Home A B C. [Toy-book.] ill. roy. 8°. per gross, $48 ....(?) *McLoughlin.*
Home advice, with whispers to epicures: receipt book by a lady; with notes for dyspeptics by a physician. 12°. $1.25.........................*Harper.*
Home affections portrayed by the poets. Mackay, C. $5; $10; $12......................*Routledge.*
Home altar. Deems, C. F. $1.25........*Hurd & H.*
Home amid the snow. ill. 12°. $1............*Nelson.*
Home and abroad. 16°. $1.50............*Am. Bapt.*
Home and abroad. Taylor, B. $1.50; $2..*Putnam.*
Home and foreign birds: book for young children. ill. 16°. '73. 50c......................*Routledge.*
Home and heaven. Sangster, M. E. M. $1. *Bost. Am. Tr.*
Home and home thoughts. 18°. 75c.......*Pres. Bd.*
Home and no home. *See* Mudge, Z. A.
Home and school. ill. 16°. 50c...........*Routledge.*
Home and school lib. 5 v. ill. 16°. $2.50..*Routledge.*
Cont.: Home and school.—Little drummer.—Daddy Dacre's school, by Mrs. A. M. Hall.—Holiday rambles, by E. Grant.—A hero; Philip's book; by Mrs. Craik.
Home arts. Smith, C. L. 60c.; 75c........*Lee & S.*
Home as found. *See* Cooper, Ja. F.
Home as it should be. Barrows, L. D. 35c. *Meth. Bk. Conc.*
Home ballads; by our home poets. ill. 16°. pap., 30c. *Huntington.*
— *See also* Cottage lib.
Home ballads and poems. Whittier, J. G. $1.. *Osgood.*
Home book of hymns; — of songs. *See* Pretty picture ser.
Home book of wonders. Abbott, J. L. *$5 ....*Case.*
Home chat with our young folks. Mateaux, C. L. $2.50. *Cassell.*
Home chemist and perfumer. sq. 18°. '74. pap., 20c. (?) *F. M. Reed.*
Home circle. Paschall, A. S. *net*, $1. *Friends Bk. Assoc.*
Home companion: vocal and instrumental music. f°. $3; $4; bds., $2.50..................*Gordon.*
Home cook book. Waggoner, J. F. $1.50. *J. F. Waggoner.*
Home cook book; comp. from recipes contributed by ladies of Toledo, etc. ('74.) 2d ed. 8°. '76. $1.50.......................*Brown, E. & Co.*
Home duties: book for girls. 32°. 40c. *Scribner, W. & A.*
Home duties; or, how to cultivate sisterly affection. 18°. 35c...........................*Am. S. S.*
Home echo ser. 3 v. ill. 12°. ea., $1.50....*Lee & S.*
Cont.: Chimes for childhood.—Echoes from home.—Light at eventide.
Home fairy tales. *See* Grimm, J. L. *and* W. C.
Home fairy tales. Macé, J. $1.75; $2.25...*Harper.*
Home for all. Fowler, O. S. $1.25.......... *Wells.*
Home for a holiday. Gordon, W. 15c.......*French.*
Home for the homeless. Field, H. $3.75..*Lippincott.*
Home for the million; with plans and directions. ('57.) New ed. ill. 12°. '70. 60c.........*Pounsford.*
Home games. Smith, C. L. 60c.; 75c.......*Lee & S.*
Home in humble life. 16°. $1.............*Am. S. S.*
Home in a rough suburb. Moore, J. F. $1.25..*Hoyt.*
Home in the sea. *See* Goodrich, S. G.
Home in the west. Thurston, L. M. $1.....*Lee & S.*
Home influence. Aguilar, G. $1..*Appleton; Harper.*
Home jewels; or, Maggie Ella Colton and her brothers. 18°. 45c...........................*Pres. Bd.*
Home kindness. 4°. 50c.; pap., 25c.........*Nelson.*
Home lib. 6 v. ill. 18°. $3.60..........*Lippincott.*
Cont.: Home story book.—Grandfather's visit.—The lily.—Faithful dog.—Pet squirrel.—Pet lamb.
Home library. 20 v. 18°. $6.50...........*Am. Tr.*
Home lib. of poetry and song. 4 v. 12°. $4.50..*Lothrop.*
Cont.: Auld Scotch mither, by J. E. Rankin.—Legend of the White Hills, by Mrs. V. G. Ramsey.—Ivy leaves, by M. E. Atkinson.—Architect of Cologne, by M. E. Atkinson.
Home life. Brown, J. B. 75c............*Appleton.*
Home life. Hague, W. 90c.............*Am. Bapt.*
Home life. Sewell, E. M. $1.25..........*Appleton.*
Home life. Ware, J. F. W. $1.25 ....*Lee & S.*
Home life; or, how to make home happy. ill. 16°. '70. 90c...........................*Meth. Bk. Conc.*
Home life at Graystone Lodge. *See* Little folk lib.
Home life in the Bible. March, D. *$3.75; $6. *McCurdy.*
Home life in Germany. Brace, C. L. $1.75..*Scribner.*
Home life ser. *See* Baker, *Mrs.* H. N. W.
Home made happy. 18°. 40c.; 50c.......*Am. Bapt.*
Home made happy; or, pictures of everyday life for the family circle. ill. 12°. $1.25.......*T. Bliss.*
Home melodist: songs and ballads. 12°. '59. 35c. *Ditson.*
Home missionary. *See* Dunning, *Mrs.* A. K.
Home nook. Douglas, A. M. $1.50........*Lee & S.*
Home nursing. 16°. 20c................*Routledge.*
Home of the Gileadite, and other tales. 18°. 50c. *Am. S. S.*
Home of God's people. Gage, W. L. *$3; $3.50; $4; $6..............................*Dustin.*
Home of the lost child. Stewart, A. M. 60c. *Cath. Pub.*
Home of the mutineers; or, the history of John Adams and the other mutineers of the "Bounty." 18°. 85c............................*Am. S. S.*
Home of one's own. Lucas, W. J. 15c......*French.*
Home of the tulip. 18°. 60c...............*Dutton.*
Home picture book. Newman, E. E. $1......*Hoyt.*
Home pictures. ill. 18°. '64. 35c..........*Am. Tr.*
Home pictures. Denison, M. A. $1.50.....*Harper.*
Home pictures. *See* Little learners' toys.
Home pictures of English poets. Sanborn, K. A. $1. *Appleton.*
Home pleasures. Thurston, C. $1.25......*Am. Tr.*
Home pleasures. Windle, S. A. 40c. *Scribner, W. & A.*
Home recreations. Clarke, W. H. $1.50.. *G. D. Russell.*
Home recreations; or, how to amuse the young folks. ill. 12°. pap., 25c.....................*Haney.*
Home recreations and foreign travel. ill. 12°. $1.25. *Scribner, W. & A.*
Home religion. Mackenzie, W. B. 50c. *Carter; Cassell.*
Home scenes. Arthur, T. S. $1.50.....*J. E. Potter.*
Home scenes. Furman, C. C. $1; 80c.....*Darrow.*
Home scenes: 14 photographs. sm. 4°. '65. $3; mor., $5..............................*Am. Tr.*
Home scenes and heart studies. Aguilar, G. $1. *Appleton.*
Home scenes and home influence. *See* Arthur, T. S.
Home scenes in the Norwood family. 18°. 60c. *Cong. Pub.*
Home scenes of the New Test. Stork, T. $1; $1.25. (?) *Luth. Pub.*
Home ser. of juvenile books. *See* Haven, *Mrs.* A. B.

Home sketches in France. Field, H. M. $1.50 .. *Putnam.*
Home songs. ('59.) 2d ed. ill 16°. '65. $1 .. *Burnham.*
Home songs. Ward, M. O. 70c.; 80c. .... *Am. Tr.*
Home songs; with piano-forte accomp. 4°. '73. $2.50; bds., $2 .... *Ditson.*
Home songs for home-birds. Breed, W. P. $1 .. *Pres. Bd.*
Home songs for little people. ill. 16°. 90c. .... *Miller.*
Home stories. 16°. $1.50 .... *Graves.*
Home stories. *See* Arthur, T. S.
Home stories. *See* Grimm, J. L. *and* W. C.
Home stories. Haven, A. B. $1.25 .... *Appleton.*
Home stories for boys and girls. ill. sq. 12°. $1. *Bost. Am. Tr.*
Home story book. *See* Home lib.
Home story ser. *See* Larned, A.
Home sunshine. Bell, C. D. $1.75 .. *Scribner, W. & A.*
Home sunshine; or, bear and forbear. ill. 16°. '72. 75c. .... *Lothrop.*
Home sunshine ser. 6 v. 16°. $4.50 .... *Lothrop.*
Cont.: Home sunshine. — Alice Benson's trials. — Grace's visit. — Charley Hope. — Maggie's message. — Log house.

Home, sweet home; by author of "Little Dot." ill. 18°. 50c. .... *Nelson.*
Home tales. 4 v. 16°. $3 .... *Nelson.*
Cont.: Carry your parcel, sir? by M. Onley. — Violet Russell. — My brother Harold, by Miss Brightwell. — One of the least, by S. R. Sharman.

Home teachings in science. 16°. 50c. .. *Scribner, W. & A.*
Home tour with Aunt Bessie. *See* Books for the children's hour.
Home treasure: piano music for four hands. f°. $3; $4; bds., $2.50 .... *Gordon.*
Home truths. Ryle, J. C. 75c. *Meth. Bk. Conc.; So. Meth.*
Home twilight stories. 4 v. ill. 18°. $4 ...... *Miller.*
Cont.: Briery wood, and other stories. — Much ado about nothing. — Hero without courage. — Young fortune seekers.

Home views of the picturesque and beautiful: 68 steel eng. imp. 8°. mor., $20 ... *Cin. Meth. Bk. Conc.*
Home vineyard. Davis, C. E. K. 80c. .... *Garrigues.*
Home work. Chesebrough, A. S. $1; 40c. *Bost. Am. Tr.*
Home worship. Thompson, J. *$4 .... *Osgood.*
Home wreck. Coyne, J. S. *and* J. D. 15c. .. *French.*
Homely hints. Mogridge, G. 60c. .... *So. Meth.*
Homely scenes from great painters: 24 eng.; with text by G. W. Turner. demy 4°. $7.50 ...... *Cassell.*
Homer. [*Gk.* Homeros.] Works: Iliad, Odyssey and Hymns; tr. by G. Chapman; with introd. by Rev. R. Hooper. 5 v. 12°. (Lond.) '74. $12.50; hf. cf., $25 .... *Little, B. & Co.*
— Iliad [Gk.]; with Eng. notes, ed. by C. C. Felton. 12°. $1.75 .... *Dennet.*
— *Same;* with notes by T. H. L. Leary. 4 pts. 16°. (Weale.) ea., 60c. .... *Allyn.*
— *Same;* ed. by J. J. Owen. 12°. $2 ...... *Appleton.*
— — First 6 bks.; [with] Eng. notes, index and gloss. by C. Anthon. 12°. shp., $1.75 .... *Harper.*
— — First 6 bks.; with notes and ref. by J. R. Boise. ('68.) 7th ed. 12°. '76. $1.75 .... *Griggs.*
— *Eng.* The Iliad; tr. [into blank verse] by W. C. Bryant. 2 v. roy. 8°. '70. $9; hf. cf., $18; mor., $25. — (Roslyn ed.) 2 v. 16°. $4.50; hf. cf., $9; mor., $12; — in 1 v. 12°. $3.50; hf. cf., $6; mor., $8 .... *Osgood.*
— *Same;* lit. tr. by T. A. Buckley. 12°. $1.50 .. *Harper.*
— — *Same.* 12°. (Bohn.) $1.75 ..... *Little, B. & Co.*
— — *Same.* 12°. (Bohn.) $2. *Lippincott; Scribner, W. & A.*
— *Same;* tr. into Eng. verse by W. G. Caldcleugh. 12°. $3 .... *Lippincott.*
— *Same;* interl. tr. by T. Clark. roy. 12°. $2.75. *Desilver.*

Homer, *continued.*
— *Same;* tr. into blank verse by W. Cowper. 12°. (Bohn.) $1.25 .... *Little, B. & Co.*
— — *Same.* 12°. (Bohn.) $1.40 .... *Scribner, W. & A.*
— — *Same.* 12°. (Bohn.) $1.50 .... *Lippincott.*
— — *Same;* rev. by Southey, with notes by Dwight. sm. 8°. $2; mor., $5 .... *Appleton.*
— *Same;* [tr.] into blank verse by Edward, Earl of Derby. ('64.) New ed. 2 v. 8°. '69. $5; hf. cf., $9; — in 1 v. ('67.) New ed. cr. 8°. '71. $2.50; hf. cf., $4.50 .... *Scribner.*
— — *Same;* with biog. of Derby by R. S. Mackenzie; ill. with Flaxman's designs. 2 v. cr. 8°. $3.50; hf. cf., $7 .... *Porter.*
— *Same;* in rhymed verse by C. Merivale. 2 v. demy 8°. $8 .... *Routledge.*
— *Same;* tr. by W. Munford. 2 v. por. 8°. '46. $4. *J. W. Randolph.*
— *Same;* tr. by A. Pope. 24°. '75. 80c. .... *Barnes.*
— — *Same.* ill. 12°. $1.50 .... *World Pub.*
— — *Same.* (Chandos classics.) cr. 8°. $1; pap., 75c. *Scribner, W. & A.*
— — *Same.* (Scribner's pop. poets.) ill. 12°. $1.50. *Scribner, W. & A.*
— — *Same;* ed. by H. F. Cary. 12°. '72. $1. *Routledge.*
— — *Same;* with introd. by J. S. Watson; ill. by Flaxman's designs. 12°. (Bohn.) $1.75. *Little, B. & Co.*
— — — *Same.* 12°. (Bohn.) $2. *Lippincott; Scribner, W. & A.*
— *Same;* [condensed and expl.] by W. L. Collins. (Anc. classics for Eng. readers.) 16°. $1. *Lippincott; Little, B. & Co.*
— — Key to Iliad, by W. R. Smith. ('71.) New ed. 8°. '72. $3 .... *Claxton.*
— *Same;* [also] Odyssey; tr. by A. Pope. 3 v. 18°. $2.25 .... *Harper.*
— — — *Same.* (Chandos lib.) 12°. $1.75; hf. cf., $3.75; cf., $5 .... *Scribner, W. & A.*
— — — *Same.* (Chandos poets.) ill. cr. 8°. $3.75; cf., $7.50; mor., $8 .... *Scribner, W. & A.*
— — — *Same;* ed. by H. F. Cary. (Globe lib.) cr. 8°. '72. $1.75; hf. cf., $3.50; cf., $5. *Routledge.*
— Odyssey [Gk.]; with notes by T. H. L. Leary. 4 pts. 16°. (Weale.) pts. 1-3, ea., 60c.; 4, 80c. *Allyn.*
— *Same;* ed. by J. J. Owen. 12°. $2 ...... *Appleton.*
— *Same:* bks. 9-12 (The narrative of Odysseus); with commentary by J. E. B. Mayor. pt. 1. 18°. '73. pap., $1 .... *Macmillan.*
— *Eng.* The Odyssey; tr. [into blank verse] by W. C. Bryant. 2 v. roy. 8°. '71. $9; hf. cf., $18; mor., $25. — (Roslyn ed.) 2 v. 16°. $4.50; hf. cf., $9; mor., $12. — in 1 v. 12°. $3.50; hf. cf., $6; mor., $8 .... *Osgood.*
— *Same;* tr. into blank verse by W. Cowper. 12°. (Bohn.) $1.25 .... *Little, B. & Co.*
— — *Same.* 12°. (Bohn.) $1.40 .... *Scribner, W. & A.*
— — *Same.* 12°. (Bohn.) $1.50 .... *Lippincott.*
— *Same;* tr. into verse by A. Pope. ill. 12°. $1.50. *World Pub.*
— — *Same.* (Chandos classics.) cr. 8°. $1; pap., 75c. .... *Scribner, W. & A.*
— — *Same.* (Scribner's pop. poets.) ill. 12°. $1.50. *Scribner, W. & A.*
— — *Same;* ed. by H. F. Cary. 12°. '72. $1 .. *Routledge.*
— *Same;* and Hymns, Epigrams, and Battle of the frogs and mice; lit. tr. with notes, by T. A. Buckley. 12°. $1.50 .... *Harper.*
— — — *Same.* 12°. (Bohn.) $1.75 ... *Little, B. & Co.*
— — — *Same.* 12°. (Bohn.) $2. *Lippincott; Scribner, W. & A.*
— — *Same;* tr. [into verse] by A. Pope, and others; with introd. and notes by J. S. Watson; ill. by Flaxman's designs. 12°. (Bohn.) $1.75. *Little, B. & Co.*
— — — *Same.* 12°. (Bohn.) $2. *Lippincott; Scribner, W. & A.*

Homer, *continued.*
— *Same;* [condensed and expl.] by W. L. Collins. (Anc. classics for Eng. readers.) 16°. $1. *Lippincott; Little, B. & Co.*
— Achilles' wrath: composite tr. of bk. 1 of Iliad; by P. R. Johnson. 12°. '75. pap., 25c......*Colby.*
— Minor poems; tr. by Parnell, Chapman, Shelley, etc.; with introds. by H. N. Coleridge and tr. of life attributed to Herodotus. 12°. '72. $1.50..*Denham.*
Homer, S. J. M. Lessons on Epistle to the Hebrews; with introd. by Rev. A. L. Stone. 18°. '71. hf. bd., 15c.......*Hoyt.*
— Lessons on Gospel of John; for adults. 18°. '63. hf. bd., 18c.......*Hoyt.*
— *Same;* for younger scholars. 18°. '63. hf. bd., 15c. *Hoyt.*
— New question-book on Epistle to the Romans. 18°. '62. hf. bd., 15c.......*Hoyt.*
Homer, W. B. Writings; with introd. essay and memoir by E. A. Park. 12°. '49. $1.25..*Draper.*
Homeric synchronism. Gladstone, W. E. $2..*Harper.*
Homes and haunts of the Brit. poets. *See* Howitt, W.
Homes and hospitals; or, two phases of woman's work as exhibited in labors of Amy Dutton and Agnes E. Jones. 12°. $1.50.......*Bost. Am. Tr.*
Homes and how to make them. Gardner, E. C. $2. *Osgood.*
Homes for the people. Wheeler, G. $3..*Woodward.*
Homes homely and happy. 12°. 75c.......*Nelson.*
Homes of the birds. Grandfather Percy. 50c...*Nelson.*
Homes of the new world. Bremer, F. 2 v. $3..*Harper.*
Homes of Ober-Ammergau. Greatorex, E. $12.50. *Putnam.*
Homes of other days. Wright, T. $7.50; $10..*Appleton.*
Homes of the west, and how they were made happy; by author of "Johnny Wright." 18°. 75c. *Pres. Bd.*
Homes without hands. Wood, J. G. $4.50; $5; $6.75. *Harper.*
Homespun, So. (*pseud.*) *See* Monmouth, *Mrs.* L. H.
Homespun; or, five and twenty years ago. Lackland, T. $1.50.......*Hurd & H.*
Homespun lib. 5 v. 16°. $5.......*Lothrop.*
Cont.: Blue-eyed Jimmy.—Ruthie Shaw.—Johnny Jones.—Nettie Nesmith.—Much fruit.
Homestead on the hillside. Holmes, M. J. $1.50. *Carleton.*
Homeward bound. *See* Cooper, Ja. F.
Homeward path; by author of "Beginning and growth of the Christian life." ('56.) 5th ed. 16°. '73. 50c.......*Am. Unit.*
Homeyer, —. Responses at high mass. 4°. $1.25. *Ditson.*
Homilist. House, E. $1.75.......*Meth. Bk. Conc.*
Homilist. Thomas, D. $1.50.......*Tibbals.*
Homme (L') qui rit. *See* Hugo, V.
Homo versus Darwin: examination of "Descent of man." 12°. '71. $1.......*Claxton.*
Homœopathic cookery. 18°. 50c.......*Boericke.*
Homœopathic Medical Soc. of State of N. Y. Transactions, 1863–'76. 13 v. 8°. '63–'76. v. 1–10, ea., $1; v. 11–13, ea., $2.....*N. Y. Hom. Med.*
Homœopathic provings. Metcalf, J. W. $1.50. *Boericke.*
Honcharenko, Agapius. Russian and Eng. phrase book; for traders, travellers and teachers. 12°. '68. $1.......*Roman.*
Hone, W: Works. 4 v. 8°. $25.......*Appleton.*
Cont.: Every-day book; or, guide to the year, 2 v.—Table-book.—Year book.
— Ancient mysteries described. 8°. $1.50. *Scribner, W. & A.*
— Apocryphal New Test. 8°. $1.50..*Scribner, W. & A.*
Honest Abe's jokes. 12°. pap., 50c.......*Hurst.*

Honest and earnest. Floyd, C. $1.......*Randolph.*
Honest Gabriel. Howitt, M. $1.......*Perkinpine.*
Honest Jim ser. *See* Finley, M. F.
Honest thieves. Knight, T. 15c.......*French.*
Honesty the best policy. 18°. 17c.; 22c...*Am. Bapt.*
Honesty the best policy. Lemon, M. 15c....*French.*
Honey blossoms. Trimmer, S. K. 90c.......*Miller.*
Honey brook lib. ('67.) 3d ed. 6 v. ill. 16°. '72. $6. *Perkinpine.*
Cont.: Julius Farley.—Larry Lockwell.—True manliness.—Boy of Mt. Rhigi.—Romantic Belinda.—Blind Nellie's boy.
Honey drops: texts. 64°. 15c.; 20c.......*Am. S. S.*
Honey from the rock. [Religious verses.] 18°. 25c. *U. P. Bd. of Pub.*
Honey makers: habits of bees. ill. 18°. 60c. *Bost. Am. Tr.*
— *See also* Library of curious things in nature.
Honey out of the rock. 18°. 60c.......*Whittaker.*
Honeymoon. *See* Medina-Pomar.
Honeymoon. Tobin, J. 15c.......*French.*
Honeysuckle Cottage. *See* Baker, *Mrs.* H. N. W.
Höninghaus, Jul. V. Protestant evidences of Catholicity. *See* Bible question fairly tested.
Honor and glory. Herring, J. 50c. ......*Routledge.*
Honor bright; or, the faithful daughter. 18°. 55c. *Pres. Bd.*
Honor bright lib. 4 v. 18°. $3.40.....*Bost. Am. Tr.*
Cont.: Honorable club, by Mrs. M. L. Peebles.—Jerry and his friends, by A. A. Dodge.—Medicine shelf, by Mrs. H. E. Brown.—Progress, by A. A. Dodge.
Honorable club (The). *See* Peebles, *Mrs.* M. L.
Honoring God in the daily life of childhood. 18°. 50c. *Am. S. S.*
Honour before wealth. Feuillet, O. 15c.....*French.*
Hood, *Mrs.* D. M. Maud Mansfield. 12°. '76. $1.50; pap., $1.......*Burke.*
Hood, Edn. Paxton. Blind Amos and his velvet principles. 18°. 50c.......*Am. S. S.*
— *Same.* 16°. $1.......(?)*Martien.*
— Bye-path meadow. 16°. '70. $1.50.......*Lothrop.*
— Lamps, pitchers and trumpets: lectures on vocation of the preacher. New ed. 12°. '69. $1.75..*Dodd.*
— Villages of the Bible. ill. 12°. $1.25...*Lippincott.*
— World of anecdote lib. 4 v. 12°. $6...*Lippincott.*
Cont.: Anecdotes of ways of doing good; adventures; science.—Clerical adventures; lawyers; human folly.—Anecdotes of martyrs; the Bible; prayer.—Anecdotes of Christian life; preachers; noble women.
Hood, G: Musical manual: text-book in vocal or instrumental music. 12°. '63. bds., 40c...*Ditson.*
Hood, P. Treatise on gout, rheumatism and allied affections. cr. 8°. '71. $4.25.......*Lindsay.*
Hood, T: Works. 5 v. ill. 12°. ea., $1.50; per set, hf. cf., $16.25; hf. mor., $20.......*Porter.*
Cont.: Poet. works, 2 v.—Miscellanies; Hood's own.—Up the Rhine.—Whimsicalities, whims and oddities.
— *Same.* (Aldine ed.) 7 v. ill. cr. 8°. $15.75; hf. cf., $28.......*Putnam.*
— Prose works. 4 v. cr. 8°. $9.......*Putnam.*
— Prose and poet. works. (People's ed.) 2 v. 12°. $6.......*Putnam.*
— Poetical works. 32°. 60c.–$1.50.—(Red line ed.) sq. 16°. $1.50–$3.......*Porter.*
— *Same.* 3 v. cr. 8°. $6.75.......*Putnam.*
— *Same.* (Chandos classics.) cr. 8°. $1; pap., 75c. *Scribner, W. & A.*
— *Same.* (Household ser.) ill. 16°. $1.50; mor., $3. *Lee & S.*
— *Same.* (Household ed.) 3 v. 16°. $3.75; hf. cf., $7.50; mor., $11.25.......*Miller.*
— *Same.* (People's ed.) 12°. $3.......*Putnam.*
— *Same;* with memoir. (Blue and gold ed.) 3 v. por. 32°. $3.75; hf. cf., $7.50; mor., $10.50..*Miller.*
— *Same;* with memoir and notes. (Chandos poets.) por. and ill. cr. 8°. $3.75–$8..*Scribner, W. & A.*

Hood, T: *continued.*
— *Same;* with memoir. (Red line ed.) por. and ill. sm. 4°. $4.50; hf. cf., $6; mor., $8.....*Miller.*
— *Same;* with memoir by R. M. Milnes. 32°. $1.50; hf. cf., $3; cf., $3.75..................*Miller.*
— *Same;* with memoir by W. M. Rossetti. (Presentation poets.) ill. 12°. $1.75; $3; mor., $3.50. *Routledge.*
— *Same;* with biog. and notes, ed. by E. Sargent. 8°. shp., $3.50; mor., $10...............*Appleton.*
— Poems. 12°. $1.50........................*Locke.*
— *Same.* (Blue and gold ed.) 18°. $1.25..*Nichols & H.*
— *Same.* (Cabinet ed.) 16°. $1.50......*Nichols & H.*
— *Same.* (Scribner's pop. poets.) ill. 12°. $1.50. *Scribner, W. & A.*
— *Same.* (Wanstead ed.) ill. sm. 4°. '72. $5; mor., $10...................................*Putnam.*
— *Same;* with memoir. 5 v. por. 18°. $5...*Osgood.*
— Choice works in prose and verse. por. and ill. 12°. $3..........................*Scribner, W. & A.*
— Comicalities: ser. of pictures. obl. 4°. hf. mor., $1.50.................................*Porter.*
— Hood's own; or laughter from year to year. 2 ser. ill. 8°. hf. cf., $10.50; cf., $12.......*Appleton.*
— Song of the shirt. ill. 16°. pap., 30c...*Huntington.*
— *Same;* and other poems. (Cottage lib.) ill. 16°. pap., 30c...........................*Huntington.*
— Tales and extravaganzas. ill. 12°. $2....*Putnam.*
— Tylney Hall. ill. 12°. $2; $2.25.........*Putnam.*
— Up the Rhine. ill. cr. 8°. $1.75..........*Putnam.*
— Whims and oddities. ill. 12°. $1.75......*Putnam.*

Hood, T: (*the younger*). Book of Eng. anecdotes. 16°. '72. bds., 50c.......................*Routledge.*
— Cream of fun. ill. 8°. pap., 50c...*Scribner, W. & A.*
— From nowhere to the North Pole: a Noah's ark-æological narrative. ill. sq. 8°. '75. $3..*Routledge.*
— Illustrated readings: sel. from the Eng. literature of all ages. 2 v. ill. cr. 4°. ea., $3.50; $5..*Cassell.*
— Love and valor. 8°. $1.25; pap., 75c.......*Estes.*
— Petsetilla's posy: fairy tale for young and old. ill. sq. 12°. $1.75......................*Routledge.*
— Pleasant tale of Puss and Robin, and their friends Kitty and Bob. ill. cr. 4°. '71. $1.50..*Macmillan.*
— *See also* Griset, E., Comical pictures.
— *and* Kennedy, P., *and* Mair, J. A. Book of mod. anecdotes, Eng., Irish and Scotch. cr. 8°. '72. $1.75............................*Routledge.*

Hood, Wharton. On bone-setting (so-called) and its rel. to the treatment of joints crippled by injury, rheumatism, inflammation, etc. cr. 8°. '71. $1.75.............................*Macmillan.*

Hood's own. *See* Hood, T:

Hook, R. *and* G. D. Through dust and foam: journeyings toward the setting sun. ill. 8°. *$2.75; $3.50; shp., $3.25; hf. mor., $4.......*Col. Bk.*

Hook, Thdr. Novels. 15 v. 16°. hf. roxb., $18.75. *Routledge.*

Cont.: All in the wrong.—Cousin Geoffrey.—Cousin William.—Fathers and sons.—Gervase Skinner.—Gilbert Gurney.—Gurney married.—Jack Brag.—Man of many friends.—Maxwell.—Merton.—Parson's daughter.—Passion and principle.—Peregrine Bunce.—Widow and the marquess.

— *Same.* (Railway lib.) 12 v. 16°. ea., bds., 80c. *Routledge.*

Cont.: Cousin Geoffrey.—Cousin William.—Fathers and sons.—Gervase Skinner.—Gilbert Gurney.—Gurney married.—Jack Brag.—Man of many friends.—Maxwell.—Parson's daughter.—Peregrine Bunce—Widow and the marquess.

— [Plays]. 4 v. 16°. ea., pap., 15c.............*French.*

Cont.: Catch him who can: farce.—Excha ge no robbery: comedy.—Invisible girl: farce.—Killing no murder: farce.

— Choice humorous works, ludicrous adventures, bon mots, etc.; with life of author. por. and ill. cr. 8°. $3; hf. cf., $5............*Scribner, W. & A.*
— Humorous works; with life. por. and ill. 12°. $3. *Routledge.*
— Ned Musgrave; or, the most unfortunate man in the world. 8°. pap., 75c...................*Peterson.*

Hook, Thdr., *continued.*
— Sayings and doings. 5 v. 16°. hf. roxb., $6.25. *Routledge.*

Cont.: Passion and principle.—Man of many friends.—Cousin William.—Gervase Skinner.—Merton.

Hook, Wa. Farquhar. Church dictionary. 7th ed. 8°. '75. $3.75..............................*Tibbals.*
— Meditations for every day in the year. 2 v. 16°. '74. $2....................................*Pott.*

Hooker, E: W. Life of T. Hooker. *See* Lives of chief fathers of New Eng.

Hooker, Hm. Portion of the soul; [also] Christian life. 18°. 70c.....................*McCauley.*
— Uses of adversity. 32°. 30c............*McCauley.*

Hooker, Hor. Child's book on the Sabbath. ('35.) New ed. ill. 18°. 40c.................*Am. Tr.*
— John and Paul. ill. 18°. '56. 60c.........*Am. Tr.*
— *See also* Gallaudet, T. H., *and* Hooker, H.

Hooker, *Mrs.* Is. Beecher. Womanhood: its sanctities and fidelities. 16°. '75. pap., 40c......*Lee & S.*

Hooker, J: *See* Connecticut, Sup. Court reports.

Hooker, Jos. Dalton. General system of descriptive and analytical botany; ill. from designs by L. Stenheil and A. Riocroux. roy. 8°. $25..*Lee & S.*
— Student's flora of the British islands. 12°. '70. $3.50...........................*Macmillan.*

Hooker, Ma. Anne. Memoir. 18°. 55c.....*Am. S. S.*

Hooker, R: Complete works; ed. by Keble. 2 v. 8°. $6.................................*Appleton.*

Hooker, *Sir* W: Jackson. Garden ferns: col. figures and descriptions. 64 col. pl. roy. 8°. (Lond.) $21..................................*Putnam.*
— *and* Baker, J: Gilb. Every known fern. ill. 8°. (Lond.) $11; col., $14..............*Putnam.*

Hooker, Worthington. Child's book of common things. 16°. '58. *net*, 30c.......................*Peck.*
— Child's book of nature. 3 pts. ill. sm. 4°. 1, 60c.; 2, 3, ea., 65c.; — in 1 v., $1.60..........*Harper.*
— First book in chemistry. ill. sq. 4°. 90c.....*Harper.*
— First book in physiology. 12°. 90c.......*Sheldon.*
— Human physiology and hygiene. 12°. $1.75..*Sheldon.*
— Natural history. ill. 12°. $1.50...........*Harper.*
— New physiology; rev. by J. A. Sewall. 12°. $1.60. *Sheldon.*
— Primary geography. 16°. *net*, 40c...........*Peck.*
— Science for the school and family. 3 pts. ill. 12°. ea., $1.50.............................*Harper.*

Cont.: Natural philosophy.—Chemistry.—Geology and mineralogy.

Hooper, E. J. Western fruit book: facts from notes and experience of successful fruit culturists. ('57.) New ed., rev. ill. 12°. '59. $1.50......*Wilstach.*

Hooper, H: The lost model: romance. 12°. $1.75. *Lippincott.*

Hooper, Jane Winnard. Arbell: tale for young people. ill. 12°. $1.........................*Routledge.*
— Arbell's school days. 16°. $1.25......*Nichols & H.*

Hooper, J: Life and writings. *See* British reformers.

Hooper, Johnson J. Adventures of Capt. Simon Suggs. ill. 12°. pap., 75c......................*Peterson.*
— Dog and gun. 12°. 60c.; pap., 30c..........*Judd.*
— Simon Suggs' adventures and travels. ill. 12°. $1.75. *Peterson.*
— Widow Rugby's husband. ill. 12°. pap., 75c. *Peterson.*

Hooper, Lucy. Poems. por. 12°. $1.75..*Lippincott.*
— (*ed.*) Lady's book of flowers and poetry; with floral dict. and chapter on plants in rooms. 12°. '68. $1.50; mor., $2.50................*Claxton.*

Hooper, Rob. Lexicon medicum; or, medical dictionary. 16th ed., enl. by S. Akerly. 8°. shp., $3...*Harper.*

Hoopes, Josiah. Book of evergreens; incl. propagation, cultivation, description of varieties, and their adaptability to different situations. 12°. $3..*Judd.*

Hoose, Ja. H. Studies in articulation. 16°. '76. 30c.; 50c. . . . . *Bardeen.*
Hoosier mosaics. Thompson, M. $1.25. . . . . . *Hale.*
Hoosier schoolmaster. Eggleston, E. $1.25. . . *Judd.*
Hooton, F. C. Supervisor's guide: manual of the road laws of Penna., with decisions. 8°. shp., $1.50 . . . . *Kay.*
Hop blossoms. (Fatherland ser.) ill. 16°. 85c. (?)*Luth. Pub.*
Hop garden: story of town and country life. ill. fp. 8°. 60c. . . . . *Cassell.*
Hop of fashion: Ethiop. drama. 16°. pap., 15c. *French; Happy.*
Hop o' my thumb. *See* Cruikshank, G.
Hop pickers. Hazlewood, C. H. 15c. . . . . . . *French.*
Hopagog's leg. ill. cr. 16°. 25c. . . . . *Cassell.*
Hope, Ascott Rob. (*pseud.*) *See* Moncrieff, A. R. H.
Hope, Cecil. Seabury Castle: a tale. 12°. $1. *Lippincott.*
Hope, F. T. L. The three homes: tale for fathers and sons. ill. 12°. '74. $1.75. . . . . *Dutton.*
— *Same.* cr. 8°. $2.50. . . . . *Cassell.*
Hope, G: A. Till the doctor comes and how to help him; rev. with add. by a N. Y. physician. 12°. '71. 60c. . . . . *Putnam.*
Hope, Stanley. A new Godiva. 12°. $1.50. . *Lippincott.*
Hope, T. Anastasius; or, memoirs of a Greek. [Fiction.] 12°. $1.50. . . . . *Harper.*
Hope and have. Adams, W. T. $1.25 . . . . . . *Lee & S.*
Hope Campbell. *See* Bell, C. D.
Hope Darrow. Townsend, V. F. 75c. . . . . . . *Loring.*
Hope deferred. Pollard, E. F. 50c. . . . . *Harper.*
Hope Douglass. Flint, S. A. $1.25. . . . . . *Cong. Pub.*
Hope for the fallen. 18°. 50c. . . . . *Am. S. S.*
Hope for the Jews. Janeway, J. J. 50c. *N. Y. Ref. Ch. Bd.*
Hope Foster's mistake. 18°. 70c. . . . . *Pres. Bd.*
Hope in Jesus. Reid, W. 40c. . . . . *Hoyt.*
Hope Leslie. Sedgwick, C. M. 2 v. $3. . . . *Harper.*
Hope lib. 4 v. ill. 18°. $3. . . . . *Hoyt.*
Cont.: Hannah Lee. — Harrie Lee, by Mrs. M. F. Wood. — Little May. — Moorcroft hatch, by C. Tucker.
Hope Meredith. Tabor, E. 50c. . . . . *Harper.*
Hope of the family. Coyne, J. S. 15c. . . . . . . *French.*
Hope of the Gospel. Loughborough, J. N. 10c. *Sev. Day Adv.*
Hope on. ill. 16°. 50c. . . . . *Nelson.*
— *See also* Adirondack stories; — Snow-drop ser.
Hope on; or, the house that Jack built. 18°. 60c. *Cong. Pub.*
— *See also* Little Aggie's lib.
Hope on, hope ever. *See* Howitt, Ma.
Hope Raymond. Richmond, E. J. $1. . *Meth. Bk. Conc.*
Hope Wallace; or, earnest living. 16°. $1.50. *Cong. Pub.*
— *See also* Lenny's lib.
Hopedale tavern. Van Namee, J. W. $1. . *Nat. Temp.*
Hopeful words for the sick and suffering. sq. 24°. '71. $1. . . . . *Whittaker.*
Hopefully waiting. Randolph, A. D. F. $1.50. *Scribner.*
Hopeless passion. Morton, J. M. 15c. . . . . . . *French.*
Hopes and fears. Baker, H. N. W. $1.25. . *H. A. Young.*
Hopes and fears. Yonge, C. M. $1.75. *Appleton; Macmillan.*
Hopes and helps for the youth of both sexes. Weaver, G. S. $1.25. . . . . *Wells.*
Hopes crowned in death: memoir of Alexander Brown. ill. 18°. 50c. . . . . *N. Y. Ref. Ch. Bd.*
Hopes of Hope Castle. Martyn, S. T. $1.25. . *Am. Tr.*
Hopes of the human race. Cobbe, F. P. $1.50. . *Miller.*

Hopfenblüthen (Die). Schmid, C. v. 20c. . . *Morwitz.*
Hopkins, Alph. A. Newspaper poets; or, waifs and their authors. sq. 16°. '76. $1.75. (?)*Rural Home.*
Hopkins, Arch. *See* Nott, C. C., *and* Hopkins, A; — United States, Court of Claims reports.
Hopkins, C. J. Sacred songs. [Church music.] 8°. $1.25; bds., $1. . . . . *Gordon.*
Hopkins, C. T. Manual of American ideas; for instruction of foreigners and use of citizens. (Citizen's ed.) 8°. '73. $2.25. . . . . *Bancroft.*
— *Same.* (School ed.) 12°. '73. $1.50. . . . . *Bancroft.*
Hopkins, Evan H. The holy life. 18°. '75. 75c. . . *Revell.*
Hopkins, Ezekiel. Works; ed. by Rev. C. W. Quick. 3d Am., from Pratt's Lond. ed. 3 v. 8°. '74. $4.50. . . . . *Leighton.*
— Exposition of the ten commandments. 12°. '46. 80c. *Am. Tr.*
Hopkins, G: Ralph's possession. ill. 16°. '73. $1.50. *Lothrop.*
Hopkins, I. H., *and* Mahan, M. The revival system; [also] The paraclete, by Rev. J. C. Tracy. 12°. pap., 12c. . . . . *Claremont.*
Hopkins, *Miss* I. T. Christmas at the Beeches. ill. 18°. 60c. . . . . *Bost. Am. Tr.*
— — *See also* Cozy house stories.
— Cozy house tales: sequel to "Christmas at the Beeches." ill. 18°. 60c. . . . . *Bost. Am. Tr.*
— — *See also* Cozy house stories.
— Floy Lindsley. ill. 16°. '75. $1.25. . . . . *Am. Tr.*
— Ruthie's venture. ill. 16°. '76. $1.25. . . . . . *Am. Tr.*
— Summer in the forest. ill. 16°. '71. $1.10. . *Am. Tr.*
Hopkins, *Rev.* J: H: End of controversy controverted. 2 v. 12°. $2. . . . . *Claremont.*
— History of the confessional. 12°. $1.50. . . . *Harper.*
— Law of ritualism examined in its rel. to the word of God, to the primitive church, to the Church of Eng. and to the Prot. Episc. Ch. in the U. S. cr. 8°. '66. $1.25. . . . . *Hurd & H.*
— Life; by his sons. por. 12°. $2.50. . . . *Huntington.*
Hopkins, *Rev.* J: H: The three kings of Orient: a Christmas carol. [Words and music.] 4°. '65. $2.50; mor., $5. . . . . *Hurd & H.*
— *Same;* [also] Twenty-third psalm. 4°. $3. . *Hurd & H.*
Hopkins, Josiah. Christian instructor: explanation and defense of Christian religion. 5th ed. 12°. '60. $1. . . . . *Barnes.*
Hopkins, Livingston. Comic centennial hist. of the U. S. ill. 12°. $1.50. . . . . *Carleton.*
Hopkins, L: Payson. Guiding star. *See* Pioneer lib.
— Henry Langdon. ('63.) New ed. ill. 18°. '68. 55c. *Hoyt.*
— Silent comforter. 24°. '74. 25c.; 40c. — 16°. $1. *Lothrop.*
Hopkins, Manley. Handbook of average. 8°. $9. *Lippincott.*
— Manual of marine insurance. 8°. $6. . . . *Lippincott.*
Hopkins, M: Evidences of Christianity: lectures. ('63.) New ed., rev. 8°. '76. $1.50. . . *Marvin.*
— Law of love, and love as a law; or Christian ethics; with strictures by Dr. McCosh, with replies. ('70.) New ed. 12°. '75. $1.75. . . . . *Scribner.*
— Lectures on moral science, Lowell institute, Bost. roy. 12°. $1.50 . . . . *Sheldon.*
— Outline study of man; or, the body and mind in one system; with diagrams. ('73.) New ed. 12°. '76. $1.75. . . . . *Scribner.*
— Prayer and the prayer gauge. 16°. '74. 75c. . . *Dodd.*
— Strength and beauty: discussions for young men. 12°. $1.75. . . . . *Dodd.*
— Temperance and education. 18°. pap., 10c. *Nat. Temp.*
Hopkins, S. M. *See* New York, Chancery reports.
Hopkins, S: The Puritans and Queen Elizabeth: the church, court and parliament of Eng., [1553–1603]; with introd. note by M. Hopkins. ('59–'61.) 2d ed. 3 v. cr. 8°. '75. $7.50. . . . *Randolph.*

Hopkins, *Rev.* S: Works. 3 v. por. 8°. $6.. *Cong. Pub.*
— On slavery. 8°. pap., 15c............ *Cong. Pub.*
— Treatise on the millennium. 8°. pap., 10c. *Cong. Pub.*

Hopkinson, Fs. The old farm and new farm: a polit. allegory; with introd. and notes by B. J. Lossing. 16°. '67. $1.25.................... *Randolph.*
— *See also* United States, Judgments.

Hopley, Cath. C. Aunt Jenny's American pets. ill. 12°. $1.50.......................... *Nelson.*
— — *See also* Bouquet lib.

Hoppe, C: Percussion and auscultation as diagnostic aids; tr. by L. C. Lane. 12°. $1.50.. *Lippincott.*

Hoppin, A: (*ill.*) Crossing the Atlantic. obl. f°. '72. $5................................ *Osgood.*
— Hay fever. obl. f°. '73. $3 .... *Osgood.*
— On the Nile. ill. obl. f°. '74. $10. — 48 pl. in portfolio. large pap., $25............... *Osgood.*
— Ups and downs on land and water. obl. f°. '71. $10. *Osgood.*

Hoppin, Ja. M. Life of Admiral Foote. por. and ill. cr. 8°. $3.50....................... *Harper.*
— Notes of a theological student. 12°. $1... *Appleton.*
— Office and work of the Christian ministry. 8°. $3.50. *Sheldon.*
— Old England: its scenery, art and people. 16°. '67. $1.75............................ *Hurd & H.*

Hoppin, W. J. Circumstances alter cases: drama. 16°. pap., 15c........................ *French.*

Horace. [Quintus Horatius Flaccus.] Works [Lat.]; with notes. New ed., rev. and enl., with life of H., etc. 12°. shp., $1.75 .... *Harper.*
— *Same;* with notes by J. Currie. ill. 16°. (Lond.) $2 .... *Little, B. & Co.*
— *Same;* interpretatione et notis ill. L. Desproz. 8°. hf. roan, $2.80.................. *Lippincott.*
— *Same;* with notes, etc., by J. L. Lincoln. 12°. '51. $1.75............................ *Appleton.*
— *Same;* rec. A. J. Macleane. 18°. 75c..... *Harper.*
— *Same;* with notes by A. J. Macleane, rev. and ed. by R. H. Chase. ('56.) 14th ed. 12°. '74. $1.75.. *Allyn.*
— *Same;* with Stirling's interlin. tr. arranged by P. A. Nuttall. New ed., rev. by T. Clark. roy. 12°. hf. leath., $2.25.................... *Desilver.*
— *Eng.:* prose tr., with notes, index, etc., by J. Lonsdale and S. Lee. (Globe ed.) 12°. '74. $1.50............................ *Macmillan.*
— *Same;* lit. tr. by C. Smart. New ed., rev. with notes by T. A. Buckley. 12°. $1.50.. *Harper.*
— — — *Same.* 12°. (Bohn.) $1.25 .... *Little, B. & Co.*
— — — *Same.* 12°. (Bohn.) $1.40.. *Scribner, W. & A.*
— — — *Same.* 12°. (Bohn.) $1.50 ...... *Lippincott.*
— *Same;* [condensed and expl.] by T. Martin. (Anc. classics for Eng. readers.) 16°. $1. *Lippincott; Little, B. & Co.*
— Eclogue ex poematibus; rec. L. Schmitz et C. G. Zumpt. roy. 18°. '66. 70c.; hf. bd., 80c... *Lea.*
— Odes, satires and epistles [Lat.]; with notes, key, index of names, etc., by T. Chase. ('69.) 5th ed. 16°. '75. hf. leath., $1.50........... *Eldredge.*
— Odes, satires, letters, etc., [Lat.]; ed. by L. Schmitz and C. G. Zumpt. 16°. $1........... *Sheldon.*
— *Eng.* Odes: metrical tr. by T. Martin. (Blue and gold ed.) 32°. $1.50 .... * *Osgood.*
— *Same;* in a metrical paraphrase by R. M. Hovenden. 12°. '74. $1.50..................... *Macmillan.*
— Odes and epodes; tr. by W. Sewell. (Bohn.) $1.25. *Little, B. & Co.*
— — *Same.* 12°. (Bohn.) $1.40... *Scribner, W. & A.*
— — *Same.* 12°. (Bohn.) $1.50........ *Lippincott.*
— *Same:* metrical tr. by Lord Lytton; with commentaries and text from eds. of Orelli, Macleane and Yonge. 12°. $1.75 .... *Harper.*
— Odes, satires and epistles; tr. by P. Francis; with versions of various odes, by Milton, Dryden, Pope, etc.; [also] Fables by Phædrus; with app. of Gudius; tr. by C. Smart. 2 v. 18°. $1.50. *Harper.*

Horace. *See* Corneille, P.

Horace and May. *See* Bell, C. D.

Horace Carlton's essay. ill. 18°. '74. 40c... *Am. Tr*

Horace Hazelwood; or, little things. 18°. 60c.; 70c *Am. Bapt*
— *See also* Hazelwood ser.

Horace Templeton. Lever, C. $2; 75c..... *Peterson*

Horace Welford. *See* Erickson, D. S.

Horace Wilde. *See* Mallary, M. J.

Horæ Hellenicæ. Blackie, J. S. $4..... *Macmillan*

Horæ Lucanæ. Baynes, H. S. $2.50.... *Lippincott*

Horæ lyricæ. *See* Watts, I.

Horæ Paulinæ. *See* Paley, W.

Horæ sacræ. Chandler, J. 50c.; 75c.; $2.25.. *Dutton*

Horæ Tennysonianæ. Church, A. J. $1.75.. *Macmillan*

Horatius Flaccus, Q. *See* Horace.

Hord, O. B. *See* Indiana, Statutes.

Hörmann, Alto. Die Tochter Tehuan's, od. Texas im vorigen Jahrh. 12°. 35c.; pap., 15c... *Benziger.*

Horn, E: T. The Christian year. 12°. '76. $1. *Luth. Bk. St.*

Horn, W. O. v. (*pseud.*) *See* Oertel, P. F. W.

Horn of plenty of home poems and pictures; by J. Ingelow, D. M. Craik, G. MacDonald, D. Greenwell, etc. ill. sm. 4°. '75. $2.25.... *W. F. Gill.*

Horne, A. R. Pennsylvania German manual for pronouncing, speaking and writing English. 12°. '76. bds., $1.......................... (?) *Urick.*

Horne, G: Introduction to the Bible; abridg. 12°. '37. $1.50..................... *Meth. Bk. Conc.*
— On the Psalms. 8°. '69. $2.50........... *Carter.*

Horne, Lenox. Two heads better than one: farce. 16°. pap., 15c............... *French; Lee & S.*

Horne, R: H: Death of Marlowe: tragedy. 16°. pap., 15c.................................. *French.*
— (*ed.*) New spirit of the age. 12°. $1...... *Harper.*

Horne, T: Hartwell. Diplomacy; [also] Law of nations, by A. Polson. 8°. '53. $1.50. *T. & J. W. Johnson.*
— — *See also* Law lib.
— Introduction to crit. study and knowledge of Scripture. 2 v. 8°. '72. $5. — in 1 v., shp., $5.. *Carter.*
— *Same;* ed. by J. Ayre and S. P. Tregelles. 13th ed. 4 v. ill. and maps. 8°. $20............. *Pott.*

Hornehurst rectory. Clare, M. F. $2.50; $3.. *Sadlier.*

Horner, Su. *and* J. Walks in Florence. 2 v. ill. 12°. '73. $6............................ *Routledge.*

Horner, W: E. Special anatomy and histology. 8th ed., rev. 2 v. ill. 8°. $6................ *Lea.*
— The United States dissector: lessons in pract. anatomy. 5th ed., rev. by H. H. Smith. ('53.) ill. 12°. shp., $2.............. *Claxton; Lippincott.*
— *See also* Smith, H. H., *and* Horner, W: E.

Hornihold, J: The commandments and sacraments explained in 52 discourses. 12°. $2.... *Cath. Pub.*

Hornor, R. Stockton. Rhyme and reason. [Poetry.] 16°. $1.50.............................. *Claxton.*

Horoscop (Das). *See* Van der Velde, K. F.

Horrigan, L. D., *and* Thompson, S. D. Select Am. cases on the law of self-defence. 8°. '74. shp., $7 .... *Soule.*

Horrors of Paris. *See* Dumas, A.

Horsburgh, Matilda. Children of the great king. ill. 16°. $1.25.......................... *Crowell.*
— Henry Morgan; or, the sower and the seed. 18°. 50c.............................. (?) *Martien.*
— Mary Mansfield; or, no time to be a Christian. 18°. 35c.; 45c.......................... *Am. Bapt.*
— *Same.* 18°. 50c...................... (?) *Martien.*
— Nothing to do; or, the influence of a life. 18°. 35c.; 45c.............................. *Am. Bapt.*

Horse-owner's companion: hints on selection, purchase and management of the horse. 16°. '72. bds., 50c. . . . . *Happy.*

Horse-owner's guide and complete horse doctor. 12°. pap., 50c. . . . . *Hurst.*

Horse-shoe Robinson. Kennedy, J. P. $2.25 . . *Putnam.*

Horse-shoe Robinson. Tayleure, C. W. 15c. . . *French.*

Horse-shoer's manual. 12°. pap., 25c. . . . . . *Haney.*

Horst, Ja. Merlo. Paradise of the Christian soul. 18°. $1.25–$5 . . . . *O'Shea.*

— *Same;* ed. by Dr. Pusey. 2 v. 16°. '71. $2.25 . . *Pott.*

Horstmann, I. F. History of the Cath. Bible. *See* Bible [Whole], *Cath.*

Hort, Fenton J: Ant. Two dissertations: 1, on μονογενὴς Θεὸς in Scripture and tradition; 2, on the Constantinopolitan creed and other east. creeds of the 4th century. 8°. '76. $3 . . . . . . *Macmillan.*

Hortense; or, pride corrected. 18°. '60. 40c.; 60c. *Kelly, P. & Co.*

Horton, A. Melodeon without a master. obl. 8°. 75c. *Brainard.*

— Melopean without a master. obl. 8°. 75c. . . *Brainard.*

Horton, Caro. W. Architecture for general students. ill. 16°. '74. $1.50 . . . . *Hurd & H.*

Horton, D. P. *See* Tillinghast, W., *and* Horton, D. P.

— *and* Tillinghast, W: Vocal music reader. 16°. '73. bds., 15c. . . . . *Ivison.*

Horton, J. G. Youth's or people's hist. of the [Am.] Civil war. 12°. $1.50 . . . . *Van Evrie.*

Horton, M. B. The wife's messenger. [Fiction.] 12°. $1.75 . . . . *Lippincott.*

Horton, *Mrs.* W. R. Divine law of birth. 18°. '62. 30c. . . . . *H. H. Carter.*

Hosanna (The). Marshall, L. $1.38 . . . . *Ditson.*

Hosanna of the little ones. Duehrmig, G. 50c. *Benziger.*

Hoskiær, V. Guide for the electric testing of telegraph cables. pl. 8°. '73. $1.50 . . . . *Spon.*

Hoskins, Fs. R. Blossom of Churnington Green: burlesque. 16°. pap., 15c. . . . . *French.*

Hoskins, G: Gordon. Clerk of works: [on] building operations. 12°. '76. 60c. . . . . *Spon.*

— Designs for chimney pieces. 56 lith. pl. roy. f°. (Darlington, Eng.) '71. $25 . . . . *Spon.*

Hoskins, T: H. Adulteration of food and drink; with tests. 16°. 75c. *Burnham.*

Hosmer, G: H. Every-day doctor: household book of pract. medicine. 8°. leath., *3.50 . . . . *Appleton.*

Hosmer, *Mrs.* Marg. Back court; or, how to help the poor. 18°. 75c. . . . . *Pres. Bd.*

— Blanche Gilroy: girl's story. 12°. $1.50 . . *Lippincott.*

— Caddy's three dresses. 16°. $1.50 . . . . . (?) *Martien.*

— Child captives. 18°. 75c. . . . . *Pres. Bd.*

— Courts and corners. 16°. 90c. . . . . *Cong. Pub.*

— Dismal Castle brightened. 16°. $1.15 . . *Cong. Pub.*

— John Hartman. ill. 16°. $1 . . . . *J. A. Moore.*

— Juliet, the heiress. ill. 18°. 80c. . . . . *J. A. Moore.*

— Lenny, the orphan; or, trials and triumphs. ill. 16°. '69. $1.25 . . . . *Porter.*

— Lily's hard words: story for little people. 18°. '72. 75c. . . . . *Claxton.*

– Little Rosie ser. 3 v. ill. 18°. '69. ea., 75c. . . *Porter.*

Cont.: Little Rosie's first play days. — Little Rosie's Christmas times. — Little Rosie in the country.

— Morrisons (The). 12°. $1.75; pap., $1.50 . . *Peterson.*

— Rich and poor. 16°. $1.15 . . . . *Pres. Bd.*

— Rough boy's story. 16°. $1 . . . . (?) *Martien.*

— Story of a week. 16°. $1 . . . . (?) *Martien.*

— Subtle spell: temp. story. 16°. $1.25 . . (?) *Martien.*

– Three times lost; or, Patty Norris. ill. 18°. 80c. *J. A. Moore.*

— *and* Dunlap, *Miss* Jla. Under the holly; or, Christmas at Hopeton House; by "a pair of hands." ill. 16°. '69. $1.25 . . . . *Porter.*

Hospital boy (The). 18°. 50c. . . . . (?) *Martien.*

Hospital life: incidents from army hospitals; in the Fulton St. [N.Y.] prayer meeting. ill. 18°. 50c. *N. Y. Ref. Ch. Bd.*

Hospital plans: five essays rel. to construction, organization and management of hospitals. ill. roy. 8°. $6 . . . . *W. Wood.*

Hospital sketches. Alcott, L. M. $1.50 . . . . *Roberts.*

Hostages to fortune. Braddon, M. E. 75c. . . *Harper.*

Hotchkin, B. B. Infidelity against itself. 18°. 40c. *Pres. Bd.*

— Manliness. 18°. 35c. . . . . *Pres. Bd.*

— Upward from sin through grace to glory. 16°. $1.20. *Pres. Bd.*

Hotchkiss, Jed., *and* Allan, W: Battle-fields of Virginia. [Civil war.] por. and maps. 8°. '67. $5. *Van Nostrand.*

Hotel charges. Selby, C. 15c. . . . . *French.*

Hotspur. Walworth, M. T. $1.75 . . . . *Carleton.*

Hotten, J: Camden. *See* Sadler, L. R., *and* Hotten, J. C.

Hotten's ill. books. 32 v. 12° . . . . *Routledge.*

Cont.: History of advertising, $3. — Balzac's Droll stories, $5. — Bocaccio's Decameron, $3. — History of booksellers, $3. — Coleman's Broad grins, $3. — Moore's Life of Lord Byron, $3. — Mothers of great men, $3. — English surnames, $3. — Golden treasury of thought, $3. — Greenwood's Wilds of London, $3. — Hall's Sketches of Irish character, $3. — Hogarth's Works, 3 v., $9. — Jerrold's The barber's chair, $3. — Life, etc., of Gen. Lee, $3. — Mayhew's London characters, $3. — Muses of Mayfair, $3. — Napoleon III. the man of his time, $3. — Rabelais, $3. — Remarkable trials and notorious characters, $3. — Sheridan's complete works, $3. — Signboards, $3. — Slang dictionary, $3.25. — Story of the London parks, $3. — Hook's Choice humorous works, $3. — Thackerayana, $5. — Timbs' Clubs and club life, $3. — Walton and Cotton's Complete angler, $3. — Wonderful characters, $3. — Wright's Caricature history of the Georges, $3. — Wright's History of caricature and the grotesque in art, $3.

Hotze, C. L. First lessons in physics. ('71.) 16°. '75. 90c. . . . . *Cen. Pub.*

— First lessons in physiology. ill. 16°. '75. $1 . . *Ward.*

Houck, L: Treatise on law of navigable rivers. 8°. '68. shp., $3 . . . . *Little, B. & Co.*

— *See also* Missouri, Reports.

Houdin, Rob. Robert Houdin, the great wizard, French conjurer, author and ambassador; tr., with index, by R. S. Mackenzie. 12°. $1.50 . . . . . . *Desilver.*

— Houdin, the conjurer. ill. 8°. pap., 50c. . . . . *Haney.*

Hough, Franklin B. American biog. notes. 8°. '75. $5 . . . . *Munsell.*

— American constitutions. 2 v. 8°. ea., shp., $7.50. *Weed.*

— Proclamations for Thanksgiving, by the continental Congress, Washington and others; with hist. introd. roy. 8°. '58. hf. shp., $2.50 . . . *Munsell.*

— Siege of Charleston by the Brit. fleet and army under Arbuthnot and Sir Henry Clinton. por. sq. 8°. '66. $5 . . . . *Munsell.*

— Siege of Savannah by the Am. and French forces, under Gen. Lincoln and Count D'Estaing, 1779; with notes and index. por. sq. 8°. '66. $5 . . *Munsell.*

Houghton, *Lord.* [R: Moncton Milnes.] Monographs, personal and social. por. 12°. '73. $2 . . . . *Holt.*

Houghton, W. Wonders near home. ill. 18°. 50c. *Nelson.*

— *Same.* ill. 16°. '73. $1 . . . . *Lothrop.*

Hounslow Jack. 8°. pap., 25c. . . . . *De Witt.*

Houpt, J: Improvements in the steam engine; with diagrams. 16°. $2 . . . . *Lippincott.*

Hour and the man. *See* Martineau, H.

Hour in fairy land. Schoeller, H. 75c.; 60c. . . *Peters.*

Hour in Seville. Selby, C. 15c. . . . . *French.*

Hour of praise. Root, G. F. 50c. . . . . *Church.*

Hour of singing. Emerson, L. O., *and* Tilden, W. S. $1 . . . . *Ditson.*

Hour of sorrow. Maclear, G. F. $1 . . . . *Macmillan.*

Hour which cometh. Clarke, J. F. $1.50 . . . *Lee & S.*

Hour with the devil. Bennett, D. M. 10c. *D. M. Bennett.*
Hours among the Gospels. Burt, N. C. $1.50. *Claxton; Lippincott.*
Hours in a library. Stephen, L. $1.75.....*Scribner.*
Hours of amusement. Weaver, W. T. G. $2. *E. H. Cushing.*
Hours of Christian devotion. *See* Tholuck, A.
Hours of communion. Chapin, E.H. 60c...*Universalist.*
Hours of exercise in the Alps. Tyndall, J. $2..*Appleton.*
Hours of idleness. Conway, J. D. $1......*Conway.*
Hours of the passion. *See* Neale, J. M.
Hours of prayer in the noon prayer meeting. Chambers, T. W. $1....................*N. Y. Ref. Ch. Bd.*
Hours of song. Fillmore, J. H. 50c.......*Fillmore.*
Hours with the evangelists. Nichols, J. 2 v. ea., $1.50............................*Am. Unit.*
Hours with the Lord. Theremin, L. F. F. 35c...*Dutton.*
Hours with mamma. Dawes, S. E. $1......*Am. Tr.*
Hours with my picture book. ill. 4°. $1....*Am. S. S.*
Hours with the toiling: book for women. 18°. pap., 10c. ....*Bost. Am. Tr.*
Hours with working women. 18°. '65. 25c...*Am. Tr.*
— *Same.* 18°. 45c.......................*Am. S. S.*
Hours with the youngest. Gill, M. H. 2 v. ea., $1.25. *Randolph.*
House, Erwin. Homilist: sermons for preachers and laymen. 12°. '60. $1.75.......*Meth. Bk. Conc.*
— Literary and religious sketches. 18°. 60c. *Cin. Meth. Bk. Conc.*
— Missionary in many lands. 12°. '60. $1.25. *Meth. Bk. Conc.*
— Scripture cabinet. 12°. $1.75...*Cin. Meth. Bk. Conc.*
— Sketches for the young. 18°. 60c...*Cin. Meth. Bk. Conc.*
— Sunday-school handbook. 12°. $1.25. *Cin. Meth. Bk. Conc.*
House and home papers. Stowe, H. B. $1.75..*Osgood.*
House at Elmore. Robinson, F. W. 50c. ...*De Witt.*
House beautiful. *See* Tucker, *Mrs.* C.
House dog. Higgie, T. 15c................*French.*
House in Balfour St. Denutry, C. $1.50..(?) *O'Kane.*
House in town. Warner, S. *and* A. B. $1.25..*Carter.*
House of cards. Hoey, C. 75c...... ....*Littell & G.*
House of God. Everts, W. W. $1.50 ......*Am. Tr.*
House of gold. *See* Marie Josephine.
House of Israel. Warner, S. $1.50.........*Carter.*
House of Lords. *See* England, Law reports.
House of prayer. De Teissier, G. F. $1..*Macmillan.*
House of the seven gables. *See* Hawthorne, N.
House of York. Tincker, M. A. $2......*Cath. Pub.*
House on the corner of Broad St.: book for girls. ill. 16°. '75. 75c. ....*Hoyt.*
House on the heights. McKeever, H. B. $1.50. *McKinney.*
House on the hill. sq. 16°. '68. $1; pap., 50c...*Randolph.*
House on the moor. Oliphant, M. O. W. $1.50. *Harper.*
House on wheels. *See* Bégon, F. (*Comtesse*) de.
House or the home. Taylor, T. 15c.........*French.*
House out of window. Brough, W. 15c.....*French.*
House talks. Noyes, J. H. $1.50...........*Oneida.*
House that Jack built. *See* Wonderful history.
House to let. *See* Dickens, C:
House we live in. *See* Picture puzzle toy-books.
Houseful of children. Sanford, D. P. $2.25..*Dutton.*
Household (The). Wilkes, T. 60c. ......*West. Tr.*
Household angel in disguise. Baker, H. N. W. $1.50. *Lee & S.*
Household book of Eng. poetry. Trench, R. C. $2.25. *Macmillan.*
Household book of Irish eloquence; by a member of the N. Y. bar. ill. 12°. $2.50; shp., $4; hf. cf., $4.50..............................*McGee.*
Household book of poetry. Dana, C. A. $5; $8; $10 ....*Appleton.*
Household book of songs. Dana, C. A., *and* Bowman, F. A. $1.50; $2.50.................*Appleton.*
Household cyclopedia of gen. information. ('71.) New ed. ill. 8°. '76. *$4; shp., $4.50..*C. H. Davis.*
Household editions. 6 v. 12°..............*Osgood.*
Cont.: Longfellow's Poems, $2.—Owen Meredith's Poems, $2.—Tennyson's Idyls of the king, $1.50.—Tennyson's Poems, $2.—Whittier's Poems, $2.—Whittier's Songs of three centuries, $2.
Household editions of the standard poets. 16 v. 16°. ea., $1.25.................................*Miller.*
Cont.: Burns, 2 v.—Campbell.—Gray.—Hood, 3 v.—Keble's Christian year.—Keats.—Macaulay's Lays of ancient Rome.—Scott, 3 v.—Shelley, 3 v.
Household elegancies. Williams, H. T., *and* Jones, C. S. $1.50.......................*H. T. Williams.*
Household English dictionary. ill. 18°. 75c...*Nelson.*
Household fairy. Talfourd, F. 15c..*De Witt; French.*
Household friends: book for all seasons. por. sm. 4°. '63. $3; mor., $6...................*Osgood.*
Household guide: encyclopædia of domestic and social economy. 4 v. col. pl. and ill. cr. 4°. ea., $3; —in 2 v., hf. cf., $18.................*Cassell.*
Household lib. 3 v. 12°. $4.50...........*Lothrop.*
Cont.: Household puzzles.—Modern prophets.—Those boys.
Household lib. 6 v. 16°. $7.50.........*Randolph.*
Cont.: Hope Campbell.—Horace and May.—Lily Gordon.—Orphan nieces.—Rest and unrest.—Sir Genevieve.
Household lib. *See* Adams, W. T.
Household manuals. 25 v. 16°. ea., 20c...*Routledge.*
Cont.: Lady's letter-writer.—Gentleman's letter-writer.—Lover's letter-writer.—Hill's Cook's own book.—Routledge's every-day blunders in speaking.—Francatelli's Cookery book.—Hill's How to cook [preserve or make] in a hundred different ways: apples—rabbits—salads—puddings—onions—fish—fruit—game—pickles—vegetables—soups—cakes—eggs.—Victor's Routledge's recipe book.—Home nursing.—Ready remedies for common complaints.—Guila's Invalid's cook book.—Lady housekeeper's poultry yard.—Dinners and housekeeping.
Household melodies. [Songs.] 2 v. 4°. ea., $3; bds., $2.50..............................*Peters.*
Household mysteries; by author of "Light and darkness." 12°. $1.......................*Appleton.*
Household of Bouverie. *See* Warfield, C. A.
Household of peace. Newell, W. W. 20c...*Am. Tr.*
Household of Thomas More. Manning, A. $1..*Dodd.*
Household physician. Warren, I., *and* Small, A. E. *$6................................*I. Bradley.*
Household puzzle. *See* Alden, *Mrs.* I. M.
Household ser. 54 v. ill. 16°. ea., $1.50; mor., $3. *Lee & S.*
Cont.: Ainsworth's Ballads.—Arabian nights.—Bloomfield's Poems.—Book of wit and humor.—Book of humorous poetry.—Bulwer Lytton's Dramas.—Bulwer Lytton's Poems.—Burns' Poetical works.—Byron's Poetical works.—Campbell's Poetical works.—Chaucer's Poetical works.—Choice poems and lyrics.—Coleridge's Poetical works.—E. Cook's Poetical works.—Cowper's Poetical works.—Dodd's Beauties of Shakespeare.—Don Quixote.—Dryden's Poetical works.—Evenings at home.—Familiar quotations.—Goldsmith, Johnson, Shenstone and Smollett.—Gulliver's travels.—Hemans' Poetical works.—Hood's Poetical works.—Hunt's Poetical works.—Keat's Poetical works.—Keble's Christian year.—Southey's Kirke White.—Lives of the poets.—Lover's Poetical works.—"L. E. L." (Miss Landon).—Milton's Poetical works.—Montgomery's Poetical works.—Moore's Poetical works.—Percy's Reliques.—Pilgrim's progress.—Pope's Poetical works.—Roger's Poetical works.—Sacred poems.—Sanford and Merton.—Herbert's Works.—Scott's Poetical works.—Scottish and English ballads.—Shakespeare's Gems.—Shakespeare's Complete works.—Shelley's Poetical works.—Southey's Poetical works.—Spenser's Poetical works.—Swiss family Robinson.—Tennyson's Poetical works.—Thomson's Poetical works.—Tupper's Proverbial philosophy.—Wise sayings of great and good.—Wordsworth's Poetical works.
Household stories. *See* Grimm, J. L. *and* W. C.
Household stories. *See* Wildermuth, *Mme.* O.

Household tales and fairy stories. ill. cr. 8°. '71. $2.50 ... *Routledge.*
Household treasure: domestic receipts. [In Eng. or Germ.] 8°. pap., 25c. ... *Barclay.*
Household words for boys and girls; ed. by F. Dale. ill. 18°. '59. 63c. ... *Perkinpine.*
Household worship, partly responsive: book of family prayers, by a layman; with introd. by Rev. D. March. 12°. '73. $1.25 ... *Porter.*
Housekeeper, M. R. My husband's crime. [Fiction.] ill. 8°. pap., 75c. ... *Harper.*
Housekeeper. Jerrold, D. 15c. ... *French.*
Housekeeper and health keeper. Beecher, C. E. $1.50 ... *Harper.*
Housekeeper's friend: cook-book comp. by a lady of Zanesville. 8°. '76. $1.25 ... *Wiley.*
Housewife. Elliott, S. A. $1.50 ... *Hurd & H.*
Housewife's domestic science. (Reason why ser.) 12°. $1.25 ... *Lippincott.*
Housewife's treasure: information [conc.] household economics. 8°. '74. pap., 30c. ... (?) *F. M. Reed.*
Houssaye, Arsene. Life in Paris. New ed., rev. and enl. sm. 16°. '75. $1.50 ... *W. F. Gill.*
— Men and women of the 18th cent. 2 v. por. 12°. $3; hf. cf., $6 ... *Widdleton.*
— Philosophers and actresses. 2 v. por. 12°. $3; hf. cf., $6 ... *Widdleton.*
Houston, Edn. J. Elements of phys. geog. ('75.) 2d ed. 8°. '76. hf. mor., $1.75 ... *Eldredge.*
Houston, J. Arching Bergen Tunnel, Erie R. R. *See* McAlpine, W. J., Repair of earthen dam.
Houston, J: Principles of law of stoppage in transitu, retention and delivery. 8°. $4.25 ... *Callaghan.*
Houston, J: W. *See* Delaware, Reports.
Houston, S: Life. ill. 12°. $1.75 ... *J. E. Potter.*
Houston, T: Divine commendations of Abraham; or, parental duties, and blessings resulting from their faithful performance. 18°. 60c. ... *Pres. Bd.*
Hoven, Erniest. Man with two shadows. 16°. 90c. *Pres. Bd.*
— Neither Rome nor Judah. 16°. $1.10 ... *Pres. Bd.*
Hovey, Alvah. God with us; or, the person and work of Christ; with exam. of "Vicarious sacrifice" by H. Bushnell. ('72.) New ed., enl. 12°. '76. $1.50 ... *H. A. Young.*
— Scriptural law of divorce. 16°. 60c. ... *Am. Bapt.*
— State of the impenitent dead. 16°. '75. 75c. ... *Lothrop.*
— State of man after death. 18°. pap., 10c. ... *Am. Bapt.*
— *and* Gregory, J. M. Normal class manual for Bible teachers. 16°. $1 ... *Am. Bapt.*
How, W. W. New Test. according to the authorized version; with brief comment. by W. W. How and others. 2 v. maps and plans. 12°. '70. $4 .. *Pott.*
— Pastor in parochia: handbook for parish visiting. 16°. '71. $1.50; mor., $2.50 ... *Pott.*
How and why. 16°. 90c. ... *West. Tr.*
How and why. Felice, G. de. $1 ... *Lothrop.*
How Bennie did it. Wood, W. S. $1.50 .. *Hoyt, F. & D.*
How the boys spent their vacation. *See* Witt, *Mme.*
How a bride was won. Gerstäcker, F. $1.50; $1. *Appleton.*
How Charley helped his mother. *See* Lamb, *Mrs.* Jos.
How Charley Roberts became a man. Thurston, L. M. $1 ... *Lee & S.*
How could he escape? Wright, J. McN. $1.25. *Nat. Temp.*
How could he help it? Roe, A. S. $1.50 ... *Carleton.*
How crops feed; — grow. Johnson, S. W. ea., $2. *Judd.*
How do you manage? Bayly, T. H. 15c. ... *French.*
How Eva Roberts gained her education. Thurston, L. M. $1 ... *Lee & S.*
How gamblers win; or, the secrets of advantage-playing exposed. 16°. pap., 30c.; bds., 50c. *Dick & F.*
How he won her. Southworth, E. D. E. N. $1.75; $1.50 ... *Peterson.*
How I became a homœopath. Holcombe, W. H. 15c. *Boericke.*
How I came out of Rome. Thrivier, C. L. $1.25. *Nelson.*
How I found Livingstone. Stanley, H. M. $3.50. *Scribner.*
How I got my riches. 18°. 35c. ... *Am. S. S.*
How is this for high comicalities. ill. 4°. pap., 25c. *De Witt.*
How's your uncle? Wilks, T. E. 15c. ... *French.*
How it all happened. Parr, L. 15c. ... *Lippincott.*
How it was paid. Bates, L. $1.50 ... (?) *Martien.*
How Jennie found her Lord. Mathews, J. A. 35c. *Carter.*
How Jessie came out of the shadow. McLeod, G. A. H. 15c. ... *D. H. Carroll.*
How Jim did it. *See* Finley, M. F.
How the kingdom came to little Joy. 16°. 85c. *Am. S. S.*
How Lisa loved the king. Eliot, G. 50c. ... *Osgood.*
How Maggie helped her father. 18°. 40c. ... *Am. S. S.*
How Maggie's prayer was answered. 18°. 35c. *Am. S. S.*
How Maria's curls made the bracelet. *See* Witt, *Mme.*
How Marjorie watched. 12°. '73. 80c. *Meth. Bk. Conc.*
How Marjory helped. Carroll, M. $1.50 ... *Lee & S.*
How Mary Edmonds did what she could, and what came of it. ill. 18°. 60c. ... *N. Y. Ref. Ch. Bd.*
How money is lost and made in Wall Street. Lapsley and Bazley. 30c. ... (?) *Lapsley.*
How Nellie found the fairies: a grandmother's Christmas story. 16°. $1 ... *Lippincott.*
How not to be sick. Bellows, A. J. $2 .. *Hurd & H.*
How old art thou? Pingry, I. F. 20c. ... *Randolph.*
How Patty learnt the alphabet. ill. sq. 16°. 75c. *Nelson.*
How Paul Arnold made his fortune: tale of Peruvian adventure. 16°. '73. 50c. ... *Routledge.*
How Paul became an artist; or, looking out and looking in. 18°. 50c. ... *Am. S. S.*
How Paul's penny became a pound. 18°. 45c. *Am. S. S.*
How Peter's pound became a penny. 18°. 40c. *Am. S. S.*
How plants behave. Gray, A. 75c. ... *Ivison.*
How plants grow. Gray, A. $1.12 ... *Ivison.*
How shall I teach? Mason, L. 38c. ... *Ditson.*
How shall I woo thee? 16°. '75. pap., 30c. ... *Happy.*
How shall we order our worship? Seiss, J. A. 25c. *Luth. Bk. St.*
How shall we paint our houses? Masury, J. W. $1.50. *Appleton.*
How stout you 're getting. Morton, J. M. 15c. *Ames; French.*
How they made a man of him. Smith, J. R. $1. *J. D. Gill.*
How Tiptoe grew. Buck, L. A. $1 ... *Am. Tr.*
How 'tis done. Hunter, H. E. 20c. ... *Hunter.*
How to amuse an evening party. ill. large 16°. pap., 30c.; bds., 50c. ... *Dick & F.*
How to answer objections to revealed religion. 16°. 75c. ... *Nelson.*
How to be beautiful. 18°. 30c. ... *Am. S. S.*
How to be happy. Culverwell, R. J. 25c. ... *U. P. James.*
How to be happy; or, every day work. ill. 16°. $1. *Scribner, W. & A.*
How to be healthy. 16°. 10c. ... *Dick & F.*
How to be a hero. Lay, E. E. 45c. ... *Bost. Am. Tr.*
— *See also* Young hero stories.
How to be a lady. *See* Choice lib.
How to be a lady. Newcomb, H. $1 ... *Graves.*

How to be a man. *See* Choice lib.
How to be a man. Newcomb, H. $1........*Graves.*
How to be an orator. 12°. pap., 15c..........*Hurst.*
How to be saved. Brookes, J. H. 50c.; 20c...*McIntyre.*
How to become a clairvoyant. 16°. '74. 50c. *Un. Pub. Co.*
— *Same.* 12°. pap., 50c....................*Hurst.*
How to behave: pocket manual of republican etiquette, and guide to correct personal habits. 12°. '56. 75c..............................*Wells.*
How to behave; or, the spirit of etiquette. 16°. 10c. *Dick & F.*
How to behave, and how to write letters. 32°. 50c. *Fisher.*
How to behave; — do business; — talk; — write. *See* Handbook for home improvement.
How to build hot-houses. Leuchars, R. B. $1.50..*Judd.*
How to carve. ill. 16°. pap., 15c............*Locke.*
How to choose a husband; by author of "How to choose a wife." 16°. pap., 15c.........*Happy.*
How to choose a wife. 16°. pap., 15c........*Happy.*
How to conduct a debate. Rowton, F. 50c.; 75c. *Dick & F.*
How to conquer. Trowbridge, C. M. $1.25..(?) *Martien.*
How to conquer lib. 3 v. 16°. $4......(?) *Martien.*
Cont.: How to conquer. — Tom and Sarah Neal. — A mended life.

How to cook and how to carve. 16°. pap., 30c.; bds., 50c...............................*Dick & F.*
How to cook potatoes, apples, eggs and fish, 400 different ways. 16°. pap., 30c.; bds., 50c...*Dick & F.*
How to cut and contrive children's clothes. 16°. 10c. *Dick & F.*
How to detect adulteration in our daily food. sm. 4°. pap., 10c..........................*Dick & F.*
How to die for love. Kotzebue, A. F. F. 15c...*French.*
How to die happy; by author of "Learn to say no." 18°. 35c...........................*Pres. Bd.*
How to do business: pocket manual of pract. affairs and guide to success in life. 12°. '57. 75c... *Wells.*
How to do it. Hale, E. E. $1.25...........*Osgood.*
How to do it the best way. Blanchard, C. 25c. *D. Thomas.*
How to do right; or, Charley Grant. 32°. 30c. *Am. S. S.*
— *See also* Child's lib.
How to dress on 15 *l.* a year; by a lady. 16°. '74. bds., 50c.........................*Routledge.*
How to dress well. 32°. 20c............*Routledge.*
How to dress with taste. 16°. 10c... ......*Dick & F.*
How to economize like a lady. 16°. '74. bds., 50c. *Routledge.*
How to educate yourself. Eggleston, G. C. 75c. *Putnam.*
How to enjoy life. Cornell, W. N. C. $1.50..*Challen.*
How to entertain a social party: tableaux, games, etc. ill. sq. 18°. '74. pap., 25c.......(?) *F. M. Reed.*
How to farm profitably. Mechi, J. J. 2 v. ea., $2.50. *Routledge.*
How to get a divorce; [with] compilation of laws of the U. S. upon divorce; by a member of the N. Y. bar. 12°. '59. pap., 25c.......*D. Thomas.*
How to get a farm. *See* Morris, E.
How to get out of Newgate. 16°. '73. 25c...*Routledge.*
How to get rich in California: hist. of [its] industrial interests, etc. 8°. '76. pap., 50c.....*McMorris.*
How to give: the Bible way; by author of "The Episcopal invitation." 18°. 25c...........*Pres. Bd.*
How to grow rich. Reynolds, F. 15c.......*French.*
How to live. Robinson, S. $1.25........... *Wells.*
How to live long. Hall, W. W. $1.50....*Hurd & H.*
How to make the best of it. Bowman, A. $1.25. *Routledge.*
How to make the best of it. *See* Mackarness, *Mrs.* M. A.
How to make candy. 12°. 50c................*Judd.*
How to make the farm pay. *See* Dickerman, C. W., *and* Flint, C. L.
How to make home happy. Brough, W. 15c...*French.*
How to make a living. Eggleston, G. C. 75c...*Putnam.*
How to make money. Davies, T. A. $1.50..*Carleton.*
How to make a will. Lee, J. B. 40c.; 50c.; 90c. *Am. Tr.*
How to manage gas. Wilkins, F. 20c.........*Spon.*
How to nurse sick children. West, C. 50c... *W. Wood.*
How to paint. 12°. $1.......................*Judd.*
How to pay off the national debt. Green, D. $1.50. *Claxton.*
How to pay the rent. Power, T. 15c........*French.*
How to pronounce difficult words. 12°. pap., 15c. *Hurst.*
How to read a book in the best way; by a graduate of Oxford. 12°. '73. 75c.; pap., 50c.......*Philes.*
How to read character: a handbook of phrenology and physiognomy; with chart by S. R. Wells. ill. 12°. '68. $1.25; pap., $1.............. *Wells.*
How to settle accounts with your laundress: farce. 16°. pap., 15c.............................*Happy.*
How to shine in society; or, the science of conversation. 16°. pap., 25c................*Dick & F.*
How to speak and write with elegance and ease. 12°. pap., 15c..............................*Hurst.*
How to speak in public; or, the art of extempore oratory. 16°. pap., 25c................*Dick & F.*
How to succeed. 18°. 35c.; 45c...........*Am. Bapt.*
How to talk: pocket manual of conversation and debating. 12°. '57. 75c................... *Wells.*
How to talk and debate. 16°. 10c. ....*Dick & F.*
— *Same.* 12°. pap., 15c....................*Hurst.*
How to teach chemistry. Frankland, E. $1.25..*Lindsay.*
How to teach the little folks; by J. B. Tyler, Mrs. I. M. Alden, F. Latimer and Mrs. G. Partridge. 18°. 30c...............................*Pres. Bd.*
How to treat the sick without medicine. Jackson, J. C. $2..................................*Austin.*
How to win and how to woo. 16°. 10c. ....*Dick & F.*
How to work with the microscope. Beale, L. S. $7.50. *Lindsay.*
How to write: pocket manual of composition and letter writing. 12°. '57. 75c.................. *Wells.*
How to write clearly. Abbott, E. A. 60c....*Roberts.*
How to write a composition. 16°. pap., 30c.; bds., 50c.................................*Dick & F.*
How to write letters. Westlake, J. W. $1; $1.50. *Sower.*
How Violet's prayer was answered. *See* Locust grove stories.
How we managed our private theatricals: guide to the amateur stage. ill. 16°. '72. pap., 25c...*Happy.*
How we spend our years. Paxton, W. M. 35c. *Randolph.*
How will it end? Heywood, J. C. $1.50; 75c. *Lippincott.*
How will they get out of it? Rose, G. 15c...*French.*
How women can make money. Penny, V. $2. *J. E. Potter.*
How the world was peopled. Fontaine, E. $2..*Appleton.*
Howadji in Syria. Curtis, G. W. $1.50....*Harper.*
Howard, A. P. Christmas and Easter carols. 8°. '71. pap., 50c............................*Ditson.*
— Collection of carols for Christmas, Epiphany, Easter, etc.; with music. 8°. '60. pap., 60c...*Dutton.*
— Easter carols. 8°. '71. pap., 20c..........*Ditson.*
— Eight Easter carols. 8°. '76. pap., 20c.....*Ditson.*
— Ten Christmas carols. 8°. '73. pap., 20c...*Ditson.*

Howard, *Mrs.* B. C. Fifty years in a Maryland kitchen. 12°. '73. $1.50 .... *Turnbull.*

Howard, B: Chew. *See* United States, Sup. Court reports.

Howard, Blanche Willis. One summer. [Fiction.] (Saunterer's ser.) 18°. '75. $1.50 .... *Osgood.*

Howard, Caro. (*pseud.*) *See* Jervey, *Mrs.* Caro. H.

Howard, Clar. J. Book of conundrums and riddles. 16°. pap., 30c.; bds., 50c. .... *Dick & F.*
— Book of drawing-room theatricals. 16°. pap., 30c.; bds., 50c. .... *Dick & F.*
— Recitations, comic, serious and pathetic. 16°. pap., 30c.; bds., 50c. .... *Dick & F.*
— *and* Hudson, F. Twenty-six short plays for private theatricals; [compr.] Howard's "Drawing-room theatricals," and Hudson's "Private theatricals." 16°. $1.50 .... *Dick & F.*

Howard, Conway R. Earthwork mensuration on the basis of the prismoidal formulæ. ill. 8°. '74. $1.50 .... *Van Nostrand.*

Howard, D. H. Journey of the Israelites in the wilderness, spiritually considered. 16°. '64. 50c. *H. H. Carter.*

Howard, E: The penitent boy, and other tales. 18°. 70c. .... *Pres. Bd.*

Howard, Fk. Key. Fourteen months in American bastiles. 8°. '63. 50c. .... *Kelly, P. & Co.*

Howard, H: *See* Surrey, *Earl of.*

Howard, H: *See* Bible, Pentateuch.

Howard, Horton. Domestic medicine; or, family companion. ill. 8°. leath., *$6 ..... *Quak. City.*
— Improved system of botanic medicine. ('48.) New ed. ill. 8°. '54. shp., $3 .... *Wilstach.*
— Improved system of midwifery. 8°. '52. shp., $2. *Wilstach.*

Howard, J: John Howard; or, the prison world of Europe. 16°. $1.25 .... *Carter.*
— Life. 18°. 50c. .... *Pres. Bd.*

Howard, J: Practical chemistry. (Element. sci. ser.) ill. 16°. '74. 75c. .... *Putnam.*

Howard, *Rev.* J: Illustrated Scripture hist. for the young. ('52.) 30th ed. 2 v. steel eng. roy. 16°. '76. $10 .... *Virtue.*

Howard, Marion. Annie's influence; or, she hath done what she could. 18°. 75c. ...... *Pres. Bd.*
— Fred's hard fight. ('73.) New ed. 12°. '75. $1.25. *Nat. Temp.*
— Mr. Warner's household. 18°. 55c. ...... *Pres. Bd.*
— Oriel: tale of boarding-school life. 16°. $1.25. *Pres. Bd.*
— Two terms at Olney. 18°. 75c. .... *Pres. Bd.*

Howard, Nath., *jr.* *See* New York, Court of Appeals cases; Practice reports.

Howard, T. E. *See* Excelsior; — Zander, H. J., *and* Howard, T. E.

Howard, V. E. *See* Mississippi, High Court of Errors and Appeals reports.

Howard, W. W. Aids to French composition. 12°. '54. $1.25 .... *Ivison.*

Howard and his teacher. Baker, H. N. W. $1.50. *Lee & S.*

Howard Ashley. Trowbridge, C. M. 75c. (?) *Martien.*

Howarth, *Mrs.* Ellen Clementine. Poems. ('67.) 2d ed. 12°. '75. $1.25; mor., $3 ...... *Dennis.*

Howe, A. Jackson. Manual of eye surgery. 8°. '74. $2.50 .... *Wilstach.*
— Practical treatise on dislocations and fractures. ('70.) 2d ed. ill. 8°. '75. shp., $4 .... *Wilstach.*

Howe, Cupples. The deserted ship: story of the Atlantic. ill. 16°. $1.25 .... *Routledge.*

Howe, D. P. Science of language; or, seven hour system of grammar. New ed., rev. 16°. '74. $1; pap., 50c. .... (?) *Howe.*

Howe, El. ["Gumbo Chaff."] Accordion songster. obl. 8°. '60. pap., 60c. .... *Ditson.*
— Accordion [; — flute; — violin] without a master. obl. 8°. '51. ea., pap., 50c. .... *Ditson.*
— Ball-room handbook: three hundred dances, with ill. and explan. of figures. 12°. '58. 60c.; bds., 50c.; pap., 40c. .... *Ditson.*
— Complete preceptor for the accordion. sm. 8°. '50. pap., 30c. — roy. 8°. pap., 50c. .... *Ditson.*
— Ethiopian accordion instructor: with Ethiop. melodies. 8°. '51. pap., 50c. .... *Ditson.*
— Ethiopian flute instructor; with minstrel melodies. obl. 8°. '50. pap., 50c. .... *Ditson.*
— Family circle glee book. 2 v. obl. 4°. '57. ea., bds., $2 .... *Ditson.*
— German accordion preceptor. New ed., rev. and enl. obl. 8°. '66. pap., 50c. .... *Ditson.*
— Instructor for the guitar. 8°. '51. pap., 50c. .. *Ditson.*
— New Am. accordion [; — banjo; — flute; — guitar; — piano; — reed organ and melodeon; — violin] school without a master. obl. 8°. ea., 50c. *Gordon.*
— New clarionet [; — cornet; — fife; — flageolet] instructor without a master. obl. 8°. '60. ea., pap., 50c. .... *Ditson.*
— New German accordion without a master. obl. 8°. 50c. .... *Gordon.*
— New school for the German concertina. obl. 8°. '60. pap., 50c. .... *Ditson.*
— Piano-forte instructor; with collection of music. obl. 16°. pap., 50c. .... *Ditson.*
— Pocket ball-room prompter: calls for the different changes and figures to all the principal quadrilles, etc. 12°. '58. pap., 12c. .... *Ditson.*
— School for the clarionet; — fife; — flageolet; — flute; — violin. obl. 8°. '51–'60. ea., pap., 50c. .. *Ditson.*
— Self instructor for the flute; — violin. obl. 8°. '51. ea., pap., 50c. .... *Ditson.*
— Seraphine and melodeon instructor; with collection of music. 8°. '51. pap., 50c. .... *Ditson.*
— Young America instructor for the flute. obl. 8°. 50c. *Gordon.*
— Young America violin instructor. obl. 8°. 50c. *Gordon.*

Howe, Elisha P. Young citizen's catechism: duties of district, county, state and U. S. officers; with parliam. rules. 12°. '60. 75c. ..... *Barnes.*

Howe, Fisher. Oriental and sacred scenes, from notes of travel in Greece, Turkey and Palestine. ill. 16°. '53. $1.25 .... *Dodd.*
— True site of Calvary; and suggestions relative to the resurrection. map. 8°. '71. $1; bds., 75c. *Randolph.*

Howe, G: History of the Presbyterian Church in South Carolina. 8°. '70. $4 .... *Duffie.*

Howe, H: Historical collections of Ohio; with descrip. of its counties, cities, towns and villages. ill. 8°. '76. $6 .... *Clarke.*
— Lives of eminent mechanics. ill. 12°. $1.25 .. *Harper.*

Howe, J. Burdette. British slave: drama. 16°. pap., 15c. .... *French.*
— Golden eagle: drama. 16°. pap., 15c. ..... *French.*

Howe, J: Works. 2 v. 8°. '75. $5 .... *Carter.*
— Redeemer's tears wept over lost souls, and other essays; with life of author by Rev. W. Urwick. 16°. '74. $1 .... *Draper.*

Howe, Jos. W. Breath (The) and the diseases which give it a fetid odor; with directions for treatment. 12°. $1 .... *Appleton.*
— Emergencies, and how to treat them. 8°. $3 .. *Appleton.*
— Winter homes for invalids. 12°. $1.25 .... *Putnam.*

Howe, *Mrs.* Jla. Ward. From the oak to the olive. 12°. $2 .... *Lee & S.*
— Later lyrics. 16°. $2; hf. cf., $4; mor., $6. *Lee & S.*
— Passion-flowers. 3d ed. 16°. $1 .... **Osgood.*
— Trip to Cuba. 16°. $1.25 .... **Osgood.*
— Words for the hour. 16°. $1 .... **Osgood.*
— World's own. 16°. 75c. .... **Osgood.*
— (*ed.*) Sex and education: reply to E. H. Clarke's "Sex in education." 16°. '74. $1.25 .. *Roberts.*

Howe, M. A. de W. Memoirs of life and services of Alonzo Potter. cr. 8°. $3; shp., $3.50..*Lippincott.*

Howe, W. W. Pasha papers. [*anon.*] 12°. '59. $1.25. *Scribner.*

Howell, E. E. Report on geol. of Utah, etc. *See* United States, *Corps of Eng.*

Howell, R. B. C. Deaconship: its nature, qualification and duties. 18°. 40c............*Am. Bapt.*
— Early Baptists of Virginia. 12°. $1.25..*Am. Bapt.*
— Forms of communion at the Lord's table. 16°. 90c. *So. Bapt.*
— Terms of communion. 12°. 90c........*Am. Bapt.*

Howells, W: Dean. Works. 6 v. 12°. '71-'74. ea., $2; per set, hf. cf., $24................*Osgood.*
Cont.: Chance acquaintance. — Foregone conclusion. — Italian journeys. — Suburban sketches. — Their wedding journey. — Venetian life.
— Chance acquaintance. 18°. $1.25..........*Osgood.*
— Day's pleasure. (Vest pock. ser.) ill. 32°. '76. 50c.................................*Osgood.*
— Italian journeys. 12°. '67. $1.75.......*Hurd & H.*
— Poems. (Saunterer's ser.) 18°. '73. $1.25..*Osgood.*
— Suburban sketches. cr. 8°. '71. $1.75..*Hurd & H.*
— Their wedding journey. (Saunterer's ser.) 18°. $1.25...............................*Osgood.*

Howie, J: The Scots worthies. ill. 8°. $3.50..*Carter.*

Howison, G: H. Ray's analytic geometry. 8°. '69. shp., $2.50....................*Wilson, H. & Co.*

Howitt, Marg. Birds of a feather; or, the two school boys. 32°. 40c..............*Scribner, W. & A.*

Howitt, Ma. Author's daughter. 8°. pap., 25c. *Harper.*
— Birds and flowers; or, lays and lyrics of rural life. ill. sm. 4°. '72. $3....................*Nelson.*
— Birds and their nests. ill. sm. 4°. '71. $2..*Routledge.*
— Bright days. ill. 16°. '69. $1.25..........*Lothrop.*
— Child's delight; or, the three wishes and other entertaining stories. ill. 4°. $1.50...........*Miller.*
Note. First pub. under title of Jack and Harry.
— Dick and the angel. ill. 4°. '73. pap., 25c.; bds., 50c.................................*Lothrop.*
— Fireside tales; in prose and verse. 16°. '63. 75c. *Roberts.*
— Gabriel: a story of Wichnor Wood. ill. 16°. '67. $1...........................*Collins & Bro.*
— Heir of Wast-Wayland. 12°. $1.50.......*Harper.*
— Honest Gabriel; or, the reward of perseverance. ill. 16°. '66. $1......................*Perkinpine.*
— Lillieslea; or, lost and found. ill. 16°. $1.25. *Routledge.*
— — *See also* Young ladies' lib.
— Natural history stories for my juvenile friends. ill. sm. 4°. '75. $2.....................*Routledge.*
— Our cousins in Ohio; from the diary of an Am. mother. ill. 16°. '67. $1........*Collins & Bro.*
— Our four-footed friends. ill. sm. 4°. $2..*Routledge.*
— Pictorial calendar of the seasons. ill. 12°. (Bohn.) $1.75..........................*Little, B. & Co.*
— *Same.* ill. 12°. (Bohn.) $2. *Lippincott; Scribner, W. & A.*
— Picture book for the young. ill. sq. 12°. 63c. *Claxton; Lippincott.*
— Pictures for the young. ill. 4°. '69. $1.25..*Lothrop.*
— Poems. *See* Scott, *Sir* W., Lady of the lake.
— Poems of natural hist. for the young; ill. by Giacomelli. sm. 4°. '73. $3..............*Nelson.*
— Popular history of the U. S. 2 v. ill. 12°. $3.50. *Harper.*
— Series of popular juv. works. 14 v. 16°. $7..*Appleton.*
Cont.: Alice Franklin. — Hope on, hope ever. — Little coin, much care. — Love and money. — My own story. — My uncle. — No sense like common sense. — Sowing and reaping. — Story of a genius. — Strive and thrive. — Two apprentices. — Which is wiser? — Who is greatest? — Work and wages.
— Sketches of natural history; or, songs of animal life; ill. by Giacomelli. sm. 4°. $2.50......*Nelson.*
— Tales from natural hist. 18°. 60c.........*Harper.*
— Tales in prose. ill. 18°. 60c. ....*Harper.*
— Tales in verse. ill. 18°. 60c. ....*Harper.*

Howitt, Ma., *continued.*
— Who shall be greatest? 18°. 75c. ....*Harper.*
— *and* W: Jack and his pets. ill. sm. 4°. *net*, 40c. *Hamersley.*
— — Stories of Eng. and foreign life. ill. 12°. (Bohn.) $1.75..........................*Little, B. & Co.*
— — *Same.* ill. 12°. (Bohn.) $2. *Lippincott; Scribner, W. & A.*

Howitt, W: Boy's (A) adventures in the wilds of Australia. ill. 12°. $1.50...........*Eastman.*
— Country year-book; or, the field, forest and fireside. 12°. $1.50.............................*Harper.*
— Fireside stories lib. 3 v. ill. 12°. ea., $1.75. *Routledge.*
Cont.: Jack o' the mill. — Boy's adventures in the wilds of Australia. — Country book for the field, forest and fireside.
— Homes and haunts of the British poets. 2 v. ill. 12°. $3.50.................................*Harper.*
— *Same.* ill. cr. 8°. $3; hf. cf., $5; cf., $8..*Routledge.*
— Life and adventures of Jack of the mill, commonly called Lord Othmill: a fireside story. 8°. pap., 25c.....................................*Harper.*
— Woodburn Grange. 12°. $1.75; pap., $1.50..*Peterson.*
— *See also* Howitt, M. *and* W.
— *and* Milman, H. H., *and* Keats, J. Poetical works. 8°. $3.............................*Desilver.*

Howland, E: Adventures beneath the sea. *See* Goodrich, F. B., Ocean's story.

Howland, F. *See* United States, District Court reports.

Howland, J: D. *See* Barbour, L., *and* Howland, J. D.

Howland, Marion. Bert Ashley. 16°. 60c...*West. Tr.*

Howland, S. E. American economical housekeeper. [Cook-book.] 16°. pap., 50c...........*Locke.*

Howls from the owl train: Ethiop. drama. 16°. pap., 15c..........................*French; Happy.*

Hows, J: A. (*ill.*) Forest pictures in the Adirondacks; with poems by A. B. Street. 4°. '64. $3..*Hurd & H.*
— *See also* Christmas carol; — Forest scenes; — In the woods.

Hows, J: W. S. Historical Shakespearian reader. 12°. hf. bd., $1.50.........................*Appleton.*
— Junior ladies' reader. 12°. $1.50..........*Butler.*
— Ladies' book of reading and recitations. 12°. $1.88. *Butler.*
— Ladies' reader. 12°. $1.75................*Butler.*
— Primary ladies' reader. 18°. 60c...........*Butler.*
— Shakespearian reader. 12°. $1.50.......*Appleton.*
— (*ed.*) Golden leaves from American poets. 12°. '65. $1.50..............................*Randolph.*
— Golden leaves from British poets. 12°. '65. $1.50. *Randolph.*
— Golden leaves from British and American dram. poets. 12°. '65. $1.50.............*Randolph.*
— *See also* Golden leaves ser.

Howson, H. *and* C. Brief inquiry into principles, effect and present state of the Am. patent system. 2d ed. 8°. '72. hf. shp., $2..*J. Campbell & Son.*
— — Brief treatise on U. S. patents for inventors and patentees. 16°. '76. $1................*Porter.*

Howson, J: Saul. Before the table: inquiry into the true meaning of the consecration rubric in the communion service of the Church of Eng. 8°. '75. $2.75........................*Macmillan.*
— Character of St. Paul. 12°. '73. $1.75......*Dodd.*
— Companions of St. Paul. 12°. '71. $1.75..*Routledge.*
— Metaphors of St. Paul. 12°. $1.50......*Routledge.*
— Proportion in religious belief and religious practice. 8°. pap., 50c.......................*Routledge.*
— Sacramental confession. 12°. '74. $1....*Routledge.*
— Scenes from life of St. Paul, and their relig. lessons. ill. 16°. $1......................*Bost. Am. Tr.*
— *See also* Conybeare, W. J., *and* Howson, J. S.

Hoyle, Edm. Games. 18°. $1. 32°. 63c...*Lippincott.*
— *Same.* ill. 16°. $1.........................*Locke.*
— *Same.* 16°. $1.25; pap., 50c.; bds., 75c...*Dick & F.*
— *Same;* modernized by G. F. Pardon. ill. 24°. $1; bds., 80c..........................*Routledge.*

Hoyt, —. Family and social melodies. [Hymn book.] 8°. 58c. ... *Meth. Bk. Conc.*

Hoyt, Edm. S. *See* Maine State year book.

Hoyt's Sunday-school speakers. 2 ser. 18°. '76. ea., 60c. ... *Hoyt.*

Hozier, H: M. The British expedition in Abyssinia. 8°. '69. $3.50 ... *Macmillan.*

— The seven weeks' war [bet. Austria and Prussia, 1866]: its antecedents and its incidents. 2 v. 8°. '68. $4.50 ... *Claxton.*

— *Same.* New [chp.] ed. maps and plans. cr. 8°. '71. $2.50 ... *Macmillan.*

Hubback, *Mrs.* J. Kate Penrose; or, life and its lessons. 8°. pap., 25c. ... *De Witt.*

— Love and duty. 12°. $1.75; pap., $1.50 .. *Peterson.*

— May and December: a tale of wedded life. 12°. $1.50; pap., $1 ... *Claxton.*

— The wife's sister. 8°. pap., 50c. ... *Harper.*

Hubbard, F. M. *See* North Carolina readers.

Hubbard, Gardiner G. American railroads; read before Am. Soc. Sci. Assoc., May 20, 1874. 8°. '74. pap., 10c. ... *Williams.*

Hubbard, Ste. New temperance melodist. [Song book.] 16°. '59. bds., 50c. ... *Ditson.*

Hubbard, W. *See* Maine, Sup. Court reports.

Hubbard, W. G. Capital punishment; with extracts from Judge Bovee, Bright, Quimby, etc. 32°. '75. pap., 10c. ... *Friends Pub. H.; Peace.*

Hubbell, G: A. The chapel hymn book. 5th ed. 24°. '74. 50c. ... *Tibbals.*

Hubbell, J: H. Legal directory for lawyers and business men: names of lawyers in U. S. and Canada, etc. ('69.) [Annual.] 8°. shp., $5 .. *Hubbell.*

Huber, Anne L. The nursery rattle; for little folks. ill. sm. 4°. $1.75 ... *Lippincott.*

Huber, Vct. Aimé. The pope and the council; tr. from the Germ. 16°. '69. $1 ... *Roberts.*

— *Same.* 12°. '70. $1 ... *Pott.*

Hubert. Abbott, J. $1 ... *Dodd.*

Hubert Lee; or, how a child may do good. 18°. 35c. *Am. S. S.*

Hubert's wife. Lee, M. M. $1.50 ... *Kelly, P. & Co.*

Hubner, C: W. Historical souvenirs of Martin Luther. ill. 16°. $1 ... *Cin. Meth. Bk. Conc.*

— Wild flowers. [Poems.] 12°. '76. $1.25; $1.75. *Authors.*

Hübner, J: Biblische Historien; bearb. v. C. A. Körner. 12°. 60c.–$1.50 ... *Kohler.*

— *Same.* (Schulausgabe.) ill. 8°. 62c.; — (Alte unveränd. Ausg.) 50c. ... *Schäfer.*

— *Eng.* Biblical stories; tr. by J. C. Oehlschläger. 12°. 60c.–$1.50 ... *Kohler.*

— *Same.* ill. 8°. 62c. ... *Schäfer.*

— Zweimal 52 auserlesene bibl. Historien. ('64.) 33d ed. 16°. '76. bds., 40c. ... *Barthel; Brobst.*

— *Same.* 18°. 45c. ... *Radde.*

Hübner, Jos. Alex. (*Baron*) v. Ramble round the world; tr. by Lady Herbert. cr. 8°. $2.50. *Macmillan.*

Hübner, Jul. *See* Dresden gallery.

Huc, Evariste Regis. Christianity in China and Japan. 2 v. 12°. $3–$5 ... *Sadlier.*

— Journey through the Chinese empire. 2 v. map. 12°. $3 ... *Harper.*

— Travels in Tartary, Thibet and China. ill. 18°. 75c. *Nelson.*

Hudibras. *See* Butler, S:

Hudson, A. Lectures on study of fever. 8°. $2.50. *Lea.*

Hudson, C: F. Critical Gk. and Eng. concordance of New Test.; rev. and completed by E. Abbot. ('70.) 3d ed. 16°. '75. $2.50 ... *Hastings.*

Hudson, Eliz. Harriot. Life and times of Louisa, Queen of Prussia. 2 v. 12°. '74. $6 .. *Routledge.*

Hudson, Erasmus Darwin, *jr.* Anniversary discourse before N. Y. Acad of Med. 8°. '76. pap., 20c. *N. Y. Acad. Med.*

Hudson, Fs. Private theatricals for home performance. 16°. pap., 30c.; bds., 50c. ... *Dick & F.*

— *See also* Howard, C. J., *and* Hudson, F.

Hudson, F: Journalism in the U. S., 1690–1872. cr. 8°. $5 ... *Harper.*

Hudson, H. R. Poems. 16°. '74. $1.50 ... *Osgood.*

Hudson, H: Norm. Life, art and characters of Shakespeare; with crit. discourses on some of his plays. ('72.) 2d ed. 2 v. 12°. '75. $4 ... *Ginn.*

— — *See also* Shakespeare, W.

— Sermons. 16°. '74. $1.50 ... *Ginn.*

— (*ed.*) Pamphlet sections of "Text books of prose and poetry." 7 pts. 12°. '76. ea., pap., 40c. .. *Ginn.*
Cont.: Burke, 2 pts. — Webster, 2 pts. — Bacon. — Wordsworth. — Coleridge and Burns.

— Text-book of poetry; with sketches of authors' lives. 12°. '75. $2 ... *Ginn.*

— Text-book of prose; with notes and sketches of authors' lives. 12°. '76. $2 ... *Ginn.*

Hudson (The) from the wilderness to the sea. Lossing, B. J. $5; $9 ... *Virtue.*

Hudson River by daylight: New York to Albany, Saratoga springs, Lake George, etc. ('73.) [Annual.] 16°. pap., 25c. ... (?) *G. Watson.*

Hufeland, Chr. W: Art of prolonging life, tr.; ed. by E. Wilson. 12°. '70. $1.25 ... *Lindsay.*

— Enchiridion medicum; or, manual of the practice of medicine; tr. 12°. hf. mor., $2.50 ... *Radde.*

Hüffer, Fz. Richard Wagner and the music of the future: history and æsthetics; tr. 12°. $3.50. *Scribner, W. & A.*

Hugenotten (Die). 12°. pap., 15c. ... *Radde.*

Hugessen. *See* Knatchbull-Hugessen.

Hugger mugger: farce. 16°. pap., 15c. ... *French.*

Huggins, W. *See* Roscoe, H. E., Huggins, W., *and* Lockyer, J. W.

Hugh Cheston's vow. Spottswood, L. A. $1.25. *Meth. Epis.*

Hugh Fisher. *See* Reuben Kent ser.

Hugh Fisher; or, home principles carried out. 18°. 65c. *Am. S. S.*

Hugh Melton. King, R. 25c. ... *Harper.*

Hugh Taylor; or, the desert island. 18°. 25c. *Scribner, W. & A.*

Hugh Wellwood's success. *See* Cupples, *Mrs.* A. J.

Hugh Worthington. Holmes, M. J. $1.50 .. *Carleton.*

Hugh Wynford; or, the cousin's revenge. 16°. $1. (?) *Martien.*

Hughan, W. J. Masonic sketches and reprints. 12°. '72. $3 ... *Masonic.*

Hughes, E: Outlines of Scripture geog. and hist. maps. roy. 12°. '54. $1 ... *Lea.*

Hughes, Hu. Female characters of Holy Writ. ill. 16°. $1.75 ... *Scribner, W. & A.*

Hughes, Ja. *See* Kentucky, Court of Appeals reports.

Hughes, *Abp.* J: Works; ed. by L. Kehoe. 3d ed. 2 v. 8°. '66. $8 ... *Cath. Pub.*

— Kirwin unmasked: review of Kirwin in six letters, addressed to Rev. N: Murray. 18°. 12c. .. *Strong.*

— Life. 12°. pap., 25c. ... *Peterson.*

— Life, correspondence and writings. *See* Hassard, J. R. G.

— War in America. *See* Train, G. F., On downfall of England.

— *See also* Brooks, E., *and* Hughes, J.; — Carpenter, G. T., *and* Hughes, J.

— *and* Breckenridge, J: Is the Protestant religion the relig. of Christ? [Debate.] 8°. $2 .. *Cummiskey.*

— — Is the Rom. Cath. religion inimical to civil or relig. liberty? [and] Is the Presb. relig. inimical to civil or relig. liberty? [Debate.] 8°. '56. $2.50; $3 ... *Murphy.*

Hughes, J: T. Doniphan's expedition: cont. account of conquest of New Mexico; Kearney's expedition to California; Doniphan's campaign against the Nevajos, etc. ill., plans and map. 12°. $1.50. 8°. pap., 50c. . . . . *U. P. James.*

Hughes, Margie S. Annetta; or, the story of a life. ill. large 16°. $1.25 . . . . *Cin. Meth. Bk. Conc.*

Hughes, R. W. Question of interest during the war: opinion and decision of H. enforcing the [Va.] act of Assembly abating war interest. 8°. '74. pap., 25c. . . . . *West, J. & Co.*

Hughes, S: *See* Coventry, T., *and* Hughes, S.

Hughes, S: Treatise on gas works and practice of manufacturing and distributing coal gas. 5th ed., rev. by W. Richards. ill. 12°. $1.75 . . . . *Baird.*

— Treatise on water works for the supply of cities and towns. 12°. $2 . . . . *Baird.*

Hughes, T. The acolyte; or, the Christian scholar. [Fiction.] 12°. '76. $1.50 . . . . . *Cuninngham.*

Hughes, T: Alfred the Great. map and ill. 16°. '71. $1.25 . . . . *Osgood.*

— *Same.* cr. 8°. '69. $1.75 . . . . *Macmillan.*

— *Same.* 12°. '73. $1.50 . . . . *So. Meth.*

— Memoir of a brother. 4th ed. por. cr. 8°. '73. $1.75 . . . . *Macmillan.*

— *Same.* 12°. '73. $1.25; hf. cf., $3 . . . . *Osgood.*

— Scouring of the White Horse; or, the long vacation ramble of a London clerk. (chp. ed.) ill. 16°. '69. $1.25 . . . . *Macmillan.*

— Struggle for Kansas. *See* Ludlow, J. M., Sketch of hist. of U. S.

— Tom Brown at Oxford. ill. 8°. pap., 75c. . . *Harper.*

— *Same.* New ed. ill. 12°. '71. $1.75 . . . . *Macmillan.*

— *Same.* 2 v. por. 16°. '60. $2.50; hf. cf., $6 . . *Osgood.*

— Tom Brown's school days. ill. 8°. pap., 50c. *Harper.*

— *Same.* 18°. '73. $1.25; 75c. — ill. 12°. $1.75. — ill. sm. 4°. $3.50 . . . . *Macmillan.*

— *Same.* ill. 16°. $1.25; hf. cf., $3 . . . . *Osgood.*

— — *See also* Chalmers, *Mrs.* A. M., Brown and Arthur.

— *Same;* [also] Tom Brown at Oxford. ill. 8°. $1.50. *Harper.*

Hughes, W: Modern atlas of the world. maps. 4°. $6.25 . . . . *Scribner, W. & A.*

— Philips' Scripture atlas. maps. 18°. '72. pap., 25c. *Lippincott; Randolph.*

— *Same.* maps. 18°. 50c. . . . . *Un. Bk. Conc.*

— Scripture atlas. 8°. (Bagster.) $3.25 . . . . . . *Wiley.*

Hughes, W: Carter. American miller and millwright's assistant. (cop. '55.) '58. 5th ed. 12°. '76. $1.50 . . . . *Baird.*

Hughey, G. W. Political Romanism; or, the secular policy of the papal church. 16°. $1. — 12°. $1.25. *Cin. Meth. Bk. Conc.*

— *See also* Braden, C., *and* Hughey, G. W.

Hugh's fire on the mountain. Pritchard, S. J. 75c. *Randolph.*

Hughs, *Mrs.* Ma. The ornaments discovered. ill. 18°. 75c. . . . . *Harper.*

— The two schools. 12°. $1 . . . . *Cath. Pub.*

Hugo, Vct. [Plays; tr.] 4 v. 16°. ea., pap., 15c. *French.*

Cont.: Angelo: tragedy. — Hernani: tragedy. — Ruy Blas. — Tour of Nesle.

— Brigand; or, the demon of the north; tr. 8°. pap., 75c. . . . . *Peterson.*

Note. Tr. of "Han d'Islande."

— Destroyer of the second republic, being Napoleon the little; tr. 12°. $1.50 . . . . *Sheldon.*

— Gavroche, the gamin of Paris; tr. and adapted by M. C. Pyle, from "Les misérables." 16°. '72. $1. *Porter.*

— Homme (L') qui rit. 8°. pap., 75c. . . . . . . *Appleton.*

— *Eng.* Man who laughs. 8°. $1.50; pap., $1 . . *Appleton.*

— Hunchback of Notre Dame; tr. 8°. pap., 75c. *Dick & F.*

Hugo, Vct., *continued.*

— *Same.* ill. 8°. '74. $3. — 12°. $1.25. — (chp. ed.) 12°. pap., 25c. . . . . *Routledge.*

— Life. 12°. $2 . . . . *Carleton.*

— Mer (La) et la nuit. 8°. pap., 50c. . . . . . . *Appleton.*

Note. Comprises pt. 1 of "Quatre-vingt-treize."

— Misérables (Les); tr. 8°. $2.50 . . . . *Carleton.*

— *Span.* Los miserables; tr. al castellano, por J. S. Flores. 8°. $2.50 . . . . *Appleton.*

— — *Same.* 2 v. $5 . . . . *Carleton.*

— Ninety-three; tr. by F. L. Benedict. 12°. $1.75. 8°. pap., 25c. . . . . *Harper.*

— Notre Dame; tr. 12°. pap., 25c. . . . . . . *Lippincott.*

— *Same.* ill. 8°. $3 . . . . *Routledge.*

— Par ordre du roi. 8°. pap., 50c. . . . . *Appleton.*

Note. Comprises pt. 2 of "Quatre-vingt-treize."

— Rhine. 12°. $1.75 . . . . *Estes.*

— Ruy Blas; tr. 12°. pap., 15c. . . . . *De Witt.*

— Toilers of the sea; tr. 8°. pap., 75c.; ill., $1.50. *Harper.*

Hugo and Franz. Finley, M. F. 75c. . . . . . . *Pres. Bd.*

Huguenot (The). *See* James, G. P. R.

Huguenot captain. Phillips, W. 15c. . . . . *French.*

Huguenot exiles. Dupuy, E. A. $1.25 . . . . . *Harper.*

Huguenot family; or, help in time of need. ill. 12°. $1.25 . . . . *Scribner, W. & A.*

Huguenot family in the English village. *See* Keddie, H.

Huguenot galley-slave. Marteilhe, J. $1.50 . . . *Holt.*

Huguenot galley-slaves. Barth, C. G. 35c. *Pres. Bd.*

Huguenot potter: historic tale. ('61.) New ed. ill. 16°. '74. $1 . . . . *Hoyt.*

Huguenots (Les). *See* Meyerbeer, G.

Huguenots (The). ill. 18°. '57. 35c. . . . . *Am. Tr.*

Huguenots (The). Smiles, S. $1.50 . . . . . . *So. Meth.*

Huguenots in France. Smiles, S. $2 . . . . *Harper.*

Huguet, Jos. Month of St. Joseph; arr. for each day of March; tr. 18°. '60. 50c. . . . . *Cunningham.*

— *Germ.* Der Monat März der Verehrung d. hl. Joseph. 18°. 50c. . . . . *Benziger.*

Huish, Rob. Memoirs of George IV. por. cr. 8°. '75. $1.50; pap., $1.25 . . . . *Adams, V. & Co.*

Hulda. Lewald, F. $1.75 . . . . *Lippincott.*

Hulen, *Mrs.* S. E. Clara Dwight in the home of her adoption. 18°. 75c. . . . . *Cong. Pub.*

— Mrs. Marshall's key, and what it unlocked. 16°. $1.15 . . . . *Cong. Pub.*

— Sunbeams in the home of Leonard Kingsley. 18°. 60c. . . . . *Cong. Pub.*

— Young teacher: sequel to "Clara Dwight." 18°. 75c. . . . . *Cong. Pub.*

Hull, —. *See* Jelliff, —, *and* Hull, —.

Hull, Amos G. Treatise on duties of town and county officers in N. Y. 8°. shp., $5 . . . . . . *W. C. Little.*

— *and* Mc Call, H: S. New York supervisor's guide. 8°. shp., $1.50 . . . . *W. C. Little.*

Hull, Asa. Casket hymns. 16°. '70. bds., 20c. . . *Ditson.*

— Casket of Sunday school melodies. obl. 12°. '69. bds., 45c. . . . . *Ditson.*

— Devotional chimes. 12°. '73. 75c. . . . . *Ditson.*

— Pilgrim's harp: sacred music. 16°. '69. 60c.; bds., 50c. . . . . *Ditson.*

— Star of the east: hymns and tunes. 16°. bds., 30c. *G. D. Russell.*

— Temperance glee book. 12°. '75. bds., 40c. . *Pond.*

— *and* Sanders, Harry. Sparkling rubies: S.-school music. obl. 12°. '71. bds., 35c. . . . . *Ditson.*

Hull, D. W. The hereafter: scientific, phenomenal and Biblical demonstration of a future life. 12°. '73. 75c.; pap., 50c. . . . . *Colby.*

Hull, E: Treatise on ornamental and building stones. photos and ill. 8°. '72. $4.50 . . . . *Macmillan.*

Hull, H: Journal. 12°. 75c. . . . . *Friends Bk. St.*

Hull, Mos. Contrast: evangelicalism and spiritualism compared. ('73.) 2d ed. 12°. '74. $1.50 . . *Colby.*

Hull, Mos., *continued.*
— Question settled: comparison of Biblical and modern spiritualism. ('69.) 2d ed. 12°. '75. $1.50..*Colby.*
— That terrible question. ('74.) 3d ed. 12°. '75. pap., 10c. . . . . *Colby.*
— *and* Parker, W. F. Which: spiritualism or Christianity? correspondence bet. H. and P. ('73.) 2d ed. 12°. '74. 75c.; pap., 50c. . . . . *Colby.*

Hullah, J: Song book. 18°. '66. $1.25..*Macmillan.*
— *See also* Wilhelm; — Palmer, *Sir* R.

Hulls, Jona. Description and draught of machine for carrying vessels out of or into harbour, 1737. [Reprint.] 12°. bds., 80c. . . . . *Spon.*

Hulme, F. E: Principles of ornamental art. 32 pl. roy. 4°. $12. . . . . *Cassell.*

Hulsean lectures, 1845–6. Fitness of Holy Scripture for unfolding the spiritual life of man: Christ the desire of all nations; or, the unconscious prophecies of heathendom; by R. C. Trench. 12°. $1.25. . . . . *Widdleton.*
— 1848. Lectures on the Apocalypse; by Rev. C. Wordsworth. 8°. $2.50. . . . . *McCauley.*
— 1859. Historical lectures on the life of Christ; by C. J. Ellicott. ('61.) New ed. cr. 8°. '74. $1.75. *Draper.*
— 1865. By J. Moorhouse. cr. 8°. $1.75..*Macmillan.*
— 1868. Immortality; by J. J. S. Perowne. 12°. '70. $1. . . . . *Randolph.*
— 1869. On some characteristics of belief, scientific and religious; by Rev. J. Venn. 8°. $2. *Macmillan.*
— 1870. Witness of history to Christ; by F. W. Farrar. New ed. cr. 8°. '75. $1.50. . . . . *Macmillan.*
— 1875. Some reasons of our Christian hope; by E. T. Vaughan. 8°. $2.50. . . . . *Macmillan.*

Hult, A. A.-B.-C.-bok för de swenska barnen i Norra Amerika. 8°. bds., 15c. . . . . *Engberg.*

Human life. Wette, W. M. de. 2 v. $2.50..*Dennet.*

Human life in Shakespeare. Giles, H. $2...*Lee & S.*

Human nature in its fourfold state. *See* Boston, T.

Human nature unveiled. Blanchard, C. 75c. *D. Thomas.*

Human sadness; — sorrows. *See* Gasparin, V. B.

Human temperaments. Powell, W. P. $2..*Widdleton.*

Humanity immortal. *See* Hickok, L. P.

Humanity in the city. Chapin, E. H. $1.25..*De Witt.*

Humber, W: Practical treatise on cast and wrought iron bridges and girders. 58 pl. imp. 4°. '57. hf. mor., $15. . . . . *Spon.*

Humbert, Aimé. Japan and the Japanese; tr. by Mrs. C. Hoey, and ed. by H. W. Bates. 4°. $12; hf. mor., $18. . . . . *Appleton.*

Humboldt, F: H: Alex. v. Works; tr. 9 v. 12°. hf. cf., $36. . . . . *Appleton.*
Cont.: Cosmos, 5 v. — Narrative of travels in Am., 3 v. — Views of nature.
— Briefe an Varnhagen v. Ense, 1827–'58, nebst Auszügen aus Varnhagen's Tagebüchern u. Briefen v. V. u. andern an H. 12°. '61. $1; pap., 60c. *Steiger.*
— *Same.* 12°. '60. pap., 50c. . . . . *Zickel.*
— Kosmos. 5 v. 8°. $3.50–$6; in 2 v., $4.50; hf. mor., $5. . . . . *F. W. Thomas.*
Note. v. 1-3, $3; pap., $2.50; hf. mor., $3.25: v. 4, 5, $1.50; pap., $1; hf. mor., $1.75.
— *Eng.* Cosmos: sketch of a physical descript. of the universe; tr. by E. C. Otté. 5 v. 12°. $6.25; shp., $8.25; hf. cf., $15. . . . . *Harper.*
— *Same;* tr. by E. C. Otté and W. S. Dallas. 5 v. 12°. (Bohn.) v. 1–4, ea., $1.25; v. 5, $1.75. *Little, B. & Co.*
— — *Same.* 5 v. 12°. (Bohn.) v. 1–4, ea., $1.40; v. 5, $2. . . . . *Scribner, W. & A.*
— — *Same.* 5 v. 12°. (Bohn.) v. 1–4, ea., $1.50; v. 5, $2.50. . . . . *Lippincott.*

Humboldt, F: H: Alex. v., *continued.*
— Travels and researches: narrative of his journeys in the equinoctial regions of Am. and Asiatic Russia; tr., with analyses of his important investigations by W. Macgillivray. ill. 18°. 75c. . . . . . *Harper.*
— *Same;* tr. and ed. by T. Ross. 3 v. 12°. (Bohn.) ea., $1.75. . . . . *Little, B. & Co.*
— — *Same.* 3 v. 12°. (Bohn.) ea., $2. *Lippincott; Scribner, W. & A.*
— Views of nature; or, contemplations of the sublime phenomena of creation; tr. by E. C. Otté and H. G. Bohn; with index. 12°. (Bohn.) $1.75. *Little, B. & Co.*
— — *Same.* 12°. (Bohn.) $2. *Lippincott; Scribner, W. & A.*

Humboldt, K: W: v. Letters to a lady; tr., with introd. by C. G. Leland. ('64.) New ed. 16°. '73. $1.25. . . . . *Holt.*

Humbug. Burnand, F. C. 15c. . . . . *French.*

Hume, D: Essays, literary, moral and political. 12°. $1.75. . . . . *Scribner, W. & A.*
— Essays and treatises; with life. 8°. $1.50..*Mendum.*
— History of England to 1688. 2 v. 8°. $4.50; shp., $6. *Polock.*
— *Same.* 3 v. 12°. $5.25. . . . . *Scribner, W. & A.*
— *Same;* with [autobiog.] 6 v. 12°. $6–$16.50..*Harper.*
— — *Same.* 6 v. 12°. $6–$18. . . . . . *Claxton; Porter.*
— — *Same.* 6 v. cr. 8°. $9–$19.50. . . . . . *Lippincott.*
— — *Same.* 6 v. 8°. '72. $15–$33...*Little, B. & Co.*
— *Same;* contin. by T. Smollett and J. R. Miller. 4 v. ill. 8°. shp., $12. . . . . *Polock.*

Hume-Rothery, *Mrs.* Ma. C. The wedding guests; or, the happiness of life. 12°. $1.25..*H. H. Carter.*

Humiliation of Christ. Bruce, A. B. $6. *Scribner, W. & A.*

Humility. Hofland, B. $1. . . . . *Nelson.*

Humility before honor. *See* Tonna, *Mrs.* C. E.

Humor, wit and wisdom: manual of table-talk. 12°. $1.75. . . . . *Routledge.*

Humorous chap-books of Scotland. Fraser, J. 2 v. ea., $1.25. . . . . *Hinton.*

Humorous phases of the law. Browne, I. $1.50. *Claxton; S. Whitney.*

Humorous speaker. Oldham, O. $1.50. . . . . . *Ivison.*

Humors of Falconbridge. Kelley, J. F. $1.75; $1.50. *Peterson.*

Humors of the railroad kings. Small, G. G. 25c. *Collin & S.*

Humors of the strike. Baker, G. M. 15c....*Lee & S.*

Humors of ventriloquism. 12°. pap., 15c. . . . . *Haney.*

Humpbacked lover. Mathews, C., *jr.* 15c. *French.*

Humpbacked Rhoda; by author of "Three Christmas days." 18°. '71. 40c. *N. Y. Ref. Ch. Bd.; Pres. Com.*

Humphrey, *Mrs.* E. J. Gems of India; or, sketches of distinguished Hindoo and Mahommedan women. ill. 12°. '75. $1.25. . . . . *Meth. Bk. Conc.*
— Six years in India; or, sketches of India and her people. ill. 12°. '66. $1.25. . . . . *Meth. Bk. Conc.*

Humphrey, E. P. Our theology in its developments. 18°. 35c. . . . . *Pres. Bd.*
— *See also* Preparing to teach.

Humphrey Clinker. Dibdin, T. 15c. . . . . *French.*

Humphrey Clinker. *See* Smollett, T.

Humphrey Merton. *See* Brother's lib.

Humphreys, A. A. Reports upon the physics, etc., of Mississippi River. *See* United States, *Corps of Eng.*
— *See also* Ives, J. C., Memoir to accompany milit. map of Florida.

Humphreys, F. Cholera and its homœop. treatment. 18°. 38c. . . . . *Boericke.*
— Dysentery and its homœop. treatment. 18°. 50c. *Boericke.*

Humphreys, H. N. Coin collector's manual. 2 v. 12°. (Bohn.) ea., $1.75 ....*Little, B. & Co.*
— *Same.* 2 v. 12°. (Bohn.) ea., $2. *Lippincott; Scribner, W. & A.*
Humphreys, *Mrs.* Laura B. Art of reading music. ('74.) 3d ed. 8°. '75. bds., 75c...*Schermerhorn.*
Humphreys, W. H. *See* Tennessee, Sup. Court reports.
Humphry, G. M. Observations in myology. 8°. '72. $2.50 .... *Macmillan.*
— On the human foot and hand. fp. 8°. '61. $1.50. *Macmillan.*
— On the human skeleton, including the joints. ill. roy. 8°. '58. $10 .... *Macmillan.*
Humpty Dumpty, and other sensational dramas. 16°. '73. bds., 50c..................... *Routledge.*
Humpty Dumpty trick book. 24°. 30c....... *Fisher.*
Humpy Dumpy. Dana, J. J. $1.25. ..... *Nat. Temp.*
Hun, Mc. T. *See* New York, Sup. Court reports.
Hunchback. Knowles, J. S. 15c...*De Witt; French.*
Hunchback of Notre Dame. *See* Hugo, V.
Hundred fold (An). *See* Vinegar Hill stories.
Hundred pound note. Peake, R. B. 15c..... *French.*
Hundred thousand dollars in gold. Burnham, G. P. *(?) .... (?)*Holland.*
Hundred thousand pounds. Byron, H. J. 15c... *French.*
Hundred years ago. E., B. E. 75c......... *Lothrop.*
Hundssattler (Die). 12°. pap., 15c......... *Radde.*
Hungarian brothers. Porter, A. M. 25c... *Lippincott.*
Hungary: its hist. and revolutions; with memoir of Kossuth. 12°. (Bohn.) $1.25..*Little, B. & Co.*
— *Same.* 12°. (Bohn.) $1.40......*Scribner, W. & A.*
— *Same.* 12°. (Bohn.) $1.50........... *Lippincott.*
Hungerford, Ja. Old plantation, and what I gathered there in an autumn month. 12°. $1.50... *Harper.*
Hungering and thirsting. ('69.) New ed. ill. 16°. '73. 75c. .... *Hoyt.*
Hungering and thirsting after righteousness. 18°. 40c. *Am. S. S.*
Hunk's wedding day: Ethiop. drama. 16°. pap., 15c. *Happy.*
Hunnewell, Ja. W. Lands of Scott. maps and por. 12°. '71. $2.50; hf. cf., $5; mor., $6..*Osgood.*
Hunt, C. H. Life of E: Livingstone; with introd. by G: Bancroft. por. 8°. $4; hf. cf., $6.50..*Appleton.*
Hunt, D: Essays on religious subjects. 12°. '74. 65c. *Friends Pub. H.*
Hunt, E. Literature of the English language. 8°. '70. $2.50 .... *Ivison.*
Hunt, Ez. M. Bible notes for daily readers. 2 v. maps. roy. 8°. '70–'72. $7; — in 1 v., $5. *Scribner.*
— Grace culture; or, thoughts on grace, growth and glory. 12°. $1.20 .... *Pres. Bd.*
— Physician's (A) counsels to his professional brethren. 18°. 45c.......................... *Pres. Bd.*
Hunt, F. W. *See* Marcy, E. E., *and* Hunt, F. W.
Hunt, Ht. Cecil. Christ bearer; or, the hermit of the ford. 18°. 40c....................... *Dutton.*
Hunt, *Mrs.* Helen. See Jackson, *Mrs.* H.
Hunt, H: G. B. Golden gate. ill. fp. 8°. 75c... *Cassell.*
Hunt, Ja. Negro's place in nature. 8°. pap., 10c. *Van Evrie.*
Hunt, Ja. H. Legend of Florence: play. 16°. pap., 15c.. *French.*
Hunt, J: Contemporary essays in theology. 8°. '73. $5 .... *Routledge.*
— Religious thought in England, from reformation to end of last century. 3 v. 8°. '73. $15..*Routledge.*
Hunt, Leigh. Autobiography; with reminiscences of friends and contemporaries. 2 v. 12°. $3; hf. cf., $6.50 .... *Harper.*

Hunt, Leigh, *continued.*
— Book for a corner. 12°. (Bohn.) $2. *Lippincott; Scribner, W. & A.*
— Book of the sonnet. 2 v. 16°. '66. $3...*Roberts.*
— Day by the fire, and other papers; ed. by "Tom Folio." 16°. '69. $1.50.............. *Roberts.*
— Foster-brother: tale of the war of Chiozza. 8°. pap., 50c.................................. *Harper.*
— Men, women and books: sel. from his uncoll. prose writings. 2 v. 12°. $3; hf. cf., $6.50..*Harper.*
— Poetical works. (Blue and gold ed.) 2 v. por. 32°. $3 .... **Osgood.*
— *Same;* ed. by T. Hunt. (Household ser.) ill. 16°. $1.50; mor., $3 .... *Lee & S.*
— — *Same.* (Presentation ed.) ill. 12°. $1.75; $3; $3.50 .... *Routledge.*
— The seer; or, common places refreshed. 2 v. 16°. '64. $3 .... *Roberts.*
— Wishing-cap papers; ed. by J. E. Babson. 12°. $1.50 .... *Lee & S.*
Hunt, R: M. Designs for gateways of south. entrances to the Central Park [N. Y.]; with descript. 4°. '66. $5 .... *Van Nostrand.*
Hunt, Rob. Coal as a reservoir of power; [also] Atoms, by — Clifford. cr. 8°. '74. pap., 25c. *Estes.*
— Poetry of science; or, studies of the phys. phenomena of nature. 12°. (Bohn.) $1.75..*Little, B. & Co.*
— *Same.* 12°. (Bohn.) $2..*Lippincott; Scribner, W. & A.*
Hunt, Sandford. Compilation of statutes of the states in rel. to incorporation and maintenance of relig. societies. 12°. '76. shp., $1.50..*Meth. Bk. Conc.*
— Handbook for trustees of religious corporations in N. Y. ('73.) 2d ed. 12°. 50c............. *Otis.*
Hunt, Sara Keables. Arthur and Bessie in Egypt. 16°. 75c. .... *Cin. Meth. Bk. Conc.*
— The brook; [also] The tide turning, by L. Bates. 12°. $1 .... *Nat. Temp.*
Hunt, T: P. The Bible Baptist. 18°. pap., 15c. *Pres. Bd.*
Hunt, T: Sterry. Address before the Am. Assoc. for Adv. of Sci., Aug., 1871. 8°. pap., 25c. *Am. Assoc. Adv. Sci.*
— Chemical and geological essays. cr. 8°. $3..**Osgood.*
— Origin of metalliferous deposits. cr. 8°. '74. pap., 25c. .... *Estes.*
Hunt, W: *See* Pennsylvania Hospital reports.
Hunt, *Rev.* W: History of Italy. ('74.) New ed. 16°. '75. $1 .... *Holt.*
Hunt, W: M. Talks on art. 8°. '75. $1.50..*Hurd & H.*
Hunt for a husband. Wooler, J. P. 15c. .... *French.*
Hunt ribbon (The). *See* Yonge, C. M.
Hunted chief; or, the female ranchero. 8°. pap., 25c. *Dick & F.*
Hunted down. *See* Dickens, C:
Hünten, Fz. Celebrated instructions for the piano-forte; with Fr. and Eng. text. 4°. '72. bds., $1.25; pap., 75c. .... *Pond.*
— Celebrated piano-forte school. 4°. $1.25; — abridg., pap., 75c.................................. *Ditson.*
— *Same;* with add. by W. C. Peters. 4°. bds., $2; — abridg. 4°. bds., $1.50.............. *Peters.*
— Piano method; with Eng. and Fr. text. f°. $2; — abridg. f°. $1.50.......................... *Gordon.*
Hunter, B: *and* Myer, W: G. Index to Iowa reports, incl. Morris and Greene's and the series v. 1–34. 16°. '74. *net*, shp., $4........................ *Mills.*
— — *Same.* 8°. '74. shp., $5.................... *Gilbert.*
— — Index to Missouri reports (v. 1–50). 8°. shp., $5. *Gilbert.*
— — *Same;* [also] Index to Missouri reports (v. 50–60), by W. G. Myer. 8°. shp., $8.50. *Gilbert.*
— — Index to Ohio reports. 8°. '74. shp., $5. *Gilbert.*
— — Index to Tenn. reports, from Overton to 7th Heiskell. 8°. '75. shp., $5.................. *Gilbert.*

Hunter, Fanny. Western adventures: what Fanny Hunter saw and heard in Kansas and Missouri. ill. 12°. $1.75 .... *J. E. Potter.*

Hunter, H: Sacred biography; or, hist. of the patriarchs; with hist. of Deborah, Ruth and Hannah; also hist. of Christ. 8°. $2; hf. cf., $4.25. *Harper.*

Hunter, H: E. How 'tis done; or, the secret out: exposition of tricks practised by gamblers with cards and dice. ('64.) New ed. 12°. '73. pap., 20c. .... *Hunter.*

— Hunter's guide and trapper's companion. ('68.) New ed. 12°. '76. 50c.; pap., 25c. .... *Hunter.*

— Prestidigitation; or, magic made easy. ('65.) New ed. 12°. '76. pap., 20c. .... *Hunter.*

— Tricks and traps of America; or swindlers, quacks and humbugs exposed. ('72.) 5th ed. 8°. '75. pap., 25c. .... *Hunter.*

— Ventriloquist's guide; or, how to learn ventriloquism. ('70.) 5th ed. 12°. '76. pap., 20c. ..... *Hunter.*

Hunter, R. F. Manual for quartermasters and commissaries. 12°. '64. $1.25; mor., $1.50. *Van Nostrand.*

Hunter, Rob. Popular treatise on bronchitis. 12°. 75c. *Miller.*

— Popular treatise on colds and affections of the air-passages and lungs. 12°. 50c. .... *Miller.*

Hunter, S. J. Elementary view of proceedings in suit in equity. 8°. '60. $1.50 .... *T. & J. W. Johnson.*

— — *See also* Law lib.

Hunter, S: J. Hunters' and trappers' ill. hist. guide. 8°. '69. $1; $1.50 .... *S. J. Hunter.*

Hunter, T: Elements of plane geometry; with app. on mensuration for beginners. 12°. $1 .. *Harper.*

Hunter and Tom. Abbott, J. $1.50 .... *Dodd.*

Hunter and trapper. Revoil, B. $1.25 .... *Nelson.*

Hunter and trapper. Thrasher, H. $1 .... *Judd.*

Hunter and trapper's guide. ill. 18°. pap., 20c... *Haney.*

— *Same.* 12°. pap., 25c. .... *Hurst.*

Hunter of the Alps. Dimond, W. 15c... *Ames; French.*

Hunter's daughter. Turner, J. W. $2 .. *G. D. Russell.*

Hunter's feast. Reid, M. $1.50 .... *Carleton.*

Hunter's lib. of adventure. *See* Bowman, Anne.

Hunters of the west; or, adventures of Kit Carson. 8°. pap., 25c. .... *De Witt.*

Hunting grounds of the old world. Leveson, *Maj.* —. $1.75 .... *Routledge.*

Hunting scenes in wilds of Africa. ill. 12°. $1.75. *J. E. Potter.*

Hunting the slippers. Becher, M. 15c. .... *De Witt.*

Hunting sports in the west. Hartley, C. B. $1.75. *J. E. Potter.*

Hunting a turtle. Selby, C. 15c. .... *French.*

Huntingdon (Henry of). *See* Henry *of Huntingdon.*

Huntingdons (The). Boggs, M. L. $1.25 .. *H. A. Young.*

Huntingdons. Hayward, M. L. $1.25 .. *H. A. Young.*

Huntington, C: B. Trial of H. for forgery; from stenog. notes by Roberts and Warburton. 8°. hf. shp., $3 .... *Baker, V. & Co.*

Huntington, D. Manual of the fine arts, critical and historical; with introd. 12°. '50. $1.75 .. *Barnes.*

Huntington, Emily. Little lessons for little housekeepers. sq. 18°. '75. 25c.–15c. ..... *Randolph.*

Huntington, Faye (*pseud.*) *See* Foster, *Mrs.* I. H.

Huntington, F: Dan. Christ and the world: secularism the enemy of the Church. sm. 4°. '74. 75c.; pap., 25c. .... *Dutton.*

— Christian believing and living: sermons. 5th ed. 12°. '60. $1.75 .... *Dutton.*

— Divine aspects of human society. 8°. $2.25 .. *Carter.*

— Elim; or, hymns of holy refreshment. 3d ed. 16°. '61. $1.50; hf. mor., $4; mor., $5 ..... *Dutton.*

— Helps to a holy Lent. 16°. '73. $1.25 .... *Dutton.*

Huntington, F: Dan., *continued.*

— Massachusetts a field for church missions. 16°. pap., 10c. .... *Dutton.*

— New helps to a holy Lent. 16°. '76. $1.25 .. *Dutton.*

— Our Lord's parables: lessons for instruction of children in the Christian life. 16°. 30c... *Dutton.*

— Religious and moral sentences culled from the works of Shakespeare and compared with Holy Writ. 16°. 75c. .... *Dennet.*

— Righteousness of God the authority for uprightness in man: sermon. 18°. '75. pap., 15c... *Dutton.*

— Sermons for the people. 8th ed. 12°. '60. $1.75. *Dutton.*

— Steps to a living faith: letters to an indifferent believer. sm. 4°. '70. 75c.; pap., 25c... *Dutton.*

— *See also* Celebration.

Huntington, Jed. Vincent. Alban; or, the hist. of a young Puritan. 2 v. in 1. 12°. $2.50 .. *O'Shea.*

— Lady Alice; or, the new Una. 8°. pap., 60c. *Appleton.*

— Pretty plate. 18°. 50c.; 75c. .... *Sadlier.*

— Rosemary. 12°. $2; $2.50 .... *Sadlier.*

Huntington, Josh. Gropings after truth: a life-journey from New Eng. Congregationalism to the one Cath. apostolic church. 16°. 75c.... *Cath. Pub.*

Huntington, S: H. *See* United States, Court of Claims reports.

Huntington, W: R. Church porch (The): service book and hymnal for S.-schools; with music. 16°. 50c.; — without music, 30c.; — without hymns and music, 20c. .... *Dutton.*

— Follow thou me: questions for the first half of the Christian year. 16°. hf. bd., 20c. ...... *Dutton.*

— Questions on both Testaments, for the two divisions of the Christian year. 16°. 30c. .... *Dutton.*

— Questions on the 4th Gospel, for advanced classes. 18°. 20c. .... *Dutton.*

— Waiting world: questions for last half of the Christian year. 16°. 20c. .... *Dutton.*

Huntington, W: S. Roadmaster's assistant and section master's guide. ('71.) 2d ed. 16°. '72. $1. *R. R. Gazette.*

Huntoon, B. B. American speaker: no. 1. 12°. '74. 65c. .... *Morton.*

Hurd, Carlton. Recollections of Marion Lyle Hurd. 18°. 35c. .... *Pres. Bd.*

Hurd, J: C. Law of freedom and bondage in the U. S. 2 v. 8°. shp., $10 .... *Baker, V. & Co.*

Hurd, Rollin C. Treatise on right of personal liberty, and on writ of habeas corpus. 2d ed. 8°. '76. shp., $7.50 .... *W. C. Little.*

Hurdy gurdy. *See* Busch, W.

Hurlbut, J. L. *See* Vincent, J. H., *and* Hurlbut, J. L.

Hurlstone, E. T. *See* England, Exchequer reports.

Hurrah for the holidays; or, the pleasures and pains of freedom. ill. 16°. $1.25 .... *O'Shea.*

Hurrah for New England. ill. 18°. '68. 65c. *Perkinpine.*

Hurricane Hurry. Kingston, W. H. G. $2.50 .. *Pott.*

Hurry-graphs. Willis, N. P. $1.75 .... *Scribner.*

Hurst, Cath. E. Queen Louisa of Prussia; or, goodness in a palace; from Germ. sources. 16°. '74. $1 .... *Meth. Bk. Conc.*

Hurst, J: F. History of rationalism; embracing a survey of the present state of Prot. theology; with app. of literature. ('65.) 9th ed., rev. 8°. '75. $3.50 .... *Scribner.*

— Life and literature in the fatherland. ('74.) New ed. 8°. '75. $2.25 .... *Scribner.*

— Martyrs to the tract cause. 12°. '72. 75c. *Meth. Bk. Conc.*

— Outline of church history. maps. 12°. '75. 80c. *Meth. Bk. Conc.*

— Outlines of Bible history. maps. 12°. '73. 50c. *Meth. Bk. Conc.*

Hurst, J: T: Handbook of formulæ, rules and memoranda, for arch. surveyors and others engaged in building. 9th ed. roy. 32°. '75. roan, $2 .. *Spon.*

Hurst, J: T: *continued.*
— *Same.* obl. 32°. $2.50 ... *Baird.*
— Spon's tables and memoranda for engineers. 2d ed. 64°. '76. roan, 40c. ... *Spon.*
— Wages tables. 18°. '70. 50c. ... *Ingham.*
— *See also* Molesworth, G. L., *and* Hurst, J. T.

Hürte, Norbert. Johann v. Leyden. 12°. pap., 15c. *Radde.*
— — *See also* Glaubrecht, O., Die Stumme v. Portici.
— Tannhäuser. *See* Norden, F., Nachtlager in Granada.

Husband at sight. Buckstone, J. B. 15c. ... *French.*

Husband for an hour. Falconer, E. 15c. ... *French.*

Husband in clover: farce. 16°. pap., 15c. ... *French.*

Husband of my heart. Selby, C. 15c. ... *French.*

Husband to order. *See* Morton, J. M.

Husbands and homes. Harland, M. $1.50 .. *Carleton.*

Husenbeth, F. C. *See* Bible [Whole], *Cath.*

Hush money: drama. 16°. pap., 15c. ... *French.*

Hush money. [Fiction.] *See* Ross, C. H.

Husmann, G: Grapes and wine: cultivation of the native grape, and manufacture of Am. wine. 12°. $1.50 ... *Woodward.*

Huss, J: Memoir; tr. from the Germ. ('55.) 2d ed. 18°. '75. 40c. ... *So. Meth.*
— *and* Jerome *of Prague.* Memoirs. 18°. '67. 65c. *Pres. Com.*

Hussey, E. C. National cottage architecture; or, homes for every one; with plans, designs, etc. roy. 4°. $6 ... *Woodward.*

Huston, C: Essay on hist. and nature of orig. titles to land in Penn. 8°. '49. $3 ... *T. & J. W. Johnson.*

Huston, R. G. Journey in Honduras, and jottings by the way: interoceanic railway. 8°. '75. 50c. *Clarke.*

Hut of the Red Mountain. Milner, H. M. 15c. ... *French.*

Hutchings, *Mrs.* E. C. Life of Charles L. Winslow. 18°. '48. 25c. ... *Am. Tr.*
— *Same.* ill. 18°. '66. 50c. ... *Am. Tr.*
Note. Issued under title of "Cinnamon-Isle boy."

Hutchings, Ja. M. Scenes of wonder and curiosity in California. ('62.) 4th ed. ill. 4°. '76. $1.75; $2.50 ... *Roman.*
— Tourist's guide to Yosemite valley. eng. 4°. $3; mor., $6 ... *Widdleton.*

Hutchings, S: Pearls of wisdom. 32°. '69. 30c.; 75c.; mor., $1.75 ... *Am. Tr.*

Hutchings, W. H. Person and work of the Holy Ghost. New ed. 12°. '76. $2 ... *Pott.*

Hutchins, C: L. (*ed.*) Church hymnal; rev. to conform to Hymnal of the Prot. Epis. Ch. in the U. S. 12°. '72. *$1.50 ... *Belknap.*

Hutchinson, Ja. H. Inflammatory origin of phthisis. *See* Seguin, E. C., Ser. of Am. clin. lect.

Hutchinson, Jona. Illustrations of clinical surgery: pl., photographs, etc., with letter-press. pts. 1–7. 4°. ea., $2.50 ... *Lindsay.*

Hutchinson, Josh. Brief narrative of the Hutchinson family. 16°. pap., 35c. ... *Lee & S.*

Hutchinson, *Mrs.* Lucy. Memoir of Col. Hutchinson; with siege of Latham House. 12°. (Bohn.) $1.25 ... *Little, B. & Co.*
— *Same.* 12°. (Bohn.) $1.40 ... *Scribner, W. & A.*
— *Same.* 12°. (Bohn.) $1.50 ... *Lippincott.*

Hutchinson, W: Spirit of Freemasonry; with notes by Rev. G. Oliver. 12°. '71. $1.50 ... *Masonic.*

Hutchinson, W: Nelson. *See* Herbert, H. W., Mayhew, E., *and* Hutchinson, W: N.

Hutchison, J: R. Reminiscences, sketches and addresses during a ministry of 45 years in Miss., La. and Texas. 12°. '74. $2 ... *E. H. Cushing.*

Hutchison, Jos. C. Treatise on physiology and hygiene. ('70.) New ed. ill. 12°. '76. $1.50. *Clark & M.*

Hutchison, W: Illustrated hist. of Washington and his times. ('72.) New ed. ill. 8°. '76. *$3.75. *Henry Bill.*

Hüte dich vor dem ersten Fehltritt. *See* Hoffmann, F.

Hütte (Die) wieder aufgebaut. 32°. '65. 15c. .. *Am. Tr.*

Hutter, Leon. Compend of Lutheran theology; tr. by H. E. Jacobs and G. F. Spieker. 12°. '75. $1.50. *Luth. Bk. St.*

Hutton, Hu. Pocket book of private devotions for every morning and evening. 32°. 50c. .. *Lee & S.*

Hutton, N. H. Paper on cement and concrete. *See* American Inst. of Arch.

Hutton, R. S. A present Saviour. 18°. '63. 25c.; pap., 10c. ... *Am. Tr.*

Hutton, W. Book of nature laid open; rev. by J. L. Blake; with questions. 18°. 75c. ... *Harper.*

Huxley, T: H. Critiques and addresses. 12°. $1.50. *Appleton.*
— *Same.* 8°. '73. $3.50 ... *Macmillan.*
— Essays; sel. from Lay sermons. 2d ed. cr. 8°. '74. pap., 50c. ... *Macmillan.*
— Lay sermons, addresses and reviews. 12°. $1.75. *Appleton.*
— *Same.* cr. 8°. $2 ... *Macmillan.*
— Lessons in element. physiology. New ed. ill. 18°. '69. $1.50 ... *Macmillan.*
— — Questions; by T. Alcock. 18°. '69. 50c. *Macmillan.*
— Man's place in nature. 12°. $1.25 ... *Appleton.*
— Manual of anat. of vertebrated animals. ill. 12°. $2.50 ... *Appleton.*
— More criticisms on Darwin, and administrative nihilism. 12°. 50c. ... *Appleton.*
— On the origin of species. 12°. $1 ... *Appleton.*
— On the physical basis of life; with introd. 12°. '71. pap., 25c. ... *Van Nostrand.*
— On yeast. cr. 8°. '74. pap., 25c. ... *Estes.*
— *and* Martin, H. N. Course of pract. instruction in element. biology. cr. 8°. '75. $2.50 .. *Macmillan.*
— *and* Roscoe, H. E., *and* Stewart, Balfour (*ed.*) Science primers. v. 1–7. 18°. ea., 50c. .. *Macmillan.*
Cont.: Roscoe's chemistry. — Stewart's Physics. — Geikie's Physical geography. — Geikie's Geology. — Foster's Physiology. — Lockyer's Astronomy. — Hooker's Botany.
— *and* Youmans, W. J. Elements of physiol. and hygiene. 12°. $1.75 ... *Appleton.*
— — *Span.* Elementos de fisiología é higiene; tr. por D. T. Quintero. ill. 12°. $2 ... *Appleton.*

Hyacinthe, *Father.* [C: Loyson.] Catholic reform; tr. by Mme. Loyson Hyacinthe; with pref. by Dean Stanley. cr. 8°. '74. $2 ... *Macmillan.*
— Family (The), discourses; [also] Education of the working classes; [also] The Church — six conferences; [also] Speeches and addresses; tr., with hist. introd. by J. Bigelow. 12°. '72. $1.50. *Putnam.*
— Life, speeches and discourses, tr.; ed. by Rev. L. W. Bacon. 12°. '72. $1.25 ... *Putnam.*

Hyacinthe. Grey, E. C. 25c. ... *Peterson.*

Hyacinthe and her brothers. Mathews, J. H. 60c. *Carter.*

Hyatt, Alpheus. Cephalopods of the Museum-embryology. ill. 8°. '72. pap., $1.25 .. *Mus. Comp. Zool.*
— Fossil cephalopods of the Museum of Comp. Zool. 8°. '67. pap., 20c. ... *Mus. Comp. Zool.*
— Observations on fresh-water polyzoa. ill. 8°. '68. $2.50 ... *Essex.*
— Revision of No. Am. poriferæ. pt. 1. ill. 4°. pap., 75c. ... *Bost. Soc. Nat. Hist.*

Hyatt, T. Hart. Grape culture and wine making in California. ('67.) 2d ed. 12°. '76. $2 .. *Bancroft.*

Hyde, Alex. Agriculture: 12 lectures before the Lowell Institute, Boston. 12°. *$1.50 .. *Am. Pub.*

Hyde, Alex., Baldwin, A. C., *and* Gage, W. L. Frozen zone and its explorers. ill. and maps. 8°. '74. *$3.50; $4.50; shp., $4; hf. mor., $5 .. *Col. Bk.*
— *and* Bliss, F. C., *and* Tyler, J. Life and life-work of David Livingstone. ill. and maps. 8°. '75. *$3.50; $4.50; shp., $4; hf. mor., $5 .. *Col. Bk.*

Hyde, *Mrs.* Anna M. Boyhood and manhood of Washington and Franklin. ill. 12°. '76. $1.50. *World Pub.*
— English history condensed and simplified for schools. 18°. '71. 50c. . . . . *Claxton.*
— Ladder (A) to learning for little climbers. 18°. '73. 50c. . . . . *Claxton.*
— Work, play and profit; or, gardening for young folks expl. in a story. ill. 12°. $1.25 . . *Lippincott.*
Hyde, C: Life of Caroline Hyde. 18°. '36. 25c. *Am. Tr.*
Hyde, E. W. Skew arches. ill. 18°. '75. bds., 50c. *Van Nostrand.*
Hyde, Fanny. Trial for murder of George W. Watson, 1872. 8°. '72. 75c. . . . . *Campbell & Co.*
Hyde, J: Our eternal homes. 18°. 62c. *H. H. Carter.*
Hydrographic Office. *See* United States.
Hygiene of the sewing machine; by a physician. ill. 12°. '74. pap., 50c. . . . . *Turnbull.*
Hymn and tune book, for the church and the home, and services for cong. worship. ('68.) 28th ed. sq. 16°. '76. $1.50; — without services, $1.25; — service book alone, 80c. . . . . *Am. Unit.*
— *See also* Hymn, tune and service book.
Hymn and tune book for Meth. Epis. Ch. *See* New.
Hymn book. 24°. 75c.–$6. — 12°. $1.50–$4. (?) *Cumberland.*
Hymn book. [Cherokee.] 32°. 25c. . . . . . *Am. Bapt.*
Hymn book. [Spanish.] 18°. '74. 40c. . . . *So. Meth.*
Hymn book; with prayers. [Catholic.] 32°. '52. 20c.; pap., 13c. . . . . *Cunningham.*
Hymn (The) my mother taught me. *See* Tucker, Ctte.
Hymn of praise. Mendelssohn-Bartholdy, F. 75c.; 60c. . . . . *Ditson.*
Hymn stories; by author of "Aunt Annie's stories." 16°. '70. $1. . . . . *Dutton.*
Hymn, tune and service book for S.-schools. ('69.) 16th ed. sq. 16°. '76. 50c. . . . . *Am. Unit.*
— *See also* Hymn and tune book.
Hymnal. *See* New; — Prot. Episc. Ch.; — Reformed Episc. Ch.
Hymni ecclesiæ; [ed. by J. H. Newman]. fp. 8°. '65. $2. . . . . *Macmillan.*
Hymnist (The). Hayden, A. S. 25c. . . . . *Chase.*
Hymns. *See also* Psalms.
Hymns, ancient and modern. 32°. '73. 20c.; 25c.; — with app., 30c.; 35c. . . . . *Claxton.*
— *Same.* 18°. 60c.; — with tunes, 90c.; mor., $2.50; cf., $2.75. — sq. 12°. $1.75 . . . . *Lippincott.*
— — Appendix, with tunes. 16°. $1; $1.25; — words only, 32°. 20c. . . . . *McCauley.*
Hymns and choirs. Phelps, A. P., Edwards, A., *and* Furber, D. L. $1.75 . . . . *Hamersley.*
Hymns and poems for little folks. ill. roy. 16°. $1.50. *Cassell.*
Hymns and poetry for the young. 18°. 45c. *Whittaker.*
Hymns and songs for Cath. children. 64°. '69. pap., 15c. . . . . *Cath. Pub.*
Hymns and spiritual songs; for the suffering and sorrowing. 12°. 75c. . . . . *Nelson.*
Hymns for the children of the Church; with a liturgy for S.-schools and prayers. 18°. '75. 12c. . . *Pott.*
Hymns for church and home; comp. chiefly by Bp. Burgess, Dr. Muhlenberg and Dr. Howe. 18°. 50c.; shp., 63c. . . . . *Lippincott.*
Hymns for the church and the home: Portland collection. 18°. '65. shp., $1.50; mor., $2; $2.50; $5 . . . . *Universalist.*
Hymns for the higher life. Peirce, B. K. $1.50; $3. *Crowell.*
Hymns for infant minds. *See* Taylor, Jane.
Hymns for little children. 12°. $1. . . . . *Nelson.*
Hymns for little children. *See* Alexander, C. F.

Hymns for mothers and children. 1st ser.; comp. by author of "Violet." sm. 8°. '60. $2 . . *Nichols & H.*
— *Same.* 2d ser.; by ed. of "Hymns of the ages." sm. 8°. '65. $2. . . . . *Nichols & H.*
Hymns for the sick room. 16°. '59. $1 . . . *Randolph.*
Hymns for social worship. 32°. '40. 40c. . . . . *Am. Tr.*
Hymns for worship. [Span.] 16°. pap., 10c. . . *Am. Bapt.*
Hymns for youth. *See* New.
Hymns from land of Luther. 24°. '58. 75c. . . *Randolph.*
Hymns in prose. *See* Barbauld, *Mrs.* A. L.
Hymns of the ages; with steel vignettes after Turner. 3 v. 12°. '60–'64. ea., $1.50; hf. cf., $3; mor., $4. . . . . *Osgood.*
Hymns of Christ and the Christian life. Smith, W. C. $1.50. . . . . *Macmillan.*
Hymns of the church, with tunes; by Z. Eddy, J. B. Thompson, A. G. Vermilye, A. R. Thompson and U. C. Burnap. 8°. '69. $2.50; $4.50; $6.50; — with liturgy, $3; $5; $7.50; — hymns only. 18°. $1.75; $3.25; $4.75; — hymns and liturgy only, $2; $3.75; $5.25. . . . . *Barnes.*
Hymns of the church militant. Warner, A. B. $1.50. *Carter.*
Hymns of the church on earth. Ryle, J. C. $1. *Randolph.*
Hymns of Denmark. Tait, G. $1.75. . . . . *Routledge.*
Hymns of devotion. Doane, W. H. 20c. . . . *Biglow.*
Hymns of faith and hope. *See* Bonar, H.
Hymns of happy voices. 32°. '67. pap., 20c.; bds., 25c. . . . . *Am. Tr.*
Hymns of my holy hours. Palmer, R. $1.50. *Randolph.*
Hymns of praise. *See* Boardman, H. A.
Hymns of prayer and praise. 18°. '71. 75c. . . *Barnes.*
Hymns of salvation. Doane, W. H. 20c. . . . *Biglow.*
Hymns, prayers and psalms. [Eng. and Germ. portion of Jewish service for Sabbath and holy days.] 16°. '68. $1.50; $2; $2.50. . . . . *Bloch.*
— *See also* Machsorim.
Hymns to Jesus; from the early English. 32°. '75. 75c. . . . . *Dutton.*
Hymns to our king. Leavitt, J. M. 60c. . . *Whittaker.*
Hyneman, Leon. Freemasonry in England. 12°. $1. *R. Worthington.*
— Fundamental principles of science: essays. 8°. '76. pap., 25c. . . . . (?) *D. M. Bennett*; (?) *Colby.*
Hypatia. Kingsley, C. $1.75 . . *Macmillan; Nichols & H.*
Hyperion. Keats, J. $1.25. . . . . *Macmillan.*
Hyperion. Longfellow, H. W. $1.50. . . . . . . *Osgood.*
Hypochondriac. Baker, G. M. 15c. . . . . . . *Lee & S.*
Hypochondriac: Ethiop. drama. 16°. pap., 15c. *French; Happy.*
Hypocrite. Bickerstaff, I. 15c. . . . . *French.*

I., A. M. d'. Inez and Emmeline; or, the adopted sister. 16°. 75c. . . . . *Routledge.*
I am afraid I have a soul. ill. 32°. '53. 30c. . . *Am. Tr.*
I am learning to read. 18°. 50c. . . . . *Am. S. S.*
I'm not mesilf at all. Maltby, C. A. 15c. . . . *De Witt.*
I'm not myself at all: farce. 16°. pap., 15c. . . *French.*
I am so happy. 18°. 12c. . . . . *Cong. Pub.*
I couldn't help it. Oxenford, J. 15c. . . . . . . *French.*
I dine with my mother. Decourcelle, A., *and* Thiboust, L. 15c. . . . . *French.*
I don't feel like it. Jackson, E. A. 50c. . . . . *Dutton.*
I don't know how. *See* Phelps, *Miss* E. S.
I go afishing. Prime, W. C. $2.50; $4.25 . . . *Harper.*
I have, and oh had I; or, lessons in contentment. 18°. 55c. . . . . *Pres. Bd.*
I've been thinking. Roe, A. S. $1.50. . . . . *Carleton.*

I've eaten my friend. Bridgeman, J. 15c.....*French.*
I've written to Browne. Williams, T. J. 15c. *French; Lee & S.*
I love you: comedietta. 16°. pap., 15c.......*French.*
I love your wife: musical [dram.] sketch. 16°. pap., 15c. ....*Happy.*
I must keep the chimes going. Brock, C. 75c...*Dutton.*
I shall write the major. Moser, G. v. 15c.....*De Witt.*
I told you so. Small, G. G. 25c..........*Collin & S.*
I want to be rich. 18°. 15c.; 20c..........*Am. Bapt.*
I will be a gentleman; — a lady. Tuthill, L. C. ea., 65c..............................*Perkinpine.*
I'll be your second. Rodwell, G. H. 15c. ....*French.*
I'll do as I please. 18°. 35c. ....*Cong. Pub.*
I'll tell your wife: farce. 16°. pap., 15c.. ....*Happy.*
I'll try. Baker, H. N. W. $1.50.............*Lee & S.*
I'll write to the "Times." Wooler, J. P. 15c...*French.*
I wills of Christ. Power, P. B. $1.50 ....*Carter.*
I wills of the Psalms. Power, P. B. $1.50 ....*Carter.*
I wish. *See* Infant school lib.
I wish I was poor. Sheldon, E. M. 20c......*Am. Tr.*
I won't play; or, who shall be captain? 18°. 60c. *Am. S. S.*
I would not live alway. *See* Muhlenberg, W. A.
Ice maiden. *See* Andersen, H. C.
Ice raft. Guernsey, C. F. $1.25........(?) *Martien.*
Ice raft ser. 4 v. 16°. $5.50............(?) *Martien.*
Cont.: Ice raft. — New boy. — Friends in need. — Tutor and teamster.

Iceland: hist. and descript. account of Iceland, Greenland and the Faroe Islands. 18°. 75c...*Harper.*
Ich sehe dich schon. *See* Hoffmann, J.
Ici on parle français. Williams, T. J. 15c...*French.*
Iconoclast (*pseud.*) *See* Collins, T:
Ida and baby Bell. Sanford, D. P. $1......*Dutton.*
Ida and the beggar. *See* Baker, *Mrs.* H. N. W.
Ida Goldwin. Derby, A. 75c. ....*De Witt.*
Ida Kleinvogle and the two millers. 18°. 60c. (?) *Martien.*
Idaho. Compiled laws to 1875. 8°. shp., $7.50. *Bancroft.*
— Statutes, 1863–'75. 8 v. 8°. hf. shp., $24..*Bancroft.*
— Supreme Court reports ('66–'67); by J. Cummins. 8°. shp., $7.50..........*Bancroft; S. Whitney.*
Idaho Tom. Coomes, O. 20c..............*Beadle.*
Idalia. La Rame, L. de. $1.50..........*Lippincott.*
Idalia. Roberts, G. 15c......... ....*French.*
Idaline. Denison, M. A. $1..............*Am. Bapt.*
Ida's little library. *See* Witt, *Mme.* H. de.
Ida's new shoes. *See* Baker, *Mrs.* H. N. W.
Ide, G: B. Bible pictures. 12°. '75. $2; ill., $3. *Lothrop.*
— Green Hollow; or, the power of kindness. 18°. 70c.; 85c. ....*Am. Bapt.*
— Ministry demanded by the present crisis. 18°. pap., 10c. ....*Am. Bapt.*
Ideal Sunday school. Crafts, W. F. 75c.; 30c...*Hoyt.*
Ideen, Marie A. Changing the crosses and winning the crown. 16°. $1....................*Lippincott.*
Identity of the church. Anderson, J. 60c. (?) *Cumberland.*
Idiot of the mountain. Suter, W. E. 15c.....*French.*
Idiot witness. Haines, J. T. 15c...........*French.*
Idle boy. 18°. 60c.....................*Cong. Pub.*
Idle Dick and the poor watchmaker. Malan, C. 40c. *N. Y. Ref. Ch. Bd.; Pres. Com.*
Idle hands. Arthur, T. S. $2..............*Porter.*
Idle Harry. 18°. 60c.....................*Cong. Pub.*
— *See also* River-bank stories.

Idle Jane. 18°. 35c.; 40c..................*Dutton*
Idle word. Goulburn, E. M. 75c.....*Appleton; Pott*
Idle words. Reed, E. 90c...................*Claxton*
Idle words ser. 3 v. ill. 16°. '69. $2.40....*Claxton*
Cont.: Idle words, by E. Reed. — Twice tried, by Mrs. E. S Courtney. — She hath done what she could, by E. Reed.
Idleness. 16°. 45c....................*Cummiskey*
Idleness; or, the double lesson; tr. by Mrs. J. Sadlier 18°. 50c.; 75c.........................*Sadlier*
Idler. *See* Chalmers, A., British essayists.
Idolatry. Hawthorne, J. $2................*Osgood*
Idols in the heart. Tucker, C. 75c...*Carter; Dutton*
Idothea. Salyards, J. $1.50; $2.50.........*Henkel*
Idstone. *See* Pearce, T:
Idyl of work. Larcom, L. $1.50...........*Osgood*
Idyls and legends of Inverburn. Buchanan, R. $1.75 *Routledge*
Idyls of the king. *See* Tennyson, A.
Idyls of Strawberry Bank. Drown, D. A. $2; $2.50 *Williams*
Ierne of Armorica. Bateman, J. C. $1.50; $2. *Sadlier*
If the cap fits. Harrington, N. H., *and* Yates, E. 15c *French*
If I had a 1000 a-year. Morton, J. M. 15c. *De Witt; French*
If, yes and perhaps. Hale, E. E. $1.50......*Osgood*
Igdrasil. Challen, J. $1.50 ....*Challen*
Ignatius de Loyola. *See* Loyola.
Ignatius *of Jesus.* School of Jesus crucified; tr. fror the Italian. [Cath. prayer book.] 18°. 75c.- $5 ....*Sadlier*
Ignorant philosopher. *See* Voltaire, F. M. A. de.
Ignotus (*pseud.*) The Christian Sabbath vindicate and the Sabbath in its political aspect. 12°. '69 $1.50 ....*Claxton*
Ike McCandliss, and other stories. ill. 8°. pap., 25c. *U. P. James*
Ildrewe, *Miss* —. Language of flowers; with introd by T. Miller. 16°. 75c.; hf. bd., 60c...*Lee & S*
Iliad. *See* Homer.
Iliad of the east. *See* Richardson, F.
Ill-treated Il Trovatore. Byron, H. J. 15c...*French*
Illinois. Act of 1872–'73, for incorporation of cities an villages. 8°. '73. pap., 50c.......*E. B. Myers*
— Constitution, 1870. 8°. pap., 30c......*E. B. Myers*
— *Same.* roy. 8°. pap., 35c..................*Gross*
— Digest of criminal laws. *See* Gross, E. L.
— General statutes on law of corporations. *See* Root J. P.
— Index to laws. *See* Gross, E. L. *and* W. L.
— Laws rel. to township organization. *See* Haines E. M.
— Organic laws. roy. 8°. '75. pap., 35c.......*Gross*
— Real estate laws. *See* Adams, J. B., *and* Durham W. J.
— Session laws, 1871–2. roy. 8°. shp., $4. — Same 1873. $2.50. — Same, 1874. $3.....*E. B. Myers*
— Statutes; embr. rev. laws of 1871–'74. roy. 8° shp., $5.............................*E. B. Myers*
— *Same;* embr. all the gen. laws in force (1818–'73) comp. by E. L. and W. L. Gross. 3 v. roy. 8° $16..*Gross*
— *Same;* with notes by W. H. Underwood. 2 v. in 1 8°. '73–'75. shp., $8.50 ....*Gilbert*
— — Digest. *See* Gross, E. L. *and* W. L.
— Supreme Court examination for admission of attor neys. *See* Bradwell, M.
— Supreme Court reports, 1819–'31; by S. Breese. 8° '31 ....*State*
— *Same.* v. 2–5 (1832–'43); by T. Y. Scammon. 4 v 8°. shp., $24..........*Callaghan; E. B. Myers*
— *Same.* v. 6–10 (1844–'48); by C. Gilman. 5 v. 8° shp., $30 ....*Callaghan; E. B. Myers*

Illinois, *continued.*
— *Same.* v. 11-30 (1849-'63); by E. Peck. [Reprint.] 20 v. 8°. ea., shp., $6............*E. B. Myers.*
— *Same.* v. 31-77 (1863-'76); by N. L. Freeman. 47 v. 8°. shp., v. 31-38, ea., shp., $6; v. 39-77, ea., shp., $5 ....*Callaghan; E. B. Myers.*
— — Digest. *See* Wood, C. H., *and* Long, J. D.
— — Index. *See* Wendling, G. R.
— Supreme Court rules of practice. *See* Chicago.

Illinois Geol. survey. Geological survey of I. v. 1-3. pl. 4°. '66-'68.......................*State.*
Cont.: 1. Geology, by J. D. Whitney, L. Lesquereux and H. Engelmann. — 2. Palæontology, by J. S. Newbury, A. H. Worthen, F. B. Meek and L. Lesquereux. — 3. Geol. and palæont., by A. H. Worthen, H. Engelmann, H. C. Freeman and H. M. Bannister.

Illinois State atlas. f°. $15................*Warner.*

Illinois State Horticultural Society. Transactions. [Annual.] 8°. ea., $1.20............*Ill. Hort.*

Illuminated book of nursery rhymes. 4°. bds., 50c. *Hurd & H.*

Illuminated Scripture text-book. [Interleaved.] ill. 32°. 75c.-$1.75..............*Scribner, W. & A.*

Illustrated anecdotes and pithy pieces. sq. 12°. $1.25. *Routledge.*

Illustrated anecdotes, and stories in prose and verse. ill. 12°. '74. $1...................*Routledge.*

Illustrated book of pigeons; by R. Fulton [and others], ed. by L. Wright; with col. pl. by J. W. Ludlow, and ill. demy 4°. $15; hf. mor., $20..*Cassell.*

Illustrated book of songs for children. sq. 12°. 60c. *Hurd & H.*

Illustrated Boston poets. 7 v. ill. 8°. ea., shp., $3.50; mor., $10 ....*Lee & S.*
Cont.: Burns. — Byron. — Hemans. — Milton. — Moore. — Scott. — Shakespeare.

Illustrated Catholic story-book. 8°. '74. $1.25. *Routledge.*

Illustrated Catholic S.-school library. 8 ser. 18°. ea., $3; $4.......................*Cath. Pub.*

Illustrated child's Bible: consec. arrang. of narrative, etc., of the Scriptures, with hist. of the Eng. Bible and account of children of the Bible. ill. and maps. 4°. '76. mor., *$6.50.....*Nat. Pub.*
— *See also* Child's Bible.

Illustrated festival of song. Saunders, F. *$3.75-$8. *Scammell.*

Illustrated flying sheets; ill. by O. Pletsch, W. Busch and others; with text. 2 v. f°. ea., bds., $1.25. — col. ill. 3 v. ea., bds., $2.........*Stroefer.*

Illustrated flying sheets for old and young. roy. f°. bds., $1.25; col., $2.....................*Estes.*

Illustrated history of England. 9 v. ill. post 4°. ea., $5 ....*Cassell.*

Illustrated homes. Gardner, E. C. $2 .....*Osgood.*

Illustrated library of travel, etc. *See* Taylor, B.

Illustrated lib. of wonders. 21 v. 12°. '72. ea., $1.25; per set, $25-$50....................*Scribner.*
Cont.: Wonders of optics, by F. Marion. — Wonders of acoustics, by R. Radou. — Phenomena and laws of heat, by Achille Cazin. — Wonders of bodily strength and skill, by G. Depping. — Egypt 3,300 years ago. — Rameses the Great, by F. de Lanoye. — Intelligence of animals, by E. Menault. — Sublime in nature, by F. de Lanoye. — Wonders of the heavens, by C. Flammarion. — Wonders of European art, by L. Viardot. — Wonderful escapes, by F. Bernard. — Wonders of Pompeii, by M. Monnier. — Wonderful balloon ascents, by F. Marion. — Wonders of glass-making, by A. Sauzay. — Thunder and lightning, by W. De Fonvielle. — Adventures on the great hunting grounds of the world, by V. Meunier. — Wonders of architecture, by M. Lefevre. — Bottom of the sea, by L. Sonrel. — Wonders of the human body, by A. Le Pileur. — Wonders of Italian art, by L. Viardot. — The sun, by A. Guillemin.

— *Same.* 2d ser. v. 1-8. 12°. ea., $1.50..*Scribner.*
Cont.: Wonders of engraving, by G. Duplessis. — Wonders of the moon, by A. Guillemin. — Wonders of electricity, by J. B. Baile. — Wonders of sculpture, by L. Viardot. — Meteors, aerolites, storms and atmospheric phenomena, by F. Zürcher and E. Margolle. — Wonders of vegetation, by F. Marion. — Wonders of water, by G. Tissandier. — Arms and armor in antiquity and the middle ages, by M. P. Lacombe.

Illustrated Philadelphia and Fairmount Park: pocket guide and street directory of Phila. map. 32°. '75. 75c.; 50c.; pap., 25c...............*Hunt.*

Illustrated poetical album. Rothwell, J. S. $2.50. *Stroefer.*

Illustrated primer. 16°. '75. 40c..........*Lothrop.*

Illustrated primers. [French, Germ. and Spanish eds.] 3 nos. 4°. '52. ea., pap., 10c.........*Barnes.*

Illustrated primers. 4 v. sq. 16°. ea., 25c. *Routledge.*
Cont.: The alphabet. — Little words. — Spelling made easy. — Easy lessons in reading.

Illustrated progressive ser. [of readers, etc.] *See* O'Shea, P.

Illustrated rambles in Bible lands. Newton, R. $2.50; $3 ....*Am. S. S.*

Illustrated reward ser. 3 v. 18°. $1.50....*Lothrop.*
Cont.: Fall of Jerusalem. — Eastern manners and customs. — The Jordan, its history, etc.

Illustrated self-instructor in phrenol. *See* New.

Illustrated sketches of the countries and places mentioned in the Bible. map. 18°. 85c...*Am. S.S.*

Illustrated sketches of nat. hist. 2 v. ill. 16°. '74. ea., $1.25 ....*Pott.*

Illustrated songs and hymns for the little ones. S., T. B. $1.25.......................*Am. News.*

Illustrated story book. sm. 4°. pap., 25c...*Am. S. S.*

Illustrated stranger. Kenney, J., *and* Millingen, J. V. 15c.....................................*French.*

Illustrated wonder books. 8°. ill. 12°. ea., $1..*Lee & S.*
Cont.: Alice's adventures in wonderland, by L. Carroll. — Prairie Crusoe. — Young Crusoe. — Willis, the pilot. — House on wheels. — Letters everywhere. — Inn of the Guardian Angel. — Arctic Crusoe.

Illustrated wonders lib. 5 v. ill. 16°. $8..*Am. Bapt.*
Cont.: Wonders of insect life. — Curiosities of heat. — Great wonders in little things. — Home and abroad. — Black diamonds.

Illustrations of the Cornish and Boulton and Watt engines, erected at the East London Water-works, Old Ford: pls. with explan. 4°. (Weale.) '42. $5.......................................*Spon.*

Illustrations of divine government. Smith, T. S. $1.25 ....*Williamson.*

Illustrations of law of kindness. Montgomery, G. W. 65c.............................*Universalist.*

Illustrations of universal progress. Spencer, H. $2.50. *Appleton.*

Illustrative gatherings for preachers and teachers. Bowes, G. S. 2 v. ea., $1.75......*Perkinpine.*

Illustrative teaching. 18°. 20c.; pap., 10c. *Am. Bapt.*

Illustrious stranger. *See* French's comic dramas.

Illustrious women of France. Challice, A. E. $3. *Scribner, W. & A.*

Illustrirte Erzählungen. 12°. '63. 65c......*Am. Tr.*

Illustrirtes Anfangsbuch. 16°. bds., 20c...*Ev. Assoc.*

Im Eckfenster. Gerstäcker, F. 50c........*Morwitz.*

Im Herzen v. Deutschland. Berneck, C. G. v. 30c. *F. W. Thomas.*

Im Schnee begraben. *See* Hoffmann, F.

Im Wartesalon erster Klasse. *See* Müller, H.

Image-boys. ill. 32°. '53. 30c..............*Am. Tr.*
— *Germ.* Die kleinen Gypsfigurenhändler. ill. 32°. '59. 25c................................*Am. Tr.*

Image of his father. 8°. pap., 25c..........*Dick & F.*

Imaginary conversations. Landor, W. S. 4 v. ea., $2.......................................*Roberts.*

Imitation of the blessed Virgin. 18°. 60c...*Cath. Pub.*

Imitatione Christi. *See* Thomas *a Kempis.*

Immen-See. *See* Storm, T.

Immisch, Moritz. Prize essay on the balance spring, and its isochronal adjustments. (Baroness Burdett Couts' prize.) ill. cr. 8°. '72. $1....*Spon.*

Immortelles of love. Barrett, J. O. $1; $1.50..*Colby.*

Imogene. Egan, P. $1.50................*Dick & F.*

Imogene. Holt, E. S. $1.50 .... *Carter.*
Imogen: story of the introd. of Christianity into Britain. 18°. 35c. .... *Dutton.*
Imogen, the orphan princess. ill. 18°. '73. 45c. *N. Y. Ref. Ch. Bd.; Pres. Com.*
Imogen Hartland. Reynolds, G. W. M. 50c. .. *De Witt.*
Imperfect instruments. Gatty, M. 15c. ... *Randolph.*
Imperia. Lexow, F. 75c.; 50c. .... *Steiger.*
Imperial (The). Murray, J. R. 75c. ..... *Brainard.*
Important questions. Smith, J. 10c. ...... *Pres. Bd.*
Impressions of England. Coxe, A. C. $1.25. *Lippincott.*
Impressions of London social life. Nadal, E. S. $1.50. *Scribner.*
Impressions of Spain. Herbert, M. E. (*Lady*). $2. *Cath. Pub.*
Impromptu speaker. 12°. pap., 25c. .... *Haney.*
Improved question book, and studies on Parables and other instruc. of the Saviour. 24°. 16c. .. *Am. S. S.*
Improved question book on life of Christ. 24°. 16c. *Am. S. S.*
Improvement of memory. 18°. pap., 15c. ... *Haney.*
Improvement of time. Foster, J. $1.25 ..... *Carter.*
Improvisatore. *See* Andersen, H. C.
Impulse and principle. Ellery, M. T. $1.50 .. *Cong. Pub.*
Imray, Keith. Popular cyclopedia of modern domestic medicine. 8°. '66. shp., $5 ..... *Collins & Bro.*
In and out. Leavitt, A. J. 15c. .... *De Witt.*
In and out of place. Johnson, S. D. 15c. .... *French.*
In both worlds. Holcombe, W. H. $1.25 .. *Lippincott.*
In the Camargue. Bowles, E. $1.25; 75c. ... *Loring.*
In camp and field. Taylor, B. F. $1.50 ...... *Griggs.*
In Christ. Gordon, A. J. $1.50 .... *H. A. Young.*
In the clearings. Wells, K. G. 80c. .... *Am. Unit.*
In the clouds: extravaganza. 16°. pap., 15c. .. *French.*
In a crucible. Pugh, E. L. $1.50 .... *Claxton.*
In the days of my youth. Edwards, A. B. $1.50; $1.25; 75c. .... *Porter.*
In demselben Hause. *See* Hoffmann, F.
In doors. Elliott, A. $1.50 .... *Nelson.*
In doors and out. Adams, W. T. $1.75 ...... *Lee & S.*
In doors and out of doors. McCalla, M. 75c. .. *Pres. Bd.*
In duty bound. [Fiction.] ill. 8°. pap., 50c. .. *Harper.*
In earnest. *See* Foster, I. H.
In the eastern seas. *See* Kingston, W. H. G.
In exile. St., W. v. $2 .... *Lippincott.*
In exitu Israel. Baring-Gould, S. $1.50 .. *Macmillan.*
In extremis. Greenough, S. D. $1.50 ...... *Roberts.*
In for a holiday. Burnand, F. C. 15c. .. *De Witt; French.*
In the forecastle; or, twenty-five years a sailor. ill. 12°. $1.50 .... *World Pub.*
In the golden shell. Mazini, L. $1.50 .... *Macmillan.*
In heaven we know our own. Blot, F. R. 60c. .. *Cath. Pub.*
In His name. *See* Hale, E. E.
In the Holy Land. *See* Thomson, A.
In the home of the presidents. Holloway, L. C. $3.50. *U. S. Pub.*
In honor bound. Gibbon, C. 50c. .... *Harper.*
In India. Michelet, J. $1.25 .... *Nelson.*
In the kitchen. Miller, E. S. $2.50 .... *Lee & S.*
In memoriam. *See* Tennyson, A.
In the midst of the North Sea. (Fatherland ser.) ill. 16°. 75c. .... (?) *Luth. Pub.*
In possession: farce. 16°. pap., 15c. .... *French.*
In the power of the spirit. Boardman, W. E. $1. *Willard.*
In the prairie. *See* Prairie books.
In praise of folly. *See* Erasmus, D.
In the ranks. Douglas, A. M. $1 .... *Lee & S.*
In the rapids. Irving, T. J. $1.50 .... *Lippincott.*
In school and out. Adams, W. T. $1.25 .... *Lee & S.*
In the school-room. Hart, J. S. $1.25 ..... *Eldredge.*
In search of the castaways. *See* Verne, Jules.
In search of a wife. *See* More, H.
In self and out of self. *See* Winifred Leigh lib.
In silk attire. Black, W. 50c. .... *Harper.*
In six months. Meline, M. M. $1.25; $1.75. *Kelly, P. & Co.*
In Spain and Portugal. *See* Andersen, H. C.
In strange company. Greenwood, J. $1.75 .. *Routledge.*
In three volumes: farce. 16°. pap., 15c. ..... *French.*
In trust. Douglas, A. M. $1.50 .... *Lee & S.*
In war-time. Whittier, J. G. $1.25 .... *Osgood.*
In the wilds of Africa. *See* Kingston, W. H. G.
In a winter city. La Rame, L. de. $1.50 .. *Lippincott.*
In the woods with Bryant, Longfellow and Halleck; ill. by J. A. Hows. 4°. '62. $3 ..... *Hurd & H.*
In the world. Darling, M. G. $1.50 .... (?) *Shepard.*
In the world, but not of the world. 18°. 75c. .. *Dutton.*
In the world, not of the world. Adams, W. 25c. .. *Am. Tr.*
In the wrong box. Clifton, M. D. 15c. .... *Ames.*
In the wrong house. Becher, M. 15c. .... *De Witt.*
Ina. *See* Washburn, K. S.
Inalienable possession. Thompson, J. P. 20c. *Randolph.*
Incentive to doing good. Allen, R. W. 35c. *Meth. Bk. Conc.*
Incentives and aids to labors in Christ's vineyard. 24°. 30c. .... *Bost. Am. Tr.*
Inchbald, *Mrs.* Eliz. [Plays.] 4 v. 16°. ea., pap., 15c. .... *French.*
Cont.: Animal magnetism: farce. — Child of nature. — Wedding day: comedy. — Wives as they were and maids as they are: comedy.
— Nature and art. *See* British pocket classics.
— Simple story. [Fiction.] 8°. pap., 50c. ... *Harper.*
Inchcape Bell. Ball, E. 15c. .... *French.*
Incidental illustrations. Palmer, P. $1.50 .. *Palmer.*
Incidents in the life of a pastor. ('55.) 2d ed. 18°. '75. 40c. .... *So. Meth.*
Incidents in my life. Home, D. D. $1.50 .. *Somerby.*
Incidents of travel in Yucatan. Stephens, J. L. 2 v. $6 .... *Harper.*
Incog: farce. 16°. pap., 15c. .... *French.*
Incompatibility of temper. Suter, W. E. 15c. *French.*
Inconstant Farquhar, G. 15c. .... *French.*
Independence day. 18°. 30c.; 40c. ...... *Am. Bapt.*
Independence, true and false. 18°. 55c. .. *Am. S. S.*
Index (The). *See* Chalmers, A., British essayists.
Index rerum. Todd, J. $3 .... *Bridgman.*
Index to the Holy Scriptures. 8°. (Bagster.) pap., 63c. — fp. 8°. pap., 50c. — 16°. pap., 50c. — 32°. pap., 50c. .... *Wiley.*
Index to persons, places and subjects occurring in the Holy Scriptures. maps. 16°. '75. 50c.; roan, 85c. .... *Pott.*
India. Southworth, E. D. E. N. $1.75; $1.50. *Peterson.*
India. *See* Land and sea.
India, pictorial, descript. and historical. *See* Corner, Jla.
Indian boy. Adams, H. C. 75c. .... *Routledge.*
Indian chief. Aimard, G. 75c. .... *Peterson.*
Indian melodies. Commick, T. 50c. .. *Meth. Bk. Conc.*
Indian pass. Street, A. B. $1.50 .... *Hurd & H.*
Indian pilgrim. *See* Sherwood, *Mrs.* M. M.
Indian saint. Mills, C. D. B. $1.50 .... *Miller.*
Indian scout. Aimard, G. 75c. .... *Peterson.*

Indian summer. Johnson, J. C. 30c. .... *Ditson.*
Indian traits. Thatcher, B. B. $1.50 ...... *Harper.*
Indiana. Statutes; with notes and ref. by J. Gavin and O. B. Hord. 2 v. 8°. '62. .... *State.*
— — Supplement, 1861-'70; by E. A. Davis. 8°... *State.*
— Supreme Court reports, 1817-'47; by I. Blackford. 8 v. 8°. shp., $40 .... *Merrill.*
— *Same*, 1848-'76. 51 v. 8°. shp., $230.... *Merrill.*
Cont.: v. 1-2 ('48-'51), by H. Carter. — 3-7 ('51-'57), by A. G. Porter. — 8-14 ('57-'61), by G. Tanner. — 15-17 ('61-'62), by B. Harrison. — 18-22 ('62-'64), by M. C. Kerr. — 23-29 ('64-'68), by B. Harrison. — 30-51 ('69-'76), by J. B. Black.
— — Digest. *See* Davis, E. A.
Indiana. Sand, G. $1.50 .... *Peterson.*
Indiana geological survey. First and second reports, 1869-'70; by E. T. Cox. 2 v. pl. and maps. 8°. '69-'71 .... *State.*
— Report of a geol. reconnoissance of I., in 1837; by D. D. Owen. 8°. '39 .... *State.*
— *Same.* Second report, 1838. 8°. .... *State.*
Indianapolis [Ind.] Superior Court reports, v. 1; by O. M. Wilson. 8°. '76. shp., $5.50..(?) *Journal Co.*
Indian's cloak. *See* Library of good example.
Indians' friend. *See* Wright, *Mrs.* J. McN.
Industrial A B C drawing book. 12°. '73. per doz., $2.50 .... (?) *Slote.*
Industrial arts (The): hist. sketches. ill. 12°. '76. $1.50 .... *Scribner, W. & A.*
Industrial biography. Smiles, S. $1.50 .... * *Osgood.*
Industrial men of note. *See* Italian boy.
Inez. Evans, A. J. $1.75 .... *Carleton.*
Inez, the forest bride. 12°. pap., 20c. .... *Hurst.*
Inez and Emmeline. I., A. M. d'. 75c..... *Routledge.*
Infant bridal. De Vere, A. $1.50 .... *Macmillan.*
Infant reader; or, easy lessons in reading. sq. 16°. 50c. .... *Pres. Bd.*
Infant school girl: memoir of Mary Elizabeth Crook. 18°. 22c. .... *Am. S. S.*
Infant school hymn-book. 32°. bds., 10c... *Whittaker.*
Infant school lib. 12 v. 32°. $2.50 .... *Am. Bapt.*
Cont.: Willie and his dogs. — Nellie and her beads. — Power of love. — Goldey Mew. — Mary's mistake. — Pet lamb. — What makes corn grow? — Robert and his dove. — Bertha's trial. — I wish. — Robbing the orchard. — Mabita.
Infant teacher's [S.-school] manual. 18°. 45c.; — in 4 pts., ea., per doz., pap., 72c... *Meth. Bk. Conc.*
Infant voyagers. 18°. 70c. .... *Pres. Bd.*
Infantry tactics for schools expl. and ill. 12°. '62. hf. bd., 75c. .... *Barnes.*
Infant's delight: pictures and stories for wee ones. ill. sm. 4°. $1.25; bds., 75c. .... *Lee & S.*
Infant's prayer. *See* Bunbury, S.
Infant's progress. 18°. 75c. .... *Carter.*
Infant's progress. *See* Sherwood, *Mrs.* M. M.
Infelice. Evans, A. J. $2 .... *Carleton.*
Infelicia. Menken, A. I. $1 .... *Lippincott.*
Infidel reclaimed. *See* Clergyman's orphan.
Infidelity; compr. Jenyn's Internal evidence, Leslie's Method, Lyttelton's Conversion of Paul, Watson's reply to Gibbon and Paine, etc. 18°. '36. 70c. *Am. Tr.*
Infidelity against itself. Hotchkin, B. B. 40c. *Pres. Bd.*
Infidelity dissected. Pierson, T. $1.50..... *Tibbals.*
Infidel's confession. Taylor, B. T. $1.50.. *So. Bapt.*
Infidel's daughter. Dayton, A. C. $1.50. *Am. Bapt.; So. Bapt.*
Infidel's or inquirer's text-book. Cooper, R. $1. *Mendum.*
Infinite (The) and the finite. Parsons, T. $1.. *Roberts.*
Influence. Mackarness, M. A. $1.25..... *Routledge.*
Influence. Pakenham, F. J. $1.35 .... *Pres. Bd.*
Influence; or, the little silk winder. 18°. 40c. *Am. S. S.*
Ingalls, *Mrs.* M. B. Ocean sketches of life in Burmah. 18°. 70c.; 85c. .... *Am. Bapt.*
Ingaretha. Malen, M. E. O. 30c. .... *Am. News.*
Ingelow, Jean. Poems. (Blue and gold ed.) 2 v. 32°. '66-'67. $2.50 .... *Roberts.*
— *Same.* (Cabinet ed.) ('68.) New ed., enl. 16°. '74. $2.25 .... *Roberts.*
— *Same.* (Diamond ed.) sq. 18°. '73. $1.50.. *Roberts.*
— *Same.* (Ill. ed.) 8°. '68. $7.50; mor., $12.. *Roberts.*
— *Same.* (Lib. ed.) 2 v. 16°. '63-'67. $3.. *Roberts.*
— *Same.* (Red line ed.) sq. 12°. '73. $3.75; mor., $7 .... *Roberts.*
— Fated to be free. [Fiction.] 16°. '75. $1.75.. *Roberts.*
— Monitions of the unseen: poems; [also] Poems of love and childhood. ill. 16°. '70. $1.50.. *Roberts.*
— Mopsa, the fairy: a story. ill. 16°. '69. $1.25.. *Roberts.*
— *Same.* ill. cr. 8°. '72. $2.50 .... *Routledge.*
— Off the Skelligs. [Fiction.] 16°. '72. $1.75.. *Roberts.*
— Poor Matt; or, the clouded intellect. 18°. '66. 60c. *Roberts.*
— *Same.* ('72.) 3d ed. 16°. '76. 75c. ...... *So. Meth.*
— Shepherd lady, and other poems; with eng. from designs by Hughes, Miss Hallock, Eytinge, etc. roy. 8°. '75. $4.50; mor., $9 .... *Roberts.*
— Sister's bye-hours (A). ill. 16°. '68. $1.25.. *Roberts.*
— *Same.* cr. 8°. $1.50. .... *Routledge.*
— Songs of seven. [Poem.] ill. 8°. '65. $2.50.—roy. 8°. mor., $8.—(chp. ed.) 20c.; 30c.... *Roberts.*
— Stories told to a child. ill. sq. 16°. $1.50.. *Routledge.*
— *Same.* 2 v. ill. 16°. '66-'71. ea., $1.25.... *Roberts.*
— Studies for stories. ill. 16°. '64. $1.25.... *Roberts.*
— *Same.* ill. cr. 8°. $1.75 .... *Routledge.*
Ingenue. Dumas, A. 50c. .... *Routledge.*
Ingersleben, *Frau* v. ["E. v. Rothenfels."] Eleonore: a romance; [tr.] by F. E. Bennett. 12°. $1.50. *Lippincott.*
Ingersoll, C: Fears for democracy regarded from Am. point of view. 8°. $1.75; pap., $1.25.. *Lippincott.*
Ingersoll, L. D. Life of Horace Greeley. ill. and por. roy. 12°. $2.50 .... *J. E. Potter.*
Ingersoll, Rob. G. The gods, and other lectures. 18°. '76. 50c.; pap., 30c.; 10c. ...... *D. M. Bennett.*
Ingham, *Col.* F: (*pseud.*) *See* Hale, E: Everett.
Ingham, Harvey A. Glad tidings; or, walks with the wonderful; with introd. by Rev. W. L. Parsons. 18°. '68. 50c. .... *Darrow.*
Ingham, *Miss* Marietta. *See* Staunton, P., *and* Ingham, *Miss* M.
Ingham, R. Handbook on Christian baptism. 8°. '65. $5 .... *Tibbals.*
Ingham lectures. Williams, W. G. $1.75.. *Ingham.*
Ingham papers. Hale, E. E. $1.50 .... *Osgood.*
Inglenook. Booth, M. 75c. .... *Roman.*
Inglis, J. The Sabath-school. 12°. $1.. *Meth. Bk. Conc.*
Inglises (The). Robertson, M. M. $1.50.. *Randolph.*
Ingo. Freytag, G. $1.25 .... *Holt.*
Ingoldsby, T: (*pseud.*) *See* Barham, R: H.
Ingoldsby legends. *See* Barham, R: H.
Ingomar, an awful warning: burlesque. 16°. pap., 15c. .... *Happy.*
Ingomar, the barbarian. Lovell, M. 15c..... *French.*
Ingraban. Freytag, G. $1.25 .... *Holt.*
Ingraham, —. Das Leben Jesu. 12°. $1.50; leath., $2 .... *Kohler.*
Ingraham, Jos. H. Works. 3 v. 12°. '63. ea., $2. *Roberts.*
Cont.: Prince of house of David. — Pillar of fire. — Throne of David.
— Annie Temple. 8°. 25c. .... *Beadle.*
— Beautiful cigar girl; or, the mysteries of Broadway. 8°. pap., 25c. .... *De Witt.*
— Captain Kyd; or, the wizard of the sea. 8°. pap., 50c. .... *De Witt.*

Ingraham, Jos. H., *continued.*
— Frank Rivers; or, the dangers of the town. 8°. pap., 25c. .... *De Witt.*
— Lafitte, the pirate of the gulf. 8°. pap., 50c. *De Witt.*
— Life and adventures of Percival Maberry. 12°. pap., 75c. .... *Peterson.*
— Montezuma, the serf. 8°. pap., 75c...... *Dick & F.*
— Rivingstone; or, the young ranger hussar. 8°. pap., 25c. .... *De Witt.*
— Surf skiff; or, the heroine of the Kennebec. 8°. pap., 25c. .... *De Witt.*
— Theodore, the child of the sea. 8°. pap., 25c. *De Witt.*
— Will Terrill; or, the adventures of a gentleman born in a cellar. 8°. pap., 25c. .... *De Witt.*
Ingulphus. Chronicle of the Abbey of Croyland; with contin. by Peter of Blois and others; tr. by H. T. Riley. 12°. (Bohn.) $1.75..... *Little, B. & Co.*
— *Same.* 12°. (Bohn.) $2.. *Lippincott; Scribner, W. & A.*
Inheritance (The). *See* Ferrier, Ma.
Inheritance (The). *See* Priest's sister.
Inherited task. Eden, C. H. 50c........ *Pott.*
Initials (The). Tautphoeus, I. (*Baroness*) v. $1.75; $1.15 .... *Peterson.*
Initiatory seal. Winfield, A. B. 25c. *N. Y. Ref. Ch. Bd.*
Injun Dick. Aiken, A. W. 20c........ *Beadle.*
Inkle and Yarico. Colman, G., *jr.* 15c. ..... *French.*
Inlets and outlets. Smith, C. A. $1....... *Pres. Bd.*
Inman, T: Ancient faiths and modern: dissertation upon worships, legends and divinities. 8°. '76. $5........ *Bouton.*
— Ancient pagan and modern Christian symbolism. 2d ed. ill. 8°. '75. $3 .... *Bouton.*
Inn album (The). Browning, R. $1.50..... *Osgood.*
Inn of the Guardian Angel. Segur, S. $1.25; $1.50; $2........ *Lee & S.*
Inner life. Davis, A. J. $1.50........ *A. J. Davis.*
Inner life. Rauch, F. A. $1.25........ *Ref. Ch. Pub.*
Inner Rome. Butler, C. M. $1.75.. *Claxton; Lippincott.*
Innes, H: Elocution: its principles and practice. 16°. $1 .... *French.*
Innkeeper of Abbeville. Ball, E. 15c....... *French.*
Innocency with her open face. *See* Penn, W.
Innocent. Oliphant, M. O. W. 75c........ *Harper.*
Innocents abroad. Clemens, S. L. *$3.50; $4; $5; $8 .... *Am. Pub.*
Inquire within: 3700 facts for the people. 12°. $1.50; hf. mor., $2.50........ *Dick & F.*
Inquirer (The). 18°. 75c........ *Cong. Pub.*
Inquirer. *See* Young, R.
Inquirer's library. Kimball, C. 7 v. $2.50.. *Cong. Pub.*
Inquiring Christian's lib. 4 v. 12°. $8. *Cin. Meth. Bk. Conc.*
Cont.: Bible and modern thought, by T. R. Birks. — Literary characteristics and achievements of the Bible, by W. Trail. — Man all immortal, by D. W. Clark. — Domestic life in Palestine, by M. E. Rogers.
Inquisition; rev. by T. O. Summers. ('55.) 2d ed. 18°. '73. 50c........ *So. Meth.*
Inquisition in Spain and other countries. 18°. '66. 60c. .... *N. Y. Ref. Ch. Bd.; Pres. Com.*
Inquisitive boy; [also] The little ragman. 18°. 50c. *O'Shea.*
Insects at home. *See* Wood, J. G.
Inselfräulein (Das). Steffens, A. 50c....... *Zickel.*
Inside. Baker, W. M. $1.75; $1.25........ *Harper.*
Inside the gates. M'Carty, J. H. $1. *Cin. Meth. Bk. Conc.*
Inside Paris during the siege; by an Oxford graduate. cr. 8°. '71. $2........ *Macmillan.*
Inside views of Methodism. Reddy, W. 50c. *Meth. Bk. Conc.*
Inskip, J: S. Methodism explained and defended. ('55.) New ed. 12°. '60. $1........ *Pounsford.*

Instant glory. Winslow, O. 30c........ *Carter.*
Institute melodies. Clapp, N. B. 50c....... *Gordon.*
Instructions for field artillery; prep. by a board of artillery officers; [also] Evolutions of batteries; tr. by R. Anderson. pl. 12°. '64. $3.. *Van Nostrand.*
Instructions for officers on outpost and patrol duty; with skirmish drill for mounted troops. 12°. '61. pap., 25c........ *Claxton.*
Instructive letter writer. 32°. bds., 35c... *U. P. James.*
Instruments (The). Groser, W. H. 10c... *Perkinpine.*
Insubordination. Arthur, T. S. 50c...... *Peterson.*
Insurance year book for 1874: hist. of the fire, marine, life and accident insurance business of the U. S. for 1873; with abstracts of statutes and decisions, etc. 8°. '74. $1.50........ (?) *Hayden.*
Integrity. Hofland, B. $1........ *Nelson.*
Intellectual life (The). Hamerton, P. G. $2.. *Roberts.*
Intelligence office: Ethiop. drama. 16°. pap., 15c. *French.*
Intercessory prayer; by a lady. sq. 24°. '74. 50c.; 75c........ *Am. Tr.*
Interesting lib. 4 v. ill. 16°. $5........ *Lippincott.*
Cont.: Old Merry's travels. — Israel Mort. — Scottish orphans. — Wonderful adventures among native tribes of Am.
Interesting narratives; or, religion the great concern. 18°. 65c........ *Pres. Bd.*
Interior Christian. Louvigny, M. B. de. 60c. *Cath. Pub.*
International atlas, political, classical and historical; with letter-press by W. F. Collier and L. Schmitz; with indices. 8°. '73. $6........ *Putnam.*
International Exhibition, 1876: official catalogue. sm. 8°. '76. $1.50........ (?) *Nagle.*
International Musical Festival. *See* World's peace jubilee.
International scientific ser. v. 1–20. 12°... *Appleton.*
Cont.: Forms of water, by J. Tyndall, $1.50. — Physics and politics, by W. Bagehot, $1.50. — Foods, by E. Smith, $1.75. — Mind and body, by A. Bain, $1.50. — Sociology, by H. Spencer, $1.50. — The new chemistry, by J. P. Cooke, jr., $2. — Conservation of energy, by B. Stewart, $1.50. — Animal locomotion, by J. B. Pettigrew, $1.75. — Responsibility in mental disease, by H. Maudsley, $1.50. — Science of law, by S. Amos, $1.75. — Animal mechanism, by E. J. Marey, $1.75. — Religion and science, by J. W. Draper, $1.75. — Descent and Darwinism, by O. Schmidt, $1.50. — Chemistry of light, by Prof. Vogel, $2. — Fungi, by M. J. Berkeley, $1.50. — Life and growth of language, by W. D. Whitney, $1.50. — Money and the mechanism of exchange, by W. S. Jevons, $1.75. — Nature of light, by E. Lommel, $2. — Animal parasites and messmates, by P. J. Van Beneden, $1.50. — On fermentation, by P. Schützenberger, $1.50.
International Sunday school commentary. v. 2–6. 8°. '73–'76. ea., $1........ *Am. Bib. Un.*
Cont.: Matthew, by F. Johnson. — Moses and Israel, by F. Johnson. — Mighty worker [in Mark], by G. W. Clark. — Heroes and judges, by F. Johnson. — Kings and apostles, by T. A. T. Hanna.
Interprète (L') américain en anglais et en français. 18°. 50c........ *Radde.*
Interpreter, od. deutscher u. engl. Uebersetzer. 5th ed. 12°. 50c........ *Schäfer.*
Interviews, memorable and useful. Cox, S. H. $1.50. *Harper.*
Intimate friend: drama. 16°. pap., 15c...... *French.*
Into the highways. Davis, C. E. K. $1.50..... *Hoyt.*
Into the light. 16°. $1.50........ *Lothrop.*
Intrigue. Poole, J. 15c........ *French.*
Introduction to Bible chronology. 18°. 45c. *Am. S. S.*
Introduction to a devout life. *See* François de Sales, *St.*
Introduction to geometry, and science of form; from the Prussian text books. ill. 12°. $1.... *Dennet.*
Introduction to hist. of France; with questions. ill. 12°. '72. $1.75........ *Kelly, P. & Co.*
Introduction to pract. organic chemistry. *See* Small books.

Introduction to resources of Tenn.; by J. B. Killebrew, J. M. Safford, etc. 8°. '75. $5..(?) *Tavel.*
Introduction to vegetable physiol. *See* Small books.
Introits. Hastings, T. $1 ... *Randolph.*
Inundation. Archer, T. 15c. ... *French.*
Invalide (Der). Spindler, C. $1.25; pap., $1; hf. mor., $1.50 ... *F. W. Thomas.*
Invalid's cook-book. Guila. 20c. ... *Routledge.*
Invalid's work. F., M. E. 50c. ... *Pres. Bd.*
Invaluable companion. [Receipts.] 24°. 50c.; pap., 40c. ... *Miller.*
Invasion (The). *See* Griffin, Ger.
Invasion of France in 1814. Erckmann, E., *and* Chatrian, A. $1.25; 75c. ... *Scribner.*
Invasion of Russia. Amherst, J. A. 15c. ... *French.*
Invincibles. Morton, T. 15c. ... *French.*
Invisible girl. Hook, T. 15c. ... *French.*
Invisible hand. Sadlier, M. A. 25c. ... *Sadlier.*
Invisible prince. Planché, J. R. 15c. ... *French.*
Invitation heeded. Stone, J. K. $1.50 ... *Cath. Pub.*
Invitation to little children. 18°. 60c. ... *Cong. Pub.*
Invitations to true happiness. Parker, J. 50c. ... *Harper.*
Ion. *See* Euripides.
Ion. Talfourd, *Sir* T. N. 15c. ... *French.*
Ion: burlesque. 16°. pap., 15c. ... *French.*
Iona. Alexander, W. L. 60c. ... *So. Meth.*
Iona. Argyll, *Duke of.* $1.25 ... *Routledge.*
Ione. *See* Ditson.
Iota (*pseud.*) Adventures of a Protestant in search of a religion. 12°. $1.50; $2 ... *Sadlier.*
Iowa. Code of 1873. imp. 8°. shp., $4; interleaved, shp., $7; — in 2 v., shp., $8 ... *Mills.*
— Compendium of repeals and amend. to laws. *See* Templin, J. W.
— Railroad tariff law, and herd law, as enacted and amended by the 12th Gen. Assembly. 8°. '74. pap., 25c. ... *Mills.*
— Supreme Court reports, 1839–'45; by E. Morris. 8°. shp., $5 ... *Mills.*
— — *Same.* 8°. shp., $5 ... *Callaghan.*
— *Same*, 1847–'52; by G. Greene. 4 v. 8°. shp., $30. *Callaghan; Mills.*
— *Same.* v. 1–3 (1855–'56). 2d ed., ed. by C. C. Cole. 3 v. 8°. '74–'76. ea., shp., $6 ... *Mills.*
Note. A reprint; to form 21 v., incl. Clarke (v. 1–8) and Withrow (v. 9–21).
— *Same.* v. 9–21 (1860–'66); by T. F. Withrow. 13 v. 8°. ea., shp., $7.50 ... *Mills.*
— *Same.* v. 22–37 (1867–'73); by E. H. Stiles. 16 v. 4°. '67–'75. ea., shp., $5. *Callaghan; Mills; E. B. Myers; Stiles.*
— *Same.* v. 38–40 (1873–'75); by J. S. Runnells. 3 v. 8°. ea., shp., $5 ... *Callaghan; Mills.*
— — Abridgment. *See* Templin, J. D.
— — Digest. *See* Withrow, T. F., *and* Stiles, E. H.
— — Index. *See* Hunter, B., *and* Myer, W. G.
Iowa band. Adams, E. $1.25 ... *Cong. Pub.*
Iowa geological survey. First and second report of progress on geol. survey of I. 8°. '68 ... *State.*
— Report of geol. survey, 1866–9; by C. A. White. 2 v. pl. and maps. 8°. '70 ... *State.*
— *See also* Owen, D. D.
Iphigenia in Aulide; — in Tauris. *See* Euripides.
Iphigenie. *See* Racine, J.
Iphigenie auf Tauris. *See* Goethe, J. W. v.
Irasule, and other stories. 18°. 70c. ... *Pres. Bd.*
Iredell, J. *See* North Carolina, Reports.
Ireland, W: H. Shakespeare forgeries: confessions of W. H. Ireland. New ed., with add. fac similes and introd., by R. G. White. 12°. '74. $2; large pap., $3.50 ... *Bouton.*
Ireland. Chancery reports during the time of Lord Chancellor Manners; by T. Ball and F. Beatty. 2 v. in 1. 8°. shp., $5.50 ... *Kay.*
— *See also* England, Law reports.
Ireland among the nations. O'Leary, J. $1 .. *McGee.*
Ireland and America: drama. 16°. pap., 15c. *French.*
Ireland and the Irish. Burke, T. N. $1...(?) *Lynch.*
Ireland as it is; — as it was. Amherst, J. A. ea., 15c. *French.*
Ireland's Catholicity and what saved it. Burke, T. N. 10c. ... *Coddington.*
Irenæus, *St.* Writings; tr. by A. Roberts and W. H. Rambaut. (Ante-Nicene Christ. lib.) 2 v. 8°. ea., $3 ... *Scribner, W. & A.*
Irene: tale of south. life. *See* Fairfield, G. G.
Irene; or, beach-broken billows. Baer, B. F. $1.25. *Authors.*
Irene Page. St. John, E. $1.75 ... *Berry.*
Iriarte, Tomas de. Fabulas literarias. 18°. 60c. *Appleton.*
Irish abroad and at home. Byrne, M. $1.50 .. *Haverty.*
Irish ambassador. Kenney, J. 15c. ... *French.*
Irish-American almanac for 1875. 12°. '74. pap., 25c. — for 1876. 12°. '75. pap., 25c. ... (?) *Lynch.*
Irish-American lib. 4 v. por. 12°. '73. $4. (?) *Lynch.*
Cont.: English misrule in Ireland, by T. N. Burke. — Ireland and the Irish, by T. N. Burke. — Sermons and lectures on moral and hist. subjects, by T. N. Burke. — Crusade of the period, by J. Mitchel.
Irish Amy. Guernsey, L. E. $1.10; 80c. .. *Am. S. S.*
Irish anecdotes. Kennedy, P. 50c. ... *Routledge.*
Irish assurance: farce. 16°. pap., 15c. ... *French.*
Irish attorney. Bernard, B. 15c. ... *French.*
Irish broom maker. Wood, C. A. F. 15c. ... *French.*
Irish bulls. *See* Edgeworth, Mar.
Irish confederates. Field, H. M. $1.50 ... *Harper.*
Irish doctor. Wood, G. 15c. ... *French.*
Irish dragoon. Selby, C. 15c. ... *French; Happy.*
Irish emigrant. Brougham, J. 15c. ... *French.*
Irish engagement: farce. 16°. pap., 15c. *French; Happy.*
Irish Jem's three trials. *See* Books about boys who fought and won.
Irish lion. Buckstone, J. B. 15c. ... *French.*
Irish melodies. *See* Moore, T:
Irish mission scenes. ('66.) New ed. ill. 18°. '72. 50c. ... *Hoyt.*
Irish national songster. ('74.) 5th ed. ill. 16°. '76. $1 ... *Kenedy.*
Irish odes. De Vere, A. $2 ... *Cath. Pub.*
Irish on the prairies, and other poems. 12°. $1.50; $2. *Sadlier.*
Irish peasant; or, the history of Peter Lacy. 18°. 17c.; 22c. ... *Am. Bapt.*
Irish post. Planché, J. R. 15c. ... *French.*
Irish race in the past and present. Thebaud, A. J. $3.50 ... *Appleton.*
Irish rebels in English prisons. Rossa, O'D. $1.50; $1 ... *Sadlier.*
Irish scholar; or, the shipwrecked boy. 18°. 50c.; 60c. ... *Am. Bapt.*
Irish singer's own book. 24°. $1 ... *Noonan.*
Irish sketch-book. *See* Thackeray, W. M.
Irish stories. 18°. 75c. ... *Pres. Bd.*
Irish stories and legends. *See* Lover, S:
Irish stories for thoughtful readers. ill. 18°. '66. 75c. *N. Y. Ref. Ch. Bd.; Pres. Com.*
Irish tiger. Morton, J. M. 15c. ... *French.*
Irish tutor. Glengall, *Lord.* 15c. ... *French.*
Irish widow. Garrick, D. 15c. ... *French.*

Irish wit and humor: witty sayings of Swift, Curran, O'Leary and O'Connell. por. 12°. $1... *McGee.*

Irish wit and wisdom; [compr.] Haverty's "Irish-American almanac," [1871-'75], without the calendars. 12°. '76. $1.50............*Haverty.*

Irish Yankee. Brougham, J. 15c...........*French.*

Irishman in London. Macready, W. 15c....*French.*

Irishman's manœuvre: comedy. 16°. pap., 15c. *French.*

Iron, *Mrs.* N. C. [" Stella."] Minna Monte. [Fiction.] 12°. $1.25 ....*Lippincott.*

Iron age of Germany. (Fatherland ser.) ill. 16°. $1.10...........................*Luth. Pub.*

Iron chest. Colman, G., *jr.* 15c. ....*French.*

Iron cousin. *See* Clarke, M. C.

Iron cross. Cobb, S., *jr.* 25c............*Peterson.*

Iron furnace; or, slavery and secession. Aughey, J. H. $1.25.......................(?)*Martien.*

Iron hand. *See* Dumas, A.

Iron head. ill. 16°. $1.15.............(?)*Luth. Pub.*

Iron mask. *See* Dumas, A.

Iron rule. Arthur, T. S. 50c. ....*Peterson.*

Iron Thorpe. *See* Trowbridge, J. T.

Irons, W. J. Bible and its interpreters, miracles and prophecy. 8°. '76. $2.75................*Pott.*

— Christianity as taught by St. Paul. *See* Bampton lectures.

— Church of all ages. 12°. '76. $3.75.............*Pott.*

Irreconcilable records. Denton, W. 50c....*Denton.*

Irrepressible conflict between labor and capital. Green, B. E. 30c...................*Claxton.*

Irrfahrt (Die) des Philhelenen. *See* Zschokke, H.

Irvin, D. *See* Georgia, Annotated code.

Irving, C. [Text-books]; rev. by M. J. Kerney. 11 v. ill. 18°. ea., 20c............*Kelly, P. & Co.*
Cont.: Astronomy. — Botany. — Classical biog. — Grecian antiquities. — Grecian hist. — Hist. of Eng. — Jewish antiquities. — Mythology. — Practical chemistry. — Roman antiquities. — Roman hist.

Irving, E: Miscellanies from [his] collected writings. 8°. $2.50....................*Routledge.*

Irving, J: T. Attorney (The); or, the correspondence of John Quod. 12°. $1.50...........*De Witt.*

— Harry Harson; or, the benevolent bachelor. 12°. $1.50 ....*De Witt.*

Irving, Jos. Annals of our time: a diurnal of events, [1837]-1871. 4th ed. 8°. hf. bd., $6. — Supplement, 1871-1874. hf. bd., $1.75.....*Macmillan.*

Irving, T. J. [" Ger. Hart."] In the rapids: a romance. 12°. $1.50........................*Lippincott.*

Irving, Thdr. Fountain of living waters. 18°. '56. 60c. ....*Randolph.*

— History of De Soto's conquest of Florida. 12°. $2.25 ....*Putnam.*

— March of De Soto. 12°. $2.50; pap., $1.50..*C. Drew.*
Note. Same as Conquest of Florida.

— More than conqueror; or, memorials of Col. J. Howard Kitching. 12°. $1.50...... *Whittaker.*

— Tiny footfall (A) within the golden gate. 32°. '65. 25c...............................*Randolph.*

— *Same.* 32°. '69. 30c. .... *Whittaker.*

Irving, Wash. Works. (Knickerbocker ed.) 27 v. 12°. ea., $2.50; per set, hf. cf., $108..*Putnam.*
Cont.: Alhambra. — Astoria. — Bonneville. — Bracebridge Hall. — Life of Columbus, 3 v. — Crayon miscellany. — Life of Goldsmith. — Conquest of Granada. — Mahomet and his successors, 2 v. — History of N. Y. — Salmagundi. — Sketch book. — Tales of a traveller. — Wolfert's roost. — Life of Washington, 5 v. — Life and letters, 3 v. — Spanish papers. — Biographies and miscellanies.

— *Same.* (People's ed.) 26 v. 16°. ea., $1.25; per set, hf. cf., $71.50......................*Putnam.*
Contents the same as above with omission of Biog. and misc.

— *Same.* (Riverside ed.) 26 v. 16°. ea., $1.75; per set, hf. cf., $84.50 ....*Putnam.*
Contents the same as in People's ed.

Irving, Wash., *continued.*

— *Same.* (Sunnyside ed.) 28 v. 12°. ea., $2.25; per set, hf. cf., $112.........................*Putnam.*
Cont.: Alhambra. — Astoria. — Bonneville. — Bracebridge Hall. — Life of Columbus, 3 v. — Crayon miscellany. — Oliver Goldsmith. — Conquest of Granada. — Mahomet and his successors, 2 v. — History of N. Y. — Salmagundi. — Sketch book. — Tales of a traveller. — Wolfert's roost. — Life of Washington, 5 v. — Life and letters, 4 v. — Spanish papers, 2 v.

— Christmas in England. ill. sm. f°. $2.50; mor., $6.50.................................*Putnam.*

— Crayon reader: sel. from writings, for schools, etc. 12°. $1.25...............................*Putnam.*

— History of N. Y. ill. roy. 8°. $9; mor., $15; large pap., $18...............................*Putnam.*

— Legend of Sleepy Hollow. ill. sm. f°. $1.25..*Putnam.*

— Life and voyages of Columbus. (Popular ed.) ill. 12°. $1.75 ....*Putnam.*

— Life of George Washington. (Mount Vernon ed.) 2 v. ill. 8°. '75. $7; hf. cf., $12. — (Popular ed.) ill. 12°. '69. $2.50; hf. cf., $4.50. — (School ed.) 12°. $2.25.............*Putnam.*

— Life of Goldsmith; with sel. from his writings. 2 v. 18°. $1.50.............................*Harper.*

— Lighter works. (Riverside ed.) 8 v. ill. 16°. ea., $1.75...................................*Putnam.*
Cont.: Knickerbocker. — Hist. of N. Y. — Tales of a traveller. — Wolfert's roost. — Crayon miscellany. — Bracebridge Hall. — Alhambra. — Oliver Goldsmith. — Sketch-book.

— Rip Van Winkle. ill. sm. f°. $1.50......*Putnam.*

— *Same.* (Booth's Theatre ed.) ill. 8°. pap., 50c. *Hinton.*

— *Same.* (Jefferson ed.) ill. 8°. $2.50 .....*Hinton.*

— Sketch book. (Artist's ed.) ill. sm. 4°. $10; mor., $16; $18.................................*Putnam.*

— *Same.* (Blue and gold ed.) 18°. $1.50..*Putnam.*

Irwin, E. King O'Toole's goose: extravaganza. 16°. pap., 15c. ....*French.*

Irwin, J. C. God's word for inquirers. 18°. '76. pap., 10c. ....*Am. Tr.*

Is the Bible true? *See* Pioneer lib.

Is Christian baptism for the remission of sins? pap., 10c. (?) *Cumberland.*

Is Christianity from God? Cumming, J. 75c...*Pres. Bd.*

Is "eternal" punishment endless? answered by a re-statement of orig. Script. doct. sq. 16°. $1; pap., 75c..................*Lockwood, B. & Co.*

Is he jealous? Beaseley, S. 15c..... ......*French.*

Is it the despair of science? Gunning, W. D. 15c...*Colby.*

Is it I? Storer, H. R. $1; 50c..............*Lee & S.*

Is it true? *See* Craik, D. M.

Is she his daughter? drama. 16°. pap., 15c....*French.*

Is spiritualism true? Denton, W. 15c........*Denton.*

Is there a devil? Baldwin, J. 25c.............*Colby.*

Isa Greame's world. 16°. $1.25...........*Am. S. S.*

Isaac Phelps. Boardman, M. M. $1.25.........*Hoyt.*

Isabel. ill. 18°. '51. 25c......................*Am. Tr.*

Isabel. Jeaffreson, J. C. $1.50..............*Harper.*

Isabel; or, influence. 18°. 60c............*Pres. Bd.*

Isabel; or, trials of the heart. 18°. 75c......*Harper.*

Isabel of Bavaria. *See* Dumas, A.

Isabella Orsini. Mosenthal, S. H. 15c......*De Witt.*

Isabella Vincent. Reynolds, G. W. M. 75c...*Peterson.*

Isabelle. Buckstone, J. B. 15c.............*French.*

Isabelle de Verneuil. Snell, C. $1; $1.50. *Kelly, P. & Co.*

Isabel's birth-day, and other tales. 18°. 70c...*Pres. Bd.*

Isabel's difficulties. Cary, M. R. $1.50.....*Dutton.*

Isabel's secret; or, a sister's love; by author of "Story of a happy girl." ill. 12°. $1.50........*Nelson.*

Isaiah. *See* Bible.

Isai's Erfahrungen, od. Anfang u. Fortgang in d. Gnade. 18°. 35c.......................*Ev. Assoc.*

Iseulte. Dempster, C. 50c..................*Harper.*

Isherwood, B. F. Engineering precedents for steam machinery. ill. 8°. '58. $2.50.. *Van Nostrand.*

Ishmael. Southworth, E. D. E. N. $1.75; $1.50. *Peterson.*

Ishmael, the Yezidee. Webb, J. D. $1.75...*Routledge.*

Island hermitage; or, the little castaways. 16°. 50c. *Scribner, W. & A.*

Island home. *See* Keene, *Mrs.* S. F.

Island home. Romaunt, C. $1.50..........*Lothrop.*

Island home; or, the adventures of six young Crusoes. ill. 16°. $1.25......................*Routledge.*

Island home lib. 4 v. 16°. $5.50........*Cong. Pub.*
Cont.: Island home, by Mrs. S. F. Keene.—Ben Farrar's experience.—White Robes, by Mrs. J. B. R. Walker.—Sunset Hill, by Miss C. E. Haywood.

Island home ser. 3 v. 16°. $4............*Lothrop.*
Cont.: Island home.—Young Americans abroad.—Captive in Patagonia.

Island neighbors. Blackwell, A. B. 75c....*Harper.*

Island of fire. Headley, P. C. $1.50.......*Lee & S.*

Island of the giant fairies. Challen, J. 10c...*Challen.*

Island of jewels. Planché, J. R. 15c........*French.*

Island of life; by a clergyman. 18°. 40c.....*Dutton.*

Island of the rainbow. Crossland, N. 50c...*Routledge.*

Island pearl. Farjeon, B. L. 35c...........*Harper.*

Island world of the Pacific. Cheever, H. T. $1.50. *Harper.*

Isländischen Briefe (Die). *See* Zschokke, H.

Islands in the Pacific. Goodrich, S. G. 50c...*Desilver.*

Isle of the dead. Souvestre, E. 40c........*Kenedy.*

Isle of St. Tropez. Williams, M., *and* Burnand, F. C. 15c..............................*French.*

Isle of Wight. *See* Abbott, Jac.

Isles of Shoals. Jenness, J. S. $1.50....*Hurd & H.*

Ismailïa. *See* Baker, *Sir* S. W.

Isocrates. Fourth oration, called Panegyric. 16°. '75. pap., 75c..........................*Sever.*

— Panegyricus; from the text of Bremi, with Eng. notes by C. C. Felton. New ed., rev. by W. W. Goodwin. ('47.) 6th ed. 16°. '72. $1.....*Allyn.*

— *Eng.* Panegyricus; lit. tr. from text of Felton. 12°. *net,* 50c...............................*Peck.*

Isolina. S., E. O. $2.................*Lippincott.*

Isoline of Bavaria. Suter, W. E. 15c.......*French.*

Isoult Barry. Holt, E. S. $1.50............*Carter.*

Israel in Egypt. Clark, E. L. $5....*Meth. Bk. Conc.*

Israel in Egypt. *See* Handel, G. F.

Israel Mort, overman. Saunders, J. $1.25..*Lippincott.*

Issues of the age. Pedder, H. C. $1.50....*Somerby.*

It is the fashion. Auer, A. v. $1.50......*Lippincott.*

It's his way. 16°. '74. 50c..................*Nelson.*

It's his way. *See* Bank notes.

It is I. *See* Hall, N.

It is never too late to mend. *See* Reade, C:

It isn't right. Ladd, J. $1.25...........(?)*Martien.*

It isn't right; or, Frank Johnson's reasons. 16°. $1.10. *Am. S. S.*

It is your life. Johnstone, J. B., $1.25....*Routledge.*

It won't hurt you. *See* Kennedy, *Mrs.* M. G.

Italian boy (The); [also] Industrial men of note. 16°. 50c........................*Scribner, W. & A.*

Italian girl (The). Washburn, K. S. $1.50..*Lee & S.*

Italian girl (The); or, the victory that overcometh the world; by author of "Broken idols." 18°. 65c...................................*Pres. Bd.*

Italian journeys. *See* Howells, W. D.

Italian legends and sketches. Cummings, J. W. $1. *Strong.*

Italian pictures. Manning, S. $3.50........*Nelson.*

Italians (The). Elliot, F. $1.50.........*Appleton.*

Italy and her church. Gladstone, W. E. 40c. *Brentano*

Italy in transition. Arthur, W. $1.50......*Harper.*

Itinerant preaching in early days of Methodism. Tucker, M. $1.......................*Russell.*

Itinerant side. Babcock, S. A. $1..*Meth. Bk. Conc.*

Itinerant's wife. Eaton, H. M. 30c...*Meth. Bk. Conc.*

Ivah and Llugwy: tale of north Wales. 18°. '64. 50c. *Challen.*

Ivan. *See* Choice little lib.

Ivan, the leper's son; tr. by Miss A. T. Sadlier. 18°. 50c.; 75c...........................*Sadlier.*

Ivan and Vasilesa; or, modern life in Russia. 18°. 70c. *Pres. Bd.*

Ivan De Biron. Helps, *Sir* A. $2.25.......*Roberts.*

Ivan Papof. ill. 16°. '74. 75c................*Nelson.*

Ivanhoe. *See* Scott, *Sir* W.

Ivanhoe: burlesque. Byron, H. J. 15c.....*French.*

Ivanhoe: drama. 16°. pap., 15c...........*French.*

Ivanhoe: melodrama. 16°. pap., 15c........*French.*

Ivanhoe: opera. *See* Ditson.

Ivar; or, the Skjuts-boy. Carlen, E. F. 50c...*Harper.*

Ives, C: L. Bible doct. of the soul. 5th ed. 12°. 50c.; pap., 25c..........................*Judd & W.*

Ives, E., *jr.* Musical recreations; or, a relief from study: two-part songs. 8°. bds., 63c...*Ditson.*

— Operatic album: music in parts for ladies' voices. obl. f°. '57. bds., $1.25..............*Ditson.*

— *and* Alpers, W., *and* Timm, H. C. Beethoven collection of sacred music in four parts; with organ accomp. obl. 4°. '37. bds., $2.25......*Ditson.*

Ives, Jos. C. Memoir to accompany a milit. map of peninsula of Florida, south of Tampa Bay, under direction of A. A. Humphreys. 8°. '56..*U. S. Govt.*

— Report upon the Colorado River of the west, explored in 1857–8. 4°. '61...........*U. S. Govt.*
Cont.: General report; Hydrographic report; Geol. report, by J. S. Newberry; Botany, by A. Gray, J. Torrey, G. Thurber and G. Engelmann; Zoology (birds), by S. F. Baird; Appendix, astron. obs.

Ives, W: The sure teacher; or, child's first course for the piano-forte. 4°. '72. $1.25; pap., 75c...*Pond.*

Ivors. Sewell, E. M. 2 v. $2............*Appleton.*

Ivy Fennhaven; or, womanhood in Christ. 12°. '72. $1.25..............................*Lothrop.*

Ivy leaves. Atkinson, M. E. $1..*Lippincott; Lothrop.*

Iwan, der Leibeigene. Weber, K. $1; 75c.; $1.25. *F. W. Thomas.*

Ixion. Burnand, F. C. 15c................*French.*

Izard, A. A. New treatment of venereal diseases and of ulcerative syphilitic affections by iodoform; tr. by H. F. Damon. 16°. '72. pap., 50c. *Jas. Campbell.*

Izax, Ikabod. My satchel and I; or, literature on foot. ill. 12°. *$1.50.....................*D. E. Fisk.*

— Sport in brief chapters. *See* Roberts, L. A.

J., E. A. *See* Jackson, E. A.

J., E. M. Autumn leaf stories. ill. 18°. 60c. *J. A. Moore.*

J., L. B. Heavenly watchwords; or, promises and countersigns. 12°. 55c..............*Pres. Bd.*

J., S. Ferncliffe. 12°. '72. $1.50......*Cunningham.*

J. H. and his nurse; [also] The child's prayer. 18°. 30c. *Pres. Bd.*

Jack, the chimney sweeper. Baker, H. N. W. $1.50. *Lee & S.*

Jack, the conqueror. *See* Bowen, C. E.

Jack, the dumb boy. Tonna, C. E. 20c......*Am. Tr.*

Jack, the giant-killer. ill. f°. pap., 15c.; 20c. *J. E. Potter.*

Jack, the giant-killer. [Toy-book.] ill. 4°. $1; 50c. *Routledge.*

Jack, the giant killer. Byron, H. J. 15c.....*French.*

Jack, the giant-killer: burlesque. 16°. pap., 15c. *Happy.*

Jack, the giant-killer's picture-book. 16°. '73. $1. *Routledge.*
Jack, the sailor boy. Sherwood, M. M. 35c... *Carter.*
Jack, the shoeblack. *See* Truth and love.
Jack Adams. *See* Chamier, F.
Jack and the bean stalk. ill. f°. pap., 15c.; 20c. *J. E. Potter.*
Jack and the bean stalk. [Toy-book.] ill. 4°. $1; 50c. .... *Routledge.*
Jack and the bean stalk. *See* Cruikshank, G:
Jack and the bean stalk: juvenile drama. 16°. pap., 40c. .... *French.*
Jack and Florie. McKeever, H. B. 75c.; $1; 50c.; 25c. .... *Claxton.*
Jack and his bride. 8°. pap., 25c. .... *De Witt.*
Jack and his pets. ill. 4°. '73. pap., 25c.; bds., 50c. *Lothrop.*
Jack and his pets. Howitt, M. *and* W. *net*, 40c. *Hamersley.*
Jack and Jill. Gobright, L. A. 50c. .... *Claxton.*
Jack and Rosy. Floyd, C. $1 .... *Randolph.*
Jack Arcombe. *See* Bradley, W. I.
Jack Ariel; or, life on board an East Indiaman. 8°. pap., 75c. .... *Peterson.*
Jack Brag. *See* Hook, Thdr.
Jack Brag: farce. 16°. pap., 15c. .... *French.*
Jack Bryson. Boyd, E. E. 80c. .... *J. A. Moore.*
Jack Cade. Conrad, R. T. 15c. .... *French.*
Jack Cade; or, the bondsman's struggle. [Fiction.] 8°. pap., 25c. .... *De Witt.*
Jack Downing's letters. 8°. pap., 25c. ...... *Peterson.*
Jack Harkaway ser. *See* Hemyng, B.
Jack Harold. 8°. pap., 25c. .... *De Witt.*
Jack Harold ser. 12 nos. 8°. ea., pap., 25c... *De Witt.*
Cont.: Jack Harold. — Spaniard's crime. — Criminal. — Outlaw. — Road to ruin. — Bristol Bill. — Brigands. — Dashington. — Virgin wife. — Fast life in London and Paris. — Grace Wilard. — Alice Wade.
Jack Hazard and his fortunes. Trowbridge, J. T. $1.25. *Porter.*
Jack Hazard ser. *See* Trowbridge, J. T.
Jack Hinton. *See* Lever, C:
Jack Huckaback. *See* Busch, W.
Jack in a box. Simpson, J. P. 15c. .... *French.*
Jack in the forecastle. Sleeper, J. S. $1.75. *Nichols & H.*
Jack in the green. Lemon, M. 15c. .... *French.*
Jack in the water. Rede, L. 15c. .... *French.*
Jack's the lad: Ethiop. drama. 16°. pap., 15c. *French; Happy.*
Jack Johnson's jokes for the jolly. 16°. pap., 25c. *Dick & F.*
Jack Junk; or, the tar for all weathers. 8°. pap., 50c. *Peterson.*
Jack Ketch. *See* Life of.
Jack Long. *See* Johnstone, J. B.
Jack Manly. *See* Grant, Ja.
Jack Mason, the old sailor. *See* Theodore Thinker.
Jack Masters. *See* Mills, L. A.
Jack Myers. Dunning, A. K. 35c. .... *Pres. Bd.*
Jack of all trades. *See* French's comic dramas.
Jack of all trades. Miller, T. 75c. .... *Routledge.*
Jack of all trades. Parker, R. A. $1 .... *Lee & S.*
Jack o' the hedge. Suter, W. E. 15c. .... *French.*
Jack of the mill. Howitt, W. $1.25 ...... *Routledge.*
Jack of the mill. *See* Life and adventures of.
Jack Rann. 8°. pap., 25c. .... *De Witt.*
Jack Rann's life and adventures. 8°. pap., 50c. *Peterson.*
Jack Robinson and his monkey. Thompson, C. P. 15c. .... *French.*

Jack Sheppard. *See* Ainsworth, W: H.
Jack Sheppard. Buckstone, J. B. 15c. .... *French.*
Jack Spraggle's history of Robinson Crusoe: comic ill. and narrative to his school-fellows at Tobey Academy. ill. 4°. per gross, $15....(?) *McLoughlin.*
Jack Story and Paul Stanley. *See* Locust grove stories.
Jack Tar at sea. *See* Herd boy ser.
Jack Thorn's knife; how he lost it, and how he found it. 18°. 45c. .... *Am. S. S.*
Jack Tier. *See* Cooper, Ja. F.
Jackdaw in the borrowed plumes. *See* Stories about animals ser.
Jacket of blue: drama. 16°. pap., 15c. ..... *French.*
Jack's delight. Williams, T. J. 15c. .... *French.*
Jack's kite. *See* Johnson, V. W.
Jack's sister. Havers, D. 75c. .... *Harper.*
Jack's story. V., G. L. $1.25 ..... *N. Y. Ref. Ch. Bd.*
Jack's ward. Alger, H., *jr.* $1.50 .... *Loring.*
Jackson, A. M. *See* Texas, Sup. Court reports.
Jackson, Abner. Discourses. 12°. '75. $1.50. *Whittaker.*
Jackson, Adolphus. Gems of four-part songs. 12°. '65. $1.25 .... *Ditson.*
Jackson, And. Life. ill. 16°. $1.25 .... *Lee & S.*
— Pictorial life. ill. roy. 8°. *net*, $1.85 ... *Hamersley.*
Jackson, C: D. Suffering here, glory hereafter: Lenten sermons. por. 12°. '71. $1.50 ..... *Dutton.*
Jackson, C: T. *See* Maine geol. survey; — New Hampshire geol. survey.
Jackson, Dan. Religious experience and Gospel labors. [Autobiog.] 16°. '59. 75c. .... *Freewill.*
Jackson, Dan. J. Alonzo and Melissa; or, the unfeeling father. 8°. pap., 25c. .... *U. P. James.*
— *Same.* 18°. '70. 75c. .... *Claxton.*
Jackson, E. A. Christine Thornton; or, who is my neighbor? 16°. '70. 75c. .... *Dutton.*
— Christmas tapers, and other stories. ill. 16°. '69. 75c. .... *Dutton.*
— Explanations of the Church service: thoughts on the lessons, collects, etc. for young readers; with questions. 16°. '69. $1 .... *Dutton.*
— I don't feel like it, and other stories. 18°. 50c. *Dutton.*
Jackson, *Mrs.* Helen. ["H. H.;" *formerly Mrs.* Hunt.] Bits of talk about home matters. sq. 18°. '73. $1 .... *Roberts.*
— Bits of travel. sq. 16°. '75. $1.50 .... *Roberts.*
— Story of Boon. [Poetry.] sq. 16°. '74. pap., 30c. *Roberts.*
— Verses. Enl. ed. sq. 18°. '73. $1.25 .... *Roberts.*
Jackson, H: Analytical index of Georgia reports. v. 1–40. 8°. '72 .... *State.*
— *See also* Georgia, Reports.
Jackson, H: Arithmetic. ('40.) New ed. 12°. '66. hf. bd., 31c. .... *Bailey.*
Jackson, H: Dangerous guest (A). 8°. pap., 50c. *Harper.*
— First friendship (A). 8°. pap., 50c. .... *Harper.*
— Gilbert Rugge. 8°. pap., $1 .... *Harper.*
Jackson, J. O. Jesus only. 18°. 40c. ...(?) *Martien.*
Jackson, J. Stuart. Geometrical conic sections. cr. 8°. '72. $1.75 .... *Macmillan.*
— Problems. *See* Cambridge Senate-House.
Jackson, Ja. C. American womanhood: its peculiarities and necessities. 12°. '70. $1.25 .... *Austin.*
— Consumption: how to prevent it, and how to cure it. 12°. '62. $2.25 .... *Austin.*
— Dancing: its evils and its benefits. 16°. '68. pap., 10c. .... *Austin.*
— Debilities of our boys and early decay of our young men. 12°. '74. pap., 30c. .... *Austin.*
— Hints on the reproductive organs: their diseases, causes and cures on hydropathic principles. 12°. '52. pap., 25c. .... *Wells.*

Jackson, Ja. C., *continued.*
— How to treat the sick without medicine. ('68.) 7th ed. 12°. '74. $2 .... *Austin.*
— Sexual organism (The), and its healthful management. ('61.) New ed. 12°. '70. $1.75..*Austin.*
— Tobacco, and its effect upon the health and character of those who use it. 16°. '68. pap., 15c...*Austin.*
— Training of children; or, how to have them healthy, handsome and happy. 12°. '72. 60c....*Austin.*
Jackson, J: Dissertation, historical and critical, on the Christian ministry. 8°. *net*, pap., 30c. *Friends Bk. Assoc.*
— Reflections on peace and war. 2d ed. 18°. *net*, pap., 15c.......... *Friends Bk. Assoc.*
— Sermons. 12°. *net*, 25c.......... *Friends Bk. Assoc.*
Jackson, *Bp.* J: Sinfulness of little sins. 18°. '69. 50c.......... *Pott.*
— *Same.* 16°. '63. 75c.......... *Randolph.*
— Witness of the Spirit: sermons preached [at] Oxford. 16°. '71. $1.50.......... *Pott.*
Jackson, *Mrs.* Lucretia E. Health reformer's cook-book. 16°. '76. pap., 30c.......... *Austin.*
Jackson, S: Complete Episcopal funeral service. f°. pap., $1.50 .... *Schirmer.*
— Guide to practice. *See* Burrowes, J. F., Piano forte primer.
— Sacred harmony: songs and music. 8°. '48. $1.25. *Meth. Bk. Conc.*
— Supplement to "Children's church." obl. 16°. '72. pap., 15c.......... *Randolph.*
Jackson, *Stonewall.* *See* Jackson, T: J.
Jackson, *Rev.* T. Questions on the lessons, collects, etc. 3 pts. in 1. 18°. 30c.......... *Dutton.*
Jackson, T: Our dumb companions: conversations about dogs, horses, donkeys and cats. ill. sm. 4°. $2 .... *Routledge.*
- Our dumb neighbors: conversations on domestic and other animals. ill. sm. 4°. $2....... *Routledge.*
Our feathered companions: conversations about sea-birds, song-birds, etc. ill. sm. 4°. $2..*Routledge.*
— Stories about animals. ill. 8°. *$2.50....*Am. Pub.*
Jackson, *Rev.* T: Centenary of Wesleyan Methodism. 12°. 90c.......... *Cin. Meth. Bk. Conc.*
— Life of Charles Wesley. por. 8°. '42. $2.70. *Meth. Bk. Conc.*
— Life of Richard Watson. 8°. '37. $2.75. *Meth. Bk. Conc.*
— Life of Robert Newton. 12°. '58. $1.50..*So. Meth.*
— Methodists vindicated: a letter to Dr. Pusey. 18°. 40c.......... *Cin. Meth. Bk. Conc.*
Jackson, T: Jona. ["Stonewall" Jackson.] *See* Davis, J., *and* Jackson, T. J.
Jackson, W. H. Descriptive catalogue of the photog. of the survey of the territories. *See* United States, *Geog. and geol. survey.*
Jackson, W: Doctrine of retribution. (Bampton lectures.) 8°. '76. $3.......... *Randolph.*
— Philosophy of natural theology. [Essay.] 8°. '75. $3 .... *Randolph.*
Jackson, W: Singing class manual. 8°. bds., 75c. *Peters.*
Jacky Nory. Malet, H. 40c....... *Scribner, W. & A.*
Jacob, Arth. Designing and construction of storage reservoirs; with tables and ill. 18°. '73. bds., 50c.......... *Van Nostrand.*
— Practical designing of retaining walls. ill. 18°. '73. bds., 50c.......... *Van Nostrand.*
Jacob, F. Greek reader; ed. by P. S. Casserly. 12°. hf. roan, $1.13.......... *Lippincott.*
— Latin reader; ed. by J. D. Ogilby. 12°. hf. roan, $1.13 .... *Lippincott.*
Jacob, *Rev.* G: And. Ecclesiastical polity of the New Test.: study for present crisis in the Church of Eng. ('72.) 4th Am. ed. 8°. '74. $2. *Whittaker.*
— *Same.* 8°. '71. $5.......... *Routledge.*
Jacob, J. Alex. Building in silence, and other sermons. 12°. '75. $2.......... *Macmillan.*
Jacob, P. W. Hindoo tales; or, the adventures of ten princes; tr. from the Sanscrit of the Dasakumaracharitam. 12°. '73. $2.......... *Routledge.*
Jacob. Moorhouse, J. $1.......... *Macmillan.*
Jacob Brown. Stanton, H. T. $1.50........ *Clarke.*
Jacob Faithful. *See* Marryat, F:
Jacob u. seine Söhne. Nieritz, G. 25c..... *Morwitz.*
Jacobi, A. Acute rheumatism in infancy and childhood. *See* Seguin, E. C., Ser. of Am. clin. lect.
— Infant diet; rev. and enl. by M. P. Jacobi. 12°. '74. 75c.......... *Putnam.*
Jacobite. Planché, J. R. 15c.......... *French.*
Jacob's ladder. Merrifield, J. $4..(?) *Townsend & Co.*
Jacob's smallness and enlargement. Reinke, A. A. 15c.......... *Clauder.*
Jacobs, *Miss* Esther. *See* Levy, *Mrs.* E.
Jacobs, F: *See* Anthon, C: Greek reader.
Jacobs, H. E. Doctrine of the ministry as taught by the dogmaticians of the Lutheran Church. 8°. pap., 25c.......... *Luth. Bk. St.*
Jacobs, J. A. Learning to spell, to read, to write, to compose—all at the same time. 18°. 75c.; — in 2 v., $1.20.......... *Appleton.*
Jacobs, S. S. White Oak and its neighbors. 12°. $1.50 .... *Cong. Pub.*
Jacobus, Melancthon W: Catechetical question book. 6 v. 18°. ea., per doz., $1.80..*Carter; Pres. Bd.*
Cont.: Matthew — Mark — Luke — John — Acts — Genesis.
— [Commentaries.] ('48–'73.) New ed. 5 v. 12°. '71–'76 .... *Carter.*
Cont.: Notes on Exodus, $1.—on Acts—on Genesis—on Luke and John—on Matthew and Mark, *ea.*, $1.50.
— Notes on Acts. 12°. $1.50.......... *Pres. Bd.*
— Notes on Genesis. 2 v. 12°. ea., $1.50...*Pres. Bd.*
— Notes on John. 12°. $1 .... *Carter.*
— Popery against common school education: four letters to Bp. O'Conner, and Gov. Bigler. 18°. pap., 10c.......... *Pres. Bd.*
Jacolliot, L: Bible in India: Hindoo origin of Heb. and Christian revelation. 12°. $2.... *Carleton.*
Jacox, Fs. At nightfall and midnight: musings after dark. 12°. '75. $3.......... *Randolph.*
— Bible music: variations in many keys on musical themes from Scripture. 16°. '72. $1.75..*Roberts.*
— Cues from all quarters; or, literary musings of a clerical recluse. 16°. '71. $1.50......*Roberts.*
— Literary life (The); or, aspects of authorship. 8°. '74. $2.50 .... *Randolph.*
— Scripture texts illustrated by general literature. 2 v. 12°. $3.50.......... *Nelson.*
— Shakespeare diversions: a medley of motley wear. 8°. $4.......... *Scribner, W. & A.*
Jacquemart, Alb. History of the ceramic art; ed. and tr. by Mrs. B. Palliser; with etchings, woodcuts and marks. roy. 8°. $18; hf. mor., $22.50. *Scribner, W. & A.*
Jacquerie (The). James, G. P. R. $1.50...*Harper.*
Jacques, D. H. Manual of the garden, farm and barn-yard. 12°. $1.75.......... *Woodward.*
— Manual of the house; with designs and plans. 12°. $1.50.......... *Woodward.*
Jacques Bonneval. Manning, A. $1.......... *Dodd.*
Jacques' strop: drama. 16°. pap., 15c....... *French.*
Jaeger, Ab. Mind and heart in religion; or, Judaism and Christianity: a heart's experience and a popular research into the true relig. of the Bible. 12°. '73. $1.25 .... *Blackall.*
Jaeger, Benedict. Class book in zoology. 18°. 50c. *Appleton.*
— *and* Preston, H. C. North American insects. ill. 12°. '59. $1.50.......... *Harper.*

Jäger, C. (*ill.*) Gallery of great composers: eng. and woodcuts, with biog. sketches by E. F. Rimbault. roy. 4°. $15. 8°. $10 .... *Stroefer.*

— German poets and their times: por. with biog. and tr. by J. Gostwick. 8°. $10 .... *Stroefer.*

— *See also* Gostwick, J.; — Gallerie deutscher; — Schiller, J. F. v.

Jäger, E: Test-types for determination of acuteness of vision, myopia, range of accommodation, etc. 4°. 75c. .... *W. Wood.*

Jagor, F. Travels in the Philippines. ill. and map. 8°. $4.50 .... *Scribner, W. & A.*

Jahr, G. H. G. Clinical guide: pocket repertory for treatment of acute and chronic diseases; tr. by C. J. Hempel. 2d Am. ed., rev. and enl. by S. Lilienthal. [Hom.] 12°. $3 .... *Boericke.*

— Diseases of the skin; tr. and ed. by C. J. Hempel. [Hom.] 18°. $1.50 .... *Boericke.*

— Homœopathic treatment of diseases of females and infants; tr. by C. J. Hempel. 8°. hf. mor., $2.50 .... *Boericke.*

— New manual of homœop. materia medica, with Possart's add., and repertory; tr. and ed. by C. J. Hempel. 5th ed., rev. and enl. 12°. hf. mor., $4.50 .... *Boericke.*

— New mannal of homœop. practice; ed. with add. by F. G. Snelling; tr. by Hull. 6th Am. ed., with new remedies by C. J. Hempel. ('40.) New ed. 2 v. 8°. '74–'76. hf. mor., $11 .... *Boericke.*

— Therapeutic guide; tr. with notes and new remedies by C. J. Hempel. [Hom.] 8°. $3.50. *Boericke.*

— Venereal diseases, their pathol. nature, correct diagnosis and homœop. treatment; tr. and enl. by C. J. Hempel. 8°. $4 .... *Boericke.*

Jahr (Das) in Blüthen. *See* Stilke, H.

Jahrbuch d. Deutschen in Amerika f. 1873. 12°. '72. 80c.; pap., 40c. .... *Steiger.*

Jahrbuch d. Nützlichen u. Unterhaltenden. 18°. 20c. *Radde.*

Jail-bird. ill. 18°. '59. 35c. .... *Am. Tr.*

Jail journal. Mitchel, J. $1.50 .... *Haverty.*

Jailer of Norwich; or, "the eighth commandment." 18°. 60c. .... *Dutton.*

Jakey Wolfenstein songster. 32°. '76. pap., 10c. *De Witt.*

Jamaica, enslaved and free. 18°. 50c. *Cin. Meth. Bk. Conc.*

Jamba, the black pirate. 8°. pap., 25c. .... *De Witt.*

James, *St.* *See* Lives of the saints.

James II., *of Gt. Brit.* Commission to Sir Edmund Andros, June 3, 1686. [Reprint.] 4°. pap., 25c. *Sabin.*

James, A. M. The upward path; or, holiness unto the Lord. 18°. $1.25 .... *Nelson.*

James, Edn. Bankrupt law of the U. S., 1867; with notes, decisions, indexes, etc., [of] U. S. Sup. Court. 8°. $4; shp., $5 .... *Harper.*

James, G: P. R. [Works.] 61 v. .... *Harper.*

Cont.: Chivalry and the crusades. — Life of Charlemagne, *ea.*, 18°, 75c. — String of pearls, 12°, $1.25. — Ancient régime. — Attila. — Charles Tyrrel. — Club-book. — Corse de Leon. — Dark scenes of history. — Darnley. — De l'Orme. — Desultory man. — Gentleman of the old school. — Gipsy. — Henry Masterton. — Henry of Guise. — Huguenot. — Jacquerie. — John Marston Hall. — King's highway. — Life of Henry IV., King of France and Navarre, 2 v. — Man at arms. — Mary of Burgundy. — Morley Ernstein. — One in a thousand. — Philip Augustus. — Richelieu. — Robber, *ea.*, 12°, $1.50. — Stepmother, 8°, pap., $1.25. — Commissioner, 8°, pap., $1. — Last of the fairies. — Margaret Graham, *ea.*, 8°, pap., 25c. — Beauchamp. — Smuggler. — Thirty years since. — Woodman, *ea.*, 8°, pap., 75c. — Agincourt. — Agnes Sorel. — Aims and obstacles. — Arabella Stuart. — Arrah Neil. — Castle of Ehrenstein. — Convict. — False heir. — The fate. — Forest days. — Forgery. — Gowrie. — Heidelberg. — Henry Smeaton. — Leonora d'Orco. — Life of vicissitudes. — Old dominion. — Old oak chest. — Pequinillo. — Rose d'Albret. — Russell. — Sir Theodore Broughton. — Ticonderoga. — Whim and its consequences, *ea.*, 8°, pap., 50c.

James, G: P. R., *continued.*

— [Novels.] (Railway lib.) 24 v. 16°. ea., bds., 80c. *Routledge.*

Cont.: Agincourt. — Arabella Stuart. — Brigands. — Castle of Ehrenstein. — Convict. — Darnley. — Forest days. — Forgery. — Gentleman of the old school. — Gipsy. — Gowrie. — Heidelberg. — Huguenot. — King's highway. — Man-at-arms. — Morley Ernstein. — Philip Augustus. — Richelieu. — Robber. — Russell. — Smuggler. — Stepmother. — Whim and its consequences. — Woodman.

— Ancient régime; or, Annette de St. Morin. 8°. pap., 50c. .... *U. P. James.*

— Arrah Neil. 8°. pap., 75c. .... *Peterson.*

— Cavalier (The): hist. romance. 12°. $1.75; pap., $1.50 .... *Peterson.*

— Convict (The). 16°. $1 .... *Routledge.*

— Eva St. Clair, and other tales. 8°. pap., 50c. *Peterson.*

— Gentleman of the old school. 8°. pap., 50c. *U. P. James.*

— Gipsy (The). 8°. pap., 50c. .... *U. P. James.*

— Lord Montagu's page. 12°. $1.75; pap., $1.50. *Peterson.*

— Louis XIV. 2 v. por. 12°. (Bohn.) ea., $1.25. *Little, B. & Co.*

— *Same.* 2 v. por. 12°. (Bohn.) ea., $1.40. *Scribner, W. & A.*

— *Same.* 2 v. por. 12°. (Bohn.) ea., $1.50 .. *Lippincott.*

— Man in black. 8°. pap., 75c. .... *Peterson.*

— Mary of Burgundy. 8°. pap., 75c. .... *Peterson.*

— Memoirs of celebrated women. ill. 12°. $2.50. *Routledge.*

— Memoirs of great commanders. ill. 12°. $2. *Routledge.*

— One in a thousand; or, the days of Henry IV. 8°. pap., 50c. .... *U. P. James.*

— Philip Augustus; or, the brothers in arms. 8°. pap., 50c. .... *U. P. James.*

— Richard Cœur de Lion, King of England. 2 v. 12°. (Bohn.) ea., $1.25 .... *Little, B. & Co.*

— *Same.* 2 v. 12°. (Bohn.) ea., $1.40 .. *Scribner, W. & A.*

— *Same.* 2 v. 12°. (Bohn.) ea., $1.50 ... *Lippincott.*

— Richelieu, tale of France. 8°. pap., 50c. . *U. P. James.*

— Robber (The). 8°. pap., 50c. .... *U. P. James.*

— Smuggler (The). 16°. $1 .... *Routledge.*

James, H: Secret of Swedenborg: elucidation of his doct. of the divine natural humanity. 8°. '69. $2.50 .... *Osgood.*

— Substance and shadow; or, mortality and religion in their relation to life. 12°. '63. $2 ..... *Osgood.*

James, H: *jr.* Passionate pilgrim, and other tales. 12°. '75. $2 .... *Osgood.*

— Roderick Hudson. [Fiction.] 12°. '75. $2 .. *Osgood.*

— Transatlantic sketches. 12°. '75. $2 ...... *Osgood.*

James, J: American household book of medicine; or, every one's guide in sickness. ('66.) 3d ed. ill. 8°. '68. $5 .... *R. W. Carroll.*

James, J: Angell. Anxious inquirer (The) after salvation directed and encouraged. 18°. 40c. *Am. Tr.; U. P. Bd. of Pub.*

— *Same.* 18°. 50c. .... *Carter; Pres. Bd.*

— *Same;* abridg. 18°. pap., 12c. ...... *Bost. Am. Tr.*

— *Swedish.* 18°. '53. 30c. .... *Am. Tr.*

— *Welsh.* 18°. '42. 35c.; pap., 15c. .... *Am. Tr.*

— Christian father's present to his children; rev. by T. O. Summers. ('58.) 8th ed. 18°. '74. 75c. *So. Meth.*

— Christian progress. 18°. '54. 50c. .... *Am. Tr.*

— *Same.* 18°. 60c. .... *Sheldon.*

— Church (The) in earnest. 18°. 75c. ...... *Sheldon.*

— Church-member's guide. 18°. 60c. ...... *Sheldon.*

— Course of faith. 16°. $1.25 .... *Carter.*

— Earnest ministry (An) the want of the times; with introd. by J. B. Condit. sm. 12°. 90c. .. *Pres. Bd.*

— Family monitor. 16°. 75c. .... *U. P. Bd. of Pub.*

— Life of Clementine Cuvier. ill. 18°. '48. 25c. *Am. Tr.*

— Life of Elizabeth Bales. ill. 18°. '46. 25c. *Am. Tr.*

— *Same.* 18°. 35c. .... *Pres. Bd.*

— Marriage ring (The); or, how to make home happy. 24°. '74. 25c.; 40c. 16°. $1 .... *Lothrop.*

— Widow directed. 18°. 50c. .... *Carter.*

James, J: Angell, *continued.*
— Young man from home. 18°. '45. 45c.....*Am. Tr.*
— Young man's friend. 16°. $1.25..........*Carter.*
— Young woman's friend. 16°. $1.25.........*Carter.*
James, Marian. Diamond on the hearth; or, the story of sister Anne. 8°. pap., 50c.........*Appleton.*
James, *Mrs.* Ma. E. Infant school lesson book. 18°. 40c.........................*Meth. Bk. Conc.*
James, S: B. Morals of mottoes. imp. 16°. '74. $1.75. *Nelson.*
James, T: P. *See* Dickens, C: Mystery of Edwin Drood.
James, W: Complete dict. of the Eng. and German lang. 12°. '75. hf. roan, $2..............*Holt.*
— *Same.* 12°. $2.......................*Routledge.*
— *and* Grassi, Gius. Dictionary of the Eng. and Italian lang. 8°. '73. hf. roan, $2...........*Holt.*
— *and* Molé, A. Dictionary of the Eng. and French lang. 8°. '75. hf. roan, $2..............*Holt.*
James, *Rev.* W: Grace for grace: letters on the higher Christian life. 12°. '74. $1.50..........*Dodd.*
James II. *See* Ainsworth, W: H.
James Ford, the heedless boy. 18°. 30c.....*Dutton.*
James Gordon's wife. 8°. pap., 50c........*Appleton.*
James Haswell. 18°. 30c..................*Dutton.*
James Keyworth; or, a witness for Jesus. 16°. '72. 75c................................*Hoyt.*
James, the Lord's brother, whose son was he? 12°. pap., 15c........................*Claremont.*
James Rogers. *See* Maple grove stories.
James' River guide. New ed.; cont. descript. of cities, towns, etc., of Mississippi valley. maps. 8°. pap., 35c........................*U. P. James.*
Jameson, *Mrs.* Anna. Works. 10 v. ill. 32°. ea., $1.50; per set, hf. cf., $25; mor., $35..*Osgood.*
Cont.: Characteristics of [Shakespeare's] women. — Diary of an ennuyée. — Legends of the Madonna. — Legends of the monastic orders. — Loves of the poets. — Memoirs of the early Ital. painters. — Sacred and legendary art, 2 v. — Sketches of art, literature and character. — Studies and stories.

— Works on art; with etchings and wood-eng. 6 v. demy 4°. $40–$100..................*Lee & S.*
Cont.: Sacred and legendary art, 2 v. — Legends of the monastic orders. — Legends of the Madonna. — History of our Lord, 2 v.
— *Same.* 6 v. demy 4°. $65–$100........*Appleton.*
— *Same.* 6 v. 8°. (Lond.) '65–'67. $40–$125. *Little, B. & Co.*
— Characteristics of [Shakespeare's] women. cr. 8°. $2.50..........................*Routledge.*
— Lives of celebrated female sovereigns. 2 v. 18°. $1.50...............................*Harper.*
— *Same.* cr. 8°. $2.50.................*Routledge.*
— *Same;* ed. by M. E. Hewitt. New ed. por. 12°. '70. $1.25..............................*Porter.*
— Memoirs of early Ital. painters. New ed. por. cr. 8°. (Lond.) '68. $4.50.......*Little, B. & Co.*
Jameson, Fs. J. Brotherly counsels to students: sermons. fp. 8°. '59. 75c. ....*Macmillan.*
— Life's work in preparation and in retrospect: sermons. fp. 8°. '63. 75c. ....*Macmillan.*
— Riders. *See* Cambridge Senate-House.
Jameson, J: A. Constitutional convention: its hist., powers and modes of proceeding. ('66.) 3d ed., rev. 8°. '73. $6; shp., $6.50......*Callaghan.*
Jameson, R: S. Basis of arithmetic. (cop. '67.) '71. 3d ed. 12°. '74. bds., 20c.......*Schermerhorn.*
Jameson, Rob. *See* Historical, etc., account of Brit. India; — Leslie, *Sir* J., Jameson, R., *and* Murray, H.
— *and* Wilson, J., *and* Murray, H. Discovery and adventure in Africa. 18°. 75c.........*Harper.*
Jamie, the English boy; or, only an hour of Sunday-school. 18°. 50c. ....*Am. S. S.*
Jamie and his pony. *See* Baker, *Mrs.* H. N. W.

Jamie and Jennie. Child, L. M. 75c.......*Lothrop.*
Jamie by the lake. *See* Finley, M. F.
Jamie Gordon; or, the orphan. 18°. 75c. ...*Carter.*
Jamie Noble. Mudge, Z. A. $1.25....*H. A. Young.*
Jamie's mittens; by author of "Willie's voyage to India." ('65.) New ed. ill. 16°. '72. 60c. *Lockwood, B. & Co.*
Jamie's wagon. 32°. 20c.; 15c. ....*Dutton.*
Jamieson, Alex. Grammar of logic and intellectual philos. 12°. $1.25 ....*Mason.*
— Grammar of rhetoric and polite literature. 12°. $1.25. *Mason.*
— Mechanics of fluids. ill. and diagrams. 8°. (Lond.) '37. $2.50...............................*Spon.*
Jamieson, Rob. Eastern manners, ill. of Old Test. hist. ill. 12°. 70c. ....*Pres. Bd.*
— On hist. books of the Bible. 12°. $1.50..(?)*Martien.*
— On Pentateuch and Joshua. 12°. $1.50..(?)*Martien.*
— *and* Fausset, A. R., *and* Brown, D. Commentary on Old and New Test. ill. roy. 8°. $7.50; leath., $9; hf. mor., $10; — in 2 v. ill. roy. 8°. $9; leath., $10.50; hf. mor., $12.50.......*Scranton.*
— — — *Same.* 4 v. 16°. '75. $6.50......*Routledge.*
— — — *Same.* 6 v. maps and plans. roy. 8°. $30; shp., $36..........................*Lippincott.*
Cont.: Pentateuch, by J. — Joshua to Esther, by J. — Job to Isaiah, by F. — Jeremiah to Malachi, by F. — Matthew to John, by B. — Acts to Romans, by B.; 1st Corinthians to Revelation, by F.
— — — Portable comment. on the Old and New Test. 2 v. cr. 8°. '76. $6........*Estes; H. A. Young.*
— — — Practical pocket comment. and Bible dictionary. 10 v. maps and ill. 16°. ea., $1.25..*Tibbals.*
Jamieson, W. F. Clergy (The) a source of danger to the Am. republic. ('71.) 3d ed. 12°. '74. $1.50; $2 ....*Colby.*
— Origin and progress of movement for recognition of the Christian God, Jesus Christ and the Bible, in the U. S. Const. 12°. '74. pap., 10c.....*Colby.*
— *See also* Brittan, S. B., *and* Jamieson, W. F.
Jamison, D. F. Life and times of Bertrand du Guesclin: hist. of 14th cent. 2 v. 8°. $14..*Lippincott.*
Jamison, G. Revolutionary soldier: farce. 16°. pap., 15c. ....*French.*
Jan Harmsen, the Dutch orphan. ill. 24°. 25c. *Perkinpine.*
Jane, *St.* *See* Lives of the saints.
Jane and her teacher; or, the Sunday-school of Ellington. 18°. 30c.......................*Am. S. S.*
Jane and Willy's visit to the farm. 18°. 30c...*Am. S. S.*
Jane Bouverie. Sinclair, C. 60c..........*McCauley.*
Jane Catharine (*pseud.*) Still happy in Jesus; or, the dying hours of Emily F—, a Kelso Sabbath scholar. 18°. 25c...................*Pres. Bd.*
Jane Clark, the orphan. *See* Clergyman's orphan.
Jane Eyre. *See* Brontë, C.
Jane Eyre. Brougham, J. 15c.............*French.*
Jane Hart. *See* Finley, M. F.
Jane Hopkins. 32°. 20c.; 15c...............*Dutton.*
Jane Hudson; or, the secret of getting on in the world. 18°. 55c..........................*Am. S. S.*
— *See also* Reuben Kent ser.
Jane Scott. 18°. 22c.......................*Am. S. S.*
Jane Seton. *See* Grant, Ja.
Jane Shore, Rowe, N. 15c........... ....*French.*
Jane Sinclair. *See* Carleton, W:
Jane Talbot. Brown, C. B. $1.............*Polock.*
Jane Taylor. Knight, H. C. 80c............*Am. Tr.*
Jane Thorne. *See* Bell, C. D.
Janes, Edm. Storer. Address to class-leaders. 12°. '62. 20c.........................*Meth. Bk. Conc.*
— Christian ministry: sermon. 12°. '76. pap., 20c. *Meth. Bk. Conc.*

Janes, Edm. Storer, *continued.*
— Death of Dr. Bangs: sermon. 18°. pap., 15c. *Meth. Bk. Conc.*
Janes, Edn. L. Character and career of Francis Asbury. 12°. '72. $2 .... *Meth. Bk. Conc.*
— Mementos of Rev. Edward Payson. 12°. '73. $1.50. *Meth. Bk. Conc.*
— Wesley, his own historian: ill. of his character, labors and achievements; from his diaries. 12°. '70. $1.50 .... *Meth. Bk. Conc.*
Janes, F. Genealogy of the descendants of Wm. Janes, the emigrant ancestor of 1637. 8°. '68. hf. shp., $3 .... *Munsell.*
Janet Cameron; or, the light-house: tale of Scottish life. ill. 12°. '75. $1.50 .... *Routledge.*
Janet Darney: tale of fisher life in Thale Bay. ('74.) New ed. 16°. '75. $1.25 .... *Hoyt.*
Janet et ses amis. With ill. from designs by Mrs. C. Hoyt. 4°. $3 .... *Appleton.*
Janet's boots; by author of "Finette." 18°. 25c. *Scribner, W. & A.*
Janet's bun, and other stories. 18°. 60c..... *Am. S. S.*
Janet's home. Keary, A. $1.25 .... *Macmillan.*
Janet's love and service. Robertson, M. M. $1.75. *Randolph.*
Janeway, Jac. J. Antidote to poison of popery. 8°. pap., 25c .... *N. Y. Ref. Ch. Bd.*
— Communicant's manual. 18°. 65c .... *Pres. Bd.*
— Exposition of Acts: questions and answers, for Bible classes, etc. 18°. 40c .... *Pres. Bd.*
— Exposition of Hebrews: questions and answers, for S.-schools. 18°. 20c .... *Pres. Bd.*
— Exposition of Romans: questions and answers, for S.-schools, etc. 18°. 20c .... *Pres. Bd.*
— Hope for the Jews. 18°. 50c ...... *N. Y. Ref. Ch. Bd.*
— Internal evidences of the Bible. 12°. 80c... *Pres. Bd.*
— *See also* Miller, S., *and* Janeway, J. J.
Janeway, Ja. Holy life and triumphant death of John Janeway. 18°. 40c .... *Pres. Bd.*
Janeway, J: Life. *See* Orme, W., Life of J. Owen.
Janeway, T. L. Memoir of J. J. Janeway. por. 12°. 85c .... *Pres. Bd.*
Janneton u. Amalie. *See* Schmid, C. v.
Janney, S: M. Conversations on religious subjects between a father and his sons. 16°. *net*, 50c. *Friends Bk. Assoc.*
— Examination of causes which led to the separation of Friends in America in 1827–8. 12°. *net*, $1. *Friends Bk. Assoc.*
— History of Friends to 1828. 4 v. 12°. '59–'67. *net*, shp., $6 .... *C. H. Davis.*
— Life of George Fox. 12°. *net*, $1 .. *Friends Bk. Assoc.*
— Life of William Penn; with sel. from his correspondence and autobiog. 12°. *net*, $1. *Friends Bk. Assoc.*
— Peace principles exemplified in the early hist. of Penna. 12°. *net*, 75c. .... *Friends Bk. Assoc.*
— Summary of Christian doctrines as held by the Friends. 24°. *net*, 15c.; pap., 10c. *Friends Bk. Assoc.*
— Vital religion and the means of promoting it. 16°. *net*, 10c. .... *Friends Bk. Assoc.*
Jansen, Ad. Twenty-five "Klavier Studien;" [for the piano]; with Germ. fingering. (op. 32.) 3 bks. f°. ea., $1.25 .... *Brainard.*
January and June. Taylor, B. F. $1.50 .... *Mason.*
Janus (*pseud.*) *See* Huber, V. A.
Janvier, *Mrs.* Emma N. Agnes Morton's trial; or, the lost diamonds; [also] The young governess. 16°. $1.25 .... *Cin. Meth. Bk. Conc.*
— Esther Maxwell's mistake. 12°. '74. $1 .. *Nat. Temp.*
Janvier, Fs. de H. Poems. 12°. $1.50 .. *Lippincott.*
Japan in our day. Taylor, B. $1.50 .... *Scribner.*
Japanese in America. Lanman, C. $1.50 .. *Univ. Pub.*

Japhet in search of a father. *See* Marryat, F.
Jaques, D. H. Domestic animals: manual of cattle, sheep and horse husbandry. 12°. '58. 75c... *Wells.*
— Rural manuals: house, farm, garden and domestic animals. 12°. '58. $2.25 .... *Wells.*
Jaques, J: Croquet: laws and regulations of the game, rev.; with descript. of implements, etc. ill. 8°. '66. 50c .... *Williams.*
Jaquett, Jos. *See* Bible [Whole], *Hebrew.*
Jardine, Rob. Elements of the psychology of cognition. cr. 8°. '74. $2 .... *Macmillan.*
Jardine, *Sir* W: (*ed.*) Naturalist's lib.; with memoirs of naturalists. 42 v. col. pl. and por. 12°. $56. *Scribner, W. & A.*

Cont.: British birds, 4 v. — Sunbirds. — Humming birds, 2 v. — Game birds. — Pigeons. — Parrots. — Birds of west Africa, 2 v. — Fly catchers. — Pheasants, peacocks, etc. — Animals: introduction. — Lions and tigers. — British quadrupeds. — Dogs, 2 v. — Horses. — Ruminating animals, 2 v. — Elephants, etc. — Marsupialia. — Seals, etc. — Whales, etc. — Monkeys. — Insects: introduction. — British butterflies. — British moths, etc. — Foreign butterflies. — Foreign moths. — Beetles. — Bees. — Fishes: introduction, and foreign fishes. — British fishes, 2 v. — Perch, etc. — Fishes of Guiana, 2 v. — Smith's Natural history of man. — Gould's Humming birds.

Jarnagin, Milton P. *See* Scott, W. L., *and* Jarnagin, M. P.
Jarrel, W. A. Liberty of conscience, and the Baptists. 18°. '76. 30c.; pap., 10c .... *So. Bapt.*
Jarves, Ja. Jackson. Art hints: architecture, sculpture and painting. 12°. $1.50 .... *Harper.*
— Art idea (The); incl. account of Am. architecture, sculpture and painting; with notices of artists, etc. 18°. $1.75; hf. cf., $3.50 ...... *Hurd & H.*
— Art thoughts: observations and experiences of an Am. amateur in Europe. cr. 8°. '69. $2.50; hf. cf., $4.50 .... *Hurd & H.*
— Glimpse at the art of Japan; ill. in fac-simile from Jap. designs. cr. 8°. '75. $2.50; $3 .. *Hurd & H.*
— Italian sights and papal principles seen through Am. spectacles. ill. 12°. $1.50 .... *Harper.*
— Parisian sights and French principles seen through Am. spectacles. 2 ser. ill. 12°. ea., $1.50 .. *Harper.*
— Why and what am I? confessions of an enquirer. 12°. '57. $1.50 .... *D. Thomas.*
Jarvis, C: Chants of the Prot. Episc. Church. obl. 8°. '44. bds., 75c .... *Ditson.*
— New and improved method of instruction for the piano-forte; with popular airs and orig. compositions. 4°. bds., $1.50 .... *Ditson.*
— Young folks' glee book. obl. 8°. '56. bds., $1.50. *Ditson; Gordon.*
— *and* Getze, J. A. Tip-top glee and chorus book. obl. 8°. '56. bds., $1.50 .... *Ditson.*
Jarvis, C: H. Chiming bells: collection of popular melodies. 12°. hf. bd., 45c .... *Sower.*
Jarvis, E: Elements of physiology; for schools. 18°. '65. 75c .... *Barnes.*
— Physiology and laws of health; for schools, etc. 12°. '65. $1.65 .... *Barnes.*
Jarvis, S: F. Union or unity: letter in answer to a proposal for a union meeting. 8°. 10c... *Claremont.*
Jarwin and Cuffy. Ballantyne, R. M. $1. *Scribner, W. & A.*
Jasmine Leigh. Tytler, C. C. F. $1.75... *Routledge.*
Jason. *See* Life and death of.
Jasper, Thdr. Birds of No. Am., drawn from nature: pl. with letter-press. [To form 36 pts.] nos. 1–16. roy. 4°. '74–'76. ea., *$1 .... *Clarke.*
— *See also* Studer, J. H., Popular ornithology.
Jasper. Abbott, J. 90c .... *Harper.*
Jasper and Lucy. Knight, H. C. 45c .... *Am. Tr.*
Jaudon, Dan., Watson, T: *and* Addington, Ste. English orthog. expositor. 12°. hf. roan, 60c... *Desilver.*
Javelin (The); by a Lutheran. 12°. $2 .. *Luth. Bk. St.*
Jay, J: *See* Federalist.
Jay, W. M. L. (*pseud.*) *See* **Woodruff, J. L. M.**

Jay, W: Works. 3 v. 8°. $6; shp., $7.50; hf. cf., $12.75 .... Harper.
— Christian contemplated. 18°. 60c .... Carter.
— Evening exercises for the closet; for every day in the year. 12°. '75. $1 .... Carter.
— *Same.* 8°. '63. $1.75; $2.75; mor., $5 .... Am. Tr.
— Evenings with Jesus: devotional readings. 12°. $1.75. J. E. Potter.
— Morning and evening exercises for the closet. 8°. $2; hf. cf., $4.25 .... Harper.
— *Same.* 4 v. 12°. '68. $5 .... Carter.
— Morning exercises for the closet; for every day in the year. 12°. '75. $1 .... Carter.
— *Same.* ill. 8°. '44. $1.75; $2.75; mor., $5 .. Am. Tr.
— Mornings with Jesus: devotional readings. 12°. $1.75 .... J. E. Potter.
— Prayers for the use of families. New ed. 12°. '53. $1 .... Dodd.

Jeaffreson, J: Cordy. Book about doctors. 12°. $2. Carleton.
— Book about lawyers. 12°. $2 .... Carleton.
— Isabel, the young wife and the old love. 12°. $1.50. Harper.
— Live it down: story of the light lands. 8°. pap., $1. Harper.
— Lottie Darling. 8°. pap., 75c .... Harper.
— Not dead yet. 8°. $1.75; pap., $1.25 .... Harper.
— Olive Blake's good work. 8°. pap., 75c .... Harper.

Jeaffreson, Jos. C. Pleasantries of English courts and lawyers. 4th ed. 8°. '76. $3.50 .... Cockcroft.

Jealous husband. Maillard, A. $1.75; $1.50. Peterson.

Jealous husband. White, C. 15c .... De Witt.

Jealous wife. Colman, G. 15c .... French.

Jealous wife. Pardoe, J. 50c .... Peterson.

Jealousy. Sand, G. $1.50 .... Peterson.

Jean. Newman, M. W. 50c .... Harper.

Jean Baudry. Vacquerie, A. 40c .... Holt.

Jean Belin. Bréhat, A. de. $1.25 .... Loring.

Jean *de Troyes*. Chronicle. *See* Comines, P. de.

Jeanie (*pseud.*) Drops of truth from the fountain of wisdom. 18°. 75c .... Pres. Bd.

Jeanie Darley. *See* McLain, *Miss* Ma.

Jeanie Morrison. 18°. 75c .... Carter.

Jeanie Nesbit. *See* Guilford Street stories.

Jeanie's new thoughts, and other stories. 18°. 40c. Am. S. S.

Jeanie's quiet life. Tabor, E. 50c .... Harper.

Jeanie's scrap-book. 18°. 65c .... Pres. Bd.

Jeannette's wedding. Buckingham, L., *and* Harris, A. 15c .... French.

Jeannette's wedding day. Carré, M., *and* Barbier, J. 15c .... French.

Jeannie Barker. *See* Seamer, *Mrs.* F.

Jeans, T: Tommiebeg shootings. (Railway lib.) 16°. bds., 80c .... Routledge.

Jebb, R. *See* England, Crown cases.

Jebb, R. C. Attic orators from Antiphon to Isacos. 2 v. 8°. '76. $9 .... Macmillan.

Jeder ist seines Glückes Schmied. *See* Hoffmann, F.

Jeemes, the poet: Ethiop. drama. 16°. pap., 15c. French.

Jefferds, J. A. Bessie and her little brothers. 18°. 50c .... Cong. Pub.
— Just right; or, a little wrong. 16°. $1.15. Cong. Pub.
— Lame Willie: story of a Sabbath-school boy. ill. 18°. 45c .... Bost. Am. Tr.
— — *See also* Young hero stories.
— Poor-house Sam. 12°. $1.25 .... Cong. Pub.
— — *See also* Mossy dell ser.

Jeffers, W: N. Nautical surveying. pl. and ill. 8°. '71. $5 .... Van Nostrand.

Jeffers, W: N., *jr.* *See* Murphy, J. McL., *and* Jeffers, W. N., *jr.*

Jefferson, T: Writings; ed. by H. A. Washington. 9 v. 8°. $27; shp., $33; hf. cf., $45 .. Lippincott.
— Correspondence and miscellanies. *See* Randolph, T. J.
— Manual of parliamentary practice; brought down to practice of present day; with rules and orders of both houses of Congress. ('40.) New ed. 12°. '76. $1 .... Clark & M.
— Notes on Virginia. maps and pl. 8°. '53. $10. J. W. Randolph.
— *See also* Madison, J., *and* Jefferson, T.; — Virginia, General Court reports.
— *and* Cabell, J. C. Letters on early hist. of Univ. of Va. 8°. '56. $5 .... J. W. Randolph.

Jefferson Medical College. Interlineal, literal and free translation of [its] diploma, by T. J. Mullen. 12°. '74. 50c .... Hamilton.

Jeffrey, Fs. (*Lord*). Contributions to "Edinburgh Review." large 8°. $2.50–$5 .... Appleton.
— — *See also* Modern Brit. essayists.

Jeffrey, *Mrs.* Rosa Vertner. Daisy Dare and baby power: poems. ill. 4°. '70. $2.50; $3; mor., $5.50 .... Claxton.

Jeffries, B. Joy. Animal and vegetable parasites of the human skin and hair, and false parasites of the human body. 12°. '72. $1 .... A. Moore.
— Diseases of the skin: recent advances in their pathology and treatment. 8°. '71. $1 .... A. Moore.
— Eye (The) in health and disease. ill. 8°. '71. $1.50. A. Moore.

Jehovah Jireh. Plumer, W. S. $1.50 .... Lippincott.

Jehovah unveiled; or, the character of the Jewish deity delineated. 12°. pap., 35c .... Mendum.

Jehovahblumen. *See* Buddenbrock, J. v.

Jejana; [also] Congo's Kraal; [also] The little missionary. 18°. 25c .... Pres. Bd.

Jelf, R. W. Secret trials of the Christian life. 12°. '75. $2.50 .... Pott.

Jelf, W. E. Greek grammar. 2 v. 8°. $12 .. Lippincott.

Jellet, J: H. Treatise on theory of friction. 8°. '72. $4 .... Macmillan.

Jelliff, —, *and* Hull, —. Patent pocket interest tables at 6 and 7 per cent. 32°. per doz., bds., $2.50; — ea., per doz., pap., $1 .... Mason.

Jelliffe, W: M. Good sel. in prose and poetry. ('72.) 5th ed. 12°. '75. $1–30c. .... Schermerhorn.

Jem Morrison. *See* Lamb, J.

Jenings, *Mrs.* Edm. ["Wycliffe Lane."] My good for nothing brother. 8°. pap., 25c .... Burnham.

Jenkin, *Mrs.* C: [Novels.] (Leis. hour ser.) 6 v. 16°. '68–'75. ea., $1.25 .... Holt.

Cont.: Jupiter's daughters.— Madame de Beaupré.— Psyche (A) of to-day. — Skirmishing. — Who breaks, pays. — Within an ace.

Jenkin, F. Electricity and magnetism. 12°. $1.50. Appleton.
— Report to the Royal Society on units of electrical resistance. *See* British Association.

Jenkins, C: W. (*ed.*) American educational cyclopædia. 8°. '74. $2; pap., $1.50 ... Schermerhorn.

Jenkins, E: Blot on the queen's head; or, how little Ben, the head waiter, changed the sign of the "Queen's Inn" to "Empress Hotel, limited," and the consequences thereof. [Polit. satire.] 12°. '76. pap., 25c .... (?) Routledge.
— Coolie (The), his rights and wrongs. 12°. '71. $1.25; pap., 50c .... Routledge.
— Devil's (The) chain: a temperance story. 16°. 75c.; pap., 50c .... Harper.
— Ginx's baby. [Polit. satire.] 16°. 50c .... *Osgood.
— *Same.* 12°. '70. $1.75 .... Routledge.
— Little Hodge. 12°. '73. $1.25 .... Dodd.
— Lord Bantam: a satire. 8°. pap., 25c .... Appleton.
— *Same.* 12°. '71. 75c .... Routledge.

Jenkins, J. Foster. Tent hospitals; read before the Am. Soc. Sci. Assoc., May 21, 1874. ill. 8°. '74. pap., 25c. . . . . *Williams.*

Jenkins, Jabez. Handy lexicon: dict. of [unfamiliar] words. 18°. '69. $1; roan, $1.25 . . . . *Claxton.*

— Vest-pocket lexicon: dict. of [unfamiliar] words. 64°. $1; roan, 75c. . . . . *Lippincott.*

Jenkins, J: D: Age of the martyrs; or, the first three centuries of the work of the church of Christ. 12°. '69. $2.50 . . . . *Pott.*

Jenkins, J: S. Heroines of history. ill. 8°. '71. *$3; $3.50; mor., $6 . . . . *Betts.*

— New clerk's assistant, or book of forms. 8°. '55. $3.50 . . . . *W. C. Little.*

Jenkins, O. L. Student's manual of Eng. literature. demy 8°. '75. $2; hf. mor., $3 . . . . *Murphy.*

Jenkinses. Planché, J. R. 15c. . . . . *French.*

Jenks, W: Address [before] the Am. Antiq. Soc., at King's Chapel, Boston, on [its] 1st anniversary, Oct. 23, 1813. 8°. '13. $1 . . . . *Am. Antiq.*

— Address [before] the N. E. Historic Geneal. Soc., Mar. 1, 1852. 8°. '52. pap., 25c. *N. E. Hist. Gen.*

— Comprehensive commentary on the Bible; adapted to the views of Baptists by Rev. J. A. Warne. ('35.) New ed. 6 v. 8°. '74. shp., $20 . . . . *Claxton.*

Jenness, J: Scribner. Isles of Shoals: hist. sketch. 2d ed. ill. 16°. '73. $1.50 . . . . *Hurd & H.*

Jennette. *See* Aunt Gracie's lib.

Jennie, the water-cress girl. ill. 24°. '69. 30c. *Lothrop.*

Jennie Carter. Bell, C. D. 40c. . . . . *Hoyt.*

Jennie Carter; or, trust in God. 18°. 30c.; 35c. *Am. Bapt.*

Jennie Gray; or, a woman's vengeance. ill. 8°. (Lond.) pap., 30c. . . . . *Am. News.*

Jennie McClintock. Cornelison, I. A. 60c. . . *Pres. Bd.*

Jennie Wellington. P., H. A. 50c. . . . . *Dutton.*

Jennie White; or, the lovely fruits of early piety. 18°. 30c.; 40c. . . . . *Am. Bapt.*

Jennie's Bible verses. Trowbridge, C. M. 60c. (?) *Martien.*

Jennie's waterproof. *See* Little Dot ser.

Jennings, A. C. *See* Bible, Psalms.

Jennings, A. G. (*ed.*) Last days of Jesus Christ on earth. 16° '74. 60c.; 90c. . . . . *Tibbals.*

Jennings, Hargrave. The Rosicrucians, their rites and mysteries. ill. 12°. $4.20 . . . . . . *Scribner, W. & A.*

Jennings, L: J. Eighty years of repub. government in the U. S. 12°. '68. $1.75 . . . . *Scribner.*

Jennings, Rob. Cattle and their diseases. ('63.) New ed. ill. 12°. '71. $1.75 . . . . *J. E. Potter.*

— Horse (The) and his diseases; [also] Rarey's method of taming horses, and law and form of warranty. ('60.) New ed. ill. 12°. '75. $1.75 . . *J. E. Potter.*

— Horse (The) and other live stock. ill. and por. 8°. leath., *$5 . . . . *J. E. Potter.*

— Horse training made easy. ('66.) New ed. ill. 16°. '72. $1.25 . . . . *J. E. Potter.*

— Sheep, swine and poultry: their history, varieties, breeding, etc. ill. 12°. $1.75 . . . . . . *J. E. Potter.*

Jennison, S: *See* Newton, R., *and* Jennison, S.

Jennison, W: *See* Michigan, Sup. Court reports.

Jenny, the crochet-worker. Fry, S. M. 55c. . . *Pres. Bd.*

Jenny Ambrose; or, life in the eastern states. 8°. pap., 50c. . . . . *Peterson.*

Jenny and the birds. Guernsey, L. E, 75c. . . *Am. S. S.*

Jenny and the insects. Guernsey, L. E. $1.10. *Am. S. S.*

Jenny Boardman. Denison, M. A. $1.50 . . *Am. Bapt.*

Jenny Diver. 8°. pap., 25c. . . . . *De Witt.*

Jenny Foster. Hazlewood, C. H. 15c. . . . . . *French.*

Jenny Geddes. Breed, W. P. $1.50 . . . . . . *Pres. Bd.*

Jenny Lind at last. Reach, A. B. 15c. . . . . . *French.*

Jenny Wade of Gettysburg. [Poetry.] 12°. 75c. *Lippincott.*

Jenny's geranium; or, the prize flower of a London court. ill. 12°. 50c. . . . . *Lippincott.*

— *Same.* ('69.) New ed. ill. 16°. '75. 80c. . . *Hoyt.*

Jenny's trials. *See* Bell, C. D.

Jensen, W: Die braune Erika: Novelle. With Eng. notes. 12°. '69. pap., 40c. . . . . *Holt.*

Jenyns, S. *See* Evidences of Christianity.

Jephson, R. M. Tom Bulkley. 16°. bds., $1 . . *Routledge.*

Jephson, Rob. Two strings to your bow: farce. 16°. pap., 15c. . . . . *French.*

Jepson, B. Elementary music readers; for public schools. 3 nos. 8°. '71. ea., 75c. . . . . . *Barnes.*

Jerauld, *Mrs.* Ctte. A. Poetry and prose; with memoir by H: Bacon. 12°. '50. $1.50 . . . . *Universalist.*

Jerdan, W: Men I have known; with fac-simile autographs. cr. 8°. $2 . . . . *Routledge.*

— *See also* Stoddard, R. H., Bric-a-brac ser.

Jeremiah. Life and prophecies. 18°. 35c. . . *Am. S. S.*

Jeremiah Saddlebag's journey to the gold diggings. ill. 8°. pap., 25c. . . . . *U. P. James.*

Jeremy, G: Treatise on the equity jurisdiction of the Court of Chancery. 8°. shp., $4 . . *Baker, V. & Co.*

Jerningham journals (The); compr. "Mrs. Jerningham's journal," and "John Jerningham's journal." 12°. '76. $1.25 . . . . *Scribner.*

Jerome *of Prague.* *See* Huss, J., *and* Jerome *of Prague.*

Jerram, C: Tribute to a daughter. 18°. 50c. . . *Carter.*

Jerrell, *Miss* Annie R. Randolph children. ill. 16°. $1 . . . . *Am. S. S.*

— Three girls of the revolution. 16°. '76. $1.50. *Am. S. S.*

Jerrmann, E: St. Petersburg: its people, their character and institutions; tr. by F. Hardman. 12°. $1. . . . . *Barnes.*

Jerrold, Blanchard. Best of all good company: a day with Dickens, a day with Scott, a day with Thackeray, a day with Douglas Jerrold. por. and ill. sm. 8°. $2.50 . . . . (?) *Shepard.*

— Cool as a cucumber: farce. 16°. pap., 15c. . . *French.*

Jerrold, Douglas. [Plays.] 25 v. 16°. ea., pap., 15c. *French.*

Cont.: Ambrose Gwinnett: melodrama. — Beau Brummel: farce. — Black-eyed Susan: naut. drama. — Bride of Ludgate. — Catspaw: comedy. — Devil's ducat. — Doves in a cage: comedy. — Gertrude's cherries: comedy. — Golden calf: comedy. — Housekeeper: comedy. — John Overy. — Martha Willis. — Mrs. Caudle's lecture: bagatelle. — Mutiny at the Nore. — Nell Gwynne: comedy. — Painter of Ghent. — Paul Pry: comedy. — Prisoner of war: comedy. — Rent day. — St. Cupid: comedy. — Sally in our alley. — Schoolfellows: comedy. — Smoked miser: farce. — Time works wonders: comedy. — White milliner: comedy.

— Barber's chair; [also] The hedgehog letters; ed., with introd., by B. Jerrold. por. 12°. '74. $3. *Routledge.*

— Chronicles of Clovernook, with some account of the hermit of Bellyfulle. 8°. pap., 25c. . . . *Harper.*

— Fireside saints, Mr. Caudle's breakfast talk and other papers; comp. by J. E. Babson. 16°. $1.50. *Lee & S.*

— Man (A) made of money. 8°. pap., 25c. . . *U. P. James.*

— Mrs. Caudle's curtain lectures. 12°. pap., 25c. *U. P. James.*

— *Same.* (Cabinet ed.) ill. 16°. $1.25; $1.75; hf. roxb., $3; mor., $4.50 . . . . *Hurd & H.*

— Painter of Ghent: play. 16°. pap., 15c. . . . . . *Ames.*

Jerry. Simonds, W. $1.25 . . . . *Miller.*

Jerry and his friends. *See* Dodge, A. A.

Jersey girl. Pitt, G. D. 15c. . . . . *French.*

Jerusalem delivered. *See* Tasso, T.

Jervey, *Mrs.* Caro. H. ["Caro. Howard."] *See* Gilman, *Mrs.* C., *and* Jervey, *Mrs.* C. H.

Jervis, J. *See* England, Exchequer reports.

Jervis, J: B. Address at first annual convention of Am. Soc. of Civil Eng., June 16, 1869. 8°. pap., 40c. . . . . *Am. Soc. of C. E.*
— Railway property: treatise on construction and management of railways. ('63.) 4th ed. 12°. '72. $2 . . . . *Baird.*
Jery u. Bätely. *See* Goethe, J. W. v.
Jess, Zach. Arithmetic. 12°. 37½c. — Key. 18°. shp., 75c. . . . . *Polock.*
Jessamine. Harland, M. $1.50 . . . . *Carleton.*
Jesse, G: R. Anecdotes of dogs. ill. 12°. (Bohn.) $1.75; $2.75 . . . . *Little, B. & Co.*
— *Same.* ill. 12°. (Bohn.) $2; $3. *Lippincott; Scribner, W. & A.*
Jesse, J: Heneage. Memoirs of the court of Eng. under the Stuarts and Cromwell. 3 v. por. 12°. (Bohn.) ea., $1.75 . . . . *Little, B. & Co.*
— *Same.* 3 v. por. 12°. (Bohn.) ea., $2. *Lippincott; Scribner, W. & A.*
— Memoirs of the pretenders and their adherents. por. 12°. (Bohn.) $1.75 . . . . *Little, B. & Co.*
— *Same.* por. 12°. (Bohn.) $2. *Lippincott; Scribner, W. & A.*
Jesse, *Uncle (pseud.)* *See* Babb, C. E.
Jesse Thornton and his friends; or, the hist. of a missionary box. 18°. 35c. . . . . *Pres. Bd.*
Jessica's first prayer. *See* Smith, Hannah.
Jessica's mother. *See* Smith, Hannah.
Jessie. Simonds, W. $1.25 . . . . *Miller.*
Jessie and her cousins. *See* Bright eye ser.
Jessie and her friend: story of a lost purse. 18°. 75c. *Whittaker.*
Jessie and her friends. 18°. 90c. . . . . (?) *Martien.*
Jessie at the spring, and other stories. ('62.) New ed. ill. 18°. '70. 30c. . . . . *Hoyt.*
Jessie books. 5 v. 18°. '60. $3.75 . . . *Meth. Bk. Conc.*
Cont.: Jessie Ross. — Jessie says so. — Jessie a pilgrim. — Jessie's golden rule. — Jessie's place.
Jessie Bower. Bamford, M. $1.25 . . . . *Hoyt.*
Jessie Brown. Boucicault, D. 15c. . . . . *French.*
Jessie Brown, the Moorland girl. 18°. 18c. . . *Am. S. S.*
Jessie Burton; or, danger in delay. 16°. $1.25 . . *Am. S. S.*
Jessie Cameron: a Highland story. 8°. pap., 25c. *De Witt.*
Jessie Carey: a story of early piety. 18°. 20c.; 25c. *Am. Bapt.*
Jessie Carlton. *See* Wise, D.
Jessie Gordon. ('70.) New ed. ill. 16°. '75. $1.50. *Hoyt.*
Jessie Graham. *See* New juvenile lib.
Jessie Grey. G., L. $1 . . . . *Nelson.*
Jessie in Switzerland. ill. 16°. '75. 90c. *Meth. Bk. Conc.*
Jessie Morrison. McKeever, H. B. 50c. . . . *Pres. Bd.*
Jessie of Dunblaine: operetta. 16°. pap., 15c. . . *French.*
Jessie a pilgrim. *See* Jessie books.
Jessie Ross. *See* Jessie books.
Jessie says so. *See* Jessie books.
Jessie Trim. Farjeon, B. L. 50c. . . . . *Harper.*
Jessie Vere. Hazlewood, C. H. 15c. . . . . *French.*
Jessie Wells. *See* Alden, *Mrs.* I. M.
Jessie Wilson. 18°. 70c. . . . . *Pres. Bd.*
Jessie Wright, or, bear ye one another's burdens. 18°. '60c. . . . . *Cong. Pub.*
— *See also* Dana Hill stories.
Jessie's birthday. *See* Bright eye ser.
Jessie's flirtations. 8°. pap., 50c. . . . . *Harper.*
Jessie's golden rule. *See* Jessie books.
Jessie's holiday. *See* Baker, *Mrs.* H. N. W.
Jessie's parrot. Mathews, J. H. $1 . . . . *Carter.*
Jessie's place. *See* Jessie books.
Jessie's work. *See* Shipley, M. E.

Jessup, H: Harris. Children of the east. 16°. 90c. *Cong. Pub.*
— Syrian home-life; comp. by I. Riley. 12°. '74. $1.50. *Dodd.*
— Women of the Arabs; with chapter for children. ill. 12°. '73. $2 . . . . *Dodd.*
Jessy Allan. *See* Kennedy, G.
Jessy Moore's four gifts. 18°. 35c.; 40c. . . . . . *Dutton.*
Jest book. Lemon, M. 75c.; $1.25 . . . . *Allyn.*
Jesuit (Der). Spindler, C. $1–75c. . . . *F. W. Thomas.*
Jesus Christ. History of our Lord; in easy verse for children. 18°. 40c.; pap., 10c. . . . . *Dutton.*
— Life. 18°. 25c. . . . . *Am. S. S.*
— Life. 34 pts. pl. 4°. $14.50–$20; ea., 25c. . . *Sadlier.*
— Life; by editor of "Kind words." 12°. '74. $1.75. *Nelson.*
— *Same.* ill. 12°. $2 . . . . *Routledge.*
— Life for youth; tr. from the Fr. by Mrs. J. Sadlier. 18°. 75c. . . . . *Sadlier.*
— Life in words of evangelists: harmony of Gospel hist. of our Saviour. ill. 16°. $1.50 . . . . *Harper.*
— Life of Christ; or, the Gospel story for the little ones. ill. 18°. 75c. . . . . *Am. S. S.*
— Life of our Lord: his life, death and resurrection. 12°. 35c. . . . . *Benziger.*
— *See also* Mary, *Virgin, and* Christ.
Jesus: histor. Schauspiel. Schnake, F. 25c. . . *Steiger.*
Jesus all in all. 16°. 60c. . . . . *West. Tr.*
Jesus l'ami des enfants: petites heures à l'usage de la jeunesse catholique. 48°. *net,* 14c.; 20c. *Benziger.*
Jesus and the coming glory. Jones, J. $3.50. (?) *Martien.*
Jesus and the common people. Headley, P. C. 25c.; 30c. . . . . *J. E. Potter.*
Jesus and his beloved disciple. Headley, P. C. 25c.; 30c. . . . . *J. E. Potter.*
Jesus and the little ones. 18°. 45c.; 55c. . . *Am. Bapt.*
Jesus as a child among children. ill. 4°. 75c. . . *Am. S. S.*
Jesus the child's best teacher. 18°. 22c. . . . . *Am. S. S.*
Jesus Christ's alluring love. Flavel, J. 50c. . . *Am. Tr.*
Jesus the cure of skepticism. Matson, H. $1 . . *Goodrich.*
Jesus in Bethany. Martyn, S. T. 25c. . . . . . . *Am. Tr.*
Jesus marks. *See* Kennedy, *Mrs.* M. G.
Jesus on earth. ill. sq. 8°. 75c. . . . . *Pres. Bd.*
Jesus on the holy mount. Sanderson, J. $1.25; 80c. *Am. Tr.*
Jesus only. Jackson, J. O. 40c. . . . . (?) *Martien.*
Jesus upon earth. 18°. '64. 60c. . . . . *Randolph.*
Jesus the way. 18°. 35c.; 45c. . . . . *Am. Bapt.*
Jesus the way. Hammond, E. P. 50c. . . . . *Nelson.*
Jesus' lambs. 18°. 40c.; 50c. . . . . *Am. Bapt.*
Jesus' seat. *See* Little Will.
Jeter, J. B. An American woman in China and her missionary work there. 16°. '75. $1.25 . . . *Lothrop.*
— Campbellism examined and re-examined. 12°. $1.50. *Sheldon.*
— Christian mirror (The). 18°. 65c. . . . . *Sheldon.*
— Life of Rev. Dan. Witt. 12°. '75. $1 . . . . . *Ellyson.*
— Seal of heaven. 12°. '71. 75c. . . . . *Am. Tr.*
— *and* Sherwood, Adiel. True mission of Baptists. 18°. pap., 10c. . . . . *So. Bapt.*
Jettatrice. Craven, A. $1.25; 75c. . . . . *Estes.*
Jeune, Marg. S. My school days in Paris. ill. 12°. $1.50 . . . . *Nelson.*
— — *See also* Bouquet lib.
Jeune savante (La). *See* Curo, *Mlle.* —.
Jevons, W. Stanley. Coal question (The). 2d ed., rev. 8°. '66. $4 . . . . *Macmillan.*
— Elementary lessons in logic, deductive and inductive. 2d ed. 18°. $1.25 . . . . *Macmillan.*
— Money and the mechanism of exchange. (Intern. sci. ser.) 12°. $1.75 . . . . *Appleton.*

Jevons, W. Stanley, *continued.*
— Principles of science: treatise on logic and scientific method. 2 v. 8°. '74. $6 .... *Macmillan.*
— Substitution of similars the true principle of reasoning; derived from modification of Aristotle's dictum. fp. 8°. '69. $1 .... *Macmillan.*
— Theory of polit. economy. 8°. '71. $3.50 .. *Macmillan.*
Jew (The). Cumberland, R. 15c .... *French.*
Jew (The). Spindler, K. 75c .... *Harper.*
Jew (The) and the doctor. Dibden, T. 15c ... *French.*
Jew (The) at home and abroad. 18°. 60c ... *Am. S. S.*
Jew Fagin. *See* Dickens, C:
Jewel. Leslie, E. 75c .... *G. D. Russell.*
Jewel case. *See* Newton, R:
Jewel case juveniles. 6 v. ill. 16°. $7.50 .... *O'Shea.*
Cont.: Pearls. — Popular tales, by Mme. Guizot. — Well begun is half done. — Many a little makes a mickle. — Will and a way. — Nannie's jewel case, by A. Moritz.
Jeweled chain; or, Jessie or Anna. 18°. 45c.; 55c. *Am. Bapt.*
Jewell, F: S. Grammatical diagrams defended and improved. 12°. '67. $1 .... *Barnes.*
— School government: discussion of its facts, principles and their application. 12°. '66. $1.50 .. *Barnes.*
Jewell, J. Grey. Among our sailors; with extracts from laws and consular regulations gov. U. S. merchant service. 12°. $1.50 .... *Harper.*
Jewell, J. S. Certain forms of morbid nervous sensibility. *See* Sequin, E. C., Ser. of Am. clin. lect.
Jewell, J: Life and writings. *See* British reformers.
Jewelled serpent. Richmond, E. J. $1 .. *Nat. Temp.*
Jeweller of St. James. Suter, W. E. 15c ... *French.*
Jewelry, silversmith and watchmakers' reference book. ('71.) New ed. 4°. '74. $25 .... *J. A. Murphy.*
Jewels. ill. 16°. 40c .... (?) *Cumberland.*
Jewels; or, Michael Ashdell's trial. 18°. 35c ... *Dutton.*
Jewels for the household. Edwards, T. *$2 ..... *Case.*
Jewels from the quarry of the mind. Head, J. H. $2.50 .... *H. A. Young.*
Jewels gathered from painter and poet. ill. fp. 4°. $2.50 .... *Cassell.*
Jewels of the Lord. 18°. 50c .... *Dutton.*
Jewels of Virginia. Munford, G. W. 50c. *J. W. Randolph.*
Jewess (The). Bourdon, M. F. 30c .... *O'Shea.*
Jewess (The). *See* Ditson.
Jewess (The). Lacy, T. H. 15c .... *French.*
Jewess and her daughter: account of former times. 18°. '72. 35c .... *N. Y. Ref. Ch. Bd.; Pres. Com.*
Jewett, C: Bound and how; or, alcohol as a narcotic. 12°. pap., 10c .... *Nat. Temp.*
— Forty years' fight with the drink demon. ('72.) New ed. 12°. '76. $1.50 .... *Nat. Temp.*
Jewett, C: C. Construction of catalogues of libraries. 8°. '53. pap., 50c .... *Smith. Inst.*
— Public libraries of U. S. 8°. '51. pap., 50c. *Smith. Inst.*
Jewett, Helen. Life; [also] Life of R: P. Robinson. 8°. pap., 50c .... *Peterson.*
Jewett, J. P., and Co. (*pub.*) National flute teacher. obl. 8°. '50. pap., 75c .... *Ditson.*
— National violin teacher. obl. 8°. pap., 75c ... *Ditson.*
Jewett, S. A. W. Livingstone in Africa: his explorations and missionary labors. ill. 16°. $1.25. *Cin. Meth. Bk. Conc.*
Jewish family papers. Herzberg, W. *$3 .. *Am. Jew.*
Jewish heroes. Colton, T. G. 80c .... *Cong. Pub.*
Jewish persecutor. Colton, T. G. 75c .... *Cong. Pub.*
Jewish prisoner. Bird, I. 35c .... *Bost. Am. Tr.*
Jewish Synagogue. Mohl and Sh'chida books. [Explanation of circumcision and sacrifices.] 12°. 50c.-$1 .... *Frank.*

Jewish Synagogue, *continued.*
— Sepher chayim: book of life; in Hebrew and German. [Prayers.] 8°. $2 .... *Frank.*
— T'filoth. [Hebrew prayers.] Pocket ed. 24°. 50c.-$5 .... *Frank.*
— Tikun leil Sh'vuoth: book of Pentecost. [Prayers.] 12°. 75c .... *Frank.*
— Tikun torah. [Expl. of Jewish law and ritual.] 12°. $1 .... *Frank.*
— *See also* Leeser, I.
Jewish tabernacle. Newton, R. $1.25 .... *Carter.*
Jewish temple (The) and the Christian church. Dale, R. W. $2 .... *Tibbals.*
Jewish twins. 18°. 60c .... *Carter.*
Jewitt, Llewellyn. Descriptive handbook of Eng. coins. ill. 24°. 75c .... *Scribner, W. & A.*
— William Hutton and the Hutton family. (Chandos lib.) 12°. $1.75-$5 .... *Scribner, W. & A.*
— *and* Hall, S. C. Stately homes of England; with 210 wood-eng. fp. 4°. $7.50; hf. cf., $12; mor., $15 .... *Porter.*
Jew's daughter. Judson, E. Z. C. 25c ..... *Dick & F.*
Jew's daughter. Stirling, E. 15c .... *French.*
Jewsbury, Geraldine E. Adopted child. 16°. $1. *Harper.*
— Constance Herbert. 8°. pap., 50c .... *Harper.*
— Zoe; or, the history of two lives. 8°. pap., 50c. *Harper.*
Jewsbury, Mar. Jane. Letters to the young. ill. 12°. $1 .... *Pres. Bd.*
Jex-Blake, So. Visit to some American schools and colleges. cr. 8°. '67. $1.75 .... *Macmillan.*
Jilt (The). Smythies, *Mrs.* G. 50c .... *Harper.*
Jim, the newsboy. Porter, A. E. $1.50 ... *Cong. Pub.*
Jim Bludso. Hay, J. 25c .... *Osgood.*
Jim Fagan. 18°. 50c.; 75c .... *Sadlier.*
Jimeson, Allen Alex. Notes on the 25 articles of relig. as received and taught by Methodists. ('57.) New ed. 12°. '75. $1.50 .... *Pounsford.*
— Sacred literature of the Lord's prayer. ('58.) New ed. 12°. '60. $1 .... *Pounsford.*
Jimmy a Christian. 18°. 45c .... *Cong. Pub.*
Jimmy Don. Smith, F. I. B. 60c. *Bost. Am. Tr.; Lothrop.*
Jimmy's shoes. Chellis, M. D. $1.25 .... *Hoyt.*
Jinks, Josh. Jed. (*pseud.*) *See* Dick, W. B.
Joachim, *St.* Life. *See* Mary, *Virgin*, Life.
Joan, the trusty. *See* Sherwood, *Mrs.* M. M.
Joan of Arc. *See* Little Katie's little lib.
Joan of Arc. *See* Southey, R.
Joan of Arc: burlesque. Brough, W. 15c .... *French.*
Joan of Arc: drama. Ball, E. 15c .... *French.*
Joanna. *See* Hazen, M. P.
Joanna Darling. Townsend, V. F. 75c ..... *Loring.*
Joannes *Secundus*. Basia; [also, Pancharis] by Jean Bonnefons; with sel. from [other] authors. 32°. '55. 60c .... *D. Thomas.*
— *See also* Propertius, P. A., *and* Joannes.
Joaquin, the Claude Duval of California; or, the marauder of the mines. 8°. pap., 50c ..... *De Witt.*
Job. *See* Bible.
Job Tufton's rest. Balfour, C. L. $1.25 .. *Nat. Temp.*
Job's comforters; or, scientific sympathy. Parker, J. 25c .... *Randolph.*
Jobsiad (The). Kortum, C. A. $1.50 .... *Holt.*
Jobson, F: J. A mother's portrait: memorial of filial affection; with sketches of Wesleyan life and of relig. services; in letters to a younger sister. ill. 12°. '58. $1.50; $2 .... *So. Meth.*
— *See also* Hannah, J., *and* Jobson, F. J.
Jocelin. [Jocelinus *monachus de Furnesio.*] *See* O'Leary, J., Most ancient lives of St. Patrick.

Jocelyn's mistake. *See* Spender, J. K.
Jock Craufurt. Kennedy, J. $1 .... *Robertson.*
Joconde. Moncrieff, W. T. 15c. .... *French.*
Jocrisse, the juggler. Dennery, A. P., *and* Bresil, J. 15c. .... *French.*
Joe and Jim. Pritchard, S. J. 50c. .... *Randolph.*
Joe and Neddy. 16°. '75. 50c. .... *Hoyt.*
Joe and Sally. ill. 18°. '75. 40c. .... *Am. Tr.*
Joe Blake's temptation. ill. 18°. '74. 25c. ... *Am. Tr.*
Joe Carton; or, the lost key. ('60.) New ed. ill. 18°. '70. 55c. .... *Hoyt.*
Joe Fulwood; or, honesty and perseverance triumphant. ill. 16°. $1 .... *Perkinpine.*
Joe Miller, jr.: joke book. 8°. pap., 10c. .... *Happy.*
Joe Witless; or, the call to repentance. 16°. $1. *Am. Bapt.*
— *See also* Little door-keeper's lib.
Johann v. Leyden. *See* Hürte, N.
Johanna, od. durch Nacht zum Licht. Nieritz, G. 25c. *Morwitz.*
Johannes Olaf. Wille, E. de. $2 .... *Roberts.*
John, *Uncle* (*pseud.*) *See* Aikin, J.
John *of the cross, St.* Life. 16°. '75. $1.25 .. *Cath. Pub.*
— — *See also* Lives of the saints.
John *of Fidanza or Fidenza.* *See* Bonaventura, *St.*
John of Enon (*pseud.*) *See* Benedict, D.
John, D. C. Guiding star: S.-school songs. obl. 12°. '72. bds., 35c. .... *Ditson.*
John, Eugenia. ["E. Marlitt."] At the councillor's; or, a nameless history; tr. by Mrs. A. L. Wister. 12°. $1.75 .... *Lippincott.*
— Countess Gisela; tr. by A. Nahmer. 8°. pap., 35c. *Harper.*
— *Same;* tr. 12°. $1.25 .... *Macmillan.*
— *Same;* tr. by Mrs. A. L. Wister. 16°. $1.50. *Lippincott.*
— Gold Elsie; tr. by Mrs. A. L. Wister. 16°. $1.50. *Lippincott.*
— Little Moorland princess; tr. by Mrs. A. L. Wister. 12°. $1.50 .... *Lippincott.*
— Magdalena; tr. by Mrs. Elgard. ill. 8°. pap., 35c. *Lippincott.*
— Old Mam'selle's secret; tr. by Mrs. A. L. Wister. 16°. $1.50 .... *Lippincott.*
— Over yonder; tr. by Mrs. Elgard. 8°. pap., 30c. *Lippincott.*
— The second wife; tr. by Mrs. A. L. Wister. 12°. $1.75 .... *Lippincott.*
John. *See* Bible.
John. Carlen, E. F. 25c. .... *Dick & F.*
John. Oliphant, M. O. W. 50c. .... *Harper.*
John, the ploughman. 18°. 18c. .... *Am. S. S.*
John and the demijohn. Wright, J. McN. $1.50 .. *Hoyt.*
John and his four cousins. *See* Very little tales.
John and Paul. Hooker, H. 60c. .... *Am. Tr.*
John Andross. Davis, R. H. $1.50 .... *Judd.*
John Barrow. Phillpots, M. C. 25c. .. *Scribner, W. & A.*
John Bentley's mistake. Holt, M. A. 50c. .. *Nat. Temp.*
John Brent. *See* Winthrop, T.
John Brett's household. Davis, C. E. K. 90c. *Garrigues.*
John Bull. Colman, G., *jr.* 15c. .... *French.*
John Campbell. 18°. 20c. .... *Cong. Pub.*
John Carey. Tucker, C. 75c. .... *Carter; Dutton.*
John Dane. Denison, M. A. $1.50 .... *Hoyt.*
John Dobbs. Morton, J. M. 15c. ... *French; Lee & S.*
John Dorrien. Kavanagh, J. $1.25 .... *Appleton.*
John Frink; or, the third commandment. 18°. 28c.; 35c. .... *Am. Bapt.*
John Gay; or, work for boys. Abbott, J. 4 v. $4. *Hurd & H.*
John Godfrey's fortunes. Taylor, B. $1.50; $2. *Putnam.*
John Godsoe's legacy. Kellogg, E. $1.25 .... *Lee & S.*
John Halifax, gentleman. *See* Craik, D. M.
John Hands. [German.] ill. 32°. '59. 25c. .. *Am. Tr.*
John Harmsen. [German.] ill. 32°. '59. 25c. .. *Am. Tr.*
John Hartley. Adams, C. 75c. .... *Routledge.*
John Hartman. Hosmer, M. $1 .... *J. A. Moore.*
John Hatherton; by author of "Effie's friends." 18°. '74. 75c. .... (?) *Martien.*
John Heppell. 18°. 60c. .... *Cong. Pub.*
— *See also* River-bank stories.
John Howard. *See* Howard, J:
John Jack. Peebles, M. L. $1.25 .... *Nims.*
John Jasper's secret. Morford, H. $1.50 ... *Peterson.*
John Jerningham's journal. ('70.) New ed. 16°. '73. 75c. .... *Scribner.*
— *See also* Mrs. Jerningham's journal.
John Jones. Buckstone, J. B. 15c. .... *French.*
John Kitto ser. 6 v. ill. 12°. $9 .... *So. Meth.*

Cont.: Life of John Kitto, by J. Eadie. — Huguenots, by S. Smiles. — Self-help, by S. Smiles. — Wanderings over Bible lands and seas, by Mrs. E. Charles. — Life and times of Alfred the Great, by T. Hughes. — Thomas Chalmers, by J. Dodds.

John Lennard. ('68.) New ed. ill. 18°. '75. 50c. .. *Hoyt.*
John Marchmont's legacy. Braddon, M. E. 75c. *Harper.*
John Marston Hall. James, G. P. R. $1.50 .. *Harper.*
John Marten. *See* Sherwood, *Mrs.* M. M.
John Maurice; or, the effects of a passionate temper. 18°. 18c. .... *Am. S. S.*
John Milton and his times. [Fiction.] Ring, M. $1.50; $1 .... *Appleton.*
John Moore. St. John, E. $1.75 .... *Berry.*
John Mytton. 16°. bds., $1 .... *Routledge.*
John of Paris. Pocock, I. 15c. .... *French.*
John Oriel's start in life. *See* Little folk lib.
John Overy. Jerrold, D. 15c. .... *French.*
John Paul (*pseud.*) *See* Webb, C: H.
John Paul's book. Webb, C. H. *$3.50–$5 .. *Col. Bk.*
John Phillips. *See* Sunshine and shadow lib.
John Ploughman's talk. Spurgeon, C. H. 90c. .. *Sheldon.*
John Pounds and his pupils. *See* My own lib.
John Richmond. Taylor, T. $1 .. *Cin. Meth. Bk. Conc.*
John Smith. Hancock, W. 15c. ..... *Ames; French.*
John Smith's funny adventures on a crutch. Hill, A. F. $1.75 .... *J. E. Potter.*
John Stafford: drama. 16°. pap., 15c. .... *French.*
John Street Adelphi: farce. 16°. pap., 15c. .. *French.*
John Swig. Carswell, E. 15c. .... *Nat. Temp.*
John Thompson, blockhead. Parr, L. $1.25. *Lippincott.*
John Thompson's nursery. *See* Little Dot ser.
John Tompkins; or, the end of the dram-drinker; in verse. 18°. 18c. .... *Am. S. S.*
John Trevlyn's revenge. Phillips, E. 30c. .. *Am. News.*
John True. Abbott, J. 90c. .... *Harper.*
John Wesley in company with high churchmen; by an old Methodist. 12°. '72. $1.25 .... *Pott.*
John Whopper's adventures. 16°. '70. 75c. .. *Roberts.*
John Wopps. Suter, W. E. 15c. ... *French; Lee & S.*
John Worthington's name. Benedict, F. L. $1.50; $1. *Harper.*
Johnnie, the railroad boy. *See* Poole, *Mrs.* M. E.
Johnny. Knight, H. C. 40c. .... *Am. Tr.*
Johnny and his mother. *See* Robin Ranger's lib.
Johnny Jones. Monmouth, L. H. $1 ...... *Lothrop.*
Johnny Jordan and his dog. Eiloart, C. J. $1.25. *Routledge.*

Johnny Ludlow: collection of Eng. stories. 12°. $1.50. *Carleton.*

Johnny McKay; or, the sovereign. ('58.) 2d ed. 18°. '75. 50c. .... *So. Meth.*

— *Same.* ('60.) New ed. ill. 18°. '70. 60c. .. *Hoyt.*

— *Same.* ill. 18°. '66. 65c. *N. Y. Ref. Ch. Bd.; Pres. Com.; Pres. Bd.*

Johnny Rider, the little English basket-maker. 18°. 40c.; 50c. .... *Am. Bapt.*

Johnny Weston. *See* Marshall, E.

Johnny Wilks; or, the old home and the new. 18°. 60c. .... (?) *Martien.*

Johnny Wright; or, the boy who tried to do right; by author of "Little Bob True." 18°. 75c. .. *Pres. Bd.*

Johnny's captain. Davis, C. E. K. 55c. .... *Hoyt.*

Johnny's first boots. *See* Maple grove stories.

Johns, J., *and* Sparrow, W: Memoir of Rev. W: Meade. por. 12°. '67. $2 ..... *J. W. Randolph.*

Johns, R: *and* Nicolas, P. H. Naval and military heroes of Gt. Brit. por. 12°. (Bohn.) $2.25. *Little, B. & Co.*

— — *Same.* por. 12°. (Bohn.) $2.40 .. *Scribner, W. & A.*

— — *Same.* por. 12°. (Bohn.) $2.50 .... *Lippincott.*

Johns, Wa. R. *See* Cones, A., *and* Johns, W. R.

Johnson, A. *See* Maryland, Court of Appeals reports.

Johnson, A. H. The Norman kings and the feudal system. 16°. $1 .... *Estes.*

Johnson, Alex. Bryan. Lectures to young men on relig. in its rel. to the present life. 18°. 75c. .. *Harper.*

— Meaning of words. 12°. $1.25 .... *Appleton.*

— Treatise on banking. *See* Banker's common place book.

Johnson, Alvin J. (*pub.*) New illustrated family atlas; with treatise on physical geog. by A. Guyot. f°. '68. *$20 .... (?) *A. J. Johnson.*

— and Son (*pub.*) New universal cyclopædia. *See* Barnard, F. A. P., *and* Guyot, A.

Johnson, And. Impeachment and trial of J. 12°. $1.50. 8°. pap., 50c. .... *Peterson.*

— Life, speeches and services. 12°. $1; pap., 75c. *Peterson.*

Johnson, Artemas N. Choir chorus book. 8°. '48. bds., $2 .... *Ditson.*

— Domestic concert collection. 8°. 35c. ...... *Church.*

— Keystone collection of church music. ('56.) New ed. obl. 8°. '75. hf. bd., $1.50 .... *Claxton.*

— Melodeon, organ and harmony instruction book. obl. 8°. $2.50 .... *Gordon.*

— Practical instruc. on harmony upon the Pestalozzian or inductive system. 8°. '55. bds., $1.25 .. *Ditson.*

— Singing school banner. obl. 8°. 75c. ...... *Gordon.*

— Standard anthem and chorus book. obl. 8°. $1.38. *Gordon.*

— Standard glee book. obl. 8°. $1.38 .... *Gordon.*

— Theoretical works. 3 v. obl. 8°. .... *Gordon.*
Cont.: 1. Instructions in thorough base, $1.25. — 2. Instructions in art of playing church music, $1.25. — 3. Melodeon, organ and harmony instruction book, $2.50.

— True choir. obl. 8°. '70. $1.50 .... *Church.*

— True juvenile song book. obl. 12°. 50c. .... *Church.*

— True psalmist. obl. 8°. $1.50 .... *Church.*

— True singing school text book. 8°. 75c. .... *Church.*

— *See also* White, E. L., *and* Johnson, A. N.; — Woodbury, I. B., *and* Johnson, A. N.

— *and* White, J. Young minstrel. obl. 16°. 50c. *Gordon.*

Johnson, Bradley T. *See* United States, Circuit Court decisions.

Johnson, C: Cobbler of Preston: farce. 16°. pap., 15c. .... *French.*

Johnson, Cuthbert W: Farmer's and planter's encyclopædia; adapted to the U. S. by G. Emerson. roy. 8°. $6 .... *Lippincott.*

Johnson, E. The judge's pets. ill. 16°. '71. $1. *Hurd & H.*

Johnson, E: Domestic practice of hydropathy; with form of a report. ill. 12°. $1.50 .... *Wells.*

Johnson, *Capt.* E: Wonder-working Providence of Sion's Saviour in New Eng. Lond., 1654. [Reprint.] With hist. introd. and index by W. F. Poole. 4°. '67. pap., $10 .... *Draper.*

Johnson, Edm. Mouth of gold: dramatic sketches illustrating life and times of Chrysostom. sm. 4°. 75c.; $1 .... *Barnes.*

Johnson, Fk. G. Natural philosophy and key to philos. charts. 8°. '72. $3.50 .... *Schermerhorn.*

Johnson, Franklin. Heroes and judges. *See* International S.-school comment.

Johnson, G. B. The four Gospels and the one Christ: a study and a guide. 12°. 75c. .... *Nelson.*

Johnson, G: Lectures on Bright's disease; with special ref. to pathology; with diagnosis and treatment. ill. 8°. $2.25 .... *Putnam.*

Johnson, G: H: S., Cook, F. C., *and* Elliot, C. I. Comment. on Psalms. *See* Cook, F. C., Bible comment.

Johnson, G: W: Cottage gardener's dict.; with sup. ill. 12°. hf. bd., $3.25 .... *Scribner, W. & A.*

Johnson, Helen Kendrick. Roddy's romance: story for the young folks. 16°. '74. $1.25 .. *Putnam.*

Johnson, J. Essays on some of the testimonies of truth as held by the Friends. 3d ed. 18°. *net*, 25c. .... *Friends Bk. Assoc.*

Johnson, J. A. Offertory sentences. [Church music.] obl. 4°. 75c. .... *Gordon.*

Johnson, J. C. Carmina meloda: song book for schools and seminaries. obl. 12°. '55. bds., 45c. .. *Ditson.*

— Cherub (The): songs for S.-schools. obl. 12°. '63. bds., 35c.; pap., 30c. .... *Ditson.*

— Children of Jerusalem: juvenile oratorio. obl. 12°. pap., 30c. .... *Ditson.*

— Flower festival; or, banks of the Rhine: cantata. obl. 12°. '57. bds., 45c. .... *Ditson.*

— Indian summer: juvenile oratorio. obl. 12°. pap., 30c. .... *Ditson.*

— Juvenile oratorios: collection of songs. obl. 12°. '49. bds., 60c. .... *Ditson.*

— May festival: musical recreation for flower time. 16°. pap., 20c. .... *Ditson.*

Johnson, J. D. Therapeutic key: guide for homœop. treatment of acute diseases. 2d ed. 18°. $1.50; $2 .... *Boericke.*

Johnson, Ja. Economy of health; or, the stream of human life from the cradle to the grave. 18°. 75c. .... *Harper.*

— *and* Martin, J. R. Influence of tropical climates on European constitutions; from 6th Lond. ed., with notes by an Am. physician. 8°. $3 .... *W. Wood.*

Johnson, Jane. Devotional poetry for children. 32°. *net*, 20c. .... *Friends Bk. Assoc.*

— Primary lessons for first day schools. 2 pts. 18°. *net*, 1, 12c.; 2, 20c. .... *Friends Bk. Assoc.*

— Talks with the children; or, questions and answers for family use or first day schools. 2 pts. 16°. *net*, 1, 25c.; 2, 35c. .... *Friends Bk. Assoc.*

— Treasury of facts. 6 nos. 48°. *net*, 75c. *Friends Bk. Assoc.*

— (*ed.*) A daily Scriptural watchword and Gospel promise. 32°. *net*, 75c. ..... *Friends Bk. Assoc.*

Johnson, J: *See* Maryland, Court of Appeals reports.

Johnson, J: Lipscomb. University memorial: sketches of alumni of Univ. of Va. who fell in Confederate war. ill. 8°. '71. $5; hf. cf., $7 ..... *Turnbull.*

Johnson, Jos. Living in earnest; with lessons and incidents from the lives of the great and the good. 16°. $1.25 .... *Cin. Meth. Bk. Conc.*

— *Same.* 12°. $1.75 .... *Nelson.*

— Living to purpose; or, making the best of life. 12°. $1.50 .... *Nelson.*

Johnson, Laura W. Poems of twenty years. 12°. $1.50 .... *Lent.*

Johnson, *Mrs.* M. A. Stoddard. Memorial of Charles Stoddard. 12°. $1.75 .... *Cong. Pub.*

Johnson, M. O. Elms homestead. 16°. $1..*Lippincott.*

Johnson, M. R. *See* Powers, M. R., *and* Johnson, M. R.

Johnson, Mar. L. Lucy's fair, and other tales. ill. 18°. 60c. .... *Bost. Am. Tr.*

— — *See also* Cozy house stories.

Johnson, P. Roosevelt. *See* Homer, Achilles' wrath.

Johnson, R. M. English classics: hist. sketch of literature of England. 12°. '60. 75c.... *Claxton.*

Johnson, R: Seven champions of Christendom. ill. sq. 12°. '74. $1 .... *Routledge.*

Johnson, Rossiter (*ed.*) Condensed classics [v. 1]: Ivanhoe by Sir W. Scott. 18°. '76. $1...*Holt.*

— Little classics. 16 v. 18°. '74–'75. ea., $1; per set, hf. mor., $40 .... *Osgood.*

Cont.: Exile. — Intellect. — Tragedy. — Life. — Laughter. — Love. — Romance. — Mystery. — Comedy. — Childhood. — Heroism. — Fortune. — Narrative poems. — Lyrical poems. — Minor poems. — Authors.

— *See also* Stories by Mrs. L. C. Moulton, etc.; — Two fortune-seekers.

Johnson, *Mrs.* S. O. ["Daisy Eyebright."] Every woman her own flower gardener. 12°. '71. $1; pap., 50c. .... *H. T. Williams.*

— Manual of etiquette; with hints on politeness, good breeding, etc. 12°. '73. 75c .... *Putnam.*

Johnson, S: *LL.D.* Works; with essay on his life and genius by A. Murphy. 2 v. 8°. $4; shp., $5; hf. cf., $8.50 .... *Harper.*

— Dictionary of the Eng. lang.; ed. by R. G. Latham. 8°. $8 .... *R. Worthington.*

— *Same;* ed. by J. H. Murray. 12°. 50c...*Routledge.*

— *Same;* [ed.] by H. J. Todd with J. Walker's pronounc. dict. and Walker's key to class. pronunc.; ed. and rev. by J. E. Worcester. roy. 8°. hf. mor., $5 .... *Desilver.*

— — Illustrated pocket dict.; ed. by P. A. Nuttall. 18°. 25c. .... *Routledge.*

— History of Rasselas, prince of Abyssinia. 32°. 38c. *Appleton.*

— *Same.* 16°. 75c. .... *Carter.*

— *Same.* 12°. $1 .... *Lippincott.*

— *Same.* 16°. $1.25 .... *Scribner, W. & A.*

— *Same;* [also] Elizabeth; or, the exiles of Siberia, by S. R. Cottin. ill. 12°. '76. $1.50.. *World Pub.*

— — *See also* British pock. class.; — Goldsmith, O., Vicar of Wakefield.

— Life and writings; sketched and arranged by W. P. Page. 2 v. 18°. $1.50 .... *Harper.*

— Lives of the English poets. ill. 12°. $1.50. *Scribner, W. & A.*

— *Same.* (Chandos classics.) cr. 8°. $1; pap., 75c. *Scribner, W. & A.*

— *Same.* (Household ser.) ill. 16°. $1.50; mor., $3. *Lee & S.*

— *Same;* with crit. obs. on their works and sketch of J. by Sir W. Scott. (Chandos lib.) 12°. $1.75; hf. cf., $3.75; cf., $5 .... *Scribner, W. & A.*

— *Same;* with crit. obs. on their works; with notes by P. Cunningham, and life of J. by Macaulay. 2 v. 12°. '70. $3–$6.50 .... *Claxton.*

— Memoir of Gay. *See* Gay, J.

— Poems. *See* Tupper, M. F., Poems.

— Poetical works. *See* Goldsmith, O., Johnson, S., Shenstone, W., *and* Smollett, T.

— Religious life and death of J. 12°. $1.50.. *Harper.*

— Table talk. *See* Lippincott's pock. treas.

Johnson, *Rev.* S: (*of Lynn, Mass.*) Oriental religions, and their relation to universal religion: India. 8°. '72. $5; hf. cf., $8 .... *Osgood.*

— *See also* Longfellow, S., *and* Johnson, S.

Johnson, S: D. [Plays.] 4 v. 16°. ea., pap., 15c. *French.*

Cont.: Fireman. — In and out of place: burletta. — Our gal: farce. — Shaker lovers.

Johnson, S: W. How crops feed. ill. 12°. $2..*Judd.*

— How crops grow. ill. 12°. $2 .... *Judd.*

— Peat and its uses. ill. 12°. $1.25 .... *Judd.*

Johnson, *Mrs.* Susannah. Recollections of Rev. John Johnson and his home. 12°. '69. $1.50.. *So. Meth.*

Johnson, Thdr. T. California and Oregon; or, sights in the gold region, and scenes by the way; with instructions to emigrants by S. R. Thurston; [with] Oregon land bill. map and ill. 12°. '51. $1.25 .... *Claxton.*

Johnson, Virg. W. ["Cousin Virginia."] Calderwood secret. 8°. pap., 50c. .... *Harper.*

— Catskill fairies; ill. by A. Fredericks. sq. 8°. $3. *Harper.*

— Christmas stocking. ill. 12°. $1.50....(?) *O'Kane.*

— Doll's club ser. 4 v. ill. 16°. '70. $3.... *Claxton.*

Cont.: Katy's Christmas. — Jack's kite. — Patty's pranks. — Jo's doll.

— Joseph the Jew: story of an old house. 8°. pap., 50c. .... *Harper.*

— Kettle Club ser. 4 v. ill. 16°. '66–'69. $4. *Lockwood, B. & Co.*

Cont.: Kettle Club; Christmas tales for children. — The cricket's friends: tales told by the cricket, the teapot and saucepan. — Grandfather's pocket-book. — The kettle's birthday party.

— Sack of gold. 8°. pap., 50c. .... *Harper.*

— Travels of an Am. owl. [Satire.] ill. demy 8°. '70. $2.50 .... *Claxton.*

Johnson, W: *See* New York, Chancery reports; Supreme Court reports.

Johnson, W: Woolsey. Elementary treatise on analyt. geom. of three dimensions. 12°. $2..*Lippincott.*

— *See also* Rice, J. M., *and* Johnson, W. W.

Johnston, Alex. Keith. Atlases: middle school ser., with index. 3 v. 12°. ea., $1.25.. *Scribner, W. & A.*

Cont.: Historical atlas. — Physical atlas. — Political atlas.

— Bible atlas; to illustrate Old and New Test. 4°. 50c. *Scribner, W. & A.*

— Scripture atlas; to illustrate Old and New Test. 4°. $2.50 .... *Scribner, W. & A.*

— Surface zones of the globe: a handbook to accompany a physical chart. maps and ill. 12°. $1.75. *Scribner, W. & A.*

— Unrivalled atlas: maps, charts and index. 4°. $1.75; $2.50 .... *Scribner, W. & A.*

— *See also* Johnston, W. *and* A. K.

Johnston, *Miss* Emma M. *See* Boyd, *Mrs.* E. E., *and* Johnston, *Miss* E. M.

Johnston, J. B. The prayer meeting. 12°. $1. *U. P. Bd. of Pub.*

Johnston, Ja. D. China and Japan: cruise of the U. S. steam-frigate Powhatan, 1857–'60; incl. account of Japanese embassy to the U. S. por. 12°. $1.50 .... *Desilver.*

Johnston, Ja. F. W. Agricultural chemistry: lectures on applic. of chem. and geology to agric. 12°. $1.75 .... *Judd.*

— Chemistry of common life. 2 v. 12°. $3..*Appleton.*

— Elements of agric. chem. and geol.; with index and Am. pref. by S. Brown. 12°. $1.50 ...... *Judd.*

Johnston, J: Elements of chemistry. 12°. $1.50. *Desilver.*

— Manual of chemistry; on basis of E. Turner's Elements. ill. 12°. hf. leath., $2.50.... *Desilver.*

— Manual of natural philos. ill. 12°. $1.75.. *Desilver.*

— Primary nat. philos. ill. 18°. hf. roan, 80c... *Desilver.*

Johnston, J: History of Bristol and Bremen (Me.), incl. anc. Eng. settlement of Pemaquid. 8°. '73. $3.50; hf. mor., $4.50 .... *Munsell.*

Johnston, Jos. Willing hearts and ready hands. 12°. $1.50 .... *Nelson.*

Johnston, Jos. E. Narrative of [his] milit. operations during the late war between the states. ill. and maps. 8°. '74. *$5–$7.50 .... *Appleton.*

Johnston, R: M. ["Philemon Perch."] Dukesborough tales. ('71.) 2d ed. sq. 12°. '74. $1.50.. *Turnbull.*
— *and* Browne, W: H. Historical sketch of Eng. literature. 12°. '72. $1.50.............. *Univ. Pub.*
Note. An enl. ed. of Johnston's Eng. classics.

Johnston, Rob. Lectures on Epistle to James; with new tr. and notes on the Gk. text. 8°. '73. $2.25.......................... *Randolph.*

Johnston, W: *and* A. K. The globe atlas. 8 pts. 36 maps. 4°. $7-$4...................... *Estes.*

Johnstone, Ja. B. [Plays.] 7 v. 16°. ea., pap., 15c. *French.*
Cont.: Ben Bolt. — Gale Breezeley. — Gipsy farmer. — Jack Long; or, the shot in the eye. — Pedrillo. — Sailor of France. — Tufelhausen.

— Jack Long; or, the shot in the eye: drama. 16°. pap., 15c.......................... *De Witt.*

Johnstone, *Rev.* Ja. Barbour. "It is your life:" preach. for the people. 16°. '72. $1.25.. *Routledge.*

Johnstone, J: Mode of draining land accord. to system [of] J. Elkington. 19 pl. 8°. $2........ *Spon.*

Johnstone, *Mrs.* J: Experiences of Richard Taylor. [Fiction.] 8°. pap., 25c. .... *Littell & G.*

Johnstone's farm. Samuels, S. B. C. 75c. .. *Lee & S.*

Johonnot, Ja. School houses; [with] arch. designs by S. E. Hewes. ('71.) 2d ed. 8°. '72. $3. *Schermerhorn.*

Joie (La) fait peur. Girardin, D. de. 30c....... *Holt.*

Joining the grangers. Small, G. G. 25c... *Collin & S.*

Joinville, J: de. Memoirs of Louis IX. *See* Bohn, H. G., Chronicles of the crusades.
— St. Louis, King of France. 16°. $1.25. *Scribner, W. & A.*
— *and* Froissart, J: Stories of the olden time; arranged by M. Jones. 16°. '70. $1............ *Cassell.*

Jolly, *Miss* Emily. Caste. 8°. pap., 50c..... *Harper.*
— Colonel Dacre. 8°. pap., 50c............. *Harper.*
— My son's wife. 12°. $1.75; pap., $1.50.. *Peterson.*
— Safely married. 8°. pap., 50c............ *Harper.*

Jolly and Katy in the country. Mathews, J. A. 75c. *Carter.*

Jolly bear and his friends. Shanley, C. D. 50c. *Hurd & H.*

Jolly good times. Smith, M. P. W. $1.50... *Roberts.*

Jolly millers: Ethiop. drama. 16°. pap., 15c. *French; Happy.*

Jomini, Ant. H: de. Art of war. New ed.; tr. by G. H. Mendell and W. P. Craighill. maps. 12°. '62. $1.75.......................... *Lippincott.*
— Political and military history of campaign of Waterloo; tr. by S. V. Benét. 3d ed. 12°. '64. $1.25. *Van Nostrand.*
— Treatise on grand milit. operations; ill. by hist. of wars of Frederick the Great; tr. by S. B. Holabird. 2 v. and atlas. 8°. '65. $15; hf. cf., $21; hf. mor., $22.50................ *Van Nostrand.*

Jonah, the self-willed prophet. Mitchell, S. $1.50. *Claxton.*

Jonas books. *See* Abbott, Jac.

Jonas Clare. Bates, L. 70c................ *Am. Tr.*

Jonas a judge; — on a farm. *See* Abbott, Jac.

Jonathan. Tytler, C. C. F. $1.25............. *Holt.*

Jonathan Bradford. Ball, E. 15c........... *French.*

Jonathan in England: comedy. 16°. pap., 15c. *French.*

Jonathan Frock. *See* Zschokke, H.

Jonathan Wild. 8°. pap., 25c.............. *De Witt.*
— *See also* Life and adventures.

Jonathan Wild ser. 11 nos. 8°. ea., pap., 25c... *De Witt.*
Cont.: Jonathan Wild. — Paul Clifford's revenge. — Wild in limbo. — Clifford in danger. — Wild a fugitive. — Nibbling Joe. — Paul and Dora. — Bleeding phantom. — Clifford conquers. — Wild betrayed. — Midnight Jack.

Jonathan Wild's stratagem; or, the highwayman's escape. 8°. pap., 25c................ *Dick & F.*

Jones, —. Life and adventures in the south Pacific ill. 12°. $1.50......................... *Harper*

Jones, A., *jr.* Ecclesiastical unity. 18°. pap., 10c. *So. Bapt*
— Training of children. 18°. 30c........... *So. Bapt*

Jones, *Rev.* A. D. Elements of the Hebrew lang. 8° '70. $1.75........................... *Draper*

Jones, Alfr. Proper names of Old Test., expounded and illustrated. 4°. (Bagster.) $6.25.. *Wiley*

Jones, Bence. Life and letters of Faraday. 2 v. por and ill. 8°. $10................... *Lippincott*

Jones, *Miss* C. A. Church stories for the Sundays and holy-days of the Church. 8 v. 18°. $8.... *Pott*

Jones, *Rev.* C. A. British birds and their haunts. ill 12°. '67. $4.......................... *Pott*

Jones, *Mrs.* C. S., *and* Williams, H. T. Ladies' fancy work. 8°. '76. $1.50.......... *H. T. Williams*
— *See also* Williams, H. T., *and* Jones, *Mrs.* C. S.

Jones, *Rev.* C: Alfr., *and* Cheyne, C. H. Algebraical exercises. 18°. '69. 75c............. *Macmillan*

Jones, C: C., *jr.* Account of Sergeant W: Jasper, distinguished at Fort Moultrie, S. C., 1776. 8°. '76 pap., 50c.......................... *Munsell*
— Antiquities of the south. Indians, particularly of the Georgia tribes. 8°. $6.............. *Appleton*
— Historical sketch of Chatham artillery, during the [Civil war]. plans. 8°. '67. $3....... *Munsell*
— Siege of Savannah in 1779, as descr. [by] two French officers; with notes. map. f°. '74. $4.. *Munsell*
— Siege of Savannah in December, 1864. sm. 4°. '74 $2.50.......................... *Munsell*

Jones, C: Colcock. History of the church of God during period of revelation. 8°. '67. $3.50.. *Scribner*

Jones, C: H. Africa, hist. of exploration, etc., from Herodotus to Livingston. map and ill. 8°. '75 $5.......................... *Holt*
— Davault's mills. 12°. $1.75.......... *Lippincott*
— (*ed.*) Vers de société. ('74.) New ed. ill. 8°. '75 $7.50; mor., $15. — (Leis. hour ser.) 16°. $1.25 *Holt*

Jones, C: Handfield. Clinical obs. on functional nervous disorders. 2d ed. 8°. $3.25......... *Lea*
— *and* Sieveking, E. H. Manual of pathol. anatomy. New ed., enl.; ed. by J. F. Payne. ill. demy 8°. '75. $6.......................... *Lindsay*

Jones, Cornelia. ["Jane R. Sommers."] Heavenward led; or, the two bequests. ill. 16°. '70. $1.25. *Porter.*

Jones, Darius E. Songs for the new life. [Hymn book.] 8°. $1.60; mor., $3.50........ *Church*
— Temple melodies; for public, social and private worship. 12°. $1. 8°. $1.50.......... *Hamersley.*

Jones, D: Journal of two visits to some nations of Indians on the west side of the Ohio, 1772-3. Burlington, 1774. [Reprint.] With memoir by H. G. Jones. 8°. $1.50; large pap., $3.. *Sabin.*

Jones, E. D. Aids to Sunday-school workers. 16°. 75c. *Am. Bapt.; So. Bapt.*

Jones, *Rev.* E. W. Adopted son of the princess; or, providence in a family. ill. 16°. '73. $1.. *Tibbals.*

Jones, E. Warner. Book of Psalms: questions. 18°. '63. bds., 40c. — Key. bds., 40c.; — 2 v. in 1. 12°. $1.25.......................... *Randolph.*

Jones, Elisha. Exercises in Gk. prose composition. ('72.) New ed. 12°. '75. hf. leath., $1.25.. *Griggs.*

Jones, Eliza G. Memoir. 18°. 55c.; 65c... *Am. Bapt.*

Jones, Evan Rowland. Historical sketches: Lincoln, Stanton and Grant. por. 8°. $3.. *Scribner, W. & A.*

Jones, Fs. Owen's College junior course of chemistry, with pref. by Prof. Roscoe. 2d ed. ill. 18°. $1.25. *Macmillan.*

Jones, G: Life scenes from the four Gospels. 12°. '65. $2.......................... *Garrigues.*
— Life scenes from the Old Test. 12°. '68. $2. *Garrigues.*

ones, G: *continued.*
– Observations on the zodiacal light. *See* Hawks, F. L., Narrative of expedition, etc.
'ones, H. Cadman. *See* England, Chancery reports.
ones, Hamilton C. *See* North Carolina, Law reports.
ones, *Rev.* Harry. The perfect man; or, Jesus an example of godly life. 16°. '69. $1...*Lothrop.*
– The regular Swiss round. ill. sm. 8°. $1.75..*Routledge.*
ones, H: ["Cavendish."] Guide to euchre. 12°. pap., 10c. ....*Happy.*
– Laws and principles of whist. New ed., enl. 16°. (Lond.) '75. $2...............*Little, B. & Co.*
– New and complete treatise on whist. 18°. 75c. *Appleton.*
'ones, Horatio M. *See* Missouri, Sup. Court reports.
ones, Hu. Present state of Virginia. [Reprint.] 8°. $3; large pap., $5......................*Sabin.*
ones, J. Jesus and the coming glory. 8°. $3.50. (?)*Martien.*
'ones, J. H. *See* Knell, A., *and* Jones, J. H.
'ones, *Rev.* J. H. Man, moral and physical. 12°. $2. (?)*Martien.*
'ones, J. W: Personal reminiscences, etc., of R. E. Lee. ill. 8°. *$3.50–$7.50.................*Appleton.*
'ones, Ja. Compendium of forms; with mode of procedure in courts of Illinois. 4th ed., rev. and enl. 8°. '76. shp., $5.............*E.B.Myers.*
'ones, Jl. Syllabus of law of land office titles in Penn. 8°. '50. $1.50...............*T. & J. W. Johnson.*
'ones, J: Handrailing cut square to the plank, without a falling mould. pl. f°. '74. bds., $2.50..*Spon.*
'ones, J: B. Library of adventure. 3 v. ill. 12°. ea., $1.25; pap., 75c..................*Lippincott.*
Cont.: Wild western scenes.—War path.—Life and adventures of a country merchant.
– Love and money. 12°. $1.75; pap., $1.50..*Peterson.*
– Rebel war clerk's (A) diary at the Confederate States capital. 2 v. 8°. '66. $5.50..*Claxton; Lippincott.*
– Rival belles (The); or, life in Washington. 12°. $1.75; pap., $1.50..................*Peterson.*
– Secession, coercion and civil war: a prophecy of the rebellion. 12°. $1.75...............*Peterson.*
– Wild southern scenes. 12°. $1.75; pap., $1.50. *Peterson.*
'ones, J: Hilton. Sixty-six interludes and preludes; [for the organ]. obl. 8°. 60c.......*Brainard.*
'ones, J: Mat. Visitor's guide to Bermuda; with sketch of its natural history. sm. 12°. '76. bds., $1.50............................*Brentano.*
'ones, J: Pringle. *See* Pennsylvania, Supreme Court reports.
'ones, J: Richter. The Quaker soldier; or, the British in Phila. 12°. $1.75; pap., $1.50..*Peterson.*
'ones, Jos. Investigations, chemical and physiological, rel. to certain Am. vertebrata. 4°. '56. pap., $1.50 .... *Smith. Inst.*
'ones, Jos. H. Anna Cradock; [also] Little Samuel. 18°. 45c. ....*Pres. Bd.*
– Brazen serpent (The); or, faith in Christ. ill. 18°. 25c.....................................*Am. S. S.*
– *Same.* 18°. 45c.......................*Pres. Bd.*
– Hadassah and court of Ahasuerus. 18°. 45c. *Pres. Bd.*
'ones, Jos. Stevens. ["Jefferson Scattering Batkins."] [Plays.] 6 v. 16°. ea., pap., 15c.......*French.*
Cont.: Captain Kyd.—Carpenter of Rouen.—Green Mountain boy: comedy.—Moll Pitcher.—People's lawyer: comedy.—Surgeon of Paris.
– Life of Jefferson S. Batkins, member from Cranberry Centre. por. 8°. '71. $1.50...........*Loring.*
'ones, Just. ["Harry Hazel."] The flying Yankee. 8°. pap., 50c..........................*Peterson.*
– The king's cruisers. 8°. pap., 50c.......*Peterson.*
'ones, L. E., *and* Scudder, J. M. The American eclectic materia medica and therapeutics. ('58.) 5th ed. 8°. '74. shp., $3.............. *Wilstach.*

Jones, Lloyd. *See* Ludlow, J. M., *and* Jones, L.
Jones, Ma. Life. ill. 32°. '53. 30c..........*Am. Tr.*
Jones, Meredith. Bible stories for little children. ill. 16°. 50c..............................*Nelson.*
— Biographies of great men. ill. 16°. 50c.....*Nelson.*
— Book of Bible stories. ill. 16°. 50c.........*Nelson.*
— Huc's travels in Tartary. *See* Wonder lib.
— Stories from Eng. hist. ill. 16°. 50c........*Nelson.*
— Stories from European hist. ill. 16°. 50c...*Nelson.*
— Story of Capt. Cook's three voyages around the world. ill. 4°. $2.50.........................*Lee & S.*
Jones, Pl. Life. ill. 12°. $1.25..........*Lippincott.*
Jones, Pleasant. Slaveholder abroad; or, Billy Bucks' visit with his master to England: letters to Maj. Joseph Jones, of Georgia. ill. 12°. '60. $1.25. *Claxton; Lippincott.*
Jones, R: Green man: comedy. 16°. pap., 15c...*French.*
Jones, Rob. The hidden hand: drama. 16°. pap., 15c...................................*Lee & S.*
Jones, Rob. History of the French bar, ancient and modern. 8°. '56. $1.50.....*T. & J. W. Johnson.*
— — *See also* Law lib.
Jones, S: *See* New York City, Superior Court reports.
Jones, Silas. Introduction to legal science; [with] dictionary of law terms and phrases. 12°. hf. shp., $2 ....*Baker, V. & Co.*
Jones, T. G. The Baptists: their origin, continuity, principles, etc. 16°. 90c............*Am. Bapt.*
Jones, T. Percy (*pseud.*) *See* Aytoun, W. E.
Jones, T: Book-keeping and accountantship: double entry. 8°. 75c......................... *Wiley.*
— Book-keeping and accountantship; element. and pract. 8°. $2.50.—(School ed.) 8°. $1.50.. *Wiley.*
Jones, T: G. *See* Alabama, Sup. Court reports.
Jones, T: Rymer. Natural history of birds. ill. 16°. '67. $2.50..............................*Pott.*
Jones, T: Wharton. Defects of sight and hearing: their nature, causes, prevention, etc. 2d ed. 12°. '66. $1.25...........................*Lindsay.*
Jones, W: Broad, broad ocean (The), and some of its inhabitants. ill. cr. 8°. $2.50. *Scribner, W. & A.*
— Treasures of the earth: mines, minerals and metals. ill. 16°. $1.75. cr. 8°. $2.50...*Scribner, W. & A.*
— *Same.* ill. large 12°. '72. $2.50.........*Putnam.*
Jones, W: *See* Russell, W.
Jones, *Rev.* W: (*ed.*) New Testament illustrations: sel., anecdotes, etc., explan. of New Test. ill. 8°. *$3.50; leath., $4.........................*Burr.*
Jones, W: A. Report on the reconnoissance of Wyoming. *See* United States, *Corps of Eng.*
Jones, W: Basil. Peace of God: sermons on reconciliation of God and man. cr. 8°. $2.....*Routledge.*
— *See* Bible, New Test.
Jones, W: P. Myth of Stone Idol: love legend of Dakota. sm. 4°. '75. $1.25...........*Griggs.*
Jonquil (*pseud.*) Was she engaged? 12°. $1.25. *Lippincott.*
Jonson, Ben. Works; with memoir by W. Gifford. 8°. shp., $3.50.....................*Appleton.*
— — *Same.* roy. 8°. $6...................*Routledge.*
— Every man in his humor: comedy. 16°. pap., 15c. *French.*
Jonveaux, Emile. Two years in east Africa: adventures in Abyssinia and Nubia, with journey to sources of the Nile. ill. 12°. '75. $1.25..*Nelson.*
Jordan, *Miss* C. J. M. Richmond, her glory and her graves: poem. 8°. '67. pap., 50c. *J. W. Randolph.*
Jordan, C: H. Tabulated weights of angle T, bulb, and flat iron; for naval architects and ship builders. 2d ed. 18°. pap., 60c...................*Spon.*
Jordan, *Mrs.* D. M. Rosemary leaves: poems. 18°. '73. $1.50..........................*Clarke.*

Jordan, D: Starr. Manual of the vertebrates of the northern U. S., east of the Mississippi and north of North Carolina and Tennessee; exclusive of marine species. 12°. '76. $2 .... *Jansen.*

Jordan, G. Foundations under water; [also] Ellis' Formation of bars at the mouths of rivers; [also] Crosby's Economy of railroad curvature; [also] Maurice's Erection of a draw-bridge without false works; [also] Macdonald's Proportions of the heads of eye-bars; [also] Richards' Tensile strength of bar iron and boiler plate. 8°. '74. pap., 80c. .... *Am. Soc. of C. E.*

Jordan, R: Life. 12°. 62c. .... *Friends Bk. St.*

Jordan, T: *and* Pryor, J. P. Campaigns of Gen. N. B. Forrest, and of Forrest's Cavalry. por., maps and ill. 8°. '68. $4; hf. cf., $6 .... *Eyrich.*

Jordan (The): its hist., monuments, etc. ill. 18°. '71. 50c. .... *Lothrop.*

Jorrocks' jaunts and jollities. Surtees, R. S. $1. *Routledge.*

Jo's doll. *See* Johnson, V. W.

Joseph, *St.* Life. 16°. 75c.; $1.25 .... *Sadlier.*

— — *See also* Lives of the saints; — Mary, *Virgin.*

Joseph II. and his court. Mundt, *Mrs.* C. M. $1.50; $1; $3.50 .... *Appleton.*

Joseph. *See* History of.

Joseph; in Bible lang. 18°. 35c. .... *Pres. Bd.*

Joseph; or, humility before honor. 18°. 25c. *Scribner, W. & A.*

Joseph, the Jew. [Juvenile.] 16°. $1.25 .. (?) *Martien.*

Joseph, the Jew. Johnson, V. W. 50c. ..... *Harper.*

Joseph, the model young man. Sprague, W. B. $1. *Randolph.*

Joseph and his brethren. ill. sq. 18°. '58. 25c. *Am. Tr.*

— *Same.* 16°. 75c. .... *Graves.*

— *Same.* demy 4°. $1; bds., 50c. ... *Scribner, W. & A.*

— *See also* Life story ser.

Joseph and his brethren. *See* Three dramas.

Joseph and his friend. Taylor, B. $1.50; $2. *Putnam.*

Joseph Andrews. *See* Fielding, H:

Joseph in Egypt. *See* French's serio-comic dramas.

Joseph in the snow. Auerbach, B. $1.25 ...... *Holt.*

Joseph Martin. 18°. 60c. .... (?) *Martien.*

Joseph Murray, the young prodigal. 18°. 60c.; 70c. *Am. Bapt.*

Joseph Noirel's revenge. Cherbuliez, V. $1.25 .. *Holt.*

Joseph Pilmore. ill. 12°. 90c. .... *Nelson.*

Joseph Wilmot. Reynolds, G. W. M. $1.75; $1. *Peterson.*

Josephine, *Empress.* Life. 12°. $1.50; $2 .. *Sadlier.*

Josephine (*pseud.*) Our children's pets. ill. sm. 4°. $2 .... *Routledge.*

Josephine. Aguilar, G. 50c. .... *Peterson.*

Josephine; or, the maid of the gulf. 8°. pap., 25c. *Dick & F.*

Josephine gallery. Cary, P. *and* A. $5; $10 .. *Lippincott.*

Josephus, Flav. Works; tr. ill. 8°. $3–$7.50. *Lippincott.*

— *Same;* with notes, obs. and index. (Lib. ed.) 4 v. cr. 8°. $9; shp., $10; hf. cf., $18 ...... *Mason.*

— *Same.* (Pop. ed.) 2 v. cr. 8°. $4.50; shp., $5; hf. cf., $9 .... *Mason.*

— *Same;* tr. by W. Whiston. 8°. $2; shp., $2.75. *World Pub.*

— — *Same.* por. demy 8°. $2.50 .. *Appleton; Lee & S.*

— — *Same.* 8°. $3; shp., $3.50; hf. cf., $6.50 .. *Porter.*

— — *Same.* 8°. '71. shp., $3.50 .... *Claxton.*

— — *Same.* (Globe lib.) cr. 8°. '73. $1.75; hf. cf., $3.50; cf., $5. .... *Routledge.*

— — *Same;* with notes by I. Taylor. 2 v. ill. roy. 8°. cf., $20; — in 1 v., cf., $18 .... *Appleton.*

Josephus, Flav., *continued.*

— — *Same;* with introd. by Rev. H. Stebbing. ('49.) 6th ed. ill. and pl. roy. 8°. '74. hf. mor., $12. *Virtue.*

— *Germ.* Werke; Ausg. v. C. R. Demme. 7th ed. 8°. leath., $6.50 .... *Schäfer.*

Josey, the runaway. *See* Books about boys who fought and won.

Joshua. *See* Handel, G. F.

Joshua and his successors. Groser, W. H. 2 v. ea., 90c. .... *Nelson.*

Joshua Davidson. Linton, E. L. $1.25 .. *Lippincott.*

Joshua Marvel. *See* Farjeon, B. L.

Josie and Rosie. *See* Sunbeam ser.

Joslin, B. F. Homœopathic treat. of epidemic cholera. 3d ed., enl. 12°. $1 .... *Boericke.*

— Principles of homœopathy: lectures. 12°. 75c. *Boericke.*

Joslin, Tit. Life of St. Francis of Assisium. 18°. 45c. *O'Shea.*

— Life of the Virgin Mary. ill. 12°. $1; $1.50; mor., $3 .... *O'Shea.*

— Star of Bethlehem. [Cath. prayer book.] 18°. $1.25–$10. — 24°. 75c.–$20 .... *O'Shea.*

Josse, M. *See* Sales, F.

Jottings from life. Cutler, H. R. $1 .. *Cin. Meth. Bk. Conc.*

Jouanne, L. E. Gender of French nouns. 12°. '56. 60c. .... *G. R. Lockwood.*

Joubert, Jos. Some of the thoughts of J.; ed., with biog. notice, by G. H. Calvert. 16°. $1.50 .. *Lee & S.*

Jouffroy, T. Introduction to ethics; tr. by Rev. W. H. Channing. 2 v. 12°. $2.50 .... *Dennet.*

Jourdan, Bce. A. Chances and changes: stories of the past and present. ill. 12°. '73. $2 ... *Routledge.*

Journal abroad. Kennedy, J. P. $2 .... *Putnam.*

Journal of a home life. Sewell, E. M. $2 .. *Williams.*

Journal of a residence on a Georgia plantation. Kemble, F. A. $1.50 .... *Harper.*

Journal of a summer tour. Sewell, E. M. $1 .. *Appleton.*

Journal of a young lady of Virginia. Mason, E. V. $1. *Murphy.*

Journée du chrétien. [Prayer book.] 24°. 50c.–$15. *Sadlier.*

Journey (The). *See* Champney stories.

Journey from Cornhill to Grand Cairo. *See* Thackeray, W. M.

Journey home. Monro, E. 60c. .... *Dutton.*

Journey in Brazil. Agassiz, L. *and* E. C. $5; $8. *Osgood.*

Journey in Honduras. Huston, R. G. 50c. .. *Clarke.*

Journey of disc. all round our house; or, the interview. (Reason why ser.) 12°. $1.25 ...... *Lippincott.*

Journey over the region of fulfilled prophecy. Wylie, J. A. 50c. .... *Carter.*

Journey round my room. Maistre, X. de. $1.50. *Hurd & H.*

Journey through the Chinese empire. Huc, E. R. $3. *Harper.*

Journey to Ashango land. DuChaillu, P. B. $5 .. *Harper.*

Journey to the centre of the earth. *See* Verne, Jules.

Journey to the north pole. *See* Verne, Jules.

Journeys and labors of St. Paul. Tarbox, I. N. 15c. *Cong. Pub.*

Jousse, J. Catechism of music; for the piano. 12°. 20c. .... *Brainard.*

— *Same.* 24°. 25c. .... *Gordon.*

— *Same;* with app. New ed. 12°. '66. pap., 20c. *Ditson.*

— *Same;* with modulations from the various major and minor keys, by W. Coard. 32°. '66. pap., 25c. *Pond.*

— — *Same.* 24°. '66. bds., 35c.; pap., 25c. .. *Holmes.*

— *Same;* [also] J. F. Burrowes' Guide to practice; with dict. of musical terms. 12°. pap., 20c. *Church.*

Jousse, J., *continued.*
— — *Same;* [also] Albretschberger's Forty-six modulations; arrang. by O. B. Brown. 16°. 45c.; bds., 35c. . . . . *G. D. Russell.*
— The piano-forte made easy and the art of fingering clearly explained; with lessons. 1st Am. from 11th Lond. ed., rev. and enl. 4°. bds., $3. . *Ditson.*
Jovinian. *See* Library of good example.
Jowett, B. (*tr.*) *See* Plato, Dialogues.
Joy (The). Bliss, P. P. 75c. . . . . *Church.*
Joy House and its treasures. *See* Gerty and May books.
Joy in God. Stevenson, J. 50c. . . . . . . *Wiley.*
Joy is dangerous. Mortimer, J. 15c. . . . . *De Witt.*
Joy of the Christian soul. Lombez, A. de. 40c. *Kelly, P. & Co.*
Joy of morning. 18°. 35c. . . . . *Pres. Bd.*
Joyas de la poesia castellana. 12°. 75c. *G. R. Lockwood.*
Joyce, Jer. Introduction to the arts and sciences. 12°. (Bohn.) $1.25 . . . . *Little, B. & Co.*
— *Same.* 12°. (Bohn.) $1.40 . . . . *Scribner, W. & A.*
— *Same.* 12°. (Bohn.) $2 . . . . *Lippincott.*
— Scientific dialogues; rev. to present time by Dr. Griffith. 12°. (Bohn.) $1.75 . . . *Little, B. & Co.*
— *Same.* 12°. (Bohn.) $2 . . *Lippincott; Scribner, W. & A.*
Joyce, W: Law and pract. of injunctions. 2 v. 8°. '72. *net*, shp., $22.50 . . . . *Clarke.*
Joyful notes. Fillmore, J. H. 50c. . . . . . *Fillmore.*
Joyful songs. Murray, J. R. 35c. . . . . . *Brainard.*
Joyful sufferer: memorial of Mrs. James E—. 32°. 20c. . . . . *Pres. Bd.*
Joyful tales. [Toy-books.] 6 nos. ill. 8°. per gross, $36 . . . . (?) *McLoughlin.*
Cont.: King Donkey's doings.—Old Dame Trot.—Jingles and jokes.—Queen of hearts.—Bright thoughts.—Joyful tales.
Joynes, E: S. Practical introd. to Fr. pronunc. ('67.) 3d ed., rev. 12°. 30c. . . . . *Barnes.*
Joynson, Fs. H. Mechanic's and student's guide in designing and construction of general machine gearing. pl. 8°. $2 . . . . . . *Van Nostrand.*
— Metals used in construction: iron, steel, Bessemer metal, etc. 12°. 75c. . . . . . *Van Nostrand.*
Joys and sorrows of the ecclesiastical year. Milward, M. G. $1; $1.25; $2.50 . . . . . . *McCauley.*
Juba: Ethiop. drama. 16°. pap., 15c. . . . . *Happy.*
Jube Hawkins: Ethiop. drama. 16°. pap., 15c. *Happy.*
Jubeltöne. Yeokel, R., *and* Hoffmann, E. A. 40c.; 50c.; 75c. . . . . *Ev. Assoc.*
Jubilant voices. Baker, B. F., *and* Hodges, D. F. $1.50 . . . . *Lee & S.*
Jubilate (The). Emerson, L. O. $1.50 . . . . *Ditson.*
Jubilee (The). Bradbury, W. B. $1.50 . . . . *Ditson.*
Jubilee book: instructions on the jubilee encyclical letter of Pius IX. 32°. 10c. . . . . . *Sadlier.*
Jubilee collection of standard glees and choruses; for male voices. 56 nos. 8°. ea., pap., 6c.–10c.;— for mixed voices. 100 nos. 8°. ea., pap., 6c.–10c. . . . . *Ditson.*
Jubilee days: humorous record of the world's peace jubilee; ill. by Hoppin. 8°. '72. pap., $1.50; bds., $2 . . . . *Osgood.*
Jubilee service: order of divine worship for 7th jubilee of reformation. 12°. 30c.; pap., 20c. . . *Lippincott.*
Jubilee singers (The). Pike, G. D. $1.25 . . *Lee & S.*
Jubilee songs. Seward, T. F. 25c. . . . . . *Biglow.*
Jud Süss. *See* Hauff, W.
Judah's lion. Tonna, C. E. 90c. . . . . . . *Dodd.*
Judas, the Maccabee. Blackburn, W. M. 75c. . . *Pres. Bd.*
Judas Maccabeus. *See* Handel, G. F.
Judd, Sylvester. Margaret: tale of the real and the ideal. 16°. '70. $1.50 . . . . *Roberts.*

Judd, Sylvester, *continued.*
— *Same;* ill. by 30 outline compositions by F. O. C. Darley. imp. f°. $15; hf. mor., $20; mor., $25 . . . . *Widdleton.*
— Richard Edney, and the governor's family. 16°. $1.50 . . . . *Roberts.*
Judd family. Scotford, J. $1 . . . . . . *R. A. Beal.*
Jude (Der). Spindler, C. $1.25; $1; $1.50. *F. W. Thomas.*
Jude Cain; [also] Little Ann; [also] Escape of the dove. 18°. 30c. . . . . *Am. S. S.*
Judea capta. Tonna, C. E. 90c. . . . . . . *Dodd.*
Juden (Die). *See* Lessing, G. E.
Judge, Hu. Memoirs and journal. 12°. '41. *net*, shp., $1 . . . . *Friends Bk. Assoc.*
Judge Branard's infantry. 16°. $1.50 . . . (?) *Martien.*
Judge Justin. Abbott, J. 90c. . . . . . . *Harper.*
Judge's pets. Johnson, E. $1 . . . . . . *Hurd & H.*
Judge's sons. Kendall, E. D. $1.50 . . . . . *Lothrop.*
Judges of Israel. Adams, H. C. $1 . . *Scribner, W. & A.*
Judicial puzzles. Paget, J. $1.50 . . . . . *S. Whitney.*
Judson, *Mrs.* A. H. Life. 18°. 70c. . . . . . *Am. S. S.*
Judson, E. Z. C. ["Ned Buntline."] Beautiful nun. 8°. pap., 75c. . . . . *Peterson.*
— B'hoys of New York. 8°. pap., 75c. . . . . *Dick & F.*
— Buccaneer's daughter. 8°. pap., 25c. . . . . *Dick & F.*
— Conspirator's victim. 8°. pap., 75c. . . . . *Dick & F.*
— G'hals of New York. 8°. pap., 50c. . . . . *De Witt.*
— Jew's daughter. 8°. pap., 25c. . . . . . *Dick & F.*
— Life yarn. 8°. pap., 75c. . . . . . . *Dick & F.*
— Mysteries and miseries of New York. 2 v. in 1. 8°. pap., $1.50 . . . . *Dick & F.*
— Three years after. 8°. pap., 75c. . . . . . *Dick & F.*
— White cruiser. 8°. pap., 25c. . . . . . . *Dick & F.*
Judson, *Mrs.* Emily C. ["Fanny Forester."] Anna Bailey; or, the second commandment. 18°. 25c.; 30c. . . . . *Am. Bapt.*
—Memoir of Sarah B. Judson. 16°. 75c. . . . . *Sheldon.*
Judson, J. C. Life. ill. 18°. '53. 35c. . . . . . *Am. Tr.*
Judson, L. Carroll. Moral probe (The): 102 common sense essays on nature of men and things. 12°. '72. $1.75 . . . . *J. M. Stoddart.*
— Sages and heroes of the Am. revolution. por. 8°. $2.50 . . . . *Lee & S.*
Jug-or-not. Wright, J. McN. $1.25 . . . . . *Nat. Temp.*
Juive (La). *See* Ditson.
Jukes, And. Differences of the four Gospels. 16°. 75c. . . . . *Willard.*
Jukes, *Mrs.* M. Memoir. 18°. 75c. . . . . . *Carter.*
Jules Gerard, the lion slayer. 12°. pap., 20c. . . *Hurst.*
Julia, *St.* *See* Lives of the saints.
Julia, *Mother.* Life of J., foundress of Sisters of Notre Dame. por. 12°. '72. $1.50 . . . . . . *Cath. Pub.*
Julia. Lamb, M. J. 60c. . . . . *Lothrop.*
Julia. Sadlier, M. A. 25c. . . . . *Sadlier.*
Julia. Vahey, J. W. $1 . . . . *Pustet.*
Julia Bicknell; or, love and murder. 8°. pap., 25c. *De Witt.*
Julia changed; or, the true secret of a happy Christmas. 18°. 30c. . . . . *Am. S. S.*
Julia Chase; or, memoirs of pious children. 18°. 30c. *Am. S. S.*
Julia Howard. Bell, M. 50c. . . . . *Harper.*
Julia Mansfield. Bradbury, O. 25c. . . . . . *Dick & F.*
Julia Ried. *See* Alden, *Mrs.* I. M.
Julian, Evan. Interest tables. 12°. $1. *Appleton; Ingham.*
Julian, G: W. Speeches on political questions. por. 8°. '71. $3 . . . . *Hurd & H.*
Julian. Mitford, M. R. 15c. . . . . *French.*
Julian. Ware, W. $2 . . . . *Miller.*

Julian Home. Farrar, F. W. $1.75..*Dutton; Mason.*
Juliana. 18°. 60c........................*Cong. Pub.*
Juliana Johnson: Ethiop. drama. 16°. pap., 15c. *Happy.*
Juliana Oakley. *See* Sherwood, *Mrs.* M. M.
Juliane, *Electress Palatine.* Life. 12°. $1.25...*Carter.*
Julia's mistake; or, the fairy valley. 18°. 25c. *Scribner, W. & A.*
Julia's visit to the asylum. Wallace, S. S. T. 35c. *Pres. Bd.*
Julie and Gilbert. Sanford, D. P. 20c.; 15c...*Dutton.*
Juliet, the heiress. Hosmer, M. 80c.....*J. A. Moore.*
Julius. Alger, H., *jr.* $1.25................*Loring.*
Julius and his parrot. *See* Bertie and Amy books.
Julius Cæsar. *See* Shakespeare, W:
Julius Farley. Tuthill, L. C. $1........*Perkinpine.*
Jumbo Jum: farce. 16°. pap., 15c...........*French.*
June, Jennie (*pseud.*) *See* Croly, *Mrs.* J. C.
Junge Frau (Eine). *See* Wartenburg, K.
Junge Pilger (Der), od. die Pilgerreise nach d. Berge Zion. 18°. 80c.; $1................*Ev. Assoc.*
Junge Sänger (Der). *See* Robyn, H., *and* Berg, F.
Junge Trommelschläger (Der). Nieritz, G. 25c. *Steiger.*
Jungfrau v. Orleans. *See* Schiller, J. F. v.
Jungle boy, and other stories. 18°. 17c.; 22c. *Am. Bapt.*
Juniata ballads. Sullivan, M. D. 35c.......*Gordon.*
Junior clerk. *See* Hodder, E.
Junior college atlas. sq. imp. 8°. $1.25..*Scribner, W. & A.*
Junius. Letters; with essay, notes, fac-similes, etc. (Globe lib.) cr. 8°. '74. $1.75; hf. cf., $3.50; cf., $5.............................*Routledge.*
— *Same.* New ed., enl. with notes. 2 v. 12°. $3. *Lippincott.*
— *Same;* ed. by G. Woodfall. 8°. $2.50..*World Pub.*
— *Same;* incl. letters under other signatures; add., correspondence with Wilkes and Woodfall. Enl. ed., with anal. by Sir H. Nicolas; [ed.] by J: Wade. 2 v. 12°. (Bohn.) ea., $1.25...*Little, B. & Co.*
— — *Same.* 2 v. 12°. (Bohn.) ea., $1.40. *Scribner, W. & A.*
— — *Same.* 2 v. 12°. (Bohn.) ea., $1.50..*Lippincott.*
Junkin, D. X. Good steward: systematic beneficence an essential element of Christianity. 12°. 60c. *Pres. Bd.*
— Life of G: Junkin. por. cr. 8°. $2.50..*Lippincott.*
Junkin, G: Commentary on Epistle to the Hebrews. 12°. '73. $2...................*Smith, E. & Co.*
— On justification. 12°. $1.50...........(?)*Martien.*
— One baptism, as found in the Bible. 18°. pap., 12c. *Pres. Bd.*
— Tabernacle (The); or, the Gospel according to Moses. 12°. 85c...........................*Pres. Bd.*
— Treatise on sanctification. 12°. 80c......*Pres. Bd.*
Juno and Georgie. Abbott, J. $1.............*Dodd.*
Juno on a journey. Abbott, J. $1............*Dodd.*
Jupiter's daughters. Jenkin, C. $1.25........*Holt.*
Jurka, Antony. Americký besedník. 32°. '76. $1.25. *Geringer.*
Just like Roger: farce. 16°. pap., 15c.......*French.*
Just right; or, a little wrong. Jefferds, J. A. $1.15. *Cong. Pub.*
Justice and judgment. *See* Cupples, *Mrs.* A. J.
Justified believer. Mackenzie, W. B. 60c...*Pres. Bd.*
Justin *Martyr* [Justinus] *and* Athenagoras. Writings; tr. by M. Dods, G. Reith and B. P. Pratten. (Ante-Nicene Christ. lib.) 8°. $3. *Scribner, W. & A.*
Justin [Justinus], Nepos, Corn., *and* Eutropius. Literally tr. by J. S. Watson. 12°. (Bohn.) $1.75. *Little, B. & Co.*
— — — *Same.* 12°. (Bohn.) $2. *Lippincott; Scribner, W. & A.*
— *See also* Gardner, F., Gay, A. M., *and* Buck, A. M.

Justin Harley. Cooke, J. E. $1.75........*Claxton.*
Justina, the avenger. 12°. pap., 20c.........*Hurst.*
Justinianus, Flav. Anicius. Institutes; tr. with notes by T. Cooper. 3d ed., rev. by A. S. Garr. 8°. $6.50...........................*Baker, V. & Co.*
— *Same;* with Eng. introd., tr. and notes by T. C. Sandars. 1st Am., from 5th Lond. ed., with introd. by W. G. Hammond. 8°. '76. shp., $7.50. *Callaghan.*
Jutland series. 4 v. ill. 16°. ea., $1.50.....*Lee & S.*
Cont.: Sand hills of Jutland, by H. C. Andersen. — Yarns of an old mariner, by Mrs. M. C. Clarke. — Schoolboy days, by W. H. G. Kingston. — Great men and gallant deeds, by J. G. Edgar.
Juvenal [Juvenalis], Decimus Junius. Satires [Lat.]; with notes by T. H. S. Escott. 16°. (Weale.) 60c..*Allyn.*
— *Same;* with a comment. by J. E. B. Mayor. v. 1. cr. 8°. '72. $2.50................*Macmillan.*
— *Same;* with notes by A. J. Macleane; rev. and ed. by S. Hart. ('73.) 2d ed. 16°. '75. $1.50..*Allyn.*
— *Same;* [excl. 2d, 6th, and 9th]; ed. by G. A. Simcox. 2d ed. 12°. '73. $1.50......................*Allyn.*
— *Same;* with lit. tr. by W. Gifford; [arr.] for schools, etc., by H. Corson. roy. 12°. hf. leath., $2.25. *Desilver.*
— — Selections [Lat.]; [also] Fifth satire of Persius; with notes by T. Chase. 16°. '76. $1.25..*Eldredge.*
— *Eng.* Satires; tr. by C. Badham; with imitations of 3d and 10th satires by S. Johnson; [also] Satires by Persius; tr. by Sir W. Drummond. 18°. 75c..................................*Harper.*
— — [Satires condensed and expl.] by E. Walford. (Anc. classics for Eng. readers.) 16°. $1. *Lippincott; Little, B. & Co.*
— *and* Persius, Flaccus A. Satires [Lat.]; with notes by C. Anthon. 12°. shp., $1.50........*Harper.*
— — Satiræ expurgatæ; with notes by F. P. Leverett. 12°. hf. roan, $1.25..................*Lippincott.*
— — *Eng.* Satires; lit. tr. by Rev. D. Madan. 12°. 95c.......................*Claxton; Lippincott.*
— — *and* Sulpicia *and* Lucilius, C. Satires; lit. tr., with notes, etc., by L. Evans; with met. version of Juvenal and Persius by W. Gifford. 12°. $1.50................*Harper; Scribner, W. & A.*
— — — — — *Same.* 12°. (Bohn.) $1.75. *Little, B. & Co.*
— — — — — *Same.* 12°. (Bohn.) $2. *Lippincott; Scribner, W. & A.*
Juvenile budget opened; — reopened. Aikin, J. ea., 75c...*Harper.*
Juvenile classic ser. 4 v. 18°. $3.........*Lothrop.*
Cont.: Unexpected pleasures. — Æsop's Fables. — Sandford and Merton. — Evenings at home.
Juvenile companion. Blake, J. L. 75c......*Harper.*
Juvenile gift book; by authors of "Parents' cabinet." ill. 16°. $1.75.................*Scribner, W. & A.*
Juvenile instructions for the piano-forte; with waltzes, etc. 4°. pap., 75c...........................*Ditson.*
Juvenile libraries. 2 sets. ea., 75 v. 18°. per set, $10. *Am. S. S.*
Juvenile library. 8 v. ill. 32°. '69. hf. bd., $1..*Am. Tr.*
Juvenile library. 50 v. 18°. hf. bd., $13..*So. Meth.*
— *See also* Banvard, Jos.; — Lovechild, L.; — New.
Juvenile picture books. 1st ser. 10 v. ill. 8°. ea., 25c...*Pres. Bd.*
Cont.: Good shepherd. — My birthday present. — My mother's gift. — Sea stories. — Bible stories. — My father's gift. — Book about animals. — Book about birds. — My Christmas present. — Missionary stories.
— *Same.* 2d ser. 10 v. ill. 8°. ea., 25c....*Pres. Bd.*
Cont.: Winter stories. — Summer stories. — Holy Land. — Good boy's book. — Seaside scenes. — Good girl's book. — Book about flowers. — My teacher's gift. — Country scenes. — City scenes.
Juvenile sports and occupations. ill. 16°. pap., 10c. *U. P. James.*
Juventus mundi. *See* Gladstone, W. E.
Juvinell, *Uncle* (*pseud.*) *See* Thayer, W. M.

K., A. (*ed.*) Alexander v. Humboldt: biog. Erinnerungsblätter. 12°. '69. pap., 15c. . . . . . *Steiger.*

K., A. H. Our two lives; or, Graham and I. 16°. '73. $1.25 . . . . . . *Randolph.*

K., J. T. Legends of King Arthur and his knights of the round table. 16°. $1 . . . . . . *Routledge.*

Kabale u. Liebe. *See* Schiller, J. F. v.

Kaim, Adolph. Missa: Sancte Cæcilia. 4°. $1.25; — voice parts, 25c. . . . . . *Church.*

— Vespers. 4°. $1 . . . . . . *Church.*

Kain und Abel. 18°. 30c. . . . . . *Ev. Assoc.*

Kaines, Jos. Last words of eminent persons. cr. 8°. $2 . . . . . . *Routledge.*

Kainszeichen (Die). Hackländer, F. W. 2 v. ea., 50c. . . . . . *Morwitz.*

Kaiser Octavianus. 12°. pap., 20c. . . . . . *Radde.*

Kaisermörder (Der). 12°. pap., 15c. . . . . . *Radde.*

Kalevala: selections, tr. by J. A. Porter, from a Germ. version; with introd. and analysis. ('67.) New ed. 16°. '73. $1.50 . . . . . . *Holt.*

Kalisch, Isidor. Guide for rational inquirers into the Biblical writings. 16°. $1.25 . . . . . . *Bloch.*

Kalkbrenner, F. Piano method. 4°. bds., $2.50. *Ditson.*

Kalmis, —. *See* Luthardt, C. E., Kalmis, —, *and* Bruckner, —.

Kaloolah. *See* Mayo, W. S.

Kaltschmidt, J. H. Latin-English and Eng.-Lat. lexicon. 16°. $2.50 . . . . . . *Sheldon.*

Kames, *Lord.* [H: Home.] Elements of criticism; with analysis. New ed., rev. and enl. 12°. '55. $1.75 . . . . . . *Barnes.*

— *Same;* ed. by Ab. Mills. cr. 8°. $1.75 . . . *Sheldon.*

Kanarienvogel (Der) u. das Johanniskäferchen. *See* Schmid, C. v.

Kane, Elisha Kent. Arctic explorations. ill. 8°. *$4.50; shp., $5; hf. mor., $7.50 . . . . . . *Col. Bk.*

— Physical obs. in the Arctic seas. 4°. '60. pap., $4; — in 4 pts. 4°. '59–'60. pap. . . . *Smith. Inst.*

Cont.: Astronomical obs., $1. — Magnetic obs., $1. — Meteorological obs., $1.25. — Tidal obs., $1.50.

Kane, Rob. Elements of chemistry, with applic. to medicine, pharmacy and the arts. Am. ed., enl. by J. W. Draper. 8°. $2; shp., $2.50 . . *Harper.*

Kangaroo hunters. *See* Bowman, A.

Kansas. General statutes; rev. by J. M. Price, S. A. Riggs and Jas. McCahon; with notes, ref., index, etc. 8°. '68 . . . . . . *State.*

— Supreme Court reports, v. 1–15 (1862–'75). 8° . . *State.*

Cont.: 1–5 ('62–'70), by E. N. Banks. — 6–15 ('70–'75), by W. C. Webb.

— — Digest. *See* Dassler, C. F. W.

Kansas geological survey. Report of a geol. survey of Miami Co., Kan.; by G. C. Swallow and F. Hawn. 8°. '65 . . . . . . *State.*

Kant, Im. Critique of pure reason; tr. by J. M. D. Meiklejohn. 12°. (Bohn.) $1.75 . . *Little, B. & Co.*

— — *Same.* 12°. (Bohn.) $2. *Lippincott; Scribner, W. & A.*

— Metaphysic of ethics; tr. by J. W. Semple. 3d ed., with introd. by H. Calderwood. 12°. $3. *Scribner, W. & A.*

Kapelle (Die) beim Wolfsbühl. *See* Schmid, C. v.

Kapf, S. C. Warnung e. Jugendfreundes vor d. gefährlichsten Jugendfeind, od. Belehrung üb. geheime Sünden. 18°. 25c. . . . . . *Radde.*

Kapp, F: European emigration to the U. S. 8°. '69. 25c. . . . . . *Williams.*

— Geschichte d. deutschen Einwanderung in Amerika. 1. Bd.: Die Deutschen im Staate New York. ('67.) 3d ed. 8°. '69. $1.75; pap., $1.20. *Steiger.*

Kappe, E. Kleine Weltgeschichte. 12°. 50c. . . *Ludwig.*

Kappes, J. H. First steps on the piano. 4°. pap., 75c. *Brainard.*

Karaman, the bandit chief. Reynolds, G. W. M. 50c. *De Witt.*

Kardec, Allan. Experimental spiritism — book on mediums; or, guide for mediums and invocators; tr. by E. A. Wood. ('73.) 2d ed. 12°. '75. $1.50. *Colby.*

— Spirit's book; tr. by A. Blackwell. por. 12°. $1.25. *Colby.*

Karen. Mason, F. 35c. . . . . . *Mason.*

Karl Keigler; or, the fortunes of a foundling. ill. 16°. 80c. . . . . . *Lee & S.*

Karr, J. B. A. Tour around my garden. ill. sm. cr. 8°. $3.75 . . . . . . *Scribner, W. & A.*

Karslake, W. H. Theory of prayer. 18°. '73. 50c. *Pott.*

Karthäuserkloster. Schmid, C. v. 30c.; 10c. *Benziger.*

Kasem, the miser; and other stories. 18°. 50c. . . *O'Shea.*

Kasey, J. W. Young man's guide to true greatness. 12°. '58. $1.25 . . . . . . *Wilstach.*

Kästner, C. A. Auszug a. d. Choralbuch d Evang. Brüder; mit Zwischenspielen. obl. 8°. '61. bds., $1.65 . . . . . . *Clauder.*

Kata Phusin (*pseud.*) *See* Ruskin, J:

Kätchen v. Heilbronn. 12°. pap., 15c. . . . . . *Radde.*

Kate, *Cousin* (*pseud.*) *See* Bell, C. D.

Kate and Charlie; or, Thanksgiving day. 18°. 18c. *Am. S. S.*

Kate and Effie. Pinchard, M. D. 75c. . . . . . *Dutton.*

Kate and her brother; or, the young orphans. ('69.) New ed. ill. 16°. '74. 75c. . . . . . *Hoyt.*

Kate and her cousins. *See* Ellerslie House lib.

Kate Aubrey's birthday. ill. 24°. 25c. . . . . *Perkinpine.*

Kate Aylesford. Peterson, C. J. $1.75; $1.50 . . *Peterson.*

Kate Beaumont. De Forest, J. W. $1.25; 75c. . . *Estes.*

Kate Carlton. *See* Wise, D.

Kate Clarendon. Bennett, E. $1.75; $1.50 . . *Peterson.*

Kate Coventry. Melville, J. G. Whyte. 38c. . . *Littell & G.*

Kate Darley. *See* Baker, S.

Kate Elmore. Robbins, S. S. $1.15 . . . . . . *Hoyt.*

Kate Jameson. Cragin, M. A. $1.25 . . . . . *Cong. Pub.*

Kate Kemp. Hall, A. M. $1 . . . . . . *Perkinpine.*

Kate Kennedy. Newby, C. J. 50c. . . . . . *Peterson.*

Kate Kilborn. 18°. 75c. . . . . . *Carter.*

Kate Lovell's school days. 18°. 35c. . . . . . *Nelson.*

— *See also* Uncle Barnaby's budget.

Kate O'Donoghue. Lever, C. $2; 75c. . . . . *Peterson.*

Kate Parker. Wilkins, S. F. $1.50 . . . . . . *Cong. Pub.*

Kate Penrose. Hubback, J. 25c. . . . . . *De Witt*

Kate Stanley. Eldridge, A. 65c. . . . . . *Pres. Bd*

Kate Vaugh. Day, C. H. 15c. . . . . . *Hunter.*

Kate Walsingham. Pickering, E. 50c. . . . . . *Peterson.*

Kate Weston. De Witt, J. $1.50 . . . . . . *De Witt.*

Kate Woodman. Dodge, A. A. 80c. . . . *Bost. Am. Tr.*

Katerfelto. *See* Melville, G. J. W.

Kate's new home. *See* Little Katie's little lib.

Katharine and Petruchio: burlesque. 16°. pap., 15c. *Happy.*

Katharine and Petruchio: comedy. Garrick, D. 15c. *French.*

Katharine Ashton. *See* Sewell, E. M.

Katharine Walton. Simms, W. G. $1.75; 75c. *Widdleton.*

Katharine's experience. Biscoe, E. L. $1.50 . . *Lothrop.*

Käthe Seymour. *See* Katie Seymour.

Katherine Earle. Trafton, A. $1.75 . . . . . . *Lee & S.*

Kathie Brande. Parr, H. $1.50 . . . . . . *Harper.*

Kathie's Aunt Ruth; — harvest days; — soldiers; — stories; — summer at Cedarwood; — three wishes. *See* Douglas, A. M.

Kathleen; by author of "Raymond's heroine." 8°. pap., 50c. . . . . *Harper.*

Kathleen mavourneen: drama. 16°. pap., 15c. . . *French.*

Katholisches Lesebuch f. d. Mittelklassen d. deutschen Schulen. 8°. hf. bd., 35c. . . . . *Vering.*

Katholisches Missionsbuch. [Redemptoristen.] 18°. 75c.; leath., $1; $1.25; $1.50. . . . . *Benziger.*

Kathrina. *See* Holland, J. G.

Katie, a clock; — a cross-bearer; — a lamb; — a servant; — a soldier; — a steward. *See* Katie Evelyn stories.

Katie and the cup of cold water. *See* Aunt Hattie's stories.

Katie and her mother. *See* Meadowside stories.

Katie Evelyn stories. 3 v. 32°. ea., 15c.; 20c. . . *Dutton.*
Cont.: Katie, a clock; Katie, a servant. — Katie, a lamb; Katie, a soldier. — Katie, a steward; Katie, a cross-bearer.

Katie Hildreth. 18°. 50c. . . . . *Cong. Pub.*

Katie Johnstone's cross. *See* M., A. M.

Katie Johnstone's lib. 5 v. 16°. '71. $5.50. *Meth. Bk. Conc.*
Cont.: Katie Johnstone's cross. — Grocer's boy. — One of the Billingses. — Emily Milman. — Cottagers of Glencarran.

Katie Lawford's victory. M., L. C. 60c. . . (?) *Martien.*

Katie Lee; or, little duties for little people. 18°. 35c. *Am. S. S.*

Katie Lee lib. 5 v. ill. 18°. $1.95. . . . . . *Am. S. S.*
Cont.: Katie Lee; or, little duties for little people. — Little light: sequel to "Katie Lee." — Nic at the tavern; or, nobody's boy. — A little leaven in a little lump. — Little nurse of Cape Cod.

Katie Seymour; or, how to make home happy. ill. 18°. '63. 45c. . . . . *Am. Tr.*

— *Same.* 18°. 75c. . . . . *Pres. Bd.*

— *Germ.* Käthe Seymour, od. wie Andere glücklich zu machen. 18°. 35c. . . . . *Ev. Assoc.*

— *Same.* Kätie Seymour. ill. 18°. '71. 35c. . . *Am. Tr.*

Katie Stewart. Oliphant, M. O. W. 25c. . . . . *Harper.*

Katie Summers. Hall, C. 2 v. $1.50. . . . . . *Nelson.*

Katie's secret; or, the boys and girls of Otter Creek. 18°. 90c. . . . . *Cong. Pub.*

Katie's work. Marshall, E. 50c. . . . . *Carter.*

— *See also* My holiday books.

Katsch, A. E. Under the stork's nest; tr. by E. R. Steinestel. 12°. $1.25 . . . . *Lippincott.*

Katte, W. Plan for erecting superstructure of Illinois and St. Louis bridge. 8°. pap., 60c. *Am. Soc. of C. E.*

Katty O'Sheal. Pilgrim, J. 15c. . . . . *French.*

Katy, brief sketch of a gentle lamb. 18°. 30c. *Whittaker.*

Katy Hunter's home. Livingstone, C. M. 75c. *Lothrop.*

Katy's Christmas. *See* Johnson, V. W.

Kaub, —. *See* Audin, J. M. V., *and* Kaub, —.

Kaufmann, Thdr. American painting book. col. ill. 4°. '71. $5. . . . . *Prang.*

Kaufmann v. Venedig. *See* Shakespeare, W.

Kaulbach, W: v. (*ill.*) Female characters of Goethe: eng. with text by G. H. Lewes. f°. $36; mor., $50; proofs, $250; artist's proofs, $500. . *Stroefer.*

— *Same:* photos. with text by Lewes. large 8°. $18. — sm. 4°. mor., $12; — without text. sm. 4°. mor., $8 . . . . *Stroefer.*

— *Same.* Goethe's Frauengestalten: engrav. with [Germ.] text by F. Spielhagen. f°. $36; mor., $60. — 8°. mor., $18. — sm. 4°. mor., $12. *Stroefer.*

— *See also* Goethe, J. W. v., Hermann and Dorothea; Reynard, the fox; — Schiller gallery.

Kautz, A: V. The company clerk: how to keep the records of a company, troop, or battery, in the U. S. army. 12th ed. 12°. '63. $1.25. *Claxton; Lippincott.*

— Customs of service for non-commissioned officers and soldiers, as practised in the U. S. army. 18°. '64. $1.25 . . . . *Claxton; Lippincott.*

Kavanagh, Jla. [Novels.] 13 v. . . . . *Appleton.*
Cont.: Bessie. — Silvia, *ea.*, 8°, pap., 75c. — Adele. — Beatrice. — Daisy Burns. — Grace Lee. — John Dorrien. — Madeline. — Nathalie. — Queen Mab. — Rachel Grey. — Seven years, etc. — Sybil's second love, *ea.*, 12°, $1.25.

— Dora. ill. 8°. $1.50; pap., $1. . . . . *Appleton.*

— Women of Christianity, exemplary for piety and charity. 12°. $1. . . . . *Appleton.*

Kavanagh. Longfellow, H. W. $1.25 . . . . . *Osgood.*

Kavanaugh, H. H. Semi-centennial sermon. 12°. '74. pap., 15c. . . . . *So. Meth.*

Kavanaugh, *Mrs.* Russell. Original dramas. 16°. '67. 90c. . . . . *Morton.*

Kay, Jos. Social condition and education of the people in England. 12°. $1.50. . . . . *Harper.*

Kay, W. Commentary on Isaiah. *See* Cook, F. C., Bible comment.

Kaye, J: W: Lives of [East] Indian officers; illustrative of history of civil and military services of India. 2 v. 8°. $12. — New [chp.] ed. 3 v. cr. 8°. $7.50. . . . . *Routledge.*

Kaye, W: Essays of an optimist. 16°. $1.50. *Lippincott.*

Kay's infant and primary school reader and definer. 3 v. ill. 18°. '40–'42. . . . . *C. H. Davis.*
Cont.: 1. In words of two and three letters, 25c. — 2. In words of one syllable, 30c. — 3. In words of one and two syllables, 37c.

Keach, O. W., *and* Burditt, B. A. Modern school for the drum. obl. 8°. '61. pap., 75c. . . *Ditson.*

— — *and* Cassidy, J. Army drum and fife book. obl. 8°. '61. pap., 75c. . . . . *Ditson.*

Keam, P: *and* Mickleborough, J. Handbook of map drawing. 4°. pap., 80c. . . . . *Butler.*

Keary, Annie. Castle Daly. [Fiction.] 12°. $1.50; pap., $1; — (Intern. ed.), $1.25 . . . . *Porter.*

— Clemency Franklyn. [Fiction.] 12°. $1.25. *Macmillan.*

— Janet's home. [Fiction.] 12°. $1.25. . *Macmillan.*

— Nations around. cr. 8°. '70. $1.75. . . . *Macmillan.*

— Oldbury. [Fiction.] 12°. $1.50; pap., $1; — (Intern. ed.), $1.25. . . . . *Porter.*

— *Same.* cr. 8°. $1.75. . . . . *Macmillan.*

— *and* E. Heroes of Asgard: tales from Scandinavian mythol. 2d ed. ill. fp. 8°. '70. $1.50. . *Macmillan.*

— — Little Wanderlin, and other fairy tales. 18°. '64. 75c. . . . . *Macmillan.*

Keary, E. *See* Keary, A. *and* E.

Keary, Ma. Hetty; or, fresh water cresses. 16°. 50c. *Scribner, W. & A.*

— Phillis Phil; or, alone in the world. ill. 16°. $1. *Scribner, W. & A.*

— Sam; or, a good name. 16°. 50c. . . *Scribner, W. & A.*

Keating, *Miss* E. H. [Plays.] 10 v. 16°. ea., pap., 15c. . . . . *French.*
Cont.: Aladdin: burlesque. — Ali Baba: extravaganza. — Beauty and the beast: extravaganza. — Blue Beard: fairy play. — Cinderella: fairy play. — Little Red Riding Hood: fairy play. — Puss in boots: fairy play. — Sleeping beauty: extravaganza. — White cat: fairy play. — Yellow dwarf: fairy play.

— Charade dramas for the drawing room. 2 pts. 16°. ea., pap., 40c. . . . . *French.*

— Dramas for boys. 16°. pap., 40c. . . . . *French.*

— Plays for the parlor. 2 pts. 16°. ea., pap., 40c. *French.*

Keating, G. History of Ireland; ed. by J. O'Mahony. 8°. $4. . . . . *Strong.*

Keats, J: Poems; with life by J. R. Lowell. por. 18°. $1. . . . . *Osgood.*

— Poetical works. por. and ill. 16°. $1.50. . *Lee & S.*

— *Same.* por. 12°. $2; mor., $5. . . . . *Appleton.*

— *Same.* (Chandos classics.) cr. 8°. $1; pap., 75c. *Scribner, W. & A.*

— *Same.* (Household ed.) 16°. $1.25; hf. cf., $2.50; cf., $3.75. . . . . *Miller.*

— *Same.* (Household ser.) por. and ill. 16°. $1.50; mor., $3. . . . . *Lee & S.*

Keats, J: *continued.*
— *Same.* (Scribner's pop. poets.) ill. 12°. $1.50. *Scribner, W. & A.*
— *Same;* with memoir by Lord Houghton. ill. sm. 4°. $5 .... *Routledge.*
— *Same;* with memoir by J. R. Lowell. (Blue and gold ed.) ill. 32°. $1.25; hf. cf., $2.50; cf., $3.50. — (Red line ed.) ill. sm. 4°. $3.50; hf. cf., $5; cf., $7 .... *Miller.*
— *Same;* with memoir by W. M. Rossetti. ill. 12°. hf. cf., $3; cf., $5 .... *Pott.*
— *Same;* with memoir by W. B. Scott. (Presentation ed.) ill. 12°. $1.75; $3 .... *Routledge.*
— — *See also* Coleridge, S. T.; — Howitt, W., Milman, H. H., *and* Keats, J.
— Eve of St. Agnes. ill. 12°. '75. $1.25 .... *Putnam.*
— *Same.* ill. 12°. $2.50; mor., $5 .... *Appleton.*
— Hyperion; [tr.] into Latin verse by C. Merivale. 2d ed. fp. 8°. $1.25 .... *Macmillan.*

Keble, J: Christian year (The): thoughts in verse for the Sundays and holy days throughout the year. 48°. 50c.-$2.25 .... *Rutter.*
— *Same.* 18°. $1; cf., $2.25; — with photo., mor., $6. *Lippincott.*
— *Same.* por. 16°. $1.50 .... *Lee & S.*
— *Same.* 16°. '59. $1.50; mor., $4.50. — 24°. $1.25. — 48°. 25c .... *Dutton.*
— *Same.* ill. 16°. '73. $1.50; mor., $6. — 18°. $1; $1.25. — 24°. 25c.; 50c .... *Routledge.*
— *Same.* ill. 8°. $2.50-$6. — 12°. $1.50. — 18°. 90c.; $1.50 .... *McCauley.*
— *Same.* ill. cr. 4°. $3.50; $5 .... *Cassell.*
— *Same.* ill. 4°. '73. $7; mor., $15 .... *Routledge.*
— *Same.* 12°. mor., $7. — 18°. mor., $5. — 8°. mor., $10 .... *Appleton.*
— *Same.* (Household ed.) 16°. $1.25; hf. cf., $2.50; mor., $3.75 .... *Miller.*
— *Same.* (Household ser.) ill. and por. 16°. $1.50; mor., $3 .... *Lee & S.*
— *Same.* (London ed.) 32°. 50c.-$2.50 .... *Dutton.*
— *Same.* (Presentation ed.) ill. 12°. '73. $1.75; $3. *Routledge.*
— *Same.* (Red line ed.) 16°. $1.50; mor., $3.50. *Porter.*
— *Same.* (Red line ed.) ill. 12°. '73. $2.50 .. *Routledge.*
— *Same.* (Red line ed.) ill. sm. 4°. $3.50; hf. cf., $5; mor., $7 .... *Miller.*
— — Concordance. 12°. '71. $2 .... *Pott.*
— Devotions before and after communion. 32°. '75. 50c.; mor., $2 .... *Pott.*
— Evening hymn. ill. 4°. $5 .... *Routledge.*
— Letters of spiritual counsel and guidance. 12°. '70. $2; cf., $5 .... *Pott.*
— On eucharistical adorations; with considerations suggested by a late pastoral letter (1858) on doct. of the eucharist. 16°. '67. $1.25; pap., $1 .. *Pott.*
— Sermons for the Christian year. 6 v. 8°. '75-'76. ea., $2.50 .... *Pott.*
Cont.: Advent to Christmas eve. — Christmas and Epiphany. — Holy week. — Lent to Passiontide. — Easter to Ascension day. — Ascension day to Trinity Sunday.
— Village sermons on the baptismal office. 8°. '68. $2. *Pott.*

Keddie, *Miss* Henrietta. ["Sa. Tytler."] [Works.] 7 v. cr. 8°. ea., $2 .... *Routledge.*
Cont.: Citoyenne Jacqueline: a woman's lot in the Fr. rev. — Days of yore. — Diamond rose: life of love and duty. — Girlhood and womanhood. — Heroines in obscurity: 2d ser. of Papers for thoughtful girls. — Noblesse oblige. — Papers for thoughtful girls.
— Huguenot family in the English village. 12°. $1.50. *Harper.*
— *Same.* ill. cr. 8°. $2.50 .... *Routledge.*
— Lady Bell: story of the last century. ill. 12°. $1.75. *Lippincott.*
— Modern painters and their paintings. 16°. '74. $1.50. *Roberts.*
— Musical composers and their works. 16°. '75. $2. *Roberts.*

Keddie, *Miss* Henrietta, *continued.*
— Old masters and their pictures. 16°. '74. $1.50. *Roberts.*
— Papers for thoughtful girls; with sketches of some girls' lives. ('72.) 2d ed. 16°. '76. 75c... *So. Meth.*
— *Same.* 16°. $1.25 .... *Nichols & H.*
— *and* Watson, J. L. Songstresses of Scotland. 2 v. 8°. '71. $5 .... *Routledge.*

Keddie, W: Literary and scientific anecdotes, ill. of characters, habits and conversations of men of letters and science. ill. 8°. $2.50; $3.50 .. *Routledge.*

Kedge-anchor. Brady, W. N. $3.50 .... *Appleton.*

Kedzie, A. S. Success of evil. 12°. $1.25 .. *Cong. Pub.*

Keel and saddle. Revere, J. W. $2 .... **Osgood.*

Keeler, Ralph. Vagabond adventures. 16°. $1.50. **Osgood.*

Keen, W: W. History of the Phila. School of Anatomy. 16°. '75. pap., 30c .... *Lippincott.*
— Sketch of early hist. of practical anatomy. 12°. 50c.; pap., 25c. .... *Lippincott.*

Keenan, Ste. Doctrinal catechism: enl. edition of Scheffmacher's Catechism. 16°. 50c.; 75c .... *Strong.*

Keene, Ja. B. Handbook of practical gauging; with chapter on distillation. 8°. '68. $1.25 .. *Baird.*

Keene, Luther. Sermons; with introd. by Rev. S. E. Herrick. 12°. '76. $1.25 .... (?) *Cong. Pub.*

Keene, *Mrs.* S. F. Artists' children. 16°. $1.15. *Cong. Pub.*
— Billy's Christmas tree, and chimes for childhood. ('73.) New ed. ill. 16°. '74. 75c .... *Hoyt.*
— Grace Irving's friends. 16°. $1.15 .... *Cong. Pub.*
— Grace Irving's vacation. 16°. $1.25 .... *Cong. Pub.*
— — *See also* Mossy dell ser.
— Island home. 16°. $1.25 .... *Cong. Pub.*
— — *See also* Island home lib.
— Mac Donald ser. ('70-'75.) New ed. 5 v. 16°. '75-'76. $7.50 .... *Hoyt.*
Cont.: Orient boys. — Lyle Mac Donald. — Guy's life lesson. — Led. — Viking heir.

Keene, Surrey. Sophie Krantz; or, the cottage and the castle. 18°. 90c .... (?) *Martien.*

Keener, J. C. Post-oak circuit; ed. by T. O. Summers. 18°. '57. 90c .... *So. Meth.*

Keep good company. Smiles, S. 20c ... *Meth. Bk. Conc.*

Keep a good heart. Cousin Carrie. $1 .... *Appleton.*

Keep your temper. Wooler, J. P. 15c .... *French.*

Keeper of the seals: comedietta. 16°. pap., 15c. *French.*

Keeper's travels in search of his master. 18°. '68. 45c .... *Routledge.*
— *Same.* ill. 18°. '68. 65c .... *Perkinpine.*

Keeping house and house keeping. Hale, S. J. 75c. *Harper.*

Keeping open house. McLain, M. W. $1 .... *Dutton.*

Keeping up appearances. Arthur, T. S. 75c. *Collins & Bro.*

Keepsake. 18°. 20c .... *Cong. Pub.*

Keepsake for the young. ill. sm. 4°. $1.75. *Scribner, W. & A.*

Keepsake lib. 4 v. ill. 16°. $3 .... *Nelson.*
Cont.: Grandpa's keepsakes, by Mrs. Cupples. — Stories from Jewish hist., by Mrs. C. Tucker. — Under the microscope. — Fisherman's children.

Keese, J: (*ed.*) Words of peace; or, the mourner's chaplet. [Poetry.] 24°. '74. 25c.; 40c. 16°. $1 .... *Lothrop.*

Keetels, J: Gst. Analytical and pract. French grammar. ('72.) New ed. 12°. '76. $2 .. *Clark & M.*
— — Key to the Eng. exercises. ('73.) New ed. 12°. '76. 75c .... *Clark & M.*
— Child's ill. first book in French. ('75.) New ed. 12°. '76. $1 .... *Clark & M.*
— Elementary French grammar. ('73.) New ed. 12°. '76. $1.25 .... *Clark & M.*

Keetels, J: Gst., *continued.*
— New method of learning French. 12°. hf. roan, $1.75. —Key. 12°. 60c. . . . . *Sheldon.*
— Oral French course. 12°. $1.75; — in 3 pts., ea., 75c. . . . . *Sheldon.*
— Oral method with German. ('71.) New ed., rev. and enl. 12°. '76. hf. roan, $1.75 . . . . *Holt.*
Kehoe, Ja. The expiation: drama. 12°. '71. pap., 40c. . . . . *Murphy.*
Keighley Hall; [also] Maltese cross. 18°. 50c.; 75c. *Sadlier.*
Keightley, T: Fairy mythology. 12°. (Bohn.) $1.75. *Little, B. & Co.*
— *Same.* 12°. (Bohn.) $2 . . *Lippincott; Scribner, W. & A.*
— History of Eng. to 1839; with notes, etc., by J. T. Smith. ill. 8°. $2; shp., $2.75 . . . . . *World Pub.*
— *Same.* 5 v. 18°. $3.75 . . . . *Harper.*
— Mythology of anc. Greece and Italy. 12 pl. 8°. $6; hf. cf., $8 . . . . *Appleton.*
Keil, K: F: Biblical commentaries. 7 v. 8°. ea., $3. *Scribner, W. & A.*
Cont.: Chronicles. — Daniel. — Kings. — Jeremiah, 2 v. — Introd. to Old Test., 2 v.
— *and* Delitzsch, F. J. Commentaries. 8 v. 8°. ea., $3 . . . . *Scribner, W. & A.*
Cont.: Ezra, Nehemiah and Esther. — Joshua, Judges and Ruth. — Minor prophets, 2 v. — Pentateuch, 3 v. — Samuel.
Keiley, W: S. Law and practice of insolvent assignments in N. Y. State; with forms. 8°. '76. shp., $2 . . . . (?) *Banks.*
Keim, De Benneville Randolph. San Domingo: pen pictures and leaves of travel. 12°. '70. $1.50 . . *Claxton.*
— Sheridan's troopers on the borders: a winter campaign on the plains. ill. 12°. '70. $1.75 . . *Claxton.*
— Washington guide. maps. 12°. $1 . . . . . *Hopkins.*
Kein Hüsung. Reuter, F. $1; 75c. . . . . *Steiger.*
Keith, Alex. Demonstration of truth of the Christian religion. ill. 12°. $1.50 . . . . *Harper.*
— Evidence of the truth of the Christian religion. ill. 12°. $1.10 . . . . *Pres. Bd.*
— *Same.* 12°. $1.50 . . . . *Harper.*
— Evidences of prophecy. 18°. '33. 25c. . . . . *Am. Tr.*
— *Germ.* Erfüllung des proph. Schriftwortes. ill. 18°. '46. 50c. . . . . *Am. Tr.*
— Harmony of prophecy; or, Scriptural ill. of the Apocalypse. 12°. $1.50 . . . . *Harper.*
— Land of Israel; according to the covenant with Abraham, with Isaac and with Jacob. 12°. $1.50. *Harper.*
Keith, T: Treatise on globes. *See* Guy, Ja., Elements of astronomy.
Kelas, C. J. Little Josie; or, try and succeed. ill. 16°. $1 . . . . *Locke.*
Kelland, P., *and* Tait, P. G. Introduction to quaternions; with examples. cr. 8°. '73. $3 . . *Macmillan.*
Keller, Fz. The Amazon and Madeira rivers: sketches and descrip. from note-book of an explorer. '68 wood-eng. f°. $7.50 . . . . *Appleton.*
— *Same.* New ed. wood eng. 8°. $5 . . . . *Lippincott.*
Kelley, D. C. Go, or die: essay on missions; ed. by T. O. Summers. 12°. '74. pap., 20c. . . *So. Meth.*
Kelley, H: S. Probate guide for Missouri. 8°. '71. shp., $5 . . . . *Gilbert.*
— Treatise for justices of the peace in Missouri. 8°. '69. shp., $7.50 . . . . *Gilbert.*
Kelley, J. F. Humors of Falconbridge. 12°. $1.75; pap., $1.50 . . . . *Peterson.*
Kelley, Ol. Hudson. Origin and progress of the Patrons of Husbandry in the U. S., 1866–'73. ill. 12°. '75. $1.50 . . . . *Wagenseller.*
Kelley, W: D. Speeches, addresses and letters on indust. and financ. questions. 8°. '72. $3 . . *Baird.*
Kellogg, E: New monetary system; rev. from "Labor and other capital," with add.; ed. by M. K. Putnam, with biog. sketch of author. 12°. (cop. '61.) '75. $1.50; pap., $1 . . . . *Baird.*
Kellogg, Elij. Elm Island stories. 6 v. ill. 16°. ea., $1.25 . . . . *Lee & S.*
Cont.: Lion Ben of Elm Island. — Charlie Bell, the waif of Elm Island. — Ark of Elm Island. — Boy farmers of Elm Island. — Young shipbuilders of Elm Island. — Hardscrabble of Elm Island.
— Forest glen ser. v. 1–3. ill. 16°. ea., $1.25 . . *Lee & S.*
Cont.: Sowed by the wind. — Wolf run. — Brought to the front.
— Norman Cline. 16°. $1.50 . . . . *Cong. Pub.*
— Pleasant Cove ser. 6 v. ill. 16°. ea., $1.25 . . *Lee & S.*
Cont.: Arthur Brown, the young captain. — Young deliverers. — Cruise of the Casco. — Child of the island glen. — John Godsoe's legacy. — Fisher boys of Pleasant Cove.
— Whispering pine ser. 6 v. ill. 16°. ea., $1.25 . . *Lee & S.*
Cont.: A stout heart. — Spark of genius. — Sophomores of Radcliffe. — Whispering pine. — Turning of the tide. — Winning his spurs.
Kellogg, H. L. College secret societies: their customs, character and efforts for their suppression. 12°. pap., 35c. . . . . *E. A. Cook.*
Kellogg, J: H. Alcoholic poison. 16°. 20c. *Sev. Day Adv.*
— Evils of fashionable dress, and how to dress healthfully. 16°. pap., 10c. . . . . *Sev. Day Adv.*
— Healthful cookery. 16°. 25c. . . . . . . *Sev. Day Adv.*
— Household manual of domestic hygiene. 16°. 75c. *Sev. Day Adv.*
— Proper diet for man. 16°. pap., 15c. . . *Sev. Day Adv.*
Kellogg, Merritt G. Hygienic family physician. 16°. $1 . . . . *Sev. Day Adv.*
Kellogg, S. W. The Livelies, and other short stories. 8°. pap., 40c. . . . . *Lippincott.*
Kelly, C. E. *See* Davis, *Mrs.* C. E. K.
Kelly, F. F. Sermons on special duties; for children. 18°. '73. 75c. . . . . *Pott.*
Kelly, *Mrs.* Fanny. My captivity among the Sioux. 12°. *$1.50 . . . . *Am. Pub.*
Kelly, J. M. *See* Georgia, Sup. Court reports.
Kelly, Ja. American catalogue of books pub. in the U. S., 1861–'66; with sup. of pamphlets, etc., on the Civil war, and app. of learned societies, etc., with their publications. 8°. '66. *net*, $4. — Same; for 1866–'71. 8°. '71. *net*, $6 . . *Publishers' Weekly.*
Kelly, Ja. Birch. Summary of hist. and law of usury. 8°. '53. $1.50 . . . . *T. & J. W. Johnson.*
— — *See also* Law lib.
Kelly, J: *vs.* Marsh, L. R., *and* Wallis, A. H. Copy [of] judgment roll on dismissal of the complaint. [In verse.] 12°. '75. pap., 50c. . . *Campbell & Co.*
Kelly, M. *See* Stoddard, R. H., Bric-a-brac ser.
Kelly, Wa. B. Collection of the proverbs of all nations. 16°. '69. $1.25 . . . . *Draper.*
Kelly, Wa. Keating. History of Russia. 2 v. 12°. (Bohn.) ea., $1.25 . . . . *Little, B. & Co.*
— *Same.* 2 v. 12°. (Bohn.) ea., $1.40. *Scribner, W. & A.*
— *Same.* 2 v. 12°. (Bohn.) ea., $1.50 . . *Lippincott.*
Kelly Nash. Baker, S. S. 45c. . . . . *Am. Tr.*
Kellys and the O'Kellys. *See* Trollope, A.
Kelt, T: Mechanic's text book, and engineer's guide. 16°. '66. 75c. . . . . *Nichols & H.*
Kelton, J. C. New manual of the bayonet. 5th ed., rev. pl. 12°. '64. $2 . . . . *Van Nostrand.*
Kemble, C: Plot and counterplot: farce. 16°. pap., 15c. . . . . *French.*
— Point of honour: comedy. 16°. pap., 15c. . . *French.*
Kemble, *Mrs.* C: Day after the wedding: interlude. 16°. pap., 15c. . . . . *French.*
Kemble, *Mrs.* Fes. Ann. Journal of a residence on a Georgia plantation. 12°. $1.50 . . . . *Harper.*
Kemble, J. P. Lodoiska: opera. 16°. pap., 15c. *French.*
Kemlo, F. Watch-repairers' handbook. ('69.) New ed. ill. 12°. '72. $1.25 . . . . *Williams.*
Kemp, E: Landscape gardening; or, how to lay out a garden. ill. 12°. $2.50 . . . . *Wiley.*

Kempis, Thomas a. *See* Thomas *a Kempis.*

Kempters, —. Mass in D; for four voices. 4°. $1.50 .... *Ditson.*

Kemptons (The). Potwin, H. K. $1 .... *Dodd.*

Kemshead, W. B. Elements of inorganic chemistry. (Element sci. ser.) ill. 16°. '74. 75c... *Putnam.*

Kendall, Amos. Autobiography; ed. by W. Stickney. por. and ill. 8°. $5 .... *Lee & S.*

Kendall, *Rev.* E. D. The last judgment, and the second coming of the Lord. ill. 12°. $1. *H. H. Carter.*

Kendall, *Mrs.* E. D. The judge's sons. ill. 16°. '70. $1.50 .... *Lothrop.*

— The Stanifords of Staniford's Folly. ill. 16°. '72. $1.50 .... *Lothrop.*

Kendall, G: Wilkins. *See* Nebel, C., War between U. S. and Mexico.

Kendall, Ja. Clarionet instruction book. obl. 8°. '51. pap., 60c. .... *Ditson.*

Kendall, J: *See* Letters on religious subjects.

Kendo, T. A. Treatise on silk and tea culture and other Asiatic industries, adapted to soil and climate of California. 16°. '70. 50c.... *Roman.*

Kendrick, Asahel Clark. Complete vocab. and notes to the 7 bks. of the Anabasis; with introd. map. 12°. $1.25 .... *Sheldon.*

— Greek Ollendorf: progressive exhibition of principles of Gk. grammar. 12°. $1.75 .... *Appleton.*

— Introduction to Gk. 12°. '59. 80c. .... *Ivison.*

— Life and letters of Mrs. Emily C. Judson. por. 12°. $1.75 .... *Sheldon.*

— (*ed.*) Our poetical favorites. 2 v. 12°. ea., $2; $2.75; mor., $5 .... *Sheldon.*

Cont.: 1st ser. Minor Eng. poems. — 2d ser. Longer Eng. poems.

— *See also* Bullions, P., *and* Kendrick, A. C.

Kenedy's juv. lib. 6 v. 18°. $2.50 .... *Kenedy.*

Cont.: Blanche. — Adelmar. — Isle of the dead. — Young captives. — Maltese cross. — Life of St. Louis.

Kenelm Chillingly. *See* Bulwer-Lytton, *Sir* E. G. E. L.

Kenilworth. *See* Scott, *Sir* W.

Kenilworth: burlesque. 16°. pap., 15c. ...... *French.*

Kenilworth: drama. Dibdin, T., *and* Bunn, A. 15c. .... *French.*

Kenly, J: R. Memoirs of a Maryland volunteer in the war with Mexico, 1846–8. 8°. $3.50 .. *Lippincott.*

Kennan, G: Tent life in Siberia, and adventures among the Koraks and other tribes in Kamtchatka and northern Asia. 5th ed. map. 12°. '70. $2. *Putnam.*

Kennard, J. Spencer. Memorial of J. H. Kennard. 12°. $1.50 .... *Am. Bapt.*

Kennaway, C: E: Consolatio; or, comfort for the afflicted. 16°. '70. $1.50 ...... *Pott; Randolph.*

Kennedy, Arch., *and* Hackwood, R. H. Tables for setting out curves for railways, canals, roads, etc., varying from a radius of five chains to three miles. 32°. '73. $1 .... *Spon.*

Kennedy, Crammond. Close communion, or open communion. 12°. 25c. .... *Freewill.*

Kennedy, Grace. Abbey of Innismoyle. 8°. pap., 25c. *Peterson.*

— Anna Ross; or, the orphan of Waterloo. 16°. 50c. *Scribner, W. & A.*

— *Same.* 18°. 50c. .... *Carter.*

— *Same.* 18°. 55c. .... *Am. S. S.*

— Decision. 18°. 35c. .... *Carter.*

— Dunallan; or, know what you judge. 12°. $1.50. *Nelson.*

— *Same.* ill. 16°. $1.75 .... *Scribner, W. & A.*

— Father Clement. 12°. 75c. 8°. pap., 50c... *Peterson.*

— *Same.* 16°. $1 .... *Carter.*

— *Same.* ill. 12°. $1.25 .... *Scribner, W. & A.*

Kennedy, Grace, *continued.*

— Grace Kennedy stories. 3 v. 12°. ea., $1.75. (?) *Martien.*

Cont.: Anna Ross; Philip Colville; Jessy Allan. — Father Clement; Profession is not principle; The decision. — Dunallan.

— Jessy Allan. 18°. 35c. .... *Carter.*

— Profession is not principle. 18°. 50c. ...... *Carter.*

Kennedy, Ja. Jock Craufurt: poem in Scottish dialect. 8°. $1 .... *Robertson.*

Kennedy, J: American polite letter-writer. 24°. 15c. *I. N. Whiting.*

Kennedy, *Rev.* J: Divine life. 12°. $1.10... *Pres. Bd.*

— Sunday school speaker. ('56.) 11th ed. 18°. '71. 60c. *Cin. Meth. Bk. Conc.; Perkinpine.*

— Work and conflict; or, the divine life in its progress: facts and histories. 12°. $1.25 ...... *Pres. Bd.*

Kennedy, J: Pendleton. [" Sol. Secondthoughts."] Works. 10 v. 12°. $20; hf. cf., $40 .. *Putnam.*

Cont.: Horse-shoe Robinson. — Rob of the bowl. — Life of William Wirt, 2 v. — Political papers. — Swallow-barn. — Quodlibet. — Occasional addresses. — Journal abroad. — Life and letters by Tuckerman.

— Memoirs of William Wirt. 2 v. 12°. $2. — 2 v. 8°. $3 .... *Lea.*

— Quodlibet, some annals thereof; with account of the origin, growth of borough, and sayings and doings of sundry of the townspeople. 12°. '60. $1.25. *Claxton; Lippincott.*

— Rob of the bowl: a legend of St. Inigoe's. 12°. '54. $1.75 .... *Claxton; Lippincott.*

Kennedy, *Mrs.* M. G. Clarence and Hallie books. 10 v. 24°. $3.25 .... *Am. Bapt.*

Cont.: Coming to Jesus. — Trusting in Jesus. — Praying to Jesus. — Learning of Jesus. — Giving to Jesus. — Working for Jesus. — Stand up for Jesus. — Living for Jesus. — Jesus marks. — Growing like Jesus.

— Library for little children. 10 v. 32°. $3.75 .. *Am. Bapt.*

Cont.: Bessie's light. — Nellie's birthday. — Treasures above. — Welcome home. — Water of life. — My mother's Bible. — Only five cents. — Unto me. — It won't hurt you. — Ned Morton's sled.

Kennedy, Pat. Irish anecdotes. 16°. '72. bds., 50c. *Routledge.*

— *See also* Hood, T., Kennedy, P., *and* Mair, J. A.; — Legends and fairy tales of Ireland.

Kennedy, W. S. Messianic prophecy and life of Christ. 12°. '60. $1.25 .... *Draper.*

Kenneth. Reynolds, G. W. M. $1.75; $1... *Peterson.*

Kenneth. Yonge, C. M. $1 .... *Appleton.*

Kenneth, my king. Brock, S. A. $1.75 .... *Carleton.*

Kenneth and Hugh. *See* Bell, C. D.

Kenneth Forbes; or, fourteen ways of studying the Bible. 18°. 75c. .... *Am. S. S.; Pres. Bd.*

— *Same.* 18°. '66. 75c... *N. Y. Ref. Ch. Bd.; Pres. Com.*

Kenney, C: Lamb. Memoir of M. W. Balfe. ill. and por. 8°. '75. $3 .... *Routledge.*

Kenney, Ja. [Plays.] 12 v. 16°. ea., pap., 15c. *French.*

Cont.: Alcaid: opera. — Blind boy. — Ella Rosenberg. — False alarms: opera. — Fighting by proxy: burletta. — Irish ambassador: comedy. — Love, law and physic: farce. — Matrimony: comedy. — Raising the wind: farce. — Spring and autumn: comic drama. — Sweethearts and wives: comedy. — Turn out: farce.

— *and* Millingen, J. V. Illustrious stranger: farce. 16°. pap., 15c. .... *French.*

Kenney, W. S. Manual of chess. 18°. 50c... *Appleton.*

Kenney. *See* Taylor, G. B.

Kenny Carl's uniform. *See* Pritchard, *Miss* S. J.

Kennyington Crosse. Wilks, T. E. 15c.... *French.*

Kenny's mills; or, the earnest worker. 18°. '53. 60c. *Randolph.*

Kenrick, Fs. P: Primacy of the apostolic see vindicated. 7th ed., rev. and enl. 8°. '55. $3; $3.50 .... *Murphy.*

— *See also* Bible [Whole], *Cath.*; New Test., *Cath.*; Job, *Cath.*; Pentateuch, *Cath.*; Psalms, *Cath.*; — Catholic Church, Form of consecration.

Kenrick, P. R. Holy house of Loretto. 12°. $1.25. *Cummiskey.*
— Month of May: reflections for each day on the different titles applied to the mother of God in the litany of Loretto. 18°. 55c.....*Cummiskey.*
Kensington gardens. Brough, R. B. 15c. ..*French.*
Kent, C: Charles Dickens as a reader. ill. 12°. $1.50. *Lippincott.*
Kent, Ja. Commentaries on Am. law; ed. and rev. by O. W. Holmes, jr. 12th ed. 4 v. 8°. '73. shp., $20..........................*Little, B. & Co.*
— *Same;* for colleges and academies. v. 1. 8°. '73. shp., $5.....................*Little, B. & Co.*
— *Same;* reduced to questions and answers by A. Kinne. 4th ed., rev. and enl. by J. C. Devereux. 8°. shp., $3.50.................*Baker, V. & Co.*
— — *See also* Dickson, F. S.
Kent, S. H. Gath to the Cedars: experiences of travel in the Holy Land and Palmyra. ill. 12°. $2.50. *Scribner, W. & A.*
Kentish, T: Treatise on a box of instruments and the slide rule; with theory of trigonom. and logarithms, etc. ('52.) 4th ed. 12°. '72. $1.25..*Baird.*
Kentuck, the sport. Aiken, A. W. 20c......*Beadle.*
Kentucky. Codes of practice in civil and criminal cases, with amendments and notes of decisions; by H. Myers. 8°. '67. shp., $7.50.....*Clarke.*
— Court of Appeals reports, 1785–1817. 7 v. 8°. *net*, shp.....................................*Clarke.*
Cont.: 1785–1801, by J. Hughes, $6.50.—1801–'05 (Pr. decisions), by A. Sneed, $5.50.—1805–'08, by M. D. Hardin, $6.—1808–'17, by G. M. Bibb, 4 v., $10.
— *Same.* 1817–'40. 19 v. 8°..................*State.*
Cont.: 1817–'21, by A. K. Marshall, 3 v. in 2.—1822–'24, by W. Littell, 5 v.—1824–'28, by T. B. Monroe, 7 v. in 3.—1829–'32, by J. J. Marshall, 7 v. in 4.—1833–'40, by J. Dana, 9 v. in 5.
— *Same.* 1840–'58; by Ben Monroe. 18 v. 8°. *net*, shp., v. 1–12, $30; v. 13–18, $30........*Clarke.*
— *Same.* 1859–'63; by J. P. Metcalfe. 4 v. 8°. v. 3, 4, ea., shp., $5.......................*Clarke.*
Note. v. 1 and 2 are o. p.
— *Same.* 1864–'66; by A. Duvall. 2 v. 8°. ea., $6.*Morton.*
— *Same.* 1868–'74; by W. P. D. Bush. 10 v. 8°. ea., $6....................................*Morton.*
— *Same:* select cases, 1795–1821; by W. Littell. 8°. '24......................................*State.*
— — Digest. *See* Monroe, B., *and* Harlan, J.; — Trimble, W. W.
— — Supplemental digest. *See* Cofer, M. H.
Kentucky geological survey. Report on geol. reconnoissance of K. in 1838; by W. W. Mather. 8°. '39......................................*State.*
— Report on geol. survey in K. in 1854–9; by D. D. Owen, R. Peter and S. S. Lyon. 4 v. 8°. '56–'61. *State.*
Kentucky tragedy. Thompson, J. J. 25c...*U. P. James.*
Kentucky's love. King, E. $1.50..........*Lee & S.*
Kenyon, Fannie. Safe home. *See* Pioneer lib.
Kenyon, Ja. B. The fallen, and other poems. 12°. '76. $1.50...........................*Curtiss & C.*
Kenyon, W: C. Elements of Eng. grammar. ('49.) New ed., rev. 12°. '71. $1...........*Darrow.*
Keon, Miles Ger. Dion and the sibyls. [Fiction.] 8°. '72. $1.50...........................*Cath. Pub.*
Keppel, H: Expedition to Borneo of [the] "Dido" for suppression of piracy; with extracts from journal of J. Brooke. 12°. $1.......*Harper.*
Kept from idols. Denison, M. A. $1.50.......*Hoyt.*
Ker, J: The day dawn and the rain, and other sermons. 12°. '75. $2..................*Carter.*
Kercheval, S. History of the valley of Virginia. ('33.) 2d ed., enl. 12°. '50. shp., $5..*J. W. Randolph.*
Kerl, Bru. Practical treatise on metallurgy; from last Germ. ed. by W. Crookes and E. Rohrig. 3 v. 8°. $30......................................*Wiley.*
— *See also* Bodemann, T., *and* Kerl, B.
Kerl, Sim. Common school [Eng.] grammar. 12°. '65. $1......................................*Ivison.*
— Comprehensive Eng. gram. 12°. '61. $1.25..*Ivison.*
— Elements of composition and rhetoric. 12°. '69. $1.25.....................................*Ivison.*
— First lessons in Eng. gram. 16°. '65. 45c...*Ivison.*
— Shorter course in Eng. gram. 12°. '70. 75c...*Ivison.*
— System of arithmetic on an original plan. 18°. hf. roan, 40c...............................*Desilver.*
Kern, G. M. Practical landscape gardening. ('55.) New ed. ill. 12°. '65. $1.50..........*Wilstach.*
Kernan, F. *See* New York, Court of Appeals reports.
Kerney, Mt. J. Catechism hist. of U. S.: a chronol. table, 1492–1873. ('50.) New ed., rev. and enl. 16°. '73. 25c..................*Kelly, P. & Co.*
— Columbian arithmetic. 12°. '52. 50c.—Key. 12°. '59. 40c......................................*Murphy.*
— Compendium of anc. and mod. hist. ('51.) 44th ed., rev. and contin. to 1867. 12°. $1.25...*Murphy.*
— First class-book of hist. 18°. '51. 60c....*Murphy.*
— Introduction to Columbian arithmetic. 12°. '51. 20c. *Murphy.*
— *See also* Murray, L., Grammar.
Kerr, J: Lessons from a shoemaker's stool. 24°. pap., 25c.......................................*Routledge.*
Kerr, Mich. C. *See* Indiana, Reports.
Kerr, Orpheus C. (*pseud.*) *See* Newell, R. H.
Kerr, Rob. Malcolm. An action at law: outline of jurisdiction of superior courts of common law. 8°. '53. $2.50.............*T. & J. W. Johnson.*
— — *See also* Law lib.
Kerr, W: Williamson. Treatise on law and practice as to receivers appointed by Court of Chancery; with Am. notes by G. T. Bispham. 2d ed. 8°. shp., $4.50...............................*Kay.*
— Treatise on the law and practice of injunctions in equity; with notes and add. from Am. cases by W. A. Herrick. 8°. '71. shp., $6..*Little, B. & Co.*
— Treatise on the law of fraud and mistake, misrepresentation, concealment, etc.; with notes to Am. cases by O. F. Bump. 8°. shp., $6..*Baker, V. & Co.*
Kersey, Jesse. Narrative of [his] early life, travels and gospel labors. [Autobiog.] 12°. *net*, shp., 50c........................*Friends Bk. Assoc.*
Keshub Chunder Sen. English visit; ed. by S. D. Collet. 12°. '71. $3...............*Routledge.*
Ketchum, W: Authentic and comprehensive hist. of Buffalo, with account of its early inhabitants and historic notices of the Iroquois Indians. 2 v. maps. 8°. '64–'65. $6............(?) *Rockwell.*
Ketteler, W. E. Freiheit, Autorität u. Kirche. 12°. 50c.....................................*Benziger.*
Kettell, T: Prentice. Southern wealth and northern profit. 8°. pap., 25c...............*Van Evrie.*
Kettle Club ser. *See* Johnson, V. W.
Kettle's birth-day party. Johnson, V. W. $1. *Lockwood, B. & Co.*
Key note. Bradbury, W. B. $1.50..........*Ditson.*
Key of heaven. [Cath. prayer book.] 48°. 25c.–$4. —32°. $1; $1.25.—24°. 50c.–$1.65..*Benziger.*
— *Same.* 24°. 38c.–$40.—18°. 75c.–$50.—48°. 38c.–$25..*Sadlier.*
— *Same.* 32°. 45c.–$2.50.—24°. 50c.–$7.50.—18°. 75c.–$6....................................*O'Shea.*
— *Same.* 24°. 50c.–$2.50................*T. Kelly.*
— *Same.* 24°. 50c.–$15......................*Strong.*
— *Same.* 24°. 75c.–$9................*Cunningham.*
— *Same.* ('67.) New ed. 24°. '76. 50c.–$6...*Kenedy.*
— *Same.* ('70.) 6th ed. ill. 18°. '75. 75c.–$8..*Kenedy.*
— *Same;* [with] Epistles and Gospels. 48°. 38c.–$5. *Sadlier.*
— — *Same.* 32°. 50c.–$25......................*Noonan.*
— — *Same.* 24°. 60c.–$18....................*Benziger.*
— — *Same.* 24°. '69. 50c.–$25.......*Kelly, P. & Co.*
— *See also* Little key; — Milner, J.; — Pocket key.

Key of life lib. 4 v. ill. 16°. '76. $3.60. ea., 90c. *Tibbals.*
Cont.: Old oak farm.—Herbert's keys.—Breaking the rules.—High and low.

Key to Christian doctrine and practice. Blunt, J. H. $1 .... *Lippincott.*

Key to composition; or, how to write a book. 12°. pap., 30c. .... *Hurst.*

Key to fortune. McCurdy, A. C. 25c. ..... *Barclay.*

Key to self-improvement and happiness. Hamilton, D. H. 10c. .... *D. H. Hamilton.*

Keyes, E. L. *See* Van Buren, W. H., *and* Keyes, E. L.

Keyes, E. R. Wesley and Swedenborg: appeal to Methodist ministers. 12°. 75c. ..... *Lippincott.*

Keyes, E. W. *See* New York, Court of Appeals reports.

Keyes, Wade. Essay on the learning of remainders. 8°. '52. pap., 75c. .... *T. & J. W. Johnson.*
— On chattels. 8°. '53. $3.50 .... *J. White.*
— On realty. 8°. '53. $2 .... *J. White.*

Keyl, E. W. G. Katechismusauslegung, aus Luthers Schriften u. d. symbolischen Büchern zusammengestellt. 4 v. 12°. '53–'68. $4 .... *Barthel.*

Keys, C: C. Class leader's manual. 18°. '51. 50c. *Meth. Bk. Conc.*

Keys, W: W. *See* Meignen, L., *and* Keys, W: W.

Keys of the creeds. 12°. $1.25 .... *Putnam.*

Keys of Poictiers. *See* Library of good example.

Keyser, C. C. F. Mehemet Ali's Oriental interpretation of dreams, and Bismarck's wheel of fortune. [In Eng. or Germ.] 8°. pap., 25c. .... *Barclay.*

Keyser, C: S. Fairmount Park and the International Exhibition at Philadelphia. ('71.) 6th ed. 12°. '75. $1; pap., 75c. .... *Claxton.*

Keyser, Ja. Leitfaden f. d. Religions Unterricht; bearb. v. Jos. Kilian. 32°. 12½c. .. *Germ. Bapt.*

Keystone collection of church music. Johnson, A. N. $1.50 .... *Claxton.*

Keystone of the Masonic arch. Scott, C. $1.50 .. *Moss.*

Kibrizli-Mehemet-Pasha, Melek-Hanum. Thirty years in the harem. 12°. $1.50 .... *Harper.*

Kick him down hill. Smith, M. M. $2.50 .. *U. S. Pub.*

Kidd, J: On adaptation of external nature to phys. condition of man. (Bridgewater treatises.) 12°. (Bohn.) $1.25 .... *Little, B. & Co.*
— *Same.* 12°. (Bohn.) $1.40 ..... *Scribner, W. & A.*
— *Same.* 12°. (Bohn.) $1.50 .... *Lippincott.*

Kidd, Rob. Elocution and vocal culture: exercises in reading and speaking, with rules, etc. 12°. '70. $1.35 .... *Wilson, H. & Co.*
— Rhetorical reader. 12°. '70. $1.25 .. *Wilson, H. & Co.*

Kidder, Dan. P. Christian pastorate: its character, responsibilities and duties. 12°. $1.75. *Cin. Meth. Bk. Conc.*
— Helps to prayer. 12°. '74. $3.50 ... *Meth. Bk. Conc.*
— Mormonism and the Mormons. 18°. '42. 60c. *Meth. Bk. Conc.*
— Questions on the New Test.; — on the Old Test. 18°. ea., per doz., $2.16 .... *Meth. Bk. Conc.*
— Treatise on homilectics. 12°. '64. $1.75. *Meth. Bk. Conc.*

Kidder, F: First New Hampshire regiment in war of the revolution. 8°. '68. $2.50 .... *Munsell.*
— History of the Boston massacre, March 5, 1770. map and pl. 8°. '70. $3 .... *Munsell.*
— Military operations in eastern Maine and Nova Scotia during the revolution; chiefly from papers of J: Allen. map. 8°. '67. $4 .... *Munsell.*

Kidder, J. L. Natural hist. of Kerguelen Island; by J. L. Kidder and others. (Bull. of Nat. Museum, no. 3.) 8°. '76. pap., 25c. .... *Smith. Inst.*
— — *See also* United States, *National Mus.*
— *and* Coues, E. Birds of Kerguelen Island. (Bull. of Nat. Museum, no. 2.) 8°. '75. pap., 25c. *Smith. Inst.*

Kiddle, H: New manual of elements of astronomy. ill. 12°. '67. $1.50 .... *Ivison.*
— Short course in astronomy and use of globes. ill. 12°. '70. 90c. .... *Ivison.*
— *and* Harrison, T: F., *and* Calkins, Norm. A. How to teach: methods for a graded course of instruction. ('73.) 6th ed. 12°. '75. $1.25 .. *Schermerhorn.*
— *and* Schem, Alex. J. (*ed.*) Cyclopædia of education. 8°. '76. $5–$10 .... *Steiger.*

Kieffer, J. M. The pearl. [S.-school music.] obl. 12°. 35c. .... *Brainard.*
— The welcome. [S.-school music.] obl. 12°. bds., 35c. .... *Brainard.*

Kiehl, Emilie M. Golden grains. [Poetry.] por. 12°. $1.50 .... *Lippincott.*

Kill the fiend. Ritchie, A. 40c. .... *West. Tr.*

Kill or cure. Dance, C. 15c. .... *French.*

Killebrew, J. B. *See* Introduction to resources of Tenn.; — Safford, J. M., *and* Killebrew, J. B.

Killen, J. M. Our companions in glory. 12°. '62. $1.75 .... *Randolph.*
— Our friends in heaven: recognition of the redeemed in glory demonstrated. 12°. 65c. ..... *Pres. Bd.*
— *Same.* 16°. $1 .... *Cin. Meth. Bk. Conc.*

Killen, W. D. Ecclesiastical hist. of Ireland. 2 v. 8°. '75. $10 .... *Macmillan.*
— Old Catholic Church: hist., doctrine, etc., of Christians, to establishment of the pope as a temporal sovereign. 8°. $5 .... *Scribner, W. & A.*

Killing the giants. *See* Maple grove stories.

Killing no murder. Hook, T. 15c. .... *French.*

Kilmahoe. Shairp, J. C. $1.50 .... *Macmillan.*

Kilmeny. Black, W. 50c. .... *Harper.*

Kilpatrick, Judson. Allatoona: drama. 16°. pap., 15c. *French.*

Kilpin, S: Wyke. Life. 18°. 20c.; 25c. .. *Am. Bapt.*

Kimball, Clb. Inquirer's lib. 7 v. 18°. $2.50 .. *Cong. Pub.*

Kimball, D: [Works.] 6 v. 18° .... *Cong. Pub.*
Cont.: Awakened sinner directed, 45c.—Child assisted in giving the heart to God, 35c.—Happy choice, 40c.—Holy Spirit resisted, 40c.—View of Christ, 40c.—Young Christian directed, 60c.

Kimball, *Miss* Ht. McEwen. Hymns. 12°. '67. $1.25. *Dutton.*
— Swallow flights of song. sq. 16°. '75. $1.25 .. *Dutton.*

Kimball, Hor. E. New method for reed organ. obl. 4°. $2.50 .... *Brainard.*

Kimball, Ja. Destruction of tea in Boston harbor. 8°. '74. 30c. .... *Essex.*
— Journal of Rev. Dan. Shute. 8°. '74. pap., 15c. *Essex.*
— Journey to the west in 1817. 8°. pap., 15c. .. *Essex.*

Kimball, Ja. W: Beloved disciple. 18°. pap., 15c. *Bost. Am. Tr.*
— Encouragements to faith. 16°. 75c. ...... *Willard.*
— Friendly words with fellow pilgrims. sm. 18°. 60c. *Willard.*
— *Same.* 18°. 75c. .... *Bost. Am. Tr.*
— Only believe. 18°. '74. 50c. .... *Am. Tr.*
— Ten helps to joy and peace in believing. 32°. 30c. *Bost. Am. Tr.*

Kimball, R: B. [Works.] 7 v. 12° ...... *Carleton.*
Cont.: Henry Powers, banker, $1.75.—Life in San Domingo, $1.50.—Romance of student life, $1.75.—Saint Leger, $1.75.—To-day, $1.75.—Undercurrents of Wall St., $1.75.—Was he successful? $1.75.

Kimpton, F. He lies like truth: farce. 16°. pap., 15c. *French.*

Kinane, C. H. Dove of the tabernacle; or, love of our Lord in the most holy sacrament. 18°. '74. 75c.; $1 .... *Haverty.*

Kind (Das). *See* Grimm, H.

Kind (Das) der Sünde. Pitawall, E. $1.50; $1 .. *Zickel.*

Kind action. *See* Edmond Darley ser.

Kind friend. *See* Prairie books (The).

Kind seaman and his young friends. 18°. 22c. .. *Am. S. S.*

Kind to a fault. Brough, W. 15c.... *De Witt; French.*
Kind words. 18°. 60c.................... *Cong. Pub.*
Kind words. [Annual.] 4°. bds., $1.50..... *Nelson.*
Kind words. *See* Newcomb, H.
Kind words awaken kind echoes. ill. 12°. $1.50.. *Nelson.*
Kind words for his young friends. Uncle William. 40c. *Pres. Bd.*
Kind words in melody. 18°. 25c........... *So. Bapt.*
Kinder der Kirche. ill. 32°. '61. 25c........ *Am. Tr.*
Kinder (Die) v. Hameln. Nieritz, G. 25c... *Steiger.*
Kinderfreude (Die). 24°. 15c............ *Ev. Assoc.*
Kindergarten (Der) in Amerika. [Fröbel's system.] 12°. '72. pap., 15c.................... *Steiger.*
Kinderlust. 2 ser. 24 v. 32°. ea., 15c.... *Ev. Assoc.*
Kindest friend. 18°. 22c.................. *Am. S. S.*
Kindness. *See* Boys and boys; — Little folks ser.
Kindness to animals. 4°. 50c.; pap., 25c.... *Nelson.*
Kindness to animals; or, the sin of cruelty exposed and rebuked. 18°. 40c............... *Am. S. S.*
Kindness wins, and other stories. 18°. 70c... *Pres. Bd.*
King, A. Good fight; or, G. D. Boardman and the Burman mission; with introd. by W. R. Williams. New ed. 16°. '75. $1.25............. *Lothrop.*
King, C: W: Handbook of engraved gems. ill. 12°. (Bohn.) $2.25 .... *Little, B. & Co.*
— *Same.* ill. 12°. (Bohn.) $2.40... *Scribner, W. & A.*
— *Same.* ill. 12°. (Bohn.) $2.50........ *Lippincott.*
— Natural hist. of gems, or decorative stones. ill. 12°. (Bohn.) $2.25 .... *Little, B. & Co.*
— *Same.* ill. 12°. (Bohn.) $2.40... *Scribner, W. & A.*
— *Same.* ill. 12°. (Bohn.) $2.50....... *Lippincott.*
— Natural hist. of precious stones and metals. ill. 12°. (Bohn.) $2.25................ *Little, B. & Co.*
— *Same.* ill. 12°. (Bohn.) $2.40... *Scribner, W. & A.*
— *Same.* ill. 12°. (Bohn.) $2.50........ *Lippincott.*
King, Clar. Mountaineering in the Sierra Nevada. New ed., enl. maps. 12°. '72. $2...... *Osgood.*
— Report of geol. exploration of 40th parallel. *See* United States, *Corps of Eng.*
King, Dan. Quackery unmasked. 12°. '58. $1.. *D. Clapp.*
King, D: On the ruling eldership of the Christian church. 18°. 60c........... *U. P. Bd. of Pub.*
— *Same.* 16°. '51. 75c. .... *Carter.*
King, Edm. Fillingham. Ten thousand wonderful things. ill. 12°. $1.50............... *Dick & F.*
— *Same.* (Globe ed.) ill. cr. 8°. $1.75; hf. cf., $3.50; cf., $5......................... *Routledge.*
King, E: French political leaders. 16°. '76. $1.50. *Putnam.*
— Great south (The); ill. from sketches by J. W. Champney: record of journeyings in 1872–3. ill. and maps. 8°. *$6–$12............. *Am. Pub.*
— Kentucky's love; or, roughing it around Paris. 12°. $1.50.................................. *Lee & S.*
— My Paris: French character sketches. 12°. $1.50. *Lee & S.*
King, G. A. *See* Allen, J., *and* King, G. A.
King, H: Clay. Digest of Tenn. decisions, 1796–1868; with notes. 4 v. 8°. '69 .... *State.*
King, Homer A. *See* King, N. H. *and* H. A.
King, J: American dispensatory. ('59.) 8th ed., rev. roy. 8°. '76. shp., $10............... *Wilstach.*
— American eclectic obstetrics. ('55.) 3d ed., rev. and enl. ill. roy. 8°. '75. shp., $6.50.. *Wilstach.*
— Causes, symptoms, diagnosis, pathology and treatment of chronic diseases. roy. 8°. '66. shp., $15 .... *Wilstach.*
— Woman: her diseases and their treatment. ('58.) 4th ed. 8°. '75. shp., $3.50.......... *Wilstach.*
King, J: Commentary on law and true construction of the federal Constitution. 8°. '71. $2.50.. *Clarke.*
King, Jonas. Bible prayers. 32°. '67. 25c.; 50c. *Am. Tr.*

King, Kath. Hugh Melton. ill. 8°. pap., 25c... *Harper.*
— Off the roll. 8°. pap., 75c.................. *Harper.*
— Our detachment. 8°. pap., 75c............ *Harper.*
— Queen of the regiment. 8°. $1.25; pap., 75c... *Estes.*
King, *Mrs.* Mar. M. [Lectures.] ('70.) 2d ed. 5 v. 12°. '76. ea., pap., 25c................. *Colby.*
Cont.: Brotherhood of man, and what follows from it. — God the father, and man the image of God. — Social evils: their causes and cure. — Spiritualism vs. diabolism. — What is spiritualism? and shall spiritualists have a creed?
— Principles of nature as disc. in develop. and structure of the universe; given inspirationally. ('65.) 2d ed. 8°. '71. $1.75.................... *Colby.*
— Real life in spirit land; given inspirationally. ('70.) 4th ed. 12°. '74. $1...................... *Colby.*
King, Ma. Memoir. 18°. 22c............. *Am. S. S.*
King, Ma. B. Allen. Looking backward; or, memories of the past. 12°. '70. $1.75........ *Randolph.*
King, N. H., *and* H. A. Bee-keeper's text-book; with index. ('64.) New ed., rev. 12°. '74. 75c.; pap. 40c.. *King.*
King, P: (*1st Baron*). Constitution of the primitive church. 12°. '41. $1........... *Meth. Bk. Conc.*
King, P: (*7th Baron*). Life and letters of J: Locke with extracts from his common-place book. 12° (Bohn.) $1.25.................. *Little, B. & Co.*
— *Same.* 12°. (Bohn.) $1.40..... *Scribner, W. & A.*
— *Same.* 12°. (Bohn.) $1.50.......... *Lippincott.*
King, Su. P. Lily. [Fiction.] 12°. $1.25.. *Harper.*
King, T. Lovers' quarrels: farce. 16°. pap., 15c. *French.*
King, T: Starr. The White Hills: their legends, landscapes and poetry. cr. 8°. $3............. *Gill.*
King, W. M. *See* Louisiana, Reports.
King, W: A. New collection of church music; with sep. organ accomp. obl. 4°. '62. $2.25.. *Ditson.*
— *See also* Grace Church collection.
King, W: R. Lessons and pract. notes on steam, steam engine, propellers, etc.; rev. by J. W. King. 19th ed. 8°. '75. $2..... *Van Nostrand.*
— Report on certain investigations, etc. *See* United States, *Corps of Eng.*
King Alfred and the cakes. *See* Brough, Rob. B.
King Arthur. Brough, W. 15c............. *French.*
King Arthur. *See* Bulwer-Lytton, *Sir* E. G. E. L.
King and cloister; or, legends of the dissolution. 16° $1; $1.50................................ *Sadlier.*
King and the commons: Cavalier and Puritan poems. 16°. $1.25............... *Scribner, W. & A.*
King and commonwealth. Cordery, B. M., *and* Phillpotts, J. S. $1.75...................... *Coates.*
King and deserter. Maddox, J. M. 15c...... *French.*
King and his servants. 18°. 30c............. *Dutton.*
King and I. Morton, J. M. 15c............ *French.*
King and rebel: drama. 16°. pap., 15c....... *French.*
King and the robber. *See* Stories of the good shepherd.
King bee's dream. Maxwell, T. $1........ *Searcy.*
King Charming. Planché, J. R. 15c......... *French.*
King Christmas: burlesque. 16°. pap, 15c... *French.*
King Cuffee: Ethiop. drama. 16°. pap., 15c... *Happy.*
King Henry IV., V., VI., VIII. *See* Shakespeare, W:
King in his beauty. Armstrong, F. C. 75c... *Randolph.*
King Jack of Haylands: tale of school life; by author of "Hope on." ill. 18°. 75c........... *Nelson.*
— *Same.* 16°. 85c............................ *Tibbals.*
— *See also* Golden secret lib.
King John. *See* Shakespeare, W:
King Jollyboy's royal story book for young folks. 4° 75c.. *Lee & S.*
King Lear. *See* Shakespeare, W:
King of the Alps. Buckstone, J. B. 15c..... *French.*
King of commons. White, J. 15c.......... *French.*

King of day. Urmy, W. S. 90c......*Meth. Bk. Conc.*
King of the earth. Kingsley, C. $1.25...*Macmillan.*
King of the Golden River. *See* Ruskin, J:
King of love; by author of "How to enter into rest." 18°. 75c............................*Willard.*
– *Same.* 12°. '74. $1....................*Routledge.*
King of the Merrows. Burnand, F. C. 15c...*French.*
King of No-land. Farjeon, B. L. 25c......*Harper.*
King of the peacocks. Planché, J. R. 15c...*French.*
King of the swans. Grimm, J. L. *and* W. C. $1..*Miller.*
King of the winds. 8°. pap., 25c...........*Dick & F.*
King O'Neill. Gore, C. G. 15c..............*French.*
King O'Toole's goose. Irwin, E. 15c........*French.*
King Pippin: sequel to "Giant land." 8°. (Lond.) 75c..............................*Am. News.*
King René's daughter. *See* Hertz, H.
King Richard II. *See* Shakespeare, W:
King Solomon's dream-book. 12°. '74. pap., 30c. *Happy.*
King Tarantula, and other stories. 18°. 40c...*Dutton.*
King Thrushbeard. Talfourd, F. 15c........*French.*
Kingdom, J: M. Fountain of beauty: extravaganza. 16°. pap., 15c.........................*French.*
– Marcoretti; or, the brigand's sacrifice: drama. 16°. pap., 15c...........................*De Witt.*
Kingdom of Christ. Whately, R. $1.50 ....*Carter.*
Kingdom of Christ on earth. Harris, S. $1.75..*Draper.*
Kingdom which shall not be destroyed. Oswald, J. $1..............................*Lippincott.*
Kinglake, Alex. W: Eothen; or, traces of travel brought home from the east. 12°. $1.50..*Mason.*
– Invasion of the Crimea. 3 v. maps and plans. 12°. ea., $2..............................*Harper.*
Kingman, Bradford. History of North Bridgewater, Mass., 1645–1866; with family registers. por., map and pl. 8°. '66. $5.............*Munsell.*
King's bell. Stoddard, R. H. $2.50 ....*Huntington.*
King's Bench reports. *See* England, Common law reports; Law reports.
King's cruisers. Jones, J. 50c............*Peterson.*
King's daughter. *See* Alden, *Mrs.* I. M.
King's daughter. Gardner, H. C. $1.25..*Meth. Bk. Conc.*
King's daughter: allegory. 18°. 75c.........*Strong.*
King's daughters. Harwood, A. 80c......*Randolph.*
King's godchild, and other tales; tr. by M. A. T. 18°. '71. 90c............................*Claxton.*
King's highway. Hewit, A. F. $1.50.....*Cath. Pub.*
King's highway. *See* James, G. P. R.
King's highway. Newton, R. $1.25.........*Carter.*
King's lily and rosebud. Diaz, A. M. $1.50..*Osgood.*
King's messenger. ill. 18°. 50c.; — in French. ill. 18°. 50c. .... *Dutton.*
King's namesake: tale of Carisbrook Castle. 12°. $1.25....................................*Pott.*
King's own. *See* Marryat, F:
King's own borderers. *See* Grant, Ja.
King's pine apple. R., E. 90c..........(?) *Martien.*
King's rival. Taylor, T., *and* Reade, C. 15c...*French.*
King's servants. *See* Smith, Hannah.
King's wager. Wilks, T. E. 15c............*French.*
Kings and apostles. *See* Hannah, T. A. T.
Kings and queens. Abbott, J. S. C. $1.75..*Harper.*
Kings of Israel; — of Judah. *See* Mortimer, *Mrs.* M.
Kingsbury, B: *jr.* Maine townsman: laws for regulation of towns, with forms and decisions, adapted to rev. statutes of Maine. ('44.) New ed. 12°. '72. shp., $2.50..............*Bailey; Dresser.*
Kingsbury, *Rev.* H. Garden prayer. 64°. '75. 15c.; 50c. ....*Am. Tr.*
Kingsbury, Howard, *and* Graley, A. A. Happy hours: song-book for schools, etc. 12°. 75c.; bds., 50c. *Taintor.*
Kingsbury, J: H. Pine grove doings: sketches. ill. 12°. $1.50.........................*Carleton.*
Kingsbury, O. A. Alfred Warriner. ill. 18°. 75c. *Am. Tr.*
— Hints for living. ill. 16°. '71. $1.25......*Lothrop.*
Kingsbury, T. Commentary on Song of Solomon. *See* Cook, F. C., Bible comment.
Kingsbury, T. L. Spiritual sacrifice and holy communion: sermons, 1867. fp. 8°. $1..*Macmillan.*
Kingsford, Jane (*pseud.*) *See* Barnard, C: F., *jr.*
Kingsley, Calv. Resurrection of the dead. 18°. 40c. *Cin. Meth. Bk. Conc.*
— Round the world: series of letters. 2 v. 16°. $2.50; $3........................*Cin. Meth. Bk. Conc.*
Kingsley, C: Alton Locke, tailor and poet: an autobiography. [Fiction.] 12°. $1.50.....*Harper.*
— *Same.* New ed., with pref. by T. Hughes. cr. 8°. '75. $1.75 ....*Macmillan.*
— At last: a Christmas in the West Indies. ill. 12°. $1.50...............................*Harper.*
— *Same.* New ed. ill. cr. 8°. '73. $2.....*Macmillan.*
— David: four sermons. 2d ed., enl. fp. 8°. '74. $1. *Macmillan.*
— Discipline, and other sermons. fp. 8°. '74. $1.25. *Macmillan.*
— Glaucus; or, the wonders of the sea shore. New ed., rev. col. ill. cr. 8°. '73. $1.75....*Macmillan.*
— Good news of God. 4th ed. fp. 8°. '74. $1.25. *Macmillan.*
— Gospel of the Pentateuch. 2d ed. fp. 8°. '64. $1.25. *Macmillan.*
— Health and education. 12°. $1.75.......*Appleton.*
— *Same.* 12°. '74. $2...................*Routledge.*
— Hereward, the wake: last of the English. [Fiction.] 2d ed. cr. 8°. $1.75. ....*Macmillan.*
— Hermits (The): their lives and works. ill. 12°. $1.75 ....*Lippincott.*
— *Same.* cr. 8°. '68. $1.75.............*Macmillan.*
— Heroes; or, Greek fairy tales for my children. New ed. col. ill. fp. 8°. '68. $1.50......*Macmillan.*
— Hypatia; or, new foes with an old face. [Fiction.] 6th ed. cr. 8°. $1.75...............*Macmillan.*
— *Same.* 12°. $1.75...................*Nichols & H.*
— King of the earth, and other sermons: 2d ser. of Sermons on national subjects. 2d ed. fp. 8°. '72. $1.25.............................*Macmillan.*
— Lectures delivered in America in 1874; ed. by Mrs. Kingsley. 12°. '75. $1.25.............*Porter.*
— Madame How and Lady Why; or, first lessons in earth lore for children. 3d ed. ill. 12°. '73. $2. *Routledge.*
— Phæthon; or, loose thoughts for loose thinkers. 12°. 25c.......... ....*McCauley.*
— *Same.* 3d ed. cr. 8°. '59. 75c........*Macmillan.*
— Plays and Puritans, and other hist. essays. por. cr. 8°. '73. $1.75....................*Macmillan.*
— Poems. fp. 8°. '75. $2...............*Macmillan.*
— Prose idylls, new and old. cr. 8°. '74. $1.75. *Macmillan.*
— Selections from writings. por. 12°. '73. $2..*Routledge.*
— Sermons for the times. 3d ed. fp. 8°. '74. $1.25. *Macmillan.*
— Sermons on national subjects. 2d ed. fp. 8°. '72. $1.25 ....*Macmillan.*
— Three lectures on the ancient régime. cr. 8°. '67. $1.75 ....*Macmillan.*
— Town and country sermons. 2d ed. fp. 8°. '68. $1.25. *Macmillan.*
— Town geology. 12°. $1.50..............*Appleton.*
— Two years ago. [Fiction.] 5th ed. cr. 8°. $1.75. *Macmillan.*
— Village sermons. 8th ed. fp. 8°. '73. $1.25..*Macmillan.*
— Water babies (The): fairy tale. 2d ed. 4°. '63. $1.50. *Burnham.*

Kingsley, C: *continued.*
— *Same.* New ed. ill. cr. 8°. '71. $1.75..*Macmillan.*
— Water of life, and other sermons. 2d ed. fp. 8°. '73. $1.25..........*Macmillan.*
— Westminster sermons. chp. ed. fp. 8°. '74. $1.50. *Macmillan.*
— Westward ho! or, the voyages and adventures of Sir Amyas Leigh. [Fiction.] 8th ed. cr. 8°. $1.75. *Macmillan.*
— Yeast: a problem. [Fiction.] 12°. $1.50. *Harper; Macmillan.*
Kingsley, G. H. *See* Herbert, G. R. C., *and* Kingsley, G. H.
Kingsley, G: New templi carmina. [Music.] obl. 8°. $1.75; bds., $1.38..........*Gordon.*
— School room choir: sel. of church melodies. 8°. '71. bds., 60c..........*Barnes.*
— Social choir. 3 v. f°. '35–'42. ea., $1.25..*Crocker.*
- Young ladies' harp: secular and sacred music with piano accomp. 4°. '47. hf. bd., $1....*Barnes.*
Kingsley, H: [Novels.] 5 v. 12°. ea., $1.75..**Osgood.*
Cont.: Austin Elliot. — Recollections of Geoffry Hamlyn. — Hillyars and Burtons. — Leighton Court. — Ravenshoe.
— *Same.* 8 v. 12°. hf. roxb., $10........*Routledge.*
Cont.: Austin Elliot. — Geoffry Hamlyn. — Leighton Court. — The Harveys. — Stretton. — Ravenshoe. — Hillyars and the Burtons. — Silcote of Silcotes.
— Boy in grey: fairy story. ill. 12°. '71. $1.50. *Routledge.*
— Harveys (The): romance. 12°. $1.50..*Lippincott.*
— Hetty. 8°. pap., 25c..........*Harper.*
— Lost child (The). ill. cr. 4°. '71. $1.50..*Macmillan.*
— Old Margaret. 12°. '75. 50c.; bds., 35c...*Donnelley.*
— Silcote of Silcotes. 8°. pap., 75c.........**Osgood.*
— Stretton. 8°. pap., 40c..........*Harper.*
— *Same.* ill. 8°. $1.25; pap., 75c..........*Estes.*
— Tales of old travel, re-narrated. 4th ed. ill. cr. 8°. $1.75..........*Macmillan.*
— Valentin: French boy's story of Sedan. ill. 16°. '74. $1.25..........*Routledge.*
Kingston, E: P. Genial showman: reminiscences of Artemus Ward. 8°. pap., 75c.........*Harper.*
Kingston, W: H. G. Adrift in a boat. ill. 16°. $1. *Scribner, W. & A.*
— *Same;* [also] Washed ashore. ill. cr. 8°. $2.50. *Scribner, W. & A.*
— Adventure lib. 3 v. ill. 8°. ea., $2.50.....*Nelson.*
Cont.: In the eastern seas. — In the wilds of Africa. — On the banks of the Amazon.
— Adventures of Dick Onslow among the redskins. 12°. '70. $1.50..........*Tilton.*
— African trader (The). 16°. $1.50......*Cong. Pub.*
— *Same.* 16°. '74. $1.50..........*H. A. Young.*
— Antony Waymouth; or, the gentlemen adventurers. 12°. $1.50..........*Tilton.*
— At the south pole; or, adventures of Richard Pengelly, mariner. ill. cr. 8°. $2..........*Cassell.*
— Charley Laurel: story of adventure by sea and land. ill. 12°. $1.50..........*Nelson.*
— *Same.* ill. 16°. '75. $1.25..........*Lothrop.*
— Count Ulrich. 18°. 50c.; 60c..........*Am. Bapt.*
— Cruise of the Frolic: a sea story. ill. 16°. *net*, $1.20. *Hamersley.*
— *Same.* 12°. $1.50..........*Tilton.*
— *Same.* ill. 12°. $1.75..........*Routledge.*
— Digby Heathcote; or, the early days of a country gentleman's son and heir. ill. 16°. $1.50. *Routledge.*
— Fisher boy (The); or, Michael Penguyne. ill. 16°. '74. $1..........*Lothrop.*
— — *See also below* Michael Penguyne.
— Fisher life. 16°. $1..........*Cong. Pub.*
— Fred Markham in Russia; or, the boy travelers in the land of the czar. ill. sm. 4°. 75c...*Harper.*
— Great African travelers; from Mungo Park to Livingstone and Stanley. ill. and map. 12°. '73. $2..........*Routledge.*
— Here, there and everywhere: boy's book of adventures. ill. 12°. '76. $1.50.........*World Pub.*

Kingston, W: H. G., *continued.*
— Heroic wife (The); or, the wanderers on the Amazon. ill. 16°. 75c..........*Pott.*
— Hurricane Hurry; or, the adventures of a naval officer afloat and on shore. ill. sm. 4°. $2.50..*Pott.*
— Kingston lib. of adventure. 5 v. ill. 16°. $2.50. *Routledge.*
Cont.: Trapper's son. — African trader. — Archibald Hughson. — Waihoura. — Mary Liddiard.
— Library of adventure. 5 v. ill. 12°. $6.25..*Lippincott.*
Cont.: Round the world. — Salt water. — Peter, the whaler. — Mark Seaworth. — Midshipman.
— Little Ben Hadden; or, do right whatever comes of it. ill. 16°. '70. $1.25..........*Lothrop.*
— Little Peter, the ship boy. ill. 16°. '74. $1..*Lothrop.*
— Log house (The). ill. 16°. '72. 75c.....*Lothrop.*
— Michael Penguyne. ill. 12°. 75c..........*Pott.*
— — *See also above* Fisher boy.
— Millicent Courtenay's diary; or, experiences of a young lady at home and abroad. ill. 12°. $1.75. *Routledge.*
— Off to sea; or, adventures of jovial Jack Junkeron on his road to fame. ill. roy. 16°. $1.50..*Cassell.*
— *Same.* ill. 4°. $1.50..........*Lee & S.*
— Paul Gerrard, the cabin boy. ill. 16°. $1.25. *Routledge.*
— Pioneer lib. 3 v. ill. 8°. ea., $2.50.......*Nelson.*
Cont.: My first voyage to southern seas — Old Jack. — Voyage round the world.
— Ralph and Dick. ill. 16°. '75. $1.......*Lothrop.*
— Ralph Clavering. 32°. 40c.......*Scribner, W. & A.*
— *Same.* 16°. '69. 40c..........*Dutton.*
— Roger Kyffyn's ward. ill. 12°. '73. $1.75..*Routledge.*
— Ronald Morton. ill. 12°. $1.75.........*Routledge.*
— Saved from the sea; or, loss of the "Vesper" and her crew in the Great Sahara. ill. cr. 8°. $1.75. *Nelson.*
— School-boy days. ill. 16°. $1.50.........*Lee & S.*
— School friends, and other tales. 16°. '73. 75c. *Routledge.*
— Shipwrecks and disasters at sea. ill. 12°. '72. $1.75. *Routledge.*
— South-sea whaler (The). ill. 12°. $1.75....*Nelson.*
— Stories of animal sagacity. ill. cr. 8°. $1.50...*Nelson.*
— Sunshine Bill. 16°. $1..........(?) *Martien.*
— Three hundred years ago; or, the martyr of Brentwood. 16°. 75c..........*Luth. Pub.*
— Three lieutenants; or, naval life in 19th cent. ill. sm. 4°. $2.50..........*Pott.*
— Trapper's son. 16°. $1.50..........*Cong. Pub.*
— *Same.* 16°. '74. $1.50..........*H. A. Young.*
— Two shipmates. ill. 16°. 50c..........*Pott.*
— Virginia. ill. 16°. '76. $1.25..........*Lothrop.*
— Washed ashore; or, the tower of Stormount Bay. sq. 12°. $1.50..........*Claxton.*
— *Same.* ill. 16°. $1..........*Scribner, W. & A.*
— — *See also above* Adrift in a boat.
— Western world (The): picturesque sketches of nature and natural hist. in No. and So. Am. ill. 8°. $2.50..........*Nelson.*
— Young whaler (The). 16°. '73. 75c.....*Lothrop.*
Kingston lib. of adventure. *See* Kingston, W. H. G.
Kington-Oliphant, T. L. Duke and the scholar, and other essays. 8°. $2..........*Macmillan.*
Kinkel, C: Forty-three scales, exercises, and solfeggios for mezzo-soprano or tenor voices. 4°. bds., $2.50..........*Peters.*
— New method for the reed organ. obl. 4°. bds., $2.50..........*Peters.*
Kinnaman, F. C. Arrah De Baugh: drama. 16°. pap., 15c..........*Ames.*
Kinne, Asa. *See* Kent, J., Commentaries.
Kinnear, D: Christian holiness; ed. by T. O. Summers. ('57.) 2d ed. 18°. '75. 40c..........*So. Meth.*
— Divine Providence; ed. by T. O. Summers. ('56.) 2d ed. 18°. '75. 50c..........*So. Meth.*
Kinney, Eliz. C. Bianca Cappello: tragedy. 16°. '73. $1.50..........*Hurd & H.*
— Poems. 16°. $1.50..........*Hurd & H.*

Kinsale family. 18°. 22c. . . . . *Am. S. S.*
Kinsey, O. P. Normal debater. 12°. '74. 75c. . . *Stevens.*
Kinsley, C: Self-instructor on lumber surveying. ('70.) 2d ed. 12°. '73. $2. . . . . *Baird.*
Kinsley, Jos. *and* Ma. Memoir. 18°. 25c. . . *Am. S. S.*
Kinzie, *Mrs.* J. H. Walter Ogilby. [Fiction.] 12°. $2. . . . . *Lippincott.*
– Wau Bun. [Fiction.] 12°. $1.75. . . . . . *Lippincott.*
Kip, Fs. M. Discourse, Sept. 12, 1866, at celebration of 150th anniv. of 1st Ref. Dutch Ch., Fishkill, N. Y. ill. 8°. pap., 75c. . . . . *N. Y. Ref. Ch. Bd.*
Kip, Leon. Dead marquise: tale of the chateau Sainte-Maure. 12°. '74. $1.50. . . . . *Putnam.*
Kip, W: Ingraham. Catacombs of Rome. 18°. $1. *Dutton.*
– Christmas holy days in Rome. 12°. '60. $1.50. *Dutton.*
– Double witness of the church. 12°. $1.50. . *McCauley.*
– Early Jesuit missions in No. Am. map. 12°. '73. $1.50. . . . . *Munsell.*
– Historical sc:nes from the old Jesuit missions. 12°. '75. $1.75. . . . . *Randolph.*
– History, object and proper observance of Lent. 11th ed. 12°. '75. $1.25. . . . . *Pott.*
– Olden time in New York. ill. roy. 8°. $3. . *Putnam.*
– Unnoticed things of Scripture. 16°. '68. $1.50. *Roman.*
Kippis, And. Cook's voyages around the world; with account of his life during the previous and intervening periods. 2 v. in 1. 16°. '71. $1.50. *Claxton; J. E. Potter.*
– *Same.* 18°. hf. roan, 90c. . . . . *Harper.*
Kirby, E. A. On the administration and value of phosphorus as a remedy for loss of nerve power, neuralgia, etc.; with formulæ for combinations with iron, quinine, etc. 2d ed. 12°. '75. 50c. *Lindsay.*
Kirby, Ma. *and* Eliz. Aunt Martha's corner cupboard; or, stories about tea, coffee, sugar, rice, honey, etc. ill. 12°. '75. $1.25. . . . . *Nelson.*
— — Beautiful birds in far-off lands: their haunts and homes. ill. 12°. $2.50. . . . . *Nelson.*
— — Bundle of sticks; or, love and hate. ill. 16°. 75c. . . . . *Routledge.*
— — Humming birds. ill. 16°. 75c. . . . . *Nelson.*
— — Sea and its wonders. ill. sm. 4°. '71. $3. . *Nelson.*
— — Stories about birds. ill. f°. *$2.50. . . . *Am. Pub.*
— — Talks about trees. ill. cr. 8°. $2.50. . . . . *Cassell.*
— — Things in the forest. ill. 18°. 75c. . . . . . *Nelson.*
— — Truth is always best; or, a fault confessed is half redressed. 18°. 35c. . . . . *Carter.*
— — *Same.* 18°. 50c. . . . . *Dutton.*
— — *Same.* ill. 18°. 75c. . . . . *Nelson.*
— — World at home: pictures and scenes from far off lands. ill. sm. 4°. '71. $3. . . . . *Nelson.*
Kirby, W: Power, wisdom and goodness of God in the creation of animals; ed. with notes by T. R. Jones. 2 v. ill. 12°. (Bohn.) ea., $1.75. *Little, B. & Co.*
– *Same.* 2 v. ill. 12°. (Bohn.) ea., $2. *Lippincott; Scribner, W. & A.*
Kirche (Die) in der Tiefe. ill. 32°. '61. 25c. . . *Am. Tr.*
Kirchen-Agende f. ev.-luth. Gemeinden, U. A. C., a. d. alten sächsischen Kirchen-Agenden; [also] Ev.-luth. Perikopenbuch. ('55.) New ed. 4°. '76. $3; $4. . . . . *Barthel.*
– Taschen-Agende. [Pocket ed. without Perikopenbuch.] 8°. 60c. . . . . *Barthel.*
Kirchengesangbuch f. ev.-luth. Gemeinden. ('65.) 12th ed. 16°. '76. 75c.–$3. . . . . *Barthel.*
– *Same.* ('47.) 45th ed. sm. 8°. '75. 85c.–$3. . *Barthel.*
– *Same.* large 8°. '72. leath., $1.10; $2.75. . *Barthel.*
Kirchhoff, C. Researches on solar spectrum, and spectra of chem. elements; tr. by H: Roscoe. 2d ed. ill. 4°. $2.50. . . . . *Macmillan.*
Kirk, —. Catholic harp. obl. 12°. 50c. . . . . *Sadlier.*
Kirk, Alfr., *and* Belfield, H. H. Model arithmetic. ('75.) New ed. 12°. '76. $1. . . . . . *Sherwood.*
— — Model element. arith. 12°. '76. 60c. . . *Sherwood.*
Kirk, E: Norris. Behold the lamb of God. 24°. 50c. *Bost. Am. Tr.*
— Revival lectures. 12°. $1.50. . . . . *Cong. Pub.*
— Songs for social and public worship. sq. 16°. '58. 75c. . . . . *Hoyt.*
Kirk, J: Mother of the Wesleys. 12°. $2. *Cin. Meth. Bk. Conc.*
Kirk, J: Foster. History of Charles the Bold. 3 v. 8°. '63–'68. $9; shp., $11.25. — (Fine pap. ed.) $10.50; hf. cf., $15. . . . . . . *Claxton; Lippincott.*
Kirkaldy, D: Results of experim. inquiry into comparative tensile strength of various kinds of wrought iron and steel. 2d ed. pl. and diagrams. 8°. $9. . . . . *Spon.*
Kirke, Edm. (*pseud.*) *See* Gilmore, J. R.
Kirker, Ja. B. *See* Chateau Lescure.
Kirkes, W: Senhouse. Manual of physiology; ed. by W. M. Baker. New Am., from 8th Lond. ed., rev. ill. roy. 12°. $3.25; leath., $3.75. . . . *Lea.*
Kirkham, S: English grammar in familiar lectures. New ed. 12°. '74. hf. bd., 70c. . . *Collins & Bro.*
— Exercises in elocution. 12°. $1.25. . . . . *Sheldon.*
Kirkham, S: *See* Fowler, O. S. *and* L. N., *and* Kirkham, S.
Kirkland, *Mrs.* Caro. Mta. ["*Mrs.* Ma. Clavers."] Garland of poetry for the young. ('63.) New ed. 2 v. in 1. 12°. '72. $2.25. . . . . . . *Scribner.*
— Patriotic eloquence. ('65.) New ed. 12°. '66. $1.75. *Scribner.*
Kirkus, W: Prayer-book churchmanship: essay on Prayer-book revision. 12°. '75. pap., 50c. *Turnbull.*
Kirkwood, Dan. Comets and meteors. 12°. $1.25. *Lippincott.*
— Meteoric astronomy. 12°. $1.50. . . . . . . *Lippincott.*
Kirkwood, Ja. P. Address to Am. Soc. of Civil Eng., Dec. 4, 1867. 8°. pap., 30c. . . . *Am. Soc. of C. E.*
— Collection of reports (condensed) and opinions of chemists [on] use of lead pipe for service pipe in distribution of water. 8°. $1.50. . . . . . *Wiley.*
— Report of filtration of river waters for supply of cities, as practised in Europe, made to Board of Water Commissioners, St. Louis. 30 pl. 4°. '69. $15. . . . . *Van Nostrand.*
Kirtland, Frazer. Cyclopædia of commercial and business anecdotes. por. and ill. 8°. *$5; shp., $6; hf. mor., $7.50. . . . . *Appleton.*
Kirtley, J. A. Design of baptism; with exegeses and quotations. 12°. $1.25. . . . . *Stevens.*
Kirton, J: W. Bunch of cherries. ill. 12°. $1.50. *Routledge.*
— *Same.* 12°. $1.75. . . . . *Nelson.*
— Buy your own cherries. 8°. pap., 10c. . . . . *Pres. Bd.*
— *Same.* 12°. pap., 20c. . . . . *Nat. Temp.*
— *Same.* 18°. '65. 25c. . . . . *Am. S. S.*
— *Same;* [also] Poor little Ellen, the drunkard's daughter. 18°. 30c. . . . . *Pres. Bd.*
— Buy your own goose. 18°. 25c. . . . . *Am. S. S.*
— Four pillars of temperance. ('69.) New ed. 18°. '73. 75c. . . . . *Nat. Temp.*
— Frank Spencer's rule of life. ('71.) New ed. 18°. '75. 50c. . . . . *Nat. Temp.*
Kirwan (*pseud.*) *See* Murray, N:
Kirwan, A. V. *See* England, Common law reports.
Kirwan, D. J. Palace and hovel; or, phases of London life. ill. and map. 8°. *$3.50; shp., $4; hf. mor., $5. . . . . *Col. Bk.*
Kirwan unmasked. Hughes, J. 12c. . . . . *Strong.*
Kiss (A) for a blow. Wright, H. C. $1.50; 60c. *Lee & S.*
Kiss (A) in the dark. Buckstone, J. B. 15c. . . *French.*
Kissing the rod. *See* Yates, Edm.

Kit, the street boy. 18°. 40c. . . . . *Whittaker.*

Kit Clayton: sequel to "Jack Rann." 8°. pap., 50c. *Peterson.*

Kit, Fan, Tot and the rest of them. Wadsworth, O. A. $1.25 . . . . *Bost. Am. Tr.*

Kitchell, H. D. Suppression of the liquor traffic. 12°. pap., 10c. . . . . *Nat. Temp.*

Kitchener, F. E. Geometrical note book. New ed. 4°. '72. pap., 75c. . . . . *Macmillan.*

Kitchiner, W: Directions for invigorating and prolonging life; or, the invalid's oracle; with improvements by T. S. Barrett. 18°. 60c. *Harper.*

Kite story; [also] Birthday festival. ill. 18°. 25c. *N. Y. Ref. Ch. Bd.*

Kitten cousins. f°. pap., 15c.; 20c.; 30c. . . *J. E. Potter.*

Kitten in the well; or, one sinner destroyeth much good. ill. 18°. '67. 40c. *N. Y. Ref. Ch. Bd.; Pres. Com.*

Kitto, J: Bible hist. of the Holy Land. maps and ill. 8°. $3.25; $3.50 . . . . *Routledge.*

— Bible illustrations: orig. readings on sacred hist., biog., geog., antiq. and theology. 4 v. 12°. '74. $7; hf. cf., $12 . . . . *Carter.*

— Biblical cyclopædia and index. 3d ed., rev. and enl. by W. L. Alexander. 3 v. maps and eng. roy. 8°. $25; shp., $27 . . . . *Lippincott.*

— Cyclopedia of Biblical literature. 2 v. maps and ill. roy. 8°. '45. hf. cf., $10 . . . . *Ivison.*

— Family Bible, with notes; with introds. to the books of the Old and New Test. by T. R. Birks. 40 pts. ill. 4°. '72. ea., *50c. . . . . *S. Walker.*

— History of Palestine. ill. 16°. $1.25 . . . *J. E. Potter.*

— Illustrated hist. of the Bible; ed. by A. Bond, assisted by C. H. Hitchcock. ill. 8°. '68. *$4.75; $5.25; $6.25 . . . . *Henry Bill.*

— Land of promise: description of Palestine, etc. ill. and maps. 12°. '51. $1.25 . . . . . *Meth. Bk. Conc.*

— Popular Biblical encyclopedia; for S.-schools. ill. and maps. 8°. '75. *$4.50; $5; $6 . . *Henry Bill.*

— Scripture lands and Biblical atlas. 12°. (Bohn.) $1.75; col. maps, $2.75 . . . . *Little, B. & Co.*

— *Same.* 12°. (Bohn.) $2; col. maps, $3. *Scribner, W. & A.*

— *Same.* 12°. (Bohn.) $2.50; col. maps, $3.50. *Lippincott.*

Kittredge, C. B. Harvestings. 16°. 75c. . . *Cong. Pub.*

Kitty, *Aunt (pseud.)* *See* McIntosh, *Miss* M. J.

Kitty. Edwards, M. B. 50c. . . . . *Harper.*

Kitty and Lulu books. *See* Mathews, J. H.

Kitty at the seaside. ill. 18°. '75. 40c. . . . . *Dodd.*

Kitty Barton. Gray, H. 60c. . . . . *Lee & S.*

Kitty books. 5 v. ill. 24°. $2 . . . *Cin. Meth. Bk. Conc.*

Kitty books. 5 v. ill. 18°. '75. $2 . . . . *Dodd.*
Cont.: Kitty's victory. — Kitty at the seaside. — Kitty's illness. — Sugar camp. — Kitty's journey.

Kitty Bourne. ill. 16°. '75. $1.25 . . . . *Dodd.*

Kitty Bright, the flower girl. ill. 18°. 50c. . . . *Nelson.*

Kitty Brown ser. *See* Phelps, *Mrs.* E. S.

Kitty Collins. ill. 24°. '70. 30c. . . . . *Lothrop.*

Kitty Dale. 18°. 35c.; 45c. . . . . *Am. Bapt.*

Kitty Dennison and her Christmas gifts; by author of "Madeline." 18°. 35c. . . . . *Pres. Bd.*

Kitty Farnham's letters. Foster, I. H. 75c. . . *J. A. Moore.*

Kitty Foote; or, the true way to peace. 18°. 60c. *Pres. Bd.*

Kitty Grafton as a medicine. *See* Sargent, L. M.

Kitty Kent's troubles. Eastman, J. A. $1.50 . . *Lothrop.*

Kitty King. Knight, H. C. 30c. . . . . *Am. Tr.*

Kitty lib. 6 v. ill. 18°. $2.40 . . . . *Hoyt.*
Cont.: Jane Thorne, by C. D. Bell. — Ned, the shepherd boy. — Leonard Dobbin. — Carrie Allison, by Mrs. C. E. K. Davis. — Willie and Charlie. — Kitty's knitting needles.

Kitty Maynard; or, "to obey is better than sacrifice." 18°. 75c. . . . . *Am. S. S.*

Kitty Swindon's text. *See* Little folk lib.

Kitty Trevylyan. *See* Charles, *Mrs.* E.

Kitty Willis; or, the naughty girl won. 18°. 45c. *Am. S. S.*

Kitty's choice. Davis, R. H. 40c. . . . . *Lippincott.*

Kitty's Christmas tree; or, the net of the flatterer. 18°. 50c. . . . . *Am. S. S.*

Kitty's class day at Harvard. Alcott, L. M. 75c.; 50c. *Loring.*

Kitty's illness. ill. 18°. '75. 40c. . . . . *Dodd.*

Kitty's journey. ill. 18°. '75. 40c. . . . . *Dodd.*

Kitty's knitting-needles. 18°. 35c. . . . . *Pres. Bd.*

— *Same.* ('61.) New ed. ill. 18°. '75. 40c. . . . *Hoyt.*

— *See also* Head and heart ser.

Kitty's pearls; [also] Robert Spencer's revenge. 32°. 20c.; 15c. . . . . *Dutton.*

Kitty's robins. Mathews, J. H. $1 . . . . *Carter.*

Kitty's scrap-book. Mathews, J. H. $1 . . . . . . *Carter.*

Kitty's tableaux. Clark, M. L. 30c. . . . . *Lothrop.*

Kitty's victory. ill. 18°. '75. 40c. . . . . *Dodd.*

Kitty's victory. 18°. 75c. . . . . *Carter.*

Kitty's visit to grandmamma. Mathews, J. H. $1. *Carter.*

Klaczko, Julian. Two chancellors: Gortchakof and Bismarck; tr. by F. P. Ward. cr. 8°. '76. $2. *Hurd & H.*

Klausenburg (Die). *See* Tieck, L.

Kleeblatt (Das). Nieritz, G. 25c. . . . . *Morwitz.*

Klein, E. *See* Handbook for the physiol. laboratory.

Klein, H: Rudiments of Germ. etymology. 8°. '75. 60c. . . . . *M. Taylor.*

Klein, K. A. Die Mutter als Erzieherin ihrer Kinder. 12°. '73. pap., 75c. *Zickel.*

Kleine Gebets-Schatz (Der). *See* Evangelisch-luth. Gebets-Schatz.

Kleine geistliche Harfe (Die) der Kinder Zions. [Hymns.] 12°. leath., $1.50 . . . . *Baer.*

Kleine illustrirte Kalender (Der) f. 1873–'76. 4 v. 12°. '72–'75. ea., pap., 10c. . . . . *Steiger.*

Kleine Lautenspielerin (Die). Schmid, C. v. 20c. *Morwitz.*

Kleine New Yorker Köchin (Die). May, A. 30c. *Steiger.*

Kleine Samariter (Der). *See* Nieritz, G.

Kleine Sprachlehre f. Volksschulen; v. e. Schwester d. Benediktiner Ordens. 12°. 35c. . . . . *Benziger.*

Kleine Thiergarten (Der). 24°. 15c. . . . . . . *Ev. Assoc.*

Kleine Ursachen. *See* Zschokke, H.

Kleinen goldenen Schlüssel (Die). 18°. 35c. . . *Ev. Assoc.*

Kleinen Gypsfigurenhändler (Die). *See* Image-boys.

Kleinert, P. On the minor prophets. *See* Lange, J. P., Commentary.

Kleines ist die Wiege des Grossen. *See* Hoffmann, F.

Klencke, P. F. H., *and* Schlesier, G. Lives of A. and W. v. Humboldt; tr. by J. Bauer. 12°. $1.50. *Harper.*

Klindworth, P. Fibel f. christliche Schulen. 8°. '73. bds., 20c. . . . . *Germ. Ev. Luth. Syn. of Iowa.*

Kling, Chr. F. On Corinthians. *See* Lange, J. P., Commentary.

Klippart, J: H. Principles and practice of land drainage. 2d ed. ill. 12°. '67. $1.75 . . . . *Clarke.*

— The wheat plant: its origin, culture, etc., with remarks on Indian corn. ill. 12°. '59. $1.75 . . . . *Wilstach.*

— *See also* Ohio geol. survey.

Klob, Jul. M. Pathological anatomy of the female sexual organs; tr. by J. Kammerer and B. F. Dawson. v. 1: Affections of the uterus. 8°. $3.50 . . . . *W. Wood.*

Kluge, E. T. A faithful and effective ministry: sermon. 8°. '70. pap., 15c. *Clauder.*

Klugheit (Die) u. Gelehrigkeit d. Thiere. ill. 12°. '69. 75c. .... *Witter.*

Kmanyo, or John Wesley, son of a noted chief of the Bassa tribe. [Biog.] 18°. 40c. ...... *Am. S.S.*

Knapp, *Mrs.* —. *See* Vincent, J. H., *and* Knapp, *Mrs.* —.

Knapp, F. Technology; or, chemistry applied to the arts and to manufactures; with Am. add. by W. Johnson. 2 v. ill. 8°. $6 .... *Lea.*

Knapp, G. Chr. Lectures on Christian theology; tr. by L. Woods, jr. 8°. '75. $3 .... *Tibbals.*

Knapp, H. Treatise on intra-ocular tumors; tr. by S. Cole. ill. 8°. $3.75 .... *W. Wood.*

Knapp, H. S. History of the Maumee valley, [since] 1680. ill. 8°. '72. $6.50 .... (?) *Locke & J.*

Knapp, J. C. Erstes deutsches systematisches Lesebuch. 16°. '66. bds., 25c. .... *Knoefel.*

Knapp, *Mrs.* Jos. F. Notes of joy; for the S.-school, etc. obl. 16°. '69. bds., 35c. .... *Biglow.*

Knapp, S: L. Female biography. ill. 12°. $1.50. *Sower.*

Knapp, W: H. Autobiography; with essays. 2d ed. 12°. $1.50 .... *Williams.*

Knapp, W: I. Chrestomathie française. 12°. hf. leath., $1.75 .... *Harper.*

— Practical grammar of the French lang.; with exercises, reading lessons and vocab. 12°. hf. leath., $1.75. *Harper.*

Knapsack full of fun; or, one thousand rations of laughter. ill. 12°. pap., 25c. .... *Dick & F.*

Knatchbull-Hugessen, E. H. [Juveniles.] 5 v. ill. cr. 8°. ea., $1.75 .... *Macmillan.*

Cont.: Crackers for Christmas. — Moonshine: fairy stories. — Queer folk: fairy stories. — Stories for my children. — Tales at tea-time: fairy stories.

— Pussy-cat mew, and other fairy stories. ill. 12°. $1.25 .... *Harper.*

— River legends; or, Father Thames and Father Rhine. ill. sm. 4°. '74. $3 .... *Routledge.*

Knatchbull-Hugessen, Louisa. History of Prince Perrypets: a fairy tale. New ed. cr. 4°. '72. $1.50 .... *Macmillan.*

Kneeland, Abner. National hymns. 18°. '34. 35c. *Mendum.*

— Review of evidences of Christianity; with extract from Wyttenbach's Opuscula on the anc. notices of the Jewish nation. 12°. $1 .... *Mendum.*

Kneeland, S. F. Law of liens: treatise upon the principles gov. acquisition and enforcement of mechanics' liens. 8°. $4.50 ..... *Campbell & Co.*

Kneeland, S: An American in Iceland. map and ill. 12°. '75. $2.50 .... *Lockwood, B. & Co.*

— Wonders of the Yosemite Valley and of California. photos. and maps. 8°. '71. $4 ...... *A. Moore.*

— *See also* Annual of scientific discovery.

Knell, A., *and* Jones, J. H. Phonic reader. 16°. '68. 27c. .... *Wilson, H. & Co.*

Knevels, *Mrs.* D. C. ["Fes. Eastwood."] Geoffrey, the Lollard. ill. 16°. '70. $1.25 .... *Dodd.*

— Marcella, the fearless Christian maiden: tale of the early church. ill. 16°. '71. $1.25 .... *Dodd.*

Knickerbacker, Jos. Foster. Vision of the arch of truth, allegory; and add. poems. sq. 12°. '76. $1.50 .... *W. H. Young.*

Knickerbocker, *jr.* (*pseud.*) The wreckmaster. ill. 16°. '70. $1.25 .... (?) *Daughaday.*

Knickerbocker, Diedrich (*pseud.*) *See* Irving, Wash.

Knife grinder's son. [Fiction.] 18°. 50c. .. *So. Bapt.*

Knight, *Dr.* —. Indian atrocities: narratives of the sufferings of Dr. Knight and J. Slover, during the rev. war. 12°. '67. pap., $1.25 ... *U. P. James.*

Knight, Cameron. Mechanician and constructor for engineers: forging, planing, lining, slotting, etc. 96 pl. 4°. '69. hf. mor., $20 .... *Spon.*

Knight, C: English cyclopædia. 12 v. 4°. *net*, $75; hf. mor., $100 .... *Scribner, W. & A.*

— Half hours with the best authors; with notices. (Household ed.) 3 v. cr. 8°. $6; hf. cf., $12; hf. mor., $15. — (Lib. ed.) 6 v. cr. 8°. $9; hf. cf., $18; hf. mor., $21 .... *Porter.*

— *Same.* 4 v. por. post 8°. $10; hf. cf., $16; cf., $25 .... *Lippincott.*

— *Same.* 4 v. ill. and por. sm. 8°. $9; hf. cf., $15; cf., $20; $25 .... *Appleton.*

— *Same.* 4 v. por. 12°. $10; hf. cf., $15; cf., $21; — in 2 v. 8°. $5 .... *Scribner, W. & A.*

— Half hours with the best letter writers and autobiographers. cr. 8°. $3 .... *Routledge.*

— History of England. 8 v. ill. 8°. $25 .... *Routledge.*

— Knowledge is power: manual of polit. economy. 12°. '75. $2 .... *Lothrop.*

— *Same.* 12°. (Bohn.) $1.75 .... *Little, B. & Co.*

— *Same.* 12°. (Bohn.) $2 .. *Lippincott; Scribner, W. & A.*

— Old England: a pictorial museum. 33 pts. ill. 4°. '72. ea., *50c. .... *S. Walker.*

— *Same.* 2 v. ill. f°. $20 .... *Routledge.*

— Once upon a time. cr. 8°. $3 .... *Routledge.*

— Passages from life of K.: [autobiog.]; rev. and abridg. 12°. '74. $2.25 .... *Putnam.*

— Popular hist. of England; with app., 1849–'67. 8 v. ill. 8°. $25–$60 .... *Estes; Lippincott.*

— Studies of Shakespeare. 8°. $3 .... *Routledge.*

— *See also* Shakespeare, W.

Knight, Cornelia. *See* Stoddard, R. H., Bric-a-brac ser.

Knight, E: H. American mechanical dict. [To form 3 v.] v. 1, 2. eng. roy. 8°. ea., *$8; shp., $9; hf. mor., $10 .... *Hurd & H.*

Knight, *Mrs.* Helen C. [Juveniles.] 10 v. ill. '53–'72 .... *Am. Tr.*

Cont.: Golden threads, 4°, $2; $2.50; hf. mor., $3. — Jane Taylor, 16°, 80c. — Jasper and Lucy, 18°, 45c. — Johnny, 18°, 40c. — Kitty King, 18°, 30c. — Lady Huntington, 12°, $1.10. — Life of Hannah Moore, 12°, $1.10. — No pains, no gains, 18°, 35c. — Old paths, 18°, 35c. — The rocket, 18°, 40c.

— Taking a stand. ('65.) New ed. ill. 18°. '70. 45c. *Hoyt.*

— True and false courage. 18°. 50c. .... *Cong. Pub.*

Knight, Ja. Improvement of health by natural means. 12°. '74. $1.50 .... *Putnam.*

— Orthopædia and its treatment. ill. 8°. '74. $4. *Putnam.*

Knight, J: Collyer. Pentateuchal narrative vindicated from the absurdities charged against it by the Bishop of Natal. 8°. (Bagster.) pap., 35c. *Wiley.*

Knight, R: Payne. Inquiry into symbolical lang. of anc. art and mythology; with introd., notes, glossary, etc. 8°. '76. $2.50 .... *Bouton.*

Knight, Rob. Plurality of worlds. cr. 8°. (Bagster.) $1.50 .... *Wiley.*

— Scriptural predestination. 8°. (Bagster.) $2.25. *Wiley.*

Knight, *Mrs.* S. G. ["Grandmother Hope."] Lottie Wilde's picnic. ill. 18°. '67. 75c. .... *Crowell.*

— — *See also* Bright eye lib.

— Pete, the cunner boy. ('62.) New ed. ill. 18°. '75. 60c. .... *Hoyt.*

— Tit bits; or, how to prepare a nice dish at a moderate expense. 12°. '64. $1 .... *Nichols & H.*

Knight, T: Honest thieves: farce. 16°. pap., 15c. *French.*

— Turnpike gate: farce. 16°. pap., 15c. ..... *French.*

Knight and peasant. ill. 16°. $1 .... (?) *Luth. Pub.*

Knight of Arva. Boucicault, D. 15c. .... *French.*

Knight of the cross: drama; by a Franciscan Brother. 12°. '76. 40c. .... (?) *O'Shea.*

Knight of Gwynne. *See* Lever, C:

Knightly heart. Coleman, J. F. $2 .... *Estes.*

Knightly soldier. Trumbull, H. C. $1.25. *Lockwood, B. & Co.*

Knights (The). *See* Aristophanes.

Knights and sea kings. Smith, S. F. $1.75..*Lothrop.*
Knights of the cross. Beazley, S., *jr.* 15c....*French.*
Knights of Pythias shown up. Small, G. G. 25c. *Collin & S.*
Knights of St. John. Almer, G. 15c.........*French.*
Knights Templar. Official proceedings of triennial conclave of the grand encampment, New Orleans, Dec., 1874. 8°. '75. $3................*Day.*
— *See also* Freemasons.
Knights' round table. Planché, J. R. 15c....*French.*
Knill, R: Farmer and family. ill. 18°. '57. 25c...*Am. Tr.*
Kniselʳ. U. Jesse. Arithmetical questions. 12°. '70. bds., 42c.....................*Cowperthwait.*
Knitze, —. Mass pastorale in G; arrang. by W. C. Peters. 4°. pap., $1.25...............*Peters.*
Knœfel, H: [Lesebücher.] 4 v. '66–'67. bds...*Knœfel.*
Cont.: Vorschule, 16°, 15c.—Zweites deutsches Lesebuch, 16°, 40c.—Drittes deutsches Leseb., 12°, 65c.—Viertes deutsches Leseb., 12°, $1.
Knollys, W. W. Handy dict. of milit. terms. 18°. 80c...............................*Spon.*
Knopfmacher-Geselle Pechmann. *See* Höchst wunderbaren Schicksale.
Knopp, Gst. Schulvorschriften. 9 nos. obl. 4°. ea., pap , 10c...........................*Benziger.*
— *Eng.* Practical system of penmanship. 9 nos. obl. 4°. ea., pap., 10c.......................*Benziger.*
Knorr, Jul. B. Guide for the piano-forte. 4°. $3..*Ditson.*
— Guide to young pianists. f°. $3........*Brainard.*
— Methodical guide for teachers of music on the piano forte; tr. by G. A. Schmidt. 12°. '54. 75c...*Ditson.*
Knorring, So. Marg. (*Baroness*) v. Peasant and his landlord; tr. by M. Howitt. [Fiction.] 12°. $1.50................................*Harper.*
Knortz, C. American Shakespeare bibliography. 12°. pap., 30c..........................*Schoenhof.*
Knots untied. McWatters, G. S. *$2.75; $3.25..*Burr.*
Knotting 'em brothers: farce. 16°. pap., 15c...*French.*
Knout (The): tale of Poland; tr. by Mrs. J. Sadlier. 16°. '59. $1............*Cunningham; Sadlier.*
Knout and the Russians. Lagny, G. de. $1.25..*Harper.*
Know your own mind. Murphy, A. 15c.....*French.*
Knowledge is power. *See* Knight, C:
Knowledge of God. *See* Breckinridge, R. J.
Knowles, D. C. A life that speaketh: biog. of Rev. G. P. Wilson. 12°. '74. $1.....*Meth. Bk. Conc.*
Knowles, *Mrs.* E. J. *See* Toy, *Miss* A. J., *and* Knowles, *Mrs.* E. J.
Knowles, J. P. *See* Rhode Island, Sup. Court reports.
Knowles, Ja. Critical pronounc. Eng. dictionary. 8°. $2.50...........................*Routledge.*
Knowles, Ja. D. Ann H. Judson: memoir. 16°. $1. *Am. Bapt.*
Knowles, Ja. Sheridan. Dramatic works. por. post 8°. $3; hf. cf., $5....................*Routledge.*
— [Plays.] 11 v. 16°. ea., pap., 15c.........*French.*
Cont.: Alfred the Great: extravaganza.—Brian Boroihme.—Bridal: tragedy.—Caius Gracchus: tragedy.—Daughter.—Hunchback.—Love.—Love chase: comedy.—Virginius: tragedy.—Wife.—William Tell: historical play.
— Fortescue. [Fiction.] 8°. pap., $1......*Harper.*
— Hunchback: drama. 12°. '76. pap., 15c...*De Witt.*
— True unto death: drama. 16°. pap., 15c...*Lee & S.*
Knowlson, J: C. Complete cow, or cattle doctor. 8°. pap., 25c..........................*Peterson.*
— Complete farrier, or horse doctor. 8°. pap., 25c. *U. P. James; Peterson.*
— Farrier and horse doctor. 18°. pap., 15c...*Dick & F.*
— *See also* Rarey, J., *and* Knowlson, J. C.
Knowlton, C: B. Gems of pen art. 8°. '72. $1.50. *Knowlton.*
— Practical lessons in penmanship. 2d ed. 8°. '72. 60c.; bds., 40c.....................*Knowlton.*

Knowlton, M. J. The foreign missionary: his field and work. 12°. $1.25..............*Am. Bapt.*
Knox, *Mrs.* Alice W. *and* C. E. The infant Sunday school; with app. by J. H. Vincent. 12°. '70. 75c..............................*Meth. Bk. Conc.*
Knox, C: E. David the king; with study on location of the Psalms in the order of David's life. maps. 12°. '75. $2........................*Randolph.*
— Love to the end: book for communion Sabbath. 12°. 60c.................................*Pres. Bd.*
— Primary year of the graduated S.-school text books. ill. 16°. '63. 20c.—2d year. '64. 20c.—3d year. '65. 25c.—4th year. '65. 30c.—5th year. '67. 35c...............................*Randolph.*
— Year with St. Paul: lessons on life. maps. 16°. '62. $1.50................................*Randolph.*
— *See also* Knox, *Mrs.* A. W. *and* C. E.
Knox, Isa Craig. Esther West. ill. imp. 16°. $2..*Cassell.*
— Little folks' hist. of Eng. ill. fp. 8°. $1....*Cassell.*
— Songs of consolation. fp. 8°. '74. $1.50..*Macmillan.*
— Young folks' hist. of Eng. ill. 16°. $1.25..*Lee & S.*
Knox, J: Life. 18°. 50c.................*Am. S. S.*
— Life and writings. *See* British reformers.
Knox, *Rev.* J: Church glorious (The): discourse on opening Ref. Prot. Dutch Ch., 4th St. and Lafayette Place, N. Y., May 9, 1839. 8°. pap., 25c. *N. Y. Ref. Ch. Bd.*
Knox, Kathleen. Fairy gifts; or, a wallet of wonders. ill. 16°. $1............................*Pott.*
Knox, Rob. The Ulster revival: an address to Sabbath scholars. 18°. 35c.................*Pres. Bd.*
Knox, T: W. Backsheesh; or, life and adventures in the Orient. ill. and por. roy. 8°. '75. *$3; leath., $3.50......................*A. D. Worthington.*
— Overland through Asia. ill. 8°. *3.50; $4; hf. mor., $5; mor., $8.......................*Am. Pub.*
— Underground; or, life below the surface. ill. 8°. $3.50; leath., $4; hf. mor., $5..................*Burr.*
Kobboltozo. Cranch, C. P. $1.25...........*Lee & S.*
Kobell, F. v. Mineralogy simplified; tr. with additions by H. Erni. 12°. '67. $2.50...........*Baird.*
— Sketches from mineral kingdom. *See* Schouw, J. F., Earth, plants and man.
Koch, J. J. Leben. 18°. '50. 30c..........*Am. Tr.*
Koch, Rosalie. Seed-time and harvest; tr. from the Germ. ill. 16°. $1.25.................*O'Shea.*
Kock, H. de. *See* Barrière, T., *and* Kock, H. de.
— *and* Witter, C. Pronouncing dict. of the Eng. and Germ. lang.; with Eng. [or Germ.] pronunciation. 2d ed. 16°. '74. ea., $1.50............*Witter.*
Koeppen, Adph. L: History of the middle ages. 2 v. 12°. $3.50..........................*Appleton.*
Kœuba. Ball, E. 15c.......................*French.*
Kohl, J. G. *See* Maine Hist. Soc.
Köhl, J: Die Taufe. 12°. '71. 75c........*Ev. Assoc.*
Köhler, Aug. Die neue Erziehung: Fröbel's pädag. Ideen u. deren Anwendg. 12°. '74. pap., 15c. *Steiger.*
Köhler, F: Dictionary of the Eng.-Germ. and Germ.-Eng. lang. 8°. '70. hf. roan, $3.50......*Holt.*
Kohlrausch, H: F: Thdr. History of Germany; tr. by J. D. Haas. 8°. '45. $2.50; hf. cf., $4.50..*Appleton.*
— Introduction to physical measurements; tr. by T. H. Waller and H. Richardson. 8°. $2.50..*Appleton.*
Koinonia. *See* Challon, J.
Kolk. *See* Schröder van der Kolk.
Kolliker, A. Anatomy of the human body; tr. by J. M. Da Costa. ill. 8°. shp., $3.50...*Lippincott.*
— Manual of human microscop. anat.; tr. by G. Busk and T. Huxley; with notes and add. by J. M. Da Costa. wood eng. 8°. shp., $3.50....*Claxton.*
Kollock, Su. Memoir. 18°. 35c...........*Am. S. S.*
Kolping, Ad. Katholisches Volksbuch. 12°. pap., 25c.................................*Benziger.*

Koner, W. *See* Guhl, E., *and* Koner, W.

Konewka, Pl. (*ill.*) Black Peter: 20 pictures in silhouette; with rhymes from the German. 4°. '70. bds., 60c. . . . . *Hurd & H.*

— *Same;* [also] Pictures in black. 4°. bds., $1. *Hurd & H.*

— Evening amusement. 16°. '70. $1.25. . . . *Roberts.*

— Falstaff and his companions. 8°. '71. $3; mor., $6. *Roberts.*

— Goethe's Faust. 4°. '70. $3; mor., $8. . . *Roberts.*

— Pictures in black. 4°. '71. bds., 60c. . . . *Hurd & H.*

— — *See also above* Black Peter.

— Silhouettes; with verse. roy. 4°. bds., $1. . *Stroefer.*

— *See also* Bund, L., Puck's nightly pranks; — Catastrophe of the hall; — Shakespeare, W., Midsummer-night's dream.

König, E. A. Verstossen. 12°. '74. pap., 25c. . . *Zickel.*

König Eginhard. 12°. pap., 15c. . . . . *Radde.*

König (Der) u. d. Müller. Nieritz, G. 25c. . . *Morwitz.*

Königliche Weg (Der). 12°. '72. $1; $1.25. *Ev. Assoc.*

Königsmark. Boker, G. H. $1.75. . . . . . *Lippincott.*

Konings, A. *See* Liguori, *St.* A. de, Theologia moralis.

Konstanzer Hans (Der). 12°. 20c. . . . . *Radde.*

Kopf (Der) oder das Herz. 18°. 30c. . . . . . . *Ev. Assoc.*

Koran (The); tr. by G: Sale. 12°. $1.50. . *Burnham.*

— *Same.* 8°. $2.75; shp., $3.25. . . . . *Lippincott.*

Körber, Ph. Herdsman of Dambach; tr. from the Germ. 16°. '75. 80c. . . . . (?)*Luth. Pub.*

Korfmacher, W. H. Rechenbuch f. Elementarschulen; nach d. Methode v. A. Richter u. J. Gröning, f. deutsche Schulen in d. Ver St. bearb. 5 v. 8°. *Vering.*

Cont.: Erster Theil, hf. bd., 25c. — Zweiter Theil, hf. bd., 50c. — Antwortenheft, hf. bd., 40c. — Dritter Theil, hf. leath., 90c. — Antwortenheft, hf. bd., 40c.

Körner, C. A. *See* Hübner, J., Biblische Historien.

Körner, C: Thdr. Zriny: Trauerspiel. With introd. and notes by E. R. Ruggles. ('66.) New ed. 12°. '76. pap., 60c. . . . . *Holt.*

Körner, H. J. A. Lebenskämpfe in der alten u. neuen Welt. [Selbstbiog.] 2 v. 8°. '66. pap., $2.50. *Schmidt.*

Korsaren (Die) a. d. Morgenland. 12°. 35c.; pap., 15c. . . . . *Benziger.*

Kortum, C. A. The Jobsiad: a grotesco-comico-heroic poem; tr. by C. T. Brooks. 16°. '63. $1.50. *Holt.*

Kost, J: Elements of materia medica and therapeutics; adapted to Am. eclectic practice. ill. 8°. '58. shp., $4.50. *Wilstach.*

Köstering, F. F. Lebenslauf v. E. D. L. Böse. 8°. 15c. . . . . *Barthel.*

Köstering, J. F. Auswanderung der sächsischen Lutheraner im, J., 1838; ihre Niederlassung in Perry Co., Mo., etc. 8°. 75c. . . . . *Volkening.*

Köstliche Gedanken f. junge Leute. 24°. 25c. *Ev. Assoc.*

Kostoweta, Mar. Inmitten der Nordsee. 18°. '71. 35c. . . . . *Am. Tr.*

Kotzebue, A: F. F. v. [Plays; tr.] 4 v. 16°. ea., pap., 15c. . . . . *French.*

Cont.: How to die for love: farce. — Lovers' vows. — Pizarro: tragedy. — Stranger.

Kotzka, St. Stanislaus. *See* Stanislaus Kotzka, *St.*

Kraft u. Stoff. Büchner, L. $1; 75c. . . . . . *Steiger.*

Kramer, H., *and* Wallis, H. Liederbuch f. deutsch-engl. Schulen in d. Ver. Staaten. 2 pts. 8°. pt. 1, hf. bd., 25c.; pt. 2, hf. bd., 35c. . . . *Vering.*

Kramer, J: W. Myndeful of hym; or, our heavenly Father and his children. 4°. '74. $4. . *Whittaker.*

Krämer, P. (*ill.*) English poets: photos., with essays by J. Gostwick. 8°. $10; mor. $15. . *Stroefer.*

Krasinski, *Count* Zygmund Napoleon. Undivine comedy, and other poems; tr. by M. W. Cook. 12°. '75. $2.25. . . . . *Lippincott.*

Krauss, E. C. F. Elements of German grammar. 12°. $1.10. . . . . *Thompson.*

— First book in German. 12°. $1.10. . . . . *Thompson.*

— German manual: first instruction in Germ. ('64.) New ed. 12°. '72. $1. . . . . *Holt.*

Krauth, C: Porterfield. Augsburg Confession; lit. tr. from the Lat., with the add. of the Germ. text. 12°. '69. 80c. . . . . *Luth. Bk. St.*

— Cæsar and God; or, politics and religion: sermon. 16°. pap., 10c. . . . . *Luth. Bk. St.*

— Christ and his kingdom in shadows. *See* Bible [Whole].

— Conservative reformation and its theology. 8°. $5. *Lippincott.*

— Infant baptism and infant salvation in the Calvinistic system: review of Hodge's "Systematic theology." 8°. '74. $1. . . . . *Luth. Bk. St.*

— Origin and result of theses of Luther. *See* Mann, W. J., Great reformation.

— *See also* Bible [Whole].

Krauth, Ht. Reynolds. Church book with music; for congregations. 8°. '72. $3. . . . . . *Luth. Bk. St.*

Krebsfänger (Der). 18°. 30c. . . . . *Ev. Assoc.*

Kreissmann, A: The sanctuary. [Sacred music.] obl. 4°. $3; bds., $2.50. . . . . *G. D. Russell.*

Kremer, R. E. Bible gems: manual of Scripture lessons. ill. 16°. '70. $1; hf. bd., 60c. . . . . . . *Lippincott*

— Easy lessons in natural science. ill. 12°. '73. hf. roan, $1.50 . . . . *Claxton.*

Kreussler, E. Homœopathic treatment of acute and chronic diseases; tr. and enl. by C. J. Hempel. 12°. 75c. . . . . *Boericke.*

Kreutzer, R. *See* Baillot, P., Rode, P., *and* Kreutzer, R.

Kreuz u. Schwert. Meding, G. 2 v. $1. . . *Morwitz.*

Kreuzfahrer (Die). 12°. pap., 15c. . . . . *Radde.*

Kreuzzug (Der) der Unschuldigen im Dienste d. göttlichen Herzens Jesu. 18°. pap., 10c. . . *Hoffmann.*

Krez, Konr. Aus Wiskonsin: Gedichte. 16°. '75. $1. *Steiger.*

Kriege, *Miss* Alma L. (*ed.*) Rhymes and tales for the kindergarten and nursery. 12°. '76. $1; pap., 50c. . . . . *Steiger.*

Kriege, *Mrs.* Mta. H. Life of Friedrich Fröbel. por. 12°. '76. 50c.; pap., 25c. . . . . *Steiger.*

— *See also* Marenholtz-Bülow, *Baroness*, The child.

Kriegerische Abenteuer e. Friedfertigen. *See* Zschokke.

Krilof and his fables. Ralston, W. R. S. $2.50; $5.50. *Routledge.*

Kriss Kringle's lib. 12 v. ill. 24°. pap., $1.80. *Pounsford.*

Kröger, A. E. The minnesinger of Germany. 16°. '72. $2.25. . . . . *Hurd & H.*

Krotel, G. J. *See* Luther, M., Kleiner Katechismus.

Krug, Jos. Erstes Lesebüchlein. 32°. 12½c. *Germ. Bapt.*

Krummacher, F: Adph. Parables; tr. from the Germ. 12°. 75c. . . . . *McCauley.*

— *Same.* 12°. (Bohn.) $2. . *Lippincott; Scribner, W. & A.*

— *Same.* 12°. (Bohn.) $1.75. . . . . *Little, B. & Co.*

Krummacher, F: W: Autobiography; tr. from the Germ. 8°. '69. $2. . . . . *Carter.*

— David, the king of Israel; tr. by Rev. M. G. Easton. 12°. $1.75. . . . . *Harper.*

— *Same.* cr. 8°. $3.75. . . . . *Scribner, W. & A.*

— Elisha; tr., with introd. remarks by E. Bickersteth. 32°. 75c. . . . . *Nelson.*

— Elias, der Thisbiter. 12°. '44. $1.10. . . . . . *Am. Tr.*

— *Eng.* Elijah, the Tishbite. 16°. 75c. . . . *Routledge.*

— *Same.* 18°. '38. 80c. . . . . *Am. Tr.*

— Risen Redeemer; tr. 12°. '74. $1.25. . . . . . *Carter.*

— The suffering Saviour; tr. 12°. '75. $1.50. . *Carter.*

— *Same.* cr. 8°. $2.25. . . . . *Scribner, W. & A.*

Kruna (*pseud.*) Apples of gold in pictures of silver: stories and poems for children. ill. 18°. 60c. *Bost. Am. Tr.*

— Broken rock. ('68.) New ed. 18°. '72. 50c... *Nat. Temp.*

Krüsi, Hm. Inventive drawing: ser. of draw. books, [with teachers' manuals]. [To form 4 pts.] pts. 1–3, and manuals. obl. f°. and 8°...... *Appleton.*

Cont.: 1. Synthetic ser., 4 pts., ea., 20c. — Manual for teachers, 75c. — 2. Analytic ser., 6 pts., ea., 25c. — Manual, 75c. — 3. Perspective ser., 4 pts., ea., 30c. — Manual, 75c.

— *Span.* Dibujo inventivo. pts. 1, 2, and manuals. obl. f°. and 8°. .... *Appleton.*

Cont.: Parte primera, ó sea sintética, 4 nos., ea., 20c.— Manual del maestro, 75c.— Parte segunda, ó sea analítica, 6 nos., ea., 25c. — Manual, 75c.

— Pestalozzi: his life, work and influence. por. and ill. 8°. '75. $2.25 .... *Wilson, H. & Co.*

Kuchenmichel (Der). Stöber, K. 15c..... *Ludwig.*

Kuffner, J. Sixty lessons for two guitars. f°. pap., $1.75 .... *Ditson.*

Kugler, Fz. Thdr. Handbook of painting: German, Flemish and Dutch schools; based on handbook of K. by G. F. Waagen. New ed., rev. by J. A. Crowe. 2 v. ill. cr. 8°. (Lond.) '74. $9. *Little, B. & Co.*

— *Same:* Italian schools; based on the handbook of Kugler, ed. by Sir C. L. Eastlake. 4th ed., rev. by Lady Eastlake. 2 v. eng. cr. 8°. (Lond.) '74. $11 .... *Little, B. & Co.*

Kuhn, R. K. Executor's account-book; with instructions how to settle an estate. 3d ed. 18°. '74. 35c.; roan, 50c. .... *Claxton.*

Kühner, Raph. Elementary gram. of the Greek lang.; tr. by S. H. Taylor. 12°. '46. $1.60.... *Ivison.*

— Greek grammar; [tr. and ed.] by Edwards and Taylor. 12°. $2 .... *Appleton.*

Kummer, C. Flute school. [Eng., Germ. and Fr. text.] 4°. bds., $3 .... *Peters.*

Kummer, F. A. Violoncello school for introd. instruction; with prog. studies. (op. 60.) f°. *net*, pap., $6 .... *Schirmer.*

Kunst, P. J. American dict. of the Eng. and Germ. lang. 12°. hf. mor., $2.50 .... *Kohler.*

Kuntze, E. J. Mystic bell: wonder book for young people. ill. 16°. '69. $1 .... *Putnam.*

Kunz, H. Auszug aus d. Choralbuch d. Evang. Brüder Gemeine. obl. 4°. $1.75 .... *Clauder.*

Kunz, J. G. Liederbuch f. christlichr. Schulen: (zwei u. dreistimmig.) 12°. 40c. .... *Volkening.*

Küpfer, B. S. Kanzelvorträge. 12°. 65c... *Germ. Bapt.*

Kupfermünzen u. Goldstücke. *See* Schmid, C. v.

Kurr, J. G. v. Mineralogy illustrated: 24 pl. with text. f°. $6 .... *Schoenhof.*

Kurtz, J: H: History of the old covenant; tr. from the Germ. 3 v. 8°. ea., $3... *Scribner, W. & A.*

— Manual of sacred hist.; tr. by C. E. Schaffer. ('54.) 15th ed. 12°. '76. $1.50........ *Smith, E. & Co.*

— Sacrificial worship of the Old Testament; tr. 8°. $3. *Scribner, W. & A.*

— Text book of church hist.; rev. and enl. from the Germ. ('60.) New ed. 2 v. in 1. 12°. '75. $3. *Smith, E. & Co.*

Kurzenknabe, J. H. The reward: hymns and music. obl. 12°. bds., 35c. .... *Ditson.*

Küss, E. Lectures on physiology; tr. by R. Amory; ed. by M. Duval. ill. 12°. '75. $2.50. *Jas. Campbell.*

Kustel, Guido. Nevada and California processes of gold and silver extraction. 8°. '63. $4; leath., $5. *Roman.*

Kyburg, od. die Zelle der Leiden. 12°. 35c.; pap., 15c. .... *Benziger.*

Kynaston, Herbert [*formerly* Snow]. Sermons preached in Cheltenham College. 1874–'5. cr. 8°. '76. $2.25 .... *Macmillan.*

Kyriale. *See* Maugin, C.

L., E. E. *See* Lay, E. E.

L., H. Table showing the screws that can be cut on slide lathes. 8°. '73. bds., 40c. .... *Spon.*

L., H. E. Hymns and poems. ill. sq. 16°. 75c. *Nelson.*

L., H. L. Christian remembrancer: daily text-book. [Interleaved.] 18°. 90c. .... *Nelson.*

— Moravian missions in Greenland and Labrador. ill. 18°. 50c. .... *Nelson.*

— Words of comfort for days of trial. [Interleaved.] 18°. 90c. .... *Nelson.*

L., J. C. W. Astronomische Unterredung. 8°. '73. bds., 15c. .... *Barthel.*

L., J. W. Brockley moor. [Fiction.] 12°. $1.50. *Appleton.*

L., L. (*pseud.*) *See* Pratt, I. Loring.

L., L. E. *See* Landon, Letitia E.

L., Katie. Elmwood; or, the withered arm. 16°. '76. $1.25 .... *Kelly, P. & Co.*

Labadye, Fs. de. Baron of Hertz: tale of the Anabaptists; tr. from the Fr. 12°. $2..... *O'Shea.*

La Barré Duparcq, N: E: de. Elements of military art and history; tr. by G. W. Cullum. 8°. '63. $5 .... *Van Nostrand.*

Labberton, Rob. A. Historical atlas: chronol. ser. of 100 maps. ('71.) 5th ed. obl. 4°. '74. $3.50. *Claxton.*

— Historical chart; or, hist. taught by the eye. f°. '74. hf. bd., $3.50; $4.50 .... *Claxton.*

— Historical questions, logically arranged and divided. ('71.) 3d ed. obl. 4°. '75. $1.75 .... *Claxton.*

— Outlines of hist.; with tables, chronol., geneal. and literary. ('70.) New. ed. obl. 4°. '75. $2. *Claxton.*

La Bedollière, Emilie de. Histoire de la mère Michel et de son chat. ('64.) New ed., with vocab. by L. Pylodet. 16°. '76. 75c. .... *Holt.*

— *Eng.* Mother Michel and her cat; tr. by F. Fuller. ill. 16°. 60c. .... *Hurd & H.*

Labiche, Eug. Marin, *and* Delacour, A. Cagnotte (La): comédie-vaudeville. 12°. '75. pap., 40c. *Holt.*

— — Petites oiseaux (Les): comédie. With Eng. notes by F. Bôcher. ('64.) New ed. 12°. '76. pap., 40c. .... *Holt.*

— *and* Martin, E: La poudre aux yeux: comédie. With Eng. notes by F. Bôcher. ('64.) New ed. 12°. '76. pap., 40c. .... *Holt.*

Lablache, L: Complete method of singing; tr. and enl. f°. bds., $3; — abridg., $2. *Church; Ditson; Gordon.*

— Fourteen vocalizes for soprano or tenor; tr. f°. $1.75. *Brainard.*

— Method of singing for the bass voice; tr. f°. bds., $4. *Ditson; Peters.*

Labor lost. *See* Abbott, Jac., Rollo story books.

Labor stands on golden feet. Zschokke, H. $1.. *Cassell.*

Laborde, J: Jos. Impossibility of the immaculate conception as an article of faith; tr. by A. C. Coxe. 12°. 60c. .... *McCauley.*

Laborer's daughter; or, relig. training in humble life: autobiog. sketch, by author of "Pearl of days." 18°. 30c. .... *Pres. Bd.*

Laborers in the east: memoirs of Dr. Buchanan, H: Martyn and D: Brown. 18°. 65c...... *Pres. Bd.*

Labors of Jesus. Headley, P. C. 25c.; 30c. *J. E. Potter.*

Labors of love. *See* Poplar Dell lib.

Labouchère, H: Diary of the besieged resident in Paris. 8°. pap., 60c. .... *Harper.*

— *Same.* 3d ed. cr. 8°. '72. $2.50 .... *Macmillan.*

Labouchere, P. A. (*ill.*) Illustrations of life of Luther: eng. after paintings by L., with descrip. by J. H. Merle d'Aubigne. sm. 4°. '68. $5; mor., $9 .... (?) *Luth. Pub.*

La Bouillerie, F. A. R. de. Hours before the altar; or, meditations on the sacrament; tr. 24°. 50c. *Strong.*

Laboulaye, E: Abdallah and the four-leaved shamrock; tr. 16°. $1.25 .... *Scribner, W. & A.*

— Fairy tales of all nations; tr. by M. L. Booth. ill. 12°. $2; $2.50 .... *Harper.*

— Finette: a fairy story; tr. sq. 12°. $1 ...... *Tilton.*

La Bree, L. Ebenezer Venture: farce. 16°. pap., 15c. *French.*

Labree, Lawrence. The rebels and Tories; or, the blood of the Mohawk. 8°. pap., 50c.... *De Witt.*

Lacey, E: Picture primer. 18°. 10c....... *Am. S. S.*

Lacey, G: S. Doctrinal and ritualistic view of the eucharist. 12°. '69. $1.50 .... *Claxton.*

Lacey, J: F. Digest of railway decisions. imp. 8°. '75. shp., $10 .... *Callaghan.*

Lachende Kinder: drollige Geschichten, lustige Bilder, etc. ill. 4°. '68. bds., $1 .... *Witter.*

Lackland, T: Homespun; or, five and twenty years ago. 16°. '67. $1.50 .... *Hurd & H.*

Lacombe, M. P. Arms and armour in antiquity and the middle ages; also, notice of modern weapons; tr. by C. Bartlett. ill. 12°. '76. $1.50.. *Scribner.*

Lacombe, Pl. Petite histoire du peuple français. 12°. 90c. .... *Schoenhof.*

— *Same.* With notes by J. Bué. sm. 8°. $1.. *Lippincott.*

— *See also* Sprague, A, P., *and* Lacombe, P.

Lacon; or, many things in few words. *See* Colton, C. C.

Laconics. Tegg, W. 50c. .... *Scribner, W. & A.*

Lacordaire, J: Bapt. H: Conferences on the church; [also] Panegyric on Daniel O'Connell; tr. 8°. $5; hf. mor., $6.50 .... *O'Shea.*

— Conferences on life: tr. 8°. $3; hf. mor., $5.. *O'Shea.*

— God: conferences delivered at Notre Dame, Paris; tr. 16°. $2 .... *Scribner, W. & A.*

— *Same.* 8°. $3; hf. mor., $5 .... *O'Shea.*

— God and man: conference delivered at Notre Dame, Paris; tr. 16°. $2 .... *Scribner, W. & A.*

— Historical sketch of Order of St. Dominic; tr. 12°. $1 .... *O'Shea.*

— Jesus Christ: conferences at Notre Dame, Paris; tr. 16°. $2 .... *Scribner, W. & A.*

— *Same.* 8°. $3; hf. mor., $5 .... *O'Shea.*

Lacour, P. On the manufacture of liquors, wines and cordials without distillation. 12°. $2.50.. *Dick & F.*

Lacroix, J: P. Life of Rudolfe Stier; from German sources. 12°. '73. $1.50 ...... *Meth. Bk. Conc.*

Lacroix, Pl. Arts in the middle ages; with 19 chromolith. prints by F. Kellerhoven, and 400 wood-eng. imp. 8°. $12; hf. cf., $15; cf., $18; mor., $25 .... *Appleton.*

— Manners, customs and dress during the middle ages; with 15 chromolith. prints and 400 wood-eng. imp. 8°. $12–$25 .... *Appleton.*

— Military and religious life in the middle ages; with 14 chromolith. prints by F. Kellerhoven, Regamey and L. Allard, and 400 wood-eng. imp. 8°. $12; hf. cf., $15; cf., $18; mor., $25 ...... *Appleton.*

Lactantius. [Lucius Cœlius Firmianus.] Works; tr. by W. Fletcher. (Ante-Nicene Christ. lib.) 2 v. 8°. $3 .... *Scribner, W. & A.*

Lacy, Rophino. Cinderella: opera. 16°. pap., 15c. *French.*

— Doing for the best: drama. 16°. pap., 15c. *De Witt; French.*

— Doing my uncle: farce. 16°. pap., 15c. .... *French.*

— Maid of Judah: opera. 16°. pap., 15c. .... *French.*

Lacy, T: Hailes. Amateur's [dram.] guide, handbook and manual. 10th ed. 16°. '75. pap., 25c... *French.*

— Dramatic costumes: plates. 68 pts. 16°. ea., $1; — in 1 v., $60 .... *French.*

— Jewess: drama. 16°. pap., 15c. .... *French.*

— Silent woman: farce. 16°. pap., 15c. *De Witt; French.*

Lacy, T: Hailes, *continued.*

— Winning a wife: comedy. 16°. pap., 15c... *French.*

— *See also* Higgie, T., *and* Lacy, T. H.; — Robertson, T. W., *and* Lacy, T. H.

— *and* Courtney, J. Clarissa Harlowe: tragic drama. 16°. pap., 15c. .... *French.*

Lacy diamonds. Coulson, J. G. A. $1.25; 75c... *Hale.*

Lacy's acting ed. of plays. 106 v. 16°. ea., hf. cf., $2.75; — 1590 nos. 16°. ea., pap., 15c... *French.*
Note. Specific entries under authors and titles.

Lacy's comic reciter. 5 pts. 16°. ea., pap., 15c.; — in 1 v., 75c. .... *French.*

Lacy's home plays for ladies. 5 pts. 16°. ea., pap., 40c. .... *French.*
Cont.: School for daughters; Mrs. Willis' will; Duchess of Mansfeldt. — Slighted treasures; Slight mistake; La rosiere; Who is to inherit? — Christmas gambol; Gaffer Grey's legacy; Harvest queen; Mystery of Muddlewitz. — Lina and Gertrude; Wonderful cure; My aunt's heiress. — Quarrel of the flowers; Choosing a bride; My daughter's daughter.

Lad from the country: farce. 16°. pap., 15c... *French.*

Ladd, *Mrs.* J. It isn't right; or, Frank Johnson's reason. 16°. $1.25 .... (?) *Martien.*

Ladder of life. *See* Edwards, A. B.

Ladder to learning. Hyde, A. M. 50c. ..... *Claxton.*

Ladies at home. Millingen, J. V. 15c. ...... *French.*

Ladies, beware: farce. 16°. pap., 15c. ...... *French.*

Ladies of St. Cyr. Dumas, A. 15c. .... *French.*

Ladies' and gentlemen's letter-writer and guide to politeness. 16°. 60c. .... *Locke.*

Ladies' battle: comedy. 16°. pap., 15c. ..... *French.*

Ladies' book of anecdotes. Smith, D. 75c. *Meth. Bk. Conc.*

Ladies' book of etiquette and manual of politeness. 12°. $1.50 .... *Lee & S.*

Ladies' club. Lemon, M. 15c. .... *French.*

Ladies' complete guide to needlework and embroidery. ill. 12°. $1.75 .... *Peterson.*

Ladies' guide to beauty. large 16°. pap., 30c. *Dick & F.*

Ladies' guide to gentility. 16°. $1 .... *Lippincott.*

Ladies' handbook of etiquette, and manual of politeness. 16°. 75c. .... *Miller.*

Ladies' letter-writer. 16°. 35c. .... *Porter.*

Ladies' letter-writer. 18°. 60c. .... *Miller.*

Ladies' prize lib. 5 v. 16°. $6 .... *Am. Bapt.*
Cont.: Minnie Loyle. — Ada Emory. — Ella's battles. — Elsie Lee. — Ursula's girlhood.

Ladies' science of etiquette. 8°. pap., 25c... *Peterson.*

Ladies' vase; by a lady. 32°. *net*, 19c... *Hamersley.*

Ladies' work-table book. ill. 12°. $1.50; pap., 50c. *Peterson.*

Ladreyt, Cas. Chrestomathie de la littérature française; avec notices biog., litt. et bibliog. New ed., enl. 12°. '45. $1.60.. *Claxton; Lippincott.*

Ladreyt, E. M. Livre de lectures. [French reader.] 16°. $1 .... *Lee & S.*

Lads of Heatherwood. 18°. 60c. .... (?) *Martien.*

Lady Alice. Huntington, J. V. 60c. ...... *Appleton.*

Lady Alice Lisle. Martyn, S. T. 80c. .... *Am. Tr.*

Lady Amabel. Stewart, A. M. 50c.; 75c.... *Sadlier.*

Lady and the devil. Dimond, W. 15c. ...... *French.*

Lady and gent in a perplexing predicament. Selby, C. 15c. .... *French.*

Lady and the priest. Maberly, K. C. 50c. .. *Harper.*

Lady Anna. Trollope, A. 50c. .... *Harper.*

Lady artist. ill. 18°. 50c. .... *Crowell.*

— *See also* Annie Marlowe ser.

Lady Ashleigh. Smith, J. F. 75c. .... *Dick & F.*

Lady at home. Arthur, T. S. 50c. .... *Peterson.*

Lady Audley's secret. Braddon, M. E. 50c. *Dick & F.*

Lady Audley's secret. Hazlewood, C. H. 15c. *French.*

Lady Audley's secret. Suter, W. E. 15c. ..... *Ames.*

Lady Bell. Keddie, H. $1.75 .... *Lippincott.*
Lady Belle Belle. Byron, H. J. 15c. .... *French.*
Lady Betty's governess. Guernsey, L. E. $1.50. *Whittaker.*
Lady-bird. Fullerton, *Lady* G. $1.50; $2 .. *Murphy.*
Lady Blanche. Egan, P. 50c. .... *De Witt.*
Lady Ernestine. Warfield, C. A. $1.75 ... *Peterson.*
Lady Geraldine's courtship. Browning, E. B. $4; $8 .... *Miller.*
Lady Godiva: burlesque. 16°. pap., 15c. ... *French.*
Lady Green-satin and her maid Rosette. Martineau des Chesnez, E. $1.50 .... *Porter.*
Lady Hester. Yonge, C. M. $1.75 ...... *Macmillan.*
Lady housekeeper's poultry-yard. 16°. 20c. *Routledge.*
Lady Huntington and her friends. Knight, H. C. $1.10 .... *Am. Tr.*
Lady in difficulties. Planché, J. R. 15c. .... *French.*
Lady Judith. McCarthy, J. $1.75; $1 ..... *Sheldon.*
Lady Lee's widowhood. Hamley, E. B. 50c. .. *Harper.*
Lady Linnet. Chester, S. E. 25c. .... *Am. Tr.*
Lady Lisle. Braddon, M. E. 50c. .... *Dick & F.*
Lady Lucy's secret. *See* Guernsey, L. E.
Lady Mary. Tayler, C. B. $1 .... *Leighton.*
Lady Maud. Egan, P. $1.75; $1.50 .... *Peterson.*
Lady of the bedchamber: farce. 16°. pap., 15c .. *French.*
Lady of Belle Isle: drama. 16°. pap., 15c. .. *French.*
Lady of the camellias: drama. 16°. pap., 15c. .. *French.*
Lady of the ice. De Mille, J. $1.25; 75c. .. *Appleton.*
Lady of the isle. Southworth, E. D. E. N. $1.75; $1.50 .... *Peterson.*
Lady of La Garaye. *See* Norton, C.
Lady of the lake. *See* Scott, *Sir* W.
Lady of the lake: burlesque. Reece, R. 15c. .. *French.*
Lady of the lake: drama. Dibdin, T. 15c. ... *French.*
Lady of the lake: travestie. Thomson, M. 15c. .. *French.*
Lady of Lawford, and other Christmas stories. Warren, N. B. $2.50; $3 .... *Nims.*
Lady of the lions. Durivage, O. F. 15c. ..... *French.*
Lady of Lyndon. Blake, *Lady* —. $1.25; 75c. .. *Estes.*
Lady of Lyons. *See* Bulwer-Lytton, *Sir* E. G. E. L.
Lady of Lyons. Byron, H. J. 15c. .... *French.*
Lady of the manor. *See* Sherwood, *Mrs.* M. M.
Lady of Milan. Thomson, K. B. 75c. ...... *Harper.*
Lady of Provence. *See* Tucker, *Mrs.* C.
Lady preacher. Brown, G. $1.25 .... (?) *Daughaday.*
Lady Rosamond's book. Guernsey, L. E. $1.50. *Whittaker.*
Lady superior (The). Pollard, E. F. 50c. .. *Harper.*
Lady Susan. *See* Austen, Jane.
Lady Sweetapple. Dasent, G. W. 75c. ..... *Appleton.*
Lady Wedderburn's wish. *See* Grant, Ja.
Lady Willacy's protégées. Gray, A. $1.50 .... *Nelson.*
Lady's almanac. ('52.) [Annual.] 32°. 50c. .. *Coolidge.*
Lady's book of knitting and crochet; comp. and ed. by a lady expert. 12°. '76. pap., 50c. .. *Symonds.*
Lady's companion lib. 4 v. 16°. $2.85 ...... *Miller.*
Cont.: Ladies' book of etiquette. — Ladies' letter-writer. — Young wife's book. — Handbook of etiquette.
Lady's historical lib. 5 v. 12°. $8.75 ... *J. E. Potter.*
Cont.: Empress Josephine, by M. A. Le Normand. — Marie Antoinette, by Mme. Campan. — Mary, Queen of Scots, by Miss Benger. — Queens of France, by Mrs. F. Bush. — Anne Boleyn, by Miss Benger.
Lady's letter-writer. 16°. 20c. .... *Routledge.*
Lady's love oracle; or, counselor to the fair sex: fortune-teller. 12°. pap., 30c. .... *Dick & F.*
Lady's mile (The). Braddon, M. E. 50c. .. *Dick & F.*
Lady's oracle: pastime for social parties and the family circle. ill. 12°. $1.25 .... *T. Bliss.*
Lady's (A) second journey round the world. Pfeiffer, I. $1.50 .... *Harper.*
Lafayette, Marie J: P. R. Y. G. M. (*Marquis*) de. Life. ill. 16°. $1.25 .... *Lee & S.*
Laferrière, A. *See* Pierron, E., *and* Laferrière, A.
Lafitte, J. P. Red doctor; tr. by H. d' Aramis. 12°. '66. $1.75 .... *Claxton.*
Lafitte. Ingraham, J. H. 50c. .... *De Witt.*
La Fontaine, J: de. Les fables. ill. 18°. 60c. *G. R. Lockwood.*
— *Same.* Avec 80 grand dessins et 250 vignettes par G. Doré. 2 v. f°. $100; hf. mor., $150 ... *Appleton.*
— — *Eng.* 2 v. f°. $100 .... *Appleton.*
— *Same;* with notes by F. Tarver. 16°. $1 .. *Lippincott.*
— *Same;* [avec] notes par M. M. Coste, C. Nocher, etc. 18° hf. roan, 75c. .... *Kelly, P. & Co.*
— *Eng.;* tr. into verse by W. Thornbury; with ill. by Doré. roy. 4°. $15; mor., $20; $25 .... *Cassell.*
— *See also* Masterpieces of foreign literature.
Laforet, N. J. Why men do not believe: principal causes of infidelity. 16°. '68. $1 ... *Cath. Pub.*
Lagarde, Ern. French verb book. 12°. '72. hf. leath., $1 .... *Eldredge.*
La Gattina, F. P. de. *See* Gattina, F. P. della.
La Gironière, Pl. de. Twenty years in the Philippines; tr. ill. 12°. $1.50 .... *Harper.*
Lagny, Germain de. The knout and the Russians; or, the Muscovite empire, the czar and his people. ill. 12°. $1.25 .... *Harper.*
La Grange, *Mme.* A. K. de. Ferryman of the Tiber: hist. tale; tr. 12°. $1.25 .... *O'Shea.*
— Last days of Jerusalem; tr. 12°. $1.25 ... *O'Shea.*
— Malediction (The); tr. 12°. $1.25 .... *O'Shea.*
— Vestal (The): hist. tale of 1st cent. of the church; tr. 12°. $2 .... *O'Shea.*
La Guard, Thdr. de (*pseud.*) *See* Ward, Natl.
La Hache, Thdr. v. Missa pro pace. 8°. $1.50; pap., $1; bds., $1.25 .... *Gordon.*
— Unison mass. f°. pap., $1.25 .... *Ditson.*
— Unison mass in G. 4°. pap., 60c. .... *Peters.*
Laid up in port: drama. 16°. pap., 15c. ..... *French.*
Laidlaw, Alex. H. American pronounc. dict. of the Eng. lang. sq. 8°. hf. roan, $2 .... *Desilver.*
Laighton, Alb. *See* Payson, A. M., *and* Laighton, A.
Laila. Stratton, G. W. 60c.; 70c. .... *Stratton.*
Laing, *Mrs.* C. H. B. Conquests of the seven hills. ill. 16°. '75. $1.25 .... *Porter.*
— Heroes of the seven hills. ill. 16°. '73. $1.25 .. *Porter.*
— Seven kings of the seven hills: anc. hist. of Rome for children. ill. 16°. '72. $1 .... *Porter.*
Laird of Norlaw. *See* Oliphant, M. O. W.
Lajétchnikoff, —. The heretic; tr. by T. B. Shaw. [Fiction.] 8°. '64. pap., 50c. .... *Harper.*
Lake Cottage; or, the found treasures; tr. by M. Shannon. ill. 16°. $1 .... *Locke.*
— *See also* Better path stories.
Lake of Galilee. Hamilton, J. 50c. .... *Carter.*
Lake of the woods. Tucker, C. 75c. .... *Carter.*
Lake shore ser. *See* Adams, W. T.
Lakes and rivers of the Bible: 12 views with letterpress. obl. 24°. 50c.; 75c. .... *Nelson.*
Lakeside ser. 4 v. 16°. $5.75 .... *Graves.*
Cont.: Mabel Ross. — Broken pitcher. — Luke Darrell. — Sloppy Dingle, by C. Percy.
Lakeville. Healy, M. $1.50; $1 .... *Appleton.*
Lakey, C: D. Village and country houses. ill. 4°. $6. *Judd.*
Lalla Rookh. *See* Moore, T:
Lalla Rookh: burlesque. 16°. pap., 15c. ..... *French.*
Lallemant, Rob. Ari. *See* Lowenburg, J., Lallemant, R. A., *and* Dore, A.
Lalor, J. J. *See* Mason, A. B., *and* Lalor, J. J.

Lalor, M. *See* New York, Supreme Court reports.

Lalor, T. M. Law of real property in N. Y. 8°. '55. *net*, shp., $2.50 .... *Ward & P.*

— *See also* New York, Supreme Court and Court of Errors reports.

Lamar, J. S. Organon of Scripture: inductive method of Biblical interpretation. 12°. $1 .. *Lippincott.*

— *Same.* 12°. $1.50 .... *Chase.*

Lamar, P. F. Practical grammar of the Eng. lang. 16°. '58. hf. bd., 90c. .... *Challen.*

Lamartine, Alph. de. Additional memoirs of my youth; tr. 8°. pap., 25c. .... *Harper.*

— Fior d'Aliza; tr. by G. Perry. 16°. '68. $1.25 .. *Hurd & H.*

— French revolution of 1848; tr. 12°. (Bohn.) $1.25. *Little, B. & Co.*

— *Same.* 12°. (Bohn.) $1.40 ...... *Scribner, W. & A.*

— *Same.* 12°. (Bohn.) $1.50 .... *Lippincott.*

— Geneviève; or, the history of a servant; tr. 8°. pap., 25c. .... *Harper.*

— *Same;* tr. by A. R. Scoble. 12°. (Bohn.) 60c. *Scribner, W. & A.*

— Graziella. [French.] 12°. 90c. ... *G. R. Lockwood.*

— *Eng.* Graziella; tr. by S. C. B. 12°. $1; pap., 60c. *Lippincott.*

— — *Same;* tr. by J. B. Runnion. ('75.) 2d ed. sm. 4°. '76. $2 .... *Jansen.*

— History of the Girondists; or, personal memoirs of the patriots of the French revolution. 3 v. 12°. $4.50 .... *Harper.*

— *Same.* 3 v. 12°. (Bohn.) ea., $1.25 ... *Little, B. & Co.*

— *Same.* 3 v. 12°. (Bohn.) ea., $1.40 .. *Scribner, W. & A.*

— *Same.* 3 v. 12°. (Bohn.) ea., $1.50 ...... *Lippincott.*

— Homer and Socrates; with biog.; tr. by Mrs. E. W. Smith. 12°. $1 .... *Lippincott.*

— Memoirs of celebrated characters; tr. 3 v. 12°. $4.50 .... *Harper.*

— Memoirs of my youth; tr. 8°. pap., 25c. .. *Harper.*

— Raphael. [French.] 12°. 90c. .... *G. R. Lockwood.*

— *Eng.* Raphael; or, pages from the book of life at twenty. 12°. $1.25 .... *Harper.*

— Restoration of the monarchy; tr. 4 v. 12°. (Bohn.) ea., $1.25 .... *Little, B. & Co.*

— *Same.* 4 v. 12°. (Bohn.) ea., $1.40 .. *Scribner, W. & A.*

— *Same.* 4 v. 12°. (Bohn.) ea., $1.50 ...... *Lippincott.*

— Stone mason of Saint Point: a village tale; tr. 12°. $1.25 .... *Harper.*

— *Same.* 12°. (Bohn.) 60c. .... *Scribner, W. & A.*

— Three months in power; tr. 12°. (Bohn.) 80c. *Scribner, W. & A.*

— *See also* Stoddard, R. H., Bric-a-brac ser.

Lamb, C: Works. (Moxon's ed.) 4 v. por. 12°. hf. cf., $16; cf., $18; $25 .... *Appleton.*

— *Same;* ed. by C. Kent. (Globe lib.) cr. 8°. '76. $1.75; hf. cf., $3.50; cf., $5 .... *Routledge.*

— *Same;* ed. and pref. by R. H. Shepherd. por. cr. 8°. (Lond.) '75. $3 .... *Little, B. & Co.*

— *Same;* ed. by Sir T. N. Talfourd. 8°. $2.75; shp., $3.50; hf. cf., $4.75 .... *Lippincott.*

— — *Same.* 2 v. por. 12°. $3 .... *Harper.*

— — *Same.* 5 v. por. cr. 8°. $9. *Nichols & H.; Widdleton.*

— Dramatic poets of time of Elizabeth; incl. sel. from the Garrick plays. 12°. (Bohn.) $1.75. *Little, B. & Co.*

— *Same.* 12°. (Bohn.) $2. *Lippincott; Scribner, W. & A.*

— Eliana: uncollected writings of L. cr. 8°. $1.75; hf. cf., $3.50 .... *Putnam; Widdleton.*

— Essays of Elia. 12°. pap., 25c. .... *Lippincott.*

— *Same.* cr. 8°. $1.75. *Nichols & H.; Putnam; Widdleton.*

— *Same;* with reminiscences of L. and his friends by E. Ollier. (World-wide lib.) 2 ser. 12°. ea., pap., 25c. .... *Routledge.*

— *Same;* [also] Last essays of Elia. 12°. 75c.; pap., 50c. .... *Routledge.*

— *Same;* [also] Eliana. 12°. (Bohn.) $1.25. *Little, B. & Co.*

Lamb, C: *continued.*

— — *Same.* 12°. (Bohn.) $1.40 ... *Scribner, W. & A.*

— — *Same.* 12°. (Bohn.) $1.50 .... *Lippincott.*

— Poetical works. *See* Rogers, S., Poet. works.

— *See also* Stoddard, R. H., Bric-a-brac ser.

— *and* Ma. Tales from Shakespeare for the young. ill. 16°. $1.25 .... *Hurd & H.; Routledge.*

Lamb, *Mrs.* Jos. ["Ruth Buck."] Captain Christie's granddaughter. ill. 16°. '65. $1 .... *Dodd.*

— — *See also* Little door-keeper's lib.

— Dick Fraser; or, the travels of a village artist. 18°. 60c. .... (?) *Martien.*

— How Charlie helped his mother. 18°. 75c. (?) *Martien; Whittaker.*

— Jem Morrison. ill. 16°. '73. 75c. .... *Am. Tr.*

— *Same.* 16°. $1 .... (?) *Martien.*

— Master and servant; or, Richard Owen's choice. 18°. 25c. .... *Nelson.*

— Mended life; or, the carpenter's family. 16°. $1.50. (?) *Martien.*

— Sturdy Jack. ill. 16°. '72. 80c. .... *Lothrop.*

Lamb, *Mrs.* Martha J. Play school stories. 4 v. 18°. '74. ea., 60c. .... *Lothrop.*

Cont.: Julia. — Mattie. — Fanny. — Harry.

— Spicy. ill. 8°. $1.50; pap., $1 .... *Appleton.*

Lamb, Ma. *See* Lamb, C: *and* M.

Lamb of Christ's flock. 18°. 22c. .... *Am. S. S.*

Lambert, Etienne, *and* Sardou, Alfr. All the French verbs at a glance. 12°. '74. 50c. ..... *Mason.*

— — Idiomatic key to French. 12°. '74. $1.50 .. *Mason.*

Lambert, T. S. Primary systematic human physiol., anatomy and hygiene. ill. 12°. 85c. ... *W. Wood.*

Lambillotte, L. Paschal mass in D. f°. '70. bds., $2.50 .... *Ditson.*

Lambla, Hattie Lena. Bewitched closet: [dram.] sketch. 16°. pap., 15c. .... *Ames.*

— Domestic felicity: [dram.] sketch. 16°. pap., 15c. *Ames.*

— Obedience: comedietta. 16°. pap., 15c. .... *Ames.*

— That mysterious bundle: farce. 16°. pap., 15c. *Ames.*

Lambruschini, L. Immaculate conception. 16°. $1. *Sadlier.*

Lambs of the flock. *See* Pet lamb.

Lamé Fleury, Jules Raymond. Histoire ancienne; racontée à la jeunesse. With notes by S. M. Lane. ('69.) New ed. 12°. '72. 90c. .. *Holt.*

— Histoire de France; racontée à la jeunesse. ('63.) New ed. 12°. '76. $1.50 .... *Holt.*

Lame Allan; or, cast thy burden on the Lord. ('69.) New ed. 16°. '73. 65c. .... *Hoyt.*

Lame beggar. Strong, J. D. 25c. .... *Lothrop.*

Lame Bessie. 18°. 65c. .... *Cong. Pub.*

Lame Bessie. F., H. H. $1 .... *Lothrop.*

Lame boy; or, filial love rewarded. 18°. 17c.; 22c. *Am. Bapt.*

Lame excuse. Hay, F. 15c. .... *De Witt; French.*

Lame Felix. *See* Bruce, C:

Lame Jock's carol. 18°. 40c. .... *Am. S. S.*

Lame John; or, the charitable poor man. 18°. 45c. *Am. S. S.*

Lame Letty. Finlay, M. F. 60c. .... *Pres. Bd.*

Lame Sam; or, Walter Castle's work. 18°. 50c. (?) *Martien.*

Lame Willie. *See* Jefferds, J. A.

Lämmchen (Das). Schmid, C. v. 20c. ... *Morwitz.*

Lamon, W. H. Life of Abraham Lincoln to [1861]. por. and ill. 8°. $5 .... *Osgood.*

Lamont, Ja. Seasons with the sea-horses; or, sporting adventures in the northern seas. map and ill. 8°. $3 .... *Harper.*

— Yachting in the Arctic seas: notes of 5 voyages in neighborhood of Spitzbergen and Novaya Zemlya. maps and ill. 8°. '76. $6.75 .. *Scribner, W. & A.*

La Motte Fouqué, F: H: K: (*Freiherr*) de. Four seasons; tr. ill. 16°. '75. $1.25.... *Routledge.*
— Romantic fiction; tr. ill. 16°. '75. $1.25.. *Routledge.*
— Thiodolph, the Icelander; tr. 12°. 75c.; $1.25.. *Miller.*
— Undine; mit Wörterb. ('64.) New ed. 12°. '76. pap., 50c. .... *Holt.*
— *Eng.* Undine, and other tales. ill. 16°. $1.50; $2; hf. mor., $3.50; mor., $5 .... *Hurd & H.*
— — Undine, and other tales; ill. by H. W. Herrick. cr. 8°. $2–$6 .... *Hurd & H.*
— — Undine and Sintram. 12°. $1.25; pap., 75c.; —ill. 12°. $1.75 .... *Miller.*
— — Loves of Undine and Sintram; [also] Paul and Virginia, by J. H. de Saint Pierre. ill. 12°. '76. $1.50 .... *World Pub.*
— *Same;* [also] The two captains; tr. by F. E. Bunnett. 12°. $1.25; pap., 50c... *Scribner, W. & A.*
La Motte, *Mme.* Gabrielle de. Piano and musical matter. 8°. $3; bds., $2; $2.50 .... *Lee & S.*
Lamp and the lantern. *See* Hamilton, Ja.
Lamp for the feet. 24°. 20c.; 25c. .... *Am. S. S.*
Lamp of the sanctuary. Wiseman, N. 50c... *Coddington.*
Lamp to the path; or, the Bible in the heart, the home, and the market place. 16°. '74. $1.25. *Lothrop.*
Lampadius, W. A. Life of Mendelssohn; with sup. sketches by J. Benedict, H. F. Chorley, Bayard Taylor, etc.; ed. and tr. by W. L. Gage. 12°. '65. $1.75 .... *Ditson.*
Lampe, F. A. Compendium of the Christian religion. [German.] 18°. 15c. .... *N. Y. Ref. Ch. Bd.*
Lamplighter (The). Cummins, M. S. $1.75.. *Osgood.*
Lamplighter's story. *See* Dickens, C:
Lamson, Alvan. Church of the first three centuries. 8°. $3 .... *Fuller.*
Lamson, Warren H. Writing-books: Grammar school ser. 4 nos. obl. 8°. per doz., $1.80... *Harper.*
Lancashire lass. Byron, H. J. 15c. .... *De Witt.*
Lancashire witches. *See* Ainsworth, W. H.
Lancaster, Alb. Note additionnelle au "Volcanic manifestations in New England." 4°. pap., 35c. *Bost. Soc. Nat. Hist.*
— — *See also* Brigham, W. T.
Lancaster, C. S. Advice to husbands: comedietta. 16°. pap., 15c. .... *French.*
Lancaster, E. Young actress: interlude. 16°. pap., 15c. .... *French.*
Lancaster, J: Life of Lady Maxwell. 12°. '37. $1.25. *Meth. Bk. Conc.*
Lancelott, F: Queens of England and their times. 2 v. por. sm. 8°. $4; hf. mor., $8 .... *Appleton.*
Lancers. Vernon, L. 15c. .... *French.*
Lances of Lynwood. *See* Yonge, C. M.
Lancewood, Law. (*pseud.*) *See* Wise, Dan.
Land and the book. Thomson, W. M. 2 v. $5; $6; $8.50 .... *Harper.*
Land and its story. Burt, N. C. *$3.50; $5.. *Appleton.*
Land and ocean adventure lib. 5 v. ill. 12°. $6.25. *Lippincott.*
Cont.: Red Eric, by R. M. Ballantyne. — Privateersman, by F. Marryat. — Tiger prince, by W. Dalton. — Life of Daniel Boone. — Life of Paul Jones.
Land and sea. 5 v. ill. 16°. '76. ea., 75c. .... *Dodd.*
Cont.: India. — Builders of the sea. — Ancient Egypt. — Frozen north. — Ocean.
Land and sea tales; by "the old sailor." 16°. bds., 80c. .... *Routledge.*
Land at last. *See* Yates, Edm.
Land battles from Hastings to Inkermann. V., L. $1.25. *Scribner, W. & A.*
Land of Cid. *See* Ozanam, A. F.
Land of the czar. Wahl, O. W. $5.25.. *Scribner, W. & A.*
Land of desolation. Hayes, I. I. $1.75 .... *Harper.*
Land of Israel. Keith, A. $1.50 .... *Harper.*
Land of the lion; or, adventures among the wild animals of Africa. ill. 4°. '75. $1.75 .... *Nelson.*
Land of Moab. Tristram, H. B. $2.50 .... *Harper.*
Land of mystery; or, scenes and incidents in central Africa. 18°. 65c. .... *Am. S S.*
Land of the Nile. Adams, W. H. $1.50.... *Lothrop.*
Land of the Pharaohs. Manning, S. $3.50... *Nelson.*
Land of the pigtail. Clarke, B. $1.50 .... *Nelson.*
Land of promise. Kitto, J. $1.25.... *Meth. Bk. Conc.*
Land of the Saracen. Taylor, B. $1.50; $2.. *Putnam.*
Land of shadowing wings. Loomis, H. $1.25. *Meth. Bk. Conc.*
Land of Thor. Browne, J. R. $2 .... *Harper.*
Land of the Veda. *See* Butler, W.
Land of the white elephant. *See* Bacon, G. B.
Land of the white elephant. Vincent, F., *jr.* $3.50. *Harper.*
Land-war in Ireland. Godkin, J. $2.50.. *Macmillan.*
Landels, W. Young man in the battle of life. 3d ed. 12°. $1.50 .... *Cassell.*
Landenberger, C. J. Choralbuch f. d. Orgel. 4°. $1.50 .... *Kohler.*
— Kirchenchöre. 4°. $2 .... *Kohler.*
Lander, R. *and* J. Journal of expedition to explore course and termination of the Niger. 2 v. ill. 18°. $1.50 .... *Harper.*
Lander, Sa. W. Fairy bells; and what they tolled us; from the German. ('67.) New. ed. ill. 16°. '76. $1.25 .... *Lockwood, B. & Co.*
— Spectacle series; for young eyes. 8 v. ill. 16°. $8 .... *Sheldon.*
Cont.: Boston and vicinity. — St. Petersburg. — Zurich. — Pekin. — Moscow. — Berlin. — Rome. — New York.
Landing of the pilgrim fathers. Singer, O. $1.. *Church.*
Landis, Jesse. Supplement to Linn's Analytical index of references to [Penna.] cases. 8°. '73. shp., $6. *J. Campbell & Son.*
Landis, Rob. Wharton. Immortality of the soul and final condition of the wicked carefully considered. 12°. '59. $1.75 .... *Meth. Bk. Conc.*
— Rabbah taken: theological system of Alex. Campbell examined and refuted. 8°. '44. pap., 50c. *Wilstach.*
Landlord and tenant's lawyer; by an attorney-at-law. 12°. '72. $1.50; shp., $1.75 .... *Tibbals.*
Landmarks, and other poems. Piatt, J. J. $1.50. *Hurd & H.*
Landmarks of history. *See* Yonge, C. M.
Landmarks of truth. Evans, D. M. *$3; $5. *Quak. City.*
Landon, *Miss* H. Nora, and thoughts about Christ. 16°. 75c. .... *Cong. Pub.*
Landon, Letitia Eliz. [*now Mrs.* Maclean]. Works. 8°. shp., $3.50; mor., $10 .... *Appleton.*
— Poetical works. (Household ser.) ill. 16°. $1.50; mor., $3 .... *Lee & S.*
— *Same;* with memoir by W. B. Scott. (Presentation ed.) 12°. $1.75; ivorine, $3 .... *Routledge.*
Landon, Melville D. ["Eli Perkins."] Eli Perkins (at large): his sayings and doings, etc. ill. 12°. '75. $1.25 .... *Ford.*
— Saratoga in 1901: a book of satire, love, fun and statistics. ill. 12°. $2 .... *Sheldon.*
Landor, Wa. Savage. Works. New ed., with rev. ed. of life by J. Forster. [To form 8 v.] 4 v. por. and ill. demi 8°. ea., $4; hf. cf., $6.. *Lippincott.*
— Cameos: sel. from [his] poems; with introd. essay by E. C. Stedman and T. B. Aldrich. sm. 4°. '73. $2 .... *Osgood.*
— Imaginary conversations. 4 v. sq. 12°. '76. ea., $2. *Roberts.*
— Pericles and Aspasia. 16°. '70. $1.50.... *Roberts.*
— Selections from [his] writings; ed. by G. S. Hillard. 16°. $1.25; $1.75. 8°. $2.50 .... *Osgood.*

Landrin, M. H. C. Treatise on steel; tr., with notes, by A. A. Fesquet; with app. on the Bessemer and Martin processes, from report of A. S. Hewitt. 12°. '68. $3 .... *Baird.*

Landriot, J. F. Sins of the tongue and jealousy in woman's life; tr. by H. Lyons. 12°. $1.50 .. *Noonan.*

— The valiant woman: discourses for women living in the world; tr. by H. Lyons. 12°. $1.50 .. *Noonan.*

Lands of Scott. Hunnewell, J. W. $2.50; $5; $6. *Osgood.*

Landschaftsmaler (Der). *See* Grimm, H.

Landseer, *Sir* Edn. Engravings from L.: 24 heliot. pl., with sketch of his life and works. 4°. '75. $10. *Osgood.*

— Pictures by L.; with descriptive text and biog. sketch by J. Dafforne. f°. '74. $15 .... *Routledge.*

Lane, *Miss* A. Thrilling and strange adventures of L. [In Eng. or Germ.] 8°. pap., 20c..... *Barclay.*

Lane, B: I. Refuge of lies, and the covert from the storm: lectures on doctrine of future punishment. 12°. '44. $1 .... *W. H. Young.*

Lane, E: W: Account of the manners and customs of the modern Egyptians. 5th ed. 2 v. ill. post 8°. (Lond.) '71. $5 .... *Little, B. & Co.*

— *See also* Arabian nights' entertainments; — Thousand and one nights.

Lane, Lafayette. *See* Oregon, Organic and general laws.

Lane, Wycliffe (*pseud.*) *See* Jenings, *Mrs.* E.

Laneside stories. 4 v. 18°. $2.50 .... (?) *Martien.*
Cont.: Mother's warm shawl. — Dick Fraser. — Margaret and her friends. — Oliver Dale's decision.

Laneton parsonage. *See* Sewell, E. M.

Lanfrey, P. History of Napoleon I.; tr. v. 1, 2. 8°. '71–'72. ea., $3.50 .... *Macmillan.*

Lang, B: J. Youthful voices: hymns and tunes. 16°. 60c.; bds., 50c .... *Ditson.*

Langalerie, P. H. G. de. Month of St. Joseph; or, exercises for each day; tr. by a Sister of St. Joseph. 16°. 75c.; $1 .... *Sadlier.*

Langbein, G. F., *and* J. C. J. District courts of N. Y. City: their organization, jurisdiction and practice; with forms. 8°. '72. shp., $4.50 .... *Ward & P.*

Langbridge, F. Fair Rosamond's bower: burletta. 16°. pap., 15c .... *French.*

Langdell, C. C. Selection of cases on law of contracts; with ref. and citations. 8°. '71. shp., $6. *Little, B. & Co.*

— Selection of cases on law of sales of personal property; with ref. and citations. v. 1. 8°. '72. shp., $6. *Little, B. & Co.*

Langdon, C: W. Treatise on justices of the peace, sheriffs and constables in Cal.; [also] supplement to same, from Supreme Court reports ('70–'74), with amendments to code of civil procedure, since 1869, applicable to justices' courts; by J. C. Bates. 2 v. 8°. '70–'75. pap., $7.50 .. *Bancroft.*

Langdon, Ma. (*pseud.*) *See* Pike, *Mrs.* M. H.

Langdon lib. 5 v. ill. 18°. $2.75 .... *Hoyt.*
Cont.: Matty Frost, by Mrs. C. E. K. Davis. — Robin, the runner. — Lime burner. — Willie Maitland. — Our Father in heaven.

Lange, C. H. B. Lehrbuch d. engl. Sprache f. deutsche Schulen in Am. 8°. $1 .... *Siemon.*

Lange, J: P: Life of Christ, tr.; ed., with add. notes, by M. Dode. 4 v. 8°. '72. $12.50 .. *Smith, E. & Co.*

— (*ed.*) Commentary on the Scriptures; tr. and ed. by P. Schaff. Old Test. v. 1, 2, 4, 6, 8–11, 16. 9 v. 8°. '68–'76. ea., $5; shp., $6.50; hf. cf., $7.50 .... *Scribner.*
Cont.: 1. General introd.: Genesis, by J. P. Lange. — 2. Exodus, by C. M. Mead; Leviticus, by F. Gardiner; with gen. introd. by S. Osgood. — 4. Joshua, by F. R. Fay; Judges and Ruth, by P. Cassel. — 6. Kings, by C. W. F. Bähr. — 8. Job, a rhythmical version, by T. Lewis, and comment. by O. Zöckler. — 9. Psalms, by C. B. Moll, with new version by T. J. Conant. — 10. Proverbs, Ecclesiastes and Song of Solomon, by O. Zöckler. — 11. Jeremiah and Lamentations, by C. W. E. Naegelsbach. — 16. Minor prophets, by P. Kleinert, O. Schmoller, T. W. Chambers, J. F. McCurdy and J. Packard.

Lange, J: P: *continued.*

— *Same.* New Test. 10 v. 8°. '64–'76. ea., $5; shp., $6.50; hf. cf., $7.50 .... *Scribner.*
Cont.: 1. General introd.: Matthew, by J. P. Lange. — 2. Mark, by J. P. Lange; Luke, by J. J. van Oosterzee. — 3. John, by J. P. Lange. — 4. Acts, by G. V. Lechler and C. Gerok. — 5. Romans, by J. P. Lange and F. R. Fay. — 6. Corinthians, by C. F. Kling. — 7. Galatians, by O. Schmoller; Ephesians, Philippians and Colossians, by K. Braune. — 8. Thessalonians, by C. A. Auberlen and C. J. Riggenbach; Timothy, Titus and Philemon, by J. J. van Oosterzee; Hebrews, by C. B. Moll. — 9. James, by J. P. Lange and J. J. van Oosterzee; Peter and Jude, by G. F. C. Fronmüller; John, by K. Braune. — 10. Revelations, by J. P. Lange.

Lange, Rud. Kleines Lehrbuch d. engl. Sprache. ('73.) 3d ed. 8°. '76. 40c. .... *Barthel.*

Langham revels. Guernsey, L. E. $1.50 .. (?) *Martien.*

Langhorne, G. W. Proselytism and proselyters; ed. by T. O. Summers. 18°. '60. 60c....... *So. Meth.*

Langhorne, J. *and* W. *See* Plutarch, Lives.

Langille, J. H. Among the willows. ill. 16°. '65. 60c. *Am. Tr.*

— Lighthouse boy. ill. 18°. '64. 25c......... *Am. Tr.*

— Save the erring. ill. 18°. '65. 45c......... *Am. Tr.*

— Secrets revealed. ill. 16°. '70. 80c......... *Am. Tr.*

— Snail-shell harbor. ('70.) New ed. ill. 16°. '73. $1.25 .... *Hoyt.*

Langl, Jos. Modern art education; from the Austrian report on Vienna Exposition, 1873; tr. with notes by S. R. Köhler, with introd. by C. B. Stetson. 8°. '75. pap., 75c .... *Prang.*

Langley, J. Baxter. Life [insurance] agents' vademecum; or, practical guide to success. Am. ed., rev. and enl. sq. 16°. 75c .... *Wynkoop.*

Langridge, N. T. Rambles among mountains. ('56.) 2d ed. 18°. '75. 40c. .... *So. Meth.*

Langstaff, Lancelot (*pseud.*) *See* Paulding, J. K.

Langstroth, L. L. Practical treatise on the hive and honey bee; with introd. by R. Baird. 12°. $2. *Judd; Lippincott.*

Language and poetry of flowers. ill. 16°. $1.25; $1.50 .... *World Pub.*

Language of flowers. 32°. 20c .... *Routledge.*

Language of flowers. 48°. 25c..... *Scribner, W. & A.*

Language of flowers. 32°. '75. 25c.; 50c... *Nelson.*

Language of flowers. 24°. $1.50 .... *Locke.*

Language of flowers and alphabet of floral emblems. 32°. 35c .... *U. P. James.*

Languellier, L: A. *See* Monsanto, H. M., *and* Languellier, L. A.

Languet, Jos. Reflections on the confidence in the mercy of God. 18°. 50c............ *Cath. Pub.*

Lanier, Clifford. Thorn-fruit. 8°. '67. pap., 50c... *Eyrich.*

Lanier, Sidney. Florida: its scenery, climate and history. ill. 12°. $1.75 .... *Lippincott.*

Lankester, Ctte. Marian and her pupils. ill. 12°. $1.25 .... *Scribner, W. & A.*

— The Medwins of Wykeham: tale of home life. ill. 12°. $1 .... *Routledge.*

Lankester, E. Ray. Comparative longevity in man and the lower animals. cr. 8°. '70. $1.50 .. *Macmillan.*

— Zoology. (Adv. sci. ser.) 12°. '74. $1.50 .. *Putnam.*

Lankester, Edn. Half hours with the microscope. ill. 18°. '73. $1.25 .... *Putnam.*

Lanman, C: Biographical annals of the civil government of the U. S. 8°. '76. $7; hf. mor., $8; mor., $10 .... *Anglim.*

— Dictionary of the U. S. Congress aad the general government. 5th ed., rev. 8°. '68. *$4 .. *Belknap.*

— The Japanese in Am. ill. 12°. '72. $1.50 .. *Univ. Pub.*

Lanman, Ja. H. History of Michigan. 18°. 75c. *Harper.*

Lanoye, Fd. de. Rameses the Great; or, Egypt 3300 years ago; tr. from the French. ill. 12°. '75. $1.25 .... *Scribner.*

— The sublime in nature. ill. 12°. '75. $1.25 .. *Scribner.*

Lanphier, J. C. Alone with Jesus: gleanings for closet reading. ('72.) 6th ed. 16°. '76. 85c.; $1.. *Tibbals.*

Lansdale lib. 6 v. 18°. $5.50........(?) *Martien.*
Cont.: Clifton Rice; or, thou God seest me.—Blind Tom; or, the lost found.—Duties and difficulties; or, Mary Mathieson.—Pastors' widows.—Working and waiting; or, patience in well-doing.—Raphael, the blind boy.

Lansing, Ab. *See* New York, Supreme Court reports.

Lantern journeys. Wilson, E. L. $2.... *Benerman.*

Lanthurn, W: H. Hymns for the sanctuary and social worship; with tunes. sq. 12°. $1.35; $1.75; $2.75; mor., $4.................. *Un. B. Pub.*

Lanzi, Luigi. History of painting in Italy; tr. by T: Roscoe. 3 v. 12°. (Bohn.) ea., $1.25. *Little, B. & Co.*

— *Same.* 3 v. 12°. (Bohn.) ea., $1.40.. *Scribner, W. & A.*

— *Same.* 3 v. 12°. (Bohn.) ea., $1.50....... *Lippincott.*

— Sacred heart of Jesus and the sacred heart of Mary; tr., with introd. by C. P. Meehan. 24°. 60c. *Cath. Pub.*

Laocoon. *See* Lessing, G. E.

Lape, T: The early saved. 2d ed. 18°. '73. 35c.; 50c.; pap., 15c..................... *Tibbals.*

La Peltrie, *Mme.* de —. Life. 18°. 50c..... *Strong.*

Lapham, I. A. Antiquities of Wisconsin. 4°. '55. pap., $6 .... *Smith. Inst.*

Lapointe, Savinien. Faerie gold for young and old; tr. by H. F. Chorley. ill. 12°. $1... *Routledge.*

Laporte, Laurent. Sailing on the Nile; tr. by V. Vaughan. 16°. '72. $1.50........... *Roberts.*

Lapsley and Bazley (*pub.*) How money is lost and made in Wall Street. 24°. '74. 30c...(?) *Lapsley.*

Lapstone. Abbott, J. 90c............... *Harper.*

La Rabbiata. *See* Heyse, P.

La Rame, Louise de. ["Ouida."] Novels. 14 v. 12°. ea., $1.50 .... *Lippincott.*
Cont.: Beatrice Boville, etc.—Bebee.—Cecil Castlemaine's gage, etc.—Chandos.—Folle-Farine.—Granville De Vigne.—Idalia.—In a winter city.—Pascarel.—Puck.—Randolph Gordon, etc.—Strathmore.—Tricotrin.—Under two flags.

— Cecil Castlemaine's gage, and other stories. 12°. $1.50 .... *Claxton.*

— Leaf (A) in the storm, and other novelettes. 8°. pap., 50c. .... *Lippincott.*

— Signa. 12°. $2..................... *Lippincott.*

Larboard fire. Wills, W. H. 15c.......... *French.*

Larcom, Lucy. Breathings of the better life. sm. 4°. '66. $2.50; hf. cf., $3.75; mor., $5.... *Osgood.*

— Childhood songs. ill. 12°. '74. $2.25; mor., $5. *Osgood.*

— Idyl (An) of work. [Poems.] 16°. '75. $1.50.. *Osgood.*

— Leila among the mountains. ('61.) New ed. ill. 16°. '74. 80c. .... *Hoyt.*

— Poems. 16°. '68. $1.50; hf. cf., $3....... *Osgood.*

— Ships in the mist. ('60.) New ed. ill. 18°. '68. 30c. *Hoyt.*

— Similitudes. ('60.) New ed. ill. 16°. '63. 65c... *Hoyt.*

— Sunbeam (The), and other stories. ('60.) New ed. ill. 16°. '72. 65c..................... *Hoyt.*

— (*ed.*) Roadside poems for summer travellers. 18°. '76. $1 .... *Osgood.*

Lard, Mos. E. Commentary on Romans; with rev. Gk. text. 2d ed. 8°. '75. $3; hf. mor., $5; mor., $8 .... *Tr. P. & P. Co.*

— Reply to a Baptist; or, what baptism is for. 32°. '70. pap., 10c. .... *Tr. P. & P. Co.*

— Review of "Campbellism examined." ('57.) 2d ed. 8°. $1.50 .... *Tr. P. & P. Co.*

L'Ardèche, Laurent de. Life of Napoleon; tr. from the French. ill. 8°. $3;—ill. by Cruikshank. sm. ill 8°. hf. cf., $5; cf., $6.50 .... *Appleton.*

Lardner, Dionysius. History of the world. ('69.) New ed., enl. ill. 12°. '74. $1.50.......... *Claxton*

— One thousand and ten things worth knowing. 12°. pap., 50c. .... *Peterson.*

— The steam engine. ill. 12°. 50c......... *Baird.*

Large letters. [Toy-book.] sq. 12°. per gross, $28.80. — 8°. per gross, $12.................. *Porter.*

Large letters for the little ones. [Toy-book.] ill. 8°. 15c.; 25c.; bds., 30c............... *Hurd & H.*

Large print stories. 6 v. ill. 16°. $2.40.... *Lothrop.*
Cont.: Illustrated primer.—Easy reading.—Birds and fishes.—Book of animals.—Book of birds.—Book of nat. hist.

Larimer, *Mrs.* Sa. L. The capture and escape; or, life among the Sioux. ill. 12°. '69. $1.50.. *Claxton.*

Larkin, Ja. Practical brass and iron founder's guide; [with] improvements by the Bessemer process. ('55; cop. '66.) 11th ed., rev. and enl. 12°. '76. $2.25 .... *Baird.*

Larkin, Mt. Rival collection of prose and poetry. ('72.) 2d ed. 8°. '73. $2...... *Schermerhorn.*

Larkin's love letters. Williams, T. J. 15c. *De Witt; French.*

Larkins, W: G: Handbook of Eng. literature. 16°. $1.25 .... *Routledge.*
Compr. Handbook of Eng. poet. lit., *and* Handbook of Eng. prose lit.

— Handbook of English poetical literature. 16°. bds., 50c. .... *Routledge.*

— Handbook of English prose literature. 16°. bds., 50c. .... *Routledge.*

Lark's (The) nest. 18°. 18c.............. *Am. S. S.*

Larned, Augusta. Home story series: no. 1. 3 v. 12°. '73. $4.................... *Meth. Bk. Conc.*
Cont.: Country stories.—Holiday stories.—Stories for leisure hours.

— *Same:* no. 2. 3 v. 12°. '73. $4.... *Meth. Bk. Conc.*
Cont.: Vacation stories.—Stories for little people.—Fireside stories.

— Talks with girls. 12°. '74. $1.50.. *Meth. Bk. Conc.*

Laroche, G. Abel. Fables. [Poems.] 18°. '69. $1.50. *Payot.*

La Roche, R. On pneumonia. 8°. $3......... *Lea.*

— On yellow fever: its hist., pathol., etiological and therapeutical relations. 2 v. 8°. $7...... *Lea.*

La Rochefoucauld, François (*Duc*) de. Maxims and moral reflections; also Shakespearian aphorisms; tr. por. 18°. $1.25.................... *Miller.*

Larrabee, C. S. Cipher and secret letter and telegraphic code, with Hogg's improvements. 18°. '70. $1....................... *Van Nostrand.*

Larrabee, W. H. Helps to speak and write correctly. 2d ed. 12°. '76. $1................ *Tibbals.*

Larrabee, W: C. Asbury and his coadjutors. 2 v. 12°. $2.25 .... *Cin. Meth. Bk. Conc.*

— Wesley and his coadjutors. 2 v. 16°. $2.25. *Cin. Meth. Bk. Conc.*

Larrazábal, Felipe. Vida de Bolívar. *See* Bolivar, S., Correspondencia general.

Larry Connor's charge. ill. 18°. '73. 60c.... *Lothrop.*

Larry Lockwell. Tuthill, L. C. $1..... *Perkinpine.*

Lars. Taylor, B. $1.50..................... *Osgood.*

Larwood, Jac. (*pseud.*) *See* Sadler, L. R.

Larwood, Ja. Story of the London parks. ill. 12°. $3 .... *Routledge.*

La Salle, J: B. de. Duty of a Christian towards God; tr. by Mrs. J. Sadlier. 12°. hf. bd., 63c... *Sadlier.*

— True friend of youth: life and virtues of La S. 18°. 60c. .... *O'Shea.*

Lasar, Sgsm. The Cæcilia: vocal music, with lessons in vocal training and musical notation. obl. 16°. '60. bds., $1 .... *Ditson.*

— The hymnary; with tunes. obl. 16°. '72. bds., 50c. *Biglow.*

Lascaris. *See* Villemain, A. F.

Las Casas, Bart. de. *See* Casas, B. de las.

Las Cases, Marin J. E. D. (*Comte*) de. Memoirs of life, exile and conversations of Napoleon I.; tr. 4 v. por. 12°. $7; $12.......... *Widdleton.*

Lascine; by an Oxford man. [Fiction.] 12°. $1.50. *Appleton.*

Lasker, R. Hebrew primer; tr. into Eng. 12°. bds., 20c. . . . . *Frank.*

Laslett, T: Timber and timber trees, native and foreign. ill. cr. 8°. '75. $3.50 . . . . *Macmillan.*

Lasselle, *Mrs.* N. P. Belle of Washington. 12°. $1.75; pap., $1.50 . . . . *Peterson.*

— High life in Washington. 12°. $1.75; pap., $1.50. *Peterson.*

Lassenius, Joh. Zwei-u. achtzig kurze Trostreden an Angefochtene aller Art. 8°. hf. leath., $1.15. *Volkening.*

Lasserre, Henri. Our lady of Lourdes; tr. [Historical.] 12°. $2; $2.50 . . . . *Sadlier.*

Last Aldini. Sand, G. 50c. . . . . *Peterson.*

Last Athenian. Rydberg, V. $2; $1.50 . . . *Peterson.*

Last Christmas. 18°. 25c.; 30c.; pap., 10c. . . *Dutton.*

Last chronicle of Barset. Trollope, A. $2; $1.50. *Harper.*

Last command. Charlesworth, M. L. 30c. . . . *Carter.*

Last day of the week. 18°. 35c. . . . . *Am. S. S.*

Last day of the week. Cheap, *Mrs.* —. 40c. *So. Meth.*

Last days of Christian martyrs. Bonar, A. R. 50c. *U. P. Bd. of Pub.*

Last days of Emma. 18°. 22c. . . . . *Am. S. S.*

Last days of Jerusalem. La Grange, A. K. de. $1.25. *O'Shea.*

Last days of Jesus. Moore, T. V. 90c. . . . . *Pres. Bd.*

Last days of Jesus Christ on earth. Jennings, A. G. 60c.; 90c. . . . . *Tibbals.*

Last days of a king. *See* Hartmann, M.

Last days of the papal army: siege and occupation of Rome in September, 1870. 18°. 15c. . . *Benziger.*

Last days of Pompeii. *See* Bulwer-Lytton, *Sir* E. G. E. L.

Last days of Pompeii. Medina, L. 15c. . . . . *French.*

Last drop: temperance drama. 16°. pap., 15c. *Happy.*

Last essays of Elia. *See* Lamb, C.

Last gift. 18°. 30c.; 35c. . . . . *Am. Bapt.*

Last gladiatorial show. Short, J. T. $1.25. *Cin. Meth. Bk. Conc.*

Last inhabitants of an old house. ill. 16°. '72. $1. *Dutton.*

Last knight. Auersperg, A. A. $2.50 . . . . *Hurd & H.*

Last leaf from Sunny-side. *See* Phelps, *Mrs.* E. S.

Last leap. 8°. pap., 25c. . . . . *De Witt.*

Last life: Irish drama. 16°. pap., 15c. . . . . . *French.*

Last lily: comedietta. 16°. pap., 15c. . . . . . *Happy.*

Last loaf. Baker, G. M. 15c. . . . . *Lee & S.*

Last man. Pitt, G. D. 15c. . . . . *French.*

Last of the barons. *See* Bulwer-Lytton, *Sir* E. G. E. L.

Last of the Catholic O'Malleys. Taunton, M. $1.25; $1.75 . . . . *Kelly, P. & Co.*

Last of the fairies. James, G. P. R. 25c. . . . *Harper.*

Last of the Huggermuggers. Cranch, C. P. $1.25. *Lee & S.*

Last of the legends: extravaganza. 16°. pap., 15c. *French.*

Last of the Mohicans. *See* Cooper, J. F.

Last of the Mohicans. Stewart, J. C. 15c. . . *De Witt.*

Last of the Mortimers. Oliphant, M. O. W. $1.50. *Harper.*

Last of the pigtails. Selby, C. 15c. . . . . *French.*

Last passover. Whitney, J. R. $1 . . . . *Claxton.*

Last sheaf. Hazen, M. $1.25 . . . . *Cong. Pub.*

Last shilling. Power, P. B. 60c. . . . . *Carter.*

Last shilling; or, the selfish child. 18°. 60c. . *Am. S. S.*

Last Sunday school lesson remembered; or, story of Harriet Russell. 18°. 60c. . . . . *Am. S. S.*

Last times and the great consummation. Seiss, J. A. $1.50 . . . . *Smith, E. & Co.*

Last tournament. *See* Tennyson, A.

Last travels of Ida Pfeiffer. 12°. $1.50 . . . . . *Harper.*

Last week of Davis Johnson, jr. 18°. 60c. . . . . *Carter.*

Last witness. Baker, O. C. 30c. . . *Cin. Meth. Bk. Conc.*

Last words of eminent persons. Kaines, J. $2. *Routledge.*

Late visitation of typhoid fever in Uppingham [England]. f°. '76. pap., $1 . . . . *Spon.*

Later lyrics. Howe, J. W. $2; $4; $6 . . . . *Lee & S.*

Later years. Prime, W. C. $1.50; $3.25 . . . *Harper.*

Latham, Bald. Scheme of sewage and sewage utilization for Hornsey [Eng.] map. 8°. pap., 40c. . . *Spon.*

Latham, H. Sertum Shaksperianum subnexis aliquot aliunde excerptis floribus; Latine reddidit. fp. 8°. '64. $1.50 . . . . *Macmillan.*

Latham, Rob. Gordon. Dictionary of the Eng. language; founded on that of Johnson as ed. by J. H. Todd. New ed., rev. and enl. 4 v. 4°. (Lond.) '66–'70. $45; hf. mor., $60 . . . . . *Little, B. & Co.*

— Handbook of the Eng. lang. 12°. $1.75 . . *Appleton.*

Latham, W: H. First lessons for deaf mutes. ill. 16°. '74. 27c. . . . . *Wilson, H. & Co.*

— Primary reader for deaf mutes. 16°. '76. bds., 45c. *Wilson, H. & Co.*

Lathan, J: Howard. Currency rates of sterling exchange; also tables of equivalent quotations, etc. med. 18°. '74. $2 . . . . *Clayton.*

— Sterling conversion tables: pounds into dollars and dollars into pounds; also table of equivalents and one of shillings and pence expressed decimally. roy. 8°. '74. hf. bd., $10 . . . . *Clayton.*

— Stock equivalents: tables giving equiv. quotations of London prices for Am. securities. 8°. '74. hf. bd., $5 . . . . *Clayton.*

— Tables of arbitrations of exchanges, comprising francs, reichsmarks and florins through sterling, francs through marks, and francs through florins (and their converse); also a table of equivalent thalers, reichsmarks and florins. roy. 8°. '74. hf. bd., $5 . . . . *Clayton.*

Lathe and its uses: instruction in turning wood and metal; with supplement. ill. 8°. $7. — Supplement and index. 8°. pap., 90c. . . . . *Wiley.*

Lathes, *Mrs.* Stanley. Morning clouds; or, Penelope. ill. 16°. '73. $1 . . . . *Dodd.*

Lathrop, G: P. Rose and roof-tree. [Poems.] 16°. '75. $1.50 . . . . *Osgood.*

— Study of Hawthorne. 18°. '76. $1.25 . . . . . *Osgood.*

Lathrop, *Mrs.* H: Allerton homes. ill. 16°. $1. *J. A. Moore.*

— Elm Grove cottage; or, a sister's influence. ('66.) New ed. ill. 16°. '74. $1.25 . . . . *Hoyt.*

Lathrop, J: *See* Massachusetts, Supreme Court reports.

Lathrop, Jos. Exposition of Epistle to the Ephesians; with memoir by W. B. Sprague. 8°. $2.75. *Pres. Bd.*

Lathrop, *Mrs.* Ma. A. Bethlehem and her children. ill. sq. 18°. '59. 30c. . . . . *Am. Tr.*

— Child's history of Paul. ill. sq. 18°. '61. 30c. . . *Am. Tr.*

— That sweet story of old. ill. sq. 18°. '57. 35c. . . *Am. Tr.*

Latimer, Faith. Children's church. 18°. 60c. . . *Pres. Bd.*

— *See also* How to teach the little folks.

Latimer, Hu. Life and writings. *See* British reformers.

Latimer family; or, principles and results. 18°. 85c. *Am. S. S.*

Latouche, J: Travels in Portugal. ill. 8°. '75. $3.50. *Putnam.*

Latour, T. New and improved method of instruction for the piano-forte. 4°. bds., $2.25 . . . . . *Ditson.*

— *Same.* f°. bds., $2 . . . . *Willig.*

Latreaumont. Sue, E. 50c. . . . . *U. P. James.*

La Trobe, Chr. Ign. Letters to my children, written at sea in 1815. 12°. $1 . . . . *Clauder.*

— Moravian tune book. New ed., enl.; with introd. by P. La Trobe. sm. f°. (Lond.) '67. $2.25. sm. 32°. $1.25 . . . . *Clauder.*

Latrobe, J. H. B. First steamboat voyage on the west. waters; — Lost chapter in hist. of the steamboat. *See* Maryland Hist. Soc.

La Trobe, Ja. The merits of Christ. [Lenten lectures.] 12°. (Lond.) '71. $1 .... *Clauder.*

Latta, S. A. Chain of sacred wonders: a connected view of Scripture scenes and incidents. ('58.) New ed. ill. 8°. '75. $3.50 .... *Pounsford.*

Latter-day pamphlets. *See* Carlyle, T:

Lattmann, I. Lateinisches Lesebuch. 8°. $1.20. . *Siemon.*

— Lateinisches Uebungsbuch. 8°. 85c. .... *Siemon.*

— Vorschule f. d. lateinischen Elementar Unterricht. 8°. 20c. .... *Siemon.*

— *and* Müller, H. D. Kurzgefasste lateinische Grammatik. 8°. $1.20 .... *Siemon.*

Lauda Sion. *See* Mendelssohn-Bartholdy, F.

Laugel, A: England, political and social; tr. by J. M. Hart. 12°. '74. $1.50 .... *Putnam.*

Laugh when you can. Reynolds, F. 15c. ..... *French.*

Laughable A B C. [Toy-book.] ill. 4°. $1; 50c. *Routledge.*

Laughing gas. White, C. 15c. .... *De Witt.*

Laughing gas: encyclopedia of wit, wisdom and wind. ill. 12°. pap., 25c. .... *Dick & F.*

Laughing hyena. Webster, B. 15c. .... *French.*

Laughing Kittie and Purring Kittie. *See* Aunt Lottie.

Laughing Kittie stories. 5 v. 18°. $3 . . . *Bost. Am. Tr.*

Cont.: Apples of gold. — Grandpa's Carlie, by Gano. — Laughing Kittie and Purring Kittie, by Aunt Lottie. — Our birds, by Mrs. F. I. B. Smith. — There's time enough.

Laughter-book for little people. ill. 4°. $2 . . . *Miller.*

Laune (Die) d. Verliebten. *See* Goethe, J. W. v.

Laura and Anna; or, the effect of faith on the character; tr. by MS. 18°. '71. 60c. .... *Cunningham.*

Laura and Lucy. Adams, C. $1.25 . . *Scribner, W. & A.*

Laura Clifford. Chase, M. G. 90c. .... *Dutton.*

Laura Temple. Bowman, A. 75c. .... *Routledge.*

Laura's garden. *See* Cousin Belle.

Laura's impulses; or, principle a safer guide than feeling. 18°. 40c. .... *Am. S. S.*

Laure. Hill, L. C. $1.50 .... *Claxton.*

Laurel leaves: poems, stories and essays by H. W. Longfellow, O. W. Holmes, J. R. Lowell, J. G. Whittier, W. C. Bryant and others; with ill. by Fredericks, S. Eytinge, jr., and others. 4°. '75. $6; mor., $12 .... *W. F. Gill.*

Laurel ser. 4 v. 16°. $5 .... *Lothrop.*

Cont.: Charley Laurel. — Alice Sutherland. — Tom's opinion. — Barbara.

Laurel ser. 8 v. 16°. '75. $2.80 .... *Nelson.*

Cont.: Lonely dove. — Boys who could not read. — Cottage door. — Wood cutter of Gutech. — Mary Wharton. — Divided money. — Charlotte, the Hindoo orphan. — Striving for the mastery.

Laurel wreath. Perkins, W. O. $1 . . *Pond; G. D. Russell.*

Laurels and jewels; compr. Bradbury's "Fresh laurels;" and Allen's, Sherwin's and Lowry's "Bright jewels." obl. 16°. '69. bds., 65c. ..... *Biglow.*

Laurence, J: Z. Handy-book of ophthalmic surgery. 2d ed., rev. and enl. ill. 8°. $2.75 .... *Lea.*

Laurence Bronson's victory. Mathews, J. A. 75c. *Carter.*

Laurence Monroe; or, lights and shades of New Eng. life. 16°. $1.25 .... *Cong. Pub.*

Laurence's love suit. Wooler, J. P. 15c. .... *French.*

Lauretta and the fables. 18°. '66. 50c. . . *Cunningham.*

Laurie, Jos. Elements of homœop. practice of physics. 12°. hf. mor., $1.25 .... *Boericke.*

— Homœopathic domestic medicine; rev. and enl. by A. G. Hull. 18°. 60c. .... *Boericke.*

— *Same;* rev. and enl. by R. J. McClatchey. 8°. hf. mor., $5 .... *Boericke.*

Laurie, Jos., *continued.*

— Parent's guide: diseases of infancy and childhood and their homœop. treatment; ed. and enl. by W. Williamson. 12°. $1 .... *Boericke.*

Laurie, T: Dr. Grant and the mountain Nestorians. ill. and maps. 16°. '74. $1.50 .... *Lothrop.*

Laus Veneris. Swinburne, A. C. $1.50 ..... *Carleton.*

Läuschen un Rimels. Reuter, F. 2 v. ea., $1; 75c. *Steiger.*

Lautenschlager, —. The young crusaders; from the Germ. 18°. 50c. .... *Strong.*

Lavater, J: C. Essays on physiognomy; tr. by T. Holcroft. 400 eng. 8°. hf. cf., $7.50 . . *Appleton.*

— *Same;* abridg. ill. 12°. hf. cf., $2.50; cf., $3. *Appleton.*

Lavater. Planché, J. R. 15c. .... *French.*

Lavengro. Borrow, G. 75c. .... *Harper.*

Lavinia and Lily; or, life at boarding-school. 18°. 60c. .... *Am. S. S.*

Law, H: W. Simplified interest tables. 4°. '74. $3. (?) *Kendall.*

Law, Ja. Farmer's veterinary adviser: guide to prevention and treatment of disease in domestic animals. ill. 12°. '76. $3 .... *Law.*

Law, J: Colonial hist. of Vincennes, Ind., under French, British and Am. governments, to admin. of Gen. Harrison. 12°. '58. $1.50 ..... *Clarke.*

Law, Ste. D. Digest of Am. cases rel. to patents and copyrights; also, cases in respect to trade-marks. v. 1 (1789–1862). roy. 8°. '62. shp., $8 . . *Cockcroft.*

— Patent and copyright laws of the U. S., 1790–1872; with decisions, forms and indexes. 12°. hf. shp., $2.50 .... *Baker, V. & Co.*

— United States courts practice. 8°. shp., $6.50. *W. C. Little.*

Law, W: Serious call to a devout and holy life. 18°. '37. 55c. .... *Meth. Bk. Conc.*

— *Same.* 16°. $1.25 .... *Routledge.*

— — Call to Christians. 18°. $1; 75c. .... *Am. Bapt.*

Law (The) allows it: musical monologue. 16°. pap., 15c. .... *Happy.*

Law (The) and the lady. *See* Collins, Wilkie.

Law lib. [Repub. of Eng. element. treatises.] 31 v. 8°. $93 .... *T. & J. W. Johnson.*

Cont.: 1. Wharton's Principles of conveyancing; Macnaghten's Select equity cases. — 2. Smith's Master and servant; Kelly's Usury. — 3. Tapping's Mandamus. — 4. Norman's Patents; Collier's Mines; Moore's Abstracts of title; Pollock's Production of documents. — 5. Woolrych's Treatise on law of waters; Polson's Law of nations; Horne's Diplomacy. — 6. Bunyon's Life assurance; Locke's Law of attachment; Supplement to Drewry's Injunctions. — 7. Grant's Corporations. — 8. Kerr's Action at law; Dearsley's Criminal process. — 9. Ross' Bills and promissory notes. — 10. Phillimore's International law; Pothier's Partnership. — 11. Bowyer's Universal public law; Levi's Mercantile law. — 12. Ross' Law of contracts. — 13. Thibaut's Introduction to jurisprudence; Parson's Wills. — 14. Coryton's Patents; Macnamara's Nullities — 15. Phillimore's International law, v. 2. — 16. Smith's real and personal property. 17. Cornish's Purchase deeds; Jones' History of the French bar. — 18. Brown's Commentaries on the common law. — 19. Mayne's Damages; Bucknell's Criminal lunacy. — 20. Grant's Banking. — 21. Fisher's Mortgages; Grapel's Roman civil law. — 22. Phillimore's International law, v. 3. — 23. Roberts' Principles of chancery; Powell's Evidence. — 24. Lewin's Trusts and trustees. — 25. Haynes' Outlines of equity. — 26. Ross' Suretyship, agency partnership and insurance. — 27. Fry's Specific performance; Phear's Treatise on the rights of waters. — 28. Westlake's Private international law; Appleton's Evidence. — 29, 30. Lindley's Partnership, v. 1, 2; Beaumont's Bills of sale. — 31. Trower's Debtor and creditor; Hunter's Suit in equity.

Law of God explained and enforced. Plumer, W. S. $2 .... *Pres. Bd.*

Law of love. 18°. 50c. .... *Pres. Bd.*

Law of love, and love as a law. Hopkins, M. $1.75. *Scribner.*

Law of nature. *See* Volney, C. F. C.

Law of the road. Rogers, R. V., *jr.* $1.50 . . *S. Whitney.*

Law versus love. Linley, G. 15c. .... *French.*

Lawford, Louisa. Dream-book and fortune-teller. 16°. '72. bds., 40c. .... *Routledge.*

Lawford, Louisa, *continued.*
— Every girl's book: amusements for recreation in home circles. ill. 16°. $1.25........*Routledge.*
Lawrence, Annie M. Olive Loring's mission. ill. 16°. '71. $1.25..........................*Lothrop.*
Lawrence, E. A. Life of Rev. Joel Hawes; with introd. by T. D. Woolsey. 8°. $2.75..*Hamersley.*
Lawrence, F. E. Manual of devotions for the holy communion. 24°. '70. 35c.; 50c....*Randolph.*
Lawrence, G: Alfr. Novels. 8 v. 12°. hf. roxb., $10. *Routledge.*
Cont.: Anteros. — Barren honor. — Brakespeare. — Breaking a butterfly. — Guy Livingstone. — Maurice Dering. — Sans merci. — Sword and gown.
— *Same.* 7 v. 8°. pap....................*Harper.*
Cont.: Anteros, 50c. — Brakespere, 50c. — Breaking a butterfly, 35c. — Hagarene, 75c. — Maurice Dering, 50c. — Sans merci, 50c. — Sword and gown, 25c.
— Breaking a butterfly. ill. 16°. $1.25....*Lippincott.*
— Guy Livingstone; or, "thorough." 12°. $1.25; bds., $1..................................*Routledge.*
— *Same.* 12°. $1.50.....................*Harper.*
Lawrence, G: N. Birds of Mexico. (Bull. of Nat. Mus., no. 4.) 8°. '76. pap., 25c...*Smith. Inst.*
— — *See also* United States, *National Mus.*
— List of birds of west. Mexico; with notes on their habits, etc., by A. J. Grayson. 4°. pap., $1.25. *Bost. Soc. Nat. Hist.*
Lawrence, J: History of the Church of the United Brethren in Christ. 8°. shp., $2.50..*Un. B. Pub.*
— Manual of rules of order for conducting deliberate assemblies. 18°. 30c. ....*Un. B. Pub.*
Lawrence, J: *See* New Am. pocket farrier.
Lawrence, M. W. Light on the dark river: memorials of Mrs. H. A. L. Hamlin. 12°. $1.50..**Osgood.*
Lawrence, Ph. The Lawrence speaker. 12°. $2. *Peterson.*
— The model speaker. ('69.) 9th ed. 12°. '75. hf. mor., $1.50.........................*Eldredge.*
— *See also* Comstock, A., *and* Lawrence, P.
Lawrence, R. H. Tables of earned and unearned fire premiums at pro-rata and short rates. roy. 4°. '69. $10..........................*Spectator.*
Lawrence, S: Moral design of Freemasonry. 12°. '71. $1....................................*Masonic.*
Lawrence, Slingsby. [Plays.] 6 v. 16°. ea., pap., 15c.................................*French.*
Cont.: Buckstone's adventure: farce.— Cozy couple: farce. — Game of speculation: comedy. — Give a dog a bad name: farce. — Lawyers: comedy. — Sunshine through the clouds.
— Give a dog a bad name: farce. 16°. pap., 15c...*Lee & S.*
— Sunshine through the clouds: drama. 16°. pap., 15c. *Lee & S.*
— *and* Mathews, C. Strange history: drama. 16°. pap., 15c...............................*French.*
Lawrence, W: Lectures on comparative anat., physiol., zoology and nat. hist. of man. 12°. (Bohn.) $1.75.................*Little, B. & Co.*
— *Same.* 12°. (Bohn.) $2..*Lippincott; Scribner, W. & A.*
Lawrence, W: *See* Ohio, Sup. Court reports.
Lawrence, W: Beach. Foreign treaties of U. S. in conflict with state laws rel. to transmission of real estate to aliens; with laws of various countries affecting property of married women. 8°. $1.50.........................*Baker, V. & Co.*
— Visitation and search: hist. sketch of British claim to exercise maritime police over vessels of all nations. 8°. '58. $1..........*Little, B. & Co.*
Lawrence, W: H. Caroline Morin. ill. 18°. '54. 20c. *Am. Tr.*
Lawrence, W: R. Life of Amos Lawrence. New ed. ill. 16°. '75. $1.50.................*Lothrop.*
Lawrence speaker. Lawrence, P. $2.....*Peterson.*
Lawrence's adventures. *See* Trowbridge, J. T.
Lawrences (The). Turnbull, C. $2......*U. S. Pub.*

Lawry, W. Missions in Tonga and Feejee. 12°. $1.50. *Cin. Meth. Bk. Conc.*
Laws and polity of the Jews. 12°. 50c...*Meth. Bk. Conc.*
Laws and practice of game of euchre and draw poker. 32°. $1..............................*Peterson.*
Laws from heaven for life on earth. Arnot, W. $2.50. *Nelson.*
Laws of the kingdom. Dykes, J. O. $1.25..*Carter.*
Laws of love. 12°. pap., 30c.............*Dick & F.*
Lawson, G: Diseases and injuries; with formulary, test types and ill. 12°. '69. $2.50....*Lindsay.*
— Injuries of the eye, orbit and eyelids. ill. 8°. $3.50. *Lea.*
Lawson, *Rev.* G: Reflections on the illness and death of a beloved daughter. 32°. 25c......*Pres. Bd.*
Lawson, H: Manual of popular physiology. ill. 18°. '74. $1 ....*Putnam.*
Lawson, J. A. Wanderings in the interior of New Guinea. map. 8°. $3......*Scribner, W. & A.*
Lawton, —. *See* Beck, —, *and* Lawton, —.
Lawyer abroad. Day, H. $2...............*Carter.*
Lawyer and his clients. Stickney, A. 50c...*Osgood.*
Lawyer in the school room. Walsh, M. McN. $1. *Schermerhorn.*
Lawyer's daughter. Alden, J. 75c.........*Harper.*
Lawyer's secret. Braddon, M. E. 25c.....*Peterson.*
Lawyer's story. Maitland, J. A. $1.75; $1.50. *Peterson.*
Lawyers. Lawrence, S. 15c...............*French.*
Laxton, H: Builders and contractors' tables; for engineers, architects, surveyors, builders, etc.: 53 tables. 4°. $2..........................*Spon.*
Lay, E. Eliz. How to be a hero. 18°. 45c...*Bost. Am. Tr.*
— — *See also* Young hero stories.
Lay, H: Champlin. Letters to a man bewildered. 12°. pap., 10c...............................*Dutton.*
— Studies in the church: letters to an old-fashioned layman. 16°. '72. $1....................*Pott.*
— *See also* Tracts for missionary use.
Lay of the bell. *See* Schiller, J. F. v.
Lay of the last minstrel. *See* Scott, *Sir* W.
Lay sermons. Huxley, T. H. $2........*Macmillan.*
Layard, Aust. H: Discoveries among the ruins of Nineveh and Babylon, with travels in Armenia, etc. 2d ed. 12°. '75. $1.75...............*Barnes.*
— *Same;* abridg. by author. ill. 12°. $1.75..*Harper.*
— Fresh discoveries at Nineveh and Babylon; with travels in Armenia, Kurdistan and the desert. maps and ill. 8°. $4; hf. cf., $6.25....*Harper.*
Laycock, T: Lectures on principles and methods of med. obs. and research. roy. 12°. $1.....*Lea.*
Laying the keel. *See* Silverbeach lib.
Layman's breviary. Schefer, L. $1.50; $2.25..*Roberts.*
Layman's story. Abbott, L. $1.25...........*Dodd.*
Layriz, F. Evangelisch-luth. Choralbuch f. Kirche u. Haus. 8°. hf. leath., $2......... *Volkening.*
— Vor- u. Zwischenspiele zu d. gangbarsten Choralmelodien; aus "Kern d. deutschen Kirchengesangs." 8°. hf. leath., $2.50........ *Volkening.*
— Zwei hundert u. fünf u. zwanzig Melodien deutscher Kirchengesänge, meist a. d. 16. u. 17. Jahrh. ('62.) 4th ed. 8°. '76. 30c..........*Barthel.*
Lays and lyrics of ancient Palestine: ill. of Old Test. hist. ill. 8°. $4.......................*Nelson.*
Lays of ancient Rome. *See* Macaulay, T. B.
Lays of the Holy Land. ill. 8°. $4.50; $7.50..*Carter.*
Lays of the Hudson. Hoffman, C. F. 38c...*Appleton.*
Lays of the Scottish cavaliers. Aytoun, W. E. $1.50; $3 .... *Widdleton.*
Lays of Sweden and Finland: Scandinavian songs. f°. '76. $4...........................*L. Meyer.*
Lazar house. 18°. 50c.; 55c...............*Dutton.*

Lazare, C: Champion school for the flute [*or* pianoforte, *or* violin]: instructions with music. obl. 8°. ea., pap., 60c. . . . . . *G. D. Russell.*

Lazarus, Emma. Admetus, and other poems. cr. 8°. $2 . . . . . . *Hurd & H.*

— Alide: romance of Goethe's life. 12°. $1.25. *Lippincott.*

— Poems. cr. 8°. $2.25 . . . . . . *Hurd & H.*

Lazarus, and other poems. Plumptre, E. H. $1.75. *Routledge.*

Lazelle, H. M. One law in nature: unity of force, identity of matter, and its multiple atom constitution, applied to phys. affections or modes of energy. 12°. '73. $1.50 . . . . . . *Van Nostrand.*

Lazy Arthur. 32°. 15c. . . . . . *Dutton.*

Lazy birds; or, the result of idleness. ill. cr. 4°. pap., 20c.; 25c. . . . . . *J. E. Potter.*

Lazy Lawrence. *See* Edgeworth, M.

Lazy Robert. *See* Baker, *Mrs.* H. N. W.

Lazy Stephen. McKeever, H. B. 30c. . . . . . *Hoyt.*

Lazy tour of two idle apprentices. *See* Dickens, C.

Lea, Eliz. E. Domestic cooking: receipts and hints to young housekeepers. 12°. '73. $1.25. *Cushings & B.*

Lea, H: Carey. Historical sketch of sacerdotal celibacy in the Christian church. 8°. '67. $3.75. *Claxton; Lea; Lippincott.*

— Studies in church hist.: rise of temporal power, benefit of clergy, excommunication. 12°. $2.75 . . *Lea.*

— Superstition and force: essays on wager of law, wager of battle, ordeal and torture. 12°. $2.75 . . *Lea.*

— Synopsis of the fresh-water bivalves. imp. 4°. bds., $5 . . . . . . *Lea.*

Lea, I: Contributions to geology. 8°. pl. $5. *Acad. of Nat. Sci.*

— Fossil foot-marks: text and pl. f°. $1; — without text, 50c. . . . . . *Acad. of Nat. Sci.*

— Observations on the genus unio. v. 1–13. lith. pl. 4°. $60; — v. 2, 3, 5–11, 13, ea., $5. *Acad. of Nat. Sci.*

— *and* Carpenter, P. P. Check list of shells in No. Am. 8°. '60. pap., 25c. . . . . . *Smith. Inst.*

Lea, *Rev.* W. Catechising on the Prayer book. 18°. '73. pap., 15c. . . . . . *Pott.*

Lea, W: Tables of strength and deflection of timber. post 8°. (Lond.) '50. 75c. . . . . . *Spon.*

Leach, Dan. Complete spelling book. ('56.) New ed. 16°. '76. bds., 32c. . . . . . *Cowperthwait.*

— Geographical quest. book. ('63.) New ed. 16°. '74. bds., 32c. . . . . . *Cowperthwait.*

Leach, G: Church and home: sacred music. obl. 4°. '57. $2.75; bds., $2.50 . . . . . . *Ditson.*

— Laus Domino. [Church music.] obl. 4°. $2.75; bds., $2.50 . . . . . . *Gordon.*

Leach Club (The). Owen, G. W. $1.50 . . . . *Lee & S.*

Leader (The). Palmer, H. R., *and* Emerson, L. O. $1.38 . . . . . . *Ditson.*

Leaders of the old bar of Philadelphia. Binney, H. $5 . . . . . . *J. Campbell & Son.*

Leaders of public opinion in Ireland. Lecky, W. E. H. $1.75 . . . . . . *Appleton.*

Leading ideas of the Gospels. Alexander, W. $1.75. *Macmillan.*

Leading strings. Troughton, A. C. 15c. . . . . . *French.*

Leading strings to knowledge. Trimmer, S. K. $1. *Miller.*

Leaf in the storm. La Rame, L. de. 50c. . . *Lippincott.*

League of the Miami. Bennett, E. 25c. . . *U. P. James.*

Leah; or, the forsaken: romance of a Jewish maiden. 8°. pap., 50c. . . . . . *Peterson.*

Leah, the forsaken: play. 16°. pap., 15c. . . . . *French.*

Leah, a woman of fashion. Edwards, A. $1.75; $1. *Sheldon.*

Leah and Rachel. Hammond, J. 75c. . . . . . *Sabin.*

Leah Mordecai. Abbott, B. K. $1.50 . . *Baker, P. & Co.*

Leahy, J. P. Art of swimming in the Eton style. ill. cr. 8°. '75. $1 . . . . . . *Macmillan.*

Leake, I: Q. Memoir of Gen. John Lamb and his correspondence with Washington, Clinton, etc. por. and maps. 8°. '50. $2.50 . . . . . . *Munsell.*

Leal (*pseud.*) *See* Disosway, E.

Leander, R: Fantastic stories; tr. by P. B. Granville. ill. 12°. $1.75 . . . . . . *Routledge.*

Leandro. S., J. $1.50 . . . . . . *Cunningham; Sadlier.*

Leap year. Buckstone, J. B. 15c. . . . . . *French.*

Leap year. Sedgwick, A. B. 15c. . . . . . *De Witt.*

Lear, E: Book (A) of nonsense. col. ill. obl. 8°. $2; bds., $1.50 . . . . . . *Miller.*

— Books of nonsense. 4 nos. ill. demy 4°. ea., 50c.; in 1 v., $2.50 . . . . . . *Scribner, W. & A.*

— Nonsense songs: stories, botany and alphabets. ill. sq. 12°. $2 . . . . . . **Osgood.*

Lear, *Mrs.* Sidney. Bossuet and his contemporaries. 12°. '75. $3.50 . . . . . . *Pott.*

— Dominican artist (A): sketch of Père C. J. B. Besson. cr. 8°. $1.75 . . . . . . *Lippincott.*

— *Same.* 12°. '72. $2 . . . . . . *Kelly, P. & Co.*

— Life of Louise de France, daughter of Louis XV. 12°. '72. $3 . . . . . . *Pott.*

— Life of St. François de Sales. 12°. $3 . . . . . . *Pott.*

— Light of the conscience; with introd. by Rev. T. T. Carter. 12°. '76. $2 . . . . . . *Pott.*

— Revival of priestly life in France in 17th cent. 12°. '73. $2.50 . . . . . . *Pott.*

— *See also* Grou, N: J: Hidden life of the soul.

Lear. *See* Shakespeare, W:

Lear of private life. Moncrieff, W. T. 15c. . . *French.*

Lear of the steppe. *See* Turgenieff, I.

Leared, Arth. Imperfect digestion: its causes and treatment. 6th ed., rev. and enl. 12°. '70. $1.75 . . . . . . *Lindsay.*

Learn of me: words of truth and love from the best teacher. 12°. 75c. . . . . . *Nelson.*

Learn to say no; or, the city apprentice. 18°. 40c. *Pres. Bd.*

Learning about common things; — about right and wrong. Abbott, J. ea., 90c. . . . . . *Harper.*

Learning better. *See* Good child's lib.

Learning of Jesus. *See* Kennedy, *Mrs.* M. G.

Learning to act; — to converse; — to feel. *See* Mogridge, G:

Learning to live. 16°. 90c. . . . . . *Am. Bapt.*

Learning to read; — to talk; — to think. Abbott, J. ea., 90c. . . . . . *Harper.*

Learning to think. *See* Mogridge, G:

Learning with pleasure. *See* Big type stories.

Leary's reckoner and form book: the trader's [etc.,] assistant for buying and selling commodities, [etc.]; with tables, etc. ('43.) New ed. 32°. '76. bds., 25c. . . . . . *Leary; McDowell.*

Leask, W: Footsteps of the Messiah. 12°. $1.50. (?) *Martien.*

Leather Lungos the Great: extravaganza. 16°. pap., 15c. . . . . . *French.*

Leather stocking and silk. Cooke, J. E. $1.50 . . *Harper.*

Leather-stocking tales. *See* Cooper, Ja. F.

Leatherman, P. R. Elements of moral science. 12°. '58. $1.75 . . . . . . *Challen.*

Leathes, Stanley. Religion of the Christ. *See* Bampton lectures.

— Structure of the Old Testament: essays. 16°. '73. $1.25 . . . . . . *Smith, E. & Co.*

Leave it to me: farce. 16°. pap., 15c. . . . . . *French.*

Leavens, B. F. Service of song: church music, arranged for four voices; with piano or organ accomp. f°. '49. $3.50 . . . . . . *Ditson.*

Leaves and flowers. Wood, A. $1.50 ......*Barnes.*

Leaves from the book of human life. Arthur, T. S. $1.75 ......*J. E. Potter.*

Leaves from the book of life. 18°. 55c.; 65c. *Am. Bapt.*

Leaves from a Christmas bough. Bond, A. L. $3. *Routledge.*

Leaves from a family journal. Souvestre, E. $1. *Appleton.*

Leaves from the note-book of a naturalist. 8°. pap., 50c. ......*Littell & G.*

Leaves from the note-book of a N. Y. detective. 8°. pap., 75c. ......*Dick & F.*

Leaves from a summer book. Allen, F. B. $6..*Estes.*

Leaves from Sunday school and mission fields. Hale, M. P. 75c. ......*Bost. Am. Tr.*

Leaves from the tree of life. *See* Newton, R:

Leaves gathered in the daily walks of life. Thomas, J. H. $1.50 ......*H. A. Young.*

Leaves of comfort. 12°. '69. 75c. ......*Lothrop.*

Leaves of consolation for the afflicted. Williams, H. D. $1 ......*Pres. Bd.*

Leaves of grass. Whitman, W. $5 ...... *Whitman.*

Leaves of life. 18°. '69. 40c. ......*Am. Tr.*

Leaves that never fade; or, records of teachings and help. 24°. '60. 35c. ......*Meth. Bk. Conc.*

Leaving home. Grosvenor, H. S. 35c. ......*Hoyt.*

Leavitt, A. J. [Plays.] 13 v. 16°. ea., pap., 15c...*De Witt.*
Cont.: Big mistake. — Bruised and cured. — Cremation. — High Jack, the heeler. — In and out. — Lost will. — Remittance from home. — Rigging a purchase. — Sleep-walker: farce. — Squire for a day. — Stranger: burlesque. — Them papers. — Who died first?

— Sleep walker: farce. 16°. pap., 17c. ......*French.*

Leavitt, Hum. H. *See* United States, Circ. and Dist. Court reports.

Leavitt, J: M. Faith: poem. 16°. 40c. *Cin. Meth. Bk. Conc.*

— Hymns to our king. 18°. '72. 60c..... *Whittaker.*

Leavitt, T: H. Facts about peat as an article of fuel. 12°. $1.75 ......*Lee & S.*

Leavitt, W: B. Farmer's almanac. [Annual.] 12°. pap., 10c. ......*Eastman.*

Le Bas, C: W. Life of Cranmer. 2 v. 18°. $1.50. *Harper.*

— Life of Wiclif. 18°. 75c. ......*Harper.*

Leben u. Treiben in New York. Griesinger, T. 50c.; 25c. ......*Zickel.*

Lebensbilder a. d. Westen. Ruppius, O. 75c.; 70c. *Zickel.*

Lebenskämpfe. *See* Hoffmann, F.

Lebenskämpfe in d. alten u. neuen Welt. Körner, H. J. A. 2 v. $2.50 ......*Schmidt.*

Lebenslauf eines Dollars. Gruhler, J. 20c...*Pilger.*

Lebensversicherung (Die). *See* Hoffmann, F.

Leber, —, *and* Rottenstein, —. Dental caries and its causes: investigation into influence of fungi in destruction of teeth; tr. by T. H. Chandler. ill. 8°. '73. $1.50 ......*Lindsay.*

Lebert, Sgsm., *and* Stark, L: Grand theoret. and pract. piano school; tr. by C. E. R. Müller. 4°. $4; — in 4 pts. pap. 1, 2, ea., $1.50; 3, 4, ea., $1.75 ......*G. D. Russell.*

— — *Same.* 2 pts. 4°. ea., bds., $4; — bks. 1, 3 and 4, ea., $1.50; 2, $1.75 ......*Ditson.*

— — *Same.* [In Eng. or Germ.] (Cotta ed.) nos. 1–3. f°. ea., $4.80; 4, $6.30 ......*Gordon.*

Lebeurier, P. F. Life of Mother St. Joseph; tr. from the Fr. 12°. $2; $2.50 ......*Sadlier.*

Le Bon, Hub. Beauties of the sanctuary; from the Fr. ('60.) 2d ed. 18°. '70. 75c.; $1.25..*Kelly, P. & Co.*

— The holy communion, it is my life! tr. by M. A. Garnett. 2d ed., rev. 18°. '71. $1; $1.50..*Murphy.*

Le Boys des Guays, J. F. E. Letters to a man of the world; from the Fr. 16°. $1.50....*Lippincott.*

Le Brun, Pigault. *See* Pigault Le Brun, C. A. G.

Le Carpentier, Adph. Elementary school for the piano-forte; tr. with add. by H. Daum; with Am. and foreign fingering. obl. 4°. bds., $1..*G. D. Russell.*

— First method for the piano forte. 4°. '70. bds., $1; pap., 80c. ......*Ditson.*

— *Same:* Am. fingering. obl. 4°. pap., 80c.; bds., $1. — Same: foreign fingering. obl. 4°. pap., 80c.; bds., $1 ......*Gordon.*

Lechler, Gth. Vct. On Acts. *See* Lange, J. P., Commentary.

Lecky, W: E: Hartpole. History of European morals. 2 v. 8°. $6; hf. cf., $10 ......*Appleton.*

— History of rise and influence of spirit of rationalism in Europe. 2 v. sm. 8°. $4; hf. cf., $8..*Appleton.*

— Leaders of public opinion in Ireland: Swift, Flood, Grattan, O'Connell. 12°. $1.75......*Appleton.*

Leclerq, Thdr. Trois proverbes; avec vocab. ('65.) New ed. 12°. '68. pap., 40c. ......*Holt.*

Lecocq, C: My new maid: opera for amateurs. 16°. pap., 40c. ......*French.*

Lecomte, Fd. War in the U. S.: report to the Swiss military department; tr. from the Fr. 12°. '63. $1 ......*Van Nostrand.*

Le Conte, J: Lawr. Address before Am. Assoc. for Advanc. of Sci., Aug., 1874. 8°. pap., 25c. *Am. Assoc. Adv. Sci.*

— Classification of coleoptera of No. Am. 8°. '62. pap., $1.50 ......*Smith. Inst.*

— *Same.* pt. 2. 8°. '73. pap., 50c......*Smith. Inst.*

— Coleoptera of Kansas and New Mexico. 4°. '59. pap., $1.25 ......*Smith. Inst.*

— List of coleoptera of No. Am. pt. 1. 8°. '66. pap., 75c. ......*Smith. Inst.*

— New species of No. Am. coleoptera. 8°. '66. pap., $1. — pt. 2. 8°. '73. pap., 50c.....*Smith. Inst.*

Le Conte, Jos. Religion and science: Sunday lectures on relation of natural and revealed religion. 12°. $1.50 ......*Appleton.*

Lectures, historical, expository and practical upon communion office of the Prot. Episc. Ch.; by a presbyter of the church. 12°. $1.25...*Lippincott.*

Lectures on the evidences of Christianity, 1850–1, at Univ. of Va. ('51.) New ed. 8°. '59. $3..*Carter.*

Lectures on painting by the Royal Academicians; with introd. essay and notes by R. Wornum. 12°. (Bohn.) $1.75 ......*Little, B. & Co.*

— *Same.* 12°. (Bohn.) $2..*Lippincott; Scribner, W. & A.*

Lectures to children; rev. by T. O. Summers. ('57.) 2d ed. 18°. '75. 50c. ......*So. Meth.*

Lectures to ladies on practical subjects. 3d ed., rev. cr. 8°. '57. $2 ......*Macmillan.*

Lectures to my students. Spurgeon, C. H. $1.25. *Sheldon.*

Led. Keene, S. F. $1.50 ......*Hoyt.*

Led astray. [Fiction.] Feuillet, O. $1.75..*Carleton.*

— *Same:* drama. 15c. ......*French.*

Led astray. Wilmer, L. A. 25c. ......*Barclay.*

Led to the light. Denison, M. A. $1.25..(?)*Martien.*

Ledderhose, C: T. Life of A. G. Spangenberg; tr. from the Germ. 12°. (Lond.) '55. $1..*Clauder.*

Ledge rock lib. 10 v. 18°. $4 ......*Randolph.*
Cont.: Right way. — Two heaps. — Lost and found. — Lost pearl. — Lydia's duty. — Clover glen. — Gentle Gracie. — Gleaners. — Painstaking. — Black Judy.

Ledgeside series. 6 v. 16°. $7.50 ......*Carter.*
Cont.: Squire Downing's heirs. — Margaret Russell's school. — Busy bees. — Grandfather's Nell. — Conant farm. — Down the steps.

Ledru, Fs. Comprehensive grammar of French. 12°. '66. $1 ......*Barnes.*

— Fables in French. 12°. '66. 75c. ......*Barnes.*

— French reader. 12°. '66. $1 ......*Barnes.*

Ledyard, Laura W. Very young Americans. ill. sq. 16°. '72. $1 ......*Roberts.*

Lee, Alfr. A life hid in Christ with God: memoir of Susan Allibone, chiefly from her diary and letters. 8°. '55. $2.25 .... *Claxton; Lippincott.*

Lee, B. Correct principles of treatment for angular curvature of the spine. ill. 12°. $1 .. *Lippincott.*

Lee, C: A. Elements of geology for popular use; with descript. of geol. formations and mineral resources of U. S. ill. 18°. 75c. .... *Harper.*

— Human physiology; for element. schools. 12°. '47. hf. roan, $1.13 .... *Claxton; Lippincott.*

Lee, Day K. Master builder; or, life at a trade. 12°. $1.25 .... *Williamson.*

— Summerfield; or, life on a farm. 12°. $1.25. *Williamson.*

Lee, Edith (*pseud.*) *See* Burckett, *Miss* F.

Lee, Fes., *and* Locke, Una. Eggs that were never peacocks. *See* Bertie and Amy books.

Lee, F: G: Christian doctr. of prayer for the departed; with notes and app. 8°. '72. $4 .. *Pott; Routledge.*

— Validity of the holy orders of the Church of Eng. maintained and vindicated; with foot-notes, tables and app. 8°. '69. $7 .... *Pott.*

Lee, G. *See* England, Ecclesiastical reports.

Lee, G: Mantle of Elijah. [Juvenile.] 16°. $1.50. (?) *Martien.*

Lee, Harvey. *See* California, Sup. Court reports.

Lee, H: Memoirs of the war (of '76) in the south. dept. of the U. S. New ed., rev. with life of author by R. E. Lee. ill., por., maps, plans, etc. 8°. '69. $4; hf. cf., $6 .... *Univ. Pub.*

Lee, H: Lectures on syphilis and some forms of local disease affecting principally the organs of generation. 8°. $2.25 .... *Lea.*

Lee, *Maj.* H: Observations on writings of T: Jefferson; with particular ref. to [their] attack on memory of Gen. H: Lee. 8°. '32. bds., $3. *J. W. Randolph.*

Lee, H: W. Baptized child. 18°. 30c.; pap., 10c. *Dutton.*

— Family prayers. 16°. '59. $1.25 .... *Dutton.*

— Prayers for children. 32°. 25c. .... *Dutton.*

Lee, Herb. Avenger: melodrama. 16°. pap., 15c. *French.*

Lee, Holme (*pseud.*) *See* Parr, Ht.

Lee, J. B. How to make a will. 18°. '73. 40c.; 50c.; shp., 90c. .... *Am. Tr.*

Lee, J. F. *See* Cohen, J. I., *and* Lee, J. F.

Lee, Jud. S. Nature and art in the old world. 12°. $1.50 .... *Williamson.*

— Sacred cities. 12°. $1.25 .... *Williamson.*

Lee, Leila. Wee-wee songs for our little pets. ill. sq. 32°. 75c. .... *Mason.*

Lee, Leroy M. Advice to a young convert. 12°. '38. $1.25 .... *So. Meth.*

— Great supper (The) not Calvinistic: reply to Fairchild's discourses on parable of the great supper; ed. by T. O. Summers. ('55.) 2d ed. 18°. '75. 75c. .... *So. Meth.*

— Life and times of Jesse Lee. 8°. '59. $2 .. *So. Meth.*

Lee, *Miss* M. E. Emily Ashton. ill. 16°. '72. $1.10. *Am. Tr.*

Lee, Ma. B. Lucien Guglieri. 16°. '75. 60c. *Meth. Bk. Conc.*

Lee, Ma. Eliz. Historic tales for youth; or, social evenings. 18°. 75c. .... *Harper.*

Lee, Ma. P., *and* Hadley, H. English grammar. ('73.) 4th ed. 12°. '75. $1 .... *Hadley.*

Lee, Minnie Ma. Hubert's wife: story for you. 12°. '75. $1.50 .... *Kelly, P. & Co.*

— Myrrha Lake; or, into the light of Catholicity. 2d ed. 16°. '73. $1 .... *Cath. Pub.*

Lee, N. H. Immersionists against the Bible; ed. by T. O. Summers. ('56.) 2d ed. 18°. '73. 75c. *So. Meth.*

Lee, *Mrs.* R. Young hunter's lib. 4 v. ill. 16°. ea., $1.50 .... *Lee & S.*

Cont.: Australian wanderers. — African Crusoes. — Anecdotes of animals. — Anecdotes of birds, fish, reptiles, etc.

Lee, Rob. E. The Christian soldier: life of R. E. Lee. 18°. '73. $1 .... *Claxton.*

Lee, S: Prologomena in Biblia polyglotta. 4°. (Bagster.) $3.25 .... *Wiley.*

Lee, S: Bible (The) regained, and the God of the Bible ours; or, system of religious truth in outline. 12°. $1.50 .... *Lee & S.*

— Eschatology; or, Scripture doctrine of the coming of the Lord, the judgment and the resurrection. 12°. '59. $1.50 .... *Tilton.*

Lee, *Miss* So. Chapter of accidents: farce. 16°. pap., 15c. .... *French.*

Lee, T: J. Tables and formulæ [for] surveying, etc. *See* United States, *Corps of Eng.*

Lee, W: On inspiration of the Scriptures: its nature and proof. 8°. '76. $2.50 .... *Carter.*

Lee and Walker's juvenile melodeon instructor. 8°. '69. pap., 60c. .... *Ditson.*

Lee and Walker's juvenile piano instructor. Bellak, J. 60c. .... *Ditson.*

Lee Avenue collection; or, the young singer's friend: hymns and songs, comp. by the superintendent. 24°. '57. 75c. .... *Barnes.*

Leech, Harry Harewood. Letters of a sentimental idler, from Greece, Turkey, Egypt, Nubia and the Holy Land. por. and ill. 12°. $2.50 .. *Appleton.*

Leech, J: (*ill.*) Pictures of life and character: sketches from "Punch." 5 v. in 3. obl. f°. (Lond.) hf. mor., $30 .... *Little, B. & Co.*

— *Same.* 5 v. in 3. f°. hf. mor., $35 ..... *Lippincott.*

Leedle mistake (A): Dutch [dram.] sketch. 16°. pap., 15c. .... *Happy.*

Leeds, Alb. *See* Morton, H., *and* Leeds, A.

Leeds, Josiah W. (*ed.*) Primitive Christian's estimate of war and self-defence. 12°. '76. 25c. .. *Peace.*

Leeds, Lew. W. Treatise on ventilation: lectures. ill. 8°. $2.50 .... *Wiley.*

Lees, Flo. S. Handbook for hospital sisters; ed. by H. W. Ackland. 12°. '74. $2 .... *Routledge.*

Lees, F: R: Text book of temperance. ('69.) New ed. 12°. '74. $1.50 .... *Nat. Temp.*

— *and* Burns, D. Temperance Bible commentary. ('70.) New ed. 12°. '75. $2.50 .... *Nat. Temp.*

Lees, W: Acoustics: light and heat. (Element. sci. ser.) ill. 16°. '73. 75c. .... *Putnam.*

Leeser, I: (*ed.*) Book of daily prayers according to the custom of the Germ. and Polish Jews. 12°. leath., $3.50; mor., $6 .... *Frank.*

— *Same;* according to the custom of the Span. and Port. Jews. 12°. leath., $3.50; mor., $6 .. *Frank.*

— Form of prayers for all the [Jewish] festivals. 7 v. 12°. leath., $20; mor., $28 .... *Frank.*

— *See also* Bible [Whole], *Hebrew.*

Le Fanu, Ja. Sheridan. Novels. 5 v. 8°. pap. *Harper.*

Cont.: Uncle Silas: tale of Bartram-Haugh, 75c. — All in the dark. — Guy Deverell. — Lost name. — Tenants of Malory, *ea.*, 50c.

— Checkmate; or, the Longcluse mystery. 8°. pap., 50c. .... *De Witt.*

— *Same.* 8°. $1.25; pap., 75c. .... *Estes.*

— Shamus O'Brien, [poem]; [also] Father Roach, by S. Lover. 12°. '71. pap., 25c. .... *Claxton.*

Lefèvre, André. Beauties of modern architecture; tr. 40 pl. 8°. hf. mor., $6 .... *Appleton.*

— Wonders of architecture, tr.; with chapter on Eng. arch. by R. Donald. ill. 12°. '75. $1.25 .. *Scribner.*

Lefferts, G: M. Modern methods of examining upper air-passages. *See* Seguin, E. C., Series of Am. clin. lect.

Left at home. *See* Library of pleasant stories.

Left handed Elsa. sq. 16°. '76. pap., 50c....*Loring.*
Left in a cab. Stirling, E. 15c.............*French.*
Left on Labrador. Stephens, C. A. $1.25....*Porter.*
Left the stage. Siraudin, P. 15c.............*French.*
Left the stage: farce. 16°. pap., 15c.........*French.*
Leftwich, W. M. Martyrdom in Missouri. 2 v. 12°. *net*, $2.50......................*S. W. Bk. & Pub.*
Legacies to parsons. Cobbett, W. 60c......*Sadlier.*
Legacy of historical gleanings. Bonney, C. V. R. 2 v. $10...................................*Munsell.*
Legacy of honour. Stirling, E. 15c.........*French.*
Legacy to the friends of free discussion. Offen, B. $1. *Mendum.*
Le Gal, Eug. School of the guides; for the militia of the U. S. 16°. '64. 60c........*Van Nostrand.*
Legal adviser. *See* Freedley, E. T.
Legal anecdotes. Timbs, J. 50c..........*Routledge.*
Legal Gazette reports. *See* Campbell, J. H.
Legal impediment. Oxenford, J. 15c.........*French.*
Legal outlines. Hoffman, D. $4......*Baker, V. & Co.*
Legal recreations. 4 v. 12°. ea., $1.50...*S. Whitney.*
Cont.: Humorous phases of the law, by I. Browne.—Curiosities and law of wills, by J. Proffatt.—Judicial puzzles, by J. Paget.—Law of the road, by R. V. Rogers, jr.

Legal remembrancer. Abbott, A. $2.50..*Baker, V. & Co.*
Legend of Don Munio. *See* Buck, D.
Legend of Florence. Hunt, J. H. 15c.......*French.*
Legend of Jubal. Eliot, G. $1.50; $3; $4..*Osgood.*
Legend of Montrose. *See* Scott, *Sir* Wa.
Legend of Sleepy Hollow. *See* Irving, Wash.
Legend of the wandering Jew. Doré, G. $6.50; $8. *Cassell.*
Legend of the White Hills. Ramsey, V. G. $1.50. *Lothrop.*
Legendary ballads of England and Scotland. *See* Roberts, J. S.
Legenden a. d. amerik. Revolution. *See* Lippard, G.
Legendre, Adr. Marie. Elements of geometry; tr. (School ed.) 12°. $1.................*T. Bliss.*
— *Same;* with add. and modifications by M. A. Blanchet; tr. by F. H. Smith. 8°. '67. hf. leath., $2.25.........................*Kelly, P. & Co.*
— *See also* Davies, C., Elements of geometry;—Thompson, J. B.
Legends and fairy tales of Ireland; by P. Kennedy, J. C. Croker and others. ill. 12°. '71. $2..*Haverty.*
Legends and lyrics. Hayne, P. H. $1.50..*Lippincott.*
Legends and memories of Scotland. Aitken, C. K. $1.50.............................*Williams.*
Legends from fairy land. ill. 8°. '76. $1.50...*Miller.*
Legends from fairy land. Parr, H. $1.25. *Scribner, W. & A.*
Legends of the Am. revolution. *See* Lippard, G.
Legends of the birds. Leland, C. G. $2.......*Holt.*
Legends of the black watch. *See* Grant, Ja.
Legends of Brittany. Souvestre, E. $1.25....*O'Shea.*
Legends of Charlemagne. Bulfinch, T. $3. *Lee & S.; Tilton.*
Legends of fairy land. Bache, A. 75c.......*Claxton.*
Legends of the flowers. *See* Fireside lib.
Legends of King Arthur and his knights of the round table. K., J. T. $1.................*Routledge.*
Legends of Mexico. Lippard, G. 50c......*Peterson.*
Legends of Michigan and the old north-west. Littlejohn, F. J. *$3.50–$7......................*N. W. Bible.*
Legends of Number Nip. Lemon, M. $1..*Macmillan.*
Legends of Old Test. characters. Baring-Gould, S. $2.......................................*Macmillan.*
Legends of the patriarchs and prophets. Baring-Gould, S. $2...................................*Holt.*
Legends of St. Joseph; tr. by Mrs. J. Sadlier. 16°. $1; $1.50............................*Sadlier.*
Legends of savage life. Greenwood, J. $2..*Putnam.*
Legends of the west. Hall, J. $2...........*Clarke.*
Le Geyt, C. J. Supper of the Lord and holy communion. 32°. 75c...........................*Pott.*
Legg, J. Wickham. Guide to the examination of the urine. 3d ed. 16°. '76. 75c.........*Lindsay.*
Legge, Alfr. O. Growth of the temporal power of the papacy. cr. 8°. '70. $2............*Macmillan.*
— Pius IX.: story of his life, to 1850, with glimpses at the national movement in Italy. 2 v. 8°. $12. *Scribner, W. & A.*
Legge, Ja. Chinese classics; incl. the works of Confucius and Mencius. 8°. '70. $3.50...*Hurd & H.*
— Confucius, his life and teachings; with explan. notes. cr. 8°. $4.........................*Lippincott.*
— Life of Mencius. *See* Mencius, B.
Leggett, W: *See* Tales of Glauber Spa.
Legion; or, feigned excuses; by author of "Letter to a member of a church choir." 12°. pap., 15c. *Claremont.*
Legouix, I. E. Crimson scarf. [Opera.] 4°. '74. pap., $1.................................*Pond.*
Legouvé, Ern. Medea: tragedy; tr. 16°. pap., 15c. *French.*
— *See also* Denaux, P., *and* Legouvé, E.;—Scribe, E., *and* Legouvé, E.
Lehmann, C: Gotliff. Manual of chemical physiol.; tr., with notes and add., by J. C. Morris; with essay on vital force by S. Jackson. ill. 8°. $2.25..*Lea.*
— Physiological chemistry; tr. by G. E. Day and ed. by R. E. Rogers. 2 v. ill. and pl. 8°. $6....*Lea.*
Lehmann, Ign. Geist d. amerik. Gesetze. 12°. '58. 50c.....................................*Witter.*
— Regeln (Die) d. Anstands. 16°. 20c.......*Witter.*
Lehrreiche Kamingeschichten. 18°. 30c....*Ev. Assoc.*
Leib, C: Nine months in the quartermaster's department; or, the chances for making a million. 12°. '62. 75c.; pap., 50c.................*Wilstach.*
Leib, J. Der wohlerfahrene Pferde-Arzt. 12°. $1. *Kohler.*
Leiden des jungen Werther. *See* Goethe, J. W. v.
Leidy, Jos. Ancient fauna of Nebraska. 4°. '53. pap., $5..........................*Smith. Inst.*
— Contributions to extinct vertebrate fauna of west. territories. *See* United States, *Geog. and geol. survey.*
— Cretaceous reptiles of the U. S. 4°. '65. pap., $4. *Smith. Inst.*
— Elementary text-book on human anatomy. ill. 8°. '60. shp., $5.............*Claxton; Lippincott.*
— Extinct American ox. 4°. '52. pap., $1..*Smith. Inst.*
— Extinct mammalian fauna of Dakota and Nebraska; with introd. on geol. of tertiary formations of Dakota and Nebraska, with map by F. V. Hayden. pl. f°. bds., $20............*Lippincott.*
— Extinct sloth tribe of North America. 4°. '55. pap., $3.................................*Smith. Inst.*
Leifchild, J: Remarkable facts, ill. and confirmative of portions of Scripture; with pref. by his son. 12°. $1.50..........................*Claxton.*
Leifchild, J: R. The great problem: higher ministry of nature in the light of modern science; with introd. by H. Crosby. 12°. '72. $2.25..*Putnam.*
Leigh, B. W. *See* Virginia, Court of Appeals and General Court reports.
Leigh, Edn. Independent first reader; in phonetic type. 16°. 25c..........................*Barnes.*
— McGuffey's new eclectic primer; in phonetic pronouncing orthography. ('64.) New ed. 16°. '68. 20c..........................*Wilson, H. & Co.*
— McGuffey's new primary reader; in phonetic pronouncing orthography. ('64.) New ed. 16°. '68. 35c.....................*Wilson, H. & Co.*

Leigh, Edn., *continued.*
— National primer; in phonetic type. 16°. 25c. *Barnes.*
— *See also* Hillard, G. S.; — Hillard, G. S., *and* Campbell, L. J.

Leigh, Larrie. The true Grecian bend. ill. 12°. 75c. *Redfield.*

Leighton, J: (*ill.*) *See* Pigott, R.

Leighton, R. F. Greek lessons; to accompany Goodwin's Greek grammar. ('71.) 5th ed. 12°. '75. hf. leath., $1.56 .... *Ginn.*
— Latin lessons; to accompany Allen and Greenough's Latin grammar. ('72.) 7th ed. 12°. '75. hf. leath., $1.56 .... *Ginn.*
— *See also* Harvard examination papers.

Leighton, Rob. Scotch words; [also] Bapteesement o' th' bairn. 24°. pap., 25c. .... *Routledge.*

Leighton, *Abp.* Rob. Works. 8°. '74. $3 ... *Carter.*
— *Same;* with life. 8°. $3 .... *Nelson.*
— Commentary upon 1st Peter; with memoir of author. 2 v. 8°. $4 .... *Pres. Bd.*
— Rules for a holy life. *See* Scougal, H., Life of God.

Leighton children. 10 v. ill. 18°. $3; $3.50 .. *Am. S. S.*
Cont.: Theodore's trouble. — Berty's visit. — Chip and Kitty. — Mark's composition. — Aunt Priscilla's story. — Sunday school picnic. — Coveted bonnet. — Stingy Lewis. — Stone house. — Hem-stitched handkerchief.
— *See also* Cobden, H. E. C.

Leighton Court. *See* Kingsley, H:

Leighton Grange. Braddon, M. E. 25c. .... *De Witt.*

Leightons (The). *See* Bremer, F.

Leila. *See* Bulwer-Lytton, *Sir* E. G. E. L.

Leila. Reynolds, G. W. M. 50c. .... *De Witt.*

Leila; or, the island. Tytler, A. F. $1.25 ... *Porter.*

Leila Ada. *See* Heighway, O. W. T.

Leila Ada's relatives. *See* Heighway, O. W. T.

Leila among the mountains. Larcom, L. 80c. ... *Hoyt.*

Leila at home. Tytler, A. F. $1 .... *Porter.*

Leila books. *See* Tytler, A. F.

Leila in England. Tytler, A. F. $1 .... *Porter.*

Leishman, W: System of midwifery, incl. diseases of pregnancy and the puerperal state. 2d ed., with add. by J. S. Parry. ill. 8°. $5; leath., $6 .. *Lea.*

Leisure day rhymes. Saxe, J. G. $2–$4.50 .. *Osgood.*

Leisure hour book. *See* Chambers, W. *and* R.

Leisure hour series.
Note. Entered specifically under authors and titles.

Leisure hour work for ladies: instructions for flower and shell work, etc. sq. 18°. '74. pap., 20c. (?) *F. M. Reed.*

Leisure hours. Boyd, A. K. H. $1.25 ...... * *Osgood.*

Leisure moments. Nunes, H. H. $2 ...... *Lippincott.*

Leisure moments improved. *See* Fireside lib.

Leitch, R: P. Water colour painting; with 24 col. pl. 2d ed. obl. 4°. $2.50 .... *Cassell.*
— *See also* Course of painting; — Course of sepia drawing.

Leitch, W: God's glory in the heavens. ill. cr. 8°. $2.25 .... *Routledge.*

Lejeal, Alois F. Mass in D; with Lat. and Eng. text, and with accomp. for organ or piano. ('70.) New ed. 8°. '76. $1.50; bds., $1.25 .... *Pond.*
— Vespers, for 4 voices; with Lat. text, and accomp. for organ or piano. 8°. '70. $1.50; bds., $1.25. *Pond.*

Leland, C: Godf. Egyptian sketch book. 16°. '73. $1.75 .... *Hurd & H.*
— Fusang; or, discovery of Am. by Chinese Buddhist priests in 5th cent. 12°. '75. $1.75 .... *Bouton.*
— Hans Breitmann books: ballads. 5 v. 12°. ea., pap., 75c. .... *Peterson.*
Cont.: Hans Breitmann about town — as an Uhlan — in church — in Europe. — Hans Breitmann's party.
— Hans Breitmann's ballads. 2 v. 12°. $5; in 1 v., $4. *Peterson.*
— Legends of the birds. ill. 4°. '63. $2 .... *Holt.*

Leland, C: Godf., *continued.*
— Meister Karl's sketch book. 12°. $2.50; mor., $3.50 .... *Peterson.*
— Music lesson of Confucius, and other poems. sq. 16°. '72. $1.50 .... *Osgood.*
— *See also* Eichendorff, Jos. v.; — English gipsy songs; — Heine, H.

Leland, H: P. The grey mare, and other sketches. ill. 12°. '70. $1.50 .... *Claxton.*

Leland, O. S. Beatrice: drama. 16°. pap., 15c. .. *French.*
— Blue and cherry; or, appearances are deceitful: comedy. 16°. pap., 15c. .... *Lee & S.*
— Rights of man: comedy. 16°. pap., 15c. ... *French.*

Le Maout, Emm. Flower object lessons; or, first lessons in botany; tr. by A. L. Page. ill. 12°. '73. 70c. .... *Black*

Le Marchand, *Mme.* —. Fortune-teller and dreamer's dict. ill. 16°. bds., 35c. .... *Dick & F.*

Lemoine, Gst. *See* Bayard, J. F. A., *and* Lemoine, G.

Lemon, Harry. [Plays.] 4 v. 16°. ea., pap., 15c. *French.*
Cont.: Gertrude's money-box: farce. — Go to Putney: farce. — Up for the cattle show: farce. — Wait for an answer: dram. sketch.
— Gertrude's money-box: farce. 16°. pap., 15c. *De Witt.*
— Go to Putney: farce. 16°. pap., 15c. ...... *De Witt.*
— Up for the cattle show: farce. 16°. pap., 15c. *De Witt.*

Lemon, M: [Plays.] 11 v. 16°. ea., pap., 15c. *French.*
Cont.: Domestic economy: farce. — Grandfather Whitehead. — Gwynneth Vaughan. — Honesty the best policy. — Jack in the green: farce. — Ladies' club. — Mind your own business. — Moving tale: farce. — Railway belle: farce. — Self accusation. — Slow man: farce.
— Christmas hamper: tale for the season. 12°. pap., 50c. .... *Routledge.*
— Jest book: anecdotes and sayings. 18°. '75. $1.25. *Macmillan.*
— *Same.* (Golden treasury ser.) 18°. 75c. 16°. $1.25 .... *Allyn.*
— Legends of Number Nip. [Fairy stories.] ill. fp. 8°. '70. $1 .... *Macmillan*
— Leyton Hall. 8°. pap., 75c. .... *Peterson.*
— Petticoat parliament: extravaganza. 16°. pap., 15c. *De Witt*

Lemoyne d'Iberville, P. Narrative of Lemoyne, an artist who accompanied the French expedition to Florida, under Laudonnière in 1564; tr. from the Latin of De Bry. heliot. ill. 4°. '75. bds., $10 .... *Osgood*

Lemprière, J: Classical dictionary. 16°. $1.50 .. *Putnam*
— *Same.* 8°. shp., $3.75; — abridg. 12°. $1.50. *Lippincott*

Lena; or, the Stark family. Hofsten, H. $1. *Cin. Meth. Bk. Conc*

Lena Cameron. Grey, E. C. 50c. .... *Peterson*

Lena Landon; by a Virginia Baptist minister. 16°. $1.25 .... *Am. Bapt*

Lena Leslie: hist. of an orphan; by a lady of Kentucky. 18°. 35c. .... *Pres. Bd*

Lena Rivers. Holmes, M. J. $1.50 .... *Carleton*

Lend me five shillings. Morton, J. M. 15c. ... *French*

Lending a hand. A'Beckett, G. A. 15c. *French; Lee & S*

Lenguage (El) de las flores y de las frutas. 18°. 60c. *Appleton*

Lenhart, —. Elements of music: rules for the pianoforte; [also] Burrowes' Guide to practice; [also] Czerny's Letters on art of playing the piano. 12°. '64. bds., 50c. .... *Ditson*

Leni Leoti. Bennett, E. 25c. .... *U. P. James*

Lening, G. Die Nachtseiten von. New York. 2d ed. 8°. '75. $3 .... *Zickel*

Lennie's Bible. ill. 18°. 50c. .... *Pott*

Lennox, Ma. (*pseud.*) *See* Cook, *Mrs.* M. L.

Lenny, the orphan. Hosmer, M. $1.25 ...... *Porter*

Lenny's lib. 4 v. 16°. $6 .... *Cong. Pub*
Cont.: Lenny's search, by Mrs. C. Drew. — Ada Hovey's idols, by Miss M. Newhall. — Bertha's journal, by E. M. Harris. — Hope Wallace.

Lenny's search. Drew, C. $1.50 .... *Cong. Pub.*

Lenoir, Pl. The Fayoum; or, artists in Egypt. ill. 12°. $2.50 .... *Routledge.*

Lenore. Bürger, G. A. $1.50 .... *Kohler.*

Le Normand, *Mme.* Camille. Fortune-telling by cards; or, cartomancy made easy. ill. 12°. 75c. 32°. bds., 50c. .... *De Witt.*

— Napoleon's complete dream-book. 12°. 75c. 32°. bds., 50c. .... *De Witt.*

— Unerring fortune-teller. ill. 16°. bds., 35c. *Dick & F.*

Le Normand, *Mlle.* M. A. Historical and secret memoirs of Empress Josephine; tr. by J. M. Howard. 12°. $1.75 .... *J. E. Potter.*

Lenormant, François, *and* Chevallier, E. Student's manual of Oriental hist.: anc. hist. of the east to the Median wars; tr. 2 v. cr. 8°. $5.50; hf. cf., $8.50; v. 2, sep., $2.50 .... *Lippincott.*

Lenormont, *Mme.* Amélie Cyvoct. Memoirs and correspondence of Mme. Recamier; tr. and ed. by I. M. Luyster. 16°. '67. $1.50 .... *Roberts.*

Lent arm-chair. 18°. 35c. .... *Cong. Pub.*

Lent jewels. sq. 12°. '71. bds., 50c. .... *Routledge.*

Lent, a precious season. 32°. 25c.; pap., 10c. .. *Dutton.*

Lent readings from the fathers. Pusey, E. B. $2 .. *Pott.*

Lente, F. D. Neurotic origin of disease. 8°. pap., 25c. .... *Campbell & Co.*

Lenten lessons from Lenten services: readings for every day in Lent. 16°. 50c. .... *Pott.*

Lenten thoughts: meditations on the Collects, Epistles and Gospels for Lent. 12°. $1.25 ... *Whittaker.*

Leo (*pseud.*) *See* Pemberton, *Col.* —.

Leo x. Life and times; rev. by T. O. Summers. ('58.) 3d ed. 18°. '75. 50c. .... *So. Meth.*

Leo the terrible. Coyne, J. S. 15c. .... *French.*

Leofwine, the Saxon. Leslie, E. $1.50 .. *Meth. Bk. Conc.*

Leon and Zephie. Wildermuth, O. 75c. ..... *Dutton.*

Leonard, C. H. Book of prayer for the church and the home; with sel. from the Psalms, and coll. of hymns. 12°. '64. $1.75; mor., $5; — without hymns, $1.25 .... *Universalist.*

— First steps in the open path: book of worship and instruction for children and youth. 32°. '65. pap., 10c. .... *Universalist.*

Leonard, H: C. Pigeon Cove and vicinity. 12°. '73. $1 .... *Searle.*

Leonard, Silas W. New Christian psalmist. 16°. '70. bds., 50c. .... *R. W. Carroll.*

— *and* Fillmore, A. D. The Christian psalmist. 16°. '54. hf. roan, $1.25 .... *Morton.*

Leonard, W: A. Christmas festival: its origin, hist. and customs; with carols. 12°. '76. 75c. *Somerby.*

— Music in the western church: lecture on hist. of psalmody, with examples of music of various periods. 12°. '76. $1 .... *Somerby.*

— Summary of Herbert Spencer's first principles. 12°. '76. pap., 50c. .... *Somerby.*

Leonard, *Rev.* W: A. Via sacra; or, footprints of Christ: descriptive of the great themes of holy week; with introd. by C. H. Hall. 32°. '75. $1. *Dutton.*

Leonard, the lion heart; or, bravery put to the test. 18°. 35c. .... *Am. S. S.*

Leonard Barton. *See* Casket of juveniles.

Leonard Dobbin; or, the one moss rose. ('61.) New ed. ill. 18°. '75. 40c. .... *Hoyt.*

Leonards (The); or, the cobbler, the clerk, etc. ill. post 18°. 75c. .... *Scribner, W. & A.*

Leonette; or, truth sought and found. 18°. 65c.; 75c. *Am. Bapt.*

Leonhard, the runaway. (Fatherland ser.) ill. 16°. 50c. .... (?) *Luth. Pub.*

Leonhardt, Josephus. Confessions of a minister. 16°. '74. 50c. .... *H. Peterson.*

Leonhart, R. Der geheimnissvolle Pedlar. 12°. '74. pap., 75c. .... *Zickel.*

Leonora Casaloni. Trollope, T. A. $1.75; $1.50. *Peterson.*

Leonora d'Orco. James, G. P. R. 50c. ..... *Harper.*

Leonore. 12°. pap., 15c. .... *Radde.*

Leonore's trials. 16°. $1.25 .... *Cong. Pub.*

— *Same.* ill. 16°. '72. $1.25 .... *Am. Tr.*

Leonowens, *Mrs.* Anna Harriette. English governess at the Siamese court. ill. 12°. '70. $1.50. *Coates.*

— Romance of the harem. ill. 12°. '72. $1.50 .. *Coates.*

Leontine. Maberly, K. C. 50c. .... *Harper.*

Le Pileur, A. Wonders of the human body; tr. from the Fr. ill. 12°. '73. $1.25 .... *Scribner.*

L'Epine, Ern. Days of chivalry: legend of Croquemitaine; tr. by Tom Hood; with 177 designs by Doré. roy. 4°. $5 .... *Cassell.*

Le Play, F. Organization of labor; with causes of [present] evils and means to effect reform; tr. by G. Emerson. 12°. '71. $2 .... *Claxton.*

Leppere, Ad. Hamilton. The rainbow creed. 12°. '75. $1.50 .... *W. F. Gill.*

Lepsius, C. R: Letters from Egypt, Ethiopia and Sinai; tr. by L. and S. B. Horner. 12°. (Bohn.) $1.75 .... *Little, B. & Co.*

— *Same.* 12°. (Bohn.) $2 .. *Lippincott; Scribner, W. & A.*

Lermant, J. L. Pronouncing Germ. grammar and conversational phrase-book for beginners. 18°. '55. pap., 25c. .... *Wilstach.*

Lermontoff, Mich. The Circassian boy; tr. by S. S. Conant. [Poem.] sq. 16°. $1.50 .... * *Osgood.*

Le Ros, Chr. Great gun trick: farce. 16°. pap., 15c. *French.*

Leroux, C: Practical treatise on manufacture of worsteds and carded yarns; tr. by H. Paine and A. A. Fesquet; with app. on woolen and worsted machinery and fabrics exhibited in the Paris exposition in 1867. pl. 8°. '68. $5 .... *Baird.*

Lesage, Alain René. Gil Blas de Santillane. [French.] 12°. $2 .... *Routledge.*

— *Same.* 12°. $1.50 .... *G. R. Lockwood.*

— *Eng.* Adventures of Gil Blas. ill. 12°. (Bohn.) $2.40 .... *Scribner, W. & A.*

— *Same.* ill. 12°. (Bohn.) $2.50 .... *Lippincott.*

— *Same;* with memoir. ill. roy. 8°. $3.50; hf. cf., $6. *Appleton.*

— *Same;* tr. by T. Smollett. 12°. $1 .... *Lippincott.*

— — *Same.* (Globe ed.) ill. cr. 8°. $1.75; hf. cf., $3.50; cf., $5 .... *Routledge.*

— — *Same.* 2 v. ill. 12°. '64. $1 .... *D. Thomas.*

— — *Same.* New ed., rev. 3 v. 12°. '65. $3.75; hf. cf., $7.50; cf., $9 .... *Little, B. & Co.*

— — *Same;* with memoir by T. Roscoe. 12°. $1.50. *Harper.*

— *Span.* Historia de Gil Blas de Santillana; trad. por el Padre Isla. 12°. $1.50 .... *Appleton.*

— Bachelor of Salamanca; tr. by J. Townsend. 2 v. 18°. '68. $1.50 .... *Claxton.*

— Devil (The) on two sticks; tr. 18°. 75c. .... *Sower.*

— *Same;* [also] Asmodeus' crutches; [also] Dialogues between two chimneys of Madrid; tr. 18°. 75c. *U. P. James.*

Lesbos. Pember, E. H. $1.50 .... *Macmillan.*

Lescher, F. Harwood. Elements of pharmacy. 4th ed., rev. and enl. 8°. '76. $3 .... *Lindsay.*

Lesebuch f. die deutschen kathol. Schulen in den Ver. St. [New ser.] 4 v. 12°. Erstes (Fibel) Lesebuch, 15c.; Zweites, 30c.; Drittes, 60c.; Viertes, $1 .... *Benziger.*

Lesebuch f. die Primar-Schulen der Ver. St. [Old ser.] 4 v. 12°. Erstes Lesebuch, 12c.; Zweites, 22c.; Drittes, 50c.; Viertes, 85c. .... *Benziger.*

Lesebuch f. evangelisch-lutherische Schulen. ('62.) 12th ed. 8°. '75. 50c.; — für Unter-Classen. 12°. '76. 25c.; — für Mittel-Classen. 8°. '76. 50c. .... *Barthel.*

Lesebuch f. katholische Schulen. 4 v. 8°. .. *Vering.*

Cont.: Erstes Lesebuch, hf. bd., 15c. — Zweites, hf. bd., 20c. — Drittes, hf. leath., $1. — Kathol. Lesebuch., hf. bd., 35c.

Lesebuch, od. Leseübungen f. die unteren Klassen. 16°. 18c. .... *Benziger.*

Lese-Elementar Uebungen. With Eng. vocab. 8°. bds., 20c. .... *Enderis.*

Lesley, J. P. Man's origin and destiny; sketched from the platform of the sciences: lectures before Lowell Institute, Boston. cr. 8°. $4 .. *Lippincott.*

Leslie, C. *See* Evidences of Christianity.

Leslie, C: Rob. (*ill.*) Pictures by L.; with text and biog. by J. Dafforne. f°. '72. $7.50 .. *Routledge.*

Leslie, *Miss* Eliza. Complete cookery. (cop. '37.) '51. 60th ed., enl. 12°. '70. $1.50 ..... *Baird.*

— Ladies' guide to true politeness and perfect manners. 12°. $1.75; pap., $1.50 .... *Peterson.*

— New cook book. 12°. $1.75 .... *Peterson.*

— New receipts for cooking. 12°. $1.75 ..... *Peterson.*

Leslie, Emma. Captives (The). ill. 12°. $1 .. *Nelson.*

— Church history stories. 6 v. ill. 12°. '75. ea., $1.50 .... *Meth. Bk. Conc.*

Cont.: Glaucia: a story of Athens in 1st cent. — Flavia; or, loyal to the end: tale of the church in 2d cent. — Quadratus: tale of the world in the church. — Ayesha: tale of times of Mohammed. — Leofwine, the Saxon: story of hopes and struggles. — Elfreda: sequel to "Leofwine."

— Eliza Metcalf's basket; or, policy not principle. 12°. $1 .... *Nelson.*

— Eliza's basket. ill. 12°. $1 .... *Nelson.*

— Ellerslie House; or, stick to your principles. 16°. $1 .... *Am. Bapt.*

— Elsie's dowry: tale of the Franco-German war. 12°. $1 .... *Nelson.*

— Esther's regret. *See* Gem cluster.

— Ferryman's family. ill. 16°. 75c. .... *Nelson.*

— Harry Lawley. ill. 12°. $1 .... *Nelson.*

— Hayslop Grange. ill. 12°. $1 .... *Nelson.*

— Marian's mission; or, influence of Sunday-schools. 16°. '75. $1 .... *Meth. Bk. Conc.*

— Orphan (The) and the foundling. ill. 12°. $1 .. *Nelson.*

— Percy Raydon; or, self-conquest. ill. 12°. $1 .. *Nelson.*

— *Same.* ill. 16°. '72. $1 .... *Lothrop.*

— Squire Lynn's will. ill. 12°. '75. $1.50 .... *Nelson.*

— Sunbeam Susette: story of the siege of Paris. ill. 16°. $1 .... *Cong. Pub.; Nelson.*

— Sunshine of Blackpool. 16°. '75. $1 .. *Meth. Bk. Conc.*

— Teddy's dream; or, a little sweep's mission. 18°. 50c. .... *Carter; Dutton.*

— Tom Perry's venture. ill. 16°. 50c. .... *Nelson.*

Leslie, Ern. Complete course of instruc. for cabinet organ; with music. obl. 8°. pap., 75c. *G. D. Russell.*

— Jewel. [Choruses, etc.] 8°. bds., 75c. *G. D. Russell.*

— Meteor: melodies for schools, etc. obl. 12°. bds., 50c. .... *G. D. Russell.*

Leslie, Frank. *See* Frank Leslie's.

Leslie, H: Elementary manual of music. fp. 8°. 50c. *Cassell.*

— Songs for little folks; with music. ill. roy. 4°. $1.50. *Cassell.*

Leslie, H: [Plays.] 4 v. 16°. ea., pap., 15c. .. *French.*

Cont.: Adrienne. — Mariner's compass. — Sin and sorrow. — Time and tide.

— Adrienne: drama. 16°. pap., 15c. .... *De Witt.*

— Time and tide: drama. 16°. pap., 15c. ... *De Witt.*

— *and* Rowe, N: Orange girl: drama. 16°. pap., 15c. *De Witt; French.*

Leslie, J. H., *and* Ogden, W. A. Silver carols: new music for district schools, seminaries, etc. obl. 16°. 50c. .... *W. W. Whitney.*

Leslie, *Sir* J: Jameson, R., *and* Murray, H. Discovery and adventure in the polar seas and regions. ill. 18°. 75c. .... *Harper.*

Leslie, M. E. Dawn of light. 18°. 65c. ... *Pres. Bd.*

Leslie, *Mrs.* Madeline (*pseud.*) *See* Baker, H. N. W.

Leslie Goldthwaite. Whitney, A. D. T. $1.50 .. *Osgood.*

Lesquereux, Leo. Pacific coast mosses. 4°. $1. *Cal. Acad. Sci.*

— *See also* Arkansas geol. survey; — California Acad. of Nat. Sci.; — Illinois geol. survey.

Lesser lights. Bourdillon, F. $1.25 .... *Pott.*

Lessing, Ghld. Eph. Dramatische Werke. 7 v. 12°. ea., pap., 10c. .... *F. W. Thomas.*

Cont.: Die Juden. — Der Freigeist. — Miss Sara Sampson. — Philotas. — Emilia Galotti. — Minna v. Barnhelm. — Nathan der Weise.

— Sämmtliche Werke. 2 v. 8°. $2.25; pap., $1.50; hf. mor., $2.50 .... *F. W. Thomas.*

— Emilia Galotti: Tragödie. With Eng. notes. ('69.) New ed. 12°. '73. pap., 40c. .... *Holt.*

— Laocoon (The): essay on limits of painting and poetry; tr. by E. Frothingham. 16°. '73. $1.50. *Roberts.*

— *Same;* tr., with pref. and add. notes, by Sir R. J. Phillimore. 8°. '74. $4 .... *Macmillan.*

— Minna von Barnhelm: Lustspiel; zum Uebers. in's Eng. mit Noten v. W. C. Wrankmore. ('64.) New ed. 12°. '76. pap., 50c. .... *Holt.*

— *Eng.* Minna von Barnhelm; or, a soldier's fortune: comedy; tr. for students of German, with notes in German by W. C. Wrankmore. ('64.) New ed. 12°. '76. pap., 50c. .... *Holt.*

— Nathan the wise; tr. by E. Frothingham; [with] Kuno Fischer's essay on the poem. ('67.) New ed. 16°. '73. $1.50 .... *Holt.*

Lesson for gentlemen: drama. 16°. pap., 15c. .. *French.*

Lesson in love. Cheltnam, C. S. 15c. .... *French.*

Lessons for children about themselves. Newton, A. E. 50c. .... *Colby.*

Lessons for every Sunday in the year. 4 ser. 18°. ea., per doz., $1.80 .... *Meth. Bk. Conc.*

Lessons for infant schools. 18°. 25c. ...... *Am. S. S.*

Lessons for the little ones. Hildeburn, M. J. 20c. *Pres. Bd.*

Lessons for schools. 12°. 45c.; 60c. ...... *Am. S. S.*

Lessons from biog. for young men. 18°. 60c. .. *Am. S. S.*

Lessons from daily life. Hildreth, E. E. $1 .. *Lippincott.*

Lessons from heathen lands. *See* Bechuana girl.

Lessons from insect life. ill. 18°. 60c. .. *Bost. Am. Tr.*

— *See also* Library of curious things.

Lessons from Jesus. Balfern, W. P. $1 .... *Sheldon.*

Lessons from life of Christ. *See* Golden secret lib.

Lessons from nature. Cheap, *Mrs.* —. 60c. .. *So. Meth.*

Lessons from a shoemaker's stool. Kerr, J. 25c. *Routledge.*

Lessons in Bible hist.; by a teacher. ill. 12°. $1.25; — in 3 pts., ea., 50c. .... *O'Shea.*

Lessons in flying for our home birds. Breed, W. P. 55c. .... *Pres. Bd.*

Lessons in German. 2 pts. 8°. ea., $1.25; — in 1 v. 8°. $2. — Key, 75c. .... *Cassell.*

Lessons in life. *See* Arthur, T. S.

Lessons in life. Holland, J. G. $1.75 .... *Scribner.*

Lessons in right and wrong. Rogers, W. P. 75c. *H. H. Carter.*

Lessons of the cross and passion. Vaughan, C. J. $1. *Macmillan.*

Lessons of a disciple: chapters in life of a young lady. ('56.) 3d ed. 18°. '73. 50c. .... *So. Meth.*

— *See also* Young disciples' lib.

Lessons of experience; or, tales from real life. 16°. $1.50 .... *Pres. Bd.*

Lessons of life and death. Ritchie, E. 40c. .. *Pres. Bd.*

Lessons of life and godliness. Vaughan, C. J. $1.25. *Macmillan.*

Lessons of love. Marshall, E. $1 .... (?) *Martien.*

Lessons on life of Christ; by author of "Hymns from the land of Luther." ill. 18°. 75c.....*Nelson.*
— *Same.* 16°. 85c. ....*Tibbals.*
Lessons on the Lord's prayer. 18°. 40c......*Am.S.S.*
Lessur, R. J. Sixty seven chants. obl. 8°. pap., 30c. *G. D. Russell.*
Lestelle. Crow, *Mrs.* —. 30c............*Am. News.*
Lester, A. H. The pre-Adamite; or, who tempted Eve? Scripture and science in union resp. antiquity of man. 12°. $1.25........*Lippincott.*
Lester, C: Edwards. America's advancement: progress of the U. S. during their 1st century. eng. 4°. '76. mor., $50.......................*Virtue.*
— Life and public services of Charles Sumner. por. and ill. 8°. '74. $3.75–$8..........*U.S.Pub.*
— Napoleon dynasty: hist. of the Bonaparte family; by the Berkeley men (*pseud.*) ('60.) New ed., enl. por. 8°. $2.50................*Sheldon.*
— Our first hundred years: life of the U. S., ill. in its 4 great periods, colonization, consolidation, development, achievement. 2 v. roy. 8°. '75. $4. *U.S.Pub.*
Lester, G. N. *See* Georgia, Annotated code; Supreme Court reports.
Lester, J. Erastus. Atlantic to the Pacific: what to see and how to see it. ill. 16°. $1.50..(?)*Shepard.*
Lester, W. W. Decisions of the Interior Dept. in public land cases, and land laws passed by Congress, with regulations of the General Land Office. 2 v. 8°. shp., $12.50........................*Kay.*
Lestocq. Macfarren, G. 15c...............*French.*
Lestrange family. 16°. $1.................*Carter.*
Let not your heart be troubled. sq. 12°. '75. pap., 75c. ....*Williams.*
Let those laugh who win: musical [dram.] sketch. 16°. pap., 15c........................*Happy.*
Let us read ser. 5 v. ill. 8°. ea., 50c.........*Pott.*
Cont.: Miriam's trials, by A. A. — Pieces of silver. — Alice Neville, by C. E. Bowen. — Looking up, by F. C. A. — Lennie's Bible.

Let well alone; by author of "But once." 16°. '74. $1.25........................... (?) *Martien.*
Letheby, H: Food: its varieties, chemical composition, nutritive value, etc. 2d ed. 12°. '72. $2.25..............................*W. Wood.*
Letourneur, Augustin J: Little month of the holy infancy; or, the first mysteries of the life of Christ; tr. from the Fr. 18°. 63c.............*O'Shea.*
Letter and spirit. Metcalf, R. 60c. ....*Am. Unit.*
Letter bag of the Great Western. *See* Haliburton, T. C.
Letter of marque. Low, C. R. $1........*Routledge.*
Letter of redemption. Gurney, J. J. 15c...*Lippincott.*
Letter to Annie. 18°. 30c................*Am. S. S.*
Letter to the Catholic bishop of Boston, proving that the Rom. Cath. relig. is opposed to a repub. form of government; by an independent Irishman. 12°. pap., 15c. ....*Mendum.*
Letter to Santa Claus. Avard, E. A. 50c.; 75c. *D. H. Carroll.*
Letter-writer. *See* New.
Letter-writer etiquette. 16°. bds., 50c. — 18°. 50c. — 32°. 40c.......................*Lippincott.*
Letter-writing made easy, and composition simplified. 12°. pap., 20c. ....*Hurst.*
Letteris, M. L. *See* Bible [Whole], *Hebrew.*
Letterman, J. Medical recollections of the army of the Potomac. 8°. $1...............*Appleton.*
Letters everywhere; or, rhymes and stories for children. ill. 12°. $1.25; $1.50; $2......*Lee & S.*
Letters from abroad to kindred at home. Sedgwick, C. M. 2 v. $3.........................*Harper.*
Letters from the east. Bryant, W. C. $1.50; $2.50. *Putnam.*
Letters from a father to his sons in college. Miller, S. 75c...............................*Pres. Bd.*
Letters from the frontier. McCall, G. A. $2.50. *Lippincott.*
Letters from Rome in 1838; by author of "Clouds and sunshine." 12°. $1..............*Appleton.*
Letters from Rome on the Council. *See* Quirinus.
Letters of the British spy. Wirt, W. $1.25..*Harper.*
Letters of life. Sigourney, L. H. $4; $2; $1.50. *Appleton.*
Letters of a sentimental idler. Leech, H. H. $2.50. *Appleton.*
Letters of a traveller. Bryant, W. C. $2 ..*Putnam.*
Letters on ecclesiastical hist. from 13th to 18th cent. 18°. 60c............................*Am. S. S.*
— *Same;* progress of the Gospel in 19th cent. 18°. 35c. *Am.S.S.*
Letters on religious subjects written by divers Friends, deceased; compiled by a committee; ed. by J. Kendall. 12°. 75c.............*Friends Bk. St.*
Letters to the aged. Alexander, A. 35c....*Pres.Bd.*
Letters to an anxious inquirer. Henry, T. C. 65c. *Pres. Bd.*
Letters to Eugenia. Holbach, P. T. d'. $1..*Mendum.*
Letters to the Joneses. Holland, J. G. $1.75..*Scribner.*
Letters to little children. ill. 18°. '47. 25c...*Am. Tr.*
Letters to a man bewildered. Lay, H. C. 10c...*Dutton.*
Letters to a man of the world. Le Boys des Guays, J. F. E. $1.50.....................*Lippincott.*
Letters to married women. [In Eng. or Germ.] ill. 8°. 75c.; pap., 25c....................*Barclay.*
Letters to the members of a Bible class. 18°. 35c. *Am.S.S.*
Letters to mothers. Sigourney, L. H. $1.50..*Harper.*
Letters to my children. La Trobe, C. I. $1..*Clauder.*
Letters to the people on health and happiness. Beecher, C. E. $1...........................*Harper.*
Letters to a recent convert; by a pastor. 18°. 35c. *Pres.Bd.*
Letters to a school-boy. 16°. '67. $1..*Meth. Bk. Conc.*
Letters to school-girls. Mathews, J. M'D. 60c. *Cin. Meth. Bk. Conc.*
Letters to students: importance of a fixed belief in divine revelation, and of an elevated relig. character. 18°. 35c. ....*Am. S. S.*
Letters to a very young lady. 18°. 70c. ...*Am. S. S.*
Letters to the young. Jewsbury, M. J. $1..*Pres. Bd.*
Letters to a young Christian. 16°. 40c. .... *West. Tr.*
Letters to a young communicant. 18°. 50c. *Cong. Pub.*
Letters to young ladies. Sigourney, L. H. $1.50. *Harper.*
Letters to a young lady. Bennett, J. 75c...*Claxton.*
Letters to a younger brother on various subjects. 18°. 55c. ....*Am. S. S.*
Lettice Arnold. Marsh-Caldwell, A. 25c...*Harper.*
Lettice Lisle. 8°. '69. pap., 38c.........*Littell & G.*
Lettie Sterling. *See* Shaw, J. R.
Lettie Sterling ser. 3 v. 16°. $4.50 ....*Crowell.*
Cont.: Lettie Sterling, by J. R. Shaw. — Nix's offerings, by M. H. Henry. — Words and deeds, by E. L. Biscoe.

Letty Hyde's lovers. *See* Grant, Ja.
Letzte Bombardier (Der). Hackländer, F. W. 50c. *Morwitz.*
Letzten Ritter (Die) von Marienburg. *See* Hauff, W.
Leuchars, Rob. B. How to build hot houses, greenhouses, graperies, etc., and how to ventilate them. ill. 12°. $1.50.....................*Judd.*
Leuchtthurmwächters (Des) Tochter. 18°. 30c. *Ev. Assoc.*
Leusden, J. *See* Bible, New Test., *Greek and Lat.*
Levana. Richter, J. P. $2................**Osgood.*

Lever, C: Novels. 27 v. 16°. $35; hf. cf., $80. *Routledge.*
Cont.: Arthur O'Leary. — Barrington. — Bramleighs. — Charles O'Malley. — Con Cregan. — Cornelius O'Dowd. — The Daltons. — Davenport. — Day's ride. — Dodd family abroad. — Fortunes of Glencore. — Harry Lorrequer. — Jack Hinton. — Knight of Gwynne. — Lord Kilgobbin. — Luttrell of Arran. — Martins of Cro' Martin. — Maurice Tiernay. — The O'Donoghue. — One of them. — Rent in the cloud. — Roland Cashel. — Sir Brook Fossbrooke. — Sir Jasper Carew. — That boy of Norcott's. — Tom Burke of ours. — Tony Butler.

— *Same.* 17 v. 8°. pap.; — in 5 v. 8°. $15..*Harper.*
Cont.: Barrington, 75c. — Bramleighs of Bishop's Folly, 50c. — The Daltons, $1.50. — Day's ride, 50c. — Dodd family abroad, $1.25. — Gerald Fitzgerald, 50c. — Glencore and his fortunes, 50c. — Lord Kilgobbin, $1. — Luttrell of Arran, $1. — Martins of Cro' Martin, $1.25. — Maurice Tiernay, $1. — One of them, 75c. — Roland Cashel, $1.25. — Sir Brook Fossbrooke, 50c. — Sir Jasper Carew, 75c. — That boy of Norcott's, 25c. — Tony Butler, $1.

— *Same.* 17 v. ill. 8°. ea., $3............*Routledge.*
Cont.: Barrington. — Bramleighs of Bishop's Folly. — Charles O'Malley. — Con Cregan. — The Daltons. — Davenport Dunn. — Dodd family. — Harry Lorrequer. — Jack Hinton. — Knight of Gwynne. — Lord Kilgobbin. — Luttrell of Arran. — Martins of Cro' Martin. — O'Donoghue. — One of them. — Roland Cashel. — Tom Burke.

— *Same.* 10 v. 8°. ea., $2; pap., 75c......*Peterson.*
Cont.: Arthur O'Leary. — Charles O'Malley. — Con Cregan, the Irish Gil Blas. — Davenport Dunn. — Harry Lorrequer. — Horace Templeton. — Jack Hinton, the guardsman. — Kate O'Donoghue. — Knight of Gwynne. — Tom Burke of ours.

— Adventures of Arthur O'Leary. 12°. $1.25. — (Railway lib.) 16°. bds., $1........*Routledge.*
— Charles O'Malley, the Irish dragoon. 12°. $1.25. *Routledge.*
— Con Cregan's confessions. 12°. $1.25. — (Railway lib.) 16°. bds., $1................*Routledge.*
— Lord Kilgobbin. ill. 8°. $1.50............*Harper.*
— Luttrell of Arran. 8°. $1.50 ....*Harper.*
— Rent in the cloud. 8°. pap., 50c. ....*Peterson.*
— Roland Cashel. ill. 8°. $1.75 ....*Harper.*
— Saint Patrick's eve. 8°. pap., 50c........*Peterson.*
— Sir Brook Fossbrooke. 8°. '66. pap., 50c..*Littell & G.*
— Tony Butler. 8°. $1.50...................*Harper.*

Leverett, F. P. Latin lexicon. New ed., embr. class. distinct. of words, and the etymolog. index of Freund's Lexicon. 8°. shp., $6.25..*Lippincott.*

Le Vert, *Mme.* Octa. Walton. Souvenirs of travel. 12°. $2..............................*Carleton.*

Leveson, *Maj.* —. Hunting grounds of the old world. ill. 12°. $1.75.........................*Routledge.*

Levey, —. South American, Asiatic and Oceanic business directory of principal cities and towns; [with] products [etc., of each], etc. 8°. '74. $8 ....(?) *For. Dir.*

Levey, E. M. *See* Baptist praise book.

Levi, Leone. Manual of mercantile law of Gt. Brit. and Ireland. 8°. '54. $1.50.....*T. & J. W. Johnson.*
— — *See also* Law lib.

Levien, Fanny. Little Ada's jewels. 2 v. ill. 18°. '75. $1.50 ....*Nelson.*

Levin's treasure in bank. Reed, E. 75c.....*Claxton.*

Levinski, J. L. *See* Bible [Whole], *Heb. and Eng.*

Levizac, J: P. V. L. French grammar; tr. and ed. by A. Bolmar. 12°. $1.50............*Sheldon.*
— Theoretical and pract. grammar of Fr.; rev. by S. Pasquier; with tables on formation of verbs, etc., from grammar of J. Mouls. 12°. '35. $1.13. *Claxton; Lippincott.*

Levy, *Mrs.* Esther [*formerly Miss* Jacobs]. Jewish cookery book. [Hebrew.] 12°. $1.25..*Souder.*

Levy, U. P. Manual of internal rules and regulations for men-of-war. 3d ed., rev. and enl. 18°. '62. 50c.................................*Van Nostrand.*

Lewald, Fanny. Hulda; tr. by Mrs. A. L. Wister. [Fiction.] 12°. $1.75 ....*Lippincott.*

Lewes, G: H: Biographical hist. of philosophy. 8°. $3.50; — in 2 v., $4 ....*Appleton.*
— Comte's philosophy of the sciences: exposition of the "Cours." 12°. (Bohn.) $1.75 ..*Little, B. & Co.*

Lewes, G: H: *continued.*
— *Same.* 12°. (Bohn.) $2..*Lippincott; Scribner, W. & A.*
— Noble heart: tragedy. 16°. pap., 15c......*French.*
— Physiology of common life. 2 v. 12°. $3..*Appleton.*
— Problems of life and mind: the foundations of a creed. v. 1, 2. 8°. '74–'75. ea., $3............*Osgood.*
— Story of Goethe's life. por. 12°. '73. $1.50..*Osgood.*
— Studies in animal life. ill. 12°. $1.........*Harper.*
— Three sisters and three fortunes; or, Rose, Blanche and Violet. [Fiction.] 8°. pap., 75c...*Harper.*
— *See also* Kaulbach, W., Female characters of Goethe.

Lewes, *Mrs.* M. E. *See* Eliot, George (*pseud.*)

Lewie; or, the bended twig. Bradford, S. H. $1.25. *Hurd & H.*

Lewin, G: Treatment of syphilis by subcutaneous sublimate injections; tr. by C. Prögler and E. H. Gale. ill. 8°. '72. $2.25..............*Lindsay.*

Lewin, Raph. What is Judaism? or, a few words to the Jews. 16°. $1..................*Appleton.*

Lewin, T: Life and epistles of St. Paul. 2 v. maps, ill., etc. demy 4°. $18–$40...*Scribner, W. & A.*
— Practical treatise on law of trusts and trustees. 2d Am. ed. 8°. '58. $5.50.....*T. & J. W. Johnson.*
— — *See also* Law lib.

Lewis, A. H. ["L: Henry."] Boston boy (The). 16°. '71. $1.25........................*Graves.*
— Only ask; or, avenue and alley. 16°. '71. $1.25. *Graves.*

Lewis, C: B. ["M. Quad."] Goaks and tears. ill. 12°. '75. pap., 50c................(?) *Shepard.*

Lewis, Charlton T. Gnomon of the New Test. *See* Bengel, J. A.
— History of Germany; founded on D. Müller's "History of the German people." ill. cr. 8°. $2.50. *Harper.*

Lewis, *Rev.* D. Sketches of a superannuate. 12°. $1.25.....................*Cin. Meth. Bk. Conc.*

Lewis, Dio. Chastity; or, our secret sins. 12°. '74. *$2; $2 50; hf. mor., $3............*Maclean.*
— Five-minute chats with young women and certain other parties. 12°. $1.50.............*Harper.*
— New gymnastics for men, women and children. ('62.) 17th ed. ill. 12°. $1.50.............*Osgood.*
— Our digestion; or, my jolly friend's secret. ill. 12°. '72. *$2; $2.75.....................*Maclean.*
— Our girls. 12°. $1.50......................*Harper.*
— Prohibition a failure: true solution of the temperance question. 16°. '75. $1.50...........*Osgood.*
— Weak lungs, and how to make them strong. ('63.) 12th ed. ill. 12°. $1.50..............*Osgood.*

Lewis, E. J. The American sportsman. ill. 8°. $2.75 ....*Lippincott.*

Lewis, Ellis. Romance of matrimony. ill. 12°. '61. $1.50 ....*Challen.*

Lewis, Enoch. Treatise on plane and spherical trigonometry, incl. construction of the auxiliary tables. 8°. '44. hf. roan, $1.75...............*Porter.*

Lewis, Estelle A. Records of the heart, and other poems. pl. 8°. '66. $3.................*Bouton.*

Lewis, G. B. Life of John Thomas, first Baptist missionary to Bengal. 8°. $4.........*Macmillan.*

Lewis, J: N. Presbyterian manual. 18°. 50c. *Pres. Bd.*

Lewis, *Mrs.* Ma. ["Mtea."] Heart echoes. 12°. '73. $1.25 ....*Turnbull.*

Lewis, Mat. Greg. [Plays.] 6 v. 16°. ea., pap., 15c. *French.*
Cont.: Adelgitha: tragedy. — Castle spectre. — One o'clock; or, the knight and the wood demon: operetta. — Raymond and Agnes: melodrama. — Timour, the Tartar. — Venoni.
— The monk. [Fiction.] 8°. pap., 50c.....*Peterson.*

Lewis, Meriwether, *and* Clarke, W. *See* Biddle, N., Hist. of expedition.

Lewis, R: History of the life-boat and its work. 2d ed. ill. cr. 8°. '74. $1.75 ....*Macmillan.*

Lewis, S: Biography. 12°. $1.25..*Cin. Meth. Bk. Conc.*

Lewis, Tayler. Divine human in the Scriptures. ('59.) New ed. 12°. '60. $1.50 .... *Carter.*
— Light (The) by which we see light; or, nature and the Scriptures. (Vedder lectures, Rutgers Coll., 1875.) 12°. $1.25 .... *N. Y. Ref. Ch. Bd.*
— Rhymthical version of Job. *See* Lange, J. P., Commentary.
— *See also* Plato; — Van Santwood, C., *and* Lewis, T.

Lewis, W. G. Trades and industrial occupations of the Bible. 12°. $1.25 .... *Nelson.*

Lewis, W: H. Interleaved book of family prayers. 18°. '75. 50c. .... *Dutton.*
— Sermons for the Christian year. 6th ed., rev. and enl. 2 v. 12°. '75. $3.50 .... *Dutton.*

Lewis, W: M. People's practical poultry book. ('71.) 7th ed. ill. 8°. '76. $1.50 .... *Rural.*

Lewis, Winslow. Address at annual meeting of the N. E. Historic-Geneal. Soc., Jan. 7, 1863. 8°. '63. pap., 25c. .... *N. E. Hist. Gen.*
— Annual address of president of N. E. Hist.-Geneal. Soc., Jan. 6, 1864. 8°. '64. pap., 25c. *N. E. Hist. Gen.*

Lewis Arundel. *See* Smedley, F. E.

Lewsiana. Smith, W. A. $3 .... *Routledge.*

Lexow, F: Novellistisches. 3 v. 12°. '72. ea., 75c.; pap., 50c. .... *Steiger.*
Cont.. Auf dem Geierfels. — Imperia. — Vornehm u. Gering.
— Gedichte. por. 16°. '72. $1 .... *Steiger.*

Lexow, Rudolph. Romane u. Novellen. 2 v. 12°. '72. ea., 75c.; pap., 50c. .... *Steiger.*
Cont.: Annie's Prüfungen. — Der Rubin.

Leyendas morales (Ó): tratados españoles. 12°. '52. 60c. .... *Am. Tr.*

Leypoldt, F: ["L. Pylodet."] (*ed.*) Beginner's French reader. Premières lectures. With vocab. ('68.) New ed. 16°. '76. bds., 60c. .... *Holt.*
— Beginning French: exercises arranged from 140th ed. of Ahn's French course, and 10th Paris ed. of Belèze's Syllabaire. ('66.) New ed. ill. 16°. '76. bds., 60c. .... *Holt.*
— Gouttes de rosée: petit trésor poétique des jeunes personnes. ('65.) New ed. 18°. '76. 75c. .. *Holt.*
— La littérature française classique, précédée de leçons sur la litt. franç. depuis ses origines. ('67.) New ed. 12°. '76. $1.75 .... *Holt.*
— La littérature française contemporaine: recueil en prose et en vers de morceaux; avec notices biog. et litt., par P. Poitevin, M. Roche, L. Grangier, etc. ('67.) New ed. 12°. '76. $1.50 ... *Holt.*
— Mère l'oie: poésies, énigmes, chansons et rondes enfantines. ('63.) New ed. ill. 8°. '74. bds., 50c. .... *Holt.*
— New guide to German conversation; arranged from Witcomb, E. Otto, Flaxman and others. ('69.) New ed. 18°. '76. 75c. .... *Holt.*
— Secondes lectures. Second French reader; with vocab. ('70.) New ed. ill. 12°. '76. $1.25 .. *Holt.*
— *See also* Alphabetical ref. list; — American catalogue; — Annual Am. catal.; — Eia Popeia; — Publisher's trade list ann.; — Trade circular ann.

Leyser, P. *See* Chemnitz, M., Leyser, P., *and* Gerhard, J.

Leyton Hall. Lemon, M. 75c. .... *Peterson.*

L'Homond, C: François. De viris illustribus urbis Romæ; a Romulo ad Augustum. 12°. '59. 75c. *Kelly, P. & Co.*
— *Same;* with a dict. by J. Hardie. 18°. 75c. .. *Butler.*
— Elements of French grammar; tr. with notes and exercises by H. W. Longfellow. 12°. $1 .. *Dennet.*
— Epitome historiæ sacræ. 12°. '59. 50c. *Kelly, P. & Co.*
— *Same;* with notes, etc., by G. Ironsides. 20th ed., rev. and enl. by T. S. Joy. 18°. 63c. .. *Butler.*

L'Hote, J. B. Book of Revelation explained by history. 12°. $1 .... *Lippincott.*

Liar. Foote, S. 15c. .... *De Witt; French.*

Libbey, W. H. Use and abuse of tobacco. 16°. '76. pap., 25c. .... *Williams.*

Liber librorum, its structure, limitation and purpose: friendly communication to a reluctant sceptic. 16°. '67. $1.50 .... *Scribner.*

Liber musicus. Woodbury, I. B. $1.50 .. *Huntington.*

Liber primus. *See* New.

Liberia. Hale, S. J. $1.25 .... *Harper.*

Liberty bell. Tucker, H. 75c.; 50c. .... *Pond.*

Liberty, equality, fraternity. Stephen, J. F. $2 .. *Holt.*

Liberty of conscience and the Baptists. Jarrel, W. A. 30c.; 10c. .... *So. Bapt.*

Liberty or slavery: essays on Am. slavery by R. B. Thurston, A. C. Baldwin and T. Williston. 18°. 30c. .... *Cong. Pub.*

Library (The); or, what books to read, and how to buy them: practical hints by an old book buyer. 16°. '74. pap., 20c. .... *Porter.*

Library atlas of modern, historical and classical geography, incl. 8 railway maps and 4 astron. charts; with descrip. letter-press of mod. geog. by J. Bryce, of hist. geog. by W. F. Collier, and of class. geog. by L. Schmitz, and indices. 8°. '75. hf. mor., $14; $16 .... *Putnam.*

Library for happy hours. 5 v. ill. 18°. '68. $2.50. *Meth. Bk. Conc.*
Cont.: Charlotte and her enemy. — Three half-dollars. — Paul's mountain home. — Harry and Phil. — Little medicine-carrier.

Library for little children. *See* Kennedy, *Mrs.* M. G.

Library for the little folk. *See* Cousin Belle.

Library for little folks. 6 v. 32°. $1.85 ... *Am. S. S.*
Cont.: Bible stories, 2 v. — Fanny and her brothers. — My little library. — Stories for boys. — Stories for girls.

Library for little lads and lasses. 5 v. ill. 18°. '70. $3 .... *Meth. Bk. Conc.*
Cont.: Archie and his sisters. — Archie and Nep. — Stories about the little ones. — More stories about the little ones. — Fisher boy's secret.

Library for students. 3 v. 12°. $4.50 ..... *Lothrop.*
Cont.: Bremen lectures. — Salvation by Christ. — Flashes of thought.

Library notes. Russell, A. P. $2 .... *Hurd & H.*

Library of adventure. 2 v. 16°. $3 .... *Lothrop.*
Cont.: African adventure and adventurers. — First explorers of North America.

Library of adventure. *See* Ballantyne, R. M.

Library of adventure. *See* Jones, J. B.

Library of Am. hist. ill. imp. 8°. $3 ... *U. P. James.*

Library of Am. linguistics. Shea, J. G. 15 v. $75 .. *Shea.*

Library of the beatitudes. 13 v. 18°. ea., 30c. .. *O'Shea.*
Cont.: Two roads. — Gabriel. — Martha. — Flowers from heaven. — Jewess. — Patient mourner. — Bread of forgiveness. — Henrietta; Gretchen. — Episode of the campaign in Russia. — Cornelio; Valentine. — Thousand francs; Fairy's well. — Secret of riches. — Adventures and misfortunes of a Saxon schoolmaster.

Library of celebrated books. 4 v. ill. 12°. $4 .. *Lippincott.*
Cont.: Robinson Crusoe. — Arabian nights. — Swiss family Robinson. — Gulliver's travels.

Library of Christian devotion. 3 v. 16°. $3 ... *Lothrop.*
Cont.: Hours of Christian devotion. — Perfect man. — Search the Scriptures.

Library of curious things in nature. 5 v. 18°. $3. *Bost. Am. Tr.*
Cont.: Honeymakers. — Lessons from insect life. — Plants. — Rambles after land-shells, by Mrs. H. T. Parker. — The senses.

Library of education. 6 v. 24°. ea., pap., 25c. *Schermerhorn.*
Cont.: Some thoughts conc. education, by J. Locke. — *Same;* [also] Treatise of education, by J. Milton. — Study of physiology in schools, by H. Mann. — Scottish university addresses, by J. S. Mill and others. — Bible in the public schools. — *Same;* by A. D. Mayo and T. Vickers.

Library of elegant pastime. 3 v. ill. 12°. $3.75; $6. *T. Bliss.*
Cont.: Floral offering. — Book of parlor games. — Lady's oracle.

Library of exemplary women. 8 v. ea., $1.50.. *Roberts.*
Cont.: Memoirs and correspondence of Mme. Récamier, 16°. — Madame Récamier and her friends, by Miss Luyster, 16°. — Friendships of women, by W. R. Alger, 16°. — Life and letters of Mme. Swetchine, by Count de Falloux, 16°. — Sainte-Beuve's Portraits of celebrated women, 16°. — Memoirs of Mme. Desbordes-Valmore, by C. A. Sainte-Beuve, 16°. — Letters of Mme. de Sévigné, 12°. — Letters of Lady Mary Wortley Montagu, 12°.

Library of famous fiction. ill. 8°. *$4 .... *Ford.*

Library of foreign poetry. 6 v. 16° .... *Holt.*
Cont.: Hertz's King René's daughter, $1.25. — Tegnér's Frithiof's saga, $1.50. — Lessing's Nathan the wise, $1.50. — Selections from the Kalevala, $1.50. — Heine's Book of songs, $1.50. — Goethe's Poems and ballads, $1.50.

Library of general knowledge. ill. imp. 8°. $1.50. *U. P. James.*

Library of good example. 12 v. 18°. ea., 40c... *O'Shea.*
Cont.: Indian's cloak. — Poor priest. — Battle of Lepanto. — Sister Beatrice. — Keys of Poictiers. — Guendaline. — Young communicants. — Seraph of Assisium. — Traveler. — Jovinian. — Dark valley. — Way of heaven.

Library of instructive amusement. *See* Chambers, W. *and* R.

Library of little gems for little readers. 10 v. ill. 16°. $2.50 .... *Routledge.*
Cont.: Little gems for little readers. — Æsop's little fable-book. — Reasons in rhyme. — Visit to grandmother. — Noble Joe. — Holidays at Wilton. — Favorite animals. — Lucy Vernon. — Among the mountains. — Do your duty.

Library of mesmerism and psychology. 2 v. in 1. 12°. '52. $3.50 .... *Wells.*

Library of pleasant stories. 5 v. ill. 16°. $2.50. *Routledge.*
Cont.: Charlie and Lucy. — Little Nan. — Happy land. — Wandering May. — Left at home.

Library of relig. knowledge. 5 v. 8°. shp., $22.. *Scranton.*
Cont.: Practical and devotional family Bible. — Smith's Bible dictionary. — Jamieson, Fausset and Brown's Commentary on the Bible. — Conybeare and Howson's Life of St. Paul. — Pond's History of God's church.

Library of romantic books. 5 v. ill. 12°. $6.25. *Lippincott.*
Cont.: Dick Rodney, by J. Grant. — Frank Wildman's adventures, by F. Gerstäcker. — Wild sports in the far west, by F. Gerstäcker. — Clayton rangers. — Young islanders.

Library of standard and classical works. 11 v. ill. 8°. ea., $3.50 .... *Routledge.*
Cont.: Arabian nights. — Boswell's Johnson. — Poetical works of Burns and Scott. — Goldsmith's works. — Poetical works of Milton and Young. — Poetical works of Gray, Beattie, Blair, Collins, Thomson and Kirke White. — Masterpieces of foreign literature. — Robinson Crusoe. — Literary and scientific anecdotes. — Cruden's Concordance. — Chaucer and Crabbe.

Library of story. *See* Ballantyne, R. M.

Library of travel and adventure. 3 v. 16°. $1.80. *Appleton.*
Cont.: Fast in the ice. — Away in the wilderness. — Fighting the whales.

Library of travel and adventure. *See* Baker, *Sir* S. W.

Libro primario de los niños. ill. 8°. per doz., pap., $2. *Appleton.*

Libro primario de ortografía. 12°. 50c..... *Appleton.*

Lichtenstein. *See* Hauff, W.

Lichtensteiner (Die). *See* Van der Velde, K. F.

Liddell, H: G. Life of Julius Cæsar. 16°. 75c. *Hurd & H.*
— School hist. of Rome to establishment of the empire; with chapters on hist. of literature and art. ill. 12°. $2 .... *Harper.*
— *and* Scott, Rob. Greek-English lexicon, based on that of F. Passow; rev. and enl. by H. Drisler. roy. 8°. shp., $6 .... *Harper.*
— — *Same.* 6th Oxford ed., unabridg. 4°. mor., $12; shp., $13 .... *Ginn.*
— — *Same;* abridg. sm. 8°. $3......... *Nichols & H.*
— — — *Same.* sq. 12°. hf. bd., $3 .... *Appleton.*
— — — *Same.* 4°. hf. leath., $3.50 .... *Claxton.*
— — — *Same;* with app. of proper and geog. names by J. M. Whiton. sq. 12°. mor., $3; shp., $3.50. *Ginn.*

Liddon, H: Parry. Divinity of Jesus Christ. (Bampton lectures, 1866.) 12°. $2.50. *Dutton; Pott; Scribner, W. & A.*
— Sermons before Univ. of Oxford. 12°. '73. $1.50. *Pott; Scribner, W. & A.*
— Some elements of religion. [Lectures.] 12°. '71. $1.50........... *Dutton; Pott; Scribner, W. & A.*
— University sermons. 12°. '68. $1.25 ...... *Dutton.*

Lidell, J: A. Treatise on apoplexy, cerebral hemorrhage, cerebral embolism, cerebral gout, cerebral rheumatism and epidemic cerebro-spinal meningitis. 8°. $4 .... *W. Wood.*

Lie, Jonas. The pilot and his wife: a Norse love story; tr. by Mrs. Ole Bull. 12°. '76. $1.50.. *Griggs.*

Liebe (Die) d. Ausgewanderten. *See* Zschokke, H.

Liebe zum Heiland. 18°. 30c. .... *Ev. Assoc.*

Lieber, Fs. Character of the gentleman. 3d. ed., enl. 16°. '63. 75c.; $1 .... *Claxton; Lippincott.*
— Essays on property and labor; with essay by Bp. Potter. 18°. 75c. .... *Harper.*
— Great events described by distinguished historians, chroniclers and other writers. 12°. $1.50. *Harper.*
— Instructions for government of armies of the U. S. in the field. 12°. '63. pap., 25c. .. *Van Nostrand.*
— Manual of political ethics; ed. by T. D. Woolsey. 2 v. 8°. $6 .... *Lippincott.*
— On civil liberty and self-government. New ed.; ed. by T. D. Woolsey. 8°. $3.50...... *Lippincott.*
— Vocal sounds of Laura Bridgeman. 4°. '50. pap., $1............................ *Smith. Inst.*

Lieber, Osc. M. Assayer's guide. ('52.) 5th ed. 12°. '75. $1.25 .... *Baird.*

Liebes Leid u. Lust. *See* Shakespeare, W:

Liebet eure Feinde. *See* Hoffmann, F.

Liebhaber-Theater (Das). *See* Van der Velde, K. F.

Liebig, J: Just. v. Works on chemistry. 8°. $2. *Peterson.*
— Animal chemistry. 8°. pap., 25c......... *Peterson.*
— Chemistry and its applic. to physiology, agriculture and commerce; ed. by J. Gardner. 8°. '50. pap., 50c.............................. *Wells.*
— Chemistry in its applic. to agric. 12°. $1... *Wiley.*
— Letters on modern agriculture; ed. by J. Blyth; with add. by a pract. agriculturist. 12°. $1. *Wiley.*
— Potato disease (The). 8°. pap., 25c..... *Peterson.*
— Principles of agric. chemistry, with special ref. to late researches in Eng. 12°. 75c. ...... *Wiley.*
— *Same.* 8°. pap., 25c. .... *Peterson.*

Liebreich, R: Atlas of opthalmoscopy: normal and pathol. conditions of the fundus oculi as seen with the ophthalmoscope: 12 chromo-lith. plates, with text. tr. into Eng. 2d ed., rev. and enl. 4°. $15 .... *Lindsay.*
— On a new method for extraction of cataract. 12°. '72. pap., 25c. .... *Claxton.*

Liechtenstein, *Princess* Marie. History of Holland House. New [chp.] ed. ill. 8°. '75. $7.50. *Same.* Large pap. ed., with Woodbury-type ill. 2 v. 4°. hf. mor., $40 .... *Macmillan.*

Lied (Das) von der Glocke. *See* Schiller, J. F. v.

Lieder e. Wandervogels. Winckler, W. $1.50.. *Steiger.*

Lieder für Soldaten. 32°. '62. 15c........... *Am. Tr.*

Liederbuch für die Jugend. 32°. '54. 30c.; 35c. *Am. Tr.*

Lieder-Cyclus: 24 beliebte. Männerchöre. 12°. pap., 75c. .... *Schirmer.*

Liederkranz f. christl. Schulen. Haas, J. C. 2 pts. ea., 15c.; in 1 v., 25c................ *Schäfer.*

Liederliche Kleeblatt (Das). *See* Böse Geist (Der).

Liedersammlung: festliche Gesänge, nebst e. Anhange v. Schulliedern f. d. Jugend. 24°. 18c. *Benziger.*

Liefde. *See* De Liefde.

Liénard, E: Specimens of the decoration and ornamentation of the 19th cent.: 127 pl. reprod. by heliot. process. 4°. '74. bds., $27; hf. mor., $30. . . . . *Osgood.*
Liethe, W. Anna Lavater; or, pictures of Swiss pastoral life; tr. by C. E. Hurst. 16°. $1. *Cin. Meth. Bk. Conc.*
Lieutenant Falstaff. Winterfeld, A. v. 25c. . . *Steiger.*
Lieut. Messenger. Denison, M. A. 65c. . . . . *Hoyt.*
Liezen-Mayer, A. (*ill.*) *See* Goethe, J. W. v.
Life (The). ('73.) 2d ed. 12°. '74. 50c. . . . . *Colby.*
Life among the Apaches. Cremony, J. C. $2 . . *Carmany.*
Life among the Chinese. Maclay, R. S. $1.75. *Meth. Bk. Conc.*
Life among the Indians. Finley, J. B. $1.75. *Cin. Meth. Bk. Conc.*
Life and adventures of an Arkansaw doctor. Byrn, M. L. 50c. . . . . *U. P. James.*
Life and adventures of Baron Munchausen. *See* Raspe, R. E.
Life and adventures of Ben Brace, the sailor. 8°. pap., 75c. . . . . *Peterson.*
Life and adventures of Captain Singleton. *See* Defoe, D.
Life and adventures of a country merchant. Jones, J. B. $1.25; 75c. . . . . *Lippincott.*
Life and adventures of Dick Clinton. 8°. pap., 25c. *Dick & F.*
Life and adventures of Don Quixote. *See* Cervantes.
Life and adventures of Hajji Baba. Morier, J. $1.50. *Quak. City.*
Life and adventures of Jack Adams. 8°. pap., 75c. *Peterson.*
Life and adventures of Jack of the mill. Howitt, W. 25c. . . . . *Harper.*
Life and adventures of Jonathan Wild. 8°. pap., 25c. *Peterson.*
Life and adventures of a little bird. Watts, J. G. 50c. *Cassell.*
Life and adventures of Paul Periwinkle. 8°. pap., 75c. *Peterson.*
Life and adventures of Percival Maberry. Ingraham, J. H. 75c. . . . . *Peterson.*
Life and adventures of a Quaker among the Indians. Battey, T. C. $1.50 . . . . . *Lee & S.*
Life and adventures of Robinson Crusoe. *See* Defoe, D.
Life and adventures of Tom Bowling, the sailor. 8°. pap., 75c. . . . . *Peterson.*
Life and alone. [Fiction.] 12°. $1.50 . . . . . *Lee & S.*
Life and death. Flemming, D. L. *$2.50; $3; $4. (?) *Gootee.*
Life and death eternal. Bartlett, S. C. $1.50. *Bost. Am. Tr.*
Life and death of Jason. Morris, W. $1.50 . . *Roberts.*
Life and liberty in Am. Mackay, C. $1.50 . . *Harper.*
Life and light. Ritchie, A. $1.25 . . . . . *West. Tr.*
Life and light; or, every-day religion; by author of "George Miller." 18°. 65c. . . . . *Pres. Bd.*
Life and light of men. Young, J. $2.25 . . . *Routledge.*
Life and nature under the tropics. Myers, H. M. *and* P. V. N. $2 . . . . . *Appleton.*
Life and times of Conrad the squirrel; by author of "Wandering Willie." cr. 8°. $1.25 . . *Macmillan.*
Life and the true light. Blaikie, W. G. $1.75 . . *Tibbals.*
Life and work of earnest men. Tweedie, W. K. $1.75. *Cin. Meth. Bk. Conc.*
Life at a farm house. *See* Chat in the playroom.
Life at the fireside. Thayer, W. M. $1.50 . . *Cong. Pub.*
Life at home. Aikman, W. $1.50; $2 . . . . . *Wells.*
Life at threescore and ten. Barnes, A. 35c. . . *Am. Tr.*
Life boat. Ballantyne, R. M. $1.50 . . . . . *Tilton.*
Life by the Ganges. Mullens, *Mrs.* —. 80c. . . *Pres. Bd.*
Life chase. Belot, A. 15c. . . . . *De Witt.*
Life chase. Oxenford, J., *and* Wigan, H. 15c. . . *French.*
Life cruise of Capt. Bess Adams. Wright, J. McN. $1.50 . . . . . *Nat. Temp.*
Life for a life. *See* Craik, D. M.
Life here and there. Willis, N. P. $1.75 . . . *Scribner.*
Life hid in Christ with God. Lee, A. $2.25. *Claxton; Lippincott.*
Life histories for the Sabbath school. 18°. 75c. *Cong. Pub.*
Life histories of animals. *See* Packard, A. S., *jr.*
Life illustrated lib. 75 v. ill. 18°. *net*, $20 . . . *Am. Tr.*
Life in the army. Gregg, J. C. $1.25 . . . . *Perkinpine.*
Life in the backwoods: guide to the successful hunting and trapping of all kinds of animals. sq. 18°. '74. pap., 20c. . . . . (?) *F. M. Reed.*
Life in Brazil. Ewbank, T. $3; $5.25 . . . . . *Harper.*
Life in the camp: incidents of Am. camp life. 12°. pap., 30c. . . . . *Hurst.*
Life in the clearing *vs.* the bush. Moodie, S. $1.50. *De Witt.*
Life in the cloister. Stewart, A. M. $1.25; $1.75. *Kelly, P. & Co.*
Life in Danbury. Bailey, J. M. $1.50 . . . . . *Lee & S.*
Life in earnest. *See* Hamilton, J.
Life in earnest; or, Christian activity and ardour ill. and commended. 18°. 50c. . . . . *Am. S. S.*
Life in the East Indies. Thomes, W. H. $1.50 . . *Lee & S.*
Life in the exode. Pollock, A. D. $2 . . . . . *Univ. Pub.*
Life in the far west. Ruxton, G. F. $1.50 . . . . *Harper.*
Life in the forest. 18°. 17c.; 22c. . . . . *Am. Bapt.*
Life in heaven. 16°. '65. $1.25 . . . . . *Roberts.*
Life in India; or, sketches of Madras, the Neilgherries and Calcutta; by a returned missionary. 18°. $1 . . . . . *Am. S. S.*
Life in the itinerancy. Davis, L. D. $1.50. *Meth. Bk. Conc.*
Life in Judea. 16°. $1.25 . . . . . *Am. Bapt.*
Life in the laity. Davis, L. D. 75c. *Cin. Meth. Bk. Conc.*
Life in London. Reynolds, G. W. M. $1.50 . . *Dick & F.*
Life in Lyntonville. *See* Lyntonville lib.
Life in narrow streets. Thompson, J. C. $1.15. *Pres. Bd.*
Life in New York. Brougham, J. 15c. . . . . *French.*
Life in New York. Small, G. G. 25c. . . . . *Collin & S.*
Life in the old world. Bremer, F. $3.50 . . . *Peterson.*
Life in the open air. Winthrop, T. $1.25 . . . . . *Holt.*
Life in Paris. Houssaye, A. $1.50 . . . . . *W. F. Gill.*
Life in Paris. Reynolds, G. W. M. 50c. . . . . *Peterson.*
Life in the prairie land. Farnham, E. W. $1 . . *Harper.*
Life in the Red Brigade. Ballantyne, R. M. $1.25. *Routledge.*
Life in San Domingo. Kimball, R. B. $1.50 . . *Carleton.*
Life in Spain: past and present. Thornbury, W. $1.50. *Harper.*
Life in Utah. Beadle, J. H. *$2.75; $3.25 . . *Nat. Pub.*
Life in the west. Meeker, N. C. $2 . . . . . *Wells.*
Life in the west; or, the Moreton family. 18°. 75c. *Am. S. S.*
Life in the woods. Geikie, J. C. $2 . . . . . *Routledge.*
Life-incidents of home, school and church. Stone, R. C. $1 . . . . . *S. W. Bk. & Pub.*
Life inexplicable except as a probation. Olin, S. 15c.; 25c. . . . . *Cin. Meth. Bk. Conc.*
Life's a lottery: farce. 16°. pap., 15c. . . . . *French.*
Life lessons from Proverbs. Perry, W. S. $1.75. *Whittaker.*
Life lessons in the school of Christian duty. Gillett, E. H. $1.10 . . . . . *Pres. Bd.*
Life-line of the lone one. Chase, W. $1 . . . . . *Colby.*
Life of an actress. Boucicault, D. 15c. . . . . *French.*

Life of Arthur Vandeleur. Marsh, C. $1.25..*Carter.*
Life of a Berlin doll. 18°. 25c......*Scribner, W. & A.*
Life of Billy Vidkins. Stephens, H. L. 25c...*Peterson.*
Life of Daniel. 18°. 65c..................*Am. S. S.*
Life of Dick Parker, the pirate. 8°. pap., 25c. *Peterson.*
Life of Elijah. 18°. 60c..................*Am. S. S.*
Life of Elisha. 18°. 60c..................*Am. S. S.*
Life of faith. 32°. pap., 10c..................*Dutton.*
Life of faith. Upham, T. C. $1.50..........*Harper.*
Life of faith; with pref. notice by [Rev. M. Dix]. 24°. pap., 10c......................*Huntington.*
Life of galloping Dick, the highwayman. 8°. pap., 25c. *Peterson.*
Life of Gideon. ill. 18°. '66. 45c. *N. Y. Ref. Ch. Bd.; Pres. Com.*
Life of God in the soul of man. *See* Scougal, H.
Life of Grace O'Malley. Maxwell, W. H. 50c. *Peterson.*
Life of human souls. Cochran, W. $1...*Perkinpine.*
Life of Jack Ketch, the murderer. 8°. pap., 25c. *Peterson.*
Life of Jack Sheppard. *See* Ainsworth, W. H.
Life of Jacob and his son Joseph. 18°. 60c...*Am. S. S.*
— *Same.* 18°. '66. 60c...*N. Y. Ref. Ch. Bd.; Pres. Com.*
Life of Lopez, the Cuban patriot and martyr. 8°. pap., 10c..............................*De Witt.*
Life of man symbolized by the months of the year. Pigott, R. $15; $20................*Appleton.*
Life of Mother Brownrigg. 8°. pap., 25c.....*Peterson.*
Life of peace. Brown, R. C. L. $1............*Pott.*
Life of a sailor. *See* Chamier, F.
Life of a showman. Miller, D. P. 40c. ......*French.*
Life of trust. Muller, G. $1.75............*Sheldon.*
Life of vicissitudes. James, G. P. R. 50c....*Harper.*
Life on the deep. 12°. $1..................*Nelson.*
Life on the ocean. Nordhoff, C. $2.50 ....*Wilstach.*
Life pictures. 18°. 35c.; 45c.............*Am. Bapt.*
Life pictures; or, by-gone scenes remembered. 18°. 65c..............................*Am. S. S.*
Life pictures from the Bible. Halsey, Le R. J. $1.65. *Pres. Bd.*
Life preserver. *See* Sargent, L. M.
Life, real and unreal; or, living to some purpose. 18°. 75c..............................*Am. S. S.*
Life scenes. 18°. 50c....................*Cong. Pub.*
Life scenes from the four Gospels; — from the Old Test. Jones, G. ea., $2..................*Garrigues.*
Life scenes in the mountains of Ararat. Parmalee, M. P. $1.25..........................*Cong. Pub.*
Life sketches from Scottish hist.: brief biog. of Scottish Presbyterian worthies. 18°. 40c...*Pres. Bd.*
Life story boys. *See* Newcomb, H.
Life story girls. *See* Newcomb, H.
Life story ser. 4 v. 16°. $3.................*Graves.*
Cont.: Life story boys, by H. Newcomb. — Life story girls, by H. Newcomb. — Kind words, by H. Newcomb. — Joseph and his brethren.

Life studies. *See* Baillie, J.
Life that now is. Collyer, R. $1.50 ....*Lee & S.*
Life that speaketh. Knowles, D. C. $1..*Meth. Bk. Conc.*
Life thoughts. Beecher, H. W. $1.75 ......*Sheldon.*
Life truths. 18°. 60c.; 75c................*Am. S. S.*
Life under glass. Shove, G. A. $1..........*Osgood.*
Life voyage. Daryl, S. $1.25......*Scribner, W. & A.*
Life, walk and triumph of faith. *See* Romaine, W.
Life within and life without. Fuller, M. $1.50..*Roberts.*
Life work. Ranyard, E. $1.25...............*Carter.*
Life work of the Saviour. Ball, G. H. 18c...*Lothrop.*
Life yarn. Judson, E. Z. C. 75c..........*Dick & F.*
Life's aftermath. Marshall, E. $1.50 ....*Dutton.*
Life's assize. Riddell, J. H. 50c. ....*Harper.*
Life's battle lost and won. ill. 16°. '68. 90c...*Am. Tr.*
Life's changes. Browne, S. H. 60c........*Cong. Pub.*
Life's evening; or, thoughts for the aged. 16°. $1.25; $1.50; mor., $4.50........................*Lee & S.*
Life's lessons. Grosvenor, *Mrs.* —. 75c.....*Cong. Pub.*
Life's lessons. Thomas, M. M. $1.50.......*Harper.*
Life's lottery; or, life and its aims. [Fiction.] 12°. '68. $1.50 ....*Claxton.*
Life's morning; or, counsel and encouragement for youthful Christians. 16°. $1.25; $1.50; mor., $4.50..................................*Lee & S.*
Life's quiet hours: quiet hints for the young and old. 16°. $1.25; $1.50; mor., $4.50........*Lee & S.*
Life's ransom. Marston, W. 15c............*French.*
Life's revenge. Suter, W. E. 15c......*Ames; French.*
Life's secret. Wood, E. P. 50c. ....*Peterson.*
Life's struggle. Pardoe, J. $1.75; $1.50...*Peterson.*
Life's struggles; or, one who came up through much tribulation. ('74.) New ed. 16°. '75. $1..*Hoyt.*
Life's trial. Bernard, W. B. 15c............*French.*
Life's work and God's discipline. Vaughan, C. J. $1. *Macmillan.*
Life's work in preparation and in retrospect. Jameson, F. J. 75c. ....*Macmillan.*
Lift a little. *See* Ballard, *Mrs.* J. P.
Lifted up; or, Walter Douglas. 16°. '72. 80c...*Hoyt.*
Lifting the veil. McLain, M. W. $1.75....*Scribner.*
Light, Aust. Shipper's directory for the north-west. 8°. '73. hf. bd., $4 ....*Griggs.*
Light and cloud in the dark valley: sketches of remarkable cases of hope in death. 18°. 50c. *Am. S. S.*
Light and a dark Christmas. Wood, E. P. 25c. *Peterson.*
Light and dark path: hist. of Mary Lester and Eliza Bruce. ill. 18°. 65c. ....*Am. S. S.*
Light and hope ser. 4 v. 16°. $6......(?)*Martien.*
Cont.: Nanny and I. — Caddy's three dresses. — Lucy's two lives. — How it was paid.

Light and love for the nursery group. 18°. 60c. *Am. S. S.*
Light and shade. Baker, H. N. W. $1.25.....*Hoyt.*
Light and support for the dark valley. 18°. 30c. *Pres. Bd.*
Light at evening time. Holme, J. S. $2.50–$8..*Harper.*
Light at eventide: religious poems; by author of "Chimes for childhood." 12°. $1.50; $2..*Lee & S.*
Light-bearer (The); or, Lucy's visit; by author of "Story of a pocket Bible." 18°. 50c. *Am. S. S.*
Light-bearers and beacons. *See* Little Lottie ser.
Light for the line. Marsh, C. 35c..........*Carter.*
Light for little ones. Waterbury, M. F. 50c. *Hoyt, F. & D.*
Light from beyond to cheer the Christian pilgrim. Geikie, J. C. $1......................*Routledge.*
Light from the cross. *See* Tholuck, A.
Light in the dark. Caughey, J. $1.50.......*Palmer.*
Light in dark places. *See* Neander, J. A. W.
Light in darkness. Hewit, A. F. 75c......*Cath. Pub.*
Light in the east. *See* Hayes, A. P.
Light in the valley. *See* Annesley, *Miss* M.
Light in the window. 18°. 35c.; 45c.......*Am. Bapt.*
— *See also* Little folks ser.; — Neddie and Maggie.
Light of all ages. Carlyle, G. $1.75......*Routledge.*
Light of the conscience. Lear, S. $2 ....*Pott.*
Light of the forge; or, counsels drawn from the sick bed of E. M. 16°. 90c......................*Am. S. S.*
Light of light. ill. 32°. '57. 30c. ....*Am. Tr.*
Light of the world. Wilkins, A. S. $1.50..*Macmillan.*
Light of the world, and other poems and hymns; by eminent poets. ill. 4°. $5; mor., $9..*Lippincott.*

Light of the world: repository of relig. knowledge [giving] hist. of transactions connected with life of Christ, etc. ('71.) 2d ed. ill. 4°. '72. *$5; $6; $7.50 .... *Flint.*

Light of the world; or, footprints of Christ our Lord. 18°. 40c. .... *Dutton.*

Light on the dark river. Lawrence, M. W. $1.50. * *Osgood.*

Light on Freemasonry. Bernard, D. $1.75.. *Un. B. Pub.*

Light on the last things. Hayden, W. B. $1.25. *Lippincott.*

Light on little graves: thoughts for parents bereaved of young children. 18°. 50c. .... *Am. S. S.*

Light on the ocean. Hanks, S. W. 75c. .. *Cong. Pub.*

Light on the pathway. 5 v. in 1. 16°. 90c... *West. Tr.*

Light on the pathway of holiness. M'Cabe, L. D. 75c. *Meth. Bk. Conc.*

Light on shadowed paths. Arthur, T. S. $1.50. *J. E. Potter.*

Light science for leisure hours. Proctor, R. A. $1.75. *Appleton.*

Light shining. 18°. 60c. .... *Cong. Pub.*

Light shining in darkness; or, illustrations of the power of the Gospel. 16°. $1.50 .... *Pres. Bd.*

Lighted valley. 16°. 90c. .... *Carter.*

Lighted way; or, loving words about Jesus. 18°. 40c.; 50c. .... *Am. Bapt.*

Lightfoot, Jos. Barber. On a fresh revision of the Eng. New Test. 2d ed., rev. cr. 8°. '72. $2. *Macmillan.*

— St. Clement of Rome: two epistles to the Corinthians; rev. text, with introd. and notes. 8°. '69. $4.25. *Macmillan.*

— St. Paul's Epistles to the Colossians and to Philemon: rev. text, with introds., notes and dissertations. 8°. '75. $6 .... *Macmillan.*

— St. Paul's Epistle to the Galatians: rev. text, with introd., notes, etc. 8°. '70. $3 .... *Draper.*

— *Same.* 4th ed. 8°. '74. $6 .... *Macmillan.*

— St. Paul's Epistle to the Philippians: rev. text, with introd., notes and dissertations. 2d ed. 8°. '73. $6 .... *Macmillan.*

— *and* Trench, *Rev.* R. C., *and* Ellicott, *Rev.* J. C. Revision of the Eng. version of the New Test.; with introd. by Rev. P. Schaff. cr. 8°. $3.. *Harper.*

Lighthall, G. E. Analysis, parsing and composition. 12°. bds., 35c. .... *Waldteufel.*

Light-headed pussy: a story in rhymes; ill. by F. Lossow. 8°. bds., 50c.; 75c. .... *Stroefer.*

Light-hearted girl. Alden, J. 50c. .... *Lee & S.*

Lightheart's pilgrimage. Baker, G. M. 15c... *Lee & S.*

Lighthouse (The). Bullard, A. 25c. .... *Lee & S.*

Lighthouse boy (The). Langille, J. 25c.... *Am. Tr.*

Lighthouse keeper's daughter. 64°. 20c. *Bost. Am. Tr.*

— *Same.* ('62.) New ed. 16°. '70. 30c. .... *Hoyt.*

Lighthouse series. 4 v. 18°. $3.60 ..... (?) *Martien.*

Cont.: Children of the lighthouse. — Mere piece of mischief. — Edith Vaughan's victory. — Sophie Krantz.

Lightning: its causes and effects, familiarly explained. 18°. 22c. .... *Am. S. S.*

Lightning express. Adams, W. T. $1.25... *Lee & S.*

Lighton, F. Modern school for the fife. 8°. 50c. *Gordon.*

Lights and shadows. 16°. $1 .... *Carter.*

Lights and shadows of Freemasonry. Morris, R. $2. *Masonic.*

Lights and shadows of New York life. McCabe, J. D. *$2.75; $3.75 .... *Nat. Pub.*

Lights and shadows of real life. Arthur, T. S. $1.75. *J. E. Potter.*

Lights and shadows of sacred story. Wright, J. McN. *$3.50; $5.50 .... *McCurdy.*

Lights and shadows of Scottish life. *See* Wilson, J.

Lights of the world. Stoughton, J. $1. *Cin. Meth. Bk. Conc.*

Ligny, Fs. de. History of the life of Jesus Christ; also hist. of the acts of the apostles; tr. by Mrs. J. Sadlier. 8°. $4; hf. mor., $5; $6.. *Sadlier.*

Liguori, Alf. Marie de, *St.* Advice to Catholic girls; tr. 24°. pap., 10c. .... *Coddington.*

— Christian virtues, and means of obtaining them; tr. 16°. $1 .... *Strong.*

— Clock of the passion; tr. 18°. 45c. .... *Sadlier.*

— Four principal gates of hell; tr. 24°. pap., 10c. *Coddington.*

— Glories of Mary; tr. 18°. $1.25; $1.75 .... *O'Shea.*

— *Same.* 16°. $1.25; $2 .... *Strong.*

— *Germ.* Die Herrlichkeiten Marias. 18°. '52. $1.75; $2; $2.50 .... *Murphy.*

— Holy way of the cross; tr. 32°. pap., 10c... *Benziger.*

— Hours of the passion; or, pathetic reflections on sufferings and death of our Redeemer; tr. by Rev. W. Walsh, with sketch of L. 18°. 60c. *Cath. Pub.*

— Instructions on the commandments and sacraments; tr. 48°. 40c. .... *O'Shea.*

— *Same.* 24°. 50c. .... *Noonan.*

— Life; by a Sister of Mercy. por. 18°. $2.50; $3. *O'Shea.*

— Love of Christ; or, the practice of the love of Jesus; tr. 32°. 50c. .... *Strong.*

— Love of Jesus Christ reduced to practice; tr. by Rev. W. Walsh. 18°. 60c. .... *Cath. Pub.*

— Manual: prayers, devotional exercises, etc., from works; sel. by M. Müller. 12°. '76. 75c... *Pustet.*

— Means of acquiring perfection; tr. 32°. '67. 25c. *Murphy.*

— Meditations and discourses on the incarnation; tr. 16°. 75c. .... *Strong.*

— Preparations for death; or, considerations on the eternal maxims; tr. by a Cath. clergyman. 12°. '69. 75c.; $1.25 .... *Murphy.*

— *Same.* 12°. 75c. .... *Strong.*

— Sacerdos sanctificatus; or, discourses on the mass and office; with a preparation and thanksgiving before and after mass for every day in the week; tr. by Rev. J. Jones. 18°. '61. $1..... *Cunningham.*

— Short treatise on prayer adapted to all classes of Christians; tr. 24°. 40c. .... *Cath. Pub.*

— Spirit of L.: sel. from his shorter spiritual treatises; tr. by Rev. J. Jones, with memoir of L. 24°. 60c. .... *Cath. Pub.*

— Spiritual retreat of eight days; tr. by a member of the Order of Mercy. 32°. 40c. .... *O'Shea.*

— Theologia moralis; in compendium red. et usui venerabilis cleri Am. accom. A. Konings. 4°. *net,* hf. mor., $5 .... *Benziger.*

— Treatise on prayer; tr. 48°. 40c. .... *O'Shea.*

— *Same.* 24°. 50c. .... *Strong.*

— True spouse of Christ; or, the nun sanctified; tr. 12°. *net,* $2.25 .... *Sadlier.*

— Visits to the blessed sacrament; tr. 32°. 38c. *Strong.*

— *Same.* 24°. 60c. .... *Cath. Pub.*

— *Same;* [also] Spirit. 16°. 75c. .... *Strong.*

— Way of salvation, in meditations for every day in the year; tr. by Rev. J. Jones. 24°. 75c. .. *Cath. Pub.*

— *See also* Golden treasury; — Livre des missions; — Mission book.

Like unto Christ. *See* Thomas *a Kempis.*

Lila. *See* Goethe, J. W. v.

Lili, the doctor's daughter; or, the bunch of violets, and what became of them. 16°. '74. 75c... *Routledge.*

Lilian: story of the days of martyrdom in England. 16°. '65. 90c. .... *Meth. Bk. Conc.*

Lilian: tale for children, in verse. 18°. 22c... *Am. S. S.*

Lilian: tale of 300 years ago. ill. 18°. 60c. *Bost. Am. Tr.*

— *See also* Winter school stories.

Lilian; or, persecutions in England. ill. 18°. '65. 60c. .... *Am. Tr.*

Lilian Gordon. Dunning, A. K. 50c. ..... *Pres. Bd.*

Lilian Grey. Holt, M. H. $1.25 .... *Lothrop.*

Lilian Grey lib. 4 v. 16°. $5 .... *Lothrop.*
Cont.: Lilian Grey. — Ivy Fennhaven. — Signet ring. — Lame Bessie.

Lilian's prayer. *See* Holt, M. H.

Lilias and her cousins. 18°. '58. 80c. ...... *Challen.*

Lilias Gray, and other stories. 32°. 40c. *Scribner, W. & A.*

Lilienthall, M. E., *and* Allyn, R. Object lessons: instruction in composition and object lessons. 16°. '62. 25c. .... *Wilson, H. & Co.*

Lilies and thistledown. Mathews, J. A. $1.25 .. *Carter.*

Liliesleaf. Oliphant, M. O. W. $1 .... *Burnham.*

Lille, Hub. As like as two peas: farce. 16°. pap., 15c. .... *French.*

Lillian. Smith, J. F. 75c. .... *Dick & F.*

Lillian Gervaise. Barnett, J. 15c. .... *French.*

Lillian's fate. Egan, P. 25c. .... *De Witt.*

Lillian's golden hours. Meteyard, E. $1.50. *Routledge.*

Lillie, J. *See* Curtis, J. T., *and* Lillie, J.

Lillie, *Rev.* J: Lectures on 1st and 2nd Peter; with introd. by P. Schaff. ('68.) New ed. 8°. '69. $3.50 .... *Scribner.*

— On Thessalonians. 8°. $2 .... *Carter.*

Lillie; or, the little Christian's toilet. Brown, H. E. $1 .... *Am. Tr.*

Lillie's visit. 18°. 30c. .... *Dutton.*

Lillieslea. *See* Howitt, M.

Lillingstones of Lillingstone. *See* Worboise, E. J.

Lilliput lectures; by author of "Lilliput levee." ill. sq. 12°. '71. $1.50 .... *Routledge.*

Lilliput legends; by author of "Lilliput levee." ill. sq. 12°. '72. $1.50 .... *Routledge.*

Lilliput levee: book of rhymes for children. ill. sq. 16°. $1 .... *Routledge.*

Lilliput revels; by author of "Lilliput levee." ill. sq. 12°. '71. $1.25 .... *Routledge.*

Lillo, G: George Barnwell: tragedy. 16°. pap., 15c. *French.*

Lilly, W. S. *See* Newman, J. H., Characteristics from writings.

Lilly, W: Introduction to astrology; with emendations by Zadkiel. 12°. (Bohn.) $1.75 .... *Little, B. & Co.*

— *Same.* 12°. (Bohn.) $2. *Lippincott; Scribner, W. & A.*

Lilly's birthday. *See* Baker, *Mrs.* H. N. W.

Lily (The). *See* Home lib.

Lily. King, S. P. $1.25 .... *Harper.*

Lily among thorns. Marshall, E. $1.50 ..... *Dutton.*

Lily among thorns; [also] Old Gabriel. 32°. 20c. *Pres. Bd.*

Lily and the cross. De Mille, J. $1.50 ...... *Lee & S.*

Lily Bell, the culprit fay. Saroni, H. S. $1 ... *Church.*

Lily gathered; or, the conversion of James Laing. 18°. 20c.; 25c. .... *Am. Bapt.*

— *Same.* 18°. 35c. .... *Am. S. S.*

Lily Gordon. *See* Bell, C. D.

Lily Norris' enemy. Mathews, J. H. $1 ..... *Carter.*

Lily of France: drama. 16°. pap., 15c. .... *French.*

Lily of Israel. Gerbet, O. P. 75c.; $1 .... *Kenedy.*

Lily of Israel. *See* Mary, *Virgin*, Life.

Lily of Lumley. Milner, E. $1.50 .... *Macmillan.*

Lily of St. Joseph. [Cath. prayer book.] 32°. 45c. -$3 .... *O'Shea.*

Lily of Tiflis. 18°. 45c. .... *Dutton.*

Lily of the valley. Gray, A. $1.50 ... *Kelly, P. & Co.*

Lily of the valley. *See* Flower garlands for little gleaners.

Lily series. *See* Sherwood, *Mrs.* M. M.

Lily white. Goodwin, E. $1 .... *Lippincott.*

Lily's hard words. Hosmer, M. 75c. .... *Claxton.*

Lily's home. Barker, S. 50c. .... *Routledge.*

Lily's lesson. Mathews, J. H. 60c. .... *Carter.*

Lily's looking glasses. Boyd, E. E. 45c. .. *J. A. Moore.*

Lime-burner, and other stories. ('63.) New ed. ill. 16°. '75. 55c. .... *Hoyt.*

Lime-kiln man; or, victim of misfortune. 8°. pap., 25c. .... *De Witt.*

Lime-street lectures: defence of important doctrines of the Gospel: sermons. 8°. $2 ...... *Pres. Bd.*

Limerick boy. Pilgrim, J. 15c. .... *French.*

Limerick veteran. Stewart, A. M. $1.50; $2. *Kelly, P. & Co.*

Limits of religious thought. *See* Mansel, H. L.

Lina and Gertrude. *See* Lacy's home plays for ladies.

Lincoln, *Mrs.* A. H. *See* Phelps, *Mrs.* A. H. Lincoln.

Lincoln, Ab. Illustrated life, speeches, martyrdom and funeral. 12°. $1.75. 8°. pap., $1.50 ..... *Peterson.*

— Our martyr president, Abraham Lincoln: voices from the pulpit of New York and Brooklyn, oration by G. Bancroft, burial oration by Bp. Simpson, eulogy by R. S. Storrs, jr. 12°. '65. $2 .. *Tibbals.*

— Tribute of respect of citizens of Troy, to memory of L. 8°. '65. $3; large pap., $12 .. *W. H. Young.*

— Vida de Abram Lincoln; con una introd. por D. F. Sarmiento. 12°. $1.75 .... *Appleton.*

Lincoln, D. F. Electro therapeutics: manual of medical electricity. ill. roy. 12°. $1.50 ...... *Lea.*

— Report on school hygiene; [also] Hygiene in schools and colleges, by A. L. Carroll. 8°. '74. pap., 10c. *Williams.*

Lincoln, Ensign. Aids to devotion. 16°. $1. 18°. 80c. .... *Am. Bapt.*

Lincoln, Heman (*ed.*) The quiet hour: a book of prayers. 18°. '71. 50c. .... *Lothrop.*

Lincoln, W: Address, Worcester [Mass.], upon the character and services of C. C. Baldwin, late librarian of the Society. 8°. '35. 50c. *Am. Antiq.*

— History of Worcester, to 1836; contin. to 1860 by C. Hersey. ill. 8°. '60. $2.50 .... (?) *C. Hersey.*

Lincolniana. sm. 4°. $6 .... *Lee & S.*

Linda. Hentz, C. L. $1.75; $1.50 .... *Peterson.*

Linda di Chamounix. *See* Donizetti, G.

Linda of Chamouni. Edwardes, C. 15c. ..... *French.*

Linda Tressel; by author of "Nina Balatka." 8°. '68. pap., 38c. .... *Littell & G.*

Lindau, Pl. Maria and Magdalena: play. 16°. pap., 15c. .... *De Witt.*

Lindemann, J. C. W. Dr. Martin Luther als Erzieher der Jugend. ('66.) 3d ed. 16°. 35c. ..... *Dette.*

Linden, A: Children's trials; or, the little rope-dancers, and other tales; tr. ill. 16°. $1.25 ..... *O'Shea.*

— Tales and legends; tr. ill. 16°. $1.25 ..... *O'Shea.*

Linden, C. Our general. [In Eng. or Germ.] ill. 8°. pap., 50c. .... *Barclay.*

Lindendale stories. *See* Wise, D.

Lindenwood. Dawes, S. E. $1.25 .... *Am. Tr.*

Lindisfarn Chase. Trollope, T. A. $2; $1.50. *Harper.*

Lindley, J: Theory of horticulture; with add. by A. J. Downing. 12°. $2 .... *Wiley.*

— *and* Moore, T: Treasury of botany: popular dict. of the vegetable kingdom. 2 v. ill. 18°. $6; hf. cf., $8 .... *Appleton.*

Lindley, Natl. Introduction to study of jurisprudence. *See* Law lib.

— Treatise on law of partnership; incl. its application to joint-stock and other companies. 2 v. 8°. '60. $6.50 .... *T. & J. W. Johnson.*

Lindsay, A. W. C. (*Lord*). [Alex. W. Crawford.] Letters on Egypt, Edom and the Holy Land. ill. and maps. 12°. (Bohn.) $1.75 .. *Little, B. & Co.*

— *Same.* ill. and maps. 12°. (Bohn.) $2. *Lippincott; Scribner, W. & A.*

Lindsay, W. S. History of merchant shipping and ancient commerce; ill. by J. D. Cooper with charts and maps. 4 v. 8°. $35..*Scribner, W. & A.*

Lindsay Lee and his friends. 12°. '74. 75c. *Meth. Bk. Conc.*

Lindslay, Wa. M. Poems. 12°. 75c.......*Appleton.*

Lindsley, D: P. Elements of tachygraphy. ('69.) 5th ed. ill. 12°. '76. $1.75; bds., $1.50. *O. Clapp.*

— The note taker: pt. 2 of Elements of tachygraphy. 12°. '73. $2.75......................*O. Clapp.*

Lindsley, Ph. Works; ed. by L. J. Halsey; with notices of life and labors. 3 v. 8°. $12..*Lippincott.*

Line upon line. *See* Mortimer, *Mrs.* M.

Lineage of language. Fradenburgh, J. N. $3..*Authors.*

Lines in pleasant places. Shillaber, B. P. $1.50. *Williams.*

Lines left out. Mortimer, M. 75c...........*Harper.*

Ling Bank Cottage. ill. 18°. '73. 75c........*Am. Tr.*

Lingard, J: History of England; with a contin. to 1854 by J. Burke, and app. to 1873; with memoir and notes. por. 8°. '75. $3.50; $4.........*Murphy.*

— *Same.* (School ed.) 12°. '55. $1.50......*Murphy.*

— *Same.* 13 v. por. and ill. 12°. $20; shp., $24; hf. cf., $32............................*O'Shea.*

Lingard, W: H. On the beach at Long Branch song book. 16°. 25c....................*Dick & F.*

Link, and other stories. Cousin Zilpha. 60c. *Bost. Am. Tr.*

Link your chain; by author of "Blue bell." [Fiction.] ill. 8°. (Lond.) pap., 30c...........*Am. News.*

Links in a golden chain. *See* Golden chain lib.

Linley, G: Law versus love: comedietta. 16°. pap., 15c. ....*French.*

Linley Rochford. McCarthy, J. $1.75; $1..*Sheldon.*

Linn, E. A., *and* Sargent, N. Life and public services of Lewis F. Linn, U. S. Senator from Missouri. por. 8°. $2........................*Appleton.*

Linn, S. Landscape photography. 18°. pap., 75c. *Benerman.*

Linn, S. Pollock (*ed.*) Living thoughts of leading thinkers; with dict. of authors, with their real and assumed signatures. 12°. '75. $2..*Johnson & M.*

Linn, S: Index of parallel references to cases in Penna. courts; with cases overruled, etc. 8°. shp., $6.50..................................*Kay.*

Linnet. *See* Our song birds.

Linnet's trial. *See* Smedley, M. B.

Linny Lockwood. Crowe, C. 80c.........*Routledge.*

Linsday, Owen. The Baldwinsville homicide: report of trial of L. for murder of F. A. Colvin. 8°. '75. $1; pap., 50c.........................*Tinsley.*

Linside farm. Moore, J. F. $1.25............*Hoyt.*

Linton, *Mrs.* Eliza Lynn. Atonement of Leam Dundas. 8°. $1.50; pap., $1.................*Lippincott.*

— Girl of the period. 12°. '69. pap., 10c....*Redfield.*

— Lizzie Lorton of Greyrigg. 8°. pap., 75c...*Harper.*

— Ourselves: essays on women. 12°. $1.50. *Routledge.*

— Patricia Kemball. 12°. $1.75..........*Lippincott.*

— Sowing the wind. 8°. pap., 50c. ....*Harper.*

— True history of Joshua Davidson, communist. 12°. '72. $1.25.....................*Lippincott.*

Linton, H. P. Psalms of David and Solomon. fp. 8°. (Bagster.) $1.25......................*Wiley.*

— Scriptures arranged, in the order of time as written. fp. 8°. (Bagster.) $2.50...............*Wiley.*

Linwoods (The). Sedgwick, C. M. 2 v. $3..*Harper.*

Lion and the lamb. *See* Aunt Alice's lib.

Lion and other beasts. *See* Stories about animals ser.

Lion at bay. Phillips, W. 15c. ....*French.*

Lion Ben of Elm Island. Kellogg, E. $1.25..*Lee & S.*

Lion heart lib. 5 v. ill. 16°. $2.50 ....*Nelson.*
Cont.: Dick's robins, by Mrs. F. Seamer. — Poacher's sons, by H. Hill. — Marion's three crowns, by S. Doudney. — Tom Perry's venture, by E. Leslie. — Treasure on the beach, by M. A. P.

Lion-hearted (The). Grey, E. C. 75c.....*Peterson.*

Lion of Flanders. Conscience, H. $1.25..*Kelly, P. & Co.*

Lion slayer. Williams, T. J. 15c............*French.*

Lionel Jocelyn. Egan, P. 50c..............*De Witt.*

Lionel Lincoln. *See* Cooper, Ja. F.

Lionel St. Clair. Moncriefe, L. A. 75c. *Carter; Dutton.*

Lionello. Bresciani, A. $1.50; $2...*Kelly, P. & Co.*

Lionel's courage. Wise, D. $1.25......*Perkinpine.*

Lion's den. *See* Dunning, *Mrs.* A. K.

Lion's reception. [Toy-book.] ill. 4°. $1; 50c. *Routledge.*

Lipowitz, M. A. *See* Reid, H.

Lippard, G: [Novels.] 12 v. 8°..........*Peterson.*
Cont.: Empire city; or, New York by night and day. — Memoirs of a preacher; or, the mysteries of the pulpit. — Nazarene (The). — Washington and his men, *ea.*, pap., 75c. — Bank director's son. — Entranced (The); or, the wanderer of 18 centuries, *ea.*, pap., 25c. — Legends of Mexico, pap., 50c. — Blanche of Brandywine. — Legends of the Am. rev. — Paul Ardenheim, the monk of Wissahickon. — Quaker city (The); or, monks of Monk Hall, *ea.*, $2; pap., $1.50. — Mysteries of Florence, $2; pap., $1.

— Legenden a. d. amerik. Revolution; a. d. Engl. 8°. pap., 50c. ....*F. W. Thomas.*

— New York: its upper ten and lower million. 8°. '53. $1..............................*Mendenhall.*

Lippe, A. Key to the materia medica. [Hom.] 8°. pap., 75c. ....*Boericke.*

Lippincott, *Mrs.* Sara J. ["Grace Greenwood."] Bonnie Scotland. ill. 16°. $1.50......**Osgood.*

— Forest tragedy. 16°. $1.25..............**Osgood.*

— Greenwood leaves. 12°. $1.75..........**Osgood.*

— Haps and mishaps. 12°. $1.75...........**Osgood.*

— Heads and tails: studies and stories of pets. ('74.) New ed. ill. sq. 16°. '76. $2 ....*Ford.*

— History of my pets. ill. 16°. $1..........**Osgood.*

— Merrie England. ill. 16°. $1.50.........**Osgood.*

— New life in new lands: notes of travel across the Am. continent, from Chicago to the Pacific and back. 12°. '72. $2.............................*Ford.*

— Poems. por. 16°. $1.25.................**Osgood.*

— Recollections of my childhood. ill. 16°. $1..**Osgood.*

— Records of five years. 16°. $1.50........**Osgood.*

— Stories and legends of travel and history. ill. 16°. $1.50 ....**Osgood.*

— Stories and sights of France and Italy. ill. 16°. $1.50. **Osgood.*

— Stories from famous ballads. ill. 16°. $1..**Osgood.*

— Stories of many lands. ill. 16°. $1.50....**Osgood.*

— *See also* Greatorex, Eliza.

Lippincott's dictionary of biography. *See* Thomas, J.

Lippincott's pocket treasuries. 6 v. sm. 4°. $4.50. *Lippincott.*
Cont.: Treasury of table talk. — Epigrams and literary follies. — Treasury of poetic gems. — Table talk of Samuel Johnson. — Gleanings from the comedies of Shakespeare. — Beauties of the British dramatists.

Lippincott's pronouncing gazetteer of the world. *See* Thomas, J., *and* Baldwin, T.

Lippitt, Fs. J. Field service in war. 12°. '69. $10. *Van Nostrand.*

— Intrenchments. ill. 12°. '66. $1.25..*Van Nostrand.*

— Special operations of war. ill. 18°. '68. $1. *Van Nostrand.*

— Tactical use of the three arms. 12°. '65. $1. *Van Nostrand.*

Liquefaction of the blood of St. Januarius. 8°. '74. $1. *Cath. Pub.*

Lisco, F: Gst. On the parables. fp. 8°. $2.50. *Scribner, W. & A.*

L'Isera, Colombat de. Treatise upon diseases and hygiene of organs of the voice. 12°. '45. 50c...*Burnham.*

List, F. National system of political economy. 8°. $2. *Claxton; Lippincott.*

Listemann, B. Method of modern violin playing. f°. '69. bds., $3 .... *Ditson.*

Liszt, Fz. Life of Chopin; tr. by M. W. Cook. 4th ed. 12°. '63. $1.50 .... *Ditson.*

— Prometheus. [Music.] 8°. $1.50; pap., $1; bds., $1.25 .... *Church.*

Litch, J. Complete harmony of Daniel and the Apocalypse. 12°. '72. $1.50 .... *Claxton.*

Literary and social judgments. Greg, W. R. $2 .. *Holt.*

Literary life (The). Jacox, F. $2.50 ..... *Randolph.*

Literary selections for students of the Normal Coll. of N. Y. City. 12°. hf. bd., $1.50 .... *Harper.*

Literature and dogma. *See* Arnold, Mat.

Literature and life. Whipple, E. P. $1.50 .. *Osgood.*

Literature, art and song: melodies, etc., by T. Moore, biog. of Moore by R. S. Mackenzie, and collection of melodies arranged by Sir J. Stevenson and others. ill. 4°. '66. *$4; $5; $6 .... *Intern.*

Literature for the little folks. Lloyd, E. 75c.; 50c. *Sower.*

Literature in letters. Holcombe, J. P. $2; $4.50. *Appleton.*

Literature of kissing. Bombaugh, C. C. $1.75; $2.50. *Lippincott.*

Literature primers. *See* Green, J. R.

Littell, E. D. *See* Cottrell, C. C., *and* Littell, E. D.

Littell, W. *See* Kentucky, Court of Appeals reports; Select cases.

Little, *Mrs.* —. Memorial of Rev. Geo. B. Little. 16°. $1 .... *Cong. Pub.*

Little, *Mrs.* H. M. Aunt Katie's talks at bedtime. ill. 24°. 40c. .... *Bost. Am. Tr.*

— Sunday alphabet of animals. ill. 18°. 60c. *Bost. Am. Tr.*

Little, J: Life of Mrs. Jessie Little. 18°. '51. 40c. *Am. Tr.*

Little Ada. Henry, H. L. $1 .... *Claxton.*

Little Ada's jewels. Levien, F. 2 v. $1.50 .. *Nelson.*

Little Ada's lib. 3 v. ill. 18°. '71. $3 ...... *Claxton.*

Cont.: Little Ada, by H. L. Henry.—Little gems for little people, by S. H. Pierce. — King's godchild, and other tales.

Little Addie's lib. *See* Cousin Belle.

Little Aggie's fresh snowdrops. 18°. 60c. .. *Cong. Pub.*

— *Same.* ill. 16°. 50c. .... *Nelson.*

— *See also* Little Aggie's lib.; — Snowdrop ser.

Little Aggie's lib. 4 v. ill. 18°. '65. $2.25 .. *Meth. Bk. Conc.*

Cont.: Matty's hungry missionary box. — Motherless Martha's home. — Hope on; or, "The house that Jack built." — Little Aggie's fresh snow-drops.

— *Same.* 4 v. ill. 16°. $2 .... *Nelson.*

Little Agnes. Baker, H. N. W. $1.50 ...... *Lee & S.*

Little Agnes. *See* Bradley, *Mrs.* M. E.

Little Agnes' lib. for girls. *See* Baker, *Mrs.* H. N. W.

Little Alice. 32°. 40c. .... *Scribner, W. & A.*

Little Alice's lib. 9 v. ill. 18°. $3 .... *Nelson.*

Cont.: Eyes for everything. — Little stories for little people. — Little reading book. — Fine pictures, etc. — Harry's escape. — Simple tales. — Young child's picture book. — Maggie's windows. — Short stories for little people.

Little Alice's palace; or, the sunny heart. 18°. 25c. *Am. S. S.*

Little Amy. 32°. 20c.; 15c. .... *Dutton.*

Little Amy's stories. *See* Myrtle, *Mrs.* H.

Little animals described for little people. *See* Dove ser.

Little Ann. *See* Jude Cain.

Little Ann; or, every day lessons on interesting subjects. 18°. 40c. .... *Am. S. S.*

Little Ann and her mamma. [Toy-book.] ill. 4°. $1; 50c. .... *Routledge.*

Little Anna. *See* Aunt Grace's lib.

Little Anna. Stein, A. 50c. .... *Lee & S.*

Little Anna; or, a mother's memory. ill. 18°. '71. 25c. *N. Y. Ref. Ch. Bd.; Pres. Com.*

Little Anna stories. 6 v. ill. 18°. ea., 60c. .. *Lee & S.*

Cont.: Little Anna. — Alice Learmont. — A thousand a year. — Estelle's stories about dogs. — Cheerful heart. — The little helper.

Little Annie. *See* Baker, *Mrs.* H. N. W.

Little Annie and her nurse. 18°. 30c. .... *Dutton.*

Little Annie's birthday. Suter, W. E. 15c. *De Witt; French.*

Little Annie's first and second books. sq. 16°. ea., 60c. *Carter.*

Little Annie's first Bible lessons. 18°. 60c. .. *Pres. Bd.*

Little Annie's first thoughts about God. Dunning, A. K. 40c. .... *Pres. Bd.*

Little apple blossom. Davis, C. E. K. 50c. .... *Hoyt.*

Little Arthur's history of Eng. New ed. 16°. '75. 75c.; pap., 50c. .... *Routledge.*

Little Baptist. Martin, J. M. $1; $2 ..... *So. Bapt.*

Little barefoot (The). *See* Auerbach, B.

Little barefoot. Waldauer, A. 15c. .... *French.*

Little beauty. Grey, E. C. $1.75; $1.50 .. *Peterson.*

Little beggar boy; or, thou shalt not covet. 18°. 55c. *Am. S. S.*

Little beggars. *See* Sherwood, *Mrs.* M. M.

Little Ben, the motherless boy. Brewster, M. M. 50c. *Randolph.*

Little Ben Hadden. Kingston, W. H. G. $1.25 .. *Lothrop.*

Little Ben Hadden ser. 4 v. 16°. $5 .... *Lothrop.*

Cont.: Little Ben Hadden. — Stories from the moorland. — Archy Hamilton. — Boat builders.

Little Bertie. Strong, J. D. 25c. .... *Lothrop.*

Little Bertie. *See* Bertie's lib.; — Moss rose ser.

Little Bertie's picture lib. 12 v. 24°. ill. $3 .. *Lothrop.*

Cont.: Little Bertie. — Lame beggar. — Wilful waste. — Minna's proud heart. — Little Nora. — Brown pony. — The blacksmith. — Beauty Benson. — Trust and try. — Too late. — Gregory Gold. — Truthful Jenny.

Little Bessie. ill. 18°. '56. 35c. .... *Am. Tr.*

Little Bessie. Franklin, J. 83c. .... *Thompson.*

Little Bessie, and how she kept the wolf from the door. 16°. 90c. .... *Hoyt.*

— *See also* Aunty Lee lib.

Little Bessie's country stories. Miller, T. 6 v. $1.50. *Sheldon.*

Little Bill at the pump; by a pastor of the Episc. Church. 18°. '66. 35c. *N. Y. Ref. Ch. Bd.; Pres. Com.*

— *Same;* and sequel. 18°. 35c. .... *Am. S. S.*

Little Billy. *See* Gerty and May books.

Little Bird Red and Little Bird Blue. Edwards, M. B. 60c. .... *Hurd & H.*

Little black hen. *See* Books of blessing.

Little Blackcap. ill. fp. 8°. 60c. .... *Cassell.*

Little blind girl. sq. 16°. '67. 50c.; pap., 30c. *Randolph.*

Little Blossom. Clark, M. L. 30c. .... *Lothrop.*

Little Blossom's reward. Hare, E. 80c. ..... *Lee & S.*

Little Blue Bell. 18°. 17c.; 22c. .... *Am. Bapt.*

Little blue eyes, and other field and flower stories; by the author of "My young days." ill. 12°. '74. $1.50 .... *Nelson.*

Little Blue Hood. Miller, T. 60c. .... *Hurd & H.*

Little Blue Hood books. 5 v. ill. sq. 12°. '66. $3; ea., 60c. .... *Hurd & H.*

Cont.: Little Blue Hood, by T. Miller. — Little Bird Red and Little Bird Blue, by M. B. Edwards. — Pet lamb, etc. — Illustrated book of songs. — The water-lily.

Little Blue Mantle lib. 10 v. ill. 18°. '72. $3.75. *Meth. Bk. Conc.*

Cont.: Little Blue Mantle. — Pleasant words for little folks. — Our new baby, and other stories. — Eugene, the little rag-picker. — Widow's cow, and other stories. — Young potato-roasters. Young colt, and other stories. — Mother's staff, and other stories — Truant, and other stories. — Sam's friend, and other stories.

Little boarding-school girls. *See* Aunt Gracie's lib.

Little Bob True, the driver boy; by author of "Stories on petitions of Lord's prayer." ill. 18°. 60c. *Pres. Bd.*
Little Bobin Hood: burlesque. 16°. pap., 15c. *French.*
Little Bobtail. Adams, W. T. $1.50 .... *Lee & S.*
Little book for little folks about the book of books. 18°. 35c. .... *Pres. Bd.*
Little book of knowledge. Novere, E. G. 50c. *So. Meth.*
Little books for little readers. *See* Finley, M. F.
Little Boots. Harrison, J. $1.25 .... *Dodd.*
Little boy of Bethlehem. *See* Emily Somerville.
Little boy's story. Gouraud, J. $1.50 .... *Hurd & H.*
Little boy's treasury of precious things. Addie. 60c. *Pres. Bd.*
Little boys' lib. 6 v. 32°. '75. $1.50... *H. A. Young.*
Cont.: Sandy Duncan. — Terence Moran. — Little trapper boy. — Boy not made to mind. — Poor Pat. — Word in season.
Little brook and its travels. 18°. 18c....... *Am. S. S.*
Little brother. Ludlow, F. H. $1.50 .... *Lee & S.*
Little brother and sister. Wildermuth, O. $1.25. *Cin. Meth. Bk. Conc.*
Little brothers and sisters. Marshall, E. $1.25 .. *Carter.*
Little brown Bible. Llewellyn, B. L. 60c. *Pres. Bd.*
Little brown house. 18°. 25c. .... *Am. S. S.*
— *See also* Children of Blackberry Hollow.
Little brown jug. Baker, G. M. 15c. .... *Lee & S.*
Little buds. *See* Morning glory lib.
Little burnt girl: memoir of Cath. Howell. 18°. 35c. *Am. S. S.*
Little Buttercup and Jenny Wren. Hamilton, *Miss* —. 75c.; $1; 50c. .... *Gospel.*
Little by little. Adams, W. T. $1.25 .... *Lee & S.*
Little by little: a tale. 18°. 90c. .... (?) *Martien.*
Little camp on Eagle Hill. Warner, S. $1.25 .. *Carter.*
Little Canary. Osgood, M. A. 75c. .... *Lee & S.*
Little Canary ser. *See* Osgood, *Mrs.* M. A.
Little Canary's black Cato; — country life; — daisy. Osgood, M. A. ea., 75c. .... *Lee & S.*
Little captain. *See* Aunt Hattie's stories.
Little captain. Peebles, M. L. 60c. ... *Bost. Am. Tr.*
Little cares. 32°. '73. 25c. .... *Randolph.*
Little Carl. *See* Bright eye ser.
Little castle maiden. Greene, L. L. $1 .. *Scribner, W. & A.*
Little Catholic hymn book. 32°. 30c.; pap., 15c. *Strong.*
Little Catholic piety. [Prayer book.] 48°. '75. 40c. -$5 .... *Cunningham.*
Little Cathy; or, will no one come? 18°. 35c. *Whittaker.*
Little change (A): farce. 16°. pap., 15c...... *French.*
Little Charley's Christmas amusements and stories of great men. 2 v. in 1. ill. 4°. 50c... *J. E. Potter.*
Little Charley's puzzle: the singular letter he wrote, and what became of him. 18°. 25c. .. *Am. S. S.*
Little Charley's rhymes and jingles and games and sports. 2 v. in 1. ill. 4°. 50c. ...... *J. E. Potter.*
Little Charley's summer rambles in the fields and woods. ill. 4°. 50c. .... *J. E. Potter.*
Little Charlie, and other stories. 32°. 40c. *Scribner, W. & A.*
Little Charlie, the winner. 18°. 20c.; 25c... *Am. Bapt.*
Little Charlotte's home. 18°. 50c. .... (?) *Martien.*
Little children in Eden. Wheeler, C. H. 75c. *Hoyt, F. & D.*
Little children's lib. 24 v. ill. 32°. hf. bd., $2.25. *Am. Tr.*
Little child's Bible picture book. *See* Sanford, *Mrs.* D. P.
Little child's lib. 9 v. 32°. $2.50 .... *Dutton.*
Little Chinaman. *See* Daisy lib.
Little choristers. 18°. 30c.; pap., 10c. .... *Dutton.*
Little Christie. 16°. '76. $1.25 .... *Hoyt.*
Little Christie and her friends: book for girls. 16°. '75. $1.25 .... *Hoyt.*
Little cider merchant. Porter, A. E. 75c... *Cong. Pub.*
Little Clara. Bache, A. 75c. .... *Tibbals.*
Little classics. *See* Johnson, Rossiter.
Little cloister ruin. (Fatherland ser.) ill. 16°. 70c. (?) *Luth. Pub.*
Little coin, much care. *See* Howitt, Ma.
Little companion of the Sisters of Mercy; [also] The little office of the Virgin Mary; [also] The little office of the immaculate conception; in Lat. and Eng. 32°. '75. *net*, 50c. .... *Kelly, P. & Co.*
Little confectioner. Hicks, S. 60c....... *N. Y. News.*
Little conqueror. Davis, C. E. K. 50c. .... *Hoyt.*
Little conqueror's ser. *See* Davis, *Mrs.* C. E. K.
Little Conscience. *See* Baker, *Mrs.* H. N. W.
Little Content. Walford, E. 50c. .... *Cassell.*
Little cricket. Samuels, A. F. 50c. .... *Lee & S.*
Little crown of Jesus. [Cath. prayer book.] 32°. '69. 40c.-$15 .... *Kelly, P. & Co.*
— *See also* Crown of Jesus.
Little crown of St. Joseph. [Cath. prayer book.] 24°. $1; mor., $2; cf., $2.50 .... *Sadlier.*
Little crowns. Collier, J. A. 75c. .... *Carter.*
Little Cuba. Barclay, G. L. 25c. .... *Barclay.*
Little Daisy. Williams, T. J. 15c. .... *French.*
Little Daisy's letter. *See* Baker, *Mrs.* H. N. W.
Little diadem. Tillinghast, W. 30c... *Schermerhorn.*
Little Dick and the angel. *See* Howitt, Ma.
Little Dick Positive. *See* Finley, M. F.
Little dog Trusty. [Toy-book.] ill. 4°. $1; 50c. *Routledge.*
Little Don Giovanni. Byron, H. J. 15c. .... *French.*
Little donkey drivers. 32°. 20c.; 15c. .... *Dutton.*
Little doorkeeper. C., S. T. 90c. .... (?) *Martien.*
Little door-keeper lib. 5 v. 16°. '66. $6 .. *Meth. Bk. Conc.*
Cont.: Little door-keeper. — Captain Christie's granddaughter. — False shame. — Joe Witless. — Miracles of heavenly love in daily life.
Little Dora. 18°. 40c. .... *Dutton.*
Little Dora. Alden, J. 75c. .... *Tibbals.*
Little Dorrit. *See* Dickens, C.
Little Dot. ill. 18°. '74. 30c. .... *Am. Tr.*
— *See also* Mattie's home.
Little Dot ser. 12 v. ill. 18°. $3 .... *Nelson.*
Cont.: Book of books. — Little Dot. — Two ways to begin life. — Little gooseberry. — Gamekeeper's daughter. — Old Humphrey's study table. — Springfield stories. — John Thompson's nursery. — Ethel Ripon, by G. E. Sargent. — Fanny Ashley. — Fred Kenny. — Jennie's water proof.
Little drops of rain. 16°. $1 .... *Carter.*
Little drummer; or, filial affection: story of the Russian campaign. ill. 16°. 50c. .... *Routledge.*
Little drummer boy: child of the 13th Reg't., N. Y. S. M. ill. 16°. 55c. .... *Hoyt.*
Little drummer boy: sketch of life of Clarence D. McKenzie. ill. 12°. 40c. .... *N. Y. Ref. Ch. Bd.*
Little duke. Yonge, C. M. 75c. .... *Macmillan.*
Little Edward. 18°. 25c. .... *Am. S. S.*
Little Effie's home; by author of "Donald Fraser." 16°. $1.25 .... *Carter.*
Little Ellie. Andersen, H. C. $1 .... *Miller.*
Little Elly's first visit. Parmelee, H. L. 50c. *Randolph.*
Little Emma. *See* Tub night.
Little Episcopalian. Cruse, M. A. 90c. .... *Dutton.*
Little Eppie, and other tales. 18°. 70c...... *Pres. Bd.*
Little Ernest; or, the land beyond the river. 18°. 25c. *Am. S. S.*
Little Estella, and other fairy tales. 18°. '72. 75c. *Macmillan.*
Little fables for little folks. ill. fp. 8°. 60c..... *Cassell.*

Little facts for little people. *See* Dove ser.

Little Fan. *See* Little Fan's lib.

Little Fanny. ill. sq. 16°. 50c........*Meth. Bk. Conc.*

Little Fan's lib. 6 v. ill. 18°. '74. $2.40.....*Nelson.*
Cont.: Little Fan. — Sam Silva. — Young exile. — Robbie's Christmas eve. — Sketches of my childhood. — The young comforters.

Little favorites' lib. *See* Baker, *Mrs.* H. N. W.

Little ferns. *See* Parton, *Mrs.* S. P.

Little fir tree. Bradley, M. E. 40c. ....*Dutton.*

Little fish peddler; or, mackerel Will and his friend Emma; by author of "School boys." ill. 18°. '72. 45c. ....*N. Y. Ref. Ch. Bd.; Pres. Com.*

Little flirt. ill. 64°. pap., 25c................*Fisher.*

Little Florentine. *See* Baker, *Mrs.* H. N. W.

Little flower garden. [Cath. prayer book.] 48°. '64. 25c.–$3 ....*Cunningham.*

— *See also* Flower garden.

Little flower gatherer. *See* My own lib.

Little flowers of piety. [Cath. prayer book.] 64°. $1.50–$6 ....*Strong.*

— *Same.* 64°. $1.50–$15..................*T. Kelly.*

— *See also* Flowers of piety.

Little Floy. Smith, F. I. B. 50c. ....*Lothrop.*

Little Flyaway. *See* Baker, *Mrs.* H. N. W.

Little folk lib. 6 v. ill. 18°. '70. $3.75..*Meth. Bk. Conc.*
Cont.: Alone in London. — Kitty Swindon's text. — Happy half hours. — John Oriel's start in life. — Willie and Lucy at the seaside. — Home life at Graystone Lodge.

Little folk life. Dodge, M. A. 90c. ....*Harper.*

Little folk life ser. Dodge, M. A., *and* Stoddard, R. H. 3 v. ea., $1.........................*W. F. Gill.*

Little folk songs. White, A. B. $1.......*Hurd & H.*

Little folks. [Annual] ill. 4°. (Lond.) $2; bds., $1.50 ....*Am. News.*

Little folks. *See* Dickens, C:

Little folks astray. Clarke, R. S. 75c.......*Lee & S.*

Little folks at Redbow. Denison, M. A. $1.50. *H. A. Young.*

Little folks in feathers and fur. Thorne, O. *$2.50; $3 ....*Dustin.*

Little folks' A B C. [Toy-book.] ill. roy. 8°. per gross, $48.....................(?) *McLoughlin.*

Little folks' colored picture book. [Toy-book.] ill. roy. 8°. $1....................(?) *McLoughlin.*

Little folks' letters. Emerson, N. S. $1.50..*Carleton.*

Little folks' lib. 10 v. 32°. '66. $2.50.......*Hoyt.*

Little folks' own book. ill. 4°. $1; $1.25..*J. E. Potter.*

Little folks' own lib.: tales for children. 7 v. ill. cr. 16°. ea., 25c...........................*Cassell.*
Cont.: Everybody's boy. — Crooked sixpence. — Never afraid. — Hopagog's leg. — Nelly. — Lucky Tym. — Little Tom Stirling.

Little folks' picture album. Mateaux, C. L. $2.50. *Cassell.*

Little folks' picture book. Frost, S. A. 30c...*Am. Tr.*

Little folks' picture-gallery. ill. 4°. (Lond.) $2.50. *Am. News.*

Little folks' picture-gallery. Mateaux, C. L. $2.50. *Cassell.*

Little folks' ser. 12 v. 18°. $1.80.........*Lothrop.*
Cont.: Boys and boys. — Among the mountains. — Willie Graham. — Kindness. — The victory. — Even grip. — Elsie Wood. — Light in the window. — The prize. — Forgiven. — Naomi's home. — Neddie and Maggie.

Little folks' ser. [Toy-books.] 12 nos. ill. sm. 4°. per gross, $30................(?) *McLoughlin.*
Cont.: Babes in the wood. — My first alphabet. — Diamonds and toads. — Little Bo-peep. — Dame Trot and her cat. — Sing a song of sixpence. — Jack and the bean stalk. — Story of three little pigs. — Five little pigs. — Old woman who lived in a shoe. — Old Mother Goose. — Three bears.

Little footprints in Bible lands. Vincent, J. H. 60c. *Meth. Bk. Conc.*

Little footprints on the old church path. 18°. 35c.; 40c..................................*Dutton.*

Little forest girl. ill. 24°. 25c...........*Perkinpine.*

Little fox. Trimmer, S. K. 90c..............*Miller.*

Little foxes. 18°. 40c....................*Cong. Pub.*

Little foxes. Stowe, H. B. $1.75...........*Osgood.*

Little foxes; by author of "How Marjorie watched." ill. 16°. '75. 90c...............*Meth. Bk. Conc.*

Little Frank. ill. sq. 16°. 75c...............*Nelson.*

Little Frank. *See* Conscience, H.

Little Frank and the rat, and other tales. ill. 4°. 50c. *J. E. Potter.*

Little Frank Harley. ill. sq. 16°. pap., 40c. *Meth. Bk. Conc.*

Little Frankie and his cousins; — and his father; — and his mother; — at his plays; — at school; — on a journey. Baker, H. N. W. ea., 35c...(?) *Shepard.*

Little Frankie ser. *See* Baker, *Mrs.* H. N. W.

Little Frank's story book. Sanford, D. P. 50c. *Dutton.*

Little Freddie feeding his soul. 18°. 50c......*Carter.*

Little Freddy. 32°. 20c.; 15c..............*Dutton.*

Little friends. *See* Bright eye ser.

Little friends at Glenwood. Mathews, J. H. $1.25. *Carter.*

Little Frisky. *See* Aunt Alice's lib.

Little Fritz. *See* Baker, *Mrs.* H. N. W.

Little gardeners. 16°. 45c.............*Cummiskey.*

Little gardeners. *See* May, A.

Little gems for boys and girls. 18°. 70c. ...*Pres. Bd.*

Little gems for little people. Pierce, S. H. $1..*Claxton.*

Little gems for little readers. ill. 16°. 25c...*Routledge.*

Little gems from the "Children's hour." Arthur, T. S. $1 ....*J. M. Stoddart.*

Little gems in the Saviour's crown. Stryker, P. 60c. *N. Y. Ref. Ch. Bd.*

Little Gennette. 18°. 20c.; 25c...........*Am. Bapt.*

Little gentleman in green. Hepworth, G. H. 75c. *Loring.*

Little George. *See* Flower transplanted.

Little George's first journey. 18°. 55c.....*Am. S. S.*

Little German drummer-boy (The). ('66.) 6th ed. ill. 16°. '72. $1.......................*Perkinpine.*

Little Gertrude. *See* Bright eye ser.

Little Gerty. *See* Prairie books.

Little girl in black. Wilmer, M. E. 90c...*Nat. Temp.*

Little girls' habits. O'Brien, H. 35c.......*Pres. Bd.*

Little girls' lib. 6 v. 32°. '75. $1.50 ..*H. A. Young.*
Cont.: Tiny's musical box. — Ruth Dean's birthday. — Marie's reward. — Waking up. — Bound girl. — Caught in her own trap.

Little girls' missionary meeting. 18°. 25c...*Am. S. S.*

Little girls' treasury. Brooks, A. 50c. ....*Pres. Bd.*

Little Giselle: burlesque. 16°. pap., 15c.....*French.*

Little gleaner. *See* Maple grove stories.

Little gold keys. Ballard, J. P. 50c...*Bost. Am. Tr.*

Little Goody Two Shoes. ill. f°. pap., 15c.; 20c.; 30c. *J. E. Potter.*

Little gooseberry. *See* Little Dot ser.

Little Gracie. Barrows, J. S. 45c. ....*Hoyt.*

Little grandfather. Clarke, R. S. 75c. .....*Lee & S.*

Little grandmother. Clarke, R. S. 75c. ....*Lee & S.*

Little Granite. *See* Good boy's lib.

Little graves: sel. of poetry and prose; with introd. by J. G. Holland. sq. 16°. '75. $1.50..*Meth. Bk. Conc.*

Little Gretchen. *See* Fireside stories.

Little Grig and the tinker's letter. *See* Books for the children's hour.

Little Gwen's story. *See* Alice Leigh's mission.

Little gypsy. Sauvage, E. $1.25...........*Roberts.*

Little hands. Farrand, H. S. 75c. ....*Cong. Pub.*

Little Happy-heart. *See* Chaplin, *Mrs.* J. D.

Little Harry's troubles. *See* Silvertone lib.

Little haymakers. 12°. $1.50 .... Locke.
Little helper. *See* Finley, M. F.
Little helper. Goodwin, L. S. 50c.......... Lee & S.
Little helps for our little ones; or, reading a pleasure, not a task. [One syllable.] ill. 16°. 50c. *Routledge.*
Little Henry and his bearer. *See* Sherwood, *Mrs.* M. M.
Little herdsman. 32°. 40c. .... *Am. S. S.*
— *See also* Child's lib.
Little Hindoo baby. *See* Mr. Moffat and the Bechuanas.
Little Hodge. Jenkins, E. $1.25 .... *Dodd.*
Little home lib. 10 v. 32°. '64. $2.50....... *Hoyt.*
Little home missionary. Smith, M. J. P. 25c. *Am. Tr.*
Little home missionary; or, how to make others happy. ill. 18°. '60. 60c.................... *Am. S. S.*
Little house in the hollow; by author of "Shenac's work at home." 16°. 90c. .... *Am. S. S.*
— *See also* Glen Elder lib.
Little Humpy. ('70.) 4th ed. ill. 18°. '74. 50c. *Perkinpine.*
Little Indian. *See* Baker, *Mrs.* H. N. W.
Little iron wheel. Bascom, H. B. 60c. .... *So. Bapt.*
Little Italian boy. 18°. 45c.............. *Whittaker.*
Little Italian boy. Cousin Mary. 25c...... *Pres. Bd.*
Little Jack. *See* Children's prize stories;—Go-ahead lib.
Little Jack; or, mend your nets. ('69.) New ed. ill. 16°. '73. $1.......................... *Hoyt.*
Little jacket stories. 3 v. ill. 4°. ea., $1.25.. *Lee & S.*
Cont.: Kobboltozo. — Last of the Huggermuggers. — King of the Golden River.

Little Jackie. Ray, R. 45c.............. *J. A. Moore.*
Little Jack's four lessons. Warner A. B. 50c. *Carter.*
Little James. *See* Bertie's lib.; — Moss rose ser.
Little Jamie. Ritchie, A. 25c............. *West. Tr.*
Little Jane; or, feed my lambs. 18°. 45c.; 55c. *Am. Bapt.*
Little Jane; or, the reward of well-doing. ill. 16°. $1. *Perkinpine.*
Little Janie; or, sunshine in the house. 18°. 50c. *Pres. Bd.*
Little Jennie. *See* Dana Hill stories.
Little Jennie, the minister's daughter. *See* Warren, *Mrs.* J. S.
Little Jenny, the water-cress seller. 18°. 60c. *Cong. Pub.*
Little Jenny Wren books. 3 nos. ill. 4°. ea., pap., 10c.; 15c........................ *J. E. Potter.*
Little Jerry. Grosvenor, H. S. 35c........... *Hoyt.*
Little Jessie's mission. 18°. 17c.; 22c..... *Am. Bapt.*
Little Jessie's work. 18°. 25c............. *Am. S. S.*
Little Jewess; [also] The ransomed child; [also] Time to seek the Lord. 18°. 25c..... *Pres. Bd.*
Little Jim, the rag merchant. 18°. 30c..... *Am. S. S.*
Little Jimmy. *See* Maple grove stories.
Little Joanna. Bellamy, E. W. 60c....... *Appleton.*
Little Joe, and his strawberry plant. 18°. 30c.; 35c. *Am. Bapt.*
— *Same.* 18°. 50c.................... (?) *Martien.*
Little Joe Ashton; or, forbidden ground. 18°. '66. 45c............. *N. Y. Ref. Ch. Bd.; Pres. Com.*
Little Joe Carter, the cripple. Finley, M. F. 50c. *Pres. Bd.*
Little Johnnie. ill. 24°. 30c........... *Bost. Am. Tr.*
Little Johnny, the idiot boy. 18°. 25c.; 30c. *Am. Bapt.*
Little Joseph. ill. 32°. '55. 30c............ *Am. Tr.*
Little Josephine. 18°. 35c................ *Am. S. S.*
Little Josie. Kelas, C. J. $1................ *Locke.*
— *See also* Better path stories.
Little Julia and the cripple. *See* Witt, *Mme.* H. de.
Little Kadore; [also] The royal beggar boy; [also] Maurice Sullivan. 18°. 30c......... *Pres. Bd.*

Little Karin. Schwartz, M. S. *$1 .... *Col. Bk.*
Little Kate Kirby. Robinson, F. W. 75c.... *Harper.*
Little Katie. *See* Little Katie's little lib.
Little Katie's little lib. 10 v. 18°. $3.50... *Routledge.*
Cont.: Little Katie. — Dick Barford. — Lost ruby. — Perilous adventures. — Kate's new home. — Little Maggie. — Magic glass. — Peace and war. — Joan of Arc. — Brave days of old.

Little Katy and jolly Jim. Mathews, J. A. 50c. *Carter.*
Little keepsake lib. *See* Cousin Belle.
Little key of heaven. [Cath. prayer book.] 64°. 20c.–$5.................................. *Sadlier.*
— *See also* Key of heaven.
Little king. *See* Wright, *Mrs.* J. McN.
Little Kit. *See* Choice little lib.
Little kitten ser. *See* Ballantyne, W.
Little kitten stories. ill. f°. $1.50; $2.. *J. E. Potter.*
Little Kitty's knitting needles, and other stories. 18°. 50c. .... *Am. S. S.*
Little Kitty's lib. 6 v. 18°. $3............. *Carter.*
Cont.: Kitty's victory. — Hubert's rooster. — Annie Price. — Lost spectacles. — Happy Charlie. — What Elise loved best.

Little knitter. *See* Power, P. B.
Little ladders to learning. 2 v. ill. 12°. ea., $1.50. *Routledge.*
Little laddie; by author of "Little mother." ill. 8°. '73. $2 .... *Nelson.*
Little lame prince. *See* Craik, D. M.
Little lays for little folk. ill. sm. 4°. '68. $2.50; mor., $5.................................. *Routledge.*
Little learner series. *See* Abbott, Jac.
Little learner's toy-book. ill. 4°. $2. *Nelson; Scribner, W. & A.*
Little learner's toys. 4 v. 8°. ea., 50c.; pap., 25c. *Nelson.*
Cont.: A B C picture book. — Bible pictures. — First lessons in reading. — Home pictures.

Little leaven (A) and what it wrought. 18°. '58. $1. *Randolph.*
Little leaven (A) in a little lump. 18°. 40c. .. *Am. S. S.*
— *See also* Katie Lee lib.
Little lessons for little folks. 18°. 13c..... *Hurd & H.*
Little lessons for little housekeepers. Huntington, E. 25c.; 20c.; 15c. .... *Randolph.*
Little library. 16 v. 32°. 20c. .... *Pres. Bd.*
Little library. 40 v. ill. 32°. $6............ *Nelson.*
Little library. *See* Trimmer, *Mrs.* S. K.
Little library of true stories. *See* Goodrich, S. G.
Little life. Ballard, J. P. 50c.............. *Crowell.*
Little light. Bruce, E. M. 75c......... *Universalist.*
Little light: sequel to "Katie Lee." 18°. 40c. *Am. S. S.*
— *See also* Katie Lee lib.
Little lights. 18°. 70c. .... *Pres. Bd.*
Little lights. 18°. 30c.................... *Am. S. S.*
— *See also* Children of Blackberry Hollow.
Little Lilla. *See* Dove ser.
Little Lily's picture-book. ill. sq. 12°. '72. $1.. *Routledge.*
Little Lily's travels. ill. 18°. 75c........... *Nelson.*
— *Same.* ill. 16°. '70. $1................. *Lothrop*
Little Lisette. 16°. $1.................. *Cong. Pub.*
Little Lizzie; or, what does it mean? 18°. 20c.; 25c. *Am. Bapt.*
Little Lottie ser. 6 v. ill. 18°. $2.......... *Nelson.*
Cont.: Holy well. — Travelling sixpence. — Three flowers. — Lost and rescued. — Little Lottie. — Light-bearers and beacons.

Little Lou's sayings and doings. Prentiss, E. $1.50. *Hurd & H.*
Little Louvre. Abbott, J. 90c. .... *Harper.*
Little Lucy Harris, and other stories. ill. 24°. 25c. *Bost. Am. Tr.*
— *See also* Banner stories.
Little Lucy's wonderful globe. *See* Yonge, C. M.
Little Lychetts. 18°. 75c.................. *Carter.*

Little Mabel ser. 4 v. 16°. $3............*Lothrop.*
Cont.: Mabel's faith. — Three little brothers. — Lost purse. — Davy's jacket.
Little Madelon; or, maternal love. (Fatherland ser.) ill. 16°. $1....................(?) *Luth. Pub.*
Little Maggie. *See* Baker, *Mrs.* H. N. W.
Little Maggie. *See* Little Katie's little lib.
Little Maggie's lib. *See* Baker, *Mrs.* H. N. W.
Little Maggie's trials and triumphs. 18°. 55c. *Am. S. S.*
Little maid. *See* Bright eye ser.
Little maid. *See* Tucker, *Mrs.* C.
Little maid of Oxbow. Nowell, H. P. H. $1..*Lee & S.*
Little Maidie. Davis, C. E. K. $1.75; in 3 v., ea., 75c..............................*Hoyt.*
Little Maja and Charley learning to read; or, alphabet with short words. ill. 4°. 50c.....*J. E. Potter.*
Little manual for use of the sodality of the Holy Child Jesus. 32°. '71. 20c...........*Kelly, P. & Co.*
Little manual of the blessed Trinity. [Cath. prayer book.] ('71.) 12th ed. ill. 24°. '76. 75c.–$8. *Kenedy.*
Little manual of devotions to the sacred heart of Jesus, and spiritual bouquet. 32°. 50c......*Cath. Pub.*
Little manual of St. Aloysius. [Cath. prayer book.] ill. 32°. 30c.–$2.75. — 24°. 50c.–$5.....*T. Kelly.*
Little manual of the sodality of the Holy Angels Society. [Cath. prayer book.] 32°. '71. 20c. *Kelly, P. & Co.*
Little Margery. *See* Mathews, J. A.
Little Margery. Miller, M. E. 90c.........*Am. Tr.*
Little Marian's pilgrimage. 18°. 25c.......*Am. S. S.*
Little Marie. 32°. 20c.; 15c. ....*Dutton.*
Little Mary and the fairy. *See* McKeever, H. B.
Little Mary's first and last falsehood. Waller, F. 20c. *Am. Tr.*
Little Mary's first going to church. Fitzroy, *Lady* C. 70c.; 75c...........................*Dutton.*
Little Mary's pet. 32°. 20c.; 15c...........*Dutton.*
Little Mary's three homes. 18°. 25c.......*Am. S. S.*
Little Mary's troubles. 18°. 30c...........*Dutton.*
Little match girl. *See* Andersen, H. C.
Little Mattie. 18°. 15c.; 20c.............*Am. Bapt.*
Little May. *See* Parrott, M.
Little May; or, of what use am I? 18°. 60c...*Am. S. S.*
— *Same.* ('60.) New ed. ill. 18°. '75. 75c...*Hoyt.*
Little May's legacy. *See* Marshall, E.
Little May's picture. Pratt, L. M. 50c.....*Lothrop.*
Little medicine carrier: boyhood of George Wayland. 18°. 40c..............................*Am. S. S.*
— *Same.* 18°. '73. 45c....*N. Y. Ref. Ch. Bd.; Pres. Com.*
— *See also* Library for happy hours.
Little Meg's children. *See* Smith, H.
Little Meg's lib. 3 v. 18°. $2.25.......(?) *Martien.*
Cont.: Little Meg's children. — Minnie Gray. — Nellie Walters.
Little men. Alcott, L. M. $1.50.............*Roberts.*
Little merchant. Adams, W. T. 45c.......*Lee & S.*
Little merchants. Edgeworth, M. 25c....*Routledge.*
Little messmates, and other stories. 16°. '72. 75c. *Dutton.*
Little miner; or, truth and honesty. 16°. 50c. *Scribner, W. & A.*
Little Minnie. *See* Alden, *Mrs.* I. M.
Little Minnie. *See* Minnie's lib.; — Moss rose ser.
Little Minnie's thinking-cap. 18°. 18c......*Am. S. S.*
Little minstrel. Fillmore, A. D. 35c. ..*R. W. Carroll.*
Little Mirabel's fair. Waring, S. M. 40c.....*Dutton.*
Little Mischief. *See* Hildeburn, *Mrs.* M. J.
Little Miss Fret. *See* Baker, *Mrs.* H. N. W.
Little missionary. *See* Aunt Deborah's lib.
Little missionary. *See* Jejana.
Little missionary: biog. sketch of Gratia Olive Leonard. 18°. 40c. ....*Am. S. S.*
Little mittens. *See* Barrow, *Mrs.* F.
Little month of the holy infancy. Letourneur, A. J. 63c. ....*O'Shea.*
Little Moorland princess. John, E. $1.50..*Lippincott.*
Little more. 18°. '65. 30c. ....*Am. Tr.*
— *Same.* 18° 70c........................*Pres. Bd.*
Little more cider. Baker, G. M. 15c........*Lee & S.*
Little mother: farce. 16°. pap., 15c. ....*French.*
Little mother; by author of "Little Rosy's travels." 16°. 75c...............................*Am. S. S.*
— *Same;* ill. by L. Frölich. sq. 12°. $2.50..*Appleton.*
Little mother and her Christmas. McKeen, P. F. $1. *Lothrop.*
Little mother ser. 4 v. 16°. $4............*Lothrop.*
Cont.: Papa's boy, by Mrs. C. E. K. Davis. — Double story, by G. MacDonald. — Little mother, etc., by P. McKeen. — Robbie Meredith, by Mrs. J. J. Colter.
Little mountain guide; or, how to be happy. ('60.) New ed. ill. 18°. '75. 90c. ....*Hoyt.*
Little musicians. *See* Baker, Sa.
Little Nan. *See* G., F. F.
Little Nan. *See* Library of pleasant stories.
Little Nazloo. *See* Daisy lib.
Little Nell. *See* Dickens, C:
Little Nellie. Bell, C. D. 25c......*Scribner, W. & A.*
Little Nellie. W., F. M. C. $1.25........... *Hoyt.*
Little Nellie. *See* Yonge, C. M.
Little Nellie's velvet carpet. 18°. 35c. .....*Pres. Bd.*
Little Nell's story book. Sanford, D. P. 50c...*Dutton.*
Little Nelly; [also] Dying Irish girl. 18°. 40c. *Pres. Bd.*
Little nightcaps. *See* Barrow, *Mrs.* F.
Little Nobody, and how God cared for her. 18°. 45c.; 55c. ....*Am. Bapt.*
Little Nora. Strong, J. D. 25c...........*Lothrop.*
Little Nortons. Martin, C. B. $1.25...*Loring, S. & H.*
Little Norwegian (The); [also] The young woodcutter; by author of "Annie Lorimer." 18°. 45c. ....*Pres. Bd.*
Little nurse of Cape Cod. 18°. 40c.........*Am. S. S.*
— *See also* Katie Lee lib.
Little oaths. *See* Tonna, *Mrs.* C. E
Little office of the immaculate conception. 32°. '75. per doz., 50c. ....*Kelly, P. & Co.*
— *See also* Little companion of the Sisters of Mercy.
Little office of the Virgin Mary, accord. to Roman ritual, in Lat. and Eng; [also] Little office of the immaculate conception. 18°. '75. *net*, 30c. *Kelly, P. & Co.*
— *See also* Little companion of the Sisters of Mercy; — Office of the Virgin Mary.
Little Oh-dear-me! 12°. '70. pap., 15c....*Randolph.*
Little ones gone before. Thurston, J. R. 50c. *Cong. Pub.*
Little ones in the fold. Hammond, E. P. 75c. ..*Hoyt.*
Little ones' lib. 10 v. 32°. '67. $2.50 ....*Hoyt.*
Little ones' lib. 25 v. 32°. $6 ....*Cong. Pub.*
Little orange sellers. *See* Fry, S. M.
Little orator. Donaldson, S., *jr.* 30c.; 20c...*Murphy.*
Little orator. Northend, C. 60c...........*Barnes.*
Little Orleys. Burton, W. D. 45c. ......*Routledge.*
Little orphan. ill. fp. 8°. 75c.............*Cassell.*
Little page. 32°. 20c.; 15c...............*Dutton.*
Little partners. *See* Pretty little lib.
Little passion. Prime, W. C. $10..........*Bouton.*
Little path to heaven. [Cath. prayer book.] 48°. 30c.–$4 ....*Benziger.*
Little path to paradise. [Cath. prayer book.] 48°. 30c.–$2.50..........................*O'Shea.*
Little Patie. C., M. A. L. 30c.......*Bost. Am. Tr.*

Little Patience. *See* Finley, M. F.
Little Paul. Abbott, J. 90c. .... *Harper.*
Little Paul. *See* Dickens, C:
Little peace maker. 18°. 20c.; 25c. ...... *Am. Bapt.*
Little Peachblossom. Wise, D. $1.25 .. *Meth. Bk. Conc.*
Little peanut merchant. 16°. '69. $1.25 .. *H. A. Young.*
Little pearls from the ocean of divine truth. 18°. 70c. *Pres. Bd.*
Little peat cutters. *See* Marshall, E.
Little people of God. *See* Austin, *Mrs.* G. L.
Little people of the snow. Bryant, W. C. $5; $9. *Appleton.*
Little people whom the Lord loved. *See* Flagg, E. E.
Little people's home lib. 12 v. 24°. $3.60 .. *Lothrop.*
Cont.: My birthday. — Water cress girl. — Christmas tales. — Young fisherman. — Young Sapphira. — Two fawns. — School life. — Ellen's May-day. — Tom Thornhill. — Pleasure and profit. — Crown jewels. — Truth and love.
Little Perseverance; or, industry rewarded. ill. cr. 4°. pap., 20c.; 25c. .... *J. E. Potter.*
Little pet books. *See* Barrow, *Mrs.* F.
Little Pete. 18°. 35c. .... *Whittaker.*
Little Peter. ill. 18°. '74. 50c. .... *Nelson.*
Little Peter. Kingston, W. H. G. $1 .... *Lothrop.*
Little Peter, the ship-boy. 18°. 50c. .... *Am. S. S.*
Little Peter and his sister Patty. 18°. 17c.; 22c. *Am. Bapt.*
Little Peter's lib. 6 v. ill. 18°. '74. $3 ..... *Nelson.*
Cont.: Little Peter. — Geordie's tryst. — Uncle Max. — The two friends. — What we saw in Egypt. — Helen's victory.
Little Pet's book. *See* Nursery lib.
Little philosopher. 18°. 40c. .... *Am. S. S.*
Little pickles. Hering, J. 50c. .... *Cassell.*
Little pieces for little speakers. Priest, S. M. 60c.; 75c. .... *Lee & S.*
Little Pierre, the pedlar of Alsace; tr. from the Fr. 6th ed. ill. 12°. '71. $1.50 .... *Cath. Pub.*
Little pig's lib. ill. sq. 12°. per doz., pap., $1.50; col. ill., per doz., $2.50 .... *Thompson.*
Little pilgrim. 18°. 22c. .... *Am. S. S.*
Little pilgrims. 18°. '63. 25c. .... *Am. Tr.*
Little pilgrims in the Holy Land. Osborn, H. S. $1.25. *Challen.*
Little pillows. Havergal, F. R. 35c. .... *Dutton.*
Little plays for little people. 12°. pap., 30c. .. *Happy.*
Little prattler. ill. 4°. '75. 90c. .... *Nelson.*
Little prattler: good words for the young. ill. 8°. '74. $2.50 .... *Routledge.*
Little prayer. *See* Aunt Alice's lib.
Little preacher. Prentiss, E. $1 .... *Randolph.*
Little priest. Breed, W. P. 75c. .... *Pres. Bd.*
Little Primrose. Marshall, E. 50c. .... *Carter.*
Little princess. Babb, H. 65c. .... *Meth. Bk. Conc.*
Little Prudy. Clarke, R. S. 75c. .... *Lee & S.*
Little Prudy stories. *See* Clarke, R. S.
Little Prudy's Captain Horace; — Cousin Grace; — Dotty Dimple; — Sister Susy; — story book. Clarke, R. S. ea., 75c. .... *Lee & S.*
Little Prudy's Flyaway series. *See* Clarke, R. S.
Little Pussy Willow. Stowe, H. B. $1.50 ... *Osgood.*
Little queen: story for children. 18°. 22c. .. *Am. S. S.*
Little Queen Bess, and other stories. ill. 24°. 25c. *Bost. Am. Tr.*
— *See also* Banner stories.
Little questioners. 18°. 35c. .... *Am. S. S.*
Little rabbit-keepers. *See* Violet stories.
Little ragman. *See* Inquisitive boy.
Little rag-pickers. Baker, H. N. W. 55c. ..... *Hoyt.*
Little Rattler: good things for the young. 8°. '74. $2.50 .... *Routledge.*

Little reading book. *See* Little Alice's lib.; — Pretty picture ser.
Little rebel. Coyne, J. S. 15c. ..... *De Witt; French.*
Little red book. 18°. 45c. .... *Whittaker.*
Little Red Cloak. McKeever, H. B. 75c. .. *Pres. Bd.*
Little Red Riding Hood. ill. f°. pap., 15c.; 20c.; 30c. *J. E. Potter.*
Little Red Riding Hood. [Toy-book.] ill. 4°. $1; 50c. .... *Routledge.*
Little Red Riding Hood. Buckingham, L. 15c. .. *French.*
Little Red Riding-hood. Keating, E. H. 15c. .. *French.*
Little Red Riding Hood: burlesque. 16°. pap., 15c. *Happy.*
Little Red Riding Hood. [Verse.] Stoddard, R. H. 25c. .... *Hurd & H.*
Little Red Shoes; by two friends. col. ill. fp. 8°. 60c. *Cassell.*
Little Redcap. ill. 16°. '71. 80c. .... *Lothrop.*
Little Robbie. Dunning, A. K. 50c. .... *Am. Tr.*
Little Robert. 16°. 30c. .... *West. Tr.*
Little robins in the nest; — in trouble; — learning to fly. Baker, H. N. W. ea., 35c. .... (?) *Shepard.*
Little robins' friends. Baker, H. N. W. 35c. (?) *Shepard.*
Little robins' love one to another. Baker, H. N. W. 35c. .... (?) *Shepard.*
Little roebuck: story in rhyme; ill. by F. Lossow. [Juvenile.] 8°. bds., 50c.; 75c. ...... *Stroefer.*
Little Rookwood. ('69.) New ed. ill. 16°. '73. 80c. *Hoyt.*
Little Rosebud's album. ill. sm. 4°. '74. $2 .. *Routledge.*
Little Rosie in the country. Hosmer, M. 75c. .. *Porter.*
Little Rosie ser. *See* Hosmer, M.
Little Rosie's Christmas times. Hosmer, M. 75c. *Porter.*
Little Rosie's first play-days. Hosmer, M. 75c. *Porter.*
Little Rossie. 16°. 80c. .... *Cong. Pub.*
Little Rosy's pet. ill. 12°. $1.25 .... *Nelson.*
Little Rosy's pets; by author of "Little Rosy's travels." ill. 16°. '76. $1 .... (?) *Cong. Pub.*
Little Rosy's picture book; ill. by L. Frölich. 8°. $1.50. *Appleton.*
Little Rosy's travels. ill. 4°. '68. $1.50 .. *Randolph.*
Little Rosy's travels; by T: Miller and others. 6 v. 32°. $1.50 .... *Sheldon.*
Cont.: On the journey. — A walk and a drive. — The ducks and the pigs. — Wounded bird. — Sad adventure. — Doctor's visit.
Little Rosy's travels; or, country scenes in south of France; ill. by L. Frölich. 12°. $2.50 .. *Appleton.*
Little Ruby. Wallace, J. J. 15c. .... *De Witt.*
Little Samaritan. *See* Ravenswood stories.
Little Samuel. *See* Jones, J. H.
Little sanctuary, and other meditations. Raleigh, A. $1.75 .... *Dodd.*
Little Sarah; or, perfumes of early piety. 18°. 60c. *Whittaker.*
Little savage. *See* Marryat, F.
Little savage. Morton, J. M. 15c. .... *French.*
Little Scotch Menie. *See* Daisy lib.
Little sea-bird; by author of "Mackerel Will." ill. 18°. 60c. .... *Am. S. S.; Pres. Bd.*
— *Same.* ill. 18°. '64. 60c. .... *Am. Tr.*
Little seed, and how it grew: origin of Bible Society. 18°. 18c. .... *Am. S. S.*
Little seed-sowers. *See* M., *Mrs.* A. S.
Little sentinel. Williams, T. J. 15c. .... *French.*
Little seraph. [Singing book.] 16°. 50c.; bds., 35c. *So. Bapt.*
Little sermon talks. Davis, C. E. K. 65c. ..... *Hoyt.*
Little sheaves for little gleaners. Perkins, E. M. 75c. *Bost. Am. Tr.*

Little shoemaker. Myers, S. A. 70c. *N. Y. Ref. Ch. Bd.; Pres. Com.*

Little silver barrel. *See* Silver barrel lib.

Little Silver Hair and the three bears: pastoral drama. 16°. pap., 15c. *Happy.*

Little singer. Curtis, G. H. 60c. *Barnes.*

Little sins and pretty sinners: farce. 16°. pap., 15c. *French.*

Little slate-picker. Boyd, E. E. 50c. *J. A. Moore.*

Little Snowdrop and her golden casket; by author of "Little Hazel, the king's messenger." 12°. '75. $1.25. *Nelson.*

Little songs. Follen, E. L. 50c. *Lee & S.*

Little songs for little people. 16°. '58. $1.25. *Randolph.*

Little songs for little readers. 12°. 60c. *Meth. Bk. Conc.*

Little songs for little singers. Mason, L. 40c. *Ditson.*

Little sower. Rosecrans, J. H. 35c. *Crandall.*

Little Spaniard. Nowell, H. P. H. $1. *Lee & S.*

Little Splendid's vacation. Fry, C. W. T. 80c. *Am. Unit.*

Little standard-bearer. ill. 18°. 60c. *Crowell.*

Little standard-bearer. *See* Go ahead lib.

Little stories for good children. ill. sq. 12°. '71. bds., 50c. *Routledge.*

Little stories for little folks. 18°. 22c. *Am. S. S.*

Little stories for little folks. Doughty, S. P. 50c. *H. H. Carter.*

Little stories for little people. *See* Little Alice's lib.; — Picture stories for little folks; — Pretty little lib.

Little story book. ill. 18°. 35c. *Bost. Am. Tr.*
— *See also* Uncle Reuben ser.

Little straw-plaiter; or, the triumph of truth. 18°. 40c. *Am. S. S.*

Little street-sweeper. 32°. 20c.; 15c. *Dutton.*

Little street-sweeper. 18°. 50c. *Pres. Bd.*

Little street-sweeper. Halliday, S. B. $1.25. *Ford.*

Little Sue and her friends. *See* Charlesworth, M. L.

Little sunbeam. Doane, W. H. 25c. *Church; Ditson.*

Little sunbeam; or, Lizzie's orange. 18°. 25c. *Scribner, W. & A.*

Little sunbeams. *See* Mathews, J. H.

Little Sunshine's holiday. *See* Craik, D. M.

Little Susan: memoir of Susan Kollock. 18°. 35c. *Am. S. S.*

Little Susan and her lamb. 32°. 20c.; 15c. *Dutton.*

Little Susy lib. *See* Prentiss, *Mrs.* E.

Little Susy's little servants; — six birthdays; — six teachers. Prentiss, E. ea., 85c. *Randolph.*

Little Syd. ill. 18°. 50c. *Crowell.*
— *See also* Annie Marlowe ser.

Little Syracuse boy: memoir of Scovell H. McCollum. ill. 18°. 60c. *N. Y. Ref. Ch. Bd.*

Little talks for little folks. 18°. 35c. *Pres. Bd.*

Little teacher. Graham, A. J. 75c.; 50c. *Graham.*

Little teacher: 1st book in reading, on word method. 16°. '55. pap., 10c.; bds., 16c. *Wilson, H. & Co.*

Little teachers. *See* Swallow stories.

Little teetotaler; or, true liberty. 18°. 18c. *Am. S. S.*

Little testaments of Jesus, Mary and Joseph: rosary of the sacrament and devotions for every day in the week. 32°. 25c. *Sadlier.*

Little testaments of Jesus Christ and the Virgin; or, an admonition, aspiration and practice for each day. 32°. '68. 20c. *Kelly, P. & Co.*

Little thing. Dunning, A. K. *Pres. Bd.*

Little things. 16°. 25c. *West. Tr.*

Little things. 18°. 35c. *Am. S. S.*

Little things are the germs of greatness. *See* Hoffmann, F.

Little things in every day life. 18°. 50c. *Whittaker.*

Little things of nature. *See* Grindon, L. H.

Little Thoughtless. 18°. 17c.; 22c. *Am. Bapt.*

Little threads. Prentiss, E. $1. *Randolph.*

Little Three Year Old. Davis, C. E. K. 75c.; $1.25. *Lothrop.*

Little Three Year Old lib. 3 v. 4°. $3.75. 16°. $2.25. *Lothrop.*
Cont.: Little Three Year Old. — Little Lucy's wonderful globe. — Babes in the basket.

Little Toddlekins. Mathews, C. J. 15c. *French.*

Little Tom, the ploughman's boy. 32°. 20c.; 15c. *Dutton.*

Little Tom Stirling. ill. cr. 16°. 25c. *Cassell.*

Little Toss. Cummings, M. J. $1.25. *Lothrop.*

Little Tot's lesson. *See* Baker, *Mrs.* H. N. W.

Little toy-maker. *See* Patience and her friend.

Little tract girl. *See* My own lib.

Little trapper boy. *See* Bright gems for boys and girls; — Little boy's lib.

Little travels. *See* Thackeray, W. M.

Little treasure. Harris, A. 15c. *French.*

Little treasure. Valentine, R. $1.50. (?) *McLoughlin.*

Little treasures for little children. Mayser, F. P. 20c. *Baer.*

Little treatise on little virtues. Roberti, F. 45c. *Cath. Pub.*

Little Trix; or, grandma's lessons. 16°. 60c. *Carter.*

Little trowel. Waddy, E. 90c. *Meth. Bk. Conc.*

Little Ursuline manual: collection of [Cath.] prayers and spiritual exercises; with Epistles and Gospels. 18°. 80c.-$8. 24°. 70c.-$6. *T. Kelly.*

Little vade mecum: manual of prayer for mass and vespers. 64°. 30c.-$13. *Cummiskey.*

Little vesper book: supplement to the manual of Roman chant. 12°. '60. 75c. *Kelly, P. & Co.*

Little voice within. 18°. 18c. *Am. S. S.*

Little Walter of Wyalusing. 18°. 35c. *Carter.*

Little Walter's stories about autumn; — about spring; — about summer; — about winter. ill. 16°. '65. ea., 75c. *Universalist.*

Little wanderers. ill. 16°. $1.50. *Carleton.*

Little wanderlin. Keary, A. *and* E. 75c. *Macmillan.*

Little watchman; by author of "Annie Lincoln's lesson." 18°. 75c. *Pres. Bd.*

Little watercress sellers. *See* Fry, S. M.

Little Wavie. *See* Temple, C.

Little weed; or, Ralph and his grandfather. 18°. 18c. *Am. S. S.*

Little weed; or, self will. 18°. 20c.; 25c. *Am. Bapt.*

Little white mice boy. Clark, M. L. 30c. *Lothrop.*

Little wide-awake. ill. 4°. $1.50. *Locke.*

Little wide-awake. Barker, S. $1.25; $2. *Routledge.*

Little wife. Grey, E. C. 50c. *Peterson.*

Little Will; [also] Jesus' seat; [also] Alpine cross. [Poems.] 64°. '70. 15c. *Am. Tr.*

Little Willie. 18°. 50c. *Carter; Dutton.*

Little Willie. Atkinson, *Miss* —. 25c. *Am. Tr.*

Little Willie's lib. 10 v. 32°. $2.25. *Cong. Pub.*
Cont.: Irreparable loss. — Lost child. — Faith. — True friend. — Ten years old. — Birthday wishes. — Truant boys. — John of the Rackets. — Didier, the vagabond. — He who is not for me.

Little Willie's lib. *See* Baker, *Mrs.* H. N. W.

Little woman. Farman, E. $1. *Lothrop.*

Little women. Alcott, L. M. 2 v. $3. *Roberts.*

Little woodman. *See* Sherwood, *Mrs.* M. M.

Little words, and little talks about them; by author of "Little Bob True." 18°. 65c. *Pres. Bd.*

Little words for little folks. ill. 4°. pap., 10c.; 15c. *J. E. Potter.*

Little wrinkled old man. Thurston, E. A. 75c. *Lee & S.*

Little yellow jacket ser. 5 v. 18°. $3.75..(?) *Martien.*
Cont.: Two little yellow jackets. — Big dots and little dots. — Once upon a time. — The P. D. S. — Cobbler and his rose.

Littledale, R. F. Commentary on the Song of songs; from anc. and mediæval sources. 16°. $2.75..*Pott.*

— *See also* Neale, J. M., *and* Littledale, R. F.

Littlejohn, Flav. J. Legends of Michigan and the old north west. 8°. '75. *$3.50–$7....*N. W. Bible.*

Littlejohn, Wolcott H. Position and work of the true people of God under the third angel's message. 16°. '71. pap., 10c..............*Sev. Day Adv.*

— Seventh part of time: sermon on the Sabbath question. 16°. '72. pap., 10c. ......*Sev. Day Adv.*

— *See also* Constitutional amendment.

Littleton, H. A., *and* Blatchley, J. S. Digest of law of fire insurance as decided by courts of Gt. Brit. and the U. S. 3d ed., rev. by C. Bates. 8°. shp., $6.50........................*Baker, V. & Co.*

Littlewood, W. E. Essentials of New Test. study: compr. account of the Gk. and Eng. texts, with lives of writers and introd. to each book; with tables and vocab. maps and plans. cr. 8°. '72. $2.50............................*Randolph.*

Litton, E: Arth. The church of Christ in its idea, attribute and ministry; with ref. to the controversy between Romanists and Protestants. ('56.) 4th Am. ed., rev. by Rev. C. W. Quick. 8°. '69. $1.25. *Leighton; Smith, E. & Co.*

Liturgical "reason why." Williams, A. $2....*Pott.*

Liturgies and other documents of the ante-Nicene period. (Ante-Nicene Christ. lib.) 8°. $3. *Scribner, W. & A.*

Live and learn. Baker, H. N. W. 16°. '60. $1.25. *Graves.*

Live and learn: guide for all who wish to speak and write correctly. 16°. 75c...........*Dick & F.*

Live and let live. Sedgwick, C. M. 75c. ....*Harper.*

Live Injun. Bryant, D. 15c...............*De Witt.*

Live it down. Jeaffreson, J. C. $1 ....*Harper.*

Live woman in the mines. "Old Block." 15c. *French.*

Liveing, E: Megrim, sick-headache and some allied disorders. col. pl. 8°. '73. $6......*Lindsay.*

Livelies (The). Kellogg, S. W. 40c....*Lippincott.*

Livermore, Abiel A. Commentary on Acts. 12°. $1.25. *Miller.*

— Commentary on Epistle to the Romans. ('54.) 3d ed. 12°. '61. $1.25...............*Am. Unit.*

— Commentary on the Gospels. 2 v. 12°. $2.50..*Miller.*

— Commentary on Romans. 12°. $1.25 ......*Miller.*

— Marriage offering. 18°. $1.25 ....*Nichols & H.*

Lives and deeds of our self-made men. Stowe, H. B. *$3.50; $4; $5 ....*Dustin.*

Lives and deeds worth knowing about. *See* Stevenson, W. F.

Lives made sublime by faith and works. *See* Steel, R.

Lives of apostles and early martyrs of the church. ill. 18°. 75c............................*Harper.*

Lives of the chief fathers of New Eng. 6 v. 12°. $5; — in 5 v. 18°. $3..................*Cong. Pub.*
Cont.: Increase Mather and Sir William Phipps, by E. Pond. — Thomas Shepard, by J. A. Albro. — John Cotton, by A. W. McClure. — John Eliot, by N. Adams. — Wilson, Norton and Davenport, by A. W. McClure. — Life of Thomas Hooker, by E. W. Hooker.

Lives of distinguished females. 18°. 75c.....*Harper.*

Lives of distinguished men of modern times. 2 v. 18°. $1.50 ....*Harper.*

Lives of the early martyrs. 12°. $1.25; $1.75..*Sadlier.*

Lives of eminent Anglo Saxons; ill. dawn of Christianity and civilization in Great Britain. 2 v. 18°. '57. $1.25 ....*So. Meth.*

Lives of eminent individuals in Am. hist. por. and autographs. 3 v. 12°. $4.50...........*Harper.*

Lives of the fathers of the church; by author of "Tales of Kirkbeck." 2 v. 12°. '75. $5........*Pott.*

Lives of the fathers of the desert; tr. from the Fr. ill. 18°. 60c..........................*Cath. Pub.*

Lives of the felons. ill. 8°. pap., 25c.......*Peterson.*

Lives of great and eccentric characters of all ages. ill. 8°. $2; shp., $2.75...............*World Pub.*

Lives of Mlle. de la Fayette, Theresa de Bourk, Mary Theresa Weld, and other Sisters of the Visitation; [with] hist. of the foundation of the Order. 12°. '69. $1.50; $2............*Kelly, P. & Co.*

Lives of the patriarchs. 18°. 60c. ....*Pres. Bd.*

Lives of the popes. 12°. '53. $1.75..*Meth. Bk. Conc.*

Lives of the popes. ('56.) 3d ed. 4 v. 18°. '76. $1.75. *So. Meth.*

Lives of prominent saints. *See* Mary, *Virgin*, Life.

Lives of remarkable youth. 18°. 45c. .....*Pres. Bd.*

Lives of the saints. 22 v. ill. 18°. ea., 75c...*McGee.*
Cont.: St. Margaret. — St. Catharine. — St. Julia. — St. Anne. — St. Mary. — St. Teresa. — St. Bridget. — St. Agnes. — St. Jane. — St. Helen. — St. Elizabeth. — St. Peter. — St. Patrick. — St. John. — St. Andrew. — St. Henry. — St. James. — St. Michael. — St. William. — St. Joseph. — St. Thomas. — St. Charles.

Living and loving. Townsend, V. F. $1.25..*J. E. Potter.*

Living and loving ser. 6 v. 16°. $7.50..*J. E. Potter.*
Cont.: Living and loving, by V. F. Townsend. — While it was morning, by V. F. Townsend. — Anna Clayton, by Mrs. H. J. Moore. — Christian gift, by R. W. Clark. — Woman's mission and woman's influence. — Enchanted beauty, by W. Elder.

Living authors at the N. Y. bar. Guernsey, R. S. $1.50; $1......................*Campbell & Co.*

Living Christ (The). 24°. 50c.; pap., 10c. *Crowell.*

Living faith (A). Merriam, G. S. $1.50. *Lockwood, B. & Co.*

Living for Jesus. *See* Kennedy, *Mrs.* M. G.

Living in earnest. *See* Johnson, Jos.

Living jewels. *See* Tucker, *Mrs.* C.

Living letters: alphabet, with short stories on each letter. 18°. 25c......................*Am. S. S.*

Living life. Andrews, E. $1.25; $1.50......*Earle.*

Living link. De Mille, J. $1.50; $1.......*Harper.*

Living or dead. Ryle, J. C. $1 ....*Carter.*

Living oracles. *See* Campbell, A.

Living present and dead past. Wright, H. C. 75c.; 50c...................................*Colby.*

Living questions of the age. Walker, J. B. $1.50. *Lippincott.*

Living statue. Dilley, J. J., *and* Allen, J. 15c. *De Witt.*

Living temple. Stowe, J. S. $2.50 ......*Randolph.*

Living temple: memoir of Jane Bethel. 18°. 40c. *Am. S. S.*

Living thoughts. Means, C. A. $2–$4.50...*Lee & S.*

Living thoughts of leading thinkers. Linn, S. P. $2. *Johnson & M.*

Living to Christ. 18°. 60c. ....*Carter.*

Living to purpose. Johnson, J. $1.50 ......*Nelson.*

Living too fast. Troughton, A. C. 15c. .....*French.*

Living voices: sel., with pref. by the Abp. of Canterbury. 16°. '74. $2................*Routledge.*

Living water. 18°. 17c.; 22c............*Am. Bapt.*

Living waters. Hodges, D. F. 30c.; 25c....*Ditson.*

Living waters for daily use. 24°. '50. 35c. *Meth. Bk. Conc.*

Living way. Atkinson, J. 55c....*Cin. Meth. Bk. Conc.*

Living Wesley. Rigg, J. H. $1.25...*Meth. Bk. Conc.*

Living word. Parsons, J. C. $1 ....*Ginn.*

Living words. M'Clintock, J. $1.75; $4. *Meth. Bk. Conc.*

Living words: experiences of infidel men related in Fulton St. [N. Y.] prayer meeting. ill. 18°. 50c. *N. Y. Ref. Ch. Bd.*

Livingston, D: Treatise on the setting out of railway curves, with tables of angles, distances and offsets required. cr. 8°. '73. $4.25........*Spon.*

Livingston, J: H: Memoirs. 12°. $1; mor., $3. *N. Y. Ref. Ch. Bd.*

Livingstone, *Mrs.* C. M. Katy Hunter's home. ill. 16°. '76. 75c. .... *Lothrop.*
— Night before Christmas. [Drama.] 16°. pap., 10c. *Lothrop.*

Livingstone, C: *See* Livingstone, D. *and* C.

Livingstone, D: Last journals in central Africa, 1865 to his death; contin. by narrative of his last moments from his servants Chuma and Susi; ed. by H. Waller. maps and ill. 8°. $5; chp. ed., $2.50 .... *Harper.*
— *Same.* maps and ill. 8°. *$2.50–$4 .... *Col. Bk.*
— Life. 16°. 75c. .... *Routledge.*
— Life hist. of L.; incl. his last letters. maps and ill. roy. 12°. $2.50 .... *J. E. Potter.*
— Missionary travels and researches in south Africa; with por., maps by Arrowsmith, and ill. 8°. $4.50; shp., $5; hf. cf., $6.75 .... *Harper.*
— Travels and researches in south Africa; from the personal narrative; [with] sketch of discoveries in Africa. ('68.) New ed. ill. 12°. '76. $1.75. *J.E.Potter.*
— *and* C: Narrative of an expedition to the Zambesi and its tributaries, and of the disc. of lakes Shirwa and Nyassa, 1858–1864. map and ill. 8°. $5; shp., $5.50; hf. cf., $7.25 .... *Harper.*

Livingstone and his African explorations. ('72.) New ed. map. 12°. '73. $1.50 .... *Adams, V.& Co.*

Livingstone's discoveries and adventures in Africa; [also] The Stanley expedition. [In Eng. or Germ.] 8°. pap., 25c. .... *Barclay.*

Livius *Patavinus*, Tit. [History of Rome; *Lat.*] Books 1, 2, 21, 22; ed. by Schmitz and Zumpt. 16°. $1 .... *Sheldon.*
— *Same.* Books 1, 21 and 22; with extracts from bks. 9, 24, 35, 38, 39 and 45; with notes, index, etc., by T. Chase. (cop. '70.) '72. 3d ed. 16°. '75. hf. leath., $1.50 .... *Eldredge.*
- *Same.* Books 21, 22; with notes by W. B. Smith. 16°. (Weale.) 60c. .... *Allyn.*
— *Same.* Selections from first 5 books, with 21st and 22d entire; with Eng. notes by J. L. Lincoln. map and plan. 12°. $1.75 .... *Appleton.*
— *Eng.* History of Rome; tr. by G. Baker. 5 v. 18°. $3.75 .... *Harper.*
— *Same;* lit. tr. by Spillan and others. 4 v. 12°. (Bohn.) ea., $1.75 .... *Little, B. & Co.*
Cont.: 1. Bks. 1-8. — 2. Bks. 9-26. — 3. Bks. 27-36. — 4. Bk. 37 to end; index.
— — *Same.* 4 v. 12°. (Bohn.) ea., $2. *Lippincott; Scribner, W.& A.*
— *Same.* Books 1–30; tr. by D. Spillan and C. Edmonds. 2 v. 12°. $3 .... *Harper.*
— *Same.* Selections from first 5 books, with 21st and 22d entire; interlin. tr. by I. W. Bieber. roy. 12°. $2.25 .... *Desilver.*
— Seven kings of Rome; abridg. from first bk. of L. by J. Wright. New ed., rev. with vocab. fp. 8°. $1.25 .... *Macmillan.*
— *See also* Collins, W. L., New ser. of anc. classics.

Livonian tales. 8°. pap., 25c. .... *Harper.*

Livre des missions: instructions et prières tirées en partie des œuvres de St. Alphonse de Liguori. 18°. *net*, 47c.; 62c. .... *Benziger.*
— *See also* Mission book.

Livre des petit enfants. Reader for little children; with vocab. 16°. '46. 75c. .... *G.R.Lockwood.*

Liza. Turgénieff, I. $1.25 .... *Holt.*

Lizars, J: Use and abuse of tobacco. 12°. '73. 60c. *Lindsay.*
— — *See also* Miller, Ja., Alcohol.

Lizzie. *See* Swallow stories.

Lizzie, the girl soldier. *See* Wright, *Mrs.* J. McN.

Lizzie Blake. ill. 18°. '73. 40c. .... *Am. Tr.*

Lizzie Claire; or, the last penny. 18°. 22c. .... *Am.S.S.*

Lizzie doing good. 18°. 60c. .... *Cong. Pub.*

Lizzie Eames. 18°. 30c. .... *Am.S.S.*

Lizzie Ferguson. Egliseau, S. S. 60c. .... *Pres. Bd.*

Lizzie French; or, pleasant memories. 18°. 40c. *Cong. Pub.*

Lizzie Glenn. Arthur, T. S. $1.75; $1.50 .. *Peterson.*

Lizzie Leigh. Gaskell, E. C. $1.75 .. *Scribner, W. & A.*

Lizzie Leigh: drama. 16°. pap., 15c. .... *French.*

Lizzie Lorton of Greyrigg. Linton, E. L. 75c. .. *Harper.*

Lizzie Lovell; or, what a little girl can do. 18°. 17c.; 22c. .... *Am. Bapt.*

Lizzie Lyle. Hazlewood, C. H. 15c. .... *French.*

Lizzie Maitland. Clarke, D. W. C. $1 .... *Strong.*

Lizzie Weston's mission. *See* W., A. L.

Lizzie's secret. Maguire, A. A. 75c. .... *Dutton.*

Lizzie's visit to New York. 18°. 60c. .... *Whittaker.*

Lizzy Johnson; or, mutual help. 16°. 50c. *Scribner, W.& A.*

Llewellyn, B. L. Little brown Bible. 18°. 60c. *Pres. Bd.*

Llewellyn, E. Walter Stockton; or, my father's at the helm. 18°. 70c. .... *Pres. Bd.*

Llewellyn, E. L. Agnes Lysle; or, sowing and reaping. 16°. $1.25 .... *Am. Bapt.*
— Deserted mill; or, the reward of industry. 16°. $1.25. *Graves.*
— Dove's nest lib. 4 v. 18°. '74. $2 .... *Meth. Epis.*
Cont.: Dove's nest. — Fido and Frank. — Uncle John. — Visit to the woods.
— Flowers in the grass. 18°. 75c. .... *Pres. Bd.*
— What to do. 18°. 55c. .... *Pres. Bd.*

Llewellyn, *Mrs.* E. V. C. Heavenly dews. 12°. '75. $1.25 .... *Turnbull.*

Lliano, H: St. A. v. Church of God and the bishops; suggested by the convocation of the Vatican Council; tr. 16°. '70. $1 .... *Pott.*

Llorente, Juan Ant. History of the inquisition in Spain; tr. 8°. pap., 75c. .... *Peterson.*

Lloyd, Eliz. Literature for little folks: sel. from standard authors and easy lessons in composition. 16°. 75c.; hf. bd., 50c. .... *Sower.*

Lloyd, J: Analysis of first 11 chapters of Gesenius' Heb. grammar. sm. 4°. (Bagster.) $1.50. *Wiley.*
— — *See also* Gesenius, F. H. W.

Lloyd, S: H. Glimpses of the spirit land: sonnets, addresses and other poems. 16°. $1.50 .. *Widdleton.*
— Wayside thoughts. 16°. $1 .... *Widdleton.*

Lloyd, W. Watkyss. Age of Pericles: hist. of arts and politics of Greece from the Persian to the Peloponnesian war. 2 v. 8°. '75. $8 .. *Macmillan.*

Lloyd Dalan. Densel, M. $1.25 .... *Dutton.*

Lloyd's (American) register of Am. and foreign shipping. [Annual.] 4°. mor., $15 ... *Hartshorne.*

Load of chips. *See* Baker, *Mrs.* H. N. W.

Loan of a lover. Planché, J. R. 15c. .... *French.*

Loan of a wife: drama. 16°. pap., 15c. .... *French.*

Loango. *See* Hoffmann, F.

Löb, H. Road to faith, for Jewish element. schools; tr. from the Germ. 32°. 30c. .... *Bloch.*

Lob Gottes. Ahrens, J. B. A. *net*, 35c. .... *So. Meth.*

Lobe, J. C. Catechism of music; tr. by F. R. Ritter. New ed. 12°. '76. bds., 50c. .... *North.*
— *Same.* 12°. *net*, pap., $1.50; 75c. .... *Schirmer.*

Löber, Chr. Evangelisch-lutherische Dogmatik; mit Vorwort v. C. F. W. Walther. 8°. '72. hf. mor., $2.25 .... *Dette.*

Lobster boy. Mudge, Z. A. 50c. .... *Bost. Am. Tr.*

Loch (Das) im Aermel. *See* Zschokke, H.

Loch (Das) in d. Hose. Gerstäcker, F. 25c. .. *Steiger.*

Lochner, F. Chorgesänge zur Liturgie f. e. Charfreitags-Gottesdienst. 12°. pap., 10c. .. *Volkening.*

Lock, A. G. Agriculturists their own superphosphate makers. 2d ed. ill. 8°. '72. pap., 40c. .. *Spon.*

Lock and key. Hoare, P. 15c. .... *French.*

Locke, D: Ross. ["Petroleum V. Nasby."] Ekkoes from Kentucky. ill. 12°. $1.50 .... *Lee & S.*

— The morals of Abou Ben Adhem: eastern fruit on western dishes. 12°. $1.50 .... *Lee & S.*

— On inflation. [Burlesque.] 8°. pap., 25c. .. *Barclay.*

— Swingin' round the cirkle. ill. 12°. $1.50 .. *Lee & S.*

Locke, E., *and* Nourse, S. School melodist: song book for school and home. ('54.) New ed. sq. 16°. '59. bds., 40c. .... *Wilstach.*

— — School vocalist: system of element. instruc. in music; with exercises. ('48.) New ed. sq. 16°. '53. bds., 40c. .... *Wilstach.*

Locke, J: Philosophical works; with notes and index by J. A. St. John. 2 v. 12°. (Bohn.) ea., $1.25. *Little, B. & Co.*

Cont.: 1. Of the conduct of the understanding; Essay conc. the human understanding. — 2. Exam. of Malebranche's opinion of seeing all things in God; Elements of nat. philos.; Reading for a gentleman; Index.

— — *Same.* 2 v. 12°. (Bohn.) ea., $1.40. *Scribner, W. & A.*

— — *Same.* 2 v. 12°. (Bohn.) ea., $1.50 .. *Lippincott.*

— Commonplace book of the Bible. 8°. '58. $1.25. *Am. Tr.*

— Conduct of the understanding. *See* Bacon, F., Essays.

— Essay conc. the human understanding; and treatise on the conduct of the understanding. 8°. shp., $2.85 .... *C. H. Davis.*

— *Same.* New ed., rev. sm. 8°. hf. cf., $4.50; cf., $6 .... *Appleton.*

— — *See also* British pocket classics.

— Some thoughts conc. education. ('69.) 2d ed. 24°. '75. pap., 25c. .... *Schermerhorn.*

— *Same;* [also] Treatise of education by J. Milton. 24°. '69. pap., 25c. .... *Schermerhorn.*

Locke, J: Law and practice of foreign attachment; [also] Supplement to On injunctions by C. S. Drewry. 8°. '54. $1.50 ..... *T. & J. W. Johnson.*

— — *See also* Law lib.

Locke, Una. *See* Lee, F., *and* Locke, U.

Locke Amsden. *See* Thompson, D. P.

Locked in. Wooler, J. P. 15c. .... *De Witt.*

Locked in with a lady. Addison, H. R. 15c. *De Witt; French.*

Locked out. Paul, H. 15c. .... *De Witt; French.*

Locker, Arth. (*pseud.*) *See* Forbes, J. H.

Lockerby, Dan. F. Acrostical pen portraits of the 18 presidents of the U. S.: biog., hist., descrip. and eulogistic. 16°. '76. $1; mor., $2 ..... *Sibole.*

Locket ser. 3 v. 18°. per double set, $6 .... *Nelson.*

Cont.: Ella's locket and what it brought her, by G. E. Dartnell. — Our games, by M. Hamilton. — Twin brothers of Everdale, by C. H. Eden.

Lockhart, J: Bible manual: handbook of leading facts of the Bible; with epitome of anc. hist. 12°. $1.25 .... *Nelson.*

Lockhart, J: Gibson. Ancient Spanish ballads; with biog. por. 16°. $1 .... **Osgood.*

— *Same.* (Scribner's pop. poets.) ill. 12°. $1.50. *Scribner, W. & A.*

— *Same;* [also] Chronicle of the Cid, by R. Southey. (Chandos classics.) cr. 8°. $1; pap., 75c. *Scribner, W. & A.*

— — *Same.* (Chandos lib.) 12°. $1.75; hf. cf., $3.75; cf., $5 .... *Scribner, W. & A.*

— Life of Napoleon Bonaparte. 2 v. por. 18°. $1.50. *Harper.*

— Life of Scott. por. 8°. $2.50 .... *Peterson.*

— *Same.* 2 v. cr. 8°. (Lond.) $2.50 .. *Little, B. & Co.*

— *Same.* 9 v. in 3. ill. 12°. $6.75 .... **Osgood.*

— — *See also* Scott, *Sir* W., Works.

— *See also* Noctes ambrosianæ.

Lockhart, Law. W. M. Fair to see. [Fiction.] 8°. pap., 75c. .... *Harper.*

Lockroy, —, *and* Michel, M. Tompkins, the troubadour: farce. 16°. pap., 15c. .... *De Witt.*

Locksley Hall. *See* Tennyson, Alfr.

Lockwood, D. W. Preliminary report upon a recon. in s. and s. w. Nev. *See* United States, *Corps of Eng.*

Lockwood, Howard (*ed.*) Directory of the paper trade in the U. S. and Canadas. ('73.) 2d ed. 8°. '75. $2 .... *H. Lockwood.*

Lockwood, Ingersoll. Washington: heroic drama of the rev. 12°. '76. pap., *50c. .. (?) *I. Lockwood.*

Lockwood, Lew. C. Mary S. Peake, colored teacher at Fortress Monroe. 18°. 35c. .... *Bost. Am. Tr.*

Lockwood, Luke A. Masonic law and practice. 12°. '67. $1 .... *Masonic; Redding.*

Lockwood, R. *See* New York, Synopsis of cases.

Lockwood's ladies' angular-hand copy books. 6 nos. obl. 18°. per doz., $2.40 ...... *G. R. Lockwood.*

Lockyer, Jos. Norm. Astronomy. (Science primer.) 18°. 50c. .... *Appleton.*

— Contributions to solar physics. col. pl. and woodcuts. roy. 8°. '73. $10 .... *Macmillan.*

— Elementary lessons in astronomy. 12°. $1.75. *Appleton.*

— *Same.* ill. 18°. $1.75 .... *Macmillan.*

— — Questions; by J. F. Robertson. 18°. '70. 50c. *Macmillan.*

— Spectroscope and its applications. 2d ed. ill. 12°. '73. $1.25 .... *Macmillan.*

— *See also* Roscoe, H. E., Huggins, W., *and* Lockyer, J. N.

Lockyer, Lisa. Child's influence; or, Kathleen and her great uncle. ill. 16°. '72. $1 ...... *Dutton.*

Locust grove stories. 6 v. 18°. $1.80; $2.10. *Am. S. S.*

Cont.: Unruly tongue, etc. — How Violet's prayer was answered, etc. — Jack Story and Paul Stanley, etc. — Dick Mason and Harry Slack, etc. — Earnest boy, etc. — Birthday party at the Hall, etc.

Lodeman, A: German conversation tables; with notes. 12°. '71. bds., 40c. .... *Holt.*

— Grundriss d. Geschichte d. deutschen Literatur. 12°. '74. 75c. .... *Schoenhof.*

Loder, G: Philadelphia and New York glee book; with piano-forte accomp. 8°. '57. $1.50 .... *Ditson.*

Lodge, Edm. Portraits of illustrious personages of Gt. Brit., with memoirs. 8 v. por. 12°. (Bohn.) ea., $1.75 .... *Little, B. & Co.*

— *Same.* 8 v. por. 12°. (Bohn.) ea., $2. *Lippincott; Scribner, W. & A.*

Lodgers and dodgers. Hay, F. 15c. .. *De Witt; French.*

Lodgings at Knightsbridge. *See* Witch-Hampton Hall.

Lodgings for single gentlemen: drama. 16°. pap., 15c. *French.*

Lodoiska. Kemble, J. P. 15c. .... *French.*

Loebell, J: W: *See* Bunsen, C. C. J., Brandis, C. A., *and* Loebell, J. W.

Loew, H. Monograph of the diptera of No. Am. pt. 2. 8°. '64. pap., $2.50 .... *Smith. Inst.*

— *Same.* pt. 3. 8°. '73. pap., $2 ..... *Smith. Inst.*

— *and* Osten-Sacken, C. R. R. Monograph of the diptera. pt. 1. 8°. '62. pap., $1.50 .. *Smith. Inst.*

Loew, O. Report upon mineral., etc., conditions. *See* United States, *Corps of Eng.*

Lofsånger och åndeliga wisor i nådene. 12°. 20c. *Engberg.*

Loftie, W. J. *See* Rowbotham, F. L., Water-color albums.

Lofton, G. A. Drunkenness and its remedy. 16°. 60c. *So. Bapt.*

Lofty aims and lowly efforts. Shipley, M. E. $1.50. *Pott.*

Lofty aims lib. 4 v. ill. 12°. ea., $1.50 ...... *Pott.*

Cont.: Lofty aims and lowly efforts, by M. E. Shipley. — Stories of success, by J. F. Cobb. — Village beech tree. — New stories, by C. E. Bowen.

Lofty and lowly. McIntosh, M. J. 2 v. $2.50 .. *Appleton.*

Lofty projects. Lunn, J. 15c. .... *French.*

Log-book of a fisherman and zoologist. Buckland, F. T. $3 .... *Lippincott.*

Log house. Kingston, W. H. G. 75c....... *Lothrop.*

Log house by the lake. *See* Variety lib.

Logan, C. A. Yankee land: comedy. 16°. pap., 15c. *French.*

Logan, J. B. Carrie Holmes. 16°. 50c. (?) *Cumberland.*

— Heavenly birth (The). 25c....... (?) *Cumberland.*

— Plain and Scriptural guide in reference to the doctrines of baptism. 20c......... (?) *Cumberland.*

Logan, Ja. *See* Historical Soc. of Penna.; —Penn, W., *and* Logan, J.

Logan, Olive. Get thee behind me, Satan: home-born book of home truths. ('72.) New ed. 12°. '73. $1.50 .... *Adams, V. & Co.*

— Mimic world. 8°. '71. *$3.75; mor., $5.. *New World.*

— They met by chance: a society novel. 12°. '73. $1.50. *Adams, V. & Co.*

Logan, W: Words of comfort for bereaved parents. 12°. $1............................ *Nelson.*

— *Same.* 16°. $1.25...................... *Carter.*

Logic of accounts. Folsom, E. G. $2....... *Barnes.*

Logic of death; — of life. *See* Holyoake, G. J.

Logical praxis. Day, H. N. $1 .... *Putnam.*

Login, T. Roads, railways and canals for India; with pract. suggestions. 8°. pap., 40c........ *Spon.*

Lohbeck, P: Peter Lohbeck, der fromme Soldat. [Biog.] 32°. '62. 15c................ *Am. Tr.*

Lohengrin. *See* Wagner, W. R.

Lohn (Der) e. guten That. Oertel, P. F. W. 25c. *Steiger.*

Lois Mead. *See* Bradley, *Mrs.* M. E.

Loitering Linus. *See* Finley, M. F.

Lokka. *See* Sophie's dream.

Lola Montes. *See* Montes, *Mme.* Lola.

Lolla; or, the sin of greediness. 18°. 45c.... *Am. S. S.*

Lolly Dinks' doings. Stoddard, R. H. $1... *W. F. Gill.*

Lomax, E. V. ["Byrd Lyttle."] Mary Austin; or, the new home. 18°. 90c........... (?) *Martien.*

Lomax, J. T. Digest of laws resp. real property in the U. S., especially in Va.; incl. code of 1850 and decisions of Supreme Court. 2d ed., enl. 3 v. 8°. '55. shp., $22.50 .... *J. W. Randolph.*

— Treatise on law of executors and administrators in the U. S., particularly in Va. 2d ed., enl. 2 v. 8°. '57. shp., $25 .... *J. W. Randolph.*

Lombard Street. Bagehot, W. $1.75..... *Scribner.*

Lombardi (I). *See* Verdi, G.

Lombez, Amb. de. Joy of the Christian soul; tr. by E. Domphoux. 18°. '64. 40c.... *Kelly, P. & Co.*

Loménie, L: de. Beaumarchais and his times: sketches of French society in the 18th cent.; tr. by H. S. Edwards. 12°. $1.50 .... *Harper.*

Lommel, Eug. Nature of light; with general account of phys. optics. ill. 12°. '76. $2..... *Appleton.*

Lonas, H: Choralbuch d. evang. Brüder Kirche: Auszug a. C. Gregor's Choralbuch von 1784. 8°. $2............................ *Clauder.*

London apprentice. *See* Good boy's lib.

London apprentice and the goldsmith's daughter. Egan, P. 25c...................... *De Witt.*

London Art Journal. *See* One hundred gems.

London assurance. *See* Boucicault, D.

London boy; or, a visit to an Am. Sunday-school. 18°. 22c. .... *Am. S. S.*

London bridge: drama. 16°. pap., 15c...... *French.*

London characters. Mayhew, H. $3 .... *Routledge.*

London Daily News. *See* Daily News.

London in miniature. map and ill. 48°. 25c. *Scribner, W. & A.*

London in modern times: sketches of L. during last two centuries; rev. by T. O. Summers. ('57.) 2d ed. 18°. '76. 50c................. *So. Meth.*

London in the olden time: sketches of L. to end of 16th cent.; rev. by T. O. Summers. ('57.) 2d ed. 18°. '76. 50c. .... *So. Meth.*

London's heart. *See* Farjeon, B. L.

Lone house on the bridge: drama. 16°. pap., 15c. *French.*

Lonely dove. *See* Laurel ser.

Lonely life; by author of "Wise as a serpent." 12°. $1.75; pap., $1.50.................. *Peterson.*

Lonely Lily; by author of "Twice found." 18°. 35c. *Carter.*

— *Same.* ill. 16°. '75. 75c.................. *Dodd.*

— *See also* Aunt Deborah's lib.

Lonely man of the ocean. Blake, T. G. 15c... *French.*

Lonely pollywog of the mill-pond: drama. 16°. pap., 15c. .... *Happy.*

Long, Edn. M. Illustrated hist. of hymns and their authors. 8°. '75. *$3.50.......... (?) *Jaggars.*

Long, G: Classical atlas, with geog. introd. 52 maps. 8°. $4.............................. *Sheldon.*

Long, H. A. Names we bear: compendium of Biblical, classical and common names; with pref. by J. McCann. 8°. '75. $1.50 .... *Williams.*

Long, Ht. S. First lessons in grammar: introd. to Eng. grammar. 16°. hf. roan, 25c........ *Lippincott.*

Long, J. D. *See* Wood, C. H., *and* Long, J. D.

Long, J: H., *and* Buel, R. H. The cadet engineer; or, steam for the student. 8°. '65. $2.25. *Claxton; Lippincott.*

Long, Jos. W. American wild fowl shooting. ill. 12°. '74. $2................................ *Ford.*

Long, R. H. Hunt's gazetteer of the border and southern states. map. 36°. '63. 75c.; 50c. *Hunt.*

Long, S: P. Art: its laws and the reasons for them. ill. 12°. $3........................... *Lee & S.*

Long (The) and the short of it. Small, G. G. 25c. *Collin & S.*

Long-hand shortened. 12°. pap., 15c....... *Happy.*

Long look ahead. Roe, A. S. $1.50....... *Carleton.*

Long strike: drama. 16°. pap., 15c. .... *French.*

Longden, H: Life. 18°. '37. 50c.... *Meth. Bk. Conc.*

Longfellow, H: Wadsworth. Poems. (Blue and gold ed.) 2 v. 32°. $2.50; hf. cf., $5; mor., $6. *Osgood.*

— *Same.* (Cabinet ed.) 2 v. por. 16°. $3; hf. cf., $6; mor., $8......................... *Osgood.*

— *Same.* (Cambridge ed.) 4 v. 16°. '65. $9; hf. cf., $18; mor., $24; — in 2 v. 12°. $7; hf. cf., $12; mor., $16 .... *Osgood.*

— *Same.* (Centennial ed.) ill. 8°. '76. pap., $1. *Osgood.*

— *Same.* (Diamond ed.) 16°. '67. $1; hf. cf., $2.25; mor., $3 .... *Osgood.*

— *Same.* (Household ed.) 12°. '73. $2; hf. cf., $4; mor., $5 .... *Osgood.*

— *Same.* (Ill. octavo ed.) por. and ill. 8°. '72. $10; hf. cf., $14; mor., $16 .... *Osgood.*

— *Same.* (Red line ed.) por. and ill. sm. 4°. '69. $3.50; hf. cf., $5; mor., $7 .... *Osgood.*

— Prose works. (Blue and gold ed.) 2 v. por. 32°. $2.50; hf. cf., $5; mor., $6 .... *Osgood.*

— *Same.* (Cabinet ed.) 2 v. por. 16°. $3; hf. cf., $6; mor., $8........................ *Osgood.*

— *Same.* (Cambridge ed.) 3 v. 16°. '65. $6.75; hf. cf., $13.50; mor., $18.............. *Osgood.*

— Aftermath. 16°. '73. $1.50; hf. cf., $3; mor., $4. *Osgood.*

Note. Part 3 of Wayside Inn.

— Building of the ship. (Ill. red line ed.) sm. 4°. '69. $3; mor., $5.50................. *Osgood.*

Longfellow, H: Wadsworth, *continued.*
— Christus: a mystery. 3 v. 12°. '72. $4.50; hf. cf., $9; mor., $13.50 .... *Osgood.*
Cont.: Divine tragedy. — Golden legend. — New England tragedies.

— *Same.* 3 v. in 1. 8°. $3; hf. cf., $5.50; mor., $7. — (Red-line ed.) ill. sm. 4°. $3.50; hf. cf., $5; mor., $7. — (Cabinet ed.) 16°. $1.50; hf. cf., $3; mor., $4. — (Blue and gold ed.) 32°. $1.25; hf. cf., $2.50; mor., $3. — (Diamond ed.) 18°. '73. $1; hf. cf., $2.25; mor., $3 ...... *Osgood.*
— Courtship of Miles Standish. (Vest pocket ser.) ill. 32°. '76. 50c. .... *Osgood.*
— *Germ.* Miles Standish's Brautwerbung; übers. v. F. E. Baumgarten. 16°. '59. pap., 25c. .. *Witter.*
— Divine tragedy. 16°. '71. $1.50. — (Holiday ed.) 8°. $3 .... *Osgood.*
— Evangeline. 16°. '47. $1.25. — ill. sm. 4°. $3; mor., $5.50. — (Vest pocket ser.) ill. 32°. '75. 50c. .... *Osgood.*
— Flower-de-luce. ill. sm. 4°. '66. $2.50 .... *Osgood.*
— Hanging of the crane. 8°. '74. $5; mor., $9. — ill. 16°. $1.50; mor., $4 .... *Osgood.*
— Household poems. ill. sm. 4°. '65. 75c. ... *Osgood.*
— Hyperion. [Fiction.] 16°. $1.50 .... *Osgood.*
— Kavanagh. [Fiction.] 16°. $1.25 .... *Osgood.*
— Masque of Pandora, and other poems. 16°. '75. $1.50; hf. cf., $3; mor., $4 .... *Osgood.*
— New England tragedies. 16°. '68. $1.50; hf. cf., $3; mor., $4 .... *Osgood.*
— Outre-mer. 16°. $1.50 .... *Osgood.*
— Song of Hiawatha. 16°. '55. $1.50; large pap., $2.50 .... *Osgood.*
— Three books of song. 16°. '72. $1.50; hf. cf., $3; mor., $4 .... *Osgood.*
— Wayside Inn, and other poems. 16°. '63. $1.50. — ill. 8°. mor., $10 .... *Osgood.*
— (*ed.*) Poets and poetry of Europe. roy. 8°. $6; hf. cf., $11; mor., $14 .... *Osgood.*
— *See also* Companion poets; — Dante Alighieri; — Forest scenes; — Laurel leaves; — L'Homond, C. F.; — Winter poems.

Longfellow, S: Hymns of the spirit. 16°. '64. $1.25. *Osgood.*
— *and* Higginson, T. W. Thalatta: a book for the seaside. 16°. $1 .... *Osgood.*
— *and* Johnson, *Rev.* S. Book of hymns. 16°. '48. $1.25 .... *Osgood*

Longking, Jos. Notes on Galatians and Ephesians. 18°. '63. 60c. .... *Meth. Bk. Conc.*
— Notes on Gospels. 4 v. 18°. ea., 75c. .. *Meth. Bk. Conc.*
— Notes on Hebrews. 18°. '67. 75c. .. *Meth. Bk. Conc.*
— Questions on Galatians and Ephesians. 18°. per doz., $1.80 .... *Meth. Bk. Conc.*
— Questions on the Gospels. 4 v. 18°. per doz., $1.80. *Meth. Bk. Conc.*
— Questions on Hebrews. 18°. per doz., $1.80. *Meth. Bk. Conc.*

Longley, El. Phonetic first reader. 16°. '57. pap., 20c. .... *Stevens.*
— Phonetic primer. 16°. '57. pap., 10c. ..... *Stevens.*

Longman, F. W. Frederick the Great and the seven years' war. 16°. $1 .... *Estes.*

Longmore, T. Treatise on gunshot wounds. 12°. $1.25 .... *Claxton.*

Longstreth, M. A. Young student's companion: element. lessons and exercises in tr. from Eng. into Fr. ('53.) 7th ed. 12°. '74. $1 .. *Eldredge.*

Longus. *See* Heliodorus *Emesenus*, Longus, *and* Tatius, A.

Longworth, N. Directions for cultivation of the strawberry. *See* Buchanan, R., Culture of the grape.

Lonnie, our little lamb. Brown, H. E. 45c. *Bost. Am. Tr.*

Lonsdale, H: Sketch of life and writings of Robert Knox, anatomist. por. cr. 8°. '70. $2.50. *Macmillan.*

Lonsdale, J: (*Lord*). Memoir of reign of James II. *See* Carrel, A., Hist. of counter-revolution.

Look, H: M. Treatise upon law and practice of Masonic trials. 12°. $2 .... *Masonic; Redding.*

Look after Brown. Stuart, G. A. 15c. ...... *Lee & S.*

Look before you leap. Lovell, G. W. 15c. .. *French.*

Look before you leap. *See* French's comic dramas.

Look to the end. Ellis, S. S. 50c. .... *Harper.*

Look to Jesus. Reid, W. 40c. .... *Hoyt.*

Look up; or, girls and flowers. 18°. 45c. .. *Am. S. S.*

Look up lib. 3 v. 16°. $3.75 .... (?) *Martien.*
Cont.: Philip in Palestine. — Take, but earn. — Joseph, the Jew.

Look upward; or, the working boy's own book. ill. 16°. 60c. .... *Bost. Am. Tr.*

Looker-on. *See* Chalmer, A., British essayists.

Looking backward. King, M. B. A. $1.75 .. *Randolph.*

Looking beyond. Barrett, J. O. 75c. .... *Colby.*

Looking to the cross. Bonar, H. 40c. .. (?) *Martien.*

Looking toward sunset. Child, L. M. $3; $5; $6.50. *Osgood.*

Looking unto Jesus. 16°. '53. 75c. .... *Dutton.*

Looking unto Jesus. Ambrose, I. $3 .. (?) *Martien.*

Looking unto Jesus. Monod, T. 15c.; 50c. .. *Am. Tr.*

Looking up. A., F. C. 50c. .... *Pott.*

Looking upward; or, the story of Wilhelm Deremen; tr. by H. G. Blythe. 18°. '75. 60c. .. *H. A. Young.*

Looking-glass for the mind. *See* Happy child's lib.

Loomis, *Rev.* A. W. Confucius and the Chinese classics; or, readings in Chinese literature. 12°. '67. $1.50 .... *Roman.*
— English and Chinese lessons. 12°. '72. $1 .. *Am. Tr.*

Loomis, Alfr. L. Lectures on diseases of the respiratory organs, heart and kidneys. 8°. $5; leath., $6 .... *W. Wood.*
— Lessons in physical diagnosis. 8°. $2 ..... *De Witt.*
— *Same.* New ed., rev. and enl. ill. 8°. $3 .. *W. Wood.*
— Peritonitis. *See* Seguin, E. C., Series of Am. clin. lect.

Loomis, El. Elements of algebra. 26th ed. 12°. shp., $1.25 .... *Harper.*
— Elements of analytical geometry. Rev. ed. 12°. shp., $1.50 .... *Harper.*
— *Same;* [also] Elements of calculus. 2 v. in 1. 12°. shp., $2.50 .... *Harper.*
— Elements of arithmetic. 16°. hf. shp., 40c. *Harper.*
— Elements of astronomy. 12°. shp., $1.50 .. *Harper.*
— Elements of the differential and integral calculus. Rev. ed. 12°. shp., $1.50 .... *Harper.*
— Elements of natural philosophy. 8th ed. 12°. shp., $1.50 .... *Harper.*
— Geometry, conic sections and plane trigonometry. 12°. shp., $1.50 .... *Harper.*
— Introduction to pract. astronomy; with astron. tables. 8th ed. 8°. shp., $2 .... *Harper.*
— Recent progress of astronomy, especially in the U. S. Rev. ed. ill. 12°. $1.50 .... *Harper.*
— Storms in Europe and America, Dec., 1836. 4°. '60. pap., $1.25 .... *Smith. Inst.*
— Treatise on algebra. 12°. shp., $1.50 ..... *Harper.*
— Treatise on arithmetic, theoretical and practical. 12th ed. 12°. shp., $1.25 .... *Harper.*
— Treatise on astronomy. ill. 8°. shp., $2 .. *Harper.*
— Treatise on meteorology; with meteorol. tables. 8°. shp., $2 .... *Harper.*
— Trigonometry and tables. 28th ed. 8°. shp., $2; — ea., sep., $1.50 .... *Harper.*

Loomis, G: B. First steps in music. 4 v. 16°. '71. bds., bks. 1, 2, ea. 15c.; 3, 35c.; 4, 60c. .. *Ivison.*
— Progressive music lessons; rev. from "First steps." 3 v. 16°. '75. bds., bk. 1, 20c.; 2, 25c.; 3, 35c. .... *Ivison.*

Loomis, H. Great conflict: Christ and antichrist, the church and apostasy. 12°. '74. $1..*Meth. Bk. Conc.*
— Land of shadowing wings; or, the empire of the sea. 12°. '73. $1.25..........*Meth. Bk. Conc.*
Loomis, J. R. Elements of anatomy, physiology and hygiene. 12°. $1.25..........*Sheldon.*
— Elements of geology. 12°. $1.25..........*Sheldon.*
Loomis, Lafayette C. Home book-keeping. obl. 12°. '67. pap., 25c..........*Schermerhorn.*
— Mental and social culture. ('67.) 2d ed. 12°. '76. 75c..........*Schermerhorn.*
— Mizpah: friends at prayer: prayer or meditation for every day. 12°. $2..........*Lippincott.*
Loomis, Silas L. Analytical arithmetic; for beginners. 18°. '59. hf. roan, 38c.....*Claxton; Lippincott.*
— Normal arithmetic, theoretical and practical. 12°. '58. hf. roan, 63c..........*Claxton; Lippincott.*
— — Key. 12°. '60. 50c..........*Claxton.*
Loos, I: K. Life of Cain. ill. 16°. 75c...*Ref. Ch. Pub.*
— Salome, the dancer. ill. 16°. 40c......*Ref. Ch. Pub.*
Lope de Vega. *See* Vega.
Lord, C. E. Evidences of natural and revealed theology. 8°. $3.50..........*Lippincott.*
Lord, *Mrs.* C: Grace Harriet. ill. 18°. '49. 25c. *Am. Tr.*
Lord, E. Psalter readjusted: in its rel. to the temple services and the anc. Jewish faith. 12°. '60. $1.25..........*Randolph.*
Lord, I. S. P. On intermittent fever and other malarious diseases. [Hom.] 8°. $3 ....*Boericke.*
Lord, J: Ancient states and empires. map. cr. 8°. '69. $3; hf. cf., $5; — chp. ed. 12°. $1.50..*Scribner.*
— History of modern Europe [1483–1821]. 12°. $2.25. *Desilver.*
— History of the U. S. 12°. $1.75..........*Desilver.*
— Life of Emma Willard. por. 12°. $2....*Appleton.*
— Old Roman world: the grandeur and failure of its civilization. cr. 8°. $3 ....*Scribner.*
Lord, Lucy T. Memoir. 18°. 60c.; 75c. ..*Am. Bapt.*
Lord, Ma. Life. ill. 32°. '54. 30c..........*Am. Tr.*
Lord, Otis P. Memoir of Asahel Huntington. 8°. '71. 25c..........*Essex.*
Lord, W. W. André: tragedy. 12°. '56. $1..*Scribner.*
Lord, Willis. Christian theology for the people. ('74.) New ed. 8°. '75. $4..........*Carter.*
— Men and scenes before the flood. ill. sq. 12°. 50c. *Pres. Bd.*
Lord (The) our shepherd. 12°. 80c...*N. Y. Ref. Ch. Bd.*
Lord (The) our shepherd. Stevenson, J. $1.50.. *Wiley.*
Lord Bantam. *See* Jenkins, E.
Lord Bateman. Byron, H. J. 15c..........*French.*
Lord Bateman. *See* Ballad of.
Lord Darnley. Wilks, T. E. 15c. ....*French.*
Lord Hope's choice. Stephens, A. S. $1.75; $1.50. *Peterson.*
Lord Kilgobbin. *See* Lever, C:
Lord Lisle's daughter. Braeme, C. M. 30c...*Am. News.*
Lord Lovell and Lady Nancy Bell. Burnand, F. C. 15c..........*French.*
Lord Montagu's page. James, G. P. R. $1.75; $1.50. *Peterson.*
Lord Oakburn's daughters. Wood, E. P. $1.75; $1.50. *Peterson.*
Lord of himself. Underwood, F. H. $1.75 ..*Lee & S.*
Lord of the isles. *See* Scott, *Sir* W.
Lord of the manor. Burgoyne, *Gen.* —. 15c...*French.*
Lord Roldan. Cunningham, A. $1.50.......*Harper.*
Lord Saxondale. Reynolds, G. W. M. $1.75; $1. *Peterson.*
Lord will provide. Randolph, S. N. 90c...*Randolph.*
Lord's day. 18°. pap., 10c..........*Am. Tr.*
Lord's prayer. 18°. 40c.; 50c..........*Am. Bapt.*
— *See also* Picture page lib.
Lord's prayer ser. 6 v. 18°. $2.25 ....*Pres. Bd.*
Cont.: Annie Lee. — Blind Ruth. — Hazel Glen. — Christmas eve. — Seventy times seven. — Charlie.
Loreley. Mendelssohn Bartholdy, F. 65c...*Ditson.*
Lorenz, Edm. S. Songs of the cross. sq. 8°. '76. 35c. *Un. B. Pub.*
Lorenzo; or, the empire of religion. sq. 16°. '51. 60c.; 80c..........*Murphy.*
Lorgnette (The). Mitchell, D. G. $3.50...*Scribner.*
Lorimer, G: C. Under the evergreens; or, a night with St. Nicholas. ill. sq. 16°. $1.50..(?) *Shepard.*
Lorimer, Ja. Institutes of law. 8°. $7. *Scribner, W. & A.*
Lorimer, J: G. Historical sketch of the Protestant church of France, with notices of the church of Scotland. 12°. $1.30..........*Pres. Bd.*
Lorimer, Ma. Among the trees: journal of walks in the woods, and flower-hunting through field and by brook. ill. 4°. $2.25; mor., $5...*Hurd & H.*
Loring, E: G. Determination of the refraction of the eye with the ophthalmoscope. sm. 4°. 50c... *W. Wood.*
Loring, F: W. Boston dip (The), and other verses. sq. 16°. 50c..........*Loring.*
— Two college friends. 12°. $1 ....*Loring.*
— *See also* Six of one by half a dozen of the other.
Loring, Laurie (*pseud.*) *See* Pratt, L. Maria.
Lorna Doone. Blackmore, R. D. 75c.......*Harper.*
Lorne, *Marquis of.* [J. H. E. H. D. S. Campbell.] Guido and Lita: a tale of the riviera. sm. 4°. '75. $1.50..........*Macmillan.*
Lorraine (*pseud.*) Why she refused him. [Fiction.] 12°. $1.75..........*Lippincott.*
Lorraine, Alf. M. Helm, cross and sword. 12°. $1.75. *Meth. Bk. Conc.*
— Sea sermons. 16°. 60c. ....*Meth. Bk. Conc.*
Lorrimer Littlegood. Smedley, F. E. $1.75; $1.50. *Peterson.*
Löser, Pl. Vollständige Geschichte d. grossen amerik. Bürgerkrieges; nach d. Engl. 2 v. 12°. '65. $2 ....*Zickel.*
Losing to win. Davies, T. $1.50; $1......*Sheldon.*
Losing the way. 18°. 75c..........*Dutton.*
Loss and gain. 18°. 60c..........*Cong. Pub.*
Loss and gain. Haven, A. B. $1.25 ......*Appleton.*
Loss of the "Australia." 18°. 35c. ....*Carter.*
Loss of the "Kent," East-Indiaman. 18°. 30c...*Dutton.*
Losses and gains. Moore, J. F. $1.50........*Hoyt.*
Lossing, Benson J. Account of Mount Vernon. *See* Headley, J. T., Illustrated life of Washington.
— American centenary: hist. of the progress of the U. S. 55 eng. 4°. '76. *$15; — in 30 pts., ea., *50c. *Porter.*
— Common school hist. of the U. S. 12°. $1.75..*Sheldon.*
— Grammar school hist. of the U. S. 16°. $1.25..*Sheldon.*
— History of England. 3 maps. 12°. '71. $2.50; hf. cf., $4.50..........*Putnam.*
— History of our wars with Gt. Brit. 3 v. ill. 8°. '76. ea., *$5.50; hf. mor., $6.50; mor., $11; — in 56 pts., ea., *25c. ....*N. Y. Bk. Conc.*
— History of the U. S., to [1876]. (Centennial ed.) ill. 8°. '76. *$5; $5.50; hf. mor., $6..*Belknap.*
— *Germ.;* übers. v. L. Simonson. ill. 8°. *$5; $5.50; hf. mor., $6 ....*Belknap.*
— — *See also* Spencer, J. A., *and* Lossing, B. J.
— Home of Washington; or, Mount Vernon and its associations: hist., biog. and pictorial. eng. sq. 8°. '73. *$3; $4; mor., $7.........*Virtue.*
— Hudson (The), from the wilderness to the sea. ('66.) 3d ed. ill. sq. 8°. '72. $5; mor., $9 ... *Virtue.*
— Life of Gen. Philip Schuyler; [with papers of Gen. S.] 2 v. por. and ill. cr. 8°. $5 ......*Sheldon.*
— Lives of the signers of the Declaration of independence. (Centennial ed.) por., ill., etc. 12°. $2. *Souder.*

Lossing, Benson J., *continued.*
— Our country: [hist. to 1876]; ill. by Darley. [To form 48 pts.] pts. 1–24. 4°. '76. ea., 25c. *Johnson & M.*
— Outline hist. of the U. S. ill. 12°. $1.25 .. *Sheldon.*
— Outline of hist. of the fine arts. ill. 18°. 75c. *Harper.*
— Pictorial field-book of the civil war in the U. S. 3 v. ill. 8°. '69. *$15–$30; — 3 v. in 1., hf. mor., $10. *Belknap.*
— Pictorial field-book of the revolution. 2 v. 8°. $14–$22 .... *Harper.*
— Pictorial field-book of the war of 1812. ill. 8°. $7–$12 .... *Harper.*
— Pictorial hist. of the U. S. ill. 12°. $2 .... *Sheldon.*
— *Same.* [In Eng. or Germ.] ('67.) (Centennial ed.) wood-eng. roy. 8°. '76. *$5; leath., $5.50; hf. mor., $6.......... *Scammel.*
— Primary hist. of the U. S. ill. 16°. $1 .... *Sheldon.*
— Vassar College and its founder. imp. 8°. '75. $4.75. (?) *Alvord.*
— Washington and the Am. republic. ('71.) 7th ed. 3 v. steel eng. roy. 8°. '76. $22.50 .... *Virtue.*
Lossow, F. (*ill.*) *See* Light-headed pussy; — Little roebuck.
Lost among the wild men. Dalton, W. $1.50 .. *Routledge.*
Lost and found. 18°. '63. 40c. .... *Randolph.*
Lost and found. Urmy, W. S. $1.25 .. *Cin. Meth. Bk. Conc.*
Lost and found. *See* Ravenswood stories.
Lost and found: operetta. March, G. 15c. .. *French.*
Lost and found; or, the adopted daughter. 18°. 25c. *Scribner, W. & A.*
Lost and rescued. *See* Little Lottie ser.
Lost and saved. Norton, C. $1.25 .... *Lippincott.*
Lost and won: a rhyme of dark and daybreak. 12°. '74. $1.......... *Turnbull.*
Lost bank-note. Wood, E. P. 50c.......... *Peterson.*
Lost beauties of the English language. Mackay, C. $1.75 .... *Bouton.*
Lost beauty; by a lady of the Spanish court. 12°. $1.75; pap., $1.50.......... *Peterson.*
Lost blessing. Shipton, A. 75c.; 10c...... *Crowell.*
Lost boy. *See* Arthur, T. S.
Lost bracelet; by author of "Little Flora." 18°. 45c. *Pres. Bd.*
Lost bride. Arthur, T. S. 50c.......... *Peterson.*
Lost but found. Baker, H. N. W. $1.25 .. *H. A. Young.*
Lost cause. Pollard, E. A. *$5; $6; $8..... *Treat.*
Lost chamois hunter: tale of the Matterhorn. ill. 18°. 45c.......... *Routledge.*
Lost child. 18°. 35c.......... *Carter.*
Lost child. 16°. 45c.......... *Cummiskey.*
Lost child. *See* Cousin Belle.
Lost child. *See* Little Willie's lib.
Lost child. Suter, W. E. 15c.......... *French.*
Lost child. *See* Yonge, C. M.
Lost children. *See* Arthur, T. S.
Lost children. Snyder, S. J. H. 40c...... *Ev. Assoc.*
Lost children; or, Harry and his torch; by author of "Widow's sixpence." 18°. 40c...... *Pres. Bd.*
Lost daughter. Hentz, C. L. $1.75; $1.50 .. *Peterson.*
Lost despatch. Friedrich, F. $1.25; 50c...... *Estes.*
Lost diamond: drama. 16°. pap., 15c....... *French.*
Lost father: story of a Phila. boy; by author of "Chinaman in California." 18°. 75c... *Pres. Bd.*
Lost for love. Braddon, M. E. 75c. .... *Harper.*
Lost forever. Townsend, L. T. $1.75....... *Lee & S.*
Lost (The) found. Giberne, A. 60c....... *Lothrop.*
Lost (The) found. Taylor, W. M. $1.50 .. *Scribner.*
Lost found; [also] Clara C.; or, usefulness attainable by all. 18°. 45c.; 55c.......... *Am. Bapt.*
Lost Genoveffa. 16°. 60c.; $1.......... *Sadlier.*

Lost geranium. 18°. 30c.; 35c.......... *Am. Bapt.*
Lost Gip. *See* Smith, Ha.
Lost Gospel. Sadler, M. F. $3.......... *Pott.*
Lost half crown. ('62.) New ed. 16°. '69. 30c... *Hoyt.*
Lost heir; or, truth and falsehood. ill. post 18°. 75c. *Scribner, W. & A.*
Lost heir of Linlithgow. Southworth, E. D. E. N. $1.75; $1.50.......... *Peterson.*
Lost heiress. Southworth, E. D. E. N. $1.75; $1.50. *Peterson.*
Lost husband: drama. 16°. pap., 15c....... *French.*
Lost in the fog. De Mille, J. $1.50......... *Lee & S.*
Lost in the jungle. Du Chaillu, P. B. $1.50 .. *Harper.*
Lost in London. *See* Phillips, W.
Lost jewel. Tucker, C. 75c.......... *Carter.*
Lost key. *See* Fry, S. M.
Lost Kittie. *See* Baker, *Mrs.* H. N. W.
Lost knife; or, the first theft. 18°. 18c.... *Am. S. S.*
Lost lamb. Alden, J. 50c.......... *Lee & S.*
Lost legends of the nursery songs. Clark, M. S. $2. *Routledge.*
Lost light. 18°. 70c.......... *Pres. Bd.*
Lost lilies. Marshall, E. 50c.......... (?) *Martien.*
— *See also* Silvertone lib.
Lost love. Ogle, A. $1 .... *Loring.*
Lost love. Oliphant, M. O. W. $1.75; $1.50 .. *Peterson.*
Lost manuscript. Freytag, G. 75c......... *Appleton.*
Lost model. Hooper, H. $1.75 .... *Lippincott.*
Lost name. Le Fanu, J. S. 50c.......... *Harper.*
Lost note. 18°. 60c. .... *Cong. Pub.*
Lost on the line. *See* Yonge, C. M.
Lost opportunities. 18°. 17c.; 22c........ *Am. Bapt.*
Lost palace. Hale, E. E. 25c..... *Lockwood, B. & Co.*
Lost pearl. M., E. A. 40c. .... *Randolph.*
Lost piece of silver; or, struggles into a better life. ('70.) New ed. ill. 16°. '73. $1.25 ..... *Hoyt.*
Lost principles. *See* Scott, J.
Lost purse; or, Bessie Bleak. ill. 16°. '74. 75c. *Lothrop.*
Lost rabbit. *See* Edmond Darley ser.
Lost ride. 18°. 18c.......... *Am. S. S.*
Lost rifle. Adams, H. C. 75c.; $1.25 .... *Routledge.*
Lost ruby. *See* Little Katie's little lib.
Lost sailor. 16°. '75. 50c. .... *Hoyt.*
Lost ship. Neale, W. J. 75c.......... *Harper.*
Lost ship. Townsend, T. 15c.......... *French.*
Lost Sir Massingberd. Payn, J. $1.75; $1.50. *Peterson.*
Lost son; tr. by Mrs. J. Sadlier. 16°. 75c.; $1.25. *Sadlier.*
Lost spectacles. 18°. 50c. .... *Carter.*
Lost tales of Miletus. *See* Bulwer-Lytton, *Sir* E. G. E. L.
Lost tar. Samuels, A. F. 50c.......... *Lee & S.*
Lost thimble. 18°. 45c.......... *Whittaker.*
Lost ticket; or, is your life insured? ('61.) New ed. ill. 32°. '64. 25c. .... *Hoyt.*
Lost tongue; [also] Four important words; [also] Begin now. 18°. 30c.......... *Am. S. S.*
Lost wife: drama. 16°. pap., 15c.......... *French.*
Lost will. Leavitt, A. J. 15c. .... *De Witt.*
Lost will. Porter, A. E. $1.15.......... *Hoyt.*
Lost will. Wood, E. P. 50c. .... *Peterson.*
Lost Willie. 18°. '69. 40c. .... *Randolph.*
Loterie (La) de Francfort. *See* Souvestre, E.
Loth, C. E: Practical stair-builder. pl. 4°. '67. $10. *Bicknell.*
Loth, Moritz. The forgiving kiss. 12°. $1.75 .. *Carleton.*
Lothair Disraeli, B. $2; $1.......... *Appleton.*

Lothrop, Amy (*pseud.*) *See* Warner, Anna B.
Lothrop, Ma. Memoir. (cop. '28.) New ed. ill. 18°. '36. 25c. .... *Am. Tr.*
— *Germ.* Leben. ill. 18°. '45. 25c. .... *Am. Tr.*
Lotos leaves; by A. Tennyson, J. Hay, Mark Twain, W. Collins and others; with ill. by Fredericks, Lumley and La Farge. 4°. '74. $6... *W. F. Gill.*
Lot's wife. McCord, W. J. 40c. .... *Pres. Bd.*
Lotta Schmidt. *See* Trollope, Ant.
Lottery ticket. Beasley, S. 15c. .... *French.*
Lottie. 32°. 20c.; 15c. .... *Dutton.*
Lottie and Jennie. *See* Aunty Ray's little lib.
Lottie Darling. Jeaffreson, J. C. 75c. .... *Harper.*
Lottie Eames; or, do your best and leave the rest. ill. 16°. $1.50 .... *Lee & S.*
Lottie Freeman's word; or, always be truthful. 16°. $1 .... (?) *Martien.*
Lottie Lane. Berry, M. E. $1.25 .... *Am. Tr.*
Lottie Lonsdale. Worboise, E. J. $1.75 .. *Routledge.*
Lottie Wilde's picnic. *See* Knight, *Mrs.* S. G.
Lottie's white frock, and other stories. ill. fp. 8°. 50c. *Cassell.*
Lotty's Christmas eve. *See* Austin, C.
Lotus eating. Curtis, G. W. $1.50 .... *Harper.*
Lotus flower. 18°. 40c. .... *Dutton.*
Louage, A. History of Greek and Roman classical literature. 12°. $1.25 .... *Appleton.*
— Moral philosophy: logic, metaphysics and ethics. 12°. '73. hf. roan, $1.50 .... *Kelly, P. & Co.*
Loubat, Alph. The American wine-dresser's guide. New ed., rev. 16°. $1.50 .... *Appleton.*
Loubat, J. F. Narrative of the mission to Russia, 1866, of G. V. Fox; from the journal and notes of L.; ed. by J. D. Champlin, jr. 8°. $5 .... *Appleton.*
Loud, Jer. The orphan boys; or, lights and shadows of humble life. 12°. $1.75 .... *J. E. Potter.*
Loudolphe, J. H. Book of scrolls and ornaments; for painters, etc. obl. 8°. '73. $1 .... *Haney.*
Loudon, J: Cls. Encyclopædia of agriculture. 6th ed. wood eng. 8°. (Lond.) '66. $12; hf. cf., $14.50. *Little, B. & Co.*
— Encyclopædia of cottage, farm and villa architecture and furniture. New ed., ed. by Mrs. Loudon. wood eng. 8°. (Lond.) '67. $15; hf. cf., $17.50. *Little, B. & Co.*
— Encyclopædia of gardening; with wood eng. by Branston. New ed., ed. by Mrs. Loudon. 8°. (Lond.) '65. $12; hf. cf., $14.50 .... *Little, B. & Co.*
— Encyclopædia of plants; ed. by Mrs. Loudon, assisted by G. Don and D. Wooster. woodcuts. 8°. (Lond.) '66. $15; hf. cf., $17.50. *Little, B. & Co.*
— Encyclopædia of trees and shrubs; abridg. from Arboretum et fruticetum. wood eng. 8°. (Lond.) '53. $12; hf. cf., $14.50 .... *Little, B. & Co.*
Loudon, *Mrs.* J. W. Entertaining naturalist; rev. by W. S. Dallas. ill. 12°. (Bohn.) $2.50. *Little, B. & Co.*
— *Same.* ill. 12°. (Bohn.) $2.75 .... *Lippincott.*
— *Same.* ill. 12°. (Bohn.) $2.80 ... *Scribner, W. & A.*
— Gardening for ladies, and companion to the flower-garden. 2d Am. from 3d Lond. ed.; ed. by A. J. Downing. 12°. $2 .... *Wiley.*
— Young naturalist; or, the travels of Agnes Merton and her mamma. ill. 16°. 50c. ..... *Routledge.*
— — *See also* Harry and Lucy lib.
Loughborough, J: N. Hope of the Gospel: what it is and when it will be consummated. 16°. '73. pap., 10c. .... *Sev. Day Adv.*
— The saints' inheritance; or, the earth made new. 16°. '73. pap., 10c. .... *Sev. Day Adv.*
Louie's last term at St. Mary's. Harris, M. C. $1.50. *Carleton.*
Louis IX., *of France* [*St.* Louis.] Life; tr. from the Fr. ('71.) 3d ed. 18°. '75. 40c. .... *Kenedy.*
— — *See also* Kenedy's juvenile lib.
Louis XI. Delavigne, C. 15c. .... *French.*
Louis XIV. and court of France in 17th cent. Pardoe J. 2 v. $4; $5 .... *Harper.*
Louis XV. and his times. Bungener, L. F. $1.50. *Lothrop.*
Louis Napoleon. Pitawall, E. $2.25; $1.75; $2.50. *F. W. Thomas.*
— *See also* Napoleon III.
Louis, J: Boston musical treasure: duets, trios, etc. 16°. '73. bds., 60c. .... *Ditson.*
— Easy and elementary course of singing. sq. 12°. '69. pap., 10c. .... *Ditson.*
— Manual of music lessons; for primary and secondary schools. 16°. '71. bds., 15c.; — for grammar schools. 12°. '72. bds., 30c. .... *Ditson.*
Louis de Blois. *See* Blosius, Louis de.
Louis and Frank. 18°. 75c. .... *Carter.*
Louis De Sacy. 18°. 30c.; 40c. .... *Am. Bapt.*
Louis Michaud; or, the little French Protestant. 18°. 50c.; 60c. .... *Am. Bapt.*
— *Same.* ('68.) New ed. ill. 16°. '71. 85c. ... *Hoyt.*
Louis Sinclair. Wise, D. $1.25 .... *H. A. Young.*
Louis' school days. *See* May, E. J.
Louisa, *Aunt* (*pseud.*) *See* Valentine, *Mrs.* R.
Louisa. Dumas, A. 50c. .... *U. P. James.*
Louisa; or, the virtuous villager: Cath. tale. 18°. 60c. *Cath. Pub.*
Louisa, my first born: a sketch for mothers. 18°. 35c. .... *Am. S. S.*
Louisa Murray. Baker, L. M. 50c. .... *Williamson.*
Louisa of Prussia. Mundt, C. M. $1.50; $1; $3.50. *Appleton.*
Louise de Lignerolles. Denaux, P., *and* Legouvé, E. 15c. .... *French.*
Louise Field, od. d. Werk e. jungen Lebens. 18°. 25c. *Ev. Assoc.*
Louise la Vallière. *See* Dumas, A.
Louise of France, daughter of Louis XV. [Life.] 12°. '73. $2 .... *Kelly, P. & Co.*
Louise's mistake. Foster, I. H. 50c. .... *H. A. Young.*
Louisiana. Civil code, 1874; [ed.] by A. Voorhies. 8°. '75 .... *State.*
— Supreme Court reports, 1809–'30; by F. X. Martin. 20 v. in 10. 8° .... *State.*
— — *Same;* condensed. 20 v. in 4. 8° .... *State.*
— *Same.* 1830–'40; by B. W. Miller and T. Curry. 19 v. 8° .... *State.*
— — *Same;* with ref. by T. G. Morgan. 19 v. in 10. 8°. '54 .... *State.*
— *Same.* 1841–'46; by M. M. Robinson. 12 v. 8° .. *State.*
— *Same.* Annual reports, 1846–'74. 26 v. 8° .. *State.*
Cont.: 1–4 (1846–'49), by M. M. Robinson. — 5, 6 (1850–'51), by W. M. King. — 7–11 (1852–'56), by W. M. Randolph. — 12–15 (1857–'60), by A. N. Ogden. — 16–18 (1861–'66), by S. F. Glenn. — 19–24 (1867–'72), by J. Hawkins. — 25, 26 (1873–4), by C. Gayarre.
— — Digest. *See* Hennen, W. D.; — Walker, S. R. *and* C. L.
Louisiana geological survey. Preliminary report of a geol. reconnoissance of L.; by E. W. Hilgard. 8°. '69 .... *State.*
Louisiana swamp doctor; by author of "Cupping on the sternum." ill. 12°. pap., 75c. .... *Peterson.*
Louisville debate. Wilkes, L. B., *and* Ditzler, J. $3. *Tr. P. & P. Co.*
Loutron; or, water baptism. Fuller, S. 20c. *Claremont.*
Louvigny, Bernier de. Interior Christian; with supplement. 18°. 60c. .... *Cath. Pub.*
Love, —. Difference between Cumberland Presbyterian and other denominations. 25c. (?) *Cumberland.*

Love, J. D. Copy-book primer: elements of reading and writing combined. 12°. 30c. ...... *Barnes.*
Love, T: Art of dyeing, cleaning, scouring and finishing. ('60; cop. '68.) 2d ed. 8°. '69. $5 .. *Baird.*
Love. *See* Herbert, M. E. (*Lady*).
Love. Knowles, J. S. 15c. .... *French.*
Love. Michelet, J. $1.50 .... *Carleton.*
Love: burlesque. 16°. pap., 15c. .... *Happy.*
Love afloat. Sheppard, F. H. $1.50; $1 ... *Sheldon.*
Love after marriage. Hentz, C. L. $1.75; $1.50. *Peterson.*
Love-a-la-mode. Macklin, C. 15c. .... *French.*
Love and charity: drama. 16°. pap., 15c. ... *French.*
Love and duty. Buckland, A. J. 75c. .... *Cassell.*
Love and duty. Hubbach, J. $1.75; $1.50 .. *Peterson.*
Love and fear. 32°. 20c.; 15c. .... *Dutton.*
Love and fortune. Planché, J. R. 15c. ...... *French.*
Love and honor. Davenant, *Sir* W. 15c. .... *French.*
Love and hunger. Morton, J. M. 15c. ...... *French.*
Love and intrigue. *See* Schiller, J. F. v.
Love and its hidden history. Randolph, P. B. $2.50. *Colby.*
Love and liberty. *See* Dumas, A.
Love and life in Norway. Bjornson, B. $1 .. *Cassell.*
Love and loyalty. Robson, W. J. 15c. ...... *French.*
Love and mesmerism. Smith, H. 75c. ...... *Harper.*
Love and money. *See* Howitt, Ma.
Love and money. Jones, J. B. $1.75; $1.50 .. *Peterson.*
Love and murder. Brougham, J. 15c. ...... *French.*
Love and parentage. Fowler, O. S. $1; 50c. .. *Wells.*
Love and rain: farce. 16°. pap., 15c. .... *French.*
Love and valor. Hood, T. $1.25; 75c. .... *Estes.*
Love at first sight. Curling, H. 50c. ...... *Peterson.*
Love birds. 32°. 20c.; 15c. .... *Dutton.*
Love by lantern light. Carré, M., *and* Battu, L. 15c. *French.*
Love chase. Knowles, J. S. 15c. .... *French.*
Love enthroned. Steele, D. $1.50 ... *Meth. Bk. Conc.*
Love for love. Congreve, W. 15c. .... *French.*
Love in a cottage. Arthur, T. S. 50c. ..... *Peterson.*
Love in high life. Arthur, T. S. 50c. ...... *Peterson.*
Love in humble life. Payne, J. H. 15c. ..... *French.*
Love in livery. Wooler, J. P. 15c. .... *French.*
Love in marriage. Guizot, F. P. J. 85c. *Meth. Bk. Conc.*
Love in a maze. Ellet, E. F. 25c. .... *Beadle.*
Love in the 19th cent. Preston, H. W. $1.25 .. *Roberts.*
Love in '76. Bunce, O. 15c. .... *French.*
Love in Spain, and other poems. 16°. $1.50 .. *Lee & S.*
Love in a village. Bickerstaff, I. 15c. ...... *French.*
Love is blind: drama. 16°. pap., 15c. ...... *French.*
Love is enough. Morris, W. $1.25; $2 .... *Roberts.*
Love laughs at locksmiths. Colman, G., *jr.* 15c. *French.*
Love, law and physics. Kenney, J. 15c. .... *French.*
Love makes a man. Cibber, C. 15c. .... *French.*
Love-making secrets. 12°. pap., 20c. .... *Hurst.*
Love match. *See* Cockton, H:
Love me, leave me not. Egan, P. 50c. ..... *De Witt.*
Love me little love me long. *See* Reade, C:
Love not: drama. 16°. pap., 15c. .... *French.*
Love of a bonnet. Baker, G. M. 15c. ...... *Lee & S.*
Love of Christ. Liguori, *St.* A. M. de. 50c. .. *Strong.*
Love of country; tr. from the Fr. ill. 16°. $1.25 .. *O'Shea.*
Love of dress. 18°. 35c. .... *Am. S. S.*
Love of Jesus. *See* Gilbert, D.
Love of Mary. Roberto, D. 50c. .... *Strong.*
Love of a prince. Gayler, C. 15c. .... *French.*
Love of religious perfection. Bayma, J. 75c.; $1.25. *Murphy.*
Love one another. *See* Children's prize stories.
Love or marriage? Black, W. 50c. .... *Harper.*
Love revealed. Bowen, G. $1.50 .... *Pres. Bd.*
Love scrapes of Fudge Fumble; by author of "Arkansaw doctor." 12°. pap., 75c. .... *Peterson.*
Love spell: opera. 16°. pap., 15c. .... *French.*
Love test: comedietta. 16°. pap., 15c. ...... *French.*
Love that lived. Eiloart, C. J. 50c. .... *Harper.*
Love thy neighbor. *See* Head and heart ser.
Love to Christ. Vincent, T. 30c. .... *Pres. Bd.*
Love to the end. Knox, C. E. 60c. .... *Pres. Bd.*
Love to enemies; or, good for evil. 18°. 55c.; 65c. *Am. Bapt.*
Love token for children. Sedgwick, C. M. 75c. *Harper.*
Love wins: comedy. 16°. pap., 15c. .... *French.*
Lovechild, Lucy. New juvenile lib. 12 v. ill. 16°. $3.75; pap., $1.50 .... *T. Bliss.*
Cont.: Easy stories for children. — Indian chief and the little white boy. — Archy Sommerville, etc. — Charley's pets. — Kind father, etc. — Charley's museum. — Little Pilgrim's progress, 2 v. — Little Æsop. — Little Robinson Crusoe. — Country sights for little folks. — City sights for little folks.
Lovel, the widower. *See* Thackeray, W: M.
Lovell, Alb. A. Worcester [Mass.] in the revolution: acts of the town, 1765–1783; with app. ill. 8°. '76. $1.50 .... (?) *A. A. Lovell.*
Lovell, C. S. Manual of Methodism. ('58.) New ed. 12°. '60. $1 .... *Pounsford.*
Lovell, G: Life. ill. 18°. '51. 25c. .... *Am. Tr.*
Lovell, G: W. Look before you leap: comedy. 16°. pap., 15c. .... *French.*
— Provost of Bruges: tragedy. 16°. pap., 15c. .. *French.*
— Wife's secret: play. 16°. pap., 15c. .. *French; Lee & S.*
Lovell, J: Love's sacrifice: play. 16°. pap., 15c. *French.*
Lovell, J: E. New school dialogues. New ed., rev. and enl. 12°. '71. $1.40 .... *Collins & Bro.*
— Progressive ser. of readers. 5 v. '55–'57. *net* .. *Peck.*
Cont.: No. 1. 16°, 28c. — 2. 16°, 40c. — 3. 12°, 75c. — 4. 12°, 85c. — 5. 12°, $1.15.
— United States speaker. New ed., rev. 12°. '75. $1.40 .... *Collins & Bro.*
— Young speaker: introduction to "United States speaker." 12°. '45. *net*, 85c. .... *Peck.*
Lovell, Mar. Ingomar, the barbarian: play. 16°. pap., 15c. .... *French.*
Lovels of Arden. Braddon, M. E. 75c. .... *Harper.*
Lover, S: Works. 5 v. 12°. ea., $1.50; per set, hf. mor., $10; hf. cf., $12 .... *Sadlier.*
Cont.: Handy Andy. — Rory O'More. — Legends and stories of Ireland. — Treasure trove; or, he would be a gentleman, *ea.*, 8°, pap., 75c. — Songs and ballads.
— Novels. 4 v. 12°. hf. roxb., $5 .... *Routledge.*
Cont.: Handy Andy. — Rory O'More. — Irish stories and legends. — He would be a gentleman.
— *Same.* 4 v. 8°. ea., pap., 75c. .... (?) *Am. News.*
Cont.: Handy Andy. — Rory O'More. — Treasure trove. — White horse of the Peppers.
— *Same.* 5 v. 8°. ea., pap., 75c. .... *Dick & F.*
Cont.: Handy Andy. — Legends and stories of Ireland. — Rory O'More. — Tom Crosbie. — Treasure trove.
— [Plays.] 4 v. 16°. ea., pap., 15c. .... *French.*
Cont.: Happy man: farce. — Mac Carthy. — Rory O'More. — White horse of the Peppers.
— Poems; ed. by R. A. Willmott; with biog., etc. (British poets.) ill. 12°. $2.25; hf. cf., $3.50; mor., $5 .... *Routledge.*
— Poetical works. (Household ser.) ill. 16°. $1.50; mor., $3 .... *Lee & S.*
— *Same.* (Presentation poets.) por. and ill. 16°. $1.75 .... *Routledge.*
— Father Roach. *See* Le Fanu, J. S., Shamus O'Brien.
— Handy Andy. ill. 8°. $3. 12°. $1.25; bds., $1. *Routledge.*

Lover, S: *continued.*
— He would be a gentleman; or, treasure trove. ill. 8°. $3 .... *Routledge.*
— Rory O'More. 12°. $1.25; bds., $1 .... *Routledge.*
— Selection from papers and correspondence. *See* Bernard, B., Life of L.
Lover (The). *See* Addison, Jos.
Lover by proxy. Boucicault, D. 15c........ *French.*
Lovering, Jos. Address before the Am. Assoc. for the Advancement of Sci., Aug., 1873. 8°. pap., 25c. *Am.Assoc.Adv.Sci.*
Lover's companion. sq. 18°. '74. pap., 25c. (?) *F.M.Reed.*
Lover's diary. Cary, A. $3 .... * *Osgood.*
Lover's dictionary: poetical treasury. post 8°. $3.50; hf. cf., $5 .... *Harper.*
Lover's revenge. Thigpen, J. $1 .... *Burke.*
Lover's stratagem. Carlen, E. F. 50c....... *Harper.*
Lover's trials. Denison, M. A. $1.75; $1.50 .. *Peterson.*
Lovers of Gudrun. Morris, W. $1 .... *Roberts.*
Lovers' letter-writer. 16°. 20c. .... *Routledge.*
Lovers' letter-writer. 32°. 50c. .... *Fisher.*
Lovers' own lib. 3 v. 12°. ea., pap., 20c..... *Hurst.*
Cont.: Love making secrets. — Confidential advice to a lover. — Bashfulness cured.
Lovers' quarrels. King, T. 15c. .... *French.*
Lovers' telegraph. 32°. pap., 15c. .... *Fisher.*
Lovers' vows. Kotzebue, A. F. F. v. 15c.... *French.*
Love's labor. Eldridge, A. 75c. .... *Pres. Bd.*
Love's labor won. Southworth, E. D. E. N. $1.75; $1.50 .... *Peterson.*
Love's labour's lost. *See* Shakespeare, W.
Love's labyrinth. Emden, W. S. 15c. ...... *French.*
Love's lesson. 18°. 75c. .... *Dutton.*
Love's martyr. Buckingham, L. 15c....... *French.*
Love's meine. Ruskin, J. $1 .... *Wiley.*
Love's sacrifice. Lovell, J. 15c. .... *French.*
Love's telegraph: comedy. 16°. pap., 15c.... *French.*
Love's victory. Farjeon, B. L. 25c........ *Harper.*
Loves and adventures. Hogg, J. $1.50 .. *World Pub.*
Loves of the early poets. Stoddard, R. H. $5; $10. *Lippincott.*
Loves of famous men. Fitzgerald, P. 75c.; 50c. *J.M.Stoddart.*
Loves of the harem. Reynolds, G. W. M. 75c. *Peterson.*
Loves of Jonathan and Virginia. Boswell. 50c. *Lippincott.*
Loves of a lawyer. Shuman, A. $1 .... *Keen.*
Loves of little Bo-Peep and little Boy-Blue: pastoral drama. 16°. pap., 15c. .... *Happy.*
Loves of Lord Bateman and fair Sophia: drama. 16°. pap., 15c. .... *French.*
Loves of Paris. Sue, E. 75c. .... *Dick & F.*
Loves of the poets. Jameson, A. $1.50 ..... *Osgood.*
Loves of Undine and Sintram. *See* La Motte Fouqué, F.
Lovett, Rob. Sermons on several important subjects connected with the Gospel of Christ. 8°. pap., 50c. .... *N. Y. Ref. Ch. Bd.*
Loving cup. Halliday, A. 15c. .... *French.*
Loving heart and helping hand lib. 5 v. 16°. '72. $5.50 .... *Meth. Bk. Conc.*
Cont.: Nettie and her friends. — Philip Moore, the sculptor. — Orphan's story. — Carrie Williams and her scholars. — Story of a moss rose.
Loving Jesus early. 18°. 55c. .... *Pres. Bd.*
Loving kindness. Russell, S. 50c. .... *Dutton.*
Loving kindness; or, the Ashdown flower show. 18°. 45c. .... *Am. S. S.*
Loving words. Monod, A. 40c. .... *Pres. Bd.*
Loving words; or, how to make others happy. ('60.) New ed. 16°. '75. $1 .... *Hoyt.*

Loving words and loving deeds. *See* Golden stories.
Low, C. R. Adventures of Joshua Hawsepipe: a ta of sea and land. ill. 16°. 75c. .... *Routledg*
— Captain Cook's voyages. 16°. '75. $1.25; $1; 75 —ill. 12°. $1.50 .... *Routledg*
— Great battles of the British navy. ill. 12°. '72. $ *Routledg*
— Letter of marque, and other tales. ill. 12°. '72. $ *Routledg*
— Man-o'-war's bell: tale of the sea. 12°. '74. $1.7 *Routledg*
— Tales of naval adventure. ill. 12°. '71. $1 .. *Routledg*
— Tales of old ocean. 12°. $1.50 .... *Claxto*
— *Same.* 16°. $1.75 .... *Scribner, W. &*
Low, G. P., *jr.* Statistics of cost and work of pum ing engines. *See* Hamilton, S., Fabrication, et
Low, J. Instructor for the dulcimer. 8°. '58. pa 50c. .... *Ditso*
Low life deeps. Greenwood, J. $3 .. *Scribner, W. &*
Lowe, *Sir* Hudson. History of the captivity of Nap leon at St. Helena; from the letters and journa of L., by W. Forsyth. 2 v. por. and map. 1 $3.50 .... *Harpe*
Lowe, W. H. *See* Bible, Psalms.
Lowell, *Mrs.* A. C. Posies for children. sq. 16°. '7 75c. .... *Robert*
Lowell, Ja. Russell. Poems. 2 v. por. 16°. $3. (Blue and gold ed.) 2 v. 32°. $2.50; hf. c $5; mor., $6. — (Cabinet ed.) 2 v. 16°. $ hf. cf., $6; mor., $8. — (Diamond ed.) 18°. '6 $1; hf. cf., $2.25; mor., $3. — (Red.line ed.) i sm. 4°. '70. $3.50; hf. cf., $5; mor., $7 .. *Osgoo*
— Among my books. 2 ser. 12°. '70–'76. ea., $ hf cf., $4; mor., $5. .... *Osgoo*
— Biglow papers. 2 ser. 16°. ea., $1.50 ..... *Osgoo*
— Cathedral (The). 16°. '69. $1.25 .... *Osgoo*
— Courtin' (The); ill. in silhouette by W. Homer. 4 '73. $3; mor., $7 .... *Osgoo*
— Fable for critics. 16°. 75c. .... *Osgoo*
— Fireside travels. 16°. '64. $1.50 .... *Osgoo*
— My study windows. ('71.) 8th ed. 12°. $2; hf. c $4; mor., $5 .... *Osgoo*
— Under the willows, and other poems. 16°. '68. $1.5 hf. cf., $3.50; mor., $4.50 .... *Osgoo*
— Vision of Sir Launfal. ('61.) 8th ed. 16°. 75c. (Vest pocket ser.) ill. 32°. 50c. — ill. sm. 4 $3; mor., $5.50 .... *Osgoo*
— *See also* Keats, J: Poems; — Laurel leaves; Winter poems.
Lowell, J: *See* United States, Dist. and Circ. Cou reports.
Lowell, Rob. T. S. Antony Brade. [Fiction.] 16 '74. $1.75 .... *Robert*
— Poems. 16°. '59. $1.25 .... *Dutto*
— Story of the new priest in Conception Bay. New e ill. 16°. '59. $1.75 .... *Dutto*
Löwenritter (Die). 12°. pap., 20c. .... *Radd*
Lowenstein. Emil. Trial for the murder of J. I Weston, Aug. 5, 1873; [by N. C. Moak]. 8 '74. pap., $2; hf. bd., $2.50 .... *Goul*
Löwenthal, J. Chess Congress of 1862: collection games played and selection of problems; wi account of proceedings and memoir of the Bri Chess Assoc. by G. W. Medley. 12°. (Bohn. $2.75 .... *Lippincot*
— *Same.* 12°. (Bohn.) $2.80 ..... *Scribner, W. & A*
Lowly ways. B., F. E. $1 .... *Claxto*
Lowndes, R: Our vows: baptism, confirmation an communion. 18°. 30c.–$3 .... *Dutto*
Lowndes, W: T: Bibliographer's manual of En literature: account of rare, etc., books pub. in rel. to Gt. Brit. and Ireland. New ed., rev. b H. G. Bohn. 11 pts. 12°. (Bohn.) '57–'64. 1–1 ea., $1.25; 11, $1.75; — in 4 v., hf. mor., $15. *Little, B. & C*

Lowndes, W: T: *continued.*
— *Same.* 11 pts. 12°. (Bohn.) 1–10, ea., $1.40; 11, $2; — in 4 v., hf. mor., $16.80.. *Scribner, W. & A.*
— *Same.* 4 v. 12°. (Bohn.) ea., hf. mor., $4.25. *Lippincott.*
Lowrey, A. Positive theology. 12°. $1.25. *Cin. Meth. Bk. Conc.*
Lowrie, J: M. [Works.] 8 v. 12°........*Pres. Bd.*
Cont.: Adam and his times, $1. — Esther and her times, $1. — Hebrew lawgivers, 2 v., $2.50. — Life of David, $1.50. — Prophet Elisha; with memoir by W. D. Howard, $1.15. — Translated prophet, $1.25. — Week with Jesus, $1.50.
Lowrie, Wa. M. Memoir; ed. by his father. 12°. $1.25..............................*Pres. Bd.*
Lowry, Rob. Question book: Christ in promise and prophecy. 18°. '70. bds., 15c..........*Tibbals.*
— *See also* Vail, S. J., *and* Lowry, R.
— *and* Doane, W: H. Brightest and best: coll. of songs. obl. 16°. '75. 50c.; 75c.; bds., 35c.....*Biglow.*
— — Gold and diadem: [compr.] "Pure gold" and "Royal diadem." obl. 16°. '73. bds., 65c. *Biglow.*
— — Pure gold for the Sunday school. [Sing. book.] obl. 16°. '71. 75c.; bds., 35c..........*Biglow.*
— — Royal diadem for the Sunday school. [Sing. book.] obl. 16°. '73. 75c.; bds., 35c...*Biglow.*
— — Temple anthems; for service of the sanctuary. obl. 4°. '73. bds., $1.25...............*Biglow.*
— — Tidal wave: temperance songs, etc. obl. 4°. '74. bds., 30c..............................*Biglow.*
— — *Same;* [also] The revellers, by J. H. Hewitt. obl. 4°. '74. bds., 50c.................*Biglow.*
— *and* Sherwin, W. F., *and* Allen, C. G. Bright jewels for the Sunday school: Sunday school songs. obl. 16°. '69. bds., 35c.........*Biglow.*
Lowry, S. A. Earnest search for truth; letters from a son to his father. 18°. 50c............*Pres. Bd.*
Lowthorp, F. C. Cast iron for compressive members of iron bridges. *See* Craven, A. W., Address, etc.
Loyal Charlie Bentham. 18°. 35c.........*Routledge.*
— *See also* Moss wreath lib.
Loyal unto death. 12°. $1.75.............*Carleton.*
Loyd, J. F. Wine as a beverage. 16°. 40c. *Cin. Meth. Bk. Conc.*
Loyd, *Miss* Ma. A. Child's life of Luther. ill. 18°. '68. 35c...............................*Am. Tr.*
Loyola, *St.* Ign. de. Manresa; or, spiritual exercises of St. Ignatius [Loyola]. 3d ed. 12°. '73. $1.50............................*Cath. Pub.*
Loyola and jesuitism. Taylor, I. 12°. $1.25..*Carter.*
Loyson, C: *See* Hyacinthe, *Father.*
Lubbock, *Sir* J: On British wild flowers; considered in rel. to insects. ill. 12°. '75. $1.50..*Macmillan.*
— Origin and metamorphoses of insects. 2d ed. ill. 12°. '74. $1..........................*Macmillan.*
— Origin of civilization, and the primitive condition of man. 12°. $2.........................*Appleton.*
— Pre-historic times, as ill. by anc. remains, and manners and customs of mod. savages. ill. 8°. $5; hf. cf., $10...............................*Appleton.*
Lübke, W: History of art; tr. by F. E. Bunnett. 2 v. 415 ill. imp. 8°. $18; mor., $25....*Lippincott.*
— History of sculpture; tr. 2 v. 377 ill. imp. 8°. $18; mor., $25..........................*Lippincott.*
— *See also* Monuments of art.
Lucanus, Mcs. Annæus. Pharsalia; tr., with notes, by H. T. Riley. 12°. (Bohn.) $1.75..*Little, B. & Co.*
— *Same.* 12°. (Bohn.) $2..*Lippincott; Scribner, W. & A.*
Lucas, D. R. Apostolic hymns and songs for the S.-school, etc. 12°. 30c....................*Chase.*
— Conversion of Paul Darst; or, the conflict of love and duty. 12°. '76. $1.25............*Cen. Bk.*
Lucas, Dan. Bedinger. Wreath of elgantine, and other poems. ill. 12°. '68. $1.50..*Kelly, P. & Co.*
Lucas, Jos. R. *See* Ray, D. B., *and* Lucas, J. R.
Lucas, W. J. Home of one's own: farce. 16°. pap., 15c...................................*French.*

Lucas, W. J., *continued.*
— Man with iron mask: drama. 16°. pap., 15c...*French.*
— White farm: melodrama. 16°. pap., 15c...*French.*
Lucas Garcia, and other stories. 8°. '76. $1.50. *Cath. Pub.*
Lucchesi, F. Vocal exercises; for singing classes. f°. '54. pap., 60c.........................*Ditson.*
Luce, Enos T. Maine probate practice. 8°. '72. shp., $2.50.................................*Dresser.*
Luce, S. B. Seamanship, with designs; for U. S. Naval Acad. 5th ed., rev. ill. cr. 8°. '73. hf. roan, $7.50.....................*Van Nostrand.*
Lucia: her problem. Douglas, A. M. $1.50..*Sheldon.*
Lucia di Lammermoor. *See* Donizetti, G.
Lucia di Lammermoor: burlesque. Byron, H. J. 15c. *French.*
Lucia di Lammermoor: opera. 16°. pap., 15c...*French.*
Lucian. [Lucianus *Samosatensis.*] [Outlined and expl.] by W. L. Collins. (Anc. classics for Eng. readers.) 16°. $1....*Lippincott; Little, B. & Co.*
Lucie. Riodu, A. 75c...........................*Holt.*
Lucien Guglieri. Lee, M. B. 60c. ...*Meth. Bk. Conc.*
Lucile. *See* Bulwer-Lytton, E. R.
Lucile; ou, la lecture de la Bible. *See* Monod, A.
Lucilius, Caius. *See* Juvenal, D. J., Persius, F. A., Sulpicia, *and* Lucilius, C.
Lucilla; or, reading the Bible. *See* Monod, A.
Lucille. Bernard, W. B. 15c. ....*French.*
Lucille; or, the young flower maker; tr. by A. T. Sadlier. 18°. 50c.; 75c...............*Sadlier.*
Lucinda's wedding: Ethiop. drama. 16°. pap., 15c. *Happy.*
Luck and pluck ser. *See* Alger, H., *jr.*
Luck is everything. *See* Maxwell, W: H.
Luck of Alden Farm. Mudge, Z. A. $1.50...*Lothrop.*
Luck of Ladysmede. 8°. pap., 50c.......*Littell & G.*
Luck of Roaring Camp. Harte, B. $1.50; $3; $8. *Osgood.*
Luckey, S: Ethic hymns and Script. lessons for children. 18°. '68. 45c..............*Darrow.*
— Lord's supper. 18°. '59. 60c. ......*Meth. Bk. Conc.*
Luckock, H. M. The tables of stone: sermons. fp. 8°. '68. $1.25 ....*Macmillan.*
Lucky disappointment. Marryat, F. 35c....*Loring.*
Lucky escape. Cheltnam, C. S. 15c. ....*French.*
Lucky hit. Stirling, E. 15c...............*French.*
Lucky horseshoe. Parry, T. 15c. ....*French.*
Lucky job. White, C. 15c.................*De Witt.*
Lucky number: Ethiop. drama. 16°. pap., 15c. *French.*
Lucky penny. Hall, A. M. $1 ....*Routledge.*
Lucky penny lib. 4 v. ill. 16°. $4........*Routledge.*
Cont.: Lucky penny. — Young artists. — Sir Wilfred's seven flights. — Heroes of the workshop.
Lucky sixpence: farce. 16°. pap., 15c. .....*French.*
Lucky stars: burletta. 16°. pap., 15c. ......*French.*
Lucky Tym. ill. cr. 16°. 25c. ....*Cassell.*
Lucretia. *See* Bulwer-Lytton, *Sir* E. G. E. L.
Lucretia and her garden. *See* Maple grove stories.
Lucretia Borgia: burlesque. Byron, H. J. 15c. *French.*
Lucretius Carus, Tit. De rerum natura libri sex; recog. H. A. I. Munroe. 18°. 75c............*Harper.*
— *Eng.* On the nature of things; tr. by J. S. Watson; with metrical version by J. M. Good. 12°. (Bohn.) $1.75................*Little, B. & Co.*
— — *Same.* 12°. (Bohn.) $2. *Lippincott; Scribner, W. & A.*
Lucrezia Borgia. *See* Donizetti, G.
Lucrezia Borgia: burlesque. Buckingham, L. 15c. *French.*
Lucy, the light bearer. *See* Sargent, G. E.

Lucy and Arthur; or, the little cousins. ill. post 18°. 75c. *Scribner, W. & A.*
Lucy and Bell, and how they overcame. ill. 18°. 35c. *Bost. Am. Tr.*
— *See also* Aunty Ray's little lib.
Lucy and her dhaye. 18°. 30c. *Am. S. S.*
Lucy and her friends. 18°. 50c. *Am. S. S.*
Lucy Arden. *See* Grant, Ja.
Lucy at home. O'Brien, H. 35c. *Pres. Bd.*
Lucy at play. *See* Abbott, Jac.
Lucy books. *See* Abbott, Jac.
Lucy Clifton. Eldridge, A. 75c. *Pres. Bd.*
Lucy Crofton. Oliphant, M. O. W. $1.50 ... *Harper.*
Lucy Dunlevy. Egliseau, S. S. 50c. *Pres. Bd.*
Lucy Elton; or, home and school. ill. 16°. 50c. *Routledge.*
Lucy Forrester's triumphs. McKeever, H. B. $1. *Porter.*
Lucy Howard's journal. Sigourney, L. H. $1.25. *Harper.*
Lucy Jackson. ill. 18°. '53. 35c. *Am. Tr.*
Lucy Lee. Fuller, J. G. 90c. *Dodd.*
Lucy Maria. Diaz, A. M. $1.50. *Osgood.*
Lucy Mason; or, the peacock butterfly. ('67.) New ed. ill. 16°. '72. 75c. *Hoyt.*
Lucy Maynard; or, judge not by appearances. 18°. 40c. *Cong. Pub.*
Lucy of the west. ill. 18°. '64. 35c. *Am. Tr.*
Lucy on the mountains; — on the sea shore. *See* Abbott, Jac.
Lucy Randolph. Bates, S. B. $1.15. *Hoyt.*
Lucy Raymond. Machar, A. M. $1.25 ... *Am. Tr.*
Lucy Sandford. Arthur, T. S. 50c. *Peterson.*
Lucy Seymour. 18°. 35c.; 45c. *Am. Bapt.*
Lucy Thornton. 8°. pap., 25c. *De Witt.*
Lucy Vernon. ill. 16°. 25c. *Routledge.*
Lucy West; or, the orphans of Highcliffe. ill. 12°. $1.25. *Scribner, W. & A.*
Lucy Woodville's temptation. ill. 16°. '70. $1.25. *Am. Tr.*
Lucy's conversations. *See* Abbott, Jac.
Lucy's fair. *See* Johnson, M. L.
Lucy's life story; by author of "Lonely Lily." ill. 16°. '75. 75c. *Dodd.*
Lucy's love lesson: comedietta. 16°. pap., 15c. *Happy.*
Lucy's pet. Baker, S. S. 30c. *Am. Tr.*
Lucy's stories; — studies. *See* Abbott, Jac.
Lucy's two lives. McKeever, H. B. $1.50 .. (?) *Martien.*
Lucy's visit. *See* Abbott, Jac.
Lucy's way out of the dark. 16°. $1.25 .... *Cong. Pub.*
Ludden, T. *See* Maine, Sup. Court reports.
Ludden, W. Pronouncing dictionary of musical terms. 8°. $1.50; bds., $1.25. *Peters.*
— Sacred lyrics. 8°. 80c.; cf., $4. *Church.*
— School for the voice. 4°. bds., $3.50 ... *Peters.*
— School lyrics. 8°. 80c.; bds., 50c. *Church.*
— Thorough base. 8°. $1.50. *Church.*
Ludlam, R. Lectures, clinical and didactic, on the diseases of women. 8°. '73. $7; leath., $7.50. (?) *Halsey.*
Ludlow, Anna D. Madge Graves. ill. 16°. $1. *Bost. Am. Tr.*
Ludlow, Fitz Hugh. Heart of the continent: record of travel across the plains and in Oregon. ill. 8°. '70. $3.75. — por. 8°. $2.50 ... *Hurd & H.*
— Little brother, and other stories. 12°. $1.50 .. *Lee & S.*
Ludlow, Helen W. *See* Armstrong, *Mrs.* M. F., *and* Ludlow, H. W.
Ludlow, J. L. Manual of examinations upon anatomy, physiology, surgery, etc.; with medical formulary. ill. roy. 12°. $3.25; leath., $3.75. *Lea.*
Ludlow, J. M. *See* Illustrated book of pigeons; — Wright, L., Illustrated book of poultry.
Ludlow, Ja. A. Our creeds. [Sermon.] 16°. pap., 10c. *N. Y. Ref. Ch. Bd.*
Ludlow, J: Malcolm. Sketch of hist. of U. S., [1776–1861]; [also] Struggle for Kansas, by T. Hughes. cr. 8°. '62. $2.50. *Macmillan.*
— War of Am. independence. 16°. $1. *Estes.*
— Woman's work in the church. 16°. $2 .. *Routledge.*
— *and* Jones, Lloyd. Progress of the working classes, 1832–1867. cr. 8°. bds., $1. *Routledge.*
Ludlow, Park (*pseud.*) *See* Brown, Theron.
Ludlow, W: Report of a reconnoissance of the Black Hills. *See* United States, *Corps of Eng.*
Ludovic and Gertrude. Conscience, H. $1; $1.25. *Murphy.*
Ludwig, der Auswanderer. Schmid, C. v. 20c. *Morwitz.*
Luebbers, H. L. Manufacture of coke from Illinois coal. 8°. pap., 25c. *Am. Soc. of C. E.*
Lugarto, the mulatto. O'Brien, C. 15c. ... *French.*
Luisa Miller. *See* Verdi, G.
Luke, the labourer. Buckstone, J. B. 15c. .. *French.*
Luke, the lurker. 8°. pap., 25c. *De Witt.*
Luke Darrell, the Chicago news boy. 16°. '65. $1.50. *Graves.*
Luke Sharp. 18°. 75c. *Dutton.*
Lüken, D. H. Deutsche Sprachschüler (Der). 16°. '73. bds., 45c.; — in 2 pts., 1, 20c.; 2, 30c. *Cen. Pub.*
— Fibel für den ersten Schreib- und Leseunterricht. sq. 16°. '73. bds., 30c. *Cen. Pub.*
Lullabies. *See* Lullaby ser.
Lullabies, ditties and tales. Sproat, N. 60c. .. *Am. Tr.*
Lullaby: heart songs for baby and mamma; set to music. 4°. '70. $1.50. *Randolph.*
Lullaby ser. 4 v. 8°. ea., 50c.; pap., 25c. .. *Nelson.*
Cont.: Lullabies. — Nursery play-hour. — Pretty book for good child. — My new book.
Lulu. Walworth, M. T. $1.75. *Carleton.*
Lulu Reed's pupil. Baker, H. N. W. $1 .. *H. A. Young.*
Lum, Dyer D. Early social life of man: man in geology; or, the antiquity, art and social life of prehistoric man. ('72.) 2d ed. 12°. '74. pap., 25c. *Colby.*
— The spiritual delusion: its methods, teachings and effects: philosophy and phenomena crit. examined. 12°. $1.50. *Lippincott.*
Lumbey, E. *See* England, Law reports.
Luminary. Powell, J. P. $2. *Chase.*
Luminous unity. Miller, M. R. $1.50 ... *Lippincott.*
Lumpaci Vagabundus. 12°. pap., 15c. *Radde.*
— *See also* Böse Geist (Der); — Pariser Taugenichts.
Lunarius: a visitor from the moon. 18°. '69. 35c. *Nat. Temp.*
Lunatic (The), and his keepers, and other narratives. ('61.) New ed. ill. 32°. '64. 25c. *Hoyt.*
Lund, T: *See* Snowball, J. C., *and* Lund, T:
Lundie, R. H. The crown without the conflict. 32°. 25c. *Carter.*
Lundy, J. P. Monumental Christianity; or, the art and symbolism of the primitive church as witnesses and teachers of the one catholic faith and practice. ill. 4°. '76. $7.50; hf. mor., $10; mor., $15. *Bouton.*
Lunettes, H: American gentleman's guide to politeness and fashion: familiar letters to his nephews. ('63.) New ed. 12°. '76. $1.50 ... *Claxton.*
Lunn, Jos. [Plays.] 9 v. 16°. ea., pap., 15c. .. *French.*
Cont.: False and constant: comedy. — Family jars: farce. — Fish out of water: farce. — Hide and seek: opera. — Lofty projects: farce. — Management: farce. — Roses and thorns: comedy. — Sharp practice. — Shepherd of Derwent vale.
Lunt, G: Old New England traits. 16°. '73. $1.50. *Hurd & H.*

Lunt, W: P. Gleanings. 12°. '74. $1.50.....*Lunt.*
Luola (*pseud.*) Basket of chips for the little ones. 18°. 65c.....*Pres. Bd.*
— Willow Bend; or, school influence. 18°. 70c. *Pres. Bd.*
Lurline. Dalrymple, J. S. 15c.....*French.*
Lust und Lehre. [Tales.] 12°. '73. $1; $1.25. *Ev. Assoc.*
Lustigen Weiber (Die) v. Windsor. *See* Shakespeare, W.
Lute Falconer. ill. 16°. '70. $1.50.....*Lothrop.*
Lute of Zion (New). *See* Woodbury, I. B.
Luthardt, Cp. Ern. Apologetic lectures on the moral truths of Christianity; tr. from the Germ. cr. 8°. $3.....*Scribner, W. & A.*
— Apologetic lectures on the saving truths of Christianity; tr. cr. 8°. $3.....*Scribner, W. & A.*
— Creation and the fall: defence of the first 3 chapters of Genesis; tr. 8°. $6.....*Scribner, W. & A.*
— Grundwahrheiten des Christenthums. 12°. '74. $1.25. *Am. Tr.*
— St. John, the author of the fourth Gospel; tr. by C. R. Gregory. 8°. $3.75.....*Scribner, W. & A.*
— *and* Kalmis, —, *and* Bruckner, —. The church: its origin, its history, and its present position. cr. 8°. $2.50.....*Scribner, W. & A.*
Luther, Mt. Aeusserst merkwürdige Weissagungen. 12°. bds., 50c.....*Radde.*
— Auslegung d. Epistel Pauli an d. Galater; nebst Luther's Leben. 4th ed. 8°. $2.50.....*Schäfer.*
— *Eng.* Commentary on Galatians; with Tischer's Life of L. abridg., and sketch of Zwingli; [also] Essay on reformation by S. S. Schmucker. ill. 8°. *$2.50; $3; $3.50; mor., $4.50..*Quak. City.*
— Auslegung des Vaterunser. 18°. '45. 30c....*Am. Tr.*
— Biblisches Schatzkästchen. 18°. '53. 70c...*Am. Tr.*
— Epistle of St. Peter and St. Jude expl.; tr. by E. H. Gillette. 12°. '58. 75c.....*Randolph.*
— Grosse u. kleine Katechismus (Der). 16°. 20c. *Ludwig.*
— *Eng.* Smaller and larger catechism, with hist. introd.; [also] Augsburg confession and sel. of hymns and prayers; tr. and ed. by D. Henkel. ('12.) 2d ed., rev. 12°. '66. 75c.....*Henkel.*
— Kleine lutherische Katechismus (Der) f. Sonntagschulen. 32°. pap., 10c.....*Ludwig.*
— *Same;* bearb. v. W. J. Mann u. G. J. Krotel. 18°. 25c.....*Kohler.*
— *Same;* [with Bible extracts]. 12°. 25c. *Germ. Ev. Luth. Syn. of Iowa.*
— *Same;* mit Zusätzen u. unveränd. Augsburger Confession. 18°. 25c.....*Brobst; Kohler.*
— *Same;* mit Bibelstellen, Ordnung des Heils, Confirmations u. andern Liedern, Augsburger Confession, etc. 32°. pap., 20c.....*Ludwig.*
— — Enchiridion: der kleine Katechismus. 12°. '68. 10c.....*Barthel.*
— — *Same.* 12°. bds., 10c.....*Brumder.*
— *Same;* in Fragen u. Antworten erklärt v. K. H. Caspari. 12°. bds., 40c.....*Brumder.*
— — *Same;* mit Anh. d. würtemb. Confirmanden Examens. 12°. bds., 45c.....*Brumder.*
— *Same;* in Frage u. Antwort ausgelegt; v. J. C. Dieterich. ('60.) 22d ed. 12°. '76. 35c...*Barthel.*
— — Auszug aus d. Katechismus; v. J. C. Dieterich. ('68.) 6th ed. 12°. '75. 20c.....*Barthel.*
— — *See also* Bohm, E., Katechismus; — Keyl, E. W. G.
— *Eng.* Smaller catechism, with explan. Bible texts, and Augsburg confession. 32°. pap., 20c. *Ludwig.*
— — *Same;* with Scripture texts. 16°. '74. bds., 20c. *Luth. Bk. St.*
— — *Same.* pt. 1: Ten commandments; with explanations. 16°. 15c.....*Luth. Bk. St.*
— — Enchiridion: the smaller catechism of L. 2d ed. 18°. '67. 25c.....*Henkel.*
— *Swedish.* Lilla cateches, med dertill utwalda bibelspråk. 12°. bds., 25c.....*Engberg.*

Luther, Mt., *continued.*
— *Swedish and Eng.* Lilla cateches, på Swenska och Engelska. 12°. bds., 15c.....*Engberg.*
— Hauspostille. 8°. leath., $2.50.....*Kohler.*
— *Same;* v. Veit Dieterich. 8°. $2.....*Ludwig.*
— *Eng.* Church postil: sermons on the Epistles for the Sundays and festivals; tr. 3 v. in 1. 16°. '69. $2.50; shp., $2.75.....*Henkel.*
— Hochzeitsgeschenk: aus Luthers Schriften zusammengestellt v. C. P. H. Brandt. 12°. '69. $1.25; $2.50.....*Barthel.*
— Life by himself; collected and arr. [with add.] by J. Michelet; tr. by W. Hazlitt. 12°. (Bohn.) $1.25.....*Little, B. & Co.*
— *Same.* 12°. (Bohn.) $1.40.....*Scribner, W. & A.*
— *Same.* 12°. (Bohn.) $1.50.....*Lippincott.*
— Life of L., and the reformation in Germany; with introd. by T. Stork. ill. 8°. $2.50; $3. (?)*Luth. Pub.*
— — *See also* Golden chain lib.
— Ninety five theses. *See* Mann, W. J., Great reformation.
— Scripture pearls. [Dutch.] 32°. '53. 20c...*Am. Tr.*
— Table talk; tr. by W. Hazlitt. 12°. (Bohn.) $1.25. *Little, B. & Co.*
— *Same.* 12°. (Bohn.) $1.40.....*Scribner, W. & A.*
— *Same.* 12°. (Bohn.) $1.50.....*Lippincott.*
— *Same.* 3d ed. cr. 8°. $2–$5.....(?)*Luth. Pub.*
— Volksbibliothek: ausgew. Schriften; hrsg. v. d. am. Lutherverein. v. 1–28 in 14 v. 8°. '59–'75. ea., 50c.....*Barthel.*
— Watchwords for the warfare of life; sel. [and tr.] by Mrs. E. Charles. 12°. '68. $1.75.....*Dodd.*
— *See also* Bible [Whole], *Germ.;* — Dieterich, C., Institutiones catecheticae; — Evangelisch-lutherischer Gebets-Schatz; — Lindemann, J. C. W.; — Morris, J. G.; — Pontoppidan, E.; — Story of Martin Luther.
— *and* Calvin, J: Selection of [their] most celebrated sermons; with sketch of lives. ill. 12°. $1.75. *Desilver.*
Luther and the Bible; — and his times. *See* Stork, T.
Luther as a hymnist. *See* Pick, B.
Luther at home. Stork, T. $1.....(?)*Luth. Pub.*
Luther-Lied. Hasta, O. S. v. $1.....*Brumder.*
Lutheran. *See* Evangelical; — German Evangelical.
Lutheran Church. Book of worship of the General Synod. 24°. 80c.–$3.50. — 16°. $1–$4.50. — (Pulpit ed.) 12°. $1.75–$6.....(?)*Luth. Pub.*
— Church book for evang. Lutheran congregations. 16°. '68. $1–$5.....*Luth. Bk. St.*
— Church forms for performance of ministerial acts. 12°. 50c.....*Luth. Bk. St.*
— Symbolical books of the Evang. Luth. Ch. 12°. pap., 10c.....*Luth. Bk. St.*
— *See also* Evangelical Lutheran.
Lutheran Evangelical Assoc. [or Church]. *See* Evangelical Assoc.
Lutheran Sunday school hymn books. per doz., *net*, hf. bd., $2; $3.....(?)*Luth. Pub.*
Lutheran Synod. *See* Evangelical Lutheran.
Lutherthum vor Luther. Pfeiffer, A. 75c....*Dette.*
Luttrell of Arran. *See* Lever, C:
Luttrells (The). Williams, R. F. 50c.....*Harper.*
Lutze, Arth. Manual of homœopathic theory and practice; tr. by C. J. Hempel. 8°. hf. mor., $2.50.....*Boericke.*
Lützow, C. F. A. v. *See* Monuments of art.
Luyster, Miss I. M. Madame Récamier and her friends. 16°. '75. $1.50.....*Roberts.*
Lyall, A. C. Relation of witchcraft to religion. 12°. 15c.....*Somerby.*
Lyceum boys. *See* Glen Elder books.
Lydia: tale of 2d cent. Geiger, H. $1.50..*Cummiskey.*
Lydia Harper; or, the lost child. 18°. 22c...*Am. S. S.*

Lydia's duty. 18°. '69. 40c. . . . . *Randolph.*
Lydias (The). Philip, R. 60c. . . . . *Carter.*
Lyell, *Sir* C: Elements of geology. ill. 12°. '39. $1.60. . . . . *C. H. Davis.*
— *Same.* 6th ed., enl. wood-cuts. 8°. $3.50. . *Appleton.*
— Geological evidences of the antiquity of man, with remarks on origin of species by variation. woodcuts. 8°. $5 . . . . *Lippincott.*
— Principles of geology; or, the modern changes of the earth and its inhabitants. 2 v. maps, pl. and woodcuts. roy. 8°. $8. *Appleton.*
— Second visit to the U. S. 2 v. 12°. $3. . . *Harper.*
— Student's elements of geology. ill. 12°. $2. . *Harper.*
Lying in ordinary: farce. 16°. pap., 15c. . . . . *Happy.*
Lying Jim. *See* Baker, *Mrs.* H. N. W.
Lyle MacDonald. Keene, S. F. $1.50. . . . . *Hoyt.*
Lyman, Azel S. Historical chart. 4°; key, 12°. '73. *$3.50; hf. mor., $4.50. . . . . *Jones.*
Lyman, Darius. Reference index to the revised statutes of the U. S. roy. 8°. pap., $1.25. . *Little, B. & Co.*
Lyman, H: Memoir. 12°. $1.50 . . . . *Carter.*
Lyman, Jos. B. Cotton culture; with chapter on cotton seed and its uses by J. R. Sypher. map and ill. 12°. $1.50 . . . . *Judd.*
Lyman, Jos. B. *and* L. E. Philosophy of housekeeping. ill. 12°. '69. *$2. . . . . *Betts.*
Lyman, Laura E. *See* Lyman, J. B. *and* L. E.
Lyman, Mar. Bruce. Secret of strength. ill. 16°. $1. *Bost. Am. Tr.*
— Work and wages. 16°. $1.25 . . . . *Cong. Pub.*
Lyman, S. P. Public and private life of Daniel Webster; with his speeches and letters. 2 v. in 1. ill. 12°. $1.75. . . . . *J. E. Potter.*
Lyman, Thdr. Ophiuridæ and astrophytidæ. ill. imp. 8°. '64. pap., $3.50. . . . . *Mus. Comp. Zool.*
— Ophiuridæ and astrophytidæ, new and old. ill. 8°. '74. pap., $1.75 . . . . *Mus. Comp. Zool.*
— Ophiuridæ and astroph., incl. those dredged by the late Dr. Stimpson [in Hassler exped.] ill. 4°. '75. pap., $1.50 . . . . *Mus. Comp. Zool.*
— Preliminary report on the oph. and astroph. dredged by L. F. De Pourtalès. 8°. '69. pap., 35c. *Mus. Comp. Zool.*
— Supplement to the oph. and astroph. ill. imp. 8°. '71. pap., 75c. . . . . *Mus. Comp. Zool.*
Lyman, Wyllys. Selection of tactical studies. 12°. $1.25. . . . . *Appleton.*
Lynch, T: J. Rose of Ettrick vale: drama. 16°. pap., 15c. . . . . *French.*
Lynch, T: T. Moral of accidents, and other discourses; ed. by S. Cox. cr. 8°. $1.75. . . . . *Routledge.*
Lynch, W: F. Narrative of the U. S. expedition to the Dead Sea and River Jordan. maps and ill. 8°. '49. $3. 12°. $1. . . . . *Lea.*
— Official report of the U. S. expedition to explore the Dead Sea and River Jordan. 4°. '52. $5. . *Murphy.*
Lynch, W: R. Manual for notaries public of N. Y.; with forms. 8°. '76. bds., $1.50 . . . . *Ward & P.*
— Manual of the law of real estate brokers. 12°. '76. hf. shp., $1.50. . . . . *Ward & P.*
Lynd, Ja. First book of etymology. 12°. '47. hf. bd., 65c. . . . . *Fortescue.*
Lynda Newton. Frost, L. J. H. $1.50. . . . . . *Graves.*
Lynde Weiss. Throop, G. H. $1.50. . . . . . . *Claxton.*
Lyndon (*pseud.*) *See* Bright, Mta. A.
Lynn, Ethel. General Frankie: story for little folks. 18°. '63. 60c. *Randolph.*
Lynn's Creek; or, two days' experience in the life of Willie Grey. 18°. 35c. . . . . *Am. S. S.*
Lyntonville; or, the Irish boy in Canada. ill. 18°. 60c. . . . . *Bost. Am. Tr.*
— *Same.* ill. 16°. '66. 70c. . . . . *Am. Tr.*
— *See also* Winter school stories.

Lyntonville lib. 4 v. 16°. '68. $4.50. . *Meth. Bk. Conc.*
Cont.: Life in Lyntonville. — Miss Carrol's school. — Fishers of Derby Haven. — Grace's visit.
Lynx hunting. Stephens, C. A. $1.25. . . . . . . *Porter.*
Lyon, Sydney S. *See* Kentucky geol. survey.
Lyonel Harlington. *See* Zschokke, H:
Lyons, —. Village lawyer: farce. 16°. pap., 15c. *French.*
Lyons, J. G. Selections from sermons and poems. 8°. $5 . . . . *Lippincott.*
Lyons, Jos. A. American elocutionist and dramatic reader; with introd. on elocution and vocal culture by M. B. Brown. 3d ed., rev. 12°. $1.65. . *Butler.*
Lyons, Rob. D. Handbook of hospital practice: introd. to pract. study of medicine at the bedside. 12°. $1.25 . . . . *W. Wood.*
— Treatise on fever. 8°. $2.25 . . . . *Lea.*
Lyra Americana. Rider, G. T. $1.50; $3.50; $4. *Appleton.*
Lyra Anglicana. Rider, G. T. $1.50; $3.50; $4. *Appleton.*
Lyra Catholica. 24°. 75c. . . . . *Strong.*
Lyra Catholica. Wilcox, J. H., *and* Southard, L. H. $2.75; $2.50. . . . . *Ditson.*
Lyra cœlestis. Thompson, A. C. $1.75. . . . . *Sheldon.*
Lyra Devoniensis. Wollaston, T. V. $1.25. . *Macmillan.*
Lyra domestica. Spitta, C. J. P. $1.50; $4.50. . *Dutton.*
Lyra Germanica: hymns for the Sundays and chief festivals of the Christian year. 16°. '61. $1.25; mor., $4.50. . . . . *Dutton.*
Lyra Germanica: songs of the Christian life. 2d ser. 16°. '64. $1.50. *Randolph.*
Lyra sacra Americana. Cleveland, C. D. $3. . *Scribner.*
Lyre française. Masson, G. $1.25. . . . . . . *Macmillan.*
Lyret. Tyler, J. $1.25. . . . . *Lothrop.*
Lyric drama: choruses and concerted pieces from operas. 8 nos. 4°. '57. ea., pap., 75c. . . *Ditson.*
Lyric gems. Smith, S. F. 25c.; 40c.; $1. . . *Lothrop.*
Lyrical lover: comedietta. 16°. pap., 15c. . . . *Happy.*
Lyrical recreations. Ward, S. $2. . . . . *Appleton.*
Lyrics of life. Browning, R. 75c. . . . . *Osgood.*
Lysias. Select orations [Gk.]; with introd. and notes by W. A. Stevens. 12°. '76. $1.50. . . . *Griggs.*
— *Same;* ed. by J. M. Whiton. 12°. '75. $1.50. . *Ginn.*
Lysistrata. *See* Aristophanes.
Lyte, H. C. Maxwell. History of Eton College, 1440–1875. ill. 8°. '76. $12 . . . . *Macmillan.*
Lyte, H: Fs. Miscellaneous poems. 16°. $2.50. . *Pott.*
— Poems. 16°. '70. $1.25; $1.50. . . . . *Randolph.*
Lyttelton, G: (*Lord*). Ueber die Bekehrung Pauli. 18°. '45. 30c. . . . . *Am. Tr.*
Lyttelton, G: W: (*Lord*). *See* Milton, J.
Lyttle, Byrd (*pseud.*) *See* Lomax, E. V.
Lyttleton, W. H. Sins of trade and business; [also] Morals of trade, by H. Spencer. 12°. '74. $1. *Routledge.*
Lytton, *Lord.* *See* Bulwer-Lytton, *Sir* E. G. E. L.
Lytton, *Lord.* *See* Bulwer-Lytton, E: Rob.

M., A. C. Elsie: a lowland sketch. cr. 8°. $1.75. *Macmillan.*
M., A. M. Katie Johnstone's cross: Canadian tale. ill. 12°. $1 . . . . *Nelson.*
— — *See also* Katie Johnstone's lib.
— Whither bound? 18°. 55c. . . . . *Pres. Bd.*
M., *Mrs.* A. S. Cedar brook stories; or, the Clifford children. 5 v. ill. 18°. '63. $3.25. . . . . *Graves.*
Cont.: Little seed sowers. — Seed growing. — Seed bearing fruit. — Sowing in new fields. — Frank gone to the war.
M., B. *See* Macandrew, *Mrs.* B.
M., B. A. Essay contributing to a philosophy of literature. ('74.) New ed. 12°. '76. $1.50. . *Claxton.*

M., B. V. Two ways. 16°. 40c. . . . . *West. Tr.*
M., C. J. Alice Sherwin: hist. tale. 12°. $1.25; $1.75. *Sadlier.*
M., E. Edith Hinton; or, twice blest. ill. 18°. 75c. *Nelson.*
M., E. A. Lost pearl. 18°. '71. 40c. . . . . . *Randolph.*
M., E. B. Word pictures. 6 v. 18°. $2.10. . *Pres. Bd.*
M., E. L. Stars in a stormy night: story of early Christians in Rome. ill. 12°. $1.25. . . . . *Nelson.*
M., K. *See* M'Clellan, Kate.
M., L. C. Katie Lawford's victory. 18°. 60c. (?) *Martien.*
M., M. A. S. Daily watchwords: morning thoughts on Scripture texts. 12°. $1.50. . . . . *Nelson.*
M., M. E. Philip Brantley's life work, and how he found it. ill. 16°. '69. $1. . . . . *Dodd.*
M., M. K. The birds we see. ill. 16°. 75c. . . . *Nelson.*
— Wild flowers. ill. 16°. 75c. . . . . *Nelson.*
— With the birds. ill. 16°. 75c. . . . . *Nelson.*
M., M. de. La petite maman: comédie; [also] Le bracelet: drame, par Mme. de Gaulle. ('64.) New ed. 12°. '76. pap., 25c. . . . . *Holt.*
M., Rog. de. Eight months on duty: diary of a young officer in Chanzy's army; from the Fr., with pref. by C. J. Vaughan. cr. 8°. '72. $1.75. *Routledge.*
M., S. W. *See* S., E. W., *and* M., S. W.
M., T. J. Life of St. Thomas of Villanova; with sketch of men, manners and morals of 16th cent. 12°. '74. $1.50. . . . . *Cunningham.*
M..., *Mme.* —. Madame de Lavalle's bequest: counsels to young ladies. 12°. '75. $1.50. . *Cunningham.*
Maas für Maas. *See* Shakespeare, W.
Mabel (*pseud.*) *See* Hazen, Ma. P.
Mabel; or, the bitter root. *See* Guernsey, L. E.
Mabel and Tura. Wright, J. McN. $1.25. . (?) *Martien.*
Mabel Clark; or, looking unto Jesus. 18°. 70c. *Pres. Bd.*
Mabel Clifton. Brierwood, F. $1.50. . . . . . . *Claxton.*
Mabel Grant. Ballantyne, R. H. 75c. . . . . *Carter.*
Mabel Hazard's thoroughfare. Robbins, S. S. $1.25. *Carter.*
Mabel Lee. Fisher, F. C. $1.50; $1. . . . . . *Appleton.*
Mabel Lee. Willard, *Mrs.* —. 60c. . . . . . . *Cong. Pub.*
Mabel lib. 5 v. 16°. $5.75. . . . . *Hoyt.*
Cont.: Mabel's message. — Wee Donald. — Tom Green. — Newell boys, by C. Whipple. — Robert Joy's victory.
Mabel Livingstone. Titterington, S. B. $1.25. . *Lothrop.*
Mabel Martin. Whittier, J. G. $1.50–$9. . . *Osgood.*
Mabel Ross, the sewing girl. 16°. '66. $1.50. . *Graves.*
Mabel Vaughan. Cummins, M. S. $1.75. . *Nichols & H.*
Mabel Walton's experiment. Mathews, J. H. $1.25. *Carter.*
Mabel's confirmation. 32°. '74. 20c. . . . . . . *Williams.*
Mabel's experience. 18°. 75c. . . . . *Carter.*
Mabel's faith. ill. 18°. '75. 50c. . . . . *Nelson.*
— *Same.* ill. 16°. '75. 75c. . . . . *Lothrop.*
Mabel's message and the happy land. ('72.) New ed. 16°. '74. $1.25. . . . . *Hoyt.*
Mabel's mistake. Stephens, A. S. $1.75; $1.50. *Peterson.*
Mabel's new year. *See* Bradley, *Mrs.* M. E.
Mabel's pets. *See* Sunbeam lib.
Mabel's progress. Trollope, F. E. 50c. . . . . . *Harper.*
Maberly, *Mrs.* —. Art of conversation; with remarks on fashion and dress. 8°. pap., 25c. . . *Dick & F.*
Maberly, G: Sayings of the great forty days; with exam. of Mr. Newman's theory of developments. New ed. 12°. '72. $2.50. . . . . *Dutton.*
Maberly, *Mrs.* Kate C. Lady (The) and the priest. 8°. pap., 50c. . . . . *Harper.*
— Leontine; or, the court of Louis XV. 8°. pap., 50c. *Harper.*

Mabire, J. L. Conversational phrases; or, French synonyms. 16°. '45. 60c. . . . . . . *G. R. Lockwood.*
Mabita. *See* Infant school lib.
Mabon, W. V. V. Our duties to the young in the home and in the church. [Sermon.] 8°. pap., 25c. . . . . *N. Y. Ref. Ch. Bd.*
McAdam, D: Marine Court of N. Y. City: its organization, jurisdiction and practice; with forms. ('72.) 2d ed. 8°. '74. shp., $4.50. . . *Ward & P.*
— On terms of court: essay on dies juridici, or law days. 8°. '75. pap., 50c. . . . . *Ward & P.*
— The rights, remedies and liabilities of landlord and tenant; with forms. 8°. '75. shp., $5.50. *Ward & P.*
Macallan, Emma. Miner's hut. 18°. 25c.; 30c. *Dutton.*
McAllister, Cutler. *See* United States, Circuit Court reports.
McAllisters (The). Richmond, E. J. 50c. *Nat. Temp.*
M'Allum, D. Remains: essays, lectures, etc. 12°. '40. 60c. . . . . *Meth. Bk. Conc.*
McAlpine, W: J. Address to Am. Soc. of Civil Engineers, Dec. 2, 1868. 8°. pap., 35c. *Am. Soc. of C. E.*
— Corrosion of iron; [also] Durability of cast iron water-mains, by J. B. Francis; [also] Sketch of improvements in suspension bridges, by C. Bender. 8°. pap., 50c. . . . . *Am. Soc. of C. E.*
— Engineers in courts of law. *See* Craven, A. W., Address to Am. Soc. Civ. Eng.
— Foundations of new Capitol at Albany. *See* Allen, T., Iron hulls for western river steamboats.
— Repair of earthen dam of storing reservoir, New Bedford water works; [also] Arching Bergen Tunnel, Erie R. R., by J. Houston. 8°. pap., 50c. . . . . *Am. Soc. of C. E.*
— Waves of translation in fresh water. 8°. pap., 40c. *Am. Soc. of C. E.*
M'Anally, D. R. Life and times of S: Patton. 12°. $1.50 . . . . *S. W. Bk. & Pub.*
— Scripture manual; for opening and closing schools. 18°. hf. bd., 35c. . . . . *S. W. Bk. & Pub.*
— Western harp: prayer meeting and revival hymn book. 24°. shp., 65c.–$2 . . . . . . *S. W. Bk. & Pub.*
Macandrew, *Mrs.* B. Ezekiel and other poems. 12°. '73. $1.25 . . . . *Nelson.*
— Religious poems. 24°. '71. $1.50. . . . . . . *Randolph.*
Macaria. Evans, A. J. $1.75. . . . . *Carleton.*
Macarius (*pseud.*) Quay of the Dioscuri. 18°. 55c. *Dutton.*
MacArthur, A. *See* District of Columbia, Sup. Ct. reports.
Macarthur, Marg. History of Scotland. ('73.) New ed. 16°. '74. $1 . . . . *Holt.*
Macarthy, Harry. Barney's courtship; or, Mollie dear: Ethiop. mus. interlude. 16°. '76. pap., 15c. . . . . *De Witt.*
Macaulay, Ja. Plea for mercy to animals. sq. 16°. '75. $1.25 . . . . *Nelson.*
Macaulay, T: Babington (*Lord*). Works; ed. by Lady Trevelyan. 4 v. sm. 8°. $9; hf. cf., $16; cf., $24. — 8 v. 8°. $32; hf. cf., $48; $52. . *Appleton.*
— *Same.* 16 v. cr. 8°. $32; hf. cf., $64 . . . . *Putnam.*
— *Same;* with indices, memoir by Dean Milman, and biog. sketch by E. P. Whipple; also appendices and notes. (Riverside ed.) 16 v. por. cr. 8°. $32; hf. cf., $64. — (Student's ed.) 8 v. cr. 8°. $16; hf. cf., $32. — (Popular ed.) 6 v. cr. 8°. $12.50 . . . . *Hurd & H.*
— Miscellaneous works; incl. essays, poems and speeches; with index, app. and biog. sketch by E. P. Whipple. (Riverside ed.) 8 v. cr. 8°. $16; hf. cf., $32. — (Student's ed.) 4 v. cr. 8°. $8; hf. cf., $16 . . . . *Hurd & H.*
— Miscellaneous writings contributed to "Knight's Quarterly Magazine," etc. 12°. '74. 75c.; pap., 50c. . . . . *Routledge.*

Macaulay, T: Babington (*Lord*), *continued.*
— Biographical sketches; designed as a reader for schools. 12°. $1 .... *Appleton.*
— Critical and historical essays. por. 12°. '74. $2.50; shp., $3; hf. cf., $5 .... *Mason.*
— *Same.* 8°. $2.50; shp., $3.50; hf. cf., $5 .. *Appleton.*
— *Same.* cr. 8°. (Lond.) '74. $2 .... *Little, B. & Co.*
— *Same.* 7 v. sm. 8°. $8.75; hf. cf., $24; cf., $31.50. *Appleton.*
— *Same.* (Riverside ed.) 6 v. por. cr. 8°. $12; hf. cf., $24.—(Student's ed.) 3 v. cr. 8°. $6; hf. cf., $12.—(Popular ed.) cr. 8°. $2.50 .. *Hurd & H.*
— *Same.* 1st ser. 12°. '74. 75c.; pap., 50c. *Routledge.*
— — *See also* Modern Brit. essayists.
— History of Eng. from accession of James II.; ed. by Lady Trevelyan. 5 v. por. 12°. $5; shp., $7.50; hf. cf., $15;—in 1 v. 8°. $3; shp., $3.50 .. *Porter.*
— *Same.* 5 v. 8°. $10.—5 v. 12°. $5; shp., $7; hf. cf., $13.75.—(chp. ed.) 5 v. 8°. pap., $1.50. *Harper.*
— *Same.* 8 v. post 8°. (Lond.) '71. $14; hf. cf., $28. *Little, B. & Co.*
— *Same.* (Riverside ed.) 8 v. por. cr. 8°. $16; hf. cf., $32.—(Student's ed.) 4 v. cr. 8°. $8; hf. cf., $16 .... *Hurd & H.*
— *Same;* [with] memoir by Milman, and add. notes, sketch of life and index by S. A. Allibone. (Crown ed.) 5 v. por. 12°. '75. $5; shp., $7.50; hf. cf., $15 .... *Claxton; Lippincott.*
— *Same;* [also] Critical and historical essays. 4 v. post 8°. (Lond.) '74. $7.—12 v. post 8°. (Lond.) 1871–4. $21; hf. cf., $42; cf., $60. *Little, B. & Co.*
— Lays of ancient Rome, and other poems. ill. 4°. $5–$9.—(Household ed.) 16°. $1.25–$3.75.—(Red line ed.) ill. sm 4°. $3.50–$7 .... *Miller.*
— Life of Frederick the Great. 16°. 75c. ... *Hurd & H.*
— Life of William Pitt. 16°. 75c. .... *Hurd & H.*
— Selected essays, and miscellaneous writings. 16°. '74. $1.25 .... *Routledge.*
— Speeches. 2 v. cr. 8°. $3; hf. cf., $6 .. *Widdleton.*
— Speeches and poems; with papers upon Indian penal code. (Riverside ed.) 2 v. cr. 8°. $4; hf. cf., $8.—(Student's ed.) cr. 8°. $2; hf. cf., $4. *Hurd & H.*

McAuley, Cath. Life. cr. 12°. $2.50; $3.50 .. *Sadlier.*

Macbeth, J: Walker Vilant. Might and mirth of literature: treatise on figurative language. cr. 8°. $2.50 .... *Harper.*

McBeth, Sue. Practical talks with sinners, inquirers and Christians. 18°. '68. $1 .... *McIntyre.*

Macbeth. *See* Shakespeare, W:

Macbeth: travestie. Talfourd, F. 15c. .... *French.*

McBride, H. Elliott. All kinds of dialogues. 16°. pap., 30c.; bds., 50c. .... *Dick & F.*
— Comic dialogues. 16°. pap., 30c.; bds., 50c. *Dick & F.*

McBride, Ja. Pioneer biography: sketches of lives of early settlers of Butler Co., Ohio. 2 v. por. 8°. '69–'71. v. 1, $3.50; large pap., $7; 2, $3; large pap., $6 .... *Clarke.*

McBride, P. H. *See* Missouri, Sup. Court reports.

McC., *Mrs.* A. L. Old rope maker; or, the house of divine grace. 18°. 65c.; 75c. .... *Am. Bapt.*

McCabe, C. C., *and* Macfarlan, D. F. Winnowed hymns: collection of sacred songs. 16°. '73. 35c.; pap., 25c.; bds., 30c. *Biglow; Meth. Bk. Conc.*

McCabe, Ja. D. Centennial book of Am. biography. por. 8°. '76. *$2.75; leath., $3.50 .... *Ziegler.*
— Centennial history of the U. S. [In Eng. or Germ.] ill. and por. 8°. '75. *$3.75; $4.50 .. *Nat. Pub.*
— Centennial view of our country and its resources. ill. 8°. '76. *$4; leath., $5 .... *Hubbard.*
— Cross and crown: the sufferings and triumphs of heroic men and women who were persecuted for the religion of Jesus Christ. ill. 8°. '74. *3.75; mor., $6 .... *Jones.*

McCabe, Ja. D., *continued.*
— Great fortunes, and how they were made; or, the struggles and triumphs of our self-made men. ill. 8°. '71. *$3.50; $4.50; mor., $7 .. *Maclean.*
— History of the war between Germany and France; with biog. sketches. ill. and maps. 8°. '71. *$3.50 .... *Nat. Pub.*
— Lights and shadows of New York life; or, the sights and sensations of the great city. [In Eng. or Germ.] ill. 8°. '72. *$2.75; leath., $3.75. *Nat. Pub.*
— Pathways of the Holy Land; or, Palestine and Syria. ill. and maps. roy. 8°. *$3.75; $4.50; mor., $6 .... *Nat. Pub.*
— Planting the wilderness; or, the pioneer boys. ill. 16°. $1.25 .... *Lee & S.*

M'Cabe, L. D. Light on the pathway of holiness. 16°. '71. 75c. .... *Meth. Bk. Conc.*

McCaffery, Mich. J. A. Siege of Spoleto: poem. 12°. 75c.; $1 .... *O'Shea.*

McCaffrey, J. Catechism for general use. 18°. pap., per 100, $5.—24°. pap., per 100, $2.75;—abridg. 24°. pap., per 100, $1.75 .... *O'Shea.*

McCahon, Ja. *See* Kansas, Gen. statutes.

McCall, Anderson. On the treatment of diseases of the skin; with analysis of cases. 8°. $1 ... *Lea.*

McCall, G. A. Letters from the frontier; during 30 years' service in the U. S. army. cr. 8°. $2.50. *Lippincott.*

McCall, H: S. Clerk's assistant; with forms and instruments adapted to county and town offices, etc. ('60.) 3d ed., rev. 8°. '72. $3.50 .. *Gould.*
— Treatise on civil, criminal and special powers and duties of justices of the peace in N. Y.; with forms. 5th ed., rev. and enl. 8°. '73. shp., $7.50. *Gould.*
— Treatise on powers and duties of constables in N. Y.; with forms. ('73.) 3d ed. 12°. $2 .... *Gould.*
— *See also* Hull, A. G., *and* McCall, H. S.

McCall, S. Culture and the Gospel; or, a plea for the sufficiency of the Gospel to meet the wants of an enlightened age. 16°. '70. 75c.; $1; bds., 60c. *Randolph.*

McCalla, Ma. In doors and out of doors; or, life among the children. sq. 16°. 75c. .... *Pres. Bd.*
— Twin sisters. ill. 18°. 50c. .... *Pres. Bd.*
— Why was I left? or, he hath done all things well. sq. 16°. 60c. .... *Pres. Bd.*

McCarter, T. N. *See* New Jersey, Court of Chanc. reports.

McCarthy, Denis Florence. Book of Irish ballads. 12°. $1 .... *Noonan.*

M'Carthy, Just. Dear Lady Disdain. 8°. '76. $1.75; pap., $1 .... *Sheldon.*
— Fair Saxon (A). 12°. $1.75; pap., $1 .... *Sheldon.*
— Lady Judith: tale of two continents. 8°. $1.75; pap., $1 .... *Sheldon.*
— Linley Rochford. 8°. $1.75; pap., $1 .... *Sheldon.*
— Modern leaders: biog. sketches. 8°. $1.75 .. *Sheldon.*
— My enemy's daughter. ill. 8°. pap., 75c. .. *Harper.*
— Paul Massie. 12°. $1.50; pap., $1 .... *Sheldon.*
— Waterdale neighbors. 8°. pap., 50c. .... *Harper.*

MacCarthy More. Lover, S. 15c. .... *French.*

MacCarthy More. Sadlier, M. A. $1; $1.50 .. *Sadlier.*

M'Carty, J. Hendrickson. Black horse and carryall. 16°. $1.25 .... *Cin. Meth. Bk. Conc.*
— Inside the gates. 16°. $1 .... *Cin. Meth. Bk. Conc.*

McCaskey, J: P. Pennsylvania song collection. 8°. '75. bds., $1; 60c.; pap., 40c.;—words only, pap., 15c. .... *McCaskey.*

McCauley, Ja. A. The nation and the church. [Sermon.] 8°. pap., 25c. .... *D. H. Carroll.*

McCausland, Dominick. Adam and the Adamite; or, the harmony of Scripture and ethnology. 12°. $2.50 .... *Scribner, W. & A.*

McCausland, Dominick, *continued.*
— Builders of Babel. 12°. $2.50..... *Scribner, W.&A.*
— Sermons in stones; or, Scripture confirmed by geology. 12°. $3.................. *Scribner, W.&A.*
McCheyne, Rog. Murray. Works; compr. life, letters, lectures and sermons. 2 v. in 1. 8°. $3... *Carter.*
— Bethany; or, the sickness, death and resurrection of Lazarus. 18°. 35c.................... *Pres. Bd.*
— McCheyne's gems. 64°. '58. 20c.; 25c..... *Am. Tr.*
— To a boy anxious about his soul. *See* Cripple (The).
Macchiavelli, Nicolo. *See* Machiavelli.
McCleland, T. *See* England, Exchequer reports.
McClellan, Ely. History of cholera epidemic of 1873; — History of the travels of Asiatic cholera. *See* United States, *Surgeon-General's Office.*
McClellan, G: Principles and practice of surgery; ed. by J. H. B. McClellan. 8°. '48. shp., $2. *Claxton; Lippincott.*
McClellan, G: B. Armies of Europe: descript. of their military systems. ill. 8°. '61. $3.50. *Claxton; Lippincott.*
— European cavalry; incl. organization of cavalry service among principal nations. ill. 12°. '61. $1.25. *Claxton.*
— Life, battles, reports and public services. 12°. 75c.; pap., 50c.......................... *Peterson.*
— Manual of bayonet exercise; prep. for U. S. army. 12°. '52. $1.25...................... *Claxton.*
— Regulations and instructions for field service of the U. S. cavalry in war. ill. 12°. '61. $1.50.. *Claxton.*
— Report and campaigns. 12°. $1.75; bds., $1.25. *Sheldon.*
— Report of army of Potomac, of its operations while under his command. maps and plans. 8°. '64. $1; pap., 50c.................... *Van Nostrand.*
McClellan, J: Brown. New Testament: new tr. on basis of authorized version from a crit. rev. Gk. text; newly arranged in paragraphs; with analyses, ref. and ill., chronol. and anal. harmony of the Gospels, notes and dissertations. [To form 2 v.] v. 1: 4 Gospels. 8°. '75. $12.. *Macmillan.*
M'Clellan, Kate. Annie and Pierre; or, our father's letter. 16°. $1..................... *Whittaker.*
— Easter day, and other stories. 18°. 50c... *Whittaker.*
— Edith Leigh's prayer book. 18°. '68. 90c. *Whittaker.*
— Theo. Gray's first years out of school. 12°. '70. $1.50. *Whittaker.*
— Two Christmas gifts. 18°. 60c......... *Whittaker.*
— Willie's hyacinth, and other stories. 18°. 40c. *Whittaker.*
Maclellan, Malcolm. Benoni Blake, M.D., surgeon at Glenaldi. [Fiction.] cr. 8°. '71. $1.75.. *Routledge.*
McClellan, R. Guy. The golden state: hist. of region west of the Rocky Mts. maps and eng. 12°. '72. *$3.50; $4........................ *F. Scofield.*
— *Same.* ('73.) New ed. 8°. '76. *$4; $4.50; hf. mor., $5.50.................................. *Flint.*
— Republicanism in America. ill. cr. 8°. '72. $3.50. *J. M. Stoddart.*
McClellan, Rob. H. Jurisdiction of surrogates' courts and the remedies offered thereby. 8°. '75. shp., $6.50................................ *Gould.*
— Manual for executors, administrators and guardians, with exposition of their rights, privileges, etc., and of rights of widows in personal estate and to dower. 2d ed., rev. and enl. 8°. '73. $3.50. *Gould.*
McClelland, Alex. Sermons. 12°. $2....... *Carter.*
McClelland, M. A. Civil malpractice. 8°. '73. $2. *Keen.*
McClenachan, C: T. Book of the ancient and accepted Scottish rite of Freemasonry. ill. 12°. '65. $3. *Masonic.*
— *Same.* ill. 12°. $5.......................... *Redding.*
— Manual of the lodge of perfection. [Freemasonry.] 12°. '73. $1.50..................... *Masonic.*

McClintock, *Sir* Fs. L. Meteorological obs. in the Arctic seas. 4°. '62. pap., $1.50... *Smith. Inst.*
— Voyage of the "Fox" in the Arctic seas: narrative of the discovery of the fate of Sir John Franklin and his companions. 12°. $1.25........ *Porter.*
McClintock, J: Analysis of Watson's Institutes. 18°. '42. 55c.......................... *Meth. Bk. Conc.*
— Biographical sketches of Methodist ministers. 8°. $5. *Cin. Meth. Bk. Conc.*
— Living words; or, unwritten sermons. 12°. '70. $1.75; mor., $4................ *Meth. Bk. Conc.*
— Methodology lectures on theological encyclopedia and methodology. 12°. $1.50.. *Cin. Meth. Bk. Conc.*
— Second book in Greek. 12°. hf. bd., $1.50.. *Harper.*
— Second book in Latin. 12°. hf. bd., $1.50.. *Harper.*
— Temporal power of the pope. 12°. '55. 60c. *Meth. Bk. Conc.*
— *and* Crooks, G. R. First book in Greek. 12°. hf. bd., $1.50.......................... *Harper.*
— — First book in Latin. 12°. hf. bd., $1.50.. *Harper.*
— *and* Strong, J. Cyclopædia of biblical, theological and ecclesiastical literature. v. 1–5. maps and ill. 8°. ea., $5; shp., $6; hf. mor., $8.. *Harper.*
McClung, J: A. Sketches of western adventure, 1755–1794; with add. sketches by [R. H. Collins], and biog. of McC. by H. Waller. 12°. '72. $2. *R. H. Collins.*
McClure, A. K. Three thousand miles through the Rocky Mts. ill. 12°. $2........... *Lippincott.*
McClure, Alex. W. Translators revived. 12°. 80c. *N. Y. Ref. Ch. Bd.*
— John Cotton; — Wilson, Norton and Davenport. *See* Lives of chief fathers of New Eng.
McClure, Hepburn. Lumberman's assistant: tables determining cubical and superficial contents of hewn timber. 12°. leath., $2.......... *Souder.*
McClure, Rob. American gentleman's stable guide. 16°. '70. $1.......................... *Porter.*
— Diseases of the Am. horse, cattle and sheep. ill. 12°. '70. $2........................... *J. E. Potter.*
— Percheron horse. *See* Walsh, J. H., Every horse-owner's encyclopedia.
McCollum, Scovell H. Little Syracuse boy: memoir of McC. ill. 18°. 60c.......... *N. Y. Ref. Ch. Bd.*
McConaughy, *Mrs.* J. E. Clarence; or, self-will and principle. ('66.) 2d ed. ill. 18°. '68. 60c. *Perkinpine.*
— Fire fighters. ('72.) New ed. 12°. '75. $1.25. *Nat. Temp.*
— Hannah's lesson, and what it cost. ill. 18°. 60c. *Perkinpine.*
— Hard master. ('67.) New ed. 18°. '73. 85c. *Nat. Temp.*
— One hundred gold dollars. 18°. '66. 90c. *Garrigues.*
M'Conkey, *Miss* Reb. True stories of the American fathers. ill. 12°. '74. $1.50.... *Meth. Bk. Conc.*
McConnell, J. S. J. Where is he? or, the doctrine of an intermediate place. 16°. '68. 50c. *Perkinpine.*
McCook, G. W. *See* Ohio, Sup. Court reports.
McCook, H: C. Object and outline teaching: guide book for S.-school workers. ('71.) 2d ed. 12°. $1.50................................ *McIntyre.*
— Westminster Sabbath-school lessons. 12°. *net*, 18c. *Pres. Bd.*
— *See also* Tercentenary book.
McCoomb, Flo. (*pseud.*) *See* Meline, M. M.
MacCord, C. W. Practical treatise on the slide valve by eccentrics, etc. ill. 4°. '73. $3. *Van Nostrand.*
McCord, D: J. *See* South Carolina, Reports.
McCord, W: J. Lot's wife: warning against bad examples. 18°. 40c.................... *Pres. Bd.*
— Our Passover; or, the great things of the law. 12°. 60c................................ *Pres. Bd.*
— Redeemer's legacy; or, peace from the Saviour's hands and side. 18°. 35c............ *Pres. Bd.*

McCord, W: J., *continued.*
— Salvation; or, the sinner directed in the way of life. 18°. 35c. *Pres. Bd.*
— *Germ.* 18°. 20c. *Pres. Bd.*
— Why will ye die? expostulation with self-destroyers. 18°. 35c. *Pres. Bd.*

McCorkle, J. M. *See* North Carolina, Reports.

M'Cormick, S. J. M'Cormick's almanac; [with] statistics of Oregon, Washington [Territory] and Idaho, etc. ('56.) [Annual.] 18°. pap., 15c. *M'Cormick.*

M'Cosh, Ja. Christianity and positivism: lectures, 1871, Union Theol. Sem., N. Y. 12°. '75. $1.75. *Carter.*
— Examination of J. S. Mill's philosophy. 8°. '75. $3. *Carter.*
— Intuitions of the mind, inductively investigated. 8°. '75. $3 *Carter.*
— Laws of discursive thought: text book of formal logic. ('70.) New ed. 12°. '76. $1.50 *Carter.*
— Method of divine government, physical and moral. 8°. '74. $2.50 *Carter.*
— Reply to Tyndall: ideas in nature overlooked by Dr. Tyndall: examination of Belfast address. 12°. '75. 50c. *Carter.*
— Royal law of love. [Sermon.] 12°. '75. pap., 25c. *Carter.*
— Scottish philosophy, biog., expository, crit.; from Hutcheson to Hamilton. ('74.) New ed. 8°. '75. $4 *Carter.*
— Typical forms and special ends in creation. 8°. '72. $2.50 *Carter.*
— *See also* Prayer gauge debate.

McCrary, G: W. Treatise on the Am. law of elections. 8°. '75. *net*, shp., $5 *E. B. Myers.*

M'Creath, A. S. *See* Pennsylvania geol. survey.

M'Crie, T: History of the reformation in Italy in 16th cent.; with sketch of reformation in the Grisons. 12°. $1 *Pres. Bd.*
— Life of Andrew Melville; abridg. 18°. 40c. *Pres. Bd.*
— Life of John Knox. por. 8°. $2; — abridg. 18°. 60c. *Pres. Bd.*

M'Crindell, *Miss* Rachel. Convent. 18°. 75c. *Carter.*
— English governess. 12°. 90c. *McCauley.*
— School girl in France. 16°. 90c. *McCauley.*
— *Same.* 16°. $1 *Carter.*

McCulloch, J. Distillation, brewing and malting. 12°. '67. $1 *Roman.*

McCulloch, J: Ramsay. Dictionary of commerce and commercial navigation. New ed., rev. with two supplements; ed. by H. G. Reid. maps and plans. 8°. $20; hf. mor., $25 *Scribner, W. & A.*
— Principles of polit. economy; with sketch of [its] rise and progress. 12°. $2.50 *Scribner, W. & A.*
— Universal gazetteer; enl. by D. Haskel. 2 v. maps. roy. 8°. shp., $10 *Harper.*

McCulloch, R. S. Elementary treatise on mechan. theory of heat, and its applic. to air and steam engines. 8°. '76. $3.50 *VanNostrand.*

McCune, W. C. Desecration of the Sabbath. *See* Sabbath (The).

McCurdy, A. C. Key to fortune: likenesses and biog. sketches of successful business men, showing how they became rich. [In Eng. or Germ.] 8°. pap., 25c. *Barclay.*

M'Curdy, C. L. Band of hope speaker. 18°. 60c. *Cin. Meth. Bk. Conc.*

McCurdy, J. F. On the minor prophets. *See* Lange, J. P., Commentary.

Macdermots of Ballycloran. *See* Trollope, Ant.

McDill, D: Blanchard, Jona., *and* Beecher, E. Secret societies. 16°. 40c. *U. P. Bd. of Pub.; West. Tr.*

Macdonald, C. Proportions of heads of eye-bars. *See* Jordan, G., Foundations.

McDonald, D: Treatise on law rel. to powers and duties of justices of the peace and constables in Indiana; with forms and essays on various titles of the common law. New ed., rev. to 1863 by E. A. Davis. 8°. '71. shp., $6 *Clarke.*

Macdonald, Don. Introduction to Pentateuch. 2 v. 8°. $10 *Scribner, W. & A.*

Macdonald, Frederika. Nathaniel Vaughan, priest and man. [Fiction.] 12°. '74. $1.50 *Somerby.*

MacDonald, G: Works of fancy and imagination. 10 v. 24°. '71. $15 *Routledge.*
— Adela Cathcart. 12°. $1.75 *Loring.*
— Alec Forbes of Howglen. 8°. pap., 75c. *Harper.*
— Annals of a quiet neighborhood. 12°. $1.25 *Harper.*
— *Same.* cr. 8°. '65. $1.75 *Routledge.*
— *Same.* ill. 12°. '73. $1.75 *Lothrop.*
— At the back of the north wind. ill. 12°. '71. $2. *Routledge.*
— Cure for thought-taking. sm. 18°. 50c.; pap., 10c. *Crowell.*
— David Elginbrod. 12°. $1.75 *Loring.*
— Dealings with the fairies. ill. sq. 16°. $1.25 *Routledge.*
— Double story. ill. 16°. '76. $1 *Lothrop.*
— *Same.* 16°. '75. $1.25 *Dodd.*
— England's antiphon: review of relig. poetry of Eng. ill. 12°. $1.75 *Lippincott.*
— *Same.* cr. 8°. '68. $1.75 *Macmillan.*
— Guild Court. 8°. pap., 50c. *Harper.*
— Gutta percha Willie. ('73.) 16°. New ed. '76. $1.25. *Hoyt.*
— Hidden life. 12°. '72. $1.50 *Scribner.*
— Malcolm: romance. 8°. $1.50; pap., $1 *Lippincott.*
— On the miracles of our Lord. ill. 16°. $1 *Lippincott.*
— *Same.* cr. 8°. $1.25 *Routledge.*
— *Same.* 12°. '70. $1.25 *Randolph.*
— Phantastes. 12°. $1.75 *Loring.*
— Portent (The). 12°. $1.75 *Loring.*
— Princess and the goblin. ill. 16°. $1.25 *Lippincott.*
— *Same.* ill. 12°. '71. $1.50 *Routledge.*
— — *See also* Enchanting fairy lib.
— Ranald Bannerman's boyhood. ill. 12°. $1.25. *Lippincott.*
— *Same.* ill. cr. 8°. '71. $1.75 *Routledge.*
— Robert Falconer. 12°. $1.75 *Loring.*
— St. George and St. Michael: tale of the civil wars in Eng. ('75.) ill. 12°. '76. $1.75 *Ford.*
— Seaboard parish: sequel to "Annals of a quiet neighborhood." cr. 8°. '68. $1.75 *Routledge.*
— *Same.* ill. 12°. '73. $1.75 *Lothrop.*
— Thomas Wingfold, curate. 12°. '76. $1.75. (?) *Routledge.*
— Unspoken sermons. cr. 8°. $1.50 *Routledge.*
— Vicar's daughter. ill. 16°. '71. $1.50 *Roberts.*
— Wilfred Cumbermede. 12°. $1.50 *Lippincott.*
— *Same.* 12°. '72. $1.75. — New [chp.] ed. ill. 12°. $1.25; pap., 75c. *Scribner.*
— Within and without. 12°. '72. $1.50 *Scribner.*

Macdonald, J. D. Guide to microscopical examination of drinking water. ill. 8°. '75. $3 *Lindsay.*

Macdonald, Ja. Book of Ecclesiastes explained, critically and popularly. 12°. $1.75 *Dodd.*

Macdonald, Jona. S. Vital philosophy: survey of substance and exposition of natural religion. 12°. $1.75 *Lippincott.*

McDonald, W. N. *See* Blackburn, J. S., *and* McDonald, W. N.

M'Donald, W: Annihilation of the wicked. 12°. '72. 50c. *Meth. Bk. Conc.*
— New Testament standard of piety. 12°. $1 *Palmer.*
— Spiritualism; with testimony of God and man against it. 12°. '66. $1.25 *Meth. Bk. Conc.*
— Wesleyan minstrel. [Hymn book.] 12°. '53. 75c. *Meth. Bk. Conc.*

Macdonald; or, the great mistake. 18°. 30c. *Am. S. S.*

MacDonald ser. *See* Keene, *Mrs.* S. F.

Macdonell, Agnes. For the king's dues. [Fiction.] cr. 8°. '74. $1.75 *Macmillan.*

Macdonell, J: Land question; with particular ref. to Eng. and Scot. 8°. '73. $3.50 .... *Macmillan.*

McDonnell, W: Exeter Hall: a theolog. romance. ('69.) 7th ed. 8°. '73. 80c.; pap., 60c... *Colby.*

— Heathens of the heath: romance. 12°. '74. $1.50; pap., $1 .... *D. M. Bennett.*

Macduff, J: Ross. Altar incense. 18°. $1.. *Carter.*

— Bow in the cloud. 18°. 40c....... *U.P.Bd. of Pub.*

— *Same.* 18°. 50c.; 75c.................... *Carter.*

— *Same;* [also] First bereavement. 18°. '66. 50c. *N. Y. Ref. Ch. Bd.; Pres. Com.*

— Child's book of divinity. 18°. 35c......... *Carter.*

— Cities of refuge. 18°. 50c................ *Carter.*

— Clefts of the rock. 16°. $1.50........... *Carter.*

— Comfort ye, comfort ye. 16°. $1.50....... *Carter.*

— Curfew chimes. 18°. 75c................. *Carter.*

— Evening incense. 18°. 25c.............. *McCauley.*

— Exiles of Lucerna; or, sufferings of the Waldenses during persecution of 1686. 16°. '70. 75c... *Dutton.*

— Faithful promiser. 32°. '52. 15c.; 20c..... *Am. Tr.*

— *Same.* 18°. '70. 40c................ *H. A. Young.*

— *Same.* 18°. '69. 50c.................... *Lothrop.*

— *Same.* ('60.) New ed. 16°. '75. 75c...... *Hoyt.*

— — *See also below* Mind of Jesus.

— Family prayers. 16°. $1.25................ *Carter.*

— Fergus Morton: story of a Scottish boy. 18°. 35c. *Am. S. S.; Carter.*

— First bereavement. *See above* Bow in the cloud.

— Footsteps of St. Paul. 12°. $1.50......... *Carter.*

— Gates of praise and other orig. hymns and poems and fragments of verse. 24°. '76. $1...... *Carter.*

— Gates of prayer. 24°. $1.................. *Carter.*

— Golden sunset. 18°. 35c.................. *Carter.*

— Grapes of Eshcol. 16°. $1................ *Carter.*

— Great journey (The). 18°. 50c........... *Carter.*

— Hart (The) and the water-brooks. 16°. $1.. *Carter.*

— Healing waters of Israel. 16°. $1.25...... *Carter.*

— Memories of Bethany. 16°. $1........... *Carter.*

— Memories of Gennesaret. 12°. $1.50...... *Carter.*

— Memories of Olivet. 12°. $2............. *Carter.*

— Memories of Patmos. 12°. $2............ *Carter.*

— Mind of Jesus. 18°. '68. 30c............. *Am. Tr.*

— *Same.* 32°. '62. 35c.................... *Dutton.*

— *Same.* 18°. '70. 50c................ *H. A. Young.*

— *Same;* [also] Faithful promiser. 32°. '62. 50c. *Dutton.*

— *Same;* [also] Words of Jesus. 24°. 50c. *N. Y. Ref. Ch. Bd.*

— — *Same.* 18°. '70. 75c.; $1.25.......... *Lothrop.*

— — *Same;* [also] Faithful promiser. 24°. '67. 50c. *Pres. Com.*

— — — *Same.* 32°. 50c.; 60c................ *Carter.*

— — — *Same.* 32°. '62. 60c................ *Dutton.*

— — — *Same.* sq. 18°. 75c........... *Estes; Graves.*

— — — *Same.* 18°. '70. 75c............ *H. A. Young.*

— — — *Same.* 18°. 75c. — 32°. 50c......... *Mason.*

— — — *Same;* [also] Morning and night watches. 16°. $1.50.................................. *Carter.*

— *Germ.* Jesu Sinn. 18°. '70. 30c......... *Am. Tr.*

— Morning and night watches. 24°. '67. 50c. *N. Y. Ref. Ch. Bd.; Pres. Com.*

— *Same.* 32°. 50c.; 60c..................... *Carter.*

— *Same.* 18°. '70. 75c.; $1.25............. *Lothrop.*

— — *See also above* Mind of Jesus.

— Noontide at Sychar. 16°. $1.50........... *Carter.*

— Prophet of fire. 12°. $1.50............... *Carter.*

— St. Paul in Rome. 16°. $1.25............. *Carter.*

— Shepherd and his flock. 12°. $1.50....... *Carter.*

— Story of Bethlehem. 16°. $1.............. *Carter.*

— Sunsets on Hebrew mountains. 12°. $1.50.. *Carter.*

— Tales of warrior judges. 16°. $1.......... *Carter.*

— Thoughts of God. 32°. 50c................ *Carter.*

— Wells of Baca; or, solaces of the Christian mourner, and other thoughts on bereavement. obl. 32°. '76. 50c.................................... *Carter.*

— Woodcutter and exiles. 18°. 75c.......... *Carter.*

— Words of Jesus. 18°. '68. 30c............ *Am. Tr.*

— *Same.* 32°. '62. 35c..................... *Dutton.*

Macduff, J: Ross, *continued.*

— *Same.* 18°. '70. 50c................. *H. A. Young.*

— — *See also above* Mind of Jesus.

— *Germ.* Worte Jesu an die Müden. 18°. '70. 25c. *Am. Tr.*

— *Span.* Palabras de Jesus. 18°. '74. 45c... *Am. Tr.*

Macé, J: Histoire d'une bouchée de pain: l'homme. With vocab. and list of idiomatic expressions. ('67.) New ed. 12°. '76. $1.25 .... *Holt.*

— *Eng.* History of a mouthful of bread, and its effect on the organization of men and animals; tr. by Mrs. A. Gatty. 12°. $1.75............ *Harper.*

— Home fairy tales; tr. by M. L. Booth. ill. 12°. $1.75; $2.25......................... *Harper.*

— Servants of the stomach. 12°. $1.75...... *Harper.*

McElgun, J: Annie Reilly; or, the fortunes of an Irish girl in New York. 12°. $1........ *McGee.*

McElhinney, J: J. Doctrine of the church: hist. monograph; with bibliog. of subject. 8°. '71. $3. *Claxton.*

McElligott, Ja. N. American debater: exposition of public debate, and law and practice of parliamentary assemblies, etc. 12°. '55. $1.50.. *Ivison.*

— Analytical and synthetical manual of orthography and definition. 8°. '46. 90c. .... *Ivison.*

— Young analyzer: spelling book and dict. for younger classes. 12°. '45. 30c................ *Ivison.*

— *See also* Sanders, C. W., *and* McElligott, J. N.

McElrath, T: Dictionary of words and phrases used in commerce. 8°. hf. mor., $6 .... *Taintor.*

Maceuen, Malcolm. Celebrities of the past and present; chiefly adapted from Sainte-Beuve. 12°. '74. $1.50............................ *Porter.*

McFadder, *Mrs.* C. Parsonage in the Hartz. 16°. $1.15 .... *Pres. Bd.*

Macfarlan, D. F. *See* M'Cabe, C. C., *and* Macfarlan, D. F.

McFarland, D. *See* Richardson, A. D., *vs.* McFarland, D.

Macfarlane, C: Great battles of the Brit. army. ill. post 8°. $2......................... *Routledge.*

— History of Brit. India. ill. cr. 8°. $2... *Routledge.*

— Italy. *See* Romance of history.

— Life of Duke of Wellington. ill. 12°. $1.. *Routledge.*

— Life of Napoleon Bonaparte. ill. 16°. $1.. *Routledge.*

— Turkey and its destiny. 2 v. 12°. $2 .... *Lea.*

Macfarlane, Ja. Coal regions of Am.: their topog., geol. and development. ill. and maps. 8°. $5; shp., $6; hf. mor., $7.50............. *Appleton.*

Macfarlane, J: Hiding place; or, the sinner found in Christ. 12°. $1.50................ (?) *Martien.*

— Night lamp; or, the deathbed of Agnes M. Macfarlane. 12°. $1.50 .... (?) *Martien.*

Macfarlane, Rob. *See* Practical treatise on dyeing and calico printing.

Macfarren, G: [Plays.] 7 v. 16°. ea., pap., 15c. *French.*

Cont.: Gil Blas. — Guy Faux. — Lestocq: opera. — Malvina: opera. — March of intellect: farce. — My old woman: farce. — Winning a husband: burletta.

McFerrin, J: Berry. Methodism in Tennessee. 3 v. 12°. '70–'72. ea., $2................. *So. Meth.*

— Witnessing church. [Sermon.] 8°. '75. pap., 15c. *So. Meth.*

McFingal. Trumbull, J. $1.75 .... *Putnam.*

MacGahan, J. A. Campaigning on the Oxus, and the fall of Khiva. map and ill. cr. 8°. $3.50.. *Harper.*

McGarvey, J: W. Commentary on Acts; with a rev. of the text. 8°. '59. $1.50....... *Tr. P. & P. Co.*

— Commentary on Matthew and Mark. cr. 8°. *$2; shp., $2.50; hf. cf., $3 .... *Chase.*

— Eldership: treatise on church government. 32°. '72. pap., 10c......................... *Tr. P. & P. Co.*

— Fifty-two Bible lessons. 16°. '75. pap., 20c. *Tr. P. & P. Co.*

McGarvey, J: W., *continued.*
— Midway question book. 2 v. 12°. '60. ea., 15c. *Tr.P.&P.Co.*
Cont.: 1. Matthew, Mark and Luke. — 2. John and Acts.

McGary, W: L. Missouri pleading in civil actions. 8°. shp., $4 .... *Gilbert.*
— — *See also* Whittelsey, C. C.

McGee, Ja. E. Lives of Irishmen's sons and their descendants. 12°. $1 .... *McGee.*
— Men of '48. 12°. $1 .... *McGee.*

McGee, T. D'Arcy. History of Ireland. 2 v. 12°. $3; hf. mor., $4.50; hf. cf., $6 .... *Sadlier.*
— Poems. 12°. $2.50–$4.50 .... *Sadlier.*
— Sebastian; or, the Roman martyr: drama. 18°. 40c. *Sadlier.*
— Star of the north: life of Bp. Maginn. 12°. $1.50. *O'Shea.*

McGeoghegan, Jacques. *See* Mitchel, J., *and* McGeoghegan, J.

McGhee, Rob. J. On Ephesians. 8°. $3 .... *Carter.*

M'Gilchrist, J: Richard Cobden, the apostle of free trade: his political career and public services. ill. 16°. $1.50 .... *Harper.*

McGill, A. T. (*ed.*) American slavery as viewed and acted on by the Presbyterian Church in the U. S. 12°. 20c. .... *Pres. Bd.*

McGill, Ja. Secret prayer and its accompanying exercises. 18°. 65c. .... *Pres. Bd.*

Macgill, J: Our faith the victory: view of principal doctrines of Christian relig. 8°. '65. $2; hf. mor., $3.50 .... *Kelly, P.& Co.*

MacGinley, T: C. Introduction to general biology. (Element. sci. ser.) ill. 16°. 75c. .... *Putnam.*

McGlynn, E: *See* O'Hagan, *Lord*, McGlynn, E., *and* O'Gorman, R.

McGranahan, Ja., *and* Case, C. C. Choice. [Sing. book.] obl. 8°. 75c. .... *Church.*

Macgregor, Annie L. Professor's wife; or, it might have been. 12°. $1.75 .... *Lippincott.*

MacGregor, Dunc. Mariner's progress; or, Captain Christian's voyage to the promised land. 16°. '76. $1.25 .... *Carter.*
— Shepherd of Israel. 16°. $1.25 .... *Carter.*

MacGregor, J: Eastern traveler: places and customs mentioned in the Bible. ill. 18°. 30c. .. *Pres. Bd.*
— Rob Roy (The) on the Baltic. ill. 16°. '67. $1.25. *Roberts.*
— Rob Roy (The) on the Jordan, Nile, Red Sea and Gennesareth, etc. maps and ill. cr. 8°. $2.50. *Harper.*
— Thousand miles in the Rob Roy canoe; or, rivers and lakes of Europe. map and ill. 16°. '67. $1.25 .... *Roberts.*
— Voyage alone in the yawl Rob Roy, from London to Paris, and back by Havre, etc. 16°. '68. $1.25 .... *Roberts.*

McGregor, P. System of logic: compr. discussion of various means of acquiring and retaining knowledge and avoiding error. 12°. $1.50 ... *Harper.*

Macgregor, W. Tables for computing contents of earthwork in cuttings and embankments of railways. roy. 8°. '71. $2.50 .... *Spon.*

McGuffey, W: H. [New eclectic ser.] ('49–'67.) New ed. 11 v. '58–'67 .... *Wilson, H.& Co.*
Cont.: New eclectic primer, 16°, 16c. — spelling book, 16°, 18c. — first reader, 16°, 18c. — second reader, 16°, 35c. — third reader, 16°, 50c. — fourth reader, 12°, 60c. — fifth reader, 12°, 95c. — sixth reader, 12°, $1.15 — speaker, 12°, $1.35 — juvenile speaker, 16°, 75c. — Pictorial eclectic primer, 16°, 12c.

— New high school reader. 12°. '57. $1.25. *Wilson, H.& Co.*
— Rhetorical guide. 12°. '70. $1.35 .. *Wilson, H.& Co.*
— *See also* Leigh, Edn.

Machar, *Miss* A. M. Lucy Raymond. ill. 16°. '71. $1.25 .... *Am. Tr.*

McHenry, Ja. Pleasures of friendship. *See* Poems of pleasures.

McHenry, J: *See* Maryland, Important cases.

Machiavelli, Nicolo. History of Florence, etc.; with the Prince and various hist. tracts. 12°. (Bohn.) $1.25 .... *Little, B.& Co.*
— *Same.* 12°. (Bohn.) $1.40 ...... *Scribner, W.& A.*
— *Same.* 12°. (Bohn.) $1.50 .... *Lippincott.*

Machinists and Blacksmiths' Union. Ritual. *See* Grand Army of the Republic, Ritual.

Machinists and iron founders' reference book. 4°. '72. $30 .... *J.A. Murphy.*

Machpelah: book for the cemetery. 24°. '65. $1.50. *Randolph.*

Machsor: form of [Hebrew] prayers for New Year, Atonement, Passover, Pentecost and Tabernacles; with Eng. transl. 5 v. 12°. $8; mor., $12.50; $16 .... *Frank.*
— *Same;* for New Year and Atonement; with Eng. transl. 2 v. 12°. $4.50; mor., $6.50; $8 .. *Frank.*
— *Same;* for New Year and atonement; without transl. 12°. $1.50 .... *Frank.*

Machsorim: prayers for the holy days. [Hebrew.] 2 v. 16°. '68. $4; $5; mor., $6 .... *Bloch.*
Compr. Rosh hashona *and* Your kippur.

— *Same;* [also] Thefiloth [and] Hymns, prayers and psalms. 4 v. 16°. $6; $8; mor., $10 ... *Bloch.*

Macht (Die) des Gewissens. *See* Hoffmann, F.

Macht (Die) des Glaubens, od. die Bekehrung v. Fräulein Sarah Jordan. 18°. 30c. .... *Ev. Assoc.*

McIlvain, Ctte. L. Ebon and gold. 12°. $1.50 .. *Carleton.*

M'Ilvaine, C: Pettit. Evidences of Christianity: lectures. (cop. '32.) 12°. '53. 90c. .... *Am. Tr.*
— *Same.* ('32.) New ed., with pref. by O. Gregory. 12°. '71. 75c. .... *Leighton; Smith, E.& Co.*
— *Germ.* 12°. $1 .... *Leighton.*
— Justification by faith. 18°. '40. 30c. .. *I. N. Whiting.*
— Righteousness by faith: a new ed., rev., of "Oxford divinity." 2d ed. 8°. '64. $1.25 ..... *Leighton.*
— Select family and parish sermons. 2 v. roy. 8°. '48. $3.50 .... *I. N. Whiting.*
— True temple (The); or, the holy catholic church and communion of saints, in its nature, structure and unity. 16°. '61. 50c. .... *Leighton.*
— Truth and life. 8°. $2.50 .... *Carter.*
— Work of preaching Christ. 12°. '70. 30c.; 40c. *Gospel.*
— *Same.* 12°. '64. 35c. .... *Randolph.*

M'Ilvaine, J. H. Directions to inquiring souls. 32°. 25c. .... *Carter.*
— Elocution: sources and elements of its power. ('70.) New ed. 12°. '74. $1.75 .... *Scribner.*

Macilwain, G: Memoirs of John Abernethy. 12°. $1.50 .... *Harper.*

McIlwraith, T. List of birds of Hamilton, Canada West. 8°. '66. pap., 15c. .... *Essex.*

McIntire, Ja. Treatise on astronomy and the use of the globes. 12°. '50. $1.50 .... *Barnes.*

McIntosh, C: H. Notes on Genesis, Exodus, Leviticus, Numbers. ('72.) New ed. 4 v. 8°. '76. ea., $1.25; per set, $4 .... *Revell.*
— Regeneration: what is it? ('75.) New ed. 16°. '76. 25c.; pap., 10c. .... *Revell.*

McIntosh, *Miss* Mar. Jane. ["Aunt Kitty."] Tales. 4 v. 18°. ea., 75c. .... *Harper.*
Cont.: Conquest and self-conquest; or, which makes the hero? — Cousins: tale of early life. — Praise and principle; or, for what shall I live? — Woman an enigma; or, life and its revealings.

— *Same.* 9 v. 12° .... *Appleton.*
Cont.: Lofty and lowly, 2 v., $2.50. — Aunt Kitty's tales. — Charms and countercharms. — Two lives; or, to seem and to be, *ea.*, $1.25. — Meta Gray; or, what makes home happy. — Year with Maggie and Emma, *ea.*, 75c. — Evenings at Donaldson Manor. — Two pictures; or, how we see ourselves and how the world sees us, *ea.*, $1.

McIntosh, R. M. Good news: songs and tunes for Sunday schools. obl. 12°. '76. bds., 35c.; pap., 30c. ... Ditson.
— Hermon: collection of sacred music. obl. 8°. bds., $1.34 ... Huntington.
— Tabor: Richmond collection of sacred music. obl. 8°. bds., $1.34 ... Huntington.

McJilton, J: N. *See* Monmonier, J. F., *and* McJilton, J. N.

Mack, E. Analytical method for the violin. obl. 4°. '76. bds., $1 ... Ditson.
— Eclectic school for parlor or cabinet organ. obl. 4°. '76. $2.50 ... North.
— New and improved piano method. 4°. bds., $2 .. Peters.
— New melodeon method. 4°. '67. pap., $1.50 .. Ditson.
— One dollar analyt. method for the cabinet organ. 8°. '72. bds., $1 ... Ditson.

Mack, J: Weston the walkist: Dutch [dram.] sketch. 16°. pap., 15c. ... De Witt.

Mack, Rob. C. (*ed.*) Exercises on 150th anniversary of settlement of old Nutfield, comprising Londonderry, Derry, Windham and parts of Manchester, Hudson and Salem, N. H. ill. 8°. '70. $2. *J. B. Clarke.*

Mackarness, *Mrs.* Mta. Anne [*formerly Miss* Planché]. Acting charades for the drawing room. 16°. bds., 50c. ... Routledge.
— Children of the olden time; with pref. by J. R. Planché. ill. 12°. $1.25 ... *Scribner, W. & A.*
— Children's Sunday album. ill. roy. 16°. $1.50. *Cassell.*
— *Same.* ill. 4°. $1.75 ... *Lee & S.*
— Girl of the family. ill. 16°. $1.25 ... Routledge.
— Golden rule: stories ill. of the ten commandments. ill. 16°. $1.25 ... Routledge.
— Granny's spectacles, and what she saw through them. ill. fp. 8°. 60c. ... Cassell.
— How to make the best of it. *See* Young ladies' lib.
— Influence. ill. 16°. $1.25 ... Routledge.
— New charades. 16°. bds., 50c. ... Routledge.
— Old saws new set. ill. 16°. $1.25 ... Routledge.
— Sunbeam stories. ill. 12°. $1.50 ... World Pub.
— Sunbeam stories lib. 4 v. ill. 16°. $5 .. Routledge.
Cont.: Trap to catch a sunbeam. — Cloud with the silver lining. — Dream chintz. — Minnie's love.
— Sweet violets lib. 4 v. ill. 16°. '73–'74. ea., 75c. *Routledge.*
Cont.: Sweet violets. — Sweet flowers. — Snow drop, etc., — Wild rose, etc.
— Tell mamma. ill. 16°. '73. $1.25 ... Routledge.
— Village idol. ill. 16°. $1.25 ... Routledge.
— When we were young. ill. 18°. '70. 55c. .. Lothrop.
— Young ladies' book: occupations, games and amusements. ill. 12°. '75. $3.50 ... Routledge.

Mackay, *Mrs. Col.* Family at Heatherdale. 18°. 75c. *Carter.*
— The Wycliffites. 16°. $1.25 ... Carter.

Mackay, C: Life and liberty in Am.: sketches of a tour in the U. S. and Canada in 1857–8. ill. 12°. $1.50 ... Harper.
— Lost beauties of the English language. 12°. '74. $1.75 ... Bouton.
— Medora Leigh: a hist. and autobiog.; with introd. and commentary on charges brought against Byron by Mrs. Stowe. 8°. pap., 25c. .. Harper.
— Memoirs of extraordinary popular delusions, and the madness of crowds. ill. cr. 8°. '72. $1.75; hf. cf., $3.50; cf., $5 ... Routledge.
— (*ed.*) Home affections portrayed by the poets. ill. 4°. $5; cf., $10; mor., $12 ... Routledge.
— Thousand and one gems of English poetry. ill. 4°. '71. $5. — cr. 8°. $1.75; hf. cf., $3.50; mor., $5. *Routledge.*
— Thousand and one gems of English prose. cr. 8°. $1.75; hf. cf., $3.50; cf., $5 ... Routledge.

McKay, *Mrs.* Ctte. Eliz. Stories of hospital and camp. 12°. '76. $1.50 ... Claxton.

Mackay, W. P. Grace and truth; under twelve different aspects. 12°. '75. $1; pap., 50c. *Gospel; Randolph; Revell.*

McKean, Kate. Manual of social science; condensed from Carey's "Principles of social science." ('64.) 8th ed. 12°. '74. $2.25 ... Baird.

McKean, *Miss* May F. Agnes and Mattie. 16°. $1. *Am. Bapt.*

McKee, Jos. *See* Abeel, G., Murdoch, D., *and* McKee, J.

McKee, W. History of Sherbro mission, west Africa. 16°. 75c. ... Un. B. Pub.

McKeen, Phebe F. Little mother and her Christmas, and other stories. ill. 16°. '75. $1 ... Lothrop.
— Theodora: a home story. 12°. '75. $1.75 .. Randolph.
— Thornton Hall; or, old questions in young lives. 12°. '72. $1.50 ... Randolph.

McKeever, Ht. B. Aunt Harriet's tales about little words. 18°. 75c. ... Pres. Bd.
— Breakers ahead; or, Larry Dalton. ill. 16°. $1. *J. A. Moore.*
— Children with the poets. ('68.) 5th ed. 12°. '70. $1.50–$4.50 ... Claxton.
— Diamond cross ser. 3 v. 18°. $1.75 ... Pres. Bd.
Cont.: Diamond cross; or, story of Florence Clifton, 60c. — May Castleton's mission, 60c. — Rose Delaney's secret, 55c.
— Edith's ministry. 12°. $1.50 ... J. A. Moore.
— Eleanor's three birthdays; or, "charity seeketh not its own." ill. 16°. '67. $1 ... Porter.
— Flounced robe, and what it cost. ('60.) New ed. ill. 16°. '75. 85c. ... Hoyt.
— Frederick Latimer. 16°. $1.25 ... Am. Bapt.
— Good-bye stories for little children. 18°. 70c. Pres. Bd.
— Heavenward earthward. 16°. '67. $1.25 .. Garrigues.
— House on the heights. 12°. $1.50 ... McKinney.
— Jack and Florie; or, the pigeons' wedding. ill. sq. 12°. '69. 75c.; $1; pap., 50c.; — without ill., pap., 25c. ... Claxton.
— Jessie Morrison; or, the mission flower. 18°. 50c. *Pres. Bd.*
— Lazy Stephen, and what made him a valuable man. ('60.) New ed. ill. 16°. '71. 30c. ... Hoyt.
— Little Mary and the fairy. 18°. 50c. ... Pres. Bd.
— *Same.* ill. sq. 12°. '70. 75c.; $1; pap., 50c.; — without ill., pap., 25c. ... Claxton.
— Little Red Cloak: tale in rhyme. ill. sq. 8°. 75c. *Pres. Bd.*
— Lucy Forrester's triumphs; or, "thinketh no evil, believeth all things, hopeth all things." 16°. '67. $1 ... Porter.
— Lucy's two lives. 16°. $1.50 ... (?) Martien.
— Mary Leslie's trials; or, "not easily provoked." ill. 16°. '67. $1 ... Porter.
— Maude and Miriam; or, the fair crusader. ('71.) New ed. 12°. '74. $1.50 ... Claxton.
— Milly's taper; or, what can I do? ('63.) New ed. ill. 16°. '73. $1.15 ... Hoyt.
— Nothing but leaves. ill. 16°. $1 ... J. A. Moore.
— Nursery treasury. ill. 12°. '72. 75c.; $1; pap., 50c.; — without ill., pap., 25c. ... Claxton.
— Old château. 16°. $1.50 ... Pres. Bd.
— Rupert Lawrence; or, a boy in earnest. ill. 16°. $1.25 ... J. A. Moore.
— Silver threads. ('68.) 6th ed. 12°. '75. $1.50. Claxton.
— Sunshine; or, Kate Vinton. ill. 16°. $1.25. *J. A. Moore.*
— Twice crowned: story of the days of Queen Mary. ('73.) 2d ed. 12°. '75. $1.50 ... Claxton.
— Westbrook parsonage. 12°. '69. $1.50 ... Claxton.
— Will Collins. ('60.) New ed. ill. 16°. '72. $1 .. Hoyt.
— Woodcliff. 12°. $1.50 ... J. A. Moore.
— Woodcliff children. ill. 16°. $1 ... J. A. Moore.

Mackellar, T: Rhymes atween times. 12°. $2. *Lippincott.*

MacKenna, Ste. J. At school with an old dragoon. ill. 12°. $2 ... Routledge.
— Plucky fellows. *See* Plucky fellows lib.

McKenney, J. A. Devotional guide for youth. 32°. '70. 25c. . . . . *Dutton.*

M'Kenney, T: L. History of the Indian tribes of N. A. 3 v. 12°. col. por. f°. hf. mor., $120. — text, 2 v., roy. 8°; pl., 1 v., f°. hf. mor., $75; — in 3 v. imp. 8°. hf. mor., $30; mor., $35; — in 2 v. imp. 8°. mor., $33; — in pts., $25. . . . *Rice.*

MacKenzie, —. Problems and riders. *See* Cambridge Senate-House.

Mackenzie, *Mrs.* Adelheid Shelton. Aureola; or, the black sheep: story of Germ. social life. 12°. '71. $1.50. . . . . *Claxton.*

McKenzie, *Rev.* Alex. National series for 1875. [S.-school quest. book.] 18°. bds., 15c. *Cong. Pub.*

— Notes for [S.-school] teachers and scholars. 12°. 50c. . . . . *Cong. Pub.*

— Two boys, and what they did with a year. 16°. $1.25 . . . . *Cong. Pub.*

Mackenzie, Alex. Slidell. American (The) in England. 2 v. 12°. $2.50. . . . . *Harper.*

— Life of Paul Jones. 2 v. 12°. $2. . . . . *Harper.*

— Life of O. H. Perry; with reply to J. F. Cooper's account of the battle of Lake Erie. 2 v. por. 18°. $1.50. . . . . *Harper.*

— Spain revisited. 2 v. ill. 12°. $3.50. . . . . . *Harper.*

— Year in Spain. 3 v. ill. 12°. $3.75. . . . . . . *Harper.*

McKenzie, Clar. D. Little drummer boy: sketch of [his] life. ill. 12°. 40c. . . . . . . *N. Y. Ref. Ch. Bd.*

Mackenzie, Colin A. The Waterloo soldier: life of Farquhar Mackay; with introd. by W. M. Hetherington. 18°. 40c. . . . . *Pres. Bd.*

Mackenzie, H: Novels and misc. works; with memoir by Sir W. Scott. 12°. $1.50. . . . . *Harper.*

Mackenzie, Ja. History of Scotland. 12°. 75c. *Nelson.*

Mackenzie, Morell. Growths in the larynx: their hist., causes, symptoms, diagnosis, etc., with reports of cases. ill. 8°. '71. $3. . . . . . . *Lindsay.*

— Pharmacopœia of the hospital for diseases of the throat; with formulæ for gargles, etc. 18°. '76. $1.25 . . . . *Lindsay.*

Mackenzie, Rob. Shelton. Biography of T. Moore. *See* Literature, art and song.

— Bits of blarney. 12°. $1.50; $2 . . . . *Sadlier.*

— Life of C: Dickens; with his uncoll. pieces, personal recollections and anecdotes. 12°. $2. . *Peterson.*

— Life of Sir Walter Scott. por. 12°. $2. . . . * *Osgood.*

— Tressilian and his friends. 12°. $1.25. . *Lippincott.*

McKenzie, W. S. Sabbath-school studies on life of Christ. 4 v. 18°. '59. ea., pap., 15c. . . *Graves.*
Cont.: 1, 2. For children. — 3, 4. For adults.

Mackenzie, W: Bell. Home religion. 24°. 50c. *Carter.*

— The justified believer: his security, conflicts and triumphs. 12°. 60c. . . . . *Pres. Bd.*

Mackerel Will, the cheating fisher-boy; by author of "Gilbert Gresham." ill. 18°. '61. 40c. . . *Am. Tr.*

— *Same.* ('60.) New ed. ill. 18°. '75. 55c. . . *Hoyt.*

— *Same.* ill. 18°. 65c. . . . . *Pres. Bd.*

Mackey, —. Ghost in a pawnshop: Ethiop. [dram.] sketch. 12°. pap., 15c. . . . . *De Witt.*

Mackey, Alb. G. Book of the chapter: monitorial instructions in [Masonic] degrees of mark, past and most excellent master, and the holy royal arch. ('58.) New ed. ill. 12°. '71. $1.60. . *Clark & M.*

— Cryptic Masonry: monitorial instructions in degrees of royal and select master; with add. section on the super excellent master's degree. ('67.) New ed. 12°. '76. $2 . . . . *Clark & M.*

— Encyclopædia of Freemasonry, and its kindred sciences. ill. 8°. *$9–$15. . . . . *Moss.*

— Lexicon of Freemasonry. por. 12°. $3. . . *Redding.*

— Manual of the lodge. 8°. $1.60 . . . *S. W. Bk. & Pub.*

— *Same.* ('62.) New ed., rev. ill. cr. 8°. '76. $2. *Clark & M.*

— Manual of parliament. law applied to government of Masonic bodies. 12°. *$2; shp., $2.75. . . *Moss.*

Mackey, Alb. G., *continued.*

— Masonic lexicon. por. 12°. $3; hf. cf., $4.50; cf. $5.50 . . . . *Moss*

— Masonic ritualist. 32°. $1.60. . . . . *Redding*

— *Same.* ('67.) New ed. ill. 32°. '76. $1.25; $1.6[0] *Clark & M*

— Mystic tie. [Masonic.] 12°. '75. $1.50. . *Masonic*

— Symbolism of Freemasonry. ('69.) New ed. 12° '76. $2.25 . . . . *Clark & M*

— Text-book of Masonic jurisprudence. 12°. $2.75. *Redding*

— *Same.* ('59.) New ed. 12°. '76. $2.50. . *Clark & M*

Mackey, Jos. Index to the N. Y. dry goods market obl. 8°. '73. $1 . . . . (?) *Mackey*

McKinney, Mordecai. Pennsylvania justice of th[e] peace. 2 v. 8°. '74. . $6. . . *T. & J. W. Johnson*
Cont.: Criminal jurisdiction. — Civil jurisdiction.

Mackintosh, C. H. Life and times of David. 12°. '76 *net*, 45c. . . . . (?) *Longstreth*

Mackintosh, *Sir* Ja. Argument in case of Petier. *Se[e]* Chatham, *Earl of*, Burke, E., *and* Erskine, T.

— Critical and misc. essays. 8°. $2.50; shp., $3.50 hf. cf., $5 . . . . *Appleton*

— — *See also* Modern Brit. essayists.

— History of Eng. to 17th cent. 3 v. 12°. $3. . *Harper*

Macklin, C: Man of the world: comedy. 16°. pap. 15c. . . . . *French*

McKnight, C: Old Fort Duquesne; or, Captain Jack the scout. [Fiction.] ('74.) New ed. ill. 12° '75. $2.50 . . . . *S. A. Clarke*

— Our western border one hundred years ago. ill. 8° '75. *$3 . . . . *McCurdy; McKnight*

McLain, Ma. W. Bearing our burdens. 16°. $1.25. *Cong. Pub*

— Broken idols. 16°. $1.50. . . . . *Cong. Pub*

— Daisy Ward's work. 16°. $1.25. . . . . *Loring*

— Jeanie Darley; or, in the darkness, and in the light 16°. $1.25 . . . . *Cong. Pub.; H. A. Young*

— Keeping open house. ill. 16°. '73. $1. . . . . *Dutton*

— Lifting the veil. ('70.) New ed. 12°. '75. $1.25. *Scribner*

— Wedding garments; or, Bessie Morris' diary. 12° '75. $1.25. . . . . *Scribner*

McLandburgh, *Miss* Flo. Automaton-ear, and othe[r] sketches. 12°. '76. $1.50. . . . . *Jansen*

Maclaren, *Rev.* Alex. Sermons preached at Manchester. 3d ed. fp. 8°. '74. $1.50. . . . *Macmillan*

— *Same.* 2d and 3d ser. 2 v. fp. 8°. '73–'75. ea. $1.50 . . . . *Macmillan*

Maclaren, Arch. Fairy family: ballads and metrica[l] tales ill. fairy mythology of Europe. cr. 8°. '74 $1.75 . . . . *Macmillan*

— Training (for oarsmen), in theory and practice. 2[d] ed., enl. ill. cr. 8°. '74. $2.25. . . . *Macmillan*

McLauchlan, T: Early Scottish church. 8°. $5. *Scribner, W. & A*

McLaurin, J: The model potato: exposition of prope[r] cultivation of the potato, with notes by R. T Trall. 12°. '72. pap., 50c. . . . . *Wells*

McLaurin, *Rev.* J: Essays. 12°. 90c. . . . . *Pres. Bd*

— Glorying in cross of Christ. 18°. '58. 35c. *Randolph*

MacLaurin, Rob. Pious shepherd: life and characte[r] of James Wait. 32°. 30c. . . . . *Pres. Bd*

Maclay, R. S. Life among the Chinese. 12°. '61 $1.75 . . . . *Meth. Bk. Conc*

McLean, Alex., *and* Eaton, W: H. Penuel; or, fac[e] to face with God. 8°. $1.50 . . . . . . *Palmer*

M'Lean, Arch. Commission given by Jesus Christ t[o] his apostles. ill. 12°. 75c.; pap., 30c. . . *Chase*

McLean, J: Sketch of Rev. P. Gatch. 18°. 50c. *Cin. Meth. Bk. Conc*

— *See also* United States, Circuit Court reports.

Maclean, *Mrs.* L. E. *See* Landon, L. E.

Maclear, G: F: Apostles of mediæval Europe. cr. 8°. '69. $1.75 .... *Macmillan.*
— Class-book of the catechism of the Church of Eng. 2d ed. 18°. '75. 75c. .... *Macmillan.*
— Class-book of New Test. history; incl. the connection of Old and New Test. 4th ed. 18°. '75. $1.50. *Macmillan.*
— Class-book of Old Test. hist. 7th ed. maps. 18°. '74. $1.50 .... *Macmillan.*
— First class book of catechism of Church of Eng., with Scripture proofs. New ed. 18°. '68. pap., 20c. *Macmillan.*
— First communion; with prayers and devotions. 32°. '74. 25c. .... *Macmillan.*
— Hour of sorrow. 32°. '75. $1 .... *Macmillan.*
— Manual of instruction for confirmation; with prayers and devotions. 32°. '74. $1 .... *Macmillan.*
— Manual of New Test. hist.; abridg. from Class-book. New ed. 18°. '74. 50c. .... *Macmillan.*
— Manual of Old Test. hist.; abridg. from Class-book. New ed. 18°. '74. 50c. .... *Macmillan.*
— Order of confirmation, with prayers and devotions. 32°. '74. 25c. .... *Macmillan.*
— *See also* Procter, F., *and* Maclear, G. F.

McLees, Arch. Series of alphabets and fancy letters: text book for designers, engravers, etc. 8°. '55. $2.50 .... *Ivison.*
— *Same:* smaller alphabets. 16°. $1 .... *Ivison.*

Macleod, Alex. Christus consolator; or, the pulpit in rel. to social life. 12°. '71. $1.75 .. *Randolph.*
— The wonderful lamp. 16°. $1 .... *Carter.*

Macleod, G: H. B. Notes on surgery of war in Crimea; with remarks on treatment of gunshot wounds. 12°. $1.50 .... *Claxton; Lippincott.*

Macleod, *Mrs.* Georgia A. Hulse. How Jessie came out of the shadow. 16°. pap., 15c. .. *D. H. Carroll.*
— Sea drifts. 16°. $1.25 .... *Carter.*

Macleod, H: Dunning. Elements of banking. cr. 8°. '76. $3.75 .... *Scribner, W. & A.*

Macleod, Norm. Character sketches. ill. 12°. '75. $1.50 .... *Dodd.*
— *Same.* ill. cr. 8°. '72. $2 .... *Routledge.*
— *Same;* incl. "Wee Davie." ill. 12°. '72. $1.50. *Randolph.*
— Days in north India. ill. 12°. $1.50 .... *Lippincott.*
— Earnest student. 12°. $1.50 .... *R. Worthington.*
— Gold thread. 18°. 50c. .... *Carter.*
— *Same.* 18°. '66. 50c. .. *N. Y. Ref. Ch. Bd.; Pres. Com.*
— *Same.* ill. 12°. $1 .... *Routledge.*
— *Same.* ill. 12°. $1.50 .... *R. Worthington.*
— Heaven anticipated. sq. 24°. '75. 35c. .... *Am. Tr.*
— Memoirs. 8°. $2 .... *R. Worthington.*
— Old lieutenant and his son. ill. 12°. $1.50. *Routledge; R. Worthington.*
— Parish papers. 12°. $1.25 .... *Carter.*
— Peeps at the far east: familiar account of a visit to India. ill. 4°. '71. $7.50 .... *Routledge.*
— Reminiscences of a Highland parish. 16°. $1.25. *Carter.*
— *Same.* cr. 8°. $3 .... *Routledge.*
— Simple truths spoken to working people. sm. 8°. $1.25 .... *Routledge.*
— Starling: Scotch story. 8°. '69. pap., 38c. *Littell & G.*
— *Same.* ill. 12°. '74. $1.50 .... *Dodd.*
— *Same.* ill. 12°. $2 .... *Routledge.*
— Temptation of our Lord. 12°. '73. $1.25. *Routledge.*
— Wee Davie. 18°. pap., 15c. .... *R. Worthington.*
— *Same.* 24°. pap., 25c. .... *Routledge.*
— *Same.* 18°. '66. 30c. .... *Am. Tr.*
— *Same.* 18°. 35c. .... *Carter.*
— *Same.* 18°. '66. 35c. .. *N. Y. Ref. Ch. Bd.; Pres. Com.*
— *Same.* 16°. 40c. .... *West. Tr.*
— — *See also above* Character sketches.
— *and* Guthrie, T: (*ed.*) Wind-wafted seed. cr. 8°. $2. *Routledge.*

Macleod, Xav. Don. History of devotion to the Virgin Mary in No. Am.; with memoir of M. by J. B. Purcell. ('66.) 5th ed. 8°. '68. $2.50 ... *Virtue.*
— — *See also* Orsini, M., Life of Virgin.
— Life of Sir Walter Scott. ill. 12°. $1.50 .... *Mason.*
— Memoir of Norman Macleod. 2 v. 8°. '76. $4.50. *Scribner.*

Maclise, Dan. Gallery of illustrious literary characters; with notes by W. Maginn, ed. by W. Bates. 83 por. 4°. $12.60; mor., $28 .. *Scribner, W. & A.*
— Pictures by M.; with descrip. text and biog. sketch by J. Dafforne. f°. '72. $7.50 .... *Routledge.*

Maclise, Jos. Surgical anatomy; with 68 col. pl. and explan. letter-press. imp. 4°. $14 .... *Lea.*

McMaster, J: Bach. Bridge and tunnel centres. ill. 18°. '76. bds., 50c. .... *Van Nostrand.*
— High masonry dams. ill. 18°. '76. bds., 50c. *Van Nostrand.*

McMaster, Rob. Bach. *See* New York, Act to provide for organization of business corporations; Statute law rel. to railroads.

McMasters, S. Y. Methodist in search of the church. 16°. '72. 75c. .... *Dutton.*

Macmillan, Hu. Bible teachings in nature. 7th ed. 12°. $2 .... *Appleton; Macmillan.*
— First forms of vegetation. 2d ed., rev. and enl. ill. 12°. '74. $2 .... *Macmillan.*
— Holidays on high lands; or, rambles and incidents in search of Alpine plants. 2d ed., rev. and enl. 12°. '73. $2 .... *Macmillan.*
— Ministry of nature. 3d ed. 12°. $2 .... *Macmillan.*
— Our Lord's three raisings from the dead. 16°. '75. $1.50 .... *Dutton.*
— Sabbath of the fields: sequel to "Bible teachings in nature." 2d ed. fp. 8°. '76. $2 ..... *Macmillan.*
— The true vine; or, the analogies of our Lord's allegory. 2d ed. 12°. $2 .... *Macmillan.*

Macmillan's globe editions. 12 v. 18°. ea., $1.50; $2; hf. cf., $3 .... *Macmillan.*
Cont.: Shakespeare, ed. by Clark and Wright. — Mallory's Morte d'Arthur. — Scott's Poetical works, with essay by F. T. Palgrave. — Burns' Poetical works, ed. by A. Smith. — Robinson Crusoe, ed. by H. Kingsley. — Goldsmith, with essay by Masson. — Pope's Poetical works, ed. by Ward. — Spenser, ed. by Morris. — Dryden, ed. by Christie. — Cowper's Poetical works, ed. by Benham. — Virgil, tr. by Lonsdale and Lee. — Horace, tr. by Lonsdale and Lee.

Macmillan's lib. of travel. 6 v. ill. cr. 8°. $15 .. *Macmillan.*
Cont.: Baker's Nile tributaries of Abyssinia. — Baker's Albert N'yanza great basin of the Nile. — Palgrave's Narrative of a year's journey through central and eastern Arabia. — Dilke's Greater Britain. — Kingsley's At last. — Wallace's Malay archipelago.

Macmillan's reading books. 7 v. 16°. '75 .. *Macmillan.*
Cont.: Primer, 10c. — Bk. 1, 15c. — 2, 20c. — 3, 25c. — 4, 40c. — 5, 50c. — 6: introd. to Eng. literature, 12°, $1.

McMullan, J. *See* South Carolina, Reports.

MacMullen, J: History of Canada. 8°. $3.50; hf. cf., $5.50 .... *Lippincott.*

McMullen, Jos. F. Compendium of Wisconsin forms. 4th ed., rev. and enl. 8°. shp., $3 .. *E. B. Myers.*

McMullen, *Miss* Ma. A. ["Una."] Snatches of song. 12°. '74. $1.50 .... *Fox; Sadlier.*

McMurtrie, H: Domestic medicine. 18°. '71. $1. *Porter.*
— Woman's medical companion and nursery adviser. 18°. '71. $1 .... *Porter.*

McMurtrie, R. C. *See* Biddle, G. W., *and* McMurtrie, R. C.

Macnaghten, Stuart. Select equity cases. *See* Law lib.
— *See also* England, High Court of Chancery reports.

McNally, Fs. Improved system of geography. 4°. '66. hf. bd., $2 .... *Barnes.*
— — *See also* Allen, J.

McNally, T: Apostolic canons; in Greek, Lat. and Eng., with notes. 8°. (Bagster.) pap., $1.25 .. *Wiley.*

Macnamara, C. Manual of the diseases of the eye. 2d ed., rev. and enl. pl., ill. and diagrams. 12°. $4.50 .... *Lindsay.*

Macnamara, H. Practical treatise on nullities and irregularities in law: their character, distinctions and consequences. 8°. '55. $1.50. *T. & J. W. Johnson.*

— — *See also* Law library.

McNary, Rob. B. Woman her own doctor: treatise upon diseases peculiar to women. 12°. '71. $1.25 .... *S. W. Bk. & Pub.*

Macnaught, J: Doctrine of inspiration: inquiry conc. infallibility, inspiration and authority of Holy Writ. 12°. $1.50 .... *Mendum.*

McNevin, T: Confiscation of Ulster. 12°. $1 .. *Noonan.*

MacNie, J. Treatise on theory and solution of algebraical equations. 8°. '76. $2.50 .... *Barnes.*

M'Owan, P: Memoirs of Mary Fishwick. 18°. '43. 40c. *Meth. Bk. Conc.*

— Practical considerations on the Christian Sabbath. 18°. 60c. .... *Cin. Meth. Bk. Conc.*

Macoy, Rob. Adoptive rite: manual of instruction in the Eastern Star degree. 16°. '75. $1 .. *Masonic.*

— General history, cyclopaedia and dictionary; [with] dict. of symbolical Masonry by G. Oliver. ill. 8°. '75. *$5 .... *Masonic.*

— History of, and how to see, New York and its environs. 2d ed. 12°. '76. 50c.; pap., 25c. .. *Macoy.*

— Manual of the order of the Eastern Star. ill. 12°. '72. $1 .... *Masonic; Redding.*

— Masonic manual. ('58.) New ed., rev. ill. 32°. '76. $1; $1.50 .... *Clark & M.*

— Masonic vocal manual. [Music.] 16°. '62. per doz., $3 .... *Masonic.*

— Master workman: elucidations of degrees of entered apprentice, fellow-craft and master Mason. ('53.) New ed. ill. 32°. '76. 60c. .... *Clark & M.*

— Obituary rites of Freemasonry. 16°. '65. 30c. *Masonic.*

— Ritual of the order of the Eastern Star. ill. 18°. '76. $1 .... *Macoy.*

— True Masonic guide: elucidations of the fundamental principles of Freemasonry. ('52.) New ed. ill. 12°. '73. $1.75 .... *Clark & M.*

— *and* Sickels, Dan. Freemason's monitor. 32°. '75. $1.50 .... *Masonic.*

McPheeter, J. New and improved six per ct. interest table; showing interest on any amount for from 1 to 360 days. 8°. $1 .... *Lippincott.*

McPherson, E: Handbook of politics for 1872. 8°. '72. $2.50; — for 1874. 8°. '74. $2.50 .. *Solomons.*

— Political hist. of U. S. during the period of reconstruction. ('71.) 2d ed. 8°. '76. $5 .. *Solomons.*

— Political hist. of U. S. during the rebellion, 1860–1865. ('64.) 3d ed. 8°. '76. $5 ..... *Solomons.*

Macpherson, Ja. Poems of Ossian. (Blue and gold ed.) ill. 18°. $1.25. — (Cabinet ed.) ill. 16°. $1.50 .... *Nichols & H.*

— *Same;* in Gaelic and Eng.; ed. by A. Clerk. 2 v. imp. 8°. $15.75 .... *Scribner, W. & A.*

Macpherson, J: Baths and wells of Europe: their action and uses, with notices of climatic resorts and diet cures. 2d ed. 12°. '73. $2 ... *Macmillan.*

— Our baths and wells: mineral waters of the Brit. islands; with list of sea-bathing places. 12°. '71. $1.25 .... *Macmillan.*

Macpherson, *Rev.* J: Life and labors of Duncan Matheson, the Scottish evangelist. 16°. '76. $1.25 .... *Carter.*

MacPherson, W. *See* England, Law reports.

Macplin, C: Love-a-la-mode: farce. 16°. pap., 15c. *French.*

McQuaid, B. J., *and* Abbot, F. E. Public school question as understood by a Cath. Am. citizen and by a liberal Am. citizen. 12°. '76. pap., 20c. .... *Free Rel.*

McQueen, Hu. Orator's touchstone; or, eloquence simplified: system for improvement of the voice. 12°. $1.25 .... *Harper.*

Macquoid, *Mrs.* Kath. S. Charming widow (A). 12°. $1.75 .... *Carleton.*

— Hester Kirton. 16°. $1 .... *Lippincott.*

— My story. ill. 8°. pap., $1 .... *Appleton.*

— Patty. 8°. pap., 50c. .... *Harper.*

— *Same.* cr. 8°. $1.75 .... *Macmillan.*

— Rookstone. ill. 8°. $1.25; pap., 75c. ... *Lippincott.*

— Through Normandy. ill. 12°. '75. $1.50 .. *Randolph.*

— *Same.* ill. 12°. '74. $3 .... *Routledge.*

— Too soon. 8°. pap., 50c. .... *Harper.*

MacRae, Archibald. The Andes and pampas. *See* Gilliss, J. M.

Macready, W: Irishman in London: farce. 16°. pap., 15c. .... *French.*

Macready, W: C: Reminiscences and diary; ed. by Sir F. Pollock. 2 v. por. 8°. '75. $12 .. *Macmillan.*

— *Same;* condensed. por. cr. 8°. $1.50. *Harper; Macmillan.*

McRoberts, J: A. Self-instructing model Eng. grammar. 12°. hf. roan, 75c. .... *Desilver.*

Macrum, Ja. M. The new piano: lyric poem. sq. 16°. '71. 75c. .... *R. S. Davis (P.)*

M'Sherry, Ja. Father Laval; or, the Jesuit missionary: tale of the No. Am. Indians. sq. 16°. '60. 60c.; 80c. .... *Murphy.*

— History of Maryland to 1848, and other essays. 8°. '69. $1.25 .... *Kelly, P. & Co.*

Macturk, J: Elements of physical geography. (Element. sci. ser.) ill. 16°. '73. 75c. .... *Putnam.*

McTyeire, Holland N. Catechism of Bible hist. ('74.) 5th ed. ill. 18°. '76. hf. bd., 25c. ..... *So. Meth.*

— Duties of Christian masters. 18°. '59. 75c. .. *So. Meth.*

— Manual of the discipline of the M. E. Church, south; incl. decisions of college of bishops, and rules of order, application to ecclesiastical courts and conferences. ('70.) 6th ed. 16°. '76. $1 .. *So. Meth.*

McVey, A. H. Digest of Ohio reports. 2 v. roy. 8°. '75. shp., $15 .... *Callaghan; Ingham.*
Compr. Ohio reports (20 v.); Ohio State reports (v. 1–24); Tappan; Wright; Handy; Disney, etc.

MacVicar, M. Teacher's handbook of arithmetic. 12°. $1.50 .... *Taintor.*

McVickar, W: A. Life of John McVickar. por. cr. 8°. '71. $2 .... *Hurd & H.*

McWatters, G: S. Knots untied; or, ways and byways in the hidden life of Am. detectives. ill. 8°. $2.75; leath., $3.25 .... *Burr.*

McWhorter, G: Cumming. Church essays. 12°. $1. *Appleton.*

— Popular handbook of the New Test. 16°. $1 .. *Harper.*

Macy, Sylvanus J. Genealogy of the Macy family, 1653–1868. por. and pl. fp. 4°. $8 ... *Munsell.*

Mad as a hatter. Marshall, F. A. 15c. ...... *French.*

Mad astronomer: musical [dram.] sketch. 16°. pap., 15c. .... *Happy.*

Mad bard; or, the mysteries of Melrose Castle. 12°. pap., 20c. .... *Hurst.*

Mad dogs. Moore, J. 15c. .... *French.*

Mad folk of Shakespeare. Bucknill, J. C. $2.50. *Macmillan.*

Mad marriage. Fleming, M. A. $1.75 ..... *Carleton.*

Mad Monkton. *See* Collins, W.

Mada (*pseud.*) *See* Clarke, M. L.

Madagascar and its martyrs. ill. 18°. 50c. .. *Pres. Bd.*

Madam is abed: vaudeville. 16°. pap., 15c. .. *Lee & S.*

Madame Agnes. *See* Farm of Muiceron.

Madame Angot: opera bouffe. 16°. pap., 15c. *French.*

Madame Beliott's ball. Burnand, F. C. 15c. .. *French.*

Madame de Beaupré. Jenkin, C. $1.25 ...... *Holt.*

Madame de Chamblay. *See* Dumas, A.

Madame de Fleury. *See* Edgeworth, Mar.

Madame de Lavalle's bequest. M. . ., *Mme.* $1.50. *Cunningham.*

Madame de Stäel: hist. novel. Bölte, A. $1.50. *Putnam.*
Madame de Verceil. Bourdon, M. F. 30c...*O'Shea.*
Madame How and Lady Why. Kingsley, C. $2. *Routledge.*
Madame Mobcap, and other stories. ill. 4°. '76. pap., 25c. ....*Lothrop.*
Madame Therese. Erckmann, E., *and* Chatrian, A. $1.25; 75c....................*Scribner.*
Mädchen (Das) von Treppi. *See* Heyse, P.
Maddalena, the orphan of the Via Appia: tale of Rome in 19th cent. 16°. $1; $1.50....*Sadlier.*
Madden, H: R. Uterine diseases; with app. [Hom.] 8°. 50c....................*Boericke.*
Madden, R: R. Literary life and correspondence of Countess of Blessington. 2 v. por. 12°. $3. *Harper.*
— Lives of Robert and Thomas A. Emmet. por. 12°. '57. $1.50....................*Haverty.*
Maddest marriage ever was. Burton, J. D. 25c. *Beadle.*
Maddie and Lolly: sequel to "Little Alice's palace." 18°. 25c....................*Am.S.S.*
Maddock, H: *See* England, Chancery reports.
Maddox, F: More. Frederick the Great: drama. 16°. pap., 15c....................*French.*
Maddox, J. M. King and deserter: drama. 16°. pap., 15c....................*French.*
Made for it. *See* Golden chain lib.
Made up stories. Follen, E. L. 50c........*Lee & S.*
Madelaine. Cunningham, V. 15c..........*French.*
Madelaine's voyage. ill. 18°. '75. 30c.......*Dodd.*
Madeleine's trial. Pressensé, E. de. $1.25. *Scribner, W. & A.*
Madeline. Elmwood, R. 30c..............*Am. Tr.*
Madeline. Kavanagh, J. $1.25..........*Appleton.*
Madeline Graham. Robinson, J. 80c.....*Routledge.*
Madeline Hascall's letters. *See* Gardner, *Mrs.* H. C.
Mademoiselle de la Seiglière. Sandeau, J. 40c...*Holt.*
Mademoiselle Fifty Millions. Saint-Mars, N. C. de C. 60c....................*Appleton.*
Madge. Talcott, H. B. $1.25..........*Appleton.*
Madge Graves. Ludlow, A. D. $1....*Bost.Am.Tr.*
Madge, Kate and Dick. Dudleigh, A. $1..*Pres.Bd.*
Madison, Ja. Letters and other writings. 4 v. 8°. '65. $16..................*Claxton; Lippincott.*
— *See also* Federalist.
— *and* Jefferson, T: Virginia and Kentucky's resolutions and debates, 1798–9. 8°. '35. hf. shp., $1.50....................*J. W. Randolph.*
Madison, Ja. M. Exposition of Odd-fellowship. ill. 8°. pap., 25c....................*Peterson.*
Madison, Virg. (*pseud.*) *See* Brock, Sallie A.
Madison Ave. lectures on Baptist principles; by eighteen ministers. 12°. $1.50..........*Am.Bapt.*
Madison Avenue [N. Y.] Reformed Church. Exercises at the laying of the corner stone, May 23, 1870. ill. 8°. pap., 25c..............*N.Y.Ref.Ch.Bd.*
Madison Sq. Church collection. Coe, S.W. $2.75.*Pond.*
Madonna Mary. Oliphant, M. O. W. 50c. *Harper; Littell & G.*
Madvig, J: N: Latin grammar; rev. by T. A. Thacher. ('70.) 3d ed. 12°. '75. hf. mor., $3...*Ginn.*
Mae Madden. Mason, M. M. $1.25........*Jansen.*
Maffei, J: P. *See* Bartoli, D., *and* Maffei, J: P.
Maffit, J: N. Life. 8°. pap., 13c........*Peterson.*
Magazin d. merkwürdigsten u. interessantesten Criminalgeschichten u. Länder. 8°. '74. $3.25..*Zickel.*
Magdala and Bethany. Malan, S. C. 60c....*Dutton.*
Magdalen. *See* David Hewson.
Magdalena. John, E. 35c..............*Lippincott.*
Magdalena Goldschlager. 12°. pap., 15c.....*Radde.*
Magdalene and Raphael; or, the wonder of vision; tr. from the Germ. 18°. 45c..........*Routledge.*
Magee, Irving. Rise of Protestantism, with the growth and doctrines of the Lutheran Church: sermon. 8°. '75. pap., 50c....................*Munsell.*
Magee's illustrated guide of Phila. and the Centennial Exhibition. sq. 16°. '76. 75c.; $1; pap., 50c. *R. Magee.*
Magendie, François. Treatise on human physiology; tr. and enl. by J. Revere. ill. 8°. $2.50..*Harper.*
Maggie. Eggleston, N. H. 50c..........*Cong.Pub.*
Maggie, the fisherman's daughter. 18°. 60c...*Crowell.*
— *See also* Bright eye lib.
Maggie and Bessie; or, lame Jemmy's chair. 18°. 60c. *Am.S.S.*
Maggie and her friends. Brown, M. R. 75c...*Randolph.*
Maggie and the mice. *See* Baker, *Mrs.* H. N. W.
Maggie and the sparrows. 18°. 50c..........*Carter.*
Maggie and Willie. 18°. 60c............*Cong.Pub.*
Maggie Fuller lib. 5 v. ill. 18°. '66. $2.50. *Meth.Bk.Conc.*
Cont.: Maggie Fuller. — China cup. — Miss Howard's school. — Boy artist. — Great things done by little people.
Maggie Lisle. 18°. '70. pap., 12c..........*Dutton.*
Maggie Manealy. Browne, S. H. 60c.....*Cong.Pub.*
Maggie's message; by the author of "Soldier Fritz." ill. 16°. '72. 75c....................*Lothrop.*
Maggie's mistake: school girl's story. ill. 16°. $1.25. *Carter.*
Maggie's rosary, and other tales; by author of "Marion Howard." 2d ed. 12°. '73. $1....*Cath. Pub.*
Maggie's windows. *See* Little Alice's lib.
Maggy Spencer; or, how to reach the erring and the lost. 18°. 50c....................*Am.S.S.*
Magic circle. Harmistoun, J. $2.25; $1.75..*Peters.*
Magic flute. *See* Ditson.
Magic glass. *See* Little Katie's little lib.
Magic lantern. *See* Cousin Belle; — Robin Ranger's lib.
Magic mirror. 18°. 30c. ....*Dutton.*
Magic mirror. Ford, T. 20c..........*Claremont.*
Magic mirror. Gilbert, W. $2..........*Routledge.*
Magic of kindness. Mayhew, H. *and* A. 75c. *Harper.*
Magic penny: Ethiop. drama. 16°. pap., 15c. *French; Happy.*
Magic, pretended miracles and remarkable natural phenomena; rev. by T. O. Summers. ('56.) 2d ed. ill. 18°. '75. 65c..............*So.Meth.*
Magic shoes. Giles, C. $1..............*New Ch.*
Magic spectacles. 18°. 65c..............*Cong.Pub.*
Magic spectacles. Giles, C. $1............*New Ch.*
Magic spectacles, and other stories. 18°. 40c. *Dutton.*
Magic staff. Davis, A. J. $1.75 ........*A.J.Davis.*
Magic toys. Oxenford, J. 15c..............*French.*
Magician's guide; or, conjuring made easy. ill. 12°. pap., 25c. ....*Hurst.*
Magician's own book: sleight-of-hand and card tricks, puzzles, etc. ill. 12°. $1.50..........*Dick & F.*
Magician's show box. ill. 16°. $1.50......**Osgood.*
Magicians of Palestine. Headley, P. C. 25c.; 30c. *J.E.Potter.*
Magie, D: Spring-time of life. ill. 18°. '55. 60c. *Am.Tr.*
Magill, E: H. First lessons in French; with vocab. 12°. 75c....................*Potter, A.& Co.*
— French grammar; with vocab. 12°. $1.50. *Potter, A.& Co.*
— Introductory French reader. 12°. $2..*Potter, A.& Co.*
— Key to French grammar. 12°. $1...*Potter, A.& Co.*
— Prose and poetry. [French.] 12°. $2..*Potter, A.& Co.*

Magill, Ma. Tucker. History of Virginia; for schools. ill. 12°. '73. hf. roan, $1.25 .... *Turnbull.*
— Holcombes: story of Virginia home-life. 12°. $1.50. *Lippincott.*
— Women; or, chronicles of the late [civil] war. 12°. '71. $1.75 .... *Turnbull.*
Maginn, W: *See* Noctes ambrosianæ.
Maglathlin, H. B. National speaker. 29th ed. 12°. $1.25 .... *R.S.Davis (B.)*
Magnet stories. *See* Peebles, *Mrs.* M. L.
Magoon, Elisha L. Distinguished Am. orators. ill. 12°. $1.75 .... *Mason.*
— Orators of the Am. revolution. ill.12°. $1.75 .. *Mason.*
— Westward empire; or, the great drama of human progress. 12°. $1.50 .... *Harper.*
Magpie; or, the maid. Pocock, I. 15c ...... *French.*
Magruder, A. C. *See* Maryland, Court of Appeals reports.
Magruder, W. H. N. Young minister: life of S. B. Bangs. 12°. $1.25 .... *Cin.Meth.Bk.Conc.*
Maguire, A. A. Lizzie's secret. ill. 16°. '73. 75c. *Dutton.*
Maguire, J: Fs. Works. 3 v. 12°. ea., $2 .. *Sadlier.*
Cont.: Irish in America. — Life of Father Matthew. — Rome and its ruler.
— Young Prince Marigold. ill. fp. 8°. '73. $1.50. *Macmillan.*
Maguire, S. *See* Pope, R. T. P., *and* Maguire, S.
Maguire, T. H. Art of figure drawing. pl. f°. '74. $8. *Routledge.*
Mahaffy, J: Pentland. Social life in Greece, from Homer to Menander. 2d ed., rev. and enl. cr. 8°. '75. $2 .... *Macmillan.*
Mahan, Asa. Baptism of the Holy Ghost. 8°. $1.25. *Palmer.*
— Natural theology. 12°. '67. $1.50 .... *Hoyt.*
— Science of logic: analysis of laws of thought. 8°. '56. $2 .... *Barnes.*
— System of intellectual philosophy. ('54.) New ed., rev. and enl. 12°. $1.75 .... *Barnes.*
— The true believer: his character, duty and privileges elucidated. 16°. 75c. .... *Harper.*
Mahan, Dennis Hart. Advanced guard, outpost and detachment service of troops; with principles of strategy and grand tactics. ill. 18°. $1.50 .. *Wiley.*
— Descriptive geometry; as applied to drawing of fortifications and stone cutting; for cadets of U. S. Milit. Acad. pl. 8°. $1.50 .... *Wiley.*
— Elementary course of civil engineering; for cadets of the U. S. Milit. Acad.; with app. and index, ed. by De V. Wood. ill. 8°. $5 .... *Wiley.*
— Elements of permanent fortifications. New ed., rev. and ed. by J. B. Wheeler. pl. 8°. $6.50 .. *Wiley.*
— Industrial drawing. 20 pl. 8°. $3 .... *Wiley.*
— Treatise on field fortifications; with outlines of arrangement, etc., of permanent fortifications. pl. 8°. $3.50 .... *Wiley.*
Mahan, Milo. Church hist. of first 7 centuries, to close of 6th general council. 8°. '73. $4; hf. cf., $6 .... *Pott.*
— Exercise of faith, in its rel. to authority and private judgment. 18°. 50c. .... *McCauley.*
— On confession: introd. to C. N. Gray's Statement on confession. 8°. '73. pap., 25c. .... *Pott.*
— Spiritual point of view; or, the glass reversed: answer to Bp. Colenso. 12°. 75c. .... *Appleton.*
— Who was James, the Lord's brother? *See* Seabury, S: Mary the Virgin.
— *See also* Hopkins, I. H., *and* Mahan, M.
Maher, W: H. On the road to riches: hints for clerks and young business men. 12°. '76. $1.25; pap., 50c. .... *Brown, E. & Co.*
Mahlon, —. Letters; ed. by A. J. Baird. 60c. (?) *Cumberland.*
Mahomet. *See* Goethe, J. W. v.
Mahomet. *See* Mohammed.
Mahon, *Lord.* *See* Stanhope, *Earl.*

Mahony, Fs. ["Father Prout."] Reliques of Fath[e] Prout; coll. by O. Yorke [*pseud.*] ill. 12°. h[f.] cf., $5 .... *Appleto[n].*
— *Same.* ill. 12°. (Bohn.) $2.75 ..... *Little, B. & C[o].*
— *Same.* ill. 12°. (Bohn.) $3. *Lippincott; Scribner, W. & A.*
Maiblumen (Die). Schmid, C. v. 20c. .... *Morwitz.*
Maid and magpie. Byron, H. J. 15c. .... *French.*
Maid and magpie. Pocock, I. 15c. .... *French.*
Maid ob de Hunkpuncas: Ethiop. drama. 16°. pap. 15c. .... *Happy*
Maid of Croissey. Gore, C. G. 15c. .... *French.*
Maid of honor; or, the massacre of St. Bartholomew. 8°. pap., 50c. .... *Harper.*
Maid of honour. Wooler, J. P. 15c. .... *French.*
Maid of Judah. Lacy, R. 15c. .... *French.*
Maid of Killeena. *See* Black, W:
Maid of the mill. Beaumont, F., *and* Fletcher, J. 15c. *French.*
Maid of Orleans. Calvert, G. H. $1.50 .... *Putnam.*
Maid of Orleans. *See* Schiller, J. F. v.
Maid of Orleans: romantic chronicle. 8°. pap., 75c. *Harper.*
Maid of Sker. Blackmore, R. D. 75c. ..... *Harper.*
Maid or wife: comedy. 16°. pap., 15c. ...... *French.*
Maid with milking pail. Buckstone, J. B. 15c. .. *French.*
Maiden and married life of Mary Powell. Manning, A. $1 .... *Dodd.*
Maiden martyr of Scotland. Mowat, M. 65c. .. *Pres.Bd.*
Maiden mother. Zurnow, C. 25c. .... *Barclay.*
Maiden of Treppi. Heyse, P. 75c. .... *Hinton.*
Maiden widow. Southworth, E. D. E. N. $1.75; $1.50 .... *Peterson.*
Maidenhood ser. 5 v. ill. 12°. $8 .... *Lee & S.*
Cont.: Seven daughters, by A. M. Douglas. — Running to waste, by G. M. Baker. — Our Helen, by S. May. — That queer girl, by V. F. Townsend. — The Asbury twins, by S. May.
Maierstein, M. First lessons in German. 16°. '7[?] bds., 30c. .... *Knœfel.*
Mail-bag. 18°. 65c. .... *Cong.Pub.*
Mail-bag ser. 7 v. 18°. $4.50 .... *Cong.Pub.*
Cont.: Mail-bag. — Old homestead. — Magic spectacles. — Old school-house. — Only a pin. — Village doctor. — Lame Bessie.
Mail coach. *See* Sherwood, M. M.
Maillard, *Abbé* —. Grammar of the Mikmaque lang. *See* Shea, J. G., Library of Am. linguistics.
Maillard, Annette Marie. The jealous husband. 12°. $1.75; pap., $1.50 .... *Peterson.*
— Zingra, the gipsy. 8°. pap., 50c. .... *U.P.James.*
Main, Hub. P. *See* Bell, G: A., *and* Main, H. P.
Main, Sylvester. *See* Bell, G: A., *and* Main, S.; — Bradbury, W. B., Bell, G. A., *and* Main, S.
Main, T: J., *and* Brown, T: Indicator and dynamometer; with their applic. to steam engine. ('64.) 3d ed. ill. 8°. '74. $1.50 .... *Baird.*
— — Marine steam engine. ('64.) 7th ed. ill. 8°. '74. $5 .... *Baird.*
— — Questions on subjects connected with the marine steam-engine, and examination papers; with hints for their solution. ('63.) 5th ed. 12°. '75. $1.50 .... *Baird.*
Maine, *Sir* H: Sumner. Ancient law: its connection with early hist. of society, and its rel. to modern ideas. 5th ed. 8°. (Lond.) '74. $5 .. *Little, B. & Co.*
— *Same;* with introd. by T. W. Dwight. 8°. '7[?]. $3.50 .... *Holt.*
— Lectures on early hist. of institutions. 8°. (Lond.) '75. $5 .... *Little, B. & Co.*
— *Same.* 8°. '75. $3.50 .... *Holt.*
— Village communities in the east and west: lectures at Oxford. 2d ed. 8°. (Lond.) '72. $3.75. *Little, B. & Co.*
— *Same.* 8°. '76. $3.50 .... *Holt.*

Maine. Revised statutes, 1871; [with] U. S. Const. and Const. of Me.; with app. roy. 8°. '71. shp., $4 .... *Bailey*.
— Supreme Court reports, v. 1–56 (1820–1869). 56 v. 8°. ea., shp., $5.50 .... *Dresser*.
Cont.: 1-9 (1820-'32), by S. Greenleaf. — 10-12 (1833-'35), by J. Fairfield. — 13-18 (1836-'41), by J. Shepley. — 19, 20 (1841), by J. Appleton. — 21-30 (1842-'49), by J. Shepley. — 31-35 (1849-'53), by A. Redington. — 36-40 (1853-'55), by S. Heath. — 41, 42 (1856), by J. M. Adams. — 43, 44 (1857-8), by T. Ludden. — 45-51 (1859-'65), by W. Hubbard. — 52-56 (1865-'69), by W. W. Virgin.
— *Same*. v. 57–61 (1870–'74). 5 v. 8°. ea., shp., $5. *Loring, S. & H.*
Cont.: 57-60 (1870-'73), by W. W. Virgin. — 61 (1874), by E. B. Smith.
— *Same*. v. 62–65 (1874–'76). 4 v. 8°. ea., shp., $5.50. *Dresser*.
Cont.: 62-64 (1874-5), by E. B. Smith. — 65 (1876), by J. D. Pulsifer.
— — Digest. *See* Virgin, W. W.
Maine geological survey. First–third reports on geol. of M.; by C: T. Jackson. 3 v. 8°; and atlas, 4°. '37–'39 .... *State*.
— Preliminary report upon the natural history and geol. of M. 8°. '61 .... *State*.
Note. Bd. with 6th ann. rpt. of Me. Bd. of Agric.
— *Same*. Second report. 8°. '62 .... *State*.
Maine Historical Soc. Collections. 7 v. 8°. '31–'76. $14 .... *Me. Hist.*
— Documentary ser. v. 1: Discovery, by J. G. Kohl; with app. on the voyages of the Cabots by M. d'Avezac. 8°. '69. $4 .... *Me. Hist.*
Maine state year book and legislative manual; by E. S. Hoyt. [Annual.] (Business ed.) 16°. $1.25; with map, $1.50. — (Legislative ed.) 16°. $1.50; with map, $1.75 .... *Hoyt, F. & D.*
Maine woods. Thoreau, H. D. $1.50 .... *Osgood*.
Mainstone's housekeeper. Meteyard, E. $1.50 .. *Loring*.
Maintenance of health. Fothergill, J. M. $2; $5. *Putnam*.
Mair, Ja. Allan (*ed.*) Scotch anecdotes. 16°. bds., 50c. .... *Routledge*.
— *See also* Hood, T., Kennedy, P., *and* Mair, J. A.
Mair, J: Introduction to Latin syntax. 12°. hf. roan, 75c. .... *Lippincott*.
Maison (La) de Penarvan. Sandeau, J. 40c... *Holt*.
Maistre, Xav. de. Œuvres complètes. Nouv. ed., [avec] notice biog. 12°. '75. $1.50 .... *Holt*.
— Les prisonniers du Caucase. *See* Achard, A., Le clos pommier.
— Voyage autour de ma chambre. 12°. '75. pap., 50c. *Holt*.
— *Eng.* Journey round my room; tr. with notice of M. by H. A. 16°. '71. $1.50 .... *Hurd & H.*
Maitland, E: [" Herb. Ainslie."] By and by: hist. romance of the future. 12°. '74. $1.75 .. *Putnam*.
— Higher law: romance. 12°. '71. $1.75 .. *Putnam*.
— Pilgrim and the shrine. 3d ed. 12°. '71. $1.50. *Putnam*.
Maitland, Ja. A. [Novels.] 7 v. 8°. ea., $1.75; pap., $1.50 .... *Peterson*.
Cont.: Diary of an old doctor.— Lawyer's story.— Old patroon. — Sartaroe: tale of Norway.— Three cousins.— Wanderer.— Watchman.
Maius, Angelus. *See* Bible, New Test., *Greek*.
Major John André. Haid, L. 50c. .... *Murphy*.
Major Jones' chronicles of Pineville; — courtship; — scenes in Georgia; — sketches of travel. *See* Thompson, W. T.
Major O'Regan's adventures. Brackenridge, H. H. 75c. .... *Peterson*.
Make the best of it. *See* Goodrich, S. G.
Make home happy. Weidenmann, J. $15 .... *Judd*.
Make or break. Adams, W. T. $1.25 .... *Lee & S.*
Make your wills. *See* Mayhew, E., *and* Smith, G.
Making the best of it. Brock, C. 50c.... (?) *Martien*.
Making haste to be rich. Arthur, T. S. 75c. *Collins & Bro.*
Making honey. Flint, S. A. 60c. .... *Cong. Pub.*
Making honey; or, Francis Stuart. 16°. '69. $1.25. *H. A. Young*.
Making something. Child, L. M. 75c. ..... *Lothrop*.
Makins, G: H. Manual of metallurgy. 2d ed., enl. ill. 8°. '73. $6.50 .... *Roberts*.
Malade imaginaire (Le). *See* Molière, J. B. P.
Malan, César. Arme Genfer Uhrmacher (Der). 32°. '64. 15c. .... *Am. Tr.*
— — *See also below* Idle Dick.
— Clara de Monthely; tr. 18°. '67. 35c. *N. Y. Ref. Ch. Bd.; Pres. Com.*
— Doubts removed; tr. 32°. '76. pap., 10c.... *Revell*.
— Fox hunters; tr. 18°. '69. 25c. *N. Y. Ref. Ch. Bd.; Pres. Com.*
— *Same*. ('62.) New ed. ill. 18°. '69. 40c..... *Hoyt*.
— Idle Dick; [also] Poor watchmaker; tr. ill. 18°. '67. 40c. .... *N. Y. Ref. Ch. Bd.; Pres. Com.*
— Mort (La) du fils ainé. 18°. '45. 25c.; pap., 10c. *Am. Tr.*
— Ralph; [also] Simon the rebel; tr. 18°. '67. 40c. *N. Y. Ref. Ch. Bd.; Pres. Com.*
— Sieg (Der) der Gnade. 18°. '51. 30c. .... *Am. Tr.*
— Sketches for youth; tr. ('56.) 2d ed. 18°. '74. 40c. *So. Meth.*
— — *See also* Village lib.
— Theobald, the iron-hearted; tr. 18°. '67. 40c. *N. Y. Ref. Ch. Bd.; Pres. Com.*
— Vraie croix (La). 18°. '46. pap., 8c. ...... *Am. Tr.*
— *Eng.* The true cross. 18°. '65. 30c.; pap., 15c. *Randolph*.
— Wonderful letter; tr. 32°. '64. 20c. .... *Randolph*.
Malan, H. Family guide to administration of homœop. remedies. 24°. 30c. .... *Boericke*.
— *Span.* 12°. 75c. .... *Boericke*.
Malan, Solomon Cæsar. Magdala and Bethany. 18°. 60c. .... *Dutton*.
Malcolm, H: F: History of the war in India; with memoir of Sir H. Havelock. maps and ill. 12°. $1.75 .... *J. E. Potter*.
Malcolm, Howard. Christian rule of marriage. 16°. 75c. .... *Lippincott*.
— Extent and efficacy of the atonement. 16°. 75c. *Lippincott*.
— Index to principal works in every dept. of relig. literature. 8°. $4 .... *Lippincott*.
— New Bible dict. 16°. $1.25 .... *Sheldon*.
— Travels in s. e. Asia. 12°. $1.50 .... *Am. Bapt.*
Malcolm, Lydia M. Life. 18°. 35c.; 45c... *Am. Bapt.*
Malcolm. MacDonald, G. $1.50; $1..... *Lippincott*.
Malcolm Dykes. *See* Guilford Street stories.
Malcolm's cottage, and Malcolm's friend. Wright, J. McN. $1.25 .... (?) *Martien*.
Male life among the Mormons. Ward, A. N. $1.75. *J. E. Potter*.
Malediction. La Grange, A. K. de. $1.25.. *O'Shea*.
Malen, M. E. O. [Novels.] 5 v. ill. 8°. (Lond.) ea., pap., 30c. .... *Am. News*.
Cont.: Ingaretha.— Naomi, the gipsey girl.— Rachel, the miser's daughter.— The shadow hand.— The white lady.
Malet, H. Jacky Nory; or, do your best. 32°. 40c. *Scribner, W. & A.*
Malgaigne, Jos. François. Treatise on fractures; tr., with notes and add., by J. H. Packard. ill. 8°. '58. shp., $4 .... *Claxton; Lippincott*.
Malicious trespass. White, C. 15c. .... *De Witt*.
Malkin, B: Heath. *See* England, Common law reports.
Mallary, *Mrs.* M. Jeanie. Elsie Lee. 16°. $1.25. *Am. Bapt.*
— Horace Wilde. 16°. $1.25 .... *Am. Bapt.*
— *Same*. 12°. $1.50 .... *Lippincott*.
Mallet, A. Compound engines; tr. from the Fr. ill. 18°. '73. bds., 50c. .... *Van Nostrand*.

Mallet, Pl. H: Northern antiquities: account of anc. Scandinavians; tr. by Bp. Percy, with abstract of the Eyrbiggia saga by W. Scott; ed. by J. A. Blackwell. 12°. (Bohn.) $1.75..*Little, B.& Co.*
— *Same.* 12°. (Bohn.) $2..*Lippincott; Scribner, W.& A.*
Malleville. Abbott, J. 90c..................*Harper.*
Mallory, D: Life and speeches of Henry Clay; with add. 2 v. 8°. '53. $4.50..............*Barnes.*
Mallory, J: A. *See* Truman, J. H., Mallory, J. A., *and* Shipman, H. A.
Mallory girls. Guernsey, C. F. $1.50.......*Am. S. S.*
Malmene, W. Freemason's hymnal. 18°. 40c. *S. W. Bk. & Pub.*
Malory, *Sir* T: Morte d'Arthur: original ed. of Caxton rev., with introd., by Sir E. Strackey. (Globe ed.) 12°. '68. $1.50...............*Macmillan.*
— *Same;* ed. from Harleian MS. in British Museum, by J. J. Furnivall; with essay by H. Coleridge. fp. 8°. '64. $2....................*Macmillan.*
Malot, Hect. Romain Kalbris: his adventures by sea and land; tr. by Mrs. J. McN. Wright. ill. 12°. '73. $1.50..........................*Porter.*
Maltby, C. A. I'm not mesilf at all: farce. 16°. pap., 15c...............................*De Witt.*
— Somebody's nobody: farce. 16°. pap., 15c...*Ames.*
— *and* Stamforth, F. Sea gulls: farce. 16°. pap., 15c. *French.*
Maltese cross, and other tales. 18°. '72. 40c...*Kenedy.*
— *See also* Keighley Hall.
Maltheser (Der). *See* Van der Velde, K. F.
Malvina. Macfarren, G. 15c................*French.*
Malý katechismus pro katolické školy. [Small catechism for Cath. schools.] 16°. '76. 25c. *Geringer.*
Mambi-land (The). O'Kelly, J. J. $1.75..*Lippincott.*
Mamie's watchword. Mathews, J. H. $1....*Carter.*
Mamma's Bible stories, and sequel. 2 v. sq. 18°. ea., 75c..........................*Carter.*
Mamma's journal from Maple grove. *See* Maple grove stories.
Mamma's little friend. Adams, C. 40c......*Dutton.*
Mamma's microscope. 32°. 20c.; 15c.......*Dutton.*
Mamma's return. ill. sq. 12°. '71. bds., 50c. *Routledge.*
Mamma's talks with Charlie. Woodbridge, S. 50c. *Hoyt.*
Mammon. *See* Harris, J.
Man all immortal. *See* Clark, D. W.
Man and apes. Mivart, St. G. $1.50......*Appleton.*
Man and beast here and hereafter. *See* Wood, J. G.
Man and the Gospel. *See* Guthrie, T.
Man and his dwelling place. Hinton, J. $1.75..*Appleton.*
Man and his motives. Moore, G. $1........*Harper.*
Man and the marquis. Dibdin, T. 15c. .....*French.*
Man and wife. *See* Collins, Wilkie.
Man and wife. Webber, H. A. 15c...*Ames; French.*
Man and woman. *See* Reed, J.
Man and woman. Slaughter, P. $1......*Slaughter.*
Man and woman in their rel. to each other, and to the world. Pedder, H. C. $1..............*Wells.*
Man-at-arms. *See* James, G. P. R.
Man eaters. Reid, M. $1.50................*Miller.*
Man from Texas. Aiken, A. W. 20c........*Beadle.*
Man in black. James, G. P. R. 75c. ......*Peterson.*
Man in earnest. Collyer, R. $1.50..........*Lee & S.*
Man in Genesis and geology. Thompson, J. P. $1. *Wells.*
Man in the moon. Raymond, R. W. $2 ......*Ford.*
Man in search of a wife. Seaton, W. 25c...*De Witt.*
Man is love: an Am. story; by one who knows. 12°. $1.75...........................*Lippincott.*
Man lost and saved. 18°. 18c..............*Am. S. S.*
Man (A) made of money. Jerrold, D. 25c. *U. P. James.*
Man, moral and physical. Jones, J. H. $2..(?) *Martien.*
Man of God. Winslow, O. 75c.............*Carter.*
Man of honor. Eggleston, G. C. $1.25.......*Judd.*
Man of like passions. Platt, S. H. 25c.; 15c...*Hope.*
Man of many friends. *See* Hook, Thdr.
Man of the north and man of the south. Bonstetten, C. V. $1 ....*Christern.*
Man of one book. Marsh, C. $1.50..*Meth. Bk. Conc.*
Man of two lives. Bernard, W. B. 15c. ....*French.*
Man-o'-war's bell. Low, C. R. $1.75....*Routledge.*
Man-of-war's-man. Sue, E. 50c.........*Peterson.*
Man of the world. Macklin, C. 15c.........*French.*
Man of the world. North, W. $1.75; $1.50..*Peterson.*
Man on the ocean: a book for boys. ill. 12°. $1.25. *Nelson.*
Man proposes: comedietta. 16°. pap., 15c...*French.*
Man responsible for his belief. Breed, W. P. 10c. *Pres. Bd.*
Man that follows the ladies: drama. 16°. pap., 15c. *French.*
Man who kept himself in repair. 18°. 30c...*Am. S. S.*
Man who laughs. *See* Hugo, V.
Man who ran away from himself. 18°. 30c...*Am. S. S.*
Man with the book. *See* Waylland, J. M.
Man with the broken ear. About, E. $1.25....*Holt.*
Man with the carpet bag. A'Beckett, G. A. 15c. *French.*
Man with the demijohn. Baker, G. M. 15c...*Lee & S.*
Man with the five wives. *See* Dumas, A.
Man with the iron mask. Lucas, W. J. 15c...*French.*
Man with many friends: comedy. 16°. pap., 15c. *French.*
Man with two shadows. Hoven, E. 90c.....*Pres. Bd.*
Man without a head. Wooler, J. P. 15c.....*French.*
Man-woman. *See* Dumas, A.
Maná diario. 64°. '66. 15c.................*Am. Tr.*
Management. Lunn, J. 15c.................*French.*
Manager in distress: [dram.] prelude. 16°. pap., 15c. *French.*
Manager in a fix: Ethiop. drama. 16°. pap., 15c. *French; Happy.*
Manahan, Amb. Triumph of the Cath. Church in the early ages. 8°. $3.................*Appleton.*
Manchester, *N. H.* Brief record of its past and a picture of its present. ill. 8°. $2.50...*J. B. Clarke.*
Mandeville, H: [Readers.] 7 v..........*Appleton.*
Cont.: First reader, 16°, 20c.—Second, 16°, 40c.—Third, 12°, 60c.—Fourth, 12°, 60c.—Fifth, 12°, $1.—Course of reading, 12°, $1.25.—Elements of reading and oratory, 12°, $1.25.
— [Spanish readers.] 3 v. ill. 12°..........*Appleton.*
Cont.: Libro primario, 25c.—Libro segundo, 35c.—Libro tercero de lectura, 50c.
Manesca, L. French grammar: serial and oral method of teaching lang. 12°. hf. leath., $1.50..*Desilver.*
— French reader; [with] a table of verbs arr. on new plan. 12°. $1.50....................*Desilver.*
Manfred. A'Beckett, G. A. 15c............*French.*
Manfred. Byron, *Lord.* 15c...............*French.*
Manfred. Guerazzi, F. D. $1.75..........*Carleton.*
Mangan, Ja. Clar. Poems. 12°. $2; $2.50..*Sadlier.*
— *Same;* with biog. and crit. introd. by J. Mitchell. 12°. '61. $2.........................*Haverty.*
Mangin, Arth. Desert world (The); tr. ill. imp. 8°. '71. $6; hf. cf., $8.50; mor., $12.....*Nelson.*
— Earth (The) and its treasures: descript. of metallic and mineral wealth of nature; tr. ill. 12°. $1.25. *Nelson.*
— Jardins (Les); histoire et descriptions; avec dessins par Anastasi, d'Aubigny, Foulquier, etc. f°. $60. *Appleton.*
— Mysteries of the ocean, tr.; ill. by Freeman and Noel. imp. 8°. '70. $5–$10.50 ....*Nelson.*

Mangnall, *Miss* Richmal. Historical questions; with Am. add. 12°. $1.50................*Appleton.*

Manigault, G. St. Cecilia, pt. 1: Adversity. [Fiction.] 12°. $1.50..................*Lippincott.*

Manley, Ja. R. Anniversary discourse before N. Y. Acad. of Med. 8°. '48. pap., 25c. *N. Y. Acad. Med.*

Manliness. Hotchkin, B. B. 35c..........*Pres. Bd.*

Manly, Basil *and* B., *jr.* Baptist psalmody. [Hymn book.] 32°. $1–$2.75. — 18°. shp., $1.25–$4. *Sheldon; So. Bapt.*

Manly independent thinker. Demarest, D. D. 25c. *N. Y. Ref. Ch. Bd.*

Manly piety in its spirit. Philip, R. 55c....*Pres. Bd.*

Mann, C: A. Paper money, the root of evil: examin. of currency of the U. S., with suggestions for restoring specie payment without robbing debtors. 12°. $2..........................*Appleton.*

Mann, Hor. Annual reports on education, 1839–1848. cr. 8°. $3..........................*Lee & S.*

— Lectures and annual reports on education. cr. 8°. $3..................................*Lee & S.*

— Study of physiology in schools. ('69.) 3d ed. 24°. '72. pap., 25c...................*Schermerhorn.*

— Thoughts; sel. from writings. 16°. $1.25..*Lee & S.*

Mann, *Mrs.* Hor. *See* Mann, *Mrs.* Ma.

Mann, Hor., *jr.* Flora of the Hawaiian Islands. 8°. '68. 50c..............................*Essex.*

Mann, Jona. B. Life of H: Wilson. por. and ill. 8°. pap., 50c. ....* *Osgood.*

Mann, *Mrs.* Ma. Christianity in the kitchen: a physiol. cook book. 16°. $1.25...............* *Osgood.*

— Flower people (The). ill. sq. 16°. $1.50..* *Osgood.*

— Life of Horace Mann. cr. 8°. $3..........*Lee & S.*

— *and* Peabody, *Miss* Eliz. P. Moral culture of infancy, and kindergarten guide. ('69.) 5th ed. 12°. '74. $1.25........................*Schermerhorn.*

Mann, Nellie A. (*pseud.*) *See* Manville, Helen A.

Mann, Rob. Ja. Guide to the knowledge of life. 12°. $1.50 .... (?)*Francis.*

Mann, W. J. The great reformation, address, Oct. 31, 1872; [also] Origin and result of the 95 theses of Luther by C. P. Krauth, with Eng. tr. of the theses. 16°. pap., 20c............*Luth. Bk. St.*

— *See also* Bible [Whole], *Germ.;* — Luther, M., Kleiner Katechismus.

Mann (Der), der seinen Nachbar unschädlich machte. 32°. '65. 15c. ....*Am. Tr.*

Mann (Der) im Monde. *See* Hauff, W.

Manna für die Kleinen. 24°. 15c..........*Ev. Assoc.*

Manna-crumbs for hungry souls. Rutherford, S. 80c. *Pres. Bd.*

Männerchor (Der). Hartmann, W. 9 nos. ea., 25c.; in 1 v., $1.50....................*Schäfer.*

Männerchor. Root, G. F. 75c.............*Church.*

Mannering, E. Christian consistency: connection between experimental and practical religion. 18°. 60c. ....*Pres. Bd.*

Mannering, May (*pseud.*) *See* Nowell, H. P. H.

Manners and customs of the Japanese in 19th cent.; from accounts of recent Dutch residents and from the work of Ph. Fh. v. Siebold. 18°. 75c. *Harper.*

Manners and customs of the Jews. 12°. 50c. *Meth. Bk. Conc.*

Manners of modern society. fp. 8°. $1.25...*Cassell.*

Mannheimer, S. Hebrew reader and grammar; with exercises for translation. 2d ed., enl. 12°. '76. $1.25.......................*Frank; Roeslein.*

— *Same;* in 4 pts. 12°. 1, 30c.; 2–4, $1....*Roeslein.*

— *See also* Hebrew grammar.

Manning, Anne. Cherry and Violet. 18°. '65. $1..*Dodd.*

— Colloquies of Edward Osborne: tale of the Elizabethan period. ('70.) New ed. 8°. '75. pap., 25c...........................*Tompkins.*

Manning, Anne, *continued.*

— Deborah's diary. 8°. pap., 17c.........*Littell & G.*

— Faire gospeller: Anne Askew. 18°. '66. $1..*Dodd.*

— Heroes of the desert. ill. 12°. '75. $1.50..*Nelson.*

— Household of Sir T: More. 18°. '67. $1...*Dodd.*

— Jacques Bonneval: tale of the Huguenots. 16°. '67. $1 ....*Dodd.*

— Maiden and married life of Mary Powell. 18°. '66. $1 ....*Dodd.*

— One trip more, and other stories. sq. 16°. '70. $1. *Cassell.*

— Sower's reward: domestic novel. 8°. pap., 25c. *Peterson.*

— Spanish barber: tale of the Bible in Spain. ill. 16°. '69. $1.25..............................*Dodd.*

Manning, C: P. *See* Osborne, R. B., *and* Manning, C. P.

Manning, H: E: Glories of the sacred heart. 12°. $1 ....*Sadlier.*

— *Same.* 12°. '76. $1.50................*Cath. Pub.*

— Internal mission of the Holy Ghost. 12°. $1. *Sadlier.*

— *Same.* 2d ed. 12°. '75. $1............*Cath. Pub.*

— Lectures on the four great evils of the day. 16°. '72. $1.25; $1.75 ....*Kelly, P. & Co.*

— Lectures on the grounds of faith. 18°. '67. 40c.; pap., 20c.........................*Kelly, P. & Co.*

— Reunion of Christendom: pastoral letter. 8°. pap., 50c...................................*Appleton.*

— Sermons on ecclesiastical subjects. ('72.) New ed. 2 v. 12°. '73. ea., $2..............*Cath. Pub.*

— Sin and its consequences. 12°. $1........*Sadlier.*

— Temporal mission of the Holy Ghost; or, reason and revelation. 12°. $1.....................*Sadlier.*

— Vatican council. 12°. $1....................*Sadlier.*

— *See also* Gladstone, W. E., Vatican decrees.

— *and* Newman, J: H. Reply in the Gladstone controversy. 12°. '75. $1.50; pap., 50c...*Cath. Pub.*

Manning, *Rev.* Jac. Half truths and the truth. 12°. $2.......................................*Lee & S.*

— Helps to a life of prayer. 16°. $1.25......*Lee & S.*

Manning, Ja. *See* England, Common law reports.

Manning, R. *See* Michigan, Sup. Court reports.

Manning, S: [Works.] 6 v. imp. 8°. '72–'75...*Nelson.*

Cont.: Egypt to Sinai. — Swiss pictures, drawn with pen and pencil, *ea.*, $4. — Italian pictures, drawn with pen and pencil. — Land of the Pharaohs. — Spanish pictures, drawn with pen and pencil. — Those holy fields, Palestine ill. by pen and pencil, *ea.*, $3.50.

Mannock, J: Poor man's catechism: Christian doctrine expl. with short admonitions. 24°. 50c.; pap., 25c..............................*Cath. Pub.*

— *Same.* 18°. 40c.; pap., 25c...............*Sadlier.*

— *Same.* 12°. 75c.; hf. bd., 50c............*Strong.*

Manns, Jean. New elementary school for the piano. 4°. '67. bds., $2.50..........................*Pond.*

Manœuvring. *See* Edgeworth, Mar.

Manœuvring mother. Grey, E. C. 50c....*Peterson.*

Manor house exhibition. 16°. 50c...*Scribner, W. & A.*

Man's contract with God in baptism; tr. by J. M. Cullen. 18°. '59. 50c..............*Cunningham.*

Man's gift to God. Monod, A. 12c...*Cin. Meth. Bk. Conc.*

Man's labour and God's harvest. Rowsell, T. J. $1. *Macmillan.*

Man's nature and development. Atkinson, H. G., *and* Martineau, H. $1.50..............*Mendum.*

Man's origin and destiny. Lesley, J. P. $4. *Lippincott.*

Man's place in nature. Huxley, T. H. $1.25..*Appleton.*

Man's power over himself to prevent or control insanity. *See* Small books on great subjects.

Man's rights. Cridge, A. D. 15c...........*Denton.*

Man's story. *See* Barker, M. A. (*Lady*).

Man's thoughts. Friswell, J. H. $3..*Scribner, W. & A.*

Man's true saviours. Denton, W. 10c. *Denton; Mendum.*

Mansel, H: L. Limits of religious thought. (Bampton lectures, 1858.) 12°. $1.50..........*Pott.*
— *Same.* 12°. '59. $1.75..............*H.A. Young.*
— *Same.* sm. 8°. $3.75............*Scribner, W. & A.*
— Metaphysics: philos. of consciousness, phenomenal and real. 12°. $1.75..............*Appleton.*
— Philosophy of the conditioned; compr. remarks on Hamilton's philosophy, and on J. S. Mill's exam. of that philosophy. 8°. '71. $2.50...*Routledge.*

Mansfield, C. B. A theory of salts: treatise on the constitution of bipolar (two-membered) chemical compounds. cr. 8°. '65. $4.......*Macmillan.*

Mansfield, D. H. American vocalist. 8°. hf. bd., $1.12..............................*Thompson.*

Mansfield, E: D. American education: its principles and elements. 12°. '50. $1.50........*Barnes.*
— Life and military services of Winfield Scott. 12°. '61. $1.75..........................*Barnes.*
— Memoir of life of Daniel Drake; with notices of early settlement of Cincinnati, and of its pioneer citizens. por. 12°. '57. $1.50......*Pounsford.*
— Mexican war. ('48.) 10th ed. 12°. $1.50..*Barnes.*
— Political manual: theory and practice of the general and state governments of the U. S. 12°. '73. $1.25..............................*Barnes.*

Mansfield, Jose. Life. *See* Stokes, E. S., Life.

Mansfield, L. W. The congregation; from studies in the Hebrew and Greek Scriptures. 16°. '71. 75c.............................*Routledge.*

Mansfield, the noble boy. 18°. 20c.; 25c...*Am. Bapt.*

Mansfield Park. *See* Austen, Jane.

Mant, R: Happiness of the blessed. New ed. sm. 8°. '70. $1.50...........................*Dutton.*
— *See also* Bible [Whole].

Mantell, Gid. Algernon. Geological excursions thro' Isle of Wight and Dorsetshire. New ed., ed. by T. R. Jones. ill. and map. 12°. (Bohn.) $1.75. *Little, B. & Co.*
— *Same.* ill. and map. 12°. (Bohn.) $2. *Lippincott; Scribner, W. & A.*
— Medals of creation: first lessons in geol. 2 v. pl. and ill. 12°. (Bohn.) ea., $2.75..*Little, B. & Co.*
— *Same.* 2 v. pl. and ill. 12°. (Bohn.) ea., $3. *Lippincott; Scribner, W. & A.*
— Petrifactions and their teachings. ill. 12°. (Bohn.) $2.25.........................*Little, B. & Co.*
— *Same.* ill. 12°. (Bohn.) $2.40....*Scribner, W. & A.*
— *Same.* ill. 12°. (Bohn.) $2.50.........*Lippincott.*
— Wonders of geology: familiar expos. of geol. phenomena. New ed., enl. by T. R. Jones. 2 v. ill. and map. 12°. (Bohn.) ea., $2.75....*Little, B. & Co.*
— *Same.* 2 v. ill. and map. 12°. (Bohn.) ea., $3. *Lippincott; Scribner, W. & A.*

Mantilla, Luis Felipe. Cartilla de fisica. 16°. '75. 60c.........................*G. R. Lockwood.*
— Cartilla ó silabario. 18°. 20c.....*G. R. Lockwood.*
— Elementos de fisiologia é higiene. 16°. '74. 60c. *G. R. Lockwood.*
— Libro primario para traducir el francés, con un vocabulario. 16°. 50c..............*G. R. Lockwood.*
— Nocionos de lengua francesa. 16°. '75. 60c. *G. R. Lockwood.*
— Nuevo método para aprender inglés y español. 12°. $1.25..............................*Appleton.*
— [Spanish readers.] 3 v. 12°. '65...........*Ivison.*
Cont.: No. 1, bds., 30c. — No. 2, 85c. — No. 3: ó sea autores selectos españoles é hispano-americanos, $1.10.
— *See also* Goodrich, S. G., Universal hist.

Mantle of Elijah. Lee, G. $1.50.......(?)*Martien.*

Manual concordance of the New Test. 18°. (Bagster.) $1..................................*Wiley.*

Manual for the sick. 16°. 40c.; 50c.........*Dutton.*

Manual of the arch confraternity of the holy family; comp. by a clergyman of the Redemptorist Order. [Cath. prayer book.] 32°. 30c.......*Noonan.*
— *Same.* 32°. 45c............................*O'Shea.*

Manual of the blessed sacrament. [Cath. prayer book.] ill. 18°. 80c.–$8. — 24°. 70c.–$6.......*T. Kelly.*

Manual of the blessed Trinity. [Cath. prayer book.] ('71.) 15th ed. ill. 18°. '76. $1–$12..*Kenedy.*

Manual of Catholic devotion. ill. 24°. '59. 75c.–$10. *Murphy.*

Manual of Catholic prayers; with Epistles and Gospels. ('68.) 8th ed. 48°. '76. 37c.–$5......*Kenedy.*

Manual of ceremonies; for Catholic churches in the U. S. 12°. '52. 75c................*Murphy.*

Manual of the children of Mary. *See* Sisters of Charity.

Manual of controversy: cont. Grounds of the Catholic doctrine, Papist misrepresented and truly represented; [also] Fifty reasons why the Roman Cath. relig. ought to be preferred to all others [by J. Gother]. 16°. 88c..............*Strong.*

Manual of the crucifixion: guide to Catholic devotion. [Prayer book.] ('71.) 15th ed. ill. 24°. '76. 63c.–$7..............................*Kenedy.*

Manual of devotion. [Cath. prayer book.] 32°. '70. 35c.–$4.........................*Cunningham.*

Manual of devotion to the sacred heart; for sodalities and for general use. [Cath. prayer book.] 18°. 50c. — 32°. 50c.; 75c.................*O'Shea.*

Manual of edeography: easy lessons in short-hand writing. 12°. '74. 75c.; pap., 50c...(?)*Evans.*

Manual of flax culture and manufacture. ('63.) 4th ed. ill. 8°. '64. pap., 25c.............*Rural.*

Manual of hair ornaments for jewelry or souvenirs. ill. 12°. pap., 50c.......................*Haney.*

Manual of histology; by S. Stricker, T. Meynert, F. v. Recklinghausen, M. Schultze, W. Waldeyer, etc.; tr. by H. Power, etc.; ed. by A. H. Buck. ill. 8°. $10; leath., $11..............*W. Wood.*

Manual of the holy angels' sodality. [Cath. prayer book.] 32°. '60. per doz., $1.50..*Cunningham.*

Manual of the holy cross. [Cath. prayer book.] ill. 32°. 40c.–$2.75; — with Epistles and Gospels. 24°. 60c.–$6..........................*T. Kelly.*

Manual of the holy family sodality, Jesus, Mary and Joseph. *See* Sisters of Notre Dame.

Manual of homœopathic veterinary practice. 8°. hf. mor., $5............................*Boericke.*

Manual of the immaculate conception. [Cath. prayer book.] 18°. $1.50–$20...............*O'Shea.*

Manual of matrimony. ill. 32°. 38c.......*Appleton.*

Manual of the passion: guide to Cath. devotion. 18°. $1–$60................................*Sadlier.*

Manual of piety: Catholic prayers and devotions, with the Epistles and Gospels; comp. by a father of the Soc. of Jesus. 32°. 50c.–$5.....*Benziger.*

Manual of piety; for use of seminaries. [Cath. prayer book.] 32°. '56. 60c.–$1.50.........*Murphy.*

Manual of piety for clients of the sacred heart of Jesus; with the Epistles and Gospels. [Cath. prayer book.] ill. 16°. $1.50–$10. — 18°. $1.25–$9..................................*T. Kelly.*

Manual of politeness. 18°. 60c.........*Lippincott.*

Manual of the queen of angels; comp. by a religious of the Order of Mercy. [Cath. prayer book.] 18°. $1.25–$5........................*O'Shea.*

Manual of the queen of angels. *See* Sisters of Mercy.

Manual of Roman chant; for [Cath.] churches, seminaries, etc. 4°. '60. $1.75.......*Kelly, P. & Co.*

Manual of the sacred heart of Jesus. *See* New.

Manual of St. Aloysius. [Cath. prayer book.] 24°. $1–$3................................*O'Shea.*

Manual of St. Bridget: Cath. prayers and devotions; with the Epistles and Gospels. ill. 16°. $1–$10. — 18°. 90c.–$9........................*T. Kelly.*

Manual of sign, carriage and decorative painting. 12°. 50c..............................*Haney.*

Manual of the Sisters of Charity. 24°. '75. $1–$14. *Murphy.*

Manual of the sodality; [also] Sacred wreath. 18°. $1.25–$4.50 .... *Cummiskey.*

Manual of the sodality of the sacred heart of Jesus. [Cath. prayer book.] 3d ed., enl. 32°. '74. 50c.; 75c. .... *Murphy.*

Manual of the sodality of Virgin Mary; by a father of the Soc. of Jesus. 32°. 50c.–$3.50 .. *Benziger.*
- *Same.* 18°. '62. 90c. .... *Cummiskey.*
- *Same.* 30th ed., rev. and enl.; with hymns set to music, etc. 32°. '51. 45c.; 60c. ..... *Murphy.*
- *See also* New.

Manual of the Virgin; with the Epistles and Gospels. [Cath. prayer book.] ill. 18°. 80c.–$8. — 24°. 70c.–$6 .... *T. Kelly.*

Manual of weathercasts and storm prognostics. 16°. bds., 40c. .... *Routledge.*

Manuel du fervent chrétien. [Cath. prayer book.] 18°. *net*, 45c. .... *Benziger.*

Manufacturing, agricultural and industrial resources of Iowa. 16°. '73. *(?) .... (?)*Hyatt.*

Manuscript man. *See* Walshe, E. H.

Manuscript manual: how to prepare MSS. for the press. ('75.) 3d ed. 8°. pap., 10c ... *Authors.*

Manville, Helen A. ["Nellie A. Mann."] Heart echoes: book of poems. 12°. '74. $1; $1.25. *Wells.*

Many happy returns of the day. Clarke, C. C. *and* M. C. $1.75 .... *Routledge.*

Many lands and many people: sketches of travel in all parts of the world; by J. L. T. Phillips, F. R. Feudge, G. C. Musters and E. W. Howland. ill. 8°. '75. $2.50 .... *Lippincott.*

Man a little makes a mickle; tr. from the Germ. ill. 16°. $1.25 .... *O'Shea.*

Many teachers, but one lesson. Bennett, M. L. 60c. *Lee & S.*

Many thoughts of many minds. Southgate, H. 2 v. $12; $20 .... *Routledge.*

Manzoni, *Count* Alessandro. I promessi sposi. With Eng. notes. 12°. $1.75; pap., $1.25 .. *Schoenhof.*
- *Eng.* The betrothed. 12°. $1.50 .... *Cath. Pub.*
- — *Same.* ill. 12°. (Bohn.) $1.75 ... *Little, B. & Co.*
- — *Same.* ill. 12°. (Bohn.) $2. *Lippincott; Scribner, W. & A.*

Maple grove stories. 10 v. 24°. $2.50 .. *Meth. Bk. Conc.*

Cont.: Little Jimmy. — Johnny's first boots. — Flag of truce. — Lucretia and her garden. — Nanny's epitaph, — Happy hearts. — God's little boy that went home. — Children's providence. — Mamma's journal from Maple grove. — Bitter medicine.

- *Same.* 2d ser. 8 v. 24°. $3 .... *Meth. Bk. Conc.*

Cont.: Little gleaner. — Children's post-office at Maple grove. — Garden lesson. — Where is Rosa? — Killing the giants. — James Rogers. — Under the vine and under the snow. — Babble brook.

Maple hill. Chaplin, J. D. 45c. .... *Bost. Am. Tr.*

Maple leaves. Perk, A. $1.50 .... *Dutton.*

Mapleville boys. Trowbridge, C. M. $1 .. (?)*Martien.*

Mapleville lib. 4 v. 16°. $3.80 .... (?)*Martien.*

Cont.: Jem Morrison. — Mapleville boys. — Snowstorms and sunbeams. — Red crosses.

Marache, N. Manual of chess: games for beginners, openings, etc. 16°. 75c.; bds., 50c. ... *Dick & F.*

Marble bride. Hazlewood, C. H. 15c. ...... *French.*

Marble faun. *See* Hawthorne, Natl.

Marble heart. Selby, C. 15c. .... *French.*

Marble Isle. Bridges, S. $1.25 .... *Lippincott.*

Marble preacher. Clarke, H. S. $1.50 .... *Lothrop.*

Marble prophecy. Holland, J. G. $1.50; $2 .. *Scribner.*

Marble worker's manual. 16°. $1 .... *Sheldon.*

Marble worker's manual; tr. by M. L. Booth; with app. (cop. '56.) '65. 3d ed. 12°. '76. $1.50 .. *Baird.*

Marbles. *See* Conduct book.

Marbleside; or, the widow and her family. ill. 18°. 60c. .... *Bost. Am. Tr.*

Marcel, Cl. Rational method, following nature step by step, to learn how to read, hear, speak and write Fr. 18°. 50c. .... *Appleton.*
— Study of languages brought back to its true principles. 12°. $1.25 .... *Appleton.*

Marceleau, J. H. C. Lajoie de. Dictées corrigées of orthog. exercises; with gram. and logical analysis. 12°. 50c. .... *Appleton.*

Marcella. Knevels, D. C. $1.25 .... *Dodd.*

Marcellinus, Ammianus. *See* Ammianus Marcellinus.

Marcet, *Mrs.* Jane. Mary's grammar; for use of children. 12°. $1.25 .... *Appleton.*

March, Anne. Old stone house. ill. 16°. '73. $1.50. *Lothrop.*

March, C: W. Daniel Webster and his contemporaries. 12°. $1.50 .... *Mason.*

March, Dan. Home life in the Bible. ill. 8°. *$3.75; mor., $6 .... *McCurdy*
— Night scenes in the Bible, portrayed, studied and ill. 8°. *$3.75; mor., $6 .... *McCurdy.*

March, Fs. A. Anglo-Saxon reader. 8°. $1.50. *Harper.*
— Comparative grammar of Anglo-Saxon. cr. 8°. $2.50 .... *Harper.*
— Latin hymns with Eng. notes; for schools and colleges. 12°. $1.75 .... *Harper.*
— Method of philological study of the Eng. language. 12°. 75c.; pap., 60c. .... *Harper.*
— — *See also* Fowler, W. C., English lang. in its elements and forms.
— Parser and analyzer for beginners; with diagrams and pictures. 16°. 50c. .... *Harper.*
— (*ed.*) Douglas ser. of Christian Gk. and Lat. writers; for schools and colleges. v. 1–4. 12°. ea., $1.75. *Harper.*

Cont.: Latin hymns, with Eng. notes. — Ecclesiastical hist. of Eusebius. — Select works of Tertullian. — Athenagoras.

March, G: Lost and found: operetta. 16°. pap., 15c. *French.*
— Who's the heir? operetta. 16°. pap., 15c. .. *French.*

March of De Soto. Irving, T. $2.50; $1.50 .. *C. Drew.*

March of intellect. Macfarren, G. 15c. ..... *French.*

Märchen, f. Söhne u. Töchter gebildeter Stände. *See* Hauff, W.

Märchen (Das) ohne Ende. Carové, F. W. 25c. .. *Holt.*

Marchena, A. A. de. Compendio de la historia antigua. 18°. 75c. .... *Appleton.*

Märchennovellen. *See* Tieck, L.

Marchesi, Malthilde Gastrone. Exercises elementaires gradues for development of the voice. f°. '72. pap., $2 .... *Ditson.*
— Twenty-four vocalises for soprano or mezzo-soprano. (op. 2.) 4°. pap., $2.50 .... *G. D. Russell.*
— Vocal exercises; tr. by J. C. D. Parker. (op. 1.) 4°. pap., $2.50 .... *G. D. Russell.*

Marchesi, Salv. C. Twenty vocalises. f°. $2. *Brainard; Gordon.*

Marchioness of Brinvilliers. *See* Smith, Alb.

Marcia. ill. 32°. '54. 30c. .... *Am. Tr.*

Marcia and Ellen. Smith, M. J. P. 40c. .... *Am. Tr.*

Marcia's faith. Berry, M. E. 75c. .... *Cong. Pub.*

Marco Paul's voyages and travels in the pursuit of knowledge. *See* Abbott, Jac.

Marco Spada. Simpson, J. P. 15c. .... *French.*

Marcoartu, Arturo de. Internationalism; [also] Prize essays on intern. law, by A. P. Sprague and Paul Lacombe. 8°. hf. shp., $3.50; shp., $4. *Baker, V. & Co.*

Marcoretti. Kingdom, J. M. 15c. .... *De Witt.*

Marcos Steadman. *See* Mark Steadman.

Marcoy, Pl. Journey across South America from the Pacific to the Atlantic; ill. with 600 eng. on wood, and ten col. maps. ('74.) New ed. 2 v. roy. 4°. '75. $15 .... *Scribner.*
Marcus Aurelius Antoninus. *See* Antoninus, M. A.
Marcus. Simonds, W. $1.25 .... *Miller.*
Marcus Blair. Wright, C. E. $1.25 .... *Lippincott.*
Marcus Warland. Hentz, C. L. $1.75; $1.50 .. *Peterson.*
Marcy, E. E. Homœopathy and allopathy: reply to Examination of the doctrines and evidences of homœopathy, by W. Hooker. 12°. 50c... *Boericke.*
Life duties. 12°. $1.50; $2 .... *Sadlier.*
— *and* Hunt, F. W. Homœopathic theory and pract. of medicine. 2 v. 8°. hf. mor., $12 .. *Boericke.*
Marcy, Lorenzo J. Sciopticon manual; expl. Marcy's new magic-lantern and light, etc. 5th ed. 16°. '74. 75c.; pap., 50c .... (?) *Marcy.*
Marcy, Randolph Benton. Border reminiscences. ill. 12°. $2 .... *Harper.*
— Prairie traveller. [Guide book.] maps and ill. 16°. $1 .... *Harper.*
— Thirty years of army life on the border. 8°. $3. *Harper.*
Marden, G: A. Poem. *See* Patterson, J. W., Address before Phi Beta Kappa Soc.
Mardi. Melville, H. $3 .... *Harper.*
Marenholtz-Bülow, *Baroness.* The child, its nature and relations: elucidation of Fröbel's principles of education: free [tr.] from the Germ. by Mrs. M. H. Krieze. 2d ed. 12°. '72. $1 .... *Steiger.*
Marett, P. R. Yachts and yacht-building. 2d ed., enl. 12 pl. 8°. '72. $5 .... *Spon.*
Marey, Etienne Jules. Animal mechanism. (Intern. sci. ser.) 12°. $1.75 .... *Appleton.*
Margaree. Massor, H. 75c. .... *Lippincott.*
Margaret *of Cortona, St.* Life. 12°. $1 .... *Sadlier.*
— *Same;* tr. by J. G. Shea. 16°. '58. $1 .. *Cunningham.*
— — *See also* Lives of the saints.
Margaret *d'Angoulême, Queen of Navarre.* Heptameron; tr. with memoir by W. K. Kelly. 12°. $1.50; hf. cf., $3 .... *Appleton.*
— *Same.* 12°. (Bohn.) $1.25 .... *Little, B. & Co.*
— *Same.* 12°. (Bohn.) $1.40 .... *Scribner, W. & A.*
— *Same.* 12°. (Bohn.) $1.50 .... *Lippincott.*
— *Same;* ill by L. Flameng. cr. 8°. '76. $3.75 ... *Gebbie.*
Margaret. ill. 32°. '54. 30c. .... *Am. Tr.*
Margaret. Bright, M. A. $1.50 .... *Scribner.*
Margaret. Fraser, C. C. F. $1.25 .... *Dodd.*
Margaret. *See* Judd, S.
Margaret. Tayler, C. B. $1 .... *Leighton.*
Margaret, the pearl of Navarre. Martyn, S. T. 80c. *Am. Tr.*
Margaret, the young wife. ill. 18°. 85c. .... *Am. S. S.*
Margaret and Bessie. Savage, M. S. 90c ... *Cong. Pub.*
Margaret and Henrietta. Sigourney, L. H. 25c. *Am. Tr.*
Margaret and her bridesmaids. Stretton, J. $1.50. *Loring.*
Margaret and her friends. 18°. 60c. .... (?) *Martien.*
Margaret Ashton. Myers, S. A. 75c. .... *Pres. Bd.*
Margaret at home; or, the leaven still working. 18°. '62. $1 .... *Randolph.*
Margaret Brown. *See* Changed cross (The).
Margaret Catchpole. Stirling, E. 15c. .... *French.*
Margaret Cecil. Bell, C. D. $1.75 .. *Scribner, W. & A.*
Margaret Chester. *See* Beebe, Marg. N.
Margaret Claire. Burnett, A. 75c. .... *Cong. Pub.*
Margaret Craven. Fry, S. M. 60c. *N. Y. Ref. Ch. Bd.; Pres. Com.*
Margaret Denzil's history. Greenwood, F. 75c. *Harper.*
Margaret Gordon. Myers, S. A. $1.50 .... *Pres. Bd.*
Margaret Graham. James, G. P. R. 25c. .. *Harper.*
Margaret Hamilton. Newby, C. J. 50c .... *Peterson.*
Margaret Lawrence, and other stories. 18°. 70c. *Pres. Bd.*
Margaret McDonald. 18°. 45c. .... *Cong. Pub.*
Margaret Maitland. Oliphant, M. O. W. $1.75; $1.50. *Peterson.*
Margaret Moncrieffe. Burdett, C. $1.75 .. *J. E. Potter.*
Margaret Percival. Sewell, E. M. 2 v. $2 .. *Appleton.*
Margaret Roper. Stewart, A. M. $2 .. *Kelly, P. & Co.*
Margaret Russell's school. 16°. $1.25 .... *Carter.*
Margaret Vernon. *See* Pollard, M. M.
Margaret Warner. Sumner, G. 75c. .... *Carter.*
Margaret Worthington. Provost, K. $1.50 .. *Lothrop.*
Margaretha Blümchen. *See* Schmid, C. v.
Margarethe and Waldemar. Conwell, S. G. 90c. *Dutton.*
Margaret's choice. 16°. $1.50 .... *Cong. Pub.*
Margaret's engagement. 8°. pap., 50c. .... *Harper.*
Margaret's old home. *See* Shaw, J. R.
Margaret's secret and its success. Brock, C. $1.25. (?) *Martien.*
Margaret's trial; or, a sister's influence. 18°. 75c. (?) *Martien.*
Margate sands. Hancock, W. 15c. .... *French.*
Margery Daw. Morton, J. M. 15c. .... *French.*
Margery Keith. Townsend, V. F. 75c. .... *Loring.*
Margery's Christmas box: story for girls. 16°. '75. 75c. .... *Hoyt.*
Margery's city home. *See* Mathews, J. A.
Margie. Bulfinch, M. H. 50c. .... *Dutton.*
Margie Hopkins. Bates, S. B. $1.15 .... *Hoyt.*
Margie's matches. Pritchard, S. J. 60c ... *Randolph.*
Margoliouth, Mos. Poetry of the Hebrew Pentateuch: four essays on Moses and the Mosaic age. 8°. (Bagster.) $1.50 .... *Wiley.*
Margollé, E. *See* Zurcher, F., *and* Margollé, E.
Marguerite. Girardin, D. de. 25c. .... *Appleton.*
Marguerite. Taylor, T. $1 ..... *Cin. Meth. Bk. Conc.*
Marguerite, Baroness Leichenstein, and other poems; by author of "Zelica." 12°. $1.50 .. *Lippincott.*
Marguerite de Valois. *See* Dumas, A.
Marguerite Kent. Wayne, M. W. $2 ... *Lippincott.*
Marguerite's colours. Archer, T. 15c. .... *French.*
Marguerite's journal; [with] introd. by author of "Rutledge." 12°. $1.50 .... *Carleton.*
Margy and her feather. *See* Sunshine and shadow lib.
Maria. *See* Bible pictures.
Maria and Magdalena. Lindau, P. 15c. .... *De Witt.*
Maria Cheeseman; or, the candy-girl. 18°. 55c. *Am. S. S.*
Maria di Rohan. *See* Donizetti, G.
Maria immaculata. Dooley, E. J. $2.50; $2.25 .. *Ditson.*
Maria Monk's daughter. Eckel, L. St. J. $1.75. *U. S. Pub.*
Maria Olliviero, the female brigand. 12°. pap., 20c. *Hurst.*
Maria Stuart. *See* Schiller, J. F. v.
Maria Theresa and her fireman. *See* Mundt, *Mrs.* C. M.
Mariamne. Osborn, L. 75c. .... *Hinton.*
Marian; or, a day without prayer. 18°. 22c ... *Am. S. S.*
Marian and her pupils. Lankester, C. $1.25. *Scribner, W. & A.*
Marian Ellis; or, unfading flowers; by a clergyman's wife. 18°. '73. 45c. .... *Routledge.*
Marian Grey. Holmes, M. J. $1.50 .... *Carleton.*
Marian Temple's work. *See* Poplar Dell lib.
Marianische Sodal (Der). Polk, J. 75c.; $1 .. *Benziger.*
Marianne: drama. 16°. pap., 15c. .... *French.*
Marianne, the vivandière. Phillips, L. 15c ... *French.*
Marian's history. 18°. 50c. .... *O'Shea.*

Marian's mission. Leslie, E. $1 .... *Meth. Bk. Conc.*
Maria's two vacations; or, principle in pleasure. 18°. 70c. .... *Am. S. S.*
Maricourt, René de. Viva perpetua; or, the martyrs of Carthage; tr. from the Fr. 12°. $2.. *O'Shea.*
Marie Antoinette. Giacometti, P. 15c. ...... *French.*
Marie Antoinette. Mundt, C. M. $1.50; $1; $3.50. *Appleton.*
Marie Celeste, *Sister.* Estelle Russell. [Fiction.] 8°. pap., 75c. .... *Harper.*
— *Same.* New ed. cr. 8°. '71. $1.75... *Macmillan.*
Marie Derville. Witt, H. G. de. $1.50... *Lippincott.*
Marie Ducange. Bernard, W. B. 15c. ...... *French.*
Marie Josephine (*pseud.*) House of gold; [also] Saint of Nazareth: poetical life of St. Joseph. 12°. '73. $2; $2.50 .... *Kelly, P. & Co.*
— Rosa immaculata; or, tower of ivory in the house of Anna and Joachim. [Poem.] 12°. $2; $3. *O'Shea.*
— Rosa mystica; or, Mary of Nazareth: the lily of the house of David. 12°. $2; $3 .... *O'Shea.*
Marie Louise. Carlen, E. F. 25c. .... *Dick & F.*
Marienbild (Das). *See* Schmid, C. v.
Marie's reward. *See* Bright gems for boys and girls; — Little girls' lib.
Marietta. Trollope, T. A. $1.75; $1.50... *Peterson.*
Marietta; or, the maid and the miser. 8°. pap., 25c. *De Witt.*
Mariner's compass. Leslie, H. 15c. .... *French.*
Mariner's progress. Macgregor, D. $1.25... *Carter.*
Marion, Fs. Life. ill. 16°. $1.25 .... *Lee & S.*
Marion, Fulgence. Wonderful balloon ascents; or, the conquest of the skies; tr. from the Fr. ill. 12°. '74. $1.25 .... *Scribner.*
— Wonders of optics; tr. and ed. by C. W. Quin. ill. 12°. '75. $1.25 .... *Scribner.*
— Wonders of vegetation; tr. from the Fr.; ed. with add. by S. De Vere. ('71.) New ed. ill. 12°. '74. $1.50 .... *Scribner.*
Marion; or, the picture in my uncle's drawing-room. 16°. '70. $1; $1.50 .... *Kelly, P. & Co.*
Marion and his men; or, the Tory prisoner. 8°. pap., 25c. .... *De Witt.*
Marion and Jessie; or, children's influence. ill. 16°. $1 .... *Cin. Meth. Bk. Conc.*
Marion Barnard. Smith, J. F. 75c. .... *Dick & F.*
Marion Berkley. Comins, L. B. $1.50 .... *Loring.*
Marion Elwood. Brownson, S. A. $1.25; $1.75. *Sadlier.*
Marion Grey. *See* Gem cluster.
Marion Harvie. Finley, M. F. 65c. .... *Pres. Bd.*
Marion Howard. S., M. $2 .... *Cunningham.*
Marion Leslie; or, the light at home; with introd. by H. A. Boardman. 18°. 75c. .... *Pres. Bd.*
Marion Lester. Davis, M. S. $1 .... *Universalist.*
Marion Martin. 18°. 40c. .... *Dutton.*
Marion through the brush. 18°. 90c. .... (?) *Martien.*
Marion's jewels. *See* Baker, *Mrs.* H. N. W.
Marion's lib. *See* Baker, *Mrs.* H. N. W.
Marion's little sister. Drinkwater, J. M. $1.. *Cong. Pub.*
Marion's path through shadow to sunshine. 16°. $1.25. (?) *Martien.*
Marion's Sundays. *See* Neely, *Miss* K.
Marion's three crowns. Doudney, S. 50c. .. *Nelson.*
Maritana. *See* Ditson.
Maritana: opera. 16°. pap., 15c. .... *French.*
Marjorie Daw. Aldrich, T. B. $1.50; $1 .. *Osgood.*
Marjorie Fleming. *See* Brown, *Dr.* J:
Marjorie's quest. Gould, J. T. $1.50 .... *Osgood.*
Marjorie's work. *See* Ravenswood stories.

Marjory. Deane, M. $1.50 .... *Macmillan.*
Mark, the fisher boy. Sanford, D. P. 75c. .. *Dutton.*
Mark, the match boy. Alger, H., *jr.* $1.25.. *Loring.*
Mark Barnett; or, to every one his work. ('64.) New ed. ill. 16°. '75. $1.15 .... *Hoyt.*
Mark Churchill. ill. 16°. '72. $1.25 .... *Lothrop.*
Mark Dunning's enemy. Chellis, M. D. $1.50. *H. A. Young.*
Mark Hurdlestone. Moodie, S. $1.25 .... *De Witt.*
Mark Jarrett's daisy. Egan, P. $1 .... *De Witt.*
Mark Noble; or, the button necklace. 18°. 60c. (?) *Martien.*
Mark Peters; or, a lesson on contentment. 18°. 25c.; 30c. .... *Am. Bapt.*
Mark Raffles. *See* Dalton, W:
Mark Rowland. Sleeper, J. S. $1.25 .... *Loring.*
Mark Seaworth. Kingston, W. H. G. $1.25.. *Lippincott.*
Mark Steadman; or, show your colours. ill. 18°. 60c. *Am. Tr.; Am. S. S.*
— *Same.* ('68.) New ed. ill. 16°. '75. $1.15.. *Hoyt.*
— *Span.* Marcos Steadman. ill. 18°. '70. 50c... *Am. Tr.*
Mark Thoresby; or, the evangelist among the Indians. 16°. $1.35 .... *Pres. Bd.*
Mark Wilton, the merchant's clerk. Tayler, C. B. $1. *Leighton*
Mark Woodford's promise; or, a boy's obedience. ill. 18°. '73. 60c. .... *Lothrop.*
Markby, T: Practical essays on education. cr. 8°. $2. *Routledge.*
Markby, W: Elements of law. cr. 8°. $2.50. *Macmillan.*
— — Supplement. cr. 8°. '75. $1 .... *Macmillan.*
Markham, *Mrs.* (*pseud.*) *See* Penrose, Eliz.
Markham, Clements Rob. History of the Abyssinian expedition; incl. account of physical geog., geol. and botany of the region traversed. maps, etc. 8°. '69. $4 .... *Macmillan.*
— Life of Lord Fairfax, commander-in-chief of the army of the parliament of England. por., maps, plans, etc. 8°. '70. $5 .... *Macmillan.*
Markhams of Ollerton. Glaister, E. $1 .... *Pott.*
Markoe, F. H. *See* Marquand, F. A., Markoe, F. H., *and* Henderson, W. J.
Markoe, T: M. Treatise on diseases of the bones. ill. 8°. $4.50 .... *Appleton.*
Mark's composition. *See* Leighton children.
Marks, Bernh. First lessons in geometry, objectively presented. 12°. '58. 90c. .... *Ivison.*
Marks, E. M. Events in life of Miss Dollikins. ill. obl. 32°. 50c. .... *Nelson.*
Marks, J: J. Peninsula campaign in Virginia: incidents and scenes on the battle-fields and in Richmond. 12°. '63. $1.75; pap., $1.25. *Claxton; Lippincott.*
Marks, *Mrs.* Marrilla. Memoirs of David Marks. ('46.) New ed. 12°. '47. $1 .... *Freewill.*
Marksman (*pseud.*) The dead shot; or, sportsman's complete guide. 12°. $1.75 .... *Woodward.*
Marlay, J: F. Life of Bp. T. A. Morris. 12°. $1.75. *Cin. Meth. Bk. Conc.*
Marlitt, E. (*pseud.*) *See* John, Eugenia.
Marlowe, Cp. Complete works; with account of author and notes by A. Dyce. por. roy. 8°. $4.50. *Routledge.*
Marmaduke Multiply; or, multiplication table in rhyme. ill. sq. 16°. 50c.; 20c. .... *Miller.*
Marmion. *See* Scott, *Sir* Wa.
Marmont, A: F: L: V. de. Spirit of milit. institutions; or, essential principles of art of war; tr. with notes by H. Coppée. 12°. '62. $1.25.. *Claxton.*
Marnie's angel. *See* Swallow stories.
Marooner's Island. Goulding, F. R. $1.50.. *Claxton.*

Marooner's Island stories. 3 v. ill. 16°. '66–'69. $4.50 .... *Claxton.*
Cont.: Marooner's Island, by F. R. Goulding. — Young marooners, by F. R. Goulding. — Young wrecker, by R. M. Bache.

Marquand, F. A., Markoe, F. H., *and* Henderson, W. J. Carmina Princetonia: songs of Princeton College. 8°. '76. $1.50 .... *Dennis.*

Marquart, J: Key for mathematical self-instruction on the mechanical sliding or carpenter's rule. 18°. 37½c. .... *Polock.*

— Six hundred [misc.] receipts; with gauging tables. 12°. $1.75 .... *J. E. Potter.*

Márquez, J. *See* Bello, A., Compendio de la gramática castellana.

Marquis and merchant. Collins, M. 50c. ... *Appleton.*

Marquis de Villemer. *See* Sand, G.

Marquis of Carabas. [Toy-book.] ill. obl. 4°. bds., 50c. .... *Routledge.*

— *See also* Routledge's.

Marquis of Létorière. Sue, E. $1.25 ... *Nichols & H.*

Marr, Fannie H. Heart life in song. 12°. '74. $1. *Turnbull.*

Marriage. *See* Ferrier, Ma.

Marriage and married life. Cates, J. M. D. $1.25. *So. Bapt.*

Marriage at any price. Wooler, J. P. 15c. *De Witt; French.*

Marriage gift. Petrie, J. 60c. .... *Pres. Bd.*

Marriage in high life. Feuillet, O. $1.50; $1.25; 75c. .... *Porter.*

Marriage in high life. Grey, E. C. 50c. ... *Peterson.*

Marriage a lottery. Dance, C. 15c. .... *French.*

Marriage of Figaro. *See* Mozart, J. C. W. A.

Marriage of Moira Fergus. *See* Black, W:

Marriage offering. Livermore, A. A. $1.25. *Nichols & H.*

Marriage ring. James, J. A. 25c.; 40c.; $1 .. *Lothrop.*

Marriage verdict. *See* Dumas, A.

Married. Newby, C. J. 50c. .... *Peterson.*

Married and single. Poole, J. 15c. .... *French.*

Married at last. Thomas, A. $1.75; $1.50 .. *Peterson.*

Married bachelor. O'Callaghan, P. P. 15c. .. *French.*

Married belle. Smith, J. P. $1.75 .... *Carleton.*

Married beneath him. Payn, J. $1.75; $1.50 .. *Peterson.*

Married daughters: drama. 16°. pap., 15c. .. *French.*

Married for both worlds. Porter, A. E. $1.50 .. *Lee & S.*

Married in haste. Stephens, A. S. $1.75; $1.50. *Peterson.*

Married life. *See* Arthur, T. S.

Married life. Belcher, J. 50c. .... *Am. Bapt.*

Married life. Buckstone, J. B. 15c. .... *French.*

Married or single? Sedgwick, C. M. 2 v. $3 .. *Harper.*

Married rake. Selby, C. 15c. .... *French.*

Married unmarried. Barnett, M. 15c. .... *French.*

Married women. Child, L. M. $1.25 ... (?) *Francis.*

Marrow of modern divinity. Fisher, E. $1.50 .. *Pres. Bd.*

Marry in haste and repent at leisure: comedietta. 16°. pap., 15c. .... *Happy.*

Marryat, Emilia. Among the Maoris: book of adventure. ill. 16°. $1.75 .... *Scribner, W. & A.*

Marryat, Flo. [*now Mrs.* Ross Church]. Her lord and master. 8°. pap., 50c. .... *Harper.*

— Life of F: Marryat. 2 v. 12°. $4 .... *Appleton.*

— Lucky disappointment. sq. 16°. '76. pap., 35c. *Loring.*

— No intentions. 8°. pap., 75c. .... *Appleton.*

— Open! Sesame! 12°. '75. $1; bds., 75c. .. *Donnelley.*

— *Same.* ill. 8°. $1.25; pap., 75c. .... *Estes.*

— Poison of asps. 8°. pap., 30c. .... *Appleton.*

— Prey of the gods. 8°. pap., 30c. .... *Harper.*

— Sybil's friend, and how she found him. ill. 16°. '73. $1.25 .... *Routledge.*

Marryat, Fk. S. Mountains and mole hills; or, recollections of a burnt journal. ill. 12°. $1.25 .. *Harper.*

Marryat, F: Works. 5 v. ill. 12°. (Bohn.) ea., $1.75. *Little, B. & Co.*
Cont.: Masterman Ready. — Mission; or, scenes in Africa. — Pirate; Three cutters. — Privateer's-man. — Settlers in Canada.

— *Same.* 5 v. ill. 12°. (Bohn.) ea., $2. *Lippincott; Scribner, W. & A.*

— *Same.* 16 v. 12°. ea., 25c. — ill. 12°. $20; hf. roxb., $24; hf. cf., $48; — in 4 v. 12°. $5. — (Railway lib.) 16°. ea., bds., 40c. .... *Routledge.*
Cont.: King's own. — Frank Mildmay. — Percival Keene. — Phantom ship. — Dog fiend. — Jacob Faithful. — Poacher. — Pacha of many tales. — Japhet in search of a father. — Rattlin, the reefer. — Midshipman Easy. — Peter Simple. — Newton Foster. — Valerie. — Olla podrida. — Monsieur Violet.

— *Same.* • 15 v. 8°. ea., pap., 50c. .... *Peterson.*
Cont.: Frank Mildmay. — Jacob Faithful. — Japhet in search of a father. — King's own. — Midshipman Easy. — Naval officer. — Newton Foster. — Pacha of many tales. — Percival Keene. — Peter Simple. — Phantom ship. — Pirate; Three cutters. — Poor Jack. — Sea king. — Snarleyow.

— *Same.* 12 v. 12°. ea., pap., 50c. .... *Appleton.*
Cont.: Peter Simple. — Jacob Faithful. — Naval officer. — King's own. — Japhet in search of a father. — Newton Foster. — Midshipman Easy. — Pacha of many tales. — Poacher. — Phantom ship. — Snarleyow. — Percival Keene.

— *Same.* 12 v. 12°. $15; hf. cf., $36 .... *Appleton.*

— *Same.* 17 v. 8°. ea., pap., 25c. .... *De Witt.*
Cont.: Newton Foster. — Midshipman Easy. — Peter Simple. — Pacha of many tales. — Pirate; Three cutters. — King's own. — Japhet in search of a father. — Snarleyow. — Jacob Faithful. — Frank Mildmay. — Percival Keene. — Phantom ship. — Rattlin, the reefer. — Poacher. — Poor Jack. — Masterman Ready. — Valerie.

— *Same.* (Standard ed.) 13 v. 16°. $13; hf. cf., $30. .... *Routledge.*
Cont.: King's own. — Frank Mildmay. — Percival Keene. — Phantom ship. — Japhet in search of a father. — The dog fiend. — Jacob Faithful. — Poacher. — Newton Foster. — Pacha of many tales. — Rattlin, the reefer. — Midshipman Easy. — Peter Simple.

— Children of the New Forest. 12°. $1.25 .. *Harper.*

— *Same.* ill. 12°. $1.50 .... *Routledge.*

— Japhet in search of a father. 12°. $1.25 ... *Harper.*

— Juvenile stories. 3 v. ill. 12°. $3 .... *Appleton.*
Cont.: Masterman Ready. — Settlers in Canada. — Scenes in Africa.

— Little savage: hist. of a boy left alone upon an uninhabited island. 12°. $1.25 .... *Harper.*

— *Same.* ill. 12°. $1.50 .... *Routledge.*

— Masterman Ready. 16°. $1.25 .... *Appleton.*

— Pirate; [also] Three cutters. ill. sq. 16°. $1 .. *Eastman.*

— Privateersman. ill. 12°. $1.25 .... *Lippincott.*

— *Same.* ill. 16°. '65. $1.25 .... *Roberts.*

— Three cutters. 8°. pap., 25c. .... *Dick & F.*

— — *See also above* Pirate.

Marryat, Jos. History of pottery and porcelain, mediæval and modern. col. pl. and wood-cuts. 8°. $21; cf., $27 .... *Scribner, W. & A.*

Marrying beneath your station. Wood, E. P. 25c. *Peterson.*

Marrying for money. Pickering, E. 75c. .. *Peterson.*

Marsden, Alex. New and successful mode of treating cert in forms of cancer. 2d ed. col. pl. 8°. '74. $3.50 .... *Lindsay.*

Marsden, F: Clouds: comedy. 16°. pap., 15c. .. *De Witt.*

Marsh, And. J. Manual of reformed phonetic shorthand. 16°. '68. $2 .... *Bancroft.*

Marsh, *Miss* Caro. [Juveniles.] 13 v. .... *Carter.*
Cont.: Life of Arthur Vandeleur, 12°, $1.25. — Crossing the river, 60c. — English hearts and hands, $1.25. — Golden chain, 90c. — Life of Dr. Marsh, $1.75, *ea.*, 16°. — Haven and prize. — Light for the line. — Midnight chimes. — Rift in the clouds. — Victory won, *ea.*, 18°, 35c. — Prince and the prayer, 18°, 10c. — Shining light, 18°, 50c. — Life of Capt. Vicars, 18°, 60c.

— Life of Capt. Hedley Vicars. 18°. '62. 30c. *Am. Tr.*

— Life of Maj. Arthur Vandeleur. 18°. '63. 25c. *Am. Tr.*

— Man of one book: life of Rev. W: Marsh. 12°. '74. $1.50 .... *Meth. Bk. Conc.*

— Victory won: memorial of G. R. 18°. 35c. *N. Y. Ref. Ch. Bd.*

Marsh, Cp. C. Course of practice in single entry book-keeping. 8°. $2 .... *Appleton.*
— *Span.* Curso práctico de teneduría de libros: partida sencilla. 8°. $2 .... *Appleton.*
— Science of double entry book-keeping. 8°. $2.50. *Appleton.*
— *Span.* La ciencia de la teneduría de libros: partida doble. 8°. $2 .... *Appleton.*
— Theory and practice of bank book-keeping and joint stock accounts. 4°. $6 .... *Appleton.*

Marsh, Dwight W. Tennessean in Persia and Koordistan: scenes and incidents in life of S: A. Rhea. 12°. $2 .... *Pres. Bd.*

Marsh, *Mrs.* E. F. Bible gems: texts. 16°. 30c. *West. Tr.*

Marsh, G: P. Earth (The) as modified by human action: new ed. of Man and nature. cr. 8°. '74. $4.50 .... *Scribner.*
— Lectures on the Eng. lang. ('59.) 4th ed., rev. and enl. '74. cr. 8°. $3; hf. cf., $5 ... *Scribner.*
— Origin and hist. of the Eng. lang. and of the early literature it embodies. ('62.) New ed. cr. 8°. '72. $3; hf. cf., $5 .... *Scribner.*

Marsh, J. Piano method. obl. 4°. 75c. .... *Gordon.*

Marsh, J: Epitome of ecclesiastical hist. 16th ed., rev. and brought down to present time. 12°. '64. $2 .... *Barnes.*
— — Questions; by J. Emerson and others. 18°. '64. 75c. .... *Barnes.*
— Putnam and the wolf. ill. 18°. '38. 25c. ... *Am. Tr.*

Marsh, J: B. For liberty's sake: story of Robert Ferguson. 8°. '73. $2 .... *Routledge.*
— Stories of Venice and the Venetians. ill. 12°. '73. $2 .... *Routledge.*

Marsh, J: B. Music of the chapter; for royal arch Masons. 8°. '69. $1 .... *Ditson; Masonic.*

Marsh, Leon. *See* Shadow of Christianity.

Marsh, Luther R. *See* Kelly, J.

Marsh, W. H. H. Modern Sunday school. 16°. $1. *Am. Bapt.*

Marsh-Caldwell, *Mrs.* Anne. [Tales.] 15 v. 8°. pap. .... *Harper.*

Cont.: Adelaide Lindsay. — Castle Avon. — Evelyn Marston. — Heiress of Haughton. — Mordaunt Hall. — Norman's bridge. — Ravenscliffe. — Rose of Ashurst. — Time the avenger. — The Wilmingtons., *ea.*, 50c. — Aubrey. — Emilia Wyndham. — Father Darcy. — Triumphs of time, *ea.*, 75c. — Lettice Arnold, 25c.

— Admiral's daughter. 8°. pap., 50c. ...... *Peterson.*
— Angela. 12°. $1.50 .... *Harper.*
— Deformed (The). 8°. pap., 25c. .... *Peterson.*
— Helen's fault. 18°. 45c. .... *Routledge.*
— History of the Protestant reformation in France. 2 v. roy. 12°. $2 .... *Lea.*
— Orphan sisters. 8°. pap., 50c. .... *Peterson.*

Marsh king's daughter. *See* Andersen, H. C.

Marshal Vavasour. Sadler, S. W. 75c. .... *Pott.*

Marshall, Alex. K. *See* Kentucky, Court of Appeals reports.

Marshall, C: *See* England, Common law reports.

Marshall, C: F. True hist. of the Brooklyn scandal: account of trial of H. W. Beecher upon charges preferred by T. Tilton. por. 8°. '74. *$2.50 .. *Nat. Pub.*

Marshall, E: C. Book of oratory. 12°. $1.50 .. *Appleton.*
— First book of oratory. 12°. $1.25 .... *Appleton.*

Marshall, *Mrs.* Emma. Between the cliffs. 16°. $1. *Carter.*
— Brook Silvertone and its message. 18°. 75c. (?) *Martien.*
— — *See also* Silvertone lib.
— Brothers and sisters; or, true of heart. 16°. $1.25. (?) *Martien.*
— Crofton cousins. 32°. 40c. .... *Scribner, W. & A.*
— Edith Prescot; or, lessons of love. ill. 16°. '71. $1.25 .... *Lothrop.*
— Grandma's wardrobe. 18°. 75c. ...... (?) *Martien.*
— Happy days at Fern Bank. 16°. $1 ... (?) *Martien.*

Marshall, *Mrs.* Emma, *continued.*
— Johnny Weston; or, Christmas eve at the White House. 18°. 75c. .... *Whittaker.*
— *Same.* 18°. 90c. .... (?) *Martien.*
— Lessons of love; or, Aunt Bertha's visit to the Elms. 16°. $1 .... (?) *Martien.*
— Life's aftermath: story of a quiet people. 12°. '76. $1.50 .... *Dutton.*
— Lily among thorns. 12°. '74. $1.50 ...... *Dutton.*
— Little brothers and sisters. 16°. $1.25 ..... *Carter.*

Comprising Three little brothers *and* Three little sisters.

— Little May's legacy; or, the gipsy boy. 18°. 50c. (?) *Martien.*
— *Same;* [also] Story of a basket. 18°. 50c. .. *Am. S. S.*
— *Same;* and other stories. 18°. 60c. .... *Whittaker.*
— Little peat-cutters; or, song of love. 18°. 50c. .. *Dutton.*
— *Same.* 18°. 60c.; 70c. .... *Am. Bapt.*
— *Same.* ('69.) New ed. ill. 16°. '73. 75c. .. *Hoyt.*
— Lost lilies. 18°. 50c. .... (?) *Martien.*
— Matthew Frost, carrier; or, little Snowdrop's mission. 16°. $1 .... *Carter; Dutton.*
— Millicent Legh. 16°. $1.25 .... (?) *Martien.*
— Mrs. Mainwaring's journal. 12°. '73. $1.50 .. *Dutton.*
— Now-a-days; or, kings' daughters. 12°. '74. $1.50. *Dutton.*
— Primrose ser. 6 v. 18°. ea., 50c. .... *Carter.*

Cont.: Little peat-cutters. — Roger's apprenticeship. — Katie's work. — Consideration for others. — Little Primrose. — Two Margarets.

— Stellafont Abbey; or, nothing new. 18°. $1. *Carter; Dutton.*
— Story of a basket. 18°. 50c. .... (?) *Martien.*
— — *See also above* Little May's legacy.
— Theodora's childhood. 16°. 50c. .. *Scribner, W. & A.*
— Three little brothers. 18°. 50c. .... *Carter.*
— *Same.* ill. 16°. 75c. .... *Lothrop.*
— — *See also above* Little brothers and sisters.
— Three little sisters. 18°. 50c. .... *Carter; Dutton.*
— — *See also above* Little brothers and sisters.
— Two holidays. 18°. 50c. .... *Carter.*
— Violet Douglas; or, the problems of life. ill. 16°. '72. $1.50 .... *Lothrop.*

Marshall, Fs. A. Mad as a hatter: farce. 16°. pap., 15c. .... *French.*

Marshall, J. M. Report of celebration of centennial of incorporation of Buxton, Maine, Aug. 14, 1872. 8°. $1.50 .... *Hoyt, F. & D.*

Marshall, J. M. Table of irregular Greek verbs. roy. 8°. '66. 40c. .... *Macmillan.*

Marshall, Ja. A. Rise and progress of Chicago. *See* Brown, H: Present and future of Chicago.

Marshall, J: Life of Washington. 2 v. 8°. shp., $6. *Claxton.*
— *See also* United States, Circ. Court reports.

Marshall, J: Description of the human body: its structure and functions; with diagrams. 2 v. text, 4°; pl., f°. bds., $8.50 .... *Putnam.*
— Key to "Physiological diagrams." 8°. 50c. *Lindsay.*
— Outlines of physiology, human and comparative; with add. by F. G. Smith. ill. 8°. $6.50; leath., $7.50 .... *Lea.*

Marshall, J: Ja. *See* Kentucky, Court of Appeals reports.

Marshall, Leon. Clarion (The): anthems, motets, etc. obl. 8°. bds., 50c. .... *G. D. Russell.*
— Harp of praise: music for choirs, congregations, etc. obl. roy. 8°. '75. bds., $1.25 .... *Pond.*
— Hosanna (The): collection of psalm and hymn tunes, etc. obl. 8°. '56. bds., $1.38 .... *Ditson.*
— New sacred star; or, union collection of church music. obl. 8°. '65. bds., $1.38 .... *Ditson.*
— Sacred star; or, union collection of church music. obl. 8°. '61. bds., $1.38 .... *Ditson.*
— Vestry melodies; with sup. 12°. '74. 90c. ... *Graves.*
— *and* Proctor, J. C., *and* Burnham, S. Sabbath songs for children's worship. 4°. pap., 30c.; bds., 35c. .... *Lee & S.*

Marshall, T. A. *See* Mississippi, Chancery reports; Law reports.

Marshall, T. W. M. Christian missions. 2 v. 12°. $4; hf. mor., $6; hf. cf., $7.50........*Sadlier.*

— Order and chaos: lecture. 8°. '69. pap., 25c. *Murphy.*

Marshall, T: F. Speeches and writings. ('58.) New ed. por. 8°. '65. cf., $2............*Pounsford.*

Marshall, W. S. Farmer's handbook; with receipts and tables. ('57.) New ed. 12°. '68. $1.50. *Pounsford.*

Marshall, Wa. Gospel mystery of sanctification opened in sundry practical directions. 18°. 60c. *U.P.Bd.of Pub.*

Marshman, J. R. *See* England, Common Law reports.

Marston, C. D. *See* Moore, D., Marston, C. D., *and* Bayley, *Sir* E.

Marston, Westland. [Plays.] 7 v. 16°. ea., pap., 15c. *French.*

Cont.: Anne Blake. — Hard struggle. — Life's ransom. — Patrician's daughter: tragedy. — Pure gold. — Strathmore: tragic play. — Wife's portrait: farce.

Marston of Dunoran. 8°. pap., 25c.......*Littell & G.*

Marteilhe, Jean. The Huguenot galley-slave; tr. from the Fr. [Autobiog.] 12°. '76. $1.50.......*Holt.*

Martel, C: Henry Arden; or, it is only a pin. ('66.) 6th ed. ill. 16°. '72. $1 ....*Perkinpine.*

Marten, E: Bindon. Records of steam boiler explosions. ill. 8°. '72. $2 ....*Spon.*

Marten and his two little scholars at a Sunday school. 18°. 50c..........................*Am.S.S.*

Martensen, Hs. Lassen. Christian dogmatics. 8°. $3. *Scribner, W. & A.*

— Christian ethics. 8°. $3..........*Scribner, W. & A.*

Martha, *Cousin.* *See* Cousin Martha.

Martha. 12°. pap., 15c....................*Radde.*

Martha. Bourdon, M. F. 30c. ....*O'Shea.*

Martha. *See* Flotow, F. v.

Martha. Reed, A. $1.25 ....*Harper.*

Martha Willis. Jerrold, D. 15c... ....*French.*

Martha's gift: story for the freed children; by a teacher. 18°. 50c.....................*Am.S.S.*

Martha's home. ill. 16°. 50c...............*Nelson.*

— *Same.* 18°. 60c. ....*Cong.Pub.*

— *See also* Adirondack stories; — Snow-drop ser.

Martha's hooks and eyes. 18°. 50c. ....*Appleton.*

Martha's hymn. *See* Books of blessing.

Martha's school days. Nelson, H. C. $1.25. *Cong. Pub.*

Marthas (The). Philip, R. 60c............*Carter.*

Martial [Martialis], Mcs. Valerius. Epigrams; lit. tr., with verse tr. from Eng. poets, etc., and index. 12°. (Bohn.) $2.75.............*Little, B. & Co.*

— *Same.* 12°. (Bohn.) $3..*Lippincott; Scribner, W. & A.*

Martial deeds of Pennsylvania. Bates, S. P. *$6.75; $8.75; $15.............................*Rutter.*

Martien's cheap Sunday-school lib. 50 v. ill. 18°. *net*, $20.........................(?) *Martien.*

Martin, B. Y. *See* Georgia, Sup. Court reports.

Martin, Bon L: Henri. Popular hist. of France from 1789; tr. 30 pts. 8°. pap., *$15; — in 3 v. 8°. *$16.50–$30 ....*Estes.*

Martin, C. A. F. Natural history; tr. by S. A. Myers. ill. cr. 8°. '60. $4...................*Mason.*

Martin, *Mrs.* Clara B. Little Nortons (The): a summer's life. ill. 12°. '70. $1.25...*Loring, S. & H.*

— Mount Desert on the coast of Maine. maps and ill. 16°. '74. bds., 75c. ....*Loring, S. & H.*

Martin, E: Directory of Watsonville [Cal.] for 1873; with description of the Pajaro Valley, its climate, resources, etc. 16°. '73. pap., 50c. (?) *White & B.*

Martin, E: *See* Labiche, E. M., *and* Martin, E.

Martin, E: *See* Smith, W., *and* Martin, E.

Martin, E: Winslow. Behind the scenes in Washington. ill. 8°. $2.75 ....*Tibbals.*

— History of the grange movement: farmers' war against monopolies. ill. 8°. '73. *$2.75......*Nat.Pub.*

Martin, Fs. X. *See* Louisiana, Sup. Court reports; — North Carolina, Law reports.

Martin, Fes. Angèlique Arnauld, Abbess of Port Royal. [Biog.] cr. 8°. '73. $1.75..*Macmillan.*

Martin, F: History of Lloyd's and of marine insurance in Great Britain; with statistics rel. to marine insurance. 8°. '76. $4.50..........*Macmillan.*

— Statesman's year-book: statistical and hist. annual of the civilized world. cr. 8°. $3.50...*Macmillan.*

Martin, G: H. Text book on civil government in the U. S. 12°. '75. $1.25...............*Barnes.*

Martin, G: W. Interest and average tables. 4°. '76. $3 ....*Darrow.*

Martin, H. N. *See* Huxley, T. H., *and* Martin, H. N.

Martin, Hu. The atonement in its rel. to the covenant, the priesthood, the intercession of our Lord. 12°. '71. $1.50 ....*Smith, E. & Co.*

— The prophet Jonah, and his mission to Nineveh. cr. 8°. $2.50.............................*Routledge.*

Martin, I: Journal of life, travels, labours and relig. exercises. 12°. *net*, shp., 40c...*Friends Bk.Assoc.*

Martin, J. H. *See* Tennessee.

Martin, J. L. Voice of the seven thunders: lectures on Revelations. 8th ed. por. 12°. '76. $1.50. *Cen.Bk.*

Martin, J. M. Little Baptist; rev. by M. P. Lowrey. 12°. '76. $1; mor., $2..................*So.Bapt.*

Martin, Ja. Ranald. *See* Johnson, J., *and* Martin, J. R.

Martin, J: H. Manual of microscopic mounting; with notes on collection and examination of objects. ill. 8°. '72. $3 ....*Lindsay.*

Martin, J: Hill. Historical sketch of Bethlehem and the Moravians. 8°. '73. $3 ....*Clauder.*

Martin, *Mrs.* M. Dayspring; or, light to them that sit in darkness. ('54.) 3d ed. 18°. '73. 40c...*So.Meth.*

— Methodism; or, Christianity in earnest. ('59.) 2d ed. 18°. '75. 50c.........................*So.Meth.*

— Sabbath-school offering; or, true stories and poems. 18°. '60. 50c. ....*So.Meth.*

— — *See also* Young disciples lib.

Martin, *Mrs.* M. *and Miss* —. Heroines of early Methodism. 18°. '75. 50c...........*So.Meth.*

Martin, S. W. Festival chimes. [Sing. book.] obl. 8°. bds., $1.50 ....*Peters.*

— *and* Towne, T. M., *and* Stillman, J. M. The cluster. obl. 8°. bds., $1.50 ....*Peters.*

Martin, S: Youthful Christianity: its characteristics, dangers and excellences. ('55.) 2d ed. 18°. '75. 40c...................................*So.Meth.*

Martin, Thdr. Life of the prince consort. v. 1. por. and ill. 12°. $2..................*Appleton.*

— *and* Aytoun, W. E. Book of ballads; ed. by Bon Gaultier [*pseud.* for M. and A.] New ed.; incl. Firmilian, by T. Percy Jones [*pseud.*] 16°. $1.50; hf. cf., $3 ....*Widdleton.*

Martin, W. A. Screw-cutting tables; for the mechanical engineers. 8°. 50c.................*Baird.*

— *Same.* 2d ed. obl. roy. 8°. '74. 50c........*Spon.*

Martin, W: Chang-Ching-Fou: burlesque. 16°. pap., 15c. ....*French.*

Martin, W: C. L. Cattle: their breeds, management and diseases; rev. and ed. by W. and H. Raynbird. ill. 16°. bds., 50c............*Routledge.*

— Sheep: our domestic breeds and their treatment. ill. 16°. bds., 50c...................*Routledge.*

— *See also* Youatt, W., *and* Martin, W. C. L.

Martin. Franklin, J. 83c..............*Thompson.*

Martin, the foundling. Sue, E. $2; $1.50..*Peterson.*

Martin and the miller; — and Nelly. Franklin, J. ea., 83c. . . . . *Thompson.*
Martin Chuzzlewit. *See* Dickens, C:
Martin Chuzzlewit: drama. 16°. pap., 15c. . . *French.*
Martin Merrivale. Trowbridge, J. T. $2 . . . . *Tilton.*
Martin on the mountain. Franklin, J. 83c. *Thompson.*
Martin Paz. *See* Verne, Jul.
Martin Pole. Saunders, J. 50c. . . . . *Harper.*
Martin stories. *See* Franklin, J.
Martindale, Ja. B. Martindale's U. S. law directory. [Annual.] 2d ed. 8°. '76. shp., $5 . . *Martindale.*
Martindale, Jos. C. Anatomy, physiology and hygiene. ('72.) 3d ed. 12°. '75. hf. leath., $1.30 . . *Eldredge.*
— Common school speller. 12°. hf. bd., 25c. . . *Butler.*
— Complete speller. 12°. hf. bd., 30c. . . . . *Butler.*
— First lessons in natural philosophy. ('72.) 5th ed. 16°. '76. 60c. . . . . *Eldredge.*
— History of the United States. ('66.) 21st ed. 16°. '76. 60c. . . . . *Eldredge.*
— Primary speller. 16°. hf. bd., 20c. . . . . *Butler.*
Martine, Arth. Droll dialogues and laughable recitations. 16°. pap., 30c.; bds., 50c. . . . . *Dick & F.*
— Handbook of etiquette and guide to true politeness. 16°. 75c.; bds., 50c. . . . . *Dick & F.*
— Sensible letter writer. 16°. 75c.; bds., 50c. . . *Dick & F.*
— *Same;* [also] Book of etiquette. 16°. $1.50 . . *Dick & F.*
Martineau, Ht. Billow and the rock. ill. 16°. '74. 50c. . . . . *Routledge.*
— Biographical sketches, 1852–'68. 8°. '69. $1.50 . . *Holt.*
— *Same.* 3d ed. 12°. '70. $1.25 . . . . . *Macmillan.*
— Chicago in 1836. *See* Brown, H: Present and future prospects of Chicago.
— Eastern life: past and present. cr. 8°. '76. $3 . . *Roberts.*
— History of the peace: hist. of Eng., 1816–'54. 4 v. post 8°. $10 . . . . . (?) *Francis.*
— Hour and the man: hist. romance. 8°. pap., 50c. *Harper.*
— *Same.* 16°. $1 . . . . . *Routledge.*
— Martineau library. 5 v. ill. 16°. ea., 50c. *Routledge.*
Cont.: Peasant and the prince. — Crofton boys. — Feats on the fiord. — Settlers at home. — Traditions of Palestine.
— Our farm of two acres. 16°. '63. pap., 25c. *Huntington.*
— Peasant and prince. *See* Happy child's lib.
— Playfellow (The): juvenile stories. ill. 12°. '72. $2.50 . . . . . *Routledge.*
— *See also* Atkinson, H. G., *and* Martineau, Ht.
Martineau, Ja. Essays, philosophical and theological. ('66–'68.) New ed. 2 v. 8°. '75. $5 . . . *Holt.*
— Modern materialism: its attitude towards theology. 8°. '76. pap., 25c. . . . . *Ellis.*
— New affinities of faith: plea for free Christian union. 12°. '69. pap., 25c. . . . . *Holt.*
— Religion as affected by modern materialism; with introd. by H. W. Bellows. 12°. '75. 75c. *Putnam.*
— Studies of Christianity; or, timely thoughts for religious thinkers; ed. by W. R. Alger. ('58.) 5th ed. 12°. '74. $1.25 . . . . . *Am. Unit.*
Martineau library. *See* Martineau, Ht.
Martineau des Chesnez, E. (*Baronne*). Lady Green-Satin and her maid Rosette; or, the history of Jean Paul and his little white mice; tr. ill. 12°. '73. $1.50 . . . . . *Porter.*
— Uncle Grandesir's matches: a fairy tale; tr. 12°. '73. $1.25 . . . . . *Claxton.*
Martingale, Hawser (*pseud.*) *See* Sleeper, J. S.
Martin's pet robins. *See* Yonge, C. M.
Martins of Cro' Martin. *See* Lever, C:
Martiri (I). *See* Ditson.
Martyn, Fs. Homilies on the book of Tobias: explan. of duties of domestic life. 12°. $1 . . . *Cath. Pub.*
Martyn, H: Journal and letters. 12°. $1.25 . . *Leighton.*
— Life. 18°. 70c.; 75c. . . . . *Dutton.*
— — *See also* Laborers in the East.
— *Same;* with account of Abdool Messech, a Hindoo convert. 18°. 70c. . . . . *Am. S. S.*
— Memoir of J. Sargent. ill. 18°. '34. 60c. *Am. Tr.*
Martyn, *Mrs.* S. T. [Juveniles.] 15 v. '60–'70 . . *Am. Tr.*
Cont.: Allan Cameron, 50c. — Effie Morison, 45c. — Happy fireside, 50c. — Huguenots of France, 60c. — Jesus in Bethany, 25c., *ea.*, 18°. — Crescent and the cross, 90c. — Daughters of the cross, 80c. — Dora's mistake, 90c. — Hopes of Hope Castle, $1.25. — Lady Alice Lisle, 80c. — Life of W: Tyndale, 80c. — Margaret, the pearl of Navarre, 80c. — Netty and her sister, 70c. — Sybil Grey; or, a year in the city, 90c. — Wilford parsonage, 90c., *ea.*, 16°.
— Hillside cottage. 16°. 75c. . . . . *Cong. Pub.*
— Winnie and her grandfather; or, the way to overcome evil with good. ill. 18°. 60c. . . *Bost. Am. Tr.*
— — *See also* Cozy house stories.
— Women of the Bible. ill. sq. 12°. '68. $3; mor., $5 . . . . . *Am. Tr.*
Martyn, W: Carlos. Great reformation. 5 v. 12°. '66–'68. $7; hf. mor., $12 . . . . . *Am. Tr.*
Cont.: Luther and his times, $1.50. — Dutch reformation, $1.75; $2.25. — Hist. of the Huguenots, $1.50. — Eng. Puritans, $1.50; $1.75. — Pilgrim fathers of New Eng., $1.25.
Martyn Ware's temptation. Wood, E. P. 25c. *Peterson.*
Martyr of Lebanon. Bird, I. 80c. . . . . *Bost. Am. Tr.*
Martyr people. ill. 18°. '55. 35c. . . . . *Am. Tr.*
Martyr to science. *See* French's comic dramas.
Martyr wife. Arthur, T. S. $1.50 . . . . . *J. E. Potter.*
Martyrdom of Jesus of Nazareth. *See* Wise, I. M.
Martyrdom of man. Reade, W. $3 . . . . . *Somerby.*
Martyrdom of St. Cecily. Christie, A. 25c. . . *Sadlier.*
Martyred church. Gill, W. F. $2 . . . . . *W. F. Gill.*
Martyr's daughter. Butler, M. 70c. . . . . *Pres. Bd.*
Martyrs (The). *See* Chateaubriand, F. A. de.
Martyrs and heroes of the covenant. Gilfillan, G. $1. *Carter.*
Martyrs and sufferers for the truth. Plumer, W. S. 65c. . . . . *Pres. Bd.*
Martyrs for the word. 18°. 60c. . . . . *Cong. Pub.*
Martyrs of Bohemia: memoirs of John Huss and Jerome of Prague. 18°. '67. 65c. *N. Y. Ref. Ch. Bd.; Pres. Com.*
Martyrs of the catacombs. 16°. '65. 90c. *Meth. Bk. Conc.*
Martyrs of the Coliseum. O'Reilly, A. J. $1.50; $2. *Sadlier.*
Martyrs of Madagascar. ill. 18°. '53. 35c. . . *Am. Tr.*
Martyrs of the mutiny: trials and triumphs of Christians in the Sepoy rebellion in India. 18°. 60c. *Pres. Bd.*
Martyrs of science. *See* Brewster, *Sir* D.
Martyrs of Spain. Charles, E. $1 . . . . . *Carter.*
Martyrs of Vilvorde. *See* Good boy's lib.
Martyrs to the tract cause. Hurst, J. F. 75c. *Meth. Bk. Conc.*
Marvel, Ik. (*pseud.*) *See* Mitchell, Donald G.
Marvellous country. Cozzens, S. W. $3.50; $4.50; $6 . . . . . *Lee & S.*
Marvin, Enoch M. God in Old Test. hist.: sermon. 16°. pap., 25c. . . . . *S. W. Bk. & Pub.*
— Life of W. G. Caples. 12°. $1.50 . . *S. W. Bk. & Pub.*
— Methodist Episc. churches, north and south. 16°. 60c. *S. W. Bk. & Pub.*
— Sermons. 12°. '76. $2 . . . . . *So. Meth.*
Marvin, F: R. Epidemic delusions. 12°. '74. 50c. *Somerby.*
— Philosophy of spiritualism, and the pathology and treatment of mediomania. 12°. '74. $1 . . *Somerby.*
Marvin, *Mrs.* H. N. Rabbit-snares, and other stories. ill. 18°. 50c. . . . . *Bost. Am. Tr.*
— — *See also* Gay cottage stories.
Marvin, W: Treatise on law of average. 8°. '66. shp., $3.50 . . . . . *Ward & P.*
Marvine, A. R. Report on geol. from St. George to Gila River. *See* United States, *Corps of Eng.*
Marwin, *Mrs.* M. J. Parish hall, and what was done there. ('60.) New ed. ill. 18°. '73. 50c. . . *Hoyt.*

Marx, Adph. Bernh. General musical instruction; tr. by G. Macirone. 8°. $2.50 .... *Ditson.*
— Musical compositions; with app. by E. Girax. 12°. $2.50; bds., $2 .... *Gordon.*
— — Appendix. 12°. $1 .... *Gordon.*
Mary, *Virgin.* Lily of Israel: life of the Virgin. 16°. 75c.; $1.25 .... *Sadlier.*
— Life; from her conception to her assumption. 12°. 35c. .... *Benziger.*
— *Same;* [also] Lives of the prominent saints. ill. 4°. $5–$20; — in 36 pts., ea., 25c. .... *T. Kelly.*
— *Same;* [also] Lives of St. Joseph, St. Joachim and St. Ann. 16°. $7.50–$40 .... *Strong.*
— *and* Christ. Lives; tr. by Mrs. J. Sadlier. ill. 4°. $16–$18; — in 34 pts. pl. 4°. $14.50–$20; ea., 25c. .... *Sadlier.*
Mary, *Cousin.* *See* Cousin Mary.
Mary, *Queen of Scots.* Life. 12°. $1.50; $2.. *Sadlier.*
Mary *of Egypt, St.* Life; [also] Lives of St. Cecilia and St. Bridget. 18°. '71. 60c........ *Kenedy.*
Mary *of Jesus of Agreda.* Divine life of the Virgin Mary: abridgment of Mystical city of God. 12°. '72. $2 .... *Cunningham; Sadlier.*
— — *See also* Lives of the saints.
Mary, the handmaid of the Lord. Charles, E. $1.. *Dodd.*
Mary, Queen of Scots. Murray, W. 15c..... *French.*
Mary, star of the sea. Thompson, E. W. $1.50. *Cath. Pub.*
Mary Alden. 18°. 50c.................... *Cong. Pub.*
Mary Ames; or, true beauty. 18°. 60c... *Cong. Pub.*
Mary and Archie Graham. 18°. 25c........ *Am. S. S.*
Mary and Dick; or, the beauty of kindness. ill. cr. 4°. pap., 20c.; 25c...................... *J. E. Potter.*
Mary and Frank. 18°. 50c............. (?) *Martien.*
Mary and Henry Day ser. *See* Phelps, P. H.
Mary and her doll. *See* Prairie books.
Mary and Norah; or, Queen Catharine's school. 18°. 25c.......................... *Scribner, W. & A.*
Mary and Willie. *See* Baker, *Mrs.* H. N. W.
Mary, Anna and Nina. *See* Aunt Gracie's lib.
Mary Austin. Lomax, E. V. 90c....... (?) *Martien.*
Mary Bartlett; or, the young home missionary. 8°. 20c.; 25c............................ *Am. Bapt.*
Mary Barton. *See* Gaskell, *Mrs.* E. C.
Mary Bell. Abbott, J. 90c................ *Harper.*
Mary Boyd; or, flower transplanted. 18°. 22c. *Am. S. S.*
Mary Bruce; or, the two physicians. ('66.) New ed. ill. 16°. '71. $1.25 .... *Hoyt.*
Mary Bunyan. Ford, S. R. $1.50......... *Sheldon.*
Mary Burns. Baker, S. 60c............. *Randolph.*
Mary Carrow's school. 2 pts. sq. 16°. ea., 80c. *Am. S. S.*
Mary Corner. 18°. 45c.................. *Whittaker.*
Mary Day forming good habits. Phelps, P. H. 90c. *Thompson.*
Mary Day's story book. Phelps, P. H. 90c... *Thompson.*
Mary Derwent. Stephens, A. S. $1.75; $1.50.. *Peterson.*
Mary Edmonstone: drama. 16°. pap., 15c... *French.*
Mary, Ellen and Lucy: the sick girl, the cross girl and the happy girl. 18°. 22c........ *Am. S. S.*
Mary Elliot. Bell, C. D. $1....... *Scribner, W. & A.*
Mary Ellis. 18°. '49. 40c................ *Am. S. S.*
Mary Ellis. Arthur, T. S. $1.50........ *J. E. Potter.*
Mary Elton. Paul, H. B. 50c...... *Scribner, W. & A.*
Mary Erskine. Abbott, J. 90c.............. *Harper.*
Mary Gay; or, work for girls. Abbott, J. 4 v. $4. *Hurd & H.*
Mary Glautonbury. Ball, E. 15c........... *French.*
Mary Glenworth. Reynolds, G. W. M. 75c... *Dick & F.*
Mary Grant; or, the secret fault. 18°. 30c... *Am. S. S.*
Mary Gresley. *See* Trollope, Ant.
Mary Grey's perplexities. Dunning, A. K. $1.25. *Cong. Pub*
Mary Grover. Burdett, C. 75c............. *Harper*
Mary Hallman. 18°. 28c.; 35c........... *Am. Bapt*
Mary Howson; or, a new creature. 18°. 35c.; 45c. *Am. Bapt*
Mary Humphreys; or, light shining in a dark place 18°. 45c................................ *Pres. Bd*
Mary Lee. Boyce, J. $1.50 .... *Noonan*
Mary Lee. *See* Fireside lib.
Mary Leeson. ill. 18°. '68. 65c........ *Perkinpine*
Mary Leigh. Geldart, T. $1....... *Scribner, W. & A*
Mary Leslie's trials. McKeever, H. B. $1... *Porter*
Mary Liddiard. *See* Kingston, W. H. G.
Mary Lyndsay. Ponsonby, *Lady* E. 50c.... *Harper*
Mary Mansfield. *See* Horsburgh, M.
Mary Moo. Suter, W. E. 15c............... *Lee & S*
Mary Moreton. Arthur, T. S. 50c.......... *Peterson*
Mary Morne and her friend. Boyd, E. E. 75c. *J. A. Moore*
Mary of Burgundy. *See* James, G. P. R.
Mary of Lorraine. *See* Grant, Ja.
Mary of Toulouse. ill. 18°. '51. 25c......... *Am. Tr*
Mary Osborn. Abbott, J. $1................ *Dodd*
Mary Price. Reynolds, G. W. M. $1.75; $1.. *Peterson*
Mary Price: drama. 16°. pap., 15c.......... *French*
Mary Raymond. Dunning, A. K. 30c...... *Pres. Bd*
Mary Ray's faith; or, Tom's return. 18°. 40c. *Am. S. S*
Mary Seaham. Grey, E. C. 75c........... *Peterson*
Mary searching for Jesus. Drummond, J. 20c. *Pres. Bd*
Mary Staunton. Uncle Ben. $1.......... *Appleton*
Mary Stuart. *See* Schiller, J. F. v.
Mary Stuart, Queen of Scots. Reynolds, G. W. M 75c. .... *Peterson*
Mary Turner. Burnand, F. C. 15c......... *French*
Mary Wharton. *See* Laurel ser.
Maryland. Code: general and local laws in force adopted 1860. 2 v. 8°. '60. shp., $6.. *Murphy*
— — Supplement [to 1867]; with notes, etc. 8°. '68 shp., $6................................ *Murphy*
— Constitution, adopted 1867; with notes and ref. by E O. Hinkley. 8°. '67. $1.50; pap., $1.. *Murphy*
— Court of Appeals reports, 1800–1851. 30 v. 8°.. *State*
Cont.: 1800–'26, by T. Harris and R. Johnson, 7 v. — 1826–'29 by T. Harris and R. W. Gill, 2 v. — 1829–'42, by R. W. Gill an J. Johnson, 12 v. — 1843–'51, by R. W. Gill, 9 v.
— *Same.* 1851–'74. 41 v. 8°. '52–'75. ea., shp., $5 *Cushings & B*
Cont.: v. 1, 2 (1851–2), by A. C. Magruder. — v. 3–18 (1852 '62), by O. Miller. — v. 19–26 (1863–'66), by N. Brewer. — v. 27 41 (1867–'74), by J. S. Stockett.
Note. Known as the Maryland reports.
— *Same.* v. 27–36 (1867–'72); by J. S. Stockett. 10 v 8°. ea., $5................................ *Murphy*
— — Digest. *See* Cohen, J. I., *and* Lee, J. F.; — Norris, W. H., Brown, G. W., *and* Brune, F. W. *jr.;* — Stockett, J. S., Merrick, R. T., *an* Miller, O.
— Debates of constitutional convention, 1864. 8° shp., $10................................ *Murphy*
— Digest of decisions. *See* Mayer, L.
— High Court of Chancery reports, 1811–'32; by T Bland. 3 v. 8°. '36–'41. shp., $15.. *Cushings & B*
— *Same.* 1846–'54; by J. Johnson. 4 v. 8°. '51–'54 *State*
— Important cases determined in Provincial Court an Court of Appeals, and in the General Court 1700–'99; by T. Harris, jr., and J. McHenry 4 v. 8°. $16.................. *T. & J. W. Johnson*
— Law of attachment. *See* Hinkley, E. O., *an* Mayer, L.
— Laws. 6 v. 8°. '64, '66, ea., $4; '67, '70, '72, '74 ea., $5................................ *Murphy*

Maryland, *continued.*
— Laws and rules of the Land Office; by J. M. Brewer and L. Mayer. 8°. '71. shp., $3.50. *Kelly, P. & Co.*
— Statutory testamentary law, with decisions; by C. Dorsey. 8°. '38. shp., $2....... *Cushings & B.*

Maryland geological survey. Reports. 13 v. in 2. 8°. '34–'40.................................... *State.*

Cont.: Engineers' reports on the topog. survey for 1834–'36; by J. H. Alexander. — Reports of geologist, 1834–'40; by J. T. Ducatel.

— First report of Ph. T. Tyson. 8°. '60....... *State.*

Maryland Historical Society. Fund publications. 9 v. 8°. '67–'76. nos. 1–3, 5, 6, ea., $1; nos. 4, 8, ea., $1.50; nos. 7, 9, ea., $2.50....... *Md. Hist.*

Cont.: 1. History, possessions and prospects of the Md. Hist. Soc., by B. Mayer. — 2. First commander of Kent Island, by S. F. Streeter. — 3. Maryland Hist. Soc.: in memory of Geo. Peabody. — 4. Brief account of settlement of Ellicott's Mills, by M. E. Tyson. — 5. A lost chapter in the hist. of the steamboat, by J. H. B. Latrobe. — 6. First steamboat voyage on the west. waters, by J. H. B. Latrobe. — 7. Relatio itineris in Marylandiam, a Patre A. White; Declaratio coloniæ Domini Baronis de Baltimoro; Excerpta ex diversis litteris missionariorum, 1635–1638, ed. by Rev. E. A. Dalrymple. — 8. The Lords Baltimore, by J. G. Morris. — 9. Papers rel. to early hist. of Md., by S. F. Streeter.

Mary's garden, and where the flowers went. col. ill. sq. 12°. $1.50........................ *Appleton.*
Mary's grammar. Marcet, *Mrs.* J. $1.25.. *Appleton.*
Mary's mistake. *See* Infant school lib.
Mary's new friends. Dunning, A. K. 35c... *Pres. Bd.*
Mary's patience bank. Davis, C. E. K. $1.15.. *Hoyt.*
Marys (The). Philip, R. 60c.............. *Carter.*
Masaniello: burlesque. Brough, R. B. 15c... *French.*
Masaniello. [Fiction.] Dumas, A. 25c.... *De Witt.*
Masaniello: opera. *See* Auber, D. F. E.
Masius, D. H. G. Kurzer Bericht v. d. Unterschied der wahren ev.-luth. u. der reformirten Lehre. 8°. 65c.......................... *Volkening.*
Masius, H. *See* Fischbach, J., Deutscher Wald und Hain.
Mask lifted. Pratt, J. L. $1.25.............. *Hoyt.*
Masked ball. *See* Ditson.
Maskell, W: Ivories, ancient and mediæval. ill. cr. 8°. '75. $1................. *Scribner, W. & A.*
— (*ed.*) South Kensington Museum art handbooks. 5 v. ill. cr. 8°. '75. ea., $1.... *Scribner, W. & A.*

Cont.: Rock's Textile fabrics. — Maskell's Ivories, ancient and mediæval. — Pollen's Ancient and modern furniture and wood work. — Fortnum's Majolica. — Engel's Musical instruments.

Maskelyne, Antonia Story. True and false riches; or, the ore-seeker. ill. 12°. $1.25.. *Scribner, W. & A.*
Maskelyne, J. N. Modern spiritualism: its rise and progress, with some exposures of so-called spirit media. 16°. '76. bds., 50c.... *Scribner, W. & A.*
Masks and faces. Taylor, T., *and* Reade, C. 15c. *French.*
Mason, A. B., *and* Lalor, J. J. Primer of polit. economy; in 16 definitions and 40 propositions. ('75.) 2d ed. 12°. '76. 75c............ *Jansen.*
Mason, C. Welsh. Rape of the gamp. [Fiction.] ill. 8°. pap., $1.......................... *Harper.*
Mason, C: Sermons; with sketch of life. por. 8°. '69. $4.............................. *Dutton.*
Mason, D: Essay on Scott. *See* Scott, *Sir* Wa.
Mason, *Miss* Emily V. Journal of a young lady of Virginia in 1782. sm. 4°. '71. $1.... *Murphy.*
— Popular life of Rob. E. Lee. 2d ed., rev. demi 8°. '71. *$2.50; $3; hf. mor., $3.50...... *Murphy.*
— Southern poems of the [civil] war. 12°. '67. $2; $3.................................... *Murphy.*
Mason, F. H. The 42d Ohio Infantry. por. cr. 8°. $2....................................... *Cobb.*
Mason, Fs. Karen, the apostle. 18°. 35c... *Mason.*
— Story of a workingman's life; with sketches of travel. ill. 12°. '70. $1.50.................. *Mason.*

Mason, G: C. Newport [R. I.] and its cottages. 45 views. large 4°. $50................. *Osgood.*
— Newport ill. in ser. of pen and pencil sketches. map and ill. 16°. '75. 75c.; pap., 50c... *C. E. Hammett.*
Mason, H. H. A common sense view of King David and his times. 12°. '69. $1.50.......... *Colby.*
Mason, I. L. Analytical investigation of resistance of piles. *See* United States, *Corps of Eng.*
Mason, Ja. Old fairy tales. ill. roy. 16°. $1.25.. *Cassell.*
Mason, *Maj.* J: Brief hist. of the Pequot war; with introd. and expl. notes by T. Prince. [Reprint.] 8°. '69. $1.............................. *Sabin.*
Mason, *Rev.* J: Select remains. 32°. '53. 25c. *Am. Tr.*
— Treatise on self-knowledge. 18°. '43. 55c. *Meth. Bk. Conc.*
Mason, *Rev.* J: M. Gospel for the poor. 18°. '61. 20c..................................... *Am. Tr.*
— Life. 8°. $2.............................. *Carter.*
Mason, Lowell. Book of chants. 16°. '42. $1.. *Ditson.*
— Boston anthem book: sel. of anthems, collects, motets, etc. obl. 8°. '39. bds., $2..... *Ditson.*
— Carmina sacra; or, Boston collection of church music. obl. 8°. '69. bds., $1.50........ *Ditson.*
— — *See also below* New carmina.
— Gentleman's glee book. obl. 8°. '41. bds., $1.50. *Ditson.*
— Hallelujah (The); [also] The singing school; [also] Musical notation in a nutshell. obl. 8°. '54. bds., $1.50.............................. *Ditson.*
— How shall I teach? or, hints to teachers as to the use of music and its notation. 12°. '75. pap., 38c....................................... *Ditson.*
— Little songs for little singers. 12°. bds., 40c. *Ditson.*
— Manual of the Boston Acad. of Music; for instruction in elements of vocal music on the system of Pestalozzi. ('36.) 8th ed. 12°. $1.... *Ditson.*
— New carmina sacra; or, Boston collection of church music. obl. 8°. '69. bds., $1.50....... *Ditson.*
— — *See also above* Carmina.
— Normal singer. obl. 16°. '56. bds., 60c.... *Ditson.*
— People's tune book: class book of church music for choirs. obl. 8°. '60. bds., $1.38....... *Ditson.*
— Song garden: ser. of school music bks. 3 v. obl. 12°. '64–'66. bds., bk. 1, 50c.; bk. 2, 80c.; bk. 3, $1.................................... *Ditson.*
— Vocal exercises and solfeggios; with piano-forte accomp. sel. from Ital., Fr. and Germ. composers, and adapted to treble and tenor, or alto and bass voices. obl. 4°. '50. $1.50........... *Ditson.*
— *See also* Park, E. A., Phelps, A., *and* Mason, L.; — Root, G. F., *and* Mason, L.; — Seward, T. F., Allen, C. G., *and* Mason, L.; — Seward, T. F., Mason, L., *and* Bradbury, W. B.; — Webb, G. J., *and* Mason, L.
— *and* T. B. The harp: collection of sacred music. ('41.) 2d ed. 8°. '59. hf. bd., $1.25.. *Wilstach.*

Note. Formerly pub. as v. 1 of "Sacred harp."

— *and* W: Asaph; or, the choir book: collection of vocal music. obl. 8°. '61. bds., $1.50... *Ditson.*
— *and* Green, D. Church psalmody: psalms and hymns adapted to public worship. ('59.) New ed. 16°. '73. 90c.–$3.75.......................... *Marvin.*
— *and* Seward, T. F. Pestalozzian music teacher; or, class instructor in element. music; with ill. lessons on form, number, etc., by J. W. Dickinson. 8°. '71. $2................................ *Ditson.*
— *and* Webb, G: J. Boston glee book. obl. 4°. '38. bds., $1.50............................ *Ditson.*
— — Cantica laudis; or, the Am. book of church music. obl. 8°. '50. bds., $1.50............. *Ditson.*
— — Glee hive: collection of glee quartets, etc. obl. 8°. '53. 75c............................ *Ditson.*
— — National psalmist: collection of psalm and hymn tunes. obl. 8°. '48. bds., $1.50....... *Ditson.*
— — Primary school song book. obl. 12°. '46. bds., 40c....................................... *Ditson.*
— — Psaltery (The): collection of church music. obl. 8°. '45. bds., $1.50................. *Ditson.*

Mason, Lowell, *continued.*
— — Song book of the school room. obl. 12°. '47. bds., 75c. . . . . *Ditson.*
— — The vocalist: short and easy glees or songs in parts. obl. 8°. '44. bds., $1.50 . . *Ditson; Gordon.*
Mason, Luther Whiting. National music teacher: guide for teaching vocal music to young children. ('70.) 2d ed. 8°. '72. hf. bd., 60c. . . . . *Ginn.*
— *See also* National music course for public schools.
Mason, *Mrs.* Ma. Springtime for sowing. 18°. 90c.; $1. . . . . *Dutton.*
— Young housewife's counsellor and friend. 12°. $1.75. *Hale; Lippincott.*
Mason, *Mrs.* Ma. Murdoch. Mae Madden, story; with poem by Joaquin Miller. 16°. '75. $1.25 . . *Jansen.*
Mason, *Mrs.* Ma. W. Life; with introd. by Bp. Janes. 12°. '70. $1.50. . . . . *Meth. Bk. Conc.*
Mason, R: Farrier and stud-book. ('32.) New ed. 12°. '76. hf. roan, $1.50. . . . . *Claxton.*
— Gentleman's new pocket farrier; with essay on domestic animals by J. S. Skinner. ('48.) New ed. 12°. '76. hf. roan, $1.50. . . . . *Claxton.*
Mason, S. W. Manual of gymnastic exercises for schools and families. 12°. 40c. . . *Potter, A. & Co.*
Mason, T. B. Sacred harp; or, beauties of church music. v. 2. ('43.) New ed., rev. and enl. 8°. '76. hf. bd., $1.25. . . . . *Wilstach.*
Note. — For v. 1 *see* Mason, L. *and* T. B.
— *See also* Shawm.
Mason, T: Zion's songster: hymns and spiritual songs. 32°. shp., 50c. . . . . *Harper.*
Mason, W: Crumbs from the Master's table. 64°. '30. 15c.; 20c. . . . . *Am. Tr.*
— Parlor preacher: short addresses to those who are determined to win Christ. 18°. 40c. . . . . *Pres. Bd.*
— Perfect in Christ. 18°. 35c. . . . . *Am. Bapt.*
— Spiritual treasury for children of God: meditations for morning and evening. 2 v. 12°. ea., $1.50. *Pres. Bd.*
Mason, W: *See* Mason L. *and* W.
— *and* Bancroft, Silas A. Social glee book. obl. 8°. '47. $1.50. . . . . *Ditson.*
— *and* Hoadly, E. S. Method for piano forte. 4°. '67. bds., $4; — with foreign fingering, $4 . . . *Ditson.*
— — System for beginners in the art of playing upon the piano forte. 4°. '71. $3; — with foreign fingering, $3. . . . . *Ditson.*
Mason, W: P. *See* United States, Circ. Court reports.
Mason of Buda. Planché, J. R. 15c. . . . . *French.*
Masonic choir. Dadmun, J. W. 75c. . . *G. D. Russell.*
Masonic harp. Chase, G. W. 75c. . . . . *Ditson.*
Masonic token. Anderson, W. T. $2.50 . . . *Masonic.*
Mason's first book for the reed organ or melodeon. obl. 8°. pap., 75c. . . . . *Peters.*
Masons. *See* Freemasons.
Masque of the gods. Taylor, B. $1.25 . . . . . *Osgood.*
Masque of Pandora. Longfellow, H. W. $1.50; $3; $4. . . . . *Osgood.*
Masquerade. Saxe, J. G. $1.75. . . . . *Osgood.*
Masquerade: farce. 16°. pap., 15c. . . . . *French.*
Mass. *See* Catholic church.
Massachusetts. General statutes, 1860; ed. by W. A. Richardson and G. P. Sanger. 8°. '73. shp., $2.50. . . . . *Wright.*
— — Supplement, 1860–'72. 8°. '73. shp., $4 . . *Wright.*
— General statutes and add. laws to the present time; reduced to questions and answers, with index, by C. U. Bell. 2d ed., enl. 12°. '75. $1 . . *Reed.*
— Superior Court reports (1761–'72); by J. Quincy, jr.; ed by S. M. Quincy. 8°. '65. shp., $6. *Little, B. & Co.*
— Supreme Court reports, 1804–'22; with notes by B. Rand. 17 v. 8°. '38–'40. shp., $51 . . *Little, B. & Co.*
Cont.: 1804–5, by E. Williams. — 1805–'22, by S. A. Tyng, 16 v.

Massachusetts, *continued.*
— *Same.* v. 18–90 (1822–'64). 73 v. 8°. '24–'66. ea., shp., $4 . . . . *Little, B. & Co.*
Cont.: v. 18–41 (1822–'40), by O. Pickering. — v. 42–54 (1840–'47), by T. Metcalf. — v. 55–66 (1848–'53), by L. S. Cushing. — v. 67–82 (1854–'60), by H. Gray, jr. — 83–90 (1860–'64), by C. Allen.
— *Same.* v. 91–118 (1864–'76). 28 v. 8°. ea., shp., $5.50 . . . . *Hurd & H.*
Cont.: v. 91–96 (1864–'67), by C. Allen. — v. 97–114 (1867–'76), by A. G. Browne, jr. — v. 115–118 (1874–'76), by J. Lathrop.
— — Digest. *See* Bennett, E. H., *and* Heard, F. F.; — Bennett, E. H., *and* Holland, H. W.
— — Index. *See* Bell, C. U.
Massachusetts a field for church missions. Huntington, F. D. 10c. . . . . *Dutton.*
Massachusetts geological survey. Report on geol., mineral., botany and zoology of M.; by E. Hitchcock. ill. and atlas of pl. 8°. '33. . . . . . . *State.*
— Final report of geol. of Mass.; by E. Hitchcock. 4°. '41 . . . . *State.*
Massachusetts Historical Society. Collections. ser. 1–5. 35 v. 8°. 1806–'76. . . . . *Mass. Hist.*
Cont.: v. 1, 4–7, 9, 10 (ser. 1), v. 1–6, 10 (ser. 2), v. 1–8 (ser. 3), v. 1, 2, 4 (ser. 4), ea., $2; v. 3 (ser. 4), $3; v. 5 (ser. 4), v. 2, 3, (ser. 5), ea., $2.50; v. 7, 8, 10 (ser. 4), v. 1 (ser. 5), ea., $4; v. 6, 9 (ser. 4), ea., $3.50.
Note. v. 2, 3, 8 (ser. 1), v. 7–9 (ser. 2), v. 9, 10 (ser. 3), o. p.
— Proceedings, 1855–'76. 12 v. ill. 8°. '59–'76. *Mass. Hist.*
Cont.: 1855–'65, ea., $3; '66–'73, ea., $3.50; '73–'75, $4; '75–'76, $3.
Massachusetts zoological and botanical survey. Reports on the fishes, reptiles and birds of M. 8°. '39 . . . . *State.*
— Reports on the herbaceous plants and on the quadrupeds of M. 8°. '40. . . . . *State.*
— Report on the insects of M. injurious to vegetation. 8°. '41. . . . . *State.*
— Report on the invertebrates of M. 8°. '41 . . . . . *State.*
Massacre in Syria: account of the outrages suffered by the Christians of Mount Lebanon. ill. 8°. pap., 25c. . . . . *De Witt.*
Massacre of Glencoe. Reynolds, G. W. M. 75c. *Peterson.*
Massaniello. Milner, H. M. 15c. . . . . *French.*
Masse, J. N. Pocket anatomical atlas of the descript. anat. of the human body; tr. and ed. by G. S. Pattison. ill. 12°. $3.75. . . . . *Harper.*
Massey, C: Exhibition reciter and drawing room entertainments. 2 nos. 16°. ea., pap., 30c.; — in 1 v. 16°. $1 . . . . *French.*
Massey, Ger. Poetical works. (Blue and gold ed.) por. 32°. $1.50.—(Cabinet ed.) 16°. $2 . . * *Osgood.*
— Tale of eternity, and other poems. 16°. $2 . . * *Osgood.*
— *Same.* 12°. '73. $2. . . . . *Routledge.*
Massinger, Ph. Plays; with notes by W. Gifford. 8°. $2.25 . . . . *Barnes.*
— Fatal dowry: tragedy. 16°. pap., 15c. . . . . . *French.*
— New way to pay old debts: play. 16°. pap., 15c. *French.*
— Roman actor: drama. 16°. pap., 15c. . . . . . . *French.*
— *and* Ford, J: Complete works; with introd. by H. Coleridge. por. roy. 8°. $5. . . . . *Routledge.*
Masson, D: British novelists and their styles. New ed. 16°. '75. $1.25. . . . . *Lothrop.*
— Chatterton, and other essays. cr. 8°. '74. $1.75. *Macmillan.*
— Life of John Milton; narrated in connexion with the political, ecclesiastical and literary hist. of his time. New ed. 3 v. 8°. '71–'75. v. 1, 3, ea., $6; v. 2, $5. . . . . *Macmillan.*
— Recent British philosophy. 12°. $1.25 . . . *Appleton.*
— *Same.* New [chp.] ed. 12°. '67. $2 . . . *Macmillan.*
— Three devils, Luther's, Milton's and Goethe's; and other essays. cr. 8°. '74. $1.75 . . . . *Macmillan.*
— William Drummond of Hawthornden. [Biog.] por. cr. 8°. '73. $3.50. . . . . *Macmillan.*
— Wordsworth, Shelley, Keats; and other essays. cr. 8°. '74. $1.75. . . . . *Macmillan.*

Masson, Gst. Compendious dict. of the French lang., French-Eng., Eng.-French. sm. 4°. '74. hf. bd., $2.50 .... *Macmillan.*
— Lyre française. 18°. '67. $1.25 .... *Macmillan.*
— *See also* Brette, P. H. E., *and* Masson, G.
Masson, Mich. Celebrated children of all ages and nations; tr. by Mrs. L. Burke. ill. 16°. $1.25. *Routledge.*
Massor, Hampden. Margaree. [Poetry.] 16°. 75c. *Lippincott.*
Mast, I: The gun, rod and saddle. 16°. '76. $1.25. *Meth. Epis.*
Master and pupil. ill. 16°. '69. $1.50 .... *Lothrop.*
Master and scholar. Plumptre, E. H. $2 .. *Routledge.*
Master and servant. Lamb, J. 25c. .... *Nelson.*
Master builder. Lee, D. K. $1.25 .... *Williamson.*
Master Cæsar. Stahl, P. J. 75c. .... *Appleton.*
Master Charlie; or, the little captain. 18°. 60c. (?) *Martien.*
Master Gregory's cunning, and what he got by it. 16°. 50c. .... *Scribner, W. & A.*
Master Hathorne's family. Merrill, G. E. $1.50. *Am. Bapt.*
Master Hector's adventure. Stahl, P. J. 75c. *Appleton.*
Master Humphrey's clock. *See* Dickens, C:
Master Jack. ill. sq. 12°. '71. bds., 50c. ... *Routledge.*
Master Jack ser. of picture books. 22 v. ill. sq. 12°. '71. ea., bds., 50c. .... *Routledge.*
Cont.: Master Jack. — Cousins. — Mamma's return. — Nellie and Bertha. — My best frock. — Tiger lily. — Bible stories. — Lent jewels. — Canary bird. — For want of a nail. — Two neighbours. — Three envious men. — Old Test. A B C. — Little stories for good children. — History of Moses, the lawgiver. — History of Joseph. — Farm-yard A B C. — Child's book of trades. — Nursery rhymes, songs and legends. — A B C picture-book. — Pussy's picture-book. — Animals and birds.

Master Jones' birthday. Morton, J. M. 15c. *De Witt; French.*
Master key; or, power of sympathy. 18°. 40c. *Am. S. S.*
— *See also* Child's lib.
Master mechanic; or, Joshua Taylor's passion. ('65.) New ed. ill. 16°. '72. $1.25 .... *Hoyt.*
Master of Greylands. Wood, E. P. $1.75; $1.50. *Peterson.*
Master passion. Phillips, A. 15c. .... *French.*
Master Peter. ill. 12°. 90c. .... *Nelson.*
Masterman Ready. *See* Marryat, F:
Masterpieces in English literature. Sprague, H. B. $2.25 .... *Schermerhorn.*
Masterpieces of foreign literature; tr. from Schiller, Goethe, La Fontaine and Saintine. 8°. $3.50. *Routledge.*
Master's home call. Bickersteth, E. H. 50c. .. *Carter.*
Master's rival. Peake, R. B. 15c. .... *French.*
Masters, *Miss* Eliz. Life. [In Eng. or Germ.] 8°. pap., 25c. .... *Barclay.*
Masury, J: W. How shall we paint our houses? art of house painting. 12°. '68. $1.50 .... *Appleton.*
Mat and Sofie. 18°. 35c. .... *Carter.*
Mat Warner. Dunning, A. K. 45c. .... *Pres. Bd.*
Match in the dark. Dance, C. 15c. .... *French.*
Match-maker. Reynolds, B. $1.75; $1.50 .. *Peterson.*
Match-maker: drama. 16°. pap., 15c. .... *French.*
Match-making. Poole, J. 15c. .... *French.*
Matched but not mated: comedietta. 16°. pap., 15c. *Happy.*
Matéaux, C. L. Home chat with our young folks on people and things they see and hear about. ill. fp. 4°. $2.50 .... *Cassell.*
— Little folks' picture album. cr. 4°. $2.50 ... *Cassell.*
— Little folks' picture gallery with simple rhymes. ill. cr. 4°. $2.50 .... *Cassell.*
— Peeps abroad for folks at home. ill. fp. 4°. $2.50. *Cassell.*

Matéaux, C. L., *continued.*
— Raggles, Baggles and the emperor. ill. fp. 8°. 50c. *Cassell.*
— Sunday chats with sensible children. ill. 4°. $2.50. *Cassell; Lee & S.*
— Through picture land. ill. fp. 4°. $1.50 .... *Cassell.*
Mather, Natl. Early piety exemplified in life and death of M.; with introd. by J. T. Tucker. 18°. 45c. *Cong. Pub.*
Mather, R: Journal; [also] Life and death of M. [Reprint.] 12°. '50. bds., 50c. ... *Dorch. Antiq.*
— *Same.* 12°. '74. 50c. .... *D. Clapp.*
Mather, *Mrs.* Sa. A. Young life; or, boys and girls of Pleasant Valley. 16°. $1.25 .. *Cin. Meth. Bk. Conc.*
Mather, W: W. *See* Kentucky geol. survey; — New York geol. survey; — Ohio geol. survey.
Mathes, Ja. M. Morris' letters; or, seven reasons for not being a Methodist: letters to T. Morris. New ed. 24°. '76. 40c.; pap., 25c. .... *Cen. Bk.*
— (*ed.*) Western preacher: 30 sermons by 24 leading preachers. por. 12°. '71. $2 .... *Cen. Bk.*
Matheson, Dunc. Life and labours. 16°. '76. $1.25. *Carter.*
Matheson, Ewing. Cotton baling presses; with descript. of accumulator cotton press. 8°. '70. pap., 40c. .... *Spon.*
— Vocabulary of technical terms used in design, etc., of iron structures: Eng., Fr., Germ., Ital. and Span. 8°. '73. pap., 80c. .... *Spon.*
— Works in iron bridge and roof structures. 150 eng. roy. 8°. '73. $6 .... *Spon.*
Mathews, C. *See* Lawrence, S., *and* Mathews, C.
Mathews, C: Ja. [Plays.] 11 v. 16°. ea., pap., 15c. *French.*
Cont.: Adventures of a love letter: comedy. — Bachelor's bed-room: farce. — Dowager: comedy. — His excellency: comedy. — Humpbacked lover: interlude. — Little Toddlekins: comic drama. — My wife's mother: comic drama. — Paul Pry married and settled: farce. — Two in the morning: comic dram. scene. — Used-up: comedy. — Who killed Cock Robin? farce.

— Bull in a china shop: comedy. 16°. pap., 15c. *Lee & S.*
Mathews, G: D. Coinages of the world, ancient and modern. ill. 8°. '76. $2.50; $3.50 .. *J. W. Scott.*
Mathews, H: M. *See* West Virginia, Sup. Court reports.
Mathews, Joanna H. Benny. ill. 18°. '74. 20c. .. *Am. Tr.*
— Bessie books. ('67–'70.) New ed. 6 v. 16°. '74–'75. ea., $1.25 .... *Carter.*
Cont.: Bessie at the seaside. — Bessie in the city. — Bessie and her friends. — Bessie among the mountains. — Bessie at school. — Bessie on her travels.

— Flowerets (The). ('70.) New ed. 6 v. 18°. '73–'74. ea., 60c. .... *Carter.*
Cont.: Violet's idol. — Daisy's work. — Rose's temptation. — Lily's lesson. — Hyacinthe and her brother. — Pinkie and the rabbits.

— Kitty and Lulu books. 6 v. 16°. '72–'73. ea., $1 .. *Carter.*
Cont.: Touton and pussy. — Kitty's robins. — The white rabbit. — Rudie's goat. — Kitty's visit to grandmamma. — Kitty's scrap-book.

— Little friends at Glenwood. 16°. '76. $1.25 .. *Carter.*
— Little sunbeams. ('71–'72.) New ed. 6 v. '75–'76. 16°. ea., $1 .... *Carter.*
Cont.: Belle Powers' locket. — Dora's motto. — Lily Norris' enemy. — Jessie's parrot. — Mamie's watchword. — Nellie's housekeeping.

— Miss Ashton's girls. New ed. 6 v. 16°. '73–'75. $7.50 .... *Carter.*
Cont.: Fanny's birthday gift. — The new scholars. — Rosalie's pet. — Eleanor's visit. — Mabel Walton's experiment. — Elsie's Santa Claus.

Mathews, Jos. M'D. Letters to school-girls. 18°. 60c. .... *Cin. Meth. Bk. Conc.*
Mathews, Jla. A. Dare to do right ser. 5 v. 16°. $5.50 .... *Carter.*
Cont.: Grandfather's faith. — Our four boys. — Giuseppe's home. — Nellie's stumbling block. — Susy's sacrifice.

Mathews, Jla. A., *continued.*
— Drayton Hall ser. 6 v. 16°. $4.50........*Carter.*
Cont.: Laurence Bronson's victory. — Christy's grandson. — Allan Haywood. — Frank Austin's diamond. — Eagle crag. — True to his flag.
— Golden ladder ser. 6 v. 16°. $3..........*Carter.*
Cont.: Nettie's mission. — Crossing sweeper. — Little Margery. — Margery's city home. — Rosy Conroy's lesson. — Ned Dolan's garret.
— How Jennie found her Lord. 16°. 35c......*Carter.*
— Jolly and Katy in the country. 16°. 75c....*Carter.*
— Lilies and thistledown. 16°. '76. $1.25....*Carter.*
— Little Katy and jolly Jim. 16°. 50c........*Carter.*
Mathews, W. S. B. Outline of musical form. 12°. 60c..................................*Ditson.*
— *See also* Emerson, L. O., *and* Mathews, W. S. B.
Mathews, W: Getting on in the world; or, hints on success in life. ('72.) New ed. 12°. '76. $2; $2.50; hf. cf., $3.50; cf., $5............*Griggs.*
— Great conversers and other essays. ('74.) New ed. map. 12°. '75. $1.75...............*Griggs.*
— Words: their use and abuse. 12°. '76. $2; $2.50. *Griggs.*
Mathias, G. H. D. En avant, messieurs: a tutor's counsels to his pupils. 16°. $1. *Claxton; Lippincott.*
Mathilda of Canossa. *See* Bresciani, A.
Matilda. Sue, E. $1.50..................*Dick & F.*
Matilda Lonsdale. Adams, C. $1.25.....*Routledge.*
Matilda Montgomery. Richardson, J. 50c...*De Witt.*
Matins and vespers. Bowring, J. $1.50...* *Osgood.*
Matricide's daughter. 8°. pap., 25c........*Dick & F.*
Matrimonial. Bridgeman, I. V. 15c........*French.*
Matrimonial infelicities. Coffin, R. B. $1.50. *Hurd & H.*
Matrimonial misfortunes of Peter Clancy. Maxwell, W. H. 75c..........................*Dick & F.*
Matrimonial prospectuses. Simpson, J. P. 15c. *French.*
Matrimony. Kenney, J. 15c...............*French.*
Matson, *Mrs.* —. Morning stars; or, childhood of Jesus. ill. sq. 18°. '56. 40c...........*Am. Tr.*
Matson, H: Jesus the cure of skepticism. 16°. $1. *Goodrich.*
Mattei, Pasquale de. Devotions to the holy guardian angels: prayers, pious practices and examples; tr. 32°. '67. 50c. ....*Kelly, P. & Co.*
Matteo Falcone. Oxberry, W. H. 15c......*French.*
Matter and manner for Christian workers. Ritchie, A. $1.75 .... *West. Tr.*
Mattes, H. L. (*ed.*) Christtags-Harfe. obl. 4°. pap., 10c......................................*Brobst.*
Matteson, J: G. Bibelske Salmar og Lovsange. 16°. '70. $1 ....*Sev. Day Adv.*
— Hellige's Arv. 16°. '74. 20c. ......*Sev. Day Adv.*
— Liv og Död. 16°. '75. $1 ....*Sev. Day Adv.*
— Liv og Uforkrænkelighed. 16°. '74. 20c. *Sev. Day Adv.*
— Nye Testamente's Sabbat. 16°. '74. pap., 15c. *Sev. Day Adv.*
— Ugudelige's Straf. 16°. '74. pap., 15c. *Sev. Day Adv.*
Matteson, W. N. *See* Connecticut, Sup. Court reports.
Matthew Merchant (*pseud.*) *See* Wood, W. S.
Matthew *of Westminster.* Flowers of history to 1307; tr. by C. D. Yonge. 2 v. 12°. (Bohn.) ea., $1.75............................*Little, B. & Co.*
— *Same.* 2 v. 12°. (Bohn.) ea., $2. *Lippincott; Scribner, W. & A.*
Matthew *Paris* (*ed.*) Chronicle; tr. 5 v. 12°. (Bohn.) ea., $1.75..........................*Little, B. & Co.*
Cont.: Roger of Wendover's Flowers of Eng. hist. to 1235; tr. by Dr. Giles, 2 v. — 1235-1273, with index to work, 3 v.
— *Same.* 5 v. 12°. (Bohn.) $2. *Lippincott; Scribner, W. & A.*

Matthew Frost. Marshall, E. $1..*Carter; Dutton.*
Matthews, F. J. A guide, with forms, for guardians of minors and probate Courts in Ohio. 8°. '59. shp., $1 ....*I. N. Whiting.*
Matthews, J. E. The sapling and the tree; or, results of early training. ill. 18°. '71. 35c. *N. Y. Ref. Ch. Bd.; Pres. Com.*
Matthews, *Rev.* J. M. Fifty years in New York: discourse. 8°. pap., 25c........*N. Y. Ref. Ch. Bd.*
Matthews, Ja. M. Digest of the laws of Va. of a civil nature, ill. by judicial decisions; [with] U. S. Const. and New Bill of Rights and Const. of Va. 2 v. 8°. '56-'57. shp., $20....*J. W. Randolph.*
— Digest of laws of Va. of a criminal nature, ill. by judicial decisions; with new Const. 2d ed., rev. and enl. 8°. '71. shp., $5.......*J. W. Randolph.*
— Guide to commissioners in chancery; with forms for discharge of their duties; adapted to the statute law of Va. 2d ed., rev. and enl. 8°. '71. hf. cf., $4 ....*J. W. Randolph.*
Matthews, J: Divine purpose displayed in works of providence and grace. 18°. 50c........*Pres. Bd.*
— The influence of the Bible in improving the understanding and moral character; with memoir of author by J. Wood. 8°. 75c.........*Pres. Bd.*
Matthews, Stanley. Summary of the law of partnership; for business men. 12°. '64. $1.25; shp., $1.50 ....*Clarke.*
Matthews, W. Grammar and dict. of lang. of the Hidatsa; — Hidatsa (Minnotaree) Eng. dict. *See* Shea, J. G., Library of Am. linguistics.
Matthews, W: B. Forms of pleadings in civil and criminal cases, and of deeds, wills, etc., and proceedings in bankruptcy. 8°. '73. shp., $5. *J. W. Randolph.*
— Guide for executors and administrators in Virginia. 8°. '72. bds., 75c..............*J. W. Randolph.*
Mattie, *Aunt.* *See* Aunt Mattie.
Mattie. Lamb, M. J. 60c..................*Lothrop.*
Mattie. Robinson, F. W. 75c..................*Harper.*
Mattie Carson. Berry, M. E. 75c.......*Cong. Pub.*
Mattie Sherwood. *See* Wise, D.
Mattie's flowers. *See* New Year lib.
Mattie's home; [also] Little Dot. ill. 16°. '74. 75c. *Lothrop.*
Mattie's story; or, the blessing of the pure in heart. 18°. 50c..............................*Pres. Bd.*
Mattison, Hiram. Bible doctrine of immortality. 12°. '68. pap., 25c.................*Meth. Bk. Conc.*
— Doctrine of the Trinity, and of the divinity of Christ; as against the various forms of modern Unitarianism. 16°. '67. 60c.....................*Tibbals.*
— High school astronomy. 12°. $1.25.......*Sheldon.*
— Immortality of the soul. ('64.) 7th ed. 12°. '75. $1.50 ....*Perkinpine.*
— Minister's pocket ritual: handbook of Scripture lessons and forms of service. ('64.) 5th ed. 12°. '76. mor., $1............................*Perkinpine.*
— Popular amusements. 12°. '67. pap., 25c. *Meth. Bk. Conc.*
— Primary astronomy. ill. 12°. 80c..........*Sheldon.*
— Resurrection of the dead; with introd. by Bp. Simpson. ('66.) 6th ed. 12°. '74. $1.50. *Perkinpine.*
— Romanism: its decline and its present condition and prospects in the United States. 8°. pap., 50c. *Cin. Meth. Bk. Conc.*
— Select lessons from the Scripture; adapted to responsive readings in S.-schools. ('66.) 2d ed. 18°. bds., per doz., $3.60...............*Perkinpine.*
Mattocks, Brewer. Minnesota as a home for invalids. 12°. $1.25 ....*Lippincott.*
Matt's follies. Prescott, M. N. $1.50.........*Miller.*
Matty Frost. Davis, C. E. K. 55c..............*Hoyt.*
Matty Gregg. *See* Fry, S. M.

Matty's hungry missionary box, and other stories; by author of "Village missionaries." ill. 18°. 50c. *Bost.Am.Tr.; Nelson.*
— *Same.* ill. 16°. 50c. ... *Nelson.*
— *Same.* ill. 18°. '73. 50c. *N.Y.Ref.Ch.Bd.; Pres.Com.*
— *Same.* ill. 18°. 60c. ... *Cong.Pub.*
— *See also* Chip-basket stories; — Little Aggie's lib.; — Snow-drop ser.

Maturin, C: Rob. Bertram: tragedy. 16°. pap., 15c. *French.*

Maturin, E: Bianca: tale of Erin and Italy. 12°. $1.25 ... *Harper.*
— Viola: play. 16°. pap., 15c. ... *French.*

Mätzner, —. English grammar, methodical, analytical and historical; tr. by C. J. Grece. 3 v. 8°. '75. $15 ... *Roberts.*

Maud, the maniac; or, the fratricide. 8°. pap., 25c. *De Witt.*

Maud Irving. Cooper, G. 75c.; 60c. ... *Peters.*

Maud Latimer; or, patience and impatience. ill. post 18°. 75c. ... *Scribner, W. & A.*

Maud Mansfield. Hood, D. M. $1.50; $1 ... *Burke.*

Maud Mohan. Thomas, A. 25c. ... *Harper.*

Maud Muller. Whittier, J. G. $3.50; $7 ... *Osgood.*

Maud or Nina. Melville, G. J. W. $1.25; 75c. ... *Estes.*

Maud Summers, the sightless. 18°. 75c. ... *Carter.*

Maude and Miriam. McKeever, H. B. $1.50 .. *Claxton.*

Maude Grenville lib. 5 v. 16°. '66. $6 .. *Meth.Bk.Conc.*
Cont.: Maude Grenville. — Heroism of boyhood. — Enoch Roden's training. — Victor and Hilaria. — Children of the great king, by N. Horsburgh.

Maude Maynard. 16°. $1 ... *Am.Bapt.*

Maud's peril. Phillips, W. 15c. ... *De Witt; French.*

Maud's two homes. *See* Finley, M. F.

Maud's visit. *See* Present for my darling lib.

Maudsley, H: Body and mind: inquiry into their connection and mutual influence, specially in ref. to mental disorders. 12°. $1.50 ... *Appleton.*
— *Same.* cr. 8°. '73. $2 ... *Macmillan.*
— Physiology and pathology of the mind. 8°. $3. *Appleton.*
— Responsibility in mental disease. (Intern. sci. ser.) 12°. $1.50 ... *Appleton.*
— Sex in mind and in education. 16°. pap., 25c. .. *Miller.*

Maugin, C. Holy week: music book; with chant in Gregorian notation. 12°. '61. $1.25 .. *Murphy.*
— *Same;* with the chant in modern notation. 12°. '61. $1.25 ... *Murphy.*
— Kyriale; or, ordinary of mass: liturgical collection of Gregorian chants for Cath. choirs, etc. 5th ed., with app. and masses and obsequies for the dead. 12°. '57. $1 ... *Murphy.*
— *Same;* with Gregorian chants in modern notation. 8th ed. 12°. $1 ... *Murphy.*
— The Roman vesperal; with Gregorian chants in modern notation. 12°. '57. $1.50 ... *Murphy.*

Maum Guinea. Victor, M. V. F. 20c. ... *Beadle.*

Maunder, C. F. Operative surgery. 2d ed. ill. 12°. '73. $2.50 ... *Lindsay.*
— Surgery of the arteries, incl. aneurisms, wounds, hæmorrhages, etc. ill. 12°. '76. $2 .. *Lindsay.*

Maunsell, H: The Dublin practice of midwifery. ill. 12°. (Lond.) $1.75 ... *Jas. Campbell.*

Mauprat. Sand, G. $1.50 ... *Roberts.*

Maureen Dhu. Sadlier, M. A. $1.25; $1.75 .. *Sadlier.*

Maurette, J. J. Des adieux à Rome. 18°. '45. pap., 8c. *Am.Tr.*
— *Germ.* Abschied von Rom. 18°. '51. 30c. .. *Am.Tr.*

Maurice, C. S. Erection of a draw-bridge without false works. *See* Jordan, G., Foundations under water.

Maurice, F: Denison. Conscience: lectures on casuistry. New [chp.] ed. cr. 8°. '72. $1.75 .. *Macmillan.*
— Dialogues on family worship. cr. 8°. '62. $1.50. *Macmillan.*

Maurice, F: Denison, *continued.*
— Epistles of St. John: lectures on Christian ethics. 2d [chp.] ed. cr. 8°. '67. $2.25 ... *Macmillan.*
— Expository sermons on the Prayer-book; especially in ref. to the Romish system. 2d ed. 12°. '61. $1.50 ... *Macmillan.*
— Friendship of books, and other lectures; ed., with pref., by T. Hughes. cr. 8°. '74. $2.50 .. *Macmillan.*
— Gospel of St. John: discourses. 3d [chp.] ed. cr. 8°. '67. $2.25 ... *Macmillan.*
— Ground and object of hope for mankind. 16°. 75c. *Lee & S.*
— Lectures on Apocalypse. cr. 8°. '61. $2.50 .. *Macmillan.*
— Lectures on ecclesiast. history. 8°. $3.50 .. *Macmillan.*
— Lord's prayer (The), the creed and the commandments: manual for parents and schoolmasters; [also] The order of the Scriptures. 18°. '70. 50c. ... *Macmillan.*
— Moral and metaphysical philosophy. 2 v. 8°. '73. $9 ... *Macmillan; Scribner, W. & A.*
Cont.: 1. Ancient philos. and 1st–13th centuries. — 2. 14th cent. and the Fr. rev., with a glimpse into the 19th cent.
— On the Lord's prayer. 4th ed. fp. 8°. '61. 75c. *Macmillan.*
— *Same.* 16°. '72. $1.25 ... *Hurd & H.*
— On the Sabbath day; [also] The character of the warrior; [also] On the interpretation of history. fp. 8°. '53. 75c. ... *Macmillan.*
— Patriarchs and lawgivers of the Old Test. 3d [chp.] ed. 12°. '67. $2 ... *Macmillan.*
— Prophets and kings of the Old Test. 3d ed., with new pref. cr. 8°. '71. $3.50 ... *Macmillan.*
— Religions of the world, and their relations to Christianity. 5th ed. 12°. '76. $1.50 ... *Macmillan.*
— Sequel to What is revelation? letters in reply to Mensel's Examination of Strictures on the Bampton lectures. cr. 8°. '60. $1.50 ... *Macmillan.*
— Sermons preached in country churches. cr. 8°. '73. $3.50 ... *Macmillan.*
— Social morality: lectures. 2d [chp.] ed. cr. 8°. '72. $3.50 ... *Macmillan.*
— Theological essays. 3d ed., with new pref. cr. 8°. '71. $3.50 ... *Macmillan.*
— What is revelation? sermons on the Epiphany; [also] Letters to a theological student on the Bampton lectures of Mansel. cr. 8°. '59. $2.50 .. *Macmillan.*
— *See also* Worship of God and fellowship among men.

Maurice Dering. *See* Lawrence, G: A.

Maurice Favell. 18°. 40c. ... *Dutton.*

Maurice Guildford; or, the trials of a small boy. 18°. 45c. ... *Am.S.S.*
— *Same.* ('68.) New ed. ill. 16°. '70. 80c. .. *Hoyt.*

Maurice Sullivan. *See* Little Kadore.

Maurice Tiernay. *See* Lever, C:

Maurine. Wheeler, E. $1.50 ... *Cramer.*

Maury, J: Siffrein. Principles of eloquence. 18°. '37. 55c. ... *Meth.Bk.Conc.*
— *Same;* with introd. by Bp. A. Potter. 18°. '75c. *Harper.*

Maury, Mat. Fontaine. Elementary, practical and theoretical treatise on navigation. 3d ed., rev. and enl. 8°. '45. shp., $4.50 ... *Fortescue.*
— First lessons in geography. ('68.) Rev. ed. ill. sm. 4°. '70. hf. bd., 63c. ... *Univ.Pub.*
— Manual of geography: mathematical, civil and physical geog. ill. 4°. '70. hf. bd., $2 .. *Univ.Pub.*
— Physical geography. maps and ill. imp. 8°. '73. hf. bd., $2.25 ... *Univ.Pub.*
— Physical geography of the sea, and its meteorology. 8th ed. 8°. $4 ... *Harper.*
— Physical survey of Virginia. 2d ed. map. 8°. '69. pap., $1 ... *J. W. Randolph.*
— The world we live in. ('68.) Rev. ed. ill. 4°. '70. hf. bd., $1.25 ... *Univ.Pub.*

Maury, Mat. Fontaine, *jr.* Resources of the coal field of the upper Kanawha; with sketch of the iron belt of Va. 8°. '73. pap., 50c. .. *J. W. Randolph.*

Mavor's alphabet, spelling and reading book. 12°. 25c. *Scribner, W.&A.*
Mavor's ill. linen primer. 12°. 25c... *Scribner, W.&A.*
Mavor's ill. primer. cr. 8°. 25c. .... *Scribner, W.&A.*
Max and Maurice. Busch, W. $1.25 .... *Roberts.*
Max Fleming. Bates, L. 30c. .... *Am. Tr.*
Max Frere. Pinchard, M. D. 50c. .... *Routledge.*
Max Kromer. Smith, H. 75c. .... *Dodd.*
Max Meredith's millennium. Townsend, V. F. 75c. *Loring.*
Maxims and hints for an angler; [with] maxims and hints for a chess-player. ill. 18°. '68. 40c. *Claxton.*
Maxims and instructions on the art of war; tr. by Capt. Lendy. 18°. '64. 75c.... *Van Nostrand.*
Maxson, Edn. R. Practice of medicine. 8°. '61. $4. *Lindsay.*
Maxwell, Cecil. Story of three sisters. (Leis. hour ser.) 16°. '76. $1.25 .... *Holt.*
Maxwell, Ja. Clerk. Theory of heat. 12°. $1.50. *Appleton.*
Maxwell, *Mrs.* J: *See* Braddon, *Miss* M. E.
Maxwell, Sidney D. Suburbs of Cincinnati: sketches, hist. and descript. sm. 4°. $2 .... *Stevens.*
Maxwell, T: King bee's dream. [Poem.] 12°. $1. *Searcy.*
Maxwell, W: Hamilton. Novels and tales. 4 v. 8°. pap. .... *Peterson.*
Cont.: Life of Grace O'Malley, 50c. — Brian O'Lynn; or, luck is everything. — Stories of Waterloo. — Wild sports in the west, *ea.*, 75c.
— *Same.* 5 v. 8°. pap. .... *Dick & F.*
Cont.: Hector O'Halloran, 2 v. in 1, $1. — Adventures of Capt. Blake. — Adventures of Mick Costigan. — Bivouac. — Matrimonial misfortunes, *ea.*, 75c.
— *Same.* (Railway lib.) 5 v. 16°. ea., bds., 80c. *Routledge.*
Cont.: Bivouac. — Capt. Blake. — Hector O'Halloran. — Luck is everything. — Stories of Waterloo.
— *Same.* 10 v. 16°. hf. roxb., $12.50 .... *Routledge.*
Cont.: Hector O'Halloran. — Stories of Waterloo. — Captain Blake. — Wild sports of the west. — Bivouac. — Luck is everything. — Highlands of Scotland. — Flood and field. — Peninsular war. — Captain O'Sullivan.
— Grace Willoughby: a tale of the wars of King James. 8°. pap., 50c. .... *U. P. James.*
— Victories of Wellington and the Brit. armies. ill. 12°. (Bohn.) $1.75 .... *Little, B. & Co.*
— *Same.* ill. 12°. (Bohn.) $2. *Lippincott; Scribner, W.&A.*
Maxwell. *See* Hook, Thdr.
Maxwell Drewitt. Riddell, J. H. 75c. .... *Harper.*
May, Amasa. *See* New American ser. [of readers, etc.]
May, Anna. Die kleine New Yorker Köchin. 24°. '59. bds., 30c. .... *Steiger.*
May, Annie. Sunny nook stories. 5 v. 18°. '70. $3.75. *H. A. Young.*
Cont.: Tony and his rabbit. — Old oak chest. — Little gardeners. — Old bureau. — Casket of gems.
May, Caro. Hymns on the collects. 16°. '72. $1.25; $1.75 .... *Randolph.*
— (*ed.*) Female poets of America: sel. with notes. ill. 12°. '76. $1.50 .... *World Pub.*
May, Carrie L. Bertie's telegraph. 18°. '67. 75c. *H. A. Young.*
— Charlie's calico rooster. 18°. '69. 75c... *H. A. Young.*
— Four little pitchers. 18°. '67. 75c.... *H. A. Young.*
— Grandma's strong box. 18°. '69. 75c... *H. A. Young.*
— Sweet clover stories. 4 v. 16°. '65–'66. ea., $1.25. *H. A. Young.*
Cont.: Nellie Milton's housekeeping. — Brownie Sanford. — Sylvia's burden. — Ruth Lovell.
— Trials of the baby pitcher. 18°. '69. 75c... *H. A. Young.*
— Uncle Barney's fortune. 18°. '67. 75c... *H. A. Young.*
May, D. M. H. New violin school. f°. '70. pap., $1.25 .... *Ditson.*
— Practical school for violin. f°. '68. pap., $1.. *Willig.*

May, Edith. ["Anna Drinker."] Poems. ill. 12°. $2.50 *Miller*
May, Edith J. Louis' school days. *See* Winter evening lib.
— School and college lib. 3 v. ill. 16°. ea., $1.75. *Routledge*
Cont.: Louis' school-days. — Saxelford. — Dashwood Priory or, Mortimer's college days.
May, H. W. Treatise on statutes of Elizabeth against fraudulent conveyances and law of voluntary dispositions of property. 8°. $6.50; shp., $7.50 *Callaghan*
May, J: Journal and letters rel. to two journeys to the Ohio country in 1788–9; with biog. sketch by R. S. Edes and ill. notes by W. M. Darlington. 8° '73. $2 .... *Clarke*
May, J: W. Treatise on the law of insurance, as applicable to fire, life, accident and other risks not maritime. 8°. '73. shp., $6 ...... *Little, B. & Co*
May, Kath. S. Alfred and his mother; or, seeking the kingdom. 18°. '75. 60c. .... *H. A. Young.*
May, S: J. Memoirs. por. 16°. '73. 75c. ... *Roberts*
— Recollections of our anti-slavery conflict. 16°. '69 $1.50 .... * *Osgood*
May, Sophie (*pseud.*) *See* Clarke, Rebecca Sophia.
May, T: Erskine. Constitutional history of England 1760–1860. 2 v. cr. 8°. $3.50; hf. cf., $7. *Nichols & H.; Widdleton*
May. Oliphant, M. O. W. $1.50; $1 ..... *Scribner.*
May; or, Dolly's delusion: drama. 16°. pap., 15c. *French.*
May; or, grandpa's pet. *See* Smith, F. I. B.
May and December. Hubback, J. $1.50; $1.. *Claxton.*
May and Tom stories. *See* Smith, *Mrs.* F. I. B.
May Bell. Herbert, S. A. F. $1.50 .... *Lothrop.*
May blossoms; comp. by the Sisters of Notre Dame. [Music.] 12°. bds., 40c. — Enl. ed. 4°. bds. $1.25 .... *Peters.*
May Carleton's story; [also] The miller's daughter. 18°. '66. 50c. .... *Cunningham.*
May carols. DeVere, Aubrey. $1.25 ..... *Cath. Pub.*
May Castleton's mission. McKeever, H. B. 60c. *Pres. Bd.*
May Chester. Willard, C. A. 75c. .... *Randolph.*
May chimes; comp. by Sisters of Notre Dame. 4°. bds., $1.25 .... *Peters.*
Note. An enl. ed. of "May blossoms."
May Christians dance? Brookes, J. H. 60c.; 25c. *McIntyre.*
May Chumleigh and her friend Conscience. 18°. 40c *Am. S. S.*
May Coverly, the young dressmaker. ill. 18°. '61. 60c. .... *Am. Tr*
— *Same.* ill. 18°. '66. 70c. *N. Y. Ref. Ch. Bd.; Pres. Com.*
— *Same.* 18°. $1 .... *Tilton.*
May-day. Emerson, R. W. $1.50 .... *Osgood.*
May-day ramble. *See* Casket of juveniles.
May Dundas. Geldart, T. 75c. .... *Routledge.*
May festival. Johnson, J. C. 20c. .... *Ditson.*
May-flower. Stowe, H. B. $2 .... *Osgood.*
May-flower ser. *See* Clark, Ma. L.
May Horton. Grosvenor, H. S. $1.25 .... *Hoyt*
May I believe? Hamilton, A. 50c. .... *Pres. Bd*
May I not? or, two ways of looking through a telescope; by author of "What can I do?" 18° 35c. .... *Am. S. S*
May Martin. *See* Thompson, D. P.
May Middleton. Reynolds, G. W. M. 75c... *Peterson.*
May party. Bruce, E. M. 75c. .... *Universalist*
May queen. *See* Banner stories.
May queen. *See* Bennett, W. S.
May queen. *See* Tennyson, A.
May queen, and other stories. ill. 24°. 25c. *Bost. Am. Tr.*

May Templeton: tale of faith and love. 12°. $1.50; $2 .... *O'Shea.*
May Thornton; or, of what use am I? 18°. 60c.; 70c. *Am. Bapt.*
May wreath. 18°. 50c .... *Cong. Pub.*
Mayer, A. M. The earth a great magnet. 12°. '72. 50c.; pap., 25c. .... *VanNostrand.*
Mayer, Brantz. History, etc., of Md. Hist. Soc. *See* Maryland Hist. Soc.
— Mexican history and archæology. 4°. '56. pap., $1. *Smith. Inst.*
— Vindication of Capt. Cresap against charge of murdering family of Logan. 8°. '67. $2 .. *Munsell.*
Mayer, *Rev.* I: Source of salvation: catechism of the Jewish religion; with the confirmation service. 12°. 50c. .... *Frank.*
— *See also* Hebrew grammar.
Mayer, J: Metallurgy. (Element. sci. ser.) 2 pts. ill. 16°. ea., 75c. .... *Putnam.*
Mayer, Lew. Digest of decisions construing statutes of Maryland. 8°. '66. shp., $8 .... *Murphy.*
— *See also* Hinkley, E. O., *and* Meyer, L.; — Maryland, Laws and rules of the Land Office.
Mayer, Nath. Differences. [Fiction.] 16°. 50c... *Bloch.*
Mayer, Wendelin Mar. St. Benedict's manual. [Cath. prayer book.] 12°. '76. $1.25; $2 .... *Pustet.*
Mayfield, Millie. Wreath of rhymes. [Poetry.] 12°. $2 .... *Lippincott.*
Mayfield lib. 3 v. 18°. $3.25 .... *Randolph.*
Cont.: Little leaven. — Margaret at home. — Watson's Woods.
Mayhew, A: *See* Mayhew, Hor. *and* A:
— *and* Edwards, Sutherland. Christmas boxes: farce. 16°. pap., 15c. .... *French.*
— — Goose with the golden eggs: farce. 16°. pap., 15c. .... *De Witt; French.*
Mayhew, E: Dogs: their management. ill. 16°. bds., 75c. .... *Routledge.*
— Illustrated horse doctor. ill. 8°. $3 .... *Lippincott.*
— *Same;* [also] Practical horse-shoeing, by G. Fleming, and chapter on the late horse epidemic. ill. 8°. $3.50 .... *Appleton.*
— Illustrated horse management. 8°. $3. *Claxton; Lippincott.*
— Wandering minstrel: farce. 16°. pap., 15c... *French.*
— *See also* Herbert, H: W: Mayhew, E: *and* Hutchinson, W. N.
— *and* Smith, G. Make your wills: farce. 16°. pap., 15c. .... *French.*
— — — *See also* French's comic dramas.
Mayhew, H: Boyhood of Martin Luther. ill. 16°. $1.25 .... *Harper.*
— London characters: ill. of the humor, pathos and peculiarities of London life. ill. 12°. $3 .. *Routledge.*
— Story of the peasant-boy philosopher. 16°. $1.25. *Harper.*
— *Same.* ill. 16°. $1.50 .... *Routledge.*
— Wonders of science; or, young Humphrey Davy. 16°. $1.25 .... *Harper.*
— *Same.* ill. 16°. $1.50 .... *Routledge.*
— Young Benjamin Franklin; or, the right road through life. ill. 16°. $1.25 .... *Harper.*
Mayhew, Hor. *and* A: Charades in action; or, plays without words. 16°. 40c. .... *French.*
— — Good genius that turned everything into gold; or, the queen bee and the magic dress. ill. 16°. 75c. *Harper.*
— — Greatest plague of life: adventures of a lady in search of a good servant. ill. 16°. bds., 80c.; $1. *Routledge.*
— — Magic of kindness; or, the wondrous story of the good Huan. ill. 16°. 75c. .... *Harper.*
— — Whom to marry and how to get married: adventures of a lady in search of a good husband. 8°. pap., 25c. .... *Dick & F.*
— — *Same.* ill. 12°. bds., $1 .... *Routledge.*
Mayhew, Ira. Means and ends of universal education. 12°. '56. $1.75 .... *Barnes.*
— Practical book-keeping: single and double entry. 12°. '51. 84c. — Key. 12°. '60. 84c... *Nichols & H.*
— University book-keeping. 8°. '67. $2.50. — Key. 8°. $2.50 .... *Nichols & H.*
Mayhew, T: Ambition: drama. 16°. pap., 15c. *French.*
Mayhew's image of his father. ill. 12°. (Bohn.) 80c. *Scribner, W. & A.*
Maynard, G: W. Iron analysis record; for use in blast furnaces. sm. 32°. '75. shp., $1 .. *W. H. Young.*
Maynard, Michel Ulysse. Studies and teachings of the Society of Jesus at the time of its suppression, 1750–1775; tr. from the Fr. 12°. '55. $1 .. *Murphy.*
Mayne, J. *See* Mayne, R. G. *and* J.
Mayne, J: D. Treatise on the law of damages. 8°. '57. $3 .... *T. & J. W. Johnson.*
— — *See also* Law lib.
Mayne, Leger D. (*pseud.*) *See* Dick, W: Brisbane.
Mayne, Rob. Gray *and* J. Medical vocabulary. 4th ed., rev. and enl. post 8°. '75. $3... *Lindsay.*
Mayo, Amory Dwight. The balance; or, moral arguments for Universalism. 32°. '46. 60c. *Universalist.*
— *and* Vickers, T: The Bible in the public schools: addresses. 24°. '70. pap., 25c... *Schermerhorn.*
Mayo, C: Lessons on objects in a Pestalozzian school. 12°. '76. $1.75 .... *Roman.*
Mayo, Is. F. ["Edward and Ruth Garrett."] [Works.] 8 v. ill. 12°. '73–'76 .... *Dodd.*
Cont.: Doing and dreaming, $1.25. — By still waters. — Crooked places. — Crust and the cake. — Dead sin, etc. — Gold and dross. — Occupations of a retired life. — Premiums paid to experience, *ea.*, $1.75.
— Occupations of a retired life. 8°. '68. pap., 50c. *Littell & G.*
— Quiet Miss Godolphin; [also] A chance child. ill. 16°. 75c.; pap., 50c. .... *Lippincott.*
— White as snow. 12°. '70. $1 .... *Randolph.*
Mayo, Jos. Guide to magistrates; with forms and precedents. 8°. '60. cf., $3 ...... *J. W. Randolph.*
Mayo, Osc. Finger training [for the piano]. 4°. $1.50. *Church.*
Mayo, W: Starbuck. The Berber; or, the mountains of the Atlas: tale of Morocco. New ed. 12°. '73. $1.75 .... *Putnam.*
— Kaloolah: autobiography of Jonathan Romer of Nantucket. 12°. '72. $1.75 .... *Putnam.*
— Kaloolah; or, journeyings to the djebel kumel. 8°. pap., 50c. .... *De Witt.*
— Never again. ill. '73. $2 .... *Putnam.*
Mayor, *Rev.* J: E. B. First Greek reader; ed. after Karl Halm, with corrections and add. 2d [chp.] ed. fp. 8°. $1.50 .... *Macmillan.*
Mayor, Jos. B. Greek for beginners. fp. 8°. '69. $1.50 .... *Macmillan.*
Mayor of Garratt. Foote, S. 15c. .... *French.*
Mayor of Windgap. *See* Banim, J. *and* M.
May's Advent. Radcliffe, A. G. 40c. .... *Dutton.*
Mayser, F. P. Little treasures for little children; or, elementary lessons for smaller scholars in S.-schools. 24°. 20c. .... *Baer.*
Maysie's star. Wyeth, M. E. C. 25c. ...... *Am. Tr.*
Mayweed blossoms. Waisbrooker, L. $1.25 .. *Colby.*
Maze of life. Richmond, D. $1 .... *Routledge.*
Mazeppa: burlesque. 16°. pap., 15c... *French; Happy.*
Mazeppa: drama. Milner, H. M. 15c. ..... *French.*
Mazères, É: Le collier de perles: comédie. With vocab. ('65.) New ed. 12°. '76. pap., 30c... *Holt.*
Mazini, Linda. In the golden shell: story of Palermo. ill. fp. 8°. '72. $1.50 .... *Macmillan.*
Mazourka. Byron, H. J. 15c. .... *French.*
Mazzini, Jos. Life, writings and political principles; chiefly from autobiog. sources; with introd. by W. L. Garrison. por. cr. 8°. '72. $1.75 .. *Hurd & H.*

Mazzoni, —. Solfeggi; arr. for the present Am. pitch by E. S. f°. '68. pap., $1.25.........*Ditson.*

Me-a-ow; or, good advice to cats. *See* Ballantyne, W.

Meacham, A. B. Wi-ne-ma (the woman-chief) and her people. ill. 12°. '76. *$1........*Am.Pub.*

Mead, C. M. On Exodus. *See* Lange, J. P., Commentary.

Mead, E: C. Genealogical hist. of the Lee family of Virginia and Maryland, 1300–1866; with notes. ill. sm. 4°. '68. $5; mor., $10 .....*Univ.Pub.*

Mead, F. L. Report upon diurnal lipidoptera. *See* United States, *Corps of Eng.*

Mead, J: Mooney. Memoir. ('32.) New ed. ill. 18°. '36. 35c..................................*Am. Tr.*

Mead, *Mrs.* M. E. The hard problem. ill. 16°. '73. $1.25 ....*Am. Tr.*

Mead, M. Gert. Nannie and our boys. 16°. $1.50. *Cong. Pub.*

Mead, Mat. The almost Christian discovered; or, the false professor tried and cast. 18°. 55c...*Pres. Bd.*

Mead, P: B. Elementary treatise on Am. grape-culture and wine-making. ill. 8°. $3.....*Harper.*

Meade, *Mrs.* Anna. *See* Chalmers, *Mrs.* A. M.

Meade, G: Life and public services of Gen. Meade, the hero of Gettysburg. 12°. pap., 25c...*Peterson.*

Meade, R: W. Naval construction: treatise on naval architecture and ship-building. ill. cr. 8°. $10. *Lippincott.*

Meade, W: Bible and classics. 8°. $2.50....*Carter.*

— Old churches, ministers and families of Virginia. 2 v. ill. 8°. $5..........................*Lippincott.*

Meadow brook. Holmes, M. J. $1.50....*Carleton.*

Meadows, Alfr. Manual of obstetrics. 3d ed., rev. and enl. ill. 8°. '76. $3.25.........*Lindsay.*

Meadows, F. C. French and Eng. pronouncing dictionary. 16°. '55. $1.50......*G. R. Lockwood.*

— French-Eng. and Eng.-French dict. 12°. $2..*Appleton.*

— Italian-Eng. dict. 16°. hf. bd., $2. — New ed., rev. hf. bd., $2.50..........................*Appleton.*

— Spanish-Eng. and Eng.-Span. dict. 18°. hf. roan, $2.50 ....*Appleton; Desilver.*

Meadowside stories. 8 v. ill. 18°. '61. $4. *Meth. Bk. Conc.*

Cont.: Meadowside; or, Aunt Grace and Dora. — Sally Grafton and her teacher. — The book. — Faithful Lina. — Katie and her mother; or, the widow's trust. — Victor; or, Paris troubles and province roses. — Good daughters; or, the sea-shore and the cottage. — Anton, the peasant boy.

Meagher, T: Fs. Commercial agency system of the U. S. and Canada exposed: is the secret inquisition a curse or a benefit? 8°. '76. $3..(?)*Meagher.*

— Life. 12°. $2; $2.50 ....*Sadlier.*

— Speeches on the legislative independence of Ireland; [also] R. O'Gorman's oration. por. 12°. '69. $1.50 ....*Haverty.*

Meaney, *Miss* Ma. L. Confessors of Connaught; or, the tenants of a lord bishop. sm. 12°. '68. $1. *Cunningham.*

— Grace Morton; or, the inheritance. 18°. '66. $1. *Cunningham.*

Means, *Mrs.* Ctte. A. Golden truth ser. 3 v. 4°. ea., $2; mor., $4.50..................*Lee & S.*

Cont.: Golden truths. — Words of hope. — Living thoughts.

— Ring (The) and its motto. 16°. $1.....*Cong. Pub.*

Means, *Mrs.* J. H. Auntie's secret. 16°. 90c. *Cong. Pub.*

Means, *Mrs.* Jane C. Consolation, in conflict, sickness and sorrow: poems. 18°. 75c. ...*Bost. Am. Tr.*

Means and ends. Sedgwick, C. M. 75c.....*Harper.*

Means of acquiring perfection. *See* Liguori, A. M. de, *St.*

Mearns, P: Memoir of Mrs. Agnes Andrew of Paisley. 18°. 45c. ....*Pres. Bd.*

Mears, J: W. Beggars of Holland and grandees of Spain: the reformation in the Netherlands. 16°. $1.50.................................*Pres. Bd.*

Mears, J: W., *continued.*

— Martyrs of France. 18°. 50c.............*Pres. Bd.*

— Story of Madagascar. 16°. $1.25........*Pres. Bd.*

Measure for measure. *See* Shakespeare, W:

Mecca. Pratt, J. L. $1.25 ....*Hoyt.*

Mechanism in thought and morals. Holmes, O. W. $1.......................................*Osgood.*

Mechener, Ez. *See* Hartman, W. D., *and* Mechener, E.

Mechi, J: Jos. How to farm profitably. 2 v. ill. fp. 8°. ea., hf. bd., $2.50......................*Routledge.*

— Liquid manure. *See* Stöckhardt, J. A., Agricultural chemistry.

Mecklenbörg'schen Montecchi (De) un Capuletti. Reuter, F. $1; 75c.....................*Steiger.*

Medals of creation. *See* Mantell, G. A.

Medbery, Ja. K. Men and mysteries of Wall Street. ill. 12°. $2............................**Osgood.*

Meddaugh, Elij. W. *See* Michigan, Sup. Court reports.

Meddling Matt. *See* New Year lib.

Medea. *See* Euripides.

Medea. Legouvé, E. W. 15c...............*French.*

Medea: burlesque. Brough, R. B. 15c. ....*French.*

Médecin malgré lui (Le). *See* Molière, J. B. P.

Medhurst, Wa. H: The foreigner in Far Cathay. 12°. '73. $1.50 ....*Scribner.*

Mediation: the function of thought. 16°. '71. $1.25. *Draper.*

Mediatorial sovereignty. Steward, G. 2 v. $10. *Scribner, W. & A.*

Medical and surgical knowledge: pract. guide on health and disease. (Reason why ser.) 12°. $2.50 ....*Lippincott.*

Medical Assoc. of the State of Alabama. Transactions, 1868–'76. 9 v. 8°. ea., pap., $2.50 ..*Ala. Med.*

Medical jurisprudence; by F. Wharton, S. Ashhurst, R. Amory and W. Sinkler. 3d ed. 2 v. in 3. 8°. shp., $19.50.............................*Kay.*

Medical man (A): comedietta. 16°. pap., 15c...*Happy.*

Medical Soc. of State of N. Y. Transactions, 1807–'31, 1840–'43, 1860–'62, 1864–'75. 16 v. 8°..*N. Y. Med.*

Cont.: 1807–'31 (reprint), 50c. — 1840–'43 (reprint), 50c. — 1860, 1862, 1864, 1865, 1867, ea., $1. — 1861, 1866, 1868–'72, 7 v., ea., 50c. — 1873–4, $1.50. — 1875, $1.55.

Medicine shelf. Brown, H. E. 85c. ...*Bost. Am. Tr.*

Medico-Legal Society of N. Y. Papers read from its organization in 1868. 8°. $4.50; shp., $5. *Campbell & Co.*

Medina, *Miss* Louisa. Ernest Maltravers: drama. 16°. pap., 15c. ....*French.*

— Last days of Pompeii: spectacle. 16°. pap., 15c. *French.*

— Nick of the woods: drama. 16°. pap., 15c...*French.*

Medina-Pomar, *Count* de. The honey-moon: a remembrance of a bridal tour through Scotland; tr. from the Spanish by author. 2 v. 12°. $3. *Lippincott.*

Meding, Guido. ["Greg. Samarow."] Europäische Minen u. Gegenminen: Fortsetzg. v. "Um Szepter u. Kronen;" [also] Die Ehre des Herzens, v. E. M. Vacano. 3 v. 8°. ea., pap., 50c. *Morwitz.*

— Held u. Kaiser. 2 v. 8°. ea., pap., 50c...*Morwitz.*

— Kreuz u. Schwert. 2 v. 8°. ea., pap., 50c...*Morwitz.*

— Um Szepter u. Kronen. 2 v. 8°. ea., pap., 50c. *Morwitz.*

— — *See also above* Europäische Minen.

— Zwei Kaiserkronen. 2 v. 8°. ea., pap., 50c. *Morwitz.*

Meditation of Columbia. *See* Centennial meditation.

Meditations and considerations for a retreat of one day in each month. 18°. '65. 60c. — 2d ed. 24°. '76. 60c.......................*Kelly, P. & Co.*

Meditations of a Christian mother. 18°. 50c...*Pres. Bd.*

Meditations of the litany of the Virgin. *See* Orsini, M., Life of the Virgin.

Meditations on St. Joseph. [Cath. prayer book.] 12°. $1.50; $2 .... *Sadlier.*

Meditative hours. 16°. '65. $1.25 ...... *Randolph.*

Mediums and mediumship. Hazard, T. R. 10c... *Colby.*

Medley, Jul. G: India and Indian engineering: lectures, Royal Engineer Inst., Chatham, July, 1872. cr. 8°. '73. $1.25 .... *Spon.*

Medwins of Wykeham. Lankester, C. $1.. *Routledge.*

Meech, L. W. Relative intensity of heat and light of the sun. 4°. '56. pap., $1.25 ..... *Smith. Inst.*

Meehan, C. H. W. Law and practice of the game of euchre. 32°. $1 .... *Peterson.*

Meehan, C. P. Confederation of Kilkenny. 12°. $1. *Noonan.*

Meehan, T: American handbook of ornamental trees. 18°. '53. 75c .... *Claxton; Lippincott.*

Meek, A. R. *See* Florida, Sup. Court reports.

Meek, F. B. Report on invertebrate, etc., fossils of upper Missouri country. *See* United States, *Geol. Survey of the Ter.*

— *See also* California geol. survey; — Illinois geol. survey.

— *and* Hayden, F. V. Palæontology of the upper Missouri. pt. 1. 4°. '65. pap., $2.50.. *Smith. Inst.*

Meeker, N. C. Life in the west: stories of the Mississippi valley. 12°. '68. $2 .... *Wells.*

Meeson, R. *See* England, Exchequer reports.

Meet for heaven. 16°. '64. $1.25 .... *Roberts.*

Meeting of the travellers. 18°. 40c .... *Dutton.*

Meggie of the Pines. Baker, S. 60c ...... *Randolph.*

Meg's diversion. Craven, H. T. 15c .... *French.*

Mehetabel. Gardner, H. C. $1.25... *Meth. Bk. Conc.*

Meignen, Lp. Vocal method. 4°. $3 ...... *Church.*

— *and* Keys, W: W. The music reader. 4th ed. 12°. '65. bds., $1 .... *Ditson.*

Meigs, C: D. On the nature, signs and treatment of childbed fever. 8°. $2 .... *Lea.*

Meigs, H. Our summer at Sunnybrook. 16°. '60. $1. *Randolph.*

Meigs, J: Forsyth, *and* Pepper, W. Practical treatise on the diseases of children. 5th ed., rev. and enl. roy. 8°. $6; leath., $7 .... *Lindsay.*

Meigs, Return Jona. *See* Tennessee, Code; Sup. Court reports.

Meikle, Ja. Solitude sweetened. 12°. $1. *U. P. Bd. of Pub.*

Meiklejohn, J. M. D. *See* Sonnenschein, R., *and* Meiklejohn, J. M. D.

Meilhac, Henri, *and* Halévy, Ludovic. Frou-Frou: drama. 16°. pap., 15c .... *French.*

Meille, J. P. General Beckwith: his life and labors among the Waldenses of Piedmont; with introd. note by W. Arnot. 12°. $1.25 .... *Nelson.*

Mein Bruder Benjamin. *See* My brother Ben.

Mein erstes Buch in Sonntags-Schule u. Haus. ('75.) 2d ed. 16°. '76. 20c.; bds., 18c .... *Pilger.*

Mein Onkel Fischer in Baltimore. *See* Dilthey, K.

Mein zweites Buch in Sonntags-Schule u. Haus Lernbuch f. d. Mittelklasse. 16°. '76. 30c.; bds., 25c .... *Pilger.*

Meinecke, C. Frühlings-Kuren: e. mineralwäss'rige Centralpark- u. Charakter-Studie, in schlechten Hexametern abgefasst. 8°. '69. pap., 20c. *Steiger.*

Meineke, C. New instruction for the piano-forte. ('40.) 30th ed., rev. and enl. 4°. pap., $1 .... *Ditson.*

Meinhold, J. W. Sidonia, the sorceress. [Fiction.] 8°. pap., $1 .... *Harper.*

Meissner, A. L. Philology of the Fr. lang.: chp. ed. of "Palæstra Gallica." sm. 8°. $1.50.. *Lippincott.*

Meister Karl's sketch book. Leland, C. G. $2.50; $3.50 .... *Peterson.*

Melancholy anatomized; with anecdotic ill.; princip. founded on Burton's "Anatomy of melancholy." 12°. hf. cf., $2.50; cf., $3 .... *Appleton.*

Melancthon, Ph. Life. 18°. 55c. .... *Pres. Bd.*

Melbourne House. Warner, S. $2 .... *Carter.*

Melek-Hanum. *See* Kibrizli-Mehemet-Pasha.

Mélesville (*pseud.*) *See* Duveyrier, A. H. J.

Melinda, the caboceer. Sketchly, J. A. $1.75.. *Appleton.*

Meline, Ja. F. Mary, Queen of Scots, and her late English historian [Froude]. 4th ed. 12°. '73. $1.75. *Cath. Pub.*

— Two thousand miles on horseback, Santa Fé and back: a summer tour through Kansas, Nebraska, Colorado and New Mexico, in 1866. cr. 8°. '67. $1.75 .... *Hurd & H.*

— *Same.* 12°. '68. $1.50 .... *Cath. Pub.*

Meline, *Miss* Ma. Miller. ["Flo. McCoomb."] Charteris: romance. 12°. $1.50 .... *Lippincott.*

— In six months; or, the two friends. 16°. '74. $1.25; $1.75 .... *Kelly, P. & Co.*

— The Montarges legacy. 12°. '69. $1.. *Cunningham.*

Mell, Pat. H. Doctrine of prayer: its utility and its rel. to Providence. 16°. 60c .... *Sheldon.*

— Manual of parliamentary practice. 16°. 75c. *Sheldon.*

Mellichampe. Simms, W. G. $1.75; 75c. *Widdleton.*

Melodeon (The): songs, duets, quartettes, rounds and marches; with hist. of music and musical instruments. imp. 8°. pap., 35c .... *U. P. James.*

Melodica. Baumbach, A. 75c .... *Peters.*

Melodies for childhood. 16°. $1.50 ..... (?) *Martien.*

Melodies of heaven. St. John, T. E. 50c. *Williamson.*

Melodist. Buckley, F. 40c .... *Gordon.*

Melpomene divina. Pindar, C. L. $1.50.. *Lippincott.*

Melsheimer, F: Ernst. Catalogue of coleoptera. 8°. '53. pap., $2 .... *Smith. Inst.*

Melvill, H: B. Lectures. 8°. $2 .... *McCauley.*

Melvill family and their Bible readings. ill. 16°. $1. *Hoyt, F. & D.*

Melville, Fk. Industrial drawing book in graded numbers. 4 nos. 8°. '73. per doz., $2.50. (?) *Slote.*

Melville, G: J: Whyte. [Novels.] 7 v. .... *Appleton.*

Cont.: The Brookes of Bridlemere. — Cerise. — Uncle John. — White rose, *ea.*, 12°, $1.25. — Gladiators. — Good for nothing. — Sarchedon: legend of the great queen, *ea.*, 8°, pap., 60c.

— Cerise: tale of the last century. 12°. $1.50.. *Claxton.*

— Kate Coventry: an autobiography. 8°. pap., 38c. *Littell & G.*

— Katerfelto: story of Exmoor. 12°. '75. $1; bds., 75c .... *Donnelley.*

— *Same.* 12°. $1.50; pap., 75c. — (Intern. ed.) 12°. $1.25 .... *Porter.*

— Maud or Nina. 8°. $1.25; pap., 75c .... *Estes.*

Melville, H: Sermons; ed. by Rev. C. P. M'Ilvaine. 2 v. 8°. $5 .... *Miller.*

Melville, Hm. Battle pieces and aspects of the war. 12°. $1.75 .... *Harper.*

— Clarel: pilgrimage in the Holy Land: narrative poem. 2 v. 12°. '76. $3 .... *Putnam.*

— Mardi, and a voyage thither. 2 v. 12°. $3.. *Harper.*

— Moby-Dick; or, the whale. 12°. $1.75 .... *Harper.*

— Omoo: narrative of adventures in the south seas. 12°. $1.50 .... *Harper.*

— Pierre; or, the ambiguities. 12°. $1.50... *Harper.*

— Redburn: his first voyage. 12°. $1.50.... *Harper.*

— Refugee (The). 12°. $1.75; pap., $1.50. *Peterson.*

— Typee: peep at Polynesian life, during a four months' residence in the Marquesas. Rev. ed., with sequel. 12°. $1.50 .... *Harper.*

— White-jacket; or, the world in a man-of-war. 12°. $1.50 .... *Harper.*

Melville lib. 6 v. ill. 18°. $3 .... *Hoyt.*
Cont.: Stella, by Mrs. M. A. Dennan. — Parish ball, by Mrs. M. J. Marwin. — Mamma's talks with Charlie, by Miss Sarah Woodbridge. — Fisher Bill. — The violet. — Why the mill was stopped, by Mrs. H. S. Grosvenor.

Melzar; or, beloved disciple. 18°. 60c.; 70c. *Am. Bapt.*

Member for Paris. *See* Murray, G.

Memes, J: S. Memoirs of the Empress Josephine. 18°. 75c. .... *Harper.*

Memminger, Rob. Withers. Present issues; or, facts observable in the consciousness of the age. 12°. '72. $1.50 .... *Claxton.*

— What is religion? protest against "the spirit of the age." 12°. '71. $1.50 .... *Claxton.*

Memmler, Louise. Bunte Blätter. 16°. '66. bds., 25c. *Steiger.*

Memoir of a late officer in the army of the U. S. 18°. 30c. .... *Am. S. S.*

Memoir of the pilgrimage to Va. of the Knights Templars of Mass. and R. I., 1859; pub. by authority of the De Molay Encampment. 12°. '59. $1.25. *Williams.*

Memoir of Wesleyan preachers. 12°. '43. 90c. *Meth. Bk. Conc.*

Memoirs of a cavalier. *See* Defoe, D.

Memoirs of the devil; or, the black book of Rouquerolles: drama. 16°. pap., 15c. .... *French.*

Memoirs of a doll. 16°. '64. 60c. .... *Am. S. S.*

Memoirs of a doll. Besset, J. M. 50c. ... *Routledge.*

Memoirs of a guardian angel. Chardon, G. $1.50. *Murphy.*

Memoirs of a Huguenot family. Fontaine, J. $1:75. *Putnam.*

Memoirs of my youth. Lamartine, A. de. 25c. *Harper.*

Memoirs of a physician. *See* Dumas, A.

Memoirs of a preacher. Lippard, G. 75c... *Peterson.*

Memoirs of Sergeant Dale, his daughter and the orphan Mary. 18°. 40c. .... *Am. S. S.*

Memoirs of Yellowplush. *See* Thackeray, W: M.

Memoranda during the [civil] war. Whitman, W. $1.50 .... *Whitman.*

Memorare (The). Werner, A. $2.75 ...... *Ditson.*

Memorial days of the renewed church of the Brethren; tr. from the Germ. 12°. (Lond.) 65c... *Clauder.*

Memorial for Sunday school boys. 18°. 30c... *Am. S. S.*

Memorial hour. Chaplin, J. $1.25 .... *Lothrop.*

Memorial of the Intern. Exhibition at Phila.: views of principal buildings. obl. 24°. '76. 50c. *T. Hunter.*

Memorials of deceased Friends, members of Phila. yearly meeting, to 1787. 12°. 75c... *Friends Bk. St.*
— *Same;* to 1849. 12°. 75c. .... *Friends Bk. St.*
— *Same;* to 1868. 12°. pap., 15c..... *Friends Bk. St.*
— *Same;* to 1874. 12°. pap., 35c..... *Friends Bk. St.*

Memorials of English martyrs; from Wyckliffe to end of reign of Mary. ill. 12°. $1.75. *Bost. Am. Tr.*

Memorials of Harrow Sundays. Vaughan, C. J. $3. *Macmillan.*

Memorials of prison life. Finley, J. $1.25. *Meth. Bk. Conc.*

Memorials of a quiet life. *See* Hare, A. J. C.

Memories. Müller, M. $1; $2 .... *Jansen.*

Memories of Bethany. Macduff, J. R. $1... *Carter.*

Memories of fifty years. Sparks, W. H. $2.50.. *Claxton.*

Memories of Gennesaret. Macduff, J. R. $1.50.. *Carter.*

Memories of home. 18°. 30c.; 40c. ..... *Am. Bapt.*

Memories of many men and of some women. Field, M. B. $2 .... *Harper.*

Memories of Olivet; — of Patmos. Macduff, J. R. ea., $2 .... *Carter.*

Memories of Westminster Hall [Lond.]; with hist. introd. by E. Foss. 2 v. ill. 8°. '74. $7. *Cockcroft; Estes.*

Memory. 18°. pap., 10c. .... *Nelson.*

Memory and hope. Silsbee, *Mrs.* —. $7 ... *Osgood.*

Memphian's (A) trip to Europe. Watson, S. $1.50. *So. Meth.*

Men and memories of San Francisco. Barry, T. A., *and* Patten, B. A. .... *Bancroft.*

Men and mysteries of Wall Street. Medbery, J. K. $2. * *Osgood.*

Men and scenes before the flood. Lord, W. 50c. *Pres. Bd.*

Men and things as I saw them in Europe. Murray, N. $1.50 .... *Harper.*

Men and women. Browning, R. $1.50 ..... *Osgood.*

Men are what women make them. Belot, A. $1.50. *McKinney.*

Men I have known. Jerdan, W. $2...... *Routledge.*

Men of '48. McGee, J. E. $1 .... *McGee.*

Men of mark. Brightwell, C. L. $1.75...... *Nelson.*

Men of mark. Greer, F. H. $6; $25.. *N. Y. & H. Pub.*

Men of progress. Patten, J. $6; $25.. *N. Y. & H. Pub.*

Men of the third republic; or, the present leaders of France. 12°. $1.75 .... *Porter.*

Men of the time: biog. dict. of eminent characters. 9th ed., rev. post 8°. '75. $6........ *Routledge.*

Men of worth. *See* Pioneer lib.

Men of Wycombe. *See* Austin, C.

Men, women and books. Hunt, L. $3; $6.50.. *Harper.*

Men, women and ghosts. Phelps, E. S. $1.50.. *Osgood.*

Men worth imitating. Groser, W. H. $1.... *Nelson.*

Menagerie (The) improved. ill. 18°. 22c... *Am. S. S.*

Menard, René. French artists of the present day; with biog. notes. pl. f°. '76. $10.... *Bouton.*

Menault, Ern. Intelligence of animals; with ill. anecdotes. ill. 12°. '75. $1.25......... *Scribner.*

Mencius, Balt. Works; with life, essays and notes by J. Legge. 12°. $4 .... *Lippincott.*

— *See also* Legge, J.

Mend your nets; or, little Jack. ill. 18°. 65c... *Crowell.*

— *See also* Go ahead lib.

Mended life. Lamb, J. $1.50 .... (?) *Martien.*

Mendell, G: H. Treatise on military surveying. ill. 12°. '64. $2 .... *Van Nostrand.*

Mendelssohn-Bartholdy, C: Goethe and Mendelssohn; tr. by M. E. v. Glehn; with por., facsimile and letters of Mendelssohn of later date. New ed., with add. letters. cr. 8°. '74. $2. *Macmillan.*

Mendelssohn-Bartholdy, Fel. As the hart pants: 42d Psalm. [Oratorio.] 8°. pap., 40c.; bds., 50c. .... *Ditson; Gordon.*

— Athalie, by Racine; tr. by M. Bartholomew. [Oratorio.] 8°. bds., $1; pap., 80c. — Libretto, pap., 10c. .... *Ditson.*

— Come let us sing: 95th Psalm; with piano-forte accomp. [Cantata.] 8°. pap., 40c.; bds., 50c. *Ditson.*

— Elijah; with words from Old Test.; tr. by W. Bartholomew. [Oratorio.] 8°. $1.50; pap., $1; bds., $1.25 .... *Ditson; Gordon.*

— *Same.* 8°. $1.75; pap., $1; bds., $1.38.. *Church.*

— — Choruses. 8°. bds., 80c....... *Ditson; Gordon.*

— Four part songs for male voices; tr. by C. J. Sprague. 5 bks. 8°. $3; — vocal pts., ea., 75c.; — piano score, $1 .... *G. D. Russell.*

— Four part songs for mixed voices; with Germ. words, and with Eng. words by J. C. D. Parker. 8°. '56. bds., $1; — for men's voices, 75c; — 2 pts. in 1, $1.25; — Selections, pap., 25c.......... *Ditson.*

— Hear my prayer: hymn for soprano and chorus. 4°. pap., 40c. .... *Ditson.*

— Hymn of praise. [Cantata.] 8°. bds., 75c.; pap., 60c. .... *Ditson.*

— Lauda Sion. [Cantata.] 8°. $1.25; pap., 80c. *Ditson.*

Mendelssohn-Bartholdy, Fel., *continued.*
— Letters, 1833–'47; ed. by P. and C. Mendelssohn Bartholdy; with catalogue of his musical compositions by J. Rietz; tr. by Lady Wallace. 12°. $1.75 .... *Ditson.*
— Letters from Italy and Switzerland; tr. by Lady Wallace; with biog. notice by J. de Marguerittes. 12°. $1.75 .... *Ditson.*
— Loreley: an unfinished opera; tr. by W. Bartholomew. 8°. pap., 65c. .... *Ditson.*
— Ninety-eighth Psalm: Sing to the Lord; for double chorus: Eng. version adapted by W. Bartholomew. 8°. bds., 75c.; pap., 60c. .... *Ditson.*
— St. Paul. [Oratorio.] Novello's rev. ed. 8°. $1.25; bds., $1; pap., 80c. .... *Ditson.*
— — Choruses. 8°. bds., 65c. .... *Ditson.*
— Three motets for female voices. 3 nos. 4°. pap., 1, 30c.; 2, 3, ea., 50c. .... *Ditson.*
— Twenty-four four-part songs for singing in the open air; with Germ. words, and with Eng. words by J. C. D. Parker. 8°. '56. pap., 40c. ..... *Ditson.*
— Walpurgis night, by Goethe; tr. by W. Bartholomew. 8°. $1.25; bds., $1; pap., 80c. .. *Ditson.*
Mendenhall, E. Ninth census of the population of the United States. sq. 16°. '71. 40c.; pap., 25c. *Mendenhall.*
— Shipping atlas of the western and southern states. 15 maps. 4°. '76. $5 .... *Mendenhall.*
Mendenhall, G: Medical student's vade mecum: compend. of anatomy, physiology, chemistry, etc. 11th ed., rev. and enl. ill. 12°. '76. $2.50 .. *Lindsay.*
Mendenhall, W: History, correspondence and pedigrees of the Mendenhalls of England and the U. S., rel. to their common origin and ancestry. New ed., enl. by E. Mendenhall. 8°. '64. roan, $5 .... *Mendenhall.*
Mendicant. A'Beckett, G. A. 15c. .... *French.*
Mengarini, Greg. Selish, or flat-head grammar. *See* Shea, J. G., Library of Am. linguistics.
Menghi-D'Arville, *Abbé.* The year of Mary; or, the true servant of the blessed Virgin; tr. by Mrs. J. Sadlier. 12°. $1.50 .... *Sadlier.*
— *Same.* 12°. '68. $1.50 .... *Cunningham.*
Menken, Adah Isaacs. Infelicia. [Poetry.] 18°. $1. *Lippincott.*
Menno, Sim. Works; tr. from the Dutch. 8°. leath., $4.50 .... *Baer.*
— *Germ.* Schriften. 12°. $2 .... *Baer.*
— Foundation and plain instruction of the saving doctrine of Christ; tr. 12°. leath., $1.25 .... *Baer.*
— Life and times. [German.] 18°. 30c. ... *Am. Bapt.*
Mennonite Brothers. Collection of Psalms, hymns and spiritual songs; with app. of Germ. hymns; [comp.] by a committee. 32°. leath., 60c. .. *Baer.*
— Confession of faith. *See* Christian spiritual conversation.
— Unpartheyische Gesangbuch (Das). [Hymn book.] 12°. leath., $1.50 .... *Baer.*
Mensch u. Natur. Erlenkötter, G. 90c. .... *Schäfer.*
Mental hygiene. Ray, I. $1.50 .... *Osgood.*
Mental medicine. *See* Evans, W. F.
Mentor in the granges and homes of Patrons of Husbandry. Grosh, A. B. *$2 .... *Clark & M.*
Menzel, Wolfg. History of Germany; tr. by Mrs. G. Horrocks. 3 v. por. 12°. (Bohn.) ea., $1.25. *Little, B. & Co.*
— *Same.* 3 v. por. 12°. (Bohn.) ea., $1.40. *Scribner, W. & A.*
— *Same.* 3 v. por. 12°. (Bohn.) ea., $1.50 .. *Lippincott.*
Menzel der Franzosenfresser. *See* Börne, L.
Menzies, *Mrs.* Ste. Hints on Bible marking; with pref. note by D. L. Moody. ill. 16°. pap., 25c. *Nelson.*
— *Same.* ill. sq. 18°. '76. 25c.; pap., 15c. .. *Randolph.*
— — *See also* Moody, D. L., How to study the Bible.

Mephistopheles. Brough, R. B., *and* Edwards, S. 15c. .... *French.*
Mer (La) et la nuit. Hugo, V. 50c. ...... *Appleton.*
Mercadante, Saverio. Four voice mass. 8°. $1; pap., 75c. .... *Gordon.*
— Mass in B flat; for 3 voices; with Lat. and Eng. words. 8°. '70. $1; pap., 75c. .. *Ditson; Gordon.*
— Third mass in G minor; arrang. by W. Dressler. 4°. pap., $1.50 .... *Peters.*
— Vespers, no. 8; arrang. by W. Dressler. 4°. pap., $1.25 .... *Peters.*
Mercedes; or, the outlaw's child. 12°. pap., 20c. *Hurst.*
Mercedes of Castile. *See* Cooper, Ja. F.
Mercein, Imogen. Garden of the Lord. 48°. '46. 20c. .... *Meth. Bk. Conc.*
Mercein, T. F. R. Natural goodness. 12°. '60. 75c. *Randolph.*
— *Same.* 12°. '54. $1 .... *Meth. Bk. Conc.*
Mercer, Jesse. Mercer's cluster: spiritual songs, hymns and sacred poems. 18°. shp., 75c. *Desilver.*
Merchant, Mat. (*pseud.*) *See* Wood, W. S.
Merchant and farmer. 18°. 50c.; 60c. .... *Am. Bapt.*
Merchant of Antwerp. Conscience, H. $1.50; $2. *Kelly, P. & Co.*
Merchant of Berlin. *See* Mundt, *Mrs.* C. M.
Merchant of Venice. *See* Shakespeare, W.
Merchant of Venice: extravaganza. 16°. pap., 15c. *French.*
Merchant's clerk. Alexander, J. W. 35c. .. *Randolph.*
Merchant's daughter. Barr, J. T. 60c. *Cin. Meth. Bk. Conc.*
Merchant's daughter. Hall, A. M. $1.25. *Scribner, W. & A.*
Merchant's wedding. Planché, J. R. 15c. .. *French.*
Merchant's widow. Hofland, B. 50c. ...... *Porter.*
Merchant's widow. Sawyer, C. M. 50c. .. *Williamson.*
Merchants', manufacturers' and importers' business register of N. Y. City for 1873–4; with list of leading business houses of Phila. and Boston. 12°. '73. $2.50 .... (?) *Phillips, A. & Co.*
Mercier, *Mrs.* Jerome. Campanella; or, the teachings of life. ill. 12°. $1.25 ...... *Scribner, W. & A.*
— Christabel Hope; or, the beginnings of life. ill. 12°. $1.25 .... *Scribner, W. & A.*
— Only a girl's life. ill. 16°. $1 .... *Scribner, W. & A.*
— Our mother church: simple talks on high topics. 16°. '75. $1.50 .... *Dutton.*
— *Same.* 12°. '75. $3.50 .... *Pott.*
Mercury and the woodman. *See* Stories about animals ser.
Mercy and truth: brief narratives of real life. ill. 12°. $1 .... *Nelson.*
Mercy Elwood's work; or, the cup of cold water. 18°. 18c. .... *Am. S. S.*
Mercy Glidden's work. Phelps, E. S. $1.25 .. *Hoyt.*
Mercy seat. Thompson, A. C. $1.50; $2.50; $3.50. *Sheldon.*
Mercy to babes. Adams, W. $1 .... *McCauley.*
Mère Michel. *See* La Bedollière, E. de.
Mère (La) l'oie. Leypoldt, F. 50c. .... *Holt.*
Mere piece of mischief. Guernsey, C. F. 90c. (?) *Martien.*
Meredith, Evan Powell. Prophet of Nazareth: crit. inquiry into prophetical, intellectual and moral character of Jesus Christ. 8°. $4 .... *Mendum.*
Meredith, G: Evan Harrington; or, he would be a gentleman. 12°. $1.50 .... *Harper.*
Meredith, Is. Grant. Old house on Briar Hill. ill. 16°. '75. $1.25 .... *Dodd.*
Meredith, L. P. Every-day errors of speech. 16°. 75c. .... *Lippincott.*
— The teeth, and how to save them. 16°. $1.25. *Lippincott.*

Meredith, Owen (*pseud.*) *See* Bulwer-Lytton, E: Rob.

Merewether, H: Atworth. By sea and by land: a trip through Egypt, India, Ceylon, Australia, New Zealand and America all round the world. cr. 8°. '74. $2.50 .... *Macmillan.*

Meridiana. *See* Verne, Jul.

Mérimée, Prosper. Colomba. *See* Schmidt, W., Vier Blüthen, etc.

— *See also* Stoddard, R. H., Bric-a-brac ser.

Merits of Christ. La Trobe, J. $1 .... *Clauder.*

Merivale, C: Conversion of the northern nations. (Boyle lectures, 1865.) 12°. $1.50 ... *Appleton.*

— Conversion of the Roman Empire. (Boyle lectures, 1864.) 12°. $1.50 .... *Appleton.*

— General hist. of Rome, B. C. 753–A. D. 476. maps and plans. 12°. '76. $2 .... *Harper.*

— History of the Romans under the empire. 7 v. sm. 8°. $14; hf. cf., $28. — in 8 v. sm. 8°. hf. cf., $35 .... *Appleton.*

Note. v. 8 contains "Conversion of the north. nations" and "Conversion of the Roman empire."

— (*tr.*) *See* Keats, J: Hyperion.

Merle d'Aubigné, J. H. *See* Aubigné.

Merman (The). *See* Enchanting fairy lib.

Merman (The) and the figure head. *See* Guernsey, C. F.

Meroke; or, missionary life in Africa. 18°. 65c. *Am. S. S.*

Mérope. *See* Voltaire.

Merrett, H. S. Practical treatise on science of land and engineering surveying, levelling, estimating quantities, etc. 41 pl. roy. 8°. '71. $5 .. *Spon.*

Merriam, E. E. William, Prince of Orange; or, the king and the hostage. 12°. '74. $1.75 .... *Hoyt.*

Merriam, G: S. A living faith. 16°. '76. $1.50. *Lockwood, B. & Co.*

Merrick, D. A. Lectures on the Church. 12°. $1.50. *O'Shea.*

— Sermons for the times. 12°. $1.50 .... *O'Shea.*

Merrick, J. M. The strawberry and its culture. 12°. '70. $1; pap., 50c. .... *Tilton.*

Merrick, J: Mudge. Nugæ inutiles: Mother Goose in Latin, with tr. from the Latin and German. 12°. '74. $1.25 .... (?) *Shepard.*

Merrick, R: T. *See* Stockett, J. S., Merrick, R. T., *and* Miller, O.

Merrie England. Lippincott, S. J. $1.50 ... * *Osgood.*

Merrie England in the olden time. Daniel, G. $1.75; $3.75; $5 .... *Scribner, W. & A.*

Merrifield, Ja. Jacob's ladder; or, more than leaves. 4°. '75. $4 .... (?) *Townsend & Co.*

— Royal road to learning; or, the finger-post to knowledge. New ed. 4°. '75. $2.50 .. (?) *Townsend & Co.*

Merrifield, *Mrs.* Ma. Philadelphia. Female costume; or, dress as a fine art. ill. 16°. pap., 40c. .. *French.*

Merrill, Cath. Indiana in the war for the union. 2 v. 8°. shp., $10 .... *Merrill.*

Merrill, G: E. Battles lost and won. ill. 16°. '72. $1.50 .... *Lothrop.*

— Master Hathorne's family. 16°. $1.50 .. *Am. Bapt.*

Merrill, H. T. Golden crown. [S.-school music.] obl. 12°. pap., 10c. .... *Church.*

— Harmonic method for German concertina. obl. 8°. pap., 60c. .... *Peters.*

Merrill, *Miss* Jenny B. *See* Crafts, *Mrs.* W. F., *and* Merrill, J. B.

Merrill, S: Oblong definition book. obl. 12°. hf. bd., 25c. .... *Merrill.*

Merrill, Ste. M. Christian baptism: its subjects and modes. 16°. '76. $1.25 .... *Cin. Meth. Bk. Conc.*

Merrill, W: E. Iron truss bridges for railroads. 3d ed. 9 pl. 4°. '75. $5 .... *Van Nostrand.*

Merriman, Mansfield. Theory and calculations of continuous bridges. ill. 18°. '76. bds., 50c. *Van Nostrand.*

Merritt, Tim. Christian's manual: treatise on Christian perfection. 24°. '37. 40c. .... *Meth. Bk. Conc.*

— Convert's guide and preacher's assistant. 18°. '41. 55c. .... *Meth. Bk. Conc.*

Merry, *Old.* *See* Old Merry (*pseud.*)

Merry, Rob. Book of puzzles. 12°. pap., 30c. *Thompson.*

— Rhymes and puzzles. ill. 12°. $1.50 ... (?) *O'Kane.*

Merry chimes. Emerson, L. O. 50c. .... *Ditson.*

Merry Christmas. Aunt Mattie. 18°. 75c. .. *Graves.*

Merry Christmas of the old woman who lived in her shoe. Baker, G. M. 15c. .... *Lee & S.*

Merry elves. Murray, C. O. $1.50 .... *Nelson.*

Merry heart lib. 8 v. 16°. $4 .... *Nelson.*

Cont.: Bertha Marchmont, by Mrs. Cupples. — Fanny Sylvester, by Mrs. Cupples. — Vea and her cousins, by Mrs. Cupples. — Carry's rose, by Mrs. Cupples. — Bluff cragg, by Mrs. Cupples. — Hugh Wellwood's success, by Mrs. Cupples. — Alice Leighton, by Mrs. Cupples. — Little May, by M. Panott.

Merry Madge. Bruce, E. M. 75c. .... *Universalist.*

Merry mice, and other stories. ill. 4°. '76. pap., 25c. *Lothrop.*

Merry stories. Goodrich, S. G. $2 .... *Miller.*

Merry voices. Stewart, N. C. 50c. ...... *Brainard.*

Merry widow. Buckingham, L. 15c. .... *French.*

Merry wives of Windsor. *See* Ditson.

Merry wives of Windsor. *See* Shakespeare, W:

Merton. *See* Hook, Thdr.

Mervyn Clitheroe. *See* Ainsworth, W: H.

Méry, Jos. Through thick and thin; or, "La guerre du Nizam;" tr. by O. Vibeur. 12°. $1.75 .. *Carleton.*

— *See also* Cross of Berny.

Merz, K: Method for reed organ. obl. 4°. $2.50. *Brainard.*

— Miriam's song of triumph. [Cantata.] f°. $1.50. *Brainard.*

— Musical hints for the million. 12°. $1; 50c. *Brainard.*

— — *See also* Brainard, G. W., New method for pianoforte.

— Runaway flirt. [Operetta.] roy. 8°. $1 .. *Brainard.*

Mess, J. Speller and first German reader. 16°. '60. bds., 25c. .... *Ivison.*

— *See also* Sanders, C. W., *and* Mess, J.

Message from the sea. *See* Dickens, C:

Message to a sick child. 32°. 20c.; 15c. .... *Dutton.*

Message to the "sovereign people" of the U. S. Blanchard, C. 25c. .... *D. Thomas.*

Messages of the presidents. *See* United States.

Messenger ser. 8 v. 12°. '71–'76. ea., $1.50. *Cunningham.*

Cont.: Leandro, by J. S. — Simon Peter and Simon Magus, by J. J. Franco. — Acts of the early martyrs, by J. A. M. Fastre, 4 v. — Tigranes, by J. J. Franco. — Acolyte, by T. Hughes.

Messiah. *See* Handel, G. F.

Messiahship of Jesus. Frey, J. S. C. F. 90c. *Am. Bapt.*

Meta (*pseud.*) *See* Lewis, *Mrs.* Ma.

Meta Gray. McIntosh, M. J. 75c. .... *Appleton.*

Metamora. Brougham, J. 15c. .... *French.*

Metaphors of St. Paul. Howson, J. S. $1.50. *Routledge.*

Meta's faith. Tabor, E. 50c. .... *Harper.*

Metcalf, A. *See* Pickert, C., *and* Metcalf, A.

Metcalf, Ja. W. Homœopathic provings. 8°. $1.50. *Boericke.*

Metcalf, R: Letter and spirit. (Winchester lectures.) ('70.) 6th ed. 16°. '76. 60c. .... *Am. Unit.*

Metcalf, Theron. Principles of law of contracts; with examples of their application. 8°. '67. shp., $4.50 .... *Hurd & H.*

— *See also* Massachusetts, Sup. Court reports; — United States, Digest.

Metcalfe, J. P. *See* Kentucky, Court of Appeals reports.

Metcalfe, S: L. Caloric: its mechanical, chemical and vital agencies in the phenomena of nature. 2 v. 8°. '59. $5 ... *Claxton; Lippincott.*

Metcalfe, W: Out of the clouds into the light: 17 discourses upon leading doctrines of the Christian church. 12°. $1.75 ... *Lippincott.*

Meted out: drama. 16°. pap., 15c. ... *French.*

Meteor. Leslie, E. 50c. ... *G.D.Russell.*

Meteyard, Eliza. ["Silverpen."] Doctor's little daughter. ill. 12°. '72. $2 ... *Routledge.*

— Dora and her papa. ill. 12°. $1.75 ... *Routledge.*

— Josiah Wedgwood and his works: selection of his choicest plaques, medallions, cameos, etc., from designs by Flaxman and others; reproduced in photog.; with sketch of life of Wedgwood, and of progress of his art manufacture. imp. 4°. ill. $30 ... *Macmillan.*

— Lillian's golden hours. ill. 12°. $1.50 ... *Routledge.*

— Mainstone's housekeeper. 12°. $1.50 ... *Loring.*

Methfessel, A. G. Arithmetical primer. 4°. pap., 15c. ... *Lee & S.*

Methinks I see my father. Morton, T. 15c. ... *French.*

Method for the melodeon. *See* New.

Method of grace. Flavel, J. 90c. ... *Am. Tr.*

Method of grace. *See* Hollatz, D.

Methodism and its methods. Crane, J. T. $1.50. *Meth. Bk. Conc.*

Methodism forty years ago and now. Culver, N. $1.25 ... *Meth. Bk. Conc.*

Methodism in earnest; with introd. by T. O. Summers. 12°. '58. $1.50 ... *So. Meth.*

Methodist almanac. ('36.) [Annual.] 12°. pap., 10c. *Meth. Bk. Conc.*

Methodist Episcopal Church. Catechism. 4 nos. in 1 v. 24°. 40c. ... *Meth. Bk. Conc.*

— Centenary singer; comp. by committee of Gen. Conf. sq. 12°. $1 ... *Meth. Bk. Conc.*

— Changes in discipline made by Gen. Conf. of 1868. 12°. '71. pap., 20c. ... *Meth. Bk. Conc.*

— Discipline. 16°. '59. 50c.; leath., $1.10 .. *Dulany.*

— *Same.* 24°. '44. 25c.; 50c.; mor., $1. — 12°. $1.25; mor., $1.75 ... *Meth. Bk. Conc.*

— *Swedish.* 24°. 60c. ... *Cin. Meth. Bk. Conc.*

— General Conference journals, 1796–1856. 3 v. 8°. ea., shp., $3. — 1860–'64. 2 v. ea., $3.50. — 1868–'72. 2 v. ea., $4 ... *Meth. Bk. Conc.*

— General rules. 24°. '69. 10c.; — with ritual, 20c. *Meth. Bk. Conc.*

— Hymnal. 24°. ('59.) 75c.–$2.25. — 18°. $1.25–$3.50. — 12°. $1.80–$4.50 ... *Dulany.*

— Hymns. 48°. '61. 65c.–$4.75. — 24°. '37. 80c.–$10. — 18°. '49. $1.20–$7. — 12°. '38. $1.75–$5. — 8°. $3.50–$8 ... *Meth. Bk. Conc.*

— Lesser hymnal. 18°. 45c.; 50c. ... *Meth. Bk. Conc.*

— Minutes of the annual conferences, v. 2, 3, 5, 6 (1829–'57). 4 v. 8°. ea., shp., $3. — v. 7–9 ('58–'63). 3 v. ea., $3. — v. 10–15 ('64–'75). 6 v. ea., $4. — '52–'53. 2 v. ea., pap., 35c. — '54–'56. 3 v. ea., 40c. — '57–'62. 6 v. ea., 70c. — '63–'65. 3 v. ea., $1. — '66–'68. 3 v. ea., $1.50. — '69–'74. 6 v. ea., $1 ... *Meth. Bk. Conc.*

— *Same.* 1845–'58, 1858–'65. 2 v. 8°. '70. ea., $3; shp., $3.50. — 1866–'69. 8°. '70. pap., $1.50. — 1870–'74. 5 v. 8°. '71–'75. ea., pap., 50c. *So. Meth.*

— Pictorial catechism. sq. 8°. $1 ... *Meth. Bk. Conc.*

— Report of the N. Y. State convention. 8°. '70. $1. *Meth. Bk. Conc.*

— Ritual. 12°. '50. 50c.; 75c. 8°. $1.50; mor., $2. *Meth. Bk. Conc.*

— *See also* New hymn and tune book.

Methodist Episcopal Church, *South.* Discipline; ed. by T. O. Summers. ('46.) New ed., rev. 24°. '74. 50c. — 12°. $1.25; $1.75; mor., $3 .. *So. Meth.*

Methodist Episcopal Church, *South, continued.*

— *Span.* 24°. '74. 50c. ... *So. Meth.*

— Journal of the Gen. Conf., 1858; ed by T. O. Summers. 12°. pap., 50c. — 1866. 12°. pap., 50c. — 1870. 12°. pap., 75c. — 1874. 12°. pap., 75c. *So. Meth.*

Methodist in search of the church. McMasters, S. Y. 75c. ... *Dutton.*

Methodist social hymn book. 24°. 50c. .. *Meth. Bk. Conc.*

Methodius, Alexander *of Lycopolis, and* Peter *of Alexandria.* Writings, with other fragments; [tr. by W. R. Clark and others]. (Ante-Nicene Christ. lib.) 8°. $3 ... *Scribner, W. & A.*

Methods of human science and divine revelation. Wilkinson, G. $5 ... *Lippincott.*

Método fácil para aprender á escribir. 5 nos. 8°. per doz., pap., $2.40 ... *Appleton.*

Metrical romances. Ellis, G. $2 ... *Lippincott.*

Métromanie (La). Piron, A. 50c. ... *Lippincott.*

Metropolitan [old ser. of readers]. 4 v. 16° .. *Sadlier.*
Cont.: First reader, 25c. — Second reader, 45c. — Speller and definer, 45c. — Spelling book, 25c.

Metropolitan [new ser. of readers]. 6 v. ... *Sadlier.*
Cont.: New first reader, 16°, 25c. — New second, 16°, 45c. — New third, 16°, 60c. — New fourth, 12°, 75c. — New fifth, 12°, $1.13. — New sixth, 12°, $1.50.

Mettenheimer, H. J. Safety book-keeping: exposition of book-keeper's frauds. 18°. '75. $1 .. *Clarke.*

Metz, A. Anatomy and physiology of the human eye. ill. 8°. $2 ... *Brinton.*

Metz, Conrad Mart. Studies for drawing the human figure: copper-pl. engravings, eng. by E. Scott, R. Gilchrist, T. Barrow, etc. f°. hf. mor., $7.50. *Porter.*

Meunier, Vct. Adventures on the great hunting grounds of the world. ill. 12°. '73. $1.25 .. *Scribner.*

Mexico. Mining laws. *See* Congdon, H. B.

Meyer, E. *See* Gorling, A., Meyer, E., *and* Woltman, A.

Meyer, H: A: W: Critical and exegetical comment. on New Test. v. 1–6. 8°. ea., $3 .. *Scribner, W. & A.*
Cont.: Galatians — Romans, 2 v. — St. John, 2 v. — Philippians and Colossians.

Meyer, J: G: *See* Meyer von Bremen.

Meyer, Moritz. Electricity in its rel. to practical medicine; tr., with notes and add., by W. A. Hammond. ill. 8°. $4.50 ... *Appleton.*

Meyer von Bremen gallery: photos. with por., biog. and descript. text by D. O'C. Townley. f°. $36; mor., $50 ... *Stroefer.*

Meyerbeer, Giac. Africaine (L'). *See* Ditson.

— Dinorah: Le pardon de Ploërmel; with Ital. words, and Eng. words by H. F. Chorley. [Opera.] 4°. bds., $4 ... *Ditson.*

— — *See also* Ditson.

— Etoile (L') du nord; — Huguenots (Les); — Prophète (Le); — Robert, le diable. *See* Ditson.

Meynert, T. *See* Manual of histology.

Meyr, M. Zwei Freier; [also] Auf d. Universität, v. Theod. Storm. 12°. '64. pap., 30c. ... *Steiger.*

Meystre, Ja. E: Life of Meystre, the blind, deaf mute. 18°. 30c. ... *Am. S. S.*

Mi abuela facil: colleccion nueva de historias para niños. 12 v. ill. 8°. $2 ... *Appleton.*

Mi hermano Ben. *See* My brother Ben.

Mia and Charlie. Keary, A. 75c. ... *Carter; Dutton.*

Mice at play. Floyd, C. $1.50 ... *Roberts.*

Mice in council. *See* Stories about animals ser.

Michael, *St.* *See* Lives of the saints.

Michael, der Bergmann. 18°. 30c. ... *Ev. Assoc.*

Michael, the miner. *See* Craik, *Mrs.* D. M.

Michael Dwyer. Campion, J. T. $1 ... *Kenedy.*

Michael Erle. Wilks, T. E. 15c. ... *French.*

Michael Graham. 18°. 50c. . . . . *McCauley.*
Michael Kemp. 18°. 60c. . . . . *Carter.*
Michael Lorio's cross. *See* Smith, H.
Michael Penguyne. *See* Kingston, W. H. G.
Michael Rudolph. Dupuy, E. A. $1.75. . . *Peterson.*
Michaelis, O. E. The Le Boulengé chronograph. pl. 4°. '72. $3. . . . . *Van Nostrand.*
Michaux, François And. North Am. sylva: descript. of forest trees of U. S., Canada and Nova Scotia (3 v.); contin. by T: Nuttall (2 v.) 5 v. col. pl. imp. 8°. hf. mor., $70; mor., $75. *Lippincott; Rice.*
— *Same.* 5 v. col. pl. imp. 8°. '65. hf. mor., $75. . *Estes.*
Michel, Fernand. Story of the stick. 16°. '75. $1.50. *Bouton.*
Michel, M. *See* Lockroy, —, *and* Michel, M.
Michelet, *Mme.* Athanaise. Nature; or, poetry of earth and sea, tr.; ill. by Giacomelli. imp. 8°. '72. mor., $6; $12. . . . . *Nelson.*
Michelet, Jul. Bird (The), tr.; ill by Giacomelli. imp. 8°. '69. $5; mor., $10.50. . . . . *Nelson.*
— Elements of mod. hist.; tr., with introd., notes, etc., by A. Potter. 18°. 75c. . . . . *Harper.*
— Historical view of Fr. rev.; tr. by C. Cocks. 12°. (Bohn.) $1.25. . . . . *Little, B. & Co.*
— *Same.* 12°. (Bohn.) $1.40. . . . . *Scribner, W. & A.*
— *Same.* 12°. (Bohn.) $1.50. . . . . *Lippincott.*
— History of France; tr. by W. K. Kelley. 2 v. 8°. $4; hf. cf., $8. . . . . *Appleton.*
— In India; tr. 8°. $1.25. . . . . *Nelson.*
— Insect (The), tr.; ill. by Giacomelli. imp. 8°. '74. $5; mor., $10.50. . . . . *Nelson.*
— Life of Luther. *See* Luther, Mt.
— Love; tr. 12°. $1.50. . . . . *Carleton.*
— Mountain (The), tr.; ill. by P. Skelton and C. Stanton. imp. 8°. '72. $5; mor., $10.50. . . . *Nelson.*
— Roman republic; tr. by W. Hazlitt. 12°. (Bohn.) $1.25. . . . . *Little, B. & Co.*
— *Same.* 12°. (Bohn.) $1.40. . . . . *Scribner, W. & A.*
— *Same.* 12°. (Bohn.) $1.50. . . . . *Lippincott.*
— Romish confessional; tr. 8°. pap., 50c. . . *Peterson.*
— Seal (The), tr.; ill. by Giacomelli. imp. 8°. '75. $5. . . . . *Nelson.*
— Summary of modern history; tr. and contin. to present time by M. C. M. Simpson. 12°. '75. $1.75. . . . . *Macmillan.*
— Woman; tr. 12°. $1.50. . . . . *Carleton.*
Micheline. Bersier, E. 75c. . . . . *Dutton.*
Michels, Ph. Lesefibel. [Henze's Schrift.] 12°. '72. bds., 25c. . . . . *Knœfel.*
Michie, P: S. Report on fabrication of iron, etc. *See* United States, *Corps of Eng.*
Michigan. Court of Chancery reports [1838-'42]; by E. B. Harrington. 2d ed.; with notes and ref. to late decisions by T. M. Cooley. 8°. '72. $5. *Richmond.*
— *Same.* 1842-'45; by H. N. Walker. [Reprint.] 8°. shp., $6. . . . . *Richmond.*
— Laws. *See* Dewey, J. S.
— Nisi prius reports, 1869-'71; by C. R. Brown. 2 v. 8°. . . . . *State.*
— Probate law. *See* Cheever, N. W.
— Supreme, Circuit, Chancery and Superior Court rules; rev. by H. Post. 8°. '76. shp., $3. . *Richmond.*
— Supreme Court reports, 1843-'47; by S. T. Douglass. 2 v. 8°. '46-'49. $14. . . . . *Richmond.*
— *Same.* v.1-31 (1847-'75). 31 v. 8°. '52-'76. . *Richmond.*

Cont.: 1 (1847-'50), by R. Manning, $12. — 2-4 (1851-'57), by G. C. Gibbs, $28. — 5-12 (1858-'64), by T. M. Cooley, $72. — 13 (1864-5), by E. W. Meddaugh, $6. — 14-18 (1865-'69), by W. Jennison, $27.50. — 19 (1869-'70), by H. R. Clarke, $7.50. — 20-22 (1870-1), by H. K. Clarke, $12. — 23-31 (1871-'75), by H. Post, ea., $3.

— — Digest. *See* Chaney, H. A.; — Cooley, E. A.
Michigan geological survey. Report of State geologist, 1838-9. 8°. . . . . *State.*
Michigan lawyer (The). 2 v. 8°. '75-'76. ea., shp., $2. . . . . *Richmond.*
Michigan State Medical Soc. Transactions, 1868-'76. 9 v. 8°. ea., pap., 50c. . . . . *Mich. Med.*
Mick Healy. Gregg, J. 40c. . . . . *So. Meth.*
Mick Tracy. C., W. A. $1.50. . . . . *Am. Bapt.*
Mickle, I: Reminiscences of old Gloucester, N. J. 12°. '76. $2. . . . . *Chew.*
Mickleborough, J: *See* Keam, P., *and* Mickleborough, J:
Microcosm (The). Coles, A. $2.25. . . . . . *Appleton.*
Midas. O'Hara, K. 15c. . . . . *French.*
Middle kingdom. Williams, S. W. 2 v. $4. . *Wiley.*
Middle life. Graves, J. R. 75c. . . . . *So. Bapt.*
Middle temple (The): farce. 16°. pap., 15c. . . *Happy.*
Middlemarch. *See* Eliot, G:
Middleton, A. C. Festival of Ashtaroth: a tale of Palestine. 12°. pap., 15c. . . . . *Mendum.*
Middleton, J. G. *See* England, Law reports.
Middy ashore. Bernard, W. B. 15c. . . . . *French.*
Midnight banquet: drama. 16°. pap., 15c. . . *French.*
Midnight chimes. Marsh, C. 35c. . . . . *Carter.*
Midnight harmonies. Winslow, O. $1. . . . . . *Carter.*
Midnight hour. Inchbald, E. S. 15c. . . . . *French.*
Midnight Jack. 8°. pap., 25c. . . . . *De Witt.*
Midnight queen. 8°. pap., 25c. . . . . *Dick & F.*
Midnight sea. 18°. 30c. . . . . *Dutton.*
— *See also* Revellers.
Midnight sun. Bremer, F. 25c. . . . . *Harper.*
Midnight, 13th chime: melodrama. 16°. pap., 15c. *French.*
Midnight watch. Morton, J. M. 15c. *De Witt; French.*
Midshipman (The). Kingston, W. H. G. $1.25. *Lippincott.*
Midshipman Easy (*pseud.*) David Watson; or, the pirate cutter. 8°. pap., 25c. . . . . *Dick & F.*
Midshipman Easy. *See* Marryat, F:
Midshipman in China: recollections of the Chinese. 18°. 45c. . . . . *Am. S. S.*
Midsummer eve. Hall, A. M. 50c. . . . . *Harper.*
Midsummer fays. *See* Fireside lib.
Midsummer night's dream. *See* Shakespeare, W:
Mietzka, G: A. Columbia: patriotic cantata. 8°. 38c. . . . . *Gordon.*
Miffitt, *Mrs.* A. S. Only a pauper. ('59.) New ed. ill. 16°. '75. $1.25. . . . . *Hoyt.*
Might and mirth of literature. Macbeth, J. W. V. $2.50. . . . . *Harper.*
Might and right books. *See* Cupples, *Mrs.* A. J.
Mighty worker. *See* Clark, G. W.
Mignet, François Auguste Alexis. History of the French revolution, 1789-1814; tr. 12°. (Bohn.) $1.25. . . . . *Little, B. & Co.*
— *Same.* 12°. (Bohn.) $1.40. . . . . . . *Scribner, W. & A.*
— *Same.* 12°. (Bohn.) $1.50. . . . . *Lippincott.*
Mignon. *See* Ditson.
Mignon; tr. from the Fr. 12°. $1.25; $1.75. . *O'Shea.*
Mignonette. Bingham, H. A. $1.50. . . *Universalist.*
Mijatovics, *Mme.* Elodie Lawton. Serbian folk lore: popular tales sel. and tr. by Mme. M.; ed. by W. Denton. 8°. '74. $3. . . . . *Routledge.*
Mike Fink. Bennett, E. 25c. . . . . *U. P. James.*
Mike Marble. *See* Woodworth, F. C.
Mikseh, —. Solfeggi; adapted by E. S. f°. '68. pap., 60c. . . . . *Ditson.*
Mildenhall, T. Governor's wife: comedy. 16°. pap., 15c. . . . . *French.*
— Post of honour: drama. 16°. pap., 15c. . . . *French.*
Mildred. Craik, G. M. 50c. . . . . *Harper.*

Mildred Arkell. Wood, E. P. $1.75; $1.50.. *Peterson.*
Mildred Gwynne; or, soi-meme: story of a wilful life. ('69.) New ed. 16°. '76. $1.25........ *Hoyt.*
Mile-stones in our life-journey. Osgood, S. $1.50. *Dutton.*
Miles, *Miss* E. E. *See* Hanaford, *Mrs.* P. A., *and* Miles, E. E.
Miles, G: H. Christine, and other poems. 12°. '66. $2........ *Cath. Pub.*
— Review of Shakespeare's Hamlet. 8°. '70. 50c. *Kelly, P. & Co.*
— The truce of God: tale of 11th cent. 18°. '71. $1; $1.50........ *Murphy.*
Miles, H: A. Words of a friend on the foundation, difficulties, helps and triumphs of a religious life. 16°. '70. $1.25........ *Lockwood, B. & Co.*
— *See also* Altar at home.
Miles, J: *See* Philadelphia, Dist. Court Reports.
Miles, S. P., *and* Sherwin, T: Mathematical tables. 8°. hf. bd., $1.10........ *Thompson.*
Miles, W: On the horse's foot. 12°. 75c...... *Judd.*
Miles Lawson; or, the yews. ('60.) New ed. ill. 18°. '75. 55c........ *Hoyt.*
Miles Standish. *See* Longfellow, H: W.
Miles Wallingford. *See* Cooper, Ja. F.
Milet, Pierre. Relation de sa captivité parmi les Onneiouts en 1690-'91. 8°. '64. pap., $2....... *Shea.*
Miley, J: Class-meetings. 18°. 70c. *Cin. Meth. Bk. Conc.*
Milford, Flo. Holiday tales. ill. 16°. 75c.... *Nelson.*
Military anecdotes. 16°. '73. bds., 50c... *Routledge.*
Milk and honey. Norton, J. N. $1.25...... *Dutton.*
Milk for babes. *See* Schieffelin, S. B.
Milk for babes: texts for every day. 64°. '48. 15c.; 20c........ *Am. Tr.*
— *See also* Children's bread.
Milk-white dove; or, little Jacob's temptation. 18°. 30c........ *Am. S. S.*
Milky white. Craven, H. T. 15c... *De Witt; French.*
Mill, J. *See* South Carolina, Constitutional Court reports.
Mill, J: *See* Bible, New Test., *Greek.*
Mill, J: Stuart. Miscellaneous works. 12 v. large 12°. '73-'75. ea., $2.50........ *Holt.*
Cont.: Autobiography. — Considerations on representative government. — Dissertations and discussions, polit., philos. and historical, 5 v. — Examinations of Sir W: Hamilton's philosophy, 2 v. — On liberty; Subjection of women. — Three essays on religion. — Positive philosophy of Auguste Comte, $1.50.
— Inaugural address at Univ. of St. Andrews on university education. 8°. '67. pap., 25c... *Littell & G.*
— Inexpediency of an irredeemable paper currency. 8°. '75. 20c........ *Hinton.*
— Memorial volume, his life and works: sketches by Fox, H. Spencer, H. Fawcett, F. Harrison and others. 16°. '73. $1........ *Holt.*
— Principles of polit. economy. cr. 8°. $2.50 .. *Lee & S.*
— *Same.* cr. 8°. (Lond.) '67. $2.50 .. *Little, B. & Co.*
— *Same.* 2 v. 8°. $6; hf. cf., $10; cf., $12.. *Appleton.*
— Subjection of women. 12°. '70. $1.25....... *Holt.*
— System of logic, ratiocinative and inductive. 8°. $3; shp., $3.50........ *Harper.*
— *and* Froude, J. A., *and* Carlyle, T: Scottish University addresses. ('69.) 3d ed. 24°. '72. pap., 25c........ *Schermerhorn.*
Mill girls at Roswell's paper mill. 18°. 55c... *Am. S. S.*
Mill on the Floss. *See* Eliot, G:
Millar, W. J. Principles of mechanics, and their applic. to prime movers, naval architecture, iron bridges, water supply, etc.: lectures, Univ. of Glasgow, 1872-3. cr. 8°. '74. $2........ *Spon.*
Millard, Harrison. Mass in G. 8°. $1.25; pap., $1. *Gordon.*
— Sacred quartet. obl. 4°. $2.75; bds., $2.50.. *Gordon.*
— Silver threads of song. 12°. 60c......... *Gordon.*
Millard, Harrison, *continued.*
— Vespers. f°. $2........ *Gordon.*
— Vocalist's text book. ('69.) New ed. 4°. '76. $3.75. *Pond.*
— *See also* Cooper, G., *and* Millard, H.
Millard, H: B. Climate and statistics of consumption. 12°. 75c........ *Boericke.*
— Guide for emergencies: homoeop. treatment of diseases requiring immediate attention, without a physician. 3d ed. obl. 18°. '71. 75c... *Hurlburt.*
Millbank. Holmes, M. J. $1.50........ *Carleton.*
Millennial experience. Underwood, A. $1.50.. *Hoyt.*
Miller, B. W. *See* Louisiana, Sup. Court reports.
Miller, C. C. *See* Cummings, M. F., *and* Miller, C. C.
Miller, *Mrs.* C. S. The victory won. ill. 16°. '76. $1. *Am. Tr.*
Miller, C. W. Apostolical succession. 18°. '72. 60c. *So. Meth.*
— Baptismal regeneration. 16°. pap., 25c. *S. W. Bk. & Pub.*
— Infant baptism. 16°. 75c. .... *S. W. Bk. & Pub.*
— Points of controversy on mode of baptism. 16°. 75c. *S. W. Bk. & Pub.*
— Southern review and infant baptism; or, Methodist literature vindicated against attacks of A. T. Bledsoe. 12°. '74. pap., 25c........ *So. Meth.*
Miller, Cincinnatus Hiner. *See* Miller, Joaquin.
Miller, D: Prince. Life of a showman, and the managerial struggles of D. P. Miller. 16°. pap., 40c. *French.*
Miller, E. Christian assurance. 18°. '75. 35c.; bds., 40c........ *Meth. Epis.*
Miller, *Mrs.* Eliz. S. In the kitchen. [Cook book.] 4°. $2.50........ *Lee & S.*
Miller, Emily Huntington. Parish of Fair Haven. 16°. '76. 15c........ *Un. Bk. Conc.*
— Royal road to fortune. ill. 12°. '75. $1.50. *Meth. Bk. Conc.*
Miller, G. Practical Christianity. 18°. '71. 50c. *Ev. Assoc.*
— *Germ.* Das thätige Christenthum. 18°. 40c. *Ev. Assoc.*
Miller, *Rev.* G: History philosophically considered. 4 v. 12°. (Bohn.) ea., $1.25.... *Little, B. & Co.*
— *Same.* 4 v. 12°. (Bohn.) ea., $1.40.. *Scribner, W. & A.*
— *Same.* 4 v. 12°. (Bohn.) ea., $1.50...... *Lippincott.*
Miller, Hu. Works. 10 v. 12°. ea., $1.50 .. *Carter.*
Cont.: Cruise of the Betsey. — Essays. — First impressions of England. — Footprints of the Creator. — Headship of Christ. — My schools and schoolmasters. — Old red sandstone. — Popular geology. — Tales and sketches. — Testimony of the rocks.
— *Same.* 13 v. 12°. hf. cf., $45........ *Routledge.*
— Scenes and legends of the north of Scotland. ('52.) New ed. 12°. '60. $1.50........ *Wilstach.*
Miller, *Mrs.* Hu. *See* Miller, *Mrs.* L. F.
Miller, J. D: Treasury pictures. ill. 16°. 60c. *Ref. Ch. Pub.*
Miller, J. R. *See* Hume, D:
Miller, Ja. Alcohol: its place and power. 12°. '73. 75c........ *Lindsay.*
— *Same;* [also] Use and abuse of tobacco, by J. Lizars. 12°. '73. $1........ *Lindsay.*
— — *Same.* ('67.) New ed. 12°. '75. $1.. *Nat. Temp*
— Practice of surgery. ill. 8°. $3.75........ *Lea.*
— Principles of surgery. ill. 8°. $3.75........ *Lea.*
Miller, Joaquin. [Cincinnatus Hiner Miller.] First fam'lies of the Sierras. [Fiction.] 3d ed. 12°. '76. $1.50........ *Jansen.*
— One fair woman (The). [Fiction.] 12°. $2.. *Carleton.*
— Ship in the desert. [Poem.] 16°. '75. $1.50.. *Roberts.*
— Songs of the Sierras. 16°. '71. $1.50.... *Roberts.*
— Songs of the sun lands. 16°. '73. $1.50.. *Roberts.*
— Unwritten history; or, life among the Modocs. ill. 8°. *$3; $3.50; hf. cf., $4.50........ *Am. Pub.*
Miller, J: Commentary on Proverbs; with new tr., and some of the orig. expositions re-exam. in a classified list. 8°. '73. $4........ *Randolph.*
— Fetich in theology; or, doctrinalism akin to ritualism. 12°. '74. $1.25........ *Dodd.*

Miller, J: *continued.*
— Metaphysics, the science of perception. 8°. '74. $2.50. *Dodd.*

Miller, Josiah. Singers and songs of the church: biog. sketch of hymn-writers; with notes on their psalms and hymns. 12°. '74. $4 .... *Randolph.*

Miller, Leo. Woman and the divine republic. 8°. '74. $1.25 .... (?) *Haas.*

Miller, *Mrs.* Lydia Falconer. Anecdotes of animals; or, two great families of the animal kingdom. ill. 12°. '69. $1.50 .... *Lothrop.*

Miller, M. R. The luminous unity: letters to A. Guinzburg on Is Unitarianism, as opposed to Trinitarianism, a principle of heathenism rather than of specific Judaism? 12°. $1.50 .... *Lippincott.*

Miller, *Miss* Ma. Christina. Ned and Sydney. 16°. '74. 75c. .... (?) *Cumberland.*

Miller, *Mrs.* Ma. E. Bertie's fall. ill. 18°. '74. 45c. *Am. Tr.*
— Bessie Kirkland. ill. 18°. '74. 60c. ...... *Am. Tr.*
— Holly books. 6 v. ill. 32°. '73. $1.50 ... *Am. Tr.*
— Little Margery. ill. sm. 4°. '73. 90c. .... *Am. Tr.*
— Old Mr. Pro. 16°. 75c. .... *Cong. Pub.*
— Riverside farmhouse. ill. 18°. '76. 45c. .. *Am. Tr.*

Miller, *Mrs.* O. D. Twilight stories. 16°. '66. $1. *Universalist.*

Miller, Ol. *See* Stockett, J. S., Merrick, R. T., *and* Miller, O.; — Maryland, Court of Appeals reports.

Miller, R. H. Doctrine of the Brethren defended: faith and practise of the Brethren proven by the Gospel to be true. 12°. '76. $1.60 .... *Brumbaugh.*

Miller, R. Kalley. Romance of astronomy. 2d ed., rev. and enl. cr. 8°. '75. $1.25 ..... *Macmillan.*

Miller, S: Life of Rev. S: Miller. 2 v. por. 12°. '69. $4.50 .... *Claxton.*
— Life of J. Edwards. *See* Sparks, J., Lib. of Am. biog.

Miller, *Rev.* S: Christian ministry; or, the primitive and apostolic order of the church of Christ vindicated. 12°. $1 .... *Pres. Bd.*
— Essay on warrant, nature and duties of ruling elder in the Presb. Church. 18°. 75c. ...... *Pres. Bd.*
— *Same.* 18°. 40c. .... (?) *Martien.*
— Letters from a father to his sons in college. por. 12°. 75c. .... *Pres. Bd.*
— Letters on clerical manners and habits. por. 12°. $1.25 .... *Pres. Bd.*
— Letters on observance of the monthly concert in prayer. 18°. 35c. .... *Pres. Bd.*
— Memoir of Rev. J: Rodgers. por. 18°. 60c. .. *Pres. Bd.*
— Mercersburg and modern theology compared. 16°. 60c. .... *Ref. Ch. Pub.*
— Presbyterianism the primitive constitution of the church of Christ; [also] Infant baptism Scriptural and reasonable; [also] Baptism by sprinkling the most suitable mode. 12°. 70c. .... *Pres. Bd.*
— Thoughts on public prayer. por. 12°. $1. *Pres. Bd.*
— Utility and importance of creeds and confessions. 18°. 40c. .... *Pres. Bd.*
— *and* Janeway, J. J. Christian educ. of children and youth in the Presb. Church. 18°. 30c. ... *Pres. Bd.*

Miller, S: F. *See* United States, Circ. Court reports; Sup. Court decisions.

Miller, Ste. F. Bench and bar of Georgia: memoirs and sketches. 2 v. 8°. '58. $5 .. *Claxton; Lippincott.*
— Wilkins Wylder; or, the successful man. 12°. $1. *Lippincott.*

Miller, T: [Juveniles.] 7 v. ill. .... *Routledge.*

Cont.: Boy's country book, 16°, $2.50. — British wolf hunters, 16°, 50c. — Child's country book, sq. 12°, $1.50. — Child's country story book, sq. 12°, $1.50. — Fred and the gorillas, 16°, $1.25. — Jack of all trades, 16°, 75c. — My father's garden, cr. 8°, $2.50.

— Common wayside flowers. col. ill. sm. 4°. $5. *Routledge.*

Miller, T: *continued.*
— History of the Anglo-Saxons; on the basis of S Turner. ill. 12°. (Bohn.) $1.75 .. *Little, B. & Co*
— *Same.* ill. 12°. (Bohn.) $2. *Lippincott; Scribner, W. & A*
— Little Bessie's country stories. 6 v. 32°. $1.50. *Sheldon*
— Little Blue Hood. ill. sq. 12°. '66. 60c. .. *Hurd & H*
— *See also* Little Rosy's travels; — Violet stories.

Miller, W. G. Thirty years in the itinerancy. ('75.) 2d ed. 12°. '76. $1.50 .... *Hauser*

Miller, W: Allen. Elements of chemistry. 3 v. 8° $18 .... *Wiley*

Cont.: Chemical physics, $4. — Inorganic chemistry, $6. — Organic chemistry, $10.

— Introduction to study of inorganic chemistry. ill 12°. $1.50 .... *Appleton*
— Magnetism and electricity. 8°. $2.50 .... *Wiley*

Miller, W: E. Treatise on pleading and practice in Iowa, under code of 1873. New ed., rev. 8°. '75 shp., $7.50 .... *Mills*

Miller and his men. Pocock, I. 15c. .... *French*

Miller and his men. Talfourd, F., *and* Byron, H. J. 15c. .... *French*

Miller and his men; or, the secret robbers of Bohemia. 8°. pap., 25c. .... *U. P. James*

Miller of Angibault. Sand, G. $1.50 .... *Roberts*

Miller of Derwent-water. Ball, E. 15c. .. *Ames; French.*

Miller of Mansfield. Dodsley, R. 15c. ...... *French*

Miller of New Jersey. Brougham, J. 15c. ... *French.*

Miller of Silcott mill. Deslonde, M. D. $1.75. *Carleton.*

Miller of Whetstone. Wilks, T. E. 15c. .... *French.*

Miller's daughter. *See* May Carleton's story.

Miller's guide to Central Park [N. Y.] ill. and maps. 16°. $1 .... *Miller.*

Miller's guide to the Hudson River. ill. and map. 16°. $1; pap., 50c. .... *Miller.*

Miller's guide to Saratoga Springs and its vicinity. ill. 16°. 75c. .... *Miller.*

Miller's maid. Saville, J. F. 15c. .... *French.*

Miller's story of the war. Erckmann, E., *and* Chatrian, A. $1.25; bds., 75c. .... *Scribner.*

Millhouse, J: New English-and-Italian pronounc. and explan. dict. 2 v. sm. 8°. hf. bd., $6 .. *Appleton.*

Millicent Courtenay's diary. Kingston, W. H. G. $1.75 .... *Routledge.*

Millicent Legh. Marshall, E. $1.25 .... (?) *Martien.*

Millicent's home. Temple, C. 70c. .... *Am. Tr.*

Millie and her two friends. *See* New holiday lib.

Millie Lee. Porter, A. E. $1.50 .... *Lothrop.*

Milligan, Rob. Analysis of the four Gospels and Acts; with queries and ill. for Sunday schools, families, etc. 8°. $2 .... *Chase.*
— Brief treatise on prayer. 24°. 50c. 32°. pap., 10c. *Chase.*
— Commentary on Hebrews. cr. 8°. *$2; shp., $2.50; hf. cf., $3 .... *Chase.*
— Grace and good works; or, the divine and human agency in the work of human redemption. 24°. pap., 10c. .... *Chase.*
— Reason and revelation: province of reason in matters pertaining to divine revelation defined and ill. cr. 8°. $2 .... *Chase.*
— Scheme of redemption, as revealed and taught in the Holy Scriptures. cr. 8°. $2 .... *Chase.*

Milliner's holiday. Morton, J. M. 15c. ..... *French.*

Millingen, J. V. Bee hive: farce. 16°. pap., 15c. *French.*
— Ladies at home: dram. interlude. 16°. pap., 15c. *French.*
— *See also* Kenney, J., *and* Millingen, J. V.

Million too much. Wright, J. McN. $1.25 .. *Porter.*

Millionär (Der). *See* Zschokke, H.

Mills, Ab. Ancient Hebrews (The); with essay on the world before the flood. 12°. '56. $1.75..*Barnes*.
— Literature and literary men of Great Britain and Ireland. 2 v. 8°. $4; shp., $5; hf. cf., $8.25. *Harper*.
— *See also* Blair, H., Rhetoric and belles-lettres.
Mills, C: D. B. The Indian saint; or, Buddha and Buddhism. cr. 8°. '75. $1.50 ....*Miller*.
Mills, F: Ja. Life of John Carter. ill. cr. 8°. '68. $1.50 ....*Hurd & H.*
Mills, Ja. D. Art of money making; or, the road to fortune. ill. 8°. '72. $2 ....*Intern*.
Mills, J: *See* Farmer's barn-book.
Mills, Lucy A. Jack Masters; or, the berry-pickers. ill. 16°. '72. $1.50 ....*Crowell*.
— — *See also* Father Merrill ser.
— Peter's strange story. ill. 16°. '73. $1.50..*Lothrop*.
Mills, Ma. Truth; or, Frank's choice. 32°. 40c. *Scribner, W. & A.*
Mills, W: *See* England, Law reports.
Mills of the gods. Twells, J. H. $1.50 ..*Lippincott*.
Mills of Tuxbury. Townsend, V. F. $1.25 ..*Loring*.
Milly. *See* Finley, M. F.
Milly; or, the hidden cross. Guernsey, L.E. $1..*Loring*.
Milly Moyne. Smith, J. F. 75c. ....*Dick & F.*
Milly's doves. *See* Minnie's lib.; — Moss rose ser.
Milly's errand; or, saved to save. 18°. 60c. (?)*Martien*.
Milly's lib. 5 v. 18°. $3 ....(?)*Martien*.
Cont.: Milly's errand. — Johnny Wilks. — Ruth Lee. — Lads of Heatherwood. — Katie Lawford's victory.

Milly's taper. McKeever, H. B. $1.15 ....*Hoyt*.
Milman, E. H. Arthur Conway; or, scenes in the tropics. [Fiction.] 8°. pap., 50c.....*Harper*.
— The wayside cross; or, the raid of Gomez: a tale of the Carlist war. 8°. pap., 25c..........*Harper*.
Milman, H: Hart. Works. 14 v. 12° ea., $1.75. *Nichols & H.; Pott; Putnam; Widdleton*.
Cont.: History of Christianity, 3 v. — History of the Jews, 3 v. — History of Latin Christianity, 8 v.

— *Same*. 15 v. post 8°. (Lond.) '66–'67. ea., $1.75; per set, hf. cf., $52.50; cf., $75...*Little, B. & Co.*
Cont.: History of Christianity, 3 v. — History of the Jews, 3 v. — History of Latin Christianity, 9 v.

— Fazio: tragedy. 16°. pap., 15c..........*French*.
— History of Christianity, from the birth of Christ to the abolition of paganism in the Roman empire; with notes by J. Murdock. 8°. $2; hf. cf., $4.25..........*Harper*.
— History of the Jews. 3 v. maps and ill. 18°. $2.25. *Harper*.
— Poetical works. *See* Howitt, W., Milman, H. H., *and* Keats, J.
Milner, Edith. The lily of Lumley. [Fiction.] cr. 8°. '69. $1.50 ....*Macmillan*.
Milner, H. M. [Plays.] 7 v. 16°. ea., pap., 15c...*French*.
Cont.: Fair maid of Perth. — Frankenstein. — Gambler's fate. — Hut of the Red Mountain. — Massaniello: opera. — Mazeppa. — Veteran of 102.

Milner, J: End of religious controversy: correspondence between a relig. soc. of Protestants and a Cath. divine. 12°. 75c..........*Strong*.
— *Same*. 12°. 75c.; pap., 50c..........*Cath. Pub.*
— *Same*. 12°. $1; pap., 50c..........*Sadlier*.
— *Same*. 8°. '51. $1; pap., 75c. ....*Murphy*.
— Key of heaven; or, manual of [Cath.] prayer. ill. 16°. $1.50–$10. — 18°. 90c.–$9......*T. Kelly*.
— *Same*. 32°. '64. 45c.–$9 ....*Murphy*.
— Letters to a prebendary: answer to "Reflections on popery," by J. Sturgis. 24°. 75c. ...*Cath. Pub.*
Milner, T: Half-hour readings for Sunday afternoons; in prose and verse. 12°. $1.25 ....*Nelson*.
— The heavens and the earth: popular book of astronomy. 12°. $1.25..........*Nelson*.

Milner, Vincent L. History of all relig. denominations of the world, with sketches of the founders. New ed., rev. and enl. by J. N. Brown. por. 8°. '74. *$2.75; mor., $3; $3.50..*Bradley, G. & Co.*
Milner, Vincent W. Blessings of an open Bible as shown in the history of Christianity; with add. by J. F. Berg. ill. 12°. $1.75 .....*J. E. Potter*.
Milnes, R: Moncton. *See* Houghton, *Lord*.
Milo, W: Notes on beauty, vigor and development. 12°. '67. pap., 10c..........*Wells*.
Milton, J: Works. ill. 8°. shp., $4.50; mor., $10..*Mason*.
— *Same;* with memoirs. por. 8°. (Dick.) 50c.; pap., 25c..........*Am. News*.
— *Same;* with memoir and crit. remarks by J. Montgomery. ill. 8°. $2; shp., $2.75. 12°. $1.50. *World Pub.*
— Poems. 12°. $1.50 ....*Locke*.
— *Same*. ill. 16°. $1.12; $1.35. — 32°. 85c.; $1.12. *World Pub.*
— *Same*. (Aldine ed.) 3 v. 16°. ea., 75c...*Lippincott*.
— *Same*. (Blue and gold ed.) 18°. $1.25..*Nichols & H.*
— *Same*. (Boston ed.) 8°. shp., $4.50; mor., $10. *Mason*.
— *Same*. (Cabinet ed.) 16°. $1.50 ....*Nichols & H.*
— *Same*. (Scribner's pop. poets.) ill. 12°. $1.50. *Scribner, W. & A.*
— *Same;* ed. by R. A. Willmott, with biog., etc. (Brit. poets.) ill. 12°. $2.25; hf. cf., $3.50; mor., $5 ....*Routledge*.
— *Same;* with memoir by J. Mitford. 3 v. por. 18°. $3.75 ....*Osgood*.
— Poetical works; with life. ill. 16°. $1.25; hf. cf., $3.25; mor., $4. — (chp. ed.) 16°. pap., 60c. — ill. 8°. shp., $3.50; mor., $10.....*Appleton*.
— *Same*. (Chandos classics.) cr. 8°. $1; pap., 75c. *Scribner, W. & A.*
— *Same;* with notes. (Chandos poets.) ill. cr. 8°. $3.75; cf., $7.50; mor., $8 ....*Scribner, W. & A.*
— *Same;* with biog., notes, etc. (Presentation poets.) ill. 12°. $1.75; $3; mor., $3.50.....*Routledge*.
— *Same;* ed. by Sir E. Brydges. (Boston ed.) ill. 8°. shp., $3.50; mor., $10 ....*Lee & S.*
— *Same;* ed. by C. D. Cleveland; with life of M., dissertations on poems, notes, etc. 12°. '64. $2.50 ....*Barnes*.
— *Same;* ed. with life and notes by Prof. Masson. (Golden treas. ed.) 2 v. 18°. '74. $3..*Macmillan*.
— *Same;* ed. with text collated from best authorities; with introd. and notes by D. Masson. 3 v. 8°. '74. $15..........*Macmillan*.
— *Same;* with life and notes by J. Mitford. (Standard ed.) 2 v. 12°. $4; hf. cf., $8..........*Porter*.
— *Same;* with memoir and crit. remarks by J. Montgomery. 12°. $1.50.......... *World Pub.*
— *Same;* with memoir by J. Montgomery, Todd's verbal index and notes. 2 v. ill. 12°. (Bohn.) ea., $1.75 ....*Little, B. & Co.*
— — *Same*. 2 v. ill. 12°. (Bohn.) ea., $2. *Lippincott; Scribner, W. & A.*
— *Same*. New ed., rev. from the text of T. Newton. (Household ser.) ill. 16°. $1.50; mor., $3. *Lee & S.*
— *Same;* [also] Poetical works by E. Young. ill. 8°. $3.50..........*Routledge*.
— *Same;* [also] Poetical works of Young, Gray, Beattie and Collins. ill. 8°. $3; mor., $7; $7.50. *Lippincott*.
— — Concordance. *See* Cleveland, C. D.
— Prose works; with index. 5 v. 12°. (Bohn.) ea., $1.25 ....*Little, B. & Co.*
— *Same*. 5 v. 12°. (Bohn.) ea., $1.40..*Scribner, W. & A.*
— *Same*. 5 v. 12°. (Bohn.) ea., $1.50.......*Lippincott*.
— Allegro (L'). ill. 12°. '75. $1.25..........*Putnam*.
— *Same*. ill. 12°. $2.50; mor., $5..........*Appleton*.
— *Same*. ill. 8°. '74. $3 ....*Routledge*.
— Comus. 16°. pap., 15c. ....*French*.
— *Same;* rendered into Gk. verse by Lord Lyttelton. 2d ed. fp. 8°. '65. $1.75..........*Macmillan*.
— Paradise lost. (School ed.) 18°. 38c....*Clark & M.*
— *Same*. (School ed.) 18°. 38c.......*Nichols & H.*

Milton, J: *continued.*
— *Same;* with notes, by J. R. Boyd. 12°. '50. (Lib. ed.), $1.50. — (School ed.), hf. bd., $1.25. *Barnes.*
— *Same;* with notes and life of author by H. Stebbing and analysis. 32°. 35c. . . . . *U.P.James.*
— *Same;* with notes and life by H. Stebbing. (Lib. ed.) 12°. $1.50. — (School ed.) 18°. 65c. — (Blue and gold ed.) $1.15 . . . . *C.H.Davis.*
— *Same;* with notes prep. under the advice of Prof. Torrey. (Cabinet ed.) ill. 16°. $1.25; $1.75; hf. roxb., $3; mor., $4.50 . . . . *Hurd & H.*
— *Same;* with drawings by Doré; ed., with notes and life of M., by R. Vaughan. New ed. cr. f°. $25; mor., $40; $60 . . . . *Cassell.*
— Samson Agonistes rendered into Gk. verse by Lord Lyttelton. fp. 8°. '67. $2.50 . . . . . . *Macmillan.*
— Treasures from prose writings of M. por. 16°. $2. **Osgood.*
— Treatise of education. *See* Locke, J: Some thoughts conc. education.

Milward, Mar. G. Joys and sorrows of the ecclesiastical year: meditations and poetry. 12°. $1; $1.25; mor., $2.50 . . . . *McCauley.*

Milwood. Porter, A. E. 45c. . . . . *Cong.Pub.*

Mimi; or, the parsonage. Smith, F. I. B. 75c. *Bost. Am. Tr.; Lothrop.*

Mimic (The). Edgeworth, M. 25c. . . . . . . *Routledge.*

Mimic stage. Baker, G. M. $1.50 . . . . *Lee & S.*

Mimic world. Logan, O. *$3.75; $5 . . . . *New World.*

Mimpriss, Rob. Gospel treasury and expository harmony of the four evangelists. cr. 8°. '68. $1.75. — 4°. $7.50 . . . . *Dodd.*
— Gospels in harmony; with notes, ref. and charts. 16°. $1.25. — 18°. 75c.; pap., 60c. . . . . *Dodd.*
— Lessons on life of Christ; harmonized from the four evangelists. 3 grades. 18°. '69. ea., 20c. — Teacher's manuals. 3 grades. 18°. '69. ea., 40c. — Studies. 18°. '69. 40c. . . . . *Dodd.*
— Steps of Jesus: four evangelists combined and arr. in chronol. order, and as a consecutive narrative; with chart. 18°. '68. 75c. . . . . *Dodd.*

Mind and heart in religion. Jaeger, A. $1.25. *Blackall.*

Mind and matter. Brodie, *Sir* B. $1.25 . . . . *W. Wood.*

Mind in nature. Clark, H. J. $3.50 . . . . . . *Appleton.*

Mind of Jesus. *See* Macduff, J. R.

Mind of my own, and the mind of Christ. 18°. 40c.; 50c. *Am.Bapt.*

Mind your own business. Lemon, M. 15c. . . *French.*

Mind your stops; or, punctuation made plain. 16°. 10c. *Dick & F.*

Miné, A. Mass, solennelle, in E flat. 4°. pap., $1.25. *Peters.*

Mine (The). *See* Goodrich, S. G.

Mine (The). *See* Tucker, *Mrs.* C.

Mine explored. Nicholls, B. E. $1.50 . . . . . *Am. S. S.*

Mine of wealth. Fitzgibbon, W. 50c. . . . . . . *Barclay.*

Miner, Alonzo Ames. Bible exercises; or, the Sunday-school one class. 16°. '54. per doz., bds., $3. *Universalist.*

Miner, T. B. Domestic poultry book. ill. 12°. $1.50. *Dick & F.*

Mineral riches of the earth. 18°. 85c. . . . . . *Am.S.S.*

Minerali. Plunkett, H. G. 15c. . . . . *French.*

Miner's children. 18°. 45c. . . . . *Am.S.S.*

Miner's daughter. Caddell, C. M. 60c.; $1 . . *Sadlier.*

Miner's daughter; or, the messenger of truth. 18°. 50c. *Am.S.S.*

Miner's hut. Macallan, E. 25c.; 30c. . . . . . . *Dutton.*

Miner's son. *See* Pollard, M. M.

Mines, Flavel S. Presbyterian clergyman looking for the church. New ed. 12°. '72. $2 . . . *Dutton.*

Miniature blue and gold poets. 6 v. 18°. ea., 75c. *Appleton.*
Cont.: Thomson's Seasons. — Young's Night thoughts. — Moore's Lalla Rookh. — Pollok's Course of time. — Moore's Melodies. — Gems of American poets.

Miniature English classics. 28 v. ill. 32°. $10.50; ea., 38c. . . . . *Appleton.*
Cont.: Bond's Golden maxims. — Clarke's Scripture promises. — Cottin's Elizabeth; or, the exiles of Siberia. — Gems of American poets. — Goldsmith's Vicar of Wakefield. — Goldsmith's Essays. — Hannah More's Private devotions. — Hannah More's Practical piety, 2 v. — Hemans' Domestic affection. — Hoffman's Lays of the Hudson. — Johnson's History of Rasselas. — Manual of matrimony. — Moore's Lalla Rookh. — Moore's Melodies. — St. Pierre's Paul and Virginia. — Poetic Lacon. — Pollok's Course of time. — Pure gold from the rivers of wisdom. — Thomson's Seasons. — Token of the heart. — Token of affection. — Token of remembrance. — Token of love. — Token of friendship. — Useful letter-writer. — Wilson's Sacra privata. — Young's Night thoughts.

Miniature fruit garden. *See* Rivers, T.

Miniature lib. *See* Routledge's miniature lib.

Minifie, W: Geometrical drawing; abridg. for schools. New ed., enl. ill. 12°. '75. $2 . . *Van Nostrand.*
— Text-book of geometrical drawing. 9th ed. ill. roy. 8°. '73. $4 . . . . *Van Nostrand.*

Minigo. Abbott, J. 90c. . . . . *Harper.*

Minister of Christ for the times. Adams, C. 70c. *Cin. Meth. Bk. Conc.*

Ministering children. *See* Charlesworth, *Mrs.* M. L.

Ministering Nellie. 18°. 30c. . . . . *Am.S.S.*

Minister's family. *See* Happy child's lib.

Minister's wife. 16°. $1 . . . . *Cong. Pub.*
— *See also* Silver spray lib.

Minister's wife. Dunning, A. K. $1 . . . . *Am.S.S.*

Minister's wife. Oliphant, M. O. W. 75c. . . *Harper.*

Minister's wooing. Stowe, H. B. $2 . . . . *Osgood.*

Ministers who switched off; or, lights and shadows of ministerial life. 12°. $1.50 . . *Cin. Meth. Bk. Conc.*

Ministration of angels. Canright, D. M. 20c. *Sev. Day Adv.*

Ministry of angels realized. Newton, A. E. 25c. *Colby.*

Ministry of evil. Warren, W. F. 15c. *Cin. Meth. Bk. Conc.*

Ministry of life. Charlesworth, M. L. $1.25. *Appleton; Meth. Bk. Conc.*

Ministry of nature. Macmillan, H. $2 . . *Macmillan.*

Ministry of song. Havergal, F. R. $1.50; $2.50; $3.50 . . . . *Lent.*

Ministry of the word. Taylor, W. M. $1.50 . . *Randolph.*

Ministry we need. Sweetser, S. 75c. . . *Bost. Am. Tr.*

Mink Curtiss; or, life in the backwoods, and other stories. ill. 12°. $1.50 . . . . *Miller.*

Minn (*pseud.*) Neddie's care. *See* G., F. F., Little Nan.

Minna Crosswell. Dunning, A. K. 50c. . . . *Pres. Bd.*

Minna in the wonderland. *See* Pyle, M. C.

Minna Monte. Iron, N. C. $1.25 . . . . *Lippincott.*

Minna Raymond; or, self-sacrifice. ill. 16°. $1. *Routledge.*

Minna Raymond lib. 4 v. ill. 16°. $4 . . . *Routledge.*
Cont.: Minna Raymond. — Helena Bertram. — Maze of life. — Sunshine and clouds.

Minna v. Barnhelm. *See* Lessing, G. E.

Minna's proud heart. Strong, J. D. 25c. . . . *Lothrop.*

Minnehaha glee-book. Cady, C. M. $1.50 . . . *Peters.*

Minnesinger of Germany. Kröger, A. E. $2.25. *Hurd & H.*

Minnesota. Analytical index to general and special laws. *See* Shaw, J. C., *and* West, J. B.
— Railroad laws. *See* Edgerton, A. J.
— Statutes at large to 1873; with ref. comp. by A. H. Bissell. 2 v. roy. 8°. '73. shp., $15 . . *Callaghan.*
— Supreme Court reports, v. 1–9 (1851–'64); by H. Officer. 9 v. 8°. ea., shp., $5 . . . . *E. B. Myers.*
— *Same.* v. 10, 11 (1865, '66); by W. A. Spencer. 2 v. 8°. ea., shp., $5 . . . . *E.B.Myers.*

Minnesota, *continued*.
— *Same*. v. 12–20 (1867–'74); by W. A. Spencer. 9 v. 8°. ea., shp., $5 .... *Combs*.
— — Digest. *See* Searles, J. N.
Minnesota geological survey. *See* Owen, D. D.
Minnesota Historical Society. Collections. 8°. '72. $2.50 .... *Minn. Hist.*
Minnie; or, the little woman: fairy story; by author of "Violet." ill. 16°. 80c. .... *Lee & S.*
Minnie and her pets. *See* Baker, *Mrs.* H. N. W.
Minnie Brown. *See* Wise, D.
Minnie Carleton. Bartlett, M. B. 75c. .... *Dodd.*
Minnie Gray. Phillips, R. 75c. .... (?) *Martien.*
Minnie Grey. Smith, J. F. 75c. .... *Dick & F.*
Minnie Loyle; or, the brush-cabiners. 16°. $1.50. *Am. Bapt.*
Minnie Watson. 16°. $1.25 .... *Cong. Pub.*
Minnie Weston; or, the ins and outs of Doubting Castle. 16°. 90c. .... *Am. Bapt.*
Minnie's doll's house. 32°. 20c.; 15c. .... *Dutton.*
Minnie's legacy; by author of "Rose and Kate." 18°. 45c. .... *Routledge.*
Minnie's lib. 6 v. 32°. '70. $1.50 .... *H. A. Young.*
Cont.: Little Minnie. — Afraid of the dark. — Birthday present. — Real victory. — Sowing little seeds. — Milly's doves.
Minnie's love. *See* Mackarness, *Mrs.* M. A.
Minnie's pet cat; — dog; — lamb; — monkey; — parrot; — pony. Baker, H. N. W. ea., 75c. .. *Lee & S.*
Minnie's picnic; — play-room. *See* Wise, D.
Minnows (The). 32°. 20c.; 15c. .... *Dutton.*
Minor, H. *See* Alabama, Sup. Court reports.
Minor, J: B. Institutes of common and statute law. 2 v. 8°. '75. shp., v. 1, $9; 2, $13 .. *West, J. & Co.*
Cont.: 1. The rights which relate to persons. — 2. The rights which relate to things real.
— *Same*. 2 v. 8°. '75. shp., $15 .... *McKennie.*
Minor, J: D. *et al.*, *v.* Board of Education of Cincinnati. Arguments [on the Bible in the public schools] in the Superior Court of Cincinnati; with the opinions and decision of the Court. 8°. '70. $2; shp., $3 .... *Clarke.*
— — *Same*. Arguments of Ramsey, etc., in favor of the use of the Bible. 8°. '70. pap., 50c. .. *Clarke.*
— — *Same*. Arguments of Stallo, etc., against the use of the Bible. 8°. '70. pap., 50c. .... *Clarke.*
Minor, T: C. Child-bed fever: erysipelas and puerperal fever; as they prevailed sporadically in the U. S. during 1870; with app. 8°. '74. $2 .. *Clarke.*
Minor characters of the Bible. Hall, J. 35c. *Pres. Bd.*
Minot, G: *See* United States, Circ. Court reports.
Minstrel gags, and end-men's handbook. 16°. '75. pap., 30c. .... *Happy.*
Minton, H: Domestic practice of medicine. [Hom.] 8°. $3 .... *Agar.*
Mintorn, *Mrs.* J. H. Handbook of paper flower making. ill. 16°. '71. 50c. .... *Routledge.*
— Lessons in flower and fruit modeling in wax. ill. 16°. $1.50 .... *Routledge.*
— Modeling in leather. ill. 16°. '71. bds., 50c. *Routledge.*
Minturn lib. 5 v. ill. 18°. $2.75 .... *Hoyt.*
Cont.: Addie Ansley. — Henry Minturn. — Pete, the cunner boy, by Mrs. S. J. Knight. — Rose cottage. — Sophie De Brentz.
Minutes of trial and examination of certain persons in province of New York charged with being engaged in a conspiracy against the authority of the congress and the liberties of America. Lond., 1786. [Reprint.] f°. '65. pap., $20. — 4°. $10. — 8°. $5 .... *J. Campbell & Son.*
Mirabeau: a life history. roy. 12°. 75c. .... *Lea.*
Miracle of the roses. Bordèse, L. $1.50 .. *Schirmer.*
Miracles (The). [Quest. book.] 18°. bds., 15c. *Am. Bapt.*
Miracles of Christ; with explan. obs. and ill. from modern travels. ill. 18°. 65c. .... *Pres. Bd.*
Miracles of faith. Weitbrecht, M. 75c. .... *Dodd.*
Miracles of heavenly love in daily life. *See* Tucker, *Mrs.* Ctte.
Miracles, past and present. Mountford, W. $2. * *Osgood.*
Mirage of life. 18°. 53c. .... *U. P. Bd. of Pub.*
— *Same*. ill. sq. 18°. '69. 70c. .... *Am. Tr.*
— *Germ.* Trugbilder des Lebens. 18°. '70. 50c. *Am. Tr.*
Miralda. Ballou, M. M. 15c. .... *French.*
Mireio. Mistral, F. $1.50; $2 .... *Roberts.*
Mirella. *See* Ditson.
Mirelle. Mistral, F. $2 .... *Macmillan.*
Miriam. Harland, M. $1.50 .... *Carleton.*
Miriam, the avenger. Southworth, E. D. E. N. $1.75; $1.50 .... *Peterson.*
Miriam, and other poems. Whittier, J. G. $1.50; $4. *Osgood.*
Miriam Alroy. Disraeli, B. 50c. .... *Peterson.*
Miriam and Rosette; or, the trials of faith. ill. 16°. '71. 50c. .... *Routledge.*
Miriam Brandon. Moore, J. F. $1.25 .... *Hoyt.*
Miriam Coffin. Hart, J. C. $2 .... *Coleman.*
Miriam Gray; or, scenes from the true history of a life. 18°. '66. 35c. .. *N. Y. Ref. Ch. Bd.; Pres. Com.*
Miriam Monfort. Warfield, C. A. $2 ..... *Appleton.*
Miriam Rosenbaum: story of Jewish life. ('73.) New ed. 16°. '75. $1.25 .... *Hoyt.*
Miriam's crime. Craven, H. T. 15c. *De Witt; French.*
Miriam's memoirs. Warfield, C. A. $1.75 .. *Peterson.*
Miriam's reward. 18°. 25c. .... *Am. S. S.*
Miriam's song of triumph. Merz, K. $1.50 .. *Brainard.*
Miriam's song of triumph. Schubert, F. 50c. *Ditson.*
Miriam's trial. A., A. 50c. .... *Pott.*
Mirror (The). *See* Chalmers, A., British essayists.
Mirror of Johannite Masons. *See* Oliver, G.
Mirror of truth. Hamerton, E. $2 .... *Roberts.*
Mirthfulness and its exciters. Clark, B. F. $1.50. *Lee & S.*
Misanthrope (Le). *See* Molière, J. B. P.
Miscellaneous sermons. 12°. $1 .. *Cin. Meth. Bk. Conc.*
Mischief. *See* My own lib.
Mischief making. Buckstone, J. B. 15c. ..... *French.*
Mischief's Thanksgiving. Woolsey, S. C. $1.50. *Roberts.*
Mischievous Bob: comic drama. 16°. pap., 15c. *Happy.*
Mischievous boy. *See* New Year lib.
Mischievous nigger: Ethiop. drama. 16°. pap., 15c. *French; Happy.*
Mischievous puppy. f°. pap., 15c.; 20c.; 30c. *J. E. Potter.*
Miser. Conscience, H. $1; $1.25 .... *Murphy.*
Miser. Fielding, H. 15c. .... *French.*
Miser of Shoreditch. Prest, T. P. 15c. ..... *French.*
Miserables (Les). *See* Hugo, V.
Miserables (Les): Ethiop. drama. 16°. pap., 15c. *French; Happy.*
Miseries of human life: farce. 16°. pap., 15c. .. *Happy.*
Miser's daughter. *See* Ainsworth, W. H.
Miser's daughter: drama. 16°. pap., 15c. ... *French.*
Miser's heir. Myers, P. H. 75c.; 50c. .... *Peterson.*
Miser's will. Reynolds, G. W. M. 50c. ..... *De Witt.*
Misfortune of Peter Faber. Neal, J. C. 75c. *Peterson.*
Mishaps and adventures of Obadiah Oldbuck. ill. obl. 8°. 30c. .... *Dick & F.*
Mishaps of Cæsar Crum: Ethiop. drama. 16°. pap., 15c. .... *Happy.*
Mishaps of Mr. Ezekiel Pelter. Higgins, A. S. $1.50. *Griggs.*

Misread passages of Scripture. Brown, J. B. 2 v. $1.75 .... *Meth. Bk. Conc.*
Misrepresentation. Drury, A. H. $1...... *Harper.*
Miss Adelaide's school. *See* Sunbeam ser.
Miss Alice's story. *See* Aunt Alice's lib.
Miss Angel. Thackeray, A. I. 75c. .... *Harper.*
Miss Ashton's girls. *See* Mathews, J. H.
Miss Carew. Edwards, A. B. 50c.......... *Harper.*
Miss Carrol's school. *See* Lyntonville lib.
Miss Charlotte. 18°. 40c.................... *Dutton.*
Miss Chester: drama. 16°. pap., 15c........ *French.*
Miss Clare's party. *See* Hildeburn, *Mrs.* M. J.
Miss Dollikins (Events in life of). Marks, E. M. 50c. *Nelson.*
Miss Dorothy's charge. Benedict, F. L. $1.50; $1. *Harper.*
Miss Eily O'Connor. Byron, H. J. 15c. .... *French.*
Miss Forrester. Edwards, A. $1.75; $1... *Sheldon.*
Miss Gilbert's career. Holland, J. G. $2 .. *Scribner.*
Miss Grey's text, and how it was learned. ill. 18°. '76. 50c.................................. (?) *Nelson.*
Miss Hitchcock's wedding dress; by author of "Mrs. Jerningham's journal." sq. 12°. '76. $1.25. *Scribner.*
Miss Howard's school. *See* Maggie Fuller lib.
Miss Katy's little maid. 18°. 60c.......... *Am. S. S.*
Miss Laura's wedding day. 18°. 40c.......... *Dutton.*
Miss Lilly's voyage round the world; tr. by I. M. Luyster; ill. by Frölich. 8°. '68. $3.. *Roberts.*
Miss Mackenzie. *See* Trollope, Ant.
Miss Marjoribanks. *See* Oliphant, M. O. W.
Miss Mary and her scholars. Henderson, M. P. 75c. *N. Y. Ref. Ch. Bd.; Pres. Com.*
Miss Matty. *See* Hazelwood ser.
Miss Matty; or, our youngest passenger. 16°. '66. 75c. .... *Dutton.*
Miss Molly. Butt, B. M. $1.25 .... *Holt.*
Miss Moore. Craik, G. M. 90c............ *Harper.*
Miss Muff and Little Hungry. Warner, A. B. 75c. *Pres. Bd.*
Miss or Mrs.? *See* Collins, W.
Miss Patience Hathaway. Bradley, W. I. $1.50. *H. A. Young.*
Miss Prouncer's visit. *See* Daisy lib.
Miss Ravenel's conversion from secession to loyalty. De Forest, J. W. $1.50.............. *Harper.*
Miss Roberts' fortune. 12°. '71. $1.50.... *Randolph.*
Miss Rosy. *See* Swallow stories.
Miss Rovel. Cherbuliez, V. $1.25; 50c. ..... *Estes.*
Miss Sara Sampson. *See* Lessing, G. E.
Miss Thistledown. Clarke, R. S. 75c....... *Lee & S.*
Miss Tibbit's back hair. Robinson, W. 15c... *French.*
Miss Tiller's vegetable garden. Warner, A. B. 90c.; 30c. .... *Randolph.*
Miss Touchall. 16°. 45c.............. *Cummiskey.*
Miss Van Kortland. Benedict, F. L. $1.50; $1.. *Harper.*
Miss Wealthy's hope. Davis, C. E. K. $1.50.. *Lothrop.*
Missiles of truth. Gardner, W. W. $1.... *So. Bapt.*
Missing boat. ill. 18°. '64. 30c.............. *Am. Tr.*
— *Same.* ill. 18°. 40c. .... *Bost. Am. Tr.*
— *Same.* 18°. '67. 40c... *N. Y. Ref. Ch. Bd.; Pres. Com.*
— *Same.* 18°. 70c. .... *Pres. Bd.*
— *Germ.* Das vermisste Boot. 24°. 20c... *Ev. Assoc.*
— — *Same.* ill. 18°. '70. 25c. .... *Am. Tr.*
Missing boat stories. 5 v. 18°. $2.... *Bost. Am. Tr.*
Cont.: The Clevelands, by Mrs. E. M. Sheldon. — Elton Wheatley, by E. Derby. — Happy home. — Lift a little, by Mrs. J. P. Ballard. — Missing boat.
Missing link. 12°. $1.25.................. *Carter.*
Missing links in Jewish hist. Tucker, C. 90c. *Am. Bapt.*

Mission; or, scenes in Africa. *See* Marryat, F.
Mission book. [Cath. prayer book.] 24°. 50c.-$2.5 *Strong*
— *Same.* 18°. '62. 75c.-$5 .... *Kelly, P. & C*
— *Same.* 18°. 75c.-$3. — 24°. 50c.-$2.50.. *T. Kelly*
— *Same.* 18°. $1.50-$9. — 24°. 75c.-$5.... *O'Shea*
— *Same.* 18°. 75c.-$20. — 24°. 60c.-$15 .. *Sadlier*
— *Same.* 16°. 75c.-$4.50. — 32°. 60c.-$3.50. — 48 30c.-$2 .... *Benziger*
— *See also* Redemptorist mission book.
Mission book: [Cath.] manual of instruction and praye chiefly from works of St. Alphonsus Liguori. 18 75c.-$3 .... *Strong*
— *Same.* 18°. $1-$7.75 .... *Cummiskey*
— *Same.* 18°. 75c.-$40. — 24°. 60c.-$60.... *Sadlier*
— *See also* Livre des missions.
Mission book of the sacred passion. [Cath. praye book.] 24°. 75c.-$3. — 18°. 75c.-$3.50.. *O'Shea*
Mission of death. Walworth, M. T. 75c.; $1.25. *Sadlier*
Mission of the North American people. Gilpin, W $4.50 .... *Lippincot*
Mission of sorrow. Spring, G. 35c.......... *Am. T*
Mission of the spirit. Dunn, L. R. $1.25. *Meth. Bk. Con*
Mission prayer book for church and Sunday schoo 32°. '72. 15c...................... *Woodhous*
Mission school in Mill Village. Hazen, M. P. $1.1 *Bost. Am. T*
Mission Sunday-school hymn book. 32°. 10c... *Am. S.*
Missionär (Der) in Afrika. *See* Belohnte Treue.
Missionary among cannibals. Rowe, G. S. $1. *Meth. Bk. Con*
Missionary anecdotes. ill. 16°. 90c........ *Am. S.*
Missionary book for the young. 18°. 40c. *U. P. Bd. of Pu*
Missionary box. 18°. 50c................. *Pres. B*
Missionary converts. 18°. 30c.; 40c...... *Am. Bap*
Missionary doctor. Wilmer, M. E. 80c. *N. Y. Ref. Ch. B*
Missionary gems for the young. 18°. 40c.; 50c. *Am. Bap*
Missionary in many lands. House, E. $1.25. *Meth. Bk. Con*
Missionary in the wilderness. Brainerd, D. 40c. *Pres. B*
Missionary kite. 18°. 25c................. *Am. S.*
Missionary letters; relating to the Greeks and Arme nians. 18°. 25c. .... *Am. S.*
Missionary patriots. Tarbox, I. N. $1.25.. *Cong. Pu*
Missionary picture gallery: ill. from British Americ Mohammedan countries, Africa and New Zealan ill. 4°. 50c.............................. *Hurd & H*
Missionary prince. *See* Better than diamonds.
Missionary printer. 18°. 18c............... *Am. S.*
Missionary records: northern countries [Greenlan Labrador, etc.] 18°. 75c............ *Pres. B*
Missionary sisters. Benjamin, M. G. $1.25. *Bost. Am. T*
Missionary sketches for children. 32°. 25c... *Pres. B*
Missionary stories. *See* Juvenile picture books.
Missionary stories; or, sketches of Moravian mission 18°. 55c.................................. *Am. S.*
Missionary tales for little listeners. Barber, M. A. 50c. .... *Pres. B*
Missionary world: encyclop. of information conc. mi sions of all denominations in all parts of the worl cr. 8°. '73. $2.50........................ *Randolp*
Missionary's daughter. 18°. 25c.; 30c.... *Am. Bap*
— *Same.* (cop. '42.) New ed. 18°. '49. 45c... *Am. T*
Missionary's mother. Adams, W. 20c...... *Am. T*
Missions in Japan and Paraguay. 12°. $1; $1.50. *Sadlie*

Mississippi. Chancery reports, 1839–'43; by J. D. Freeman. 8°. '44 ... *State*.
— *Same*, 1840–'43; by W. C. Smedes and T. A. Marshall. 8°. '44 ... *State*.
— Criminal cases decided in the High Court of Errors and Appeals, and in Supreme Court, 1818–'72; with notes of Eng. and Am. decisions and authorities and manual of forms; by J. S. Morris. 2 v. 8°. '73. shp., $20 ... *Callaghan*.
— Law reports, 1818–'32; by R. J. Walker. 8°. *net*, shp., $8 ... *Gould*.
— *Same*. v. 2–8 (1834–'43); by V. E. Howard. 7 v. 8°. '39–'44 ... *State*.
— *Same*. v. 9–22 (1843–'50); by W. C. Smedes and T. A. Marshall. 14 v. 8°. '44–'51 ... *State*.
— *Same*. v. 23–29 (1851–'55); by J. F. Cushman. 7 v. 8°. shp., $38.50 ... *Little, B. & Co*.
— *Same*. v. 30–50 (1855–'73). 21 v. 8°. '51–'75 .. *State*.
Cont.: v. 30–39 (1855–'63), by J. Z. George. — v. 40–42 (1864–'69), by R. O. Reynolds. — v. 43–48 (1870–'73), by J. S. Morris. — v. 49–50 (1873–4), by G. E. Harris and G. H. Simrall.
— *Same*. v. 43–48 (1870–'73); by J. S. Morris. 6 v. 8°. shp., $45 ... *Callaghan*.
— — Digest. *See* George, J. Z.
— Revised code of the statute law as adopted, 1871. 4°. '71 ... *State*.
Missippippi agricultural and geological survey. Preliminary report on geol. and agric. of M.; by L. Harper. 8°. '57 ... *State*.
— Report on the agric. and geol. of M., embr. sketch of the social and nat. hist. of the state; by B. L. C. Wailes. 8°. '54 ... *State*.
— Report on the geol. and agric. of M.; by E. W. Hilgard. 8°. '60 ... *State*.
Mississippi und Rhein. Ende, H. 75c.; 30c.; 50c. *Doerflinger*.
Missouri. Constitution; annotated. 8°. '75. bds., $1. *Gilbert*.
— Index to session laws. 8°. '69. shp., $5 ... *Gilbert*.
— Statutes; with notes, ref. and index; by D. Wagner. 2 v. 8°. '70. shp., $15 ... *Gilbert*.
— Supreme Court reports, v. 1–41 (1821–'67). 41 v. 8°. shp., $300 ... *Gilbert*.
Cont.: 1 (1821–'28), by P. H. McBride. — 2, 3 (1828–'35), by J. C. Edwards. — 4 (1835–'37), by W. P. Napton. — 5–8 (1837–'45), by S. M. Bay. — 9–11 (1845–'48), by B. F. Stringfellow. — 12, 13 (1848–'50), by W. A. Robards. — 14, 15 (1851–'52), by J. B. Gardenshire. — 16–21 (1852–'55), by S. A. Bennett. — 22–30 (1855–'60), by H. M. Jones. — 31 (1860–'62), by H. M. Jones, D. R. Barclay and C. C. Whittelsey. — 32–41 (1862–'67), by C. C. Whittelsey.
— *Same*. v. 42–61 ('67–'76); by T. A. Post. 20 v. 8°. ea., shp., $4 ... *Gilbert*.
— *Same*. v. 1–15; ed. by L. Houck. 15 v. 8°. shp., $75 ... *Gilbert*.
— — Digest. *See* Pattison, E. W.
— — Index. *See* Hunter, B., *and* Myer, W. G.; — Myer, W. G.
Missouri geological survey. First and second reports of geol. survey of M.; by G. C. Swallow. 8°. '55. $5 ... *Swallow*.
— Geographical report of country along line of southwest. branch of Pacific Railroad, Mo.; by G. C. Swallow, with memoir of Pacific Railroad. 8°. '57. $1 ... *Swallow*.
Missouri harmony. Carden, A. D. 75c. ... *Wilstach*.
Missouri sermons; by ministers of the Meth. Episc. Church, south. 12°. $1.50 ... *S. W. Bk. & Pub*.
Mistaken. Fuller, L. $1.50 ... *Lippincott*.
Mistaken story: farce. 16°. pap., 15c. ... *French*.
Mistakes of educated men. Hart, J. S. 50c. *Garrigues*.
Mr. and Mrs. Peter White. Raymond, R. J. 15c. *French*.
Mr. and Mrs. Pringle. Trueba y Cosio, T. de. 15c. *Ames; French*.
Mr. Blake's walking stick. Eggleston, E. 50c. *Adams, B. & L*.
Mr. Caudle's breakfast talk. *See* Jerrold, D.
Mr. Clipstock's clock, and what it made him think about the old year. 18°. 18c. ... *Am. S. S*.
Mister Fox. *See* Ballantyne, W.
Mr. Joffin's latch-key: farce. 16°. pap., 15c. .. *French*.
Mr. Johnson's school; or, the new master. 32°. 40c. *Scribner, W. & A*.
Mr. McKenzie's answer. Foster, I. H. $1.25 .. *Nat. Temp*.
Mr. Moffat and the Bechuanas; [also] The little Hindoo baby. 18°. 25c. ... *Pres. Bd*.
Mr. Pendleton's cup. Bradley, W. I. $1.25 .. *H. A. Young*.
Mr. Pisistratus Brown, M.P., in the Highlands: reprinted, with add., from the "Daily News." New ed. ill. cr. 8°. '73. $1.50 ... *Macmillan*.
Mr. Rutherford's children. Warner, S. *and* A. B. 75c. *Scribner, W. & A*.
Mr. Scroggins. Hancock, W., *and* Moore, A. 15c. *De Witt; French*.
Mr. Smith. Walford, L. B. $1.25 ... *Holt*.
Mr. Stewart's intentions. Robinson, F. W. 25c. *Burnham*.
Mr. Vaughan's heir. Benedict, F. L. $1.50; $1 .. *Harper*.
Mr. Wallingford's mistake. Dunning, A. K. $1 .. *Pres. Bd*.
Mr. Warner's household. Howard, M. 55c. .. *Pres. Bd*.
Mr. Wind and Madam Rain. Musset, P. de. 75c. *Harper*.
Mr. Wynyard's ward. Parr, H. 50c. ... *Harper*.
Mr. X. Rosenfeld, S. 15c. ... *De Witt*.
Mistletoe bough. Somerset, C. 15c. .. *Ames; French*.
Mistral, F: Mirelle, a pastoral epic of Provence; tr. by H. Crichton. fp. 8°. '68. $2 ... *Macmillan*.
— Mireio, a provençal poem; tr. by H. W. Preston. sq. 12°. '72. $2. — 16°. $1.50 ... *Roberts*.
Mistress and maid. *See* Craik, D. M.
Mrs. Armington's ward. Wright, D. T. $1.50 .. *Lee & S*.
Mrs. Brown series. *See* Rose, G.
Mrs. Brown's stories. 18°. 40c. ... *Cong. Pub*.
Mrs. Caudle Sterling: farce. 16°. pap., 15c. .. *French*.
Mrs. Caudle's curtain lectures. *See* Jerrold, D.
Mrs. Cooper's story; or, the golden mushroom. 18°. 60c. ... *Am. S. S*.
Mrs. Deane's way. Foster, I. H. $1.25 ... *Lothrop*.
Mrs. Gerald's niece. *See* Fullerton, *Lady* G.
Mrs. Gordon's household. G., B. C. 50c. *Scribner, W. & A*.
Mrs. Green's snug little business. Cheltnam, C. S. 15c. ... *French*.
Mrs. Halliburton's troubles. Wood, E. P. $1.25; 75c. *Dick & F*.
Mrs. Herbert and the villagers. 18°. $1.50 .. *O'Shea*.
Mrs. Hurd's niece. Farman, E. $1.50 ... *Lothrop*.
Mrs. Jarley's wax works. 2 pts. 16°. ea., pap., 25c. *French*.
Mrs. Jerningham's journal. [Poem.] 2d ed. fp. 8°. '70. 75c. ... *Macmillan*.
— *Same*. ('70.) New ed. 12°. '73. 75c. .. *Scribner*.
— *See also* John Jerningham's journal.
Mistress Judith. Tytler, C. C. F. $1.25 ... *Holt*.
Mrs. Latimer's meetings. Dunning, A. K. 35c. *Pres. Bd*.
Mrs. Lee and her boy Bertie. *See* Hildeburn, *Mrs.* M. J.
Mrs. Limber's raffle; or, a church fair and its victims. 18°. 75c.; pap., 50c. ... *Appleton*.
Mrs. Lirriper's legacy. *See* Dickens, C:
Mrs. Lirriper's lodgings. *See* Dickens, C:
Mrs. Mainwaring's journal. Marshall, E. $1.50 .. *Dutton*.
Mistress Margery. *See* Holt, E. S.
Mrs. Marshall's key. Hulen, L. S. $1.15 .. *Cong. Pub*.
Mrs. Marsh's help. *See* Dana, J. J.
Mrs. Matthews. Trollope, F. $1 ... *Routledge*.
Mistress of the manse. Holland, J. G. $1.50 .. *Scribner*.
Mistress of the mill. Moncrieff, W. T. 15c. .. *French*.
Mistress of novices enlightened upon her duties; tr. by a Sister of Mercy. 16°. '74. $1.50 .. *Cath. Pub*.

Mrs. Partington's carpet-bag of fun. Shillaber, B. P. $1.25; 75c. . . . . *Dick & F.*

Mrs. Partington's edition of Mother Goose. Tilton, S. W. 60c. . . . . *Tilton.*

Mrs. Partington's knitting work. Shillaber, B. P. $1.75. *J. E. Potter.*

Mrs. Sarah Gamp's tea and turnout: farce. 16°. pap., 15c. . . . . *Happy.*

Mrs. Skaggs' husbands. Harte, B. $1.50; $3 . . *Osgood.*

Mrs. Smith. Payne, J. H. 15c. . . . . *French.*

Mrs. Thorne's guests. Capron, M. J. $1.50 . . *Lothrop.*

Mrs. White. Raymond, R. J. 15c. . . . . *French.*

Mrs. Wiggins. Allingham, J. T. 15c. . . . . *French.*

Mrs. Willis' will. *See* Lacy's Home plays for ladies.

Mists of the valley. Giberne, A. $1 . . . . . *Dodd.*

Misunderstood. Montgomery, F. $1.25 . . *Randolph.*

Mit eiserner Hand. *See* Dedenroth, E. H. v.

Mitchel, J: Crusade of the period, and last conquest of Ireland (perhaps). por. 12°. '73. $1.25. (?) *Lynch.*

— Jail journal; or, four years in British prisons. por. 12°. '68 $1.50 . . . . . *Haverty.*

— Life of Hugh O'Neill, Earl of Tyrone. por. 12°. '70. $1 . . . . . *Haverty.*

— *and* McGeoghegan, Jacques. History of Ireland. 4°. '68. $15–$22; — in 2 v. 4°. $20. — (chp. ed.) 2 v. 8°. $7–$10; — in 1 v. 8°. $3.50–$5. — ill. 8°. mor., $18; — in 40 pts. ill. 8°. ea., 25c. . . . . *Sadlier.*

Mitchel, Ormsby McKnight. Works. 3 v. 12°. '48–'63. ea., $1.75 . . . . . *Mason; Scribner.*

Cont.: Astronomy of the Bible. — Planetary and stellar worlds. — Popular astronomy.

Mitchell, *Miss* Anne Mar. Crystals. 18°. 70c. *Pres. Bd.*

— Freedboy in Alabama. 18°. 65c. . . . . *Pres. Bd.*

— Golden first reader. ill. 12°. 25c. . . . . *Pres. Bd.*

— Golden primer. ill. 12°. 20c. . . . . *Pres. Bd.*

Mitchell, Don. G. ["Ik. Marvel."] Dr. Johns: narrative of certain events in life of an orthodox minister in Connecticut. [Fiction.] ('66.) New ed. 2 v. 12°. '72. $3.50 . . . . . *Scribner.*

— Dream life: fable of the seasons. ('63.) New ed. 12°. '76. $1.75; mor., $4. — (Cabinet ed.) 16°. $1.75; hf. cf., $3 . . . . . *Scribner.*

— Fresh gleanings; or, a new sheaf from the old fields of continental Europe. 12°. $1.75 . . . . *Scribner.*

— Lorgnette (The); or, studies of the town; by an opera-goer. 2 v. ill. 12°. $3.50 . . . . . *Scribner.*

— My farm of Edgewood. ('63.) New ed. 12°. '72. $1.75. — New [chp.] ed. sq. 12°. $1.25 . . *Scribner.*

— Pictures of Edgewood: photog. views by Rockwood, with text and diagrams. ('68.) New ed. 4°. '69. $12 . . . . . *Scribner.*

— Reveries of a bachelor; or, a book of the heart. ('63.) New ed. 12°. '76. $1.75; mor., $4. — (Cabinet ed.) 16°. $1.75; hf. cf., $3. — ill. ed. ('50.) New ed. sq. 8°. '52. $5 . . . . . *Scribner.*

— Rural studies; with pract. hints for country places. ('67.) New ed. ill. 12°. '73. $1.75 . . *Scribner.*

— Seven stories, with basement and attic. 12°. $1.75. *Scribner.*

— Wet days at Edgewood, with old farmers, old gardeners and old pastorals. ('64.) New ed. 12°. '70. $1.75 . . . . . *Scribner.*

Mitchell, Ja. Y. History and directory of Temple Presb. Ch. ill. 16°. '73. $2 . . . (?) *Daughaday.*

Mitchell, J: Manual of practical assaying. 4th ed., ed. by W. Crookes. 8°. $10 . . . . . *Wiley.*

Mitchell, J: K. Five essays on the cryptogamous origin of malarious and epidemic fevers, etc.; ed. by S. W. Mitchell. 12°. $1.25 . . . . . *Lippincott.*

Mitchell, M. S. Manual of elocution. ('67.) 9th ed. 12°. '75. $1.50 . . . . . *Eldredge.*

Mitchell, S: A: Ancient atlas, classical and sacred; with maps, tables and descriptive geog. ill. 4°. $1.35 . . . . . *Butler.*

Mitchell, S: A: *continued.*

— Ancient geography, classical and sacred. [Old ed.] ill. 12°. 90c.; — with 4° atlas, $2.25 . . . . *Butler.*

— *Same.* New ed. ill. 12°. $1.75 . . . . . *Butler.*

— Biblical and Sabbath school geography. col. maps and ill. 12°. $1.25 . . . . . *Butler.*

— Elements of physical geog.; with treatise on physical phenomena of the U. S.; [ed.] by J. Brocklesby. ill. and maps. 4°. $1.88 . . . . . *Butler.*

— First lessons in geography. ill. and maps. sm. 4°. 50c. . . . . *Butler.*

— Geographical question book. 12°. 56c. . . . . *Butler.*

— Key to outline maps. 12°. 60c. . . . . *Butler*

— Modern atlas; to ill. New school geography. 4°. $1.50 . . . . . *Butler.*

— Modern atlas; with index by H. D. Gregory. 4°. $2 . . . . . *Butler.*

— New intermediate geog.; with system of map-drawing. New ed., rev. maps and ill. 4°. $1.80 . . *Butler.*

— New primary geography. ill. and col. maps. sm. 4°. 80c. . . . . *Butler.*

— New school geog., physical, political and descript. ill. 12°. $1; — with 4° atlas, $2.50 . . . . . *Butler.*

— Primary geography. [Old ed.] 4°. 75c. . . . *Butler.*

— School atlas: maps and tables to accompany School and family geography. 4°. $1.20 . . . . . *Butler.*

— School geography. Rev. ed. ill. 12°. 80c.; — with 4° atlas, $2 . . . . . *Butler.*

Mitchell, S: Weir. Injuries of the nerves and their consequences. 8°. $3 . . . . . *Lippincott.*

— Rest in the treatment of nervous disease. *See* Seguin, E. C., Series of Am. clin. lect.

— Venom of the rattlesnake. 4°. '60. pap., $1.75. *Smith. Inst.*

— Wear and tear; or, hints for the overworked. 18°. 50c.; pap., 30c. . . . . *Lippincott.*

— *and* Morehouse, G. R. Anatomy and physiology of respiration in chelonia. 4°. '63. pap., $1. *Smith. Inst.*

Mitchell, Stuart. Church (The), its constitution and government. 18°. 50c. . . . . *Pres. Bd.*

— Jonah, the self-willed prophet: expos. of Book of Jonah; with tr. and notes. 12°. '75. $1.50 . . *Claxton.*

Mitchell, T: Stepping stones to architecture: questions and answers expl. principles and progress of architecture. ill. 12°. 60c. . . . . *Judd.*

Mitchell, *Rev.* T: Old paths: treatise on perfect love. 16°. '69. 50c. . . . . *Tibbals.*

— Philosophy of God and the world. 8°. '71. $4. *Tibbals.*

— Philosophy of spiritualism. 16°. '72. 40c. . . *Tibbals.*

Mitchell, T: D. Materia medica and therapeutics; with ill. of practice, and notices of toxicology. 8°. '50. shp., $4 . . . . . *Claxton; Lippincott.*

Mitchell, Wa. Bryan Maurice; or, the seeker. 12°. '67. $1.75 . . . . . *Claxton; Lippincott.*

Mitford, A. B. Tales of old Japan. ill. cr. 8°. $2.50. *Macmillan.*

Mitford, *Miss* Ma. Russell. Works, prose and verse. 8°. shp., $3 . . . . . *Desilver.*

— Foscari: tragedy. 16°. pap., 15c. . . . . *French.*

— Julian: tragedy. 16°. pap., 15c. . . . . *French.*

— Life; told in letters to her friends, with anecdotes and sketches of her contemporaries; ed. by A. G. K. L'Estrange. 2 v. 12°. $3.50 . . . . . *Harper.*

— Our village. 2 v. ill. 12°. (Bohn.) ea., $1.25. *Little, B. & Co.*

— *Same.* 2 v. ill. 12°. (Bohn.) ea., $1.40. *Scribner, W. & A.*

— *Same.* 2 v. ill. 12°. (Bohn.) ea., $1.50 . . *Lippincott.*

— Recollections of a literary life; or, books, places and people. 12°. $1.50 . . . . . *Harper.*

— Rienzi: tragedy. 16°. pap., 15c. . . . . *French.*

— Tales and stories. ill. 16°. $1.75 . . *Scribner, W. & A.*

Mitschuldigen (Die). *See* Goethe, J. W. v.

Mittendorf, W. Kirchengeschichte der Vereinigten Brüder in Christo. 12°. $1 . . . . . *Un. B. Pub.*

Mittendorf, W., *continued.*
— Spiritualismus im Licht Heiliger Schrift. 18°. 35c. *Un.B.Pub.*
Mittens. *See* Barrow, *Mrs.* F.
Mittheilungen a. d. Memoiren d. Satans. *See* Hauff, W.
Mivart, St. G: Common frog (The). ill. 12°. '74. $1. *Macmillan.*
— Genesis of species. ill. 12°. $1.75; hf. cf., $4. *Appleton.*
— *Same.* 2d ed., with notes in ref. to Darwin's Descent of man. ill. cr. 8°. '71. $2..*Macmillan.*
— Lessons on elementary philosophy. ill. 18°. '73. $2. *Macmillan.*
— Man and apes: exposition of structural resemblances and differences, bearing upon questions of affinity and origin. 12°. $1.50..............*Appleton.*
Mixer, A. H. Manual of French poetry. 12°. '74. $2. *Ivison.*
Mixing in society: manual of manners; by Countess of —. 12°. $1.50....................*Routledge.*
Mixture for low spirits. Tegg, W. 50c. *Scribner, W.& A.*
Mizpah. Loomis, L. C. $2.............*Lippincott.*
Mliss. Harte, B. 50c.....................*De Witt.*
Moak, Natl. C. Reports of cases decided in the English courts, with notes and ref. v. 1–11. 8°. '72–'76. ea., shp., $6.....................*Gould.*
— Statutes rel. to the Albany [N. Y.] Penitentiary. 8°. '72. $1...........................*Munsell.*
Moase, C: Church member's monitor. 8°. '68. pap., 10c...............................*Darrow.*
Mob cap. Paul, H. 15c...................*French.*
Moberly, G: Administration of the Holy Spirit in the body of Christ. *See* Bampton lectures.
Moby-Dick. Melville, H. $1.75...........*Harper.*
Mock marriage. Bickley, C. P. 25c.....*U.P.James.*
Mocking bird. Perkins, W. O. 50c. *Pond; G.D.Russell.*
Mode of baptism. 18°. 75c..............*Cong.Pub.*
Mode of keeping the Sabbath. 18°. pap., 10c...*Am. Tr.*
Mode of man's immortality. Goodwin, T. A. $1.25..*Ford.*
Model architect (The). Sloane, S. $25..*Lippincott.*
Model for men of business. 16°. '55. 80c. *Meth.Bk.Conc.*
Model for a wife. Wigan, F. 15c..........*De Witt.*
Model husband. Wooler, J. P. 15c.........*French.*
Model landlord. Holt, M. A. 60c........*Nat. Temp.*
Model letter-writer. ill. 48°. 25c....*Scribner, W.& A.*
Model letter-writer; with forms. 32°. 45c...*Nichols & H.*
Model liberality. Seiss, J. A. 10c.....*Luth.Bk.St.*
Model lib. 4 v. ill. 12°. $4..................*Nelson.*
Cont.: Percy Raydon, by E. Leslie. — Under grey walls, by S. Doudney. — One by herself, by Mrs. C. L. Balfour. — Golden mill.
Model melodeon instructor. 4°. '51. bds., $1.50..*Ditson.*
Model merchant. Arthur, W. 70c.........*Pres. Bd.*
Model mother; or, the mother's mission. ill. 12°. $1.25.................................*Hoyt.*
Model of a wife. Wigan, A. 15c............*French.*
Model pastor. Stockbridge, J. C. $1.75....*Lee & S.*
Model prayer. Baldwin, G. C. $1.50.......*Lee & S.*
Model preacher. Taylor, W. $1.50..*Cin.Meth.Bk.Conc.*
Model school for the piano-forte. 4°. '55. bds., $1.50. *Ditson.*
Model Sunday school speaker. Monroe, A. 60c.; 75c...................................*Lee & S.*
Model town. Pinkerton, A. $1.50........*Carleton.*
Model town and the detectives. Pinkerton, A. $1.50. *Keen.*
Model women. Anderson, W. $1.75........*Nelson.*
Modern antiques. O'Keeffe, J. 15c..........*French.*
Modern atheism. Tiffany, C. C. 20c. ... *Whittaker.*
Modern babes in the wood. *See* Smith, H. P., *and* Wallace, E. R.

Modern British essayists. 6 v. 8°. ea., $2.50..*Appleton.*
Cont.: Miscellaneous essays, by Sir A. Alison; Recreations of Christopher North, by J. Wilson. — Crit. and misc. essays by T. Carlyle. — Contributions to the Edinburgh Review, by Lord Jeffrey. — Essays, by Lord Macaulay. — Crit. and misc. essays, by Sir J. Macintosh. — Works of S. Smith; Crit. and misc. essays of T. N. Talfourd and J. Stephens.
Modern British Plutarch. Taylor, W. C. $1..*Harper.*
Modern chivalry. Brackenridge, H. H. 2 v. ea., $1.75...............................*Peterson.*
Modern classics: stories from the "Atlantic Monthly." 12°. $1.25.............................*Porter.*
Modern cook. Francatelli, C. E. $5......*Peterson.*
Modern Cressida (A). *See* Asheton, F.
Modern diabolism. Williamson, M. J. $2 ...*Miller.*
Modern doubt and Christian belief. *See* Christlieb, T.
Modern Edinburgh; rev. by T. O. Summers. ('57.) 2d ed. 18°. '69. 50c.................*So. Meth.*
Modern genesis. Slaughter, W. B. $1..*Meth.Bk.Conc.*
Modern harp. White, E. L., *and* Gould, J. E. $1.50. *Ditson.*
Modern householder: manual of dom. economy; ed. by a com. of ladies. ill. 12°. $3.75..*Scribner, W.& A.*
Modern infidelity. *See* Hall, R.
Modern inquiries. Bigelow, J. $2.50..*Little, B.& Co.*
Modern Jerusalem; rev. by T. O. Summers. ('56.) 2d ed. 18°. '76. 50c. ....*So. Meth.*
Modern Job (The). Peterson, H. 75c...*H.Peterson.*
Modern leaders. McCarthy, J. $1.75......*Sheldon.*
Modern magic. Devere, M. S. $2 ....*Putnam.*
Modern materialism. Martineau, J. 25c. .....*Ellis.*
Modern Othello; or, the guilty wife. 8°. pap., 25c. *De Witt.*
Modern painters. *See* Ruskin, J.
Modern painters and their paintings. Keddie, H. $1.50. *Roberts.*
Modern palmistry. Craig, A. R. $1.75 ....*Redfield.*
Modern Pentecost (A). Wallace, A. $1..*A. Wallace.*
Modern playmate. *See* Wood, J. G.
Modern pocket Hoyle. Trumps. $1.25; 50c.; 75c. *Dick & F.*
Modern prophets. Alden, I. M., *and* Foster, I. H. $1.50 ....*Lothrop.*
Modern revivalism. Dungan, D. R. 15c....*Cen.Bk.*
Modern skepticism. Barker, J. $1.75..*Smith, E.& Co.*
Modern speaker. 3 pts. 16°. ea., pap., 15c.; — in 1 v., 75c. ....*French.*
Modern utilitarianism. Birks, T. R. $2.25..*Macmillan.*
Modern vassal. Wilmer, J. 25c. ....*Littell & G.*
Modern women and what is said of them: reprint. from "Saturday Review;" with introd. by Mrs. L. G. Calhoun. 2 ser. 12°. ea., $2.........*Redfield.*
Modesty and merit. Eppendorff, M. 75c. ...*Fuller.*
Moe, Adelaide Reynolds. Old Fountain Inn, and other poems. 12°. $1.50 ....*Lippincott.*
Moelling, C. E. Faust's death: tragedy. 12°. pap., 75c. ....*Lippincott.*
Moens, W. J. C. English travelers and Italian brigands: a narrative of capture and captivity. ill. 12°. '66. $1.75 ....*Harper.*
Moffat, Ja. C. Alwyn: a romance of study. [Poetry.] 16°. '75. $1.50..................*Randolph.*
— Comparative hist. of religions. 2 v. 12°. '73–'74. ea., $1.75...............................*Dodd.*
Cont.: Pt. 1. Anc. Scriptures. — 2. Latin Scriptures.
— Introduction to study of æsthetics. ('56.) New ed. 12°. '60. $1.25...................... *Wilstach.*
— Life of T: Chalmers. por. 12°. '53. $1.25. *Wilstach.*
— Song and scenery; or, a summer ramble in Scotland. 16°. $1.50; $2.......................*Robertson.*

Moffat, Rob. Missionary scenes and labors in southern Africa. por. 12°. '56. $1 .... *Wilstach.*
— Scenes and adventures in Africa; from "Labors in Africa." 18°. 35c....... .... *Pres. Bd.*
— Stories about Africa. 18°. 35c. .... *Pres. Bd.*

Moffatt, *Mrs.* A. S. One-armed Hugh, little corn-merchant; or, Ralph and Tib. 16°. '66. $1.50 .. *Graves.*

Mogridge, G: ["Old Humphrey."] Cheerful chapters; adapted to youth and not unsuited to age. ill. 18°. '67. 55c..................... *Pres. Com.*
— Half-hours with Old Humphrey. 16°. '50. $1. *Meth. Bk. Conc.*
— Learning to act; — to converse; — to feel; — to think. 4 v. 18°. ea., 55c........... *Pres. Bd.*
— *Same.* 4 v. 18°. ea., 60c............... *Am. S. S.*
— Memoir of Old Humphrey; with gleanings from his portfolio, in prose and verse. 18°. 70c... *Am. S. S.*
— Old Humphrey lib. 1st pt. ('55–'58.) 3d ed. 10 v. 18°. '74–'75. $6 .... *So. Meth.*

Cont.: Memoir, 65c. — Observations, 65c. — Walks in London. — Thoughts for the thoughtful. — Owen Gladdon's wanderings in the Isle of Wight. — Pleasant tales. — Old sea-captain. — Addresses. — Pithy papers, *ea.*, 60c. — Old Michael and young Maurice, 50c.

— *Same.* 2d pt. ('55–'58.) New ed. 12 v. 18°. '68–'75. $6.20 .... *So. Meth.*

Cont.: Chapters for children, 50c. — Country strolls, 60c. — Country tales, 50c. — Homely hints, 60c. — Grandfather Gregory, 40c. — Grandmother Gilbert, 40c. — Cheerful chapters, 60c. — Manners and customs of No. Am. Indians, 60c. — Learning to act — to converse — to feel — to think, *ea.*, 50c.

— Old Humphrey's friendly appeals. 18°. '67. 60c. *N. Y. Ref. Ch. Bd.; Pres. Com.*
— Old Humphrey's study table. *See* Little Dot ser.
— Tales in rhyme for girls. ill. 18°. 50c..... *Pres. Bd.*

Mogul tale. Peake, R. B. 15c. .... *French.*

Mohamed Ali Bey. *See* Ali Bey.

Mohammed *or* **Mahomet**. Life; rev. by T. O. Summers. ('55.) 3d ed. 18°. '75. 50c... *So. Meth.*
— *See also* Koran.

Mohammed and Mohammedanism. Smith, R. B. $1.50................................. *Harper.*

Mohammed Ali and his house. Mundt, C. M. $1.50; $1; $3.50 .... *Appleton.*

Mohan, Milo. Collected works; ed. by J. H. Hopkins. v. 1, 2. sm. 8°. '75. $10................ *Pott.*

Mohicans of Paris. *See* Dumas, A.

Mohr, F: On the grape-vine; tr. by "Horticola." 12°. $1...................................... *Judd.*

Mohun. Cooke, J. E. $2.25 .... *Huntington.*

Moister, W: Missionary memorials in west Africa. 12°. '42. 90c......................... *Meth. Bk. Conc.*

Molé, A. French-English and English-French dictionary. cr. 8°. $2................ *Routledge.*
— *See also* James, W., *and* Molé, A.

Molesworth, Guilford L. Pocket-book of useful formulæ and memoranda for civil and mechanical engineers. ('66.) 5th ed. 32°. '73. $2.. *Baird.*
— *Same;* rev. and enl. roy. 32°. '75. roan, $2.. *Spon.*
— *and* Hurst, J. T. Pocket book of pocket books for engineers. roy. 32°. '76. mor., $5...... *Spon.*

Molière, J: Bapt. P. de. Œuvres complètes. 2 v. 12°. $3.......................... *G. R. Lockwood.*
— Dramatic works; tr. into Eng. prose, with introds. and notes, by C. H. Wall. [To form 3 v.] v. 1. por. 12°. (Bohn.) '76. $1.25 .... *Little, B. & Co.*
— *Same.* v. 1. por. 12°. (Bohn.) '76. $1.40. *Scribner, W. & A.*
— *Same.* v. 1. por. 12°. (Bohn.) '76. $1.50.. *Lippincott.*
— *Same;* tr. by H. Van Laun; with introds., app. and etchings. [To form 6 v.] v. 1–4. demy 8°. '75. ea., $7.50.................. *Scribner, W. & A.*
— Selected pieces. [Fr.] 18°. 75c... *G. R. Lockwood.*
— Avare (L'). Ed. by G. Masson. 16°. 50c.; pap., 25c. .... *Lippincott.*
— Bourgeois gentilhomme (Le). Ed. by F. Tarver. 16°. 50c.; pap., 25c.................. *Lippincott.*

Molière, J: Bapt. P. de, *continued.*
— Femmes savantes (Les). Ed. by A. Roche. 16°. 50c.; pap., 25c. .... *Lippincott.*
— Fourberies (Les) de Scapin. Ed. by M. De Candole. 16°. 50c.; pap., 25c............... *Lippincott.*
— *Eng.* Rogueries of Scapin: comedy; tr. by L. F. Moorehead. 12°. '70. 20c.................. *Fox.*
— Malade (Le) imaginaire. Ed. A. E. Ragon. 16°. 50c.; pap., 25c. .... *Lippincott.*
— Médecin (Le) malgré lui. Ed. by H. Lallemand. 16°. 50c.; pap., 25c.................. *Lippincott.*
— Misanthrope (Le). Ed. by P. H. E. Brette. 16°. 50c.; pap., 25c. .... *Lippincott.*
— *Same;* ed. with notes by E. S. Joynes. ('72.) New ed. 12°. '76. pap., 50c.................. *Holt.*
— Tartuffe (Le). Ed. by J. Bué. 16°. 50c.; pap., 25c. *Lippincott.*

Moll, Carl Bernhard. On Hebrews; — Psalms. *See* Lange, J. P., Commentary.

Moll Flanders. *See* Defoe, D.

Moll Pitcher. Jones, J. S. 15c. .... *French.*

Möller, J: Der vertheidigte Luther. 8°. '68. 75c. *Barthel.*

Möllhausen, Bald. Der Piraten-Lieutenant. 8°. pap., 50c. .... *Morwitz.*

Mollie's Christmas stocking. S., M. H. 60c... *Dutton.*

Molloy, Ger. Geology and revelation. 12°. $1.50. *Noonan.*
— *Same;* with introd. to Am. ed., and Prof. Dana's chapter on cosmogony. ill. 12°. '70. $2.. *Putnam.*

Molly and Kitty; or, peasant life in Ireland, and other tales. ill. 16°. $1.25.................. *O'Shea.*

Molly and Kitty juveniles. 6 v. ill. 16°. $7.50.. *O'Shea.*

Cont.: Molly and Kitty. — Children's trials, by A. Linden. — Tales and legends, by A. Linden. — Seed time and harvest, by R. Koch. — Belle and Lily. — Holly and mistletoe.

Molly and the wineglass. *See* Baker, *Mrs.* H. N. W.

Molly's Bible. Chellis, M. D. $1.50... *H. A. Young.*

Molly's verse. *See* Sunbeam lib.

Momentous question. Ball, E. 15c......... *French.*

Mommsen, Thdr. History of Rome; tr. with add. by W. P. Dixon, with introd. by L. Schmitz. ('68.) New ed., with index. 4 v. cr. 8°. '76. ea., $2; per set, hf. cf., $16.................. *Scribner.*

Mona, the vestal. *See* Dorsey, *Mrs.* A. H.

Monachesi, Herb. D., *and* Yohn, Alb. B. (*ed.*) Stationers' handbook; with alphabet. indexes of subjects, firms and trade specialties. roy. 8°. '76. *net*, $1.50 .... *Publishers' Weekly.*

Monarch of Mincing-Lane. Black, W. 50c... *Harper.*

Monastery. *See* Scott, *Sir* Wa.

Monastery of St. Just. Delavigne, C. 15c... *French.*

Monastier, Ant. History of the Vaudois church; tr. 12°. '49. $1.20................ *Meth. Bk. Conc.*

Monckton, Ja. H. National carpenter and joiner; with col. diagrams. roy. 4°. $6.... *Woodward.*
— National stair-builder: complete work on stair-building and hand-railing; with col. diagrams, etc. roy. 4°. $6.................................. *Woodward.*

Moncriefe, L. A. Lionel St. Clair. 18°. 75c. *Carter; Dutton.*

Moncrieff, Rob. Hope. ["Ascott Hope."] Book about boys. 16°. '68. 75c.................. *Roberts.*
— *Same.* 16°. $1.......................... *Miller.*
— Book about dominies. 16°. '68. 75c...... *Roberts.*
— Day after the holidays. ill. 12°. $1.50... *Appleton.*
— Oudendale: story of school-boy life. ill. 16°. $1.25. *Sheldon.*
— School-boy hero; or, Arthur Fortescue. 18°. 50c. (?) *Martien.*

Moncrieff, W: T: [Plays.] 22 v. 16°. ea., pap., 15c. *French.*

Cont.: All at Coventry: farce. — Bashful man: farce. — Beggar of Cripplegate. — Cataract of the Ganges. — Diamond arrow: comedy. — Eugene Aram. — Giovanni in London: extravaganza. — Gipsy Jack: extravaganza. — Joconde: comedy. — Lear of

Moncrieff, W: T: *continued.*

private life. — Mistress of the mill: comedietta. — Monsieur Tonson: farce. — Ravens of Orleans. — Reform. — Rochester: comedy. — Scamps of London. — Shakespeare's festival. — Shipwreck of the Medusa. — Somnambulist: farce. — Spectre bridegroom: farce. — Tom and Jerry: burletta. — Van Dieman's land.

— All at Coventry. *See* French's comic dramas.

Moncure, *Mrs.* M. B. Art of good living. [Cook book.] 12°. '70. $1.25 .... *West, J. & Co.*

Monday Club. Sermons on the International Sunday school lessons for 1876. ('75.) New ed. cr. 8°. '76. $1.50 .... *Lockwood, B. & Co.*

Monday work. Putnam, E. T. H. $1.50... *Cong. Pub.*

Monell, J. J. Washington's head-quarters, Newburgh [N. Y.]: handbook of revolutionary localities embraced in ten miles around N. 12°. 75c.; pap., 50c.......... *Ruttenber.*

Money. *See* Bulwer-Lytton, *Sir* E. G. E. L.

Money. Hildeburn, M. J. 60c. .... *Pres. Bd.*

Money: its history, nature, use, etc. ('56.) 2d ed. 18°. '75. 50c. .... *So. Meth.*

Money and its capabilities. Seiss, J. A. 10c. *Luth. Bk. St.*

Money and the mechanism of exchange. Jevons, W. S. $1.75 .... *Appleton.*

Money God. Quinton, M. A. $1.50; $2.. *Kelly, P. & Co.*

Money in the garden. Quinn, P. T. $1.50.... *Judd.*

Money king. Saxe, J. G. $1.......... *Osgood.*

Money-maker. Adams, W. T. $1.50....... *Lee & S.*

Money makes the man: comedietta. 16°. pap., 15c. *Happy.*

Money question. Berkey, W. A. $1.50; $1.. *Berkey.*

Moneyless man. Stanton, H. T. $1.75... *Turnbull.*

Monfort Hall. Warfield, C. A. $1.75..... *Peterson.*

Monge, Gaspard. Elementary treatise on statics; with biog. notice of author; tr. by W. Baker. 12°. '51. $1.50 .... *Fortescue.*

Monica, mother of St. Augustine; from the Germ. by R. Shiveley. 16°. 50c.......... *Ref. Ch. Pub.*

Monikins. *See* Cooper, J. F.

Monitions of the unseen. *See* Ingelow, J.

Monitory letters to church members. 12°. 60c. *Pres. Bd.*

Monk, Mar. Awful disclosures of Maria Monk, of the Hotel Dieu Nunnery of Montreal. 12°. $1.50. *De Witt.*

Monk, T: National drawing books. 6 nos. obl. 24°–obl. f°. '67. per doz., pap., $4.50.... *Barnes.*

Monk, W: H: Hymns, anc. and mod.; for use in the services of the church; with tunes. 12°. '71. 55c.; 60c.; — with app., 90c.; $1 ...... *Claxton.*

Monk (The). Lewis, M. G. 50c. .... *Peterson.*

Monk of Cimies. *See* Sherwood, *Mrs.* M. M.

Monkey (The): conversation about monkeys. 18°. 18c. .... *Am. S. S.*

Monkey of Porto Bello. Shanley, C. D. 50c. *Hurd & H.*

Monkhouse, W. Cosmo. *See* Sheepshanks gallery.

Monkland, *Mrs.* —. The nabob at home; or, the return to England. 8°. pap., 50c...... *Harper.*

Monk's revenge. Spring, S. 50c.......... *De Witt.*

Monmonier, J: F., *and* Mc Jilton, J: N. High school literature: selection of readings. ('52.) 3d ed. 12°. $1.75 .... *Barnes.*

Monmouth, *Mrs.* Lizzie Harpe. ["So. Homespun."] [Juveniles.] 5 v. ill. 16°. '70–'71. ea., $1.. *Lothrop.*

Cont.: Blue-eyed Jimmy; or, the good boy. — Johnny Jones; or, the bad boy. — Much fruit. — Nettie Nesmith; or, the bad girl. — Ruthie Shaw; or, the good girl.

Monnier, M: Wonders of Pompeii; tr. from the Fr. ill. 12°. '74. $1.25.......... *Scribner.*

Monnin, Alfr. Mater admirabilis; or, the first fifteen years of Mary immaculate; tr. 12°. $1.50.. *Strong.*

Monod, Adph. Dance (The) and the martyr; tr. 18°. '71. 25c.......... *Am. Tr.*

— Five discourses on St. Paul; [also one] on fatalism; tr. by J. H. Myers. ('59.) New ed. 12°. '76. 90c. *Draper.*

— Loving words in two sermons to children; tr. 18°. 40c.......... *Pres. Bd.*

— Lucile, ou la lecture de la Bible. 18°. 30c. *Pres. Bd.*

— *Same.* 18°. '52. 30c.......... *Am. Tr.*

— *Eng.* Lucilla; or, reading the Bible. 16°. 75c. *Carter.*

— *Germ.* Ist die Bibel von Gott eingegeben? 18°. '59. 35c. .... *Am. Tr.*

— *Span.* Lucila, ó la lectura de la Biblia. 18°. '58. 45c. .... *Am. Tr.*

— Man's gift to God; tr. 18°. pap., 12c. *Cin. Meth. Bk. Conc.*

— Parting words to [his] friends and the church, 1855–6; tr. por. 12°. '75. $1.50.......... *Dutton.*

— Pouvez-vous mourir tranquille? 18°. '45. pap., 8c. *Am. Tr.*

Monod, Thdr. Christian (The) and his cross; tr. from the Fr. sq. 24°. '74. 50c.; 35c.......... *Am. Tr.*

— *Same;* [also] Christianity and discipline; tr. 2 v. in 1. 16°. 40c.......... *West. Tr.*

— Looking unto Jesus; tr. 64°. '75. 15c.; 50c... *Am. Tr.*

Monopolies and the people. Cloud, D. C. $2.50; $3. *Day.*

Monro, E: Dark mountains: sequel to "Journey home." New ed. 16°. '65. 60c....... *Dutton.*

— Dark river: allegory. New ed. 16°. '65. 60c... *Dutton.*

— Journey home: allegory. New ed. 18°. '69. 60c. *Dutton.*

Monroe, Anna. The model Sunday-school speaker. 16°. 60c.; 75c.......... *Lee & S.*

Monroe, Ben. *See* Kentucky, Court of appeals reports.

— *and* Harlan, Ja. Digest of Kentucky Court of appeals cases (1792–1853). 2 v. 8°. '53. shp., $12 .... *Clarke.*

Monroe, J. Light infantry, company and skirmish drill. 32°. '63. 75c.......... *Van Nostrand.*

Monroe, J. A. Removal of broken piles from Connecticut River. 8°. pap., 25c.... *Am. Soc. of C. E.*

— Replacing a stone pier on a pile foundation. *See* Nickerson, L., Experiments, etc.

Monroe, J. R. Dramas and miscellaneous poems. 8°. '75. $1.50.......... *J. R. Monroe; Williams.*

Monroe, Ja. The people the sovereigns: comparison of the government of the U. S. with those of previous republics; ed. by S. Gouverneur. 12°. '67. $1.75.......... *Claxton; Lippincott.*

Monroe, Lew. B. [Spellers and readers.] 8 v. '71–'75.......... *Cowperthwait.*

Cont.: First steps in spelling, 16°, bds., 25c. — Advanced spell. book, 12°, bds., 35c. — First reader, 16°, bds., 30c. — Second, 16°, 50c. — Third, 16°, bds., 70c. — Fourth, 12°, $1; bds., 84c. — Fifth, 12°, $1.25. — Sixth, 12°, $1.50.

— Dialogues and dramas. 12°. $1.50....... *Lee & S.*

— Humorous readings in prose and verse. 12°. $1.50. *Lee & S.*

— Physical and vocal training. ('69.) New ed. 12°. '73. $1.......... *Cowperthwait.*

Monroe, *Mrs.* Ma. C. Souvenirs of Notre Dame: dramas and poems. 12°. '76. $2.... *Cath. Pub.*

Monroe, T: B. *See* Kentucky, Court of Appeals reports.

Monsanto, H. M. *See* Ollendorff, H. G.; — Wrage, H. D., *and* Monsanto, H. M.

— *and* Languellier, L. A. Practical course with the French language on Woodbury's plan with the German. 12°. '73. $2.......... *Ivison.*

— — Practical course with the Spanish lang. on Woodbury's plan with the German; with vocab. 12°. $1.75 .... *Ivison.*

Monseigneur. Archer, T. 15c.......... *Lee & S.*

Monsell, J. S. B. Our new vicar: plain words about ritualism and parish work. 16°. '75. $1.50.. *Pott.*

Monser, J. W. Follies of free thoughts; written against spiritualism and every form of infidelity. 24°. '72. pap., 20c. . . . . *Cen. Bk.*

Monsieur Antoine. Sand, G. $1; 75c. . . . . *Peterson.*

Monsieur Jacques. Barnett, M. 15c. . . . . *French.*

Monsieur Pierre: drama. 16°. pap., 15c. . . . *Happy.*

Monsieur Sylvestre. Sand, G. $1.50 . . . . . . *Roberts.*

Monsieur Tonson. Moncrieff, W. T. 15c. . . . *French.*

Monsieur Violet. *See* Marryat, F:

Monson, E: Advantages of the separate system of drainage, with description of works at Halstead, Essex, [Eng.] 8°. '75. pap., 40c. . . . . *Spon.*

— Sewage no value. 8°. pap., 80c. . . . . *Spon.*

Monsters of the deep. ill. 12°. $1.25 . . . . *Nelson.*

Monstrelet, Enguerrand de. Chronicles, 1400–1467, and contin. by others to 1516; tr. by T. Johnes. 2 v. ill. roy. 8°. hf. roxb., $9 . . . . *Routledge.*

Montagu, E: Wortley. Autobiography. 12°. $1.75; pap., $1.50 . . . . *Peterson.*

Montagu, *Lady* Ma. Wortley. Letters; ed. with memoir by Mrs. S. J. Hale. 12°. '68. $1.50 . . *Roberts.*

Montague, W. L. Comparative grammar of the Span. lang. 12°. $1.25 . . . . *Schoenhoff.*

Montaigne, Mich. Eyquem de. Works; compr. Essays, Journey into Italy and Letters; tr., with notes, etc., by W. Hazlitt. New ed., rev.; ed. by O. W. Wight. 4 v. por. cr. 8°. $9; hf. cf., $16 . . . . *Hurd & H.*

— Essays, tr.; ed. by author of "Gentle life." 16°. $3. 12°. $1.75 . . . . *Scribner, W. & A.*

Montaine. Vinet, A. $1.75 . . . . *Dodd.*

Montalembert, C: Forbes (*Comte*) de. Monks of the west, from St Benedict to St. Bernard; tr. 2 v. 8°. $6; hf. cf., $10 . . . . *Noonan.*

Montana. Codified laws, 1868–'72. 8°. '72. shp., $7.50 . . . . *Bancroft.*

— Supreme Court reports, 1868–'73; by H. N. Blake. 2 v. 8°. shp., $15 . . . . *Bancroft; S. Whitney.*

Montarges legacy. Meline, M. M. $1 . . *Cunningham.*

Montcalm: romantic drama. 16°. pap., 15c. . . *French.*

Monte Cristo. *See* Dumas, A.

Monte Cristo: drama. 16°. pap., 15c. . . . . *French.*

Monteiro, Joac. J: Angola and the river Congo. ill. and maps. cr. 8°. '76. $2.50 . . . . *Macmillan.*

Monteith, A. H. French [; — German; — Spanish; — Latin; — Italian] without a master. 12°. ea., pap., 40c.; — in 1 vol., $2 . . . . *Peterson.*

Monteith, Ja. Comprehensive geography. 4°. '72. hf. bd., $1.60 . . . . *Barnes.*

— Elementary geography. sm. 4°. '74. hf. bd., 80c. *Barnes.*

— First lessons in geog.; on plan of object teaching. sm. 4°. '72. hf. bd., 35c. . . . . *Barnes.*

— Introduction to "Manual of geog." sm. 4°. '67. hf. bd., 63c. . . . . *Barnes.*

— Manual of geog. comb. with hist. and astron. 4°. '68. hf. bd., $1.10 . . . . *Barnes.*

— Manual of map-drawing (Allen's system). sm. 4°. 25c. . . . . *Barnes.*

— Map-drawing and object-lessons. 4°. '69. bds., 75c. *Barnes.*

— Map-drawing made easy. 4°. '75. pap., 20c. *Barnes.*

— Physical and intermediate geography. 4°. '66. hf. bd., $1.75 . . . . *Barnes.*

— Physical and political geography. 4°. '66. hf. bd., $1.88 . . . . *Barnes.*

— Physical geog.; on plan of object teaching. 4°. '73. hf. bd., $1 . . . . *Barnes.*

— Youth's hist. of the U. S.; for intermediate classes. 4°. '58. hf. bd., 75c. . . . . *Barnes.*

— *See also* Allen, J.

Montépin, Xav. Aymon de. *See* Basté, E. P., *and* Montépin, X. A. de.

Montesano, R. R. Redstick; or, scenes in the south. ill. 8°. pap., 25c. . . . . *U. P. James.*

Montesquieu, C: de Secondat (*Baron*) de. De l'esprit des lois. 12°. $1.50 . . . . *G. R. Lockwood.*

— *Eng.* Spirit of laws; tr. by T. Nugent. New ed., rev. with memoir of author and analysis of the work by d'Alembert. 2 v. 8°. '73. $6 . . *Clarke.*

— Grandeur et décadence des Romains. 12°. $1.50. *G. R. Lockwood.*

Montez, Lola Mar. [*Countess Landsfeldt.*] Anecdotes of love. 12°. $1.50 . . . . *Dick & F.*

— Arts of beauty; or, secrets of a lady's toilet; with hints to gentlemen on art of fascinating. 16°. 75c. *Dick & F.*

— Lectures and life. 12°. $1.75; pap., $1.50 . . *Peterson.*

Montezuma, the serf. Ingraham, J. H. 75c. *Dick & F.*

Montfort, the roué; or, the French incendiary. 8°. pap., 25c. . . . . *De Witt.*

Montgomery, Flo. Misunderstood. 12°. '70. $1.25. *Randolph.*

— Thrown together. 12°. $1.50 . . . . *Lippincott.*

— Thwarted; or, ducks' eggs in a hen's nest. 12°. $1.25 . . . . *Lippincott.*

— Very simple story. ill. 16°. '71. 60c. . . . . *Randolph.*

Montgomery, G. W. Illustrations of law of kindness. 18°. '41. 65c. *Universalist.*

Montgomery, H: W. Handy Andy: drama. 16°. pap., 15c. . . . . *French.*

Montgomery, J. H. The Christian. 18°. 40c. *U. P. Bd. of Pub.*

Montgomery, Ja. Poems. 12°. $1.50 . . . . *Locke.*

— *Same;* with memoir. 5 v. por. 18°. $5 . . . *Osgood.*

— *Same;* with memoir and notes. (Chandos poets.) por. and ill. cr. 8°. $3.75–$8 . . *Scribner, W. & A.*

— Poetical works. (Household ser.) ill. 16°. $1.50; mor., $3 . . . . *Lee & S.*

— *Same;* with memoir. (Presentation poets.) ill. 16°. $1.75 . . . . *Routledge.*

— — *See also* Pollok, R., Poems; — Rogers, S., Poetical works.

— Lectures on general literature, poetry, etc. 18°. 75c. *Harper.*

Montgomery, W. F. Exposition of the signs and symptoms of pregnancy. ill. 8°. $3.75 . . . . *Lea.*

Month at Brighton. Shipley, M. E. 50c. . . . . . . *Pott.*

Month of the holy angels; or, the month of October consecrated to the holy angels. [Catholic prayer book.] 32°. 50c. . . . . *Cummiskey.*

Month of Mary: meditations, etc., in honor of the Virgin, arr. for each day of the month. 32°. 40c. . . . . *Cath. Pub.*

— *See also* Beckx, P. J.

Month of the sacred heart of Jesus: devotions for June. [Cath. prayer book.] 24°. 50c. . . *Strong.*

— *Same;* [also] Arch confraternity of sacred heart; [also] Borgo's Novena to the sacred heart of Jesus. 24°. '59. 50c. . . . . *Cunningham.*

Month of St. Joseph: exercises for March. [Cath. prayer book.] 16°. 75c. . . . . *Sadlier.*

Months and seasons. Gutterson, A. C. 20c. . . *Church.*

Monti, — de. Favorite mass in B flat. 8°. '56. $1; bds., 80c.; pap., 65c. . . . . *Ditson.*

Montolieu, Jeanne Is. P. de B. (*Baronne*) de. Enchanted plants: fables in verse. 32°. 35c. *U. P. James.*

— *See also* Wyss, J. R. v., *and* Montolieu.

Montreal, Ma. Wings or weights. 18°. 45c. . . *Am. S. S.*

Montreal: 12 views with descript. letter press. obl. 24°. 75c. . . . . *Nelson.*

Montreuil, *Baron* Alfr. de. Life of St. Zita, a servant girl of Lucca, in 13th cent.; [also] Life of Catherine Teaghoknita, the Iroquois virgin, by Father de Charlevoix, tr. from the Fr. 18°. 60c.; 90c. . . . . *O'Shea.*

Monument of parental affection. 18°. 35c...*Am.S.S.*

Monumental Christianity. Lundy, J. P. $7.50; $10; $15...*Bouton.*

Monumental city [Baltimore]: its past history and present resources. ill. 8°. '74. $2.50; $3. *Howard.*

Monuments of art; with text by W. Lübke and von Lützow. 3 v.: engr., 2 v., obl. f°.; text, 1 v., 8°. hf. mor., $50...*Stroefer.*

Monzert, L. Independent liquorist: art of manufacturing syrups, bitters, cordials, extracts, etc. 12°. $3...*Dick & F.*

Mooar, G: Historical manual of the South Church, Andover, Mass. por. 12°. '59. $1.25..*Draper.*

Mood, F. A. Methodism in Charleston, [S. C.] ('55.) 2d ed. 18°. '75. 65c...*So.Meth.*

Moodie, *Mrs.* Susannah. [Novels.] 5 v. 12°..*De Witt.*

Cont.: Flora Lyndsay; or, passages in an eventful life.—Geoffrey Moncton; or, the faithless guardian.—Mark Hurdlestone; or, the two brothers, *ea.*, $1.25.—Life in the clearing vs. the bush, $1.50.—Roughing it in the bush, pap., $1.

Moods. Alcott, L. M. $1.25...*Loring.*

Moody, Clement. New Testament expounded and illustrated. 8°. '51. $4...*Meth.Bk.Conc.*

Moody, Dwight Lyman. Addresses. 8°. 75c.; pap., 50c...*Niver.*

— *Same.* ('75.) New ed. 12°. '76. $1.25; 75c.; pap., 50c...*Revell.*

— Addresses and lectures; with narr. of the awakening in Liverpool and London. (Supplement. issue.) 8°. '75. pap., 50c...*Randolph.*

— Best thoughts and discourses of M.: work of Moody and Sankey as evangelists, with sketches of their lives by A. C. Morrow; introd. by E. J. Haynes. 16°. '76. 75c.; $1; pap., 40c...*Tibbals.*

— Glad tidings. [Discourses.] 12°. '76. $2; pap., $1. *Treat.*

— How to study the Bible. 16°. '75. 25c.; pap., 15c. *Randolph; Revell.*

— *Same;* [also] Hints on Bible marking, by Mrs. S. Menzies. sq. 18°. '76. 40c...*Randolph.*

— *See also* Clark, R. W., Work of God in Gt. Brit.

— *and* Sankey, I. D. Narrative of labors in Great Britain and Ireland; with addresses and lectures. 8°. '75. $1; pap., 75c...*Randolph.*

Moody, Granville. Popery and its aims. 12°. 50c. *Cin.Meth.Bk.Conc.*

Moody, Loring. Problem of life and immortality: inquiry into origin, composition and destiny of man: lecture, Boston Y. M. C. Union. ('72.) 2d ed., enl. 12°. '75. 75c...*Colby.*

Moody, Sophy. The fairy tree; or, stories from far and near. ill. 12°. $1.50...*Nelson.*

Moody, W: *See* England, Common law reports; Crown cases.

Moody Mike. Sewall, F. $1...*Lippincott.*

Moon, G: Wash. Dean's (The) English: crit. on Alford's "Queen's English." 16°. $1.25. *Routledge.*

— Soul's (The) inquiries answered in words of Scripture: year book of texts. 32°. '70. 75c...*Pott.*

— *Same;* with introd. by T. L. Cuyler. sq. 32°. '73. 25c...*Randolph.*

— — *Same.* 24°. '72. 50c.; —with diary, $1...*Crowell.*

— What the Bible says about prayer. sq. 24°. pap., 10c. *Dutton.*

Moonfolk. Austin, J. G. $2...*Putnam.*

Moonlight Jack. 8°. pap., 25c...*De Witt.*

Moonshine. Knatchbull-Hugessen, E. H. $1.75. *Macmillan.*

Moonstone (The). *See* Collins, Wilkie.

Moorcroft Hatch. Tucker, C. 75c...*Hoyt.*

Moore, A. *See* Hancock, W., *and* Moore, A.

Moore, A. Y. Life of Schuyler Colfax. por. 12°. $1.50...*Peterson.*

Moore, Alex. First help in accidents and in sickness: guide in absence of medical assistance. ill. 12°. '71. $1.50; pap., $1...*A.Moore.*

— Gas consumer's guide. ill. 12°. $1; pap., 75c. *A.Moore.*

— (*ed.*) Good health lib. 4 v. 8°. '70–'73. ea., $2.50. *A.Moore.*

Moore, *Mrs.* C. J. Miscellaneous poems. 12°. '75. $1.50...*Porter.*

— On dangerous ground; or, Agatha's friendship: romance of Am. society. 12°. '76. $1.50; pap., $1; —(Intern. ed.) 12°. $1.25...*Porter.*

Moore, C: W. New Masonic trestle-board. 12°. '50. $1.50...*Williams.*

Moore, Clem. C. Visit from Santa Claus. ill. f°. pap., 15c.; 20c...*J.E.Potter.*

— *Same.* ill. 4°. bds., 40c...*Miller.*

— Visit from St. Nicholas. ill. 4°. pap., 50c...*Hurd & H.*

Moore, Dan., Marston, C. D., *and* Bayley, *Sir* E. Three lectures on preaching. 16°. '74. $1..*Pott.*

Moore, E. F. *See* England, Law reports.

Moore, E: Gamester: tragedy. 16°. pap., 15c...*French.*

Moore, Fk. Women of the war: their heroism and self-sacrifice. ill. 8°. '66. $3; $3.50..*Scranton.*

— (*ed.*) Cyclopædia of Am. eloquence. 2 v. por. 8°. $7; shp., $8; hf. mor., $10...*Appleton.*

— Diary of the Am. rev., 1775–1781, as described by contemporaries. ill. 8°. '76. *$3.75..*Burr; Lloyd.*

— Illustrated ballad history of the Am. revolution by contemporary poets and prose writers. [To form 30 pts.] pts. 1–6. por., map, ill., etc. 4°. ea., 50c...*Johnson & M.*

— Portrait gallery of the [civil] war, civil, military and naval: a biog. record. 60 por. roy. 8°. '65. $6; hf. cf., $7.50...*Van Nostrand.*

— Spirit of the Bible: ill. with Scriptural sel. in English, French and German. ill. 12°. '74. $5; $6; hf. mor., $7.50; mor., $10...*U.S.Pub.*

Moore, G. F. *See* Texas, Sup. Court reports.

Moore, G: Elements of science. 16°. 75c...*Sheldon.*

— Health, disease and remedy in a few of their relations to the blood. 18°. 75c...*Harper.*

— Man and his motives. 12°. $1...*Harper.*

— Power of the soul over the body, in rel. to health and morals. 12°. $1...*Harper.*

— Use of the body in rel. to the mind. 12°. $1..*Harper.*

Moore, *Mrs.* H. J. Anna Clayton; or, the mother's trial. 16°. $1.25...*J.E.Potter.*

Moore, H: Instructions for prep. abstracts of titles; with precedents, etc.; [also] Treatise on power of courts to compel production of documents, by C. E. Pollock. 8°. '53. $1.50. *T. & J. W. Johnson.*

— — *See also* Law lib.

Moore, *Rev.* H: Life of J: Fletcher. 12°. '36. $1.25. *Meth.Bk.Conc.*

— Life of Mrs. Ma. Fletcher. ('57.) 2d ed. 18°. '75. $1...*So.Meth.*

— *Same.* 12°. '37. $1.50...*Meth.Bk.Conc.*

Moore, Ira M. Treatise on jurisdiction of justices of the peace in civil actions in Ill.; with forms. 8°. '75. shp., $7.50...*Callaghan.*

— Treatise on jurisdiction of justices of the peace, and in courts of record, in criminal cases in Ill.; with forms. 8°. '76. shp., $7.50...*Callaghan.*

Moore, *Mrs.* J. F. [Juveniles.] ('69–'74.) New ed. 7 v. 16°. '71–'76...*Hoyt.*

Cont.: Home in a rough suburb.—Linside farm.—Miriam Brandon; or, trials and triumphs, *ea.*, $1.25.—Losses and gains; or, birthdays.—Nanny Davenport; or, work for the master.—Rescued.—Tom Bentley, *ea.*, $1.50.

Moore, J. G: That blessed baby: farce. 16°. pap., 15c...*French.*

Moore, J. H. Perfect plan of salvation. 8°. '74. pap., 15c...*Brumbaugh.*

Moore, J. H. Political condition of Indians and resources of the Indian territory. 12°. pap., 50c. *S. W. Bk. & Pub.*

Moore, J. T. The Clifford household. ill. 16°. '69. $1 .... *Dodd.*

Moore, Ja. Complete hist. of the great rebellion; with introd. by R. S. Mackenzie. por. and ill. 12°. *$2.50; mor., $3; $4.......... *Quak. City.*

— Kilpatrick and our cavalry: account of raids, etc., during rebellion. ill. 12°. $1.25.... *Widdleton.*

Moore, J: Mad dogs: farce. 16°. pap., 15c... *French.*

Moore, J: Bayly. *See* England, Common law reports.

Moore, J: H. Tom Stapleton. 8°. pap., 50c. *Dick & F.*

Moore, J: W. Dictionary of musical information; with vocab. of mus. terms and list of mus. works pub. in the U. S., 1640–1875. 12°. '76. $1.50; bds., $1.25 .... *Ditson.*

— Encyclopædia of music; with app. to 1876. ('52.) New ed. 8°. '75. $6; — app. alone, bds., 50c. *Ditson.*

Moore, Natl. Ancient mineralogy: inquiry resp. mineral substances mentioned by the ancients; with remarks on uses to which they were applied. 16°. $1 .... *Harper.*

Moore, Ra. Wilson. Journal during a tour to the West Indies and South Am. in 1863–4; with notes from the diary of her husband, and his memoir by G. Truman. 12°. *net*, $1....... *Friends Bk. Assoc.*

Moore, R: Artisan's guide, and everybody's assistant. 16°. '75. $2.......... *Murray.*

Moore, R: Channing. Life. 18°. 55c.; 60c... *Dutton.*

Moore, S. Grandmother's stories for her children. 24°. *net*, 15c.; pap., 10c.......... *Friends Bk. Assoc.*

Moore, Smith W. Our church in Sandburg. 3d ed. 12°. '74. $1.25.......... *So. Meth.*

Moore, T. V. Corporate life of the church. 18°. '68. 25c. .... *N. Y. Ref. Ch. Bd.; Pres. Com.*

— Culdee church (The): hist. connection of modern Presb. churches with those of apostolic times, through the church of Scotland. ill. 18°. '68. 40c.......... *N. Y. Ref. Ch. Bd.; Pres. Com.*

— Last days of Jesus; or, appearances of our Lord during the forty days between the resurrection and ascension. 16°. 90c.......... *Pres. Bd.*

Moore, T: British ferns and their allies. ill. 16°. '74. $1.25; bds., 50c.......... *Routledge.*

— *See also* Lindley, J., *and* Moore, T.

Moore, T: Works. ill. 12°. $2; mor., $5.. *Claxton.*

— *Same.* 8°. $2.75.......... *Lee & S.*

— *Same.* ill. 8°. $3; mor., $7; $7.50.... *Lippincott.*

— *Same.* 8°. shp., $4.50; mor., $10 .... *Mason.*

— *Same.* ill. 8°. (Dick.) 50c.; pap., 25c... *Am. News.*

— Poems. 12°. $1.50.......... *Locke.*

— *Same.* (Blue and gold ed.) 18°. $1.25... *Nichols & H.*

— *Same.* (Boston ed.) 8°. shp., $4.50; mor., $10. *Mason.*

— *Same.* (Cabinet ed.) 16°. $1.50 .... *Nichols & H.*

— *Same.* (Scribner's pop. poets.) ill. 12°. $1.50. *Scribner, W. & A.*

— *Same;* with memoir. 6 v. por. 18°. $6.. *Osgood.*

— *Same;* ed. by R. A. Willmott, with biog., etc. (British poets.) ill. 12°. $2.25; hf. cf., $3.50; mor., $5 .... *Routledge.*

— Poetical works. ill. 12°. $1.50........ *World Pub.*

— *Same.* por. 8°. $2.50.......... *Lee & S.*

— *Same.* 8°. $3 .... *Desilver.*

— *Same.* (Boston ed.) 8°. shp., $3.50; mor., $10. *Lee & S.*

— *Same.* (Chandos classics.) cr. 8°. $1; pap., 75c. *Scribner, W. & A.*

— *Same.* (Chandos poets.) ill. and por. cr. 8°. $3.75; cf., $7.50; mor., $8.......... *Scribner, W. & A.*

— *Same.* (Shamrock ed.) ill. 12°. $2; mor., $5.. *Claxton.*

— *Same;* with biog. sketch and index. ill. 8°. $2; shp., $2.75.......... *World Pub.*

Moore, T: *continued.*

— *Same;* with memoir by M. Balmanno. 2 v. in 1. ill. 4°. $13.50–$16.......... *Johnson & M.*

— *Same;* ed. by Sir E. Brydges; ill. by Martin and Turner. 8°. mor., $10. — (chp. ed.) por. and ill. 16°. shp., $3.50.......... *Appleton.*

— *Same;* with memoir by D. Herbert. por. and ill. roy. 8°. $2.50; shp., $3; mor., $7 .... *Claxton.*

— *Same;* with biog. by W. Howitt. (Household ser.) ill. 16°. $1.50; mor., $3.......... *Lee & S.*

— *Same;* ed. by R. A. Willmott. (Presentation poets.) ill. 12°. $1.75; $3; mor., $3.50..... *Routledge.*

— Epicurean: romance. 12°. $1.25.......... *Miller.*

— History of Ireland. 2 v. 8°. $5.......... *Strong.*

— Irish melodies. 32°. 38c.......... *Appleton.*

— *Same.* 24°. 50c.; pap., 25c.......... *Routledge.*

— *Same.* 16°. $1.25.......... *Mason; Osgood.*

— *Same.* (Blue and gold ed.) 18°. 75c... *Appleton.*

— *Same;* with pref. letter on music. 32°. 50c. *U. P. James.*

— *Same;* with symphonies and accomp. by Sir J. Stevenson. New ed., ed. by J. W. Glover. 4°. $4.50.......... *Sadlier.*

— — *Same.* 4°. '52. $3; $4; bds., $2.50... *Ditson.*

— *Same;* with names of the old Irish airs [and sel.] poems. 32°. 50c.; pap., 25c. .... *Noonan.*

— *Same;* [also] Lalla Rookh. 16°. $3.50.... *Mason.*

— *Same;* [also] national airs, sacred songs, etc.; with memoirs and notes by J. Savage. 32°. 75c.; mor., $1.25; $2.......... *Sadlier.*

— *Same;* [also] songs. (Emerald ser.) 32°. '74. 50c.; bds., 25c. .... *Routledge.*

— — *See also* Literature, art and song.

— Lalla Rookh, an Oriental romance: poem. 32°. 37c. 24°. 75c. .... *Appleton.*

— *Same.* 32°. 50c.......... *U. P. James.*

— *Same.* 24°. 50c.; pap., 25c. .... *Routledge.*

— *Same.* 16°. $1.25.......... *Mason; Osgood.*

— *Same.* ill. 12°. $1.50 .... *World Pub.*

— *Same.* ill. 4°. $4.......... *Routledge.*

— *Same.* (Blue and gold ed.) 18°. 75c.... *Appleton.*

— *Same.* (Emerald ser.) 32°. '74. 50c.; bds., 25c. *Routledge.*

— *Same;* with notes. ill. cr. 8°. $1.75–$6.. *Hurd & H.*

— *Same;* with notes. (Cabinet ed.) ill. 16°. $1.25; $1.75; hf. roxb., $3; mor., $4.50 .... *Hurd & H.*

— *Same;* [also] Poems, by J. Thomson. ill. 16°. $1.12; $1.35. 32°. 85c.; $1.12 .... *World Pub.*

— Life and letters of Lord Byron. New ed. ill. 12°. '74. $3 .... *Routledge.*

— *Same.* 2 v. 8°. $4; hf. cf., $8.50....... *Harper.*

— *Same.* 2 v. 8°. '72. $4; shp., $5...... *Claxton.*

— — *See also* Byron, *Lord.*

— Memoirs of R. B. Sheridan. 2 v. por. cr. 8°. $3; hf. cf., $6 .... *Widdleton.*

— Moral and beautiful from [his] poems; ed. by W. Colton. 32°. 60c.–$1.50. — (Red line ed.) sq. 16°. $1.50–$3.50.......... *Porter.*

— Travels of an Irish gentleman in search of a religion. 12°. '52. $1.50.......... *Murphy.*

— *See also* Anacreon, Odes; — Stoddard, R. H., Bric-a-brac ser.

Moore, W. D. *See* Carlton, S. P., *and* Moore, W. D.

Moore, W: E. Digest of acts and deliverances of General Assembly of Presb. Church; with index. 8°. $4 .... *Pres. Bd.*

— Presbyterian digest: compend of acts and deliverances of the Gen. Assem. of Presb. Church in the U. S. 8°. $5 .... *Pres. Bd.*

Moore, W: T: Church of the future. 8°. pap., 10c. *Chase.*

— Our strength and our weakness. 8°. pap., 10c. *Chase.*

— Views of life: addresses on social and relig. questions of the age. 12°. $1.50.......... *Chase.*

— Woman's work in the church. 12°. pap., 10c... *Chase.*

— (*ed.*) Living pulpit of the Christian church: discourses, with brief biog. sketch. por. 8°. $3; $4; mor., $8.......... *Chase.*

— *See also* New Testament commentary.

Moorhead, —. Tau-go-ru-a: hist. drama in prose. 12°. $1 .... *Peterson.*
Moorhouse, Ja. Jacob: three sermons, Univ. of Camb., 1870. fp. 8°. '70. $1 ..... *Macmillan.*
— Some modern difficulties resp. facts of nature and revelation. [Sermons.] fp. 8°. $1.. *Macmillan.*
— *See also* Hulsean lectures.
Moorland cottage. Gaskell, E. C. 75c. .... *Harper.*
Moorman, J: J. Mineral springs of North America: how to reach and how to use them. ill. 12°. $2. *Lippincott.*
— Mineral waters of the U. S. and Canada. 12°. '67. $1.50 .... *Kelly, P. & Co.*
Moorson, J. M. *See* England, Law reports.
Moos, H. M. Carrie Harrington: sequel to "Hannah." 16°. 50c. .... *Bloch.*
— Hannah; or, a glimpse of paradise. 16°. $2.50; pap., $1 .... *Bloch.*
— Mortara; or, the pope and his inquisitors: drama. 16°. 75c. .... *Bloch.*
Moosrose (Die): e. Erzählung. 24°. 25c... *Ev. Assoc.*
Moo-Yai, the little Hindoo captive. 18°. 45c. *Cong. Pub.*
Mop and Frisk. *See* Barrow, *Mrs.* F.
Mopsa, the fairy. *See* Ingelow, J.
Mora, A. H. de. La iglesia de Jesu Cristo en España. 12°. '69. 60c. .... *Am. Tr.*
Morag. Gibb, *Miss* —. $1.25.. *Carter; Meth. Bk. Conc.*
Moral and religious anecdotes. 2 v. 12°. $1.50. *Pres. Bd.*
Moral aspects of city life. Chapin, E. H. $1. *Williamson.*
Moral heroism; or, the triumphs of the great and good. 18°. 85c. .... *Am. S. S.*
Moral lessons. ('56.) 2d ed. 18°. '75. 50c... *So. Meth.*
— *See also* Village lib.
Moral nursery tales for children. ill. 12°. $1.75. *Scribner, W. & A.*
Moral of accidents. Lynch, T. T. $1.75.. *Routledge.*
Moral probe. Judson, L. C. $1.75 ... *J. M. Stoddart.*
Moral system. Gillett, E. H. $1.25 .... *Scribner.*
Moral uses of dark things. Bushnell, H. $2.. *Scribner.*
Moral wreck. East, T. 75c. .... *Nelson.*
Morales, Augustin José. Progressive Spanish reader, with analytical study of the Span. language. 12°. $1.50 .... *Appleton.*
Morality of the Sabbath. Canright, D. M. 15c. *Sev. Day Adv.*
Morality of the Turks. Ropes, C. J. H. 75c... *Taintor.*
Morals of Abou Ben Adhem. Locke, D. R. $1.50.. *Lee & S.*
Morals of manners. Sedgwick, C. M. 60c... *Putnam.*
Morals of mottoes. James, S. B. $1.75..... *Nelson.*
Moralt, W. Method for the zither without a master; rev. and enl. by E. Heindl. 4°. '74. bds., $1.50. *Ditson.*
— Zither school. 4°. bds., $1.50 .... *Peters.*
Moran, C: Money. 12°. '63. $1.25 .... *Appleton.*
— Money, currencies and banking. 8°. '75. pap., 40c. *Brentano.*
Moran, Pat. Fs. Life of Rev. Oliver Plunkett. 16°. $1 .... *O'Shea.*
Moravian almanac and year book. [Annual.] 24°. (Lond.) pap., 20c. .... *Clauder.*
Moravian atlas; compr. statistics of the church of the United Brethren to 1853; comp. by teachers in Fulneck Acad., Eng. sm. 4°. (Fulneck.) '53. $1 .... *Clauder.*
Moravian Indian boy. Farrand, H. A. 75c. *Pres. Bd.*
Moravian life. 18°. $1 .... *Dutton.*
Moravian missionaries; [also] Old Jessie; [also] Sin found out. 18°. 25c. .... *Pres. Bd.*
Moravian tune book. La Trobe, C. I. $2.25; $1.25. *Clauder.*

Moravians. Church constitutions of the Bohemian and Moravian Brethren; tr. from the Lat., with notes and introd., by B. Seifferth. sm. 8°. (Lond.) '66. $2.50 .... *Clauder.*
— Journal of the General Synod of 1857; — of 1869. [In Germ. or Eng.] 2 v. 12°. v. 1, 50c.; v. 2, 75c. .... *Clauder.*
— Journal of the provincial synods of 1858, 1864, 1868, 1873. 8°. ea., pap., 50c. .... *Clauder.*
— Text book [of the United Brethren]. [In Eng. or Germ.] 32°. 35c.; 75c.; pap., 25c... *Clauder.*
Mordaunt Hall. Marsh-Caldwell, A. 50c... *Harper.*
Mordecai, Alfr. *See* United States, *Ordnance Department.*
Mordecai and Esther. Headley, P. C. 25c.; 30c. *J. E. Potter.*
More, Ha. Works. 2 v. por. 12°. $3; shp., $4; hf. cf., $6.50 .... *Lippincott.*
— *Same.* ill. 8°. shp., $3; — in 2 v. 8°. $4; shp., $5; — in 7 v. 12°. $8.75; hf. cf., $21...... *Harper.*
— Book of private devotion; chiefly from writings of H. More. 32°. 35c. .... *U. P. James.*
— *Same.* 32°. 40c.; 50c.; 75c. .... *Clark & M.*
— Cœlebs in search of a wife. 12°. $1.25.. *Lippincott.*
— — *See also* Stapleton lib.
— Parley, the porter. ill. 18°. '51. 25c...... *Am. Tr.*
— *Same.* 32°. 30c. .... *Am. S. S.*
— — *See also* Child's lib.
— Practical piety. 32°. 38c. .... *Appleton.*
— *Same.* 18°. 85c. .... *Am. S. S.*
— Private devotions. 32°. 38c. .... *Appleton.*
— *Same.* 32°. 50c.; 60c. .... *Carter.*
— Shepherd of Salisbury Plain: account of D: Saunders. 18°. '38. 30c. .... *Am. Tr.*
— *Same.* 18°. 35c. .... *Am. S. S.*
— Spirit of prayer. 32°. 50c. .... *Carter.*
— Stories for the young. 8 v. ill. 18°. '51. $3. *Am. Tr.*
— Tales and allegories for the people. 12°. $1.25. *Lippincott.*
— — *See also* Stapleton lib.
More, Mt. Pastoral reminiscences. 18°. '66. 15c. *Am. Tr.*
More, Thomas (Household of). Manning, A. $1.. *Dodd.*
More about Jesus. Mortimer, M. 75c...... *Harper.*
More bed-time stories. Moulton, L. C. $1.50.. *Roberts.*
More blunders than one. Rodwell, T. G. 15c... *French.*
More excellent way (A). Winslow, M. E. $1.. *Nat. Temp.*
More free than welcome. Suter, W. E. 15c... *French.*
More happy thoughts. Burnand, F. C. $1.. *Roberts.*
More lights. Breed, D. R. 20c.; 10c. .... *Am. Tr.*
More mittens. *See* Barrow, *Mrs.* F.
More precious than gold. Cheltnam, C. S. 15c. *French.*
More stories about the little ones. *See* Library for little lads and lasses.
More talks with Amy Dudley. *See* Bertie and Amy books.
More than conqueror. Irving, T. $1.50.. *Whittaker.*
More than she could bear. Archer, G. W. $1.50.. *Claxton.*
More victories. Flint, S. A. 75c. .... *Cong. Pub.*
More ways than one. Brock, C. 50c. ... (?) *Martien.*
More worlds than one. Brewster, *Sir* D. $2.25. *Routledge.*
Moreau, Jos. N. (*ed.*) Testimonials to Thomas Paine. 16°. pap., 15c. .... *Mendum.*
Moredun. *See* Scott, *Sir* Wa.
Morehead, *Mrs.* L. M. Christmas is coming, and other poems. 12°. 75c. .... *Lippincott.*
Morehouse, G: R. Anatomy and physiol. of respiration in chelonia. *See* Mitchell, S. W., *and* Morehouse, G. R.
Morehouse, L. P. Concerning the cost of transportation on railroads. 24°. '74. pap., 25c. *R. R. Gazette.*

Morelet, Arth. Travels in Central America, incl. accounts of regions unexplored since the conquest; tr. by Mrs. M. F. Squier, with introd. and notes by E. G. Squier. ill. post 8°. '71. $2.... *Holt.*

Moreley, Su. Throstlethwaite. 12°. $1.50.. *Lippincott.*

Morell, J: D. Complete manual of spelling, on the principles of contrast and comparison. cr. 8°. 50c.... *Cassell.*

— Modern philosophy: hist. and crit. view of the speculative philos. of Europe in the 19th cent. 8°. '72. $3.50.... *Carter.*

Morell, J. R. *See* Tennemann, W. A., Manual of history of philosophy.

Morenos, Ojos. What will the world say? novel of every-day life; [also] Only a woman. 12°. $1.50.... *Lippincott.*

Moreton Hall; or, the spirits in a haunted house. 8°. pap., 50c.... *Peterson.*

Morey, A. B. Crime of intemperance. 16°. '76. pap., 10c.... *West. Tr.*

Morey, Cornell. Practical arithmetic. ('51.) New ed. 12°. '74. 75c.... *Darrow.*

Morey, J. H. *See* Emerson, L. O., *and* Morey, J. H.

Morfit, Campbell. Practical treatise on manufact. of soaps; with wood-cuts and ill. 8°. $20.. *Wiley.*

— *See also* Booth, J. C., *and* Morfit, C.

Morford, H: ["The governor."] Coward (The): novel of society and the field in 1863. 12°. '64. $1.75; pap., $1.50.... *Peterson.*

— Days of shoddy: novel of the great rebellion of 1861. 12°. '63. $1.75; pap., $1.50.... *Peterson.*

— John Jasper's secret: conclusion of Dickens' "Edwin Drood." ill. 12°. '71. $1.50.... *Peterson.*

— Short trip guide to America. ('72.) [Annual.] 16°. $1.... *Porter.*

— Short trip guide to Europe. ('68.) [Annual.] 12°. $1.50.... *Porter.*

— Shoulder straps: novel of N. Y. and the army in 1862. 12°. '63. $1.75; pap., $1.50... *Peterson.*

— Spur of Monmouth; or, Washington in arms; by an ex-pension agent. 12°. '76. $1.75.... *Claxton.*

Morgan, A. P. Student's plant record; adapted to Wood's botanies. 12°. '72. 75c.... *Barnes.*

Morgan, C: E. Electro-physiology and therapeutics. ill. 8°. $6.50.... *W. Wood.*

Morgan, C: F. Manual of Ohio practice; cont. civil procedure, justice's act and other statutes; with ref. 12°. shp., $2.... *Gould.*

Morgan, H: Ned Nevins, the newsboy; or, street life in Boston. 12°. '66. $1.... *Lee & S.; Morgan.*

— Shadowy hand; or, life struggles. 12°. '74. $1.. *Morgan.*

— Sketches and sermons. 18°. '59. $1.50... *Morgan.*

Morgan, J. C. Diet of infants and young children. [Hom.] 8°. pap., 15c.... *Boericke.*

Morgan, J: P. *See* Roberts, E., *and* Morgan, J. P.

Morgan, Ja. Appleton. Law of literature; with Am., Eng., Fr. and Germ. statutes of copyright. 2 v. 8°. '75. $12; shp., $15.... *Cockcroft.*

— (*ed.*) Specimens of macaronic poetry. cr. 8°. '72. $2.75.... *Hurd & H.*

Morgan, J: Practical lessons in nature and treatment of affections produced by contagious diseases; with chapters on syphilitic inoculation, infantile syphilis, etc. ill. 12°. $1.75.... *Lippincott.*

Morgan, *Rev.* J: Gift of the Holy Ghost according to the teaching of the Scripture; with introd. by C. G. Finney. 18°. 25c.... *Goodrich.*

— The holiness acceptable to God. 16°. 75c. *Goodrich.*

Morgan, J: E: University oars: inquiry into after-health of men who rowed in Oxford and Cambridge race, 1829–'69. cr. 8°. '73. $3.. *Macmillan.*

Morgan, Lew. H. American beaver (castor Americanus) and his works; with lith. pl. and wood-cuts. 8°. $5.... *Lippincott.*

Morgan, Lew H., *continued.*

— Systems of consanguinity and affinity. 4°. '69. pap. $12.... *Smith. Inst*

Morgan, P. B. Aggressive work in the church o Christ; with directions for conducting mission and organizing brotherhoods and guilds, and introd. by Bp. Huntingdon. 16°. '74. $1.. *Dutton*

Morgan, R: W: Christianity and modern infidelity their relative intellectual claims compared. 12° $1.50; pap., 60c.... *Claremont*

Morgan, S: T. United States import duties under existing laws and decisions, and digest of tariff laws April 1, 1875. 8°. '75. $2.50; pap., $2.. *Turnbull*

Morgan, *Lady* Sydney Owenson. Florence McCarthy 8°. pap., $1.50.—12°. $2.... *Sadlier*

— The O'Briens and O'Flaherties. 2 v. in 1. 12°. '69 $1.50.... *Haverty*

— The wild Irish girl. 2 v. in 1. 12°. '55. $1.50.. *Haverty.*

Morgan, W: Homœopathic treatment of indigestion, constipation, hæmorrhoids; ed. with notes by A. E. Small. 12°. 75c.... *Boericke.*

— The text-book for domestic practice. [Hom.] 24°. 60c.... *Boericke.*

Morgan, *Capt.* W: Freemasonry exposed and explained. 8°. pap., 25c.... *E. A. Cook; De Witt; Dick & F.*

— History of [his] abduction and murder; prep. by seven committees of citizens, appointed to ascertain the fate of M. 12°. pap., 25c.... *E. A. Cook.*

— Masonry revealed and illustrated by eleven seceding members. 8°. pap., 25c.... *U. P. James.*

Morgan, the buccaneer; or, the freebooters. 8°. pap., 50c.... *Peterson.*

Moriah. Fraser, R. W. $1.... *Pres. Bd.*

Moriarty, J. J. Wayside pencilling, with glimpses of sacred shrines. 18°. '75. 75c.. (?) *Van Benthuysen.*

Moriarty, P. E. Life of St. Augustine. 12°. '72. $1.50.... *Cunningham.*

Morier, Ja. Life and adventures of Hajji Baba. [Fiction.] ill. 12°. $1.50.... *Quak. City.*

Morison, G. S. New portage bridge; [also] Strength and other properties of materials of construct., by R. H. Thurston. 8°. '76. pap., 70c. *Am. Soc. of C. E.*

Morison, G: *See* Chanute, O., *and* Morison, G.

Morison, Ja. C. Life and times of St. Bernard. ('63.) New [chp.] ed. cr. 8°. '68. $2.... *Macmillan.*

Morison, J: Counsels to young men on modern infidelity. 18°. '37. 40c.... *Am. Tr.*

Morison, J: H. Disquisitions and notes on the Gospels: Matthew. ('60.) 3d ed. 12°. '72. $1.25.. *Am. Unit.*

Morison, J: S. Scenes from life of Jesus. 16°. 25c. *Un. S. S.*

Moritz, A: Nannie's jewel case; tr. from the Germ. 16°. $1.25.... *O'Shea.*

Morley, H: Bartholomew Fair: its history, etc. (Chandos lib.) 12°. $1.75; hf. cf., $3.75; cf., $5.... *Scribner, W. & A.*

— Fairy tales. ill. 16°. $1.25.... *Routledge.*

— First sketch (A) of Eng. literature. 2d ed. cr. 8°. $3.50; — in 3 pts., ea., $1.50.... *Cassell.*

Morley, J: Edmund Burke: hist. study. cr. 8°. '67. $2.50.... *Macmillan.*

— Rousseau: biog. 2 v. 8°. $5.... *Scribner, W. & A.*

— Voltaire. 12°. $2.... *Appleton.*

Morley, Ralph. School days at Mount Pleasant; incl. sketches and legends of the "neutral ground." ill. 12°. $1.50.... *Hinton.*

Morley, Su. Aileen Ferrers. [Fiction.] 8°. pap., 50c.... *Harper.*

Morley Ernstein. *See* James, G. P. R.

Mormon country. Codman, J. $1.50.... *U. S. Pub.*

Mormons. English, T. D. 15c.... *French.*

Morning. 18°. 50c.... *Carter.*

Morning. *See* Ries, F.

Morning and night watches. *See* Macduff, J. R.
Morning bells. Havergal, F. R. 35c........*Dutton.*
Morning by morning. Spurgeon, C. H. $1.75. *Sheldon; So.Bapt.*
Morning call. Dance, C. 15c..............*French.*
Morning clouds. Leathes, S. $1............*Dodd.*
Morning communions with God. *See* Sturm, C. C.
Morning gleam: story of Maggie Bond. 16°. $1. *Am.Bapt.*
Morning glories. Alcott, L. M. $1.50.....*Carleton.*
Morning glory. 18°. '57. 35c..............*Am.Tr.*
Morning glory lib. 6 v. 18°. $1.80.......*Randolph.*
Cont.: Autumn leaves. — Elmer's morning glory. — Little buds. — Uncle Jerry's blossom. — Wayside flowers. — White rose.

Morning glory stories. Harrison, J. 75c...*Randolph.*
Morning hour. *See* Sunbeam lib.
Morning hours in Patmos. Thompson, A. C. $1.25. *Am.Tr.*
Morning improved. v. 1: Old Testament. 18°. 35c.; 40c. — v. 2: New Testament. 18°. 45c....*Dutton.*
Morning, noon and night; or, Christ in every page: manual of devotion. 8°. '62. $2.50..*Randolph.*
Morning notes of praise. Pepys, *Lady* C. M. $1.25. *Dutton.*
Morning of joy. Bonar, H. 60c............*Carter.*
Morning of the reformation. 18°. 80c......*Am.S.S.*
Morning portion. Hawker, R. 75c. ......*Routledge.*
Morning ride. Perry, C. T. 50c. ......*H.H.Carter.*
Morning ride. *See* Bible pictures.
Morning star. Hodges, D. F., *and* Foster, G. W. $1.50................................*Lee & S.*
Morning star. Matson, *Mrs.* —. 40c.........*Am.Tr.*
Morning star. Newton, W. $1.50; $2; $4.50. *Claxton.*
Morning star. Thayer, W. M. $1.25.....*J.E.Potter.*
Morning star. Warren, J. S. $1.......*Bost.Am.Tr.*
Morning star. Woodard, L. $1.75; $2.25. *Friends Pub. H.*
Morning star lib. 8 v. 12°. $5 ....*Cong.Pub.*
Cont.: Lost note. — Sleigh ride. — Idle boy. — Stick gatherers. — Hattie Preston. — Flower girl. — Frozen ears. — Golden rule.

Morning stars sang together. Blake, J. V. 35c.; 30c. *Ditson.*
Morning tale. Lemon, M. 15c. ....*French.*
Morning thoughts: daily text-book. 32°. 20c...*Nelson.*
Morning thoughts for every day in the year. 32°. 50c. *Am.Bapt.*
Morning walk. 18°. 22c. ....*Am.S.S.*
Mornings among the Jesuits at Rome. Seymour, M. H. $1.25...........................*Harper.*
Mornings at Bow Street. ill. 12°. bds., $1..*Routledge.*
Mornings in Florence. *See* Ruskin, J:
Mornings with Jesus. Jay, W. $1.75 ...*J.E.Potter.*
Morphis, J. M. History of Texas. ill., por. and map. 8°. '74. $3.50...........................*U.S.Pub.*
Morphy, Pl. C: Games of chess: matches and best games played by the Am. champion; with analytical notes by J. Löwenthal, and memoir. por. 12°. (Bohn.) $1.75.............*Little,B.& Co.*
— *Same.* por. 12°. (Bohn.) $2. *Lippincott; Scribner, W.& A.*
— Match games. [Chess.] 18°. 50c. ....*De Witt.*
Morrell, L. A. The American shepherd: hist. of sheep, with their breeds, management and diseases; with letters from wool-growers. ill. 12°. $1.75...................................*Harper.*
Morren, Natl. Paradise of children. 18°. 35c. *Pres.Bd.*
Morrill, C: Physiology of woman and her diseases from infancy to old age. 11th ed. 12°. '64. $1.50...........................*Jas.Campbell.*

Morris, B. Wistar. Presbyterian, Baptist and Methodist testimony to confirmation. 12°. 20c.; 40c. *Dutton.*
Morris, C: d'Urban. Grammar of Attic Greek; with exercises. 12°. $1.75 ....*Huntington.*
— Latin grammar. 12°. $1.75..........*Huntington.*
— Latin reading book. 12°. $1.75 ......*Huntington.*
— Parsing and reading lessons; adapted to Attic Greek grammar. 12°. 38c...............*Huntington.*
— Parsing and reading lessons adapted to Latin grammar. 12°. 38c..................*Huntington.*
— Principia Latina. 12°. $1.50............*Sheldon.*
— Probatio Latina: questions to test progress of learners in Lat. 12°. 50c..................*Huntington.*
— *See also* Bullions, P., *and* Morris, C: d'Urban.
Morris, Eastin. *See* Iowa, Sup. Court reports.
Morris, Edm. Farming for boys. ill. sq. 16°. $1.50. **Osgood.*
— How to get a farm, and where to find one; with homestead laws, etc. 12°. $1.25; pap., 75c. *Miller.*
— *Same.* 12°. $1.75...................... *Woodward.*
— Ten acres enough. 12°. $1.25; pap., 75c...*Miller.*
— *Same.* 12°. $1.50..................... *Woodward.*
Morris, E: E. Age of Anne. 16°. $1.........*Estes.*
— (*ed.*) Epochs of history. 15 v. 16°. ea., $1..*Estes.*
Cont.: Era of the Prot. rev., by F. Seebohm. — Crusades, by G. W. Cox. — Thirty years' war, 1618–'48, by S. R. Gardiner. — Beginning of the middle ages, by R. W. Church. — Norman kings and the feudal system, by A. H. Johnson. — French rev., by B. M. Cordery. — Early Plantagenets, by W. Stubbs. — Edward III., by W. Warburton. — Houses of Lancaster and York, by J. Gairdner. — Age of Elizabeth, by M. Creighton. — Stuarts and the Puritan rev., by J. L. Sanford. — Fall of the Stuarts, by E. Hale. — Age of Anne, by E. E. Morris. — Frederick the Great and the seven years' war, by F. W. Longman. — War of Am. independence, by J. M. Ludlow.

— *Same.* v. 1–8. 16°. ea., $1 ....*Scribner.*
Cont.: Era of the Prot. rev., by F. Seebohm. — Crusades, by G. W. Cox. — Thirty years' war, 1618–'48, by S. R. Gardiner. — Houses of Lancaster and of York, by J. Gairdner. — French rev., by W. O'C. Morris. — Age of Elizabeth, by M. Creighton. — Fall of the Stuarts and western Europe, 1678–'97, by E. Hale. — First two Stuarts and Puritan rev., by S. R. Gardiner.

Morris, Edn. Practical treatise on shock after surgical operations and injuries; with especial ref. to shock after railway accidents. 12°. $1.25. *Claxton; Lippincott.*
Morris, Elwood. Easy rules for measurement of earthworks by means of the prismoidal formula. ill. 8°. '72. $1.50......................*VanNostrand.*
Morris, Fs. Orpen. Anecdotes in natural history. ill. sm. 4°. '73. $2.................*Routledge.*
— Dogs and their doings. ill. sq. 8°. $1.75 ..*Harper.*
— *Same.* ill. sm. 4°. '71. $2 ....*Routledge.*
Morris, H: Early history of Springfield [Mass., 1636–1675]: address, Oct. 16, 1875, on 200th anniv. of burning of the town by the Indians; with app. por. 8°. '76. $1.25.................(?)*Morris.*
— History of 1st church of Springfield, Mass.: address, June 22, 1875; with app. ill. and por. 8°. '75. $1.50; pap., 60c.; $1.25.........*Whitney & A.*
Morris, Herb. W. Present conflict of science with the Christian religion: modern skepticism met on its own ground. ill. 8°. '75. *$3.50; leath, $4.25; mor., $5.50...........................*Ziegler.*
Morris, Josh. S. *See* Mississippi, Criminal cases; Law reports.
Morris, J: G. Bibliotheca Lutherana: list of publications of Lutheran ministers in the U. S. 16°. '76. 85c. ....*Luth.Pub.*
— Catalogue of lepidoptera of No. Am. 8°. '60. pap., $1.................................*Smith.Inst.*
— Lords Baltimore (The). 8°. '74. $1.....*Murphy.*
— — *See also* Maryland Hist. Soc.
— Quaint sayings and doings of Martin Luther. 12°. '76. $1.........................(?)*Luth.Pub.*
— Synopsis of lepidoptera of No. Am. pt. 1. 8°. '62. pap., $2...........................*Smith.Inst.*
Morris, J: H. Illustrated cities of the Bible. *See* Bible [Whole].

Morris, Lew. *See* New Jersey Hist. Soc.

Morris, R: Elementary lessons in historical English grammar. 18°. '75. $1.25 .... *Macmillan.*

— English grammar. *See* Green, J. R., Literature primers.

— Historical outlines of English accidence. 3d ed. 12°. '75. $1.75 .... *Macmillan.*

Morris, Rob. Courtship and matrimony. 12°. $1.75; pap., $1.50 .... *Peterson.*

Morris, Rob. Lights and shadows of Freemasonry. 12°. '75. $2 .... *Masonic.*

Morris, T: A. Church polity. 18°. '59. 40c. *Cin. Meth. Bk. Conc.*

— Death of Bp. Waugh. [Sermon.] 12°. pap., 12c. *Meth. Bk. Conc.*

— Miscellany: essays, sketches, etc. 12°. '37. $1.50. *Meth. Bk. Conc.*

— Sermons. 12°. $1.50 .... *Cin. Meth. Bk. Conc.*

Morris, W: Defence of Guenevere, and other poems. cr. 8°. '75. $2 .... *Roberts.*

— Earthly paradise. 3 v. 16°. '68–'71. $6. — cr. 8°. $9. — (Popular ed.) 16°. $4.50 .... *Roberts.*

— Life and death of Jason: poem. 16°. '67. $1.50. *Roberts.*

— Love is enough; or, the freeing of Pharamond: a morality. 16°. '72. $1.25. — cr. 8°. $2 .. *Roberts.*

— Lovers of Gudrun. 16°. '70. $1 .... *Roberts.*

— *See also* Virgil.

Morris, W: Gouverneur. *See* California, Sup. Court reports.

Morris, W: H. Field tactics for infantry. ill. 18°. '64. 75c. .... *Van Nostrand.*

— Infantry tactics. 2 v. 24°. '65. $2; — in 1 v., $1.50. *Van Nostrand.*

Morris, W: O'Conner. The French revolution and first empire: hist. sketch, with bibliog. course of study by A. D. White. 16°. '75. $1 .... *Scribner.*

Morrison, A. B. Spiritualism and necromancy. 16°. $1.25 .... *Cin. Meth. Bk. Conc.*

Morrison, C: R. Digest of N. H. reports (46 v.) 8°. '68. shp., $10 .... *Sanborn.*

— Digest of N. H. school laws. New ed., rev. 12°. '76. bds., 50c. .... *Sanborn.*

— New Hampshire justice and sheriff and attorney's assistant. 8°. '72. shp., $2.50 .... *Sanborn.*

— New Hampshire probate directory: statutes, with notes, forms, etc. sm. 8°. '70. shp., $2 .. *Sanborn.*

— The town officer; with directions, forms, decisions, etc., adapted to statutes of N. H. sm. 8°. '76. shp., $2.50 .... *Sanborn.*

— *See also* New Hampshire, General statutes.

Morrison, J: Rock of faith in contrast with the quicksands of mod. skepticism. 18°. 65c. .. *Am. Bapt.*

Morrison, R. S. Mining rights in Colorado: acts of Congress, statutes of the state, district rules, etc. ('74.) 2d ed. 12°. '75. pap., $1.25 .. *Richards.*

Morrisons (The). Hosmer, M. $1.75; $1.50. *Peterson.*

Morrow, J: Voice from the newsboys. 18°. '60. 75c. *Barnes.*

Morse, D. A. Mind (The): lecture. 8°. '75. pap., 25c. .... *Steiger.*

— Report on dipsomania and drunkenness. 8°. '73. pap., 25c. .... *Steiger.*

— Report on general paralysis: critical review, [with] analysis of case of J. S. Blackburn. 8°. '74. pap., 50c. .... *Steiger.*

— Report on monomania. 8°. '74. pap., 25c. .. *Steiger.*

Morse, *Mrs.* E. H. Three Christmas days. ('68.) New ed. ill. 18°. '75. 40c. .... *Hoyt.*

Morse, E: S. Early stages of terebratulina. ill. 4°. pap., $1 .... *Bost. Soc. Nat. Hist.*

— Embryology of terebratulina. ill. 4°. pap., $1. *Bost. Soc. Nat. Hist.*

Morse, Fs. Working for God, and other practical sermons. 2d ed. fp. 8°. $1.25 .... *Macmillan.*

Morse, J: T., *jr.* Famous trials. por. cr. 8°. '74 $2.25 .... *Little, B. & Co*

— Law of arbitration and award. 8°. '72. shp., $6. *Little, B. & Co*

— Life of Alex. Hamilton. 2 v. 12°. '76. $4.50. *Little, B. & Co*

— Treatise on law of banks and banking; with app. 8° '70. shp., $5 .... *Little, B. & Co*

Morse, Sidney Edwards. System of geography for schools. maps and ill. 4°. hf. bd., 90c. .. *Harper*

Morsels of mirth for funny fellows. 12°. pap., 20c. *Hurst.*

Morss, *Mrs.* L. H. Nest of stories. 6 v. 16°. $3. *Cong. Pub.*

Mortara. Moos, H. M. 75c. .... *Bloch.*

Morte d'Arthur. *See* Malory, *Sir* T.

Mortimer, Grace (*pseud.*) *See* Stuart, M. B.

Mortimer, Ja. Joy is dangerous: comedy. 16°. pap., 15c. .... *De Witt.*

Mortimer, *Mrs.* M. Geschichten aus dem Leben Jesu. 32°. '60. 25c. .... *Am. Tr.*

— Great truths in simple words. ill. 18°. '48. 25c. *Am. Tr.*

— *Same.* 18°. 40c. .... *Am. S. S.*

— Here a little and there a little. ill. 18°. '74. 50c. *Am. Tr.*

— Line upon line. ill. 18°. '67. 45c. *N. Y. Ref. Ch. Bd.; Pres. Com.*

— *Fr.* Ligne après ligne. ill. 18°. '52. 50c. .. *Am. Tr.*

— Lines left out: some of the histories left out in "Line upon line." ill. 16°. 75c. .... *Harper.*

— More about Jesus. map and ill. 16°. 75c. .. *Harper.*

— Near home; or, the countries of Europe described. 18°. 75c. .... *Carter.*

— Peep of day: early relig. instruct. for the infant mind. ill. 18°. '67. 40c. *N. Y. Ref. Ch. Bd.; Pres. Com.*

— *Same.* ill. sq. 12°. $2.50 .... *Routledge.*

— *Germ.* Der erste Morgenschimmer. ill. 18°. '45. 40c. .... *Am. Tr.*

— *Port.* Lembrança do passado. pts. 1 and 2. 18°. '43. 35c. .... *Am. Tr.*

— *Span.* El romper del alba. 18°. '56. 35c. .. *Am. Tr.*

— Peep of day lib. 4 v. ill. 18°. '48–'49. $1.75; ea., 45c. .... *Am. Tr.*

Cont.: Line upon line. — Night of toil. — Peep of day. — Precept upon precept.

— *Same.* 4 v. ill. 18°. $5 .... *Routledge.*

Cont.: Peep of day. — Precept upon precept. — Line upon line, 2 v.

— *Same.* 5 v. 16°. '76. $5 .... *Carter.*

Cont.: Peep of day, 75c. — Sequel to Peep of day, 60c. — Story of the Apostles, $1. — Kings of Israel and Judah, $1.50. — Captivity of Judah, $1.

— Peep of day ser. 3 v. 16°. ea., 50c. .. *Hurd & H.*

Cont.: Peep of day. — Precept upon precept. — Line upon line.

— *Same.* 4 v. 18°. '71. $2 .... *Claxton.*

Cont.: Peep of day. — Line upon line. — Precept upon precept. — Here a little, there a little.

— Precept upon precept. ill. 18°. '67. 45c. *N. Y. Ref. Ch. Bd.; Pres. Com.*

— Reading without tears; or, a pleasant mode of learning to read. ill. sm. 4°. $1.25; — in 2 pts., 1, 60c.; 2, 75c. .... *Harper.*

— Scripture facts. 4 v. ill. 32°. '49. ea., 30c. .. *Am. Tr.*

— Streaks of light: 52 facts from the Bible for 52 Sundays of the year. ill. 16°. 75c. .... *Harper.*

Mortimer, *Mrs.* T: *See* Mortimer, *Mrs.* M.

Mortimer's college life. *See* Winter evening lib.

Morton, E: Eton boy: farce. 16°. pap., 15c. .. *French.*

— Windmill: farce. 16°. pap., 15c. .... *French.*

Morton, H: *and* Leeds, Alb. Student's pract. chemistry. 12°. '65. $2 ...... *Claxton; Lippincott.*

Morton, J. W. Vindication of the true Sabbath. 16°. '72. pap., 10c. .... *Sev. Day Adv.*

Morton, J: Maddison. [Plays.] 5 v. 16°. ea., pap., 15c. .... *Ames.*

Cont.: Capital match: comic drama. — Desperate game: comic drama. — How stout you're getting: farce. — On the sly: farce. — Thirty-three next birthday: farce.

Morton, J: Maddison, *continued.*
— *Same.* 7 v. 16°. ea., pap., 15c. .... *De Witt.*
Cont.: Atchi: comedietta. — Aunt Charlotte's maid: farce.— If I had a thousand a year: farce. — Master Jones' birthday: farce. — Midnight watch. — Which of the two? comedietta. — Woodcock's little game: farce.
— *Same.* 11 v. 16°. ea., pap., 15c. .... *Lee & S.*
Cont.: Aunt Charlotte's maid: farce. — Brother Ben: farce. — Don't judge by appearances: farce. — Done on both sides: farce. — Husband to order: serio comic drama. — John Dobbs: farce.— My precious Betsy: farce. — Old Honesty: comic drama. — Slice of luck: farce. — Two Puddifoots: farce. — Your life's in danger: farce.
— *Same.* 80 v. 16°. ea., pap., 15c. .... *French.*
Cont.: Atchi: comedietta. — Attic story: farce. — Aunt Charlotte's maid: farce. — Away with melancholy: farce.— Betsy Baker: farce. — Box and Cox: farce. — Brother Ben: farce. — Capital match: farce. — Catch a weasel: farce. — Chaos is come again. — Day's fishing: farce. — Desperate game. — Don't judge by appearances: farce. — Done on both sides: farce. — Double-bedded room: farce. — Drawing room, 2d floor and attics: farce. — Dying for love: comedy. — Englishman's house is his castle: farce. — Fitzsmythe of Fitzsmythe Hall: farce. — Friend Waggles: farce. — From village to court. — Game of romps: farce.— Going to the Derby: farce. — Grimshaw, Bagshaw and Bradshaw: farce. — Hopeless passion: comedy. — How stout you're getting: farce. — Husband to order. — If I had a thousand a year: farce. — Irish tiger: farce. — John Dobbs: farce. — King and I: farce. — Lend me five shillings: farce. — Little savage: farce. — Love and hunger: farce. — Margery Daw: farce. — Master Jones' birthday: farce. — Midnight watch. — Milliner's holiday: farce. — Muleteer of Toledo. — My first fit of the gout: farce. — My husband's ghost: farce. — My precious Betsy: farce. — My wife's bonnet: farce. — My wife's second floor: farce. — Newington butts: farce. — Old Honesty. — On the sly: farce. — Our wife; or, the rose of Amiens: comic drama. — Pacha of Pimlico: extravaganza. — Poor Pillicoddy: farce. — Pouter's wedding: farce. — Prince for an hour. — Regular fix: farce. — Rights and wrongs of women: farce. — Seeing Warren: farce.— Sent to the tower: farce — She would and he wouldn't: comedy. — Slasher and Crasher: farce. — Slice of luck: farce. — Steeple-chase: farce. — 'Take care of Dowb—': farce. — Three cuckoos: farce. — Thirty-three next birthday: farce. — Thumping legacy: farce. — Ticklish times: farce. — To Paris and back for £5: farce. — Two Bonnycastles: farce. — Two Buzzards: farce. — Two Puddifoots: farce. — Unwarrantable intrusion: comic interlude. — Waiting for an omnibus: farce. — Where there's a will there's a way. — Which of the two? comedietta. — Whitebait at Greenwich: farce. — Who's my husband? farce. — Who stole the pocket-book? farce. — Woman I adore: farce. — Woodcock's little game: farce. — Wooing one's wife: farce. — Your life's in danger: farce.
— *See also* Morton, T. *and* J. M.

Morton, Natl. New England's memorial; with Bradford's history, Prince's chronology, etc. 8°. '55. $3 .... *Cong. Pub.*

Morton, S: G: Illustrated system of human anatomy, special, general and microscopic. ill. 8°. '48. shp., $4.50 .... *Claxton; Lippincott.*

Morton, T: New English Canaan, or New Canaan; cont. abstract of New England, written upon ten years knowledge and experiment of the country: 1632. [Reprint.] 4°. pap., $2 .... *Sabin.*

Morton, T: [Plays.] 15 v. 16°. ea., pap., 15c. .. *French.*
Cont.: Angel of the attic: comic drama. — Children in the wood: opera. — Cure for the heart-ache: comedy. — Education: comedy. — Go-to-bed Tom: farce. — Invincibles: farce. — Methinks I see my father: farce. — Pretty piece of business: comedy. — Roland for an Oliver. — School of reform: comedy. — Secrets worth knowing: comedy. — Sketches in India: farce. — Speed the plough: comedy. — Town and country: comedy. — Way to get married: comedy.
— Another glass: drama. 16°. pap., 15c. ...... *Lee & S.*
— *and* J: M. All that glitters is not gold: drama. 16°. pap., 15c. .... *French.*
— — Writing on the wall: drama. 16°. pap., 15c. *French.*

Morton House. Fisher, F. C. $1.50; $1 .. *Appleton.*

Mosaics of human life. Thurston, E. A. $2. *Claxton; Lippincott.*

Moschele. *See* Hoffmann, F.

Moscheles, Ignace. Life of Beethoven; incl. biog. by Schindler, correspondence with his friends, traits and remarks on works, and H. Döring's Life and characteristics; tr. 12°. $2 .... *Ditson.*
— Recent music and musicians, as described in [his] diaries and correspondence; selected by his wife and adapted from Germ. by A. D. Coleridge. ('73.) New ed. 12°. '75. $2 .... *Holt.*

Moschus. *See* Theocritus, Bion *and* Moschus.

Mose Evans. Baker, W. M. $1.50 .... *Hurd & H.*

Moseley, H: Illustrations of mechanics; ed. by J. Renwick. ill. 18°. 75c. .... *Harper.*
— Mechanical principles of engineering and architecture. New ed., enl. by D. H. Mahan. ill. 8°. $5 .. *Wiley.*

Mosenthal, Jos. Anthems; for quartette choirs for the service of Episc. Church. ('70.) New ed. 4°. '76. $2.75 .... *Pond.*

Mosenthal, Salomon Hm. Isabella Orsini: drama. 16°. pap., 15c. .... *De Witt.*

Moser, G. v. I shall invite the major: comedy. 16°. pap., 15c. .... *De Witt.*

Moses. Leben. 18°. 70c.; 90c. .... *Ev. Assoc.*
— *See also* History of Moses.

Moses, Halsey H. Law of mandamus and the practice connected with it; with forms. 8°. '66. $3.50 .... *Gould.*

Moses, H: *See* Canova, A., Works in sculpture and modelling.

Moses, the man of God. Hamilton, J. $1.50 .. *Carter.*

Moses and modern science. Weaver, G. S. $1. *Williamson.*

Moses in Egypt. *See* Rossini, G.

Mosheim, J: Lorenz v. Ancient and modern ecclesiastical hist.; tr., with notes, by A. Maclaine. New ed., contin. to 1826 by C. Coote. 2 v. 8°. $4; shp., $5 .... *Harper.*
— *Same.* 4°. shp., $4.50 .... *So. Bapt.*
— *Same.* 4°. shp., $5 .... *Pounsford.*
— *Same;* tr. by J. Murdock. 3 v. 8°. '74. $5 .. *Carter.*

Moss, Lem. Annals of the U. S. Christian Commission. ill. 8°. $4.50 .... *Lippincott.*
— Baptists and the national centenary: record of Christian work, 1776–1876. 8°. '76. $1.75 .. *Am. Bapt.*

Moss lib. 4 v. ill. 18°. '75. $2 .... *Nelson.*
Cont.: Seed and fruit. — Another's burden. — Forest crossing. — Mabel's faith.

Moss rose. *See* Power, P. B.

Moss rose ser. 12 v. ill. 32°. '70. $3 .. *H. A. Young.*
Cont.: Willie's wish. — Curious Tom. — Two mottoes. — Little James. — Old Ben's stockings. — Little Bertie. — Afraid of the dark. — Little Minnie. — Birthday present. — A real victory. — Sowing little seeds. — Milly's doves.

Moss rose stories. 6 v. 18°. $2 .... *Bost. Am. Tr.*
Cont.: Head and the heart, by C. D. Bell. — Little knitter, by P. B. Power. — Moss rose, by P. B. Power. — Trust in God, by C. D. Bell. — Two ways, by C. D. Bell. — Way to be happy, by C. D. Bell.

Moss side. Harland, M. $1.50 .... *Carleton.*

Moss wreath lib. 8 v. 18°. $2.75 .... *Routledge.*
Cont.: Paul's moss wreath. — Robinson Crusoe. — Simple stories for children. — Stories from English history. — Loyal Charlie Bentham. — Henrietta and the ayah. — Ally's schoolfellows. — A winter's wreath.

Mosses from an old manse. *See* Hawthorne, Natl.

Mossy dell ser. 5 v. 16°. $6.25 .... *Cong. Pub.*
Cont.: Grace Irving's vacation, by Mrs. S. F. Keene. — Poor house Sam, by J. A. Jefferds. — Margaret Chester, by M. N. Beebe. — Prince Paul, by Mrs. E. Pearson. — New clerk, by T. Talmon.

Mot, Maur. Adolphe. French grammar and dictionary; with method for learning pronunciation. 12°. '56. 75c. .... *Gleason.*

Motes in the sunbeam. Gatty, M. 50c. *Carter; Dutton.*

Moth and rust. Wright, J. McN. $1.60 ...... *Hoyt.*

Mother and child are doing well: farce. 16°. pap., 15c. .... *Happy.*

Mother and her offspring. Tracy, S. $1.50 .. *Harper.*

Mother and her work. Brown, H. E. 60c. .. *Bost. Am. Tr.*

Mother Anne and her little Maggie. sq. 16°. '73. 75c. *Randolph.*

Mother Anthony's family; or, not to ourselves. 16°. $1.50 .... *Cong. Pub.*

Mother at home. *See* Abbott, J. S. C.

Mother Carey's dream book and fortune teller. 16°. pap., 15c. .... *Dick & F.*

Mother dove. *See* Todd, J.

Mother Goose. ill. roy. 8°. [Linen toy-book.] per gross, $48..........(?) *McLoughlin.*
Note. Various other styles from $4 up.

Mother Goose. Dibdin, T. 15c..........*French.*

Mother Goose; or, harlequin and the golden egg: shadow pantomime. sq. 18°. '74. pap., 30c. (?) *F. M. Reed.*

Mother Goose for grown folks. Whitney, A. D. T. $1.50..........*Loring.*

Mother Goose from Germany. New ed. ill. 8°. '73. 75c..........*Putnam.*

Mother Goose in hieroglyphics. Atwater, J. J. per doz., $5; $2.50..........*Thompson.*

Mother Goose in Latin. *See* Merrick, J. M.

Mother Goose melodies. ill. sq. 16°. 90c.; 75c.; 60c.; pap., 30c..........*Miller.*

Mother Goose melodies; with music for singing. ill. 12°. $1.50..........*Carleton.*

Mother Goose set to music. *See* Elliot, J. W.

Mother Goose's melodies. ill. sq. 16°. 50c.; pap., 25c..........*Locke.*

— *Same.* ill. sq. 18°. 60c.; pap., 20c..........*Miller.*

— *Same.* (chp. ed.) ill. sq. 12°. per gross, $9; col., $15. — (Nursery ed.) sq. 12°. per gross, $24; col., $36. — (Complete ed.) sq. 12°. per gross, $48..........*Porter.*

Mother Goose's melodies. Uncle Solomon. 15c...*Happy.*

Mother Goose's melodies for children; [with] full-page ill. by H. L. Stephens, music by C. Moulton and ill. by G. Faye. 4°. '71. $2.25; $3..*Hurd & H.*

Mother Goose's pocket of pleasure. ill. 12°. $1.50..*Locke.*

Mother Goose's rhymes, chimes and melodies. sq. 12°. '71. 75c.; bds., 60c..........*Porter.*

Mother, home and heaven. Newman, J. P. $1.50. *Meth. Bk. Conc.*

Mother Hubbard and Cock Robin. [Toy-book.] ill. 4°. $1; 50c..........*Routledge.*

Mother Hubbard's picture-book. ill. sq. 12°. '72. $1. *Routledge.*

Mother Michel and her cat. La Bedollière, E. de. 60c. *Hurd & H.*

Mother of Washington. Donaldson, S., *jr.* 30c.; 20c. *Murphy.*

Mother of the Wesleys. Kirk, J. $2..*Cin. Meth. Bk. Conc.*

Mother Pitcher for young folks. New ed. ill. 8°. '73. 75c..........*Putnam.*

Mother Ross. *See* Defoe, D.

Mother Shipton's fortune-teller. 16°. pap., 30c. *Dick & F.*

Mother Shipton's Oriental dream book. 16°. pap., 30c. *Dick & F.*

Mother West's neighbors. Chaplin, J. D. 90c. *Bost. Am. Tr.*

Mother-in-law. Boardman, M. M. $1.25..*Perkinpine.*

Mother-in-law. Southworth, E. D. E. N. $1.75; $1.50..........*Peterson.*

Motherless. Witt, H. G. de. $1.50..........*Harper.*

Motherless children. Baker, H. N. W. $1.50..*Lee & S.*

Motherless Martha's home. *See* Little Aggie's lib.

Motherless Maud. Atkins, M. A. $1....*Cong. Pub.*

Motherless Meg. *See* My holiday books.

Motherly talks with young housekeepers. Beecher, *Mrs.* H. W. $2..........*Ford.*

Mother's dying child. Hazlewood, C. H. 15c. *French.*

Mother's fairy rhymes. sq. 16°. pap., 25c.....*Locke.*

Mother's (A) gift. Palmer, P. $1.50..........*Palmer.*

Mother's (A) gift: texts. 64°. 15c.; 20c. ..*Am. S. S.*

Mother's gift to her little ones at home. sq. 16°. '59. 65c..........*Meth. Bk. Conc.*

Mother's hymn book. Hastings, T. 35c...*Randolph.*

Mother's journal during the last illness of her daughter, Sarah Chisman. 18°. 50c..........*Am. S. S.*

Mother's last words. *See* Sewell, *Mrs.* Ma.

Mother's lessons on the Lord's prayer. ill. 4°. $1.50. *Am. Bapt.*

Mother's mission. 12°. '59. $1.25....*Meth. Bk. Conc.*

Mother's pearl. *See* Smith, *Mrs.* F. I. B.

Mother's pearl ser. 3 v. 18°. $2.50...*Bost. Am. Tr.*
Cont.: Little Happy-heart, by Mrs. J. D. Chaplin. — Mother's pearl, by Mrs. F. I. B. Smith. — Two granddaughters, by Mrs. J. D. Chaplin.

Mother's picture alphabet. sq. 8°. $2.50..*Meth. Bk. Conc.*

Mother's portrait. Jobson, F. J. $1.50; $2..*So. Meth.*

Mother's prayers answered. 18°. 65c......*Pres. Bd.*

Mother's recompense. *See* Aguilar, G.

Mother's return; [also] The friend in need. 18°. 17c.; 22c..........*Am. Bapt.*

Mother's ship. Hazen, M. P. $1..........*Cong. Pub.*

Mother's ship. *See* Blue shawl ser.

Mother's staff. *See* Little Blue Mantle lib.

Mother's stories. Bullard, A. 25c..........*Lee & S.*

Mother's treasure: stories for the young. ill. 12°. '75. $1.50..........*Routledge.*

Mother's trials. [Fiction.] 12°. $1.25......*Harper.*

Mother's tribute. 18°. 25c..........*Am. S. S.*

Mother's true stories. sq. 18°. 60c......*Nichols & H.*

Mother's warm shawl. 18°. 60c. ....(?) *Martien.*

Mother's work with sick children. Fonssagrives, J. B. $1.25..........*Putnam.*

Mothers of great men. Ellis, S. S. $3...*Routledge.*

Mothers of the wise and good. Burns, J. $1.25..*Tibbals.*

Motherwell, W: Poetical works; with memoir. por. 32°. $1.50..........* *Osgood.*

Motley, J: Lothrop. Historic progress and American democracy. 8°. '69. pap., 50c.......*Scribner.*

— History of the United Netherlands, [1584–1609]. 4 v. por. 8°. '61–'68. $14–$23..........*Harper.*

— Life and death of John of Barneveld; with a view of primary movements of the Thirty Years' war, [1609–1623]. 2 v. ill. 8°. $7; shp., $8; hf. cf., $11.50..........*Harper.*

— Rise of the Dutch republic, [1555–1584]. 3 v. 8°. '56. $10.50; shp., $12; hf. cf., $17.25..*Harper.*

Mott, G: S. Perfect law (The). 18°. '68. 40c. *Am. Tr.*

— *Port.* A lei perfeita. 18°. '71. 35c.......*Am. Tr.*

— *Span.* La ley perfecta. 18°. '71. 35c. ...*Am. Tr.*

— Prodigal son. sm. 12°. 60c..........*Pres. Bd.*

— Resurrection of the dead. 16°. '67. $1..*Randolph.*

Mott, Ja. Hints to young people on duties of civil life. 16°. *net*, 40c..........*Friends Bk. Assoc.*

— Observations on education. 16°. *net*, 25c. *Friends Bk. Assoc.*

— *Same;* [also] The duties of civil life. 16°. *net*, 40c. *Friends Bk. Assoc.*

Mott, T. F. Elementary methods [for the piano]. 3 pts. f°. $5.25..........*Brainard.*

Mott, Val. Eulogy on J. W. Francis. 8°. '61. pap., 25c..........*N. Y. Acad. Med.*

— Inaugural address before N. Y. Acad. of Med. 8°. '49. pap., 10c..........*N. Y. Acad. Med.*

— Surgical cliniques. *See* Francis, S. W.

Motten und Rost. 12°. '71. $1; $1.25....*Ev. Assoc.*

Motto: I am "all there." Byron, H. J. 15c...*French.*

Moulton, *Mrs.* Louise Chandler. Bed-time stories. ill. sq. 16°. '73. $1.50..........*Roberts.*

— More bed-time stories. ill. sq. 16°. '74. $1.50..*Roberts.*

— My third book. 12°. $1.25..........*Harper.*

— Some women's hearts: love stories. 16°. '74. $1.50. *Roberts.*

— *See also* Stories, by Mrs. L. C. Moulton, etc.; — Two fortune-seekers.

Mound builders. *See* Force, M. F.

Mount Lebanon and Syria: 12 views with letter-press. obl. 24°. 50c.; 75c..........*Nelson.*

Mount of Olives. *See* Hamilton, J.

Mount St. Vincent (Sisters of Charity). *See* Sisters of Charity.
Mount Sinai. Neukomm, S. $2............*Ditson.*
Mount Vernon. Rice, H. $1; $3; $4....*Appleton.*
Mt. Vernon juveniles. 6 v. ill. 16°. $7.50...*O'Shea.*
Cont.: Life of Washington, by E. Cecil. — Life of Lafayette, by E. Cecil. — Love of country. — Legends of Brittany, by E. Souvestre. — Bears of Augustusburg, by G. Nieritz. — Hurrah for the holidays.
Mount Zion coll. Perkins, T. E. $1.25.....*Barnes.*
Mountain. ('58.) 3d ed. 18°. '71. 35c....*So. Meth.*
Mountain bard. *See* Hogg, J.
Mountain daisy. 18°. 55c................*Am. S. S.*
— *See also* Select lib. for girls.
Mountain flowers. Todd, J. $1..*Bridgman; Cong. Pub.*
Mountain gem ser. *See* Todd, J:
Mountain in the plain. *See* Hamilton, J.
Mountain lamb. *See* Todd, J:
Mountain of the lovers. Hayne, P. H. $1.50..*Hale.*
Mountain outlaw; or, the secret password. 8°. pap., 25c..............................*Dick & F.*
Mountain patriots: tale of the reformation in Savoy. ('69.) New ed. 16°. '70. $1.50..........*Hoyt.*
Mountain snow storm. ill. 4°. 30c.........*Am. Bapt.*
Mountain sylph: opera. 16°. pap., 15c......*French.*
Mountaineering in the Sierra Nevada. King, C. $2. *Osgood.*
Mountaineers. Colman, G., *jr.* 15c.........*French.*
Mountains and molehills. Doughty, S. P. 50c. *H. H. Carter.*
Mountains and molehills. Marryat, F. S. $1.25. *Harper.*
Mountains of the Bible: 12 views with letter press. obl. 24°. 50c.; 75c...................*Nelson.*
Mountains of Palestine. *See* Alexander, J. H.
Mounted riflemen; or, the girl of the robber's pass. 8°. pap., 25c.........................*De Witt.*
Mountford, W: Euthanasy; or, happy talk towards the end of life. 12°. '50. $2..........*Osgood.*
— Miracles, past and present. 12°. $2......**Osgood.*
— Thorpe, a quiet English town, and human life therein. 16°. $1.50.........................**Osgood.*
Mouse and the frog. *See* Stories about animals ser.
Moustache movement. Brough, R. B. 15c...*French.*
Mouth harmonica instructor. obl. 8°. '70. pap., 50c. *Ditson.*
Mouth of gold. Johnson, E. 75c.; $1......*Barnes.*
Mowat, Mat. Maiden martyr of Scotland. 18°. 65c. *Pres. Bd.*
Mowatt, *Mrs.* A. C. *See* Ritchie, *Mrs.* A. C.
Mowbray, Bonington. *See* Dickson, W. B., *and* Mowbray, B.
Mowbray, G: M. Tri-nitro-glycerine as applied in the Hoosac tunnel, and to submarine blasting, torpedoes, quarrying, etc.; with ill., tables and app. 3d ed., rev. 8°. '74. $3.......*Van Nostrand.*
Mowrey, Ph. H. The musical servant: Ethiop. drama. 16°. pap., 15c................*De Witt.*
Mowry, Sylvester. Arizona and Sonora: geog., hist. and resources of the silver regions of North America. 12°. $1.50..................*Harper.*
Mozart, Wolfg. Amadeus. Don Giovanni. *See* Ditson.
— First mass in C; with Lat. words and organ accomp.; ed. by V. Novello. obl. roy. 8°. bds., 80c.; pap., 65c. ....*Peters.*
— *Same;* with Latin and Eng. text. 8°. '64. $1; pap., 65c.......................................*Ditson.*
— Second mass in C; with Lat. words and organ accomp.; ed. by V. Novello. obl. roy. 8°. bds., 80c.; pap., 65c..........................*Peters.*
— *Same;* with Lat. and Eng. text. 8°. $1; pap., 65c. *Ditson.*
Mozart, Wolfg. Amadeus, *continued.*
— Seventh mass in B flat; with organ or piano accomp. by V. Novello; with Lat. and Eng. text. 8°. '64. $1; pap., 65c..........................*Ditson.*
— Ninth mass in G; with organ or piano forte accomp. by V. Novello; with Lat. and Eng. text. 8°. '64. $1; pap., 65c...........................*Ditson.*
— Twelfth mass in G; with Lat. words and organ accomp.; ed. by V. Novello. obl. roy. 8°. bds., $1; pap., 80c..........................*Peters.*
— *Same;* with Lat. and Eng. text. 8°. $1.12; bds., $1; pap., 80c................*Ditson; Gordon.*
— Letters, 1769–1791; tr. by Lady Wallace. 2 v. por. 12°. ea., $1.75.........................*Ditson.*
— Marriage of Figaro; with orig. Ital. libretto, and Eng. version by G. Soane; with piano forte accomp. by H. West. 4°. bds., $1.50.............*Ditson.*
— — *See also* Ditson.
— Praise of friendship. [Cantata.] 4°. pap., 38c. *Ditson.*
— Requiem (15th) mass; with organ or piano forte accomp. by V. Novello; with Lat. and Eng. text. 8°. $1; pap., 65c.......................*Ditson.*
Mozart and Mendelssohn. Barnard, C. F., *jr.* $1.25. *Lee & S.*
Mozart's early days. Hoffmann, F. $1.......*Hoyt.*
Mozley, Ja. Bowling. Eight lectures on miracles. *See* Bampton lectures.
Much ado about merchant of Venice: comedy. 16°. pap., 15c..............................*French.*
Much ado about nothing. *See* Shakespeare, W:
Much ado about nothing. *See* Home twilight stories.
Much fruit. Monmouth, L. H. $1.........*Lothrop.*
Mudborough. Brough, W., *and* Halliday, A. 15c. *French.*
Muddy River and Brookline [Mass.] records, 1634–1838. 8°. '75. $3..................*Williams.*
Mudge, Zach. A. [Juveniles.] 8 v. 12°. '57–'75. *Meth. Bk. Conc.*
Cont.: Arctic heroes: facts and incidents of Arctic explorations. — Footprints of Roger Williams. — Forest boy: life of A. Lincoln. — Lady Huntington portrayed. — Life of T. F. Buxton. — North Pole voyages: from 2d Grinnell expedition to Polaris. — Witch Hill: hist. of Salem witchcraft, *ea.*, $1.25. — Views from Plymouth Rock, $1.50.
— Boat-builder's family. ill. 16°. '71. $1.25..*Lothrop.*
— Casket lib. 6 v. 18°. '67. $3........*H. A. Young.*
Cont.: Forest boy. — Right, and about right. — Home and no home. — A will and a way. — George Perley's lesson. — English Harry.
— Jamie Noble. 16°. '68. $1.25........*H. A. Young.*
— Luck of Alden Farm. ill. 16°. '73. $1.50..*Lothrop.*
— Pure gold ser. 12 v. 18°. '67. $6....*H. A. Young.*
Compr. Casket lib. *and* Rustic lib.
— Rustic lib. 6 v. 18°. '67. $3.........*H. A. Young.*
Cont.: Rodney Dennis. — Chester Florence. — Gracie Goodwin. — Plantation Jim. — Carrie Prince. — Prairie boys.
— Seaside lib. 4 v. ill. 18°. ea., 50c....*Bost. Am. Tr.*
Cont.: Fisher boy; or, the son who made a glad father. — Fisherman's daughter; or, Sebie's lessons and the way she learned them. — Lobster boy; or, the son who was a heaviness to his mother. — Reef village; or, what a few can do.
— Shell cove. ill. 16°. '71. $1.50..........*Lothrop.*
Mudie, Rob. Feathered tribes of the British islands. 4th ed., rev. by W. C. L. Martin. 2 v. ill. 12°. (Bohn.) ea., $1.75; col. pl., ea., $2.75......*Little, B. & Co.*
— *Same.* 2 v. ill. 12°. (Bohn.) ea., $2; col. pl., ea., $3................*Lippincott; Scribner, W. & A.*
— Popular guide to obs. of nature. ill. 18°. 75c. *Harper.*
Muenscher, Jos. Introduction to the orthography and pronunciation of the Eng. lang. 12°. $1..*Chase.*
Mugby Junction. *See* Dickens, C:
Mügge, Thdr. Afraja; or, life and love in Norway; tr. by E. J. Morris. 12°. $1.50; pap., $1; — (Intern. ed.), $1.25....................*Porter.*
— Neues Leben: Novelle. 12°. 75c.; pap., 50c. *F. W. Thomas.*
— Riukan Voss: Novelle. 12°. '69. pap., 40c...*Holt.*
— Signa die Seterin: Novelle. 12°. '69. pap., 40c. *Holt.*
Mühlarzt (Der). *See* Stöber, K.

Mühlbach, Louise (*pseud.*) *See* Mundt, *Mrs.* C. M.

Mühle (Die), od. wie Böses mit Gutem zu vergelten. 18°. 30c. .... *Ev. Assoc.*

Mühle (Die) am schwarzen Meer. *See* Temme, J. D. H.

Muhlenberg, W: A: Christ and the Bible: not the Bible and Christ. 16°. '69. 60c. ...... *Randolph.*

— Evangelical catholic papers; comp. by Anne Ayres. 1st ser. 8°. '75. $2 .... *Whittaker.*

— Evangelical sisterhoods; in two letters to a friend. sq. 18°. '67. 75c.; pap., 50c. .... *Whittaker.*

— I would not live alway, and other pieces. 18°. '61. 75c. .... *Randolph.*

— *Same;* with story of the hymn and account of St. Johnland. sq. 8°. '71. $1 .... *Whittaker.*

— *See also* Hymns for church and home.

Mulcahy's cat: Irish dram. sketch. 16°. pap., 15c. *Happy.*

Muleteer of Toledo. Morton, J. M. 15c. .... *French.*

Mulford, Elisha. The nation: foundations of civil order and political life in the United States. 8°. '72. $2.50 .... *Hurd & H.*

Mulholland, Rosa. Eldergowan. ill. 16°. $1 .. *Pott.*

— First Christmas for our dear little ones. ill. 4°. '76. $1.50 .... *Pustet.*

— Prince and Saviour: story of Jesus, simply told for the young. ill. sq. 18°. 25c. .... *Noonan.*

— Wicked woods of Tobereevil. [Fiction.] 8°. $1.25; pap., 75c. .... *Estes.*

Mullan, J: Report on military road. *See* United States, *Corps of Eng.*

Mullens, *Mrs.* (*of Calcutta*). Life by the Ganges; or, faith and victory. 16°. '67. 80c. ...... *Pres. Bd.*

Mullens, Jos. Twelve months in Madagascar. ill. 12°. $1.75 .... *Carter.*

Müller, A. *See* Schiller, J. F. v., Song of the bell.

Müller, A. E. First lesson for piano; with Am. or foreign fingering; tr. f°. 75c. .... *Gordon.*

— Method for the piano-forte; rev. by J. Knorr; tr. by G. A. Schmidt. 4°. '54. bds., $3.75 .. *Ditson.*

— Twenty-four elementary exercises [for the piano]; tr. f°. 60c. .... *Brainard.*

Müller, Adolph. Praktische Bruchrechnung. *See* Witter's [Arithmetics].

Muller, Christine (*pseud.*) *See* Walrée, E. C. W. van.

Müller, Erdm. Zwei Weihnachtsabend-Erzählungen f. d. Jugend. 32°. bds., 15c. .... *Ludwig.*

Müller, F: Max. Works. ('62–'74.) New ed. 7 v. cr. 8°. '74–'76. hf. cf., $31.50 .... *Scribner.*

Cont.: Chips from a German workshop, 4 v., *ea.*, $2.50: 1. Essays on science of religion. — 2. Essays on mythol., traditions and customs. — 3. Essays on literature, biographies, etc. — 4. Comparative philology, mythology, etc. — Lectures on science of lang., 1st ser., $2.50. — *Same*, 2d ser., $3.50. — Lectures on science of religion, $2.

— Lecture on Buddhist nihilism. 12°. pap., 10c. *Somerby.*

— Memories: story of German love; tr. by G. P. Upton. 3d ed. sm. 4°. '74. $2. — 16°. $1 .. *Jansen.*

— On missions: lecture, Westminster Abbey, Dec. 3, 1873; with introd. sermon by A. P. Stanley. 8°. '74. $1 .... *Scribner.*

Müller, F: Paludan. Fountain of youth; tr. from the Danish by H. W. Freeland. [Juvenile.] ill. cr. 8°. $1.50 .... *Macmillan.*

— *Same.* ill. 12°. $1.75 .... *Lippincott.*

Muller, G: Life of trust: narr. of dealings of God with M.; ed., with introd., by F. Wayland. ill. 12°. $1.75 .... *Sheldon.*

Müller, H. Im Wartesalon erster Klasse. *See* Elz, A., Er ist nicht eifersüchtig.

Müller, H. D. *See* Lattmann, I., *and* Müller, H. D.

Müller, J: Physics and meteorology; tr. ill. and pl. 8°. $4.50 .... *Lea.*

Müller, Js. v. History of the world, to 1783, tr.; rev. by A. Everett. 4 v. 12°. $6 .... *Harper.*

Müller, Jul. Christian doctrine of sin; tr. by W. Urwick. 2 v. 8°. $6 .... *Scribner, W. & A.*

Müller, Mich. Arch-confraternity under title of Our Lady of the Assumption; for relief of souls in purgatory. 18°. pap., 10c. .... *Kreuzer.*

— Blessed eucharist (The) our greatest treasure. 8th ed. 8°. '76. $1.50 .... *Pustet.*

— Catechism of Christian doctrine; for beginners. 24°. '76. pap., 8c. — (old series.) 24°. '75. pap., 10c. *Pustet.*

— *Same;* for parochial and Sunday schools. New ed., rev. sm. 16°. '76. 15c. — (old series.) sm. 16°. '75. 45c. .... *Pustet.*

— Catholic priest (The). 18°. 50c. .... *Kreuzer.*

— Discourse to promote charity towards souls in purgatory. 18°. pap., 10c. .... *Kreuzer.*

— *Same.* 24°. 60c.; 80c.; $1; $1.50 .... *Noonan.*

— Familiar explan. of Christian doctrine; for family and adv. students. sm. 16°. '75. 60c. .... *Pustet.*

— Golden rule; or, the book for all. 18°. $2 .. *Kreuzer.*

— Holy mass: sacrifice for the living and the dead. 2d ed. 8°. '75. $2.50 .... *Pustet.*

— "Our Father" (The). 18°. 50c. .... *Kreuzer.*

— Our lady of perpetual help in work of our redemption and sanctification. 24°. '76. 40c. .... *Kreuzer.*

— Prayer the key of salvation. 4th ed. 8°. '76. $1.50. *Pustet.*

— Prodigal son; or, the sinner's return to God. 3d ed. 8°. '76. $2 .... *Pustet.*

— Public school education. 12°. $1.50 ...... *Sadlier.*

— Religious state (The). 18°. '73. 75c. .... *Kreuzer.*

— Triumph of the blessed sacrament; or, history of Nicola Aubry. 2d ed. 18°. '73. 50c. .. *Kreuzer.*

Müller, O: Charlotte Ackerman; tr. by Mrs. C. Coleman and her daughters. [Fiction.] 12°. '71. $1.50; pap., $1; — (Intern. ed.), $1.25 ... *Porter.*

Müller, S. *See* Part songs for female voices.

Müller, W. Die schöne Müllerin. *See* Försterling, O.

Mulligan, J: Exposition of the grammatical structure of the Eng. lang. 12°. $2 .... *Appleton.*

Mullinger, Ja. Bass. Cambridge [Eng.] characteristics in the seventeenth century. cr. 8°. '67. $1.50 .... *Macmillan.*

Mullock, J. T. Life of St. Alphonsus Liguori. 18°. '74. 75c. .... *Kenedy.*

Mullois, Isidore. Clergy and the pulpit, and their rel. to the people. 12°. '68. $1.50 .. *Cath. Pub.*

Muloch, *Miss* Dinah. *See* Craik, *Mrs.* D. M.

Mulready, W: Pictures by M.; with text and biog. sketch by J. Dafforne. f°. '72. $7.50 .. *Routledge.*

Mulrenan, P. History of the Catholic Church in the diocese of Brooklyn. 12°. $1 .... *O'Shea.*

Multanowsky, E. Ist Methodismus u. Lutherthum einerlei? 8°. pap., 15c. .... *Volkening.*

Mulvany, E: Practical dictation spelling book. 12°. hf. bd., 30c. .... *O'Shea.*

Mumbo Jum: Ethiop. drama. 16°. pap., 15c. .. *Happy.*

Mumford, Ma. E. A born romp. ill. 16°. $1.50. *Souder.*

Mumford, T: J. Memoir of Samuel Joseph May. ('73.) New [chp.] ed. 16°. '75. 75c. ...... *Am. Unit.*

Mumler, W: H. Personal experiences in spirit-photography. 12°. '75. pap., 15c. .... *Colby.*

Mummy. Bernard, W. B. 15c. .... *French.*

Münch, F: Amerikanische Weinbauschule u. Weinbereitungslehre. 2d ed. 12°. '67. $1 .. *Witter.*

— *Eng.* American school for the cultivation of the grape and preparation of its juice. 2d ed. 12°. '67. $1 .... *Witter.*

— Erinnerungen aus Deutschlands trübster Zeit: Lebensbilder v. K. u. P. Follen u. F. Münch. por. 12°. '73. pap., 50c. .... *Witter.*

— Fünf Reden üb. Religion, Aberglauben u. vernünftiges Menschenthum, an d. Deutschen in Nord Amerika. 12°. '75. pap., 35c. .... *Witter.*

Münch, F: *continued.*
— Geisteslehre f. d. heranreifende Jugend; f. höhere Lehranstalten. 12°. '72. 50c. .... *Witter.*
— Sinnliche (Die) u. d. geistige Lebensansicht od. Materialismus u. Dualismus. 8°. pap., 50c. *F. W. Thomas.*
Münchhausen. 12°. pap., 25c. .... *Radde.*
Munday, Eug. H. Cost of paper; computed and tabulated for the printer and the publisher. f°. '75. $1.25 .... *Claxton; Collins & M'L.*
Munde, C: Hydriatic treatment of scarlet fever in its different forms. 4th ed. 12°. 50c..... *Boericke.*
Mundt, *Mrs.* Clara Miller. ["Louise Mühlbach."] [Historical novels; tr.] 18 v. ill. 8°. ea., $1.50; pap., $1; hf. cf., $3.50 .... *Appleton.*
Cont.: Andreas Hofer. — Berlin and Sans-souci; or, Frederick the Great and his friends. — Daughter of an empress. — Empress Josephine. — Frederick the Great and his court. — Frederick the Great and his family. — Goethe and Schiller. — Henry VIII. and Catherine Parr. — Joseph II. and his court. — Louisa of Prussia and her times. — Marie Antoinette and her son. — Merchant of Berlin; Maria Theresa and her fireman. — Mohammed Ali and his house. — Napoleon and Blucher. — Napoleon and the queen of Prussia. — Old Fritz and the new era. — Prince Eugene and his times. — Queen Hortense.
— Bernthal; or, the son's revenge; tr. 8°. pap., 50c. *Harper.*
— Maria Antonieta y su hijo: novela hist.; tr. por Villaverde. 8°. pap., 75c .... *Appleton.*
— Story of a millionnaire; tr. 12°. $1.50... *Appleton.*
— Two life-paths; tr. 8°. pap., 60c........ *Appleton.*
Mundt, Thdr. Count Mirabeau: hist. novel. ill. 8°. $1.50; pap., $1 .... *Appleton.*
Munera pulveris. Ruskin, J. $1; $2; $2.50.. *Wiley.*
Munford, G: Wythe. Lecture: the jewels of Virginia. 8°. '57. pap., 50c....... *J. W. Randolph.*
— *See also* Virginia, Code.
Munford, W: Index to Virginia reports with notes; from Washington to 6th Munford. 8°. '19. shp., $2 .... *J. W. Randolph.*
— *See also* Virginia, Court of Appeals and Court of Chancery reports.
Municipal and Sanitary Engineers. *See* Association.
Munnell, T: Evangelists, and their work in the churches. 24°. pap., 10c.............. *Chase.*
— *and* Sweeney, J: S. Shall Christians go to war? discussion. 12°. $1 .... *Chase.*
Munro's ten cent novels. 335 nos. 16°. ea., pap., 10c. *Munro.*
Münscher, Jos. Church choir: sacred music arr. for organ or piano forte. obl. 8°. '39. $1.75; bds., $1.60 .... *Ditson.*
Munsell, C: (*ed.*) Collection of songs of the Am. press, and other poems relating to art of printing. 16°. $2 .... *Munsell.*
Munsell, Fk. Chips for the chimney corner. ill. 16°. '71. 60c. .... *Munsell.*
Munsell, Jl. (*ed.*) Annals of Albany [N. Y.] 10 v. por., pl. and maps. 12°. '48–'59. $20.. *Munsell.*
— Chronology of paper-making; with account of materials used, and hist. of rise and progress of the art. pl. 8°. '70. $2 .... *Munsell.*
— Collections on hist. of Albany [N. Y.] 4 v. por., pl. and maps. roy. 8°. '65–'71. $30.. *Munsell.*
— Every day book of hist. and chronology: anniversaries of memorable persons and events. 8°. '58. $2.50 .... *Munsell.*
Munsell, Ol. S. Psychology; or, the science of the mind. 12°. $2 .... *Appleton.*
Munson, *Mrs.* C. A. Oline; or, one year at the nest. 2d ed. ill. 16°. '76. $1.25 .... *Tibbals.*
Munson, Ja. E. The complete phonographer: inductive exposition of phonog. 12°. $2 .... *Harper.*
— Dictionary of pract. phonog. 12°. '74. $3... *Hurd & H.*
Munson, Myron A. Duty contemplated as duety, that which is due. 8°. '76. pap., 20c. ... *Williams.*
Munster festivals. *See* Griffin, Gerald.

Münter, C: Das Oekumenische Concil im Lichte d. Reformation d. Zukunft. 8°. pap., 35c. *F. W. Thomas.*
Murch, E. M. Child's [Eng.] grammar. 16°. '74. bds., 65c. .... *Morton.*
Murchison, C: On the functional derangement of the liver. (Croonian lectures, 1874.) 12°. '75. $1.75 .... *Putnam; W. Wood.*
Murdered mother. 18°. 22c. .... *Am. S. S.*
Murderer and the fortune teller. *See* Pinkerton, A.
Murdoch, D: Royalist's daughter and the rebels; or, the Dutch dominie of the Catskills. 12°. $1.75. *J. E. Potter.*
— *See also* Abeel, G., Murdock, D., *and* McKee, J.
Murdoch, Ja. E. Patriotism in poetry and prose; [with] poems by T. B. Read, G. H. Boker, F. De H. Janvier and others. 12°. $1.. *Lippincott.*
— *and* Russell, W. Orthophony; or, cultivation of human voice in elocution; with sup. on purity on tone by G. J. Webb. 12°. 1.25 .... *Osgood.*
Murdock, Ja. *See* Bible, New Test.
Mure, B. Materia medica: provings of principal animal and vegetable poisons of Brazilian empire and their application in disease; tr. and arr. according to Hahnemann's method by C. J. Hempel. [Hom.] 12°. $1 .... *Boericke.*
Murel, J: A. Life and hist. of detection, conviction and designs of M., the great western land pirate. ill. 8°. pap., 25c. .... *U. P. James.*
Murillo and the Spanish school of painting; with account of the school and its great masters. 15 steel eng. and woodcuts. f°. '72. $10.. *Routledge.*
Murphey, A. D. *See* North Carolina, Reports.
Murphy, Arth. [Plays.] 6 v. 16°. ea., pap., 15c. *French.*
Cont.: All in the wrong: comedy. — Citizen: farce. — Grecian daughter: tragedy. — Know your own mind: comedy. — Three weeks after marriage: comedy. — Way to keep him: comedy.
Murphy, Ja. G. Critical commentary on Exodus. cr. 8°. $2.25 .... *Estes.*
— *Same.* ('67.) New ed. 8°. '68. $3 .... *Draper.*
— Critical commentary on Genesis; with introd. by A. Hovey and pref. by J. P. Thompson. cr. 8°. '73. $2.50 .... *Estes.*
— *Same.* ('66.) New ed. 8°. '73. $3.50.. *Draper.*
— Critical commentary on Leviticus; with new tr. 8°. '72. $2.50 .... *Draper.*
— Critical commentary on Psalms; with new tr. 8°. '75. $4 .... *Draper.*
Murphy, J: G. Review of chemistry for students; adapted to courses in principal med. schools of the U. S. 12°. '51. $1.25 .... *Lindsay.*
Murphy, J: McLeod, *and* Jeffers, W: N., *jr.* Nautical routine and stowage; with short rules in navigation. 8°. '61. $2.50 .... *Van Nostrand.*
Murphy, Jos. J: Habit and intelligence, in connection with laws of matter and force: scientific essays. 2 v. 8°. '69. $5 .... *Macmillan.*
— Scientific bases of faith. 8°. '73. $5... *Macmillan.*
Murphy's master. Payn, J. 25c. .... *Harper.*
Murray, A. W. Missionary work in Polynesia and New Guinea. 12°. '76. $2.50 .... *Carter.*
Murray, Alex. S. Manual of mythology. pl. cr. 8°. '75. $2.25 .... *Scribner.*
Murray, C. O. Merry elves; or, little adventures in fairy land. ill. sm. 4°. $1.50. .... *Nelson.*
Murray, C: A: The prairie bird. [Fiction.] 8°. pap., $1 .... *Harper.*
— *Same.* ill. 12°. $2 .... *Routledge.*
Murray, D: Manual of land surveying; with tables. ('72.) 4th ed. 12°. '75. $2... *Schermerhorn.*
Murray, *Mrs.* Eliz. Modern system of painting in water-colors from the living model. 12°. '68. pap., 50c. .... *Hurd & H.*

Murray, Grenville. ["Trois Étoiles."] Boudoir cabal. 8°. '75. pap., 75c. . . . . *Brentano.*
— Member for Paris. 8°. $1.75; pap., 75c. . . . *Estes.*
— Young Brown. ill. 8°. $1.25; pap., 75c. . . . *Estes.*

Murray, Hu. Encyclopædia of geog.; rev. and enl. by T. G. Bradford. 3 v. maps and ill. med. 8°. $5 . . . . *Lea.*
— Historical and descriptive account of Brit. America. 2 v. ill. 18°. $1.50 . . . . *Harper.*
— *See also* Historical and descrip. account of Brit. India; — Jameson, R., Wilson, J., *and* Murray, H.; — Leslie, *Sir* J., Jameson, R., *and* Murray, H.

Murray, J. B. C. History of usury. 8°. '66. $2. *Claxton; Lippincott.*

Murray, J. Clark. Ballads and songs of Scotland; in view of their influence on character of the people. cr. 8°. '74. $2.25 . . . . *Macmillan.*

Murray, Ja. R. Imperial (The) singing book. obl. 8°. 75c. . . . . *Brainard.*
— Joyful songs. [S.-school sing. book.] obl. 12°. bds., 35c. . . . . *Brainard.*
— Pure diamonds. [S.-school sing. book.] obl. 12°. bds., 35c. . . . . *Brainard.*
— School chimes. obl. 12°. bds., 50c. . . . . *Brainard.*
— *See also* Root, F. W., *and* Murray, J. R.

Murray, J: Handbook of travel talk: questions, phrases and vocab. in Eng., Germ., Fr. and Ital. New ed., rev. 16°. (Lond.) '74. $1.50. *Little, B. & Co.*
— Handbook to London as it is. New ed., rev. maps and plans. 16°. (Lond.) '74. $1.50 . . *Little, B. & Co.*

Murray, J: Observations on the pathology and treatment of cholera: the result of forty years' experience. 12°. '74. $1 . . . . *Putnam.*

Murray, *Rev.* J: Autobiography; contin. by Mrs. J. S. Murray. New ed.; with notes by G. L. Demarest. ill. 12°. '69. $1; $1.25 . . . . . . *Universalist.*

Murray, J: Fisher. Father Tom and the pope; or, a night in the Vatican. 12°. 75c. . . . . *Lippincott.*
— *Same.* ill. 12°. 75c. 8°. pap., 50c. . . . . *Peterson.*

Murray, J: O'Kane. Popular hist. of the Cath. Ch. in the U. S. cr. 8°. *$2.50; $3.50 . . . . *Sadlier.*

Murray, Lindley. Compendium of religious faith and practice; for young persons of the Soc. of Friends. 18°. 25c. . . . . *Friends Bk. St.*
— English grammar. 12°. '51. 40c. . . . . . . *Murphy.*
— *Same.* 12°. shp., 70c. . . . . *Lippincott.*
— *Same;* ed. by I. Alger. 16°. 25c. . . . *R. S. Davis (B.)*
— *Same;* abridg. 18°. 15c. . . . . *C. H. Davis.*
— *Same;* abridg. by Putnam. 16°. 20c. . . . . . *Sadlier.*
— *Same;* [also] Exercises; abridg. by M. J. Kerney. 18°. '51. 25c. . . . . *Murphy.*
— English reader. 18°. '56. 35c. . . . . *Murphy.*
— *Same.* 12°. hf. roan, 45c. . . . . *Lippincott.*
— Exercises. 12°. 42c. — Key. 12°. 42c. . . *Lippincott.*
— *Same;* ed. by I. Alger. 4°. 42c. . . . *R. S. Davis (B.)*
— Introduction to English reader. 16°. hf. bd., 31c. *Sadlier.*

Murray, N: ["Kirwan."] Dying legacy to the people of his charge: "Things unseen and eternal." 8°. 75c. . . . . *Harper.*
— Happy home. 16°. 75c. . . . . *Harper.*
— Letters to Bp. Hughes. 18°. 70c. . . . . *Pres. Bd.*
— *Same.* 12°. $1.50 . . . . *Harper.*
— *Span.* Las cartas de Kirwan. 18°. '49. pap., 10c. *Am. Tr.*
— Men and things as I saw them in Europe. 12°. $1.50. *Harper.*
— Parish and other pencilings. 12°. $1.50 . . . *Harper.*
— Preachers and preaching. 12°. $1.50 . . . . . *Harper.*
— Romanism at home: letters to R. B. Taney. 12°. $1.50 . . . . *Harper.*

Murray, Pat. J. Life of John Banim. 12°. $1.50; $2. *Sadlier.*

Murray, T: Bogles. Christmas tide. 18°. 40c. . . *Dutton.*
— Kalli: memoir of an Esquimaux Christian. 18°. 35c.; 40c. . . . . *Dutton.*

Murray, W: Mary, Queen of Scots: drama. 16°. pap., 15c. . . . . *French.*
— No! operetta. 16°. pap., 15c. . . . . *French.*
— Phillippe; or, the secret marriage: drama. 16°. pap., 15c. . . . . *French.*

Murray, W: H. Cramond brig: drama. 16°. pap., 15c. . . . . *French.*
— Diamond cut diamond: interlude. 16°. pap., 15c. *French; Lee & S.*
— Dominique, the deserter: drama. 16°. pap., 15c. *French.*
— Gilderoy: drama. 16°. pap., 15c. . . . . *French.*

Murray, *Rev.* W: H: Harrison. Lecture on deacons. ill. 12°. '75. $1.50 . . . . (?) *Shepard.*
— Music Hall [Boston] sermons. 2 v. 12°. '73. ea., $1.50 . . . . *Tibbals.*
— Park Street [Boston] pulpit sermons. 2 v. 12°. $4.50 . . . . *Tibbals.*
— Perfect horse (The). 12°. $4 . . . . *Judd.*
— Vacation adventures in the wilderness; or, camp life in the Adirondacks. ill. 16°. $1.50; $2 . . * *Osgood.*

Murrel, J: A. Life and adventures. 8°. pap., 50c. *Peterson.*

Musard ball. Brougham, J. 15c. . . . . *French.*

Muses of Mayfair. Pennell, H. C. $3 . . . . *Routledge.*

Museum (The). Abbott, J. 90c. . . . . *Harper.*

Museum of Comparative Zoology.

For Bulletins, Catalogues and Memoirs *see under* names of authors.

Music and morals. *See* Haweis, H. R.

Music and piano dealers' and manufacturers' reference book. ('71.) New ed. 4°. '73. $25 . . *J. A. Murphy.*

Music governess. ill. 18°. '69. 50c. . . . . *Hoyt.*

Music hath charms. Fisher, D. 15c. . . . . *French.*

Music in the western church. Leonard, W. A. $1. *Somerby.*

Music lesson of Confucius. Leland, C. G. $1.50. *Osgood.*

Music of nature. Gardiner, W. $5 . . . . *Ditson.*

Musical album. Root, G. F. $1 . . . . *Ditson.*

Musical blossoms: marches, waltzes, etc., for pianoforte. 4°. $2; $2.50; bds., $1.50 . . . . . . *Ditson.*

Musical bouquet and institute choir. Bradbury, W. B., *and* Converse, C. C. $1 . . . . *Ivison.*

Musical casket. Bellak, J. $1.25; 75c. . . . . *Gordon.*

Musical casket. Woodman, J. C. $1 . . . . *Ditson.*

Musical chimes. Dressler, W. $1 . . . . *Peters.*

Musical class book; for adult singing classes. obl. 16°. 75c. . . . . *Gordon.*

Musical drama. 3 bks. 4°. ea., 50c. . . . . *Gordon.*

Musical echo. Blaisdell, L. G. 75c. . . . . *Gordon.*

Musical enthusiast. Hewitt, J. H. 50c. . . . . *Ditson.*

Musical fountain. Root, G. F. 35c. . . . . *Church.*

Musical friend: collection of vocal and instrumental music. f°. $3; $4; bds., $2.50 . . . . *Gordon.*

Musical gathering: fantasies, reveries, etc., for pianoforte. 4°. '73. $2; $2.50; bds., $1.50 . . *Ditson.*

Musical gems. Bradbury, W. B. 56c. . . . . . *Ivison.*

Musical gift: collection of piano-forte music. 4°. '72. $2; $2.50; bds., $1.50 . . . . *Ditson.*

Musical hints for the million. Merz, K. $1; 50c. *Brainard.*

Musical leaves. [Hymn book.] sm. 8°. bds., 35c. *Cin. Meth. Bk. Conc.*

Musical lyra. Pease, F. H. $1.50 . . . . *Ditson.*

Musical mirror. Phipps, S. B. 75c. . . . . *Ditson.*

Musical monitor. Curtis, G. H. $1 . . . . *Pond.*

Musical recreations. Ives, E., *jr.* 63c. . . . . *Ditson.*

Musical recreations: sel. from Kinkel Mack, Vilbré, Frey, Pacher, Wyman, etc. 4°. $2.25; bds., $1.75 . . . . *Peters.*

Musical servant. Mowrey, P. H. 15c. . . . . . . *De Witt.*

Musical treasure: vocal and instrumental music for piano-forte and reed organ. 4°. '71. $3; $4; bds., $2.50 ... *Ditson.*
Musings and memories: anecdotes and reflections of a religious character on various subjects. 12°. $1. *Friends Bk. St.*
Musings of a middle-aged woman. Strykor, C. $1.50. *Claxton.*
Musings over the "Christian year" and "Lyra innocentium." Yonge, C. M. $2 ... *Appleton.*
Muskberry, W: Atonement: drama. 16°. pap., 15c. *French.*
Muskingum legends. Powers, S. $1.75 .. *Lippincott.*
Muspratt, Sheridan. Chemistry, as applied to the arts and manufactures. 2 v. 8°. *net*, $19; hf. mor., $25 ... *Wiley.*
Mussehl, W. Amerikanische Bei-Spitz- u. Spottnamen. 16°. '69. pap., 25c. ... *Zickel.*
Musset, L: C: Alfr. de. Un caprice: comédie. 12°. '75. pap., 30c. ... *Holt.*
— *Eng.* Caprice: comedy. 16°. pap., 15c... *French.*
Musset, Pl. de. Mr. Wind and Madam Rain; tr. by E. Makepeace. ill. 4°. 75c. ... *Harper.*
Must; or, Ann Holbrook's girlhood. Atkins, M. A. $1.25 ... *Cong. Pub.*
Must I not strive? or, the poor man's dinner. ill. 32°. 25c. ... *Hoyt.*
Must it be? Bauer, K. $1.25; 75c. ... *Lippincott.*
Mustang Gray. Clemens, J. $1.25 ... *Lippincott.*
Mute Christian under the smarting rod. Brookes, T. 55c. ... *Pres. Bd.*
Mutineer; or, heaven's vengeance. 8°. pap., 25c. *De Witt.*
Mutineers of the Bounty. Hanks, S. W. 65c. *Cong. Pub.*
Mutiny at the Nore. Jerrold, D. 15c. ... *French.*
Mutterliebe. *See* Hoffmann, F.
Mutton trial (The). White, C. 15c. ... *De Witt.*
Mützelburg, Adf. Zwei heitere Geschichten. 8°. pap., 50c. ... *Morwitz.*
Muzzarelli, Alf. Method of spending vacation profitably; tr. from the Ital. 32°. '68. 20c... *Waldteufel.*
Muzzey, Artemas B. Blade and the ear: thoughts for a young man. 16°. $1.50; $1.25 ... *Lee & S.*
— Christ in the will, the heart and the life. [Discourses.] 12°. $1.25 ... *Am. Unit.*
— Fireside (The). 12°. $1.25 ... *Nichols & H.*
— Young maiden. 12°. $1.25 ... *Nichols & H.*
Muzzled ox. Beach, C. F. 25c.; 10c. ... *Pres. Bd.*
My affinity. Doten, L. $1.50 ... *Colby.*
My angel. Bulfinch, M. H. 25c. ... *Dutton.*
My Apingi kingdom. Du Chaillu, P. B. $1.50 .. *Harper.*
My aunt. Arnold, S. J. 15c. ... *French.*
My aunt's heiress. *See* Lacy's home plays for ladies.
My aunt's husband. Selby, C. 15c. ... *French.*
My beautiful lady. Woolner, T. $1.50 ... *Macmillan.*
My best friend. *See* Pretty little lib.
My best frock. ill. sq. 12°. '71. bds., 50c... *Routledge.*
My Bible class: ten specimen lessons, with essay on Bible-class teaching; by a teacher. 18°. '69. 50c. ... *Perkinpine.*
My birthday; or, a lesson well taught on the sin of disobedience. ill. 24°. '69. 30c. ... *Lothrop.*
My birthday present. *See* Juvenile picture books.
My boys. Alcott, L. M. $1 ... *Roberts.*
My brother Ben; by author of "Mackerel Will." ill. 18°. '63. 45c. ... *Am. Tr.*
— *Same.* ill. 18°. 50c. ... *Am. S. S.*
— *Same.* ill. 18°. '66. 50c. *N. Y. Ref. Ch. Bd.; Pres. Com.*
— *Same.* ill. 18°. 55c. ... *Pres. Bd.*
— *Germ.* Mein Bruder Benjamin. ill. 18°. '70. 35c. *Am. Tr.*
— *Span.* Mi hermano Ben. 18°. '73. 30c... *Am. Tr.*

My brother Harold. 16°. $1 ... *Cong. Pub.*
My brother Harold. Brightwell, C. L. 75c... *Nelson.*
My brother Willie. Cragin, M. A. 75c. ... *Cong. Pub.*
My brother's keeper. Baker, G. M. 15c. ... *Lee & S.*
My brother's keeper. Warner, S. $1.50 .. *Lippincott.*
My brother's wife. Edwards, A. B. 50c. ... *Harper.*
My campaign in America. Deux-Ponts, Gu. de. $3. *Lunt.*
My captivity among the Sioux. Kelly, F. *$1.50. *Am. Pub.*
My childhood. 18°. 45c. ... *Dutton.*
My Christmas present. *See* Juvenile picture books.
My circular notes. Campbell, J. F. 2 v. $7.50. *Macmillan.*
My class. Aunt Abbie. 45c.; 55c. ... *Am. Bapt.*
My clerical friends, and their relations to modern thought. 3d ed. 12°. '72. $1.50 ... *Cath. Pub.*
My comical puss. *See* Herd boy ser.
My comrades. Hinton, H. $1.50 ... *Hinton.*
My cousin Caroline's wedding. Wood, E. P. 25c. *Peterson.*
My cousin Hester. 18°. 18c. ... *Am. S. S.*
My Danish days. Griffin, G. W. $1.50 ... *Claxton.*
My darling's album. ill. sm. 4°. $2 ... *Nelson.*
My daughter Elinor. Benedict, F. L. $1.50; $1 .. *Harper.*
My daughter, sir! *See* Planché, J. R.
My daughter's daughter. *See* Lacy's home plays for ladies.
My days and nights on the battlefield. Coffin, C. C. $1.50 ... * *Osgood.*
My diary during the last great war. Russell, W. H. $3.50 ... *Routledge.*
My diary north and south. *See* Russell, W. H.
My dog match. Parr, H. $1.25 ... *Scribner, W. & A.*
My dog Rover. Blackburn, W. M. 50c. ... *Pres. Bd.*
My dress boots. Williams, T. J. 15c. ... *French.*
My early days. 8°. 50c. ... *Am. S. S.*
My enemy's daughter. McCarthy, J. 75c. ... *Harper.*
My farm of Edgewood. Mitchell, D. G. $1.75; $1.25. *Scribner.*
My father's garden. Miller, T. $2.50 ... *Routledge.*
My father's gift. *See* Juvenile picture books.
My father's God. 18°. 35c. ... *Pres. Bd.*
My favorite lib. ('63.) New ed. 12 v. ill. 18°. '71. $7.50 ... *Perkinpine.*
Cont.: Ethel's story of patience. — Ethel's story of cheerfulness. — Ethel's story of contentment. — Hilda. — Susan Hawthorne. — Good grandson. — Two brothers. — Rosa. — Cottagers of Glenburnie. — Sequel to "Cottagers of Glenburnie." — Household words for boys and girls. — Golden rule for boys and girls.

My favorite's library. *See* Edgeworth, Mar.
My feathered friends. Wood, J. G. $1.25 .. *Routledge.*
My fellow clerk. Oxenford, J. 15c. ... *French.*
My first fit of the gout. Morton, J. M. 15c... *French.*
My first pennies. Cousin Kate. $1.15 ... *Cong. Pub.*
My first pennies. *See* Adirondack stories.
My first picture book. ill. sq. 12°. '71. $1 .. *Routledge.*
My first school book for reading and spelling. Bumstead, J. F. 25c. ... *Marvin.*
My first Sunday-school. *See* Cousin Anna's lib.
My first voyage to southern seas. Kingston, W. H. G. $2.50 ... *Nelson.*
My first white hair; from the Germ. 18°. 50c. *Whittaker.*
My five wards. Wright, J. McN. 90c. ... *Un. B. Pub.*
My friend from Leatherhead. Yates, E., *and* Harrington, N. H. 15c. ... *French.*
My friend in the straps: farce. 16°. pap., 15c... *Happy.*
My friend the major. Selby, C. 15c. ... *French.*
My friend Thompson. Barclay, J. B. 15c. ... *French.*

My friend's family. *See* Good boy's lib.
My friend's friend: a lumberman's story. 18°. 35c. *Am.S.S.*
My garden, its plan and culture. Smee, A. $8.50; $12.50; $13.50 .... *Little, B. & Co.*
My good-for-nothing brother. Jenings, E. 25c. *Burnham.*
My grandfather Gregory; or, familiar lessons from daily incidents. 18°. 50c. .... *Am.S.S.*
My grandmother. Hoare, P. 15c............ *French.*
My grandmother. *See* Pretty little lib.
My great aunt. Planché, J. R. 15c. .... *French.*
My health. Burnand, F. C. $1 .... *Roberts.*
My heart's in the Highlands. *See* Brough, W., *and* Halliday, A.
My heart's idol. Planché, J. R. 15c........ *French.*
My hero. Forrester, *Mrs.* —. $1.75; $1.50.. *Peterson.*
My hero. Porter, A. E. $1.50............ *Lothrop.*
My heroine. [Fiction.] 8°. pap., 50c...... *Appleton.*
My holiday books. 5 v. 18°. '70. $3.. *Meth. Bk. Conc.*
Cont.: Motherless Meg.—My little friends.—Katie's work.—The two Bens.—Elsie and Gatty.
My holiday gift. ill. sq. 12°. '61. $1.25.. *Meth. Bk. Conc.*
My husband's crime. Housekeeper, M. R. 75c. *Harper.*
My husband's first love. Wood, E. P. 25c... *Peterson.*
My husband's ghost. Morton, J. M. 15c..... *French.*
My husband's mirror. Clapp, W. W., *jr.* 15c... *French.*
My husband's secret: farce. 16°. pap., 15c.. *French.*
My inquiry meeting. Boyd, R. 25c.; 15c..... *Revell.*
My joy and crown. 18°. 28c.; 35c.......... *Am. Bapt.*
My Kalulu. Stanley, H. M. $2.......... *Scribner.*
My Lady Ludlow. Gaskell, E. C. 25c....... *Harper.*
My last cruise. Haversham, A. W. $2.50.. *Lippincott.*
My life on the plains. Custer, G. A. $2.... *Sheldon.*
My little corner; [also] Wandering May. ('73.) New ed. 16°. '74. $1.50.................... *Hoyt.*
My little friends. *See* My holiday books.
My little girl. Besant, W., *and* Rice, J. 75c. * *Osgood.*
My little guide; for young children. 24°. pap., 20c. *New Ch.*
My little lady. Poynter, E. F. $1.25.......... *Holt.*
My little library. 32°. 30c................ *Am.S.S.*
— *See also* Library for little folks.
My little library. 16 v. ill. 32°. '69. hf. bd., $1.50. *Am. Tr.*
My little love. Harland, M. $1.50........ *Carleton.*
My little schoolmates. *See* Pretty little lib.
My little servant-maids, and other tales. ill. 18°. 35c. *Bost. Am. Tr.*
— *See also* Alice and Willie stories.
My little sister. *See* Aunt Alice's lib.
My lord and lady. Planché, J. R. 15c....... *French.*
My love Kate. Egan, P. 50c.............. *De Witt.*
My married life at Hillside. Coffin, R. B. $1.50. *Hurd & H.*
My mates and I. ill. 16°. '73. $1.......... *Lothrop.*
My ministerial experiences. Buchsel, C. $1.50. *Routledge.*
My miscellanies. *See* Collins, Wilkie.
My mother. Taylor, A. $1.75.............. *Nelson.*
My mother. [Toy-book.] ill. 4°. $1; 50c. *Routledge.*
My mother; or, the child's affection. ill. cr. 4°. pap., 20c.; 25c.......................... *J. E. Potter.*
My mother and I. *See* Craik, D. M.
My mother-in-law. Small, G. G. 25c..... *Collin & S.*
My mother's Bible. *See* Kennedy, *Mrs.* M. G.
My mother's chair. 18°. 35c............... *Carter.*
My mother's gift. *See* Juvenile picture books.
My mother's gold ring. *See* Sargent, L. M.
My mother's picture-book. [Toy-book.] ill. demy 4°. $2.50 .... *Routledge.*
My mother's stories. 2 v. 18°. ea., 40c.... *Am.S.S.*
— *See also* Picture lib. for the little ones at home.
My native village: recollections of twenty-five years. 18°. 50c. .... *Am.S.S.*
My neighbor's shoes. *See* Tucker, *Mrs.* C.
My neighbour's wife. Bunn, A. 15c......... *French.*
My new book. *See* Lullaby ser.
My new home. Robbins, S. S. $1.25 .... *Carter.*
My new maid. Lecocq, C. 40c. .... *French.*
My novel. *See* Bulwer-Lytton, *Sir* E. G. E. L.
My old woman. Macfarren, G. 15c. .... *French.*
My opinions and Betsey Bobbet's. Holley, M. *$2.50; $3; $4 .... *Am. Pub.*
My own Bible. *See* Story of William Tyndal.
My own book: sel. narratives and instructions suitable for youth. ill. sq. 16°. 50c........... *Pres. Bd.*
My own hymn-book. ill. sq. 16°. 40c....... *Pres. Bd.*
My own lib. 10 v. 32°. $2.50 .... *Am.S.S.*
Cont.: Wonderful machine.—John Pounds and his pupils.—Spring bonnet; or, quite ready.—Little tract girl.—Mischief; or, Harry and Lizzie.—Wooden spoon.—Ragged Tom and his three foes.—Little flower gatherer.—Turning aside.—Always tell the truth.
My own story. *See* Howitt, Ma.
My own toy-book. *See* Pearl ser.
My Paris. King, E. $1.50................ *Lee & S.*
My pet library. 10 v. 32°. '63. $2.50 ...... *Hoyt.*
My pet's album. ill. sm. 4°. '72. $2..... *Routledge.*
My pet's picture book. Raffensperger, A. F. 30c. *Am. Tr.*
My pets, and other stories. 18°. '75. 25c... *Lothrop.*
My picture book. ill. 18°. '63. 30c......... *Am. Tr.*
My poll and partner Joe. Haines, J. T. 15c... *French.*
My precious Betsey. Morton, J. M. 15c. *French; Lee & S.*
My preserver. Craven, H. T. 15c. .... *French.*
My pretty scrap book. *See* Cupples, *Mrs.* A. J.
My pretty story book. ill. 4°. 25c. .... *Am. Bapt.*
My prisons. Pellico, S. $1.50; $2.25 ...... *Roberts.*
My recollections of Lord Byron. Boissy, T. G. $1.75. *Harper.*
My roses. French, L. V. $1.50 .... *Claxton.*
My Sabbath school scrap-book. Reed, J. J. $1.50. *Tibbals.*
My satchel and I. Izax, I. *$1.50 .... *D. E. Fisk.*
My Saviour. East, J. 75c................. *Carter.*
My Saviour and my home. Ritchie, A. 60c... *West. Tr.*
My scarlet shawl: a wife's story. 18°. 35c.... *Am.S.S.*
My scholars: account of some of the girls who are or have been in my day-school. 18°. 22c... *Am.S.S.*
My school-boy days. 18°. 50c.............. *Carter.*
— *Same;* and sequel. 18°. 75c............... *Carter.*
My school days in Paris. *See* Jeune, M. S.
My schools and schoolmasters. Miller, H. $1.50. *Carter.*
My shooting box. Herbert, H. W. 75c..... *Peterson.*
My sister Fanny. 18°. 22c. .... *Am.S.S.*
My sister Jeannie. Sand, G. $1.50......... *Roberts.*
My sister Kate and my man Tom: drama. 16°. pap., 15c.................................. *French.*
My sister Margaret. Edwards, C. M. $1.25. *Meth. Bk. Conc.*
My sister's confession. Braddon, M. E. 50c. *W. F. Gill.*
My sketch book. Cruikshank, G. $6; $12... *Sabin.*
My son Diana. Harris, A. 15c............. *French.*
My son's a daughter. Parselle, J. 15c....... *French.*
My son's wife. Jolly, E. $1.75; $1.50..... *Peterson.*

My soul's religious history. Hamilton, D. H. 10c. *D.H.Hamilton.*
My spouse and I. Dibdin, C., *jr.* 15c........*French.*
My station and its duties. 18°. 55c..........*Dutton.*
My step-mother. *See* Roberts, S. J.
My story. Macquoid, K. S. $1............*Appleton.*
My study windows. Lowell, J. R. $2; $4; $5. *Osgood.*
My summer in a garden. Warner, C. D. $1; $3. *Osgood.*
My Sunday book of pictures. ill. roy. 16°. 50c. *Cassell.*
My teacher's gem. Bullard, A. 25c.........*Lee & S.*
My teacher's gift. *See* Juvenile picture books.
My third book. Moulton, L. C. $1.25.......*Harper.*
My time and what I've done with it. Burnand, F. C. $1.75; $1..........................*Macmillan.*
My time's in God's hands. *See* Winslow, O.
My trip to France. Donelan, J. P. $1.......*Strong.*
My turn next. Williams, T. J. 15c...*French; Lee & S.*
My twenty-fifth year jubilee. Platt, S. H. 15c...*Hope.*
My two Sunday scholars. 18°. 30c..........*Dutton.*
My uncle. *See* Howitt, Ma.
My uncle and the parsonage. ('66.) 2d ed. ill. 18°. '68. 60c..........................*Perkinpine.*
My uncle the captain. Baker, G. M. 15c.....*Lee & S.*
My uncle the curate. Savage, M. W. 50c...*Harper.*
My Uncle Toby's lib. *See* Wise, Dan.
My uncle's lib. ('66.) 2d ed. 6 v. ill. 18°. '68. $3.75. *Perkinpine.*

Cont.: Our Willie. — Boy of spirit. — My uncle and the parsonage. — Hannah's lesson. — Clarence. — People of Bleaburn.

My uncle's suit. Becher, M. 15c............*De Witt.*
My uncle's will: drama. 16°. pap., 15c......*French.*
My vacation. Webb, C. H. $1.50.........*Carleton.*
My very last proposal: farce. 16°. pap., 15c...*French.*
My vineyard at Lake View. 12°. $1.25........*Judd.*
My visit to the sun. Benson, L. S. $2.25..*Burnton.*
My walking photograph. Sedgwick, A. B. 15c. *De Witt.*
My wedding gift: a man's idea of perfect love. 18°. '73. 50c. ....*Brentano.*
My wife — what wife? farce. 16°. pap., 15c...*French.*
My wife and I. Stowe, H. B. $1.75...........*Ford.*
My wife's come: drama. 16°. pap., 15c......*French.*
My wife's out. Rodwell, G. H. 15c...*De Witt; French.*
My wife's baby: farce. 16°. pap., 15c........*French.*
My wife's bonnet. Morton, J. M. 15c.........*French.*
My wife's daughter. Coyne, J. S. 15c........*French.*
My wife's dentist. Wilks, T. E. 15c.........*French.*
My wife's diary. Dennery, A. P., *and* Clairville, L. F. N. 15c.......................*De Witt; French.*
My wife's husband. Challis, F. 15c..........*French.*
My wife's maid. Williams, T. J. 15c.........*French.*
My wife's mirror. Wilkins, E. G. P. 15c.....*French.*
My wife's mother. Mathews, C. 15c.........*French.*
My wife's portrait. Marston, W. 15c........*French.*
My wife's relations. Gordon, W. 15c...*Ames; French.*
My wife's second floor. Morton, J. M. 15c...*French.*
My winter in Cuba. Woodruff, J. L. M. $1.50..*Dutton.*
My winter on the Nile. Warner, C. D. *$2.50–$7. *Am. Pub.*
My witness. Winter, W. $1.50; $3; $4....*Osgood.*
My young Alcides. Yonge, C. M. $1.75..*Macmillan.*
My young days; by author of "Evening amusements." ill. 16°. '69. $1.25..........................*Dutton.*
My young wife and old umbrella. Webster, B. 15c. *French.*
My youthful companions. 18°. 50c. ....*Carter.*

Myer, Alb. J. Manual of signals; for signal officers in the field, and for military and naval students, etc. New ed., enl. 48 pl. 12°. '74. roan, $5. *Van Nostrand.*
Myer, W: G. Index to Missouri reports (v. 50–60). 8°. shp., $4..........................*Gilbert.*
— *See also* Hunter, B: *and* Myer, W: G.; — Whittelsey, C.
Myers, E: H. Disruption of the Meth. Episc. Church, 1844–1846. 12°. '75. $1.25..........*So. Meth.*
Myers, Ernest. The Puritans: poem. fp. 8°. '69. 75c. *Macmillan.*
Myers, F. Catholic thoughts on the Bible and theology. 12°. '74. $3.........................*Routledge.*
— Catholic thoughts on the church of Christ and the Church of Eng. 12°. '74. $3.......*Routledge.*
Myers, F: W. H. Poems. fp. 8°. '70. $1..*Macmillan.*
— Saint Paul: a poem. sq. 24°. '68. pap., 25c. *Randolph.*
Myers, H. M. *and* P. V. N. Life and nature under the tropics: sketches of travel among the Andes, and on the Orinoco, Rio Negro and Amazons; with introd. by A. Hopkins. maps and ill. 12°. $2 ....*Appleton.*
Myers, Harvey. *See* Kentucky, Codes.
Myers, P. Hamilton. Bell Brandon, and the withered fig tree. 8°. pap., 50c...............*Peterson.*
— Emigrant squire. 8°. pap., 50c. ....*Peterson.*
— Miser's heir. 12°. 75c. — 8°. pap., 50c...*Peterson.*
Myers, P. V. N. Remains of lost empires: sketches of ruins of Palmyra, Nineveh, Babylon and Persepolis; with notes on India and the Cashmerian Himalayas. ill. cr. 8°. $3.50..........*Harper.*
— *See also* Myers, H. M. *and* P. V. N.
Myers, *Mrs.* Sa. A. [Juveniles.] 6 v. 18°..*Pres. Bd.*

Cont.: Aunt Carrie's budget: fireside stories, 60c. — Gulf stream; or, Harry Maynard's Bible, 70c. — Margaret Ashton; or, work and win, 75c. — Poor Nicholas; or, man in the blue coat, 75c. — Railroad boy, 60c. — Young recruit; or, under which king? 70c.

— Little shoemaker; or, the orphan's victory. ill. 18°. '67. 70c..............*N. Y. Ref. Ch. Bd.; Pres. Bd.*
— Margaret Gordon; or, can I forgive? 16°. $1.50. *Pres. Bd.*
— Self-sacrifice; or, the pioneers of Fuegia. 12°. $1. *Pres. Bd.*
Myers, W. Bostwick. The "Schwedler" bridge: compar. of various forms of girder bridges, showing advantages of "Schwedler": read before Inst. of Civ. Eng. pl. 8°. '76. pap., $1..*Spon.*
Mylius, Otfried. Die weisse Frau. 12°. '74. $1.50; pap., $1..............................*Zickel.*
Mylius, W: F. History of Eng., for schools; contin. by J. G. Shea. 12°. $1.25..........*Cath. Pub.*
Mylne, G: W. Intercessory prayer: its duties and effects. 32°. '61. 50c. ....*Dutton.*
— Reposing in Jesus; or, the true secret of grace and strength. 16°. 80c..............*Bost. Am. Tr.*
Myndeful of hym. Kramer, J. W. $4...*Whittaker.*
Myra. Egan, P. 25c. ....*De Witt.*
Myra Sherwood's cross, and how she bore it. ill. 16°. '71. $1.50 ....*Lothrop.*
Myra's pink dress. *See* Gem cluster.
Myria. Ritchner, W. D. 25c..............*Barclay.*
Myrrha Lake. Lee, M. M. $1 ....*Cath. Pub.*
Myrtis. Sigourney, L. H. $1.50...........*Harper.*
Myrtle, *Mrs.* Ht. Aunt Maddy's diamonds: tale for little girls. 18°. 45c.....................*Routledge.*
— Little Amy's stories. 6 v. 32°. $1.50 ....*Sheldon.*
— Ocean child; or, showers and sunshine: tale of girlhood. ill. 16°. 75c.................*Routledge.*
— Pet lamb stories. 6 v. 32°. $1.50 ....*Sheldon.*
— Rose bud ser. 12 v. ill. 32°. $3.........*Sheldon.*

Cont.: Going to the cottage. — Duck house. — Two dear friends. — Adventures of a kite. — Scene in spring. — Bertha and the bird. — Eggs and chickens. — Goat and her kid. — Little Amy's birthday. — Pet lamb. — Day in the woods. — May-day at the cottage.

Comprises Little Amy's stories *and* Pet lamb stories.

Myrtle, Lew. (*pseud.*) *See* Hill, G: Canning.
Myrtle branch. Baker, H. N. W. $1....... *Graves.*
Myrtle question-book. Weaver, J. M. 25c... *So. Bapt.*
Myself. Emery, E. $2................. *Lippincott.*
Mysie's work. Finley, M. F. 75c. .... *Pres. Bd.*
Mysteries and miseries of the great metropolis. P., A. *$3.50; $4.50...................... *Appleton.*
Mysteries and miseries of New York. Judson, E. Z. C. $1.50.......................... *Dick & F.*
Mysteries of the backwoods. Owen, T. 75c... *Peterson.*
Mysteries of Bedlam. 8°. pap., 25c........ *Peterson.*
Mysteries of Christianity. Crawford, T. J. $3.75. *Scribner, W. & A.*
Mysteries of a convent. 8°. pap., 25c...... *Peterson.*
Mysteries of the court of London. Reynolds, G. W. M. $1.75; $1.................... *Peterson.*
Mysteries of the court of Naples. Reynolds, G. W. M. $1.75; $1...................... *Peterson.*
Mysteries of the court of Queen Anne. Ainsworth, W. H. 50c. .... *Peterson.*
Mysteries of the court of the Stuarts. Ainsworth, W. H. 75c........................ *Peterson.*
Mysteries of Florence. Lippard, G. $2; $1. *Peterson.*
Mysteries of the head and the heart explained. Grimes, J. S. $2.......................... *Keen.*
Mysteries of London. Reynolds, G. W. M. $1.50. *Dick & F.*
Mysteries of New Orleans. 8°. pap., 50c... *Peterson.*
Mysteries of the ocean. Mangin, A. $5; $7.50; $10.50. *Nelson.*
Mysteries of old London. Reynolds, G. W. M. $1.50. *Dick & F.*
Mysteries of Paris. *See* Sue, E.
Mysteries of the people. Sue, E. 75c..... *Dick & F.*
Mysteries of San Francisco. Williams, H. T. 75c. *Dick & F.*
Mysteries of three cities. Duganne, A. J. H. 75c. *Peterson.*
Mysteries of Udolpho. Radcliffe, A. $1.50.. *Claxton.*
Mysteries of the voice and ear. Rood, O. N. 25c. *Van Nostrand.*
Mysterious cavern. 8°. pap., 25c.......... *De Witt.*
Mysterious foundling. 8°. pap., 25c........ *De Witt.*
Mysterious guest. Dupuy, E. A. $1.75... *Peterson.*
Mysterious hermit; tr. by Mrs. J. Sadlier. 18°. 50c.; 75c................................ *Sadlier.*
Mysterious island. *See* Verne, Jul.
Mysterious lady. Planché, J. R. 15c....... *French.*
Mysterious marksman; or, the outlaws of New York. 8°. pap., 25c..................... *U. P. James.*
Mysterious marriage. *See* Ward, *Mrs.* C. G.
Mysterious stranger: Ethiop. drama. 16°. pap., 15c. *Happy.*
Mystery (The). Crosby, G. S. $1.75... *Lippincott.*
Mystery (The). Wood, E. P. 75c........ *Peterson.*
Mystery of dark hollow. Southworth, E. D. E. N. $1.75; $1.50....................... *Peterson.*
Mystery of Edwin Drood. *See* Dickens, C:
Mystery of Holly Tavern. Collis, L. 40c. *Lippincott.*
Mystery of the lodge. Chellis, M.D. $1.50.. *Lothrop.*
Mystery of matter. Picton, J. A. $3.50.. *Macmillan.*
Mystery of medicine explained. Byrn, M. L. $2.50. *Hurst.*
Mystery of Metropolisville. Eggleston, E. $1.50.. *Judd.*
Mystery of Muddlewitz. *See* Lacy's home plays for ladies.
Mystery of Orcival. *See* Gaboriau, E.
Mystery of pain. Hinton, J. $1....... *Appleton.*
Mystery of Providence. Flavel, J. 60c.... *Pres. Bd.*
Mystery of suffering. Pressensé, E. de. $1.25. *Meth. Bk. Conc.*
Mystic bell. Kuntze, E. J. $1............ *Putnam.*
Mystic spell: Ethiop. drama. 16°. pap., 15c. *French; Happy.*
Mystic tie. Mackey, A. G. $1.50......... *Masonic.*
Mystic tie; or, Freemasonry a league with the devil: account of the church trial of Peter Cook and wife for refusing to support a reverend Freemason. 12°. pap., 20c.......................... *E. A. Cook.*
Mystic vial; or, the last demoiselle of Charrebourg, and other tales. 8°. pap., 25c...... *U. P. James.*
Mystical presence. Nevin, J. W. $1... *Ref. Ch. Pub.*
Myth of Hiawatha. Schoolcraft, H. R. $1.25. *Claxton; Lippincott.*
Myth of Stone Idol. Jones, W. P. $1.25.... *Griggs.*
Mythological fables; tr. 12°. $1....... *Lippincott.*
Myths and heroes. Smith, S. F. $1.50..... *Lothrop.*
Myths and myth-makers. Fiske, J. $2...... *Osgood.*
Myths of the new world. Brinton, D. G. $2.50; $6. *Holt.*
Myths of the Rhine. Saintine, X. B. $10; $18.. *Scribner.*

N., E. V. Alice Herbert; [also] Emily's choice. ill. 12°. $1................................ *Nelson.*
N., H. N. Phil Kennedy. ill. 16°. '66. 60c... *Am. Tr.*
Naaké, J: T. (*ed.*) Slavonic fairy tales, collected and tr. from the Russian, Polish, Servian and Bohemian. ill. 12°. $1.75................ *Routledge.*
Naaman. *See* Costa, M.
Naaman and Elisha. Alden, J. 35c........ *Pres. Bd.*
Nabob at home. Monkland, *Mrs.* —. 50c... *Harper.*
Nabob for an hour: drama. 16°. pap., 15c... *French.*
Nacht (Die) in Breczwezmcisl'. *See* Zschokke, H.
Nachtigall (Die). *See* Schmid, C. v.
Nachtlager in Granada. *See* Norden, F.
Nachtlager v. Granada. 12°. pap., 15c....... *Radde.*
Nachtseiten (Die) v. New York. Lening, G. $3.. *Zickel.*
Nacoochie. *See* Goulding, F. R.
Nadal, Bernard H. New life dawning, and other discourses. 12°. '73. $1.75....... *Meth. Bk. Conc.*
Nadal, E. S. Impressions of London social life; with other papers suggested by an Eng. residence. 12°. '75. $1.50....................... *Scribner.*
Nägelsbach, C. W. E: On Jeremiah and Lamentations. *See* Lange, J. P., Commentary.
Naiad queen. Dalrymple, J. S. 15c......... *French.*
Nails driven home. ('71.) New ed. 16°. '75. $1.25.. *Hoyt.*
Nairne, C: Murray. Oration before Philoclean and Peithessophian Societies of Rutgers College, 1857. 8°. pap., 25c................. *N. Y. Ref. Ch. Bd.*
Naisby, *Mrs.* V. What became of Thomas Munce: mysterious disappearance of strangers in great cities. [In Eng. or Germ.] 12°. pap., 20c. *Barclay.*
Nal u. Damajanti. *See* Schmidt, F.
Nall, Jose. The widow's sixpence; or, go thou and do likewise. 18°. 60c.................. *Pres. Bd.*
Name above every name. Cutler, S. $1; $1.50; $2. *Lothrop.*
Names and their meanings. Sanford, D. P. 75c. *Dutton.*
Names and titles of Jesus Christ. 32°. (Bagster.) 15c. *Wiley.*
Names of the owners or occupants of buildings in Providence [R. I.], 1749–1771. 12°. '70. hf. bd., $1.................................... *Rider.*
Names we bear. Long, H. A. $1.50...... *Williams.*
Nampon, A. Catholic doctrine as defined by the council of Trent: conferences delivered in Geneva; tr. 8°. '69. $3.50............... *Cunningham.*
Nan Darrel. Pickering, E. 38c............ *Peterson.*
Nancy. Broughton, R. $1.50; 75c........ *Appleton.*

Nannie and our boys. Mead, M. G. $1.50..*Cong. Pub.*

Nannie Barton; by author of "Blind Annie Lorimer." 18°. 75c....*Pres. Bd.*

Nannie's adventures. *See* Sunbeam ser.

Nannie's experiment. *See* Alden, *Mrs.* I. M.

Nannie's jewel case. Moritz, A. $1.25......*O'Shea.*

Nanny and I. 16°. $1.50....(?) *Martien.*

Nanny Davenport. Moore, J. F. $1.50......*Hoyt.*

Nanny Thorn. 18°. 40c....*Dutton.*

Nanny's Christmas. ('69.) 2d ed. 18°. '75. 75c. *Claxton.*

Nanny's Christmas books. 3 v. 18°. '69–'70. $2.25. *Claxton.*

Cont.: Nanny's Christmas. — Velvet-coat, the cat, by Mme. M. Dumont. — Coco, the monkey, by Mme. M. Dumont.

Nanny's epitaph. *See* Maple grove stories.

Nanon. *See* Dumas, A.

Nante im Verhör. 12°. pap., 10c....*Radde.*

Nantucket receipts; chiefly from Nantucket sources. 16°. '75. pap., 25c....*Williams.*

Naomi. *See* Webb, J. B.

Naomi, the gipsey girl. Malen, M. E. O. 30c...*Am. News.*

Naomi's home. *See* Little folks ser.

— *Same;* [also] The prize. ill. 18°. '72. 50c...*Lothrop.*

Naphegyi, Gabor. Album of lang.; ill. by the Lord's prayer in 100 languages. ill. 4°. $20; $25; mor., $30....*Lippincott.*

— Among the Arabs: narrative of adventures in Algeria. por. 12°. $1.75....*Lippincott.*

Napheys, G: H. Body (The) and its ailments: handbook of directions for care and medical aid in common complaints and injuries of adults and children. ill. 12°. '76. *$2....*Watts.*

— *Same.* ill. 12°. *$2.50....*So. Pub.*

— Physical life of woman: advice to the maiden, wife and mother. ('71.) New ed., rev. and enl. 12°. '76. *$2....*Watts.*

— *Same.* [In Eng. or Germ.] 12°. '69. *$2. *Maclean.*

— Prevention and cure of disease: treatise on nursing and home treatment of the sick. ill. 8°. '72. *(?)....(?) *Holland.*

— Transmission of life: counsels on the nature and hygiene of the masculine function. ('73.) New ed. 12°. '76. *$2....*Watts.*

Napier, Ja. Manual of dyeing and dyeing receipts; with receipts for dyeing any color on cotton, silk and wool. ill. 8°. $9....*Scribner, W. & A.*

— Manual of electro-metallurgy; incl. applic. to manufacturing processes. ('53.) 7th ed. ill. 8°. '74. $2....*Baird.*

— System of chemistry applied to dyeing; with add. by A. A. Fesquet, and app. on dyeing and calico printing as shown at the Paris Exposition, in 1867. ('53.) 2d ed. ill. 8°. '69. $5..*Baird.*

Napier, Ja. Rob. *See* Ship building.

Napier, *Sir* W: F. P. History of the Peninsular war. 8°. $4; hf. mor., $6; hf. cf., $7.50....*Sadlier.*

Napoleon Bonaparte. [Napoleon I.] Anecdotes of Napoleon. 32°. 60c....*Sadlier.*

— Life. ill. 12°. $1.25....*Scribner, W. & A.*

— *Same.* ill. 16°. $1.25....*Lee & S.*

— Sketches from [his] history. 18°. 45c....*Am. S. S.*

— Table talk and opinions. 16°. $1.25..*Scribner, W. & A.*

Napoleon III. [Louis Napoleon.] L'histoire de Jules César. 2 v. 12°. $2.50; — with maps and por., $4....*Appleton.*

— *Eng.* History of Julius Cæsar. v. 1, 2. 8°. $7; hf. mor., $11.50. — (chp. ed.) 2 v. 12°. ea., $2; pap., $1.50....*Harper.*

Napoleon III. the man of his time: story of N. as told by J. M. Haswell, [and] as told by the popular caricatures of the past thirty-five years. ill. 12°. $3....*Routledge.*

Napoleon, his army and his generals; with sketch of the Am. revolution by an American. ill. 12°. '75. $1.50....*World Pub.*

Napoleon and Blucher. Mundt, C. M. $1.50; $1; $3.50....*Appleton.*

Napoleon and the marshals of the empire. ('55.) New ed. por. demy 8°. '75. $2.50...*Claxton.*

Napoleon and the queen of Prussia. Mundt, C. M. $1.50; $1; $3.50....*Appleton.*

Napoleon in exile. O'Meara, B. E. 2 v. $3.50; $6. *Widdleton.*

Napoleon's complete dream book. *See* Le Normand, *Mme.* C.

Napoleon's oraculum. 32°. '76. pap., 10c...*De Witt.*

Napoleon's oraculum and book of dreams. 16°. 30c. *Locke.*

Napoleon's oraculum and book of fate. 16°. pap., 10c....*Happy.*

— *Same.* 12°. pap., 15c....*Hurst.*

— *See also* Everlasting fortune-teller.

Napton, W. P. *See* Missouri, Sup. Court reports.

Naquet, Alfr. Legal chemistry: guide to detection of poisons, falsification of writing, etc., applied to chemical jurisprudence; tr., with list of books on toxicology, etc., by J. P. Battershall, with pref. by C. F. Chandler. ill. 12°. '76. $2. *Van Nostrand.*

Naramore, G. Queen Loo, and other poems. 16°. $1. *Lippincott.*

Nares, E: Thinks-I-to-myself: a serio-ludicro, tragico-comico tale. 12°. $1.25....*Miller.*

Narr (Ein) d. neunzehnten Jahrhunderts. *See* Zschokke, H.

Narragansett Club. Reprints. *See* Cotton, J: — Williams, Rog.

Narrative of Emily Graham. 18°. 22c......*Am. S. S.*

Narrative of a journey round the world. Gerstäcker, F. $1.50....*Harper.*

Narrative of a mission of inquiry to the Jews from the Church of Scotland in 1839. ill. and map. 12°. $1.25....*Pres. Bd.*

Narrative of a new and unusual Am. imprisonment of two Presb. ministers, and persecution of Mr. Francis Makemie for preaching one sermon at New York, 1707. [Reprint.] 4°. pap., 75c....*Sabin.*

Narrative of proceedings of people of South Carolina, 1719: Lond., 1726. [Reprint.] 4°. pap., 50c. *Sabin.*

Narratives of revivals of religion in Scotland, Ireland and Wales. 18°. 75c....*Pres. Bd.*

Narrow escape. Thomas, A. 75c. ......*W. F. Gill.*

Narrow way. 18°. 40c....*Cong. Pub.*

Nasby, Petroleum V. (*pseud.*) *See* Locke, D: Ross.

Nash, A. C. Remarks on Mansard roofs. *See* American Inst. of Arch., Proceedings of 6th ann. conv.

Nash, Alb. Perseverance and apostacy: argument in proof of the Armenian doctrine on that subject. 2d ed. 12°. '71. $1.50....*Tibbals.*

Nash, Fs. H: *See* Curtis, G. H., *and* Nash, F. H.

— *and* Bristow, G: F. Cantara; or, teacher of singing. 2 v. 12°. '66–'68. 1, $1.15; 2, $1.40..*Barnes.*

Nash, Gilb. Bay leaves, and other poems. 16°. '69. $1.50....*Lockwood, B. & Co.*

Nash, Sim. Crime and the family. 12°. '76. $1.25..*Clarke.*

— Pleading and practice under civil codes of Ohio, N. Y., Kansas and Nebraska; with forms. 4th ed., enl. 2 v. 8°. '74. shp., $15....*Clarke.*

Nash, Willard G. Century of gossip: the real and the seeming of New England life. ill. 12°. '76. $1.50. *Keen.*

Nasmyth, Ja., *and* Carpenter, J. The moon; considered as a planet, a world and a satellite. 24 pl., woodcuts, etc. 4°. $15....*Scribner, W. & A.*

Nason, El. Carmina cœli; or, songs on heaven. ('69.) New ed. sq. 16°. '70. $1.50 .... *Hoyt.*
— Life and public services of C: Sumner. por. and ill. 12°. *$1.50; hf. mor., $2 .... *Russell.*
— Memoir of Mrs. Susannah Rowson; with extracts from her writings in prose and poetry. por. 8°. '70. $2.50 .... *Munsell.*
— Monogram on our national song. 8°. '69. $1 .. *Munsell.*
— Sir Charles Henry Frankland; or, Boston in the colonial times. 8°. '65. $2.50 .... *Munsell.*
— *and* Russell, T: Descriptive circular of life and public services of H: Wilson. ill. 12°. *$1.50; hf. mor., $2 .... *Russell.*
Nason, H: B. Table of reactions for qualitative chemical analysis. col. ill. 8°. '71. *63c. .... *Baird.*
Nassau, Rob. H. Crowned in palm-land: story of African mission life. ill. 12°. $1.75 .. *Lippincott.*
Nast, W: Commentary on Matthew and Mark. v. 1. 4°. '76. $6 .... *Meth. Bk. Conc.*
— Introduction to the Gospel record. 12°. $1.75. *Cin. Meth. Bk. Conc.*
— Larger catechism. 18°. 30c. .... *Meth. Bk. Conc.*
— Smaller catechism. 18°. 25c.; pap., 10c. *Meth. Bk. Conc.*
Nat, the navigator: memoir of Nathaniel Bowditch. ill. 16°. $1 .... *Lee & S.*
Nat and his chum. Wise, D. $1.25 ..... *Perkinpine.*
Nat Blake, the doomed highwayman. 8°. pap., 50c. *Peterson.*
Nata, A. *See* Goldoni, C., Giraud, G., *and* Nata, A.
Natchez (Les). *See* Chateaubriand, F. A.
Nate's gold ring. ('70.) 4th ed. ill. 18°. '74. 50c. *Perkinpine.*
Nathalie. Kavanagh, J. $1.25 .... *Appleton.*
Nathan der Weise. *See* Lessing, G. E.
Nathan Bird. St. John, E. $1.75 .... *Berry.*
Nathaniel Vaughan. Macdonald, F. $1.50 .. *Somerby.*
Nathusius, Marie. Tagebuch eines armen Fräuleins. ('66.) New ed. 12°. '76. pap., 75c. .... *Holt.*
Nation (The) and the church. McCauley, J. A. 25c. *D. H. Carroll.*
National American songster. 32°. 25c. .. *U. P. James.*
National Assoc. for Protection of the Interests of the Am. Trotting Turf. By-laws and rules and regulations. 12°. 25c. .... *Judd.*
National bankruptcy register reports. v. 1–12. 8°. shp., $78 .... *Campbell & Co.*
— Digest (v. 1–10). 8°. shp., $7.50 ... *Campbell & Co.*
National chorus book. Emerson, L. O. $1.50 .. *Ditson.*
National cook book. Bouvier, H. M. $1.75 .. *Peterson.*
National cookery book; comp. from orig. receipts for Women's Centennial Com. of the Intern. Exhib. of 1876. 12°. '76. $2 .... (?) *Wom. Cent.*
National Educational Assoc. Addresses and journal, 1875; ed. by W. D. Henkle. 8°. $1.50 .. *Nat. Ed.*
— Proceedings. ('72.) [Annual.] 8°. $1.50–$1.75. *Nat. Ed.*
National fairy tales. ill. f°. $1.50; $2 ... *J. E. Potter.*
National Gallery. *See* Etchings.
National gallery of Am. landscape: 24 eng. on steel from paintings by Am. artists. [Portfolio.] '71. $40 .... *Putnam.*
National hymn and tune book. 12°. '75. 60c.; bds., 40c. .... *Ditson.*
National lyrics. Whittier, J. G. 50c.; 75c. .. *Osgood.*
National Museum. *See* United States.
National music course for public schools; by J. Eichberg, J. B. Sharland, L. W. Mason and H. E. Holt. 7 v. '70–'75 .... *Ginn.*
Cont.: Primary reader, 16°, hf. bd., 30c. — Second reader, 16°, hf. bd., 40c. — Third, 16°, hf. bd., 40c. — Intermediate [incl. Second and Third], 16°, hf. bd., 70c. — Fourth, 8°, hf. bd., $1.50. — *Same*, abridg, 8°, $1.25. — Fifth, 8°, hf. bd., $1.25.
National music teacher. Mason, L. W. 60c. .. *Ginn.*
National natural history. ill. sm. 4°. $1.75. *Scribner, W. & A.*
National nursery book. ill. sm. 4°. $1.75. *Scribner, W. & A.*
National nursery tales. ill. f°. $1.50; $2 .. *J. E. Potter.*
National Pharmaceutical Conv. Minutes. *See* American Pharm. Assoc.
National portrait gallery: chromo-lith. por. of celebrities, with memoirs. [To form 4 v.] v. 1, 2. demy 4°. ea., $6; $7.50 .... *Cassell.*
National portrait gallery of distinguished Americans; with biog. sketches. 3 v. imp. 8°. '68. hf. mor., $25; mor., $30 .... *Rice.*
National psalmist. Mason, L., *and* Webb, G. J. $1.50. *Ditson.*
National school singer. Root, N. W. T. 35c. .. *Barnes.*
National Sunday School Convention. Third report, 1869. 8°. $1; pap., 50c. .... *Garrigues.*
National temperance orator. Penney, L. $1. *Nat. Temp.*
National text book: life of Washington, Washington's Farewell address, etc. 18°. 25c. .... *Fisher.*
National thanksgiving. Stanley, A. P. $1. *Macmillan.*
Nation's (A) birth. Calvert, G. H. $1.50 .. (?) *Lee & S.*
Nation's (The) defenders. Barber, J. 35c. .. *Dennis.*
Nations around. Keary, A. $1.75 ...... *Macmillan.*
Natt, G. W. Plain sermons on personal religion. 12°. $2 .... *Lippincott.*
Natty, a spirit. Putnam, A. 75c.; 50c. .... *Colby.*
Natural goodness. *See* Mercein, T. F. R.
Natural hist. for children. 18°. 45c. .... *Am. S. S.*
Natural history of the ballet girl. Smith, A. 15c. *French.*
Natural history of enthusiasm. Taylor, I. $1.25 .. *Carter.*
Natural history of insects. 2 v. ill. 18°. $1.50 .. *Harper.*
Natural history of land birds. ill. 16°. pap., 10c. *U. P. James.*
Natural hist. of N. Y. *See* New York geol. survey.
Natural history of quadrupeds. ill. 16°. pap., 10c. *U. P. James.*
Natural history of water birds. ill. 16°. pap., 10c. *U. P. James.*
Natural history scrap-book. ill. obl. 4°. $2. *Scribner, W. & A.*
Natural history scrap-book: eng. and letter-press. 2 v. imp. obl. 8°. '75. ea., 90c.; — in 1 v., $1.75. *Nelson.*
Natural history ser. of toy books. 8 v. ill. 8°. per doz., $1.50 .... *Nelson.*
Cont.: Beasts of prey. — Remarkable animals. — Birds of the tropics. — Birds of the north. — Wild animals. — Birds of prey. — Sea birds. — Monsters of the deep.
Natural history stories for my juvenile friends. Howitt, M. $2 .... *Routledge.*
Naturalist's directory. *See* Essex Institute.
Naturalist's lib. *See* Jardine, *Sir* W.
Nature and art in the old world. Lee, J. S. $1.50. *Williamson.*
Nature and the Bible. Dawson, J. W, $1.75 .. *Carter.*
Nature and culture. Rice, H. $1.50 .... *Lee & S.*
Nature and life. Collyer, R. $1.50 .... *Lee & S.*
Nature and life. Papillon, F. $2 .... *Appleton.*
Nature and philosophy: farce. 16°. pap., 15c. .. *French.*
Nature in disease. Bigelow, J. $1.25 ..... *W. Wood.*
Nature's aristocracy. Collins, J. $1.50 ...... *Lee & S.*
Nature's laws in human life: exposition of spiritualism; by author of "Vital magnetic cure." ('72.) 2d ed. 12°. '73. $1.50 .... *Colby.*
Nature's nobleman. Pardey, H. O. 15c. .... *French.*
Nature's nobleman; by author of "Rachel's secret." [Fiction.] 8°. pap., 50c. .... *Harper.*
Nature's school; or, lessons from the garden and the field. 16°. $1.25 .... *Am. S. S.*

Nature's testimony to nature's God. Newton, W. $1. *Claxton.*

Nature's voice in the holy catholic church: designs for church decoration throughout the year. obl. 12°. pap., 50c. *Pott.*

Nature's wonders. Newton, R. $1.25. *Carter.*

Nature's wonders. *See* Wonder lib.

Natürliche Tochter (Die). *See* Goethe, J. W. v.

Nauenberg, G. Twenty singing exercises; for all voices. f°. pap., 40c. *Ditson.*

Naughty girl won. 18°. '63. 45c. *Am. Tr.*

Naughty Jack. *See* Robin Ranger's lib.

Naughty Nix; or, the vain kitten. 32°. 40c. *Scribner, W. & A.*

Nauman, Ma. D. Clyde Wardleigh's promise. 12°. '72. $1.50. *Claxton.*

— Enchanted princess. 16°. '71. $1. *Claxton.*

— Eva's adventures in Shadowland. ill. 16°. $1.25. *Lippincott.*

— — *See also* Enchanting fairy lib.

— Sidney Elliott. 12°. '69. $1.50; pap., $1. *Claxton.*

— Twisted threads. 12°. '69. $1.50; pap., $1. *Claxton.*

Nautical almanac. *See* United States, *Bureau of Navigation.*

Nava, Gaetano. Repertorio di solfeggi; for soprano or mezzo soprano, with Lat., Ital. and Eng. words. 5 bks. f°. ea., pap., $1.50. *Ditson.*

— Twelve vocalises for mezzo soprano. f°. pap., $1.50. *Ditson.*

Naval anecdotes. Timbs, J. 50c. *Routledge.*

Naval engagements. Dance, C. 15c. *French.*

Naval Observatory. *See* United States.

Naval officer. *See* Marryat, F:

Naval surgeon. 16°. bds., $1. *Routledge.*

Navarro, Angel. Life of José Antonio Navarro. 8°. '76. pap., 25c. *E. H. Cushing.*

Naville, Ern. Heavenly Father: lectures on mod. atheism; tr. by H. Dornton. 16°. $1.75. *Lee & S.*

— Problem of evil; tr. by J. P. Lacroix. 12°. '71. $1.50. *Meth. Bk. Conc.*

— *Same.* cr. 8°. $5. *Scribner, W. & A.*

Navy Department. *See* United States.

Nayler, G: Practical and theoret. treat. on diseases of the skin. 2d ed., rev. and enl. 8°. $5. *Putnam.*

Naylor, *Mrs.* R. S. Affection's tribute: poems. 12°. '74. $1.25. *Cen. Bk.*

Nazarene (The). Lippard, G. 75c. *Peterson.*

Ne plus ultra glee and chorus book. Dressler, W. $1.50. *Peters.*

Nead, P: Theological works: vindication of primitive Christianity. 8°. '50. $1.25. *Brumbaugh.*

Neal, Dan. History of the Puritans; or, Protestant non-conformists, 1518–1688; with notes by J. O. Choules. 2 v. 8°. $4; shp., $5; hf. cf., $8.25. *Harper.*

Neal, E. Diet for the sick and convalescent. 12°. '60. 75c. *Challen.*

Neal, J: Great mysteries and little plagues: story-book for young and old. 16°. '69. 75c. *Roberts.*

— Wandering recollections of a somewhat busy life: autobiog. 16°. '69. $1.50. *Roberts.*

Neal, Jos. C. Charcoal sketches. ill. 12°. $2.50; pap., 75c. *Peterson.*

— Misfortunes of Peter Faber. ill. 12°. pap., 75c. *Peterson.*

— Peter Ploddy. ill. 12°. pap., 75c. *Peterson.*

Neal Malone. *See* Carleton, W:

Neale, Corn. Emblems. 18°. 40c. *Dutton.*

Neale, Erskine. Closing scene; or, Christianity and infidelity contrasted in the last hours of remarkable persons. ill. 12°. $1.50. *Sower.*

— Scenes where the tempter has triumphed. 18°. 75c. *Harper.*

Neale, Erskine, *continued.*

— Shadows and sunshine, as ill. in hist. of notable characters. ill. 18°. '52. 85c. *Dodd.*

Neale, H: *See* Romance of history.

Neale, J: Mason. Catechetical notes and class questions chiefly on earlier books of Scripture. 12°. '69. $2. *Pott.*

— Commentary on the Psalms. 4 v. 12°. '74. $16. *Pott.*

— History of the Holy Eastern Church: general introduction. 2 v. 8°. '50. $12. *Pott.*

— *Same:* Patriarchate of Alexandria. 2 v. 8°. '57. $10. *Pott.*

— *Same:* Patriarchate of Antioch (a posthumous fragment); with Memoirs of the patriarchs of Antioch by Constantius, Patriarch of Constantinople, tr. from the Gk., and app.; ed. with introd. by G. Williams. 8°. '73. $5. *Pott.*

— History of the so-called Jansenist church of Holland. 8°. '58. $3. *Pott.*

— Hymns of the Eastern Church; with notes and introd. 16°. '70. $1.25. *Pott.*

— Litanies; [also] The way to the cross; [also] The hours of the passion. 16°. '72. $1. *Pott.*

— Liturgies in Greek of S. Mark, S. James, S. Clement, S. Chrysostom, S. Basil; or, according to the use of the churches of Alexandria, Jerusalem, Constantinople, and formula of apostolical const., pref. by Dr. Littledale. 16°. '68. $2.50. *Pott.*

— Mediæval hymns and sequences. 32°. '67. 75c. *Pott.*

— Sermons for children: 33 short readings addressed to the children of S. Margaret's Home, East Grinstead. 16°. '75. $1.25. *Pott.*

— Sermons on passages of the Psalms. 12°. $2.50. *Pott.*

— Sermons preached in a religious house. 2 v. 12°. '61. $4. — 2d ser. 2 v. 12°. '74. $4. *Pott.*

— Sermons preached in Sackville College chapel. 3 v. 12°. '74. $9. *Pott.*

— Three groups of sermons on portions of the Apocalypse. 16°. $2.50. *Pott.*

— *and* Littledale, R. F. Translations of the primitive liturgies. 16°. $2. *Pott.*

Neale, S: *and* Ma. Some account of their lives. 12°. 75c. *Friends Bk. St.*

Neale, W. Johnson. The lost ship; or, the Atlantic steamer. [Fiction.] 8°. pap., 75c. *Harper.*

Neally, A. R. Children's Bible story-book. ill. sm. 4°. '75. $1.50. *Dutton.*

Neander, J: A: W: General hist. of the Christian religion and church; tr. by J. Torrey. 5 v. 8°. '47–'54. $18. *Crocker.*

— History of the planting and training of the Christ. church by the Apostles; [also] Antignosticus; or, spirit of Tertullian; tr. by J. E. Ryland. 2 v. 12°. (Bohn.) ea., $1.25. *Little, B. & Co.*

— *Same.* 2 v. 12°. (Bohn.) ea., $1.40. *Scribner, W. & A.*

— *Same.* 2 v. 12°. (Bohn.) ea., $1.50. *Lippincott.*

— *Same:* tr. rev. by E. G. Robinson. 8°. $4; hf. cf., $6.50. *Sheldon.*

— Lectures on hist. of Christian dogmas; ed. by J. L. Jacobi; tr. by J. E. Ryland. 2 v. 12°. (Bohn.) ea., $1.25. *Little, B. & Co.*

— *Same.* 2 v. 12°. (Bohn.) ea., $1.40. *Scribner, W. & A.*

— *Same.* 2 v. 12°. (Bohn.) ea., $1.50. *Lippincott.*

— Life of Christ; tr. from 4th Germ. ed. by J. M'Clintock and C. E. Blumenthal. 8°. $2.50; shp., $3; hf. cf., $4.75. *Harper.*

— *Same.* 12°. (Bohn.) $1.25. *Little, B. & Co.*

— *Same.* 12°. (Bohn.) $1.40. *Scribner, W. & A.*

— *Same.* 12°. (Bohn.) $1.50. *Lippincott.*

— Light in dark places; tr. 16°. '51. 60c. *Meth. Bk. Conc.*

— Memorials of Christ. life in the early and middle ages; incl. his "Light in dark places"; tr. by J. E. Ryland. 12°. (Bohn.) $1.25. *Little, B. & Co.*

— *Same.* 12°. (Bohn.) $1.40. *Scribner, W. & A.*

— *Same.* 12°. (Bohn.) $1.50. *Lippincott.*

— Scriptural expositions; compr. 1 John, Philippians and James; tr. by Mrs. H. C. Conant. 8°. $3. *Sheldon.*

Near and heavenly horizons. *See* Gasparin, V. B.
Near home. Mortimer, M. 75c. . . . . *Carter.*
Nearer, my God, to thee. Adams, S. F. $2 . . *Lee & S.*
Nearing home. Schenck, W. E. $2 . . . . *Pres. Bd.*
Neaves, C: (*Lord*). Greek anthology. (Anc. classics for Eng. readers.) 16°. $1. *Lippincott; Little, B. & Co.*
Nebel, C: War between U. S. and Mexico: 11 col. drawings, with descrip. of battles by G. W. Kendall. f°. hf. mor., $40 . . . . *Appleton.*
Nebelin, Ctte. Eliz. Gethsemane: meditations and prayers on the last hours of Jesus Christ; ed. by Mrs. C. Mackenzie. 16°. '74. $1.25 . . *Lothrop.*
Nebraska. General statutes in force, Sept. 1, 1873; by G. A. Brown. 8°. '73 . . . . *State.*
— Supreme Court reports to 1874; by J. M. Woolworth and L. Crounse. 3 v. 8°. '71–'74. shp., $15 . . . . *Callaghan.*
Nebulæ, meteoric showers and comets. cr. 8°. '74. pap., 25c. . . . . *Estes.*
Necessity of preaching doctrine. Coit, T. W. 25c. *W. H. Young.*
Necromancer. Reynolds, G. W. M. $1.75; $1. *Peterson.*
Ned, the shepherd boy. *See* Bell, C. D.
Ned, the shepherd boy, changed to the young Christian. ('61.) New ed. ill. 18°. '75. 40c. . . . . *Hoyt.*
Ned Allen. Hannay, D. 50c. . . . . *Harper.*
Ned and Sydney. Miller, M. C. 75c. . . (?) *Cumberland.*
Ned Dolan's garret. *See* Mathews, J. A.
Ned Franks. Tucker, C. 50c. . . . . *Carter.*
Ned Grahame. *See* Choice little lib.
Ned Grant's quest. Bissell, M. L. $1 . . . . *Dutton.*
Ned Hastings; or, the terror of the road. 8°. pap., 50c. . . . . *Peterson.*
Ned Manton. Tucker, C. 75c. . . . . *Carter.*
Ned Morton's sled. *See* Kennedy, *Mrs.* M. G.
Ned Musgrave. Hook, T. 75c. . . . . *Peterson.*
Ned, Nellie and Amy. Seymour, M. H. $1.25 . . *Dutton.*
Ned Nevins, the newsboy. Morgan, H. $1. *Lee & S.; Morgan.*
Ned Scarlet, the daring highwayman. 8°. pap., 25c. *Dick & F.*
Ned Turner. Dunning, A. K. 50c. . . . . *Pres. Bd.*
Ned Valentine, the honest fisher boy. 18°. 30c.; 40c. . . . . *Am. Bapt.*
Neddie and Maggie. *See* Little folks ser.
— *Same;* [also] Light in the window. ill. 18°. '72. 50c. . . . . *Lothrop.*
Neddie and Maggie lib. 12 v. ill. 18°. $3.60 . . *Lothrop.*
Comprises Elsie Wood lib. *and* Boys and boys lib.

Neddie's care. *See* Minn.
Neddie's temptation. 18°. 30c. . . . . *Am. S. S.*
Ned's motto. Robbins, S. S. $1.25 . . . . *Carter.*
Ned's search. ('74.) New ed. 16°. '76. $1.50 . . *Hoyt.*
Need of the church. Scott, A. T. 30c. . . *Perkinpine.*
Needham, Dan. *See* New England Agric. Soc.
Needle and the rat. Tucker, C. 75c. . . . . *Carter.*
Neely, *Miss* Kate J. Ellie Randolph; or, the good part. 18°. 75c. . . . . *Carter; Dutton.*
— Marion's Sundays. 18°. 60c. . . . . . *Carter; Dutton.*
— *See also* Bradley, *Mrs.* M. E., *and* Neely, *Miss* K. J.
Neely, Ph. P. Discourses. 12°. '59. $2; mor., $3. *So. Meth.*
Neff, Fel. Memoir. 18°. 40c. . . . . *Am. S. S.*
Neffe (Der) als Onkel. *See* Picard, L. B.
Neftel, W: B. Galvano-therapeutics: physiol. and therapeut. action of the galvanic current upon the acoustic, optic, sympathetic and pneumogastric nerves. 12°. $1.50 . . . . *Appleton.*

Neger u. Weisse. *See* Hoffmann, F.
Negerkönig (Der) Zamba. 18°. '73. 50c. . . . *Am. Tr.*
Neglected spelling lesson. 18°. '71. 45c. . . *Whittaker.*
Neglected wife. *See* Nurse Grand's reminiscences.
Negligence. 16°. 45c. . . . . *Cummiskey.*
Negro forget-me-not songster. *See* New.
Negro in the American rebellion. Brown, W. W. *$2. *Lee & S.*
Negro melodist. 32°. 25c. . . . . *U. P. James.*
Negro servant. *See* Richmond, L.
Negro's place in nature. Hunt, J. 10c. . . *Van Evrie.*
Neidhard, C: Diphtheria, as it prevailed in the U. S., 1860–1866; with its phenomena, its nature and homœop. treatment. 8°. $1.75 . . . . *Boericke.*
— On the efficacy of crotalus-horridus in yellow fever, also in malignant, bilious and remittent fevers. [Hom.] 8°. $1 . . . . *Boericke.*
Neighbor Jackwood. *See* Trowbridge, J. T.
Neighborly love: tale. 18°. 45c. . . . . *Routledge.*
— *Same*. 18°. 60c. . . . . *Whittaker.*
— *Same*. ill. 16°. '70. $1 . . . . *Lothrop.*
Neighbor's house. Shaw, J. R. $1.50 . . . . . . *Lothrop.*
Neighbors (The). *See* Bremer, F.
Neighbors' wives. Trowbridge, J. T. $1.50 . . *Lee & S.*
Neighbours. Oxenford, J. 15c. . . . . *French.*
Neil, S: Art of public speaking. 16°. pap., 25c. *Happy.*
Neill, E: D. English colonization of Am. during 17th cent. 8°. '71. $4 . . . . *Routledge.*
— Fairfaxes of Eng. and Am. in 17th and 18th centuries; with pedigrees. 8°. '68. $3 . . . . *Munsell.*
— History of Minnesota. 8°. $2.50 . . . . *Lippincott.*
— History of the Virginia Company of London; with letters to and from the first colony. sq. 8°. '69. $5 . . . . *Munsell.*
— Terra Mariæ; or, threads of Maryland colonial history. 12°. $2 . . . . *Lippincott.*
Neill, J: *and* Smith, Fs. G. Analytical compendium of the various branches of medical science. ill. roy. 12°. $4; leath., $4.75 . . . . *Lea.*
Neill, W: Autobiography; with sel. of sermons. por. 12°. 75c. . . . . *Pres. Bd.*
Neilson, W: H., *jr.* Gathered leaves of Sunday school song. 18°. '76. 30c. . . . . *Biglow.*
Neiremurg, Eus. Treatise on difference between temporal and eternal. 12°. $2 . . . . *O'Shea.*
Neither Rome nor Judah. Hoven, E. $1.10 . . *Pres. Bd.*
Neitz, Sol. Bischof Johannes Seybert's Leben u. Wirken. 12°. '62. $1.50 . . . . *Ev. Assoc.*
Nelaton, A: Clinical lectures on surgery; from notes by W. F. Atlee. 8°. shp., $3 . . . . . . *Lippincott.*
Neligan, J. Moore. Atlas of cutaneous diseases. col. pl. 4°. $5.50 . . . . *Lea.*
— Materia medica. 12°. $2 . . . . *Lippincott.*
— Medicines, their uses and mode of administration; with conspectus of the three British pharmacopœias, account of new remedies and formulæ; with notes and add. by D. M. Reese. 8°. $1.50; shp., $2 . . . . *Harper.*
Nell Gwynn. Jerrold, D. 15c. . . . . *French.*
Nellie and Bertha. ill. sq. 12°. '71. bds., 50c. *Routledge.*
Nellie and her beads. *See* Infant school lib.
Nellie Gates. Boardman, M. M. $1.25 . . *Perkinpine.*
Nellie Green; or, the way to be happy. 18°. 30c.; 35c. *Am. Bapt.*
Nellie Grey; or, ups and downs of every-day life, and their lessons. 18°. 60c. . . . . *Am. S. S.*
Nellie Greyson. 18°. '68. 50c. . . . . *Randolph.*
Nellie Holmes. 16°. 70c. . . . . *West. Tr.*
Nellie Milton's housekeeping. May, C. L. $1.25. *H. A. Young.*
Nellie Netterville. Caddell, C. M. $1.50 . . *Cath. Pub.*

Nellie Newton. 18°. 40c.; 50c. . . . . *Am. Bapt.*
— *See also* Gay cottage stories.

Nellie Newton; or, patience and perseverance, and the way to Mount Zion. ('66.) New ed. ill. 16°. '72. $1 . . . . *Hoyt.*

Nellie Nowlan. ill. 12°. $1 . . . . *Nelson.*

Nellie of Truro. 16°. $1.50 . . . . *Carter.*

Nellie Rodney's sorrows. *See* Aunt Deborah's lib.

Nellie Russell, the little girl who was easily frightened. ill. 18°. '67. 45c. . . . *N. Y. Ref. Ch. Bd.; Pres. Com.*

Nellie Walters. Denison, M. A. 75c. . . . (?) *Martien.*

Nellie Warren. Wise, D. $1.25 . . . . *H. A. Young.*

Nellie Wells. *See* Sunbeam lib.

Nellie West from ten to twenty. Graham, M. $1. *Am. S. S.*

Nellie's birthday. *See* Kennedy, *Mrs.* M. G.

Nellie's housekeeping. Mathews, J. H. $1 . . . *Carter.*

Nellie's neighbor. 18°. 70c. . . . . *Pres. Bd.*

Nellie's stumbling block. Mathews, J. A. $1.10 . . *Carter.*

Nellie's sunbeam. *See* Robbie's pets.

Nellie's trial, and how she became one of Christ's little ones. 18°. 50c. . . . . *Am. S. S.*

Nellie's work for Jesus. Blackall, C. R. 40c.; 10c. *Blackall.*

Nelligan, W: H. Rome: its churches, its charities and its schools. por. 12°. $1.25 . . . . . . *Strong.*
— Saintly characters recently proposed for canonization. 18°. $1 . . . . *Strong.*

Nell's mission. 18°. 50c. . . . . *Carter; Dutton.*

Nelly. ill. cr. 16°. 25c. . . . . *Cassell.*

Nelly; or, the best inheritance. *See* Guernsey, L. E.

Nelly, the gypsy girl. 18°. 50c. . . . . *Dutton.*

Nelly, the gipsy girl. Valentine, R. 45c. . . *Routledge.*

Nelly and her boat. Franklin, J. 83c. . . . *Thompson.*

Nelly and her friends. Franklin, J. 83c. . . *Thompson.*

Nelly stories. *See* Franklin, J.

Nelly's dark days. Smith, H. 75c. . . . . *Dodd.*

Nelly's first school days. Franklin, J. 83c. . . *Thompson.*

Nelly's lib. *See* Guernsey, L. E.

Nelly's rhymes. ill. 64°. 50c. . . . . *Nelson.*

Nelly's visit. Franklin, J. 83c. . . . . *Thompson.*

Nelson, D: Cause and cure of infidelity. ill. 12°. '41. 75c. *Am. Tr.*
— *Fr.* La cause et la remède de l'incrédulité. 18°. '61. 50c. . . . . *Am. Tr.*
— *Germ.* Ursachen des Unglaubens. 12°. '47. 70c. *Am. Tr.*
— *Span.* La causa y el remedio de la incredulidad. 12°. '68. 70c. . . . . *Am. Tr.*

Nelson, Ht. C. Martha's schooldays. 16°. $1.25. *Cong. Pub.*

Nelson, H: A. Seeing Jesus. 18°. 65c. . . . . *Pres. Bd.*

Nelson, J: Extract from journal. ('55.) 2d ed. 18°. '75. 50c. . . . . *So. Meth.*
— *Swed.* 12°. '54. 50c. . . . . *Meth. Bk. Conc.*

Nelson, R: Book-keeping. 8°. '70. $1.50 . . . *Morton.*

Nelson, Rob. Companion for the fasts and festivals of the Church of Eng.; with collects and prayers for each solemnity. por. 16°. $1.50 . . . . *Pott.*

Nelson, T: *jr.* Letters, relating to siege of Yorktown and surrender of Cornwallis. 4°. '74. pap., $5. *J. W. Randolph.*

Nelson's kitten ser. 4 v. 4°. ea., 50c.; pap., 25c. *Nelson.*
Cont.: Nursery rhymes. — Fancies and flowers for nursery hours. — Three little kittens. — Picture pages bright and gay.

Nelson's picture alphabet ser. 5 v. 4°. '75. ea., 50c.; pap., 25c. . . . . *Nelson.*
Cont.: Picture alphabet of nations of the world. — Picture alphabet of beasts. — Picture alphabet of birds. — Scripture picture alphabet. — Child's picture alphabet.

Nelson's picture primer. 18°. 25c. . . . . *Nelson.*

Nelthropp, H. L. Treatise on watch work, past and present. ill. cr. 8°. '73. $2.50 . . . . *Spon.*

Nemesis. *See* Friedrich, F.

Nemesis. Harland, M. $1.50 . . . . *Carleton.*

Nemesis. *See* Hoffmann, F.

Nemos, W: Artificial memory: method of making a bad memory good, and a good memory better. 16°. '73. pap., $1 . . . . *Bancroft.*

Nennius, *Abbot of Bangor*. History of the Britons. *See* Giles, J. A., Six old Eng. chronicles.

Nephew Frankie. 18°. 40c. . . . . *Cong. Pub.*

Nepos, Corn. [*Lat.*] With notes by C. Anthon. 12°. '73. shp., $1.50 . . . . *Harper.*
— *Same.* With notes, lexicon, etc., by G. Stuart. ('73.) 2d ed. 16°. '75. hf. mor., $1.25 . . *Eldredge.*
— *Same.* With questions and imitative exercises by T. K. Arnold; rev., with notes, by E. A. Johnson. 12°. $1.50 . . . . *Appleton.*
— De excellentibus ducibus ex terrarum gentium, cum vitis Catonis et Attici; ed. by L. Schmitz and C. G. Zumpt. roy. 18°. '63. 60c.; hf. bd., 70c. *Lea.*
— Life of Atticus. *See* Cicero, M. T., De senectute, etc.
— *See also* Gardner, F., Gay, A. M., *and* Buck, A. M.; — Justinus, Nepos, C., *and* Eutropius.

Neptune (The) afloat; — at the Golden Horn; — outward bound. Rover, W. ea., $1.50 . . . . *O'Shea.*

Neptune's defeat. Brougham, J. 15c. . . . . *French.*

Nepveu, Fs. Spirit of Christianity; or, conformity of the Christian with Jesus Christ. 16°. 75c. *Strong.*

Nero. Story, W. W. $3 . . . . *Scribner, W. & A.*

Nervous man. Bernard, W. B. 15c. . . . . *French.*

Nesbits (The); or, a mother's last request, and other tales. 16°. '73. $1.25 . . . . *Cath. Pub.*

Nest in the honeysuckles, and other stories. 18°. 60c. *Am. S. S.*

Nest of stories. Morss, L. H. 6 v. $3 . . . *Cong. Pub.*

Nestorian biography: sketches of pious Nestorians who have died at Oroomiah, Persia; by missionaries of the A. B. C. F. M. 12°. $1.25 . . *Cong. Pub.*

Nestorians (The) of Persia. 18°. 60c. . . . . . *Am. S. S.*

Nether side of N. Y. Crapsey, E. $1.75; $1 . . *Sheldon.*

Netherclift. Bates, L. $1.25 . . . . *Bost. Am. Tr.*

Netley Abbey. Pearce, W. 15c. . . . . *French.*

Nettie and her friends. *See* Loving heart and helping hand lib.

Nettie, Connie and Silas. *See* Sunberry Dale lib.

Nettie Loring. Downs, E. $1.25 . . . . *Nat. Temp.*

Nettie Nesmith. Monmouth, L. H. $1 . . . . . *Lothrop.*

Nettie Renton; or, the ghost. O'Connor, W. D. $1. *Putnam.*

Nettie Wallace. Trowbridge, C. M. 75c. . . (?) *Martien.*

Nettie's mission. *See* Mathews, J. A.

Nettie's trial. Samuels, S. B. C. 75c. . . . . *Lee & S.*

Nettlewig Hall. Westmacott, C. M. 15c. . . . *French.*

Netty and her sister. Martyn, S. T. 70c. . . . . *Am. Tr.*

Netty's acorn frames; or, a little girl's work. 18°. 50c. *Am. S. S.*

Neu vermehrtes geistliches Lust-Gärtlein frommer Seelen. 18°. leath., 75c. . . . . *Baer.*

Neubekehrte, od. Anfänger in Zion's Wegen. 18°. 40c. *Ev. Assoc.*

Neue amerikanische Advokat (Der), od. the new American lawyer; in engl. u. deutscher Sprache. 8°. $2 . . . . *Radde.*

Neue Fibel, od. erstes Lesebuch f. die deutschen kathol. Schulen in den Ver. St. 12°. 15c. . . . . *Benziger.*
— *See also* Fibel.

Neues Bilder A B C- u. Buchstabirbuch. 12°. 20c.; linen, 38c. *Radde.*

Neues Buchstabirbuch, nebst Lese- u. Denkübungen. 12°. bds., 20c. . . . . *Ludwig.*

Neues gemeinschaftliches Gesangbuch d. luth. u. reformirten Gemeinden in Nordam., nebst Sonntag-Episteln u. Gebeten. 18°. '75. leath., 75c.; $1.40; $1.65. — Taschenausg. sm. 18°. '75. leath., 60c.; $1.20; $1.45 .... *Radde.*

Neues Gesangbuch d. evang. luth. Kirche, nebst Gebeten, u. d. sonn- u. festägl. Evangelien u. Episteln, etc. 12°. '76. $1.40–$3. — Taschenausg. 32°. '76. leath., 75c. .... *Radde.*

Neues Leben. Mügge, T. 75c.; 50c... *F. W. Thomas.*

Neues Lesebuch f. Schulen, od. zweites Lesebuch. 12°. bds., 30c. .... *Ludwig.*

Neues vollständiges Traumbuch u. Punktirbuch; a. d. Arab. v. T. Horst. 18°. pap., 15c. .... *Radde.*

Neukomm, Sgsm. David; with words by J. Webb. [Oratorio.] obl. 8°. bds., $1 .... *Ditson.*

— Mount Sinai; or, the ten commandments. [Oratorio.] f°. bds., $2 .... *Ditson.*

Neuman, H: *and* Baretti, J. J. Pocket dict. of the Span. and Eng. languages: Span.-Eng. and Eng.-Span. 12°. shp., $1.88 .... *Lippincott.*

Neumann, Bern. Kurzgefasste Geographie f. deutsche Schulen Nordamerikas. 3d ed., rev. 8°. '74. 50c. .... *Herder.*

Neumann, Isidor. Handbook of skin diseases; tr. by L. D. Bulkley. 66 wood-eng. 8°. $4; shp., $5 .... *Appleton.*

Neumann, *Bp.* J: Nep. Biblische Geschichte. 12°. 40c. .... *Kreuzer.*

— Grosser Katechismus. 18°. 30c. .... *Kreuzer.*

Neun Reisen e. Sonambüle. Stohlmann, F. 75c... *Radde.*

Neupert, G: Zeugniss der Wahrheit. 18°. '51. 25c. *Am. Tr.*

Neuverbessertes u. vermehrtes Glücksrad, od. Enthüllung d. Zukunft nach Art d. alten Astrologen. 18°. 25c. .... *Radde.*

Nevada. Compiled laws; with notes of Sup. Court decisions by M. S. Bonnifield and T. W. Healy. 2 v. 8°. shp., $20 .... *Bancroft.*

— Mining laws. *See* Congdon, H. B.

— Statutes, 1861–'73; with notes of Sup. Court decisions by M. S. Bonnifield and T. W. Healy. 2 v. 8°. shp., $16 .... *S. Whitney.*

— Supreme Court reports, v. 1–10 (1865–'76). 10 v. 8°. '66–'76. shp., $78 .... *Bancroft.*

Cont.: 1–4 (1865–'69), by A. Helm. — 5–9 (1869–'74), by A. Helm and T. H. Hittell. — 10 (1874–'76), by C. F. Bicknell and T. P. Hawley.

Note. v. 1–3 not sold sep.; 4–7, ea., $7.50; 8, 9, ea., $6.50; 10, $4.50.

— *Same.* v. 1–9. 8°. shp., $66; — v. 1, *net*, shp., $10 .... *S. Whitney.*

Never afraid. ill. cr. 16°. 25c. .... *Cassell.*

Never again. Mayo, W. S. $2 .... *Putnam.*

Never give up. Baker, H. N. W. $1... *H. A. Young.*

Never give up ser. *See* Tucker, *Mrs.* C.

Never reckon your chickens, etc. *See* Reeve, W.

Never say die. Baker, G. M. 15c. .... *Lee & S.*

Never too late. *See* Happy child's lib.

Never too late to mend. *See* Reade, C:

Nevers (The). *See* Blackburn, W. M.

Nevers (The). *See* Frank's victory.

Nevile, Sandford. *See* England, Common law reports.

Neville, Edm. Questions on biblical antiquities. 24°. 16c. .... *Am. S. S.*

Neville, J: Hydraulic tables, coefficients and formulæ, for finding the discharge of water from orifices, notches, weirs, pipes and rivers. 12°. $7.. *Baird.*

Nevin, Alfr. Book opened: analysis of the Bible. 12°. '69. *$1.75 .... *Maclean.*

— *Same.* 12°. '73. *$1.75 .... *Am. Fam.*

— Improved pict. dict. of Bible. *See* Bible [Whole].

— Notes, exegetical, practical and devotional, on Exodus. ('73.) 3d ed. 12°. '74. $1.50 ...... *Claxton.*

Nevin, Alfr., *continued.*

— Popular expositor: Gospel and Acts. 4 v. ill. and maps. 8°. '72. ea., $1.50; — in 2 v., ea., *$2.25 — in 1 v., leath., *4.25; hf. mor., $5 .... *Ziegler*

— Sabbath school help: exposition of the international lessons (Mark) for 1874. ('73.) 3d ed. 12°. '74. bds., 50c. .... *Claxton*

— Words of comfort for doubting hearts. 24°. '67. 50c. *Randolph*

Nevin, D. R. B. Continental sketches of distinguished Pennsylvanians; with state papers, etc. 12°. $1.50 *Porter*

Nevin, J: W. Biblical antiquities. ill. 12°. $1.50. *Am. S. S.*

— Liturgical discussion: answer to Dorner. 12°. pap. 25c. .... *Ref. Ch. Pub.*

— The mystical presence. 12°. $1 ...... *Ref. Ch. Pub.*

Nevin, Rob. P. Black-robes: sketches of missions and ministers in the wilderness and on the border. 12°. $1.50 .... *Lippincott*

Nevins, W: Army regulations for drum, fife and bugle. obl. 8°. 40c. .... *Church*

Nevins, *Rev.* W: Practical thoughts. ill. 18°. '36. 45c. .... *Am. Tr.*

Nevius, *Mrs.* Helen S. C. Our life in China. ('68.) New ed. 16°. '76. $1.50 .... *Carter*

Nevius, J: L. China and the Chinese. map and ill. 12°. $1.75 .... *Harper*

— San-Poh; or, north of the hills: missionary work in an out-station in China. 18°. 55c. ...... *Pres. Bd.*

New affinities of faith. Martineau, J. 25c. ...... *Holt*

New age and its messenger. Evans, W. F. 38c. *H. H. Carter*

New American pocket farrier and farmer's guide; from the writings of Youatt, Lawrence, Hinds, White, Clater and others. 18°. 75c. .... *Sower*

New American ser. [of spellers, readers, etc.] 9 v. 12°. .... *Butler*

Cont.: Primary speller, hf. bd., 20c. — Pronouncing speller, hf. bd., 30c. — First reader, by E. Sargent and A. May, hf. bd. 20c. — Second, by E. Sargent and A. May, hf. bd., 30c. — Third, by E. Sargent and A. May, hf. bd., 50c. — Fourth, by E. Sargent and A. May, hf. bd., 60c. — Fifth, by E. Sargent and A. May, 90c. — Etymological reader, by E. Sargent and A. May, $1.50. — School manual of Eng. etymology, by E. Sargent, 90c.

New and complete dream-book, fortune teller, dial of fate and oraculum. 16°. bds., 35c... *U. P. James*

New and improved system of educating the horse; also treatise on shoeing; with recipes for diseases of horses, etc. sq. 18°. '74. pap., 25c... (?) *F. M. Reed*

New atmosphere. Dodge, M. A. $1.50 .... *Estes*

New baby. ill. sq. 8°. $1 .... *Nelson*

New Bible class lesson-book; on life of Paul. 18°. 16c. .... *Am. S. S.*

New Bible stories. 32°. 50c. .... *Nelson*

New Biblical atlas and Scripture gazetteer: maps and letterpress. 8°. $1.25 .... *Am. S. S.*

New biblical atlas and Scripture gazetteer; rev. by T. O. Summers. ('58.) 2d ed. 8°. '75. $1.50 .. *So. Meth.*

New birth. Phelps, A. $1.25 ..... *Graves; Lothrop*

New boat, and other tales. 18°. 70c. .... *Pres. Bd.*

New bonnet. 18°. 25c. .... *Am. S. S.*

— *See also* Children of Blackberry Hollow.

New book of 200 pictures. 16°. $1.25; $1.75. *Am. S. S.*

New boots. Phelps, P. H. 45c. .... *Cong. Pub.*

New boy. Guernsey, C. F. $1.25 ...... (?) *Martien*

New brooms sweep clean. Baker, G. M. 15c... *Lee & S.*

New buggy. *See* Baker, *Mrs.* H. N. W.

New carmina sacra. Mason, L. $1.50 .... *Ditson*

New casket (The). Robinson, G. O. $1.50... *Duffie*

New censer; — New chain. *See* Bradbury, W. B.

New chair. ('70.) 4th ed. ill. 18°. '74. 50c. *Perkinpine*

New Christian psalmist. Leonard, S. W. 50c. *R. W. Carroll*

New Church. Book of worship; prep. by order of Gen. Conv. 12°. $1.25; leath., $1.50..*New Ch.*
— Consecutive service. 12°. 40c...*Lippincott; New Ch.*
— Liturgy; with [or without] Consecutive service. 12°. $1.25....................*Lippincott; New Ch.*
— Sabbath school manual; prep. by a com. of Gen. Conv. 12°. pap., 40c..................*New Ch.*
— *See also* Centenary.
New church catechism. 18°. '62. 20c...*H. H. Carter.*
New church doctrinal class-book concerning the Lord. 16°. '62. 40c........................*H. H. Carter.*
New classical lib. *See* Harper's.
New clerk. *See* Putnam, *Mrs.* E. T. H.
New cobwebs to catch little flies. 18°. 60c....*Carter.*
New colored ill. primer. sq. 16°. 50c......*Routledge.*
Compr. Alphabet and easy words, *and* Easy spelling and reading.
New comic songster. 8°. '70. bds., 60c.....*Ditson.*
New commandment. Shaw, J. R. $1.50....*Lothrop.*
New congregational harp and chapel. Barnes, L. B. $1.38..................................*Ditson.*
New convert. *See* Young, R.
New coronet. Root, G. F. $1.25...........*Church.*
New crisis. Blanchard, C. 15c..........*D. Thomas.*
New crystal spring. Whiting, S. K. 35c...*G. D. Russell.*
New Cvriasvm Urbis. Wood, S. $2..........*Cook.*
New day. Gilder, R. W. $1.50...........*Scribner.*
New dictionary of quotations, from the Gk., Lat. and mod. lang.; tr. with notes by author of "Live and learn" and index. cr. 8°. $2...*Lippincott.*
New Don Quixote. Daudet, A. $1........*W. F. Gill.*
New elements from old subjects. Gaskell, J. $2.50. *Claxton.*
New England. Abstract of the lawes of N. E. as they are novv established: London, 1641. [Reprint.] 4°. pap., 25c..............................*Sabin.*
New England Agricultural Soc. Transactions: first annual exhibition, Springfield, Sept., 1864, [with] address of Jno. A. Andrew; [by Chas. L. Flint]. ill. 8°. '64. pap., 50c..............*N. E. Agri.*
— Second annual report, 1865; [by Dan'l Needham]. ill. sm. 8°. '66. $1..................*N. E. Agri.*
New England and Bay State glee book. Woodbury, I. B., *and* Johnson, A. N. 75c...........*Gordon.*
New England conservatory method for the piano forte: foreign and Am. fingering. 4°. bds., $3.25; — in 3 pts., ea., bds., $1.50...........*G. D. Russell.*
New England Historic, Genealogical Society. Brief hist. of the "New Eng. Hist. and Geneal. Register." 8°. '76. pap., 50c........*N. E. Hist. Gen.*
— Proceedings, Jan. 4, 1871; — Jan. 3, 1872; — Jan. 1, 1873; — Jan. 7, 1874; — Jan. 6, 1875; — Jan. 5, 1876. 6 v. 8°. '71-'76. ea., pap., 25c. *N. E. Hist. Gen.*
— — *See also* Andrew, J. A.; — Slafter, E. F.; — Wilder, M. P.
Note. Other publications of the Soc. entered under names of their authors.
New England legends. Spofford, H. E. $1; 50c.* *Osgood.*
New England primer. [Fac-simile reprint.] 32°. 12c. *Cong. Pub.*
— *Same;* with hist. sketch. 24°. '75. 25c....*Munsell.*
New England tragedies. *See* Longfellow, H: W.
New England's first fruits; with divers and other special matters conc. that country. [Reprint.] 4°. $1; large pap., $2..........................*Sabin.*
New England's Jonas cast up at London. Childe, J. 50c..*Sabin.*
New explanatory question book. 2 nos. 24°. ea., 16c. *Am. S. S.*
New fashioned girl. 16°. 40c.; pap., 30c.....*Miller.*
New fifty vol. lib. 50 v. 18°. $8; $10....*So. Bapt.*
New footman. Selby, C. 15c..................*French.*

New fruits from an old field. Whitaker, E. $1.50; $2.25..................................*Randolph.*
New gift book. ill. sm. 4°. pap., 25c.......*Am. S. S.*
New glories of the Catholic Church; tr. from the Italian, with pref. by N. Wiseman. 12°. '60. $1.50; $2...*Murphy.*
New God (The). Bischoff, J. E. 75c.; 25c...*Pustet.*
New Godiva. Hope, S. $1.50...........*Lippincott.*
New golden censer; — New golden chain; — New golden shower. Bradbury, W. B. ea., 35c.....*Biglow.*
New graded readers. 7 v. ill. 12°. '73.......*Ivison.*
Cont.: No. 1, bds., 25c. — *Same;* in Leigh's orthog., 30c. — 2, bds., 40c. — *Same;* in Leigh's orthog., 50c. — 3, bds., 50c. — 4, 80c.; bds., 70c. — 5, $1.20.
New Hampshire. Digest of school laws. *See* Morrison, C. R.
— General statutes, with U. S. and State constitutions; with glossary and index by C. R. Morrison. 8°. '67. shp., $5.........................*Sanborn.*
— — Supplement, 1867-'71. 8°..................*State.*
— Law reports, v. 1-20 (1816-'50). 8°. ea., shp., $7. *Eastman.*
Cont.: 1 (1816-'19), by N. Adams. — 2 (1819-'23), by W. M. Richardson and L. Woodbury. — 3-5 (1823-'32), by the judges. — 6 (1832-'34), by B. B. French. — 7-18 (1834-'48), by the judges. — 19 (1848-'49), by W. L. Foster. — 20 (1849-'50), by W. E. Chandler.
Note. v. 1, 2, 4, 6, 7, 9-12 are o. p.
— Superior Court reports, v. 21-56 (1850-'76). 36 v. 8°. ea., shp., $5.....................*Sanborn.*
Cont.: 21-31 (1850-'55), by W. L. Foster, — 32-38 (1856-'59), by G. G. Fogg. — 39-43 (1859-'63), by W. E. Chandler. — 45-48 (1864-'68), by A. Hadley. — 49-55 (1869-'73), by J. M. Shirley. — 56 (1874, '75), by D. Hall.
— — *Same.* 36 v. 8°. shp., 21-42, ea., $5; 43, 44, ea., $6; 45-56, ea., *net*, $3.50.............*Eastman.*
— — Digest. *See* Morrison, C. R.
New Hampshire Board of Agriculture. Reports; by J. O. Adams. 5 v. 8°. '71-'76. ea., $1-$2. *N. H. Agri.*
New Hampshire geological survey. First report on geol. of N. H.; by C. T. Jackson. 8°. '41..*State.*
— First-third reports upon the geol. and mineral. of the state; by C. H. Hitchcock. 3 v. 8°. '69-'71..*State.*
— Final report on geol. and mineral. of N. H., with contrib. towards improvement of agric. and metallurgy; by C. T. Jackson. 4°. '44.....*State.*
— Geology of N. H.; by C. H. Hitchcock. pt. 1: Physical geog. pl. and maps. 8°. '74...*State.*
New Hampshire Historical Soc. Collections. v. 1-3, 5, 7, 8. 8°. '24-'66. v. 1-3, 5, 7, ea., $2; v. 8, $2.50............................*N. H. Hist.*
Note. v. 4, 6 are o. p. — v. 7 contains Records of the N. H. Committee of Safety; History of Chester; Valley of the Merrimack; Changes in the Merrimack River. — v. 8 contains Province records and court papers, 1680-1692; Notices of provincial councilors and other papers rel. to early hist. of state.
New Hampshire register, farmers' almanac and business directory. [Annual.] 18°. pap., 25c. *Claremont.*
New Hampshire tax collectors' book and warrant, and decisions of courts in rel. to their powers and duties. 16°. '73. pap., $1..........*Sanborn.*
New harp of Zion. Fillmore, A. D. *and* J. H. $1.25. *R. W. Carroll.*
New Haven, *Conn.* *See* Attractions of N. H.
New Haven Colony Historical Soc. Papers. 8°. '65. $3.................................*N. Hav. Hist.*
New history of Sandford and Merton. Burnand, F. C. $1.75...................................*Roberts.*
New holiday lib. for boys and girls. 9 v. ill. 24°. $2.90. *Am. S. S.*
Cont.: Arthur Maitland's holidays. — Annie Leighton. — Blind Effie's trial. — Corner houses; or, kindness wins. — Frank's victory. — Susie's mistake. — Millie and her two friends. — Elsie Lee; or, impatience cured. — Who is my neighbor?
New homes; or, where to settle: guide [to west. states] for intending settlers and those in search of health. 12°. '74. $1............................*Am. News.*

New hope; or, the rescue. 2 v. 12°. ea., pap., 75c. *Peterson.*

New hymn and tune book for the Meth. Episc. Ch. 8°. $2.50; mor., $6. — 12°. $1.75; $2.50; mor., $4.50 .... *Meth. Bk. Conc.*

New hymnal; [without music]. 18°. 50c.; 75c.; bds., 40c. .... *Huntington.*

New hymns for youth; for Sabbath schools and families. 32°. 20c.–90c. .... *Pres. Bd.*

New Hyperion. Shinn, E. $3; $3.50 .... *Lippincott.*

New illustrated self-instructor in phrenology and physiology. ill. 12°. '59. 75c.; pap., 50c. .... *Wells.*

New Jersey. Court of Chancery reports, v. 1–26 (1830–'75). 26 v. 8° .... *State.*
Cont.: 1 (1830–'32), by N. Saxton. — 2–4 (1833–'45), by H. W. Green. — 5–8 (1845–'52), by G. B. Halsted. — 9–11 (1852–'58), by J. P. Stockton. — 12, 13 (1858–'60), by M. Beasley. — 14–15 (1861–2), by T. N. McCarter. — 16–26 (1863–'75), by C. E. Green.

— Digest of laws; by L. Q. C. Elmer. 4th ed.; cont. all laws in force, 1709–1868, with rules, etc., of courts, by J. T. Nixon. 8°. '68 .... *State.*

— Laws, 1869–'73. 5 v. 8° .... *State.*

— Statutes; rev. by P. D. Vroom, H. W. Green, W. L. Dayton and S. G. Potts. 8°. '47 .... *State.*

— Supreme Court reports, 1790–1795; by R. S. Coxe. 8°. '16. $5 .... *T. & J. W. Johnson.*

— *Same.* 1806–'13; by W. S. Pennington. 2d ed. 2 v. 8°. '73. shp., $15 .... *Ward & P.*

— *Same.* v. 4–37 (1816–'74). 34 v. 8° .... *State.*
Cont.: 4, 5 (1816–'20), by S. L. Southard. — 6–12 (1821–'31), by W. Halsted, jr. — 13–15 (1831–'36), by J. S. Green. — 16–19 (1837–'42), by J. Harrison. — 20 (1842–'46), by R. D. Spencer. — 21–24 (1847–'55), by A. O. Zabriskie. — 25–29 (1855–'62), by A. Dutcher. — 30–37 (1863–'74), by P. D. Vroom.

— — Index. *See* Halsted, W.

New Jersey Central Railroad, and its connections through the coal fields of Pennsylvania. 12°. $1; pap., 75c. .... *Harper.*

New Jersey conference memorial: sketches of deceased members; [by E. H. Stokes and others]. 12°. '65. $1.75 .... *Perkinpine.*

New Jersey geological survey. Description of geol.: final report by H. D. Rogers. 8°. '40 ..... *State.*

— Third report on geol. survey of N. J. for 1856. 8°. '57 .... *State.*

— Geology of N. J.; [by] G. H. Cook, state geologist. maps. 8°. '68 .... *State.*

New Jersey Historical Soc. Collections. v. 1–8; with sup. to v. 6. 7 v. ill., por. and maps. 8°. '46–'72. *N. J. Hist.*
Cont.: v. 1. East Jersey under the provinc. gov., by W. A. Whitehead; A model of the gov. of East New Jersey, by Geo. Scot, $4. — 2. Life of W. Alexander, Earl of Stirling, Major-gen. in the U. S. army during the rev., with sel. from his corresp., by W. A. Duer, $1. — 3. Provincial courts of N. J., with sketches of bench and bar, by R. S. Field, $2. — 4. Papers of Lewis Morris, ed. by W. A. Whitehead, $2. — 5. Analytical index to colonial doc. of N. J., in State Paper Offices of Eng., by H. Stevens; ed., with notes and ref., by W. A. Whitehead, $2.50. — 6. Records of Newark, 1666–1836, $2. — Sup.: Proceedings commemorative of settlement of Newark, $1.50. — 7. Constitution and gov. of N. J., with biog. sketches of governors, 1776–1845, and reminiscences of the bench and bar, by L. Q. C. Elmer, $3.

— Proceedings. 1st ser. 10 v. 8°. '45–'66. pap., 1–9, ea., $1.50; 10, $1.75. — 2d ser. v. 1–3. 8°. '67–'74. ea., pap., $1.75 .... *N. J. Hist.*

New Jerusalem and its heavenly doctrine. Swedenborg, E. 12c. .... *New Ch.*

New Jerusalem Church. *See* New Church.

New juvenile lib. 7 v. ill. 16°. $3 .... *Appleton.*
Cont.: Grace and Clara. — Florence Arnot. — Blind Alice. — Emily Herbert. — Ellen Leslie. — Rose and Lillie Stanhope. — Jessie Graham.

New juvenile lib. *See* Lovechild, Lucy.

New letter writer. 32°. '75. 35c. .... *Clark & M.*

New liber primus. 12°. 95c. .... *Thompson.*

New life. 18°. 35c. .... *Cong. Pub.*

New life. *See* Dante.

New life. Parsons, J. U. 35c. .... *Am. Tr.*

New life dawning. Nadal, B. H. $1.75 .. *Meth. Bk. Conc.*

New life in new lands. Lippincott, S. J. $2 ... *Ford.*

New lights. Sadlier, M. A. $1; $1.50 ...... *Sadlier.*

New little mittens. *See* Barrow, *Mrs.* F.

New lute of Zion. Woodbury, I. B. $1.50 .. *Huntington.*

New Magdalen. *See* Collins, Wilkie.

New manual of the sacred heart of Jesus. [Cath. prayer book.] 24°. '74. 75c.–$4.50 .. *Kelly, P. & Co.*

New manual of the sodality of the Virgin, and office of the dead; tr. by P. Kenricks. [Cath. prayer book.] 32°. '64. 50c. .... *Fox.*

— *See also* Manual.

New men and old acres. Taylor, T., *and* Durbourg, A. W. 15c. .... *De Witt; French.*

New method for the melodeon, harmonium, etc. 4°. '59. bds., $1.50 .... *Ditson.*

New names. Franks, M. B. 30c. .... *Dutton.*

New negro forget-me-not songster. 32°. pap., 25c. *U. P. James.*

New nightcaps. *See* Barrow, *Mrs.* F.

New nonsense rhymes. Beckett, W. H. $1 .. *Carleton.*

New odeon. Webb, G. J., *and* Mason, L. $1.50 .. *Ditson.*

New olive branch. Cook, T. J., *and* Perkins, T. E. $1.50 .... *Huntington.*

New oratorio chorus book. 8°. bds., $1.38 ... *Ditson.*

New origin and doctrines. 75c. .... (?) *Cumberland.*

New Orleans sketch book. 12°. pap., 75c. .. *Peterson.*

New parasol. Baker, S. S. 30c. .... *Am. Tr.*

New pet's picture book. ill. 4°. '75. $2 ...... *Nelson.*

New piano. Macrum, J. M. 75c. ...... *R. S. Davis (P.)*

New picture lib. 5 v. ill. 16°. $2.50 .... *Hoyt.*
Cont.: Ellie and Archie. — Joe and Neddy. — Danger ahead. — Brave boy. — Lost sailor.

New picture reading book. Newman, E. E. $1.50 .. *Hoyt.*

New planet. 18°. 18c. .... *Am. S. S.*

New pocket Hebrew and Eng. lexicon. 18°. (Bagster.) hf. bd., $2 .... *Wiley.*

New popular forget-me-not songster. 32°. pap., 25c. *U. P. James.*

New praises of Jesus. Hammond, E. P. 25c. .. *Biglow.*

New priest in Conception Bay. Lowell, R. T. S. $1.75. *Dutton.*

New provings of cistus canadensis, cobaltum, zingiber and mercurius protoiodatus. [Hom.] 8°. pap., 75c. .... *Boericke.*

New readings of old parables. Anderson, C. 75c. *Whittaker.*

New sacred star. Marshall, L. $1.38 .... *Ditson.*

New scholar; or, advantages of youthful piety. 18°. 40c. .... *Am. S. S.*

New scholars. Mathews, J. H. $1.25 .... *Carter.*

New school and home. Partridge, W. W. 60c. *Brainard.*

New shining star. Perkins, T. E. 40c.; 33c. *Huntington.*

New shoes. *See* Abbott, Jac.

New shower. *See* Bradbury, W. B.

New silver song. Ogden, W. A. 35c. .. *W. W. Whitney.*

New sketches of every-day life. Bremer, F. 50c. *Harper.*

New sled. *See* Hildeburn, *Mrs.* M. J.

New society. *See* Baker, *Mrs.* H. N. W.

New songs. Follen, E. L. 75c. .... *Lee & S.*

New songs for little people. Anderson, M. E. $1.50. *Lee & S.*

New spirit of the age. Horne, R. H. $1 .... *Harper.*

New standard atlas of Canada: topog., geol., postal, railway and timber land maps; with letter-press. f°. '75. mor., $25 .... *Williams.*

New stories. *See* Tucker, *Mrs.* C.

New stories and old legends. Hervey, E. L. 75c. *Cassell.*

New stories for little folks. *See* Theodore Thinker.

New stories from an old book. Hammond, H. L. 70c. *Bost. Am. Tr.*

New stories on old subjects. Bowen, C. E. $1.50..*Pott.*
New story book. *See* Parton, *Mrs.* S. P.
New Sunday school reward books. 32°. 50c...*Nelson.*
New Sunday school singer. 18°. pap., 25c. *Meth. Bk. Conc.*
New tale of a tub. Bailey, F. W. N. 75c..... *Wiley.*
New tale of a tub. [Toy-book.] ill. 4°. $1; 50c. *Routledge.*
New temperance melodist. Hubbard, S. 50c...*Ditson.*
New templi carmina. Kingsley, G. $1.75; $1.38. *Gordon.*
New Testament. *See* Apocryphal; — Bible.
New Testament alphabet. [Toy-book.] ill. 4°. $1; 50c. ....*Routledge.*
New Testament commentary; by W. K. Pendleton, W. T. Moore, etc. [To form 11 v.] v. 1, 9. 2 v. cr. 8°. ea., *$2; shp., $2.50; hf. cf., $3..*Chase.*
Cont.: v. 1. Matthew and Mark. — v. 9. Hebrews.
New Testament pictures. Caunter, H. 75c. *Scribner, W. & A.*
New Testament standard of piety. McDonald, W. $1. *Palmer.*
New theory of population; deduced from general law of animal fertility; with introd. by R. T. Trall. 12°. '57. pap., 25c. .... *Wells.*
New Timothy (The). Baker, W. M. $1.50..*Harper.*
New token for children. 18°. 55c. ....*Pres. Bd.*
New union hymns; or, hymns for Sabbath schools, Bible classes, etc. 32°. 20c.........*Am. S. S.*
New universal letter-writer. ('64.) New ed. 12°. '74. $1; bds., 50c. ....*Claxton.*
New view of hell. Barrett, B. F. $1.......*Claxton.*
New violet. Fillmore, A. D. 35c......*R. W. Carroll.*
New way to pay old debts. Massinger, P. 15c...*French.*
New way to win a fortune. Dupuy, E. A. $1.75. *Peterson.*
New world compared with the old. Townsend, G. A. *$3.50; $4; $5 ....*Betts.*
New year. Strong, M. D. 75c............*Lothrop.*
New year lib. 15 v. ill. 18°. $3..........*Lothrop.*
Cont.: Mattie's flowers. — Grandmother's story. — Grace's rose. — Bessie's temptation. — Bessie's reward. — The squirrels. — Meddling Matt. — Bird nesting. — True heroism. — Mischievous boy. — Discontented bird. — Christmas story. — Wonderful bear. — Teasing Tom. — New year.
New Year's bargain. Woolsey, S. C. $1.50..*Roberts.*
New Year's calls: Ethiop. drama. 16°. pap., 15c. *French; Happy.*
New Year's eve. Schöller, H. 75c.; 60c.....*Peters.*
New York, *City.* Marine court practice. 8°. '75. pap., 25c. ....*Campbell & Co.*
— Superior Court reports, v. 1–30 (1828–'68). 30 v. 8°. ea., shp., $7 ....*W. C. Little.*
Cont.: 1, 2 (1828–'29), by J. P. Hall. — 3–7 (1847–'52), by L. H. Sandford. — 8–13 (1852–'57), by J. Duer. — 14–23 (1857–'63), by J. S. Bosworth. — 24–30 (1863–'68), by A. L. Robertson.
— *Same.* v. 31, 32 (1869–'70); by J. M. Sweeny. 2 v. 8°. ....*State.*
— *Same.* v. 33–40 (1871–'76); by S. Jones and J. C. Spencer. 8 v. 8°. shp., $56........ *Ward & P.*
— Thirty-Fourth St. Reformed Church: 50th anniversary of its organization, Dec. 14–21, 1873. ill. 8°. $1 ....*N. Y. Ref. Ch. Bd.*
— *See also* Rogers, D.; — Wheeler, J. D.
New York, *City and County.* Court of Common Pleas reports, 1850–'54; by E. D. Smith. 4 v. 8°. shp., $26 ....*Baker, V. & Co.*
— *Same.* 1855–'60; by H. Hilton. 2 v. 8°.....*State.*
— *Same.* 1860–'76; with notes, ref. and index; by C. P. Daly. 5 v. 8°. ea., shp., $6.50..*Baker, V. & Co.*
New York, *County.* Surrogate reports, 1849–'57; by A. W. Bradford. 4 v. 8°. shp., $24. *Baker, V. & Co.; W. C. Little.*
— *Same.* 1857–'63; by A. A. Redfield. 8°. shp., $6. *Baker, V. & Co.*
— *Same.* 1864–'69; by G. J. Tucker. 8°......*State.*

New York, *State.* Act authorizing formation of corporations for manufacturing, mining, chemical and other purposes, with amendments since 1851. 12°. pap., 50c..................*Baker, V. & Co.*
— Act to provide for organization and regulation of certain business corporations, June 21, 1875. 8°. pap., 25c. ....*Campbell & Co.*
— *Same;* with introd., index and forms by R. B. McMaster. 12°. pap., 50c.........*Baker, V. & Co.*
— Analytical index of ref. to cases. *See* Stone, C. F.
— Chancery reports, 1814–'23; by W. Johnson. 7 v. 8° ....*State.*
— *Same.* 1823–'26; by S. M. Hopkins. 8°.....*State.*
— *Same.* 1828–'45; by A. C. Paige. 11 v. 8°. shp., $62 ....*W. C. Little.*
— *Same.* 1831–'50; by C. Edwards. 4 v. 8°...*State.*
— *Same.* 1839–'40; by M. Hoffman. 8°........*State.*
— *Same.* 1839–'41; by C: L. Clarke. New ed., with notes and ref. by N. C. Moak. 8°. '69. shp., $7.50.............................*W. C. Little.*
— *Same.* 1843–'47; by L. H. Sandford. 4 v. 8°..*State.*
— *Same.* 1845–'48; by O. L. Barbour. 3 v. 8°..*State.*
— Code of procedure; with rules of Supr. Court and Court of Appeals and art. 6 of Const.; with amend. of 1875. 8°. shp., $7.50. — (Diamond ed.) 32°. $1.50 .... *Weed.*
— *Same.* (Diamond ed.) 12°. $1.50..*J. D. Parsons.*
— *Same.* (Diamond ed.) sm. 8°. $1; — with rules, $1.50 ....*Ward & P.*
— *Same;* with notes, table of cases and index by W. Wait. 8°. shp., $7.50 ....*Gould.*
— — Voorhies' code of procedure, with notes, app. and index by J. Townshend. 10th ed., enl. to 1876. 8°. shp., $6 ....*Baker, V. & Co.*
— — Code as it now is; with art. 6 of Const., and notes, etc., by W. Wait. 8°. '74. $1.50 .....*Gould.*
— Constitution, 1875. 8°. 50c.........*Campbell & Co.*
— Court of Appeals reports, 1847–8; with notes and ref. by N. Howard, jr. 8°. shp, $7.50. *Baker, V. & Co.; Ward & P.*
— *Same.* v. 1–62 (1847–'76). 62 v. 8°........*State.*
Cont.: 1–4 (1847–'51), by G. F. Comstock. — 5–10 (1851–'54), by H. R. Selden. — 11–14 (1854–'56), by F. Kernan. — 15–27 (1857–'63), by E. P. Smith. — 28–39 (1863–'68), by J. Tiffany. — 40–45 (1869–'72), by S. Hand. — 46–62 (1871–'76), by H. E. Sickels.
— *Same.* 1863–'68; by E. W. Keyes. 4 v. 8°..*State.*
— *Same.* 1850–'69; by A. Abbott. 4 v. roy. 8°. '73–'74. shp., $24.....................*Ward & P.*
Note. Contains decisions incl. in Howard's Appeal cases; Selden's Notes; Keyes' Reports (4 v.); Transcript Appeals (7 v.)
— Digest of reports. *See* Brightly, F. C.; — Clinton, G. W., *and* Wait, W.; — Tiffany, J., *and* Barbour, O. L.; — Wait, W:
— Digest of statutes. *See* Fay, J. D.
— Digest of statutes and reports. *See* Abbott, B. V. *and* A.
— Documentary history. *See* O'Callaghan, E. B.
— Draft of a civil code; prep. by the commissioners of the code. 8°. '62. $3 .... *Weed.*
— Excise law, with civil damage act and amend.; with notes of decisions by W. W. Saxton. 16°. '73. pap., 50c.......................*Herrick.*
— Game laws as amended to 1872; with forms and proceedings. 16°. '72. 75c.............*Herrick.*
— General statutes, 1871–'75. 5 v. 8°. ea., $2.50.. *Weed.*
— Law of voluntary assignments. *See* Hawes, G. P.
— New York Code reporter, 1848–'51. 3 v. 8°..*State.*
— New York Code reports (new ser.), 1851–'2. 8°..*State.*
— Penal code. 8°. '65. $3......................... *Weed.*
— Political code. 8°. '65. $3 .... *Weed.*
— Reports of decisions in criminal cases in courts of Oyer and Terminer; by A. J. Parker. 6 v. 8°. shp., $45 ....*W. C. Little.*
— Reports of practice cases, 1844–'76; by N. Howard, jr. 50 v. 8°. shp., $225 ....*Gould.*
— *Same.* 1854–'65; by B. V. and A. Abbott. 19 v. 8°. ea., shp., $5...............*Baker, V. & Co.*
— — New ser., 1865–'75; by B. V. and A. Abbott. 16 v. roy. 8°. $80....*Baker, V. & Co.; Ward & P.*

New York, *State, continued.*
— Reports of select cases in Supreme Court, not heretofore reported; by J. W. Edmonds. 8°. '68. shp., $7.50 .... *Ward & P.*
— Revised statutes; ed. by J. W. Edmonds. 7 v. 8°. '69–'70. ea., shp., $6. — Index. 8°. '72. $3.50. *Weed.*
— Revised statutes, with gen. laws to 1875; ed., with ref., notes and index, by G. W. Cothran. 6th ed. 3 v. 8°. '76. *net*, shp., $18 .... *Banks.*
— Select cases adjudged in courts of N. Y., cont. case of J. V. N. Yates and case of journeymen cordwainers of N. Y. City. 8°. '11 .... *State.*
— Statute law relating to rail-roads analytically arrang. to 1875; with notes by R. B. McMaster. 8°. shp., $4 .... *Baker, V. & Co.*
— Statutes rel. to Albany Penitentiary. *See* Moak, N. C.
— Statutes rel. to limited partnerships, with the statutes rel. to compromises by partners and joint debtors and to partnership names and signs; by A. Abbott. 8°. pap., 75c. .... *Baker, V. & Co.*
— Supreme Court reports, 1794–1875 .... *State.*
Cont.: 1794–1800, by W. Coleman. — 1794–1805, by W. Coleman and G. Caines. — 1799–1803, by W. Johnson, 3 v. — 1803–5, by G. Caines, 3 v. — 1806–'23, by W. Johnson, 20 v. — 1808–'18, by J. Anthon. — 1823–'29, by E. Cowen, 9 v. — 1828–'41, by J. L. Wendell, 26 v. — 1841–'44, by N. Hill, jr., 7 v. — 1845–'48, by H. Denio, 5 v. — 1842–'44, by T. M. Lalor (sup. to Hill and Denio). — 1847–'75, by O. L. Barbour, 66 v.

— *Same.* 1869–'75. 13 v. 8°. shp., $32.50 .. *Banks.*
Cont.: 1869–'73, by A. Lansing, 7 v. — 1873–'75, by M. T. Hun, 6 v.
— *Same.* 1873–'75; by I. G. Thompson and R. D. Cook. 6 v. 8°. shp., $21 .... *J. D. Parsons.*
— Supreme Court rules; with special rules of all courts of N. Y. City. 8°. 75c. .... *Campbell & Co.*
— Synopsis of cases argued and reversed, 1799–1847; by R. Lockwood. 8°. '48 .... *State.*
— *See also* Caines, G.; — New York weekly digest.

New York: history of the metropolitan city. 16°. '53. $1.25 .... *Meth. Bk. Conc.*

New York: its upper ten and lower million. Lippard, G. $1 .... *Mendenhall.*

New York Acad. of Medicine. Bulletin. 4 v. 8°. '60–'71. ea., pap., $2 .... *N. Y. Acad. Med.*
— Transactions. 3 v. 8°. '57–'72. ea., pap., $2.50. *N. Y. Acad. Med.*
— *Same.* 2d ser. 2 v. 8°. '74–'76. ea., $4.50; pap., $4 .... *N. Y. Acad. Med.*

New York after dark; or, gleams and shadows of city life. 8°. pap., 25c. .... *De Witt.*

New York and Erie Railroad guide book. map and ill. 12°. 75c.; pap., 60c. .... *Harper.*

New York as it is: guide book to New York, Brooklyn and vicinity. map and ill. 18°. $1; pap., 75c. *Miller.*

New York Bible-women. Wright, J. McN. $1.10. *Pres. Bd.*

New York by gaslight. Foster, G. G. 25c... *De Witt.*

New York geological survey. Annual reports. 5 v. in 3. 8°. '37–'41 .... *State.*
— Natural hist. of N. Y. 22 v. pl. 4°. '42–'61 .. *State.*
Cont.: Zoology, by J. E. DeKay, 5 v. — Flora, by J. Torrey, 2 v. — Mineralogy, by L. C. Beck. — Geology, by W. W. Mather, E. Emmons, L. Vanuxem and J. Hall, 4 v. — Palæontology, by J. Hall, 5 v. — Agriculture, by E. Emmons, 5 v.

New York glee and chorus book. Bradbury, W. B. $1.50 .... *Ditson.*

New York Herald almanac and financial, commercial and polit. register for 1873. 12°. '73. pap., 25c.; — for 1874. 12°. '74. pap., 25c... (?) *N. Y. Herald.*

New York Homœopathic Med. Soc. *See* Homœopathic Med. Soc.

New York illustrated: ill. of buildings, street scenes, and suburban views; [with] maps and guide. ill. imp. 8°. pap., 50c.; — in Germ. or Spanish, ea., pap., 50c. .... *Appleton.*

New York in alter Zeit. *See* Dilthey, K.

New York in slices. 8°. pap., 50c. .... *Dick & F.*

New York Med. Soc. *See* Medical Soc. of N. Y.

New York Medico-Legal Soc. *See* Medico-Legal Soc. of N. Y.

New York naked. Foster, G. G. 50c. ...... *De Witt.*

New York Ned; or, wreck and refuge. 18°. 90c. (?) *Martien.*

New York needle-women. Wright, J. McN. 80c. *Pres. Bd.*

New York [readers and spellers]. ('23–'39.) New ed. 4 v. '71–'75. hf. bd. .... *Claxton.*
Cont.: No. 1, 18°, 25c. — 2, 18°, 35c. — 3, 12°, 45c. — New York spelling bk., or 4th bk., 18°, 21c.

New York State Med. Soc. *See* Medical Soc. of the State of N. Y.

New York Times receipts: information for the household. 8°. '76. pap., 50c. .... (?) *Am. News.*

New York Tombs. Sutton, C. $3.50; $4.25 .. *U. S. Pub.*

New York Tribune. *See* Tribune.

New York vor zwanzig Jahren. Griesinger, T. $1.50; $1 .... *Zickel.*

New York weekly digest of cases decided in [N. Y.] state and city courts, supreme courts of other states, U. S. courts, etc. v. 1. roy. 8°. '76. shp., $6.50 .... *Campbell & Co.*

New York World almanac for 1873. 12°. '73. pap., 25c.; — for 1874. 12°. '74. pap., 25c... (?) *N. Y. World.*

Newberry, J: S. *See* Ives, J. C., Report on Colorado River; — Illinois geol. survey; — Ohio geol. survey; — United States, Reports; *Corps of Eng.*

Newbery, Rob. Gleanings from ornamental art, from examples in the British, South Kensington and other museums, etc.: 100 pl. 4°. $15 .. *Baird.*

Newbury, *Mrs.* F. E. Coming to the light. ill. 16°. '73. $1.50 .... *Lothrop.*

Newbury, Herbert (*pseud.*) *See* Herbert, S. A. F.

Newby, *Mrs.* C. J. [Novels.] 9 v. 8°. ea., pap., 50c. *Peterson.*
Cont.: Common sense. — Kate Kennedy. — Margaret Hamilton. — Married. — Only temper. — Right and left. — Sunshine and shadow. — Trodden down. — Wondrous strange.

Newcastle, *Duke and Duchess of.* [W: and Marg. Cavendish.] Cavalier and his lady: sel. from their works, with introd. essay by E. Jenkins. 18°. '72. $1.25 .... *Macmillan.*

Newcomb, Harvey. Harvest and the reapers: home work for all, and how to do it. 16°. '75. $1. *Lothrop.*
— How to be a lady. 16°. $1 .... *Graves.*
— How to be a man. 16°. $1 .... *Graves.*
— Kind words; — Life story boys; — Life story girls. *See* Life story ser.
— Young ladies' guide to harmonious development of character. 12°. '53. $1.50 .... *Dodd.*

Newcomb, Sim. Critical exam. of our financ. policy during the southern rebellion. 16°. $1 .. *Appleton.*
— Orbit of Neptune. 4°. '66. pap., $2 ... *Smith. Inst.*
— Orbit of Uranus. 4°. '73. pap., $3 .... *Smith. Inst.*
— Planetary motion. 4°. '74. pap., 75c. .. *Smith. Inst.*

Newcomes (The). *See* Thackeray, W: M.

Newdigate, A. L. Scale for ready comparison of British and metric weights and measures. [In case.] '72. $2 .... *Spon.*

Newell, *Mrs.* Ht. Life and writings. 18°. 75c. .. *Am. S. S.*

Newell, Jos. K. History of 10th Regt., Mass. Vol. ill. 8°. '75. *$3.50; hf. mor., $5 ... *C. A. Nichols.*

Newell, M. A., *and* Creery, W: R. [Readers.] 6 v. ill. 12°. '68 .... *Kelly, P. & Co.*
Cont.: First reader, 25c. — Second, 50c. — Third, 75c. — Fourth, 90c. — Fifth, $1.25. — Sixth, $1.50.

Newell, Rob. H: ["Orpheus C. Kerr."] Orpheus C. Kerr papers. 4 v. in 1. 12°. $2 ...... *Carleton.*
— Versatilities: poems, patriotic, sentimental and humorous. 16°. $2 .... *Lee & S.*

Newell, W. W. Household of peace. 18°. '70. 20c. *Am. Tr.*
— The rescue. sq. 18°. '76. 25c.; pap., 10c. *Bost. Am. Tr.*
Newell boys. Whipple, C. $1.25............ *Hoyt.*
Newes [Nevves] of Sir Walter Rauleigh; with the true description of Gviana: London, 1618. [Reprint.] 4°. pap., 50c.................. *Sabin.*
Newfoundland fisherman. ill. 18°. '53. 35c. *Am. Tr.*
Newgate of Connecticut. Phelps, R. H. *75c. *Am. Pub.*
Newhall, C. S. ["Carl."] Joe and the Howards; or, armed with eyes. ill. 16°. $1.25.... *Graves.*
Newhall, F. H. *See* Warren, W. F., Newhall, F. H., *and* Haven, E. O.
Newhall, *Miss* M. Ada Hovey's idols. 16°. $1.25. *Cong. Pub.*
Newhouse, S. Trapper's guide; ed. by the Oneida Community. ill. 8°. $1.50.............. *Judd.*
Newington butts. Morton, J. M. 15c...... *French.*
Newland, W. A. Vespers, no. 1. [Cath. music.] 4°. pap., $1.25.......................... *Peters.*
Newlin, E. J. Sunday school expositor. 18°. '75. 25c. .... *Ward.*
Newlyn House, the home of the Davenports. ill. 16°. $1.50 .... *Crowell.*
— *See also* Triplet ser.
Newman, —. Young captives. 18°. '72. 50c... *Kenedy.*
Newman, *Mrs.* E. E. Home picture book. ('73.) New ed. ill. 16°. '75. $1 .... *Hoyt.*
— New picture reading-book. ('72.) New ed. ill. 16°. '75. $1.50.............................. *Hoyt.*
Newman, J: Iron cylinder bridge piers: calcul. and investig. in designing them, etc.: paper, April, 1873, Inst. of Civil Eng. 8°. '75. pap., 60c... *Spon.*
Newman, J: B. Fascination; or, the philosophy of charming. ('47.) New ed. 12°. '75. $1.. *Wells.*
— Philosophy of generation: its abuses with their causes, prevention and cure. 12°. '55. pap., 50c... *Wells.*
Newman, J: E. Treatise on pleading and practice under civil code of Kentucky. 8°. shp., $7.50. *Morton.*
Newman, J: H: Apologia pro vita sua: reply to "What, then, does Dr. Newman mean?" 4th ed. 12°. '65. $2....................... *Cath. Pub.*
— Calista: sketch of the 3d century. 12° $1.25; $1.75 .... *Sadlier.*
— Characteristics from writings: selections, personal, hist., philos. and religious; ed. by W. S. Lilly. 12°. $1.50; mor., $3.50................ *Sadlier.*
— *Same.* post 8°. $2.50............. *Scribner, W. & A.*
— Essay in aid of a grammar of assent. 12°. '70. $2.50. *Cath. Pub.*
— Hymni ecclesiæ. fp. 8°. '65. $2 .... *Macmillan.*
— Idea of a univ. defined and ill. 12°. $3.50 .... *Pott.*
— Parochial and plain sermons. 8 v. 12°. '75. $18. *Pott.*
— Reply to Gladstone. 12°. pap., 50c...... *Cath. Pub.*
Newman, J: P. From Dan to Beersheba; or, the land of promise as it now appears. maps and ill. 12°. $1.75...................... *Harper.*
— Thrones and palaces of Babylon and Nineveh, from the Persian Gulf to the Mediterranean: a thousand miles on horseback. ill. 8°. $5.... *Harper.*
Newman, *Mrs.* J. P. (*ed.*) Dewdrops and sunshine: poems about little children. sq. 18°. '72. $1.50. *Meth. Bk. Conc.*
— Mother, home and heaven. [Poetry.] sq. 18°. '72. $1.50 .... *Meth. Bk. Conc.*
Newman, *Mrs.* May Wentworth. Fairy tales from gold lands. ('67–'68.) New ed. 2 v. ill. 16°. '70. ea., 75c.............................. *Roman.*
— Golden dawn, and other stories. ('69.) 2d ed. ill. 16°. '70. 75c. .... *Roman.*
— Jean. 8°. pap., 50c......................... *Harper.*
News. *See* Daily News.
News of Sir Walter Rauleigh. *See* Newes.

Newspaper poets. Hopkins, A. A. $1.75. (?) *Rural Home.*
Newstead, Rob. Advice to one who meets in class. 72°. '43. 15c.; 20c............. *Meth. Bk. Conc.*
— Rules for holy living. 72°. '42. 15c... *Meth. Bk. Conc.*
Newton, A. E. Better way: appeal to men in behalf of human culture through a wiser parentage. 2d ed. 16°. '75. 50c.; pap., 25c........ *Wood & H.*
— Lessons for children about themselves. [Hygienic.] ('72.) 3d ed. 16°. '74. 50c.............. *Colby.*
— Ministry of angels realized: letter to the Edwards Cong. Church, Boston. ('55.) 8th ed. 12°. '73. pap., 25c................................ *Colby.*
— *and Mrs.* A. E. Answer to charges of belief in modern revelations, etc. ('54.) 2d ed. 12°. '74. pap., 15c. *Colby.*
Newton, Adelaide L. Epistle to the Hebrews. 16°. $1.50 .... *Carter.*
— Heavenly life (The). 16°. $1.75........... *Carter.*
— Memoir. 16°. $1.25...................... *Carter.*
— Song of Solomon; compared with other parts of Scripture. 16°. $1.25................. *Carter.*
Newton, B: Wills. Perfect sacrifice. 16°. 75c. *Am. Bapt.*
Newton, C: E. Cast upon the world: drama. 16°. pap., 15c. .... *De Witt.*
— Out at sea: drama. 16°. pap., 15c. ...... *De Witt.*
Newton, *Sir* I: Life; rev. by T. O. Summers. ('55.) 3d ed. 18°. '75. 50c................. *So. Meth.*
— Principia; ed. by Sir W. Thomson and H. Blackburn. 4°. '71. $12................ *Macmillan.*
— *Same:* first three sections, with notes and problems by Percival Frost. 8°. '63. $3.50 .. *Macmillan.*
Newton, J: Works. 8°. $3 .... *Carter.*
— Cardiphonia; or, the utterance of the heart in the course of a real correspondence; with introd. by D. Russel. por. 12°. $1.20 .... *Pres. Bd.*
— Letters to an adopted daughter. 18°. '46. 25c. *Am. Tr.*
— Life. 18°. '43. 45c...................... *Am. Tr.*
— Memoir; with selections from correspondence. 18°. 75c. .... *Pres. Bd.*
— Memoirs of Eliza Cunningham; [also] of Jane L. Benn, by B. Woodd; [also] of Caroline E. Smelt, by Dr. Waddell. 18°. 35c........... *Am. S. S.*
Newton, R. Heber. The children's church. [Service book and hymnal.] sm. 18°. '72. 40c... *Randolph.*
— — Supplement, by S. Jackson. obl. 16°. '72. pap., 15c. .... *Randolph.*
Newton, Rejoice, *and* Jennison, S: Brief report at annual meeting of the Am. Antiq. Soc., Oct., 1821. 8°. '22. pap., 25 .... *Am. Antiq.*
Newton, R: Bible bulwarks; or, a sevenfold argument in defence of the Scriptures. 18°. 40c.; pap., 20c. .... *Am. S. S.*
— Bible illustrations: similes, allegories and anecdotes; with introd. 12°. $1.50 .... *Sheldon; So. Bapt.*
— Child's life of Jesus. ill. 4°. '76. 40 pts. ea., *25c. .... *Gebbie.*
— Illustrated rambles in Bible lands. ill. 12°. $2.50; $3 .... *Am. S. S.*
— Jewel case. ('59–'68.) New ed. 6 v. 16°. '74–'76. ea., $1.25........................ *Carter.*
Cont.: Best things. — King's highway. — Safe compass. — Bible blessings. — Great pilot. — Bible jewels.
— Leaves from the tree of life. 18°. 65c..... *Am. S. S.*
— Rays from the sun of righteousness. 16°. '76. $1.25. *Carter.*
— Voice from Olivet; or, the warning sign. 12°. pap., 10c.................................. *Am. S. S.*
— Wonder case. ('56–'74.) New ed. 6 v. 16°. '73–'76. ea., $1.25......................... *Carter.*
Cont.: Bible wonders. — Nature's wonders. — Leaves from the tree of life. — Rills from the fountain of life. — Jewish tabernacle. — Giants and wonderful things.
— *See also* Schweinitz, E. de, Berg, J. F., *and* Newton, R.
Newton, Rob. Sermons. 12°. $1.75. *Cin. Meth. Bk. Conc.*

Newton, T: Dissertations on the prophecies, which have been fulfilled and are fulfilling; rev. by W. S. Dobson. 8°. shp., $3............*Desilver.*

Newton, W: Morning star; or, wayside musings, and other poems. 12°. '73. $1.50–$4.50...*Claxton.*

— Nature's testimony to nature's God. [Sermons.] 12°. '73. $1 ....*Claxton.*

— On the first two visions of Book of Daniel. 12°. $1.50. (?)*Martien.*

Newton, W: Wilberforce. Bible outlines: hist. chart of principal events of Old and New Test. 18°. '73. pap., 10c. ....*Whittaker.*

— Coming to confirmation. 12°. '75. pap., 15c...*Williams.*

— Gate of the temple: prayers for children. 32°. '76. 40c. ....*Whittaker.*

Newton Foster. *See* Marryat, F:

Newtonensis (*pseud.*) Handbook of shooting. roy. 32°. bds., 25c....................*Routledge.*

Next of kin. Falconer, E. 15c.............*French.*

Niagara and vicinity: 12 views with letter-press. obl. 24°. 25c.; 50c. ....*Nelson.*

Niaise (La) de Saint-Flour. Bayard, J. F. A., *and* Lemoine, G. 25c...........................*Holt.*

Nibbling Joe. 8°. pap., 25c. ....*De Witt.*

Nibelungen-Saga. *See* Schnorr, J.

Nic at the tavern; or, nobody's boy. 18°. 40c...*Am.S.S.*

— *See also* Katie Lee lib.

Nicaise, —. Belgian field artillery; tr. with app. and notes by O. E. Michaelis. 16°. '72. $2. *W.C.& F.P. Church.*

Nice firm. Taylor, T. 15c. ....*French.*

Nice quiet day: farce. 16°. pap., 15c. ......*French.*

Nice secret. *See* Herd boy ser.

Nichol, J: Hannibal: historical drama. fp. 8°. '72. $2.50 ....*Macmillan.*

Nicholas, S: Smith. Conservative essays, legal and political. 8°. $3.25 ....*Lippincott.*

Nicholas; or, the reward of a good action. 18°. 15c. *Benziger.*

Nicholas Flam. *See* Buckstone, J. B.

Nicholas Nickleby. *See* Dickens, C:

Nicholas Nickleby. Stirling, E. 15c........*French.*

Nicholls, B: Elliott. Help to the reading of the Bible. 16°. $1 ....*Pott.*

— *Same.* maps. 12°. '69. $1; $1.25.......*Dutton.*

— Mine (The) explored; or, help to the reading of the Bible. maps. 12°. '53. $1.50 ......*Am.S.S.*

Nicholls, *Mrs.* Ctte. *See* Brontë, Ctte.

Nicholls, G. F. Samaritan grammar. post 8°. (Bagster.) $2.50 ....*Wiley.*

Nichols, G: Ward. Sanctuary (The): story of the civil war. ill. 12°. $1.50............*Harper.*

— Story of the great march: diary of Sherman's campaign through Georgia and the Carolinas. map and ill. 12°. $2.......................*Harper.*

Nichols, J. Hours with the evangelists. 2 v. 12°. '59. ea., $1.50..........................*Am. Unit.*

Nichols, Ja. R. Chemistry of the farm and the sea, with other familiar chem. essays. 12°. $1.25..*Judd.*

— Fireside science: popular scientific essays. 12°. '72. $1.50 ....*Hurd & H.*

Nichols, T: L. Supramundane facts in the life of Rev. J. B. Ferguson. 12°. '65. $1.75......*Colby.*

Nichols, W: A. Life of S. T. Nichols. ill. 18°. '53. 25c...................................*Am. Tr.*

Nicholson, C. Celebrated beauties for the flute. 8°. '60. pap., 75c..........................*Ditson.*

Nicholson, H: Alleyne. Introduction to study of biology. ill. 12°. 75c....................*Appleton.*

— Manual of zoology; with gen. introd. to principles of zoology. ill. 12°. $2.50............*Appleton.*

— Text book of geology. 12°. hf. roan, $1.50..*Appleton.*

— Text-book of zoology. 12°. hf. roan, $1.75..*Appleton.*

Nicholson, Ja. B. Manual of art of book-binding. ('56.) 3d ed. ill. 12°. '74. $2.25........*Baird.*

Nicholson, N. A. Science of exchanges. 4th ed., rev. and enl. demy 4°. '73. $2.50..........*Cassell.*

Nicholson, P: Carpenter's new guide; rev. by N. K. Davis, and cont. improved and original designs for roofs, domes, etc. 20th ed., rev. by S. Sloane. 4°. hf. roan, $4.50.................*Lippincott.*

Nick Hardy. Brown, T. $1.50.........*H.A. Young.*

Nick of the woods. Bird, R. M. $1.75...*Widdleton.*

Nick of the woods. Medina, L. 15c.........*French.*

Nick Whiffles: drama. 16°. pap., 15c.......*French.*

Nickerson, L. Experiments showing neutral axes by polarized light; [also] Replacing a stone pier on a pile foundation, by J. A. Monroe; [also] European railways, by W. H. White. 8°. '74. pap., 70c......................*Am. Soc. of C. E.*

Nickerson, *Miss* Su. D. Bees and hornets. 16°. $1.50. *Cong. Pub.*

— Station master's daughter. 16°. $1.25...*Cong. Pub.*

Nickey Nimble; or, the night prowlers. 18°. pap., 25c. ....*De Witt.*

Nicodemus. Evangelium, od. histor. Bericht von d. Leben Jesu Christi. 12°. 75c............*Baer.*

Nicolaie, L: François. *See* Clairville, L. F. N.

Nicolas, *Sir* H. *See* Walton, I., *and* Cotton, C.

Nicolas, Pl. Harris. *See* Johns, R., *and* Nicolas, P. H.

Nicolette and Aucassin. *See* Hale, E. E.

Nicolini, Gi. B. History of the Jesuits: their origin, progress, doctrines and designs. por. 12°. (Bohn.) $1.75 ....*Little, B. & Co.*

— *Same.* por. 12°. (Bohn.) $2. *Lippincott; Scribner, W. & A.*

Nicollet, Jos. N: Report to ill. map of hydrog. basin of Upper Missouri River. *See* United States, *Corps of Eng.*

Nidworth and his three magic wands. Prentiss, E. $1.25 ....*Randolph.*

Niebuhr, Barthold G. History of Rome; tr. 12°. $3. *Routledge.*

— Lectures on anc. history; tr. by L. Schmitz. 3 v. cr. 8°. $5.................................*Lea.*

Niedermeyer, L. Messe solennelle in B minor; for four voices. 8°. '71. $1.50; pap., $1.25..*Ditson.*

Niemeyer, Fel. v. Text-book of pract. medicine, with particular ref. to physiology and pathol. anatomy; tr. by G. H. Humphreys and C. E. Hackley. 2 v. 8°. $9; shp., $11...................*Appleton.*

Nienvort, G: W: (*Count*). Prayers and meditations; tr. by an American. 18°. 75c.......*Whittaker.*

Nieremberg, Juan Eusebio. Treatise on difference between temporal and eternal. 12°. $2..*O'Shea.*

Nieritz, Gst. Erzählungen. 21 v. 16°. ea., 25c. *Morwitz.*

Cont.: Das Standrecht. — Die Deportirten. — Die Auswanderer nach Afrika. — Schneider u. Geiger. — Christoph Columbus. — Clarus u. Maria. — Brand v. Hamburg. — Unrecht Gut gedeihet nicht. — Die Erfindung des Porcellans. — Die Grossmutter. — Der alte Krieger u. s. Sohn. — Die Rosenmühle; Der kleine Samariter. — Die Waise. — Johanna, od. durch Nacht zum Licht. — Der arme Gottfried. — Der König u. d. Müller. — Das Kleeblatt. — Die Guckgucksuhr. — Jacob u. s. Söhne. — Eine freie Seele. — Wahres u. falsches Wohlthun.

— Erzählungen. (Steiger's Jugend-Bibliothek.) 7 v. 16°. '66–'67. ea., bds., 25c...............*Steiger.*

Cont.: Der blinde Knabe. — Die Schwanenjungfrau. — Der Strohhalm u. d. Schatz. — Der Findling, od. die Schule d. Lebens. — Betty u. Toms, od. Doctor Jenner u. s. Entdeckg. — Der junge Trommelschläger. — Die Wunderpfeife, od. die Kinder v. Hameln.

— Bears of Augustusburg: episode in Saxon hist.; tr. 16°. $1.25 ....*O'Shea.*

— Erna, the forest princess; or, pilgrimage of the three wise men to Bethlehem; tr. by Mrs. H. C. Conant. 12°. '55. 60c...........................*Darrow.*

— Gustavus Vasa; tr. (Fatherland ser.) ill. 16°. $1.20. (?)*Luth. Pub.*

Nieritz, Gst., *continued.*
— Rich man (The) and the poor man; tr. (Fatherland ser.) 16°. '75. 65c. ....(?) *Luth. Pub.*
— Three kings (The); tr. (Fatherland ser.) ill. 16°. $1.15 ....(?) *Luth. Pub.*
Niessen, J. *See* Vinci, L. da, Das Abendmahl des Herrn.
Niff and his dogs, and other tales. 18°. 35c... *Pres. Bd.*
Nigel Bartram's ideal. Wilford, F. 50c.... *Appleton.*
Night and morning. Brougham, J. 15c...... *French.*
Night and morning. *See* Bulwer-Lytton, *Sir* E. G. E. L.
Night at Notting Hill. *See* Yates, E., *and* Harrington, N. H.
Night at sea. *See* Griffin, Ger.
Night before Christmas. Livingstone, C. M. 10c. *Lothrop.*
Night in prison. *See* Two prisoners.
Night in a strange hotel. White, C. 15c..... *De Witt.*
Night lamp. Macfarlane, J. $1.50......(?) *Martien.*
Night lessons from Scripture. Sewell, E. M. $1. *Appleton.*
Night of suspense: monologue. 16°. pap., 15c. *French.*
Night of toil. Mortimer, M. 45c............ *Am. Tr.*
Night of weeping. *See* Bonar, H.
Night scenes in the Bible. March, D. *$3.75; $6. *McCurdy.*
Night side of nature. *See* Crowe, C.
Night thoughts. *See* Young, E:
Night to light. 16°. $1.25.................. *Lothrop.*
Night wid Brudder Bones: Ethiop. drama. 16°. pap., 15c. .... *Happy.*
Nightcap series. *See* Barrow, *Mrs.* F.
Nightcaps; — New nightcaps. *See* Barrow, *Mrs.* F.
Nightingale, *Mrs.* Flo. Notes on nursing: what it is, and what it is not. 12°. 75c.......... *Appleton.*
— *Germ.* Anmerkungen zur Krankenpflege. 12°. '67. 50c.; pap., 30c.............. *Zickel.*
Nightingale. Fillmore, A. D. 60c....... *Pounsford.*
Nightingale. Perkins, W. O. *and* H. S. 50c... *Ditson.*
Nightingale. *See* Schmid, C. v.
Nightingale songster; or, lyrics of love. 16°. bds., 50c. .... *Dick & F.*
Nightingale's nest. Reichardt, G. $1.... *Brainard.*
Nightshade. 8°. pap., 25c................ *De Witt.*
Nightshade on the heath. 8°. pap., 25c..... *De Witt.*
Nightshade ser. 9 nos. 8°. ea., pap., 25c... *De Witt.*
Cont.: Nightshade. — Nightshade on the heath. — Claude and the countess. — Hounslow Jack. — Claude in the cathedral. — Girl of the gibbet. — Highwayman's doom. — Fatal tree. — Last leap.
Nile journal. Appleton, T. G. $2.25........ *Roberts.*
Nile notes of a howadji. Curtis, G. W. $1.50.. *Harper.*
Niles, Hezekiah. Principles and acts of the revolutionary war. ('22.) New ed. roy. 8°. '76. $3; shp., $4.50; hf. cf., $6.............. *Barnes.*
Nimrod of the sea. Davis, W. M. $2...... *Harper.*
Nina. Bremer, F. 50c.................. *Harper.*
Nina and Pippo; or, the lost children of Mount St. Bernard. 18°. 15c................ *Benziger.*
Nina Balatka. Trollope, A. 38c......... *Littell & G.*
Nina Gordon. Stowe, H. B. $2.............. *Osgood.*
Nina Grey: a Christmas story. 18°. 60c.... *Pres. Bd.*
Nina's atonement. Fisher, F. C. $1.50; $1.. *Appleton.*
Nine days' wonder. Aide, H. $1.25; 50c...... *Estes.*
Nine little busters. Etheridge, K. 75c.; 25c... *Authors.*
Nine little goslings. Woolsey, S. C. $1.50... *Roberts.*
Nine months in the quartermaster's department: Leib, C. 75c.; 50c............ *Wilstach.*
Nine o'clock in the morning. Tucker, H. 50c... *Pond.*
Nine points of the law. Taylor, T. 15c. *French; Lee & S.*
Nine prizes. Wilmer, M. E. 90c.... *N. Y. Ref. Ch. Bd.*
Nine Saturdays. Chester, S. E. 60c....... *Randolph.*
Nine years old. Tabor, E. $1.50........ *Macmillan.*
Nineteen beautiful years; or, sketches of a girl's life; by her sister, with introd. by R. S. Foster. 16°. $1 .... *Harper.*
Ninety three. Hugo, V. $1.75; 25c........ *Harper.*
Nineveh and its palaces. *See* Bonomi, J.
Nissen, J. Die Rüstzeit des neuen Bundes. 18°. '76. 30c.............. *Am. Tr.*
Nitschke, A. Choralbuch d. Evang. Brüder Gemeine: Auszug a. C. Gregor's Choralbuch. obl. 4°. '68. hf. bd., $2.50 .... *Clauder.*
— *See also* Gregor, C., Choralbuch.
Nixon, J. E. Parallel extracts, arranged for tr. into Eng. and Lat., with notes on idioms, pt. 1: Historical and epistolary. 12°. '74. $1.50.. *Macmillan.*
Nixon, J: T. *See* New Jersey, Digest of laws.
Nix's offering. *See* Henry, Ma. H.
No! Murray, W. 15c.................. *French.*
No alternative. Thomas, A. $1.50–$1.25 .... *Porter.*
No baby in the house. Dolliver, C. G. 75c... *Roman.*
No cross no crown. Davis, C. E. K. 80c....... *Hoyt.*
No cross no crown. Penn, W. 75c. *Friends Bk. Assoc.; Friends Bk. St.*
No cure no pay. Baker, G. M. 15c......... *Lee & S.*
No cure no pay: Ethiop. drama. 16°. pap., 15c. *French; Happy.*
No fiction. Reed, A. $1.25................ *Harper.*
No followers: drama. 16°. pap., 15c......... *French.*
No intentions. *See* Marryat, Flo.
No lie thrives. 18°. 90c................(?) *Martien.*
No man's friend. Robinson, F. W. 75c..... *Harper.*
No moss. Fosdick, C. A. $1.50............ *Porter.*
No name. *See* Collins, Wilkie.
No pains no gains. Knight, H. C. 35c....... *Am. Tr.*
No pains no gains, and other stories. 32°. 15c... *Am. S. S.*
No Sabbath school. 32°. 15c............ *Cong. Pub.*
No Sabbath school lessons. 32°. 15c....... *Cong. Pub.*
No Sabbath school to-day. 32°. 15c....... *Cong. Pub.*
No sects in heaven. Cleaveland, H. J. $1.25.. *Clark & M.*
No sense like common sense. *See* Howitt, Ma.
No sex in education. Duffey, E. B. $1.. *J. M. Stoddart.*
No song no supper. Hoare, P. 15c.......... *French.*
No such word as fail. *See* Haven, *Mrs.* A. B.
No tator; or, man fish: Ethiop. drama. 16°. pap., 15c. *French.*
No thoroughfare. *See* Dickens, C: *and* Collins, W.
No thoroughfare: drama. 16°. pap., 15c..... *French.*
No work, and other stories. 18°. 60c. ...... *Pres. Bd.*
Noble, Annette L. St. Augustine's ladder. ill. 16°. '73. $1.50 .... *Lothrop.*
Noble, S: Appeal on behalf of the doctrines of the New Church. cr. 8°. $1.......... *H. H. Carter.*
Noble, W. F. P. Century of Gospel work: hist. of the growth of evang. religion in U. S. ill. 8°. '76. *$3.50; $4.25; mor., $5.50............. *Watts.*
— Great men of God: biog. of patriarchs, prophets, kings and apostles; with introd. by I. W. Wiley. ill. 8°. *$3.75; mor., $5.50.... *St. L. B. & B. Pub.*
— Prophets of the Bible and the seven churches. ill. 8°. '72. *$3; hf. bd., $4........... *New World.*
Noble aims for boys; — for girls. Tuthill, L. C. ea., $1.50.............. *World Pub.*
Noble deeds lib. 5 v. 16°. $2.50............ *Nelson.*
Cont.: Stories from European hist., by M. Jones. — Stories from Eng. hist., by M. Jones. — Biographies of great men, by M. Jones. — Scenes and sights of Bible lands, by A. M. S. — Book of Bible stories, by M. Jones.
Noble deeds of American women. Clement, J. $1.50. *Lee & S.*

Noble deeds of our forefathers. Watson, H. C. $1.25. *Lee & S.*
Noble deeds of women. *See* Starling, E.
Noble heart. Lewes, G. H. 15c. .... *French.*
Noble Joe. ill. 16°. 25c. .... *Routledge.*
Noble life. *See* Craik, D. M.
Noble lord. Southworth, E. D. E. N. $1.75; $1.50. *Peterson.*
Noble printer and his adopted daughter; tr. with add. by C. Overend. ill. 16°. '73. $1.50 ... *Lothrop.*
Noble rivers. Buckland, A. J. $1 .... *Am. Bapt.*
Noble sister. Denison, M. A. $1.50 .... (?) *Martien.*
Noble woman. Stephens, A. S. $1.75; $1.50 .. *Peterson.*
Noble workers. Smith, S. F. $1.50 .... *Lothrop.*
Noble workers. Yapp, A. $2 .... *Routledge.*
Nobleman of "89." Quinton, M. A. $2; $3. *Kelly, P. & Co.*
Nobleman's daughter. 8°. pap., 25c. ...... *Peterson.*
Nobleman's wife. Wood, E. P. 25c. ...... *Peterson.*
Noblesse oblige. Keddie, H. $2 .... *Routledge.*
Nobody but Nan. P., E. L. $1 ..... *Meth. Bk. Conc.*
Nobody cares. Temple, C. 60c. .... *Lothrop.*
Nobody's child. Phillips, W. 15c. .. *De Witt; French.*
Nobody's child. *See* Silver penny ser.
Nobody's fortune. *See* Yates, E.
Nobody's son: Ethiop. drama. 16°. pap., 15c. *French; Happy.*
Noctes ambrosianæ; by J. Wilson, J. G. Lockhart, J. Hogg and W. Maginn; ed. with notes by R. S. Mackenzie; with life of W. by his daughter. 6 v. por. cr. 8°. $10.50; hf. cf., $21. *Nichols & H.; Widdleton.*
Noel, *Lady* Augusta. Owen Gwynne's great work. [Fiction.] 8°. pap., 50c. .... *Harper.*
— *Same.* cr. 8°. '75. $1.25 .... *Macmillan.*
— Story of Wandering Willie. [Fiction.] 3d ed. cr. 8°. $1.50 .... *Macmillan.*
Noel, Bapt. W. Meditations in sickness and old age. 18°. 50c. .... *Pres. Bd.*
Noel, François Jos., *and* Chapsal, G. P. Abrégé de la grammaire française. 12°. $1.25. *G. R. Lockwood.*
— — *Eng.* Abridgment of French grammar. 12°. '69. $1.25 .... *G. R. Lockwood.*
— — *French and Eng.* 12°. '69. $1.75. — Key. 12°. $1.25 .... *G. R. Lockwood.*
— — Exercises français. 16°. 60c. .... *Appleton.*
— — — Corrigé. 16°. $1 .... *Appleton.*
— — Grammaire française. 16°. 60c. .... *Appleton.*
— — *Same.* 12°. $1.75. — Corrigé. 12°. $1.25. *G. R. Lockwood.*
— — Leçons et modèles de littérature française; par Chapsal. 12°. '46. $1.75 ...... *G. R. Lockwood.*
— — New French grammar; rev. by A. Vaillant. pt. 1. 12°. $1 .... *Moss.*
— — *Same;* [with exerc.] 12°. $1.75. — Key. $1 .. *Moss.*
— — New system of French grammar; with questions, Eng. key, lessons in reading and speaking, etc., by S. E. Saymore; rev. and enl. by C. P. Bordenave. 12°. $1.25 .... *Harper.*
Noel, Roden. Beatrice. [Poem.] 16°. $1 .. *Lippincott.*
— *Same;* and other poems. fp. 8°. '69. $1.75 .. *Macmillan.*
— The red flag, and other poems. 16°. '73. $2. *Routledge.*
Noémie. Dennery, A. P., *and* Clement, —. 15c. *De Witt; French.*
Noise (The). 18°. 30c. .... *Dutton.*
Noisy Herbert. Whitmarsh, C. S. 75c. ...... *Fuller.*
Nolan, Alice. Byrnes of Glengoulah. 12°. $1.50. *O'Shea.*
Nolan, Lew. E: System for training cavalry horses; [ed. and enl.] by Kennar Garrard. pl. 12°. '62. $2 .... *Van Nostrand.*
Noll, C: B. On Hebrews. *See* Lange, J. P., Comment.
Noll, the beggar boy. *See* Finley, M. F.
Noll in the country. *See* Finley, M. F.
Nomistake (*pseud.*) Science of money. 12°. $1.75. *Lippincott.*
None like Christ. *See* Winslow, O.
Nonsense. Pomeroy, M. M. $1.50 .... *Carleton.*
Nonsense rhymes (New). *See* Beckett, W. H.
Nonsense songs. Lear, E. $2 .... **Osgood.*
Nonsuch professor. Secker, W. $1 ..... *Pounsford.*
Nooks and corners of the New Eng. coast. Drake, S. A. $3.50 .... *Harper.*
Noontide at Sychar. Macduff, J. R. $1.50 .. *Carter.*
Noque, Oro (*pseud.*) Historicals for young folks. ill. 12°. '74. $1.25 .... *Lothrop.*
Nora. Landon, H. 75c. .... *Cong. Pub.*
Nora and Archibald Lee. 8°. pap., 50c. ..... *Harper.*
Nora Brady's vow. *See* Dorsey, *Mrs.* A. H.
Nora Creina. Stirling, E. 15c. .... *French.*
Norah, the flower girl. ill. 18°. '73. 50c. .... *Lothrop.*
Norah and her Kerry cow; or, the Bible the best guide. 18°. 50c. .... *Pres. Bd.*
Norah and Winnie. 18°. 60c. .... *Dutton.*
Norah Neill. Hamilton, K. W. 60c. ...... *Pres. Bd.*
Norah's neighbor. *See* Sunbeam ser.
Nora's life at Derncleugh. 18°. 60c. .... *Am. S. S.*
Nora's lilies. *See* Sunbeam lib.
Nordamerikanische Dolmetscher (Der), u. Rathgeber f. Einwanderer u. Eingewanderte. 15th ed. 16°. 50c. .... *Morwitz.*
Norden, Fr. Nachtlager in Granada; [also] Tannhäuser, v. N. Hürte. 16°. 25c. .... *Morwitz.*
Nordhoff, C: California; for health, pleasure and residence: book for travelers and settlers. ill. 8°. $2.50; pap., $2 .... *Harper.*
— Cape Cod and all along shore: stories. 12°. $1.50. *Harper.*
— Communistic societies of the U. S. ill. 8°. $4. *Harper.*
— Cotton states in the spring and summer of 1875. 8°. pap., 50c. .... *Appleton.*
— Life on the ocean. ill. sm. 8°. '74. $2.50 .. *Wilstach.*
— Northern California, Oregon and the Sandwich Islands. ill. 8°. $2.50 .... *Harper.*
— Politics for young Americans. 12°. $1.25. — (School ed.) 12°. hf. leath., $1 .... *Harper.*
— Stories of the island world. ill. 12°. $1 .... *Harper.*
Norine's revenge. *See* Fleming, M. A.
Norma. Bellini, V. $1.50 .... *Ditson.*
Norma. Oxberry, W. H. 15c. .... *French.*
Norma. Planché, J. R. 15c. .... *French.*
Norma Danton; or, the lighthouse murder. 12°. pap., 20c. .... *Hurst.*
Normal (The). Suffern, J. W. 75c. ..... *Brainard.*
Normal collection. Palmer, H. R. $1.50 ... *Church.*
Normal diadem of school songs. Tillinghast, W. 75c. *Schermerhorn.*
Normal school song book. obl. 16°. 50c. .... *Gordon.*
Normal singer. Mason, L. 60c. .... *Ditson.*
Norman, J: Paxton. Treatise on law and practice relating to letters patent for inventions. 8°. '53. $2.50 .... *T. & J. W. Johnson.*
— — *See also* Law lib.
— *See also* England, Exchequer reports.
Norman and Ada; or, the first visit. 18°. 50c. (?) *Martien.*
Norman Brill's life-work. Eldridge, A. $1 .. *Nat. Temp.*
Norman Cline. Kellogg, Elijah. $1.50 ... *Cong. Pub.*
Norman Fleming; by author of "Christus victor." 12°. 75c. .... *Lee & S.*
Norman's bridge. Marsh-Caldwell, A. 50c. .. *Harper.*

Normandy, A. Commercial handbook of chemical anal.: instruction for determining intrinsic value of substances used in manufactures, etc. New ed., rev. and enl. by H. M. Noad. 12°. $6.25. *Baird.*

Normandy picturesque. Blackburn, H. $1.50. **Osgood.*

Nöroth, J. Blüthen der neuen englischen u. amerikanischen Poesie, ins Deutsche übertragen. 12°. '74. $1.25; pap., 75c. .... *Schoenhof.*

Norris, Emilia M. Sea-side home and smuggler's cave. ill. 16°. $1 .... *Pott.*

— Snowed up; or, the hut in the forest. ill. 16°. '71. $1 .... *Dutton.*

— Week (A) by themselves. ill. sq. 8°. $1 .... *Nelson.*

Norris, G: W. Contributions to pract. surgery, incl. clinical histories from a hospital service of 30 years. 8°. '73. $4 .... *Lindsay.*

Norris, J: Pilkington. Key to narrative of Acts. 16°. $1 .... *Lippincott.*

— Key to narrative of four Gospels. 16°. $1. *Lippincott.*

— — *See also* Blunt, J. H., Key to knowledge and use of Bible.

— Rudiments of theology: a first book for students. 16°. '76. $1.25 .... *Dutton; Pott.*

Norris, *Miss* Ma. H. Fraulein Mina; or, life in an American German family. 12°. '72. $1.25. *Meth. Bk. Conc.*

Norris, Septimus. Handbook for locomotive engineers and machinists. ('52.) 12th ed. ill. 12°. '74. $2. *Baird.*

Norris, Thad. American angler's book; [also] Dies piscatoriæ. New ed., with sup. ill. 8°. '64. $5.50 .... *Porter.*

— American fish culture: artificial breeding and rearing of trout, culture of salmon, shad and other fishes. cr. 8°. '68. $1.75 .... *Porter.*

Norris, W. H., Brown, G. W., *and* Brune, F. W., *jr.* Digest of Maryland reports. 8°. '47. shp., $10. *Cushings & B.*

Compr. Harris and McHenry (4 v.), Harris and Johnson (7 v.), Harris and Gill (2 v.), Gill and Johnson (12 v.), Bland, (3 v.)

Norse folk. Brace, C. L. $1.75 .... *Scribner.*

Norseman's pilgrimage. Boyesen, H. H. $1.50. *Sheldon.*

Norske Maalsag (Den). *See* Anderson, R. B.

North, Cp. (*pseud.*) *See* Wilson, J:

North, E. P. Blasting with nitro glycerine. 8°. pap., 35c. .... *Am. Soc. of C. E.*

— Memoranda of blasts on the Union Pacific R. R. *See* Steele, J. D., Construction of the Falls skew-bridge.

North, Ingoldsby. Book of love letters: directions and forms. 16°. 75c.; bds., 50c. .... *Dick & F.*

North, J. M. *See* Stewart, N. C., *and* North, J. M.

North, Levi. Treatise on practice in probate courts in Ill.; with forms of wills, codicils, petitions, etc. 8°. '73. shp., $5 .... *Callaghan.*

North, Ma. E. Early crowned: memoir of M. E. North. 16°. '66. $1.25 .... *Meth. Bk. Conc.*

North, W: Man of the world. 12°. $1.75; pap., $1.50. *Peterson.*

North American spelling book. 12°. '76. 20c. *Murphy.*

North and south. *See* Gaskell, *Mrs.* E. C.

North Carolina. Equity reports, 1828–'34; by T. P. Devereux. 2 v. 8°. shp., $15 .... *Hale.*

— *Same.* 1834–'40; by T. P. Devereux and W. H. Battle. 2 v. 8°. shp., $15 .... *Hale.*

— *Same.* 1840–'52; by J. Iredell. 8 v. 8°. v. 4, 5, ea., shp., $6.50; 7, shp., $5 .... *Hale.*

Note. v. 1, 2, 3, 6 and 8 are o. p.

— *Same.* 1852–'53; by P. Busbee. 8°. shp., $4 .. *Hale.*

— *Same.* 1853–'62; by H. C. Jones. 6 v. 8°. ea., shp., $4.50–$7 .... *Hale.*

North Carolina, *continued.*

— *Same.* 1863–'64; by — Winston. 8° .... *State.*

— *Same.* 1866–'68; by S. F. Phillips. 8°. $4.50 .. *Hale.*

Note. Distinction of Law and Equity has been abolished.

— Law reports, 1789–1798; by J. Haywood. 8°. shp., $7 .... *Hale.*

— *Same.* 1797–1806; by F. X. Martin and J. Haywood. 8°. shp., $7 .... *Hale.*

— *Same.* 1799–1802; by J. L. Taylor; [also] Conference reports, 1800–4; by D. Cameron and W. Norwood. 8°. shp., $7 .... *Hale.*

— *Same.* 1804–'19; by A. D. Murphey. v. 3. 8°. shp., $7.50 .... *Hale.*

Note. v. 1 and 2 are o. p.

— *Same.* North Carolina law repository, 1813–'16; [also] Term reports, 1816–'18. 8°. shp., $8.50. *Hale.*

— *Same.* 1820–'26; by F. L. Hawks. 3 v. 8°. 2, 4, ea., shp., $7.50; 3, $5.50 .... *Hale.*

Note. v. 1 is o. p.

— *Same.* 1826–'34; by T. P. Devereux. v. 1. 8°. shp., $6.50 .... *Hale.*

Note. v. 2-4 are o. p.

— *Same.* 1834–'39; by T. P. Devereux and W. H. Battle. 4 v. in 3. 8°. 1, 2, ea., shp., $7.50 .... *Hale.*

Note. v. 3 is o. p.

— *Same.* 1840–'52; by J. Iredell. 13 v. 8°. shp., 7, 9, 10, 11. ea., $7.50; 12, $5.50 .... *Hale.*

Note. v. 1-6, 8, 13 are o. p.

— *Same.* 1852–'53; by P. Busbee. 8°. shp., $6 .. *Hale.*

— *Same.* 1853–'62; by H. C. Jones. 8 v. 8°. shp., 1, 6, 7, ea., $7.50; 2, $6; 3, 4, 5, ea., $6.50; 8, $7. *Hale.*

— *Same.* 1863–'64; by — Winston. 8° .... *State.*

— *Same.* 1866–'68; by S. F. Phillips. 8°. shp., $6.50. *Hale.*

— Reports, v. 63–74 (1868–'75). 12 v. 8°. shp. .. *Hale.*

Cont.: 63-4 (1868–'70), by S. F. Phillips, 63, $7.50; 64, $8. — 65 (1871), by J. M. McCorkle, $7.75. — 66-7 (1872), by W. M. Shipp, 66, $8; 67, $6. — 68-74 (1873–'75), by T. L. Hargrave, 68-9, ea., $7.50; 70, 74, ea., $8; 71-3, ea., $7.

Note. Distinction of Law and Equity was abolished with v. 63.

— — Digest. *See* Battle, W. H.

— Revisal of public statutes, 1872–'3; by W. H. Battle. 8°. '73 .... *State.*

North Carolina form book. 12°. shp., $1.50. *Lippincott.*

North Carolina geological and natural history survey. Report of Prof. Emmons on his geol. survey of N. C. 8°. '52 .... *State.*

— Pt. 3: Botany; by M. A. Curtis. 8°. '60 ... *State.*

North Carolina readers. 3 v. '55 .... *Barnes.*

Cont.: No. 1, by F. M. Hubbard, 18°, hf. bd., 40c. — 2, by F. M. Hubbard, 18°, hf. bd., 65c. — 3, by C. H. Wiley, 12°, $1.

North coast, and other poems. Buchanan, R. $10; $15. *Routledge.*

North star and the southern cross. Weppner, M. 2 v. $5 .... *Weppner.*

North west coast. Swan, J. G. $1.50 .... *Harper.*

Northanger Abbey. *See* Austen, Jane.

Northcote, J. Spencer. Celebrated sanctuaries of the Madonna. 12°. '68. $1.50 .... *Cunningham.*

— Roman catacombs. maps and ill. 16°. '57. $1. *Cunningham.*

Northend, C: American speaker. New ed., rev. 12°. '72. $1.05 .... *Collins & Bro.*

— Child's speaker. 16°. '70. 60c. .... *Barnes.*

— Choice extracts for recitations in schools and families. 16°. pap., 12c. .... *Brown & G.*

— Entertaining dialogues. 12°. '59. $1 .... *Barnes.*

— Exercises for dictation and pronunciation. 12°. '62. hf. bd., 63c. .... *Barnes.*

— Little orator; or, primary school speaker. 16°. '59. 60c. .... *Barnes.*

— Little speaker and juvenile reader. 18°. '73. 56c. *Collins & Bro.*

— National orator. 12°. '59. $1 .... *Barnes.*

— School dialogues. New ed., enl. 12°. '72. $1.05. *Collins & Bro.*

Northend, C: *continued.*
— Selections for analysis and parsing. 12°. bds., 31c. *Ware.*
— Teacher and the parent: treatise upon common school educ. ('56.) 8th ed., enl. 12°. $1.50.. *Barnes.*
— Teacher's assistant; or, hints and methods in school discipline and instruct. 12°. '59. $1.50.. *Barnes.*
— Young declaimer. 18°. '72. 75c.......... *Barnes.*
Northern harp. Shindler, M. S. B. D. $1.50.. *Ditson.*
Northern lands. Adams, W. T. $1.50...... *Lee & S.*
Northern lights. Borg, S., *and* Brown, M. A. $1.50. *Porter.*
Northern travel. Taylor, B. $1.50; $2.... *Putnam.*
Northrop, Birdsey Grant. Education abroad, and other papers. 8°. '73. $1.50............... *Barnes.*
Norton, Andrews. Internal evidences of the genuineness of the Gospels. 8°. '55. $1.... *Am. Unit.*
— *Same;* abridg. ('67.) 5th ed. 12°. '74. $1.50.. *Am. Unit.*
— Statement of reasons for not believing doctrines of Trinitarians conc. nature of God and person of Christ; with memoir of author by W. Newell. ('56.) 11th ed., enl. 12°. '76. $1.25.. *Am. Unit.*
Norton, *Mrs.* Caro. E. S. Lady of La Garaye. 16°. '66. 90c. .... *Randolph.*
— *Same.* 7th ed. fp. 8°. $1.25.......... *Macmillan.*
— Lost and saved. 12°. $1.25........... *Lippincott.*
— Old Sir Douglas. 8°. '67. pap., 75c... *Littell & G.*
— *Same.* 12°. $1.25................... *Macmillan.*
— Poems. *See* Sigourney, L. H., Poems.
— Stuart of Dunleath. 8°. pap., 50c........ *Harper.*
Norton, C: Eliot. Notes of travel and study in Italy. 16°. '59. $1.25.................... *Osgood.*
— *See also* Blake, W., Illustrations of Job.
Norton, C: L. American sea-side resorts: handbook for health and pleasure seekers. 16°. $1.25.. *Taintor.*
Norton, J. H. Life of David. 12°. 50c.... *McCauley.*
Norton, J: N. Every Sunday: sermons for the Christian year. ('71.) 2d ed. 8°. '75. $2.. *Whittaker.*
— Full proof of the ministry: sequel to "Boy trained to be a clergyman." 12°. 75c....... *Claremont.*
— Golden truths: course of sermons for the Christian year, with special series for holy week. 8°. '75. $2................................ *Whittaker.*
— Life of Abp. Cranmer. 18°. $1........... *Dutton.*
— Life of Abp. Laud. 16°. '63. $1.25...... *Dutton.*
— Life of Bp. Berkeley. 18°. 90c.; $1...... *Dutton.*
— Life of Bp. Bowen. 18°. 70c.; 75c........ *Dutton.*
— Life of Bp. Freeman. 18°. 70c.; 75c...... *Dutton.*
— Life of Bp. Provoost. 18°. 60c.; 75c...... *Dutton.*
— Life of Bp. Stewart. 18°. 50c.; 60c....... *Dutton.*
— Life of Bp. Wilson. 18°. $1............. *Dutton.*
— Life of Washington. 18°. 90c............. *Dutton.*
— Milk and honey; or, Sunday evenings with the children. 2d ed., enl. ill. 16°. '70. $1.25.. *Dutton.*
— Phelps and Nash: lives of two pioneer missionaries. 18°. 70c.; 90c........................ *Dutton.*
— Short sermons. 12°. $2.................. *McCauley.*
Norton, J: P. Scientific agriculture: treatise on connection between science and art of pract. farming. 12°. 75c........................... *Judd.*
Norton, Lem. Autobiography. 12°. 75c... *Freewill.*
Norton, Sidney A. Elements of natural philosophy. ill. 12°. '70. $1.50............ *Wilson, H. & Co.*
— Elements of physics. ill. 12°. '74. $1.15. *Wilson, H. & Co.*
— *and* Weld, Allen H., *and* Quackenbos, G: P. English grammar. ('63.) New ed. 12°. '76. hf. leath., $1.13 .... *Bailey.*
Norton, W: A. First book of natural philosophy and astronomy. 12°. '58. $1............. *Barnes.*
— Treatise on astronomy, spherical and physical; with problems and tables. 4th ed., rev. and enl. pl. 8°. $3.50.............................. *Wiley.*
— *and* Porter, J. A. First book of science. 12°. '73. $1.75 .... *Barnes.*

Norton Hargrave. 18°. 40c............... *Dutton.*
Norval (*pseud.*) Steamship notes: manual of information for those who contemplate a trip to Europe. 12°. '75. 50c.; pap., 25c........... *Patterson.*
Norwood, R. Voyage to Virginia, 1649. [Reprint.] 4°. pap., 50c.......................... *Sabin.*
Norwood, W. Conference reports. *See* North Carolina, Law reports.
Norwood. Beecher, H. W. $2.............. *Ford.*
Nossa casa terrestre. *See* Our earthly house.
Not anything for peace. *See* Arthur, T. S.
Not at all jealous: farce. 16°. pap., 15c..... *French.*
Not a bad judge. Planché, J. R. .... *French.*
Not beggars. *See* Bright eye ser.
Not a bit jealous. Robertson, T. W. 15c..... *De Witt.*
Not bread alone. Drinkwater, J. M. $1.25 .. *Carter.*
Not dead yet. Jeaffreson, J. C. $1.75; $1.25.. *Harper.*
Not easily jealous. 8°. $1.25; pap., 75c....... *Estes.*
Not exactly so. O'Brien, H. 75c........... *Pres. Bd.*
Not forsaken. Giberne, A. $1.25 .... *Hoyt.*
Not guilty. Phillips, W. 15c....... *De Witt; French.*
Not a hero. Pugh, E. L. 50c............... *Eyrich.*
Not lost, but laid aside. 18°. 40c. .... *Dutton.*
Not a minute to spare. *See* C., S.
Not pretty but precious, and other stories. ill. 8°. pap., 50c. .... *Lippincott.*
Not so bad after all. Reeve, W. 15c... *Ames; French.*
Not so bad as we seem. *See* Bulwer-Lytton, *Sir* E. G. E. L.
Not such a fool as he looks. Byron, H. J. 15c... *De Witt.*
Not to be done: farce. 16°. pap., 15c. ...... *French.*
Not wisely, but too well. Broughton, R. $1.50; 60c. *Appleton.*
Not without thorns. Graham, E. $1.25; 75c.... *Estes.*
Nota, Alberto. La fiera: commedia. With notes by Prof. Torricelli. 12°. '64. pap., 75c..... *Holt.*
Notable shipwrecks. Uncle Hardy. $2 ..... *Cassell.*
Notable women of olden time. 18°. 85c..... *Am. S. S.*
Notaries' and commissioners' handbook: manual of forms and fees allowed in N. Y.; with suggestions, ref. and notes of statutes. 8°. $1.25; pap., 75c....................... *Baker, V. & Co.*
Notary's nose. About, E. $1.25............... *Holt.*
Note book sketches of an architect in Europe. Peabody, R. S. $6 .... *Osgood.*
Note taker. Lindsley, D. P. $2.75........ *O. Clapp.*
Notes from life. Taylor, H. $1.25.......... *Osgood.*
Notes from Nineveh. Fletcher, J. P. 75c. ..... *Lea.*
Notes of the Christian life. Reynolds, H. R. $2.50. *Macmillan.*
Notes of a collector. 18°. 40c. .... *Cong. Pub.*
Notes of hospital life, Nov., 1861–Aug., 1863; with introd. by Bp. Potter. 12°. $1.25 .. *Lippincott.*
Notes of joy. Knapp, J. F. 35c........... *Biglow.*
Notes of Livermore. Washburn, I., *jr.* $1.25. *Hoyt, F. & D.*
Notes of a theological student. Hoppin, J. M. $1. *Appleton.*
Notes on building construction; arr. to meet requirements of Committee on Education, South Kensington, London. pt. 1. ill. 8°. $3.50.. *Lippincott.*
Notes, questions and answers on the Collects. 16°. '72. 20c. .... *Pott.*
Notes, questions and answers on the Gospels. 16°. '72. 50c. .... *Pott.*
Nöthen, Thdr. History of the Catholic Church, to the Œcumenical Council of the Vatican. 2d ed. 12°. '71. $1.25 .... *Murphy.*
— *Same.* demi 8°. *$2–$3.50................ *Murphy.*
— *See also* History of the Bible for Cath. schools.

Nothing but leaves. *See* McKeever, H. B.
Nothing but money. Arthur, T. S. $1.50..*J.E.Potter.*
Nothing like it. Waisbrooker, L. $1.50......*Colby.*
Nothing like paste. Rae, C. M. 15c........*De Witt.*
Nothing new. *See* Craik, D. M.
Nothing to do. Horsburgh, M. 35c.; 45c...*Am.Bapt.*
Nothing to drink. *See* Wright, J. McN.
Nothing to nobody. Brenda. 90c. ....*Dodd.*
Nothing to nurse. Walcott, C. M. 15c. .....*French.*
Nothing to say. Thomson, M. 75c........*Peterson.*
Nothing venture, nothing have. *See* Haven, *Mrs.* A. B.
Nothing venture, nothing win. Coyne, J. S. 15c. *French.*
Notice to quit. Wells, W. G. 50c.........*Harper.*
Notley, *Mrs.* —. ["Fs. Derrick."] Beneath the wheels: a romance. 8°. pap., 50c. ....*Harper.*
— Olive Varcoe; or, true to the last. 8°. pap., 50c. *De Witt.*
Notoriety. Reynolds, F. 15c..............*French.*
Notre Dame. *See* Hugo, V.
Notre Dame. *See* Sisters of Notre Dame.
Nott, Abner Kingman. Memoir; by his brother. por. 18°. $1.50..........................*Sheldon.*
Nott, C: C. Treatise on the mechanic's lien laws of N. Y. 8°. shp., $3................ *W.C.Little.*
— *See also* United States, Court of Claims reports.
— *and* Hopkins, A. Digest of U. S. Court of Claims reports, 1863–'75, and of appealed cases in Supreme Court. 8°. shp., $6 ....*Morrison.*
Nott, Eliphalet. Counsels to young men on formation of character, and principles which lead to success and happiness in life. 18°. 75c. ....*Harper.*
— Resurrection of Christ: discourses, with introd. and notes by T. Lewis. 12°. '72. $1.50...*Scribner.*
Nott, H: Junius. *See* South Carolina, Reports.
Nott, Josiah C., *and* Gliddon, G: R. Indigenous races of the earth; or, new chapters of ethnological inquiry. pl. and ill. roy. 8°. $5 ....*Lippincott.*
— — Types of mankind; or, ethnological researches; ill. by selections and contributions. 9th ed. col. maps and ill. roy. 8°. $5...........*Lippincott.*
Notting'm brothers: farce. 16°. pap., 15c....*French.*
Nouet, Jacques. Life of Jesus Christ in glory: daily meditations. 12°. '72. $2.25.............*Pott.*
— *Same;* [also] Meditations on sacred heart of Jesus, by C. Borgo. 12°. $2.50............*Cath.Pub.*
Nourishment of the Christian soul. Pinart, D. $2..*Pott.*
Nourse, *Mrs.* Cora S. (*ed.*) Sunset hours of life. [Devotional.] sq. 24°. '75. $1.; $1.25.....*Am.Tr.*
Nourse, S. *See* Locke, E., *and* Nourse, S.
Novello, Sabilla. Vocal school. 4°. bds., $1.50. *Ditson.*
Novels and novelists of the 18th cent. Forsyth, W. $1.50..............................*Appleton.*
Novelties of the new world. 16°. $1.25 ....*Lothrop.*
Novelty fair: burlesque. 16°. pap., 15c. ....*French.*
Novelty ser. 4 v. 16°. $5................*Lothrop.*

Cont.: The tropics. — Wonders of the plant world. — Novelties of the new world. — Willie's money box.

Novena, and prayers to our lady of Lourdes; for the sick and afflicted. 32°. '73. 40c.; pap., 25c. *Murphy.*
Novere, Eliz. G. Little book of knowledge; ed. by T. O. Summers. ('58.) 2d ed. 18°. '76. 50c...*So.Meth.*
Now. Hall, N. 35c.......................*Carter.*
Now and forever. Baker, H. N. W. $1.50..*Lee & S.*
Now and then. Warren, S. $1.25 ....*Harper.*
Now and then picture books. *See* Warne's.
Now is Christ risen. Wright, S. L. $1.25.....*Hoyt.*
Now or never. Adams, W. T. $1.25.......*Lee & S.*
Now-a-days. Marshall, E. $1.50..........*Dutton.*

Nowell, H. P. H. ["May Mannering."] Helping hand ser. 6 v. ill. 16°. ea., $1.............*Lee & S.*

Cont.: Climbing the rope. — Billy Grimes' favorite. — Cruise of the Dashaway. — Little Spaniard. — Salt water Dick. — Little maid of Oxbow.

Noye, W: Treatise of principal grounds and maxims of the laws of Eng.; with biog. sketch of author and index by C. S. Sims. 16°. '70. $2..*Munsell.*
Noyes, Dan. P. Church work. 18°. 30c...*Cong.Pub.*
Noyes, Eli. Lectures on truth of the Bible. 8°. '53. $1 ....*Freewill.*
Noyes, G: F. The bivouac and battle-field; or, campaign sketches in Virginia and Maryland. 12°. $1.50 ....*Harper.*
Noyes, G: R. Translation of the Hebrew prophets; with introd. and add. notes. New ed. 2 v. 12°. '74. $2.50..........................*Am. Unit.*
— (*ed.*) Theological essays from various authors; with introd. ('56.) 6th ed. 12°. '73. $1.25..*Am. Unit.*
— *See also* Bible, New Test.; Job; Psalms.
Noyes, H: D. Diagnosis of diseases of the eye. *See* Seguin, E. C., Series of Am. clin. lect.
Noyes, J: Humphrey. Dixon and his copyists. 8°. pap., 25c. ....*Oneida.*
— History of American socialisms. 8°. '70. $3. *Lippincott; Oneida.*
— House-talks; ed. by A. Barron and G. N. Miller. v. 1. 12°. '75. $1.50.................*Oneida.*
— Male continence, or self control in sexual intercourse. 8°. pap., 25c.........................*Oneida.*
— Salvation from sin, the end of Christian faith. 8°. pap., 25c. ....*Oneida.*
— Scientific propagation. 8°. pap., 25c.......*Oneida.*
Noyes, W: Lord. Memorial; ed. by T. W. Bicknell. 12°. '69. $1.50.........................*Rider.*
Nueva biblioteca de la visa, por una sociedad de literatos de buen humor. 12°. $1.75..........*Appleton.*
Nuevo canton (El) cristiano y caticismo. 18°. 15c. *Strong.*
Nugæ inutiles. Merrick, J. M. $1.25...(?) *Shepard.*
Nugee, G: Words from the cross as applied to our own death-beds. 16°. '65. $1................*Pott.*
Nugel, Louise. Das Vaterunser in Erzählungen u. Gedichten. 16°. '69. bds., 25c.........*Steiger.*
Nugent, *Lord.* [G. N. T. Grenville.] Memorials of Hampden, his party and times. por. 12°. (Bohn.) $1.75 ....*Little, B. & Co.*
— *Same.* por. 12°. (Bohn.) $2. *Lippincott; Scribner, W. & A.*
Nugent, E. Treatise on optics; or, light and sight, theoretically and practically treated; with applic. to fine art and industrial pursuits. ill. 12°. $1.50. *Van Nostrand.*
Nugent, Edm. C. Burlesque and musical acting charades. 16°. pap., 30c.; bds., 50c......*Dick & F.*
Nugent, T: French-English and Eng.-French dictionary. 18°. $1......................*Routledge.*
— Pocket dictionary of the French and Eng. lang. 5th Am., from last Lond. ed., enl. by J. Ouiseau. 16°. $1.25..........................*Butler.*
Nuitter, C: *and* Derley, J. Cup of tea: comedietta. 16°. pap., 15c...............*De Witt; French.*
Number one: farce. 16°. pap., 15c..........*French.*
Number one around the corner. Brough, W. 15c. *French.*
No. 6 Duke Street: farce. 16°. pap., 15c.....*French.*
Numismatic and Antiquarian Soc. of Phila. Proceedings, May 4, 1865–Dec. 31, 1866. 8°. '67. $3. *Phila.Num.*
Nun (The). *See* Sherwood, *Mrs.* M. M.
Nun of Kenmare (*pseud.*) *See* Cusack, Ma. F.
Nunes, Helen H. Day dreams. [Poetry.] 12°. 75c. *Lippincott.*
— Leisure moments. [Poetry.] 12°. $2..*Lippincott.*

Nunes, Jos. A. Aristocracy; or, life among the upper ten. 8°. pap., 75c. . . . . *Peterson.*

Nuovo tesoro di scherzi, massime, proverbi, etc. 12°. $1.75 . . . . *Appleton.*

Nur immer brav. *See* Hoffmann, F.

Nur Kleinigkeiten. *See* Hoffmann, F.

Nurse Brame. *See* Charlesworth, M. L.

Nurse Grand's reminiscences; [also] The neglected wife. 16°. $1.35 . . . . *Pres.Bd.*

Nurse Grand's stories. 18°. 75c. . . . . *Am.S.S.*

Nursery album. Heaton, C. $1.75 . . . . *Routledge.*

Nursery colored picture book. ill. roy. 8°. $1. (?) *McLoughlin.*

Nursery for youngest readers. 4 v. sm. 8°. ea., $1.25. *Nichols & H.*

Nursery lib. 6 v. ill. 18°. $3.60 . . . . *Lippincott.*

Cont.: Songs and stories. — Little Pet's book. — Nursery songs. — Gifts for little ones. — Dew drop. — Widow's cottage.

Nursery lib. 2 ser. ea., 12 v. ill. 64°. '70–'71. per ser., 50c. . . . . *Routledge.*

Nursery noonings. Dodge, M. A. $1.25 . . . . *Harper.*

Nursery picture-book. ill. f°. bds., $2; col. ill., $4.50. *Routledge.*

Nursery play book. *See* Picture puzzle toy book.

Nursery play hour. *See* Lullaby ser.

Nursery primer and self-teaching reader, for beginners. ill. sq. 16°. '75. bds., 30c. . . . . *Shorey.*

Nursery rattle. Huber, A. L. $1.75 . . . . *Lippincott.*

Nursery reading book. ill. 16°. '73. 75c. . . *M. Taylor.*

Nursery rhymes. [Toy-book.] ill. sm. 4°. per gross, $24 . . . . (?) *McLoughlin.*

Nursery rhymes. 3 nos. 8°. ea., 15c. . . . . *Hurd & H.*

Cont.: Aunt Mary's nursery rhymes. — Aunt Kitty's nursery rhymes. — Aunt Jenny's nursery rhymes.

Nursery rhymes for the little ones. 4 nos. ill. 4°. ea., pap., 10c.; 15c. . . . . *J.E. Potter.*

Nursery rhymes of England. Halliwell, J. O. $1; 50c. . . . . *Scribner, W.& A.*

Nursery rhymes, songs and legends. ill. sq. 12°. '71. bds., 50c. . . . . *Routledge.*

Nursery rhymes, tales and jingles. Valentine, R. $3.75 . . . . *Scribner, W.& A.*

Nursery rhymes with music. 16°. 90c. . . . . *Nelson.*

Nursery songs. *See* Nursery lib.

Nursery tales. Valentine, R. 75c. . . *Scribner, W.& A.*

Nursery tales for her little friends. Finley, M. F. 40c. . . . . *Pres.Bd.*

Nursery treasury. McKeever, H. B. 75c.; $1; 50c.; 25c. . . . . *Claxton.*

Nurseryman's general catalogue. 8°. pap., 20c. *Dewey.*

Nurseryrhymia. Paxton, A. 25c. . . . . *French.*

Nurses for the needy in the homes of the London poor. Ranyard, E. $1.25 . . . . *Carter.*

Nursey chickweed. Williams, T. J. 15c. *French; Lee & S.*

Nüsse für Knaben. 18°. 65c.; 85c. . . . . *Ev.Assoc.*

Nutcracker and mouseking. Hoffmann, E. T. 75c. *Lockwood, B.& Co.*

— *See also* Grandmother's lib.

Nuts for boys to crack. Todd, J. 90c. . . . . *Am.Tr.*

Nuts for Christmas cracking. Hall, T.O. $2 . . *Whittaker.*

Nuts ready cracked. Phelps, P. H. 60c. . . *Cong.Pub.*

Nutshell of knowledge. Tucker, C. 75c. . . . . *Carter.*

Nuttall, P. Aust. Dictionary of scientific terms. 12°. $2.50 . . . . *Routledge.*

— Routledge's diamond pocket dictionary. 64°. 40c.; roan, 60c. . . . . *Routledge.*

Nuttall, T: *See* Michaux, F. A., North Am. sylva.

Nuttall Ornithological Club. Bulletin. v. 1, nos. 1, 2. 8°. '76. ea., pap., 30c. . . . . *Nuttall.*

Nutting, J. K. Rocky hill and rolling prairie. 16°. $1.50 . . . . *Cong.Pub.*

— Tilman Loring; or, minister or merchant? 18°. '67. 90c. . . . . *Garrigues.*

Nymph of the Lurleyburg. Byron, H. J. 15c. . . *French.*

Nystrom, J: W. On force of falling bodies, and dynamics of matter, classified with precision to the meaning of dynamical terms. 8°. pap., 25c. *Lippincott.*

— On technological education and the construction of ships and screw propellers. 2d ed., rev. and enl. ill. 12°. '66. $1.50 . . . . *Baird.*

— Pocket book of mechanics and engineering. ill. 16°. $3.50 . . . . *Lippincott.*

— Tonal system: new system of arithmetic, weight, measure and coins, with 16 to the base. 8°. $1.50. *Lippincott.*

— Treatise on elements of mechanics; establishing strict precision in the meaning of dynamical terms; with app. on duodenal arithmetic and metrology. ill. 8°. '75. $4 . . . . *Porter.*

— Treatise on parabolic construction of ships, and other marine engineering subjects. 8°. $1.25. *Lippincott.*

O., G. E. River of dreams, and other poems. 16°. $1.25. *Lee & S.*

— Thurid, and other poems. 12°. $2 . . . . *Lee & S.*

O. T. *See* Andersen, H. C.

O mother dear Jerusalem! Prime, W. C. $1.50. *Randolph.*

Oak glen stories. 5 v. 18°. $3 . . . . (?) *Martien.*

Cont.: Gold dollar. — Edna Willis. — Arthur Morland. — Wishing and choosing. — Harry's battles.

Oak-mot. Baker, W. M. $1 . . . . *Pres.Bd.*

Oak openings. *See* Cooper, Ja. F.

Oak ser. 3 v. 12°. $4.50 . . . . *Nelson.*

Cont.: Lady Willacy's protégées, by Agnes Gray. — Young Brahmin's story, by Auguste Glandon. — Scenes and sketches of Eng. hist., by S. M. S. Clarke.

Oakeley, F: Canon. Catholic worship: instruction on ceremonies and devotions of the [Cath.] Church. 3d ed. 16°. '72. 60c. . . . . *Cath.Pub.*

— Ceremonial of sacrifice of the mass explained in a dialogue between a priest and a catechumen; with app. on mass, vespers, compline and benediction of the sacrament. 3d ed. 18°. '72. 60c. . . . . *Cath.Pub.*

Oakfield Lodge. ill. 18°. '74. 40c. . . . . *Am.Tr.*

Oakland stories. *See* Taylor, G: B.

Oakley, Juliana. Memoir. 18°. 40c. . . . . *Am.S.S.*

Oakridge. Smith, J. E. $2 . . . . *Osgood.*

Oakshaw. Goggeshall, W. T. 75c. . . . . *U.P.James.*

Oakville dove's nest. Trowbridge, C. M. $1.75. (?) *Martien.*

Oakwood and its lessons. Worth, A. A. $1.25. *Cong.Pub.*

Oakwood lib. 4 v. ill. 16°. $4 . . . . *Hoyt.*

Cont.: Old oak farm. — Tempter and the tempted, by Miss M. F. Wood. — Life's struggles. — Loving words.

Oarsman's manual; ill. by G. T. Balch. 4°. $10 . . *Nims.*

Oates, G: Interest tables at 7 per cent. demy 4°. '64. hf. bd., $5 . . . . *Clayton.*

— Sterling interest tables at 5 per cent. demy 4°. '70. hf. bd., $8 . . . . *Clayton.*

Obadiah Oldbuck. *See* Mishaps and adventures of.

Obedience. Lambla, H. L. 15c. . . . . *Ames.*

Oberholtzer, *Mrs.* Sara Louisa. Violet Lee, and other poems. 12°. $1.25 . . . . *Lippincott.*

Oberlin, J: F: Life. 18°. 45c. . . . . *Am.S.S.*

— Memoir. 18°. 35c. . . . . *Pres.Bd.*

— *Same.* 18°. '55. 60c. . . . . *Carter.*

— *Same;* with introd. by H. Ware, jr. 2d ed., enl. 12°. '45. 75c. . . . . *Burnham.*

Oberon. Planché, J. R. 15c. . . . . *French.*

Obeying orders. Arnold, J. 15c. . . . . *De Witt.*

Obi; or, three-fingered Jack. 8°. pap., 50c...*Peterson.*

Object of interest. Stocqueler, J. H. 15c. ..*French.*

Object of life: narr. ill. insufficiency of the world, and sufficiency of Christ. ill. 16°. $1.25..*Bost. Am. Tr.*

— *Same.* ill. 12°. '57. $1.25........*Meth. Bk. Conc.*

Obligations of the world to the Bible. Spring, G. 90c. *Pres. Bd.*

Obliging a friend: farce. 16°. pap., 15c. ...*French.*

Obookiah, H: Memoir. 18°. 40c. ....*Am. S. S.*

— Memoir of Edn. W. Dwight. ill. 18°. '37. 35c. *Am. Tr.*

O'Brian family; or, fruits of Bible reading. 18°. 30c.; 40c. ....*Am. Bapt.*

O'Brien, FitzJames. Gentleman from Ireland: comedy. 16°. pap., 15c. ....*French.*

O'Brien, *Mrs.* H. [Juveniles.] 8 v. 18°....*Pres. Bd.*

Cont.: Aunt Betsy's rule, and how it worked, 75c. — Little girls' habits, 35c. — Lucy at home, 35c. — Not exactly so, 75c. — Social influence; or, take care of the boys, 75c. — Talks with little Emily, 35c. — Two little cousins, 35c. — Two wallets, 50c.

O'Brien, *Rev.* Ja. H. The Franciscan way to the heavenly Jerusalem: prayers, litanies, etc. 24°. roan, 75c.; mor., $1; $1.50 ....*Strong.*

O'Brien, *Bp.* Ja. T: Attempt to explain and establish the doctrine of justification by faith only. 3d ed. 8°. $4 ....*Macmillan.*

— Sermons on prayer. 8°. '75. $2......*Macmillan.*

O'Briens and O'Flaherties. Morgan, *Lady* S. O. $1.50. *Haverty.*

O'Bryan, C. Lugarto, the mulatto: drama. 16°. pap., 15c...............................*French.*

Observation and flirtation. Wigan, H. 15c...*French.*

Observations on the authenticity of the Gospels; by a layman. 2d ed. 16°. $1..........*Lippincott.*

Observer. *See* Chalmers, A., British essayists.

Obstinate family: farce. 16°. pap., 15c.....*French.*

O'Callaghan, Edm. B. History of New Netherlands; or, New York under the Dutch. 2 v. pl. and maps. 8°. $6 ....*Appleton.*

— List of editions of the Scriptures and parts thereof, printed in Am. previous to 1860; with introd., bibliog. notes, facsimiles, etc. roy. 8°. '61. pap., $8 ....*Munsell.*

— (*ed.*) Documentary hist. of N. Y., [1600–1800]. 4 v. 4° *or* 8° ....*State.*

— Documents rel. to colonial hist. of N. Y. 11 v. 4°. '56–'58 ....*State.*

Cont.: 1, 2. Holland documents. — 3–8. London documents. — 9, 10. Paris documents. 11. Index.

O'Callaghan, J: C. History of the Irish brigades in service of France. ill. 8°. $5..*Haverty; O'Shea.*

O'Callaghan, P. P. Married bachelor: farce. 16°. pap., 15c. ....*French.*

Occupations of a retired life. *See* Mayo, I. F.

Ocean (The). *See* Land and sea.

Ocean born. Adams, W. T. $1.50..........*Lee & S.*

Ocean child. Myrtle, H. 75c............*Routledge.*

Ocean lanes for steamships. Peirce, B. 10c... *Williams.*

Ocean life series. *See* Thomes, W. H.

Ocean monarch. 8°. pap., 25c..............*De Witt.*

Ocean of life. Haines, J. T. 15c...........*French.*

Ocean queen. 8°. pap., 25c..............*Dick & F.*

Ocean sketches of life in Burmah. Ingalls, M. B. 70c.; 85c. ....*Am. Bapt.*

Ocean to ocean: Pacific Railroad and adjoining territories; with distances and fares from Am. cities. maps. 16°. 50c.....................*Lippincott.*

Ocean waif. Reid, M. $1.50..................*Miller.*

Ocean work. *See* Happy child's lib.

Ocean world. *See* Figuier, L.

Ocean's story. Goodrich, F. B. *$3–$4.50..*Hubbard.*

Ockley, Sim. Fall of the Saracens. cr. 8°. $1; pap., 75c.......................*Scribner, W. & A.*

Ockley, Sim., *continued.*

— History of the Saracens. 12°. (Bohn.) $1.25. *Little, B. & Co.*

— *Same.* 12°. (Bohn.) $1.40......*Scribner, W. & A.*

— *Same.* 12°. (Bohn.) $1.50 ....*Lippincott.*

O'Connell, Dan. Life and speeches. ill. 8°. $2. *McGee.*

— Popular life; incl. funeral oration of Padre Ventura at Rome, Father Burke's sermon at Glasnevin, and W. Phillips' centennial oration. ill. 12°. '76. $1 ....*Noonan.*

O'Connor, Flo. J. Heroine of the Confederacy; or, truth and justice. 12°. '69. $2........*Eyrich.*

O'Connor, W: D. Nettie Renton; or, the ghost: Christmas story. ill. 16°. '72. $1....*Putnam.*

Octoroon. *See* Boucicault, D.

Octoroon. Braddon, M. E. 50c............*De Witt.*

Odd couple. Oliphant, M. O. W. $1.50–75c...*Porter.*

Odd five minutes. Bourdillon, F. $1.25.....*Nelson.*

Odd gentleman. 16°. $1.25..............*Am. Bapt.*

Odd hours of a physician. Garretson, J. E. $1.50. *Lippincott.*

Odd lot. Gordon, W. 15c....................*French.*

Odd one. Payne, A. M. $1.25..............*Carter.*

Odd people. Reid, M. 75c..................*Harper.*

Odd stories about animals. ill. sq. 8°. $1....*Nelson.*

Odd trump. Coulson, J. G. A. $1.25; 75c.....*Hale.*

Oddfellowship examined in light of Scripture and reason. 12°. '56. 75c..............*Perkinpine.*

Oddfellowship exposed. ill. 8°. pap., 13c...*Peterson.*

Oddfellowship exposed. Small, G. G. 25c. *Collin & S.*

Oddities of humanity. 16°. 60c.; $1.......*Sadlier.*

Odenheimer, W: H: Private prayer book; for daily and hourly use. 16°. 75c...........*McCauley.*

— *and* Bird, F. M. Songs of the spirit. [Hymns.] sm. 4°. '71. $3.........................*Randolph.*

Odeon (New). *See* Webb, G. J., *and* Mason, L.

Odious Captain Cutter: farce. 16°. pap., 15c...*French.*

Odling, W: Course of practical chemistry; arranged for medical students. roy. 12°. $2........*Lea.*

O'Donnells of Glen Cottage. Conyngham, D. P. $1.50; $2.......................................*Sadlier.*

O'Donoghue (The). *See* Lever, C:

Odyssey. *See* Homer.

Œcolampadius, J: Biographical sketch. *See* Zwingli, M., Life.

Œdipus tyrannus. *See* Sophocles.

Oehler, Gst. F: Theology of the Old Test.; tr. v. 1. 8°. $3......................*Scribner, W. & A.*

Oehlschläger, Ja. C. Englisch-deutsches u. deutsch-engl. Taschenwörterbuch, nebst engl. Aussprache. 36th ed. 16°. $1.50..................*Schäfer.*

— English-German and German-Eng. school dict. 10th ed. 16°. $1..............................*Schäfer.*

— German-Eng. and Eng.-German dict.; with Germ. pronunc. 19th ed. 16°. $1.50........*Schäfer.*

— Lesebuch, no. 1. 12°. 25c......................*Kohler.*

— Pronouncing Germ. reader. 12°. $1.25..*Appleton.*

— Zweites Lesebuch. 12°. 50c..................*Kohler.*

— *See also* Ahn, F.; — Grieb, C. F.

O'er moor and fen. Walsingham, C. $1.50..*Claxton.*

Oersted, Hs. Chr. The soul in nature; tr. by Leonora and J. B. Horner. 12°. (Bohn.) $2. *Lippincott; Scribner, W. & A.*

Oertel, Mx. Neues und Altes. por. 8°. $2..*Benziger.*

Oertel, P. F. W. ["W. O. v. Horn."] Erzählungen. 14 v. 12°. $10; pap., $8.40; ea., 75c.; pap., 60c.; — in 7 v., $8.75; hf. mor., $12; $14; ea., $1.25; hf. mor., $2.........................*Kohler.*

— Goldkörner, od. Bilder u. Beispiele. 8°. '75. $1.50; $2 ....*Ev. Assoc.*

Oertel, P. F. W., *continued.*
— Jugend u. Volkschriften. (Steiger's Jugend-Bibliothek.) 11 v. 16°. '65–'66. ea., bds., 25c. . . *Steiger.*
Cont.: Johann Jacob Astor. — Benjamin Franklin. — James Watt. — George Stephenson. — Von d. Neffen der seinen Onkel sucht. — Das Pathengeschenk. — Das Büchlein v. Feldmarschall Blücher. — Prinz Eugenius, d. edle Ritter. — Der Brand v. Moskau. — Der Lohn e. guten That. — Wie einer e. Wallfischfänger wurde.
— Olaf Thorlaksen: an iceland narative; tr. (Fatherland ser.) ill. 16°. $1 . . . . (?) *Luth. Pub.*
— Schoolmaster of Albach, and other tales; tr. 12°. '70. $1.50; pap., $1 . . . . *Claxton.*
Oesten, Thdr. Piano instructor; with Eng. and Germ. text. 4°. bds., $2.50 . . . . *Peters.*
Of age tomorrow. Dibdin, T. 15c. . . . . *French.*
Off the roll. King, K. 75c. . . . . *Harper.*
Off the Skelligs. Ingelow, J. $1.75 . . . . *Roberts.*
Off the stage. Rosenfeld, S. 15c. . . . . *De Witt.*
Off to the Geysers. Stephens, C. A. $1.25 . . . *Porter.*
Off to sea. Kingston, W. H. G. $1.50 . . *Cassell; Lee & S.*
Off the track. Denison, M. A. $1.50 . . . . (?) *Martien.*
Offen, B: Legacy to the friends of free discussion: review of the principles, hist. facts and personages of the books known as Old and New Test.; with remarks on morality of nature. 12°. $1 . . *Mendum.*
Offenbach, Jacques. Blind beggars, opera; arr. for amateurs. 16°. pap., 40c. . . . . *French.*
— Breaking the spell. [Opera.] 4°. '74. pap., $1 . . *Pond.*
— Opera bouffe: vocal and instrumental gems from Offenbach's operas. 4°. '68. $4–$2.50 . . . . *Ditson.*
— Rose of Auvergne; or, spoiling the broth. [Opera.] 4°. '74. $1 . . . . *Pond.*
— *Same;* arr. for amateurs. 16°. pap., 40c. . . *French.*
Offering. Southard, L. H. $1.50 . . . . *Ditson.*
Offering. *See* Diamond miniatures.
Offerings to the Lord. Cole, E. 10c. *N. Y. Ref. Ch. Bd.*
Offhand sketches. *See* Arthur, T. S.
Offhand takings. Bungay, G. W. $2 . . . . *De Witt.*
Office of the immaculate conception. *See* Little office.
Office of the Virgin Mary; for the three seasons of the year; according to the Roman breviary in Lat. 24°. '65. *net*, 50c. . . . . *Kelly, P. & Co.*
— *Same;* in Lat. and Eng. 18°. 40c. . . . . *Sadlier.*
— *See also* Little office.
Officer, Harvey. *See* Minnesota, Sup. Court reports.
Officer, M. African Bible pictures: Script. scenes and customs in Africa. 18°. 35c. . . . . . (?) *Luth. Pub.*
Officer's widow and her young family. Hofland, B. 50c. *Porter.*
Offsprings of fancy. Post, J. H. 75c. . . . . . . *Dennis.*
O'Flanagan, Pat. Hibernia collection: Irish jigs, etc., arr. for the violin, flute, cornet, etc. 8°. '60. pap., 50c. . . . . *Ditson.*
O'Flanagan and the fairies. Brougham, J. 15c. *French.*
Oft-told tales. [Toy-book.] ill. 4°. $1.50. (?) *McLoughlin.*
Ogden, A. N. *See* Louisiana, Sup. Court reports.
Ogden, J: Science of education and art of teaching. 12°. $1.50 . . . . *Wilstach.*
Ogden, Rob. N. Who did it? [Fiction.] 8°. '69. pap., 50c. . . . . *Claxton.*
Ogden, W. A. Anthem choir: anthems, choruses, opening and closing pieces, etc. obl. 12°. $1.25. — Appendix, 30c. . . . . *W. W. Whitney.*
— Convention choruses. 8°. 75c. . . . . *Brainard.*
— Crown of life: collection of songs, for Sunday schools, etc. obl. 18°. bds., 35c. . . . . *W. W. Whitney.*
— New silver song; for the Sunday school. obl. 18°. bds., 35c. . . . . *W. W. Whitney.*
— *See also* Leslie, J. H., *and* Ogden, W. A.
— *and* Abbey, A. J. Songs of the Bible: gems for the Sunday school. obl. 18°. bds., 35c. *W. W. Whitney.*
Ogilby, J: D. Lay baptism. 12°. 50c. . . . . *Appleton.*
Ogilvies (The). *See* Craik, D. M.
Ogle, Annie. ["Ashford Owen."] A lost love. sq. 16°. $1; pap., 50c. *Loring.*
O'Gorman, *Miss* Edith. Convent life unveiled; or, six years a nun: trials and persecutions of Miss Edith O'Gorman, otherwise Sister Teresa de Chantal of St. Joseph's Convent; by herself. 12°. '71. *$1.50 . . . . *Conn. Pub.*
O'Gorman, R: Oration. *See* Meagher, T. F., Speeches on legislative independence of Ireland.
— *See also* O'Hagan, *Lord*, McGlynn, *Rev.* E., *and* O'Gorman, R:
Oh hush; or, the Virginy cupids: Ethiop. drama. 16°. pap., 15c. . . . . *French; Happy.*
Oh! I see you. *See* Hoffman, J.
Oh! if I were the squire. 18°. 18c. . . . . *Am. S. S.*
O'Hagan, *Lord*, McGlynn, *Rev.* E: *and* O'Gorman, R: O'Connell centenary: speeches delivered on the occasion. 18°. pap., 25c. . . . . *Sadlier.*
O'Hara, J: P. *See* Wigram, *Sir* Ja., *and* O'Hara, J: P.
O'Hara, Kane. Midas: comic opera. 16°. pap., 15c. *French.*
O'Hara, P. Forty-five players' manual: rules for the game as laid down by the Forty-five Players' Congress, N. Y., Sept., 1875. 24°. '75. pap., 25c. . . . . (?) *Donnell.*
Oheim u. Neffe. *See* Hoffmann, F.
Ohio. Code of civil procedure and amend., sup. acts and statutes reg. practice, with notes; by G. E. Seney. 2d ed., rev. and enl. 8°. '74. shp., $7.50 . . . . *Clarke.*
— Digest of decisions. *See* McVey, A. H.; — Walker, J. B., *and* Bates, C.
— General railroad laws. *See* Wilcox, J. A.
— Nisi prius reports, 1831–'34; by J. C. Wright. 8°. shp., $5 . . . . *I. N. Whiting.*
— *Same.* 8°. '35. shp., $7.50 . . . . *Clarke.*
— Public statutes at large, 1833–'60, arranged in chronol. order, with ref.; ed. by M. E. Curwen. 4 v. roy. 8°. *net*, shp., $20 . . . . *Clarke.*
— Reports of cases (Common Pleas), 1816–'19; [with] opinion of Judge McLean in case of Lauderback *v.* Moore (1876); by B. Tappan. 8°. *net*, shp., $3.50 . . . . *Ingham.*
— Revised statutes of a general nature in force, Aug. 1, 1860, collated by J. R. Swan; with notes and ref. by L. J. Critchfield. New ed. 2 v. roy. 8°. '70. shp., $15 . . . . *Clarke.*
— Statutes. *See* Chase, S. P.
— Statutes, 1860–'75, arr. in chronol. order, with ref. and index; ed. by J. R. Sayler. 4 v. roy. 8°. '76. *net*, shp., $20 . . . . *Clarke.*
— Supreme Court reports, 1821–'51 (Ohio reports). 20 v. 8°. ea., *net*, shp., $2.50 . . . . *Clarke.*
Cont.: 1–9 (1821–'39), by C. Hammond. — 10 (1840–'41), by P. B. Wilcox. — 11–13 (1841–'44), by A. M. Stanton — 14–19 (1845–'50), by H. Griswold. — 20 (1851), by W. Lawrence.
— *Same.* (Ohio state reports), v. 1–25 (1852–'75). 25 v. 8°. ea., *net*, shp., $2.50 . . . . *Clarke.*
Cont.: 1 (1852), by G. W. McCook. — 2–4 (1853–'55), by R. B. Warden. — 5–21 (1855–'71), by L. J. Critchfield. — 22, 23 (1871–'73), by M. M. Granger. — 24, 25 (1874–'75), by E. L. DeWitt.
— — Digest. *See* McVey, A. H.; — Wilcox, P. B.
— — Index. *See* Hunter, B., *and* Meyer, W. G.
Ohio ark and how it floated. Wright, J. McN. $1.15. *Pres. Bd.*
Ohio ark ser. 7 v. 16° . . . . *Pres. Bd.*
Cont.: Ohio ark, by Mrs. J. McN. Wright, $1.15. — Craythorns of Stony Hollow, by Mrs. M. J. Hildeburn, $1.15. — Madge, Kate and Dick, by A. Dudleigh, $1. — Rich and poor, by Mrs. M. Hosmer, $1.15. — Man with two shadows, by E. Hoven, 90c. — Mr. Wallingford's mistake, by Mrs. A. K. Dunning, $1. — Virgilia, by G. Grey, $1.15.
Ohio canals. *See* Documentary hist.
Ohio geological survey. Agricultural survey; by J. H. Klippart. 8°. '71 . . . . *State.*
— First report on geol. survey of O.; by W. W. Mather. 8°. '38 . . . . *State.*

Ohio geological survey, *continued.*
— Second report. 8°. '38 .... *State.*
— Report of progress in 1869; by J. S. Newberry, E. B. Andrews [and] E. Orton. maps. 8°. '71.. *State.*
— Report of progress in 1870; by J. S. Newberry and others. pl. 8°. '71 .... *State.*
Ohio in the war. Reid, W. 2 v. $10–$15... *Wilstach.*
Ohio valley hist. ser. 8 v. 8°. '67–'71 ...... *Clarke.*
Cont.: Bouquet's expedition against the Ohio Indians, 1764, by W. Smith, $3. — History of Athens Co., Ohio, by C. M. Walker, $6. — Campaign in the Illinois, 1778–9, by G. R. Clark, $2. — Pioneer biog., by J. McBride, 2 v., $6.50. — Captivity with the Indians, 1755–'59, by J. Smith, $2.50. — Pioneer life in Kentucky, by D. Drake, $3. — Miscellanies; Tour in Ohio, etc., by J. Esky; Two western campaigns in the war of 1812, by S. Williams; The Leatherwood god, by R. H. Taneyhill, $2.50.
Ohnewald, Jos. Requiem mass no. 1, in F. 4°. pap., $1.25 .... *Peters.*
— Requiem mass no. 2, in B flat. 4°. pap., 80c... *Peters.*
Oiled feather. 18°. 25c. .... *Am.S.S.*
Oiled feather series: nos. 1, 2. *See* Power, P. B.
— *Same:* no. 3. 5 v. 18°. $1.75; pap., 50c... *Am.S.S.*
Cont.: Born with a silver spoon in his mouth. — Experiences of a church plate. — "We" versus I. — On letting one's self alone; On looking seedy. — Reports and the mischief they do; On not knowing when one is well off; Upon crawling.
O'Kane, Ja. Notes on the rubrics of the Roman ritual, regarding the sacraments in general, etc. 12°. $2.50 .... *Noonan; O'Shea.*
O'Kane, T. C. Every Sabbath. [S.-school music.] obl. 16°. '74. 35c. .... *Church.*
— Songs for worship. 18°. 35c....... *Meth.Bk.Conc.*
O'Keeffe, J: [Plays.] 9 v. 16°. ea., pap., 15c... *French.*
Cont.: Agreeable surprise: comic opera. — Castle of Andalusia: opera. — Farmer: opera. — Fontainebleau: opera. — Highland reel: farce. — Modern antiques: farce. — Poor soldier: farce. — Prisoner at large: comedy. — Wild oats: comedy.
— *See also* Stoddard, R. H., Bric-a-brac ser.
O'Kelly, Ja. J. Mambi-land: adventures of a "Herald" correspondent in Cuba. 12°. $1.75.. *Lippincott.*
Olaf Thorlaksen. Oertel, P. F. W. $1..(?) *Luth.Pub.*
Olcott, E: R. *See* United States, Dist. Court reports.
Olcott, H: S. People from the other world: wonderful doings of the "Eddy Brothers" and other noted spiritualists; with tests applied by the author. ill. 12°. *$2.50; $3; mor., $4......... *Am.Pub.*
Old Abe. Barrett, J. O. $1; 50c........... *Atwood.*
Old Ambrose. 32°. 20c.; 15c............. *Dutton.*
Old and new. Sadlier, M. A. $1.25; $1.75.. *Sadlier.*
Old and the new; or, the past and present of the parish of St. Ann's, Brooklyn, [N. Y.] sq. 12°. '69. $1. *DeSelding.*
Old and new home. ill. 12°. $1.............. *Nelson.*
Old and new London. Thornbury, W., *and* Walford, E. 3 v. ea., $5 .... *Cassell.*
Old and young. Salmon, J. 15c............ *French.*
Old Anthony's hints to young people to make them both cheerful and wise. 18°. 50c.......... *Pres.Bd.*
Old back room. Harrison, J. $1.25.......... *Dodd.*
Old barracks. Davis, C. E. K. $1.25.......... *Hoyt.*
Old battle ground. *See* Trowbridge, J. T.
Old beggar. 16°. 45c.................. *Cummiskey.*
Old Ben's stockings. *See* Bertie's lib.; — Moss rose ser.
Old Bible. Wynne, E. $1......... *Scribner, W. & A.*
Old Block (*pseud.*) Live woman in the mines: play. 16°. pap., 15c.................... *French.*
Old boy's stories. *See* Gordon, C.
Old Bright. Cragin, M. A. 45c........... *Cong.Pub.*
Old brown book. ill. 16°. '76. 60c.......... *Lothrop.*
Old brown house. Hamilton, K. W. 50c.... *Pres.Bd.*
Old brown pitcher. Prentiss, E. $1....... *Nat.Temp.*
Old bureau. *See* May, A.
Old cabinet. Pierson, H. W. 85c.......... *Challen.*
Old Catholics at Cologne: sketch in three scenes; by author of "Comedy of convocation." 18°. '73. 75c. .... *Cath.Pub.*
Old château. Coyne, J. S. 15c............ *French.*
Old château. McKeever, H. B. $1.50...... *Pres.Bd.*
Old château ser. 5 v. 16°................. *Pres.Bd.*
Cont.: Old château, by Miss H. B. McKeever, $1.50. — Happy light, by Miss E. N. Beebe, $1.50. — Gertrude Terry, by M. Grahame, $1.35. — Cast out, by A. Eldridge, $1.35. — Influence, by F. J. P., $1.30.
Old chest. Aunt Elizabeth. 85c............. *Dodd.*
Old chest; tr. by Miss A. T. Sadlier. 12°. $1.50; $2. *Sadlier.*
Old church bell. *See* Andersen, H. C.
Old church door. ill. 16°. '76. $1........... *Carter.*
— *See also* Vinegar Hill stories.
Old church in the corner. 18°. 60c.......... *Dutton.*
Old churches of Virginia. Meade, W. $5.. *Lippincott.*
Old corner lib. 4 v. 16°. $4................ *Dutton.*
Cont.: Ned Grant's quest, by M. L. Bissell. — Frank Stirling's choice, by M. H. Bulfinch. — Boy artists, by M. E. Foa. — Grandmother's curiosity cabinet.
Old countess. Höfer, E. $1............. *Lippincott.*
Old countess. Stephens, A. S. $1.75; $1.50.. *Peterson.*
Old curiosity shop. *See* Dickens, C:
Old curiosity shop. Stirling, E. 15c......... *French.*
Old dad's cabin: Ethiop. drama. 16°. pap., 15c. *French; Happy.*
Old dame and her silver sixpence. ill. 4°. pap., 10c.; 15c. .... *J.E.Potter.*
Old Deccan days. Frere, M. $1.25...... *Lippincott.*
Old distillery. Avery, J. G. $1.50........... *Hoyt.*
Old doctor's son. Chellis, M. D. $1.50.. *H.A.Young.*
Old dog Tray. *See* Swallow stories.
Old dominion. James, G. P. R. 50c....... *Harper.*
Old dower house. Grey, E. C. 50c....... *Peterson.*
Old dramatists and poets. (Moxon's ed.) 13 v. por. roy. 8°. $65 .... *Routledge.*
Cont.: Shakespeare. — Jonson. — Massinger and Ford. — Wycherly, Congreve, Vanbrugh and Farquhar. — Beaumont and Fletcher, 2 v. — Webster. — Marlowe. — Greene and Peele. — Spenser. — Chaucer. — Dryden. — Pope.
Old Edinburgh: hist. sketch; rev. by T. O. Summers. ('57.) 2d ed. 18°. '69. 50c.......... *So.Meth.*
Old England worthies. Brougham, H. (*Lord*). 15 pts. ea., *50c. .... *S. Walker.*
Old English baron. *See* Reeve, C.
Old fairy tales. Mason, J. $1.25 .... *Cassell.*
Old faith and the new. Strauss, D. F. $2 ..... *Holt.*
Old farm and new farm. Hopkinson, F. $1.25. *Randolph.*
Old-fashioned boy. Finley, M. F. $1.50... *Souder.*
Old-fashioned ethics. Thornton, W. T. $3.50. *Macmillan.*
Old-fashioned girl. Alcott, L. M. $1.50 ... *Roberts.*
Old-fashioned lives. Todd, S. D. $1.25.. *Cong.Pub.*
Old flag. 16°. $1.25 .... *Am.S.S.*
Old forest ranger. Campbell, W. $2...... *Routledge.*
Old forget-me-not songster. 32°. 40c.......... *Locke.*
Old Fort Duquesne. McKnight, C. $2.50.. *S.A.Clarke.*
Old Fountain Inn. Moe, A. R. $1.50.... *Lippincott.*
Old friends. ill. 16°. '70. $1.............. *Lothrop.*
Old friends and new friends. Dulcken, H. W. $1.75. *Scribner, W. & A.*
Old friends with new faces. *See* Tucker, *Mrs.* C.
Old Fritz. Mundt, C. M. $1.50; $1; $3.50.. *Appleton.*
Old Gabriel. *See* Lily among thorns.
Old gems in new settings. *See* Coles, Ab.
Old Gingerbread and the school-boys. 18°. 35c. *Carter; Dutton.*
— *Same.* 16°. 50c................ *Scribner, W. & A.*
Old Gooseberry. Williams, T. J. 15c. *French; Lee & S.*

Old Granny Tift. *See* Aunty Ray's little lib.
Old gray rosary. Dorsey, A. H. $1 .... *O'Shea.*
Old Grimes. Greene, A. G. $1.50........... *Rider.*
Old Grips and little Tid. Banvard, J. 75c.... *Ward.*
Old guard: drama. 16°. pap., 15c........... *French.*
Old gum game: Ethiop. drama. 16°. pap., 15c. *Happy.*
Old heads and young hearts. Boucicault, D. 15c. *French.*
Old helmet. Warner, S. $2.25 .... *Carter.*
Old Herbert, and little Alice. 18°. 35c...... *Am. S. S.*
Old Hicks, the guide. Webber, C. W. $1.50.. *Harper.*
Old home by the river. Dutcher, J. C. $1.25.. *Tibbals.*
Old homestead. 18°. 65c................ *Cong. Pub.*
Old homestead. Stephens, A. S. $1.75; $1.50.. *Peterson.*
Old Honesty. Morton, J. M. 15c.... *French; Lee & S.*
Old horseshoe; or, Sammy's first cent. 16°. $1.25. *Cong. Pub.*
Old house at home: drama. 16°. pap., 15c... *French.*
Old house by the Boyne. Sadlier, M. A. $1.25; $1.75. *Sadlier.*
Old house by the river. Prime, W. C. $1.50.. *Harper.*
Old house on Briar Hill. Meredith, I. G. $1.25.. *Dodd.*
Old house on the bridge of Notre Dame. Barrière, T., *and* Kock, H. de. 15c................ *French.*
Old Humphrey (*pseud.*) *See* Mogridge, G:
Old Humphrey lib. *See* Mogridge, G:
Old Humphrey's friendly appeals; — study table. *See* Mogridge, G:
Old Hunks: Ethiop. drama. 16°. pap., 15c. *French; Happy.*
Old Indian root and herb doctor. 16°. 50c... *Claremont.*
Old Jack. Kingston, W. H. G. $2.......... *Nelson.*
Old Jacob; or, a friend in need. 18°. 25c. *Scribner, W. & A.*
Old James, the Irish pedlar. [Rhyme.] 18°. 40c. *Am. S. S.*
Old Jessie. *See* Moravian missionaries.
Old Joe and young Joe. Courtney, J. 15c. .. *French.*
Old Jolly. Small, G. G. 25c.............. *Collin & S.*
Old judge. Haliburton, T. C. 75c.......... *Dick & F.*
Old Kentucky home: Ethiop. drama. 16°. pap., 15c. *Happy.*
Old Kensington. Thackeray, A. I. $1.50; $1.. *Harper.*
Old kitchen fire. Parker, C. E. R. 30c...... *Am. Tr.*
Old landmark reset. Pendleton, J. M. 10c... *So. Bapt.*
Old landmarks. Drake, S. A. $3.......... * *Osgood.*
Old leaves. Wills, W. H. $1.25 .... *Harper.*
Old lieutenant and his son. Macleod, N. $1.50. *Routledge; R. Worthington.*
Old mam'selle's secret. John, E. $1.50 .. *Lippincott.*
Old man of the cliff. Dyer, F. J. 90c. .... *Hoyt.*
Old man of the hill-side. *See* Rogers, G:
Old man of the woods. 12°. '74. pap., 15c... *Ellyson.*
Old manor house, and sequel. ('66.) New ed. 2 v. ill. 16°. '73. ea., $1.50 .... *Hoyt.*
Old man's bride. Arthur, T. S. $1.25.... *J. E. Potter.*
Old man's home. 18°. 40c.................. *Dutton.*
Old man's prayer. Baker, G. M. $1.50...... *Lee & S.*
Old man's stories: when I was young; or, Gideon and his grandchildren. 18°. 55c........... *Am. S. S.*
Old Margaret. Kingsley, H. 50c.; 35c. .. *Donnelley.*
Old Margie's flower stall. 18°. 50c.......... *Carter.*
Old market cart. Smith, F. I. B. 75c. *Bost. Am. Tr.; Lothrop.*
Old masters (The) and their pictures. Keddie, H. $1.50 .... *Roberts.*
Old meeting-house. *See* Tarbox, I. N.
Old merchants of N.Y. Scoville, J. A. 4 v. $6.. *Miller.*
Old Merritt. *See* Aunt Gracie's lib.
Old Merry (*pseud.*) *See* Hodder, E.
Old Merry's travels on the continent. *See* Hodder, E.
Old Michael and his little friend; by author of "Blind Annie Lorimer." 18°. 60c............ *Pres. Bd.*
Old Michael and young Maurice. Mogridge, G. 50c. *So. Meth.*
Old mill. Chellis, M. D. $1.50........... *Cong. Pub.*
Old Mr. Pro. Miller, M. E. 75c.......... *Cong. Pub.*
Old Mortality. *See* Scott, *Sir* Wa.
Old Mother Hubbard and her dog. ill. 4°. pap., 10c.; 15c. .... *J. E. Potter.*
Old Myddelton's money. Hay, M. C. 50c. .. *Harper.*
Old New England traits. Lunt, G. $1.50 .. *Hurd & H.*
Old New York. Francis, J. W. $2.25–$10.. *Widdleton.*
Old New York. Greatorex, E. $30; $50 ... *Putnam.*
Old Noll. Robinson, F. W. 50c. .... *De Witt.*
Old nursery rhymes. G., M. E. $1.50 ...... *Cassell.*
Old nursery rhymes with old tunes. [Toy-book.] ill. 4°. $1; 50c. .... *Routledge.*
Old oak chest. James, G. P. R. 50c........ *Harper.*
Old oak chest. *See* May, A.
Old oak farm. *See* Haverfield, T. T.
Old offender. Planché, J. R. 15c. .... *French.*
Old, old story. ill. 16°. '72. 20c. .... *Dutton.*
Old, old story. Clark, M. L. 15c. .... *Lothrop.*
Old, old story. Hankey, *Miss* —. 50c.; 25c... *Am. Tr.*
Old, old story. Roy, G. 25c................ *Clarke.*
Old parsonage; or, recollections of a minister's daughter. 18°. 70c............................ *Pres. Bd.*
Old paths. Berg, J. F. 75c.; 50c. .. *N. Y. Ref. Ch. Bd.*
Old paths. Cracraft, J. W. $1.50........... *Clarke.*
Old paths. Knight, H. C. 35c. .... *Am. Tr.*
Old paths. Mitchell, T. 50c. .... *Tibbals.*
Old patroon. Maitland, J. A. $1.75; $1.50.. *Peterson.*
Old pauper; [also] The beautiful villa. 18°. 17c.; 22c. *Am. Bapt.*
Old Philip's moral stories. 18°. 40c.; 50c... *Am. Bapt.*
Old Phil's birthday. Wooler, J. P. 15c. ..... *French.*
Old picture Bible. ill. 16°. $1.25 .... *Carter.*
Old pine farm; or, southern ministerial life; by a southern country minister. 12°. $1........ *So. Bapt.*
Old plantation. Hungerford, J. $1.50....... *Harper.*
Old Poz: juvenile drama. 16°. pap., 40c. ... *French.*
Old Put; or, the days of '76. 8°. pap., 50c... *Peterson.*
Old red house. Grosvenor, H. S. $1.50........ *Hoyt.*
Old red sandstone. Miller, H. $1.50........ *Carter.*
Old régime and the revolution. Tocqueville, A. de. $1.50 .... *Harper.*
Old régime in Canada under Louis XIV. Parkman, F. $2.50; $4.50 .... *Little, B. & Co.*
Old regimentals. Bernard, W. B. 15c. ...... *French.*
Old revolutionary soldier. Alden, J. 75c. ... *Tibbals.*
Old Robin and his proverb. 16°. '74. 50c. ... *Nelson.*
Old Roman world. Lord, J. $3 .... *Hurd & H.*
Old Rome and new Italy. Castelar, E. $1.75.. *Harper.*
Old rope maker. McC., *Mrs.* A. L. 65c.; 75c. *Am. Bapt.*
Old sailor's story. Sargent, G. E. $1.25.. *Hoyt; Nelson.*
Old St. Paul's. *See* Ainsworth, W: H.
Old saws new set. Mackarness, M. A. $1.25.. *Routledge.*
Old schoolhouse. 18°. 65c. .... *Cong. Pub.*
Old schoolfellows. ill. 16°. '72. 90c......... *Am. Tr.*
Old schoolfellows and what became of them. 16°. $1.25................................ *Cong. Pub.*
— *Same.* ill. 16°. '72. $1.25.............. *Lothrop.*
Old schoolmaster. Hoffmann, F. 90c.... *Ref. Ch. Bd.*
Old score. Gilbert, W. S. 15c............. *French.*
Old sea captain. Mogridge, G. 60c.......... *So. Meth.*

Old secrets and new discoveries. 8°. '74. pap., 50c. (?)*F.M.Reed.*
Old sergeant, and other poems. Willson, F. $1.50. *Osgood.*
Old shag. *See* Todd, J:
Old shepherd. *See* Short stories lib.
Old showman and the old London fairs. Frost, T. $2. *Routledge.*
Old Sir Douglas. *See* Norton, C.
Old Skekarry (*pseud.*) *See* Leveson, *Maj.* —.
Old song and new. [Poems.] Preston, M. J. $2. *Lippincott.*
Old stone chimney. Pritchard, S. J. 75c...*Randolph.*
Old stone farm house. 18°. 60c. ....*Am.S.S.*
Old stone house. *See* Alden, J.
Old stone house. March, A. $1.50.........*Lothrop.*
Old stone mansion. Peterson, C. J. $1.75; $1.50. *Peterson.*
Old stories for young people. [Toy-book.] ill. roy. 16°. 75c. ....(?)*McLoughlin.*
Old story. Byron, H. J. 15c.................*French.*
Old streets of New York. Gerard, J. W. $1..*Patterson.*
Old Sunapee. Chellis, M. D. $1.50...........*Hoyt.*
Old tales for the young. Palmer, F. P. $1.25..*Routledge.*
Old tales newly told. ill. 18°. 35c.......*Bost.Am.Tr.*
— *See also* Uncle Reuben ser.
Old Testament. *See* Bible.
Old Testament A B C. ill. sq. 12°. bds., 50c. *Routledge.*
Old Testament alphabet. [Toy-book.] ill. 4°. $1; 50c. ....*Routledge.*
Old Testament pictures. Caunter, H. 75c. *Scribner, W. & A.*
Old Testament shadows of New Test. truths. Abbott, L. $3; $3.50; $5.25.................*Harper.*
Old theology turned upside down, or right side up. Taylor, T. B. $1.25; $1...............*Colby.*
Old-time pictures and sheaves of rhyme. Taylor, B. F. $2; $2.50..........................*Griggs.*
Old times. Chellis, M. D. $1.25.........*Nat.Temp.*
Old Trusty. Gordon, W. 15c...............*French.*
Old uncle Billy: Ethiop. drama. 16°. pap., 15c. *Happy.*
Old Vigilance and his pet. 18°. 75c........*Pres.Bd.*
Old wells dug out. Talmage, T. DeW. $2...*Harper.*
Old Whitey's Christmas trot. Hall, A. O. $1..*Harper.*
Old words newly spoken. Dickson, A. F. $1..*Pres.Bd.*
Old world in its new face. Bellows, H. W. $3.50..*Harper.*
Old year and the new year: selected verses. 16°. '71. pap., 15c..........................*Randolph.*
Old Zip Coon: Ethiop. drama. 16°. pap., 15c. *Happy.*
Oldbury. *See* Keary, *Miss* A.
Olden time in New York. Kip, W. J. $3...*Putnam.*
Olden's mission: a tale of famine in Leyden; by author of "Chronicles of four little Christmas stockings." 18°. 45c.................................*Pres.Bd.*
Older than Adam. Whitmarsh, C. S. 90c...*Thompson.*
Oldest and the newest empire. Speer, W. $3.50; $4; $5 ....*Scranton.*
Oldham, Ol. The humorous speaker: pieces for schools. 12°. '53. $1.50.........................*Ivison.*
Oldschool, Ol. (*pseud.*) *See* Dennie, Jos.
Oldschool, Ol. (*pseud.*) *See* Sargent, W.
Oldtown folks. Stowe, H. B. $2 ....*Osgood.*
Ole Bull violin instruction book. obl. 8°. '51. pap., 60c...............................*Ditson.*
O'Leary, Ja. Ellie Laura: drama. 18°. 40c...*Sadlier.*
— History of the Bible; with Script. tables and glossary. ill. and maps. 12°. $2.50.......*Sadlier.*
— Ireland among the nations: faults and virtues of the Irish compared with those of other races. 12°. $1 ....*McGee.*

O'Leary, Ja., *continued.*
— Most ancient lives of St. Patrick; incl. [that] by Jocelin and his extant writings; with pref. and chronol. table. ('74.) 3d ed. ill. 16°. '76. $1. *Kenedy.*
— Treatise on the sixteen names of anc. Ireland. ill. 18°. '74. 50c........................*Kenedy.*
— *See also* Bible [Whole], *Cath.*
Olfers, Mar. v. Erzählungen. 8°. pap., 50c...*Morwitz.*
Olier, Jean Jacques. Christian catechism of an interior life; tr. 32°. 50c.; 75c..............*Murphy.*
Olin, Jla. M. The perfect light: biog. sketches of remarkable women in various walks of life. cr. 8°. '66. $2..........................*Randolph.*
Olin, Ste. Works. 2 v. 12°. $3...........*Harper.*
— Call to the ministry. ('60.) 2d ed. 12°. '74. pap., 10c.................................*So.Meth.*
— Christian principle and mental culture. 18°. '48. 30c. *Meth.Bk.Conc.*
— College life: its theory and practice. 12°. $1.50. *Harper.*
— Life and letters. 2 v. 12°. $3............*Harper.*
— Life inexplicable except as a probation. 18°. pap., 15c.; 25c..................*Cin.Meth.Bk.Conc.*
— On youthful piety. 18°. '51. 35c...*Meth.Bk.Conc.*
— Religious training of children. 18°. '49. 20c. *Meth.Bk.Conc.*
— Resources and duties of Christian young men. 18°. '46. 30c. ....*Meth.Bk.Conc.*
— Travels in Egypt, Arabia Petræa and the Holy Land. 2 v. ill. 8°. $3; hf. cf., $6.50........*Harper.*
Oline. Munson, C. A. $1.25...............*Tibbals.*
Olio (The); or, speaker's companion. 3 pts. 16°. ea., pap., 15c. ....*French.*
Oliphant, Laur. Narrative of the Earl of Elgin's mission to China and Japan in 1857–'59. ill. 8°. $3.50; shp., $4 ....*Harper.*
Oliphant, *Mrs.* Marg. O. W. [Novels.] 23 v...*Harper.*
Cont.: Days of my life.—House on the moor.—Laird of Norlaw.—Last of the Mortimers: story in two voices.—Lucy Crofton, *ea.*, 12°, $1.50.—Chronicles of Carlingford, 8°, $1.75; pap., $1.25.—Son of the soil.—Perpetual curate, *ea.*, 8°, $1.50; pap., $1.—Katie Stewart.—Quiet heart, *ea.*, 8°, pap., 25c.—Curate in charge.—John.—Madonna Mary.—Miss Marjoribanks, *ea.*, 8°, pap., 50c.—Agnes.—Athelings; or, the three gifts.—Brownlows.—For love and life.—Innocent.—Minister's wife.—Ombra.—Squire Arden.—Story of Valentine and his brother, *ea.*, 8°, pap., 75c.
— [Select works.] 6 v. 8°. '66–'69. pap...*Littell & G.*
Cont.: Brownlows, 37c.—Chronicles of Carlingford, 25c.—Historical sketches of reign of George II., $1.—Madonna Mary, 50c.—Miss Marjoribanks, 75c.—Zaidee, 75c.
— Agnes Hopetoun's schools and holidays. New ed. ill. fp. 8°. '72. $1.50 ....*Macmillan.*
— At his gates. ill. 8°. '73. $1.50; pap., $1..*Scribner.*
— Francis of Assisi. cr. 8°. '71. $1.75 ..*Macmillan.*
— Laird of Norlaw. 12°. $1.50...........*Lippincott.*
— Life of Edward Irving; ill. by his journals and correspondence. por. 8°. $3.50 ....*Harper.*
— Liliesleaf. 16°. '64. $1 ....*Burnham.*
— Lost love (The). 12°. $1.75; pap., $1.50..*Peterson.*
— Margaret Maitland. 12°. $1.75; pap., $1.50..*Peterson.*
— May: a novel. 8°. '73. $1.50; pap., $1..*Scribner.*
— Odd couple (An). 12°. $1.50; pap., 75c.—(Intern. ed.), $1.25..............................*Porter.*
— Orphans; [also] Caleb Field. 8°. pap., 50c...*Peterson.*
— Rose (A) in June. ill. 8°. $1.25; pap., 50c...*Estes.*
— Self-sacrifice. 12°. $1.75; pap., $1.50...*Peterson.*
— Son of the soil. 12°. $1.25 ....*Macmillan.*
— Three brothers. 8°. pap., $1..........*Appleton.*
— Trials and triumphs. 16°. '76. $1.25 ....*Tibbals.*
— Whiteladies. (Leis. hour ser.) 16°. '75. 1.25..*Holt.*
Oliphant, T. L. Kington. *See* Kington-Oliphant, T. L.
Olive (*pseud.*) Annie Grey, and other sketches. 18°. 35c. ....*Pres.Bd.*
Olive. *See* Craik, D. M.
Olive Blake's good work. Jeaffreson, J. C. 75c...*Harper.*
Olive branch. Tucker, C. 50c.............*Nelson.*

Olive branch (New). *See* Cook, T. J., *and* Perkins, T. E.

Olive branch lib. 7 v. 16°. '74. $3.50.....*Nelson.*

Cont.: Olive branch, by Mrs. C. Tucker. — Good for evil. — Friend in need, by Mrs. C. Tucker. — It's his way. — Two watches. — Old Robin and his proverb. — Upwards and downwards, by Mrs. C. Tucker.

Olive Lacey. Argyle, A. $1.75..........*Lippincott.*

Olive leaves. Sigourney, L. H. 75c.........*Carter.*

Olive Loring's mission. Lawrence, A. M. $1.25..*Lothrop.*

Olive Varcoe. Notley, *Mrs.* —. 50c.........*De Witt.*

Oliver, B: L. Forms of practice; or, American precedents in personal and real actions. 4th ed., rev. and enl. by a member of Cumberland bar. 8°. '74. shp., $7.50 ....*Dresser.*

Oliver, C. D. St. Peter's chain of Christian virtues. ('56.) 2d ed. 18°. '72. 75c...........*So. Meth.*

Oliver, Dan. First book of Indian botany. ill. 12°. '69. $2.50..........................*Macmillan.*

— Lessons in elementary botany. New ed. ill. 18°. '74. $1.50 ....*Macmillan.*

Oliver, E: B. New manual of thorough bass and text book of musical theory. 12°. '64. 67c.; bds., 50c. *Ditson.*

— Practical text book of music as connected with art of playing the piano-forte. 12°. '53. 67c...*Ditson.*

— Vocalist's companion: exercises for developing, strengthening and equalizing the voice. f°. pap., $1 ....*Ditson.*

Oliver, F. E. Ancient psalm melodies; adapted to canticles of the Church. 3d ed. 8°. '64. pap., 35c. ....*Dutton.*

Oliver, G: Antiquities of Freemasonry. 12°. '65. $1. *Masonic.*

— Historical landmarks and other evidences of Freemasonry. [Lectures.] 2 v. por. large 12°. $5. *Masonic; Redding.*

— History of initiation. [Masonic lectures.] 12°. '65. $1.50 ....*Masonic; Redding.*

— History of Masonic persecutions and Masonic institutes. 12°. '71. $2........*Masonic; Redding.*

— Illustrations of Masonry. 12°. '71. $1.75..*Masonic.*

— Mirror of Johannite Masons; [also] The star in the east. 12°. '65. $1.50...............*Masonic.*

— Revelations of a square: sayings and doings of eminent Masons. 12°. '71. $1.50..*Masonic; Redding.*

— Signs and symbols: lectures on Freemasonry. 12°. '71. $1.50................*Masonic; Redding.*

— Symbol of glory; showing object and end of Freemasonry. 12°. '71. $1.50............*Masonic.*

— Theocratic philosophy of Freemasonry. 12°. '71. $1.50 ....*Masonic.*

— *See also* Ashe, J., Masonic manual.

Oliver, H: K. Collection of hymn and psalm tunes, etc. obl. 8°. '60. bds., $1.50.........*Ditson.*

— Original hymn tunes, chants, etc. obl. 8°. '75. $1; bds., 80c..............................*Ditson.*

Oliver Dale's decision. [Juvenile.] 18°. 60c. (?) *Martien.*

Oliver Ellis. *See* Grant, Ja.

Oliver Kirby. 18°. 35c.; 40c..............*Dutton.*

Oliver of the mill. Charlesworth, M. L. $1.50..*Carter.*

Oliver Twist. Almar, G. 15c..............*French.*

Oliver Twist. *See* Dickens, C:

Oliver's oath. Doudney, S. $1............*Nelson.*

Oliver's prisoner. Guernsey, C. F. $1..(?) *Martien.*

Olivers, T: Full refutation of the doctrine of unconditional perseverance. ('54.) 4th ed. 18°. '75. 65c. ....*So. Meth.*

Olive's rescue, and other tales. 16°. 50c.; 75c. *Sadlier.*

Olive's world. 18°. 60c..................*Am. S. S.*

Olivia. Reynolds, G. W. M. 50c..........*De Witt.*

Olla podrida. *See* Marryat, F:

Olle Kamellen. Reuter, F. 7 v. ea., $1; 75c...*Steiger.*

Ollendorff, Henri Godefroy. Companion in French gram.; by G. W. Greene. 12°. $1.25..*Appleton.*

— First lessons in French; by G. W. Greene. 18°. 75c.................................*Appleton.*

— Maestro (El) de inglés [Eng. gram. for Spaniards]; por F. J. Vingut. 12°. '69. $2. — Clave, $1. *G. R. Lockwood.*

— Maître (Le) d'espagnol [Span. gram. for Frenchmen]; par F. J. Vingut. 12°. $2. — Corrigé, $1 ....*G. R. Lockwood.*

— Method of learning French; by V. Value. 12°. $1.25. — Key, $1..................*Appleton.*

— Método para aprender frances; por T. Simonné. 12°. $1.50. — Clave, 12°. $1.........*Appleton.*

— Método para aprender inglés; por R. Palenzuela y J. de la C. Carreño. 12°. $1.50. — Clave, 12°. $1 ....*Appleton.*

— Neue Methode spanisch zu lernen, v. H. D. Wrage u. H. M. Monsanto. 12°. $1.50. — Schlüssel, $1. *Appleton.*

— New gram. for Germans to learn Eng.; by P. Gands. 12°. $1.50. — Key, $1.......*Appleton.*

— New method of learning French; by J. L. Jewett. 12°. $1.25. — Key, $1................*Appleton.*

— New method of learning Germ.; by G. J. Adler. 12°. $1.25. — Key, $1...................*Appleton.*

— New method of learning Italian; by F. Foresti. 12°. $1.50. — Key, $1..................*Appleton.*

— New method of learning Span. on the Ollendorff system, by M. Velásquez and T. Simonné. 12°. $1.50. — Key, $1...................*Appleton.*

— Primary lessons. [Italian.] 18°. 75c...*Appleton.*

— *See also* Vingut, F. J., Spanish teacher.

Ollie and the boys. *See* Chester, S. E.

Ollie lib. 4 v. 16°. $5....................*Crowell.*

Cont.: Ollie and the boys, by S. E. Chester. — Bashie's service, by M. Alden. — Mrs. Marsh's help, by J. J. Dana. — Bessie Hartwell, by C. J. Freeland.

Ollier, Edm. History of the U. S.; with wood-eng., maps, plans, etc. v. 1. cr. 4°. $5......*Cassell.*

— Memoirs of Doré. *See* Doré gallery.

— Our British portrait painters, 1617–1872: 16 eng. with descrip. and hist. notices. 4°. $10; mor., $20 ....*Lippincott.*

— — *See also* Gallery of pictures.

Olmsted, Alex. Fisher. Chemistry. 12°. '54. $1.25. *G. R. Lockwood.*

Olmsted, Denison. Compendium of astronomy. New ed., rev. by E. S. Snell. ill. 12°. '73. $1.18. *Collins & Bro.*

— Compendium of natural philosophy; rev. by E. S. Snell. ('63.) New ed. 12°. '76. $1.65..*Clark & M.*

— Introduction to astronomy. 3d ed., rev. by E. S. Snell. ill. 8°. '75. $2.25........*Collins & Bro.*

— Introduction to natural philosophy. 2d ed., rev. by E. S. Snell. ill. 8°. '75. $3.75...*Collins & Bro.*

— Letters on astronomy: elements of the science expl. in connection with biog. sketches of the eminent astronomers. ill. 12°. $1.50...........*Harper.*

— Rudiments of natural philosophy and astronomy. Rev. ed. ill. 18°. '64. hf. bd., 94c...*Collins & Bro.*

— Secular period of aurora borealis. 4°. '56. pap., $1. *Smith. Inst.*

Olmsted, F: Law. Walks and talks of an Am. farmer in England. 12°. '59. $1.50...........*Gleason.*

Olney, E: Complete school algebra. 12°. $1.50. — Key, hf. leath., $1.50 ....*Sheldon.*

— Elements of arithmetic. ill. 12°. hf. bd., 85c. *Sheldon.*

— Elements of geometry. 8°. hf. leath., $1.50..*Sheldon.*

— Elements of trigonometry. 8°. hf. leath., $1.50. *Sheldon.*

— General geometry and calculus. 8°. hf. leath., $2.50. *Sheldon.*

— Geometry. (Univ. ed.) 8°. hf. leath., $2..*Sheldon.*

— Geometry and trigonometry. (School ed.) 8°. hf. leath., $2.50 ....*Sheldon.*

— *Same.* (Univ. ed.) 8°. hf. leath., $2.50; — with tables of logarithms. 8°. hf. leath., $3..*Sheldon.*

Olney, E: *continued.*
— Introduction to algebra. 12°. $1 .... *Sheldon.*
— Introduction to geometry. 8°. hf. leath., 75c. *Sheldon.*
— Pictorial primary arithmetic. 16°. hf. bd., 35c. *Sheldon.*
— Science of arithmetic. 12°. $1.25 .... *Sheldon.*
— Tables of logarithms. 8°. 75c. .... *Sheldon.*
— Teacher's handbook of arith. exercises, with duplicate examples. 12°. hf. bd., 75c. .... *Sheldon.*
— Test examples in algebra. 12°. 75c. ...... *Sheldon.*
— University algebra. 8°. hf. leath., $2. — Key, hf. leath., $2 .... *Sheldon.*

Olney, Jesse. History of the U. S.; for schools and academies. 18°. *net*, 50c. .... *Peck.*
— *and* Barber, J. W. Family book of history. ill. 8°. *net*, $2.25 .... *Peck.*

Olney, Warren. *See* California, Code of civil procedure.

Olonois, the buccaneer. 8°. pap., 25c. ...... *Dick & F.*

Olph; or, pirates of the shoals. 8°. pap., 25c. .. *Dick & F.*

Olrig Grange: a novel in verse. 16°. $1.50 .. **Osgood.*

Olshausen, Hm. Biblical comment. on New Test.; contin. by Ebrard and Wiesinger; rev. after Germ. ed. by A. C. Kendrick. 6 v. 8°. $18. *Sheldon; So. Bapt.*

Olver, J. S. Tables for setting-out curves on railways and other public works. cr. 8°. $2 ...... *Spon.*
— Tables for setting-out half-widths on railways, roads, canals, etc. 12°. '70. $1.50 .... *Spon.*

Olympic devils. Planché, J. R., *and* Dance, C. 15c. *French.*

Olympic revels. Planché, J. R., *and* Dance, C. 15c. *French.*

Omar; to ill. Jewish hist. from B. C. 63 to birth of Christ. 18°. 70c. .... *Am. S. S.*

Omar pasha. Reynolds, G. W. M. 50c. ...... *De Witt.*

Ombra. *See* Ditson.

Ombra. Oliphant, M. O. W. 75c. .... *Harper.*

O'Meara, Barry E: Napoleon in exile: a voice from St. Helena. 2 v. por. and ill. 12°. $3.50; hf. cf., $6 .... *Widdleton.*

Omi. Robinson, F. W. 50c. .... *De Witt.*

Omnibus: farce. 16°. pap., 15c. .... *French.*

Omoo. Melville, H. $1.50 .... *Harper.*

On the Amazons. Stephens, C. A. $1.25 .... *Porter.*

On and off. Williams, T. J. 15c. .... *French.*

On the banks of the Amazon. *See* Kingston, W. H. G.

On the border. Gilmore, J. R. $1.75 .... *Lee & S.*

On both sides of the sea. Charles, E. $1 ...... *Dodd.*

On bread and water. Rosenfeld, S. 15c. .... *De Witt.*

On a candlestick. *See* Aunty Lee lib.

On the church steps. *See* Hallowell, S. C.

On a coral reef. Forbes, J. H. $1.50 .... *Cassell.*

On dangerous ground. Moore, C. J. $1.50; $1.25; $1. *Porter.*

On the edge of the storm. Roberts, M. $1.50; $2. *Putnam.*

On the eve. Turgenieff, I. $1.25 .... *Holt.*

On the ferry-boat. Harrison, J. 60c. ..... *Hurd & H.*

On the frontiers. Pearson, H. C. $1.25 .. *Cong. Pub.*

On guard. Thomas, A. 50c. .... *Harper.*

On guard: comedy. 16°. pap., 15c. .... *French.*

On the heights. Auerbach, B. $2; in 2 v., $2.50 .. *Holt.*

On holy ground. Hodder, E. $1.50 ... *Meth. Bk. Conc.*

On the imitation of Christ. *See* Thomas *a Kempis.*

On inflation. Locke, D. R. 25c. .... *Barclay.*

On the journey. *See* Little Rosy's travels.

On letting one's self alone; or, Mr. Whinnyfret's book of troubles. 18°. 25c. .... *Am. S. S.*

On looking seedy. 18°. 25c. .... *Am. S. S.*

On the mountain. *See* Guernsey, L. E.

On the Nile. Hoppin, A. $10; $25 .... *Osgood.*

On not knowing when one is well off. 18°. 25c. .. *Am. S. S.*

On papa's lap. Gladwyn, G. 60c. ...... *Bost. Am. Tr.*

On the road to riches. Maher, W. H. $1.25; 50c. *Brown, E. & Co.*

On the rock. Dungan, D. R. $1.50 .... *Cen. Bk.*

On the rock and on the sand. 18°. 50c. ..... *Am. S. S.*

On the seas. ill. 16°. '70. 80c. .... *Lothrop.*

On the seas: book for boys. ill. 16°. 50c. .. *Routledge.*

On the sly. Morton, J. M. 15c. ...... *Ames; French.*

On time. Adams, W. T. $1.25 .... *Lee & S.*

On the trail of the German and French war. Shand, A. I. 35c. .... *Harper.*

On the wave. Samuels, A. F. 50c. .... *Lee & S.*

On the way. *See* Tucker, *Mrs.* C.

On the white horse. Swedenborg, E. 10c. .. *Lippincott.*

On the wing. Bumstead, J. $1.50 .... *Happy.*

On the wing. Eyster, N. $1.25 .... *Meth. Epis.*

Once on a time. Baker, G. M. 15c. .... *Lee & S.*

Once upon a time. 18°. 75c. .... (?) *Martien.*

Once upon a time. Knight, C. $3 .... *Routledge.*

Once upon a time: extravaganza. 16°. pap., 15c. *French.*

Onderdonk, H: History of Maryland, to 1867; with the Const. of Md. ill. 18°. '68. 75c. .. *Murphy.*

One and twenty. Robinson, F. W. 50c. ..... *De Witt.*

One armed Hugh. Moffatt, A. S. $1.50 ..... *Graves.*

One baptism as found in the Bible. Junkin, G. 12c. *Pres. Bd.*

One big pop-gun. *See* Barrow, *Mrs.* F.

One by herself. Balfour, C. L. $1 .... *Nelson.*

One by one. Dulcken, H. W. $1.75 ...... *Routledge.*

One coat for two suits. Walcot, C. M. 15c. .. *French.*

One day's weaving. Peebles, M. L. $1.25 ..... *Nims.*

One dollar bill (The), and what was done with it. 18°. 22c. .... *Am. S. S.*

One dollar dreamer and fortune teller. 18°. $1 .. *Fisher.*

One fair woman (The). Miller, J. $2 ...... *Carleton.*

One good turn deserves another. Neely, K. J. $1. *Lee & S.*

One hour a week. 18°. '64. 75c. .... *Randolph.*

One hundred and seventeen Arundel Street. Addison, H. R. 15c. .... *French.*

One hundred and sixteen games. 32°. 50c. ... *Fisher.*

One hundred beautiful melodies for the violin. 8°. '60. pap., 75c. .... *Ditson.*

One hundred comic songs; by J. W. Turner, E. T. Bates and others. [Music and words.] 8°. '58. pap., 50c.; bds., 60c. .... *Ditson.*

One hundred gems from the London Art Journal. ill. 4°. $6 .... *Lee & S.*

One hundred gold dollars. McConaughy, J. E. 90c. *Garrigues.*

One hundred Irish airs; arr. for the piano. 3 ser. f°. '57–'58. ea., $1.50; in 1 v., $6; $7.50 .. *Haverty.*

One hundred large type hymns. 12°. '75. $1 .. *Revell.*

One hundred ministers. Flood, T. L. $1.50 ... *Estes.*

One hundred operatic melodies for the flute. 8°. '60. pap., 75c. .... *Ditson.*

One hundred picture fables. Speckter, O. $1.75. *Routledge.*

One hundred songs of Ireland. [Music and words.] 8°. '59. bds., 60c.; pap., 50c. .... *Ditson.*

One hundred songs of praise. Connor, G. C. per doz., $1.50; $1.80 .... *Burke.*

One hundred songs of Scotland. [Music and words.] 8°. '59. bds., 60c.; pap., 50c. .... *Ditson.*

One hundred tales. Schmid, C. v. 60c.; $1 .. *Sadlier.*

One hundred thousand pounds. Byron, H. J. 15c. *De Witt.*

One hundred years achievement of a free people. Taylor, C. B. *$2.50 .... *H. S. Allen.*

One hundred years ago. Baker, G. M. 15c...(?)*Lee & S.*
One hundred years ago. Hale, E. E. 25c. *Lockwood, B. & Co.*
One hundredth night of Hamlet. White, C. 15c. *De Witt.*
One in a thousand. *See* James, G. P. R.
One key singer. Packard, J. B. 25c........*Ditson.*
One law in nature. Lazelle, H. M. $1.50..*VanNostrand.*
One night in a bar-room. White, C. 15c.....*De Witt.*
One night's mystery. Fleming, M. A. $1.75..*Carleton.*
One o'clock. Lewis, M. G. 15c............*French.*
One of the Billingses. *See* Katie Johnstone's lib.
One of the family. Payn, J. 25c...........*Harper.*
One of the least. Sharman, S. R. 75c. *Cong. Pub.; Nelson.*
One of our soldiers. 18°. 60c.; 70c. ......*Am. Bapt.*
One of them. *See* Lever, C:
One of you must marry: drama. 16°. pap., 15c. *French.*
One offering (The). Sadler, M. F. $1.........*Pott.*
One poor girl. Sikes, W. $1.50.........*Lippincott.*
One quiet life. Colter, J. J. $1.50........*Lothrop.*
One religion, many creeds. Winans, R. $1.50. *DesForges.*
One step; or, to what will it lead? 18°. 55c...*Am. S. S.*
— *See also* Select lib. for boys.
One summer. Howard, B. W. $1.50........*Osgood.*
One summer's dream. Gunnison, E. N. $1.50; $1.75; $2; $3.50 ....*Hiram Young.*
One-syllable books. *See* Godolphin, Ma.
One talent and other tales. 18°. 70c.......*Pres. Bd.*
One thousand and one days. *See* Enchanted keys.
One thousand and one lives. Goodrich, S. G. $1.50. *World Pub.*
One thousand and ten things worth knowing. Lardner, D. 50c................................*Peterson.*
One thousand francs. 18°. pap., 15c.........*O'Shea.*
Note. Same as "Sebastian."
— *Same;* [also] Fairy's well. 18°. 30c......*O'Shea.*
One thousand gems. Talmage, T. DeW. $1.50..*Tibbals.*
One thousand meditations. *See* Daily food ser.
One thousand questions and propositions for S.-schools and Bible classes. 24°. 16c. — Key, 16c. *Am. S. S.*
One too many: farce. 16°. pap., 15c........*French.*
One too many for him. Williams, T. J. 15c. *De Witt; French.*
One touch of nature. Webster, B. 15c......*French.*
One tree hill. Craven, H. T. 15c...........*French.*
One trip more. Manning, A. $1.............*Cassell.*
One, two, buckle my shoe. [Toy book.] ill. 8°. 20c. *Hurd & H.*
One, two, three. Wild, J. 15c.............*De Witt.*
One-two-three-four-five by advertisement: farce. 16°. pap., 15c.........................*French.*
One woman's mission. Arnold, A. N. $1.25. *H. A. Young.*
One woman's two lovers. Townsend, V. F. $1.50. *Lippincott.*
One year at our boarding school. Phelps, A. $1. *Loring.*
One year of my life. ill. 16°. '70. $1.25....*Lothrop.*
O'Neal the great. Clarke, N. H. B. 15c......*French.*
Oneida Community. *See* Handbook of.
O'Neill, C: Dictionary of dyeing and calico printing; with essay on coal tar colors and their applic. to dyeing and calico printing by A. A. Fesquet, and app. on dyeing and calico printing as shown at the Paris exposition in 1867. 8°. '69. $6....*Baird.*
O'Neill, J. W. Glimpses of animated nature: descript. of birds, animals, etc., with sketches of habits, etc. ill. demi 8°. $3.50–$4 ....*Desilver.*
— New standard letter writer for the people. roy. 18°. bds., 50c..............................*Desilver.*

O'Neill, J. W., *continued.*
— (*ed.*) Handbook of family knowledge for the people; compr. "Standard handbook of household economy," Soyer's "Standard cookery," and O'Neill's "Standard letter writer." 12°. $2....*Desilver.*
Ongaro, Francesco dall'. Rosa dell' Alpi: novella. With notes. 12°. pap., 75c..............*Hoyt.*
— *Germ.* Die weisse Rose; übers. v. A. Koch. 8°. pap., 40c..........................*F. W. Thomas.*
Onions: how to raise them profitably; by seventeen practical onion-growers. ill. 12°. 20c.....*Judd.*
Onkel Tom's Hütte. *See* Stowe, H. B.
Onley, Ma. Above the breakers: tale for the young. ill. 18°. 75c...........................*Nelson.*
— "Carry your parcel, sir?" ill. 16°. 75c.....*Nelson.*
Only ask. Lewis, A. H. $1.25..............*Graves.*
Only ask ser. 4 v. 16°. $5...............*Graves.*
Cont.: Boston boy, by A. H. Lewis. — Only ask, by A. H. Lewis. — Richard Peters, by P. Curtiss. — For better, for worse.

Only a beggar boy, and other stories. ill. 18°. '76. 50c...............................(?)*Nelson.*
Only believe. Hamilton, A. 30c...........*Pres. Bd.*
Only believe. Kimball, J. W. 50c...........*Am. Tr.*
Only a child. Dunning, A. K. 35c.........*Pres. Bd.*
Only a clod. Braddon, M. E. 50c.........*Dick & F.*
Only a clod. Simpson, J. P. 15c....*French; Lee & S.*
Only a dandelion. Prentiss, E. $1.25.....*Randolph.*
Only an ensign. *See* Grant, Ja.
Only a fiddler. *See* Andersen, H. C.
Only five cents. *See* Kennedy, *Mrs.* M. G.
Only a girl. Hillern, W. v. $2..........*Lippincott.*
Only a girl's life. Mercier, J. $1...*Scribner, W. & A.*
Only girls. Townsend, V. F. $1.50.........*Lee & S.*
Only a halfpenny. Oxenford, J. 15c...*De Witt; French.*
Only herself. Thomas, A. 50c..............*Harper.*
Only in fun. Hildeburn, M. J. 50c.........*Pres. Bd.*
Only just once, and other stories. ill. fp. 8°. 50c. *Cassell.*
Only love. ('70.) 4th ed. ill. 18°. '74. 50c. *Perkinpine.*
Only me. *See* Up to fifteen.
Only Ned. Drinkwater, J. M. $1.25........*Carter.*
Only one way of salvation. *See* Ryle, J. C.
Only a pauper. Miffitt, A. S. $1.25 ....*Hoyt.*
Only a penny. ('70.) 4th ed. ill. 18°. '74. 50c. *Perkinpine.*
Only a penny. Dunning, A. K. 50c........*Pres. Bd.*
Only a penny-a-liner: comedietta. 16°. pap., 15c. *French.*
Only a pin. 18°. 60c...................*Cong. Pub.*
Only a pin; tr. by a graduate of St. Joseph's Acad., Emmittsburg. 2d ed. 16°. '74. $1..*Cath. Pub.*
Only rule of faith. Hall, J. 35c...........*Pres. Bd.*
Only sister. Witt, P. de. 90c..............*Harper.*
Only somebody. Edwardes, C. 15c.........*De Witt.*
Only son. 8°. pap., 38c. ....*Littell & G.*
Only son; or, the history of Jonah Ross and his mother. 18°. 65c...........................*Am. S. S.*
Only temper. Newby, C. J. 50c. ....*Peterson.*
Only this once. Dunning, A. K. 35c.......*Pres. Bd.*
Only three weeks. 8°. $1.25; pap., 50c........*Estes.*
Only a woman. *See* Morenos, O., What will the world say?
Onondaga and French dict. *See* Shea, J. G., Lib. of Am. ling.
Onward. Winscom, J. A. $1.50..........*Dutton.*
Onward: the mountain clamberers. 16°. $1.50. *Am. Bapt.*
Onward and upward ser. *See* Adams, W. T.
Onward, right onward. Tuthill, L. C. 65c. *Perkinpine.*

Oosterzee, J. J. van. Christian dogmatics; tr. by J. W. Watson and M. J. Evans. ('74.) New ed. 2 v. 8°. '76. $6 .... *Scribner.*
— Geschichte oder Roman? eine Beleuchtung des Lebens Jesu v. Renan. 18°. '66. 25c. .... *Am. Tr.*
— On James; — Luke; — Timothy, Titus and Philemon. *See* Lange, J. P., Commentary.
— Theology of the New Test.; tr. by M. J. Evans. 12°. '73. $1.75 .... *Dodd.*
— *Same;* tr. by G. E. Day. 8°. '71. $2 ... *Judd & W.*
— Year of salvation: words of life for every day; tr. cr. 8°. $3.75 .... *Scribner, W. & A.*
O'Pagus, Arry (*pseud.*) *See* Sommer, H. B.
Open door. Pollard, J. 65c. .... *Pres. Bd.*
Open door. Smith, J. H. $1.50 .... *Holmes.*
Open doors. Bruce, E. M. 75c. .... *Universalist.*
Open house. Buckstone, J. B. 15c. .... *French.*
Open polar sea. Hayes, I. I. $2.50–$6 ... *Hurd & H.*
Open question. De Mille, J. $1.50; $1 ... *Appleton.*
Open! Sesame! *See* Marryat, Flo.
Open way. Weaver, G. S. $1.25 .... *Williamson.*
Opening of the chestnut burr. Roe, E. P. $1.75 .. *Dodd.*
Opera (The): trios, quartettes and choruses from operas. 22 nos. obl. 4°. '57. ea., pap., 25c. *Ditson.*
Opera at home. Peters, J. L. $4; $3 .... *Peters.*
Opera dancer. Reynolds, G. W. M. 75c. .. *Peterson.*
Opera librettos. *See* Ditson.
Operatic album. Ives, E., *jr.* $1.25 .... *Ditson.*
Operatic bouquet. Bruce, E. $2.50; $2; $1.50 .. *Ditson.*
Operatic pearls: songs from operas, with Eng., Fr. and Ital. words. 4°. '63. $3; $4; bds., $2.50 .. *Ditson.*
Opie, *Mrs.* Amelia. Works. 3 v. 8°. shp., $9. *Desilver.*
— On lying. 18°. 60c. .... *Carter.*
— *Same;* ed. by T. O. Summers. ('59.) 3d ed. 18°. '74. 75c. .... *So. Meth.*
Opinions concerning the Bible law of marriage; by one of the people. 12°. '70. $1.50 .... *Claxton.*
Opinions of the attorneys general of the U. S. advising the president and heads of the departments in rel. to their official duties; comp. with notes and ref. by B. F. Hall, C. C. Andrews, J. H. Ashton and A. J. Bentley. 14 v. 8°. '52–'72. $31 .. *Morrison.*
Opinions of celebrated men on true and false religion. 12°. pap., 10c. .... *Mendum.*
Opium-eater. *See* De Quincey, T:
Opium eating: autobiog. sketch by an habituate. 12°. '75. $1 .... *Claxton.*
Oppen, E: A. French reader; for colleges and schools. 12°. '64. $1.50 .... *Macmillan.*
Opportunities. Warner, S. $1.25 .... *Carter.*
Opportunities for industry. Freedley, E. T. $1. *Lippincott.*
Opportunity. Seemuller, A. M. $2 .... * *Osgood.*
Opposite the jail. Denison, M. A. $1.25 ..... *Hoyt.*
Opposite neighbours. Paul, H. 15c. .... *French.*
Opposite neighbours; or, two lives and their end. 16°. $1.25 .... *Am. S. S.*
Optic, Ol. (*pseud.*) *See* Adams, W: T.
Optical delusion: farce. 16°. pap., 15c. ..... *French.*
Oracles: daily Scripture text-book. 32°. 35c. .. *Am. S. S.*
Oraculum; or, book of fate. 16°. pap., 10c. *U. P. James.*
Oraculum; or, Napoleon's book of fate. *See* Connoisseur, *Mme.* —.
Oram, E. Table book; or, stepping-stones to intellect. and pract. arithmetic. 16°. 20c. ...... *Sadlier.*
Oramaika: an Indian story. 16°. 75c. .... *Strong.*
Orange blossoms. Arthur, T. S. $2.50; $3; $4.50. *J. M. Stoddart.*
Orange blossoms. Wooler, J. P. 15c. *De Witt; French.*
Orange girl. Leslie, H., *and* Rowe, N. 15c. *De Witt; French.*
Orange girl of Venice. 8°. pap., 25c. .... *Dick & F.*
Orange grove. 32°. 20c.; 15c. .... *Dutton.*
Orange seed. *See* Baker, S.
Orange tree: extravaganza. 16°. pap., 15c. .. *French.*
Oratorio chorus book. *See* New.
Oratorio librettos. 10 nos. 8°. ea., pap., 25c. .. *Ditson.*
Orator's touchstone. McQueen, H. $1.25 ... *Harper.*
Orators of the age. Francis, G. H. $1 ..... *Harper.*
Oratory of the faithful soul. Blosius, L. de. 50c. *Cath. Pub.*
Orbs around us. Proctor, R. A. $3 .. *Scribner, W. & A.*
Orchard, G. H. History of Baptists. 2 v. 12°. ea., $1.50 .... *So. Bapt.*
Orcutt, Hiram. Parent's manual. 12°. '75. $1.25. *Thompson.*
— Teacher's manual. 12°. $1 .... *Thompson.*
— *See also* Rickard, T., *and* Orcutt, H.
Orcutt, S: History of Wolcott, Conn., 1731–1874; with account of centennial meeting, Sept. 10, 11, 1873, and genealogies of families of the town. 8°. '74. $5 .... (?) *Am. Print.*
Ordeal for wives. Edwards, A. $1.50; $1 .. *Sheldon.*
Order and chaos. Marshall, T. W. M. 25c. .. *Murphy.*
Order of daily service; with the musical notation as used in Eng. and cathedral churches; with communion services and chants for the Psalms for the day and canticles. 8°. $1.50 ..... *W. H. Young.*
Order of music for festival of parish choirs to be held in Emmanuel Church, Boston, Easter-tide, 1876. 8°. '75. pap., 50c. .... *Williams.*
Ordericus Vitalis. Ecclesiastical hist. of Eng. and Normandy; tr. by T. Forester. 4 v. 12°. (Bohn.) ea., $1.75 .... *Little, B. & Co.*
— *Same.* 4 v. 12°. (Bohn.) ea., $2. *Lippincott; Scribner, W. & A.*
Orders and constitvtions partly collected out of his maiesties letters patents and partly ordained vpon mature deliberation by the treasvror, covnseil and companie of Virginia for the better gouerning of the said companie here in England residing, 1619–1620. [Reprint.] 4°. pap., 25c. .... *Sabin.*
Ordnance Department. *See* United States.
Ordnance manual; for officers of the army and others. ill. 12°. '61. $3 .... *Claxton; Lippincott.*
Ordo divini officii recitandi, missaeque celebrandae; ad usum cleri saecularis Dioec. Cincinnati, Columbus, Fort Wayne, etc. [Annual.] 24°. 50c. *Pustet.*
Ordronaux, J: Code of health of the school of Salernum. cr. 8°. $1.50; large pap., mor., $5. *Lippincott.*
— Hints on the preservation of health in armies; for volunteer officers and soldiers. 18°. 38c. *Appleton.*
— *Same.* New ed. 18°. '63. 75c. ... *Van Nostrand.*
— Jurisprudence of medicine in its rel. to law of contracts, torts and evidence; with sup. on liabilities of vendors of drugs. 8°. '69. $3.50; shp., $4. *T. & J. W. Johnson.*
— Manual of instructions for milit. surgeons in examination of recruits and discharge of soldiers; with official regulations of the provost marshal general's bureau, and for formation of invalid corps, etc. 12°. '63. hf. mor., $1.50 .. *Van Nostrand.*
— Proper legal status of the insane and feeble minded; with notes. 8°. 75c. .... *Campbell & Co.*
Ore bank. 18°. '60. 35c. .... *Am. Tr.*
Ore from precious mines: daily readings from various authors. 24°. '66. $1.50 .... *Randolph.*
Oregon. Organic and general laws, 1843–'72; compiled by M. P. Deady and L. Lane. 8°. '74. shp., $8.50 .... *Bancroft.*
— Statutes, 1866–'74. 5 v. 8°. hf. shp., $15 ... *Bancroft.*

Oregon, *continued.*
— Supreme Court reports, v. 1–5 (1853–'76). 5 v. 8°. shp., $30 .... *Bancroft.*
Cont.: 1–3 (1853–'70), by J. G. Wilson. — 4, 5 (1870–'76), by C. B. Bellinger.
Note. v. 1, not sold separately; 2, $7.50; 3–5, ea., $6.

Oregon and California in 1848. Thornton, J. Q. 2 v. $3 .... *Harper.*
Oregon and Eldorado. Bulfinch, T. $2.50 ... *Tilton.*
Oregon trail. Parkman, F. $2.50; $4.50 .. *Little, B. & Co.*
O'Reilly, A. J. Alvira, the heroine of Vesuvius: tale of the 17th cent. 12°. $1.50 .... *Sadlier.*
— Double triumph: drama. 18°. 40c. ...... *Sadlier.*
— Martyrs of the Coliseum. 12°. $1.50; $2 .. *Sadlier.*
— Victims of the Mamertine prison. 12°. $2; $2.50. *Sadlier.*
O'Reilly, E. R. Children of the Church; or, lessons on the Church catechism for infant children. 18°. 50c. .... *Pott.*
O'Reilly, J: Boyle. Songs from the southern seas, and other poems. 16°. $1 .... *Noonan.*
— *Same.* 16°. '73. $1.50 .... *Roberts.*
O'Reilly, Miles (*pseud.*) *See* Halpine, C. G.
O'Reilly, Myles. Memorials of those who suffered for the Catholic faith in Ireland during 16th–18th centuries. cr. 8°. '70. $2.50 .... *Cath. Pub.*
O'Reilly, *Mrs.* Rob. Cicely's choice. 16°. '74. $1. *Dutton.*
— Doll world lib. 3 v. ill. 16°. '74. $3 .... *Dutton.*
Cont.: Doll world; or, play and earnest. — Daisy's companions; or, scenes from child life. — Deborah's drawer.

— Giles's minority; or, scenes at the red house. ill. 16°. '74. $1 .... *Dutton.*
— Stories they tell me; or, Sue and I. ill. 16°. '74. $1.25 .... *Dutton.*
Orestes. *See* Euripides.
Orestes in Argos. Bayley, P. 15c. .... *French.*
Organ at home: collection of new and standard music. 4°. '73. $3; $4; bds., $2.50 .... *Ditson.*
Organ grinder. Baker, H. N. W. $1.15 ...... *Hoyt.*
Organ grinder: juvenile drama. 16°. pap., 40c. .. *French.*
Organ manual for amateurs and church committees; with hist. and construction of the organ by H. D. Nicholson, and app. 12°. '66. 75c. .... *Ditson.*
Organic affection. Phillips, A. 15c. .... *French.*
Organon of Scripture. *See* Lamar, J. S.
Oriel. Howard, M. $1.25 .... *Pres. Bd.*
Orient. 18°. 40c. .... *Bost. Am. Tr.*
Orient and its people. Hauser, I. L. $1.75 .. *Hauser.*
Orient boys. Keene, S. F. $1.50 .... *Hoyt.*
Oriental (The). Wetmore, W. J. $1.25 .. *Schermerhorn.*
Oriental and sacred scenes. Howe, F. $1.25 .. *Dodd.*
Oriental glee and anthem book. Cook, T. J., Perkins, T., *and* Hastings, T. 80c. .... *Huntington.*
Oriental pearl. *See* Dorsey, A. H.
Oriental picture gallery; or, illustrations from India, China and Japan. ill. 4°. 50c. ...... *Hurd & H.*
Origenes Adamantius. Writings; tr. by F. Crombie. (Ante-Nicene Christ. lib.) 2 v. 8°. ea., $3. *Scribner, W. & A.*
Origin and progress of language. ('58.) 2d ed. 18°. '76. 50c. .... *So. Meth.*
Origin of the appellation Keystone State, as applied to Pennsylvania. 12°. '74. $1.50 .... *Claxton.*
Origin of species. Darwin, C. R. $2; $4.50 .. *Appleton.*
Origin of sprinkling for baptism. 12°. pap., 10c. *So. Bapt.*
Original (The): interlude. 16°. pap., 15c. .. *Happy.*
Original and present state of man. Phipps, J. 45c. *Friends Bk. St.*
Original and selected beauties for the flute. 8°. 60c. *Ditson.*
Original church of Christ. Bangs, N. 75c. *Meth. Bk. Conc.*
Original idea (An). Baker, G. M. 15c. ..... *Lee & S.*
Original penny readings. Fenn, G. M. 2 v. $2.50. *Routledge.*
Original poems for infant minds; by several young persons. 16°. 75c. 18°. 45c. .... *Routledge.*
— *See also* Taylor, Jane.
Orio. Bradbury, W. B. 25c. .... *Wilstach.*
Oriola. Bradbury, W. B. 60c. .... *Wilstach.*
Orkney. Abbott, J. 90c. .... *Harper.*
Orkney islands. *See* Abbott, Jac.
Orlando Furioso. *See* Ariosto, L.
Orleans, *Bp. of.* *See* Dupanloup, F.
Orley Farm. *See* Trollope, Ant.
Ormathwaite, *Lord.* [J: Benn-Walsh.] Astronomy and geology compared. 18°. $1 ...... *Appleton.*
Orme, Ma. Uncle John; or, "it is too much trouble." 18°. 60c. .... *Harper.*
Orme, W: Life of Rev. J: Owen, abridg.; [also] Life of Rev. J: Janeway. 18°. 60c. .... *Pres. Bd.*
— Life of R: Baxter; abridg. 18°. 50c. ..... *Pres. Bd.*
— Memoir of the controversy resp. the three heavenly witnesses, 1 John, v, 7; incl. crit. notices of the principal writers. New ed., with notes and app. by E. Abbot. 16°. '72. $1.25 .. *Lockwood, B. & Co.*
Orme, W: Memoirs of J: Urquhart; incl. letters and sel. remains. por. 12°. $1.10 .... *Pres. Bd.*
Ormond, J. J. *See* Alabama, Sup. Court reports.
Ormond. *See* Brown, C. B.
Ornamental designs for fret-work, scroll-sawing, fancy carving and home decorations. 3 pts. 4°. '75. 1, pap., 75c.; 2, 3, ea., pap., $1 ... *H. T. Williams.*
Ornaments (The) discovered. Hughs, M. 75c. *Harper.*
Orono [Me.] centennial: proceedings, March 3, 1874: historical address, poems, etc., with index. 8°. $1.25 .... *Hoyt, F. & D.*
Oroonoko. Southerne, T. 15c. .... *French.*
Orphan (The). *See* Göhren, C. v.
Orphan (The). *See* Patty Parsons.
Orphan and the foundling. Leslie, E. $1 .... *Nelson.*
Orphan Anne. Denison, M. A. 60c. .... (?) *Martien.*
Orphan boys. Loud, J. $1.75 .... *J. E. Potter.*
Orphan brothers. 16°. 90c. .... *Cong. Pub.*
Orphan children. Arthur, T. S. 50c. .... *Peterson.*
Orphan girl. 18°. 22c. .... *Am. S. S.*
Orphan girls. Peacocke, J. S. $1.75 .... *J. E. Potter.*
Orphan niece. Pickering, E. 50c. .... *Peterson.*
Orphan nieces. Guernsey, L. E. $1.25 ... *Randolph.*
Orphan of Moscow; tr. by Mrs. J. Sadlier. 16°. 75c.; $1.25 .... *Sadlier.*
Orphan of the old dominion. Suddorth, H. A. B. $2. *Lippincott.*
Orphan of Pimlico. *See* Thackeray, W: M.
Orphan of Waterloo. Blake, *Mrs.* —. 75c. .. *Routledge.*
Orphan seamstress. 8°. pap., 25c. .... *Dick & F.*
Orphan sisters. ill. 18°. 50c. .... *Nelson.*
Orphan sisters. Hoffman, M. I. $1.50; $2 .. *Sadlier.*
Orphan sisters. Marsh-Caldwell, A. 50c. .. *Peterson.*
Orphan sisters; or, pupils of the common school: drama. ('62.) New ed. 12°. '70. 20c. *Kelly, P. & Co.*
Orphan's home mittens. *See* Barrow, *Mrs.* F.
Orphan's story. *See* Loving heart and helping hand lib.
Orphan's trials. Bennett, E. $1.75; $1.50 .. *Peterson.*
Orphans (The). 16°. 40c. .... *West. Tr.*
Orphans (The). Edgeworth, M. 25c. .... *Routledge.*
Orphans of Glen Elder. 16°. 90c. .... *Am. S. S.*
— *See also* Glen Elder lib.
Orphans of Glenulva. ill. 12°. 90c. .... *Nelson.*
Orphans' triumphs. Potwin, H. K. $1 .... *Dodd.*

Orphean (The). Perkins, W. O., *and* Hallett, A. R. $1 .... *Ditson.*

Orpheus. *See* Ditson.

Orpheus. *See* Glück, C. W. v.

Orpheus and Eurydice. *See* Brough, Rob. B.

Orpheus and Eurydice. Byron, H. J. 15c...*French.*

Orpheus C. Kerr papers. Newell, R. H. $2..*Carleton.*

Orpheus in the Haymarket. Planché, J. R. 15c. *French.*

Orr, *Mrs.* Alex. S. Twins of St. Marcel. ill. 12°. $1.50............................(?) *Shepard.*

Orr, *Mrs.* N. De Witt's Connecticut cook book, and housekeeper's assistant. 16°. '71. 75c.; bds., 50c................................*De Witt.*

Orrin Pierce. *See* History of.

Orsay, *Count* d', *and* Calabrella, *Countess* de. The lady's and gentleman's science of etiquette and guide to perfect manners. 8°. 50c....*Peterson.*

Orsay, *Comtesse* d'. Clouded happiness; tr. from the Fr. 8°. pap., 50c. .... *Harper.*

Orsini, Mathieu. Life of the Virgin Mary; tr. 18°. 75c.; —with pl., $1.25................*Strong.*

— *Same;* tr. by Mrs. J. Sadlier. 8°. $4; hf. mor., $5; $6. — 32°. 40c.; 60c..............*Sadlier.*

— *Same;* with hist. of the devotion to her; [also] Meditations of the litany of the Virgin; tr. ill. 4°. $3–$18 ....*T. Kelly.*

— *Same;* with hist. of the devotion to her, [and] calendar of [her] feasts by E. Barthe; tr. by F. C. Husenbeth; also devotion to the Virgin in N. Am. by Rev. X. D. Macleod. ('61.) 24th ed. eng. 4°. '76. hf. mor., $12.50......... *Virtue.*

— *Same;* [also] Life of Christ, by Rev. H. Rutter. ill. 4°. $8–$20; —in 46 pts., ea., 25c....... *T. Kelly.*

— — *Same;* with introd. on devotion to M. by N. Wiseman and lives of St. Joseph, St. Joachim and St. John. ill. 4°. '69. hf. mor., $19; mor., $21; $22...........................*Johnson & M.*

Orthodoxy: its truth and its errors. Clarke, J. F. $1.25 ....*Am. Unit.*

Orthos (*pseud.*) Chimasia: reply to Longfellow's Theologian, and other poems. 12°. $1.... *Lippincott.*

Ortiz, Pedro P. Principios elementales de física experimental y aplicada, incl. la meteorología y la climatología. ill. 12°. $1.75......... *Appleton.*

— Principios fundamentales sobre educacion popular y los nuevos métodos de enseñanza. 12°. $1.75. *Appleton.*

Orton, E: *See* Ohio geol. survey.

Orton, Ja. Andes (The) and the Amazon; or, across the continent of South America. 3d ed., rev. and enl.; with notes of a second journey across the continent from Parà to Lima and Lake Titicaca. maps and ill. 8°. '76. $3...... *Harper.*

— Comparative zoology, structural and systematic; for schools and colleges. ill. cr. 8°. '76. $3.. *Harper.*

— Liberal education of women: the demand and method: current thoughts in America and England. 12°. '73. $1.50 .... *Barnes.*

Orville College. Wood, E. P. 50c......... *Peterson.*

Orvis, W: B. Coming of Christ in his kingdom: adventism, millenarianism, etc., refuted. 2d ed. 12°. '76. $1.50.......................... *Tibbals.*

— Ritualism dethroned and the true church found. 12°. '75. $1.50.......................(?) *Longstreth.*

Orwig, W: W. Geschichte der Evangelischen Gemeinschaft. 12°. '57. $1.50......... *Ev. Assoc.*

— *Eng.* History of the Evangelical Association. 12°. '58. $1.25............................ *Ev. Assoc.*

— Heilsfülle (Die). ('72.) 2d ed. 12°. '75. $1.50. *Ev. Assoc.*

— Katechismus üb. d. Hauptlehren der christl. Religion. 32°. 30c............................ *Ev. Assoc.*

— *Eng.* Catechism of the principal doctrines of the Christian religion; with prayers and hymns. 32°. 30c................................. *Ev. Assoc.*

Osbon, B. S. Handbook of the U. S. navy: principal events in hist. of every vessel of the U. S. navy, 1861–1864. 12°. '64. $1.50..... *Van Nostrand.*

Osborn, H. S. Metallurgy of iron and steel. pl. and wood-eng. 8°. '69. $15............... *Baird.*

Osborn, H: S. Biblical tables: handbook of reference for teachers. 8°. $1.50 .... *Am. Bapt.*

— Little pilgrims in the Holy Land. ill. 16°. '59. $1.25. *Challen.*

— Palestine, past and present; with Biblical, scientific and literary notes. ill. roy. 8°. '58. $5.. *Challen.*

— Teachers' guide to Palestine: list of names of all the cities of Palestine, etc. 18°. '68. 65c... *Garrigues.*

Osborn, Laughton. Mariamne: tragedy of Jewish hist. 12°. '73. 75c. .... *Hinton.*

Osborn, Sherard. The Polar regions: search after Sir John Franklin's expedition. 12°. '71. $1.25. *Barnes.*

Osborne, *Mrs.* D: *See* Osborne, Fannie.

Osborne, E. H. Lectures: Mission of the young men of the south, Sphere and mission of women, Genius of Masonry. 18°. 30c........ *So. Bapt.*

Osborne, Fannie. The world of waters; or, a peaceful progress o'er the unpathed sea. 18°. '51. 75c.. *Carter.*

— *Same;* rev. by T. O. Summers. ('56.) 2d ed. 2 v. ill. 18°. '74. $1.25................... *So. Meth.*

Osborne, R: B., *and* Manning, C: P. Report on their investigation of the merits of narrow gauge railways as applicable to long main lines. 12°. '71. 25c. .... *Kelly, P. & Co.*

Oscar. Simonds, W. $1.25................. *Miller.*

Oscar Bertrand. Braddon, M. E. 50c....... *De Witt.*

Oscar Shanghai. *See* Extraordinary and mirth provoking adventures of.

Osceola, the Seminole. Reid, M. $1.50.... *Carleton.*

Osgood, *Mrs.* Fes. S. Works. ill. 12°. '76. $1.50. *World Pub.*

— (*ed.*) Poetry of flowers and flowers of poetry. ill. 12°. '69. $1.50; mor., $2.50.......... *Claxton.*

Osgood, G: L. Guide to art of singing; based on traditions of the Ital. school of vocalization and practical develop. of modern science. f°. '74. bds., $4 .... *Ditson.*

Osgood, Josiah. American school melodist. obl. 16°. 50c.. *Gordon.*

Osgood, Lucius. American [ser. of spellers and readers]. 9 v. 12°. '70–'73.............. *English.*

Cont.: American adv. speller, 35c. — Am. primary speller, 20c. — Am. primer, 20c. — Am. first reader, 30c. — second, 50c. third, 70c. — fourth, 80c. — fifth, $1.25. — sixth, $1.50.

— Progressive [readers and spellers]. ('55–'58.) New ed. 7 v. '68............................ *English.*

Cont.: Progressive primer, 16°, bds., 8c. — Prog. first reader, 16°, 23c. — second, 16°, 45c. — third, 12°, 70c. — fourth, 12°, $1.15 — fifth, 12°, $1.35. — Prog. speller, 16°, 22c.

Osgood, *Mrs.* M. A. Little Canary ser. 4 v. ill. 24°. ea., 75c.................................. *Lee & S.*

Cont.: Little Canary's daisy. — Little Canary. — Little Canary's country life. — Little Canary's black Cato.

Osgood, S: American leaves: familiar notes of thought and life. 12°. $1.75.................. *Harper.*

— Good man's legacy. [Sermon.] 12°. '66. pap., 10c. *Wells.*

— Gospel among the animals; or, Christ with the cattle. 12°. '67. 25c.; pap., 10c................ *Wells.*

— Hearthstone (The): thoughts upon home life in our cities. 12°. $1.50.......................... *Dutton.*

— Mile-stones in our life-journey. 12°. $1.50.. *Dutton.*

— On Leviticus. *See* Lange, J. P., Commentary.

— Studies in Christian biog. 12°. $1.50....... *Miller.*

— *and* Farley, F. A. Book of vespers: order of evening worship, with psalms and hymns. 12°. $1.25. *Miller.*

— — Christian worship: services for the church, with order of vespers and hymns. 12°. $2; mor., $4. *Miller.*

Osgood's Am. guide books. 4 v. maps and plans. 16°. '73–'76. ea., $2 .... *Osgood.*

Cont.: New England. — Middle states. — Maritime provinces. — White Mountains.

Osgood's (Baedeker's) European guide books. 11 v. maps and ill. 16° .... *Osgood.*

Cont.: Belgium and Holland, $1.75. — The Rhine, $2. — Northern Germany, $2. — Southern Germany and Austria, $3.50. — Northern Italy and Corsica, $2.50. — Central Italy and Rome, $2.50. — Southern Italy, Athens, Malta, etc., $2.50. — Paris and Northern France, $2. — Switzerland, etc., $2.50. — Palestine and Syria, $7.50. — Traveller's manual of conversation in Eng., Germ., Fr. and Ital., $1.25.

O'Shaughnessy, Arth. *and* Eleanor. Toyland. sm. 4°. '75. $2 .... *Routledge.*

O'Shea, Pat. Illustrated progressive ser. [of readers and spellers]. 9 v. '71–'75 .... *O'Shea.*

Cont.: Primer, 16°, bds., 12c. — Primary spelling and reading book, 12°, bds., 20c. — Spelling book, 12°, bds., 25c. — First reader, 12°, bds., 25c. — Second reader, 12°, hf. roan, 40c. — Third reader, 12°, hf. roan, 65c. — Fourth reader, 12°, hf. roan, 90c. — Fifth reader, 12°, hf. roan, $1.20. — Sixth reader; or, oratorical class book, 12°, hf. roan, $1.50.

Ossawatomie Brown. Swayze, J. C. 15c... *French.*

Ossian. *See* Macpherson, Ja.

Ossian's harp. Dodge, O. E. 25c. .... *Ditson.*

Osswald, H. F. Californien u. seine Verhältnisse. 18°. 25c. .... *Radde.*

Osten-Sacken, Carl Rob. Romanoff (*Baron*) v. Catalogue of diptera of North America. 8°. '58. pap., 75c. .... *Smith. Inst.*

— Monograph of diptera of No. Am. pt. 4. 8°. '69. pap., $2 .... *Smith. Inst.*

— — *See also* United States, *Corps of Eng.*

— Monograph of the tabanidæ. pt. 1. 4°. pap., 65c. *Bost. Soc. Nat. Hist.*

— *See also* Loew, H., *and* Osten-Sacken.

Ostereier (Die). *See* Schmid, C. v.

Ostern im Himmel. Weninger, F. X. $1.. *Benziger.*

Ostervald, Jean F: *See* Bible, New Test., *French.*

Ostrolenka. *See* Bonawitz, J. H.

Oswald, *Rev.* J. The kingdom which shall not be destroyed: expos. of prophecy. 12°. $1.. *Lippincott.*

Oswald, J: Etymological dict. of the Eng. lang.; with essay on mode of teaching Eng. composition by J. M. Keagy. New ed., enl. 12°. '52. hf. roan, $1.65 .... *Fortescue.*

Oswald Cray. Wood, E. P. $1.75; $1.50.. *Peterson.*

Oswyn Dudley. Herndon, M. E. 50c.... *U. P. James.*

Otec La Ruine. Dumas, A. 90c. .... *Geringer.*

Otello. *See* Rossini, G.

Otey, Ja. H. Doctrine, discipline and worship of the Am. branch of the Cath. Church, expl. and defended in three sermons. 12°. pap., 50c... *Dutton.*

Othello. *See* Shakespeare, W.

Othello: burlesque. 16°. pap., 15c. .... *French.*

Othello: Ethiop. drama. 16°. pap., 15c..... *Happy.*

Othello. [Fiction.] *See* Hauff, W.

Othello: travestie. Dowling, M. G. 15c..... *French.*

Otheman, E: Christian student. 18°. '43. 55c. *Meth. Bk. Conc.*

Other folks' lives. Smedley, M. B. $2 ... *Routledge.*

Other girls. Whitney, A. D. T. $2 .... *Osgood.*

Other life. Holcombe, W. H. $1.50 .... *Lippincott.*

Other people's money. *See* Gaboriau, E.

Other people's windows. Friswell, J. H. $3. *Scribner, W. & A.*

Other shore. *See* Warner, A. B.

Other worlds than ours. Proctor, R. A. $2.50.. *Appleton.*

Otis, Calv. Sacred and constructive art. 12°. '69. $1.25 .... *Putnam.*

Otis, F. N. Drawing books of animals. 5 pts. obl. 8°. 1, 2, ea., 45c.; 3, 50c.; 4, 5, ea., 65c.; — in 1 v., $3 .... *Appleton.*

Otis, F. N., *continued.*

— Drawing books of landscape. 6 pts. obl. 8°. 1–3, ea., 40c.; 4–6, ea., 50c.; — in 1 v., $3.. *Appleton*

— Estudios sobre los animales, con instrucciones para el uso del lápiz de plomo y de creyon. obl. 4°. $3.50 .... *Appleton*

— Lecciones fáciles de paisaje con instrucciones para el uso del lápiz de plomo y de creyon. obl. 4°. $3.50 *Appleton*

Otis, Fessenden N. Gleet and its relations to urethra stricture. *See* Seguin, E. C., Series of Am. clin. lect.

— History of the Panama Railroad, and of the Pacific Mail Steamship Co.; with traveller's guide and business man's handbook. ill. 12°. $2.. *Harper*

Otis, G: A. Medical and surg. hist. of rebellion; — Report of surg. cases in the U. S. army; — Report on amputations of hip-joints; — Report on excisions of the head of the femur. *See* United States, *Surgeon-General's Office.*

Ottalie's stories for the little folks. Wildermuth, *Mme* O. $1.25 .... *Dutton*

Otté, Elise C. Scandinavian history. maps. 12°. '75. $2.50 .... *Macmillan*

Ottley, H: Biographical and crit. dict. of recent and living painters and engravers: sup. to Bryant's Dictionary of painters and engravers. roy. 8°. $6 .... *Scribner, W. & A.*

Otto, Emil. First book in Germ.; rev. by E. S. Joynes. ('74.) New ed. 16°. '76. bds., 40c. .... *Holt*

— French conversation-gram.; rev. by F. Bôcher. ('64.) New ed. 12°. '76. hf. roan, $1.75. — Key. ('65.) New ed. 12°. '76. pap., 75c. .... *Holt*

— German conversation-gram. ('64.) New ed., with vocab. by L. Pylodet. 12°. '76. hf. roan, $1.75. — Key. 12°. pap., 75c. .... *Holt*

— Introductory Germ. lessons. ('68.) New ed., with vocab. by E. S. Joynes. 12°. '76. $1.... *Holt*

— Introductory Germ. reader; with notes and vocab. by E. S. Joynes. ('74.) New ed. 12°. '76. $1.25 .... *Holt*

— Practical and easy course of the Germ. lang. 16°. '68. bds., 50c. .... *Knœfel*

Otto, W: T. *See* United States, Sup. Ct. reports.

Otto's Missionsbüchse. 18°. 35c. .... *Ev. Assoc*

Otway, T: Venice preserved: tragedy. 16°. pap., 15c. *French*

Oudendale. Moncrieff, R. H. $1.25 .... *Sheldon*

Ought Christians to debate? Jamieson, W. F. 10c. *Mendum*

Ought we to visit her? Edwards, A. $1.75; $1.. *Sheldon*

Ouida (*pseud.*) *See* La Rame, Louise de.

Ould man's (The) coat-tails: Irish [dram.] sketch. 16°. pap., 15c. .... *Happy*

Oulita, the serf. Helps, *Sir* A. $1.75 .... *Routledge*

Ouno (*pseud.*) *See* Ashworth, T. M.

Our artist ser. *See* Carleton, G. W.

Our baby. Warner, S. E. $1.25; $1.50; $3.. *Am. Tr*

Our baby. *See* Harland stories.

Our barren lands. Hazen, W. B. 50c. ...... *Clarke*

Our baths and wells. Macpherson, J. $1.25.. *Macmillan*

Our behavior. Duffey, E. B. $2 ..... *J. M. Stoddart*

Our Bertie. Pratt, L. M. 75c. .... *Lothrop*

Our best. Draper, E. E. 30c. .... *Williams*

Our Bible. Hewitt, J. O. M. $1.25 .... *Jansen*

Our bird's nest, and other stories. 24°. 25c. *Bost. Am. Tr*

— *See also* Banner stories.

Our birds. *See* Smith, *Mrs.* F. I. B.

Our birthday trip. *See* Aunt Gracie's lib.

Our bodies. Davidson, E. A. 50c. .... *Cassell*

Our boys. Hill, A. F. $1.75 .... *J. E. Potter*

Our boys; or, we're off to the diggings. 18°. 60c. *Cong. Pub*

Our boys and girls ser. *See* Adams, W: T.
Our boys' holiday lib. 6 v. ill. 16°. $3......*Lothrop.*
Cont.: Sturdy Jack. — On the seas. — Every man in his place. — Robin, the runner. — Soldier Fritz. — Little Redcap.
Our British portrait painters, 1617–1872. Ollier, E. $10; $20........................*Lippincott.*
Our campaigns. Woodward, E. M. $1.75..*J.E.Potter.*
Our Charlie. *See* Southworth, *Mrs.* A. S.
Our Chatham Street uncle. Wright, J. McN. $1.50. *Hoyt.*
Our children. Gardner, A. K. $2.........*Carleton.*
Our children. Haygood, A. G. $1.50..*S. W.Bk.& Pub.*
Our children: how to rear and train them. cr. 8°. $1.50 ....*Cassell.*
Our children in heaven. Holcombe, W. H. $1.25. *Lippincott.*
Our children's pets. Josephine. $2.......*Routledge.*
Our church and her services. Oxenden, A. 75c. *Dutton.*
Our church in Sandburg. Moore, S. W. $1.25. *So. Meth.*
Our class. *See* Wright, *Mrs.* J. McN.
Our clerks. Coyne, J. S. 15c......*De Witt; French.*
Our companions in glory. Killen, J. M. $1.75. *Randolph.*
Our country: its trial and triumph. Peck, G. $1.50. *Meth. Bk. Conc.*
Our country and government for one hundred years; with Declaration of independence, lives and por. of presidents, etc. ill. 16°. *$1.......*Col. Bk.*
Our cousins in Ohio. Howitt, M. $1..*Collins & Bro.*
Our creeds. Ludlow, J. A. 10c.....*N. Y. Ref. Ch. Bd.*
Our daily trials, and how to bear them. sq. 24°. '76. 50c. ....*Am. Tr.*
Our darling Nellie. *See* Tarbox, I. N.
Our daughter's lib. 4 v. 16°. $6..........*Lothrop.*
Cont.: New commandment. — Mrs. Thorne's guest. — Neighbor's house. — Katharine's experience.
Our dear Eddie. Pease, D. G. 45c...........*Hoyt.*
Our detachment. King, K. 75c............*Harper.*
Our distant cousins. ('71.) New ed. ill. 16°. '74. $1.50 ....*Hoyt.*
Our domestic pets. Wood, J. G. $1.25...*Routledge.*
Our domestics. Hay, F. 15c.......*De Witt; French.*
Our dumb companions. Jackson, T. $2..*Routledge.*
Our dumb neighbors. Jackson, T. $2....*Routledge.*
Our earthly house and its builder. ill. 18°. '69. 60c. *Am. Tr.*
— *Port.* Nossa casa terrestre. ill. 18°. '70. 50c. *Am. Tr.*
Our English Bible; rev. by T. O. Summers. ('55.) 3d ed. 18°. '75. 60c. ....*So. Meth.*
Our English Bible and its ancestors. Walden, T. $1.25. *Porter.*
Our English surnames. *See* Bardsley, C. W.
Our eternal home. Hayden, W. B. 50c...*H. H. Carter.*
Our eternal homes; by a Bible student. 2d Am. ed. 16°. '68. $1.25 ....*Lockwood, B. & Co.*
Our excellent women: biog. sketches. ill. 4°. $5..*Miller.*
Our eyes and how to take care of them. Williams, H. W. $1..........................*Hurd & H.*
Our faith and hope. White, J. 20c....*Sev. Day Adv.*
Our faith the victory. Macgill, J. $2; $3.50. *Kelly, P. & Co.*
Our farm of four acres, andthe mon ey we made by it. 12°. $1..........................*Woodward.*
— *Same.* 12°. $1; pap., 50c.................*Miller.*
Our farm of two acres. Martineau, H. 25c...*Huntington.*
Our farm-yard alphabet. [Toy-book.] ill. 4°. $1; 50c. *Routledge.*
Our Father. ill. 18°. 50c.....................*Nelson.*
Our Father. Alden, J. 35c...................*Prés. Bd.*
Our Father. Dunning, A. K. 25c...........*Am. Tr.*

Our Father (The). Müller, M. 50c........*Kreuzer.*
Our Father in heaven. ('64.) New ed. ill. 18°. '75. 55c. ....*Hoyt.*
Our Father in heaven. Wilson, J. H. $1.25..*Carter.*
Our Father's business. *See* Guthrie, T:
Our Father's care. *See* Sewell, *Mrs.* M.
Our Father's house. ('60.) New ed. ill. 18°. '68. 45c. ....*Hoyt.*
Our favorite. Danks, H. P. 60c........*G. D. Russell.*
Our favorite nursery rhymes. ill. 12°. pap., 50c. *Scribner, W. & A.*
Our favorite toy books. 4 nos. ill. f°. ea., pap., 20c.; 25c.; 30c...........................*J. E. Potter.*
Our feathered companions. Jackson, T. $2..*Routledge.*
Our first hundred years. Lester, C. E. 2 v. $4. *U. S. Pub.*
Our flag on the ocean. Frost, J. $1.50... *World Pub.*
Our folks at home. Toliver, E. $1.50....*J. E. Potter.*
Our forest home and its inmates. ('73.) New ed. 16°. '75. $1.50...................................*Hoyt.*
Our four boys. Mathews, J. A. $1.10........*Carter.*
Our four-footed friends. Howitt, M. $2...*Routledge.*
Our fresh and salt tutors. *See* Gordon, C.
Our friends in heaven. *See* Killen, J. M.
Our future life. *See* Holcombe, W. H.
Our gal. Johnson, S. D. 15c................*French.*
Our games. Hamilton, M. $1................*Nelson.*
Our general. Linden, C. 50c...............*Barclay.*
Our girls. Lewis, D. $1.50................*Harper.*
Our girls' holiday lib. 6 v. ill. 16°. $3.....*Lothrop.*
Cont.: Home sunshine. — Alice Benson's trials. — Grace's visit. — Charley Hope. — Maggie's message. — The log house.
Our girls' lib. 3 v. 16°. $2.50.............*Dutton.*
Cont.: Eunice Somers, by Mrs. D. P. Sanford. — White castles. — Little messmates.
Our Guy. Boyd, E. E. $1......................*Hoyt.*
Our heavenly Father. Smith, J. 50c.; 75c...*Am. Tr.*
Our Helen. Clarke, R. S. $1.75...........*Lee & S.*
Our heroes. Renauld, J. B. 15c...........*De Witt.*
Our holidays. *See* Picture puzzle toy books.
Our holy Christianity. Swartz, C. W. 65c......*Day.*
Our home beyond the tide. Hanaford, P. A., *and* Miles, E. E. $1.50......................*Locke.*
Our home counsellor. Yaggy, L. W. $2.50.. *West. Pub.*
Our inheritance in the great pyramid. Smyth, P. $6. *Routledge.*
Our Irish boys songster. 32°. '76. pap., 10c... *De Witt.*
Our Jemimy. Conway, H. J. 15c............*French.*
Our Katie. 18°. '63. 20c.....................*Am. Tr.*
Our keepsake. Haygood, A. G. $1.........*So. Meth.*
Our king. Wise, D. $2..............*Meth. Bk. Conc.*
Our kings and queens. *See* Picture puzzle toy books.
Our lady of Lourdes. Lasserre, H. $2; $2.50..*Sadlier.*
Our library. 55 v. 18°. '61. $20....*Meth. Bk. Conc.*
Our library of books about wonderful and curious things. *See* Books about wonderful and curious things.
Our life in China. Nevius, H. S. C. $1.50....*Carter.*
Our little Comfort. 18°. 75c..................*Dutton.*
Our little fruit-gatherers. 18°. 35c.........*Pres. Bd.*
Our little girls. 18°. '58. 40c...........*Randolph.*
Our little one. ill. 16°. 75c. — 12°. $1.50..*Sheldon.*
Our little ones. ill. 4°. 75c...............*Am. Bapt.*
Our little ones in heaven. [Verse and prose.] 18°. 90c.; $1.25...........................*Sheldon.*
Our little people's lib. 5 v. 16°. $2.25.....*So. Meth.*
Our little pet's own picture-book. sq. 12°. $1..*Appleton.*
Our looking-glasses. *See* Aunt Hattie's stories.
Our Lord's three raisings from the dead. Macmillan, H. $1.50.............................*Dutton.*

Our lost home, and how to find it. 18°. 30c.; 35c. *Am. Bapt.*
Our martyr president. *See* Lincoln, A.
Our Mary Anne: farce. 16°. pap., 15c....... *Happy.*
Our Max: memoir of a four-footed friend; by his chief mourner. ill. 8°. bds., 50c............ *Loring.*
Our morals and manners. Brown, J. B. 75c... *Nelson.*
Our mother church. *See* Mercier, J.
Our mutual friend. *See* Dickens, C:
Our national house. Remington, E. F. $1.25.. *Tibbals.*
Our national obligation: essay. 12°. 60c.... *West. Tr.*
Our neighbors in the corner house. Arthur, T. S. $1.50. *J. E. Potter.*
Our new baby, and other stories. *See* Little Blue Mantle lib.
Our new crusade. Hale, E. E. $1.25; 75c... *Roberts.*
Our new departure. Brooks, E. G. $1.75.. *Universalist.*
Our new man. Suter, W. E. 15c........... *French.*
Our new masters. Wright, T. $2.50...... *Routledge.*
Our new minister. Perryman, E. G. $1.. *Whittaker.*
Our new vicar. Monsell, J. S. B. $1.50....... *Pott.*
Our new way round the world. Coffin, C. C. $2.50. * *Osgood.*
Our new west. Bowles, S. *$3; $3.50.. *C.A. Nichols.*
Our next-door neighbor. Haven, G. $3.50.. *Harper.*
Our next-door neighbors. 18°. '67. 50c. *N. Y. Ref. Ch. Bd.; Pres. Com.*
Our Nina's pet stories. ill. f°. $1.50; $2.. *J.E. Potter.*
Our nurse's picture-book. [Toy-book.] ill. demy 4°. $2.50.............................. *Routledge.*
Our old home. *See* Hawthorne, N.
Our old men. 50c.................. (?) *Cumberland.*
Our only brother; by author of "Jessie Burton." 16°. $1.50 .... *Am. S. S.*
Our opposite neighbour. 18°. 40c........... *Dutton.*
Our Oriental missions. Thomson, E. $2.50; $3. *Cin. Meth. Bk. Conc.*
Our own ser. 3 v. 16°. $4.50................. *Souder.*
Cont.: Two boys, by J. McN. Wright. — Old-fashioned boy, by M. Finley. — A born romp, by M. E. Mumford.
Our parish. Hill, G. C. $1.75........... *J.E. Potter.*
Our parish. Pearson, E. C. 75c.......... *Nat. Temp.*
Our Passover. McCord, W. J. 60c........ *Pres. Bd.*
Our pet: comedy. 16°. pap., 15c............ *French.*
Our pets: sketches of the furred and feathered favorites. ill. sq. 12°. $1.75....... *Scribner, W. & A.*
Our picture-book. 18°. 35c.; 45c.......... *Am. Bapt.*
Our picture-book. ill. roy. 16°. 50c.......... *Cassell.*
Our place among infinities. Proctor, R. A. $1.75. *Appleton.*
Our planet: its past and future. Denton, W. $1.50. *Denton.*
Our plea and our mission. Dungan, D. R. 10c. *Cen. Bk.*
Our poetical favorites. Kendrick, A. C. 2 v. ea., $2; $2.75; $5 .... *Sheldon.*
Our ponds and our fields. 16°. 50c... *Scribner, W. & A.*
Our poor neighbors. Perring, *Mrs.* —. 45c. *Routledge.*
Our poor relations. Hamley, E. B. $1.25.... *Tilton.*
Our pretty alphabets. 3 nos. ill. f°. ea., pap., 15c.; 20c.; 30c.......................... *J.E. Potter.*
Cont.: A. of objects; A B C made easy. — A. of costumes; or, the dress of all nations. — A. of Bible history.
Our representatives abroad. Rogers, A. C. $10; $15; $20.................................. *Atlantic.*
Our revenue system and the civil service: shall they be reformed? 12°. pap., 25c..... *Intern. Fr. Tr.*
Our roadways. Viator. 20c. .... *Spon.*
Our Rosie; or, the little Owens. 18°. 40c... *Am. S. S.*
Our rules and our rights: outlines of the U. S. government. 6th ed. 12°. '69. $2; shp., $2.50.. *Tibbals.*
Our Saturday nights. Pomeroy, M. M. $1.50.. *Carleton.*
Our Saviour. 18°. 40c.; 50c. .... *Am. Bapt.*
Our Saviour. *See* Williams, W:
Our seamen. Plimsoll, S. $1.25 .... *Routledge.*
Our seven churches. Beecher, T. K. $1; $1.25; 50c. *Ford.*
Our show. Cohen, D. S., *and* Sommer, H. B. $1; 50c. *Claxton.*
Our sister republic, Mexico. Evans, A. S. *$3; $3.50; $4.50 .... *Col. Bk.*
Our sketching club. Tyrwhitt, R. St. J. $2.50.. *Roberts.*
Our song birds. Root, N. W. T. 4 nos. ea., 20c. *Barnes.*
Our song birds. [School music.] 6 nos. 12°. '66. ea., pap., 18c.; — in 1 v., 60c. .... *Church.*
Cont.: Snowbird. — Robin. — Red bird. — Dove. — Blue bird. — Linnet.
Our standard-bearer. Adams, W. T. $1.50.. *Lee & S.*
Our strength and our weakness. Moore, W. T. 10c. *Chase.*
Our Sue. *See* Woodworth, F. C.
Our Summer at Hillside farm. *See* Barrett, M.
Our summer at Sunnybrook. Meigs, H. $1.. *Randolph.*
Our summer house. Whitmarsh, C. S. 90c. *Thompson.*
Our Sunday school and how we conduct it. Abbott, W. $1.15.............................. *Hoyt.*
Our Sunday school scrap-book. Wise, D., *and* Vincent, J. H. 25c................. *Meth. Bk. Conc.*
Our sympathizing high priest. *See* Tucker, C.
Our Tabby and her travels. *See* Guernsey, L. E.
Our temple. Seiss, J. A. 10c........... *Luth. Bk. St.*
Our theology in its developments. Humphrey, E. P. 35c. .... *Pres. Bd.*
Our three boys. Chester, S. E. $1.25....... *Am. Tr.*
Our two lives. K., A. H. $1.25.......... *Randolph.*
Our vacations and how to enjoy them. Clark, F. E. $1....................................... *Estes.*
Our village. *See* Mitford, M. R.
Our village. Rede, W. L. 15c. .... *French.*
Our village. Watson, J. L. 75c............ *Nelson.*
Our village girls. *See* Sunshine and shadow lib.
Our vows. Lowndes, R. 30c.–$3 .... *Dutton.*
Our wasted resources. Hargreaves, W. $1.25. *Nat. Temp.*
Our western border one hundred years ago. *See* McKnight, C.
Our western home: story from life; by author of "Daniel Tracey's store." 16°. 75c. ... *Am. S. S.*
Our wife. Morton, J. M. 15c. .... *French.*
Our Willie. Coates, W. H. 60c......... *Perkinpine.*
Our woodlands, heaths and hedges. Coleman, W. S. $1.25; 50c. .... *Routledge.*
Our work. Groser, W. H. 75c.............. *Nelson.*
Our work and our blessings. Havergal, F. R. $1. *Randolph.*
Our work in Palestine. *See* Palestine Exploration Fund.
Our work-shop. Thorold, T. 80c......... *Routledge.*
Our world in a nutshell. Blake, J. L. $1.50.. *World Pub.*
Our year. *See* Craik, D. M.
Our young ladies from girlhood to womanhood. Tuthill, L. C. $1.50 .... *World Pub.*
Ours. Robertson, T. W. 15c.............. *De Witt.*
Ourselves. Linton, E. L. $1.50 .... *Routledge.*
Out and all about. Yapp, A. $2 .... *Routledge.*
Out at sea. Emma. 55c................. *Pres. Bd.*
Out at sea. Newton, C. E. 15c............ *De Witt.*
Out from the shadows. Giles, E. A. $1.50. *Atwood; Jansen.*
Out in the garden. *See* Robin Ranger's lib.
Out in the playground. Pease, F. W. 40c. .. *Am. Tr.*

Out in the storm; by author of "Leighton children." 18°. 60c. .... *Am.S.S.*
Out in the streets. Cook, S. N. 15c. .... *Ames.*
Out in the world. Arthur, T. S. $1.50 .. *J.E.Potter.*
Out in the world. Wolfe, H. J. $1.25 .. *Cin.Meth.Bk.Conc.*
Out of the clouds, into the light. Metcalfe, W. $1.75. *Lippincott.*
Out of the dark. 16°. $1.20 .... *Pres.Bd.*
Out of darkness into light; or, true ground of peace. ill. 18°. 50c. .... *N.Y.Ref.Ch.Bd.*
Out of debt out of danger. *See* Haven, *Mrs.* A. B.
Out of the deep. Wood, E. P. $1.50; 75c... *W.F.Gill.*
Out of the depths: story of a woman's life. 12°. $1.75; pap., $1.50 .... *Peterson.*
Out of the fire. Chellis, M. D. $1.25 .... *Nat.Temp.*
Out of the foam. Cooke, J. E. $1.50 ...... *Carleton.*
Out of the frying pan: comedy. 16°. pap., 15c... *French.*
Out of harness. *See* Guthrie, T.
Out of the heart. Andersen, H. C. $1.50 .. *Routledge.*
Out of her sphere. Harbert, L. B. $1.50 ...... *Mills.*
Out of the hurly-burly. Clark, C. H. *2.50; $3; $4. *Maclean.*
Out of the orphan's asylum; or, sketches in a country parish. 16°. $1.25 .... *Am.S.S.*
Out of the past. Godwin, P. $2 .... *Putnam.*
Out of prison. Denison, M. A. $1.50... *H.A. Young.*
Out of school. *See* Robin Ranger's lib.
Out of the streets. Gayler, C. $1.50 .... *De Witt.*
Out of town. Burnand, F. C. $1.25 .... *Roberts.*
Out of town. Coffin, R. B. $1.50 .... *Hurd & H.*
Out of the wilderness. Chaplin, J. D. $1.25 .. *H.A. Young.*
Out to nurse. Williams, T. 15c. .... *French.*
Out west. *See* Very little tales.
Outcast. Reade, W. 30c. .... *D.M.Bennett.*
Outcast. Watson, J. W. $2; $3; $4 ..... *Peterson.*
Outcast boy rescued. 18°. 18c. .... *Am.S.S.*
Outcast daughter: story of the west. 18°. 20c.; 25c. *Am.Bapt.*
Outcroppings: selections of California verse. sm. 4°. '66. $1 .... *Roman.*
Out-doors at Idlewild. Willis, N. P. $1.75 .. *Scribner.*
Outis (*pseud.*) Hiatus: the void in modern education, its cause and antidote. 8°. '69. $3 .. *Macmillan.*
Outlaw. 8°. pap., 25c. .... *De Witt.*
Outlaw of the Adriatic. Sejour, V. 15c. .... *French.*
Outlaw's daughter. Bennett, E. $1.50; $1 .. *Claxton.*
Outline questions on connections of sacred and profane history; with tables and maps. 18°. '74. pap., 50c. .... *Randolph.*
Outline study of man. Hopkins, M. $1.75 .. *Scribner.*
Outlines of chronology, anc. and mod.: introd. to study of hist. on the plan of D. Blair. 18°. '48. bds., 50c. .... *Ware.*
Outlines of history of Great Britain, [1702–1820]. 12°. 20c. .... *Nelson.*
Outlines of men, women and things. Clemmer, M. $1.50 .... *Hurd & H.*
Outlines of New Testament history for youth. 16°. 90c. .... (?) *Luth.Pub.*
Outlines of Old Testament history for youth. 16°. 90c. .... (?) *Luth.Pub.*
Outlines of sacred hist.; with questions for examination. ill. 18°. '43. hf. bd., 50c. ..... *Fortescue.*
Outlines of Sunday school lectures. ('55.) 2d ed. 18°. '75. 50c. .... *So.Meth.*
Outpost: sequel to "Dora Darling." 12°. '76. $1.50. *Tilton.*
Outpost and patrol duty: instruct. for officers and non-commissioned officers. 32°. pap., 25c. *Lippincott.*
Outposts of Zion. Goode, W. H. $1.75. *Cin.Meth.Bk.Conc.*
Outre-mer. Longfellow, H. W. $1.50 ...... *Osgood.*
Outside and inside, and other tales. 18°. 65c... *Pres.Bd.*
Outward bound. Adams, W. T. $1.50 ..... *Lee & S.*
Over Forty (*pseud.*) The tall man of Winton and his wife. 16°. '72. 75c. .... (?) *Cumberland.*
Over the hedge; or, the gate opened. 18°. 60c... *Am.S.S.*
Over the ocean. Guild, C. $2.50 .... *Lee & S.*
Over the plains songster. Dumont, F. 20c... *Barclay.*
Over the river. Thayer, T. B. $1–$3 .. *Universalist.*
Over the sea. 18°. 50c.; 60c. .... *Am.Bapt.*
Over the sea; or, letters from an officer in India to his children at home. 18°. 70c. .... *Am.S.S.*
Over yonder. John, E. 30c. .... *Lippincott.*
Overberg, Bern. A B C- Buchstabir- u. Lesebuch. 12°. hf. bd., 10c. .... *Vering.*
— Neues A B C- Buchstabir- u. Lesebuch. 16°. 12c. *Benziger.*
Overcoming. Churchill, E. K. $1.25 ...... *Lothrop.*
Overcoming. Underwood, R. S. 20c. .... *Palmer.*
Overend, *Mrs.* Campbell. *See* Besieged city.
Overland. De Forest, J. W. $1.75; $1 .... *Sheldon.*
Overland Kit. Aiken, A. W. 20c. .... *Beadle.*
Overland route. Taylor, T. 15c. .... *De Witt.*
Overland through Asia. Knox, T. W. *$3.50; $4; $5; $8 .... *Am.Pub.*
Overman, F: Manufacture of steel. New ed., rev. and enl. by A. A. Fesquet. 12°. '73. $1.50 .. *Baird.*
— Mechanics for the millwright, machinist, engineer, etc. ('51.) New ed. ill. 12°. '75. $1.50 .. *Claxton.*
— Moulder and founder's pocket-guide; with receipts for alloys, etc., and tables on strength, etc., of cast metals. (cop. '51.) '72. 4th ed. ill. 12°. '75. $1.50 .... *Baird.*
— Practical mineralogy, assaying and mining. 12°. '75. $1.25 .... *Lindsay.*
— Treatise on metallurgy. ill. 8°. $5 ...... *Appleton.*
Overton, Dan. Y. Code of practice in Iowa and Wisconsin. imp. 8°. '75. shp., $7.50 .. *Callaghan.*
Overton, J: *See* Tennessee, Superior Courts reports.
Overture of angels. Beecher, H. W. $1.50 ... *Ford.*
Ovid [*Lat.* Ovidius] Naso, Publius. Works; lit. tr. by H. T. Riley. 3 v. 12°. (Bohn.) ea., $1.75. *Little, B. & Co.*
Cont.: 1. Fasti; Tristia; Epistles, etc.—2. Metamorphoses.—3. Heroides; Art of love, etc.
— *Same.* 3 v. 12°. (Bohn.) ea., $2. *Lippincott; Scribner, W. & A.*
— Art of love; Remedy of love; Art of beauty; Court of love; History of love and amours; tr., with life and notes. ('55.) New ed. ill. 32°. 60c. *D. Thomas.*
— Excerpta ex libris Fastorum, ex Tristium et ex De Ponto. 16°. '67. 75c. .... *Kelly, P. & Co.*
— Four books of the Metamorphoses expurgated [*Lat.*]; [with] explan., notes and dict. by N. C. Brooks. ('72.) 2d ed. ill. demi 8°. '74. $1.75 .. *Claxton.*
— Metamorphoses, and Elegiac verses [*Lat.*]; ed. by Schmitz and Zumpt. 16°. $1 .... *Sheldon.*
— Metamorphoses and Epistles; tr. by Dryden, Pope, Addison, Congreve and others. 2 v. 18°. $1.50. *Harper.*
— Selectæ fabulæ ex libris Metamorphoseon. 16°. '59. 50c. .... *Kelly, P. & Co.*
— Selections from Metamorphoses and Heroides [*Lat.*]; with notes, ref. and exercises in scanning by E. A. Andrews. 12°. '51. $1.25 .... *Crocker.*
— *Same;* with lit. and interl. tr. by G. W. Heilig. roy. 12°. hf. leath., $2.25 .... *Desilver.*
— Selections from poems, chiefly the Metamorphoses [*Lat.*]; with introd., notes and index of proper names by J. H. Allen and J. B. Greenough. ('75.) 3d ed. 12°. '76. hf. leath., $1.50. *Ginn.*

Ovid [*Lat.* Ovidius] Naso, Publius, *continued.*
— *See also* Collins, W. L., New ser. of anc. classics; — Gardner, F., Gay, A. M., *and* Buck, A. M.
— *and* Virgil. Selections [*Lat.*]; with vocab. by J. H. Hanson and W. J. Rolfe. 12°. $2.. *Potter, A. & Co.*

Ovingdean Grange. *See* Ainsworth, W: H.

Owen, Ashford (*pseud.*) *See* Ogle, Annie.

Owen, D: Dale. Report of a geol. survey of Wisconsin, Iowa and Minnesota. 2 v. ill. 4°. $7.50. *Claxton; Lippincott.*
— *See also* Arkansas geol. survey; — Indiana geol. survey; — Kentucky geol. survey.

Owen, F. Ritter Bell, the cripple. 18°. 90c. (?) *Martien.*

Owen, F. M. The soldier and patriot: story of Geo. Washington. ill. cr. 8°. $1.50 .... *Cassell.*

Owen, Farleigh. Aden Power; or, the cost of a scheme. 8°. '62. $1 .... *Burnham.*

Owen, G: W. The Leach Club; or, the mysteries of the Catskills. 12°. $1.50.......... *Lee & S.*

Owen, J: Works; ed. by W. H. Goold and C. W. Quick, with memoir and index. 17 v. 8°. '71. ea., $1.50.......... *Leighton.*
— Discourse conc. the Holy Spirit; [also] Nature and necessity of Gospel holiness and difference bet. grace and morality. por. 12°. $1.10 .. *Pres. Bd.*
— Doctrine of justification by faith, through the imputation of the righteousness of Christ, explained, confirmed and vindicated. 8°. $2..... *Pres. Bd.*
— Nature, power, deceit and prevalency of indwelling sin in believers. 18°. 65c. .... *Pres. Bd.*
— On temptation and the mortification of sin in believers. por. 12°. $1.......... *Pres. Bd.*

Owen, J: J. Acts of the apostles in Greek; with lexicon. 12°. $1.75 .... *Appleton.*
— Commentary, critical, expository and practical. ('56–'67.) New ed. 3 v. 12°. '73–'75 ...... *Scribner.*
Cont.: Matthew and Mark, $1.25. — Luke, $1.75. — John, $1.75.
— *Same.* (Sunday school ed.) ('60.) New ed. 2 v. 12°. ('73–'74) .... *Scribner.*
Cont.: Matthew, $1.25. — Mark, $1.
— Greek reader. 12°. $2 .... *Appleton.*
— *See also* Homer; — Thucydides; — Xenophon.

Owen, *Mrs.* Oct. Freire. Heroines of domestic life. ill. 16°. $1.25.......... *Routledge.*
— Heroines of history. 16°. $1.25.......... *Routledge.*
— *Same.* 12°. '54. $1.25.......... *Meth. Bk. Conc.*

Owen, R: Comparative anatomy and physiol. of vertebrate animals. 3 v. ill. 8°. $25.. *Jas. Campbell.*
Cont.: Fishes and reptiles. — Warm blooded vertebrates. — Mammalia, incl. man; with indexes.
— *Same.* 3 v. 8°. $30 .... *Lippincott.*
— Principal forms of the skeleton and teeth; as a basis for a system of nat. history and comp. anatomy. ill. 12°. 75c. .... *W. Wood.*

Owen, Rob., *and* Campbell, Alex. Evidences of Christianity: debate cont. an examination of the "social system" and all systems of skepticism. 12°. $1.50 .... *Chase.*

Owen, Rob. Dale. Beyond the breakers: story of the present day. ill. 8°. $1.50; pap., $1.. *Lippincott.*
— Debatable land (The) between this world and the next. 12°. $2 .... *Carleton.*
— Footfalls on the boundary of another world. 12°. $1.75 .... *Lippincott.*
— Hints on public architecture. 4°. '49. pap., $5. *Smith. Inst.*
— Law of divorce. *See* Greeley, H., Recollections of a busy life.
— Moral physiology: plain treatise on population. 12°. 68c.......... *Mendum.*
— Threading my way: twenty-five years of autobiog. 12°. $1.50.......... *Carleton.*
— Wrong (The) of slavery, the right of emancipation, and the future of the African race in the U. S. 12°. '64. $1.25.......... *Claxton; Lippincott.*

Owen, S: Treatise on law and practice in bankruptcy; with U. S. bankrupt act, 1841. 8°. shp., $3.50. *Baker, V. & Co.*

Owen, T. T. Questions on history, biography and antiquity of the Bible. 18°. '55. per doz., pap., $1.35 .... *So. Meth.*

Owen, Tom (*Bee hunter*). Mysteries of the backwoods. 12°. pap., 75c.......... *Peterson.*

Owen, W: Pictorial Sunday readings: sel. from Old and New Testaments. 20 pts. ill. 8°. '72. ea., *30c. .... *S. Walker.*
— *Same.* 2 v. col. pl. 8°. hf. mor., $10.. *Routledge.*

Owen Carstone; or, a youth's first steps on the journey of life; by author of "Holidays at Llandudno." ill. fp. 8°. 75c.......... *Cassell.*

Owen Evans (Adventures of). *See* Anderdon, W. H.

Owen Gladdon's wanderings in the Isle of Wight. Mogridge, G. 60c.......... *So. Meth.*

Owen Gwynne's great work. *See* Noel, *Lady* A.

Owen's College essays: essays and addresses by professors and lecturers of Owen's College, Manchester. 8°. '73. $5.......... *Macmillan.*

Ox and the sheep. *See* Stories about animals ser.

Oxberry, W. H. Matteo Falcone: drama. 16°. pap., 15c. .... *French.*
— Norma: travestie. 16°. pap., 15c.......... *French.*

Oxenden, Ashton. Confirmation; or, are you ready to serve Christ? 16°. pap., 10c.......... *Dutton.*
— Course of preparation for the Lord's table. 32°. 20c.; pap., 10c.......... *Pres. Bd.*
— Earnest communicant. 24°. '64. 35c.; 75c. *Randolph.*
— Family prayers. 16°. '64. $1.......... *Randolph.*
— Fervent prayer. 32°. '75. 50c.......... *Hammond.*
— Lord's supper simply expl. 32°. '64. 35c... *Randolph.*
— Our church and her services; adapted to Prot. Episc. Church in the U. S. by F. D. Huntington. 18°. '69. 75c.......... *Dutton.*
— Pastoral office (The): its duties, difficulties, privileges and prospects. 12°. $1....... *Whittaker.*
— Pathway of safety; or, counsel to the awakened. 18°. 75c.......... *Whittaker.*
— *Same;* with introd. by C. D. Cooper. 18°. '76. 75c. *Hammond.*
— Private prayers. 24°. '68. 35c.; 50c.... *Randolph.*
— Thoughts for Lent. 16°. '73. 75c....... *Randolph.*

Oxenford, J: [Plays.] 22 v. 16°. ea., pap., 15c. *French.*
Cont.: Adrienne, the actress. — Beauty; or, the beast: farce. — Billing and cooing: comedy. — Bristol diamonds: farce. — Cleft stick: comedy. — Day well spent: farce. — Doctor Dilworth: farce. — Doubtful victory: comedy. — Family failing: farce. — I couldn't help it: farce. — Legal impediment: farce. — Magic toys: farce. — My fellow clerk: farce. — Neighbours: comedy. — Only a halfpenny: farce. — Porter's knot. — Reigning favourite. — Retained for the defence: farce. — Sam's arrival: farce. — Twice killed: farce. — Uncle Zachary. — World of fashion: comedy.
— Cleft stick: comedy. 16°. pap., 15c........ *Lee & S.*
— Doubtful victory: comedy. 16°. pap., 15c... *Lee & S.*
— Only a halfpenny: farce. 16°. pap., 15c... *De Witt.*
— Porter's (The) knot: drama. 16°. pap., 15c. *De Witt.*
— Twice killed: farce. 16°. pap., 15c....... *De Witt.*
— *See also* Tales from the German.
— *and* Brooks, C. S. Timour, the Tartar: burlesque. 16°. pap., 15c.......... *French.*
— *and* Wigan, H. Life chase: drama. 16°. pap., 15c. *French.*

Oxford, W: Junior speaker: exercises in declamation, recitation and representation. ill. 12°. 75c. *Butler.*
— Senior speaker: exercises in declamation, recitation and representation. ill. 12°. $1.50...... *Butler.*

Oxford Methodists (The). Tyerman, L. $2.50.. *Harper.*

Oxford union meeting. 12°. '75. $1; bds., 75c... *Revell.*

Oxley. Bright, M. A. $1.50.......... *Sribner.*

Oxonians (The). *See* Bulwer-Lytton, *Sir* E. G. E. L.

Ozanam, Alph. F: A pilgrimage to the land of Cid; tr. by P. S. 2d ed. 18°. '75. $1..... *Cath. Pub.*

P., *Abbé*. Life of St. Joseph; tr., [with] prayers and devotions for the month of March. 12°. $1.50; $2 .... *O'Shea.*

P., A. (*Amateur vagabond*). Mysteries and miseries of the great metropolis. 8°. *3.50; shp., $4.50. *Appleton.*

P., A. S. *See* Paschall, Ann S.

P., B. K. Chaplain with the children. 8°. $1.25 .. *Palmer.*

P., E. H. The word and the teacher. 16°. 75c. *Willard.*

P., E. L. Nobody but Nan. 16°. '76. $1 .. *Meth. Bk. Conc.*

P., F. J. *See* Pakenham, F. J.

P., H. A. Jennie Wellington; or, the lost ring. 18°. 50c. .... *Dutton.*

P., H. F. *See* Parker, *Mrs.* H. F.

P., M. A. Treasures on the beach. ill. 16°. 50c. *Nelson.*

P., R. Ambas Américas: contrastes. ill. 12°. $2.50. *Appleton.*

P. D. S. (The). 18°. 75c. .... (?) *Martien.*

P. P.; or, man and the tiger. Parry, T. 15c. .. *French.*

P's and Q's. Yonge, C. M. $1.50 .... *Macmillan.*

Pacha of many tales. *See* Marryat, F:

Pacha of Pimlico. Morton, J. M. 15c. ...... *French.*

Pachthof (Der). *See* Hoffmann, F.

Pacific coast [readers and spellers]. ('73.) New ed. 7 v. 12°. '75 .... *Bancroft.*

Cont.: Pacific coast first reader, bds., 25c. — second, bds., 50c. — third, bds., 75c. — fourth, bds., $1 — fifth, $1.25 — instructive reader, $1.25 — speller, bds., 35c.

Pacific glee book. Root, T. W., *and* Murray, J. R. $1.25 .... *Church.*

Pacific tourist. Williams, H. T. $1.50; $2. *H. T. Williams.*

Packard, Alpheus Spring, *jr.* Development of limulus polyphemus. ill. 4°. pap., $2. *Bost. Soc. Nat. Hist.*

— Embryological studies on diplax, perithemis and the thysanurous genus isotoma. ill. imp. 8°. '71. pap., $1 .... *Peabody Acad. of Sci.*

— Embryological studies on hexapodous insects. ill. imp. 8°. '72. pap., $1 .... *Peabody Acad. of Sci.*

— Guide to the study of insects; with treatise on those injurious and beneficial to crops. ('69.) 5th ed. pl. and ill. 8°. '76. $5 .... *Estes; Holt.*

— *Same.* pl. and ill. 8°. '72. $5 .... *Nat. Agcy.*

— Gynandromorphism in lepidoptera; [also] Structure and transformation of eumæus atala, by S. H. Scudder. ill. 4°. pap., 75c. .. *Bost. Soc. Nat. Hist.*

— Half hours with insects: habits, modes of life, etc. 12 pts. ill. 12°. ea., 25c.; — in 1 v., $2.50. *Estes.*

— Life histories of animals, including man. ill. 8°. '76. $2.50 .... *Estes; Holt.*

— Monograph of the geometrical moths of the U. S. *See* United States, *Geol. Survey of the Ter.*

— Our common insects. ill. 16°. '73. $2.50 .... *Estes.*

— Salt water insects. 8°. '69. pap., 15c. .... *Essex.*

— *See also* Putnam, F. W., *and* Packard, A. S.

Packard, F: A. Life of Robert Owen. 2d ed. 12°. '68. 75c. .... *Leighton.*

Packard, J. B. One key singer: hymns and tunes for Sabbath schools. obl. 12°. bds., 25c. ... *Ditson.*

Packard, J: H. Handbook of operative surgery. pl. and wood-cuts. 8°. $5; shp., $5.75 .. *Lippincott.*

— Lectures on inflammation. 12°. $2.50 .. *Lippincott.*

— Manual of minor surgery. ill. 12°. '63. $1.25. *Claxton; Lippincott.*

Packard, Jos. On the minor prophets. *See* Lange, J. P., Commentary.

— Questions on the Gospels in harmony. 18°. bds., 25c. .... *Whittaker.*

Packard, Silas S. Complete course of business training: instruction in book-keeping, arithmetic, commercial law and correspondence. ('72.) New ed. 8°. '76. 75c. .... *Packard.*

Packard, Silas S., *continued.*

— Manual of theoretical training; for use in the International Business College Association. ('67.) New ed. 8°. '76. 50c. .... *Packard.*

— Packard's complete course of business training and key. 8°. '73. $3 .... *Packard.*

— Programme of study in Packard's complete course. 8°. '73. 40c. .... *Packard.*

— *See also* Bryant, H. B., Stratton, H. D., *and* Packard, S. S.; — Williams, J. D., *and* Packard, S. S.

Packington parish and the diver's daughter. Paull, M. A. $1.25 .... *Nat. Temp.*

Paddle your own canoe. 18°. 30c. .... *Am. S. S.*

Paddock, Zach. Memoir of Rev. B: Paddock. 12°. '74. $1.50 .... *Meth. Bk. Conc.*

Paddock: opera. 16°. pap., 15c. .... *French.*

Paddy, the piper. Pilgrim, J. 15c. .... *French.*

Paddy Carey. Power, T. 15c. .... *French.*

Paddy Miles: farce. 16°. pap., 15c. .... *French.*

Paden, I: History of the devil. 16°. pap., 10c. *D. M. Bennett.*

Paer, F. Twenty-four exercises for soprano or tenor. f°. $2 .... *Brainard.*

Paez, Ramon. Libro segundo de geografía descriptiva, destinado á seguir al primero de Smith. New ed., rev. and enl. 4°. $1.75 .... *Appleton.*

— Travels and adventures in South and Central America; with life in the llanos of Venezuela. 12°. '73. *$2 .... *Belknap.*

Pagani, J. B. Anima divota; or, devout soul; tr. from the Ital. 24°. 60c. .... *Cath. Pub.*

Page, D: P. Elements of geology. 12°. '60. $1.25. *Barnes.*

— Theory and practice of teaching; with sketch of author. ('58.) 19th ed. 12°. $1.50 ... *Barnes.*

Page, H. A. (*pseud.*) *See* Yapp, Alex.

Page, Harlan. Memoir of W: A. Hallock. ill. 18°. '35. 45c. .... *Am. Tr.*

Page, T: J. La Plata, the Argentine Confederation and Paraguay: narrative of exploration in 1853–'56. New ed., with account of explorations, 1859–'60. map and ill. 8°. $5 .... *Harper.*

Page (The), and other stories. 18°. 50c. ..... *O'Shea.*

Page of the Duke of Savoy. Dumas, A. 50c. *Routledge.*

Paget, F. A. Report on the economical road maintenance and horse-draught through steam-road rolling. 8°. '70. pap., 80c. .... *Spon.*

Paget, F. E. Faith and patience; in work and warfare, triumph and reward. 12°. '75. $2.50 ..... *Pott.*

— Plain village sermons. 2 v. 12°. '75. $4.50 .. *Pott.*

Paget, Ja. Surgical pathology: lectures. 3d Lond. ed., rev. by W. Turner. ill. 8°. '70. $7.50; leath., $8.50 .... *Lindsay.*

Paget, J: Hungary and Transylvania. 2 v. 12°. $2 .. *Lea.*

Paget, J: Judicial puzzles gath. from state trials: v. 3 of Legal recreations. 12°. $1.50 ... *S. Whitney.*

Paige, Alonzo C. *See* New York State, Chancery reports.

Paige, Elbridge Gerry. ["Dow, *jr.*"] Short patent sermons. 4 ser. 12°. ea., $1.50; pap., $1 .. *Peterson.*

Paige, *Mrs.* J. B. New inductive and eclectic method for the piano-forte. 4°. '70. bds., $3.75 .. *Ditson.*

Paige, Lucius R. Commentary on New Test. 6 v. 12°. '44–'69. ea., $1 .... *Universalist.*

Cont.: Matthew and Mark. — Luke and John. — Acts. — Romans. — Corinthians. — Corinthians to Revelation.

Pain quotidien pour les chrétiens. *See* Daily food for Christians.

Paine, C: Iron rails on the Michigan Southern and Northern Indiana Railway. 8°. pap., 55c. *Am. Soc. of C. E.*

Paine, D: Social minstrel; for the domestic circle, schools, etc. f°. '44. $1; bds., 75c. ... *Crocker.*

Paine, Elij., *jr.* *See* United States, Circuit Court reports.

Paine, J: A. Questions on Romans. 12°. '70. 35c. *Randolph.*

Paine, J: Knowles. St. Peter. [Oratorio.] 8°. '72. $2; bds., $1.75; pap., $1.60 .... *Ditson.*

— — Choruses. 8°. '72. bds., $1.25 .... *Ditson.*

Paine, Levi Leonard. *See* Book of praise.

Paine, Martyn. Institutes of medicine. 8°. shp., $5. *Harper.*

— Physiology of the soul and instinct as distinguished from materialism; with demonstrations of the divine communication of the narratives of creation and the flood. 8°. $5 .... *Harper.*

Paine, Rob. Life and times of William McKendree. ('70.) 2d ed. 2 v. 12°. '75. ea., $2 .. *So. Meth.*

Paine, T. O. Temple of Solomon, the tabernacle and last temple described. pl. 8°. $2.50 .. *H. H. Carter.*

Paine, T: Works; with memoir. 3 v. 8°. $7 .. *Mendum.*

— Age of reason: investigation of true and fabulous theology. 12°. *net*, 50c.; pap., 25c. ... *Mendum.*

— *Same;* [also] Examination of the prophecies; with essay on character and services of P. by G. J. Holyoake. 12°. '76. 75c.; pap., 50c. .. *Somerby.*

— *Same;* [also] Examination of the prophecies; [also] Essay on dreams, etc. 18°. *net*, 75c. .. *Mendum.*

— Common sense. 12°. '60. pap., 15c. ... *D. Thomas.*

— *Same;* with brief sketch of author's life. 12°. pap., 20c. .... *Mendum.*

— Political writings; with sketch of the author's life. 2 v. 8°. $5 .... *Mendum.*

— *Germ.* Politische Werke. 2 v. 12°. $3; hf. mor., $3.50 .... *F. W. Thomas.*

— Rights of man: answer to Burke's attack on the French revolution. 12°. 50c. .... *Mendum.*

— Theological and misc. writings. 12°. $2.50 .. *Mendum.*

— *Germ.* Theologische Werke. 12°. $1.50; hf. mor., $1.75 .... *F. W. Thomas.*

— Thomas Paine, the author hero of the Am. revolution. 8°. pap., 10c. .... *Mendum.*

Paine, W: Address to members of Am. Antiq. Soc., King's Chapel, Boston, on 3d anniv., Oct. 23, 1815; with list of officers. 8°. '15. 50c. ... *Am. Antiq.*

Paine, W: New school remedies, and their applic. to cure of diseases, incl. those of women, children and surgery. 2d ed. 12°. '68. $3 ... *Claxton.*

— Treatise on principles and practice of medicine and pathology, diseases of women and children, and medical surgery. ('66.) 3d ed. 8°. '75. shp., $6 .... *Claxton.*

Painstaking. 18°. '62. 40c. .... *Randolph.*

Painter, gilder and varnisher's companion; with app. on colors and coloring; [and] Chevreul's Principles of harmony and contrast of color. ('50; cop. '69.) 27th ed. 12°. '75. $1.50 ... *Baird.*

Painter of Ghent. Jerrold, D. 15c. .. *Ames; French.*

Painter's camp. Hamerton, P. G. $1.50; $2 .. *Roberts.*

Painter's handbook: instructions for house and ornamental painting. 12°. '68. pap., 25c. ... *Happy.*

Painter's manual: guide to house and sign painting, graining, varnishing, etc. 12°. pap., 50c. .. *Haney.*

Pair of blue eyes. Hardy, T. $1.25 .... *Holt.*

Pair of pigeons. Stirling, E. 15c. .... *French.*

Pair of shoes. ill. 18°. '75. 30c. .... *Dodd.*

Pakenham, F. J. Influence. 16°. $1.30 ... *Pres. Bd.*

Palace and cottage. Adams, W. T. $1.50 ... *Lee & S.*

Palace and hovel. Kirwan, D. J. *$3.50–$5 .. *Col. Bk.*

Palace of infamy. Reynolds, G. W. M. 50c.; 25c. *De Witt.*

Palaces and prisons. Stephens, A. S. $1.75; $1.50. *Peterson.*

Palafox, J: de. Christmas nights' entertainments; tr. from the Span. 18°. '72. 75c. .... *Kenedy.*

Palais Royal. *See* Story of.

Palatinate catechism; tr. by H. Harbaugh. 16°. 50c.; — in Germ., 12c. .... *Ref. Ch. Pub.*

— *See also* Heidelberg catechism.

Paleario, Aonio. Beneficio della morte di Cristo. 18°. '51. 25c. .... *Am. Tr.*

— *Eng.* Benefit of Christ's death. 18°. 40c. .. *Pres. Bd.*

— — *See also* Blackburn, W. M., Aonio Paleario and his friends.

— *Fr.* Bienfaits de Jésus Christ crucifié. 18°. '58. 30c.; pap., 10c. .... *Am. Tr.*

— — *Same.* 18°. 15c. .... *Pres. Bd.*

Palenzuela, Ramon. *See* Ollendorff, H. G.

Palestine after the Messiah's advent. Headley, P. C. 25c.; 30c. .... *J. E. Potter.*

Palestine Exploration Fund. Our work in Palestine: account of expeditions sent to the Holy Land by the committee since 1865. maps, plans and ill. cr. 8°. $1.50 .... *Scribner, W. & A.*

— Recovery of Jerusalem: explor. and disc. in city and Holy Land, by C. W. Wilson, C. Warren, etc.; with introd. by A. P. Stanley; ed. by W. Morrison. ill. 8°. $3.50; hf. cf., $6.50 ..... *Appleton.*

Palestine under pagan kings. Headley, P. C. 25c.; 30c. .... *J. E. Potter.*

Paley, W: Works. por. 8°. $3 .... *Desilver.*

— Horæ Paulinæ. 12°. '51. 60c. .... *Am. Tr.*

— Natural theology; ed. by D. E. Bartlett. 2 v. ill. 12°. $3 .... *Harper.*

— *Same;* ed. by J. Ware. ill. 12°. $1.50 ... *Sheldon.*

— *Same;* with notes, etc., by Lord Brougham and Sir C. Bell, and obs. and notes by Bp. Potter. 2 v. ill. 18°. $1.50 .... *Harper.*

— *Same;* rev. to harmonize with mod. science by F. Le G. Clark. 12°. '75. $1.75 .... *Pott.*

— *Same;* [also] Horæ Paulinæ. ill. 12°. '48. $1.50. *Am. Tr.*

— Principles of moral and political philosophy; with questions for students. 12°. $1.50 .... *Harper.*

— View of evidences of Christianity. 18°. 75c. .. *Harper.*

— *Same;* with memoir. por. 18°. 65c. ... *C. H. Davis.*

— *Same;* with notes, app. and pref. by E. A. Litton. 16°. $1.50 .... *Pott.*

— *Same;* with notes and add. by C. M. Nairne. ('54.) New ed. 12°. '74. $1.50 .... *Carter.*

— *Same;* with annot. by R. Whately. 8°. $2.50 .. *Miller.*

Palfrey, J: Gorham. History of New England during the Stuart dynasty. v. 4. maps and pl. 8°. '76. $4 .... *Little, B. & Co.*

Note. v. 1-3 are o. p.

Palfrey, Sa. H. ["E. Foxton."] Agnes Wentworth. 12°. $1.50 .... *Lippincott.*

— Hermann; or, young knighthood. 2 v. 12°. $3.50; — in 1 v. 12°. $1.50 .... *Lee & S.*

Palgrave, *Sir* Fs. History of the Anglo-Saxons. 12°. $3 .... *Scribner, W. & A.*

— History of Normandy and of England, to death of William Rufus. 4 v. 8°. ea., $6.50 .. *Macmillan.*

Palgrave, Fs. Turner. Essays on art. fp. 8°. '66. $1.50 .... *Macmillan.*

— *Same.* 16°. '67. $1.75; hf. cf., $3.50 ... *Hurd & H.*

— Five days' entertainments at Wentworth Grange: book for children. ill. sm. 4°. '68. $2 .. *Macmillan.*

— Gems of English art of 19th century. ill. 4°. $10; mor., $15 .... *Routledge.*

— Lyrical poems fp. 8°. '71. $1.75 .... *Macmillan.*

— Original hymns. 3d ed., enl. 18°. 50c. .. *Macmillan.*

— *Same.* sq. 24°. '68. pap., 25c. .... *Randolph.*

— Remarks upon Sir W. Scott. *See* Scott, *Sir* W.

— (*ed.*) Children's treasury of Eng. song; with notes. 18°. '75. $1.25 .... *Macmillan.*

— Golden treasury of the best songs and lyrical poems in the Eng. lang. 18°. '75. $1.25 ... *Macmillan.*

— *Same.* 18°. 75c. — 16°. $1.25 .... *Allyn.*

Palgrave, Reg. F. D. House of Commons: illustrations of its history and practice: lectures. cr. 8°. '69. $1.25 .... *Macmillan.*

Palgrave, W: Gifford. Essays on eastern questions. 8°. '72. $3.50 ..... *Macmillan.*
— Hermann Agha: an eastern romance. (Leis. hour. ser.) 16°. '72. $1.25 ..... *Holt.*
— Narrative of a year's journey through central and eastern Arabia, 1862–3. 6th [chp.] ed. map, plans and por. cr. 8°. '73. $2.50 ... *Macmillan.*

Palissy, the Huguenot potter. *See* Brightwell, C. L.

Pallett, H: The miller's, millwright's and engineer's guide. ('66.) 5th ed. ill. 12°. '74. $3 .. *Baird.*

Palliser, *Mrs.* Bury. China collector's pocket companion. 2d ed., enl., with marks. 16°. $2.50. *Scribner, W.& A.*
— Historic devices, badges and war cries. ill. 8°. $9. *Scribner, W. & A.*
— History of lace. New ed., rev. ill. and col. designs. 8°. $10.50 ..... *Scribner, W. & A.*

Palliser, J: Solitary hunter; or, sporting adventures on the prairies. 8°. pap., 25c. ..... *De Witt.*
— *Same.* 16°. bds., 80c. ..... *Routledge.*

Palm (The). Wyman, C. M. $1.50 ..... *Church.*

Palm land. Samuels, A. F. 50c. ..... *Lee & S.*

Palm of victory. Dowling, L. H. 20c. .... *Dowling.*

Palm tribes. ('56.) 2d ed. 18°. '71. 50c. ... *So. Meth.*

Palmer, A. B. Four lectures on homœopathy. 8°. '69. pap., 25c. ..... *Fiske & D.*

Palmer, B: Morgan. Christianity and law. 18°. '71. 25c. ..... *N. Y. Ref. Ch. Bd.; Pres. Com.*
— Family (The); in its civil and churchly aspects. 16°. '76. $1 ..... *N. Y. Ref. Ch. Bd.; Pres. Com.*
— Life and letters of Ja. H. Thornwell. por. 8°. '76. *net*, $3 ... *N. Y. Ref. Ch. Bd.; Pres. Com.; Whittett.*
— Pious physician. 18°. '70. 25c. *N. Y. Ref. Ch. Bd.; Pres. Com.*

Palmer, E: H: Desert of the exodus: journeys on foot in the wilderness of the forty years' wanderings; undertaken in connection with the Ordnance Survey of Sinai and the Palestine Exploration Fund. maps and ill. cr. 8°. $3 ..... *Harper.*
— History of the Jewish nation. ill. and map. 12°. '74. $1.50 ..... *Pott.*
— *Same;* with introd. by S. F. Smith. ill. 16°. $1.25. *Lothrop.*
— Outlines of Scripture geog. maps. 18°. 40c. ... *Nelson.*

Palmer, Fs. Pl. Old tales for the young. ill. 16°. $1.25. *Routledge.*

Palmer, H. R. Collection of concert choruses. 8°. 75c. ..... *Church.*
— Elements of musical composition. 16°. 50c. ... *Church.*
— Normal collection. [Hymn book.] obl. 8°. $1.50. *Church.*
— Rudimental class teaching. [Music.] 16°. 50c. *Church.*
— Sabbath school songs. 12°. '72. bds., 25c. *Adams, B. & L.*
— Song herald. obl. 12°. '76. bds., 75c. .... *Church.*
— Song king. 8°. 75c. ..... *Church.*
— Song queen. 8°. pap., 50c.; bds., 60c. ..... *Church.*
— Songs of love. obl. 12°. 35c. ..... *Church.*
— Theory of music: guide to study of thorough-bass, harmony, etc. 16°. '76. $1 ..... *Church.*
— *See also* Emerson, L. O., *and* Palmer, H. R.
— *and* Emerson, L. O. The leader: sacred and secular music. obl. 8°. '74. bds., $1.38 ..... *Ditson.*
— — The song monarch: collection of secular and sacred music. obl. 8°. '74. bds., 75c. .. *Ditson.*

Palmer, H. V. The younger son. [Fiction.] ill. 8°. (Lond.) pap., 30c. ..... *Am. News.*

Palmer, Jos. H. Practical book-keeping; with business papers. 12°. $1. — Key, 10c. .... *Sheldon.*

Palmer, *Mrs.* J. W. Stratford gallery; or, the Shakespeare sisterhood; compr. forty-five ideal por. imp. 8°. mor., $15 ..... *Appleton.*

Palmer, J: Williamson (*ed.*) Folk songs: book of golden poems for the popular heart. ('66.) New ed. ill. and fac-similes. 8°. '67. $15; mor., $18. *Scribner.*

Palmer, J: Williamson (*ed.*), *continued.*
— Poetry of compliment and courtship. 12°. $4; mor., $6.50. — 16°. $1.50 ..... *Osgood.*

Palmer, Lynde (*pseud.*) *See* Peebles, *Mrs.* Ma. L.

Palmer, P: S. History of Lake Champlain, 1609–1814. roy. 8°. '66. hf. shp., $5 ..... *Munsell.*

Palmer, *Mrs.* Phœbe. [Works.] 13 v. ..... *Palmer.*
Cont.: Crowning testimony, 8°, 25c. — Entire devotion, 16°, 40c. — Faith and its effects, 12°, 75c. — Four years in the old world, 8°, $3.50. — Incidental illustrations, 8°, $1.50. — Mother's gift, 12°, $1.50. — Pioneer experiences, 8°, $1.50. — Promise of the Father, 8°, $1.50. — Sweet Mary, 16°, 40c. — Tongue of fire on the daughter of the Lord, 16°, pap., 10c. — Useful disciple, 12°, 65c. — Way of holiness, 12°, 70c. — Life and letters; ed. by R. Wheatley, 8°, $2.50.

Palmer, Ray. Earnest words on true success in life; addressed to young men and women. 12°. '73. $1.50 ..... *Barnes.*
— Hints on the formation of religious opinions. 12°. '68. $1.25; $1.75 ..... *Randolph.*
— Home; or, the unlost paradise. sq. 16°. '72. $1.25. *Randolph.*
— Hymns and poems. 16°. '65. $1.75 .... *Randolph.*
— Hymns of my holy hours. 16°. '67. $1.50. *Randolph.*
— Poems: sacred poetry. 8°. '76. $4; hf. cf., $6; mor., $8 ..... *Barnes.*
— Poetical works. 8°. '75. $4 ..... *Barnes.*
— Remember me; or, the holy communion. 12°. '65. $1.25 ..... *Barnes; Bost. Am. Tr.*

Palmer, *Sir* Roundell. *See* Selborne, *Lord.*

Palmer, T: H. Arithmetic, oral and written, applied by means of suggestive questions. 12°. '54. 90c. ..... *Crocker.*

Palmer, W: Compendious ecclesiastical history. 12°. '75. $1.25 ..... *Pott.*

Palmer, W: Calendar of Virginia state papers, and other MSS., 1652–1781, preserved in Capitol at Richmond. v. 1. 4°. '75. pap., $4 .. *J. W. Randolph.*
— *Same.* 4°. '76. $3.50 ..... *West, J. & Co.*

Palmetto leaves. Stowe, H. B. $2 ..... *Osgood.*

Palmquest, G. *and* P. Pilgrims-Sanger pa wägen till det himmelskasion. 32°. '67. 45c. .... *Am. Tr.*

Palvinita; or, veiled songstress. Glover, H. $2 .. *Peters.*

Pamela. *See* Richardson, S:

Pan. Byron, H. J. 15c. ..... *French.*

Panama in 1855. Tomes, R. 75c. ..... *Harper.*

Pancharis. *See* Bonnefons, J:

Panckoucke, C. L. F. *See* Arnault, M. A., *and* Panckoucke, C. L. F.

Pancoast, Seth. Blue and red light. cr. 8°. $2. *J. M. Stoddart.*
— Ladies' medical guide and marriage friend. ('64.) New ed. ill. 12°. '76. $1.75 ..... *J. E. Potter.*
— *Same.* ill. 12°. '75. *$2.25 ..... *Hubbard.*

Pancoast, W: H. Report of the autopsy on the Siamese twins; with other information conc. their life. ill. sm. 12°. pap., 25c. .. *Lippincott.*

Pandora's box. Byron, H. J. 15c. ..... *French.*

Pandosy, M. C. Grammar and dictionary of the Yakama lang. 4°. '62. pap., $3 ..... *Shea.*
— — *See also* Shea, J. G.

Panofka, H. Twelve vocalises progressives, pour contralto. (op. 89.) f°. pap., $4 ... *Schirmer.*
— Twenty-four vocalises for alto or baritone. (op. 81 bis.) f°. pap., $4; — in 2 bks., ea., $2 .. *Schirmer.*
— Twenty-four vocalises for soprano, mezzo-soprano, or tenor. (op. 81.) New ed. f°. pap., $3; — in 2 bks., ea., $1.50 ..... *Schirmer.*

Panseron, A. A B C of music; or, progressive lessons in the rudiments of music and solfeggi; tr. by J. R. Fry, with add. by F. Dorigo and J. Concone. f°. '47. bds., $4; — abridg., $1 ..... *Ditson.*
— *Same;* abridg. 8°. $1.25; bds., $1 ..... *Gordon.*
— Method of vocalization. f°. '47. bds., $3.50; — abridg., $1.25 ..... *Ditson.*

Panseron, A., *continued.*
— Méthode complète de vocalisation pour mezzo soprano. 8°. *net*, pap., $6............*Schirmer.*
Pansies. Whitney, A. D. T. $1.50; $3; $4..*Osgood.*
Pansy (*pseud.*) *See* Alden, *Mrs.* I. M.
Pansy lib.; — picture lib.; — ser. *See* Alden, I. M.
Pansy's picture book. Alden, I. M. $2; $2.25..*Lothrop.*
Pantomime Joe. Brett, —. 75c. ....*Am. News.*
Pão quotidiano (O). *See* Daily food for Christians.
Papal system (The). 16°. 10c.............*Pres. Bd.*
Papa's boy. Davis, C. E. K. 75c. ....*Lothrop.*
Papa's little soldiers. Davis, C. E. K. 45c. ...*Hoyt.*
Papa's pet. *See* Swallow stories.
Papa's present. *See* Baker, *Mrs.* H. N. W.
Papa's pretty gift book. ill. sm. 4°. $1.75. *Scribner, W. & A.*
Paper mill reference book. 4°. '71. $30..*J. A. Murphy.*
Paper money, the root of evil. Mann, C. A. $2. *Appleton.*
Paper wings. Phillips, W. 15c.............*French.*
Papers for home reading. Hall, J. $1.75.....*Dodd.*
Papers for thoughtful girls. *See* Keddie, *Miss* H.
Papers from Overlook House. *See* Beasley, F. W.
Paphian bower. Planché, J. R., *and* Dance, C. 15c. *French.*
Papillon, Fernand. Nature and life: facts and doctrines rel. to const. of matter, new dynamics and philosophy of nature; tr. by A. R. Macdonough. 12°. $2..........................*Appleton.*
Papillonetta. Brough, W. 15c.............*French.*
Papist misrepresented and truly represented. *See* Gother, J.
Papy, Mariano D. *See* Florida, Supreme Court reports.
Paquita: comic opera. 16°. pap., 15c.......*French.*
Par ordre du roi. Hugo, V. 50c...........*Appleton.*
Parable of the raindrop. 16°. '70. $1........*Hoyt.*
Parable of the ten virgins. Seiss, J. A. $1. *Luth. Bk. St.; Smith, E. & Co.*
Parables. [Quest. book.] 18°. bds., 15c...*Am. Bapt.*
Parables for children. Abbott, E. A. $1.25..*Macmillan.*
Parables from nature. Gatty, M. 75c. ......*Carter.*
Parables of animals. *See* Sunberry Dale lib.
Parables of our Lord; ill. by J. Franklin. 4°. mor., $7 ....*Claxton; Lippincott.*
— *See also* Gleichnisse.
Parables of our Lord explained. Bourdillon, F. $1.50. *Meth. Bk. Conc.*
Paraclete (The). Parker, J. $1.50 ....*Scribner.*
Paraclete (The). *See* Tracy, J. C.
Paradies Gärtlein (Das). [Cath. prayer book.] 32°. 35c.–$1...........................*Strong.*
— *Same.* 32°. 50c.–$2 ....*T. Kelly.*
Paradise. Patterson, R. M. $1.25.........*Pres. Bd.*
Paradise in the Pacific. Bliss, W. R. $1.25..*Sheldon.*
Paradise lost. *See* Milton, J:
Paradise lost; or, the great dragon cast out! 12°. 70c. *Mendum.*
Paradise of childhood. Wiebe, E. $3; $2.50. *M. Bradley.*
Paradise of children. Morren, N. 35c. ....*Pres. Bd.*
Paradise of the Christian soul. *See* Horst, J. M.
Paradise of doctors. *See* Bigelow, J.
Paradise of God; or, the virtues of the sacred heart of Jesus; by a father of the Soc. of Jesus. 18°. '74. $1; $1.50..........................*Murphy.*
Paradise regained. *See* Milton, J:
Paradise row and Violet: temperance story. ('65.) New ed. ill. 16°. '68. 80c..............*Hoyt.*
Parasit (Der). *See* Schiller, J. F. v.
Parasite (The). Picard, L. B. 75c. .....*Lippincott.*

Pardee, R: G. Sabbath school index: hist. and progress of S.-schools, with modes of instruction, etc. 16°. '68. $1.25................*Garrigues.*
— Strawberry culture. 12°. 75c. ....*Judd.*
Pardey, H. O. Nature's nobleman: comedy. 16°. pap., 15c..................................*French.*
Pardoe, *Miss* Jla. Works. 8°. $4; — in 5 v., pap. *Peterson.*

Cont.: Confessions of a pretty woman. — Rival beauties. — Romance of the harem. — Wife's trials, *ea.*, 75c. — Jealous wife, 50c.

— Adopted heir. 12°. $1.75; pap., $1.50...*Peterson.*
— Earl's secret. 12°. $1.75; pap., $1.50...*Peterson.*
— Episodes of French hist. during the consulate and first empire. 12°. $1.50 ....*Harper.*
— Life's struggle. 12°. $1.75; pap., $1.50..*Peterson.*
— Louis XIV. and the court of France in 17th cent. 2 v. ill. 12°. $4; $5..................*Harper.*
— Parental instruction for young persons; sel. mainly from writings of a physician. 8°. 75c...*Harper.*
Pardon, G: F: ["Capt. Crawley."] [Handbooks.] 5 v. roy. 32°. ea., bds., 20c.............*Routledge.*

Cont.: Handbook of billiards and bagatelle — of chess — of draughts and backgammon — of whist. — The card-player.

— Guide to London and its suburbs. maps and ill. 16°. bds., 50c. ....*Routledge.*
— Manly games for boys. ill. 12°. $3..*Scribner, W. & A.*
Parents and children. Witt, C. de. $1......*Nelson.*
Parents' assistant. *See* Edgeworth, M.
Parents' friend. Smith, D. 50c.......*Meth. Bk. Conc.*
Parents' gift. Collins, R. 60c..............*Claxton.*
Parents' guide. Laurie, J. $1 ....*Boericke.*
Parents' text-book for little children; by author of "Thoughtful hours." 18°. 90c.........*Nelson.*
Parenty, *Abbé* —. Life of St. Angela Merici of Brescia, foundress of Order of St. Ursula; tr., with hist. of the Order in Ireland, Canada and the U. S. by J. G. Shea. 16°. '57. $1...*Cunningham.*
Paris, J: Ayrton. Pharmacologia: inquiry into operation of medicinal bodies upon which are founded the theory and art of prescribing. New ed., rev. with notes by C. A. Lee. 8°. $1.50....*Harper.*
Paris, L: P. d'Orléans (*Comte*) de. History of the civil war in Am.; tr. by L. F. Tasistro; ed. by H. Coppée. v. 1–2. col. maps. 8°. '75–'76. ea., $3.50; shp., $4.50; hf. mor., $6 ....*Coates.*
Comprises v. 1–4 of Fr. ed.
Paris. Burnand, F. C. 15c. ....*French.*
Paris, ancient and modern; rev. by T. O. Summers. ('58.) 2d ed. 18°. '75. 50c...........*So. Meth.*
Paris and back for £5: farce. 16°. pap., 15c...*French.*
Paris and London: farce. 16°. pap., 15c. ...*French.*
Paris and pleasure. Selby, C. 15c...........*French.*
Paris in Blut u. Feuer. Homburg, C. 50c...*F. W. Thomas.*
Paris in December, 1851. Tenot, E. $2.50..*Hurd & H.*
Paris sketch-book. *See* Thackeray, W: M.
Pariser Taugenichts. 12°. pap., 15c.........*Radde.*
— *Same;* [also] Lumpaci Vagabundus. 16°. 25c. *Morwitz.*
Parish, T. Parish will case. *See* Delafield, H.
Parish and other pencillings. Murray, N. $1.50..*Harper.*
Parish hall. Marwin, M. J. 50c.............*Hoyt.*
Parish of Fair Haven. Miller, E. H. 15c...*Un. Bk. Conc.*
Parish papers. Macleod, N. $1.25..........*Carter.*
Parisian sights and French principles seen through Am. spectacles. Jarves, J. J. 2 v. ea., $1.50..*Harper.*
Parisians. *See* Bulwer-Lytton, *Sir* E. G. E. L.
Park, Edwards A. Address at funeral of S. H. Taylor. cr. 8°. '71. pap., 25c. ....*Draper.*
— Memoir of life and character of S: Hopkins. 8°. $1.25..........................*Cong. Pub.*
— Memoir of Natl. Emmons; with sketches of his friends and pupils. por. 8°. $3.50..*Cong. Pub.*

Park, Edwards A., *continued.*
— (*ed.*) The atonement: discourses and treatises by Edwards, Smalley, Maxcy, Emmons, Griffin, Burge and Weeks; with introd. by E. A. Park. 8°. $4 .... *Cong. Pub.*
— Preacher and pastor. 12°. '45. $1.25.... *Draper.*
— *See also* Phelps, A., Park, E. A., *and* Furber, D. L.
— *and* Phelps, Aust., *and* Mason, Lowell. New Sabbath hymn and tune book; prep. for Baptist churches by F. Wayland. 16°. $1.38–$2.90; — with index. 8°. $2.25–$10 .... *Hamersley.*
— — — Sabbath hymn book; prep. for Baptist churches by Francis Wayland. sm. 4°. $1–$1.70. — 16°. $2–$6. — 12°. $8–$10 .... *Hamersley.*
— — — *Same;* cont. tunes only. 16°. 75c... *Hamersley.*

Park, Mungo. Travels, with account of his death; from journal of Isaaco, and later discoveries rel. to his fate and the termination of the Niger. 18°. 75c. .... *Harper.*

Parke, Uriah. Farmers' and mechanics' practical arithmetic; rev. and enl. by H. F. Percy. 12°. '70. hf. roan, 60c. — Key. 16°. hf. roan, 60c. *Cushings & B.*
— Philosophy of arithmetic. 8°. $2 .... *Moss.*

Parker, *Mrs.* —. Annals of the Christian church. 18°. '43. 60c. .... *Meth. Bk. Conc.*

Parker, Amasa J. *See* New York State, Reports of criminal cases.

Parker, *Mrs.* Caro. E. R. [Juveniles.] 6 v. ill. 18°. '69–'73 .... *Am. Tr.*
Cont.: Grandmamma's trunkful of stories, 50c. — Old kitchen fire, 30c. — Pleasant pictures, 50c. — Stories for the little ones, 50c. — Twenty stories and twenty poems, 80c. — Wilson's kindling depot, 60c.
— Stories for the little ones. 2 v. ill. 32°. ea., 30c. *Bost. Am. Tr.*

Parker, C: H. Digest of California Sup. Court reports (v. 1–34). 2 v. 8°. '69. shp., $22.50.. *Bancroft.*
— *Same;* [also] Digest of v. 34–46; by R. Desty. 3 v. 8°. shp., $25 .... *S. Whitney.*
— *See also* California, Civil pract. act; General laws.

Parker, E. P. Song flowers. obl. 16°. bds., 35c. *Hamersley.*
— Sunday school songs. sq. 18°. 35c.; 40c... *Hamersley.*
— *See also* Book of praise.

Parker, E: H. Handbook for mothers: guide in care of young children. 12°. '57. $1.50.. *Hurd & H.*

Parker, Foxhall A. Fleet tactics under steam. ill. 18°. '70. $2.50 .... *VanNostrand.*
— Naval howitzer afloat. pl. 8°. '66. $4.. *VanNostrand.*
— Naval howitzer ashore. pl. 8°. '65. $4.. *VanNostrand.*
— Squadron tactics under steam. pl. 8°. '64. $5. *VanNostrand.*

Parker, Fs. J. Colonel W: Prescott, commander in battle of Bunker Hill. 8°. '75. pap., 25c... *Williams.*

Parker, H. M. Proceedings of 1st reunion of 11th Regt., Ill. Vol. Inf., Ottawa, Ill., Oct. 27, 1875; [with] brief hist. of regt., etc. sm. 8°. '75. 75c.; pap., 50c. .... *Osman.*

Parker, *Mrs.* Helen F. Arthur's aquarium. 16°. 75c. *Cong. Pub.*
— Blind Florette. 16°. $1.25 .... *Cong. Pub.*
— Constance Aylmer: story of 17th cent. ('68.) New ed. 12°. '69. $1.50 .... *Scribner.*
— Frank's search for sea-shells. ill. 16°. $1.15. *Bost. Am. Tr.*
— Missions and martyrs in Madagascar. ill. 16°. 80c. *Bost. Am. Tr.*
— Rambles after land shells. ill. 18°. 60c... *Bost. Am. Tr.*
— — *See also* Library of curious things.

Parker, J. C. D. Manual of harmony. 16°. $1.. *Gordon.*
— Sacred chorus book. obl. 4°. $1.75 ...... *Gordon.*
— Seven-part songs. 8°. '75. bds., 60c.; per pt., 10c. *Ditson.*
— Theoretical and pract. harmony; with treatment of thorough bass by B. F. Baker. 8°. '70. $2.. *Ditson.*

Parker, Jenny Marsh. [Juveniles.] 7 v. 18°.. *Dutton.*
Cont.: Around the manger, 40c. — Dick Wortley; or, choosing a profession, 50c. — Life of St. Paul; or, "the soldier of the cross," 35c.; 40c. — Seed for spring time, 40c. — Simple lessons, 35c.; 40c. — Story of Andy, 60c. — Under his banner, 90c.
— Barley wood. 16°. 75c. .... *Claremont.*

Parker, Jl. Invitations to true happiness, and motives for becoming a Christian. 18°. 50c.... *Harper.*
— *and* Smith, T. R. Presbyterian's handbook of the Church. 16°. 90c. .... *Harper.*

Parker, J: A. Quadrature of the circle: demonstrations of errors of geometers in finding approximations in use; incl. lectures on polar magnetism and non-existence of projectile forces in nature. 8°. $2.50. .... *Wiley.*

Parker, J: H: Concise glossary of terms used in Grecian, Roman, Italian and Gothic architecture. New ed., rev. ill. 16°. (Oxford.) '69. $3. *Little, B. & Co.; Scribner, W. & A.*
— Introduction to study of Gothic architecture. ill. 16°. $2.50 .... *Scribner, W. & A.*

Parker, Jos. Ad clerum: advices to a young preacher. 16°. '71. $1.50 .... *Roberts.*
— Ecce Deus: essays on life and doctrine of Jesus Christ; with controversial notes on "Ecce homo." 16°. '67. $1.50 .... *Roberts.*
— Job's comforters; or, scientific sympathy; with introd. and notes by G. Z. Gray. sq. 18°. '75. pap., 25c. .... *Randolph.*
— Paraclete (The): essay on personality and ministry of the Holy Ghost, with some ref. to current discussions. ('74.) New ed. 12°. '76. $1.50.. *Scribner.*
— Pulpit notes; with essay on preaching of Jesus Christ. 8°. '73. $2 .... *Routledge.*
— Springdale Abbey; from diaries and letters of an English preacher. 12°. '69. $1.50.... *Claxton.*

Parker, Jos. E. *See* Goddard, P. B., *and* Parker, J. E.

Parker, Langston. Modern treatment of syphilitic diseases; with cases, formulæ, etc. 5th ed., enl. 8°. '71. $4.25 .... *Lindsay.*
— Treatment of syphilitic diseases by the mercurial vapor baths; ed. by J. W. Foye. 12°. '74. $1.50. *Williams.*

Parker, Nath. H. Missouri as it is in 1867: historical gazetteer. ill. 8°. '67. $3.50.. *Claxton; Lippincott.*
— Missouri handbook. 16°. '65. 50c.; pap., 25c. *S. W. Bk. & Pub.*

Parker, R: Green. [School readers: old ed.] 6 v. '49–'52 .... *Barnes.*
Cont.: School primer, 18°, hf. bd., 12c. — First school reader, 18°, hf. bd., 20c. — Second, 18°, hf. bd., 35c. — Third, 18°, hf. bd., 50c. — Fourth, 18°, 75c. — Rhetorical, 12°, $1.
— Aids to Eng. composition. 12°. $1.25 .... *Harper.*
— Geographical questions. 12°. 50c. .... *Harper.*
— Juvenile philosophy; or, philos. in familiar conversations. (Parker's philosophy, pt. 1.) 18°. '71. hf. bd., 38c. .... *Collins & Bro.*
— *Same.* pt. 2. 16°. '75. hf. bd., 56c. .. *Collins & Bro.*
— Outlines of general hist. 12°. shp., $1.50.. *Harper.*
— Progressive exercises in Eng. composition. 12°. 50c. New ed., rev. and enl. 12°. $1.. *R. S. Davis (B.)*
— School compend. of natural and experimental philos. (Parker's philos., pt. 3.) New ed., enl. by G. W. Plympton. ill. 12°. '74. $1.75 .. *Collins & Bro.*
— *and* Fox, C: Progressive exercises in Eng. grammar. 12°. '34. shp., $1 .... *Crocker.*
— *and* Watson, J. M. [National ser. of readers.] 7 v. '57–'66. .... *Barnes.*
Cont.: Nat. first reader, 18°, hf. bd., 38c. — second, 18°, hf. bd., 63c. — third, 12°, hf. bd., $1 — fourth, 12°, $1.50 — fifth, 8°, $1.88 — Nat. pronounc. speller, 12°, hf. bd., 50c. — Nat. school primer, 18°, hf. bd., 25c.
— *and* Zachos, H. Introductory lessons in reading and elocution. 12°. '68. 75c. .... *Barnes.*

Parker, Rosa Abbott. ["Rosa Abbott."] Rosa Abbott stories. 6 v. ill. 16°. ea., $1 .... *Lee & S.*
Cont.: Jack of all trades. — Alexis, the runaway. — Tommy Hickup. — Up side down. — Young detective. — Pinks and blues.

Parker, Thdr. Additional speeches, addresses and occasional sermons. 2 v. 12°. $3.......*Fuller.*
— Critical and misc. writings. 12°. $1.50....*Fuller.*
— Discourse of matters pertaining to religion. 12°. $1.50. *Fuller.*
— Historic Americans: Franklin, Washington, Adams, Jefferson. 12°. $1.50.................*Fuller.*
— Sermons of theism, atheism and popular theology. 12°. $1.50..........................*Fuller.*
— Speeches, addresses and occasional sermons. 3 v. 12°. $4.50..............................*Fuller.*
— Transcendentalism. 12°. pap., 10c.......*Free Rel.*
— Trial of Parker for a speech against kidnapping before Circuit Court of the U. S., at Boston, April 3, 1855; with the defence. 8°. $1.50...*Fuller.*
— Two Christmas celebrations, A. D. 1 and 1855: Christmas story. sq. 16°. 60c. ....*Fuller.*

Parker, W. F. *See* Hull, M., *and* Parker, W. F.

Parker, W. H. Instructions for naval light artillery, afloat and ashore. 3d ed., rev. by S. B. Luce. pl. 8°. '64. $3...............*VanNostrand.*

Parkes, Bessie Raynor. Essays on woman's work. 16°. $1.50..............................*Routledge.*
— La belle France. ill. 8°. $3...........*Routledge.*
— Vignettes: 12 biog. sketches. cr. 8°. $2.50..*Routledge.*

Parkes, E: A. Manual of pract. hygiene; for medical officers of the army, civil med. officers, boards of health, etc. 4th ed., rev. and enl. ill. 8°. '73. $6. *Lindsay.*

Parkes, *Mrs.* F. W. Domestic duties: instructions to young married ladies on management of their households and regulation of their conduct. 12°. $1.25..............................*Harper.*

Parkes, H: Australian views of England: letters, 1861–'62. cr. 8°. $1.25.................*Macmillan.*

Parkes-Belloc, Bessie. *See* Belloc, B. P.

Parkhurst, C. H. The Latin verb; ill. by the Sanskrit. 12°. '74. 50c....................*Ginn.*

Parkinson, S. Treatise on elementary mechanics. 5th ed., rev. cr. 8°. '74. $3........*Macmillan.*
— Treatise on optics. 3d ed., rev. and enl. cr. 8°. '70. $3.50...........................*Macmillan.*

Parkman, Fs. Works. New ed. 7 v. cr. 8°. '74–'75. ea., $2.50; hf. cf., $4.50........*Little, B. & Co.*
Cont.: Conspiracy of Pontiac and Indian war after conquest of Canada, 2 v. — Oregon trail: sketches of prairie and Rocky Mt. life. — Discovery of the great west. — Jesuits in No. Am. in 17th cent. — Old régime in Canada under Louis XIV. — Pioneers of France in the new world: 1, Huguenots in Florida; 2, Samuel de Champlain.
— Book of roses. 12°. '66. $1.50...........*Tilton.*

Parks, Rob. *See* Paul, H., *and* Parks, R.

Parks, W. J. Essay on apostasy. 18°. '59. 50c. *So. Meth.*

Parkwater. Wood, E. P. 75c...........*Peterson.*

Parlate Italiano? or, do you speak Italian? manual of Ital. and Eng. conversation. ('64.) New ed. 18°. '76. bds., 60c.........................*Holt.*

Parley, P: (*pseud.*) *See* Goodrich, S: G.

Parley, the porter. *See* More, H.

Parley's Columbus, Washington and Franklin. New ed., rev. ill. 16°. $1.50..............*Desilver.*

Parley's fireside lib. 3 v. ill. 8°. $6.........*Miller.*
Cont.: Watson's Camp fires of the revolution. — Goodrich's Merry stories. — Goodrich's Thousand and one stories.

Parley's present. Goodrich, S. G. $1.50..*Appleton.*

Parlez-vous français? or, do you speak French? pocket manual of Fr. and Eng. conversation. ('64.) New ed. 18°. '76. bds., 60c......*Holt.*

Parliament in the playroom. Tucker, C. 50c...*Carter.*

Parloa, *Miss* Marie. Appledore cook-book. 12°. '72. $1.25..............................*Graves.*

Parlor and kitchen; or, the story of Ann Conover at service. 18°. 60c....................*Am. S. S.*

Parlor and playground amusements. 12°. $1.50..*Locke.*

Parlor book. *See* Chambers, W. *and* R.

Parlor glee book; arranged for piano-forte. f°. '59. bds., $1.38...............................*Ditson.*

Parlor letter-writer. 16°. $1................*Miller.*

Parlor lute. Higgins, H. M. 50c. ....*Peters.*

Parlor magician; or, one hundred tricks for the drawing-room. ill. 16°. pap., 30c.; bds., 50c. *Dick & F.*

Parlor poetic lib. 10 v. 32°. $6; $9; mor., $15..*Porter.*
Cont.: Bloomfield's Farmer's boy. — Burns' Poetical works. — Moral and beautiful in poems of Byron. — Griswold's Gems from Am. poets. — Hogg's Mountain bard, and Forest minstrel. — Hood's Poetical works. — Moral and beautiful in poems of Moore. — Dodd's Beauties of Shakespeare. — Shakespeare's Poems. — Shelley's Poetical works.

Parlor preacher. Mason, W. 40c. ....*Pres. Bd.*

Parlor theatricals; or, winter evenings' entertainment. ill. 16°. pap., 30c.; bds., 50c..........*Dick & F.*

Parlor tricks with cards. ill. 16°. pap., 30c.; bds., 50c. *Dick & F.*

Parlour magic. 16°. pap., 60c..............*French.*

Parmalee, M. P. Life scenes in the mountains of Ararat. 16°. $1.25................*Cong. Pub.*

Parmelee, *Mrs.* Helen L. Little Elly's first visit. 18°. '64. 50c. ....*Randolph.*

Parnassus. Emerson, R. W. $4; $7.50; $10..*Osgood.*

Parnell, T: Hermit: poem. ill. sq. 16°. $1.25. *Am. S. S.*
— Poems. (Aldine ed.) 16°. 75c.......*Lippincott.*
— *Same;* [also] Poems by T: Tickel; with memoirs. 18°. $1..............................*Osgood.*

Paroissien des petits enfans pieux. [Cath. prayer book.] 48°. 25c.–$10...............*Sadlier.*

Paroissien romain; contenant l'office des dimanches et fêtes. [Cath. prayer book.] 18°. $2.50–$50. *Strong.*

Parr, Ht. ["Holme Lee."] Annis Warleigh's fortunes. 8°. pap., 75c..........................*Harper.*
— Fairy tales. 12°. $1.75. ill. cr. 8°. $2.50. *Scribner, W. & A.*
— Kathie Brande: fireside story of a quiet life. 12°. $1.50...............................*Harper.*
— Legends from fairy land. ill. 12°. $1.25. *Scribner, W. & A.*
— Mr. Wynyard's ward. 8°. pap., 50c.........*Harper.*
— My dog match. ill. 12°. $1.25.....*Scribner, W. & A.*
— Poor match. 16°. '71. $1.25.............*Dutton.*
— Sylvan Holt's daughter. 12°. $1.50.......*Harper.*
— Tuflongbo and Little Content: their wonderful adventure in the enchanted forest. ill. 12°. $1.25. *Scribner, W. & A.*
— Tuflongbo's life and adventures, and how his shoes got worn out. ill. 12°. $1.25..*Scribner, W. & A.*
— Vicissitudes of Bessie Fairfax. 12°. $1.50; pap., 75c. — (Intern. ed.), $1.25..............*Porter.*

Parr, Louisa. Blue bell of Red-Neap: Christmas story. 12°. '71. $1.......................*Routledge.*
— Dorothy Fox. ill. 8°. $1.25; pap., 75c...*Lippincott.*
— Hero Carthew. (Leis. hour ser.) ('73.) New ed. 16°. '75. $1.25..............................*Holt.*
— How it all happened. 12°. pap., 15c....*Lippincott.*
— John Thompson, blockhead; and companion portraits. 12°. $1.25...................*Lippincott.*

Parr, R: Life and writings. *See* British reformers.

Parricide (The). Reynolds, G. W. M. 75c...*Peterson.*

Parrish, E: Phantom bouquet: art of skeletonizing leaves and seed-vessels. 12°. $1...*Lippincott.*
— Treatise on pharmacy; with formulæ and prescriptions. 4th ed., rev. by T. S. Wiegand. ill. 8°. $5.50; leath., $6.50..........................*Lea.*

Parrott, F: Ascent of Mt. Ararat; tr. 35c.(?)*Luth. Pub.*
— *Same;* tr. by W. T. Cooley. map and ill. 12°. $1. *Harper.*

Parrott, M. A. Harry's mistakes. 18°. 75c.(?)*Martien.*

Parrott, Marianne. Little May. *See* Merry heart lib.

Parry, J: S. Extra-uterine pregnancy: its clinical hist., diagnosis, prognosis and treatment. 8°. $2.50..*Lea.*

Parry, T: Cure for love: comedy. 16°. pap., 15c. *French.*
— Lucky horseshoe: drama. 16°. pap., 15c...*French.*
— P. P.; or, the man and tiger: farce. 16°. pap., 15c. *French.*
Parry, *Sir* W: E. Three voyages for the disc. of a n. w. passage from the Atlantic to the Pacific, and narr. of attempt to reach the North Pole. 2 v. 18°. $1.50..................... *Harper.*
Parselle, J. My son's a daughter: drama. 16°. pap., 15c................................. *French.*
Parson and people. Spooner, E. $1.... *Huntington.*
Parson Beecher and his horse. Small, G. G. 25c. *Collin & S.*
Parson of the islands. Wallace, A. $1.50..*A. Wallace.*
Parsonage in the Hartz. McFadder, C. $1.15..*Pres. Bd.*
Parsonage of Mora. Bremer, F. 25c.......*Harper.*
Parson's daughter. *See* Hook, Thdr.
Parsons, Anson V. Select cases. *See* Law lib.
— *See also* Pennsylvania, Court of Com. Pleas reports.
Parsons, Arth. Treatise on law of wills. 8°. '55. $1.50....................... *T. & J. W. Johnson.*
Parsons, F. M. Treatise on law of costs as settled in N. Y. and adapted to the code of Ohio. 8°. '76. shp., $5 .... *Cockcroft.*
Parsons, Flora T. Calisthenic songs. ill. 16°. '69. bds., 40c. .... *Ivison.*
Parsons, H: Moore. Christ in the desert; or, the tempter foiled. 18°. 50c............ *Pres. Bd.*
Parsons, J. U. New life. ill. 18°. '71. 35c.; pap., 20c.............................. *Am. Tr.*
— *Same.* pt. 2: Counsels to converts. 18°. '71. pap., 15c.............................. *Am. Tr.*
Parsons, Ja. Essays on legal topics. 8°. '76. shp., $2; pap., $1.50 .... *Welsh.*
Parsons, Ja. C. The living word; or, Bible truths and lessons. 12°. '72. hf. bd., $1 .... *Ginn.*
Parsons, Laura S. Gem of dialogues. ('71.) 2d ed. 8°. '75. pap., 40c.............. *Schermerhorn.*
Parsons, P. M. *See* Adams, W. B., *and* Parsons, P. M.
Parsons, Reuben. Biographical dictionary. 12°. $1.50. *Sadlier.*
Parsons, S: B. History and culture of the rose. 12°. $1.25 .... *Wiley.*
— Treatise on propagation, culture and hist. of the rose. ill. 12°. $1.50........................ *Judd.*
Parsons, Thph. Deus homo: God-man. cr. 8°. $2.50. *Lippincott.*
— Elements of mercantile law. 2d ed., rev. and enl. 8°. shp., $6..................... *Little, B. & Co.*
— Essays. 3 v. 16°. '55–'62. ser. 1, $1.50; ser. 2, 3, ea., 50c. .... *H. H. Carter.*
— Infinite (The) and the finite. 16°. '72. $1..*Roberts.*
— Laws of business for all the states. 8°. '69. $2.50; shp., $3...................... *Little, B. & Co.*
— *Same;* for all the states and Canada. 8°. '69. hf. leath., $3.75; leath., $4.25... *W. Gill; Scranton.*
— Outlines of the religion and philosophy of Swedenborg. 16°. '76. $1.25 .... *Roberts.*
— Political, personal and property rights of a citizen of the U. S.; with rules of procedure in deliberative assemblies, also glossary of law terms. ('74.) New ed. 8°. '76. cf., *$4........... *Scranton.*
— *Same.* 8°. '75. $4; shp., $4.50 .... *W. Gill.*
— Treatise on law of contracts. 6th ed., rev. and enl. 3 v. 8°. '73. shp., $18 .... *Little, B. & Co.*
— Treatise on law of marine insurance and general average. 2 v. 8°. '68. shp., $12..*Little, B. & Co.*
— Treatise on law of partnership. 2d ed. 8°. '70. shp., $6 .... *Little, B. & Co.*
— Treatise on law of promissory notes and bills of exchange. 2 v. roy. 8°. shp., $15.... *Lippincott.*
— Treatise on law of shipping and law and practice of admiralty. 2 v. 8°. '69. shp., $12..*Little, B. & Co.*
Parsons, T: W: Poems. 12°. $1.25.......* *Osgood.*

Parsons, W. L. Believer's victory over Satan's devices. 12°. '76. $1.25......... *Meth. Bk. Conc.*
Part songs for female voices; sel. [mostly] from S. Müller's collection; tr. by F. M. Raymond. 12°. '61. 75c.; bds., 60c..................... *Ditson.*
Particular providence; ill. by life of Joseph. 12°. $2. *N. Y. Ref. Ch. Bd.*
Parties and their principles. Holmes, A. $1.50. *Appleton.*
Parting gift to a Christian friend; or, true sources of peace and protection. 18°. 40c........ *Am. S. S.*
Parting spirit's address to his mother. *See* Wyatt, W. E.
Parting word. Hall, N. 60c.............. *Sheldon.*
Partington, *Mrs.* (*pseud.*) *See* Shillaber, B. P.
Partingtonian patchwork. Shillaber, B. P. $1.75. *Lee & S.*
Partisan. Simms, W. G. $1.75; 75c. .... *Widdleton.*
Partisan life with Mosby. Scott, J. $3.50... *Harper.*
Parton, Ja. Works. 12 v. 8°. '54–'74. ea., $3; per set, hf. cf., $65......................... *Osgood.*

Cont.: Famous Americans of recent times. — Gen. Butler in New Orleans. — Life of Aaron Burr, 2 v. — Life of Andrew Jackson, 3 v. — Life of Benj. Franklin, 2 v. — Life of Horace Greeley. — Life of T: Jefferson. — Humorous poetry of the Eng. lang., with notes.

— Life of Horace Greeley. (chp. ed.) 12°. $2; — in Germ. ill. 8°. pap., 75c............ *Osgood.*
— People's book of biography: short lives of interesting persons of all ages and countries. ill. 8°. '73. *$3.50.............................. *Virtue.*
— Smoking and drinking. 16°. '68. $1; pap., 50c. *Osgood.*
— Topics of the time. 12°. '71. $2......... *Osgood.*
— Triumphs of enterprise, ingenuity and public spirit. ('72.) 2d ed. med. 8°. '74. *$3.50... *Virtue.*
— Words of Washington. 18°. $1............ *Estes.*
— *See also* Eminent women of the age; — Parton, *Mrs.*
Parton, *Mrs.* Sara Parker. ["Fanny Fern."] Fanny Fern, a memorial volume: her select writings and memoir by J. Parton. 12°. '73. $2..*Carleton.*
— Fanny Fern lib. ('53–'64.) New ed. 3 v. ill. 16°. '72. $4.50........................ *Clark & M.*

Cont.: Little ferns. — Play-day book. — New story-book.

— Life and beauties of Fanny Fern. 12°. $1.75; pap., $1.50 .... *Peterson.*
Partridge, *Mrs.* G. *See* How to teach the little folks.
Partridge, W. W. New school and home [singing book]. obl. 16°. 60c.............. *Brainard.*
— School and home [singing book]. obl. 12°. bds., 50c. .... *Brainard.*
Partridge's ill. juveniles. 15 v. ill. sm. 4°. ea., $2. *Routledge.*

Cont.: Our dumb neighbours. — Our four-footed friends. — Clever dogs, horses, etc. — Our dumb companions. — Birds and their nests. — Animal sagacity. — Our children's pets. — Jack, the conqueror. — Our feathered companions. — Dogs and their doings. — Anecdotes in natural history. — My pet's album. — Little Rosebud's album. — Animals and their young. — Natural history stories.

Party spirit in the church. Robins, S. 75c.; 50c. *Dutton.*
Parvin, Rob. J. Union notes on the Gospels. 2 v. 18°. ea., 70c.; — in 1 v., $1................ *Am. S. S.*

Cont.: Matthew and Mark. — Luke and John.

Parvin, Z. M. Songs of delight for the Sunday school. 16°. '75. hf. bd., 35c................. *Barnes.*
Pas de fascination. Coyne, J. S. 15c......... *French.*
Pascal, Blaise. Provincial letters; tr. with introd. and notes by T. McCrie; [with] life of P., essay and biog. notice; ed. by O. W. Wight. cr. 8°. $2.25; hf. cf., $4......................... *Hurd & H.*
— Thoughts, letters and opuscules; tr. by O. W. Wight; with introd. notices and notes from all the commentators. cr. 8°. $2.25; hf. cf., $4..*Hurd & H.*
Pascal, Jacqueline. Life. 12°. $1.25........ *Carter.*
Pascarel. La Rame, L. de. $1.50....... *Lippincott.*
Pascha (Der) v. Buda. *See* Zschokke, H.

Paschal, G: W. Constitution of the U. S. defined and carefully annotated. ('68.) 2d ed., rev. and enl. 8°. leath., $4 ... *Morrison.*
— Digest of laws of Texas, 1754–1875. ('66.) 4th ed. 2 v. 8°. '75. shp., $25; ea., $15 .. *E. H. Cushing.*
— Digest of Texas Supreme Court decisions and of U. S. Sup. Court decisions upon Texas law. 3 v. 8°. shp., $45 ... *E. H. Cushing.*
— *See also* Texas, Sup. Court reports.
Paschall, Ann S. Home circle (The). 12°. *net*, $1. *Friends Bk. Assoc.*
— Scripture lessons for the little ones. 16°. *net*, 33c. *Friends Bk. Assoc.*
— Story of T: Ellwood. 18°. *net*, 25c. *Friends Bk. Assoc.*
Pascoe, C: E. London directory for Am. travellers. [Annual.] 12°. '75. $1.50 ... *Lee & S.*
Pasha papers. Howe, W. W. $1.25 ... *Scribner.*
Pasquino (*pseud.*) American Cyclops (B. F. Butler), the hero of New Orleans and spoiler of silver spoons, dubbed LL. D. [Poem.] ill. 4°. '67. $1.50 ... *Kelly, P. & Co.*
Passage to India. Whitman, W. $1 ... *Somerby.*
Passages from the diary of Lady Willoughby. Rathbone, H. M. $1 ... *Barnes.*
Passages from the diary of a late physician. *See* Warren, S:
Passages in the maiden and married life of Rose Bryant. 18°. 55c. ... *Am. S. S.*
Passavant, J: D: Raphael of Urbina and his father Giovanni Santi. photos. roy. 8°. '71. $12. *Macmillan.*
Passetout; or, the new fishing smack. *See* Peasants of the Alps.
Passing bell; or, "he died rich." 18°. 22c... *Am. S. S.*
— *Same.* 18°. '66. 25c... *N. Y. Ref. Ch. Bd.; Pres. Com.*
Passing cloud. Bernard, W. B. 15c. ... *French.*
Passing clouds. 18°. 75c. ... *Carter; Dutton.*
Passing the portal. Victor, M. V. F. $1.50 .. *Carleton.*
Passing thoughts on religion. Sewell, E. M. $1. *Appleton.*
Passion and principle. Grey, E. C. 75c.... *Peterson.*
Passion and principle. *See* Hook, Thdr.
Passion flowers. Howe, J. W. $1 ... *Osgood.
Passion (A) in tatters. Thomas, A. 75c. ... *Harper.*
Passion music (accord. to Gospel of Matthew): Eng. and Germ. words; Eng. tr. and adaptation by J: S. Dwight; [with] full vocal score, and piano accomp. mainly by J. Stern. 8°. '69. $2; bds., $1.60; pap., $1.25 ... *Ditson.*
Passionate pilgrim. James, H., *jr.* $2 ... *Osgood.*
Passmore, W: Compendium of evangelical theology; in words of Scripture. 16°. '75. $3.50 .. *Randolph.*
— Short hand in a day. 2 pts. 12°. '71. ea., pap., 25c. *Randolph.*
Past and present. *See* Carlyle, T:
Past and present: drama. 16°. pap., 15c. ... *French.*
Past and present of the Irish race. Thébaud, A. J. $3.50 ... *Sadlier.*
Past meridian. Sigourney, L. H. $1.50 .. *Brown & G.*
Past, present and future. Carey, H. C. $2.50 .. *Baird.*
Past successes, future possibilities. Warren, H. W. 25c. ... *Meth. Bk. Conc.*
Past ten o'clock. Dibdin, T. 15c. ... *French.*
Pastor, Tony. Book of six hundred comic songs and speeches. 18°. bds., $1 ... *Dick & F.*
— Complete budget of comic songs. 18°. $1.25 .. *Dick & F.*
Pastor (The). Ziegler, H. $1.50–$3 .. (?) *Luth. Pub.*
Pastor in his closet. Armstrong, J. 60c... *McCauley.*
Pastor in parochia. How, W. W. $1.50; $2.50 .. *Pott.*
Pastor of the desert. Pelletan, E. 90c. ... *Dodd.*
Pastor of Gegenburg; tr. from the Germ. 18°. 40c. *Pres. Bd.*
Pastoral reminiscences. More, M. 15c. ... *Am. Tr.*
Pastorate (The). Burnet, D. S. 10c. ... *Chase.*
Pastorini, *Sig.* (*pseud.*) *See* Walmesley, C.
Pastor's Bible class: familiar conversations conc. sacred mountains. 18°. 65c. ... *Pres. Bd.*
Pastor's counsel. 32°. '53. 15c. ... *Am. Tr.*
Pastor's daughter. 18°. '46. 25c. ... *Am. Tr.*
Pastor's family. 18°. 35c. ... *Carter.*
Pastor's fireside. *See* Porter, J.
Pastor's household. *See* Bradley, *Mrs.* M. E.
Pastor's jottings. Belcher, J. $1 ... *Am. Tr.*
Pastor's manual. 16°. 50c. ... *Cong. Pub.*
Pastor's reasonings with the young of his flock on the claims of the Gospel. 18°. 55c. ... *Am. S. S.*
Pastor's recollections. Dashiell, T. G. $1.25 .. *Appleton.*
Pastor's selection of hymns and tunes. Burt, N. C. $1. *Lippincott.*
Pastor's sketches. Spencer, I. S. $2 ... *Dodd.*
Pastor's son. 18°. 60c. ... (?) *Martien.*
Pastor's story. Gay, M. A. H. $1.50 ... *Turnbull.*
Pastor's testimony. Clark, J. A. $1.25 ... *Carter.*
Pastor's wedding gift. Thayer, W. M. $1. *Lockwood, B. & Co.*
Pastor's wife. *See* Sherman, J.
Pastors' widows. 18°. 90c. ... (?) *Martien.*
Pat, the little emigrant. 16°. 45c. ... *Cummiskey.*
Pater, Wa. H. Studies in hist. of the renaissance. cr. 8°. '73. $2.50 ... *Macmillan.*
Pater mundi. Burr, E. F. 2 v. $3.50. *Lockwood, B. & Co.*
Paterson, Alex. Smith. Concise system of theology on basis of the Shorter catechism. 18°. 75c. *Carter.*
Path and the lamb; by author of "Blind Annie Lorimer." 18°. 75c. ... *Pres. Bd.*
Path of holiness. Carter, T. T. 75c. ... *Pott.*
Path of life. Rowland, H. A. 60c. ... *Dodd.*
Path of life. Wise, D. $1; $1.30 ... *Meth. Bk. Conc.*
Path of the Pilgrim Church. Waddington, J. 75c. *Cong. Pub.*
Path she chose. S., M. F. $1.25 ... *Routledge.*
Path to heaven: collection of [Cath.] prayers and instructions. 32°. $1–$13 ... *Benziger.*
Path to paradise; or, the way of salvation. [Cath. prayer book.] 48°. 31c.–$40. — 32°. 38c.–$50. *Sadlier.*
Path to salvation: manual of [Cath.] prayer. ('68.) 4th ed. 32°. '73. 35c.–$4 ... *Kenedy.*
Path which led a Prot. lawyer to the Cath. Church. Burnett, H. $2 ... *Benziger.*
Pathengeschenk (Das). Oertel, P. F. W. 25c. *Steiger.*
Pathfinder. *See* Cooper, Ja. F.
Pathological Soc. of Phila. Transactions, 1871–'75; ed. by J. Tyson. 2 v. 8°. ea., $4 .. *Lippincott.*
Paths of the Lord. Reid, W. 50c. ... *Bost. Am. Tr.*
Pathway of promise. 32°. 50c. ... *Carter.*
Pathway of promise. 24°. 75c. ... *Routledge.*
Pathway of safety. Oxenden, A. 75c. *Hammond; Whittaker.*
Pathways of the Holy Land. McCabe, J. D. *$3.75; $4.50; $6 ... *Nat. Pub.*
Patience. Charlesworth, M. L. 50c. ... *Bost. Am. Tr.*
Patience. Cheney, E. D. 75c. ... *Lee & S.*
Patience and her friend. 24°. 25c. ... *Perkinpine.*
— *Same;* [also] Little toy maker. 18°. 35c. *Bost. Am. Tr.*
— — *See also* Uncle Reuben ser.
Patience of hope. *See* Greenwell, D.
Patience removes mountains, and other tales. 18°. 50c. *O'Shea.*
Patience Strong's outings. Whitney, A. D. T. $1.50. *Loring.*

Patient Gracie. *See* Swallow stories.
Patient Johnny. Bruce, E. M. 75c. ... *Universalist.*
Patient mourner. Bourdon, M. F.. 30c. .... *O'Shea.*
Patient Penelope. Burnand, F. C. 15c...... *French.*
Patient Susie; or, paying the mortgage. ill. 16°. $1.25. *Cin. Meth. Bk. Conc.*
Patient waiting no loss. *See* Haven, *Mrs.* A. B.
Patmore, Coventry. Angel in the house; compr. The betrothal, and The espousal. 12°. $1.50. *Dutton.*
— Faithful forever. 16°. $1.25 .... *Osgood.*
— Victories of love. 16°. '62. 50c...... *H. H. Carter.*
— (*ed.*) Children's garland from the best poets. 18°. '71. $1.25. — ill. cr. 8°. $2.50 ..... *Macmillan.*
— *Same.* 18°. 75c. 16°. $1.25.............. *Allyn.*
Patmos. Smith, J. A. $1.25............... *Griggs.*
Patoo, T. H. Life. ill. 18°. '53. 35c....... *Am. Tr.*
Patriarchs; or, Bible histories for children. 18°. 30c.; 40c. .... *Am. Bapt.*
Patriarchs and lawgivers of the Old Test. Maurice, F. D. $2 .... *Macmillan.*
Patriarchs of Palestine. Headley, P. C. 25c.; 30c. *J. E. Potter.*
Patricia Kemball. Linton, E. L. $1.75.. *Lippincott.*
Patrician's daughter. Marston, W. 15c. .... *French.*
Patrick, *St.* Life. 12°. 35c. .... *Benziger.*
— *See also* Lives of the saints.
— *Same;* [also] Lives of St. Bridget and St. Columba. 12°. '51. 75c.............................. *Murphy.*
Patrick, S. Book for beginners. 18°. 40c. .. *Dutton.*
Patrignani, Jos. Ant. A novena in honor of St. Joseph; tr. from the Ital.; [with] litany of St. Joseph, etc. 32°. '73. 25c.; pap., 20c......... *Murphy.*
Patriot and Tory. Wright, J. McN. $2.50; $3.. *Jones.*
Patriot soldier. Taylor, J. 65c.............. *Hoyt.*
Patriotic eloquence. Kirkland, C. M. $1.75.. *Scribner.*
Patriotic glee book. Higgins, H. M. $1.50 .. *Peters.*
Patriotic speaker. 32°. '76. pap., 10c...... *De Witt.*
Patriotism in poetry and prose. Murdoch, J. E. $1. *Lippincott.*
Patriots and statesmen one hundred years ago. ill. 12°. $1.50 .... *World Pub.*
Patrizier (Die). *See* Van der Velde, K. F.
Patronage. *See* Edgeworth, Mar.
Patsy's first glimpse of heaven. Byrne, J. 50c. *Cassell.*
Patten, B. A. *See* Barry, T. A., *and* Patten, B. A.
Patten, G: Army manual: instructions for officers in preparation of rolls, returns, etc. 8°. '65. $2. *Van Nostrand.*
— Artillery drill. 12°. '71. pap., 50c... *Van Nostrand.*
— Cavalry drill. 12°. '64. pap., 50c... *Van Nostrand.*
— Infantry tactics. 12°. '65. pap., 50c. — New ed., rev. 12°. pap., 75c............ *Van Nostrand.*
Patten, J. Men of progress. 8°. '72. $6. — 4°. mor., $25 .... *N. Y. & H. Pub.*
Patten, J. Alex. Lives of the clergy of New York and Brooklyn. ill. roy. 8°. '75. $5; roan, $7; hf. cf., $8.50; mor., $10.................... *Atlantic.*
Patterson, Alex. S. Explanation of the Shorter catechism. 18°. 60c.; shp., 75c..... *U. P. Bd. of Pub.*
Patterson, Calv. Common school speller. 16°. hf. bd., 25c. .... *Sheldon.*
— New method of map drawing. obl. f°. 20c. *Potter, A. & Co.*
— Speller and analyzer for advanced classes. 16°. hf. bd., 40c.......................... *Sheldon.*
Patterson, J. W. Address before Phi Beta Kappa Soc., Dartmouth Coll.; [also] Poem, by G. A. Marden. 8°. pap., 25c............... *Hardy.*
Patterson, Rob. Narrative of the campaign in the valley of the Shenandoah in 1861. por. 8°. '65. pap., $1. 4°. pap., $5............. *J. Campbell.*
Patterson, *Rev.* Rob. Christianity the only republican religion. 16°. pap., 10c............. *West. Tr.*
— Fables of infidelity and facts of faith. 12°. $1.75. *H. E. Simmons; West. Tr.*
Patterson, Rob. M. Historical sketch of the synod of Phila.; [with] biog. sketches of members of the synod of Phila. by Rob. Davidson. 16°. 30c.; 50c. .... *Pres. Bd.*
— Paradise. 16°. $1.25 .... *Pres. Bd.*
— *See also* Tercentary book.
Patterson, W. M. Manual of architecture; with introd. by R. A. Young. pl. 4°. '74. $5.. *So. Meth.*
Patteson, W. N. Forms for clerks, sheriffs, constables, notaries, coroners, commissioners and attorneys. 8°. '69. $1.50; pap., $1.25..... *J. W. Randolph.*
Pattison, Everett W. Digest of Missouri reports (v. 1–49). 2 v. 8°. '73. shp., $15; — in 1 v., shp., $14 .... *Gilbert.*
— Lay preaching. 18°. pap., 10c........... *McIntyre.*
Patton, F. *See* Preparing to teach.
Patton, Fs. L. Inspiration of the Scriptures. 16°. 65c. .... *Pres. Bd.*
Patton, J. Harris. History of the U. S. 8°. $3; with por., shp., $5; hf. cf., $6.50; mor., $10.. *Appleton.*
Patton, Jac. H. Concise history of the Am. people, to 1876. por., maps, etc. 8°. '76. *$3.75; $4.75; hf. mor., $6 .... *Ford.*
Patton, J: M. *See* Virginia, Court of Appeals reports.
— *and* Heath, R. B. Index to Virginia reports (2d to 11th Grattan). 8°. '56. hf. shp., $5.. *J. W. Randolph.*
Patton, T: Appendix to Bourdon's Algebra. 8°. $1. *Keystone.*
Patton, W: Bible wines; or, laws of fermentation, and wines of the ancients. ('71.) New ed. 12°. '74. 60c.; pap., 30c................. *Nat. Temp.*
— *See also* Bible [Whole].
Patton, W: W. Prayer and its remarkable answers: statement of facts in the light of reason and revelation. 12°. '75. $2.................. *Goodman.*
— Spiritual victory. 32°. $1.............. *Cong. Pub.*
— *vs.* Swing, *Rev.* D: World's ed. of the great Presbyterian conflict: Patton vs. Swing. por. 8°. '74. $1.25; pap., 75c................ (?) *MacDonald.*
Patty. *See* Macquoid, K. S.
Patty; or, beware of meddling. 18°. 18c. ... *Am. S. S.*
Patty and Bob; or, the little orange-sellers. 18°. 30c.; 35c.................................. *Am. Bapt.*
Patty Bailey; or, who knows best. ill. 18°. 80c. *J. A. Moore.*
Patty Grant, the English work house girl. 18°. 60c.; 70c. .... *Am. Bapt.*
Patty Gray's journey to Cotton Islands. *See* Dall, C. H.
Patty Parsons; [also] Fanny's return; [also] The orphan. 18°. 30c...................... *Am. S. S.*
Patty Williamson's voyage. *See* Silver penny ser.
Patty's pranks. *See* Johnson, V. W.
Paul *of the cross, St.* Life. 12°. $1.50; $2.. *Sadlier.*
Paul, *St.* Vincent de. *See* Vincent de Paul.
Paul, B: H. Manual of technical analysis. *See* Bolley, P. A.
— On liquid fuel. 8°. pap., 40c............... *Spon.*
Paul, C. Kegan. William Godwin: his friends and contemporaries. 2 v. ill. and por. 8°. '76. $6. *Roberts.*
Paul, Hiland, *and* Parks, Rob. History of Wells. 8°. '69. $1............................. *Tuttle.*
Paul, Howard. [Plays.] 7 v. 16°. ea., pap., 15c. *French.*
Cont.: Change of system: comedy. — Locked out: farce. — Queen of Arragon: comedy. — Mob cap. — Opposite neighbours: farce. — Rapping and table movings: farce. — Thrice married: farce.
— Book of theatrical anecdotes. 16°. '73. bds., 50c. *Routledge.*
— Locked out: farce. 16°. pap., 15c........ *De Witt.*

Paul, Howard, *continued.*
— Thrice married: farce. 16°. pap., 15c. .... *De Witt.*
— *and* Timbs, J., *and* Fitzgerald, P. (*ed.*) Book of modern anecdotes: American, legal and theatrical. cr. 8°. '73. $1.75 .... *Routledge.*
Paul, Ja. L. Pennsylvania's soldier's orphan schools. 8°. '76. *$3; mor., $6 .... *Claxton.*
Paul, J: (*pseud.*) *See* Webb, C: H.
Paul, *Mrs.* Sara T. Cookery from experience. 12°. '75. $1.50; — interleaved, $1.75 .... *Porter.*
Paul, T: Cooke. Sketch of life and character. 18°. 65c. .... *Am. S. S.*
Paul, *Uncle* (*pseud.*) *See* Burnham, S., *jr.*
Paul, the peddler. Alger, H., *jr.* $1.25 ..... *Loring.*
Paul, the pilot: drama. 16°. pap., 15c. .... *French.*
Paul, the poacher: drama. 16°. pap., 15c. ... *French.*
Paul and the chief cities of his labors. 18°. $1.25. *Cong. Pub.*
Paul and Dora. 8°. pap., 25c. .... *De Witt.*
Paul and Harry Fane; or, the two sons, with other stories. 18°. '67. 50c. *N. Y. Ref. Ch. Bd.; Pres. Com.*
Paul and Margaret. Potwin, H. K. 90c. .... *Dodd.*
Paul and Virginia. Cobb, J. 15c. .... *French.*
Paul and Virginia. *See* Saint Pierre, J. H. B., de.
Paul Ardenheim. Lippard, G. $2; $1.50 ..... *Peterson.*
Paul Arnold's fortune. ill. 16°. 50c. ...... *Routledge.*
Paul Arnold's lib. of stories. 5 v. ill. 16°. $2.50. *Routledge.*

Cont.: Paul Arnold's fortune. — On the seas. — Year at school. — British wolf-hunters. — Billow and the rock.

Paul Barton. Baker, H. N. W. 16°. '68. $1.25 .. *Graves.*
Paul Blake. *See* Elwes, A.
Paul Brewster and son. Chapman, H. E. $1 .. *Nat. Temp.*
Paul Clifford. *See* Bulwer-Lytton, *Sir* E. G. E. L.
Paul Clifford. Webster, B. 15c. .... *French.*
Paul Clifford; or, hurrah for the road. 8°. pap., 25c. *Dick & F.*
Paul Clifford's revenge. 8°. pap., 25c. .... *De Witt.*
Paul Darst. *See* Conversion of.
Paul Deverell; or, two judgments for one crime. 8°. pap., 25c. .... *Dick & F.*
Paul Fane. Willis, N. P. $1.75 .... *Scribner.*
Paul Gerrard, the cabin boy. Kingston, W. H. G. $1.25 .... *Routledge.*
Paul Grey's light. 18°. 65c. .... *Cong. Pub.*
Paul Hawthorne. 18°. 30c.; 40c. .... *Am. Bapt.*
Paul Jones. Dibdin, T. 15c. .... *French.*
Paul Jones. Dumas, A. 25c. .... *Dick & F.*
Paul Loring. Boyd, E. E. 80c. .... *J. A. Moore.*
Paul Massie. McCarthy, J. $1.50; $1 ..... *Sheldon.*
Paul of Tarsus: inquiry into the times and the Gospel of the apostles of the Gentiles; by a graduate. 16°. '72. $1.50 .... *Roberts.*
Paul Periwinkle. *See* Life and adventures of.
Paul Prescott's charge. Alger, H., *jr.* $1.25 .. *Loring.*
Paul Preston. Campbell, E. $1.15 .... *Hoyt.*
Paul Preston's voyages, travels and remarkable adventures. ill. 16°. '72. $1.25 .... *Roberts.*
Paul Pry. Jerrold, D. 15c. .... *French.*
Paul Pry married and settled. Mathews, C. J. 15c. *French.*
Paul Venner. Bates, L. $1.25 .... *Am. Tr.*
Paul Winslow. Chapman, H. E. 45c. .... *Pres. Bd.*
Paulding, Ja. K. ["Lancelot Langstaff."] Book of vagaries, compr. "The new mirror for travellers and other whim-whams": sel. from papers of a retired common councilman; ed. by W. I. Paulding. ('67.) New ed. cr. 8°. '68. $2.50. *Scribner.*
Paulding, Ja. K., *continued.*
— Bulls (The) and the Jonathans; compr. "John Bull and Brother Jonathan," "John Bull in America"; ed. by W. I. Paulding. cr. 8°. '67. $2.50 .. *Scribner.*
— Dutchman's fireside. cr. 8°. $2.50 .... *Scribner.*
— Life of Washington. 2 v. 18°. $1.50 ...... *Harper.*
— Tales of the good woman, by a doubtful gentleman; ed. by W. I. Paulding. ('61.) New ed. cr. 8°. '67. $2.50 .... *Scribner.*
— *See also* Tales of Glauber Spa.
Paulding, W: I. Literary life of James K. Paulding. por. cr. 8°. '67. $2.50 .... *Scribner.*
Pauli, Rhld. Life of Alfred the Great; tr. by B. Thorpe. 12°. (Bohn.) $1.75 .... *Little, B. & Co.*
— *Same.* 12°. (Bohn.) $2 .. *Lippincott; Scribner, W. & A.*
Pauline. *See* Bright eye ser.
Pauline. *See* Dumas, A.
Pauline: drama. 16°. pap., 15c. .... *French.*
Pauline; or, the belle of Saratoga. Danks, H. P. $2. *Peters.*
Pauline question book; or, questions on life of Paul. 2 v. 18°. ea., bds., 15c. .... *Am. Bapt.*
Pauline Seward. Bryant, J. D. $2; $2.50 .. *Murphy.*
Pauline Warden. Tappan, L. W. $1.15 .. *Cong. Pub.*
Paull, *Mrs.* H. B. Children of elfland. ill. post 18°. 75c. *Scribner, W. & A.*
— Mary Elton; or, self-control. 16°. 50c. *Scribner, W. & A.*
— Pride and principle. 16°. 50c. .... *Scribner, W. & A.*
Paull, M. A. Packington parish and the diver's daughter. ('72.) New ed. 12°. '74. $1.25 ..... *Nat. Temp.*
— Tim's troubles. ill. 12°. $1.50 .... *Nelson.*
— *Same.* ('70.) New ed. 12°. '74. $1.50 .. *Nat. Temp.*
Paul's moss wreaths. 18°. 35c. .... *Routledge.*
— *See also* Moss wreath lib.
Paul's mountain home: an orphan's story. 18°. '73. 45c. .... *N. Y. Ref. Ch. Bd.; Pres. Com.*
— *Same.* 18°. 60c. .... *Whittaker.*
— *See also* Library for happy hours.
Paul's penny. *See* Bowen, *Mrs.* C. E.
Paul's return. Phillips, W. 15c. .... *French.*
Paul's speech to the Bishop of Crete. Turford, H. 20c. *Friends Bk. Assoc.*
Pausanias, the Spartan. *See* Bulwer-Lytton, *Sir* E. G. E. L.
Pausinger, F. v. (*ill.*) Waidmann's Erinnerungen. Photos. and woodcuts with [German] text by K. Stieler. roy. 4°. $16 .... *Stroefer.*
Pauvre Jacques (Le). Ryan, R. 15c. .... *French.*
Pauvrette. Boucicault, D. 15c. .... *French.*
Pavy, F. W. Treatise on food and dietetics, physiologically and therapeutically considered. 8°. $4.75 .... *Lea.*
— Treatise on function of digestion: its disorders and their treatment. sm. 8°. $2 .... *Lea.*
Paws and claws: stories for clever creatures, tame and wild; by one of the authors of "Poems written for a child." ill. fp. 4°. $2.50 .... *Cassell.*
Paxton, Alfr. Fairy land; or, the riddle and the key: fairy extravaganza. 16°. pap., 15c. ..... *French.*
— Nurseryrhymia; or, the party, the prince and the pie: juvenile drama. 16°. pap., 25c. .... *French.*
Paxton, *Sir* Jos. Botanical dictionary: names, hist. and culture of all plants known in Britain. 8°. $12.50 .... *Scribner, W. & A.*
Paxton, W. E. Apostolic church. 12°. '76. $1.50; mor., $2.50 .... *So. Bapt.*
Paxton, W: Two discourses upon life of Francis Herron. 12°. $1; pap., 50c. .... *R. S. Davis (P.)*
Paxton, W: M. How we spend our years. 24°. '74. 35c. .... *Randolph.*
Pay thy vows. Bedell, G. T. 30c. .... *Whittaker.*
Pay your debts. ill. sq. 16°. 75c. .... *Nelson.*

Payable at sight: farce. 16°. pap., 15c...... *French.*
Payable on demand. Taylor, T. 15c... *French; Lee & S.*
Paying dear for it. Tucker, C. 50c......... *Carter.*
Paying investment. Dickinson, A. E. $1... *Osgood.*
Payn, Ja. [Novels.] 14 v. 8°. pap......... *Harper.*
Cont.: Carlyon's year. — Gwendoline's harvest. — Murphy's master. — One of the family, *ea.*, 25c. — At her mercy. — Best of husbands. — Bred in the bone. — Cecil's tryst. — Found dead. — Halves. — Woman's (A) vengeance. — Won, not wooed, *ea.*, 50c. — Beggar on horseback, 35c. — Walter's word, 75c.
— A county family. 8°. '69. pap., 50c..... *Littell & G.*
— Lost Sir Massingberd. 12°. $1.75; pap., $1.50. *Peterson.*
— Married beneath him. 12°. $1.75; pap., $1.50. *Peterson.*
Payne, Annie Mitchell. Cash-boy's trust. 16°. $1. *Carter.*
— Odd one. 16°. $1.25..................... *Carter.*
— Rhoda's corner. 18°. $1.25....... *Carter; Dutton.*
Payne, Buckner H. The negro: what is his ethnological status? by Ariel [*pseud.*] 2d ed. 12°. '67. pap., 25c.............................. *Setliff.*
Payne, C. H. Daniel, the uncompromising young man. 12°. '72. pap., 20c.............. *Meth. Bk. Conc.*
Payne, J: Howard. [Plays.] 10 v. 16°. ea., pap., 15c. *French.*
Cont.: Ali Pacha: melodrama. — Charles II.: comedy. — Clari; or, the maid of Milan. — Fall of Algiers: opera. — Love in humble life. — Mrs. Smith: farce. — Peter Smink. — Therese. — 'Twas I: farce. — Two galley slaves: melodrama.
— Tragedy of Brutus; or, the fall of Tarquin; with original cast of characters in 1833. 8°. '75. hf. shp., $1.50........................... *Munsell.*
— — *See also* Hinton, H. L., Acting plays of Edwin Booth.
Payne, Jos. *See* England, Common law reports.
Payne, Jos. Fröbel and the kindergarten system of element. educ. 12°. '74. pap., 15c..... *Steiger.*
— Science and art of educ. 12°. '76. pap., 15c.. *Steiger.*
Payne, W: H. Chapters on school supervision. 12°. '75. $1.25 .... *Wilson, H. & Co.*
Payot's first French reader. 18°. '69. bds., 35c. *Payot.*
Payson, Aurin M., *and* Laighton, Alb. (*ed.*) Poets of Portsmouth, N. H.; with introd. by A. P. Peabody. 8°. '65. $2.50; $3 .... *Williams.*
Payson, E: Complete works. 3 v. 8°. $7.50. (?) *Martien.*
Payson, J. W. *See* Hanaford, L. B. H., *and* Payson, J. W.
— *and* Dunton, S., *and* Scribner, W. M. Copy books. 12 nos. obl. 8°. per doz., $1.80.. *Potter, A. & Co.*
— — — New manual of penmanship. 12°. $1.25. *Potter, A. & Co.*
— — — New mounted tablets. $3.75 ... *Potter, A. & Co.*
— — — New sheet tablets. $2.50 ...... *Potter, A. & Co.*
— — — Primary tracing books. nos. 1, 2. obl. f°. per doz., $1.20.................. *Potter, A. & Co.*
— — — *Same.* nos. 3, 4: primary short course. obl. 8°. per doz., $1.20 .... *Potter, A. & Co.*
Payson, the model boy. 18°. '65. 45c... *Meth. Bk. Conc.*
Pea Ridge and Prairie Grove. Baxter, W. $1. *Cin. Meth. Bk. Conc.*
Peabody, Alfr. Early California voyages. 8°. '74. 25c.................................. *Essex.*
Peabody, And. P. Christian belief and life. 16°. '75. $1.50................................ *Roberts.*
— Christian consolations: sermons. ('57.) 6th ed. 16°. '72. $1 .... *Am. Unit.*
— Christianity and science: lectures, 1874, Union Theol. Sem., N. Y. 16°. '74. $1.75............ *Carter.*
— Christianity the religion of nature. roy. 12°. $1.50. *Sheldon.*
— Conversation, its faults and its graces. 16°. 75c. *Dennet.*
— Manual of moral philosophy. 12°. '73. $1.25.. *Barnes.*
— Reminiscences of European travel. 16°. '68. $1.50. *Hurd & H.*
— Sermons for children. ('65.) 2d ed. 16°. '67. 60c. *Am. Unit.*

Peabody, C: Twenty years with colporteurs. ('65.) New ed. 18°. '67. 25c.; pap., 10c..... *Am. Tr.*
Peabody, *Miss* Eliz. P. Lectures on the nursery and kindergarten. 2 v. 16°. '74-'75. ea., pap., 15c. *Williams.*
— *Same.* 2 v. 12°. '75. ea., pap., 25c....... *Steiger.*
— *See also* Mann, *Mrs.* H., *and* Peabody, *Miss* E. P.
Peabody, *Mrs.* M: (*pseud.*) *See* Victor, *Mrs.* M. V. F.
Peabody, Rob. S. Note-book sketches of an architect in Europe. obl. f°. '74. $6.......... *Osgood.*
Peabody, Selim H. Cecil's books of nat. hist. ('69.) New ed. 3 v. ill. 16°. '71. $3.75.... *Claxton.*
— Ray's elements of astronomy. ill. and maps. 8°. '69. shp., $2 .... *Wilson, H. & Co.*
— *See also* Felter, S. A.
Peabody, W: Bourn Ol. Life of D. Brainerd; — of C. Mather; — of I. Putnam; — of A. Wilson. *See* Sparks, J., Lib. of Am. biog.
Peabody Acad. of Science. Annual reports, 1-6. 8°. '69-'74. 1, 2-3, 6, ea., pap., 50c.; 4, 5, ea., pap., 75c......................... *Peabody Acad. of Sci.*
Includes Record of Am. entomology, 1872-'74.
Note. 2 and 3 are bd. together.
— Memoirs. 4 v. ill. imp. 8°. '69-'75. ea., pap., $1. *Peabody Acad. of Sci.*
Cont.: Revision of the large, stylated, fossorial crickets, by S. H. Scudder. — Embryological studies on diplax, perithemis and the thysanurous genus isotoma, by A. S. Packard, jr. — Embryological studies on hexapodous insects, by A. S. Packard, jr. — Fresh water shell mounds of the St. John's River, Fla., by J. Wyman.
Peabody Museum of Am. Archæology and Ethnology. Reports. nos. 1-9. ill. 8°. '68-'76. ea., pap., 25c.; — in 1 v. 8°. $2.50.. *Peabody Mus. Am. Arch.*
Peace. *See* Aristophanes.
Peace. White, J. J. $1.50.............. *Lippincott.*
Peace and quiet. Williams, T. J. 15c....... *French.*
Peace and war. Hemmenway, J. 75c... *Friends Pub. H.*
Peace and war. *See* Little Katie's little lib.
Peace at any price. *See* Robertson, T. W.
Peace, be still. Ryle, J. C. 15c............. *Am. Tr.*
Peace for the troubled. Heck, D. 25c.; 10c.. *Pres. Bd.*
Peace in death exemplified in youthful believers; by author of "Little Kadore." 18°. 35c... *Pres. Bd.*
Peace of God. Jones, W. B. $2......... *Routledge.*
Peace of the soul and the happiness of the heart. *See* Scupoli, L.
Peacemaker. *See* Arthur, T. S.
Peacemaker; or, little Gretchen. 18°. '72. 50c. *Lothrop.*
Peacemaker and watchtowers. 32°. 15c.; 20c. *Dutton.*
Peach, E: Pious biography; or, models of piety. 18°. 60c. .... *Cummiskey.*
Peach orchard robbery. 18°. 18c........... *Am. S. S.*
Peacock, T: Brower. Poems. 12°. '72. $1.. *Peacock.*
— Vendetta, and other poems. 8°. '76. $1.50.. *Peacock.*
Peacock, T: Love. Works; with preface by Lord Houghton and biog. notice by E. Nichols; ed. by H. Cole. 3 v. por. post 8°. $8; hf. cf., $14. *Scribner, W. & A.*
Peacock at home. [Toy-book.] ill. 4°. $1; 50c. *Routledge.*
Peacocke, Ja. S. Orphan girls. 12°. $1.75.. *J. E. Potter.*
Peake, Eliz. History of the German emperors and their contemporaries. ill. 8°. $3.... *Lippincott.*
— Pen pictures of Europe: where and how we went, and what we saw during a seventeen months' tour. ill. cr. 8°. $3.50............ *Lippincott.*
Peake, H. Boys' book of heroes. ill. 12°. $1.25. *Scribner, W. & A.*
Peake, R: Brinsley. [Plays.] 9 v. 16°. ea., pap., 15c.................................. *French.*
Cont.: Amateurs and actors: farce. — Comfortable lodgings: farce. — Duel: farce — Evil eye: musical drama. — Haunted inn: farce. — Hundred pound note: farce. — Master's rival: farce. — Mogul tale: farce. — Uncle Rip: farce.

Peaks of Otter: monograph of the relig. experiences of a young man. 18°. 25c. . . . . *Pres. Bd.*

Peale, R. Graphics, the art of accurate delineation: school exercise. 12°. '45. hf. bd., 45c. . . *Fortescue.*

Pearce, C. E. The golden island. ill. 8°. (Lond.) 50c. . . . . *Am. News.*

Pearce, Ja. Chants and responses. 12°. '67. $1.75. *Ditson.*

— Hymn music; adapted to the Hymnal of the Episc. Church. ('72.) New ed. 8°. '75. $2 . . . *Pond.*

— The service: Episc. service arranged to music. ('72.) New ed. '75. 8°. $1.25 . . . . *Pond.*

Pearce, T: The dog; with directions for his treatment and notices of the best dogs of the day and their breeders or exhibitors. ill. cr. 8°. $1.75 . . *Cassell.*

Pearce, W: Hartford bridge: farce. 16°. pap., 15c. *French.*

— Netley Abbey: farce. 16°. pap., 15c. . . . . . . *French.*

Peard, Fes. M. Rose garden (The): novelette. 16°. '72. $1.50 . . . . *Roberts.*

— Thorpe Regis. 16°. '74. $2 . . . . *Roberts.*

— Unawares: novelette. 16°. '72. $1.50 . . . . *Roberts.*

Pearl, Christie (*pseud.*) *See* Perkins, Ellen M.

Pearl (The). Kieffer, J. M. 35c. . . . . *Brainard.*

Pearl necklace, and other stories. ('70.) New ed. ill. 16°. '75. $1.25 . . . . *Hoyt.*

Pearl of Orr's Island. Stowe, H. B. $2 . . . . . *Osgood.*

Pearl of parables. Hamilton, J. $1.25 . . . . *Carter.*

Pearl of Savoy: drama. 16°. pap., 15c. . . . . . *French.*

Pearl of story books. 12°. $1.50 . . . . *Nelson.*

Pearl ser. 4 v. 8°. ea., 50c.; pap., 25c. . . . . . *Nelson.*

Cont.: Pretty pictures for little eyes. — Child's Noah's ark. — Gift for a pet. — My own toy book.

Pearl ser. *See* Baker, *Mrs.* H. N. W.

Pearls, and other tales; tr. from the Germ. ill. 16°. $1.25 . . . . *O'Shea.*

Pearls for the little ones. 18°. 45c.; 55c. . . *Am. Bapt.*

Pearls for prayer meetings. 32°. '69. 25c. . . *Randolph.*

Pearls of thought: sel. from old authors. 24°. '58. $1.50 . . . . *Randolph.*

Pearls of wisdom. Hutchings, S. 30c.–$1.75 . . *Am. Tr.*

Pearls reset. Clark, E. 75c. . . . . *Graves.*

Pearly gates. Rosecrans, J. H. 25c. . . . . *Cen. Bk.*

Pearse, M: Guy. Daniel Quorm and his religious notions. ill. 12°. '75. $1 . . . . *Meth. Bk. Conc.*

Pearson, *Mrs.* C. H. On the frontiers; or, scenes in the west. 16°. $1.25 . . . . *Cong. Pub.*

— Prince Paul, the freedman soldier. 16°. $1.25. *Cong. Pub.*

Pearson, C: H. Cabin on the prairie. ill. 16°. $1.25. *Lee & S.*

Pearson, *Mrs.* E. Prince Paul. *See* Mossy dell ser.

Pearson, *Miss* Eliz. H. The three passovers. sq. 24°. 50c. . . . . *Willard.*

Pearson, *Mrs.* Emily C. Gutenberg, and the art of printing. ill. 12°. '71. $2 . . . . *Lockwood, B. & Co.*

— Our parish. ('68.) New ed. 18°. '73. 75c. . . *Nat. Temp.*

Pearson, Helen C. Roy's search. ('70.) New ed. 12°. '74. $1.25 . . . . *Nat. Temp.*

Pearson, J: Exposition of the Apostles' creed. 12°. (Bohn.) $1.75 . . . . *Little, B. & Co.*

— *Same.* 12°. (Bohn.) $2 . . *Lippincott; Scribner, W. & A.*

— *Same;* ed. by Dobson. 8°. $2.50 . . . . *Appleton.*

Pearson, Jona. Contributions for genealogies of descendants of first settlers of Schenectady [N.Y.], 1662–1800. sm. 4°. '73. hf. shp., $6 . . *Munsell.*

— Genealogies of first settlers of anc. co. of Albany [N. Y.], 1630–1800. sm. 4°. '72. $5 . . . . *Munsell.*

Peasant and guest. ill. 8°. 50c. . . . . *Am. S. S.*

Peasant and his landlord. Knorring, S. M. v. $1.50. *Harper.*

Peasant and the prince. *See* Martineau, H.

Peasant boy philosopher. Mayhew, H. $1.50 . . *Routledge.*

Peasant life in the north: sketches of villagers and field-laborers in Glenaldie. 2 v. cr. 8°. '72. ea., $2 . . . . *Routledge.*

Peasants of the Alps; [also] Passetout; or, the new fishing smack. 16°. 50c. . . . . *Scribner, W. & A.*

Pease, A. G. Philosophy of Trinitarian doctrine. 12°. '75. $1.50 . . . . *Putnam.*

Pease, D. G. Our dear Eddie. ('61.) New ed. ill. 18°. '68. 45c. . . . . *Hoyt.*

Pease, *Miss* F. W. Out in the playground. ill. 18°. '73. 40c. . . . . *Am. Tr.*

Pease, F: H. Crystal (The). [Music.] 8°. $1.50. *Brainard.*

— Musical lyra: glees, quartettes, etc. 8°. '62. bds., $1.50 . . . . *Ditson.*

— *See also* Perkins, E. A., *and* Pease, F. H.

Peaslee, Edm. Randolph. Anniversary discourse: progress and the spirit of medical science. 8°. '58. pap., 50c. . . . . *N. Y. Acad. Med.*

— Treatise on ovarian tumors. ill. 8°. $5; shp., $6. *Appleton.*

Peat, J. B. Baptists examined; or, common sense on baptism, close communion and the Baptists: dialogue between a Presbyterian and a Methodist. ('68.) 4th ed. 12°. '70. $1.50 . . . . . *Blackall.*

Peat makers. *See* Bright eye ser.

Pebbles and pearls. Richardson, A. S. *1.25 . . *Am. Pub.*

Pebbles from the sea-shore. Bache, A. 75c. . . *Tibbals.*

Peck, Ann Thane. Memoir. 18°. 40c. . . . *Cong. Pub.*

Peck, D: Peace for the troubled; or, friendly words for earnest seekers. 18°. 25c.; pap., 10c. . . *Pres. Bd.*

Peck, E. *See* Illinois, Sup. Court reports.

Peck, Ellen. ["Cuyler Pine."] Ecce femina; or, the woman Zoe. 12°. $1.50 . . . . *Carleton.*

Peck, G: Early Methodism within bounds of old Genesee conference. 12°. '60. $1.75 . . *Meth. Bk. Conc.*

— Episcopacy and slavery. 8°. 35c. . . *Cin. Meth. Bk. Conc.*

— Formation of a manly character. 16°. '53. 75c. *Meth. Bk. Conc.*

— Life and times: autobiog. 12°. '74. $1.75. *Meth. Bk. Conc.*

— Our country: its trial and triumph. 12°. '65. $1.50. *Meth. Bk. Conc.*

— Rule of faith: appeal from tradition. 12°. '44. $1.25. *Meth. Bk. Conc.*

— Scripture doctrine of Christian perfection. 12°. '42. $1.75 . . . . *Meth. Bk. Conc.*

— Why are you a Methodist? 18°. '42. 60c. *Meth. Bk. Conc.*

— Wyoming: its hist., stirring incidents and romantic adventures. ill. 12°. $1.75 . . . . *Harper.*

Peck, Hiram D. Law of municipal corporations in Ohio; with notes of decisions. 8°. '75. $3.50; leath., $4 . . . . *Clarke.*

— Manual of law rel. to formation and government of townships, and the rights and duties of township officers in Ohio; with forms and annotations. 12°. '74. $2; shp., $2.50 . . . . *Clarke.*

Peck, Jac. *See* Tennessee, Sup. Court reports.

Peck, Jesse T. History of the great republic. 8°. $4; shp., $5; hf. mor., $6 . . . . *Palmer.*

— True woman. 12°. '57. $1.75; $2.25 . . *Meth. Bk. Conc.*

— What must I do to be saved? 18°. '58. 60c. *Meth. Bk. Conc.*

Peck, J: A short poem. 24°. '51. pap., 10c. . . *Perkinpine.*

Peck, Jos. E. Soul problems; with papers on the theolog. amend. and the state personality idea. 12°. '75. 75c.; pap., 50c. . . . . *Somerby.*

Peck, W: G. Complete arithmetic, theoretical and practical. 12°. '74. hf. bd., 90c. . . . . *Barnes.*

— — Key. 12°. '76. 90c. . . . . *Barnes.*

— Elementary treat. on mechanics. 12°. '70. $2 . . *Barnes.*

— Elements of mechanics; with calculus. 12°. '59. $1.40 . . . . *Barnes.*

Peck, W: G., *continued.*
— First lessons in numbers. 16°. '74. hf.bd.,25c. *Barnes.*
— Introductory course of nat. philosophy; from Ganot's "Popular physics." 12°. '75. $1.75.. *Barnes.*
— — *See also* Ganot, A., Popular physics.
— Manual of algebra. 12°. '75. $1.60...... *Barnes.*
— Manual of geometry and conic sections; with applic. to trigonometry and mensuration. 12°. '76. $1.10 ...... *Barnes.*
— Manual of practical arithmetic. 18°. '74. hf. bd., 50c. ...... *Barnes.*
— Practical treatise on differential and integral calculus; with applic. to mechanics and astronomy. 12°. '70. $1.75 ...... *Barnes.*
— Treatise on analyt. geometry. 12°. '73. $1.75.. *Barnes.*

Peckham, *Mrs.* Ma. C. Father Gabrielle's fairy. ('69.) 2d ed. ill. 16°. '70. 80c. ...... *Am. Unit.*

Pecksy and Flapsy. sq. 16°. pap., 25c.; 35c... *Am. S. S.*

Peculiar position: farce. 16°. pap., 15c..... *Happy.*

Peculiarly perplexing predicament: burlesque. 16°. pap., 15c. ...... *French.*

Pedder, H: C. Issues of the age; or, consequences involved in mod. thought. 12°.'74. $1.50.. *Somerby.*
— Man and woman considered in their rel. to each other and to the world. 12°. '70. $1 ... *Wells.*
— Religion and progress. 16°. '75. $1...... *Dutton.*

Pedder, Ja. Land-measurer for farmers. 18°. 60c. *Judd.*

Peddler boy. *See* Woodworth, F. C.

Peddler of dust sticks. Follen, E. L. 50c. .. *Lee & S.*

Peddler of La Grave. Finley, M. F. 55c... *Pres. Bd.*

Pedestrianism: health, training, etc. ill. 48°. 25c. *Scribner, W. & A.*

Pedlar boy. Harrington, R. 15c. ...... *French.*

Pedlar of Very Nice. Baker, G. M. 15c.... *Lee & S.*

Pedlar's acre. Almar, G. 15c. ...... *French.*

Pedley, *Mrs.* G. Practical housekeeping. 16°. bds., 40c. ...... *Routledge.*

Pedrillo. Johnstone, J. B. 15c. ...... *French.*

Peebles, Ja. M. Seers of the ages: ancient, mediaeval and modern spiritualism. ('69.) 6th ed. 8°. '74. $2 ...... *Colby.*
— Spiritual teacher and songster. [Sing. book.] 12°. '74. 15c. ...... *Colby.*
— Spiritualism defined and defended: lectures. 12°. '75. pap., 15c. ...... *Colby.*
— Travels around the world. ('74.) 2d ed. large 8°. '75. $2 ...... *Colby.*
— *See also* Barrett, J. O., *and* Peebles, J. M.; — Tuttle, H., *and* Peebles, J. M.
— *and* Barrett, J. O. Spiritual harp: vocal music for the choir, congregation and social circles; E. H. Bailey, musical ed. ('68.) 7th ed. 8°. '76. $2; $3; — abridg., $1 ...... *Colby.*

Peebles, *Mrs.* Ma. L. Good fight (The). ill. 18°. 75c. ...... *Bost. Am. Tr.*
— — *See also* Pleasant Grove ser.
— Helps over hard places; for boys. 18°. 90c... *Nims.*
— *Same.* 2 v. ill. 18°. ea., 75c. ...... *Bost. Am. Tr.*
— *Same;* for girls. ill. 18°. 75c. ...... *Bost. Am. Tr.*
— Honorable club (The), and other tales. ill. 18°. 90c. *Bost. Am. Tr.*
— — *See also* Honor bright lib.
— Little captain: temperance tale. ill. 18°. 60c. *Bost. Am. Tr.*
— Magnet stories. 4 v. ill. 16°. $5 ...... *Nims.*
Cont.: Drifting and steering. — One day's weaving. — Archie's shadow. — John Jack.

Peele, G: *See* Greene, R., *and* Peele, G.

Peep at my neighbors; or, the houses in Kingston Court turned inside out. 18°. 60c..... *Am. S. S.*

Peep at "number five." *See* Phelps, *Mrs.* E. S.

Peep into sacred tradition. Abbott, O. 50c. (?) *Emerson.*

Peep o' day. *See* Banim, J. *and* M.

Peep o' day. Falconer, E. 15c...... *De Witt; French.*

Peep of day. *See* Mortimer, *Mrs.* M.

Peep of day lib.; — ser. *See* Mortimer, *Mrs.* M.

Peep ser. of juvenile books. ill. 16°. per doz., $3.. *Nelson.*

Peep show. ill. 4°. '75. $2; bds., $1.50..... *Nelson.*

Peep show man. Williams, T. J. 15c. ...... *French.*

Peep show ser. 4 v. ill. 18°. $2 ...... *Nelson.*
Cont.: Walks and talks with grandpapa, by Mrs. A. J. Cupples. — Shadows on the screen. — Sights at a peep show, by Mrs. A. J. Cupples. — My pretty scrap book, by Mrs. A. J. Cupples.

Peeping Tom of Coventry: farce. 16°. pap., 15c. *French.*

Peeps abroad for folks at home. Mateaux, C. L. $2.50 ...... *Cassell.*

Peeps at the far east. Macleod, N. $7.50.. *Routledge.*

Peeps at the "little bells." 18°. 45c. ...... *Cong. Pub.*

Peeps at our Sunday school. Taylor, A. $1.25. *Meth. Bk. Conc.*

Peeps from the wainscot. 18°. 60c.; 70c... *Am. Bapt.*

Peers and parvenus. Gore, C. J. 50c. ...... *Harper.*

Peet, Harvey Prindle. Course of instruction for the deaf and dumb. ('45-'46.) New ed. pts. 1, 3. 16°. '75. 1, 75c.; 3, $1 ...... *Baker, P. & Co.*
Note. pt. 2 not pub.
— History of the U. S. 12°. '69. $1.50.. *Baker, P. & Co.*
— Manual of inorganic chemistry for students. 24°. '68. 75c. ...... *Baker, P. & Co.*
— Scripture lessons. ('47.) New ed. ill. 18°. '49. 30c.; bds., 20c. ...... *Am. Tr.*

Peet, I: Lew. Language lessons; to instruct young learners, deaf mutes and foreigners in Eng. 12°. '75. $1.25 ...... *Baker, P. & Co.*
— Manual of vegetable physiology adapted to use of the deaf and dumb. 16°.'69. pap., 25c... *Baker, P. & Co.*

Peg Woffington. *See* Reade, C:

Pegg, J. G. B. New eschatology; showing indestructibility of the earth and difference bet. letter and spirit of the Scripture. 12°. 75c.... *Lippincott.*

Peggy Green. Selby, C. 15c...... *De Witt; French.*

Peggy Ward's canaries. 18°. 40c. ...... *Dutton.*

Peile, J: Introduction to Greek and Latin etymology. 2d ed., rev. cr. 8°. '75. $3.50...... *Macmillan.*

Peirce, B: Address before Am. Assoc. for Advancement of Sci., July, 1853. 8°. pap., 25c. *Am. Assoc. Adv. Sci.*
— Elementary treatise on algebra; [with] Exponential equation and logarithms. 12°. $1.25.... *Dennet.*
— Elementary treatise on plane and solid geometry. 12°. $1 ...... *Dennet.*
— Elementary treatise on sound. 8°. $1.50.. *Dennet.*
— Ocean lanes for steamships; read before Am. Soc. Sci. Assoc., May 20, '74. 8°. '74. pap., 10c. *Williams.*
— System of analytic mechanics. 4°. '72. $10. *Van Nostrand.*

Peirce, Bradford Kinney. Bay state questions upon uniform lessons for 1873. 18°. bds., 15c. *Cong. Pub.*
— Bible scholar's manual. 18°. '47. 60c. *Meth. Bk. Conc.*
— Faith and works harmonized: question-book on Ephesians and James. 18°. hf. bd., 15c... *Hoyt.*
— Hymns for the higher life. sm. 4°. '67. $1.50; mor., $3 ...... *Crowell.*
— Infant question-book; or, little child's pathway to Jesus. 18°. '64. hf. bd., 15c. ...... *Hoyt.*
— Notes on Acts. 12°. '48. $1.25 .... *Meth. Bk. Conc.*
— Questions on Acts. 18°. per doz., $2.16.. *Meth. Bk. Conc.*
— Questions on Exodus. 18°. per doz., $1.80. *Meth. Bk. Conc.*
— Questions on Genesis. 18°. per doz., $1.80. *Meth. Bk. Conc.*
— Stories from life which the chaplain told. ('66.) New ed. ill. 16°. '68. $1 ...... *Hoyt.*
— Trials of an inventor: life and discoveries of Charles Goodyear. 12°. '66. $1.25...... *Meth. Bk. Conc.*
— Under the cross. ('69.) New ed. ill. 16°. '74. $1.50. sq. 12°. $4.25 ...... *Hoyt.*

Peirce, Bradford Kinney, *continued.*
— Word of God opened. 12°. '64. $1.25.. *Meth. Bk. Conc.*
— Young Shetlander and his home: biog. sketch of T: Edmonston. ill. 12°. '70. $1.25.. *Meth. Bk. Conc.*
Peirce, Ja. Mills. Elements of logarithms; with explanation of author's three and four place tables. 12°. '74. $1 .... *Ginn.*
— Tables of logarithmic and trigonometric functions to three and four places of decimals. ('71.) 2d ed. 4°. '74. 75c. .... *Ginn.*
Peissner, El. English-German grammar. 12°. $1.75. *Sheldon.*
Pelayo. Beach, E. T. P. $2; $2.50; $4.50. *Appleton.*
Pelham. *See* Bulwer-Lytton, *Sir* E. G. E. L.
Pellarin, C: Life of Charles Fourier; tr. by F. G. Shaw. 2d ed., with app. por. 12°. '48. $1.50; pap., $1 .... *D. Thomas.*
Pellegrin, V. Theory and practice of linear perspective, applied to landscapes, interiors and the figure. 12°. '74. $1.......... *Putnam.*
Pellegrino, G. R. (*ed.*) The Christian trumpet; or, previsions and predictions about impending general calamities, the universal triumph of the Church, the coming Christ, the last judgment and the end of the world. 12°. $1.50.. *Noonan.*
Pelletan, Eug. The pastor of the desert, Jean Jarousseau; tr. from the Fr. ill. 16°. '72. 90c... *Dodd.*
Pellico, Silvio. Francesca da Rimini: tragedia. 12°. '64. pap., 75c.......... *Holt.*
— My prisons: memoir of P., with introd. by E. Sargent. 12°. '67. $1.50; $2.25.......... *Roberts.*
Peloubet, F. N. International question book. ('75.) [Annual.] 3 grades. 18°. ea., 15c.......... *Hoyt.*
— Select notes on International lessons. ('75.) [Annual.] maps, tables, etc. 8°. $1.25 .... *Hoyt.*
Pelouze, Théophile Jul., *and* Fremy, E. General notes on chemistry; tr. by E. C. Evans. ill. 12°. $1.75 .... *Lippincott.*
Pelton, C. Key to maps. 8°. hf. bd., 80c..... *Sower.*
Pember, E: H: Tragedy of Lesbos: dramatic poem. fp. 8°. '70. $1.50 .... *Macmillan.*
Pemberton, *Col.* —. ["Leo."] The scapegoat. 12°. $1.50 .... *Lippincott.*
Pemberton. Peterson, H. $1.25 .... *Lippincott.*
Pembroke, *Earl of.* *See* Herbert, G. R. C.
Pen photographs of Charles Dickens and his readings. Field, K. $1.50 .... *Osgood.*
Pen pictures of Europe. Peake, E. $3.50.. *Lippincott.*
Pencil sketches. 18°. 35c. .... *Cong. Pub.*
Pencillep, Harry. Sunlight and shadow; or, the poetry of home. 12°. $1.75 .... *J. E. Potter.*
Pencillings by the seashore. Gilman, B. F. $1.25. *Cong. Pub.*
Pencillings by the way. Willis, N. P. $1.75.. *Scribner.*
Pendennis. *See* Thackeray, W: M.
Pendleton, Edm. Monroe. Text book of scientific agriculture; with practical deductions. 12°. '74. $2.50 .... *Barnes.*
Pendleton, *Mrs.* Hester. The parents' guide; or, human development through inherited tendencies. 2d ed., rev. and enl. 12°. '71. $1.25 ..... *Wells.*
Pendleton, J. M. Church manual; for use of Baptist churches. 18°. 50c.......... *Am. Bapt.*; *So. Bapt.*
— Old landmark reset. 18°. pap., 10c.......... *So. Bapt.*
— Questions to the impenitent. 18°. 30c.; pap., 15c. *So. Bapt.*
— Sermons. 12°. $1.50.......... *So. Bapt.*
— Thoughts on Christian duty. 18°. 30c.; pap., 15c. *So. Bapt.*
— Three reasons why I am a Baptist. 16°. '53. 50c. *Wilstach.*
— *Same.* 18°. 60c.......... *So. Bapt.*

Pendleton, W. K. Baptism for the remission of sins. 8°. pap., 10c. .... *Chase.*
— *See also* New Test. commentary.
Pendleton, W: N. Science a witness for the Bible. 12°. '60. $1 .... *Claxton; Lippincott.*
Penelope Anne: farce. 16°. pap., 15c. ...... *Happy.*
Penetralia. Davis, A. J. $1.75.......... *A. J. Davis.*
Pengilly, R: Scripture guide to baptism. 18°. 40c. *Am. Bapt.*
— *French.* 18°. 40c.; pap., 25c.......... *Am. Bapt.*
— *German.* 12°. 30c.; pap., 10c.......... *Am. Bapt.*
Penington, I: Works. 4 v. 8°. $5.. *Friends Bk. St.*
— Letters. 12°. 75c.......... *Friends Bk. St.*
Peninsular war. *See* Maxwell, W: H.
Penitent boy. Howard, E. 70c.......... *Pres. Bd.*
Penley, Aar. Sketching from nature in water colours; with chromo-lith. roy. 4°. $7.50 ...... *Cassell.*
Penley, Sampson. Sleeping draught: farce. 16°. pap., 15c.......... *French.*
Penn, W: Correspond. and autobiog. *See* Janney, S. M.
— Journal while visiting Holland and Germany. 12°. 40c. .... *Friends Bk. St.*
— Life. ill. 16°. $1.25.......... *Lee & S.*
— No cross, no crown: discourse [on] nature and discipline of the holy cross of Christ. 12°. 75c. *Friends Bk. Assoc.*; *Friends Bk. St.*
— *German.* 12°. 50c.......... *Friends Bk. St.*
— Rise and progress of the people called Quakers. 12°. 35c. .... *Friends Bk. St.*
— *Same;* [also] Sandy foundation shaken; [also] Innocency with her open face; with letter to his wife and children. 16°. *net*, 25c. *Friends Bk. Assoc.*
— *and* Logan, Ja. Correspondence, 1700–1750; with notes by Mrs. D. Logan; ed. with add. notes by E. Armstrong. v. 1–2. 8°. $5..... *Lippincott.*
— — — *See also* Historical Soc. of Penna.
Pennell, H. Cholmondeley. The modern practical angler. 12°. $3 .... *Scribner, W. & A.*
— The muses of Mayfair: sel. from vers de société of the 19th cent. 12°. '74. $3 .... *Routledge.*
Pennell, R. F. History of anc. Greece. ('74.) 2d ed. map and plans. 16°. '76. 75c.......... *Allyn.*
— The Latin subjunctive. ('75.) 2d ed. 16°. '76. pap., 30c.......... *Allyn.*
Penney, *Miss* L. National temperance orator. ('74.) New ed. 12°. '76. $1 .... *Nat. Temp.*
Penniman, *Maj.* (*pseud.*) *See* Denison, C: W.
Pennington, W: S. *See* New Jersey, Superior Court reports.
Pennmaen-maur: a Welsh Christmas story. 18°. 30c. *Dutton.*
Pennot, P: (*pseud.*) *See* Round, W. M. F.
Pennsylvania. Cases decided by federal and state courts (1842–'61); with ref. to [subsequent] cases by J. A. Clark. 5 v. 8°. shp., $30.. *Welsh.*
— Constitution as amended in 1874; with notes and ref. by F. C. Brightly; [also] Constitution of 1838. (Binns' justice ed.) 8°. pap., 25c... *Kay.*
— *Same.* (Purdon's digest ed.) imp. 8°. pap., 25c. *Kay.*
— *Same;* with introd., notes and ref. by H. E. Wallace and D. Sanders. 2d ed. 8°. '74. 75c.. *Welsh.*
— Court of Common Pleas reports, 1st district, 1806–'14; by P. A. Browne. 2 v. in 1. 8°. shp., $12.. *Gilbert.*
— — Reports of cases in Courts of Common Pleas, Quarter Sessions, Oyer and Terminer and Orphans' Court, 1st district; with notes and ref. by J. W. Ashmead. New ed. 2 v. 8°. '71. shp., $15 .... *J. Campbell & Son.*
— — *Same.* v. 2. 8°. '41. $7.50.. *T. & J. W. Johnson.*
— *Same.* 1841–'51; by A. V. Parsons. 8°. '53. $5.50. *T. & J. W. Johnson.*
— Digest of acts of Assembly. *See* Dunlop, J.
— Digest of titles of corporations. *See* Beitel, C. G.

Pennsylvania, *continued.*
— Laws, 1700–1829; with notes and ref. by — Smith and — Reed. 10 v. 8°. shp., $25 ....*Kay.*
— — Digest. *See* Purdon, J.
— Nisi prius reports. *See* Campbell, J. H., Legal Gazette reports.
— Supreme Court reports, with sel. cases at nisi prius and in circuit courts, 1791–1808; by J. Yeates. New ed. 4 v. 8°. '71. shp., $30..*J. Campbell & Son.*
— *Same.* 1754–1814; condensed by T. J. F. Alden. 3 v. 8°. shp., $15.......................*Kay.*
Includes Dallas (1754–1806), 4 v.; Yeates (1791–1808), 4 v.; Binney (1799–1814), 6 v.; Addison (1791–1799), 1 v.
— *Same.* 1814–'28; by T. Sergeant and W. Rawle, jr. 17 v. 8°. *net*, shp., $102................*Kay.*
— *Same.* 1828–'35; by W. Rawle, jr. New ed., with notes by W. W. Wister. 5 v. 8°. '69. $40. *T. & J. W. Johnson.*
— *Same.* 1829–'32; by W. Rawle, jr., C. B. Penrose and F. Watts. 3 v. 8° ....*State.*
— *Same.* 1832–'40; by F. Watts. 10 v. 8°....*State.*
— *Same.* 1835–'41; by T. I. Wharton. New ed., with notes by J. Sword. 6 v. 8°. '70. $48. *T. & J. W. Johnson.*
— *Same.* 1841–'45; by F. Watts and H. J. Sergeant. 9 v. 8°. shp., $54.......................*Kay.*
— *Same.* Penn. reports, v. 1–10 (1845–'49); by R. M. Barr. 10 v. 8°. $45.......*T. & J. W. Johnson.*
— *Same.* v. 11, 12 (1849); by J. P. Jones. 2 v. 8°. $9. *T. & J. W. Johnson.*
— *Same.* v. 13–24 (1849–'55); by G. W. Harris. 12 v. 8°. shp., $54...........................*Kay.*
— *Same.* v. 25–36 (1855–'60); by J. Casey. 12 v. 8°. shp., $54 ....*Kay.*
— *Same.* v. 37–50 (1860–'65); by R. E. Wright. 14 v. 8°. shp., $63............................*Kay.*
— *Same.* v. 51–77 (1865–'76); by P. F. Smith. 27 v. 8°. shp., $121...........................*Kay.*
— *Same.* 1852–'63; by B. Grant. v. 2, 3. 8°. '59–'64. ea., shp., $10 ....*J. Campbell & Son.*
Note. v. 1 is o. p.
— — Digest. *See* Brewster, F. C.; — Wharton, H.; — Wharton, T. J.
— — Index. *See* Wright, R. E.
— — Rules, adopted Jan. 3, 1876; with rules of equity practice adopted, Jan. 27, 1865. 8°. '76. bds., $1 ....*J. M. P. Wallace.*
— — Rules of equity practice adopted May 27, 1865; with report of commissioners and index. 8°. pap., 50c. ....*Kay.*
— — *See also* Brightly, F. C.; — Pittsburgh reports; — United States, Sup. and Circ. Court reports.
Pennsylvania choral harmony. Weber, T. R. $1.50. *Clauder.*
Pennsylvania geological survey. First–sixth reports of state geologist. 6 v. 8°. '36–'42......*State.*
— Geology of P.: a government survey by H. D. Rogers. v. 1, 2. 4°. '58 ....*State.*
— — *See also* Rogers, H: D.
Pennsylvania second geological survey. Reports of progress; by F. Prime, jr., J. F. Carll, H. E. Wrigley [and] A. S. M'Creath. 8°. '75..*State.*
Pennsylvania Hist. Soc. *See* Historical Soc. of Penn.
Pennsylvania Hospital reports; ed. by J. M. Da Costa and W. Hunt. v. 1, 2. ill. 8°. '68–'69. ea., $4. *Lindsay.*
Pennsylvania illustrated: sketch of the state, its scenery, history and industries. ill. 8°. '74. pap., 50c. ....*Porter.*
Pennsylvania pilgrim. Whittier, J. G. $1.50; $4. *Osgood.*
Pennsylvania scenery: handbook for tourists. ill. 8°. pap., 25c. ....*Lippincott.*
Pennsylvania scenery, and Philadelphia and its environs. 8°. $1....................*Lippincott.*
Pennsylvania song collection. *See* McCaskey, J. P.

Penny, *Miss* Virg. Five hundred employments adapted to women; with average rate of pay in each. 12°. $1.75 ....*J. E. Potter.*
— How women can make money, married or single, in all branches of the arts, sciences, etc. ill. 12°. $2. *J. E. Potter.*
— Think and act: articles pertaining to men and women, work and wages. 12°. '68. $1.50....*Claxton.*
Penny readings in prose and verse. Carpenter, J. E. 10 v. ea., 50c................*Scribner, W. & A.*
Penny Rust's Christmas. Davis, C. E. K. $1.15..*Hoyt.*
Penny saved and penny earned. Drinkwater, J. M. 65c. ....*Cong. Pub.*
Penny tract. 18°. '53. 35c................*Am. Tr.*
Penny wise and pound foolish. Brock, C. $1.25. (?) *Martien.*
Penrose, C. B. *See* Pennsylvania, Sup. Court reports.
Penrose, Eliz. ["*Mrs.* Markham."] History of France, from conquest of Gaul by Julius Cæsar to reign of Louis Philippe; prep. for schools by J. Abbott. map. 12°. $1.75 ....*Harper.*
— School history of Eng.; ed. by Eliza Robbins. 12°. $1.50..................................*Appleton.*
Penrose, Fs. Cranmer. On a method of predicting, by graphical construction, occultations of stars by the moon and solar eclipses for any given place; with more vigorous methods for accurate calculation of longitude; with charts, tables, etc. 4°. '69. $6 ....*Macmillan.*
Penruddocke. Aide, H. $1.25; 75c.........*Estes.*
Pens and types. Drew, B. $1.50; 75c.; 60c...*Lee & S.*
Pentateuch. *See* Bible.
Penuel. McLean, A., *and* Eaton, W. H. $1.50..*Palmer.*
People from the other world. Olcott, H. S. *$2.50; $3; $4...............................*Am. Pub.*
People I have met. Willis, N. P. $1.75....*Scribner.*
People of Bleaburn. ill. 18°. '68. 65c...*Perkinpine.*
People of China; or, a summary of Chinese history. 18°. 65c. ....*Am. S. S.*
People of Poplar Dell. *See* Poplar Dell lib.
People (The) the sovereigns. Monroe, J. $1.75. *Claxton; Lippincott.*
People's chorus book: choruses and four-part songs for mixed voices. 8°. '76. bds., $1 ....*Ditson.*
People's history of America. ill. roy. 4°. '76. *$5.50–$12 ....*H. S. Allen.*
People's lawyer. Jones, J. S. 15c..........*French.*
People's tune book. Mason, L. $1.38.......*Ditson.*
Peoples of the world. Belloc, B. P. $2.50..*Cassell.*
Pepper, J: H: Chemistry, electricity, light. ill. 12°. $2.50 ....*Scribner, W. & A.*
— Cyclopædic science simplified: light, heat, electricity, magnetism, etc. ill. cr. 8°. $4.50. *Lippincott; Routledge; Scribner, W. & A.*
— Play-book of metals. ill. 8°. $2.25.....*Routledge.*
— Play-book of science; incl. arrangements of apparatus for experiments in natural history. ill. cr. 8°. $2..............................*Routledge.*
— Scientific amusements for young people. ill. 16°. 75c.; bds., 50c. ....*Routledge.*
— — *See also* Boys' treasury of sports and pastimes; — Peterson, R. E., Familiar science.
— *and* Routledge, Rob. Discoveries and inventions of 19th cent. ill. post 8°. '75. $4.50...*Routledge.*
Pepper, W: *See* Meigs, J. F., *and* Pepper, W:
Peppergrass, Pl. (*pseud.*) *See* Boyce, J.
Peppermint drops. Small, G. G. 25c. ...*Collin & S.*
Pepys, *Lady* Ctte. Mar. Morning notes of praise: meditations upon the morning psalms. New ed. sm. 8°. '72. $1.25 ....*Dutton.*
— Quiet moments: a four weeks' course of thought and meditations, before evening prayer and at sunset. New ed. 16°. '71. $1.25..............*Dutton.*

Pepys, S: Diary and correspondence. 12°. '70. $2; hf. cf., $4.50 .... *Putnam.*
— *Same.* (Chandos lib.) 12°. $1.75; hf. cf., $3.75; cf., $5 .... *Scribner, W. & A.*
— *Same;* with life and notes by Lord Braybrooke. 4 v. por. 8°. $7 .... *Lippincott.*
— — *Same.* 4 v. ill. 12°. hf. cf., $14; cf., $16; — in 1 v. 12°. $1.75; hf. cf., $4 .... *Appleton.*
— — *Same;* with add. letters. 4 v. por. 12°. (Bohn.) ea., $1.75 .... *Little, B. & Co.*
— — *Same.* 4 v. 12°. (Bohn.) ea., $2. *Lippincott; Scribner, W. & A.*
Pequinillo. James, G. P. R. 50c. .... *Harper.*
Perabo, M. Guitar method. 4°. 50c. .... *Brainard.*
Perch, Philemon (*pseud.*) *See* Johnston, R. M.
Percie; or, the conspirators. *See* Shaw, *Miss* C. E.
Percival, Emily. Wreath of gems. 16°. $1.50. *J. E. Potter.*
Percival, Fes. E. Angel visitor; or, voices of the heart. 16°. $1.25 .... *J. E. Potter.*
— Sweet home; or, friendship's golden altar. 16°. $1.25. *J. E. Potter.*
Percival, Ja. G. Poems. 2 v. por. 32°. $2.50 .. *Osgood.*
— *See also* Connecticut geol. survey; — Wisconsin geol. survey.
Percival Keene. *See* Marryat, F:
Percival Maberry. *See* Ingraham, J. H.
Percy, Flo. (*pseud.*) *See* Allen, *Mrs.* E. A.
Percy, J: Manufacture of Russian sheet-iron. ill. 8°. '71. pap., 50c. .... *Baird.*
— Metallurgy: refractory metals and fuel. New ed., rev. and enl. ill. 8°. (Lond.) '75. $12. *Little, B. & Co.*
Percy, Sholto *and* Reub. (*pseud.*) *See* Byerley, T: *and* Robertson, Ja. Cragie.
Percy, Ste. Robin Hood and his merry foresters. 16°. $1 .... *Miller.*
— Tales of the kings and queens of England. ill. 16°. $1.25 .... *Routledge.*
Percy, T: Reliques of ancient English poetry; with supplement, glossary and notes. imp. 8°. $3.75. *Porter.*
— *Same.* (Household ser.) ill. 16°. $1.50; mor., $3. *Lee & S.*
— *Same;* ed. by J. V. Prichard. 2 v. 12°. (Bohn.) $2.50 .... *Little, B. & Co.*
— — *Same.* 2 v. 12°. (Bohn.) $2.80 .. *Scribner, W. & A.*
— — *Same.* 2 v. 12°. (Bohn.) $3 .... *Lippincott.*
— *Same;* ed. by R. A. Willmott, with biog., etc. (British poets.) ill. 12°. $2.25; hf. cf., $3.50; mor., $5 .... *Routledge.*
— — *Same.* (Presentation ed.) ill. 12°. $1.75; $3. *Routledge.*
— *See also* Mallet, P. H.
Percy anecdotes (The). Byerley, T., *and* Robertson, J. C. $2; shp., $2.50 .... *Harper.*
— *Same.* 2 v. $3.50; hf. cf., $10 .... *Appleton.*
— *Same.* 3 v. ea., $1.75; $3.75; $5 .. *Scribner, W. & A.*
Percy Effingham. Cockton, H. 75c. .... *Peterson.*
Percy family. *See* Eddy, D. C.
Percy Raydon. Leslie, E. $1 ..... *Lothrop; Nelson.*
Percy's holidays. Guernsey, L. E. 40c. .... *Am. S. S.*
Percy's visit to Maple Shade. 18°. 60c. .. *Cong. Pub.*
Percy's year of rhymes. Richardson, A. S. 50c. *Hurd & H.*
Percys (The). Prentiss, E. $1.25 .... *Randolph.*
Perdita. Balfour, F. 50c. .... *De Witt.*
Perdita. Brough, W. 15c. .... *French.*
Peregrine Bunce. *See* Hook, Thdr.
Peregrine Pickle. *See* Smollett, T.
Pereira, Jona. Elements of materia medica and therapeutics; abridg. and adapted by R. Bentley and T. Redwood. roy. 8°. $7; shp., $8 .. *Appleton.*

Pereira, Jona., *continued.*
— *Same;* arranged and adapted by F. J. Farre, assisted by R. Bentley and R. Warington; with add. and ref. to the U. S. pharmacopœia by H. C. Wood. ill. 8°. $7; leath., $8 .... *Lea.*
— Lectures on polarized light; with lecture on the microscope; ed. by B. Powell. ill. 12°. (Lond.) '54. $1.25 .... *Spon.*
— Physician's prescription book: lists of terms, phrases, abbreviations, etc., with notes; with key of unabbreviated prescriptions. 32°. '74. $1.25; leath., $1.50 .... *Lindsay.*
— Treatise on food and diet; with obs. on dietetical regimen suited for disordered states of digestive organs; ed. by C. A. Lee. 8°. '43. $1.50. *Wells.*
Peres, Jac. J. Child's arithmetical example book and teacher's key. 16°. '69. bds., 15c. ... *A. F. Dod.*
Perfect Adonis (A). Harris, M. C. $1.50 .. *Carleton.*
Perfect description of Virginia: London, 1649. [Reprint.] 4°. pap., 20c. .... *Sabin.*
Perfect gentleman: book of American etiquette. 12°. $1.50 .... *Dick & F.*
Perfect in Christ. Mason, W. 35c. .... *Am. Bapt.*
Perfect law. Mott, G. S. 40c. .... *Am. Tr.*
Perfect life. Channing, W. E. $1.50 .... *Roberts.*
Perfect light. Olin, J. M. $2 .... *Randolph.*
Perfect love. Reece, R. 15c. .... *French.*
Perfect love. Stevenson, J. 50c. .... *Wiley.*
Perfect love casteth out fear. Washburn, K. S. $1.50. *Lee & S.*
Perfect man. Jones, H. $1 .... *Lothrop.*
Perfect sacrifice. Newton, B. W. 75c. .... *Am. Bapt.*
Perfection. Bayly, T. H. 15c. .... *French.*
Perichole. *See* Ditson.
Pericles and Aspasia. Landor, W. S. $1.50 .. *Roberts.*
Perico the sad, and other stories. 8°. '76. $1.50. *Cath. Pub.*
Perilous adventures. Davenport, R. A. 75c. .. *Harper.*
Perilous adventures. *See* Little Katie's little lib.
Perilous incidents in lives of sailors and travellers; tr. from the Germ. ill. sm. 4°. $2 .... *Porter.*
Perils among the heathen. Ridgeway, J. $1 .. *Nelson.*
Perils and pleasures of a hunter's life. Herne, P. $1.75 .... *J. E. Potter.*
Perils in the desert. *See* Ragged scholars.
Perils of the sea: narratives of remarkable disasters upon the deep. ill. 18°. 75c. .... *Harper.*
— *See also* Harper's boys' and girls' lib.
Perk, Abner. Maple leaves; or, a summer in the the country. ill. sm. 4°. '72. $1.50 ... *Dutton.*
Perkins, A: T. Losses to literature and the fine arts of the great fire in Boston. 8°. '73. pap., 50c. *N. E. Hist. Gen.*
— Name of Perkins as found on the Essex Co. [Mass.] records. 8°. '76. pap., 15c. .... *Essex.*
Perkins, C: C. Art in education; reprinted from Journal of Am. Social Science Association. 8°. '70. pap., 10c. .... *Williams.*
— Italian sculptors: hist. of sculpture in northern, south. and east. Italy; with etchings and wood-eng. imp. 8°. (Lond.) '68. $16 .. *Little, B. & Co.*
— Tuscan sculptors: their lives, works and times; with etchings and wood eng. 2 v. imp. 8°. (Lond.) '64. $22.50 .... *Little, B. & Co.*
Perkins, C. O. *and* F. Farmer's accountant. 12°. $3. *Judd.*
Perkins, E. E. Gas and ventilation. ('56.) 2d ed. ill. 12°. '69. $1.25 .... *Baird.*
Perkins, E: A., *and* Pease, F: H. Western bell: glees, quartettes and choruses. obl. 8°. '57. bds., $1.50. *Ditson.*
Perkins, Eli (*pseud.*) *See* Landon, M. D.

Perkins, Ellen M. ["Christie Pearl."] Every day lessons: children's stories. ill. 18°. 60c. *Bost.Am.Tr.*
— Little sheaves for little gleaners. ill. 18°. 75c. *Bost.Am.Tr.*
— — *See also* Golden sheaves lib.
Perkins, F. *See* Perkins, C. O. *and* F.
Perkins, F: B. Life and works of Charles Dickens. 12°. $1 .... *Putnam.*
— Scrope; or, the lost library. [Fiction.] 8°. '74. $1.50 .... *Roberts.*
— *See also* Six of one by half a dozen of the other.
Perkins, F: W. *See* Essex Institute, Naturalists' directory.
Perkins, G. H., *and* Stowe, J. G. New guide to the sheet-iron and boiler plate roller: series of tables. obl. roy. 8°. '67. $2.50 .... *Baird.*
Perkins, G: A. Record of the Perkins of Ipswich. 8°. '72. pap., 15c. .... *Essex.*
Perkins, G: R. Elementary arithmetic. 12°. 75c. *Appleton.*
— *Span.* Lecciones de aritmética elemental. 18°. 50c. *Appleton.*
— Elementary geometry; with applications. 12°. '47. shp., $1.25 .... *Appleton.*
— Elements of algebra. 12°. '44. shp., $1.50 .. *Appleton.*
— Higher arithmetic. 12°. $1.75 .... *Appleton.*
— Plane and solid geometry. (College ed.) 8°. '54. $2 .... *Appleton.*
— Plane trigonometry and surveying; with tables. 8°. '51. $2 .... *Appleton.*
— Practical arithmetic. 12°. $1.25. — Key. 12°. $1.50. *Appleton.*
— Primary arithmetic; comb. mental and written exercises. 16°. 30c. .... *Appleton.*
— Treatise on algebra. (College ed.) 8°. '41. shp., $2 .... *Appleton.*
Perkins, H. S. Advance (The). [Church music.] 8°. $1.25 .... *Brainard.*
— College hymn and tune book. 12°. bds., 30c. .. *Peters.*
— The song echo. cr. 8°. bds., 75c. .... *Peters.*
— *See also* Perkins, W. O. *and* H. S.; — Wendeté, C. W., *and* Perkins, H. S.
— *and* W. O. The shining river: collection of music for Sunday schools. obl. 12°. '75. bds., 35c.; pap., 30c. .... *Ditson.*
— *and* Bentley, W: W. River of life: collection of music. obl. 12°. '73. bds., 35c.; pap., 30c. *Ditson.*
Perkins, Jona. C. *See* England, Chancery reports; — United States, Digest.
Perkins, Just. Missionary life in Persia: glimpses of a quarter of a century's labor among the Nestorian Christians. ill. 16°. $1 ...... *Bost.Am.Tr.*
Perkins, Maur. Elementary manual of qualitative chemical analysis. 12°. $1 .... *Wiley.*
Perkins, *Mrs.* S. M. Eugene Cooper; or, the motherless boy. ('69.) New ed. ill. 16°. '75. $1.15 .. *Hoyt.*
Perkins, *Mrs.* S. M. C. Alice and her friends. 16°. '66. $1.50 .... *Universalist.*
Perkins, S: E. Indiana practice. [Law.] 8°. shp., $3 .... *Merrill.*
Perkins, Thdr. E. Mount Zion coll. of tunes, etc., for S.-schools. roy. 8°. '69. bds., $1.25 ... *Barnes.*
— New shining star; for S.-schools. obl. 16°. bds., 40c.; pap., 33c. .... *Huntington.*
— Psalm king. obl. 8°. bds., $1.50 ...... *Huntington.*
— Sabbath carols. 12°. '68. pap., 30c.; bds., 35c. *Barnes.*
— Sacred lute: music, sacred and secular, cont. all metres of the Methodist hymn book. obl. 8°. bds., $1.50 .... *Huntington.*
— *See also* Cook, T. J., *and* Perkins, T. E.; — Cook, T. J., Perkins, T. E., *and* Hastings, T.; — Robinson, C. S., *and* Perkins, T. E.
— *and* Taylor, Alfr. Songs of salvation. obl. 16°. '70. bds., 35c. .... *Biglow.*

Perkins, Thdr. E., *continued.*
— — *and* Sanders, C: W. Songs for to-day; for day schools. obl. 16°. '72. bds., 40c. ...... *Biglow.*
Perkins, W. O. Anthem book; for opening and closing relig. service. 8°. '74. bds., $1.50 .. *Ditson.*
— Chorister; for choirs, schools and conventions. ('70.) New ed. obl. roy. 8°. '76. bds., $1.50. *Pond; G.D.Russell.*
— Church welcome; for choirs, classes and conventions. ('73.) New ed. obl. roy. 8°. '76. bds., $1.50. *Pond; G.D.Russell.*
— Golden robin. [Sing. book.] obl. 12°. '68. bds., 50c. .... *Ditson.*
— Laurel wreath; for female seminaries, etc. ('70.) New ed. obl. roy. 8°. '76. bds., $1. *Pond; G.D.Russell.*
— Mocking bird: element. music for schools. ('71.) New ed. obl. 12°. '76. bds., 50c. .. *Pond; G.D.Russell.*
— Seminary album: exercises in vocal culture and music for female voices. ('73.) New ed. obl. roy. 8°. '76. bds., $1 ...... *Pond; G.D.Russell.*
— Singing school; for public and private sing. classes. obl. 8°. bds., 75c. .... *G.D.Russell.*
— Starry crown: hymns, anthems, etc. ('69.) New ed. obl. 12°. '76. bds., 35c. .... *Pond; G.D.Russell.*
— Zion: music for choirs, etc. obl. 8°. bds., $1.25. *G.D.Russell.*
— *See also* Baker, B. F., *and* Perkins, W. O.; — Perkins, H. S. *and* W. O.
— *and* H. S. Church bell. obl. 8°. bds., $1.25. *G.D.Russell.*
— — Nightingale: collection of songs, chants and hymns. obl. 16°. '60. bds., 50c. ...... *Ditson.*
— — Sabbath school trumpet: collection of hymns and tunes. obl. 12°. '64. bds., 35c.; pap., 30c. *Ditson.*
— *and* Hallett, A. R. The orphean: element. course in music with sel. 8°. '71. bds., $1 .... *Ditson.*
Perlen der Andacht: Gebetbuch f. Katholiken. 32°. 10c.–85c. .... *Hoffmann.*
Perlenschnur von Gottes Führungen. 18°. 35c. *Ev.Assoc.*
Perles, Jos. Interment of the dead in post biblical Judaism; — Jewish marriages. *See* Hebrew characteristics.
Perley, Mt. Van Buren. Cape Ann family almanac and centennial year book. ill. 8°. '76. pap., 50c. *Perley.*
Perowne, J: Ja. Stewart. Book of psalms; with introd. and notes: new tr. 3d ed., rev. 2 v. 8°. $3 .. *Pott.*
— Immortality. *See* Hulsean lectures.
— Sermons. 8°. '74. $3 .... *Routledge.*
Perpetual curate. Oliphant, M. O. W. $1.50; $1. *Harper.*
Perranzabuloe: the lost church found. Trelawney, C. T. C. $1.75 .... *Pott.*
Perreyve, Henri. Daily life of the sick; from the Fr., with introd. by L. Petétot. 12°. '75. $1.50. *Cunningham.*
Perrier, Amelia. A good match. 12°. '73. $1.50 .. *Ford.*
Perrin, J. B. French and English conversations. 18°. hf. bd., 38c. .... *Sadlier.*
— French fables. 18°. hf. bd., 38c. .... *Sadlier.*
— *Same;* with key, ed. by A. Bolmar. 12°. $1.25. *Sheldon.*
Perring, *Mrs.* —. [Juveniles.] 9 v. 18°. ea., 45c. *Routledge.*

Cont.: Blanche and Agnes. — Ellen and Frank. — Our poor neighbors. — Story of a cat. — Story of a dog. — Story of a mouse. — Story of a penny. — Three sisters. — Village school.

— Castle and the cottage; or, life as it should be. 16°. 50c. .... *Routledge.*
— — *See also* Harry and Lucy lib.
Perrodin, J: C. Conversations of a Catholic missionary with Americans. 12°. '68. $1.25; pap., 50c. *Hoffmann.*
Perry, Arth. Latham. Elements of political economy. ('73.) 14th ed., rev. and enl. cr. 8°. '76. $2.50. *Scribner.*

Perry, Bela C. Human hair and the cutaneous diseases which affect it. 12°. $2 .... *Miller.*

Perry, *Mrs.* C. T. Effie Gray. 16°. '66. 50c. *H. H. Carter.*

— Morning ride. 16°. '66. 50c. .... *H. H. Carter.*

Perry, F: Dulce domum: essays on home life. 8°. '73. $2.50 .... *Routledge.*

Perry, H. J. Sketch of Ann Eliza, Hester Jane and Laura Washington Perry. ('54.) 3d ed. 18°. '76. 60c. .... *So. Meth.*

Perry, J. Instructions; comp. by a priest of the mission. 12°. '75. $1 .... *Fox; Sadlier.*

Perry, J. P. Sermons on the Lord's prayer. 8°. '68. 50c.; 30c. .... *H. H. Carter.*

Perry, Jairus Ware. Treatise on trusts and trustees. 2d ed. 2 v. 8°. '74. shp., $12 .... *Little, B. & Co.*

Perry, J: Elementary treatise on steam. ill. 18°. '74. $1.50 .... *Macmillan.*

Perry, Mat. C. *See* Hawks, F. L., Narrative of expedition, etc.

Perry, Nora. After the ball, and other poems. sm. 4°. '74. $1.50; hf. cf., $3; mor., $4 .... *Osgood.*

— Bessie's trials at boarding school. ill. 16°. '75. $1.25. *Lothrop.*

Perry, *Mrs.* S. A. Blind Graham. 18°. 90c. *Cong. Pub.*

Perry, *Mrs.* S. B. Bible responsive exercises. 18°. 30c. .... *Lee & S.*

— Manual of Bible selections and responsive exercises for public and private schools, etc. 16°. $1 .. *Lee & S.*

Perry, T: Erskine. *See* England, Common law reports.

Perry, W: Stevens. Handbook of general convention of Prot. Epis. Church, giving hist. and const., 1785–1874. 12°. '74. $1.50; bds., $1 .... *Whittaker.*

— Life lessons from Proverbs. 12°. '72. $1.75. *Whittaker.*

— Questions on life and labors of the great apostle (Paul). 16°. 30c. .... *Dutton.*

Perryman, E. G. Our new minister. 12°. '75. $1. *Whittaker.*

Persecuted but not forsaken. *See* Philip Martin.

Persecuted Dutchman. Barry, S. 15c. ..... *French.*

Persecuted family. *See* Pollok, Rob.

Persecutions in Scotland. B., M. M. 20c. .. *Am. Tr.*

Perseus and Andromeda. Brough, W. 15c. .. *French.*

Persevere and prosper. *See* Goodrich, S: G.

Perseverance and apostacy. Nash, A. $1.50 .. *Tibbals.*

Perseverance of the saints. 18°. 35c. ..... *Pres. Bd.*

Persevering Dick. 18°. 35c. .... *Pres. Bd.*

Persius Flaccus, A. Satires [*Lat.*]; ed. by B. L. Gildersleeve. 12°. $1.25 .... *Harper.*

— *Same*; with notes by S. Hart. 16°. '75. 90c. .. *Allyn.*

— — *See also* Juvenal.

Person of Christ. *See* Schaff, P.

Personages. Young, R. A. $1.25 .... *So. Meth.*

Personal beauty; or, the art of attaining bodily vigor, etc. ill. 12°. pap., 25c. .... *Hurst.*

Personal effort explained and enforced. Wise, D. 30c. *Meth. Bk. Conc.*

Personal experience of Roman Catholicism. Richardson, E. $1.25 .... *Lippincott.*

Personal experiences in spirit-photography. Mumler, W. H. 15c. .... *Colby.*

Personal names in the Bible. Wilkinson, W. F. $2.50 .... *Routledge.*

Personal piety: a help to Christians to walk worthy of their calling. 18°. '68. 75c. .... *Whittaker.*

Personal recollections. *See* Tonna, *Mrs.* C. E.

Personal recollections of distinguished generals. Shanks, W. F. G. $2 .... *Harper.*

Personation. Decamp, M. T. 15c. .... *French.*

Personne (*pseud.*) *See* De Fontaine, F. G.

Persuasion. *See* Austen, Jane.

Persuasives to early piety. Pike, J. G. 70c. .. *Am. Tr.*

Perverse pussy; by author of "Leighton children." 18°. 50c. .... *Am. S. S.*

Pestalozzian school song book. obl. 16°. 50c. .. *Gordon.*

Pestilence of Marseilles: drama. 16°. pap., 15c. *French.*

Pet. Haweis, H. R. $1.50 .... *Harper.*

Pet bird. *See* Grandmother's lib.

Pet Dayton and Pet Dayton's patient. 18°. '63. 40c. *Randolph.*

Pet lamb. [Toy-book.] ill. 4°. $1; 50c. .. *Routledge.*

Pet lamb. *See* Home lib.

Pet lamb. *See* Infant school lib.

Pet lamb. *See* Selby, C.

Pet lamb, and other stories for our little friend. ill. sq. 12°. 60c. .... *Hurd & H.*

Pet lamb; [also] Lambs of the flock. 18°. 35c. *Pres. Bd.*

Pet lamb picture-book. demy 4°. '73. $2.50 .. *Routledge.*

Pet lamb stories. *See* Myrtle, *Mrs.* H.

Pet lib. 4 v. 16°. $3 .... *Dutton.*

Cont.: Uncle Rod's pet, by S. E. Emery. — Miss Matty. — Redesdale. — Fannie and Robbie, by A. G. Hale.

Pet of the petticoats. Buckstone, J. B. 15c. .. *French.*

Pet of the public. Stirling, E. 15c. .... *Ames; French.*

Pet rabbits. 18°. 75c. .... *Carter.*

Pet sparrow. *See* Baker, *Mrs.* H. N. W.

Pet squirrel. *See* Home lib.

Pete, the cunner boy. Knight, S. G. 60c. ..... *Hoyt.*

Pete and Ephraim: Ethiop. drama. 16°. pap., 15c. *Happy.*

Pete Ogle; or, a hasty temper mastered. ill. 18°. '69. 75c. .... *Lothrop.*

Peter, *St.* Der Apostel Petrus. 18°. 45c. .. *Ev. Assoc.*

— Life and writings. 18°. 65c. .... *Am. S. S.*

— *See also* Lives of the saints.

Peter *of Alexandria.* Writings. *See* Methodius.

Peter *of Blois.* *See* Ingulphus, Chronicle of the Abbey of Croyland.

Peter, Rob. *See* Arkansas geol. survey; — Kentucky geol. survey.

Peter, the apprentice. ('73.) New ed. 16°. '76. $1.25. *Hoyt.*

Peter, the apprentice: tale of reformation in Eng. 16°. '74. 90c. .... *Meth. Bk. Conc.*

Peter the Great. *See* Atlantic lib.

Peter, the whaler. Kingston, W. H. G. $1.25 .. *Lippincott.*

Peter and his pony. *See* Sylvan stories.

Peter Clinton. Wise, D. $1.25 .... *H. A. Young.*

Peter Ducket. 18°. 35c. .... *Am. S. S.*

Peter Killip's king. Smith, H. $1.25 .... *Hoyt.*

Peter Midler. Bristol, M. C. 40c. .... *Am. Tr.*

Peter of the castle. *See* Banim, J. *and* M.

Peter Parley (*pseud.*) *See* Goodrich, S. G.

Peter Parley's little library of true stories. *See* Goodrich, S. G.

Peter Parley's own story. Goodrich, S. G. $1.25. *Sheldon.*

Peter Ploddy. Neal, J. C. 75c. .... *Peterson.*

Peter Schlemihl. Chamisso, A. v. $2 ...... *Denham.*

Peter Simple. *See* Marryat, F:

Peter Smink. Payne, J. H. 15c. .... *French.*

Peter Thompson; [also] The dying sheep; [also] The Bible the best book. 18°. 45c. .... *Pres. Bd.*

Pteer Wilkins: spectacle. 16°. pap., 15c. ... *French.*

Peterchen and Gretchen. Prentiss, E. $1 .. *Randolph.*

Petermann, K: Lesebücher der deutsch-amerik. Schule. 6 ser. 8°. '75. .... *Schmidt.*

Cont.: Erstes Leseb., bds., 30c. — Zweites Leseb., bds., 60c. — Drittes Leseb., bds., 75c. — Leseb. f. die oberen Klassen, bds., $1. — Literaturgeschichtliches Leseb., 2 v., ea., bds., $1; in 1 v., hf. leath., $2.

Petermann, K: G. Aufgabenbuch f. schriftl. Gedanken-Ausdruck. 8°. 25c. .... *Schäfer.*

Peter's adventures. Greenwood, J. $1.50..*Routledge.*

Peter's journey, and other tales. 12°. $1.50..*Cath.Pub.*

Peter's pound. *See* Bowen, C. E.

Peter's strange story. Mills, L. A. $1.50...*Lothrop.*

Peters, Absalom. On baptism: sprinkling the only Scripture mode of baptism. 18°. '56. 85c...*Dodd.*

Peters, Chr. H: F: Observations of solar spots. *See* Harvard Coll. Astron. Observ.

Peters, DeWitt C. Kit Carson's life and adventures; from facts narr. by himself. ill. roy. 8°. '74. *$3; $4; leath., $3.50 .... *Dustin.*

Peters, J. L. Brilliant gems: piano pieces. 4°. $2.25; bds., $1.75 .... *Peters.*

— Opera at home: standard opera songs. 4°. $4; bds., $3 .... *Peters.*

— Opera chorus book; for mixed voices. 2 v. 8°. ea., bds., $2 .... *Peters.*

— Reed organ or melodeon instructor. obl. roy. 8°. bds., $1.50 .... *Peters.*

— Sweet sounds. [Songs.] 4°. $2.25; bds., $1.75. *Peters.*

Peters, J: C: Diseases of females and married females. [Hom.] 2d ed. 8°. $1.50 .... *Boericke.*

— Diseases of married females. [Hom.] 8°. $1..*Boericke.*

— History of the travels of Asiatic cholera. *See* United States, *Surgeon-General's Office.*

— On sects in medicine. 8°. pap., 25c...*Campbell & Co.*

— Treatise on apoplexy; with app. on softening of the brain and paralysis; based on T. J. Rückert's "Clinical experience in homœopathy." 8°. $1. *Boericke.*

— Treatise on headaches and diseases of the head; based on T. J. Rückert's "Clinical experience in homœop." 8°. $3 .... *Boericke.*

— Treatise on inflammatory and organic diseases of the brain; based on T. J. Rückert's "Clinical experience in homœop." 8°. $1 .... *Boericke.*

— Treatise on internal diseases of the eyes; based on T. J. Rückert's "Clinical experience in homœop." 8°. $1 .... *Boericke.*

— Treatise on nervous derangements and mental disorders; based on T. J. Rückert's "Clinical experience in homœop." 8°. $1 .... *Boericke.*

— Treatise on principal diseases of the eyes; based on T. J. Rückert's "Clinical experience in homœop." 8°. $1.50 .... *Boericke.*

Peters, R: *See* United States, Admiralty decisions.

Peters, R: *jr.* *See* United States, Circuit Court reports; Sup. Ct. reports.

Peters, W: C. Art of singing. 4°. bds., $3..*Peters.*

— Catholic choir. [Masses.] 2 v. 4°. ea., bds., $3.50. *Peters.*

— Catholic harmonist. [Choir music.] obl. 8°. $1.50. *Peters.*

— Catholic harp; with Eng. and Lat. text. [School music.] obl. 8°. $1.25 .... *Peters.*

— Eclectic piano forte instructor. 4°. $4; bds., $3.25. *Peters.*

— Eclectic vocal instructor; for female voices. cr. 8°. 50c. .... *Peters.*

— Elements of thorough bass. 12°. bds., 50c...*Peters.*

— Evening service. [Cath. music.] 4°. bds., $4..*Peters.*

— Improved flute instructor. obl. 8°. pap., 75c...*Peters.*

— Improved violin instructor. obl. 8°. pap., 75c. *Peters.*

— Jubilee mass in G. 4°. pap., $2 .... *Peters.*

— Mass in D. sm. f°. '75. bds., $1.25 .... *Willig.*

— Mass in G. obl. 8°. pap., 80c. .... *Peters.*

— Method for French accordion. obl. 8°. pap., 75c. *Peters.*

— Missa de angelis in C; with chorus in unison. 4°. pap., 70c. .... *Peters.*

— Morning service. [Cath. music.] 4°. bds., $3.50. *Peters.*

Peters, W: C., *continued.*

— Vespers no. 2: Gregorian in G and magnificat. 4°. pap., 40c. .... *Peters.*

— Vespers no. 3: plain chant. 4°. pap., 50c...*Peters.*

— Young Catholic's vocal class book. 12°. bds., 50c.. *Peters.*

Peters' Catholic melodist. Dressler, W. $1.50..*Peters.*

Peters' octavo choruses. 10 nos. 8°. ea., pap., 25c. *Peters.*

Peters' sacred selections. [Church music.] 10 nos. 8°. ea., pap., 25c. .... *Peters.*

Peters' sodality hymn book; compiled by Sisters of Notre Dame, Cincinnati. cr. 8°. bds., 40c...*Peters.*

Peterson, C. I. P. Norwegian-Danish grammar and reader; with vocab. 12°. '72. $1.25..*Griggs.*

Peterson, C: J. [Novels.] 5 v. .... *Peterson.*

Cont.: Kate Aylesford. — Old stone mansion, *ea.*, 12°, $1.75; pap., $1.50. — Cruising in the last war [1812], 8°, pap., 75c. — Grace Dudley; or, Arnold at Saratoga, 8°, pap., 50c. — Valley farm, 8°, pap., 25c.

Peterson, H: Faire-mount. [Poetry.] 12°. '73. $1. *Claxton.*

— Modern Job (The): dramatic poem. 12°. '69. 75c. *H. Peterson.*

— Pemberton; or, one hundred years ago. 12°. $1.25. *Lippincott.*

Peterson, *Mrs.* M. E. Manual of preserving, pickling and canning fruits. 18°. 50c.; bds., 35c...*Fisher.*

Peterson, Rob. E. Familiar science; or, scientific explan. of common things. 18°. hf. bd., 80c...*Sower.*

— *Same;* [also] Scientific amusements for young people, by J. H. Pepper. 12°. $1.60 .... *Sower.*

— The Roman Catholic not "the only true religion," not "an infallible church." 16°. 75c...*Lippincott.*

Peterson's complete coin book. f°. pap., $1..*Peterson.*

Peterson's new cook book. 12°. $1.75 ..... *Peterson.*

Pete's luck: Ethiop. drama. 16°. pap., 15c...*Happy.*

Petit paroissien; ou, recueil de prières. 12°. *net,* 53c. *Benziger.*

Petit Robinson (Le) de Paris. Foa, E. 90c. .... *Holt.*

Petite. Bray, R. M. $1.25 .... *Lothrop.*

Petite fadette (La). Sand, G. $1.25 .... *Holt.*

Petite maman (La). *See* M., M. de.

Petites causeries. Sauveur, L. $1.25; $2 ..... *Holt.*

Petites filles modèles (Les). *See* Ségur, *Comtesse* E. de.

Petites misères de la vie humaine. Clairville, L. F. N. 25c. .... *Holt.*

Petites oiseaux (Les). Labiche, E., *and* Delacour, A. 40c. .... *Holt.*

Petits livres pour les enfants. 32°. '54. 30c...*Am. Tr.*

Peto, *Sir* S. Morton. Resources and prospects of America. cr. 8°. $2 .... *Routledge.*

Petra; or, the rock city and its explorers. ill. 18°. 35c. *Pres. Bd.*

Petrarch, Francesco. Sonnets and other poems; tr. into Eng. verse by various hands; with life by T. Campbell. 12°. (Bohn.) $1.75..*Little, B. & Co.*

— *Same.* 12°. (Bohn.) $2..*Lippincott; Scribner, W. & A.*

Petrel (The). Fisher, W. 75c. .... *Peterson.*

Petrie, Ja. Marriage gift. 18°. 60c. .... *Pres. Bd.*

Petrifactions and their teachings. Mantell, G. A. $2.40 .... *Scribner, W. & A.*

Petrolia. Cones, A., *and* Johns, W. R. $3..*Appleton.*

Petronius Arbiter, Tit. The satyricon; tr. [with notes, etc., by C. Blanchard]. 16°. '66. $1. *D. Thomas.*

— *See also* Propertius, Petronius Arbiter, *and* Joannes *Secundus.*

Petros. Seiss, J. A. 25c. .... *Luth. Bk. St.*

Petrucelli Gattina, F. de. *See* Gattina, F. P. de.

Petrus in Rom u. Rom ohne Petrus. Brandes, K. 75c. *Benziger.*

Pet's picture book. sm. 4°. $2 .... *Nelson.*

Pets of the parterre. Coyne, J. S. 15c. ..... *French.*

Petsetilla's posy. Hood, T. $3 .... *Routledge.*

Pettengill, Peletiah. Perfect fortune-teller and dream-book. 16°. bds., 35c. .... *Dick & F.*

Pettengill, S: M. Advertiser's handbook: list of newspapers, periodicals and magazines pub. in the U. S. and Brit. possessions. ('70.) [Annual.] 8°. $3 .... *Pettengill.*

Petticoat government. Dance, G. 15c...... *French.*

Petticoat government. Trollope, F. 50c. .. *Harper.*

Petticoat parliament. Lemon, M. 15c...... *De Witt.*

Pettigrew, Ja. Bell. Animal locomotion; or, walking, swimming and flying; with dissertation on aëronautics. (Intern. sci. ser.) ill. 12°. $1.75. *Appleton.*

— Physiology of the circulation in plants, in the lower animals and in man: lectures, 1872. ill. 8°. '74. $4 .... *Macmillan.*

Pettigrew, T: J. Chronicles of the tombs: collection of remarkable epitaphs. 12°. (Bohn.) $1.75. *Little, B. & Co.*

— *Same.* 12°. (Bohn.) $2 .. *Lippincott; Scribner, W. & A.*

Peveril of the Peak. *See* Scott, *Sir* Wa.

Peveril of the Peak: drama. 16°. pap., 15c... *French.*

Peyrac, *Mme.* — de. Comment on parle à Paris: guide for learning to speak French quickly. 12°. $1.50. *Appleton.*

— French children at home: introd. to "Comment on parle à Paris." 12°. 90c. .... *Appleton.*

Pfarrerstochter v. Taubenheim. 12°. pap., 15c. *Radde.*

Pfarrhaus (Das). *See* Hoffmann, F.

Pfarrhaus (Das). *See* Zschokke, H.

Pfeiffer, A: Lutherthum vor Luther: Beantwortung dreier v. Arnold Engel ausgestreuten Fundamentalfragen wider die lutherische Religion. 8°. '72. 75c. .... *Dette.*

Pfeiffer, Ida. Lady's (A) second journey round the world; tr. 12°. $1.50 .... *Harper.*

— Last travels, incl. visit to Madagascar; with autobiog. memoir; tr. by H. W. Dulcken. por. 12°. $1.50 .... *Harper.*

Pfeufer, K: v. Zum Schutze wider d. Cholera; hrsg. v. Max Herzog. 12°. '66. pap., 20c.... *Steiger.*

Pflanzer (Der) in Cuba. *See* Zschokke, H.

Phædo (The). *See* Plato.

Phädra. *See* Racine, J.

Phædrus. Fables. 16°. '59. 50c...... *Kelly, P. & Co.*

— — *See also* Horace, Odes.

— *See also* Gardner, F., Gay, A. M., *and* Buck, A. M.; — Terence *and* Phædrus.

Phæthon. *See* Kingsley, C.

Phantasien im Bremer Rathskeller. *See* Hauff, W.

Phantasmion. Coleridge, S. H. $2........ *Roberts.*

Phantastes. MacDonald, G. $1.75 .... *Loring.*

Phantom. Boucicault, D. 15c............. *French.*

Phantom bouquet. Parrish, E. $1...... *Lippincott.*

Phantom breakfast. Selby, C. 15c... *French; Lee & S.*

Phantom bride: melo-drama. 16°. pap., 15c... *French.*

Phantom of the forest. *See* Bennett, E.

Phantom regiment. *See* Grant, Ja.

Phantom ship. *See* Marryat, F:

Pharsalia. *See* Lucanus, M. A.

Phear, J. Budd. Elementary hydrostatics. 3d ed. cr. 8°. $2 .... *Macmillan.*

— Treatise on rights of water, incl. public and private rights to the sea and sea-shore. 8°. '59. $1.50. *T. & J. W. Johnson.*

— — *See also* Law lib.

Phelan, Mich. Game of billiards. 12°. $1.50.. *Appleton.*

Phelps, Agnes. One year at our boarding-school. 12°. $1 .... *Loring.*

Phelps, *Mrs.* Almira Hart Lincoln. Botany for beginners. ('63.) New ed. 18°. '74. hf. roan, 65c. *Claxton.*

— Caroline Westerley; or, the young traveler from Ohio. ill. 18°. 75c. .... *Harper.*

— Chemistry for beginners. 16°. hf. roan, 63c. *Lippincott.*

— Chemistry for collegiate institutions, etc. New ed., with discoveries and improvements to 1866. 12°. hf. roan, $1.50 .... *Lippincott.*

— Discipline of life; or, Ida Norman. 2 v. in 1. 12°. '68. $1.75 .... *Barnes.*

— Educator; or, hours with my pupils. 12°. '68. $1.50. *Barnes.*

— Fireside friend; or, female student: advice to young ladies on education. 12°. $1.50 .... *Harper.*

— Lincoln's lectures on botany. New ed., with introd. to natural orders, and artificial key for analysis of the same. 12°. hf. roan, $1.75 ... *Lippincott.*

— Natural philosophy for beginners. 16°. hf. roan, 63c. .... *Lippincott.*

— Natural philosophy for schools, families and private students. 12°. hf. roan, $1.50 ...... *Lippincott.*

— Reviews and essays in art, literature and science. 12°. '72. $1.50 .... *Claxton.*

— Student; or, fireside friend; with app. on moral and religious education. 12°. '68. $1.50 ... *Barnes.*

— Whispers to a bride; [also] Christian households; with hist. of order of deaconesses. ('58.) 3d ed. 16°. '69. $1; cf., $3 .... *Claxton.*

Phelps, Aust. Ministerial culture. 18°. '68. pap., 10c. *Draper.*

— New birth (The); or, work of the Holy Spirit. 16°. $1.25 .... *Graves.*

— *Same.* 16°. '75. $1.25 .... *Lothrop.*

— Sabbath hours. 32°. 75c. .... *Cong. Pub.*

— Solitude of Christ. 18°. 50c.; pap., 15c. *Bost. Am. Tr.*

— Still hour; or, communion with God. New ed. 16°. '75. 60c.; $1 .... *Lothrop.*

— *See also* Park, E. A., Phelps, A., *and* Mason, L.

— *and* Park, E. A., *and* Furber, D. L. Hymns and choirs; or, matter and manner of service of song in the house of the Lord. 12°. '60. $1.50.. *Draper.*

— — — *Same.* 12°. $1.75 .... *Hamersley.*

Phelps, C: A. Life and public services of U. S. Grant and biog. sketch of H. Wilson. ill. and por. 12°. $1; pap., 50c. .... *Lee & S.*

Phelps, *Miss* Eliz. Stuart. Gates ajar. 16°. '68. $1.50; hf. cf., $3. —ill. 4°. '69. $3.50; mor., $7.. *Osgood.*

— — *See also* Antidote.

— Gipsy books. ('67.) New ed. 4 v. ill. 16°. '75. ea., $1 .... *Dodd.*

Cont.: Gypsy Breynton. — Gypsy's cousin Joy. — Gypsy's sowing and reaping. — Gypsy's year at the Golden Crescent.

— Hedged in. 16°. '70. $1.50 .... *Osgood.*

— Men, women and ghosts. 16°. '69. $1.50 .. *Osgood.*

— Mercy Glidden's work. ('66.) New ed. ill. 16°. '73. $1.25 .... *Hoyt.*

— Poetic studies. sq. 16°. '75. $1.50; hf. cf., $3; mor., $4 .... *Osgood.*

— Silent partner. ('70.) 10th ed. 16°. $1.50; hf. cf., $3 .... *Osgood.*

— Tiny ser. 4 v. 18°. '64–'67. $3 .... *Cong. Pub.*

Cont.: Tiny, 75c. — Tiny's Sunday nights, 65c. — I don't know how, 85c. — Ellen's idol, 75c.

— Tiny's lib. 4 v. 18°. '66. $3 .... *H. A. Young.*

Contents same as above.

— Trotty book. ('69.) 7th ed. ill. sm. 4°. $1.50 .. *Osgood.*

— Trotty's wedding-tour. ill. sm. 4°. '73. $1.50.. *Osgood.*

— Up hill; or, life in the factory. ('65.) New ed. ill. 16°. '75. $1.25 .... *Hoyt.*

— What to wear? 16°. '73. $1; pap., 50c.... *Osgood.*

— *See also* Stories by Mrs. L. C. Moulton, etc.; — Two fortune-seekers.

Phelps, *Mrs.* Eliz. Stuart. ["H. Trusta."] Angel over the right shoulder; or, the beginning of a new year. ('52.) 15th ed. 16°. '75. 40c... *Draper.*

Phelps, *Mrs.* Eliz. Stuart, *continued.*
— Kitty Brown ser. 4 v. 18°. '50. $1.85....*Am.S.S.*
Cont.: Kitty Brown and her Bible verses, 40c. — Kitty Brown and her little school, 40c. — Kitty Brown and her city cousins, 50c. — Kitty Brown beginning to think, 55c.
— Sunny-side (The); or, the country minister's wife. ('51.) 2d ed. 18°. '52. 60c..........*Am.S.S.*
— Sunny-side ser. ('51–'53.) New ed. 3 v. 18°. '64. $2.40 .... *Sheldon.*
Cont.: Tell-tale. — Peep at "number five." — Last leaf from Sunny-side.
Phelps, Ja. R., *and* Silver, Ednah C. Sunday school service. 16°. '76. bds., 30c...*Lockwood,B.& Co.*
Phelps, J: W. Secret societies, ancient and modern. ('73.) 2d ed. 12°. '75. pap., 50c....*E.A.Cook.*
Phelps, *Miss* L. L. ["Alpha."] The veil on the heart. ill. 16°. '71. $1.25..................*Lothrop.*
Phelps, Lavinia H. Dramatic stories for home and school entertainment. 12°. '73. $1.... *Griggs.*
Phelps, *Miss* Lucy. Sketches for my Sabbath school class. 18°. 50c....................*Cong.Pub.*
Phelps, *Mrs.* Phebe H. Mary and Henry Day ser. 4 v. ill. 16°. $3.60...............*Thompson.*
Cont.: Mary Day's story book. — Henry Day learning to obey Bible commands. — Mary Day forming good habits. — Henry Day's story book.
— New boots. 16°. 45c..................*Cong.Pub.*
— Nuts ready cracked. 16°. 60c..........*Cong.Pub.*
— Some coats that fit. 18°. 60c..........*Cong.Pub.*
Phelps, R: H. Newgate of Connecticut: hist. of the Simsbury mines, the historical prison during the revolution. ill. 12°. '76. *75c........*Am.Pub.*
Phelps, *Mrs.* S. B. Sister Eleanor's brood. ill. 16°. '72. $1.50...........................*Lothrop.*
Phelps, Sylvanus Dryden. Travels in Holy Land. ('71.) 10th ed. ill. 12°. $1.25................ *Ward.*
— *See also* Baptist praise book.
Phelps, W. D. ["Webfoot."] Fore and aft; or, leaves from the life of an old sailor. 16°. '70. $1.50. *Nichols & H.*
Phelps, W: F. Teacher's handbook for the institute and the class room. 12°. '74. $1.50....*Barnes.*
Phemie Frost's experiences. Stephens, A. S. $1.75. *Carleton.*
Phemie Keller. Riddell, J. H. 50c.........*Harper.*
Phemie's temptation. Harland, M. $1.50..*Carleton.*
Phenomena of plant life. *See* Grindon, L. H.
Phenomenon: comic drama. 16°. pap., 15c...*French.*
Phenomenon in smock frock. Brough, W. 15c. *French.*
Phil, the fiddler. Alger, H., *jr.* $1.25.......*Loring.*
Phil Derry, the western boy who became a Sunday school missionary. 16°. $1.25........*Am.S.S.*
Phil. Foghorn. [Bohemian.] 16°. '75. 30c...*Geringer.*
Phil Kennedy. N., H. N. 60c...............*Am.Tr.*
Philadelphia, *City.* Court of Nisi Prius reports. *See* Brightly, F. C.
— Reports: decisions pub. in the "Legal Intelligencer," 1850–'74; by H. E. Wallace. 9 v. 8°. v. 1–5, ea., $5; 6–9, ea., $6.................*J.M.P. Wallace.*
— — *See also* Brewster, F. C.; — Campbell, J. H.
— *See also* International exhibition.
Philadelphia, *City and County.* District Court reports, 1835–'40; by J. Miles. New ed. 2 v. 8°. '71. shp., $15.....................*J. Campbell & Son.*
Philadelphia, *County.* Rules of the Court of Common Pleas. 8°. '75. pap., $1........*J.M.P. Wallace.*
— Rules of the Court of Oyer and Terminer. 8°. '75. pap., 25c. .....................*J.M.P. Wallace.*
— Rules of the Orphans' Court. 8°. '75. pap., 25c. *J.M.P. Wallace.*
Philadelphia Acad. of Natural Sciences. *See* Academy of Nat. Sci. of Phila.
Philadelphia and its environs: descript. of the city and its surrounding points. ill. 8°. pap., 50c.; — in Germ., pap., 75c....................*Lippincott.*

Philadelphia and New York glee book. Loder, G. $1.50...............................*Ditson.*
Philadelphia anthem book. Beckel, J. S. 25c. *Ditson.*
Philadelphia Baptist Assoc. Minutes, 1707–1807. 8°. $2.50 ....*Am.Bapt.*
Philadelphia College of Physicians. *See* College of Phys. of Phila.
Philadelphia First Day School Union. Selected poems for first day schools. 2d ed. 16°. *net*, 50c. *Friends Bk.Assoc.*
Philadelphia housewife; by a lady of Philadelphia. 12°. $1........................*Lippincott.*
Philadelphia illustrated. 8°. pap., 25c.......*Porter.*
Philadelphia Numis. and Antiq. Soc. *See* Numismatic and Antiq. Soc. of Phila.
Philadelphia Pathological Soc. *See* Pathological.
Philadelphia Yearly Meeting. *See* Friends (Society of).
Philalethe (*pseud.*) Righteousness, the divinely appointed rule of life: book of collated Scriptures. sm. 4°. '74. pap., 50c. ....*Tompkins.*
Philanthropy; or, my mother's Bible. 18°. 50c...*Harper.*
Philaret, *Bp. of Moscow.* Select sermons. 8°. '73. $3.......................................*Pott.*
Philbrick, E: S. Defects in house drainage and their remedies. ill. 8°. '76. pap., 25c. ... *Williams.*
Philbrick, J: D. American union speaker. cr. 8°. $2.25 ....*Thompson.*
— Primary union speaker. ill. 16°. 65c...*Thompson.*
Philip, J: Rays of light; or, church themes and life problems. 12°. $1.50 ....*Hoyt,F.& D.*
Philip, Rob. Devotional guides. 12°. $2....*Carter.*
— Hannahs (The); or, maternal influence on sons. 18°. 60c.......................................*Carter.*
— Life of John Bunyan; with introd. by S. D. Phelps. 8°. '66. $3.50; shp., $4 .... *Wilstach.*
— Lydias (The); or, development of female character. 18°. 60c..............................*Carter.*
— Manly piety in its spirit; with introd. by A. Barnes. 18°. 55c. ....*Pres.Bd.*
— Marthas (The); or, varieties of female piety. 18°. 60c. ....*Carter.*
— Marys (The); or, beauties of female holiness. 18°. 60c. ....*Carter.*
Philip, *Uncle* (*pseud.*) *See* Hawks, F. L.
Philip. *See* Thackeray, W: M.
Philip Alderton's temptation. 18°. 75c....*Cong.Pub.*
Philip and Bessie; or, wisdom's way. ('60.) New ed. ill. 18°. '68. 40c.........................*Hoyt.*
Philip and Emma, the little gardeners. 18°. 25c. *Scribner, W.& A.*
Philip and his garden. *See* Tonna, *Mrs.* C. E.
Philip Augustus. *See* James, G. P. R.
Philip Blandford. Smith, J. F. 75c........*Dick & F.*
Philip Brantley's life work. M., M. E. $1....*Dodd.*
Philip Colville. *See* Kennedy, G.
Philip Earnscliff. Edwards, A. $1.75; $1..*Sheldon.*
Philip Eckert's struggles and triumphs; by author of "Margaret Clair." ('68.) New ed. 18°. '75. 60c..............................*Nat.Temp.*
Philip English's two cups. 12°. '69. 75c...*Randolph.*
Philip Garland; or, love one another. 18°. 35c.; 45c. *Am.Bapt.*
Philip Hartley; or, a boy's trials and triumphs. 18°. '66. 50c. ....*Cunningham.*
Philip in Palestine. Edwards, M. A. $1.25..(?)*Martien.*
Philip in search of a wife. 8°. pap., 25c....*Peterson.*
Philip Martin; [also] Persecuted but not forsaken. 16°. $1 ....*Hoyt.*
Philip Moore, the sculptor. *See* Loving heart and helping hand lib.
Philip Oakover; [also] Robbie and his mother. 16°. 90c.......................................*Hoyt.*

Philip Rollo. *See* Grant, Ja.

Philip Van Artevelde. Taylor, H. $1.50...* *Osgood.*

Philippe, *Brother.* *See* Braussi, M.

Philip's book. ill. 16°. 50c. .... *Routledge.*

Philips' Scripture atlas. 32°. pap., 25c. ..... *Nelson.*
— *Same.* 12 maps. 18°. '72. pap., 25c... *Randolph.*
— *See also* Hughes, W.

Phillimore, C. M. Pictures from Venice. ill. 16°. 50c. .... *Pott.*

Phillimore, J: G: Private law among the Romans; from the Pandects. 8°. '63. $5 ... *Macmillan.*

Phillimore, Rob. Commentaries upon international law. 3 v. in 2. 8°. '54. $11.. *T.&J. W. Johnson.*
— — *See also* Law lib.

Phillipine. *See* Silver Grange.

Phillippe. Murray, W. 15c.................. *French.*

Phillips, *Mrs.* Alfr. Master passion: comedy. 16°. pap., 15c.................................. *French.*
— Organic affection: farce. 16°. pap., 15c... *French.*
— Uncle Crotchet: farce. 16°. pap., 15c..... *French.*

Phillips, Arth. Elements of metallurgy. ill. 8°. (Lond.) '74. $14 .... *Spon.*

Phillips, C: Curran and his contemporaries. 12°. $1.50. *Harper.*

Phillips, E. John Trevlyn's revenge. [Fiction.] ill. 8°. (Lond.) pap., 30c. .... *Am. News.*

Phillips, F: Bird in the hand is worth two in the bush: farce. 16°. pap., 15c.................. *French.*

Phillips, G: S. ["January Searle."] Origin of churches: divine evolution of the churches; or, the New Church as the church of humanity: its position and prospects considered. 12°. pap., 25c. .... *Lippincott.*

Phillips, J: Drainage and sewage of towns. 8°. pap., 60c. .... *Spon.*

Phillips, J: Arth., *and* Darlington, J: Records of mining and metallurgy; or, facts and memoranda for use of the mine agent and smelter. ill. cr. 8°. '67. $1.50.............................. *Spon.*
— — *Same.* ill. 12°. $2 .... *Baird.*

Phillips, Josiah S: Explorer's, miner's and metallurgist's companion. ('71.) 2d ed. ill. 8°. '73. $10.50; cf., $12........................... *J.S. Phillips.*

Phillips, L. Marianne, the vivandière: drama. 16°. pap., 15c................................. *French.*

Phillips, Lawr. B. Dictionary of biographical reference; with index of works on biography. 8°. hf. mor., $13.50........................ *Scribner, W.&A.*

Phillips, Ph. Statutory jurisdiction and practice of the Supreme Court of the U. S. 2d ed. 8°. '76. shp., $5.............................. *Morrison.*

Phillips, Ph. Day-school singer. 8°. '69. 50c. *Wilson, H.& Co.*
— Gospel singer; for Sabbath schools, etc. obl. 12°. '74. bds., 35c.......................... *Ditson.*
— International singing annual for Sabbath schools. sm. 4°. '73. pap., 25c.................. *Barnes.*
— Metrical tune book. 18°. '73. $1........ *Barnes.*
— New hymn and tune book for the Meth. Episc. Church. 8°. $2.50; mor., $6. 12°. $1.75.. *Meth. Bk. Conc.*
— Singing pilgrim. 8°. 50c.......... *Meth. Bk. Conc.*
— Song life; ill. journey of Christiana and her children from earth to the Celestial City. 4°. 50c. *Harper.*
— *Same.* 18°. 50c.................. *Meth. Bk. Conc.*
— Spring blossoms: music for Sunday schools, with rudiments. sq. 16°. '65. bds., 30c.; pap., 25c. *Wilstach.*

Phillips, Rose. Minnie Gray; or, merit rewarded. 18°. 75c. .... (?) *Martien.*
— Sketches for the fireside. 18°. '68. 75c... *Claxton.*

Phillips, S. The Christian home as it is in the sphere of nature and of the church. ill. 12°. *$1.75. *C.A. Nichols.*

Phillips, S. F. *See* North Carolina, Reports.

Phillips, S: Voice of blood. 12°. $2 .. *Ref. Ch. Pub.*

Phillips, S: L. Treatise on the law of mechanics' liens on real and personal property. 8°. '74. shp., $6. *Little, B. & Co.*

Phillips, S: March. Famous cases of circumstantial evidence; with introd. on theory of presumptive proof. ('73.) 2d ed., enl. 8°. '75. $3.50; shp., $4.50 .... *Cockcroft.*
— *and* Amos, A. Treatise on law of evidence; with notes and ref. to Am. decisions. 2 v. 8°. shp., $7 .... *Banks.*

Phillips, Waldorf H. The world to blame. [Fiction.] 12°. '73. $1.50 .... *Claxton.*

Phillips, Watts. [Plays.] 4 v. 16°. ea., pap., 15c. *De Witt.*
Cont.: Fettered. — Maud's peril. — Nobody's child. — Not guilty.
— *Same.* 15 v. 16°. ea., pap., 15c.......... *French.*
Cont.: Camilla's husband. — Dead heart. — Fettered. — His last victory. — Huguenot captain. — Lion at bay. — Lost in London. — Maud's peril. — Nobody's child. — Not guilty. — Paper wings: comedy. — Paul's return: comedy. — Ticket of leave: farce. — White cockade. — Woman in mauve.
— For a woman's sake. [Fiction.] ill. 8°. (Lond.) pap., 30c. .... *Am. News.*
— Lost in London: drama. 16°. pap., 15c..... *Lee & S.*
— Ticket of leave: farce. 16°. pap., 15c. ..... *Ames.*
— Wandering heiress. [Fiction.] 8°. pap., 75c. (?) *O'Kane.*
— Wentworth mystery. [Fiction.] ill. 8°. (Lond.) pap., 30c. .... *Am. News.*

Phillips, Wendell. Daniel O'Connell. [Lecture.] 12°. '72. pap., 10c........................ *O'Brien.*
— Review of Froude. *See* Burke, T. N., Final answer.
— Speeches, lectures and letters. por. cr. 8°. $2.50. *Lee & S.*

Phillips, Willard. Treatise on law of insurance. 5th ed. 2 v. 8°. '67. shp., $15....... *Hurd & H.*

Phillips, W: Campbellism exposed. 18°. 70c. *Cin. Meth. Bk. Conc.*

Phillips, W: H. H. Elements of geometry. 12°. '74. $1.50 .... *Schermerhorn.*

Phillis, Phil. Keary, M. $1........ *Scribner, W.&A.*

Phillpots, M. C. John Barrow; or, coals of fire. 32°. 25c.......................... *Scribner, W.&A.*

Phillpotts, J. Surtees. *See* Cordery, B. M., *and* Phillpotts, J. S.

Philo Judæus. Works; tr. by C. D. Yonge. 4 v. 12°. (Bohn.) ea., $1.75............... *Little, B. & Co.*
— *Same.* 4 v. 12°. (Bohn.) ea., $2. *Lippincott; Scribner, W.&A.*

Philobiblius (*pseud.*) *See* Brockett, L. P.

Philomena, *St.* Life and miracles of St. P., virgin and martyr; tr. from the Fr. 18°. 60c.; 90c... *O'Shea.*

Philosophe (Un) sous les toits. *See* Souvestre, E.

Philosopher's stone. Coyne, J. S. 15c...... *French.*

Philosophers and actresses. Houssaye, A. $3; $6. *Widdleton.*

Philosophers and fools. Duhring, J. $2.. *Lippincott.*

Philosophical theories and experience. *See* Small books on great subjects.

Philosophy of eating. Bellows, A. J. $2.. *Hurd & H.*

Philosophy of the future state. Dick, T. 75c... *Sower.*

Philosophy of God and the world. Mitchell, T. $4. *Tibbals.*

Philosophy of the infinite. Calderwood, H. $3.50. *Macmillan.*

Philosophy of living. Ticknor, C. 75c..... *Harper.*

Philosophy of mystery. Dendy, W. C. $1.. *Harper.*

Philosophy of the plan of salvation. Walker, J. B. $1.50 .... *Griggs.*

Philostorgius. Ecclesiastical history. *See* Sozomenus, H., Ecclesiastical history.

Philotas. *See* Lessing, G. E.

Philpot, J: Life and writings. *See* British reformers.

hin, J: Chemical history of the six days of creation. 12°. '71. 75c. . . . . *Indust.*
- Open air grape culture; or, garden and vineyard culture of grapes and wine. 12°. $1.50. *Woodward.*
- Plain directions for construct. and erection of lightning rods. 2d ed., enl. ill. 12°. '73. 50c. . . *Indust.*
- Practical hints on selection and use of the microscope; for beginners. ill. 12°. '75. 75c. . . *Indust.*

hineas Finn. *See* Trollope, Ant.

hineas redux. *See* Trollope, Ant.

hinney, El. History of the battle of Lexington, April 19, 1775. ('25.) New ed. 8°. '75. pap., 25c. . . . . *Lockwood, B. & Co.*

hipps, J: Original and present state of man briefly considered. 12°. 45c. . . . . *Friends Bk. St.*

hipps, Jos. True Christian baptism and communion. 12°. pap., 15c. . . . . *Friends Bk. St.*

hipps, Sireno B. Musical mirror: elementary instructions in vocal music, with exercises. obl. 16°. '62. bds., 75c. . . . . *Ditson.*

hipson, T: Lambe. Phosphorescence; or, the emission of light by minerals, plants and animals. 16°. $1.75 . . . . *Appleton.*

hocylides. Poema admonitorium [*Gk.*]; recog. notis J. B. Feulling. 16°. '69. pap., 30c.; 40c. *Draper.*

hœbe; or, the hospital. 18°. 40c. . . . . *Dutton.*

hœnician. *See* Euripides.

hœnix, J: (*pseud.*) *See* Derby, G: H.

hœnixiana. Derby, G. H. $1.25; 50c. . . *Appleton.*

honographic handbook; for self-instruction in the mod. system. 12°. pap., 25c. . . . . *Haney.*

hotograph (The). G., L. 25c. . . . . *Coddington.*

hotographic fix. Hay, F. 15c. . . . *De Witt; French.*

hotographic views. Weninger, F. X. $2. . *O'Shea.*

hrenological guide; for students of their own character. ('44.) 25th ed. 12°. pap., 25c. . . . *Wells.*

hrenology and the Scriptures. Pierpont, J. 25c. *Wells.*

hysical atlas: maps and index. 12°. $1.25. *Scribner, W. & A.*

hysical basis of immortality. Blackwell, A. B. $1.50. *Putnam.*

hysical history of the earth. 12°. (Bagster.) $1.12. *Wiley.*

hysical life of man and woman; or, advice to both sexes. 8°. *$2; leath., $2.50 . . . . *Nat. Pub.*

hysical theory of another life. Taylor, I. $1.50. *Tibbals.*

hysician's counsels to his professional brethren. Hunt, E. M. 45c. . . . . *Pres. Bd.*

hysician's (A) problems. *See* Elam, C.

hysician's wife. Spangler, H. K. $1.50. . *Lippincott.*

hysicians and dentists' reference book. 4°. '69. $50. *J. A. Murphy.*

hysics and politics. Bagehot, W. $1.50. . *Appleton.*

hysics of the ether. Preston, S. T. $3. . . . *Spon.*

hysiology of common life. Lewes, G. H. 2 v. $3. *Appleton.*

hysiology of health. 18°. 10c. . . . . *Dick & F.*

hysiology of the soul and instinct. Paine, M. $5. *Harper.*

iano at home: music arranged for four hands. 4°. '74. $3; $4; bds., $2.50 . . . . *Ditson.*

iano treasures. 4°. $3; $4; bds., $2.50. . *Brainard.*

iano-forte gems. 4°. '69. $4–$2.50 . . . . *Ditson.*

iatt, J: J. Landmarks, and other poems. 12°. '72. $1.50 . . . . *Hurd & H.*
– Western windows, and other poems. 12°. $1.50. *Hurd & H.*

iatt, *Mrs.* S. M. B. A voyage to the Fortunate Isles, and other poems. 16°. '74. $1.50. . . . . *Osgood.*
– A woman's poems. 16°. '71. $1.50. . . . . . . *Osgood.*

Picard, L: Benoît. Neffe (Der) als Onkel. *See* Schiller, J. F. v.
— Parasite (The); or, how to make one's fortune: comedy; tr. from the Fr. 12°. pap., 75c. . . *Lippincott.*
— — *See also* Schiller, J. F. v.

Picciola. *See* Saintine, X. B.

Piccolissima. Follen, E. L. 50c. . . . . *Lee & S.*

Piccolomini (Die). *See* Schiller, J. F. v.

Pick, Aar. The Bible student's [Hebrew] concordance. sm. 4°. (Lond.) $10 . . . . *Wiley.*

Pick, Bern. Luther as a hymnist: [compilation of Luther's hymns]. 12°. '75. $1.25. . *Luth. Bk. St.*

Picked up adrift. De Mille, J. $1.50 . . . . *Lee & S.*

Pickering, C: Gliddon mummy case in Smithsonian Institution. 4°. '69. pap., 50c. . . . . *Smith. Inst.*
— History of the races of man; with analyt. synopsis of the nat. hist. of man by J: C: Hall. por. 12°. (Bohn.) $2; col. ill., $3 . . . . . *Scribner, W. & A.*
— — *See also* Wilkes, C: U. S. explor. expedition.

Pickering, E: C. Elements of physical manipulation. 2 v. ill. 8°. '73. v. 1, $3; v. 2, $4. . *Hurd & H.*

Pickering, *Miss* Ellen. [Novels.] 9 v. 8°. pap. *Peterson.*

Cont.: Ellen Wareham. — Nan Darrell. — The squire. — Who shall be heir? *ea.*, 38c. — Kate Walsingham. — Orphan niece. — Poor cousin, *ea.*, 50c. — The grumbler. — Marrying for money, *ea.*, 75c.

— Charades. 16°. pap., 40c. . . . . *French.*
— The grandfather. 8°. pap., 50c. . . . . *Harper.*
— The grumbler. 8°. pap., 50c. . . . . *Harper.*

Pickering, J: Greek and English lexicon. 8°. shp., $6.25 . . . . *Lippincott.*

Pickering, Oct. *See* Massachusetts, Sup. Court reports.
— *and* Upham, C: W. Life of Timothy Pickering. 4 v. por. 8°. '67–'73. $14 . . . . *Little, B. & Co.*

Pickert, C: *and* Metcalf, A. Art of graining. 42 col. pl. 4°. '72. $10 . . . . *Van Nostrand.*

Picket (The); [also] Watch. 18°. 25c. . . . . *Am. S. S.*

Picket guard. 18°. 40c. . . . . *Whittaker.*

Pickett, Alb. Juvenile spelling book. 16°. *net*, per doz., $2 . . . . *Ferry.*
— *and* J: W. Analyzer and expositor: exercises in Eng. etymology, definition and reading. 12°. '47. hf. bd., 50c. . . . . *U. P. James.*

Pickett's men. Harrison, W. $2 . . . . *Van Nostrand.*

Pickings from the "Picayune." 12°. pap., 75c. *Peterson.*

Pickney, W: A flower of faith: memoir of E. O. Holtzman. 18°. 20c. . . . . *McCauley.*

Pickwick abroad. Reynolds, G. W. M. 75c. . . *Peterson.*

Pickwick papers. *See* Dickens, C:

Pickwickians: comic drama. 16°. pap., 15c. . . *French.*

Picnic (The). *See* Thomas, J. R.

Picnic (The). *See* Witt, *Mme.* H. de.

Picnic papers. *See* Dickens, C:

Picnic party. Adams, W. T. 45c. . . . . *Lee & S.*

Picnic party. *See* Baker, *Mrs.* H. N. W.

Pictet, Bened. Christian theology; tr. by F. Reyroux. 12°. $1.10 . . . . *Pres. Bd.*

Picton, J. Allanson. Mystery of matter, and other essays. cr. 8°. '73. $3.50 . . . . *Macmillan.*

Picton, T: [Plays.] 6 v. 16°. ea., pap., 15c. . . *De Witt.*

Cont.: Cupid's eye-glass: comedy. — A hard case: farce. — A tell-tale heart: comedietta. — Tempest in a teapot: comedy. — There's no smoke without fire: comedietta. — 'Tis better to live than to die: farce.

Pictor Ignotus (*pseud.*) *See* Blake, W:

Pictorial catechism of the Meth. Episc. Church. sq. 12°. '54. $1 . . . . *Meth. Bk. Conc.*

Pictorial field-book of the revolution. *See* Lossing, B. J.

Pictorial first book for little boys and girls. sq. 16°. 50c. . . . . *Pres. Bd.*

Pictorial gatherings. sq. 8°. '54. $1. . *Meth. Bk. Conc.*

Pictorial handbook of mod. geog. 12°. (Bohn.) $1.25; ill., $2.25; col. ill., $2.75.. *Little, B. & Co.*
— *Same.* ill. 12°. (Bohn.) $2.40; col. ill., $3. *Scribner, W. & A.*
— *Same.* ill. 12°. (Bohn.) $2.50; col. ill., $3. *Lippincott.*
Pictorial hist. of the Am. revolution. ill. 8°. $2.. *Lee & S.*
Pictorial history of Indian wars and captivities. ill. 8°. $3.50 .... *J. G. Wells.*
Pictorial letter book. 18°. 40c.......... *Am. S. S.*
Pictorial letter book. *See* Picture lib.
Pictorial life; or, man's life illustrated; by H. Crosby, G. B. Cheever, E. H. Gillett and others. ill. 8°. '70. $2.50; $3.50; shp., $3.......... *Tibbals.*
Pictorial narratives. ill. 12°. '50. 70c.......... *Am. Tr.*
— *See also* Illustrirte Erzählungen.
Pictorial primer; or, first reader for parochial schools. 8°. '76. 25c.......... *Barthel.*
Pictorial scenes and incidents ill. of Christian missions. ill. sq. 16°. 50c. .... *Pres. Bd.*
Pictorial second book. Cousin Mary. 50c... *Pres. Bd.*
Pictorial Sunday readings. *See* Owen, W.
Pictorial teaching. 18°. pap., 10c.......... *Nelson.*
Pictorial teaching and Bible illustration. Hartley, F. J. 10c.......... *Perkinpine.*
Pictorial world. *See* Frost, J.
Picture (The); [also] The country cousins. 18°. 50c. *O'Shea.*
Picture A B C book. *See* Theodore Thinker.
Picture book. 18°. 45c.......... *Whittaker.*
Picture book; with designs by L. Frölich. sm. 4°. '68. $2.......... *Roberts.*
Picture book for the young. *See* Howitt, M.
Picture book of animals and birds. ill. 16°. '71. 50c. *Routledge.*
Picture books for little children. 18°. 50c.; 35c... *Nelson.*
Picture clock. *See* Baker, *Mrs.* H. N. W.
Picture fables. Speckter, O. $2.......... *Appleton.*
Picture gallery. Bache, A. 75c.......... *Tibbals.*
Picture lessons. 18°. 18c.......... *Am. S. S.*
Picture lessons. *See* Picture page lib.
Picture lessons for young readers. ill. 16°. 75c. *Lothrop.*
Picture lib.; — reading book. *See* New.
Picture lib. for the little ones at home. 8 v. ill. 18°. $3.15 .... *Am. S. S.*
Cont.: Round picture stories. — Select poetry for children. — Stories which sister Alice told her little brother Johnny. — Book of one hundred pictures. — Second book of one hundred pictures. — My mother's stories, 2 v. — Pictorial letter book.
Picture of St. John. Taylor, B. $2.......... *Osgood.*
Picture page lib. 12 v. [2 sets of 6 v. ea.] ill. 18°. $3 .... *Nelson.*
Cont.: A child's duty. — Lord's prayer. — Scrap-book. — Picture pages. — Picture lessons. — Picture show.
Picture pages. *See* Picture page lib.
Picture poems for young folks. Greene, A. D. $1.50 *Osgood.*
Picture posies. [Poems.] ill. 4°. '74. $8; mor., $20. *Routledge.*
Picture puzzle toy-book. 7 nos. ill. demy 4°. ea., 50c.......... *Scribner, W. & A.*
Cont.: House we live in. — Nursery play book. — Our holidays. — Holiday fun. — Our kings and queens. — Book of trades. — The horse.
Picture-reading book. ill. 16°. 75c.......... *Hoyt.*
Picture room. 18°. 40c. .... *Am. S. S.*
Picture ser. 6 v. ill. 16°. $3.......... *Lothrop.*
Cont.: Christmas morning. — Bert's confession. — Sailor brother. — The concert. — Little May's picture. — Effie's friends.
Picture show. *See* Picture page lib.
Picture stories for little folks. 6 v. 32°. '70. $1.50. *H. A. Young.*
Cont.: Little stories for little people. — Scenes in the city and country. — Rhymes and stories for little folks. — Frank's pet rooster, and other stories. — White swan, and other stories. — Picture stories for little folks.

Picture story book. ill. 4°. $1.......... *Am. Bap*
Picture story book. ill. sq. 12°. $2.......... *Routledg*
Picture story book. ill. 12°. 75c. .... *Bost. Am. T*
Picture story book. Tucker, C. $1.10 .... *Nelso*
Picture teaching for young and old. Byrne, J. $1.5 *Cassel*
Pictures and flowers for child lovers. *See* Thurston, *Mr*
Pictures and lessons for little readers. ill. 12°. 80 *Bost. Am. T*
Pictures and painters: gems of modern art, with d scriptive text by T. A. Richards. roy. 4°. '6 mor., $30.......... *Virtu*
Pictures and reading. *See* Pretty picture ser.
Pictures and songs. 12 v. 18°. $3.......... *Lothro*
Pictures and songs for the little ones. 18°. '73. 25 *Lothro*
Pictures and stories. 18°. 45c.......... *Whittake*
Pictures and stories for little ones. Dawes, S. E. 70 *Am. T*
Pictures and stories for the young. 18°. 60c... *Am. S.*
Pictures and stories of animals. *See* Tenney, *Mrs.*
Pictures and stories of natural history. 2 v. ill. 4 ea., $1.25.......... *Nelso*
Pictures by Ital. masters; with introd. essay, notic of painters and subjects by W. B. Scott. ill. f '74. $10.......... *Routledg*
Pictures by Venetian painters; with notices of artis and subjects by W. B. Scott. ill. f°. '74. $1 *Routledg*
Pictures for happy hours: short stories. ill. 16°. $ *Cassel*
Pictures for the little ones; with stories. 18°. 75c. *Whittake*
Pictures for our darlings. 4°. '76. $1.25... *Lothro*
Pictures for our pets. 2 v. ill. roy. 4°. ea., 90c.; 2 v. in 1, $1.75.......... *Nelso*
Cont.: Birds, beasts and fishes. — Home and country scen
Pictures for our pets. ill. 4°. $1.75.. *Scribner, W. &*
Pictures for the young. Howitt, M. $1.25.. *Lothro*
Pictures from Bobby's life. *See* Alden, *Mrs.* I. M.
Pictures from English literature. Waller, J. F. $3.5 $5 .... *Cassel*
Pictures from Italy. *See* Dickens, C.
Pictures from prison life. Haynes, G. $1.50.. *Lee &*
Pictures from Venice. Phillimore, C. M. 50c... *Pot*
Pictures in black. *See* Konewka, P.
Pictures of Christian heroism. 16°. $1; $1.50.. *Sadlie*
Pictures of cottage life in the west of Eng. Pool M. E. $1.50.......... *Macmilla*
Pictures of country life. Cary, A. $2 .... *Hurd & I*
Pictures of early life. Embury, E. C. 75c... *Harpe*
Pictures of Edgewood. Mitchell, D. G. $12.. *Scribne*
Pictures of English history. 2 v. ill. 4°. ea., $1; 50 *Routledg*
Pictures of English history. [Toy-book.] ill. demy 4 $2.50.......... *Routledg*
Pictures of heroes, and lessons from their lives. 12 $1.50.......... *Routledg*
Pictures of Hindoo life; or, India without the Gospe ill. 18°. 55c. .... *Pres. B*
Pictures of Italy and America. *See* Dickens, C.
Pictures of John and George. 18°. 30c.......... *Am. S.*
Pictures of life and character. *See* Leech, J.
Pictures of life, with pen and pencil. ill. sq. 12°. '6 $1.50; $1.75.......... *Am. T*
Pictures of travel. *See* Andersen, H. C.
Pictures of travel. *See* Heine, H.
Pictures of travel in far off lands: companion to stu of geog. 2 v. ill. 12°. ea., $1.25.......... *Nelso*
Cont.: Central America. — South America.

Pictures of truth. ill. 18°. 70c. .... *Pres. Bd.*
Picturesque people of the world. Simpson, W. $20. *Cassell.*
Picturesque world. *See* Colange, L.
Pieces of a broken-down critic. Bristed, C. A. $2.50. *Holt.*
Pieces of pleasantry. Planché, J. R. 40c.... *French.*
Pieces of silver. ill. 18°. 50c................. *Pott.*
Pierce, E: L. Treatise on Am. railroad law. 8°. shp., $5....................... *Baker, V. & Co.*
Pierce, E: M. (*ed.*) Cottage cyclopedia of history and biography. 12°. '74. *$5............... *Case.*
Pierce, G: Foster. Devotedness to Christ: sermon in memory of W: Capers. 12°. '55. pap., 20c. *So. Meth.*
Pierce, Gilb. A. The Dickens dictionary; with add. by W. A. Wheeler. por. and ill. 12°. $3. **Osgood.*
Pierce, R. V. People's common sense medical adviser in plain English; or, medicine simplified. ('75.) 3d ed. ill. 12°. *$1.50.................. *Pierce.*
Pierce, S. H. Little gems for little people. ('71.) 2d ed. 18°. '72. $1 .... *Claxton.*
Pierette. Ball, E. 15c...................... *French.*
Pierpont, J: American first class book. 12°. hf. roan, 95c......................... *Lippincott.*
— National reader. 12°. hf. roan, 63c..... *Lippincott.*
— New reader: introd. to the National reader. 12°. hf. roan, 45c...................... *Lippincott.*
— Phrenology and the Scriptures. 12°. '50. pap., 25c. *Wells.*
— The young reader. 18°. hf. roan, 15c.... *Lippincott.*
Pierre. Melville, H. $1.50 .... *Harper.*
Pierre and Annette. ill. 18°. 60c........... *Crowell.*
— *See also* Bright eye lib.
Pierre and his family: story of the Waldenses; by author of "Lilly Douglas." 18°. 60c..... *Am. S. S.*
— *Same.* 18°. '66. 60c. ..*N. Y. Ref. Ch. Bd.; Pres. Com.*
Pierron, Eug., *and* Laferrière, A. Book 3, chapter 1; or, the subterfuge: comedy; tr. 16°. pap., 15c. *French.*
Pierson, A. T. C. Traditions of Freemasonry and its coincidence with the ancient mysteries. ill. 12°. '75. $2................... *Masonic; Redding.*
Pierson, D: H. System of questions in geog. adapted to any modern atlas. New ed., rev. 12°. '74. 75c. .... *Mason.*
Pierson, Helen Wall. Bertha; or, the only fault. 18°. 60c.............................. *Dutton.*
— Edith Vaughan's victory; or, how to conquer. 18°. 90c............................. (?) *Martien.*
— Gracie's mission: tale of Norway. 16°. $1.25. (?) *Martien.*
— Old cabinet. 16°. '58. 85c. .... *Challen.*
Pierson, T: Infidelity dissected. 12°. '72. $1.50.. *Tibbals.*
Piesse, G. W. Septimus. Whole art of perfumery. ill. 12°. $3.............................. *Lindsay.*
Pietas quotidiana: private prayers and meditations. 32°. '59. 60c.; mor., $2.............. *Dutton.*
Pietro v. Albano. *See* Tieck, L.
Piety and pride. Crispin, L. H., $1.......... *Hoyt.*
Piffard, H: G. Urine examinations; for medical students and practitioners. ill. 8°. $1.25.. *W. Wood.*
Pigault-LeBrun, Gu. C: Ant. Citateur; [also] Doubts of infidels. ('71.) New ed. 12°. '73. 75c.; pap., 50c. .... *Colby.*
Pigeon Cove and vicinity. Leonard, H. C. $1.. *Searle.*
Pigeon pie. Yonge, C. M. $1 .... *Roberts.*
Pigeon's bronze boots. ('70.) 4th ed. ill. 18°. '74. 50c. *Perkinpine.*
Pigeons and rabbits. ill. 16°. bds., 50c.... *Routledge.*
Piggott, A. Snowden. Copper mining and copper ore; descrip. of some of the copper mines of the U. S., art of mining, etc. 12°. '58. $1.50.... *Lindsay.*

Pigott, R: Life of man symbolized by the months of the year, with passages from ancient and modern authors; ill. by J. Leighton. 4°. $15; mor., $20. *Appleton.*
Pike, Alb. Morals and dogma of Freemasonry. 4°. '72. $5.............................. *Masonic.*
— *See also* Arkansas, Sup. Court reports.
Pike, Gst. D. The Jubilee singers and their campaign for $20,000; with music. 12°. $1.25.. *Lee & S.*
Pike, Ja. S. The prostrate state; or, South Carolina under negro government. 12°. $1.... *Appleton.*
Pike, J: Bud, blossom and fruit. 16°. $1.. *Cong. Pub.*
Pike, J: Greg. Divine origin of Christianity. 32°. '36. 50c............................. *Freewill.*
— Guide to young disciples. 18°. 70c. .... *Am. Tr.*
— Persuasives to early piety. 18°. '31. 70c... *Am. Tr.*
— Religion and eternal life. 18°. '34. 50c.... *Am. Tr.*
— True happiness. 18°. 45c......... *U. P. Bd. of Pub.*
— *Same.* 18°. 50c......................... *Carter.*
Pike, *Mrs.* Ma. H. ["Ma. Langdon"; "Sydney A. Story, *jr.*"] Climbing and sliding: book for boys. ('66.) New ed. ill. 16°. '73. $1.25. *Lockwood, B. & Co.*
— Every day: book for young ladies. 12°. '70. $1.25. *Lockwood, B. & Co.*
— Striving and gaining: book for girls. ('67.) New ed. ill. 16°. '73. $1.25...... *Lockwood, B. & Co.*
Pike, N: Sub-tropical rambles in the land of the Aphanapteryx: personal experiences, adventures and wanderings in and about the island of Mauritius. ill. cr. 8°. $3.50................ *Harper.*
Pike, S: *and* Hayward, S: Religious cases of conscience answered in an evangelical manner. 12°. $1 .... *U. P. Bd. of Pub.*
— — *Same;* [with] introd. by H. A. Boardman. New ed. 12°. '59. $1.25 .... *Smith, E. & Co.*
Pike, Ste. Arithmetic. 12°. 37½c. — Key. 18°. leath., 75c..................................... *Polock.*
Pike county ballads. Hay, J. $1.50; $3.... *Osgood.*
Pilgrim, J. [Plays.] 8 v. 16°. ea., pap., 15c... *French.*
Cont.: Eveleen Wilson. — Katty O'Sheal: farce. — Limerick boy: farce. — Paddy, the piper: comic drama. — Robert Emmet. — Servants by legacy: farce. — Shandy Maguire. — Wild Irish girl.
Pilgrim. *See* Seaboy's grave.
Pilgrim and the shrine. Maitland, E. $1.75.. *Putnam.*
Pilgrim boy. Cross, J. 40c. .... *Am. Tr.*
Pilgrim boy of Monghyr, and other stories. 18°. 25c. *Pres. Bd.*
Pilgrim fathers. *See* Root, G. F.
Pilgrim melodies. Sweetser, J. E. $1.25.... *Barnes.*
Pilgrim memories. Stuart-Glennie, J. S. $3.. *Appleton.*
Pilgrim of love. Byron, H. J. 15c.......... *French.*
Pilgrim path: incidents from experience of Christians. ill. 16°. 70c..................... *Bost. Am. Tr.*
Pilgrim psalms. Cox, S. $5............. *Routledge.*
Pilgrim Street. *See* Smith, Ha.
Pilgrim Street ser. *See* Smith, Ha.
Pilgrimage of grace. Emery, M. $2 .... *O'Shea.*
Pilgrimage to Jerusalem. Strauss, F. $1.25. *Lippincott.*
Pilgrimage to the land of Cid. Ozanam, A. F. $1. *Cath. Pub.*
Pilgrimage to Palestine. Smith, J. V. C. $1.. *D. Clapp.*
Pilgrimage to Rome. *See* Cabinet lib. of household reading.
Pilgrimage to the shrine of St. Teresa at Alba de Tormes in Spain. 32°. '65. pap., 15c... *Murphy.*
Pilgrim's harp. Hull, A. 60c.; 50c. .... *Ditson.*
Pilgrim's harp: hymn book. [German.] 24°. 75c. -$2.75 .... *Am. Bapt.*
Pilgrim's lib. 6 v. 18°. $4.90............ *So. Meth.*
Cont.: Pilgrim's progress, by J. Bunyan. — Tongue of fire, by W. Arthur. — Christian father's present to his children, by J. A. James. — Home truths, by Rev. J. C. Ryle. — Successful merchant, by W. Arthur. — Post oak circuit.

Pilgrim's progress. *See* Bunyan, J:
Pilgrim's progress. Faurot, R. $1 .... *Chase.*
Pilgrim's progress. *See* Godolphin, M. A.
Pilgrim's wallet. Haven, G. $1.75 .... *Hurd & H.*
Pilgrims of fashion. Cornwallis, K. $1 ..... *Harper.*
Pilgrims of the Rhine. *See* Bulwer-Lytton, *Sir* E. G. E. L.
Pilgrims-Sanger. Palmquest, G. *and* P. 45c... *Am. Tr.*
Pilkington, Ja. Mechanic's own book. 12°. $1.50. *Nichols & H.*
Pillar of fire. Ingraham, J. H. $2 .... *Roberts.*
Pillars in the temple. Smith, W. C. $1.25 .. *Meth. Bk. Conc.*
Pillars of Hercules. Urquhart, D. 2 v. $3 .. *Harper.*
Pillars of the house. Yonge, C. M. 2 v. $3.50. *Macmillan.*
Pillars of truth. Haven, E. O. $1.25 .. *Meth. Bk. Conc.*
Pillon, Alex. J: Bapt. A. Greek synonyms. *See* Yonge, C. D., English-Greek lexicon.
Pillow of stones. Sewall, F. $1.50 ...... *Lippincott.*
Pilon, Mt. R. Day's (A) work; or, the base and balance of a fair trade: pt. 1 of bk. 1 of "Yanko-Sequor." 8°. '76. pap., 35c .... *Authors.*
— Gold and free banks: bk. 2 of "Yanko-Sequor." 2d ed. 8°. '75. pap., $1 .... *Authors.*
Pilot. Ball, E. 15c. .... *French.*
Pilot. *See* Cooper, Ja. F.
Pilot and his wife. Lie, J. $1.50 .... *Griggs.*
Pilot's daughter. Doudney, S. $1 .... (?) *Nelson.*
Pilpay. [Bidpai.] Fables. ill. 16°. '75. $1.50. *Hurd & H.*
— *Same.* ill. cr. 8°. '71. $3.50 .... *Hurd & H.*
Pinart, Désiré. Meditations on the suffering life on earth of [Christ]; tr. by A. P. Forbes. 12°. '75. $2 .... *Pott.*
— Nourishment of the Christian soul; or, mental prayer rendered easy by meditations on the passion of Christ; tr. by A. P. Forbes. 12°. '76. $2 .. *Pott.*
Pinchard, *Miss* Marg. Douglass. Kate and Effie; or, prevarication. 18°. 75c .... *Dutton.*
— Max Frere; or, overcome evil with good. 16°. 50c. *Routledge.*
Pindar [*Lat.* Pindarus]. Odes; rendered into Eng. prose, with introd. notes, etc., by E. Myers. cr. 8°. '74. $1.50 .... *Macmillan.*
— *Same;* lit. tr. by D. W. Turner, and metrical version by A. Moore. 12°. (Bohn.) $1.75 .. *Little, B. & Co.*
— — *Same.* 12°. (Bohn.) $2. *Lippincott; Scribner, W. & A.*
— *Same;* tr. by C. A. Wheelwright; [also] Anacreon's Odes; tr. by T. Bourne. 18°. 75c. ... *Harper.*
Pindar, Cp. L. Alleghania; or, praises of American heroes. [Poetry.] 12°. $1.25 ..... *Lippincott.*
— Melpomene divina: poems on Christian themes. 16°. $1.50 .... *Lippincott.*
Pindar, Su. Cooper. The Wentworths. ill. 16°. '76. $1.25 .... *Lothrop.*
Pine, Cuyler (*pseud.*) *See* Peck, Ellen.
Pine cottage. Chapman, H. E. 60c .... *Cong. Pub.*
Pine grove doings. Kingsbury, J. H. $1.50 .. *Carleton.*
Piney Woods tavern; or, Sam Slick in Texas. 12°. $1.75; pap., $1.50 .... *Peterson.*
Pingry, I. F. How old art thou? 32°. '62. 20c... *Randolph.*
Pink and white tyranny. Stowe, H. B. $1.50 .. *Roberts.*
Pink slippers; or, cure of vanity. 18°. 22c... *Am. S. S.*
— *Same.* 18°. '66. 25c... *N. Y. Ref. Ch. Bd.; Pres. Com.*
Pinkerton, Allan. [Detective stories.] 4 v. 12°. '74–'76. ea., $1.50 .... *Keen.*
Cont.: Claude Melnotte as a detective, etc. — Detective and the somnambulist; Murderer and the fortune-teller. — Expressman and the detective. — Model town and the detective; Byron as a detective.
— Model town and the detective. 12°. $1.50 .. *Carleton.*
Pinkerton, J: J. Practical guide to administrators, guardians and assignees. 18°. '70. shp., $1.50. *J. Campbell & Son.*
Pinkerton, Lew. L. Bible questions for Sunday schools, Bible-classes, etc. 18°. 25c .... *Chase.*
— Life, letters and addresses; ed. by J. Shackelford. por. 12°. $1.50 .... *Chase.*
Pinkie and the rabbits. Mathews, J. H. 60c... *Carter.*
Pinks and blues. Parker, R. A. $1 .... *Lee & S.*
Pinneo, T. S. Analytical [English] grammar. ('50.) New ed. 12°. '59. 60c .... *Wilson, H. & Co.*
— English teacher: structure of sentences by analysis and synthesis. 12°. '64. 60c... *Wilson, H. & Co.*
— Exercises for parsing and analysis. 12°. '67. 50c. *Wilson, H. & Co.*
— Exercises in false syntax. 12°. 45c... *Wilson, H. & Co.*
— Guide to composition. 12°. '64. 75c... *Wilson, H. & Co.*
— Hemans young ladies' reader (The). 12°. '47. $1.25. *Wilson, H. & Co.*
— Primary grammar. 16°. '54. 40c. .. *Wilson, H. & Co.*
Pinney, Norm. Easy lessons in French. 12°. 80c. *Sheldon.*
— Elementary French reader. 12°. $1 ...... *Sheldon.*
— First book in French. 16°. 60c.; — with key, 75c. *Sheldon.*
— Progressive French reader. 12°. $1.50 ... *Sheldon.*
— *and* Arnoult, Émile. French grammar. 8°. $2. — Key, $1 .... *Sheldon.*
— *and* Badois, C. Practical French teacher. 12°. $1.50. — Key, $1 .... *Sheldon.*
— *and* Barcelo, Juan. Practical Spanish teacher. 12°. $1.50. — Key, $1 .... *Sheldon.*
Pinney, S. M. *See* Wisconsin, Reports.
Pinnock, W: History of France and Normandy; ed. by W. C. Taylor. ill. 12°. hf. roan, $1.75 .. *Desilver.*
— *See also* Goldsmith, Cl.
Pinnock, W: H: Analysis of ecclesiastical hist., 1–A. D. 325; with examination questions. 18°. '73. $1.75 .... *Pott.*
— Analysis of Eng. church hist.; compr. reformation period and subsequent events; with questions of exam. 18°. '70. $2.25 .... *Pott.*
— Analysis of New Test. hist.; with questions for exam. 18°. '74. $2.25 .... *Pott.*
— Analysis of Old Test. hist.; with maps, index. and exam. questions. 18°. '75. $1.75 .... *Pott.*
Pinsuti, Ciro. Six four-part songs for mixed voices. 8°. ap., 50c.; pea., 10c. .... *Ditson.*
Pint of ale: temperance [dram.] sketch. 16°. pap., 15c .... *Happy.*
Pioneer experiences. Palmer, P. $1.50 .... *Palmer.*
Pioneer lib. 10 v. 18°. $5 .... *Un. B. Pub.*
Cont.: Little gate, by A. S. Spalding. — Safe home, by F. Kenyon. — Little Mary, by B. Stowe. — Men of worth. — May Earnest, by C. Bellmont. — Is the Bible true? — Counsels to young men, by J. Haws. — City cousins. — Guiding star, by L. P. Hopkins. — Introduction to Bible study, by S. Green.
Pioneer lib. *See* Thayer, W. M.
Pioneer life in the west. ill. 12°. $1.75 .. *J. E. Potter.*
Pioneer mothers of the west. Frost, J. $1.50 .. *Lee & S.*
Pioneer women of the west. Ellet, E. F. $1.25 .. *Porter.*
Pioneer's daughter. Bennett, E. 75c ...... *Peterson.*
Pioneers. *See* Cooper, Ja. F.
Pioneers. Seton, W. $1.50 .... *O'Shea.*
Pioneers and founders. Yonge, C. M. $1.75. *Macmillan.*
Pioneers in the settlement of America. Crafts, W. A. 24 pts. ea., *50c. .... *S. Walker.*
Pioneers of Maryland. *See* Pioneers of the new world.
Pioneers of the new world. 4 v. 16°. $5 .. *Lothrop.*
Cont.: Plymouth and the pilgrims. — Southern explorists and colonists. — Pioneers of Maryland. — Soldiers and patriots of the rev.
Pioneers of the west. Strickland, W. P. $1.75. *Meth. Bk. Conc.*

Pioneers of the world's progress. Simpson, A. L. $2. *Nelson.*

Piot, B. S. Considerations on the ministry; with a rule of life for pastors. ('60.) 2d ed. 18°. '70. *net*, 50c. . . . . *Kelly, P. & Co.*

Pious biography. Peach, E. 60c. . . . . . *Cummiskey.*

Pious children. 18°. '49. 20c. . . . . *Am. Tr.*

Pious exercises and practices in honor of the sacred heart of Mary. 32°. '56. 15c. . . . *Kelly, P. & Co.*

Pious guide: manual of prayers and devotions for Cath. Christians. 18°. 90c.–$9 . . . . *Benziger.*

Pious Jemima: humorous sketch in verse. ill. 12°. '72. $1.50 . . . . *Routledge.*

Pious physician. Palmer, B. M. 25c. *N. Y. Ref. Ch. Bd.; Pres. Com.*

Pious remembrancer. Collins, R. 15c. . . . . *Claxton.*

Pious shepherd. MacLaurin, R. 30c. . . . . . *Pres. Bd.*

Pipkins' rustic retreat. Williams, T. J. 15c. . . *French.*

Pippins and pies. Coyne, J. S. 50c. . . . . *Routledge.*

Pique: tale of English aristocracy. 12°. $1.50; pap., $1 . . . . *Loring.*

Pirata (Il). *See* Bellini, V.

Pirate. *See* Marryat, F:

Pirate. *See* Scott, *Sir* Wa.

Pirate chief. 8°. pap., 25c. . . . . *Dick & F.*

Pirate city. Ballantyne, R. M. $1.75 . . . . . . *Nelson.*

Pirate doctor. 8°. pap., 25c. . . . . *Dick & F.*

Pirate of the isles. Clarke, N. H. B. 15c. . . . *French.*

Piraten-Lieutenant (Der). Möllhausen, B. 50c. *Morwitz.*

Pirate's bride. 8°. pap., 25c. . . . . *De Witt.*

Pirate's legacy. Saunders, C. H. 15c. . . . . . *French.*

Pirate's son. ill. 8°. pap., 25c. . . . . *Peterson.*

Pirates of the Mississippi. 8°. pap., 25c. . . . *De Witt.*

Pirates of the prairies. Aimard, G. 75c. . . . *Peterson.*

Pirates of Putney. Selby, C. 15c. . . . . *French.*

Pirates of Savannah. Bourgeois, A., *and* Dugué, F. 15c. . . . . *French.*

Pirie, G. Lessons on rigid dynamics. cr. 8°. '75. $2.25 . . . . *Macmillan.*

Pirithous. Burnand, F. C. 15c. . . . . *French.*

Piron, Alexis. La métromanie. Ed. by F. Tarver. 16°. 50c.; pap., 25c. . . . . *Lippincott.*

Pirrie, W: Principles and practice of surgery; ed. by J. Neill. ill. 8°. $3.75 . . . . *Lea.*

Pise, C: C. Acts of the Apostles rendered into Eng. verse. *See* Rutter, H., Life, etc., of Christ.

Pisgah views. Winslow, O. $1.25 . . . . *Carter.*

Pison. *See* French's comic dramas.

Pistol (The) as a weapon of defence in the house and on the road. 12°. '75. 50c. . . . . *Indust.*

Pitawall, Ern. 500,000 Thaler, od. Fabrikarbeiter u. Millionär. 8°. $2.25; pap., $1.75; hf. mor., $2.50. *F. W. Thomas.*

— Gabriele, das Weib des Spielers; [also] Die Franctireurs, Erzählung a. d. deutsch-franz. Kriege, v. F. Gerstäcker. 8°. pap., 50c. . . . . *Morwitz.*

— Kind (Das) der Sünde: Roman a. d. Hamburger Leben. 12°. pap., $1 . . . . *Zickel.*

— Louis Napoleon, od. Schicksalskampf u. Kaiserkrone. 8°. $1.75–$2.50 . . . . *F. W. Thomas.*

Pitcher of cool water. Arthur, T. S. 50c. . . *Nat. Temp.*

Pithy papers. Mogridge, G. 60c. . . . . *So. Meth.*

Pitman, Benn. Assassination of Lincoln and trial of the conspirators. por. roy. 8°. '65. $3; $3.50; hf. cf., $5 . . . . *Wilstach.*

— First phonographic reader. ('60.) New ed. 24°. '76. 25c. . . . . *Pitman.*

— First reporter's reader. ('60.) New ed. 24°. '76. 25c. . . . . *Pitman.*

Pitman, Benn, *continued.*

— Manual of phonography. ('54.) New ed. 12°. '71. $1; pap., 80c. . . . . *Appleton; Pitman.*

— Phrase book: vocab. of phraseography, with engraved phonographic forms. ('57.) New ed. 12°. '76. $1 . . . . *Pitman.*

— Plain talk; comp. from Spurgeon. [Phonog.] ('72.) New ed. 12°. '76. 50c. . . . . *Pitman.*

— Reporter's companion: guide to verbatim reporting. ('54.) New ed. 12°. '76. $1.25; bds., $1. *Appleton; Pitman.*

— Second phonographic reader. ('60.) New ed. 24°. '76. 25c. . . . . *Pitman.*

— Trials for treason at Indianapolis; disclosing the plans for establishing a north-western confederacy; [with] report of Judge-Advocate-General Holt on the Order of American Knights, *alias* the Sons of Liberty. por. 8°. $3–$2 . . . . *Wilstach.*

Pitt, G: D. [Plays.] 7 v. 16°. ea., pap., 15c. . . *French.*

Cont.: Beggar's petition. — Drunkard's doom. — Eddystone elf: melodrama. — Jersey girl. — Last man. — Simon Lee. — Susan Hopley.

Pitt, W: *See* Chatham, *Earl of.*

Pittenger, W: Oratory, sacred and secular; or, the extemporaneous speaker; with introd. by J. A. Bingham, and app. 12°. '68. $1.25 . . . . . . *Wells.*

Pitts, F. E. Zion's harp. 16°. '52. shp., 60c. . . *Morton.*

Pittsburgh Convention of Freemasons. Proceedings. 12°. pap., 25c. . . . . *E. A. Cook.*

Pittsburgh pulpit: sermons by fourteen clergymen of Pittsburgh, Penn. 8°. '76. $1 . . *R. S. Davis (P.)*

Pittsburgh [Penn.] reports: cases decided by the federal and state courts, chiefly at Pittsburgh, 1853–'73; ed. with ref. by B. Crumrine. 3 v. 8°. '72–'73. shp., $22.50 . . . . *J. Campbell & Son.*

Pitzmaroon. Beach, C. A. $1.25 . . . . . . *Whitney & A.*

Pius VI., *Pope.* History of [his] pontificate and captivity; with glance at the Cath. church; tr. by Miss H——th. 18°. 60c. . . . . *O'Shea.*

Pius IX., *Pope.* History and captivity. 18°. 40c. *Sadlier.*

— Pius IX. and temporal rights of the holy see. 18°. 40c. . . . . *Sadlier.*

Pius, *Father* —. Life of St. Paul of the cross; tr. by Father Ignatius. 12°. $1; $1.50 . . . . . . *O'Shea.*

Pivot words of Scripture. Power, P. B. $1.50 . . *Carter.*

Pizarro, Francisco. *See* Balboa, V. N. de, Cortes, H., *and* Pizarro, F.

Pizarro. Kotzebue, A. F. F. v. 15c. . . . . *French.*

Place for everything. *See* Haven, *Mrs.* A. B.

Plague of my life: farce. 16°. pap., 15c. . . . *French.*

Plague of the village. *See* Cluster gem.

Plaid pincushion. Guernsey, C. F. 45c. . . *Whittaker.*

Plaideurs (Les). *See* Racine, J:

Plaidy, L: Piano teacher; tr. by J. S. Dwight. 12°. bds., 38c.; pap., 30c. . . . . *Ditson.*

— Pianoforte teacher's guide; tr. by F. R. Ritter. 8°. '76. bds., 40c. . . . . *Schuberth.*

— Technical studies for the piano: Am. fingering; tr. 4°. $2; bds., $1.50 . . . . *Brainard.*

— *Same*: Am. or foreign fingering. f°. $2; bds., $1.50; — foreign fingering, 75c. . . . . *Gordon.*

— *Same.* 4°. '74. $2; bds., $1.50; — Germ. fingering. 4°. $2; bds., $1.50 . . . . *Pond.*

— *Same*; enl. by K. Klauser. f°. pap., $3 . . *Schirmer.*

— *Same*; tr. by H. Daum: Germ. fingering. 4°. $2. *G. D. Russell.*

— — Tabular scheme to piano studies. 16°. pap., 15c. *Ditson.*

Plain account of the English Bible. Blunt, J. H. $1. *Dutton.*

Plain chant (?) 50c. . . . . *Dooley.*

Plain commentary on the four Gospels; for devotional reading. 2 v. 8°. $6; hf. cf., $8.50; — 2 v. in 1, hf. cf., $7.50; mor., $10 . . . . *McCauley.*

Plain directions for accidents, emergencies and poisons and care of the sick; by a fellow of the Coll. of Physicians of Phila. 12°. '75. $1..... *Claxton.*

Plain directions for acquiring art of shooting on the wing; by an old game keeper. ill. 12°. '73. 75c. ..... *Indust.*

Plain educational talks with teachers and parents. Raub, A. N. $1.50..... *Claxton.*

Plain home talk. Foote, E. B. $3.25; $3.75..*J. G. Wells.*

Plain paths onward and heavenward. 18°. 50c...*Nelson.*

Plain preaching for a year. Fowle, E. 3 v. $6..*Pott.*

Plain sermons on personal religion. Natt, G. W. $2. *Lippincott.*

Plain-song reason why. Walker, C. $1.75.....*Pott.*

Plain talk about insanity. Fisher, T. W. $1.50. *A. Moore.*

Plain talk about the Protestantism of today. Segur, L. G. de. 60c.; 25c..... *Noonan.*

Plain talks. Greenough, J. 75c..... *Cong. Pub.*

Plain talks on familiar subjects. Holland, J. G. $1.75. *Scribner.*

Plain thoughts on art of living. Gladden, W. $1.50. **Osgood.*

Plain words. Seiss, J. A. 60c..... *Luth. Bk. St.*

Plain words on Christian living. *See* Vaughan, C. J.

Plain words to a young communicant. Alexander, J. W. 40c..... *Randolph.*

Plaine description of the Barmvdas, now called Sommer Ilands: Lond., 1613. [Reprint.] 4°. pap., 50c. *Sabin.*

Planché, *Mrs.* E. Pleasant neighbor: farce. 16°. pap., 15c..... *French.*

Planché, F: D'Arros. Evening amusements for every one. ill. 12°. $1.50..... *Porter.*

Planché, Ja. Robinson. [Plays.] 64 v. 16°. ea., pap., 15c..... *French.*

Cont.: Amoroso, king of little Britain: farce.—Beauty and the beast: extravaganza.—Bee and the orange tree: farce.—Birds of Aristophanes: extravaganza.—Brigand.—Cabinet question: comic drama.—Camp at the Olympic: extravaganza.—Captain of the watch: farce.—Charles XII.—Child of the wreck.—Cymon and Iphigenia: extravaganza.—Court beauties: dram. sketch.—Daughter to marry: comedietta.—Day of reckoning.—Discreet princess: extravaganza.—Faint heart never won fair lady: comedy.—Fair one with golden locks: extravaganza.—Follies of a night: comedy.—Fortunio: extravaganza.—Garrick fever: farce.—Golden branch: extravaganza.—Golden fleece: extravaganza.—Good woman in the wood: extravaganza.—Graciosa and Percinet: extravaganza.—Green eyed monster: farce.—Grist to the mill: comic drama.—Hold your tongue.—Invisible prince: extravaganza.—Irish post.—Island of jewels: extravaganza.—Jacobite.—Jenkinses: farce.—King Charming: extravaganza.—King of the peacocks: extravaganza.—Knights of the round table.—Lady in difficulties.—Lavater; or, not a bad judge.—Loan of a lover: comedy.—Love and fortune: burlesque.—Mason of Buda: farce.—Merchant's wedding: comedy.—My great aunt: comedy.—My heart's idol: comedy.—My lord and lady: comedy.—Mysterious lady: comedy.—Norma: opera.—Not a bad judge: comic drama.—Oberon: opera.—Old offender: comic drama.—Orpheus in the Haymarket: opera bouffe.—Pride of the market: comic drama.—Printer's devil: farce.—Promotion: vaudeville.—Queen Mary's bower: comedy.—Queen of frogs: extravaganza.—Romantic idea.—Secret service.—Seven champions of Christendom: spectacle.—Somebody else: farce.—Theseus and Ariadne: extravaganza.—Vampire.—White cat: extravaganza.—Yellow dwarf: extravaganza.—Young and handsome: extravaganza.

Note. "Daughter to marry," formerly pub. under title of "My daughter, Sir!"

— Cyclopædia of costume; or, a dictionary of dress. [To form 24 pts.] pts. 1–10. ill. 4°. ea., pap., $2 ..... *Scribner, W. & A.*

— Garrick fever: farce. 16°. pap., 15c..... *De Witt.*

— History of British costume. 16°. bds., $1.50..*French.*

— *Same.* ill. 12°. (Bohn.) $1.75..... *Little, B. & Co.*

— *Same.* ill. 12°. (Bohn.) $2..... *Scribner, W. & A.*

— Pieces of pleasantry: juvenile dramas. 16°. pap., 40c..... *French.*

— Sleeping beauty in the wood. ill. sm. 4°. $1.75. *Routledge.*

— (*ed.*) Four-and-twenty fairy tales; tr. from Perrault, etc. ill. post 8°. $2–$3.50..... *Routledge.*

Planché, Ja. Robinson, *continued.*

— *See also* Stoddard, R. H., Bric-a-brac ser.

— *and* Dance, C: [Plays.] 6 v. 16°. ea., pap., 15c. *French.*

Cont.: Blue Beard: musical burlesque.—Deep, deep sea: burletta.—High, low, Jack and game: burlesque.—Olympic devils: burlesque.—Olympic revels: burletta.—Paphian bower: extravaganza.

— *and* Dance, G: Telemachus: extravaganza. 16°. pap., 15c..... *French.*

Planché, *Mrs.* Jos. Robinson. Handsome husband: comic drama. 16°. pap., 15c..... *French.*

— The Welsh girl: comedy. 16°. pap., 15c...*Lee & S.*

Planché, *Miss* Mta. A. *See* Mackarness, *Mrs.* M. A.

Planchette mystery: inquiry into nature, origin, import, etc., of mod. signs and wonders; by a truth seeker. 12°. '69. pap., 20c..... *Wells.*

Planchette's diary. Field, K. 50c..... *Redfield.*

Plancy, Colin de. Legends of the Virgin; tr. from the Fr. 12°. 90c.; $1.50..... *O'Shea.*

Plane and plank. Adams, W. T. $1.25..... *Lee & S.*

Planetary and stellar worlds. Mitchel, O. McK. $1.75. *Mason.*

Plant hunters (The). Reid, M. $1.50..... *Miller.*

Plantation Jim. *See* Mudge, Z. A.

Planter's daughter. Dupuy, E. A. $1.75...*Peterson.*

Planter's northern bride. Hentz, C. L. $1.75; $1.50. *Peterson.*

Planters plea; or, the grounds of plantations examined, and vsual objections answered; with a manifestation of the causes mooving such as have lately vndertaken a plantation in New England: London, 1630. [Reprint.] 4°. pap., $1....*Sabin.*

Planting the wilderness. McCabe, J. D. $1.25..*Lee & S.*

Plants. *See* Library of curious things in nature.

Plants, ill. in their structure the wisdom and goodness of God. ill. 18°. 60c..... *Bost. Am. Tr.*

Plants and trees of Scripture; rev. by T. O. Summers. ('57.) 3d ed. 18°. '75. 65c..... *So. Meth.*

Plassmann, E. Modern Gothic ornaments: 32 photolith. pl. f°. '76. hf. shp., $12.... *Lindemann.*

Plate, E. Th. Prakt. Lehr- u. Uebungsbuch f. d. Unterricht in d. deutschen Sprache. 1. u. 2. Stufe. 2 v. 8°. hf. bd., 1, 35c.; 2, 45c... *Vering.*

Plate, H. German studies: course of instruction in the Germ. lang. 12°. '70. $1.35..... *Knœfel.*

Plate of chowder: a dish for funny fellows. ill. 12°. pap., 30c..... *Dick & F.*

Plato. Works; tr. by H. Cary and others. 6 v. 12°. (Bohn.) ea., $1.75 ..... *Little, B. & Co.*

Cont.: 1. Apology of Socrates, Crito, Phædo, Gorgias, Protagoras, Phædrus, Theætetus, Euthyphron, Lysis.—2. The republic, Timæus, and Critias.—3. Meno, Euthydemus, The sophist, Statesman, Cratylus, Parmenides, and The banquet.—4. Philebus, Charmides, Laches, The two Alcibiades, and ten other dialogues.—5. The laws.—6. Doubtful works with general index.

— *Same.* 6 v. 12°. (Bohn.) ea., $2. *Lippincott; Scribner, W. & A.*

— Apology and Crito [*Gk.*]; with notes by J. Davies. 16°. (Weale.) 80c..... *Allyn.*

— — *Same;* with Eng. notes by L. Tyler. 12°. $1.50. *Appleton.*

— Dialogues; tr. with analyses and introductions by B. Jowett. ('72.) New ed. 4 v. cr. 8°. '74. $12; hf. cf., $20; hf. mor., $22.50.—New [chp.] ed. 4 v. cr. 8°. $8..... *Scribner.*

— — Analysis and index to Dialogues, by A. Day. 12°. (Bohn.) $1.75..... *Little, B. & Co.*

— — *Same.* 12°. (Bohn.) $2. *Lippincott; Scribner, W. & A.*

— Divine and moral works; tr. with introd. dissertations and notes. 12°. $2.50..... *Mendum.*

— Gorgias [*Gk.*]; with notes by T. D. Woolsey. 12°. $1.75..... *Hamersley.*

— Phædo [*Gk.*]; with notes by W. Wagner. 3d ed. 16°. '75. $1.50..... *Allyn.*

lato, *continued.*
- *Eng.* Phædo; or, the immortality of the soul; tr. by C. S. Stanford; with life of Plato by Fenélon, and catalogue of books rel. to future state. por. 12°. $1.25 .... *Miller.*
- Plato contra Atheos: 10th bk. of the Dialogue on laws [*Gk.*]; with notes and dissertations on the Platonic philosophy by T. Lewis. 12°. $1.75. *Harper.*
- Republic [*Gk.*]; with notes by J. L. Davies and D. J. Vaughan. 18°. '66. $1.25 ...... *Macmillan.*
- Select dialogues: lit. version by H. Cary. 12°. $1.50 .... *Harper.*
- [Outlined and expl.] by C. W. Collins. (Anc. classics for Eng. readers.) 16°. $1. *Lippincott; Little, B. & Co.*
- Best thoughts; comp. from Jowett's tr. by Rev. C. H. A. Buckley. 8°. '76. $2.50 .... *Scribner.*

latonic attachments. Bernard, W. B. 15c... *French.*

latt, A. H. Human life prolonged; or, five thousand facts for physical existence. ill. 8°. *$3.50; leath., $4 .... *Quak. City.*

latt, *Mrs.* Adeline E. Star of Bethlehem. ill. 18°. '69. 70c.; pap., 30c. .... *Am. Tr.*

latt, C: H: Sermons; ed. by J. G. Webster. 8°. '72. $2 .... *Sickels.*

latt, Smith H. Christ and adornments. ('57.) 4th ed. 16°. '67. 40c. .... *West. Tr.*
- Gift of power; or, special influences of Holy Spirit the need of the church; with introd. by N. Bangs. ('56.) 5th ed. 12°. '76. $1.25. *Hope; Meth. Bk. Conc.*
- Man of like passions; or, Elijah the Tishbite. ('70.) 4th ed. 18°. '74. 25c.; pap., 15c. .... *Hope.*
- My 25th year jubilee; or, cure by faith after 25 years of lameness. 16°. '75. pap., 15c. .... *Hope.*
- Power of grace over acquired habits, special inborn perversities and the natural appetites; [also] The wondrous name. 6th ed. '74. $1; 60c.; pap., 35c.; — with por., $1.10 .... *Hope.*
- Princely manhood: treatise on the procreative instinct as related to moral and Christian life. ('74.) 6th ed. 16°. '76. 60c.; pap., 50c. .... *Hope.*
- Queenly womanhood: treatise on the sexual instinct as related to moral and religious life. 16°. '75. 65c.; pap., 50c. .... *Hope.*
- Wondrous name (The): sermon. 8°. '73. 12°. '74. pap., 10c. .... *Hope.*

lattner, C: F: Manual of qualitative and quantitative analysis with the blow-pipe; rev. and enl. by T. Richter; tr. by H. B. Cornwall and J. H. Caswell. 2d ed., rev. ill. 8°. '75. $5 ...... *Van Nostrand.*

latts, J. Cyclopædia of curiosities. ill. 8°. $2; shp., $2.75 .... *World Pub.*

lautus, Tit. Maccius. Comedies; lit. tr. with notes by H. T. Riley. 2 v. 12°. (Bohn.) ea., $1.75. *Little, B. & Co.*
- *Same.* 2 v. 12°. (Bohn.) ea., $2. *Lippincott; Scribner, W. & A.*
- Captives [*Lat.*]: comedy; with Eng. notes by J. Proudfit. 18°. 75c. .... *Harper.*
- Captivi, Trinummus et Rudens; with Eng. notes by C. S. Harrington. 12°. $1.25 .... *Harper.*
- Mostellaria; with notes, prolegomena and excursus by W: Ramsay, ed. by G. G. Ramsay. 8°. '69. $4. *Macmillan.*
- *and* Terentius Afer, Publius. [Writings; outl. and expl.] by W. L. Collins. (Anc. classics for Eng. readers.) 16°. $1 ... *Lippincott; Little, B. & Co.*

lay and profit in my garden. Roe, E. P. $1.50 .. *Judd.*

lay and study. Baker, H. N. W. $1.50 .... *Lee & S.*

lay and study ser. *See* Baker, *Mrs.* H. N. W.

lay book of science. Pepper, J. H. $2 .. *Routledge.*

lay day. *See* Swallow stories.

lay day book. *See* Parton, *Mrs.* S. P.

lay ground; or, out-door games for boys. ill. 16°. 75c.; bds., 50c. .... *Dick & F.*

Play hours and half holidays. Atkinson, J. C. $1.25. *Routledge.*

Play school stories. *See* Lamb, *Mrs.* M. J.

Played out. Thomas, A. 75c. .... *Harper.*

Playfair, J. *See* Euclid.

Playfellow. Hofland, B. $1 .... *Nelson.*

Playfellow. Martineau, H. $2.50 .... *Routledge.*

Playing for high stakes. Thomas, A. 25c. .. *Harper.*

Playing the mischief. De Forest, J. W. 75c... *Harper.*

Playing Robinson Crusoe. *See* Sylvan stories.

Playing Santa Claus. Doughty, S. P. 50c. *H. H. Carter.*

Playing trades. Grey, H. $1.50 .... *Cassell.*

Playing with fire. Brougham, J. 15c. ...... *French.*

Plays and Puritans. Kingsley, C. $1.75 .. *Macmillan.*

Plays of the Kindergarten. Richter, C. J. 30c... *Peters.*

Plea for Bible in schools. Ritchie, A. 10c... *West. Tr.*

Plea for mercy to animals. Macaulay, J. $1.25 .. *Nelson.*

Plea for a new English version of the Scriptures; by a licentiate of the Church of Scotland. 8°. '64. $2. *Macmillan.*

Plea for peasant proprietors. Thornton, W. T. $2.25. *Macmillan.*

Pleading Saviour. Smith, J. $1.50 .... *Nelson.*

Pleadings of the sacred heart. Comeford, M. 60c. *Cath. Pub.*

Pleasant boy: opera. 16°. pap., 15c. .... *French.*

Pleasant Cove series. *See* Kellogg, E.

Pleasant dreams. Dance, C. 15c. .... *French.*

Pleasant grove. *See* Dodge, A. A.

Pleasant grove ser. 5 v. 18°. $3 ..... *Bost. Am. Tr.*
Cont.: Ansdale Hall, by C. J. G. — Good fight, by Mrs. M. L. Peebles. — Holiday tales, by U. L. Bailey and F. L. Pratt. — Pleasant grove, by Alice A. Dodge. — Pleasant tales.

Pleasant hours in an eventful life. Stewart, W. F. $1. *Carmany.*

Pleasant neighbor. Planché, E. 15c. .... *French.*

Pleasant paths for little feet. Ballard, A. 65c. *Randolph.*

Pleasant paths for little feet. Collier, J. A. 60c. *Am. Tr.*

Pleasant pathways. Wise, D. $1.25 .. *Meth. Bk. Conc.*

Pleasant picnic. *See* Gerty and May books.

Pleasant pictures. Parker, C. E. R. 50c.... *Am. Tr.*

Pleasant pictures and stories; by the foremost Eng. writers. ill. f°. '75. $3 .... *Routledge.*

Pleasant reading. Flint, S. A. 45c. ...... *Cong. Pub.*

Pleasant stories. *See* Big type stories.

Pleasant stories for the young. 16°. 60c.... *Am. S. S.*

Pleasant surprises. ('60.) New ed. ill. 18°. '75. 55c. *Hoyt.*

Pleasant tale of puss and robin. Hood, T. $1.50. *Macmillan.*

Pleasant tales. Mogridge, G. 60c. .... *So. Meth.*

Pleasant tales. *See* Pleasant grove ser.

Pleasant tales by popular authors. ill. 8°. $2. *Routledge.*

Pleasant tales in prose and verse. ill. 18°. 60c. *Bost. Am. Tr.*

Pleasant talk about fruits, flowers and farming. Beecher, H. W. $2 .... *Ford.*

Pleasant words for little folks. *See* Little Blue Mantle lib.

Pleasantries of English courts and lawyers. Jeaffreson, J. C. $3.50 .... *Cockcroft.*

Pleasants, Jla. Callamura. [Fiction.] 12°. '68. $1.75. *Claxton.*

Pleasonton, A. J. Influence of the blue ray of the sunlight and of the blue color of the sky in developing animal and vegetable life, in arresting disease and in restoring health, etc. cr. 8°. '76. $2 .... *Claxton.*

Pleasure and profit. 18°. 28c.; 35c. ...... *Am. Bapt.*

Pleasure and profit. *See* Big type stories.

Pleasure and profit. *See* Grandmother's lib.

Pleasure and profit: how Fanny Welmore overcame a hasty temper. ill. 24°. '69. 30c. .... *Lothrop.*

Pleasures of angling. Dawson, G. $1.50 ... *Sheldon.*

Pleasures of friendship. *See* McHenry, J.

Pleasures of hope. *See* Campbell, T:

Pleasures of memory. *See* Rogers, S:

Pleasures of old age. Souvestre, E. $2 .. *Routledge.*

Pleasures of religion. Burder, H. F. 60c. .. *Pres. Bd.*

Pleasures of taste. Taylor, J. 75c. .... *Harper.*

Pledge (The); or, the first step to fortune. 8°. pap., 25c. .... *De Witt.*

Plenary council. *See* Baltimore.

Pleyel, Ign. Duets. *See* Wichtl, G., Young violinist.

Plimsoll, S: Our seamen: an appeal. 12°. '73. $1.25. *Routledge.*

Pliny *the elder*. [Caius Plinius Secundus.] Natural history; tr., with notes, by J. Bostock and H. T. Riley. 6 v. 12°. (Bohn.) ea., $1.75 .. *Little, B. & Co.*

— *Same.* 6 v. 12°. (Bohn.) ea., $2. *Lippincott; Scribner, W. & A.*

Pliny *the younger*. [Caius Plinius Cæcilius Secundus.] Letters; [condensed and expl.] by W. J. Brodribb. (Anc. classics for Eng. readers.) 16°. $1. *Lippincott; Little, B. & Co.*

Plomteaux, H. J. Dental register, to indicate exact location of operations; with index. demi 4°. '76. hf. mor., $5 .... *Strickland.*

Plon, Eug. Thorvaldsen: his life and works; tr. by Miss Luyster. ill. 8°. '72. $4 .... *Roberts.*

Plönnies, Louisa v. Prinzessin Ilse: Märchen aus dem Harzgebirge. With Eng. notes by J. M. Merrick, jr. ('64.) New ed. 12°. '76. pap., 50c. .. *Holt.*

— *Eng.* Princess Ilse: story of the Hartz Mountains. 18°. $1.25 .... *Tilton.*

— *Same;* tr. by an Am. lady, with introd. by J. L. Lincoln. ill. 4°. '74. $2 .... *Lothrop.*

Plot (The): [also] Falsely accused. ill. 16°. '72. 50c. *Lothrop.*

Plot and counterplot. Kemble, C. 15c. ...... *French.*

Plot and passion. Taylor, T. 15c. ... *De Witt; French.*

Plot of Portzentausend: drama. 16°. pap., 40c. .. *French.*

Plots for petticoats: farce. 16°. pap., 15c. .... *French.*

Plötz, C. Easy and practical French grammar; for Am. schools, etc., by J. Nöroth. ('71.) New ed. 12°. '76. $1.25 .... *Schoenhof.*

— Elementarbuch d. französ. Sprache; nach Seidenstücker's Methode. 12°. '65. bds., 60c. .. *Steiger.*

Plouvier, E. *See* Barrière, T., *and* Plouvier, E.

Plucky fellows. *See* Mackenna, S. J.

Plucky fellows lib. 3 v. ill. 16°. $3.75 ... *Routledge.*
Cont.: Plucky fellows, by S. J. Mackenna. — Brave men's footsteps, by C. Doyle. — Seeking his fortune.

Plues, Marg. British grasses: introd. to study of grasses found in British isles. col. pl. and ill. cr. 8°. (Lond.) $5.25 .... *Putnam.*

Plumb, P. B. *See* Swan, J. R., *and* Plumb, P. B.

Plumer, W: S. Bible (The) true. 18°. '48. 25c. .. *Am. Tr.*

— Church (The) and her enemies. 18°. 40c. .. *Am. Bapt.*

— Commentary on Hebrews. 8°. '72. $4 .. *Randolph.*

— Commentary on Romans; with introd. on life, times, etc., of Paul. 8°. '70. $4 .... *Randolph.*

— Earnest hours. 12°. '69. $1.25. *N. Y. Ref. Ch. Bd.; Pres. Com.*

— Grace of Christ; or, sinners saved by unmerited kindness. 12°. $1.40 .... *Pres. Bd.*

— Hints and helps in pastoral theology. 12°. $2 .. *Harper.*

— Jehovah Jireh: treatise on Providence. 12°. '67. $1.50 .. *Lippincott; N. Y. Ref. Ch. Bd.; Pres. Com.*

— Law of God, as contained in the ten commandments, expl. and enforced. 12°. $2 .... *Pres. Bd.*

— Martyrs and sufferers for the truth. 18°. 65c. *Pres. Bd.*

— Promises of God: their nature and properties, variety and value. 24°. 40c. .... *N. Y. Ref. Ch. Bd.*

Plumer, W: S., *continued.*

— Ribbon room, and other stories. 18°. 40c. .. *Pres. Bd.*

— Rock of our salvation. 12°. '67. $1.50; $1.75. *Am. Tr.*

— Rome against the Bible, and the Bible against Rome. 18°. 40c. .... *Am. Bapt.*

— Saint and sinner. 18°. 25c. .... *Pres. Bd.*

— Sermons for the people. 12°. '71. $1.10 .... *Am. Tr.*

— Sinless character of Christ. 16°. '76. 65c. .. *Pres. Com.*

— Studies in Psalms: critical and expository commentary, with remarks on entire Psalter. roy. 8°. '6[illegible] $6 .... *Claxton; Lippincott.*

— Truths for the people. 12°. '75. $1 ...... *Am. Tr.*

— Vital godliness. ('64.) New ed. 12°. '66. $1.50; $2 .... *Am. Tr.*

— Word to the weary. 32°. '74. 40c.; 60c. .. *Randolph.*

— Words of truth and love. 18°. 55c. ...... *Pres. Bd.*

Plummer, J: I: Practical astronomy. (Element. sc. ser.) ill. 16°. '73. 75c. .... *Putnam.*

Plummer, P. W. The carpenters' and builders' guide. ill. 8°. hf. bd., $1 .... *Hoyt, F. & L.*

Plummer Hall. Proceedings upon dedication. *See* Salem, Mass.

Plumtre, E: H. Biblical studies. 8°. $2 .. *Routledge.*

— Christ and Christendom: Boyle lectures for 1866. demy 8°. $3.50 .... *Routledge.*

— Commentary on Proverbs. *See* Cook, F. C., Bible commentary.

— Lazarus, and other poems. cr. 8°. $1.75 .. *Routledge.*

— Master and scholar, and other poems. cr. 8°. $2. *Routledge.*

— Spirits in prison: sermon on state of the dead. 8°. '71. pap., 50c. .... *Routledge.*

— Theology and life: sermons. sm. 8°. $2 .. *Routledge.*

— *See also* Bible educator.

Plunket, Is. Children's band; or, the trial of Paul's faith. 16°. '72. 50c. .. *Dutton; Scribner, W. & A.*

— Hester's fortune; or, pride and humanity. ill. 12°. $1.25 .... *Scribner, W. & A.*

Plunkett, H: G. Minerali: romantic drama. 16°. pap., 15c. .... *French.*

Plurality of worlds. Knight, R. $1.50 ...... *Wiley.*

Plurality of worlds. New ed., with supplementary dialogue in which the author's reviewers are reviewed. 16°. '74. $1.50 .... *Lothrop.*

Plu-ri-bus-tah. Thomson, M. $1.75; $1.50 .. *Peterson.*

Plutarch. [*Lat.* Plutarchus.] Lives; tr., with notes and life of author, by J. and W. Langhorne. roy. 8°. shp., $3 .... *Pounsford.*

— — *Same.* 8°. $2; — in 4 v. 12°. $5 ...... *Harper.*

— *Same;* tr. and ed. for youth by E. Robbins. 18°. hf. roan, 63c. .... *Lippincott.*

— *Same:* the tr. called Dryden's, corrected from the Greek and rev. by A. H. Clough; with new life of Plutarch. 2d ed., rev. 5 v. 8°. '75. $15; hf. cf., $25; cf., $30 .... *Little, B. & Co.*

— Morals; tr. by several hands; corrected and rev. by W. W. Goodwin; with introd. by R. W. Emerson. 5 v. 8°. '74. $15–$30 .... *Little, B. & Co.*

— On the delay of the deity in the punishment of the wicked [*Gk.*]; with notes by H. B. Hackett. 12°. '44. 60c. .... *Draper.*

— *Same.* New ed., rev. with notes by H. B. Hackett and W. S. Tyler. 12°. $1.50 .... *Appleton.*

— Shakspeare's Plutarch: sel. from lives in North's Plutarch, which ill. Shakespeare's plays; ed. with pref., notes and index by W. W. Skeat. cr. 8°. '75. $2.50 .... *Macmillan.*

Pluto and Proserpine. Talfourd, F. 15c. .... *French.*

Plutus. *See* Aristophanes.

Plymouth and the Pilgrims. Banvard, J. $1.25. *Lothrop.*

Plymouth Church, *Brooklyn, N. Y.* Proceedings of the Advisory Council called by Plymouth Church. [Official stenog. report.] 8°. '76. $2; pap. $1.25 .... *Barnes.*

Plymouth Church and its pastor. Doyle, J. E. P. *$2.50 .... (?) *Park Pub.*

Plymouth coll. of hymns and tunes. *See* Beecher, H. W.

Plympton, G: W. Blow pipe: guide to its use in determination of salts and minerals. 12°. '74. $1.50. *Van Nostrand.*

Poacher. *See* Marryat, F:

Poacher. Tucker, C. 75c. .... *Carter.*

Poacher; tr. by Mrs. J. Sadlier. 18°. 50c.; 75c. *Sadlier.*

Poacher's doom. Ames, A. D. 15c. .... *Ames.*

Poacher's sons. Hill, H. 50c. .... *Nelson.*

Po-ca-hon-tas. Brougham, J. 15c. .... *French.*

Pocahontas. Sigourney, L. H. $1.25; $1.75 .. *Harper.*

Pocket Catholic manual. [Prayer book.] 64°. 25c.–50c. .... *T. Kelly.*

Pocket Hebrew and Eng. lexicon. *See* New.

Pocket key of heaven. [Cath. prayer book.] 64°. 25c.–$2 .... *Noonan.*

— *Same.* ('75.) 4th ed. ill. 48°. '76. 25c.–$1.25 .. *Kenedy.*

— *See also* Key of heaven.

Pocket manual. [Cath. prayer book.] 48°. 25c.–$8. *Sadlier.*

Pocket or popular letter writer. 32°. bds., 35c. *U. P. James.*

Pocket pictorial dictionary of the Eng. lang. Rev. ed. 32°. '71. 50c.; 75c. .... *Claxton.*

Pocket remembrancer; or, first book of relig. instruction. 18°. '66. 25c. .... *H. H. Carter.*

Pocket ser. of the poets. (World ed.) 12 v. ill. 32°. ea., 85c.; $1.12 .... *World Pub.*
Cont.: Sigourney and Norton. — Scott and Coleridge. — Scott's Lady of the lake, and Howitt. — Milton. — Hemans and Wordsworth. — Goldsmith and Southey. — Pollok and Montgomery. — Young and Campbell. — Cowper and Rogers. — Moore's Lalla Rookh, and Thomson. — Tupper and Johnson. — Pope and Sterne.

Pocock, I: [Plays.] 8 v. 16°. ea., pap., 15c. .. *French.*
Cont.: For England, ho! opera. — Hit or miss: farce. — John of Paris: opera. — Magpie; or, the maid. — Maid and magpie. — Miller and his men: melodrama. — Robber's wife. — Robinson Crusoe: romantic drama.

Poe, Edg. Allan. Works; with memoir by J. H. Ingram and notices of his life by Lowell, Willis and others. (Lib. ed.) 4 v. cr. 8°. $9; hf., cf., $16. *Nichols & H.; Putnam; Widdleton.*

— Poems. (Blue and gold ed.) por. 24°. $1.25. *Nichols & H.; Widdleton.*

— — *Same.* 24°. $1.50 .... *Putnam.*

— *Same.* (Cabinet ed.) por. 16°. $1.75. *Nichols & H.; Putnam; Widdleton.*

— *Same;* with new memoir and vindication. (Diamond ed.) 16°. $1.25 .... *Widdleton.*

— *Same;* with memoir, por., etc. 32°. cf., $3 .. *Widdleton.*

— *Same;* ill. by Paton, Whirter, Stanton, Hay, Palmer, etc. 4°. $5; mor., $8 .... *Widdleton.*

— Poems and essays: memorial volume, cont. the Ingram memoir and vindication, tributes of J. R. Lowell and others and monumental proceedings at Baltimore. ill. and por. cr. 8°. $2.25 .. *Widdleton.*

— Prose tales. 2 v. 16°. ea., $1.75. *Nichols & H.; Putnam; Widdleton.*

— Selected works; with memoir and por. (Household ed.) cr. 8°. $2.50 .... *Widdleton.*

— Raven. [English and German text.] ill. 8°. pap., 50c. .... *Barclay.*

Poems for little folks. ill. sq. 16°. 50c. .. *Perkinpine.*

Poems from eastern sources. *See* Trench, R. C.

Poems from the inner life. Doten, L. $1.50; $2 .. *Colby.*

Poems of home life. Warner, H. P. $1; $1.25; $3; $3.50 .... *Am. Tr.*

Poems of love and childhood. *See* Ingelow, J.

Poems of the pleasures; compr. Akenside's Pleasures of imagination, Rogers' Pleasures of memory, Campbell's Pleasures of hope, McHenry's Pleasures of friendship. ('40.) New ed. 18°. '70. 75c. .... *Claxton.*

Poems of progress. Doten, L. $1.50; $2 ..... *Colby.*

Poems of twenty years. Johnson, L. W. $1.50 .. *Lent.*

Poems of the war. Boker, G. H. $1.50 .. *Lippincott.*

Poems written for a child; by two friends. ill. sq. 16°. $1.50 .... *Routledge.*

Poesien des Urwalds. Giorg, K. $1 ...... *Benziger.*

Poesies. Cauwet, P. $2 .... *Payot.*

Poet and painter: poems and engravings. 8°. $12; mor., $20 .... *Appleton.*

Poet at the breakfast table. *See* Holmes, O. W.

Poetic fate book. Gilman, C. 75c.; 60c. .... *Lee & S.*

Poetic gift. Smith, E. O. *net,* 19c. ...... *Hamersley.*

Poetic Lacon: aphorisms from the poets. ill. 32°. 38c. *Appleton.*

Poetic proposal: farce. 16°. pap., 15c. ..... *French.*

Poetic studies. Phelps, E. S. $1.50; $3; $4 .. *Osgood.*

Poetical tributes to the memory of Abraham Lincoln. 12°. $2 .... *Lippincott.*

Poetry for home and school. Eliot, I. M., *and* Brackett, A. C. $1.25 .... *Putnam.*

Poetry from the best authors. Bowman, A. $1. *Scribner, W. & A.*

Poetry of the age of fables. Bulfinch, T. $2 .. *Tilton.*

Poetry of architecture. Ruskin, J. $1.50 ..... *Wiley.*

Poetry of flowers, and flowers of poetry. Osgood, F. S. $1.50; $2.50 .... *Claxton.*

Poetry of nature. ill. 12°. '75. $1.25 ...... *Putnam.*

Poetry of nature; ill. by Birket Foster. 12°. $2.50; mor., $5 .... *Appleton.*

Poetry of the Orient. Alger, W. R. $1.50 .. *Roberts.*

Poetry of reason and conscience. Walker, J. B. $1.50. *Lippincott.*

Poetry of science. *See* Hunt, R.

Poetry of the vegetable world. Schleiden, M. J. $1.50. *Wilstach.*

Poet's bazaar. *See* Andersen, H. C.

Poet's companion: dict. of all allowable rhymes in the Eng. lang. 16°. pap., 25c. .... *Dick & F.*

Poet's journal. Taylor, B. $1.25 .... *Osgood.*

Poets and novelists. Smith, G. B. $2 ..... *Appleton.*

Poets of the Elizabethan age: songs and sonnets. ill. cr. 8°. $3 .... *Huntington.*

Poets of the nineteenth century. (Chandos poets.) ill. cr. 8°. $3.75; cf., $7.50; mor., $8. *Scribner, W. & A.*

Poets' gallery: 36 ideal portraits from Eng. poems. imp. 8°. $7.50; mor., $10 .... *Appleton.*

Poets' gift of consolation to sorrowing mothers. sm. 4°. '73. $1.50 .... *Barnes.*

Point-lace and diamonds. Baker, G. A., *jr.* $1; $1.50; $3 .... *Patterson.*

Point of honor. *See* Edwards, *Mrs.* A.

Point of honour. Kemble, C. 15c. .... *French.*

Points of controversy. Smarius, C. F. $1.50 .. *O'Shea.*

Points of history: Galileo and the inquisition, massacre of St. Bartholomew, etc. 18°. 60c.; pap., 25c. *Noonan.*

Poison of asps. *See* Marryat, Flo.

Poisoned letter; or, the lost and redeemed. 8°. pap., 25c. .... *De Witt.*

Poitevin, Maur. Cours théorique et pratique de langue française; ed. par M. B. Maurice. 12°. '65. $1. *Barnes.*

Poke and her sisters; or, a peep at the Clyde family. 16°. $1.10 .... *Am. S. S.*

Poland, J: S. Digest of military laws of the U. S., 1860–'67. 8°. '68. $3; shp., $3.50 .. *Little, B. & Co.*

Pole, W: Iron as a material of construction: handbook for students in engineering. ill. post 8°. '72. $2.50 .... *Spon.*

Pole, W: *continued.*
— Theory of the modern scientific game of whist. New ed., enl. 16°. '72. $1 . . . . *Carleton.*
— *Same.* 6th ed. 16°. (Lond.) '73. $1 . . *Little, B. & Co.*
Polhemus, Ab. Address before Alumni Association of Rutger's College, July 27, 1852. 8°. pap., 25c. *N. Y. Ref. Ch. Bd.*
Policy player. White, C. 15c . . . . *De Witt.*
Polish spy. Dumas, A. 50c . . . . *De Witt.*
Polished pearls. Shelton, T. J. *and* J. H. 10c. *Fillmore.*
Polite learning: epitome of arts and sciences; for schools. 18°. shp., 50c . . . . *Polock.*
Polite letter writer. 32°. 40c . . . . *Locke.*
Polite philosopher. *See* Chesterfield, *Lord.*
Politeness, the true and the false. 18°. 17c.; 22c. *Am. Bapt.*
Political atlas: maps and index. 12°. $1.25. *Scribner, W. & A.*
Political cyclopedia. 4 v. 12°. (Bohn.) ea., $1.25. *Little, B. & Co.*
— *Same.* 4 v. 12°. (Bohn.) ea., $1.40 . . *Scribner, W. & A.*
— *Same.* 4 v. 12°. (Bohn.) ea., $1.50 . . . . . . *Lippincott.*
Political economy of art. Ruskin, J. $1 . . . . . *Wiley.*
Political lyrics of 1854. 12°. pap., 13c . . . . . *Peterson.*
Political portraits. Hill, F. H. $1.50 . . . . *Lippincott.*
Political Romanism. Hughey, G. W. $1; $1.25. *Cin. Meth. Bk. Conc.*
Politics as a science. Reemelin, C. $1.50 . . . *Clarke.*
Politics for young Americans. Nordhoff, C. $1.25; $1. *Harper.*
Politics in religion. Wadsworth, C. 12c . . . *Peterson.*
Politzer, Ad. The membrana tympani in health and disease; tr. by A. Mathewson and H. G. Newton. ill. 8°. $2.50 . . . . *W. Wood.*
Poliuto. *See* Ditson.
Polk, Jos. Der marianische Sodal: Satzungen, Andachtsübungen u. Gesänge. 32°. 75c.; leath., $1. *Benziger.*
Polko, Elise. Musical sketches; tr. by F. Fuller. 12°. '63. $1.75 . . . . *Ditson.*
— Reminiscences of Mendelssohn: a social and artistic biog.; tr. by Lady Wallace; with add. letters to Eng. correspondents. 12°. $1.75 . . . . . . *Ditson.*
Poll and partner Joe. *See* Burnand, F. C.
Poll parrot picture book. demy 4°. '71. $2.50 . . *Routledge.*
Pollard, E: A. Life and times of R. E. Lee. ('67.) New ed. ill. and por. 8°. '71. *$3.75; mor., $5 . . . . *Treat.*
— Lost cause (The): south. hist. of the [civil] war. ('66.) New ed. por. 8°. '68. *$5; shp., $6; hf. cf., $8 . . . . *Treat.*
— Virginia tourist: sketches of springs and mountains of Virginia. ill. and map. 12°. $1.75; pap., $1 . . . . *Lippincott.*
— (*ed.*) Echoes from the south: Confederate government documents, speeches and public acts during the late struggle. 12°. '66. *$1.25 . . . . . . *Treat.*
Pollard, Eliza F. Hope deferred. [Fiction.] 8°. pap., 50c. . . . . *Harper.*
— The lady superior. [Fiction.] 8°. pap., 50c. *Harper.*
Pollard, Jose. Gipsy books. 5 v. ill. 16°. '73. ea., 90c. . . . . *Meth. Bk. Conc.*
Cont.: Gipsy's early days. — Gipsy in New York. — Gipsy's travels. — Gipsy's adventures. — Gipsy's quest.
— The open door. 18°. 65c . . . . *Pres. Bd.*
Pollard, M. M. A brother's legacy; or, better than gold. 16°. 35c . . . . . . *Cin. Meth. Bk. Conc.*
— Miner's son; [also] Margaret Vernon. 16°. 90c. *Meth. Bk. Conc.*
Pollen, J: Hungerford. Ancient and modern furniture and wood-work. ill. cr. 8°. '75. $1 . . *Scribner, W. & A.*
Pollie and Jack. Hepburn, A. $1.25 . . . . . . *Nelson.*
Pollock, A. D. Life in the exode. 12°. '71. $2. *Univ. Pub.*
Pollock, C: E. Treatise on power of courts to compel production of documents. *See* Law lib.; — Moore, H., Instructions for prep. abstracts of titles.
Pollock, E: Poems. por. 12°. $1.75 . . . . . *Lippincott.*
Pollock, R. H. The Saviour's claim. 18°. 40c. *U. P. Bd. of Pub.*
Pollock, T: C. Ivanhoe Masonic quartettes. ('67.) New ed. 8°. '76. $2 . . . . *Pond.*
Pollok, Rob. Course of time. 18°. hf. bd., 38c. *Clark & M.*
— *Same.* 18°. 75c. 16°. $1.25 . . . . *Carter.*
— *Same.* 12°. $1.50 . . . . *Stevens.*
— *Same.* (Blue and gold ed.) 18°. 75c . . . . *Appleton.*
— *Same.* (School ed.) 18°. 38c . . . . *Nichols & H.*
— *Same;* with memoir of author. 32°. 38c. — 24°. 75c. *Appleton.*
— *Same;* with index, memoir, introd. notice and analyses. ('33.) New ed. 18°. '73. 75c.; hf. bd., 40c . . . . *Claxton.*
— *Same;* with notes by J. R. Boyd. (Lib. ed.) 12°. '54. $1.50. — (School ed.), hf. bd., $1.25 . . *Barnes.*
— *Same;* with memoir by W. L. Prall, index and analyses. 32°. 50c . . . . *U. P. James.*
— — *Same.* 24°. 35c. — (Blue and gold ed.) 24°. 75c. *C. H. Davis.*
— Helen of the glen: tale of the Scottish Covenanters. 18°. 35c . . . . *Carter.*
— *Same.* 18°. '66. 35c . . . *N. Y. Ref. Ch. Bd.; Pres. Com.*
— Persecuted family: narr. of sufferings of the Covenanters in reign of Charles II. 18°. 35c . . . *Carter.*
— *Same.* 18°. '66. 55c . . . *N. Y. Ref. Ch. Bd.; Pres. Com.*
— Poems; [also] Poems, by J. Montgomery. ill. 16°. $1.12; $1.35. — 32°. 85c.; $1.12 . . . *World Pub.*
— Ralph Gemmell; or, banks of the Irvine: tale of the Scot. Covenanters. 18°. 35c . . . . *Carter.*
— *Same.* 16°. '66. 35c . . . *N. Y. Ref. Ch. Bd.; Pres. Com.*
— Tales of the Covenanters. 18°. 75c . . . . *Carter.*
Polly and her friends. *See* Hildeburn, *Mrs.* M. J.
Polly and Winnie. G., F. F. 75c . . . . *Dodd.*
Polly Grey's jewels. ill. 18°. 50c. . . . . *Bost. Am. Tr.*
— *See also* Chip-basket stories.
Polly Peablossom's wedding. Thompson, W. T. 75c. *Peterson.*
Polo, Marco. Travels; tr. by W. Marsden and ed. by T. Wright. 12°. (Bohn.) $1.75 . . *Little, B. & Co.*
— *Same.* 12°. (Bohn.) $2 . . *Lippincott; Scribner, W. & A.*
— *Same.* New ed., rev. with notes by H. Murray. maps. 18°. 75c . . . . *Harper.*
Polson, Archer. Principles of law of nations; with notes and essays on law of blockade and on contraband of war. 8°. '53. $1.50 . . *T. & J. W. Johnson.*
— — *See also* Horne, T. H., Diplomacy; — Law lib.
Polyeucte. *See* Corneille, P.
Polyglot of foreign proverbs. *See* Bohn, H. G.
Polyphonic. Fillmore, A. D. *and* C. L. 35c. *R. W. Carroll.*
Polytechnic. Burnap, U. C., *and* Wetmore, W. J. $1.25; $1 . . . . *Schermerhorn.*
Pomar, *Count* de Medina. *See* Medina-Pomar, Count de.
Pomeroy, E. C. Introductory reading book. 4th ed. 12°. '73. 50c . . . . *M. Taylor.*
— Introductory spelling book. 5th ed. 12°. '72. 25c. *M. Taylor.*
Pomeroy, J: Norton. Introduction to const. law of the U. S. ('68.) 3d ed., rev. and enl. 8°. '75. shp., $5 . . . . *Hurd & H.*
— Introduction to municipal law. 8°. $3; shp., $4. *Appleton.*
— Treatise on civil remedies and remedial rights. 8°. '76. shp., $6 . . . . *Little, B. & Co.*
Pomeroy, M: M. ["Brick Pomeroy."] Works. 5 v. 12°. ea., $1.50 . . . . *Carleton.*
Cont.: Brick dust. — Gold-dust. — Nonsense. — Our Saturday nights. — Sense.
Pompey's patients. White, C. 15c . . . . *De Witt.*
Pomponia. Webb, J. B. $1.50 . . . . *Pres. Bd.*

Ponapé. Thompson, H. S. $1 .... *Am. Bapt.*

Poncelet, J: Vct. Sustaining walls. *See* United States, *Corps of Eng.*

Pond, Enoch. Conversion, its nature and importance, with examples from real life. 16°. 90c. *Cong. Pub.*

— History of God's church from its origin to the present time. maps and ill. 8°. '71. $4.50; leath., $5; hf. mor., $6 .... *Scranton.*

— Lectures on Christian theology. 8°. $4 .. *Cong. Pub.*

— Lectures on pastoral theology. 12°. $1.75 .. *Draper.*

— Lives of Increase Mather and Sir W. Phipps. *See* Lives of chief fathers of New Eng.

— Seals opened; or, the Apocalypse explained. por. cr. 8°. $1.50 .... *Hoyt, F. & D.*

— Swedenborgianism examined. 16°. 80c. *Bost. Am. Tr.*

Pond lily stories. sm. 4°. $1 .... *Am. S. S.*

Ponsonby, *Lady* Emily. Discipline of life. [Fiction.] 8°. pap., 50c .... *Harper.*

— Mary Lyndsay. [Fiction.] 8°. pap., 50c ... *Harper.*

— Pride and irresolution: new ser. of "Discipline of life." 8°. pap., 50c .... *Harper.*

Pontmartin, Alex. de. Clotilde; or, the secret of three generations; tr. by K. C. Barton. 12°. '72. $1.75 .... *J. M. Stoddart.*

Pontoppidan, Er. Explanation of Luther's Smaller catechism; abridg. 12°. 25c. .... *Engberg.*

Pook, S: M. Shipbuilding: method of comparing the lines, and draughting vessels propelled by sail or steam; incl. chapter on laying off on the mould-loft floor. ill. 8°. '66. $5 ...... *Van Nostrand.*

Pool, Mat. Annotations on the Bible. 3 v. 8°. '63. $15 .... *Carter.*

Poole, C. Tribulation: comedy. 16°. pap., 15c. *French.*

Poole, J: [Plays.] 11 v. 16°. ea., pap., 15c. *French.*

Cont.: Deaf as a post: farce. — Hamlet: travestie. — Intrigue: dram. interlude. — Married and single: comedy. — Match making: farce. — Paul Pry: comedy. — Scapegoat: farce. — Simpson and Co.: comedy. — Soldier's courtship: comedy. — Turning the tables: farce. — T'would puzzle a conjurer: comic drama.

— Turning the tables: farce. 16°. pap., 15c ... *De Witt.*

Poole, *Mrs.* Marg. E. Johnnie, the railroad boy. ill. 16°. '71. $1.15 .... *Crowell.*

— — *See also* Queer people ser.

— Pictures of cottage life in the west of England. [Fiction.] cr. 8°. $1.50 .... *Macmillan.*

Poole, W: Life. 8°. pap., 25c .... *De Witt.*

Poole, W: F. Anti-slavery before 1800, essay; [with] fac-simile reprint of George Buchanan's Oration on the moral and political evil of slavery, 1791. 8°. '73. $1.25; pap., 75c .... *Clarke.*

Pooler, C. T. Test speller. 12°. '75. hf. bd., 30c. .. *Barnes.*

Poor, H: V. Manual of the railroads of the United States. ('68.) [Annual.] 8°. $5 .... *Poor.*

Poor and proud. Adams, W. T. $1.25 ...... *Lee & S.*

Poor blind beggar. *See* Stories of the good shepherd.

Poor boy. Egan, P. 50c .... *De Witt.*

Poor Bridget. 18°. 17c.; 22c. .... *Am. Bapt.*

Poor clerk. Sargent, G. E. $1.25 .... *Nelson.*

Poor clerk and the crooked sixpence. ('75.) New ed. 16°. '76. $1.25 .... *Hoyt.*

Poor cousin. Pickering, E. 50c. .... *Peterson.*

Poor cousin Walter. Simpson, J. P. 15c. ... *French.*

Poor gentleman. Colman, G., *jr.* 15c .... *French.*

Poor gentleman. Conscience, H. $1; $1.25 ... *Murphy.*

Poor girl. Egan, P. 75c .... *Dick & F.*

Poor Henry. Barth, C. G. 50c. .... *Pres. Bd.*

Poor humanity. Robinson, F. W. 50c. ..... *Harper.*

Poor Jack. *See* Marryat, F:

Poor little Ellen. *See* Kirton, J. W.

Poor little Joe. *See* Baker, S.

Poor man's catechism. *See* Mannock, J.

Poor man's controversy. Mannock, J. 50c ... *Cath. Pub.*

Poor match. Parr, H. $1.25 .... *Dutton.*

Poor Matt. *See* Ingelow, J.

Poor Miss Finch. *See* Collins, Wilkie.

Poor Nelly. Fry, S. M. 70c. *N. Y. Ref. Ch. Bd.; Pres. Com.*

Poor Nicholas. Myers, S. A. 75c .... *Pres. Bd.*

Poor nobleman. Selby, C. 15c. .... *French.*

Poor of New York: drama. 16°. pap., 15c. .. *French.*

Poor organ grinder. *See* Woodworth, F. C.

Poor orphan's legacy: counsels to a young generation. 18°. 35c .... *Pres. Bd.*

Poor Pat. *See* Bright gems for boys and girls; — Little boys' lib.

Poor Pillicoddy. Morton, J. M. 15c .... *French.*

Poor priest. *See* Library of good example.

Poor prisoner. 18°. 30c .... *Am. S. S.*

— *See also* Champney stories.

Poor Rachel; or, who is happy? 18°. 25c. .. *Am. S. S.*

Poor relations: drama. 16°. pap., 40c. ...... *French.*

Poor rich man and the rich poor man. Sedgwick, C. M. 75c .... *Harper.*

Poor Sarah, the Indian woman. 18°. 17c.; 22c. *Am. Bapt.*

Poor scholar. Carleton, W. 75c.; $1.25 .... *Sadlier.*

Poor soldier. O'Keeffe, J. 15c .... *French.*

Poor watchmaker. *See* Malan, C:

Poor weaver's family. 18°. 60c .... (?) *Martien.*

Poor woodcutter. *See* Arthur, T. S.

Poor young man: drama. 16°. pap., 15c. .... *French.*

Poorhouse; or, who maketh us to differ. 18°. 25c. *Am. S. S.*

Poorhouse Sam. *See* Jefferds, J. A.

Pop-gun stories. *See* Barrow, *Mrs.* F.

Pop-guns. *See* Barrow, *Mrs.* F.

Pope, Alex. Poetical works. 8°. $3 ...... *Desilver.*

— *Same.* (Presentation poets.) ill. 12°. $1.75; $3. *Routledge.*

— *Same;* with memoir and notes by W. C. Armstrong. ill. 8°. $2; shp., $2.75. — ill. 12°. $1.50. *World Pub.*

— *Same;* ed. by R. Carruthers. 2 v. ill. 12°. (Bohn.) ea., $1.75 .... *Little, B. & Co.*

— — *Same.* 2 v. ill. 12°. (Bohn.) ea., $2. *Lippincott; Scribner, W. & A.*

— *Same;* ed. by H. F. Cary, with biog. notice. (Globe ed.) 16°. $1.25; hf. cf., $3.25; mor., $4. — (chp. ed.), pap., 60c .... *Appleton.*

— — *Same.* (Household ser.) ill. 16°. $1.50; mor., $3 .... *Lee & S.*

— — *Same.* (Old poets.) roy. 8°. $4.50 .... *Routledge.*

— *Same;* with notes by J. Marten and others. ill. 8°. (Dick.) $1; pap., 50c .... *Am. News.*

— *Same;* ed. with notes and memoir by A. W. Ward. (Globe ed.) 12°. '69. $1.50 ...... *Macmillan.*

— — Concordance. *See* Abbott, E. A.

— Poems. 12°. $1.50 .... *Locke.*

— *Same.* (Aldine ed.) 3 v. 16°. ea., 75c ... *Lippincott.*

— *Same.* (Blue and gold ed.) 18°. $1.25 .. *Nichols & H.*

— *Same.* (Cabinet ed.) 16°. $1.50 ..... *Nichols & H.*

— *Same;* with memoir by A. Dyce. 3 v. por. 18°. $3. *Osgood.*

— *Same;* ed. by R. A. Willmott, with biog., etc. (British poets.) ill. 12°. $2.25; hf. cf., $3.50; mor., $5 .... *Routledge.*

— *Same;* [also] Poems, by L. Sterne. ill. 16°. $1.12; $1.35. — 32°. 85c.; $1.12 .... *World Pub.*

— Essay on man; with Clark's gram. notes. ('24.) New ed. 18°. '75. hf. bd., 20c. .... *Clark & M.*

— *Same;* with notes, ed. by W. B. Fowle. 12°. '43. 30c.; 20c .... *Barnes.*

— *Same;* with notes by S. R. Wells. ill. 12°. '67. $1. *Wells.*

— *Same;* [also] Universal prayer, etc. 18°. 18c. *I. N. Whiting.*

Pope, Alex., *continued.*
— — *Same.* (School ed.) 32°. 15c...... *U.P.James.*
— *Same;* with misc. poems, epitaphs, etc. 32°. 35c.; pap., 10c.............................. *U.P.James.*
— — *See* also British pocket classics.
— Universal prayer. *See* Practical morality; — *and above* Essay on man.
— *See also* Homer; — Ovid.

Pope, Fk. L. Modern practice of the electric telegraph. New ed., rev. and enl. ill. 8°. '74. $2. *Van Nostrand.*

Pope, Ma. E. Poems. por. 16°. $1.50..*Lippincott.*

Pope, R. T. P., *and* Maguire, S. Discussion on infallibility, purgatory and transubstantiation. 12°. $1.25.................................*Sadlier.*

Pope, T: C. Holy week in the Vatican. 12°. $1.50. *Noonan.*

Pope and the council. *See* Huber, V. A.

Pope Joan. Reynolds, G. W. M. 75c.......*Dick & F.*

Popery against common school education. Jacobus, M. W. 10c. ....*Pres. Bd.*

Popery and its aims. Moody, G. 50c. *Cin. Meth. Bk. Conc.*

Popery exposed. Gattina, F. P. della. $1.75; $1.50 *Peterson.*

Pope's niece, and other tales; tr. by Mrs. J. Sadlier. 18°. 50c.; 75c. ....*Sadlier.*

Popes. *See* Lives of the popes.

Poplar Dell lib. 4 v. 16°. '70. $3.25..*Meth. Bk. Conc.*
Cont.: People of Poplar Dell. — Labors of love. — Marian Temple's work. — Aunt Margery's maxim.

Poplar grove. *See* Happy child's lib.

Popocatapetel: extravaganza. 16°. pap., 15c...*French.*

Poppet. *See* Very little tales.

Popping the question. Buckstone, J. B. 15c. ..*French.*

Popping the question; or, the belle of the ball. 8°. pap., 75c...........................*Peterson.*

Popping the question, and other tales. 12°. $1.25. *T. Bliss.*

Poppleton's predicament. Rae, C. M. 15c...*De Witt.*

Popsy Dean: Ethiop. drama. 16°. pap., 15c...*Happy.*

Popular amusements. Hills, O. A. 10c..... *West. Tr.*

Popular expositor. *See* Nevins, A.

Popular fairy tales. 2 v. ill. 16°. '63. ea., $1.25..*Roberts.*

Popular fairy tales; ill. by Doré and others. 4°. $3. *Miller.*

Popular fairy tales for little folks. ill. sq. 16°. $1..*Miller.*

Popular forget-me-not songster. *See* New.

Popular ignorance. Foster, J. $1.25........*Carter.*

Popular juvenile lib. *See* Arthur, T. S.

Popular library of history. 4 v. ill. 16°. '70. $4.50. *Meth. Bk. Conc.*
Cont.: Stories of Old England. — History of the crusades. — Count Ulrich of Lindburg. — Hero of Brittany.

Popular library of wit and humor. 5 v. 12°. ea., 50c. *Scribner, W. & A.*
Cont.: Mixture for low spirits. — Epitaphs and epigrams. — Proverbs from far and near. — Laconics; or, good words of the best authors. — Wills of their own, curious, eccentric and benevolent.

Popular manual of Catholic Church history; with chronol. tables and questions. New ed. 12°. '70. $1.25 ....*Kelly, P. & Co.*

Popular nursery tales and rhymes. ill. sm. 4°. $2. *Routledge.*

Popular objections to revealed truth. [Lectures.] 12°. '73. $1.75..............................*Randolph.*

Popular resorts. *See* Bachelder, J. B.

Popular superstitions. 18°. 35c............*Am. S. S.*

Population of an old pear tree. Van Ruyssel, E. $1.50 ....*Macmillan.*

Porchat, J: Jacques. Trois mois sous la neige. ('63.) New ed. 12°. '76. pap., 90c.............*Holt.*

Porgy Joe: Ethiop. drama. 16°. pap., 15c...*Happy.*

Pork chops. Blanchard, E. L. 15c..........*French.*

Porney, M: Ant. Syllabaire français; or, French spelling book; rev. and enl. by J. Meier. 12°. 60c.....................................*Butler.*

Port-admiral: amateur drama. 16°. pap., 15c...*French.*

Port wine vs. jealousy. Carter, W. 15c.....*De Witt.*

Portal, F: Comparison of Egyptian symbols with those of the Hebrews; tr. by J. W. Simons. [Masonic.] ill. 12°. $1; hf. mor., $2..*Redding.*

Porte Crayon (*pseud.*) *See* Strother, D: H.

Portent (The). MacDonald, G. $1.75 .....*Loring.*

Porter, A. N. Iowa probate manual; cont. probate act and homestead law and that of the separate property of husband and wife; with decisions and forms. 2d ed., rev. 8°. '76. shp., $3 ..*Mills.*

Porter, Alb. G. *See* Indiana, Reports.

Porter, *Mrs.* Ann E. Captain John. ('70.) New ed. ill. 16°. '74. $1.50 ....*Hoyt.*
— Frank May, the minister's son. 16°. $1.25..*Cong. Pub.*
— Glencoe parsonage. ill. 16°. '70. $1....*Lothrop.*
— Jim, the newsboy, and his friends. 16°. $1.50. *Cong. Pub.*
— Little cider merchant. 18°. 75c........*Cong. Pub.*
— Lost will. ('60.) New ed. ill. 16°. '75. $1.15..*Hoyt.*
— Married for both worlds. 16°. $1.50 ......*Lee & S.*
— Millie Lee. ill. 16°. '73. $1.50 ....*Lothrop.*
— Milwood; or, the influence of early impressions. 18°. 45c. ....*Cong. Pub.*
— My hero. ill. 16°. '72. $1.50...........*Lothrop.*
— Sunset Mountain. ill. 16°. '72. $1.50...*Lothrop.*
— This one thing I do. 18°. 30c...........*Pres. Bd.*
— *Same.* ill. 16°. '71. $1.50 ....*Lothrop.*
— White Mountain cottage. 18°. 50c. .....*Cong. Pub.*
— Winnie Malone. 18°. 60c. ....*Cong. Pub.*

Porter, Anna M. The Hungarian brothers. cr. 8°. pap., 25c. ....*Lippincott.*

Porter, B: F. *See* Alabama, Sup. Court reports.

Porter, C: T. Treatise on the Richards steam-engine indicator and development and application of force in the steam-engine. 3d ed., rev. and enl. ill. 8°. $3.50 ....*VanNostrand.*
— *Same;* with notes and add. as developed by Am. practice by F. W. Bacon. 2d ed. ill. 12°. '73. $1; mor., $1.50 ....*Van Nostrand.*

Porter, D: D. Memoir of Com. D: Porter. por. and pl. 8°. '75. $6......................*Munsell.*

Porter, Duvall. Poems. 12°. $1.50 ....*Bell.*

Porter, E. C. *See* Celebration of 200th anniv. of settlement of Hadley.

Porter, Eb. Letters on relig. revivals which prevailed about the beginning of the present century. 12°. 50c..................................*Cong. Pub.*
— *Same.* 16°. '50. 50c...............*Meth. Bk. Conc.*

Porter, Elbert S., *and* Elmendorf, Joac. Commemorative discourses on life, character and services of I. N. Wyckoff, April 11, 1869. 8°. pap., 25c. *N. Y. Ref. Ch. Bd.*

Porter, G: P. From atheism to Christianity. 16°. '72. 60c.........................*Meth. Bk. Conc.*

Porter, G: R. Nature and properties of the sugar cane; with chapter on manufacture of sugar from beet root. pl. 8°. (Lond.) '43. $3.........*Spon.*

Porter, Ja. Violin instructor for the million. f°. 75c. *Gordon.*

Porter, *Rev.* Ja. Camp-meetings: their history, etc. 24°. '49. 25c...................*Meth. Bk. Conc.*
— Chart of life. 12°. '56. $1.........*Meth. Bk. Conc.*
— Compendium of Methodism: hist. and condition, with defence of its doct., government and prudential peculiarities. 12°. '56. $1.75..*Meth. Bk. Conc.*
— *Swedish.* 12°. '56. $1.25 ....*Meth. Bk. Conc.*
— True evangelist (The). 16°. '59. 60c...*Meth. Bk. Conc.*

Porter, Jane. Pastor's fireside. 16°. $1; bds., 80c. *Routledge.*

Porter, Jane, *continued.*
– Scottish chiefs. 12°. $1 .... *Hurd & H.*
– *Same.* 12°. $1; pap., 25c. .... *Lippincott.*
– *Same.* 12°. $1.25 .... *Sadlier.*
– *Same.* 12°. $1.25; bds., 80c. .... *Routledge.*
– *Same.* ill. 8°. $2.50; hf. cf., $4.50. — 12°. $1.50. *Appleton.*
– *Same.* ill. 12°. $1; hf. cf., $3 .... *Porter.*
– Shipwreck of Sir Edward Seaward, and disc. of certain islands in the Caribbean Sea; with details of his residence there, etc. 18°. 75c. .... *Harper.*
– Thaddeus of Warsaw. 12°. $1 .... *Hurd & H.*
– *Same.* 12°. $1; pap., 25c. .... *Lippincott.*
– *Same.* ill. 12°. $1; hf. cf., $3 .... *Porter.*
– *Same.* ill. 12°. $1.50 .... *Sadlier.*

Porter, J: A. First book of chemistry and allied sciences. 12°. '57. hf. bds., $1 .... *Barnes.*
– Principles of chemistry enlarged. ill. 12°. '68. $2. *Barnes.*

Porter, J: L. Giant cities of Bashan. 16°. $1 .. *Am. Bapt.*
– *Same.* 12°. $1.50 .... *Nelson.*
– *See also* Bible [Whole].

Porter, *Mrs.* M. E. New southern cookery book. 12°. $1.75 .... *J. E. Potter.*

Porter, Noah. Books and reading; or, what books shall I read and how shall I read them? ('70.) 5th ed., with index. cr. 8°. '76. $2; hf. cf., $4.50 .... *Scribner.*
– Elements of intellectual science; abridg. from "The human intellect." ('71.) New ed. cr. 8°. '76. $3. *Scribner.*
– Human intellect; with introd. upon psychology and human soul. ('68.) New ed. 8°. '76. $5. *Scribner.*
– Sciences of nature versus the science of man. 12°. '71. $1 .... *Dodd.*
– Two sermons: on leaving the old chapel, and on entering the new. 8°. 25c. .... *Judd & W.*
– *See also* Addresses at inauguration.

Porter, Rose. Foundations; or, castles in the air. 12°. '71. $1 .... *Randolph.*
– Summer driftwood for the winter fire. 12°. '70. $1. *Randolph.*
– Uplands and lowlands; or, three chapters in a life. 12°. '72. $1.25 .... *Randolph.*
– Winter fire: sequel to "Summer driftwood." 12°. '74. $1.25 .... *Randolph.*
– Years that are told. 12°. '75. $1.25 .... *Randolph.*

Porter, Ste. Daily walk with God in his own ordinances; or, the Bible standard of duty as exemplified in the primitive Christians; with memoir by his son. 12°. '71. 60c. .... *Darrow.*

Porter, T: C. Synopsis of the flora of Colorado. *See* United States, *Geog. and geol. survey.*

Porter, W: T. Big bear's adventures and travels. ill. 12°. $1.75; pap., 75c. .... *Peterson.*
– Quarter race in Kentucky. ill. 12°. pap., 75c. *Peterson.*

Porter's knot. Oxenford, J. 15c. ... *De Witt; French.*

Porter's troubles. Harrigan, E. 15c. .... *De Witt.*

Porteus, Beilby. Evidences of Christianity. 32°. '50. 15c. .... *Am. Tr.*

Portfolio of engineering engraving: examples in civil, hydraulic and mechanical engineering: plates with explan. details and sectional parts, etc. 4°. (Weale.) '58–'59. $5 .... *Spon.*

Portfolio of entertainment and instruction. 4°. $2.75. *Pres. Bd.*

Portion of the soul. *See* Hooker, H.

Portland collection. *See* Hymns for the church and home.

Portrait. Riddle, A. G. $1.50 .... *Cobb; Nichols & H.*

Portrait gallery of the war. Moore, F. $6; $7.50. *Van Nostrand.*

Portrait in my uncle's dining-room. *See* Fullerton, *Lady* G.

Portrait of a Christian drawn from life. Robbins, C. 60c. .... *Am. Unit.*

Portrait painter: Ethiop. drama. 16°. pap., 15c. *French; Happy.*

Portraits of celebrated women. Sainte-Beuve, C. A. $1.50 .... *Roberts.*

Portraits of North American Indians. Stanley, J. M. 50c. .... *Smith. Inst.*

Portraiture of true devotion. Grow, F. 30c. *Cath. Pub.*

Posie, the minister's daughter. *See* Washington, E.

Posie ser. 5 v. 16°. $6 .... *Crowell.*
Cont.: Posie, the minister's daughter, by E. Washington. — Boys and girls of Beech Hill, by J. G. Avery. — Little people whom the Lord loved, by E. E. Flagg. — Grace Courtney, by M. H. Henry. — Children of the great king, by M. Horsburgh.

Posies for children. Lowell, A. C. 75c. .... *Roberts.*

Position and power of the Sunday school. 18°. 80c. *Am. S. S.*

Possum fat: Ethiop. drama. 16°. pap., 15c. .. *Happy.*

Post, Alfr. C. Anniversary oration before N. Y. Acad. of Med. 8°. '49. pap., 25c. .... *N. Y. Acad. Med.*
— Eulogy on Valentine Mott. por. 8°. '65. pap., 50c. *N. Y. Acad. Med.*

Post, G. B. Fire-proof floors compared. 48°. pap., 10c. .... *Am. Inst. Arch.*

Post, Hoyt. *See* Michigan, Sup. Court reports; Sup. Court rules.

Post, J. H. Offsprings of fancy. [Poems.] 12°. '70. 75c. .... *Dennis.*

Post, *Mrs.* Loretta J. Scenes in Europe. ill. 16°. $1.50 .... *Cin. Meth. Bk. Conc.*

Post, Lydia Minturn. Grace Barclay's diary; or, personal recollections of the American revolution. 12°. '67. $1.50 .... *Randolph.*

Post, Truman A. *See* Missouri, Reports.

Post boy. Craven, H. T. 15c. .... *De Witt; French.*

Post oak circuit. Keener, J. C. 90c. .... *So. Meth.*

Post of honor. 16°. $1.25 .... *Carter.*

Post of honour. Mildenhall, T. 15c. .... *French.*

Post office pop-guns. *See* Barrow, *Mrs.* F.

Postal directory; comp. from official records, to Oct. 1, 1874. 4°. bds., $2 .... *Lippincott.*

Postillion du Lonjumeau. *See* Ditson.

Postman's bag. De Liefde, J. $1.50 .... *Routledge.*

Postman's knock: farce. 16°. pap., 15c. .... *French.*

Posy Vinton's picnic. Seymour, M. H. 75c. .. *Dutton.*

Potato roaster. *See* Bowen, C. E.

Pothier, Rob. J. Treatise on contract of partnership; tr. with ref. to Eng. decisions by O. D. Tudor. 8°. '54. $1.50 .... *T. & J. W. Johnson.*
— — *See also* Law lib.
— Treatise on law of obligations and contracts; tr., with notes ill. of the Eng. law, by W. D. Evans. 3d Am. ed. 2 v. 8°. shp., $10 .... *Kay.*

Potiphar papers, Curtis, G. W. $1.50 .... *Harper.*

Potter, —. Eloquence. 75c.; $1.50 .... *Dooley.*

Potter, Alonzo. Handbook for readers and students in sel. works for reading and investigation. 18°. 75c. .... *Harper.*
— Political economy: its objects, uses and principles, considered with ref. to the condition of the Am. people. 18°. 75c. .... *Harper.*
— Principles of science applied to the domestic and mechanic arts, and to manufacture and agriculture. ill. 12°. $1.50 .... *Harper.*
— Religious philosophy: lectures before the Lowell Institute, 1845–1853. cr. 8°. $3 .... *Lippincott.*
— *and* Emerson, G: B. The school and the schoolmaster: manual for teachers, employers, etc. 12°. $1.50 .... *Harper.*

Potter, H. L. D. Manual of reading. 12°. $1.40. *Harper.*

Potter, H: C. Choked life: some thoughts for Lent. sq. 24°. pap., 10c. . . . . *Dutton.*
— Shams in Lent; or, the real and the false in Lenten duties. sq. 24°. pap., 10c. . . . . *Dutton.*
— Sisterhoods and deaconesses at home and abroad: hist. of their rise and growth in the Prot. Epis. Church; with rules for their organization and government, etc. 16°. '71. $1.50. . . . . . *Dutton.*
Potter, Jos. Lew. English-Hebrew lexicon: index to Gesenius' Hebrew lexicon. 8°. '72. $2. . *Crocker.*
Potter, Rob. A voice from the church in Australia: sermons. fp. 8°. '64. $1.25. . . . . *Macmillan.*
Potter, S. A., *and* Hammond, W. P. Copy books. 15 nos. obl. 8°. per doz., $1.80 . . . . . *Potter, A. & Co.*
— — Penmanship explained. obl. 8°. $1. . *Potter, A. & Co.*
— — System of practical book-keeping by single and double entry. (Common school ed.) 8°. $1.15. — (High school ed.): double entry. 12°. $1.25. — Key. 12°. 70c. . . . . *Potter, A. & Co.*
Potter, T: Evangelical economy developed: discourses on facts, institutions, appliances, effects and final results of the Christian system. 12°. '48. $1.50. *Wilstach.*
Potter, T: J. Rupert Aubrey, of Aubrey Chase. sq. 16°. $1. . . . . *Noonan.*
— Two victories: Catholic tale. 16°. $1; $1.50. *Sadlier.*
Potter, W: J. Reason and revelation. 12°. pap., 10c. *Free Rel.*
Pottleton legacy. *See* Smith, Alb.
Potts, Alex. W. Hints towards Latin prose composition. 3d ed., enl. fp. 8°. $1. . . . . *Macmillan.*
Potts, *Mrs.* Arth. Catechism for little children. 12°. '75. pap., 10c. . . . . *H. E. Simmons.*
Potts, O. G. *See* New Jersey, Statutes.
Potwin, *Mrs.* H. K. Kemptons (The). ill. 16°. '65. $1 . . . . *Dodd.*
— Orphans' (The) triumphs; or, story of Lily and Harry Grant. ill. 16°. '68. $1 . . . . *Dodd.*
— Paul and Margaret, the inebriate's children. ill. 16°. '68. 90c. . . . . *Dodd.*
— Robert, the cabin boy. ill. 16°. '63. $1 . . . . . *Dodd.*
— Ruby Duke. 16°. $1.50. . . . . *Lee & S.*
Pouchet, Felix Archimèdes. The universe; or, the infinitely great and the infinitely little; tr. from the Fr.; with add. and introd. by A. Guyot. ('72.) New ed. col. ill. roy. 8°. $8; hf. cf., $15; hf. mor., $16; mor., $20 . . . . *Scribner.*
Poudre (La) aux yeux. Labiche, E. M., *and* Martin, E. 40c. . . . . *Holt.*
Poughkeepsie [N. Y.] Society of Natural Science. Proceedings. v. 1. pt. 1. 8°. '76. pap., $1. *Poughkeepsie Soc. of Nat. Sci.*
Poul a dhoil. Hazlewood, C. H. 15c. . . . . *French.*
Poultry Meg's family. *See* Andersen, H. C.
Pounceford Hall. Clarke, B. $1.50. . . . . *Nelson.*
Pour une épingle. Tardieu, J. de. $1. . . . . *Holt.*
Pourtalès, L: F. de. Contributions to the fauna of the gulf stream at great depths. 8°. '67. pap., 10c. — 2d ser. 8°. '68. pap., 15c. . . *Mus. Comp. Zool.*
— Deep-sea corals. ill. imp. 8°. '71. pap., $3. *Mus. Comp. Zool.*
— Echini, crinoids and corals; — Recent corals from Tilibiche. *See* Agassiz, A., *and* Pourtalès, L. F. de.
Pouter's wedding. Morton, J. M. 15c. . . . . . . *French.*
Pouton, Mungo. Earthquakes and volcanoes: their hist., phenomena and probable causes. ill. 12°. '71. $1.50. . . . . *Lothrop.*
Poverty: its cause and cure. H., M. G. 10c. . . *Somerby.*
Poverty of Jesus the wealth of the saints. Burnet, D. S. 10c. . . . . *Chase.*
Powder and gold. Schücking, L. 75c. . . . . . *Hinton.*
Powder monkey. Dalton, W. $2. . . . . *Routledge.*

Powell, Edm. Practice of law of evidence; with chapter on measure of damages. 8°. '58. $3. *T. & J. W. Johnson.*
— — *See also* Law lib.
Powell, F. York. Early England to the conquest. (Epochs of hist.) maps. 16°. 50c. . . . . . *Estes.*
Powell, F: Bacchus dethroned: prize essay. ('73.) New ed. 12°. '75. $1. . . . . *Nat. Temp.*
Powell, J. H. Life of W: Denton, geologist and radical. ('70.) 3d ed. 12°. '73. pap., 25c. . . *Colby.*
— Mediumship: its laws and conditions. ('70.) 3d ed. 8°. '73. pap., 25c. . . . . *Colby.*
Powell, J. P. The luminary: anthems for quartet and chorus choirs. 4°. $2. . . . . *Chase.*
Powell, Ja. W. Exploration of the Colorado River; — Report on geol. of Uinta Mts. *See* United States, *Geog. and* geol. survey.
Powell, T: Essay on apostolical succession. 12°. '42. $1.10 . . . . *Meth. Bk. Conc.*
— *Same;* with introd. by T. O. Summers. 12°. '57. $1.25 . . . . *So. Meth.*
Powell, T: W. Analysis of American law. 8°. $4.50; shp., $5.50 . . . . *Lippincott.*
— Law of appellate proceedings. 8°. '72. $5.50. *T. & J. W. Johnson.*
Powell, Warington Baden. Canoe travelling: log of a cruise in the Baltic, and hints on building and fitting canoes. ill. sq. 12°. $3. . *Scribner, W. & A.*
Powell, W: Byrd. Human temperaments: their natural hist., laws of consequences of violation, etc. ill. 8°. $2. . . . . *Widdleton.*
Powell, Willis J., *and* Rarey, J. S. The secret revealed: art of taming horses. 16°. '74. *$1.50. *Hubbard.*
Power, H: Holmes, T., Anstie, F. E., *and* Barnes, Rob. Reports on the progress of medicine and surgery, physiology, etc.; ed., for the Sydenham Soc. of Lond. 8°. '67. $2. . . . . *Lindsay.*
Power, J. L. Blue Lodge text book, adapted to the work, lectures and jurisprudence of the Grand Lodge of Mississippi. [Masonic.] 8°. '75. $2 . . . . *Power & B.*
— *See also* Webb, G. F., *and* Power, J. L.
Power, Ja. F. Virginia veteran: drama. 16°. pap., 25c. *Lee & S.*
Power, J: Carroll. History of early settlers of Sangamon Co., Illinois. 8°. '76. $5; hf. cf., $6.50. *E. A. Wilson.*
— Life of Abraham Lincoln. 12°. '75. $2; hf. cf., $3. *E. A. Wilson.*
— Rise and progress of Sunday schools: biog. of Robert Raikes and Wm. Fox. 16°. $1. . . . . . . *Sheldon.*
Power, *Rev.* J: H. Domestic piety and family government. 18°. 40c. . . . . *Cin. Meth. Bk. Conc.*
— Letters to Dr. Smith on slavery. 12°. $1.75. *Cin. Meth. Bk. Conc.*
Power, J: Hatch. Anatomy of the arteries of the human body; with descriptive anatomy of the heart. 12°. $2.50. . . . . *Lippincott.*
Power, Ph. Bennett. Babe at the wedding. 18°. 60c. *Carter.*
— Bag of blessings. 18°. 60c. . . . . *Carter; Dutton.*
— Breathings of the soul. 32°. '64. 20c. . . *Randolph.*
— Croaking Kate. 18°. 30c. . . . . *Am. S. S.*
— I wills of Christ. 12°. $1.50 . . . . *Carter.*
— I wills of the Psalms. 12°. $1.50 . . . . *Carter.*
— Little knitter. 18°. '67. 30c. *N. Y. Rf. Ch. Bd.; Pres. Com.*
— *Same.* 18°. 35c. . . . . *Bost. Am. Tr.*
— — *See* also Moss rose stories.
— Moss rose. 18°. '67. 30c. *N. Y. Ref. Ch. Bd.; Pres. Com.*
— *Same.* 18°. 35c. . . . . *Bost. Am. Tr.*
— — *See also* Moss rose stories.
— Oiled feather ser.: no. 1. 5 v. 18°. $1.75; pap., 50c. . . . . *Am. S. S.*
Cont.: Oiled feather; Mr. Clipstock's clock. — Chirping Jane and Croaking Kate. — Talking fire irons. — Stamp-on-it John. — Eye doctor.

Power, Ph. Bennett, *continued.*
— *Same:* no. 2. 6 v. 18°. $2.10; pap., 50c... *Am.S.S.*
Cont.: Man who ran away from himself. — This day month. — Paddle your own canoe. — Use of a child. — He's overhead. — Man who kept himself in repair.
— Pivot words of Scripture. 12°. $1.50 .... *Carter.*
— Rainbow ser. 5 v. 18°. ea., 60c.......... *Carter.*
Cont.: Last shilling. — Three cripples. — Two brothers. — Fagot of stories. — Stamp-on-it, John.
— Sambo's legacy. 18°. 60c.............. *Carter.*
— *Same.* 18°. 35c.; pap., 10c............. *Am.S.S.*
— This day month. 18°. 30c............... *Am.S.S.*
— Truffle nephews. 16°. $1................ *Carter.*
— Use of a child. 18°. 30c................ *Am.S.S.*

Power, Tyrone. [Plays.] 4 v. 16°. ea., pap., 15c. *French.*
Cont.: Born to good luck: farce. — How to pay the rent: farce. — Paddy Carey: dram. interlude. — St. Patrick's eve.

Power of Christ to save. Campbell, A. J. 75c. *Carter.*

Power of faith: narrative of Sarah Jordan. ('60.) New ed. 18°. '68. 45c.................. *Hoyt.*

Power of gentleness. Stanley, F. 70c..... *Pres.Bd.*

Power of gold. 18°. 90c............... (?) *Martien.*

Power of grace. Platt, S. H. $1.10–35c....... *Hope.*

Power of instruction; or, the guilty tongue; by author of "Last day of the week." 18°. 45c... *Pres.Bd.*

Power of the keys. Clay, W. L. $1.... *Macmillan.*

Power of kindness. ill. 18°. 50c............ *Nelson.*

Power of love. *See* Infant school lib.

Power of prayer. Prime, S. I. $1.50 ..... *Scribner.*

Power of song. Romberg, A. 65c. .... *Gordon.*

Power of soul over body. Moore, G. $1 ... *Harper.*

Powers, *Mrs.* A. H. The tar man; or, the fox and the hare: a Virginian nursery story. ill. 8°. '75. pap., 25c......................... *West, J. & Co.*

Powers, Horatio N. Through the year. 16°. '75. $1.50. *Roberts.*

Powers, M. R., *and* Johnson, M. R. Complete accountant; for schools and private study. 8°. '74. $2.50............................ *Keen.*

Powers, *Mrs.* S. D. Ugly-girl papers; or, hints for the toilet. 16°. $1.................. *Harper.*

Powers, Ste. Afoot and alone: walk from sea to sea by the southern route. [So. Cal., New Mexico, Texas, etc.] ill. 12°. *$2; $2.50; hf. mor., $3.50 .... *Col.Bk.*
— Muskingum legends; with other papers descrip. of the young men of Germany and the old boys of America. 12°. $1.75............. *Lippincott.*

Powers, T. N. Catechism, moral, theological and doctrinal. roy. 8°. '76. $4........... *Haverty.*

Poynter, E. F. Ersilia. (Leis. hour ser.) 16°. '76. $1.25.................................. *Holt.*
— My little lady. (Leis. hour ser.) ('72.) New ed. 16°. '76. $1.25......................... *Holt.*

Pracht-Bilder-Fibel, mit Erzählungen u. Gedichten. 8°. 25c. .... *Kohler.*

Practical astronomer. Dick, T. $1....... *Harper.*

Practical guide to the Greek New Test. fp. 8°. (Bagster.) 88c. .... *Wiley.*

Practical guide to treatment of common disorders with homœop. remedies. 64°. 20c. .... *Boericke.*

Practical housewife: papers on cookery, food, treatment of the sick, etc. 12°. $1.25... *Lippincott.*

Practical lessons in reconnoitring, outpost duty, etc. 2 v. 8°. '72–'73. ea., pap., 60c......... *Spon.*

Practical letter writer. 18°. hf. bd., 31c..... *Sadlier.*

Practical magician and ventriloquist's guide. ill. 12°. pap., 25c. .... *Hurst.*

Practical man. Bernard, W. B. 15c........ *French.*

Practical morality; or, a guide to men and manners; [compr.] Lord Chesterfield's letters to his son, The polite philosopher, Blair's Advice to youth, Fordyce On honor as a principle, Lord Burghley's Ten precepts to his son, Franklin's Way to wealth, Pope's Universal prayer. 18°. 75c... *U.P.James.*

Practical religion. Solomon, F. $1..(?) *F.Solomon.*

Practical sanctification. Boynton, J. 75c... *Palmer.*

Practical talks with sinners, inquirers and Christians. McBeth, S. $1..................... *McIntyre.*

Practical thoughts. Nevins, W. 45c........ *Am.Tr.*

Practical treatise on dyeing and calico-printing; with app. of definitions of chemical terms, with tables of weights, measures, etc.; by an experienced dyer; with sup. by R. Macfarlane. 8°. $5. *Wiley.*

Practical truths. Alexander, A. 75c........ *Am.Tr.*

Practical view. Wilberforce, W. $1.25 ..... *Carter.*

Praed, Winthrop Mackworth. Poems. (Blue and gold ed.) 2 v. 32°. $2.50............. *Widdleton.*
— *Same;* with memoir by Rev. D. Coleridge. 2 v. por. cr. 8°. $3.50; hf. cf., $7; mor., $10. *Widdleton.*

Prairie (The). *See* Cooper, J. F.

Prairie (The); rev. by T. O. Summers. ('55.) 3d ed. 18°. '75. 30c. .... *So.Meth.*

Prairie and forest. Gillmore, P. $1.50...... *Harper.*

Prairie bird. *See* Murray, C. A.

Prairie books. 12 v. ill. 16°. per doz., $2... *Nelson.*
Cont.: Stories for the winter. — Shepherd boy. — Pretty Mar-mo-set. — Grandpapa's adventure. — Kind friend. — Cat and the rat. — Pretty Betty. — In the prairie. — Happy family. — Little Gerty. — Hold him please. — Mary and her doll.

Prairie boys. *See* Mudge, Z. A.

Prairie breaking. Holbrook, J. C. 45c........ *Hoyt.*

Prairie Crusoe; or, adventures in the far west. ill. 16°. $1.50 .... *Lee & S.*

Prairie flower. Aimard, G. 75c. .... *Peterson.*

Prairie flower. Baker, H. N. W. 55c. .... *Hoyt.*

Prairie flower. Bennett, E. 25c......... *U.P.James.*

Prairie flower-boy. ill. 18°. '60. 40c. ...... *Am.Tr.*

Prairie lib. 4 v. 16°. $4............. *Bost.Am.Tr.*
Cont.: Daughters of the prairie, by Mrs. N. H. Eggleston. — Our summer at Hillside farm, by Mary Barrett. — A sister's story. — Sunshine, by Mrs. Prosser.

Prairie Mazeppa. Aiken, A. W. 20c........ *Beadle.*

Prairie missionary. 18°. 60c. .... *Am.S.S.*

Prairie traveller. Marcy, R. B. $1 .... *Harper.*

Praise and principle. McIntosh, M. J. 75c... *Harper.*

Praise Jehovah. *See* Mendelssohn-Bartholdy, F.

Praise of friendship. Mozart, W. A. 38c.... *Ditson.*

Praise of Zion. Wilder, S., *and* Davenport, F. S. $1.50...................................... *Ditson.*

Praise offering. [Music.] 12°. '76. 35c... *Un.B.Pub.*

Praise offering. Taylor, V. C. $1.50......... *Mills.*

Praise to God. Bristow, F. $2.25........... *Ditson.*

Praises of Jesus (New). *See* Hammond, E. P.

Praktische Rechner (Der); f. deutsch-amerik. Volksschulen; bearb v. e. prakt. Schulmanne. 1. Thl. 3d ed. 16°. bds., 15c. — Key. 16°. bds., 25c. — 2. Thl. 16°. bds., 20c............... *Wiebusch.*

Praktisches Rechenbuch f. deutsche Elementarschulen in. d. Ver. St. 12°. bds., 40c. .... *Ludwig.*

Prang's alphabets, plain, ornamental and illuminated. pl. obl. 8°. $2.50...................... *Prang.*

Prank. Abbott, J. 90c. .... *Harper.*

Prasca Loupouloff. 18°. 40c. .... *Dutton.*
— *See also* Yonge, C. M., Star of hope ser.

Prass, F. *See* Gilbert, T., *and* Prass, F.

Pratt, Anne. Ferns of Great Britain and their allies, the club mosses, the pepperworts and horse tails. col. pl. 8°. $6.25............. *Scribner, W. & A.*
— Flowering plants, grasses and ferns of Great Britain. 300 col. pl. 6 v. 8°. $37.50... *Scribner, W. & A.*
— Haunts of the wild flowers. ill. 16°. $1.25; bds., 80c. .... *Routledge.*

Pratt, Dan. J. (*ed.*) Regents' questions, 1866–'76: questions for prelim. examination for admission to Univ. of State of N. Y. ill. 16°. '76. $1; — in 4 pts., ea., 25c........................*Bardeen.*
Cont.: Arithmetic. — Geography. — Grammar. — Spelling and penmanship.

Pratt, Foster. Compiled law of the Grand Lodge of Free and Accepted Masons of Mich. 12°. '74. *45c.; pap., 30c..................(?)*F. Pratt.*

Pratt, Fes. Lee. Agnes and her neighbors. 16°. '72. $1.50..............................*Lothrop.*
— *See also* Bailey, U. L., *and* Pratt, F. L.

Pratt, G. W. *See* Southard, L. H., *and* Pratt, G. W.

Pratt, H. B. Presbyterian baptism. 8°. 50c...*Pres. Com.*

Pratt, I. Loring. ["L. L."] Juveniles. 4 v. ill. 16°. '72–'75. ea., $1.50..................*Lothrop.*
Cont.: Bonnie Aerie. — Branches of palm. — Broken fetters. — Evening rest.

Pratt, J. L. Mask lifted. ('73.) New ed. 16°. '76. $1.25..............................*Hoyt.*
— Mecca; or, a summer vacation. 16°. '75. $1.25..*Hoyt.*

Pratt, J: H: Treatise on attractions, Laplace's functions, and the figure of the earth. 4th ed. cr. 8°. $2.25..............................*Macmillan.*

Pratt, Josiah. Remains of R: Cecil; with view of his character. 18°. 75c.................*Pres. Bd.*

Pratt, L. Mar. ["Laurie Loring."] Juveniles. 12 v. ill. 16°. '74–'75......................*Lothrop.*
Cont.: Children's picture story book. — Stella and the priest; or, the star of Rockburn, *ea.*, $1.50. — Christmas visit. — Our Berty, etc. — Queer carriage, etc. — Somebody's darlings, etc., *ea.*, 75c. — Berty's confession. — Christmas morning, etc. — Concert, etc. — Effie's friends, etc. — Little May's picture, etc. — Sailor brother, etc., *ea.*, 50c.

Pratt, *Mrs.* Ma. E. Rhoda Thornton's girlhood. ill. 16°. $1.50............................*Lee & S.*

Pratt, T. W. Trusses and trussed arches. 8°. pap., 25c. *Am. Soc. of C. E.*

Pratt, W. W. Ten nights in a bar room: drama. 16°. pap., 15c..............................*French.*

Pray, Lew. G. Memoir of Rev. S: Barrett; with sel. from his discourses. 16°. $1.50........*Lee & S.*

Pray for the Holy Spirit. Scribner, W. $1.25; 50c. *Randolph.*

Pray for your children. Scribner, W. 40c...*Pres. Bd.*

Prayer: its nature and design; with forms for children and Sunday schools. 18°. 35c.........*Am. S. S.*

Prayer and business. Taylor, W. M. 35c.; 15c. *Randolph.*

Prayer book and hymnal for use of the New Church. 16°. '67. $1.50; — abridg. 16°. '67. $1..*Claxton.*

Prayer book and its story. Abercrombie, R. M. $1.25. *Dutton.*

Prayer-gauge debate; by Tyndall, F. Galton and others, against Littledale, McCosh and others. 12°. '76. $1.75....................*Cong. Pub.*

Prayer meeting. Johnston, J. B. $1..*U. P. Bd. of Pub.*

Prayer meeting hymn-book.. 24°. pap., 12c. *Bost. Am. Tr.*

Prayer meeting tune book. 16°. 40c........*Am. S. S.*
— *See also* Union prayer meeting hymns.

Prayer of faith. Halpine, M. G. 45c......*Cong. Pub.*

Prayer test lib. *See* Boyd, *Mrs.* E. E.

Prayers, ancient and modern; adapted to family use. 12°. '73. $1.75..............................*Pott.*

Prayers for little children; from "Steps to the throne of grace." sq. 16°. '75. 20c...........*Nelson.*

Prayers for the sick-chamber. 16°. $1.25..*Routledge.*

Prayers for the young; from "Steps to the throne of grace." sq. 16°. '75. 20c............*Nelson.*

Prayers of Israel [Heb.]; with Eng. or Germ. tr. 12°. $1.25–$6..............................*Frank.*
— *Same;* with Eng. tr. 12°. $1.50–$7.......*Frank.*

Prayers of St. Gertrude. 32°. 50c.–$2.50...*Sadlier.*

Praying and working. *See* Stevenson, W. F.

Praying to Jesus. *See* Kennedy, *Mrs.* M. G.

Preacher (The). Ziegler, H. $1.50; $2; $3. (?) *Luth. Pub.*

Preacher and pastor. Park, E. A. $1.25....*Draper.*

Preacher's text-book: biblical digest. ('54.) 6th ed. 18°. '75. shp., $1......................*So. Meth.*

Preachers and preaching. Murray, N. $1.50..*Harper.*

Preaching required by the times. Stevens, A. $1. *Meth. Bk. Conc.*

Preaching to the masses. Talmage, T. DeW. 20c. *Meth. Bk. Conc.*

Pre-Adamite (The). Lester, A. H. $1.25..*Lippincott.*

Pre-Adamite man. Randolph, P. B. $1.50...*Colby.*

Preble, G: H: First cruise of the U. S. frigate Essex. 8°. pap., $1..............................*Essex.*

Precaution. *See* Cooper, Ja. F.

Precept upon precept. *See* Mortimer, *Mrs.* M.

Precepts in practice. *See* Tucker, *Mrs.* C.

Preciosa. 12°. pap., 15c....................*Radde.*

Preciosa. Weber, C. M. v. 75c. ....*Ditson.*

Precious blood (The). *See* Faber, F. W.

Precious gleanings from the field of truth. 18°. 70c. *Pres. Bd.*

Precious pickle. Baker, G. M. 15c. ....*Lee & S.*

Precious Saviour. Waterbury, J. B. $1.25..*Randolph.*

Precious stones. Zabriskie, F. N. 75c....*Randolph.*

Precious stones of the heavenly foundations. Garret, A. B. $1.50..............................*Sheldon.*

Precious things. Winslow, O. $1.25 ....*Carter.*

Precious things of St. Peter. Rogers, E. P. $1.25; $1.50..............................*Randolph.*

Precious thoughts. Ruskin, J. $1.50; $2....*Wiley.*

Precious truths in plain words. 18°. 50c.....*Nelson.*
— *Same.* 16°. 60c.....................*Bost. Am. Tr.*

Precious words. Clark, M. L. 15c. ....*Lothrop.*

Predigt-Studien über alttestamentl. Texte im Anschluss an das Kirchenjahr; f. evang. Prediger, etc. 8°. '72. $1.50..........................*Pilger.*

Premium (The). 18°. '53. 35c. ....*Am. Tr.*

Premium lib. 3 v. 16°. '70. $2.70 ....*Lothrop.*
Cont.: Premium stories for boys. — Premium stories for girls. — Premium stories for young folks.

Premiums paid to experience. Mayo, I. F. $1.75. *Dodd.*

Prendergast, J. P. Curse of Cromwell: Cromwellian settlement of Ireland. maps. 12°. '69. $1.50. *Haverty.*

Prendergast, T: Mastery ser. [for learn. lang. without grammars]. 4 v. 12°. ea., 50c...*Appleton.*
Cont.: French. — German. — Manual para aprender inglés. — Handbook to the ser.

Prentice, G: D. Poems; collected and ed. with biog. sketch by J. J. Piatt. 12°. '75. $2....*Clarke.*
— Prenticeana; or, wit and humor in paragraphs; with biog. sketch by G. W. Griffin. ('70.) 2d ed. 12°. '71. $1.50..............................*Claxton.*

Prentiss, *Mrs.* Eliz. ["Aunt Susan."] Aunt Jane's hero. 12°. '71. $1.50................*Randolph.*
— Flower of the family ser. 4 v. 16°. '54–'70. $5.25. *Randolph.*
Cont.: Flower of the family, $1.50. — Nidworth and his three magic wands. — The Percys. — Only a dandelion, etc., *ea.*, $1.25.
— Fred, Maria and me. ('67.) New ed. ill. sq. 12°. '75. $1.50..............................*Scribner.*
— Golden hours: hymns and songs of the Christian life. 12°. '73. $1.50..................*Randolph.*
— Golden thread ser. 3 v. 16°. '56–'64. ea., $1. *Randolph.*
Cont.: Henry and Bessie. — Little threads. — Peterchen and Gretchen.
— Little Lou's sayings and doings. ill. sm. 4°. '68. $1.50. *Hurd & H.*
— Little preacher. 16°. '67. $1..........*Randolph.*

Prentiss, *Mrs.* Eliz., *continued.*
— Little Susy lib. 3 v. sq. 16°. '54. ea., 85c...*Randolph.*
Cont.: Little Susy's six birthdays. — Little Susy's little servants. — Little Susy's six teachers.
— Old brown pitcher. ('68.) New ed. 12°. '76. $1. *Nat. Temp.*
— Six little princesses. ill. sq. 16°. '71. 75c.; pap., 50c. *Randolph.*
— Stepping heavenward. 12°. '69. $1.75; $2.50. *Randolph.*
— Story Lizzie told. sq. 16°. '70. 60c.; pap., 35c. — (S.-school ed.) 16°. 75c...............*Randolph.*
— Urbané and his friends. 12°. '74. $1.50..*Randolph.*
Prentiss, G: L. Discourse in memory of T. H. Skinner. 8°. '73. pap., 75c........*Randolph.*
Preparations for death. *See* Liguori, *St.* A. M. de.
Preparing to teach; by J. Hall, E. P. Humphrey, W. H. Green and F. Patton. 12°. $1.75.....*Pres. Bd.*
Presbyterian Church. Confession of faith. 50c.-$1.50. (?) *Cumberland.*
— *Same;* [also] Psalms and hymns. 24°. 65c.-$2.75. — 18°. $1-$3 ....*Pres. Com.*
— Constitution; [also] Confession of faith, Larger and shorter catechisms, Form of government, Book of discipline, and Directory of worship as ratified by the Gen. Assembly, 1861. 18°. and 24°. '69. 50c.; shp., 60c.; pap., 30c. ....*Pres. Com.*
— — *Same.* 18°. 75c.; $1.25 ....*Pres. Bd.*
— *Germ.* 18°. 65c.; 75c. ....*Pres. Bd.*
— Digest of acts of Gen. Assembly. *See* Moore, W. E.
— Form of government, Discipline, and Directory for worship. 18°. 40c. ....*Pres. Bd.*
— Hymnal; comp. by a com. appointed by Gen. Assembly of 1864. 12°. $1.50-$5. — 18°. $1-$3.25. — 32°. 75c.-$2 ....*Pres. Bd.*
— Minutes of the Gen. Assembly, 1789-1820. 8°. $2.50. *Pres. Bd.*
— *Same.* 1821-1835. 8°. $2..............*Pres. Bd.*
— *Same.* 1870-'76. [Annual.] 8°. ea., $1.50; pap., $1...........................*Gen. Assembly.*
— Records. *See* Engles, W: M.
— *See also* United Presb. Church.
Presbyterian Church throughout the world: hist. and biog. sketches. ill. 8°. '74. *$4; hf. mor., $5; mor., $7; $9...........................*Lent.*
Presbyterian clergyman looking for the church. Mines, F. S. $2.........................*Dutton.*
Presbyterian cook book; by the ladies of the 1st Presb. Ch., Dayton, O. [Interleaved.] ('73.) 3d ed. 12°. '74. $1.50..........*J. H. Thomas.*
Presbyterian digest. *See* Moore, W. E.
Presbyterian minister's letters to a Methodist preacher. Smith, J. 63c......................*Lippincott.*
Presbyterianism three hundred years ago. Breed, W. P. $1 ....*Pres. Bd.*
Presbyterians and the revolution. Breed, W. P. 75c. ....*Pres. Bd.*
Prescott, Alb. B. Chemical examination of alcoholic liquors. 12°. '75. $1.50 ......*Van Nostrand.*
— Outlines of proximate organic analysis. 12°. '75. $1.75. *Van Nostrand.*
— *See also* Douglas, S. H., *and* Prescott, A. B.
Prescott, G: B. History, theory and practice of the electric telegraph. ill. 12°. $2.50 ....**Osgood.*
Prescott, *Miss* Ht. Eliz. *See* Spofford, *Mrs.* H. E.
Prescott, H: R. Strong drink and tobacco-smoke: structure, growth and uses of malt, hops, yeast and tobacco. ill. 8°. $3.............*W. Wood.*
Prescott, J: Eustace. The threefold cord: sermons. fp. 8°. $1 ....*Macmillan.*
Prescott, Ma. N. Matt's follies, and other stories. ('75.) 3d ed. ill. sm. 4°. '76. $1.50..*Miller.*
Prescott, W: Hickling. Works. 15 v. cr. 8°. ea., $2.50; hf. cf., $4.50. — 15 v. med. 8°. per set, $50; hf. cf., $78.75 ....*Lippincott.*

Prescott, W: Hickling, *continued.*
Cont.: Biog. and crit. miscellanies. — History of conquest of Mexico, 3 v. — History of conquest of Peru, 2 v. — History of reign of Ferdinand and Isabella, 3 v. — History of reign of Philip II., 3 v. — Robertson's History of reign of Charles V., with life of the Emperor after his abdication, by Prescott, 3 v.
— *Same;* ed. by J. F. Kirk. 15 v. 12°. $33.75; shp., $41.25; hf. cf., $67.50..............*Lippincott.*
— *Same;* incl. Life by G: Ticknor. 16 v. cr. 8°. $40; $44; shp., $48; hf. cf., $72.........*Lippincott.*
— Life of C. B. Brown. *See* Sparks, J., Library of American biography.
Prescotts (The). Whipple, C. 60c......*Garrigues.*
Presence of Christ. *See* Thorold, A. W.
Presence of God in his temple. Vaughan, C. J. $1.25. *Routledge.*
Present day papers. Ewing, A. 5 v. ea., $3..*Routledge.*
Present for my darling. [Toy-book.] ill. 4°. $1.75. *Routledge.*
Present for my darling lib. 8 v. 32°. $2..*Routledge.*
Cont.: Simple Susan, by M. Edgeworth. — Contrast, by M. Edgeworth. — Maud's visit. — Barring out, by M. Edgeworth. — Waste not, want not, by M. Edgeworth. — A drop of water, by M. Edgeworth. — Dairyman's daughter, by L. Richmond. — Birthday present.
Present heaven. *See* Greenwell, D.
Present issues. Memminger, R. W. $1.50..*Claxton.*
Present problem. Bolton, S. K. $1 ....*Putnam.*
Present Saviour. Hutton, R. S. 25c.; 10c...*Am. Tr.*
Presentation edition. *See* Routledge's British poets.
Presentation lib. for a good boy. 4 v. ill. 16°. $3. *Routledge.*
Cont.: Ernie Elton at home. — Ernie Elton at school. — Harry and his homes. — Robinson the younger.
Presentation lib. for a good girl. 4 v. ill. 16°. $3. *Routledge.*
Cont.: Amy Carleton. — Laura Temple. — May Dundas. — Inez and Emmeline.
Presented at court: comedy. 16°. pap., 15c...*Happy.*
Preserving and manufacturing secrets: directions for preserving fruits and vegetables and for manufacturing liquors, wines and summer beverages. 8°. '74. pap., 50c................(?) *F. M. Reed.*
President's daughter. *See* Bremer, F.
Pressensé, Edm. de. Early years of Christianity; tr. 3 v. 12°. '73. ea., $1.75........*Meth. Bk. Conc.*
Cont.: Apostolic era. — Martyrs and apologists. — Heresy and Christian doctrine.
— Jesus Christ: his times, life and work; tr. 12°. $3.75. *Scribner, W. & A.*
— *Same;* abridg. 12°. $1.50.....*Cin. Meth. Bk. Conc.*
— Mystery of suffering, and other discourses; tr. 12°. '69. $1.25 ....*Meth. Bk. Conc.*
— Redeemer (The): sketch of hist. of the redemption; tr. by J. H. Myers. 12°. $1.50...*Bost. Am. Tr.*
— Religion and the reign of terror; or, the church during the French rev.; from the French by J. P. Lacroix. 12°. '68. $1.75 ...*Meth. Bk. Conc.*
— Religions (The) before Christ: introd. to hist. of the first three centuries of the church; tr. by L. Corkran. 8°. $3.75 ....*Scribner, W. & A.*
— Rome and Italy at the opening of the Œcumenical Council; tr. 12°. '70. $1.50....*Meth. Bk. Conc.*
Pressensé, *Mme.* E. de. Madeleine's trial, and other stories; tr. ill. 12°. $1.25....*Scribner, W. & A.*
— Rosa [*Fr.*] With vocab. by L. Pylodet. ('69.) New ed. 12°. '76. $1.25...................*Holt.*
— *Eng.* Rosa; or, the Parisian girl; tr. by Mrs. J. C. Fletcher. 16°. 75c...................*Harper.*
— *Same.* 16°. $1.40 ....*Pres. Bd.*
— Theresa's journal; tr. 16°. $1.10........*Am. S. S.*
— Two years of school life; tr. ill. 12°. $1.25. *Scribner, W. & A.*
Pressly, J. T. Church fellowship. 18°. 25c. *U. P. Bd. of Pub.*
Prest, T: Prescott. Miser of Shoreditch: drama. 16°. pap., 15c...............................*French.*

Preston, *Miss* —. Summer with the little Grays. ill. sq. 16°. 75c. .... *Fuller*.

Preston, H. C. *See* Jaeger, B., *and* Preston, H. C.

Preston, Ht. W. Aspendale: essay and a story. 16°. '70. $1.25 .... *Roberts*.

— Love in the 19th century. [Fiction.] 16°. '73. $1.25. *Roberts*.

Preston, *Mrs.* I. S. Gaboon stories. ill. 16°. '72. 80c. *Am. Tr.*

Preston, Laura. A boy's trip across the plains. ('68.) 5th ed. 16°. '75. 75c. .... *Roman*.

Preston, Lyman. Interest tables: 8, 10 and 12 per cent. 8°. $2 .... *Sheldon*.

— Six per cent. interest tables. 8°. $3.50 .... *Sheldon*.

— *Same*. roy. 8°. $2.50 .... *Huntington*.

— Seven per cent. interest tables. 8°. $3.25 .. *Sheldon*.

— Treatise on book-keeping, by double and single entry. New ed., rev. and enl. roy. 8°. '67. $1.88. *Collins & Bro.*

Preston, *Mrs.* Marg. J. Beechenbrook, a rhyme of the war, and other poems. ill. sm. 4°. '66. $3.50; hf. cf., $4.50. — (People's ed.) 12°. $1. *Kelly, P. & Co.*

— Cartoons, from the life of the old masters, from the life of the legends, from the life of to-day. 2d ed. 16°. '75. $1.50 .... *Roberts*.

— Old song and new. [Poems.] 12°. $2 .. *Lippincott*.

Preston, *Miss* Ma. Studies in Shakespeare: essays. 16°. '69. $1 .... *Claxton*.

Preston, Pl. The fireside magician; or, the art of natural magic made easy. ill. 16°. pap., 30c.; bds., 50c. .... *Dick & F.*

— *See also* Paul Preston's voyages.

Preston, S. Tolver. Physics of the ether. 8°. '75. $3. *Spon*.

Preston, T: S. Ark of the covenant: discourses upon the joys, sorrows and glories of the mother of God. 18°. 60c. .... *Coddington; O'Shea*.

— Catholic view of the public school question. [Lecture.] 8°. pap., 20c. .... *Coddington*.

— Christ and the church. [Lectures.] 12°. '70. 50c. *Cath. Pub.*

— Church (The) and the world. [Address.] 8°. pap., 20c. .... *Coddington*.

— Lectures on Christian unity. 12°. $1.50 ... *Sadlier*.

— Lectures upon the devotion to the sacred heart of Jesus Christ. 12°. $1 .... *Coddington*.

— Life and times of St. Vincent de Paul. [Lecture.] 8°. pap., 20c. .... *Coddington*.

— Life of Mary Magdalen; or, the path of the penitents. 18°. 60c. .... *O'Shea*.

— Purgatorian manual: prayers and devotions, with reflections. ill. 18°. $1–$3.50 .... *O'Shea*.

— Reason and revelation: lectures, St. Ann's Church, N. Y., Advent, 1867. 12°. '68. $1.50 .. *Cath. Pub.*

— Sermons. 12°. $2.50 .... *Sadlier*.

— Vicar of Christ. [Lectures.] 18°. $1.50 .. *Coddington*.

Presumptive evidence. Buckstone, J. B. 15c. *French*.

Pretty Betty. *See* Prairie books.

Pretty book for good child. *See* Lullaby ser.

Pretty flower alphabet. ill. sq. 12°. per gross, $18. *Porter*.

Pretty girls of Stillberg: farce. 16°. pap., 15c. .. *French*.

Pretty horsebreaker. Brough, W., *and* Halliday, A. 15c. .... *De Witt; French*.

Pretty Jane: drama. 16°. pap., 15c. .... *French*.

Pretty little lib. 10 v. 24°. '59. $2.50 .. *Meth. Bk. Conc.*
Cont.: Wilbur's trip to the sea-shore. — Blackberry girl. — My little school-mates. — Bessie's three teachers. — Bessie's new heart. — Little stories for little people. — My grandmother. — My best friend. — Little partners, etc. — English Mary.

Pretty Mar-mo-set. *See* Prairie books.

Pretty Miss Bellew. Havers, D. $1.25 .... *Holt*.

Pretty Mrs. Gaston. Cooke, J. E. $1.50 ...... *Judd*.

Pretty name alphabet. ill. sq. 12°. per gross, $18. *Porter*.

Pretty picture book. ill. 4°. 25c. .... *Am. Bap*

Pretty picture ser. ill. 18°. '73. $3 .... *Nelson*
Cont.: Little reading book. — Pictures and reading. — Child picture book. — Home book of hymns. — Pretty pictures, etc. Home book of songs.

Pretty pictures. *See* Pretty picture ser.

Pretty pictures and pleasant stories. ill. roy. 16°. 50 *Cassel*

Pretty pictures for little eyes. *See* Pearl ser.

Pretty piece of business. Morton, T. 15c. .... *French*

Pretty plate. Huntington, J. V. 50c.; 75c. .. *Sadlie*

Pretty Poll. 4°. 50c.; pap., 25c. .... *Nelson*

Pretty Poll ser. 6 v. 4°. ea., 50c.; pap., 25c. .. *Nelson*
Cont.: Six good dogs. — Kindness to animals. — Sunny day — Pretty Poll. — Home kindness. — Pussie's mischief.

Pretty primer for good children. ill. 4°. pap., 10c 15c. .... *J. E. Potte*

Pretty puss ser. 12 nos. sq. 16°. 50c. .... *Nelson*

Pretty stories for little boys. sq. 16°. '48. 55c. *Meth. Bk. Con*

Pretty tales. ill. sq. 16°. 75c. .... *Nelso*

Pretty tales for the nursery. ill. 4°. 80c. .. *Am. Bap*

Preu, M. T. First steps in German. 8°. '71. $1.25 *Putnam*

— German primer. ill. sq. 16°. '70. $1 .... *Putnam*

Prey of the gods. Marryat, F. 30c. .... *Harpe*

Price, Bonamy. Currency and banking. 12°. $1.50 *Appleto*

— Error of an inflated currency; abridg. from "Princ ples of currency." 8°. '75. 20c. .... *Hinto*

Price, D: English speller. 18°. hf. bd., 15c. .. *Barne*

Price, E. Sick calls; from the diary of a missiona priest. [Fiction.] 18°. 75c.; $1.25 .... *Sadlie*

Price, Edm. E. Science of self-defense. ill. 16°. bds 75c. 12°. $1.25 .... *Dick &*

Price, E: Extracts from papers. 18°. 35c. *Friends Bk. S*

Price, Eli K. History of the consolidation of the Ci of Philadelphia. 12°. 75c. .... *Lippinco*

— Of the limitation of actions and of liens against re estate in Penna. 8°. shp., $3.50 .... *Ka*

— Pennsylvania act of 1853, for sale of real estate. c 8°. $2.25; shp., $2.75 .... *Ka*

Price, G: R. Hermit of the Chesapeake and his lesso of a life-time. [In Eng. or Germ.] 8°. pa 25c. .... *Barcla*

Price, J: M. *See* Kansas, Gen. statutes.

Priceless gems. [Ballads.] 4°. $2.25; bds., $1.75 *Peter*

Prichard, Iltudus T: Administration of India, 185 1868: the first ten years of administration und the crown. 2 v. 8°. '69. $7 .... *Macmilla*

Pride; or, six months at my uncle's in New Englan 18°. 40c. .... *Pres. B*

Pride and his prisoners. Tucker, C. 75c. .... *Carte*

Pride and irresolution. Ponsonby, E. 50c. .. *Harpe*

Pride and prejudice. *See* Austen, Jane.

Pride and principle. Paull, H. B. 50c. .. *Scribner, W. &*

Pride and prudence. Arthur, T. S. 50c. .... *Peterso*

Pride of the downes. Blount, M. 25c. .... *Bead*

Pride of Lexington. Seton, W. $2 .... *O'She*

Pride of life. Scott, C. L. $1.75; $1.50 ... *Peterso*

Pride of the market. Planché, J. R. 15c. .... *Fren*

Prideaux, Hum. Connection of the Old and N Test., in the hist. of the Jews, etc., from decle sion of kingdoms of Israel and Judah to time Christ. 2 v. 8°. $4; shp., $5 .... *Harp*

Pridham, Arth. Notes and reflections on Roma Ephesians and Hebrews. 3 v. 16°. ea., $2 .. *Gosp*

Priest, *Miss* S. M. Little pieces for little speake primary school teacher's assistant. ill. 16°. 60 75c. .... *Lee &*

Priest and nun. Wright, J. McN. $2.25 ... *West.*

Priest and Puritan. Ryle, J. C. $1 .... *Carter*.
Priest of Auvrigny. *See* Catholic premium-book lib.
Priesthood and clergy unknown to Christianity. Campaginator. 75c. .... *Claxton*.
Priestley, Josh. Memorials of Eliza Hessel. 16°. '60. $1.25 .... *Meth.Bk.Conc.*
Priestly, Jos. *See* Volney, C. F. C. (*Comte*) de.
Priest's prayer-book; with brief pontifical. 12°. '76. $2.50 .... *Pott*.
Priest's sister; [also] The inheritance; tr. by Mrs. J. Sadlier. 16°. 50c.; 75c. .... *Sadlier*.
Priests to the altar; or, aids to the devout celebration of communion; chiefly after ancient English use of Sarum. 8°. '69. $3.50 .... *Pott*.
Prima donna. Boucicault, D. 15c. .... *French*.
Primary grammar of the Eng. language; by a member of the Ursuline Community. 18°. 30c... *O'Shea*.
Primary lessons. 16°. pap., 10c. .... *West.Tr.*
Primary school hymn book. 32°. 30c... *Potter,A.& Co.*
Primary spelling book. 12°. 25c. .... *O'Shea*.
Primary truths of religion. Clark, T. M. $1.. *Appleton*.
Prime, E: D. G. Around the world. ill. cr. 8°. $3. *Harper*.
— Forty years in the Turkish empire: memoirs of W: Goodell. ('75.) New ed. 12°. '76. $2.50.. *Carter*.
Prime, F., *jr.* *See* Pennsylvania geol. survey.
Prime, S. Irenæus. Alhambra and the Kremlin: journey from Madrid to Moscow, including Spain, Switzerland, etc. ill. 8°. '73. $3 .... *Randolph*.
— Fifteen years of prayer in the Fulton St. [N. Y.] meeting. 12°. $1.50 .... *N.Y.Ref.Ch.Bd.*
— *Same.* ('72.) New ed. 12°. '73. $1.50 .. *Scribner*.
— Five years of prayer; with the answers. 12°. $1.50. *Harper*.
— Letters from Switzerland. 12°. $1.25 ..... *Sheldon*.
— Life of S: F. B. Morse. ill. 8°. *$5; shp., $6; hf. mor., $7.50; mor., $10 .... *Appleton*.
— Memoirs of Rev. N: Murray. por. 12°. $1.50.. *Harper*.
— Power of prayer ill. in wonderful displays of divine grace at the Fulton St. and other meetings in N. Y. and elsewhere in 1857–8. ('66.) New ed., enl. 12°. '73. $1.50 .... *Scribner*.
— Songs of the soul; gath. out of many lands and ages. ('73.) New ed. 8°. '74. $5; mor., $9.. *Carter*.
— Thoughts on the death of little children; with sel. poems. 12°. '53. $1.50 .... *Randolph*.
— Travels in Europe and the east. 2 v. ill. 12°. $3; hf. cf., $6.50 .... *Harper*.
— Under the trees. cr. 8°. $2 .... *Harper*.
— Walking with God: life hid with Christ. 24°. '72. 40c.; 60c.; pap., 25c. .... *Randolph*.
— *See also* Evangelical Alliance Conf.; — Smith, H. B., *and* Prime, S. I.; — Smitten household.
Prime, Temple. Monograph of Am. corbiculadæ. 8°. '65. pap., 75c. .... *Smith.Inst.*
Prime, W: Cowper. Boat-life in Egypt and Nubia. ill. 12°. $2; hf. mor., $3.75 .... *Harper*.
— I go a fishing. cr. 8°. $2.50; hf. cf., $4.25.. *Harper*.
— Later years. 12°. $1.50; hf. cf., $3.25 ... *Harper*.
— Little passion (The): complete set of the 37 wood cuts by A. Dürer reprod. in fac-simile. 37 pl. roy. 4°. '68. hf. vellum, $10 .... *Bouton*.
— O mother dear, Jerusalem! the old hymn, its origin and genealogy. 16°. '65. $1.50.... *Randolph*.
— Old house by the river. 12°. $1.50 .... *Harper*.
— Tent-life in the Holy Land. ill. 12°. $2; hf. mor., $3.75 .... *Harper*.
Prime minister. *See* Trollope, A.
Primeval world of Hebrew tradition. Hedge, F. H. $1.50 .... *Roberts*.
Primitive culture. Tylor, E. B. 2 v. $5.. *Estes; Holt*.
Primitive piety revived. Fish, H. C. $1.25.. *Cong.Pub.*
Primrose (The). Everest, C. W. *net*, 19c... *Hamersley*.
Primrose series. *See* Marshall, E.

Primroses. 18°. 40c. .... *Dutton*.
Prince, D: Galvano-therapeutics. ill. 8°. '74. $1.25. *Lindsay*.
— Plastic and orthopedic surgery. ill. 8°. '71. $4.50. *Lindsay*.
Prince, H. New method for reed organ. obl. 4°. $2. *Gordon*.
Prince, T: *See* Morton, N., New England's memorial.
Prince (The). Cockton, H. 75c. .... *Peterson*.
Prince Alcohol. 18°. 50c.; 60c. .... *Am.Bapt.*
Prince Amabel. Brough, W. 15c. .... *French*.
Prince and the page. Yonge, C. M. 75c... *Macmillan*.
Prince and the pilgrim. 18°. 35c. .... *Cong.Pub.*
Prince and the prayer. Marsh, C. 10c. ...... *Carter*.
Prince and saviour. Mulholland, R. 25c.... *Noonan*.
Prince Camaralzaman. Bellingham, H., *and* Best, —. 15c. .... *French*.
Prince Charles. Smith, J. F. 75c. .... *Dick & F.*
Prince Charlie. *See* Winter evening lib.
Prince Dorus. Coyne, J. S. 15c. .... *French*.
Prince Eugene. Mundt, C. M. $1–$3.50 .. *Appleton*.
Prince Florestan. *See* Dilke, *Sir* C: W.
Prince for an hour. Morton, J. M. 15c. ..... *French*.
Prince in disguise. *See* Books of blessing.
Prince Marigold. *See* Young Prince Marigold.
Prince of darkness. Southworth, E. D. E. N. $1.75; $1.50 .... *Peterson*.
Prince of the house of David. Ingraham, J. H. $2. *Roberts*.
Prince of pulpit orators. Wakeley, J. B. $1.25. *Meth.Bk.Conc.*
Prince Paul. *See* Pearson, *Mrs.* E.
Prince Perrypets (History of). Knatchbull-Hugessen, L. $1.50 .... *Macmillan*.
Princely manhood. Platt, S. H. 60c.; 50c.... *Hope*.
Princes of art. Urbino, S. R. $2 .... *Lee & S.*
Princess (The). Gilbert, W. S. 15c. .... *French*.
Princess (The). *See* Tennyson, A.
Princess and the goblin. *See* MacDonald, G:
Princess Charming. Arden, H. T. 15c. ..... *French*.
Princess Ilse. *See* Plönnies, L. v.
Princess Narina. *See* Silver penny ser.
Princess of Hansfeld. Sue, E. 25c. ..... *U.P.James*.
Princess of Silverland. Strivelyne, E. $1.50. *Macmillan*.
Princess of Thule. *See* Black, W:
Princess Primrose. Bellingham, H., *and* Best, —. 15c. .... *French*.
Princesse de Trebizonde. *See* Ditson.
Principia; or, basis of social science. Wright, R. J. $3.50 .... *Lippincott*.
Principles form character. Wehner, J. H. 15c. *French*.
Principles of coal mining. (Element. sci. ser.) ill. 16°. '76. 75c. .... *Putnam*.
Principles of courtesy. Hervey, G. W. $1.50.. *Harper*.
Principles of criminal law. *See* Small books on great subjects.
Principles of the interior or hidden life. Upham, T. C. $1.50 .... *Harper*.
Principles of nature. Davis, A. J. $3.50.. *A.J.Davis*.
Printer boy: life of Benjamin Franklin. 16°. '60. $1.50 .... *Tilton*.
Printer's devil. Planché, J. R. 15c. .... *French*.
Printers' and newspaper publishers' reference book. 4°. '72. $30 .... *J.A.Murphy*.
Prinz Eugenius, d. edle Ritter. Oertel, P. F. W. 25c. *Steiger*.
Prinz Friedrich. *See* Van der Velde, K. F.
Prinz Gerbino. 12°. pap., 15c. .... *Radde*.

Prinzessin Ilse. *See* Plönnies, L. v.
Prinzessin (Die) v. Wolfenbüttel. *See* Zschokke, H.
Prior, *Sir* Ja. Life of Edm. Burke. 12°. (Bohn.) $1.25 .... *Little, B. & Co.*
— *Same.* 12°. (Bohn.) $1.40 ...... *Scribner, W. & A.*
— *Same.* 12°. (Bohn.) $1.50 .... *Lippincott.*
Prior, Mat. Poems. (Aldine ed.) 2 v. 16°. ea., 75c. *Lippincott.*
— *Same;* with memoir by J. Mitford. 2 v. por. 18°. $2 .... *Osgood.*
Priscilla. Banvard, J. $1.50 .... *Am. Bapt.*
Priscilla, the beautiful. Wise, D. $1.25 .. *Perkinpine.*
Prison chaplain. Clay, W. S. $4 .... *Macmillan.*
Prison life in the south. Abbott, A. O. $2 ... *Harper.*
Prisoner. 18°. 20c. .... *Cong. Pub.*
Prisoner at large. O'Keeffe, J. 15c. .... *French.*
Prisoner of war. Jerrold, D. 15c. .... *French.*
Prisoner released. *See* Two sons.
Prisoner's child. *See* Bradley, *Mrs.* M. E.
Prisoners (The). Breed, W. P. 75c. ..... *Pres. Bd.*
Prisonniers du Caucase. *See* Maistre, X. de.
Pritchard, G. S. *See* Edgar, J. H., *and* Pritchard, G. S.
Pritchard, *Miss* Sa. J. Aunt Saidee's cow. 16°. $1.25. *Carter.*
— Hugh's fire on the mountain. 18°. '66. 75c. *Randolph.*
— Joe and Jim under the roof and elsewhere. 18°. '65. 50c. .... *Randolph.*
— Kenny Carle's uniform. ill. 18°. 45c. .. *Bost. Am. Tr.*
— — *See also* Young hero stories.
— Margie's matches. 18°. '67. 60c. .... *Randolph.*
— Old stone chimney. 18°. '68. 75c. ..... *Randolph.*
— Rose Marbury. 16°. $1.25 .... *Carter.*
— Shawny and the lighthouse. 16°. 60c. ...... *Carter.*
Pritchard, W: Tarn. Digest of English admiralty cases; with app. of American equity cases. 8°. shp., $3.50 .... *Kay.*
Pritchett, J. H., *and* Sweeney, J: S. Baptism, its mode, subjects, etc., and conversion. [Debate.] 12°. $1 .... *S. W. Bk. & Pub.*
Private inquiry: farce. 16°. pap., 15c. ...... *Happy.*
Private law among the Romans. Phillimore, J. G. $5. *Macmillan.*
Private life of Galileo. *See* Galilei, G.
Private life of a king. Banvard, J. $2.50. (?) *Lit. and Art Pub.*
Private thoughts on religion. Adam, T. 65c. *Pres. Bd.*
Privateer's-man. *See* Marryat, F:
Prize. 18°. 60c. .... *Am. S. S.*
Prize. 18°. 30c. .... *Dutton.*
Prize. Root, G. F. 35c. .... *Church.*
Prize. *See* Little folks ser.; — Naomi's home.
Prize: farce. 16°. pap., 15c. .... *French.*
Prize; or, story of George Benson and William Sandford. 18°. 22c. .... *Am. S. S.*
Prize Bible. Baker, H. N. W. $1.15 .... *Hoyt.*
Prize Bible, and other tales. 18°. 50c. ...... *Pres. Bd.*
Prize essays on the temporal advantages of the Sabbath considered in relation to the working classes. ill. 12°. 80c. .... *Pres. Bd.*
Prize garden; or, the present results of good and evil principles. 18°. 40c. .... *Am. S. S.*
Prize lib. 4 v. 16°. $5.75 .... *Am. Bapt.*
Cont.: Christ's cadets. — Helen Egerton. — Eastern side. — Horace Wilde.
Prize lib. 4 v. 16°. $6 .... *Cong. Pub.*
Cont.: Deacon Sims' prayers, by Mary D. Chellis. — Donald Deane and his cross, by W. J. Bradley. — Highways and hedges. — Cobbler's daughter, by Mrs. M. E. Berry.
Prize medal. Frost, S. A. 50c. .... *Am. Tr.*
Pro and con. [Juvenile.] ill. 16°. '71. $1.25 .. *Lothrop.*
Pro and con of supernatural religion. Guild, E. E. 75c.; 40c. .... *D. M. Bennett.*
Pro and con of Universalism. Rogers, G. $1.25. *Williamson.*
Pro and con ser. 4 v. 16°. $5 .... *Lothrop.*
Cont.: Pro and con. — Tried in the fire. — Carolina. — Edith Prescot.
Pro aris et focis. Van Kortland, *Miss* —. $1.25 .. *Virtue.*
Probasco, S. R. Operation of the gunpowder pile driver. *See* Clarke, J. G., Reduction of ruling.
Probationer's manual. 18°. 30c. .. *Cin. Meth. Bk. Conc.*
Problem of evil. *See* Naville, E.
Problem of health. Greene, R. $1.50 .. *Jas. Campbell.*
Problem of human destiny. Dewey, O. $2.50 .. *Miller.*
Problem of life and immortality. Moody, L. 75c. *Colby.*
Problematic characters. Spielhagen, F. $1.50 .. *Holt.*
Problems of the age. Hewit, A. F. $2 ... *Cath. Pub.*
Problems of life and mind. Lewes, G. H. 2 v. ea., $3 .... *Osgood.*
Probst, Ant. Life, trial and execution of P., murderer of the Dearing family; with his two confessions. 8°. pap., 50c. .... *Peterson.*
Probyn, J. W. *See* Cobden Club essays.
Proceedings at centennial anniv. of dedication of North Dutch Church, May 25, 1869, and at laying of corner stone of new church [N. Y. City]. ill. 8°. pap., 50c. .... *N. Y. Ref. Ch. Bd.*
Proceedings at centennial celebration of battle of Lexington, April 19, 1875. ill. 8°. '75. $2.50; pap., $2 .... *Lockwood, B. & Co.*
Proceedings at the centennial celebration of Concord fight, April 19, 1875. ill. imp. 8°. '76. pap., $1.50. *Lockwood, B. & Co.*
Procter *Brothers* (*ed.*) Fisherman's ballads and songs of the sea. 16°. '74. pap., 50c. .... *Procter.*
Procter, Adelaide Ann. Legends and lyrics; with memoir by Dickens. por. and ill. 4°. mor., $15. *Osgood.*
— Poems. (Blue and gold ed.) por. 32°. '62. $1.25; hf. cf., $2.50; mor., $3. — (Cabinet ed.) por. 16°. $1.50; hf. cf., $3; mor., $4. — (Diamond ed.) 18°. '73. $1; hf. cf., $2.25; mor., $3. — (Red line ed.) por. and ill. sm. 4°. $3.50 hf. cf., $5; mor., $7 .... *Osgood.*
Procter, Bryan Waller. ["Barry Cornwall."] Memoir of Charles Lamb. 16°. '66. $1.50 ..... *Roberts.*
Procter, Fs. History of the Book of common prayer, with a rationale of its offices. 10th ed., rev. and enl. cr. 8°. '72. $3.50 .... *Macmillan.*
— *and* Maclear, G. F. Elementary introduction to Book of common prayer. 4th ed., rev. and enl. 18°. 75c. .... *Macmillan.*
Procter, G: H. Fisherman's memorial and record book; containing list of vessels lost from Gloucester, 1830–1873, statistics, sketches, etc. 8°. '73. $1.50; pap., $1 .... *Procter.*
Proctor, *Maj.* —. Fighting their way; or, the crusaders. ill. 12°. $1.50 .... *World Pub.*
Proctor, Barn. S. Practical pharmacy: lectures. ill. 8°. '73. $5 .... *Lindsay.*
Proctor, *Miss* Edna Dean. Poems. 16°. '66. $1.25; $1.50 .... *Hurd & H.*
— Russian journey (A). 16°. '71. $1.50. — (Ill. holiday ed.) 12°. $3 .... *Osgood.*
Proctor, Fk. Pocket book of useful tables and formulæ for marine engineers. 18°. $2. ...... *Baird.*
Proctor, J. C. *See* Marshall, L., Proctor, J. C., *and* Burnham, S.
Proctor, L. B. The bench and bar of N. Y.: biographical sketches, etc. 8°. '70. shp., $5.50; hf. cf., $6.50 .... *Ward & P.*
Proctor, R: Ant. Borderland of science. 12°. $4. *Lippincott.*
— Elementary astronomy; with hints for young telescopists. ill. 16°. 75c. .... *Lippincott.*

Proctor, R: Ant., *continued.*
— Elementary physical geog. ill. 16°. 75c...*Lippincott.*
— Essays on astronomy. pl. and ill. 8°. $4.50. *Appleton; Scribner, W.&A.*
— Expanse of heaven: essays on the wonders of the firmament. 12°. $2................*Appleton.*
— Half hours with the stars: maps with introd. and text. 5th ed. 4°. (Lond.) '74. bds., $2..*Little, B. & Co.*
— *Same.* demy 4°. '73. $2.25............*Putnam.*
— Half hours with the telescope. ill. 18°. '73. $1.25. *Putnam.*
— Handbook of the stars; showing places of 1500 stars, with hints on mapping, etc. maps and diagrams. 12°. $2.50..................*Scribner, W. & A.*
— Light science for leisure hours. 12°. $1.75..*Appleton.*
— Moon (The): her motions, aspect, scenery and physical conditions; with 3 lunar photos., plates, charts, etc. 8°. $5.................*Appleton.*
— New star atlas: 12 circular maps with two index plates; with letter-press introd. on study of the stars. 8°. $2.50.....................*Putnam.*
— *Same.* f°. $12.50. — 4°. $2.50...*Scribner, W.&A.*
— Orbs around us: familiar essays on moon, planets, etc. 12°. $3.................*Scribner, W.&A.*
— Other worlds than ours: the plurality of worlds, studied under light of recent scientific researches. ill. 12°. $2.50......................*Appleton.*
— Our place among the infinities. 12°. $1.75..*Appleton.*
— Saturn and its system. ill. 8°. $7..*Scribner, W.&A.*
— Science byways; [also] Money is science. por cr. 8°. $4.......................*Lippincott*
— Strange discoveries resp. the aurora and recent solar researches. cr. 8°. '74. pap., 25c........*Estes.*
— Sun (The): ruler, fire, light and life of the planetary system. col. pl. and ill. cr. 8°. $5.50. *Scribner, W.& A.*
— Sun views of the earth; or, the seasons illustrated. pl. 4°. '73. $3....................*Putnam.*
— Universe (The) and the coming transits: researches and views resp. const. of the heavens; with investigation of conditions of coming transits of Venus. 23 charts. 8°. $6.........*Lippincott.*
— *See also* Tribune popular science.

Prodigal son. Brendle, D. F. $1......*Ref. Ch. Pub.*
Prodigal son. Mott, G. S. 60c...........*Pres. Bd.*
Prodigal son. Müller, M. $2...............*Pustet.*
Prodigal son. Punshon, W. M. 25c...*Meth. Bk. Conc.*
Prodigal son. Rogers, E. P. 25c...........*Am. Tr.*
Prodigal son. Sullivan, A. S. $1.50–$1.....*Ditson.*
Produce tables. 12°. $1.50..................*Mason.*
Profession is not principle. *See* Kennedy, G.
Profession of faith of a Savoyard vicar. Rousseau, J. J. 10c..........................*Mendum.*
Professor. *See* Brontë, Ctte.
Professor at the breakfast table. *See* Holmes, O. W.
Professor's lady; tr. by M. Howitt. [Fiction.] 8°. pap., 25c...........................*Harper.*
Professor's wife. Macgregor, A. L. $1.75. *Lippincott.*
Proffatt, J: Curiosities and law of wills: v. 2 of "Legal recreations." 12°. $1.50...........*S. Whitney.*
— Law of private corporations under civil code of California; with annotations and forms. 8°. '76. shp., $4.50........................*Bancroft.*
— Treatise on trial by jury, including questions of law and fact; with origin and history of jury trial. 8°. $7.50.........................*S. Whitney.*
— Women before the law. 12°. '74. $1; hf. bd., $1.25. *Putnam.*
Profile House. Cox, W. N. $1.50..........*Graves.*
Profit and loss. Quigley, H. $1.50......(?) *O'Kane.*
Profits of godliness; by author of "Scenes in Chusan." 18°. 50c...........................*Pres. Bd.*
Progress. *See* Dodge, A. A.
Progress and prejudice. Gore, C. G. $1....*De Witt.*
Progress of religious ideas. Child, L. M. $6.75; $13.50. *Miller.*
Progress of the working classes. Ludlow, J. M., *and* Jones, L. $1......................*Routledge.*
Progressionists. *See* Bischoff, J. E.
Progressive petticoats. Roosevelt, R. B. $1.50. *Carleton.*
Prohibition does prohibit. Stearns, J. N. 10c. *Nat. Temp.*
Prohibition a failure. Lewis, D. $1.50.....*Osgood.*
Prohibition vs. license. Dungan, D. R. 15c...*Cen. Bk.*
Promessi sposi (I). *See* Manzoni, A.
Prometheus. Liszt, F. $1.50; $1; $1.25...*Church.*
Prometheus. Reece, R. 15c...............*French.*
Prometheus bound; — chained. *See* Æschylus.
Promise and the promiser. *See* Shipton, A.
Promise of the Father. Palmer, P. $1.50...*Palmer.*
Promised one. ill. sq. 18°. '61. 25c........*Am. Tr.*
Promises and precepts: texts of Scripture for every day. 64°. 25c........................*Nelson.*
Promises of God. Plumer, W. S. 40c...*N. Y. Ref. Ch. Bd.*
Promises of God. Wines, E. C. 50c........*Pres. Bd.*
Promotion. Planché, J. R. 15c............*French.*
Pronouncing Bible dictionary; with hist. of the books of the B., and Brown's Concordance; with tables, index, etc. ill. 8°. $2; $2.50.......*Harding.*
Pronouncing dictionary of Scripture proper names. 18°. 25c.............................*Nelson.*
Proof palpable of immortality. Sargent, E. $1; 75c. *Colby.*
Proper lessons. *See* Protestant Episcopal Church.
Propertius, Petronius Arbiter, *and* Joannes *Secundus.* Works; tr. with poetical versions from various sources. 12°. (Bohn.) $1.75...*Little, B. & Co.*
— — — *Same.* 12°. (Bohn.) $2. *Lippincott; Scribner, W.&A.*
Property consecrated. *See* Fry, B. St. J.
Prophecies of St. Columbkille. 18°. 60c....*Sadlier.*
Prophecy, a preparation for Christ. *See* Smith, R. P.
Prophecy and the times. Berg, J. F. $1..*Perkinpine.*
Prophet. Taylor, B. $2...................*Osgood.*
Prophet Daniel: lectures for a Sabbath school; tr. from the Fr. ill. 18°. 75c............*Pres. Bd.*
Prophet heroes of Palestine. Headley, P. C. 25c.; 30c. *J. E. Potter.*
Prophet of fire. Macduff, J. R. $1.50.......*Carter.*
Prophet of the highest. Gale, N. $1...*Bost. Am. Tr.*
Prophet of Nazareth. Meredith, E. P. $4..*Mendum.*
Prophète (Le). *See* Meyerbeer, G.
Prophetic abstract from proceedings of the Trojan Society for retardation of science, for 1870. 8°. pap., 10c.........................*W. H. Young.*
Prophetic vision of Daniel. Tregelles, S. P. $2.25. *Wiley.*
Prophetic voice concerning America. Sumner, C. $2. *Lee & S.*
Prophet's guard. 18°. 30c................*Dutton.*
Prophets (The). 18°. 30c.; 40c.........*Am. Bapt.*
Prophets and kings of the Old Testament. Maurice, F. D. $3.50......................*Macmillan.*
Prophets of the Bible and the seven churches. Noble, W. F. P. *$3; $4...............*New World.*
Proportion in religious belief and religious practice. Howson, J. S. 50c................*Routledge.*
Prose idylls. Kingsley, C. $1.75........*Macmillan.*
Proserpina. Ruskin, J. $1..............(?) *Wiley.*
Prosper. Cherbuliez, V. $1.25...............*Holt.*
Prosser, *Mrs.* —. Cheery chime of Garth, and other stories. 18°. '74. 75c...............*Nelson.*
— Cicely Brown's trials: how she got into them, and how she got out of them, and what they did for her. ill. 16°. '71. $1..............*Lothrop.*

Prosser, *Mrs. —, continued.*
— Clackitts of Inglebrook Hall. sq. 16°. '72. 75c.; pap., 50c. .... *Randolph.*
— Day after to-morrow; or, hoping and fearing. ('71.) New ed. 16°. '75. $1.50 .... *Hoyt.*
— Door without a knocker, and other tales. ill. 12°. $1.50 .... *Nelson.*
— Fables for the young folks. ill. 12°. 75c. *Bost. Am. Tr.*
— Sunshine; or, cures for all ills. ill. 16°. $1. *Bost. Am. Tr.*
— — *See also* Prairie lib.

Prosser, T. Application of new system of distillation; [also] Béton coignet, by L. F. Beckwith. 8°. pap., 90c. .... *Am. Soc. of C. E.*

Prostrate state. Pike, J. S. $1 .... *Appleton.*

Proteaux, A. Practical guide for manufacture of paper and boards; with add. by L. S. Le Normand; tr. with notes by H. Paine; with chapter on the manufacture of paper from wood in the U. S. by H. T. Brown. pl. 8°. '66. $10 .... *Baird.*

Protection against fire. Bird, J. $1.50 ... *Hurd & H.*

Protestant Episcopal almanac and Church directory. [Annual.] 18°. pap., 25c. .... *Whittaker.*

Protestant Episcopal Church. Additional hymns, set forth by House of Bishops, 1865. 32°. pap., 10c. — 18°. 25c. .... *Rutter.*
— *Same.* 18°. 13c.–$1.75 .... *Lippincott.*
— — *See also below* Book of common prayer; Church service.
— Book of common prayer. 48°. 62½c.–$1.50 .. *Wiley.*
— *Same.* 24°. $1–$7 .... *Hurd & H.*
— *Same.* 16°. $1–$6. — 18°. 75c.–$5 .... *Lippincott.*
— *Same.* 32°. 25c.; shp., 30c. — 18°. 30c.; shp., 35c. — 24°. mor., $1; — without Psalms and hymns. 32°. 20c.; shp., 25c. — 18°. 25c.; shp., 30c. .... *Claremont.*
— *Same.* ("Brevier" ed.) 32°. 30c.–$4.50 .. *Lippincott.*
— *Same.* ("Diamond" ed.) 48°. 30c.–$1 .. *Lippincott.*
— *Same.* ("Pica" ed.) roy. 12°. $1.25–$5 .. *Lippincott.*
— *Same;* with notes and introd. hist. of the Liturgy. ill. 8°. $6; mor., $12 .... *Routledge.*
— *Same;* with Additional hymns. 48°. 88c.–$5 .. *Rutter.*
— — *Same.* 32°. 25c.–$6.50.—18°. $1.20–$8.50 .. *Rutter.*
— — *Same.* 16°. $4.50–$11. — 12°. $5–$6.50. — 8°. $1.75–$2.75 .... *Rutter.*
— — *Same.* ("The gem prayer book.") 48°. $1.25–$3. *J. E. Potter.*
— — *Same.* ("The medium prayer book.") 18°. $1.25–$4 .... *J. E. Potter.*
— — *Same.* ("The royal prayer book.") 8°. $2–$7. *J. E. Potter.*
— — *Same.* ("Rubricated Book of common prayer.") 16°. $1.75–$12 .... *Hurd & H.*
— *Same;* and Hymnal revised. 2 v. [in case]. 32°. $1.25–$6 .... *Lippincott.*
— — *See also* Blunt, J. H.; — Campion, W. M., *and* Beamont, W. J.; — Reformed Episc. Ch.; — *and below* Hymnal.
— *French.* fp. 8°. (Bagster.) $1.12. — (Polymicrian ed.) 32°. $1.12. — (Large print ed.) 8°. $3. *Wiley.*
— *Germ.* fp. 8°. (Bagster.) $1.12. — (Polymicrian ed.) 32°. $1.12 .... *Wiley.*
— *Greek.* fp. 8°. (Bagster.) $1.12. — 32°. $1.12 .. *Wiley.*
— *Ital.* fp. 8°. (Bagster.) $1.12. — (Polymicrian ed.) 32°. $1.12 .... *Wiley.*
— *Latin;* ed. by John Carey. fp. 8°. (Bagster.) $1.12. — (Polymicrian ed.) 32°. $1.12 .. *Wiley.*
— *Mod. Gk.* 32°. (Bagster.) $1.12 .... *Wiley.*
— *Port.* fp. 8°. (Bagster.) $1.12. — (Polymicrian ed.) 32°. $1.12 .... *Wiley.*
— *Span.* fp. 8°. (Bagster.) $1.12. — (Polymicrian ed.) 32°. $1.12 .... *Wiley.*
— *Octaglot* Book of common prayer. [Eng., Fr., It., Germ., Span., anc. and mod. Gk., and Lat.) fp. 8°. (Bagster.) $5 .... *Wiley.*

Protestant Episcopal Church, *continued.*
— Calendar of the Prayer book; with app. of chief Christian emblems, from early and mediæval monuments. 12°. '70. $2.50 .... *Pott.*
— *Same.* ill. 16°. '67. $3; cf., $6 .. *Scribner, W. & A.*
— Canticles; with music. 8°. 60c. .... *Dutton.*
— — *See also below* Hymnal.
— Church service. 18°. $2–$5 .... *Lippincott.*
— *Same;* with Additional hymns. 48°. $2.50–$7. — 32°. $3–$7. — 18°. mor., $6.50 .... *Rutter.*
— — *See also below* The evening service.
— Collects for the several Sundays, and holy days and in occasional offices prescribed in Book of common prayer. 16°. 35c.; pap., 15c. .. *Dutton.*
— *Same;* with col. floral designs. cr. 8°. '70. $4. *Macmillan.*
— 1st Congress, N. Y., Oct. 6, 7, 1874. Proceedings. 8°. pap., 50c. .... *Whittaker.*
— 2d Congress, Phila., Nov. 9–12, 1875. Proceedings. 8°. $1; pap., 75c. .... *Whittaker.*
Note. The above 2 in 1 v., $1.50.
— Free evening service: order of daily evening prayer, with select. from authorized Psalms and hymns. 18°. '65. 20c. .... *Dutton.*
— Hymnal revised. 32°. 20c.–75c. — 18°. 40c.; 50c. *Pott.*
— *Same.* ('71.) 15th ed. 32°. '75. 20c.–$2.25. — 16°. 40c.–$2.50 .... *Claxton.*
— *Same.* 16°. 75c.; $4 .... *Hurd & H.*
— *Same.* 16°. 75c.–$3. — 18°. 50c.–$1.50 .. *Lippincott.*
— *Same.* 16°. $1; mor., $4. — 18°. 50c. ... *Appleton.*
— *Same.* ("Pearl" ed.) 48°. 15c.; 20c. — ["Nonpareil" ed.) 32°. 15c.; 20c. — ("Bourgeoise" ed.) 32°. 35c.–$2.75. — 16°. 40c.–75c. .. *Dutton.*
— *Same;* with tunes new and old; ed. by J. Ireland Tucker. 12°. $1.85; $1.90 .... *Pott.*
— *Same;* [also] Book of common prayer. 32°. '65. $2.50–$10 .... *Dutton.*
— *Same;* [also] Canticles with music; prep. by A. B. Goodrich and W. B. Gilbert. 8°. '75. $1.75; mor., $5. — 4°. $3.50–$9 .... *Dutton.*
— — First ed. of music hymnal. 8°. 75c. .... *Dutton.*
— — *Same;* and Canticles. 8°. $1 .... *Dutton.*
— Lessons of Holy Scripture to be read at morning and evening prayer on Sundays and other holy days throughout the year. 18°. $1.50–$3.75 .. *Rutter.*
— Liturgy and hymns, chants and Church catechism. 32°. bds., 20c. .... *Whittaker.*
— *Same;* for common schools. 18°. '69. pap., 12c. *Pott.*
— *Same;* for Sunday schools. 18°. 12c. .... *Whittaker.*
— — Emphasized liturgy: morning, evening, communion and burial services and collects marked for emphasis and clause; with essay on emphasis, etc., by A. M. Bell. 12°. '66. $1 .... *Burbank.*
— Manuscript chant book. obl. 4°. $1.50 .... *Gordon.*
— Prayer book psalter; in eight languages. fp. 8°. (Bagster.) $1.75 .... *Wiley.*
— Proper lessons to be read at morning and evening prayer, on the Sundays and other holy days throughout the year. 48°. $1.75–$2. — 32°. $1–$2 .... *Rutter.*
— *Same.* 18°. 75c.–$3 .... *Lippincott.*
— *Same.* 12°. '61. $1–$2.50.—18°. $2–$2.75 .. *Dutton.*
— Psalter pointed for singing and set to music; according to use of Trinity Parish, N. Y. 16°. '76. $1.25. obl. 8°. $2 .... *Pott.*
— Tune book. obl. 12°. $1.50 .... *Gordon.*
— *See also* Certain sermons; — Church of England; — Concordance; — Reformed Episcopal Church.

Protestant Episcopal Sunday school book. 4 nos. 18°. pap., 24c. .... *Dutton.*

Protestant gems of the Prayer book. Du Hamel, J. P. 50c.; $1 .... *Claxton.*

Protestantism or Catholicism: "Lenten pastoral" of Bp. Gilmour, with discourses in reply by T. B. Forbush; with letters of G. and Father Thorpe. 8°. pap., 50c. .... *Ingham.*

Protesting Christian standing before the judgment seat of Christ to answer for the protest against that patient church which Christ built upon a rock. 18°. 30c. .... *Coddington.*

Proud and lazy. Adams, W. T. 45c........ *Lee & S.*

Proud girl (The), and how she was cured. 18°. 22c. *Am.S.S.*

Proud little Dody. Chester, S. E. $1.25.... *Am.Tr.*

Proud Miss MacBride. Saxe, J. G. $2.50; $5.50. *Osgood.*

Proudfit, J: Remarks on history, structure and theories of the Apostles' creed. 8°. pap., 25c. *N.Y.Ref.Ch.Bd.*

Proudfoot, J: The Scotchman in America. [Poems and addresses.] 12°. '73. $2......... *Ingham.*

Proudhon, Pierre Jos. Works. v. 1: What is property? inquiry into principles of right and of government; tr. by B. R. Tucker. 8°. '76. $3.50; cf., $6.50 .... *B.R.Tucker.*

Prout, *Father (pseud.)* *See* Mahony, Fs.

Prout, W: Treatise on chemistry, meteorology and digestion; ed. by J. W. Griffith. (Bridgewater treatise.) 12°. (Bohn.) $1.75... *Little, B. & Co.*

— *Same.* 12°. (Bohn.) $2. *Lippincott; Scribner, W. & A.*

Proverb stories. *See* Bradley, M. E., *and* Neely, K. J.

Proverbial philosophy. *See* Tupper, M. F.

Proverbs. *See* Bible.

Proverbs and other remarkable sayings of Solomon. 18°. 60c........ *Am.S.S.*

Proverbs and their lessons. Trench, R. C. $1. *Macmillan.*

Proverbs from far and near. Tegg, W. 50c. *Scribner, W.&A.*

Proverbs illustrated. Gatty, M. 50c......... *Carter.*

Proverbs of Solomon. demy 4°. $1; bds., 50c. *Scribner, W.&A.*

Providence and life. Chapin, E. H. $1.50. *Williamson.*

Providence of God displayed in a series of interesting facts. 18°. 55c........ *Pres.Bd.*

Provincial Council. *See* Baltimore.

Provine, J. C. The blind man's cottage. 16°. 50c. (?) *Cumberland.*

Provings of cistus canadensis. *See* New.

Provision for passing over Jordan. Scudder, J. 25c. *Am.Tr.*

Provoked husband. Van Brugh, *Sir* J., *and* Cibber, C. 15c........ *French.*

Provost, Kath. Margaret Worthington. ill. 16°. '73. $1.50 .... *Lothrop.*

Provost Marshal-General's Bureau. *See* United States.

Provost of Bruges. Lovell, G. W. 15c...... *French.*

Prudence Palfrey. Aldrich, T. B. $1.50; $1.. *Osgood.*

Prudy books. *See* Clarke, R. S.

Prudy keeping house. Clarke, R. S. 75c..... *Lee & S.*

Prue and I. Curtis, G. W. $1.50........ *Harper.*

Prüfet die Geister. Brobst, S. K. 15c. .... *Brobst.*

Prüfungen. *See* Hoffmann, F.

Prying Polly, and other stories. ill. 18°. 60c... *Crowell.*

— *See also* Bright eye lib.

Pryor, J. P. *See* Jordan, T., *and* Pryor, J. P.

Psalm book. 48°. shp., 20c. — 32°. 25c.-40c. — 24°. 40c.-$1. — 12°. shp., 90c.; roan, $1; — with Brown's notes. 12°. $1-$2.25.. *U.P.Bd.of Pub.*

Psalm king. Perkins, T. E. $1.50 ..... *Huntington.*

Psalmist. *See* Stow, B., *and* Smith, S. F.

Psalms. Psalms in metre. 12°. $1.25; $1.50. — 18°. 60c.; 75c. — 48°. 30c.; 40c.; — with Brown's notes. 18°. 75c. .... *Carter.*

— *Same.* 32°. '72. shp., 30c.; mor., 75c. — 18°. shp., 50c.; mor., $1.25........ *Claxton.*

Psalms, *continued.*

— *Germ.* Die Psalmen Davids, nebst einer Sammlung geistlicher Lieder für öffentlichen und Privat-Gottesdienst. 12°. $1.10. — 18°. 90c... *Pres.Bd.*

— *Span.* Salmos en verso. 32°. '55. 40c. ... *Am.Tr.*

— *See also* Bible, Psalms.

Psalms and hymns adapted to worship in Presb. Ch. 12°. $1.75-$4.50. — 18°. $1.25-$3.40. — 24°. 75c.-$5.50. — 64°. 45c.-$1.75 .... *Pres.Bd.*

— *Same.* 24°. 50c.-$6. — 18°. 75c.-$7. — 12°. $1.25-$4.80. — (Pulpit ed.) 8°. $3.50-$5.. *Pres.Com.*

— *See also* Congregational churches in Conn.; — Hymns; — Presbyterian Church.

Psalms of life. Adams, J. S. $1; 80c. ...... *Ditson.*

Psalter (The): Book of Psalms in different metres, with music. 16°. 50c.-$2.50 ... *U.P.Bd.of Pub.*

Psalter (The): sel. from the Book of Psalms; arr. [for] public worship. 8°. '65. 90c.; $2.50; $4.50. — 16°. 60c........ *Barnes.*

— *See also* Bible, Psalms; — Protestant Episc. Ch.

Psaltery (The). Mason, L., *and* Webb, G. J. $1.50. *Ditson.*

Psyche (A) of to-day. Jenkin, C. $1.25........ *Holt.*

Public benefactor. Baker, G. M. 15c. ...... *Lee & S.*

Public men and events. Sargent, N. 2 v. $6.. *Lippincott.*

Public school singing book. Bower, J. 25c... *Fortescue.*

Public worship, partly responsive, for any Christian denomination; with introd. by D. March. 8°. '74. $1........ *Barnes.*

Publicans and sinners. Braddon, M. E. 75c. *Harper.*

Publishers' trade list annual; embr. trade lists of Am. publishers, with alphab. ref. list of books recorded in "Publishers' Weekly," Jan. 16, 1873-June 27, 1874; also American educ. catalogue for 1874; with indexes of firms and trade specialties. [2d year.] roy. 8°. '74. *net*, $1.50.. *Publisher's Weekly.*
Note. That for 1873 is o.p.

Publishers' trade list annual; embr. trade lists of Am. publishers, with alphab. indexes to principal books; also American educ. catalogue for 1875; with indexes of firms and trade specialties. [3d year.] roy. 8°. '75. *net*, $2........ *Publishers' Weekly.*

Publishers' trade list annual; embr. trade lists of Am. publishers; with indexes of firms and specialties in annuals for 1873-'76, a publishers' directory, etc. [4th year.] roy. 8°. '76. *net*, $1.50. *Publishers' Weekly.*

— *See also* Trade circular annual.

Publishers' Weekly. *See* Alphabetical reference list.

Puck. La Rame, L. de. $1.50........ *Lippincott.*

Puck novels. 5 v. 16°. ea., 75c........ *Hinton.*
Cont.: Bulwer's Coming race. — Erckmann-Chatrian's Bells. — Schücking's Powder and gold. — Fulton's Brown stone front. — Heyse's Maiden of Treppi.

Puckle, G: Hale. Elementary treatise on conic sections and algebraic geometry. 4th ed., enl. cr. 8°. $2.50 .... *Macmillan.*

Puck's nightly pranks. Bund, L. 50c....... *Roberts.*

Puddleford papers. Riley, H. H. $1.50..... *Lee & S.*

Pugh, *Mrs.* Eliza Lofton. In a crucible. 12°. '71. $1.50 .... *Claxton.*

— Not a hero. 8°. '67. pap., 50c........ *Eyrich.*

Pugh, Selina. Life and happy death of Selina Pugh. 18°. 22c........ *Am.S.S.*

Pujol, L: *and* Van Norman, D. C. Complete French class-book. 8°. '60. $2.25; $2.40; — in 3 v., ea., $1.25. — Key. 8°. '62. $1.50 .... *Barnes.*

Pullan, *Mrs.* Mta. Marian. Lady's manual of fancy work. ill. 8°. $2 .... *Dick & F.*

Pullen, H: W: Psalter and Canticles pointed for chanting; with marks of expression and list of appropriate chants. 8°. '67. $1.50........ *Macmillan.*

— Stones through glass houses; or, modern Christianity a civilized heathenism. 12°. '74. $1.25; pap., 75c. *W.F.Gill.*

Pulpit cyclopedia and Christian minister's companion: sketches and skeletons of sermons and essays. 8°. $2.50 .... *Appleton.*
— *Same.* 8°. $3 .... *So. Bapt.*
Pulpit eloquence of 19th century. Fish, H. C. $4 .. *Dodd.*
Pulpit germs. Wythe, W. W. $1.50 .... *Lippincott.*
Pulpit ministrations. Spring, G. 2 v. $6 ... *Harper.*
Pulpit notes. Parker, J. $2 .... *Routledge.*
Pulpit of the American revolution. Thornton, J. W. $2.50 .... *Lothrop.*
Pulpit of the Methodist Church, south. Smithson, W. T. $4.50; $5; $6.50; $10 .... *Wilstach.*
Pulpit themes, and preacher's assistant: outlines of sermons; [also] Art of preaching, practically developed. 12°. $2 .... *Sheldon; So. Bapt.*
Pulsifer, D: Account of battle of Bunker Hill; with Burgoyne's account of the battle. map. 16°. (cop. '72.) '75. 50c.; 75c. .... *Williams.*
— Guide to Boston and vicinity. maps and ill. 12°. (cop. '66.) '71. $1 .... *Williams.*
Pulsifer, Josiah D. *See* Maine, Reports.
Pulszky, Theresa. Memoirs of an Hungarian lady: [autobiog.] roy. 12°. $1 .... *Lea.*
Pummill, Ja. Russet leaves: poems and sketches. ill. 12°. $2 .... *Lippincott.*
Pumpelly, Raph. Across America and Asia: notes of a five years' journey around the world and of residence in Arizona, Japan and China. ('69.) New ed. maps and ill. roy. 8°. '70. $5.—(chp. ed.) post 8°. $2.50 .... *Holt.*
— Geological researches in China, Mongolia, etc. 4°. '66. pap., $3.50 .... *Smith. Inst.*
— *and* Brooks, T. B., *and* Schmidt, A. Iron ores of Missouri and Michigan; with ill. in text and geol. and topog. atlas. 3 v.: text, 2 v., 8°; atlas, f°. '76. $10 .... *Putnam.*
Punch and Judy picture-book. sq. 12°. '73. 75c.; bds., 60c. .... *Routledge.*
Punchard, G: View of Congregationalism: its principles and doctrines; with introd. by R. S. Storrs. 12°. $1.25 .... *Cong. Pub.*
— *Same.* ('43.) New ed. 16°. '44. 60c. ... *Draper.*
Punot, S. Tim's little mother. 12°. $1.25 .... *Carter.*
Punshon, W: Morley. Lectures and sermons. 12°. $1.25 .... *R. Worthington.*
— *Same.* cr. 8°. $2.50; mor., $4 .... *Estes.*
— New handbook of illustration; or, treasury of themes, anecdotes, etc. 8°. $3.75 ..... *Scribner, W. & A.*
— Prodigal son: four discourses. 12°. '68. 25c. *Meth. Bk. Conc.*
— Sabbath chimes. 12°. '68. $2–$5 .. *Meth. Bk. Conc.*
— Select lectures and sermons of the Wesleyan Conference, England. 12°. '60. $1.25 .. *Pounsford.*
— Sermons and lectures. 12°. $2; $2.50. *Cin. Meth. Bk. Conc.*
Pupil of the legion of honor. *See* Enault, L:
Pupil's daily exercises; for piano. 5 nos. f°. $1.40; ea., 20c.–30c. .... *Gordon.*
Pupils of St. John. *See* Yonge, C. M.
Purcell, J: B. Marriage and family duties in general: a pastoral letter. 24°. 25c. .... *Benziger.*
— *See also* Campbell, Alex., *and* Purcell, J: B.
Purday, C: H. *See* Tucker, W. G., *and* Purday, C: H.
Purdon, J: Digest of laws of Penna., 1700–1872. 10th ed., rev. and enl., with notes, tables and index by F. C. Brightly. 2 v. imp. 8°. shp., $15 .. *Kay.*
Pure Christianity (A) the world's only hope. Cushman, R. W. 75c. .... *Sheldon.*
Pure diamonds. Murray, J. R. 35c. .... *Brainard.*
Pure gold. 18°. 45c.–55c. .... *Am. Bapt.*
Pure gold. Marston, W. 15c. .... *French.*
Pure gold for the Sunday school. Lowry, R., *and* Doane, W. H. 75c.; 35c. .... *Biglow.*

Pure gold from rivers of wisdom. ill. 32°. 38c. *Appleton.*
Pure gold ser. *See* Mudge, Z. A.
Pure light. Whiting, S. K. 50c. .... *G. D. Russel*
Purgatory opened to the piety of the faithful; or, the month of November consecrated to relief of souls in purgatory. 12°. 38c. .... *Strong*
Puritani (I). *See* Bellini, V.
Puritans (The). Myers, E. 75c. .... *Macmillan*
Puritans (The) and Queen Elizabeth. Hopkins, S. 3 v. $7.50 .... *Randolph*
Purple, S: S. Inaugural address. See Flint, A. Valedictory address.
Purple and fine linen. Fawcett, E. $1.75 .. *Carleton*
Purple jar. Edgeworth, M. 25c. .... *Routledge*
Purpose. Bates, L. $1.25 .... *Am. Tr*
Purry, J: P: Description of province of South Carolina drawn up at Charlestown, in Sept., 1731: Washington, 1837. [Reprint.] 4°. pap., 25c. .. *Sabin*
Purse and pistol. *See* Galloping Gus.
Pursuit of holiness. Goulburn, E. M. 75c. *Appleton; Pott*
Pursuit of knowledge under difficulties. *See* Craik, G. L.
Purty shure cure: Irish dram. sketch. 16°. pap., 15c. *Happy*
Pusey, E: Bouverie. Advent readings from the fathers. 16°. '70. $2 .... *Pott*
— Collegiate and professional teaching and discipline answer to Vaughan. 8°. '54. $1 .... *Pott*
— Councils of the church, 51–381. 8°. '57. $3.50 .. *Pott*
— Daniel, the prophet: lectures, Oxford; with answer to R. Williams. New ed. 8°. '68. $3 .... *Pott*
— Doctrine of the real presence as contained in the fathers. 8°. '55. $4 .... *Pott*
— Eirenicon (An): letter to author of "Christian year." 12°. $1.50 .... *Appleton*
— Lent readings from the fathers. 16°. '72. $2 .. *Pott*
— Lenten sermons; chiefly to young men at the universities, 1858–1874. 8°. '74. $2.25 .... *Pott*
— Minor prophets; with comment. and introd. to the books. 4 v. 4°. ea., $1.75 .... *Pott*
Cont.: Hosea–Joel, introd.—Joel, introd.; Amos, vi., 6.—Amos, vi., 6 to the end.—Obadiah, Jonah, Micah, i., 12.—Micah i., 13; Nahum.
— Occasional parochial sermons. 8°. '65. $2.50 .. *Pott*
— On the clause, "and the Son." 8°. '76. $2 .. *Pott.*
— Parochial sermons. 2 v. 8°. '68. $4.25 .... *Pott.*
— *Same.* 12°. $1.75 .... *McCauley*
— Real presence (The): the doctrine of the Eng. church. 8°. '69. $3 .... *Pott.*
— Royal supremacy not an arbitrary authority, but limited by the laws of the church of which kings are members. 8°. '50. $1.25 .... *Pott.*
— Sermons before Univ. of Oxford, 1859–1872. 8°. '72. $2.25 .... *Pott.*
Puss and John. *See* Barrow, *Mrs.* F.
Puss and robin. *See* Hood, T.
Puss in boots. ill. f°. pap., 15c.; 20c. ... *J. E. Potter.*
Puss in boots. [Toy-book.] ill. 4°. $1; 50c. .. *Routledge.*
Puss in boots. *See* Cruikshank, G.
Puss in boots. Keating, E. H. 15c. .... *French.*
Puss in the corner ser. 4 nos. ill f°. ea., pap., 15c.; 20c.; 30c. .... *J. E. Potter.*
Pussie's mischief. 4°. 50c.; pap., 25c. ...... *Nelson.*
Pussy, *Mme.* Fouqueau de. Le grand-père et ses quatre petit-fils: livre de lecture à l'usage des écoles. 11th Am. ed., rev. with notes by F. S. Williams. 12°. hf. roan, $1.50 .... *Ware.*
Pussy-cat mew. Knatchbull-Hugessen, E. H. $1.25. *Harper.*
Pussy Tip-Toe's family. Sanford, D. P. $2.25 .. *Dutton.*
Pussy's picture-book. ill. sq. 12°. '74. $1; bds., 50c. .... *Routledge.*
Put off is not done with. *See* Andersen, H. C.

Put through. Small, G. G. 25c. . . . . *Collin & S.*

Put to the test. Chamberlain, C., *jr.* $1.50 . . *Hinton.*

Put yourself in his place. *See* Reade, C:

Puterbaugh, Sabin D. Treatise on forms of chancery suits, pleading and practice in Ill. 8°. '74. shp., $7.50 . . . . *Callaghan.*

— Treatise on forms of common law actions, pleading and practice in use in Ill. ('63.) 3d ed. 8°. '73. shp., $7.50 . . . . *Callaghan.*

Putkins. Emerson, W. R. 15c. . . . . *Lee & S.*

Putlitz, Gst. H: zu. Badekuren: Lustspiel. ('66.) New ed. 12°. '76. pap., 50c. . . . . *Holt.*

— Herz (Das) vergessen: Lustspiel. 12°. pap., 40c. *Holt.*

— Vergissmeinnicht: eine Arabeske. With Eng. notes. 12°. '71. pap., 50c. *Holt.*

— Was sich der Wald erzählt: ein Märchenstraus. ('64.) New ed. 12°. '70. pap., 50c. . . . . *Holt.*

— *Eng.* Forest voices, tr.; ed. by C. A. Smith. sq. 8°. '66. $2.50 . . . . *Munsell.*

— *See also* Stilke, H., Das Jahr in Blüthen.

Putnam, Alfr. P. Singers and songs of the liberal faith: sel. with biog. sketches. 8°. '74. $3. *Roberts.*

Putnam, Allen. Agassiz and spiritualism, involving investigation of Harvard Coll. professors in 1857. 12°. '73. 25c. . . . . *Colby.*

— Bible marvel-workers, and the power which helped perform mighty works, etc. ('73.) 2d ed. 12°. '74. $1.25 . . . . *Colby.*

— Flashes of light from the spirit land; through the mediumship of Mrs. J. H. Conant. 12°. '72. $1.50 . . . . *Colby.*

— Mesmerism, spiritualism, witch-craft and miracle. 12°. '73. pap., 30c. . . . . *Colby.*

— Natty, a spirit: his portrait and his life. 12°. '74. 75c.; pap., 50c. . . . . *Colby.*

— Spirit invocations: prayers and praises publicly offered by more than one hundred spirits, through vocal organs of Mrs. J. H. Conant. 16°. '76. $1.25 . . . . *Colby.*

— Tipping his tables: ramblings after a rambler, exposure of an exposer, elicited by an "Exposé of spiritualism, by J. G. Northfield, Vt., 1872." 16°. '73. 25c. . . . . *Colby.*

Putnam, *Mrs.* Eliz. H. Receipt book, and young housekeeper's assistant. 12°. $1.50 . . . . *Sheldon.*

Putnam, *Mrs.* Ellen T. H. ["Thrace Talmon."] Hero girl (The), and how she became a captain in the army. ill. 12°. $1.75 . . . . *J. E. Potter.*

— Monday work; or, how the minister's family built them a house. 16°. $1.50 . . . . *Cong. Pub.*

— New clerk. 16°. $1.25 . . . . *Cong. Pub.*

— — *See also* Mossy dell ser.

— Red bridge (The). ('67.) New ed. 18°. '75. 90c. *Nat. Temp.*

— Where is the city? experience of a young man in search of the true church. 16°. '68. $1.25 . . *Roberts.*

Putnam, F: Ward. List of the fishes sent by Mus. of Comp. Zool. in exchange for other specimens; with annotations. 8°. '63. pap., 15c. *Mus. Comp. Zool.*

— *and* Packard, A. S. Notes on humble bees, wild bees of New Eng., etc. ill. 8°. '65. pap., 75c. . . *Essex.*

Putnam, G: Palmer. Best reading: hints on sel. of books; with classified bibliography. ('72.) New ed., rev. and enl. 12°. '75. $1.50; pap., $1. *Putnam.*

— World's progress: dict. of dates. New ed. 12°. '72. $3.50; hf. cf., $5.50 . . . . *Putnam.*

— (*ed.*) Sunnyside book; by popular authors. ill. f°. $4.50; mor., $8 . . . . *Putnam.*

Putnam, *Miss* H. A. Through trials to triumphs. [Juvenile.] ill. 12°. '73. $1.25 . . . *Meth. Bk. Conc.*

Putnam, J. P. International or metric system of weights and measures. 8°. '74. bds., 50c. — (Teacher's ed.) 8°. pap., 35c. . . . . . . *Hurd & H.*

— *See also* United States, Digest.

Putnam, Ma. Lowell. Fifteen days. 16°. '66. $1.50. *Osgood.*

— Record of an obscure man. 16°. '61. $1 . . . *Osgood.*

— Tragedy of errors. 16°. '61. $1 . . . . *Osgood.*

— Tragedy of success. 16°. '62. $1 . . . . *Osgood.*

Putnam, Ruf. *See* Finley, I. J., *and* Putnam, R.

Putnam, Worthy. Elocution and oratory. 12°. $1.50. *Mason.*

Putnam. Bannister, N. H. 15c. . . . . *French.*

Putnam and the wolf. Marsh, J. 25c. . . . . . . *Am. Tr.*

Putnam's advanced science series. 27 v. ill. 12°. ea., $1.50 . . . . *Putnam.*

Cont.: Practical plane and solid geometry, by F. A. Bradley. — Machine construction and drawing, by E. Tomkins, 2 v. — Building construction, by R. S. Burn, 2 v. — Naval architecture, by S. J. P. Thearle, 2 v. — Pure mathematics, by E. Atkins, 2 v. — Theoretical mechanics, by P. G. Tait. — Applied mechanics, by O. Reynolds. — Acoustics, light and heat, by W. S. Davis. — Magnetism and electricity, by F. Guthrie. — Inorganic chemistry, by J. E. Thorpe, 2 v. — Organic chemistry, by J. Dewar. — Geology, by J. Young. — Animal physiology, by J. Cleland. — Zoology, by E. R. Lankester. — Vegetable anatomy and physiology, by J. H. Balfour. — Systematic and economic botany, by J. H. Balfour. — Metallurgy, by W. H. Greenwood, 2 v. — Navigation, by H. Evers. — Nautical astronomy, by H. Evers. — Steam and steam engine, by H. Evers. — Physical geography, by J. Young.

Putnam's elementary science series. 30 v. ill. 16°. ea., 75c. . . . . *Putnam.*

Cont.: Practical plane and solid geometry, by H. Angel. — Machine construction and drawing, by E. Tomkins. — Building construction by R. S. Burn, text, 2 v.; plates, 2 v. — Naval architecture, by S. J. P. Thearle, 2 v., $1.75. — Pure mathematics, by L. Sergeant. — Theoretical mechanics, by W. Rossiter. — Applied mechanics, by W. Rossiter. — Acoustics, light and heat, by W. Lees. — Magnetism and electricity, by J. Angell. — Inorganic chemistry, by W. B. Kemshead. — Organic chemistry, by W. M. Watts. — Geology, by W. S. Davis. — Mineralogy, by J. H. Collins. — Animal physiology, by J. Angell. — Zoology, by M. Harbison. — Vegetable anatomy and physiology, by J. H. Balfour. — Systematic and economic botany, by J. H. Balfour. — Metallurgy, by J. Mayer. — Navigation, by H. Evers. — Nautical astronomy, by H. Evers. — Steam and the steam engine, by H. Evers, 2 v. — Physical geography, by J. Macturk. — Practical chemistry, by J. Howard. — Astronomy, by J. J. Plummer. — Principles of coal mining.

Putnam's handy-book ser. 15 v. 12°. . . . . *Putnam.*

Cont.: Best reading, by G. P. Putnam, $1; $1.50. — Hand-book of statistics of the U. S., by M. C. Spaulding, $1. — What shall we eat? 75c.; 50c. — 'Till the doctor comes, by G. H. Hope, 60c. — Stimulants and narcotics, by G. M. Beard, 75c. — Eating and drinking, by G. M. Beard, 75c. — Students' own speaker, by P. Reeves, 90c.; 75c. — How to educate yourself, by G. C. Eggleston, 75c. — Manual of etiquette, by Mrs. S. O. Johnson, 75c. — Hints on dress, by E. C. Gale, 75c. — The home, by F. R. Stockton, 75c. — The mother's work with sick children, by J. B. Fonssagrives, $1.25. — Manual of thermometry, by E. Seguin, 75c. — Infant diet, by A. Jacobi, 75c. — How to make a living, by G. C. Eggleston, 75c.

Putnam's popular manuals. 14 v. . . . . *Putnam.*

Cont.: Half hours with the microscope, by E. Lankester, ill. 12°, $1.25. — Half hours with the telescope, by R. A. Proctor, ill. 12°, $1.25. — Half hours with the stars, by R. A. Proctor, maps, demi 4°, $2.25. — Manual of popular physiology, by H. Lawson, ill. 18°, $1.25. — Women before the law, by J. Proffatt, 12°, $1; hf. bd., $1.25. — Sophisms of protection, by F. Bastiat, 12°, $1. — What is free trade? by E. Walter, 12°, 75c. — Essays on political economy, by F. Bastiat, 12°, $1. — Social economy, by J. E. T. Rogers, 16°, 75c. — Method of learning to draw from memory, by Mme. E. Cavé, 12°, $1. — Method of teaching color by Mme. E. Cavé, 12°, $1. — Perspective, by V. Pellegrin, 12°, $1. — Microscopic objects, by T. Davies, 12°, $1.25. — The taxidermist's manual, by T. Brown, ill. 12°, $1.25.

Putnam's [ser. of atlases]. *See* Academic; — Atlas; — Bartholomew, J.; — Collegiate; — International; — Library; — Student's; — Thomson, A.

Putz, W: *and* Arnold, T. K. Manual of ancient geography and history. 12°. $1.50 . . . . *Appleton.*

— — Mediæval geography and history. 12°. $1.50. *Appleton.*

— — Modern geography and history. 12°. $1.50. *Appleton.*

Pycroft, Ja. Course of English reading; rev. and enl. by J. A. Spencer. 12°. $1.25 . . . . *Miller.*

Pygmalion and Galatea: comedy. 16°. pap., 15c. *French.*

Pyke, E. Catechism of religious and moral instructions. 16°. bds., 25c. . . . . *Frank.*

— Scriptural questions for the use of [Hebrew] Sabbath schools. 16°. pap., 15c. . . . . *Bloch.*

Pyke, E., *continued.*
— Scripture history simply arranged for Jewish schools. 16°. 60c. ... *Frank.*
Pyke O'Callaghan: drama. 16°. pap., 15c. ... *French.*
Pyle, M. C. Minna in the wonderland; [also] Roland and his friend. ill. 16°. '71. 75c. ... *Porter.*
Pylodet, L. (*pseud.*) *See* Leypoldt, F:
Pynchon, T: R. Introduction to chemical physics. New ed., rev. and enl. ill. 8°. '74. $3. *Van Nostrand.*
Pyne, J. B. Lake scenery of England. pl. sm. 4°. $5 ... *Routledge.*
Pyramus and Thisbe: drama. 16°. pap., 15c. *French.*
Pyrotechny; or, the art of making fire works at little cost, and with complete safety and cleanliness. ill. 12°. $2.50 ... *Baird.*
Pythagoras in India. *See* Voltaire.

Quack doctor: Ethiop. drama. 16°. pap., 15c. *French; Happy.*
Quackenbos, G: Payne. Advanced course of composition and rhetoric. 12°. $1.50 ... *Appleton.*
— Elementary arithmetic; upon basis of works of G. R. Perkins. 12°. 50c. ... *Appleton.*
— Elementary hist. of the U. S. 12°. 75c. ... *Appleton.*
— English grammar. 12°. 90c. ... *Appleton.*
— First lessons in Eng. composition. 12°. 90c. *Appleton.*
— Higher arithmetic. 12°. $1.25. — Key. 12°. 75c. *Appleton.*
— Historia ilustrada de los Estados Unidos y países adyacentes de América. 12°. $1.75 ... *Appleton.*
— History of the U. S. ill. 12°. $1.50 ... *Appleton.*
— Mental arithmetic. 18°. 45c. ... *Appleton.*
— Natural philosophy. 12°. $1.75 ... *Appleton.*
— Practical arithmetic; upon basis of works of G. R. Perkins. 12°. $1. — Key, 20c. ... *Appleton.*
— Primary arithmetic; upon basis of works of G. R. Perkins. 18°. 30c. ... *Appleton.*
— Primary grammar of Eng. lang. 18°. 50c. ... *Appleton.*
— Primary hist. of the U. S. sm. 4°. 90c. ... *Appleton.*
— *See also* Norton, S. A., Weld, A. H., *and* Quackenbos, G: P.; — Weld, A. H., *and* Quackenbos, G: P.
Quackenbos, J: D. Illustrated school history of the world. maps and ill. 12°. $1.75 ... *Appleton.*
Quackery unmasked. King, D. $1 ... *D. Clapp.*
Quad, M. (*pseud.*) *See* Lewis, C: B.
Quadratus. Leslie, E. $1.50 ... *Meth. Bk. Conc.*
Quadroona; přel. J. A. Oliverius. 16°. '74. $1. *Geringer.*
Quadros juvenis. 18°. '70. 30c. ... *Am. Tr.*
Quadrupani, Carlos José. Christian instructed; tr. 32°. 40c. ... *Sadlier.*
— Spiritual consoler; tr. 18°. 50c. ... *Cath. Pub.*
Quadrupeds: drama. 16°. pap., 15c. ... *French.*
Quain, Jones. *See* Sharpey, W., *and* Quain, J. *and* R.
— *and* Wilson, W. J. E. Anatomical plates, with ref. and physiol. comments; rev. with notes by J. Pancoast. 4th ed. pl. 4°. hf. mor., $20 .. *W. Wood.*
Quain, R: On some defects in general education. cr. 8°. '70. $1.25 ... *Macmillan.*
— *See also* Sharpey, W., *and* Quain, J. *and* R.
Quaker: operetta. Dibdin, C. 15c. ... *French.*
Quaker among the Indians. *See* Battey, T: C.
Quaker city; or, the monks of Monk Hall. Lippard, G. $2; $1.50 ... *Peterson.*
Quaker soldier. Jones, J. R. $1.75; $1.50 .. *Peterson.*
Quakers. *See* Friends (Society of).
Quality Fogg's old ledger. ('69.) New ed. ill. 16°. '74. $1 ... *Hoyt.*
Quantrell, the terror of the west. [Fiction.] 12°. pap., 20c. ... *Hurst.*
Quarles, Fs. Emblems, divine and moral. 18°. '54. 75c. ... *Carter.*
— *Same*; ill. by C. Bennett and W. H. Rogers. (Lond.) 4°. '70. $6; mor., $10 ... *Tibbals.*

Quarles, Ja. M. *See* Tennessee, Criminal code.
Quarrel among the flowers. *See* Schöller, H.
Quarrel of the flowers. *See* Lacy's home plays for ladies.
Quarrelsome servants: Ethiop. drama. 16°. pap., 15c. ... *French; Happy.*
Quarter race in Kentucky. Porter, W. T. 75c. *Peterson.*
Quartet and chorus choir. Holbrook, J. P. $2.50; $3. *Barnes.*
Quartette. Dyer, S. O. 7 v. ea., $1; — in 5 v., $5. *Pond.*
Quash. Brookes, G. 15c. ... *French.*
Quatrefages de Bréau, J: L: A. de. Natural history of man; tr. by E. A. Youmans. 12°. $1 .. *Appleton.*
Quatremère de Quincy, Ant. C. Life and works of Raffaello. *See* Duppa, R., Life and works of Michael Angelo.
Quaw, Ja. E. Bible baptism; or, the immerser instructed. 12°. 60c. ... *N. Y. Ref. Ch. Bd.*
Quay of the Dioscuri. Macarius. 55c. ... *Dutton.*
Quebec: 12 views with letter press. obl. 24°. 75c. *Nelson.*
Queechy. Warner, S. $1.75 ... *Lippincott.*
Queen (A). Wildermuth, O. 75c. ... *Dutton.*
Queen Hortense. Mundt, C. M. $1–$3.50 .. *Appleton.*
Queen Krinaleen's plagues. Jonquil. 50c. ... *Lippincott.*
Queen lib. 5 v. 16°. $3.75 ... *Dutton.*
Cont.: A queen, by Mme. O. Wildermuth. — Leon and Zephie, by Mme. O. Wildermuth. — Bertha Weisser's wish, by M. L. Bissell. — Contraband Christmas, by Rev. N. W. T. Root. — Posy Vinton's picnic, by Mrs. M. H. Seymour.
Queen Loo. Naramore, G. $1 ... *Lippincott.*
Queen Louisa of Prussia. Hurst, C. E. $1. *Meth. Bk. Conc.*
Queen love and the fairies. 16°. 35c. ... *Williamson.*
Queen Mab. Kavanagh, J. $1.25 ... *Appleton.*
Queen Mab. Shelley, P. B. 50c. ... *Mendum.*
Queen Mary. *See* Tennyson, A.
Queen Mary's bower. Planché, J. R. 15c. ... *French.*
Queen mother and Rosamond. Swinburne, A. C. $2. **Osgood.*
Queen of the Adriatic. Adams, W. H. D. $1.75 .. *Lothrop.*
Queen of the air. Ruskin, J. $1 ... *Wiley.*
Queen of Arragon. Paul, H. 15c. ... *French.*
Queen of Connaught. [Fiction.] 8°. pap., 50c. ... *Harper.*
Queen of the country. Stretton, J. $1.50 ... *Loring.*
Queen of Denmark. Gore, C. G. 50c. ... *Harper.*
Queen of frogs. Planché, J. R. 15c. ... *French.*
Queen of hearts. *See* Collins, W.
Queen of hearts. Greenough, J. B. 50c. ... *Sever.*
Queen of the kitchen. Tyson, M. L. $1.75 .. *Peterson.*
Queen of the regiment. *See* King, K.
Queen of spades. Boucicault, D. 15c. ... *French.*
Queen Rhoda. Beech, A. A. $1.50 ... *Hoyt.*
Queenly womanhood. Platt, S. H. 65c.; 50c. ... *Hope.*
Queen's bench. Rede, L. 15c. ... *French.*
Queen's cadet. Grant, J. 80c. ... *Routledge.*
Queen's daughter; or, the orphan of La Granja. 18°. '68. 50c. ... *Cunningham.*
Queen's English. Alford, H. $1.25 ... *Routledge.*
Queen's favorite; or, price of a crown. 12°. $1.75; pap., $1.50 ... *Peterson.*
Queen's heart: comedy. 16°. pap., 15c. ... *French.*
Queen's necklace. *See* Dumas, A.
Queen's revenge. *See* Collins, Wilkie.
Queens. Emery, E. B. $1.50 ... *Estes.*
Queens and princesses of France. White, G. 60c.; 80c. ... *Murphy.*
Queens of Am. society. *See* Ellett, E. F.
Queens of society. *See* Wharton, G. *and* P.

Queens of song. Clayton, E. C. $3; $4.75..*Harper*.
Queer carriage. 75c. Pratt, L. M. ....*Lothrop*.
Queer characters. [Toy-book.] ill. 4°. $1; 50c. *Routledge*.
Queer folk. Knatchbull-Hugessen, E. H. $1.75. *Macmillan*.
Queer little people. Stowe, H. B. $1.50....*Osgood*.
Queer people. *See* Bennett, M. E.
Queer people ser. 3 v. 16°. $3.75 ....*Crowell*.
Cont.: Queer people, by M. E. Bennett. — Smith's saloon, by Mrs. Ellsworth. — Johnnie, the railroad boy, by Mrs. M. E. Poole.
Queerest courtship. Sedgwick, A. B. 15c...*De Witt*.
Quench not the Spirit. *See* Hall, N.
Quentin Durward. *See* Scott, *Sir* Wa.
Queries of highest consideration. *See* Williams, R.
Querner, Emil. Anleitung zur Pflege u. Heilung d. Kranken: Behandlg. v. Schwangerschaft, etc., u. erste Pflege d. Kinder. 2d ed. 8°. $1..*Schäfer*.
— Der Selbstarzt, od. Doctor u. Apotheker im eigenen Haus. 3d ed. ill. 8°. hf. bd., $1.......*Schäfer*.
Quesnel, Pasquier. Gospels, with moral reflections on each verse; with introd. by D. Wilson, rev. by H. A. Boardman. 2 v. cr. 8°. '67. $5..*Randolph*.
Question of hell: essay on new orthodoxy; by a Puritan. 16°. '73. $1..............(?) *Wilson & Co*.
Question settled. Hull, M. $1.50............*Colby*.
Questions and answers on the books of the Bible. 18°. '58. bds., 25c.......................*Randolph*.
Questions and notes on Matthew; for parents and teachers. 2 v. 18°. per doz., hf. bd., $1.80. *N. Y. Ref. Ch. Bd.*
Questions and stories on the commandments, with graces and prayers. 18°. 18c.........*Am. S. S.*
Questions of the age. Baker, J. S. 30c.; 15c. *So. Bapt.*
Questions of the day. Elder, W. $3........*Baird*.
Questions of the day. Hall, J. $1.75 ....*Dodd*.
Questions of the soul. Hecker, I. T. $1.50..*Cath. Pub.*
Questions on Acts. 3 pts. 18°. ea., bds., 10c...*Dutton*.
Questions on the Collects. 18°. bds., 10c....*Dutton*.
Questions on Genesis. 4 pts. 18°. ea., bds., 10c. *Dutton*.
Questions on Matthew. 3 pts. 18°. ea., bds., 10c.; — in 1 v., 25c...........................*Dutton*.
Questions on natural hist. of the Bible. 18°. per doz., 72c. — Key, per doz., 72c........*Meth. Bk. Conc.*
Questions on principles of geography. 12°. pap., 18c. *Thompson*.
Questions on St. Paul's Epistles. 16°. 30c...*Un. S. S.*
Questions to the impenitent. Pendleton, J. M. 30c.; 15c. ....*So. Bapt.*
Quétin, —. *See* Audin, J. M. V., *and* Quétin, —.
Quick, Rob. Herb. Essays on educational reformers. 12°. '74. $2 ....*Clarke*.
Quiddities of an Alaskan trip. Bell, W. H. $3.50. *Lippincott*.
Quiet corner of England. Champney, B. $5...*Bouton*.
Quiet day: drama. 16°. pap., 15c. ....*French*.
Quiet family. Suter, W. E. 15c. ....*French*.
Quiet heart. Oliphant, M. O. W. 25c.......*Harper*.
Quiet hour. Lincoln, H. 50c. ....*Lothrop*.
Quiet hour lib. 6 v. 18°. $3...............*Lothrop*.
Cont.: Quiet hour, ed. by H. Lincoln. — Mind of Jesus, by J. R. Macduff. — Morning watches, by J. R. Macduff. — Words of Jesus, by J. R. Macduff. — Night watches, by J. R. Macduff. — Faithful promiser, by J. R. Macduff.
Quiet hours: poems. sq. 18°. '74. $1.25 ....*Roberts*.
Quiet life, and other poems. R., E. D. 60c...*Randolph*.
Quiet Miss Godolphin. *See* Mayo, I. F.
Quiet moments. Pepys, *Lady* C. M. $1.25..*Dutton*.
Quiet resting-places, and other sermons. Raleigh, A. $4.......................................*Routledge*.

Quigley, Hu. Cross and the shamrock; or, how to defend the faith. 12°. $1.50 ....*Noonan*.
— Profit and loss. [Fiction.] 12°. $1.50..(?) *O'Kane*.
Quimby, I. F. Elements of differential and integral calculus. 8°. '67. shp., $2.50.........*Ivison*.
Quinby, G: W. Marriage and the duties of the marriage relations: six lectures. 16°. 75c. *U. P. James; Williamson*.
Quinby, M. Practical bee-keeping. ill. 12°. $1.50..*Judd*.
Quincy, Edm. Life of Josiah Quincy. 12°. '67. $1. *Williams*.
— *Same*. ('67.) 6th ed. por. 8°. '74. $3..*Little, B. & Co.*
Quincy, Josiah, *jr*. *See* Massachusetts, Superior Court reports.
Quincy, Josiah, 3*d*. Essays on soiling of cattle; with memoir of author by E. Quincy. 12°. $1.25..*Judd*.
— Memoir of life of Josiah Quincy, jr.; ed. by E. S. Quincy. 2d ed. 8°. '74. $3......*Little, B. & Co.*
— Speeches delivered in the U. S. Congress; ed. by E. Quincy. 8°. '74. $3..........*Little, B. & Co.*
Quincy, Josiah Phillips. Protection of majorities: considerations rel. to electoral reform; with other papers. 16°. '75. $1 ....*Roberts*.
Quincy, Quatremère de. *See* Quatremère de Quincy.
Quinn, J. Life and labors. 12°. 75c...*Cin. Meth. Bk. Conc.*
Quinn, P. T. Money in the garden: vegetable manual, prepared with a view to economy and profit. 12°. $1.50 ....*Judd*.
— Pear culture for profit. ill. 12°. $1..........*Judd*.
Quintard, *Rev.* C: Todd. Preparation for confirmation. 18°. 50c.; 60c.; pap., 12c.......*Dutton*.
Quinten Matsys. Egan, P. 75c..........*Dick & F.*
Quinter, Ja. Collection of psalms, hymns, etc., adapted to the fraternity of the Brethren. [In Eng. or Germ.] 32°. '67. 75c.; mor., $1..*Brumbaugh*.
Quintilian [*Lat.* Quintilianus], Mcs. Fabius. Institutes of oratory; lit. tr., with notes, etc., by J. S. Watson. 2 v. 12°. (Bohn.) ea., $1.75. *Little, B. & Co.*
— *Same*. 2 v. 12°. (Bohn.) ea., $2. *Lippincott; Scribner, W. & A.*
— *See also* Cicero *and* Quintilian; — Frieze, H. S.
Quinton, M. A. Money God; or, the empire and the papacy: tale of 3d cent.; tr. 12°. '72. $1.50; $2............................*Kelly, P. & Co.*
— Nobleman of '89: episode of the French rev.; tr. by E. Legarde. sm. 8°. '74. $2; $3..*Kelly, P. & Co.*
Quirinus (*pseud.*) Letters from Rome on the Council; tr. from "Allgemeine Zeitung." 12°. '76. $2..*Pott*.
Quite alone. Sala, G. A. 75c..............*Harper*.
Quite at home. Rose, G. 15c. ....*De Witt*.
Quite at home. Ryan, R. 15c. ....*French*.
Quits. Tautphœus, *Baroness* I. v. $1.75..*Lippincott*.
Quixstar. Taylor, E. $1.75..............*Putnam*.
Quodlibet. *See* Kennedy, J. P.
Quorndon hounds. Herbert, H. W. 75c...*Peterson*.
Quotations from the Brit. poets; alphabet. arr. accord. to subjects. 16°. '69. 75c............*Claxton*.

R., A. G. *See* Radcliffe, A. G.
R., C. H. Will Phillips. ill. 16°. '73. $1.50..*Lothrop*.
R., E. *See* Reed, E.
R., E. D. A quiet life, and other poems. 24°. '74. 60c. ....*Randolph*.
R., F. W. True to him ever. 12°. $1.50...*Carleton*.
R., L. N. *See* Ranyard, Ellen.
R., V. R. *See* Excelsior; or, essays on politeness.
R. B. R.'s (The). Child, *Miss* —. 75c........*Fuller*.
Rab and his friends. *See* Brown, *Dr.* J:
Rabaut and Bridaine. Bungener, L. F. $1.50..*Lothrop*.
Rabbah taken. Landis, R. W. 50c....... *Wilstach*.

Rabbi Agur's school and its four teachers. ill. sq. 18°. 60c. . . . . *Nelson.*

Rabbit snares. *See* Marvin, *Mrs.* H. N.

Rabelais, François. Works; tr., with variorum notes. ill. 12°. $3 . . . . . *Routledge.*

— *Same;* tr. by Sir T. Urquhart and Le Motteux; with notes by Duchat, Ozell and others. 2 v. 12°. hf. cf., $6 . . . . . *Appleton.*

— — *Same.* 2 v. 12°. (Bohn.) ea., $1.25 . . *Little, B. & Co.*

— — *Same.* 2 v. 12°. (Bohn.) ea., $1.40. *Scribner, W. & A.*

— — *Same.* 2 v. 12°. (Bohn.) ea., $1.50 . . . . *Lippincott.*

Raccolta (The); or, collection of indulgenced prayers; tr. by Ambrose St. John. 24°. 63c.–$6 . . *Sadlier.*

— *See also* Way of the cross.

Race ball: farce. 16°. pap., 15c. . . . . *Happy.*

Race for a dinner. Rodwell, T. G. 15c. *De Witt; French.*

Race for wealth. Riddell, J. H. 75c. . . . . *Harper.*

Race for a widow. Williams, T. J. 15c. *French; Lee & S.*

Race for a wife. Smart, H. 50c. . . . . *Appleton.*

Rachel. *See* Aunty May's children.

Rachel, the miser's daughter. Malen, M. E. O. 30c. *Am. News.*

Rachel Bovill. 18°. 50c. . . . . *Whittaker.*

Rachel Cardingford's book. *See* Silverbeach lib.

Rachel comforted: thoughts for the consolation of bereaved parents. 16°. '66. 50c. . . . . *Pott.*

Rachel Grey. Kavanagh, J. $1.25 . . . . *Appleton.*

Rachel Johnson; by author of "Widow's son." 18°. 40c. . . . . *Claremont; Dutton.*

Rachel Noble's experience. Edwards, B. 90c. *Nat. Temp.*

Rachel Ray. *See* Trollope, Ant.

Rachel White's fault. ill. 18°. '74. 40c. . . . . *Am. Tr.*

Rachel's Easter offering. 18°. 75c. . . . . *Dutton.*

Rachel's lilies. 18°. '72. 20c. . . . . *Am. Tr.*

Rachel's secret; by author of "Master of Marton." 8°. pap., 75c. . . . . *Harper.*

Rachel's water-lilies. *See* Daisy lib.

Racine, J: Œuvres complètes. 12°. $1.50. *G. R. Lockwood.*

— *Same.* 12°. $2 . . . . . *Routledge.*

— Théâtre complet. 12°. pap., $1; hf. bd., $2 . . *Appleton.*

— Andromaque [Fr.]; ed. by H. Tarver. 16°. 50c.; pap., 25c. . . . . *Lippincott.*

— Athalie [Fr.]; ed. by P. H. E. Brette. 16°. 50c.; pap., 25c. . . . . *Lippincott.*

— *Same;* with notes by E. S. Joynes. ('71.) New ed. 12°. '76. pap., 50c. . . . . *Holt.*

— — *See also* Mendelssohn-Bartholdy, F.

— Britannicus [Fr.]; ed. by G. Masson. 16°. 50c.; pap., 25c. . . . . *Lippincott.*

— Chefs-d'œuvre. With notes by Fasquelle. 12°. '56. $1.25 . . . . . *Ivison.*

— Esther [Fr.]; ed. by A. Roche. 16°. 50c.; pap., 25c. . . . . *Lippincott.*

— Iphigenie [Fr.]; ed. by J. Bué. 16°. 50c.; pap., 25c. . . . . *Lippincott.*

— Phädra. *See* Schiller, J. F. v.

— Plaideurs (Les). Ed. by F. Tarver. 16°. 50c.; pap., 25c. . . . . *Lippincott.*

— Selected pieces [Fr.] 16°. 75c. . . . *G. R. Lockwood.*

— Suitors (The): comedy; tr. by I. Browne. '70. 16°. $1.—8°. $2 . . . . . *Putnam.*

Rack, J: French wine and liquor manufacturer. ill. 12°. $3 . . . . . *Dick & F.*

Radau, Rod. Wonders of acoustics; tr. from the Fr.; rev. by R. Ball. ill. 12°. '72. $1.25 . . *Scribner.*

Radcliffe, A. G. Daily hymns: hymns for every day in Lent. 32°. '67. 75c. . . . . *Dutton.*

— May's Advent. 18°. 40c. . . . . *Dutton.*

Radcliffe, *Mrs.* Anne. Ellena. 8°. pap., 50c. *U. P. James.*

— Mysteries of Udolpho. 12°. '69. $1.50 . . . *Claxton.*

— Romance of the forest. 12°. '72. $1.50 . . . *Claxton.*

Radcliffe, C: Bland. Dynamics of nerve and muscle. cr. 8°. '71. $3 . . . . . *Macmillan.*

— Lectures on epilepsy, pain, paralysis and other disorders of nerv. system. ill. 12°. '66. $2 . . *Lindsay.*

Radical Club. Woods, K. T. 25c. . . . . *W. F. Gill.*

Radical discourses. *See* Denton, W.

Radical problems. Bartol, C. A. $2 . . . . *Roberts.*

Radical rhymes. Denton, W. $1.25 . . . . *Denton.*

Rae, C: M. Nothing like paste; or, Billy Doo, the bill-sticker: farce. 16°. pap., 15c. . . . . *De Witt.*

— Poppleton's predicaments: farce. 16°. pap., 15c. *De Witt.*

Rae, W: F. Westward by rail: new route to the east. 12°. $2 . . . . . *Appleton.*

— Wilkes, Sheridan, Fox: opposition under George III. 12°. $2 . . . . . *Appleton.*

Raff, G: W. Guide for executors and administrators in settlement of estates of deceased persons in Ohio; with comment on statute. 3d ed. 8°. '71. shp., $2 . . . . . *Clarke.*

— Law relating to roads and highways in Ohio; with forms. 2d ed., rev. and enl. 12°. '71. shp., $2 . . . . . *Clarke.*

— Manual of laws, regulations, instructions, etc., rel. to pensions, bounty pay, etc., and prosecution of claims against the government growing out of the war of 1861–'65. 12°. '66. shp., $4 . . . *Clarke.*

— Manual of pensions, bounty and pay, 1789–1863; with notes and ref. 12°. '64. shp., $2 . . *Clarke.*

Raffaelle, the reprobate. Wilks, T. E. 15c. . . *French.*

Raffensperger, *Mrs.* A. F. My pet's picture book. ill. 18°. '73. 30c. . . . . *Am. Tr.*

Raffles, T: Memoirs of Thomas Spencer of Liverpool. ('57.) 2d ed. 18°. '74. 50c. . . . . *So. Meth.*

Rafinesque, Const. Schmaltz. Complete writings on conchology; ed. by W. G. Binney and G. W. Tryon, jr. 8°. '64. $2.50 . . . . *Acad. of Nat. Sci.*

Rag-bag. Willis, N. P. $1.75 . . . . *Scribner.*

Ragged Dick. Alger, H., *jr.* $1.25 . . . . *Loring.*

Ragged Dick ser. *See* Alger, H., *jr.*

Ragged Franz; or, temptation resisted. 18°. 17c.; 22c. *Am. Bapt.*

Ragged homes and how to mend them. 16°. $1.10. *Am. S. S.*

Ragged scholars; [also] Perils in the desert; [also] The avenger stayed. 18°. 25c. . . . . *Pres. Bd.*

Ragged Tom and his three foes. *See* My own lib.

Ragged Tommy; or, the boy and the bishop. 18°. 30c. *Pres. Bd.*

Raggles, Baggles and the emperor. Mateaux, C. L. 50c. . . . . *Cassell.*

Ragpicker of Paris. Stirling, E. 15c. . . . . *French.*

Rah-Tah-Bah, the Chihuahua chief. 12°. pap., 20c. *Hurst.*

Raikes, Rob. Life. 18°. 60c.; 75c. . . . . *Am. Bapt.*

— *See also* Stoddard, R. H., Bric-a-brac ser.

Railroad boy. Myers, S. A. 60c. . . . . *Pres. Bd.*

Railroad problem. Adams, C. F., *jr.* 15c. . . *R. R. Gazette.*

Railroad station. Wilks, T. E. 15c. . . . . *French.*

Railway anecdote-book. 16°. pap., 50c. . . *Appleton.*

Railway belle. Lemon, M. 15c. . . . . *French.*

Rainbow (The). Bristow, F. L. 50c. . . . . *Church.*

Rainbow and Lucky series. *See* Abbott, Jac.

Rainbow around the tomb. Thornwell, E. $1.50. *J. E. Potter.*

Rainbow creed. Leppere, A. H. $1.50 . . *W. F. Gill.*

Rainbow in the north. Tucker, E. 75c. . . . *Carter.*

Rainbow lib. 3 v. 12°. $3.75 . . . . . *Nelson.*

Cont.: Old sailor's story, by G. E. Sargent. — Poor clerk, by G. E. Sargent. — Frances Leslie, by Miss E. Bickersteth.

Rainbow ser. *See* Arthur, T. S.

Rainbow ser. *See* Power, Ph. B.

Rainbow side. Edwards, C. M. $1.25..*Meth. Bk. Conc.*

Rainbow stories; by various authors. 3 v. ill. 12°. ea., $1.50..........*Scribner, W. & A.*

Rainbow's journey. Abbott, J. 90c.........*Harper.*

Rainbows for children. Child, L. M. $1.50..*Osgood.*

Rainbows in springtide. Sadie. 50c. ....*Routledge.*

Rainer, Jos. Dr. Joseph Salzmann's Leben u. Wirken. 12°. '76. $1 ....*Herder.*

Rainford ser. *See* Bradley, W. I.

Rainy, R. Delivery and development of Christian doctrine. 8°. $5 ....*Scribner, W. & A.*

Rainy afternoon; or, how to bear disappointment. 18°. 30c..........*Am. S. S.*

Rainy day. 18°. 18c..........*Am. S. S.*

Rainy day at school. Clark, M. L. 75c.....*Lothrop.*

Rainy day in the nursery. Carter, *Mrs.* 75c...*Lee & S.*

Rainy day stories. 18°. 35c.; 45c. ....*Am. Bapt.*

Rainy day stories. *See* Whitmarsh, C. S.

Raising of Lazarus. 18°. '45. 25c. ....*Am. Tr.*

Raising the wind. Kenney, J. 15c..........*French.*

Rake's progress. Rede, W. L. 15c. ....*French.*

Raleigh, Alex. Little sanctuary, and other meditations. 12°. '72. $1.75 ....*Dodd.*

— Quiet resting-places, and other sermons. 8°. '74. $4 ....*Routledge.*

Ralph. *See* Malan, C:

Ralph, the heir. *See* Trollope, Ant.

Ralph and Bruno. Bramston, M. $1.25..*Macmillan.*

Ralph and Dick. Kingston, W. H. G. $1 ..*Lothrop.*

Ralph and Robbie; by author of "Roland Rand." ill. 18°. '67. 50c. ....*N. Y. Ref. Ch. Bd.; Pres. Com.*

Ralph Berrien: tales of the French revolution. 18°. '66. 50c..........*Cunningham.*

Ralph Clavering. *See* Kingston, W. H. G.

Ralph Elmwood. Vosburg, J. H. $1.......*Claxton.*

Ralph Gemmell. *See* Pollok, R.

Ralph Harding's success. ('72.) New ed. 16°. '74. $1.25 ....*Hoyt.*

Ralph Luttrell's fortunes. Corbet, R. St. J. $1.75. *Scribner, W. & A.*

Ralph Moore, the profane boy. 18°. 18c....*Am. S. S.*

Ralph Rattler. *See* Wise, D.

Ralph Runnion; or, the outlaw's doom. 8°. pap., 50c. *Peterson.*

Ralph Waring's money. Dunning, A. K. $1.25. *Am. S. S.*

Ralph Wilton's weird. Hector, A. F. $1.25....*Holt.*

Ralph's possession. Hopkins, G. $1.50 ....*Lothrop.*

Ralston, T: N. ["Eureka."] Ecce unitas; or, a plea for Christian unity. 16°. 80c. *Meth. Bk. Conc.*

— Elements of divinity. ('71.) 3d ed. 8°. '75. shp., $6 ....*So. Meth.*

Ralston, W. R. S. Krilof and his fables. 8°. $2.50; $5.50..........*Routledge.*

Ram, Ja. Science of legal judgment. New ed., enl. by J. Townshend. 8°. shp., $4.50..*Baker, V. & Co.*

— Treatise on facts as subjects of inquiry by a jury. 3d Am. ed., with notes by J. Townshend. 8°. shp., $4.50..........*Baker, V. & Co.*

Ram, Stopford J. *See* Vernon, Ruth (*pseud.*)

Ram-Krishna-Punt, the boy of Bengal. sq. 8°. 75c. *Pres. Bd.*

Ramage, Craufurd Tait. Beautiful thoughts from [foreign] authors; with Eng. tr., indexes, etc. 4 v. 16°. $10.50; hf. cf., $18......*Scribner, W. & A.*

Cont.: 1. French and Ital. authors. — 2. Germ. and Span. authors. — 3. Greek authors. — 4. Lat. authors.

— *Same.* 4 v. 16°. v. 1, 4, ea., $3.50; v. 2, 3, ea., $3. *Routledge.*

Ramaley, D: Employing printers: price list for job printing based on new plan of measurement and with detailed prices for all classes of work. fp. 8°. '73. pap., 60c..........*Ramaley.*

Rambach, J: Jac. Das Leiden Christi. 8°. '54. $2.50. *Ev. Assoc.*

— Wohlunterrichteter Katechet. 12°. 60c... *Volkening.*

Ramble around the world. Hübner, *Baron* J. A. $2.50. *Macmillan.*

Rambler (*pseud.*) Guide to Florida. ill. and map. 12°. (cop. '73.) '75. 50c..........*Jenkins.*

Rambler. *See* Chalmers, A., British essayists.

Rambles about the country. Ellet, E. F. 75c...*Harper.*

Rambles about Portsmouth. Brewster, C. W. 2 v. ea., $2.50..........*Williams.*

Rambles after land-shells. *See* Parker, *Mrs.* H. T.

Rambles among the Alps. Abbott, J. 90c...*Harper.*

Rambles among mountains. Langridge, N. T. 40c. *So. Meth.*

Rambles among words. Swinton, W. $1 ....*Ivison.*

Rambles in old pathways. *See* Tarbox, I. N.

Rambles of a rat. *See* Tucker, *Mrs.* C.

Rambling chats and chatty rambles. Black, S. S. $1. *Dutton.*

Rambling story. Clarke, M. C. $1.50......*Roberts.*

Rambosson, J. Astronomy; tr. by C. B. Pitman. ill., maps and pl. 8°. $6..........*Appleton.*

Rame, Louise de la. *See* La Rame, L. de.

Rametti, J. Flute scales. f°. pap., 20c...*Brainard.*

Ramière, H: Manual of apostleship of prayer. 2d ed. 32°. '66. 35c. 12°. $1.50..........*Murphy.*

Rammelsberg, C. F. Guide to course of quantitative chemical analysis, especially of minerals and furnace products; tr. by J. Towler. 8°. '72. $2.25 ....*Van Nostrand.*

Ramsay, Arth. Catechiser's manual; or, the Church catechism ill. and expl. 18°. 50c...*Macmillan.*

Ramsay, D: History of South Carolina, to 1808. 2 v. in 1. 8°. '67. $4; hf. cf., $5..........*Duffie.*

Ramsay, E: Bannerman. Reminiscences of Scottish life and character. por. 16°. $1.50; $2..*Robertson.*

Ramsay, Grace. Are you my wife? story of the times. 8°. '76. $2..........*Cath. Pub.*

Ramsay, Martha Laurens. Memoirs. 18°. 70c. *Am. S. S.*

Ramsbotham, Fs. H. Principles and practice of obstetric medicine and surgery in ref. to process of parturition. New ed., rev. and enl.; with add. by W. V. Keating. pl. and ill. imp. 8°. leath., $7 ....*Lea.*

Ramsey, G: M'Ilvaine. Cosmology. ('69.) 3d ed. 12°. '73. $1.50..........*Colby.*

Ramsey, J. G. M. Annals of Tennessee. 8°. $2.50. *Lippincott.*

Ramsey, Ja. B. Questions on Bible doctrine for the closet, the family and Bible-classes. 18°. '74. hf. bd., 30c..........*Pres. Com.*

— Spiritual kingdom. 8°. '73. $3..........*Pres. Com.*

Ramsey, *Mrs.* V. G. Facts and reflections on condition of the heathen world and importance of missions. 32°. '48. 25c..........*Freewill.*

— Legend of the White Hills, and other poems. 12°. '71. $1.50..........*Lothrop.*

Ramseyer, F: A: *and* Kühne, Js. Four years in Ashantee. ill. 12°. $1.75..........*Carter.*

Ramshorn, Lew. Dictionary of Latin synonymes; tr. by F. Lieber. 12°. $1.88..........*Butler.*

Ran away to sea. Reid, M. $1.50..........*Miller.*

Ranald Bannerman's boyhood. *See* MacDonald, G:

Ranck, G: W. History of Lexington, Ky.; with biog. sketches, etc. 8°. '72. $4..........*Clarke.*

Rand, B. Howard. Elements of medical chemistry. ill. 12°. $2; shp., $2.50..........*Lippincott.*

Rand, C. H. ["Mabel Hazelton."] Aunt Matty. ill. 16°. '69. $1.50 . . . . *Lothrop.*

Rand, E: Sprague, *jr.* Bulbs: treatise on hardy and tender bulbs and tubers; with two app. New ed., rev. and enl. ill. 8°. '76. $2.50 . . . . *Hurd & H.*

— Flowers for the parlor and garden. New ed. ill. 8°. '76. $2.50 . . . . *Hurd & H.*

— Garden flowers: how to cultivate them. New ed., rev. and enl. ill. 8°. '76. $2.50 . . . . *Hurd & H.*

— Orchids: species and varieties grown at Glen Ridge near Boston, with lists and descrip. of others. New ed. cr. 8°. '76. $3.50 . . . . *Hurd & H.*

— Popular flowers and how to cultivate them; with appendix. New ed., rev. and enl. ill. sq. 8°. '76. $2 . . . . *Hurd & H.*

— Rhododendrons. New ed., rev. 8°. '76. $1.50. *Hurd & H.*

— Window gardener. 5th ed., enl. sq. 8°. '76. $1.25. *Hurd & H.*

Rand, W. W. Dictionary of the Bible. maps and ill. 12°. '59. $1.50–$4 . . . . *Am. Tr.*

Randall, *Mrs.* Anna T. *See* Diehl, *Mrs.* Anna T.

Randall, D: Aust. Handwriting of God in Egypt, Sinai and the Holy Land: records of a journey. ('62.) New ed. maps, diagrams and ill. roy. 8°. '74. $3.50; roan, $4 . . . . *Goodspeed; Randall.*

Randall, G: M. Observations on the nature, duty and benefits of the apostolic rite of confirmation. 6th ed. 16°. '68. 10c. . . . . *Dutton.*

— Why I am a churchman. 18°. pap., 12c. . . *Dutton.*

Randall, H: S. Fine wool sheep husbandry. 12°. $1. *Judd.*

— Life of Thomas Jefferson. 3 v. 8°. $10; shp., $12.50; hf. cf., $15.50 . . . . *Lippincott.*

— Practical shepherd: breeding, management and diseases of sheep. ('63.) 29th ed. ill. 12°. $2. *Rural.*

— Sheep husbandry; with G. W. Kendall's letter on sheep raising in Texas. por. and ill. 8°. $1.50. *Judd.*

Randall, J: Montague. Titles of Our Lord adopted by himself in New Test. 12°. 75c. . . . . *Pres. Bd.*

Randall, J: W. Mission of the Holy Spirit. 24°. pap., 10c. . . . . *Chase.*

— *See also* Sleeth, A., *and* Randall, J. W.

Randall, P. M. Quartz operator's handbook. ill. 12°. '71. $2 . . . . *Van Nostrand.*

Randall, S: S. First principles of popular educ. and public instruction. 12°. $1.50 . . . . *Harper.*

— History of common school system of State of N. Y., 1795–1871. ill. 8°. '70. $3 . . . . *Ivison.*

— History of the State of N. Y. ('69.) New ed. ill. 12°. '71. $1.50 . . . . *Ford.*

Randall's thumb: comedy. 16°. pap., 15c. . . *French.*

Randolph, *Mrs.* —. Gentianella. [Fiction.] 12°. $1.50; pap., 75c.; — (Intern. ed.), $1.25. *Porter.*

— Wild hyacinthe. [Fiction.] 12°. $1.75 . . *Lippincott.*

Randolph, Anson D. F. Hopefully waiting, and other verses. ('66.) New ed. 16°. '67. $1.50 . . *Scribner.*

Randolph, Cornelia J. Parlor gardener: house culture of ornamental plants. 24°. '61. $1 . . *Tilton.*

Randolph, J. Thornton. Cabin and parlor. 12°. $1.75; pap., $1.50 . . . . *Peterson.*

Randolph, *Mrs.* Ma. Virginian housewife; or, methodical cook. 12°. '73. $1 . . . . *Claxton.*

Randolph, Paschal B. After death, disembodiment of man: location, topography and scenery of the supernal universe. ('63.) New ed., rev. and enl. 8°. '73. $2 . . . . *Colby.*

— Love and its hidden history, and the master passion. ('63.) 3d ed. 2 v. in 1. 8°. '73. $2.50 . . *Colby.*

— Pre-Adamite man; demonstrating existence of the human race upon this earth 100,000 years ago. ('63.) 4th ed. 12°. '74. $1.50 . . . . *Colby.*

Randolph, Peyton. *See* Virginia, Court of Appeals and General Court reports.

Randolph, Ph. *See* Young American's lib.

Randolph, R: Sober thoughts on staple themes. ('71.) New ed. 12°. '72. $1 . . . . *Claxton.*

— Windfalls. 12°. '70. $1 . . . . *Claxton.*

Randolph, Sa. N. Domestic life of T: Jefferson, comp. from family letters and reminiscences. ill. cr. 8°. $2.50 . . . . *Harper.*

— Life of Gen. ("Stonewall") T: J. Jackson. ill. cr. 8°. $2 . . . . *Lippincott.*

— The Lord will provide. 16°. '72. 90c. . . *Randolph.*

Randolph, T: Jefferson. Memoir, correspondence and miscellanies from papers of T: Jefferson. 4 v. por. 8°. '29. cf., $5 . . . . *J. W. Randolph.*

Randolph, W. M. *See* Louisiana, Sup. Court reports.

Randolph children. Jerrell, A. R. $1 . . . . *Am. S. S.*

Randolph Gordon. La Rame, L. de. $1.50 . . *Lippincott.*

Randolphs (The). Alden, I. M. $1.50 . . . . *Lothrop.*

Random recollections of Albany. Worth, G. A. $2.50. *Munsell.*

Random sketches. Edwards, J. E. $1.50 . . *Harper.*

Ranelagh. Simpson, J. P., *and* Wray, C. 15c. *French.*

Rangers (The). *See* Thompson, D. P.

Ranke, Lp. v. Civil wars and monarchy in France in 16th–17th centuries; tr. by M. A. Garvey. 12°. $1.50; hf. cf., $3.25 . . . . *Harper.*

— History of the popes: their church and state, especially of their conflict with Protestantism in 17th–18th centuries; tr. by E. Foster. 3 v. 12°. hf. cf., $9 . . . . *Appleton.*

— *Same.* 3 v. 12°. (Bohn.) ea., $1.25 . . . . *Little, B. & Co.*

— *Same.* 3 v. 12°. (Bohn.) ea., $1.40 . . *Scribner, W. & A.*

— *Same.* 3 v. 12°. (Bohn.) ea., $1.50 . . . . *Lippincott.*

— History of the reformation in Germany. 8°. $1; — in 3 pts., ea., 20c. . . . . *Lea.*

— History of Servia and the Servian rev.; with sketch of insurrection in Bosnia; tr. by Mrs. A. Kerr. 12°. (Bohn.) $1.25 . . . . *Little, B. & Co.*

— *Same.* 12°. (Bohn.) $1.40 . . . . *Scribner, W. & A.*

— *Same.* 12°. (Bohn.) $1.50 . . . . *Lippincott.*

— History of the Turkish and Spanish empires. 8°. pap., 25c. . . . . *Lea.*

Ranken, Fs. A. Strains and trusses; computed by means of diagrams, with 20 examples drawn to scale. 8°. $2.50 . . . . *Appleton.*

Rankin, Ja. B. Walking with God; or, the practical Christian life. 18°. 70c. . . . . *Pres. Bd.*

Rankin, Jer. E. Auld Scotch mither, and other poems. ill. 12°. '73. $1.25 . . . . *Lothrop.*

— Gems for the bridal ring. 32°. $1 . . . . *Cong. Pub.*

Rankin, J: Covenant of grace. 18°. 40c. *U. P. Bd. of Pub.*

Rankin, *Miss* Ma. Memoir. 12°. $1.25 . . *Un. B. Pub.*

Rankin, *Mrs.* Sara Burlingame. Climbing poems. 12°. '74. $1.25 . . . . *Turnbull.*

Rankine, W: J: Macquorn. Cyclopædia of machines and hand-tools. f°. hf. mor., $27.50. *Scribner, W. & A.*

— Manual of applied mechanics; with diagrams. 7th ed., rev. 12°. (Lond.) '73. $5. *Appleton; Little, B. & Co.; Scribner, W. & A.*

— Manual of civil engineering; with diagrams. 9th ed., rev. 12°. (Lond.) '73. $6.50. *Appleton; Little, B. & Co.; Scribner, W. & A.*

— Manual of machinery and millwork; with diagrams. 12°. (Lond.) '69. $5. *Little, B. & Co.; Scribner, W. & A.*

— *Same;* with tables and ill. 12°. $6.25 . . . *Appleton.*

— Manual of the steam-engine and other prime movers; with ill. and diagrams. 6th ed., rev. 12°. (Lond.) '73. $5 . . *Appleton; Little, B. & Co.; Scribner, W. & A.*

— Useful rules and tables rel. to mensuration, engineering, structures and machines. 4th ed. ill. 12°. (Lond.) '73. $3.75. *Little, B. & Co.; Scribner, W. & A.*

Rankine, W: J: Macquorn, *continued*.
— *Same*. ill. 12°. $4.50 .... *Appleton*.
— *See also* Ship building.
— *and* Bamber, E. F. Mechanical text-book: introd. to study of mechanics and engineering; with diagrams. 12°. (Lond.) '73. $3.75 .. *Little, B. & Co.*
— — *Same*. 12°. $4 .... *Appleton*.
— — *Same*. cr. 8°. $4.50 .... *Scribner, W. & A.*
Ransome, Arth. On stethometry; [with] app. on chemical and microscopical examin. of respired air. ill. 8°. '76. $3 .... *Macmillan*.
Ransomed child. *See* Little Jewess.
Ranyard, Ellen. ["L. N. R."] Book and its story. 12°. $1.50 .... *Carter*.
— Fresh leaves from the book, and its story. ill. 12°. '71. $2 .... *Carter*.
— Life work. 12°. $1.25 .... *Carter*.
— Nurses for the needy in the homes of the London poor. sq. 16°. $1.25 .... *Carter*.
Raoul de Surville. Sue, E. 25c. .... *Peterson*.
Rape of the gamp. Mason, C. W. $1 .... *Harper*.
Raphael. *See* Lamartine, A. de.
Raphael, the blind boy. 18°. 90c. .... (?) *Martien*.
Raphael engravings: 24 studies designed and eng. after 5 paintings by R.: heliotypes from the Tosti coll. in Boston Public Library. 4°. '74. $10 .. *Osgood*.
Raphalina. De Bonay, J. 25c. ... (?) *H. L. Williams*.
Raphall, Morris J. History of the Jews, 420 B.C.E.-70 C.E. 2 v. 12°. $4 .... *Appleton*.
— Post biblical hist. of the Jews. 2 v. 12°. $4; hf. cf., $6; mor., $7.50 .... *Frank*.
Rapid reckoning: system of famous lightning calculator. 12°. pap., 25c. .... *Haney*.
Rapid transit and terminal freight facilities, by O. Chanute, M. N. Forney, A. Welch, C. K. Graham and F. Collingwood; [also] Whipple's Upright arched bridges; [also] Corthell's Levees of the Mississippi; [also] Thurston's Furnaces burning wet fuel. 8°. '75. pap., $1 .. *Am. Soc. of C. E.*
Rapids of Niagara. Warner, S. $1.25 .... *Carter*.
Rapou, A. Typhoid fever and its homœop. treatment; tr. by M. Cote. 12°. '53. 50c. .... *Wilstach*.
Rapp, S: A. Digest of decisions of 2d comptroller and 2d auditor upon bounty laws of the U. S. 8°. '72. $2.50 .... *Morrison*.
Rapping and table movings. Paul, H. 15c. .. *French*.
Rare romance of Reynard the fox. Day, S. P. $1.50. *Cassell*.
Rarey, J: S. Horse taming by a new method. 18°. pap., 15c. .... *Dick & F.*
— Horse taming without a master. 16°. pap., 15c. *Happy*.
— *See also* Powell, W. J., *and* Rarey, J. S.
— *and* Knowlson, J. C. Complete horse tamer and farrier. ill. 16°. bds., 50c. .... *Dick & F.*
Rasch, Gst. Berlin bei Nacht: Culturbilder. 8°. pap., 40c. .... *F. W. Thomas*.
Rasche, F. Union piano-forte instructor; with popular tunes. 4°. '54. bds., $2 .... *Ditson*.
Raspe, Rud. Er. Travels and adventures of Baron Munchausen; tr. 12°. (Bohn.) bds., 40c. *Scribner, W. & A.*
— *Same*. ill. 16°. $1.25 .... *Porter*.
— *Same*. ill. 12°. $1.50 .... *World Pub.*
— *Same*. New ed., rev. with introd. by T. T. Shore; with eng. by G. Doré. 3d ed. roy. 4°. $5 .. *Cassell*.
— — *See also* Bravo of Perth.
Rasselas. Brough, W. 15c. .... *French*.
Rasselas. *See* Johnson, S:
Rathbone, Ha. Ma. Passages from the diary of Lady Willoughby. 12°. $1 .... *Barnes*.
Rathfelder's hotel. 18°. 70c. .... *Pres. Bd.*
Räthselbüchlein. 12°. pap., 15c. .... *Radde*.
Rational cosmology. Hickok, L. P. $2 .... *Appleton*.

Rats of the Seine; or, river thieves of Paris. 8°. pap., 25c. .... *Peterson*.
Rattlebrain (*pseud.*) Sir Guy de Guy: a romaunt. ill. sm. 4°. $2 .... *Routledge*.
Rattlehead, D: (*pseud.*) *See* Byrn, M. Lafayette.
Rattlin, the reefer. *See* Marryat, F:
Rau, C: Archæological collection: Nat. Museum. 4°. '76. pap., $2 .... *Smith. Inst.*
— Early man in Europe. ill. 8°. '76. $2.50 ... *Harper*.
Rau, Gli. L: Organon of the specific healing art of homœopathy; ed. by C. J. Hempel. 8°. $1.25. *Boericke*.
Rau, Heribert. Die Geschichte d. Menschheit nach d. Baudenkmälern, Schriften, u. Urkunden aller Völker. ill. 12°. $3.50 .... *Witter*.
— Mozart: a biog. romance; tr. by E. R. Sill. 12°. '68. $1.75 .... *Ditson*.
— Raub (Der) Strassburgs. [Fiction.] 8°. pap., 50c. *Morwitz*.
Raub, Alb. N. Normal primary speller. 12°. hf. bd., 30c. .... *Sower*.
— Normal speller. Rev. ed. 12°. hf. bd., 45c. .. *Sower*.
— Plain educational talks with teachers and parents. 12°. '69. $1.50 .... *Claxton*.
Raub (Der) Strassburgs. Rau, H. 50c. .... *Morwitz*.
Raüber (Die). *See* Schiller, J. F. v.
Raubritter, Fz. v. Staufeneck. 12°. pap., 15c. .. *Radde*.
Raubschloss (Das). *See* Schmid, C. v.
Rauch, F: A: Inner life; ed. by E. V. Gerhart. 12°. $1.25 .... *Ref. Ch. Pub.*
— Psychology; or, a view of the human soul; incl. anthropology. 12°. '53. $1.75 .... *Dodd*.
Raue, C. G. Special pathology and diagnosis; with therapeutic hints. [Hom.] 8°. hf. mor., $5. *Boericke*.
— *See also* Annual record of homœop. lit.
Rauschenbusch, A: Englisch-deutsches Anfangsbüchlein. ill. 18°. '59. 50c. .... *Am. Tr.*
— Geschichte der Erzväter, deutsch und englisch. ill. 18°. '59. 60c. .... *Am. Tr.*
— Pilgerväter (Die). 18°. '68. 30c. .... *Am. Tr.*
— Vorläufer (Die) der Reformation. 16°. 30c. *Germ. Bapt.*
Ravellings from the web of life. Cannon, C. J. $1.50; $2 .... *Sadlier*.
Raven. *See* Poe, E. A.
Raven's feather. Barth, C. G. 35c. .... *Am. S. S.*
Ravens of Orleans. Moncrieff, W. T. 15c .. *French*.
Ravenscliffe. Marsh-Caldwell, A. 50c. .... *Harper*.
Ravenscroft, J: S. Life. 18°. 50c. .... *Dutton*.
Ravensdale. 8°. pap., 25c. .... *Dick & F.*
Ravenshoe. *See* Kingsley, H:
Ravenswood stories. 5 v. 24°. $1.75 .... *Am. Bapt.*
Cont.: Ravenswood. — Marjorie's work. — Lost and found. — Little Samaritan. — Bessie Baldwin's stories.
Rawle, W: *jr*. *See* Pennsylvania, Sup. Court reports.
Rawle, W: H: Equity in Pennsylvania. [Lecture.] 8°. pap., $1.50; shp., $2 .... *Kay*.
— Practical treatise on the law of covenants for title. 4th ed., enl. 8°. '73. shp., $6 .. *Little, B. & Co.*
Rawlinson, G: Elementary statics; ed. by E: Sturges. cr. 8°. $1.75 .... *Macmillan*.
Rawlinson, *Rev*. G: Commentary on Kings, Chronicles, etc. *See* Cook, F. C., Bible comment.
— Five great monarchies (The) of the ancient eastern world: Chaldæa, Assyria, Babylon, Media and Persia. 2d ed., rev. 3 v. ill., maps and plans. 8°. (Lond.) '71. $15. *Little, B. & Co.; Scribner, W. & A.*
— *Same*; with Sixth Oriental monarchy. 4 v. 8°. hf. cf., $30; hf. mor., $35; cf., $40 .. *Scribner, W. & A.*
— Historical evidences of truth of the Scripture records stated anew. 12°. $1.75 .... *Sheldon*.

Rawlinson, *Rev.* G: *continued.*
— Historical illustrations of Old Testament. 12°. 60c. *Meth. Bk. Conc.*
— *Same;* with notes and literary ref. by H. B. Hackett. 16°. '73. $1.25 .... *H. A. Young.*
— History of Herodotus. 4 v. maps and eng. 8°. $10; hf. cf., $20 .... *Appleton.*
— Manual of ancient history to fall of western empire. 12°. $2.50 .... *Harper.*
— Modern scepticism. [Lectures.] 12°. '71. $2.50. *Randolph.*
— Sixth Oriental monarchy: Parthia. col. pl., maps and ill. 8°. (Lond.) '73. $6. *Little, B. & Co.; Scribner, W. & A.*
— Seventh great Oriental monarchy: the Sassinian, or, new Persian empire. ill. and woodcuts. 8°. '76. $9 .... *Scribner, W. & A.*

Rawson, Ja. Nature and ministry of angels. 18°. '48. 35c. .... *Meth. Bk. Conc.*

Ray, D: Burcham. Baptist succession: handbook of Bapt. hist. 12°. $2 .... *So. Bapt.; Stevens.*
— Text book on Campbellism. 12°. $1.50 ... *So. Bapt.*
— *and* Lucas, Jos. R. Debate: Baptists and disciples. 12°. $2 .... *Stevens.*

Ray, I: Contributions to mental pathology. sm. 8°. '73. $3 .... *Little, B. & Co.*
— Medical jurisprudence of insanity. 5th ed., enl. 8°. '71. $5; shp., $5.50 .... *Little, B. & Co.*
— Mental hygiene. 16°. '63. $1.50 .... *Osgood.*

Ray, J. E. Congregational manual. 16°. 35c.; pap., 10c. .... *Cong. Pub.*

Ray, J: English proverbs. *See* Bohn, H. G., Handbook of proverbs.

Ray, Jos. Elementary algebra. 12°. $1 .. *Wilson, H. & Co.*
— Elements of algebra. ('52.) New ed. 8°. '66. shp., $2 .... *Wilson, H. & Co.*
— Higher algebra. 8°. $1.40 .... *Wilson, H. & Co.*
— Higher arithmetic. 12°. '56. $1.15. — Key. 12°. '58. $1 .... *Wilson, H. & Co.*
— Intellectual arithmetic. ('57.) New ed. 16°. '60. 35c. *Wilson, H. & Co.*
— Key to Elementary and Higher algebras. ('52.) New ed. 12°. '67. $1.50 .... *Wilson, H. & Co.*
— Practical arithmetic. ('44.) New ed. 16°. '57. 67c. — Key. 16°. '45. 67c. .... *Wilson, H. & Co.*
— Primary arithmetic. 16°. '44. 23c... *Wilson, H. & Co.*
— Primary elements of algebra. ('48.) New ed. 12°. '66. $1.15 .... *Wilson, H. & Co.*
— Rudiments of arithmetic; [with or without answers]. ('44.) New ed. 16°. '66. ea., 45c. *Wilson, H. & Co.*
— Three thousand test examples in arithmetic. 16°. '62. 45c. .... *Wilson, H. & Co.*
— *See also* Clark, Ja. G.; — Howison, G: H.; — Peabody, S. H., Elements of astronomy; — Schuyler, A.; — Tappan, Eli T.

Ray, Rena (*pseud.*) Dainty Maurice; or, lost in the woods. ill. 18°. 45c. .... *J. A. Moore.*
— Little Jackie; or, the rose tree. ill. 18°. 45c. *J. A. Moore.*
— Tabitha Todd; or, love to do good. ill. 18°. 45c. *J. A. Moore.*

Ray of light. 16°. 75c. .... *Carter.*

Raybold, G. A. Methodism in west Jersey. 18°. '49. 50c. .... *Meth. Bk. Conc.*

Raymond *of Capua.* Life of St. Catherine of Sienna; tr. by the ladies of the Sacred Heart. 12°. '59. $1.50 .... *Cunningham.*

Raymond, —. Barber baron: drama. 16°. pap., 15c. *French.*

Raymond, *Prof.* —. Parlor pastimes; or, the whole art of amusing. 12°. pap., 25c. .... *Hurst.*

Raymond, C: W. Report of a reconnoissance of the Lukon River, Alaska. *See* United States, *Corps of Eng.*

Raymond, Ida (*pseud.*) *See* Tardy, *Mrs.* Ma. T.

Raymond, R. J. [Plays.] 4 v. 16°. ea., pap., 15c. *French.*
Cont.: Cherry bounce: farce. — Mr. and Mrs. Peter White: farce. — Mrs. White: farce. — Robert, the devil: opera.
— Cherry bounce. *See* French's comic dramas.

Raymond, Rob. R. Patriotic speaker. 8°. '66. $1.75. *Barnes.*

Raymond, Rossiter W. ["Robertson Gray."] Brave hearts. ill. 12°. '73. $1.75 .... *Ford.*
— Christmas angel. 18°. '69. 35c.; pap., 20c. *Randolph.*
— Man in the moon, and other people. ('74.) New ed. ill. sq. 16°. '76. $2 .... *Ford.*
— Mining industry of the states and territories west of the Rocky Mountains; incl. descrip. of quartz, placer and hydraulic mining, amalgamation, etc. eng. and maps. 8°. '74. $3.50 .... *Ford.*
— Silver and gold: account of mining and metallurgical industry of the U. S. pl. 8°. '73. $3.50 .. *Ford.*
— Statistics of mines and mining: 6th ann. report. 8°. '74 .... *U. S. Govt.*

Raymond and Agnes. Lewis, M. G. 15c.... *French.*

Raymond's heroine; by author of "Heir expectant." 8°. pap., 50c. .... *Harper.*

Raynal, F. E. Wrecked on a reef; or, twenty months among the Auckland Isles; from the French. ill. 12°. $1.75 .... *Nelson.*

Rayne, *Mrs.* M. L. Against fate. ill. 12°. '76. $1.50. *Keen.*

Rayner, B. F. Dumb man of Manchester: melodrama. 16°. pap., 15c. .... *French.*

Rayners up to town: drama. 16°. pap., 15c... *French.*

Raynolds, W. F. Report on explor. of Yellowstone River. *See* United States, *Corps of Eng.*

Rayon d'amour. Hancock, S. J. $2 ..... *Lippincott.*

Rays from the sun. Green, S. G. 50c... *Perkinpine.*

Rays from the sun of righteousness. Newton, R. $1.25 .... *Carter.*

Rays of light. 18°. 70c. .... *Pres. Bd.*

Rays of light. Philip, J. $1.50 .... *Hoyt, F. & D.*

Rays of light. *See* Bijou Bible text-books.

Rays of light for dark hours. B., J. $1.50.. *Randolph.*

Rays of sunlight for dark days: sel. with pref. by C. J. Vaughan. New ed. 18°. '65. $1.. *Macmillan.*

Reach, Angus Bethune. Jenny Lind at last: farce. 16°. pap., 15c. .... *French.*

Read, Emily T. Aytoun: a romance. 8°. pap., 40c. *Lippincott.*

Read, Hollis. The devil in history; or, the foot-prints of Satan. ('72.) New ed. ill. 8°. '75. $3; $3.50; shp., $4 .... *Treat.*

Read, J: Meredith, *jr.* Historical inquiry conc. Henry Hudson. 8°. '66. $5 .... *Munsell.*

Read, T: Buchanan. Poetical works. 3 v. 16°. $5.25; hf. cf., $9 .... *Lippincott.*
— Wagoner of the Alleghanies: poem of days of seventy-six. 12°. $1.25. — (Blue and gold ed.) 18°. $1.50 .... *Lippincott.*
— *Same;* and other poems. 16°. $1.75 .. *Lippincott.*

Read, W: Placenta prævia: its history and treatment. 8°. pap., $2 .... *Lippincott.*

Read, W: T. Life of George Read, a signer of the Dec. of ind.; with sel. from his correspondence, etc. 8°. $4 .... *Lippincott.*

Readable dictionary. Williams, J. $1.75... *Barnes.*

Reade, C: Novels. 3 v. 8°. $7 .... *Harper.*
— *Same.* 13 v. .... *Harper.*
Cont.: Cloister and the hearth, 8°, pap., 75c. — Foul play, 8°, pap., 50c. — Griffith Gaunt; or, jealousy, 8°, pap., 50c. — Hard cash, 8°, $1.25; pap., 75c. — Hero and a martyr, 8°, pap., 15c. — It is never too late to mend, 8°, pap., 75c. — Love me little, love me long, 12°, $1; 8°, pap., 50c. — Peg Woffington, Christie Johnstone, etc., 8°, pap., 75c. — Put yourself in his place, 12°, $1; 8°, $1.25; pap., 75c. — Simpleton, 8°, $1; pap., 50c. — Terrible temptation, 12°, 75c.; 8°, pap., 50c. — Wandering heir, 8°, 60c.; pap., 35c. — White lies, 8°, pap., 50c.

Reade, C: *continued.*
— *Same.* (Household ed.) 11 v. ill. 16°. ea., $1. **Osgood.*

Cont.: Hard cash. — Foul play. — White lies. — Love me little, love me long. — Griffith Gaunt. — Cloister and the hearth. — Never too late to mend. — Peg Woffington, Christie Johnstone, etc. — Put yourself in his place. — Terrible temptation. — Simpleton.

— Dora: pastoral drama. 16°. pap., 15c. .... *Lee & S.*
— Gold: drama. 16°. pap., 15c. .... *French.*
— Terrible temptation: story of to-day. 8°. pap., 25c. *De Witt.*
— *See also* Taylor, T., *and* Reade, C.
Reade, W: Winwood. Martyrdom of man. 12°. '74. $3 .... *Somerby.*
— Outcast. sm. 12°. '76. pap., 30c. .. *D. M. Bennett.*
— Western Africa: narr. of tour in equatorial, south-western and north-western Africa. ill. and map. 8°. $4; shp., $4.50; hf. cf., $6.25 .... *Harper.*
Reader, Fk. S. Moody and Sankey: account of their lives and services. por. 12°. '76. $1; pap., 50c. .... *Hale.*
Reading club and handy speaker. Baker, G. M. 3 nos. ea., 50c. .... *Lee & S.*
Reading without tears. *See* Mortimer, *Mrs.* M.
Readings from the best authors. 2 v. 12°. v. 1, 75c.; v. 2, $1 .... *Nelson.*
Ready for work. Groser, W. H. 50c. .... *Nelson.*
Ready-made speeches. Hindley, C. 50c. .. *Routledge.*
Ready money: drama. 16°. pap., 15c. .... *French.*
Ready-money Mortiboy. Besant, W., *and* Rice, J. 75c. .... **Osgood.*
Ready reckoner. 32°. 16c. .... *Fisher.*
Ready reckoner; or, federal calculator. 32°. hf. bd., 25c. .... *U. P. James.*
Ready reckoner and mercantile companion. 18°. 25c. — (Pocket ed.) 32°. 25c. .... *Lippincott.*
Ready remedies for common complaints. 16°. 20c. *Routledge.*
Ready work for willing hands; or, the story of Comfort Allison. 18°. 80c. .... *Am. S. S.*
Real and ideal. Wigan, H. 15c. .... *French.*
Real children: their sayings and doings. 4 v. ill. 18°. $1.40 .... *Am. S. S.*
Real folks. Whitney, A. D. T. $1.50 .... *Osgood.*
Real life. Bourdon, M. F. $1.50; $2 .. *Kelly, P. & Co.*
Real life in spirit land. Kings, M. M. $1 .... *Colby.*
Real Robinson Crusoes. *See* Books for the children's hour.
Real secret art and philosophy of wooing, winning and wedding. 25c. .... *Un. Pub. Co.*
Real victory. *See* Minnie's lib.; — Moss rose ser.
Realities of Irish life. Trench, W. S. $1 .. *Roberts.*
Realm of the ice king; by author of "Saved from the wreck." 12°. $1.75 .... *Nelson.*
— *Same.* ill. sq. 12°. '75. $2 .... *Putnam.*
Realmah. *See* Helps, *Sir* A.
Reapers. Stirling, E. 15c. .... *French.*
Reason and faith; or, the two lights; by author of "Struggles for life." [Fiction.] 12°. $1.50. *Lippincott.*
Reason and redemption. White, R. B. $2 .. *Lippincott.*
Reason and revelation. Milligan, R. $2 .... *Chase.*
Reason and revelation. Potter, W. J. 10c. .. *Free Rel.*
Reason and revelation. Preston, T. S. $1.50 .. *Cath. Pub.*
Reason in religion. Hedge, F. H. $1.50 .... *Roberts.*
Reason, the only oracle of man. Allen, E. 50c. *Mendum.*
Reason vs. the sword. *See* Washburn, J. M.
Reason why all Christians should read God's written word in Greek. 8°. (Bagster.) pap., 25c. .. *Wiley.*
Reason why natural history (The); by author of "Inquire within." 12°. $1.50 .... *Dick & F.*
Reason why of general science. ill. 12°. $1.50 .. *Dick & F.*
Reasonable elocution. Taverner, F. G. $1.25 .. *Barnes.*
Reasons for becoming a Baptist. Slack, W. L. 10c. *So. Bapt.*
Reasons for becoming a Methodist. Smith, I. 50c. *Meth. Bk. Conc.*
Reasons for my hope. Hastings, H. L. 25c. .. *Hastings.*
Reasons for our hope. Wilson, J. V. 75c. *Universalist.*
Reasons for returning to the Church of England. cr. 8°. '71. $1.75 .... *Routledge.*
Reasons in rhyme. 16°. 25c. .... *Routledge.*
Reavis, L. U. Saint Louis, the future great city of the world. 8°. '75. mor., $10 .... *Gray.*
— Thoughts for the young men and the young women of Am. 2d ed., rev. and enl. 12°. '71. 75c. .. *Wells.*
Reback, H. Novels. 4 v. ill. 8°. (Lond.) ea., pap., 30c. .... *Am. News.*

Cont.: Bound by a spell. — Doomed. — Tracked. — Young cavalier.

Rebel and the rover. 8°. pap., 50c. .... *Peterson.*
Rebel bride. 8°. pap., 50c. .... *Peterson.*
Rebel chief. Aimard, G. 75c. .... *Peterson.*
Rebel coaster; or, the escape from the pressgang. 8°. pap., 25c. .... *De Witt.*
Rebel general's loyal bride. *See* Avery, M. A.
Rebel prince. Blackburn, W. M. $1 .... *Pres. Bd.*
Rebel reclaimed. Tucker, C. 75c. .... *Carter.*
Rebel scout. Ashland, A. 25c. .... *U. P. James.*
Rebel war clerk's diary. *See* Jones, J. B.
Rebella. Dunning, A. K. 50c. .... *Pres. Bd.*
Rebel's recollections. Eggleston, G. C. $1.50. *Hurd & H.*
Rebels and tories. Labree, L. 50c. .... *De Witt.*
Reber, G: The Christ of Paul; or, the enigmas of Christianity. 12°. '76. $2 .... *Somerby.*
Rebe's common sense. Dodge, A. A. $1.15. *Bost. Am. Tr.*
Receipts for the million. Hale, S. J. $1.75 .. *Peterson.*
Recent art and society. Chorley, H. F. $2 .... *Holt.*
Recent British philosophy. *See* Masson, D.
Recent origin of man. Southall, J. C. $6 .. *Lippincott.*
Reck, P. G. F. v., *and* Bolzius, J. M. Extract of journals of Von Reck, who conducted the first transport of Saltzburgers to Georgia; and of the Rev. Mr. Bolzius, one of their ministers: Lond., 1734. [Reprint.] 4°. pap., 50c. .... *Sabin.*
Recklinghausen, F. v. *See* Manual of histology.
Reclus, Elisée. The earth: descrip. history of the phenomena of the life of the globe; tr. by B. B. Woodward and ed. by H. Woodward. maps and ill. 8°. $5; hf. cf., $7.25 .... *Harper.*
— The ocean, atmosphere and life: 2d ser. of a descrip. hist. of the life of the globe; tr. maps and ill. 8°. $6; hf. cf., $8.25 .... *Harper.*
Recluse of Rambouillet; tr. by Miss A. T. Sadlier. 18°. 50c.; 75c. .... *Sadlier.*
Recognition of friends in another world. Dorr, B. 40c. .... *McCauley.*
Recollections of a busy life. Greeley, H. $3. *N. Y. Tribune.*
Recollections of Eton; by an Etonian. ill. 8°. pap., 50c. .... *Harper.*
Recollections of Geoffry Hamlyn. Kingsley, H. $1.75. **Osgood.*
Recollections of an itinerant. Smith, H. $1. *Cin. Meth. Bk. Conc.*
Recollections of a literary life. Mitford, M. R. $1.50 .... *Harper.*
Recollections of men and things at Washington. Gobright, L. A. $1.75 .... *Claxton.*
Recollections of my childhood. Lippincott, S. J. $1. **Osgood.*

Recollections of our anti-slavery conflict. May, S. J. $1.50 ....*Osgood.*
Recollections of Oxford. Coxe, G. V. $2.50. *Macmillan.*
Recollections of past life. Holland, *Sir* H. $2. *Appleton.*
Recollections of seventy years. Farrar, E. W. $1.50. **Osgood.*
Recollections of a southern matron. Gilman, C. $1.75 ............................*J.E.Potter.*
Recompense. Seymour, M. H. $1.25... *Whittaker.*
Record of a happy life. Smith, H. W. $1.25; 50c. *Lippincott; Revell.*
Record of the metropolitan fair in aid of the U. S. Sanitary Com., N. Y., April, 1864: report of U. S. Sanit. Com. photos. 4°. $6; hf. cf., $9..*Hurd & H.*
Record of an obscure man. Putnam, M. L. $1..*Osgood.*
Record of a school. Alcott, A. B. $1.50....*Roberts.*
Records of five years. Lippincott, S. J. $1.50..**Osgood.*
Records of a good man's life. Tayler, C. B. $1. *Leighton.*
Records of the heart. Lewis, E. A. $3.....*Bouton.*
Records of noble lives. Adams, W.H.D. $1.50..*Nelson.*
Records of the past. *See* Birch, S.
Records of a quiet life. Hare, A. J. C. $2..*Roberts.*
Recovery of Jerusalem. *See* Palestine exploration fund.
Recreations for cabinet organ, harmonium and melodeon: sel. and arr. of popular themes. 4°. '63. $2; bds., $1.50 ....*Ditson.*
Recreations for the cornet: songs, etc., for cornopean or cornet a piston, also for valve trumpet, Kent bugle and clarionet. 4 nos. 8°. ea., pap., 50c. *Ditson.*
Recreations of Christopher North. *See* Wilson, J:
Recruiting office. White, C. 15c ....*De Witt.*
Recruiting officer.* Farquhar, G. 15c.......*French.*
Rector of Roxburgh. DeCosta, B. F. $1.25..*Dutton.*
Rector's daughter. Bowman, A. $1 .....*Routledge.*
Rector's visits. 18°. 40c....................*Dutton.*
Rector's wife. Stratton, J. $1.75; $1.50..*Peterson.*
Rectory and the manor. Brock, C. $1.50...*Dutton.*
Rectory of Valehead. Evans, R. W. $1....*Dutton.*
Recueil de pièces sur la négociation entre la Nouvelle France et la Nouvelle Angleterre ès années 1648 et suivantes. 8°. '66. pap., $3..........*Shea.*
Recueil de prières pour tous les besoins de la vie. 32°. *net*, 29c.-68c.........................*Benziger.*
Red and white roses. *See* Yonge, C. M.
Red as a rose is she. Broughton, R. $1.50; 60c. *Appleton.*
Red bird. *See* Our song birds.
Red bridge. Putnam, E. T. H. 90c.......*Nat. Temp.*
Red bridge ser. 4 v. 18°. $3.50..........*Nat. Temp.*
Cont.: Red bridge, by Mrs. E. T. H. Putnam. — Hard master, by Mrs. J. E. McConaughy. — Echo bank, by Ervie. — Rachel Noble's experience, by B. Edwards.

Red brothers. 18°. 18c.....................*Am.S.S.*
Red chignon. Baker, G. M. 15c..............*Lee & S.*
Red cotton nightcap country. Browning, R. $1.50. *Osgood.*
Red Court farm. *See* Wood, H.
Red cross. Adams, W. T. $1.50 ....*Lee & S.*
Red cross knight. *See* Tucker, *Mrs.* C.
Red cross of Constantine. Stowell, C.L. $1.50..*Masonic.*
Red crosses. Guernsey, C. F. 90c......(?)*Martien.*
Red doctor. Lafitte, J. P. $1.75...........*Claxton.*
Red Eric. *See* Ballantyne, R. M.
Red flag, and other poems. Noel, R. $2..*Routledge.*
Red Indians of Newfoundland. ill. 8°. pap., 75c. *Peterson.*
Red king; or, the corsair chieftain. 8°. pap., 50c. *Peterson.*

Red line editions. 12 v. ill. sm. 4°. ea., $3.50..*Osgood*
Cont.: Burns' Poems. — Bret Harte's Poems. — Mrs. Browning's Aurora Leigh. — Longfellow's Poems. — Longfellow's Christus. — Lowell. — Owen Meredith's Lucile. — Procter. — Saxe. — Scott. — Tennyson. — Whittier.
Red line editions of the standard poets. 11 v. ill. sm. 4° ....*Miller*
Cont.: Bailey's Festus, $3.50. — Browning's Poems, $4.50. — Browning's Aurora Leigh, $3.50. — Burns, $4.50. — Campbell, $3.50. — Gray, $3.50. — Hood, $4.50. — Keats, $3.50. — Keble's Christian year, $3.50. — Macaulay's Lays of ancient Rome, $3.50 — Shelley, $4.50.
Red line ser. 6 v. ill. 4°. ea., $5; mor., $8.. *World Pub*
Cont.: Sigourney's Poetical works. — Watson's Quotation from the poets. — Montgomery's Poetical works. — Krummacher's Parables. — Weld's Book of sacred quotations. — Mrs. Osgood's Poetical works.
Red lion. 18°. 80c......................*Cong. Pub*
— *See also* Seaside stories.
Red mask. Brougham, J. 15c..............*French*
Red plant. Guernsey, L. E. 40c...........*Am.S.S*
Red rajah. Whittaker, F. 20c..............*Beadle*
Red Riding Hood: burlesque. 16°. pap., 15c...*French*
Red Riding Hood picture-book. sm. 4°. $2.50..*Routledge*
Red Rover. Ball, E. 15c...................*French*
Red Rover. *See* Cooper, Ja. F.
Red shanty boys. Brown, T. $1.50.... *H.A. Young*
Red shoes. 18°. 25c.........................*Am.S.S*
— *See also* Children of Blackberry Hollow.
Red shoes. *See* Andersen, H. C.
Red-skins. *See* Cooper, Ja. F.
Red track. Aimard, G. 75c..............*Peterson*
Red velvet Bible. *See* Story of.
Red Wing; or, cruiser of Van Dieman's Land. 8° pap., 50c...........................*Peterson*
Red Wolf, the pirate. 8°. pap., 25c.........*De Witt*
Red Wolf ser. 8 v. 8°. ea., pap., 25c.......*De Witt*
Cont.: Red Wolf. — Black brother. — Pirate's bride. — Mysterious cavern. — Jamba. — Black eagle. — Diana. — Ocean monarch.
Redbrook. *See* Wise, D.
Redburn. Melville, H. $1.50..............*Harper*
Redden, *Miss* Laura C. *See* Searing, *Mrs.* Laura C.
Redding, Cyrus. History and descript. of wines, anc. and modern. ill. 12°. (Bohn.) $1.75..*Little, B. & Co*
— *Same.* ill. 12°. (Bohn.) $2. *Lippincott; Scribner, W. & A*
Redding, M. Wolcott. Antiquities of the Orient unveiled. [Masonic.] ill. 8°. '72. $4; leath. $4.50; mor., $6......................*Redding*
— Practical monitor and compend. of Masonic law and jurisprudence. ill. 32°. $1.35 ....*Redding*
Reddy, W: Inside views of Methodism. 18°. '59 50c. ....*Meth. Bk. Conc*
Rede, Leman T. Devil and Dr. Faustus: drama. 16° pap., 15c...............................*French*
— Guide to the stage. 16°. pap., 15c. ....*French*
— Jack in the water: burletta. 16°. pap., 15c...*French*
— Queen's Bench: farce. 16°. pap., 15c.......*French*
Rede, W: Leman. [Plays.] 7 v. 16°. ea., pap., 15c *French*
Cont.: Affair of honor: farce. — Douglas: travestie. — His first champagne: farce. — Our village; or, the lost ship. — Rake's progress. — Sixteen-string Jack. — Skeleton witness.
Redeemer. *See* Congregation of the Most Holy Redeemer.
Redeemer and redeemed. Beecher, C. $1.75..*Lee & S*
Redeemer's counsel. *See* Bijou Bible text-books.
Redeemer's legacy. McCord, W. J. 35c...*Pres. Bd*
Redeemer's tears wept over lost souls. Howe, J. $1 *Draper*
Redemption: its nature and objects illustrated. 18° 25c.....................................*Am.S.S*
Redemptorist mission book. 48°. 30c.-$2..*Noonan*
—*See also* Mission book.
Reden, K: (*pseud.*) *See* Converse, C: C.

Redesdale; by author of "Grace Houghton's story." 16°. '68. 75c. . . . . *Dutton.*

Redfield, Amasa A. Treatise on law and practice of surrogates' courts of New York. 8°. shp., $6.50. *Baker, V. & Co.*

— *See also* New York County, Surrogate reports; — Shearman, T. G., *and* Redfield, A. A.

Redfield, I: F. Law of carriers of goods and passengers; also construction, responsibility and duty of innkeepers, and law of bailments. 8°. '69. $6.50 . . . . *Hurd & H.*

— Law of railways; embr. corporations, eminent domain, contracts, etc. 5th ed., rev. and enl. 2 v. 8°. '73. shp., $12 . . . . *Little, B. & Co.*

— Law of wills. 3d ed. 3 v. 8°. '70. shp., $18. *Little, B. & Co.*

— *Same.* 4th ed. v. 1. 8°. '76. shp., $6 . . *Little, B. & Co.*

— Leading American cases and notes upon law of wills: sup. to "Law of wills." 8°. '74. shp., $6. *Little, B. & Co.*

— Leading Am. railway cases on important questions involved in law of railways; with notes and opinions. 2d ed. 2 v. 8°. '72. shp., $12 . . . . *Little, B. & Co.*

— *and* Bigelow, Melville M. Leading and select Am. cases in law of bills of exchange, promissory notes and checks; with notes and ref. 8°. '71. shp., $6 . . . . *Little, B. & Co.*

Redfield, Ja. W. Physiognomy. ill. 8°. $2.50. *Widdleton.*

Redford, Alb. H. Fred Brenning. ('72.) 7th ed. 16°. '76. 75c. . . . . *So. Meth.*

— History of Methodism in Kentucky. ('68–'70.) 3d ed. 3 v. ill. 12°. '70. ea., $2–$4 . . . . . . *So. Meth.*

— Organization of the Meth. Episc. Ch., south. ('71.) 5th ed. 12°. '76. $2 . . . . *So. Meth.*

— Russell Morton. 16°. '76. 75c. . . . . *So. Meth.*

— Western cavaliers: hist. of the Meth. Episc. Ch. in Kentucky, 1832–'44. 12°. '75. $2 . . . . *So. Meth.*

Redford, G: The great change: treatise on conversion. 18°. 60c. . . . . *Am. S. S.*

Redgauntlet. *See* Scott, *Sir* Wa.

Redgrave, R: Manual of design; comp. from his writings and addresses by G. R. Redgrave. ill. cr. 8°. '76. $1 . . . . *Scribner, W. & A.*

Redington, Asa. *See* Maine, Sup. Court reports.

Redmond, Count O'Hanlon. Carleton, W. 60c.; $1. *Sadlier.*

Redmond O'Neil. Smith, J. F. 75c. . . . . . . *Dick & F.*

Redstick. Montesano, R. R. 25c. . . . . . . *U. P. James.*

Reece, R. [Plays.] 7 v. 16°. ea., pap., 15c. . . *French.*
Cont.: Brown and brahmins: burlesque. — Dora's device: comedy. — Lady of the lake: burlesque. — Perfect love: fairy play. — Prometheus: extravaganza. — Stranger: burlesque. — Whittington junior: burlesque.

Reed, *Miss* A. Women of the covenant: their trials and triumphs. 18°. 50c. . . . . *Cong. Pub.*

Reed, *Mrs.* A. Christianity makes heroes: tale of the early days of Christianity. 16°. '52. 40c. *West. Tr.*

Reed, And. Martha: memorial of an only and beloved sister. 12°. $1.25 . . . . *Harper.*

— No fiction. 12°. $1.25 . . . . *Harper.*

— Plumbe rolls. [Biog.] ill. 18°. '49. 20c. . . *Am. Tr.*

Reed, E. Gold, frankincense and myrrh. 16°. '72. $1 . . . . *Claxton.*

— Idle words. ('69.) New ed. ill. 16°. '70. 90c. *Claxton.*

— King's pine apple. 18°. 90c. . . . . (?) *Martien.*

— Levin's treasure in bank. 2d ed. 18°. '69. 75c. *Claxton.*

— She hath done what she could. 18°. '70. 75c. *Claxton.*

Reed, F. A. Twin heroes. 12°. $1.75 . . . . *Cong. Pub.*

Reed, H: Lectures on the British poets. ('57.) New ed. 2 v. 12°. '69. $3.50 . . . . *Claxton.*

— Lectures on English history and tragic poetry as ill. in Shakespeare. ('55.) New ed. 12°. '75. $1.75. *Claxton.*

— Lectures on Eng. literature, from Chaucer to Tennyson. ('55.) 6th ed., rev. 12°. '75. $1.75 . . *Claxton.*

Reed, I: G., *jr.* Erring, yet noble: tale of and for women. 12°. $1.50; pap., $1 . . . . *Loring.*

— From heaven to New York; or, the good hearts and the brown stone fronts. 12°. '75. pap., 50c. *Murray.*

Reed, Jac. Whittemore. History of the Reed family in Europe and America. por. 8°. '61. $4. *Lockwood, B. & Co.*

Reed, Ja. Man and woman. 16°. 50c. . . *H. H. Carter.*

— *Same.* 16°. '69. 75c. . . . . *Lockwood, B. & Co.*

— Religion and life. 16°. 75c. . . . . *New Ch.*

Reed, J: C. Handbook of Georgia criminal law. 8°. '73. shp., $6 . . . . *Burke.*

— Practical suggestions for conduct of law suits in and out of court. 8°. '75. $4; shp., $5 . . *Cockcroft.*

Reed, J: J. My Sabbath school scrap-book. 3d ed. 12°. '75. $1.50 . . . . *Tibbals.*

Reed, Jos. J. Outlines of universal hist. [To form 3 pts.] pt. 1: Ancient hist. f°. $2 . . *Lippincott.*

Reed, P. Fishe. Beyond the snow: history of Trim's adventures in Nordlichtschein. ill. 12°. '73. $1.25 . . . . *Donnelley.*

— Drawing lessons, for home and school use. obl. 4°. $1.50 . . . . *Un. Bk. Conc.*

Reed, Reb. Perly. Above and below; or, why the baby died. 16°. $1.25 . . . . *Cong. Pub.*

— Ethel's gift. 18°. '74. 20c. . . . . *Am. Tr.*

— Everybody's providence. 12°. $1.75 . . . . *Cong. Pub.*

Reed, Sampson. Correspondence of heat and light. 18°. '62. 25c. . . . . *H. H. Carter.*

— Observations on growth of the mind. 16°. 62c. *H. H. Carter.*

— *Same.* 16°. $1 . . . . *Lippincott.*

Reed, W: B. World essays: among my books. 12°. $1.50 . . . . *Hale.*

Reed shaken with the wind. Faithful, E. $1.50. *Adams, V. & Co.*

Reeder, Louise. Currer Lyle; or, autobiography of an actress. 12°. $1.75; pap., $1.50 . . . . *Peterson.*

Reef, and other parables. Bickersteth, E. H. $1.25. *Carter; Dutton.*

Reef village. Mudge, Z. A. 50c. . . . . . . *Bost. Am. Tr.*

Reemelin, C: Politics as a science. 8°. '75. $1.50. *Clarke.*

— Wine-maker's manual. 12°. '68. $1.25 . . . . *Clarke.*

Rees, Ja. Footprints of a letter-carrier: hist. of the world's correspondence. 12°. $2.25 . . *Lippincott.*

— Life of Edwin Forrest; with reminisc. and personal recollections. por. 12°. $2; pap., $1 . . *Peterson.*

— Shakespeare and the Bible; with prayers on the stage, Shakespeare's use of the name of deity, etc. 16°. '75. $1 . . . . *Claxton.*

Reese, D. M. Elements of zoology; or, natural history of animals. 12°. '49. $1.50 . . . . . . *Barnes.*

Reese, J: J. American medical formulary. 12°. '50. $1.50 . . . . *Lindsay.*

— Analysis of physiology. 2d ed., enl. 12°. '52. $1.50. *Lindsay.*

— Manual of toxicology. 8°. $5; shp., $6 . . *Lippincott.*

— Syllabus of med. chemistry. 12°. '57. $1 . . *Lindsay.*

Reeve, Ann. Short account of Ann Reeve. 24°. pap., 10c. . . . . *Friends Bk. St.*

Reeve, Clara. Old English baron; [also] Castle of Otranto, by H. Walpole. cr. 8°. pap., 25c. *Lippincott.*

Reeve, Jos. Bible history. 18°. hf. bd., 90c. . . *Sadlier.*

— History of the Old and New Test.; with reflections from the fathers. 18°. 75c. . . . . *Noonan.*

— *Same.* 8°. $1 . . . . *Cath. Pub.*

— Practical discourses on perfections and works of God, and divinity and works of Christ. 8°. $2.50. *Cath. Pub.*

Reeve, Lovell. Elements of conchology: introd. to nat. hist. of shells, and of animals which form them. 2 v. col. pl. roy. 8°. (Lond.) $28 . . *Putnam.*

Reeve, Tapping. Domestic relations: law of baron and femme, of parent and child, etc., and of the powers of the Court of Chancery. 3d ed., with notes and ref. by A. J. Parker and C. E. Baldwin. 8°. '62. shp., $6 .... *Gould.*

Reeve, Wybert. Never reckon your chickens: farce. 16°. pap., 15c. .... *De Witt; French.*

— Not so bad after all: comedy. 16°. pap., 15c. *Ames; French.*

— Won at last: comedy. 16°. pap., 15c. .. *Ames; French.*

Reeves, Ja. E. Practical treatise on enteric fever, its diagnosis and treatment; embr. a partial hist. of the disease in Virginia. 12°. $1 ... *Lippincott.*

Reeves, J: History of Eng. law to end of reign of Elizabeth; with notes and introd. by W. F. Finlason. New ed. 3 v. 8°. '69. $12; hf. cf., $18 .... *Little, B. & Co.*

— *Same.* 3 v. 8°. $18; cf., $33 ... *Scribner, W. & A.*

Reeves, *Miss* M. R. L. *See* Rodney, *Mrs.* M. R. L.

Reeves, Marian. Door of escape, and what it led to. 18°. 75c. .... (?) *Martien.*

Reeves, Pl. Student's own speaker: manual of oratory. 12°. '71. 90c.; bds., 75c. .... *Putnam.*

Reference catalogue of current [Eng.] literature. cr. 8°. (Lond.) '75. *net*, $2.50 .. *Publishers' Weekly.*
Note. Published biennially.

Reffelt, H. Allgemeine deutsche Vorschriften f. Schönschreiben. 2 nos. obl. 8°. '64. ea., pap., 25c. .... *Steiger.*

— [Arithmetics, in Eng.] 9 v. 12°. '61-'73. bds. *Steiger.*
Cont.: Earliest lessons in arith., 20c. — First book of arith., 30c. — Key, pap., 8c. — Second book, 50c. — Key, 20c. — Third book, 60c. — Key, 30c. — Fourth book, *and* Key, ea., 75c.

— — Second, third and fourth books of arithmetic in 9 nos. (nos. 4-12 of series); with keys. 12 v. 12° .... *Steiger.*
Cont.: Nos. 4-6 of ser. (pts. 1-3 of 2d bk.), ea., 20c. — No. 7 (pt. 1 of 3d bk.), 25c. — Nos. 8-9 (pts. 2-3 of 3d bk.), ea., 30c. — No. 10 (pt. 1 of 4th bk.), 15c. — Key, 10c. — No. 11 (pt. 2 of 4th bk.), 30c. — Key, 35c. — No. 12 (pt. 3 of 4th bk.), *and* Key, ea., 35c.

— Buch f. Schule u. Haus. 4 v. 12°. '70-'74. bds. *Steiger.*
Cont.: Erstes Buch f. Schule u. Haus, 25c. — Zweites, 45c. — Drittes, 50c. — Viertes, 70c.; in 2 pts., ea., 40c.

— *Same;* with vocab. of German words, for use in Am. schools. 2 v. 12°. '70-'71. bds. .... *Steiger.*
Cont.: First book for school and house, 30c. — Second, 50c.

— Deutsch-eng. Liederbuch f. deutsche Schulen. 12°. '62. 50c. .... *Steiger.*

— Ersten Anfänge (Die) im Rechnen. 12°. '68. bds., 20c. .... *Steiger.*

— Exempelbuch f. d. Kopfrechnen. 2 nos. 12°. '66. bds., 1, 36c.; 2, 45c. .... *Steiger.*

— — Antworten. 12°. '66. bds., 45c. .... *Steiger.*

— Exempelbuch f. d. Unterricht im Rechnen. 4 pts. (Theile), with keys. 7 v. 12°. '71-'73. bds. *Steiger.*
Cont.: Erster Theil, 40c. — Schlüssel, pap., 8c. — Zweiter Theil, 50c. — Schlüssel, 20c. — Dritter Theil, 60c. — Schlüssel, 30c. — Vierter Theil, 75c.

— *Same;* in 12 nos. (Hefte), with keys. 15 v. 12°. pap. .... *Steiger.*
Cont.: 1. Heft, pap., 15c. — 2. u. 3. Heft, ea., pap., 12c. — 4.-6. Heft, ea., 20c. — 7. Heft, 25c. — 8. u. 9. Heft, ea., 30c. — 10. Heft, 15c. — Schlüssel, pap., 8c. — 11. Heft, 25c. — Schlüssel, 30c. — 12. Heft u. Schlüssel, ea., 35c.

— Kleine theoretisch-praktische Gesanglehre f. deutsche Schulen mit ein- u. zweistimmigen Liedern. 12°. '69. bds., 30c. .... *Steiger.*

— Kurzgefasstes Lehrbuch d. Rechnens. 12°. '66. bds., 40c. .... *Steiger.*

— Leichte Vorübungen im Lesen f. Schule u. Haus. 12°. '76. bds., 20c. .... *Steiger.*

— Lese- u. Lehrbuch f. deutsche Schulen in d. Ver. Staaten. 5 v. 12°. '61-'71. bds. .... *Steiger.*
Cont.: Erstes Lese- u. Lehrbuch, 30c. — Zweites, 50c. — Drittes, 70c. — *Same,* new ed., enl., '74, 80c. — Viertes, 70c. — Fünftes, 65c.

Reffelt, H., *continued.*

— Lesebuch f. Kirchen u. Sonntagsschulen. 3 v. 12°. '72. bds. .... *Steiger.*
Cont.: Erstes Lesebuch f. Kirchen u. S., 15c. — Zweites, 15c. — Drittes, 25c.

— Lesefibel. 12°. '62. bds., 20c. .... *Steiger.*

— Rechnenbuch f. deutsche Schulen u. zum Privatgebrauch. 3 nos. 12°. '56-'58. bds., 1, 30c.; 2, 45c.; 3, 50c. .... *Steiger.*

— — Antwortenheft. 12°. '57. bds., 36c. .... *Steiger.*

— *See also* Goldammer, H., Die Einordng. d. Kindergartens.

Refiner's fire: thoughts on affliction; sel. from works of Leighton, Rutherford, Hooker, Newton, Cecil and others. 12°. $2.25 .... *Nelson.*

Reflected light. 12°. $1.25 .... (?) *Martien.*

Reflection. Hofland, B. $1 .... *Nelson.*

Reflections and prayers for holy communion; tr., with pref. by H. E. Manning. 16°. $1.50. *Kelly, P. & Co.*

Reflections on peace and war. Jackson, J. *net*, 15c. *Friends Bk. Assoc.*

Reform. Moncrieff, W. T. 15c. .... *French.*

Reformation. *See* Young Protestant's lib.

Reformed Church in America. Book of praise: psalms and hymns set to music. 8°. hf. mor., $2. *N. Y. Ref. Ch. Bd.*

— Constitution. 32°. 25c. .... *Ref. Ch. Bd.*

— *Same.* 18°. 50c. .... *N. Y. Ref. Ch. Bd.*

— *Same;* with pref. and introd. by T. W. Chambers. 18°. 60c. .... *N. Y. Ref. Ch. Bd.*

— *Same;* and Digest. 18°. 75c. .... *N. Y. Ref. Ch. Bd.*

— *Same;* embr. Catechism, Compendium, Confession of faith, etc.; with app. 18°. 57c. *N. Y. Ref. Ch. Bd.*

— — Appendix. 8°. pap., 10c. .... *N. Y. Ref. Ch. Bd.*

— *Germ.* 18°. 35c. .... *N. Y. Ref. Ch. Bd.*

— — *Same.* 32°. 25c. .... *Ref. Ch. Pub.*

— Digest of laws of the General Synod, to 1869. 18°. 75c. .... *N. Y. Ref. Ch. Bd.*

— Evangelische Kinder-Harfe f. christliche Schulen. 18°. '60. hf. bd., 30c. .... *N. Y. Ref. Ch. Bd.*

— Evangelische Lieder. Comp. by committees of Synod. 32°. 75c.; $1; $1.50 .... *Ref. Ch. Pub.*

— Forms and hymns; comp. by committees of Synod. 12°. $1.50; $2.50; $4; mor., $5 .. *Ref. Ch. Pub.*

— Hymns; comp. by a committee of Synod. 12°. $1-$5 .... *Ref. Ch. Pub.*

— Hymns of the Church: Liturgy with tunes. 8°. $3. — Liturgy alone. 18°. $2 .... *N. Y. Ref. Ch. Bd.*

— Hymns of prayer and praise; with tunes. 12°. 75c. *N. Y. Ref. Ch. Bd.*

— Liturgy; as rev. by the committees of Gen. Synod. 12°. 50c.-$1.50 .... *N. Y. Ref. Ch. Bd.*

— Minutes of the General Synod. v. 1 (1771-1812). 8°. $2.50; pap., $2 .... *N. Y. Ref. Ch. Bd.*

— Order of worship; comp. by committees of Synod. [In Eng. or Germ.] 12°. $1.50-$4. — (Pulpit ed.), mor., $7.50. — Forms alone, 40c. *Ref. Ch. Pub.*

— *Same;* and hymns. 12°. $2-$6 .... *Ref. Ch. Pub.*

— Primary Bible questions for Sabbath schools. 5 v. 18°. ea., per doz., $1.80 .... *N. Y. Ref. Ch. Bd.*
Cont.: Genesis to Joshua v. — Joshua vi. to Daniel vi. — Harmony of the Gospels, 3 v.

— Psalms and hymns; comp. by a com. of the Maryland classes. 24°. 75c.-$7 .... *Ref. Ch. Pub.*

— *Same.* 24°. 75c.-$2.50. — 18°. $1.20-$3. — 12°. $1.60-$4 .... *N. Y. Ref. Ch. Bd.*

— *Germ.* 12°. $1.10-$2.50. — 18°. 90c.-$2.50. *N. Y. Ref. Ch. Bd.*

— Sabbath school and social hymns; adopted by Gen. Synod, June, 1843. 18°. hf. bd., 12c. *N. Y. Ref. Ch. Bd.*

— Tercentenary monument; in commemoration of 300th anniv. of the Heidelberg catechism; prep. by secretaries of Tercentenary convention. [In Eng. or Germ.] 12°. ea., $3.50 .... *Ref. Ch. Pub.*

— Tracts issued by the Board of Publication. Nos. 1-40 in 2 v, 12°. ea., 75c. .... *N. Y. Ref. Ch. Bd.*

— *See also* Heidelberg catechism.

Reformed Episcopal Church. Book of common prayer, adopted by the 2d General Council, 1874. 18°. 70c.–$2.25. — 32°. 50c.–$2.25; — with hymns. sq. 12°. $2.50; mor., $3.50 ........*J.A. Moore.*
— Hymnal. 18°. 25c....................*J.A. Moore.*
— *See also* Protestant Episc. Church.
Reformed gambler. *See* Green, J. H.
Reformed highwayman. *See* Reynolds, G. W. M.
Reformed pastor. *See* Baxter, R.
Reformed Virginian silk-worm: a rare and new disc. of a speedy way, and easie means for the feeding of silk-worms: Lond., 1655. [Reprint.] 4°. pap., 75c. ....*Sabin.*
Reformers before the reformation. Ullmann, C. 2 v. ea., $3 ....*Scribner, W.& A.*
Refuge; by author of "Guide to domestic happiness." 12°. 80c..........................*Pres. Bd.*
Refuge of lies, and the covert from the storm. Lane, B. I. $1 .... *W. H. Young.*
Refugee. Melville, H. $1.75; $1.50......*Peterson.*
Refutation of the age to come. Waggoner, J. H. 20c............................*Sev. Day Adv.*
Regeln u. Wörterverzeichniss f. d. deutsche Orthographie; [nach R. v. Raumer]. 8°. '76. pap., 50c..............................*Doerflinger.*
Regeneration: what is it? McIntosh, C. H. 25c.; 10c..................................*Revell.*
Regent's daughter. 8°. pap., 50c..........*Harper.*
Regent's daughter. Dumas, A. 50c.......*Routledge.*
Regester, Seeley (*pseud.*) *See* Victor, *Mrs.* M. V. F.
Regicide's daughter. Carpenter, W. H. 60c...*Claxton.*
Reginald Archer. Seemuller, A. M. 75c...**Osgood.*
Reginald Hastings. Warburton, E. 50c.....*Harper.*
Regnault, Vct. Elements of chemistry; tr. by T. F. Betton, and ed., with notes, by J. C. Booth and W. L. Faber. (cop. '52.) '64. 3d ed. 2 v. ill. 8°. '74. $7.50.........................*Baird.*
Regular fix. Morton, J. M. 15c............*French.*
Regular Swiss round. Jones, H. $1.75...*Routledge.*
Rehearsals. Warren, J. L. $1.75.......*Routledge.*
Reichardt, G. Nightingale's nest. [Music.] f°. $1. *Brainard.*
Reichel, Levin T. History of the Moravians in North Carolina. 24°. '57. 50c.............*Clauder.*
Reichel, W: C. The Crown Inn, near Bethlehem, Pa., 1745. sq. 8°. pap., $3..............*Clauder.*
— (*ed.*) Memorials of the Moravian Church. v. 1. cr. 8°. *$3.50 ....*Lippincott.*
Reichenau, Rud. Child life; adapted from the Germ. by C. Campbell. ill. sq. 8°. $1.75...*Routledge.*
Reichenbach, O. Einige Gedanken e. Nichtgelehrten bei Lesung d. Kosmos. 12°. 75c...*F. W. Thomas.*
Reid, Alex. New English dictionary; with derivations. 12°. hf. bd., $1.25....................*Appleton.*
Reid, Chr. (*pseud.*) *See* Fisher, F. C.
Reid, D: Boswell. Ventilation in Am. dwellings; with diagrams and outline of progress of improvement. 12°. $1.50.................... *Wiley.*
Reid, H: Practical treatise on concrete, and how to make it; with obs. on uses of cements, limes and mortars. pl. cr. 8°. '73. $2........*Spon.*
— Practical treatise on manufacture of Portland cement; with tr. of M. A. Lipowitz's descript. of a new Germ. method for manuf. that cement, by W. F. Reid. pl. and wood eng. 8°. $7.50....*Baird.*
Reid, J: Footprints of sorrow. ('69.) New ed. 12°. '75. $2.............................*Carter.*
— Voices of the soul, answered in God. ('65.) New ed. 12°. '75. $1.75.................*Carter.*
Reid, Mayne. Castaways. 16°. $1.25 ......*Sheldon.*
— Desert home. ill. 16°. $1.50..............*Miller.*
— *Span.* Casa (La) en el desierto; tr. por S. Camacho y A. Hernández. 12°. $1.50..........*Appleton.*

Reid, Mayne, *continued.*
— Flag of distress. 12°. '76. $1.75. 16°. $1.50..*Miller.*
— Hunter's feast. ill. 12°. $1.50...........*Carleton.*
— Library of travel and adventure. 10 v. ill. 16°. $15. *Miller.*
Cont.: Afloat in the forest.—Boy hunters.—Boy slaves.—Bruin.—Desert home.—Forest exiles.—Giraffe hunters.—Man eaters.—Ocean waifs.—Young voyagers.
— Odd people: popular descrip. of singular races of man. ill. 16°. 75c....................*Harper.*
— Osceola, the Seminole. ill. 12°. $1.50....*Carleton.*
— Rifle rangers. ill. 12°. $1.50...........*Carleton.*
— Scalp hunters. 8°. pap., 20c..............*Beadle.*
— *Same.* ill. 12°. $1.50....................*Carleton.*
— Tales of Am. adventure. 6 v. ill. 16°. $9..*Miller.*
Cont.: Desert home.—Forest exiles.—Boy hunters.—Man eaters.—Young voyagers.—Bruin.
— Tales of foreign adventure. 6 v. ill. 16°. $9..*Miller.*
Cont.: Bush boys.—Young yagers.—Plant hunters.—Ran away to sea.—Boy tar.—Cliff climbers.
— Tiger hunter. ill. 12°. $1.50............*Carleton.*
— Travels by sea and land. 5 v. ill. 16°. $7.50..*Miller.*
Cont.: Ocean waifs.—Afloat in the forest.—Boy slaves.—Giraffe hunters.—Flag of distress.
— War trail. ill. 12°. $1.50..............*Carleton.*
— White chief. ill. 12°. $1.50............*Carleton.*
— White squaw. 8°. pap., 20c...............*Beadle.*
— Wild huntress. ill. 12°. $1.50..........*Carleton.*
— Wild life. ill. 12°. $1.50...............*Carleton.*
— Wood rangers. ill. 12°. $1.50..........*Carleton.*
Reid, S: C., *jr.* Scouting expeditions of the Texan rangers; with sketches of the partisan chiefs, Hays, McCullough and Walker. ill. 12°. $1.75. *J. E. Potter.*
Reid, T: Essays on the intellectual powers of man, abridg. with notes; ed. by J. Walker. 10th ed. 12°. $1.88............................*Butler.*
Reid, Whitelaw. ["Agate."] After the war: a southern tour, 1865–6. ill. 12°. '66. $2.50..*Wilstach.*
— Ohio in the war: her statesmen, her generals and soldiers. 2 v. maps and por. roy. 8°. '67. $10; shp., $12; hf. mor., $15.............. *Wilstach.*
Reid, W: Blood of Jesus. 18°. 30c.; pap., 15c.*Am. Bapt.*
— *Same.* 18°. 35c..................*U. P. Bd. of Pub.*
— *Same.* ('63.) New ed. ill. 18°. '76. 40c....*Hoyt.*
— *Same.* 18°. 50c.........................*Tibbals.*
— *Same.* 18°. 50c.; pap., 15c..........*Bost. Am. Tr.*
— *Germ.* Das Blut Jesu; bearb. v. P. W. Bickel. 16°. 30c.; pap., 20c..............*Germ. Bapt.*
— Gift of Jesus. 18°. 40c......................*Hoyt.*
— Hope in Jesus. 18°. 40c......................*Hoyt.*
— Look to Jesus. 16°. 40c......................*Hoyt.*
— Paths of the Lord. 18°. 50c..........*Bost. Am. Tr.*
Reign of grace. Booth, A. 75c...........*Am. Bapt.*
Reign of law. Argyll, *Duke of.* $2......*Routledge.*
Reign of law. Salmon, G. $2.25........*Macmillan.*
Reigning belle. Stephens, A. S. $1.75; $1.50..*Peterson.*
Reigning favourite. Oxenford, J. 15c.......*French.*
Reil, A. Monograph on aconite: its therapeutic and physiological effects; tr. by H. B. Millard. [Hom.] 8°. 75c.....................*Boericke.*
Reilly, A. Adams. *See* Adams-Reilly, A.
Reilly, A. J. The juror: guide to citizens summoned to serve as jurors. New ed., rev. by E. C. Shapley. 24°. '73. 50c...........*J. Campbell & Son.*
Reilly, W: Memoir of Gideon Ouseley. 18°. '47. 65c. *Meth. Bk. Conc.*
Reimann, M. Treatise on manufacture of aniline and aniline colors; with report on col. matters from coal tar as shown at Paris exhibition, 1867, by Hofmann; ed. by W. Crookes. 8°. $2.50... *Wiley.*
Reimensnyder, J. B. Heavenward; or, the race for the crown of life. 12°. '74. 50c...*Luth. Bk. St.*
Reinagle, Alex. First lessons for the piano-forte. obl. 16°. pap., 60c..........................*Ditson.*
Reindeer, dogs and snow-shoes. Bush, R. J. $3. *Harper.*

Reinecke, C. Snowdrop: Schneewittchen. [Fairy cantata.] f°. pap., $3 .... *Schirmer.*
Reineke Fuchs. *See* Goethe, J. W. v.
Reinke, A. A. Jacob's smallness and enlargement. [Sermon.] 8°. '68. pap., 15c......... *Clauder.*
Reis' nah Belligen. Reuter, F. $1; 75c...... *Steiger.*
Reisebilder. *See* Heine, H.
Reissner, J. C. A B C-Buchstabier- u. Lesebuch. 12°. bds., 30c............................. *Ev. Assoc.*
Rejected addresses. Smith, H. *and* J. $1.25. **Osgood.*
Rejected wife. Stephens, A. S. $1.75; $1.50. *Peterson.*
Relation de la mission du Missisipi du Séminaire de Québec en 1700. 8°. '61. pap., $3....... *Shea.*
Relation des affaires du Canada en 1696, avec des lettres des Pères de la Compagnie de Jésus depuis 1696 jusqu'en 1702; [also] Relation de la mission Abnaquise de St. François de Sales, l'année 1702, par le P. Jacques Bigot, S. J.; [also] Lettre du Père Jacques Gravier, S. J., le 23 février 1708 sur les affaires de Louisiane. 3 v. in 1. 8°. '65. $4 .... *Shea.*
Relation of the colony of the Lord Baron of Baltimore in Maryland near Virginia. [Reprint.] 4°. pap., $1 .... *Sabin.*
Relation of a discovery lately made on the coast of Florida; by W: Hilton, Commander and commissioner, with Capt. Anthony Long and Peter Fabian, in the ship Adventure: Lond., 1664. [Reprint.] 4°. pap., 50c.......................... *Sabin.*
Relation of Maryland [1533-4]; reprint. from Lond. ed. of 1635, with a pref. note and app. by F. L. Hawks. 4°. '65. $3; large pap., $5... *Sabin.*
Relation of the successful beginnings of the Lord Baltemore's plantation in Maryland, A.D. 1634. [Reprint.] 4°. pap., $1.25 .... *Shea.*
Relation of witchcraft to religion. Lyall, A. C. 15c. *Somerby.*
Relations of honor to political life. Woolsey, T. D. 25c. .... *Judd & W.*
Relations of the kingdom. Dykes, J. Oswald. $1.25. *Carter.*
Religio chemici. Wilson, G. $2 .... *Macmillan.*
Religio medici. *See* Browne, *Sir* T:
Religio-political physics. Blanchard, C. 50c.; 25c. *D. Thomas.*
Religion and eternal life. Pike, J. G. 50c... *Am. Tr.*
Religion and the family. Wiley, I. W. $1. *Cin. Meth. Bk. Conc.*
Religion and its image. 18°. 25c. .... *Am. S. S.*
Religion and life. Reed, J. 75c. .... *New Ch.*
Religion and progress. Pedder, H. C. $1... *Dutton.*
Religion and the reign of terror. Pressensé, E. de. $1.75 .... *Meth. Bk. Conc.*
Religion and science. Draper, J. W. $1.75.. *Appleton.*
Religion and science. Le Conte, J. $1.50.. *Appleton.*
Religion in America. Baird, R. $3 .... *Harper.*
Religion in common life. *See* Caird, J.
Religion in society. 12°. $1.50............. *Sadlier.*
Religion of the Christ. *See* Leathes, S.
Religion of the family. Wiley, I. W. $1; $1.25. *Cin. Meth. Bk. Conc.*
Religion of good sense. Richer, E. 62c... *H. H. Carter.*
Religion of humanity. Frothingham, O. B. $1.50. *Putnam.*
Religion of inhumanity. Harrison, F. 20c... *Somerby.*
Religion of money. 18°. 17c.; 22c. ...... *Am. Bapt.*
Religion of the present and of the future. Woolsey, T. D. $2; $3 .... *Scribner.*
Religion of Protestants. Chillingworth, W. $1.40. *Scribner, W. & A.*
Religion recommended to youth. Thayer, C. M. 30c. *Cin. Meth. Bk. Conc.*
Religion the weal and need of the church. Steward, G. 90c. .... *Meth. Bk. Conc.*
Religions before Christ. Pressensé, E. de. $3.75. *Scribner, W. & A.*
Religions of China. Channing, W. H. 25c... *Free Rel.*
Religions of the world. Maurice, F. D. $1.50. *Macmillan.*
Religions of the world. Schmucker, S. M. *$2; $2.50; $3.50 .... *Quak. City.*
Religious courtship. Defoe, D. $1...... *Pounsford.*
Religious demands of the age. Cobbe, F. P. 25c... *Fuller.*
Religious denominations in the U. S.: their hist., with statistics and summary of relig. denominations in Eng. and Scotland. ill. roy. 8°. $5; leath., $5.50; hf. cf., $6 .... *Desilver.*
Religious duty. Cobbe, F. P. $1.75 .... *Lee & S.*
Religious experience and Gospel labors. Jackson, D. 75c. .... *Freewill.*
Religious philosophy. Potter, A. $3 .... *Lippincott.*
Religious positivism. Edger, H. 50c. ..... *Somerby.*
Religious progress. Williams, W. R. $1.25.. *Carter.*
Religious sentiment (The). Brinton, D. G. $2.50.. *Holt.*
Reliques of Father Prout. *See* Mahony, Fs.
Rellstab, L: Drei Jahre von Dreissigen: hist. Roman. 3 v. 12°. '58. pap., 75c....... *Steiger.*
— *Same.* 8°. $2.50; pap., $2; hf. mor., $2.75. *F. W. Thomas.*
— 1812: hist. Roman. 12°. $2; pap., $1.50; hf. mor., $2.25 .... *F. W. Thomas.*
Remains of lost empires. Myers, P. V. N. $3.50. *Harper.*
Remarkable delusions; or, ill. of popular errors; rev. by T. O. Summers. ('56.) 3d ed. 18°. '75. 50c.. *So. Meth.*
Remarkable escapes from peril; rev. by T. O. Summers. ('56.) 2d ed. 18°. '74. 50c... *So. Meth.*
Remarkable escapes from peril; ill. of divine providence. 18°. 75c. .... *Pres. Bd.*
Remarkable examples of moral recovery. 18°. '54. 50c. .... *Meth. Bk. Conc.*
Remarkable places mentioned in the Holy Scriptures. ill. 18°. 40c. .... *Pres. Bd.*
Remedial system (The). Christopher, H. $3. *Tr. P. & P. Co.*
Remember me. *See* Palmer, R.
Remembered prayer. ('60.) New ed. ill. 16°. '69. 30c. .... *Hoyt.*
Remick, Martha. Agnes Stanhope: tale of Eng. life. 12°. '62. $1.50 .... *Universalist.*
Remington, E. F. City of sin and its capture by Immanuel's army: allegory. 12°. '57. $1.25. *Meth. Bk. Conc.*
— Our national house: its founders and defenders. 12°. '73. $1.25 .... *Tibbals.*
Remington, Ste. Reasons for becoming a Baptist. [French.] 18°. 30c.; pap., 10c...... *Am. Bapt.*
Reminiscences of European travel. Peabody, A. P. $1.50 .... *Hurd & H.*
Reminiscences of fifty years. Boyd, M. $1.75. *Appleton.*
Reminiscences of Forts Sumter and Moultrie. Doubleday, A. $1 .... *Harper.*
Reminiscences of a Highland parish. Macleod, N. $3 .... *Routledge.*
Reminiscences of a voyage around the world. Davis, R. C. $1 .... *R. A. Beal.*
Remittances from home. Leavitt, A. J. 15c. *De Witt.*
Remond, A. *See* California geol. survey.
Removing mountains. Hart, J. S. $1.25.... *Carter.*
Rena. Hentz, C. L. $1.75; $1.50......... *Peterson.*

Renan, Ern. Lives of the apostles; tr. 12°. $1.75. *Carleton.*
– *Germ.* Die Apostel; übers. v. Carl Rose. 12°. (Oshkosh.) '67. pap., $1 .... *Steiger.*
– Life of Jesus; tr. 12°. $1.75 .... *Carleton.*
– Life of St. Paul; tr. 12°. $1.75 .... *Carleton.*
Renata of Este. Strack, C. $1.25 .. *Cin.Meth.Bk.Conc.*
Renauld, J: B. Our heroes: military play. 16°. pap., 15c. .... *De Witt.*
Rendezvous. Ayton, R. 15c. .... *French.*
Rendu, Le Chanoine. Theory of the glaciers of Savoy; tr. by A. Wills; [with] orig. memoir and sup. articles by P. G. Tait and John Ruskin; ed. with introd. remarks by G. Forbes. 8°. '74. $3. *Macmillan.*
René. *See* Chateaubriand, F. A.
René. *See* Hoffmann, F.
Reneau, Russell. Essays on Baptist controversy: exam. of mode and subjects of baptism. 18°. '56. 60c. .... *Perkinpine.*
– Lectures on reign of Satan. 18°. '56. 60c. *Perkinpine.*
Renegade gypsy. 8°. pap., 25c. .... *De Witt.*
Rennie, Ja. Insect architecture. New ed., rev. by J. G. Wood. 12°. (Bohn.) $1.75 .. *Little, B. & Co.*
– *Same.* 12°. (Bohn.) $2 .. *Lippincott; Scribner, W. & A.*
– Natural history of birds. ill. 18°. 75c. ..... *Harper.*
– Natural history of the elephant. ill. 18°. 75c. *Harper.*
– Natural history of quadrupeds. ill. 18°. 75c. *Harper.*
Rennie, *Sir* J: Autobiography. por. 8°. '75. $5 .. *Spon.*
Rensselaer [N. Y.] Polytechnic Institute. Semi-centennial transactions. 8°. '76. pap., $1; hf. mor., $2.50 .... *W. H. Young.*
Rent day. Jerrold, D. 15c. .... *French.*
Rent in the cloud. *See* Lever, C:
Rent veil. Bonar, H. $1.25 .... *Carter.*
Renunciation. Bedell, G. T. 30c. ...... *Whittaker.*
Renwick, Ja. Applications of science of mechanics to pract. purposes. ill. 18°. hf. shp., 90c. *Harper.*
– Familiar ill. of natural philos.; sel. principally from Daniell's Chemical philosophy. 18°. 75c. *Harper.*
– First principles of chemistry. ill. 18°. hf. shp., 90c. *Harper.*
– First principles of natural philos.; sel. principally from Daniell's Chemical philosophy. 18°. hf. shp., 90c. .... *Harper.*
– Life of De Witt Clinton; with sel. of his letters. por. 18°. 75c. .... *Harper.*
– Life of R. Fulton; — of D. Rittenhouse. *See* Sparks, J., Library of Am. biog.
– Lives of John Jay and Alexander Hamilton. por. 18°. 75c. .... *Harper.*
Reparation. Fullerton, *Lady* G. 50c.; 75c. *Kelly, P. & Co.*
Repentance explained. Walker, C. 25c. .... *Am. Tr.*
Repentance, false and true. Bradley, C. 35c. *U. P. Bd. of Pub.*
Reports.
See under names of organizations making reports; for law reports under name of country, state, etc.
Reports and the mischief they do. 18°. 25c. .. *Am. S. S.*
Reposing in Jesus. Mylne, G. W. 80c. .. *Bost. Am. Tr.*
Representative actors. Russell, W. C. 75c.–$5. *Scribner, W. & A.*
Representative men. Emerson, R. W. $1.50 .. *Osgood.*
Representative men of San Francisco. roy. 8°. '76. mor., $10 .... *N. Y. & H. Pub.*
Republican court. Griswold, R. W. $5; $6; $7.50; $15 .... *Appleton.*
Republican landmarks. Sanderson, J. P. $1.50. *Lippincott.*
Republicanism in America. McClellan, R. G. $3.50. *J. M. Stoddart.*
Republicanism vs. Grantism. Sumner, C. 25c. *Lee & S.*
Republics. Crowell, J. $1 .... *Pres. Bd.*

Rescue. Newell, W. W. 25c.; 10c. ... *Bost. Am. Tr.*
Rescued. Gilbert, C. H. 15c. .... *Ames.*
Rescued. Moore, J. F. $1.50 .... *Hoyt.*
Rescued boy. ill. 18°. '58. 35c. .... *Am. Tr.*
Rescued child. Schenck, J. W. 30c. .... *Am. Tr.*
Rescued from Egypt. *See* Tucker, *Mrs.* C.
Rescued girl. 16°. 90c. .... *Cong. Pub.*
— *See also* Blue shawl ser.
Rescued lamb. 18°. '74. 20c. .... *Am. Tr.*
— *See also* Daisy lib.
Rescued nun. 8°. pap., 25c. .... *Dick & F.*
Resignation. *See* Arbouville, S. de B.
Resources of the union. Carey, H. C. 50c. .. *Baird.*
Respect the burden. 18°. 18c. .... *Am. S. S.*
Responsibility for the gift of eternal life. Campbell, J. McL. $2 .... *Macmillan.*
Responsibility in mental disease. Maudsley, H. $1.50. *Appleton.*
Rest and unrest. Bell, C. D. $1.25 ...... *Randolph.*
Rest for the weary: words of love for the sick and sorrowing. sq. 18°. 75c. .... *Nelson.*
Rest for the weary; or, the story of Hannah. 18°. 60c. .... *Am. S. S.*
Rest in Christ. *See* Fear not.
Rest of faith. Earle, A. B. 50c.; 75c.; $1 .... *Earle.*
Rest of faith. See, I. M. $1 .... *Palmer.*
Restatements of Christian doctrine. Bellows, H. W. $1 .... *Am. Unit.*
Restoration of belief. Taylor, I. $1.50 .... *Dutton.*
Restoration of paths to dwell in. Street, B. $2.50. *Routledge.*
Result of a nap: farce. 16°. pap., 15c. ...... *Happy.*
Resurrection destinies. Buck, D. D. 20c. .. *Darrow.*
Retained for the defence. Oxenford, J. 15c. .. *French.*
Retiring from business. Arthur, T. S. 75c. *Collins & Bro.*
Retribution. Southworth, E. D. E. N. $1.75; $1.50. *Peterson.*
Retribution. Taylor, T. 15c. .... *French.*
Return of prayers. Goodwin, T. 35c. ...... *Pres. Bd.*
Return of the wanderer. Hazlewood, C. H. 15c. .. *French.*
Return ticket: farce. 16°. pap., 15c. .... *French.*
Returned father, and other stories. ill. 24°. 25c. *Bost. Am. Tr.*
— *See also* Banner stories.
Retzsch, Moritz (*ill.*) Outline ill. to Burger's Ballads. obl. f°. '72. $5; mor., $9 .... *Roberts.*
— Outline ill. to Schiller's Lay of the bell. obl. 4°. '68. $7.50; mor., $12 .... *Roberts.*
— Outline ill. to Shakespeare: pl., with explan. text. obl. f°. '71. $9; mor., $15 .... *Roberts.*
Reubelt, J. A. Scripture doctrine of the person of Christ; based on German of W. F. Gess. 12°. '76. $1.50 .... *Draper.*
Reuben Davidger (Adventures of). Greenwood, J. $1.75 .... *Harper.*
Reuben Inch (Story of). Brock, C. 75c. ... *Nelson.*
Reuben Kent at school; or, influence as it should be. 18°. 40c. .... *Am. S. S.*
Reuben Kent ser. 5 v. 18°. $2.80 .... *Am. S. S.*
Cont.: Reuben Kent at school. — Reuben Kent's first winter in the city. — Robert Dawson. — Jane Hudson. — Hugh Fisher.
Reuben Kent's first winter in the city: sequel to "Reuben Kent at school." 18°. 60c. .... *Am. S. S.*
Reuben's temptation; by author of "How little Bessie kept the wolf from the door." ill. 18°. 50c. *Nelson.*
— *Same.* ('74.) New ed. 16°. '76. 75c. ...... *Hoyt.*
Reuck, W: H. Practical examples in arithmetic. 12°. '54. hf. bd., $1 .... *Barnes.*
— Practical examples in simple and denominate numbers. 12°. '55. hf. bd., 50c. .... *Barnes.*

Reue versöhnt. *See* Hoffmann, F.

Reumont, Alfr. v. Carafas of Maddaloni, and Naples under Spanish dominion; tr. from the Germ. 12°. (Bohn.) $1.25 .... *Little, B. & Co.*

— *Same.* 12°. (Bohn.) $1.40 ...... *Scribner, W. & A.*

— *Same.* 12°. (Bohn.) $1.50 .... *Lippincott.*

Reunion of Christendom. Manning, C. E. 50c. *Appleton.*

Reuter, Fritz. Sämmtliche Werke. New ed. 13 v. 12°. '70. ea., $1; pap., 75c. .... *Steiger.*

Cont.: 1. Olle Kamellen, pt. 1: Woans ik tau'ne Fru kam; Ut de Franzosentid.—2. *Same*, pt. 2: Ut mine Festungstid.—3-5. *Same*, pts. 3-5: Ut mine Stromtid, 3 v.—6. Schurr-Murr.—7. Hanne Nüte un de lütte Pudel.—8. Reis' nah Belligen.—9, 10. Läuschen un Rimels, 2 v.—11. Kein Hüsung.—12. Olle Kamellen, pt. 6: Dörchläuchting.—13. *Same*, pt. 7: De Mecklenbörg'schen Montecchi un Capuletti, od. de Reis' nah Konstantinopel.

— Nachgelassene Schriften; hrsg. v. A. Wilbrandt. pt. 1. 12°. '75. $1; pap., 75c. .... *Steiger.*

Cont.: Briefe d. Herrn Inspectors Bräsig; Urgeschicht v. Meckelnborg, etc.; [also] Fritz Reuter's Leben u. Schriften, v. Herausg. des Nachlasses.

— Seed time and harvest; or, during my apprenticeship; tr. 8°. $1.50; pap., $1 .... *Lippincott.*

— *See also* Frehse, F., Wörterbuch.

Revelation considered as light. Ewing, A. $3. *Routledge.*

Revelation in progress from Adam to Malachi. Titcomb, J. H. $2.50 .... *Nelson.*

Revelation of law in Scripture. *See* Fairbairn, P.

Revelations of Peter Brown. Waller, J. F. $1. *Cassell.*

Revelations of a slave smuggler. Drake, R. 25c. *De Witt.*

Revelations of a square. *See* Oliver, G.

Revellers. *See* Hewitt, J. H.

Revellers; [also] The midnight sea; [also] Constant watchfulness. 18°. 60c. .... *Dutton.*

Revenge. Young, E. 15c. .... *French.*

Revenge; or, how to wipe off an old score: story for school boys. 18°. 18c. .... *Am. S. S.*

Revere, Jos. W. Keel and saddle: retrospect of 40 years' milit. and naval service. 12°. $2 ..* *Osgood.*

Rev. Dr. Willoughby and his wine. Walker, M. S. $1.50 .... *Nat. Temp.*

Reveries of a bachelor. *See* Mitchell, D. G.

Reverse of the medal: drama for girls. 16°. '74. 20c. *Cath. Pub.*

— *Same.* 12°. '73. pap., 25c. .... *Kelly, P. & Co.*

Revett, N: *See* Stuart, J., *and* Revett, N.

Review. Colman, G., *jr.* 15c. .... *French.*

Review. *See* French's comic dramas.

Reviewers reviewed. Stephens, A.H. $1.50 .. *Appleton.*

Revision of [the statutes of Ill. of] 1872: hist. of the way Hurd's revision was made, etc. pts. 1, 2. 8°. '73. pap., 50c. .... *Gross.*

Revival and camp-meeting minstrel. ('67.) 2d ed. 24°. '68. shp., 50c. .... *Perkinpine.*

Revival and its lessons. Alexander, J.W. 40c. *Am. Tr.*

Revival in school. 18°. 50c. .... *Cong. Pub.*

Revival melodist. Hammond, E. P. 15c. ..... *Hoyt.*

Revival miscellanies. Caughey, J. $1.50 ... *Palmer.*

Revival of priestly life in France. Lear, S. $2.50 .. *Pott.*

Revivalist. Hillman, J. 75c. .... *Nims.*

Revoil, Bened. Hunter and trapper in No. Am.; or, romantic adventures in field and forest; tr. by W. H. D. Adams. ill. 12°. '74. $1.25 ... *Nelson.*

Revolt of the bees. Baker, G. M. 15c. ..... *Lee & S.*

Revolt of the workhouse: opera. 16°. pap., 15c. *French.*

Revolution in New England justified and the people there vindicated from the aspersions cast upon them by Mr. John Palmer: 1691. [Reprint.] 4°. pap., $1 .... *Sabin.*

Revolutionary soldier. Jamison, G. 15c. .. *French.*

Révy, J. J. Observations and surveys on the largest rivers of the world. 8 pl. and charts. imp. 4°. '74. $17 .... *Spon.*

Reward (The). Kurzenknabe, J. H. 35c. .. *Ditson.*

Reward of merit. Bullard, A. 25c. .... *Lee & S.*

Reynal, C. French verbs. 12°. '70. $1.25. *G. R. Lockwood.*

Reynard, the fox. [Toy-book.] ill. 4°. $1; 50c. *Routledge.*

Reynard, the fox. *See* Bulwer-Lytton, *Sir* E. G. E. L.

Reynard, the fox. *See* Day, S. P.

Reynard, the fox. *See* Goethe, J. W. v.

Reynard, the fox. *See* Rare romance of.

Reynard, the fox; from the Low Germ. of the 15th cent. ill. 16°. $2.50 .... *Lee & S.*

Reynolds, Bce. Matchmaker. 12°. $1.75; pap., $1.50. *Peterson.*

Reynolds, E: Morris. Modern methods in elementary geometry. cr. 8°. '68. $1.25 ..... *Macmillan.*

Reynolds, F: [Plays.] 10 v. 16°. ea., pap., 15c. *French.*

Cont.: Blind bargain: comedy.—Confounded foreigners.—Delinquent: comedy.—Dramatist; comedy.—Exile: play.—Folly as it flies: comedy.—How to grow rich: comedy.—Laugh when you can: comedy.—Notoriety: comedy.—The will: comedy.

Reynolds, F: Mansell. The coquette. 8°. pap., 75c. *Peterson.*

Reynolds, G: W. M. Novels. 11 v. 8°. pap... *Dick & F.*

Cont.: Ellen Monroe.—Esther de Medina.—Life in London.—Mysteries of London.—Mysteries of old London.—Reformed highwayman, *ea.*, pap., $1.50.—Angela Wildon, pap., $1.—Countess of Arnheim.—Mary Glenworth.—Pope Joan.—Robert Macaire, *ea.*, pap., 75c.

— *Same.* 18 v. 8°. ea., pap., 50c. .... *De Witt.*

Cont.: Ada Arundel; or, the secret corridor.—Canonbury House; or, the queen's prophecy.—Catharine Volmar; or, a father's vengeance.—Empress Eugenie's boudoir; or, mysteries of court of France.—Ethel Trevor; or, the duke's victim.—Faust: romance of the secret tribunals.—First false step.—Imogene Hartland; or, star of the circus.—Karaman, the bandit chief.—Leila; or, star of Mingrelia.—Miser's will; or, doom of the poisoner.—Olivia; or, the maid of honor.—Omar pasha; or, the vizier's daughter.—Palace of infamy; or, the slave women of England.—Rose Somerville; or, a husband's mystery and a wife's devotion.—Wagner, the wehr wolf.—White lady.—Young duchess; or, memoirs of a lady of quality.

— *Same.* 40 v. 8° .... *Peterson.*

Cont.: Rose Foster: 2d ser. of "Mysteries of court of London," $1.75; pap., $1.50.—Banker's daughter: sequel to "Joseph Wilmot."—Caroline of Brunswick: 3d ser. of "Mysteries of court of London."—Count Christoval: sequel to "Lord Saxondale."—Eustace Quentin: sequel to "Mary Price."—Gipsy chief.—Joseph Wilmot; or, memoirs of a man servant.—Kenneth.—Lord Saxondale; or, court of Queen Victoria.—Mary Price; or, adventures of a servant maid.—Mysteries of court of London: being "Mysteries of court of George III.," with life and times of Prince of Wales.—Mysteries of court of Naples.—Necromancer: being "Mysteries of court of Henry VIII."—Rosa Lambert; or, memoirs of an unfortunate woman.—Robert Bruce.—Rye-House plot; or, Ruth, the conspirator's daughter.—Venetia Trelawney: 4th ser. of "Mysteries of court of London."—Wallace, the hero of Scotland, *ea.*, $1.75; pap., $1.—Agnes Evelyn; or, beauty and pleasure.—Child of Waterloo.—Countess and the page.—Countess of Lascelles: sequel to "Vivian Bertram."—Discarded queen.—Duke of Marchmont: sequel to "Countess of Lascelles."—Ellen Percy; or, memoirs of an actress.—Isabella Vincent; or, the two orphans.—Loves of the harem.—Mary Stuart, Queen of Scots.—May Middleton; or, history of a fortune.—Massacre of Glencoe.—Opera dancer.—The parricide.—Pickwick abroad: a [so called] companion to the "Pickwick papers."—Soldier's wife.—Vivian Bertram, *ea.*, pap., 75c.—Ciprina; or, secrets of a picture gallery.—Clifford and the actress.—Edgar Montrose.—Life in Paris.—Ruined gamester, *ea.*, pap., 50c.

Reynolds, Grindall. Concord fight, April 19, 1775. 8°. '75. pap., 15c. .... *Williams.*

Reynolds, H: Rob. Notes of the Christian life: sermons. cr. 8°. '65. $2.50 .... *Macmillan.*

Reynolds, J. L. [Readers.] 6 v. 12° .... *Duffie.*

Cont.: Pictorial primer, pap., 10c.—Primary reader, hf. bd., 25c.—Second, hf. bd., 40c.—Third, hf. bd., 60c.—Fourth, hf. bd., 80c.—Fifth, $1.25.

— Elementary spelling book. 12°. hf. bd., 15c... *Duffie.*

— Writing books. 5 nos. obl. 4°. ea., pap., 15c.. *Duffie.*

Reynolds, J: Russell. Lectures on clinical uses of electricity. 2d ed., rev. and enl. 12°. '74. $1.25. *Lindsay.*

— (*ed.*) System of medicine. 3 v. 8°. '71. ea., $9. *Lippincott; Macmillan.*

Cont.: General diseases; Local diseases. — Diseases of the nervous system. — Diseases of the digestive system.

Reynolds, *Sir* Josh. Life and discourses. ('60.) 2d ed. 12°. $1.50 .... *Barnes.*

— Literary works. 2 v. 12°. (Bohn.) ea., $1.25. *Little, B. & Co.*

— *Same.* 2 v. 12°. (Bohn.) ea., $1.40 .. *Scribner, W. & A.*

— *Same.* 2 v. 12°. (Bohn.) ea., $1.50 ...... *Lippincott.*

— *See also* Beautiful women.

Reynolds, L. Eine amerikanische Mutter, od. Glanz u. Elend in N. Y. 12°. $1; pap., 65c... *Zickel.*

Reynolds, L. E. Mysteries of Masonry: outline of a universal philos. founded upon ritual and degree of anc. Freemasonry. 12°. $2..... *Lippincott.*

— Treatise on hand-railing. pl. 8°. $2 ... *Appleton.*

Reynolds, Martha W. (*ill.*) Flowers for the altar; with text. 4°. $7.50 .... *Lippincott.*

Reynolds, Osborne. Sewer gas, and how to keep it out of houses: handbook on house drainage. 2d ed. cr. 8°. '72. 60c. .... *Macmillan.*

Reynolds, R. O. *See* Mississippi, Law reports.

Reynoldson, T: H. Curse of mammon: drama. 16°. pap., 15c. .... *French.*

— Elixir of love: opera. 16°. pap., 15c....... *French.*

— Rich man of Frankfort: drama. 16°. pap., 15c. *French.*

— Venetian: drama. 16°. pap., 15c.......... *French.*

Rheem, J. H. *See* Rosecrans, J. H., *and* Rheem, J. H.

Rhees, W: J. List of Am. libraries, and public institutions. 8°. '72. pap., $1.......... *Smith. Inst.*

Rhesus. *See* Euripides.

Rhetoric of conversation. Hervey, G. W. $1.50.. *Harper.*

Rhind, W: *See* Historical and descript. account of British India.

Rhind, W: Graeme. High priest of Israel. f°. (Bagster.) $7.50 .... *Wiley.*

— Tabernacle of Israel in the wilderness: eng. with letter-press. f°. (Bagster.) $6.25...... *Wiley.*

Rhine. Hugo, V. $1.75 .... *Estes.*

Rhine kitten. *See* Daisy lib.

Rhoads, J. Primary arithmetic for young learners. 12°. hf. bd., 28c............................ *Sower.*

Rhoads, T: Y. Battle-fields of the revolution. ill. 12°. $1.75 .... *J. E. Potter.*

Rhoda; or, the excellence of charity. 18°. 40c.; 50c. *Am. Bapt.*

Rhoda Thornton's girlhood. Pratt, M. E. $1.50.. *Lee & S.*

Rhoda's corner. Payne, A. M. $1.25.. *Carter; Dutton.*

Rhoda's education. Guernsey, L. E. $1.25.. *Am. S. S.*

Rhode Island and Providence Plantations. General statutes; with U. S. and State Constitutions. 8°. '72. shp., $3 .... *Hurd & H.*

— Supreme Court reports. v. 1–10 (1828–'74). 10 v. 8°. *State.*

Cont.: 1, 2 (1828–'53), by J. K. Angell and T. Durfee. — 3 (1853–'55), by J. P. Knowles. — 4–7 (1855–'63), by S. Ames. — 8 (1864–'67), by S. Ames, J. P. Knowles and C. S. Bradley. — 9, 10 (1868–'74), by J. F. Tobey.

— *Same.* v. 4–6 (1855–'62); by S. Ames. 3 v. 8°. shp., $15 .... *Little, B. & Co.*

— *Same.* v. 9, 10 (1868–'74); by J. F. Tobey. 2 v. 8°. '73–'75. ea., shp., $6.50 .... *Hurd & H.*

Rhode Island Freewill Baptist pulpit. Williams, A. D. $1 .... *Freewill.*

Rhodes, Alb. French at home. ill. 16°. '75. $1.25. *Dodd.*

Rhodes, W: Barnes. Bombastes furioso: burlesque. 16°. pap., 15c............................ *French.*

Rhododendron. Closs, G., *and* Fröhlicher, O. $24. *Stroefer.*

Rhyme and reason. Dulcken, H. W. $1.75.. *Routledge.*

Rhyme and reason. Hornor, R. S. $1.50.... *Claxton.*

Rhymes and jingles. Mapes, M. M. $3; $1.50. *Scribner.*

Rhymes and roundelayes in praise of a country life. ill. 4°. '74. $5 .... *Routledge.*

Rhymes and stories for little folks. *See* Picture stories for little folks.

Rhymes and tales for the kindergarten and nursery. Kriege, A. L. $1; 50c. .... *Steiger.*

Rhymes atween times. Mackellar, T. $2.. *Lippincott.*

Rhymes for the little ones. V., L. 25c... *Scribner, W. & A.*

Rhymes for the nursery. sq. 16°. pap., 25c.... *Locke.*

Rhymes for the nursery. 18°. 40c. .... *Pres. Bd.*

Rhymes for the nursery. ill. 60c.; 90c.; pap., 30c. *Miller.*

Rhymes for the nursery. sm. 4°. 75c. .... *Am. S. S.*

Rhymes for the nursery; by authors of "Original poems." 16°. 45c. .... *Routledge.*

Rhymes of contrast on wisdom and folly. Rush, J. $1.25 .... *Lippincott.*

Rhyming alphabet; or, Sarah, Bell and Fanny Blake. 18°. 50c. .... *Am. S. S.*

Rhyming story book. ill. sm. 4°. 50c...... *Hurd & H.*

Ribbon room. Plumer, W. S. 40c. .... *Pres. Bd.*

Ribbon stories. Barker, M. A. (*Lady*). $1.50. *Macmillan.*

Ribot, T. English psychology; tr. from the Fr. 12°. $1.50 .... *Appleton.*

— Heredity: psychological study on its phenomena, its laws, its causes and its consequences; tr. 12°. $2. *Appleton.*

Ricardo, D: Works; with notice of life and writings by J. R. McCulloch. por. 8°. $8.. *Scribner, W. & A.*

Rice, Anne M. Slate exercises in numbers. 18°. '74. 30c. .... *Nichols & H.*

Rice, C: Three guardsmen: drama. 16°. pap., 15c. *French.*

— Three musketeers: drama. 16°. pap., 15c... *French.*

Rice, Edn. Scholar's handbook on the International lessons; with introd. by J. Hall. 6 pts. 32°. ea., 10c. .... *Am. S. S.*

Rice, F. B. Sacred songs for social worship. 16°. 50c.; mor., 75c. .... *Goodrich.*

Rice, Harvey. Mount Vernon, and other poems. 12°. $1; hf. cf., $3; cf., $4 .... *Appleton.*

— Nature and culture. 12°. $1.50 .... *Lee & S.*

Rice, I: L. What is music? 12°. $1; pap., 50c. *Appleton.*

Rice, J. *See* Besant, W., *and* Rice, J.

Rice, J. M., *and* Johnson, W. W. On a new method of obtaining the differentials of functions; with especial ref. to the Newtonian conception of rates or velocities. 12°. '75. pap., 50c... *Van Nostrand.*

Rice, Nath. L. God sovereign and man free. 16°. 65c. *Pres. Bd.*

— Immortality of the soul. 18°. 70c. .... *Pres. Bd.*

— Modern spiritualism: what we are to think of it. 18°. pap., 10c. .... *Pres. Bd.*

— *and* Blanchard, J. Debate on slavery, Cincinnati, 1845. ('46.) New ed. 12°. '57. $1.50.. *Wilstach.*

Rice, Ph. Method for the banjo; with or without a master. 4°. '58. bds., $1.50 .... *Ditson.*

Rice, W: Digest of South Carolina Superior Court reports, 1783–1838. 8°. '39 .... *State.*

— *See also* South Carolina, Chancery reports; Court of Appeals reports.

Rice, *Rev.* W: (*ed.*) Moral and religious quotations from the poets. 8°. '60. shp., $3; hf. cf., $4. ill. 8°. mor., $7.50; $9.50 ...... *Meth. Bk. Conc.*

Rich, A. B. Gleanings from science. 18°. 45c. *Cong. Pub.*

Rich, Ant. Dictionary of Roman and Greek antiquities. ill. sm. 8°. $4 .... *Appleton.*

Rich and humble. Adams, W. T. $1.25.....*Lee & S.*
Rich and poor. Hosmer, M. $1.15.........*Pres. Bd.*
Rich and poor. Ryle, J. C. $1..............*Carter.*
Rich husband. Riddell, J. H. $1.75; $1.50..*Peterson.*
Rich man and the poor man. Nieritz, G. 65c. (?)*Luth. Pub.*
Rich man of Frankfort. Reynoldson, T. H. 15c. *French.*
Rich Medway's two loves. Gardner, C. E. $1.75. *Carleton.*
Rich men of Philadelphia: their income tax list. 8°. pap., $1..........................*Peterson.*
Richard (*pseud.*) *See* Audin, J. M. V.
Richard *of Cirencester.* Ancient state of Briton. *See* Giles, J. A., Six old Eng. chronicles.
Richard *of Devizes.* Chronicle conc. deeds of Richard I. *See* Bohn, H. G., Chronicles of the crusades.
Richard. 32°. 15c.........................*Dutton.*
Richard II. *See* Shakespeare, W:
Richard III. *See* Shakespeare, W:
Richard ye third: burlesque. 16°. pap., 15c...*French.*
Richard, the fearless. *See* Yonge, C. M.
Richard and Rover. 18°. 18c..............*Am. S. S.*
Richard Edney. Judd, S. $1.50............*Roberts.*
Richard Harvey; or, taking a stand 32°. 25c. *Scribner, W. & A.*
Richard Hurdis. Simms, W. G. $1.75; 75c. *Widdleton.*
Richard Knill. *See* Wright, *Mrs.* J. McN.
Richard Owen's choice. 18°. 45c........ *Whittaker.*
Richard Peters. Cox, W. N. $1.25.........*Graves.*
Richard Plantagenet. Haines, J. T. 15c.....*French.*
Richard Taylor (Experiences of). Johnstone, J. 25c. *Littell & G.*
Richard Vandermarck. Harris, M. C. $1.50..*Carleton.*
Richard Weaver: account of the converted collier. 16°. 50c. .... *West. Tr.*
Richards, C. B. Experiments on resistance of stones to crushing. 8°. pap., 35c......*Am. Soc. of C. E.*
— Tensile strength of bar iron and boiler plate. *See* Jordan, G., Foundations under water.
Richards, J. Economy of work-shop manipulation: logical method of learning constructive mechanics. 8°. '75. $2.......................*Spon.*
— On the arrangement, care and operation of wood-working factories and machinery. ill. cr. 8°. '73. $1.50.......................................*Spon.*
— Treatise on construction and operation of wood-working machines; incl. hist. of origin, progress and manufacture of wood-working machinery. 25 pl. and ill. 4°. '72. $6..............*Spon.*
Richards, Lucy. Memoir. 18°. '42. 55c...*Meth. Bk. Conc.*
Richards, T. Addison. *See* Pictures and painters.
Richards, W: C. Harry's vacation; or, philosophy at home. ill. 12°. $1.25 ....*Appleton.*
Richards, Wolcott. Christian physician. 18°. '62. 20c..*Am. Tr.*
Richards Entschiedenheit. 18°. 30c.......*Ev. Assoc.*
Richardson, *Mrs.* Abby Sage. History of our country to [1876]. maps, plans, por. and eng. 8°. '76. *$4.50; shp., $5; mor., $6.25. ......*Hurd & H.*
— Pebbles and pearls. ill. f°. *$1.25.......*Am. Pub.*
— Percy's year of rhymes. ill. sm. 4°. bds., 50c. *Hurd & H.*
— Stories from old English poetry. ill. 16°. '71. $1.25. *Hurd & H.*
— (*ed.*) Songs from the old dramatists; ill. by J. La Farge. 4°. '72. $2.50..........*Hurd & H.*
Richardson, Alb. Deane. Beyond the Mississippi. ill. 8°. *$3.50; $4; hf. mor., $5; mor., $8. *Am. Pub.*
— Field, dungeon and escape. ill. 8°. *$3; $3.50; hf. mor., $5...........................*Am. Pub.*
Richardson, Alb. Deane, *continued.*
— Garnered sheaves; with biog. sketch of author by [Mrs. A. S. Richardson]. ill. and por. 8°. *$2.50; hf. mor., $4 ....*Col. Bk.*
— Personal history of U. S. Grant. ill. 8°. *$3; $3.50; hf. mor., $5 ....*Am. Pub.*
— *vs.* McFarland, D. Tragedy and divorce suit. [In Eng. or Germ.] 8°. pap., 25c.......*Barclay.*
Richardson, B: Ward. Alcohol: Cantor lectures, 1875. 12°. '75. pap., 50c.........*Macmillan.*
— *Same.* 12°. '76. $1; pap., 50c........*Nat. Temp.*
— *Same;* ed. with notes by T. S. Lambert. 16°. '76. pap., 30c.................................*U. S. Pub.*
— Diseases of modern life. cr. 8°. '76. $6..*Macmillan.*
Richardson, C: New dictionary of the English language. 2 v. 4°. hf. roxb., $32..........*Pott.*
Richardson, C: Ja. House building; from a cottage to a mansion. ill. cr. 8°. '72. $3.50..*Putnam.*
Richardson, Eliza. Personal experience of Roman Catholicism; with incidents of convent life. ill. 18°. $1.25..........................*Lippincott.*
Richardson, Frederika. Iliad of the east: legends drawn from Valmiki's The Rāmāyana. [Sanskrit poem.] cr. 8°. '70. $2...........*Macmillan.*
Richardson, G: F: Geology, incl. mineralogy, palæontology; rev. and enl. by T. Wright. ill. 12°. (Bohn.) $1.75 ....*Little, B. & Co.*
— *Same.* ill. 12°. (Bohn.) $2. *Lippincott; Scribner, W. & A.*
Richardson, H. D. Dogs: their origin and varieties, directions as to their management, etc. 12°. 60c.; pap., 30c. ....*Judd.*
Richardson, J. S. G. *See* South Carolina, Reports.
Richardson, Jabez. Monitor of Freemasonry. 16°. $1.25; pap., 75c.; leath., $2..........*Dick & F.*
Richardson, Ja. Wonders of the Yellowstone. ('72.) New ed. map and ill. 12°. '75. $1.50..*Scribner.*
Richardson, Ja. American school dialogue book. no. 1. ('67.) 9th ed. 8°. '75. pap., 40c. *Schermerhorn.*
Richardson, J: Journal. 12°. 75c...*Friends Bk. St.*
— Life, ministry and travels. 12°. *net,* 75c. *Friends Bk. Assoc.*
Richardson, *Maj.* J: Ecarte; or, the salons of Paris. 8°. pap., 50c..........................*De Witt.*
— Hardscrabble; or, the fall of Chicago. 8°. pap., 25c. ....*De Witt.*
— Matilda Montgomery; or, the prophecy fulfilled: sequel to "Wacousta." 8°. pap., 50c...*De Witt.*
— Wacousta; or, the prophecy. 8°. pap., 50c...*De Witt.*
Richardson, *Rev.* J: *See* Daily readings for holy seasons.
Richardson, *Sir* J: Arctic searching expedition: journal of a boat-voyage in search of Sir John Franklin; with app. ill. 12°. $1.50...*Harper.*
Richardson, J: F. Roman orthoepy. 18°. 50c. *Sheldon.*
Richardson, Jos. Practical treatise on mechanical dentistry. 2d ed., enl. ill. 8°. '69. leath., $4.50. *Lindsay.*
Richardson, Jos. G. Handbook of medical microscopy. ill. 12°. $2.25..............*Lippincott.*
Richardson, *Mrs.* M. K. Among the Alps. ill. 16°. '71. $1.25 ....*Am. Tr.*
Richardson, Nath. Elements of music at sight. 16°. $1 ....*Gordon.*
— Modern school for the piano: foreign fingering. 4°. $3.50..*Gordon.*
— New method for the piano-forte. pl. 4°. '59. bds., $3.75; — foreign fingering, $3.75........*Ditson.*
— New modern school for the piano. 4°. $3.25; — in 2 pts., ea., $2.25 ....*Gordon.*
Richardson, Natl. S. Churchman's reasons for his faith and practice. 12°. '67. $1..............*Pott.*
Richardson, R: Memoir of Josiah White. ill. 12°. $1.25 ....*Lippincott.*

Richardson, Rob. Communings in the sanctuary. 18°. '72. $1 .... *Tr.P.&P.Co.*
— Holy Spirit: scriptural view of office of the Holy Spirit. 12°. $1.50 .... *Chase.*
— Memoirs of Alex. Campbell. 2 v. cr. 8°. ea., $2.50–$4.25; — in 1 v., $4; shp., $5 .... *Chase.*
— *Same.* 2 v. cr. 8. ea., $2.50–$4.25 ... *Lippincott.*
— Principles and objects of the relig. reformation urged by A. Campbell and others. 24°. pap., 10c. *Chase.*

Richardson, S: Novels. 3 v. 12°. $3.75 .. *Routledge.*
Cont.: Clarissa Harlowe. — Sir Charles Grandison. — Pamela.
— Clarissa Harlowe. 16°. bds., 80c. ...... *Routledge.*
— *Same;* condensed by C. H. Jones. (Leis. hour ser.) ('74.) New ed. 16°. '75. $1.25 .... *Holt.*
— Pamela. 16°. bds., $1 .... *Routledge.*
— Sir Charles Grandison. 16°. bds., $1 ... *Routledge.*

Richardson, Tobias G. Elements of human anatomy, general, descriptive and practical. ('67.) 2d ed., rev. ill. 8°. $6 .... *Claxton; Lippincott.*

Richardson, W. C. Gaspar: a romaunt. 12°. '73. 50c. .... *Searcy.*

Richardson, W: A. *See* Massachusetts, General statutes.

Richardson, W: Merchant. *See* New Hampshire, Law reports.

Richelieu. *See* Bulwer-Lytton, *Sir* E. G. E. L.

Richelieu. *See* James, G. P. R.

Richer, E: Religion of good sense. 16°. '70. 62c. *H. H. Carter.*

Riches. Burges, *Sir* J. B. 15c. .... *French.*

Riches have wings. Arthur, T. S. 75c. ... *Collins & Bro.*

Riches without wings. 16°. $1.50 .... *Pres. Bd.*

Richmond, D. [Juveniles.] 8 v. ill. 16° .. *Routledge.*
Cont.: Annie Maitland; or, the lesson of life, 50c. — Harry and his homes; or, the conquest of pride, 75c. — Helena Bertram; or, the orphan. — Maze of life, *ea.*, $1. — Children of blessing. — Doctor's ward. — Four sisters. — Through life and for life, *ea.*, $1.25.

Richmond, *Mrs.* E. J. Adopted. ('72.) New ed. 12°. '75. 60c. .... *Nat. Temp.*
— Alice Grant. 12°. '76. $1.25 .... *Nat. Temp.*
— Fatal dower. ('74.) New ed. 18°. '75. 60c. *Nat. Temp.*
— Hope Raymond; or, what is truth? ill. 16°. '75. $1. *Meth. Bk. Conc.*
— Jewelled serpent. ('72.) New ed. 12°. '75. $1. *Nat. Temp.*
— McAllisters (The). ('71.) New ed. 18°. '74. 50c. *Nat. Temp.*
— Two paths (The). 16°. '75. $1 .... *Meth. Bk. Conc.*
— Zoa Rodman. ('73.) New ed. 12°. '75. $1 .. *Nat. Temp.*

Richmond, J. F. Bright side of New York [City] and its institutions. ('71.) New ed. ill. 8°. '74. *$3; shp., $4 .... *Treat.*
— Diamonds unpolished and polished. ill. 12°. '73. $1.25 .... *Meth. Bk. Conc.*

Richmond, Legh. Annals of the poor. 18°. 45c. *Routledge.*
— *Same.* 18°. 60c. .... *Carter.*
— *Same.* 18°. '56. 60c. .... *Am. Tr.*
— *Same.* 18°. '65. 60c. .... *Meth. Bk. Conc.*
— *Same.* 12°. 75c. .... *Pres. Bd.*
— *Same.* 18°. 85c. .... *Am. S. S.*
— *Same.* 18°. 50c.; 75c. — 32°. 75c. — 12°. $1.25; $1.75 .... *Nelson.*
— *Same;* with life of author by J. Ayre. 18°. 60c. *Bost. Am. Tr.*
— Dairyman's daughter. 32°. 25c. ... *Scribner, W. & A.*
— *Same.* 18°. 40c. .... *Bost. Am. Tr.; Whittaker.*
— *Same.* 18°. '38. 40c. .... *Am. Tr.*
— *Same.* 18°. '67. 40c. .. *N. Y. Ref. Ch. Bd.; Pres. Com.*
— *Same.* 16°. 50c. .... *Scribner, W. & A.*
— *Same.* 18°. 60c. .... *Am. S. S.*
— *Same;* enl. by T. O. Summers. ('56.) 5th ed. 18°. '76. 50c. .... *So. Meth.*
— — *See also* Present for my darling lib.
— *Dutch;* [also, Young cottager]. 18°. '61. 30c. *Am. Tr.*

Richmond, Legh, *continued.*
— *Germ.* Das Milchmädchen. 18°. '51. 50c. .. *Am. Tr.*
— Domestic portraiture. 16°. $1.25 .... *Carter.*
— Letters and counsels. 18°. '49. 40c. ..... *Am. Tr.*
— Life. 18°. 60c. .... *Am. S. S.*
— Negro servant. 18°. '73. 30c. *N. Y. Ref. Ch. Bd.; Pres. Com.*
— *Same.* 18°. 35c. .... *Bost. Am. Tr.*
— *Germ.* Der bekehrte Neger. 32°. '65. 15c.; pap., 5c. .... *Am. Tr.*
— Young cottager. 32°. 25c. .... *Scribner, W. & A.*
— *Same.* 18°. '62. 40c. .... *Am. Tr.*
— *Same.* 18°. '67. 40c. .. *N. Y. Ref. Ch. Bd.; Pres. Com.*
— *Same.* 16°. 50c. .... *Scribner, W. & A.*
— — *See also* Good child's lib.; — *and above* Dairyman's daughter.
— *French.* La jeune villageoise. 18°. 10c. *Pres. Bd.*
— — *Same.* 18°. '52. 15c. .... *Am. Tr.*

Richmond, Wilberforce. Life of Legh Richmond. ill. 18°. '49. 40c. .... *Am. Tr.*

Richmond: her glory and her graves. Jordan, C. J. M. 50c. .... *J. W. Randolph.*

Richter, A. *See* Korfmacher, W. H.

Richter, C. J. Plays of the kindergarten: collection of songs. [Eng. and Germ. text.] sq. 12°. pap., 30c. .... *Peters.*

Richter, Ern. F: Manual of harmony; tr. by J. P. Morgan. 8°. *net*, $2 .... *Schirmer.*
— *Same;* tr. by J. C. D. Parker. 12°. '73. $2 .. *Ditson.*
— Treatise on counterpoint; tr. by F. Taylor. 8°. *net*, $2 .... *Schirmer.*

Richter, Eug. Co-operative stores: their hist., organization and management. ('67.) New ed. 12°. '73. pap., 50c. .... *Holt.*

Richter, Jean Paul. Campaner Thal, and other writings; tr. (Leis. hour ser.) 16°. $1.25 ... *Holt.*
— Flower, fruit and thorn pieces; tr. by E. H. Noel; with memoir of author by T. Carlyle. (Leis. hour ser.) 2 v. 16°. $2.50. .... *Holt.*
— Hesperus; or, forty-five dog-post-days; tr. by C. T. Brooks. (Leis. hour ser.) 2 v. 16°. $2.50 .. *Holt.*
— Levana; or, the doctrine of education; tr. 12°. $2. **Osgood.*
— Life. 12°. $2 .... **Osgood.*
— Titan: a romance; tr. by C. T. Brooks. (Leis. hour ser.) 2 v. 16°. $2.50 .... *Holt.*

Richthofen, F. (*Baron*). Natural system of volcanic rocks. 4°. $1.50 .... *Cal. Acad. Sci.*
— *See also* California Acad. of Sci.

Rickard, Truman, *and* Orcutt, H. Class-book of prose and poetry; with exercises for parsing. 16°. 37c. *R. S. Davis (B.)*

Ricketicketack and wooden Clara. Conscience, H. $1; $1.25 .... *Murphy.*

Rickey, S: *and* Barney, *Master.* Bad whiskey: comic Irish dram. sketch. 16°. pap., 15c. .... *De Witt.*

Ricochets (Les). *See* Souvestre, E.

Ricord, F: W. History of Rome; for schools. 12°. '58. $1.75 .... *Barnes.*
— Youth's grammar; or, easy lessons in etymology. 12°. 38c. .... *Appleton.*

Riddell, *Mrs.* J. H. ["F. G. Trafford."] Above suspicion. 8°. $1.25; pap., 75c. .... *Estes.*
— Far above rubies, 12°. '71. $1.50; pap., $1. *Claxton.*
— George Geith of Fen Court. 12°. '65. $2 .. *Burnham.*
— Life's (A) assize. 8°. pap., 50c. .... *Harper.*
— Maxwell Drewitt. 8°. pap., 75c. .... *Harper.*
— Phemie Keller. 8°. pap., 50c. .... *Harper.*
— Race for wealth. 8°. pap., 75c. .... *Harper.*
— Rich husband. 12°. $1.75; pap., $1.50 .. *Peterson.*
— Too much alone. 8°. '66. pap., 75c. ... *Burnham.*
— *Same.* 8°. $1.25; pap., 75c. .... *Estes.*

Riddell, J: Model architect: agricultural designs for model country residences. ill. and pl. 4°. $15. *Peterson.*

Riddell, Rob. Lessons on hand-railing for learners. 4°. '75. $5 .... *Claxton.*
— Mechanics' geometry. ill. 4°. '74. $5 .... *Claxton.*
— New elements of hand-railing; with 41 pl. ('71.) 2d ed., rev. f°. '75. $7 .... *Claxton.*
— Practical carpenter and joiner. ('72.) 2d ed., rev. and enl. ill. 4°. '73. $10 .... *Claxton.*

Riddle, Alb. Gallatin. Alice Brand: a romance of the Capitol. 12°. $1.50 .... *Appleton; Cobb.*
— Bart Ridgeley: story of northern Ohio. 12°. '73. $1.50 .... *Cobb; Nichols & H.*
— Portrait (The): romance of the Cuyahoga valley. 12°. '73. $1.50 .... *Cobb; Nichols & H.*
— Students and lawyers: philosophy of political parties, etc. 12°. '73. $2 .... *Morrison.*

Riddle, Jos. Esmond. *See* Hawks, F. L., Household prayers.
— *and* Arnold, T. K. English-Latin lexicon; founded on Germ.-Lat. dict. of C. E. Georges; rev. and enl. by C. Anthon. roy. 8°. shp., $5 .. *Harper.*

Riddles and jokes. Routledge, E. 50c .... *Routledge.*

Riddles, conundrums and puzzles. 12°. pap., 20c. *Hurst.*

Ride for life. 8°. pap., 25c .... *De Witt.*

Ride through the Holy Land. Adams, G. M. $1 .. *Hoyt.*

Rider, G: T. Lyra Americana: verses of praise and faith from Am. poets. 12°. $1.50; cf., $3.50; mor., $4 .... *Appleton.*
— Lyra Anglicana: hymnal of sacred poetry. 12°. $1.50; cf., $3.50; mor., $4 .... *Appleton.*

Ridgaway, H: B. Life of Alfred Cookman. por. 12°. $2; mor., $6 .... *Harper.*
— Ten days in Switzerland. 12°. '72. pap., 20c. *Meth. Bk. Conc.*

Ridgely, T: Body of divinity. 2 v. 8°. $5 .. *Carter.*

Ridgemont ser. 3 v. 16°. $4.50 .... *Lothrop.*
Cont.: Romneys of Ridgemont.—School days of Beulah Romney.—Kitty Kent's troubles.

Ridgeway, Jos. Perils among the heathen: narr. of adventure, daring and endurance for Christ's sake. ill. 16°. $1 .... *Nelson.*

Ridgway, Rob. Birds of Colorado. 8°. '73. pap., 15c .... *Essex.*
— Notes on the bird fauna of the Salt Lake valley. 8°. '73. pap., 10c .... *Essex.*
— *See also* Baird, S. F., Brewer, T. M., *and* Ridgway, R.; — Baird S. F., *and* Ridgway, R.

Ridicula rediviva. Rogers, J. E. $2 .... *Macmillan.*

Ridley, Ja. Tales of the genii. 2d ed., ed. by R. Whately. ill. 12°. hf. cf., $3.50 .... *Appleton.*
— *Same.* ill. 12°. (Bohn.) $1.75 ...... *Little, B. & Co.*
— *Same.* ill. 12°. (Bohn.) $2. *Lippincott; Scribner, W. & A.*

Ridley, N: Holy communion: its nature and benefits. 32°. '69. 35c .... *McCauley; Pott.*
— Life and writings. *See* British reformers.

Ridpath, J: Clark. History of the U. S. for schools; on a new plan embr. features of Lyman's hist. chart. maps and charts. 8°. '75. $1.75 ...... *Jones.*
— Popular hist. of the U. S. ill., maps and col. charts. 8°. '76. *$3; $3.50 .... *Jones.*

Riecke, G. A. Dr. Martin Luther: Bilder u. Scenen aus d. Leben Luther's. 3d ed. ill. large 8°. 75c; $1 .... *Schäfer.*

Riedel, Gst. Der blinde Wilhelm. 16°. 25c ... *Morwitz.*
— *Same.* 16°. 30c.; bds., 20c.; pap., 15c .... *Kohler.*
— *Eng.* Blind William. *See* American youth's lib.

Riedesel, *Mme* F. Ctte. L. v. Letters and journals rel. to the [Am.] rev. and capture of Germ. troops at Saratoga; tr. by W. L. Stone. por. and pl. 8°. '67. $3 .... *Munsell.*

Riedesel, F: A. v. Memoirs, letters and journals during his residence in Am.; tr. by W. L. Stone. 2 v. por. and ill. 8°. '68. $5 .... *Munsell.*

Rienzi. *See* Bulwer-Lytton, *Sir* E. G. E. L.

Rienzi. Mitford, M. R. 15c .... *French.*

Riepe, —. Leben u. Wirken Martin Luther's; mit Musterpredigten a. d. luth. Kirche. large 8°. 25c. *Schäfer.*

Ries, F. Morning. [Cantata.] obl. 4°. 40c ... *Gordon.*
— *Same;* with Eng. words by J. S. Dwight. obl. 4°. pap., 40c .... *Ditson.*

Ries, H. Violin school: element. instruction. f°. *net*, bds., $4 .... *Schirmer.*

Riffault, J: René Denis, Vergnaud, A. D., *and* Toussaint, G. A. Practical treatise on manufacture of colors for painting; rev. and ed. by M. F. Malepeyre; tr. by A. A. Fesquet. ill. 8°. '74. $7.50 .... *Baird.*

Riffdorf (Das), od. was Wenige thun können. 18°. 35c .... *Ev. Assoc.*

Rifle (The): its theory and practice. 12°. 50c ... *Judd.*

Rifle and hound in Ceylon. *See* Baker, *Sir* S. W.

Rifle and how to use it. Bridgeman, I. V. 15c ... *French.*

Rifle rangers. Reid, M. $1.50 .... *Carleton.*

Rifle shots at the great men of the day. 8°. pap., 25c. *Peterson.*

Rifle volunteers. Stirling, E. 15c .... *French.*

Rift in the clouds. Marsh, C. 35c .... *Carter.*

Rigby, E: Obstetric memoranda. 4th ed., rev. and enl. by A: Meadows. 32°. '72. 50c ... *Lindsay.*
— System of midwifery; with notes. 8°. $2.50 .. *Lea.*

Rigg, Ja. H. Living Wesley (The). 12°. '75. $1.25. *Meth. Bk. Conc.*
— National education in its social conditions and aspects, and public element. school educ., English and foreign. 12°. '73. $4.50 .... *Routledge.*

Riggenbach, C. J. On Thessalonians. *See* Lange, J. P., Commentary.

Rigging a purchase. Leavitt, A. J. 15c ..... *De Witt.*

Riggs, A. L. Diamond hymns. [S.-school music.] 16°. bds., 15c.; pap., 12c .... *Church.*

Riggs, El. Manual of the Chaldee lang.; cont. Chaldee grammar, chrestomathy and vocab. ('58.) 2d ed., rev. 8°. $2 .... *Randolph.*
— Suggested emendations of the authorized Eng. version of the Old Test. 12°. '73. $1 .... *Draper.*

Riggs, S: A. *See* Kansas, Gen. statutes.

Riggs, Ste. R. Gospel among the Dakotahs. 16°. $1.50 .... *Cong. Pub.*

Right, and about right. *See* Mudge, Z. A.

Right and left. Newby, C. J. 50c .... *Peterson.*

Right and wrong. 18°. 90c .... *Whittaker.*

Right at last. Gaskell, E. C. $1.50 .... *Harper.*

Right is might. *See* Goodrich, S: G.

Right lines in their right places; or, form and colour: first principles of geometry. ill. fp. 8°. 50c. *Cassell.*

Right one. Schwartz, M. S. $1.50; $1 ..... *Porter.*

Right way. Collier, J. A. 45c .... *Am. Tr.*

Right way. Crane, J. T. $1 .... *Meth. Bk. Conc.*

Right way. Harrison, J. 40c .... *Randolph.*

Right way and wrong way. 16°. $1 ...... *Cong. Pub.*

Right word in the right place: pocket dict. and ref. book; by author of "How to write." 12°. '59. 75c .... *Wells.*

Righted wrong. *See* Yates, Edm.

Righteousness by faith. M'Ilvaine, C. P. $1.25. *Leighton.*

Righteousness of God the authority for uprightness in man. Huntington, F. D. 15c .... *Dutton.*

Rightful heir. *See* Bulwer-Lytton, *Sir* E. G. E. L.

Rightheart stories. 4 v. 18°. $2 ...... *H. A. Young.*
Cont.: Archie's old desk, by S. Dodney.—Louise's mistake, by F. Huntingdon.—Binney, the beaver, by L. E. Guernsey.—Robert Rightheart.

Rightmyer, Levy. American system of penmanship. 13 nos. obl. 4°. ea., pap., 10c .... *Benziger.*

Rights and wrongs of women. Morton, J. M. 15c. *French.*
Rights of labor. Brown, L. 50c. .... *Mills.*
Rights of laymen; by a layman. 18°. pap., 10c. *So. Bapt.*
Rights of man. Leland, O. S. 15c. .... *French.*
Rights of man. Paine, T. 50c. .... *Mendum.*
Rigoletto. *See* Verdi, G.
Rilda; or, coming to Christ. 18°. 40c. .... *Cong. Pub.*
Riley, F. Preceptor for violoncello. f°. pap., $2.50. *Ditson.*
Riley, Harvey. The mule: treatise on breeding, training and uses to which he may be put. ill. 12°. '67. $1.50 .... *Claxton.*
Riley, H: Hopkins. Puddleford papers; or, humors of the west. ill. 12°. $1.50 .... *Lee & S.*
Riley, Ja. What he saw and did in Africa. ill. 12°. $1.50 .... *World Pub.*
Riley, J: C. Compend of materia medica and therapeutics. 8°. $3 .... *Lippincott.*
Riley, W. *See* South Carolina, Chancery cases; Reports.
Rills from the fountain of life. Newton, R. $1.25 .. *Carter.*
Rills from the fountain of wisdom. Engles, W. M. 75c. .... *Pres. Bd.*
Rills from the river of life. *See* Bijou Bible text-books.
Rimbault, E: F. Handbook for the piano-forte. 8°. pap., 60c. .... *Ditson.*
— Handbook of harmony. 16°. pap., 75c. .... *Ditson.*
— *See also* Jäger, C., Gallery of great composers.
Rime of the ancient mariner. *See* Coleridge, S. T.
Rinaldo Rinaldini. [German.] 12°. pap., 25c... *Radde.*
Rinaldo Rinaldini, captain of banditti. 8°. pap., 25c. *U. P. James.*
Rindfleisch, E: Text-book of pathol. histology; tr. by W. C. Kloman, assisted by F. T. Miles. ill. 8°. '72. $6; leath., $7 .... *Lindsay.*
Ring, D: Three thousand exercises in arithmetic; with app. by W. J. Lewis. 3d ed., rev. 18°. '43. 30c. — Key. 12°. 30c. .... *Fortescue.*
Ring, Max. John Milton and his times. [Fiction.] ill. 8°. $1.50; pap., $1 .... *Appleton.*
Ring and the book. Browning, R. 2 v. $3 .. *Osgood.*
Ring and its motto. Means, C. A. $1 .... *Cong. Pub.*
Ring and the keeper. Wooler, J. P. 15c. .... *French.*
Ring of Amasis. *See* Bulwer-Lytton, E. R.
Ringdoves: farce. 16°. pap., 15c. .... *Happy.*
Ringer, Sidney. Handbook of therapeutics. 5th ed. 8°. $4.25 .... *W. Wood.*
Ringleader: tale for boys. 18°. 55c. .... *Am. S. S.*
Ringwalt, J. Luther (*ed.*) American encyclopædia of printing. imp. 8°. $10 .... *Lippincott.*
Rink, C. H. First three months at the organ. 4°. pap., $1.75 .... *Ditson.*
— *Same.* f°. $1.75 .... *Gordon.*
— *Same.* 4°. 75c. .... *Brainard.*
— Instructor for beginners on the organ. 2 bks. 4°. ea., $1.50 .... *Brainard.*
— Organ school; rev. with Germ. directions and terms tr. into Eng.; ed. by W. T. Best. 4°. $6; — in 6 bks., ea., pap., $1.50 .... *Ditson.*
Riodu, *Mme.* A. Lucie: familiar conversations in French and English. ('66.) New ed. 12°. '73. 75c. *Holt.*
Rip Van Winkle. Burke, C. 15c. .... *French.*
Rip Van Winkle. *See* Irving, W.
Rip Van Winkle: Ethiop. drama. 16°. pap., 15c. *French.*
Rip Van Winkle; or, the sleep of twenty years. 8°. pap., 25c. .... *De Witt.*
Ripalda, Gerónimo. Catecismo de la doctrina cristiana. 18°. bds., 25c. .... *Appleton.*
Ripe harvest. Russell, G. B. 50c. .... *Ref. Ch. Bd.*
Ripe strawberries. *See* Baker, *Mrs.* H. N. W.
Ripley, G: Literature and the fine arts: index to terms employed in belles lettres, philosophy, mythology, painting, music, etc. 8°. $3 .... *Barnes.*
— *and* Dana, C: (*ed.*) New American cyclopædia: popular dictionary of general knowledge. ('61–'63.) 2d ed., rev. and enl. 16 v. ill. 8°. '72–'75. ea., *$5–$10 .... *Appleton.*
Ripley, H: Jones. Church polity: treatise on Christian churches and the Christian ministry. 16°. '67. 75c. .... *Graves.*
— Notes on Acts. 12°. $1.50 .... *Sheldon.*
— Notes on Epistle to the Hebrews. 12°. $1.25. *Sheldon.*
— Notes on Epistle to the Romans. 12°. $1 .. *Sheldon.*
— Notes on the Gospels. map. 12°. $2 ...... *Sheldon.*
— Sacred rhetoric; or, composition and delivery of sermons; [also] Ware's Hints on extemporaneous preaching. 12°. $1.25 .... *Sheldon.*
Ripley, Ma. A. Exercises in analysis and parsing. ('71.) 3d ed. 16°. '76. bds., 40c. ...... *Paul.*
Rippard, the outlaw. 12°. pap., 20c. .... *Hurst.*
Ripples of song. 16°. pap., 15c. .... *Nat. Temp.*
Rise and conquer lib. 3 v. ill. 12°. $4.50 .... *Nelson.*
Cont.: Constancia's household, by E. Leslie. — From tent to palace, by B: Clarke. — First heroes of the cross, by B: Clarke.
Rise and progress of religion in the soul. *See* Doddridge, Ph.
Risen from the ranks. Alger, H., *jr.* $1.50 .. *Loring.*
Rishiel, Jos. O. Odd-fellowship illustrated. ('74.) 5th ed. ill. 12°. '76. 25c. .... *E. A. Cook.*
Rising faith. Bartol, C. A. $2 .... *Roberts.*
Rising in the world. Arthur, T. S. 75c... *Collins & Bro.*
Ritchie, *Mrs.* A. I. *See* Thackeray, *Miss* A. I.
Ritchie, And. Christian friend. 16°. 40c... *West. Tr.*
— Christian Sabbath. *See* Sabbath.
— First lessons in theology. 16°. 40c. ...... *West. Tr.*
— Kill the fiend. 16°. 40c. .... *West. Tr.*
— Life and light: pt. 1 of Manner and matter for Christian workers. 12°. $1.25 .... *West. Tr.*
— Little Jamie. 16°. 25c. .... *West. Tr.*
— Matter and manner for Christian workers. 12°. $1.75 .... *West. Tr.*
— My Saviour and my home. 12°. 60c. ..... *West. Tr.*
— Pastor's gift book. 16°. 30c.; pap., 10c... *West. Tr.*
— Plea for Bible in schools. 16°. pap., 10c... *West. Tr.*
— Relation of civil government to the Sabbath. 16°. pap., 10c. .... *West. Tr.*
— Sacramental catechism, for young communicants; [also] Essay on relations of baptized youth to the church, by J. Claybaugh. 12°. '55. 50c. *Wilstach.*
Ritchie, *Mrs.* Anna Cora [*formerly Mrs.* Mowatt]. Armand: play. 16°. pap., 15c. .... *French.*
— Fashion: comedy. 16°. pap., 15c. .... *French.*
— Fortune hunter. 8°. pap., 50c. .... *Peterson.*
Ritchie, Arch. Tucker. Dynamical theory of the formation of the earth; based on assumption of its non-rotation during period called "the beginning." 8°. '74. $5 .... *Routledge.*
Ritchie, Eliz. Lessons of life and death: memorial of Sarah Ball. 18°. 40c. .... *Pres. Bd.*
Ritchie, Leitch. Romance of history: France. ill. 12°. '72. $2.50 .... *Putnam.*
— — *See also* Romance of hist.
— Weary foot common. ill. 12°. $1.25 .. *Scribner, W. & A.*
Ritchie, W: Scripture testimony against intoxicating wine. 18°. '66. 60c. .... *Nat. Temp.*
Ritchner, W. D. Life and crimes of Dr. Sefton. 8°. pap., 25c. .... *Barclay.*
— Myria, the mad actress. [In Eng. or Germ.] 8°. pap., 25c. .... *Barclay.*
Rites and worship of the Jews. 12°. 50c. *Meth. Bk. Conc.*

Ritter, A. G. Art of organ playing, 2d pt.: practical course of instruction in organ playing; text tr. by J. P. Morgan. 4°. *net*, bds., $3...*Schirmer*.

Ritter, Abram. History of the Moravian Church in Phila. from 1742; with notices of its founder, Count N. L. v. Zinzendorf, and app. 8°. '57. $1.50 .... *Clauder*.

Ritter, C: Comparative geography; tr. by W. L. Gage. 12°. $1.50 .... *Lippincott*.

— Comparative geography of Palestine and the Sinaitic peninsula; tr. and adapted to use of Biblical students by W. L. Gage. 4 v. 8°. $14; hf. cf., $24. *Appleton*.

Ritter, F: L: History of music in the form of lectures; tr. 2 v. 12°. '74. ea., $1.50 .... *Ditson*.

Ritter Bell. Owen, F. 90c............ (?) *Martien*.

Ritual "reason why." Walker, C. $1.75...... *Pott*.

Rituale Romanum. *See* Catholic Church.

Ritualism dethroned and the true church found. Orvis, W. B. $1.50 .... (?) *Longstreth*.

Riukan Voss. Mügge, T. 40c............... *Holt*.

Rival artists. White, C. 15c.............. *De Witt*.

Rival beauties. Pardoe, J. 75c........... *Peterson*.

Rival belles. Jones, J. B. $1.75; $1.50...*Peterson*.

Rival Crusoes. St. John, P. B. 50c....... *Am. News*.

Rival kings. 18°. 75c...................... *Carter*.

Rival lovers: Ethiop. drama. 16°. pap., 15c. *French; Happy*.

Rival lovers; or, the midnight murder. 8°. pap., 25c. *De Witt*.

Rival mokes: Ethiop. drama. 16°. pap., 15c. *Happy*.

Rival pages: comedy. 16°. pap., 15c........ *French*.

Rival students. 16°. $1.25 .... *Am. Bapt*.

Rival tenants. Stout, G. L. 15c........... *De Witt*.

Rival valets. Ebsworth, J. 15c............ *French*.

Rivals. 18°. 50c.; 55c. .... *Dutton*.

Rivals. Clemens, J. $1.25..... *Claxton; Lippincott*.

Rivals. *See* Griffin, Ger.

Rivals. Sheridan, R. B. 15c. .... *French*.

Rive, *Mme*. Caro. System of sight singing. 4°. $2.50. *Church*.

River. ('59.) 2d ed. 18°. '75. 30c. .... *So. Meth*.

River-bank stories. 6 v. 18°. $3.60...... *Cong. Pub*.
Cont.: Street sweeper. — Idle Harry. — Successful apprentice. — Workhouse boy. — John Heppell. — Walter and his prize.

River home lib. 3 v. ill. 16°. $3.50.......... *Tibbals*.
Cont.: Oline, by Mrs. C. A. Munson. — Adopted son of the princess, by E. W. Jones. — Old home by the river, by J. C. Dutcher.

River legends. Knatchbull-Hugessen, E. H. $3. *Routledge*.

River of dreams. O., G. E. $1.25.......... *Lee & S*.

River of life. Perkins, H. S., *and* Bentley, W. W. 35c.; 30c. .... *Ditson*.

River of life, and other poems. Carr, G. P. 75c. *Turnbull*.

River pirates: tale of N. Y. 8°. pap., 25c...*Peterson*.

Riverdale stories. *See* Adams, W. T.

Riverdale story books. *See* Adams, W. T.

Rivers, Pearl. Lyrics. 12°. $1.25....... *Lippincott*.

Rivers, R: H. Mental philosophy. ('71.) 3d ed. 12°. '76. $1.50 .... *So. Meth*.

— Moral philosophy. ('71.) 3d ed. 12°. '76. $1.50. *So. Meth*.

Rivers, T: Miniature fruit-garden; or, the culture of pyramidal and bush fruit-trees. ill. 12°. $1..*Judd*.

— *Same*. 18°. $1 .... *Tilton*.

Rivers and lakes of the Bible. *See* Tweedie, W. K.

Rivers of waters in a dry place: account of introd. of Christianity into south Africa and of Mr. Moffat's missionary labors. 16°. $1.15........ *Pres. Bd*.

Riversdale. *See* Bowen, *Mrs*. C. E.

Riverside. Butler, M. R. 75c.............. *Chase*.

Riverside classics. 8 v. ill. 16°. v. 1-7, ea., $1.25-$4.50; v. 8, $1.50-$5 .... *Hurd & H*.
Cont.: Saintine's Picciola. — Jerrold's Mrs. Caudle's curtain lectures. — Paradise lost. — Moore's Lalla Rookh. — St. Pierre's Paul and Virginia. — Haliburton's Clockmaker. — La Motte Fouqué's Undine, etc.

Riverside farmhouse. Miller, M. E. 45c.... *Am. Tr*.

Riverside juveniles. 5 v. 16°. ea., bds., 75c.; — in 1 v., $3; hf. mor., $5 .... *Hurd & H*.
Cont.: A frog he would a-wooing go. — House that Jack built. — Old Mother Hubbard and her dog. — Fox and the geese. — Five little pigs.

Riverside lib. 5 v. 16°. $6.................. *Hoyt*.
Cont.: Mildred Gwynne. — Alone in the world. — Little Nellie, by F. M. C. W. — Two books, by Mrs. C. E. K. Davis. — Two little Bruces.

Riverside press centennial guide books. 3 v. 16°. '76. ea., 35c.; pap., 15c............ *Hurd & H*.
Cont.: New York City. — Philadelphia and the Centennial. — Washington City.

— *Same*. Boston to Washington. [Eng., Germ., Fr. *and* Span. eds.] maps. 16°. '76. ea., $1; roan, $1.50; pap., 35c.......................... *Hurd & H*.

Rives, W: C. History of life and times of James Madison. 3 v. 8°. '68. $10.50; hf. cf., $16.50. *Little, B. & Co*.

Riviera (The). Alford, H. $10 .... *Routledge*.

Rivingstone. Ingraham, J. H. 25c. .... *De Witt*.

Road to faith. Loeb, H. 30c................ *Bloch*.

Road to ruin. 8°. pap., 25c. .... *De Witt*.

Road to ruin. Holcroft, T. 15c............ *French*.

Road to ruin; or, the dangers of the town. 8°. pap., 25c. .... *U. P. James*.

Roadside poems for summer travellers. Larcom, L. $1 .... *Osgood*.

Roanoke; or, where is Utopia? Wiley, C. H. 75c. *Peterson*.

Roarer. Small, G. G. 25c. .... *Collin & S*.

Rob Cobb Kennedy, the incendiary spy. 12°. pap., 20c. .... *Hurst*.

Rob of the bowl. *See* Kennedy, J: P.

Rob Roy. *See* Grant, Ja.

Rob Roy. *See* Scott, *Sir* Wa.

Rob Roy. Soane, G. 15c.................... *French*.

Rob Roy lib. of adventure. *See* Grant, Ja.

Rob Roy of the Rocky Mountains; or, the foundling. 8°. pap., 25c.......................... *De Witt*.

Rob Roy (The) on the Baltic. Macgregor, J. $1.25. *Roberts*.

Rob Roy (The) on the Jordan. Macgregor, J. $2.50. *Harper*.

Rob Roy's adventures. *See* Grant, Ja.

Roba di Roma. Story, W. W. $4....... *Lippincott*.

Robards, C: L. *See* Texas, Sup. Court reports.

Robards, W: A. *See* Missouri, Sup. Court reports.

Robb, J: S. Swamp doctor's adventures in the south-west. ill. 12°. $1.75.................. *Peterson*.

Robber (The). *See* James, G. P. R.

Robber kitten. ill. f°. pap., 15c.; 20c.; 30c. *J. E. Potter*.

Robber kitten. *See* Ballantyne, W.

Robber of the Rhine. Almar, G. 15c....... *French*.

Robber's cave. *See* Tucker, *Mrs*. C.

Robber's wife. Pocock, I. 15c............. *French*.

Robber's wife: domestic romance. 8°. pap., 50c. *Peterson*.

Robbers. *See* Schiller, J. F. v.

Robbers of the Pyrenees. Suter, W. E. 15c...*French*.

Robbie, the herd boy. 32°. 25c...... *Scribner, W. & A*.

Robbie and his mother. 16°. 75c.......... *Cong. Pub*.
— *See also* Philip Oakover.

Robbie and the stars. *See* Alden, *Mrs*. I. M.

Robbie Grey lib. 30 v. ill. 18°. $7.50...... *Lothrop*.

Robbie Meredith. Colter, J. J. $1 .... *Lothrop.*
Robbie's Christmas eve. *See* Little Fan's lib.
Robbie's light. Frost, S. A. 30c. .... *Am. Tr.*
Robbie's pets; [also] Nellie's sunbeam. ill. 18°. '72. 50c. .... *Lothrop.*
Robbing the orchard. *See* Infant school lib.
Robbins, *Mrs.* —. Frank and Amy's visit to Palestine. 18°. 75c. .... *Cong. Pub.*
Robbins, Chandler. Portrait of a Christian drawn from life: memoir of Maria Elizabeth Clapp. ('58.) 5th ed. 16°. '67. 60c. .... *Am. Unit.*
Robbins, *Miss* Eliza. American popular lessons. 18°. '48. 40c. — Introd., 30c. .... *G. R. Lockwood.*
— Class-book of poetry. 16°. $1.25 .... *Appleton.*
— Elements of mythology. 18°. 80c. .... *Moss.*
— Guide to knowledge. 18°. $1 .... *Appleton.*
— Primary dictionary. 18°. '42. 40c. .. *G. R. Lockwood.*
— School friend. 18°. hf. roan, 42c. .... *Lippincott.*
— Tales from Am. hist. 3 v. ill. 18°. $2.25 ... *Harper.*
Robbins, Gilb. Christian patriot: biog. of James McClellan. por. 12°. '65. $1 ..... *Putnam & D.*
Robbins, Royal. Outlines of history, ancient and modern. 2 v. in 1. 12°. *net,* $1.80 ...... *Hamersley.*
Robbins, *Mrs.* S. S. Benny's birds. ('60.) New ed. ill. 18°. '70. 30c. .... *Hoyt.*
— Brentford parsonage. 16°. $1.25 .... *Carter.*
— Butterfly's flights. 3 v. 18°. $2.25 .... *Carter.*
— Clifton Rice. 18°. 90c. .... (?) *Martien.*
— Comfort Strong. 16°. '76. $1.25 .... *Carter.*
— Doors outward. 16°. $1.25 .... *Carter.*
— Green Mountain stories. 5 v. 16°. $6; ea., $1.25. *Carter.*

Cont.: Binding the sheaves. — Weighed in the balance. — Edged tools. — Girding on the armor. — Robert Linton.

— Hetty's hopes; or, trust in God. ('66.) New ed. ill. 18°. '75. $1.50 .... *Hoyt.*
— Kate Elmore; or, light in darkness. ('64.) New ed. ill. 16°. '72. $1.15 .... *Hoyt.*
— Mabel Hazard's thoroughfare. 16°. $1.25 .. *Carter.*
— Village schoolmistress; or, more about Kate Elmore. ('64.) New ed. ill. 16°. '75. $1.25 .... *Hoyt.*
— Who won. 16°. $1.25 .... *Carter.*
— Win and wear series. 6 v. 16°. ea., $1.25 .. *Carter.*

Cont.: Win and wear. — Tony Starr's legacy. — Faithful and true. — Ned's motto. — My new home. — Turning a new leaf.

Robert, H: M. Rules of order for deliberative assemblies. 18°. '76. 75c. .... *Griggs.*
Robert, *Uncle.* *See* Uncle Robert.
Robert. *See* Hoffmann, F:
Robert; or, the influence of a good mother, and other stories. 8°. '76. $1.50 .... *Cath. Pub.*
Robert, the cabin boy. Potwin, H. K. $1 .... *Dodd.*
Robert, the devil. Raymond, R. J. 15c. .... *French.*
Robert, le diable. *See* Meyerbeer, G.
Robert, der Teufel. 12°. pap., 15c. .... *Radde.*
Robert, der Waisenknabe. *See* Schmid, C. v.
Robert Ainsleigh. Braddon, M. E. 2 v. $3 .. *Lippincott.*
Robert and Daisy. Finley, M. F. 45c. .... *Pres. Bd.*
Robert and his dove. *See* Infant school lib.
Robert Benton; or, let it alone 'till to-morrow. 18°. 30c. .... *Am. S. S.*
Robert Bruce. Reynolds, G. W. M. $1.75; $1 .. *Peterson.*
Robert Dawson; or, the brave spirit. 18°. 60c. .. *Am. S. S.* — *See also* Reuben Kent ser.
Robert Emmet. Pilgrim, J. 15c. .... *French.*
Robert Falconer. Mac Donald, G. $1.75 ... *Loring.*
Robert Graham. Hentz, C. L. $1.75; $1.50 .. *Peterson.*
Robert Greathouse. Swift, J. F. $2 .... *Carleton.*
Robert Hamet, the lame cobbler. 18°. 30c. .. *Am. S. S.*
Robert Joy's victory; or, life's battle lost and won. ('67.) New ed. ill. 16°. '75. $1.15 .... *Hoyt.*
Robert Linton. Robbins, S. S. $1.25 .... *Carter.*
Robert Macaire. Reynolds, G. W. M. 75c. ... *Dick & F.*
Robert Macaire. Selby, C. 15c. .... *French.*
Robert Make Airs: Ethiop. drama. 16°. pap., 15c. *French; Happy.*
Robert May. 18°. 50c.; 75c. .... *Sadlier.*
Robert Oaklands; or, the outcast orphan; by author of "Robber of the Rhine." 8°. pap., 50c. .. *Peterson.*
Robert of Woodleigh. Stoner, P. $1.25 ..... *Miller.*
Robert Rightheart. 18°. 50c. .... *H. A. Young.*
Robert Severne. Hammond, W. A. $1.75 .. *Lippincott.*
Robert Spencer's revenge. *See* Kitty's pearls.
Robert Stone. 18°. 40c. .... *Cong. Pub.*
Robert Walton; or, the great idea. ('60.) New ed. ill. 18°. '70. 60c. .... *Hoyt.*
— *Germ.* Robert Walton, od. ein grosser Gedanke u. was daraus wurde. 18°. 40c. .... *Ev. Assoc.*
Roberti, F. Little treatise on the little virtues. 32°. 45c. .... *Cath. Pub.*
Roberto, D. Love of Mary; or, readings for the month of May. 24°. 50c. .... *Strong.*
Robert's holidays. *See* D'Anvers, N.
Roberts, Alex. Discussions on the Gospels. 2d ed., rev. 8°. $4 .... *Macmillan.*
— *and* Donaldson, J. (*ed.*) Ante-Nicene Christian lib.: tr. of the writings of the fathers to A. D. 325. 24 v. 8°. ea., $3 .... *Pott; Scribner, W. & A.*

Cont.: Apostolic fathers, tr. by Roberts, Donaldson and F. Crombie. — Justin Martyr and Athenagoras, tr. by M. Dods, G. Reith and B. P. Pratten. — Tatianus and others, tr. by B. P. Pratten, M. Dods and T. Smith. — Clement of Alexandria, tr. by W. Wilson, 2 v. — Irenæus (v. 1), tr. by A. Roberts and W. H. Rambaut. — Hippolytus' Refutation of all heresies, tr. by J. H. MacMahon. — Tertullianus' Five books against Marcion, tr. by P. Holmes. — Cyprianus and others, tr. by E. Wallis, 2 v. — Irenæus (v. 2) and Hippolytus (v. 2), tr. by H. Roberts and W. H. Rambaut. — Origines, tr. by F. Crombie, 2 v. — Tertullianus and others, tr. by S. Thelwall and P. Holmes, 3 v. — Methodius and others. — Apocryphal Gospels, Acts and Revelation, tr. by A. Walker. — Clementine homilies. — Arnobius' Seven books of Adversus gentes, tr. by H. Bryce and H. Campbell. — Gregorius Thaumaturgus and others, tr. by S. D. F. Salmond. — Lactantius, tr. by W. Fletcher, 2 v. — Liturgies and other documents, by several translators.

— — *and* Crombie, F. (*tr.*) Writings of the apostolic fathers. (Ante-Nicene Christ. lib.) 8°. $3. *Scribner, W. & A.*
Roberts, D. Lloyd. Student's guide to practice of midwifery. ill. 12°. '76. $2.25 .... *Lindsay.*
Roberts, E: Apples of gold in pictures of silver: hymns and tunes. obl. 12°. '67. bds., 35c.; pap., 30c. .... *Ditson.*
— *and* Morgan, J. P. The tonart: sacred and secular music. obl. 8°. bds., $1.50 .... *Huntington.*
Roberts, F: T. Handbook of the theory and practice of medicine. New ed., enl. 8°. '76. $5; leath., $6 .... *Lindsay.*
Roberts, G: [Plays.] 6 v. 16°. ea., pap., 15c. .. *French.*

Cont.: Ample apology: farce. — Cousin Tom: comedietta. — Forty winks: farce. — Idalia. — Three furies: comedietta. — Under the rose: farce.

— Cousin Tom: comedietta. 16°. pap., 15c. .. *Lee & S.*
Roberts, J: Memoir. 18°. 50c. .... *Friends Bk. St.*
Roberts, J: S. Life and explorations of David Livingstone; incl. extracts from his last journal by E. A. Manning. map, por. and ill. 12°. $1.50; hf. mor., $2 .... *Russell.*
— (*ed.*) Legendary ballads of Eng. and Scotland. por. and ill. cr. 8°. 75c.–$8 .... *Scribner, W. & A.*
Roberts, Jos. Handbook of artillery. 10th ed., rev. and enl. 16°. '75. mor., $2 .... *Van Nostrand.*
Roberts, L: A. High art: pictures from the poets; [also] Sport in brief chapters, from the quill of Ikabod Izax. ill. 8°. *$1.50 .... *D. E. Fisk.*
Roberts, *Miss* Marg. On the edge of the storm. 12°. '69. $1.50; $2 .... *Putnam.*
— Sydonie's dowry. ill. 12°. $1.25 .. *Scribner, W. & A.*

Roberts, Nath. Ready reckoner; or, Am. measurer's guide: tables for measurement of timber, stone, boxes, etc. 12°. '73. shp., $3.... *Collins & Bro.*

Roberts, S: Digest of sel. Brit. statutes; with notes and ill. 2d ed., rev. and enl. by R. E. Wright. 8°. shp., $2.50.......................... *Kay.*

Roberts, *Miss* Sa. J. My step-mother; or, the power of love. 18°. 60c.................. *Claremont.*

— *Same.* 18°. 70c.......................... *Dutton.*

Roberts, T: A. Principles of Court of Chancery, and powers and duties of its judges. 8°. '57. $2.50. *T. & J. W. Johnson.*

— — *See also* Law lib.

Roberts, T: P. Report of a reconnoissance of the Missouri River. *See* United States, *Corps of Eng.*

Roberts, W. M. Engineering. 8°. pap., 40c. *Am. Soc. of C. E.*

— Plenum-pneumatic process: Illinois and St. Louis bridge. 8°. pap., 40c.......... *Am. Soc. of C. E.*

Roberts, W: History of the U. S., to [1865]. 12°. hf. bd., 75c.......................... *Sower.*

Roberts, W: Life and correspondence of Hannah More. 2 v. por. 12°. $2.50; shp., $3.30; hf. cf., $6.......................... *Harper.*

Roberts, W: Practical treatise on urinary and renal diseases, incl. urinary deposits; ill. by cases and eng. col. pl. 8°. $4.50.................. *Lea.*

Roberts, W: C. Anniversary discourse before N. Y. Acad. of Med. 8°. '59. pap., 25c. *N. Y. Acad. Med.*

Roberts family. 18°. 35c.................. *Am. S. S.*

Robertson, Ant. L. *See* New York City, Superior Court reports.

Robertson, Fk. Engineering notes. 8°. '73. $5.. *Spon.*

— Tables for arches. 8°. '71. $2............ *Spon.*

Robertson, F: W: Lectures and addresses on literary and social topics. 12°. $1.25.........* *Osgood.*

— Life and letters. 2 v. 12°. $3; — in 1 v., $1..* *Osgood.*

— Life, letters, lectures on Corinthians, and addresses. por. 12°. $1.50; hf. cf., $3.25......... *Harper.*

— Sermons; with memoir. 5 v. por. 12°. ea., $1.25; — in 2 v., $2 ....* *Osgood.*

— Sermons preached at Brighton. por. 12°. $1.50; hf. cf., $3.25...................... *Harper.*

Robertson, G: Outline of life, [autobiog.]; with introd. and app. by his son. 8°. '76. $2.. *Tr. P. & P. Co.*

Robertson, J. Forbes. Questions on Lockyer's Astronomy. 18°. '70. 50c.......... *Macmillan.*

Robertson, Ja. Craigie. History of the Christian church, A.D. 64 to 1517. New ed., rev. 8 v. 8°. '75. ea., $2.25...................... *Pott.*

— *See also* Byerley, T., *and* Robertson, J. C.

Robertson, J: Pastoral counsels. 3d ed. 12°. '67. $1.50.......................... *Macmillan.*

— Sermons and expositions. 8°. $3...... *Routledge.*

Robertson, Marg. M. Inglises (The); or, how the way opened. 12°. '72. $1.50...... *Randolph.*

— Janet's love and service. 12°. '70. $1.75.. *Randolph.*

Robertson, Norvell. Church member's handbook of theology. 12°. $1.50.............. *So. Bapt.*

Robertson, Thdr. Intermediate French course. 12°. '60. $1.75.................. *G. R. Lockwood.*

— Introductory French course. 12°. '61. $1.25. *G. R. Lockwood.*

— New Spanish course. 12°. '61. $1.75.. *G. R. Lockwood.*

— Nuevo curso práctico, analítico, teórico y syntético del idioma inglés; tr. por P. J. Rojas. 8°. $3. *Appleton.*

— Whole French course. 12°. '58. $2. — Key. 12°. '55. 75c.................... *G. R. Lockwood.*

Robertson, T: W: [Plays.] 13 v. 16°. ea., pap., 15c.......................... *De Witt.*

Cont.: Breach of promise: comic drama. — Caste: comedy. — Chevalier de St. George. — David Garrick: comedy. — Dreams; or, my Lady Clara. — Home: comedy. — My wife's diary: farce. — Not a bit jealous: farce. — Ours: comedy. — Peace at any price: farce. — School: comedy. — Society: comedy. — Young collegians: farce.

Robertson, T: W: *continued.*

— *Same.* 5 v. 16°. ea., pap., 15c.......... *French.*

Cont.: Cantab: farce. — Chevalier de St. George. — Ernestine. — Peace at any price: farce. — Society: comedy.

— Cantab. *See* Evening's entertainment.

— *and* Lacy, T. H. Two gay deceivers: farce. 16°. pap., 15c.................. *De Witt; French.*

Robertson, W: Desert pathway. 12°. $1.50.. *Carter.*

Robertson, W: History of disc. of Am.; with account of his life and writings; with questions by J. Frost. ill. 8°. $2.25; shp., $2.75; hf. cf., $4.50; — abridg. 18°. 75c.......... *Harper.*

— History of reign of Charles v.; with life of Emperor after his abdication, by W. H. Prescott. 3 v. cr. 8°. $7.50; hf. cf., $13.50.......... *Lippincott.*

— *Same;* with questions by J. Frost. ill. 8°. $2.25; shp., $2.75; hf. cf., $4.50; — abridg. 18°. 75c. *Harper.*

— History of Scotland during reigns of Mary and James VI., to [1603]; [also] Dissertation conc. ancient India. 8°. $2.25; shp., $2.75; hf. cf., $4.50.......................... *Harper.*

Robie Grey. *See* Fireside stories.

Robillard, V. Fit of the blues: opera arr. for amateurs. 16°. pap., 40c.................. *French*

Robin, C: *See* Bernard, C., *and* Robin, C.

Robin. *See* Our song birds.

Robin, the bold. ill. 16°. 50c.................. *Pott.*

Robin, the runner; or, the fruits of well-doing. ('65.) New ed. ill. 18°. '75. 50c.............. *Hoyt.*

— *Same.* ill. 16°. '72. 60c.................. *Lothrop.*

— *Same.* ill. 18°. 70c.................... *Pres. Bd.*

Robin Gray. Gibbon, C. 50c.............. *Harper.*

Robin Hood. Ball, E. 15c.................. *French.*

Robin Hood. Burnand, F. C. 15c.......... *French.*

Robin Hood (Story of). Heaton, W. $1.50.. *Cassell*

Robin Hood; or, the merry men of Sherwood Forest drama. 16°. pap., 15c.................. *Happy.*

Robin Hood and his merry foresters. Percy, S. $1. *Miller*

Robin Hood and his merry men. ill. f°. pap., 15c.: 20c.......................... *J. E. Potter.*

Robin nest stories. *See* Baker, *Mrs.* H. N. W.

Robin Ranger's lib. 10 v. 24°. '62. $2.50.. *Meth. Bk. Conc*

Cont.: Magic lantern. — Up in the garret. — Sunshine Hall — Summer days. — Johnny and his mother. — Out in the garden. — Naughty Jack. — Winter days. — Out of school. — Grandma Gray.

Robin Ranger's picture book. 18°. '65. 45c. *Meth. Bk. Conc*

Robin Ranger's stories about birds. 10 v. 24°. '69 $2.50.......................... *Meth. Bk. Conc*

Cont.: Cone-billed birds. — Running birds and pigeons. — Wading birds. — Vultures and eagles. — Swimming birds. — Cleft-billed birds. — Hawks and owls. — Climbing birds. — Tooth-billed birds. — Slender-billed birds.

Robin Ranger's stories about wild beasts. 10 v. 24° '66. $2.50.......................... *Meth. Bk. Conc*

Cont.: Monkeys. — Lion. — Tiger. — Leopard. — Wolves and foxes. — Weasels. — Bear. — Gnawing animals. — Antelopes. — Elephant.

Robin Redbreast picture-book. 16°. '73. 75c.; bds. 50c.......................... *Routledge*

Robin Redbreast ser. *See* Baker, *Mrs.* H. N. W.

Robin Tremayne. Holt, E. S. $1.50....... *Carter*

Robin's Christmas song. [Toy-book.] ill. 4°. $1 50c.......................... *Routledge*

Robins, Sanderson. Party spirit in the church. 16° 75c.; pap., 50c.................. *Dutton*

Robins (Story of the). *See* Trimmer, *Mrs.* S. K.

Robins' nest. Baker, H. N. W. 35c....(?) *Shepard*

Robinson, C: J. Handbook of physical training in schools. 18°. '74. 50c.................. *Payot*

Robinson, C: S. Church work: 26 sermons. 2 v. 12°. '73. $3 .... *Barnes.*
— Psalms and hymns and spiritual songs; with hymns and tunes. 8°. '75. $1.75–$6.50; — hymns only, 75c. .... *Barnes.*
— Songs for Christian worship: sel. from "Songs of the church." 8°. '69. $1.50; $3.50; $5.50 .. *Barnes.*
— Songs for the sanctuary. [Cong., Presb. and Bapt. eds.] 8°. '72. $2; — hymns only. 12°. '70. $2.50–$6.50. — 18°. '65. $1.75–$4.75. — (Chapel ed.): hymns and tunes. 8°. '72. $1.40–$5. — (Psalter ed.), $1.75 .... *Barnes.*
— Songs of the church; or, hymns and tunes for Christian worship. 8°. '62. $2.50; $4.50; $6.50. *Barnes.*
— *and* Perkins, Thdr. E. Calvary songs. 16°. '75. 35c. .... *Am. S. S.*

Robinson, Conway. Forms adapted to practice in Virginia courts of law and civil cases. 8°. '41. shp., $18 .... *J. W. Randolph.*
— Practice in courts of law and equity and criminal causes in Virginia. 3 v. 8°. '32–'39. shp., $35. *J. W. Randolph.*
— Principles and practice of courts in Eng. and U. S. 7 v. 8°. '54–'74. ea., shp., $8 .... *Woodhouse.*
— *Same.* 7 v. 8°. '54–'74. shp., $100 .. *J. W. Randolph.*
— *Same.* v. 5–7. 8°. '68–'70. $24 .. *T. & J. W. Johnson.*
Note. v. 1–4 are o. p.
— *See also* Robinson, J. *and* C.; — Virginia, Court of Appeals reports.

Robinson, E: Biblical researches in Palestine. 3 v. map. 8°. '56. $10 .... *Crocker.*
— Greek and Eng. lexicon of New Test. roy. 8°. $6; shp., $6.50; hf. cf., $8.25 .... *Harper.*
— Harmony of the four Gospels in Gk. 8°. '51. $2; — in Eng. 12°. $1 .... *Crocker.*
— Later Biblical researches in Palestine. maps. 8°. $3 .... *Crocker.*
— Physical geog. of the Holy Land: sup. to Biblical researches in Palestine. 8°. '65. $3.50 .. *Crocker.*

Robinson, Fayette. Grammar of the Spanish language, based on system of J. de Urcullu. 12°. $2. *Desilver.*

Robinson, Fk. H. Lacrosse. 48°. 25c. *Scribner, W. & A.*

Robinson, F: W: Novels. 12 v. 8°. pap... *Harper.*
Cont.: Carry's confession. — For her sake. — Little Kate Kirby. — Mattie: a stray. — No man's friend. — Second cousin Sarah, *ea.*, 75c. — Bridge of glass. — Girl's (A) romance, etc. — Her face was her fortune. — Poor humanity. — Stern necessity. — True to herself, *ea.*, 50c.
— *Same.* 13 v. 8°. ea., pap., 50c. .... *De Witt.*
Cont.: Anne Judge, spinster. — Grandmother's money. — Heads and hearts; or, my brother, the colonel. — Heirs of Derwentwater. — House at Elmore. — Old Noll; or, days of the Ironsides. — Omi. — One-and-twenty. — Secretary (The); or, circumstantial evidence. — Shira. — Sweet nineteen. — Under the spell. — Wild flowers.
— Christie's faith. 12°. $1.75 .... *Harper.*
— Mr. Stewart's intentions. 8°. pap., 25c... *Burnham.*
— Slaves of the ring. 8°. pap., 25c. ...... *Burnham.*
— *Same.* 8°. $1.25; pap., 75c. .... *Estes.*
— Woman's (A) ransom. 8°. $1.25; pap., 75c... *Estes.*
— *Same.* 12°. '64. $1.50 .... *Burnham.*

Robinson, G: C. Seed-thought: handbook of doctrine and devotion. 12°. '63. $1 .... *Meth. Bk. Conc.*
— Social hymns and tunes for the Meth. Episc. Ch. 18°. '56. 50c. .... *Meth. Bk. Conc.*

Robinson, G: O. New casket: sacred melodies for social and public worship. obl. 8°. hf. bd., $1.25. *Duffie.*

Robinson, *Mrs.* H. M. Practical cook book. 12°. '64. $1.25 .... *Baker, P. & Co.*

Robinson, H: Crabb. Diary, reminiscences and correspondence; sel. and ed. by T: Sadler. 2 v. 12°. '69. $4 .... **Osgood.*
— *Same.* 3d ed., rev. and enl. 2 v. cr. 8°. '72. $6. *Macmillan.*

Robinson, Horatio N. Concise mathematical operations. 8°. '54. shp., $3 .... *Ivison.*
— Conic sections and analytical geometry. 8°. '60. shp., $2.25 .... *Ivison.*
— First lessons in mental and written arithmetic; ed. by S. D. Barr. 18°. '70. bds., 40c. .... *Ivison.*
— Higher arithmetic. ('60.) New ed. 12°. '75. $1.38. — Key, $1.25 .... *Ivison.*
— Intellectual arithmetic. 16°. '58. bds., 40c... *Ivison.*
— Key to geometry and trigonometry, analyt. geometry and conic sections, surveying and navigation; with astron. problems. 8°. shp., $2.25 .. *Ivison.*
— New elementary algebra. 12°. '75. shp., $1.50. — Key, $1.25 .... *Ivison.*
— New geometry and trigonometry. 8°. '62. shp., $2.25; — in 2 v., ea., $1.25 .... *Ivison.*
— New surveying and navigation, with tables; ed. by O. Root. 8°. '63. shp., $2.25 .... *Ivison.*
— New university algebra. 8°. '75. shp., $2.20. — Key, $2.20 .... *Ivison.*
— Practical arithmetic. ('58.) New ed., rev. 12°. '63. bds., 94c. — Key, 90c. .... *Ivison.*
— Primary arithmetic. 16°. '58. bds., 25c. .. *Ivison.*
— Rudiments of written arithmetic. 16°. '52. bds., 43c. .... *Ivison.*
— Table-book. 16°. '62. bds., 20c. .... *Ivison.*
— University astronomy. ('49.) New ed., rev. 8°. '57. shp., $2.75 .... *Ivison.*
— *See also* Ficklin, J., Complete algebra; — Fish, D. W.

Robinson, J. *and* C. Collection of forms used by clerks of courts of law and equity in Virginia; with declarations, indictments, informations and forms o conveyances. 2d ed. 8°. '26. shp., $18. *J. W. Randolph.*

Robinson, J. B. Vines of Eshcol. 12°. 75c. *Un. B. Pub.*

Robinson, J. R. Explosions of steam boilers: how they are caused, and how they may be prevented. 12°. '70. $1.25 .... *Little, B. & Co.*

Robinson, Ja. Whole art of making British wines, cordials, and liqueurs in the greatest perfection, etc. fp. 8°. (Lond.) '48. $1 .... *Spon.*

Robinson, *Miss* Jane. Madeline Graham. 16°. 80c. *Routledge.*
— Whitefriars; or, days of Charles II. 16°. bds., 80c. *Routledge.*
— *Same.* 8°. $1 .... *Peterson.*
— Whitehall; or, times of Oliver Cromwell. 8°. pap., 75c. .... *Peterson.*
— *Same.* 16°. bds., 80c. .... *Routledge.*

Robinson, J: Ferns of Essex Co. [Mass.] 8°. '75. pap., 10c. .... *Essex.*

Robinson, *Rev.* J: Works; with memoir and annotations by Rob. Ashton. 3 v. 12°. $5 ... *Cong. Pub.*

Robinson, *Mrs.* M. Harrison. Helen Erskine. 12°. $1.50 .... *Lippincott.*

Robinson, *Mrs.* Ma. S. The brother ser. ('66–'70.) New ed. 4 v. 18°. '71. $3; ea., 75c... *Tibbals.*
Cont.: Brother soldiers. — Forward the flag. — Great battle year. — Two great captains.

Robinson, Mat. Autobiography; ed. by Rev. J. E. B. Mayor. fp. 8°. $1.75 .... *Macmillan.*

Robinson, Merritt M. *See* Louisiana, Sup. Court reports.

Robinson, Nugent. Miss Tibbit's back hair: farce. 16°. pap., 15c. .... *French.*

Robinson, R: P. Life. *See* Jewett, H., Life.

Robinson, S. H. Bengal sugar planter: cultivation of the sugar cane and date tree in Bengal, and manufacture of sugar and rum therefrom. 8°. (Calcutta.) '49. $2.50 .... *Spon.*

Robinson, S. W. Practical treatise on teeth of wheels, with theory of use of Robinson's odontograph. 18°. '76. bds., 50c. .... *Van Nostrand.*

Robinson, Solon. How to live: saving and wasting; or, domestic economy ill. by life of two families. 12°. $1.25 .... *Wells.*

Robinson, Stuart. Discourses of redemption. 12°. '74. $1.50 .... *N. Y. Ref. Ch. Bd.; Pres. Com.*
— *Same.* 8°. $3 .... *Appleton.*
Robinson, *Mrs.* Thérèse Albertina L. v. J. ["Talvi."] Fifteen years: picture from the last century. [Fiction.] 12°. $1.50 .... *Appleton.*
Robinson, T: Commentary on St. Paul's Epistle to the Romans; with notes. 2 v. 12°. $3 .. *Appleton.*
Robinson, Tod. *See* California, Sup. Court reports.
Robinson, W: S. ["Warrington."] Salary grab (The): hist. of passage of act increasing salaries of members of Congress. 16°. pap., 40c. ...... *Lee & S.*
— Warrington's manual of parliamentary practice. 16°. 75c. .... *Lee & S.*
Robinson Crusoe. *See* Defoe, Dan.
Robinson Crusoe. *See* Evening's entertainment.
Robinson Crusoe. *See* Jack Spraggle's hist. of.
Robinson Crusoe. Pocock, I. 15c. .... *French.*
Robinson Crusoe: burlesque. Byron H. J. 15c. *French.*
Robinson Crusoe. [Toy-book.] ill. 4°. $1; 50c. *Routledge.*
Robinson Crusoe, jr. Adams, W. T. 45c. ... *Lee & S.*
Robinson Crusoe picture-book. demy 4°. '73. $2.50. *Routledge.*
Robinson Crusoe's money. Wells, D. A. $1; 50c. *Harper.*
Robinson, the younger; or, the new Crusoe; tr. from the Germ. ill. 16°. 75c. .... *Routledge.*
Robinson's merkwürdige Abenteuer. 16°. pap., 20c. *Radde.*
Robinsons (The). Bissell, M. L. $1.25 ... *Lothrop.*
Robson, C: (*ed.*) Biographical encyclop. of Illinois of 19th cent. roy. 4°. '75. mor., $25 .... *Robson.*
— Biographical encyclop. of Ohio of 19th cent. roy. 4°. '76. mor., $25 .... *Robson.*
— Biographical encyclop. of Penna. of 19th cent. ('74.) 2d ed. roy. 4°. '76. mor., $25 .... *Robson.*
— Manufactories and manufacturers of Penna. of 19th cent. roy. 4°. '75. mor., $25 .... *Robson.*
Robson, W: Great sieges of history. ill. cr. 8°. $2. *Routledge.*
— Life of Cardinal Richelieu. New ed. ill. 12°. '74. $1.75 .... *Routledge.*
Robson, W: Ja. Love and loyalty: play. 16°. pap., 15c. .... *French.*
Roby, H: J: Grammar of the Lat. lang. from Plautus to Suetonius. 2 pts. 12°. '74. pt. 1, $2.50; 2, $3.50 .... *Macmillan.*
Roby, Ma. K. Story of a household, and other poems. fp. 8°. $1.50 .... *Macmillan.*
Roby family. *See* Tucker, C.
Robyn, H: The classical singer: 4th pt. of Singer's handbook. obl. 12°. 60c. .... *Witter.*
— The singer's handbook. 3 v. obl. 12°. '72-'74. bds., bk. 1, 30c.; bk. 2, 40c.; bk. 3, 50c. .... *Witter.*
— *and* Berg, F. Der junge Sänger. 2 v. obl. 12°. '72-'74. bds., 1, 35c.; 2, 50c. .... *Witter.*
Roccambole. Suter, W. E. 15c. .... *French.*
Roccus, Franciscus. Manual of maritime law; [also] Treatise on insurance; tr. with notes by J. R. Ingersoll. 8°. 1809. $1.50 .. *T. & J. W. Johnson.*
Roche, Regina Mar. Children of the abbey. 8°. pap., 25c. .... *Lippincott.*
— *Same.* 12°. $1 .... *Hurd & H.; Lippincott.*
— *Same.* 12°. $1.50 .... *Sadlier.*
— *Same.* 12°. $1; hf. cf., $3 .... *Porter.*
— *Same.* cr. 8°. $1.50; hf. cf., $3.50 ...... *Appleton.*
Rochefoucauld, François (*Duc*) de la. *See* La Rochefoucauld.
Rochester, *N. Y.* Church book of St. Peter's [Presb.] Church. 8°. '68. $2 .... *Darrow.*
Rochester. Moncrieff, W. T. 15c. .... *French.*
Rochester. Smith, J. F. 75c. .... *Dick & F.*
Rocholl, H: T. Catholic vocalist: collection of sacred music. 5 nos. 8°. '60. ea., pap., 50c. .. *Ditson.*
Rochsa, N. C. First six weeks for the harp. f°. bds., $3 .... *Willig.*
Rock, Dan. Textile fabrics. ill. cr. 8°. '75. $1. *Scribner, W. & A.*
Rock ahead. *See* Yates, Edm.
Rock Allen, the orphan. Wilkins, W. H. 15c. .. *Ames.*
Rock Cottage; or, the summer vacation. 18°. 40c. *Cong. Pub.*
Rock light. Hervey, E. L. $1 .... *Scribner, W. & A.*
Rock of ages. *See* Bickersteth, E. H.
Rock of ages. Smith, S. F. $1.50; $2 .... *Lothrop.*
Rock of ages lib. 3 v. 4°. $6 .... *Lothrop.*
Cont.: Rock of ages, by S. F. Smith. — Morning and night watches, by J. R. Macduff; Quiet hour, by H. Lincoln. — Mind and words of Jesus *and* Faithful promiser, by J. R. Macduff.
Rock of faith in contrast with quicksands of mod. skepticism. Morrison, J. 65c. .... *Am. Bapt.*
Rock of our salvation. Plumer, W. S. $1.50; $1.75. *Am. Tr.*
Rock-a-bye lib. ill. sq. 12°. per doz., pap., 90c.; col. ill., per doz., $1.50 .... *Thompson.*
Rockbourne. Weir, M. E. $1.25 .... *Carter.*
Rockburn lib. 3 v. 16°. $4.50 .... *Lothrop.*
Cont.: Stella and the priest. — Miss Wealthy's hope. — Their children.
Rocket. Knight, H. C. 40c. .... *Am. Tr.*
Rocks ahead. Greg, W. R. $2 .... * *Osgood.*
Rocks and shoals. Hepworth, G. H. 60c. .. *Am. Unit.*
Rockwell, A. D. *See* Beard, G. M., *and* Rockwell, A. D.
Rockwell, C: Catskill Mountains and the regions around: their scenery, legends and history. 16°. $1.50 .... *Taintor.*
Rockwell, J. E. Diamond in the cage. 16°. $1.15. *Pres. Bd.*
— Sheet anchor. 32°. 10c. .... *Pres. Bd.*
— Sketches of the Presb. Church. 18°. 65c. .. *Pres. Bd.*
— Visitor's [S.-school] questions. 18°. 20c. .. *Pres. Bd.*
— Young Christian warned; or, pastoral counsels against conformity to the world. 18°. 50c. *Pres. Bd.*
Rockwell, J: A. Compilation of Span. and Mexican law in rel. to mines and titles to real estate, in force in California and New Mexico, and in territories acquired under the Louisiana and Florida treaties. 8°. shp., $7.50 .... *Baker, V. & Co.*
Rockwell, *Mrs.* M. E. Rose Thorpe's ambition. 16°. '71. $1.25 .... *Garrigues.*
— Tom Miller; or, after many days. 16°. '67. $1.25. *Garrigues.*
Rocky hill and rolling prairie. Nutting, J. K. $1.50. *Cong. Pub.*
Rocky hill ser. 4 v. 16°. $6 .... *Cong. Pub.*
Cont.: Rocky hill, by J. K. Nutting. — Two boys, by A. McKenzie. — Norman Cline, by E. Kellogg. — Mother Anthony's family.
Rocky island, and other parables. 18°. 30c. .. *Dutton.*
Rocky mountain Rob. Aiken, A. W. 20c. ... *Beadle.*
Rocky mountain saints. Stenhouse, T. B. H. *$5; $6; $7.50 .... *Appleton.*
Rocky mountain ser. *See* Fosdick, C. A.
Roddy's romance. Johnson, H. K. $1.25 .. *Putnam.*
Rode, P. *See* Baillot, P., Rode, P., *and* Kreutzer, R.
Rodenbough, Thdr. F. From everglade to cañon with the 2d U. S. Cavalry: account of service in Florida, Mexico, Virginia and the Indian country, incl. recollections of officers, anecdotes, ballads, etc. ill. roy. 8°. '75. $7.50 .. *Van Nostrand.*
Roderick Hudson. James, H., *jr.* $2 ...... *Osgood.*
Roderick Random. *See* Smollett, T.
Rodgers, G: Gospel according to Moses, as seen in the tabernacle and its various services. New ed. 18°. '75. 75c.; bds., 50c. .... *Revell.*

Rodgers, M. H. Elements of mensuration. 12°. hf. bd., 60c. — Key. 12°. hf. bd., 60c. ..... *Butler.*
— Note book of arith. rules and definitions used in the Girls' High and Normal School, Philadelphia. 16°. *net*, hf. bd., 25c. .... *Butler.*
Rodman. Swerdna, A. 40c. .... *Dutton.*
Rodney, *Mrs.* Marion R. L. [*formerly Miss* Reeves; "Fadette"]. Sea drift. ('69.) New ed. 18°. '75. 90c. .... *Claxton.*
— Wearithorne; or, in the light of to-day. 12°. $1.50. *Lippincott.*
Rodney, Rob. Burton. Alboin and Rosamond, and lesser poems. sq. 16°. $1.25 .... *Lippincott.*
Rodney Dennis. *See* Mudge, Z. A.
Rodney Roverton. 18°. 45c.; 55c. .... *Am.Bapt.*
Rodolphus. Abbott, J. 90c. .... *Harper.*
Rodrigues, J. C. Chrestomathia: Eng. reader for Portuguese. 12°. '70. $1.75 .... *Barnes.*
Rodriguez, Alphonsus. Practice of Christian and religious perfection. 3 v. 8°. $4 .... *Strong.*
Rodwell, G: F. Birth of chemistry. ill. 12°. '74. $1 .... *Macmillan.*
— Dictionary of science: astronomy, chemistry, dynamics, etc.; with essay on hist. of the physical sciences. ill. 8°. $5 .... *Lea; Lippincott.*
Rodwell, G: Herb. [Plays.] 4 v. 16°. ea., pap., 15c. .... *French.*

Cont.: I'll be your second: farce. — My wife's out: farce. — Teddy, the tiler: farce. — Was I to blame? farce.

— My wife's out: farce. 16°. pap., 15c. ..... *De Witt.*
Rodwell, T: G. More blunders than one: farce. 16°. pap., 15c. .... *French.*
— Race for a dinner: farce. 16°. pap., 15c. *De Witt; French.*
— Young widow: farce. 16°. pap., 15c. ..... *French.*
Rody, the rover: a tale of Ireland. 8°. pap., 25c. *Peterson.*
Roe, Azel S. [Novels.] 6 v. 12°. ea., $1.50 .. *Carleton.*

Cont.: How could he help it?—I've been thinking; or, James Montjoy. — Long look ahead. — Star and the cloud. — To love and to be loved. — True to the last.

Roe, E: Payson. [Novels.] 4 v. 12°. '73–'75. ea., $1.75 .... *Dodd.*

Cont.: Barriers burned away. — From jest to earnest. — Opening of the chestnut burr. — What can she do?

— Manual on culture of small fruits. 8°. '76. pap., 50c. .... *Roe.*
— Play and profit in my garden. 12°. $1.50 .... *Judd.*
Roe, Fs. A. Naval duties and discipline; with the policy and principles of naval organization. 12°. '65. $1.50 .... *VanNostrand.*
Roe, W: M. Bible vs. materialism. 12°. pap., 50c. *Chase.*
Roebling, J: A. Long and short span railway bridges; with copper-pl. imp. f°. '69. $25 .. *VanNostrand.*
— Memoir of the Niagara Falls and international suspension bridge; [also] The Paddock viaduct, by J. Hawkshaw; [also] The Denby Dale viaduct, by J. Hawkshaw; [also] Newark dyke bridge, by J. Cubitt; [also] Mountain top track in Va., by E. Ellet; [also] Preliminaries to good building, by E. Garbett. ill. roy. 8°. (Weale.) '56. $5 .... *Spon.*
Roehm, Ph. *See* Witter's [arithmetics].
Roemer, J. Cavalry: its history, management and uses in war. ill. 8°. '63. $6; hf. cf., $7.50. *VanNostrand.*
— First French reader. 12°. $1.50 .... *Appleton.*
— Second French reader. 12°. $1.50 ...... *Appleton.*
— French dictionary of English idioms. 12°. '53. $2. *G.R.Lockwood.*
— Polyglot reader and guide for translation; to serve as a mutual key. 5 v. 12°. ea., $1.50 .. *Appleton.*

Cont.: 1. English text, by J. Roemer. — 2. French tr., by J. Roemer. — 3. German tr., by R. Solgez. — 4. Spanish tr., by S. Camacho. — 5. Italian tr., by V. Botta.

Rogation; or, the lightning legion: story of the Christian church in 2d cent.; tr. by F. H. Smith. ill. 16°. 75c. .... *Ref.Ch.Pub.*
Roger *of Hoveden.* Annals of Eng. hist., A.D. 732–1201; ed. by H. T. Riley. 2 v. 12°. (Bohn.) ea., $1.75 .... *Little,B.& Co.*
— *Same.* 2 v. 12°. (Bohn.) ea., $2. *Lippincott; Scribner, W.& A.*
Roger *of Wendover.* Flowers of Eng. hist. *See* Matthew *Paris*, Chronicle.
Roger, Henri. *See* Barth, J. P. B., *and* Roger, H.
Roger Bernard. Taylor, G. B. $1 .... *Am.Bapt.*
Roger Kyffyn's ward. Kingston, W. H. G. $1.75. *Routledge.*
Roger Miller. 18°. 50c. .... *Carter.*
Roger O'Donnell. 8°. pap., 25c. .... *De Witt.*
Roger's apprenticeship. Marshall, E. 50c. ... *Carter.*
Rogers, A: C. Our representatives abroad. ('74.) 2d ed. ill. 4°. '76. $10; hf. cf., $15; mor., $20 .... *Atlantic.*
— Sketches of representative men, north and south. ('72.) 3d ed. ill. 4°. '75–'76. $10; hf. cf., $15; mor., $20 .... *Atlantic.*
Rogers, *Miss* B. C. Twilight stories. ill. 18°. '75. 50c. .... *Am.Tr.*
Rogers, Dan. New York City Hall recorder, 1816–'21. [Criminal cases.] 6 v. in 3. 8° .... *State.*
Rogers, Eb. Platt. Everything in Christ. 12°. 60c.; $1 .... *N.Y.Ref.Ch.Bd.*
— Glory of New York: discourse in South Reform. Ch., Nov. 26, 1874. 8°. '74. pap., 25c. ... *U.S.Pub.*
— Precious things of St. Peter. sq. 18°. '74. $1.25; $1.50 .... *Randolph.*
— Prodigal son. 18°. '62. 25c. .... *Am.Tr.*
— Syrian leper. 18°. '67. 25c. .... *Am.Tr.*
Rogers, G: Adventures of Elder Triptolemus Tub; compr. important and startling disclosures conc. hell, etc.; [also] Old man of the hill-side. 18°. '46. 65c. .... *Universalist.*
— Pro and con of Universalism. 12°. $1.25 .. *Williamson.*
Rogers, H: Essays from "Good Words." 12°. $1.75. *Routledge.*
— Life and character of J: Howe; with anal. of his writings. 12°. $1.50 .... *Nelson.*
— Superhuman origin of the Bible inferred from itself. 12°. '75. $2 .... *Scribner.*
Rogers, H: Darwin. Geology of Penna.: gov't survey; with gen. view of geol. of U. S., essays on coal formation, etc. 3 v. and portfolio of maps. ill. and pl. 4°. '58. $30 .... *Van Nostrand.*
— *See also* New Jersey geol. survey; — Pennsylvania geol. survey.
Rogers, Hester Ann. Journal. 16°. '61. 75c. *Meth.Bk.Conc.*
— Life. 18°. '37. 65c. .... *Meth.Bk.Conc.*
— *Swed.* 18°. '54. 65c. .... *Meth.Bk.Conc.*
— Life and correspondence; with add., and with introd. by T. O. Summers. ('57.) 3d ed. 18°. '76. 75c. *So.Meth.*
Rogers, J. E. Ridicula rediviva: old nursery rhymes. col. ill. obl. f°. '70. $2 .... *Macmillan.*
Rogers, Ja. Edn. Thorold. Cobden and political opinion. 8°. '73. $4 .... *Macmillan.*
— Historical gleanings. 2 ser. cr. 8°. '69–'70. ea., $1.75 .... *Macmillan.*

Cont.: Montague, Walpole, Adam Smith, Cobbett. — Wicklif, Laud, Wilkes, Horne Tooke.

— Social economy. 12°. '71. 75c. .... *Putnam.*
Rogers, J: Biography of John T. Johnson. por. 12°. $1. *Chase.*
— Life and writings. *See* British reformers.
Rogers, Jos. M. Principles and practice of fire underwriting, systematically arranged. ('71.) 3d ed., rev. and enl. 8°. '75. $2 .... *Spectator.*

Rogers, Ma. E. Domestic life in Palestine. 12°. $1.75. *Cin. Meth. Bk. Conc.*
— — *See also* Inquiring Christian's lib.
Rogers, R. Vashon, *jr.* Law of the road; or, wrongs and rights of a traveller: v. 4 of "Legal recreations." 12°. $1.50 .... *S. Whitney.*
Rogers, S: Poetical works. ill. 12°. '76. $1.50. *World Pub.*
— *Same.* por. 12°. '71. $1.50; hf. cf., $3.50 .. *Putnam.*
— *Same.* (Household ser.) por. 16°. $1.50; mor., $3. *Lee & S.*
— *Same;* ill. by Turner and Stothard. 4°. $12; mor., $18 .... *Routledge.*
Same; [also] Poetical works of Campbell, Montgomery, Lamb and Kirke White. ill. 8°. $3; mor., $7; $7.50 .... *Lippincott.*
— Poems. (Presentation poets.) ill. 16°. $1.75; $3. *Routledge.*
— *Same;* ed. by R. A. Willmott; with biog., etc. (British poets.) ill. 12°. $2.25; hf. cf., $3.50; mor., $5 .... *Routledge.*
— — *See also* Cowper, W: Poems.
— Pleasures of memory. ill. 12°. '75. $1.25 .. *Putnam.*
— — *See also* Poems of pleasures.
Rogers, W: B. *See* Virginia geol. survey.
Rogers, W: Price. Lessons in right and wrong. 16°. '64. 75c. .... *H. H. Carter.*
Roget, P: M: Animal and vegetable physiology. 2 v. ill. 12°. (Bohn.) ea., $2.25 ...... *Little, B. & Co.*
— *Same.* (Bridgewater treatise.) 2 v. ill. 12°. (Bohn.) ea., $2.40 .... *Scribner, W. & A.*
— — *Same.* 2 v. ill. 12°. (Bohn.) ea., $2.50. *Lippincott.*
— Thesaurus of Eng. words and phrases; rev., with list of foreign words defined in Eng., etc., by B. Sears. 12°. $2 .... *Sheldon.*
Rogueries of Scapin. *See* Molière, J. B. P. de.
Rogues and rogueries of New York. ill. 12°. pap., 25c. .... *Haney.*
Rohbock, H. Instructions for the piano-forte. 4°. '44. bds., $2.50 .... *Ditson.*
Rohden, L. v. Johannes, der Täufer. *See* Duncan, W: C., Life of John the Baptist.
Röhling, A: Antichrist (Der) u. das Ende der Welt. 8°. '75. pap., 40c. .... *Herder.*
— Louise Lateau: her stigmas and ecstasy; tr. by W. J. Walsh. 8°. '76. pap., 25c. .... *Hickey.*
— Medulla theologiæ moralis. 8°. '75. $2 .... *Herder.*
Rohr, Ph. H. Catholic melodies for church, school and home. 16°. 40c. .... *Noonan.*
— First lessons in music, and book of favorite melodies for children. 12°. '53. pap., 20c. ...... *Ditson.*
Rohrer, L: Lectures on book-keeping; for teachers. 8°. '75. pap., $1 .... *Gilbert.*
— Primary book-keeping. 8°. '75. pap., 50c... *Gilbert.*
— School ed. book-keeping. 8°. '73. $1.50... *Gilbert.*
Rohrer, Mt. M. Practical calculator: pocket manual of plain rules and calculations for business operations. 18°. 63c.; $1.25 .... *Lippincott.*
Röhrig, F: L: O. Shortest road to German; for teachers and students. 12°. '74. $1.50 ...... *Andrus.*
Rojas, Marco A. El reino animal segun la clasificacion de Cuvier. ill. 12°. $2 .... *Appleton.*
Rokeby. *See* Scott, *Sir* Wa.
Rokitansky, C: Pathological anatomy: abnormal conditions of organs of respiration; tr. and enl. by J. C. Peters. 8°. 75c. .... *Boericke.*
Roland and his friend. *See* Pyle, M. C.
Roland Cashel. *See* Lever, C:
Roland for an Oliver. Morton, T. 15c. ...... *French.*
Roland Yorke. Wood, E. P. $1.75; $1.50 .. *Peterson.*
Rolfe, W: Ja. *See* Goldsmith, O.; — Gray, T.; — Hanson, J. H., *and* Rolfe, W. J.; — Ovid; — Shakespeare, W.
Rolfe, W: Ja., *continued.*
— *and* Gillet, J. H. Cambridge course of physics. 3 v. 12°. ea., $2 .... *Potter, A. & Co.*
Cont.: Chemistry. — Philosophy. — Astronomy.
— — Handbook ser. 3 v. 12° .... *Potter, A. & Co.*
Cont.: Handbook of chemistry, $1.25 — of philosophy, $1.25 — of astronomy, $1.60.
Roll of the drum. *See* Wilks, T. E.
Rolleston, G: Harveian oration, 1873. cr. 8°. $1. *Macmillan.*
Rollin, C. V. Masonic text book. ('70.) New ed. 16°. '72. $1.50. 12°. $2.50 .... *Tuttle.*
Rollin, C: Ancient history; tr. from the Fr. 4 v. in 2. ill. 8°. ea., $2; shp., $2.75 .... *World Pub.*
— *Same.* Rev. ed. 4 v. 8°. '75. $10; shp., $12; hf. cf., $18 .... *Claxton.*
— *Same;* with life of author. 2 v. roy. 8°. shp., $6. *Pounsford.*
— *Same;* with life of author by J. Bell. 2 v. maps and ill. 8°. $4.50; shp., $5.50; — in 1 v., shp., $4. *Harper.*
Rollin, *Miss* Fk. R. Life and public services of Martin R. Delany. 12°. *$2 .... *Lee & S.*
Rolling stone (A). *See* Sand, G:
Rollo books; — code of morals; — in the woods; — story books. *See* Abbott, Jac.
Rollo's garden; — tour in Europe. *See* Abbott, Jac.
Rollwyn, J. A. S. Astronomy simplified for general reading; with discoveries in spectral analysis. ill. 8°. $4.50 .... *Scribner, W. & A.*
Rolph, Hiram. Normal system of penmanship. 6 bks. obl. 4°. per doz., $1.80 .... *Adams, B. & L.*
— Review book. obl. 4°. 40c. .... *Adams, B. & L.*
— Specimen book. obl. 4°. pap., 10c... *Adams, B. & L.*
Roly and Poly story books. Chester, S. E. $1.50. *Randolph.*
Romain Kalbris. Malot, H. $1.50 .... *Porter.*
Romaine, W: Life, walk and triumph of faith. 12°. $1 .... *U. P. Bd. of Pub.*
— *Same.* 16°. $1.25 .... *Carter; Routledge.*
— On intercessory prayer; with biog. sketch by J. Forsyth. 18°. pap., 10c. .... *Pres. Bd.*
Roman actor. Massinger, P. 15c. .... *French.*
Roman Catholic church. *See* Catholic church.
Roman Catholic not "the only true religion," etc. Peterson, R. E. 75c. .... *Lippincott.*
Roman d'un jeune homme pauvre. *See* Feuillet, O.
Roman elegies. *See* Goethe, J. W. v.
Roman imperialism. Seeley, J. R. $1.50 .. *Roberts.*
Roman lawyer in Jerusalem. Story, W. W. 10c. *Colby.*
Roman martyrology. New ed. 8°. '69. *net*, $2.50. *Kelly, P. & Co.*
Roman traitor. Herbert, H. W. $1.75; $1.50 .. *Peterson.*
Roman vesperal. Maugin, C. $1.50 .... *Murphy.*
Romance after marriage. Goodrich, F. B., *and* Warden, F. L. 15c. .... *French.*
Romance and its hero; by author of "Magdalen Stafford." 12°. $1.25 .... *Harper.*
Romance and reality. Brougham, J. 15c. .. *French.*
Romance of adventure. *See* Grant, Ja.
Romance of the age. Dunbar, E. E. $1.25 .. *Appleton.*
Romance of Am. hist. DeVere, M. S. $1.50 .. *Putnam.*
Romance of astronomy. Miller, R. K. $1.25. *Macmillan.*
Romance of Beauseincourt. Warfield, C. A. $2. *Appleton.*
Romance of charity. De Liefde, J. B. $2.50 .. *Routledge.*
Romance of the charter oak: hist. novel. 12°. $2.25. *O'Shea.*
Romance of the English stage. Fitzgerald, P. $2. *Lippincott.*
Romance of the forest. Radcliffe, A. $1.50 .. *Claxton.*

Romance of the green seal. Warfield, C. A. 25c. *Beadle.*

Romance of the harem. *See* Leonowens, A. H.

Romance of the harem. Pardoe, J. 75c... *Peterson.*

Romance of history. 5 v. cr. 8°. ea., $1; $2.50; pap., 75c. .... *Scribner, W. & A.*

Cont.: England, by H. Neale. — France, by L. Ritchie. — Spain, by T. de Trueba. — Italy, by C. Macfarlane. — India, by Rev. H. Caunter.

Romance of an honest woman. Cherbuliez, V. $1.50. *W. F. Gill.*

Romance of London. Timbs, J. 2 v. ea., $1.75; $3.75; $5 .... *Scribner, W. & A.*

Romance of matrimony. Lewis, E. $1.50.. *Challen.*

Romance of missions. West, M. A. $2 .. *Randolph.*

Romance of natural history. Gosse, P. H. $1.25. *Lippincott.*

Romance of old court-life in France. Elliot, F. $2; $1.50 .... *Appleton.*

Romance of perfume lands. Clifford, F. S. $2.50; 50c.................................. *Clifford.*

Romance of a poor young man. *See* Feuillet, O.

Romance of railroad. Smith, S. $1.50.... *Carleton.*

Romance of the republic. Child, L. M. $2.. *Osgood.*

Romance of the revolution. Bunce, O. $1.25.. *Porter.*

Romance of student life. Kimball, R. B. $1.75. *Carleton.*

Romance of travel: sketches and adventures in foreign countries. ill. 12°. $1.25 .... *T. Bliss.*

Romance of war. *See* Grant, Ja.

Romance of western hist. Hall, J. $2...... *Clarke.*

Romance under difficulties. Burnand, F. C. 15c. *French.*

Romance-without fiction. Bleby, H. $1.75. *Meth. Bk. Conc.*

Romances and realities. Barr, A. E. $1.50 .. *Ford.*

Romanes, G: J. Christian prayer and general laws; with app. on physical efficacy of prayer. (Burney prize essay, 1873.) cr. 8°. $1.75.... *Macmillan.*

Romanism as it is. Barnum, S. W. *$3.50; $4; $5. *Conn. Pub.*

Romanism as it is. Cumming, J. 10c...... *Pres. Bd.*

Romanism at home. Murray, N. $1.50.... *Harper.*

Romanism the enemy of liberty. 18°. pap., 10c. *Pres. Bd.*

Romanism in Rome. *See* Alford, H.

Romanoff, H. C. Sketches of rites and customs of the Greco-Russian Church; with introd. by C. M. Yonge. 12°. '69. $3.................... *Pott.*

Romans and Danes; or, England's early days. 16°. 50c......................... *Scribner, W. & A.*

Romantic attachment. Wood, A. 15c. *Ames; French.*

Romantic Belinda. Tuthill, L. C. $1... *Perkinpine.*

Romantic fiction. La Motte Fouqué, F. H. K. $1.25. *Routledge.*

Romantic idea. Planché, J. R. 15c. .... *French.*

Romantic incidents in lives of queens of Eng. Smith, J. F. $1.50........................ *Dick & F.*

Romantic legend of Sakya Buddha. Beal, S. $6. *Scribner, W. & A.*

Romany Rye. Borrow, G. 75c........... *Harper.*

Romanzero. *See* Heine, H.

Romaunt, Cp. Island home; or, the young castaways. ill. 16°. '74. $1.50 .... *Lothrop.*

Romberg, And. Harmony of the spheres. [Music.] obl. 4°. 50c.......................... *Gordon.*

— Power of song. [Music.] obl. 4°. 65c.... *Gordon.*

— Song of the bell [by Schiller]; tr. and adapted to music of Romberg by S. A. Eliot. 2d ed. obl. 4°. '51. bds., 80c............. *Ditson; Gordon.*

— Transient and eternal; with organ or piano accomp. by V. Novello. obl. 4°. pap., 38c. *Ditson; Gordon.*

Romberg, Bern. Theoretical and practical school for the violoncello. 4°. bds., $3; — abridg. f°. '55. bds., $2.25.......................... *Ditson.*

Rome: its edifices and its people. 12°. '52. $1. *Meth. Bk. Conc.*

Rome against the Bible. Plumer, W. S. 40c. *Am. Bapt.*

Rome and the abbey. 12°. $1.25; $1.75.... *Sadlier.*

Rome and the campagna. Burn, R. $1.25.. *Macmillan.*

Rome and the council in the 19th cent. Bungener, L. F. $2.50..................... *Scribner, W. & A.*

Rome and its ruler. Maguire, J. F. $2..... *Sadlier.*

Rome and the newest fashions in religion. Gladstone, W. E. $1.75......................... *Harper.*

Rome and the papacy. Gattina, F. P. della. $1.75; $1.50................................ *Peterson.*

Rome and the popes. Brandes, K. $1.25.. *Benziger.*

Rome as it is. Scott, H. R. $1.50....... *Lippincott.*

Rome, Christian and papal. De Sanctis, L. $1.50. *Harper.*

Rome in 19th century. *See* Eaton, C. A.

Romeo and Juliet. *See* Gounod, C. F.

Romeo and Juliet. *See* Shakespeare, W:

Romeo and Juliet: burlesque. Halliday, A. 15c. *French.*

Romeo u. Julie. [Fiction.] 12°. pap., 15c... *Radde.*

Romish confessional (The). Michelet, J. 50c. *Peterson.*

Romneys of Ridgemont. Eastman, J. A. $1.50. *Lothrop.*

Romola. *See* Eliot, G:

Romp. Bickerstaff, I. 15c. .... *French.*

Romulus and Remus: burlesque. 16°. pap., 15c. *French.*

Ronald Cameron. *See* Witt, *Mme.* H. de.

Ronald Morton. Kingston, W. H. G. $1.75.. *Routledge.*

Ronald's reason; or, the little cripple. sq. 12°. '68. pap., 50c........................ *Meth. Bk. Conc.*

Ronayne, Edm. Handbook of Freemasonry. 12°. '75. pap., 50c...................... *E. A. Cook.*

Rondinella, Pasquale. Exercise du chant. f°. 35c. *Gordon.*

— Fifty vocalises; from "Art of singing." f°. pap., 60c................................ *Ditson.*

— Fundamental rules for study of harmony. obl. 12°. 40c................................ *Ditson.*

— Introduction to art of singing. f°. '54. pap., $1.25. *Ditson.*

— Preparatory lessons in art of singing. f°. bds., $3; — pt. 1, $2 .... *Ditson.*

— Seventy-six exercises of vocalization; in tables. f°. $1 .... *Gordon.*

— Sixty-five progressive exercises for cultivation of the voice: pt. 2 of "Preparatory lessons." f°. pap., $1.50 .... *Ditson.*

— Twelve vocalising melodies for study of various embellishments in singing. f°. '72. pap., $1.50. *Ditson.*

Rondthaler, E: Life of John Heckewelder; ed. by B. H. Coates. 8°. '47. 75c........... *Clauder.*

Ronger, Florimond. ["Hervé."] Chilperic. [Opera.] 4°. '74. $1............................ *Pond.*

Rood, Ogden N. Mysteries of the voice and ear. ill. 12°. '73. pap., 25c. .... *VanNostrand.*

Roof scrambler. A'Becket, G. A. 15c....... *French.*

Rook (The). 18°. 40c..................... *Dutton.*

Rookstone. Macquoid, K. S. $1.25; 75c... *Lippincott.*

Rookwood. *See* Ainsworth, W: H.

Rooms to let: Ethiop. drama. 16°. pap., 15c. *French; Happy.*

Rooper, G: Flood, field and forest. ill. 12°. '74. $2 .... *Routledge.*

Roosa, Dan. B. St. J: Anniversary discourse before N. Y. Acad. of Med. 8°. '74. pap., 15c. *N. Y. Acad. Med.*

Roosa, Dan. B. St. J: *continued.*
— Memoranda of ophthalmology and otology. 32°. $1. *W. Wood.*
— Practical treatise on diseases of the ear, incl. [its] anatomy. ill. 8°. $5; leath., $6...... *W. Wood.*
— Vest-pocket medical lexicon. 64°. 75c.; $1.. *W. Wood.*
Roosevelt, Rob. B. Five acres too much. ill. 12°. $1.50.................................. *Harper.*
— Progressive petticoats: satirical tale. 12°. $1.50. *Carleton.*
Root, F. W. School of singing. 4°. $3.... *Church.*
— Song era. [Sing. book.] 8°. 75c......... *Church.*
— *and* Murray, J. R. Pacific glee book. obl. 16°. $1.25................................ *Church.*
Root, G: F: Belshazzar's feast; or, fall of Babylon. [Cantata.] 8°. '60. pap., 50c......... *Ditson.*
— Bugle call. 8°. 35c....................... *Church.*
— Cabinet organ companion. 12°. 75c....... *Church.*
— Chapel gems. sq. 12°. bds., 35c.; pap., 30c... *Church.*
— Choir and congregation hymn book. 16°. 50c.; bds., 35c.—sq. 8°. $2; bds., $1.50.......... *Church.*
— Diapason: collection of church music. obl. 8°. '60. bds., $1.50.............................. *Ditson.*
— Flower queen; or, coronation of the rose. [Cantata.] obl. 12°. '52. bds., 75c.—Libretto, 12c... *Ditson.*
— Forest choir. [School music.] 16°. 60c... *Church.*
— Glory (The). [Hymn book.] 8°. $1.50.. *Church.*
— Guide for the piano forte. 12°. 75c........ *Church.*
— Haymakers. [Cantata.] obl. 4°. '57. pap., $1.. *Ditson.*
— Hour of praise. [Hymn book.] 8°. 50c... *Church.*
— Männerchor. obl. 8°. 75c.................. *Church.*
— Model organ method. 4°. $2.50........... *Church.*
— Musical album: vocal class book. obl. 12°. '55. bds., $1................................ *Ditson.*
— Musical fountain. [Sing. book.] 12°. 35c... *Church.*
— New coronet. 8°. $1.25..................... *Church.*
— New musical curriculum. [Piano forte method.] 4°. $3....................................... *Church.*
— Normal musical handbook. 8°. $3....... *Church.*
— Pilgrim fathers; with words by G. F. Root and Miss F. J. Crosby. [Cantata.] obl. 8°. '54. pap., 50c.. *Ditson.*
— Prize. [S.-school music.] obl. 32°. 35c... *Church.*
— Sabbath bell: music for choirs, etc. obl. 8°. '56. bds., $1.50.............................. *Ditson.*
— School for the melodeon, harmonium and cabinet organ. 4°. '63. bds., $2.50............ *Ditson.*
— Silver chime. [S.-school sing. book.] obl. 24°. 60c.; pap., 30c.; bds., 35c............ *Gordon.*
— Silver lute. [School music.] 16°. 50c.... *Church.*
— Triumph. [Hymn book.] 8°. '68. $1.50.. *Church.*
— Trumpet of reform. 12°. 50c............. *Church.*
— *See also* Shawm (The).
— *and* Bradbury, W: B. Book of cantatas. obl. 8°. bds., $1.50................................ *Ditson.*
— — Daniel; or, the captivity and restoration; with words by C. M. Cady and Miss F. J. Crosby. [Cantata.] obl. 8°. pap., 50c. .... *Ditson.*
— — Festival glee book. ('59.) New ed., rev. and enl. obl. 4°. bds., $2.25.............. *Ditson.*
— *and* Mason, Lowell. Academy vocalist; with element. instruction. obl. 16°. '52. bds., $1.. *Ditson.*
— — Young men's singing book. obl. 8°. '55. bds., $1.50.................................. *Ditson.*
Root, Ja. P. General statutes of Ill. on law of corporations; with forms for organization of joint stock companies, etc., and for religious and other corporations. 12°. '72. shp., $1.50.. *E.B.Myers.*
Root, Mcs. A. Philosophical theory and practice of penmanship. 12 nos. obl. 8°. per doz., $1.80.. *Moss.*
Root, N. W. Taylor. Contraband Christmas. ill. 16°. '60. 75c..................................... *Dutton.*
— National school singer. large 16°. '75. hf. bd., 35c. *Barnes.*
— Our song-birds. 4 nos. 16°. ea., 20c. .... *Barnes.*
— School amusements; or, how to make the school interesting. ill. 12°. '57. $1.50........ *Barnes.*

Root, O., *jr.* *See* Campbell, L. J., *and* Root, O., *jr.*
Roothaan, J: Method of meditation. 18°. 50c. *Sadlier.*
Roper, R. S. D., *and* White, H. H. Treatise on law of legacies; with ref. to Am. cases. 2d Am. ed. 2 v. 8°. *net*, shp., $15.................... *Kay.*
Roper, Ste. Catechism of high pressure, or non-condensing steam engines. ('73.) 8th ed. ill. 16°. '76. $2................................ *Claxton.*
— Handbook of land and marine engines. ill. 12°. '75. $3.50.................................... *Claxton.*
— Handbook of the locomotive. ('74.) 4th ed. ill. 16°. '75. $2.50............................ *Claxton.*
— Handbook of mod. steam fire-engines, incl. running, care and management of steam fire-engines and fire-pumps. ill. 12°. '76. $3.50....... *Claxton.*
Ropes, C: J. H. Morality of the Greeks as shown by their literature, art and life. roy. 8°. pap., 75c. *Taintor.*
Ropes of sand. *See* Hamilton, *Mrs.* C. V.
Ropp, Chr., *jr.* Commercial calculator; for farmers, mechanics, business men, etc. ('69.) 6th ed. 18°. '76. $1; mor., $1.50; leath., $2... *Ropp.*
Roquette, O. See Gallerie deutscher Dichter.
Rorer, D: Treatise on law of judicial and execution sales. 2d ed. 8°. '73. shp., $6..... *Callaghan.*
Rory O'More. *See* Lover, S:
Rosa. *Se* Peressensé, *Mme.* E. de.
Rosa: sequel to "Two brothers." ('63.) 7th ed. ill. 18°. '71. 63c.................... *Perkinpine.*
Rosa, the little cousin from India. 32°. 20c.; 15c. *Dutton.*
Rosa Abbott stories. *See* Parker, R. A.
Rosa Bell, the prince's victim. 8°. pap., 25c... *De Witt.*
Rosa dell' Alpi. Ongaro, F. dall'. 75c......... *Holt.*
Rosa immaculata. Marie Josephine. $2; $3.. *O'Shea.*
Rosa Lambert. Reynolds, G. W. M. $1.75; $1. *Peterson.*
Rosa Lane: short stories in short words. 18°. 45c. *Am.S.S.*
Rosa Lindesay, the light of Kilmain. 16°. $1.. *Am.Bapt.*
— *See also* Glen Elder books.
Rosa mystica. Marie Josephine. $2; $3.... *O'Shea.*
Rosa v. Tannenburg. *See* Schmid, C. v.
Rosa Woodville. Dumas, A. 75c.......... *Dick & F.*
Rosabella; or, the queen of May. 18°. 22c... *Am.S.S.*
Rosales, Geronimo. Caton cristiano y catecismo de la doctrina cristiana. 18°. 25c......... *Appleton.*
Rosalie; or, first communion. 18°. pap., 10c. *Claremont.*
— *Same.* 18°. 30c.; pap., 10c. .... *Dutton.*
Rosalie du Pont. Bennett, E. 25c....... *U.P.James.*
Rosalie melodist: coll. of vocal music. 24°. 35c. *Gordon.*
Rosalie's lessons. Wallace, S. S. T. 50c... *Pres.Bd.*
Rosalie's pet. Mathews, J. H. $1.25........ *Carter.*
Rosamond. *See* Addison, Jos.
Rosamond. *See* Edgeworth, Mar.
Rosamond Dayton. *See* Gardner, *Mrs.* H. C.
Rosary book: instructions on confraternity of the most holy rosary; with compend. of indulgences. 24°. pap., 10c......................... *Benziger.*
Rosary of the Virgin Mary. ill. 24°. pap., 10c... *Strong.*
Rosa's childhood; or, the influence of principle. 18°. 40c.. *Am.S.S.*
Rosa's wish, and how she attained it. Bell, C. D. $1.75. *Scribner, W.&A.*
Rosch, D. Chronic diseases, especially nervous diseases of women; tr. by C. Dunning. 12°. pap., 50c.. *Wells.*
Roscoe, H: Digest of law of evidence in criminal cases. 7th Am. ed., with add. by H. Smith; with add. notes and Am. ref., etc., by G. Sharswood. 8°. '74. $7.50.............. *T. & J. W.Johnson.*
— *See also* England, Exchequer reports.

Roscoe, *Mrs.* H: Vittoria Colonna: her life and poems. cr. 8°. '68. $3 .... *Macmillan.*

Roscoe, H: E. Chemistry. (Science primer.) 18°. 50c. *Appleton; Macmillan.*

— Lessons in element. chemistry, inorganic and organic. New ed. ill. 18°. '75. $1.50.. *Macmillan; W. Wood.*

— Spectrum analysis: lectures, 1868; with 4 app. col. pl. and ill. 8°. $9 .... *Appleton.*

— *Same.* 3d ed., rev. ill., maps and chromo-liths. 8°. '73. $9 .... *Macmillan.*

— *and* Huggins, W: *and* Lockyer, J. N. Spectrum analysis: lectures. ill. 12°. '72. pap., 25c. *Van Nostrand.*

Roscoe, W: Life and pontificate of Leo X.; with notes and index. 2 v. por. 12°. (Bohn.) ea., $1.25. *Little, B. & Co.*

— *Same.* 2 v. por. 12°. (Bohn.) ea., $1.40. *Scribner, W. & A.*

— *Same.* 2 v. por. 12°. (Bohn.) ea., $1.50.. *Lippincott.*

— Life of Lorenzo de Medici; with notes. por. 12°. (Bohn.) $1.25 .... *Little, B. & Co.*

— *Same.* por. 12°. (Bohn.) $1.40 ... *Scribner, W. & A.*

— *Same.* por. 12°. (Bohn.) $1.50 .... *Lippincott.*

Rose *of Lima, St.* Life; ed. by F. W. Faber. 16°. '55. $1 .... *Cunningham; Sadlier.*

Rose, A. C. Helps to every day holiness. 16°. 50c. *Palmer.*

— Widow's souvenir. 24°. '52. 40c.... *Meth. Bk. Conc.*

Röse, F. A. Grammar of the Germ. lang. 12°. hf. roan, $1 .... *Lippincott.*

Rose, G: ["Arth. Sketchley."] [Works.] 17 v. 16°. bds. .... *Routledge.*

Cont.: Mrs. Brown at Brighton — at the international — at Margate — at the play — at the seaside — in America — in the Highlands — in London — in Paris — on Dizzy — on the grand tour — on the liquor law — on the royal marriage — on the Tichborne case — on woman's rights, *ea.*, 50c. — Mrs. Brown on the Battle of Dorking, 25c. — Mrs. Brown's 'oliday 'outins, 50c.

— Dark cloud: drama. 16°. pap., 15c. .... *French.*

— How will they get out of it? comedy. 16°. pap., 15c. *French.*

— Quite at home: comedietta. 16°. pap., 15c... *De Witt.*

Rosé, Jul. D. Rudimenta linguæ Latinæ. 12°. '56. $1. *Dennis.*

Rose. *See* Charlesworth, *Mrs.* M. L.

Rose, the lavender girl; or, honest industry rewarded. 16°. '71. $1 .... *Whittaker.*

Rose and Annie; or, the fourth commandment. 18°. 25c.; 30c. .... *Am. Bapt.*

Rose and her pets. Dawes, S. E. 60c. .... *Am. Tr.*

Rose and her troubles. ill. 24°. 25c. ..... *Perkinpine.*

— *Same.* 18°. 35c. .... *Bost. Am. Tr.*

— *See also* Alice and Willie stories.

Rose and Kate; or, the little Howards. 16°. 50c. *Routledge.*

Rose and Kate lib. 5 v. ill. 16°. $2.50 .... *Routledge.*

Cont.: Rose and Kate. — Memoirs of a doll. — Child's natural history. — Fabulous histories, by Mrs. Trimmer. — Max Frere.

Rose and Lillie Stanhope. *See* New juvenile lib.

Rose and Millie. Atkinson, M. E. $1.25... *Lothrop.*

Rose and Millie lib. 4 v. 16°. $5 .... *Lothrop.*

Cont.: Mabel Livingstone. — Dr. Plassid's patients. — Rose and Millie. — The Robinsons.

Rose and the ring. *See* Thackeray, W: M.

Rose and roof-tree. Lathrop, G. P. $1.50... *Osgood.*

Rose and shamrock. Crow, *Mrs.* —. 30c.... *Am. News.*

Rose Carleton's reward. Frances, M. $1...... *Chase.*

Rose Cottage; or, visits to my grandmamma. ill. 18°. '66. 50c. .... *N. Y. Ref. Ch. Bd.; Pres. Com.*

— *Same.* ('60.) New ed. ill. 18°. '75. 55c.... *Hoyt.*

Rose d'Albret. James, G. P. R. 50c. .... *Harper.*

Rose Dale: Ethiop. drama. 16°. pap., 15c. *French; Happy.*

Rose Dale books. *See* Sanford, *Mrs.* D. P.

Rose Darling; or, the path of truth; by author of "Joe Carton." ('67.) New ed. ill. 18°. '75. 55c... *Hoyt.*

Rose Delaney's secret. McKeever, H. B. 55c... *Pres. Bd.*

Rose Douglas. 12°. $1.75; pap., $1.50 ..... *Peterson.*

Rose Elliott's wish; or, diamonds and toads; by author of "Nora's life at Duncleugh." 18°. 55c. *Am. S. S.*

Rose Foster. Reynolds, G. W. M. $1.75; $1.50. *Peterson.*

Rose garden. Peard, F. M. $1.50 .... *Roberts.*

Rose Hamilton. 18°. 35c. .... *Cong. Pub.*

Rose (Die) im Thal. 24°. 20c. .... *Ev. Assoc.*

Rose in the desert. *See* Books of blessing.

Rose in June. *See* Oliphant, *Mrs.* M. O. W.

Rose leaf. 18°. 22c. .... *Am. S. S.*

Rose Le Blanc. Fullerton, G. $1; $1.50... *Sadlier.*

Rose lib. v. 1–7. ill. 12°. ea., $1.25; pap., 50c. *Scribner, W. & A.*

Cont.: Seagull rock, by J. Sandeau. — House on wheels, by Comtesse F. de Bégon. — Undine *and* The two captains, by La Motte-Fouqué. — Four gold pieces, by J. Gouraud. — Picciola, by X. B. Saintine. — Two children of St. Domingo, by J. Gouraud. — Robert's holidays, by N. D'Anvers.

Rose Marbury. Pritchard, S. J. $1.25 ...... *Carter.*

Rose Mather. Holmes, M. J. $1.50 .... *Carleton.*

Rose Morton ser. 5 v. ill. 18°. $3.50 ...... *Sheldon.*

Cont.: Rose Morton's journal for January — for February — for March — for April — for May.

Rose of Ashurst. Marsh-Caldwell, A. 50c... *Harper.*

Rose of Auvergne. *See* Offenbach, J.

Rose of Castile. *See* Balfe, M. W.

Rose of Castile: opera. 16°. pap., 15c. ...... *French.*

Rose of Disentis. Zschokke, H. $1.50; $1.. *Sheldon.*

Rose of Ettrick vale. Lynch, T. J. 15c..... *French.*

Rose, Robin and little May. ('74.) New ed. 16°. '76. 90c. .... *Hoyt.*

Rose Smith; or, how a child may do good. 32°. '74. 30c. .... *Whittaker.*

Rose Somerville. Reynolds, G. W. M. 50c... *De Witt.*

Rose Thorpe's ambition. Rockwell, M. E. $1.25. *Garrigues.*

Rose, Tom and Ned. Sanford, D. P. $1.... *Dutton.*

Rose valley lib. 6 v. ill. 32°. $1.50; ea., 25c. *Porter.*

Cont.: Robinson Crusoe. — Eva Bruen. — Edith Locke. — Discontented Tom. — Willie and Ned. — Ben Benson.

Rose (Die) von Rom, od. ehre Vater u. Mutter. 12°. 35c.; pap., 15c. .... *Benziger.*

Rose Warrington. Duganne, A. J. H. 25c... *Peterson.*

Rosebud. Tonna, C. E. 35c. .... *Pres. Bd.*

Rosebud of Stinging Nettle Farm: drama. 16°. pap., 15c. .... *French.*

Rosebud ser. *See* Myrtle, *Mrs.* H.

Rosebuds. Sanford, D. P. 20c.; 15c. ...... *Dutton.*

Rosecrans, Ja. H. Little sower: music for S.-schools. 16°. '70. bds., 35c. .... *Crandall.*

— Pearly gates: songs for the S.-school. obl. 16°. bds., 25c. .... *Cen. Bk.*

— Rosecrans' lightning music reader: songs and glees, and short method for read. and sing. by note. obl. 12°. '76. bds., 60c. .... *Fillmore.*

— Three Christian graces; or, faith, hope and charity; with words by F. Church: cantata. 16°. '69. bds., 25c. .... *Crandall.*

— *See also* Shelton, T. J., *and* Rosecrans, J. H.

— *and* Rheem, J. H. The beauty: sacred and secular music for school and conventions. ('74.) 2d ed. 8°. '75. bds., 75c. .... *Crandall.*

Rosedale. Gardner, H. C. $1.75.. *Cin. Meth. Bk. Conc.*

Rosedale lib. ('66.) 6th ed. 6 v. ill. 16°. '72. $6. *Perkinpine.*

Cont.: Henry Arden. — Honest Gabriel. — Joe Fulwood. — Kate Kemp. — Little Jane. — Little German drummer boy.

Roseleur, Alfr. Galvanoplastic manipulations: guide for the gold and silver electro-plater and the galvanoplastic operator; tr. by A. A. Fesquet. ill. 8°. '72. $6 .... *Baird.*

Rosemary. Fullerton, *Lady* G. $1........*O'Shea*.

Rosemary. Huntington, J. V. $2; $2.50...*Sadlier*.

Rosemary leaves. Jordan, D. M. $1.50....*Clarke*.

Rosenberg, C. G. Wonders of the world. ill. 4°. $4; $5..........................*U.S.Pub*.

Rosenfeld, Sydney. [Plays.] 4 v. 16°. ea., pap., 15c. ....*De Witt*.

Cont.: High C: comedietta. — Mr. X: farce. — Off the stage: comedietta. — On bread and water: farce.

Rosenkranz, J: K: F. Hegel as the national philosopher of Germany; tr. by G. S. Hall. 8°. '74. $1.50; pap., $1.........................*Gray*.

— Philosophy of education; or, pedagogics as a system; tr. by A. C. Brackett. 8°. '72. $1.50; pap., $1. *Gray*.

Rosenmühle (Die). *See* Nieritz, G.

Rosenstock (Der). *See* Schmid, C. v.

Rose's temptation. Mathews, J. H. 60c. ....*Carter*.

Roses and thorns. Lunn, J. 15c............*French*.

Roses without thorns. Fleet, E. F. 2 v. $1.50..*Nelson*.

Rosette. ill. 18°. 50c. ....*Crowell*.

— *See also* Annie Marlowe ser.

Rosewald, J. H. The solfeggio: musical instruction. ('71.) 2d ed. 16°. '76. bds., 60c.......*Dulany*.

Rosewig, A. H. Cantus divinus: Catholic music. obl. 4°. '75. bds., $2.75....................*Ditson*.

— Vespers in G. f°. pap., $1.25.............*Ditson*.

Rosière (La). *See* Lacy's home plays for ladies.

Rosina. Brooke, F. 15c. ....*French*.

Rosina Meadows. English, W. B. 15c......*French*.

Ross, C: H. Hush money: a life drama. [Fiction.] ill. 8°. (Lond.) pap., 30c..........*Am.News*.

— *Same*. 8°. pap., 50c......................*De Witt*.

Ross, Charley. Abduction of Charley Ross. 8°. pap., 25c. ....*Barclay*.

Ross, Chr. K. The father's story of Charley Ross, the kidnapped child. por. 12°. '76. $2..*J.E.Potter*.

Ross, D. Barton. Rhetorical manual; or, fifth reader. ('31.) 5th ed. 12°. '53. $1.20........*Claxton*.

— Southern speaker. 12°. hf. roan, $1.50..*Lippincott*.

Ross, G: Leading cases in commercial law of England and Scotland; with notes. 3 v. 8°. '55–'58. $12. *T.& J. W.Johnson*.

Cont.: Bills of exchange. — Law of contracts. — Suretyship, agency, partnership and insurance.

— — *See also* Law lib.

Ross, Ja. Latin grammar; with idioms, prosody, etc., by N. C. Brooks. 12°. '44. $1..*Barnes; Claxton*.

Ross, Ja. M. Class book of geog. of Iowa, and of county, state and federal government; for schools. 4°. '74. bds., 60c.......................*Mills*.

Ross, J: M. (*ed.*) Globe encyclopædia of universal information. 48 pts. 4°. pap., *$24; — in 6 v. 4°. $30; shp., $36; hf. mor., $42............*Estes*.

— — Atlas; by W. and A. H. Johnston. 8 pts. 36 maps. 4°. *$7–$4............................*Estes*.

Ross, Miriam. After many years. ill. 8°. (Lond.) pap., 30c. ....*Am.News*.

— Against tide. ill. 8°. (Lond.) pap., 30c...*Am.News*.

— Counterfeit coin. ill. 8°. (Lond.) pap., 30c. *Am.News*.

Ross, Owen C. D. Air as fuel; or, petroleum and other mineral oils utilized by carburetting air and rendering it inflammable. 2d ed. cr. 8°. '74. $1.50. *Spon*.

Ross, W. A. Equatorial needle; or, compass which swings E. and W. 8°. '75. pap., 20c......*Spon*.

— Pyrology; or, fire chemistry. pl. and ill. cr. 4°. '75. $15..................................*Spon*.

Ross, W. F. Exposures in fire insurance. 12°. '75. $1.50....................................*Day*.

Rossa, O'Donovan. Irish rebels in Eng. prisons. 8°. $1.50; pap., $1 ....*Sadlier*.

Rosse, J. Willoughby. Index of dates. 2 v. 12°. (Bohn.) ea., $1.75..............*Little,B.& Co*.

— *Same*. 2 v. 12°. (Bohn.) ea., $2. *Lippincott; Scribner, W.& A*.

Rosser, W. H. Bijou gazetteer of the world. 48°. 50c.; leath., $1..............*Scribner, W. & A*.

Rossetti, Christina G. Annus Domini: prayer for each day of the year founded on text of Scripture. sq. 18°. $1.50....................*Roberts*.

— Commonplace, and other stories. 16°. '70. $1.50. *Roberts*.

— Poems. ('66.) New ed., enl. 16°. '76. $1.50..*Roberts*.

— *Same*. New ed. fp. 8°. $3............*Macmillan*.

— Sing song: a nursery rhyme book. ill. 8°. '71. $1.50. *Roberts*.

— Speaking likenesses: a Christmas story. ill. sq. 12°. '74. $1.50..............................*Roberts*.

— *Same*. ill. fp. 8°. $3..................*Macmillan*.

Rossetti, Dante Gbr. Dante and his circle; with the Ital. poets preceding him: collection of lyrics ed. and tr. in the original metres. Rev. ed. cr. 8°. '75. $3.50..............................*Roberts*.

— Poems. 16°. '70. $1.50. — cr. 8°. $2....*Roberts*.

Rossetti, Mar. Francesca. Shadow of Dante: essay towards studying himself, his world and his pilgrimage. ill. 12°. '72. $2.50.........*Roberts*.

Rossetti, W: Mich. (*tr.*) *See* Dante, A.

Rossi, L. F. Vespers no. 5; arr. by W. Dressler. 4°. pap., $1.50..........................*Peters*.

Rossignoli, C. G. Choice of a state of life. 18°. '68. 90c.; $1.25...........................*Murphy*.

Rossini, Gioacchino. Barbiere (Il) di Siviglia; — Gazza ladra (La); — Otello; — William Tell. *See* Ditson.

— Messe solennelle; with piano and organ accomp. 8°. '69. bds., $2; pap., $1.60............*Ditson*.

— Moses in Egypt: oratorio; tr. and adapted by G. S. Parker. 8°. '55. bds., $2..............*Ditson*.

— — Choruses. 8°. bds., $1.25..............*Ditson*.

— Stabat mater; with Lat. and Eng. words. 8°. $1; bds., 80c.; pap., 65c..........*Ditson; Gordon*.

— — Choruses. 8°. pap., 40c..................*Ditson*.

— Vocal exercises and solfeggios. f°. pap., $1..*Ditson*.

Rossiter, W: Theoretical mechanics. (Element. sci. ser.) ill. 16°. 75c..............*Putnam*.

Rostet nicht. *See* Hartmann, M.

Rosy Conroy's lesson. *See* Mathews, J. A.

Rosy dawn stories. *See* Baker, *Mrs.* H. N. W.

Rosy diamond story books. 6 v. ill. 16°. ea. 80c. *Lee& S*.

Cont.: Great rosy diamond. — Daisy. — Violet. — Minnie. — Angel children. — Little Blossom's reward.

Roth, E: Christus judex: a traveller's tale. ('64.) 5th ed. 16°. '74. $1 ...............*I.N.Andrews*.

Rothenfels, E. v. (*pseud.*) *See* Ingersleben, *Frau* v.

Rothery, *Mrs.* Ma. C. H. *See* Hume-Rothery.

Rothkäppchen (Das). *See* Tieck, L.

Rothwell, J. S. (*ed.*) Illustrated poetical album; ill. by Birket Foster, etc. 12°. $2.50.....*Stroefer*.

Rotteck, C: v. History of the world; with contin. by C. J. Peterson. 4 v. in 2. ill. 8°. ea., $2; shp., $2.75 ....*World Pub*.

Rottenstein, —. *See* Leber, —, *and* Rottenstein, —.

Roué (The). *See* Bulwer-Lytton, *Sir* E. G. E. L.

Rouge et noir. About, E. $1.50; $1 ......*Claxton*.

Rougegorge, and other short stories; by H. P. Spofford, A. Cary, L. H. Hooper, J. G. Austin, A. L. Wister, L. C. Davis, F. L. Benedict, etc. 8°. pap., 50c. ....*Lippincott*.

Rough and Ready. Alger, H., *jr*. $1.25....*Loring*.

Rough boy's story. Hosmer, M. $1.....(?)*Martien*.

Rough diamond. Buckstone, J. B. 15c......*French*.

Rough rhymes for country boys. 18°. 18c...*Am.S.S*.

Roughing it. Clemens, S. L. *$3.50–$8...*Am.Pub*.

Roughing it in the bush. Moodie, S. $1 ...*De Witt.*

Roughing it with Aleck Bailie. Stewart, W. J. 75c. *Carter.*

Rouillon, D. de. Guide to French conversation. 18°. '66. 60c. .... *G.R.Lockwood.*

Roulier, A. Charterhouse first book of French composition: Eng. into Fr. sm. 8°. 75c...*Lippincott.*

Round, W: M. F. ["*Rev.* P: Pennot."] Achsah: a New Eng. life study. 12°. '76. $1.50 ....(?)*Lee&S.*

Round by round. Warner, H. P. $1; $1.25 ..*Am. Tr.*

Round the fire: six stories related by six girls. 18°. 75c. .... *Carter; Dutton.*

Round the fire stories. ill. 16°. $1..*Scribner, W.&A.*

Round games for all parties. 16°. pap., 60c...*French.*

Round the Grange Farm. Watson, J. L. $1.25. *Cin. Meth. Bk. Conc.*

Round my house. Hamerton, P. G. $2 ....*Roberts.*

Round picture stories. 18°. 30c.; pap., 15c...*Am. S. S.*

— *See also* Picture lib. for the little ones at home.

Round table. *See* Hazlitt, W.

Round the table: notes on cooking and plain receipts. 12°. $2.50 .... *Lippincott.*

Round the world. Kingsley, C. 2 v. $2.50; $3. *Cin. Meth. Bk. Conc.*

Round the world. Kingston, W. H. G. $1.25. *Lippincott.*

Round the world. Smiles, S. $1.50 ....*Harper.*

Round the world. Smith, D. M. $1 ....*Nelson.*

Roundabout papers. *See* Thackeray, W: M.

Roundabout rambles. Stockton, F. R. $2 ..*Scribner.*

Roundhearts. Harris, M. C. $1.50.......*Carleton.*

Rouse, E. S. S. Bugle blast. 12°. '64. $1.75; $1.50. *Challen.*

Roussel, Nap. *See* Schaff, P., *and* Roussel, N.

Rousselet, L: India and its native princes: travels in central India and in the presidencies of Bombay and Bengal; tr. from the Fr. ill. imp. 4°. '76. $25 .... *Scribner.*

Routh, C: H. F. Infant feeding, and its influence on life. fp. 8°. $3 .... *Lippincott.*

Routh, E: J: Problems and riders. *See* Cambridge Senate-House.

— Treatise on dynamics of rigid bodies. New ed. cr. 8°. $3.50 .... *Macmillan.*

Routledge, Edm. Every-day blunders in speaking. 16°. 20c. .... *Routledge.*

— Handbook of cricket. roy. 32°. bds., 25c...*Routledge.*

— Handbook of croquet. roy. 32°. bds., 20c...*Routledge.*

— (*ed.*) Every boy's annual. ('65.) New ed. ill. 8°. '76. $3 .... *Routledge.*

— Every boy's book: encyclopedia of sports and amusements. New ed., with Am. games by H. Chadwick. ill. post 8°. $3.50; hf. cf., $5.50. *Routledge.*

— Riddles and jokes. 16°. bds., 50c.......*Routledge.*

Routledge, Rob. *See* Pepper, J. H., *and* Routledge, R.

Routledge, T: Bamboo, considered as a paper-making material. 8°. '75. pap., 80c. .... *Spon.*

Routledge's Blue Beard picture-book. ill. 8°. '75. $1.25; $2.50 .... *Routledge.*

Routledge's book of alphabets. [Toy-book.] ill. 8°. $1.25 .... *Routledge.*

Routledge's Brit. poets. (Presentation ed.) 11 v. 12°. ea., mor., $3.50 .... *Routledge.*

Cont.: Shakespeare. — Milton. — Moore. — Burns. — Wordsworth. — Scott. — Byron. — Cowper. — Hemans. — Hood. — Tennyson.

— *Same.* 24 v. 12°. ea., $3 .... *Routledge.*

Cont.: Tennyson. — Shakespeare. — Milton. — Wordsworth. — Goldsmith. — Burns. — Cowper. — Moore. — Byron. — Chaucer. — Pope. — Hemans. — Spenser. — Rogers. — Scott. — Leigh Hunt. — Keble. — Coleridge. — Dodd's Beauties of Shakespeare. — Percy's Reliques. — Shelley. — Keats. — L. E. Landon. — Hood.

Routledge's Brit. poets and selections. (Presentation ed.) 51 v. ill. 12°. ea., $1.75......*Routledge.*

Cont.: Tennyson. — Shakespeare. — Moore. — Scott. — Byron. — Burns. — Milton. — Cowper. — Wordsworth. — Chaucer. — Pope. — Goldsmith. — Campbell. — Herbert. — Kirke White. — Southey. — Humor and wit. — Sacred poems. — Choice poems. — Wise sayings. — Shakespeare gems. — Familiar quotations. — Montgomery. — Lover. — Bloomfield. — Leigh Hunt. — Dryden. — Tupper. — Shelley. — Coleridge. — Hood. — Keats. — Spenser. — Rogers. — Hemans. — Ainsworth. — Eliza Cook. — Keble. — Lytton's poems. — Lytton's dramas. — L. E. Landon. — Dodd's Beauties of Shakespeare. — Percy's Reliques. — Robinson Crusoe. — Swiss family Robinson. — Sandford and Merton. — Evenings at home. — Arabian nights. — Gulliver's travels. — Don Quixote. — Bunyan's Pilgrim's progress.

Routledge's Brit. poets; ed. by R. A. Willmott, with biog. and notes. 21 v. ill. 12°. ea., $2.25; hf. cf., $3.50; mor., $5 .... *Routledge.*

Cont.: Burns. — Byron. — Campbell. — Chaucer's Canterbury tales. — E. Cook. — Cowper. — Dryden. — Hemans. — Herbert. — Kirke White. — Lover. — Milton. — Moore. — Percy's Reliques. — Pope. — Rogers. — Scott. — Southey's Joan of Arc, etc. — Spenser's Fairy queen. — Tasso's Jerusalem delivered. — Wordsworth.

Routledge's colored A B C book. demy 4°. '71. $2.50. *Routledge.*

Routledge's colored scrap-book: stories and anecdotes. ill. 4°. $4; $6 .... *Routledge.*

Routledge's comic readings. 16°. bds., 50c...*Routledge.*

Routledge's globe lib. 23 v. cr. 8°. ea., $1.75; hf. cf., $3.50; cf., $5 .... *Routledge.*

Cont.: Arabian nights. — Cruden's Concordance. — Curiosities of literature. — Don Quixote. — Gil Blas. — Goldsmith's works. — Boswell's Johnson. — Thousand and one gems of poetry. — Blackfriars ed. of Shakespeare. — Ten thousand wonderful things. — Sterne's works. — Spectator. — Memoirs of extraordinary popular delusions. — Pope's Homer's Iliad and Odyssey. — Thousand and one gems of prose. — Book of modern anecdotes: Eng., Irish, Scotch. — Book of modern anecdotes: American, legal, theatrical. — Works of Flavius Josephus. — Book of table talk. — Junius' letters. — Family doctor. — Froissart's chronicles. — Lamb's complete works.

Routledge's handbooks: manuals on athletic and in-door sports. 19 v. roy. 32°. bds......*Routledge.*

Cont.: Forrest's Gymnastics. — Chess. — Pardon's Whist. — Pardon's Billiards and bagatelle. — Pardon's Draughts and backgammon. — Pardon's Card player. — Rowing and sailing. — Walsh's Riding and driving. — Archery, fencing and broadsword. — Brother Sam's conundrums. — Manly exercises, by Walsh, Forrest, etc. — Routledge's Croquet, *ea.*, 20c. — Fishing. — Quoits and bowls. — Swimming. — Skating. — Shooting. — Riddles. — Routledge's cricket, *ea.*, 25c.

Routledge's household manuals. *See* Household.

Routledge's ill. reading-book. ill. 12°. $1..*Routledge.*

Routledge's lib. of standard and classical works. *See* Library of.

Routledge's manual of etiquette. 16°. '75. 75c.; bds., 50c. .... *Routledge.*

Routledge's Marquis of Carabas' picture-book. 8°. '74. $1.25; $2.50 .... *Routledge.*

Routledge's miniature lib. 8 v. 32°. ea., 20c. *Routledge.*

Cont.: Etiquette for gentlemen. — Etiquette for ladies. — Etiquette of courtship and matrimony. — Ball-room companion. — Language of flowers. — How to dress well. — Handbook of carving. — Toasts and sentiments.

Routledge's new 16° toy-books. 32 v. ill. sq. 16°. ea., 25c.; pap., 12½c. .... *Routledge.*

Routledge's nursery book. [Toy-book.] ill. demy 4°. $2.50 .... *Routledge.*

Routledge's our pet's colored picture-book. 4°. '72. $1.25; $2.50 .... *Routledge.*

Routledge's picture-book. [Toy-book.] ill. 4°. $1.75. *Routledge.*

Routledge's picture-book of animals and birds. [Toy-book.] ill. 8°. $1.25 .... *Routledge.*

Routledge's picture gift-book. demy 4°. $2.50. *Routledge.*

Routledge's Scripture gift-book. [Toy-book.] demy 4°. $2.50 .... *Routledge.*

Routledge's temperance reciter. 16°. bds., 50c. *Routledge.*

Rouvroy, L: de. *See* Saint-Simon, *Duke of.*

Roux, G. (*ill.*) *See* Closs, G., Frölicher, O., *and* Roux, G.

Rover, A. (*pseud.*) Croquet: its principles and rules. 14th ed. 16°. '75. pap., 10c. .... *M. Bradley.*

Rover, Winnie. Steps through the world. 3 v. ill. 12°. ea., $1.50 .... *O'Shea.*
Cont.: The Neptune outward bound. — The Neptune afloat. — The Neptune at the Golden Horn.

Rover's bride. Almar, G. 15c. .... *French.*

Row, Aug. Masonic biography and dictionary. 12°. $3. *Lippincott.*

Row, C: Adolphus. Moral teaching of the New Test., viewed as evidential to its historical truth. 16°. '72. 75c. .... *Pott.*

Row, Nelson. Complete fractional ready reckoner. 36°. bds., 50c. .... *Dick & F.*

— National wages tables. 12°. 75c.; hf. bd., 50c.; roan, $1 .... *Dick & F.*

Row, R: Episodes in an obscure life: experiences in the tower hamlets; by a curate. ill. 8°. $1.25; pap., 75c. .... *Lippincott.*

— *Same.* 12°. '71. $1.75 ...... *Randolph; Routledge.*

— Friends and acquaintances. cr. 8°. '71. $1.75. *Routledge.*

Rowan, Frederica Maclean. Modern French reader. 12°. $1.50 .... *Appleton.*

Rowbotham, F. L. (*ill.*) Water-color albums of selected scenery; with arch., hist., poet. and descript. notes by W. J. Loftie. 4 v. ill. sm. 4°. ea., $3. *Scribner, W. & A.*
Cont.: English lake scenery. — Scottish scenery. — Views in North Wales. — Wicklow and Killarney.

Rowbotham, J: Diamond pocket dict. of the Fr. lang. 32°. '68. roan, 75c. .... *Claxton.*

Rowbotham, T: Art of sketching from nature. 12°. '60. pap., 50c. .... *Tilton.*

Rowcroft, C: Australian Crusoes; [also] Wolf boy, by Wm. Dalton. ill. 12°. $1.50 .... *World Pub.*

— Bush-ranger of Van Dieman's Land. 8°. pap., 50c. *Harper.*

Rowe, *Mrs.* Eliz. Devout exercises of the heart, in meditation and soliloquy, prayer and praise. 24°. '37. 35c. .... *Meth. Bk. Conc.*

— *Same.* 18°. '56. 50c. .... *So. Meth.*

Rowe, G: Stringer. Missionary among cannibals: life of John Hunt. 12°. '60. $1 ..... *Meth. Bk. Conc.*

Rowe, J. F. Exposition of the new birth. 8°. pap., 10c. .... *Chase.*

— Unity of the Holy Spirit. 8°. pap., 10c. .... *Chase.*

Rowe, Nicholas. Fair penitent: tragedy. 16°. pap., 15c. .... *French.*

— Jane Shore: tragedy. 16°. pap., 15c. ...... *French.*

— *See also* Leslie, H., *and* Rowe, N.

Rowell, G: P., and Co. (*pub.*) American newspaper directory. ('69.) [Annual.] 8°. $5 .... *Rowell.*

Rowell, J: W. *See* Vermont, Sup. court reports.

Rowland, H: A: Path of life. 18°. '55. 60c. .. *Dodd.*

Rowland Hill. *See* Barbary doves.

Rowley, H: Africa unveiled. 12°. '76. $2 .... *Pott.*

Rowley, Hu. Sage stuffing for green goslings; or, saws for the goose and saws for the gander. ill. sq. 8°. '71. $2.50 .... *Routledge.*

Rowley, W: Woman never vext: comedy. 16°. pap., 15c. .... *French.*

Rownie. H., M. R. 90c. .... *Pott.*

Rowsell, T: Ja. English universities and the Eng. poor: sermons. fp. 8°. $1 .... *Macmillan.*

— Man's labour and God's harvest: sermons, 1861. fp. 8°. $1 .... *Macmillan.*

Rowson, *Mrs.* Susanna. Charlotte and Lucy Temple. 16°. $1 .... *Lippincott.*

— Charlotte Temple: tale of truth. 16°. pap., 20c. *U. P. James.*

— *Same.* 18°. bds., 25c. .... *Fisher.*

— *Same.* [In Eng. or Germ.] 8°. pap., 20c. ... *Barclay.*

— Extracts from writings. *See* Nason, E.

Rowton, F: How to conduct a debate. 16°. pap., 50c.; bds., 75c. .... *Dick & F.*

Roxana. *See* Defoe, Dan.

Roxobel. *See* Sherwood, *Mrs.* Ma. Mar.

Roy, —. New and complete method for the cornet a piston with two or three pistons or valves; fingered by W. R. Bayley. 8°. '43. pap., 60c. *Ditson.*

Roy, G: Art of pleasing: lecture. 12°. '75. pap., 25c. .... *Clarke.*

— Generalship; or, how I managed my husband: tale. 18°. '75. $1; pap., 50c. .... *Clarke.*

— Old, old story: lecture. 12°. '75. pap., 25c. .. *Clarke.*

Royal, W: L. Digest of Grattan's Virginia Sup. Court reports, v. 1–21 (1844–'73). 8°. '73. shp., $8. *Ward & P.*

Royal Academicians. *See* Lectures on painting.

Royal beggar boy. *See* Little Kadore.

Royal Club series. *See* Everett, W.

Royal diadem for the S.-school. Lowry, R., *and* Doane, W. H. 75c.; 35c. .... *Biglow.*

Royal favorite (Story of a). Gore, C. G. 50c. *Harper.*

Royal illuminated legends. [Ballads with music.] 8 nos. ill. obl. 4°. ea., bds., 50c. ...... *Routledge.*
Cont.: Pocahontas. — King Alfred and Othero. — Marquis of Carabas. — Hind of the forest. — Cinderella. — Fair one with the golden locks. — Lady Ouncebell and Lord Lovell. — Sleeping beauty.

Royal illum. nursery rhymes; [with music]. 8 nos. ill. obl. 8°. ea., bds., 25c. ..... *Appleton; Routledge.*
Cont.: Sing a song of sixpence. — Little market woman. — Little Bo-Peep. — Simple Simon. — Carrion crow. — Jack and Gill. — Mother Hubbard. — Four nursery rhymes.

Royal law of love. M'Cosh, J. 25c. .... *Carter.*

Royal oak; or, the reformed village. 18°. 17c.; 22c. *Am. Bapt.*

Royal picture alphabet. 4°. bds., 50c. .... *Lee & S.*

Royal preacher. Hamilton, J. $1.25 .... *Carter.*

Royal readers. 8 v. .... *Nelson.*
Cont.: No. 1, 18°, 12½c. — *Sequel*, 18°, 20c. — 2, 18°, 25c. — *Sequel*, 18°, 40c. — 3, 12°, 50c. — 4, 12°, 75c. — 5, 12°, $1. — 6, 12°, $1.25.

Royal road to fortune. Miller, E. H. $1.50. *Meth. Bk. Conc.*

Royal road to learning. Merrifield, J. $2.50. (?) *Townsend & Co.*

Royal songs; by J. W. Suffern, W. W. Bentley, S. J. Vail and W. S. Wymer. [S.-school music book.] 16°. '75. per 100, pap., $25; bd., $30 .. *Am. Tr.*

Royal supremacy. Pusey, E. B. $1.25 .... *Pott.*

Royalist's daughter and the rebels. Murdoch, D. $1.75 .... *J. E. Potter.*

Royce, M. S. Historical sketches of the Church of Eng. and of the Prot. Episc. Church in the U.S. 18°. 75c.; pap., 25c. .... *Claremont.*

— *Same.* 18°. 70c.; 75c. .... *Dutton.*

Royle, J: Forbes. Manual of materia medica and therapeutics. 6th ed., rev. and enl. by J. Harley. ill. demy 8°. '76. $6 .... *Lindsay.*

Royo, José Manuel. Instruccion moral y religiosa, para la escuelas de la república. 18°. $1 .. *Appleton.*

Roy's search. Pearson, H. C. $1.25 ..... *Nat. Temp.*

Royse, N. K. Manual of Am. literature. ('72.) New ed. '75. $1.75 .... *Cowperthwait.*

Rubenstein, Pasach N. Life and trial. 8°. pap., 25c. *Barclay.*

— Trial for murder of Sarah Alexander, in New Lots [near Brooklyn, N.Y.], on Dec. 12, 1875. 8°. hf. shp., $2.50; pap., $2 .... *Baker, V. & Co.*

Rübezahl Sagen. Hoffmann, F. 25c. ...... *Steiger.*

Rubies. ill. 18°. '72. 75c. .... *Lothrop.*

Rubin (Der). Lexow, R. 75c.; 50c. .... *Steiger.*

Ruby Adams; or, a vocation wanted. 16°. $1 .. *Am. S. S.*

Ruby Blas righted: burlesque. 16°. pap., 15c. *French.*

Ruby Duke. Potwin, H. K. $1.50 .... *Lee & S.*

Ruby Gray's strategy. Stephens, A. S. $1.75; $1.50. *Peterson.*
Ruby lib. 20 v. ill. 24°. $3 .... *Lothrop.*
Ruby's husband. Harland, M. $1.50 ...... *Carleton.*
Rückert, E. F. (*ed.*) Therapeutics; or, successful homœop. cures; tr. by C. J. Hempel. 8°. hf. mor., $4 .... *Boericke.*
Rückert, Fried. Gedichte. 3 v. 12°. hf. mor., $5. *Kohler.*
Rückwirkungen. *See* Zschokke, H.
Rudder, W: A rationale of the Church's liturgic worship: study for the times. 16°. 75c.; $1. *Lippincott.*
Ruddiman, T: Latin grammar. 12°. '53. 75c... *Murphy.*
Rude boys reformed. *See* Haymakers.
Rude stone monuments in all countries. Fergusson, J. $8.50 .... *Little, B. & Co.*
Rudens. *See* Plautus, T. M.
Rudie's goat. Mathews, J. H. $1 .... *Carter.*
Rüdinger, N. Atlas of the osseous anatomy of the human ear; tr. and ed. with notes by C. J. Blake: 9 pl., with text and portf. 4°. '74. $5. *Williams.*
Rudo ensayo, tentativa de una prevencional descripcion geográfica de la provincia de Sonora. 4°. '63. pap., $4 .... *Shea.*
Rudolphson, —. Pupil's first book. [Piano-forte methods.] obl. 8°. pap., $1 .... *Peters.*
Rudolphy, J: Pharmaceutical directory of all crude drugs in general use. 8°. '72. $2.50 ... *Radde.*
— *Germ.* 8°. '72. $2.50 .... *Radde.*
Rue, thyme and myrtle. Spencer, C. E. $1.. *Lippincott.*
Ruffian boy. Dibdin, T. 15c. .... *French.*
Ruffini, Gi. Carlino. 8°. pap., 35c. ..... *Lippincott.*
— Doctor Antonio: love story of Italy. 12°. $1.75. *Carleton.*
Rufus the unready. Finley, M. F. $1.25... *Pres. Bd.*
Rufus and Rose. Alger, H., *jr.* $1.25...... *Loring.*
Rufus Hill, the missionary child in Siam. 18°. 40c. *Am. S. S.*
Rugantine: drama. 16°. pap., 15c. .... *French.*
Ruge, Arn. Acht Reden üb. d. Religion. 12°. (St. Louis.) '68. pap., 50c. .... *Steiger.*
Ruggles, H: J. Method of Shakespeare as an artist. 16°. '70. $1.75 .... *Hurd & H.*
Ruhkopp, Julie. Trifles: a tale. 18°. 50c... *O'Shea.*
Rühl, K: Californien: üb. dessen Bevölkerung u. gesellschaftl. Zustände, polit., relig. u. Schul-Verhältnisse, Handel, Industrie, Minen, Ackerbau, etc.; mit Berücksicht. d. Minen-Regionen d. benachbarten Staaten u. Territorien. maps. 8°. '67. pap., $2.25 .... *Steiger.*
Ruined cities of the east. ill. 12°. $1 .... *Nelson.*
Ruined gamester. Reynolds, G. W. M. 50c. *Peterson.*
Ruined statues. Spalding, L. B. $1.50... *Lippincott.*
Ruins. *See* Volney, G. F. C.
Ruins of ancient cities. Bucke, C. $1.50... *Harper.*
Rule, W: Harris. Brand of Dominick: hist. of the inquisition. 12°. '53. $1.25...... *Meth. Bk. Conc.*
— Himnos evangélicos. 18°. '49. pap., 10c... *Am. Tr.*
Rule and exercise of holy living. *See* Taylor, Jer.
Rule and misrule of the Eng. in Am. Haliburton, T. C. $1.25 .... *Harper.*
Rule Britannia. Campbell, A. L. V. 15c. ... *French.*
Rule of faith. Peck, G. $1.25 ...... *Meth. Bk. Conc.*
Rule of life. 24°. 50c. .... *Strong.*
Rule of the monk. Garibaldi, G. 50c....... *Harper.*
Rule of three. Talfourd, F. 15c. .... *French.*
Rule a wife and have a wife. Beaumont, F., *and* Fletcher, J. 15c. .... *French.*
Rules for daily life: daily text-book. 32°. 20c. *Nelson.*
Rulof and Ernestine. 18°. '69. 45c. ...... *Whittaker.*
Ruloff, E: H. Life, trial and execution. [In Eng. or Germ.] 8°. '71. pap., 25c. .... *Barclay.*
Rum. Comstock, W. 15c. .... *De Witt.*
Rum fiend. Burleigh, W. H. 20c. .... *Nat. Temp.*
Rumford, *Count.* [*Sir* B: Thompson.] Works. 4 v. 8°. '70–'75. $5 .... *Am. Acad. of A. & S.*
— *Same;* with life by G. E. Ellis. 5 v. ill. 8°. $25; hf. cf., $40 .... *Estes.*
Rumor. Sheppard, E. S. $1.25; 75c. *Burnham; Estes.*
Rumplestilskin. Burnand, F. C. 15c. ...... *French.*
Run through Europe. Benedict, E. C. $2 .. *Barnes.*
Runaway. Hanaford, P. A. $1.25..... *H. A. Young.*
Runaway. *See* Wise, D.
Runaway: story for the young; by author of "Mrs. Jerningham's Journal." ill. fp. 8°. '72. $1.50. *Macmillan.*
Runaway boy. Hanaford, P. A. $1.25.. *H. A. Young.*
Runaway boy; or, sunshine in the valleys. 18°. 35c.; 45c. .... *Am. Bapt.*
Runaway flirt. Merz, K. $1 .... *Brainard.*
Runaway match. Wood, E. P. 25c....... *Peterson.*
Runaways. Baker, G. M. 15c. .... *Lee & S.*
Runaways and the gypsies: tale. 16°. 50c. *Routledge.*
Runkle, J: D. Asteroid supplement to new tables for $b_s^{(i)}$. 4°. '57. pap., $1 .... *Smith. Inst.*
— Tables for planetary motion. 4°. '56. pap., $1. *Smith. Inst.*
Runkle, W: M. Wontus; or, the corps of observation. ill. 12°. $1.75 .... *Lippincott.*
Runnells, J: S. *See* Iowa, Sup. Court reports.
Running the blockade. Thomes, W. H. $2.50.. *Lee & S.*
Running the blockade: Ethiop. drama. 16°. pap., 15c. *French.*
Running the gauntlet. *See* Yates, Edm.
Running to waste. *See* Baker, G: M.
Ruoff, A. J. F. Repertory of homœop. medicine nosologically arranged; tr. by A. H. Okie; with add. by G. Humphrey. 12°. $1.50 .... *Boericke.*
Rupert Aubrey. Potter, T. J. $1 .... *Noonan.*
Rupert Cabel. Alden, J. 75c. .... *Tibbals.*
Rupert Godwin. Braddon, M. E. 50c...... *Dick & F.*
Rupert Lawrence. *See* McKeever, H. B.
Ruppaner, Ant. Hypodermic injections, in treatment of neuralgia, rheumatism, gout and other diseases. 12°. '65. $1.25 .... *Burnham.*
— Principles and practice of laryngoscopy and rhinoscopy in diseases of the throat, etc. ill. 8°. '68. $1.50 .... *Lindsay.*
Ruppius, O: Ein Deutscher: Roman a. d. amerik. Leben. 12°. '75. 75c.; pap., 50c. .... *Zickel.*
— Lebensbilder a. d. Westen. 12°. '74. 75c.; pap., 50c. .... *Zickel.*
— Two hemispheres: romance; tr. by C. L. W. 12°. '69. $1.50; pap., $1 .... *Claxton.*
Ruppricht, S. Der Arzt als Hausfreund. 8th ed. 8°. '76. $2 .... *Zickel.*
Rural affairs. Thomas, J. J. 7 v. ea., $1.50.. *L. Tucker.*
Rural felicity. Buckstone, J. B. 15c. .... *French.*
Rural hours. Cooper, S. F. $2 .... *Putnam.*
Rural letters. Willis, N. P. $1.75 .... *Scribner.*
Rural poems. Barnes, W. $1.25; $2; $5.. *Roberts.*
Rural studies. Mitchell, D. G. $1.75...... *Scribner.*
Rural tales. *See* Happy child's lib.
Ruschenberger, W: S. W. [Works.] 8 v. ill. 12°. '42–'50 .... *Claxton.*
Cont.: Elements of anatomy and physiology, 45c. — of botany, 55c. — of conchology, 45c. — of entomology, 45c. — of geology, 50c. — of herpetology and ichthyology, 45c. — of mammalogy, 45c. — of ornithology, 55c.

Ruschenberger, W: S. W., *continued.*
— Elements of natural history, embr. zoology, botany and geology; with glossary. ('50.) New ed. 2 v. ill. 12°. '71. hf. mor., $4.50. — Lexicon of terms used. 12°. 45c. . . . . *Claxton.*

Rush, B: *See* Rush, R. *and* B.

Rush, Ja. Brief outline of analysis of human intellect. 2 v. 8°. $7.50 . . . . *Lippincott.*
— Philosophy of the human voice. 8°. $3.75 . . *Lippincott.*
— Rhymes of contrast on wisdom and folly: narr. dialogue. cr. 8°. $1.25 . . . . *Lippincott.*

Rush, J: Veterinary surgeon: handbook to veterinary homœop.; with add. from F. E. Günther's "Homœopathic veterinary"; tr. by J. F. Sheek. 24°. 50c. . . . . *Boericke.*

Rush, R: Occasional productions, political, diplomatic and miscellaneous. 8°. $2.25 . . . . *Lippincott.*
— *and* B: Recollections of the Eng. and Fr. courts, 1817–1849. por. 8°. $6 . . . . *Lippincott.*

Ruskin, J: ["Kata Phusin."] Works. 30 v. 12°. $44; pl., $52; — in 20 v., hf. cf., $78 . . . . *Wiley.*
— Selections from writings. 12°. $2; $2.50 . . . *Wiley.*
— Aratra pentelici: lectures on elements of sculpture. 12°. $1.50; pl., $3. — 8°. $4; large pap., $4.50. *Wiley.*
— Ariadne Florentina: lectures on wood and metal eng. 12°. $1.50; — pts. 4–6, $1 . . . . *Wiley.*
— Art culture: laws of art sel. from [his] works; comp. by W. H. Platt. ill. 12°. $3. — (School ed.), $2.50 . . . . *Wiley.*
— Crown of wild olive: lectures on work, traffic and war. 12°. $1; $1.50 . . . . *Wiley.*
— Deucalion: collected studies of the lapse of waves and life of stones. pts. 1–3 in 1 v. 12°. '76. $1. *Wiley.*
— Eagle's nest: 10 lectures on relation of natural science to art. 12°. $1.50 . . . . *Wiley.*
— Elements of drawing; in 3 letters to beginners. 12°. $1 . . . . *Wiley.*
— Elements of perspective. 12°. $1 . . . . *Wiley.*
— Ethics of the dust: lectures to little housewives on the elements of crystallization. 12°. $1.25; $1.75 . . . . *Wiley.*
— Fors clavigera: letters to the workmen and labourers of Gt. Brit. pts. 1, 2. ill. 12°. ea., $1 . . . *Wiley.*
— Frondes agrestes: readings on Modern painters; chosen by the Younger Lady of the Thwaite, Coniston. 12°. hf. mor., $2.50 . . *Scribner, W. & A.*
— *Same;* [also] Mornings in Florence. 12°. $1 . . *Wiley.*
— Inquiry into some of the conditions affecting "study of archit. in our schools." 12°. pap., 15c. . . *Wiley.*
— King of the Golden River; or, the black brothers. ill. 4°. $1.25 . . . . *Lee & S.*
— Lectures before Society of Architects. 12°. pap., 15c. . . . . *Wiley.*
— Lectures on architecture and painting. ill. 12°. $1.50. *Wiley.*
— Lectures on art. 12°. $1 . . . . *Wiley.*
— Love's meine: lectures on Greek and Eng. birds. pl. 12°. $1 . . . . *Wiley.*
— Modern painters. 5 v. pl. 12°. $18; hf. cf., $27; — without pl., $12; hf. cf., $20 . . . . *Wiley.*
— Munera pulveris: essays on elements of polit. economy. 12°. $1. 8°. $2; large pap., $2.50 . . *Wiley.*
— Poetry of architecture, villa and cottage. ill. 12°. $1.50 . . . . *Wiley.*
— Political economy of art. 12°. $1 . . . . *Wiley.*
— Precious thoughts, moral and religious, sel. from [his] works by Mrs. L. C. Tuthill. 12°. $1.50; $2 . . . . *Wiley.*
— Pre-Raphaelitism; [also] Notes on construction of sheepfolds; [also] King of the Golden River; or, the black brothers: legend of Stiria. 12°. $1 . . . . *Wiley.*
— Proserpina: studies of wayside flowers, while the air was yet pure among the Alps, and in the Scotland and England which my father knew. 12°. '76. $1 . . . . *Wiley.*

Ruskin, J: *continued.*
— Queen of the air: study of the Greek myths of cloud and storm. 12°. $1 . . . . *Wiley.*
— Sesame and lilies: lectures on books, women, etc. 12°. $1.50; $1.75. — 8°. $2; large pap., $2.50. *Wiley.*
— Seven lamps of architecture. ill. 12°. $1.75 . . *Wiley.*
— Stones of Venice. 3 v. 12°. $7; hf. cf., $12 . . *Wiley.*
Cont.: Foundations. — Sea stories. — The fall.
— Time and tide by weare and tyne: letters to a workingman on the laws of work. 12°. $1 . . . . *Wiley.*
— True and the beautiful in nature, art, morals and religion; sel. from works, with notice of R. by Mrs. L. C. Tuthill. por. 12°. $2; $2.50 . . *Wiley.*
— Two paths: lectures on art, and its applic. to decoration and manufacture. ill. 12°. $1.25 . . . . *Wiley.*
— "Unto the last": essays on first principles of polit. economy. 12°. $1 . . . . *Wiley.*
— *See also* Rendu, Le C., Theory of glaciers of Savoy.

Rusling, Ja. F. Across America; or, the great west and Pacific coast. ill. large 12°. $2 . . . . *Sheldon.*

Russel family. Hastings, A. 75c. . . . . *Dodd.*

Russell, Addison P. Library notes. 12°. '75. $2. *Hurd & H.*

Russell, Fs. T. Juvenile speaker. 12°. $1.25 . . *Harper.*

Russell, Fk. What Jesus says: arrang. of words of our Saviour; with index. 12°. '75. $2 . . (?) *Kalamazoo.*

Russell, G: B. Creed and customs. 12°. $2. *Ref. Ch. Pub.*
— Ripe harvest. 16°. 50c. . . . . *Ref. Ch. Pub.*

Russell, H. Rutherford. Tom: hist. of a very little boy. ill. 16°. $1 . . . . *Pott.*

Russell, J: (*Earl*). Recollections and suggestions of public life, 1813–1873. 8°. '75. $3 . . . . *Roberts.*

Russell, J: Scott. Modern system of naval architecture. 3 v. f°. [165 pl., 2 v.; text, 1 v.] $75; hf. mor., $150 . . . . *Appleton.*

Russell, Martha. Forger's daughter; or, out of the shadow into the sun. 12°. $1.75 . . . . *J. E. Potter.*

Russell, Mich. Works. 7 v. ill. 18°. ea., 75c. *Harper.*
Cont.: History of the Barbary states. — History of Nubia and Abyssinia. — History of Palestine. — History of Polynesia. — Life of Oliver Cromwell, 2 v. — View of anc. and mod. Egypt.

Russell, So. Loving kindness; or, Ashdown flower show. 18°. '72. 50c. . . . . *Dutton.*

Russell, T. O'Neill. Dick Massey: tale of the Irish evictions. 16°. '75. $1 . . . . *Kenedy.*

Russell, T: *See* Haven, G., *and* Russell, T.; — Nason, E., *and* Russell, T.

Russell, W. H. C. Autobiography of a London detective. 8°. pap., 75c. . . . . *Dick & F.*
— Diary of a detective police officer. 8°. pap., 75c. *Dick & F.*
— Experiences of a French detective. 8°. pap., 75c. *Dick & F.*

Russell, W: American elocutionist. ill. 12°. hf. roan, $1.35 . . . . *Ware.*
— Elocutionary reader. 12°. $1.25 . . . . *Dennet.*
— Introduction to reader. 12°. 63c. . . . . *Dennet.*
— Pulpit elocution; with obs. and sel. and introd. by E. A. Park and E. N. Kirk. ('46.) New ed. 12°. '69. $1.50 . . . . *Draper.*
— University speaker. 12°. $1.50 . . . . *Dennet.*
— *See also* Murdoch, J. E., *and* Russell, W.

Russell, W: History of modern Europe, with view of progress of society to 1763; with contin. by W. Jones. 3 v. ill. 8°. $6; shp., $7.50; hf. cf., $12.75 . . . . *Harper.*

Russell, W: Clark. Book of authors: collection of criticisms, mots, etc. 12°. $1.75; hf. cf., $3.75; cf., $5 . . . . *Scribner, W. & A.*
— Book of table-talk. cr. 8°. '74. $1.75; hf. cf., $3.50; cf., $5 . . . . *Routledge.*
— Representative actors: collection of criticisms, anecdotes, etc. 12°. 75c.–$5 . . . . . . *Scribner, W. & A.*

Russell, W: Howard. Canada, its defences, condition and resources: sequel to "My diary, north and south." 12°. '65. $1.50............Burnham.
— Diary in the east, during tour of Prince and Princess of Wales. ill. 8°. '69. $5..........Routledge.
— My diary during the last great [Franco-German] war. 8°. '73. $3.50...............Routledge.
— My diary north and south [U. S.] 8°. $1..Harper.
— *Same.* 12°. '63. $1.50...............Burnham.
— Todleben's defence of Sebastopol: review of Gen. Todleben's narrative. 12°. '65. $2..Van Nostrand.
Russell, *Sir* W: Oldnall. *See* England, Crown cases.
Russell. *See* James, G. P. R.
Russell Morton. Redford, A. H. 75c......So. Meth.
Russet leaves. Pummill, J. $2.........Lippincott.
Russian boy. 32°. '53. 30c...............Am. Tr.
Russian gypsy. Dumas, A. 50c...........Routledge.
Russian journey. Proctor, E. D. 16°. $1.50.— 12°. $3..............................Osgood.
Russian tailor. 18°. '60. 30c..............Am. Tr.
Rust, G: First steps to Latin prose composition. 18°. 60c...............................Macmillan.
Rustic library. *See* Mudge, Z. A.
Rustic pictures and random rhymes. Harpel, O. H. $2.................................Harpel.
Rustic prima donna: drama. 16°. pap., 15c...French.
Rusty needle; or, how the least sin appears in the sight of God. 18°. 18c. ....Am. S. S.
Ruter, Mt. History of the Christian church. 8°. $2.50. Cin. Meth. Bk. Conc.
Ruth, *Sister*. *See* Sister Ruth.
Ruth. Gaskell, E. C. $1.75........Scribner, W. & A.
Ruth. Haines, J. T. 15c...................French.
Ruth Allan. *See* Sunshine and shadow lib.
Ruth Allerton, the missionary's daughter. 16°. $1.10. Am. S. S.
Ruth and Aunt Alice. Bulfinch, M. H. $1...Dutton.
Ruth and her friends: story for girls. 18°. 75c. Carter; Dutton; Macmillan.
Ruth and little Jane. Charlesworth, M. L. 40c. Bost. Am. Tr.
Ruth and Naomi. Damrosch, L. $1.25; $1. G. D. Russell.
Ruth at service. 32°. 20c.; 15c.............Dutton.
Ruth Chenery. Davis, C. E. K. $1.25........Hoyt.
Ruth Cummings. Dunning, A. K. 45c......Pres. Bd.
Ruth Dean's birthday. *See* Bright gems for boys and girls; — Little girls' lib.
Ruth Derwent. Freeland, C. J. $1.15..Bost. Am. Tr.
Ruth Edwards' victory. Flint, S. A. 75c...Cong. Pub.
Ruth Ellis. B., E. V. $1.25...............Palmer.
Ruth Elmer: tale for school girls. 18°. 45c...Am. S. S.
Ruth Garnet. Ainsworth, W. H. 50c........De Witt.
Ruth Hawthorne. Beebe, E. N. $1.25.....Pres. Bd.
Ruth Lee; or, the true secret of cheerfulness. 18°. 60c..............................Am. S. S.
Ruth Lee and her companions; or, working for God. 18°. 60c.........................(?) Martien.
Ruth Lovell. May, C. L. $1.25 ....H. A. Young.
Ruth Maxwell. Blake, *Lady* —. $1.25; 75c...Estes.
Ruth Oakley. Harris, A., *and* Williams, T. J. 15c. French.
Ruth und die kleine Jane. 18°. 30c.......Ev. Assoc.
Rutherford, Alex. C. Lectures on doctrine of election. 12°. '54. 75c. ....Perkinpine.
Rutherford, S: Garden of spices: extracts from [his] letters; ed. by L. R. Dunn. 12°. $2; $2.50. Cin. Meth. Bk. Conc.
— Letters. 8°. '75. $2.50.....................Carter.
— Manna crumbs for hungry souls: excerpts from letters gathered by W. P. Breed. 12°. 80c...Pres. Bd.

Rutherford, W: Outlines of practical histology. 2d ed., rev. and enl. ill. 12°. '76. $1.25..Lindsay.
Ruthie Shaw. Monmouth, L. H. $1.......Lothrop.
Ruthie's venture. Hopkins, I. T. $1.25.....Am. Tr.
Ruthven. Harris, A. 15c....................French.
Ruthvens of Cedar Grove. Seymour, M. A. $1.25. Dutton.
Rutland [Vt.] centennial celebration, Oct., 1870. 8°. pap., 75c............................Vt. Hist.
Rutledge. Harris, M. C. $1.50 ....Carleton.
Ruttenber, E: M. History of Orange Co., [N. Y.]; with hist. of City of Newburgh. ill. 8°. '76. $3.50. Ruttenber.
— History of the tribes of Hudson River Indians: their origin, manners and customs. 8°. '72. $3.50. Munsell.
Rutter, H: Life, doctrine and sufferings of Jesus Christ, as recorded by the four evangelists; with notes. ill. 4°. hf. mor., $15.50; mor., $17.50; $18.50..........................Johnson & M.
— *Same*; with pref. by C. C. Pise. ill. 4°. $3–$18; — in 24 pts., ea., 25c. ....T. Kelly.
— — *See also* Orsini, M., Life of Virgin Mary.
— *Same*; [also] Acts of the apostles rendered into blank verse with notes; by C. C. Pise. ('52.) 24th ed. eng. 4°. '74. hf. mor., $10.50.. Virtue.
Rutter, W. C. Key to interest at from 5 to 10 per cent. ('59.) New ed. 24°. '70. 75c.......Pounsford.
Ruxton, G: F. Adventures in Mexico and the Rocky Mountains. 12°. $1.50.................Harper.
— Life in the far west. 12°. $1.50...........Harper.
Ruy Blas. Hugo, V. 15c...........De Witt; French.
Ruy Blas. *See Ditson.*
Ruyssel, E. van. *See* Van Ruyssel, E.
Ryan, —. Works. 17 v. obl. 8°. ea., 75c...Church.
Cont.: True accordion instructor — banjo instructor — bugle instructor — cabinet organ instructor — clarionet instructor — concertina instructor — cornet instructor — drum instructor — fife instructor — flageolet instructor — flute instructor — flutina instructor — guitar instructor — melodeon instructor — piano instructor — violin instructor — violoncello instructor.

Ryan, C: Systematic drawing and shading. ill. post 8°. $1...............................Cassell.
Ryan, E: *See* England, Common law reports; Crown cases.
Ryan, Ja. Algebra. 12°. hf. roan, $1.05..Lippincott.
— Astronomy. 18°. hf. roan, 56c.........Lippincott.
— Treatise on gauging. *See* Bonnycastle, J., Introduction to mensuration.
Ryan, Ja. E. *See* Zundel, J., *and* Ryan, J. E.
Ryan, Mich. Philosophy of marriage, in its social, moral and phys. relations. 16°. '75. $1..Lindsay.
Ryan, Ph. J. Consolation for those who mourn; or, treasury of the sick; tr. by M. O'Reilly. 16°. '73. 50c...................................Ryan.
Ryan, R: Everybody's husband: farce. 16°. pap., 15c.....................................French.
— Le pauvre Jaques: farce. 16°. pap., 15c....French.
— Quite at home: farce. 16°. pap., 15c......French.
Rydberg, Vct. Last Athenian; tr. by W. W. Thomas, jr. 12°. $2; pap., $1.50 ....Peterson.
Ryder, W: The superannuate: sketches of W. Ryder. 18°. '45. 50c. ....Meth. Bk. Conc.
Rye-House plot. Reynolds, G. W. M. $1.75; $1. Peterson.
Ryland, Archer. *See* England, Common law reports.
Ryland, Jona. E: *See* Foster, J., Life and correspondence.
Ryle, J: C: Call to prayer. 18°. '55. 20c...Am. Tr.
— *Same*. 18°. '67. 25c...N. Y. Ref. Ch. Bd.; Pres. Com.
— — *See also* Calls to the Saviour; — Hall, N., *and* Ryle, J. C.
— *Germ.* Aufruf zum Gebet. 32°. '64. 20c.; pap., 8c. ....Am. Tr.

Ryle, J: C: *continued.*
— Expository notes on the Gospels. 7 v. 12°. ea., $1.50 .... *Carter.*
Cont.: John, 3 v. — Luke, 2 v. — Mark. — Matthew.

— Home truths. 16°. '54. 75c. .... *Meth. Bk. Conc.*
— *Same.* ('56.) 2d ed. 18°. '74. 75c. .... *So. Meth.*
— *Same.* 5 v. 16°. $5 .... *Carter.*
Cont.: Living or dead. — Wheat or chaff. — Startling questions. — Rich and poor. — Priest and Puritan.

— Hymns of the church on earth. 24°. '60. $1 .. *Randolph.*
— Lebst Du, oder bist Du todt? 32°. '65. 15c.; pap., 5c. .... *Am. Tr.*
— Only one way of salvation. 18°. '67. 25c. *N. Y. Ref. Ch. Bd.; Pres. Com.*
— — *See also* Calls to the Saviour.
— Peace, be still. 32°. '62. 15c. .... *Am. Tr.*
— Spiritual songs for a month. 32°. '64. 35c. .. *Randolph.*
— Twelve hints to young men. 18°. 10c. ... *Pres. Bd.*

S., A. G. The holly boy. ill. 18°. '75. 25c. .. *Am. Tr.*
S., A. M. Scenes and sights of Bible lands. ill. 16°. 50c. .... *Nelson.*
S., E. O. Isolina; or, the actor's daughter: romance. 12°. $2 .... *Lippincott.*
S., E. W., *and* M., S. W. Children's hour. sq. 12°. '64. $1.25 .... *Claxton; Lippincott.*
S., F. E. Revival in Harrisburg, [Pa.]; ill. four weeks' work of E. P. Hammond. por. 12°. '76. pap., 20c. .... *E. S. German.*
S., H. M. L. A few words of advice to ladies on travelling and its requirements; with vocab. in Fr. and Germ. 12°. 50c. .... *Cook.*
S., H. W. *See* Smith, H. W.
S., J. Leandro; or, the sign of the cross: tale. 12°. '74. $1.50 .... *Cunningham; Sadlier.*
S., M. Alphonso; or, the triumph of religion. sm. 12°. '66. $1 .... *Cunningham.*
— Marion Howard; or, trials and triumphs. 12°. '72. $2 .... *Cunningham.*
S., M. F. The path she chose. 16°. '72. $1.25. *Routledge.*
S., M. H. Mollie's Christmas stocking, and other stories. 16°. '66. 60c. .... *Dutton.*
S., M. L. R. *See* Satterlee, M. L. R.
S., R. P. Holiness through faith. 16°. '70. 50c.; 75c. *Randolph.*
S., T. B. Illustrated songs and hymns for the little ones. ill. 16°. (Lond.) $1.25 ...... *Am. News.*
S., W. *See* Satterlee, W.
Sabbath (The). Elliott, C. 65c. .... *Pres. Bd.*
Sabbath (The). Everest, C. $1.50 .... *Ditson.*
Sabbath (The); [compr.] Christian Sabbath, by A. Ritchie; Civil Sabbath, by B. P. Aydelott; Desecration of the Sabbath, by W. C. McCune. 16°. 25c. .... *West. Tr.*
Sabbath abroad. Waterbury, J. B. $1.25 .. *Cong. Pub.*
Sabbath and the family. 18°. pap., 10c. .... *Am. Tr.*
Sabbath bell. Root, G. F. $1.50 .... *Ditson.*
Sabbath carols. Perkins, T. E. 30c.; 35c. .. *Barnes.*
Sabbath chimes. Punshon, W. M. $2; $3; $5. *Meth. Bk. Conc.*
Sabbath day readings. Corner, J. $1.25 .. *Pres. Bd.*
Sabbath a divine institution. 18°. pap., 10c. .. *Am. Tr.*
Sabbath guest. Emerson, L. O., *and* Morey, J. H. $1.50 .... *Ditson.*
Sabbath hours. Phelps, A. 75c. .... *Cong. Pub.*
Sabbath manual. 4 v. 18°. '45–'48. ea., pap., 10c. *Am. Tr.*
Cont.: Sabbath a divine institution. — Lord's day. — Sabbath and the family. — Mode of keeping the Sabbath.

Sabbath of the fields. Macmillan, H. $2 .. *Macmillan.*
Sabbath praise. Suffern, J. W. $1.38 .... *Gordon.*
Sabbath readings. White, E. G. 60c.; in 5 v., 50c. *Sev. Day Adv.*
Sabbath school chestnuts. Bullard, A. 60c. *Cong. Pub.*
Sabbath school concert. Trumbull, H. C. 30c. .. *Hoyt.*
Sabbath school gems of music and poetry. Cruikshank, J. *and* A., *and* Fish, F. H. 50c. .. *Barnes.*
Sabbath school harp. 32°. 15c. .... *Am. Bapt.*
Sabbath school help. Nevin, A. 50c. ...... *Claxton.*
Sabbath school hosanna. 16°. 35c.; pap., 30c. *Am. S. S.*
Sabbath school hymn and tune book. [French.] 18°. 10c. .... *Pres. Bd.*
Sabbath school hymn book. 32°. 30c.; bds., 20c. *Pres. Bd.*
Sabbath school lib. 100 v. 18°. $15 .... *Cong. Pub.*
Sabbath school melodist. Adams, J. G. 35c. *Universalist.*
Sabbath school offering. *See* Martin, *Mrs.* M.
Sabbath school psalmodist: sel. from the Psalms with music. obl. 16°. *net*, 25c. ..... *U. P. Bd. of Pub.*
Sabbath school results. Bullard, A. 75c. .. *Cong. Pub.*
Sabbath school songster. *See* Vormeida, S.
Sabbath school teacher. Todd, J. $1.50 .. *Bridgman.*
Sabbath school theology. Hall, J. 40c. .... *Pres. Bd.*
Sabbath school trumpet. Perkins, W. O. *and* H. S. 35c.; 30c. .... *Ditson.*
Sabbath schools. Aunt Mattie. 18°. 75c. .. *Graves.*
Sabbath songs for children's worship. Marshall, L., Proctor, J. C., *and* Burnham, S. 30c.; 35c. *Lee & S.*
Sabbath stories. Ballard, J. P. 70c. ...... *West. Tr.*
Sabbath talks about Jesus. *See* Ashton, *Mrs.* S. G.
Sabbath talks on Psalms. *See* Ashton, *Mrs.* S. G.
Sabbaths of our Lord. Stevens, W. B. $2.50; $3; $4.50 .... *J. M. Stoddart.*
Sabbaths with my class. Green, S. G. 40c. .. *So. Meth.*
Sabin, Jos. Catalogue of library belonging to Mr. Thomas W. Field. 8°. '75. $1; with prices, $2 .... *Sabin.*
— (*ed.*) Dictionary of books rel. to America. pts. 1–44. 8°. '68–'75. ea., $2; large pap., $4 ... *Sabin.*
Sabine, Lorenzo. Loyalists of the Am. rev.; with hist. essay. 2 v. 8°. '64. $7; hf. cf., $11. *Little, B. & Co.*
Sabine, Rob. History and progress of the electric telegraph; with descript. of some of the apparatus. 12°. $1.25 .... *Van Nostrand.*
— *See also* Clark, L., *and* Sabine, R.
Sabonadière, W: Coffee planter of Ceylon. 2d ed., rev. and enl. ill. cr. 8°. '70. $3 .... *Spon.*
Sabres and spurs. Denison, F. $2 .... *Freeman.*
Sabrina Hacket. ill. 16°. '69. $1.50 ...... *Lothrop.*
Sachtleben, A. Guide to correct pronunciation of the French lang. 12°. '70. 60c. .... *Univ. Pub.*
Sack of gold. Johnson, V. W. 50c. .... *Harper.*
Sacken, C: Rob. R. O. *See* Osten-Sacken.
Sackett, J. B. Masonic service for the burial of the dead and lodge of sorrow. 18°. '70. $1; mor., $1.50 .... *E. B. Myers.*
Sackville, T: Induction to a mirrour for magistrates. [Reprint of Southey's ed., '31]. 12°. '75. pap., 25c. .... *Fiske & D.*
Sacra privata. *See* Wilson, T:
Sacrament of responsibility; or, testimony of Scripture to teaching of the church on holy baptism. 12°. pap., 12c. .... *Claremont.*
Sacramental confession. Howson, J. S. $1 .. *Routledge.*
Sacramental meditations and advices. *See* Willison, J.
Sacred allegories. Adams, W. $4 .... *Lippincott.*
Sacred chorus book. Parker, J. C. D. $1.75 .. *Gordon.*
Sacred chorus book. White, E. L., *and* Gould, J. E. $2.50 .... *Ditson.*

Sacred cities. Lee, J. S. $1.25........ *Williamson.*

Sacred crown. Hodges, D. F. $1.50 ....*Lee & S.*

Sacred gift. *See* Diamond miniatures.

Sacred harmony. Jackson, S. $1.25..*Meth. Bk. Conc.*

Sacred harp. 18°. '74. 45c. ....*Routledge.*

Sacred harp. Mason, T. B. $1.25........ *Wilstach.*

Sacred heroes and martyrs. Headley, J. T. *$3.50; $4; $6 ....*Treat.*

Sacred history: Old Test. 18°. 50c. — New Test. 18°. 55c.; 60c. ....*Dutton.*

Sacred hour. Gaddis, M. P. $1..*Cin. Meth. Bk. Conc.*

Sacred Latin poetry. Trench, R. C. $2.50. *Macmillan.*

Sacred lute. Perkins, T. E. $1.50 ....*Huntington.*

Sacred lyre. Aldrich, J. 75c..............*Graves.*

Sacred lyrics. Ludden, W. 80c.; $4.......*Church.*

Sacred lyrics from the German. 12°. $1.50..*Pres. Bd.*

Sacred meditations. Upham, P. L. 60c.....*Harper.*

Sacred melodeon. Dalby, R. M. 40c.....*Pounsford.*

Sacred melodeon. Hayden, A. S. $1.25... *Wilstach.*

Sacred melodies: hymns and songs. ('38.) New ed. 18°. '70. 35c......................*Freewill.*

Sacred philosophy of the seasons. *See* Duncan, H.

Sacred poems. ill. 16°. $1.50; mor., $3......*Lee & S.*

Sacred poems. 12°. $1.75................*Routledge.*

Sacred poetry of early religions. Church, R. W. 50c. *Macmillan.*

Sacred praise. Hastings, T. 60c...........*Barnes.*

Sacred songs. Hopkins, C. J. $1.25; $1....*Gordon.*

Sacred songs; with music. 18°. '75. 50c...*Lothrop.*

Sacred songs for social worship. Rice, F. B. 50c.; 75c. ....*Goodrich.*

Sacred songster. Carpenter, J. E. 25c. ..*Routledge.*

Sacred star. Marshall, L. $1.38...........*Ditson.*

Sacred wreath: Cath. hymns. 24°. 30c.; pap., 20c. *Cummiskey.*

— *See also* Manual of the sodality.

Sacrifice of praise; with tunes, hymns and spiritual songs; with notes on the origin of hymns. 8°. '69. hf. roan, $2.50; $2.75; $3. — (chp. ed.) 8°. $2; hf. roan, $2.25; — without tunes, $1.25; $2 ....*Randolph.*

Sacristan's household. Trollope, F. E. 75c...*Harper.*

Sad adventure. *See* Little Rosy's travels.

Sad history of James Parker. 18°. pap., 25c...*Am. S. S.*

Sadi, *the Persian.* Gulistan; or, rose garden; tr. by F. Gladwin, with pref. by R. W. Emerson. 16°. $2.50 ....**Osgood.*

Sadie (*pseud.*) Rainbows in springtide. ill. 16°. 50c. *Routledge.*

Sadler, L. R. ["Jac. Larwood"], *and* Hotten, J: Camden. Signboards, their hist.; with anecdotes of famous taverns and remarkable characters. 12°. $3 ....*Routledge.*

Sadler, Mich. F. Church doctrine, Bible truth. 12°. '69. $1.50 ....*Pott.*

— Church teacher's manual of Christian instruction: catechism expounded and expl. in question and answer. 16°. '75. $1 ....*Pott.*

— Communicant's manual. 32°. '76. 40c........*Pott.*

— Emmanuel; or, the incarnation of the Son of God the foundation of immutable truth. 8°. '67. $3. *Pott.*

— Lessons on the Church catechism; with Scripture ref. 16°. 20c.........................*Dutton.*

— Lost Gospel. 8°. '76. $3..................*Pott.*

— One offering (The). 16°. '75. $1 ....*Pott.*

— Second Adam and the new birth: doctrine of baptism as cont. in Scripture. 12°. pap., 15c...*Claremont.*

Sadler, Percy. Stepping-stones to Eng. grammar. 16°. 20c. ....*Sadlier.*

Sadler, Percy, *continued.*

— Translating Eng. into Fr. (cours de versions); rev. and annot. by C. F. Gillette. New ed., rev. and enl. by B. Maurice. ('63.) new ed. 12°. '76. $1.25..................................*Holt.*

Sadler, S. Whitechurch. African cruiser (The): a midshipman's adventures on the west coast. ill. 16°. $1.25..........................*Routledge.*

— Marshal Vavasour. ill. 12°. 75c............*Pott.*

— Ship of ice. ill. 12°. $1.50................*Nelson.*

— Slave dealer. ill. 16°. 50c.................*Pott.*

Sadler, T: Edwin Wilkins Field: memorial sketch; with address in hall of Incorporated Law Soc., by Sir R. Palmer. por. cr. 8°. '72. $1.75..*Macmillan.*

Sadlier, *Mrs.* Ja. *See* Sadlier *Mrs.* Ma. Anne.

Sadlier, *Mrs.* Ma. Anne. [Tales.] 17 v. .... *Sadlier.*

Cont.: Aunt Honor's keepsake. — Con O'Regan. — MacCarthy More. — New lights; or, life in Galway, *ea.*, 16°, $1; $1.50. — Bessy Conway; or, the Irish girl in America. — Confessions of an apostate. — Elinor Preston, *ea.*, 16°, 75c.; $1.25. — Blakes and the Flanagans. — Heiress of Kilorgan. — Hermit of the rock. — Maureen Dhu. — Old and new. — Old house by the Boyne, *ea.*, 16°, $1.25; $1.75. — Daughter of the Tyrconnell. — Father Sheehy, etc., *ea.*, 18°, 50c.; 75c. — Willy Burke, 18°, 60c. — Confederate chieftains, 12°, $2; $2.50.

— [Dramas.] 6 v. 18°. ea., 25c.............*Sadlier.*

Cont.: Babbler. — Elder brother. — Invisible hand. — Julia; or, the gold thimble. — The secret. — The talisman.

— Catechism of sacred hist. 18°. 25c........*Sadlier.*

— Young ladies' reader. 12°. $1.25..........*Sadlier.*

— (*tr.*) Ten stories from the Fr. 18°. 50c.; 75c. *Sadlier.*

Sadlier's excelsior [ser. of geographies]; by a Cath. teacher. 4 v. ill. 4°. and sm. 4°. '76. bds. *W. H. Sadlier.*

Cont.: No. 1, 40c. — No. 2, $1. — No. 3, $1.88. — Sadlier's excelsior introd. to geog., 75c.

Sadlier's excelsior [readers]; by a Cath. teacher. 4 v. '76. bds. ....*W. H. Sadlier.*

Cont.: Sadlier's excelsior first reader, 16°, 25c. — second, 16°, 50c. — third, 12°, 75c. — fourth, 12°, $1.

Sadlier's fireside lib. 12 v. 16°. $9.25; $15.25..*Sadlier.*

Saeltzer, Alex. Treatise on acoustics in connection with ventilation. 12°. '72. $2... *Van Nostrand.*

Safe compass. Newton, R. $1.25..........*Carter.*

Safely married. Jolly, E. 50c. ....*Harper.*

Safest creed. Frothingham, O. B. $1.50...*Somerby.*

Safford, Ann Eliza. Memoir of Dan. Safford. ill. 12°. $1.50..........................*Bost. Am. Tr.*

Safford, Ja. M. *See* Introduction to resources of Tenn.; — Tennessee geol. survey.

— *and* Killebrew, J. B. Elementary geology of Tennessee: being also an introd. to geology in general; for schools of Tenn. 8°. '76. $1.... *Tenn. Agri.*

Safford, O. P. Devotional melodies. [Sing. book.] 18°. '76. 40c.................... *Universalist.*

Safford, T. H. Catalogue of standard polar and clock stars. *See* Harvard Coll. Astron. Observ.

Safford, W: H. Blennerhasset papers; [incl.] private journal of H. Blennerhasset and unpub. corresp. of Burr, Alston, C. Tylor, etc.; with memoir of Blennerhasset. por. 8°. '65. $3.50.. *Wilstach.*

Safia. Beauvoir, R. de. 50c. ....*Harper.*

Sagacity of animals: stories. 18°. 30c.; 40c. *Am. Bapt.*

Sage es Jesu. 18°. 45c.................. *Ev. Assoc.*

Sage stuffing for green goslings. Rowley, H. $2.50. *Routledge.*

Sagean, Mathieu. Extrait de la relation des avantures et voyage de Mathieu Sagean. 8°. '63. pap., $2. *Shea.*

Sagen u. Märchen. Hoffmann, F. 25c.......*Steiger.*

Sagen vom Rübezahl. Hoffmann, F. 25c.....*Steiger.*

Sages and heroes of the Am. revolution. Judson, C. L. $2.50 ....*Lee & S.*

Saigey, Emile. Unity of natural phenomena: introd. to study of forces of nature; tr. from the French, with notes and introd. by T. Moses. cr. 8°. '73. $1.50 ....*Estes.*

Sail on the river. *See* Cousin Belle.

Sailing on the Nile. Laporte, L. $1.50 ...... *Roberts.*

Sailing order ser. 4 v. 16°. $3 .... *Lothrop.*
Cont.: Sailing orders. — Ben's boyhood. — Book stall boy. — Young whaler.

Sailing orders. Gladstone, G. 75c. .... *Lothrop.*

Sailing party. 18°. 30c. .... *Dutton.*

Sailor boy. 18°. 17c.; 22c. .... *Am. Bapt.*
— *See also* Better home.

Sailor boy. Adams, W. T. $1.50 .... *Lee & S.*

Sailor boy ser. *See* Adams, W: T.

Sailor boys. Hanks, S. W. 75c. .... *Cong. Pub.*

Sailor brother. Pratt, L. M. 50c. .... *Lothrop.*

Sailor of France. Johnstone, J. B. 15c. .... *French.*

Sailor's companion. Engles, W. M. 80c. .. *Pres. Bd.*

St.
Note. For names of canonized persons *see* under name following St.

St., W. v. In exile: tr. from the Germ. [Fiction.] 12°. $2 .... *Lippincott.*

St. A., J. H. Basket of flowers: tale for the young. ill. 18°. 50c.; 75c. .... *Nelson.*

Saint Abe. Buchanan, R. $1.50 .... * *Osgood.*

Saint and his Saviour. *See* Spurgeon, C. H.

Saint and sinner. Plumer, W. S. 25c. .... *Pres. Bd.*

St. Augustine's ladder. Noble, A. L. $1.50 .. *Lothrop.*

St. Cadog's well; or, the stolen dog. 18°. 25c. *Scribner, W. & A.*

Saint Cecilia. Damrosch, L. $1.50; $1.25 ... *Pond.*

St. Cecilia. Manigault, G. $1.50 .... *Lippincott.*

Saint Cecilia's day. Bree, J. J. v. $1.25; $1 .. *Ditson.*

St. Clair, C. G. Mass. 8°. $1.25; pap., $1 .. *Gordon.*

St. Clair of the Isles. Helme, E. 25c. .... *Lippincott.*

St. Cupid. Jerrold, D. 15c. .... *French.*

St. David's day. Dibdin, T. 15c. .... *French.*

St. Dominic's manual; or, tertiary's guide; by two fathers of the Order. 24°. $1–$12 .... *Sadlier.*
— *See also* Dominican manual.

St. Dominic's mission book: instructions for missions, with prayers, etc. 24°. 75c.–$3.50 ..... *O'Shea.*

St. Dominique, *Countess* Caithness de (*pseud.*) Animal magnetism (mesmerism) and artificial somnambulism. 12°. '74. $1.50 .... *Colby.*

St. Elmo. Evans, A. J. $2 .... *Carleton.*

St. Flore; or, the fatal promise. 8°. pap., 25c. *Dick & F.*

St. George and St. Michael. MacDonald, G. $1.75 .. *Ford.*

St. George's key. Coghlan, W. E. $1 .. *Scribner, W. & A.*

Saint Germain, Cp. Doctor and student: dialogues between a doctor of divinity and a student in laws of Eng.; cont. grounds of those laws, with questions conc. equity thereof; with two pieces conc. suits in chancery by subpœna. New ed., rev. by W. Muchall. 8°. '74. $3 .... *Clarke.*

Saint-Germain, J. T. de (*pseud.*) *See* Tardieu, J. de.

St. Helena; or, finding of the holy cross: drama. 12°. pap., 30c. .... *Kelly, P. & Co.*

St. James. *See* Ainsworth, W: H.

St. James lectures (The). companions for the devout life. 8°. '75. $3 .... *Pott.*

St. John, *Mrs.* Eugenia (*pseud.*) [*Mrs.* Martha E. Berry.] Bella; or, the cradle of liberty: story of insane asylums. ('73.) 3d ed. 12°. '75. $1.50. *Berry.*

— Irene Page, a life prisoner in cradle of liberty. 12°. $1.75 .... *Berry.*

— John Moore: mistakes in cradle of liberty. 12°. $1.75. *Berry.*

— Nathan Bird: true kindness in cradle of liberty. 12°. $1.75 .... *Berry.*
Note. Works written by Mrs. Berry under her real name will be found entered under Berry: the identity of the two writers not being known when that part of the Catalogue was printed.

St. John, Ja. A. Lives of celebrated travellers. 3 v. 18°. $2.25 .... *Harper.*

St. John, Percy B. Arctic Crusoe; or, sea of ice. ill. 16°. $1.50. 12°. $1 .... *Lee & S.*
— Rival Crusoes. ill. 8°. (Lond.) 50c. .... *Am. News.*
— Silent hunter. 8°. pap., 20c. .... *Beadle.*

St. John, S: Elements of geology. ill. 12°. $1.50. *Putnam.*

St. John, T. E. Melodies of heaven: hymns and tunes. 16°. 50c. .... *Williamson.*

St. John's Gospel. 32°. '62. 15c. .... *Am. Tr.*

St. John's manual: guide to public worship and services of Cath. Church, and coll. of devotions for private use. 18°. $1.50–$25 .... *Strong.*

St. Jure, J: Bapt. Treatise on knowledge and love of Jesus Christ; tr. by a Sister of Mercy. 3 v. 12°. $7.50 .... *O'Shea.*
— Union with our Lord Jesus Christ in his principal mysteries; tr. 16°. $1.25; mor., $2.50 .. *Sadlier.*

Saint Leger. Kimball, R. B. $1.75 .... *Carleton.*

St. Leonards, *Lord.* *See* Sugden, E.

St. Louis Acad. of Science. *See* Academy of Science.

St. Louis and Calvin. Guizot, F.P. G. $1.75 .. *Lippincott.*

St. Louis in chains: drama. 12°. '71. pap., 40c. *Murphy.*

Saint-Marc Girardin. *See* Girardin.

Saint-Mars, N. Cisterne de Courtiras, *Vicomtesse* de. ["*La Comtesse* Dash."] Mademoiselle Fifty Millions; tr. by Mme. Chaudron. 8°. pap., 60c. *Appleton.*

St. Martin, Menard. Defense of Jesus; tr. by P. Cobden. 16°. $1 .... *Cin. Meth. Bk. Conc.*

St. Martin's eve. Wood, E. P. $1.75; $1.50 .. *Peterson.*

St. Mary's eve. Bernard, W. B. 15c. .... *French.*

St. Maur *or* Seymour, E. A. *See* Somerset, *Duke of.*

Saint of Nazareth. *See* Marie Josephine.

St. Olave's. Tabor, E. 75c. .... *Harper.*

St. Patrick's day. Sheridan, R. B. B. 15c. ... *French.*

Saint Patrick's eve. Lever, C. 50c. .... *Peterson.*

St. Patrick's eve. Power, T. 15c. .... *French.*

St. Patrick's manual. *See* Cusack, M. F.

St. Paul. *See* Mendelssohn-Bartholdy, F.

Saint Paul. Myers, F. W. H. 25c. ...... *Randolph.*

St. Paul and Protestantism. Arnold, M. $1.75. *Macmillan.*

St. Paul in Rome. *See* Butler, C. M.

St. Paul in Rome. Macduff, J. R. $1.25 ..... *Carter.*

St. Peter. *See* Paine, J. K.

St. Peter's chain of Christian virtues. Oliver, C. D. 75c. .... *So. Meth.*

St. Philip's. Harris, M. C. $1.50 .... *Carleton.*

Saint Pierre, Jacques H: Bernardin de. Paul et Virginie. With vocab. 12°. '52. $1 .. *G. R. Lockwood.*
— *Same;* ill. par de la Charlerie. 4°. $30; hf. mor., $50 .... *Appleton.*
— *Same;* [also] La chaumière indienne. ill. roy. 8°. hf. mor., $20 .... *Appleton.*
— *Eng.* Paul and Virginia. 32°. 35c. ... *U. P. James.*
— — *Same.* ill. 32°. 38c. .... *Appleton.*
— — *Same.* 18°. '68. 75c. — ill. 12°. $1.50 .. *Claxton.*
— — *Same;* with introd. and preface now first tr. ill. cr. 8°. $1.75–$6 .... *Hurd & H.*
— — *Same;* with memoir of author. ill. 12°. $1 .. *Porter.*
— — *See also* British pocket classics; — Goldsmith, O., Vicar of Wakefield; — La Motte Fouqué, F., Loves of Undine and Sintram.
— — *Same;* [also] Elizabeth; or, the exiles of Siberia; from the Fr. of Mme. Cottin. 12°. '68. $1.25. *Claxton.*

St. Ronan's well. *See* Scott, *Sir* Wa.

Saint-Simon, *Duke of.* [L: de Rouvroy.] Memoirs during reign of Louis XIV. and the regency; tr. and ed. by B. St. John. 3 v. ill. 8°. $10.50. *Scribner, W. & A.*

St. Simon's niece. Benedict, F. L. $1.50; $1..*Harper.*

St. Vincent de Paul (Brotherhood of). Clifton tracts. 4 v. 12°. $3........................*Strong.*

— *See also* Vincent de Paul, *St.*

St. Vincent's manual. [Cath. prayer book.] 24°. '51. $1–$30............................*Murphy.*

Saint Vladimir; or, the martyrs of Kief. 18°. 50c. *Dutton.*

St. Winifred's. Farrar, F. W. $1.75..*Dutton; Mason.*

Sainte-Beuve, C: A: Celebrities of the past and present; [tr. and ed.] by M. Maceuen. 12°. '74. $1.50............................*Porter.*

— English portraits; sel. and tr. from "Causeries du lundi;" with introd. on life and writings. 12°. '75. $2................................*Holt.*

— Memoirs of Madame Desbordes-Valmore; tr. by H. W. Preston. 16°. '72. $1.50........*Roberts.*

— Portraits of celebrated women; tr. by H. W. Preston. 16°. '68. $1.50 ....*Roberts.*

Sainte-Foi, C: Mission and duties of young women; tr. by C. I. White. ('72.) 4th ed. 18°. '76. 60c..............................*Kenedy.*

Saintine, Xav. Boni. Dame Nature and her three daughters; tr. ill. 16°. '69. $1.25. *Hurd & H.*

— Myths of the Rhine; tr. by M. S. De Vere; ill. by G. Doré. 4°. '74. $10; mor., $18 ...*Scribner.*

— Picciola, the prisoner of Fenestrella; or, captivity captive; tr. ill. 12°. $1..............*Mason.*

— *Same.* 12°. $1.25 ....*Appleton.*

— *Same.* 12°. $1.25; pap., 50c. ....*Scribner, W. & A.*

— *Same.* ill. cr. 8°. $1.75–$6. — (Cabinet ed.) ill. 16°. $1.25–$4.50 ....*Hurd & H.*

— *See also* Masterpieces of foreign literature.

Saint's everlasting rest. *See* Baxter, R:

Saint's inheritance. Guthrie, T. $1.50.......*Carter.*

Saint's inheritance. Loughborough, J. N. 10c. *Sev. Day Adv.*

Sakuntala. *See* Belohnte Treue.

Sala, G: A: Quite alone. 8°. pap., 75c. ....*Harper.*

— Story of the Comte de Chambord: triology. 16°. '73. bds., 50c. ....*Routledge.*

— Terrible tales. ill. 8°. (Lond.) pap., 30c. *Am. News.*

— Two prima donnas (The). 8°. pap., 25c...*Peterson.*

Salad for the solitary and the social. *See* Saunders, F:

Salary grab. Robinson, W. S. 40c..........*Lee & S.*

Salathiel. *See* Croly, G.

Sale of Crummie. 18°. 75c..................*Carter.*

Salem, *Mass.* First church in Salem, 1634. ill. 24°. pap., 10c..............................*Essex.*

— — *See also* Sketch of founders.

— Proceedings upon dedication of Plummer Hall, Oct. 6, 1857. 8°. '58. pap., 30c. ....*Essex.*

— Town records, 1634–1659. 8°. '68. $2......*Essex.*

Salem [Mass.] English High School. Catalogue, reunion, etc. ill. 8°. '57. 50c.............*Essex.*

Salem. Castleton, D. R. $1.25 ....*Harper.*

Sales, *St.* François de. *See* François de Sales, *St.*

Sales, Fs. Josse's Spanish grammar. 12°. '69. $2. *G. R. Lockwood.*

Salisbury, S. Star spangled banner and national songs. *See* American Antiq. Soc.

Salkeld, Jos. Classical antiquities: compend. of Roman and Grecian antiquities, incl. sketch of anc. mythology. maps. 18°. 75c......*Harper.*

— First book in Spanish. 12°. shp., $1.50 ...*Harper.*

Sallust [*Lat.* Sallustius] Crispus, Caius. Opera; [with] lit. tr. by J. Hamilton; ed. by T. Clark. roy. 12°. hf. leath., $2.25 ....*Desilver.*

— Conspiracy of Catiline [*Lat.*]; ed. with introd. and notes by J. H. Allen and J. B. Greenough. ('73.) 2d ed. 12°. '75. $1 ....*Ginn.*

— *Same;* ed. by P. Bullions. 12°. $1.50 ....*Sheldon.*

Sallust [*Lat.* Sallustius] Crispus, Caius, *continued.*

— *Same;* [also] Jugurthine war; with Eng. comment. and geog. and hist. indexes by C. Anthon. 12°. shp., $1.50..........................*Harper.*

— — *Same;* with notes and vocab. by N. Butler and M. Sturges. 12°. $1.75.............*Appleton.*

— — *Same;* with Eng. notes; ed. by H. R. Cleveland. 12°. '38. hf. roan, 75c. ....*Claxton.*

— — *Same;* ed. by G. Long. 18°. 75c.......*Harper.*

— — *Same;* [ed.] by C. Merivale; with notes. 2 v. fp. 8°. ea., 75c. ....*Macmillan.*

— — *Same;* ed. by L. Schmitz and C. G. Zumpt. roy. 18°. '52. 60c.; hf. bd., 70c..............*Lea.*

— — *Same;* with notes, lexicon, etc., by G. Stuart. ('70.) 5th ed. 16°. '75. hf. leath., $1.25..*Eldredge.*

— — *Eng.* History of the Jugurthine war, and Conspiracy of Catiline; tr. by W. Rose. 18°. 75c. *Harper.*

— *and* Florus, Lucius Annæus, *and* Velleius Paterculus, Caius. Works; tr., with notes, biog. and index, by J. S. Watson. 12°. $1.50..*Harper.*

— — — *Same.* 12°. (Bohn.) $1.75...*Little, B. & Co.*

— — — *Same.* 12°. (Bohn.) $2. *Lippincott; Scribner, W. & A.*

Sally Grafton and her teacher. *See* Meadowside stories.

Sally in our alley. Jerrold, D. 15c..........*French.*

Sally Williams. Cheney, E. D. $1.50 ......*Lee & S.*

Salmagundi. *See* Irving, Wash.

Salmon, G: Reign of law, and other sermons. cr. 8°. '73. $2.25 ....*Macmillan.*

Salmon, J: Old and young: farce. 16°. pap., 15c. *French.*

Salmonia. Davy, *Sir* H. $1.50............*Roberts.*

Salmos en verso. *See* Psalms.

Salome, the dancer. Loos, I. K. 40c ...*Ref. Ch. Pub.*

Salomons, A. Handbook of the diseases of the eye. 16°. '69. $1.50.................*Jas. Campbell.*

Salon (Der). *See* Heine, H:

Saloquah. *See* Goulding, F. R.

Salt Lake City and Utah: 12 views with descript. letter-press. obl. 24°. 75c...............*Nelson.*

Salt water. Kingston, W. H. G. $1.25...*Lippincott.*

Salt water Dick. Nowell, H. P. H. $1......*Lee & S.*

Salted with fire. Cameron, R. $1............*Hale.*

Salter, Fk. Economy in use of steam. ill. cr. 8°. '74. $1.50 ....*Spon.*

Salter, Ja. A. Dental pathology and surgery. ill. 8°. $4.50...............................*W. Wood.*

Salutation. Emerson, L. O. $1.38 ....*Ditson.*

Salvation. McCord, W. J. 35c. ....*Pres. Bd.*

Salvation by Christ. Wayland, F. $1.50..*Lothrop.*

Salvation from sin. Walsh, J. T. 10c. ......*Chase.*

Salvation from sin, end of Christian faith. Noyes, J. H. 25c...................................*Oneida.*

Salvation to eternal life, not salvation to kingdom of heaven. 16°. '68. 30c.; pap., 15c....*Claxton.*

Salverte, Eusebe. Philosophy of magic, incl. prodigies, apparent miracles, etc.; tr. by A. T. Thomson. 2 v. 12°. $2. ....*Harper.*

Salyards, Jos. Idothea; or, the divine image: poem. 8°. '74. $1.50; mor., $2.50...........*Henkel.*

Salzburger exodus. (Fatherland ser.) ill. 16°. 85c. (?) *Luth. Pub.*

Salzman, Chr. Gotthilf. What God does is well done; tr. by E. T. Disosway. 16°. $1.25. *Cin. Meth. Bk. Conc.*

Sam; or, a good name. Keary, M. 50c. *Scribner, W. & A.*

Sam Bolton's cottage, and what kept his wife from church. 18°. 75c..................(?) *Martien.*

Sam Lawson's fireside stories. Stowe, H. B. 75c.; $1. *Osgood.*

Sam Silva. *See* Little Fan's lib.

Sam Slick, the clock-maker; — in England; — in search of a wife. *See* Haliburton, T. C.

Sam Slick's nature and human nature; — sayings and doings. *See* Haliburton, T. C.

Sam Weller. *See* Dickens, C:

Samarow, Greg. (*pseud.*) *See* Meding, Guido.

Sambo's legacy. *See* Power, P. B.

Sambo's return: Ethiop. drama. 16°. pap., 15c. *Happy.*

Sameness of words no hindrance to devotion. Coit, T. W. 10c. ... *W. H. Young.*

Samenkörner. Bickel, P. W. 30c. ... *Germ. Bapt.*

Sammlung von geistreichen Sterb- u. Begräbniss Liedern, f. Christen. 32°. leath., 40c. ... *Baer.*

Sammy Gill; or, the little pet mocking bird, and other stories. 18°. 35c. ... *Am. S. S.*

Sampson, Ez. Brief remarker on ways of man: essays and sketches of life. 12°. $1.50 .. *Appleton.*

— (*ed.*) Beauties of the Bible; with remarks and brief dissertations. 16°. $1 ... *Harper.*

Sampson, Fs. S. On Hebrews. ('56.) New ed. 8°. '66. $3 ... *Carter.*

Sampson, H: History of advertising; ill. by anecdotes, specimens, notes, etc. ill. cr. 8°. '75. $3. *Routledge; Scribner, W. & A.*

Sam's arrival. Oxenford, J. 15c. ... *French.*

Sam's chance. Alger, H., *jr.* $1.25 ... *Loring.*

Sam's courtship. White, C. 15c. ... *De Witt.*

Sam's friend. *See* Little Blue Mantle lib.

Samson. Das Leben Simsons. 18°. 30c. .. *Ev. Assoc.*

Samson, G: Whitefield. Elements of art criticism. 8°. $3.50; — abridg., $1.75 ... *Lippincott.*

— Physical media in spiritual manifestations; ill. from anc. and mod. testimony. 16°. $1.25 .. *Lippincott.*

Samson. *See* Handel, G. F.

Samson Agonistes. *See* Milton, J:

Samuel Gunn, the lay reader. 18°. 30c. ... *Dutton.*

Samuel in search of himself. Coyne, J. S. 15c. *French.*

Samuel J. Tilden unmasked. Buckman, B. E. $1. (?) *Buckman.*

Samuel Tyndale; or, the little hero. 18°. 22c. *Am. S. S.*

Samuels, Adelaide F. Dick and Daisy ser. 4 v. ill. 16°. ea., 50c. ... *Lee & S.*
Cont.: Adrift in the world; or, Dick and Daisy's early days. — Fighting the battle; or, Dick and Daisy's city life. — Saved from the street; or, Dick and Daisy's protégés. — Grandfather Milly's luck; or, Dick and Daisy's reward.

— Dick Travers abroad ser. 4 v. ill. 16°. ea., 50c. *Lee & S.*
Cont.: Little Cricket; or, Dick Travers in London. — Palm land; or, Dick Travers in the Chagos Islands. — Lost tar; or, Dick Travers in Africa. — On the wave; or, Dick Travers aboard the Happy Jack.

Samuels, E: A. Among the birds: sketches for young folks, ill. domestic life of our feathered friends. ill. 16°. '67. $1.25 ... *Lockwood, B. & Co.*

— Birds of New England and adjacent states. ('67.) 6th ed., rev. with app. 8°. '75. $4; — with col. pl., $7.50; $9; $15. — large pap. ed., $25; hf. mor., $30; $32; mor., $40 .... *Lockwood, B. & Co.*

— *See also* Arnold, A. C. L., *and* Samuels, E. A.

Samuels, *Mrs.* S. B. C. Cherry, the singer. ill. 16°. $1 ... *Lockwood, B. & Co.*

— Springdale stories. 6 v. ill. 16°. ea., 75c. .. *Lee & S.*
Cont.: Adele. — Herbert. — Eric. — Nettie's trial. — Johnstone's farm. — Ennisfellen.

San Domingo: pen pictures and leaves of travel. Keim, DeB. R. $1.50 ... *Claxton.*

Sanborn, E. D. History of New Hampshire. 8°. '76. $2–$3.25 ... *J. B. Clarke.*

Sanborn, F. B. Prison question in Am. *See* Wines, E. C., Prison conference at Brussels.

— Work of social science, past and present: report, Detroit, May 13, 1875. [Am. Soc. Sci. Assoc.] 8°. '75. pap., 10c. ... *Williams.*

— — *See also* American Social Science Assoc.

Sanborn, Kate A. Home pictures of Eng. poets; for fireside and school-room. ill. 12°. $1 .. *Appleton.*

Sancte Cæcilia. Kaim, A. $1.25; — voice pts., 25c. *Church.*

Sanctification. Adams, J. Q. 25c. ... *Hoyt.*

Sanctuary. Everts, W. W. 60c. ... *Sheldon.*

Sanctuary. Kreissmann, A. $3; $2.50 .. *G. D. Russell.*

Sanctuary. Nichols, G. W. $1.50 ... *Harper.*

Sanctuary: drama. 16°. pap., 15c. ... *French.*

Sanctuary: Sunday school vocal class-book. sq. 16°. per doz., *net*, $2.75 ... *Sadlier.*

Sanctuary and 2300 days. Andrews, J. N. 10c. *Sev. Day Adv.*

Sanctum sanctorum. Tilton, T. $1.50 ... *Sheldon.*

Sanctus (The). Hamilton, E. $1.38 ... *Ditson.*

Sand, George (*pseud.*) [*Mme.* A. L. A. D. Dudevant.] [Novels; tr.] 11 v. ... *Peterson.*
Cont.: Consuelo. — Countess of Rudolstadt, *ea.*, 12°, $1.50; 8°, pap., 75c. — Monsieur Antoine, 12°, $1; 8°, pap., 75c. — Fanchon, the cricket, 12°, $1.50; pap., $1. — Indiana. — Jealousy; or, Teverino, *ea.*, 12°, $1.50. — First and true love, 12°, pap., 75c. — Consuelo; [also] Countess of Rudolstadt, 8°, $2. — Corsair. — Last Aldini. — Simon, *ea.*, 8°, pap., 50c.

— *Same.* 6 v. 16°. '70–'74. ea., $1.50 ... *Roberts.*
Cont.: Antonia; tr. by V. Vaughan. — Mauprat; tr. by V. Vaughan. — Miller of Angibault; tr. by M. E. Dewey. — Monsieur Sylvestre; tr. by F. G. Shaw. — My sister Jeannie; tr. by S. R. Crocker. — Snow-man; tr. by V. Vaughan.

— *Same.* 4 v. 8°. '71. ea., $1.25; pap. ... *Estes.*
Cont.: Cesarine Dietrich. — Marquis de Villemer; tr. by R. Keeler, *ea.*, 75c. — Handsome Lawrence: sequel to "Rolling stone." — Rolling stone, *ea.*, 50c.

— La petite fadette. With Eng. notes by F. Bôcher. ('65.) New ed. 12°. '76. $1.25 ... *Holt.*

— *See also* Stoddard, R. H., Bric-a-brac ser.

Sand, Maur. (*pseud.*) [J. F. M. A. Dudevant.] Callirhoe; tr. by S. A. da Ponte. 12°. '71. $1.75. *Claxton.*

Sand hills of Jutland. Andersen, H. C. $1.50 .. *Lee & S.*

Sandars, W. C. *See* Bué, J., *and* Sandars, W. C.

Sanday, W: Authorship and hist. character of the fourth Gospel. cr. 8°. '72. $3.50 ... *Macmillan.*

— Gospels in 2d cent.: exam. of crit. part of "Supernatural religion." cr. 8°. '76. $3.75 .. *Macmillan.*

Sandeau, Jul. Mademoiselle de la Seiglière: comédie. ('65.) New ed. 12°. '76. pap., 40c. .. *Holt.*

— Maison (La) de Penarvan: comédie. With Eng. notes by F. Bôcher. ('64.) New ed. 12°. '76. pap., 40c. ... *Holt.*

— Seagull rock; tr. by R. Black. ill. cr. 8°. $3. — 12°. $1.25; pap., 50c. ... *Scribner, W. & A.*

— *See also* Cross of Berny.

Sanders, C: W. English and Germ. pictorial primer. 32°. 30c. ... *Ivison.*

— New speller, definer and analyzer. ill. 16°. '54. bds., 25c. ... *Ivison.*

— Pictorial primer. ill. 16°. '58. bds., 18c. ... *Ivison.*

— [Readers.] 5 v. ... *Ivison.*
Cont.: First, 32°, 28c. — Second, 32°, 50c. — Third, 16°, 75c. — Fourth, 12°, $1.20. — Fifth, 12°, $1.25.

— School speaker. 12°. '57. $1.50 ... *Ivison.*

— Test speller. 16°. '66. bds., 25c. ... *Ivison.*

— Union [ser. of readers and spellers]. 11 v. '58–'67. *Ivison.*
Cont.: Union reader, no. 1, 16°, bds., 28c. — *Same*, in Leigh's orthog., 32c. — No. 2, 16°, bds., 50c. — No. 3, 12°, bds., 75c. — No. 4, 12°, $1.25. — No. 5, 12°, $1.50. — No. 6; or, rhetorical reader, 12°, 1.88. — Union pictorial primer, 12°, bds., 20c. — *Same*, in Leigh's orthog., 25c. — Union primary speller, 16°, bds., 20c. — Union speller, 16°, bds., 25c.

— Union speaker. 12°. '64. 90c. ... *Ivison.*

— *See also* Perkins, T. E., Taylor, A., *and* Sanders, C. W.

— *and* McElligott, J. N. Analysis of Eng. words. 12°. '59. pap., 80c. ... *Ivison.*

— *and* Mess, J. Phonetic speller. 16°. '61. bds., 25c. *Ivison.*

Sanders, D. *See* Pennsylvania, Constitution.

Sanders, Fs. Williams. Essay on uses and trusts and on nature of conveyances at common law and of those which derive their effect from statute of uses. 2d Am. ed., ed. by G. W. Sanders and J. Warner. 2 v. in 1. 8°. shp., $5.50....*Kay.*

Sanders, G. J. Hub. French student's first book; based upon Ollendorff's method. 12°. '48. hf. bd., 60c. ....*Fortescue.*

— Practical course of French grammar; based on Ollendorff's method. 12°. '47. $1.25..*Fortescue.*

Sanders, Harry. Sweet incense: concert pieces for the Buell family. obl. 16°. pap.,15c. *D. H. Carroll.*

— *See also* Hull, A., *and* Sanders, H.

— *and* Grape, J: T. Hearts and voices: sel. of new and sacred music. obl. 16°. pap., 10c...*D. H. Carroll.*

Sanders, J. Milton. Physics of chemistry. *See* Gregory, W., Handbook of inorganic chemistry.

Sanderson, J. Burdon. *See* Burdon-Sanderson, J.

Sanderson, J. M. Complete cook. ('49.) New ed., rev. and enl. 12°. '74. $1.25.........*Claxton.*

Sanderson, J: Biography of signers to the Declaration of independence. por. 8°. hf. mor., $7.50; mor., $10..........................*Desilver.*

Sanderson, J: P. Republican landmarks: views of Am. statesmen on foreign immigration. 8°. $1.50..........................*Lippincott.*

Sanderson, Jos. Jesus on the Holy Mount. 12°. '69. $1.25; 80c..........................*Am. Tr.*

Sandford, Lew. H. *See* New York City, Superior Court reports; — New York State, Chancery reports.

Sandford, P: P. Wesley's missionaries to Am. 12°. '37. 90c....................*Meth. Bk. Conc.*

Sandford and Merton (History of). *See* Day, T:

Sandford and Merton (New history of). Burnand, F. C. $1.75..........................*Roberts.*

Sandhurst, Ph. T., *and* Stothert, Ja. (*ed.*) Masterpieces of European art. [To form 34 pts.] pts. 1–8. roy. 4°. '76. ea., *50c.; India pap. proofs, ea., $2..........................*Gebbie.*

Sands, Alex. Hamilton. Practical forms. 2d ed., enl. 2 v. 8°. '72. hf. cf., $5........*J. W. Randolph.*

Sands, B: F. Reports on solar eclipse of Dec. 22, 1870. *See* United States, *Naval Observatory.*

Sands, H. B. On tracheotomy and laryngotomy. *See* Seguin, E. C., Series of Am. clin. lect.

Sands, Natl. Philosophy of teaching: the teacher, the pupil, the school. 8°. $1..........*Harper.*

Sands, Rob. C: *See* Tales of Glauber Spa.

Sandwich Island notes; by a Häolé. ill. 12°. $1.50. *Harper.*

Sandwiches. Browne, C. F. 25c........*Carleton.*

Sandy Cameron; or, the way one looks at it; by author of "Ruth Allerton." 16°. $1..*Am. S. S.*

Sandy Duncan. *See* Bright gems for boys and girls; — Little boys' lib.

Sandy foundation shaken. *See* Penn, W:

Sandy Maclean: story of Scot. persecution. ('64.) New ed. ill. 18°. '72. 50c..............*Hoyt.*

Sanford, *Rev.* D. P. Pocket book of private prayers. 32°. 15c.; roan, 50c..................*Dutton.*

Sanford, *Mrs.* D. P. [Cora ser.] 3 v. 32°. ea., 15c.; 20c. ....*Dutton.*

Cont.: Cora and Hattie. — Cora and her cousins. — Cora and the little ones.

— Cousin Ellen's stories. 32°. 50c..........*Dutton.*

— Eddy's tickets. 32°. 15c.; 20c............*Dutton.*

— Eunice Somers, a learner in life's school. 16°. '71. $1..........................*Dutton.*

— Frisk and his flock. ill. 4°. '75. $2.25....*Dutton.*

— Grandma Berry's secret. 32°. 20c.; 15c....*Dutton.*

— Green house, and who lived in it. 32°. 20c.; 15c. *Dutton.*

Sanford, *Mrs.* D. P., *continued.*

— Houseful of children. sm. 4°. $2.25.......*Dutton.*

— Julie and Gilbert. 32°. 20c.; 15c.........*Dutton.*

— Lessons on Scripture narrative. 2 pts. 18°. ea., 20c. *Dutton.*

— Little child's Bible picture book. 3 pts. 32°. ea., 15c.; 20c.; — in 1 v., 40c..............*Dutton.*

Cont.: Old Test. through hist. of Balaam. — Old Test. from Samuel, and life of Christ. — New Test. parables, miracles, etc.

— Little Frank's story book. ill. 18°. '72. 50c. *Dutton.*

— Little Nell's story book. ill. 18°. '72. 50c...*Dutton.*

— Mark, the fisher boy; and other stories. ill. 18°. '71. 75c..........................*Dutton.*

— Names and their meanings. ill. 16°. '71. 75c. *Dutton.*

— Pussy Tip-Toe's family. New ed., rev. ill. 4°. '74. $2.25..........................*Dutton.*

— Rose buds. 32°. 20c.; 15c................*Dutton.*

— Rose Dale books. 3 v. 16°. '75. $3.......*Dutton.*

Cont.: Rose, Tom and Ned. — Ida and baby Bell. — Five happy children.

— Under the sky-light. 18°. 50c.............*Dutton.*

— [Willy ser.] 3 v. 32°. ea., 20c.; 15c......*Dutton.*

Cont.: Willy's cherry tree. — Willy's new teacher. — Willy's winter corner.

— Young laymen; or, boy workers of Wiltham parish. ill. 16°. '72. 90c. ....*Dutton.*

Sanford, J: Langton. The Stuarts and the Puritan revolution. (Epochs of hist.) 16°. $1...*Estes.*

Sanford, *Mrs.* Lucy E. History of two lives. 18°. '75. 50c..........................*Nat. Temp.*

Sanford, Lucy E. Prayer: selections. 32°. '73. 25c.; 40c. ....*Am. Tr.*

Sanford, Shelton P. Analytical common school arithmetic. 12°. hf. roan, 90c...........*Lippincott.*

— Higher analyt. arith. 12°. hf. roan, $1.40. *Lippincott.*

— Intermediate analyt. arithmetic. 16°. hf. roan, 50c. *Lippincott.*

— Primary analyt. arith. 16°. hf. roan, 30c. *Lippincott.*

Sang, E: Progressive lessons in applied science. pts. 1–3. cr. 8°. '75. ea., $1.25.............*Spon.*

Cont.: 1. Geometry on paper. — 2. Solidity, weight and pressure. — 3. Trigonometry, vision, surveying instruments.

Sanger, G: P. *See* Massachusetts, General statutes; — United States, Digest; Statutes at large.

Sanger, W: W. History of prostitution: report to Board of Almshouse Governors of N. Y. City. 8°. ('58.) $5..........................*Harper.*

Sänger (Der) am Grabe. 18°. 50c. ....*Kohler.*

Sänger-Fest. Dressler, W. $1.50 ....*Peters.*

Sängerlust: neuestes illustr. [deutsches] Taschenliederbuch, mit amerik. Volksliedern in engl. Sprache. sm. 16°. '74. 75c.; bds., 50c... *Witter.*

Sangster, *Mrs.* M. E. Five happy weeks. ill. 18°. '75. 50c..........................*Am. Tr.*

— Home and heaven: book of thoughts and sketches. ill. 16°. $1.......................*Bost. Am. Tr.*

— Splendid times. ill. sm. 4°. '75. $1.......*Am. Tr.*

Sanitary siftings; or, results of sewage systems compared; by a naval officer. 8°. pap., 20c...*Spon.*

Sankey, C: *See* Cox, G. W., *and* Sankey, C.

Sankey, Ira D. *See* Bliss, P. P., *and* Sankey, I. D.; — Moody, D. L., *and* Sankey, I. D.

Sankey, P. M. Catechism of Old Test. history. 32°. '58. 10c..........................*Pott.*

Sankey, W. H. O. Lectures on mental diseases. 8°. '66. $3.25..........................*Lindsay.*

San-Poh. Nevius, J. L. 55c..............*Pres. Bd.*

Sans merci. *See* Lawrence, G: A.

Sans-souci series. *See* Stoddard, R. H.

Sansom, Arth. Ern. Chloroform: its action and administration. 12°. '66. $2...........*Lindsay.*

— Lectures on phys. diagnosis of diseases of the heart. 12°. '76. $1.50..........................*Lindsay.*

Sanson, *Abbé.* Paradise of the earth; or, true means of finding happiness in the religious state; tr. by Ig. Sisk. 12°. '70. $1.50; $2........*Murphy.*
Santa Claus and his friend St. Nicholas. ill. 12°. '76. $1.50..............................*World Pub.*
Santa Claus' frolics. Baker, G. M. 15c......*Lee & S.*
Sapelo. *See* Goulding, F. R.
Saphit, Adph. Conversion; ill. by examples in the Bible. 16°. $1.50..................*Routledge.*
Saphir, M. G. Werke; mit Vorrede v. Friedrich d. Lachenden. 6 v. 12°. $9.50–$5........*Radde.*
Sapling and the tree. Matthews, J. E. 35c. *N. Y. Ref. Ch. Bd.; Pres. Com.*
Sappho. *See* Gounod, C. F.
Sappington, J: Theory and treatment of fevers; rev. by F. Stith. 18°. shp., $1............*Desilver.*
Sarah, the creole. Barnett, M. 15c..........*French.*
Sarah Barry's home. Eames, J. A. 70c.....*Dutton.*
Sarah Watkins; or, crumbs for the birds. 18°. 25c. *Scribner, W. & A.*
Sarah White; or, the pleasant Sabbath day. [In rhyme.] 18°. 18c.....................*Am. S. S.*
Sarah Wolston. 18°. 30c...................*Dutton.*
Sarah's young man. Suter, W. E. 15c. *French; Lee & S.*
Sarasa, Ant. Alph. de. Art of always rejoicing. 16°. '73. 75c.........................*H. A. Young.*
Saratoga: comic drama. 16°. pap., 15c......*French.*
Saratoga: Indian tale of frontier life in 1787. 12°. $1.75; pap., $1.50..................*Peterson.*
Saratoga in 1901. Landon, M. D. $2......*Sheldon.*
Sarchedon. Melville, G. J. W. 60c. .....*Appleton.*
Sardanapalus. Byron, *Lord.* 15c..........*French.*
Sardinia. ill. 16°. 50c.......................*Pott.*
Sardou, Alfr. *See* Lambert, E., *and* Sardou, A.
Sardou, Victorien. Fernande: dráma. 16°. pap., 15c. ....*De Witt.*
Sargeant, T: *See* Pennsylvania, Supreme Court reports.
Sargent, C. S. Few suggestions on tree planting; from report of Mass. State Board of Agric. for 1875. 8°. '76. pap., 50c.................. *Williams.*
Sargent, Epes. American adventure by land and sea. 2 v. 18°. $1.50.....................*Harper.*
— Arctic adventures by sea and land. ill. 12°. $2. *Thompson.*
— Intermediate standard speaker. 12°. $2..*Desilver.*
— New ser. of readers........................*Shorey.*
Cont.: Standard primer, 16°, 24c. — Standard first, 16°, 35c. — Standard second, 16°, 56c. — Standard third, 12°, 70c. — Intermediate, 12°, 80c. — Standard fourth, 12°, $1.12. — Standard fifth, 12°, $1.38.
— [Old ser. of readers.]....................*Shorey.*
Cont.: Standard primer, 16°, 24c. — Standard first, 16°, 35c. — Standard second, 16°, 56c. — Standard third, 12°, 70c. — Standard fourth, 12°, $1.12. — Standard fifth; or, first class reader, 12°, $1.38.
— Original dialogues. 12°. $1.50............*Shorey.*
— Planchette; or, despair of science: account of mod. spiritualism. 16°. '69. $1.25..........*Roberts.*
— Primary standard speaker. 16°. hf. roan, 60c. *Desilver.*
— Pronouncing speller. 16°. 32c............*Shorey.*
— Proof palpable of immortality: account of materialisation phenomena of modern spiritualism. 12°. '75. $1; pap., 75c.......................*Colby.*
— Selections in poetry; for exercises at school and at home. ill. 12°. $1.50 ....*Desilver.*
— Standard primary spelling book. 16°. 24c...*Shorey.*
— Standard speaker. cr. 8°. hf. roan, $2.50..*Desilver.*
— Standard spelling book. 16°. 38c.........*Shorey.*
— Woman who dared. [Poem.] 16°. '69. $1.50..*Roberts.*
— Wonders of the Arctic world: hist. of the discoveries, with hist. of Polaris expedition by W. H. Cunnington. ill. roy. 12°. '73. $2.50..*J. E. Potter.*
— *See also* new American ser. [of readers, etc.]
Sargent, Fitzwilliam. On bandaging and other operations of minor surgery. ill. roy. 12°. $1.75..*Lea.*
Sargent, G: E. Bedfordshire tinker: hist. of John Bunyan. ill. 18°. 35c...............*Pres. Bd.*
— Chronicles of an old manor house. 16°. $1.50..*Pres. Bd.*
— Ethel Ripon. *See* Little Dot ser.
— Faithful son; or, three Christmas eves. ill. 16°. '75. $1.25.......................................*Hoyt.*
— Grafton family, and other tales. ill. 12°. $1 ..*Nelson.*
— Letters to parents of S.-school children; rev. by T. O. Summers. ('55.) 2d ed. 18°. '76. 50c. *So. Meth.*
— Lucy, the light-bearer. ill. 18°. '72. 50c...*Am. Tr.*
— *Same.* ill. 16°. $1.........................*Crowell.*
— — *See also* Apron-strings lib.
— Old sailor's story. ('74.) New ed. 16°. '75. $1.25. *Hoyt.*
— *Same.* ill. 12°. $1.25....................*Nelson.*
— Poor clerk (The). ill. 12°. $1.25.........*Nelson.*
— Story of a child's companion. ill. 18°. '73. 60c. *Lothrop.*
— Sunday evenings at Northcourt. 16°. $1 ..*Pres. Bd.*
— *Same.* 16°. $1.50 ....*Cong. Pub.*
— Two New Year's days, and other narr. and sketches. ('66.) New ed. ill. 16°. '68. $1.15......*Hoyt.*
Sargent, H: W. Skeleton routes through England, Scotland, Ireland, Wales, Denmark, Norway, Sweden, Russia, Poland and Spain. 18°. $1. *Appleton.*
Sargent, Lucius M. Stage coach (The). ill. 18°. 75c.; pap., 30c...........................*Bost. Am. Tr.*
— Temperance tales. 6 v. ill. 18°. ea., 75c.; — in 21 v., ea., 5c.–30c. ....*Bost. Am. Tr.*
Cont.: My mother's gold ring, etc. — Fritz Hazell, etc. — A word in season, etc. — Kitty Grafton as a medicine. — The stage coach. — The life preserver, etc.
Sargent, Nath. ["Ol. Oldschool."] Public men and events from 1817 to 1853. 2 v. 8°. $6..*Lippincott.*
— *See also* Linn, E. A., *and* Sargent, N.
Sargent, Winthrop. History of the expedition against Fort Du Quesne, 1755, under Gen. E: Braddock. maps and pl. 8°. '55. $5...*Claxton; Lippincott.*
— — *See also* Historical Soc. of Penna.
Sarmiento, Domingo F. Aritmética práctica: primera parte. 12°. 50c. ....*Appleton.*
— Escuelas (Las): base de la prosperidad y de la república en los Estados Unidos. 8°. $3.50. *Appleton.*
— Método de lectura gradual. ill. 18°. pap., 20c. *Appleton.*
— *See also* Lincoln, A., Vida.
Sarmiento, F. L. Life and adventures of Miss Maj. Pauline Cushman, Union spy and scout. por. and ill. 12°. $1.75 ....*J. E. Potter.*
Saroni, A. E. Musical grammar. 16°. 75c...*Gordon.*
Saroni, Hm. S. Lily Bell, the culprit fay. [Cantata.] 8°. $1 ....*Church.*
— Twin sisters. [Operetta.] obl. 12°. '60. bds., 50c. *Ditson.*
Sartaroe. Maitland, J. A. $1.75; $1.50..*Peterson.*
Sartor resartus. *See* Carlyle, T:
Sarum missal (The). 8°. '68. $10...........*Pott.*
Sarver, J. Sermon on Odd-fellowship and other secret societies. 12°. pap., 10c.....*E. A. Cook.*
Sasnett, W: Jere. Discussions in literature and religion. 12°. '58. $2 ....*So. Meth.*
— Progress; considered with particular ref. to the Meth. Episc. Church, south. 12°. '59. $1.25..*So. Meth.*
Satan. Cranch, C. P. 75c.................*Roberts.*
Satan in Paris. Selby, C. 15c.............*French.*
Satan in society. Cook, N. F. *$2........... *Vent.*
Satanella. *See* Ditson.
Satanstoe. *See* Cooper, Ja. F.
Satanus: extravaganza. 16°. pap., 15c......*French.*
Satchel guide for vacation tourists in Europe. New ed. maps. 16°. '76. roan, $2..........*Hurd & H.*
Satchel series for leisure hours and holiday rambles; by W. Collins, M. E. Braddon and others. v. 1, 2. ill. 8°. '75. ea., 50c.............. *W. F. Gill.*

Satin dress, and other stories. 18°. 35c. ..... *Nelson.*
— *See also* Uncle Barnaby's budget.
Satisfactory portion. George, A. C. 60c. *Cin. Meth. Bk. Conc.*
Satterlee, F. LeRoy. Neuroses of the skin. 8°. pap., 25c. ..... *Campbell & Co.*
Satterlee, M. L. R. *and* W. Two legends of the Christ-child; for Christmas-tide. 4°. 60c. ..... *Lent.*
Saturday afternoon. 18°. 25c.; 30c. ..... *Dutton.*
Saturday afternoon ser. *See* Denison, *Mrs.* M. A.
Saturday evening. Smith, B. B. 25c. ..... *Whittaker.*
Saturday evenings with my children. 18°. 35c. *Cong. Pub.*
Satyricon. Petronius Arbiter, T. $1 ..... *D. Thomas.*
Saul. Heavysege, C. $2 ..... * *Osgood.*
Saunders, C. H. Pirate's legacy: drama. 16°. pap., 15c. ..... *French.*
Saunders, F: Evenings with sacred poets: quiet talks about singers and their songs; with app. on hymnology. cr. 8°. '69. $3.50. 12°. $1.75 ... *Randolph.*
— Monologue on matrimony; [from "Salad for the solitary and social"]. 8°. pap., 25c. ..... *Lent.*
— Salad for the solitary and the social; redressed and compounded with sundry add. esculents, succulents and condiments. ill. 8°. '71. $4–$10 .. *Lent.*
— Toilet (The) and its devotees; [from "Salad for the solitary and social"]. 8°. pap., 25c. ..... *Lent.*
— Woman, love and marriage. 12°. $1.50 ... *Carleton.*
— (*ed.*) Illustrated festival of song. [Selections.] ill. roy. 8°. *$3.75–$8 ..... *Scammell.*
Saunders, G: Scientific self-instructing school for the violin. 4°. '47. bds., $1.25 ..... *Ditson.*
Saunders, J: [Novels.] 4 v. 8°. pap. ..... *Harper.*
Cont.: Abel Drake's wife. — Bound to the wheel, *ea.*, 75c. — Hirell. — Martin Pole, *ea.*, 50c.
— Israel Mort, overman: story of the mine. ill. 16°. $1.25 ..... *Lippincott.*
Saunders, Kath. Gideon's rock. 16°. $1 .. *Lippincott.*
— High mills. ill. 8°. $1.25; pap., 75c. ... *Lippincott.*
Saunders, Sim. M. Domestic poultry: treatise on preferable breeds of poultry, their hist. and leading characteristics. ill. 12°. 75c.; pap., 40c. ... *Judd.*
Saunders, T: W: Treatise upon law applicable to negligence; with notes of Am. cases by H. Hooper. 8°. '72. shp., $3.75 ..... *Clarke.*
Saunders, Thorndyke. Bankruptcy practice. 8°. '68. shp., $2.50 ..... *Ward & P.*
Saunterer's series. 14 v. 18° ..... *Osgood.*
Cont.: Warner's Saunterings, $1.25. — Howells' Chance acquaintance, $1.25. — Howells' Their wedding journey, $1.25. — Holmes' Autocrat of the breakfast table, $1.50. — C. Thaxter's Among the Isles of Shoals, $1.25. — Howells' Poems, $1.25. — Exotics, $1.25. — K. Field's Haphazard, $1.25. — Howard's One summer, $1.25. — K. Field's Ten days in Spain, $1.25. — Waring's Whip and spur, $1.25. — Warner's Baddeck and that sort of thing, $1. — Stoddard's South sea idyls, $1.25. — Boyesen's Gunnar, $1.25.
Saunterings. Warner, C. D. $1.25 ..... *Osgood.*
Sauremonde: tradition of the Black Mountain. 18°. pap., 12c. ..... *O'Shea.*
— *See also* Secret of riches.
Saurin, Ja. Sermons; tr. by R. Robinson, H. Hunter and J. Sutcliffe. New ed., rev. by S. Burder; with pref. by J. P. K. Henshaw. 2 v. por. 8°. $4; hf. cf., $8.50 ..... *Harper.*
Sausage makers. White, C. 15c. ..... *De Witt.*
Sauvage, Elie. The little gypsy; tr. by I. M. Luyster. ill. sq. 12°. '68. $1.25 ..... *Roberts.*
Sauveur, Lambert. Causeries avec les enfants. 12°. '74. $1.25 ..... *Holt.*
— *Eng.* Chats with the little ones. ill. 8°. '74. $2.50. *Holt.*
— — *Same;* tr. by Mrs. S. A. Bigelow. ill. 4°. '75. $2 ..... *Estes.*
— Causeries avec mes élèves. ill. 12°. '74. $1.50 .. *Holt.*
— Entretiens sur la grammaire. 12°. '74. $1.75 .. *Holt.*

Sauveur, Lambert, *continued.*
— Introduction to teaching of living languages without gram. or dict. 12°. '74. pap., 50c. ..... *Holt.*
— Petites causeries. 12°. '74. $1.25. — ill. 12°. '74. $2 ..... *Holt.*
Sauzay, A. Wonders of glass-making in all ages. ill. 12°. '71. $1.25 ..... *Scribner.*
Savage, H: Surgery, surgical pathology and surgical anatomy of the female pelvic organs: col. plates with commentaries, notes and cases. 3d ed., enl. 4°. '76. $14 ..... *Lindsay.*
Savage, J: Life of W: Carleton. *See* Carleton, W:
— Poems. 12°. $2.25 ..... *Strong.*
Savage, Marmion W. Bachelor of the Albany. 12°. $1.50 ..... *Harper.*
— My uncle, the curate. 8°. pap., 50c. ..... *Harper.*
— Woman of business. 8°. pap., 75c. ..... *Appleton.*
Savage, Ma. S. Margaret and Bessie. 16°. 90c. *Cong. Pub.*
Savage, Minot Judson. Christianity the science of manhood: book for questioners. 16°. '73. $1.50. *Osgood.*
— *Same.* 2d ed. 12°. '74. $1.50 .. *Lockwood, B. & Co.*
Savarin, Brillat. Handbook of dining; or, corpulency and leanness scientifically considered; tr. by L. F. Simpson. 12°. $1 ..... *Appleton.*
Save the erring. Langille, J. H. 45c. ..... *Am. Tr.*
Saved from the sea. Kingston, W. H. G. $1.75. *Nelson.*
Saved from the street. Samuels, A. F. 50c. ... *Lee & S.*
Savery, W: Journal. 12°. 75c. ..... *Friends Bk. St.*
Saville, J: Faucit. Miller's maid: drama. 16°. pap., 15c. ..... *French.*
— Wapping Old Stairs: drama. 16°. pap., 15c. ... *French.*
Savin, Una (*pseud.*) *See* Hepworth, *Mrs.* G. H.
Saving and spending; or, right use of money. 18°. 75c. ..... *Whittaker.*
Saving faith. Chamberlayne, I. $1.25 .. *Meth. Bk. Conc.*
Saving knowledge. Guthrie, T., *and* Blaikie, W. G. $1.75 ..... *Routledge.*
Saviour we need. Helffenstein, J. 65c. ..... *Pres. Bd.*
Saviour's claim. Pollock, R. H. 40c. *U. P. Bd. of Pub.*
Sawyer, *Mrs.* Caro. M. Merchant's widow. 16°. 50c. *Williamson.*
Sawyer, G: A. Fret-sawing and wood-carving for amateurs. ill. sq. 16°. $1.50 ..... *Lee & S.*
Sawyer, H: E. Latin primer. 12°. bds., 40c. *Potter, A. & Co.*
Sawyer, Lorenzo S. B. *See* United States, Circ. and Dist. Court reports.
Sawyer, T. J. Flower basket. 16°. 50c. ... *Williamson.*
Saxe, J: Godfrey. Poems. 16°. $1.50. — (Blue and gold ed.) por. 32°. $1.25; hf. cf., $2.50; mor., $3. — (Cabinet ed.) por. 16°. $1.50; hf. cf., $3; mor., $4. — New ed. 16°. '68. $2.25; hf. cf., $4.50; mor., $6. — (Highgate ed.) 16°. $1.50; hf. cf., $3; mor., $4. — (Diamond ed.) 18°. $1; hf. cf., $2.25; mor., $3. — (Red-line ed.) por. and ill. sm. 4°. $3.50; hf. cf., $5; mor., $7 ..... *Osgood.*
— Clever stories of many nations rendered in rhyme. ill. sm. 4°. '64. $3.50 ..... *Osgood.*
— Fables and legends of many countries, rendered in rhyme. 16°. '72. $1.50 ..... *Osgood.*
— Leisure day rhymes. 16°. '75. $2; hf. cf., $3.50; mor., $4.50 ..... *Osgood.*
— Masquerade (The), and other poems. 16°. '66. $1.75. *Osgood.*
— Money-king, and other poems. por. 16°. '59. $1. *Osgood.*
— Proud Miss McBride; ill. by A. Hoppin. sm. 4°. '73. $2.50; mor., $5.50 ..... *Osgood.*
Saxelford. May, E. J. $1.25 ..... *Routledge.*
Saxon studies. Hawthorne, J. $2 ..... *Osgood.*

Saxton, N. *See* New Jersey, Court of Chanc. reports.
Saxton, W: W. *See* New York State, Excise law.
Say, J: Bapt. Treatise on political economy; tr. with notes by C. R. Prinsup. ('32.) New Am. ed., with add. notes by C. C. Biddle. 8°. '69. shp., $2.50 .... *Claxton.*
Say, T: Description of shells of No. Am. 68 col. pl. 8°. '34. $10.50 .... *Acad. of Nat. Sci.*
— Entomology: descript. of insects of No. Am.; ed. by J. L. Le Conte, with memoir by G. Ord. 2 v. 54 col. pl. 8°. $15; hf. cf., $20 .... *Estes.*
Say and do ser. *See* Warner, S.
Say and seal. Warner, S. $2 .... *Lippincott.*
Sayers, T: *and* Heenan, J: C. Lives. 8°. pap., 50c. *De Witt.*
Sayings and doings: farce. 16°. pap., 15c... *Happy.*
Sayings and doings of children. Smith, J. B. 75c. *Ward.*
Sayings of Dr. Bushwacker. Cozzens, F. S. $1.50. *Hurd & H.*
Sayings of the great forty days. Moberly, G. $2.50. *Dutton.*
Sayings of sages. 12°. '63. $1.50... *Meth. Bk. Conc.*
Sayler, J. R. *See* Ohio, Statutes.
Sayles, J: Book of [legal and business] forms for Texas. 8°. '76. shp., $5 .... *E. H. Cushing.*
— Notes to Texas reports (v. 1-31). 8°. '72. shp., $7.50 .... *E. H. Cushing.*
— Treatise on law and practice in justices' courts in Texas; with forms. 8°. '66. shp., $7.50. *E. H. Cushing.*
— Treatise on practice in courts of Texas; with ref. ('58.) 2d ed. 8°. '75. shp., $10.. *E. H. Cushing.*
— Treatise on principles of pleading in civil actions in Texas; with precedents. 8°. '72. shp., $6.50. *E. H. Cushing.*
— *See also* Texas, Constitutions; Probate law.
Saymore, Sa. E. *See* Noel, F. J., *and* Chapsal, G. P.
Sayre, Lew. A. On disease of the hip-joint. *See* Seguin, E. C., Series of Am. clin. lect.
Scaeva (*pseud.*) *See* Stuart, I: W.
Scalp hunters. *See* Reid, M.
Scammon, C: M. Marine mammals of the n. w. coast of No. Am.; with account of Am. whale-fishery. (cop. '72.) '74. 2d ed. 30 pl. 4°. '76. $10; pap., $5 .... *Carmany; Putnam.*
Scammon, T. Young. *See* Illinois, Sup. Court reports.
Scamp songster. 32°. '76. pap., 10c........ *De Witt.*
Scampini. White, C. 15c........ *De Witt.*
Scamps of London. Moncrieff, W. T. 15c... *French.*
Scanlan and Cronin's "Irish boys" songster. 32°. '76. pap., 10c. .... *De Witt.*
Scanzoni, F. W. v. Practical treatise on diseases of sexual organs of women; tr. from Fr. ed. of H. Dor and A. Socin by A. K. Gardner. ill. 8°. '61. $5 .... *De Witt; Lindsay.*
Scapegoat. Pemberton, *Col.* —. $1.50.. *Lippincott.*
Scapegoat. Poole, J. 15c........ *French.*
Scapegrace: comedy. 16°. pap., 15c........ *French.*
Scapegrace at sea; — of London; — of the school. Hemyng, B. ea., $1.50; 75c........ *Am. News.*
Scapular book: explan. of the scapular of Mt. Carmel. 24°. pap., 10c........ *Strong.*
Scarlet flower. Egan, P. 75c........ *Dick & F.*
Scarlet letter. *See* Hawthorne, N.
Scarlet letter: drama. 16°. pap., 15c........ *Lee & S.*
Scarlett, J: Converted infidel. 18°. '53. 60c. *Meth. Bk. Conc.*
Scattergood, D. Game of draughts or checkers simplified and explained. 16°. 50c........ *Dick & F.*
Scattergood, T: Journal. 8°. $1.25; hf. cf., $1.75. *Friends Bk. St.*
Scattergood family. *See* Smith, Alb.
Scenery on the St. Lawrence: 12 views with letter press. obl. 24°. 75c........ *Nelson.*
Scenes and legends of the north of Scotland. Miller, H. $1.50 .... *Wilstach.*
Scenes and sights of Bible lands. S., A. M. 50c. *Nelson.*
Scenes and sketches of English history. Clarke, S. M. S. $1.50 .... *Nelson.*
Scenes at Gurney's: Ethiop. drama. 16°. pap., 15c. *French; Happy.*
Scenes at the west. Pearson, C. H. $1.25.. *Cong. Pub.*
Scenes from Christian hist. Hale, E. E. 42c... *Un. S. S.*
Scenes in Africa. *See* Marryat, F:
Scenes in China. Shuck, H. 75c........ *Am. Bapt.*
Scenes in Chusan; or, missionary labors by the way. ill. 18°. 70c. .... *Pres. Bd.*
Scenes in the city and country. *See* Picture stories for little folks.
Scenes in a clergyman's life. Tayler, C. B. $1.. *Leighton.*
Scenes in Europe. Post, L. J. $1.50. *Cin. Meth. Bk. Conc.*
Scenes in the Hawaiian Islands and California. $1.15. *Bost. Am. Tr.*
Scenes in the Indian country; by author of "Scenes in Chusan." 18°. 75c. .... *Pres. Bd.*
Scenes in the Isle of Mount Desert. DeCosta, B. F. $1.50; $4 .... *Randolph.*
Scenes in Luther's life. 16°. $1........ *Am. Bapt.*
Scenes in nature: conversations for children on land and water. ill. 18°. 75c........ *Harper.*
Scenes in the New Hebrides; [also] Shesh Achurjya. 18°. 30c. .... *Pres. Bd.*
Scenes in our parish. 18°. $1.15; $1.25.... *Dutton.*
Scenes in Switzerland. Bates, L. 45c........ *Am. Tr.*
Scenes in the west; by a missionary. 16°. '76. 75c. (?) *Luth. Pub.*
Scenes in the wilderness. 18°. 18c........ *Am. S. S.*
Scenes of clerical life. *See* Fliot, G:
Scenes of the olden time. ill. 12°. $1 .... *Nelson.*
Scenes of wonder and curiosity in California. Hutchings, J. M. $1.75; $2.50 .... *Roman.*
Scenes on the Mississippi. White, C. 15c.... *De Witt.*
Scenes where the tempter has triumphed. Neale, E. 75c. .... *Harper.*
Sceptre. Everett, A. B. *and* B. H. $1...... *Biglow.*
Sceptres and crowns. Warner, S. $1.25.... *Carter.*
Schaaf, Jul. Die Harfe: relig. Gesänge f. gemischte Singchöre, mit od. ohne Orgelbegl. 4 nos. obl. 4°. ea., pap., 25c.; in 1 v., $1........ *Schäfer.*
Schabalie, Ph. Die wandelnde Seele, d. i. Gespräche [üb. d.] Erschaffung d. Welt. 12th ed. 8°. leath., $1 .... *Schäfer.*
Schäfer, J. C. Manual of homœop. veterinary medicine; tr. and enl. by C. J. Hempel. 8°. $2. *Boericke.*
Schäfer (Der) u. seine Lämmer. 24°. 15c... *Ev. Assoc.*
Schaff, Ph. Anglo-amerikanische Sonntag (Der). 32°. '64. 20c. .... *Am. Tr.*
— Catechism for S.-schools and families; in 52 lessons. Rev. ed. 18°. bds., 20c........ *Whittaker.*
— *Same*. 12°. hf. bd., 18c.; — with proof texts and notes, 50c.; hf. bd., 35c........ *Ref. Ch. Pub.*
— Christ in song, hymns of Immanuel; sel. from all ages with notes. cr. 4°. '68. $2.50; $3.. *Randolph.*
— Christlicher Katechismus. ill. 18°. '64. 25c... *Am. Tr.*
— *Same*. 18°. 20c.; — mit Erklärgn. 18°. 35c... *Kohler.*
— *Eng.* Christian catechism. 18°. '63. hf. bd., 15c. *Hoyt.*
— Christusfrage (Die). 18°. '72. 25c........ *Am. Tr.*
— Deutsches Gesangbuch f. kirchl. u. häusl. Gebrauch. 24°. $1-$3 .... *Kohler.*

Schaff, Ph., *continued.*
— *Same.* 32°. 75c.; $3. — 18°. $1; $3. — 12°. $1.50; $4.50 .... *Ref. Ch. Pub.*
— Gesangbuch f. d. Sonntagschulen. 32°. 25c. *Kohler.*
— Gesang- u. Choralbuch f. kirchl. u. häusl. Gebrauch. 12°. $2-$4.75 .... *Kohler; Ref. Ch. Pub.*
— Geschichte d. alten Kirche, bis zu Ende d. 6. Jahrh. 8°. hf. mor., $7.50 .... *Kohler.*
— *Eng.* History of the Christian church. ('58-'67.) New ed. 3 v. in 2. 8°. '73. 1, $3.50; 2, $4. *Scribner.*
Cont.: 1. Birth of Christ to 311. — 2 and 3 (in 1 v.) 311-600.
— History of the apostolic church, with general introd. to church history; tr. by E. D. Yeomans. ('63.) New ed. 8°. '74. $3.75 .... *Scribner.*
— History of the Vatican council. *See* Gladstone, W. E., Vatican decrees.
— Life of St. Augustine. post 8°. (Bagster.) $1.50. *Wiley.*
— Person (Die) Jesu Christi. 18°. '71. 60c. ... *Am. Tr.*
— *Eng.* The person of Christ, the miracle of history; with reply to Strauss and Renan, and coll. of testimonies of unbelievers. 12°. '71. $1.25. *Bost. Am. Tr.; Scribner.*
— [Principle of Protestantism; in German.] 12°. 50c. *Ref. Ch. Pub.*
— *See also* Evangelical Alliance Conf.; — Gladstone, W. E., *and* Schaff, P.; — Heidelberg catechism; — Hitchcock, R. D., Eddy, Z., *and* Schaff, P.; — Lange, J. P., Commentary; — Smith, H. B., *and* Schaff, P.
— *and* Roussel, Nap. Romance of M. Renan and the Christ of the Gospels. [Essays.] 12°. '68. $1.25. *Meth. Bk. Conc.*

Schäffer, C: W: Early history of the Lutheran Church in Am., to middle of 18th cent. ('57.) New ed. 12°. '68. 80c. .... *Luth. Bk. St.*
— Family prayers. 12°. $1; $1.25; mor., $1.50. (?) *Luth. Pub.*

Schaitberger, Jos. Evangelischer Sendbrief; an d. Landsleute in Salzburg. 8°. $1.15 .. *Volkening.*

Schalk, Emil. Campaigns of 1862 and 1863; ill. principles of strategy. ill. 12°. '63. $1.75. *Claxton; Lippincott.*
— Summary of art of war. ('62.) 2d ed. ill. 12°. '63. $1.75 .... *Claxton; Lippincott.*

Scharf, J. T: Chronicles of Baltimore: history of "Baltimore town" and Baltimore city. 8°. '74. $5; shp., $6; hf. cf., $7 .... *Turnbull.*

Schatz (Der) des Inka. *See* Hoffmann, F.

Schatzkästchen. Gossner, J. $1-$4 ...... *Kohler.*

Schatzman, —. Sax horn or cornet instructor. obl. 8°. pap., 75c. .... *Ditson; Gordon.*

Schedel, H: E. Emancipation of faith. 2 v. 8°. $4. *Appleton.*
— *See also* Cazenave, P. L. A., *and* Schedel, H. E.

Schedler, J. Illustrated manual for terrestrial and celestial globes. 12°. '75. pap., 25c. .... *Steiger.*

Schefer, Lp. Artist's (An) married life, that of A. Dürer; tr. by Mrs. J. R. Stodart, with memoir. 12°. $1.25; pap., 75c. .... *Miller.*
— Layman's breviary; or, meditations for every day in the year; tr. by C. T. Brooks. sq. 16°. '67. $1.50; $2.25 .... *Roberts.*
— World-priest; tr. by C. T. Brooks. sq. 16°. '72. $2.25 .... *Roberts.*

Scheffmacher, J. J. Controvers-Katechismus üb. d. Ursprung des Lutheranismus. 12°. 40c. *Benziger.*

Scheidermeyer, —. Mass in D; arrang. by W. C. Peters. 4°. pap., $1.50 .... *Peters.*

Scheidler, C. A. Theoretical and practical piano school. f°. '67. bds., $3.75 .... *Willig.*

Scheifele, J: G: Gedichte in schwäbischer Mundart. 12°. '70. pap., 75c. .... *Steiger.*

Schein (Der) trügt. *See* Hoffmann, F.

Schele De Vere, M. *See* De Vere, M. Schele.

Scheliha, — v. Treatise on coast defence; based on experience gained by engineers of the Confederate army, and comp. from reports of officers of U.S. navy, 1861-5. pl. imp. 8°. '68. $8 .... *Spon.*

Schell, F. P. *See* Coe, B. H., *and* Schell, F. P.

Schellen, T: Jos. H: Spectrum analysis; tr. by J. and C. Lasell; ed., with notes, by W. Huggins. wood-cuts, plates, por. and maps. 8°. $6. *Appleton.*

Schem, Alex. J. Deutsch-amerikanisches Conversations-Lexicon. 11 v. 8°. '69-'74. ea., $3.25; hf. mor., $4.25; — in 110 nos. 8°. ea., pap., 25c. *Steiger.*
— Statistics of the world: area, population, debt, imports [and] exports, weights, etc., of all countries; with side tables showing religious, postal, etc., statistics. 4th ed., rev. f°. '76. pap., 50c. *Lee & S.*
— *See also* Crooks, G. R., *and* Schem, A. J.; — Kiddle, H., *and* Schem, A. J.

Schenck, B. S. Mercersburg theology inconsistent with Protestant and reformed doctrine. 12°. $1.25. *Lippincott.*

Schenck, *Mrs.* J. W. Rescued child. ill. 18°. '68. 30c. .... *Am. Tr.*

Schenck, P. A. Gardener's text book. [Kitchen-garden.] 18°. 75c. .... *Judd.*

Schenck, W: E: Aunt Fanny's home, and her talks about God's works. 18°. 70c. .... *Pres. Bd.*
— Children in heaven; or, the infant dead redeemed by the blood of Jesus; with words of consolation to parents. 8°. $1.75 .... *Pres. Bd.*
— Nearing home; or, comforts and counsels to the aged. 12°. $2 .... *Pres. Bd.*
— Presbyterian social psalmodist. sq. 12°. 70c.-$1.25. *Pres. Bd.*
— *See also* Converse, C. C., *and* Schenck, W. E.

Scheppig, R: *See* Spencer, H., Descriptive sociology.

Scherr, J. Schiller u. seine Zeit. 12°. $1.50; hf. mor., $2 .... *Kohler.*
— *Same.* 2 v. 12°. '61. $1 .... *Steiger.*

Scherz, List u. Rache. *See* Goethe, J. W. v.

Schicksals-Braut (Die). Conrad, J. $1.50; $1. *F. W. Thomas.*

Schieferdecker, G. A. Geschichte d. ersten deutschen luth. Ansiedlung in Altenburg, Perry Co., Mo. 8°. '65. pap., 50c. .. *Germ. Ev. Luth. Syn. of Iowa.*

Schieffelin, S: B. Children's bread. [Catechism.] 18°. bds., 15c. .... *Whittaker.*
— *Same.* 16°. '75. *net*, bds., 15c. *N. Y. Ref. Ch. Bd.; Pres. Com.*
— *Same;* [also] Milk for babes. 16°. 25c. *N. Y. Ref. Ch. Bd.; Pres. Com.*
— Foundations of history: a series of first things. ill. 12°. 80c. .... *N. Y. Ref. Ch. Bd.*

Schiller, E: Handbook of progressive philosophy. 12°. '71. $1.50 .... *Redfield.*

Schiller, J: F: v. Sämmtliche Werke. 12 v. 12°. $9; hf. mor., $15; in 6 v., $10. — fine pap. ed. 12 v. 12°. $15; hf. mor., $20; in 6 v., $15 .. *Kohler.*
Cont.: 1. Gedichte. — 2. Die Räuber; Fiesco. — 3. Kabale u. Liebe; Don Carlos; Der Menschenfeind. — 4. Wallenstein. — 5. Maria Stuart; Die Jungfrau v. Orleans; Die Braut v. Messina. — 6. Tell; Iphigenie in Aulis; Macbeth, etc. — 7. Turandot; Der Parasit; Der Neffe als Onkel; Phädra; Nachlass. — 8. Abfall d. Ver. Niederlande. — 9. Der dreissigjährige Krieg. — 10. Prosaische Schriften, 1. u. 2. Periode. — 11. Kleine Schriften. — 12. Schriften vermischten Inh.
— *Same;* f. Schulen u. Lehranstalten. 12 v. 12°. ea., 75c. — fine pap. ed., ea., $1.25; $1.75 .... *Kohler.*
— *Same.* 2 v. 8°. $3; pap., $2; hf. mor., $3.50; — billige Ausgabe. 2 v. 8°. $2.25; pap., $1.25; in 1 v., $1.75 .... *F. W. Thomas.*
— *Same.* 2 v. 8°. $5.50; hf. mor., $6.50. — fine pap. ed., $7; hf. mor., $8.50; mor., $18; in 1 v., mor., $12 .... *Kohler.*
— *Same;* billige Volksausgabe. 2 v. 8°. $4; hf. mor., $4.50; in 1 v., $3.50 .... *Kohler.*

Schiller, J: F: v., *continued.*
— *Eng.* Works. 6 v. 12°. (Bohn.) ea., $1.25. *Little, B. & Co.*
Cont.: 1. Thirty years' war; Revolt of the Netherlands. — 2. Contin. of the Revolt of the Netherlands; Wallenstein's camp; Piccolomini; Death of Wallenstein; William Tell. — 3. Don Carlos; Mary Stuart; Maid of Orleans; Bride of Messina. — 4. Robbers; Fiesco; Love and intrigue; The ghost-seer. — 5. Poems. — 6. Letters and essays.
— — *Same.* 6 v. 12°. (Bohn.) ea., $1.40. *Scribner, W. & A.*
— — *Same.* 6 v. 12°. (Bohn.) ea., $1.50.. *Lippincott.*
— — *Same.* 12°. hf. cf., $15; cf., $17.50... *Appleton.*
— — *Same;* sel. from the best translations, ed. by C. J. Hempel. 2 v. roy. 8°. $6; hf. mor., $7; in 1 v., $5. — fine paper ed. 2 v. 8°. $7; hf. mor., $9; mor., $18; $20; in 1 v., mor., $12; $14.. *Kohler.*
— Dramatische Werke. 17 v. 12°. ea., pap., 10c. *F. W. Thomas.*
Cont.: Die Räuber. — Fiesco. — Kabale u. Liebe. — Iphigenie in Aulis. — Don Carlos. — Wallenstein's Lager. — Die Piccolomini. — Wallenstein's Tod. — Maria Stuart. — Tell. — Die Jungfrau v. Orleans. — Die Braut v. Messina. — Macbeth. — Turandot. — Phädra. — Der Parasit. — Der Neffe als Onkel.
— Gedichte. 12°. pap., 20c............ *F. W. Thomas.*
— *Same.* 12°. 75c.; $1.25; hf. mor., $1.25. — fine pap. ed., $1.25; $1.50; hf. mor., $1.75; mor., $3.50 .... *Kohler.*
— *Eng.* Poems; tr. by E. A. Bowring. 16°. $1.75. *Lippincott.*
— — *Same;* ed. and tr. by H. D. Wireman. 12°. $1.25; $1.50. — fine pap. ed., $1.50; $1.75; hf. mor., $1.75; mor., $3.50 .... *Kohler.*
— — *Same.* Poems and ballads; tr. by Sir E. Bulwer-Lytton. (Blue and gold ed.) por. 24°. $1.50. *Clark & M.*
— — *Same.* (Red line ed.) ill. and por. sm. 4°. $4; hf. cf., $6; mor., $7.50 .... *Clark & M.*
— — *Same.* (Cabinet ed.) por. 16°. $1.60; hf. cf., $3; mor., $4........................ *Clark & M.*
— *Germ.* ed., *and Eng.* Poems; ed. and tr. by H. D. Wireman. 12°. $2; $2.50. — fine pap., $2.50; $2.75 .... *Kohler.*
— Æsthetical essays; also philos. letters and essay on connection between animal and spiritual nature of man. 12°. $1.50................ *Lippincott.*
— Geschichte des dreissigjährigen Krieges. 12°. pap., 25c........................... *F. W. Thomas.*
— *Eng.* History of the thirty years' war; tr. by A. J. W. Morrison. 12°. $1............ *Harper.*
— History of revolt of the Netherlands: trial and execution of Counts Egmont and Horn, and siege of Antwerp; tr. by A. J. W. Morrison. 12°. $1. *Harper.*
— Jungfrau (Die) von Orleans: Tragödie. With Eng. notes. ('65.) New ed. 12°. '76. pap., 50c. *Holt.*
— Lied (Das) von der Glocks. With photos. after C. Jaeger and A. Müller. roy. 4°. $15. 8°. $10. *Stroefer.*
— *Eng.* Song of the bell; tr. by W. H. Furness; with photos. from originals of C. Jaeger and A. Müller. roy. 4°. $15; mor., $20. 8°. $10...... *Stroefer.*
— — Lay of the bell; tr. by Bulwer; with outline ill. by M. Retzsch. obl. 4°. '68. $7.50; mor., $12. *Roberts.*
— — — *See also* Romberg, A.
— Maria Stuart: Trauerspiel. With introd. and notes for tr. into Eng. by A. Bernays. ('65.) New ed. 12°. '76. pap., 60c......................... *Holt.*
— *Same;* with Eng. notes by E. C. F. Krauss. ('66.) New ed. 12°. '76. 60c......................... *Holt.*
— Piccolomini (Die). Ed. by J. M. Hart; with notes, commentary and glossary. map. 16°. '75. $1.25. *Putnam.*
— *Same;* with Eng. notes by E. C. F. Krauss. ('66.) New ed. 12°. '76. pap., 50c................. *Holt.*
— Robbers: tragedy; [tr.] 16°. pap., 15c.... *French.*
— Wallenstein [*Germ.*] With Eng. notes by E. C. F. Krauss. ('66.) New ed. 12°. '76. $1.50.. *Holt.*
— Wallenstein's Lager. With Eng. notes by E. C. F. Krauss. ('66.) New ed. 12°. '76. pap., 50c... *Holt.*

Schiller, J: F: v., *continued.*
— Wallenstein's Tod: Trauerspiel. With Eng. notes by E. C. F. Krauss. ('66.) New ed. 12°. '76. pap., 50c.................................. *Holt.*
— Wilhelm Tell: Schauspiel. With Eng. notes by E. C. F. Krauss. ('64.) New ed. 12°. '76. pap., 50c. .... *Holt.*
— *See also* Gottschall, R., Gedanken-Harmonie; — Masterpieces of foreign literature.
Schiller Gallerie. Photos after W. Kaulbach and others; with [Germ.] text by E. Förster. f°. $36; mor., $50. — 8°. mor., $18. — sm. 4°. mor., $12 .... *Stroefer.*
Schiller gallery, designed by W. Kaulbach and others: photos. with text by F. A. Schwarzenberg. f°. $36; mor., $50. — 8°. mor., $18. — sm. 4°. mor., $12; — without text. sm. 4°. mor., $8.. *Stroefer.*
Schinderhannes. 12°. pap., 15c.............. *Radde.*
Schindler, A. Biography of Beethoven. *See* Moschelles, I., Life of Beethoven.
Schinz, C: Researches on action of blast furnace; tr. by W. H. Maw and Moritz Müller. pl. cr. 8°. '70. $4...................................... *Spon.*
— *Same.* ill. 12°. $5............................ *Baird.*
Schlaraffiade. Anthropos, H. 30c.......... *Pilger.*
Schlegel, A: W: Dramatic literature; tr. por. 12°. (Bohn.) $1.25.................. *Little, B. & Co.*
— *Same.* por. 12°. (Bohn.) $1.40.. *Scribner, W. & A.*
— *Same.* por. 12°. (Bohn.) $1.50 ...... *Lippincott.*
Schlegel, C: A. Classical French reader, with notes. pt. 1. 12°. '71. hf. roan, 90c......... *Steiger.*
— Collegiate course. 3 v. 12°. '71–'74. hf. roan.. *Steiger.*
Cont.: German grammar for beginners, $1.25. — First classical German reader, $1. — Second, $1.50.
— Elementarbuch d. engl. Sprache. 8°. '76. 60c. *Schmidt.*
— First German book. 2 v. 8°. '75–'76. bds., pt. 1, 50c.; 2, 60c.; in 1 v., $1............. *Schmidt.*
— French grammar, for beginners. 12°. '71. hf. roan, $1.50 .... *Steiger.*
Schlegel, C: W: F: v. [Works; tr.] 5 v. 12°. (Bohn.) ea., $1.25.......................... *Little, B. & Co.*
Cont.: Æsthetic and misc. works. — History of literature, ancient and modern; with gen. index. — Modern history. — Philosophy of history; tr. by J. B. Robertson. — Philosophy of life and lang.; tr. by A. J. W. Morrison.
— *Same.* 5 v. 12°. (Bohn.) ea., $1.40.. *Scribner, W. & A.*
— *Same.* 5 v. 12°. (Bohn.) ea., $1.50.. *Lippincott.*
— Lectures, with questions on hist. of anc. and mod. literature. 12°. $1.75...................... *Moss.*
— Philosophy of life and philos. of lang.; tr. by A. J. W. Morrison. 12°. $1.50............ *Harper.*
Schleiden, M. J. Poetry of the vegetable world: popular exposition of botany in its rel. to man; ed. by A. Wood. ill. 12°. '53. $1.50.... *Wilstach*
Schleiden, R. Reise-Erinnerungen aus d. Ver. Staaten. 12°. '73. pap., 30c............... *Steiger*
Schlesier, Gst. *See* Klencke, P. F. H., *and* Schlesier, G.
Schlesinger, M. Historical Jesus of Nazareth. 12° '76. $1................................ *Somerby*
Schlesische Rübezahl (Der). 12°. pap., 15c... *Radde*
Schlessinger, W. Stunden der Andacht: ein Gebet u. Erbauungsbuch f. Israels Frauen u. Jungfrauen; mit mehreren Zusätzen v. Fanny Neuda 16°. 75c.. *Frank*
— *Eng.;* tr. by M. Mayer. 12°. $1............ *Frank*
Schletterer, H. M. Dornröschen: [The sleeping beauty in the wood]. [Operetta.] 8°. *net,* pap. $1.50 .... *Schirmer*
Schliemann, H: Troy and its remains: result of excavations in the Trojan plains; tr., ed. by P. Smith. maps, views, plans, etc. 8°. '75. $12.50 hf. cf., $15................................ *Scribner, W. & A.*
Schlossdiebe (Die). *See* Hiltl, G.

Schmauck, J. G. Deutsche Harmonie, od. mehrstimmige Gesänge f. deutsche Singschulen u. [protest.] Kirchen. 25th ed. obl. 4°. $1.50. *Schäfer.*

Schmid, A. F. Mass no. 1 in C; arrang. by W. C. Peters. 4°. pap., $1.25 .... *Peters.*
— Mass no. 2 in A; arrang. by A. Derleth. 4°. pap., $1 .... *Peters.*
— Mass no. 3 in C; arrang. by A. Derleth. 4°. pap., $1 .... *Peters.*
— Mass no. 4 in D; arrang. by A. Derleth. 4°. pap., $1 .... *Peters.*
— Mass no. 5 in E flat; arrang. by A. Derleth. 4°. pap., $1 .... *Peters.*
— Mass no. 6 in F; arrang. by A. Derleth. 4°. pap., $1 .... *Peters.*
— Mass no. 7 in G; arrang. by A. Derleth. 4°. pap., $1 .... *Peters.*

Schmid, Chr. F: Biblical theology of the New Test. 8°. $3 .... *Scribner, W. & A.*
— General principles of Christian ethics; abridg. by W. J. Mann. 12°. $1.25 .... *Luth. Bk. St.*

Schmid, Cp. v. Erzählungen. 8 v. 12°. ea., pap., 15c. .... *F. W. Thomas.*
Cont.: Rosa v. Tannenburg. — Fernando. — Emma v. Finkenstein. — Das Blumenkörbchen. — Der Rosenstock. — Die Ostereier. — Der Kanarienvogel u. d. Johanniskäferchen. — Heinrich v. Eichenfels.
— *Same.* 10 v. 12°. ea., pap., 15c. .... *Radde.*
Cont.: Das Blumenkörbchen. — Fernando. — Rosa v. Tannenburg. — Heinrich v. Eichenfels. — Der Canarienvogel u. das Johanniskäferchen. — Die Nachtigall. — Die Ostereier. — Der Rosenstock. — Der Weihnachtsabend. — Emma v. Finkenstein.
— — Jugendbibliothek. 33 v. 16°. ea., 20c. .. *Morwitz.*
Cont.: Heinrich v. Eichenfels. — Der Weihnachtsabend. — Der Rosenstock. — Der Kanarienvogel u. das Johanniskäferchen. — Die Ostereier. — Die Hopfenblüthen. — Eustachius. — Das Blumenkörbchen. — Rosa v. Tannenburg. — Genofeva. — Die Nachtigall. — Robert der Waisenknabe. — Ludwig der Auswanderer. — Sieben Erzählungen. — Janneton u. Amalie. — Die Maiblumen. — Emma v. Finkenstein. — Wilhelm Tell. — Das verlorene Kind. — Das Täubchen; Das Raubschloss. — Der gute Fridolin u. d. böse Dieterich. — Zweihundert Erzählungen, 2 v. — Die Gräfin Julia. — Gottfried der junge Einsiedler. — Der Christbaum. — Die kleine Lautenspielerin. — Das Lämmchen. — Fernando. — Kupfermünzen u. Goldstücke; Das Vogelnestchen; Die Kapelle beim Wolfsbühl. — Margaretha Blümchen; Die Waldkapelle; Das beste Erbtheil. — Die Feuersbrunst; Wasserfluth am Rhein. — Der Diamantring; Das Marienbild.
— Biblische Geschichte des alten u. neuen Bundes f. die Jugend. 12°. 30c. .... *Benziger; Vering.*
— Biblische Geschichte f. kathol. Schulen u. Familien. 12°. $1.35 .... *Benziger.*
— Eustachius. 12°. 35c.; pap., 15c. .... *Benziger.*
— Genovefa. 12°. 35c.; pap., 15c. .... *Benziger.*
— *Eng.* Geneviève de Brabant: tale of antiquity. 18°. 60c. .... *Cath. Pub.*
— *Swed.* Genoveva. 12°. pap., 35c. .... *Engberg.*
— Gräfin Julia, od. die kindliche Liebe. 12°. 35c; pap., 15c. .... *Benziger.*
— Gute Fridolin (Der) u. der böse Dieterich. 12°. 35c.; pap., 15c. .... *Benziger.*
— Janneton u. Amalie. 12°. 35c.; pap., 15c. .. *Benziger.*
— Karthäuserkloster. 12°. 30c.; pap., 10c. .. *Benziger.*
— Nightingale; or, a kind act is never lost: tale of the Russian war; tr. 18°. 35c. .... *Claremont.*
— *Same.* 18°. 35c.; 40c. .... *Dutton.*
— One hundred tales; tr. 16°. 60c.; $1 .... *Sadlier.*
— Ostereier (Die). 16°. '67. bds., 25c. .... *Steiger.*
— *Eng.* Easter eggs. 18°. 40c. .... *Dutton.*
— *Same;* tr. by H. Steiner. ill. 16°. 45c. .. *Ref. Ch. Pub.*
— Robert der Waisenknabe. 12°. 35c.; pap., 15c. *Benziger.*
— Tales; tr. 6 v. 18°. $3 .... *Strong.*
— Weihnachtsabend (Der). 16°. '67. bds., 25c. *Steiger.*
— Wie Heinrich v. Eichenfels zur Erkenntniss Gottes kam. 16°. '67. bds., 25c. .... *Steiger.*
— Zweihundert lehrreiche kleine Erzählungen f. Kinder. 16°. 30c.; pap., 15c. .... *Radde.*

Schmid, H: Doctrinal theology of the Luth. Church, exhib. and verified from orig. sources; tr. by C. A. Hay and H. E. Jacobs. 8°. '75. $6 .. *Luth. Bk. St.*

Schmid, Hm. Habermeister; tr. from the Germ. ('69.) New ed. (Leis. hour ser.) 16°. '75. $1.25 .... *Holt.*

Schmidt, —. New and improved instructor for the E flat cornet (sax horn); with either piston or rotary valves. 8°. '59. pap., 25c. .... *Ditson.*

Schmidt, A. F. Mass in E flat; for soprano, alto, tenor and bass; arr. by E. Spoth. f°. '55. pap., $1.50 .... *Ditson.*

Schmidt, Adf. *See* Pumpelly, R., Brooks, T. B., *and* Schmidt, A.

Schmidt, Erasmus. Greek concordance to New Test. fp. 8°. (Bagster.) $1.50. — 32°. $1.50 .. *Wiley.*

Schmidt, Fd. Nal u. Damajanti. 16°. 25c. .. *Morwitz.*
— *Same.* 16°. 30c.; bds., 20c.; pap., 15c. .... *Kohler.*

Schmidt, Fz. Heimkehr vom Himmel zur Erde. 8°. pap., 40c. .... *F. W. Thomas.*

Schmidt, Gst. Civil law of Spain and Mexico arr. on principles of mod. codes; with notes and ref. 8°. shp., $5 .... *S. Whitney.*

Schmidt, H: I. Course of ancient geography. 12°. $1.25 .... *Appleton.*
— History of education; with plan of culture and instruction based on Christian principles. 18°. 75c. *Harper.*

Schmidt, Osc. Theory of descent, and Darwinism. ill. 12°. $1.50 .... *Appleton.*

Schmidt, W: Vier Blüthen u. Eine Frucht; [also] Colomba, v. P. Merimée. 8°. pap., 50c. *Morwitz.*

Schmidt-Weissenfels, E: Die Familie Besson-Völker während der Belagerung v. Strassburg: hist. Roman. 8°. pap., 40c. .... *F. W. Thomas.*
— Die Söhne Barnevelt's. *See* Streckfuss, A., Der tolle Hans.

Schmitt, J. Method for piano. 4°. $2 .... *Gordon.*

Schmitz, J. Adph. *and* H. J. Text-book for study of the Germ. lang. 12°. hf. roan, $1.50 .. *Lippincott.*

Schmitz, Lh. Manual of ancient geography. 12°. $1.75 .... *Sheldon.*
— Manual of ancient history, to 476; with chron. tables. 12°. $1.75 .... *Sheldon.*
— *See also* Bartholomew, J., *and* Weller, E.; — International atlas; — Library atlas of geog.; — Student's atlas of class. geog.
— *and* Zumpt, C: G. Classical ser. 8 v. roy. 18°. .*Lea.*
Cont.: Elementary Lat. exercises, 50c. — Advanced Lat. exercises and reading book, 60c.; hf. bd., 70c. — Cæsar, 60c.; hf. bd., 70c. — Sallust, 60c.; hf. bd., 70c. — Virgil, 85c.; hf. bd., $1. — Horace, 70c.; hf. bd., 80c. — Quintus Curtius, 80c.; hf. bd., 90c. — Cornelius Nepos, 60c.; hf. bd., 70c.

Schmolke, B: Das himmlische Vergnügen in Gott. 8°. $2–$6 .... *Kohler.*

Schmoller, O: Minor prophets. *See* Lange, J. P., Comment.

Schmucker, S: M. [Works.] 7 v. por. 12°. ea., $1.75 .... *J. E. Potter.*
Cont.: Life and times of Alex. Hamilton — of Geo. Washington — of Henry Clay — of Thos. Jefferson. — Life of E. K. Kane and of other Am. explorers — of Nicholas I., with descript. of Russian society, etc. — Public and private hist. of Louis Napoleon.
— History of the four Georges, kings of Eng. 12°. $1.75 .... *Miller.*
— Religions of the world. New ed., enl. by C. Drew. ill. 12°. *$2; $2.50; mor., $3.50 .... *Quak. City.*

Schmucker, S: S. Essay on the reformation. *See* Luther, Mt., Commentary on Galatians.
— Psychology: elements of a new system of mental philos.; on basis of consciousness and common sense. 12°. $1.25 .... *Harper.*
— True unity of Christ's church: renewed appeal on primitive Christian union. 12°. '70. $1.25. *Randolph.*

Schnake, F: Jesus: histor. Schauspiel. 8°. (St. Louis.) '73. pap., 25c. .... *Steiger.*

Schnapps. Clifton, M. D. 15c. .... *Ames.*

Schneck, B: S. Mercersburger Theologie. 8°. 75c. *Kohler.*

Schneider, J. C. F. Practical organ school: instruct. in fingering, management of stops, pedals, etc.; with treatise on harmony and thorough base; tr. 4°. bds., $3.50 .... *Ditson.*

— Selection of organ voluntaries, preludes and interludes. 4°. pap., $2.25 .... *Ditson.*

— Treatise on thorough base and harmony; tr. and adapted to wants of young students by E. L. White. 12°. '51. bds., 50c. .... *Ditson.*

Schneider u. Geiger. Nieritz, G. 25c. .... *Morwitz.*

Schnick-schnack: trifles for the little ones. ill. sq. 8°. $1.50 .... *Routledge.*

Schnorr, Jul. The Nibelungen-Saga: photos. after frescoes in royal palace at Munich, with text by H. Holland. roy. 4°. $15 .... *Stroefer.*

Schödler, F: Book of nature: element. introd. to physics, astronomy, chemistry, geology, etc.; tr. by H. Medlock. New ed., with glossary. ill. 8°. $3 .... *Sheldon.*

— Wonders of nature: element. introd. to the sciences; tr. by H. Medlock. ill. 8°. $3 .... *Lea.*

Schoepff, J: D: Climate and diseases of Am. during the rev.; tr. by J. R. Chadwick. sm. 4°. '75. bds., 30c. .... *Hurd & H.*

Schofield, W. J., *and* Attwill, R. I. Prospector's manual for disc. of quartz and placer indications of gold and silver mines. 16°. '75. pap., 50c. *W. J. Schofield.*

Scholar. Buckstone, J. B. 15c. .... *French.*

Scholar's companion: exercises in orthog., derivation and classification of Eng. words; with introd. and index by R. W. Bailey. 12°. $1 .... *Butler.*

Scholar's text book. 18°. 15c. .... *Pres. Bd.*

Scholar's welcome. Bullard, A. 25c. .... *Lee & S.*

Schölcher, Vct. Life of Handel. 16°. $2 .... *Ditson.*

Scholefield, Ja. *See* Daily readings for holy seasons.

Schöller, H: Hour (An) in fairy land. [Cantata.] obl. 8°. bds., 75c.; pap., 60c. .... *Peters.*

— New year's eve. [Cantata.] obl. 8°. bds., 75c.; pap., 60c. .... *Peters.*

— Quarrel among the flowers; with words by Mrs. M. W. Telfair. [Cantata.] obl. 12°. '71. pap., 35c. *Ditson.*

Scholz, J. M. A. *See* Bible, New Test., *Greek.*

Schön Kätchen v. Heilbronn. Grabowski, S. (*Graf*). $2; $1.50 .... *F. W. Thomas.*

Schöne Magelone (Die). 12°. pap., 15c. ..... *Radde.*

Schöne Müllerin (Die). *See* Försterling, O. (*ill.*)

Schönsten Tage (Die) e. Tänzerin. *See* Dilthey, K.

School. Robertson, T. W. 15c. .... *De Witt.*

School and the army. Hazen, W. B. $2.50 .. *Harper.*

School and college lib. *See* May, E. J.

School and home. 16°. $1.25 .... *Carter.*

School and home; — New school and home. *See* Partridge, W. W.

School and the schoolmaster. Potter, A., *and* Emerson, G. B. $1.50 .... *Harper.*

School bell. Butler, C., *and* Southard, L. H. 50c. *Gordon.*

School boy baronet. *See* Greene, *Mrs.* L. L.

School boy courage and its reward. ill. 18°. 50c. .. *Nelson.*

School boy days. Kingston, W. H. G. $1.50 .. *Lee & S.*

School boy hero. Moncrieff, R. H. 50c. .. (?) *Martien.*

School boy honor. Adams, H. C. $1.25 .. *Routledge.*

School boy stories lib. *See* Adams, H. C.

School chimes. Baker, B. F., *and* Southard, L. H. 50c. .... *Gordon.*

School chimes. Murray, J. R. 50c. ...... *Brainard.*

School dame, and other stories for girls. 18°. 50c. *Am. S. S.*

School days at Mount Pleasant. Morley, R. $1.50. *Hinton.*

School days of Beulah Romney. Eastman, J. A. $1.50 .... *Lothrop.*

School days reviewed: stories of school boys. 18°. 60c. *Am. S. S.*

School fellows. Jerrold, D. 15c. .... *French.*

School for coquettes. Simpson, J. P. 15c. .. *French.*

School for daughters. *See* Lacy's home plays for ladies.

School for fathers. Gwynne, T. $1.25 ..... *Harper.*

School for scandal. *See* Sheridan, R. B.

School for scheming: comedy. 16°. pap., 15c. *Happy.*

School for tigers: farce. 16°. pap., 15c. .... *Happy.*

School friend. Robbins, E. 42c. .... *Lippincott.*

School friends. Kingston, W. H. G. 75c. .. *Routledge.*

School girl in France. *See* M'Crindell, *Miss* R.

School girls; or, the best of knowledge. 18°. 60c.; 70c. *Am. Bapt.*

School girls in number 40; or, principle put to the test. 18°. 40c. .... *Am. S. S.*

School girls of Elverly. Lathrop, H. $1.25. *H. A. Young.*

School girls of Queen's May. 18°. 75c. .... *Am. S. S.*

School girls' treasury. Guernsey, L. E. 90c. *Whittaker.*

School harmonist. Cleaveland, A. J. 75c. .. *Barnes.*

School harmonist. Zundel, J., *and* Ryan, J. E. $1.25; 90c .... *Harper.*

School in the woods. 18°. 35c. .... *Am. S. S.*

School is out. Colesworthy, D. C. $2.50 .... *Barry.*

School life. ill. 16°. $1.50 .... *Graves.*

School life of Ben and Bertie. 18°. 90c. *Meth. Bk. Conc.*

School life stories. 6 v. 24°. $1.80 ...... *Lothrop.*

Cont.: School life. — Ellen's May-day. — Tom Thornhill. — Pleasure and profit. — Crown jewels. — Truth and love.

School lyrics. Capron, S. M. 40c. .... *Harper.*

School lyrics. Ludden, W. 80c.; 50c. ...... *Church.*

School melodist. Locke, E., *and* Nourse, S. 40c. *Wilstach.*

School of infancy. Comenius, J. A. $1.25 .. *Clauder.*

School of Jesus crucified. *See* Ignatius *of Jesus.*

School of reform. Morton, T. 15c. .... *French.*

School of singing. Root, F. W. $3 .... *Church.*

School question (The): Catholics and education. 8°. '76. $1.25 .... *Cath. Pub.*

School recreations; or, the Catholic teacher's companion for Cath. schools. 12°. 35c. .. *Benziger.*

School stage. Venable, W. H. $1.25 .. *Wilson, H. & Co.*

School translator. Heidner, F. W. 35c. .... *Enderis.*

School vocalist. Curtis, G. H. $1 .... *Barnes.*

School vocalist. Locke, E., *and* Nourse, S. 40c. *Wilstach.*

Schoolcraft, H: R. Archives of aboriginal knowledge: orig. papers laid before Congress resp. hist., antiquities, lang., etc., of the Indian tribes of the U. S. 6 v. eng. imp. 4°. $90 .... *Lippincott.*

— Myth of Hiawatha and other oral legends, mythologic and allegoric, of the No. Am. Indians. 12°. '56. $1.25 .... *Claxton; Lippincott.*

— Personal memoirs of a residence of 30 years with the Indian tribes on the Am. frontiers, 1812–'42. 8°. '51. $3 .... *Claxton; Lippincott.*

— Summary narrative of expedition to sources of Mississippi River in 1820; resumed and completed in 1832. 8°. '54. $3 .. *Claxton; Lippincott.*

Schoolcraft, *Mrs.* Ma. H. The black gauntlet. 12°. $1.25 .... *Lippincott.*

Schooler, S: Elements of descriptive geometry: point, straight line and plane. 4°. '53. hf. bd., $1.50. *J. W. Randolph.*

Schooling of life. Tyrwhitt, R. St. J. $1..*Macmillan.*

Schoolmaster and his son. Caspari, K. H. $1. (?)*Luth. Pub.*

Schoolmaster of Albach. Oertel, P. F. W. $1.50; $1 .... *Claxton.*

Schoolmaster's stories. Eggleston, E. $1.50. (?)*Shepard.*

Schoolmaster's trunk. Diaz, A. M. $1; 50c. *Osgood.*

Schoolmates. 18°. 40c.................... *Dutton.*

Schoolmates. 18°. 30c.; 40c............ *Am. Bapt.*

Schoolroom choir. Kingsley, G. 60c. ...... *Barnes.*

Schools and schoolmasters. *See* Dickens, C:

Schools of the prophets. Thompson, H. A. 40c. *Un. B. Pub.*

Schooner Mary Ann. Abbott, J. $1.50 ...... *Dodd.*

Schorlemmer, C. Manual of the chemistry of the carbon compounds; or, organic chemistry. ill. 8°. '74. $5 .... *Macmillan.*

Schott, C: A. Tables of rain and snow in U. S. 4°. '72. pap., $3 .... *Smith. Inst.*

— Temperature tables. 4°. '76. pap., $3..*Smith. Inst.*

Schott, Thdr. Anne du Bourg: a life picture of the early days of French Protestantism, 1557–1559, and two centenaries after. (Fatherland ser.) 16°. '73. $1.10 .... (?)*Luth. Pub.*

Schouler, Ja. Law of domestic relations; embr. husband and wife, parent and child, guardian and ward, infancy, and master and servant. 2d ed. 8°. '74. shp., $6........... *Little, B. & Co.*

— Treatise on the law of personal property. 2 v. 8°. '73–'76. ea., shp., $6........... *Little, B. & Co.*

Schouler, W., *jr.* Church catechism verified by the Scriptures. 18°. '71. 10c. .... *Pott.*

Schouw, Joac. F. Earth, plants and man; [also] Kobell's Sketches from the mineral kingdom; tr. by A. Henfrey. map. 12°. (Bohn.) $1.75. *Little, B. & Co.*

— *Same.* map. 12°. (Bohn.) $2. *Lippincott; Scribner, W. & A.*

Schreckensjahre. Glaubrecht, O. 25c..... *Morwitz.*

Schroder, K: Manual of midwifery, incl. pathology of pregnancy and the puerperal state; tr. by C. H. Carter. ill. 8°. $3.50; shp., $4.50.... *Appleton.*

Schroeder van der Kolk, J. C. L. Pathology and therapeutics of mental diseases; tr. by Rudall. 8°. '70. $3 .... *Lindsay.*

Schubert, Ern. L. Details of machinery designed for free hand and mechanical drawing. pl. f°. $1.75 .... *Schoenhof.*

Schubert, Fz. Miriam's song of triumph; with words by Grillparzer. [Cantata.] 4°. pap., 50c. *Ditson.*

Schubert, G. H. v. Fifteen charts of the natural hist. of the animal kingdom. 90 pl. f°. bds., $7.50; — explan. text, tr. 12°. bds., 50c.... *Schoenhof.*

Schubert, *Rev.* G. H. Das Leben von J. J. Fabricius. 18°. '50. 25c......................... *Am. Tr.*

— Der Meeresstrom. ill. 18°. '51. 25c....... *Am. Tr.*

Schuckers, J. W. Brief account of finances and paper money of revolutionary war. 8°. '74. pap., $1.25 .... *J. Campbell & Son.*

— Finances: panics and specie payments. 8°. '74. pap., 50c.......................... *J. Campbell & Son.*

— Life and public services of S. P. Chase. ill. 8°. *$5; shp., $6; hf. mor., $7.50............ *Appleton.*

Schücking, Levin. Powder and gold: story of the Franco-Prussian war; tr. from the Germ. 16°. 75c. .... *Hinton.*

Schulmeister (Der) u. s. Sohn. Caspari, K. H. 25c. *Morwitz.*

Schulmeister (Der) v. Tannenrode. Baron, R. 25c. *Steiger.*

Schulte, J: Roman Catholicism, old and new. cr. 8°. $1.50........................ *R. Worthington.*

Schultze, B. S. Lecture diagrams for instruction in pregnancy and midwifery: 20 col. pl. with 4° v. of letter-press. '65. $15.......... *Lindsay.*

Schultze, M. *See* Manual of histology.

Schumacher, J. J. H. Kern d. hl. Geschichte d. alten u. neuen Testaments f. kathol. Schulen. 8°. hf. leath., 60c. .... *Vering.*

Schumann, Rob. Album for young pianists. (op. 68.) roy. 8°. $2; pap., $1.50............... *Ditson.*

— *Same.* 4°. $3....................... *G. D. Russell.*

— *Same.* 8°. pap., $1.50.................. *Schirmer.*

— Rules for young musicians. 16°. pap., 12c. *Church.*

— *Same.* 12°. pap., 20c...................... *Ditson.*

— Vocal album: 30 songs with Eng. and Germ. words. 8°. $3; pap., $2.50................. *Schirmer.*

— Women's love and life: [Frauenliebe und Leben]. [Songs.] f°. pap., $1.50................ *Schirmer.*

— *and* Chopin, F: Album: piano forte music. f°. 50c. *Gordon.*

Schurr-Murr. Reuter, F. $1; 75c......... *Steiger.*

Schurz, C: Eulogy of Charles Sumner. cr. 8°. $1; pap., 50c.............................. *Lee & S.*

— Speeches. 12°. $2.................... *Lippincott.*

Schüssler, —. The twelve tissue remedies and their use in trituration recommended for investigation; ed. and tr. by C. Hering. 16°. 60c.... *Boericke.*

Schuster, Ign. Abridged hist. of the Old and New Test.; tr. from the Germ. ill. 16°. '74. hf. roan, 30c. .... *Herder.*

— Illustrated Bible hist. of the Old and New Test. for Cath. schools; tr. from the Germ.; rev. by Mrs. J. Sadlier. 12°. '76. 60c... *Herder; W. H. Sadlier.*

Schuster, Sgsm. Drawing cards: 2 pts. in 1 v., with instructions. obl. 18°. $1.25........... *Ivison.*

Schützenberger, P. On fermentation; tr. ill. 12°. '76. $1.50.......................... *Appleton.*

Schuyler, Aar. Complete algebra. 12°. '70. $1.50. — Key. 12°. '74. $1.25........ *Wilson, H. & Co.*

— Elements of geometry; with exercises for students and introd. to modern geometry. 12°. '76. $1.50. *Wilson, H. & Co.*

— Higher arithmetic. 12°. '60. $1.50....... *Sheldon.*

— Plane and spherical trigonometry and mensuration and logarithmic tables. 8°. '75. $1.50. *Wilson, H. & Co.*

— Principles of logic. 12°. '69. 80c... *Wilson, H. & Co.*

— Ray's surveying and navigation; with prelim. treatise on trigonometry and mensuration. 8°. '73. shp., $2.25 .... *Wilson, H. & Co.*

Schwäbische Dorfpredigten. Dreizler, C. B. 15c. *Steiger.*

Schwanenjungfrau (Die). Nieritz, G. 25c... *Steiger.*

Schwartz, *Mme.* Marie Sophie. [Novels]; tr. by S. Borg and M. A. Brown. 8 v. 8°. '70–'74. ea., $1.50; pap., $1 .... *Porter.*

Cont.: Birth and education. — Gerda; or, the children of work. — *Same* (Intern. ed.), $1.25. — Gold and name. — Guilt and innocence. — Right one (The). — Son of the organ-grinder; with biog. sketch and por. — *Same* (Intern. ed.), $1.25. — Two family mothers. — Wife of a vain man.

— Little Karin. por. 12°. *$1.............. *Col. Bk.*

Schwarz und Weiss, od. d. Herz, nicht d. Gesicht. 18°. 35c............................ *Ev. Assoc.*

Schwarze Sam (Der). *See* Hoffmann, J.

Schwarzenberg, F. A. *See* Schiller gallery.

Schwegler, Alb. Handbook of the hist. of philosophy; tr. by J. H. Seelye. 12°. $1.50...... *Appleton.*

— *Same;* tr. and annot. by J. H. Stirling. 12°. '72. $2.25 .... *Putnam.*

Schweinfurth, G: Heart of Africa: three years' travels and adventures in unexplored regions of centre of Africa, 1868–'71; tr. by E. E. Frewer; with introd. by W. Reade. 2 v. ill. and maps. 8°. $8.............................. *Harper.*

Schweinitz, Edm. de. Historic character of the Am. Moravian Church: sermon. 8°. '67. pap., 15c. *Clauder.*
— History and mission of the Moravian Church: sermon. 8°. '71. pap., 25c. .... *Clauder.*
— Life and times of David Zeisberger, the western pioneer and apostle of the Indians. 8°. $3.50. *Lippincott.*
— Moravian episcopate. 16°. '65. pap., 20c... *Clauder.*
— Moravian manual. 2d ed., enl.; with hist. tables. 12°. '69. $1 .... *Clauder.*
— *and* Berg, J. F., *and* Newton, R. Sermons. 16°. '71. pap., 25c. .... *Clauder.*

Schweizer, Meta Heusser. *See* Heusser-Schweizer.

Schwing, H: Missa solemnis: mass in D major. f°. '62. bds., $2.50 .... *Ditson.*
— *See also* Steiner, L. H., *and* Schwing, H.

Science and health. Glover, M. B. $2.50.. *Chr. Sci.*

Science and religion. Garesché, F. P. 15c... *Benziger.*

Science and religion. Wiseman, N. 60c. ...... *Fox.*

Science byways. Proctor, R. A. $4 .... *Lippincott.*

Science for the young. *See* Abbott, Jac.

Science in story. Foote, E. B. 5 v. $7.50; $5; in 1 v., $2 .... *Murray.*

Science in theology. Farrar, A. S. $1.. *Smith, E. & Co.*

Science of common things. Wells, D. A. $1.20.. *Ivison.*

Science of happiness. Bourdon, M. F. $1.. *O'Shea.*

Science of knowledge. Fichte, J. G. $2.. *Lippincott.*

Science of money. Nomistake. $1.75... *Lippincott.*

Science of a new life. Cowan, J. *$3; $3.50; $4. (?) *Cowan.*

Science of rights. Fichte, J. G. $2 ..... *Lippincott.*

Science primers. 6 v. 18°. ea., 50c...... *Appleton.*
Cont.: Chemistry, by H. E. Roscoe.—Physics, by B. Stewart. —Physical geography, by J. Geikie.—Geology, by J. Geikie. —Physiology, by M. Foster.—Astronomy, by J. N. Lockyer.

Science primers. *See* Huxley, T. H., Roscoe, H. E., *and* Stewart, B.

Science a witness for the Bible. Pendleton, W. N. $1. *Claxton; Lippincott.*

Sciences of nature, versus science of man. Porter, N. $1 .... *Dodd.*

Scientific American reference book. ('72.) [Annual.] ill. 8°. $2.50 .... *Munn & Co.*

Scientific amusements. *See* Pepper, J. H.

Scientific bases of faith. Murphy, J. J. $5.. *Macmillan.*

Scientific London. Becker, B. H. $1.75.. *Appleton.*

Scipio Africanus: Ethiop. drama. 16°. pap., 15c. *Happy.*

Sclaverei (Die) der Liebe. Hahn, E. 50c... *Morwitz.*

Scofield, S. R. Easy lessons: key to National school tablets. 8°. '64. 25c. .... *Barnes.*

Scot, G: Model of the government of East New Jersey. *See* New Jersey Hist. Soc.

Scotch anecdotes. Mair, J. A. 50c. ..... *Routledge.*

Scotch story. *See* Barker, M. A. (*Lady*).

Scotch violinist. 4 nos. f°. ea., 25c...... *Gordon.*

Scotch words. *See* Leighton, R.

Scotchman in America. Proudfoot, J. $2.. *Ingham.*

Scotford, J: Judd family; or, an evening visit, and what came of it: elucidation of baptism, ceremonial and spiritual. 16°. '69. $1..... *R. A. Beal.*

Scotia's bards: productions of Scottish poets, with brief biog. sketches. ('53.) New ed. 8°. '69. $4.50; hf. cf., $6; mor., $7.50 .... *Carter.*

Scots worthies. Howie, J. $3.50 .... *Carter.*

Scott, Alfr. T. Hints to converts; or, the happy life begun. 24°. 25c. .... *D. H. Carroll.*
— Need of the church. 18°. 30c. .... *Perkinpine.*

Scott, *Mrs.* Anna M. Glimpses of life in Africa. ill. 18°. '57. 25c. .... *Am. Tr.*

Scott, *Lady* C. L. Pride of life. 12°. $1.75; pap., $1.50 .... *Peterson.*

Scott, C: Keystone of Masonic arch: comment. on universal laws and principles of ancient Freemasonry. 12°. $1.50 .... *Moss.*

Scott, Clem. (*ed.*) Drawing-room plays and parlour pantomimes. 16°. $1.50 .... *French.*

Scott, D: B. Manual of hist. of U. S. to [1869]; with Declaration of ind. and U. S. Const. New ed. 16°. maps. '74. hf. bd., 63c..... *Collins & Bro.*
— School hist. of the U. S., to 1870. maps and ill. 12°. hf. leath., $1.50 .... *Harper.*
— Smaller school hist. of the U. S. maps and ill. 16°. hf. leath., $1 .... *Harper.*

Scott, Eb. Greenough. Commentaries upon intestate system of Penna., and powers and jurisdiction of Orphans' Court. 8°. shp., $6.50 .... *Kay.*

Scott, Fk. J. Suburban home grounds, and best modes of laying out, planting, and keeping decorated grounds; with descript. of beautiful and hardy trees and shrubs grown in U. S. pl. and eng. 8°. *$8 .... *Appleton.*

Scott, Genio C. Fishing in American waters. New ed., enl. ill. cr. 8°. $3.50 .... *Harper.*

Scott, G: Gilbert. See Examples of mod. arch.

Scott, H. Y. D. Sewage question. 2 pts. 8°. '74. ea., pap., 80c. .... *Spon.*
Cont.: 1. Water carriage system, with account of lime and cement process.—2. Interception systems, with suggestions for extraction of concentrated manures from sewage.

Scott, H: Lee. Military dictionary; compr. technical definitions, information on raising and keeping troops, actual service, etc. ill. 8°. '64. hf. roan, $6; hf. mor., $8; mor., $10.. *Van Nostrand.*

Scott, *Mrs.* Hu. R. Rome as it is: reminiscences of a visit to the "city of the Cæsars." ill. 12°. $1.50. *Lippincott.*

Scott, *Rev.* J. W. The dove: parody on "The raven." 12°. '73. 40c.; pap., 25c...... *Claxton.*

Scott, J. Wa. Coin chart manual: sup. to Thompson's Bank note and commercial reporter. ('35.) New ed., rev. ill. 8°. '76. pap., 50c. .... *J. W. Scott.*
— Descriptive price catalogue of revenue stamps of all nations. ill. 8°. '74. pap., 25c...... *J. W. Scott.*
— Descriptive price list of Am. and foreign copper coins. 8°. '73. pap., 25c. .... *J. W. Scott.*
— Descriptive price list of Am. and foreign silver coin. 8°. '74. pap., 25c. .... *J. W. Scott.*
— Postage stamp catalogue. ('66.) New ed., rev. ill. 8°. '76. pap., 25c. — Supplement of ill. 8°. pap., 25c; — in 1 v., pap., 25c. .... *J. W. Scott.*

Scott, Job. Works. 2 v. 8°. '31. *net*, shp., $8. *Friends Bk. Assoc.*

Scott, J: ["Barbarossa."] Lost principle (The); or, the sectional equilibrium: how it was created, how destroyed, how it may be restored. 8°. '60. $1.50 .... *J. W. Randolph.*
— *Same.* 8°. '60. $2 .... *Woodhouse.*
— Partisan life with Mosby. por., ill. and maps. 8°. $3.50 .... *Harper.*

Scott, J: *See* England, Law reports.

Scott, *Rev.* J: Luther and the Lutheran reformation. 2 v. 18°. $1.50 .... *Harper.*

Scott, J: F. Brudder Bones' book of stump speeches and burlesque orations. 16°. pap., 30c.; bds., 50c. .... *Dick & F.*

Scott, Mich. Tom Cringle's log. *See* Standard sea tales.

Scott, Rob. *See* Liddell, H. G., *and* Scott, R.

Scott, Rob. Treatise on ventilation of coal mines; with a narr. of scenes and incidents from life of a miner. 2d ed. ill. 8°. pap., 40c. .... *Spon.*

Scott, S: Diary. 12°. 75c. .... *Friends Bk. St.*

Scott, T. J. Missionary life among the villages of India. 12°. '76. $1.75 .... *Cin. Meth. Bk. Conc.*

Scott, T. Parkin. Authority and free will: lecture. 8°. '63. 25c. .... *Kelly, P. & Co.*

Scott, T: Commentary on the Bible: Old and New Test.; with notes, obs., ref., indexes, etc. 3 v. roy. 8°. $9; shp., $10 .... *Lippincott.*

— Commentary on New Test. roy. 8°. $3; shp., $3.50. *Lippincott.*

— Force of truth. 18°. 75c. .... *Cong. Pub.*

— *Same;* with letters by J. Newton. 18°. 60c. *Pres. Bd.*

— *See also* Bible [Whole]; — Comprehensive comment. on the Bible.

Scott, W. Alice Wade. 8°. pap., 25c. ...... *De Witt.*

Scott, *Elder* Wa. The messiahship; or, great demonstration. 12°. $1.50 .... *Chase.*

Scott, *Sir* Wa. Complete works; with life. 100 v. ill. fp. 8°. (Edinb.) hf. cf., $225 .... *Little, B. & Co.*

Cont.: Waverley novels, 48 v. — Prose works, 30 v. — Poetical works, 12 v. — Lockhart's Life of Scott, 10 v.

— Waverley novels. 4 v. 12°. '74. $7; hf. roxb., $8; hf. cf., $12 .... *Routledge.*

— *Same.* New ed. v. 1–12. ill. 12°. '75–'76. ea., $1.50. *Routledge.*

— *Same.* 26 v. 8°. ea., pap., 25c. .... *Peterson.*

Cont.: Abbot. — Anne of Geierstein. — Antiquary. — Betrothed. — Black dwarf; Legend of Montrose. — Bride of Lammermoor. — Count Robert of Paris. — Fair maid of Perth. — Fortunes of Nigel. — Guy Mannering. — Heart of Mid Lothian. — Highland widow. — Ivanhoe. — Kenilworth. — Monastery. — Old Mortality. — Peveril of the Peak. — Pirate. — Quentin Durward. — Redgauntlet. — Rob Roy. — St. Ronan's well. — Surgeon's daughter; Castle Dangerous. — Talisman. — Waverley. — Woodstock.

— *Same.* 48 v. ill. 16°. hf. cf., $125; cf., $175. *Appleton.*

— *Same.* (Abbotsford ed.) 12 v. ill. demi 8°. $18; $21; shp., $24; hf. cf., $39 .... *Lippincott.*

— *Same.* (Black's ed.) 25 v. roy. 8°. (Edinb.) ea., pap., 25c. .... *Am. News.*

Cont.: Abbot. — Anne of Geierstein. — Antiquary. — Betrothed; Highland widow. — Black dwarf; Legend of Montrose. — Bride of Lammermoor. — Count Robert of Paris. — Fair maid of Perth. — Fortunes of Nigel. — Guy Mannering. — Heart of Mid Lothian. — Ivanhoe. — Kenilworth. — Monastery. — Old Mortality. — Peveril of the Peak. — Pirate. — Quentin Durward. — Redgauntlet. — Rob Roy. — St. Ronan's Well. — Surgeon's daughter. — Talisman. — Waverley. — Woodstock.

— *Same.* (Black's ed.) 25 v. ill. 8°. $100–$175. *Appleton.*

— *Same;* with notes, glossary and index. (Centenary ed.) 25 v. ill. cr. 8°. (Lond.) $31.25; hf cf., $68.75; cf., $100; ea., $1.25 ...... *Little, B. & Co.*

Contents same as in Black's ed. with omission of "Highland widow," and addition of "Castle Dangerous" (bd. with "Surgeon's daughter").

— *Same.* (Centenary ed.) 25 v. ill. 12°. $31.25; hf. cf., $68.75; cf., $80 .... *Appleton.*

— *Same.* (Chp. ed.) 25 v. 8°. ea., pap., 25c. *Appleton; Lippincott.*

Contents same as in Black's ed.

— *Same.* (Edinburgh ed.) 48 v. ill. fp. 8°. $84; hf. cf., $125 .... *Lippincott.*

— *Same.* (Fireside ed.) 23 v. ill. 12°. ea., $1.25; hf. cf., $2.75 .... *Porter.*

Contents same as in Globe ed.

— *Same.* (Globe ed.) 23 v. ill. 16°. ea., $1 .. *Porter.*

Cont.: Abbot. — Anne of Geierstein. — Antiquary. — Betrothed; Talisman. — Black dwarf; Old Mortality. — Bride of Lammermoor; Legend of Montrose. — Count Robert of Paris; Castle Dangerous. — Fair maid of Perth. — Fortunes of Nigel. — Guy Mannering. — Heart of Mid Lothian. — Highland widow; Surgeon's daughter; Chronicles of the Cannongate. — Ivanhoe. — Kenilworth. — Monastery. — Peveril of the Peak. — Pirate. — Quentin Durward. — Redgauntlet. — Rob Roy. — St. Ronan's well. — Waverley. — Woodstock.

— *Same.* (Household ed.) 50 v. ill. 16°. ea., $1 .. * *Osgood.*

Cont.: Abbot, 2 v. — Anne of Geierstein, 2 v. — Antiquary, 2 v. — Betrothed, 2 v. — Black dwarf, 2 v. — Bride of Lammermoor, 2 v. — Count Robert of Paris, 2 v. — Fair maid of Perth, 2 v. — Fortunes of Nigel, 2 v. — Guy Mannering, 2 v. — Heart of Mid Lothian, 2 v. — Ivanhoe, 2 v. — Kenilworth, 2 v. — Monastery, 2 v. — Old Mortality, 2 v. — Peveril of the Peak, 2 v. — Pirate, 2 v. — Quentin Durward, 2 v. — Redgauntlet, 2 v. — Rob Roy, 2 v. — St. Ronan's well, 2 v. — Surgeon's daughter, 2 v. — Talisman, 2 v. — Waverley, 2 v. — Woodstock, 2 v.

Scott, *Sir* Wa., *continued.*

— *Same;* with glossary and index. (Ill. lib. ed.) 25 v. ill. 12°. ea., $1.50 .... *Hurd & H.*

Contents same as in Black's ed., with addition of "Castle Dangerous" (bd. with "Surgeon's daughter").

— *Same.* (Lib. ed.) 6 v. ill. sm. 8°. ea., $1.75; per set, shp., $15; hf. cf., $21 .... *Appleton.*

— *Same.* (Melrose ed.) 13 v. ill. cr. 8°. '75. ea., $2. * *Osgood.*

Cont.: Bride of Lammermoor; Woodstock. — Count Robert of Paris; Betrothed. — Fortunes of Nigel; Black dwarf. — Heart of Mid Lothian; Castle Dangerous. — Ivanhoe; Talisman. — Kenilworth; Fair maid of Perth. — Monastery; Abbot. — Peveril of the Peak; Surgeon's daughter. — Pirate; St. Ronan's well. — Quentin Durward; Anne of Geierstein. — Redgauntlet; Guy Mannering. — Rob Roy; Old Mortality. — Waverley; Antiquary.

— *Same.* (National ed). 5 v. por. 8°. $15; shp., $17.50; hf. cf., $25 .... *Peterson.*

— *Same.* (Pocket ed.) 25 v. 12°. ea., 75c.; in 13 v., cf., $50 .... *Scribner, W. & A.*

— *Same;* with notes, glossary and index. (Riverside ed.) 25 v. ill. cr. 8°. ea., $1.50; per set, hf. cf., $75 .... *Hurd & H.*

Contents same as in Black's ed. with addition of "Castle Dangerous" (bd. with "Surgeon's daughter").

— *Same.* (Standard ed.) 23 v. ill. 12°. ea., $1.50; hf. cf., $3 .... *Porter.*

Contents same as in Globe ed.

— *Same.* (Thistle ed.) 48 v. ill. 12°. ea., $1.50; mor., $2.25 .... *Hale.*

Cont.: Abbot, 2 v. — Anne of Geierstein, 2 v. — Antiquary, 2 v. — Betrothed. — Bride of Lammermoor; Black dwarf, 2 v. — Count Robert of Paris; Castle Dangerous; Surgeon's daughter, 3 v. — Fair maid of Perth, 2 v. — Fortunes of Nigel, 2 v. — Guy Mannering, 2 v. — Heart of Mid Lothian, 2 v. — Highland widow. — Ivanhoe, 2 v. — Kenilworth, 2 v. — Legend of Montrose. — Monastery, 2 v. — Old Mortality, 2 v. — Peveril of the Peak, 3 v. — Pirate, 2 v. — Quentin Durward, 2 v. — Redgauntlet, 2 v. — Rob Roy, 2 v. — St. Ronan's well, 2 v. — Talisman. — Waverley, 2 v. — Woodstock, 2 v.

— Poems. 12°. $1.50 .... *Locke.*

— *Same.* (Blue and gold edition.) 18°. $1.25. — (Cabinet ed.) 16°. $1.50 .... *Nichols & H.*

— *Same.* (Holiday ed.) 5 v. 16°. $8.75; hf. cf., $12.50. — (Lib. ed.) 2 v. ill. 16°. $4; hf. cf., $7.50 .... *Mason.*

— *Same.* (Scribner's pop. poets.) ill. 12°. $1.50. *Scribner, W. & A.*

— *Same;* with biog. (Household ser.) ill. 16°. $1.50; mor., $3 .... *Lee & S.*

— *Same;* with memoir. 9 v. por. 18°. $9. — (Diamond ed.) 16°. '68. $1; hf. cf., $2.25; mor., $3. — (Red line ed.) ill. sm. 4°. '69. $3.50; hf. cf., $5; mor., $7 .... *Osgood.*

— *Same;* ed. by R. A. Willmott; with biog., etc. (Brit. poets.) ill. 12°. $2.25; hf. cf., $3.50; mor., $5. *Routledge.*

— *Same;* [also] Poems by S. T. Coleridge. ill. 16°. $1.12; $1.35. — 32°. 85c.; $1.12 .... *World Pub.*

— Poetical works. 8°. $3 .... *Desilver.*

— *Same.* ill. 8°. shp., $3.50; mor., $10 ... *Appleton.*

— *Same.* 8°. cf., $5 .... *Peterson.*

— *Same.* (Boston ed.) 8°. shp., $3.50; mor., $10. *Lee & S.*

— *Same.* (Boston ed.) ill. 8°. shp., $4.50; mor., $10. *Mason.*

— *Same.* (Centenary ed.) 2 v. cr. 8°. (Lond.) $2.50 .... *Little, B. & Co.*

— *Same.* (Chandos classics.) cr. 8°. $1; pap., 75c. *Scribner, W. & A.*

— *Same.* ill. 8°. (Dick.) 50c.; pap., 25c. .. *Am. News.*

— *Same.* (Household ed.) 3 v. 16°. $3.75; hf. cf., $7.50; cf., $11.25. — (Blue and gold ed.) 3 v. por. 32°. $3.75; hf. cf., $7.50; cf., $10.50 .. *Miller.*

— *Same.* (Pocket ed.) 6 v. 12°. ea., 75c. *Scribner, W. & A.*

— *Same;* with his introds. and notes. ill. 8°. $3; mor., $7; $7.50 .... *Lippincott.*

— *Same;* with life. (Globe ed.) ill. 16°. $1.25; hf. cf., $3.25; mor., $4. — (chp. ed.), pap., 60c. *Appleton.*

— *Same;* with memoir and notes. (Presentation poets.) 12°. $1.75; ivorine, $3; mor., $3.50 .. *Routledge.*

Scott, *Sir* Wa., *continued.*
— *Same;* with notes. ill. 8°. $2; shp., $2.75.. *World Pub.*
— *Same;* with notes. (Chandos poets.) ill. cr. 8°. $3.75; cf., $7.50; mor., $8 .... *Scribner, W.& A.*
— *Same;* with notes. (Handy vol. ed.) 7 v. ill. 18°. '76. $5 .... *Scribner, W.& A.*
— *Same;* with notes, app., memoir, etc. (Globe ed.) ill. 12°. $1.50; hf. cf., $2.75; mor., $5; — with sketch of life. (Diamond ed.) sq. 16°. $1.75. *Lippincott.*
— *Same;* ed., with biog. and memoir, by F. T. Palgrave. (Globe ed.) 12°. '69. $1.50. *Macmillan.*
— — *See also* Burns, R., Poetical works.
— Select poetical works. (Presentation ed.) 6 v. 18°. $25 .... *Appleton.*
— Abstract of the Eyrbiggia saga. *See* Mallet, P. H., Northern antiquities.
— Essays on chivalry, romance and the drama. 12°. $1.75; hf. cf., $3.75; cf., $5. — cr. 8°. $1; pap., 75c. .... *Scribner, W. & A.*
— Ivanhoe: a romance. ill. 12°. $1 .... *Porter.*
— *Same;* condensed by R. Johnson. 18°. '76. $1.. *Holt.*
— Lady of the lake. 18°. hf. bd., 38c. ...... *Clark & M.*
— *Same.* 32°. 50c. .... *U.P.James.*
— *Same.* 16°. 50c .... *Appleton.*
— *Same.* 32°. 60c.; 90c.; mor., $1.50 .... *Porter.*
— *Same.* ill. 18°. 75c. .... *Nelson.*
— *Same.* 16°. $1.25 .... *Mason; Osgood.*
— *Same.* ill. 12°. $1.50 .... *World Pub.*
— *Same.* ill. cr. 8°. $1.75; $2.25; hf. roxb., $4.50; mor., $6 .... *Hurd & H.*
— *Same.* (Cabinet ed.) ill. 16°. $1.25; $1.75; hf. roxb., $3; mor., $4.50 .... *Hurd & H.*
— *Same.* (School ed.) 18°. 38c. .... *Nichols & H.*
— *Same;* with introd. and notes. ill. 16°. $1.50; mor., $4 .... *Porter.*
— — *See also* British pocket classics.
— *Same;* [also] Poems by M. Howitt. ill. 16°. $1.12; $1.35. — 32°. 85c.; $1.12 .... *World Pub.*
— Lay of the last minstrel. 16°. 50c. ...... *Appleton.*
— *Same.* 16°. $1.25 .... *Mason; Osgood.*
— — *See also* British pocket classics.
— Letters on demonology and witchcraft; addressed to J. G. Lockhart. ill. 18°. 75c. .... *Harper.*
— Life; with remarks upon his writings by F. T. Palgrave; essay on Scott by D. Mason; and Dryburg Abbey [poem], by C. Swain. 12°. 50c.; 25c. .... *Porter.*
— Life of Napoleon Bonaparte. 5 v. 12°. ea., 75c. *Scribner, W.& A.*
— Lives of celebrated novelists and dramatists. 12°. $1.75; hf. cf., $3.75; cf., $5. — cr. 8°. $1; pap., 75c. .... *Scribner, W.& A.*
— *Same.* 12°. '72. $2 .... *Denham.*
— Lord of the isles. 16°. $1.25 .... *Mason.*
— Marmion. 16°. 50c. .... *Appleton.*
— *Same.* 16°. $1.25 .... *Mason; Osgood.*
— *Same.* ill. 18°. 75c. .... *Nelson.*
— Moredun: tale of 1210. 8°. pap., 50c. .... *Peterson.*
— Rokeby. 16°. $1.25 .... *Mason.*
— Tales of a grandfather. 4 v. 12°. ea., 75c. *Scribner, W.& A.*

Cont.: History of Scotland, 3 v. — History of France.

— *Same.* 6 v. 16°. ea., $1.25 .... **Osgood.*
— *Same.* ill. 8°. $2; shp., $2.75 .... *World Pub.*
— *Same.* (Centenary ed.) 2 v. cr. 8°. (Lond.) $2.50 .... *Little, B.& Co.*
— *Same.* (Fireside ed.) ill. 16°. $1.50; hf. cf., $2.75. *Porter.*
— *Same.* (Globe ed.) ill. 16°. $1 .... *Porter.*
— *Same.* (Ill. lib. ed.) 3 v. ill. 12°. ea., $1.50. *Hurd & H.*
— *Same.* (Riverside ed.) 3 v. ill. 12°. $4.50; hf. cf., $9 .... *Hurd & H.*
— *Same.* (Standard ed.) 4 v. ill. 12°. ea., $1.50; hf. cf., $3 .... *Porter.*
— *Same.* pt. 1. 8°. pap., 25c. .... *Peterson.*

Scott, W: Anderson. Christ of the apostle's creed: the voice of the church against Arianism, Strauss and Renan; with app. 8°. '67. $3 ...... *Randolph.*
— Giant judge (The): story of Samson, the Hebrew Hercules. 12°. $1 .... *Pres. Bd.*
— Wedge of gold; or, Achan in El Dorado. 18°. 60c. .... *Pres. Bd.*

Scott, W: B. Gems of modern art: carbon photos., with remarks and essays. 3 v. 4°. '71–'72. ea., $10 .... *Routledge.*

Cont.: Gems of mod. Belgian art, mor., $20. — Gems of mod. French art, mor., $20. — Gems of mod. Germ. art, mor., $15.

— Half-hour lectures on hist. and practice of fine and ornamental arts. ill. 16°. $3 ... *Scribner, W.& A.*
— *See also* Pictures by Ital. masters; — Pictures by Venetian painters.

Scott, W: L., *and* Jarnagin, Milton P. Treatise upon law of telegraphs; embr. gen. statutes of Eng., Canada, the U. S., and the several states on the subject. 8°. '68. shp., $5 .... *Little, B.& Co.*

Scott, Winfield. Autobiography. 2 v. ill. 12°. $4; hf. cf., $8. — large pap. ed., $10; hf. cf., $12.50. *Sheldon.*
— Infantry tactics: rules for exercise and manœuvres of the U. S. infantry. 3 v. 24°. $3 .... *Harper.*

Scottish and English ballads. ill. 16°. $1.50; mor., $3 .... *Lee & S.*

Scottish cavalier. *See* Grant, Ja.

Scottish chiefs. *See* Porter, Jane.

Scottish minister. ('65.) New ed. ill. 16°. '69. $1.15 .... *Hoyt.*

Scottish minstrel: songs and song writers of Scotland subsequent to Burns; with biog., notes, etc. demy 8°. $2.50 .... *Appleton; Lee & S.*

Scottish orphans. *See* Blackford, *Mrs.* —.

Scottish philosophy. M'Cosh, J. $4 .... *Carter.*

Scottish song. Aitken, M. C. $1.25 ..... *Macmillan.*

Scottish stories: brief accounts of persecuted Covenanters. 12°. 60c. .... *West. Tr.*

Scougal, H: Life of God in soul of man. 16°. '68. $1.25 .... *Lockwood, B.& Co.*
— *Same;* [also] Rules for a holy life, by R. Leighton. 12°. 90c. .... *Whittaker.*

Scourge of Israel. 18°. 40c. .... *Am. S. S.*

Scouring of the White Horse. Hughes, T. $1.25. *Macmillan.*

Scout. Simms, W. G. $1.75; 75c. ...... *Widdleton.*

Scouting expeditions of the Texan rangers. Reid, S. C., *jr.* $1.75 .... *J.E. Potter.*

Scovil, W. E. A short-hand legible as the plainest writing; ed. by W. E. Scovil, *jr.* 16°. $1.75. *Campbell & Co.*

Scoville, Jos. A. Old merchants of New York. New ed., rev. 4 v. ill. 12°. '76. $6 .... *Miller.*

Scrambles among the Alps. Whymper, E. $2.50; $3. *Lippincott.*

Scrap-book. Fields, W. $2 .... *Claxton.*

Scrap-book. *See* Picture page lib.

Scrap of paper. Simpson, J. P. 15c .... *French.*

Scraps of knowledge for the little ones. Byrne, J. $1.50 .... *Cassell.*

Scribe, Eug. Bertrand et Raton. Ed. by J. Bué. 16°. 75c. .... *Lippincott.*
— First love: comedy; tr. 12°. pap., 15c. .. *De Witt.*
— Glass of water; tr. *See* Evening's entertainment.
— Woman that was a cat: farce; tr. 16°. pap., 15c. *French.*
— *and* Duveyrier, A. H. J. (*Baron*) de. Valérie: comédie; avec vocab. ('65.) New ed. 12°. '75. pap., 30c. .... *Holt.*
— *and* Legouvé, E. Bataille (La) de dames: comédie. ('64.) New ed. 12°. '76. pap., 40c. .... *Holt.*
— — Doigts (Les) de fée: comédie. With Eng. notes by F. Bôcher. ('64.) New ed. 12°. '76. pap., 40c. .... *Holt*

Scribner, C: H. Treatise on the law of dower. v. 2. 8°. $7.50 .... *T. & J. W. Johnson.*
Note. v. 1 is o. p.

Scribner, J. M. Engineers' and mechanics' companion. 16°. *net*, $1.56 .... *Hamersley.*
— Engineers', contractors' and surveyors' pocket table book. 16°. *net*, $1.56 .... *Hamersley.*
— Lumber and log book; for ship builders, boat builders, etc. 12°. 30c. .... *Judd.*

Scribner, W. M. *See* Payson, J. W., Dunton, S., *and* Scribner, W. M.

Scribner, W: Pray for the Holy Spirit; with note by by W. G. T. Shedd. 12°. '75. $1.25; pap., 50c. *Randolph.*
— Pray for your children. 18°. 40c. .... *Pres. Bd.*

Scribner's popular juveniles. 7 v. ill. 12°. ea., $1.50. *Scribner, W. & A.*
Cont.: Andersen's Fairy tales.— Arabian nights.— Don Quixote. — Eastern tales. — Grimm's fairy tales. — Defoe's Robinson Crusoe. — Swiss family Robinson.

Scribner's popular poets. 22 v. ill. 12°. ea., $1.50. *Scribner, W. & A.*
Cont.: Burns. — Butler's Hudibras. — Byron. — Campbell. — Coleridge. — E. Cook. — Cowper. — Cary's Dante. — Combe's Dr. Syntax. — Hemans. — Hood. — Keats. — Roberts' Legendary ballads. — Lockhart's Spanish ballads. — Milton. — Moore. — Pope's Iliad. — Pope's Odyssey. — Scott. — Shakespeare. — Shelley. — Wordsworth.

Scriptural coincidences. Craig, J. D. $1.25 .. *Wiley.*

Scriptural doctrine of Hades. Bartle, G. $1.50. *Lippincott.*

Scriptural predestination. Knight, R. $2.25 .. *Wiley.*

Scripture atlas: maps and plans, with chronol. chart of hist. fp. 8°. (Bagster.) 50c. .... *Wiley.*

Scripture atlas to ill. Old and New Test.; with physical map of Egypt, Sinai and Palestine. 4°. $2.50. *Scribner, W. & A.*

Scripture biographical dictionary. 18°. 60c. .. *Am. S. S.*

Scripture cabinet. House, E. $1.75. *Cin. Meth. Bk. Conc.*

Scripture facts. Mortimer, M. 4 v. ea., 30c. .. *Am. Tr.*

Scripture gift book. Ellet, E. F. *net*, 75c. .. *Hamersley.*

Scripture guide to infant baptism. 16c. (?) *Cumberland.*

Scripture harmony: manual for devotional students of the Scriptures. 12°. '66. 75c. .... *Randolph.*

Scripture history. 18°. 60c. .... *Dutton.*

Scripture ill. by interesting facts. Field, C. 75c. *Harper.*

Scripture illustrations. 2 pts. 18°. ea., 40c. .. *Am. S. S.*

Scripture illustrations. 18°. 50c. .... *Nelson.*

Scripture itself the illustrator. Bowes, G. S. $1.50. *Carter.*

Scripture lessons. Peet, H. P. 30c.; 20c. .... *Am. Tr.*

Scripture lessons for the little ones. Paschall, A. S. *net*, 33c. .... *Friends Bk. Assoc.*

Scripture lessons in verse. Doddridge, P. 40c. *Pres. Bd.*

Scripture narratives of young persons. 18°. 40c.; 50c. .... *Am. Bapt.*

Scripture natural history: descript. of birds, quadrupeds, etc., mentioned in Scripture. ill. 12°. $1. *Pres. Bd.*

Scripture pearls. *See* Luther, Mt.

Scripture picture books. 6 v. 4°. ea., 50c.; pap., 25c. *Nelson.*
Cont.: Story of Joseph and his brethren. — History of Solomon. — History of Moses. — History of David. — History of Daniel. — Story of Ruth.

Scripture portions for the afflicted; with reflections from various authors. 18°. 50c. .... *Pres. Bd.*

Scripture portraits. Stanley, A. P. $2.50 .. *Routledge.*

Scripture precepts; tr. by Mrs. E. B. Stork. 2 ser. $1.50 .... (?) *Luth. Pub.*

Scripture promises. *See* Clarke, S.

Scripture questions. 22 v. 18°. v. 1, bds., 20c.; v. 2–20, ea., bds., 15c. .... *Cong. Pub.*
Cont.: Romans. — 1 Corinthians. — Gospels in harmony, 2 pts. — 2 Corinthians, Titus and Jude, 2 pts. — Genesis, 2 pts. — Gospels in harmony, 2 pts. — Parables of N. Test., 2 pts. — Gospels in harmony, 2 pts. — Acts. — Job. — Life and teachings of Christ. — Psalms. — Hist. of Christ. — Miracles of Christ. — Prophecies relating to Christ in O. Test. — Scripture biog. — Exodus and Leviticus. — Scripture biog., 2d pt. — Numbers and Deuteronomy. — Hebrews. — Isaiah. — Christian morality.

Scripture readings for devotion and study. Barrows, L. D. 20c. .... *N. E. Meth.*

Scripture readings for schools and families. *See* Yonge, C. M.

Scripture speculations. Stevens, H. R. $2 .. *Somerby.*

Scripture stories. 18°. 22c. .... *Am. S. S.*

Scripture subjects put into simple verses for the young. 18°. 40c. .... *Am. S. S.*

Scripture testimony against intoxicating wine. Ritchie, W. 60c. .... *Nat. Temp.*

Scripture types. Frey, J. S. C. F. 2 v. $1.50. *Am. Bapt.*

Scripture views of heaven. *See* Edmondson, J.

Scrivener, F: H: *See* Bible, New Test., *Greek.*

Scriver, Chr. Gotthold's emblems; or, invisible things understood by things that are made; tr. by R. Menzies. 8°. '66. $2.50 .... *Eastman.*
— *Same.* cr. 8°. $2.50 .... *Scribner, W. & A.*
— Verlorene u. wiedergefundene Schäflein (Das). 16°. '75. 50c. .... *Dette.*

Scrope. Perkins, F. B. $1.50 .... *Roberts.*

Scrub. Balfour, C. L. 50c. .... (?) *Martien.*

Scrub Hollow Sunday school: how it was started. 16°. $1.50 .... *Am. S. S.*

Scruggs, *Mrs.* M. V. ["Elsie Earnest."] Sketches. 12°. '74. $1.50 .... *Turnbull.*

Scudamore, W. E. Notitia eucharistica: comment. on order of administration of Lord's supper according to Church of England. 8°. '72. $10 .. *Dutton.*
— Steps to the altar: manual of devotions for the eucharist. 18°. '69. 25c. .... *Dutton.*
— *Same.* 32°. '75. 40c.; 50c. .... *Pott.*

Scudder, D: C. Stories about the heathen, and their children. ill. 24°. 30c. .... *Bost. Am. Tr.*

Scudder, H: Christian's daily walk in holy security and peace. 12°. 90c. .... *Pres. Bd.*

Scudder, Hor. E. Doings of the Bodley family in town and country. ill. sm. 4°. '75. $2 .... *Hurd & H.*
— Dream children. 16°. $1 .... *Hurd & H.*
— Dwellers in Five Sisters Court. 16°. '76. $1.50; pap., $1.25 .... *Hurd & H.*
— Seven little people and their friends. ill. 16°. $1.25. *Hurd & H.*
— Stories from my attic. ill. 16°. $1.50 .... *Hurd & H.*
— (*ed.*) Men and manners one hundred years ago. *See* Stoddard, R. H., Sans-souci series.

Scudder, J: Appeal to children and youth of U. S. on behalf of the heathen world. 18°. 55c. *Am. S. S.*
— Appeal to Christian mothers in behalf of the heathen. 18°. 20c. .... *Am. Tr.*
— Grandpapa's talk with his little Mary. 2 v. ill. 18°. 60c. .... *N. Y. Ref. Ch. Bd.*
— Letters to Sabbath school children on the condition of the heathen. 18°. 25c. .... *Am. S. S.*
— Provision for passing over Jordan. (cop. '46.) New ed. 64°. '52. 25c. .... *Am. Tr.*
— Tales about the heathen. ill. 18°. '49. 45c. .. *Am. Tr.*
— Voice from the east to the young. ill. 18°. 60c. *N. Y. Ref. Ch. Bd.*

Scudder, J: M. Eclectic practice in diseases of children. 8°. '69. shp., $5 .... *Wilstach.*
— Eclectic practice of medicine. ('63.) 6th ed. 8°. '75. shp., $7 .... *Wilstach.*
— Eclectic practice of medicine for families. ('65.) 17th ed. 2 v. in 1. 8°. '76. shp., $3 .. *Wilstach.*
— On reproductive organs and the venereal. ('73.) 2d ed. ill. 8°. '76. shp., $5 .... *Wilstach.*
— On use of inhalations in treatment of diseases of respiratory organs. ('66.) 3d ed. 12°. '74. $2. *Wilstach.*

Scudder, J: M., *continued*.
— Practical treatise on diseases of women. ('57.) 5th ed. ill. 8°. '74. shp., $4 .... *Wilstach.*
— Principles of medicine. 8°. '67. shp., $4 .. *Wilstach.*
— Specific diagnosis: study of diseases with ref. to administration of remedies. ('74.) 2d ed. 12°. '75. $2.50 .... *Wilstach.*
— Specific medication and specific medicines. ('70.) 2d ed. 12°. '71. $2.50 .... *Wilstach.*
— *See also* Jones, L. E., *and* Scudder, J. M.

Scudder, *Mrs.* Jos. Captain Waltham: tale of southern India. 16°. $1.10 .. *N. Y. Ref. Ch. Bd.; Pres. Bd.*

Scudder, Mos. L. American Methodism; with introd. by J. Cummings. ill. 8°. $3.50; $4 .. *Scranton.*
— Wesleyan psalmist. [Hymn book.] 18°. '49. 35c. — ill. 18°. $3 .... *Meth. Bk. Conc.*

Scudder, S: H. Catalogue of orthoptera of No. Am. 8°. '68. pap., $1 .... *Smith. Inst.*
— Fossil butterflies. ill. 4°. '75. pap., $2; hf. mor., $3.50 .... *Am. Assoc. Adv. Sci.*
— Fossil myriapods from Nova Scotia. 4°. pap., 35c. *Bost. Soc. Nat. Hist.*
— Revision of the large, stylated, fossorial crickets. ill. imp. 8°. '69. pap., $1 .. *Peabody Acad. of Sci.*
— Species of the lepidopterous genus pamphila. ill. 4°. pap., $1 .... *Bost. Soc. Nat. Hist.*
— Structure and transformations of eumæus atala. *See* Packard, A. S., *jr.*, Gynandromorphism in lepidoptera.

Sculptor's triumph. Baker, G. M. 15c. .... *Lee & S.*

Scupoli, Laur. Spiritual combat; tr. from the Ital. 18°. '75. 40c.; pap., 20c. .... *Pott.*
— *Same.* 48°. 40c.; 60c.; roan, 75c. .... *O'Shea.*
— *Same.* 32°. '51. 40c.–$2 .... *Murphy.*
— *Same;* [also] The peace of the soul and the happiness of the heart which dies to itself in order to live to God. 32°. 40c. .... *Cath. Pub.*

Scylla and Charybdis. Foote, H. S. $2.50 .. *Harper.*

Sea. ('59.) 2d ed. 18°. '75. 30c. .... *So. Meth.*

Sea. Somerset, C. A. 15c. .... *French.*

Sea and its living wonders. Hartwig, G. $6 .. *Dodd.*

Sea and its wonders. Kirby, M. *and* E. $3 ... *Nelson.*

Sea and sail: marvelous adventures on the ocean. ill. 12°. $1.50 .... *World Pub.*

Sea and sea-shore: lessons in study of nature and natural history. ill. 12°. '75. $1 ..... *Nelson.*

Sea and shore. Adams, W. T. $1.25 .... *Lee & S.*

Sea and shore. Warfield, C. A. $1.75 ..... *Peterson.*

Sea and shore: a poetical selection. sq. 18°. '74. $1.25. *Roberts.*

Sea and shore ser. 5 v. 16°. $5 .... *Lothrop.*
Cont.: Famous islands. — Wrecked, not lost. — My mate and I. — Little Wavie, the foundling. — Wonders near home.

Sea breezes; by author of "Knight of the frozen sea." ill. 12°. $1.50 .... *Nelson.*

Sea drift. Rodney, M. R. L. 90c. .... *Claxton.*

Sea drifts. Macleod, G. A. $1.25 .... *Carter.*

Sea fights and land battles. Valentine, R. $2.50 *Scribner, W. & A.*

Sea fights from Sluys to Navarino. V., L. $1.25. *Scribner, W. & A.*

Sea gift. Fuller, E. W. $1.50 .... *Hale.*

Sea gulls. Maltby, C. A., *and* Stainforth, F. 15c. *French.*

Sea king. Marryat, F. 50c. .... *Peterson.*

Sea kings and naval heroes. *See* Edgar, J. G.

Sea lions. *See* Cooper, Ja. F.

Sea of Galilee. *See* Stories of the good shepherd.

Sea of ice. Dennery, A. P., *and* Dugué, F. 15c. *French.*

Sea of troubles. Baker, G. M. 15c. .... *Lee & S.*

Sea shore. *See* Abbott, Jac.

Sea shore. Babb, C. E. 40c. .... *West. Tr.*

Sea songs. *See* Dibdin, C.

Sea stories. *See* Juvenile picture books.

Sea stories; by an old sailor. ill. 12°. $1.25 .. *Nelson.*

Sea tales. *See* Cooper, Ja. F.

Seaboard parish. MacDonald, G. $1.75. *Lothrop; Routledge.*

Seaboy's grave; [also] English boy; [also] Pilgrim. 18°. 30c. .... *Am. S. S.*

Seabury, *Bp.* S: Communion office; reprint. in facsimile, with hist. sketch and notes by S. Hart. 12°. '74. 75c. .... *Whittaker.*
— Life. 18°. 60c. .... *Dutton.*

Seabury, *Rev.* S: Discourses ill. of nature and work of the Holy Spirit, and other papers; ed. by W. J. Seabury. 8°. '74. $1.25; pap., $1 ..... *Pott.*
— Mary, the virgin, as commemorated in church of Christ; [also] Who was James, the Lord's brother? by M. Mahan. 16°. '68. 25c. ... *Pott.*
— Theory and use of Church calendar in measurement and distribution of time. 8°. '72. $2.50 .. *Pott.*

Seabury Castle. Hope, C. $1 .... *Lippincott.*

Seagull rock. *See* Sandeau, J.

Seal of heaven. Jeter, J. B. 75c. .... *Am. Tr.*

Sealed packet. Trollope, T. A. $1.75; $1.50. *Peterson.*

Sealing of the spirit. Underwood, A. 25c. .... *Hoyt.*

Seals opened. Pond, E. $1.50 .... *Hoyt, F. & D.*

Seaman, Ez. C. American system of government. 12°. '70. $1.50 .... *Scribner.*
— Progress of nations in civilization, productive industry, wealth and population. 2 v. cr. 8°. ea., $2.50 .... *Scribner.*
— Views of nature and of the elements, forces and phenomena of nature and of mind. 12°. '73. $1. *Scribner.*

Seaman and his family. 18°. 55c. .... *Am. S. S.*

Seaman's compass and chart. Bonney, S. W. 25c. *Am. Tr.*

Seamen's narratives. ill. 18°. '60. 50c. .... *Am. Tr.*

Seamer, *Mrs.* F. Dick's robins. ill. 16°. 50c. .. *Nelson.*
— Jeannie Barker. *See* Gem cluster.
— Young missionaries. ill. 16°. 75c. .... *Nelson.*

Search and manifestation. *See* Townsend, L. T.

Search for winter sunbeams. Cox, S. S. $3 .. *Appleton.*

Search the Scriptures. 16°. $1 .... *Lothrop.*

Searching the net. Warren, J. L. $1.75 .. *Routledge.*

Searing, *Mrs.* Laura C. [*formerly Miss* Redden; "Howard Glyndon."] Sounds from secret chambers. 18°. $1.50 .... *Osgood.*

Searle, Arth. Outlines of astronomy. 2d ed. 16°. '75. $2 .... *Ginn.*

Searle, January (*pseud.*) *See* Phillips, G: S.

Searle, R. *See* England, Law reports.

Searles, J. N. Digest of Minnesota Sup. Court reports (v. 1–16). 8°. '72. shp., $7.50 .. *Callaghan.*

Sears, A. F. Reducing cost of railroad construction. 8°. pap., 55c. .... *Am. Soc. of C. E.*

Sears, Barnas. Celebration of 100th anniv. of founding of Brown Univ., Sept. 6, 1864; with hist. discourse. roy. 8°. '65. 75c. .... *Rider.*
— Life of Luther; with special ref. to its earlier periods and the opening scenes of reformation. 18°. 90c.; $1. — 12°. $1.50. — 8°. $2 .... *Am. S. S.*

Sears, Edm. H. Foregleams and foreshadows of immortality. ('72.) 11th ed. 12°. $1.75. *Claxton.*
— Fourth Gospel the heart of Christ. ('72.) 4th ed. 12°. '75. $2.50 .... *Lockwood, B. & Co.*
— Regeneration. 9th ed., rev. and enl. 12°. '72. $1.25. *Claxton.*
— Sermons and songs of the Christian life. 12°. '74. $2. *Lockwood, B. & Co.*

Sears, E: S. Faxon's ill. handbook of summer travel to lakes, springs and mountains of New Eng. and N. Y. New ed., enl. ill. and maps. 16°. '75. $1 .... *Faxon.*
Sears, Rob. Family instructor: digest of general knowledge. ill. 8°. *$3.50; $4.50..*J.E.Potter.*
Seaside and fireside fairies. ill. 12°. $1.25..*Lippincott.*
Seaside home. Norris, E. M. $1 .... *Pott.*
Seaside lib. *See* Mudge, Z. A.
Seaside rambles. 18°. 35c. .... *Pres.Bd.*
Seaside scenes. *See* Juvenile picture books.
Seaside stories. 3 v. 18°. $2.50 .... *Cong.Pub.*
Cont.: Red lion. — Ferryman's child. — Fisherman's children.
Seaside studies in natural history. Agassiz, E. C. *and* A. $3 .... *Osgood.*
Seasons. 18°. 35c. .... *Am.S.S.*
Seasons. *See* Diamond miniatures.
Seasons. *See* Haydn, F. J.
Seasons. *See* Thomson, Ja.
Seasons, months and days. Summers, T. O. 40c. *So.Meth.*
Seasons with the sea-horses. Lamont, J. $3..*Harper.*
Seat of empire. Coffin, C. C. $1.50 .... *Osgood.*
Seaton, E: C. Handbook of vaccination. 12°. $1.25. *Lippincott.*
— *Same.* 12°. '68. $2.25 .... *Macmillan.*
Seaton, *Sir* T: Manual of fret-cutting and wood-carving; with diagrams. 12°. '75. $1..*Routledge.*
Seaton, Wa. A man in search of a wife; or, adventures of a bachelor in N.Y. 8°. pap., 25c...*De Witt.*
Seaton, W: Winston. Biographical sketch; by his daughter. 12°. $2 .... *Osgood.*
Seaver, Edn. P. Formulas of plane and spherical trigonometry. 16°. '72. 80c. .... *Allyn.*
Seaward, *Sir* E: *See* Porter, J., Shipwreck of Sir Edward Seaward.
Sebald, Hg. Zeichnen-Schule: praktische Anleitg. zur Erlerng. der Zeichnen-Kunst nebst e. Umriss d. plastischen Anatomie, der Lehre d. Perspective, sowie der Behandlung der Wasser- und Oel- Farben. ill. 4°. '74. $5; pap., $4......(?)*Sebald.*
Sebastian. McGee, T. D. 40c. .... *Sadlier.*
Sebastian. *See* One thousand francs.
Secession, coercion and civil war. Jones, J. B. $1.75 .... *Peterson.*
Sechste und siebente Buch (Das) Mosis. 18°. $1.50. *Radde.*
Sechter, S. Correct order of fundamental harmonies; comp. and adapted by C. C. Müller. 8°. '71. $2 .... *Pond.*
Secker, T: Five discourses against popery. 2d ed. 18°. '35. 18c. .... *I.N.Whiting.*
— Lectures on catechism of Prot. Episc. Church; with discourse on confirmation. roy. 12°. '35. 75c. *I.N.Whiting.*
Secker, W: Nonsuch professor; or, Christianity as exemplified in conduct of its sincere professors. ('55.) New ed. 12°. '60. $1 .... *Pounsford.*
Seclusaval. *See* Graves, *Mrs.* A. C
Second Adam and the new birth. Sadler, M. F. 15c. *Claremont.*
Second cousin Sarah. Robinson, F. W. 75c...*Harper.*
Second hand dress. 18°. 20c.; 25c. .... *Am.Bapt.*
Second love. Simpson, J. P. 15c. .... *French.*
Second reader; for Cath. schools. 16°. 33c..*Benziger.*
— *See also* First book; — Third reader.
Second to none. *See* Grant, Ja.
Second wife. John, E. $1.75 .... *Lippincott.*
Secondthoughts, Sol. (*pseud.*) *See* Kennedy, J: P.
Secret. 18°. 17c.; 22c. .... *Am.Bapt.*
Secret. Barrymore, W. 15c. .... *French.*
Secret. Sadlier, M. A. 25c. .... *Sadlier.*
Secret. *See* Two paths.
Secret agent. Coyne, J. S. 15c. .... *French.*
Secret art of breaking, taming and training wild and vicious horses; [also] The American horse doctor. ('69.) 10th ed. 8°. '76. pap., 25c...*Hunter.*
Secret band of brothers. Green, J. H. $1.75; $1.50. *Peterson.*
Secret despatch. Grant, J. 80c. .... *Routledge.*
Secret disciple encouraged to avow his master. Watson, J. 50c. .... *Claxton.*
Secret drawer: Italian story; by author of "Alice Middleton." ill. 12°. $1 .... *Nelson.*
Secret drawer lib. 4 v. 12°. $4 .... *Nelson.*
Cont.: Secret drawer. — Harry Lawley, by E. Leslie. — Orphan and the foundling, by E. Leslie. — Faith Harrowby, by S. Doudney.
Secret duel. Wright, S. A. 25c. .... *Sickels.*
Secret history of a votary of pleasure. Blanchard, C. $1 .... *D.Thomas.*
Secret of Christianity. Hebberd, S. S. $1.50..*Lee & S.*
Secret of the island. *See* Verne, Jul.
Secret of the Lord. *See* Shipton, A.
Secret of riches: tale of last century. 18°. 30c.; pap., 12c. .... *O'Shea.*
— *Same;* [also] Sauremonde. 18°. 30c. ..... *O'Shea.*
Secret of strength. Lyman, M. B. $1..*Bost.Am.Tr.*
Secret of success. Baker, H. N. W. $1..*H.A.Young.*
Secret of Swedenborg. James, H. $2.50....*Osgood.*
Secret orders. Bain, J.W. 40c.; 20c...*U.P.Bd.of Pub.*
Secret out; or, one thousand tricks with cards. ill. 12°. $1.50 .... *Dick & F.*
Secret passion. Williams, R. F. $1 .... *Peterson.*
Secret revealed. Powell, W. J., *and* Rarey, J. S. *$1.50 .... *Hubbard.*
Secret revealed; or, Minnie McDougal, the raspberry vender. 18°. 30c. .... *Am.S.S.*
Secret service. Planché, J. R. 15c. .... *French.*
Secret trials of the Christian life. Jelf, R. W. $2.50. *Pott.*
Secretary. Robinson, F. W. 50c. .... *De Witt.*
Secrets for farmers: information for fruit growers, house owners, dairy men, etc. 8°. '74. pap., 30c. ....(?)*F.M.Reed.*
Secrets of the convent and confessional. Wright, J. McN. *$2.75; $3.25 .... *Jones.*
Secrets of the sanctum. Hill, A. F. $1.50..*Claxton.*
Secrets revealed. Langille, J. H. 80c. ..... *Am.Tr.*
Secrets worth knowing. Morton, T. 15c....*French.*
Secrets worth knowing: 1000 manufacturers' and money-making recipes. 12°. pap., 25c....*Haney.*
Secundus, J. N. *See* Joannes *Secundus.*
Sedgemoor. *See* Atlantic lib.
Sedgwick, Ad. *See* Brougham, H: (*Lord*), Sedgwick, A., *and* Verplanck, G. C.
Sedgwick, Alfr. B. [Plays.] 4 v. 16°. ea., pap., 15c. .... *De Witt.*
Cont.: Leap year: musical drama. — My walking photograph: drama. — Queerest courtship: comic operetta. — Twin sisters: comic operetta.
— Complete instructor on German accordion. obl. 8°. 50c. .... *Gordon.*
— Complete method for cornet. obl. 8°. bds., $1..*Peters.*
— Complete method for Eng. concertina. obl. 8°. bds., $1 .... *Peters.*
— Complete method for flute or piccolo. obl. 8°. bds., $1.50; pap., 75c. .... *Peters.*
— Complete method for French accordion. obl. 8°. bds., $1 .... *Peters.*
— Complete method for German accordion. obl. 8°. bds., $1 .... *Peters.*
— Complete method for German concertina. obl. 8°. bds., $1 .... *Peters.*

Sedgwick, Alfr. B., *continued.*
— Improved and complete instructions for German concertina. obl. 8°. '65. pap., 75c. .... *Ditson.*
— New English concertina. obl. 8°. 75c. .... *Gordon.*
— New German concertina. obl. 8°. 50c. .... *Gordon.*
— Perfect method for cornet; abridg. from Complete method. obl. 8°. pap., 75c. .... *Peters.*
— Perfect method for English concertina; abridg. from Complete method. obl. 8°. pap., 75c. .... *Peters.*
— Perfect method for French accordion; abridg. from Complete method. obl. 8°. pap., 75c. .... *Peters.*
— Perfect method for German accordion; abridg. from Complete method. obl. 8°. pap., 75c. .... *Peters.*
— Perfect method for German concertina; abridg. from Complete method. obl. 8°. pap., 75c. .... *Peters.*

Sedgwick, *Mrs.* Cath. Mar. Boy of Mt. Rhigi. ill. 16°. '68. $1 .... *Perkinpine.*
— Facts and fancies for school-day reading. New ed. sq. 16°. '72. 75c. .... *Putnam.*
— Home. ('35.) New ed. 16°. '76. $1 .... *Miller.*
— Hope Leslie. 2 v. 12°. $3 .... *Harper.*
— Letters from abroad to kindred at home. 2 v. 12°. $3 .... *Harper.*
— Life of Miss L. M. Davidson. *See* Sparks, J., Library of Am. biog.
— Linwoods (The). 2 v. 12°. $3 .... *Harper.*
— Live and let live; or, domestic service illustrated. 18°. 75c. .... *Harper.*
— Love token for children. 18°. 75c. .... *Harper.*
— Married or single? 2 v. 12°. $3 .... *Harper.*
— Means and ends; or, self-training. 18°. 75c. *Harper.*
— Memoir of Joseph Curtis. 16°. 75c. ...... *Harper.*
— Morals of manners; or, hints for our young folks. sq. 16°. '73. 60c. .... *Putnam.*
— Poor rich man and the rich poor man. 18°. 75c. *Harper.*
— Stories for young persons. 18°. 75c. ...... *Harper.*
— Wilton Harvey, and other tales. 18°. 75c. .. *Harper.*
— *See also* Tales of Glauber Spa.

Sedgwick, *Mrs.* C: A talk with my pupils. 16°. $1.25 .... *Miller.*

Sedgwick, Thdr. Treatise on measure of damages: inquiry into principles which govern amount of compensation recovered in suits at law. 6th ed., enl. by H. D. Sedgwick. 8°. shp., $7.50. *Baker, V. & Co.*
— Treatise on rules which govern interpretation and applic. of statutory and constitutional law. New ed., with notes by J. N. Pomeroy. 8°. shp., $6.50. *Baker, V. & Co.*

Sedgwick, *Mrs.* Thdr. Walter Thornley; or, a peep at the past. 12°. $1.50 .... *Harper.*

Sedwick, B. F. Baptist pretensions met and confuted. 12°. '76. pap., 15c. .... *So. Meth.*

See, I: M. Rest of faith. 12°. $1 .... *Palmer.*

Seebohm, F: Era of Protestant revolution. 2d ed.; with notes on books in Eng. rel. to reformation by G. P. Fisher. (Epochs of hist.) ('74.) New ed. maps. 16°. '75. $1 .... *Scribner.*
— *Same.* 16°. $1 .... *Estes.*

Seed and fruit. ill. 18°. '75. 50c. .... *Nelson.*

Seed bearing fruit. *See* M., *Mrs.* A. S.

Seed corn ser. 6 v. 18°. $1.65 ..... *N. Y. Ref. Ch. Bd.*
Cont.: Sunlight children. — Bertha's rose; Where Daisy's doll went. — Aunt Charity's legacy; Working for Jesus. — Tub night; Little Emma. — A kite story; Birthday festival. — Croquet; or, social prayer illustrated.

Seed growing. *See* M., *Mrs.* A. S.

Seed thought. Robinson, G. C. $1 ... *Meth. Bk. Conc.*

Seed thoughts. Carryl, J. 75c. .... *Pres. Bd.*

Seed time and harvest. *See* Arthur, T. S.

Seed time and harvest. Koch, R. $1.25 .... *O'Shea.*

Seed time and harvest. Reuter, F. $1.50; $1. *Lippincott.*

Seed time and harvest. *See* Tweedie, W. K.

Seed truths. Church, P. $1.75 .... *Sheldon.*

Seeds and sheaves. Thompson, A. C. $1.75 .. *Sheldon.*

Seeds for spring time. Parker, J. M. 40c. .. *Dutton.*

Seeds for young sowers. 2 v. sq. 24°. ea., 25c. *Am. S. S.*

Seeing the elephant. Baker, G. M. 15c. .... *Lee & S.*

Seeing Jesus. Nelson, H. A. 65c. .... *Pres. Bd.*

Seeing Warren. Morton, J. 15c. .... *French.*

Seek and find. Adams, W. T. $1.25 .... *Lee & S.*

Seek Christ early. 16°. 25c. .... *West. Tr.*

Seekers after God. Farrar, F. W. $1.75. *Lippincott; Macmillan.*

Seeking and finding. Steiner, L. H. $1 .. *Ref. Ch. Pub.*

Seeking his fortune. Alger, H., *jr., and* Cheney, O. A. $1.25 .... *Loring.*

Seeking his fortune. *See* Plucky fellows lib.

Seeley, J: R. Ecce homo: survey of life and work of Jesus Christ. 16°. '66. $1.50 .... *Roberts.*
— Lectures and essays. 8°. '70. $3.50 .... *Macmillan.*
— Roman imperialism, and other lectures and essays. 16°. '71. $1.50 .... *Roberts.*
— *See also* Abbott, E. A., *and* Seeley, J. R.

Seelye, E: E. Bible emblems. 12°. '66. 80c. *Am. Tr.*

Seelye, Jul. Hawley. Christian missions: Yale lectures. 12°. '75. $1.25 .... *Dodd.*
— Way (The), the truth and the life. 16°. $1. *Cong. Pub.*

Seemuller, *Mrs.* Anne Moncure [*formerly Miss* Crane]. Emily Chester. 16°. $2 .... * *Osgood.*
— Opportunity. 12°. $2 .... * *Osgood.*
— Reginald Archer. 8°. pap., 75c. .... * *Osgood.*

Seen and heard. Heady, M. $1.50 .... *Turnbull.*

Seen and unseen. *See* Algatchie.

Seen and unseen. *See* Arthur, T. S.

Seer (The). Hunt, L. 2 v. $3 .... *Roberts.*

Seers of the ages. Peebles, J. M. $2 .... *Colby.*

Segneri, Paolo. Lenten sermons; from the Ital. 2 v. 12°. '72. $3 .... *Cath. Pub.*

Seguin, E: Idiocy, and its treatment by the physiological method. 8°. $5 .... *W. Wood.*
— Manual of thermometry; for mothers, nurses and all who have charge of sick and young. 12°. '73. 75c. .... *Putnam.*
— Medical thermometry and human temperature; with diagrams. 8°. $3.50 .... *W. Wood.*

Seguin, E: C. (*ed.*) Series of Am. clinical lectures. v. 1, in 12 nos. 8°. '75–'76. ea., pap., 30c.; in 1 v., $4 .... *Putnam.*
Cont.: Disease of the hip-joint, by L. A. Sayre. — Acute rheumatism in infancy and childhood, by A. Jacobi. — Pneumothorax, by A. Flint. — Rest in the treatment of nervous disease, by S. W. Mitchell. — Treatment of sciatica, by W. H. Thomson. — Otitis, by C. R. Agnew. — Capillary bronchitis of adults, by C. Ellis. — Inflammatory origin of phthisis, by J. H. Hutchinson. — Peritonitis, by A. L. Loomis. — Gleet and its relations to urethral stricture, by F. N. Otis. — On the diagnosis of diseases accompanied with real or apparent paraplegia without marked muscular degeneration, by H. C. Wood, jr. — Nature of the gouty vice, by W. H. Draper.

— *Same.* v. 2, nos. 1–7. 8°. '76. ea., pap., 30c. *Putnam.*
Cont.: Principle of physiological antagonism applied to the treatment of the febrile state, by R. Bartholow. — On certain forms of morbid nervous sensibility, by J. S. Jewell. — Treatment of mild cases of melancholia at home, by E. C. Seguin. — Some forms of dyspepsia, by F. Delafield. — Diagnosis of those diseases of the eye which can be seen without the ophthalmoscope, by H. D. Noyes. — The modern methods of examining the upper air passages, by G. M. Lefferts. — On tracheotomy and laryngotomy, by H. B. Sands.

Ségur, *Comtesse* Eug. de. French fairy tales; tr. by Mrs. Coleman and her daughters. ill. 12°. '69. $1.50 .... *Porter.*
— Inn of the Guardian Angel; tr. ill. 12°. $1; $1.25; $1.50; $2 .... *Lee & S.*
— Les petites filles modèles; [also] Les goûters de la grandmère, par Mme. Z. T. Carraud. With list of difficult phrases. ('69.) New ed. 12°. '72. $1. *Holt.*

Ségur, L: Gast. de. On confession; tr. 18°. 50c. *O'Shea.*
— Plain talk about the Protestantism of to-day; tr. 18°. 60c.; pap., 25c. .... *Noonan.*
— True idea of holy communion; tr. 32°. 25c.; 35c.; pap., 15c. .... *O'Shea.*
- Wonders of Lourdes; tr. by Miss A. T. Sadlier. sq. 16°. 60c. .... *Sadlier.*

Ségur, *Comte* L: Ph. de. History of the expedition to Russia undertaken by Napoleon in 1812; tr. 2 v. 18°. $1.50 .... *Harper.*

Seibertz, E. (*ill.*) *See* Goethe, J. W. v., Faust.

Seidel, Cp. Tim. Der würdige Communicant: Anweisung zum Gebrauch d. hl. Abendmahls. 8°. '73. 75c.; $1; $1.40 .... *Dette.*

Seidensticker, Oswald. Geschichte d. Deutschen Gesellschaft v. Pennsylvanien, 1764–1876. 8°. '76. $1.50; $2; $2.50 .... *Kohler.*

Seidenstücker, J. H. P. *See* Addicks, B. O'S., French elements; — Plötz, C., Elementarbuch d. französ. Sprache.

Seigneret, Pl. Life and letters; tr. from the French. 12°. $1.50 .... *O'Shea.*

Seiler, C: Micro-photographs in histology, normal and pathological. 4°. '76. $6 .... *Coates.*

Seiler, Emma. Exercises for training the female voice: original and selected; tr. f°. '68. pap., $2 .. *Ditson.*
— The voice in singing; tr. by a member of the Am. Philos. Soc. 12°. $1.50 .... *Lippincott.*
— The voice in speaking; tr. by W. H. Furness. ill. 12°. $1.50 .... *Lippincott.*

Seiss, Jos. A. Apocalypse: lectures on revelation of Jesus Christ; with rev. text. ('65.) New ed. v. 1. 12°. '72. $2.50 .... *Luth. Bk. St.*
— Bandages removed. 8°. pap., 10c. .... *Luth. Bk. St.*
— Child's catechism: first lessons for young beginners. ill. 16°. '75. 20c. .... *Luth. Bk. St.*
— Christian giving. 8°. pap., 10c. ...... *Luth. Bk. St.*
— Ecclesia Lutherana: brief survey of Luth. Church. 3d ed. 12°. '67. $1.25; mor., $5 .. *Luth. Bk. St.*
— Holy types; or, the gospel in Leviticus: lectures on the Hebrew ritual. ('59.) 3d ed. 12°. '75. $1.50. *Smith, E. & Co.*
— How shall we order our worship? sketches in liturgics. 8°. pap., 25c. .... *Luth. Bk. St.*
— Last times (The) and the great consummation. ('56.) 6th ed., enl. 12°. '70. $1.50 ... *Smith, E. & Co.*
— Lectures on the Gospels. 2 v. 8°. '76. $5. *Luth. Bk. St.*
— Lutheran Church. 12°. pap., 10c. ...... *Luth. Bk. St.*
— Model liberality. 8°. pap., 10c. ...... *Luth. Bk. St.*
— Money and its capabilities. 8°. pap., 10c. *Luth. Bk. St.*
— Our temple. 8°. pap., 10c. .... *Luth. Bk. St.*
— Parable of the ten virgins: 6 discourses and sermon on judgeship of the saints. ('62.) 3d ed. 12°. '73. $1 .... *Luth. Bk. St.; Smith, E & Co.*
— Petros, the wonderful building: sermon. 12°. pap., 25c. .... *Luth. Bk. St.*
— Plain words: Sunday sermons and lectures. 12°. '69. 60c. .... *Luth. Bk. St.*
— That alabaster box. 8°. pap., 10c. .... *Luth. Bk. St.*
— Truth made plain; or, the rudiments of the Christian religion. 16°. '70. 50c.; pap., 25c. .. *Luth. Bk. St.*
— Uriel: some occasional discourses. 12°. '74. $1.25. *Luth. Bk. St.*
— *and* Engelman, C: P. Church song. 2 pts. 4°. '75–'76. 1, 75c.; 2, $1; in 1 v., $1.75 ... *Luth. Bk. St.*

Sejour, Vct. Outlaw of the Adriatic: drama. 16°. pap., 15c. .... *French.*

Selah. Hastings, T. $1.50 .... *Barnes.*

Selborne, *Lord.* [*Sir* Roundell Palmer.] Book of praise. 18°. '71. $1.25 .... *Macmillan.*
— *Same.* 18°. 75c. — 16°. $1.25 .... *Allyn.*
— Book of praise hymnal; chiefly from Book of praise. 32°. 25c. — 18°. 50c.; — with music by John Hullah. sq. 18°. $1.25 .... *Macmillan.*
— *See also* Sadler, T., Edwin Wilkins Field.

Selby, C: [Plays.] 36 v. 16°. ea., pap., 15c. .. *French.*
Cont.: Bonnie fish wife: musical drama. — Boots at the Swan: farce. — Catching an heiress: comedy. — Caught by the ears: farce. — Day in Paris: farce. — Drapery question: farce. — Fearful tragedy in Seven Dials: dram. interlude. — Fire eater: farce. — Frederick of Prussia: burletta. — Harold Hawk. — Hotel charges: farce. — Hour in Seville: Protean dram. interlude. — Hunting a turtle: farce. — Husband of my heart. — Irish dragoon. — Lady and gent in a perplexing predicament: farce. — Last of the pigtails: petite comedy. — Marble heart. — Married rake: farce. — My aunt's husband. — My friend, the major: farce. — New footman: burletta. — Paris and pleasure. — Peggy Green: farce. — Pet lamb: comedietta. — Phantom breakfast: farce. — Pirates of Putney: extravaganza. — Poor nobleman. — Robert Macaire: melodrama. — Satan in Paris. — Spanish dancers: burletta. — Unfinished gentleman: farce. — Valet de sham: farce. — Widow's victim: farce. — Witch of Windermere: comedy. — Young mother.
— Antony and Cleopatra married and settled: burletta. 16°. pap., 15c. .... *Happy.*
— Bonnie fish wife: musical interlude. 16°. pap., 15c. *De Witt.*
— Dinner question; or, how to dine well and economically; by Tabitha Tickletooth [*pseud.*] 16°. '72. bds., 50c. .... *Routledge.*
— Fearful tragedy in the Seven Dials: dram. interlude. 16°. pap., 15c. .... *De Witt.*
— Irish dragoon: farce. 16°. pap., 15c. ..... *Happy.*
— Peggy Green: farce. 16°. pap., 15c. ...... *De Witt.*
— Pet lamb: comedietta. 16°. pap., 15c. .... *Happy.*
— Phantom breakfast: farce. 16°. pap., 15c. .. *Lee & S.*

Selden, H: R. *See* New York State, Court of Appeals reports.

Select biographies of eminent men in church and state. 18°. 65c. .... *Am. S. S.*

Select British eloquence. Goodrich, C. A. $4; $4.50; $6.25 .... *Harper.*

Select fables from Æsop and others. ill. 18°. 75c. *Sower.*

Select lib. 7 v. 16°. $8.50 .... *Lothrop.*
Cont.: Strawberry Hill. — Bright days. — Overcoming. — Sunny skies. — Hints for living. — Glencoe parsonage. — Evenings with the children.

Select lib. *See* Baker, *Mrs.* H. N. W.

Select lib. for boys. 4 v. 18°. $2 .... *Am. S. S.*
Cont.: Grandfather Merrie. — Bosses and their boys. — Stories for village lads. — One step.

Select lib. for girls. 4 v. 18°. $2.30 .... *Am. S. S.*
Cont.: Bessie Duncan. — Young envelope makers. — Mountain daisy. — Beauty of the heart.

Select poetry for children. 18°. 35c. .... *Am. S. S.*
— *See also* Picture lib. for the little ones at home.

Select readers. 3 v. hf. bd. .... *Friends Bk. St.*
Cont.: No. 1. 18°, 10c. — 2. 12°, 20c. — 3. 12°, 55c.

Select stories for little folks. Addie. 60c. .. *Pres. Bd.*

Select stories to please and to profit. 16°. $1.25. *Am. S. S.*

Select Sunday school lib. 40 v. ill. 18°. $18 .. *Am. Bapt.*

Selecta ex classicis Latinitatis; ad usam scholarum Societatis Jesu. 2 v. 18°. 1, 30c.; 2, 50c. *Strong.*

Selected hymns; from Hymns ancient and modern and Hymns for church and home. 16°. 60c. *Lippincott.*

Selected poems. 37 nos. ill. sq. 16°. '74–'75. ea., pap., 10c.; — in 3 v., ea., $2 .... *Tompkins.*

Selections for little folks. 16°. '70. 50c. .. *Eldredge.*

Selections from British poets. ill. 12°. '56. $1.50. *Meth. Bk. Conc.*

Selections from chorus books. obl. 4°. '70. bds., 60c. .... *Ditson.*

Self. Bateman, S. F. 15c. .... *French.*

Self. Gore, C. G. 75c. .... *Harper.*

Self accusation. Lemon, M. 15c. .... *French.*

Self contradictions of the Bible: 144 propositions proved affirmatively and negatively from Scripture without comment. 12°. pap., 25c. .... *Mendum.*

Self control. Brunton, M. 75c. .... *Harper.*

Self control: hints for the improvement of temper. 18°. 40c. .... *Am. S. S.*

Self convicted. Wood, E. P. 25c. .... *Peterson.*
Self cure of debility, consumption, dyspepsia, nervousness, etc. 12°. '69. pap., 75c. .... *Haney.*
Self cure of stammering. 12°. pap., 25c. ..... *Haney.*
Self dependence; or, "I'll not do so again." 18°. 30c. *Am.S.S.*
Self devotion. Campbell, H. 50c. .... *Harper.*
Self employment in secret. Corbet, J. 25c. .. *Pres.Bd.*
Self help. *See* Smiles, S.
Self love; or, the afternoon of single life. 12°. $1.75; pap., $1.50 .... *Peterson.*
Self made. Welty, E. A. $1.50 .... *Sheldon.*
Self made men. Seymour, C. C. B. $1.75 .. *Harper.*
Self made woman. Buckingham, E. M. $1.50 .. *Wells.*
Self raised. Southworth, E. D. E. N. $1.75; $1.50. *Peterson.*
Self reliance. *See* Cupples, *Mrs.* A. J.
Self reliance; or, what can be accomplished by resolute effort. 18°. 50c. .... *Am.S.S.*
Self sacrifice. Myers, S. A. $1 .... *Pres.Bd.*
Self sacrifice. Oliphant, M. O. W. $1.75; $1.50. *Peterson.*
Self taught men: ser. of biographies. 12°. $1.25 .. *Nelson.*
Self will. (Fatherland ser.) ill. 16°. $1 .. (?) *Luth.Pub.*
Selfish little girl. *See* Hid in a cave.
Selfishness: its nature and remedy. Wilson, J. 80c. *N.Y.Ref.Ch.Bd.*
Selfishness and kindness. *See* Cupples, *Mrs.* A. J.
Selin; or, the pasha of Salonica; tr. by Mrs. J. Sadlier. 18°. 50c.; 75c. .... *Sadlier.*
— *See also* Glory and sorrow.
Selkirk, G: H. Guide to the cricket ground. ill. fp. 8°. '67. $1.25 .... *Macmillan.*
Selle, C. A. T. *See* German-Evang. Luth. Church, *Synod of Mo.*
Selle, L. Vespers; for 4 voices. f°. $1.50 .. *Gordon.*
Sellers, W: and Co. (*pub.*) Treatise on machine tools, etc.: photos. and wood-eng. 12°. *net*, $6. *Lippincott.*
Selling Lucky. Abbott, J. 90c. .... *Harper.*
Selling out ye pope. Byer, —. 25c. .... *Hinton.*
Sells, *Mrs.* S. E. Amy's temptation. 16°. $1.25. *Cin.Meth.Bk.Conc.*
Selous, H. C. Gerty and May. ill. 18°. $1 .. *Lee & S.*
— *See also* Shakespeare, W:
Seltz's American boys' theatre. [Miniature plays.] 8 nos. 8°. ea., pap., 25c.; 50c. ..... *J.W.Scott.*
Selumiel; or, a visit to Jerusalem, and interesting scenes in and around it, A.D. 40. 18°. 65c. .... *Am.S.S.*
Selwyn, W: Abridgment of law of nisi prius. 7th Am. ed., with notes of Wheaton, Wharton and Law, and ref. to late Am. authorities by A. I. Fish. 2 v. 8°. shp., $13 .... *Kay.*
Semeleder, F: Rhinoscopy and laryngoscopy: their value in practical medicine; tr. by E. T. Caswell. ill. 8°. $3.25 .... *W. Wood.*
Seminary album. Perkins, W. O. $1. *Pond; G.D.Russell.*
Seminary bell. Butler, C. 75c. .... *Gordon.*
Semiramide. *See* Ditson.
Semmes, Raph. Memoirs of service afloat during the war between the states: personal memoir of cruises and services in the "Sumter" and "Alabama." ill. and por. 8°. '68. $5; $6.50; hf. mor., $7.50 .... *Kelly,P.& Co.*
Semple, Fs. Narratives and arguments showing conflict of secret societies with Const. and laws of the Union and of the states. 12°. pap., 20c. *E.A.Cook.*
Seneca, Lucius Annæus. Morals by way of abstract; [also] An afterthought; tr. by Sir Roger l'Estrange. 18°. 60c. .... *Lippincott.*
Seney, G: E. *See* Ohio, Code.
Senhouse, —. Letters of the Madiai and visits to their prisons. por. 12°. 75c. .... *Pres.Bd.*
Senior reader. post 8°. $1.25 .... *Nelson.*
Senior Sunday-school class; with chapter on best means of retaining larger scholars. 18°. '69. pap., 20c. .... *Perkinpine.*
Senour, F. The Christian soldier. 32°. 10c. .. *Pres.Bd.*
Sense. Pomeroy, M. M. $1.50 .... *Carleton.*
Sense and sensation. Taylor, T. 15c. .... *French.*
Sense and sensibility. *See* Austen, Jane.
Senses. ill. 16°. 60c. .... *Bost.Am.Tr.*
— *See also* Library of curious things in nature.
Senses and the intellect. *See* Bain, A.
Sensualistic philosophy of the 19th cent. Dabney, R. L. $2 .... *Randolph.*
Sent to the tower. Morton, J. M. 15c. ...... *French.*
Sentimental journey. *See* Sterne, L.
Sentinel: musical burletta. 16°. pap., 15c. .. *Happy.*
Separate maintenance: farce. 16°. pap., 15c. .. *French.*
Sepherchayim. *See* Jewish Synagogue.
Seppeli, the Swiss boy; tr. by A. H. Lochman. (Fatherland ser.) ill. 16°. 65c. .... (?) *Luth.Pub.*
Septem contra Thebas. *See* Æschylus.
Septimus Felton. *See* Hawthorne, N.
Sepulchre in the garden. Walker, D. 37c. *Cong.Pub.*
Seraph (Der) von Assisi: Lebensbild d. hl. Ordenstifters Franziskus. 12°. 75c. .... *Benziger.*
— *Eng.* Seraph of Assisium. *See* Library of good example.
Seraphic manual. [Cath. prayer book.] 24°. 75c.–$2.50 .... *T.Kelly; Strong.*
Seraphic staff; for members of third order of St. Francis. [Prayer book.] 32°. 25c. .... *Strong.*
Serbian folk lore. Mijatovics, E. L. $3 .. *Routledge.*
Serenade. White, C. 15c. .... *De Witt.*
Serf. Talbot, R. 15c. .... *Ames; French.*
Serf. Williams, H. L. 25c. .... *De Witt.*
Sergeant, H: J. Treatise on lien of mechanics and material men in Penna. 2d ed., ed. by E. S. Miller. 8°. shp., $3.50 .... *Kay.*
— *See also* Pennsylvania, Sup. Court reports.
Sergeant, Lew. Pure mathematics. (Element. sci. ser.) 16°. '74. 75c. .... *Putnam.*
Sergeant, T: Constitutional law: view of practice and jurisdiction of courts of U. S., and of const. points decided. 2d ed. 8°. '30. $4 .. *T.& J.W.Johnson.*
— Treatise upon law of Penna. rel. to proceeding by foreign attachment. 2d ed., rev. and enl. 8°. shp., $2.50 .... *Kay.*
— View of land laws of Penna.; with notices of its early hist. and legislation. 8°. shp., $2.50 ...... *Kay.*
Sergeant Atkins: tale of adventure, founded on fact; by an officer of the U. S. army. ill. 12°. $1.75. *Lippincott.*
Sergeant's memorial. Thompson, J. P. 60c. .. *Randolph.*
Sergeant's wedding: comic drama. 16°. pap., 15c. *French.*
Serie nueva de novelitas para diversion é instruccion de la infancia. 12 v. 8°. $2 .... *Appleton.*
Serious affair: farce. 16°. pap., 15c. .... *French.*
Serious family. Barnett, M. 15c. .... *French.*
Serjeant's wife. Banim, J. 15c. .... *French.*
Serle, T: J. Tender precautions: comedy. 16°. pap., 15c. .... *French.*
Sermons and essays; by G., W. and J. Tennent, J. Blair, R. Smith and S. Finley. por. 12°. $1.25. *Pres.Bd.*
Sermons delivered in cathedral during 2d Plenary Council of Baltimore. ill. 12°. '66. $2; hf. cf., $2.50 .... *Kelly,P.& Co.*

Sermons for Sundays and some other holy days of the Christian year. 12°. $1.50. — 2d ser. 2 v. 12°. $2.50 .... *Pott.*

Sermons for the times. Kingsley, C. $1.25 .. *Macmillan.*

Sermons from Shakespeare's text. Denton, W. 10c. *Denton.*

Sermons in stones. McCausland, D. $3. *Scribner, W.& A.*

Sermons of the Paulist fathers. 3 v. 12°. ea., $1.50. *Cath.Pub.*

Sermons on Book of common prayer; by the bishops and clergy of the Prot. Episc. Church. 16°. '74. $1 .... *Pott.*

Sermons out of church. *See* Craik, D. M.

Sermons to the clergy. Dodge, M. A. $2 .. *W.F. Gill.*

Sermons to the young; rev. by T. O. Summers. ('58.) 2d ed. 18°. '75. 50c. .... *So.Meth.*

— *See also* Village lib.

Sermons to young children. 32°. 25c. .... *Pres.Bd.*

Serpent on the hearth. Simpson, J. P. 15c. .. *French.*

Serpents in the doves' nest. Todd, J. 50c.; 15c. *Lee & S.*

Servants by legacy. Pilgrim, J. 15c. .... *French.*

Servants of the stomach. Macé, J. $1.75 ... *Harper.*

Servetus. Ford, S. H. 40c. .... *So.Bapt.*

Service for the first two nights of Passover [*Heb.*]; with Germ. or Eng. transl. 12°. bds., 25c. .. *Frank.*

— *Same;* with Eng. transl. ill. 8°. 75c.; bds., 50c. *Frank.*

Service of the poor. Stephen, C. E. $2.25 .. *Macmillan.*

Service of praise. Eustis, W. T. $1.50 .... *Scribner.*

Service of song. *See* Caldwell, S. L., *and* Gordon, A. J.

Service of song. Leavens, B. F. $3.50 ...... *Ditson.*

Service of song. Stacy, A. G. $1.50. *Barnes; S. W. Bk.& Pub.*

Service of sorrow. Hale, L. P. $1.75 ..... *Am. Unit.*

Sesame and lilies. *See* Ruskin, J:

Sessions, H. C. Clerk's, sheriff's, and constable's guide. 12°. '73. $1; leath., $1.50 .. *Richmond.*

Sestini, Bened. Elementary algebra. 12°. '54. 75c. *Murphy.*

— Elements of geometry and trigonometry. 8°. '56. $2 .... *Murphy.*

— Manual of geometrical and infinitesimal analyses. 8°. '71. $1.50 .... *Murphy.*

— Treatise on algebra. 12°. '55. $1 .... *Murphy.*

Setma, the Turkish maiden. *See* Barth, C. G.

Seton, *Mrs.* Eliz. Memoir, letters and journal; ed. by her grandson. 2 v. roy. 8°. $6; $8 ... *O'Shea.*

Seton, W: Pioneers: poem. sm. 4°. $1.50 .... *O'Shea.*

— Pride of Lexington: tale of Am. rev. 12°. $2 .. *O'Shea.*

Settlers at home. Martineau, H. 50c. .... *Routledge.*

Settlers in Canada. *See* Marryat, F:

Settling day. Taylor, T. 15c. .... *French.*

Settling the verdict. *See* French's comic dramas.

Seven ages. Baker, G. M. 15c. .... *Lee & S.*

Seven autumn leaves from fairy land. Cunningham, C. $1.50 .... *Williams.*

Seven brothers of Wyoming; or, brigands of the Am. rev. 8°. pap., 50c. .... *Peterson.*

Seven champions of Christendom. Johnson, R. $1. *Routledge.*

Seven champions of Christendom. Planché, J. R. 15c. *French.*

Seven clerks. Wilks, T. E. 15c. .... *French.*

Seven corporal works of mercy: tales. 18°. '67. 50c. *Cunningham.*

Seven curses of London. *See* Greenwood, J.

Seven daughters. Douglas, A. M. $1.50 .... *Lee & S.*

Seven decades of the Union. Wise, H. A. $2. *Lippincott.*

Seven great hymns of the mediæval church. 16°. '66. $1.75 .... *Randolph.*

Seven hills. DeMille, J. $1.50 .... *Lee & S.*

Seven historic ages. Gilman, A. $1 ...... *Hurd & H.*

Seven kings of Rome; [also] The story of Pompeii. 16°. 50c. .... *Scribner, W.& A.*

Seven kings of the seven hills. Laing, C. H. B. $1. *Porter.*

Seven lamps of architecture. Ruskin, J. $1.75 .. *Wiley.*

Seven last words of Jesus upon the cross; rev. by F. Varella. 32°. 20c. .... *Coddington.*

Seven little people and their friends. Scudder, H. E. $1.25 .... *Hurd & H.*

Seven little sisters who live on the round ball that floats in the air. ill. sq. 12°. $1.25 .... **Osgood.*

Seven months' run (A). Brooks, J. $1.75. *Appleton.*

Seven stories, with basement and attic. Mitchell, D. G. $1.75 .... *Scribner.*

Seven stormy Sundays. Hale, L. P. $1 ... *Am. Unit.*

Seven to seventeen. *See* Bell, M. M.

Seven trumpets. Smith, M. 15c. .... *Sev.Day Adv.*

Seven wives and seven prisons; or, experiences in life of a matrimonial monomaniac. ill. 16°. '75. pap., 50c. .... *Hunter.*

Seven wonders of the world. ill. 12°. '54. $1.25. *Meth. Bk. Conc.*

Seven wonders of the world; with their associations in art and history. ill. 16°. $1.25 ..... *Routledge.*

Seven words of Christ on the cross. Cure, E. C. $1.25. *Macmillan.*

Seven years, and other tales. Kavanagh, J. $1.25. *Appleton.*

Seven years from to-night. Ballard, J. P. $1.25. *Cong. Pub.*

Sevenoaks. Holland, J. G. $1.75 .... *Scribner.*

Seventh Day Baptists. Appeal for restoration of the Bible Sabbath: address to the Baptists from the Seventh Day Bapt. Gen. Conf. 16°. '73. pap., 10c. .... *Sev.Day Adv.*

Seventh part of time. Littlejohn, W. H. 10c. *Sev.Day Adv.*

Seventy six: a cook book; ed. by ladies of Plymouth Church, Des Moines, Iowa. 12°. '76. $1.50. *Mills.*

Seventy times seven; or, the law of kindness. 18°. 40c. .... *Pres.Bd.*

Sévigné, Marie de R. C. (*Marquise*) de. Lettres. 12°. $1.50 .... *G.R.Lockwood.*

— *Eng.* Letters; ed. with memoir by Mrs. S. J. Hale. 12°. '68. $1.50 .... *Roberts.*

Sewall, Fk. Christian hymnal. 16°. '66. $1.25. *Claxton; Lippincott.*

— Daily bread for every household; from word of God. sm. 4°. '76. $1 .... *Randolph.*

— Hem of his garment: spiritual lessons from life of our Lord. 12°. $1.50 .... *Lippincott.*

— Moody Mike; or, the power of love: Christmas story. ill. 16°. $1 .... *Lippincott.*

— Pillow of stones: divine allegories, their spiritual meaning. 12°. $1.50 .... *Lippincott.*

— Welcome (The); with services, catechism, Scripture questions, hymns and tunes. 12°. bds., 30c. *New Ch.*

— *and* Day, W. G. Prayer book and hymnal for use of the New Church. 16°. $1.50; roan, $1.75; $2; mor., $4; — abridg., $1 .... *Lippincott.*

Sewall, Jos. A. Botany; condensed. ('72.) New ed. 8°. '76. $1 .... *Sherwood.*

Sewall, T: Memoir of J. D. Godman. *See* Hall, Newman, Closing scenes.

Seward, Thdr. F. Jubilee songs. 8°. '72. pap., 25c. *Biglow.*

— Singer (The). obl. 4°. '70. bds., 60c. .... *Biglow.*

Seward, Thdr. F., *continued.*
— Sunnyside glee-book: secular music, for the singing-school and musical societies. obl. 8°. bds., 80c. *Huntington.*
— *See also* Allen, C. G., *and* Seward, T. F.; — Mason, L., *and* Seward, T. F.
— *and* Allen, C. G., *and* Mason, Lowell. The coronation: music for choirs, etc. obl. 4°. '72. bds., $1.50 .... *Biglow.*
— *and* Mason, L., *and* Bradbury, W: B. Temple choir: sacred and secular music. obl. 8°. '67. bds., $1.50 .... *Ditson.*

Seward, W: H. Works; with memoir. 4 v. ill. and por. 8°. $16; hf. cf., $28; cf., $32.. *Widdleton.*
— Travels round the world; ed. by O. R. Seward. ill., por. and map. 8°. *$5; shp., $6; hf. mor., $7.50; mor., $10.......... *Appleton.*

Sewell, *Miss* Eliz. Missing. [Tales.] 19 v. 12°. ea., $1 .... *Appleton.*

Cont.: Amy Herbert. — Cleve Hall. — Earl's daughter. — Experience of life. — Gertrude. — Glimpse of the world. — Ivors: story of Eng. country life, 2 v. — Journal of a summer tour. — Katharine Ashton, 2 v. — Laneton parsonage, 3 v. — Margaret Percival, 2 v. — Ursula: tale of country life, 2 v. — Home life, $1.25.

— *Same.* 9 v. cr. 8°. '55–'68. ea., $2.... *Williams.*

Cont.: After life: sequel to "Journal of a home life." — Cleve Hall. — Experience of life. — Gertrude. — Glimpse of the world. — Journal of a home life. — Katharine Ashton. — Ursula: tale of country life. — Laneton parsonage, $2.25.

— Amy Herbert. 8°. pap., 50c. .... *Harper.*
— First history of Greece. 18°. 75c.......... *Appleton.*
— First history of Rome. 18°. 75c.......... *Appleton.*
— History of the early church. 16°. $1. *Dutton; Appleton.*
— Night lessons from Scripture. 16°. $1.... *Appleton.*
— Passing thoughts on religion. 16°. $1.... *Appleton.*
— Preparation for the holy communion: the devotions chiefly from works of J. Taylor; [with] the communion service. 18°. '60. 50c...... *Dutton.*
— Principles of education drawn from nature and revelation, and applied to female education in the upper classes. 2 v. in 1. 12°. $2 .... *Appleton.*
— Readings for every day in Lent; from writings of J. Taylor. 16°. $1.25 .... *Dutton.*
— Readings for a month; preparatory to confirmation. 16°. '60. $1.25 .... *Dutton.*
— Thoughts for the age. New ed. cr. 8°. '71. $1.50. *Williams.*
— Thoughts for the holy week. 32°. '61. 50c... *Dutton.*
— *and* Urbino, *Mrs.* L. B. Dictation exercises. ('65.) New ed., rev. 16°. '76. bds., 60c. ...... *Holt.*
— *and* Yonge, Ctte. M. (*ed.*) European history: hist. sel. from the best authorities. 2 v. cr. 8°. '72–'73. ea., $1.75 .... *Macmillan.*

Sewell, J. B. Appendix to Curtius' Greek grammar: versification and list of verbs. 12°. pap., 50c. *Harper.*

Sewell, *Mrs.* Ma. Ballads for children; incl. "Mother's last words." ill. 16°. $1........ *Routledge.*
— Mother's last words: ballad. 18°. 25c..... *Am.S.S.*
— *Same.* 18°. 50c.......... *Carter.*
— *Same;* [also] Our Father's care. 18°. 30c.; 35c. *Am. Bapt.*
— — *Same.* 18°. '66. 50c. *N.Y.Ref.Ch.Bd.; Pres.Com.*
— Our Father's care: ballad. 18°. 25c...... *Am.S.S.*
— Popular ballads and stories in verse. 4 sets. 16°. ea., 50c. .... *Routledge.*
— Thy poor brother. 16°. $1.50.......... *Am.S.S.*

Sewell, Rob. Pension, bounty and prize laws. 8°. shp., $4.......... *Appleton.*

Sewell, W: History of the rise, increase and progress of the Christian people called Quakers. 8°. shp., $2.25; cf., $3 .... *Friends Bk. St.*

Sewell, W: G. Ordeal of free labor in the Brit. West Indies. 12°. $1.50.......... *Harper.*

Sewill, H. E. Student's guide to dental anatomy and surgery. ill. 12°. '76. $1.75 .... *Lindsay.*

Sex and education. Howe, J. W. $1.25 .... *Roberts.*

Sex in education. Clarke, E. H. $1.25 ..... *Osgood.*

Sex in industry. Ames, A., *jr.* $1 .... *Miller.*

Sex in nature. Grindon, L. H. $1.25.. *Lockwood, B. & Co.*

Sexes, here and hereafter. Holcombe, W. H. $1.50. *Lippincott.*

Sexes throughout nature. Blackwell, A. B. $1.25. *Putnam.*

Sexton, Maur. J: Pocket-book for boiler makers and steam users. ill. roy. 32°. '75. roan, $2... *Spon.*

Sexton's tale. Tilton, T. $1.50.......... *Sheldon.*

Sexual diseases: their causes, prevention and cure on physiological principles. 12°. $2 .... *Wells.*

Seyd, Ern. Bank of England note issue and its error. fp. 8°. $3.50 .... *Cassell.*

Seyffarth, Gst. Amerikanische Kalendermann (Der). 12°. bds., 10c.......... *Ludwig.*
— Chiliasm crit. examined according to New and Old Testament, with ref. to the most recent theory of the millennium. 8°. '61. 50c..... *Westermann.*
— Das 1,000jährige Reich im Lichte d. Offenbarung. 12°. bds., 15c.......... *Ludwig.*
— Uebersicht neuer Entdeckungen in d. biblischen Zeitrechnung, allgem. Weltgeschichte u. ägyptischen Alterthumskunde, nebst Uebersetzg. d. ersten hl. Buchs d. alten Aegypter. 12°. bds., $1 .... *Ludwig.*
— *Eng.* Summary of recent discoveries in biblical chronology, etc., with transl. of the first sacred book of the Egyptians. 2d ed. 12°. $1.. *Ludwig.*

Seymour, C. *See* Boucicault, D., *and* Seymour, C.

Seymour, C: C. B. Self-made men. por. 12°. $1.75. *Harper.*

Seymour, E: Adph. *See* Somerset, *Duke of.*

Seymour, Horatio, *and* Blair, F. P., *jr.* Lives. 12°. 75c.; pap., 50c.......... *Peterson.*

Seymour, Ma. Alice. Holiday lib. 3 v. 16°. '59–'69. $3 .... *Dutton.*

Cont.: Christmas holidays at Cedar Grove. — Easter holidays at Cedar Grove. — Ruthvens of Cedar Grove; or, the Whitsuntide holidays.

— Holly cross. 18°. 25c. .... *Dutton.*

Seymour, *Mrs.* Ma. H. Ned, Nellie and Amy: story of the White Hills. 16°. '70. $1.25....... *Dutton.*
— Posy Vinton's picnic, and other stories. 16°. '70. 75c. .... *Dutton.*
— Recompense. ill. 12°. '74. $1.25....... *Whittaker.*
— Sunshine and starlight: Scripture texts, with hymn and collect for morning and evening for a month. 32°. '59. 50c.; 60c.......... *Dutton.*

Seymour, Mich. Hobart. Mornings among the Jesuits at Rome: notes of conversation held with certain Jesuits on religion. 12°. $1.25........ *Harper.*
— *Span.* Noches con los Romanistas. [Tr. by H. B. Pratt.] 12°. '60. 70c.......... *Am. Tr.*
— *Port.* Noites com os Romanistas. 12°. '71. $1.. *Am. Tr.*

Seymours (The). Bates, L. $1.......... *Nat. Temp.*

Sforzosi, Luigi. Compendious hist. of Italy; tr. by N. Greene. 18°. 75c.......... *Harper.*

Shabalie, J: Ph. Wandering soul: conversations of the wandering soul with Adam, Noah and Simon Cleophas: epitome of facts to A. D. 109, with account of destruction of Jerusalem; tr. from the Germ. 12°. leath., $1.25 .... *Baer.*

Shades of the heroes. Cooke, T. 25c. ...... *Gordon.*

Shadow. Almar, G. 15c. .... *French.*

Shadow hand. Malen, M. E. O. 30c...... *Am. News.*

Shadow of Ashlydyat. Wood, E. P. $1.75; $1.50. *Peterson.*

Shadow of Christianity; or, genesis of the Christian state: treatise for the times; [by Leonard Marsh]. 12°. $1.25.......... *Draper.*

Shadow of crime. Cheltnam, C. S. 15c. .... *French.*

Shadow of the cross. 18°. 50c. .... *Dutton.*

Shadow of Dante. Rossetti, M. F. $2.50...*Roberts.*

Shadow of Moloch Mountain. Austin, J. G. $1.50; $1...*Sheldon.*

Shadow of the rock. Hamilton, K. W. 50c...*Pres. Bd.*

Shadow of the rock, and other religious poems. ('66.) 2d ed. 24°. '72. $1.50...*Randolph.*

— *See also* Changed cross (The).

Shadow on the hearth. 16°. $1.25...*Carter.*

Shadowed home. Bickersteth, E. H. $1.50..*Carter.*

Shadowed perils. Avery, M. A. $1.25...*Authors.*

Shadows: drama. 16°. pap., 15c...*French.*

Shadows and sunshine. Neale, E. 85c...*Dodd.*

Shadows of the past: comic drama. 16°. pap., 15c. *French.*

Shadows on the screen. ill. 18°. '75. 50c...*Nelson.*

— *See also* Peep show ser.

Shadowy hand. Morgan, H. $1...*Morgan.*

Shady Brook stories. 6 v. 18°. $3.60...(?)*Martien.*

Cont.: Boy friend; or, all can help. — Ida Kleinvogel and the two millers. — Poor weaver's family. — Pastor's son. — Mark Noble. — Jennie's Bible verses.

Shady Dell stories. *See* Bullard, A.

Shady side. 12°. $1.25...*Carter.*

Shaffer, H. M. Baptism: obligations, subjects and mode. 18°. 55c...*Cin. Meth. Bk. Conc.*

Shairp, J: Campbell. Culture and religion in some of their relations. 16°. '72. $1.25...*Hurd & H.*

— Kilmahoe, and other poems. fp. 8°. '64. $1.50. *Macmillan.*

— Studies in poetry and philosophy. 16°. '72. $1.50. *Hurd & H.*

— *and* Tait, P: G., *and* Adams-Reilly, A. Life and letters of James David Forbes. por., map and ill. 8°. '73. $5...*Macmillan.*

Shaker lovers. Johnson, S. D. 15c...*French.*

Shakespeare, W: Complete works. (Boston ed.) ill. 8°. shp., $3.50; mor., $10...*Lee & S.*

— *Same.* (Cabinet Boydell ed.) [To form 15 v.] v. 1–4. ill. and por. fp. 8°. '74–'76. ea., *$1.50; $2.50...*Gebbie.*

— *Same.* (Chandos classics.) cr. 8°. $1; pap., 75c. *Scribner, W. & A.*

— *Same.* (Diamond ed.) 16°. $2; mor., $4.50. *Lippincott.*

— *Same.* (Dick's ed.) por. and ill. 8°. (Lond.) $1.25; pap., 60c...*Am. News.*

— *Same.* (Falstaff ed.) 4 v. ill. cr. 8°. ea., $1.75; hf. cf., $3.75; hf. mor., $4.50...*Porter.*

— *Same.* (Globe ed.) 16°. '69. $1.75...*Roberts.*

— *Same.* (Handy ed.) 8 v. 16°. '69. $6; $8; hf. cf., $18...*Claxton.*

— *Same.* (Handy vol. ed.) 13 v. 18°. $9. *Little, B. & Co.; Scribner, W. & A.*

— — *Same.* 13 v. 18°. $10.50...*Estes; Routledge.*

— — *Same.* 13 v. 24°. $12...*Appleton.*

— *Same.* (Knight's ed.) 2 v. ill. 8°. '74. $10; $12; hf. cf., $15; cf., $25; — in 1 v., $10..*Routledge.*

— *Same.* (Knight's pictorial ed.) 8 v. ill. roy. 8°. $40; hf. cf., $60; cf., $90...*Routledge.*

— *Same.* (Knight's popular ed.) [To form 36 pts.] pts. 1–16. ill. and pl. 8°. ea., *50c...*Estes.*

— *Same.* (Leicester Square ed.) por. and ill. 8°. $6.50...*Appleton.*

— *Same;* ed. by H. G. Bell, with biog. introd., index and glossary. 6 v. 16°. '75. $7.50; hf. cf., $17.50...*Routledge.*

— — *Same.* 6 v. 12°. $9; mor., $20...*Appleton.*

— *Same;* adapted for reading classes and family circle by T. and S. G. Bulfinch. ('64.) New ed. 12°. '75. $3...*Tilton.*

— *Same;* ed. by T. Campbell. ill. roy. 8°. $6; hf. cf., $8.50; mor., $12...*Routledge.*

— *Same;* from text of G. Steevens; with memoir by A. Chalmers. ill. 8°. shp., $4.50; mor., $10..*Mason.*

— — *Same;* ill. 8°. $2; shp., $2.75...*World Pub.*

Shakespeare, W: *continued.*

— *Same;* ed. by W. G. Clark and W. A. Wright. (Globe ed.) 12°. '65. $1.50...*Macmillan.*

— — *Same.* (Globe ed.) 12°. $1.50; $2; hf. mor., $3.25; hf. cf., $3.75; mor., $5...*Claxton.*

— — *Same.* (Globe ed.) ill. sq. 12°. $1.75; hf. cf., $3.75; mor., $5.50...*Lippincott.*

— — *Same.* (Cambridge ed.) 9 v. 8°. ea., $4. *Macmillan.*

— *Same;* ed., with revision of the text, by C. and M. C. Clarke. 4 v. ill. 8°. $12; hf. cf., $20; tr. cf., $25...*Lippincott.*

— — *Same.* (Boydell ed.) 2 v. ill. 8°. $20; — in 1 v. ill. and por. 8°. $10...*Routledge.*

— — *Same;* ill. by H. C. Selous. (Cassell's ill. ed.) 3 v. imp. 8°. $17; $17.50; hf. mor., $25; mor., $32. *Cassell.*

Cont.: Comedies, $5.50. — Hist. plays, $5. — Tragedies, $6 50.

— *Same;* with biog. sketch and glossary by M. C. Clarke. por. and ill. demy 8°. $2.50. *Appleton; Lee & S.*

— — *Same.* ill. roy. 8°. $2.50; $3; mor., $7..*Claxton.*

— — *Same.* ill. roy. 8°. hf. bd., $9; hf. cf., $12; mor., $15; — in 2 v. 8°. hf. bd., $12; hf. cf., $18; mor., $25; — in 4 v. 8°. $12; hf. mor., $20; cf., $25; — in 1 v. 8°. mor., $10. — (chp. ed.) ill. 8°. shp., $3.50...*Appleton.*

— *Same;* with hist. of the stage, life of the poet and introd. to each play by J. P. Collier; with notes by J. L. Jewett. ('55.) New ed. ill. roy. 8°. '75. shp., $5; mor., $10...*Holmes.*

— *Same;* with life and introds., ed. by G. L. Duyckinck. [To form 20 pts.] pts. 1–9. ill. roy. 8°. '76. ea., *30c...*C. H. Davis.*

— — *Same;* with life by A. Chambers. ill. and por. 8°. $3.75...*Porter.*

— *Same;* ed. by Dyce. New ed., rev. 9 v. '75–'76. 8°. $27...*Scribner, W. & A.*

— — *Same.* 12°. (Bohn.) $1.40; ill., $2. *Scribner, W. & A.*

— — *Same.* 12°. (Bohn.) $1.75; ill., $2..*Lippincott.*

— *Same;* embr. various readings of principal editors; ed. by H. H. Furness. (Variorum ed.) v. 1–2. roy. 8°. ea., $3...*Lippincott.*

Cont.: Romeo and Juliet. — Macbeth.

— *Same;* from text of Johnson, Steevens and Reed; by W. Hazlitt. 5 v. fp. 8°. $9; hf. cf., $15..*Routledge.*

— *Same;* with introd. notes and life by H. N. Hudson. (Cabinet ed.) ('51.) New ed. 11 v. 16°. '71. $15; hf. cf., $30; — ill., $22; hf. cf., $42; mor., $55...*Lockwood, B. & Co.*

— *Same;* with life, notes, etc., from text of Johnson, Steevens and Reed. (Rowe's ed.) demy 8°. $3; hf. cf., $5...*Routledge.*

— *Same;* ed. by C. Knight. (Blackfriars ed.) cr. 8°. $1.75; hf. cf., $3.50; cf., $5...*Routledge.*

— — *Same.* (Household ser.) ill. 16°. $1.50; mor., $3...*Lee & S.*

— — *Same.* (Knight's pop. pict. ed.) 36 pts. ill. by Sir J. Gilbert, etc. 4°. '75. ea., *50c...*S. Walker.*

— — *Same.* (Presentation poets.) ill. 16°. $1.75; ivorine, $3; mor., $3.50...*Routledge.*

— — *Same.* (Red line ed.) por. and ill. sq. 8°. '75. $4...*Routledge.*

— — *Same.* (Stratford ed.) 6 v. 8°. large pap., $10; hf. cf., $20; cf., $24...*Appleton.*

— — *Same;* collated with the editions of Halliwell, Knight and Collier. ill. and por. roy. 8°. '63. hf. mor., $21; $23; mor., $27; $29...*Johnson & M.*

— *Same;* text [from] f° ed. of 1623, with [various] readings, etc., [and] notes by Knight, Douce, etc. (Windsor ed.) 8 v. 16°. ea., $1.25; hf. cf., $2.75; hf. mor., $3.25...*Porter.*

— *Same;* reprint of 1st f° ed. (1623); reprod. in facsimile by photog.; with introd. by J. O. H. Phillips. 8°. $4.20...*Scribner, W. & A.*

— *Same;* ed. with notes, glossary and life by H. Staunton. 3 v. ill. roy. 8°. $22.50; hf. cf., $30; $42.50; mor., $45...*Routledge.*

Shakespeare, W: *continued.*
— — *Same.* (Library ed.) 6 v. ill. 8°. '73. $12; hf. roxb., $13; hf. cf., $30; cf., $50.. *Routledge.*
— *Same;* ed. by S. W. Singer. (Chiswick press ed.) 10 v. ill. 16°. $12.50; mor., $25; hf. cf., $27.50; tr. cf., $40.......................... *Lippincott.*
— — *Same;* and life by C. Symmons. ill. 8°. shp., $4; — in 2 v. 8°. $4; shp., $5; hf. cf., $8.50.. *Harper.*
— *Same;* ed. from the folio ed., with various readings, notes, etc., by R. G. White. 12 v. 16°. '75. $18; hf. cf., $36; cf., $48............ *Little, B. & Co.*
— Complete poetical works; [with] life, glossary, etc. ill. 12°. $1.50.................... *World Pub.*
— Poems. 32°. 60c.; 90c.; mor., $1.50..... *Porter.*
— *Same.* 12°. $1.50...................... *Locke.*
— *Same.* (Aldine ed.) 16°. 75c........ *Lippincott.*
— *Same.* (Boston ed.) 8°. shp., $4.50; mor., $10. *Mason.*
— *Same.* (Presentation ed.) ill. 12°. $1.75; $3; mor., $3.50 .... *Routledge.*
— *Same.* (Scribner's pop. poets.) ill. 12°. $1.50. *Scribner, W. & A.*
— Songs; sel. from poems and plays. por. and ill. sq. 16°. $1.25 .... *Routledge.*
— Songs and sonnets. ill. 12°. '75. $1.25.. *Putnam.*
— *Same.* ill. cr. 8°. $3................ *Huntington.*
— Sonnets and songs; ed. by F. T. Palgrave. (Gem ed.) 32°. $1..................... *Macmillan.*
— Dramatic works; with life, notes and glossary. 4 v. demy 8°. '74. $10; $12; hf. cf., $18.. *Claxton.*
— *Same;* with biog. introd., index and glossary by H. G. Bell. (Collins ed.) 6 v. 12°. $7.50; — in 2 v. 8°. hf. mor., $8 .... *Putnam.*
— *Same;* with the corrections, etc., of Johnson, G. Steevens, etc.; rev. by I. Reed. 6 v. ill. roy. 12°. $9; shp., $11.40 .... *Harper.*
— *Germ.* Dramatische Werke. 33 v. 12°. ea., pap., 15c.......................... *F. W. Thomas.*
Cont.: Hamlet. — Kaufmann v. Venedig. — Othello. — Romeo u. Julie. — Sommernachts-Traum. — Macbeth. — Richard III. — Heinrich VIII. — Der Sturm. — Julius Cäsar. — Was Ihr wollt. — Ende gut, Alles gut. — Cymbeline. — Viel Lärmen um Nichts. — Wie es Euch gefällt. — Der Widerspenstigen Zähmung. — Heinrich IV., 2 pts. — Die Comödie d. Irrungen. — Die beiden Veroneser. — Coriolanus. — Liebes Leid u. Lust. — König Johann. — Richard II. — Heinrich VI., 3 pts. — Maass f. Maass. — Lear. — Timon v. Athens. — Troilus u. Cressida. — Heinrich V. — Die lustigen Weiber v. Windsor. — Titus Andronicus. — Das Wintermärchen. — Antonius u. Cleopatra.
— — *Same;* übers. v. Schlegel u. Tieck. 8 v. 12°. $7; pap., $4; in 4 v., $6......... *F. W. Thomas.*
— Plays. 32 v. 16°. ea., pap., 15c. .... *French.*
Cont.: All's well that ends well. — Antony and Cleopatra. — As you like it. — Coriolanus. — Cymbeline. — Hamlet; [condensed to 3 acts]. — Julius Cæsar. — King Henry IV., pt. 1. — King Henry IV., pt. 2. — King Henry V. — King Henry VI. — King Henry VIII. — King John. — King Lear. — King Richard II. — King Richard III. — Love's labour's lost. — Macbeth. — Measure for measure. — Merchant of Venice. — Merry wives of Windsor. — Midsummer night's dream. — Much ado about nothing. — Othello. — Romeo and Juliet. — Taming the shrew. — Tempest. — Timon of Athens. — Troilus and Cressida. — Twelfth-night. — Two gentlemen of Verona. — Winter's tale.
— *Same;* sel. and prep. for families and schools by H. N. Hudson [v. 1-3]; [also] Life, art and character of S. [v. 4-5]. (Hudson's family S.) ('71-'73.) New ed. 5 v. 12°. '75. $10; hf. mor., $15; cf., $20.............................. *Ginn.*
Note. v. 1-3 of above constitute Hudson's School Shakespeare. 3 v. 12°. ea., $2.
— — *Same.* (School ed.) 13 v. 12°. ea., pap., 40c. *Ginn.*
Cont.: As you like it. — Hamlet. — Julius Cæsar. — King Henry IV., pt. 1. — King Henry VIII. — King Lear. — Macbeth. — Merchant of Venice. — Midsummer night's dream. — Much ado about nothing. — Othello. — Romeo and Juliet. — Tempest.
— Plays and poems. (Chandos poets.) por. cr. 8°. $3.75; cf., $7.50; mor., $8 .... *Scribner, W. & A.*
— Select plays. (Booth's acting ed.) 9 v. 8°. ea., pap., 30c. .... *Hinton.*
Cont.: Hamlet. — Julius Cæsar. — King Richard III. — King Richard III. (Cibber's version). — Macbeth. — Merchant of Venice; in 4 acts. — Much ado about nothing. — Othello. — Romeo and Juliet.
— — *See also* Hinton, H. L.

Shakespeare, W: *continued.*
— Hamlet. 16°. pap., 15c..................... *Ames.*
— *Same;* with notes. 16°. bds., 40c...... *Routledge.*
— Julius Caesar; with notes by W. J. Rolfe. ill. sm. 4°. 90c. .... *Harper.*
— King Henry V. 16°. pap., 15c............ *De Witt.*
— King Henry VIII.; with notes by W. J. Rolfe. ill. sm. 4°. 90c.............................. *Harper.*
— King Richard III.; adapted for school reading by H. L. Hinton, with foot notes and glossary. 12°. 50c. .... *Hinton.*
— Macbeth; adapted for school reading by H. L. Hinton, with foot notes and gloss. 12°. 50c.... *Hinton.*
— — *See also* Schiller, J. F. v.
— Merchant of Venice; adapted for school reading by H. L. Hinton, with foot notes and glossary. 12°. 50c. — ill. roy. 8°. $1................ *Hinton.*
— *Same;* with notes by W. J. Rolfe. ill. sm. 4°. 90c. *Harper.*
— Merchant of Venice; Tempest; Henry VIII; Julius Cæsar; ed. with notes by W. J. Rolfe. ill. 16°. $3; — in 4 v. 16°. ea., 90c........... *Harper.*
— Midsummer night's dream: silh. ill. by Konewka. roy. 8°. '69. $4; mor., $9............ *Roberts.*
— *Same;* ill. by A. Fredericks. 4°. $7.50; mor., $12. *Appleton.*
— Othello; adapted for school reading by H. L. Hinton, with foot notes and glossary. 12°. 50c. *Hinton.*
— Romeo and Juliet; adapted for school reading by H. L. Hinton, with foot notes and glossary. 12°. 50c. .... *Hinton.*
— Tempest; with notes by J. M. Jephson. 18°. 50c. *Macmillan.*
— *Same;* with notes by W. J. Rolfe. ill. sm. 4°. 90c. *Harper.*
— Winter's tale; ed. by H. Staunton. ill. sq. 8°. $1.25. *Hinton.*
— Beauties of Shakespeare; sel. by W. Dodd. ill. 16°. $1.50; mor., $3 .... *Lee & S.*
— *Same.* ill. 12°. $1.75; ivorine, $3...... *Routledge.*
— *Same.* 32°. 60c.; 90c.; mor., $1.50. — sq. 16°. $1.50; mor., $2.25; $3.50 .... *Porter.*
— Concordance to works. *See* Clarke, *Mrs.* M. C.
— Dictionary of Shakespearian quotations. demy 8°. '71. $2; $2.50; hf. cf., $3.50; mor., $4.50.. *Claxton.*
— Falstaff and his companions: 21 ill. in silhouette by P. Konewka; with introd. by H. Kurz; tr. by C. C. Shackford. 8°. '71. $3; mor., $6.. *Roberts.*
— Gems: plates by R. Smirke, with descrip. text. sm. 4°. $4................. *Lippincott; Routledge.*
— Gleanings from [his] comedies. *See* Lippincott's pocket treasuries.
— Outline ill. to Shakespeare, by M. Retzsch: pl. with explan. text. obl. f°. '71. $9; mor., $15.. *Roberts.*
— Proverbs; or, the wise saws of our wisest poet; collected into a modern instance by M. C. Clarke. 12°. pap., 25c......................... *Happy.*
— Sertum Shaksperianum subnexis aliquot aliunde excerptis floribus; Latine reddidit H. Latham. fp. 8°. '64. $1.50..................... *Macmillan.*
— Shakespeare gems: thoughts from works. (Household ser.) ill. 16°. $1.50; mor., $3 .... *Lee & S.*
— Shakespeare's gems; by author of "Familiar quotations." (Presentation poets.) 16°. $1.75. *Routledge.*
— Tales. *See* Lamb, C. *and* M.
— Vocal music of plays; with accomp. 20 nos. 16°. ea., pap., 40c.-$1.50; — in 1 v., $10..... *French.*
Cont.: Midsummer night's dream, $1.50. — Macbeth. — Tempest, *ea.*, $1. — As you like it. — Merchant of Venice. — Merry wives of Windsor, *ea.*, 80c. — Much ado about nothing. — Twelfth night. — Winter's tale, *ea.*, 60c. — Antony and Cleopatra. — Cymbeline. — Hamlet. — Henry IV., pt. 2. — Henry VIII. — King Lear. — Love's labour's lost. — Measure for measure. — Othello. — Romeo and Juliet. — Two gentlemen of Verona, *ea.*, 40c.

Shakespeare and the Bible. Rees, J. $1... *Claxton.*

Shakespeare and the emblem writers. Green, H. $10; $16.............................. *Bouton.*

Shakespeare and his friends. Williams, R. F. $1. *Peterson.*

Shakespeare diversions. Jacox, F. $4..*Scribner, W.& A.*
Shakespeare forgeries. Ireland, W. H. $2; $3.50. *Bouton.*
Shakespeare gallery. *See* Boydell, J. *and* J.
Shakespeare treasury of wisdom and knowledge. Stearns, C. W. $2 .... *Putnam.*
Shakespeare's dream. Brougham, J. 15c...*French.*
Shakespeare's early days. Somerset, C. A. 15c. *French.*
Shakespeare's festival. Moncrieff, W. T. 15c. *French.*
Shakespeare's mental photographs. 16°. '68. pap., 15c. .... *Hurd & H.*
Shakespeare's Plutarch. *See* Plutarch.
Shakespearian grammar. Abbott, E. A. $2. *Macmillan.*
Shaking out the reef. *See* Todd, J:
Shakings: etchings from the Naval Academy; by a member of the class of '67. obl. 4°. $5..*Lee & S.*
Shaler, Natl. Southgate. Antiquity of caverns and cavern life of the Ohio valley. ill. 4°. pap., 40c. *Bost. Soc. Nat. Hist.*
— List of brachiopods from the island of Anticosti. 8°. '65. pap., 10c. .... *Mus. Comp. Zool.*
— Question guide to environs of Boston; for beginners in geology in Harvard Univ. pt. 1: Somerville and Cambridge. 12°. '75. pap., 25c...*Sever.*
— Recent changes of level on coast of Maine. 4°. pap., 40c. .... *Bost. Soc. Nat. Hist.*
Shall Christians go to war? Munnell, T., *and* Sweeney, J. S. $1 .... *Chase.*
Sham doctor: Ethiop. drama. 16°. pap., 15c. *French; Happy.*
Shameful behaviour. Troughton, A. C. 15c...*French.*
Shamrock and thistle. Adams, W. T. $1.50..*Lee & S.*
Shamrock flower; or, an Irish girl in America. 18°. 17c.; 22c. .... *Am. Bapt.*
Shamrock songster. 18°. 50c.; pap., 25c...*Sadlier.*
Shams in Lent. Potter, H. C. 10c. .... *Dutton.*
Shamus O'Brien. [Poem.] *See* Le Fanu, J. S.
Shamus O'Brien: tale of the Irish rebellion of 1798. 18°. pap., 10c. .... *Coddington.*
Shamus O'Brien, the bold boy of Glengall. [Fiction.] 8°. pap., 25c. .... *De Witt.*
Shand, Alex. Innes. On the trail of the German and French war. ill. 8°. pap., 35c. .... *Harper.*
Shandy Maguire. Boyce, J. $1.50 .... *Noonan.*
Shandy Maguire. Pilgrim, J. 15c. .... *French.*
Shankland, *Mrs.* E. R. Matron's household manual. sm. 16°. '75. 80c. .... (?) *Shankland.*
Shanks, W: F. G. Personal recollections of distinguished generals. 12°. $2 .... *Harper.*
Shanley, C: D. Truant chicken ser. 3 v. ill. sq. 8°. ea., 50c. .... *Hurd & H.*
Cont.: Truant chicken. — Monkey of Porto Bello. — Jolly bear and his friends.
Shannon, C. Youthful queen: comedy. 16°. pap., 15c. .... *French.*
Shannons (The). Finley, M. F. $1.25 .... *Pres. Bd.*
Sharland, J. B. Happy hour: songs, duets, etc. 12°. '65. bds., 25c. .... *Ditson.*
— *See also* Grammar school chorus; — National music course.
Sharman, S. Russell. One of the least. ill. 16°. 75c. *Cong. Pub.; Nelson.*
Sharp, S: *See* Bible, New Test.
Sharp, W: Tracts on homœopathy. 12°. 75c. *Boericke.*
Sharp practice. Lunn, J. 15c. .... *French.*
Sharpe, Edm. Architecture of the Cistercians. pl. imp. 4°. '74. pap., $3 .... *Spon.*
— First excursion of the Architectural Assoc.: account of Lincolnshire churches visited Aug., 1870, incl. architect. hist. of the Lincoln cathedral and [various] parish churches. lith. pl. and ill. roy. 8°. $8.50 .... *Spon.*

Sharpe, Edm., *continued.*
— Four letters on colour in churches, on walls and in windows. 2d ed. 8°. '71. pap., 20c.... *Spon.*
— Mouldings of the six periods of architecture from the conquest to the reformation. ('71.) New ed. 2 nos. pl. imp. 4°. '74. ea., pap., $8.50...*Spon.*
— Ornamentation of the transitional period of British architecture. no. 1. 42 pl. imp. 4°. $8.50. — no. 2, pt. 1, $4.25 .... *Spon.*
— Seven periods of English architecture. eng. and wood cuts. roy. 8°. $6 .... *Spon.*
Sharpey, W: *and* Quain, J. *and* R. Human anatomy. New ed., rev. and enl. by J. Leidy. 2 v. ill. 8°. $6 .... *Lea.*
Sharples, Ste. P. Chemical tables; arr. for laboratory use. 12°. '66. $2.25 .... *Allyn.*
Sharpstein, J: R. Digest of the Am., Eng., Scotch and Irish reports of life and accident insurance cases. 8°. shp., $3 .... *S. Whitney.*
Sharswood, G: Essay on professional ethics. [Law.] 4th ed. 12°. '76. $2 .... *T. & J. W. Johnson.*
— Lectures introd. to study of law. 12°. '70. $1.50. *T. & J. W. Johnson.*
Shaver, L. A. History of 60th Alabama Reg't, Gracie's Alabama Brigade. 8°. '67. $1 .... *Barrett.*
Shaw, Annie. Two families and two aims in life. ill. 16°. '72. $1.50 .... *Crowell.*
— — *See also* Father Merrill ser.
— White chrysanthemum. ill. 16°. '71. $1.50. *Crowell.*
— — *See also* Triplet ser.
Shaw, B. F. *See* Allen, F. A., *and* Shaw, B. F.
Shaw, Barnabas. Memorials of south Africa. 12°. 80c. .... *Cin. Meth. Bk. Conc.*
Shaw, *Miss* C. E. Percie; or, the conspirators; [also] Gracie, the child emancipator. 16°. 60c. *Cong. Pub.*
Shaw, C: A. Treasure trove. 8°. '74. $1.50; hf. mor., $2.50 .... *Freeman.*
Shaw, E: Civil architecture: theoret. and pract. system of building; with treatise on Gothic architecture by T. W. Silloway and G. M. Harding; with 102 copper pl. ('69.) 2d ed. 4°. '76. $10..*Baird.*
Shaw, Eyre M. Fire surveys: summary of principles to be observed in estimating risk of buildings. 4°. '72. pap., 50c. .... *Spectator.*
— Fires in theatres. 8°. '76. pap., 40c. ...... *Spon.*
Shaw, G: B. *See* Vermont, Sup. Court Reports.
Shaw, H: W. ["Josh. Billings."] Complete writings; with biog. 4 v. in 1. por. and ill. 12°. $2. *Carleton.*
— Everybody's friend; or, Josh. Billings' proverbial philosophy of wit and humor; ill. by Nast. 8°. *$3.50; $4; hf. mor., $5 .... *Am. Pub.*
Shaw, J. W. Writing and composition spelling-book. obl. 4°. pap., 15c. .... *Eastman.*
Shaw, Jennie R. Lettie Sterling. ill. 16°. '72. $1.50. *Crowell.*
— — *See also* Lettie Sterling ser.
— Margaret's old home: tale of Christian love. ill. 16°. '71. $1.50 .... *Crowell.*
— — *See also* Triplet ser.
— Neighbor's house. ill. 16°. '71. $1.50...*Lothrop.*
— New commandment; or, Ella's ministry. ill. 16°. '71. $1.50 .... *Lothrop.*
Shaw, J: C., *and* West, J: B. Analytical index to general and special laws of Minnesota, 1849–1875. 8°. '76. shp., $4 .... *J. B. West.*
Shaw, K. Golden gate. [S.-school music.] 16°. 35c. *Church.*
— Gospel trumpet. [S.-school music.] 12°. pap., 15c. *Church.*
— Shining pearls. [S.-school music.] 12°. pap., 15c. *Church.*
— Sparkling jewels. [S.-school music.] 12°. 30c. *Church.*

Shaw, Ol. Instruction book; [for the piano-forte]. f°. pap., $1.50 .... *Ditson.*

Shaw, R. Tennent. Day thoughts and commentary on the New Test. 12°. $1.50 .... *Lippincott.*

Shaw, Rob. Exposition of the Confession of faith of the Westminster Assembly. 12°. $1 .. *Pres. Bd.*

Shaw, S. Parsons. Odontalgia, commonly called toothache: its causes, prevention and cure. 16°. $1.75. *Lippincott.*

Shaw, T: B. Complete manual of English literature; ed., with notes and ill., by W. Smith; with sketch of Am. literature by H. T. Tuckerman. 12°. $2. *Sheldon.*

— New hist. of Eng. literature; rev. for text-book use by T. J. Backus. 12°. $1.50 .... *Sheldon.*

— Outlines of Eng. literature; with sketch of Am. literature by H. T. Tuckerman. 12°. $1.75 .. *Sheldon.*

— Smaller hist. of Eng. literature; ed. by W. Smith and H. T. Tuckerman. 16°. $1.25 .... *Sheldon.*

— Specimens of Am. literature and literary reader. 12°. $1.50 .... *Sheldon.*

— Specimens of Eng. literature; ed., with add., by W. Smith. Am. ed., rev. by B. N. Martin. 12°. $2 .... *Sheldon.*

Shaw, W: G. *See* Vermont, Sup. Court reports.

Shawl-straps. Alcott, L. M. $1 .... *Roberts.*

Shawm (The): library of church music; by W. B. Bradbury, G. F. Root, T. Hastings and T. B. Mason. obl. 8°. '53. bds., $1.50 .... *Ditson.*

Shawny and the light house. Pritchard, S. J. 60c. *Carter.*

She hath done what she could. Reed, E. 75c. *Claxton.*

She loved him madly. Borys, G. $1.75 .... *Carleton.*

She spake of him. Denning, H. $1.25 ...... *Carter.*

She stoops to conquer. *See* Goldsmith, Ol.

She would and he wouldn't. Morton, J. M. 15c. *French.*

She would and she wouldn't. Cibber, C. 15c... *French.*

Shea, J: Gilmary. Catechism of the hist. of U. S. 18°. 25c. .... *Sadlier.*

— Elements of hist., comb. with geog. and chronology. ill. and maps. 12°. hf. bd., 63c. ...... *Sadlier.*

— History of Catholic missions among Indian tribes of the U. S., 1592–1854. ill. 12°. $2.50 ... *Strong.*

— History of modern Europe. 12°. $1.25 .... *Strong.*

— History of Order of St. Ursula. *See* Parenty, *Abbé*, Life of St. Angela Merici.

— School hist. of U. S. 18°. 50c. .... *Strong.*

— (*ed.*) Cramoisy series of relations and memoirs on the French colonies in North America. 25 v. sm. 8°. '57–'66. sheets, $50 .... *Shea.*

— Library of Am. linguistics: grammars and dictionaries of Am. Indian lang. 15 v. 8°. '60–'75. pap., $75 .... *Shea.*

Cont.: 1. Onondaga and French dict. — 2. Selish, or flathead grammar, by G. Mengarini. — 3. Grammatical sketch of Heve lang., by B. Smith. — 4. Grammar of the Mutsun lang., by F. Arroyo de la Cuesta. — 5. Grammar of the Pima or Névome, by B. Smith. — 6. Grammar and dict. of the Yakama lang., by M. C. Pandosy. — 7. Vocabulary of the lang. of San Antonio Mission, California, by B. Sitjar. — 8. Vocabulary or phrase book of the Mutsun lang. of Alta California, by F. Arroyo de la Cuesta. — 9. Grammar of the Mikmaque lang. of Nova Scotia, by Maillard. — 10. Radical words of the Mohawk lang., with their derivatives, by J. Bruyas. — 11. Alphabetical vocabularies of the Clallam and Lummi, by G. Gibbs. — 12. Dictionary of the Chinook jargon, or trade lang. of Oregon, by G. Gibbs. — 13. Alphabetical vocab. of the Chinook lang., by G. Gibbs. — 14. Grammar and dict. of lang. of the Hidatsa (Minnetarees Grosventres of the Missouri); with introd. sketch of tribe, by W. Matthews. — 15. Hidatsa (Minnetaree) English dict., by W. Matthews.

— *See also* Courcy, H. de, Catholic Church in the U. S.

Sheaf. Des Essarts, A. S. L. 90c.; $1.20 ... *O'Shea.*

Sheaf of papers. Appleton, T. G. $1.50 .... *Roberts.*

Sheahan, Ja. W. Life of Stephen A. Douglas. por. 12°. $1.50 .... *Harper.*

Shearer, Ja. W. Combination speller. 16°. '74. bds., 30c. .... *Ivison.*

Shearman, T: G., *and* Redfield, A. A. Treatise on law of negligence and remedies for private wrongs and negligent performance of contracts. 8°. shp., $6.50 .... *Baker, V. & Co.*

Shedd, *Mrs.* Jla. A. Famous painters and paintings; with heliotypes of celebrated paintings. 8°. '75. $5; hf. cf., $8 .... *Osgood.*

Shedd, W: G. T. Works. ('67–'71.) New ed. 4 v. 8°. '75–'76. ea., $2.50; per set, hf. cf., $18 .. *Scribner.*

Cont.: History of Christian doctrine, 2 v. — Sermons to the natural man, $3. — Treatise on homiletics and pastoral theology.

— Discourses and essays. ('56.) New ed. 12°. '70. $1.50 .... *Draper.*

— Lectures upon philosophy of history. ('56.) New ed. 12°. '73. 75c. .... *Draper.*

Sheddan, S. S. Blessings in disguise: sequel to "Valley of Achor." 18°. 50c. .... *Pres. Bd.*

— Valley of Achor; or, hope in trouble. 18°. 35c. *Pres. Bd.*

Sheeleigh, Matthias (*ed.*) Herald picture books. nos. 1, 2, ea., 6 v. ea., 25c. .... (?) *Luth. Pub.*

Sheep and lambs. *See* Baker, *Mrs.* H. N. W.

Sheep in wolf's clothing. Taylor, T. 15c. *De Witt; French.*

Sheepshanks gallery: 20 autotype reproductions of pictures in the Sheepshanks Gallery in the South Kensington Museum; with descrip. letterpress by W. C. Monkhouse. imp. 4°. $20 ... *Lippincott.*

Sheer off. Tucker, C. 75c. .... *Carter.*

Sheet anchor. Rockwell, J. E. 10c. ...... *Pres. Bd.*

Sheil, R: Lalor. Apostate: tragedy. 16°. pap., 15c. *French.*

— Evadne: tragedy. 16°. pap., 15c. .... *French.*

— Sketches of the Irish bar; with memoir and notes by R. S. Mackenzie. 2 v. 12°. $3; hf. cf., $6. *Widdleton.*

— *and* Curran, J: P. Memoirs and speeches; by a member of the N. Y. bar. 8°. $1.50 ... *McGee.*

Sheldon, E. A. [Readers.] ('72–'75.) New ed. 6 v. 12°. '76 .... *Scribner.*

Cont.: Primer; adapted to phonic mode of teaching, 20c. — First reader; adapted to phonic mode of teaching, 25c. — Second reader, 50c. — Third, 75c. — Fourth, $1.25. — Fifth, $1.50.

— Lessons on objects; for children between six and fourteen. ('63.) New ed. 12°. '76. $1.75 .. *Scribner.*

— Manual of element. instruct.: object lessons for training and developing faculties of children. ('62.) New ed., rev. and enl. 12°. $1.75 .. *Scribner.*

— *and* Barlow, E. H. Teachers' manual of instruction in reading; to accompany Sheldon's readers. ('75.) New ed. 12°. '76. $1 ...... *Scribner.*

Sheldon, *Mrs.* Electra M. Clevelands (The): influence of a Christian family in a new settlement. ill. 18°. 40c. .... *Bost. Am. Tr.*

— — *See also* Missing boat stories.

— Early history of Michigan, to 1815. 8°. '56. $2.50. *Barnes.*

— I wish I was poor. ill. 18°. '63. 20c. ...... *Am. Tr.*

Sheldon, G: *See* Temple, J. H., *and* Sheldon, G.

Shelford, Leon. On law of railways. 2 v. 8°. shp., $10 .... *W. C. Little.*

Shell cove. Mudge, Z. A. $1.50 .... *Lothrop.*

Shell cove ser. 4 v. 16°. $6 .... *Lothrop.*

Cont.: Shell cove. — Bye-path meadow. — William the silent. — This one thing I do.

Shell gatherers. 18°. 60c. .... *Cong. Pub.*

Shell worker, and other stories. ('66.) New ed. ill. 16°. '69. $1.25 .... *Hoyt.*

Shelley, C. P. B. Work shop appliances. 12°. $1.50. *Appleton.*

Shelley, *Mrs.* Ma. Wollstonecraft. Beautiful widow. 12°. $1.75; pap., $1.50 .... *Peterson.*

— Frankenstein; or, the modern Prometheus. 2d ed. 12°. '69. $1; pap., 60c. .... *Allyn.*

Shelley, Percy Bysshe. Poems. 12°. $1.50...*Locke.*
— *Same.* (Scribner's pop. poets.) ill. 12°. $1.50. *Scribner, W.& A.*
— *Same;* ed. by Mrs. Shelley, with memoir. 4 v. por. 18°. $4....*Osgood.*
— Poetical works. por. and ill. 16°. $1.50....*Lee & S.*
— *Same.* 32°. 60c.; 90c.; mor., $1.50......*Porter.*
— *Same.* roy. 8°. $3......*Desilver.*
— *Same.* (Chandos classics.) cr. 8°. $1; pap., 75c. *Scribner, W.& A.*
— *Same.* (Chandos poets.) por. and ill. cr. 8°. $3.75; cf., $7.50; mor., $8......*Scribner, W.& A.*
— *Same.* (Household ed.) 3 v. 16°. $3.75; hf. cf., $7.50; cf., $11.25......*Miller.*
— *Same.* (Household ser.) por. and ill. 16°. $1.50; mor., $3......*Lee & S.*
— *Same.* (Red line ed.) ill. sm. 4°. $4.50; hf. cf., $6; cf., $8......*Miller.*
— *Same;* ed. by Mrs. Shelley, with memoir by J. R. Lowell. (Blue and gold ed.) 3 v. 32°. $3.75; hf. cf., $7.50; cf., $10.50......*Miller.*
— *Same;* ed. with introd. and memoir by W. B. Scott. (Presentation poets.) ill. 12°. $1.75; ivorine, $3......*Routledge.*
— — *See also* Coleridge, S. T., Poetical works.
— Queen Mab; with notes. 12°. 50c......*Mendum.*
Shelley, *Mrs.* Percy Bysshe. *See* Shelley, *Mrs.* Ma. W.
Shells. Wheeler, E. $1.50......*Hauser.*
Shelomith's son, the curser and blasphemer. 18°. 50c. *Am.S.S.*
Shelton, T. J., *and* Rosecrans, J. H. Polished pearls: S.-school sing. book. obl. 16°. '76. pap., 10c. *Fillmore.*
Shenac's work at home: tale of Canadian life. 16°. $1.25......*Am.S.S.*
— *See also* Glen Elder lib.
Shenstone, W: *See* Goldsmith, O., Johnson, S., Shenstone, W., *and* Smollett, T.
Shenuit, H. Mass in F, for three or four voices. 4°. $1.25; —tenor parts, 25c......*Church.*
Shepard, C: U. *See* Connecticut geol. survey.
Shepard, *Mrs.* Louisa. Dialogues and recitations adapted to children's progressive lyceums. sm. 12°. '71. 50c......*Rel.Phil.*
Shepard, T: Works; with memoir by J. A. Albro. 3 v. 12°. $5......*Cong.Pub.*
— Clear sunshine of the Gospel breaking forth upon the Indians in New Eng. [Reprint.] 4°. $1.50; large pap., $2......*Sabin.*
Shepherd, G: Sermons; with memorial by D. S. Talcott. ('68.) 2d ed. por. 12°. $2.25. *Lockwood, B.& Co.*
Shepherd, H: E. History of the Eng. language. 12°. $1.50......*Hale.*
Shepherd, J. W. *See* Alabama, Sup. Court reports.
Shepherd, S. *See* Virginia, Statutes.
Shepherd, W: Memoir of W: T. Buchanan. 18°. 35c. *Pres. Bd.*
Shepherd and his flock. Macduff, J. R. $1.50. *Carter.*
Shepherd boy. *See* Prairie books.
Shepherd boy of Bethlehem, and other stories. 18°. 25c......*Pres.Bd.*
Shepherd king. *See* Tucker, *Mrs.* C.
Shepherd lady. Ingelow, J. $4.50; $9.....*Roberts.*
Shepherd of Bethlehem. *See* Tucker, *Mrs.* C.
Shepherd of Cournailles: operetta. 16°. pap., 15c. *French.*
Shepherd of Derwent vale. Lunn, J. 15c...*French.*
Shepherd of Israel. MacGregor, D. $1.25..*Carter.*
Shepherd of the Pyrenees. 18°. '69. 25c. *N. Y. Ref. Ch. Bd.; Pres. Com.*
Shepherd of Salisbury Plain. *See* More, Ha.

Shepherd's voice; or, words of encouragement and words of warning for the ears of the young. 18°. 55c......*Am.S.S.*
Shepley, J: *See* Maine, Sup. Court reports.
Sheppard, Edg. Madness; in its medical, social and legal aspects. 8°. '73. $2.50......*Lindsay.*
Sheppard, *Mrs.* Edn. Hester Power's girlhood. 12°. $1......*Loring.*
Sheppard, Eliz. S. ["E. Berger;" "Kinkel."] Charles Auchester. 8°. $1.25; pap., 75c...*Estes.*
— *Same.* 8°. pap., 75c......*Harper.*
— Counterparts. 8°. $1.25; pap., 75c. *Burnham; Estes.*
— Rumor. 8°. $1.25; pap., 75c....*Burnham; Estes.*
Sheppard, Fs. H. Love afloat. 12°. $1.50; pap., $1. *Sheldon.*
Sheppard, Furman. Constitutional text-book: exposition of the Const. of the U. S. and of portions of the public and administrative law of the federal government. 12°. hf. bd., $1.25......*Sower.*
— First book of the Constitution: exposition of U. S. Const. 12°. hf. bd., 75c......*Sower.*
Sheppard, J: H. Brief hist. of the N. E. Historic-Geneal. Soc. 8°. '62. pap., 25c...*N.E.Hist. Gen.*
Sheppard, J: J. Fall of Rome and rise of the new nationalities. post 8°. $2.50......*Routledge.*
Sherbauer, —. Vespers no. 6. [Choral music.] 4°. pap., 80c......*Peters.*
Sherbrooke. Talcott, H. B. $1.50......*Appleton.*
Sheridan, *Mrs.* M. B. Guarded by a fear. [Fiction.] 8°. pap., 35c......*Authors.*
Sheridan, Ph. H. Illustrated life and services. 12°. $1; pap., 75c......*Peterson.*
Sheridan, R: Brinsley Butler. Works; with memoir by J. P. Browne, [and] extracts from life by T. Moore. por. 8°. $3.50......*Lippincott.*
— *Same;* with memoir of author, collection of ana, and chalk drawings; ed. by F. Stainforth. 12°. '74. $2.50......*Routledge.*
— Dramatic works and life. 12°. (Bohn.) $1.25. *Little, B.& Co.*
— *Same.* 12°. (Bohn.) $1.40......*Scribner, W.& A.*
— *Same.* 12°. (Bohn.) $1.50......*Lippincott.*
— [Plays.] 6 v. 16°. ea., pap., 15c......*French.*
Cont.: Critic. — Duenna: comic opera. — Rivals: comedy. — St. Patrick's day: farce. — School for scandal: comedy. — Trip to Scarborough: comedy.
— School for scandal; arr. by A. Daly. 16°. pap., 25c. *French.*
Sheridan's ride. *See* Read, T: B.
Sheridan's troopers on the borders. Keim, De B. R. $1.75......*Claxton.*
Sherlock, T: Trial of the witnesses of the resurrection of Jesus; with sequel. 12°. 80c...*Pres.Bd.*
— *Same;* with introd. by T. O. Summers. ('55.) 3d ed. 18°. '71. 50c......*So.Meth.*
Sherlock, W: Discourse conc. the divine providence; ed. by T. O. Summers. ('53.) 3d ed. 12°. '75. $1.50......*So.Meth.*
Sherman, D: History of revisions of Discipline of the Meth. Episc. Church. 12°. $2.50. *Cin.Meth.Bk.Conc.*
— Sketches of New England divines. 12°. '59. $1.75. *Meth.Bk.Conc.*
Sherman, *Mrs.* Ellen Ewing. Memoir of Thomas Ewing of Ohio. 4°. '74. $3......*Cath.Pub.*
Sherman, Ja. Guide to acquaintance with God. 32°. 30c......*Pres.Bd.*
— Pastor's wife: memoir of Mrs. Sherman. 18°. 75c. *Sower.*
— *Same.* ill. 18°. '54. 60c......*Am.Tr.*
Sherman, Lydia. Life, trial and confession. [In Eng. or Germ.] 8°. pap., 25c......*Barclay.*
Sherman, R. K. Musical catechism. 16°. 50c. *Gordon.*

Sherman, W: Tecumseh. Memoirs, by himself. 2 v. map. 8°. $5.50; shp., $7; hf. mor., $8.50; mor., $12 .... *Appleton.*

Sherman's historical raid. Boynton, H. V. $2. *Wilstach.*

Sherwin, T: Common school algebra. 12°. $1.10.—Key, 95c. .... *Thompson.*

— Elementary algebra. 12°. '41. $1.25.—Key, $1. *Nichols & H.*

— *See also* Miles, S. P., *and* Sherwin, T.

Sherwin, W: F. *See* Allen, C. G., *and* Sherwin, W. F.;—Lowry, R., Sherwin, W. F., *and* Allen, C. G.

— *and* Stearns, J. N. Bugle notes for the temperance army. pap., 30c.; bds., 35c. .... *Nat. Temp.*

Sherwood, Adiel. Notes on the New Test.; for Sunday-schools. 2 v. 8°. ea., $1.75 .. *So. Bapt.*

— *See also* Jeter, J. B., *and* Sherwood, A.

Sherwood, G: Primary speaker. ('63.) New ed. 18°. '75. 30c. .... *Sherwood.*

— Six column writing-speller. obl. 12°. '75. 15c. *Sherwood.*

— Speller and definer. ('63.) New ed. 12°. '76. 15c. *Sherwood.*

— Speller and pronouncer. ('62.) New ed. 12°. '76. 15c. .... *Sherwood.*

— Writing speller. ('61.) New ed. 12°. '76. 12c. *Sherwood.*

Sherwood, J: D. Comic hist. of the U. S. ill. 12°. '69. $2.50 .... *Osgood.*

Sherwood, *Mrs.* Ma. Martha. Works. 16 v. ill. 12°. ea., $1.50; per set, hf. cf., $52 .... *Harper.*
Cont.: History of Henry Milner, pt. 1-3.—Fairchild family, etc.—Little Henry and his bearer, etc.—Indian pilgrim, etc.—Infant's progress, etc.—The governess, etc.—The nun, etc.—Victoria, etc.—Lady of the manor, 4 v.—The mail coach, etc.—The monk of Cimies, etc.—History of Henry Milner, pt. 4, etc.—John Marten.

— Clever stories. sq. 16°. 75c. .... *Carter.*

— Duty is safety. sq. 16°. 35c. .... *Carter.*

— History of Susan Gray, as related by a clergyman. 18°. '73. 45c. .... *Routledge.*

— *Same.* 16°. 50c. .... *Scribner, W. & A.*

— Jack, the sailor boy. sq. 16°. 35c. .... *Carter.*

— Juliana Oakley. ill. 18°. '66. 40c. *N. Y. Ref. Ch. Bd.; Pres. Com.*

— Life; abridg. por. 12°. 60c. .... *Pres. Bd.*

— Lily ser. 6 v. 18°. $2 .... *Carter.*
Cont.: Flowers of the forest.—Little beggars.—Two orphans.—Little woodman.—Young forester.—Joan the trusty.

— Little Henry and his bearer. ill. 18°. 30c. *Am. S. S.; Am. Tr.*

— *Same.* 18°. 35c. .... *Whittaker.*

— *Same.* 18°. 40c. .... *Dutton.*

— — *See also* Good child's lib.

— *Germ.* Der kleine Heinrich und sein Träger. ill. 18°. '46. 25c. .... *Am. Tr.*

— *Ital.* Storia di Enrichetto ed il suo latore. 18°. '76. 30c. .... *Am. Tr.*

— *Port.* Henriquinho e o seu creador. 18°. '53. 15c. *Am. Tr.*

— Little woodman. 32°. 25c. .... *Scribner, W. & A.*

— Roxobel. 3 v. 18°. $2.25 .... *Harper.*

— Stories explanatory of the Church catechism. 12°. $1 .... *McCauley.*

— *Same.* 12°. '52. $1.25 .... *Whittaker.*

— Stories for Sundays, ill. the catechism; rev. and ed. by A. C. Coxe. ill. 12°. $1.25; $2.50 .. *Lippincott.*

— Think before you act. sq. 16°. 35c. .... *Carter.*

Sherwood, W: Practical speller and definer. 8°. '63. pap., 10c. .... *Barnes.*

— Self culture in reading, speaking, etc.; for schools, colleges, etc. 12°. '55. $1.50 .... *Barnes.*

— Speller and pronouncer. 8°. '62. pap., 10c. .. *Barnes.*

Shesh Achurjya. *See* Scenes in the New Hebrides.

Sheville, J: *and* Gould, Ja. Guide to the royal arch chapter. [Masonic.] ill. 12°. '67. $1.50 .. *Macoy.*

— — Manual of the chapter. [Masonic.] 32°. 75c. *Masonic.*

Shew, Jl. Children: their hydropathic management in health and disease. 12°. '52. $1.50 .... *Wells.*

— Hydropathic family physician. ill. 8°. '71. $4; leath., $5 .... *Wells.*

— Midwifery and diseases of women; showing superiority of water-treatment. 12°. '52. $1.50 .. *Wells.*

— Water-cure in pregnancy and child-birth. 12°. '49. pap., 50c. .... *Wells.*

Shield of faith. sq. 24°. 45c.; 50c. .... *Am. S. S.*

Shields, C: W. Book of common prayer. 16°. $2.50. (?) *Martien.*

— Book of remembrance. 18°. 75c. .... *Pres. Bd.*

— Religion and science in their rel. to philosophy; suggested by Tyndall's address at Belfast. 8°. '75. 75c. .... *Scribner.*

Shifting for himself. Alger, H., *jr.* $1.50 .. *Loring.*

Shifting winds. Ballantyne, R. M. $1.25. *Claxton; Porter.*

Shiftless folks. Smith, F. N. $1.75 .... *Carleton.*

Shillaber, B: P. ["*Mrs.* Partington."] Lines in pleasant places: rhythmics of many moods and quantities, wise and otherwise. 12°. '74. $1.50. *Williams.*

— Mrs. Partington's carpet-bag of fun. ill. 12°. $1.25; pap., 75c. .... *Dick & F.*

— Mrs. Partington's knitting work, and what was done by her plaguy boy, Ike: a web of many textures as woven by Ruth herself. ill. 12°. $1.75. *J. E. Potter.*

— Partingtonian patchwork. ill. 12°. $1.75 ... *Lee & S.*

Shilling day at the great exhibition. Brough, W., *and* Halliday, A. 15c. .... *French.*

Shilling song book. 3 nos. 12°. '60. ea., pap., 12c. *Ditson.*

Shilling's worth of fun. 16°. '72. 40c. .. *Routledge.*

Shiloh. Woodruff, J. L. M. $2 .... *Dutton.*

Shimeall, R: C. Our Bible chronology; harmonized with chronol. of profane writers. maps and ill. 8°. '59. $4.50 .... *Barnes.*

Shindler, *Mrs.* Ma. S. B. D. [*formerly* Ma. S. B. Dana]. Forecastle Tom; or, the landsman turned sailor. 18°. 75c. .... *Harper.*

— Northern harp: sacred and moral songs. 4°. '41. bds., $1.50 .... *Ditson.*

— Southern harp: sacred and moral songs. 4°. '41. $1.50 .... *Ditson.*

— Western harp: Sunday music. 4°. '60. $2; bds., $1.50 .... *Ditson.*

— Young sailor. 18°. 75c. .... *Harper.*

Shining hours. ill. 16°. '69. $1.50 .... *Lothrop.*

Shining light. Charles, E. 60c. .... *Pres. Bd.*

Shining light. *See* Dunning, A. K.

Shining light. Marsh, C. 50c. .... *Carter.*

Shining lights. [Sacred songs.] 4°. $2.25; bds., $1.75. *Peters.*

Shining pearls. Shaw, K. 15c. .... *Church.*

Shining river. Perkins, H. S. *and* W. O. 35c.; 30c. *Ditson.*

Shining star (New). *See* Perkins, T. E.

Shinn, Earl. ["E: Strahan."] The new Hyperion; from Paris to Marly by way of the Rhine. ill. 8°. $3; $3.50 .... *Lippincott.*

— *and* Smith, Wa., *and* Wilson, Jos. M. (*ed.*) Illustrated catalogue: the masterpieces of the U. S. Intern. Exhibition, 1876. [To form 50 pts.] pts. 1-6. pl. roy. 8°. '76. ea., *50c. ... *Gebbie.*

Shinn, G: W. Manual of instruction on church hist. 18°. '76. 60c.; bds., 30c. .... *Whittaker.*

— Manual of instruction on the Prayer book. 18°. '74. 75c.; bds., 25c. .... *Whittaker.*

— Manual of instruction upon the Collects, Epistles and Gospels for the Christian year. 18°. bds., 30c. .... *Whittaker.*

Shinn, W. P. On railroad accounts and returns. 8°. '76. pap., 60c. .... *Am. Soc. of C. E.*

Ship (The). *See* Goodrich, S: G.
Ship, ahoy! Fenn, G. M. 40c. . . . . *Harper.*
Ship building, theoretical and practical; by I. Watts, W. J. M. Rankin, F. K. Barnes, J. R. Napier, etc. 30 nos. wood-cuts and eng. f°. $37.50; bds., $35; hf. mor., $40. . . . . *Wiley.*
Ship in the desert. Miller, J. $1.50 . . . . *Roberts.*
Ship of ice. Sadler, S. W. $1.50 . . . . *Nelson.*
Shipley, Ma. E. Christmas at Annesley. ill. 12°. $1.25. . . . . *Nelson.*
— Jessie's work; or, faithfulness in little things. 16°. 90c. . . . . *Am. S. S.*
— *Same.* ill. 16°. '73. 90c. . . . . *Am. Tr.*
— *Same.* ('73.) New ed. 16°. '75. $1.25. . . . . *Hoyt.*
— *Same.* ill. 16°. '74. $1.25 . . . . *Dutton.*
— Lofty aims and lowly efforts. ill. 12°. $1.50. . *Pott.*
— Month at Brighton. ill. 16°. 50c. . . . . *Pott.*
Shipley, Orby. Glossary of terms used in theology, liturgiology, symbolism, sacred offices and vestments, architecture, etc. 8°. $8. . . . . *Pott.*
— Six short sermons on sin: Lent lectures at St. Alban, the Martyr. 16°. '68. 50c. . . . . *Pott.*
— Theory about sin, derived from facts of every day life: Lent lectures on the seven capital sins. cr. 8°. '74. $3 . . . . *Macmillan.*
Shipman, G: E. Homœopathic family guide for 28 remedies in treatment of the more simple forms of disease; [also] Directions for treatment of dengue and yellow fever, by W. H. Holcombe. 8th ed. por. 12°. '73. $2. . . . . (?) *West. News.*
Shipman, G: M. God's dealings with the Chicago Foundlings' Home: hist. of the first four years of the Home. 8°. '75. pap., 30c. . . . . *Revell.*
Shipman, Herb. A. *See* Truman, J. H., Mallory, J. A., *and* Shipman, H. A.
Shipmates: comedy. 16°. pap., 15c. . . . . . . *French.*
Shipp, W: M. *See* North Carolina, Reports.
Shippen, Rush R. (*ed.*) Daily praise and prayer. ('75.) 2d ed. sq. 16°. '76. $1; $1.25. . *Am. Unit.*
Ships and sailors. Cottrell, C. C., *and* Littell, E. D. $1.50. . . . . *Appleton.*
Ships in the mist. Larcom, L. 30c. . . . . *Hoyt.*
Shipton, Anna. Anna Shipton lib. 8 v. 16°. ea., 75c.; pap., 25c. . . . . *Crowell.*

Cont.: Tell Jesus. — Waiting hours. — Lost blessing. — Promise and the Promiser. — Wayside service. — Secret of the Lord. — Watch-tower. — Asked of God.

— Anna Shipton ser. ('72–'74.) New ed. 7 v. 16°. '76. $6.25; ea., 75c; pap., 25c. . . . . *Hoyt.*

Cont.: Following fully. — Wayside service. — Asked of God. — Cottage on the rock. — Promise and the Promiser. — Secret of the Lord. — Waiting hours.

— Following fully. 12°. $1 . . . . *Palmer.*
— Promise and the Promiser: power and presence of the Lord with his people. 16°. '74. 75c. . . *Randolph.*
— *Same.* 16°. '75. 75c.; pap., 50c. . . . . *Gospel.*
— Secret of the Lord. 16°. '71. 75c. . . . . . *Randolph.*
— *Same.* 12°. $1 . . . . *Palmer.*
— Tell Jesus: recollections of Emily Gosse. 16°. '71. 75c.; pap., 25c. *Randolph.*
— *Same.* 12°. 75c. . . . . *Palmer.*
— *Same.* 16°. '75. 50c.; pap., 20c. . . . . *Gospel.*
— Waiting hours with the hungry and weary and thirsty in the wilderness. 16°. '74. 75c. . . . *Randolph.*
— *Same.* ('74.) New ed. 16°. '76. 75c. . . . . . *Hoyt.*
— *Same.* 16°. '75. 75c.; $1; pap., 50c. . . . . *Gospel.*
— Watch tower in the wilderness. 16°. '76. 75c.; pap., 25c. . . . . *Hoyt.*
— *Same.* 16°. '75. 75c.; pap., 50c. . . . . *Gospel.*
— Wayside service; or, the day of small things. 16°. '71. 75c. . . . . *Randolph.*
— *Same.* 12°. $1 . . . . *Palmer.*
Shipwreck. 18°. 30c. . . . . *Am. S. S.*
— *See also* Champney stories.
Shipwreck; or, the desert island. 18°. 75c. . . *Strong.*
Shipwreck of the Medusa. Moncrieff, W. T. 15c. *French.*
Shipwrecked in the air. *See* Verne, Jul.
Shipwrecks and disasters at sea. 16°. bds., 80c. *Routledge.*
Shipwrecks of faith. Trench, R. C. $1. . *Macmillan.*
Shira. Robinson, F. W. 50c. . . . . *De Witt.*
Shiras, Alex. Christian festivals: a help to devout observance of the sacred seasons of the church. 12°. '69. $1.50; $2; mor., $4. . . . . *Claxton.*
Shirley, J: M. *See* New Hampshire, Law reports.
Shirley, Wa. Waddington. Elijah: four university sermons. fp. 8°. '64. 75c. . . . . *Macmillan.*
Shirley. *See* Brontë, C.
Shocking events. Buckstone, J. B. 15c. . . . . *French.*
Shoe and leather trade reference book; [also] Tanners and curriers' reference book. 4°. '68. $30. . *J. A. Murphy.*
Shoe-binders of New York. Wright, J. McN. 80c. *Pres. Bd.*
Shoemaker, J. W. Elocutionist's annual. nos. 1, 2. 12°. ea., 75c.; pap., 35c. . . . . *Lippincott.*
Shoemaker of Toulouse. Hill, F. S. 15c. . . . *French.*
Shoemaker's village. Holbeach, H. $1.75. . *Routledge.*
Shoes of fortune. Andersen, H. C. $1. . . . . . . *Miller.*
Sholl, C: Church architecture: 10 working designs for Cath. churches. f°. $15; hf. mor., $20. *Sadlier.*
Shooting the moon: drama. 16°. pap., 15c. . . *French.*
Shore, T. T. *See* Cassell's biog. dictionary.
Shores, S. Z. Poems. 12°. $1. . . . . *Lippincott.*
Short, C: Essay on order of words in Attic-Greek prose. *See* Yonge, C. D., English-Greek lexicon.
Short, J: T. Last gladiatorial show. ill. 16°. $1.25. *Cin. Meth. Bk. Conc.*
Short and sweet. Troughton, A. C. 15c. . . . . . *French.*
Short comings and long goings. ill. 16°. '70. $1.25. *Lothrop.*
Short family prayers, with hymns. 18°. 30c. *Whittaker.*
Short history of the English people. *See* Green, J. R.
Short lessons in reading. ill. 4°. pap., 10c.; 15c. *J. E. Potter.*
Short logarithmic and other tables, to facilitate pract. calculations and for solving arith. problems in class. 8°. '74. 60c. *Spon.*
Short miscellanies for young people. ill. 32°. 25c. *Pres. Bd.*
Short off-hand sermons on forgotten texts: 1st ser. on temperance; by a very plain old-fashioned preacher. ('73.) 4th ed. 18°. '74. 20c.; pap., 10c. . . . . *Claxton.*
Short poem (A). Peck, J. 10c. . . . . *Perkinpine.*
Short prayer (The); [also] Text of easy words. 32°. 20c. . . . . *Pres. Bd.*
Short prayers for little Catholics. ill. 48°. 25c.-$1. *Benziger.*
Short readings for daily use. Smith, J. 25c. . . *Nelson.*
Short sermons and true tales. *See* Capers, W:
Short sermons for plain readers and hearers. Dickson, A. F. 70c. . . . . *Pres. Bd.*
Short sermons to little children. 18°. 45c. . . *Am. S. S.*
Short stories and lessons on festivals, fasts and saints' days of the Prot. Episc. church. 4th ed. 12°. '74. $1.50. . . . . *Whittaker.*
Short stories for the little ones at home. Alexander, J. W. 80c. . . . . *Am. S. S.*
Short stories for little people. *See* Little Alice's lib.
Short stories founded on Eng. hist. 12°. $1.50. . *Pott.*
Short stories lib. 5 v. ill. 16°. $2.50. . . . *Routledge.*

Cont.: Better than rubies. — Sybil's sacrifice. — Experience teaches. — Old shepherd. — Two brothers.

Short studies on great subjects. *See* Froude, J. A.
Short tales for Sunday reading. ill. post 18°. 75c. *Scribner, W. & A.*
Shortcut, Daisy (*pseud.*) *See* Cohen, D. S.
Shorthand: all about it, how long it will take to learn it, teacher or no teacher; by a N. Y. reporter. 12°. '70. pap., 10c. .... *Hunter.*
Shorthand without a master. 16°. pap., 15c. *Happy.*
Shortrede, Rob. Latitude and declination tables. [In Eng. and French.] 8°. $3 .... *Routledge.*
Shoshie. Brittan, H. G. $1.25 .... *Whittaker.*
Should this meet the eye: farce. 16°. pap., 15c. *French.*
Shoulder knot. Tefft, B. F. $1.50 .... *Harper.*
Shoulder straps. Morford, H. $1.75; $1.50 .. *Peterson.*
Shoup, F. A. Elements of algebra. 8°. $1.50 .. *Hale.*
Shove, G: A. Life under glass. 16°. '74. $1 .. *Osgood.*
Show your colors. Fulton, J. D. $1 .... *Ward.*
Shower (The new). *See* Bradbury, W. B.
Shower of pearls: [duets]; with piano forte accomp. 4°. '58. $3; $4; bds., $2.50 .... *Ditson.*
Showers of blessings. Caughey, J. $1.50 .. *Palmer.*
Shreve, S: H. On upright arched bridges. *See* Hamilton, S., Fabrication of béton blocks.
— Treatise on strength of bridges and roofs. 87 woodcuts. 8°. '73. $5 .... *Van Nostrand.*
Shrigley, Natl. True relation of Virginia and Maryland: Lond., anno 1669. [Reprint.] 4°. pap., 25c. .... *Sabin.*
Shryock, D. Golden key. [School music.] 16°. 25c. *Church.*
— Silver clarion. [School music.] 16°. 45c... *Church.*
Shuck, *Mrs.* Henrietta. Scenes in China: sketches of the country, religion and customs. 18°. 60c.; 75c. .... *Am.Bapt.*
Shuey, W: J. Doctrine and disciplines of the United Brethren in Christ. 32°. 30c.; — in Germ. 32°. 30c. .... *Un.B.Pub.*
— *and* Hanley, W., *and* Chittenden, L. S. Collection of hymns for the use of the United Brethren in Christ. 12°. $1.50–$3.75. — 18°. 75c.–$1.75. *Un.B.Pub.*
Shufeldt, Rob. W. Reports [on] ship-canal between Atlantic and Pacific. *See* United States, *Navy Dept.*
Shuldham, E. B. Family homœopathist; or, plain directions for treatment of disease. 3d ed. 32°. 50c. .... *Cassell.*
Shuman, And. Loves of a lawyer: his quandary, and how it came out. 16°. '75. $1 .... *Keen.*
Shumard, B: Franklin. *See* Texas geol. and agric. survey.
Shunk, W: F. Practical treatise on railway curves and locations. (cop. '54.) '65. 5th ed. 12°. '73. $2 .... *Baird.*
Shurtleff, C. A. Report on army worm. 8°. '62. pap., 10c. .... *Essex.*
Shurtleff, J. B. Governmental instructor: view of the government of the U. S. and of the state governments; for schools. 3d ed., rev. by D. N. Camp. 12°. '73. hf. bd., 75c. .... *Collins & Bro.*
Shurtleff, Natl. B. Topographical and hist. descript. of Boston; with anc. maps and plans. ('71.) 2d ed., rev. roy. 8°. '72. $5 ... *Lockwood, B. & Co.*
Shuster, W: H. Flute without a master. 8°. '57. pap., 60c. .... *Ditson.*
— Violin without a master. 8°. '57. pap., 60c. *Ditson.*
Shute, S: M. Manual of Anglo-Saxon for beginners. ('67.) 3d ed., rev. and enl. 12°. '75. $1.50 .. *Holt.*
Shuttleworth, Ph. N. Consistency of revelation with itself and with human reason. 18°. 75c. *Harper.*
Shylock. Talfourd, F. 15c. .... *French.*
Shylock: Ethiop. drama. 16°. pap., 15c. .. *Happy.*
Siam, the land of the white elephant. Bacon, G. B. $1.50 .... *Scribner.*
Siamese twins. A'Beckett, G. A. 15c. .... *French.*
Siamese twins. White, C. 15c. .... *De Witt.*
Sibbes, R: Bruised reed and smoking flax; with descript. of Christ. 16°. 75c. .... *Pres.Bd.*
— The Christian's portion; or, the charter of a Christian. 32°. 25c. .... *Pres.Bd.*
Sibley, J: Langdon. Harvard graduates. 8°. '74. $5. *Sever.*
Sibree, Marie. *See* Hall, Marie.
Sibson, Alfr. Agricultural chemistry; with pref. by A. Voelcker. 16°. bds., 75c. .... *Routledge.*
Sibyl and her live snowball. ill. 4°. $1 ... *Am.Bapt.*
Sibylle. *See* Story of Sibylle.
Sibylline oracles; or, dreams and their interpretations. 32°. pap., 25c. .... *U.P.James.*
Sibyl's (The) cave. Bache, A. 25c.; 10c. ... *U.P.James.*
Sichere Compass (Der). 12°. '72. $1; $1.25 .. *Ev.Assoc.*
Sichere Weg (Der) zum Himmel. 24°. 70c.; leath., $1 .... *Benziger.*
Sick calls. Price, E. 75c.; $1.25 .... *Sadlier.*
Sick room devotions. Engles, W. M. 30c. ... *Pres.Bd.*
Sickels, Dan. Freemason's monitor. 32°. '64. $1; $1.50 .... *Macoy.*
— *Same.* ('64.) New ed. 32°. '76. $1; $1.50 .. *Clark & M.*
— — *See also* Macoy, R., *and* Sickels, D.
— General ahiman rezon and Freemason's guide. ill. 12°. '65. $2; mor., $3.50 .. *Macoy; Masonic; Redding.*
Sickels, H. E. *See* New York State, Court of Appeals reports.
Sickles, Dan. E. Trial of D. E. Sickles for shooting Philip Barton Key. 8°. pap., 50c. .... *De Witt.*
Sickness: its trials and blessings. 16°. '69. $1.50 .. *Pott.*
Sickness improved. 18°. 55c. .... *Am.S.S.*
Sidgwick, H: Methods of ethics. 8°. '74. $4. *Macmillan.*
Sidney, Edn. Field and fold: popular exposition of science of agriculture; rev. by T. O. Summers. ('56.) 3d ed. 18°. '75. 50c. .... *So.Meth.*
— Philosophy of food and nutrition in plants and animals. 12°. '50. 75c. .... *Meth.Bk.Conc.*
Sidney, *Sir* Ph. Arcadia; ed. with notes by J. H. Friswell. 16°. $3 .... *Scribner, W. & A.*
— Miscellaneous works; with life and notes by W. Grey. 8°. '60. $2.50. — ill. 8°. hf. mor., $3.50; mor., $6 .... *Burnham.*
Sidney, S: Book of the horse: encyclopædia on every subject connected with horses, carriages and stable management. 25 col. pl. and 100 wood eng. demy 4°. $15 .... *Cassell.*
— Pig (The): selecting, breeding, feeding and fattening. ill. 16°. bds., 50c. .... *Routledge.*
Sidney De Grey. Wise, D. $1.25 ...... *H.A. Young.*
Sidney Elliott. Nauman, M. D. $1.50; $1 .. *Claxton.*
Sidney Grey. Keary, A. 75c. ...... *Carter; Dutton.*
Sidonia, the sorceress. Meinhold, J. W. $1 .. *Harper.*
Siebe, H: Conquest of the sea. ill. 12°. $2 .. *Routledge.*
Sieben Erzählungen. *See* Schmid, C. v.
Sieben weisen Meister (Die). 12°. pap., 25c. ... *Radde.*
Sieber, Fd. Art of singing; tr., with add. of an orig. chapter on hygiene of the voice, by F. Seeger. 8°. '72. $1.50 .... *Pond.*
Siebold, C: Thdr. Ern. v. Anatomy of the invertebrata; tr., with add. and notes, by W. J. Burnett. 8°. '54. $5 .... *Jas. Campbell.*
Siebold, Ph. Fz. v. *See* Manners and customs of the Japanese.
Siefert, H. O. R. Liederbuch f. christl. Schulen. 12°. bds., 40c. .... *Brumder.*
Siege of Belgrade. Cobb, J. 15c. .... *French.*

Siege of Colchester. Townsend, G. F. $1.25... *Pott.*
Siege of Rochelle: opera. 16°. pap., 15c.... *French.*
Siege of Spoleto. McCaffery, M. J. A. 75c.; $1. *O'Shea.*
Siemens, C. W: Fuel; [also] Value of artificial fuels as compared with coal, by J. Wormald. 18°. '73. bds., 50c. ... *Van Nostrand.*
Siena. Swinburne, A. C. 25c. ... *Lippincott.*
Sieveking, E: H: Medical adviser in life assurance. 12°. '74. $2.25 ... *Lindsay.*
— *See also* Jones, C. H., *and* Sieveking, E. H.
Sighart, J. *See* Vinci, L. da.
Sights afoot. *See* Collins, Wilkie.
Sights and insights. Warren, H. W. $1.25. *Meth. Bk. Conc.*
Sights and insights. Whitney, A. D. T. $3.. *Osgood.*
Sights and sensations in Europe. Browne, J. H. *$3; $3.50; $4.50... *Am. Pub.*
Sights and sensations in France, Germany and Switzerland. Buffum, E. G. $1.50... *Harper.*
Sights at a peep show. *See* Cupples, *Mrs.* A. J.
Sigillologia. Didymus, I. 25c. ...(?) *Kewand.*
Siglar, H. W. Practical English grammar based on progressive exercises by use of symbols. ('74.) New ed. 12°. '76. bds., 75c. ... *Holt.*
Sign of affection: comic drama. 16°. pap., 15c. *Happy.*
Sign of the cross in the 19th cent. Gaume, J. J. $1.50. *Cunningham.*
Signa. La Rame, L. de. $2... *Lippincott.*
Signa die Seterin. Mügge, T. 40c. ... *Holt.*
Signal lights. 12°. '71. $1.25... *Randolph.*
Signal Office. *See* United States.
Signet of King Solomon. *See* Arnold, A. C. L.
Signet ring. De Liefde, J. $1.25... *Lothrop.*
Signs and symbols. *See* Oliver, G.
Signs before death: record of strange apparitions, remark. dreams, etc. 16°. $1.75.. *Scribner, W. & A.*
Signs of the times. Bunsen, C. C. J. $1.50.. *Harper.*
Signs of the times. Hastings, H. L. $1... *Hastings.*
Sigourney, *Mrs.* Lydia Howard. Boy's book. 18°. 60c. ... *Carter.*
— Child's book. sq. 16°. 50c. ... *Carter.*
— Daily counsellor. [Poetry.] 12°. $1.50. *Brown & G.*
— Faded hope. 18°. 75c. ... *Carter.*
— Girl's book. 18°. 60c. ... *Carter.*
— Letters of life. 12°. $2; hf. cf., $4.—(chp. ed.), $1.50 ... *Appleton.*
— Letters to mothers. 12°. $1.50... *Harper.*
— Letters to young ladies. 12°. $1.50... *Harper.*
— Lucy Howard's journal. 12°. $1.25... *Harper.*
— Margaret and Henrietta. ill. 18°. '52. 25c... *Am. Tr.*
— Myrtis, and other sketchings. 12°. $1.50.. *Harper.*
— Olive leaves. 18°. 75c. ... *Carter.*
— Past meridian. [Poetry.] 12°. $1.50.. *Brown & G.*
— Pocahontas, and other poems. ill. 12°. $1.25; $1.75. *Harper.*
— Poems; [also] Poems, by Mrs. C. Norton. ill. 16°. $1.12; $1.35.—32°. 85c.; $1.12.... *World Pub.*
— Select poems. ill. 12°. $1.75; $2... *J. E. Potter.*
— Voice of flowers. 32°. *net*, 19c. ... *Hamersley.*
— Water drops. 18°. 75c. ... *Carter.*
— Weeping willow. 32°. *net*, 19c. ... *Hamersley.*
— Whisper to a bride. 16°. *net*, 75c.; $1.67.. *Hamersley.*
Sigston, Ja. Memoir of life and ministry of W: Bramwell; with extracts from his correspondence; rev. by T. O. Summers. ('55.) 3d ed. '75. 75c. *So. Meth.*
Sihler, W. Evangelien Predigten. roy. 8°. $2.50; hf. mor., $3 ... *Siemon.*
— Gedanken eines Lutheraners beim Herannahen d. 100jähr. Gedächtnissfeier des nord-am. Staatenbundes. 8°. 15c. ... *Barthel.*

Sikes, Wirt. One poor girl: the story of thousands. 12°. $1.50 ... *Lippincott.*
Sikes, *Mrs.* Wirt. *See* Logan, Olive.
Silabario castellano, para los niños. 18°. '56. 20c.; — para las ninãs. 18°. '56. 20c.... *Kelly, P. & Co.*
Silas Marner. *See* Eliot, G:
Silas Narrow's lesson. *See* Todd, J:
Silber, W: B. Elementary grammar of the Lat. language. 12°. '69. 63c. ... *Barnes.*
— Latin reader; with epitome of grammar, notes, etc. 12°. '67. $1.25... *Barnes.*
— Progressive lessons in Greek. 12°. $1.25.. *Appleton.*
Silberstein, A: Glänzende Bahnen; [also] Die Sonne bringt es an den Tag. 2 v. 8°. ea., pap., 50c. *Morwitz.*
Silcote of Silcote's. *See* Kingsley, H:
Silence and voices of God. *See* Farrar, F. W.
Silence of Scripture. Wharton, F. $1... *Dutton.*
Silent comforter. Hopkins, L. P. 25c.; 40c.; $1. *Lothrop.*
Silent comforter ser. 4 v. 24°. $1. 16°. $1.60.. *Lothrop.*
Cont.: Silent comforter.—Attractions of heaven.—Words of peace.—Voices of comfort.
Silent hour. Friswell, J. H. $3.... *Scribner, W. & A.*
Silent hunter. St. John, P. B. 20c. ... *Beadle.*
Silent musings. Waldron, S. D. 60c. ... *So. Meth.*
Silent partner. Phelps, E. S. $1.50; $3.... *Osgood.*
Silent protector. Williams, T. J. 15c. *De Witt; French.*
Silent struggles. Stephens, A. S. $1.75; $1.50. *Peterson.*
Silent system. Williams, T. J. 15c. ... *French.*
Silent Tom. Edson, N. I. $1.75... *Lothrop.*
Silent witness. Yates, E. $1.50; 75c. ... *W. F. Gill.*
Silent woman. Lacy, T. H. 15c.... *De Witt; French.*
Silhouettes and songs. *See* Hind, H. M.
Silk apron. *See* Baker, *Mrs.* H. N. W.
Silken fetters. Buckingham, L. 15c. ... *French.*
Sill, J. M. B. Synthesis of the Eng. sentence: element. grammar on the synthetic method. New ed., rev. and enl. 16°. '63. bds., 75c... *Ivison.*
Silliman, B: *jr.* First principles of chemistry. ill. 8°. '52. $2... *Ivison.*
— Principles of physics of natural philosophy. ill. 8°. '60. $3.50 ... *Ivison.*
Silloway, T: W. Text-book of carpentry. 12°. $1.50. *Nichols & H.*
Silsbee, *Mrs.* — (*ed.*) Memory and hope: collection of consolatory pieces. 8°. mor., $7.... *Osgood.*
— Willie Winkie's nursery rhymes of Scotland. 16°. $1.25 ... **Osgood.*
Silsbee, S. Death, the devil and the doctor on the war. 16°. '62. 50c. ... *Wilstach.*
Silver, Abiel. Holy Word (The) in its own defence. 8°. 75c. ... *H. H. Carter.*
— *Same.* 12°. $1... *Appleton.*
— Lecture on symbolic character of Scriptures. 8°. 75c. ... *H. H. Carter.*
— *Same.* 12°. $1... *Appleton.*
— Rationality of the Christian religion. 8°. 75c. *H. H. Carter.*
Silver, Ednah C. *See* Phelps, J. R., *and* Silver, E. C.
Silver and pewter; or, life in N. Y. 8°. pap., 50c. *Peterson.*
Silver barrel lib. 3 v. ill. 12°. $3... *Routledge.*
Cont.: Little silver barrel.—Dorothy's story-book.—Happy hours at Wynford.
Silver bell. Butler, C. 50c. ... *Gordon.*
Silver buckle. 18°. 18c. ... *Am. S. S.*
Silver carols. Leslie, J. H., *and* Ogden, W. A. 50c. *W. W. Whitney.*
Silver casket. 18°. 45c. ... *Cong. Pub.*
Silver casket. *See* Tucker, *Mrs.* Ctte.

Silver castle. Wilmer, M. E. $1.25...... *Nat. Temp.*

Silver chime. Root, G. F. 60c.; 30c.; 35c... *Gordon.*

Silver chord: songs, ballads, etc., with piano-forte accomp. 4°. '62. $3; $4; bds., $2.50.... *Ditson.*

Silver clarion. Shryock, D. 45c........... *Church.*

Silver cord. Brooks, C. S. $2; $1.50...... *Harper.*

Silver cord lib. 4 v. ill. 18°. $2........... *Nelson.*
Cont.: Spare well, spend well. — Strive and thrive. — Our Father. — Power of kindness.

Silver cup. *See* Guernsey, C. F.

Silver dollar, and what a little boy did with it. 18°. 35c.............................. *Am. S. S.*

Silver Grange; [also] Phillipine. 18°. '66. 50c. *Cunningham.*

Silver keys. Tucker, C. 75c........ *Carter; Dutton.*

Silver lake. Ballantyne, R. M. $1.. *Scribner, W. & A.*

Silver lake ser. 4 v. 12°. $5............. *Nat. Temp.*
Cont.: Humpy Dumpy, by J. J. Dana. — Fred's hard fight, by M. Howard. — Mr. Mackenzie's answer, by F. Huntington. — Packington parish, by M. A. Paull.

Silver lake ser. *See* Baker, *Mrs.* H. N. W.

Silver lake stories. Bradford, S. H. 6 v. $3.60. *Hurd & H.*

Silver lib. *See* Guernsey, C. F.

Silver lining. Buckingham, L. 15c. .... *French.*

Silver lining. Flint, S. A. $1.25 .... *Cong. Pub.*

Silver lute. Root, G. F. 50c.............. *Church.*

Silver penny ser. 6 v. 18°. $3.............. *Sheldon.*
Cont.: Sunny-eyed Tim. — Child life in India. — Princess Narina. — Theda and the mountain. — Patty Williamson's voyage. — Nobody's child, etc.

Silver pitchers. Alcott, L. M. $1.25 .... *Roberts.*

Silver rifle. *See* Guernsey, C. F.

Silver sands. Crampton, G. E. E. $1.50 ... *Lothrop.*

Silver shilling. *See* Andersen, H. C.

Silver song (New). *See* Ogden, W. A.

Silver sounds. [Music.] 4°. $3; $4; bds., $2.. *Church.*

Silver spoon. 18°. 60c.................. *Cong. Pub.*

Silver spray. Doane, W. H. 40c. .... *Church.*

Silver spray lib. 5 v. 16°. $5............ *Cong. Pub.*
Cont.: Minister's wife. — Blind Graham, by S. A. Perry. — Auntie's secret, by J. H. Means. — Double fault, by M. R. Yatem. — Ring and its motto, by C. A. Means.

Silver threads. McKeever, H. B. $1.50..... *Claxton.*

Silver threads of song. Millard, H. 60c..... *Gordon.*

Silver trumpet. 16°. 50c. .... *Scribner, W. & A.*

Silver wings. Converse, C. C. 35c.; 30c..... *Ditson.*

Silver wreath: songs, ballads, etc., with piano forte accomp. 4°. '66. $3; $4; bds., $2.50... *Ditson.*

Silverbeach lib. 4 v. 16°. '72. $3.50.. *Meth. Bk. Conc.*
Cont.: Silverbeach. — Rachel Cardingford's book. — Laying the keel. — Junior clerk.

Silvermere stories. 5 v. 18°. $2.50 ... (?) *Martien.*
Cont.: Buy an orange, sir? — More ways than one. — Witless Willie. — Making the best of it. — Mary and Frank.

Silverpen (*pseud.*) *See* Meteyard, Eliza.

Silversmith, Jul. Practical handbook for miners, metallurgists and assayers. 4th ed., rev. and enl. ill. 12°. '67. $3................ *Van Nostrand.*

Silversmith of Jerusalem; by author of "Asa and his family." 18°. 75c.................. *Pres. Bd.*

Silverstone's wager. Andrews, R. R. 15c.... *Lee & S.*

Silvertone lib. 4 v. ill. 18°. '67. $2.25.. *Meth. Bk. Conc.*
Cont.: Brook Silvertone, by E. Marshall. — Lost lilies. — Grace Hall. — Little Harry's troubles.

Silvervale, Lumina (*pseud.*) *See* Suddorth, *Mrs.* H. A. B.

Silvia. Kavanagh, J. 75c................ *Appleton.*

Simcoe, G. A. Poems and romances. cr. 8°. $1.75. *Routledge.*

Sime, Ja. History of Germany. ('74.) New ed. 16°. '75. $1.............................. *Holt.*

Sime, W: History of the Covenanters in Scotland. 2 v. 18°. $1.40 .... *Pres. Bd.*

— History of the inquisition. 18°. 60c....... *Pres. Bd.*

Simeon, C: Beauty and excellency of the Liturgy. 2d Am. ed. 18°. '31. 18c. .... *I. N. Whiting.*

Simeon Green; or, the man that killed his neighbours with that potent weapon "kindness." 18°. 30c. *Am. S. S.*

Similitudes. Larcom, L. 65c................ *Hoyt.*

Simmonds, P: L. Coffee and chicory: culture, chemical composition, preparation for market, etc. ill. and por. 8°. '64. 75c................ *Spon.*

— Commercial dictionary of trade products, commercial, manufacturing and technical terms. fp. 8°. hf. bd., $2......................... *Routledge.*

Simmons, C: Scripture manual; to facilitate finding of proof texts. 12°. '45. $1.75............. *Dodd.*

Simmons, H. E. Glad tidings. ill. sm. 4°. '72. bds., 50c. .... *Am. Tr.*

Simmons, Ja. A. Digest of Wisconsin Sup. Court reports (1842–'74). 2 v. 8°. shp., $14..... *Gould.*

Simmons, Ja. P. War in heaven: disquisition, biblical and rational, conc. angels, devils and men, and the creation, fall and redemption of the human soul. 8°. '70. $1.50 .... *Claxton.*

Simms, F: W. Treatise on principles and practice of levelling. 5th Lond. ed., with Law's practical examples for setting out railway curves. pl. and wood-cuts. 12°. $2.50.......... *Van Nostrand.*

Simms, Jeptha R. Trappers of New York; or, a biography of Nicholas Stoner and Natl. Foster, with anecdotes of other hunters, etc. eng. 12°. '71. $1.50. — New ed. por. and pl. 8°. $3.. *Munsell.*

Simms, W: Gilmore. ["Fk. Cooper."] Works. 17 v. ill. 12°. ea., $1.75; pap., 75c.; per set, $30; hf. cf., $50 .... *Widdleton.*
Cont.: Partisan. — Mellichampe. — Katharine Walton. — Scout. — Woodcraft. — Forayers. — Eutaw. — Guy Rivers. — Richard Hurdis. — Border beagles. — Charlemont. — Beauchamp. — Confession. — The Yemassee. — Vasconselos. — Southward ho! — Wigwam and the cabin.

— Poems, dramatic, legendary and contemplative. 2 v. por. 12°. $3; hf. cf., $6............ *Widdleton.*

— Count Julien. 8°. pap., 75c............... *Dick & F.*

— Life of Capt. John Smith, founder of Virginia. ill. 12°. $1.75 .... *J. E. Potter.*

— Life of Chevalier Bayard. ill. 12°. $1.50.. *Harper.*

Simon, J: Filth diseases and their prevention. 16°. '76. $1.......................... *Jas. Campbell.*

Simon. *See* Sand, G.

Simon, the rebel. *See* Malan, C.

Simon Lee. Pitt, G. D. 15c................ *French.*

Simon Martin. Grosvenor, H. S. $1........... *Hoyt.*

Simon Menno. *See* Menno, Simon.

Simon Peter and Simon Magus. Franco, J. J. $1.50. *Cunningham.*

Simon Snodgrass. *See* Snipsnaps and snickerings of.

Simon Suggs. *See* Hooper, J. J.

Simonde de Sismondi, J: C: L. Historical view of literature of the south of Europe; tr., with notes by T. Roscoe. 2 v. 12°. $2.75; hf. cf., $6.25. *Harper.*

— *Same.* 2 v. 12°. (Bohn.) ea., $1.25.... *Little, B. & Co.*

— *Same.* 2 v. 12°. (Bohn.) ea., $1.40.. *Scribner, W. & A.*

— *Same.* 2 v. 12°. (Bohn.) ea., $1.50 ...... *Lippincott.*

— History of the Italian republics: view of rise, progress and fall of Ital. freedom; tr. 12°. 75c. *Harper.*

Simonds, W: ["Wa. Aimwell."] Aimwell stories. 7 v. ill. 16°. $8.75; ea., $1.25 .... *Miller.*
Cont.: Clinton. — Ella. — Jerry. — Jessie. — Marcus. — Oscar. — Whistler.

— Boys' own guide. 16°. $1.25............ *Cong. Pub.*

Simonds, W: Edg. Law of design patents: decisions of U. S. courts, cases in patent office, with digest of points decided and treatise. ill. 8°. *net*, shp., $4.50 .... *Baker, V. & Co.*

Simonds, W: Edg., *continued.*
— Manual of patent laws; with app. upon the sale of patents. 12°. '74. hf. shp., $2.50.. *G. W. Smith.*
Simonné, Thdr. Treatise on French verbs. 12°. 75c. *Appleton.*
— *See also* Ollendorff, H. G.;—Velásquez de la Cadena, M., *and* Simonné, T.
Simons, Ez. D. Divine pictures of the Christian centuries. 16°. '75. $1.25 .... *W. H. Young.*
Simons, J: W. Beauseant (The): manual for Knights Templar. 12°. '74. $1.50 ..... *Macoy; Sickles.*
— Book of the commandery: monitor for the orders of Masonic knighthood. 32°. 75c.; $1. *Masonic; Redding.*
— Comparison of Egyptian symbols with those of the Hebrews; tr. by F. Portal. 12°. '75. $1.. *Masonic.*
— Familiar treatise on principles and practice of Masonic jurisprudence. por. 12°. '64. $1.50.... *Macoy.*
— Knights Templars' manual. 12°. $1.50... *Masonic.*
Simons, M. Laird (*ed*). Sunday half hours with the great preachers; with biog. notices and index. 8°. '71. $3.75; $4.50; $4.75; mor., $6..... *Porter.*
— *See also* Bible [Whole].
Simonson, L. (*ed*). Deutsches Balladenbuch. With biog. sketches, introd. and notes. ('65.) New ed., rev. 12°. '75. $1.50.................... *Holt.*
Simonton, A. G. Os sacramentos. 12°. 15c... *Pres. Bd.*
Simonton, C: H., *and* Conner, Ja. Digest of So. Carolina equity reports (1780–1856). 8°. '57.. *State.*
Simple addition and nursery jingles. [Toy-book.] ill. 8°. $1........................ (?) *McLoughlin.*
Simple cobler of Aggawam in America. Ward, N. $1. *Sabin.*
Simple conversations. 45c............. (?) *Luth. Pub.*
Simple flower. 18°. 25c........... *Scribner, W. & A.*
Simple flower. *See* Tonna, *Mrs.* C. E.
Simple lessons. Parker, J. M. 35c.; 40c.... *Dutton.*
Simple rhymes. *See* Thomas and Ellen.
Simple Scripture biographies. 18°. 50c. .... *Am. S. S.*
Simple stories. 18°. 55c.................... *Am. S. S.*
Simple stories. *See* Simple stories lib.
Simple stories for children. 18°. 35c. .... *Routledge.*
— *See also* Moss wreath lib.
Simple stories lib. 5 v. ill. 16°. $2.50.... *Routledge.*
Cont.: Simple stories. — Happy recovery. — Young orator. — Three friends. — Gratitude and probity.
Simple stories with odd pictures; or, evening amusements for little ones. 16°. '70. 75c. *Meth. Bk. Conc.*
Simple story. Inchbald, E. 50c............ *Harper.*
Simple Susan. *See* Edgeworth, Mar.
Simple tales. *See* Little Alice's lib.
Simple truths spoken to working people. Macleod, N. $1.25............................ *Routledge.*
Simpleton. *See* Reade, C:
Simplicitie's defence against seven-headed policy. *See* Gorton, S.
Simplicity and fascination. Beale, A. $1.50.. *Loring.*
Simpson, A. L. Pioneers of the world's progress; or, illustrious pathfinders for the human race. ill. 12°. $2.............................. *Nelson.*
Simpson, E: Ordnance and naval gunnery; comp. as a text-book for U. S. Naval Acad. 5th ed., rev. and enl. ill. 8°. '71. $5........ *Van Nostrand.*
Simpson, H: *and* Canterbury, Ira. Union drum and fife book. obl. 8°. '62. pap., 75c....... *Ditson.*
Simpson, J. Palgrave. [Plays.] 19 v. 16°. ea., pap., 15c............................ *French.*
Cont.: Appearances: comedy. — Atrocious criminal: farce. — Court cards. — Dreams of delusion. — Fair pretender. — First affections: comedietta. — Heads or tails: comedietta. — Jack in a box: comedietta.— Marco Spada.— Matrimonial prospectuses: farce. — Only a clod: comic drama. — Poor cousin Walter. — School for coquettes: comedietta. — Scrap of paper. — Second love: comic drama. — Serpent on the hearth. — Sybilla. — Very suspicious: comedietta. — Without incumbrances: farce.

Simpson, J. Palgrave, *continued.*
— Only a clod: comic drama. 16°. pap., 15c... *Lee & S.*
— *and* Dale, Fel. Time and hour: drama. 16°. pap., 15c......................... *De Witt; French.*
— *and* Wray, C. Ranelagh: drama. 16°. pap., 15c. *French.*
— *and* Yates, E. Black sheep: drama. 16°. pap., 15c. *De Witt; French.*
Simpson, Ja. H. Shortest route to California: explorations of great basin of Utah, and some account of the Indian tribes. map. 12°. $1.50.. *Lippincott.*
Simpson, *Sir* Ja. Y. Anæsthesia, hospitalism, etc.; ed. by Sir W. Simpson. 8°. $3; shp., $4.. *Appleton.*
— Diseases of women; ed. by A. Simpson. 8°. $3; shp., $4.......................... *Appleton.*
— History of modern anæsthetics: reply to J. Bigelow's second letter. 8°. '72. pap., 25c. *Jas. Campbell.*
— Obstetric memoirs and contributions; ed. by W. O. Priestley and H. R. Storer. 2 v. 8°. '56. $7.50; shp., $9.......................... *Lippincott.*
— Selected obstetrical and gynæcological works; ed. by J. W. Black. 8°. $3; shp., $4.... *Appleton.*
Simpson, Jos. Cairn. Horse portraiture: breeding and management of horses. post 8°. $3.. *Woodward.*
Simpson, M. Resurrection of the dead. *See* Mattison, H.
Simpson, M. C. M. *See* Michelet, M., Summary of modern history.
Simpson, Rob. Traditions of the Covenanters; or, gleanings among the mountains. 3 v. 18°. 1st ser., 55c.; 2d ser., 65c.; 3d ser., 60c... *Pres. Bd.*
Simpson, W. Picturesque people of the world: 18 chromo-lith. pl. and descriptive letter press. 4°. $20 .... *Cassell.*
Simpson, W. H. *See* Burlinson, H., *and* Simpson, W. H.
Simpson, W: Epitome of the history of the Christian church. 5th ed. fp. 8°. $1........ *Macmillan.*
Simpson and Co. Poole, J. 15c........... *French.*
Simrall, G. H. *See* Mississippi, Law reports.
Sims, J. Marion. Anniversary discourse: silver sutures in surgery. 8°. '57. pap., 50c... *N. Y. Acad. Med.*
— Clinical notes on uterine surgery; with special ref. to management of the sterile condition. ill. 8°. $4................................ *W. Wood.*
Sin and its consequences. Manning, H. E. $1.. *Sadlier.*
Sin and penalty. Thompson, H. M. 15c..... *Dutton.*
Sin and sorrow. Leslie, H. 15c............ *French.*
Sin as set forth in Holy Scripture. Straffer, G. M. $1. *Dutton.*
Sin found out. *See* Moravian missionaries.
Sinbad, the sailor. ill. f°. pap., 15c.; 20c... *J. E. Potter.*
— *See also* Arabian nights.
Sinclair, Cath. Charlie Seymour. 18°. 50c... *Carter.*
— Flirtations in fashionable life. 12°. $1.75; pap., $1.50............................ *Peterson.*
— Holiday house. 18°. 75c................. *Carter.*
— Jane Bouverie; or, prosperity and adversity. 16°. 60c............................ *McCauley.*
— Modern accomplishments and society. 12°. $1.50. *Carter.*
— Sir Edward Graham; or, railway speculators. [Fiction.] 8°. pap., $1.................. *Harper.*
— Woman in black. 12°. $1.75; pap., $1.50.. *Peterson.*
Sinfulness of American slavery. Elliott, C. 2 v. $2.50 .... *Cin. Meth. Bk. Conc.*
Sinfulness of little sins. *See* Jackson, J:
Sing song. Rossetti, C. G. $1.50.......... *Roberts.*
Sing-u. Betbüchlein f. Kinder ev. luth. Schulen. 12°. '74. 20c. .... *Barthel.*
Singer, Edg. A. Model common school arithmetic. 12°. '76. $1. —Key, *net*, 75c....... *Eldredge.*
— Model element. arithmetic. 12°. '76. 60c. —Key, *net*, 50c............................ *Eldredge.*
— Model mental arithmetic. 16°. '76. bds., 45c. *Eldredge.*

Singer, Edg. A., *continued.*
— Model primary arithmetic. 16°. '76. bds., 30c. *Eldredge.*
— *See also* Fewsmith, W: *and* Singer, E. A.
Singer, O: Landing of the pilgrim fathers; with words of Mrs. F. D. Hemans. [Cantata.] 8°. $1. *Church.*
Singer (The). Seward, T. F. 60c. *Biglow.*
Singers and songs of the church. Miller, J. $4. *Randolph.*
Singers and songs of the liberal faith. Putnam, A. P. $3 *Roberts.*
Singet dem Herrn. Stohlmann, J. F. C. 25c. *Radde.*
Singing bird. Bradbury, W. B. 56c. *Ivison.*
Singing girl. *See* Baker, *Mrs.* H. N. W.
Singing made easy. 12°. pap., 20c. *Hurst.*
Singing pilgrim. Phillips, P. 50c. *Meth. Bk. Conc.*
Singing school. Emerson, L. O. 75c. *Ditson.*
Singing school. Perkins, W. O. 75c. *G. D. Russell.*
Singing school banner. Johnson, A. N. 75c. *Gordon.*
Singing school companion. Bird, J. *and* H. $1. *Ditson.*
Singing school echo. Stewart, N. C., *and* North, J. M. 75c. *Brainard.*
Singing teacher. Everest, C. pt. 1, 25c.; pt. 2, 20c. *Ditson.*
Singing Will. Cousin Anna. 35c. *N. Y. Ref. Ch. Bd.; Pres. Com.*
Single life: comedy. 16°. pap., 15c. *Happy.*
Singleton Fontenoy, R. N. *See* Hannay, J.
Singular creatures. Cupples, A. J. $1.50 *Lee & S.*
Singvögelein (Das). Bickel, P. W. 40c. *Germ. Bapt.*
Siniscalchi, Liborio. Meditations of St. Ignatius; or, the "spiritual exercises" expounded; tr. from the Ital. 12°. '62. $1.50 *Cunningham.*
Sink or swim. Alger, H., *jr.* $1.50 *Loring.*
Sink or swim: comedy. 16°. pap., 15c. *French.*
Sinkler, Wharton. *See* Medical jurisprudence.
Sinless one. Tucker, J. T. $1.25 *Cong. Pub.*
Sinlessness of Jesus. Ullmann, C. $3. *Scribner, W. & A.*
Sinner guided to Christ. Alexander, A. 25c. *Am. Tr.*
Sinner's friend. 18°. 35c. *Carter.*
— *Same.* 18°. '66. 35c. *N. Y. Ref. Ch. Bd.; Pres. Com.*
Sinner's progress. *See* Bunyan, J:
Sinner's Savior; by various authors. 16°. $1.25. *West. Tr.*
Sins of the tongue. Landriot, J. F. $1.50. *Noonan.*
Sins of the tongue; or, truth is everything. 18°. 55c. *Am. S. S.*
Siona. Haas, J. S. 2 v. ea., 75c.; in 1 v., $1.50. *Schäfer.*
Sir Bernard Gaston. Smith, J. F. 75c. *Dick & F.*
Sir Brook Fossbrooke. *See* Lever, C:
Sir Charles Grandison. *See* Richardson, S:
Sir Edward Graham. Sinclair, C. $1 *Harper.*
Sir Genevieve. Chester, S. E. $1.25 *Randolph.*
Sir Guy de Guy. Rattlebrain. $2 *Routledge.*
Sir Harry Hotspur of Humblethwaite. *See* Trollope, A.
Sir Jasper Carew. *See* Lever, C:
Sir Jasper's tenant. Braddon, M. E. 50c. *Dick & F.*
Sir Noel's heir. *See* Fleming, M. A.
Sir Roger de Coverly. Coyne, J. S. 15c. *French.*
Sir Theodore Broughton. James, G. P. R. 50c. *Harper.*
Sir Thomas More. *See* Three dramas.
Sir Victor's choice. Thomas, A. $1 *Routledge.*
Sir Wilfred's seven flights. Chatelaine, *Mme.* — de. $1 *Routledge.*
Siraudin, Pl. Left the stage: farce; tr. 16°. pap., 15c. *French.*
— *and* Thiboust, L. Les femmes qui pleurent: comédie. ('64.) New ed. 12°. '72. pap., 25c. *Holt.*
Siren (A). Trollope, T. A. 50c. *Harper.*
Siska von Roosemael. Conscience, H. 50c. *Strong.*
Sismondi, J: C: L. S. de. *See* Simonde.
Sissy Jupe. *See* Dickens, C:
Sister Alice's stories. 18°. 50c. *Am. S. S.*
Sister and I: drama. 16°. pap., 15c. *French.*
Sister Beatrice. *See* Library of good example.
Sister Eleanor ser. 4 v. 16°. $6 *Lothrop.*
Cont.: Sister Eleanor's brood. — Violet Douglas. — Agnes and her neighbors. — Silver sands.
Sister Eleanor's brood. Phelps, S. B. $1.50. *Lothrop.*
Sister Mary's stories. 18°. 65c. *Am. S. S.*
Sister Patience. 18°. 45c. *Dutton.*
Sister Rose. *See* Collins, Wilkie.
Sister Rose; or, St. Bartholomew's eve. 18°. 75c. *Am. S. S.*
Sister Ruth (*pseud.*) Arithmetic of life; or, the time digits. 18°. 45c. *Pres. Bd.*
Sisterly service. Wooler, J. P. 15c. *De Witt; French.*
Sister's (A) bye-hours. *See* Ingelow, J.
Sister's lib. 4 v. ill. 16°. $4 *Routledge.*
Cont.: Emily Milman. — Carrie Williams. — Happy village. — Forge on the heath.
Sister's offering. 18°. 45c. *Cong. Pub.*
Sister's penance. Taylor, T., *and* Dubourg, A. W. 15c. *French.*
Sister's story. ill. 16°. $1 *Bost. Am. Tr.*
— *See also* Prairie lib.
Sister's story. Craven, A. $2.50 *Cath. Pub.*
Sister's triumph. Boardman, M. M. $1.25. *Perkinpine.*
Sisters. Hofland, B. 50c. *Porter.*
Sisters. Warren, I. P. 80c. *Bost. Am. Tr.*
Sisters; or, reminiscences of a village teacher. 18°. 35c. *Am. S. S.*
Sisters and not sisters. Berry, M. E. 90c. *Am. Tr.*
Sisters Clare; or, preparing for confirmation. 18°. 30c.; pap., 10c. *Dutton.*
Sisters of Charity, *Mt. St. Vincent.* Manual of the children of Mary. 32°. 50c.–$2.50 *Strong.*
— — *See also* Manual.
Sisters of Mercy. Help of Christians: manual of instructions and prayers. 18°. $1.25–$60. *Sadlier.*
— Manual of the queen of angels; with introd. by T. S. Preston. 18°. $1.25–$6 *O'Shea.*
— — *See also* Manual.
Sisters of Notre Dame. Child of Mary: manual of prayers and instructions. 32°. 45c.–$5. *Benziger.*
— Manual of the holy family sodality, Jesus, Mary and Joseph. 32°. 50c.–$1.75 *Benziger.*
— Notre Dame system for the piano. 4°. $2. *Church.*
Sitgreaves, Lor. Report of exped. down Yuni and Colorado Rivers. *See* United States, *Corps of Eng.*
Sitjar, Bonaventure. Vocabulary of lang. of San Antonio Mission, California. 4°. '61. pap., $4. *Shea.*
— — *See also* Shea, J. G., Library of Am. linguistics.
Six boys. Bennett, M. E. $1.25 *Bost. Am. Tr.*
Six cushions. Yonge, C. M. $1 *Lee & S.*
Six days' wonder; or, the world as it was and is. 18°. 65c. *Am. S. S.*
Six degrees of crime. Hill, F. S. 15c. *French.*
Six good dogs. 4°. 50c.; pap., 25c. *Nelson.*
Six hundred dollars a year: a wife's effort at living under high prices. 18°. $1 **Osgood.*
Six hundred easy profitable ways to make money. Draiper, E. S. $1; 50c. *Harpel.*
Six hundred receipts. Marquart, J. $1.75. *J. E. Potter.*
Six in all. Townsend, V. F. $1.25 *Loring.*
Six little princesses. Prentiss, E. 75c.; 50c. *Randolph.*
Six mince pies. *See* Baker, *Mrs.* H. N. W.
Six mitten books. *See* Barrow, *Mrs.* F.

Six months ago. Dale, F. 15c......*De Witt; French.*
Six months hence. *See* Hamilton, *Mrs.* C. V.
Six months in the gold mines. Buffum, E. G. 50c. *Lea.*
Six months in Italy. Hillard, G. S. $2......*Osgood.*
Six months under the red cross with the French army. Boyland, G. H. $1.50..................*Clarke.*
Six nights in a block house. Watson, H. C. $1.75. *J.E.Potter.*
Six nights with the Washingtonians. Arthur, T. S. $3.50; $4.50; $6....................*Peterson.*
Six of one by half a dozen of the other: novelette; by H. B. Stowe, A. D. T. Whitney, L. P. Hale, E. E. Hale, F. B. Perkins and F. W. Loring. 16°. '72. $1.50........................*Roberts.*
Six old English chronicles. *See* Giles, J. A.
Six species of men. Van Evrie, J. H. 10c... *VanEvrie.*
Six steps to honor. Andrews, H. P. $1..*Meth.Bk.Conc.*
Six to sixteen. Ewing, H. J. $1.50.........*Roberts.*
Six weeks in the saddle. Waller, S. E. $1.75. *Macmillan.*
Six years in India. Humphrey, E. J. $1.25. *Meth.Bk.Conc.*
Six years later. *See* Dumas, A.
Sixes: drama. 16°. pap., 15c. ....*French.*
Sixpenny calico. ill. 24°. 25c..........*Perkinpine.*
Sixpenny glass of wine. 18°. 22c. ....*Am.S.S.*
Sixteen string Jack. 8°. pap., 25c. ....*De Witt.*
Sixteen string Jack. Rede, W. L. 15c......*French.*
Sixteen stringed Jack's fight for life. 8°. pap., 25c. *Peterson.*
Sixteen thousand years ago: Ethiop. drama. 16°. pap., 15c. ....*French; Happy.*
Sixtus v., *Pope.* Life and times; tr. by J. F. Meline. 2d ed. 16°. '74. $1 ....*Cath.Pub.*
Sizer, Nelson. Thoughts on domestic life; or, marriage vindicated and free love exposed. 12°. '58. pap., 25c. ....*Wells.*
Skates. Flint, S. A. 75c................*Cong.Pub.*
Skating and sliding. Wood, J. G. 25c....*Routledge.*
Skeat, Wa. W: *See* Plutarch, Shakespeare's Plutarch.
Skeleton leaves and phantom flowers, and how to prepare them. ('64.) New ed. 12°. '76. $2..*Tilton.*
Skeleton witness. Rede, W. L. 15c........*French.*
Skelton, J: Poems. 3 v. 18°. $3........*Osgood.*
Skeptic refuted and Bible vindicated. 18°. 75c. *Cong.Pub.*
Skertchly, J. A. Melinda, the caboceer; or, sport in Ashanti: tale of the gold coast. 12°. $1.75. *Appleton.*
Sketch book. Smith, W. C. $1.25...*Meth.Bk.Conc.*
Sketch book. *See* Irving, Wash.
Sketch of the founders of Salem and the First Church. 8°. '56. pap., 15c..........................*Essex.*
Sketch of my friend's family. 18°. 35c.....*Am.S.S.*
Sketches abroad with pen and pencil. Darley, F. O. C. $2.50; $3; $5 ....*Hurd & H.*
Sketches and adventures in Madeira, Portugal and the Andalusias of Spain; by author of "Daniel Webster and his contemporaries." ill. 12°. $1.50. *Harper.*
Sketches and rambles. Headley, J. T. $1.50..*Scribner.*
Sketches and skeletons of 500 sermons; by author of "Pulpit cyclopædia." 8°. $2.50.....*Appleton.*
Sketches and stories. 32°. 20c.; 15c.......*Dutton.*
Sketches by Boz. *See* Dickens, C:
Sketches for the fireside. Edwards, T. *$2.50..*Case.*
Sketches for the fireside. Phillips, R. 75c...*Claxton.*
Sketches for my Sabbath school class. Phelps, L. 50c. ....*Cong.Pub.*
Sketches for you. 18°. 40c. ....*Cong.Pub.*
Sketches for you. Egliseau, S. S. 70c. ...*Pres.Bd.*
Sketches for the young. Belcher, J. 40c. ..*Am.Tr.*
Sketches for the young. House, E. 60c. *Cin.Meth.Bk.Conc.*
Sketches for youth. *See* Malan, C.
Sketches from the Bible: account of creation and fall of man; adapted to infant minds. 18°. 30c.*Am.S.S.*
Sketches from life. Belcher, J. 3 v. ea., $1.50..*Am.Tr.*
Sketches from the study of an itinerant. Stevens, A. 90c. ....*Cin.Meth.Bk.Conc.*
Sketches from Venetian history. Smedley, E. 2 v. $1.50...................................*Harper.*
Sketches in France. *See* Dumas, A.
Sketches in India. Morton, T. 15c. ....*French.*
Sketches of character; for admonition and improvement of S.-school teachers. 18°. 40c...*Am.S.S.*
Sketches of Christian life in England. Charles, E. $1.75.....................................*Nelson.*
Sketches of creation. Winchell, A. $2....*Harper.*
Sketches of home life. 18°. 45c...........*Am.S.S.*
Sketches of illustrious soldiers. Wilson, J. G. $2.25. *Putnam.*
Sketches of incidents and adventures in the west. ill. imp. 8°. pap., 25c.................*U.P.James.*
Sketches of the Irish bar. Sheil, R. L. 2 v. $3; $6. *Widdleton.*
Sketches of Irish character. *See* Hall, A. M.
Sketches of Irish soldiers in every land. 12°. $1..*McGee.*
Sketches of Jewish life. Gersoni, H. 75c....*Bloch.*
Sketches of life and character. Arthur, T. S. $1.75. *J.E.Potter.*
Sketches of my childhood. *See* Little Fan's lib.
Sketches of my school days. 18°. 50c. ..*Cong.Pub.*
Sketches of pioneer history. Hildreth, S. P. $1. *Meth.Bk.Conc.*
Sketches of representative men, north and south. *See* Rogers, A. C.
Sketches of a superannuate. Lewis, D. $1.25. *Cin.Meth.Bk.Conc.*
Sketches of Virginia. Foote, W. H. $2....*Claxton.*
Sketches of the Waldenses. 18°. 50c......*Am.S.S.*
Sketching from nature in pencil and water colors and crayon drawing. 12°. 50c.............*Haney.*
Sketchley, Arth. (*pseud.*) *See* Rose, G:
Skey, F: C. Operative surgery. ill. 8°. $3.25..*Lea.*
Skidmore, Wa. A. Revised statutes of U. S. rel. to mineral lands and mining resources, with instructions of Gen. Land Office, digest of decisions of Dept. of Interior, and opinions of attorneys general; with special statutes rel. to mining forms and index. 8°. $1.50.............*S. Whitney.*
Skildringar och berättelser. no. 1: Hans, som kom till folkhögskolan. 15c..............*Engberg.*
Skillful housewife. Abell, L. G. 75c.........*Judd.*
Skinner, Dolphus. Episcopalianism considered in five letters from a father to a daughter. 16°. pap., 25c. ....*Williamson.*
Skinner, H. N. Monthly wages table. obl. 16°. '74. leath., 75c..........................(?)*Skinner.*
Skinner, Ht. H. Oneida Community cook-book; or, a dinner without meat. 16°. pap., 25c...*Oneida.*
Skinner, J. O. *See* Universalist register and almanac.
Skinner, J. Ralston. Key to Hebrew-Egyptian mystery in source of measures, originating British inch and anc. cubit. 8°. '75. $5............*Clarke.*
Skinner, J: Stuart. *See* Farmer's barn book.
Skinner, Jos. J. Principles of approximate computations. 16°. '76. $1.25 ....*Holt.*
Skinner, Orrin. Issues of American politics. cr. 8°. $2.25 ....*Lippincott.*

Skinner, Otis Ainsworth. Family worship: reflections and prayers for domestic devotion. 18°. '43. 65c. . . . . *Universalist.*
— Letters on moral and religious duties of parents. 18°. '43. 50c. . . . . *Universalist.*
— Sermons in defense of the doctrine of universal salvation. 18°. '42. 65c. . . . . *Universalist.*
Skinner, T: Stock exchange year-book. demy 8°. $2.50 . . . . *Cassell.*
Skinner, T: H. Discussions in theology. 12°. '68. $1.50. . . . . *Randolph.*
— Hints to Christians. 32°. '54. pap., 10c. . . *Randolph.*
Skirmishes and sketches. Dodge, M. A. $1.50. . *Estes.*
Skirmishing. Jenkin, C. $1.25. . . . . *Holt.*
Skitt. *See* Fisher's River.
Slack, Ja. H. Practical trout culture. ill. 12°. $1.50. *Woodward.*
Slack, W. L. Reasons for becoming a Baptist. 18°. pap., 10c. . . . . *So. Bapt.*
Slade, Dan. D. Diphtheria, its nature and treatment; with hist. of its prevalence in various countries. roy. 12°. $1.25 . . . . *Lea.*
Slade, F: J. Wear of rails as affected by their quality; [with] app. by F. A. Childs on comparative value of rails of different quality. ill. 8°. '75. pap., 25c. . . . . *R.R. Gazette.*
Slade, W: *See* Vermont, Sup. Court reports.
Slafter, Edm. F. Discourse before the N. E. Hist. Geneal. Soc., Mar. 18, 1870, on [its] 25th anniversary; with proceedings and app. por. 8°. '70. $1 . . . . *N.E. Hist. Gen.*
Slang and vulgar phrases and forms: coll. of objectionable words, inaccurate terms, colloquialisms, etc. 12°. pap., 15c. . . . . *Hurst.*
Slang dictionary, etymological, historical and anecdotal. ill. 12°. $3.25 . . . . *Routledge.*
Slasher and Crasher. Morton, J. M. 15c. . . . . *French.*
Slater, J. W. Manual of colors and dye wares; their properties, applications, valuations, impurities and sophistications. 12°. $3.75. . . . . *Baird.*
Slater, W: Original draught of the primitive church; in answer to "Inquiry into constitution, etc., of primitive church." roy. 12°. '33. $1. *I.N. Whiting.*
Slaughter, Ph. History of St. George's Parish, Spotsylvania Co., Virginia. 8°. '47. pap., $3. *Slaughter.*
— Man and woman; or, law of honor applied to solution of problem, Why are so many more women than men, Christians? with introd. by A. T. Bledsoe. 18°. '60. $1. . . . . *Slaughter.*
— Virginian history of African colonization. 8°. '56. $1 . . . . *Slaughter.*
Slaughter, W. B. Modern genesis: inquiry into credibility of nebular theory of origin of planetary bodies, structure of solar system, and of general cosmical history. 16°. '76. $1. . . *Meth. Bk. Conc.*
Slaughter, W: Missionary work. 18°. 25c. *Un. B. Pub.*
Slave: opera. 16°. pap., 15c. . . . . *French.*
Slave dealer. Sadler, S. W. 50c. . . . . *Pott.*
Slave, serf and the freeman: story of early Eng. history. ill. 12°. $1.50. . . . . *Nelson.*
Slave stories. 16°. 60c. . . . . *West. Tr.*
Slaveholder abroad. *See* Jones, P.
Slaver's adventures on sea and land. Thomes, W. H. $1.50 . . . . *Lee & S.*
Slaves of the ring. *See* Robinson, F. W.
Slavonic fairy tales. Naaké, J. T. $1.75. . *Routledge.*
Sleep walker. *See* Leavitt, A. J.
Sleeper, J: Sherburne. ["Hawser Martingale."] Jack in the forecastle. 12°. '60. $1.75. . . *Nichols & H.*
— Mark Rowland: sea story. 12°. $1.25. . . . . *Loring.*
— Tales of the ocean. 12°. $1.50 . . . . *Locke.*

Sleeper, J: Sherburne, *continued.*
— Wonderful adventures on the ocean. 12°. $1.50. *Locke.*
Sleeper, Martha G. Fonthill recreations. 3 v. ill. 16°. '76. $3.75 . . . . *Tibbals.*
Cont.: Mediterranean islands. — Sweden and Norway. — Two Sicilies.
Sleeper, Wa. T. ["Uncle Walter."] Walks and talks; or, Uncle Walter's conversations with the boys. ill. 18°. 50c. . . . . *Bost. Am. T.*
— — *See also* Chip-basket stories.
Sleeping beauty. ill. f°. pap., 15c.; 20c. . . *J.E. Potter.*
Sleeping beauty: burlesque. 16°. pap., 15c. . . *French.*
Sleeping beauty: extravaganza. Keating, E. H. 15c. *French.*
Sleeping beauty in the wood. [Toy-book.] ill. 4°. $1; 50c. . . . . *Routledge.*
Sleeping beauty in the wood. Planché, J. R. $1.75. *Routledge.*
Sleeping draught. Penley, S. 15c. . . . . *French.*
Sleeping hare. Dilley, J. J. 15c. . . . . *French.*
Sleepy forest, and other stories. Conder, E. R. $1.75. *Routledge.*
Sleepy Hollow (Legend of). *See* Irving, Wash.
Sleeth, Asa, *and* Randall, J. W. Holy Spirit, its influence in conversion: debate. 12°. $1. . . . *Chase.*
Sleigh ride. 18°. 60c. . . . . *Cong. Pub.*
Slenker, Elmina Drake. Studying the Bible: brief criticisms on some Script. texts. 12°. 75c. *Mendum.*
Slice of luck. Morton, J. M. 15c. . . *French; Lee & S.*
Slicer, *Mrs.* Adeline E. H. The Brainards at the Rocky Mountains. ill. 16°. '76. $1. . *Meth. Bk. Conc.*
Slicer, H: Baptism: obligation, subjects and mode. 18°. '41. 55c. . . . . *Meth. Bk. Conc.*
Slick, Jona. High life in New York. ill. 12°. $1.75; pap., $1.50. . . . . *Peterson.*
Slick, Sam (*pseud.*) *See* Haliburton, T: C.
Slight mistake. *See* Lacy's home play for ladies.
Slighted treasures. *See* Lacy's home plays for ladies.
Slighted vow. 18°. 17c.; 22c. . . . . *Am. Bapt.*
Slim Jack; or, history of a circus boy. 18°. 40c. *Am. S. S.*
Slingsby, Jona. Freke (*pseud.*) *See* Waller, J: F.
Slip in the fens. (Leis. hour ser.) ill. 16°. '73. $1.25. *Holt.*
Slippers and gown. Etheridge, K. $1.25. . . *Author.*
Slippery paths. Strout, C. W. D. 50c. . . *Hoyt, F. & D.*
Sloan, S: American houses: orig. designs for rural buildings; ill. by 26 eng., with descript. ref. 8°. '61. $2.50. . . . . *Baird.*
— City and suburban architecture: designs and details for public edifices, private residences, etc.; with 131 eng., accomp. by specifications and text. 4°. '59. $15. . . . . *Claxton; Lippincott.*
— Constructive architecture; with glossary. 66 pl. 4°. '59. $9. . . . . *Claxton; Lippincott.*
— Homestead architecture: designs for villas, cottages and farm houses; with essays on style, construction, etc. eng. 8°. $4.50. . . . . *Lippincott.*
— Model architect: designs for cottages, villas, etc. accomp. by specifications, estimates, etc. 2 v. col. pl. imp. 4°. $25. . . . . *Lippincott.*
Sloppy Dingle. Cox, W. N. $1.50. . . . . *Graves.*
Slovenly Kate, and other stories; tr. from the Germ. col. ill. 4°. $2. . . . . *Miller.*
Slovenly Peter; or, cheerful stories and funny pictures for good little folks. ill. 4°. $1.50. . . . . . *Porter.*
Slovenly Peter ser. [Toy-books.] 6 nos. ill. 18°. per gross, $18. . . . . (?) *McLoughlin.*
Cont.: Carrie and the candle. — Sammy Tickletooth. — Dirty child. — Johnny Sliderlegs. — Tom the thief. — Little Jacob.
Slow and sure. Alger, H., *jr.* $1.25 . . . . . . *Loring.*
Slow horses made fast and fast horses made faster. Elderkin, J. 50c. . . . . *Haney.*

low man. Lemon, M. 15c. . . . . *French.*
lowtop's engagements. Cheltnam, C. S. 15c. *French.*
luyter, P: *See* Dankers, J., *and* Sluyter, P.
ly Boots, the fox; or, caught at last. ill. cr. 4°. pap., 20c.; 25c. . . . . *J. E. Potter.*
mall, A. E. Diseases of the nervous system; [also] Treatise on diseases of the skin, by C. E. Toothacker. [Hom.] 8°. $1 . . . . *Boericke.*
— Manual of homœop. practice; for families. 14th ed., enl. 8°. hf. mor., $3. . . . . *Boericke.*
— *Germ.;* übers. v. C. J. Hempel. 8°. $3 . . *Boericke.*
— *See also* Warren, I., *and* Small, A. E.
mall, G: G. [Works.] 18 v. ill. '71–'76. ea., pap., 25c. . . . . *Collin & S.*
Cont.: Capers. — Comical medicine man. — Freemasonry exposed. — Humors of the railroad kings. — Odd-fellowship exposed. — "Old Jolly." — Peppermint drops. — Put through. — The roarer, *ea.*, 4°. — Farming for fun; or, back yard grangers. — Fred Douglas and his mule. — "I told you so;" or, the beats and baits of society. — Joining the grangers. — Knights of Pythias shown up. — Life in New York. — Long and short of it; or, three comical adventures of two comical men. — Parson Beecher and his horse. — Stumping it, *ea.*, 8°.
— Bricktop stories. 7 v. ill. 8°. '75–'76. ea., pap., 25c. . . . . *Collin & S.*
Cont.: Trip of the Porgie. — My mother-in-law. — "Them thar" grasshoppers. — Smith in search of a wife. — Trip to Niagara Falls. — Bald headed history of America. — "Going to the centennial:" a guy to the entire exhibition.
mall beginnings; or, the way to get on. [Brief biographies.] ill. 16°. 75c. . . . . *Porter.*
mall book for a small child. 18°. 18c. . . . . . *Am. S. S.*
mall books on great subjects. 11 nos. 18°. ea., pap., 15c.; — in 3 v., $1.50 . . . . *Lea.*
Cont.: Philosophical theories and experience. — Connection between physiology and intellectual science. — Man's power over himself to prevent or control insanity. — Introduction to practical organic chemistry. — Brief view of Greek philosophy to age of Pericles. — Brief view of Greek philosophy from Socrates to coming of Christ. — Christian doctrine and practice in 2d cent. — Exposition of vulgar and common errors. — Introduction to vegetable physiology. — Principles of criminal law. — Christian sects in the 19th century.
mall house at Allington. Trollope, A. $2; $1.50. *Harper.*
mall rain upon the tender herb. [Texts.] 128°. 25c. . . . . *Am. S. S.*
mall sins no trifles. 18°. 25c. . . . . *Am. S. S.*
malley, Dan. S. American phonetic dictionary of the Eng. lang. 8°. '55. mor., $5. . . . . *Wilstach.*
marius, C. F. Points of controversy: lectures. 12°. $1.50 . . . . *O'Shea; Sadlier.*
mart, C. H. Manual of free gymnastics and dumb-bell exercises. ill. 16°. '64. 20c. . . *Wilson, H. & Co.*
mart, C: Driven from the path. [Fiction.] 12°. $1.75 . . . . *Appleton.*
mart, Hawley. Breezie Langton. 8°. pap., 75c. *Appleton.*
— Race for a wife. 8°. pap., 50c. . . . . *Appleton.*
mart, Ja. H. Indiana schools, and the men who have worked in them. 12°. '76. $1 . . *Wilson, H. & Co.*
mart, Mos. M. Brief view of Christian doctrine. 24°. '43. 75c. . . . . *Freewill.*
mashington Goit. Williams, T. J. 15c. . . . *Lee & S.*
mead, Wesley. Guide to wealth, and pathway to health, peace and competence. 16°. '56. 75c. *Mendenhall.*
meaton, A. C. Builder's pocket companion. ('50.) 10th ed. 12°. '74. $1.50. . . . . *Baird.*
meaton, G: On doctrine of atonement as taught by the apostles. 8°. $5. . . . . *Scribner, W. & A.*
— On doctrine of atonement as taught by Christ himself. 8°. $5. . . . . *Scribner, W. & A.*
medes, —. *See* Yerger, —, Smedes, —, *and* Abbey, R.
medes, W. C. *See* Mississippi, Chancery reports; Law reports.
medley, E: History of reformed religion in France. 3 v. 18°. $2.25 . . . . *Harper.*
— Sketches from Venetian hist. 2 v. 18°. $1.50 . . *Harper.*

Smedley, Fk. E. Novels. 4 v. 12°. $6. — (Railway lib.) 16°. ea., bds., $1. . . . . *Routledge.*
Cont.: Colville family. — Frank Fairlegh. — Harry Coverdale. — Lewis Arundel.
— *Same.* 7 v. . . . . *Peterson.*
Cont.: Colville family, 8°, pap., 50c. — Tom Racquet, and his three maiden aunts, 8°, pap., 75c. — Fortunes and misfortunes of Harry Racket Scapegrace. — Frank Fairlegh. — Lewis Arundel, *ea.*, 8°, $1,75; pap., 75c. — Harry Coverdale's courtship and marriage. — Lorrimer Littlegood, *ea.*, 12°, $1.75; pap., $1.50.
— Frank Fairlegh. ill. 8°. $3. . . . . *Routledge.*
— Harry Coverdale. ill. 8°. $3 . . . . *Routledge.*
— Lewis Arundel. ill. 8°. $3 . . . . *Routledge.*
Smedley, Menella Bute. Linnet's trial. 12°. $1.25; pap., $1. . . . . *Loring.*
— *Same.* cr. 8°. '71. $2. . . . . *Routledge.*
— Other folks' lives. cr. 8°. $2. . . . . *Routledge.*
— Two dramatic poems. fp. 8°. '74. $2.25 . . *Macmillan.*
Smee, Alfr. Accidents and emergencies: directions for treatment; with alterations, corrections and app. by R. T. Trall. New ed., rev. ill. 12°. '75. pap., 25c. . . . . *Wells.*
— My garden, its plan and culture; with gen. descrip. of its geology, botany and natural history. 2d ed., rev. 1300 eng. roy. 8°. (Lond.) '72. $8.50; hf. mor., $12.50; cf., $13.50. . . . . *Little, B. & Co.*
Smellie, W: Philosophy of natural hist.; with introd. and add. by J. Ware. ill. 12°. $2 . . *Thompson.*
Smet, P: J: de. History of the western missions. 12°. $2 . . . . *Strong.*
— New Indian sketches. 16°. 60c.; $1. . . . . *Sadlier.*
Smike. *See* Dickens, C:
Smiles, S: Brief biographies. por. 16°. $1.50 . . **Osgood.*
— Character. 12°. $1.25. . . . . *Harper.*
— Huguenots (The): their settlements, churches and industries in England and Ireland; with app. on the Huguenots in America. cr. 8°. $2 . . *Harper.*
— *Same.* 12°. '73. $1.50. . . . . *So. Meth.*
— Huguenots (The) in France after revocation of edict of Nantes; with a visit to the country of the Vaudois. cr. 8°. $2. . . . . *Harper.*
— Industrial biography: iron-workers and tool-makers. 16°. $1.50 . . . . **Osgood.*
— Keep good company. 12°. '72. pap., 20c. *Meth. Bk. Conc.*
— Life of George Stephenson, railway engineer. por. 16°. $1.50 . . . . **Osgood.*
— Life of George Stephenson and of Robert Stephenson; with hist. of invention and introd. of railway locomotive. por. and ill. 8°. $3 . . . . . *Harper.*
— Lives of the engineers, with account of their principal works. New ed., rev. 5 v. por. and ill. cr. 8°. $12.50; hf. cf., $22.50; cf., $27.50; $32. *Scribner, W. & A.*
— Self-help; with ill. of character, conduct and perseverance. 12°. $1.25. . . . . *Harper.*
— *Same.* por. 16°. $1.50 . . . . **Osgood.*
— *Same.* 12°. '72. $1.50. . . . . *So. Meth.*
— Thrift. 12°. $1.25 . . . . *Harper.*
— (*ed.*) Round the world; incl. a residence in Victoria and journey by rail across North America. ill. 12°. $1.50. . . . . *Harper.*
Smiles and tears. 32°. 20c.; 15c. . . . . *Dutton.*
Smiley, S. F. Who is he? appeal to those who regard with any doubt the name of Jesus. 16°. 75c. *Lippincott.*
Smiley, T: T. Arithmetic. 16°. hf. bd., 31c. — Key. 16°. hf. bd., 63c. . . . . *Lippincott.*
— Table book. 18°. pap., 4c. . . . . *Lippincott.*
Smirke, Rob. *See* Gems from Shakespeare.
Smith, Abram D. *See* Wisconsin, Reports.
Smith, Ad. Essays: moral sentiments, astronomy, physics, etc. 12°. $1.75. . . . . . *Scribner, W. & A.*
— Theory of the moral sentiments; [also] First formation of languages. 12°. (Bohn.) $1.25 . . *Little, B. & Co.*
— *Same.* 12°. (Bohn.) $1.40. . . . . . *Scribner, W. & A.*
— *Same.* 12°. (Bohn.) $1.50 . . . . *Lippincott.*
— Wealth of nations. 12°. $1.75. . . . *Scribner, W. & A.*
— *Same.* New ed. 12°. '71. $2.50. . . . . *Putnam.*

Smith, Alb. Novels and tales. 5 v. 16°. hf. roxb., $6.25. — (chp. ed.) 16°. ea., $1. — (Railway lib.) 16°. ea., bds., 80c. . . . . *Routledge.*
Cont.: Adventures of Mr. Ledbury. — Christopher Tadpole. — Marchioness of Brinvilliers. — Pottleton legacy. — Scattergood family.
— Blanche Heriot: drama. 16°. pap., 15c. . . . . *French.*
— Cricket on the hearth: fairy tale. 16°. pap., 15c. *French.*
— Esmeralda: burlesque. 16°. pap., 15c. . . . . *French.*
— Natural history of the ballet-girl. ill. 16°. pap., 15c. *French.*

Smith, Alex. City poems. 16°. $1. . . . . * *Osgood.*
— Dreamthorpe: book of essays written in the country. cr. 8°. $1.50. . . . . *Routledge.*
— Edwin of Deira. 2d ed. fp. 8°. $1. . . . . *Macmillan.*
— Summer in Skye. 12°. '76. $1.50 . . . . *Miller.*
— *Same.* cr. 8°. $2.50. . . . . *Routledge.*

Smith, Asa. Illustrated astronomy. ('48.) New ed., rev. roy. 4°. '60. $1.25. . . . . *Nichols & H.*
— *Span.* Astronomia ilustrada; tr. por D. Paredes. 4°. $2. . . . . *Appleton.*
— *Port.* 4°. $2.50. . . . . *Appleton.*
— Primer libro de geografía elemental; tr. por T. Paredes. New ed., rev. and enl. ill. 4°. $1. . *Appleton.*

Smith, A: W. Elementary treatise on mechanics: theory of statics and dynamics, and its applic. to solids and fluids. ill. 8°. $2; shp., $2.50. . *Harper.*

Smith, B. B. Saturday evening; or, thoughts on the progress of the plan of redemption. 8°. '76. pap., 25c. . . . . *Whittaker.*

Smith, B. M. Family religion; or, the domestic relations as regulated by Christian principles. 12°. $1. . . . . *Pres. Bd.*
— Questions on the Gospel. 18°. '68. hf. bd., 20c. *Pres. Com.*
— *See also* Faussett, A. R., *and* Smith, B. M.

Smith, Barn. Arithmetic and algebra. 12th ed. cr. 8°. $3.50. . . . . *Macmillan.*
— Arithmetic for schools. New ed. 12°. '65. $1.50. —Key. 12°. '65. $3. . . . . *Macmillan.*
— Examination papers on arithmetic; with answers. 18°. '67. 75c. —Key. 18°. '67. $1.75. . *Macmillan.*
— Exercises in arithmetic; with answers. cr. 8°. 75c. *Macmillan.*
— Metric system of arithmetic. 4th ed. 18°. pap., 12c. *Macmillan.*
— School class book of arithmetic. 18°. '65. $1.50. — Key. 18°. '65. $2. . . . . *Macmillan.*
— Shilling book of arithmetic for national and elementary schools. 18°. '66. 50c. —Key. 18°. '66. $1.75. *Macmillan.*

Smith, B: G. *See* Tomes, R., *and* Smith, B. G.

Smith, Benton. The Christian way; for advanced scholars in S.-schools. 16°. '68. per doz., bds., $3. . . . . *Universalist.*

Smith, Buckingham. Grammar of the Pima or Névome; — Grammatical sketch of Heve lang. *See* Shea, J. G., Library of Am. linguistics.

Smith, Butler K. Serial discourses: 20 sermons on various subjects. 12°. $1.50. . . . . *Chase.*

Smith, C. Graham. Address on educ. of a civil engineer, Edinburgh and Leith Engin. Soc., Nov. 3, 1875. 8°. '76. pap., 60c. . . . . *Spon.*
— Engineering papers: mortar, practical ironwork and retaining walls. 8°. '75. $2. . . . . *Spon.*

Smith, C. J. Catalogue of synonymous words in the Eng. lang., shades of meaning, etc.; with quotations. 8°. $6. . . . . *Scribner, W. & A.*
— Complete collection of synonyms and antonyms. 12°. (Bohn.) $1.75. . . . . *Little, B. & Co.*
— *Same.* 12°. (Bohn.) $2. . *Lippincott; Scribner, W. & A.*

Smith, C. Shaler. Draw spans and their turn tables. *See* Chanute, O., Weight of rails.

Smith, *Mrs.* Caro. L. ["Aunt Carrie."] American home book of in-door games, recreations and occupations. ill. 16°. $1.50. . . . . *Lee & S.*

Smith, *Mrs.* Caro. L., *continued.*
— Home arts for old and young. 16°. 60c.; 75c. *Lee & S.*
— Home games for old and young. 16°. 75c.; hf. bd., 60c. . . . . *Lee & S.*

Smith, Cath. Barn. Poems. fp. 8°. '68. $1.50. *Macmillan.*

Smith, C: A. Among the lilies. 16°. $1.10. . *Pres. Bd.*
— Inlets and outlets. 16°. $1. . . . . *Pres. Bd.*

Smith, C: H. J. Parks and pleasure grounds: pract. notes on country residences, villas, public parks and gardens. 12°. $2.25. . . . . *Baird.*

Smith, C: Hamilton. Natural hist. of man. *See* Jardine, *Sir* W., Naturalists' lib.

Smith, C: M. Treatise on law of master and servant. *See* Law lib.

Smith, C: W: Actor's (The) art: its requisites and how to obtain them. 16°. pap., 15c. *French; Happy.*
— Common blunders made in speaking and writing. 16°. pap., 15c. . . . . *Happy.*
— Elocution without a master. 16°. pap., 15c. *Happy.*
— French in a fortnight without a master. 16°. pap., 15c. . . . . *Happy.*
— Hints on elocution, and how to become an actor. 16°. 20c. . . . . *Ames.*
— Mispronunciation corrected. 16°. pap., 15c. . . *Happy.*
— Reading, speaking and acting. 16°. pap., 15c. *French.*
— (*ed.*) Family theatricals: scenes from standard plays suitable for family performance. 16°. bds., 50c. . . . . *Routledge.*

Smith, Chauncy, *and* Bates, S: W. Cases rel. to railways and canals, argued and adjudged in the [Eng.] courts of law and equity, 1835–'52. 6 v. 8°. shp., $36. . . . . *Little, B. & Co.*

Smith, D. Murray. Round the world: story of travel. ill. 12°. $1. . . . . *Nelson.*

Smith, Dan. [Books of anecdotes.] 4 v. 18°. '50. ea., 75c. . . . . *Meth. Bk. Conc.*
Cont.: Anecdotes for the fireside — for the young — of the Christian ministry. — Ladies' book of anecdotes.
— Book of manners. 24°. '52. 40c. . . *Meth. Bk. Conc.*
— Gems of female biog. 18°. 75c. . . *Cin. Meth. Bk. Conc.*
— Lectures to young men. 12°. '52. 75c. *Meth. Bk. Conc.*
— Parent's friend. 18°. '38. 50c. . . . . *Meth. Bk. Conc.*
— Wisdom in miniature. [Proverbs.] 24°. 35c. *Cin. Meth. Bk. Conc.*

Smith, D: Dyer's instructor; [with] treatise on art of padding. ('53.) 6th ed. 12°. '76. $3. . *Baird.*
— Practical dyer's guide; with treatise on art of padding. 8°. $25. . . . . *Baird.*

Smith, *Rev.* D: Guide to the Lord's supper. 24°. '52. 30c. . . . . *Meth. Bk. Conc.*
— Lord's supper manual. 32°. '54. 35c.; 60c. — 64°. 15c.; 20c. . . . . *Am. Tr.*

Smith, Dexter. Blanks and prizes: farce. 16°. pap., 15c. . . . . *Lee & S.*

Smith, E. A. Collection compendium: digest of laws of every state, with banking and attorney list and stipulated rates for collection of claims. 8°. '76. shp., $6. . . . . *E. A. Smith.*
— Manual of banking laws. 8°. pap., $1. . *E. A. Smith.*

Smith, E. Delafield. *See* New York City, Court of Common Pleas reports.

Smith, E. Goodrich. Life of C: H. Porter. 18°. '49. 35c. . . . . *Am. Tr.*

Smith, *Mrs.* Eliz. Oakes. Poetic gift. 32°. *net*, 19c. *Hamersley.*

Smith, Edm. Reuel. The Araucanians: notes of a tour among the Indian tribes of southern Chili. 12°. $1.50. . . . . *Harper*

Smith, E: Foods. (Intern. sci. ser.) 12°. $1.75. *Appleton.*
— Health: handbook for households and schools. 12°. $1. . . . . *Appleton.*
— On consumption: its early and remediable stages. 8°. $2.25. . . . . *Lea*

Smith, E: P. Incidents in the U. S. Christian Com. pl. and wood eng. 8°. *$3 .... *Lippincott.*

Smith, Edn. B. *See* Maine, Reports.

Smith, Erasmus Peshine. Manual of polit. economy. 12°. $1.25 .... *Putnam.*

— *Same.* (cop. '53.) '71. 2d ed. 12°. '73. $1.25 .. *Baird.*

— *See also* New York State, Court of Appeals reports.

Smith, Eug. A. Geological survey of Alabama: report of progress for 1874. 8°. $1; — for 1875. 8°. $1.25 .... *Dr. E. A. Smith.*

Smith, Eust. Clinical studies of diseases of lungs in children. 12°. '75. $2.50 .... *Lindsay.*

— Practical treatise on wasting diseases of infancy and childhood. 8°. $2.50 .... *Lea.*

Smith, *Miss* F. M. Footprints on life's pathway: new book for the young. ill. 16°. '75. $1 .. *Routledge.*

Smith, Fannie N. ["Christabel Goldsmith."] Brazen gates. 12°. $1.50 .... *Carleton.*

— Shiftless folks. 12°. $1.75 .... *Carleton.*

Smith, *Mrs.* Fes. Irene Burge. Asleep: words of comfort to the bereaved. 16°. '76. $1 .. *Whittaker.*

— Bessie and her grandfather. ill. 18°. '67. 75c. *Crowell.*

— — *See also* Bright eye lib.

— Bishop (The) and Nanette. 12°. '73. $1.50. *Whittaker.*

— Fanfan stories. ill. 18°. 85c. .... *Bost. Am. Tr.*

— Jimmy Don; or, Judy and her baby. ill. 18°. 60c. *Bost. Am. Tr.*

— *Same.* ill. 18°. '71. 60c. .... *Lothrop.*

— Little Floy. ill. 16°. '71. 50c. .... *Lothrop.*

— May; or, grandpa's pet. ill. 16°. 75c. .. *Bost. Am. Tr.*

— May and Tom lib. 5 v. ill. 18°. '71. ea., 75c. *Lothrop.*
Cont.: May; or, grandpapa's pet. — Tom; or, the sailor boy. — Mimi; or, the parsonage. — Clem and Joyce; or, the prairie school. — Old market cart.

— Mimi; or, the parsonage. ill. 18°. 75c. *Bost. Am. Tr.*

— Mother's pearl, and other stories. ill. 18°. 75c. *Bost. Am. Tr.*

— — *See also* Mother's pearl ser.

— Old market cart. ill. 18°. 75c. .... *Bost. Am. Tr.*

— Our birds. ill. 18°. 60c. .... *Bost. Am. Tr.*

— — *See also* Laughing Kitty stories.

Smith, Fs. Gurney. *See* Neill, J., *and* Smith, F. G.

Smith, Fs. H. Elementary treatise on algebra; with examples by S. Crutchfield. demy 8°. $2 .. *Desilver.*

— Elements of descript. geometry; with its applic. to shades, shadows and perspective and topography. pt. 1. 8°. '68. $1.75 .... *Kelly, P. & Co.*

— Introduction to Smith and Duke's Arithmetic. 18°. hf. roan, 40c. .... *Desilver.*

— *and* Duke, R. T. W. American statistical arithmetic; for academies and schools. 4th ed. roy. 18°. hf. roan, 40c. — Key. 18°. hf. roan, 60c. *Desilver.*

Smith, Fs. S. The young Magdalen, and other poems. 12°. $3; $4 .... *Peterson.*

Smith, G: Assyria; from the earliest times to fall of Nineveh. ill. 16°. $1 .... *Scribner.*

— Assyrian discoveries: explorations and discoveries on site of Nineveh, 1873–4. maps, plans, ill., etc. 8°. '75. $4 .... *Scribner.*

— Chaldean account of genesis: descrip. of creation, fall of man, deluge, towel of Babel, etc.; from the cuneiform inscriptions. maps, ill., plans, etc. 8°. '76. $4 .... *Scribner.*

Smith, G: Elements of divinity. ('55.) 4th ed. 12°. '76. $2 .... *So. Meth.*

— Sacred annals. 4 v. 8°. '37–'50. .... *Meth. Bk. Conc.*
Cont.: Patriarchal age: hist. and relig. of mankind to death of Isaac, $3.25; hf. cf., $4.25. — History of the Heb. people, $3.50; hf. cf., $4.50. — History of the Gentile nations, $3.50; hf. cf., $4.50. — Harmony of divine dispensations, $3; hf. cf., $4.

Smith, G: *See* Mayhew, E., *and* Smith, G.

Smith, *Rev.* G: Narrative of explor. visit to consular cities of China and to islands of Hong Kong and Chusan, in behalf of Church Missionary Soc., in 1844–'46. 12°. $1.50 .... *Harper.*

Smith, *Capt.* G: Uses and abuses of Freemasonry. 12°. '75. $1.25; hf. mor., $2.50 .. *Masonic; Redding.*

Smith, G: Barnett. Poets and novelists: ser. of literary studies. 12°. $2 .... *Appleton.*

Smith, G: J. P. *See* England, Common law reports.

Smith, Goldwin. Lectures on study of hist.; with lecture on Univ. of Oxford. 12°. $1.75 .. *Harper.*

— Three English statesmen: Pym, Cromwell and Pitt: lectures. New [chp.] ed. fp. 8°. '67. $1.50. *Macmillan.*

— *Same.* 12°. $1.50 .... *Harper.*

Smith, Gouverneur M. Anniversary discourse before N. Y. Acad. of Med. 8°. '69. pap., 25c. *N. Y. Acad. Med.*

Smith, H. Farnam. *See* United States, Digest.

Smith, H. Perry, *and* Wallace, E. R. Modern babes in the wood: summerings in the wilderness; with a guide to the Adirondacks. ill. and map. 12°. *$2.50; hf. mor., $4 .... *Col. Bk.; Waverley.*

Smith, *Mrs.* H. W. Christians' secret of a happy life. 16°. $1 .... *Willard.*

— Holiness as set forth in the Scriptures. 24°. 20c.; pap., 15c. .... *Willard.*

— Record of a happy life: memorials of Franklin Whitall Smith; by his mother. por. 12°. '75. $1.25; pap., 50c. .... *Lippincott; Revell.*

Smith, Ha. ["Hesba Stretton."] Alone in London. ill. sq. 18°. '69. 60c. .... *Am. Tr.*

— *Same.* ('69.) New ed. ill. 16°. '75. 90c. .. *Hoyt.*

— Bede's charity. New ed. ill. 16°. '74. $1.50 .. *Dodd.*

— Brought home. 16°. '75. $1.25 .... *Dodd.*

— Cassy. 16°. '74. $1 .... *Dodd.*

— Children of Cloverly. 16°. $1 .... *Am. Bapt.*

— Clives of Burcot. 12°. bds., $1 .... *Routledge.*

— Cloverly ser. ('65–'73.) New ed. 5 v. ill. 16°. '72–'75. $6 .... *Hoyt.*
Cont.: Children of Cloverly. — Peter Killip's king; or, fishers of Derby Haven. — Young apprentice. — Lost Gip. — Pilgrim Street.

— Crew of the Dolphin. 16°. '76. $1.25 ...... *Dodd.*

— David Lloyd's last will. 16°. '73. 75c. ...... *Dodd.*

— Doctor's dilemma. 8°. pap., 75c. .... *Appleton.*

— Fern's Hollow: story of the English collieries. 18°. 70c. .... *Pres. Bd.*
Note. Same as "Collier boy."

— *Same.* ill. 18°. 75c. .... *Bost. Am. Tr.*

— Hester Morley's promise. 12°. '73. $1.75 .. *Dodd.*

— Jessica's first prayer: story of London life. ill. sq. 18°. '68. 45c. .... *Am. Tr.*

— *Same.* ('67.) New ed. ill. 16°. '75. 75c. .. *Hoyt.*

— *Same;* [also] Jessica's mother. 18°. 65c. *Pres. Bd.*

— *Germ.* Jessicas erstes Gebet. 18°. '72. 25c. *Am. Tr.*

— Jessica's mother. ('67.) New ed. ill. 16°. '75. 75c. *Hoyt.*

— King's (The) servants. 16°. '73. $1.25 .... *Dodd.*

— *Same.* 16°. '75. $1.25 .... *Hoyt.*

— Little Meg's children. 18°. 50c.; 60c. .... *Am. Bapt.*

— *Same.* ill. sq. 18°. '69. 60c. .... *Am. Bapt.*

— *Same.* 18°. 75c. .... (?) *Martien.*

— *Same.* ('69.) New ed. ill. 16°. '74. $1 .. *Hoyt.*

— Lost Gip. 18°. '75. 60c. .... *H. A. Young.*

— *Same;* [also] Michael Lorio's cross. 16°. '73. $1.25. *Dodd.*

— Max Kromer: story of seige of Strasburg. 16°. '73. 75c. .... *Dodd.*

— Nelly's dark days. 16°. '73. 75c. .... *Dodd.*

— Pilgrim Street ser. 4 v. 18°. $2.30 ...... *Am. S. S.*
Cont.: Jessica's first prayer, 40c. — Alone in London, 60c. — Collier boy, 60c. — Pilgrim Street, 70c.

— Storm of life. ill. 16°. '76. $1 .... *Am. Tr.*

— Wonderful life. 16°. '75. $1.50 .... *Dodd.*

Smith, H: *See* Tiffany, J., *and* Smith, H.

Smith, *Rev.* H: Recollections of an itinerant. 16°. $1. *Cin. Meth. Bk. Conc.*

Smith, H: Arth. Chemistry of sulphuric acid manufacture. ill. cr. 8°. '73. $1.50 .... *Spon.*

Smith, H: Boynton. History of the church of Christ, in chronological tables. ('57.) New ed., rev. f°. '75. $6.75 .... *Scribner.*

— *and* Prime, S. I. Evangelical alliance of the U. S.: report of state of relig. in U. S., and account of the ten days' conference at Amsterdam, Holland. 8°. '67. pap., 25c. .... *N. Y. Ref. Ch. Bd.*

— *and* Schaff, P. (*ed.*) Theological and philosophical lib. 4 v. 8°. '73 .... *Scribner.*
Cont.: History of philosophy, by F. Ueberweg, 2 v., $7.50.— Christian dogmatics, by J. J. van Oosterzee, 2 v., $6.

Smith, H: Fly. Handbook for midwives. ill. 16°. $1.75 .... *Jas. Campbell.*

Smith, H: H., *and* Horner, W: E. Anatomical atlas, ill. of structure of human body. ill. imp. 8°. $4.50. *Lea.*

Smith, Hor. Adam Brown, the merchant. [Fiction.] 8°. pap., 50c. .... *Harper.*

— Arthur Arundel. [Fiction.] 8°. pap., 50c... *Harper.*

— History of festivals, games and amusements, ancient and modern; with add. by S. Woodworth. ill. 18°. 75c. .... *Harper.*

— Love and mesmerism. [Fiction.] 8°. pap., 75c. *Harper.*

— The Tor hill. 8°. pap., 50c. .... *U. P. James.*

— *and* Ja. Poetical works; incl. "Rejected addresses," etc. 12°. '71. $2; hf. cf., $4; mor., $6. *Putnam.*

— — Rejected addresses; or, the new theatrum poetarum. 16°. $1.25 .... * *Osgood.*

Smith, I. Reasons for becoming a Methodist. 18°. '58. 50c. .... *Meth. Bk. Conc.*

Smith, I. Greg. Characteristics of Christian morality. *See* Bampton lectures.

Smith, J. B. Sayings and doings of children. ill. 16°. '73. 75c. .... *Ward.*

Smith, J. Brook. Arithmetic in theory and practice. cr. 8°. $2.50 .... *Macmillan.*

Smith, J. E. *See* Bible [Whole].

Smith, J. F: [Novels.] 29 v. 8°. pap.... *Dick & F.*
Cont.: Alice Arran. — Dick Tarleton, *ea.*, 25c. — Amy Lawrence. — Banker's secret. — Bella Trelawney. — Charles Vavasseur. — Dick Markham. — Fred Arden. — Fred Graham. — Gus Howard. — Harold Tracy. — Harry Ashton. — Helen De Vere.— Henry De La Tour. — Lady Ashleigh. — Lillian. — Marion Barnard. — Milly Moyne. — Minnie Grey. — Philip Blandford. — Prince Charles. — Redmond O'Neil. — Rochester. — Sir Bernard Gaston. — Temptation. — Virgin queen. — Woman and her master, *ea.*, 75c. — Fred Vernon, $1. — Stanfield Hall, $1.50.

— Adelaide Waldegrave; or, the trials of a governess. 8°. pap., 75c. .... *Peterson.*

— Romantic incidents in lives of queens of England. 12°. $1.50 .... *Dick & F.*

— Usurer's victim; or, Thomas Balscombe. 8°. pap., 75c. .... *Peterson.*

— Woman's love; or, like and unlike. 8°. $1.25; pap., 75c. .... *Estes.*

Smith, J. Lew. Practical treatise on diseases of children. 8°. $5; leath., $6. .... *Lea.*

Smith, J. Wheaton. Life of John P. Crozer. 12°. $1.50 .... *Am. Bapt.*

Smith, Ja. *See* Smith, Hor. *and* J.

Smith, *Col.* Ja. Account [by himself] of remarkable occurrences in [his] life and travels during his captivity with the Indians, 1755–'59: Lexington, 1799. [Reprint.] 8°. '70. $2.50; large pap., $5. *Clarke.*

Smith, *Rev.* Ja. Believer's daily remembrance. 18°. $1 .... *Carter.*

— Believer's triumph. 32°. 75c. .... *Nelson.*

— Better land (The). 18°. 40c. .... *Pres. Bd.*

— *Same.* sq. 24°. '74. 75c.; $1 .... *Am. Tr.*

— Book that will suit you; or, a word for every one. 32°. '56. $1 .... *Dodd.*

— Brief portions for daily use. 32°. 25c. .... *Nelson.*

— Christ alone. 32°. pap., 10c. .... *Pres. Bd.*

— Coming man (The). [Fiction.] 2 v. 8°. '73. $5. *Routledge.*

Smith, *Rev.* Ja., *continued.*

— Daily Bible readings. 18°. mor., $1.50 .... *Nelson.*

— Every day manuals. 10 v. 18°. $3 .... *Nelson.*
Cont.: Better land. — Our heavenly Father. — Do this in remembrance. — Christ alone. — Important questions. — Great Comforter. — Morning sacrifice. — Evening sacrifice. — Words of comfort. — Welcome to Jesus.

— Food for the soul. 32°. 25c. .... *Nelson.*

— God our refuge and strength. 32°. pap., 10c. *Pres. Bd.*

— Great comforter (The); or, the work of the Holy Spirit. 32°. pap., 10c. .... *Pres. Bd.*

— Green pastures; or, daily food for the Lord's flock. 32°. 40c. .... *Pres. Bd.*

— Important questions. 32°. pap., 10c. .... *Pres. Bd.*

— Our heavenly Father. sq. 24°. '74. 50c.; 75c. *Am. Tr.*

— Pleading Saviour. 18°. mor., $1.50 .... *Nelson.*

— Short readings for daily use. 32°. 25c. .... *Nelson.*

— Still waters; or, refreshment for the Saviour's flock at eventide. 32°. 40c. .... *Pres. Bd.*

— *Same.* 32°. mor., $1 .... *Nelson.*

— Strong tower (The); or, strength, salvation and joy for the believer: sel. from his works. 18°. 60c. *Pres. Bd.*

— Temperance reformation (The) and its claim upon the Christian church. 8°. '75. $2.50.. *Lothrop.*

— This do in remembrance of me; or, sacramental meditations. 32°. pap., 10c. .... *Pres. Bd.*

— Wait on the Lord. 32°. '64. 20c. .... *Randolph.*

— Welcome to Jesus. 32°. pap., 10c. .... *Pres. Bd.*

— Words of comfort. sq. 24°. '74. 50c.; 75c... *Am. Tr.*

Smith, Jerome Van Crowninshield. Pilgrimage to Palestine. 12°. '53. $1 .... *D. Clapp.*

— Ways of women in their physical, moral and intellectual relations. ill. sm. 8°. '73. *$3; $4; leath., $3.50 .... *Dustin.*

Smith, *Capt.* J: Description of New England; or, the observations and discoueries of Captaine Iohn Smith (Admirall of that country) in the north of America in 1614: Lond., 1616. [Reprint.] 4°. pap., $1 .... *Sabin.*

— New England's trials: Lond., 1622. [Reprint.] 4°. pap., 75c. .... *Sabin.*

Smith, J: Fruits and farinacea the proper food of man; with notes and ill. by R. T. Trall. 12°. '54. $1.50 .... *Wells.*

Smith, J: Ferns, British and foreign: history, organography, classification, etc. 250 woodcuts. cr. 8°. (Lond.) $3 .... *Putnam.*

Smith, *Rev.* J: A Presbyterian minister's letters to a Methodist preacher. 18°. 63c. ..... *Lippincott.*

Smith, J: C. National accountant: theory and practice of book-keeping by double and single entry. roy. 8°. $3 .... *Lippincott.*

Smith, J: Cotton. Miscellanies, old and new. 18°. '76. $1.75 .... *Whittaker.*

— *Same.* 2d [chp.] ed. 12°. '76. $1.25.. *Whittaker.*

Smith, J: Hyatt. Gilead; or, the vision of All Souls' Hospital: allegory. ('63.) New ed. 12°. '64. $1.50 .... *Scribner.*

— The open door; or, light and liberty. ('70.) New ed. ill. 12°. '74. $1.50 .... *Holmes.*

Smith, J: Lawr. Address before Am. Assoc. for Advanc. of Sci., Aug., 1873. 8°. pap., 25c. *Am. Assoc. Adv. Sci.*

— Minerals. *See* Gilliss, J. M.

Smith, J: Nelson. Science of sensibility (intelligence), or simple element of soul; and the spirit of life and origin of species, and natural cause of the constancy of each species to its type. 12°. $1.50. *Lippincott.*

Smith, J: Pye. Geology and Scripture; or, rel. between Scriptures and geological science. 12°. (Bohn.) $1.75 .... *Little, B. & Co.*

— *Same.* 12°. (Bohn.) $2.. *Lippincott; Scribner, W. & A.*

Smith, J: W: Compendium of mercantile law; with Am. add. by Holcombe and Gholson. 8°. shp., $6 .... *Appleton.*

Smith, J: W: *continued.*
— Law of contracts. 5th Am. ed., ed. by J. G. Malcolm; with notes and ref. to Eng. and Am. cases, by W. H. Rawle; and add. notes and ref. to recent Am. cases by G. Sharswood. 8°. '69. $5.50. *T. & J. W. Johnson.*
— Leading cases on various branches of law; from last Eng. ed., ed. by H. S. Keating and J. S. Willis. 7th Am. ed., with add. notes and Am. ref. by J. I. C. Hare, H. B. Wallace and J. W. Wallace. 2 v. in 3. 8°. '73. $19.50... *T. & J. W. Johnson.*

Smith, Jos. Emerson. Oakridge: old-time story of Maine. 12°. '75. $2 .... *Osgood.*

Smith, Jos. Few. Prayer of the afflicted. 32°. '64. 35c. .... *Randolph.*

Smith, Jos. Mather. Anniversary discourse before N. Y. Acad. of Med. 8°. '50. pap., 25c. *N. Y. Acad. Med.*

Smith, Josiah D. Truth in love: [sermons]; with biog. by J. M. Platt and introd. by M. W. Jacobus. por. 12°. $1.40 .... *Pres. Bd.*

Smith, Josiah W: Compendium of law of real and personal property as connected with conveyancing. 8°. '56. $4.50 .... *T. & J. W. Johnson.*
— — *See also* Law lib.
— Manual of common law; with notes and ref. by E. C. Ingersoll. 12°. '71. $4 .... *Morrison.*
— Manual of equity jurisprudence. 12°. '71. $4. *Morrison.*
— Original view of executory interests in real and personal property. 8°. shp., $3.50 .... *Kay.*

Smith, Jla. E. (*tr.*) *See* Bible [Whole].

Smith, Jla. R. How they made a man of him. 12°. '76. $1 .... *J. D. Gill.*

Smith, Julie P. Novels. 7 v. 12°. ea., $1.75.. *Carleton.*
Cont.: Chris and Otho. — Courting and farming. — His young wife. — Married belle. — Ten old maids. — Widow Goldsmith's daughter. — Widower.

Smith, Just. A. Patmos; or, the kingdom and the patience. sq. 16°. '75. $1.25 .... *Griggs.*

Smith, Leon. Guide to French conversation; ed. by F. A. Brĕgy. 16°. '75. 60c. .... *Eldredge.*

Smith, *Mrs.* M. J. P. Golden ladder. ill. 32°. '64. 25c. .... *Am. Tr.*
— Little home missionary. ill. 32°. '64. 25c... *Am. Tr.*
— Marcia and Ellen. ill. 18°. '60. 40c. ...... *Am. Tr.*

Smith, *Miss* M. M. Kick him down hill; or, ups and downs in business: story of millions. 8°. '75. $2.50 .... *U. S. Pub.*

Smith, *Rev.* M. M. History of infant baptism. 15c. (?) *Cumberland.*

Smith, *Mrs.* Ma. L. G. Among the stars; or, Minnie Weston's astronomy class. 18°. '76. 65c. *Am. Bapt.*

Smith, Ma. P. Wells. ["P. Thorne."] Jolly good times; or, child life on a farm. ill. sq. 16°. '75. $1.50 .... *Roberts.*

Smith, *Mrs.* Ma. Stuart. Heirs of the kingdom; ed. by A. G. Haygood. ('74.) 3d ed. 18°. '76. 50c. *So. Meth.*

Smith, Mat. Hale. ["Burleigh."] Bulls and bears of N. Y., with the crisis of 1873 and the cause: hist. of Wall Street during the past 200 years, incl. biog. sketches of leading speculators. ill. 8°. *$2.75; leath., $3.25 .... *Burr.*
— Sunshine and shadow in N. Y. ill. 8°. *$3; leath., $3.50 .... *Burr.*
— Universalism not of God. 18°. '48. 50c... *Am. Tr.*

Smith, Mirah. The seven trumpets. 16°. '75. pap., 15c. .... *Sev. Day Adv.*

Smith, Mos. Elements of mental science. 12°. $1.75. *Cin. Meth. Bk. Conc.*

Smith, Nath. D. Meteorological observations in Arkansas, 1840–'59. 4°. '60. pap., $1.25. *Smith. Inst.*

Smith, Nath. Ryno. Fractures of the lower extremity, and use of the anterior suspensory apparatus. ill. 8°. '67. $3 .... *Kelly, P. & Co.*

Smith, Ol. P. The domestic architect. 4°. '52. $3.75. *Mason.*

Smith, Persifor Frazer. Complete collection of forms of procedure in the several courts of Penna. 8°. shp., $7.50 .... *Kay.*
— *See also* Pennsylvania, Sup. Court reports.

Smith, Ph. Ancient hist., to fall of the western empire. 3 v. plans, maps and ill. 8°. $10.50; shp., $13.50; hf. mor., $15; hf. cf., $18.... *Appleton.*
— New Testament hist.; with introd. connecting hist. of the Old and New Test. maps and ill. 8°. $2.50 .... *Appleton.*
— Old Testament hist., to return of Jews from captivity. maps and ill. sm. 8°. $2.50 ..... *Appleton.*
— Smaller anc. hist. of the east, to conquest by Alexander the Great. ill. 16°. $1 .... *Harper.*
— Students' ancient history of the east, to conquest by Alexander the Great; ed. by W: Smith. ill. 12°. $2 .... *Harper.*

Smith, Ph. V. History of Eng. institutions: handbook of bases and structure of institutions of Eng. civilization. 12°. $1.50 .... *Lippincott.*

Smith, R. Bosworth. Mohammed and Mohammedanism: [lectures]; with E. Deutsch's Islam. 12°. $1.50 .... *Harper.*

Smith, R. H. *See* England, Chancery reports.

Smith, R. Murdoch. Persian art. map and ill. cr. 8°. '76. 75c. .... *Scribner, W. & A.*

Smith, Reub. Pastoral office: experiences and obs. for forty years. 18°. 45c. .... *Pres. Bd.*

Smith, *Mrs.* R: Life of Rev. H: Moore. 12°. '45. 90c. *Meth. Bk. Conc.*

Smith, R: Somers. Manual of linear perspective: form, shade, shadow and reflection. pl. 8°. $2.. *Wiley.*
— Manual of topographical drawing. pl. 8°. $2.. *Wiley.*

Smith, Rob. *See* Sermons and essays.

Smith, Rob. Payne. Commentary on Jeremiah and Lamentations. *See* Cook, F. C., Bible commentary.
— Prophecy a preparation for Christ. *See* Bampton lectures.

Smith, Rob. Pearsall. Walking in the light. 16°. 75c. *Willard.*

Smith, *Mrs.* Rob. Pearsall. *See* Smith, *Mrs.* H. W.

Smith, Roswell C. English grammar on the productive system. 12°. hf. bd., 56c. .... *Butler.*
— First book in geog. ('54.) New ed., rev. sm. 4°. '56. hf. bd., 60c. .... *Claxton; Lippincott.*
— Geography on the productive system; with atlas. ('40.) New ed. 2 v.: text, 12°; atlas, 4°. '53. hf. bd., $1.75 .... *Claxton; Lippincott.*
— Introductory arithmetic. ('32.) New ed. 18°. '73. hf. bd., 15c. .... *Claxton.*
— New arithmetic. 12°. hf. bd., 95c. — Key. 12°. hf. bd., 95c. .... *Lippincott.*
— New geography: map questions, text and notes. 4°. '60. hf. bd., $1.75 .... *Claxton; Lippincott.*
— Practical arithmetic. 18°. hf. bd., 56c. — Key. 18°. hf. bd., 56c. .... *Lippincott.*
— Quarto, or second book in geog. ('46.) New ed. 4°. '53. hf. bd., $1.20 .... *Claxton; Lippincott.*

Smith, S. Notes on 2d Plenary Council of Baltimore. 12°. $2 .... *O'Shea.*

Smith, S. Theyre. Cut off with a shilling: comedietta. 16°. pap., 15c. .... *De Witt; French.*
— Happy pair: comedietta. 16°. pap., 15c. *De Witt; French.*
— Uncle's will: comedietta. 16°. pap., 15c... *De Witt.*

Smith, S: Fs. Knights and sea kings; or, the middle ages. ill. 12°. '74. $1.75 .... *Lothrop.*
— Lyric gems. 24°. '74. 25c.; 40c. 16°. $1.. *Lothrop.*
— Myths and heroes; or, the childhood of the world. ill. 16°. '74. $1.50 .... *Lothrop.*
— Noble workers. ill. 12°. '76. $1.50 ...... *Lothrop.*
— Rock of ages: coll. of religious poems. 4°. '69. $1.50; $2 .... *Lothrop.*

Smith, S: Fs., *continued.*
— Stories of success. ill. 12°. '76. $1.50 .. *Lothrop.*
— *See also* Stow, B., *and* Smith, S. F.

Smith, Seba. [" *Maj.* Jack Downing."] Way down east; or, portraitures of Yankee life. ill. 12°. $1.75 .... *J.E.Potter.*

Smith, Sidney. Method for the piano-forte. 4°. '71. bds., $2 .... *Ditson.*

Smith, Sol. Sol. Smith's theatrical apprenticeship. ill. 12°. pap., 75c.......... *Peterson.*
— Theatrical journey-work and anecdotal recollections. 12°. pap., 75c.......... *Peterson.*
— Theatrical management in the west and south for thirty years. ill. and por. 8°. $2; pap., $1.50. *Harper.*

Smith, Southwood. Common nature of epidemics, and their rel. to climate and civilization; also remarks on contagion and quarantine; ed. by T. Baker. 12°. $1.50.......... *Lippincott.*

Smith, Ste. Grains for the grangers; discussing farmers' movement for emancipation of white slaves from slave power of monopoly. 12°. $1.75. *J.E.Potter.*
— Romance of railroad. 12°. $1.50.......... *Carleton.*

Smith, Sydney. Works. 3 v. 12°. $4.. *R. Worthington.*
— — *See also* Modern Brit. essayists.
— Elementary treatise on moral philosophy: [lectures] delivered in 1804–6. 12°. $1.50.......... *Harper.*
— Essays. 16°. '74. $1.25. — 1st ser., sep., 75c.; pap., 50c.......... *Routledge.*
— Wit and wisdom of Sydney Smith: sel. from his writings and passages of his letters and table-talk; with memoir and notes by E. A. Duyckinck. por. cr. 8°. $2.25; hf. cf., $4.... *Widdleton.*
— *and* Talfourd, *Sir* T. N., *and* Stephen, *Sir* J. Works and crit. and misc. essays. 8°. $2.50; shp., $3.50; hf. cf., $5.......... *Appleton.*

Smith, T. J. Interest tables. 8°. $1.50... *Appleton.*

Smith, T. Ralston. *See* Parker, J., *and* Smith, T. R.

Smith, T: Laurens. History of Windham, Maine. 8°. $1.25 .... *Hoyt,F.&D.*

Smith, T: Southwood. Illustrations of divine government; embr. letter of J. Foster against endless punishment. 12°. $1.25.......... *Williamson.*

Smith, Thornley. History of Joshua; viewed in connection with topog. of Canaan and the customs of the times. ill. 12°. '75. $1.25...... *Randolph.*
— Joshua and his times. 3d ed. ill. 18°. '75. $1.25. *Tibbals.*
— Memoir of Rev. T. L. Hodgson, with extracts from his journals; rev. by T. O. Summers. ('58.) 2d ed. 18°. '74. 60c.......... *So.Meth.*

Smith, Uriah. Destiny of the wicked. 16°. '73. 15c. *Sev.DayAdv.*
— Nature and destiny of man. 16°. '73. $1; pap., 40c. *Sev.DayAdv.*
— State of the dead; from "Nature and destiny of man." 16°. '73. 25c. .... *Sev.DayAdv.*
— Thoughts, critical and practical, on book of Daniel. 16°. '73. $1; pap., 35c.......... *Sev.DayAdv.*
— Thoughts, critical and practical, on book of Revelation. 2d ed. 16°. '75. pap., $1... *Sev.DayAdv.*
— United States in the light of prophecy: exposition of Revelation 13: 11–17. 16°. '76. 40c.; pap., 20c. *Sev.DayAdv.*
— Word for the Sabbath; or, false theories exposed. [Poem.] 3d ed. 16°. '75. 40c... *Sev.DayAdv.*

Smith, W. Anderson. Lewsiana; or, life in the outer Hebrides. ill. 12°. '75. $3 .... *Routledge.*

Smith, W. H. Charades. 16°. pap., 40c.... *French.*
— Drunkard; or, the fallen saved: drama. 16°. pap., 15c.......... *French.*

Smith, Wa. American drawing cards for drawing on slates in primary schools. 2 ser. ea., 15c. *Prang.*
— Art education, scholastic and industrial. ill. 8°. '72. $5 .... *Prang.*

Smith, Wa., *continued.*
— Drawing copies: large examples for freehand drawing in high schools, evening classes and art schools. 4 pts. 4°. ea., $5.......... *Prang.*
— Freehand drawing book. nos. 1–6. obl. 8°. ea., 25c.......... *Prang.*
— Geometrical drawing book. nos. 1–4. obl. 8°. ea., 25c.......... *Prang.*
— Industrial drawing in public schools: 3 lectures. 8°. '76. pap., 25c.......... *Prang.*
— Intermediate drawing book. nos. 1–3. obl. 12°. ea., 15c.......... *Prang.*
— Model and object drawing book. nos. 1, 2. obl. 8°. ea., 25c.......... *Prang.*
— Perspective drawing book. nos. 1–3. obl. 8°. ea., 25c. .... *Prang.*
— Teacher's manual for freehand drawing in primary schools. 12°. '74. bds., $1; — in intermediate schools. 12°. '76. bds., $1.25; — in grammar schools. 8°. bds., $2.50 .... *Prang.*
— Teacher's manual of freehand drawing and designing, and guide to self-instruction. ill. 8°. '75. bds., $2.50.......... *Prang.*
— *See also* Shinn, E., Smith, W., *and* Wilson, J. M.

Smith, Wa. C. Hymns of Christ and the Christian life. fp. 8°. '67. $1.50.......... *Macmillan.*

Smith, Wa. G. Commentary on the Brit. pharmacopœia. 8°. $5.......... *Putnam.*

Smith, W: Dictionary of the Bible: its antiquities, biog., geog. and nat. hist. 3 v. maps and wood eng. 8°. (Lond.) $18; hf. cf., $24.. *Little,B.&Co.*
— *Same.* Am. ed., rev. and ed. by H. B. Hackett and E. Abbot. 4 v. maps and ill. 8°. '69–'70. $26–$50 .... *Hurd & H.*
— *Same;* [abridg. by author]. maps and ill. 8°. $3. *Miller.*
— — *Same.* ill. and maps. 8°. $3; shp., $3.75.. *Porter.*
— — *Same.* ill. and maps. 8°. *$3; $3.50; leath., $4. *Burr.*
— — *Same.* ('70.) 6th ed. ill. and maps. 8°. '75. $3; shp., $3.50.......... *Tibbals.*
— — *Same.* ill. and maps. 8°. $3.50; shp., $4.50. *Estes.*
— — *Same.* ill. and maps. 8°. (Lond.) $4.50; shp., $5.50; hf. cf., $6.50.......... *Little,B.&Co.*
— — *Same.* ill. and maps. 8°. $4.50; leath., $5; hf. mor., $6.......... *Scranton.*
— — *Same.* New ed.; with pref. by Dr. Day and sup. by Rev. H. Lincoln. ill. and maps. 8°. '72. $4. *Lothrop.*
— — *Same;* ed. by S. W. Barnum. ill. and maps. 8°. *$5; shp., $6; hf. mor., $7.50.......... *Appleton.*
— — *See also* Bible [Whole].
— Classical dictionary of biog., myth. and geog. 10th ed. ill. 8°. (Lond.) $6; hf. cf., $8.. *Little,B.&Co.*
— *Same;* rev. with add. by C. Anthon. roy. 8°. shp., $5 .... *Harper.*
— Dictionary of Greek and Roman antiquities. 2d ed., rev. and enl. ill. 8°. (Lond.) hf. cf., $8. *Little,B.&Co.*
— *Same.* 3d Am. ed., rev. and enl. by C. Anthon. ill. roy. 8°. shp., $6.......... *Harper.*
— Dictionary of Greek and Roman biog. and mythol. 3 v. ill. 8°. (Lond.) hf. cf., $24.. *Little,B.&Co.*
— Dictionary of Greek and Roman geog. 2 v. ill. 8°. (Lond.) hf. cf., $16.......... *Little,B.&Co.*
— French principia. pt. 1: a first French course. 12°. 75c.......... *Harper.*
— *Same.* pt. 2: a first French reading book. 12°. '76. $1.25.......... *Harper.*
— German principia. pt. 1: a first German course. 12°. '76. 75c.......... *Harper.*
— History of Greece to Roman conquest, with chapters on hist. of literature and art; with notes and contin. by C. C. Felton. 8°. hf. roan, $2.75....... *Ware.*
— Illustrated hist. of the Bible to close of apostolic era; ed. by A. P. Hayes. ill. and maps. 8°. '71. *$4.75; roan, $5.50; mor., $7.50..... *Nat.Pub.*

Smith, W: *continued.*
— Principia Latina. pt. 1: first Latin course; rev. by H. Drisler. 12°. 75c. . . . . . *Harper.*
— School dict. of Greek and Roman antiquities; abridg. from larger dict., with corrections by C. Anthon. 12°. hf. shp., $1.50 . . . . . . *Harper.*
— Smaller classical dict. of biog., mythol. and geog. ill. sm. 8°. $2.50 . . . . . . *Appleton.*
— Smaller dict. of the Bible; for schools and young persons. maps, pl. and woodcuts. cr. 8°. (Lond.) $3 . . . . . . *Little, B. & Co.*
— Smaller dict. of Greek and Roman antiquities. 6th ed. ill. sm. 8°. $2.50 . . . . . . *Appleton.*
— *and* Cheetham, S: Dictionary of Christian antiquities: contin. of "Bible dictionary." [To form 2 v.] v. 1. ill. 8°. '75. $7.50 . . . . *Little, B. & Co.*
— — *Same.* [To form 2 v.] v. 1. ill. roy. 8°. '76. *$3.50; leath., $4 . . . . . . *Burr.*
— *and* Drisler, H: Principia Latina. pt. 2: first Lat. reading-book. 12°. $1.25 . . . . . . *Harper.*
— *and* Grove, G: Atlas of ancient geog., biblical and classical: 43 maps, with indices and text. 5 pts. 4°. '74. pap., $35; — in 1 v., hf. mor., $40. *Little, B. & Co.*
— *and* Hall, T. D. English-Latin dict.; with dict. of proper names. 8°. shp., $6 . . . . . . *Harper.*

Smith, W: *and* Martin, E: Book-keeping by single and double entry simplified and adapted to use of common schools. 4°. '59. hf. bd., $1.25 . . *Barnes.*

Smith, W: Gravenhurst; or, thoughts on good and evil: contribution to psychology; with memoir of author. por. cr. 8°. '76. $4 . . *Scribner, W. & A.*

Smith, *Rev.* W: Historical account of expedition against Ohio Indians in 1764 under H. Bouquet; with milit. papers cont. reflections on the war, etc., with pref. by F. Parkman and a tr. of Dumas' biog. sketch of Bouquet. map and pl. 8°. '68. $3; large pap., $6 . . . . . . *Clarke.*

Smith, W: And. Lectures on philos. and practice of slavery. 12°. '56. $1.50 . . . . . . *So. Meth.*

Smith, W: C. Pillars in the temple: lives of deceased laymen of the Meth. Episc. Church. 12°. '71. $1.25 . . . . . . *Meth. Bk. Conc.*
— Sacred memories: annals of deceased preachers of the N. Y. and N. Y. East Conferences. 12°. '70. $1.25 . . . . . . *Meth. Bk. Conc.*
— Sketch book; or, miscellaneous anecdotes. 12°. '60. $1.25 . . . . . . *Meth. Bk. Conc.*

Smith, W: D. What is Calvinism? or, the confession of faith in harmony with the Bible and common sense. 12°. 65c. . . . . . . *Pres. Bd.*

Smith, W: Herb. Charlotte Emma. ill. 18°. '56. 20c. *Am. Tr.*

Smith, W: Leland. Practice in proceedings in the probate court. ('68.) 3d ed. 12°. shp., $2.50. *Little, B. & Co.*

Smith, W: Prescott. History of Baltimore and Ohio Railroad. 8°. '53. $1.50 . . . . . . *Murphy.*

Smith, W: R. Key to Homer's Iliad. ('71.) New ed. 8°. '72. $3 . . . . . . *Claxton.*

Smith, W: Rob. Lectures on the efficient training of nurses. ill. 12°. '75. $2.25 . . . . . . *Lindsay.*

Smith, W: Russell. As it is. [Fiction.] 12°. '60. $1.25. *W. R. Smith.*
— History and debates of convention of people of Alabama, 1861. 8°. shp., $5 . . . . . . *W. R. Smith.*
— Jurisdiction of justices of the peace, and office and duties of judges of probate, etc., under laws of Alabama. ('41.) 3d ed. 8°. '60. shp., $5. *W. R. Smith.*
— Jurisdiction of justices of the peace and office and duties of judges of probate, etc., under the laws of Mississippi. 8°. '60. $5 . . . . . . *W. R. Smith.*
— *See also* Alabama, Sup. Court reports.

Smith, *Rev.* W: S. Christian faith: sermons. fp. 8°. '69. $1.25 . . . . . . *Macmillan.*

Smith, W: Sooy. Pneumatic foundations. *See* Clarke, J. G., Reduction of ruling.

Smith, W: Tyler. Course of lectures on obstetrics; with lecture on hist. of art of midwifery, and annotations by A. K. Gardner. ill. roy. 8°. '58. $5 . . . . . . *De Witt; Lindsay.*

Smith, W: W. Complete etymology of the Eng. lang. 12°. '67. $1.25 . . . . . . *Barnes.*
— Complete speller's manual. 16°. '67. 31c. . . *Keystone.*
— Condensed etymology of the Eng. lang. 12°. '70. hf. bd., 75c. . . . . . . *Barnes.*
— Definer's manual. 12°. hf. bd., 90c. . . . . . *Barnes.*
— Grammar school speller. 12°. '58. hf. bd., 50c. *Barnes.*
— Juvenile definer. 12°. '56. hf. bd., 45c. . . . *Barnes.*
— Little speller; or, first round in ladder of learning. 12°. '59. hf. bd., 20c. . . . . . . *Barnes.*

Smith, Worthington. Select sermons; with memoir by J. Torrey. 12°. '61. $1.25 . . . . . . *Draper.*

Smith in search of a wife. Small, G. G. 25c. *Collin & S.*

Smithers, J. Book of thought; or, happy thoughts of happy thinkers. ('58.) New ed. 12°. '71. $1.75. *Pounsford.*

Smith's interest tables. *See* Doty, D.

Smith's saloon. Ellsworth, *Mrs.* —. $1.25 . . *Crowell.*

Smithson, W: T. (*ed.*) Pulpit of the Methodist Church, south. 8°. '59. $4.50; $5; mor., $6.50; $10 . . . . . . *Wilstach.*

Smithsonian Institution. Annual reports, 1854–'75. 18 v. 8°. '55–'76. pap. . . . . . . *Smith. Inst.*
Cont.: 1854, 1855, 1857–1860, 1862, 1866, 1868, 9 v., *ea.*, $2. — 1869–1875, 7 v., *ea.*, $1. — 1863–1864, 2 v., *ea.*, 50c.
Note. Those for 1856, 1861, 1865, 1867 are o. p.
— Arrangement of families of birds in Smith. Inst. 8°. '66. pap., 10c. . . . . . . *Smith. Inst.*
— Catalogue of publications, etc., in [its] library. 8°. '59. pap., $2 . . . . . . *Smith. Inst.*
— Catalogue of publications of societies belonging to Smith. Inst. 8°. '66. pap., $3 . . . . . . *Smith. Inst.*
— Check list of invertebrate fossils of No. Am. 8°. '64. pap., 25c. . . . . . . *Smith. Inst.*
— Contributions to knowledge. v. 2–21. 4°. '51–'76. ea., pap., $12 . . . . . . *Smith. Inst.*
Note. v. 1 is o. p.
— Land and fresh water shells. 6 pts. 8°. pap., $5. *Smith. Inst.*
— — *See also* Binney, W. G.
— List of foreign correspondents of Smith. Inst. 8°. '69. pap., 25c. . . . . . . *Smith. Inst.*
— *Same.* [2d ed.] 8°. '75. pap., 25c. . . . *Smith. Inst.*
— Miscellaneous collections. v. 1–12. 8°. '62–'74. ea., pap., $5 . . . . . . *Smith. Inst.*
— Museum miscellanea. 8°. '62. pap., 50c. *Smith. Inst.*
— Photograph portraits of No. Am. Indians. 8°. '67. pap., 25c. . . . . . . *Smith. Inst.*
— Publications of societies in [its] library. 2 pts. 4°. '55–'56. ea., pap., 25c. . . . . . . *Smith. Inst.*
— Results of meteorological obs., 1854–'59. 2 pts. 4°. '61–'62. ea., pap., $2.50 . . . . . . *Smith. Inst.*
Note. Other publications of the Smith. Inst. are entered under names of their authors.

Smitten household: book for the afflicted; by S. I. Prime, W. B. Sprague, G. W. Bethune, J. B. Waterbury, C. M. Butler; with poet. sel. from various authors. 12°. '57. $2 . . . . . . *Randolph.*

Smoke. Turgénieff, I. $1.25 . . . . . . *Holt.*

Smoked miser. Jerrold, D. 15c. . . . . . . *French.*

Smollett, Tob. Works; with life. por. demy 8°. $2.50 . . . . . . *Appleton; Lee & S.*
— *Same;* with memoir by Sir W. Scott. ill. 8°. $2; roxb., $2.25; shp., $2.75 . . . . . . *World Pub.*
— Humphrey Clinker. 16°. bds., 80c. . . . . . *Routledge.*
— *Same;* with memoir by T. Roscoe. 12°. $1.50. *Harper.*
— Peregrine Pickle. 16°. bds., 80c. . . . . . *Routledge.*
— Roderick Random. 12°. pap., 25c. *Lippincott; Routledge.*

Smollett, Tob., *continued.*
— *Same.* 16°. bds., 80c. . . . . *Routledge.*
— *See also* Fielding, H., *and* Smollett, T.; — Goldsmith, O., Johnson, S., Shenstone, W., *and* Smollett, T.; — Hume, D: History of Eng.; — Lesage, A. R., Adventures of Gil Blas.

Smoot, R. K. Parliamentary principles in their applic. to the Presb. Church. 16°. *net*, $1 . . *N. Y. Ref. Ch. Bd.*

Smuggler. Banim, J. $1.50 . . . . *Harper.*

Smuggler. *See* James, G. P. R.

Smuggler of St. Malo. 8°. pap., 25c. . . . . . . *Dick & F.*

Smuggler's daughter: drama. 16°. pap., 15c. . . *French.*

Smuggler's daughter and other tales; by T. S. Arthur, F: Marryat, Mrs. S. C. Hall, Maxwell, Chas. Lamb, etc. 8°. pap., 25c. . . . . *U. P. James.*

Smuggler's ghost. Wood, E. P. 25c. . . . . . . *Peterson.*

Smyth, Alex. Jesus of Nazareth: true hist. of the man called Jesus Christ; given through the mediumship of A. Smyth by Paul and Judas. ('64.) 4th ed. 12°. '72. $1.50 . . . . *Rel. Phil.*

Smyth, Egb. C. Value of the study of church history in ministerial education: lecture. 8°. '74. pap., 25c. . . . . *Draper.*

Smyth, J: H. Law of homestead and exemptions. 8°. shp., $5 . . . . *S. Whitney.*

Smyth, Piazzi. Our inheritance in the great pyramid. ill. 12°. $6 . . . . *Routledge.*

Smyth, T: Calvin and his enemies: memoir of life, character and principles of Calvin. 18°. 50c. *Pres. Bd.*
— Ecclesiastical catechism of the Presbyterian Church. 18°. '68. 50c.; hf. bd., 30c. . . . . *Pres. Com.*
— Well in the valley. 16°. $1.25 . . . . *Am. S. S.*
— Why do I live? 18°. '57. 40c. . . . . *Am. Tr.*

Smyth, Warington Wilkinson. Rudimentary treatise on coal and coal mining. 4th. ed., rev. ill. 12°. $1.75 . . . . *Baird.*

Smyth, W: Lectures on French revolution. 2 v. 12°. (Bohn.) ea., $1.25 . . . . *Little, B. & Co.*
— *Same.* 2 v. 12°. (Bohn.) ea., $1.40 . . *Scribner, W. & A.*
— *Same.* 2 v. 12°. (Bohn.) ea., $1.50 . . . . . . *Lippincott.*
— Lectures on modern history. 2 v. 12°. (Bohn.) ea., $1.25 . . . . *Little, B. & Co.*
— *Same.* 2 v. 12°. (Bohn.) ea., $1.40 . . *Scribner, W. & A.*
— *Same.* 2 v. 12°. (Bohn.) ea., $1.50 . . . . . . *Lippincott.*

Smyth, W: New elementary algebra. ('50.) New ed. 12°. '68. hf. bd., $1.25 . . . . *Bailey.*

Smythe, C: R. Letters on the public school question. 12°. '70. pap., 10c. . . . . *Fox.*

Smythies, *Mrs.* Gordon. Breach of promise. [Fiction.] 8°. pap., 50c. . . . . *Harper.*
— Jilt (The). 8°. pap., 50c. . . . . *Harper.*

Snail-shell harbor. Langille, J. H. $1.25 . . . . . *Hoyt.*

Snake in the grass. Egan, P. 50c. . . . . *De Witt.*

Snakes in the grass. Buckstone, J. B. 15c. . . *French.*

Snapping turtles. Buckstone, J. B. 15c. *De Witt; French.*

Snarleyow. *See* Marryat, F:

Snarly or Sharly. 18°. 50c. . . . . *Am. S. S.*

Snatches of song. *See* McMullen, Ma. A.

Sneed, Achilles. *See* Kentucky, Court of Appeals reports.

Sneed, J: L. T. *See* Tennessee, Sup. Court reports.

Snell, *Mrs.* C: Isabelle de Verneuil; or, the convent of St. Mary's. 12°. '73. $1; $1.50 . . *Kelly, P. & Co.*

Snell, Eb. S. *See* Olmsted, D.

Snipsnaps and snickerings of Simon Snodgrass. ill. 16°. pap., 25c. . . . . *Dick & F.*

Snoblace ball. 12°. 25c. . . . . *Carleton.*

Snodgrass, W: D. Scripture doctrine of sanctification stated and defended against errors of perfectionism. 18°. 35c. . . . . *Pres. Bd.*

Snow, Herb. *See* Kynaston, Herb.

Snow, So. P., *and* Floy, H: Christmas stories about Santa Claus. ill. sq. 18°. '72. 25c. . . *Meth. Bk. Conc.*

Snow berries. Cary, A. $1.50 . . . . **Osgood.*

Snow bird. *See* Our song books.

Snow bound. Baker, G. M. 25c. . . . . *Lee & S.*

Snow bound. *See* Whittier, J. G.

Snow drop. 18°. 60c. *Cong. Pub.*

Snow drop. Burnand, F. C. 15c. . . . . *French.*

Snow drop. *See* Flower garlands for little gleaners.

Snow drop. *See* Mackarness, *Mrs.* M. A.

Snow drop. Reinecke, C. $3 . . . . *Schirmer.*

Snow drop; or, adventures of a white rabbit; written by herself. ill. 18°. 90c. . . . . *Nelson.*

Snow drop lib. 5 v. ill. 16°. $3.60 . . . . *Hoyt.*
Cont.: Jessica's first prayer, by H. Smith. — Billy's Christmas tree, by S. F. Keene. — Jessica's mother, by H. Smith. — Leila among the mountains, by L. Larcom. — Whiter than snow.

Snow drop lib. ('70). 4th ed. 6 v. ill. 18°. '74. $3. *Perkinpine.*
Cont.: Snow drops. — Only a penny. — Little Humpy. — New chair. — Only love. — Babes in the balloon.

Snow drop ser. 6 v. 18°. $3.50 . . . . *Cong. Pub.*
Cont.: Martha's home. — Little Aggie's snow drops. — Susie's flowers. — Hope on. — Golden secret. — Matty's missionary box.

Snow drops. ('70.) 4th ed. ill. 18°. '74. 50c. *Perkinpine.*

Snow drifts; or, a year of orphanage; by author of "Ella Dalton." 18°. 75c. . . . . *Pres. Bd.*

Snow flakes. Warren, I. P. $2.50 . . . . *Bost. Am. Tr.*

Snow image. *See* Hawthorne, N.

Snow man. Sand, G. $1.50 . . . . *Roberts.*

Snow storm; or, the true sources of personal and domestic enjoyment. 18°. 40c. . . . . *Am. S. S.*

Snow storms and sunbeams. 16°. 90c. . . (?) *Martien.*

Snowball, J: C. Elements of plane and spherical trigonometry. 10th ed. cr. 8°. '63. $2 . . *Macmillan.*
— *and* Lund, T: Cambridge course of element. natural philos. for degree of B.A. 5th ed., rev. and enl. cr. 8°. $1.75 . . . . *Macmillan.*

Snowden, Ja. Ross. Coins of the Bible and its money terms. 18°. 45c. . . . . *Pres. Bd.*
— Manual of coins. pl. 8°. $4.50 . . . . *Lippincott.*
— Medals: descript. of medals and other objects of interest in museum of the mint; with notices of directors of the mint, 1792–1851. ill. imp. 8°. $5.50 . . . . *Lippincott.*

Snowed in. ('70.) 4th ed. ill. 18°. '74. 50c. *Perkinpine.*

Snowed up. Fosdick, C. A. $1.25 . . . . *Porter.*

Snowed up. Norris, E. M. $1 . . . . *Dutton.*

Snyder, S. J. H. The lost children. 18°. 40c. *Ev. Assoc.*

So fair yet false. Vachette, E. $1.75 . . . . . . *Carleton.*

So runs the world away. Steele, A. C. 50c. . . *Harper.*

Soame, W. *See* Evidences of Christianity.

Soames, P: Treatise on manufacture of sugar from sugar cane. pl. and ill. 8°. '72. $5 . . . . *Spon.*

Soane, G: [Plays.] 5 v. 16°. ea., pap., 15c. . . *French.*
Cont.: Falls of the Clyde: melodrama. — Faustus. — Rob Roy. — Undine. — Young reefer: farce.

Soap maker's manual. 12°. pap., 25c. . . . . . *Haney.*

Sober thoughts on staple themes. Randolph, R. $1. *Claxton.*

Sobieski, *King of Poland, and* Hedwig, *Queen of Poland.* Lives. ill. 16°. $1.25 . . . . *O'Shea.*

Sobieski's achievements; tr. from the French. 18°. 50c. *O'Shea.*

Sociable (The); or, 1,001 home amusements. ill. 12°. $1.50 . . . . *Dick & F.*

Social and political dependence of women. 12°. pap., 30c. . . . . *Lee & S.*

Social choir. Kingsley, G. 3 v. ea., $1.25 . . *Crocker.*

Social circle. [Music.] 4°. $2; $2.50; bds., $1.75. *Church.*

Social duties considered with ref. to the organization of effort in works of benevolence and public utility; by a man of business. fp. 8°. $1.50..*Macmillan.*
Social glee book. Mason, W., *and* Bancroft, S. A. $1.50 ....*Ditson.*
Social harp. [Hymn book.] 60c.–$1.50. (?) *Cumberland.*
Social hints for young Christians. Crosby, H. 50c. *Crowell.*
Social hymn and tune book. 16°. 75c.–$2.50; — without tunes, 60c.–$2.25....*Pres. Bd.*
Social hymns. 32°. '40. 40c....*Am. Tr.*
Social hymns and tunes. Robinson, G. C. 50c. *Cin. Meth. Bk. Conc.*
Social hymns and tunes; with services and prayers; comp. by a committee, L. J. Livermore, chairman. ('68.) 9th ed. sq. 16°. '74. 60c....*Am. Unit.*
Social influence. O'Brien, H. 75c....*Pres. Bd.*
Social law of God. Washburn, E. A. $1.50. *Whittaker.*
Social lib. 6 v. 16°. $6....*Hoyt.*
Cont.: Banished daughter. — Stories from life, by B. K. Pierce. — Parable of the rain-drop. — New stories, by C. Tucker. — Philip Martin. — Caleb White.
Social morality. Maurice, F. D. $3.50..*Macmillan.*
Social pressure. Helps, *Sir* A. $2.25....*Roberts.*
Social song. [Music.] 4°. $2; $2.50; bds., $1.75. *Church.*
Social sports; or, holiday amusements. 18°. pap., 25c....*U. P. James.*
Social stage. Baker, G. M. $1.50....*Lee & S.*
Socialistic, communistic, mutualistic and financial fragments. Greene, W. B. $1.25....*Lee & S.*
Society. Robertson, T. W. 15c. ..*De Witt; French.*
Society and solitude. Emerson, R. W. $1.50; $3. *Osgood.*
Socrates *Scholasticus.* Ecclesiastical hist. in contin. of Eusebius; with the notes of Valesius; tr. 12°. (Bohn.) $1.75....*Little, B. & Co.*
— *Same.* 12°. (Bohn.) $2..*Lippincott; Scribner, W. & A.*
Sodalist's friend. T., M. A. $1; $1.50; $2; $3. *Cunningham.*
Soden, Thdr. Practical manual for acquiring art of reading, speaking and composing Germ. ('55.) New ed. 12°. '74. $1.25....*Pounsford.*
Sofge, —. Piano school. obl. 8°. bds., $1 ...*Peters.*
Softon, G: A. Baptist trophy. 12°. '76. 75c. *So. Bapt.*
— Habitual drinking and its remedy. 18°. '74. 50c. *So. Bapt.*
Söhne (Die) Barnevelt's. *See* Schmidt-Weissenfels, E.
Sohnes (Des) Heimkehr. *See* Friedrich, F.
Solace. Taylor, T. A. 40c. ....*Cong. Pub.*
Solar hieroglyphics; or, emblematic ill. of revealed doctrine of tri-personal Godhead which are discernible in the solar light; with introd. by J. G. Ralston. 16°. '74. *net,* 75c....*Smith, E. & Co.*
Soldan, L: *See* Ahn, F., Prakt. Lehrgang d. engl. Sprache; — Amerikanisches Lesebuch.
Soldier and patriot. Owen, F. M. $1.50 ....*Cassell.*
Soldier and a sailor, a tinker and a tailor: farce. 16°. pap., 15c....*Lee & S.*
Soldier and the sorceress; or, adventures of Jane Seton. 12°. $1.75 ....*J. E. Potter.*
Soldier (The), the battle and the victory: account of work of Father Rankin in settlement of slavery question. por. 12°. 50c....*West. Tr.*
Soldier boy. Adams, W. T. $1.50....*Lee & S.*
Soldier boy ser. *See* Adams, W: T.
Soldier Fritz, and the enemies he fought. ill. 16°. '72. 75c....*Lothrop.*
Soldier of the cross: memoir of Major Vandeleur, officer of Brit. army in war of Crimea. ill. 18°. 50c. ....*N. Y. Ref. Ch. Bd.*
Soldier of the Cumberland. Holmes, M. $1. *Bost. Am. Tr.*
Soldier's child. 18°. 75c. ....*Cong. Pub.*
Soldier's companion. [Manual.] 12°. 50c.; pap., 25c. *Peterson.*
Soldier's courtship. Poole, J. 15c. ....*French.*
Soldier's daughter. 18°. '43. 40c. ....*Am. S. S.*
Soldier's daughter. Cherry, A. 15c....*French.*
Soldier's daughter. Hanaford, P. A. 75c. *Universalist.*
Soldier's friend. Dulles, J. W. 10c. ....*Pres. Bd.*
Soldier's guide: manual and drill book for soldiers. 12°. 50c.; pap., 25c. ....*Peterson.*
Soldier's orphans. Stephens, A. S. $1.75; $1.50. *Peterson.*
Soldier's pocket-book. *See* Engles, W. M.
Soldier's progress. Courtney, J. 15c. ....*French.*
Soldier's return. ('63.) New ed. ill. 16°. '71. $1..*Hoyt.*
Soldier's ring. Flint, S. A. 50c. ....*Cong. Pub.*
Soldier's story of his captivity. Goss, W. L. *$2.50. *Lee & S.*
Soldier's wife. Reynolds, G. W. M. 75c...*Peterson.*
Soldiers and patriots of the revolution. Banvard, J. $1.25 ....*Lothrop.*
Soldiers and servants of Christ. 3 v. 16°. $4..*Lothrop.*
Cont.: American woman in China. — Good fight. — Dr. Grant and the mountain Nestorians.
Soldiers of the Bible. Thayer, W. M. $1.25. *Perkinpine.*
Soldiers' memorial: dedication of the soldiers' monument at Worcester, Mass., July 15, 1874. ill. 8°. '75. *net,* $1 ....*Putnam & D.*
Solger, Rhld. Anton in Amerika. [Fiction.] 2 v. 12°. '72. $1.50; pap., $1....*Steiger.*
— *See also* Roemer, J., Polyglot reader.
Soliloquy of the soul. *See* Thomas a *Kempis.*
Solitaries. Heyse, P. 25c....*Claxton.*
Solitary hunter. *See* Palliser, J.
Solitude of Christ. Phelps, A. 50c.; 15c. *Bost. Am. Tr.*
Solitude sweetened. Meikle, J. $1..*U. P. Bd. of Pub.*
Solitudes of nature and of man. Alger, W. R. $1.50; $2....*Roberts.*
Solly, N. Neal. Memoir of David Cox; with photos. from drawings by himself and fac-similes of his letters. roy. 8°. $15; mor., $20..*Scribner, W. & A.*
— Memoir of William James Miller; with orig. letters and account of his travels and of his principal works. ill. imp. 8°. $12 ....*Scribner, W. & A.*
Solly, S. Edn. Manitou, Colorado, U. S.: its mineral waters and climate. 8°. '75. pap., 25c... *Williams.*
Solomon, Fel. Practical religion. sm. 4°. '76. $1. (?) *F. Solomon.*
Solomon, *Uncle (pseud.)* *See* Uncle Solomon *(pseud.)*
Solomonic writings. Delitzsch, F. J. 3 v. ea., $3. *Scribner, W. & A.*
Soltau, H: W. Holy vessels and furniture of the tabernacle of Israel, scripturally explained, and ill. by chromo-liths. New ed. obl. 8°. (Lond.) '73. $7; hf. mor., $16 ....*Wiley.*
Solway family. [Juvenile.] 16°. 50c. (?) *Cumberland.*
Some coats that fit. Phelps, P. 60c....*Cong. Pub.*
Some elements of religion. *See* Liddon, H. P.
Some modern difficulties. Baring-Gould, S. $2..*Pott.*
Some modern difficulties resp. facts of nature and revelation. Moorhouse, J. $1....*Macmillan.*
Some talk about animals. Helps, *Sir* A. $1.75. *Routledge.*
Some week-days in Lent. Wilkinson, G. H. 75c.; 25c. ....*Dutton.*
Some women's hearts. Moulton, L. C. $1.50..*Roberts.*
Somebody. Austin, S. $1 ....*Dutton.*
Somebody else. Planché, J. R. 15c....*French.*

Somebody's nobody. Maltby, C. A. 15c.....*Ames.*
Somebody's coat: Ethiop. drama. 16°. pap., 15c. *French.*
Somebody's darlings. Pratt, L. M. 75c....*Lothrop.*
Somebody's luggage. *See* Dickens, C:
Somers, G. G., Williams, W. R., *and* Hill, L. L. (*ed.*) Baptist library: standard Baptist works. roy. 8°. $4 ....*Sheldon.*
Somers, Rob. Southern states since the war. map. 8°. '71. $3.50....................*Macmillan.*
Somerset, *Duke of.* [E: Adolphus St. Maur *or* Seymour.] Christian theology and modern skepticism. 12°. '72. $1 ....*Appleton.*
Somerset, C. A. [Plays.] 9 v. 16°. ea., pap., 15c. *French.*

Cont.: Crazy Jane: play. — Day after the fair: farce. — Female Massaroni. — Mistletoe bough. — Sea (The). — Shakespeare's early days. — Twins of Warsaw. — Yes: farce. — Zelina.

— Mistletoe bough: melodrama. 16°. pap., 15c...*Ames.*
Somerset, Ph. (*ed.*) Helping hand: cook, medical and general receipt book. [In Eng. or Germ.] 8°. pap., 25c.........................*Barclay.*
Somerville, Martha. Personal recollections from early life to old age. 8°. '74. $2.50 ....*Roberts.*
Somerville, Ma. Connection of the physical sciences. 12°. $1.............................*Harper.*
— Physical geography. New ed.; with notes and gloss. by W. S. Ruschenberger. 12°. $1.75..*Sheldon.*
Somerville Hall. *See* Happy child's lib.
Something about eyes, and other stories. ill. 24°. 25c.............................*Bost. Am. Tr.*
— *See also* Banner stories.
Something new for my little friends: stories in verse. 12°. '65. $1.............*Claxton; Lippincott.*
Something to do. [Fiction.] 8°. '71. $1.25; pap., 75c. ....*Estes.*
Sommer, H. B. *See* Cohen, D. S., *and* Sommer, H. B.
Sommer, M. M. Practical guide to double-entry bookkeeping in tabular form, and commercial calculations adapted to the comprehension of everybody. 8°. '76. pap., 75c..................*Dennis.*
Sommernachts-Traum (Ein). *See* Shakespeare, W:
Sommers, Jane R. (*pseud.*) *See* Jones, Cornelia.
Somnambula (La). Byron, H. J. 15c......*French.*
Somnambulist. Moncrieff, W. T. 15c......*French.*
Son and stranger. *See* Ditson.
Son-in-law: opera. 16°. pap., 15c..........*French.*
Son of a genius. *See* Hofland, *Mrs.* B.
Son of man. Coulin, F. $1.75..............*Claxton.*
Son of man. Wickes, T. $1...........*Bost. Am. Tr.*
Son of a night. Gayler, C. 15c............*French.*
Son of the organ-grinder. Schwartz, M. S. $1.25; $1.50; $1.............................*Porter.*
Son of the Pyrenees; or, perseverance. 18°. 25c. *Scribner, W. & A.*
Son of the soil. *See* Oliphant, *Mrs.* M. O. W.
Son of the soil: romantic play. 16°. pap., 15c...*French.*
Son of the wilderness: drama. 16°. pap., 15c...*French.*
Song and scenery. Moffat, J. C. $1.50; $2..*Robertson.*
Song basket: songs and choruses for the piano forte. 4°. '73. $2; $2.50; bds., $1.50........*Ditson.*
Song book of the school room. Mason, L., *and* Webb, G. J. 75c. ....*Ditson.*
Song cabinet. Allen, C. G. 45c.; 60c......*T. J. Hall.*
Song crown. Woodbury, I. B. $2 .....*Huntington.*
Song diamonds: songs, ballads, etc. 4°. $3; $4; bds., $2.50.........................*Brainard.*
Song echo. Perkins, H. S. 75c. ....*Peters.*
Song era. Root, F. W. 75c.................*Church.*
Song evangel. Hammond, E. P. 35c.; 30c...*Biglow.*
Song festival. Taylor, V. C. $1 ....*Ditson.*
Song flowers. Parker, E. P. 35c........*Hamersley.*
Song fountain. Tillinghast, W., *and* Horton, D. P. 40c. ....*Schermerhorn.*
Song garden. *See* Mason, L.
Song garland. Suffern, J. W. 35c........*Brainard.*
Song gift: collection of songs, etc., by different authors. 4°. '72. $2; $2.50; bds., $1.50..*Ditson.*
Song herald. Palmer, H. R. 75c. ....*Church.*
Song king. Palmer, H. R. 75c. ....*Church.*
Song land. Emerson, I. 50c............*Brown & G.*
Song life. Phillips, P. 50c...*Harper; Meth. Bk. Conc.*
Song monarch. Palmer, H. R., *and* Emerson, L. O. 75c.......................................*Ditson.*
Song of the angels. 18°. 25c................*Am. S. S.*
Song of the bell. *See* Romberg, A.; — Schiller, J. F. v.
Song of a bird. 32°. 15c. ....*Am. Bapt.*
Song of Hiawatha. Longfellow, H. W. $1.50; $2.50. *Osgood.*
Song of Italy. Swinburne, A. C. 25c......**Osgood.*
Song of the new creation. Bonar, H. $1.25..*Carter.*
Song of the redeemed. Harsha, J. W. $1.75..*Lippincott.*
Song of the shirt. *See* Hood, T:
Song of Solomon. *See* Bible.
Song of Solomon. *See* Newton, A. L.
Song of Solomon. Withington, L. $1.75 .... *Tilton.*
Song of the sower. Bryant, W. C. $5; $9..*Appleton.*
Song queen. Palmer, H. R. 50c.; 60c......*Church.*
Song tablet. Emerson, I. 50c...........*Brown & G.*
Song treasures: collection of songs. 4°. $3; $4; $2.50. *Brainard.*
Song tree. Bliss, P. P. $2.25; $1.75 ......*Church.*
Song without words. Charles, E. $1.........*Dodd.*
Songs and stories. *See* Nursery lib.
Songs by the way. Doane, G. W. $2......*Munsell.*
Songs for all seasons. *See* Tennyson, Alfr.
Songs for Cath. schools. 18°. 50c...........*Sadlier.*
Songs for Christian worship. Robinson, C. S. $1.50; $3.50; $5.50 ....*Barnes.*
Songs for little folks. ill. 16°. '74. 75c.....*Lothrop.*
Songs for little folks. Crafts, W. F., *and* Merrill, J. B. 60c.; 35c. ....*Biglow.*
Songs for little folks. Leslie, H. $1.50......*Cassell.*
Songs for the little ones at home. Ward, M. O. 70c.; 80c. ....*Am. Tr.*
Songs for my children. Chaplin, J. D. 55c. *Bost. Am. Tr.*
Songs for the new life. Jones, D. E. $1.60; $3.50. *Church.*
Songs for our darlings. Tilton, S. W. $1; 60c. *Tilton.*
Songs for the sanctuary. *See* Robinson, C. S.
Songs for social and public worship. Kirk, E. N. 75c. *Hoyt.*
Songs for social and public worship; comp. by a N. E. pastor. large 8°. '58. $1.15...........*Hoyt.*
Songs for to-day. Perkins, T. E., Taylor, A., *and* Sanders, C. W. 40c.......................*Biglow.*
Songs for the wee ones. Fillmore, J. H. 25c. *Chase; Fillmore.*
Songs from the old dramatists. Richardson, A. S. $2.50. *Hurd & H.*
Songs from the southern seas. *See* O'Reilly, J. B.
Songs in the house. 18°. 75c..............*Carter.*
Songs in many keys. Holmes, O. W. $1.50..*Osgood.*
Songs in the night; or, hymns for the sick and suffering; with introd. by A. C. Thompson. sq. 16°. $1. (?) *Shepard.*
Songs in the valley of Achor. Downing, S. E. C. 60c.; 75c...................................*Randolph.*

Songs of the affections. *See* Hemans, *Mrs.* F. D.
Songs of the Bible. Ogden, W. A., *and* Abbey, A. J. 35c. .... *W. W. Whitney.*
Songs of the church. Davies, G. C. $1..*Pounsford.*
Songs of the church. Robinson, C. S. $2.50; $4.50; $6.50 .... *Barnes.*
Songs of Columbia; with music and piano-forte accomp.; ed. by editors of "Acta Columbiana." 8°. $1.75. *Taintor.*
Songs of consolation. Knox, I. C. $1.50..*Macmillan.*
Songs of the cross. Lorenz, E. S. 35c...*Un.B.Pub.*
Songs of delight for the Sunday school. Parvin, Z. M. 35c. .... *Barnes.*
Songs of devotion for Christian associations. Doane, W. H. 75c.; $1.25; 50c.............. *Biglow.*
Songs of early and later years. Crawford, M. J. E. $1.25.............................. *Claxton.*
Songs of faith. Tenney, J. N., *and* Hoffman, E. A. 35c.............................. *Brainard.*
Songs of glory. Fillmore, J. H. 30c. *Chase; Fillmore.*
Songs of grace. Carpenter, J. E. 25c.....*Routledge.*
Songs of Ireland. Barry, M. J. $1........*Noonan.*
Songs of Ireland and other lands. 18°. $1....*Sadlier.*
Songs of joy. Demarest, G. L. 40c..... *Universalist.*
Songs of joy. Tenney, J. H. 35c.; 30c......*Lee & S.*
Songs of love. 12°. pap., 20c. .... *Hurst.*
Songs of love. Palmer, H. R. 35c.......... *Church.*
Songs of many seasons. Holmes, O. W. $2; $3.50; $4.50 .... *Osgood.*
Songs of our youth. *See* Craik, D. M.
Songs of praise. Baird, E. T. 35c. ......*Pres. Com.*
Songs of prayer and praise. 18°. 75c...*Bost.Am. Tr.*
Songs of religion and life. Blackie, J. S. $1.50. *Scribner.*
Songs of the righteous. Carpenter, J. E. 25c. *Routledge.*
Songs of salvation. Perkins, T. E., *and* Taylor, A. 35c. .... *Biglow.*
Songs of seven. *See* Ingelow, J.
Songs of the Sierras. Miller, J. $1.50......*Roberts.*
Songs of the soul. Prime, S. I. $5; $9..... *Carter.*
Songs of the spirit. Odenheimer, W. H., *and* Bird, F. M. $3 .... *Randolph.*
Songs of summer. Stoddard, R. H. $1..... *Osgood.*
Songs of the sun lands. Miller, J. $1.50 ...*Roberts.*
Songs of the temple. Baker, B. F., *and* Fargo, J. F. $1.25 .... *Lee & S.*
Songs of three centuries. *See* Whittier, J. G.
Songs of the woodland, the garden and the sea. sm. 4°. '62. $1.25 .... *Randolph.*
Songs of Yale. Elliot, C. S. $1......*H. G. Phillips.*
Songs of yesterday. Taylor, B. F. $4; $8..*Griggs.*
Songs of Zion. 18°. '64. 60c.; shp., $1; mor., $2. *Am. Tr.*
Songs of Zion. Summers, T. O. 80c.; 60c.; $1.75. *So. Meth.*
Songstresses of Scotland. Keddie, H., *and* Watson, J. L. 2 v. $5........................ *Routledge.*
Sonnambula (La). *See* Bellini, V.
Sonne (Die) bringt est an den Tag. *See* Silberstein, A:
Sonnenschein, A., *and* Meiklejohn, J. M. D. English method of teaching to read. 12°. pap., 50c. *Macmillan.*
Sonnenschein für Regentage. ill. 4°. '75. $1..*Am. Tr.*
Sonnenstrahlen, od. zwölf Kapitel üb. d. Bibel. 18°. 45c.............................. *Ev. Assoc.*
Sonntag, A. Terrestrial magnetism in Mexico. 4°. '59. pap., $1.25................... *Smith. Inst.*
Sonntagschul A-B-C-Buch. 12°. '74. bds., 12c. *Am. Tr.*
Sonntagschul-Handbuch (Das). 12°. '71. $1. *Ev. Assoc.*
Sonntagschul-Harfe. Wonnberger, C. 35c...*Pilger.*
Sonntagschulliederbuch. 32°. 25c.; 45c...*Ev. Assoc.*
Sonrel, L. Bottom of the sea; tr. and ed. by E. Rich. ill. 12°. '75. $1.25.................... *Scribner.*
Sooner or later. Brooks, C. S. $2; $1.50..*Harper.*
Sophia and the gypsies. *See* Baker, *Mrs.* H. N. W.
Sophia Bleecker; or, the girl who was always in a hurry. 18°. 45c.................... *Pres. Bd.*
Sophia's supper. Addison, H. R. 15c.......*French.*
Sophie Danforth's school life. Buhler, H. $1.25. *Dutton.*
Sophie De Brentz; or, the sword of truth; by author of "Hillside farm." ('60.) New ed. ill. 18°. '75. 60c................................ *Hoyt.*
Sophie Krantz. Keene, S. 90c........ (?) *Martien.*
Sophie's dream; [also] Lokka. 32°. 20c.; 15c. *Dutton.*
Sophie's letter-book. Baker, H. N. W. $1. *H. A. Young.*
Sophisms of protection. Bastiat, F. $1....*Putnam.*
Sophocles. Ex nov. rec. G. Dindorfii, acc. verb. et nom. index. 18°. '71. 75c........... *Harper.*
— Tragedies: Oxford tr. New ed., rev. 12°. $1.50. *Harper.*
— *Same.* 12°. (Bohn.) $1.75............ *Little, B. & Co.*
— *Same.* 12°. (Bohn.) $2..*Lippincott; Scribner, W. & A.*
— *Same;* tr. by T. Francklin. 18°. 75c.....*Harper.*
— *Same;* tr. by E. H. Plumptre, with biog. and app. cr. 8°. $3.......................... *Routledge.*
— — [Outlined and expl.] by C. W. Collins. (Anc. classics for Eng. readers.) 16°. $1. *Lippincott; Little, B. & Co.*
— Ajax [Gk.]; ed. by R. C. Jebb. 12°. '71. $1.50. *Allyn.*
— Antigone [Gk.]; with notes by J. Milner. 16°. (Weale.) 80c.......................... *Allyn.*
— *Same;* with notes by Smead. 12°. $1.75..*Appleton.*
— *Same;* with notes by T. D. Woolsey. 12°. *net,* 94c. *Hamersley.*
— Electra [Gk.]; with notes by T. D. Woolsey. 12°. *net,* 94c.......................... *Hamersley.*
— *Same;* ed. by R. C. Jebb. New ed., rev. with add. notes by R. H. Mather. ('72.) 2d ed. 16°. '75. $1.50 .... *Allyn.*
— *Eng.* Electra; tr. by J. G. Brincklé. 8°. '73. $1.50 .... *J. Campbell & Son.*
— Œdipus tyrannus [Gk.]; with notes by H. Crosby. 12°. $1.50.......................... *Appleton.*
— *Same;* with notes by H. Young. 16°. (Weale.) 40c. *Allyn.*
— *Same;* ed. with notes and explan. of metres by J. M. White. ('73.) 2d ed. 12°. '75. $1.50..*Ginn.*
Sophocles, E. A. First book in Greek. 12°. *net,* 67c. *Hamersley.*
— Greek exercises. 12°. *net,* $1......... *Hamersley.*
— Greek exercises and key. 12°. *net,* $1.30. *Hamersley.*
— Greek grammar. 12°. *net,* $1.50. — New ed., rev. 12°. *net,* $1.50 .... *Hamersley.*
— Greek lessons. 18°. *net,* 67c......... *Hamersley.*
— Greek lexicon of Roman and Byzantine periods. roy. 8°. '70. $10.................... *Little, B. & Co.*
— Romaic or modern Greek grammar. 12°. hf. roan, $2.50.............................. *Ware.*
Sophomores of Radcliffe. Kellogg, E. $1.25..*Lee & S.*
Soprano. Barnard, C. F., *jr.* $1; 60c......*Loring.*
Sordello, Strafford, Christmas-eve and Easter-day. Browning, R. $1.50.................. *Osgood.*
Sorer, B., *jr.* *See* Cincinnati, Sup. Court reports.
Soret, F: *See* Goethe, J. W. v., Conversations with Eckermann and Soret.
Sorignet, A: Sacred cosmogony; tr. by P. R. Kenrick. 8°. '62. $3........................ *Fox.*

Sorrell, W. J. Border marriage: comic drama. 16°. pap., 15c. . . . . *French.*

— *See also* French, S., *and* Sorrell, W. J.

Sorrowing yet rejoicing. 32°. 50c. . . . . *Carter.*

Sot weed factor. Cook, E. $1.25 . . . . *Shea.*

Sotheran, C: Alessandro di Cagliostro, imposter or martyr? 18°. '75. pap., 10c. *D. M. Bennett; Sabin.*

— Genealogical memoranda rel. to family of Sotheran. ill. sm. 4°. '71–'73. bds., $6 . . . . *Sabin.*

— Percy Bysshe Shelley as a philosopher and reformer; incl. sonnet by C. W. Frederickson. ill. 8°. '76. $1.25; pap., $1 . . . . *Sabin; Somerby.*

Souillard, F. A. Book of practical receipts. 16°. pap., 25c. . . . . *Dick & F.*

Soul and body. *See* Evans, W. F.

Soul gatherer; by the author of "Way home." *See* Earnest Christian's lib.

Soul in nature. *See* Oersted, H. C.

Soul of honor: drama. 16°. pap., 15c. . . . . . . *French.*

Soul of things. Denton, W. *and* E. M. F. 3 v. $5. *Denton.*

Soul on Calvary, meditating on sufferings of Jesus Christ; tr. from the Fr. 18°. 75c. . . *Coddington.*

Soul problems. Peck, J. E. 75c.; 50c. . . . . *Somerby.*

Soule, Josh. Object and nature of relig. worship: discourse, N. Y., 1818. 12°. '48. pap., 10c. *So. Meth.*

Soule R: Dictionary of Eng. synonymes and synonymous or parallel expressions. 3d ed., rev. and enl. 12°. '73. $2; hf. cf., $4 . . . . *Little, B. & Co.*

— *and* Campbell, L. J. Pronouncing handbook of words often mispronounced. 24°. 60c. — 32°. 35c. . . . . *Lee & S.*

— *and* Wheeler, W: A. First lessons in reading. 16°. bds., 35c. . . . . *Lee & S.*

— — Manual of Eng. pronunciation and spelling; with vocab. 12°. $1.50 . . . . *Lee & S.*

Soul's cry and the Lord's answer. sq. 18°. '74. 40c.; 50c. — (chp. ed.), 20c.; pap., 12c. . . . . . . *Am. Tr.*

Soul's inquiries answered in words of Scripture. *See* Moon, G. W.

Soundings from the "Atlantic." Holmes, O. W. $1.75. *Osgood.*

Sounds from secret chambers. Searing, L. C. $1.50. *Osgood.*

Source of salvation. Mayer, I. 50c. . . . . . . *Frank.*

Souter, R., *jr.* *See* Claridge, C. J., *and* Souter, R., *jr.*

South, Rob. Sermons preached upon several occasions; with memoir of author. 5 v. 8°. '66–'71. $15; shp., $20; hf. cf., $25 . . . . *Hurd & H.*

South Carolina. Chancery reports, 1784–1868. 22 v. 8°. shp. . . . . *Callaghan.*

Cont.: 1784-1816, by H. W. Desaussure, 4 v. in 2, $16. — 1824, by W. Harper, $6. — 1825–'27, by D. J. McCord, 2 v. in 1, $12. — 1830-1, by H. Bailey, $7. — 1831-2, by J. S. G. Richardson, $8. — 1833–'36, by W. R. Hill, 2 v. in 1, $12. — 1836-7, by W. Riley, $7. — 1837–8, by C. W. Dudley, $5.50. — 1839–'40, by L. Cheves, $6. — 1840–'42, by J. McMullan, $6. — 1850–'68, by J. S. G. Richardson, 11 v., $66.

— *Same.* 1784–1816; by H. W. Desaussure. 2d ed., rev. 4 v. in 2. 8°. shp., $16 . . . . *Kay.*

— *Same.* 1842–'44; by R. H. Speers. 8°. '44. . *State.*

— *Same.* 1846–'50; by J. A. Strobhart. 4 v. 8°. '48–'51 . . . . *State.*

— Constitutional Court reports, 1817–8; by J. Mill. 8°. '37 . . . . *State.*

— Reports in superior courts since the revolution [1783–1804]; by E. H. Bay. 2 v. 8°. 1809–'11. *State.*

— Reports, 1793–1838. 12 v. 8°. shp. . . . *Callaghan.*

Cont.: 1793–1816, by J. Brevard, 3 v. in 2, $18. — 1817–'20, by H. J. Nott and D. J. McCord, 2 v. in 1, $10. — 1821–'28, by D. J. McCord, 4 v. in 2, $18. — 1823–4, by W. Harper, $5. — 1828–'32, by H. Bailey, 2 v., $14. — 1833–'37, by W. R. Hill, 3 v. in 2, $14. — 1836–7, by W. Riley (law and equity), $7. — 1837–8, by C. W. Dudley, $6.50.

— *Same.* 1838–9; by W. Rice. 8°. '39 . . . . *State.*

South Carolina, *continued.*

— *Same.* 1839–'40; by L. Cheves. 8°. shp., $5. *Callagha*

— *Same.* 1840–'42; by J. McMullan. 2 v. in 1. 8°. shp $10 . . . . *Callagha*

— *Same.* 1842–'51. 11 v. 8° . . . . *Stat*

Cont.: 1842–'44, by R. H. Speers, 2 v. — 1846–'50, by J. Strobhart, 5 v. — 1844–'51, by J. S. G. Richardson (v. 1–4), 4

— *Same.* 1851–'60; by J. S. G. Richardson (v. 5–12 8 v. 8°. shp., $50 . . . . *Callagha*

— *Same.* 1860–'66; by J. S. G. Richardson. 8°. shp $8 . . . . *Callagha*

Note. Forms v. 13 (law) and 12 (equity) of Richardsor reports.

— *Same.* 1866–'68; by J. S. G. Richardson (v. 14, 15 2 v. 8°. shp., $12 . . . . *Callagha*

— *Same.* New ser., 1868–'75; by J. S. G. Richardso 5 v. 8°. shp., $30 . . . . *Callagha*

— — Digests. *See* Conner, J.; — Rice, W.; — Simonton, C. H., *and* Conner, J.

— Revised statutes; [by D. T. Corbin]. 8°. '73. . *Stat*

South Carolina geological survey. Report on geol. S. C.; by M. Tuomey. 4°. '48 . . . . *Stat*

South Carolina Medical Assoc. Transactions, 186 '76. 10 v. 8°. ea., pap., $1 . . . . *S. C. Me*

South Kensington Museum. Art books. *See* Ma kell, W.

— Handbook to special loan coll. of scientific apparatu ill. cr. 8°. '76. $1.25 . . . . *Scribner, W. &*

— Industrial arts: historical sketches. ill. cr. 8°. '7 $1.50 . . . . *Scribner, W. &*

South Meadows. Disosway, E. T. $1.50 . . . . *Porte*

South sea bubble. Ainsworth, W. H. 30c. *Am. New*

South sea bubbles. Herbert, G. R. C., *and* Kingsle G. H. $1.50 . . . . *Appleto*

South sea idyls. Stoddard, C. W. $1.25 . . . . *Osgoo*

South sea whaler. Kingston, W. H. G. $1.50 . . *Nelso*

South songs. DeLeon, T. C. $1.75 . . . . *Eyric*

Southall, Ja. C. Recent origin of man as ill. by geo ogy and pre-historic archæology. ill. 8°. $6. *Lippincot*

Southard, L. H. Course of harmony. 12°. $2.25. *Gordo*

— Elements of thorough base and harmony. 12°. '6 67c.; bds., 50c. . . . . *Ditso*

— Mass in F; for two trebles and base. obl. 4°. '6 pap., 50c. . . . . *Ditso*

— Offering: coll. of church music. obl. 8°. '66. bds $1.50 . . . . *Ditso*

— Short mass in D. obl. 4°. '67. pap., 50c. . . *Ditso*

— Standard singing school; based upon school of Ga cia with add. and adaptations to Eng. languag 4°. '68. bds., $3 . . . . *Ditso*

— *See also* Baker, B. F., *and* Southard, L. H.; — Bu ler, C., *and* Southard, L. H.; — Wilcox, J. H *and* Southard, L. H.

— *and* Pratt, G. W. Bouquet. [School sing. book obl. 16°. 75c. . . . . *Gordo*

Southard, S: L. *See* New Jersey, Sup. Court repor

Southerland, B. D. L. Arithmetical table book. 1 '73. 20c. . . . . (?) *Slo*

Southern and western pocket harmonist. Walker, $1; 84c. . . . . *Desilve*

Southern and western songster. Grigg, J. 75c. *Claxto*

Southern cookery. *See* Verstille, *Mrs.* H. W.

Southern cross. Tucker, E. 75c. . . . . *Cart*

Southern explorers and colonists. Banvard, J. $1.2 *Lothro*

Southern harp. Shindler, M. S. B. D. $1.50 . . *Ditso*

Southern life; or, inside views of slavery. 8°. pa $1 . . . . *Petersc*

Southern medical student's portfolio. Wharton, M. 75c. . . . . *Claxto*

Southern Methodist hymn and tune book. Evans, C. A. 75c. . . . . *Burke.*

Southern poems of the war. Mason, E. V. $2; $3. *Murphy.*

Southern psalmist. [Baptist.] 24°. roan, $1; mor., $2; $2.50. — 18°. roan, $1.25; mor., $2.50; $3.50 . . . . *So. Bapt.*

Southern slavery in its present aspects. Goodwin, D. R. $1.50 . . . . *Claxton.*

Southern states since the war. Somers, R. $3.50. *Macmillan.*

Southern voices. Holcombe, W.H. $1.50 . . *Lippincott.*

Southern wealth and northern profit. Kettell, T. P. 25c. . . . . *Van Evrie.*

Southerne, T: Oroonoko: tragedy. 16°. pap., 15c. *French.*

Southerner: farce. 16°. pap., 15c. . . . . *French.*

Southey, Caro. Bowles. Young grey head. 16°. '68. pap., 10c. . . . . *Randolph.*

Southey, C: Cuthbert. Life and correspondence of Rob. Southey. por. 8°. $2; shp., $2.50 . . *Harper.*

Southey, Rob. Poetical works. ill. 8°. mor., $10. — (chp. ed.), ill. and por., shp., $3.50 . . . *Appleton.*

— *Same.* (Household ser.) ill. 16°. $1.50; mor., $3. *Lee & S.*

— *Same.* (Presentation poets.) ill. 16°. $1.75. *Routledge.*

— *Same;* incl. Joan of Arc, and minor poems. ill. 16°. $1.50 . . . . *Lee & S.*

— *Same;* with memoir by H. T. Tuckerman. 10 v. por. 18°. $10 . . . . *Osgood.*

— — *See also* Goldsmith, Ol., Poems.

— Book of the church; with notes from Vindiciæ Ecclesiæ Anglicanæ. 12°. $1.75; hf. cf., $3.75; cf., $5 . . . . *Scribner, W. & A.*

— Chronicle of the Cid. *See* Lockhart, J. G., Spanish ballads.

— Common place book; ed. by J. W. Warter. 2 v. 8°. $3; hf. cf., $7.50 . . . . *Harper.*

— Doctor (The). 12°. $1.25 . . . . *Harper.*

— Joan of Arc, etc.; ed. by R. A. Willmott, with biog. and crit. notice. ill. 12°. $2.25; hf. cf., $3.50; mor., $5 . . . . *Routledge.*

— Life of J: Wesley, and rise and progress of Methodism, with notes by S. T. Coleridge, etc.; ed. by C. C. Southey. 12°. (Bohn.) $1.75. *Little, B. & Co.*

— *Same.* 12°. (Bohn.) $2 . . *Lippincott; Scribner, W. & A.*

— *Same.* 2d Am. ed., with notes, etc., by D. Curry. 2 v. 12°. $2.50; hf. cf., $6 . . . . *Harper.*

— Life of Lord Nelson. 18°. 75c. . . . . *Harper.*

— *Same.* ill. 12°. (Bohn.) $1.75 . . . . *Little, B. & Co.*

— *Same.* ill. 12°. (Bohn.) $2. *Lippincott; Scribner, W. & A.*

— Life of Oliver Cromwell. 12°. 50c. . . . . *Appleton.*

— — *See also* Young American's lib.

— Wat Tyler: dramatic poem. 12°. 20c. . . . . *Mendum.*

— *See also* Byron, *Lord, vs.* Southey, R.; — Watts, I., Horæ lyricæ; — White, H. K., Poetical works.

Southgate, H: Christus Redemptor: life, character and teachings of our Lord; ill. from anc. and mod. writers. fp. 4°. $3.50 . . . . *Cassell.*

— Gone before: manual of consolation for the bereaved, sel. from many sources. 16°. $1.50 . . *Lippincott.*

— Many thoughts of many minds: sel. from writings of celebrated authors. 2 v. 8°. ea., $6; mor., $10. *Routledge.*

— What men have said about woman: choice thoughts and sentences. ill. 12°. $2.50 . . . . . *Routledge.*

Southgate, T. L. Rudiments of vocal music; with exercises for choir boys. sq. 12°. pap., 10c. *Ditson.*

Southland writers. Tardy, M. T. 2 v. $6 . . *Claxton.*

Southward, ho! Simms, W. G. $1.15; 75c. *Widdleton.*

Southwell, G. W. Defence of forms of prayer. 16°. pap., 12c. . . . . *Dutton.*

Southwell, G. W., *continued.*

— Which is the church? or, which one of the present organized bodies is identical in hist. and doct. with the church estab. by the Apostles? 4th ed. 12°. pap., 12c. . . . . *Dutton.*

Southworth, Alvan S. Four thousand miles of African travel: personal record of a journey up the Nile and through the Soudan to Central Africa. maps and ill. 8°. '75. $2.50 . . . . *Baker, P. & Co.*

Southworth, *Mrs.* E. D. E. N. Novels. 41 v. 12°. ea., $1.75; pap., $1.50 . . . . *Peterson.*

Cont.: Allworth Abbey. — Artist's love. — Beautiful fiend. — Bridal eve. — Bride of Llewellyn. — Bride's fate: sequel to "The changed brides." — Changed brides. — Christmas guest. — Cruel as the grave. — Deserted wife. — Discarded daughter. — Fallen pride. — Family doom. — Fatal marriage. — Fortune seeker. — Fair play. — Gipsy's prophecy. — Haunted homestead. — How he won her: sequel to "Fair play." — India: the pearl of Pearl River. — Ishmael; or, in the depths. — Lady of the isle. — Lost heir of Linlithgow. — Lost heiress. — Love's labor won. — The maiden widow. — Miriam, the avenger; or, the missing bride. — The mother-in-law. — Mystery of dark hollow. — A noble lord: sequel to "Lost heir of Linlithgow." — Prince of darkness. — Retribution — Self-raised; or, from the depths. — Spectre lover. — Three beauties. — Tried for her life: sequel to "Cruel as the grave." — Two sisters. — Victor's triumph: sequel to "Beautiful fiend." — Vivia. — Widow's son. — Wife's victory.

Note. "Fallen pride" first pub. under title of "Curse of Clifton."

Southworth, *Mrs.* S. A. Hester Strong's life-work; or, the mystery solved. 16°. $1.50 . . . . *Lee & S.*

— Our Charlie; or, the little teacher. ill. 18°. 50c. *Bost. Am. Tr.*

— — *See also* Gay cottage stories.

Souvenir of baptism; by a priest of St. Sulpice of Montreal. 16°. 60c.; pap., 25c. . . . . . *Sadlier.*

Souvenir of the 19th triennial grand encampment of Knights Templar of the U. S., New Orleans, Dec. 5, 1874. 8°. '75. pap., 50c. . . . . *Waldo.*

Souvenir text-book; by author of "Thoughtful hours." [Interleaved.] 18°. 90c. . . . . *Nelson.*

Souvenirs of Notre Dame. Monroe, M. C. $2. *Cath. Pub.*

Souvestre, Emile. Au coin du feu. 12°. 75c. *G. R. Lockwood.*

— Isle of the dead; or, keeper of the lazaretto: tale of yellow fever; tr. 18°. '72. 40c. . . . . *Kenedy.*

— Leaves from a family journal; tr. ill. 12°. $1. *Appleton.*

— Legends of Brittany; tr. from the Foyer Breton by a lady. ill. 16°. $1.25 . . . . *O'Shea.*

— Loterie (La) de Francfort; [also] La jeune savante, par Mlle. Curo. ('65.) New ed. 12°. '76. pap., 25c. . . . . *Holt.*

— Philosophe (Un) sous les toits. 12°. 75c. *G. R. Lockwood.*

— *Same.* 12°. 75c.; pap., 50c. . . . . *Appleton.*

— *Same.* With table of difficulties. ('68.) New ed. 12°. '76. 75c. . . . . *Holt.*

— *Eng.* Attic philosopher in Paris; tr. 12°. 75c. *Appleton.*

— Pleasures of old age; tr. cr. 8°. $2 . . . . *Routledge.*

— Testament (Le) de Madame Patural; [also] La demoiselle de Saint-Cyr, par Comtesse Drohojowska. ('65.) New ed. 12°. '76. pap., 25c. . . . . *Holt.*

— Vieille (La) cousine; [also] Les ricochets: comédie imitée de Picard. ('65.) New ed. 12°. '76. pap., 25c. . . . . *Holt.*

Sovereign, T. American temperance spelling-book. ('67.) 14th ed. 12°. '70. per doz., hf. bd., $2.28. *Perkinpine.*

Sovereigns of the Bible. Steele, E. R. $1.25 . . *Dodd.*

Sovereigns of industry. Chamberlin, E. M. $1.25. *Lee & S.*

Sowed by the wind. Kellogg, E. $1.25 . . . . *Lee & S.*

Sower and the seed. Hall, J. 50c. . . . . *Pres. Bd.*

Sower's reward. Manning, A. 25c. . . . . . . *Peterson.*

Sowing and reaping. ('61.) New ed. ill. 18°. '72. 45c. . . . . *Hoyt.*

Sowing and reaping. *See* Howitt, Ma.

Sowing the good seed. ill. 12°. $1..........*Nelson.*

Sowing in new fields. *See* M., *Mrs.* A. S.

Sowing little seeds. *See* Minnie's lib.; — Moss rose ser.

Sowing the wind. *See* Arthur, T. S.

Sowing the wind. Linton, E. L. 50c.......*Harper.*

Soyer, Alexis. Modern domestic cookery. 12°. $1.25. *Appleton.*

— Standard cookery for the people. roy. 18°. bds., 50c. *Desilver.*

Sozomenus, Hermias. Ecclesiastical history, A. D. 324–440; [also] Ecclesiastical hist. of Philostorgius. 12°. (Bohn.) $1.75.......*Little, B. & Co.*

— *Same.* 12°. (Bohn.) $2..*Lippincott; Scribner, W. & A.*

— *See also* Greek ecclesiastical historians.

Spae wife. Boyce, J. $2..................*Noonan.*

Spain and the Spaniards. Thieblin, N. S. $1.75. *Lee & S.*

Spain revisited. Mackenzie, A. S. 2 v. $3.50..*Harper.*

Spalding, Alb. S. Little gate. *See* Pioneer lib.

Spalding, Hu. M. Jurisdiction and practice at large in city judges', mayors' and justices' courts of Indiana, and anal. of law and practice conc. personal property. 8°. '75. shp., $7.50....... *Wilstach.*

— Ohio treatise: practice and forms at large in justices' courts, and anal. of law and practice conc. personal property. 2d ed. 8°. '75. $7.50..*Wilstach.*

Spalding, J. L. Life of Rev. M. J. Spalding. por. 8°. '74. $4......................*Cath. Pub.*

Spalding, Louise Billings. The ruined statues, and other poems. 12°. $1.50...........*Lippincott.*

Spalding, Mt. J. History of the Prot. reformation in Europe: essays. 7th ed., rev. 8°. '65. $3.50; — in 2 v., $5; $6; hf. cf., $7.........*Murphy.*

— Lectures on evidences of Catholicity. 6th ed., rev. 8°. '66. $2.50; $3; $3.50; hf. cf., $4..*Murphy.*

— Miscellanea: reviews, essays and lectures. 6th ed., rev. and enl. 8°. '66. $3.50; — in 2 v., $5; $6; hf. cf., $7..........................*Murphy.*

— Papal infallibility. 8°. '70. 25c.; 50c...*Kelly, P. & Co.*

Spalding, W: History of English literature. 12°. $1.50..............................*Appleton.*

— History of Italy and the Italian islands. 3 v. ill. 18°. $2.25...............................*Harper.*

Spangenberg, A: Gli. Exposition of Christian doctrine as taught by the [Moravians]; tr. with pref. by B. La Trobe. 2d ed. 8°. (Lond.) 1796. $1.50. *Clauder.*

Note. First pub. under title of "Idea fidei Fratrum."

Spangenberg, L: Fatigue of metals under repeated strains, with various tables of results and experiments; tr. from the Germ., with pref. by S. H. Shreve. ill. 18°. '76. bds., 50c...*Van Nostrand.*

Spangler, Helen King. The physician's wife. 12°. $1.50..........................*Lippincott.*

Spaniard's crime. 8°. pap., 25c...........*De Witt.*

Spaniards in Florida. Fairbanks, G. R. $1..*C. Drew.*

Spanische Dolmetscher (Der). 18°. pap., 50c...*Radde.*

Spanish ballads. *See* Lockhart, J. G.

Spanish barber. *See* Manning, A.

Spanish brothers: tale of the 16th cent.; by author of "Dark year of Dundee." 8°. $2.50....*Nelson.*

Spanish cavalier. *See* Tucker, *Mrs.* C.

Spanish cavaliers; tr. by Mrs. J. Sadlier. 16°. 75c.; $1.25...............................*Sadlier.*

Spanish dancers. Selby, C. 15c...........*French.*

Spanish gypsy. Eliot, G. $1.50; $3; $4.... *Osgood.*

Spanish hive: select pieces from Span. authors; with a vocab. and notes. ('67.) New ed. 16°. '73. $1.25. *Holt.*

Spanish pictures. Manning, S. $3.50.......*Nelson.*

Spanking legacy. Blake, T. G. 15c.........*French.*

Spare bed: farce. 16°. pap., 15c............*French.*

Spare hours. Brown, J. 2 v. ea., $1.50; $3..*Osgood*

Spare well spend well. ill. 18°. 50c. ....*Nelson*

Sparing to spend. Arthur, T. S. $1.50....*J. E. Potte*

Spark of genius. Kellogg, E. $1.25........*Lee & S*

Sparkling jewels. Shaw, K. 30c...........*Church*

Sparkling jewels lib.: stories from the Bible. ('69. 2d ed. 4 v. ill. 18°. '72. $2.50....*Perkinpin*

Cont.: Bible portraits. — Rays from the sun. — Crumbs fro the bread of life. — My Bible-class.

Sparkling rubies. Hull, A., *and* Sanders, H. 35c. *Ditson*

Sparkling stream ser. 4 v. 12°. $5......*Nat. Tem*

Cont.: Tom Blinn's temperance society, by T. S. Arthur. — Harker family, by E. Thompson. — Job Tufton's rest, by C. Balfour. — Roy's search; or, lost in the cars, by H. C. Pearso

Sparks, Jared (*ed.*) Library of Am. biog. 10 v. po 12°. ea., $1.25; per set, hf. cf., $25.......*Harpe*

Cont.: J. Stark, by E. Everett; C. B. Brown, by W. H. Pre cott; R. Montgomery, by J. Armstrong; E. Allen, by J. Spark — A. Wilson, by W. B. O. Peabody; Capt. J. Smith, by G. Hillard. — B. Arnold, by J. Sparks. — A. Wayne, by J. Arm strong; Sir H. Vane, by C. W. Upham. — J. Eliot, by C. Franci — W. Pinkney, by H. Wheaton; W. Ellery, by E. T. Channing C. Mather, by W. B. O. Peabody. — Sir W. Phips, by F. Bowe I. Putnam, by W. B. O. Peabody; Miss L. M. Davidson, by Mi C. M. Sedgwick; D. Rittenhouse, by J. Renwick. — J. Edward by S. Miller; D. Brainerd, by W. B. O. Peabody. — Baron Ste ben, by F. Bowen; S. Cabot, by C. Hayward, jr.; W. Eaton, b C. C. Felton. — R. Fulton, by J. Renwick; H. Hudson, by H. Cleveland; J. Warren, by A. H. Everett; Father Marquette, b J. Sparks.

Sparks, W. H. Memories of fifty years: biog. notice of disting. Americans, anecdotes of remark. me etc. ('70.) 3d ed. por. 18°. '71. $2.50..*Claxto*

Sparrow, W: *See* Johns, J., *and* Sparrow, W.

Sparrowgrass papers. *See* Cozzens, F. S.

Sparry, C. Christian martyrology; or, sufferings the early Christians. ill. 8°. $2.50.....*Sowe*

Späth, A. Brosamen v. d. Herrn Tische. 18°. 25c. *Kohle*

— Evangelien (Die) des Kirchenjahrs erläutert. 16 bds., 25c....................*Brobst; Kohle*

— Zwei liturgische Andachten auf Charfreitag u. Oster 16°. pap., 10c.........................*Brobs*

— *See also* Büchner, G., Bibl. Real-u. Verbal-Han Concordanz.

Spaulding, J: Christ and the sea. 18°. '64. 25c. *Am. T*

Spaulding, M. C. Handbook of statistics of the U. 12°. '74. $1.........................*Putnam*

Spaulding, S. J. Memoir of H: C. Perkins of New buryport, [Mass.] 8°. '73. 25c. ....*Esse*

Spayth, H: American draught player: theory an practice of the scientific game of checkers. 5t ed., rev. 12°. $3....................*Dick &*

— Draughts or checkers for beginners. 16°. 75c. *Dick &*

— Game of draughts. 12°. $1.50............*Dick &*

Speak out boldly: comedy. 16°. pap., 15c...*Frenc*

Speaker's commentary. *See* Cook, F. C., Bible com mentary.

Speaker's garland. Garrett, P. 3 v. ea., $2; $2.5 *Garret*

Speaking likenesses. *See* Rossetti, C. G.

Speaking Rifle, the Indian slayer. 12°. pap., 20c. *Hurs*

Speaking to the heart. Guthrie, T. $1.50. *Carter; Routledg*

Speakman, T: H. Divisions in Society of Friend 16°. 63c............................*Lippincot*

Spear, J: Murray. Twenty years on the wing: nar of travels and labors as a missionary sent forth b the Assoc. of Beneficents in spirit-land; wit pref. by A. Putnam. 12°. '73. pap., 20c...*Colb*

Spear, S: T. Legal tender acts considered in rel. t their constitutionality and their political econom 8°. pap., 75c..................*Baker, V. & C*

Special operations of war. Lippitt, F. J. $1. *VanNostrand.*

Special performance. Harrison, W. 15c. *De Witt; French.*

Specimen of divine truths. Hellenbroek, A. per doz., $1.80 .... *N.Y.Ref.Ch.Bd.*

Specimens of macaronic poetry. Morgan, J. A. $2.75. *Hurd & H.*

Speckter, O: Fables in pictures. ill. 12°. bds., 50c. *Porter.*

— One hundred picture fables; with rhymes from the Germ. of F. Hey. sm. 8°. $1.75.... *Routledge.*

— Picture fables. ill. 12°. $2 .... *Appleton.*

Spectacle ser. *See* Lander, S. W.

Spectator Company (*pub.*) Centennial year book for 1876, and insurance register. [Annual.] imp. 8°. 75c. .... *Spectator.*

— Fire insurance register and index to resources, condition and standing of principal Am. fire ins. companies. [Annual.] 12°. pap., 25c..... *Spectator.*

— Life [insurance] agents' pocket policy register and memoranda. ('70.) 9th ed. 8°. '76. 50c. *Spectator.*

— Policy holder's pocket index to the condition and standing of Am. life insurance companies. [Annual.] 8°. pap., 25c................ *Spectator.*

— Practical hints to life insurance agents. ('70.) 15th ed. 12°. '76. pap., 25c............. *Spectator.*

Spectator (The); by Addison, Steele and others. roy. 8°. shp., $3.50................ *Pounsford.*

— *Same.* 2 v. 12°. $2.50 .... *Lippincott.*

— *Same.* 6 v. 8°. $12; shp., $18; hf. cf., $25; cf.; $35 .... *Appleton.*

— *Same.* 8 v. 16°. '72. $10; $12; hf. cf., $20; cf., $24 .... *Little,B.& Co.*

— *Same;* with introd., notes and index by H. Morley. (Globe lib.) cr. 8°. $1.75; hf. cf., $3.50; tr. cf., $5......................... *Routledge.*

— *Same;* with sketches of times of authors, index and notes. 4 v. ill. 12°. $5............. *Desilver.*

— Selected papers; with introd. essay and biog. sketches by J. Habberton. sq. 16°. '76. $1.25.. *Putnam.*

— Spectator (The) in miniature: sel. of papers of Addison, Steele, etc. 2 v. 18°. $1.50 .... *Harper.*

— *See also* Addison, J.; — Chalmers, A., British essayists.

Spectre bridegroom. *See* Irving, Wash.

Spectre bridegroom. Moncrieff, W. T. 15c... *French.*

Spectre lover. Southworth, E. D. E. N. $1.75; $1.50.............................. *Peterson.*

Spectrum analysis expl. and its uses to science illustrated. ill. cr. 8°. '74. pap., 25c. .... *Estes.*

Speeches from the dock; [also] Dock and the scaffold; [also] Wearing of the green. ill. 12°. '70. $1.50. *Haverty.*

Speechiana: coll. of speeches and recitations. 16°. '75. pap., 30c...................... *Happy.*

Speed the plough. Morton, T. 15c........ *French.*

Speer, W: God's rule for Christian giving. 16°. 75c. *Pres.Bd.*

— Great revival of 1800. 16°. 70c.......... *Pres.Bd.*

— Oldest and the newest empire: China and the U. S. ill. 8°. $3.50; leath., $4; hf. mor., $5.. *Scranton.*

Speers, R. H. *See* South Carolina, Chancery reports; Reports.

Speight, T: W. Under lock and key. 12°. $1.75. *Lippincott.*

Speke, J: Hanning. Journal of the discovery of the source of the Nile. maps, por. and ill. 8°. $4; shp., $4.50; hf. cf., $6.25............ *Harper.*

Spelling and reading book. 18°. per doz., $1.80. *Meth.Bk.Conc.*

Spelling book of the Eng. lang. 16°. 18c... *Benziger.*

Spelling made easy. ill. 4°. pap., 10c.; 15c. *J.E.Potter.*

Spelling match: musical [dram.] sketch. 16°. pap., 15c. .... *Happy.*

Spence, G: Equitable jurisdiction of the [Eng.] Court of Chancery. 2 v. 8°. '46–'50. $10. *T.&J.W.Johnson.*

Spencer, Alb. J. Book of comic speeches and humorous recitations. 16°. pap., 30c.; bds., 50c. *Dick & F.*

— *See also* Barton, J., *and* Spencer, A. J.

Spencer, Amb. Narrative of Andersonville drawn from the evidence elicited on trial of Henry Wirz, the jailer; with argument of Col. N. P. Chipman. 12°. $1.75......................... *Harper.*

Spencer, C: E. Rue, thyme and myrtle: poems and songs. 12°. $1................... *Lippincott.*

Spencer, Dwight. Church finance. 24°. '76. pap., 8c. *Am.Tr.*

Spencer, G: Latin lessons. 12°. hf. leath., $1. *Sheldon.*

Spencer, H. Ladd. Poems. 12°. $2 .... *Tuttle.*

Spencer, Herb. Works. 10 v. 8°. hf. cf., $44.. *Appleton.*

— Descriptive sociology; or, groups of sociological facts. pts. 1–3. f°. ea., bds., $4 .... *Appleton.*

Cont.: English, comp. and abstract. by J. Collier. — Ancient Mexicans, Central Americans, Chibchas and ancient Peruvians, comp. and abstract. by R. Scheppig. — Types of the lowest races; Negritto races, Malayo-Polynesian races, comp. and abstract. by D. Duncan.

— Education, intellectual, moral and physical. 12°. $1.25. *Appleton.*

— Essays, moral, political and æsthetic. 12°. $2.50. *Appleton.*

— First principles of a new system of philosophy. 12°. '73. $2.50........................ *Appleton.*

— Illustrations of universal progress: sel. of his papers. 12°. $2.50......................... *Appleton.*

— Morals of trade. *See* Lyttleton, W. H., Sins of trade.

— Philosophy of style. 12°. 50c.......... *Appleton.*

— Principles of biology. 2 v. 12°. $5..... *Appleton.*

— Principles of psychology. 2 v. 12°. $5; hf. cf., $9. *Appleton.*

— Recent discussions in science, philosophy and morals. 12°. $2 .... *Appleton.*

— Social statics; or, conditions essential to human happiness specified, and the first of them developed. 12°. $2.50 .... *Appleton.*

— Sociology. 12°. $1.50 .... *Appleton.*

Spencer, Ichabod Smith. Evidence of divine revelation; in a letter to a judge. 18°. pap., 15c. *Bost.Am.Tr.*

— Pastor's (A) sketches: conversations with anxious sinners respec. way of salvation. ('52.) New ed. 2 v. in 1. por. 12°. '55. $2............ *Dodd.*

— Sermons. ('55.) New ed. 3 v. 12°. '61. ea., $2.. *Dodd.*

Spencer, Ja. C. *See* New York City, Superior Court reports.

Spencer, Jesse Ames. Four Gospels and Acts in Greek; with Eng. notes, maps, indexes, etc.; with the Epistles and Apocalypse. 12°. $1.75; shp., $2.15......................... *Harper.*

— Greek praxis; or, Greek for beginners. 12°. '70. $1.................................. *Ivison.*

— History of the U. S. 4 v. ill. roy. 8°. '74–'76. hf. mor., $28; $30; mor., $36; $38... *Johnson & M.*

— *Germ.;* übers. v. F. Kapp. ill. roy. 8°. hf. mor., $27; $29; mor., $35; $37 .... *Johnson & M.*

— The young ruler. 12°. '71. $1.50...... *Randolph.*

Spencer, J: Things new and old; or, a storehouse of illustrations; [also] Treasury of similes, by R. Cawbray; ed. by J. G. Pilkington. 4th ed. 4°. '72. $7.50; hf. mor., $12 .... *Tibbals.*

Spencer, Ph. Jac. Kurze Katechismuspredigten. 8°. hf. leath., $4 .... *Volkening.*

Spencer, Rob. D. *See* New Jersey, Sup. Court reports.

Spencer, T: Memoirs. 18°. 45c.......... *Am.S.S.*

Spencer, W. H. Elements of qualitative chemical analysis. 4°. '66. $3 .... *Macmillan.*

Spencer, W. V. (*ed.*) Universal stage: plays. 70 nos. 16°. ea., pap., 15c.................. *Lee & S.*

Note. Entered specifically under authors and titles.

Spencer, W: A. *See* Minnesota, Sup. Court reports.

Spencerian compendium of penmanship. obl. 8°. $2.40; $3; bds., $1.75. —Key. 12°. $1.50; $2. *Ivison.*

Spencerian copy books. 14 nos. obl. 8°. ea., pap., 15c. *Ivison.*

Cont.: Nos. 1–4, 4½, 5. Common school ser. —Intermediate book.—6, 7. Business ser.—8, 9. Ladies' ser.—10–12. Exercise ser.

— *Same:* shorter course. 3 nos. obl. 16°. ea., pap., 10c. .... *Ivison.*

— *Same:* tracing books. [Penmanship.] obl. 8°. ea., pap., 10c. .... *Ivison.*

Spencerian drawing book: element. and progressive ser. 5 nos. 4°. ea., 50c. .... *Ivison.*

Spencerian key: text-book on penmanship; for teachers, pupils and professional penmen. ill. 12°. '66. $1.50 .... *Ivison.*

Spencerian theory of penmanship; by "Spencerian authors." 12°. '74. bds., 40c.; pap., 25c. .. *Ivison.*

Spencers (The). Tyng, S. H. $1.50 ...... *Am. Tr.*

Spender, J: Kent. Therapeutic means for relief of pain. 8°. '74. $2.50 .... *Macmillan.*

Spender, *Mrs.* J: Kent. Jocelyn's mistake. 8°. $1.25; pap., 75c. .... *Estes.*

Spendthrift. *See* Ainsworth, W: H.

Spenser, Edm. Complete works; ed. from orig. editions and MSS. by R. Morris; with memoir by J. W. Hales. (Globe ed.) 12°. '69. $1.50 .. *Macmillan.*

— *Same.* por. and ill. roy. 8°. $4.50 .... *Routledge.*

— Poems. 5 v. 18°. $5 .... *Osgood.*

— *Same.* (Aldine ed.) 5 v. 16°. ea., 75c. .. *Lippincott.*

— Poetical works; with sel. of notes from various commentators, and index; [with] life by H. J. Todd. roy. 8°. $4.50 .... *Routledge.*

— Faerie queene; with glossary. (Presentation poets.) ill. 12°. $1.75; ivorine, $3 .... *Routledge.*

— *Same;* ed. by R. A. Willmott, with biog. and crit. notice. (Brit. poets.) ill. 12°. $2.25; hf. cf., $3.50; mor., $5 .... *Routledge.*

— — *See also* Chaucer, G., Canterbury tales.

— *Same;* [also] Epithalamium. (Household ser.) ill. 16°. $1.50; mor., $3 .... *Lee & S.*

— *See also* Hart, J. S.

Spensers (The); or, chronicles of a country hamlet. 18°. 75c. .... *Pres. Bd.*

Sperry, A. F. History of the 33d Iowa Infantry, 1863–'66. por. 8°. '66. $1.50; shp., $2.50 .. *Mills.*

Sphinx (The). Bayer, C. R. *$2 .... *Maclean.*

Spicer, T. Beauties of Fletcher. *See* Fletcher, J. W.

Spicer, W. W. Collector's handy-book of algæ, diatoms, desmids, fungi, lichens, mosses, etc.; with instruc. for their prep. and formation of an herbarium. ill. 16°. (Lond.) $1.50 .... *Putnam.*

Spicy. Lamb, M. J. $1.50; $1 .... *Appleton.*

Spider and the fly; or, tricks, traps and pitfalls of city life; by one who knows. 12°. $1.25 .. *Miller.*

Spider spinning; or, adventures in insect-land: tale for the young. ill. 16°. 75c. .... *Routledge.*

Spiegel der Taufe (Ein); mit Geist, mit Wasser u. mit Blut. 18°. hf. bd., 30c. .... *Baer.*

Spielhagen, F: Hammer and anvil; tr. by W. H. Browne. ('70.) New ed. 16°. '73. $1.50 ... *Holt.*

— Hohensteins (The); tr. by Schele de Vere. 12°. '70. $2 .... *Holt.*

— Problematic characters; tr. by Schele de Vere. ('69.) New ed. 16°. '75. $1.50 .... *Holt.*

— Through night to light: sequel to "Problematic characters;" tr. by Schele de Vere. ('69.) New ed. 16°. '74. $1.50 .... *Holt.*

— What the swallow sang; tr. by MS. (Leis. hour ser.) 16°. '73. $1.25 .... *Holt.*

— *See also* Kaulbach, W. v., Goethe's Frauengestalten.

Spiers, Alex. French dictionary; ed. by Jewett. 8°. hf. mor., $3.50.—(School ed.) 12°. $2.50. *Appleton.*

Spiers, Alex., *continued.*

— *and* Surenné, G. Complete French-and-Eng. and Eng.-and-French dict. 8°. hf. mor., $6 .. *Appleton.*

— — Standard pronouncing dict. of French and Eng. (School ed.) 12°. $2.50 .... *Appleton.*

Spies and traitors of Hebrew history. Headley, P. C. 25c.; 30c. .... *J. E. Potter.*

Spina Christi. Hall, C. H. $1 .... *Dutton.*

Spinckes, B. F. Manual of devotions. New ed., rev. 16°. '75. $1.25 .... *Dutton.*

Spinckes, Natl. Church of England-man's companion in the closet. 16°. '67. 50c. .... *Pott.*

Spindler, C: Ausgewählte Schriften. 6 v. $6.75; pap., $5.25; hf. mor., $8.25 .... *F. W. Thomas.*

Cont.: Der Jesuit, $1; pap., 75c.; hf. mor., $1.25.—Der Bastard, $1.25; pap., $1; hf. mor., $1.50.—Der Invalide, $1.25; pap., $1; hf. mor., $1.50.—Der Jude, $1.25; pap., $1; hf. mor., $1.50.—Drei Novellen, 75c.; pap., 50c.; hf. mor., $1.—Der Vogelhändler v. Imst, $1.25; pap., $1; hf. mor., $1.50.

— The Jew; tr. [Fiction.] 8°. pap., 75c. .... *Harper.*

Spindler, F. Ten technical studies; [for the piano]. (op. 141.) 4 bks. f°. ea., 30c. .... *Brainard.*

Spinoza, Bend. de. Tractatus theologico-politicus: crit. inquiry into hist., purpose and authenticity of Hebrew Scriptures. 8°. $5.25 .. *Scribner, W. & A.*

Spirit and beauty of the Christian religion. *See* Chateaubriand, F. A.

Spirit Eye, the Indian captive. 12°. pap., 20c. .. *Hurst.*

Spirit in prison. Guernsey, C. F. $1.25 .. *H. A. Young.*

Spirit invocations. Putnam, A. $1.25 .... *Colby.*

Spirit land. Emmons, S. B. $1.25 .... *J. E. Potter.*

Spirit mysteries explained. ill. 18°. pap., 15c. .. *Haney.*

Spirit of the Bible. Moore, F. $5–$10 .... *U. S. Pub.*

Spirit of faith. Hedley, *Bp.* 60c. .... *Cath. Pub.*

Spirit of the Hebrew poetry. Taylor, I. $1.10. *Smith, E. & Co.*

Spirit of laws. Montesquieu, C: de S. de. 2 v. $6. *Clarke.*

Spirit of life. Bickersteth, E. H. $1.25 ..... *Carter.*

Spirit of the nation: ballads and songs, by writers of "The nation." 12°. $1 .... *Noonan.*

— *Same.* 18°. 50c. .... *Sadlier.*

Spirit of praise: collection of hymns. ill. cr. 8°. $3.75; cf., $7.50; mor., $8 .... *Scribner, W. & A.*

Spirit of prayer. *See* More, Ha.

Spirit of prayer. Vincent, N. 30c. .... *Pres. Bd.*

Spirit of prophecy. White, E. G. $1 .. *Sev. Day Adv.*

Spirit of the Rhine: musical drama. 16°. pap., 15c. *French.*

Spirit of seventy-six. *See* Curtis, A. W. *and* D. S.

Spirit's book. Kardec, A. $1.25 .... *Colby.*

Spirits in prison. Plumptre, E. H. 50c. .. *Routledge.*

Spiritual arithmetic. 18°. 70c. .... *Pres. Bd*

Spiritual combat. *See* Scupoli, L.

Spiritual conference. *See* Faber, F. W.

Spiritual delusion. Lum, D. D. $1.50 ... *Lippincott*

Spiritual diary. Swedenborg, E. $2.75 .. *H. H. Carter*

Spiritual garden; or, traits of Christian character delineated. 18°. 55c. .... *Pres. Bd*

Spiritual harp. *See* Peebles, J. M., *and* Barrett, J. O

Spiritual kingdom. Ramsey, J. B. $3 .... *Pres. Com*

Spiritual letters. *See* François de Sales, *St.*

Spiritual philosophy versus diabolism. King, M. M 25c. .... *Colby*

Spiritual pilgrim. Barrett, J. O. $1.50 ...... *Colby*

Spiritual point of view. Mahan, M. 75c. .. *Appleton*

Spiritual progress. Cummings, J. W. $1.50 .. *O'Shea*

Spiritual progress. Fenelon, F. $1.50 .... *Dodd*

Spiritual sacrifice and holy communion. Kingsbury T. L. $1 .... *Macmillan*

Spiritual songs. Gerhardt, P. $2.50 ...... *Routledge*

Spiritual songs and devotional hymns. 24°. '55. 75c. *Randolph.*
Spiritual songs for a month. Ryle, J. C. 35c. *Randolph.*
Spiritual struggles of a Roman Catholic. Beaudry, L. N. $1.25 .... *Meth. Bk. Conc.*
Spiritual teacher and songster. Peebles, J. M. 15c. *Colby.*
Spiritual treasury for children of God. Mason, W. 2 v. ea., $1.50 .... *Pres. Bd.*
Spiritual victory. Patton, W. W. $1 .... *Cong. Pub.*
Spiritual wives. Dixon, W. H. $2 .... *Lippincott.*
Spiritualism answered by science. Cox, E. W. 50c. *Hinton.*
Spitalfields weaver. Bayly, T. H. 15c .... *French.*
Spitfire: farce. 16°. pap., 15c .... *Happy.*
Spitta, C: J: Ph. Lyra domestica; tr. by R. Massie, with add. sel. and introd. by F. D. Huntington. 16°. '60. $1.50; mor., $4.50 .... *Dutton.*
Splendid investment. Bernard, W. B. 15c ... *French.*
Splendid times. Sangster, M. E. $1 .... *Am. Tr.*
Spofford, *Mrs.* Ht. Eliz. [*formerly Miss* Prescott]. Amber gods. 16°. $1.75 .... *Osgood.*
— Azarian. 16°. $1.50 .... *Osgood.*
— New England legends. 8°. $1; pap., 50c. *Osgood.*
— Thief in the night: novelette. 16°. '72. $1.25. *Roberts.*
— *See also* Rougegorge and other stories.
Spohr, L. Grand violin school; ed. by U. C. Hill. f°. bds., $3; — abridg., $2 .... *Ditson.*
Spoiled child. 18°. '39. 30c .... *Am. Tr.*
Spoiled child. Hoare, P. 15c .... *French.*
Spoiled child. *See* Sunbeam ser.
Spoiled children. 18°. 22c .... *Am. S. S.*
Spoiled picture. *See* Baker, *Mrs.* H. N. W.
Spon, Ern. Present practice of sinking and boring wells; with geol. considerations and examples of wells executed. diagrams. cr. 8°. '75. $3 .. *Spon.*
— Workshop receipts; for manufacturers, mechanics and scientific amateurs. ill. cr. 8°. '73. $2 .. *Spon.*
Spon's builders' pocket-book of prices and memoranda; ed. by W. Young. [Annual.] roy. 32°. '76. $1.50; roan, $1.75 .... *Spon.*
Spon's dict. of engineering, civil, mechanical, military and naval; with technical terms in French, Germ., Ital. and Span. 8 pts. ill. roy. 8°. '74. ea., $5; — in 3 v., $40; hf. mor., $50 .... *Spon.*
Spon's engineers' and contractors' ill. book of prices of machines, tools, iron-work and contractors' material. roy. 8°. '76. $3 .... *Spon.*
Spon's tables and memoranda for engineers. Hurst, J. T. 40c .... *Spon.*
Spooner, C. E. Narrow gauge railways. pl. 8°. '71. $4.50 .... *Spon.*
Spooner, E: Parson and people; or, incidents in everyday life of a clergyman. 16°. $1. *Huntington.*
Spooner, J. C., *and* Bryant, E. E. Laws rel. to organization and government of towns in Wisconsin. 8°. 75c .... *Atwood.*
Spooner, Ph. L. *See* Wisconsin, Reports.
Spooner, T: Memorial of W: Spooner, 1637, and of his descendants to the third generation; and of his great-grandson, Elnathan Spooner, and of his descendants to 1871. 8°. '71. $5 .... *Clarke.*
Spoons in a wherry. Hale, E. E. 25c. *Lockwood, B. & Co.*
Sport in brief chapters. *See* Izax, I.
Sport with a sportsman: Ethiop. drama. 16°. pap., 15c .... *Ames.*
Sports on a lark: Ethiop. drama. 16°. pap., 15c. *French; Happy.*
Sports that kill. Talmage, T. De W. $1.25; $1. *Harper.*

Sportsman's club ser. *See* Fosdick, C. A.
Spoth, E: Choral mass; in unison key of F. 4°. pap., 65c .... *Ditson.*
— Mass in B flat; for soprano, alto, tenor and bass; with offertory. f°. '55. pap., $1.50 ..... *Ditson.*
— Mass in D. 4°. pap., $1.25 .... *Peters.*
Spottiswoode, W: Polarization of light. 12°. '74. $1. *Macmillan.*
Spottswood, *Mrs.* Lucy A. Alice Dunbar. 18°. 60c. *Pres. Bd.*
— Fentons (The). ill. 16°. '74. $1.25 .... *Meth. Epis.*
— Hugh Cheston's vow; or, the trials and triumphs of a step-mother. ill. 16°. '76. $1.25 .. *Meth. Epis.*
Sprague, A. P., *and* Lacombe, P. Prize essays on international law. *See* Marcoartu, A. de, Internationalism.
Sprague, Achsa W. Poems; with memoir. 12°. '64. $1 .... *Colby.*
Sprague, C: Poetical and prose writings; with biog. sketch. ('41.) New ed. por. 12°. '76. $1.50. *Williams.*
Sprague, Homer B. Masterpieces in Eng. literature. 8°. '74. $2.25 .... *Schermerhorn.*
Sprague, I: *See* Goodale, G. L., Wild flowers of America.
Sprague, J: T. Electricity: its theory, sources and applications. ill. 8°. '75. $3 .... *Spon.*
Sprague, Peleg. *See* United States, District Court decisions.
Sprague, W: B. Annals of the Am. pulpit: notices of Am. clergymen to 1855. ('56–'68.) New ed. 9 v. 8°. '65–'73. $36; — in 11 v., ea., $2–$4 .. *Carter.*
Cont.: Annals of the Baptists — of the Congregationalists, 2 v. — of the Episcopalians — of the Methodists — of the Presbyterians, 2 v. — of the Unitarians, *ea.*, $4 — of the United Presbyterians, $3 — of the Lutherans — of the Reformed Dutch, *ea.*, $2.
— Annals of the Am. Lutheran pulpit. 8°. $1. (?) *Luth. Pub.*
— Annals of the Am. Reformed Dutch Church. 8°. $1.50 .... *N. Y. Ref. Ch. Bd.*
— Joseph, the model young man. 16°. '60. $1 .. *Randolph.*
— Letters to a daughter. ill. 18°. '55. 45c .... *Am. Tr.*
— Life of Jedidiah Morse. 8°. '75. $2.50 .. *Randolph.*
— *See also* Smitten household.
Sprechen Sie Deutsch? or, do you speak German? pocket manual of conversations in Eng. and Germ. ('64.) New ed. 18°. '76. bds., 60c ..... *Holt.*
Sprigg, D. F. Aid to those who pray in private: closet prayers. 32°. '68. 60c .... *Dutton.*
Sprigs of laurel: farce. 16°. pap., 15c .... *French.*
Spring, Arth. Life. 8°. pap., 25c .... *Peterson.*
Spring, C. F. Beiträge zur Bildung d. Jugend, gesammelt in 17 Gedichten: ein Kinderbuch. 16°. bds., 15c .... *Ludwig.*
Spring, Gardiner. Attraction of the cross. ('45.) New ed. 12°. '71. $1.10; $1.50 .... *Am. Tr.*
— Bible not of man: divine origin of Scriptures drawn from Script. themselves. 12°. '47. 75c ... *Am. Tr.*
— Doctrine of election; [also] Doctrine of perseverance of the saints, by B. Tyler. 18°. 40c ... *Cong. Pub.*
— Essays on distinguishing traits of relig. character. 12°. $1.25 .... *Cong. Pub.*
— Mission of sorrow. 18°. '63. 35c .... *Am. Tr.*
— Obligations of the world to the Bible. 18°. 90c. *Pres. Bd.*
— Personal reminiscences of [his] life and times. ('65.) New ed. 2 v. por. 12°. '66. $4; hf. cf., $7.50. *Scribner.*
— Pulpit ministrations; or, Sabbath readings: discourses on Christian doctrine and duty. 2 v. por. 8°. $6. *Harper.*
Spring, S: Monk's revenge; or, secret enemy. 8°. pap., 50c .... *De Witt.*
Spring. *See* Haydn, F. J.
Spring. Henninges, R. E. 40c .... *Brainard.*
Spring and autumn. Kenney, J. 15c .... *French.*

Spring blossom lib. 12 v. ill. 24°. $3.60..*Lothrop.*
Cont.: Daisy's mission. — Little white mice boy. — Bud and blossom. — Kitty's tableaux. — Little Blossom. — Blue violet. — Wintergreen girl. — Kitty Collins. — Susie's watch. — Fair play, and other stories. — Better than gold. — Bold as a lion.

Spring blossoms. Phillips, P. 30c.; 25c... *Wilstach.*

Spring bonnet; or, quite ready. 32°. 10c...*Am.S.S.*
— *Same.* 18°. 20c.; 25c. ....*Am.Bapt.*
— *See also* My own lib.

Spring comedies. Barker, M. A. (*Lady*). $1.50. *Macmillan.*

Spring floods. *See* Turgénieff, I.

Spring Grove Cemetery, Cincinnati: its hist. and improvements, with obs. on anc. and mod. places of sepulture. ill. 4°. '69. $15. — 8°. $2..*Clarke.*

Spring holiday. Converse, C. C. 75c. ......*Ditson.*

Spring morning, and other allegories. 18°. 50c. *Am.S.S.*

Spring ride; or, Pardington Hall. ('65.) New ed. ill. 16°. '72. $1.25 ....*Hoyt.*

Springdale Abbey. Parker, J. $1.50. .....*Claxton.*

Springdale stories. *See* Samuels, *Mrs.* S. B. C.

Springer, J: S. Forest-life and forest trees: winter camp-life among the loggers, and wild-wood adventure; with descript. of lumbering operations on rivers of Maine and New Brunswick. ill. 12°. $1.50..............................*Harper.*

Springer, Reb. R. Beechwood. [Fiction.] 12°. $1.50. *Lippincott.*

Springfield stories. *See* Little Dot ser.

Spring's message. *See* Gade, N. W.

Springtime for sowing. Mason, M. 90c.; $1..*Dutton.*

Springtime of life. Magie, D. 60c.........*Am.Tr.*

Sproat, *Mrs.* Nancy. Lullabies, ditties and tales. ill. 18°. '65. 60c....................*Am.Tr.*

Spruchbuch: Samml. v. bibl. Sprüchen. 18°. 20c. *Ludwig.*

Spruner, C: v. Historico-geographical hand atlas; from destruction of the western empire, 476. obl. 4°. $7.50 ....*Scribner, W.& A.*

Spur and encouragement to the study of Gk. Test.; with suggestions for learners. 8°. (Bagster.) pap., 25c. ....*Wiley.*

Spur of Monmouth. Morford, H. $1.75 .... *Claxton.*

Spurgeon, C: Haddon. Commenting and commentaries: lectures to students of pastor's college; with list of biblical commentaries and expositions. 12°. $1.25 ....*Sheldon.*
— Evening by evening; or, readings at eventide for the family or closet. 12°. $1.75..*Sheldon; So.Bapt.*
— Feathers for arrows. sq. 16°. $1.25 .....*Sheldon.*
— Gems: passages from sermons. 12°. $1.50..*Sheldon.*
— Gleanings among the sheaves. 16°. $1.25..*Sheldon.*
— John Ploughman's talk; or, plain advice to plain people. 16°. 90c........................*Sheldon.*
— Lectures to my students: sel. from addresses to students of pastor's college, Metropolitan Tabernacle. 12°. $1.25.....*Scribner, W.& A.; Sheldon.*
— Morning by morning; or, daily Bible readings. 12°. $1.75 ....*Sheldon; So.Bapt.*
— Plain talk; comp. by B. Pitman. [Phonog.] ('72.) New ed. 12°. '76. 50c............*Pitman.*
— Saint and his Saviour. 12°. $1.50........*Sheldon.*
— *Same.* 12°. $1.75........................*So.Bapt.*
— Sermons. 9 v. 12°. ea., $1.50..*Sheldon; So.Bapt.*
— Treasury of David: exposition of Psalms, illustrative extracts, homiletical hints and list of writers on the Psalms. 4 v. 8°. ea., $4..*Scribner, W.& A.*
— Types and emblems. [Sermons.] 12°. $1.25..*Sheldon.*

Spurzheim, J: Gaspar. Education: its element. principles founded on nature of man; with app. by S. R. Wells. ('47.) 12th Am. ed., rev. ill. 12°. $1.25 ....*Wells.*
— Natural laws of man: a philosophical catechism. 18°. 50c. ....*Wells.*
— Phrenology; or, doctrine of the mental phenomena. 2 v. in 1. ill. 8°. $2.....................*Harper.*

Spy. *See* Cooper, Ja. F.

Squibob papers. Derby, G. H. $1.50.....*Carleton.*

Squibs; or, every day life illustrated. Cox, P. *$2; $2.50; $4.............................*Am.Pub.*

Squier, Eph. G: Aboriginal monuments of N. Y. 4°. '50. pap., $4.......................*Smith.Inst.*
— Nicaragua: its people, scenery, monuments, resources, condition and proposed canal. maps and ill. 8°. $4; hf. cf., $6.25..............*Harper.*
— States of Central America: their geog., topog., etc. maps and ill. 8°. $4.....................*Harper.*
— Waikna; or, adventures on the mosquito shore. map and ill. 12°. $1.50......................*Harper.*

Squiers, Miles P. Being of God, Moral government, and Theses in theology; ed. by J. R. Boyd. por. 16°. '68. $1.25......................*Darrow.*

Squire (The). Pickering, E. 38c.........*Peterson.*

Squire Arden. Oliphant, M. O. W. 8°. 75c...*Harper.*

Squire Downing's heirs. 16°. $1.25.........*Carter.*

Squire for a day. Leavitt, A. J. 15c........*De Witt.*

Squire Lynn's will. Leslie, E. $1.50........*Nelson.*

Squire of Walton Hall. Wise, D. $1.25..*Meth.Bk.Conc.*

Squire Trevlyn's heir. Wood, E. P. $1.75; $1.50. *Peterson.*

Squire's daughter. Davis, C. E. K. $1.25 ....*Hoyt.*

Squire's legacy. Hay, M. C. 75c...........*Harper.*

Squirrels (The). *See* New Year lib.

Stabat mater. *See* Coles, Ab.

Stabat mater. Fry, W. H. $4..............*Ditson.*

Stabat mater. *See* Rossini, G.

Stable boy. 18°. 60c.........................*Cong.Pub.*

Stabler, J. L. ["Jennie Woodville."] Edith's mistake; or, left to herself. 16°. $1.25..*Lippincott.*

Stabler, Lydia C. Hints for teachers. 18°. *net,* bds., 40c. ....*Friends Bk.Assoc.*
— Questions on books of New Test.; with ref. 18°. *net,* bds., 25c. ....*Friends Bk.Assoc.*
— Questions on books of Old Test.; with ref. 18°. *net,* bds., 25c. ....*Friends Bk.Assoc.*

Stacey, W. J. Short sermons on the Psalms. 12°. '76. $2.25.................................*Pott.*

Stacy, A. G. Service of song: treatise on singing in private devotion, in the family and in the school. 2d ed., rev. 12°. '71. $1.50. *Barnes; S. W. Bk.& Pub.*

Stael-Holstein, *Mme.* A. L. G. N. (*Baronne*) de. Allemagne (L'). 12°. $1.50....*G.R.Lockwood.*
— *Eng.* Germany; with notes and app. by O. W. Wight. cr. 8°. $3; hf. cf., $4.50............*Hurd & H.*
— Corinne, ou L'Italie. 12°. $1.50. *Appleton; G.R.Lockwood.*
— *Eng.* Corinne; or, the improvisatrice. 12°. $1.75. *Appleton.*
— — Corinne; or, Italy; tr. by I. Hill. 12°. $1.75. *Mason.*
— — *Same:* poetical passages; [tr.] by L. E. L. 8°. pap., 75c.............................*Peterson.*

Staff and scrip. Barber, J. W. *$3.50; $4.50. *Bradley & G.*

Staff of diamonds: drama. 16°. pap., 15c. ..*French.*

Stag chase, and other stories. 18°. 20c.; 25c. *Am.Bapt.*

Stage coach. *See* Sargent, L. M.

Stage struck. Dimond, W. 15c............*French.*

Stage struck couple. White, C. 15c........*De Witt.*

Stage struck darkey: Ethiop. drama. 16°. pap., 15c. *French; Happy.*

Stahl, P. Versions: engl. u. deutsche Uebungsstücke. 2d ed. 2 pts. 8°. '75. ea., bds., 60c.....*Schmidt.*
— *Same:* translation exercises [into German]. 2d ed. 2 pts. 8°. '75. ea., bds., 60c.............*Schmidt.*

Stahl, P. J. (*pseud.*) [Pierre-Jules Hetzel.] Master Cæsar; tr. from the Fr. ill. 4°. bds., 75c. *Appleton.*

Stahl, P. J. (*pseud.*), *continued.*
— Master Hector's adventures; tr. from the Fr. ill. 4°. bds., 75c. . . . . *Appleton.*
Stahr, Adph. Life and works of G. E. Lessing; tr. by E. P. Evans. 2 v. 8°. '66. $5 . . . . *Holt.*
Stain upon the hand. 18°. 25c. . . . . *Am. S. S.*
Stainer, J: *See* Bramley, H. R., *and* Stainer, J.
— *and* Barrett, W. A. Dictionary of musical terms. ill. 8°. $5; bds., $4 . . . . *Ditson.*
Stainforth, F. *See* Maltby, C. A., *and* Stainforth, F.
Stale bread; or, Letta, the beggar girl. 16°. $1.25. *Am. Bapt.*
Stamm, A. *See* Amerikanisches Lesebuch.
Stamp on it John. *See* Power, P. B.
Stand and wait. Hale, E. E. 25c. . . *Lockwood, B. & Co.*
Stand by the flag. Baker, G. M. 15c. . . . . . *Lee & S.*
Stand up for Jesus. *See* Kennedy, *Mrs.* M. G.
Standard (The). Emerson, L. O., *and* Palmer, H. R. $1.50 . . . . *Ditson.*
Standard anthem and Chorus book. Johnson, A. N. $1.38 . . . . *Gordon.*
Standard atlas of Canada. *See* New.
Standard cookery for the people. Soyer, A. 50c. *Desilver.*
Standard drama. *See* Hinton, H. L.
Standard facts and figures. Sullivan, A. G. $2. *Morton & D.*
Standard fairy tales. ill. 12°. $1.50 . . . . *Porter.*
Standard glee book. Johnson, A. N. $1.38 . . *Gordon.*
Standard handbook of household economy for the people. roy. 18°. bds., 50c. . . . . . . *Desilver.*
Standard library atlas of classical geog. 12°. (Bohn.) $2.75 . . . . *Little, B. & Co.*
— *Same.* 12°. (Bohn.) $3 . . *Lippincott; Scribner, W. & A.*
Standard poets. *See* Household editions. — Red line editions.
Standard scroll book. pl. obl. 8°. $1 . . . . . . *Haney.*
Standard sea tales. 3 v. 16°. $4.50 . . . . (?) *Shepard.*
Cont.: Driven to sea, by Mrs. A. J. Cupples. — Deserted ship, by G. Cupples. — Tom Cringle's log, by M. Scott.
Standard speaker. Sargent, E. $2.50 . . . . . *Desilver.*
Standbridge, J: C. B. Celebrated piano forte method. 4°. '64. $3; bds., $2.50 . . . . *Ditson.*
— Chants of the church. obl. 8°. bds., $1 . . . . *Ditson.*
— *See also* Darley, W. H. W., *and* Standbridge, J. C. B.
Standish, G: Adventures of a Baltimore trader on coast of Pacific. 16°. pap., 30c. . . . . *Lippincott.*
Standish, the Puritan. Grayson, E. $1.50 . . *Harper.*
Standrecht (Das). Nieritz, G. 25c. . . . . . . *Morwitz.*
Stanfield, Clarkson. Pictures by S.; with text and biog. sketch by J. Dafforne. f°. $10. *Routledge.*
— Stanfield gallery; with descript. and sketch of S. by J. Dafforne. 4°. $10; mor., $20 . . . . *Lippincott.*
Stanfield gallery (The). *See* Gallery of pictures.
Stanfield Hall. Smith, J. F. $1.50 . . . . *Dick & F.*
Stanford, C: Affliction; or, the refiner watching the crucible. 24°. '71. 25c. . . . . *Randolph.*
— *Same.* sq. 18°. 50c. . . . . *Claxton.*
Stanhope, Ph. Dormer. *See* Chesterfield, *Lord.*
Stanhope, Ph. H: (*Earl*) [*formerly Lord Mahon.*] History of England, 1701–'13. 4th ed. 2 v. por. post 8°. (Lond.) '73. $3.50 . . . . . *Little, B. & Co.*
— History of England, 1713–1783. 5th ed., rev. with notes, app. and index. 7 v. post 8°. (Lond.) '58. $12.25; hf. cf., $24.50; cf., $35 . . . *Little, B. & Co.*
Staniford ser. 4 v. 16°. $6 . . . . *Lothrop.*
Cont.: The Stanifords. — My hero. — Battles lost and won. — Old school-fellows.
Stanifords (The) of Staniford's Folly. Kendall, E. D. $1.50 . . . . *Lothrop.*

Stanislaus Kotzka, *St.* Life; tr. from the Fr. 18°. 60c. . . . . *Coddington.*
— *Same.* 12°. $1.50 . . . . *Sadlier.*
Stanley, Ant. Dumond. Elementary treat. on spherical geometry and trigonometry. 12°. *net*, 75c. *Peck.*
— Tables of logarithms of numbers, and of logarithmic sines, tangents and secants; with other tables used in math. calculations. 8°. $2.50 . . . . *Peck.*
Stanley, Arth. Penrhyn. Athanasian creed; with pref. on general recommendations of the Ritual Commission. cr. 8°. '71. 75c. . . . . *Macmillan.*
— Lectures on hist. of Church of Scotland, Edinburgh, 1872. 8°. '72. $2.50 . . . . *Scribner.*
— Lectures on hist. of Eastern Church; with introd. on study of ecclesiastical hist. ('62.) New [chp.] ed. maps and plans. cr. 8°. '75. $2.50 . . *Scribner.*
— Lectures on hist. of Jewish Church. ('63.) New ed. maps and plans. cr. 8°. '76. $2.50 . . . . *Scribner.*
— National thanksgiving (The): sermons. cr. 8°. $1. *Macmillan.*
— Scripture portraits, and other miscellanies. cr. 8°. $2.50 . . . . *Routledge.*
— Sermons preached before Prince of Wales, during tour in the East, 1862; with notices of some of the localities visited. 12°. $1.50 . . . . *Porter.*
— Sinai and Palestine; in connection with their hist. ('68.) New [chp.] ed. cr. 8°. '76. $2.50 . . *Scribner.*
— *Same.* cr. 8°. $2.50 . . . . *Nichols & H.*
— *Same.* maps and ill. 8°. $4; hf. cf., $6.50. — (Popular ed.) 8°. $2.50; hf. cf., $4.50 . . *Widdleton.*
Stanley, C: H. Chess player's instructor; or, guide to beginners. 12°. 75c. 32°. 50c. . . . . *De Witt.*
Stanley, E: *See* Derby, E: (*Earl of*).
Stanley, Fk. Power of gentleness, and other tales. 18°. 70c. . . . . *Pres. Bd.*
Stanley, G: Classified synopsis of the principal painters of the Dutch and Flemish schools. 12°. (Bohn.) $1.75 . . . . *Little, B. & Co.*
— *Same.* 12°. (Bohn.) $2 . . *Lippincott; Scribner, W. & A.*
— Dictionary of painters and engravers. *See* Bryan, M.
Stanley, H: M. Coomassie and Magdala: story of two British campaigns in Africa. maps and ill. 8°. $3.50 . . . . *Harper.*
— How I found Livingstone: travels and adventures in Central Africa, incl. account of four months' residence with Dr. Livingstone. New [chp.] ed.; with memoir of Dr. Livingstone. map and ill. 8°. '73. $3.50 . . . . *Scribner.*
— My Kalulu, prince, king and slave: story of Central Africa. ('73.) New ed. ill. 12°. '74. $2 . . *Scribner.*
Stanley, J. M. Portraits of No. Am. Indians. 8°. '52. pap., 50c. . . . . *Smith. Inst.*
Stanley, Jac. Dialogues on popery. 18°. '43. 55c. *Meth. Bk. Conc.*
— *Same.* ('57.) 2d ed. 18°. '74. 60c. . . . . . . *So. Meth.*
Stanley expedition. *See* Livingstone's discoveries and adventures in Africa.
Stanley Thorne. *See* Cockton, H:
Stansbury, G: A. Interest tables at 7 per cent. roy. 8°. hf. bd., $1.50 . . . . *Harper.*
Stansbury, Howard. Expedition to valley of Great Salt Lake; with account of Mormon settlement. 2 v. maps and ill. 8°. $4 . . *Claxton; Lippincott.*
— — *See also* United States, *Corps of Eng.*
Stanton, Edn. McMasters. *See* Ohio, Sup. Court reports.
Stanton, H: T. Moneyless man, and other poems. 12°. '70. $1.75 . . . . *Turnbull.*
Stanton, R. H. Manual for executors, administrators, guardians and trustees in Kentucky; with law [of] wills and probate thereof. 2d ed., rev. to 1875. 12°. '75. shp., $1.75 . . . . *Clarke.*
— Treatise on law rel. to powers and duties of justices of the peace, clerks of circuit and county courts, sheriffs, etc., in Kentucky. 3d. ed., rev. to 1875. 8°. '75. *net*, shp., $6 . . . . *Clarke.*

Stantoun Corbet ser. (Children of). *See* Guernsey, L. E.

Stapf, E. Additions to the materia medica pura; tr. by C. J. Hempel. [Hom.] 8°. $1.50.... *Boericke.*

Staples, Nahor A. Way, truth and life: sermons, with life by J. W. Chadwick. por. 16°. '70. $1.50. *Am. Unit.*

Stapleton lib. 3 v. 12°. $3.75.......... *Lippincott.*

Cont.: Tales for the people, by H. More. — In search of a wife, by H. More. — Casella, by M. F. Finley.

Stapley, M. C. History of the English Church. 12°. '76. $2.50.......... *Pott.*

Star and the cloud. Roe, A. S. $1.50...... *Carleton.*

Star book on Christian baptism. Hiscox, E. T. 15c. *Ward.*

Star chamber. *See* Ainsworth, W: H.

Star in the dust heap. Greene, L. L. $1.75. *Scribner, W. & A.*

Star in the east. *See* Oliver, G.

Star lib. 5 v. 16°. $5.......... *Am. Bapt.*

Cont.: Children of Cloverly, by E. P. Hammond. — Fishers of Derby Haven. — Rosa Lindesay. — Giant cities, by Mrs. T. H. Griffith. — Noble rivers, by A. J. Buckland.

Star of Bethlehem. Dawes, S. E. $1.25...... *Locke.*

Star of Bethlehem. Platt, A. E. 70c.; 30c... *Am. Tr.*

Star of Bethlehem. *See* Joslin, T.

Star of Bethlehem: story. sq. 12°. '57. 40c. *Meth. Bk. Conc.*

Star of childhood. *See* Carter, T. T.

Star of the east. Hull, A. 30c......... *G. D. Russell.*

Star of the fallen. 8°. pap., 25c.......... *Dick & F.*

Star of hope. Haynes, C. *and* J. E. 35c..... *Peters.*

Star of hope ser. *See* Yonge, C. M.

Star of the north. McGee, T. D'A. $1.50.. *O'Shea.*

Star of the north: drama. 16°. pap., 15c..... *French.*

Star of our Lord. Upham, F. W. $1.75.. *Meth. Bk. Conc.*

Star of the wise men. Trench, R. C. 55c. *Cin. Meth. Bk. Conc.*

Star out of Jacob. Warner, A. B. $1.50.... *Carter.*

Star papers. Beecher, H. W. $1.75.......... *Ford.*

Starck, *Baron* J: A: de. Reunion of different Christian communions. 12°. '59. $1...... *Kelly, P. & Co.*

Stark, J: F: Gebetbuch. 12°. 75c.–$2.50.. *Ludwig.*

— Katechismus f. Erwachsene. (Praxis catechetica.) 12°. 75c.......... *Kohler.*

— Tägliches Handbuch in guten u. bösen Tagen. 8°. $1.......... *Dette; Siemon.*

— *Same.* 8°. $1–$4.50.......... *Kohler.*

— *Eng.* Daily handbook. 8°. $1.25–$4.50.. *Kohler.*

Stark, L: *See* Lebert, S., *and* Stark, L.

Stark, V. Easy mass in C. 4°. pap., 80c.... *Peters.*

Starkie, T: Law of slander and libel. 2 v. in 1. 8°. shp., $7.50.......... *W. C. Little.*

— Treatise of law of evidence. 10th Am. ed., with ref. to Am. cases by G. Sharswood. 8°. '76. $7.50. *T. & J. W. Johnson.*

— *See also* England, Common law reports.

Starkweather, L. B. *See* Emerson, L. O., *and* Starkweather, L. B.

Starlight stories. 2 v. 18°. $1.50........ *Lothrop.*

Cont.: Starlight stories. — Brother and sister.

Starling, *Miss* Eliz. Noble deeds of women: examples of female courage, fortitude and virtue. ill. 12°. (Bohn.) $1.75.......... *Little, B. & Co.*

— *Same.* ill. 12°. (Bohn.) $2. *Lippincott; Scribner, W. & A.*

Starling (The). *See* Macleod, N.

Starr, Eliza Allen. Patron saints. ill. 12°. $2.50; $3. *Murphy.*

Starr, G: O. "Forest and Stream" handbook for riflemen; with list of rifle associations in Am. maps, etc. 18°. '76. 50c.......... *Ford.*

Starr, Magnet. Halfway. 18°. 75c....... *Pres. Bd.*

Starry crown. *See* Perkins, W. O.

Starry flag. Adams, W. T. $1.25.......... *Lee & S.*

Starry flag ser. *See* Adams, W: T.

Stars and the angels. 12°. $2.......... (?) *Martien.*

Stars and the earth; or, thoughts upon space, time and eternity; with introd. by T. Hill. 4th ed., rev. 16°. '75. 75c.......... *Lockwood, B. & Co.*

Stars in a stormy night. M., E. L. $1.25..... *Nelson.*

Starting in life; or, hints to an elder scholar; [also] Going apprentice. 18°. 30c.......... *Am. S. S.*

Starting out. Clark, A. $1.25.......... *Lippincott.*

Startling facts in modern spiritualism. Wolfe, N. B. $2.......... *Rel. Phil.*

Startling questions. Ryle, J. C. $1.......... *Carter.*

State of the blessed dead. Alford, H. 75c.. *Randolph.*

State of the dead. Smith, U. 25c..... *Sev. Day Adv.*

State of the dead. West, A. $1.25...... *Lippincott.*

State of the impenitent dead. Hovey, A. 75c.. *Lothrop.*

State of man after death. Hovey, A. 10c.. *Am. Bapt.*

State prisoner: drama. 16°. pap., 15c..... *French.*

State secrets. Wilks, T. E. 15c.......... *French.*

Stately homes of England. Jewitt, L., *and* Hall, S. C. $7.50; $12; $15.......... *Porter.*

Statesman's year-book. Martin, F. $3.50. *Macmillan.*

Station house: drama. 16°. pap., 15c....... *French.*

Station life in New Zealand. Barker, M. A. (*Lady*). $1.50.......... *Macmillan.*

Station master's daughter. Nickerson, S. D.. $1.25. *Cong. Pub.*

Stations of the cross. [Cath. prayer book.] 32°. 15c.; pap., 10c.......... *Sadlier.*

Stations of Jerusalem. *See* Christian instructed.

Staunton, H: T. Jacob Brown, and other poems. 12°. '75. $1.50.......... *Clarke.*

Staunton, Howard. Chess player's companion. 12°. (Bohn.) $1.75.......... *Little, B. & Co.*

— *Same.* 12°. (Bohn.) $2.. *Lippincott; Scribner, W. & A.*

— Chess player's handbook. 12°. (Bohn.) $1.75. *Little, B. & Co.*

— *Same.* 12°. (Bohn.) $2.. *Lippincott; Scribner, W. & A.*

— Chess praxis: sup. to "Chess player's handbook." 12°. (Bohn.) $2.25.......... *Little, B. & Co.*

— *Same.* 12°. (Bohn.) $2.40...... *Scribner, W. & A.*

— *Same.* 12°. (Bohn.) $2.50.......... *Lippincott.*

— Chess tournament of 1851. 12°. (Bohn.) $1.75. *Little, B. & Co.*

— *Same.* 12°. (Bohn.) $2. *Lippincott; Scribner, W. & A.*

— *See also* Shakespeare, W:

Staunton, Phin., *and* Ingham, M. Memorial. 8°. '69. $1.......... *Darrow.*

Staunton, W: Book of common praise: music adapted to Book of common prayer. obl. 8°. $1.50. *Huntington.*

— Church chant book. obl. 4°. 75c. .... *Gordon.*

Staveley, E. F. British insects: familiar descript. of form, structure, habits and transform. of insects. ill. and col. pl. cr. 8°. (Lond.) $7.. *Putnam.*

Stayed on God. Cookman, A. 50c......... *Tibbals.*

Stayman, J: K. Flowers and fossils, and other poems. 12°. '69. $2.......... *Claxton.*

Steam engine; ed. by T. O. Summers. ('57.) 3d ed. 18°. '74. 50c.......... *So. Meth.*

Steam for the million. Ward, J. H. $1.. *Van Nostrand.*

Steamship notes. *See* Norval.

Stearns, C. C. Mass in A; with organ or piano-forte accomp., and Lat. and Eng. text. 8°. '66. $1.50. *Ditson.*

Stearns, C: W. Shakespeare treasury of wisdom and knowledge. 12°. '69. $2.......... *Putnam.*

Stearns, C: W. *See* United States, Constitution.

Stearns, Ez. S. History of Rindge, New Hampshire, 1736–1874; with geneal. register of Rindge families. 8°. '75. $4 .... *Williams.*

Stearns, J. N. Prohibition does prohibit; or, prohibition not a failure. 12°. pap., 10c.... *Nat. Temp.*

— Temperance speaker. ('69.) New ed. 18°. '75. 75c. *Nat. Temp.*

— *See also* Bradbury, W. B., *and* Stearns, J. N.;— Sherwin, W. F., *and* Stearns, J. N.

Stearns, W: A: Life of Adjutant Stearns. 16°. 60c. *Cong. Pub.*

Stebbins, G: S. Victims of ignorance; or, perils of early life: treatise on diseases and deformities of children. ill. 8°. *$2; $2.50........ *D. E. Fisk.*

Stebbins, Giles B. (*ed.*) Chapters from the Bible of the ages. ('72.) 4th ed. 12°. '74. $1.50; $2.. *Colby.*

Stebbins, Jane E. Earthly trials and glory of the immortal life. ill. 8°. '75. *$3; $3.50... *Fitch.*

— Fifty years' hist. of the temperance cause; with descript. of plan of labor by women, by T. A. H. Brown. ill. 8°. '74. *$2.50; $2.75...... *Fitch.*

— Illustrated hist. of Bible; cont. biog. sketches of noted characters in the Bible. map and ill. 8°. *$3.50; $4; mor., $6 .... *Am. Pub.*

Stedman, Edm. Clar. Alice of Monmouth. [Poem.] 16°. '64. $1.50 .... *Osgood.*

— Blameless prince, and other poems. 16°. '69. $1.50. *Osgood.*

— Poems. por. 16°. '73. $2.25............ *Osgood.*

— *Same.* 3 v. 16°. hf. cf., $9.—(Farringford ed.) 12°. hf. cf., $4.50; mor., $6.......... *Osgood.*

— Poems, lyric and idyllic. 16°. '60. $1.50.. *Osgood.*

— Victorian poets. [Essays.] 12°. '75. $2.50; hf. cf., $4.50 .... *Osgood.*

Steedman, C: Manual of swimming. ill. 16°. $1.50. *Routledge.*

Steel, Rob. Lives made sublime by faith and works. 12°. '65. $1.25................ *Meth. Bk. Conc.*

— *Same.* 12°. $1.75 .... *Nelson.*

Steel safe; or, the stains and splendor of N. Y. life. 8°. pap., 50c. .... *De Witt.*

Steele, A. Christianity in earnest as exemplified in life and labors of Hodgson Casson; ed. by T. O. Summers. ('55.) 2d ed. 18°. '70. 60c... *So. Meth.*

— Memoir of H. Casson. ('58.) 2d ed. 18°. '69. 60c. *So. Meth.*

Steele, Anna C. Broken toys. [Fiction.] 8°. $1.25; pap., 75c. .... *Estes.*

— So runs the world away. [Fiction.] 8°. pap., 50c. *Harper.*

Steele, Dan. Love enthroned: essays on evangelical perfection. 12°. '75. $1.50 ..... *Meth. Bk. Conc.*

— *See also* Binney, A., *and* Steele, D.

Steele, Eliza R. Sovereigns of the Bible. ill. 16°. '51. $1.25.................................. *Dodd.*

Steele, J. D. Compressed air as a motor for subterranean railways. *See* Craven, A. W., Address to Am. Soc. of Civ. Eng.

— Construction of the Falls skew-bridge; [also] Memoranda of blasts on the Union Pacific R.R., by E. P. North; [also] Submarine blasting, by F. Collingwood. 8°. pap., 40c. .... *Am. Soc. of C. E.*

— Early history of railways, and origin of gauge. 8°. pap., 35c....................... *Am. Soc. of C. E.*

— Nesquehonig Tunnel. 8°. pap., 70c... *Am. Soc. of C. E.*

— Railway signals. *See* Hamilton, S., Fabrication of béton blocks.

— Tests of bridge irons; [also] Notes on the crushing strength of Am. iron, by T. C. Clarke; [also] Detroit River Tunnel, by E. S. Chesbrough. 8°. '73. pap., 60c. .... *Am. Soc. of C. E.*

Steele, J. Dorman. [Text-books.] 7 v. 12°. '69–'76. ea., $1.50 .... *Barnes.*

Cont.: Fourteen weeks' course in chemistry—in descript. astronomy—in human physiology—in nat. philos.—in popular geology—in zoology.—Answers to questions and problems in "Fourteen weeks' course in chem., astron., phys., and philos."

Steele, O., *and* Terry, M. S. Commentary on Joshua —2 Samuel. 12°. $2.50.... *Cin. Meth. Bk. Conc.*

Steele, *Sir* R: *See* Spectator;—Tatler.

Steele, Silas S. Book of drawing room plays and evening amusements. 12°. $1.50......... *Desilver.*

Steele, W. C. The woman's temperance crusade; with introd. by D. Lewis. 12°. 25c...... *Nat. Temp.*

Steele, W: J: *See* Tait, P. G., *and* Steele, W. J.

Steel-McInnes patent pneumatic reaction brake, patented Jan., 1874. pl. 4°. '75. pap., $1. *Spon.*

Steeple-chase. Morton, J. M. 15c. .... *French.*

Steeple trap (The). *See* Abbott, Jac.

Steffens, Alfr. Das Inselfräulein, od. die Tochter des Schmugglers. 12°. '74. pap., 50c...... *Zickel.*

Steffens, H: German university life: story of my career as a student and professor; with personal reminiscences of Goethe, Schiller, Novalis, etc. tr. by W. L. Gage. 12°. $1.25..... *Lippincott.*

Steger, T: M. *See* Thompson, S. D., *and* Steger, T.M.

Steiger, Ern. The periodical literature of the U. S.; with index and app. 8°. '73. $1...... *Steiger.*

Steiger's Haus- Bibliothek. [Novellen.] 15 v. 12°. '64–'66. ea., pap., 25c.–45c............ *Steiger.*

Steiger's Jugendbibliothek. 32 v. 16°. '64–'70. ea, bds., 25c. .... *Steiger.*

Stein, A. Little Anna: story for pleasant little children. ill. 16°. 50c.................. *Lee & S.*

Stein, J. W. True evangelical obedience. 8°. '75. pap., 20c......................... *Brumbaugh.*

Steinbach, Fr. Zwei vornehme Ehen. 12°. '74. pap., 20c. .... *Zickel.*

Steinbrenner, G. W. Origin and early hist. of Freemasonry. 12°. '75. $1.... *Masonic; Redding.*

Steiner, Js. Compendium of children's diseases; tr. by L. Tait. 8°. $3.50; shp., $4.50. *Appleton.*

Steiner, L. H. Seeking and finding. 12°. $1. *Ref. Ch. Pub.*

Steiner, Lew. H: *and* Schwing, H: Cantate Domino: chants, hymns and tunes. 8°. '59. $2. *Ditson.*

Steinmeyer, F. L. Miracles of our Lord examined in their rel. to mod. criticism; tr. by L. A. Wheatley. 8°. $3.75............... *Scribner, W. & A.*

Steinwehr, Adph. W: F: v. Centennial gazetteer of the U. S. roy. 8°. *$4; leath., $5... *McCurdy.*

— Eclectic school geog. 4°. '70. $1.80.. *Wilson, H. & Co.*

— *and* Brinton, D. G. Eclectic intermediate geography; with lessons in map drawing. 4°. '70. $1.50 .... *Wilson, H. & Co.*

— — Eclectic primary geography. sm. 4°. '70. 80c. *Wilson, H. & Co.*

Stella (*pseud.*) *See* Iron, N. C.

Stella. Dennan, M. A. 50c. .... *Hoyt.*

Stella. *See* Goethe, J: W. v.

Stella and the priest. Pratt, L. M. $1.50... *Lothrop.*

Stella Ashton. Barlow, C. Y. 90c....... *Garrigues.*

Stellafont Abbey. Marshall, E. $1.. *Carter; Dutton.*

Stellar key to the summerland. Davis, A. J. 75c.; 50c. .... *A. J. Davis.*

Stelle, J. Parrish. Watchmaker and jeweler's manual. 12°. pap., 50c....................... *Haney.*

Stellwag von Carion, C: Treatise on diseases of the eye, including [its] anatomy; tr. and ed. by D. B. St. J. Roosa, C. S. Bull and C. E. Hackley. ill. 8°. $7; leath., $8................ *W. Wood.*

Stems and twigs; or, sermon frame work. 2 v. 12°. ea., $1.75 .... *Scribner, W. & A.*

Stenhouse, T. B. H. Rocky Mountain saints: hist. of the Mormons. ill. 8°. *$5; shp., $6; hf. mor., $7.50 .... *Appleton.*

Stenhouse, *Mrs.* T. B. H. "Tell it all": story of a life's experience in Mormonism; with introd. by Mrs. H. B. Stowe. por. roy. 8°. '74. *$3; $3.50 .... *Lloyd; A.D. Worthington.*

Step by step. 18°. 45c.................. *Cong.Pub.*

Step by step; or, child's first lesson book. 18°. hf. bd., 25c.............................. *Keystone.*

Step by step; or, Tidy's way to freedom. Brown, H. E. 50c......................... *Bost.Am.Tr.*

Stephan, R. *See* Bible, New Test., *Greek.*

Stephani's Handfibel zum Lesenlernen nach d. Lautirmethode. 12°. 15c.................... *Radde.*

Stephen, Caro. Emilia. The service of the poor: inquiry into reasons for and against establishment of relig. sisterhoods for charitable purposes. cr. 8°. '70. $2.25.................. *Macmillan.*

Stephen, *Sir* G: Adventures of an attorney in search of practice. cr. 8°. '73. $2.25...... *Cockcroft.*
Note. Erroneously credited to S. Warren.

— *Same.* cr. 8°. $2.25 .... *Estes.*

Stephen, H: J: Treatise on principles of pleading in civil actions. 9th Am. ed.; ed. by F. F. Heard. 8°. shp., $4.50........................... *Kay.*

— *Same;* with pref., introd. and notes by S. Tyler. 8°. '71. $4.50.......................... *Morrison.*

Stephen, *Sir* Ja. Critical and miscellaneous essays. *See* Modern Brit. essayists.

— Lectures on history of France. 8°. $3; hf. cf., $5.25.............................. *Harper.*

— *See also* Smith, Sydney, Talfourd, *Sir* T. N., *and* Stephen, *Sir* J.

Stephen, Ja. F. Digest of law of evidence. 16°. '76. $1.50.................................. *Soule.*

Stephen, Ja. Fitz-Ja. General view of the criminal law of England. 8°. '63. $5....... *Macmillan.*

— Liberty, equality, fraternity. ('73.) New ed. 12°. '76. $2 .... *Holt.*

Stephen, Leslie. Hours in a library. 12°. '75. $1.75. *Scribner.*

Stephen and his tempter. Wise, D. $1.25.. *Perkinpine.*

Stephen Dane. Douglas, A. M. $1.50...... *Lee & S.*

Stephen Grattan's faith; by author of "Christie." 18°. 50c............................. *Am.S.S.*

— *See also* Glen Elder lib.

Stephen Lawrence, yeoman. Edwards, A. $1.75; $1 .... *Sheldon.*

Stephens, Alex. H. Constitutional view of the late war between the states: its causes, character, conduct and results. ill. roy. 8°. '68. *$5.50; leath., $6.50; hf. cf., $8 .... *Nat.Pub.*

— History of the U. S. 12°. hf. roan, $1.50.... *Hale.*

— Review of the war between the states. 8°. $1. *Lippincott.*

— Reviewers reviewed: sup. to "War between the states." 8°. $1.50 .... *Appleton.*

Stephens, *Mrs.* Ann S. [Novels.] 22 v. 12°. ea., $1.75; pap., $1.50.................. *Peterson.*
Cont.: Bellehood and bondage.—Bertha's engagement.—Curse of gold.—Doubly false.—Fashion and famine.—Gold brick.—Heiress.—Lord Hope's choice.—Mabel's mistake.—Married in haste.—Mary Derwent.—A noble woman.—Old countess.—Old homestead.—Palaces and prisons.—Reigning belle.—Rejected wife.—Ruby Gray's strategy.—Silent struggles.—Soldier's orphans.—Wife's secret.—Wives and widows.

— Ladies' guide to crochet. obl. 12°. $1.25.. *Dick & F.*

— Phemie Frost's experiences. 12°. $1.75 .. *Carleton.*

Stephens, C: Asbury. Camping out ser. 6 v. ill. 16°. '72–'73. ea., $1.25..................... *Porter.*
Cont.: Camping out.—Left on Labrador.—Off to the geysers.—Lynx hunting.—Fox hunting.—On the Amazons.

— Young moose hunters. ill. 12°. '75. $1.50. (?) *Shepard.*

Stephens, H: L. (*ill.*) Cartoons: [ill. of familiar nursery rhymes]. 2 nos. ill. imp. 4°. $5.. *Hurd & H.*

— Cartoons: [full page ill. of familiar nursery rhymes]. imp. 4°. artist's proofs, hf. mor., $55.. *Hurd & H.*

Stephens, H: L. (*ill.*), *continued.*

— Life of Billy Vidkins: ill. of the poets taken from life of Billy Vidkins. ill. 12°. pap., 25c. *Peterson.*

— *See also* Æsop, Fables; — Mother Goose's melodies for children.

Stephens, J. B. Convict once: poem. fp. 8°. $1.50. *Macmillan.*

Stephens, J: Lloyd. Incidents of travel in Yucatan. 2 v. ill. 8°. $6 .... *Harper.*

— Travels in Central America, Chiapas and Yucatan. 2 v. map and ill. 8°. $6 .... *Harper.*

— Travels in Egypt, Arabia Petræa and the Holy Land. 2 v. ill. 12°. $3.............. *Harper.*

— Travels in Greece, Turkey, Russia and Poland. 2 v. ill. 12°. $3.......................... *Harper.*

Stephens, W. R. W. Saint Chrysostom, his life and times: sketch of the church and the empire in the 4th cent. 8°. $7.50.................. *Pott.*

Stephenson, C. H. Trombalcazar: extravaganza. 16°. pap., 15c......................... *French.*

Stephenson, M. F. Geology and mineralogy of Georgia. 16°. *$2 .... *So.Pub.*

Stephenson family; or, lessons on the Beatitudes. 18°. 50c. .... *Pres.Bd.*

Stepmother. *See* James, G. P. R.

Stepmother rewarded. 18°. 40c.......... *Cong.Pub.*

Stepmother's recompense. Dunning, A. K. $1. *Pres.Bd.*

Stepping heavenward. Prentiss, E. $1.75; $2.50. *Randolph.*

Stepping stones. *See* Brock, *Mrs.* C.

Stepping stones for little feet. ill. sm. 4°. $1.50. (?) *O'Kane.*

Stepping stones over the brook. Boyd, M. D. R. 80c. *J.A.Moore.*

Stepping stones to architecture. Mitchell, T. 60c. *Judd.*

Stepping stones to geog. 16°. 20c.......... *Sadlier.*

Steps downward. ill. 16°. '76. 60c......... *Lothrop.*

Steps in the upward way. Barrett, M. $1. *Bost.Am.Tr.*

Steps of belief. Clarke, J. F. $1 .... *Am.Unit.*

Steps of Jesus. Mimpriss, R. 75c........... *Dodd.*

Steps through the world. *See* Rover, W.

Steps to the altar. *See* Scudamore, W. E.

Steps to a living faith. Huntington, F. D. 75c.; 25c. *Dutton.*

Steps towards heaven. Arthur, T.S. $1.50.. *J.E.Potter.*

Steps up the ladder; or, the will and the way. 18°. '63. 40c. .... *Am.Tr.*

— *Same.* 18°. 50c.......................... *Pres.Bd.*

Steps upward. Gage, F. D. $1.50 ...... *Lippincott.*

Sterling, R: Southern copy books. 9 nos. obl. 12°. per doz., $1.50 .... *Burke.*

— Southern elementary spelling-book. 12°. per doz., $1. *Agar.*

— Southern little orator. 12°. 60c. .... *Agar.*

— Southern orator. 12°. $1.50.......... *Agar; Burke.*

— Southern primer. 12°. per doz., bds., $1.08; pap., 90c. .... *Agar.*

— Southern [ser. of readers]. 6 v....... *Agar; Burke.*
Cont.: Southern first reader, 24°, bds., 25c.—second, 24°, bds., 50c.—third, 12°, 60c.—fourth, 12°, 90c.—fifth, 12°, $1.25.—Southern pictorial primer, 12°, per doz., $2.40.

Stern, Adph. Andreas Heimberger; or, the miner of Berchtesgaden; tr. by Mrs. B. Mallon. 12°. '73. 85c. .... (?) *Luth.Pub.*

Stern necessity. Robinson, F. W. 50c. .... *Harper.*

Sterne, *Miss* G. M. Aunt Margaret's visit. 18°. 45c. *Routledge.*

Sterne, Laur. Complete works; with life. por. 8°. $2.50.................... *Appleton; Lee & S.*

— *Same.* (Globe ed.) cr. 8°. $1.75; hf. cf., $3.50; cf., $5 .... *Routledge.*

— *Same.* 8°. '73. $2.25; shp., $2.75 ...... *Claxton.*

Sterne, Laur., *continued.*
— *Same.* 2 v. 12°. $3; shp., $4; hf. cf., $6.50.— (Globe ed.), $1.50; hf. cf., $3.50...*Lippincott.*
— Poems. *See* Pope, A., Poems.
— Life and opinions of Tristram Shandy, gentleman. 12°. pap., 75c....*Claxton; Lippincott; Routledge.*
— *Same.* 12°. $1 ....*Lippincott.*
— Sentimental journey through France and Italy: the fragment and the history of a good warm watch-coat. 12°. '59. pap., 25c...*Claxton; Lippincott.*
— *Same.* 12°. $1 ....*Lippincott.*
— *Same;* with letters. 12°. pap., 25c......*Routledge.*
— — *See also* British pocket classics.
— Story of my Uncle Toby. 16°. $1.25. *Scribner, W. & A.*
Sterne, Sim. On representative government and personal representation; based upon T. Hare's "Election of representatives." 12°. $1.75..*Lippincott.*
Sterne, Stuart (*pseud.*) [Gert. Bloede.] Poems. 4°. '75. $2 ....*Patterson.*
Stetson, C: B. Technical education: what it is, and what Am. public schools should teach. ('73.) New ed. 12°. '76. $1.25 ....*Prang.*
Stettner, A. Praktische Aufsatzschule f. Elementar-Schüler. 12°. '74. 50c.................*Witter.*
Stevens, A. H. Electricity as a curative agent. *See* Brewster, G., New philos. of matter.
Stevens, Abel. Centenary of Am. Methodism. 12°. '65. $1.50; pap., 75c.; mor., $5..*Meth. Bk. Conc.*
— Comprehensive hist. of Am. Methodism; abridg. from "History of the M. E. Church." ill. 8°. '75. $3.50; shp., $4; mor., $6.......*Meth. Bk. Conc.*
— Essay on church polity. 12°. '47. $1..*Meth. Bk. Conc.*
— Great reform: essay. 16°. '55. 45c...*Meth. Bk. Conc.*
— — *See also* Systematic beneficence.
— History of Methodism. 3 v. 12°. '58. $5.25; hf. mor., $7.50; ill., mor., $10.50 ...*Meth. Bk. Conc.*
— History of the Meth. Episc. Church in the U. S. 4 v. 12°. '64. $7; hf. mor., $10.—4 v. 8°. $14. *Meth. Bk. Conc.*
— Life and times of Nath. Bangs. 12°. '63. $1.75; hf. mor., $2.25 ....*Meth. Bk. Conc.*
— Preaching required by the times. 12°. '55. $1. *Meth. Bk. Conc.*
— Sketches and incidents. 18°. '43. 75c...*Meth. Bk. Conc.*
— Sketches from study of an itinerant. 16°. 90c. *Cin. Meth. Bk. Conc.*
— Women of Methodism. 12°. '66. $1.50; $2. *Meth. Bk. Conc.*
Stevens, C. Wistar. College glee book. 8°. $1.50; $2. *Gordon.*
Stevens, G: E. The Queen City [Cincinnati] in 1869, historical and descriptive. 16°. $1.50..*Stevens.*
Stevens, G: T. Three years in the 6th Corps: narr. of events in Army of the Potomac, '61–5. New ed., rev. ill. and por. 8°. '70. $3..*VanNostrand.*
Stevens, Halsey R. Scripture speculations; with introd. on creation, stars, earth, primitive man, Judaism, etc. 12°. '75. $2..........*Somerby.*
Stevens, H: Analytical index to colonial documents of N. J. *See* New Jersey Hist. Soc.
Stevens, W: Bacon. Bow in the cloud. ill. 12°. '71. *$3 ....*Hubbard.*
— History of Georgia, to 1798. 2 v. maps and ill. 8°. '47. $5 ....*Claxton.*
— Sabbaths of our Lord. ill. 12°. '72. $2.50; $3; mor., $4.50....................*J. M. Stoddart.*
— Sunday at home: manual of home service; with sermons and sel. of hymns. 12°. '56. $1.50..*Porter.*
Stevenson, Dan. Bible stories; or, the little child's sacred hist.; ed. by T. O. Summers. ('59.) 6th ed. 18°. '75. 40c......................*So. Meth.*
Stevenson, E. Biographical sketch of Valentine Cook; with his discourse on baptism. 12°. '56. $1. *So. Meth.*
Stevenson, G: Offices of Christ; abridg. by W. S. Plumer. 18°. 40c..................*Pres. Bd.*

Stevenson, *Sir* J. *See* Literature, art and song;— Moore, T., Irish melodies.
Stevenson, J. M. Toils and triumphs of colportage. 18°. '67. 40c.; pap., 20c..............*Am. Tr.*
Stevenson, J: Christ on the cross. post 8°. (Bagster.) $2.25..........................*Wiley.*
— Gratitude: exposition of 103d Psalm. post 8°. (Bagster.) $1.50 ....*Wiley.*
— Joy in God. cr. 8°. (Lond.) 50c. ....*Wiley.*
— Lord (The) our shepherd: exposition of 23d Psalm. post 8°. (Bagster.) $1.50.............*Wiley.*
— Perfect love. fp. 8°. (Bagster.) 50c......*Wiley.*
— The second advent. cr. 8°. (Bagster.) 50c...*Wiley.*
Stevenson, J: J. Report on geol. of Colorado. *See* United States, *Corps of Eng.*
Stevenson, Sa. H. Boys and girls in biology: simple studies of lower forms of life; based upon lectures of T. H. Huxley. ill. 12°. $1.50 .....*Appleton.*
Stevenson, W: F. Lives and deeds worth knowing about. 12°. $1.25....................*Carter.*
— *Same.* cr. 8°. $1.50 ....*Routledge.*
— Praying and working. 18°. 60c...........*Carter.*
— *Same.* 16°. $1 ....*Routledge.*
Steward, G: Argument of Epistles to the Hebrews. 8°. $5 ....*Scribner, W. & A.*
— Mediatorial sovereignty: mystery of Christ and revelation of Old and New Testaments. 2 v. 8°. $10..........................*Scribner, W. & A.*
— Religion the weal and need of the church. 12°. '51. 90c..........................*Meth. Bk. Conc.*
Steward (The). Cockton, H. 75c........*Peterson.*
Stewart, Agnes M. Florence O'Neill; or, the siege of Limerick. 12°. '71. $1.50; $2. *Kelly, P. & Co.*
— Home of the lost child. 18°. 60c. ......*Cath. Pub.*
— Lady Amabel and the shepherd boy. 18°. 50c.; 75c. *Sadlier.*
— Life in the cloister: tale. 12°. '66. $1.25; $1.75. *Kelly, P. & Co.*
— Life of Margaret Roper; or, the chancellor and his daughter. 12°. '76. $2.........*Kelly, P. & Co.*
— Limerick veteran; or, the foster sisters. 12°. '73. $1.50; $2 ....*Kelly, P. & Co.*
— Stories on the seven virtues. 18°. 60c...*Cath. Pub.*
Stewart, And. The American system: speeches on the tariff question and on the internal improvements; principally delivered in House of Representatives of the U. S.; with biog. sketch. por. 8°. '72. $3 ....*Baird.*
Stewart, Balfour. Conservation of energy; with app. [on] the vital and mental applic. of the doctrine. (Intern. sci. ser.) 12°. $1.50.......*Appleton.*
— Lessons in elementary physics. New ed. ill. 18°. '73. $1.50 ....*Macmillan.*
— *Same.* Am. ed.; with questions and exercises by G. A. Hill. 18°. $1.75......................*Ginn.*
— Physics. (Science primer.) ill. 18°. 50c...*Appleton.*
— *See also* Huxley, T. H., Roscoe, H. E., *and* Stewart, B.;— Tait, P. G., *and* Stewart, B.
Stewart, Dugald. Philosophy of active and moral powers of man; rev. with omissions and add. by J. Walker. 12°. $1.88....................*Butler.*
— Philosophy of the human mind. New ed., rev. and abridg.; with notes for colleges and schools by F. Bowen. 12°. $1.50....................*Dennet.*
Stewart, Eliz. M. Thomas à Becket, the people's martyr. 16°. $1; $1.50..............*Sadlier.*
Stewart, F. Campbell. Anniversary discourse before N. Y. Acad. of Med. 8°. '52. pap., 25c. *N. Y. Acad. Med.*
Stewart, F. L. Sorghum and its products. 12°. '67. $1.50....................*Claxton; Lippincott.*
Stewart, G: N. *See* Alabama, Sup. Court reports.
Stewart, H: Shepherd's manual. ill. 12°. '76. $1.50. *Judd.*

Stewart, J. C. [Ethiop. dramas.] 6 v. 16°. ea., pap., 15c. .... *De Witt.*

Cont.: Baby elephant. — Eh? what is it? — Hemmed in. — Last of the Mohicans. — Tricks. — Two black roses.

Stewart, Ja. Practical treatise on diseases of children. 8°. $2; shp., $2.50 .... *Harper.*

Stewart, J: Stable book: treatise on management of horses; with notes and add. by A. B. Allen. 12°. $1.50 .... *Judd.*

Stewart, J: A. Butler's pictorial history of the U. S. maps and ill. 12°. $1.50 .... *Butler.*

Stewart, N. Coe. Merry voices. [School sing.-book.] obl. 12°. bds., 50c. .... *Brainard.*

— *and* North, J. M. Crown king (The). [Sing. book.] obl. 8°. 75c. .... *Brainard.*

— — Singing school echo. obl. 8°. 75c. .... *Brainard.*

Stewart, Rob. American farmer's horse book. ill. 8°. '66. *$3 .... *McCurdy; Vent.*

— *Germ.;* übers. v. H. Liebhart. ill. 8°. *$3 .. *McCurdy.*

Stewart, T. Grainger. Treatise on Bright's diseases of the kidneys. 2d ed. ill. 8°. $4.50 .... *W. Wood.*

Stewart, W. Fk. Pleasant hours in an eventful life. 12°. '69. $1 .... *Carmany.*

Stewart, W: J. Roughing it with Aleck Bailie. 18°. 75c. .... *Carter.*

Stick gatherers. 18°. 60c. .... *Cong. Pub.*

Stick to it. *See* Aunt Alice's lib.

Stick to the raft. Gladstone, G. 60c. ...... *Lothrop.*

Stickney, Alb. The lawyer and his clients. 8°. pap., 50c. .... *Osgood.*

Stickney, W. *See* Kendall, A., Autobiography.

Stiebeling, G: C. Naturwissenschaft gegen Philosophie: e. Widerlegung der Hartmann'schen Lehre vom Unbewussten in der Leiblichkeit, nebst e. kurzen Beleuchtung der Darwin'schen Ansicht üb. d. Instinct. 8°. '68. $1 ... *Schmidt.*

Stiegler, J: B. Modern school for the violin; accord. to system of Conservatoire de Musique at Paris. obl. 8°. '54. pap., 75c. .... *Ditson.*

Stieler, K: *See* Pausinger, F. v., Waidmann's Erinnerungen.

Stier, Rud. [Works; tr.] 10 v. 8°. ea., $3. *Scribner, W. & A.*

Cont.: Words of the Apostles expounded; tr. by G. H. Venables. — Words of the risen Saviour, and Comment. on Epistle of St. James; tr. by W. B. Pope. — On the words of Jesus; tr. by W. B. Pope, 8 v.

— *Same;* tr. by W. B. Pope, rev. by J. Strong and H. B. Smith. 4th Am. ed. 3 v. roy. 8°. '75. $13; shp., $16; hf. mor., $20 .... *Tibbals.*

Cont.: Words of Jesus. — Words of the risen Saviour. — Words of the angels.

— Words of the angels: their visits to the earth, and messages they deliver. cr. 8°. $1.25 .. *Routledge.*

Stiles, E: H. *See* Iowa, Sup. Court reports; — Withrow, T. F., *and* Stiles, E. H.

Stiles, H: R. History of Brooklyn [N. Y.], incl. Bushwick and Williamsburgh. 3 v. roy. 8°. '67–'70. $15 .... *Munsell.*

Stilke, Hermine (*ill.*) Das Jahr in Blüthen. Chromoliths.; with descript. [Germ.] poetry by E. Geibel and G. Putlitz. roy. 4°. $15 .... *Stroefer.*

Still happy in Jesus. Jane Catherine. 25c. .. *Pres. Bd.*

Still hour. Phelps, A. 60c.; $1 .... *Lothrop.*

Still waters. *See* Smith, Ja.

Still waters run deep. Taylor, T. 15c. ...... *French.*

Stille, Alfr. Epidemic meningitis, or cerebro-spinal meningitis. 8°. '67. $2 .... *Lindsay.*

— Epidemic or malignant cholera. 16°. pap., 30c. *Lippincott.*

— Therapeutics and materia medica: systematic treatise on action and uses of medicinal agents. 2 v. 8°. $10; leath., $12 .... *Lea.*

Stillé, C: J. History of the U. S. Sanitary Com.: general report of its work. 8°. '66. $3.50; hf. roxb., $8 .... *Hurd & H.*

Stille Stunde (Die), od. die rechte Gebetskunst; a. d. Engl. 16°. '76. 60c. .... *Ev. Assoc.*

Stilling, H: Autobiography; tr. by S. Jackson. 8°. 75c. .... *Harper.*

Stilling, Jung. Leben. 18°. '72. 50c. ...... *Am. Tr.*

Stillman, J. M. *See* Martin, S. W., Towne, T. M., *and* Stillman, J. M.

Stillman, Pl. Steam-engine indicator, and the improved manometer, steam and vacuum gauges: their utility and application. New ed. 12°. '64. $1 .... *Van Nostrand.*

Stillman, W: J. Cretan insurrection of 1866–8. 12°. '74. $1.50 .... *Holt.*

— (*ed.*) Poetic localities of Cambridge; with sel. from Longfellow, Lowell and Holmes. ill. 4°. '75. $3.50 .... *Osgood.*

Stimme (Die) unserer Kirche. Walther, C. F. W. $2.75. *Barthel.*

Stimpson, W: Hydrobiinæ and allied forms. 8°. '65. pap., 50c. .... *Smith. Inst.*

— Marine invertebrata of Great Manan. 4°. '53. pap., $1.50 .... *Smith. Inst.*

— Preliminary report on the crustacea dredged by L. F. De Pourtalès. 8°. '70. pap., 50c. *Mus. Comp. Zool.*

Sting of the adder. 18°. 40c.; 50c. .... *Am. Bapt.*

Stingy Lewis. *See* Leighton children.

Stirling, E: [Plays.] 26 v. 16°. ea., pap., 15c. *French.*

Cont.: Aline. — Bloomer costume: farce. — Blue jackets: farce. — Cabin boy. — Captain Charlotte: farce. — Cheap excursion: farce. — Courier of Lyons. — Grace Darling. — Jew's daughter. — Left in a cab: farce. — Legacy of honour. — Lucky hit: comic drama. — Margaret Catchpole. — Nicholas Nickleby: farce. — Nora Creina. — Old curiosity shop. — Pair of pigeons: farce. — Pet of the public: farce. — Rag-picker of Paris. — Reapers. — Rifle volunteers: farce. — Teacher taught: farce. — Teddy Roe: farce. — Trapping a tartar. — Woodman's spell. — Young scamp: farce.

— Cabin boy: drama. 16°. pap., 15c. .... *Happy.*

— Grace Darling: drama. 16°. pap., 15c. .... *Happy.*

— Pet of the public: farce. 16°. pap., 15c. ... *Ames.*

Stirling, Ja. Hutchinson. As regards protoplasm. 12°. '75. pap., 25c. .... *Van Nostrand.*

Stitch in time. Allen, C. W. $1.50 ...... *World Pub.*

Stitch in time. Webb, J. B. 40c. ... *Scribner, W. & A.*

Stith, W: History of first discovery and settlement of Virginia: essay toward general hist. of the colony. [Reprint.] 8°. $7.50; large pap., $10 .... *Sabin.*

Stith, *Miss* Zoda. ["Elloie."] Poems. 12°. '69. $1.25 .... *So. Meth.*

Stöber, K: Geschichten des Pfarrers Siebentisch. 16°. 25c. .... *Morwitz.*

— Kleine Erzählungen f. Kinder. 32°. bds., 15c. *Ludwig.*

— Kuchenmichel (Der). 32°. bds., 15c. .... *Ludwig.*

— Mühlarzt (Der); [also] Der Birkhof. 16°. 25c. *Morwitz.*

— *Same.* 16°. 30c.; bds., 20c.; pap., 15c. ... *Kohler.*

Stock, Chr. Homiletisches Reallexicon. 8°. hf. leath., $8.50 .... *Volkening.*

Stock exchange. Dance, C. 15c. .... *French.*

Stockbridge, J: Calvin. The model pastor: memoir of B. Stow. por. 12°. $1.75 .... *Lee & S.*

Stockett, J. Shaaff. *See* Maryland, Court of Appeals reports.

— *and* Merrick, R. T., *and* Miller, O. Digest of Maryland reports. 8°. '57. shp., $10 .. *Cushings & B.*

Compr. Gill (9 v.), Maryland (8 v.), Maryland chancery (4 v.)

Stöckhardt, Jul. A. Agricultural chemistry; or, chem. field lectures; tr., with notes by Prof. Henfrey, and paper on liquid manure by J. J. Mechi. 12°. (Bohn.) $1.75 .... *Little, B. & Co.*

— *Same.* 12°. (Bohn.) $2. *Lippincott; Scribner, W. & A.*

Stöckhardt, Jul. A., *continued.*
— Principles of chemistry; exemplified in series of simple experiments; tr. ill. 12°. (Bohn.) $1.75. *Little, B. & Co.*
— *Same.* ill. 12°. (Bohn.) $2. *Lippincott; Scribner, W. & A.*
— *Same;* tr. by C. H. Peirce. 16°. $2.75 .... *Butler.*
Stockly, Ht. E. Conversations with Theodore and his sister. 16°. *net*, 40c. .... *Friends Bk. Assoc.*
Stöckmar, E. v. (*Baron*). Memoirs of Baron [C. F.] Stöckmar; tr. by G. A. M.; ed. by F. M. Müller. 2 v. cr. 8°. $5 .... *Lee & S.*
Stocks up, stocks down: Ethiop. drama. 16°. pap., 15c. .... *Ames.*
Stockton, Fk. R. Roundabout rambles in lands of fact and fancy. ('72.) New ed. ill. 4°. '75. $2 .... *Scribner.*
— Tales out of school. ('75.) New ed. ill. 4°. '76. $2.50 .... *Scribner.*
— Ting-a-ling. ill. 16°. '69. $1.50 .... *Hurd & H.*
— What might have been expected. ill. 16°. '74. $1.50 .... *Dodd.*
— *and* M. E. The home: where it should be and what to put in it. 12°. '72. 75c. .... *Putnam.*
Stockton, J: P. *See* New Jersey, Court of Chanc. reports.
Stockton, Marion E. *See* Stockton, F. R. *and* M. E.
Stockton, T: Hewlings. Book above all; or, the Bible the only sensible, infallible and divine authority on earth: discourses. ('70.) 2d ed. 12°. '71. $1.50; $2 .... *Claxton.*
Stockwell, G. S. Republic of Liberia: its geog., climate, soil, hist., etc. 12°. '68. $1.25 .. *Barnes.*
Stockwell, J: N. Secular variations of orbits of planets. 4°. '72. pap., $2 .... *Smith. Inst.*
Stocqueler, J: H: Object of interest: farce. 16°. pap., 15c. .... *French.*
Stoddard, C: Warren. South sea idyls. (Saunterer's ser.) 18°. '73. $1.25 .... *Osgood.*
Stoddard, D: Tappan. Grammar of modern Syriac as spoken in Oroomiah, Persia and in Koordistan. 8°. '55. bds., $1.50 .... *Am. Orient.*
Stoddard, H. H. An egg farm: management of poultry in large numbers. ill. 12°. '76. 75c.; pap., 50c. *Judd.*
Stoddard, J: F. American intellect. arithmetic. 16°. hf. bd., 40c. — Key, hf. bd., 50c. .... *Sheldon.*
— Complete arithmetic. 12°. hf. leath., $1.25 .. *Sheldon.*
— Complete ready reckoner. 24°. $1 .... *Mason.*
— Juvenile mental arithmetic. 18°. hf. bd., 25c. *Sheldon.*
— Methods of teaching. 16°. hf. bd., 50c. .... *Sheldon.*
— New practical arithmetic. 12°. hf. bd., $1. — Key. 12°. hf. bd., $1 .... *Sheldon.*
— Old practical arithmetic. 12°. hf. bd., 90c. — Key. 12°. 75c. .... *Sheldon.*
— Pictorial primary arithmetic. 18°. hf. bd., 30c. *Sheldon.*
— Rudiments of arithmetic. 16°. hf. bd., 50c. .. *Sheldon.*
— School arithmetic, incl. written and intellectual. 16°. hf. bd., 75c. .... *Sheldon.*
— *and* Henkle, W. D. Elementary algebra. 12°. hf. leath., $1.25. — Key, $1.25 .... *Sheldon.*
— — University algebra. 12°. hf. leath., $2. — Key. 12°. $2 .... *Sheldon.*
Stoddard, R: H: Adventures in fairy land. ill. 16°. $1.25 .... * *Osgood.*
— Book of the east, and other poems. 16°. '71. $1.50; hf. cf., $3; mor., $4 .... *Osgood.*
— Children in the wood; told in verse. 4°. pap., 25c. *Hurd & H.*
— King's bell. ill. sm. 4°. $2.50 .... *Huntington.*
— Little Red Riding Hood; told in verse. ill. 4°. pap., 25c. .... *Hurd & H.*
— Loves of the early poets. por. 4°. $5; mor., $10. *Lippincott.*

Stoddard, R: H: *continued.*
— Poems. 16°. $1 .... *Osgood.*
— Songs of summer. 16°. $1 .... *Osgood.*
— Treasure-trove ser. *See* Walsh, W. S.
— (*ed.*) Bric-a-brac ser. 10 v. por. and ill. sq. 16°. '74–'76. $15; $17; hf. cf., $20; ea., $1.50 .. *Scribner.*

Cont.: 1. Personal reminiscences, by H. F. Chorley, J. R. Planché and J. C. Young. — 2. Anecdote biographies of Thackeray and Dickens. — 3. Letters to an incognita, by P. Mérimée; with recollections by Lamartine and George Sand. — 4. Personal reminiscences, by Barham, Harness and Hodder. — 5. The Greville memoirs, by C. C. F. Greville. — 6. Personal reminiscences, by Moore and Jerdan. — 7. Personal reminiscences, by Cornelia Knight and Thomas Raikes. — 8. Personal reminiscences of O'Keeffe, Kelly and Taylor. — 9. Personal reminiscences of Lamb, Hazlitt and others. — 10. Personal reminiscences, by Constable and Gillies.

— Century (A) after: picturesque glimpses of Philadelphia and Pennsylvania; with eng. from designs by T. Moran, F. O. C. Darley and others. 4°. '76. $9; hf. mor., $11; mor., $13.50 .. *Allen.*
— Golden leaves from the late English poets. 12°. '65. $1.50 .... *Randolph.*
— — *See also* Golden leaves ser.
— Melodies and madrigals, mostly from the old poets. sq. 16°. $2.50; mor., $5 .... *Huntington.*
— Sans-souci series. v. 1, 2. ill. 12°. '76. ea., $1.50. *Scribner.*

Cont.: 1. Life, letters and table talk of B. R. Haydon, by R. H. Stoddard. — 2. Men and manners one hundred years ago, by H. E. Scudder.

Stoddard, *Mrs.* R. H. Lolly Dinks' doings. sq. 16°. '74. $1 .... *W. F. Gill.*
— *See also* Dodge, Ma. A., *and* Stoddard, *Mrs.* R. H.
Stoddard, Seneca Ray. Adirondacks illustrated. ('74.) [Annual.] 4th ed. map. 12°. '76. $1.25; pap., 50c. .... *S. R. Stoddard.*
— Lake George illustrated: a book of to-day. ('73.) [Annual.] 12°. $1; pap., 50c. .... *S. R. Stoddard.*
— Ticonderoga, past and present. ill. and map. 12°. '73. 50c.; pap., 35c. .... *S. R. Stoddard.*
Stoddard, Sol. *See* Andrews, E. A., *and* Stoddard, S.
Stoddard, W: Osborn. Verses of many days. 12°. '74. $1.50 .... *Miller.*
Stoeckel, Gst. J. Sacred music: original tunes and anthems for social worship. 8°. $1.50; bds., $1. *Taintor.*
Stohlmann, F: Die Lebendigbegrabenen, u. wie Scheintodte nebst andern Verunglückten zu behandeln sind. 12°. 60c. .... *Radde.*
— Neun Reisen e. Sonambüle in die Lichtgefilde d. Seligen. 12°. 75c. .... *Radde.*
Stohlmann, J. F: Chr. Festgesänge u. andere Lieder. 12°. 25c. .... *Radde.*
— Geistliches Betkämmerlein zur Einkehr gläubiger Christen. 12°. 25c. .... *Radde.*
— Singet dem Herrn. 12°. 25c. .... *Radde.*
Stoker, —. Mass in F; for four voices. f°. pap., $1.50 .... *Ditson.*
Stokes, E. H. *See* New Jersey conf. mem.
Stokes, E: S. Life and trial; with life and assassination of Ja. Fisk and life of Josephine Mansfield. [In Eng. or Germ.] 8°. pap., 25c. .... *Barclay.*
Stokes, J. Cabinet maker's and upholsterer's companion. ('50.) 9th ed. 12°. '75. $1.25 .. *Baird.*
Stokes, W: Diseases of the heart and aorta. 8°. '55. $3 .... *Lindsay.*
— Lectures on fever; ed. by J. W. Moore. 8°. '76. $2 .... *Lea.*
Stokes, W: H., *and* Blenkinsop, Ma. Mount Hope case: report of [their] trial, Feb., 1866, before Circuit Court for Balt. Co., Md. 8°. '66. $2. *Kelly, P. & Co.*
Stokesley secret. Yonge, C. M. 60c. .... *Appleton.*
Stolen: 20*l.* reward. Hancock, W. 15c. .... *French.*
Stolen boy. Hofland, B. 25c. .... *U. P. James.*
Stolen child. Bates, L. 50c. .... *Am. Tr.*
Stolen from home. Denison, M. A. $1.50 .... *Hoyt.*

Stolen gold piece. Brigham, S. P. 40c. ...... *Hoyt.*

Stolen Jewess: drama. 16°. pap., 15c. ...... *French.*

Stolen mask. *See* Collins, Wilkie.

Stolen shilling. *See* Baker, *Mrs.* H. N. W.

Stolen waters. Gardner, C. E. $1.50 ..... *Carleton.*

Stolle, Fd. 1813: hist. Roman. 8°. $1; pap., 75c.; hf. mor., $1.25 .... *F. W. Thomas.*

Stolz, *Mme.* de (*pseud.*) *See* Bégon, F. (*Comtesse*) de.

Stolz, Alban. Der unendliche Gruss. 12°. bds., 25c. *Benziger.*

Stone, A. P. *See* England, Law reports.

Stone, And. L. Memorial discourses. 12°. $1.50; with por., $3 .... *Hoyt.*

Stone, C: Fs. Analytical index of parallel ref. to cases cited in N. Y. reports. 8°. '69. shp., $4.50. *Ward & P.*

Stone, D: Frank Forest; or, life of an orphan boy. ill. 18°. '52. 75c. .... *Dodd.*

Stone, Edn. M. Life and recollections of J: Howland. 12°. '57. $1.25 .... *Rider.*

Stone, H: D. Personal recollections of the drama. por. 12°. '73. $2 .... (?) *VanBenthuysen.*

Stone, I: Elementary and complete examiner [for teachers]; or, candidates' assistant. 12°. '64. $1.25 .... *Barnes.*

Stone, Ja. Kent. The invitation heeded: reasons for a return to Catholic unity. 10th ed. 12°. '70. $1.50 .... *Cath. Pub.*

Stone, J: S. The Christian sacraments; or, Scriptural views of baptism and the Lord's supper. 8°. '66. $3 .... *Randolph.*

— The divine rest; or, Scriptural views of the Sabbath. cr. 8°. '66. $2.25 .... *Randolph.*

— The living temple. cr. 8°. '66. $2.50 .. *Randolph.*

Stone, Livingston. Domesticated trout: how to breed and grow them. ill. 16°. '73. $2.50. *Osgood; Stone.*

Stone, R: C. Life-incidents of home, school and church. 16°. $1 .... *S. W. Bk. & Pub.*

— Miscellaneous, epic and dramatic poems. 12°. $1. *S. W. Bk. & Pub.*

Stone, W. Domett. Epitome of therapeutics. 8°. '74. $4 .... *Putnam.*

Stone, W: Leete. Border wars of the Am. revolution; with life of Jos. Brant, the Indian chief. 2 v. 18°. $1.50 .... *Harper.*

— History of Wyoming; cont. Campbell's "Gertrude." 12°. '64. $1.50; $2.50 .... *Munsell.*

— Life and times of Red Jacket [Sagoyewatha]; with memoir of author by his son. · por. and eng. 8°. '66. $3 .... *Munsell.*

— Life and times of Sir W: Johnson. 2 v. por. 8°. '65. $6 .... *Munsell.*

— Life of Joseph Brant [Thayendanegea]; incl. the border wars of the revolution, etc. 2 v. por. and pl. 8°. '65. $5 .... *Munsell.*

Stone, W: Leete, *jr.* History of New York City. roy. 8°. '72. $6 .... *Virtue.*

— Reminiscences of Saratoga and Ballston. 16°. '75. $2; hf. cf., $3.50 .... *Virtue.*

Stone age, past and present. Tyler, E. B. 25c. *Estes.*

Stone and the image. Berg, J. F. $1 .. *Perkinpine.*

Stone Edge. [Fiction.] 8°. pap., 25c. ..... *Harper.*

Stone house. *See* Leighton children.

Stone mason of Saint Point. *See* Lamartine, A. de.

Stonehenge (*pseud.*) *See* Walsh, J: H:

Stoner, D: Life. 18°. '36. 55c. .... *Meth. Bk. Conc.*

— Memoirs; with extracts from diary and correspondence; rev. by T. O. Summers. ('58.) 2d ed. 18°. '70. 65c. .... *So. Meth.*

Stoner, Ph. Robert of Woodleigh, and other poems. 12°. '72. $1.25 .... *Miller.*

Stones, Alonzo. Amateur orchestra: popular melodies for violin, flute, etc., quartets. 12 nos. 4°. ea., 40c.–60c.; — for quintets. 12 nos. 4°. ea., 50c.–75c. .... *Ditson.*

Stones and diamonds. Boyd, E. E. $1.25. (?) *Martien; H. A. Young.*

Stones of Palestine. Gray, J. C. 10c. .. *Meth. Bk. Conc.*

Stones of the temple. Field, W. $2.50 .... *Appleton.*

Stones of Venice. *See* Ruskin, J:

Stones through glass houses. Pullen, H. W. $1.25; 75c. .... *W. F. Gill.*

Stoney, Bindon B. Theory of strains in girders and similar structures; with obs. on applic. of theory to practice, and tables of strength and other properties of materials. New ed., rev. ill. roy. 8°. $12.50 .... *VanNostrand.*

Stony croft ser. for boys. 5 v. 18°. $3.25 .. *Randolph.*
Cont.: Ernest. — Joe and Jim. — Old stone chimney. — Barton Todd. — Hugh's fire on the mountain.

Stony road. 12°. '72. 85c. .... *Meth. Bk. Conc.*

Stopping the leak. Baker, H. N. W. $1.25. *H. A. Young.*

Storehouse of stories. Yonge, C. M. 2 v. ea., $1.50. *Macmillan.*

Storer, Fk. H. Cyclopædia of quantitative chemical analysis. 2 pts. 8°. '70–'73. ea., pap., $1.65 .. *Allyn.*

— Dictionary of solubilities of chemical substances. 8°. '64. $7.50; hf. mor., $9 .... *Allyn.*

— *See also* Eliot, C. W., *and* Storer, F. H.

Storer, Horatio R. Causation, course and rational treatment of insanity in women: a gynæcist's idea thereof. 16°. '71. $1.50 .... *Lee & S.*

— Female hygiene: lecture. 8°. '72. pap., 25c. *Jas. Campbell.*

— Is it I? a book for every man. 16°. '67. $1; pap., 50c. .... *Lee & S.*

— On nurses and nursing; with especial reference to management of sick women. 16°. '68. $1; pap., 50c. .... *Lee & S.*

— Why not? a book for every woman. 16°. '66. $1; pap., 50c. .... *Lee & S.*
Note. First pub. in Trans. of Am. Med. Assoc., 1865, under title of "Physical evils of forced abortions."

— *and* Heard, F. F. Criminal abortion: its nature, its evidence and its law. 8°. '68. $1.75; shp., $2. *Little, B. & Co.*

Storia di Enrichetto ed il suo latore. *See* Sherwood, *Mrs.* M. M.

Stories. *See* New.

Stories; by Mrs. L. C. Moulton, Miss E. S. Phelps, E. Farman, R. Johnson and others. ill. 16°. '76. $2 .... *Lothrop.*

Stories about. Barker, M. A. $1.50 ..... *Macmillan.*

Stories about Africa. Moffat, R. 35c. .... *Pres. Bd.*

Stories about animals. ill. 16°. $1.50 .... *Miller.*

Stories about animals. Jackson, T. *$2.50 .. *Am. Pub.*

Stories about animals ser. 12 v. ill. 18°. '75. $3 .. *Nelson.*
Cont.: Mercury and the woodman. — Wolf and the lamb. — Dog in the manger. — Jackdaw in the borrowed plumes. — Mouse and the frog. — Wolf and young goat. — Cock and the jewel. — Mice in council. — Fox and the crow. — Lap dog and the cat. — Ox and the sheep. — Lion and other beasts.

Stories about the Bible. *See* Aunt Gracie's lib.

Stories about birds. Kirby, M. *and* E. *$2.50. *Am. Pub.*

Stories about birds and beasts. *See* Theodore Thinker.

Stories about the country. *See* Theodore Thinker.

Stories about the heathen. Scudder, D. C. 30c. *Bost. Am. Tr.*

Stories about Jesus: a series for children. 18°. 50c. *So. Bapt.*

Stories about the little ones. *See* Library for little lads and lasses.

Stories about Nellie. *See* Dawes, *Mrs.* S. E.

Stories and legends of travel and hist. Lippincott, S. J. $1.50 .... * *Osgood.*

Stories and pictures from church history. ill. 12°. '70. $1.25 .... *Meth. Bk. Conc.*
Stories and rhymes for boys and girls. Doughty, S. P. 50c. .... *H. H. Carter.*
Stories and sights of France and Italy. Lippincott, S. J. $1.50 .... **Osgood.*
Stories by two sisters. 18°. 75c. .... *Pres. Bd.*
Stories explanatory of Church catechism. *See* Sherwood, *Mrs.* M. M.
Stories for Alice. Bullard, A. 25c. .... *Lee & S.*
Stories for all seasons. 18°. 50c. .... *Pres. Bd.*
Stories for beginners. ill. sq. 18°. '63. 35c... *Am. Tr.*
Stories for boys. 32°. 30c. .... *Am. S. S.*
— *See also* Library for little folks.
Stories for children. 32°. 25c. .... *West. Tr.*
Stories for children. Tonna, C. E. 35c. ..... *Am. Tr.*
Stories for Eva. Appleton, A. E. 80c. .... *Am. Unit.*
Stories for the fireside. 2 v. sq. 4°. '72. ea., bds., 60c. .... *Am. Tr.*
Stories for girls. 32°. 30c. .... *Am. S. S.*
— *See also* Library for little folks.
Stories for good boys; — for good girls. *See* Children's prize stories.
Stories for the household. Andersen, H. C. $3; $5. *Routledge.*
Stories for leisure hours. *See* Larned, A.
Stories for little ears. ill. 18°. 30c. .... *Am. S. S.*
Stories for little folks. ill. 18°. 22c. .... *Am. S. S.*
Stories for the little ones. *See* Dunning, *Mrs.* A. K.
Stories for the little ones. *See* Parker, *Mrs.* C. E. R.
Stories for little people. *See* Larned, A.
Stories for little pets. 12 bks. 18°. 50c... *Cong. Pub.*
Stories for my children. Knatchbull-Hugessen, E. H. $1.75 .... *Macmillan.*
Stories for parents. *See* Arthur, T. S.
Stories for school boys. *See* Village lib.
Stories for Sundays. Adams, H. C. $1.25.. *Routledge.*
Stories for Sundays. Sherwood, M. M. $1.25; $2.50. *Lippincott.*
Stories for village lads; by author of "Stories of school-boys." ('55.) 2d ed. 18°. '74. 60c. *So. Meth.*
— *See also* Select library for boys; — Village lib.
Stories for village lads; or, the right and wrong way of doing common duties contrasted. 18°. 50c. *Am. S. S.*
Stories for week-days and Sundays. 18°. 45c. *Routledge.*
Stories for the winter. *See* Prairie books.
Stories for the young. More, H. $3 .... *Am. Tr.*
Stories for young housekeepers. *See* Arthur, T. S.
Stories for young persons. Sedgwick, C. M. 75c. *Harper.*
Stories from Aunt Deborah's drawer. *See* Aunt Deborah's lib.
Stories from China. ill. 12°. $1.50 .... *Nelson.*
Stories from Eng. hist. 18°. 35c. .... *Routledge.*
— *See also* Moss wreath lib.
Stories from famous ballads. Lippincott, S. J. $1. **Osgood.*
Stories from Grecian history. ill. 16°. pap., 10c. *U. P. James.*
Stories from hist. Strickland, A. $1.25 .... *Porter.*
Stories from hist. of the Jews. Tucker, C. 75c. *Nelson.*
Stories from hist. of Rome. 12°. $1.50 .... *Pott.*
Stories from life. Peirce, B. K. $1 .... *Hoyt.*
Stories from the lips of the teacher. Frothingham, O. B. $1 .... *Putnam.*
Stories from the moorland. Bates, L. $1.25.. *Lothrop.*
Stories from my attic. Scudder, H. E. $1.50. *Hurd & H.*

Stories from old English poetry. Richardson, A. S. $1.25 .... *Hurd & H.*
Stories from Roman history. ill. 16°. pap., 10c. *U. P. James.*
Stories from the south seas. ill. 12°. $1.50.. *Nelson.*
Stories illustrating Shorter Catechism. Todd, J. $1.50. *Bridgman.*
Stories in prose and verse. Carter, A. A. 50c. *H. H. Carter.*
Stories of adventure. *See* Cooper, Ja. F.
Stories of adventure. *See* Verne, Jul.
Stories of animal sagacity. Kingston, W. H. G. $1.50. *Nelson.*
Stories of animals. ill. 16°. '75. 75c. ..... *Lothrop.*
Stories of animals. ill. sq. 16°. 50c. .... *Perkinpine.*
Stories of the Apostles. *See* Hadley, C.
Stories of the Beatitudes. 18°. 50c.; 75c. .. *Sadlier.*
Stories of the Bible. Tonna, C. E. 75c. *Scribner, W. & A.*
Stories of bird life. Berthone, H. $1.50 .... *Nelson.*
Stories of birds. ill. 16°. '75. 75c. .... *Lothrop.*
Stories of Canadian forests. Traill, C. P. $1.25. *Nichols & H.*
Stories of Christ the Lord. Cave, H. 90c. *Meth. Bk. Conc.*
Stories of the commandments. 18°. '67. 50c. *Cunningham.*
Stories of the creation. Thayer, W. M. $1.25. *Perkinpine.*
Stories of Eng. and foreign life. *See* Howitt, M. *and* W.
Stories of the flowers. Bates, L. 80c. ...... *Am. Tr.*
Stories of foreign countries. ill. sq. 16°. 50c. *Perkinpine.*
Stories of the good shepherd. 6 v. ill. 18°. $1.90. *Am. S. S.*
Cont.: Angel and the babe. — Woman and the traveller. — Supper on the grass. — Poor blind beggar. — King and the robber. — Sea of Galilee.
Stories of the good shepherd; or, simple Scripture narratives. ill. 18°. 90c. .... *Am. S. S.*
Stories of the gorilla country. Du Chaillu, P. B. $1.50 .... *Harper.*
Stories of a governess. 18°. 60c. .... *Dutton.*
Stories of hospital and camp. McKay, C. E. $1.50. *Claxton.*
Stories of the household. *See* Arthur, T. S.
Stories of infinity. Flammarion, C. $1.50.. *Roberts.*
Stories of inventors and discoverers. Timbs, J. $1.50. *Harper.*
Stories of the island world. Nordhoff, C. $1.. *Harper.*
Stories of Jewish hist. Tucker, C. 50c. ..... *Carter.*
Stories of the kings. Adams, H. C. $1. *Scribner, W. & A.*
Stories of many lands. Lippincott, S. J. $1.50. **Osgood.*
Stories of natural hist. ill. sq. 16°. 50c... *Perkinpine.*
Stories of the ocean. 18°. 50c. .... *Carter.*
Stories of old. *See* Hadley, C.
Stories of old Daniel; for amusement of young persons. 16°. $1 .... *Routledge.*
Stories of old England. *See* Popular lib. of hist.
Stories of an old maid. *See* Atlantic lib.
Stories of the olden time. Joinville, J. de, *and* Froissart, J. $1 .... *Cassell.*
Stories of other lands. 12°. '58. 80c. ..... *Randolph.*
Stories of our duty to God. 18°. 35c.; 40c... *Dutton.*
Stories of the patriarchs. Frothingham, O. B. $1. *Putnam.*
Stories of the patriarchs. Thayer, W. M. $1.25. *Perkinpine.*
Stories of the prairie. *See* Cooper, Ja. F.
Stories of prison life: biog. of Picciola Silvio Pellico and Baron French. 18°. 75c. .... *Barnes.*

Stories of the prophets. Adams, H. C. $1. *Scribner, W. & A.*

Stories of school boys; by author of "Stories for village lads." ('55.) 2d ed. 18°. '74. 50c...*So. Meth.*

— *Same.* 18°. 55c. ....*Am. S. S.*

— *Same.* ill. 18°. 65c.....*N. Y. Ref. Ch. Bd.; Pres. Com.*

Stories of Scotland. *See* Geldart, *Mrs.* T:

Stories of the sea. *See* Cooper, Ja. F.

Stories of success. Cobb, J. F. $1.50.........*Pott.*

Stories of success. Smith, S. F. $1.50 ....*Lothrop.*

Stories of Venice and the Venetians. Marsh, J. B. $2 ....*Routledge.*

Stories of Vinegar Hill. Warner, A. B. 6 v. $3. *Carter.*

Stories of the wars, 1574–1658. ill. 8°. $2.50. *Scribner, W. & A.*

— *See also* Beeton's boys' own lib.

Stories of Waterloo. *See* Maxwell, W: H.

Stories of the woods. *See* Cooper, Ja. F.

Stories of the world's progress. 4 v. 12°. $6..*Lothrop.*
Cont.: Myths and heroes.—Knights and sea-kings.—Stories of success.—Noble workers.

Stories old and new. 32°. 20c.; 15c. ....*Dutton.*

Stories on the Beatitudes. 18°. 55c.; 60c. ...*Dutton.*

Stories on the Lord's prayer. 18°. 50c........*Carter.*

— *See also* Head and heart ser.

Stories on parables. Tucker, C. 75c. ....*Carter.*

Stories on the seven virtues. Stewart, A. M. 60c. *Cath. Pub.*

Stories that might be true. Greenwell, D. $1.25. *Routledge.*

Stories that you will like. ill. 4°. 25c......*Am. Bapt.*

Stories they tell me. O'Reilly, R. $1.25 ....*Dutton.*

Stories to make one wise. 2 v. 32°. ea., 15c. *Am. S. S.*

Stories told to a child. *See* Ingelow, J.

Stories which sister Alice told her little brother Johnny. *See* Picture lib. for the little ones.

Stork, Thph. Afternoon: miscellaneous papers. por. 12°. $1.75; $2....................*Lippincott.*

— Children of New Test. 12°. 75c.; $1..(?) *Luth. Pub.*

— Home scenes of New Test.; or, Christ in the family. 12°. $1; $1.25..................(?) *Luth. Pub.*

— Luther and his times. v. 1, 2. ill. sq. 16°. ea., $1. (?) *Luth. Pub.*
Cont.: Luther at home.—Luther and the Bible.

— Sermons. 12°. $1.50...............(?) *Luth. Pub.*

— Unseen world in the light of the cross. 16°. $1. *Lippincott.*

— *See also* Luther, Mt., Life.

Storm, Thdr. Auf d. Universität. *See* Meyr, M., Zwei Freier.

— Immensee. With Eng. notes. ('73.) New ed. 12°. '75. pap., 40c. ....*Holt.*

— *Eng.* Immen-See; [also] Grandmother and granddaughter. 16°. '64. pap., 40c..............*Holt.*

Storm and sunshine. *See* Theodore Thinker.

Storm in a teacup. Bernard, W. B. 15c.....*French.*

Storm king. *See* Baker, B. F.

Storm of life. Smith, H. $1...............*Am. Tr.*

Storm warriors. Gilmore, J. $1.75......*Macmillan.*

Stormcliff. Walworth, M. T. $1.75.......*Carleton.*

Storme, G: Easy German reading; with foot-notes. ('68.) New ed., rev. 16°. '76. $1.....*Holt.*

— Select German stories; rev. and enl. for Am. schools. sm. 8°. '73. 65c...................*Enderis.*

Storming the fort. White, C. 15c..........*De Witt.*

Stormonth, Ja. Etymological and pronounc. dict. of the Eng. lang. 12°. $3.75.....*Scribner, W. & A.*

Stormy life. *See* Fullerton, *Lady* G.

Storrs, R: Salter. Conditions of success in preaching without notes: lectures, with app. 12°. '75. $1.25.....................................*Dodd.*

Storrs, R: Salter, *continued.*

— Early Am. spirit, and the genesis of it. 8°. '75. $1; pap., 60c.............................*Randolph.*

Story, C: A. Alcohol: its nature and effects. ('68.) New ed. 18°. '74. 90c............*Nat. Temp.*

Story, Ja. P. Choisy. [Fiction.] 8°. '72. $1.25; pap., 75c.................................*Estes.*

Story, Jos. Commentaries on conflict of laws, foreign and domestic, in regard to contracts, rights and remedies, and especially in regard to marriages, divorces, wills, etc. 7th ed., rev. and enl. by E. H. Bennett. 8°. '72. shp., $6...*Little, B. & Co.*

— Commentaries on Constitution of U. S.; with review of const. hist. of the colonies and states before adoption of the Const. 4th ed., rev. by T. M. Cooley. 2 v. 8°. '73. shp., $12..*Little, B. & Co.*

— Commentaries on equity jurisprudence as administered in Eng. and Am. 11th ed., enl. by F. V. Balch. 2 v. 8°. '73. shp., $12..*Little, B. & Co.*

— — Key. *See* Guernsey, R. S.

— Commentaries on equity pleadings and incidents thereto, accord. to practice of courts of equity of Eng. and Am.; rev. and enl. by I. F. Redfield. 8th ed. 8°. '70. shp., $6.......*Little, B. & Co.*

— Commentaries on law of agency as a branch of commercial and maritime jurisprudence; with ill. from civil and foreign law. 8th ed., enl. by N. St. J. Green. 8°. '74. shp., $6.......*Little, B. & Co.*

— Commentaries on law of bailments, with ill. from civil and foreign law. 8th ed., rev. and enl. by E. H. Bennett. 8°. '70. shp., $6..*Little, B. & Co.*

— Commentaries on law of bills of exchange, foreign and inland, as administered in Eng. and Am.; with ill. from commercial law of nations of continental Europe. 4th ed., rev. and enl. by E. H. Bennett. 8°. '60. shp., $6.......*Little, B. & Co.*

— Commentaries on law of partnership as a branch of commercial and maritime jurisprudence; with ill. from civil and foreign law. 6th ed., rev. and enl. by J. C. Gray, jr. 8°. '68. shp., $6..*Little, B. & Co.*

— Commentaries on law of promissory notes and guaranties of notes and checks on banks and bankers; with ill. from commercial law of nations of continental Europe. 6th ed., rev. and enl. 8°. '68. shp., $6.........................*Little, B. & Co.*

— Familiar exposition of U. S. Const.; with public documents ill. of the Const. 12°. $1.50..*Harper.*

Story, Rob. Herb. William Carstares: a character and career of the revolutionary epoch, 1649–1715. 8°. '74. $4..............................*Macmillan.*

Story, Sydney A., *jr.* (*pseud.*) *See* Pike, *Mrs.* M. H.

Story, W: Wetmore. Graffiti d'Italia. New ed. 12°. $3.75........................*Scribner, W. & A.*

— Nero: hist. play. 16°. $3........*Scribner, W. & A.*

— Poems. 12°. '56. $1.............*Little, B. & Co.*

— Roba di Roma; or, everything in Rome. por. demy 8°. $4.........................*Lippincott.*

— Roman lawyer (A) in Jerusalem: first century. 12°. '75. pap., 10c..........................*Colby.*

— Treatise on law of contracts. 5th ed., enl. by M. M. Bigelow. 2 v. 8°. '74. shp., $12..*Little, B. & Co.*

— Treatise on law of sales of personal property; with ill. from foreign law. 4th ed., rev. by E. H. Bennett. 8°. '71. shp., $6..........*Little, B. & Co.*

— *See also* United States, Circuit Court reports.

Story book for little boys and girls. Barrow, F. 75c. *Appleton.*

Story book for the young folks. Diaz, A. M. $1.50. *Osgood.*

Story book of country scenes. 16°. 50c. *Scribner, W. & A.*

Story Lizzie told. Prentiss, E. 60c.; 75c.; 35c. *Randolph.*

Story of Am. history. Abbott, J. 90c.......*Harper.*

Story of anc. history. Abbott, J. 90c.......*Harper.*

Story of Andy. Parker, J. M. 60c. ....*Dutton.*

Story of Annette. 32°. 20c.; 15c..........*Dutton.*

Story of the Apostles. *See* Mortimer, *Mrs.* M.
Story of an apple. Campbell, *Lady.* 50c...*Routledge.*
Story of Arthur Hunter. Crowe, C. 75c.....*Cassell.*
Story of a bad boy. Aldrich, T. B. $1.50...*Osgood.*
Story of a basket. *See* Marshall, Emma.
Story of Bethlehem. 16°. 80c............*Am. Bapt.*
Story of Bethlehem. Macduff, J. R. $1 ....*Carter.*
Story of Boon. Jackson, H. 30c. ....*Roberts.*
Story of Capt. Cook's three voyages around the world. Jones, M. $2.50.....................*Lee & S.*
Story of a cat. Perring, *Mrs.* —. 45c. ...*Routledge.*
Story of Catherine. *See* Thackeray, W: M.
Story of Chevalier Bayard. Guyard de Berville, —. $1.25 ....*Scribner, W. & A.*
Story of a child's companion. Sargent, G. E. 60c. *Lothrop.*
Story of a Chinese boy in California. 16°. $1.25. *Am. S. S.*
Story of a city Arab. 16°. $1.25...........*Am. S. S.*
Story of Columbus. Bradford, S. H. $1..*Randolph.*
Story of the Comte de Chambord. Sala, G. A. 50c. *Routledge.*
Story of a convent. Whitcher, B. W. $1...*O'Shea.*
Story of the cross. Trevor, G. $1............*Pott.*
Story of Cyril Rivers, and what he learned at college. ill. 12°. $1.25....................*Bost. Am. Tr.*
Story of a diamond: ill. of Egyptian manners and customs. 16°. $1.10....................*Am. S. S.*
— *See also* Diamond lib.
Story of a dog. Perring, *Mrs.* —. 45c....*Routledge.*
Story of Dollikins. Cupples, A. J. $1; $1.50..*Nelson.*
Story of the earth and man. Dawson, J. W. $1.50. *Harper.*
Story of Elizabeth. *See* Thackeray, A. I.
Story of Eng. history. Abbott, J. 90c. ....*Harper.*
Story of a fellow soldier. Awdry, F. $1.50..*Macmillan.*
Story of the fountain. Bryant, W. C. $5; $9. *Appleton.*
Story of four lives. Dunning, A. K. $1.50..*Lothrop.*
Story of a genius. *See* Howitt, Ma.
Story of the great march. Nichols, G. W. $2..*Harper.*
Story of the Hamiltons; or, the two sisters; by author of "Mama's new Bible stories." fp. 8°. 75c. *Cassell.*
Story of a happy little girl; by author of "Isabel's secret." ill. 12°. $1.50................*Nelson.*
Story of a house. Viollet-le-Duc, E. E. $5; $8. *Osgood.*
Story of a household. Roby, M. K. $1.50..*Macmillan.*
Story of the hymns. Butterworth, H. $2; $2.50. *Am. Tr.*
Story of James Moran. ill. 16°. $1....*Bost. Am. Tr.*
Story of Jesus. Clarke, M. L. 15c.......*Freewill.*
Story of Joseph. 18°. 35c.; 40c............*Dutton.*
Story of Joseph. Tweedie, W. K. 50c.....*Lothrop.*
Story of Kennett. Taylor, B. $1.50; $2 ..*Putnam.*
Story of the "Kersarge" and "Alabama." 8°. '68. 50c. ....*Payot.*
Story of King David. demy 4°. $1; bds., 50c. *Scribner, W. & A.*
Story of a labourer's wife. 18°. 30c........*Am. S. S.*
Story of little Flora. *See* Charlie's lessons about animals.
Story of little Gabriel. 18°. 60c............*Am. S. S.*
— *See also* Glen Elder lib.
Story of the London parks. Larwood, J. $3. *Routledge.*
Story of a lost child. Bray, R. M. $1.25 ...*Graves.*
Story of Madagascar. Mears, J. W. $1.25..*Pres. Bd.*
Story of Marcel, and other tales. 8°. '76. $1.50. *Cath. Pub.*
Story of Mark Raffles. Dalton, W. $1.50...*Nelson.*
Story of Martin Luther. 16°. $1.25 ....*Carter.*
Story of May. *See* Variety lib.
Story of a millionnaire. Mundt, C. M. $1.50..*Appleton.*
Story of a moss rose. *See* Loving heart and helping hand lib.
Story of a mouse. Perring, *Mrs.* —. 45c. *Routledge.*
Story of my life. *See* Andersen, H. C.
Story of my Uncle Toby. Sterne, L. $1.25. *Scribner, W. & A.*
Story of Ned. *See* Bell, C. D.
Story of a needle. *See* Tucker, *Mrs.* C.
Story of the new priest in Conception bay. Lowell, R. T. S. $1.75...........................*Dutton.*
Story of Nineveh: its greatness and ruins. sq. 16°. 35c. ....*Pres. Bd.*
Story of our doll. Cupples, A. J. 90c.......*Nelson.*
Story of the Palais Royal; or, loves of Louis XIV. and Mademoiselle La Valliere. 8°. '74. $2...*Sabin.*
Story of Pauline. Clunes, G. C. $1.75...*Macmillan.*
Story of the peasant-boy philosopher. Mayhew, H. $1.25 ....*Harper.*
Story of the peninsular war. Vane, C. W. $1.50; $3.25 ....*Harper.*
Story of a penny. Perring, *Mrs.* —. 45c. *Routledge.*
Story of a pin; or, the changes and chances of an eventful life. ill. 18°. 75c. ....*Nelson.*
Story of a pocket Bible. ill. 12°. $1 .... *Wiley.*
Story of a pocket Bible. ill. 12°. '60. $1.25. *Meth. Bk. Conc.*
Story of a pocket Bible. 16°. $1.50.......*Pres. Bd.*
Story of a pocket Bible. 2 v. 16°. ea., $1..*Am. Bapt.*
Story of Pompeii. *See* Seven kings of Rome.
Story of a prophet. *See* Wright, *Mrs.* J. McN.
Story of a red velvet Bible. 18°. 50c.....(?)*Martien.*
Story of Reuben Inch. Brock, C. 75c.......*Nelson.*
Story of Robin Hood. Heaton, W. $1.50 ...*Cassell.*
Story of the robins. *See* Trimmer, *Mrs.* S. K.
Story of a royal favorite. Gore, C. G. 50c..*Harper.*
Story of the Samaritans. ill. 18°. 25c. ....*Pres. Bd.*
Story of Sibylle. *See* Feuillet, O.
Story of small beginnings. *See* Warner, *Miss* S.
Story of a soul. Zabriskie, F. N. 75c. ...*Randolph.*
Story of the stick. Michel, F. $1.50.......*Bouton.*
Story of a stomach: an egotism by a reformed dyspeptic. 12°. '66. 75c. .... *Wells.*
Story of a story-book. 18°. 35c.; 40c.......*Dutton.*
Story of a summer. Bradley, M. E. 60c. *Bost. Am. Tr.; Lothrop.*
Story of a summer. Cleveland, C. $1.50 ..*Carleton.*
Story of a summer day; by author of "Busy bee." ill. sm. 4°. '74. $1.75. ....*Nelson.*
Story of Thomas Ellwood. Paschall, A. S. *net*, 25c. *Friends Bk. Assoc.*
Story of Thomas Fish. *See* Allen, *Mrs.* E. A.
Story of three sisters. Maxwell, C. $1.25.....*Holt.*
Story of the time: drama. 16°. pap., 15c....*French.*
Story of a tinker. *See* Wright, *Mrs.* J. McN.
Story of Valentine and his brother. Oliphant, M. O. W. 75c. ....*Harper.*
Story of the venerable Bede. *See* Yonge, C. M.
Story of a vocation; adapted from the French. 16°. $1 ....*Cath. Pub.*
Story of Waldemar Krone's youth. *See* Ewald, H. F.
Story of Wandering Willie. Noel, *Lady* A. $1.50. *Macmillan.*
Story of Wandering Willie. Walrée, E. C. W. van. 50c. ....*Scribner.*
Story of a week. Hosmer, M. $1 ......(?)*Martien.*

Story of William Tyndal; [also] My own Bible; [also] The ungrateful child. 18°. 25c....... *Pres. Bd.*

Story of a wonderful life. Wise, D. $1.25; $1.50. *Cin. Meth. Bk. Conc.*

Story of a workingman's life. Mason, F. $1.50.. *Mason.*

Story of the wreck of the Australian steamer "London." 16°. 75c.......................... *Am. S. S.*

Story of a young chanticleer; or, don't be discontented. ill. cr. 4°. pap., 20c.; 25c. .... *J. E. Potter.*

Story of Zadoc Hull. ill. 16°. 80c...... *Bost. Am. Tr.*

Story on the Beatitudes. 18°. 70c.......... *Am. S. S.*

Story teller. Andersen, H. C. $1........... *Miller.*

Story telling at Thanksgiving. *See* Tarbox, I. N.

Story truths. Banvard, J. $1.75........... *Am. Tr.*

Story without an end. Carové, F. W. 50c.... *Miller.*

Stothert, Ja. French and Spanish painters: etchings, with crit. and biog. text. sm. 4°. '76. $12.50; mor., $25.............................. *Gebbie.*

— *See also* Sandhurst, P. T., *and* Stothert, J.

Stoughton, J: Daily prayer-book. 12°. $1.50. *Dodd.*

— Lights of the world. 16°. $1... *Cin. Meth. Bk. Conc.*

Stout, G: L. Coal heaver's revenge: Ethiop. drama. 16°. pap., 15c......................... *De Witt.*

— Rival tenants: Ethiop. drama. 16°. pap., 15c. *De Witt.*

Stout, H. R. Our family physician; embr. allopathic, homœopathic, hydropathic, eclectic and herbal modes of treatment. ('68.) New ed., rev. and enl. 8°. *$3 .... Vent.

— *Germ.*; übers. v. H: Liebhart. 8°. *$3..... Vent.

Stout, P: F. Nicaragua, past, present and future. 12°. $1.75.......................... *J. E. Potter.*

Stout heart. Kellogg, E. $1.25 .... *Lee & S.*

Stow, Baron. Daily manna for Christian pilgrims. 24°. '74. 25c.; 40c. — 16°. $1....... *Lothrop.*

— Doctrinal question book. 18°. 15c....... *Am. Bapt.*

— History of English Baptist mission to India. 18°. 70c................................ *Am. S. S.*

— Little Mary. *See* Pioneer lib.

— *and* Smith, S. F. Psalmist: hymns for Baptist churches; with sup. of chants and sel. of Scripture for chanting. (Pulpit ed.) 12°. $2.25–$5. — (Pew ed.) 18°. $1.25–$4.50. — (Pocket ed.) 32°. 85c.–$3..... *Am. Bapt.; Sheldon; So. Bapt.*

— — *Same*; with music by B. F. Edmands. roy. 12°. $1.50 .... *Sheldon.*

Stowe, *Mrs.* Ht. Beecher. ["Christopher Crowfield."] Agnes of Sorrento: Italian romance. 12°. '62. $2.................................. *Osgood.*

— Betty's bright idea, and other tales. 12°. '75. 75c.; pap., 30c. .... *Ford.*

— Chimney-corner. 16°. '68. $1.75 .... *Osgood.*

— House and home papers. 16°. $1.75...... *Osgood.*

— Lady Byron vindicated. 16°. '70. $1.50... *Osgood.*

— Little foxes. 16°. '65. $1.75........... *Osgood.*

— Little Pussy Willow. ill. sm. 4°. '70. $1.50.. *Osgood.*

— Lives and deeds of our self-made men. por. 8°. *$3.50; leath., $4; hf. mor., $5........ *Dustin.*

— May-flower, and other sketches. 12°. $2.. *Osgood.*

— Minister's wooing. 12°. '59. $2.......... *Osgood.*

— My wife and I; or, Harry Henderson's history. ('71.) New ed. ill. 12°. '76. $1.75............ *Ford.*

— Nina Gordon. 12°. '56. $2.............. *Osgood.*

Note. First pub. under title of "Dred."

— Oldtown folks. 12°. '69. $2............ *Osgood.*

— Palmetto leaves: Florida sketches. ill. 16°. '73. $2. *Osgood.*

— Pearl of Orr's Island. 12°. '62. $2...... *Osgood.*

— Pink and white tyranny: society novel. ill. 16°. '71. $1.50............................ *Roberts.*

— Queer little people. ill. sm. 4°. '67. $1.50.. *Osgood.*

— Religious poems. ill. 16°. '67. $2 .... *Osgood.*

— Sam Lawson's fireside stories. ill. 12°. '71. pap., 75c.; bds., $1.......................... *Osgood.*

Stowe, *Mrs.* Ht. Beecher, *continued.*

— Uncle Tom's cabin. ('51.) 337th ed. 12°. '76. $2. *Osgood.*

— *German.* Onkel Tom's Hütte; frei bearb. v. A. Strodtmann. 8°. $1; pap., 75c.; hf. mor., $1.25. *F. W. Thomas.*

— We and our neighbors; or, the records of an unfashionable street: sequel to "My wife and I." ('75.) New ed. ill. 12°. '76. $1.75 ..... *Ford.*

— *See also* Beecher, C. E., *and* Stowe, *Mrs.* H. B.; — Six of one by half a dozen of the other.

Stowe, J. G. *See* Perkins, G. H., *and* Stowe, J. G.

Stowe, Phin. Phineas Stowe and Bethel work; comp. by H. A. Cooke, etc. 2d ed. 12°. '74. $1.50. *Earle.*

Stowell, C. L. Red Cross of Constantine: text-book of Christian knighthood. [Masonic.] ill. 12°. '74. $1.50.......................... *Masonic.*

Stowell, W: Hendry. History of the Puritans; [also] The pilgrim fathers, by D. Wilson. ('53.) New ed. 12°. '56. $1.50................. *Wilstach.*

Strabo. Geography; tr., with notes, by W. Falconer and H. C. Hamilton; with index. 3 v. 12°. (Bohn.) ea., $1.75.............. *Little, B. & Co.*

— *Same.* 3 v. 12°. (Bohn.) ea., $2. *Lippincott; Scribner, W. & A.*

Strachey, *Sir* E: Jewish hist. and politics in times of Sargon and Sennacherib: inquiry into hist. meaning of prophecies of Isaiah. 2d ed., rev. 8°. '74. $6......................... *Routledge.*

Strack, C: Renata of Este: chapter from hist. of reformation in France and Italy; tr. by C. E. Hurst. 16°. '73. $1.25...... *Cin. Meth. Bk. Conc.*

Stradella. *See* Ditson.

Straffen, G: M. Sin, as set forth in Scripture. (Hulsean lectures, 1874.) 12°. '76. $1...... *Dutton.*

Strahan, Alex. Memoir of Norman Macleod. 12°. pap., 50c.......................... *Lippincott.*

Strahan, E: (*pseud.*) *See* Shinn, Earl.

Straight forward. Guernsey, L. E. $1.25..... *Hoyt.*

Straight path: story of Hope Conroy. 18°. 85c. *Am. S. S.*

Straight road. *See* Tucker, *Mrs.* C.

Strait gate. Abbott, J. 90c................ *Harper.*

Strandfischer (Die). *See* Hoffmann, F.

Strange adventures of a phaeton. *See* Black, W:

Strange and wonderful adventures of Bachelor Butterfly. ill. obl. 8°. 30c................. *Dick & F.*

Strange bequest. *See* Daisy lib.

Strange history. Lawrence, S., *and* Mathews, C. 15c. *French.*

Strange stories. 16°. 50c.................. *West. Tr.*

Strange stories of a detective; or, curiosities of crime. 8°. pap., 75c.......................... *Dick & F.*

Strange story. *See* Bulwer-Lytton, *Sir* E. G. E. L.

Strange tales from humble life. Ashworth, J. 2 v. ea., 60c...................... *U. P. Bd. of Pub.*

Strange visitors: papers by spirits of Irving, Willis, Thackeray and others, dictated through a clairvoyant. ('69.) 4th ed. 12°. '73. $1.50.. *Colby.*

Strange woman. Harrington, J. A. 25c... *Collin & S.*

Strange world. Braddon, M. E. 75c........ *Harper.*

Strangely wed. Burton, J. D. 25c.......... *Beadle.*

Stranger. Kotzebue, A. F. F. v. 15c........ *French.*

Stranger. Leavitt, A. J. 15c.............. *De Witt.*

Stranger. Reece, R. 15c.................. *French.*

Stranger of Seriphos. Broome, F. N. $1.50. *Macmillan.*

Strangers and pilgrims. Braddon, M. E. 75c. *Harper.*

Strangers in Greenland. ill. sq. 18°. '61. 25c.. *Am. Tr.*

Strangers' new guide through Boston and vicinity. map. 32°. '72. pap., 10c............. *Osgood*

Strangford, *Vctss.* [Emily A. Beaufort.] Egyptian sepulchres and Syrian shrines; incl. visit to Palmyra. New ed. cr. 8°. '74. $2.50..*Macmillan.*

Strassburg auf der Schanz. Caspari, K. H. 25c. *Morwitz.*

Stratford gallery; or, the Shakespeare sisterhood. Palmer, J. W. $15..................*Appleton.*

Strathmore. La Rame, L. de. $1.50.....*Lippincott.*

Strathmore. Marston, W. 15c.............*French.*

Stratton, G. W. Fairy grotto (The): operetta. obl. 16°. '72. pap., 80c.; bds., 90c........*Stratton.*

— Genevieve: operetta. obl. 16°. '70. pap., 70c.; bds., 80c..........................*Stratton.*

— Laila: operetta. obl. 16°. '67. pap., 60c.; bds., 70c. *Stratton.*

Stratton, H. D. *See* Bryant, H. B., *and* Stratton, H. D.; — Bryant, H. B., Stratton, H. D., *and* Packard, S. S.

Stratton, W: D. Dedication memorial of the Masonic Temple, Boston. ill. 4°. *$3...........*Lee & S.*

Straub, Sol. W. Crown of glory: Sunday school music. obl. 16°. '76. bds., 35c........*Jansen.*

— Golden rule. [S.-school music.] 16°. 35c...*Church.*

— Good cheer. [Sing. book.] ('74.) New ed., rev. and enl. 8°. '76. bds., 60c...........*Jansen.*

Straubenmüller, J: *See* Wurst, R. J., Kleine Sprachdenklehre.

Strause, J. Polyglot pocket manual; [or], do you speak Eng., Germ., French, Ital., Span. and Portug.? sq. 16°. '76. $1.50...........*Radde.*
Note. Same in various combinations of three languages, as Eng., Fr. and Germ.; Eng., Fr. and Span.; Eng., Germ. and Ital.; Eng., Portug. and Germ., etc., ea., 75c.

Strauss, D: F: Life of Jesus; tr. 2 v. 8°. $12. *Scribner, W. & A.*

— Old faith (The) and the new: a confession; tr. by M. Blind. ('73.) New ed. 2 v. in 1. 12°. '74. $2......................................*Holt.*

— Ulrich Von Hutten: his life and times; tr. by Mrs. G. Sturge. 12°. '74. $4...........*Routledge.*

Strauss, F: Pilgrimage to Jerusalem: picture of Judaism in cent. which preceded advent of our Saviour. ill. 12°. $1.25...........*Lippincott.*

Strauss, J: Complete waltzes. 2 v. 4°. ea., $4; bds., $3..............................*Peters.*

— Waltzes; [for the violin]. 4°. bds., $2; pap., $1.50. *Peters.*

Strauss as a philosophical thinker. Ulrici, H. $1. *Smith, E. & Co.*

Straw bonnet maker; or, ways of usefulness. 18°. 70c.................................*Pres. Bd.*

Straw cutter's daughter. *See* Fullerton, *Lady* G.

Strawberry Hill. Denison, M. A. $1.50...*Lothrop.*

Stray arrows. Cuyler, T. L. 60c...........*Carter.*

Stray lambs. *See* Dunning, A. K.

Stray leaves from the book of nature. De Vere, M. S. $1.50.................................*Putnam.*

Stray leaves from fairy land. Grimm, J. L. *and* W. C. $1.25.................................*T. Bliss.*

Stray studies from Eng. and Italy. *See* Green, J. R.

Stray subjects arrested and bound over. ill. 12°. pap., 75c.................................*Peterson.*

Streaks of light. Mortimer, M. 75c. ......*Harper.*

Streaks of squatter life. Thompson, W. T. 75c. *Peterson.*

Streckfuss, Adf. Der tolle Hans; [also] Die Söhne Barnevelt's, v. E. Schmidt-Weissenfels. 8°. pap., 50c.................................*Morwitz.*

— Der verlorene Sohn. 8°. pap., 50c.......*Morwitz.*

Street, Alfr. B. Council of revision of N. Y.: its hist., hist. of the courts with which its members were connected, biog. sketches of its members, and its vetoes. 8°. '59. shp., $4.50...........*Gould.*

— The Indian pass; or, a tramp through the woods. 12°. $1.50.........................*Hurd & H.*

Street, Alfr. B., *continued.*

— *See also* Forest scenes; — Hows, J. A., Forest pictures in the Adirondacks.

Street, B: Restoration of paths to dwell in: essays on the re-editing and interpretation of the Old Test. Scriptures. 8°. '73. $2.50..........*Routledge.*

Street, G: Edm. *See* Examples of mod. arch.

Street sweeper. 18°. 60c................*Cong. Pub.*

— *See also* River bank stories.

Streeter, G. L. Account of newspapers and other periodicals published in Salem, [Mass.] 8°. '56. pap., 15c.................................*Essex.*

Streeter, H. R. New and correct theory for mechanical formation of the human voice. 16°. '71. $1.50.................................*Ditson.*

— Primary elements of music. 8°. '73. bds., 60c. *Ditson.*

— Voice building. 12°. '71. $1.50..........*Ditson.*

Streeter, Sebastian F. First commander of Kent Island; — Papers rel. to early hist. of Md. *See* Maryland Hist. Soc.

Streets and lakes of a city. Dutton, A. $1.25. *Macmillan.*

Streets of New York. White, C. 15c.......*De Witt.*

Strength and beauty. Hopkins, M. $1.75....*Dodd.*

Strength out of weakness; or, a glorious manifestation of the further progress of the Gospel amongst the Indians in New Eng.; with a biog. notice by the publisher. [Reprint.] 4°. $1.50; large pap., $3.................................*Sabin.*

— *See also* Farther discovery of present state of Indians.

Stretch, R: H. Report upon zygænidæ and lambycidæ. *See* United States, *Corps of Eng.*

Stretton, Hesba (*pseud.*) *See* Smith, Ha.

Stretton, Jla. Margaret and her bridesmaids. 12°. $1.50.................................*Loring.*

— Queen of the county. 12°. $1.50........*Loring.*

— Rector's (The) wife; or, valley of a hundred fires. 12°. $1.75; pap., $1.50..............*Peterson.*

Stretton. *See* Kingsley, H:

Stricker, S. *See* Manual of histology.

Strickland, Agnes. Life of Mary, Queen of Scots. 2 v. 12°. $4; hf. cf., $7.50.........*Lippincott.*

— *Same.* 2 v. 12°. (Bohn.) ea., $1.75..*Little, B. & Co.*

— *Same.* 2 v. 12°. (Bohn.) ea., $2. *Lippincott; Scribner, W. & A.*

— Lives of the queens of England from the Norman Conquest. 6 v. 12°. $12; hf. cf., $22.50; cf., $31.25.................................*Lippincott.*

— *Same.* 12°. hf. cf., $24; cf., $30; $35; — in 8 v. por. 8°. hf. cf., $40; cf., $45; $50...*Appleton.*

— *Same.* 7 v. por. 8°. $17.50; hf. cf., $35...*Miller.*

— *Same.* 7 v. por. 8°. $19.25; shp., $28; hf. cf., $35.................................*Thompson.*

— *Same.* 6 v. por. 12°. (Bohn.) ea., $1.75. *Little, B. & Co.*

— *Same.* 6 v. por. 12°. (Bohn.) ea., $2. *Lippincott; Scribner, W. & A.*

— *Same;* abridg. 12°. $2.50..............*Scribner.*

— — *Same;* rev. by C. G. Parker. 12°. $2..*Harper.*

— Lives of queens of Henry VIII. and of his mother. cr. 8°. 90c.; $1.........................*Lea.*

— Lives of queens of Scotland and Eng. princesses, connected with regal succession of Gt. Brit. 8 v. 12°. $12; hf. cf., $26.................*Harper.*

— Queen Elizabeth. cr. 8°. $1.30; $1.40.......*Lea.*

— Stories from hist. ill. 16°. $1.25..........*Porter.*

— Tales from Eng. hist. ill. 16°. $1.25.......*Porter.*

— True stories from anc. hist. ill. 16°. $1.25..*Porter.*

— True stories from mod. hist. ill. 16°. $1.25..*Porter.*

Strickland, Jane. Christmas holidays; or, a new way of spending them. 16°. 50c.........*Routledge.*

Strickland, W: P: Autobiography of Dan Young. 12°. '59. $1.75...................*Meth. Bk. Conc.*

— History of the Am. Bible Soc., from 1816; with introd. by N. L. Rice. 8°. $2; shp., $2.50....*Harper.*

Strickland, W: P: *continued.*
— History of missions of Meth. Episc. Church. 12°. $1. *Cin. Meth. Bk. Conc.*
— Life and times of Bp. Asbury. 12°. '58. $1.75. *Meth. Bk. Conc.*
— Life of Jacob Gruber. 12°. '60. $1.75.. *Meth. Bk. Conc.*
— Manual of Biblical literature. 12°. '53. $1.75. *Meth. Bk. Conc.*
— Pioneers of the west. 12°. '56. $1.75.. *Meth. Bk. Conc.*
Strife. Wallace, E. D. $1.75.............. *Claxton.*
Strife and peace. *See* Bremer, *Miss* F.
Strife and victory. 18°. 30c. .... *N. Y. Ref. Ch. Bd.*
Strike for freedom. Tuthill, L. C. 65c... *Perkinpine.*
Striking for the right. Eastman, J. A. $1.75.. *Lothrop.*
String of diamonds gathered from many mines by a gem fancier. 12°. *net,* $1.67; $2.10; $2.62; mor., $6........................ *Hamersley.*
String of pearls. [Bible texts.] ill. sq. 12°. 50c. *Meth. Bk. Conc.*
String of pearls. James, G. P. R. $1.25.... *Harper.*
Stringfellow, B: F. *See* Missouri, Sup. Court reports.
Stringfellow, Thornton. Scriptural and statistical views in favor of slavery. 12°. '56. 50c. *J. W. Randolph.*
Strive and succeed. Alger, H., *jr.* $1.50... *Loring.*
Strive and thrive. ill. 18°. 50c.............. *Nelson.*
Strive and thrive. *See* Howitt, Ma.
Strive and win ser. 3 v. ill. 16°. $3.75. *Lockwood, B. & Co.*
Cont.: Striving and gaining, by F. W. A. Pike. — Climbing and sliding, by F. W. A. Pike. — Among the birds, by E. A. Samuels.
Strivelyne, Elsie. Princess of Silverland. fp. 8°. '74. $1.50........................ *Macmillan.*
Striving and gaining. Pike, M. H. $1.25. *Lockwood, B. & Co.*
Striving for the mastery. *See* Laurel ser.; — Uncle Barnaby's budget.
Strivings for the faith. [Lectures.] 12°. '75. $1.50. *Randolph.*
Strobhart, J. A. *See* South Carolina, Chancery reports; Reports.
Strodtmann, A. *See* Heine, H., Immortellen.
Strohhalm (Der) u. d. Schatz. Nieritz, G. 25c. *Steiger.*
Strohm, Gert. (*ed.*) Word pictures; or, thoughts and descriptions from popular authors. ill. 16°. '75. $2. *Lothrop.*
Stromeyer, L: Gunshot fractures; [also] Resection in gunshot injuries, by F. Esmarch; tr. by S. F. Statham. 12°. 75c........ *Claxton; Lippincott.*
Strong, J. D. [Juveniles.] 14 v. ill. 24°. '70. *Lothrop.*
Cont.: Beauty Benson. — Blacksmith. — Brown pony. — Gregory Gold. — Lame beggar. — Little Bertie. — Little Nora. — Minna's proud heart. — Truthful Jenny, *ea.,* 25c. — Better than gold. — Bold as a lion. — Fair play, and other stories. — Wintergreen girl, and other stories, *ea.,* 30c. — Child life in many lands, $1.
— Children of many lands. ill. 16°. 60c... *Bost. Am. Tr.*
Strong, Ja. Compendium of the Gospels. 18°. '53. 40c. .... *Meth. Bk. Conc.*
— Harmony and exposition of the Gospels. maps and ill. 8°. '52. shp., $5; hf. mor., $6.. *Meth. Bk. Conc.*
— Harmony of the Gospels in the Greek of the received text; with various readings, explanations, ref., etc. 12°. $1.50........................ *Harper.*
— Manual of the Gospels. 16°. 90c.; hf. cf., $1. *Meth. Bk. Conc.*
— Question book: Christ in the Old Test. 18°. '70. bds., 15c. .... *Tibbals.*
— Questions on the Gospels. 18°. per doz., $2.40. *Meth. Bk. Conc.*
— *See also* M'Clintock, J., *and* Strong, J.
Strong, *Mrs.* M. D. New-Year, and other stories. ill. 18°. '69. 75c. .... *Lothrop.*
Strong, W: Two lectures upon rel. of civil law to church polity, discipline and property. 12°. '75. $1.. *Dodd.*
Strong, W: C. Culture of the grape. 12°. '66. $2.50 *Tilton*
Strong and steady. Alger, H., *jr.* $1.50.... *Loring*
Strong consolation. Foster, J. K. 20c. .... *Pres. Bd*
Strong drink and tobacco-smoke. Prescott, H. R. $3 *W. Wood*
Strong tower. 12°. '51. 60c.............. *Am. S. S*
Strong tower. Smith, J. 60c. .... *Pres. Bd*
Strother, D: H. ["Porte Crayon."] Virginia illustrated; cont. Visit to the Virginian Canaan, and Adventures of Porte Crayon and his cousins; ill from draw. by S. 8°. $3.50; hf. cf., $5.75.. *Harper*
Stroud, W: Harmony of the Gospels [in Greek]. 4° (Bagster.) $6.25 .... *Wiley*
— Physical cause of death of Christ, and its rel. to principles and practice of Christianity; with letter by Sir J. Y. Simpson. 12°. $2.. *Appleton*
Strout, *Mrs.* C. W. D. Slippery paths. ill. 18°. 50c *Hoyt, F. & D*
Strubberg, F. A. ["Armand."] Die alte spanische Urkunde; [also] Das Gespenst, v. E. H. v Dedenroth. 8°. pap., 50c........... *Morwitz*
Strube, Gardiner A. Drum and fife instructor. obl. 8° $1.50 .... *Appleton*
Struggle for existence. Bayer, C. R. $1.50.. *McKinney*
Struggle for Kansas. *See* Hughes, T:
Struggle for life. 8°. pap., 25c............ *De Witt*
Struggle for life. Hale, L. P. $1.50 ..... *Williams*
Struggle for neutrality in America. Adams, C. F. 50c *Scribner*
Struggle in Ferrara. Gilbert, W. $1.50; $1.. *Lippincott*
Strutt, *Mrs.* Eliz. The feminine soul: its nature and attributes; with thoughts upon marriage and friendly hints upon feminine duties. 16°. '70 50c.; pap., 25c. .... *H. H. Carter*
Strutt, Jac. G: Sylva Britannica and Scotica; with 50 etchings. imp. f°. mor., $45 .... *Estes*
Struve, Gst. Weltgeschichte. 6 v. 8°. '56–'59. hf mor., $15 .... *Steiger*
— *Same.* Alte Geschichte. 27 nos. 8°. pap., $3.. *Steiger*
— *Same.* Neue Zeit. 20 nos. 8°. pap., $2.25.. *Steiger*
Struwelpeter (Der). *See* Hoffmann, H.
Struwelpeter, enth. lustige Geschichten u. drollige Bilder. sm. 4°. 75c.................... *Kohler*
Stryker, P: Little gems in the Saviour's crown. ill. 18°. 60c...................... *N. Y. Ref. Ch. Bd*
Strykor, Cornelia. Musings of a middle-aged woman. 12°. '71. $1.50 .... *Claxton.*
Stuart, A. A. Iowa colonels and regiments: [their] history in the war of the rebellion. 8°. '65. $2; shp., $3; — with por., $3; shp., $4....... *Mills.*
Stuart, C. E. Textual criticism of the New Test., for Eng. Bible students. 2d ed., rev. 8°. (Bagster.) $1.25 .... *Wiley.*
Stuart, C: B. Civil and military engineers of Am. por. and ill. 8°. '71. $5........ *Van Nostrand.*
— Naval dry docks of the U. S. 4th ed. 24 eng. 4°. '70. $6 .... *Van Nostrand.*
Stuart, G: *See* Chase, T: Stuart, G: *and* Crowell, E. P.
Stuart, G: A. Look after Brown: farce. 16°. pap., 15c.................................. *Lee & S.*
Stuart, G: H. *See* Hall, J., *and* Stuart, G. H.
Stuart, I: W: Hartford in the olden time, its first 30 years, by Scaeva [*pseud.*]; ed. by W. M. B. Hartley; with ill. and map of H. as it was in 1640. 8°. '53. $4.50................ *J. W. Bliss.*
— Life of Jonathan Trumbull. ('49.) New ed. 8°. '59. $3 .... *Crocker.*
Stuart, Ja., *and* Revett, N: Antiquities of Athens, and other monuments of Greece. ill. 12°. (Bohn.) $1.75 .... *Little, B. & Co.*
— *Same.* ill. 12°. (Bohn.) $2. *Lippincott; Scribner, W. & A.*

Stuart, M. B. ["Grace Mortimer."] Bosom foes. 12°. $1.50 .... *Carleton.*
— The two Barbaras. 12°. $1.50 .... *Carleton.*
Stuart, Mos. Commentary on the apocalypse. 2 v. 8°. '45. $2.25 .... *Draper.*
— Commentary on Ecclesiastes; rev. by R. D. C. Robbins. ('62.) New ed. 12°. '64. $1.50 .. *Draper.*
— Commentary on Hebrews; rev. by R. D. C. Robbins. ('60.) New ed. 12°. '76. $2.25 ...... *Draper.*
— Commentary on Proverbs. ('52.) New ed. 12°. '70. $1.75 .... *Draper.*
— Commentary on Romans; rev. by R. D. C. Robbins. ('59.) New ed. 12°. '76. $2.25 ...... *Draper.*
— Critical hist. and defence of Old Test. canon. Rev. ed. 12°. '72. $1.75 .... *Draper.*
— Future punishment. 16°. 70c. .... *Pres. Bd.*
— Greek grammar of New Test. 8°. '41. $1.25 .. *Draper.*
— Miscellanies; cont. letters to Dr. Channing on the Trinity, and several sermons, notes, etc. 12°. '46. $1.25 .... *Draper.*
— Mode of Christian baptism prescribed in New Test. 12°. $1 .... *So. Bapt.*
Stuart of Dunleath. Norton, C. E. S. 50c. .. *Harper.*
Stuart-Glennie, J: S. Pilgrim memories: travels and discussion in the birth countries of Christianity with the late H. T. Buckle. 8°. $3 ... *Appleton.*
Stubbs, W: Early Plantagenets (The) and their rel. to hist. of Europe. 16°. $1 .... *Estes.*
Stuckenberg, J. H. W. History of the Augsburg confession, till adoption of Book of concord. 12°. $1.75 .... (?) *Luth. Pub.*
Student (The). *See* Bulwer-Lytton, *Sir* E. G. E. L.
Student (The). Phelps, L. $1.50 .... *Barnes.*
Student in life and philosophy. Holbeach, H. 2 v. $7 .... *Routledge.*
Student of Blenheim Forest. Dorsey, A. H. $1.50; $1.75 .... *Murphy.*
Student's atlas of classical geog.; maps, with letter-press by L. Schmitz. imp. 8°. '73. $1.50 .. *Putnam.*
Student's atlas of hist. and class. geog.: maps with descrip. letter-press. imp. 8°. '73. $2.50 .. *Putnam.*
Student's atlas of historical geog.; constructed by Weller, with descrip. letter-press by W: F. Collier, and index. imp. 8°. '73. $1.50 .... *Putnam.*
Student's atlas of mod. and classical geog.: maps with index. imp. 8°. '75. $3; hf. mor., $6 .. *Putnam.*
Student's atlas of physical geog.: maps with descrip. letter-press. imp. 8°. '73. $2.50 ...... *Putnam.*
Student's manual of Cath. devotions. 2d ed., enl. 32°. '69. 40c.; 60c. .... *Murphy.*
Student's Quarter. *See* Thackeray, W: M.
Student's walk. 18°. 35c. .... *U. P. Bd. of Pub.*
Students and lawyers. Riddle, A. G. $2 .. *Morrison.*
Studer, Jac. H. Columbus, Ohio: its hist., resources and progress. map and ill. 12°. '73. $2. *Clarke; Studer.*
— (*ed.*) Popular ornithology. v. 1: Birds of No. Am.: col. plates by T. Jasper with text. [To form 40 pts.] pt. 1. f°. '74. pap., *$1 .... *Studer.*
Studies and stories. Jameson, A. $1.50 .... *Osgood.*
Studies and teachings of the Society of Jesus. 12°. '55. $1 .... *Kelly, P. & Co.*
Studies for stories. *See* Ingelow, J.
Studies from life. *See* Craik, D. M.
Studies in animal life. Lewes, G. H. $1 .... *Harper.*
Studies in Bible lands. Gage, W. L. $2; $2.50. *Bost. Am. Tr.*
Studies in Book of Psalms. Plumer, W. S. $6; $6.75. *Lippincott.*
Studies in Christian biog. Osgood, S. $1.50 .. *Miller.*
Studies in church hist. Lea, H. C. $2.75 ...... *Lea.*
Studies in the history of the renaissance. Pater, W. H. $2.50 .... *Macmillan.*
Studies in poetry and philosophy. Shairp, J. C. $1.50. *Hurd & H.*
Studies, new and old, in ethical and social subjects. Cobbe, F. P. $3 .... *Lee & S.*
Studies of character. *See* Guthrie, T:
Studies of Christianity. Martineau, J. $1.25 .. *Am. Unit.*
Studies, pictures and fancies. Dall, C. H. $1.50 .. *Lee & S.*
Studio (The). Abbott, J. 90c. .... *Harper.*
Studio (The): Ethiop. drama. 16°. pap., 15c. .. *Ames.*
Study of the Hebrew vowel points. 4°. (Bagster.) pap., 37c. .... *Wiley.*
Studying the Bible. Slenker, E. D. 75c. .. *Mendum.*
Stumbling-blocks. Dodge, M. A. $1.50 ..... *Estes.*
Stumme (Die) v. Portici. 12°. pap., 15c. ..... *Radde.*
Stump speaker: coll. of speeches and recitations, etc. 16°. pap., 15c. .... *Happy.*
Stumping it. Small, G. G. 25c. .... *Collin & S.*
Stumps. *See* Austin, S.
Stunden der Andacht. *See* Schlessinger, W.
Stunden der Andacht. *See* Zschokke, H.
Stupid Sally. *See* Finley, M. F.
Stupid servant. White, C. 15c. .... *De Witt.*
Stupid story. *See* Barker, M. A. (*Lady*).
Sturdy Jack. Lamb, J. 80c. .... *Lothrop.*
Sturdy Jack ser. 6 v. 16°. $4.50 .... *Lothrop.*
Cont.: Sturdy Jack.— On the seas.— Every man in his place. — Robin, the runner. — Soldier Fritz. — Little Red-cap.
Sturges, Oct. Introduction to study of clinical medicine. 12°. $1.25 .... *Lea.*
Sturgis, J: H. Paper on terra cotta. *See* American Inst. of Arch., Proceedings of 5th ann. conv.
Sturm, Cp. Chr. Morning communings with God; or, devotional meditations for every day in the year. 12°. (Bohn.) $1.25 .... *Little, B. & Co.*
— *Same.* 12°. (Bohn.) $1.40 ...... *Scribner, W. & A.*
— *Same.* 12°. (Bohn.) $1.50 .... *Lippincott.*
Sturm (Der). *See* Shakespeare, W:
Sturtevant, E. Lew. *and* Jos. N. Dairy cow: monograph on Ayrshire breed of cattle; with app. on Ayrshire, Jersey and Dutch milks. ill. 12°. '75. $2 .... *Williams.*
Stuyvesant. Abbott, J. 90c. .... *Harper.*
Sua de se; or, the words of the Lord Jesus concerning himself. 12°. 50c. .... *West. Tr.*
Sub-tropical rambles. Pike, N. $3.50 ..... *Harper.*
Subjenation. Van Evrie, J. H. 25c. .... *Van Evrie.*
Sublime in nature. Lanoye, F. de. $1.25 .. *Scribner.*
Substance and shadow. James, H. $2 ..... *Osgood.*
Subtle spell. Hosmer, M. $1.25 .... (?) *Martien.*
Suburban sketches. *See* Howells, W. D.
Success and its conditions. Whipple, E. P. $1.50. *Osgood.*
Success in life. ill. 12°. $1.50 .... *Nelson.*
Success of evil. Kedzie, A. S. $1.25 .... *Cong. Pub.*
Successful apprentice. 18°. 60c. .... *Cong. Pub.*
— *See also* River-bank stories.
Successful men of modern times; rev. by T. O. Summers. ('58.) 2d ed. 18°. '73. 50c. .. *So. Meth.*
Successful merchant. *See* Arthur, W.
Successful preaching. Hall, J., Cuyler, T. L., *and* Beecher, H. W. 25c. .... *Am. Tr.*
Succession of sacred literature. Clarke, A. $1.25. *Meth. Bk. Conc.*
Such is life. Egan, P. 75c. .... *Dick & F.*
Suck, A: *See* Fries, W., *and* Suck, A.
Sudden arrival. *See* French's comic dramas.
Sudden thoughts. Wilks, T. E. 15c. .... *French.*
Suddorth, *Mrs.* H. A. B. ["Lumina Silvervale."] An orphan of the old dominion: her trials and travels. 12°. $2 .... *Lippincott.*

Sudlow, *Miss* P. W., *and* Crosby, W. E. Language lessons. ('72.) 2d ed., rev. ill. sq. 16°. '75. 35c.; — with manual for teachers, 75c...... *Day.*

Sue, *Cousin*. *See* Cousin Sue.

Sue, Eug. [Novels; tr.] 8 v. 8°.......... *Peterson.*
Cont.: Raoul de Surville, pap, 25c. — Female Bluebeard. — First love. — Man-of-war's-man. — Woman's love, *ea.*, pap., 50c. — Martin, the foundling. — Mysteries of Paris, and sequel, Gerolstein. — Wandering Jew, *ea.*, $2; pap., $1.50.

— [Novels; tr.] 5 v. 8°. pap............ *Dick & F.*
Cont.: French fortune-teller. — Gabrielle; or, pictures of the Fr. rev. — Loves of Paris. — Mysteries of the people, *ea.*, 75c. — Matilda, $1.50.

— [Novels; tr.] 4 v. 8°. pap.......... *U. P. James.*
Cont.: Commander of Malta. — Princess of Hansfeld. — Temptation; or, Duchess of Almeda, *ea.*, 25c. — Latreaumont; or, the conspiracy: romance of days of Louis XIV., 50c.

— Arthur. 8°. pap., 75c.................. *Harper.*

— Commander of Malta. 8°. pap., 50c...... *Harper.*

— De Rohan; or, the court conspirator. 8°. pap., 50c. *Harper.*

— Marquis of Létorière. sq. 18°. $1.25.. *Nichols & H.*

— Mysteries of Paris. 12°. $1.25; bds., $1.. *Routledge.*

— Wandering Jew. 12°. $1.25; bds., $1.. *Routledge.*

Sue, J: B. Exercises on the French syntax: practice of new practical method for learning French. 12°. hf. roan, 75c. .... *Lippincott.*

— First lessons in French: introd. to "Practical and intellect. method of learning French." 12°. hf. roan, $1 .... *Lippincott.*

— Key for teachers and learners to prosecute their study of French. 12°. hf. roan, 75c...... *Lippincott.*

— New practical and intellect. method of learning French, grounded on nature's teachings. 12°. hf. roan, $1.50 .... *Lippincott,*

Sue Munday, the guerilla spy. 12°. pap., 20c... *Hurst.*

Suetonius Tranquillus, Caius. Lives of the twelve Cæsars, and other works: Thomson's tr., rev. with notes by T. Forester. 12°. (Bohn.) $1.75. *Little, B. & Co.*

— *Same.* 12°. (Bohn.) $2.. *Lippincott; Scribner, W. & A.*

Suffering here, glory hereafter. Jackson, C. D. $1.50. *Dutton.*

Suffering Saviour. *See* Krummacher, F. W.

Sufferings of Jesus. *See* Emmerich, A. K.

Suffern, J. W: Normal (The). [Sing. book.] obl. 8°. 75c. .... *Brainard.*

— Sabbath praise. [Music.] obl. 8°. $1.38.. *Gordon.*

— Song garland; or, singing for Jesus. obl. 16°. 35c. *Brainard.*

— *See also* Royal songs.

Sugar camp. ill. 18°. '75. 40c................ *Dodd.*

Sugden, *Sir* E: B. Concise and pract. treatise on law of vendors and purchasers of estates. 8th ed., rev. by J. C. Perkins. 2 v. 8°. shp., $13.. *Kay.*

— Practical treatise on powers. 3d Am. ed., rev. and enl.; with notes and ref. to Am. cases by a member of the Philadelphia bar. 2 v. 8°. '56. *net*, $15 .... *T. & J. W. Johnson.*

Suggestions for the sick room; by an Am. woman. 16°. '75. 60c...................... *Randolph.*

Suil Dhuv. *See* Dibdin, T.; — Griffin, Ger.

Suit of tweeds. Hay, F. 15c.............. *French.*

Suitors. Racine, J. $1; $2................ *Putnam.*

Sulivan, Rob. Elopements in high life: comedy. 16°. pap., 15c...................... *French.*

Sullivan, A. G. Standard facts and figures; or, what you do know, what you don't know, what you want to know. 16°. '75. mor., $2.. *Morton & D.*

Sullivan, Arth. S. Church hymns with tunes. 12°. '74. 75c.......................... *Pott.*

— Prodigal son. [Oratorio.] 8°. $1.50; bds., $1.25; pap., $1 .... *Ditson.*

— Six four-part songs. 8°. 50c. ...... *Ditson; Peters.*

— *and* Gilbert, W. S. Trial by jury: opera arr. for amateurs. 16°. pap., 40c............ *French.*

— — *Same.* 8°. bds., 60c.; pap., 50c. .... *Ditson.*

Sullivan, *Sir* E: Protection to native industry. ('70.) 5th ed. 8°. '73. $1.50................ *Baird.*

Sullivan, J: T. Prayers and ceremonies of the mass. 16°. $1.50 .... *Sadlier.*

Sullivan, Marion Dix. Juniata ballads. obl. 16°. 35c. *Gordon.*

Sullivan, Rob. Sullivan's spelling-book superseded. New ed., rev. and enl. 16°. 31c...... *Sadlier.*

Sullivant, W: S. Icones muscorum: figures and descript. of most of those mosses peculiar to No. Am. ill. 8°. '64. $20. — Supplement. ill. 8°. '74. $10 .... *Sever.*

Sully, *Duke of.* [Mx. de Béthune.] Memoirs. 2 v. 12°. (Bohn.) ea., $1.25 .... *Little, B. & Co.*

— *Same.* 4 v. 12°. (Bohn.) ea., $1.40.. *Scribner, W. & A.*

— *Same.* 4 v. 12°. (Bohn.) ea., $1.50....... *Lippincott.*

Sully, T: Hints to young painters, and process of portrait painting. ill. sm. 4°. '73. $1.. *J. M. Stoddart.*

Sulpicia. *See* Juvenal, D. J., Persius Flaccus, A., Sulpicia, *and* Lucilius, C.

Sumichrast, Fs. E. Birds of southwest. Mexico. *See* United States, *National Mus.*

Summary of American history for schools. 12°. '69. 40c. .... *Barnes.*

Summary of English and French history for schools. 12°. '68. 35c........................ *Barnes.*

Summer at Marley. 18°. 75c............... *Dutton.*

Summer at White Sulphur Springs. *See* Whittlesey, E. L.

Summer by the sea. 16°. $1.10 .... *Pres. Bd.*

Summer cruise. Willis, N. P. $1.75....... *Scribner.*

Summer day book. *See* Chambers, W. *and* R.

Summer days. *See* Robin Ranger's lib.

Summer days on the Hudson. Wise, D. $2. *Meth. Bk. Conc.*

Summer driftwood for the winter fire. Porter, R. $1. *Randolph.*

Summer etchings in Colorado. Greatorex, E. $3; $6.................................. *Putnam.*

Summer gleanings. Todd, J. $1.25 .... *Bridgman.*

Summer holidays at Hillside. Aunt Cecil. 40c. *Randolph.*

Summer house stories. *See* Whitmarsh, *Miss* C. S.

Summer in Europe. Wills, M. H. $1.25.. *Lippincott.*

Summer in the forest. Hopkins, I. F. $1.10.. *Am. Tr.*

Summer in Leslie Goldthwaite's life. Whitney, A. D. T. $1.50.............................. *Osgood.*

Summer in Norway. Caton, J. D. $2.50.... *Jansen.*

Summer in Scotland. Abbott, J. $1.75 .... *Harper.*

Summer in Skye. *See* Smith, A.

Summer parish. Beecher, H. W. $1.50...... *Ford.*

Summer rest. Dodge, M. A. $1.50........... *Estes.*

Summer stories. *See* Juvenile picture books.

Summer time in the country. Willmott, R. A. $6; $9 .... *Routledge.*

Summer vacation. Hale, E. E. 50c. .... *Roberts.*

Summer vacation abroad. Ward, F. DeW. $1.25. *Darrow.*

Summer with the little Grays. Preston, *Miss* —. 75c. *Fuller.*

Summerbell, N., *and* Flood, Ja. M. Discussions on the Trinity, church constitutions and disciplines, and human depravity. ('60.) New ed. 12°. '69. $1.25.......................... *Pounsford.*

Summerfield, J: Sermons; with introd. by T. E. Bond. 8°. $2; hf. cf., $4.25.................. *Harper.*

Summerfield. Lee, D. K. $1.25....... *Williamson.*

Summerfield imbroglio. Collins, M. 25c. .. *Loring.*

Summering in Colorado. *See* Harrington, C.

Summer's dream. 32°. 20c.; pap., 15c...... *Dutton.*

Summer's romance. Healy, M. $1.50...... *Roberts.*

Summers, T: Osmond. Baptism: its nature, perpetuity, subject, etc.; with strictures on Howell's "Evils of infant baptism." ('52.) 10th ed. 12°. '76. $1.25 .... *So. Meth.*
— Catholic constitutions and relations of the Meth. Episc. Church, south. ('66.) 5th ed. 12°. '75. pap., 10c. *So. Meth.*
— Commentary on Acts. ('74.) 2d ed. 12°. '75. $1.75. *So. Meth.*
— Commentary on the Gospels. ('68–'72.) New ed. 4 v. 12°. '74–'75. v. 1, 3, 4, ea., $1.50; v. 2, $1.25 .... *So. Meth.*
Cont.: Matthew. — Mark. — Luke. — John.
— — Questions. 4 v. 18°. ea., per doz., hf. bd., $3. *So. Meth.*
— Commentary on the ritual. ('73.) 2d ed. 12°. '74. 80c. .... *So. Meth.*
— Convenient food. ('53.) 2d ed. 18°. '69. 35c. *So. Meth.*
— Golden censer: essay on prayer, with sel. of forms. ('59.) 12th ed. 18°. '76. 75c.; $1.25; mor., $3. *So. Meth.*
— Holiness: treatise on sanctification as set forth in New Test. ('56.) 2d ed. 24°. '73. 40c... *So. Meth.*
— Outline of Sunday school lectures. *See* Teacher's aid lib.
— [Question books.] 5 v. 18°. ea., per doz., hf. bd., $3 .... *So. Meth.*
Cont.: Questions on Genesis — on John — on Luke — on Mark — on Matthew.
— Refutation of theolog. works of T: Paine; not noticed by Bp. Watson in his "Apology for the Bible." ('55.) 4th ed. 18°. '74. 50c. .... *So. Meth.*
— Scripture catechism. 2 pts. 18°. '55. ea., per doz., hf. bd., $2 .... *So. Meth.*
— Seasons, months and days. ('57.) 2d ed. 18°. '74. 40c. .... *So. Meth.*
— Strictures on Dr. Howell's "Evils of infant baptism." 12°. '54. pap., 20c. .... *So. Meth.*
— Sunday-school teacher; or, the catechetical office. ('54.) 4th ed. 18°. '74. 50c. .... *So. Meth.*
— Talks, pleasant and profitable. 18°. '60. 50c. *So. Meth.*
— (*ed.*) Biographical sketches of itinerant ministers, pioneers within bounds of Meth. Episc. Church, south. ('58.) 3d ed. 8°. '76. $2; $2.50.. *So. Meth.*
— Desert. ('56.) 2d ed. 18°. '73. 40c. .. *So. Meth.*
— Fifty beautiful ballads. ('55.) 2d ed. 18°. '61. 60c. *So. Meth.*
— Fifty fine poems. ('55.) 3d ed. 18°. '75. 60c. *So. Meth.*
— Friendly talks on union between a northern and a southern Methodist. ('71.) 2d ed. 12°. '74. pap., 10c. .... *So. Meth.*
— Gate of prayer. ('56.) 2d ed. 18°. '74. 50c. *So. Meth.*
— Gathered flowerets. 18°. 50c. .... *So. Meth.*
— Songs of Zion: sup. to hymn-book of the M. E. Church, south. ('51.) 10th ed., enl. 24°. '73. roan, 80c.; shp., 60c.; mor., $1.75.... *So. Meth.*
— Sunday-school speaker. ('60.) 3d ed. 18°. '75. 60c. *So. Meth.*

Summers, T: O., *jr.* Anatomy. 24°. '75. $1.. *So. Meth.*

Sumner, C: Complete works. v. 1–11. por. 12°. '70–'76. ea., *$3; hf. cf., $5 .... *Lee & S.*
— Duel between France and Germany, with its lesson to civilization: lecture. cr. 8°. pap., 50c. *Lee & S.*
— Greeley or Grant? speech, Sept. 3, 1872. 8°. pap., 25c. .... *Lee & S.*
— Memoir and eulogies; comp. by W. M. Cornell, N. P. Banks and G. Haven: also, eulogies of C. Schurz, G. W. Curtis, etc. 12°. '74. $1.50; hf. mor., $2 .... *Earle.*
— Prophetic voices concerning Am. cr. 8°. $2.. *Lee & S.*
— Republicanism vs. Grantism: speech in U. S. Senate. 8°. pap., 25c. .... *Lee & S.*
— True grandeur of nations: oration, Boston, July 4, 1845. 12°. '70. pap., 20c. .... *Peace.*
— *See also* United States, Circuit Court reports.

Sumner, C: A. Popular use and benefits of standard phonography. 12°. pap., 15c. .... *Graham.*

Sumner, *Mrs.* G: Margaret Warner. 18°. 75c... *Carter.*

Sumner, W: Graham. American finance. 8°. '75. pap., 10c. .... *Williams.*
— History of American currency; with chapters on Eng. bank restriction and Austrian paper money; [also] The bullion report. ('74.) New ed. 12°. '76. $3 .... *Holt.*

Sumter. Allston, J. B. 50c.; 25c. .... *Turnbull.*

Sun rays from fair and cloudy skies. Cousin Carrie. $1. *Appleton.*

Sun views of the earth. Proctor, R. A. $3.. *Putnam.*

Sunbeam. Baker, B. F. 75c. .... *Brainard.*

Sunbeam. Larcom, L. 65c. .... *Hoyt.*

Sunbeam, and other stories. 18°. 50c. .... *Pres. Bd.*

Sunbeam lib. 6 v. ill. 18°. '68. $2 .... *Hoyt.*
Cont.: Mabel's pets. — Morning hour. — Dead monkey. — Nora's lilies. — Nellie Wells. — Molly's verse.

Sunbeam ser. 10 v. 24°. $3.75 .... *Am. Bapt.*
Cont.: Actions and words. — Gerty's Christmas. — Ashleigh farm. — Nannie's adventures. — Spoiled child. — Archie Lee. — Norah's neighbor. — Cloud and sunbeam. — Josie and Rosie. — Miss Adelaide's school.

Sunbeam stories. 16°. 90c. .... *Am. S. S.*

Sunbeam stories lib. *See* Mackarness, *Mrs.* M. A.

Sunbeam Susette. Leslie, E. $1.. *Cong. Pub.; Nelson.*

Sunbeams for good children. 18°. 17c.; 22c. *Am. Bapt.*

Sunbeams for human hearts, from God's own word. ('62.) New ed. 18°. 10c. .... *Hoyt.*

Sunbeams in the home of Leonard Kingsley. Hulen, S. C. 60c. .... *Cong. Pub.*

Sunberry Dale lib. 5 v. ill. 18°. '72. $3.. *Meth. Bk. Conc.*
Cont.: Christmas at Sunberry Dale. — Harry Weston's battles. — Nettie, Connie and Silas. — About common wonders. — Parables of animals.

Sunday afternoon: pictures and poems with Scripture questions. fp. 8°. (Bagster.) $3.75 ... *Wiley.*

Sunday afternoons. ill. sq. 16°. 75c. .... *Nelson.*

Sunday afternoons. Burr, E. F. 75c... *Meth. Bk. Conc.*

Sunday afternoons in the nursery. Charlesworth, M. L. 75c. .... *Carter.*

Sunday afternoons with mamma. ill. 16°. 60c. *Bost. Am. Tr.*

Sunday album for children. Heaton, C. $1.75. *Routledge.*

Sunday all the week; by author of "Pond lily stories." 16°. 60c. .... *Am. S. S.*

Sunday alphabet of animals. Little, H. M. 60c. *Bost. Am. Tr.*

Sunday at home. Stevens, W. B. $1.50 .... *Porter.*

Sunday at Oatlands. Haven, A. B. 50c. .... *Dutton.*

Sunday book of one syllable. Godolphin, M. 50c. *Routledge.*

Sunday book of poetry. *See* Alexander, *Miss* C. F.

Sunday chaplet. *See* Tucker, *Mrs.* C.

Sunday chats with sensible children. *See* Mateaux, C.L.

Sunday echoes in week day hours. *See* Brock, *Mrs.* C.

Sunday enjoyments. 18°. 40c. .... *Dutton.*

Sunday evening book. 32°. 50c. .... *Carter.*

Sunday evening readings. *See* Cousin Anna's lib.

Sunday evening thoughts. *See* Geldart, *Mrs.* T:

Sunday evenings. *See* Harper's boys and girls' lib.

Sunday evenings: Scripture stories. 3 v. ill. 18°. $2.25 .... *Harper.*

Sunday evenings at home. Adams, H. C. 2 v. ea., $2; 75c. .... *Routledge.*

Sunday evenings at home. *See* Flower garlands for little gleaners.

Sunday evenings at Northcourt. *See* Sargent, G. E.

Sunday excursion, and what came of it. ('60.) New ed. ill. 18°. '68. 35c. .... *Hoyt.*

Sunday garland of pictures and stories. ill. roy. 16°. 50c. .... *Cassell.*

Sunday half hours. ill. 12°. '74. $1.50.. *Routledge.*

Sunday half hours. ill. 8°. $1.50...*Scribner, W.&A.*

Sunday half hours with the great preachers. Simons, M. L. $3.75; $4.50; $4.75; $6........*Porter.*

Sunday hours. 18°. 55c...................*Am.S.S.*

Sunday lib. for household reading; prep. by Eng. and Am. divines. 6 v. ill. 12°. ea., $1.75..*Lippincott.*
Cont.: Pupils of St. John the divine, by C. M. Yonge. — Hermits, by C. Kingsley. — Seekers after God: lives of Seneca, Epictetus and Marcus Aurelius, by F. W. Farrar. — England's antiphon: hist. review of relig. poetry of Eng., by G. Mac Donald. — St. Louis and Calvin, by F. P. B. Guizot. — Christian singers of Germany, by C. Winkworth.

— *Same.* 13 v. cr. 8°. ea., $1.75........*Macmillan.*
Cont.: Pupils of St. John the divine. — Kingsley's Hermits. — Farrar's Seekers after God. — MacDonald's England's antiphon. — Guizot's Great Christians of France. — Winkworth's Christian singers of Germany. — Maclear's Apostles of mediæval Europe. — Hughes' Alfred the Great. — Keary's Nations around. — Church's St. Anslem. — Oliphant's Francis of Assisi. — Yonge's Pioneers and founders. — Martin's Angelique Arnauld.

Sunday morning thoughts. *See* Geldart, *Mrs.* T.

Sunday reading. 32°. 25c.; 50c............*Nelson.*

Sunday reading for good children. ill. sq. 12°. '73. $1. *Routledge.*

Sunday reading for the young. 4 v. ill. 4°. (Lond.) ea., $2.50; bds., $1.50...............*Am.News.*

Sunday readings; or, the child's Sabbath pleasantly and profitably employed. 12°. pap., 40c. *Am.S.S.*

Sunday readings for little folks. ill. roy. 16°. 50c. *Cassell.*

Sunday scholar's daily text book. 64°. 50c...*Nelson.*

Sunday school and family libraries. 4 nos. ea., 100 v. 18°. per lib., $15..................*Am.S.S.*

Sunday school anniversary. 18°. 25c.......*Am.S.S.*

Sunday school book for evang. Lutheran congregations. 16°. '73. 50c.; 60c.; 75c...*Luth.Bk.St.*

Sunday school celebration book. 18°. 60c. *Cin.Meth.Bk.Conc.*

Sunday school chant and tune book; with service. 16°. 25c. ....*Dutton.*

— *Same.* Canticles, hymns and carols; without music. 16°. 25c. ....*Dutton.*

Sunday school children. 18°. 22c..........*Am.S.S.*

Sunday school concert: general service manual for the school and congregation. 16°. '72. 75c. *Adams, B.&L.*

Sunday school days of Jennie Graham. 18°. 60c. *Pres.Bd.*

Sunday school dialogues for boys and girls. 18°. 25c. *Am.S.S.*

Sunday school exhibition and its consequences. Guernsey, L. E. 85c.......................*Am.S.S.*

Sunday school facts. 18°. 50c.; 60c. ......*Am.Bapt.*

Sunday school handbook. 18°. 50c. ....*Nelson.*

Sunday school hymn-book. 24°. roan, 40c. *Meth.Bk.Conc.*

— *Same.* 32°. '54. pap., per doz., $3......*So.Meth.*

Sunday school hymns. 24°. 20c. ....*Am.S.S.*

Sunday school idea. Hart, J. S. $1.50..*Garrigues.*

Sunday school illustrations. 18°. 55c......*Am.S.S.*

Sunday school library. no. 1. 100 v. 18°. $16. — no. 2, 100 v. 18°. $16; hf. mor., $18..*Am. Bapt.*

Sunday school liturgy; prep. under supervision of Unitarian Sunday School Soc. ('56.) 7th ed. 16°. '66. 60c......................*Am.Unit.*

Sunday school monitor. 32°. 20c..........*Am.S.S.*

Sunday school olio. Wood, R. H. 25c. *Meth.Bk.Conc.*

Sunday school photographs. Taylor, A. $1.15..*Hoyt.*

Sunday school picnic. *See* Leighton children.

Sunday school primer. ill. 24°. 10c...*Meth.Bk.Conc.*

Sunday school primer. [Baptist.] 16°. per doz., $1; pap., 60c. ....*So.Bapt.*

Sunday school primer and reader. 16°. per doz., $2. *So.Bapt.*

Sunday school reward books. *See* New.

Sunday school service and hymn-book; arr. by S.-school com. of diocese of Ohio. 16°. 25c...*Dutton.*

Sunday school singer. *See* New.

Sunday school speaker. 12°. bds., 50c......*Loring.*

Sunday school speaker. *See* Teacher's aid lib.

Sunday school teacher. 18°. 40c..........*Am. Bapt.*

Sunday school teacher's Bible stories. 8°. 50c.; 60c. *Am.S.S.*

Sunday school teacher's dream. 32°. 25c. ..*Am.S.S.*

Sunday school teacher's guide. 12°. $1.25. *Meth.Bk.Conc.*

Sunday school teacher's tracts. 18°. 60c. ..*Am.S.S.*

Sunday schools in the mountains. 18°. 40c. *Am.S.S.*

Sunday service. 12°. '66. roan, $2.25; mor., $3. *So.Meth.*

Sunday shop; or, the fourth commandment. 18°. '67. 35c. .........*N.Y.Ref.Ch.Bd.; Pres.Com.*

Sunday sketches for children; by a father. ill. 18°. '58. 85c. ....*Dodd.*

Sundays in the temple. Vaughan, C. J. $1.25. *Routledge.*

Sunderland, La Roy. Trance-dynamic cure. 12°. $1.50 ....*Mendum.*

Sunlight and shadow. Pencillep, H. $1.75..*J.E.Potter.*

Sunlight children: allegory. 18°. 30c. *N.Y.Ref.Ch.Bd.*

Sunlight of song; with orig. music by Barnby, Arthur Sullivan, etc., and ill. by celebrated artists. 4°. '75. $4.........................*Routledge.*

Sunlight through the mist; or, lessons from lives of great and good men. ill. 16°. '73. 90c...*Dodd.*

Sunny bank. Harland, M. $1.50.........*Carleton.*

Sunny bank stories. *See* Bullard, A.

Sunny Brook lib. 4 v. 16°. $3.75........*Randolph.*
Cont.: Our Tabby and her travels. — Our summer at Sunny Brook. — The Lord will provide. — Stories of other lands.

Sunny days. 4°. 50c.; pap., 25c.............*Nelson.*

Sunny days abroad. Dyer, C. C. J. $1.25.. *Whittaker.*

Sunny dell. Cousin Zilpha. 60c...........*Lothrop.*

Sunny dell ser. 5 v. 18°. $3..............*Lothrop.*
Cont.: Sunny dell. — Story of a summer. — Darkness and light. — Jimmy Don. — Blind Jakey.

Sunny eyed Tim. *See* Silver penny ser.

Sunny hour lib. *See* Eyster, N.

Sunny hours. Eyster, N. $1.25 ....*Meth.Epis.*

Sunny hours of childhood: stories for youth. 18°. '73. 75c. ....*Barnes.*

Sunny Lee stories. 4 v. 16°. $5........(?) *Martien.*
Cont.: It isn't right. — Two friends. — Charles Norwood. — Penny wise and pound foolish.

Sunny Madge; or, light of the household. 18°. 45c. *Am.S.S.*

Sunny meadow lib. 6 v. 16°. $7.50....(?) *Martien.*
Cont.: Take, but earn; or, sunny meadow. — Margaret's secret and its success. — Gracie's mission. — Charity Helstone. — Philip in Palestine. — Joseph, the Jew.

Sunny mount and its peaks. Breed, W. P. 70c. *Pres.Bd.*

Sunny nook stories. *See* May, Annie.

Sunny path. Davis, C. E. K. $1.50..........*Hoyt.*

Sunny path lib. 4 v. 16°. $5.50 ....*Hoyt.*
Cont.: Sunny path, by C. E. K. Davis. — Following on to know. — Harry Maitland, by G. F. Downs. — Arthur Lee.

Sunny scenes. *See* Sunshine and shadow lib.

Sunny shores. Adams, W. T. $1.50.......*Lee & S.*

Sunny-side (The). Phelps, E. S. 60c.....*Am.S.S.*

Sunny-side (The). Wendetè, C. W., *and* Perkins, H. S. 35c. ....*Pond.*

Sunny-side book. Putnam, G. P. $4.50; $8..*Putnam.*

Sunny-side glee-book. Seward, T. F. 80c. *Huntington.*

Sunny-side ser. *See* Phelps, *Mrs.* E. S.

Sunny skies. Channing, B. H. $1.25......*Lothrop.*

Sunset; or, the last days of William Howard; by author of "Early dawn." 18°. 60c...*Pres. Bd.*
Sunset cottage. *See* Harland stories.
Sunset Hill. *See* Haywood, *Miss* C. E.
Sunset hours of life. Nourse, C. S. $1; $1.25..*Am. Tr.*
Sunset land. Todd, J. $1.50..............*Lee & S.*
Sunset Mountain. Porter, A. E. $1.50.....*Lothrop.*
Sunset thoughts; or, Bible narratives for the evening of life; by author of "New tracts for working homes." 12°. 75c..................*Pres. Bd.*
Sunsets on Hebrew mountains. Macduff, J. R. $1.50. *Carter.*
Sunshine. Bliss, P. P. 35c...............*Church.*
Sunshine. Dall, C. H. 37c.................*Lee & S.*
Sunshine. McKeever, H. B. $1.25......*J.A. Moore.*
Sunshine. *See* Prosser, *Mrs.* —.
Sunshine and clouds in the morning of life. Bowman, A. $1..........................*Routledge.*
Sunshine and shadow. Newby, C. J. 50c...*Peterson.*
Sunshine and shadow in Kattern's life. ('72.) New ed. 16°. '75. $1.25.........................*Hoyt.*
Sunshine and shadow in New York. Smith, M. H. *$3; $3.50................................*Burr.*
Sunshine and shadow lib. 10 v. ill. 16°. $3.50. *Routledge.*
Cont.: Sunny scenes. — William Freeman. — Ruth Allan. — Allen White. — John Phillips. — Margy and her feather. — Our village girls. — Buy an orange, sir? — Don't say so. — Bob, the crossing sweeper.
Sunshine and starlight. Seymour, M. H. 50c.; 60c. *Dutton.*
Sunshine at home. *See* Arthur, T. S.
Sunshine Bill. Kingston, W. H. G. $1..(?)*Martien.*
Sunshine cottage. Denison, M. A. 75c.......*Hoyt.*
Sunshine for babyland. ill. 4°. '75. $1.75; bds., $1.25.............................*Lothrop.*
Sunshine for gloomy hours. Thornton, J. 70c. *Pres. Bd.*
Sunshine for rainy days. Frost, S. A. $1...*Am. Tr.*
Sunshine Hall. *See* Robin Ranger's lib.
Sunshine of Blackpool. Leslie, E. $1..*Meth. Bk. Conc.*
Sunshine of domestic life. Adams, W. H. D. $1.50. *Nelson.*
Sunshine of Greystone. *See* Winter evening lib.
Sunshine ser. [Toy-books.] 6 nos. ill. 18°. per gross, $18.....................(?) *McLoughlin.*
Cont.: Three little kittens. — Little old woman. — Robber kitten. — Sad fate of poor Robin. — Story of simple Simon. — Little Bo-peep.
Sunshine ser. *See* Baker, *Mrs.* H. N. W.
Sunshine story books. 4 nos. ill. 18°. per gross, $24........................(?) *McLoughlin.*
Cont.: Fairy Moonbeam's story book. — Susie Sunshine's story book. — Little slovenly Peter's story book. — Peter Prim's story book.
Sunshine through the clouds. Lawrence, S. 15c. *French; Lee & S.*
Superannuate; or, sketches of William Ryder. 18°. '45. 50c.....................*Meth. Bk. Conc.*
Superintendent's (A) addresses to the children of his Sabbath-school. 18°. 55c...........*Pres. Bd.*
Supernatural religion: inquiry into reality of divine revelation. v. 1, 2. 8°. '75. $8......*Roberts.*
Supernumerary. Woolsey, E. 50c...*Meth. Bk. Conc.*
Superstition and force. Lea, H. C. $2.75.....*Lea.*
Supper in Dixie. Triplet, A. 15c...........*French.*
Supper institution. Denison, F. 60c......*Am. Bapt.*
Supper on the grass. *See* Stories of the good shepherd.
Suppliants. *See* Euripides.
Supreme godhead of Christ. Gordon, W. R. 65c. *N. Y. Ref. Ch. Bd.*
Sure; or, it pays. ill. 16°. '72. $1.50........*Lothrop.*
Sure foundation and how to build upon it. De Witt, J. 85c. ....*N. Y. Ref. Ch. Bd.*
Sure teacher. Ives, W. $1.25; 75c..........*Pond.*
Sure way to find out the true religion. *See* Baddeley, T.
Sure words of promise. *See* Earnest Christian's lib.
Surenne, Gbr. French-and-English dictionary. 16°. $1.25...............................*Appleton.*
— French manual and traveller's companion. 16°. $1. *Appleton.*
— *See also* Spiers, A., *and* Surenne, G.
Surf skiff. Ingraham, J. H. 25c...........*De Witt.*
Surgeon-General's Office. *See* United States.
Surgeon of Paris. Jones, J. S. 15c.........*French.*
Surgeon's daughter. *See* Scott, *Sir* Wa.
Surrender of Calais. Colman, G., *jr.* 15c...*French.*
Surrey, *Col.* (*pseud.*) *See* Cooke, J. E.
Surrey, *Earl of.* [H: Howard.] Poems. (Aldine ed.) 16°. 75c..........................*Lippincott.*
— *Same*; with memoir. por. 18°. $1........*Osgood.*
Surrey of Eagle's nest. Cooke, J. E. $2.25. *Huntington.*
Surtees, Rob. Smith. Jorrocks' jaunts and jollities. 16°. bds., $1.......................*Routledge.*
Susan, *Aunt* (*pseud.*) *See* Prentiss, *Mrs.* Eliz.
Susan and Frankie. *See* Ashton, *Mrs.* S. G.
Susan Brooker; or, where there's a will there's a way. 18°. 18c...........................*Am. S. S.*
Susan Elmaker. *See* History of.
Susan Fielding. Edwards, A. $1.75; $1...*Sheldon.*
Susan Gray (History of). *See* Sherwood, M. M.
Susan Gray; or, the little runaway. 18°. 40c. *Cong. Pub.*
Susan Harvey. 18°. 40c...................*Dutton.*
Susan Hawthorne; or, avoid temptation. ('63.) 7th ed. ill. 18°. '71. 63c.............*Perkinpine.*
Susan Hopley. Pitt, G. D. 15c.............*French.*
Susan Osgood's prize. ('73.) New ed. 16°. '75. $1.50.................................*Hoyt.*
Susan Wylie; or, the smuggler's bride. 8°. pap., 25c. *De Witt.*
Susie and Rosie. *See* Big type stories.
Susie Grant. Brock, C. $1................*Dutton.*
Susie's flowers. 18°. 60c...............*Cong. Pub.*
— *See also* Adirondack stories; — Snow-drop ser.
Susie's mistake. Butler, M. 65c...........*Pres. Bd.*
Susie's mistake. *See* New holiday lib.
Susie's spectacles. ill. 16°. '71. $1.25....*Lothrop.*
Susie's thankoffering. 18°. 40c.............*Am. S. S.*
Susie's victory. *See* Baker, *Mrs.* H. N. W.
Susie's watch. ill. 24°. '70. 30c..........*Lothrop.*
Susie's watch. *See* Bright eye ser.
Suspicious husband. Hoadly, B. 15c. .....*French.*
Susy and the stray lamb. 18°. 30c.........*Am. S. S.*
Susy Hall. *See* Dot books.
Susy Lee; or, the little girl who learned to pray. 18°. 30c...............................*Am. S. S.*
Susy's flowers; or, blessed are the merciful for they shall obtain mercy; by author of "King Jack of Haylands." ill. 18°. 75c..............*Nelson.*
— *See also* Golden secret lib.; Susy's Sunday lib.
Susy's sacrifice. Mathews, J. A. $1.10......*Carter.*
Susy's Sunday lib. 5 v. ill. 16°. '73. ea., 85c. *Tibbals.*
Cont.: Brother Reginald's golden secret. — Grandpa's secret, by Mrs. A. J. Cupples. — Susy's flowers. — Lessons on life of Christ. — King Jack of Haylands.
Sut Lovingood. Harris, G. W. $1.50......*Dick & F.*
Sutcliffe, Jos. Introduction to Christianity. 18°. 55c. *Cin. Meth. Bk. Conc.*
Suter, W: E. [Plays.] 6 v. 16°. ea., pap., 15c. *Lee & S.*
Cont.: Brother Bill and me: farce. — John Wopps: farce. — Mary Moo; or, which shall I marry? farce. — Sarah's young man: farce. — Two gentlemen in a fix: farce. — Very pleasant evening: farce.

Suter, W: E., *continued.*
— *Same.* 33 v. 16°. ea., pap., 15c. .... *French.*
Cont.: Accusing spirit. — Brother Bill and me: farce. — Dick Turpin and Tom King. — Dred. — Fan Fan the tulip. — Felon's bond. — First love. — Give me my wife: farce. — Glass of water: comedy. — Highwayman's holiday: farce. — Holly Bush Hall.— Idiot of the mountain. — Incompatibility of temper: farce.— Isoline of Bavaria. — Jack o' the hedge. — Jeweller of St. James: comedy. — John Wopps: farce. — Life's revenge. — Little Annie's birthday: farce. — Lost child: farce. — More free than welcome: farce. — Our new man: farce. — Quiet family: farce. — Robbers of the Pyrenees. — Roccambole. — Sarah's young man: farce. — Syren of Paris. — Test of truth: comedy. — Two gentlemen in a fix: farce. — Very pleasant evening. — Wanted a young lady: farce. — We all have our little faults: farce. — Which shall I marry? farce.

— Catherine Howard; or, the throne, the tomb, etc.: hist. play. 16°. pap., 15c. .... *De Witt.*
— Give me my wife: farce. 16°. pap., 15c .... *Ames.*
— Lady Audley's secret: drama. 16°. pap., 15c. *Ames.*
— Life's (A) revenge: drama. 16°. pap., 15c... *Ames.*
— Little Annie's birthday: farce. 16°. pap., 15c. *De Witt.*
— Wanted, a young lady: farce. 16°. pap., 15c. *De Witt.*

Sutherlands. Harris, M. C. $1.50 .... *Carleton.*

Sutton, Amos. Guide to the Saviour. 24°. '50. 50c. *Freewill.*
— Narrative of mission to Orissa. 12°. '33. $1 .. *Freewill.*

Sutton, Anne. Poems on moral and religious subjects. 12°. 50c. .... *Cin. Meth. Bk. Conc.*

Sutton, C: New York Tombs: its secrets and its mysteries; ed. by J. B. Mix and S. A. Mackeever. ill. 8°. '74. $3.50; shp., $4.25 ...... *U.S. Pub.*

Sutton, Fs. Systematic handbook of volumetric analysis; or, quantitative estimation of chemical substances by measure, applied to liquids, solids and gases. New ed., enl. ill. 8°. $5.50 .. *Lindsay.*

Sutton, W. H. Teachers' meetings. 24°. 10c. *Meth. Bk. Conc.*

Suzanne De L'Orme: Huguenot story. 16°. $1.25. *Cin. Meth. Bk. Conc.*

Svedelius, G. Handbook for charcoal burners; tr. by R. B. Anderson, and ed. by W. J. L. Nicodemus. pl. 12°. '76. $1.50 .... *Wiley.*

Swain, C: Dryburgh Abbey. *See* Scott, *Sir* Wa.
— Poems. 18°. '63. $1 .... *Roberts.*

Swain, Leon. God's ownership of the sea. ('64.) New ed. 8°. '74. pap., 25c. .... *Draper.*

Swain, W: Pl. Surgical emergencies: concise descript. of various accidents and emergencies, with directions for their immediate treatment. ill. 12°. '74. $2 .... *Lindsay.*

Swainson, C: Ant. Authority of the New Test., and other lectures. 8°. $3.50 .... *Macmillan.*
— The creeds of the Church in their relation to Holy Scripture and the conscience of the Christian. 8°. $3 .... *Macmillan.*

Swallow, G. C. *See* Kansas geol. survey; — Missouri geol. survey.

Swallow barn. Kennedy, J. P. $2 .... *Putnam.*

Swallow flights of song. Kimball, H. McE. $1.25. *Dutton.*

Swallow stories. *See* Chester, *Miss* S. E.

Swallows of Leigh Farm. 18°. 50c. .... *Am. S. S.*

Swamp doctor's adventures in the south-west. Robb, J. S. $1.75 .... *Peterson.*

Swamp outlaws; or, the Lowery bandits of North Carolina. ill. 8°. pap., 25c. .... *De Witt.*

Swampsteed; or, the days of Marion and his merry men. 8°. pap., 50c. .... *De Witt.*

Swan, C: *See* Gesta Romanorum.

Swan, Gst. Compilation of laws, resolutions, treaties, etc., of general and state governments, rel. to lands in Ohio. 8°. '25. $2 ...... *I. N. Whiting.*

Swan, Jabez S. The evangelist: [autobiog.]; ed. by F. Denison. 12°. '73. $2; mor., $3 .. *Peckham.*

Swan, Ja. G. Haidah Indians. 4°. '74. pap., $1. *Smith. Inst.*

Swan, Ja. G., *continued.*
— Indians of Cape Flattery. 4°. '69. pap., $2. *Smith. Inst.*
— Northwest coast; or, three years' residence in Washington territory. ill. 12°. $1.50 .... *Harper.*

Swan, Jos. R. Commentaries on pleadings under Ohio code, with precedents of petitions, answers, demurrers and replies. 8°. '67. shp., $6 .. *Clarke.*
— Manual for executors and administrators; with forms, etc. 5th ed., rev. and enl. by H. C. Noble; with notes by F. J. Matthews. ('43.) 6th ed. 8°. '59. shp., $1.50 .... *I. N. Whiting.*
— Practice in civil actions and proceedings at law in Ohio, and precedents in pleading; with notes [and] forms of process and clerks' entries. 2 v. roy. 8°. '54. shp., $8 .... *I. N. Whiting.*
— Treatise on law rel. to powers and duties of justices of the peace and constables in Ohio; with forms, etc. ('36.) 5th ed. 8°. '49. shp., $2 .. *I. N. Whiting.*
— *Same.* 10th ed., rev. and enl. 8°. '75. *net*, shp., $6 .... *Clarke.*
— *See also* Ohio, Revised statutes.
— *and* Plumb, P. B. Treatise on law rel. to powers and duties of justices of the peace and constables in Kansas; with forms. 8°. '72. shp., $5 .. *Clarke.*

Swan, W: D. Large spelling book. ('48.) New ed. 16°. '72. bds., 28c. .... *Cowperthwait.*
— Primary spelling book. ('50.) New ed. 16°. '69. bds., 25c. .... *Cowperthwait.*

Swan, W: G. *See* Tennessee, Sup. Court reports.

Swank, Ja. M. American iron trade in 1876. 16°. '76. pap., $3 .... *Am. Iron.*

Swarm of B's; little children's duties explained in six charming stories. ill. 18°. 45c. *N. Y. Ref. Ch. Bd.; Pres. Com.*

Swartz, C: W. (*ed.*) Our holy Christianity: essays and sermons; with introd. by E. Miller. 18°. '73. 65c. .... *Day.*

Swayne, Jos. Griffiths. Obstetric aphorisms for students commencing midwifery practice. 2d ed., with add. by E. R. Hutchins. ill. 12°. $1.25 .. *Lea.*

Swayze, *Mrs.* J. C. Ossawattomie Brown: drama. 16°. pap., 15c. .... *French.*

Swedenborg, Em. Account of last judgment and the Babylon destroyed: relation of things heard and seen. 12°. 75c.; pap., 30c. .. *Lippincott; New Ch.*
— Angelic philos. of the divine love and wisdom; from the orig. Lat. ed. by J. F. G. Tafel; tr. by R. N. Foster. 8°. '68. $2 ...... *Claxton; Lippincott.*
— *Same.* 8°. '76. $1 .... *Am. Swed.*
— Angelic wisdom concerning the divine Providence. 12°. $1.25 ...... *Am. Swed.; Lippincott; New Ch.*
— *Same;* from Lat. ed. of J. F. I. Tafel; tr. by R. N. Foster. demy 8°. $2.25 .... *Lippincott.*
— Apocalypse revealed. 2 v. 12°. $2.75 .. *Lippincott.*
— *Same.* 2 v. 8°. '76. ea., $1.50 .... *Am. Swed.*
— Arcana cœlestia: the heavenly arcana cont. in Scriptures unfolded. 10 v. 8°. '76. ea., $1.50 .. *Am. Swed.*
— Brief exposition of doctrine of the New Church. 8°. pap., 20c. .... *Lippincott; New Ch.*
— Catechism or decalogue explained as to its external and internal senses; [from] "True Christian religion." 12°. 50c. .... *Lippincott.*
— *Same.* 12°. 50c.; bds., 40c. .... *New Ch.*
— Concerning heaven and its wonders, and concerning hell. 12°. $1.25; bds., 50c. .... *Lippincott.*
— Conjugial love and its chaste delights; also adulterous love and its sinful pleasures. 8°. '76. $1.25. *Am. Swed.*
— *Same.* 8°. $1.75 .... *Lippincott; New Ch.*
— Consecutive service (The). 12°. 40c. .. *Lippincott.*
— Dictionary of correspondences, representatives and significations derived from the word of the Lord; from writings of S. 12°. '60. $2 .. *H. H. Carter.*
— Divine attributes, incl. also the divine trinity; from the "Apocalypse explained." 12°. $2. *Claxton; Lippincott.*

Swedenborg, Em., *continued.*
— Doctrine of life for New Jerusalem; from commandments of the decalogue. 24°. 75c. . . *Lippincott.*
— *Same.* 12°. pap., 10c. . . . . *New Ch.*
— *Same.* 12°. pap., 15c. . . . . *Lippincott.*
— *Same;* tr. by T. B. Hayward. 18°. 35c. *H. H. Carter.*
— Doctrine of the New Jerusalem concerning charity. 12°. pap., 15c. . . . . *Lippincott.*
— *Same.* 12°. pap., 10c. . . . . *New Ch.*
— *Same;* [also] Doctrine concerning faith; from "Arcana cœlestia;" tr. by T. B. Hayward. 18°. 35c. *H. H. Carter.*
— Doctrine of the New Jerusalem concerning the Lord. 12°. pap., 25c. . . . . *Lippincott.*
— *Same.* 12°. pap., 20c. . . . . *New Ch.*
— *Same.* 18°. '66. 35c. . . . . *H. H. Carter.*
— Doctrine of the New Jerusalem on faith. 12°. pap., 15c. . . . . *Lippincott.*
— *Same.* 12°. pap., 10c. . . . . *New Ch.*
— Doctrine respecting the Scripture. 12°. pap., 20c. *Lippincott.*
— *Same.* 12°. pap., 15c. . . . . *New Ch.*
— *Same* 18°. '67. 35c. . . . . *H. H. Carter.*
— Doctrines of the New Jerusalem. 12°. $1.50 . . *New Ch.*
— *Same.* 12°. $1.75 . . . . *Lippincott.*
— Earths in the universe. 12°. 60c.; pap., 25c. *New Ch.*
— *Same.* 16°. 75c.; pap., 35c. . . . . *Lippincott.*
— Economy of the animal kingdom considered anatomically, physically and philosophically; tr. by A. Clissold, and ed. by J. J. G. Wilkinson. 2 v. 8°. '58. $3; in 1 v., $2.50; shp., $3 . . . *Mendenhall.*
— *Same.* 2 v. 8°. '68. $3.50; in 1 v., $2.50. *H. H. Carter.*
— Four leading doctrines (The) of the New Church: conc. the Lord, the sacred Scripture, faith and life. 8°. '76. $1 . . . . *Am. Swed.*
— *Same.* 12°. $1.25 . . . . *New Ch.*
— *Same.* 12°. $1.50 . . . . *Lippincott.*
— Heaven and its wonders, the world of spirits, and hell; from things heard and seen. 8°. '76. $1.25 . . . . *Am. Swed.*
— *Same.* demy 8°. $2.50 . . . . *Lippincott.*
— *Same.* 12°. $1.25; bds., 50c.; mor., $2.50 . . *New Ch.*
— Liturgy (The); with consecutive service. 12°. $1.25; — without consecutive service. 12°. $1.25. *Lippincott.*
— Miscellaneous theological works. 8°. '76. $1.50. *Am. Swed.*
— Of the New Jerusalem and its heavenly doctrine; [also] Some observations conc. the new heaven and the new earth. 16°. 18c. . . . . *Lippincott.*
— *Same.* 12°. pap., 12c. . . . . *New Ch.*
— *Same.* 18°. 35c. . . . . *H. H. Carter.*
— On the Athanasian creed and subjects connected with it. 12°. $1.25 . . . . *Lippincott; New Ch.*
— On the intercourse between the soul and the body. 12°. pap., 10c. . . . . *Lippincott.*
— On the white horse, mentioned in the Apocalypse. 12°. pap., 10c. . . . . *Lippincott.*
— On the worship and love of God. 16°. '56. $1. *H. H. Carter.*
— Spiritual diary. ('71.) New ed. 2 v. 12°. '72. $2.75 . . . . *H. H. Carter.*
— Summary exposition of internal sense of prophets and Psalms. 8°. pap., 20c. . . . . *New Ch.*
— *Same.* 12°. pap., 25c. . . . . *Lippincott.*
— Swedenborg lib.; ed. by B. F. Barrett. v. 1, 2. 16°. '75. ea., $1 . . . . *Claxton.*
Cont.: Death, resurrection and the judgment. — Heaven: the substance of the official report of a credible eye-witness.
— True Christian religion. 8°. $1 . . . . *H. H. Carter.*
— *Same.* 8°. $2.25 . . . . *Lippincott; New Ch.*
— *Same.* 8°. '76. $2.50 . . . . *Am. Swed.*
— *Same;* tr. from Lat. ed. of J. F. I. Tafel by R. N. Foster. 2 v. demy 8°. $5 . . . . *Lippincott.*
— Compendium of [his] theological writings; by S. M. Warren. 8°. $3.50; hf. mor., $6 . . . . . . *New Ch.*
— Gems from [his] writings; with memoir by O. P. Hiller. 2 v. 18°. $1.25 . . . . *H. H. Carter.*

Swedenborg and modern biblical criticism. Gould, E. 62c. . . . . *H. H. Carter.*
Swedenborgian Church. *See* New Church.
Swedes in Prague; or, the signal rocket: romance of the thirty years' war; tr. from the Germ. 8°. pap., 25c. . . . . *U. P. James.*
Swedish nursemaid. ill. 18°. '60. 35c. . . . . . *Am. Tr.*
Sweeney, J: S. *See* Munnell, T., *and* Sweeney, J. S.; — Prichett, J. H., *and* Sweeney, J. S.
Sweeny, Ja. M. *See* New York City, Superior Court reports.
Sweeny Todd: drama. 16°. pap., 15c. . . . . . . *French.*
Sweeny Todd, the ruffian barber. 8°. pap., 50c. *Peterson.*
Sweet, I. D. J. Elements of draughts; or, beginners' sure guide. 12°. 75c. 32°. 50c. . . . . . . *De Witt.*
— Ready reckoner. 12°. 75c. 32°. bds., 50c. *De Witt.*
Sweet, Rob. Warblers. *See* Bechstein, J. M., Cage and chamber birds.
Sweet, S. H. Special report on coal: its distribution, classification and cost delivered over different routes to various points in state of N. Y., and the principal cities on Atlantic coast. maps. 8°. '66. $3 . . . . *Van Nostrand.*
Sweet bells jangled. Hall, C. O. 50c. . . (?) *Am. News.*
Sweet brier stories. *See* Baker, *Mrs.* H. N. W.
Sweet clover stories. *See* May, *Mrs.* C. L.
Sweet flowers. *See* Mackarness, *Mrs.* M. A.
Sweet herbs. 18°. 70c. . . . . *Pres. Bd.*
Sweet home. 18°. 17c.; 22c. . . . . *Am. Bapt.*
Sweet home. Percival, F. E. $1.25 . . . . . *J. E. Potter.*
Sweet home ser. 6 v. 16°. $7.50 . . . . *J. E. Potter.*
Cont.: Sweet home, by F. E. Percival. — Angel visitor, by F. E. Percival. — Morning star, by W. M. Thayer. — Spirit land, by S. B. Emmons. — Deserted family, by P. Creyton. — Fashionable dissipation, by M. V. Fuller; Adela Lincoln, by M. F. Carey.
Sweet incense. Sanders, H. 15c. . . . . . *D. H. Carroll.*
Sweet Mary. Palmer, P. 40c. . . . . *Palmer.*
Sweet nineteen. Robinson, F. W. 50c. . . . . . *De Witt.*
Sweet sounds. Peters, J. L. $2.25; $1.75 . . *Peters.*
Sweet story of old; or, tell me about Jesus. ill. sq. 16°. '61. 75c. . . . . *Meth. Bk. Conc.*
Sweet violets. *See* Mackarness, *Mrs.* M. A.
Sweet violets lib. *See* Mackarness, *Mrs.* M. A.
Sweeter than honey. 18°. 17c.; 22c. . . . . . *Am. Bapt.*
Sweethearts and wives. Kenney, J. 15c. . . . *French.*
Sweetser, Jos. E. Pilgrim melodies: tunes adapted to "Songs for the sanctuary," and other collections. 4°. '75. $1.25 . . . . *Barnes.*
— *See also* Cheever, G. B., *and* Sweetser, J. E.
Sweetser, Mos. F. Europe for $2 a day. 16°. '75. pap., 25c. . . . . *Osgood.*
Sweetser, Seth. The ministry we need. 16°. 75c. *Bost. Am. Tr.*
Sweney, J. R. Gems of praise combined. [Music book.] 12°. '75. 25c.; pap., 20c. . . *Meth. Epis.*
Swensk och engelsk brefställare. 12°. 50c. *Engberg.*
Swenska Lutherska Tryckföreningen. Hemlandssånger. 12°. leath., $1; $1.25; mor., $1.50. *Engberg.*
— Melödier till Hemlands-sånger och ahnfelts sånger. 8°. $4.75; hf. mor., $5.25; pap., $4 . . *Engberg.*
Swept and garnished. Thompson, A. W. 30c. *Am. News.*
Swept and garnished; or, fruits meet for repentance. 16°. 90c. . . . . *Am. S. S.*
Swerdna, *Mrs.* Ambrose. Rodman: child's story. 18°. 40c. . . . . *Dutton.*
Sweringen, Hiram V. Pharmaceutical lexicon. roy. 8°. '73. $5; leath., $6 . . . . *Lindsay.*

Swetchine, *Mme.* Sophia. Life and letters; ed. by Count de Falloux; tr. by H. W. Preston. 16°. '67. $1.50 .... *Roberts.*
— Writings; ed. by Count de Falloux; tr. by H. W. Preston. 16°. '69. $1.25 .... *Roberts.*
Swete, C: *See* Trimmer, *Mrs.* S. K., History of the robins.
Swett, J: Centennial hist. of public school system of California, 1850–1876. 8°. '76. *net*, $2 .. *Bancroft.*
— Common school readings: sel. from recent literature. 12°. '67. $1.25 .... *Barnes.*
— *Same.* 12°. '67. $1.50 .... *Bancroft.*
— Questions for written examinations: aid to candidates for teacher's certificates and handbook for examiners and teachers. 12°. '72. $1 .. *Ivison.*
Swett, J: A. Treatise on diseases of the chest. 8°. $3.50 .... *Appleton.*
Swift, E. P. Memoir of Joseph W. Barr. 18°. 40c. *Pres. Bd.*
Swift, J: Franklin. Going to Jericho; or, sketches of travel in Spain and the east. ('68.) 2d ed. 12°. '74. $1.50 .... *Roman.*
— Robert Greathouse. 12°. $2 .... *Carleton.*
Swift, Jona. Works. 12°. $1.50 .... *World Pub.*
— *Same.* roy. 8°. $2.50 .... *Appleton; Lee & S.*
— *Same.* por. and ill. cr. 8°. '76. $3 .. *Scribner, W. & A.*
— *Same;* incl. life by Roscoe. 6 v. por. 12°. $12; shp., $16; hf. cf., $24 .... *O'Shea.*
— Poems. (Aldine ed.) 3 v. 16°. ea., 75c. *Lippincott.*
— *Same;* with memoir by J. Mitford. 3 v. por. 18°. $3 .... *Osgood.*
— Gulliver's travels. 8°. pap., 25c. .... *Lippincott.*
— *Same.* post 18°. 75c. .... *Scribner, W. & A.*
— *Same.* ill. 12°. $1.50 .... *World Pub.*
— *Same.* ill. 12°. '74. $1.50. — 16°. $1. — 18°. 75c. *Routledge.*
— *Same.* ill. 8°. $2.50 .... *Scribner, W. & A.*
— *Same.* (Household ser.) ill. 16°. $1.50; mor., $3. *Lee & S.*
— *Same.* (Presentation poets.) ill. 16°. '74. $1.75. *Routledge.*
— *Same.* (World wide lib.) 12°. '74. pap., 25c. *Routledge.*
— *Same;* with memoir. ill. roy. 8°. $3.50 .... *Lee & S.*
— *Same;* with life of author by J. Mitford. 12°. $1. *Lippincott.*
— — *Same.* ill. 12°. $1.25 .... *Porter.*
— *Same.* New ed.; with notes and life of author by J. F. Waller. ill. imp. 8°. $3.50; $5 .... *Cassell.*
— — *See also* Beeton's boy's own lib.; — Child's ed.; — Library of celebrated books; — Treasure-box of amusement and instruction.
— *See also* Tatler (The).
Swift, Jla. M. Field flowers. [Poetry.] ('72.) 2d ed. 16°. '73. $1.50 .... *Claxton.*
Swift, Ma. A. First lessons on natural philosophy. 2 pts. 18°. *net*, 1, 40c.; 2, 45c. .... *Hamersley.*
Swift, Owen. Boxing without a master. 32°. pap., 15c. .... *De Witt.*
Swift, Zeph. Digest of laws of Conn.; rev. by H. Dutton and N. A. Cowdrey. 2 v. 8°. *net*, $10. *Peck.*
Swift and sure. Elwes, A. $1.50 .... *Nelson.*
Swinburne, Algernon C: Atalanta in Calydon. 16°. $2 .... * *Osgood.*
— Chastelard: tragedy. 16°. '69. $1 .... *Holt.*
— Erechtheus: tragedy. cr. 8°. '76. $2.80. *Scribner, W. & A.*
— Laus Veneris, and other poems. 12°. $1.50 .. *Carleton.*
— Queen mother and Rosamond. 16°. $2 ... * *Osgood.*
— Siena. 32°. pap., 25c. .... *Lippincott.*
— Song of Italy. sm. 4°. pap., 25c. .... * *Osgood.*
— (*ed.*) French love songs. 12°. $1.50 .... *Carleton.*
Swindlers of America: who they are and how they work. 12°. '74. pap., 25c. .... (?) *F. M. Reed.*
Swing, D: Sermons. 8°. '74. $1.50; pap., $1 .. *Keen.*
Swing, D: *continued.*
— Trial before presbytery of Chicago: official report. 2d ed. 8°. '74. $1.75 .... *Jansen.*
— Truths for to-day. 2 v. 12°. '74–'76. ea., $1.50. *Jansen.*
— *See also* Patton, W. W., *vs.* Swing, D.
Swingin' round the cirkle. Locke, D. R. $1.50 .. *Lee & S.*
Swinton, W: Bible word-book: glossary of terms which have changed meaning, or are no longer in general use; ed. by T. J. Conant. 16°. '76. $1; 40c. .... *Harper.*
— Campaigns of army of the Potomac, 1861–5. ill. 8°. '66. $4 .... *Univ. Pub.*
— Complete course in geog., physical, industrial and political. 4°. '75. $2 .... *Ivison.*
— Condensed school hist. of U. S. maps, por., etc. 12°. '71. $1.25 .... *Ivison.*
— Elementary course in geog. 8°. '75. $1.20 .. *Ivison.*
— Language lessons: introd. grammar and composition for intermediate and grammar grades. 12°. 50c. *Harper.*
— Language primer: beginners' lessons in grammar and composition. 12°. 40c. .... *Harper.*
— New war book: the twelve decisive battles of the [civil] war. map and ill. 8°. $3.50; hf. cf., $6. *Dick & F.*
— New York 7th Regt.: its origin and hist. in peace and war; with biog. sketches, etc. ill. and por. 8°. '76. $3; hf. cf., $6 .... *Dillingham.*
— Outlines of the world's hist. maps and ill. 12°. '74. $2 .... *Ivison.*
— Primary hist. of U. S. ill. 16°. '72. 80c. ... *Ivison.*
— Progressive grammar of the Eng. tongue; based on results of mod. philology. 12°. 75c. ... *Harper.*
— Rambles among words: their poetry, hist. and wisdom. 12°. '72. $1 .... *Ivison.*
— School composition: advanced language-lessons for grammar schools. 12°. 50c. .... *Harper.*
— Word analysis: graded class book of Eng. derivative words with exercises. 12°. '71. bds., 40c. *Ivison.*
— Word-book of spelling, oral and written. 16°. '72. bds., 25c. .... *Ivison.*
— Word primer: beginner's book in oral and written spelling. 16°. '73. bds., 20c. .... *Ivison.*
Swiss basket maker. *See* Good boy's lib.
Swiss boy; or, the double discovery. 18°. 17c.; 22c. *Am. Bapt.*
Swiss children. Chapman, M. S. 40c. ...... *Am. Tr.*
Swiss cottage. Bayly, T. H. 15c. .... *French.*
Swiss family Robinson. *See* Wyss, J. R. v., *and* Montolieu, J. I. P. de B.
Swiss pastor: life of F. A. A. Gonthier. 18°. 50c. *Am. S. S.*
Swiss pictures. Manning, S. $4 .... *Nelson.*
Swiss swains. Webster, B. 15c. .... *French.*
Switch off. Adams, W. T. $1.25 .... *Lee & S.*
Switzerland, historical and descriptive; rev. by T. O. Summers. ('55.) 2d ed. 18°. '75. 50c. .. *So. Meth.*
Sword and garment. Townsend, L. T. $1.50 .. *Lee & S.*
Sword and gown. *See* Lawrence, G: Alfr.
Sword and sheath ser. 3 v. 12°. $4.50 ...... *Nelson.*
Cont.: Allie Stuart, by A. Grey. — Charlie Laurel, by W. H. G. Kingston. — Land of the pigtail, by B. Clarke.
Swords and shields. Connell, E. $1 .... *J. A. Moore.*
Sworn at Highgate: farce. 16°. pap., 15c. .. *French.*
Sybil and her live snow-ball. ill. 12°. bds., 50c. *Appleton.*
— *See also* Bertie and Amy books.
Sybil Grey. Martyn, S. T. 90c. .... *Am. Tr.*
Sybil Grey: romance of the opera. 8°. pap., 50c. *Peterson.*
Sybil Huntington. Dorr, J. C. R. $1.75 .. *Lippincott.*
Sybil Lennard. Grey, E. C. 50c. .... *Peterson.*
Sybilla. Simpson, J. P. 15c. .... *French.*
Sybil's book. Barker, M. A. $1.50 ...... *Macmillan.*

Sybil's friend. Marryat, F. $1.25.......*Routledge.*
Sybil's sacrifice. *See* Short stories lib.
Sybil's second love. Kavanagh, J. $1.25..*Appleton.*
Sybil's way. C., A. W. $1.25............*Lothrop.*
Syckelmoore, W: Centennial city: illustrated handbook of Phila. ill. and map. 12°. '75. $1; pap., 50c..............*Claxton;* (?)*Syckelmoore.*
Sydney Stuart. *See* Bell, C. D.
Sydnie Adriance; or, trying the world. Douglas, A. M. $1.50..........................*Lee & S.*
Sydonie's dowry. Roberts, M. $1.25..*Scribner, W. & A.*
Syllabus for the people; by a monk of St. Augustine's. 12°. pap., 25c. ....*Cath. Pub.*
Sylphide. Brough, W. 15c................*French.*
Sylvan glen ser. 3 v. 16°. $5.........*H. A. Young.*
Cont.: Breaking the rules. — Out of the wilderness, by J. D. Chaplin. — Jamie Noble, by Z. A. Mudge.
Sylvan Holt's daughter. Parr, H. $1.50....*Harper.*
Sylvan stories. 5 v. 64°. $1.12 .... *W. Wood.*
Cont.: Harry, the shrimper. — Don't touch it. — Peter and his pony. — Playing Robinson Crusoe. — Broken arm.
Sylvan year. *See* Hamerton, P. G.
Sylvana: opera. 16°. pap., 15c.............*French.*
Sylvester Daggerwood: farce. 16°. pap., 15c. *French.*
Sylvester Sound. Cockton, H. 75c.......*Peterson.*
Sylvestres (The). Edwards, M. B. $1.25; 75c. *Lippincott.*
Sylvia and Janet. D., A. C. $1.75..*Scribner, W. & A.*
Sylvia, and other dramas; by a Sister of Charity. 12°. '74. $1.50; $2; mor., $3 ....*Haverty.*
Sylvia's burden. May, C. L. $1.25....*H. A. Young.*
Sylvia's choice. Craik, G. M. 50c.........*Harper.*
Sylvia's lovers. *See* Gaskell, E. C.
Sylvia's soldier. Baker, G. M. 15c. ....*Lee & S.*
Sylvis, Ja. C. Life, speeches, labors and essays of W. H. Sylvis. ('71.) 2d ed. 12°. '72. $2..*Claxton.*
Symbol of glory. Oliver, G. $1.50........*Masonic.*
Syme, Ja. Principles and practice of surgery; ed. by R. S. Newton. ('57.) New ed. ill. 8°. '65. shp., $6 ....*Wilstach.*
— *Same;* [also] Diseases of the rectum; ed. by D. Maclean. 8°. '65. $7....*Claxton; Lippincott.*
Symington, Maggie. Working to win. ill. 12°. '74. $1.75 ....*Dutton.*
— *Same.* ill. cr. 8°. $2 ....*Cassell.*
Symington, W: On the atonement and intercession of Christ. 12°. $1 ....*U. P. Bd. of Pub.*
— *Same.* 12°. $1.25 ....*Carter.*
Symonds, J: Addington. Miscellanies; sel. and ed. by his son, with memoir. 8°. '71. $3.75. *Macmillan.*
Symons, Jellinger Cookson. Village Sunday school; with brief sketches of three of its scholars. ('55.) 2d ed. 18°. '75. 40c................*So. Meth.*
— — *See also* Village lib.
Sympathy: comedietta. 16°. pap., 15c. ....*French.*
Sympathy of Christ with man. Winslow, O. $1.25. *Carter.*
Sympathy of religions. Higginson, T. W. 10c. *Free Rel.*
Synagogue (The). *See* Harvey, C.
Synod of Dort. *See* Dort.
Synonyms of the Eng., and proverbs and phrases from the Lat., Fr., Span. and Ital. languages; with tables, etc. 16°. $1.....................*Miller.*
Synopsis of phrenology and chart; for lecturers and phrenologists. ill. 12°. '37. pap., 10c... *Wells.*
Syntagma (The). Taylor, R. $1.........*Mendum.*
Sypher, Josiah R. American popular speaker. 12°. '70. hf. bd., $1.25 ....*Porter.*
— Art of teaching school: manual of suggestions. 12°. '71. $1.50...........*Keystone; J. M. Stoddart.*
Sypher, Josiah R., *continued.*
— School hist. of Pennsylvania; with statistical tables. ill. 12°. $1.50.......................*Lippincott.*
— Young Amer. speaker. 12°. '70. hf. bd., 75c. *Porter.*
— *and* Apgar, E. H. History of New Jersey. ill. 12°. $1.25 ....*Lippincott.*
Syracuse [N. Y.] Convention of Freemasons. Minutes. 12°. pap., 25c. ....*E. A. Cook.*
Syren of Paris. Suter, W. E. 15c..........*French.*
Syriac reading lessons; with elements of Syriac grammar. fp. 8°. (Bagster.) $1.50; hf. bd., $1.75. *Wiley.*
Syrian home-life. Jessup, H. H. $1.50.......*Dodd.*
Syrian leper. Rogers, E. P. 25c. ....*Am. Tr.*
System of nature. Holbach, P. T. d'. $2..*Mendum.*
Systematic beneficence; compr. The great reform, by A. Stevens; The great question, by L. Wright; Property consecrated, by B. St. James Fry. 16°. $1..............................*Meth. Bk. Conc.*
Szabad, Emeric. Modern war, its theory and practice. maps and diagrams. 12°. $1.50.......*Harper.*

T., D. O. Walter Macdonald; or, Aunt Kitty's legacy. ill. 16°. '73. $1.50..................*Lothrop.*
T., E. C. Helen's lesson. 18°. 75c.........*Pres. Bd.*
T., H. M. Unity and its restoration. 12°. 25c...*Dutton.*
T., M. A. The sodalist's friend: coll. of meditations and prayers. 18°. '60. $1; $1.50; $2; mor., $3 .... *Cunningham.*
Tabernacle (The). Junkin, G. 85c. ......*Pres. Bd.*
Tabernacle chorus. Taylor, A. 30c.; 20c...*Biglow.*
Tabernacle of God with men. De Witt, T. 25c. *N. Y. Ref. Ch. Bd.*
Tabernacle of Israel in the wilderness. Rhind, W. G. $6.25 .... *Wiley.*
Tabernacle to Jonah. *See* Davis, *Mrs.* C. E. K.
Tabitha Todd. Ray, R. 45c.............*J. A. Moore.*
Table talk. *See* Cowper, W:
Table talk. *See* Hazlitt, W:
Table talk. *See* Luther, Mt.
Table-talk (Book of). Russell, W. C. $1.75; $3.50. *Routledge.*
Tables for facilitating the calculating of earthwork in cutting and embankments of railways, canals, etc. 2d ed., rev. and enl. by J. Mac Neil. 8°. (Dublin.) '46. $12.50..........................*Spon.*
Tables of stone. Luckock, H. M. $1.25..*Macmillan.*
Tables showing weight per yard of woolen or other fabrics; also showing the yards and fraction of yards in a pound of cotton goods; with directions for qualitative analysis of mixed fabrics. fp. 12°. '75. $3 ....*Clayton.*
Tablets. Alcott, A. B. $1.50; $2.50.......*Roberts.*
Tabor, Eliza. [Novels.] 6 v. 8°. ea., pap., 50c. *Harper.*
Cont.: Blue ribbon. — Eglantine. — Hope Meredith. — Jeanie's quiet life. — Meta's faith. — St. Olave's.
— Nine years old. ill. fp. 8°. $1.50 ......*Macmillan.*
— When I was a little girl: stories for children. ill. fp. 8°. $1.50.......................*Macmillan.*
Tabor. McIntosh, R. M. $1.34........*Huntington.*
Tacitus, Caius Corn. Works: Oxford tr., rev.; with notes. 2 v. 12°. $3 ....*Harper.*
Cont.: 1. Annals. — 2. History; Germany; Agricola; Dialogues on orators.
— *Same;* lit. tr., with notes. 2 v. 12°. (Bohn.) ea., $1.75 ....*Little, B. & Co.*
Cont.: 1. Annals. — 2. History, Germania, Agricola, etc.; with index.
— *Same.* 2 v. 12°. (Bohn.) ea., $2. *Lippincott; Scribner, W. & A.*
— Agricola and Germania [Lat.]: revised text, with notes and maps by A. J. Church and W. J. Brodribb. 2d ed. fp. 8°. '69. $1.25; — Agricola and Germania, sep., ea., 75c.............*Macmillan.*

Tacitus, Caius Corn., *continued.*
— *Same;* with notes by Tyler. 12°. $1.25..*Appleton.*
— *Same;* and selections from the Annals; with notes, ed. by C. Anthon. 12°. shp., $1.50....*Harper.*
— *Same;* and Dialogues de oratoribus; with notes by G. Stuart. 16°. '76. $1.25..........*Eldredge.*
— *Eng.* Agricola and Germania. 12°. $1..*Macmillan.*
— Annals; tr. with notes and maps by A. J. Church and W. J. Brodribb. cr. 8°. '76. $2.50..*Macmillan.*
— Histories [Lat.]; with notes by Tyler. 12°. $1.75. *Appleton.*
— *Eng.;* tr. by A. J. Church and W. J. Brodribb, with notes. map. cr. 8°. $2.50........*Macmillan.*
— Selections [Lat.]; with notes and introd. by J. T. Champlin. 16°. $1.50..................*Allyn.*
— [Outlined and expl.] by W. B. Donne. (Anc. classics for Eng. readers.) 16°. $1. *Lippincott; Little, B. & Co.*

Tafel, I. F: Im. Life of Jesus from the Gospel record, vindicated and defended against attacks of Dr. Strauss and infidelity in general. 16°. '68. $1.50. *Lockwood, B. & Co.*

Tafel, J: F: Leonh. *and* L: H. Neues vollst. englisch-deutsches u. deutsch-engl. Taschenwörterbuch, mit Aussprache, etc. 18°. $1.50........*Kohler.*
— *and* Rud. Lh. *and* L: H. Interlinear transl. of the Scriptures, with grammatical and critical notes. 8 pts. 8°. pap......................*Boericke.*
Cont.: Greek text, pts. 1-4, *ea.*, $2.—Hebrew text, pts. 1-4, *ea.*, $3.

Tafel, Rud. Lh. Emanuel Swedenborg as a philosopher and man of science. cr. 8°. $2..*Lippincott.*
— Investigations into laws of Eng. orthography and pronunciation. pt. 1. 8°. '62. $1..*Westermann.*

Taft, C: P. *See* Cincinnati, Superior Court reports.

Taft, Jona. Practical treatise on operative dentistry. ill. 8°. $4.50........................*Lindsay.*

Taft, Lyman B. Curiosities of heat. 16°. $1.25.*Am. Bapt.*

Taft, P: R. *See* Cincinnati, Superior Court reports.

Tagebuch eines armen Fräuleins. Nathusius, M. 75c. *Holt.*

Tahiti receiving the Gospel. 18°. 70c.......*Am. S. S.*

Tahiti with the Gospel. 18°. 70c. ....*Am. S. S.*

Tahiti without the Gospel. 18°. 70c.........*Am. S. S.*

Taigi, Ma. Ann. Life, prophecies and revelations of Mary Ann Taigi. 18°. 75c. ....*Cummiskey.*

Tail of a mouse. ill. 4°. $1 ....*Miller.*

Tailor and fiddler. 18°. 50c................*O'Shea.*

Taine, Hip. Adph. Ancient régime; tr. by J. Durand. 12°. '76. $2.50..........................*Holt.*
— History of English literature; tr. by H. Van Laun. New ed. 4 v. sm. 8°. (Lond.) '73-'74. $10. *Little, B. & Co.*
— *Same.* ('71.) New ed. 3 v. 12°. '76. $7.50; hf. cf., $15...................................*Holt.*
— *Same;* abridg., and ed. with chronol. table, notes and index by J. Fiske. ('72.) New ed. 12°. '76. $2.50 ....*Holt.*
— Italy: Florence and Venice; tr. by J. Durand. ('69.) New ed. 12°. '75. $2.50.........*Holt.*
— Italy: Rome and Naples; tr. by J. Durand. ('67.) New ed. large 12°. '75. $2.50............*Holt.*
— Lectures on art; tr. by J. Durand. 1st ser.: Philosophy of art; [also] Ideal in art. ('68-'73.) New ed.; in 1 v. 12°. '76. $2.50...............*Holt.*
— *Same.* 2d ser.: Philosophy of art in Italy; in the Netherlands; in Greece. ('70-'75.) New ed.; in 1 v. 12°. '76. $2.50.......................*Holt.*
— Notes on England; tr. with introd. by W. F. Rae. ('72.) New ed. por. 12°. '75. $2.50.....*Holt.*
— Notes on Paris: life and opinions of M. Frederic Thomas Graindorge [*pseud.*]; tr. with notes by J. A. Stevens. ('75.) New ed. 12°. '76. $2.50. *Holt.*
— On intelligence; tr. by T. D. Haye, and rev. with add. by the author. ('72.) New ed. 2 v. 12°. '75. $5..................................*Holt.*

Taine, Hip. Adph., *continued.*
— Tour through the Pyrenees; tr. by J. S. Fiske. 12°. '74. $2.50 ....*Holt.*
— *Same;* ill. by G. Doré. sq. 8°. '73. $10; mor., $20. *Holt.*

Taintor's route and city guides. 12 v. maps. 16°. ea., 25c...............................*Taintor.*
Cont.: Hudson River. — Erie route. — Hudson River and N. Y. Central Railway. — Shore Line route. — Newport route. — Connecticut River route. — Northern route. — Pennsylvania coal regions. — New York to Phila., Baltimore and Washington. — Delaware and Hudson route. — Long Island. — City of New York.

Tait, Gilb. Hymns of Denmark, rendered into English. 16°. $1.75..........................*Routledge.*

Tait, P: Guthrie. Lectures on some recent advances in physical science. cr. 8°. '76. $2.50..*Macmillan.*
— Theoretical mechanics. (Adv. sci. ser.) 12°. $1.50. *Putnam.*
— *See also* Kelland, P., *and* Tait, P. G.; — Rendu, Le C., Theory of glaciers of Savoy; — Shairp, J. C., Tait, P. G., *and* Adams-Reilly, A.
— *and* Steele, W. J. Treatise on dynamics of a particle. cr. 8°. $3.50.................*Macmillan.*
— *and* Stewart, Balfour. Unseen universe; or, physical speculations on immortality of the soul. 3d ed. cr. 8°. '76. $1 ....*Macmillan.*

Taittiriya-prâtiçâkhya (The) with its commentary the Tribhâshyaratna: text. [with] tr. and notes by W. D. Whitney. 8°. '72. bds., $5..*Am. Orient.*

Take, but earn. 16°. $1.25.............(?)*Martien.*

Take care of Dowb—'. Morton, J. M. 15c...*French.*

Take care of little Charley. Brough, J. 15c...*French.*

Take care of No. 1. *See* Goodrich, S: G.

Take heed. Barrow, F. 75c................*Dutton.*

Take a peep. Cobden, P. $1.25............*Lee & S.*

Take that girl away. Buckingham, L. 15c...*French.*

Taken at the flood. Braddon, M. E. 75c....*Harper.*

Taking the Bastile. *See* Dumas, A.

Taking by storm. Churchill, F. 15c. ....*French.*

Taking a stand. Knight, H. C. 45c...........*Hoyt.*

Taking up the cross. Waterbury, J. B. 40c..*Cong. Pub.*

Talbert, B. J. Gothic forms applied to furniture, metal work, and decoration for domestic purposes. 31 pl. f°. '73. $15.......................*Osgood.*

Talbot, F: Through fire and water: tale of city life. ill. 8°. pap., 25c.......................*Harper.*

Talbot, Guendaline. [*Princess Borghese.*] Life; tr. with introd. by A. F. Hewit. 18°. 45c...*O'Shea.*

Talbot, Gu. H. Philosophy of French pronunciation. 12°. '49. 90c..........................*Ivison.*

Talbot, R. The serf: tragedy. 16°. pap., 15c. *Ames; French.*

Talbot Harland. Ainsworth, W. H. 30c...*Am. News.*

Talboys, W: P. West India pickles: journal of a winter yacht cruise. ill. 16°. $1.50...*Carleton.*

Talbury girls. Denison, M. A. $1.50......*Lothrop.*

Talbury girls lib. 4 v. 16°. $6............*Lothrop.*
Cont.: Talbury girls. — Bloomfield. — Myra Sherwood's cross. — Story of four lives.

Talcott, E. N. K. Manufacture of pig iron. 8°. pap., 60c. ....*Am. Soc. of C. E.*

Talcott, *Mrs.* H. B. [*formerly Mrs.* Goodwin]. Dr. Howell's family. 12°. $1.50...........*Lee & S.*
— Madge; or, night and morning. 12°. $1.25..*Appleton.*
— Sherbrooke. 12°. $1.50...................*Appleton.*

Tale of adventure founded on facts. Sergeant, A. $1.75 ....*Lippincott.*

Tale of the epicurean. *See* Moore, T:

Tale of eternity. *See* Massey, G:

Tale of misery: drama. 16°. pap., 15c.......*French.*

Tale of a nest; by author of "Little animals." ill. 16°. '70. $1.25..............................*Dutton.*

Tale of a physician. Davis, A. J. $1 ....*A. J. Davis.*

Tale of the revolution. *See* Goodrich, S: G.
Tale of the Simplon. Hale, E. E. 25c. *Lockwood, B. & Co.*
Tale of two cities. *See* Dickens, C:
Tale of two cities. Taylor, T. 15c. .... *French.*
Tale of a tub (New). ill. 4°. $1; 50c. .... *Routledge.*
Tale of the universe. *See* Good child's lib.
Tales about the heathen. Scudder, J. 45c. .. *Am. Tr.*
Tales and illustrations. *See* Tonna, *Mrs.* C. E.
Tales and legends from hist. 16°. $1; $1.50 .. *Sadlier.*
Tales and pictures of school life. ill. 24°. '69. 30c. *Lothrop.*
Tales and sketches. Charles, E. $1 .... *Carter.*
Tales and sketches. Miller, H. $1.50 ...... *Carter.*
Tales and takings. Watson, J. V. $1.75. *Cin. Meth. Bk. Conc.*
Tales at tea-time. Knatchbull-Hugessen, E. H. $1.75. *Macmillan.*
Tales for boys and girls. ill. 12°. $1.25. *Scribner, W. & A.*
Tales for little convalescents. Bradford, S. H. 50c. *Hurd & H.*
Tales for the little ones. ill. roy. 16°. 50c. ... *Cassell.*
Tales for the people. *See* More, Ha.
Tales for rich and poor. *See* Arthur, T. S.
Tales for travellers; by E. E. Hale and others. 7 v. 8°. '70–'75. ea., pap., 25c. ... *Lockwood, B. & Co.*
Cont.: In his name. — Ten times one is ten. — Stand and wait, etc. — Tale of the Simplon, etc. — Nicolette and Aucassin, etc. — Lost palace, etc. — Spoons in a wherry, etc.

Tales for village schools. 32°. 40c. .. *Scribner, W. & A.*
Tales for the Whitsun season. 18°. 50c. ..... *Dutton.*
Tales for the young. *See* Andersen, H. C.
Tales from Alsace. 16°. $1.50 .... *Carter.*
Tales from Am. hist. Robbins, E. 3 v. $2.25 .. *Harper.*
Tales from "Blackwood." 12 v. 16°. $9; hf. cf., $15; — in 6 v., $9; hf. roxb., $12; hf. mor., $13.50 .... *Scribner, W. & A.*
— *Same.* 12 v. in 6. 16°. hf. cf., $15 .... *Appleton.*
Tales from the diary of a missionary priest. 18°. 75c.; $1.25 .... *Sadlier.*
Tales from the diary of a Sister of Mercy. Brame, C. M. $1.50 .... *Cath. Pub.*
Tales from Eng. hist. Strickland, A. $1.25 .. *Porter.*
Tales from Eng. hist. *See* Tales of many lands.
Tales from the German; tr. by I. Oxenford and C. A. Feiling. 8°. pap., 50c. .... *Harper.*
Tales from natural history. Howitt, M. 60c. *Harper.*
Tales from the operas: stories based upon opera plots. 12°. $1.50 .... *Carleton.*
Tales from the parsonage. 18°. 45c.; 55c. .. *Am. Bapt.*
Tales from Shakespeare. Lamb, C. *and* M. $1.25. *Hurd & H.*
Tales in political economy. Fawcett, M. G. $1. *Macmillan.*
Tales in prose. Howitt, M. 60c. .... *Harper.*
Tales in rhyme for girls. Mogridge, G. 50c. *Pres. Bd.*
Tales in short words; for Sunday schools. 18°. 45c. *Routledge.*
Tales in verse. Howitt, M. 60c. .... *Harper.*
Tales of Algeria. Dumas, A. $1.75 .... *Claxton.*
Tales of all countries. *See* Trollope, Ant.
Tales of Am. adventures. *See* Reid, M.
Tales of the Am. revolution. Thatcher, B. B. 75c. *Harper.*
Tales of ancient Greece. Cox, G. W. $2.75. *Little, B. & Co.*
Tales of the angels. Faber, F. W. 60c.; 80c. *Murphy.*
Tales of animals. Goodrich, S. G. $1.25 ... *Morton.*
Tales of the Argonauts. Harte, B. $1.50 ... *Osgood.*
Tales of the borders and of Scotland. *See* Wilson, J. M.

Tales of Charlton School. Adams, H. C. $1.25. *Routledge.*
Tales of Christian life. *See* Charles, *Mrs.* Eliz.
Tales of the civil war. Adams, H. C. $1.25 .. *Routledge.*
Tales of the Covenanters. Pollok, R. 75c. ... *Carter.*
Tales of the family; or, home life. ill. 16°. $1.50. *Pres. Bd.*
Tales of fashionable life. Edgeworth, M. 4 v. $3. *Routledge.*
Tales of the five senses. *See* Griffin, Ger.
Tales of foreign adventures. *See* Reid, M.
Tales of the genii. *See* Ridley, J.
Tales of Glauber Spa; by C. M. Sedgwick, W. C. Bryant, W. Leggett, R. C. Sands, J. K. Paulding. 12°. $1.50 .... *Harper.*
Tales of the good woman. Paulding, J. K. $2.50. *Scribner.*
Tales of a grandfather. *See* Scott, *Sir* Wa.
Tales of the great and brave. ill. sq. 16°. 50c. *Perkinpine.*
Tales of heroes; from Eng. hist. ill. 12°. $1.50 .. *Nelson.*
Tales of instruction and warning. 32°. 20c.; 15c. *Dutton.*
Tales of the jury room. *See* Griffin, Ger.
Tales of the kings and queens of England. Percy, S. $1.25 .... *Routledge.*
Tales of many lands. 5 v. 16°. $5 .... *Carter.*
Cont.: Tales of Sweden. — Tales from English history. — Tales of travelers. — Light and shadows. — Wood cutter and exiles.

Tales of martyr times; by author of "Days of Knox." ill. 12°. $1.50 .... *Nelson.*
Tales of a monkey. Billings, H. 50c. .... *Locke.*
Tales of the Munster festivals. *See* Griffin, Ger.
Tales of naval adventure. Low, C. R. $1 .. *Routledge.*
Tales of Nethercourt. Adams, H. C. $1.25 .. *Routledge.*
Tales of the ocean. Sleeper, J. S. $1.50 ..... *Locke.*
Tales of old Japan. Mitford, A. B. $2.50 .. *Macmillan.*
Tales of old ocean. *See* Low, C. R.
Tales of old travel, re-narrated. Kingsley, H. $1.75. *Macmillan.*
Tales of the persecuted. 16°. $1.50 .... *Pres. Bd.*
Tales of the sea. Goodrich, S. G. 50c. ..... *Desilver.*
Tales of the sea and land. *See* Goodrich, S. G.
Tales of the southern border. Webber, C. W. $2. *Lippincott.*
Tales of Sweden and the Norsemen. 16°. $1 .. *Carter.*
Tales of travelers. *See* Tales of many lands.
Tales of a traveller. *See* Irving, Wash.
Tales of truth and trust. Fullerton, *Lady* G. $1 .. *O'Shea.*
Tales of truth for the young. 18°. 40c.; 50c. *Am. Bapt.*
Tales of warrior judges. Macduff, J. R. $1 .. *Carter.*
Tales of woman's trials. Hall, A. M. 75c. ... *Harper.*
Tales out of school. Stockton, F. R. $2.50 .. *Scribner.*
Tales upon texts. Adams, H. C. $1.75 ... *Routledge.*
Talfourd, Fs. [Plays.] 11 v. 16°. ea., pap., 15c. *French.*
Cont.: Abou Hassan: farce. — Alcestis, the original strong-minded woman: travestie. — Atalanta: extravaganza. — Ganem, the slave of love: extravaganza. — Household fairy: farce. — King Thrushbeard: extravaganza. — Macbeth: travestie. — Pluto and Proserpine: extravaganza. — Rule of three: comedietta. — Shylock; or, the merchant of Venice preserved: farce. — Tell; or, strike of the cantons: extravaganza.
— Household fairy: farce. 16°. pap., 15c. ... *De Witt.*
— *and* Byron, H. J. Miller and his men: burlesque. 16°. pap., 15c. .... *French.*
— *and* Wigan, A. Tit for tat: comedietta. 16°. pap., 15c. .... *French.*
Talfourd, *Sir* T: Noon. Ion: tragedy. 16°. pap., 15c. .... *French.*
— Tragedies and poems. 12°. $1.25 .... *Nichols & H.*
— *See also* Modern British essayists; — Lamb, C.; — Smith, Sydney, Talfourd, *Sir* T. N., *and* Stephen, *Sir* J.

Talis qualis. *See* Griffin, Ger.
Talisman. Balfe, M. W. 40c. . . . . *Pond.*
Talisman. Sadlier, M. A. 25c. . . . . *Sadlier.*
Talisman. *See* Scott, *Sir* Wa.
Talisman: drama. 16°. pap., 40c. . . . . *French.*
Talk to little children. Baker, D. 30c. . . . . *Pres. Bd.*
Talk with my pupils. Sedgwick, C. $1.25 . . . . *Miller.*
Talkative wig. Follen, E. L. 50c. . . . . *Lee & S.*
Talking Bible. 18°. 18c. . . . . *Am. S. S.*
Talking fire-irons. 18°. 30c. . . . . *Am. S. S.*
Talks about Adam and his family. 18°. 40c. . . *Am. S. S.*
Talks about animals. *See* Brother's lib.
Talks about Jesus. 18°. 35c. . . . . *Pres. Bd.*
Talks about Jesus. Babb, C. E. 40c. . . . . . . *West. Tr.*
Talks about old times. *See* Tarbox, I. N.
Talks about trees. Kirby, M. *and* E. $2.50 . . *Cassell.*
Talks about the war. Babb, C. E. 40c. . . . . *West. Tr.*
Talks on art. Hunt, W. M. $1.50 . . . . *Hurd & H.*
Talks on women's topics. Croly, J. C. $1.75 . . *Lee & S.*
Talks, pleasant and profitable. Summers, T. O. 50c. *So. Meth.*
Talks to Bereans. Errett, I. $1 . . . . *Chase.*
Talks to my patients. Gleason, R. B. $1.50 . . *Wood & H.*
Talks with Amy Dudley. *See* Bertie and Amy books.
Talks with a child on the Beatitudes; by author of "Talks with a philosopher." 16°. 50c.; 75c. *Lippincott.*
Talks with the children. Johnson, J. 2 pts. *net*, 1, 25c.; 2, 35c. . . . . *Friends Bk. Assoc.*
Talks with girls. Larned, A. $1.50 . . . *Meth. Bk. Conc.*
Talks with little Emily. O'Brien, H. 35c. . . *Pres. Bd.*
Talks with a philosopher on the ways of God to man; by author of "Talks with a child on the Beatitudes." 16°. 50c.; 75c. . . . . *Lippincott.*
Tall man of Winton and his wife; by "Over Forty." 75c. . . . . (?) *Cumberland.*
Tall student; tr. by C. T. Brooks. ill. sq. 16°. '72. 75c. . . . . *Roberts.*
Tallack, W: George Fox, the Friends, and the early Baptists. por. 12°. $1.25 . . . . *Lippincott.*
Tallaferro, J. H. Which is our Saviour, Christ or the church? 18°. pap., 10c. . . . . *So. Bapt.*
Talleyrand-Périgord, C: M. de. Letter to Pius VII.; tr. by H. D. Robinson; with memoir of author. 12°. pap., 25c. . . . . *Mendum.*
Talmage, J. V. N. History and ecclesiastical relations of the churches of the presbyterial order at Amoy, China. 8°. pap., 25c. . . *N. Y. Ref. Ch. Bd.*
Talmage, T: De Witt. Abominations of modern society. ('72.) New ed. 12°. '76. $1.50. *Adams, V. & Co.*
— Around the tea-table. ill. cr. 8°. '74. *$3; $3.50; mor., $5 . . . . *Cowperthwait.*
— Crumbs swept up. ill. 12°. $2; $3; mor., $4.50. *Souder.*
— Daily thoughts; ed. by J. V. D. Shurts. 12°. '75. $2 . . . . *Dodd.*
— One thousand gems: striking passages, incidents and illustrations. ('73.) 4th ed. por. 12°. '76. $1.50. *Tibbals.*
— Preaching to the masses. 12°. '75. 20c. *Meth. Bk. Conc.*
— Sermons. 4 v. 12°. ea., $2 . . . . *Harper.*

Cont.: 1st ser. — 2d ser. — 3d ser.: Old wells dug out. — 4th ser.: Every day religion.

— Sports that kill. 12°. $1.25; pap., $1 . . . . . *Harper.*
Talmon, Thrace (*pseud.*) *See* Putnam, *Mrs.* E. T. H.
Talvi (*pseud.*) *See* Robinson, *Mrs.* T. A. L. v. J.
Tam, the oyster boy. *See* Cousin Anna's lib.
Tam O'Shanter. *See* Burns, Rob.
Tame fox. 18°. 25c.; 30c. . . . . *Am. Bapt.*
Tame turtle. Guernsey, L. E. 85c. . . . . *Am. S. S.*
Taming the shrew. *See* Shakespeare, W:
Taming a tiger: farce. 16°. pap., 15c. *De Witt; French.*
Taming a truant. Dibdin, H. 15c. . . . . *French.*
Tancred. Disraeli, B. 50c. . . . . *Appleton.*
Tancred. *See* Goethe, J. W. v.
Tandon, Moquin. World of the sea; tr. by Rev. H. M. Hart. ill. demy 8°. $5 . . . . *Cassell.*
Tandy, W. Chinese mother: drama. 12°. '70. 50c. *Kelly, P. & Co.*
— Foundling of Sebastopol: drama. 18°. 40c. . . *Sadlier.*
Taney, Rog. Brooke. *See* United States, Circuit Court decisions.
Taneywell, R. H. Leatherwood god. *See* Espy, J., Memorandums of tour in Ohio.
Tangled skein. *See* Fonblanque, A., *jr.*
Tanglewood tales. *See* Hawthorne, Natl.
Tannenreiser (Die). 16°. pap., 18c. . . . . *Germ. Bapt.*
Tanner, Gordon. *See* Indiana, Supreme Court reports.
Tanner, J: Practical midwifery and obstetrics, incl. anæsthetics. ill. 16°. $2 . . . . *Lippincott.*
Tanner, T: Hawkes. Manual of clinical medicine and physical diagnosis. 3d Am. ed., rev. and enl. by T. Fox. sm. 12°. $1.50 . . . . *Lea.*
— Memoranda of poisons. 32°. '75. 75c. . . . *Lindsay.*
— On the signs and diseases of pregnancy. col. pl. and ill. 8°. $4.25 . . . . *Lea.*
— Practical treatise on diseases of infancy and childhood. 3d Am. ed., rev. and enl. by A. Meadows. 8°. '71. $3.50 . . . . *Lindsay.*
— Practice of medicine. 6th Am. ed.; with section on diseases of women and formulæ for medicines, baths, etc. roy. 8°. '74. $6; leath., $7 . . *Lindsay.*
Tanner boy. Denison, C. W. $1.25 . . . . *Roberts.*
Tanners and curriers' reference book. *See* Shoe and leather trade reference book.
Tannhäuser. *See* Hürte, N.
Tannhaüser. *See* Wagner, R:
Tantchen Rosmarin. *See* Zschokke, H.
Tappan, B: *See* Ohio, Reports.
Tappan, Eli T. Ray's geometry and trigonometry. 8°. '69. $2 . . . . *Wilson, H. & Co.*
— Ray's plane and solid geometry. 12°. '64. $1. *Wilson, H. & Co.*
Tappan, H: P. Logic. 12°. $1.50 . . . . *Appleton.*
Tappan, *Miss* L. W. Charity chapters. 18°. 60c. *Cong. Pub.*
— Pauline Warden. 16°. $1.15 . . . . *Cong. Pub.*
Tappan, Lew Sketch of Arthur Tappan. por. 12°. $2. *Hurd & H.*
Tappan, W: Bingham. Memoir of Capt. James Wilson. 18°. 45c. . . . . *Am. S. S.*
Tapping, T: Law and practice of writ of mandamus. *See* Law lib.
Tappy's chicks. Cupples, A. J. $2 . . . . . *Routledge.*
Tar and feather outrage. *See* Dodd, P.
Tar man. Powers, A. H. 25c. . . . . *West, J. & Co.*
Tarantula (La): extravaganza. 16°. pap., 15c. *French.*
Tara's harp. Getze, J. A. 50c. . . . . *Ditson.*
Tarbell, J: A. Homœopathy simplified; or, domestic practice made easy. ('63.) New ed., rev. 12°. '74. $1.25 . . . . *O. Clapp.*
— Pocket homœopathist and family guide. ('49.) New ed. 32°. '74. 30c. . . . . *O. Clapp.*
Tarbotton, M. O. Sanitary legislation and science, with special regard to sewage and water supply. 8°. pap., 40c. . . . . *Spon.*
Tarbox, Increase N. Buried cities. 18°. '62. 75c. *Cong. Pub.*
— Journeys and labors of St Paul. 16°. 15c. *Cong. Pub.*
— Life of Israel Putnam. ill. sm. 8°. '76. $2.50. *Lockwood, B. & Co.*

Tarbox, Increase N., *continued.*
— Missionary patriots: memoirs of Ja. H. Schneider and E: M. Schneider. 16°. '67. $1.25..*Cong.Pub.*
— Tyre and Alexandria, the chief commercial cities of Scripture times. 16°. '65. $1.25 ..*Cong.Pub.*
— Uncle George's stories. 4 v. 18°. '68. $2.25..*Cong.Pub.*
Cont.: Rambles in old pathways, 2 pts., *ea.*, 60c.—Uncle George's stories.—Old meeting-house, 60c.
— When I was a boy. 18°. 50c..........*Cong.Pub.*
— Winnie and Walter ser. 4 v. 18°. '59–'69. $2.50. *Tilton.*
Cont.: Christmas stories.—Story telling at Thanksgiving.—Talks about old times.—Our darling Nellie.

Tardieu, Jul. de. ["J. T. de Saint-Germain."] Pour une épingle. With vocab. ('66.) New ed. 12°. '75. $1 ....*Holt.*

Tardy, Alex. Life. 8°. pap., 50c..........*Peterson.*

Tardy, *Mrs.* Ma. T. ["Ida Raymond."] Living female writers of the south. 4°. '71. $3.75; $4.50; mor., $8..........*Claxton.*
— Southland writers: biog. and crit. sketches of living female writers of the south, with extracts from their writings. 2 v. 8°. '69. $6.....*Claxton.*

Tarn, E. W. Science of building: element. treatise on principles of construction. 47 wood-eng. demy 8°. $4..........*Lippincott.*

Tartufe (Le). *See* Molière, J. B. P.

Tarver, H: Second French reader. sm. 8°. 75c. *Lippincott.*

Taschenliederbuch: "Wo man singt da lass dich ruhig nieder." 32°. pap., 25c..........*Radde.*

Task (The). *See* Cowper, W:

Tasso, Torquato. Gerusalemme liberata. 12°. $1.50. *G.R.Lockwood.*
— *Same:* cantos 1, 2; with introd. and notes by H. B. Cotterill. 12°. '75. $1.25 ....*Macmillan.*
— *Eng.* Jerusalem delivered; tr. into Spenserian verse, with memoir, by J. H. Wiffen. ill. 12°. (Bohn.) $1.75..........*Little,B.& Co.*
— — *Same.* ill. 12°. (Bohn.) $2. *Lippincott; Scribner, W.& A.*
— — *Same.* (Globe ed.) ill. 16°. $1.25; hf. cf., $3.25; mor., $4.—(chp. ed.), pap., 60c......*Appleton.*
— *Same;* ed. by R. A. Willmott, with biog. and crit. notice. (British poets.) ill. 12°. $2.25; hf. cf., $3.50; mor., $5 ....*Routledge.*

Tasswill, E: B. American cambist: principles and practice of foreign exchanges; [with] tables of European arbitrations. 4°. '65. hf. bd., $5. *Clayton.*

Tate, Ja. S. Surcharged and different forms of retaining walls. 18°. '73. bds., 50c..*Van Nostrand.*
— *Same.* ill. 8°. '73. $1..........*Spon.*

Tate, Jos. Digest of laws of Virginia, and index of cases in reports. 8°. '41. shp., $3..*J. W.Randolph.*
— Index to Virginia reports; from Washington to 2d Grattan. 2 v. 8°. '47. shp., $18..*J. W.Randolph.*

Tate, T: Elementary course of nat. and experiment. philos. for high schools, etc. Am. ed., rev. by C. S. Cartée. ill. 12°. hf. roan, $1.50... *Ware.*
— First lessons in philosophy; or, science of familiar things. Am. ed., rev. by C. S. Cartée. 12°. hf. roan, 75c.......... *Ware.*

Tatem, M. H. (*pseud.*) *See* Hazlett, Helen.

Tatian *and* Theophilus. Writings; [also] Clementine recognitions; tr. by B. P. Pratten, M. Dods and T. Smith. (Ante-Nicene Christ. lib.) 8°. $3. *Scribner, W.& A.*

Tatius, Achilles. *See* Heliodorus Emesenus, Longus, *and* Tatius, A.

Tatler. *See* Addison, Jos.;—Chalmers, A., British essayists.
— *Same;* [also] Guardian. 12°. $1.25....*Lippincott.*
— — *Same;* with account of authors by T. B. Macaulay. roy. 8°. shp., $3.50..........*Pounsford.*

Tattered Tom. Alger, H., *jr.* $1.25 ....*Loring.*

Tattered Tom ser. *See* Alger, H., *jr.*

Tattler (The); or, history of Patty Steele. 16°. $1.25. *Am.S.S.*

Täubchen (Das). *See* Schmid, C. v.

Taufe u. Taufkapellen. Cote, N. 55c...*Germ.Bapt.*

Tau-go-ru-a. Moorhead, —. $1 ....*Peterson.*

Taunton, M. Last of the Catholic O'Malleys: tale. 12°. '71. $1.25; $1.75..........*Kelly,P.& Co.*

Taunton, W: Pyle. *See* England, Common law reports.

Tausendjährige Reich (Das) im Lichte d. Offenbarung. Seyffarth, G. 15c..........*Ludwig.*

Tautphœus, Jemima Montgomery (*Baronin*) v. At odds; tr. from the Germ. 12°. $1.75..*Lippincott.*
— Cyrilla; or, the mysterious engagement; tr. 8°. $1.75; pap., 75c..........*Peterson.*
— Initials (The); tr. 12°. $1.75; pap., $1.50..*Peterson.*
— Quits; tr. 12°. $1.75..........*Lippincott.*

Tavern anecdotes and sayings. Hindley, C. $2. *Routledge.*

Taverner, *Mrs.* F. Graham. Reasonable elocution; for schools, clergymen, lawyers, etc. 12°. '74. $1.25. *Barnes.*

Taxidermist's guide. ill. 12°. pap., 30c......*Hurst.*

Taxidermist's manual. 12°. $1; pap., 50c...*Haney.*

Tayler, C: B. Angel's song: Christmas token. 12°. '60. $1..........*Leighton.*
— Bar of iron, and the conclusion of the matter. 18°. 50c. ....*Pres.Bd.*
— *Same.* ('50.) New ed. 18°. '65. 40c.....*Am.S.S.*
— Earnestness: sequel to "Thankfulness." 12°. $1. *Leighton.*
— Lady Mary; or, not of the world. 12°. $1..*Leighton.*
— Margaret; or, the pearl. 12°. '60. $1...*Leighton.*
— Mark Wilton, the merchant's clerk. 12°. $1. *Leighton.*
— Memorials of Eng. martyrs. ill. 12°. $1..*Harper.*
— Records of a good man's life. 12°. $1....*Leighton.*
— Scenes in a clergyman's life. 12°. $1....*Leighton.*
— Thankfulness; with passages from diary of Allan Temple. 12°. $1..........*Leighton.*
— Truth; or, Persis Clareton. 12°. $1.....*Leighton.*
— Will-forgers; or, the Church of Rome. ('58.) 2d ed. 18°. '75. 40c..........*So.Meth.*
— *Same.* 18°. '73. 40c...*N. Y.Ref.Ch.Bd.; Pres.Com.*

Tayler, T: Law glossary: sel. of foreign sentences, phrases and maxims found in Eng. and Am. reports, with notes; tr. into Eng. 4th ed., rev. and enl. 8°. shp., $4.50 ....*Baker, V.& Co.*
— Precedents of wills; with notes on construction of various clauses in a complicated will. 2 v. in 1. 8°. shp., $5 ....*Baker, V.& Co.*

Tayleure, C. W. Boy martyrs: drama. 16°. pap., 15c..........*French.*
— Horseshoe Robinson: drama. 16°. pap., 15c. *French.*

Taylor, *Miss* —. Dame Dolores. 18°. '76. 50c. *Kelly,P.& Co.*
— Wise nun of Eastonmere, and other tales. 16°. '76. $1.25 ....*Kelly,P.& Co.*

Taylor, Alfr. Peeps at our Sunday schools. 12°. '74. $1.25 ....*Meth.Bk.Conc.*
— Sunday school photographs. ('64.) New ed. ill. 16°. '67. $1.15..........*Hoyt.*
— Tabernacle chorus. [Singing book.] 32°. '74. 30c.; bds., 20c. ....*Biglow.*
— *See also* Perkins, T. E., *and* Taylor, A.;—Perkins, T. E., Taylor, A., *and* Sanders, C. W.

Taylor, Alfr. Swaine. Medical jurisprudence. 7th Am. ed.; ed. by J. J. Reese. 8°. $5; leath., $6..*Lea.*
— Poisons in relation to medical jurisprudence and medicine. 3d Am. ed., rev. 8°. $5.50; leath., $6.50 ....*Lea.*
— Principles and practice of medical jurisprudence. 2d ed., rev. 2 v. ill. 8°. $10; leath., $12...*Lea.*

Taylor, Ann. My mother. ill. sm. 4°. $1.75..*Nelson.*

Taylor, Archibald A. E. A good soldier. 32°. pap., 10c. .... *Pres. Bd.*

Taylor, B. T: The infidel's confession; or, the power of Christian union. 12°. $1.50 .... *So. Bapt.*

Taylor, Bayard. Works. (Household ed.) 16 v. 12°. $24; hf. cf., $60 .... *Putnam.*
— Beauty and the beast; [also] Tales of home. 12°. '70. $2. — (Household ed.) 12°. $1.50 .. *Putnam.*
— By-ways of Europe. 12°. '69. $2. — (Household ed.) 12°. $1.50 .... *Putnam.*
— Central Africa: life and landscape from Cairo to the White Nile. ('54.) New ed. ill. 12°. '69. $2. — (Household ed.) 12°. $1.50 ...... *Putnam.*
— Central Asia. map and ill. 12°. '74. $1.50. *Scribner.*
— Cyclopedia of modern travel: record of adventure, exploration and discovery for the past fifty years. ('56.) New ed. 2 v. in 1. ill. and maps. roy. 8°. '69. $3.50; shp., $4; hf. cf., $5.50 ... *Wilstach.*
— Egypt and Iceland in 1874. 16°. '75. $1.50. — (Household ed.) 12°. $1.50 .... *Putnam.*
— Eldorado; or, adventures in the path of empire (Mexico and California). ('50.) New ed. 12°. '69. $2. — (Household ed.) 12°. $1.50 .. *Putnam.*
— Greece and Russia; with an excursion to Crete. ill. 12°. '69. $2. — (Household ed.) 12°. $1.50. *Putnam.*
— Hannah Thurston: story of Am. life. 12°. '63. $2. — (Household ed.) 12°. $1.50 ...... *Putnam.*
— Home and abroad: sketch-book of life, scenery and men. 2 ser. ill. 12°. '59–'62. $2. — (Household ed.) 12°. $1.50 .... *Putnam.*
— Home pastorals, ballads and odes. 12°. '75. $2; hf. cf., $3.50 .... *Osgood.*
— India, China and Japan. ('55.) New ed. 12°. '69. $2. — (Household ed.) 12°. $1.50 ... *Putnam.*
— Japan in our day. ('71.) New ed. 12°. '74. $1.50. *Scribner.*
— John Godfrey's fortunes, related by himself: story of Am. life. 12°. '64. $2. — (Household ed.) 12°. $1.50 .... *Putnam.*
— Joseph and his friend: story of Pennsylvania. 12°. '70. $2. — (Household ed.) 12°. $1.50 .. *Putnam.*
— Lake regions of central Africa. map and ill. 12°. '75. $1.50 .... *Scribner.*
— Land of the Saracen; or, pictures of Palestine, Asia Minor, Sicily and Spain. ('54.) New ed. ill. 12°. '69. $2. — (Household ed.) 12°. $1.50 ... *Putnam.*
— Lars: pastoral of Norway. 16°. '73. $1.50 .. *Osgood.*
— Masque of the gods. 16°. '72. $1.25 ..... *Osgood.*
— Northern travel: summer and winter pictures of Sweden, Denmark and Lapland. ('58.) New ed. ill. 12°. '69. $2. — (Household ed.) 12°. $1.50 .... *Putnam.*
— Picture of St. John: poem. 16°. '66. $2 .. *Osgood.*
— Poems. (Blue and gold ed.) por. 32°. $1.25; hf. cf., $2.50; mor., $3. — (Cabinet ed.) por. 16°. '64. $1.50; hf. cf., $3; mor., $4 .. *Osgood.*
— Poems of home and travel. ('55.) New ed. 16°. '62. $1.25 .... *Osgood.*
— Poems of the Orient. ('55.) New ed. 16°. '62. $1.25 .... *Osgood.*
— Poet's journal (The). 16°. '62. $1.25 .... *Osgood.*
— Prophet (The): tragedy. 16°. '74. $2 ..... *Osgood.*
— School hist. of Germany, to 1871. ill. and maps. 12°. '74. hf. bd., $1.75 .... *Appleton.*
— Story of Kennett. 12°. '66. $2. — (Household ed.) 12°. $1.50 .... *Putnam.*
— Travels in Arabia. ('72.) New ed. 12°. '74. $1.50. *Scribner.*
— Travels in south Africa. ('72.) New ed. map and ill. 12°. '75. $1.50 .... *Scribner.*
— Views afoot. ('46.) New ed. 12°. '69. $2. — (Household ed.) 12°. $1.50 .... *Putnam.*
— (*ed.*) Illustrated lib. of travel, exploration and adventure. 8 v. 12°. '72–'74. ea., $1.50 .. *Scribner.*

Cont.: Japan in our day, by B. Taylor. — Wild men and wild beasts, by G. Cumming. — Travels in Arabia, by B. Taylor. — Travels in south Africa, by B. Taylor. — Wonders of the Yellowstone, by J. Richardson. — Lake regions of central Africa, by B. Taylor. — Central Asia, by B. Taylor. — Siam, by G. B. Bacon.

Taylor, Bayard, *continued.*
— *See also* Goethe, J. W. v., Faust.

Taylor, B: Cook. Annals of the classis and township of Bergen, N. J. ill. 12°. $1 .. *N. Y. Ref. Ch. Bd.*

Taylor, B: Franklin. In camp and field. 12°. '75. $1.50 .... *Griggs.*
— January and June. 12°. '60. $1.50 ...... *Mason.*
— Mission Ridge and Lookout Mountain, with pictures of life in camp and field. 12°. $2.50 .. *Appleton.*
— Old-time pictures, and sheaves of rhyme. ill. sm. 4°. '73. $2; $2.50 .... *Griggs.*
— Songs of yesterday. ill. 8°. '75. $4; mor., $8 .. *Griggs.*
— The world on wheels, and other sketches. ill. 12°. '74. $1.50 .... *Griggs.*

Taylor, C. Geometrical conics. cr. 8°. '63. $2.50. *Macmillan.*

Taylor, C. Journal of the law school and moot court at Needham, Va.; with precedents, pleadings, etc. 8°. '22. shp., $1.50 .... *J. W. Randolph.*

Taylor, C. B. Centennial hist. of the U. S. ill. 12°. '76. $1.75 .... *World Pub.*
— One hundred years' achievement of a free people: hist. of U. S. to 1876. ill. 8°. '76. *$2.50 ... *H. S. Allen.*

Taylor, *Rev.* C. B. Memorials of the English martyrs. ill. 12°. $1.75 .... *Bost. Am. Tr.*

Taylor, C: Fayette. Infantile paralysis and its attendant deformities. 12°. $1; pap., 75c. *Lippincott.*
— Spinal irritation; or, the causes of back-ache among Am. women. ill. 8°. 50c. .... *W. Wood.*

Taylor, Dan. T. The coming earthquake and the signs that betoken its approach; with other tracts. ('69.) 5th ed. 12°. '75. 80c. .... *Hastings.*
— Voice of the church on the coming and kingdom of the Redeemer: hist. of doctrine of reign of Christ on earth. ('55.) 9th ed., rev. with pref. by H. L. Hastings. 12°. '72. $1.25 .... *Hastings.*

Taylor, D: *See* Wisconsin, Revised statutes.

Taylor, *Miss* Eliz. Blindpits. [Fiction.] 12°. '68. $1.75 .... *Putnam.*
— Quixstar. 12°. '74. $1.75 .... *Putnam.*

Taylor, Emily. Ball we live on; ed. by T. O. Summers. 18°. '57. 40c. .... *So. Meth.*

Taylor, G: B. Baptists: who they are and what they have done. 18°. pap., 20c. .... *Am. Bapt.*
— Coster Grew; or, the young machinist. 16°. $1. *Am. Bapt.*
— Life and times of James B. Taylor. 12°. $1.50. *Am. Bapt.*
— Oakland stories. 4 v. ill. 16°. $3.60 ..... *Sheldon.*

Cont.: Kenny. — Claiborne. — Cousin Guy. — Gustave.

— Roger Bernard, the pastor's son. 16°. $1 .. *Am. Bapt.*
— Walter Ennis; or, the early Baptists of Virginia. 16°. $1.50 .... *Am. Bapt.*

Taylor, G: H. Diseases of women: their causes, prevention and radical cure. 12°. *$2 .... *Maclean.*
— Exposition of Swedish movement cure; with summary of principles of general hygiene. 12°. '60. $1.50 .... *Wells.*

Taylor, H: Notes from life. 16°. $1.25 .... *Osgood*
— Philip Van Artevelde. 32°. $1.50 .... * *Osgood*

Taylor, H: S. Family doctor (The). ill. 12°. $1.75 *J. E. Potter*
— Our family doctor and general receipt-book. ill. 8° *$2.50; $3 .... *J. E. Potter*

Taylor, H: W. Times of Daniel: an argument. 12° '71. $1.50 .... *Randolph*

Taylor, I: Logic in theology, and other essays. 12° '76. $1.50 .... *Tibbals*
— Loyola and jesuitism. 12°. $1.25 .... *Carter*
— Natural history of enthusiasm. 12°. $1.25 .. *Carter*
— Physical theory of another life. 12°. '76. $1.50. *Tibbals*
— Restoration of belief. 12°. '60. $1.50 ..... *Dutton*

Taylor, I: *continued.*
— Spirit of the Hebrew poetry; with sketch of author, and catalogue of his writings. ('60.) 12°. '73. $1.50 .... *Smith, E. & Co.*
— Wesley and Methodism. 12°. $1.50 ...... *Harper.*
— The world of mine. 12°. $1.50 .... *Harper.*
Taylor, *Rev.* I: Etruscan researches. cr. 8°. '74. $4. *Macmillan.*
— Words and places; or, etymological illustrations of hist., ethnology and geog. 3d ed.; compressed for schools. maps. 12°. '73. $2.. *Macmillan.*
Taylor, J. E. Geological stories: ser. of autobiographies. ill. 12°. '72. $1.75......... *Putnam.*
Taylor, J. E. J. Life. ill. 18°. '56. 35c. ... *Am. Tr.*
Taylor, Ja. History of Scotland. ('59.) 4th ed. 2 v. por. and ill. roy. 8°. '71. hf. mor., $21; mor., $24. *Virtue.*
Taylor, Ja. B. Baptist ministers of Virginia. 2 v. 12°. $2.50 .... *Sheldon.*
— Memoir. 12°. $1.50 .... *So. Bapt.*
Taylor, Jane. Hymns for infant minds. 32°. '49. 15c.; pap., 8c......................... *Am. Tr.*
— *Same.* 32°. 20c. .... *Bost. Am. Tr.*
— *Same.* 18°. 35c. .... *Am. S. S.*
— *Same.* sq. 16°. 50c. .... *Carter.*
— *Same.* ('58.) 2d ed. 18°. '74. 50c. .... *So. Meth.*
— Original poems for infant minds. 18°. 60c... *Carter.*
— *Same.* ill. 16°. $1........................ *Porter.*
— *Same.* ill. sm. 4°. $2.50 .... *Routledge.*
— Pleasures of taste, and other stories; ed. by Mrs. S. J. Hale. 18°. 75c..................... *Harper.*
Taylor, *Mrs.* Jane. Wouldst know thyself! outlines of human physiology. ill. 16°. '58. bds., 20c. *Holmes.*
Taylor, Jeffries. Young islanders; or, the school-boy Crusoes. 16°. $1.25.. *Lippincott; Nichols & H.*
Taylor, *Rev.* Jeremiah. Patriot soldier. ('63.) New ed. ill. 16°. '75. 65c.................... *Hoyt.*
Taylor, Jer. Golden grove; [also] Worthy communicant. *See* Fleetwood, J: Life of Christ.
— Preparation for holy communion. *See* Sewell, E. M.
— Readings for Lent; comp. from his writings by E. M. Sewell. 16°. $1.25................... *Dutton.*
— Rule and exercises of holy dying. 18°. 50c.; $1. *Nelson.*
— *Same.* 18°. '70. 75c.; $1.25 .... *Lothrop.*
— *Same.* 18°. $1; cf., $2.25 .... *Lippincott.*
— *Same.* 16°. $1.25; mor., $2.50. — (chp. ed.), 50c. *Lee & S.*
— — *See also below,* Rule of holy living.
— Rule and exercises of holy living. 18°. 50c.; $1. *Nelson.*
— *Same.* 18°. '70. 75c.; $1.25 .... *Lothrop.*
— *Same.* 12°. '72. $1.25.................. *Claxton.*
— *Same.* 16°. $1.25; mor., $2.50. — (chp. ed.), 50c. *Lee & S.*
— *Same.* 18°. $1; cf., $2.25............ *Lippincott.*
— *Same;* [also] Rule and exercises of holy dying. 18°. 90c.; $1.50.......................... *Nelson.*
— — *Same.* 12°. $1.50..................... *Appleton.*
— — *Same.* 2 v. in 1. 16°. $2.25; mor., $3.50.. *Lee & S.*
— — *Same.* por. 12°. (Bohn.) $1.40.. *Scribner, W. & A.*
— — *Same.* por. 12°. (Bohn.) $1.50 ...... *Lippincott.*
— — *Same.* 2 v. in 1. 32°. (Lond.) '76. $1.. *Dutton.*
— — *Same.* (Red line ed.) 2 v. in 1. 32°. '76. $2. *Dutton.*
— — *Same;* ed. by E. Abbot. 16°. '64. $2.50; hf. cf., $5 .... *Little, B. & Co.*
— Sermons. 8°. $2.50...................... *Carter.*
Taylor, J: *See* Stoddard, R: H., Bric-a-brac series.
Taylor, J: Facts and fallacies: letters, 1866, 1867, chiefly with ref. to constant service, and a future source of supply. 8°. pap., 40c.......... *Spon.*
Taylor, J: Great lessons from little things: lessons on Bible nat. hist. ill. fp. 4°. $1.50 ...... *Cassell.*
Taylor, *Col.* J: Arator: practical and political agric. essays. 12°. '17. shp., $2 ..... *J. W. Randolph.*
Taylor, *Col.* J: *continued.*
— Inquiry into principles and policy of U. S. government. 8°. '14. shp., $5.............. *J. W. Randolph.*
Taylor, J: A. Defense of insanity: address in trial of J. J. Burroughs. 8°. '76. pap., 75c... *Ward & P.*
Taylor, *Rev.* J: L. Memoir of Judge Phillips. por. 8°. $1.50.......................... *Cong. Pub.*
Taylor, J: L: *See* North Carolina, Law reports.
Taylor, J: N. Law of executors and administrators; with directions for proving a will and admin. an estate. ('51.) New ed. 18°. '74. $1.. *Baker, V. & Co.*
— Treatise on Am. law of landlord and tenant. 6th ed., rev. and enl. 8°. '73. shp., $6.. *Little, B. & Co.*
Taylor, Jos. A fast life on the modern highway: a glance into the railroad world from a new point of view. ill. 12°. $1.50; pap., $1..... *Harper.*
Taylor, R: Cowling. Statistics of coal; with incidental statistics of the iron manufacture. ('54.) 2d ed., rev. by S. S. Haldeman. maps and ill. 8°. '55. $10............................ *Baird.*
Taylor, Rob. Astro-theological lectures. 12°. $2. *Mendum.*
— Devil's (The) pulpit; with sketch of author's life and sermons. 12°. $2............... *Mendum.*
— Diegeses (The): discovery of origin, evidences and early hist. of Christianity. 8°. $2..... *Mendum.*
— Syntagma (The). 12°. $1.............. *Mendum.*
Taylor, Rob. W. Syphilitic lesions of the osseous system in infants and young children. 8°. $2.50. *W. Wood.*
Taylor, Ruf. Cottage piety exemplified. 16°. $1.25. *Lippincott.*
Taylor, S: H. Classical study: its value illustrated by selections from writings of eminent scholars. 12°. '69. $2......................... *Draper.*
— Elementary grammar of the Greek lang.; based on Kühner's grammar. 12°. '71. $1.60.... *Ivison.*
— Method of classical study; ill. by questions on selections from Latin and Greek authors. 12°. $1.25. *Thompson.*
Taylor, Sedley. Science of music. 12°. $1.. *Appleton.*
— Sound and music: a non-mathematical treatise on physical constitution of musical sounds and harmony, incl. chief acoustical discoveries of Prof. Helmholtz. cr. 8°. '73. $3........ *Macmillan.*
Taylor, *Miss* T. John Richmond; or, a sister's love. ill. 16°. $1................. *Cin. Meth. Bk. Conc.*
— Marguerite; or, the Huguenot child. 16°. $1. *Cin. Meth. Bk. Conc.*
Taylor, T. B. Old theology turned upside down, or right side up. ('71.) 2d ed. 12°. '73. $1.25; pap., $1.............................. *Colby.*
Taylor, Thdr. Charles Dickens: the story of his life. por. 8°. pap., 50c.; — with speeches, $1.50. *Harper.*
— (*ed.*) Golden treasury of thought: encyclopædia of quotations and extracts. 12°. $3. *Routledge; Scribner, W. & A.*
Taylor, T: Elusinian and Bacchic mysteries. 3d ed.; ed., with introd., notes, etc., by A. Wilder. 8°. '75. $3............................. *Bouton.*
Taylor, T: [Plays.] 5 v. 16°. ea., pap., 15c. *De Witt.*
Cont.: Henry Dunbar. — Hidden hand; or, the gray lady. — Overland route: comedy. — Plot and passion. — Sheep in wolf's clothing.
— *Same.* 21 v. 16°. ea., pap., 15c......... *French.*
Cont.: Blighted being: farce. — Fool's revenge. — Going to the bad: comedy. — Helping hands. — Henry Dunbar. — Hidden hand; or, the gray lady. — House or the home: comedy. — Nice firm: comic drama. — Nine points of the law: farce. — Payable on demand. — Plot and passion. — Retribution. — Sense and sensation. — Settling day: drama. — Sheep in wolf's clothing. — Still waters run deep: comedy. — Tale of two cities. — Ticket of leave man. — To oblige Benson: comedietta. — Up at the hills: comedy. — Victims: comedy.
— Babes in the wood: comedy. 16°. pap., 15c. *Lee & S.*
— Fool's revenge. 8°. pap., 30c.............. *Hinton.*
— — *See also* Hinton, H. L., Acting plays of Edwin Booth.

Taylor, T: *continued.*
— Nine points of the law: comedy. 16°. pap., 15c. *Lee & S.*
— Payable on demand: drama. 16°. pap., 15c... *Lee & S.*
— *and* Durbourg, A. W. New men and old acres: comedy. 16°. pap., 15c....... *De Witt; French.*
— — Sister's penance: drama. 16°. pap., 15c. *French.*
— *and* Reade, C. King's rival: drama. 16°. pap., 15c.......... *French.*
— — Masks and faces: comedy. 16°. pap., 15c. *French.*
— — Two loves and a life: drama. 16°. pap., 15c. *French.*

Taylor, T: P. Bottle (The): drama. 16°. pap., 15c. *French.*
— Chain of guilt: drama. 16°. pap., 15c..... *French.*

Taylor, Tim. Alden. Solace; or, afflictions lightened. 24°. 40c.......... *Cong. Pub.*

Taylor, V. O. Every man his own doctor. 16°. '70. pap., 50c.......... *Hunter.*

Taylor, Virgil Corydon. Chime: coll. of old and new tunes; with melodeon instructor. obl. 8°. '54. bds., $1.50.......... *Ditson.*
— Concordia: glees, quartettes, etc. obl. 8°. '52. pap., 50c.......... *Ditson.*
— Golden lyre: coll. of church music. obl. 8°. '50. bds., $1.50.......... *Ditson.*
— Praise offering: tunes with anthems. obl. 16°. '68. $1.50.......... *Mills.*
— Song festival: sel. library of psalmody. obl. 8°. '58. bds., $1.......... *Ditson.*
— Venite: coll. of chants for the Episcopal Church. obl. 8°. '65. 75c.; $1.......... *T. J. Hall.*
— Voice culture: inductive exercises for development of voice. 4°. '74. pap., 75c.......... *Mills.*

Taylor, Wa. C. A physician's counsels to man in health and disease. 12°. '72. *(?)..(?) *Holland.*
— A physician's counsels to women in health and disease. 12°. '71. *(?).......... (?) *Holland.*

Taylor, W: The model preacher. 12°. $1.50. *Cin. Meth. Bk. Conc.*

Taylor, W: A. Eighteen presidents and contemporaneous rulers. por. and ill. 12°. '76. $1; pap., 50c.......... *W. A. Taylor.*

Taylor, W: Cooke. History of Ireland, from Anglo-Norman invasion to union with Gt. Brit.; with add. by W. Sampson. 2 v. 18°. $1.50.. *Harper.*
— Manual of anc. and mod. hist.; ed. by Prof. Henry. 2 v. 8°. ea., $2; — in 1 v., $3.50.... *Appleton.*
— Modern British Plutarch: lives of men distinguished in recent hist. of Eng. 12°. $1....... *Harper.*
— Pictorial hist. of France and Normandy. ill. demy 8°. $2.50.......... *Desilver.*

Taylor, W: Ja. Romeyn. Discourse commemorative of H: G. Livingston, Feb. 18, 1855. 8°. pap., 25c.......... *N. Y. Ref. Ch. Bd.*
— Louisa: a memoir. 18°. 50c.......... *Am. S. S.*
— Reformed Protestant Dutch Church in Phila.: hist. discourse, March, 1857. 18°. 25c. *N. Y. Ref. Ch. Bd.*
— Sermon on life, character, etc., of John Ludlow, Nov. 1, 1857. 8°. pap., 25c....... *N. Y. Ref. Ch. Bd.*

Taylor, W: M. Monitor: manual of Freemasonry, adapted to the work and government of the lodges subordinate to the grand lodge of Texas. 18°. '76. $1.50; mor., $2.50; $3.50... *E. H. Cushing.*

Taylor, W: Mackergo. David, king of Israel: his life and its lessons. 12°. $2.......... *Harper.*
— Elijah, the prophet. 12°. $1.50.......... *Harper.*
— Lost (The) found and the wanderer welcomed. ('72.) New ed. 12°. '73. $1.50.......... *Scribner.*
— Ministry of the word. (Yale lectures, 1876.) 12°. '76. $1.50.......... *Randolph.*
— Prayer and business. 24°. '74. 35c.; pap., 15c. *Randolph.*

Taylor, Zach. Life. ill. 16°. $1.25.......... *Lee & S.*

Teacher (The). Abbott, J. $1.75.......... *Harper.*

Teacher (The), the class and the book. Hendryx, W. B. 50c.......... *Chase.*

Teacher (The) taught. 16°. $1.25.......... *Am. S. S.*

Teacher (The) taught. Stirling, E. 15c...... *French.*

Teacher (The) teaching. 16°. $1.25....... *Am. S. S.*

Teacher's aid lib. 10 v. 18°. $5.35.......... *So. Meth.*

Cont.: Sunday-school teacher, by T. O. Summers. — Theological compend, by A. Binney. — Sunday-school speaker. — Outline of Sunday-school lectures. — Watson's Apology. — Gate of prayer. — Work of the Holy Spirit, by Edwards. — Fletcher's appeal. — Oliver's On perseverance. — Refutation of Paine, by T. O. Summers.

Teacher's assistant in use of 3d vol. of Union questions. 18°. 60c.; — 4th vol. 18°. 75c... *Am. S. S.*

Teacher's cabinet: papers on general Sunday-school topics; by various authors. 2 v. 12°. ea., $1. *Nelson.*

Teacher's harvest; or, rewards of fidelity in Sunday-school teaching. 18°. 35c.......... *Am. S. S.*

Teacher's institute. Fowle, W. B. $1.25..... *Barnes.*

Teacher's model and the model teacher. Groser, W. H. 75c.......... *Randolph.*

Teacher's sketches. 18°. 60c.......... *Cong. Pub.*

Teachers' guide to illustration: manual [on] use of globes, outline maps, etc. 12°. '73. $1. *Andrews.*

Teaching the truth. Henry, S. M. I. $1.25. *Cin. Meth. Bk. Conc.*

Teachings of Jesus. 24°. '73. 25c...... *Collins & Bro.*

Teachings of the master. Turner, S. H. $1.25. *Randolph.*

Tears of Jesus of Nazareth. Duncan, W. C. 75c. *Sheldon.*

Teasdale, T. C. Restricted communion, as practiced by the Baptist churches. 18°. 30c.; pap., 10c. *So. Bapt.*

Teasing Tom. *See* New Year lib.

Tebay, Septimus. Elementary mensuration for schools. 12°. '68. $1.25.......... *Macmillan.*

Teddy, the bill-poster. Blackburn, W. M. 65c. *Pres. Bd.*

Teddy, the tiler. Rodwell, G. H. 15c........ *French.*

Teddy Roe. Stirling, E. 15c.......... *French.*

Teddy White; or, the little orange sellers. ('60.) New ed. ill. 18°. '69. 45c.......... *Hoyt.*

Teddy's dream. 18°. 60c.; 70c.......... *Am. Bapt.*

Teddy's dream. *See* Leslie, E.

Tees, L. C. Life, trial and execution of Anton Probst. [In Eng. or Germ.] 8°. pap., 25c..... *Barclay.*

Tefft, B: Franklin. The shoulder knot; or, sketches of the threefold life of man: story of the 16th cent. 12°. $1.50.......... *Harper.*

Tegetmeier, W: B. Homing and carrier pigeon: its hist., general management and method of training. ill. 16°. '72. bds., 50c.......... *Routledge.*
— Pigeons: their structure, varieties, habits and management. col. ill. 8°. $5.......... *Routledge.*
— Poultry book: breeding and management of profitable and ornamental poultry, their qualities and characteristics. col. ill. 8°. $9.. *Judd; Routledge.*

Tegg, T: Young man's book of knowledge. 12°. $1.50. *Sower.*

Tegg, W: (*ed.*) Dictionary of chronology. 10th ed. 12°. '71. $4.......... *Tibbals.*
— Epitaphs; with a selection of epigrams. sq. 12°. 50c. *Scribner, W. & A.*
— Laconics; or, good words of the best authors. sq. 12°. 50c.......... *Scribner, W. & A.*
— Mixture for low spirits: compound of witty sayings of many people in many climes. sq. 12°. 50c. *Scribner, W. & A.*
— Proverbs from far and near, wise sentences, etc. sq. 12°. 50c.......... *Scribner, W. & A.*
— Wills of their own, curious, eccentric and benevolent. 12°. 50c.......... *Scribner, W. & A.*

Tegnér, Esaias. Frithiof's saga; tr. by W. L. Blackley; ed. by Bayard Taylor. ('67.) New ed. 16°. '74. $1.50 .... *Holt.*
— *Same;* tr. by L. A. Sherman. ill. 4°. $7.50 .. *Osgood.*
Tekel. Bragg, H. A. $1.75 .... *Lippincott.*
Tekel. Haskell, B. D. 25c. .... (?) *Woodward.*
Tekeli: drama. 16°. pap., 15c. .... *French.*
Tel Tyler at school. Densel, M. 75c. .... *Dutton.*
Telegraph and travel. Goldsmid, *Sir* F. J. $8. *Macmillan.*
Telemachus. Planché, J. R., *and* Dance, G. 15c. *French.*
Télémaque (Les aventures de). *See* Fénelon.
Telescope (The): an allegory. ('60.) New ed. ill. 18°. '73. 40c. .... *Hoyt.*
Tell; or, strike of cantons. Talfourd, F. 15c. .. *French.*
Tell it all. Stenhouse, T. B. H. *$3; $3.50. *Lloyd; A.D. Worthington.*
Tell Jesus. *See* Shipton, A.
Tell mamma. Mackarness, M. A. $1.25 ... *Routledge.*
Tell me a story. Graham, E. $1.50 ...... *Macmillan.*
Tell the truth, and other stories. 18°. 70c. .. *Pres. Bd.*
Tell with a vengeance: burlesque. 16°. pap., 15c. *French.*
Tell-tale (The). Blanchard, C. 25c. .... *D. Thomas.*
Tell-tale (The). *See* Phelps, *Mrs.* E. S.
Tell-tale heart (A). Picton, T. 15c. .... *De Witt.*
Teller, Marg. E. Fred Lawrence; or, the world college. ill. 18°. '60. 75c. .... *Dodd.*
Temme, J. D. H. Anna Hammer: tale of contemporary Germ. life; tr. 8°. pap., 50c. .... *Harper.*
— Verworfener (Ein); [also] Das Forsthaus. 8°. pap., 50c. .... *Morwitz.*
— Wer da steht der sehe zu, dass er nicht falle; [also] Die Mühle am schwarzen Meer. 12°. '64. pap., 35c. .... *Steiger.*
Temper. Bell, R. 15c. .... *French.*
Temper and temperament. Ellis, S. S. 75c. .. *Harper.*
Temperance and education. Hopkins, M. 10c. *Nat. Temp.*
Temperance anecdotes. Bungay, G. W. $1. *Nat. Temp.*
Temperance boy. 18°. 35c. .... *Cong. Pub.*
Temperance chimes. Bradbury, W. B., *and* Stearns, J. N. 30c.; 35c. .... *Nat. Temp.*
Temperance doctor. Chellis, M. D. $1.25 .. *Nat. Temp.*
Temperance doctor: drama. 16°. pap., 15c. .. *French.*
Temperance drama. Baker, G. M. 75c.; 60c. .. *Lee & S.*
Temperance echoes. Dressler, W. 75c. ..... *Peters.*
Temperance glee book. Hull, A. 50c. .... *Pond.*
Temperance leaflet. [Singing book.] obl. 12°. pap., 10c. .... *Church.*
Temperance lib. 4 v. ill. 16°. $5.75 .... *Hoyt.*
Cont.: John and the demijohn, by Mrs. J. McN. Wright. — Upward path, by Mrs. C. E. K. Davis. — Family doctor, by Mrs. M. S. Walker. — Old distillery, by Mrs. J. S. Avery.
Temperance melodist (New). *See* Hubbard, S.
Temperance musician. Fillmore, A. D. 40c. *Pounsford.*
Temperance sermons delivered in response to an invitation of the Nat. Temp. Soc. and Pub. House. ('73.) New ed. 17 nos. in 1 v. 12°. '74. $1.50. *Nat. Temp.*
Temperance speaker. Stearns, J. N. 75c. .. *Nat. Temp.*
Temperance stories. *See* Arthur, T. S.
Temperance tales. *See* Sargent, L. M.
Temperance volume. ill. 12°. '39. 75c. ..... *Am. Tr.*
Tempest (The). *See* Shakespeare, W:
Tempest and sunshine. Holmes, M. J. $1.50. *Carleton.*
Tempest in a teapot. Picton, T. 15c. ...... *De Witt.*
Tempest-tossed. Tilton, T. $1.75 .... *Sheldon.*

Templar manual for Knights Templar: tactics and drill, with ceremonies and code of statutes and digest. 12th ed., rev. 32°. '74. $1; mor., $2. *E. B Myers.*
Temple, Allan. Thankfulness: passages from [his] diary by C. B. Tayler. 12°. $1 ...... *Leighton.*
Temple, Crona. Hill farm. ill. 16°. '75. 60c. .. *Lothrop.*
— Little Wavie, the foundling of Glenderg. 18°. 60c. *Am. S. S.*
— *Same.* ill. 16°. '73. $1 .... *Lothrop.*
— Millicent's home. ill. 16°. '73. 70c. .... *Am. Tr.*
— Nobody cares. ill. 16°. '76. 60c. .... *Lothrop.*
Temple, Dan. H. Life and letters of Dan. Temple; with introd. by R. S. Storrs. por. 12°. $1.50. *Cong. Pub.*
Temple, Eb. The Christian's daily treasury; with text for every day, and 365 short sermons. 12°. $1.50. *So. Bapt.*
Temple, F: Sermons preached in chapel of Rugby School. 3 ser. fp. 8°. '70–'71. ea., $1.50. *Macmillan.*
Temple, Josiah Howard, *and* Sheldon, G: History of Northfield, Mass., for 150 years; with account of prior Indian occupation, and with family genealogies. por. and ill. 8°. '75. $8 .... *Munsell.*
Temple, Leofric. *See* Chitty, T., *and* Temple, L.
Temple (The). Davis, A. J. $1.50; $1 .. *A. J. Davis.*
Temple (The). Edersheim, A. $1.75 .... *Nelson.*
Temple anthems. Lowry, R., *and* Doane, W. H. $1.25. *Biglow.*
Temple choir. Seward, T. F., Mason, L., *and* Bradbury, W. B. $1.50 .... *Ditson.*
Temple Emanu-el. Gottheil, G., *and* Davis, A. J. 25c. .... *Pond.*
Temple melodies. Jones, D. E. $1; $1.50 .. *Hamersley.*
Temple rebuilt. Abbe, F. R. $1.50 .. *Lockwood, B. & Co.*
Templeton, A. The great teacher. 16°. 50c. (?) *Cumberland.*
Templeton, W: Engineer's commonplace book of practical references. 6th ed. pl. 12°. (Lond.) '75. $2 .... *Spon.*
— Mechanic's, millwright's and engineer's pocket companion; with Am. additions. 16°. $2 .. *Appleton.*
— Millwright and engineer's companion. 15th ed., rev. by S. Maynard. pl. 12°. (Lond.) '74. $2 .. *Spon.*
— Operative mechanic's workshop companion and scientific gentleman's practical assistant. 11th ed., rev. and enl. ill. 12°. $2.50 .... *Baird.*
— Practical examinator on steam and the steam engine. 12°. (Lond.) '52. 75c. .... *Spon.*
— *Same.* ('53.) 10th ed. 12°. '74. $1.25 ... *Baird.*
Templi carmina (New). *See* Kingsley, G.
Templin, J. D. Abridgment of decisions in Supreme Court of Iowa, [through] v. 34 Iowa reports (1839–'72). 8°. '74. shp., $7.50 .... *Mills.*
Templin, J: W. Compendium of repeals and amendments to laws of Iowa; with ref. to Supreme Court decisions. 8°. '70. shp., $3 .... *Day.*
Temptation. Smith, J. F. 75c. .... *Dick & F.*
Temptation. Sue, E. 25c. .... *U. P. James.*
Temptation. Townsend, W. T. 15c. .... *French.*
Temptation; or, Henry Morland. 18°. 25c. *Scribner, W. & A.*
Temptation and triumph. Townsend, V. F. $1.75; $1.25 .... *Cin. Meth. Bk. Conc.*
Temptation in the desert. Dickson, A. E. 40c. *Am. Tr.*
Temptation of our Lord. Macleod, N. $1.25. *Routledge.*
Temptations and trials. 8°. pap., 25c. ..... *De Witt.*
Temptations of city life. 18°. 25c.; 30c. .. *Am. Bapt.*
Tempter. Baker, G. M. 15c. .... *Lee & S.*
Tempter and the tempted. *See* Wood, *Miss* M. F.
Ten acres enough. *See* Morris, Edm.

Ten chapters on marriage. Hayden, W. B. 50c. *H. H. Carter.*

Ten Christmas carols. Howard, A. P. 20c. .. *Ditson.*

Ten commandments (The) and thirteen creeds; or, chief principles of the Jewish religion. 16°. bds., 25c. .... *Frank.*

Ten commandments illustrated. Cross, J. 40c... *Am. Tr.*

Ten days among the Greek brigands. Van Lennep, H. J. $1.25 .... *Cong. Pub.*

Ten days in Spain. Field, K. $1.25 .... *Osgood.*

Ten days in Switzerland. Ridgaway, H. B. 20c. *Meth. Bk. Conc.*

Ten days in the tombs: Ethiop. drama. 16°. pap., 15c. *French.*

Ten great religions. Clarke, J. F. $3; $5.50 .. *Osgood.*

Ten helps to joy and peace in believing. Kimball, J. W. 30c. .... *Bost. Am. Tr.*

Ten laws of health. Black, J. R. $1.75 .. *Lippincott.*

Ten-minute talks. Burritt, E. $2.25 .... *Lee & S.*

Ten nights in a bar room. Arthur, T. S. $1.25. *J. E. Potter.*

Ten nights in a bar room. Pratt, W. W. 15c... *French.*

Ten old maids. Smith, J. P. $1.75 .... *Carleton.*

Ten thousand wonderful things. *See* King, E. F.

Ten thousand a year. *See* Warren, S:

Ten thousand a year: drama. 16°. pap., 15c. *French.*

Ten times one is ten. *See* Hale, E: E.

Ten years among the mail bags. Holbrook, J. H. *$2.50 .... *Cowperthwait.*

Ten years in Wall St. Fowler, W. W. *$3; $3.50; $4 .... *Dustin.*

Ten years in Washington. Clemmer, M. *$3; $3.50. *Lloyd; A. D. Worthington.*

Ten years old. *See* Little Willie's lib.

Ten years on the Euphrates. Wheeler, C. H. $1.25. *Bost. Am. Tr.*

Ten years on the town; or, the adventures of a played-out club. 8°. pap., 25c. .... *Dick & F.*

Ten years with spiritual mediums. Fairfield, F. G. $1.25 .... *Appleton.*

Tenant of Wildfell Hall. *See* Brontë, A.

Tenants of Malory. Le Fanu, J. S. 50c.... *Harper.*

Ten Brook, And. American state universities: their origin and progress; hist. of congressional university land-grants; with particular account of Univ. of Michigan. 8°. '75. $3.50 .... *Clarke.*

Tender attachment. Baker, G. M. 15c...... *Lee & S.*

Tender grapes for little lips. 24°. pap., 25c. *Meth. Bk. Conc.*

Tender precautions. Serle, T. J. 15c. ...... *French.*

Tennemann, W: Gli. Manual of hist. of philosophy; tr. by A. Johnson; rev. and contin. by J. R. Morell. 12°. (Bohn.) $1.75 ... *Little, B. & Co.*

— *Same.* 12°. (Bohn.) $2 .. *Lippincott; Scribner, W. & A.*

Tennent, Gilb. *See* Sermons and essays.

Tennent, J: *See* Sermons and essays.

Tennent, W: Life. 18°. 35c. .... *Carter.*

— *See also* Sermons and essays.

Tennessean in Persia and Koordistan. Marsh, D. W. $2 .... *Pres. Bd.*

Tennessee. Chancery reports, v. 1 (1872–'74); by W. F. Cooper. 8°. *net*, shp., $5 .... *G. I. Jones.*

— Code, enacted 1857–8; ed. by R. J. Meigs and W. F. Cooper. 8°. '58 .... *State.*

— Criminal code and decisions, 1858–'74; by J. M. Quarles. 8°. '74 .... *State.*

— Digest of decisions. *See* King, H. C.

— Law reports, 1791–1875. 55 v. 8°. .... *State.*

Cont.: Superior courts of law and equity, Federal Court and Supreme Court of Errors and Appeals reports, 1791–1817, by J. Overton, 2 v. — Supreme Court of Errors and Appeals and Federal Court reports, 1811–'14, by W. W. Cooke. — Supreme Court of Errors and Appeals reports, 1816–'18, by J. Haywood, 3 v. — 1822–'24, by J. Peck. — 1825–'28, by J. H. Martin and G. S. Yerger. — 1832–'37, by G. S. Yerger, 10 v. — 1838–'39, by R. J. Meigs. — 1839–'51, by W. H. Humphreys, 11 v. — 1851–'53, by W. G. Swan, 2 v. — 1853–'58, by J. L. T. Sneed, 5 v. — 1858–'59, by J. W. Head, 3 v. — 1860–'70, by T. H. Coldwell, 7 v. — 1870–'75, by J. B. Heiskell, 8 v.

— — Index. *See* Hunter, B., *and* Meyer, W. G.

— Reports of cases in highest courts of law and equity. New ed., with notes and ref. by W. F. Cooper. 9 v. in 5. 8° .... *State.*

Compr. Overton, Cooke, Haywood, Peck, Martin and Yerger, and Meigs.

— Statutes. *See* Thompson, S. D., *and* Steger, T. M.

— Supreme Court of Errors and Appeals reports; by J. Hayward; with notes and ref. by M. M. Bigelow. 8°. '70. shp., $4 .... *Hurd & H.*

Tennessee geological survey. First–eighth geol. reports, 1833–'45. 8 v. 8° .... *State.*

— Geological reconnoissance of T., by J. M. Safford. 8°. '56 .... *State.*

— Geology of T.; by J. M. Safford. map and pl. 8°. '69 .... *State.*

Tenney, *Mrs.* Abby A. Pictures and stories of animals for the little ones at home. 6 v. ill. 16°. $6. *Sheldon.*

Cont.: Quadrupeds. — Fishes and reptiles. — Sea shells, etc. — Birds. — Bees and butterflies, etc. — Sea urchins, etc.

— *See also* Tenney, S. *and* A. A.

Tenney, J. H. Songs of joy; for camp and vestry meetings, etc. 16°. 35c.; hf. bd., 30c... *Lee & S.*

— *See also* Hodges, D. F., Foster, G. W., *and* Tenney, J. H.; — Hodges, D. F., *and* Tenney, J. H.

Tenney, J. N., *and* Hoffmann, E. A. Songs of faith: coll. of sacred songs. 8°. bds., 35c... *Brainard.*

Tenney, Sanborn. Elements of zoology. ('75.) New ed. ill. 12°. '76. $2.50 .... *Scribner.*

— Geology; for teachers, classes and private students. ill. 12°. $1.75 .... *Butler.*

— Manual of zoology for schools, colleges and the general reader. ('65.) New ed., rev. ill. 12°. cr. 8°. '76. $3. — (Lib. ed.) 8°. $4.50 .. *Scribner.*

— *and* A. A. Natural history of animals. ('66.) New ed. ill. 12°. '76. $2 .... *Scribner.*

Tenney, W: J. Grammatical analyzer: derivation and definition of words. 12°. $1.50 ...... *Appleton.*

Tennyson, Alfr. Poetical works. por. and ill. 8°. $1.25; pap., 75c. .... *Harper.*

— *Same.* (Author's household ed.) por. and ill. 12°. $2 .... *Lee & S.*

— *Same.* (Cabinet ed.) 10 v. 16°. $15; mor., $20. *Scribner, W. & A.*

— *Same.* (Household ser.) ill. and por. 16°. $1.50; mor., $3 .... *Lee & S.*

— *Same.* 18°. $1 .... *R. Worthington.*

— *Same.* (Lib. ed.) 6 v. por. sm. 8°. $21; hf. cf., $33; hf. mor., $36; cf., $45; $48. *Scribner, W. & A.*

— *Same.* (Popular lib. ed.) 12°. '75. $2 .. *W. F. Gill.*

— *Same.* (Presentation poets.) ill. 16°. $1.75; hf. cf., $3; mor., $3.50; cf., $5 .... *Routledge.*

— *Same*; ill. by Creswick, Millais, Maclise, etc. 4°. $9; mor., $12 .... *Routledge.*

— Poems. 12°. $1.50 .... *Locke.*

— *Same.* ill. 12°. '65. $2. — ill. sm. 4°. '65. $9. *Tilton.*

— *Same.* (Blue and gold ed.) 2 v. por. 32°. $2.50; hf. cf., $5; mor., $6 .... *Osgood.*

— *Same.* (Cabinet ed.) 2 v. por. 16°. $3; hf. cf., $6; mor., $8 .... *Osgood.*

— *Same.* (Centennial ed.) ill. 8°. '76. pap., $1. *Osgood.*

— *Same.* (Crown ed.) 2 v. 8°. '74. $5; hf. cf., $10; mor., $13 .... *Osgood.*

— *Same.* (Diamond ed.) 16°. '66. $1; hf. cf., $2.25; mor., $3 .... *Osgood.*

— *Same.* (Farringford ed.) 2 v. por. and ill. 16°. $4.50; hf. cf., $9; mor., $12; — in 1 v. 12°. '65. $3.50; hf. cf., $6; mor., $8. — por. and ill. 8°. $10; hf. cf., $12; mor., $14 .... *Osgood.*

Tennyson, Alfr., *continued.*
— *Same.* (Fireside ed.) 10 v. 32°. '71. $10; hf. cf., $25; mor., $35 .... *Osgood.*
— *Same.* (Globe ed.) ill. 12°. $1.75 .... *Osgood.*
— *Same.* (Handy vol. ed.) 16°. '71. 75c... *Osgood.*
— *Same.* (Household ed.) por. and ill. 12°. '71. $2; hf. cf., $4; mor., $5 .... *Osgood.*
— *Same.* (People's ed.) 12°. $2.50 .... *Osgood.*
— *Same.* (Pocket ed.) por. 18°. $1.50 .... *Osgood.*
— *Same.* (Red line ed.) por. and ill. 4°. $3.50; hf. cf., $5; mor., $7 .... *Osgood.*
— — Concordance. cr. 8°. $3 .... *Routledge.*
— Enoch Arden. sm. 4°. '75. 50c.; pap., 25c. *Tompkins.*
— *Same.* ill. 16°. '64. $1.25. — por. and ill. sm. 4°. mor., $6 .... *Osgood.*
— *Same.* ill. 12°. '64. $3. — 16°. $1.25 ..... *Tilton.*
— *Same.* (Blue and gold ed.) 32°. $1.25 .... *Osgood.*
— *Same.* (Booth's Theatre ed.) roy. 8°. 50c... *Hinton.*
— *Same.* (Vest pocket ser.) ill. 32°. '76. 50c... *Osgood.*
— Gareth and Lynette. ill. 16°. '72. $1 .... *Osgood.*
— Gems from T. ill. 4°. $5. — ill. 8°. mor., $9 .. *Osgood.*
— Holy grail. 16°. '69. $1 .... *Osgood.*
— Horæ Tennysonianæ. *See* Church, A. J.
— Idylls of the king. ill. 4°. $5. — 8°. mor., $9 .. *Osgood.*
— *Same.* (New household ed.) ill. 12°. '75. $1.50; mor., $4.50 .... *Osgood.*
— *Same;* with 37 India proofs of ill. by Doré. ill. f°. mor., $125 .... *Routledge.*
— In memoriam. 16°. '61. $1.25 .... *Osgood.*
— Last tournament. ill. 16°. '71. $1; mor., $4 .. *Osgood.*
— *Same.* ill. 12°. '71. $2 .... *Tilton.*
— Locksley Hall. ill. sm. 4°. '68. $3; mor., $5.50. *Osgood.*
— *Same.* [In Eng. or Germ.] ill. 8°. pap., 50c. *Barclay.*
— May queen. ill. 12°. '75. $1.25 .... *Putnam.*
— *Same.* ill. 12°. $2.50; mor., $5 .... *Appleton.*
— Princess (The). 16°. $1 .... *Osgood.*
— Queen Mary. 16°. pap., 15c...... *De Witt; Happy.*
— *Same.* 16°. '75. $1; hf. cf., $3; mor., $4 .. *Osgood.*
— *Same.* (Popular lib. ed.) 12°. '75. 75c... *W. F. Gill.*
— *Same.* (Saunterer's ser.) 18°. 50c.; pap., 25c. *Osgood.*
— Songs for all seasons. por. and ill. 4°. 75c... *Osgood.*
— Vivien: an idyll; ill. by G. Doré. f°. mor., $30. *Routledge.*
— *See also* Companion poets; — Lotos leaves.

Tennyson, C: *See* Turner, C: T.

Tenot, Eug. Paris in December, 1851; or, the coup d'etat of Napoleon III.; tr. with notes by S. W. Adams and A. H. Brandon. cr. 8°. $2.50. *Hurd & H.*

Tent and town. Headley, P. C. 25c.; 30c... *J. E. Potter.*

Tent in the garden. *See* Golden stories.

Tent life in the Holy Land. Prime, W. C. $2; $3.75. *Harper.*

Tent life in Siberia. Kennan, G. $2 .... *Putnam.*

Tent on the beach. Whittier, J. G. $1.50; $4 .. *Osgood.*

Tercentenary book (The); by H. C. McCook, S. J. Willison, R. M. Patterson and others. 12°. $1.25 .... *Pres. Bd.*

Tercentenary monument. *See* Reformed Church in America.

Terence [*Lat.* Terentius] Afer, Publius. Adelphi, Hecyra and Phormio [Lat.]; with notes by J. Davies. 16°. (Lond.) 80c .... *Allyn.*
— Andria and Adelphœ [Lat.]; with notes by E. P. Crowell. ('74.) 2d ed. 16°. '75. hf. leath., $1.25. *Eldredge.*
— Andria and Heautontimoroumenos [Lat.]; with notes by J. Davies. 16°. (Lond.) 60c .... *Allyn.*
— Comedies; lit. tr. into Eng. prose; with notes, by H. T. Riley; [also] the blank verse tr. of G. Colman. 12°. $1.50 .... *Harper.*
— *See also* Plautus, T. M.
— *and* Phædrus. Works; tr. by H. T. Riley. 12°. (Bohn.) $1.75 .... *Little, B. & Co.*
— — — *Same.* 12°. (Bohn.) $2. *Lippincott; Scribner, W. & A.*

Terence Moran. *See* Bright gems for boys and girls; — Little boys' lib.

Terentius. *See* Terence.

Teresa, *St.* Autobiography; tr. by Canon Dalton. 12°. '60. $1.50 .... *Cunningham; Sadlier.*
— Life; by author of "Devotions before and after holy communion." cr. 8°. $3 .... *Macmillan.*
— *See also* Lives of the saints.

Terhune, *Mrs.* Ma. Virg. Hawes. *See* Harland, Marion (*pseud.*)

Terra Mariæ. Neill, E. D. $2 .... *Lippincott.*

Terrell, Alex. W. *See* Texas, Sup. Court reports.

Terrenia. Grahame, E. 50c .... *Pres. Bd.*

Terrible secret. Coyne, J. S. 15c .... *French.*

Terrible secret. Fleming, M. A. $1.75 .... *Carleton.*

Terrible tales. Sala, G. A. 30c .... *Am. News.*

Terrible temptation. *See* Reade, C:

Terrible tinker. Williams, T. J. 15c .... *French.*

Terror by night, and other stories. 18°. 25c. *Pres. Bd.*

Terry, Dan. Antiquary: play. 16°. pap., 15c... *French.*
— Guy Mannering: play. 16°. pap., 15c...... *French.*

Terry, M. S. Commentary on 1 Kings-Esther. 12°. $2.50 .... *Cin. Meth. Bk. Conc.*
— *See also* Steele, O., *and* Terry, M. S.

Terry, Rose. Poems. 16°. $1.25 .... * *Osgood.*

Tertulias de la infancia. 2 v. ill. 4°. ea., pap., 30c. *Appleton.*
Cont.: El teatro de Guiñol. — La Cenicienta.

Tertullian [*Lat.* Tertullianus], Q. S. F. Select works [Lat.]; ed. by F. A. March, with introd. by L. Coleman. 12°. '76. $1.75 .... *Harper.*
— Writings; tr. by S. Thelwall and P. Holmes. (Ante-Nicene Christ. lib.) v. 1, 2. 8°. ea., $3. *Scribner, W. & A.*
— *Same.* v. 3; [also] writings of Victorinus and Commodianus. (Ante-Nicene Christ. lib.) 8°. $3. *Scribner, W. & A.*

Tessier, J. P. Clinical remarks concerning homœop. treatment of pneumonia; tr. by C. J. Hempel. 8°. 75c .... *Boericke.*
— Clinical researches concerning homœopathic treatment of Asiatic cholera; tr. by C. J. Hempel. 8°. 75c .... *Boericke.*

Test of truth. Graham, M. J. 40c .... *Am. Bapt.*

Test of truth. Suter, W. E. 15c .... *French.*

Testament. *See* Bible.

Testament (Le) de Madame Patural. *See* Souvestre, E.

Testament (Das) Peter des Grossen. Herbert, L. 50c. *Morwitz.*

Tested. Gardner, C. E. $1.75 .... *Carleton.*

Testimony of Christ to Christianity. Bayne, P. 75c. *Tibbals.*

Testimony of an escaped novice from the sisterhood of St. Joseph. Bunkley, J. M. $1.50 .. *Harper.*

Testimony of the rocks. Miller, H. $1.50... *Carter.*

Teuffel, W: Sgsm. History of Roman literature; tr. by W. Wagner. 2 v. 8°. $10.50 .. *Scribner, W. & A.*

Texas. Constitutions, with U. S. and Confederate States Constitutions, etc.; with annotations by J. Sayles. 8°. '72. shp., $6 .... *E. H. Cushing.*
— Digest of laws. *See* Paschal, G. W.
— Legal forms for use in Texas; by a member of the Texas bar. 12°. '60. shp., $2.50 .. *E. H. Cushing.*
— Notes to reports. *See* Sayles, J.
— Probate laws; with forms and precedents by J. Sayles. ('71.) 2d ed. 8°. '73. shp., $4... *E. H. Cushing.*
— Supreme Court reports, v. 1-3, 10-13. 2d ed., with notes by J. Sayles. 7 v. 8°. '74-'76. ea., shp., $7.50 .... *E. H. Cushing.*
Cont.: 1-3 (1846-'48), by J. Webb and T. W. Duval. — 10-13 (1853-'55), by O. C. and R. K. Hartley.
— *Same.* v. 15-37 (1855-'72). 23 v. 8°. ea., shp., $7.50 .... *E. H. Cushing.*

Texas, *continued.*

Cont.: 14-21 (1855-'58), by O. C. and R. K. Hartley. — 22-25 (1858-'60), by G. F. Moore and R. S. Walker. — 26, 27 (1861-'65), by C. L. Robards and A. M. Jackson. — 28-31 (1866-'69), by G. W. Paschal. — 32-37 (1869-'72), by E. M. Wheelock.

— *Same.* v. 34 (1862-'65); by E. M. Wheelock. 8°. '73. shp., $7.50 .... (?) *Tracy.*
— *Same.* v. 38-43 (1873-'76); by A. W. Terrell and R. S. Walker. 6 v. 8°. ea., *net*, shp., $6. *E. H. Cushing.*
— — Digest. *See* Paschal, G. W.

Texas geological and agricultural survey. First report of progress; by B. F. Shumard. 8°. '59.. *State.*

Texas scrap book. Baker, D. W. C. $5; $6.. *Barnes.*

Text-book of Freemasonry; by a member of the craft. ill. 16°. $1 .... *Lippincott.*

Text of easy words. *See* Short prayer.

Thacher, E. Tables of strength of cast iron columns. *See* Allen, T., Iron hulls for western river steamboats.

Thackeray, *Miss* Anne I. [*now Mrs.* Ritchie]. Bluebeard's keys, and other stories. 8°. pap., 75c. *Harper.*
— Miscellaneous writings. ill. 8°. $1.75; pap., $1.25. *Harper.*
— Miss Angel. ill. 8°. pap., 75c. .... *Harper.*
— Old Kensington. ill. 8°. $1.50; pap., $1.. *Harper.*
— Story of Elizabeth. 16°. $1 .... * *Osgood.*
— *Same.* 12°. $1.50; pap., $1 .... *Peterson.*
— Village on the cliff. 8°. pap., 25c. .... *Harper.*
— *Same.* 8°. '67. pap., 25c. .... *Littell & G.*
— *Same.* 16°. $1 .... * *Osgood.*

Thackeray, W: Makepeace. Works. 22 v. ill. 8°. (Lond.) $66; hf. cf., $100; cf., $150; mor., $175 .... *Little, B. & Co.*

Cont.: Ballads and tales. — Barry Lyndon, etc. — Book of snobs. — Burlesques. — Catherine, etc. — Christmas books — Denis Duval, etc. — Four Georges, etc. — Henry Esmond. — Irish sketch book. — Newcomes, 2 v. — Paris sketch book. — Pendennis, 2 v. — Philip, etc., 2 v. — Roundabout papers. — Vanity fair, 2 v. — Virginians, 2 v.

— *Same.* (Crown ed.) 11 v. ill. cr. 8°. ea., $3.25. *Lippincott.*

Cont.: Book of snobs; Burlesques. — Catherine; Denis Duval; Lovel, the widower. — Christmas books; Ballads and tales. — Four Georges; English humorists; Roundabout papers. — Henry Esmond; Barry Lyndon. — Newcomes. — Paris sketch book; Irish sketch book. — Pendennis. — Philip. — Vanity Fair. — Virginians.

— *Same.* (Household ed.) 11 v. 16°. ea., $1.25. * *Osgood.*

Contents same as in Library ed.

— *Same.* (Kensington ed.) 12 v. ill. 8°. ea., $2. * *Osgood.*

Cont.: Book of snobs; Sketches. — Christmas books. — Henry Esmond; Barry Lyndon. — Hoggarty diamond; Yellowplush; Burlesques. — Newcomes. — Paris, Irish and Eastern sketch books. — Pendennis. — Philip. — Roundabout papers; Lectures. — Stories; Ballads, etc. — Vanity fair. — Virginians.

— *Same.* (Lib. ed.) 11 v. ill. 12°. ea., $2.. * *Osgood.*

Cont.: Barry Lyndon; Great Hoggarty diamond; Burlesques. — Book of snobs; Denis Duval, etc. — Catherine; Fraser miscellanies; Christmas books; Ballads, etc. — Four Georges; English humorists; Roundabout papers, etc. — Henry Esmond; Lovel, the widower. — Newcomes. — Paris sketch book; Irish sketch book, etc. — Pendennis. — Philip. — Vanity fair. — Virginians.

— *Same.* (Lib. ed.) 22 v. ill. 8°. ea., $3; per set, hf. cf., $100; cf., $125; $150 .... *Lippincott.*
— *Same.* (Lib. ed.) 22 v. ill. 8°. $60; hf. cf., $100; cf., $160; $180 .... *Scribner, W. & A.*
— *Same.* (Popular ed.) 12 v. 12°. ea., $2.50; per set, $24; hf. cf., $45; hf. mor., $60.. *Scribner, W. & A.*

Contents same as in Kensington ed.

— Adventures of Philip. ill. 8°. $1.50; pap., 75c. *Harper.*
— Ballads. 16°. $1.25 .... *Osgood.*
— Catherine. 8°. pap., 35c. .... * *Osgood.*
— Denis Duval. ill. 8°. pap., 25c. .... *Harper.*
— Early and late papers. 12°. $2 .... * *Osgood.*
— Great Hoggarty diamond. 8°. pap., 25c... *Harper.*

Thackeray, W: Makepeace, *continued.*
— History of Henry Esmond; [also] Lovel, the widower. 8°. pap., 75c.; hf. cf., $3 .... *Harper.*
— History of Pendennis. 2 v. ill. 8°. $2; hf. cf., $5; — in 1 v. 8°. pap., $1. — (chp. ed.) por. and ill. 12°. $1.25 .... *Harper.*
— Irish sketch book. 8°. pap., 75c. .... *Peterson.*
— Lectures: English humorists, Four Georges, Charity and humor. 12°. $1.25 .... *Harper.*
— Lovel, the widower. ill. 8°. pap., 25c. .... *Harper.*
— Newcomes (The). ill. 8°. $1.50; pap., $1; hf. cf., $3 .... *Harper.*
— Orphan of Pimlico, and other sketches, fragments and drawings; ed. by Miss Thackeray. ill. roy. 4°. hf. roan, $7.50; hf. mor., $9.... *Lippincott.*
— Rose and the ring; or, history of Prince Giglio and Prince Bulbo. ill. sm. 4°. $1 .... *Harper.*
— Roundabout papers: essays. ill. 12°. $1.50.. *Harper.*
— Students' Quarter; or, Paris five and thirty years since. ill. 12°. $1.75 .... *Scribner, W. & A.*
— Thackerayana: notes and anecdotes; with ill. from draw. by Thackeray. 12°. $3.75.. *Scribner, W. & A.*
— *Same.* ill. 12°. '75. $5 .... *Routledge.*
— Vanity fair: a novel without a hero. ill. 8°. pap., $1; — in 3 v. ill. and por. post 8°. $7.50; hf. mor., $12.75 .... *Harper.*
— Virginians. ill. 8°. $1.50; pap., $1; hf. cf., $3. *Harper.*

Thackerayana. *See* Thackeray, W: M.

Thaddeus of Warsaw. *See* Porter, Jane.

Thalaba: drama. 16°. pap., 15c. .... *French.*

Thalatta. Longfellow, S., *and* Higginson, T. W. $1. *Osgood.*

Thalheimer, M. E. History of England; for schools. ill. 12°. '75. $1.50 .... *Wilson, H. & Co.*
— History of the world, ancient and modern; with index. 2 v. ill., maps and charts. 8°. '72-'74. ea., $2.50; per set, hf. roxb., $6.. *Wilson, H. & Co.*
— — Eclectic historical atlas. [Maps of above.] 8°. '74. $1.50 .... *Wilson, H. & Co.*

Thaljunker (Der), od. der Heldentod. 12°. 35c.; pap., 15c. .... *Benziger.*

Thankful widow. 18°. '67. 30c. *N. Y. Ref. Ch. Bd.; Pres. Com.*

Thankfulness. Tayler, C. B. $1 .... *Leighton.*

Thankfulness and character. Wadsworth, C. 25c. *Peterson.*

Thanksgiving. Adams, W. $2 .... *Scribner.*

Thanksgiving. Chester, S. E. 25c. .... *Am. Tr.*

Thanksgiving. Wadsworth, C. 15c. ...... *Peterson.*

Thanksgiving. *See* Swallow stories.

Thanksgiving day. *See* Daisy lib.

That affair at Finchley. Coyne, J. S. 15c.... *French.*

That alabaster box. Seiss, J. A. 10c.... *Luth. Bk. St.*

That blessed baby. Moore, J. G. 15c. .... *French.*

That boy of Norcott's. *See* Lever, C:

That's it; or, plain teaching: book of universal knowledge; by author of the "Reason why" ser. ill. 12°. $1.50 .... *Dick & F.*

That mysterious bundle. Lambla, H. L. 15c... *Ames.*

That nose. Woolf, B. E. 15c. .... *French.*

That queer girl. Townsend, V. F. $1.50.... *Lee & S.*

That rascal Pat: farce. 16°. pap., 15c. .... *French.*

That sweet story of old. Lathrop, M. A. 35c. *Am. Tr.*

That terrible question. Hull, M. 10c. .... *Colby.*

Thatcher, B: Bussey. American revolution: rare and remark. passages of [its] hist. 18°. 75c. *Harper.*
— Biography of distinguished [N. A.] Indians. 2 v. 18°. $1.50 .... *Harper.*
— Indian traits: sketches of manners, customs and character of the N. A. natives. 2 v. ill. 18°. $1.50 .... *Harper.*
— Tales of the Am. revolution. ill. 18°. 75c... *Harper.*

Thätige Christenthum (Das). Miller, G. 40c. *Ev. Assoc.*

Thaumaturgus, Greg. Writings; [also] Writings of Dionysius of Alexandria; [also] Writings of Archelaus; tr. by S. D. F. Salmond. (Ante-Nicene Christ. lib.) 8°. $3.... *Scribner, W.& A.*

Thautropfen. *See* Dew drops.

Thaxter, Ad. Wallace. Grotto nymph: farce. 16°. pap., 15c. .... *French.*

Thaxter, *Mrs.* Celia. Among the Isles of Shoals. (Saunterer's ser.) ill. 18°. '73. $1.25.. *Osgood.*

— Poems. New ed., enl. sm. 4°. '76. $1.50.. *Hurd & H.*

Thayer, *Mrs.* Caro. M. Religion recommended to youth. 24°. 30c. .... *Cin. Meth. Bk. Conc.*

Thayer, Eug. Festival cantata. 8°. '72. bds., $1.25; pap., $1 .... *Ditson.*

— Mass no. 1 in E flat; with organ or piano forte accomp. 8°. '65. bds., $2 .... *Ditson.*

Thayer, M. Russell. The law; considered as a progressive science: address. 8°. pap., 30c... *Kay.*

Thayer, Sylvanus. Special report on sea-wall, Ramhead, Mass. *See* United States, *Corps of Eng.*

Thayer, T: Bald. Origin and history of doctrine of endless punishment. New ed., enl. 12°. '55. $1 .... *Universalist.*

— Over the river; or, pleasant walks into the valley of shadows and beyond. 16°. '64. $1; $1.25; mor., $3 .... *Universalist.*

— Theology of Universalism. 12°. '62. $1; $1.25. *Universalist.*

Thayer, W: Makepeace. ["Uncle Juvinell."] Abraham Lincoln, the pioneer boy. 16°. $1.50. (?) *Shepard.*

— Communion wine and Bible temperance. ('69.) New ed. 12°. '70. 50c.; pap., 20c...... *Nat. Temp.*

— Farmer boy (The) and how he became commander-in-chief. ('63.) New ed. ill. 16°. '76. $1.50. *Lockwood, B. & Co.*

— Life at the fireside. 12°. $1.50......... *Cong. Pub.*

— Morning star; or, symbols of Christ. 16°. $1.25. *J. E. Potter.*

— Pastor's wedding gift. ('54.) New ed. 16°. '72. $1.......................... *Lockwood, B. & Co.*

— Pioneer lib. 3 v. ill. 16°. '70. ea., $1.25. *Perkinpine.*

Cont.: Stories of the creation. — Soldiers of the Bible. — Stories of the patriarchs.

— Working and winning; or, the deaf boy's triumph. ('62.) New ed. ill. 16°. '75. $1.25.... *Hoyt.*

— Youth's history of the rebellion. 4 v. ill. 12°. ea., $1.50 .... *Fuller.*

Cont.: Sumter to Roanoke. — Roanoke to Murfreesboro'. — Murfreesboro' to Fort Pillow. — Fort Pillow to the end.

Thearle, S. J. P. Naval architecture, shipbuilding and laying off. (Element. sci. ser.) 16°. '74. 75c.; 4° plates, $1.25. — (Adv. sci. ser.) 12°. '74. $1.50; 4° plates, $2.50................ *Putnam.*

Theatre of the Greeks. *See* Donaldson, J. W.

Theban legion. Blackburn, W. M. $1..... *Pres. Bd.*

Thébaud, A: J. Gentilism; or, religion previous to Christianity. 8°. $3.50; hf. mor., $6; $6.50; hf. cf., $7.50.......................... *Sadlier.*

— Irish race in the past and present. 8°. $3.50. *Appleton; Sadlier.*

Theda and the mountain. *See* Silver penny ser.

Theed, Marion F. What she did with her life. 16°. $1.25 .... *Routledge.*

Theel, F. W. Hand-Fibel für den Lese-und Schreib-Unterricht. 8°. bds., 20c............. *Hoeger.*

Thefiloth: daily prayers. [Hebrew; with Eng. or Germ. tr.] 16°. '68. $1.50; $2; mor., $2.50 .. *Bloch.*

— *Same;* without tr. 16°. 50c............... *Bloch.*

— *See also* Machsorim.

Their children. Clarke, H. S. $1.50....... *Lothrop.*

Their wedding journey. Howells, W. D. $2; $1.25. *Osgood.*

Theistic conception of the world. Cocker, B. F. $2.50.............................. *Harper.*

Thelwall, Algernon Sydney. Thoughts in affliction; [also] Bereaved parents consoled, by J. Thornton; [also] Sacred poetry. 32°. 50c... *Appleton.*

Them papers. Leavitt, A. J. 15c........... *De Witt.*

Them thar grasshoppers. Small, G. G. 25c... *Collin & S.*

Theobald the iron-hearted. Malan, C. 40c. *N. Y. Ref. Ch. Bd.; Pres. Com.*

Theocritus, Bion *and* Moschus. Idylls; [also] War songs of Tyrtæus; tr. by J. Banks, with metrical versions of Chapman. 12°. (Bohn.) $1.75. *Little, B. & Co.*

— — — *Same.* 12°. (Bohn.) $2. *Lippincott; Scribner, W. & A.*

Theodelinda (*pseud.*) The Vail family; or, doing good. 18°. 75c..................... *Pres. Bd.*

Theodora. McKeen, P. F. $1.75......... *Randolph.*

Theodora: drama. 16°. pap., 15c........... *French.*

Theodora's childhood. Marshall, E. 50c. *Scribner, W. & A.*

Theodore. Wette, W. M. L. de. $1.50... *Burnham.*

Theodore: a story about baptism; by a true Baptist. 16°. $1.50 .... *Pres. Bd.*

Theodore, the child of the sea. Ingraham, J. H. 25c. *De Witt.*

Theo. Gray's first years out of school. M'Clellan, K. $1.50 .... *Whittaker.*

Theo. Leigh. Thomas, A. 50c............. *Harper.*

Theodore Thinker's new stories for little folks. ('51.) New ed. 12 v. ill. 24°. '75. $5.... *Clark & M.*

Cont.: Picture A B C book. — Boys' story book. — Girls' story book. — Two cousins; or, how to be loved. — Storm and sunshine. — Holiday book. — Tom Headstrong; or, always in trouble. — Uncle Reuben and his budget of stories. — Stories about the country. — Stories about birds and beasts. — Balloon, and other stories. — Jack Mason, the old sailor.

Theodore's trouble. *See* Leighton children.

Theodoretus *and* Evagrius *Scholasticus*. Ecclesiastical histories; from A.D. 332–427, and from A.D. 431–544. 12°. (Bohn.) $1.75... *Little, B. & Co.*

— — *Same.* 12°. (Bohn.) $2. *Lippincott; Scribner, W. & A.*

— — *See also* Greek ecclesiastical historians.

Theodosia Earnest. *See* Dayton, A. C.

Theognis. *See* Hesiodus, Callimachus Cyrenæus, *and* Theognis.

Theologia Germanica; ed. by F. Pfeiffer; tr. by S. Winkworth. 18°. '74. $1.25....... *Macmillan.*

— *Same;* with introd. by C. E. Stowe. ('55.) New ed. 16°. $1.50; cf., $2.50.............. *Draper.*

Theologian's catalogue and classified price list, to 1876. 12th ed. 8°. '76. 50c.; pap., 25c....... *Tibbals.*

Theological sketch book; or, skeletons of sermons. 2 v. in 1. 8°. '75. $3.50.............. *Carter.*

Theology of the British poets. Brooke, S. A. $2. *Appleton.*

Theology of the Greek poets. Tyler, W. S. $1.75. *Draper.*

Theophilus, Antiochenus. *See* Tatian *and* Theophilus, A.

Theophilus Americanus. Wordsworth, C. $2. *McCauley.*

Theophilus and others. Dodge, M. M. $1.50. (?) *Scribner.*

Theophilus Walton. Harrison, W. P. $1.50.. *So. Meth.*

Theophrastus. Characters: Eng. translation from a rev. text; with introd. and notes by R. C. Jebb. fp. 8°. '70. $2.......................... *Macmillan.*

Theory and practice. *See* Cupples, *Mrs.* A. J.

There's millions in it: musical [dram.] sketch. 16°. pap., 15c. .... *Happy.*

There's no place like home. Douglas, A. M. $1.50. *W. F. Gill.*

There's no smoke without fire. Picton, T. 15c. *De Witt.*

There's no time to spare: dialogue. 18°. 18c. *Am. S. S.*

There's time enough; or, the story of Charlie Scott. ill. 18°. 50c. . . . . *Bost. Am. Tr.*
— *See also* Laughing Kitty stories.
Theremin, Fs. Eloquence a virtue; or, outlines of a systematic rhetoric; tr. by W. G. T. Shedd. 3d ed., rev. with introd. essay. ('59.) New ed. 12°. '72. $1 . . . . *Draper.*
Theremin, L: F: Fz. Hours with the Lord; tr. from the Germ. 32°. '59. 35c. . . . . *Dutton.*
Theresa's journal. Pressensé, E. de. $1.10 . . *Am. S. S.*
Therese. Payne, J. H. 15c. . . . . *French.*
Thesaurus Græcæ linguæ. 16 v. f°. (Bagster.) $68. *Wiley.*
These for those. Warren, W. $1.50 . . . . *Hoyt, F. & D.*
Thesen über den Wucher. 8°. '75. 15c. . . . . *Barthel.*
Theseus and Ariadne. Planché, J. R. 15c. . . *French.*
Thesmophoriazusæ. *See* Aristophanes.
Thespian speaker. 12°. pap., 15c. . . . . *De Witt.*
Thessalonica. Hastings, H. L. $1 . . . . . . *Hastings.*
Theta (*pseud.*) *See* Henderson, Jla. Putnam.
Thetis and Peleus: extravaganza. 16°. pap., 15c. *French.*
They met by chance. Logan, O. $1.50 . . *Adams, V. & Co.*
Thibaut, Anton F: Justus. Introduction to study of jurisprudence; from "System des Pandekten Rechts"; tr., with notes, by N. Lindley. 8°. '55. $3 . . . . *T. & J. W. Johnson.*
— — *See also* Law lib.
Thiboust, Lambert. *See* Decourcelle, A., *and* Thiboust, L.; — Siraudin, P., *and* Thiboust, L.
Thiéblin, N: Léon. Spain and the Spaniards. 12°. $1.75 . . . . *Lee & S.*
Thief in the night. Spofford, H. E. $1.25 . . . *Roberts.*
Thief of time. Baker, G. M. 15c. . . . . *Lee & S.*
Thierry, Augustin. Conquest of England by the Normans; tr. by W. Hazlitt. 2 v. por. 12°. (Bohn.) ea., $1.25 . . . . *Little, B. & Co.*
— *Same.* 2 v. por. 12°. (Bohn.) ea., $1.40. *Scribner, W. & A.*
— *Same.* 2 v. por. 12°. (Bohn.) ea., $1.50 . . *Lippincott.*
— Formation and progress of the tiers état or third estate in France; tr. by F. B. Wells. 12°. (Bohn.) $2 . . . . . *Lippincott; Scribner, W. & A.*
Thiers, L: Adph. History of the consulate and empire of France under Napoleon; tr. by D. F. Campbell and H. W. Herbert; with notes and add. ('61.) New ed. 5 v. ill. 8°. '74. $12.50; shp., $15; hf. cf., $22.50 . . . . *Claxton.*
— History of the French revolution [1789–1799]; tr. by F. Shoberl. 4 v. ill. 8°. '62. $8; shp., $12; hf. cf., $16; — in 2 v. 8°. $5; shp., $7; hf. cf., $10 . . . . *Appleton.*
Thieves at the mill: Ethiop. drama. 16°. pap., 15c. *French; Happy.*
Thigpen, *Miss* J. The lover's revenge, and other poems. 12°. '76. $1 . . . . *Burke.*
Thimm, Fz. Modern languages self-taught. 4 v. 16°. ea., pap., 25c.; — in 1 v., $1.50 . . . . . . *Dick & F.*
Cont.: French. — Germ. — Span. — Ital. self-taught.

Things by their right names. Barbauld, A. L. 75c. *Harper.*
Things common and uncommon. Chellis, M. D. $1.50. *Cong. Pub.*
Things in the forest. Kirby, M. *and* E. 75c. . . *Nelson.*
Things new and old. Spencer, J. $7.50; $12 . . *Tibbals.*
Things not generally known. Wells, D. A. $1.75. *Appleton.*
Things to be thought of. 18°. 40c. . . . . *Am. S. S.*
Things unseen and eternal. Murray, N. 75c. . . *Harper.*
Think and act. Penny, V. $1.50 . . . . *Claxton.*
Think before you act. Sherwood, M. M. 35c. . . *Carter.*
Think well on't. *See* Challoner, R:
Thinker, Thdr. (*pseud.*) First lessons in botany. 16°. '50. 40c. . . . . *Barnes.*
— *See also* Theodore Thinker.
Thinker. *See* Burleigh, J. B.
Thinkers and thinking. Garretson, J. E. $1.50. *Lippincott.*
Thinks-I-to-myself. Nares, E. $1.25 . . . . *Miller.*
Thiodolph, the Icelander. *See* La Motte-Fouqué.
Thirlwall, Connop. History of Greece. 2 v. 8°. $4; shp., $5; hf. cf., $8.50 . . . . *Harper.*
Thirteen months in the rebel army; by an impressed New Yorker. 16°. '62. 75c. . . . . *Barnes.*
Thirty minutes for refreshments. Baker, G. M. 15c. *Lee & S.*
Thirty three next birthday. Morton, J. M. 15c. *Ames; French.*
Thirty two stories for children. ill. 24°. 25c. *Meth. Bk. Conc.*
Thirty years in the Arctic regions: Sir John Franklin's four expeditions to the Polar seas. 12°. $1.75. *J. E. Potter.*
Thirty years in the harem. Kibrizli-Mehemet-Pasha. $1.50 . . . . *Harper.*
Thirty years in the itinerancy. Miller, W. G. $1.50. *Hauser.*
Thirty years of army life on the border. Marcy, R. B. $3 . . . . *Harper.*
Thirty years since. James, G. P. R. 75c. . . *Harper.*
Thirty years' view. Benton, T. H. $6–$12 . . *Appleton.*
Thirza, od. die Anziehungskraft des Kreuzes. 18°. '45. 25c. . . . . *Am. Tr.*
This day month. *See* Power, P. B.
This do in remembrance of me. Smith, J. 10c. *Pres. Bd.*
This one thing I do. *See* Porter, *Mrs.* A. E.
This, our life. Anthony, C. H. $2 . . . . *Munsell.*
This present world. Arnot, W. $1.25 . . . . . . *Carter.*
Thistle blows. 18°. 40c. . . . . *Am. S. S.*
Thistledown. Boyle, E. $1.50 . . . . *Lippincott.*
Tholuck, F: A: Gottreu. Circle of human life; tr. 16°. 75c. . . . . *Carter.*
— Commentary on Sermon on the mount; tr. 8°. $3. *Scribner, W. & A.*
— Hours of Christian devotion; tr. 16°. '71. $1; $1.50; $2 . . . . *Lothrop.*
— *Same;* tr. by R. Menzies. ('74.) 2d ed. cr. 8°. '75. $3 . . . . *Scribner.*
— Light from the cross. 12°. $1.50 . . . . . (?) *Martien.*
— *Same.* ill. 16°. '69. $1.50 . . . . *Lothrop.*
— *Same.* 8°. $2.50 . . . . *Scribner, W. & A.*
— On the Gospel of John; tr. by C. J. Krauth. 8°. $3. *Scribner, W. & A.; Sheldon.*
Thom, Ad. Bisset. The upper ten thousand: alphabet. list of members of noble families, bishops, etc. 12°. '75. $4 . . . . *Routledge.*
Thomas Aquinas, *St.* Commentary on the four Gospels; [from] the works of the fathers. 6 v. 8°. '74. $21 . . . . *Pott.*
— Ninety-nine homilies upon some of the Epistles and Gospels of the Christian year. 12°. $1.50 . . *Pott.*
— Venerable sacrament of the altar; with pref. by W. J. E. Bennett; tr. by J. M. Neal. 18°. '71. $1.50. *Pott.*
Thomas à Becket. Hollister, G. H. $1.75 . . . *Lee & S.*
Thomas à Becket: play. 16°. pap., 15c. . . . . *French.*
Thomas *a Kempis*. De imitatione Christi. cr. 8°. '67. $2.50 . . . . *Macmillan.*
— *Eng.* Christian's pattern: treatise on the imitation of Christ. 24°. '37. 45c. . . . . . *Meth. Bk. Conc.*
— — Following of Christ. 32°. 40c.–$2.50 . . *O'Shea.*
— — *Same.* 48°. '52. 50c.–$3 . . . . *Murphy.*
— — *Same.* 32°. 55c.; roan, 90c.; mor., $2.50. *Cummiskey.*
— — *Same.* 24°. 60c.–$3. — 18°. $1.50–$3.50. *Sadlier.*

Thomas *a Kempis, continued.*
— — *Same;* tr. by R. Challoner. 48°. 40c.; 60c.; roan, 75c.; mor., $1.50 .... *O'Shea.*
— — — *See also* Bible, New Test.
— — Imitation of Christ. 32°. 50c.-$2.75 .... *Benziger.*
— — *Same.* 16°. 75c. .... *Mason.*
— — *Same.* 18°. '70. 75c.; $1.25 .... *Lothrop.*
— — *Same.* 16°. $1.25; mor., $2.50. — (chp. ed.), 50c. .... *Lee & S.*
— — *Same.* 8°. mor., $10. — 12°. mor., $5. — 18°. mor., $2 .... *Appleton.*
— — *Same;* tr. by W. Benham. cr. 8°. '74. $3. *Macmillan.*
— — *Same;* tr. by R. Challoner. 18°. $1.25-$5. *Benziger.*
— — *Same;* with introd. by F. W. Farrar. 16°. '70. $1.25; $1.50; mor., $4.50. — (Lond. ed.) 32°. 50c.; $1 .... *Dutton.*
— — *Same;* tr. by J. Payne; with introd. by T. Chalmers. 16°. '67. $1 .... *Collins & Bro.*
— — *Same;* with introd. by T. Chalmers; ed. by H. Malcom. New ed.; with life of author by C. Ullmann. 12°. $1.25. — sq. 8°. $2.25; $3 .. *Sheldon.*
— — Imitation; or, following of Christ. 32°. 40c.; 75c.; $1; mor., $2 .... *Strong.*
— — Like unto Christ. 16°. $3 ..... *Scribner, W. & A.*
— — Of the imitation of Christ: new tr. by Dean Goodwin. 18°. '69. 75c. .... *Pott.*
— — On the imitation of Christ. 18°. $1; cf., $2.25; mor., $6 .... *Lippincott.*
— — *Same.* 18°. 50c.; $1 .... *Nelson.*
— Garden of roses; [also] Valley of lilies; tr. 32°. '51. 50c.-$2 .... *Murphy.*
— Soliloquy of the soul; [also] Garden of roses; tr. 18°. 75c. .... *Pott.*

Thomas *of Jesus, Father.* Sufferings of our Lord Jesus Christ. 12°. $2 .... *O'Shea.*

Thomas *of Villanova, St.* Life. 12°. $1.50 .. *Sadlier.*
— *See also* Lives of the saints.

Thomas, A. A. Post mortem examination and morbid anatomy. [Hom.] 8°. $3 .... *Boericke.*

Thomas, *Miss* A. E. Hattie Powers; or, the daughter's mission. ('67.) New ed. ill. 16°. '71. $1.25. *Hoyt.*

Thomas, Abel. Life. 18°. 30c. ...... *Friends Bk. St.*

Thomas, Abel C. *See* Ely, E. S., *and* Thomas, A. C.

Thomas, *Mrs.* Annie [*now Mrs.* Pender Cudlip]. Novels. 14 v. 8°. pap. .... *Harper.*
Cont.: Called to account. — Denis Donne. — Dower house. — False colors. — He cometh not, she said. — On guard. — Only herself. — Theo. Leigh. — Two widows, *ea.*, 50c. — Passion in tatters. — Played out. — Walter Goring, *ea.*, 75c. — Maud Mohan. — Playing for high stakes, *ea.*, 25c.
— Married at last. 12°. $1.75; pap., $1.50 .. *Peterson.*
— Narrow escape. 8°. '76. pap., 75c. ..... *W. F. Gill.*
— No alternative. 12°. $1.50; pap., 75c. — (Intern. ed.), $1.25 .... *Porter.*
— Sir Victor's choice. 12°. bds., $1 ...... *Routledge.*

Thomas, Cyrus. Report on orthoptera. *See* United States, *Corps of Eng.*
— Synopsis of the acoididæ of No. Am. *See* United States, *Geog. and geol. survey.*

Thomas, D: Genius of the Gospel: commentary on St. Matthew; ed. by W. Webster. 8°. '73. $4.50. *Smith, E. & Co.*
— The homilist. 2d ed. cr. 8°. '76. $1.50 ... *Tibbals.*

Thomas, E. L. Olmstead family of New England. 16°. '69. 50c. .... *Munsell.*

Thomas, H. J. One hundred short sermons; tr. by J. A. Hamilton; with introd. by M. J. Spalding. 8°. '69. $3 .... *Murphy.*

Thomas, Isaiah. Account of the Am. Antiq. Soc., with act of incorporation, by-laws and list of officers and members. 8°. '13. $1 .. *Am. Antiq.*
— Communication [to the Am. Antiq. Soc.]; with list of officers and members and of articles presented to the Society. 8°. '15. $1 .... *Am. Antiq.*

Thomas, Isaiah, *continued.*
— History of printing in America. 2 v. 8°. '74. ea., $4 .... *Am. Antiq.*
Compr. v. 5, 6 of Transactions of Am. Antiq. Soc.

Thomas, J. E. Prize essay on encroachment of the sea between the Mersey and the Bristol Channel. 8°. '67. pap., 40c. .... *Spon.*

Thomas, *Mrs.* J. H. Drifted snow flakes. 2 ser. sm. 4°. '74. ea., $1.50; — in 1 v., $3 ... *H. A. Young.*
— Leaves gathered in the daily walks of life. sq. 18°. '74. $1.50 .... *H. A. Young.*
— Thoughts that cluster. sq. 18°. '74. $1.50. *H. A. Young.*

Thomas, Jerry. Bartender's guide; or, how to mix drinks. 12°. $2.50 .... *Dick & F.*

Thomas, J: J. American fruit culturist: directions for propagation and culture of all fruits adapted to U. S. ill. demy 8°. $3.75 .... *W. Wood.*
— Farm implements and farm machinery, and principles of construc. and use. ill. 12°. $1.50 ... *Judd.*
— Rural affairs. 7 v. ill. 12°. '57-'75. ea., $1.50. *L. Tucker.*

Thomas, J: R. Diamond cut diamond. [Operetta.] 4°. bds., $1 .... *Peters.*
— Picnic; with words by G. Cooper. [Cantata.] 8°. '69. bds., $1 .... *Ditson.*
— Sacred music: tunes, anthems, etc.; with sep. organ accomp. ('63.) New ed. 8°. '76. $1.50 .. *Pond.*
— Sacred quartets and anthems; for choirs and the home circle. obl. 4°. '74. $2.75; bds., $2.50. *Ditson.*

Thomas, Jos. Comprehensive pronouncing medical dictionary; with app. cr. 8°. '64. $3.25; shp., $3.75. *Lippincott.*
— First book of etymology. 12°. '52. hf. bd., 75c. *Fortescue.*
— (*ed.*) Lippincott's universal pronouncing dictionary of biography and mythology. roy. 8°. '70. shp., $15; hf. mor., $17; $18; — in 2 v. 8°. $22; shp., $24; hf. mor., $27-$30; mor., $36. — (Ill. ed.) 49 pts. 8°. ea., 50c.; in 3 v., $28.50; hf. mor., $31.50 .... *Lippincott.*
— *and* Baldwin, T: (*ed.*) Lippincott's complete pronounc. gazetteer of the world. 2 v. 8°. '55. shp., $12; hf. cf., $16; — in 1 v. roy. 8°. '68. shp., $10; hf. mor., $12.50 .... *Lippincott.*

Thomas, L. Museum of wonderful and gallant exploits. col. ill. 12°. *$2 .... *C. A. Nichols.*

Thomas, Lynall. Rifled ordnance: applic. of principle of the rifle to guns and mortars of every calibre; [with] new theory of initial action and force of fired gunpowder. 5th ed., rev. ill. 8°. '64. $2 .... *Van Nostrand.*

Thomas, Martha M. Life's lessons: tale. 12°. $1.50. *Harper.*

Thomas, R. Glory of America. ill. 12°. $1.50 .. *Sower.*

Thomas, R. W. Modern practice of photography. 8°. '68. 75c. .... *Baird.*

Thomas, S. A. Book-keeping: single entry. demy 4°. *net*, $1; — double entry. demy 4°. *net*, 75c. — Key. demy 4°. *net*, 25c. .... *Peck.*

Thomas, Thdr. Gaillard. Practical treatise on diseases of women. 4th ed., rev. and enl. ill. 8°. $5; leath., $6 .... *Lea.*

Thomas and Ann Thompson. 18°. 30c. ...... *Dutton.*

Thomas and Ellen; [also] Two little children; [also] simple rhymes. 18°. 30c. .... *Am. S. S.*

Thomas Brown. *See* History of.

Thomas Fish. *See* Story of.

Thomas Kenmir. 18°. 30c. .... *Dutton.*

Thomas Wingfold, curate. MacDonald, G. $1.75. (?) *Routledge.*

Thomason, T: T. Life. 18°. 45c. .... *Am. S. S.*

Thomes, W: H. Gold-hunters' lib. 3 v. ill. 12°. ea., $1.50 .... *Lee & S.*
Cont.: Gold hunters' adventures. — Bushrangers. — Gold hunters in Europe.

Thomes, W: H., *continued.*
— Ocean life ser. 3 v. ill. 12°. ea., $1.50 .... *Lee & S.*
Cont.: Whaleman's adventures in the Sandwich Islands and California. — Slaver's adventures on sea and land. — Life in the East Indies.
— Running the blockade. ill. 12°. $2.50 ...... *Lee & S.*

Thompson, A. W. Law of the farm: treatise on leading titles of law involved in farming business and litigation. 8°. shp., $7.50 .... *S. Whitney.*

Thompson, A. W. Swept and garnished. [Fiction.] ill. 8°. (Lond.) pap., 30c. .... *Am. News.*

Thompson, Alex. R. Casting down imaginations: sermon, Poughkeepsie, June 3, 1874. 8°. pap., 10c. .... *N. Y. Ref. Ch. Bd.*
— *See also* Hymns of the church.

Thompson, Ant. Todd. Conspectus of the pharmacopœias of the London, Edinburgh and Dublin lodges of physicians, and of the U. S. pharmacopœia. 18°. leath., $1.25 .... *W. Wood.*

Thompson, Arth. Bailey. The Victoria hist. of England, to 1869. ill. cr. 8°. $3 .... *Routledge.*

Thompson, A: C. Better land (The); or, the believer's journey and future home. 12°. $1.25 .. *Sheldon.*
— Christus consolator. 12°. '69. $1 .... *Am. Tr.*
— Lyra cœlestis: hymns on heaven. 12°. $1.75. *Sheldon.*
— Mercy seat; or, thoughts on prayer. 12°. $1.50. 8°. $2.50; $3.50 .... *Sheldon.*
— Morning hours in Patmos. 12°. '75. $1.25 .. *Am. Tr.*
— Seeds and sheaves; or, words of Scripture, their hist. and fruits. 12°. $1.75 .... *Sheldon.*

Thompson, *Sir* B: *See* Rumford, *Count.*

Thompson, C. P. Jack Robinson and his monkey: drama. 16°. pap., 15c. .... *French.*

Thompson, C: Delaune, the English Baptist martyr. 16°. $1.50 .... *Am. Bapt.*

Thompson, Ctte. S. Bertha Allston. ill. 18°. '66. 30c. .... *Am. Tr.*

Thompson, *Mrs.* Clara M. Hawthorndean; or, Philip Benton's family. 12°. '73. $1.50 .. *Cunningham.*

Thompson, D. W. Illustrated Bible history. ill. 8°. leath., $4 .... *J. G. Wells.*

Thompson, Dan. G. First Latin book. 12°. '72. hf. leath., $1.50 .... *Griggs.*

Thompson, Dan. Pierce. Doomed chief (The). 12°. $1.75 .... *J. E. Potter.*
— Gaut Gurley; or, the trappers of Umbagog. 12°. $1.75 .... *J. E. Potter.*
— Green Mountain ser. 4 v. 12°. '47–'52. ea., $1.25. *Nichols & H.*
Cont.: Green Mountain boys. — May Martin, and other tales of the Green Mountains. — Rangers: tale of the northern campaign of 1777. — Locke Amsden; or, the schoolmaster.

Thompson, D: Cross of Jesus. *See* Earnest Christian's lib.

Thompson, E. Wesly. Mary, star of the sea: story of Catholic devotion. 2d ed. 12°. '48. $1.50. *Cath. Pub.*

Thompson, *Miss* Edith. History of England. ('73.) New ed. 16°. '75. $1 .... *Holt.*

Thompson, E: H. Life of St. Aloysius Gonzaga. 12°. '67. $1.50 .... *Cunningham.*
— — *See also* Aloysius Gonzaga, *St.*
— Life of St. Charles Borromeo. 12°. $1.50 .. *Sadlier.*
— *Same.* 12°. '70. $1.50; $2 .... *Cunningham.*
— Life of St. Stanislaus Kostka. 12°. $1.50. *Cunningham.*

Thompson, *Mrs.* Ella W. Beaten paths; or, a woman's vacation. 16°. $1.50 .... *Lee & S.*

Thompson, Emily. The Harker family. ('70.) New ed. 12°. '74. $1.25 .... *Nat. Temp.*

Thompson, G: W. Deus semper: the norm + the germ × the conditions = the fruit. 12°. '69. $2 .... *Claxton.*

Thompson, H. A. Schools of the prophets: plea for theological training. 12°. 40c. ...... *Un. B. Pub.*

Thompson, *Mrs.* Helen S. Ponapé; or, light on a dark shore. 16°. $1 .... *Am. Bapt.*

Thompson, *Sir* H: Diseases of the prostate: their pathology and treatment. 4th ed., rev. ill. 8°. $3.75 .... *Lea.*
— Lectures on diseases of the urinary organs. 8°. $2.25 .... *Lea.*
— On pathology and treatment of stricture of urethra and urinary fistulæ. ill. 8°. $3.50 .... *Lea.*
— Practical lithotomy and lithotrity. 2d ed. ill. 8°. '71. $4 .... *Lindsay.*
— Preventive treatment of calculous disease, and use of solvent remedies. 2d ed. 12°. '76. $1 .. *Lindsay.*
— *See also* Tyndall, J:

Thompson, Hu. Miller. Absolution. 12°. 50c.; pap., 25c. .... *Dutton.*
— Concerning the kingdom of God. 12°. pap., 12c. *Dutton.*
— Copy: essays from an editor's drawer. 12°. '72. $2. *Dutton.*
— First principles. 12°. pap., 15c. .... *Dutton.*
— Sin and penalty: eternal punishment. 12°. pap., 15c. *Dutton.*
— Unity and its restoration. 12°. pap., 25c. .. *Dutton.*

Thompson, I: Grant. American reports: cases of general interest decided in the court of last resort in every State. v. 1–16. 8°. '70–'76. ea., shp., $6 .... *J. D. Parsons.*
— — Digest (v. 1–12). 8°. '75. shp., $3.50 .. *J. D. Parsons.*
— Assessors', collectors' and town clerks' manual; with forms. 8°. '75. $2.50 .... *J. D. Parsons.*
— Law and practice of provisional remedies. 8°. shp., $6.50 .... *W. C. Little.*
— Law of highways; with forms. 8°. $4.50 .. *W. C. Little.*
— Supervisor's manual [N. Y.]; with forms. 8°. '75. $3 .... *J. D. Parsons.*
— *See also* New York *State,* Supreme Court reports.

Thompson, J. J. Kentucky tragedy: history of the rencounters, fights, etc., known as the "Hill and Evans' feud." 8°. pap., 25c. .... *U. P. James.*

Thompson, J. W. Sketches, historical and descriptive, of noted Maine horses; with index, etc. 12°. $1.50 .... *Hoyt, F. & D.*

Thompson, J: B. *See* Hymns of the church.

Thompson, Jos. Parrish. Believer's refuge: meditations. 24°. '57. $1.50 .... *Randolph.*
— Bryant Gray. 18°. '64. 50c. .... *Randolph.*
— Christian graces. 16°. $1 .... *Sheldon.*
— Church and state in U. S. 16°. '73. $1.50 .. *Osgood.*
— Early witnesses; or, piety and preaching of the middle ages. 18°. '59. 75c. .... *Randolph.*
— Holy Comforter: his person and his work. 24°. '66. $1.50 .... *Randolph.*
— Home worship: sel. from the Scriptures, with meditations, prayer and song; for every day. ill. 8°. '71. *$4 .... *Osgood.*
— Inalienable possessions. 32°. '57. 20c. .. *Randolph.*
— Jesus of Nazareth: his life for the young. ill. 8°. '75. $5 .... *Osgood.*
— Man in Genesis and geology: biblical account of man's creation tested by scientific theories of his origin and antiquity. 12°. '69. $1 ... *Wells.*
— Memoir of David Tappan Stoddard, missionary to the Nestorians. ill. 12°. $1.25 .... *Bost. Am. Tr.*
— Sergeant's memorial. 18°. '64. 60c. ... *Randolph.*
— Theology of Christ, from his own words. ('70.) New ed. cr. 8°. '71. $2 .... *Scribner.*

Thompson, Jla. Carrie. Aspenridge. 16°. $1.35 . *Pres. Bd.*
— Life in narrow streets. 16°. $1.15 .... *Pres. Bd.*
— Trye's year among the Hindoos. 16°. $1.35 .. *Pres. Bd.*

Thompson, L. S. Eclectic system of penmanship: element. course. nos. 1–3. obl. 4°. ea., pap., 10c. .... *Wilson, H. & Co.*
— *and* Bowler, O. H. *and* N. E. D. Eclectic copy books. 9 nos. obl. 4°. ea., pap., 15c. *Wilson, H. & Co.*
— — — Eclectic primary copy book. 4°. pap., 10c. *Wilson, H. & Co.*

Thompson, L. S., *continued.*
— — — Handbook to accompany "Eclectic system of penmanship." ill. 16°. '70. 60c... *Wilson, H. & Co.*
— — — Sample book of Eclectic penmanship: copies sel. from all the books of the ser. obl. 4°. pap., 15c........................ *Wilson, H. & Co.*

Thompson, Lew. O. The presidents and their administrations: handbook of polit. parties. 12°. $1.75. (?)*Robinson.*

Thompson, Maur. Hoosier mosaics. 16°. $1.25.. *Hale.*

Thompson, R. A: *See* California, Sup. Court reports.

Thompson, Rezin. Medical adviser: treatise on laws of health and disease, and theory and practice of medicine. ill. 8°. '69. *$3; leath., $3.75.. *Jones.*

Thompson, Rob. Anchor. Christian theism: testimony of reason and revelation to existence of the supreme being. 12°. $1.50.......... *Harper.*

Thompson, Rob. Dundas. Food of animals: experimental researches on their food. 12°. $1.. *Judd.*

Thompson, Rob. Ellis. Social science and national economy. 12°. '75. $1.50 .... *Porter.*

Thompson, S. R. Topical outlines of chemistry; adapted to Porter's Chemistry. 16°. pap., 15c. *Barnes.*

Thompson, Seymour D. *See* Horrigan, L. D., *and* Thompson, S. D.
— *and* Steger, T. M. Compilation of statute laws of Tenn. 3 v. in 2. 8°. '71. shp., $15.... *Gilbert.*

Thompson, W. T. [Novels.] 7 v. ill. 12°... *Peterson.*
Cont.: Major Jones' courtship and travels — scenes in Georgia, *ea.*, $1.75 — chronicles of Pineville — courtship — sketches of travel. — Polly Peablossom's wedding. — Streaks of squatter life, *ea.*, 75c.
— Major Jones' courtship. ill. 12°. $1.50... *Appleton.*

Thompson, W: Outline of the necessary laws of thought. 12°. $1.75................. *Sheldon.*

Thoms, W: J. Longevity of man, its facts and its fictions; with inquiry into some of the more remarkable instances and suggestions for testing reputed cases. ill. 12°. $3.75 .. *Scribner, W. & A.*

Thomson, And. Freight charges calculator. 24°. '67. $1.25 .... *Baird.*

Thomson, And. Handbook of Scripture geography: 16 maps and plans, with hist. and geog. questions and answers. 16°. '75. 75c.......... *Putnam.*

Thomson, *Rev.* And. In the Holy Land. ill. 8°. '74. $2 .... *Nelson.*
— *Same.* ill. 12°. '75. $2................ *Randolph.*

Thomson, C. Wyville. Depths of the sea: results of dredging cruises of [the] "Lightning" and "Porcupine," 1868, '69, '70, under scientific direction of Dr. Carpenter, J. Gwyn Jeffreys and Dr. C. Wyville Thomson. ill. and maps. 8°. '73. $9......................... *Macmillan.*

Thomson, C: Inquiry into causes of alienation of the Delaware and Shawanese Indians from the British interests, and into the measures taken for recovering their friendship: Lond., 1759. [Reprint.] map. f°. '67. pap., $10. — 4°. pap., $5. — 8°. pap., $2.50 .... *J. Campbell & Son.*

Thomson, E: Biographical and incidental sketches. 12°. $1.50 .... *Cin. Meth. Bk. Conc.*
— Confederated republic of Israel: sermons and speeches. 12°. pap., 12c.... *Cin. Meth. Bk. Conc.*
— Educational essays. 12°. $1.50.. *Cin. Meth. Bk. Conc.*
— Evidences of revealed religion. 12°. $1.50. *Cin. Meth. Bk. Conc.*
— Letters from Europe. 12°. $1.50.. *Cin. Meth. Bk. Conc.*
— Moral and religious essays. 12°. $1.50. *Cin. Meth. Bk. Conc.*
— Our Oriental missions: India, China and Bulgaria. 2 v. 16°. $2.50; $3....... *Cin. Meth. Bk. Conc.*

Thomson, Ja. Poems. 2 v. por. 18°. $2.. *Osgood.*
— *Same.* (Aldine ed.) 2 v. 16°. ea., 75c... *Lippincott.*
— *Same;* with life. ill. 8°. (Dick.) 50c.; pap., 25c. *Am. News.*

Thomson, Ja., *continued.*
— *Same;* with memoir. (Household ser.) ill. and por. 16°. $1.50; mor., $3 .... *Lee & S.*
— Seasons. 32°. 38c...................... *Appleton.*
— *Same.* 18°. hf. bd., 38c. .... *Clark & M.*
— *Same.* (Blue and gold ed.) 24°. 75c.... *Appleton.*
— *Same;* with life by P. Murdoch. (Blue and gold ed.) 24°. 35c.; 75c. .... *Claxton; C. H. Davis.*
— *Same;* with crit. obs. of various authors on his genius and character, and notes by J. R. Boyd. (Lib. ed.) 12°. '52. $1.50. — (School ed.) 12°. hf. bd., $1.25........................ *Barnes.*
— *See also* British pocket classics; — Cowper, W: *and* Thomson, Ja.; — Gray, T: Poems; — Moore, T: Lalla Rookh.

Thomson, Ja. An uncle too many: drama. 16°. pap., 15c.................................. *French.*

Thomson, Ja. B. Arithmetical analysis; or, higher mental arithmetic. ('54.) New ed. 16°. '75. bds., 50c. .... *Clark & M.*
— Elements of algebra; abridg. from Day's large algebra. 12°. $1. — Key, $1 .... *T. Bliss.*
— *Same.* 12°. *net*, 85c. — Key, *net*, 85c....... *Peck.*
— Elements of geometry, on basis of Brewster's Legendre; [with] proportions, notes and illustrations. 12°. *net*, 75c........................... *Peck.*
— Higher arithmetic. ('47.) New ed. 12°. '76. bds., $1.40. — Key. ('47.) New ed. 12°. '62. bds., $1 .... *Clark & M.*
— Mental arithmetic for beginners. ('46.) New ed., rev. and enl. 16°. '76. bds., 27c..... *Clark & M.*
— New mental arithmetic for primary department. ('72.) New ed. 16°. '76. 35c. ..... *Clark & M.*
— New practical arithmetic. ('72.) New ed. 12°. '76. bds., $1. — Key. ('74.) New ed. 12°. '76. bds., $1 .... *Clark & M.*
— New rudiments of arithmetic. ('72.) New ed. 16°. '76. bds., 50c. .... *Clark & M.*
— Practical arithmetic. ('53.) New ed., rev. and enl. 16°. '76. bds., 65c. — Key. ('54.) New ed., rev. and enl. 16°. '75. bds., 65c..... *Clark & M.*
— Revised table book; for primary schools. ('74.) New ed. ill. 16°. '76. 25c.......... *Clark & M.*
— Rudiments of arithmetic; or, slate and blackboard exercises. ('53.) New ed., rev. and enl. 16°. '76. bds., 38c. .... *Clark & M.*

Thomson, J: Hats and felting: practical treatise on their manufacture. ('64.) New ed. ill. 8°. '68. $1.25 .... *Baird.*

Thomson, J: Straits of Malacca, Indo-China and China; or, ten years' travels, adventures and residence abroad. ill. 8°. $4.......... *Harper.*

Thomson, J: Cockburn. ["Ph. Wharton."] *See* Thomson, *Mrs.* K. B. *and* J. C.

Thomson, J: Lew. History of the Indian wars, and the war of the revolution. 2 v. ill. 8°. ea., $2.50 .... *Lippincott.*

Thomson, *Mrs.* Kath. B. ["Grace Wharton."] Lady of Milan; or, fidelity unto death. 8°. pap., 75c. *Harper.*
— *and* J: C. Queens of society. ill. 12°. $1.75.. *Harper.*
— — *Same.* ill. post 8°. $2.50; hf. cf., $4; cf., $6. *Routledge.*
— — Wits and beaux of society. ill. 12°. $1.75.. *Harper.*
— — *Same.* ill. post 8°. $2.50; hf. cf., $4; cf., $6. *Routledge.*

Thomson, Mortimer. ["Q. K. Philander Doesticks, P. B."] Doesticks' letters. 12°. $1.75; pap., $1.50 .... *Peterson.*
— History and records of the Elephant Club. 12°. $1.75; pap., $1.50.................. *Peterson.*
— Lady of the lake: travestie. 16°. pap., 15c. *French.*
— Nothing to say. 12°. pap., 75c.......... *Peterson.*
— Plu-ri-bus-tah. 12°. $1.75; pap., $1.50.. *Peterson.*
— Witches of New York. 12°. $1.75; pap., $1.50. *Peterson.*

Thomson, Spencer. Dictionary of domestic medicine and household surgery; rev. and enl., by H. H. Smith. demy 8°. $2 .... *Claxton.*
— Wild flowers: where to find them, and how to know them; with remarks on economical and medical uses of native plants. ill. 16°. $1.25; bds., 80c. *Routledge.*
Thomson, W. H. Treatment of sciatica. *See* Seguin, E. C., Series of Am. clin. lect.
Thomson, *Sir* W: Papers on electrostatics and magnetism. 8°. '73. $9 .... *Macmillan.*
Thomson, W: M. Land and the book; or, biblical ill. drawn from the manners, customs, scenes and scenery of the Holy Land. 2 v. maps. 12°. $5; shp., $6; hf. cf., $8.50 .... *Harper.*
Thoreau, H: D: Cape Cod. 16°. '65. $1.50.. *Osgood.*
— Excursions in field and forest. por. 16°. '63. $1.50. *Osgood.*
— Letters. 16°. '65. $1.50 .... *Osgood.*
— Maine woods. 16°. '64. $1.50 .... *Osgood.*
— Walden; or, life in the woods. 16°. '54. $1.50.. *Osgood.*
— Week on the Concord and Merrimack rivers. 16°. '67. $1.50 .... *Osgood.*
— Yankee (A) in Canada. 16°. '66. $1.50.. *Osgood.*
Thorn among the roses. Baker, G. M. 15c... *Lee & S.*
Thorn-fruit. Lanier, C. 50c .... *Eyrich.*
Thornbury, Wa. Buccaneers; or, the monarchs of the main. ill. 12°. '73. $1.75 ..... *Routledge.*
— Life in Spain, past and present. 12°. $1.50.. *Harper.*
— *and* Walford, E: Old and new London: narr. of its hist., people and places. 3 v. 4°. ea., $5.. *Cassell.*
Thornbury Abbey: tale of the times. 18°. 50c. *Strong.*
Thorne, Olive. Little folks in feathers and fur and others in neither. ill. 12°. '75. *$2.50; $3.. *Dustin.*
Thorne, P. (*pseud.*) *See* Smith, Ma. P. W.
Thornton, H: Family prayers, and prayers on the Ten commandments; with commentary on Sermon on the mount, etc.; ed. by Bp. Eastburn. 12°. $1.50. *Hurd & H.*
Thornton, J. Quinn. Oregon and California in 1848; with recent information on gold mines of Cal., etc. 2 v. map and ill. 12°. $3 ...... *Harper.*
Thornton, Jessie. Gold filings. 18°. 70c... *Pres. Bd.*
— Sunshine for gloomy hours. ill. 18°. 70c. *Pres. Bd.*
Thornton, J: Bereaved parents consoled; rev. with introd. and sel. of lyrics by T. O. Summers. ('55.) 10th ed. 18°. '76. 60c.; 70c......... *So. Meth.*
— — *See also* Thelwall, A. S., Thoughts in affliction.
Thornton, J: Wingate. Pulpit of the Am. revolution. [Reprints.] ill. 8°. '76. $2.50 ...... *Lothrop.*
Thornton, W: T: Indian public works, and cognate Indian topics. map. cr. 8°. '75. $3.. *Macmillan.*
— Old-fashioned ethics and common-sense metaphysics. 8°. '73. $3.50 .... *Macmillan.*
— On labour: its wrongful claims and rightful dues, actual present and possible future. 2d ed., rev. 8°. '70. $4.50 .... *Macmillan.*
— Plea for peasant proprietors, with the outlines of a plan for their establishment in Ireland. New ed. cr. 8°. '74. $2.25 .... *Macmillan.*
Thornton Hall. McKeen, P. F. $1.50... *Randolph.*
Thornwell, Emily. Rainbow around the tomb; or, rays of hope for those who mourn. 12°. $1.50. *J. E. Potter.*
— Young ladies' own book. 12°. $1.75... *J. E. Potter.*
— Young lady's guide to perfect gentility. 12°. $1. *Lippincott.*
Thornwell, Ja. Henley. Collected writings; ed. by J. B. Adger and J. L. Girardeau. 4 v. 8°. '70. ea., bds., $4....... *N. Y. Ref. Ch. Bd.; Pres. Com.*

Cont.: 1. Theodical. — 2. Theological and ethical. — 3. Theological and controversial. — 4. Ecclesiastical.

— Discourses on truth; delivered in chapel of the South Carolina College. ('54.) New ed. 12°. '69. $1.50. *Carter.*

Thorold, Ant. W. Presence of Christ: lectures on 23d Psalm. 12°. '71. $1.50 .... *Randolph.*
— *Same.* cr. 8°. $2 .... *Routledge.*
Thorold, Temple. Our work-shop: guide to the amateur in carpentry and joining. ill. 16°. 80c. *Routledge.*
Thorowgood, J: C. Notes on asthma; with formulæ, etc. 2d ed. 12°. '73. $1.75 .... *Lindsay.*
— Student's guide to materia medica. ill. 12°. '74. $2.50 .... *Lindsay.*
Thorpe, B: Diplomatarium Anglicum ævi Saxonici: collection of Eng. charters, 605, 1066; with tr. of the Anglo-Saxon. 8°. '65. $6.. *Macmillan.*
— Yule-tide stories: collection of Scandinavian tales and traditions. 12°. (Bohn.) $1.75.. *Little, B. & Co.*
— *Same.* 12°. (Bohn.) $2.. *Lippincott; Scribner, W. & A.*
— *See also* Bible, Gospels.
Thorpe, Kamba (*pseud.*) *See* Bellamy, *Mrs.* E. W.
Thorpe, T. E. Inorganic chemistry. (Adv. sci. ser.) 2 pts. 12°. '73. ea., $1.50 .... *Putnam.*
— Quantitative chem. analysis. ill. 18°. $1.75.. *Wiley.*
— Series of chemical problems; with pref. by Prof. Roscoe. 18°. '70. 50c. .... *Macmillan.*
Thorpe, T: Bangs. Col. Thorpe's scenes in Arkansas. ill. 12°. $1.75 .... *Peterson.*
Thorpe. Mountford, W. $1.50 .... * *Osgood.*
Thorpe Regis. Peard, F. M. $2 .... *Roberts.*
Those boys. Foster, I. H. $1.50 .... *Lothrop.*
Those holy fields. Manning, S. $3.50 .... *Nelson.*
Thought hives. Cuyler, T. L. $1.75 .... *Carter.*
Thoughtful Alice. *See* Bright eye ser.
Thoughtless Rosa, and other stories. ill. 18°. '66. 50c. .... *N. Y. Ref. Ch. Bd.; Pres. Com.*
Thoughts about art. Hamerton, P. G. $2 .. *Roberts.*
Thoughts among flowers; or, emblems of graces and defects drawn from flowers. 18°. 45c... *Am. S. S.*
Thoughts for the age. Sewell, E. M. $1.50.. *Williams.*
Thoughts for holy week. Sewell, E. M. 50c. *Dutton.*
Thoughts for Lent. Oxenden, A. 75c..... *Randolph.*
Thoughts for the old year and the new. Hall, J. 35c.; 15c. .... *Randolph.*
Thoughts for the thoughtful. Aydelott, B. P. 30c. *West. Tr.*
Thoughts for the thoughtful. Mogridge, G. 60c. *So. Meth.*
Thoughts for weary hours. 32°. 30c.; 50c. *Whittaker.*
Thoughts for the young men and the young women of Am. Reavis, L. U. 75c................ *Wells.*
Thoughts in affliction. Thelwall, A. S. 50c. *Appleton.*
Thoughts in my garden. Ware, M. E. $1.25. *Lippincott.*
Thoughts of favored hours. Copley, J. 50c. *Lippincott.*
Thoughts of God. Macduff, J. R. 50c....... *Carter.*
Thoughts of peace; or, strong hope and consolation for the bearer of the cross. ill. sq. 16°. $1.50; mor., $3.50 .... *Porter.*
Thoughts on Christian duty. Pendleton, J. M. 30c.; 15c. .... *So. Bapt.*
Thoughts on the death of little children. Prime, S. I. $1.50 .... *Randolph.*
Thoughts on the decalogue. Crosby, H. 90c. *Pres. Bd.*
Thoughts on domestic life. Sizer, N. 25c..... *Wells.*
Thoughts on the evils of drunkenness. 18°. 20c.; pap., 10c. .... *O'Shea.*
Thoughts on life and character. Herron, S. P. $1.50. *Lippincott.*
Thoughts on life science. Thring, E. $2.50.. *Macmillan.*
Thoughts on missions. Cunnyngham, W. G. E. 15c. *So. Meth.*
Thoughts on missions. Dibble, S. 40c...... *Am. Tr.*
Thoughts on personal religion. Goulburn, E. M. $1. *Appleton; Pott.*

Thoughts on prayer. Conrad, T. K. $1..*Randolph.*
Thoughts on prayer. Greenleaf, J. 60c....*Pres.Bd.*
Thoughts on preaching. Alexander, J. W. $2. *Scribner.*
Thoughts on principles of truth. Hamilton, J. $1.75. *Macmillan.*
Thoughts on prophecy. Turner, S. H. 75c. *Randolph.*
Thoughts on public prayer. Miller, S. $1..*Pres.Bd.*
Thoughts on recent scientific conclusions and their rel. to religion. 16°. '72. $2..........*Routledge.*
Thoughts on religious experience. Alexander, A. $1.60. *Pres.Bd.*
Thoughts on revelation. *See* Campbell, J. McL.
Thoughts on sacramental occasions. Doddridge, P. 40c..........................(?)*Martien.*
Thoughts on the services. *See* Coxe, A. C.
Thoughts that cluster. Thomas, J. H. $1.50. *H.A.Young.*
Thoughts through the year. Browne, J. E. A. $1. *Routledge.*
Thoughts to help and cheer. ('53.) New ed. sq. 16°. '74. $2–$6.................*Lockwood,B.&Co.*
Thoughts upon government. Helps, *Sir* A. $2.25. *Roberts.*
Thoughts worth remembering. 48°. 20c. *Cin.Meth.Bk.Conc.*
Thousand and one gems of Eng. poetry; — of Eng. prose. *See* Mackay, C.
Thousand and one nights. *See* Arabian nights' entertainments.
Thousand and one stories. Goodrich, S. G. $2..*Miller.*
Thousand lines. *See* Tupper, M. F.
Thousand miles in the Rob Roy canoe. Mac Gregor, J. $1.25.............................*Roberts.*
Thousand miles' walk across South America. Bishop, N. H. $1.25........................*Lee&S.*
Thousand (A) a year. ill. 18°. 60c.........*Lee&S.*
Thrall, Homer S. History of Methodism in Texas. 12°. '74. $1.25.....................*E.H.Cushing.*
— Mission work. 12°. '74. pap., 15c.......*So.Meth.*
Thrasher, Halsey. The hunter and trapper. ill. 12°. $1.................................*Judd.*
Threading my way. Owen, R. D. $1.50...*Carleton.*
Threads of knowledge drawn from a cambric handkerchief. Carey, A. $1.................*Cassell.*
Three (The) and the deuce: drama. 16°. pap., 15c. *French.*
Three bank-notes. Hoffmann, F. 85c...(?)*Luth.Pub.*
Three bears. ill. f°. pap., 15c.; 20c.; 30c...*J.E.Potter.*
Three bears. ill. 4°. $1; 50c............*Routledge.*
Three beauties. Southworth, E. D. E. N. $1.75; $1.50. *Peterson.*
Three Bernices. Bright, A. M. $1.75......*Claxton.*
Three black Smiths (The): Ethiop. drama. 16°. pap., 15c..........................*French; Happy.*
Three blind women. 32°. 20c............*Pres.Bd.*
Three books of song. Longfellow, H. W. $1.50; $3; $4...............................*Osgood.*
Three boys and their stories. Wilmer, M. E. 65c. *Pres.Bd.*
Three brothers. Grimm, J. L. *and* W. C. $1..*Miller.*
Three brothers. Oliphant, M. O. W. $1...*Appleton.*
Three cents. *See* Hildeburn, *Mrs.* M. J.
Three centuries of English literature. Yonge, C. D. $2...............................*Appleton.*
Three centuries of modern history. Yonge, C. D. $2. *Appleton.*
Three Christian graces. Rosecrans, J. H. 25c. *Crandall.*
Three Christmas days. Morse, E. H. 40c. ....*Hoyt.*
Three Christmas eves. V., A. $1.50....*Ref.Ch.Pub.*
Three clerks. Trollope, A. $1.50..........*Harper.*

Three courses and a dessert. *See* Cruikshank, G.
Three cousins. Maitland, J. A. $1.75; $1.50..*Peterson.*
Three cripples. Power, P. B. 60c...........*Carter.*
Three cuckoos. Morton, J. M. 15c..........*French.*
Three cutters. *See* Marryat, F:
Three days in the life of a father. Bungener, L. L. F. 40c...................................*Randolph.*
Three devils. Masson, D. $1.75........*Macmillan.*
Three distinct knocks. V *** n, W. O. 50c....*Hurst.*
Three dramas. 16°. pap., 40c.............*French.*
Cont.: Joseph and his brethren; Daniel in the lion's den; Sir Thomas More.
Three Eleanors. Berkley, C. $1...........*Strong.*
Three Elizabeths: Matron of Israel, Lily of Portugal, Queen saint of Hungary. 12°. '72. $1.25; $1.75...........................*Kelly,P.&Co.*
Three English statesmen. Smith, G. $1.50. *Harper; Macmillan.*
Three envious men. ill. sq. 12°. '71. bds., 50c. *Routledge.*
Three eras in a woman's life. Arthur, T. S. $1.50. *J.E.Potter.*
Three families. 16°. $1................*Am.Bapt.*
Three feathers. Black, W. $1.50; $1......*Harper.*
Three flowers. *See* Little Lottie ser.
Three friends. *See* Simple stories lib.
Three furies. Roberts, G. 15c..............*French.*
Three gardens. Adams, W. $2..........*Scribner.*
Three generations. Emery, S. A. $1.50; $1..*Lee&S.*
Three gifts. Cromwell, R. N. 40c...........*Am.Tr.*
Three girls. Butts, M. F. $1.25.........*Cong.Pub.*
Three girls of the revolution. Jerrell, A. R. $1.50. *Am.S.S.*
Three gold dollars. Abbott, J. 90c.........*Harper.*
Three great captains. 3 v. ill. 16°. $3....*Routledge.*
Cont.: Napoleon, by C. Macfarlane. — Wellington, by C. Macfarlane. — Nelson, by J. Allen.
Three great temptations of young men. Fisher, S. W. $1.25..............................*Wilstach.*
Three grocers: comedy. 16°. pap., 15c......*Happy.*
Three guardsmen. *See* Dumas, Alex.
Three guardsmen. Rice, C. 15c............*French.*
Three half dollars: story for boys. ill. 18°. '73. 45c. *N.Y.Ref.Ch.Bd.; Pres.Com.*
— *See also* Library for happy hours.
Three heavenly witnesses. *See* Orme, W:
Three homes. Dunning, A. K. 65c........*Pres.Bd.*
Three homes. *See* Hope, F. T. L.
Three hunchbacks: drama. 16°. pap., 15c...*French.*
Three hundred Irish airs. f°. $6; $7.50....*Haverty.*
Three hundred years ago. Kingston, W. H. G. 75c. (?)*Luth.Pub.*
Three hundred years ago; or, the story of Lilian. 18°. 60c...................................*Am.S.S.*
Three judges. Warren, I. P. $1.50........*Crowell.*
Three kingdoms of nature. Haughton, S. $2.50. *Cassell.*
Three kings. Nieritz, G. $1.15.......(?)*Luth.Pub.*
Three kings of Orient. *See* Hopkins, J: H:
Three kittens. [Toy-book.] ill. 4°. $1; 50c..*Routledge.*
Three last things. Hambleton, J. 40c. ....*Pres.Bd.*
Three lieutenants. Kingston, W. H. G. $2.50..*Pott.*
Three little brothers. *See* Marshall, E.
Three little kittens. 4 nos. ill. f°. ea., 15c.; 20c.; 30c. *J.E.Potter.*
Three little kittens. *See* Ballantyne, W.
Three little sisters. Marshall, E. 50c. *Carter; Dutton.*
Three little spades. Warner, A. B. $1......*Harper.*
Three little Tylers. Densel, M. 75c........*Dutton.*
Three martyrs: Romanus, Ignatius and Polycarp. 18°. '66. 40c...........*N.Y.Ref.Ch.Bd.; Pres.Com.*

Three messages of Revelation. Andrews, J. N. 15c. *Sev. Day Adv.*
Three months in the Orient. Bliss, O. J. $1.25. *Griggs.*
Three months in power. Lamartine, A. de. 80c. *Scribner, W. & A.*
Three months under the snow. 18°. 50c...... *Carter.*
Three months' rustication. Ballantyne, R. M. $1.25. *Claxton.*
Three musket dears: burlesque. 16°. pap., 15c. *French.*
Three musketeers. *See* Dumas, Alex.
Three musketeers. Rice, C. 15c............ *French.*
Three passovers. Pearson, E. H. 50c...... *Willard.*
Three paths in life. 16°. 90c............ *Cong. Pub.*
Three pearls; or, virginity and martyrdom. 12°. '75. $1.50 .... *Cath. Pub.*
Three-penny omnibus, and other tales. ill. 18°. 35c. *Bost. Am. Tr.*
— *See also* Alice and Willie stories.
Three people. *See* Alden, *Mrs.* I. M.
Three petitions. [Fiction.] 18°. '67. 50c.. *Cunningham.*
Three phases of Christian love. *See* Herbert, M. E.
Three Pines. Abbott, J. 90c.............. *Harper.*
Three pirates. 8°. pap., 50c.............. *Peterson.*
Three questions: what am I? whence come I? whither do I go? 18°. 40c.................. *Pres. Bd.*
Three reasons why I am a Baptist. *See* Pendleton, J. M.
Three red men. Archer, T. 15c............ *French.*
Three robes. 18°. 17c.; 22c.............. *Am. Bapt.*
Three rules. Boyd, M. D. R. $1........ *J. A. Moore.*
Three schoolmates. 18°. 40c.............. *Pres. Bd.*
Three score years and beyond. De Puy, W. H. $3.50; $7.50 .... *Meth. Bk. Conc.*
Three scouts. Trowbridge, J. T. $1.50...... *Tilton.*
Three seasons in European vineyards. Flagg, W. J. $1.50 .... *Harper; Judd.*
Three seats full. *See* Wright, *Mrs.* J. McN.
Three sermons: Human brotherhood, Curse of Meroz, Christian contentment; by a home missionary. sm. 8°. '74. pap., 25c.............. *L. Little.*
Three sisters. Perring, *Mrs.* —. 45c. .... *Routledge.*
Three sisters and three fortunes. Lewes, G. H. 75c. *Harper.*
Three sisters lib. 10 v. 18°. $4.90......... *So. Meth.*
Cont.: Three sisters. — Gathered flowerets. — Our English Bible. — Mick Healy, by J. Gregg. — Hymns for infant minds. — Field and fold, by E. Sidney. — Will forgers, by C. B. Tayler. — Sabbaths with my class, by S. G. Green. — Bible in many tongues. — Life of John Wesley.
Three strings to one bow. White, C. 15c. .. *De Witt.*
Three strong men. Dumas, A. 25c......... *De Witt.*
Three successful girls. Crouch, J. $1.50.. *Hurd & H.*
Three temptations: burlesque. 16°. pap., 15c... *Happy.*
Three thousand miles through the Rocky Mountains. McClure, A. K. $2................ *Lippincott.*
Three thousand practical words. Westlake, J. W. 50c. *Eldredge.*
Three times dead. Braddon, M. E. 50c. ... *Dick & F.*
Three times lost. Hosmer, M. 80c....... *J. A. Moore.*
Three tours of Dr. Syntax. *See* Combe, W.
Three visits to Madagascar. *See* Ellis, W.
Three voices. 18°. 40c.; 50c............ *Am. Bapt.*
Three wakings. *See* Charles, *Mrs.* E.
Three weeks after marriage. Murphy, A. 15c... *French.*
Three years after. Judson, E. Z. C. 75c. .. *Dick & F.*
Three years in the army of the Potomac. Blake, H. N. $1.50 .... *Lee & S.*
Three years in field hospitals. H., *Mrs.* —. $1.50. *Lippincott.*
Three years in a man-trap. Arthur, T. S. $2; $2.50; $4........................ *J. M. Stoddart.*
Three years in the Sixth Corps. Stevens, G. T. $3. *VanNostrand.*
Three youthful mariners. Grisét, E. 50c... *Appleton.*
Threefold cord. Prescott, J. E. $1..... *Macmillan.*
Threefold cord: texts for every day. 64°. '53. 15c.; 20c.; 50c.............................. *Am. Tr.*
Threefold cord; or, a precept, promise and prayer from the Holy Scripture for every day in the year. 32°. 30c.................... *Pres. Bd.*
Threefold grace of the Holy Trinity. Egar, J. H. $1.50 .... *Lippincott.*
Threshold of the Catholic Church. Bagshaw, F. $1.50 .... *Cath. Pub.*
Threshold of private devotion. 32°. '71. 40c. *Randolph.*
Thrice married. Paul, H. 15c. .... *De Witt; French.*
Thrift. Smiles, S. $1.25................... *Harper.*
Thrilling adventures among the early settlers. Wildwood, W. $1.75................. *J. E. Potter.*
Thrilling adventures among the Indians. Frost, J. $1.75.............................. *J. E. Potter.*
Thrilling adventures of Daniel Ellis. ill. 12°. $2.50. *Harper.*
Thrilling and exceedingly strange adventures. Lane, A. 20c.............................. *Barclay.*
Thrilling facts. 18°. 35c.; 45c........... *Am. Bapt.*
Thrilling incidents in Am. hist.; by author of "Army and navy of U. S." ill. 12°. $1.75.. *J. E. Potter.*
Thrilling scenes in social life; or, the opposite effects of vice and virtue; ed. by a son of temperance. 8°. *$2.................................. *Case.*
Thrilling stories of forest and frontier. ill. 12°. $1.25. *T. Bliss.*
Thrilling stories of the great rebellion. Greene, C. S. $1.75 .... *J. E. Potter.*
Thrilling stories of the olden time. 4 v. 16°. $5.75. *Am. Bapt.*
Cont.: Master Hathorne's family. — Walter Ennis. — From nation to nation. — De Laune.

Thring, E: Child's grammar. New ed. 18°. '66. 40c. *Macmillan.*
— Construing book. [Latin.] fp. 8°. 75c. *Macmillan.*
— Education and school. 2d ed. cr. 8°. '67. $1.75. *Macmillan.*
— Elements of grammar taught in English. 4th ed. 18°. 75c. .... *Macmillan.*
— Latin gradual: construing book for beginners. New ed. fp. 8°. '71. $1.25 .... *Macmillan.*
— Manual of mood construction. fp. 8°. '67. 75c. *Macmillan.*
— Sermons delivered at Uppingham School. cr. 8°. $2. *Macmillan.*
— Thoughts on life science. New ed., enl. and rev. cr. 8°. $2.50......................... *Macmillan.*
Thrivier, C. L. How I came out from Rome: autobiog. 12°. '73. $1.25.......................... *Nelson.*
Thron (Der) der Sünde. Barnes, A. 10c... *Ev. Assoc.*
Throne of David. Ingraham, J. H. $2 ..... *Roberts.*
Throne of grace. 18°. $1 .... *Carter.*
Throne of grace; by author of "Pathway of promise." 16°. $1 .... *Routledge.*
Thrones and palaces of Babylon and Nineveh. Newman, J. P. $5........................ *Harper.*
Throop, G: H. Lynde Weiss: autobiog. ill. 12°. '73. $1.50.............................. *Claxton.*
Throop, Montgomery H. Treatise on validity of verbal agreements as affected by the legislative enactments in England and United States. 8°. '70. shp., $7.50 .... *J. D. Parsons.*
Throstlethwaite. Moreley, S. $1.50.... *Lippincott.*
Through the air. Wise, J. *$3.50; $4..... *Maclean.*
Through and through the tropics. Vincent, F., *jr.* $1.50............................... *Harper.*
Through by daylight. Adams, W. T. $1.25.. *Lee & S.*

Through the dark to the day. Willing, J. F. $1.25. *Cin. Meth. Bk. Conc.*

Through dust and foam. Hook, R. *and* G. D. *$2.75; $3.25; $3.50; $4 .... *Col. Bk.*

Through the eye to the heart. Crafts, W. F. $1.50. *Meth. Bk. Conc.*

Through fire and water. Gordon, W. 15c.... *French.*

Through fire and water. Talbot, F. 25c..... *Harper.*

Through life and for life. Richmond, D. $1.25. *Routledge.*

Through the looking-glass and what Alice saw there. *See* Dodgson, C. L.

Through night to light. Spielhagen, F. $1.50.. *Holt.*

Through Normandy. *See* Macquoid, K. S.

Through patience. Foster, I. H. 80c..... *J. A. Moore.*

Through picture land. Mateaux, C. L. $1.50.. *Cassell.*

Through thick and thin. Méry, J. $1.75... *Carleton.*

Through trials to triumphs. Putnam, H. A. $1.25. *Meth. Bk. Conc.*

Through the wilderness. Willard, M. E. $1.. *Pres. Bd.*

Through the year. Powers, H. N. $1.50.... *Roberts.*

Thrown together. Montgomery, F. $1.50.. *Lippincott.*

Thrupp, Jos. Fs. Burden of human sin as borne by Christ: sermons, 1865. cr. 8°. $1.25.. *Macmillan.*

– Introduction to use and study of the Psalms. 2 v. 8°. $7 .... *Macmillan.*

– Song of songs; tr., with comment. and introd. cr. 8°. $1.50 .... *Macmillan.*

Thucydides. Recensuit J. G. Donaldson. [Gk.] 2 v. 18°. $1.50 .... *Harper.*

– History of the Peloponnesian war [Gk.]; ed. by J. J. Owen. map. 12°. $2.50 .... *Appleton.*

– *Same.* bks. 1, 2; ed. by C. Bigg. (Catena classicorum.) ('69.) 3d ed. 12°. '76. $2.... *Allyn.*

– *Same.* bks. 6, 7: Sicilian expedition; with notes by P. Frost. New ed. fp. 8°. '67. $1.50. *Macmillan.*

– *Eng.* History of the Peloponnesian war; tr. by W. Smith. 2 v. 18°. $1.50 .... *Harper.*

— — *Same:* literal version by H. Dale. 12°. $1.50. *Harper.*

— — — *Same.* 2 v. 12°. (Bohn.) ea., $1.25. *Little, B. & Co.*

— — — *Same.* 2 v. 12°. (Bohn.) ea., $1.40. *Scribner, W. & A.*

— — — *Same.* 2 v. 12°. (Bohn.) ea., $1.50.. *Lippincott.*

– Analysis of T. by J. T. Wheeler. 12°. (Bohn.) $1.75. .... *Little, B. & Co.*

– *Same.* 12°. (Bohn.) $2.. *Lippincott; Scribner, W. & A.*

– *See also* Herodotus *and* Thucydides.

Thudichum, J: L: W: Manual of chemical physiology, incl. its points of contact with pathology. 8°. $2.25 .... *W. Wood.*

– *and* Dupré, A: Treatise on origin, nature and varieties of wine: manual of viticulture and œnology. ill. 8°. '71. $9 .... *Macmillan.*

Thuet dies zu meinem Andenken. Beineke, P. C. $1.50. *Herder.*

Thumping legacy. Morton, J. M. 15c....... *French.*

Thurber, G: Botany. *See* Ives, J. C., Report on Colorado River.

– (*ed.*) Hop culture; by ten experienced cultivators. ill. 8°. pap., 30c. .... *Judd.*

Thurid, and other poems. O., G. E. $2..... *Lee & S.*

Thurston, *Mrs.* —. Pictures and flowers for child-lovers. ill. 16°. 75c. .... *Fuller.*

— — *See also* Union ser.

Thurston, *Miss* C. Home pleasures. 12°. '65. $1.25. *Am. Tr.*

Thurston, *Mrs.* Eliz. A. Little wrinkled old man: Christmas extravaganza, and other trifles. ill. 18°. 75c. .... *Lee & S.*

– Mosaics of human life. 12°. '66. $2. *Claxton; Lippincott.*

Thurston, J. R. Little ones gone before. 16°. 50c. *Cong. Pub.*

Thurston, *Miss* Louise M. Charley Roberts ser. [To form 6 v.] v. 1–4. ill. 16°. ea., $1.... *Lee & S.*

Cont.: How Charley Roberts became a man. — How Eva Roberts gained her education. — Home in the west. — Children of Amity Court.

— Forrest Mills: peep at child-life from within. ill. 16°. '68. 80c. .... *Am. Unit.*

Thurston, R. B. *See* Liberty or slavery.

Thurston, Rob. H: Determination of mechan. equivalent of heat. *See* Allen, T., Iron hulls for western river steamboats.

— Efficiency of furnaces burning wet fuel, pt. 1. *See* Forshey, C. G., Levees of the Mississippi River; — Rapid transit and terminal freight facilities.

— *Same,* pt. 2; [also] Upright arched bridges, by J. B. Eads. 8°. '75. pap., 70c....... *Am. Soc. of C. E.*

— Mechanical properties of materials of construction. 8°. '74. pap., 80c. .... *Am. Soc. of C. E.*

— Note on resistance of materials as affected by flow and by rapidity of distortion. *See* Bender, C., Application of theory of continuous girders.

— *Same;* [also] Production of traffic and the transportation of freight and passengers, by Coryell; [also] Backwater in streams as produced by dams, by DeV. Wood; [also] Water power of the falls of the Ohio River, by M. S. Belknap. 8°. '73. pap., 70c. .... *Am. Soc. of C. E.*

— Strength and other properties of materials of construction. *See* Morison, G. S., New portage bridge.

— *Same;* [also] Central Ave. bridge, Newark, N. J., by A. P. Boller; [also] Elements of cost of railroad freight traffic, by O. Chanute. 8°. '74. pap., $1.20 .... *Am. Soc. of C. E.*

Thwarted. Montgomery, F. $1.25...... *Lippincott.*

Thy poor brother. Sewell, M. $1.50....... *Am. S. S.*

Thy voyage. Burr, E. F. $3.50...... *Meth. Bk. Conc.*

Tia fingida (La). *See* Cervantes, Exemplary novels.

Tibbils, H. C. Amethyst: music for singing classes, etc. obl. 12°. '75. per doz., $7.50... *Benham.*

Tibbins, J. *See* Fleming, C., *and* Tibbins, J.

Tibbits, Herb. Handbook of medical electricity. ill. sm. 8°. '73. $2 .... *Lindsay.*

Tibbitts, J: S. Supervisor's manual of Michigan. 12°. '76. $1 .... *Richmond.*

Tibby, the charwoman. 18°. 50c. .... *Carter.*

Tibullus, Albius. Poems. *See* Catullus, Q. V., *and* Tibullus, A.

Tichborne, *Sir* Rog. C: Complete hist. account of the great Tichborne trial. 8°. $1.50..... *Cockcroft.*

Tickell, G: Life of blessed Margaret Mary Alacoque. 16°. $1.25; $1.75 .... *Sadlier.*

Tickell, T: Poems. *See* Parnell, T: Poems.

Ticket of leave. Phillips, W. 15c.... *Ames; French.*

Ticket of leave man. Taylor, T. 15c........ *French.*

Ticket of leave man's wife. Cheltnam, C. S. 15c. *French.*

Ticket taker: Ethiop. drama. 16°. pap., 15c. *French; Happy.*

Tickletooth, Tab. (*pseud.*) *See* Selby, C:

Ticklish times. Morton, J. M. 15c.......... *French.*

Ticknor, Almon. Columbian calculator. 16°. 42c. *Lippincott.*

— Columbian speller. 16°. 20c.......... *Lippincott.*

— Key to Columbian and Youth's calculators. 16°. 48c. *Lippincott.*

— Youth's Columbian calculator. 16°. 25c... *Lippincott.*

Ticknor, Clb. Philosophy of living; or, way to enjoy life and its comforts. ill. 18°. 75c.... *Harper.*

Ticknor, G: History of Spanish literature. 3 v. 8°. $5; hf. cf., $11.75 .... *Harper.*

— *Same.* New ed., rev. 3 v. 8°. '72. $10... *Osgood.*

— Life, letters and journals. 2 v. por. and ill. 8°. '75. $6; hf. cf., $11 .... *Osgood.*

Ticknor, G: *continued.*
— Life of W. H. Prescott. 4°. '64. large pap., $25; mor., $30 .... *Osgood.*
— *Same.* cr. 8°. $2.50 .... *Lippincott.*
Ticonderoga. James, G. P. R. 50c. .... *Harper.*
Ticonderoga, past and present. Stoddard, S. R. 50c.; 25c. .... *S. R. Stoddard.*
Tidal wave. *See* Lowry, R., *and* Doane, W. H.
Tidd, W: Practice of the courts of King's Bench and Common Pleas in personal actions and ejectment. 4th Am. ed., with notes by F. J. Troubat and A. I. Fish. 2 v. 8°. *net*, shp., $15 .... *Kay.*
Tide of time. Bernard, W. B. 15c. .... *French.*
Tide turning. *See* Bates, L.
Tides and tendencies of religious thought. Dudley, J. L. $1.50 .... *Claxton.*
Tides and tidal currents. Galbraith, J. A., *and* Haughton, S. $1.25 .... *Cassell.*
Tieck, L: Elves (The), and other tales; tr. by T. Carlyle. 8°. pap., 50c. .... *Harper.*
— Klausenburg (Die); [also] Pietro v. Albano. 12°. leath., 75c. .... *Radde.*
— Märchennovellen; [also] Die Elfen; [also] Das Rothkäppchen. With Eng. notes by L. Simonson. ('66.) New ed. 12°. '76. pap., 60c. .... *Holt.*
Tiffany, Alex. R. Treatise on criminal law of Michigan, with precedents of indictments and forms. 2d ed., rev. and enl. by A. Howell. 8°. '76. shp., $7.50 .... *Richmond.*
— Treatise on powers and duties of justices of the peace in Michigan; with forms. 2d ed., enl. by A. Howell. 8°. '75. shp., $6.50 .. *Humphrey; Richmond.*
Tiffany, C: C. Modern atheism. 18°. '74. pap., 20c. *Whittaker.*
Tiffany, Jl. On government and constitutional law. 8°. shp., $6 .... *W. C. Little.*
— *See also* New York State, Court of Appeals reports.
— *and* Barbour, O. L. Condensed digest of N. Y. Court of Appeals reports. 3 v. 8°. shp., $22 50. *W. C. Little.*
— *and* Bullard, E. F. On law of trusts and trustees. 8°. shp., $7.50 .... *W. C. Little.*
— *and* Smith, H: New York practice. 3 v. 8°. shp., $18 .... *W. C. Little.*
Tiffany, Osmond (*ed.*). Sacred biog. and hist. of the Bible; with notices of most eminent reformers. ill. 8°. '68. *$3.50; leath., $4 .... *C. A. Nichols.*
Tiger at large: comic burletta. 16°. pap., 15c. .. *Happy.*
Tiger hunter. Reid, M. $1.50 .... *Carleton.*
Tiger Jack. 18°. 35c. .... *Am. S. S.*
Tiger lily. ill. sq. 12°. '71. bds., 50c. .... *Routledge.*
Tiger prince. Dalton, W. $1.25 .. *Lippincott; Roberts.*
Tiger slayer. Aimard, G. 75c. .... *Peterson.*
Tigranes. Franco, J. J. $1.50 .... *Cunningham.*
Tikun leil Sh'ouoth. *See* Jewish Synagogue.
Tikun torah. *See* Jewish Synagogue.
Tilbury, W: H. Counter attraction: farce. 16°. pap., 15c. .... *French.*
Tilden, W. P. Buds for the bridal wreath. 18°. $1.50 .... *Lee & S.*
Tilden, W. S. Choice trios; for female voices. 12°. '73. bds., $1 .... *Ditson.*
— *See also* Emerson, L. O., *and* Tilden, W. S.
Tileston, E: G. Handbook of administrations of the U. S.; with record of contemporaneous English history. photos. 16°. $1.50; large pap., $2.50. *Lee & S.*
Till the doctor comes, and how to help him. Hope, G. A. 60c. .... *Putnam.*
Tillinghast, W: Diadem of school songs. ('69.) 6th ed. 12°. '75. bds., 60c. .... *Schermerhorn.*
— Little diadem; or, little songs for little singers. ('71.) 2d ed. 12°. '72. 30c. .... *Schermerhorn.*

Tillinghast, W: *continued.*
— Normal diadem of school songs. ('71.) 4th ed. 12°. '74. bds., 75c. .... *Schermerhorn.*
— *See also* Horton, D. P., *and* Tillinghast, W.
— *and* Horton, D. P. Song fountain: vocal music book. 2d ed. 12°. '74. bds., 40c. .. *Schermerhorn.*
Tilly Tricket; or, try. 16°. 50c. .... *Scribner, W. & A.*
Tilman, Randolph. Zion's choral: coll. of church music, with musical notation. obl. 12°. '71. bds., 75c. .... *Ditson.*
Tilman Loring. Nutting, J. K. 90c. .... *Garrigues.*
Tilt, E: J: Change of life in health and disease: treatise on nervous and other affections incidental to women at decline of life. 8°. '71. $3 .. *Lindsay.*
— Handbook of uterine therapeutics. 2d ed., rev. 8°. $3.50 .... *Appleton.*
— On preservation of health of women at critical periods of life. 18°. 50c. .... *Wiley.*
Tilton, S. Willis. ["Uncle Willis."] Mrs. Partington's edition of Mother Goose. sq. 16°. 60c. *Tilton.*
— Songs for our darlings. sq. 16°. '73. $1; pap., 60c. *Tilton.*
Tilton, Thdr. Fly (The): poem for little ones. ill. 16°. '65. per doz., $2.50 .... *Sheldon.*
— Golden-haired Gertrude: story for children. 3d ed. sq. 12°. '65. $1; bds., 75c. .... *Tibbals.*
— Sanctum sanctorum: coll. of miscellaneous papers. 12°. $1.50 .... *Sheldon.*
— Sexton's tale, and other poems. 16°. $1.50. *Sheldon.*
— Tempest-tossed. [Fiction.] 12°. $1.75 .... *Sheldon.*
— True church. [Poems.] ill. 4°. '66. $2.50; mor., $4.50; $5 .... *Claxton; Lippincott.*
— *vs.* Beecher, H: W. Beecher trial: review of evidence; reprinted from N. Y. Times of July 3, 1875; with rev. and add. 8°. '75. pap., 25c. (?) *N. Y. Times.*
— — Great Brooklyn romance: all the documents in the Beecher-Tilton case, unabridg. por. and facsimiles. 8°. '74. $1.50 .... (?) *Paxon.*
— — History, investigation and trial: letters, statements and evidence in full. [In Eng. or Germ.] 8°. pap., 25c. .... *Barclay.*
— — Pictorial hist. of the Beecher-Tilton trial. ill. and pl. 4°. $1 .... *U. S. Pub.*
— — Report of trial; with notes and ref. by A. Abbott; with account of the court, and biog. sketches of judge, parties, their counsel, etc. [To form 5 v]. v. 1, 2. 8°. '75. ea., $4; shp., $4.50. *G. W. Smith.*
— — Verbatim report of trial. 3 v. 8°. '75. $10.50; shp., $12 .... *Campbell & Co.*
— — *See also* Marshall, C. F.
Tim, the collier boy. 18°. 45c. .... *Pres. Bd.*
Tim, the scissors-grinder. *See* Baker, *Mrs.* H. N. W.
Tim Bunker papers. 12°. $1.50 .... *Judd.*
Tim Harrison. Dunning, A. K. 45c. .... *Pres. Bd.*
Tim Leeson. *See* Edmond Darley ser.
Tim Peglar's secret; or, the wonderful egg. ('69.) New ed. ill. 16°. '74. 80c. .... *Hoyt.*
Tim Pippin; or, further adventures in Giantland. ill. 8°. (Lond.) 75c. .... *Am. News.*
Tim ser. *See* Baker, *Mrs.* H. N. W.
Timanus, *Miss* Sara J. *See* Crafts, *Mrs.* W. F.
Timboo and Fanny. Abbott, J. 90c. .... *Harper.*
Timboo and Joliba. Abbott, J. 90c. .... *Harper.*
Timbs, J: Abbeys, castles and ancient halls of Eng. and Wales: their legendary lore and popular hist. (Chandos lib.) 3 v. 12°. ea., $1.75; hf. cf., $3.75; cf., $5 .... *Scribner, W. & A.*
— Century of anecdote. (Chandos lib.) 12°. $1.75; hf. cf., $3.75; cf., $5 .... *Scribner, W. & A.*
— Clubs and club life in London; with anecdotes of its famous coffee houses, hostelries and taverns. ill. 12°. $3 .... *Routledge.*

Timbs, J: *continued.*
— History of wonderful inventions, from the mariners' compass to the electric telegraph cable. ill. 12°. $2 .... *Routledge.*
— Legal anecdotes. 16°. '73. bds., 50c... *Routledge.*
— Naval anecdotes. 16°. '73. bds., 50c... *Routledge.*
— Romance of London. (Chandos lib.) 2 v. 12°. ea., $1.75; hf. cf., $3.75; cf., $5.... *Scribner, W. & A.*
— Stories of inventors and discoverers in science and the useful arts. ill. 12°. $1.50 .... *Harper.*
— *See also* Paul H., Timbs, J., *and* Fitzgerald, P.
Time, the avenger. Marsh-Caldwell, A. 50c... *Harper.*
Time about, fair play. *See* Bright eye ser.
Time and the hour. Simpson, J. P., *and* Dale, F. 15c. *De Witt; French.*
Time and tide. Leslie, H. 15c..... *De Witt; French.*
Time and tide by weare and tyne. Ruskin, J. $1.. *Wiley.*
Time as it flies. 32°. 20c.; 15c. .... *Dutton.*
Time for everything. *See* Cupples, *Mrs.* Ann Jane.
Time to seek the Lord. *See* Little Jewess.
Time tries all. Courtney, J. 15c. .... *French.*
Time will tell. Wilson, *Mrs.* —. $1...... *Nat. Temp.*
Time works wonders. Jerrold, D. 15c....... *French.*
Times. Daly, J. 15c. .... *French.*
Times (The) and the men: a satire. [Poem.] 16°. pap., 30c. .... *Lippincott.*
Times of Daniel. Taylor, H. W. $1.50.. *Randolph.*
Times receipts. *See* New York Times.
Timid lamb. 32°. 20c.; 15c. .... *Dutton.*
Timid Lucy. 18°. 75c. .... *Dutton.*
Timm, H. C. *See* Ives, E., *jr.*, Alpers, W., *and* Timm, H. C.
Timmy Top-boots. *See* Baker, *Mrs.* H. N. W.
Timon (*pseud.*) *See* Cormenin, L. M. de la H.
Timon of Athens. *See* Shakespeare, W:
Timotheus. Ein Geschenk f. die confirmirte Jugend. ('60.) 9th ed. 12°. '75. 30c. .... *Barthel.*
Timothy to the rescue. Byron, H. J. 15c. *De Witt; French.*
Timour, the Tartar: burlesque. Oxenford, J., *and* Brooks, C. S. 15c. .... *French.*
Timour, the Tartar: drama. Lewis, M. G. 15c. *French.*
Timrod, H: Poems; with memoir by P. H. Hayne. 12°. $1.50; $2 .... *Hale.*
Tim's little mother. Punot, S. $1.25....... *Carter.*
Tim's sister. Baker, H. N. W. $1.25....... *Hoyt.*
Tim's troubles. Paull, M. A. $1.50.. *Nat. Temp.; Nelson.*
Tin trumpet. Chatfield, P. $1.50; 50c..... *Appleton.*
Tincker, Ma. Agnes. House of Yorke: story of Am. life. 4th ed. 8°. '72. $2 .... *Cath. Pub.*
Tinder-box. *See* Andersen, H. C.
Ting-a-ling. Stockton, F. R. $1.50 ...... *Hurd & H.*
Tingling, J. F. B. Holiness as demanded and provided by the Gospel. 18°. pap., 15c. .... *Willard.*
Tinto, Dick (*pseud.*) *See* Goodrich, Fk. B.
Tiny. *See* Phelps, *Miss* E. S.
Tiny footfall within the golden gate. *See* Irving, T.
Tiny houses and their builders. ill. fp. 4°. $2.50. *Cassell.*
Tiny lib. 24 v. ill. 32°. $6 .... *Nelson.*
Tiny ser. *See* Phelps, *Miss* E. S.
Tiny stories in tiny words. ill. sq. 8°. $1..... *Nelson.*
Tiny Tim. *See* Dickens, C:
Tiny's lib. *See* Phelps, *Miss* E. S.
Tiny's musical box. *See* Bright gems for boys and girls; — Little girls' lib.
Tiny's Sunday nights. *See* Phelps, *Miss* E. S.
Tip Lewis and his lamp. *See* Alden, *Mrs.* I. M.
Tipperary legacy: farce. 16°. pap., 15c..... *Happy.*
Tipping his tables. Putnam, A. 25c. .... *Colby.*
Tiptoe. Williams, K. 90c. .... *Am. Tr.*
Tip-top glee and chorus book. Jarvis, C., *and* Getze, J. A. $1.50 .... *Ditson.*
Tired of housekeeping. *See* Happy child's lib.
Tis better to live than to die. Picton, T. 15c... *De Witt.*
Tis darkest hour before dawn: comedy. 16°. pap., 15c. *French.*
Tischendorf, Const. Origin of the four Gospels; tr. by W. L. Gage. Rev. and enl. ed. 16°. $1.25. *Bost. Am. Tr.*
— Wann wurden unsere Evangelien verfasst? 18°. '67. 30c. .... *Am. Tr.*
— *Eng.* When were our Gospels written? 18°. '67. 25c. .... *Am. Tr.*
— *See also* Bible, New Test.
Tischer, J. F. W. Life of Luther. *See* Luther, Mt., Commentary on Galatians.
Tissandier, Gast. Wonders of water; tr. from the Fr., ed. with add. by Schele de Vere. ('71.) New ed. ill. 12°. '74. $1.50 .... *Scribner.*
Tissot, J. Real presence (The). 18°. 60c. .. *O'Shea.*
— Scapular of Mount Carmel. 32°. 25c...... *O'Shea.*
Tit bits. Knight, S. G. $1 .... *Nichols & H.*
Tit for tat. Talfourd, F., *and* Wigan, A. 15c... *French.*
Titcomb, J. H. Cautions for doubters. 12°. $1.. *Nelson.*
— *Same.* 16°. '74. $1.25 .... *Randolph.*
— Revelation in progress from Adam to Malachi. 8°. $2.50 .... *Nelson.*
Titcomb, Tim. (*pseud.*) *See* Holland, J. G.
Titcomb's letters to young people. Holland, J. G. $1.50; $2.50; $4 .... *Scribner.*
Tithe-proctor. *See* Carleton, W:
Titles of the Holy Spirit. 64°. '66. 15c. .... *Am. Tr.*
Titles of our Lord. Randall, J. M. 75c..... *Pres. Bd.*
Titterington, *Mrs.* S. B. ["Grace Graham."] Mabel Livingstone; or, Christward led. ill. 16°. '72. $1.25 .... *Lothrop.*
Tittums and Fido. [Toy-book.] ill. 4°. $1; 50c. *Routledge.*
Titus, Tim. T. Questions on "the miracles." 16°. 20c. (?) *Luth. Pub.*
— Questions on "the parables." 16°. 20c. (?) *Luth. Pub.*
Titus Andronicus. *See* Shakespeare, W:
To the bitter end. Braddon, M. E. 50c. .... *Harper.*
To a boy anxious about his soul. *See* McCheyne, R.
To Buddlecombe and back. Burnand, F. C. 50c. *Roberts.*
To Cuba and back. Dana, R. H., *jr.* $1.25.. *Osgood.*
To-day. Kimball, R. B. $1.75 .... *Carleton.*
To learn and to know. Crabb, G. $1.50 .. *World Pub.*
To love and to be loved. Roe, A. S. $1.50.. *Carleton.*
To oblige Benson. Taylor, T. 15c. .... *French.*
To parents and guardians. Coyne, J. S. 15c... *French.*
To Paris and back for 5*l.* Morton, J. M. 15c. *French.*
To young men. Waterbury, J. B. 25c....... *Am. Tr.*
Toasts and sentiments. 32°. 20c. .... *Routledge.*
Tobacco culture; by fourteen experienced tobacco-growers; with notes on tobacco worm. ill. 8°. pap., 25c. .... *Judd.*
Tobey, Alvan. Christianity from God. 16°. $1. *Bost. Am. Tr.*
Tobey, J: F. *See* Rhode Island, Sup. Court reports.
Tobias Wilson. Clemens, J. $1.75. *Claxton; Lippincott.*
Tobin, J: Curfew: play. 16°. pap., 15c..... *French.*
— Honeymoon: comedy. 16°. pap., 15c. .... *French.*
Tobin, T: Bond tables; showing percentage of interest yielded annually. 8°. $3...... *Lippincott.*
Tobit's dog: drama. 16°. pap., 15c. .... *French.*
Toby (*pseud.*) American tour of Brown, Jones and Robinson: hist. of what they saw and did in U. S., Canada and Cuba. ill. 4°. '73. $5 .. *Appleton.*

Tochter (Die) des Fischers, od. Sebie's Lektionen. 18°. 35c. .... *Ev. Assoc.*

Tochter (Die) Tehuan's. Hörmann, A. 35c.; 15c. *Benziger.*

Tocqueville, Alexis C: H: C. de. American institutions and their influence; tr. with notes by J. C. Spencer. 12°. '51. $1.50 .... *Barnes.*
Note. A school ed. of v. 1 of "Democracy in Am."

— *Same.* ('69.) 4th ed. 12°. '75. $1.75 ..... *Allyn.*

— Democracy in Am.; tr. by Reeves, ed. with notes by F. Bowen. ('62.) 6th ed. 2 v. 8°. '76. $5 .. *Allyn.*

— Memoirs, letters and remains. 2 v. 16°. $3 .. * *Osgood.*

— Old régime and the revolution; tr. by J. Bonner. 12°. $1.50 .... *Harper.*

— Republic of the U. S. and its polit. institutions; tr. by H. Reeves, with pref. and notes by J. C. Spencer. 2 v. in 1. 8°. $3 .... *Barnes.*
Note. Same as "Democracy in Am."

Todd, C: S., *and* Drake, B: Sketches of civil and military service of W. H. Harrison. 12°. '40. 25c. *I. N. Whiting.*

Todd, H: J: Verbal index to Milton's poet. works. *See* Milton, J:

Todd, Ja. Henthorn. Books of the Vaudois: Waldensian manuscripts in library of Trinity College, Dublin; with app. cr. 8°. '65. $2 .. *Macmillan.*

Todd, J: Angel of the iceberg, and other stories. ('59.) New ed. 16°. '68. $1.25 .... *Bridgman.*

— Daughter at school. ('53.) 4th ed. 12°. '68. $1.50. *Bridgman.*

— Faithful shepherd: life of Scott, the commentator, adapted to the young. 18°. '65. 75c. *Bridgman.*

— *Same.* 18°. 75c. .... *Cong. Pub.*

— Hints and thoughts for Christians. 12°. '67. 80c. *Am. Tr.*

— Index rerum; or, index of subjects. ('33.) New ed. 4°. '76. hf. mor., $3 .... *Bridgman.*

— Lectures to children; familiarly ill. important truth. ('34–'52.) New ed. 2 v. ill. 16°. '74. ea., 75c.; — in 1 v. 16°. $1.75 .... *Bridgman.*

— *Same.* 2 v. in 1. 12°. '52. $1.75 ...... *Randolph.*

— Life. *See* Todd, J: E.

— Moral influence, dangers and duties connected with great cities. ('41.) New ed. 18°. '49. 75c. *Bridgman.*

— Mountain flowers. 16°. $1 .... *Cong. Pub.*

— *Same.* 18°. '69. $1 .... *Bridgman.*

— Mountain gem ser. ('63.) New ed. 4 v. ill. 18°. '75. $2.50 .... *Hoyt.*
Cont.: Shaking out the reef. — Cush going to mill. — Uncle Ben and Uncle Levi. — Mother dove.

— Mountain rills: stories for children. ('65.) New ed. 4 v. ill. 18°. '67. $2.75 .... *Bridgman.*
Cont.: Old Shag, etc. — Angel over the left shoulder, etc. — Mountain lamb, etc. — Silas Narrow's lesson, etc.

— Nuts for boys to crack. 16°. '66. 90c. .... *Am. Tr.*

— Question book: Joshua and Judges. ('63.) New ed. 18°. '67. per doz., $1.80 ...... *Bridgman.*

— Questions on life of Moses: Exodus, Leviticus, Numbers and Deuteronomy. ('58.) New ed. 18°. '69. per doz., $1.80 .... *Bridgman.*

— Questions on lives of the patriarchs: Genesis. ('56.) New ed. 18°. '67. per doz., $1.80 .. *Bridgman.*

— Sabbath-school teacher. ('37.) New ed. 12°. '68. $1.50 .... *Bridgman.*

— Serpents in the doves' nest. 18°. 50c.; pap., 15c. *Lee & S.*

— Stories illustrating Shorter catechism. ill. 18°. '69. $1.50. .... *Bridgman.*

— Student's manual; [for] forming and strengthening intellect. and moral character of the student. ('35.) New ed., rev. 12°. '76. $1.75 ..... *Bridgman.*

— Summer gleanings; or, sketches and incidents of a pastor's vacation; coll. and arr. by his daughter. 12°. '52. $1.25 .... *Bridgman.*

— Sunset land; or, the great Pacific slope. 16°. $1.50. *Lee & S.*

— Truth made simple. ('39.) New ed. 18°. '70. $1.25 .... *Bridgman.*

Todd, J: *continued.*

— Woman's rights. 18°. 50c.; pap., 15c. .... *Lee & S.*

— Young man (The): hints to young men of the U. S. ('44.) New ed. 18°. '56. 75c. .... *Bridgman.*

Todd, J: A. Memoir of Rev. Peter Labagh. por. 12°. $1.25 .... *N. Y. Ref. Ch. Bd.*

Todd, J: E. John Todd: the story of his life, told mainly by himself. ill. cr. 8°. $2.75 ... *Harper.*

Todd, Rob. Bentley. Clinical lectures on certain acute diseases. 8°. $2.50 .... *Lea.*

Todd, Sara D. Old-fashioned lives. 16°. $1.25. *Cong. Pub.*

Todd, Sereno Edwards. American wheat culturist: treatise upon culture of wheat. ill. 12°. '68. $1.50 .... *Rural.*

— *Same.* ill. 12°. $2 .... *Taintor.*

— Apple culturist: treatise for the practical pomologist. ill. 12°. $1.50 .... *Harper.*

— Young farmer's manual. 2 v. ill. 12°. ea., $1.75. *Woodward.*

Todhunter, I: Algebra for beginners. New ed. 18°. '67. $1.25. — Key. cr. 8°. '67. $2.25 .. *Macmillan.*

— Algebra for colleges and schools. 5th ed. cr. 8°. '70. $2.25. — Key. cr. 8°. '70. $3 .. *Macmillan.*

— Conflict of studies, and other subjects connected with education. 8°. '73. $3.50 .... *Macmillan.*

— Euclid for colleges and schools. New ed. 18°. '64. $1.25 .... *Macmillan.*

— Examples of analytical geometry of three dimensions. 3d ed. cr. 8°. $1.50 .... *Macmillan.*

— History of the mathematical theories of attraction and the figure of the earth, from the time of Newton to that of Laplace. 2 v. 8°. '73. $12 .. *Macmillan.*

— Mathematical theory of probability. 8°. '65. $8. *Macmillan.*

— Mechanics for beginners. 18°. $1.50 .. *Macmillan.*

— Mensuration for beginners. New ed., rev. 18°. $1.25. *Macmillan.*

— Plane trigonometry for colleges and schools. 5th ed. cr. 8°. '74. $1.75. — Key. cr. 8°. $3.50 .. *Macmillan.*

— Researches in the calculus of variations, principally on theory of discontinuous solutions. 8°. '71. $3.50 .... *Macmillan.*

— Treatise on analytical statics. 4th ed., rev. and enl. cr. 8°. $3.50 .... *Macmillan.*

— Treatise on differential calculus. 3d ed. cr. 8°. $3.50 .... *Macmillan.*

— Treatise on integral calculus. 3d ed. cr. 8°. $3.50. *Macmillan.*

— Treatise on plane geometry, as applied to the straight line and the conic sections. 5th ed. cr. 8°. $2.25. *Macmillan.*

— Treatise on spherical trigonometry for colleges and schools. 3d ed. cr. 8°. $1.75 ..... *Macmillan.*

— Treatise on theory of equations. New ed. cr. 8°. $2.25 .... *Macmillan.*

— Trigonometry for beginners. New ed. 18°. $1. — Key. cr. 8°. $3 .... *Macmillan.*

Todte Gast (Der). *See* Zschokke, H:

Together; or, life on the circuit. Boyd, E. E. 90c. *Cin. Meth. Bk. Conc.*

Toil and trust. 16°. 75c. .... *Dodd.*

Toilers of the sea. *See* Hugo, Vct.

Toils and triumphs of colportage. Stevenson, J. M. 40c.; 20c. .... *Am. Tr.*

Toinette. Tourjee, A. W. $1.50 .... *Ford.*

Token (New) for children. 18°. 55c. ...... *Pres. Bd.*

Token of affection; — of friendship; — of the heart; — of love; — of remembrance. ill. 32°. ea., 38c. *Appleton.*

Told in the twilight. Daryl, S. $1.25 .... *Claxton.*

Toliver, E: Hans the stranger, and other stories. ill. 16°. $1.50 .... *J. E. Potter.*

— Our folks at home; or, life at the old manor house. ill. 16°. $1.50 .... *J. E. Potter.*

Toll gate. 18°. 35c. .... *Carter; Dutton.*

Tolle Hans (Der). *See* Streckfuss, A.

Tolon, Miguel T. Elementary Spanish reader and translator; with Spanish and English vocab. 12°. $1 .... *Appleton.*

Tom. Russell, H. R. $1 .... *Pott.*

Tom. Smith, F. I. B. 75c. .... *Lothrop.*

Tom and the crocodiles. Bowman, A. $1.25 .. *Routledge.*

Tom and Jerry. Moncrieff, W. T. 15c. ..... *French.*

Tom and Sarah Neal. 16°. $1.25 ...... (?) *Martien.*

Tom Bentley. Moore, J. F. $1.50 .... *Hoyt.*

Tom Blinn's temperance society. Arthur, T. S. $1.25. *Nat. Temp.*

Tom Bowling. Campbell, A. L. V. 15c. .... *French.*

Tom Bowling. *See* Chamier, F.

Tom Bowling (Life and adventures of). 8°. pap., 75c. *Peterson.*

Tom Brian in trouble. ('62.) New ed. ill. 18°. '70. 30c. .... *Hoyt.*

Tom Brown at Oxford. *See* Hughes, T:

Tom Brown's school-days. *See* Hughes, T:

Tom Bulkley. Jephson, R. M. $1 .... *Routledge.*

Tom Burke of ours. *See* Lever, C:

Tom Burton. 16°. 75c. .... *Dodd.*

Tom Butler's trouble: cottage story. 16°. 50c. *Scribner, W. & A.*

Tom Carroll. Hazen, M. H. $1.25 .... *Cong. Pub.*

Tom Carter; or, the ups and downs in life. ('71.) New ed. 16°. '74. $1.50 .... *Hoyt.*

Tom Chips. Diekenga, I. E., *and* Ashworth, T. M. $1.50 .... *Lippincott.*

Tom Cringle. Ball, E. 15c. .... *French.*

Tom Cringle's log. *See* Scott, M.

Tom Crosbie. Lover, S. 75c. .... *Dick & F.*

Tom Dunstone's troubles. Eiloart, C. J. $1.25. *Routledge.*

Tom Folio classics. [To form 3 v.] v. 1, 2. sm. 4°. ea., $1.50 .... *Lee & S.*

Cont.: Wishing-cap papers, by L. Hunt. — Fireside saints, by D. Jerrold.

Tom Gillies. *See* Gladstone, *Mrs.* G.

Tom Green and the tinker's letter. ('72.) New ed. 16°. '76. $1.15 .... *Hoyt.*

Tom Harding. Eyster, N. $1.25 .... *Meth. Epis.*

Tom Hardy. ill. 4°. 35c. .... *Am. Bapt.*

Tom Headstrong; or, always in trouble. *See* Theodore Thinker.

Tom Jones. *See* Fielding, H:

Tom Lane's cent. 18°. 25c. .... *Am. S. S.*

— *See also* Children of Blackberry Hollow.

Tom Mather and the lost purse. ('62.) New ed. 18°. '71. 30c. .... *Hoyt.*

Tom Miller. Rockwell, M. E. 90c. ...... *Garrigues.*

Tom Newcombe. Fosdick, C. A. $1.50 ..... *Porter.*

Tom Noddy's secret. Bayly, T. H. 15c. ..... *French.*

Tom Perry's venture. Leslie, M. 50c. ...... *Nelson.*

Tom Pippin's wedding; by author of "Fight at Dame Europa's school." 16°. $1.25; pap., 75c. *Lippincott.*

Tom Racquet. Smedley, F. E. 75c. .... *Peterson.*

Tom Ray; or, the mother's prayer answered. ('63.) New ed. ill. 16°. '68. 75c. .... *Hoyt.*

Tom Ripon; or, the highwayman and housebreaker. 8°. pap., 25c. .... *Dick & F.*

Tom Smith, the young Cumbrian. 18°. 20c.; 25c. *Am. Bapt.*

Tom Stapleton. Moore, J. H. 50c. .... *Dick & F.*

Tom Thornhill, and his temptation. ill. 24°. '69. 30c. *Lothrop.*

Tom Thrasher. Harris, A. 15c. .... *French.*

Tom Thumb. Fielding, H. 15c. .... *French.*

Tom Thumb (History of). [Toy-book.] ill. 4°. $1; 50c. .... *Routledge.*

Tom Thumb (History of little). ill. f°. 15c.; pap., 20c. .... *J. E. Potter.*

Tom Thumb toys. 6 v. 4°. ea., 20c. .... *Nelson.*

Cont.: History of Tom Thumb. — Cat and fiddle. — Great A, little A and bouncing B. — Nursery rhymes. — Jack, the giant killer. — At school and at play.

Tom Thumb's alphabet. [Toy-book.] ill. 4°. $1; 50c. *Routledge.*

Tom Tiddler's ground. *See* Dickens, C:

Tom Tracy of Brier Hill. 18°. 70c. .... ∴ *Am. S. S.*

Tom Truck; or, the wizard crew. 8°. pap., 25c. *De Witt.*

Tom u. Madlein. Bürcklin, A. 45c. .... *Steiger.*

Tom Waters; or, the haunted highwayman. 8°. pap., 50c. .... *Peterson.*

Tom Watson; or, the law of kindness. 32°. 25c. *Scribner, W. & A.*

Tombler, L. O. Singing tablets; arr. in a ser. of exercises and solfeggi. f°. '52. pap., 30c. *Ditson.*

Tomes, J: System of dental surgery. 2d ed., rev. and enl. by C. S. Tomes. ill. 12°. '73. $5 .. *Lindsay.*

Tomes, Rob. Battles of Am. by sea and land; with biog. of commanders and ill. anecdotes; ill. by Darley, Chappel, etc. ('61.) 4th ed. 3 v. med. 4°. '75. hf. mor., $26 .... *Virtue.*

— Champagne country (The). 16°. $1.50 .. *Hurd & H.*

— *Same.* 12°. $1.75 .... *Routledge.*

— History of the royal dauphin, Louis XVII. ill. 16°. 75c. .... *Harper.*

— Panama in 1855: account of Panama Railroad, of cities of Panama and Aspinwall, with sketches of life and character on the isthmus. ill. 16°. 75c. .. *Harper.*

— *and* Smith, B: G. Great civil war; with biog. sketches of leading statesmen and disting. commanders. ('67.) 12th ed. 3 v. steel eng. med. 4°. '76. hf. mor., $27 .... *Virtue.*

— — *Germ.* 2 v. pl. med. 4°. hf. mor., $24 .. *Virtue.*

Tomkins, E: Machine construction and drawing. (Element. sci. ser.) 2 v. 16°. '73. ea., 75c. — (Adv. sci. ser.) 2 v. 12°. '73. ea., $1.50 .. *Putnam.*

Tomkins, *Miss* J. H. From four to fourteen. ill. 16°. '73. $1.25 .... *Am. Tr.*

Tomlinson, *Mrs.* C: First steps in general knowledge. 5 v. ill. 18°. ea., $2.50 .... *Pott.*

Cont.: Starry heavens. — Surface of the earth. — Animal kingdom. — Vegetable kingdom. — Mineral kingdom.

Tomlinson, D: G. Good way; or, why Christians of whatever name may become Churchmen. 12°. pap., 15c. .... *Claremont.*

— *Same.* 12°. 20c. .... *Dutton.*

Tommiebig shootings. Jeans, T. 80c. ... *Routledge.*

Tommy and his broom. ill. fp. 8°. 60c. ..... *Cassell.*

Tommy Hickup. Parker, R. A. $1 .... *Lee & S.*

Tommy Try, and what he did in science. ill. 12°. $1.50. *Appleton.*

Tomorrow of death. Figuier, L. $1.75 .... *Roberts.*

Tompkins, the troubadour. Lockroy, —, *and* Michel, M. 15c. .... *De Witt; French.*

Tom's geranium. *See* Witt, *Mme.* H. de.

Tom's opinion. ill. 16°. 60c. .... *Lothrop.*

Tonart (The). *See* Roberts, E., *and* Morgan, J. P.

Tone masters. *See* Barnard, C. F., *jr.*

Toner, J. M. Dictionary of elevations and climatic register of United States. 8°. '74. $3.75; pap., $3 .... *Van Nostrand.*

Tongue bridle. *See* Child's effort.

Tongue of fire. *See* Arthur, W:

Tongue of fire on the daughters of the Lord. Palmer, P. 10c. .... *Palmer.*

Tongue of time; or, the language of a church clock. 18°. '44. 75c. .... *Randolph.*

Tonna, *Mrs.* Ctte. Eliz. Baby (The), and other stories. 18°. 35c. . . . *Pres. Bd.*
— Backbiting reproved, and other sketches. 18°. 40c. *Pres. Bd.*
— Boat and the drowned officer. 18°. 30c. . . *Pres. Bd.*
— Charlotte Elizabeth stories. 8 v. ill. 16°. $8 . . *Sheldon.*
Cont.: Glimpses of the past. — Philip and his garden. — Simple flower. — Fortune teller. — Tales and illustrations. — Humility before honor. — Alice Benden. — Flower of innocence.
— Count Raymond. 18°. 90c. . . . *Dodd.*
— Deserter. 18°. 90c. . . . *Dodd.*
— Falsehood and truth. 18°. 90c. . . . *Dodd.*
— Flower garden. 18°. 90c. . . . *Dodd.*
— Glory of Israel: letters to Jewish children on early hist. of their nation. 18°. 40c. . . . *Am. S. S.*
— Jack, the dumb boy. ill. 18°. '69. 20c. . . *Am. Tr.*
— Judah's lion. 18°. 90c. . . . *Dodd.*
— Judea capta. 18°. 90c. . . . *Dodd.*
— Personal recollections. 18°. '51. 45c. . . . *Am. Tr.*
— *Same.* 18°. 90c. . . . *Dodd.*
— Philip and his garden. ill. post 18°. 75c. *Scribner, W. & A.*
— Rose-bud, and other stories. 18°. 35c. . . . *Pres. Bd.*
— Stories for children. ill. 32°. '57. 35c. . . . *Am. Tr.*
— Stories of the Bible. ill. post 18°. 75c. *Scribner, W. & A.*
— Wants and wishes. 18°. 22c. . . . *Am. S. S.*
— White lies; [also] Little oaths; [also] The bee. 18°. 30c. . . . *Pres. Bd.*
— Wrongs of women. 18°. 90c. . . . *Dodd.*

Tony, and other stories. ill. 4°. '76. pap., 25c. *Lothrop.*
Tony and his harp. *See* Baker, *Mrs.* H. N. W.
Tony and his rabbit. *See* May, A.
Tony Butler. *See* Lever, C:
Tony Pastor. *See* Pastor, Tony.
Tony Starr's legacy. Robbins, S. S. $1.25 . . . *Carter.*
Too big for Sunday school. 18°. 50c. . . . *Pres. Bd.*
Too late. ill. 24°. '70. 25c. . . . *Lothrop.*
Too late for the train. Baker, G. M. 15c. . . . *Lee & S.*
Too much alone. *See* Riddell, *Mrs.* J. H.
Too much for good nature. Falconer, E. 15c. . . *French.*
Too much of a good thing. Harris, A. 15c. . . *French.*
Too soon. Macquoid, K. S. 50c. . . . *Harper.*
Too strange not to be true. *See* Fullerton, *Lady* G.
Toodles: drama. 16°. pap., 15c. . . . *French.*
Tooke, And. Pantheon of the heathen gods and illustrious heroes; for students. ill. 12°. '69. hf. roan, $1.25 . . . *Cushings & B.*
Tooley, Larry. Dutchman's ghost: Ethiop. drama. 16°. pap., 15c. . . . *De Witt.*
— German emigrant: Ethiop. drama. 16°. pap., 15c. *De Witt.*
Toothache: drama. 16°. pap., 15c. . . . *French.*
Toothacker, C. E. Treatise on diseases of the skin. *See* Small, A. E., Diseases of nervous system.
Tootle, tootle, too: musical [dram.] sketch. 16°. pap., 15c. . . . *Happy.*
Topelius, Z. Gustav Adolf, and the thirty years' war; tr. by S. Borg and M. A. Brown. [Fiction.] 12°. '72. $1.50 . . . *Porter.*
Töpffer, Rod. Histoire de Charles; [also] Histoire de Jules. Ed. by P. H. E. Brette and G. Masson. sm. 8°. bds., 75c. . . . *Lippincott.*
Topics of the time. Parton, J. $2 . . . *Osgood.*
Toplady, A: M. Life. *See* Hervey, J., Life.
Tor hill. Smith, H. 50c. . . . *U. P. James.*
Torch-bearers. Bates, E. $1.25 . . . *Lothrop.*
Torloch O'Brien. *See* Fortunes of Torloch O'Brien.
Torn Bible. 18°. 75c. . . . *Carter.*
Torn Bible: how the prodigal was saved by it. 16°. 70c. *West. Tr.*
Torn Bible; or, Hubert's best friend. ill. post 18°. 75c. . . . *Scribner, W. & A.*

Tornos, Alberto de. Combined Spanish method: new system of learning the Castilian language. 12°. $1.75. — Key, 75c. . . . *Appleton.*
Toro, Emilio. Nueva aritmética téorico-practica con aplicaciones al comercio. 12°. 50c. . . *Appleton.*
Toronto, *Canada.* *See* City of Toronto.
Torp, O: Instructions for the Spanish guitar. f°. pap., $2.50 . . . *Ditson.*
Torpedo warfare: instructions for management of Harvey's sea torpedo. ill. 8°. '72. $1 . . . *Spon.*
Torquato Tasso. *See* Goethe, J. W. v.
Torresdale lib. 10 v. 18°. $3.25 . . . *Am. Bapt.*
Cont.: Eight years old. — Little Joe. — Nellie Green. — Mother's last words. — Our lost home. — Last gift. — Donald's hamper. — Bertie Wade. — Waterloo soldier. — Tame fox.
Torrey, J: Batis maritima. 4°. '53. pap., $1. *Smith. Inst.*
— Darlingtonia Californica. 4°. '53. pap., $1. *Smith. Inst.*
— Plantæ Fremontianæ. 4°. '53. pap., $1.50. *Smith. Inst.*
— *See also* Ives, J. C., Report on Colorado River; — New York geol. survey.
Torrey, Jos. Theory of fine art. sq. 12°. '74. $1.50. *Scribner.*
Torrey Botanical Club. Botanical directory for North America and the West Indies. 8°. '73. pap., 30c. *Torrey Bot.*
— Bulletin. v. 1–5. 8°. '70–'74. pap., $3.75 . . *Torrey Bot.*
Tortoise and the robin red-breast. 18°. 25c. . . *Am. S. S.*
Toschi's engravings; from frescoes by Correggio and Parmegiano. 4°. '74. $10 . . . *Osgood.*
Tossed on the waves. Hodder, E. 75c. . . . *So. Meth.*
Totten, B: J. Naval text-book and dictionary; for midshipmen of the U. S. navy. 2d ed., rev. 12°. '64. $3 . . . *Van Nostrand.*
Totten, Jos. Gilb. Report on firing with heavy ordnance. *See* United States, *Corps of Eng.*
Tottie's treasure. ill. sm. 4°. $1.75 . . . *Nelson.*
Toulmin, G: Hoggart. Antiquity and duration of the world. 12°. pap., 25c. . . . *Mendum.*
Tour of Dr. Syntax. *See* Combe, W.
Tour of Nesle. Hugo, V. 15c. . . . *French.*
Tour of the world in eighty days. *See* Verne, Jul.
Tour round my garden. Karr, J. B. A. $3.75. *Scribner, W. & A.*
Tourist ticket: farce. 16°. pap., 15c. . . . *French.*
Tourjee, Albion W. ["H: Churton."] Toinette: tale of transition. ('74.) New ed. 12°. '75. $1.50 . . . *Ford.*
Tourjee, Eben. Chorus choir: anthems, motettes, chants, etc. 8°. '75. bds., $2 . . . *Ditson.*
— Tribute of praise. [Hymn book.] 12°. $1. *Cong. Pub.*
— *Same.* sq. 8°. $1; — with psalter, $1.25. *Meth. Bk. Conc.*
Tournament of Idylcourt. Baker, G. M. 15c. . . *Lee & S.*
Toussaint, G. A. *See* Riffault, J. R. D., Vergnaud, A. D., *and* Toussaint, G. A.
Touton and pussy. Mathews, J. H. $1 . . . *Carter.*
Tover tangle. *See* Capron, M. J.
Toward the mark. Campbell, E. F. R. $1.25. *Garrigues.*
Toward the strait gate. Burr, E. F. $2.50. *Lockwood, B. & Co.*
Tower, Anna E. Little primer. 18°. per doz., pap., $1.25 . . . *Thompson.*
Tower, D: Bates. Common school grammar. 12°. 75c. *Lee & S.*
— Exercises in articulation. 12°. 20c. . . . *Lee & S.*
— Gradual lessons in grammar. 12°. 90c. . . . *Lee & S.*
— Gradual speller and complete enunciator. 12°. 30c. *Lee & S.*
— Grammar of [Eng.] composition. 12°. 75c. . . *Lee & S.*

Tower, D: Bates, *continued.*
— Intellectual algebra. 12°. 60c. — Key, 60c. . . *Lee & S.*
— [Readers.] 7 v. . . . . *Lee & S.*
Cont.: First reader, 16°, 25c. — Second, 16°, 45c. — Intermediate, 12°, 50c. — Third gradual, 12°, 60c. — Fourth, 12°, 75c. — Fifth, 12°, 90c. — Sixth, 12°, $1.

— *and* Tweed, B. F. First lessons in language; or, elements of Eng. grammar. 16°. 40c. . . *Lee & S.*

Tower, G. B. N. Instructions on mod. Am. bridge building; with applic. and examples, estimates of quantities and valuable tables. pl. and ill. 12°. '74. $2 . . . . *Williams.*

Tower, J: V. R. Premium tables for buying and selling gold, bonds and stocks. 4°. $3 . . . . *Claxton.*

Tower hill. Ainsworth, W. H. 30c. . . . . . . *Am. News.*

Tower mark. 18°. 22c. . . . . *Am. S. S.*
— *Same.* 18°. '66. 25c. . . *N. Y. Ref. Ch. Bd.; Pres. Com.*

Tower of constancy. Bungener, L. L. F. $1.50 . . *Lothrop.*

Tower of London. *See* Ainsworth, W: H.

Tower of London: drama. 16°. pap., 15c. . . . . *French.*

Towers of Zion; or, the evidences of Christianity illustrated. 18°. 60c. *Am. S. S.*

Towle, G: M. Glimpses of history. 16°. $1.50 . . *Lee & S.*
— History of Henry v. of England. 8°. $2.50 . . *Appleton.*

Towle, Natl. C. History and analysis of Constitution of United States. 3d ed., rev. and enl. sm. 8°. '73. $1.75 . . . . *Little, B. & Co.*

Town, Salem. Analysis of derivative words in the Eng. lang. ('35.) New ed., rev. 16°. 60c. . . *Mason.*
— New speller and definer. Rev. and enl. ed. 12°. 25c. *Mason.*
— Old spelling book. 24°. 25c. . . . . *Mason.*
— [Readers.] 6 v. . . . . *Mason.*
Cont.: First reader, 16°, hf. bd., 20c. — Second, 16°, hf. bd., 50c. — Third, 12°, hf. bd., 75c. — Fourth, 12°, $1.20. — Fifth, 12°, $1.25. — Grammar-school reader, 12°, $1.20.

Town and country. Morton, T. 15c. . . . . *French.*

Town and country sermons. Kingsley, C. $1.25. *Macmillan.*

Town geology. Kingsley, C. $1.50 . . . . *Appleton.*

Towne, Pl. Allen. Algebra. 12°. '65. $1.25. — Key, $1.25 . . . . *Morton.*
— Intermediate arithmetic. 16°. '67. bds., 55c. *Morton.*
— Mental arithmetic. 16°. '70. bds., 40c. . . . . *Morton.*
— Practical arithmetic. 12°. '66. bds., $1. — Key, $1. *Morton.*
— Primary arithmetic. 16°. '70. bds., 35c. . . *Morton.*

Towne, T. M. *See* Martin, S. W., Towne, T. M., *and* Stillman, J. M.

Townley, D. O'C. *See* Meyer von Bremen gallery.

Townley, Ja. High life below stairs: farce. 16°. pap., 15c. . . . . *French.*

Townley, *Rev.* Ja. Illustrations of Biblical literature. 2 v. 8°. $6; hf. cf., $7 . . . . *Cin. Meth. Bk. Conc.*

Townsend, A. A. Biblical hist. familiarized by questions. 4th ed. 16°. *net*, 75c. . . *Friends Bk. Assoc.*

Townsend, Aurelia W. Fugitive verses. 12°. '76. $1 . . . . *Turnbull.*

Townsend, Calv. Analysis of civil government. 12°. '68. $1.50 . . . . *Ivison.*
— Analysis of letter writing; with examples of model business letters. 12°. '72. $1.50 . . . . . *Ivison.*
— Compendium of commercial law, analytically and topically arranged. 8°. '71. shp., $4 . . . . . *Ivison.*
— Shorter course in civil government. 12°. '75 $1. *Ivison.*

Townsend, E. D. Catechism of the Bible. 2 pts. 18°. ea., 35c. . . . . *Dutton.*
Cont.: Pentateuch. — Judges and Kings.

Townsend, G: Alfr. Life, crime and capture of John Wilkes Booth; with sketch of the conspiracy. 8°. '65. pap., 25c. . . . . *Dick & F.*
— New world compared with the old: descrip. of Am. government, institutions, etc. ill. 8°. '69. *$3.50; $4; hf. mor., $5 . . . . *Betts.*

Townsend, G: Alfr., *continued.*
— Washington, outside and inside. ill. 8°. '73. *$3.50; leath., $4; hf. mor., $5 . . . . *Betts.*

Townsend, G: Fyler. Siege of Colchester; or, an event of the civil war, A. D. 1618. 12°. $1.25 . . *Pott.*

Townsend, Luther Tracy. Arena and the throne. 16°. $1.50 . . . . *Lee & S.*
— Chinese problem. 16°. '76. 75c.; pap., 50c. . . *Lee & S.*
— Controversy between real and pretended Christianity: essay. 16°. 50c.; pap., 25c. . . . . *Lee & S.*
— Credo. 16°. $1.50 . . . . *Lee & S.*
— God-man, pt. 1: Search and manifestation. 12°. $1.75. *Lee & S.*
— Lost forever. 16°. $1.75 . . . . *Lee & S.*
— Outlines of theology. 12°. '73. 50c. . . *Meth. Bk. Conc.*
— Sword and garment; or, ministerial culture. 16°. $1.50 . . . . *Lee & S.*

Townsend, Ma. Ashly. ["Xariffa."] Captain's story: poem. 12°. pap., 30c. . . . . *Lippincott.*
— Xariffa's poems. 12°. $1.50 . . . . *Lippincott.*

Townsend, Thompson. Lost ship: drama. 16°. pap., 15c. . . . . *French.*

Townsend, Virg. F. Breakwater ser. 5 v. 16°. ea., 75c. . . . . *Loring.*
Cont.: Joanna Darling; or, the home at Breakwater. — Boy at Bramley; Little newsboy. — Hope Darrow: a little girl's story. — Max Meredith's millennium. — Margery Keith.

— Darryll Gap; or, whether it paid. 12°. $1.50 . . *Lee & S.*
— Deerings of Medbury. 12°. $1.25 . . . . *Loring.*
— Elizabeth Tudor, the queen and the woman. ill. 12°. '74. $1.50 . . . . *Meth. Bk. Conc.*
— Hollands (The). 12°. $1.25 . . . . *Loring.*
— Living and loving: sketches. por. 16°. $1.25. *J. E. Potter.*
— Mills of Tuxbury. 12°. $1.25 . . . . *Loring.*
— One woman's two lovers; or, Jacqueline Thayne's choice. 12°. $1.50 . . . . *Lippincott.*
— Only girls. ill. 12°. $1.50 . . . . *Lee & S.*
— Six in all. 8°. $1.25 . . . . *Loring.*
— Temptation and triumph. 12°. $1.75. — 16°. $1.25. *Cin. Meth. Bk. Conc.*
— That queer girl. ill. 16°. $1.50 . . . . *Lee & S.*
— While it was morning. 16°. $1.25 . . . . . *J. E. Potter.*

Townsend, W. Thompson. Temptation: drama. 16°. pap., 15c. . . . . *French.*
— Whitefriars: drama. 16°. pap., 15c. . . . . . . *French.*

Townshend, Chauncey H. Facts in mesmerism, with reasons for a dispassionate inquiry into it. ill. 12°. $1.25 . . . . *Harper.*

Townshend, J: Law and practice [in N. Y.] on proceedings by landlords to recover possession of demised premises, on non-payment of rent on expiration of the term. 12°. $2 . . . . *Baker, V. & Co.*
— Treatise on wrongs called slander and libel, and their remedies. 8°. shp., $6.50 . . . . *Baker, V. & Co.*

Towzer and his troubles. ill. cr. 4°. pap., 20c.; 25c. *J. E. Potter.*

Toy, *Miss* A. J., *and* Knowles, *Mrs.* E. J. Sunday-school celebration book: dialogues, speeches, recitations, hymns, etc. ('60.) 7th ed. 18°. '76. 60c. . . . . *Perkinpine.*

Toy books of domestic animals. 4 v. ill. 4°. ea., bds., 50c. . . . . *Routledge.*
Cont.: Donkey, pet dog and goat. — Sheep, horse and cow. — Pigs, pony and cat. — Rabbits, guinea pigs and dog.

Toy books of wild animals. 4 v. ill. 4°. ea., bds., 50c. *Routledge.*
Cont.: Bear, hyena and zebra. — Bison, leopard and wolf. — Rhinoceros, hippopotamus and giraffe. — Lion, elephant and tiger.

Toy primer. ill. 4°. $1; 50c. . . . . *Routledge.*

Toyland. O'Shaughnessy, A. *and* E. $2 . . *Routledge.*

Toynbee, Jos. On diseases of the ear: their nature, diagnosis and treatment. New ed., with sup. by J. Hinton. ill. 8°. $5 . . . . *Lindsay.*

Track of the hidden church. Waddington, J. $1.25. *Cong. Pub.*

Tracked. Reback, H. 30c ... *Am. News.*

Tract Association of Friends. Series of tracts on moral and religious subjects. 3 v. 12°. '74. ea., 50c. ... *Friends Bk. St.*

Tract volumes. v. 1–14. ill. 12°. '25–'63. $12 .. *Am. Tr.*

— *German.* Traktate. 4 v. 12°. '51. ea., 90c. .. *Am. Tr.*

Tracts for missionary use; by Bp. Lay and others. 12°. $1.25 ... *Claremont.*

— *Same.* 18°. $1.50 ... *Dutton.*

Tracts on doctrines, order and polity of Presbyterian Church in the U. S. 13 v. 12°. ea., $1 .. *Pres. Bd.*

Tracts on popery. 18°. 75c. ... *Pres. Bd.*

Tracy, Ant. L: Cl. D. de. *See* Destutt de Tracy.

Tracy, Calv. Child's arithmetic. 18°. '53. hf. bd., 25c. ... *Claxton.*

— Commercial and mechanical arithmetic. 12°. '51. $1. — Key, $1 ... *Claxton.*

— Elementary arithmetic. 12°. '50. hf. bd., 35c. *Claxton.*

— Scientific and practical arithmetic. 12°. '50. hf. bd., 56c. — Key. 12°. '50. 56c. ... *Claxton.*

Tracy, J. L. American historical reader. 12°. '57. $1. *Claxton; Lippincott.*

— Elementary arithmetic. 12°. hf. roan, 35c. *Lippincott.*

— Scientific and practical arithmetic. 12°. 56c. — Key, 56c. ... *Lippincott.*

Tracy, Ja. Cole. Paraclete. *See* Hopkins, I. H., *and* Mahan, M., Revival system.

Tracy, Jos. Great awakening: hist. of revival of religion in the time of Edwards and Whitefield. por. 12°. $1.25 ... *Cong. Pub.*

Tracy, Ste. The mother and her offspring. 12°. $1.50. *Harper.*

Tracy, W: Handbook of law for business men. 8°. hf. roan, *$5.50; shp., $6.50 ... *Appleton.*

Tracy's ambition. *See* Griffin, Ger.

Trade circular annual for 1871; incl. American catalogue of books pub. in U. S. during 1870. roy. 8°. '71. *net*, $1.50 ... *Publishers' Weekly.*

— *See also* Publishers' trade-list annual.

Tradesman's son: drama. 16°. pap., 15c. ... *French.*

Trading. Warner, S. $1.25 ... *Carter.*

Traditions of the Covenanters. *See* Simpson, R.

Traditions of Palestine. Martineau, H. 50c. *Routledge.*

Traditions of Palestine. Wheelwright, A. 75c. *Cong. Pub.*

Trafford, F. G. (*pseud.*) *See* Riddell, *Mrs.* J. H.

Trafton, Adeline. An American girl abroad. ill. 16°. $1.50 ... *Lee & S.*

— Katherine Earle. ill. 16°. $1.75 ... *Lee & S.*

Trafton, M: Baptism: its subjects and mode. 16°. '70. 25c. ... *N. E. Meth.*

Tragedian. Gould, T. R. $1.75 ... *Hurd & H.*

Tragedy of errors. Putnam, M. L. $1 ... *Osgood.*

Tragedy of Lesbos. Pember, E. H. $1.50 .. *Macmillan.*

Tragedy of success. Putnam, M. L. $1 ... *Osgood.*

Tragedy transmogrified: burlesque. 16°. pap., 15c. *Happy.*

Tragic revival: farce. 16°. pap., 15c. ... *French.*

Trail, W: Guide to Christian communicants in the exercise of self-examination. 32°. 25c. *Pres. Bd.*

— Literary characteristics and achievements of the Bible. 12°. $1.75 ... *Cin. Meth. Bk. Conc.*

— — *See also* Inquiring Christian's lib.

Trail hunter. Aimard, G. 75c. ... *Peterson.*

Trail of blood: Ethiop. drama. 16°. pap., 15c. *Happy.*

Traill, *Mrs.* Cath. Parr. Afar in the forest; or, pictures of life and scenery in the wilds of Canada. ill. 18°. $1 ... *Nelson.*

— Canadian Crusoes. 16°. $1.25 ... *Nichols & H.*

— Stories of Canadian forests; or, little Mary and her nurse. 16°. $1.25 ... *Nichols & H.*

Train, G: Fs. Facts (The); or, at whose door does the sin (?) lie. [Anti-slavery.] 8°. pap., 25c. *De Witt.*

— On the downfall of England; [also] The war in Am.; by Abp. Hughes. 8°. pap., 10c. ... *Peterson.*

— On slavery and emancipation. 8°. pap., 10c. *Peterson.*

— Speech to the Fenians: views on Fenianism, Ireland and England. 8°. pap., 25c. ... *Peterson.*

— Union speeches. 2 v. 8°. ea., pap., 25c. *Peterson.*

Traine, Eliz. Twilight of faith. 12°. '73. $1. (?) *H. D. Brown.*

Training of the twelve. Bruce, A. B. $5. *Scribner, W. & A.*

Traitor. Bennett, E. 75c. ... *U. P. James.*

Traitors and assassins after Christ's advent. Headley, P. C. 25c.; 30c. ... *J. E. Potter.*

Traitors' gate: drama. 16°. pap., 15c. ... *French.*

Traits and stories of the Irish peasantry. *See* Carleton, W.

Traits of attractive women, and philosophy of love affairs. 12°. '74. $1 ... (?) *Belmont.*

Trall, Russell Thacher. Alcoholic controversy: review of the "Westminster Review" on physiol. errors of teetotalism. 12°. '55. pap., 50c. ... *Wells.*

— Bath (The): its hist. and uses in health and disease. ill. 12°. '72. 50c.; pap., 25c. ... *Wells.*

— Digestion and dyspepsia: explan. of physiology of digestive process; with symptoms and treatment of disorders. ill. 12°. '73. $1 ... *Wells.*

— Diseases of the throat and lungs. ill. 12°. '60. pap., 25c. ... *Wells.*

— Essay on tobacco using. 16°. pap., 15c. *Sev. Day Adv.*

— Health and diseases of women. 16°. pap., 15c. *Sev. Day Adv.*

— Health catechism. ill. 12°. '75. pap., 10c. .. *Wells.*

— Home treatment for sexual abuses; with their symptoms and hydropathic management. 12°. '58. pap., 50c. ... *Wells.*

— Human voice (The): its anatomy, physiology, pathology, therapeutics and training; with rules of order for lyceums. 12°. '75. 75c.; pap., 50c. *Wells.*

— Hydropathic encyclopædia: system of hydropathy and hygiene. 2 v. in 1. ill. 12°. '51. $4 .. *Wells.*

— Hygeian home cook-book; or, healthful and palatable food without condiments. 12°. '74. 50c.; pap., 25c. ... *Wells.*

— Hygienic handbook: guide for the sick room. New ed., rev. 12°. '72. $1.50 ... *Wells.*

— Hygienic system. 16°. pap., 15c. ... *Sev. Day Adv.*

— Illustrated family gymnasium. ill. 12°. '57. $1.50. *Wells.*

— Mother's hygienic handbook; for normal development and training of women and children, and treatment of their diseases with hygienic agencies. 12°. '74. $1 ... *Wells.*

— New hydropathic cook-book. ill. 12°. '53. $1.25. *Wells*

— Popular physiology: exposition of structures, functions and rel. of human system, and their applic. to preservation of health. 12°. '75. $1.25 .. *Wells.*

— Sexual physiology: fundamental problems in sociology. 12°. '66. $2 ... *Wood & H.*

— True healing art (The); or, hygienic versus drug medication. 12°. '62. 50c.; pap., 25c. .. *Wells*

— Uterine diseases and displacements. ill. 12°. '54 $5 ... *Wells*

— Water-cure for the million: processes of water-cure explained. 12°. '60. 50c.; pap., 25c. ... *Wells*

Trammell, W: Dugas. Ça ira. [Fiction.] 12°. '74 $1.50 ... *U. S. Pub*

Tramp's adventure: drama. 16°. pap., 15c. .. *French*

Tramps in New York. Weaver, *Mrs.* —. 40c. *Am. Tr*

Traneus, L. Hemläkaren, en hjelpreda för landtbor så wäl i Swerige som Amerika; med recepte enligt swenska ach amerikanska farmakopeerna 8°. 60c. ... *Engberg*

Transatlantic sketches. James, H., *jr.* $2 .. *Osgood*

Transcendentalism in New England. *See* Frothingham, O. B.

Transformation scenes in the United States. Fuller, H. $1.50 .... *Carleton.*

Transformed island: story of the south seas. 18°. 35c. .... *Pres. Bd.*

Transformed village. 18°. 60c. .... *Am. S. S.*

Transient and eternal. *See* Romberg, A.

Translated prophet. Lowrie, J. M. $1.25.. *Pres. Bd.*

Translator (The): English into French: sel. from Eng. prose writers, with principles of translation. [etc.]; by Profs. Gasc, Le Brun, etc. ('69.) New ed. 12°. '70. $1.25 .... *Holt.*

Translators revived. McClure, A. 80c. *N. Y. Ref. Ch. Bd.*

Transome lib. 4 v. 16°. $5 .... *Hoyt.*
Cont.: Gutta percha Willie, by G. Mac Donald. — King's servants. — Peter, the apprentice. — City sparrows and who feeds them.

Transplanted shamrock. Chaplin, J. D. 50c. *Bost. Am. Tr.*

Trap to catch a sunbeam. *See* Mackarness, *Mrs.* M. A.

Trapier, Pl. Catechism on the creed. 18°. bds., 10c. *Dutton.*

Trapp, J: Commentary on the Bible; ed. by H. Martin. ('62.) New ed. 5 v. 8°. '68. $37.. *Tibbals.*

Trapper ser. 3 v. ill. 12°. $3.75 .... *Nelson.*
Cont.: Hunter and the trapper. — Monsters of the deep. — Two years in east Africa.

Trapper's bride; or, the spirit of adventure; by author of "Prairie bird." 8°. pap., 50c... *U. P. James.*

Trapper's daughter. Aimard, G. 75c...... *Peterson.*

Trapper's guide; by S. Newhouse and others. ('65.) 4th ed., rev. by J. H. Noyes and T. S. Pitt. 8°. '74. $1.50 .... *Oneida.*

Trapper's niece. ill. 16°. '71. $1.25 .... *Lothrop.*

Trapper's son. *See* Kingston, W. H. G.

Trappers of New York. Simms, J. R. $1.50; $3. *Munsell.*

Trapping a Tartar. Stirling, E. 15c. .... *French.*

Traps to catch foxes. *See* Aunty Lee lib.

Trastour, E. Rudiments; [for the piano]. 16°. 75c. *Gordon.*

Trautwine, J: C. Civil engineer's pocket book of mensuration, trigonometry, surveying, hydraulics, etc. ('71.) 3d ed. ill. 12°. '74. $5.. *Claxton.*
— Field practice of laying out circular curves for railroads. ('73.) 9th ed., rev. and enl. 12°. '74. $2 .... *Claxton.*
— New method of calculating cubic contents of excavations and embankments by aid of diagrams; with directions for estimating cost of earth work. ('71.) 6th ed., rev. and enl. ill. 8°. '74. $2.. *Claxton.*

Traveler. *See* Library of good example.

Traveler's prayer. Clarke, A. 25c. *Cin. Meth. Bk. Conc.*

Travelers. Cherry, A. 15c. .... *French.*

Travelers' grab bag; or, the heart of a quiet hour: handbook for utilizing fragments of leisure. ('75.) 2d ed. 8°. '76. pap., 50c. .... *Authors.*

Traveling about over old and new ground. Barker, M. A. (*Lady*). $2 .... *Routledge.*

Traveller. *See* Goldsmith, Ol.

Traveller's inn. Chapman, H. E. 75c..... *Cong. Pub.*

Traveller's lib.: coll. of true narratives. [In Eng. or Germ.] 8°. pap., 25c. .... *Barclay.*

Traveller's manual of conversation. *See* Osgood's European guide books.

Traveller's tales; by author of "Busy bee." ill. 12°. '74. $1.50 .... *Nelson.*

Travellers' stories. Follen, E. L. 50c....... *Lee & S.*

Travelling sixpence. *See* Little Lottie ser.

Travels about home. 2 pts. 18°. ea., 35c... *Am. S. S.*

Travels and adventures of Baron Munchausen. *See* Raspe, R. E.

Travels by sea and land. *See* Reid, Mayne.

Travels in Bible lands. Andrews, E. 80c.; $1.. *Earle.*

Travels of an American owl. Johnson, V. W. $2.50. *Claxton.*

Travels of a doctor: book of travels of a doctor of physic. 12°. $2 .... *Lippincott.*

Travels of an Irish gentleman in search of a religion. Moore, T. $1.50 .... *Murphy.*

Travels of Rolando; or, a tour around the world; tr. by Miss Aikin, rev. by C. Hartley. ill. 16°. $1. *Routledge.*

Travels of true godliness. 18°. 55c.; 65c. *Am. Bapt.*

Travels of the ungodly. *See* Bunyan, J., Pilgrim's progress.

Traviata (La). *See* Verdi, G.

Travis, E: Practical organist: coll. of voluntaries for the organ. 8°. pap., $1 .... *Ditson.*

Travis, Jos. Autobiography. 12°. '59. $1.25.. *So. Meth.*
— Reasons for not joining the Baptist Church: dialogue between a Baptist and a Methodist. ('58.) 10th ed. 12°. '76. pap., 10c. .... *So. Meth.*

Treadwell, J: H. Pottery and porcelain: manual for amateurs. ill. 8°. '72. $2.75 .... *Putnam.*

Treason at home. Greenough, S. D. $1.75; $1.50. *Peterson.*

Treasure-box of amusement and instruction. 3 v. ill. 12°. $3 .... *Routledge.*
Cont.: Gulliver's travels. — Sandford and Merton. — Evenings at home.

Treasure-box of wonder and entertainment. 3 v. ill. 12°. $3 .... *Routledge.*
Cont.: Arabian nights. — Robinson Crusoe. — Swiss family Robinson.

Treasure hunters. Fenn, G. M. 40c. ...... *Harper.*

Treasure lib. for young ladies. 3 v. 12°. $4.50.. *Nelson.*
Cont.: Above rubies, by Miss Brightwell. — Early choice, by W. R. Tweedie. — Sunshine of domestic life, by W. H. D. Adams.

Treasure of the Inca. Hoffmann, F. 85c. (?) *Luth. Pub.*

Treasure of the seas. DeMille, J. $1.50.... *Lee & S.*

Treasure ser. 3 v. ill. 18°. '69. $2.50 .... *Claxton.*
Cont.: Levin's treasure in bank, by E. Reed. — Legends of fairy land, by Mrs. A. Bache. — Sea drift, by Fadette.

Treasure trove. *See* Lover, S:

Treasure trove. Shaw, C. A. $1.50; $2.50.. *Freeman.*

Treasure trove: romantic and humorous poem. ill. sm. 4°. '72. $2; mor., $5.50 .... *Osgood.*

Treasure-trove ser. *See* Walsh, W. S.

Treasured gems. Collins, R. 75c...... *Collins & Bro.*

Treasured memories for little children; by their friend Margaret. 18°. 25c. .... *Am. S. S.*

Treasured tokens. Fairlamb, J. R. $10; — Libretto, 40c. .... *Pond.*

Treasures above. *See* Kennedy, *Mrs.* M. G.

Treasures of the deep. ill. 12°. $1.50....... *Nelson.*

Treasures of the earth. *See* Jones, W.

Treasures on the beach. P., M. A. 50c...... *Nelson.*

Treasury of Bible knowledge. *See* Ayre, J.

Treasury of Christian thought. 16°. $1 .. *Lippincott.*

Treasury of David. Spurgeon, C. H. 4 v. ea., $4. *Scribner, W. & A.*

Treasury of devotion. *See* Carter, T. T.

Treasury of facts. Johnson, J. 6 nos. *net*, 75c. *Friends Bk. Assoc.*

Treasury of fairy stories. ill. sm. 4°. '71. $1.. *Hurd & H.*

Treasury of knowledge Chambers, W. *and* R. $1.25. *Barnes.*

Treasury of literature and art. ill. 4°. '72. $4.50. *Lothrop.*

Treasury of pleasure books. ill. 8°. $1.50.. *Hurd & H.*

Treasury of poetic gems. *See* Lippincott's pocket treasuries.

Treasury of the sacred heart. [Cath. prayer book.] 18°. $1-$3.50 .... *O'Shea.*

— *Same;* with Epistles and Gospels. 18°. $1.25-$4.50. *O'Shea.*

Treasury of Scripture knowledge: sel. of Scripture ref. and parallel passages, with notes, etc. fp. 8°. (Bagster.) $3.25 .... *Wiley.*

Treasury of table talk. *See* Lippincott's pocket treasuries.

Treasury of thought. Ballou, M. M. $5; $8.. *Osgood.*

Treasury of travel and adventure in North and South America, Europe, Asia and Africa. ill. 12°. $1.50 .... *Appleton.*

Treasury pictures. Miller, J. D. 60c... *Ref. Ch. Pub.*

Treat, E. B. (*ed.*) Illustrated New York and Brooklyn. [Annual guide book.] ill. and map. 8°. '74. 50c. .... *Treat.*

Treatise on general confessions: conversations between confessor and penitent. 32°. '52. 45c... *Murphy.*

Treatise on raising broom-corn and making brooms on a small or large scale; by editors of "American Agriculturist." 12°. '76. 75c.; pap., 50c... *Judd.*

Tredgold, T: Elementary principles of carpentry; rev. and partly re-written by J. T. Hurst. 48 pl. and 150 wood eng. cr. 8°. '71. $6..... *Spon.*

— (*ed.*) Tracts on hydraulics; cont. Smeaton's Experimental papers on power of water and wind to turn mills, etc., Venturé's Experiments on motion of fluids, Young's Summary of pract. hydraulics. pl. roy. 8°. (Lond.) '62. bds., $3.. *Spon.*

Tree and its fruits; or, the last hours of infidels and Christians contrasted. 18°. 45c....... *Am. S. S.*

Treffrey, R: Life of Joseph Benson. 12°. '38. 80c. *Meth. Bk. Conc.*

— Treatise on secret and social prayer. 18°. '42. 50c. *Meth. Bk. Conc.*

— *Same;* ed. by T. O. Summers. ('57.) 3d ed. 18°. '75. 60c. .... *So. Meth.*

— — *See also* Young disciples lib.

Treffrey, R: *jr.* Memoirs of Rev. John Smith. 18°. '36. 75c. .... *Meth. Bk. Conc.*

Tregelles, S: Prideaux. Account of printed text of Gk. New Test.; with remarks on its rev. upon crit. principles. 8°. (Bagster.) $4.50.. *Wiley.*

— Authenticity of Book of Daniel. fp. 8°. (Bagster.) pap., 75c. .... *Wiley.*

— Collation of crit. texts of Griesbach, Scholz, Lachmann and Tischendorf, with the received text. 8°. (Bagster.) $1.25 .... *Wiley.*

— Heads of Hebrew grammar. fp. 8°. (Bagster.) $1.25; hf. bd., $1.50........ *Wiley.*

— Hebrew reading lessons. fp. 8°. (Bagster.) $1.50; hf. bd., $1.75........ *Wiley.*

— Historic evidence of the New Test. post 8°. (Bagster.) $1.25 .... *Wiley.*

— Jansenists: their rise, persecution by the Jesuits, and existing remnant. ill. post 8°. (Bagster.) $1.50 .... *Wiley.*

— Original language of St. Matthew's Gospel; with particular ref. to Davidson's "Introduction to New Test." 8°. (Bagster.) pap., 25c........ *Wiley.*

— Prophetic visions of Daniel. post 8°. (Bagster.) $2.25 .... *Wiley.*

— *See also* Gesenius, F. H. W., Hebrew lexicon.

Trelawney, C: T. C. Perranzabuloe: the lost church found. 12°. '75. $1.75........ *Pott.*

Trench, *Capt.* F. The Russo-Indian question historically, strategically and politically considered; with sketch of central Asiatic politics. map. cr. 8°. '69. $2 .... *Macmillan.*

Trench, *Rev.* Fs. Brief notes on Greek of the New Testament for Eng. readers. cr. 8°. '64. $1.50. *Macmillan.*

Trench, *Mrs.* Melisina Chenevix. Remains: sel. from her journals, letters and other papers; ed. by R. C. Trench. New [chp.] ed. por. 8°. '68. $3.50........ *Macmillan.*

Trench, R: Chenevix. Calderon's life a dream; [also] The great theatre of the world; with essay on his life and genius. fp. 8°. $1.50 .. *Macmillan.*

— *Same.* 12°. $1.25........ *Widdleton.*

— Commentary on Epistles to the seven churches in Asia. 3d ed., rev. 8°. '66. $3.... *Macmillan.*

— *Same.* ('61.) New ed. 12°. '72. $1.50.. *Scribner.*

— Elegiac poems. 3d ed. fp. 8°. $1 .... *Macmillan.*

— English past and present: lectures. 8th ed., rev. and enl. fp. 8°. '73. $1.25 .... *Macmillan.*

— *Same.* ('68.) 7th ed., rev. 12°. '73. $1.50.. *Scribner.*

— Fitness of Scripture for unfolding spiritual life of man. *See* Hulsean lectures.

— Gustavus Adolphus in Germany, and other lectures on the thirty years' war. 2d ed., enl. fp. 8°. '72. $1.50........ *Macmillan.*

— Justin Martyr, and other poems. 5th ed. fp. 8°. $1.50........ *Macmillan.*

— Notes on miracles of our Lord. 10th ed. 8°. '74. $4.50........ *Macmillan.*

— *Same.* 8°. $2.50........ *Appleton.*

— Notes on parables of our Lord. 11th ed. 8°. '70. $4.50........ *Macmillan.*

— *Same.* 8°. $2.50; — condensed. 12°. $1.25.. *Appleton.*

— On authorized version of New Testament. 2d ed. 8°. $2.50........ *Macmillan.*

— On Bible revision. 12°. $1.25 .... *Widdleton.*

— On study of words. 15th ed., enl. and rev. fp. 8°. '74. $1.25........ *Macmillan.*

— *Same.* 12°. $1.25........ *Widdleton.*

— Plutarch: his life, his lives and his morals: lectures. New ed., enl. fp. 8°. $1........ *Macmillan.*

— Poems. New ed., rev. fp. 8°. '65. $2.50.. *Macmillan.*

— *Same.* 12°. $1.75 .... *Widdleton.*

— Poems from eastern sources; [also] Genoveva, and other poems. 2d ed. fp. 8°. $1.50.. *Macmillan.*

— Proverbs and their lessons. 6th ed., enl. fp. 8°. '69. $1 .... *Macmillan.*

— *Same.* 12°. $1 .... *Widdleton.*

— Select glossary of Eng. words used formerly in senses different from the present. 4th ed., enl. fp. 8°. '73. $1.25........ *Macmillan.*

— Sermon on the mount: an exposition drawn from the writings of St. Augustine, with essay on his merits as an interpreter of Scripture. 3d ed., enl. 8°. $4. *Macmillan.*

— Sermons on divinity of Christ. 12°. $1... *Widdleton.*

— Sermons preached for the most part in Ireland. 8°. $3.50........ *Macmillan.*

— Sermons preached in Westminster Abbey. 2d ed. 8°. $3.50 .... *Macmillan.*

— *Same.* 12°. $1.75........ *Widdleton-*

— Shipwrecks of faith: sermons before Univ. of Cambridge, 1867. fp. 8°. $1 .... *Macmillan.*

— Star of the wise men. 16°. 55c... *Cin. Meth. Bk. Conc.*

— Studies in Gospels. 2d ed. 8°. '67. $3.50.. *Macmillan.*

— *Same.* New [chp.] ed. 12°. '67. $2.50.. *Scribner.*

— Synonyms of New Testament. New ed., enl. 8°. $3.50........ *Macmillan.*

— *Same.* 2 pts. 12°. ea., $1.25 .... *Widdleton.*

— *Same.* ('64-'71.) New ed. 2 ser. 12°. '72. ea., $1.25........ *Scribner.*

— (*ed.*) Household book of Eng. poetry. 2d ed., rev. fp. 8°. $2.25........ *Macmillan.*

— Sacred Latin poetry, chiefly lyrical; with notes and introd. 3d ed., rev. fp. 8°. '74. $2.50.. *Macmillan.*

— *See also* Lightfoot, J. B., Trench, R. C., *and* Ellicott, J. C.

Trench, W. Stewart. Realities of Irish life. 16°. '69. $1........ *Roberts.*

Trenck (Freiherr v. der), od. e. verfehltes. Leben. 12°. '74. pap., 35c. .... *Zickel.*

Trent, W: Journal. *See* Goodman, A. T.

Trent (Council of). *See* Council of Trent.

Trésor de contes élémentaires. Carraud, Z. T. 75c. *Schoenhof.*

Trespassers. Wood, J. G. $3 .... *Nelson.*

Tressilian and his friends. Mackenzie, R. S. $1.25. *Lippincott.*

Treue Blut (Das). *See* Hoffmann, F.

Treue gewinnt. *See* Hoffmann, F.

Trevelyan, G: O: Life and letters of Lord Macaulay. 2 v. 8°. '76. ea., $2.50 .... *Harper.*

Trevern, J. F. Amicable discussion on Church of England and on the reformation in general; tr. by W. Richmond. 12°. $2 .... *Cath. Pub.*

Trevithick, Fs. Life of R: Trevithick (inventor of the high pressure steam engine); with account of his inventions. 2 v. por. and ill. 8°. '72. $5 .. *Spon.*

Trevor, G: Doctrine of the sacrifice and participation of the holy eucharist. 12°. '75. $5.25 ... *Pott.*

— Story of the cross; in daily contemplations of the holy week. 16°. '66. $1 .... *Pott.*

Tri-colored sketches in Paris during 1851–3. ill. 12°. $1.50 .... *Harper.*

Tri-mountain; or, the early history of Boston. 18°. 30c.; 40c. .... *Am. Bapt.*

Trial (The). *See* Yonge, C. M.

Trial and triumph. Arthur, T. S. 50c. .... *Peterson.*

Trial by jury. *See* Sullivan, A. S., *and* Gilbert, W. S.

Trial of assassins and conspirators for murder of Abraham Lincoln. 12°. $1.50. — 8°. pap., 50c. *Peterson.*

Trial of the Constitution. Fisher, S. G. $2 .. *Lippincott.*

Trial of Jesus. Dupin, A. M. J. 25c. .... *Am. Tr.*

Trial of obedience. *See* Books about boys who fought and won.

Trial of officers and crew of privateer Savannah [for] piracy, in U. S. Circ. Court for south. dist. of N.Y., Oct., 1861. 8°. shp., $3.50 ..... *Baker, V. & Co.*

Trial of Tomkins: farce. 16°. pap., 15c. .... *French.*

Trials and confessions of a housekeeper. Arthur, T. S. $1.25 .... *J. E. Potter.*

Trials and triumphs. 16°. '66. $1.10 ...... *Am. S. S.*

Trials and triumphs. Oliphant, M. O. W. $1.25 .. *Tibbals.*

Trials and trust. B., T. A. 70c. .... *Pres. Bd.*

Trials of the baby pitcher. May, C. L. 75c. *H. A. Young.*

Trials of an inventor. Peirce, B. K. $1.25. *Meth. Bk. Conc.*

Trials of the poor. 18°. 18c. .... *Am. S. S.*

Tribulation. Poole, C. 15c. .... *French.*

Tribune almanac and political register. [Annual.] 12°. pap., 25c. .... *N. Y. Tribune.*

Tribune almanac, 1838–'68; comprehending Politicians' register and the Whig almanac. 2 v. 12°. '68. hf. bd., $10 .... *N. Y. Tribune.*

Tribune essays. Congdon, C. T. $2 .... *Redfield.*

Tribune popular science; by Agassiz, Proctor, etc. ill. roy. 8°. $1.50 .... (?) *Shepard.*

Tribute of praise. *See* Tourjee, E.

Tribute of respect of citizens of Troy [N. Y] to memory of Abraham Lincoln. 8°. '65. $3; large pap., $12 .... *W. H. Young.*

Tribute to a daughter. Jerram, C. 50c. ...... *Carter.*

Tricks. Stewart, J. C. 15c. .... *De Witt.*

Tricks and diversions with cards. ill. 12°. pap., 30c. *Hurst.*

Tricks and traps of America. Hunter, H. E. 25c. *Hunter.*

Tricks on travelers. ill. 18°. pap., 15c. ...... *Haney.*

Tricotrin. La Rame, L. de. $1.50 ...... *Lippincott.*

Tried (The) and the tempted. *See* Arthur, T. S.

Tried and true. Avery, J. G. $1.15 .... *Hoyt.*

Tried for her life. Southworth, E. D. E. N. $1.75; $1.50 .... *Peterson.*

Tried in the fire. ill. 16°. '71. $1.25 .... *Lothrop.*

Trifles. Doughty, S. P. 30c. .... *H. H. Carter.*

Trifles. Dunning, A. K. $1.25 .... *Lothrop.*

Trifles. Ruhkopp, J. 50c. .... *O'Shea.*

Trifles for the Christmas holidays. Armstrong, H. S. 50c. .... *Lippincott.*

Trilemma. Graves, J. R. 60c. .... *So. Bapt.*

Trimble, Esther J. Chart of general literature. f°. '75. $3.50 .... *J. M. Stoddart.*

Trimble, I: P. Insect enemies of fruit and fruit trees. ill. 4°. $5; col. ill., $8 .... *W. Wood.*

Trimble, J. M. Memoir of Mrs. Jane Trimble. por. 16°. 75c. .... *Cin. Meth. Bk. Conc.*

Trimble, W: W. Digest of Kentucky Court of Appeals decisions, 1866–'76 (Bush 1–11). 8°. '76. shp., $6 .... *R. H. Collins.*

Trimen, H. *See* Bentley, R., *and* Trimen, H.

Trimmer, *Mrs.* Sa. Kirby. Fabulous histories for instruction of children on their treatment of animals. ill. 16°. 50c. .... *Routledge.*

— History of the robins; for instruction of children on treatment of animals. ill. sm. 4°. $3 .. *Claxton.*

— *Same.* ill. sm. 4°. '75. $2.50 .... *Nelson.*

— *Same;* written in words of one syllable by C. Swete. ill. sq. 12°. $1.50 .... *Routledge.*

— — Story of the robins. ill. 16°. $1. — ill. 12°. $1.25. *Scribner, W. & A.*

— Leading strings to knowledge. ill. sq. 16°. $1 .. *Miller.*

— Little lib. 3 v. ill. sq. 16°. $2.75 .... *Miller.*

Cont.: Leading strings. — Little fox. — Honey blossoms.

Trimmer, Tim. (*pseud.*) *See* Redford, A. H.

Trinity collection of church music. Hodges, E. $2.75; $2.50 .... *Ditson.*

Trinity hymnal; with offices of devotion for Sunday and parish schools. 18°. '70. 20c. .... *Pott.*

Trinity psalter. Cutler, H. S. $1 .... *Dutton.*

Trinuminus. *See* Plautus, T. M.

Trip in a ship. *See* Ballantyne, W.

Trip of the Porgie. Small, G. G. 25c. .... *Collin & S.*

Trip to Cuba. Howe, J. W. $1.25 .... * *Osgood.*

Trip to Niagara Falls. Small, G. G. 25c. .. *Collin & S.*

Trip to Paris: Ethiop. drama. 16°. pap., 15c. *French.*

Trip to Scarborough. Sheridan, R. B. B. 15c. .. *French.*

Tripartite nature of man. Heard, J. B. $3. *Scribner, W. & A.*

Tripler, C: S., *and* Blackman, G: C. Handbook for the military surgeon: compendium of duties of the medical officer in the field, etc.; with forms. 12°. '62. $1 .... *Clarke.*

Triplet, J. Call at no. 1–7: farce. 16°. pap., 15c. *French.*

— Supper in Dixie: farce. 16°. pap., 15c. .... *French.*

Triplet ser. 3 v. 16°. $4.50 .... *Crowell.*

Cont.: Margaret's old home, by J. R. Shaw. — Newlyn House. — White chrysanthemum, by A. Shaw.

Trippe, T. M. Birds of Minnesota. 8°. '71. 25c. .. *Essex.*

Tristram, H: Baker. Bible places. 12°. '76. $1.50 .. *Pott.*

— Land of Moab: travels and discoveries on east side of the Dead Sea and the Jordan; with chapter on the Persian palace of Mashita by J. Ferguson. map and ill. cr. 8°. $2.50 .... *Harper.*

— Natural hist. of the Bible. ill. 12°. '76. $1.50 .. *Am. Tr.*

Tristram, T: Hutchinson. *See* England, Law reports.

Tristram Shandy. *See* Sterne, L.

Triumph. Root, G. F. $1.50 .... *Church.*

Triumph (Der) der Empfindlichkeit. *See* Goethe, J: W. v.

Triumph of the blessed sacrament. Müller, M. 50c. *Kreuzer.*

Triumph of the Catholic Church in the early ages. Manahan, A. $3 .... *Appleton.*

Triumph of faith. Blackwood, S. A. 75c. .. *Willard.*

Triumph of religion: narratives. 18°. 60c. .. *Cath. Pub.*

Triumph of steam: stories from lives of Watt, Arkwright and Stephenson. ill. 12°. $1.50..*Nelson.*
— *See also* Bouquet lib.
Triumph of truth. Caughey, J. $1.75..*Perkinpine.*
Triumph over Midian. *See* Tucker, *Mrs.* Ctte.
Triumphing over death. Hall, N. $1.25. *Cin. Meth. Bk. Conc.*
Triumphlied. Brahms, J. $1.50; $1; $1.25..*Church.*
Triumphs of ancient and modern architecture. ill. 18°. 90c. ....*Nelson.*
Triumphs of industry: life of Adam Clarke. 18°. 65c. *Am. S. S.*
Triumphs of time. Marsh-Caldwell, A. 75c...*Harper.*
Troades. *See* Euripides.
Trodden down. Newby, E. J. 50c........*Peterson.*
Trödler (Der). Brachvogel, A. E. 40c......*Steiger.*
Troilus and Cressida. *See* Shakespeare, W:
Trois Ètoiles [*pseud.*] *See* Murray, Grenville.
Trois mois sous la neige. Porchat, J. J. 90c...*Holt.*
Trois proverbes. Leclerq, T. 40c............*Holt.*
Trojan sketch-book: ser. of articles contributed by clergy, and other literati of [Troy, N. Y.] 12°. $1 ....*W. H. Young.*
Trollope, Ant. [Novels.] 27 v. ill........*Harper.*
Cont.: Harry Heathcote of Gangoil: tale of Australian bush-life, 8°, pap., 25c. — Belton estate. — Brown, Jones and Robinson. — Lady Anna. — Miss Mackenzie. — Rachel Ray. — Sir Harry Hotspur of Humblethwaite, *ea.*, 8°, pap., 50c. — Prime minister. — Warden; [also] Barchester Towers, *ea.*, 8°, pap., 75c. — Claverings, 8°, $1; pap., 50c. — Golden Lion of Granpere, 8°, $1.25; pap., 75c. — He knew he was right, 8°, $1.50; pap., $1. — Eustace diamonds. — Phineas Finn. — Phineas redux. — Ralph, the heir. — Vicar of Bullhampton, *ea.*, 8°, $1.75; pap., $1.25. — Can you forgive her? — Last chronicle of Barset. — Orley Farm. — Small house at Allington. — Way we live now, *ea.*, 8°, $2; pap., $1.50. — Bertrams. — Castle Richmond. — Three clerks, *ea.*, 12°. $1.50. — Doctor Thorne, 12°, $1.50; 8°, pap., 75c. — Framley Parsonage, 12°, $1.75.
— *Same.* 17 v. 12°. $21.25 ....*Routledge.*
Cont.: He knew he was right. — Can you forgive her? — Macdermots of Ballycloran. — Kelly's and the O'Kelly's. — Tales of all countries. — Belton estate. — Bertrams. — Mary Gresley. — Doctor Thorne. — Orley Farm. — Phineas Finn. — Lotta Schmidt. — Miss Mackenzie. — Castle Richmond. — Rachel Ray. — Ralph, the heir. — Eustace diamonds.
— Barchester towers. 12°. $1.25........*Lippincott.*
— Can you forgive her? ill. 8°. $3.......*Routledge.*
— Claverings. 8°. '67. pap., 50c........*Littell & G.*
— Macdermots of Ballycloran. 12°. $1.75; pap., $1.50. *Peterson.*
— Nina Balatka: story of a maiden of Prague. 8°. '67. pap., 38c. ....*Littell & G.*
— North America. 12°. $1.50 ....*Harper.*
— Orley Farm. ill. 8°. $3........*Routledge.*
— Phineas Finn, the Irish member. ill. cr. 8°. $2.50. — ill. 8°. $3 ....*Routledge.*
— Prime minister. 12°. $1.50; pap., 75c. — (Intern. ed.), $1.25 ....*Porter.*
— Ralph, the heir. ill. 8°. $3........*Routledge.*
— Sir Harry Hotspur of Humblethwaite. 12°. '71. $1.25........*Macmillan.*
— West Indies and the Spanish main. 12°. $1.50. *Harper.*
Trollope, *Mrs.* Fes. Mrs. Matthews; or, family mysteries. 12°. bds., $1 ....*Routledge.*
— Petticoat government. 8°. pap., 50c......*Harper.*
— Widow Barnaby. 16°. bds., 80c. ......*Routledge.*
Trollope, *Mrs.* Fes. Eleanor. Anne Furness. 8°. pap., 75c........*Harper.*
— Aunt Margaret's trouble. 8°. pap., 25c...*Peterson.*
— Mabel's progress. 8°. pap., 50c..........*Harper.*
— Sacristan's (The) household: story of Lippe-Detmold. ill. 8°. pap., 75c. ....*Harper.*
— Veronica. 8°. pap., 50c........*Harper.*
Trollope, T: Adolphus. [Novels.] 7 v. 12°. ea., $1.75; pap., $1.50 ....*Peterson.*
Cont.: Beppo, the conscript. — Dream numbers. — Garstang Grange. — Gemma: tale of love and jealousy. — Leonora Casaloni; or, the marriage secret. — Marietta; or, life in Tuscany. — Sealed packet.

Trollope, T: Adolphus, *continued.*
— Diamond cut diamond: story of Tuscan life. 12°. $1.25 ....*Harper.*
— Durnton Abbey. 8°. pap., 50c..........*Harper.*
— History of commonwealth of Florence, to 1531. 4 v. cr. 8°. $12........*Macmillan.*
— Life of Columbus. 16°. 75c...........*Hurd & H.*
— Lindisfarn Chase. 8°. $2; pap., $1.50....*Harper.*
— Siren (A). 8°. pap., 50c..........*Harper.*
Trollope, *Mrs.* T: Adolphus. *See* Trollope, *Mrs.* F. E.
Trombalcazar. Stephenson, C. H. 15c.....*French.*
Trophies of song. Crafts, W. F. $1.25 ....*Lothrop.*
Tropical nature: account of the most remarkable phenomena of life in the tropics. ill. imp. 8°. '75. $5 ....*Nelson.*
Tropics (The). ill. 16°. '74. $1.25. ......*Lothrop.*
Trosse, G: Life. 18°. 40c. ....*Pres. Bd.*
Trost der armen Seelen. *See* Congregation of the Most Holy Redeemer.
Trot's letters to her doll. Bromfield, M. E. $1.25. *Nelson.*
Trotter, Lionel Ja. History of India. map and ill. 12°. '74. $3........*Pott.*
Trottie's lib. 5 v. sq. 8°. $5..........*Nelson.*
Cont.: Trottie's story book. — Odd stories about animals. — The new baby. — Tiny stories in tiny words. — A week by themselves, by E. M. Norris.
Trottie's story book. ill. sq. 8°. $1.........*Nelson.*
Trotty book. Phelps, E. S. $1.50 ....*Osgood.*
Trotty's wedding tour. Phelps, E. S. $1.50..*Osgood.*
Troubat, Fs. J. Treatise on law of limited partnership in the U. S.; with forms of deeds, statutes of different states and reports of decisions. 8°. shp., $5.50 ....*Kay.*
— *and* Haly, W: W. Practice in civil actions and proceedings in Supreme Court of Penna., in District Court and Court of Common Pleas for Philadelphia, and in courts of the U. S. 4th ed., ed. by A. I. Fish. 2 v. in 3. 8°. shp., $19.50; v. 2, 3, ea., shp., $7.50........*Kay.*
Trouble begins at nine: Ethiop. drama. 16°. pap., 15c. *French; Happy.*
Trouble on the mountain. *See* Abbott, Jac.
Troublesome secret, and what it cost. 16°. $1.25. *Am. S. S.*
Troublesome servant: Ethiop. drama. 16°. pap., 15c. *French; Happy.*
Troublesome young monkey who would see the world. ill. cr. 4°. pap., 20c.; 25c..........*J. E. Potter.*
Troughton, Adolphus C: [Plays.] 7 v. 16°. ea., pap., 15c. ....*French.*
Cont.: Fly and the web: comedy. — Leading strings: comedy. — Living too fast: comedietta. — Shameful behaviour: comedietta. — Short and sweet. — Unlimited confidence: farce. — Vandyke Brown: farce.
— Vandyke Brown: farce. 16°. pap., 15c....*De Witt.*
Trousseau, Armand. Lectures on clinical medicine; tr. by P. V. Bazire and J. R. Cormack. (Sydenham Society's ed.) 5 v. 8°. '73. v. 1–3, ea., $5; v. 4, 5, ea., $4 ....*Lindsay.*
Trouting: or, gipsying in the woods. Franklin, J. 83c. *Thompson.*
Trouvaille. Fullerton, *Lady* G. 50c.; 75c. *Kelly, P. & Co.*
Trovatore (Il). *See* Verdi, G.
Trovatore: drama. 16°. pap., 15c...........*French.*
Trowbridge, *Miss* Cath. M. [Juveniles.] 13 v. 16°. (?) *Martien.*
Cont.: Oakville dove's nest, $1.75. — Archie's keys. — Charles Norwood. — George Morton and his sister. — How to conquer; or, Allen Ware. — Two friends, *ea.*, $1.25. — Mapleville boys, $1. — Frank and Rufus, 90c. — Howard Ashley. — Nettie Wallace. — Two councils, *ea.*, 75c. — Gold dollar. — Jennie's Bible verses, *ea.*, 60c.
— Agnes Wilbur; or, a daughter's influence. 18°. '66. 90c. ....*Garrigues.*
— Bessie's visit. 18°. 60c. ....*Cong. Pub.*
— Fred Wilder; or, the golden rule. 16°. $1..*Cong. Pub.*

Trowbridge, J. C. *See* Hill, J.W., *and* Trowbridge, J.C.
Trowbridge, J: *See* Annual of scientific discovery.
Trowbridge, J: T. ["Pl. Creyton."] Brighthope ser. 5 v. 18°. $4 .... *Sheldon.*
Cont.: Old battle ground. — Iron Thorpe. — Father Brighthopes. — Burr cliff. — Hearts and faces.
— Coupon bonds, and other stories. ill. 12°. $3 .. * *Osgood.*
— Cudjo's cave. ('63.) New ed. 12°. '75. $2 .. *Tilton.*
— Deserted family; or, the wanderings of an outcast. ill. 16°. $1.25 .... *J.E. Potter.*
— Drummer boy. 12°. '63. $1.50 .... *Tilton.*
— — *See also below* Frank Manly.
— Emigrant's story, and other poems. 16°. '74. $1.50; hf. cf., $3; mor., $4 .... *Osgood.*
— Frank Manly, the drummer boy. ill. 12°. '74. $1.50. *W. F. Gill.*
— — *See also above* Drummer boy.
— Jack Hazard ser. 6 v. ill. 16°. '70–'75. ea., $1.25. *Porter.*
Cont.: Jack Hazard and his fortunes. — A chance for himself. — Doing his best. — Fast friends. — The young surveyor. — Lawrence's adventures.
— Martin Merrivale. 12°. '54. $2 .... *Tilton.*
— Neighbor Jackwood. ('56.) New ed. 12°. '75. $2. *W. F. Gill; Tilton.*
— *Same;* dramatized from Trowbridge. 16°. pap., 15c. *French.*
— Neighbors' wives. 12°. $1.50 .... *Lee & S.*
— Three scouts. ('64.) New ed. 12°. '75. $1.50 .. *Tilton.*
— Vagabonds, and other poems. por. and ill. 16°. '69. $1.50; hf. cf., $3 .... *Osgood.*
— *Same;* ill. by F. O. C. Darley. 4°. '69. $1.75; mor., $5 .... *Hurd & H.*
Trowbridge, *Mrs.* Laura. Excelsior cook-book and housekeeper's aid. 12°. $1.25 .... *Mason.*
Trowbridge, W: Petit. Heat as a source of power; with applic. of gen. principles to construction of steam generators. ill. 8°. $3.50 .... *Wiley.*
— Tables, with explanations, of non-condensing stationary steam engine, and of high-pressure steam boilers. pl. 4°. $2.50 .... *Wiley.*
Trower, C: Fs. Law of debtor and creditor. 8°. '61. $3 .... *T. & J. W. Johnson.*
— — *See also* Law lib.
Troy and its remains. Schliemann, H. $12.50; $15. *Scribner, W. & A.*
Truant. *See* Little Blue Mantle lib.
Truant boys. *See* Little Willie's lib.
Truant chicken. Shanley, C. D. 50c..... *Hurd & H.*
Truant chicken ser. *See* Shanley, C. D.
Truce of God. Miles, G. H. $1; $1.50..... *Murphy.*
True, C: Kittridge. Elements of logic. 12°. '61. 80c. *Meth. Bk. Conc.*
— John Winthrop and the great colony: settlement of Boston and of the Massachussets colony. 16°. '75. $1 .... *Meth. Bk. Conc.*
True aim stories. 5 v. 18°. $3 .... *H. A. Young.*
Cont.: Alfred and his mother, by K. S. May. — Fred Roberts' start in life, by F. Huntingdon. — Looking upward. — Lost Gip, by H. Smith. — Hildred's great work.
True and false courage. Knight, H. C. 50c. *Cong. Pub.*
True and false riches. Maskelyne, A. S. $1.25. *Scribner, W. & A.*
True as steel. Harland, M. $1.50 .... *Carleton.*
True as steel: comedy. 16°. pap., 15c....... *French.*
True basis of Christian union. Errett, I. 10c... *Chase.*
True believer. Mahan, A. 75c............. *Harper.*
True boy. Bates, L. 25c.................. *Am. Tr.*
True choir. Johnson, A. N. $1.50.......... *Church.*
True Christian religion. *See* Swedenborg, E.
True Christianity. *See* Arndt, J.
True church. Greenwald, E. 75c....... *Luth. Bk. St.*
True church. *See* Tilton, T.
True civilization. Warren, J. 30c...... *B. R. Tucker.*
True courage. 18°. 30c.................... *Am. S. S.*
True cross. Malan, C. 30c.; 15c......... *Randolph.*
True declaration of the estate of the colonies in Virginia: Lond., 1610. [Reprint.] 4°. pap., 50c. *Sabin.*
True evangelical obedience. Stein, J. W. 20c. *Brumbaugh.*
True evangelist. Porter, J. 60c...... *Meth. Bk. Conc.*
True friend. Campbell, A. J. $2.75; $3.50; $4; $4.75; $6.50.................... *A. J. Campbell.*
True friend. *See* Little Willie's lib.
True friend of youth; or, life and virtues of J. B. de la Salle. 18°. 60c..................... *O'Shea.*
True friendships. 16°. $1.25........... *H. A. Young.*
True glory of woman. Harbaugh, H. $1.25. *Ref. Ch. Pub.*
True grandeur of nations. Sumner, C. 20c... *Peace.*
True Grecian bend. Leigh, L. 75c......... *Redfield.*
True happiness. *See* Pike, J. G.
True healing art. Trall, R. T. 50c.; 25c...... *Wells.*
True heroism. *See* New Year lib.
True heroism. Tucker, C. 35c...... *Carter; Dutton.*
True history of Joshua Davidson. Linton, E. L. $1.25. *Lippincott.*
True history of a little ragamuffin. Greenwood, J. 50c.................................. *Harper.*
True idea of holy communion. Ségur, L. G. de. 25c.; 35c.; 15c............................ *O'Shea.*
True juvenile song book. Johnson, A. N. 50c. *Church.*
True life ser. 4 v. ill. 12°. ea., $1.50....... *Lee & S.*
Cont.: Bunyan's Pilgrim's progress. — Wilson's Life of the three Mrs. Judsons. — Clement's Noble deeds of American women. — Fleetwood's Life of Christ.
True love. Beauclerk, *Lady* D. DeV. $1.25.. *Lippincott.*
True manliness. Chapin, E. H. $1..... *Williamson.*
True manliness. Tuthill, L. C. $1...... *Perkinpine.*
True Mary. Browning, E. B. 90c......... *Whittaker.*
True mission of Baptists. Jeter, J. B., *and* Sherwood, A. 10c. .... *So. Bapt.*
True order of studies. Hill, T. $1.25 ...... *Putnam.*
True path. Atkinson, J. M. $1........... *Pres. Bd.*
True penitent portrayed. Wines, E. C. 60c. *Pres. Bd.*
True physician. Watson, J. 25c..... *N. Y. Acad. Med.*
True piety: Catholic prayer book, with Epistles and Gospels. 18°. $1–$9 .... *Benziger.*
True Protestant ritualism. *See* Hall, C. H.
True psalmist. Johnson, A. N. $1.50 ...... *Church.*
True psalmody; or, the Bible Psalms the church's only manual of praise; by a committee of the Reformed and United Presbyterian churches. 18°. 55c. .... *U. P. Bd. of Pub.*
True religion delineated. Bellamy, J. $2.. *Cong. Pub.*
True riches. Arthur, T. S. $1.50......... *J. E. Potter.*
True riches, and other stories. 18°. 70c. ... *Pres. Bd.*
True Robinson Crusoes. Denis, F., *and* Chauvin, V. $1.50 .... *Cassell; Lee & S.*
True sister, and other tales. 18°. 70c. ..... *Pres. Bd.*
True son, and other stories. 18°. 50c........ *O'Shea.*
True spiritual conferences. *See* François de Sales, *St.*
True spouse of Christ. *See* Liguori, A. M. de, *St.*
True stories about dogs. Follen, E. L. 50c... *Lee & S.*
True stories for little people. *See* Dove ser.
True stories from ancient history. Strickland, A. $1.25. *Porter.*
True stories from history and biograghy. *See* Hawthorne, Natl.
True stories from modern history. Strickland, A. $1.25. *Porter.*
True stories of the American fathers. M'Conkey, R. $1.50.......................... *Meth. Bk. Conc.*
True stories of brave deeds. Hoare, G. T. $1.25. *Scribner, W. & A.*

True stories of the days of Washington. ill. 16°. $1.50. *Mason.*

True stories of real pets; or, friends in fur and feathers. ill. sq. 16°. '69. $1.25 .... *Meth. Bk. Conc.*

True story lib. *See* Wright, *Mrs.* J. McN.

True story of battle of Waterloo. Gleig, G. R. $1.50. *Harper.*

True story ser. 12 v. ill. 24°. $2.40 .... *Lothrop.*

Cont.: Lame beggar. — Wilful waste. — Minna's proud heart. — Little Nora. — Brown pony. — Blacksmith. — Beauty Benson. — Trust and try. — Little Bertie. — Too late. — Gregory Gold. — Truthful Jenny.

True tales for the spare hour. *See* Clark, D. W.

True temple. M'Ilvaine, C. P. 50c. ...... *Leighton.*

True theory of Christianity. Grayson, W. S. $1.25. *Appleton.*

True to the end. Edersheim, A. $1.25 .... *Routledge.*

True to herself. Robinson, F. W. 50c. ...... *Harper.*

True to him ever. R., F. W. $1.50 .... *Carleton.*

True to his flag. Mathews, J. A. 75c. .... *Carter.*

True to the last. Roe, A. S. $1.50 .... *Carleton.*

True unity of Christ's church. Schmucker, S. S. $1.25 .... *Randolph.*

True unto death. Knowles, J. S. 15c. .... *Lee & S.*

True vine. Macmillan, H. $2 .... *Macmillan.*

True vital piety. Eshelman, M. M. $1 .. *Brumbaugh.*

True woman. Peck, J. T. $1.75; $2.25 .. *Meth. Bk. Conc.*

Trueba y Cosio, Telesforo de. Mr. and Mrs. Pringle: farce. 16°. pap., 15c. .... *Ames; French.*

— Spain. *See* Romance of history.

Truffle nephews. Power, P. B. $1 .... *Carter.*

Trugbilder des Lebens. *See* Mirage of life.

Truly noble. Chatelaine, *Mme.* — de. $1 .... *Cassell.*

Truman, G. *See* Moore, R. W., Journal.

Truman, J. H: Mallory, J. A., *and* Shipman, H. A. (*ed.*) Collection of decisions rel. to railways. v. 1–8. '73–'76. 8°. ea., shp., $6 ... *Cockcroft.*

Trumbull, G: Pocket typographia: guide to printing. 24°. '46. 35c. .... (?) *Davidson.*

Trumbull, H: Clay. Captured scout of army of the James: life of H. H. Manning, of 24th Mass. Regt. por. 16°. '68. 65c. .... *Lockwood, B. & Co.*

— Knightly soldier: biog. of Maj. H. W. Camp, 10th Conn. Vol. ('65.) 6th ed., rev. por. and ill. 16°. '76. $1.25 .... *Lockwood, B. & Co.*

— Review exercises in the Sunday-school: their value and methods. 16°. 40c.; pap., 15c. .... *Am. S. S.*

— Sabbath-school concert (The); or, children's meeting: its hist., advantages and abuses. ('61.) New ed. 18°. '64. 30c. .... *Hoyt.*

Trumbull, J: McFingal: epic poem of Am. revolution; with notes by B. J. Lossing. 16°. $1.75 .. *Putnam.*

Trumpet of freedom: collection of patriotic songs. obl. 8°. '64. pap., 40c. .... *Ditson.*

Trumpet of reform. Root, G. F. 50c. ...... *Church.*

Trumpeter's daughter. Coyne, J. S. 15c. .... *French.*

Trumpeter's wedding: drama. 16°. pap., 15c. *French.*

Trumps (*pseud.*) *See* Dick, W: Brisbane.

Trumps. Curtis, G. W. $2 .... *Harper.*

Truran, W. Iron manufacture of Gt. Brit. 2d ed., rev. by J. A. Phillips and W. H. Dorman. 84 pl. 8°. $10 .... *Appleton.*

Trusler, J: *See* Hogarth, W: Works.

Trust: or, Eaton parsonage. Herbert, S. A. F. 60c. *Randolph.*

Trust and the remittance. Clarke, M. C. $1.25 .. *Roberts.*

Trust and try. ill. 24°. '70. 25c. .... *Lothrop.*

Trust and try. ('69.) New ed. ill. 16°. '73. 80c. *Hoyt.*

Trust and try ser. 6 v. ill. 24°. $1.50 ...... *Lothrop.*

Cont.: Trust and try. — Lame beggar. — Too late. — Little Norah. — Brown pony. — Little Bertie.

Trust and try ser. 6 v. ill. 16°. $3 .... *Nelson.*

Cont.: Alicia and her aunt. — Affectionate brothers. — Elizabeth and beggar boys. — Good grandmother. — Blind farmer. — William and Uncle Ben.

Trust in God. 18°. 35c. .... *Carter.*

Trust in God. *See* Bell, C. D.

Trusta, H. (*pseud.*) *See* Phelps, *Mrs.* E. S.

Trusted and tried. *See* Bowen, *Mrs.* C. E.

Trusting in Jesus. *See* Kennedy, *Mrs.* M. G.

Truth. Mills, M. 40c. .... *Scribner, W. & A.*

Truth; or, Persis Clareton. Tayler, C. B. $1 .. *Leighton.*

Truth and error. Brann, H. A. $1 .... *Sadlier.*

Truth and grace; or, the works of Mary Jane Graham; with memoir. por. 16°. $1.10 .... *Am. S. S.*

Truth and honesty. *See* Cupples, *Mrs.* A. J.

Truth and life. McIlvaine, C. P. $2.50 ...... *Carter.*

Truth and love; [also] Jack, the shoeblack; or, the way to do good, etc. ill. 24°. '69. 30c. ..... *Lothrop.*

Truth and trust. Baker, H. N. W. $1.25 .. *H. A. Young.*

Truth finder. *See* Goodrich, S: G.

Truth found. Waggoner, J. H. 10c. .... *Sev. Day Adv.*

Truth in Christ. Whitfield, F. 50c. .... *Leighton.*

Truth in love. Smith, J. D. $1.40 .... *Pres. Bd.*

Truth is always best. *See* Kirby, M. *and* E.

Truth is everything. *See* Geldart, *Mrs.* T:

Truth made plain. Seiss, J. A. 50c.; 25c. *Luth. Bk. St.*

Truth made simple. Todd, J. $1.25 .... *Bridgman.*

Truth of Scripture. Cecil, R. 15c. .... *Am. Tr.*

Truth Seeker tracts. 3 v. 18°. '76. ea., $1; pap., 60c.; per set, $2.50; pap., $1.50 ... *D. M. Bennett.*

Truthful Jenny. Strong, J. D. 25c. .... *Lothrop.*

Truths for children. Doughty, S. P. 50c. *H. H. Carter.*

Truths for the people. Plumer, W. S. $1 ... *Am. Tr.*

Truths for to-day. Swing, D. 2 v. ea., $1.50 .. *Jansen.*

Truths illustrated by great authors: maxims, metaphors, etc. 12°. $1.50; hf. cf., $3.25 .... *Lippincott.*

Try. Finley, M. F. 70c. .... *Pres. Bd.*

Try again. Adams, W. T. $1.25 .... *Lee & S.*

Try again. *See* Tucker, *Mrs.* Ctte.

Try and trust. Alger, H., *jr.* $1.50 .... *Loring.*

Try and trust; by author of "Arthur Moreland." ill. 16°. 75c. .... *Routledge.*

Try and trust lib. 4 v. ill. 16°. $3 .... *Routledge.*

Cont.: Try and trust. — Jack of all trades. — Archie Blake. — A bundle of sticks.

Trye's year among the Hindoos. Thompson, J. C. $1.35 .... *Pres. Bd.*

Trying child: sequel to "Lucy and her friends." 18°. 40c. .... *Am. S. S.*

Trying it on. Brough, W. 15c. .... *French.*

Trying to be useful. Baker, H. N. W. $1.50 .. *Lee & S.*

Tryon, Edwards. The world's laconics: best thoughts of the best authors in prose and poetry. 12°. '52. $1.75 .... *Dodd.*

Tryon, G: Wash., *jr.* American marine conchology: descript. of shells of the Atlantic coast of U. S. col. pl. 8°. $42; — col. ed., $30; — plain ed., $20 .... *Acad. of Nat. Sci.*

— Amy Cassonet. [Opera.] f°. $5 .... *Ditson.*

— Contributions to conchology. 3 v. 8°. '60–'62. ea., $2 .... *Acad. of Nat. Sci.*

Cont.: 1. List of Am. writers on recent conchology, with titles of their memoirs and dates. — 2. Monograph of the order pholadacea, and other papers. — 3. Synonymy of the species of strepomatidæ (melanians) of the U. S., with obs. on their affinities and descript. of land, fresh-water and marine mollusca.

— Monograph of fresh water univalve mollusca. *See* Haldeman, S. S.

— Monograph of strepomatidæ. 8°. '73. pap., $2. *Smith. Inst.*

Tryon, G: Wash., *jr.*, *continued.*
— Monograph of terrestrial mollusca of U. S.; with ill. of all species. col. pl. 8°. $20; — col. ed., $13.50; — plain ed., $8.50.....*Acad. of Nat. Sci.*
— Operatic gems: coll. of melodies from operas. 4°. $3; $4; bds., $2.50..................*Ditson.*
Tschoop, the converted Indian chief. 18°. 22c. *Am. S. S.*
Tschudi, J: Jac. v. Peruvian antiquities; tr. 12°. '54. $1.50..........................*Barnes.*
— Travels in Peru; tr. 12°. '54. $1.50......*Barnes.*
Tub night; [also] Little Emma. 18°. 25c. *N. Y. Ref. Ch. Bd.*
Tuber Derg. Carleton, W. 75c.; $1.25....*Sadlier.*
Tuck, Rob. First three kings of Israel: introd. to study of reigns of Saul, David and Solomon; with notes. 2 v. 12°. ea., 90c.........*Nelson.*
Tuck, W. J. Selections for Sabbath reading, and brief miscellaneous essays, moral and religious. 12°. '56. $1..................*Claxton; Lippincott.*
Tucker, Beverly. Principles of pleading. 8°. '46. shp., $2.50......................*J. W. Randolph.*
Tucker, *Mrs.* Ctte. ["A. L. O. E."] A. L. O. E. casket. 3 v. ill. 12°. ea., $1.50...............*Nelson.*
Cont.: Giant-killer. — Young pilgrim. — Precepts in practice.
— A. L. O. E. lib. 55 v. 18°. $40..........*Carter.*
— A. L. O. E. ser. 3 v. ill. 18°. '69–'70. ea., 90c. *Lothrop.*
Cont.: Claudia. — Triumph over Midian. — Rescued from Egypt.
— Adopted son. 18°. 75c....................*Carter.*
Compr.: Walter Binning; Wings and stings; True heroism.
— Angus Tarlton. 18°. 35c..........*Carter; Dutton.*
— — *See also below* Poacher.
— Bags of gold. 18°. 50c.....................*Carter.*
— — *See also below* Christian conquests.
— Bible picture book, illustrating life of Christ. ill. 4°. $1.50................................*Nelson.*
— Black cliff. 18°. 50c......................*Carter.*
— — *See also below* Stories on parables.
— Bought with a price. ill. 18°. '74. 20c.....*Am. Tr.*
— Boy artist. *See below* Never give up ser.; Try again lib.
— Braid of cords. 18°. 75c...................*Carter.*
— Broken chain. 18°. 50c....................*Carter.*
— — *See also below* Stories on parables.
— Chief's daughter. 18°. 75c................*Carter.*
Compr.: Daybreak in Britain; Parliament in the play-room.
— *Same.* 18°. 60c..........................*Dutton.*
— Children's tabernacle. 18°. 75c...........*Carter.*
— Children's treasury. 18°. 75c.....*Carter; Dutton.*
— *Same.* ill. 18°. 90c.......................*Nelson.*
— Christian conquests. 18°. 75c.............*Carter.*
Compr.: Falsely accused; Bags of gold.
— Christian's mirror; or, words in season. 18°. 75c. *Carter; Dutton.*
— Christian's panoply. 18°. 75c.............*Carter.*
Compr.: Ned Franks; Red-cross knight.
— — *See also below* Fred Franks.
— City of No-cross. 18°. 75c................*Carter.*
— *Same.* 18°. '73. 90c..........*Lothrop; Nelson.*
— *Same.* ('73.) New ed. 16°. '75. $1.25...*Hoyt.*
— Claremont tales: illustrations of the Beatitudes. ('56.) 3d ed. 18°. '75. 50c..............*So. Meth.*
— *Same.* 18°. 75c.....................*Carter; Dutton.*
— Claudia. 18°. 75c........................*Carter.*
— *Same.* ill. 18°. 90c.......................*Nelson.*
— — *See also above* A. L. O. E. ser.
— Clouds and sunshine; [also] Forbidden ground; from "Precepts in practice." 18°. 17c.; 22c. *Am. Bapt.*
— Cortley Hall. 18°. 75c....................*Carter.*
Compr.: Straight road; Stories of Jewish history.
— Cottage by the stream. 18°. 35c..........*Carter.*
— — *See also below* Ned Manton.
— Crown of success. 18°. 75c...............*Carter.*
— Cyril Ashley. 18°. 75c...................*Carter.*

Tucker, *Mrs.* Ctte., *continued.*
— *Same.* ill. 16°. '73. 90c..............*Lothrop.*
— *Same.* ill. 18°. '74. 90c.........*Nelson; Tibbals.*
— Daybreak in Britain. 18°. 35c............*Carter.*
— — *See also above* Chief's daughter.
— Delaforce; or, war and peace. 18°. 75c...*Dutton.*
— Eddie Ellerslie. 18°. 75c..................*Carter.*
Compr.: Old friends with new faces; The mine.
— *Same.* 16°. $1.50..........................*Graves.*
— Eden in England. 16°. $1.25. — 18°. 75c...*Carter.*
— Edith. *See below* Never give up ser.; Try again lib.
— Esther Parsons. 18°. 50c..................*Carter.*
— — *See also below* Try again.
— Exiles in Babylon; or, children of light. 18°. 75c. *Carter.*
— *Same.* 12°. '65. $1.25...........*Meth. Bk. Conc.*
— Fairy Frisket. 18°. 75c...................*Carter.*
— *Same.* ill. 18°. '74. 90c...................*Nelson.*
— Falsely accused. 18°. 50c.................*Carter.*
— — *See also above* Christian conquests.
— Flora; or, self deception. 18°. 75c...*Carter; Dutton.*
— *Same.* ill. 12°. $1.25.......................*Nelson.*
— Forbidden ground. *See above* Clouds and sunshine.
— Fred Franks; or, "the Christian's panoply." 18°. 50c.................................*Dutton.*
— — *See also above* Christian's panoply.
— Friend in need. 16°. '74. 50c............*Nelson.*
— Giant killer. 18°. 50c.............*Carter; Dutton.*
— — *See also above* A. L. O. E. casket.
— *Same;* and sequel. 18°. 75c..............*Carter.*
— Giles Oldham. 18°. 75c...................*Carter.*
— Golden fleece. ill. 12°. $1.25.............*Nelson.*
— *Same;* [also] Zaida. 18°. '76. 75c.......*Carter.*
— Good for evil. 18°. 75c...................*Carter.*
— Great reformer: life of Luther. 18°. 50c...*Pres. Bd.*
— Guy Dalesford. 18°. 75c...................*Carter.*
Compr.: Wanderer in Africa; Wreath of smoke.
— Harry Dangerfield. 18°. 50c.....*Carter; Dutton.*
— — *See also below* Poacher.
— Haunted rooms. 16°. '76. $1.25. 18°. 75c....*Carter.*
— Hebrew heroes. 18°. '76. 75c.............*Carter.*
— Holiday chaplet. 18°. 75c.........*Carter; Dutton.*
— *Same.* ill. 18°. 90c.......................*Nelson.*
— House beautiful. 18°. 75c.................*Carter.*
— *Same.* ill. 18°. 90c........................*Nelson.*
— Hymn my mother taught me. *See below* Never give up ser.; Try again lib.
— Idols in the heart. 18°. 75c......*Carter; Dutton.*
— John Carey; or, what is a Christian? 18°. 75c. *Carter; Dutton.*
— Lady of Provence. 18°. 75c...............*Carter.*
— *Same.* ill. 16°. '73. 90c..................*Lothrop.*
— *Same.* ill. 18°. '74. 90c.........*Nelson; Tibbals.*
— Lake of the woods. 18°. 75c...............*Carter.*
— Little maid; [also] Living jewels. 18°. 75c. *Carter.*
— Living jewels. 18°. 50c...................*Carter.*
— — *See also above* Little maid.
— Lost jewel. 18°. 75c.......................*Carter.*
— Mine (The). 18°. 60c............*Carter; Dutton.*
— — *See also above* Eddie Ellerslie.
— *Same.* ill. 12°. $1.25......................*Nelson.*
— Miracles of heavenly love in daily life. ill. 12°. $1.25....................................*Nelson.*
— — *See also* Little door-keeper's lib.
— Missing links in Jewish history. 16°. 90c. *Am. Bapt.*
— Moorcroft hatch. ('60.) New ed. ill. 18°. '75. 75c. *Hoyt.*
— My neighbor's shoes. 18°. 50c....*Carter; Dutton.*
— — *See also below* Ned Manton.
— *Same.* ill. 12°. $1.25.......................*Nelson.*
— Ned Franks. 18°. 50c......................*Carter.*
— — *See also above* Christian's panoply; Fred Franks.
— Ned Manton. 18°. 75c....................*Carter.*
Compr.: Cottage by the stream; My neighbor's shoes.
— Needle and the rat. 18°. 75c..............*Carter.*
— Never give up ser. 4 v. ill. 18°. '73. $2.50; ea., 60c.......................................*Tibbals.*
Cont.: Edith. — Try again. — Hymn my mother taught me. — Boy artist.

Tucker, *Mrs.* Ctte., *continued.*
— New stories. 18°. 35c. .... *Dutton.*
— *Same.* 18°. 50c. .... *Nelson.*
— *Same.* ('64.) New ed. ill. 16°. '75. $1 ... *Hoyt.*
— Nutshell of knowledge. 18°. 75c. .... *Carter.*
— Old friends with new faces. 18°. 50c... *Carter; Dutton.*
— — *See also above* Eddie Ellerslie.
— Olive branch. 16°. '74. 50c. .... *Nelson.*
— On the way. 18°. 75c. .... *Carter; Dutton.*
— *Same.* ill. 18°. 90c. .... *Nelson.*
— Our sympathizing high priest: meditations on daily sorrows of the Saviour. 24°. 45c... *Bost. Am. Tr.*
— *Same.* sq. 18°. '66. 50c. .... *Am. Tr.*
— Parliament in the play-room. 18°. 50c. .... *Carter.*
— — *See also above* Chief's daughter.
— Paying dear for it. 18°. 50c. .... *Carter.*
— — *See also below* Try again.
— Picture story book. ill. roy. 4°. $1.10 .... *Nelson.*
— Poacher. 18°. 75c. .... *Carter.*
Compr.: Harry Dangerfield; Angus Tarlton.
— Precepts in practice. 18°. 75c. ... *Carter; Dutton.*
— *Same.* 16°. $1 .... *Am. Bapt.*
— — *See also above* A. L. O. E. casket.
— Pride and his prisoners. 18°. 75c. .... *Carter.*
— Rambles of a rat. 18°. 50c. .... *Carter; Dutton.*
— Rebel reclaimed. 18°. 75c. .... *Carter.*
— Red cross knight. 18°. 50c. .... *Carter; Dutton.*
— — *See also above* Christian's panoply.
— Rescued from Egypt. 18°. 75c. .... *Carter; Dutton.*
— *Same.* ill. 18°. 90c. .... *Nelson; Tibbals.*
— — *See also above* A. L. O. E. ser.
— Robber's cave. 18°. 75c. .... *Carter.*
— *Same.* ill. 12°. $1.50 .... *Nelson.*
— Roby family. 18°. 50c. .... *Carter; Dutton.*
— *Same.* ill. 12°. $1.25 .... *Nelson.*
— Sheer off. 18°. 75c. .... *Carter.*
— Shepherd king; or, a sick minister's lectures on the shepherd of Bethlehem, and the blessing that followed them. ill. 16°. $1 .... *Bost. Am. Tr.*
— *Same.* ill. 12°. '62. $1.25 .... *Meth. Bk. Conc.*
— Shepherd of Bethlehem. 18°. 75c... *Carter; Dutton.*
— Silver casket. 18°. 75c. .... *Carter.*
— *Same.* 16°. '64. $1 .... *Meth. Bk. Conc.*
— Silver keys. 18°. 75c. .... *Carter; Dutton.*
— Spanish cavalier. 18°. 75c. .... *Carter.*
— *Same.* ill. 18°. '75. 90c. .... *Nelson.*
— Stories from history of the Jews. ill. 18°. 75c. *Nelson.*
— *Same.* 18°. 50c. .... *Carter.*
— — *See also above* Cortley Hall.
— Stories on parables. 18°. 75c. .... *Carter.*
Compr.: Black Cliff; Broken chain.
— Story of a needle. 18°. 35c. .... *Carter.*
— *Same.* 18°. 40c. .... *Dutton.*
— *Same.* ill. 12°. $1.25 .... *Nelson.*
— Straight road. 18°. 35c. .... *Carter.*
— *Same.* 32°. 40c. .... *Scribner, W. & A.*
— *Same.* 16°. '69. 40c. .... *Dutton.*
— — *See also above* Cortley Hall.
— Sunday chaplet. 18°. 75c. .... *Carter.*
— *Same.* ill. 18°. 90c. .... *Nelson.*
— Triumph over Midian. 18°. 75c. .... *Carter.*
— *Same.* ill. 18°. 90c. .... *Nelson.*
— *Same.* 18°. $1 .... *Dutton.*
— — *See also above* A. L. O. E. ser.
— True heroism. 18°. 35c. .... *Carter; Dutton.*
— — *See also above* Adopted son.
— Try again. 18°. 75c. .... *Carter.*
Compr.: Esther Parsons; Paying dear for it.
— — *See also above* Never give up ser.
— Try again lib. 4 v. ill. 16°. ea., 50c. ..... *Nelson.*
Cont.: Try again. — The boy artist. — The hymn my mother taught me. — Edith and her ayah.
— Two paths. 18°. 35c. .... *Carter; Dutton.*
— Upwards and downwards. 32°. 20c.; 15c... *Dutton.*
— *Same.* 16°. '74. 50c. .... *Nelson.*
— Walter Binning. 18°. 35c. .... *Carter; Dutton.*
— — *See also above* Adopted son.
— Wanderer in Africa. 18°. 50c. .... *Carter.*
— — *See also above* Guy Dalesford.

Tucker, *Mrs.* Ctte., *continued.*
— War and peace. 18°. 75c. .... *Carter.*
— What is a Christian? 18°. 50c. .... *Nelson.*
— Wings and stings. 18°. 35c. .... *Carter; Dutton.*
— — *See also above* Adopted son.
— *Same.* ill. 18°. 75c. — 12°. $1.25 .... *Nelson.*
— Wreath of smoke. 18°. 50c. .... *Carter.*
— — *See also above* Guy Dalesford.
— Young pilgrim. 16°. 70c. .... *West. Tr.*
— *Same.* 18°. 75c. .... *Carter; Dutton.*
— — *See also above* A. L. O. E. casket.
— Zaida's note book. 18°. 50c. .... *Carter.*
— — *See also above* Golden fleece.

Tucker, *Miss* E. Abbeokuta. 18°. 75c. .... *Carter.*
— Rainbow in the north. 18°. 75c. .... *Carter.*
— Southern cross. 18°. 75c. .... *Carter.*

Tucker, G: History of the U. S., to 1841. 4 v. 8°. '56. $10 .... *Claxton; Lippincott.*

Tucker, Gideon J. *See* New York County, Surrogate reports.

Tucker, H: Liberty bell: national songs and hymns of all nations. 8°. '76. bds., 75c.; pap., 50c. *Pond.*
— Manual for the guitar. 8°. '54. 50c.; bds., 40c. *Ditson; Pond.*
— Nine o'clock in the morning: popular songs, duets, etc.; with rudimentary exercises and lessons. ('67.) New ed. 12°. '76. bds., 50c. ...... *Pond.*

Tucker, H: H. The gospel in Enoch; or, truth in the concrete: doctrinal and biographical sketch. 12°. $1.25 .... *Lippincott.*

Tucker, H: St. G. Commentaries on laws of Virginia. 3d ed. 2 v. 8°. '46. shp., $18 .. *J. W. Randolph.*

Tucker, J: Ireland. Parish hymnal. 12°. 50c.; $1. *Huntington.*
— Service book of Anglican chants and Gregorian tunes, with music adapted to offices of Book of common prayer. ('73.) New ed. 12°. '75. 60c.; 75c.; pap., 40c.; 50c. .... *Huntington.*
— Tunes, old and new, adapted to the Hymnal [of the Prot. Episc. Ch.]; with service book cont. music adapted to Book of common prayer. 8°. $1.88; $2; — for lectern and organ use. roy. 4°. $5–$10 .... *Huntington.*

Tucker, Josh. T. Christ's infant kingdom. 16°. 50c. *Cong. Pub.*
— The sinless one; or, the life manifested. 12°. $1.25. *Cong. Pub.*

Tucker, Luther. *See* Gaylord, W., *and* Tucker, L.

Tucker, *Mrs.* Ma. Itinerant preaching in early days of Methodism; ed. by T. W. Tucker. 16°. $1. *Russell.*

Tucker, Pomeroy. Origin, rise and progress of Mormonism. 12°. $1.25 .... *Appleton.*

Tucker, St. G: The devoted bride. 12°. $1.75; pap., $1.50 .... *Peterson.*

Tucker, T. W. Waifs from the way-bills of an expressman. 16°. $1 .... *Lee & S.*

Tucker, W. G., *and* Purday, C: H. Every body's song-book: popular national songs, with words and music. sq. 12°. $1 .... *Routledge.*

Tuckerman, C: K. Greeks of to-day. 12°. '72. $1.50. *Putnam.*

Tuckerman, E: Genera lichenum: arrangement of the No. Am. lichens. 8°. '72. pap., $3 .. *E. Nelson.*
— *and* Frost, C: C. Catalogue of plants growing without cultivation within thirty miles of Amherst College. 12°. '75. pap., 50c. .... *E. Nelson.*

Tuckerman, H: Thdr. America and her commentators; with crit. sketch of travel in the U. S. cr. 8°. '64. $2.50 .... *Scribner.*
— Book of the artists: biog. history of fine arts in U. S. 8°. '67. $5; hf. cf., $8 .... *Putnam.*
— Life and letters of J. P. Kennedy. 12°. $2 .. *Putnam.*
— Poems. 16°. $1.25 .... *Osgood.*

Tuckerman, Jos. On the elevation of the poor. 16°. '74. $1.25 .... *Roberts.*

'uckerman, S: Parkman. Cathedral chants. obl. f°. '58. $3; — words, 15c. ... *Ditson.*

'udor, Owen D. Leading cases on merc. and maritime law; with Am. notes by G. Sharswood. 2 v. 8°. '73. $15 ... *T.&J. W.Johnson.*

'udor, R: Decalogue viewed as the Christian's law; with special ref. to questions and wants of the times. cr. 8°. $2.50 ... *Macmillan.*

'ufelhausen. Johnstone, J. B. 15c. ... *French.*

'uflongbo and Little Content. Parr, H. $1.25. *Scribner, W.& A.*

uflongbo's life and adventures. Parr, H. $1.25. *Scribner, W.&A.*

ufts, J: Freeman. Questions on hist. and geog. of Greece. 16°. '73. pap., 25c. ... *Sever.*

- Questions on hist. and geog. of Rome. 16°. '74. pap., 25c. ... *Sever.*

- Questions on modern and physical geography. 16°. '74. pap., 25c. ... *Sever.*

'ugenden (Der) Vergeltung. *See* Hoffmann, F.

ugendkranz. 12°. 35c.; pap., 15c. ... *Benziger.*

uke, Dan. Hack. Illustrations of the influènce of the mind upon the body. 8°. $3.25 ... *Lea.*

- *Same.* 8°. '72. $4 ... *Lindsay.*

- *See also* Bucknill, J. C., *and* Tuke, D. H.

uke, H: Principles of religion, as professed by the society of Christians usually called Quakers; written for instruction of their youth, and for information of strangers. 18°. 40c. ... *Friends Bk. St.*

ulloch, J: Beginning life: chapters for young men on religion, study and business. 16°. $1.25. *Cin. Meth. Bk. Conc.*

- *Same.* cr. 8°. $1.75 ... *Routledge.*

- *Same.* 12°. '70. 90c. ... *Am. Tr.*

- Christ of the Gospels and the Christ of modern criticism: lectures on Renan's "Vie de Jésus." fp. 8°. '64. $1 ... *Macmillan.*

- *Same.* 12°. '72. $1.25 ... *Meth. Bk. Conc.*

- Christian doctrine of sin. (Croall lecture, 1876.) cr. 8°. '76. $3 ... *Scribner, W.&A.*

- Rational theology and Christian philos. in Eng. in 17th cent. 2 v. 8°. $9 ... *Scribner, W.&A.*

ully, J. C. Scriptural sanctification: exam. of doctrine of instantaneous holiness in light of Bible. 32°. pap., 10c. ... *Chase.*

umbridge, W: Wall street caricatures and information for stock speculators. 8°. '76. 10c. *Tumbridge.*

uneful hours: medley glee book. obl. 8°. '59. bds., $1.50 ... *Ditson.*

uner's guide: treat. on tuning piano forte, organ, melodeon and seraphine. 12°. '52. bds., 60c. *Ditson.*

unner, P: Treatise on roll-turning for manufacture of iron; tr. and adapted by J. B. Pearse. 2 v.: text, 8°.; pl., f°. '69. $10 ... *Van Nostrand.*

uomey, Michael. *See* Alabama geol. survey; — South Carolina geol. survey.

upper, Mt. Farquhar. Poems. ill. 16°. $1.12; $1.35. — ill. 12°. $1.50 ... *World Pub.*

- *Same.* (Blue and gold ed.) 2 v. 32°. $2.50. *Widdleton.*

- *Same.* (Presentation ed.) 12°. $1.75 .. *Routledge.*

- *Same;* [also] Poems, by S. Johnson. ill. 32°. 85c.; $1.12 ... *World Pub.*

- Crock of gold. 8°. pap., 75c. ... *Peterson.*

- Proverbial philosophy. 16°. 90c.; $1.50 .. *Sheldon.*

- *Same.* 12°. $1 ... *Wiley.*

- *Same.* ill. 4°. $5; hf. mor., $7.50; mor., $9 .. *Miller.*

- *Same.* ill. 4°. $8 ... *Routledge.*

- *Same.* (Blue and gold ed.) 32°. $1.25 .. *Widdleton.*

- *Same.* (Household ser.) ill. 16°. $1.50; mor., $3. *Lee & S.*

- *Same;* [also] A thousand lines. 12°. '56. $1.25. *Darrow.*

- — *Same.* por. 12°. $1.75 ... *J.E. Potter.*

- The twins; [also] Heart. 8°. pap., 75c. ... *Peterson.*

Tuppy, the donkey. 18°. 50c. ... *Carter.*

Turandot. *See* Gozzi, *Conte* Carlo.

Turford, Hu. Grounds of a holy life; or, the way by which many who were heathens came to be Christians, etc. 18°. '76. 20c. *Friends Bk. Assoc.*

— *Same;* [also] Paul's speech. 18°. '76. 40c. *Friends Bk. Assoc.*

— Paul's speech to the Bishop of Crete; or, the ancient Christian's principle or rule of good living revived, etc. 18°. '76. 20c. ... *Friends Bk. Assoc.*

Turgénieff, Ivan. Novels; tr. ('67–'74.) New ed. (Leis. hour ser.) 6 v. 16°. '74–'75. ea., $1.25. *Holt.*

Cont.: Dimitri Roudine. — Fathers and sons, tr. by E. Schuyler. — Liza, tr. by W. R. S. Ralston. — On the eve, tr. by C. E. Turner. — Smoke, tr. by W. F. West. — Spring-floods, tr. by S. M. Butts; [also] A Lear of the steppe, tr. by W. H. Browne.

Turkeys in season: Ethiop. drama. 16°. pap., 15c. *French; Happy.*

Turkish bath. Williams, M., *and* Burnand, F. C. 15c. ... *French; Lee & S.*

Turks in Europe. *See* Bouvet, F.

Turn him out. Williams, T. J. 15c. ... *French.*

Turn out. Kenney, J. 15c. ... *French.*

Turnaside cottage. Clark, M. S. $1.25 ... *Nelson.*

Turnbull, Ctte. The Lawrences: New England men and women as they grow up and develop. [Fiction.] 12°. $2 ... *U.S. Pub.*

Turnbull, J: Treatise on the compound engine. ill. 18°. '73. bds., 50c. ... *Van Nostrand.*

Turnbull, Lawr. Clinical manual of diseases of the ear. ill. 8°. $5 ... *Lippincott.*

Turned frock; or, story of little Violet. 18°. 40c. *Am. S. S.*

Turned head. A'Beckett, G. A. 15c. ... *French.*

Turner, Bessie. A woman in the case. [Fiction.] por. 12°. '76. $1.50 ... *Carleton.*

Turner, C: Tennyson. Small tableaux. fp. 8°. '68. $1.25 ... *Macmillan.*

— Sonnets. fp. 8°. '64. $1.25 ... *Macmillan.*

Turner, Dawson W. Notes on Herodotus. 12°. (Bohn.) $1.75 ... *Little, B. & Co.*

— *Same.* 12°. (Bohn.) $2 .. *Lippincott; Scribner, W.& A.*

Turner, E: Elements of chemistry; [ed.] by J. Johnston. ill. 12°. $1.50 ... *Desilver.*

— *See also* Johnston, J:

Turner, Godf. Wordsworth. Art studies of home life: 24 full-page photos. from paintings by great masters; with text. demy 4°. $7.50 ... *Cassell.*

— Homely scenes from great painters: 24 full-page eng. demy 4°. $7.50 ... *Cassell.*

Turner, J. A. Cotton planter's manual. 12°. $1.50. *Judd.*

Turner, J. W. Hunter's daughter. [School opera.] 4°. pap., $2 ... *G.D. Russell.*

— *See also* One hundred comic songs.

Turner, Jos. A. Handbook of punctuation. 16°. 75c. *Lippincott.*

Turner, Ned. Black jokes. 18°. pap., 10c. .. *Dick & F.*

— Circus joke book. 18°. pap., 10c. ... *Dick & F.*

— Clown joke book. 18°. pap., 10c. ... *Dick & F.*

Turner, Owen. History of the pioneer settlement of Phelps and Gorham's purchase and Morris' reserve. 8°. '51. $3 ... *Darrow.*

Turner, R. Parlor letter-writer. ('35.) New ed. 18°. '74. 50c. ... *Clark & M.*

Turner, S: H. Commentary on Hebrews in Greek and Eng. 8°. '60. $1.50 ... *Randolph.*

— Commentary on Romans in Greek and Eng. 8°. '60. $1.75 ... *Randolph.*

— Essays on our Lord's discourse at Capernaum. 12°. '60. 50c. ... *Randolph.*

— Gospels according to the Ammonian sections. 12° '60. $1.25 ... *Randolph*

Turner, S: H., *continued.*
— Spiritual things compared with spiritual. 12°. '60. 75c. .... *Randolph.*
— Teachings of the Master. 12°. '58. $1.25 .. *Randolph.*
— Thoughts on prophecy. 12°. '60. 75c. .. *Randolph.*

Turner, Sharon. Sacred hist. of the world attempted to be philosophically considered in a series of letters to a son. 3 v. 18°. $2.25 ...... *Harper.*

Turner, W: Mason. El Khuds, the holy; or, glimpses of the Orient. roy. 8°. '61. $5; mor., $8 .. *Challen.*

Turner gallery: 60 eng. from works of J. M. W. Turner; with biog. sketch and descript. text by R. N. Wornum. f°. '75. hf. mor., India pap., $110 .... *Bouton.*

Turner's companion: instructions in concentric, elliptic and eccentric turning, etc.; with patterns. ('51.) 7th ed. 12°. '72. $1.50 .... *Baird.*

Turning aside. *See* My own lib.

Turning a new leaf. Robbins, S. S. $1.25 ... *Carter.*

Turning of the tide. Kellogg, E. $1.25 ..... *Lee & S.*

Turning point. 18°. 30c. .... *Am. S. S.*

Turning points in life. Arnold, F. $1.75 ... *Harper.*

Turning the tables. Poole, J. 15c. .. *De Witt; French.*

Turning wheel. Cobden, P. $1.25 .... *Lee & S.*

Turnpike gate. Knight, T. 15c. .... *French.*

Turpin in danger. *See* Blueskin ser.

Turrettin, François. On the atonement. 12°. 75c. *N. Y. Ref. Ch. Bd.*

Tuthill, *Mrs.* Louisa Caro. Julius Farley; or, I will be a soldier. ill. 16°. $1 .... *Perkinpine.*
— Juvenile lib. 6 v. ill. 18°. '68. ea., 65c. .. *Perkinpine.*

Cont.: Anything for sport. — A strike for freedom. — Boarding school girl. — I will be a lady. — I will be a gentleman. — Onward right onward.

— Larry Lockwell; or, I will be a sailor. ill. 16°. $1. *Perkinpine.*
— Noble aims; for boys and girls. 2 v. ill. 12°. '76. ea., $1.50 .... *World Pub.*
— Our young ladies from girlhood to womanhood. ill. 12°. $1.50 .... *World Pub.*
— Romantic Belinda. ill. 16°. '67. $1 .. *Perkinpine.*
— True manliness. ill. 16°. '67. $1 .... *Perkinpine.*

Tutor and teamster. Guernsey, C. F. $1.50. (?) *Martien.*

Tutor's counsel to his pupils. Mathias, G. H. D. $1. *Lippincott.*

Tutor's ward. [Fiction.] 8°. pap., 50c. ... *Harper.*

Tuttle, C: A. *See* California, Sup. Court reports.

Tuttle, C: R. History of Indiana. 8°. '75. $3.75; leath., $4.75 .... *Peale.*
— *and* Durrie, Dan. S. History of Iowa, to 1876. 8°. '76. $4.75; leath., $5.25 .... *Peale.*
— — History of Wisconsin to 1875. por. and col. map. 8°. (Boston.) '75. $3.75 .... *Durrie.*

Tuttle, Edm. B. Boy's book about Indians. ill. 12°. $1.50 .... *Lippincott.*

Tuttle, Herb. German political leaders. 12°. '76. $1.50 .... *Putnam.*

Tuttle, Hudson. Arcana of nature. ('59.) 2d ed. 2 v. 12°. '64. ea., $1.25 .... *Colby.*

Cont.: 1. History and laws of creation. — 2. Philosophy of spiritual existence and of the spirit-world.

— Career of the Christ-idea in hist. ('70.) 2d ed. 12°. '73. $1.50 .... *Colby.*
— Origin and antiquity of physical man, scientifically considered. ('65.) 2d ed. 12°. '73. $1.50 .. *Colby.*
— *and* Peebles, J. M. (*ed.*) Year-book of spiritualism: record of its facts, science and philosophy. 12°. '71. $1.25; pap., $1 .... *Colby.*

Tuttle, Jos. F. The way lost and found. 16°. $1.15. *Pres. Bd.*

Twain, M: (*pseud.*) *See* Clemens, S. L.

Twas I. Payne, J. H. 15c. .... *French.*

Tweed, B: F. Grammar school speller. 12°. 30c. *Lee & S*
— *See also* Tower, D: B., *and* Tweed, B: F.

Tweedie, Alex. *See* Cyclopædia of practical medicine.

Tweedie, W. K. Daily duty. 18°. 50c. .... *Nelson*
— Early choice. ill. 16°. $1.25. *Am. Bapt.; Cin. Meth. Bk. Conc*
— *Same.* ill. 12°. $1.50 .... *Nelson*
— *Same.* ill. 12°. '69. $1.75 .... *Lothrop*
— Earnest men: their life and works. 12°. $1.75. *Nelson*
— — *See also below* Life and work.
— Glad tidings; or, Gospel of peace: daily meditations ill. 16°. '74. $1.25 .... *Lothrop*
— Heroes for the truth. 16°. 70c. .... *Pres. Bd*
— Home; or, parent's assistant and children's friend ill. 12°. '76. *$2.25; mor., $3.25 .. *Henry Bill*
— Jerusalem and its environs. ill. 12°. $1.25 .. *Nelson*
— Life and work of earnest men. 12°. $1.75. *Cin. Meth. Bk. Conc*
— — *See also above* Earnest men.
— Rivers and lakes of the Bible. 12°. $1.25 .. *Nelson*
— Rivers and lakes of Scripture. ill. 16°. $1.25. *Cin. Meth. Bk. Conc*
— Seedtime and harvest; or, sow well and reap well ill. 16°. '74. $1.25 .... *Lothrop*
— *Same.* ill. 12°. $1.50 .... *Nelson*
— Story of Joseph. ill. 18°. '72. 50c. ...... *Lothrop*
— Youthful diligence. ill. 12°. $1.50 .... *Nelson*

Tweedie ser. 3 v. 16°. $3.75 .... *Lothrop*

Cont.: Glad tidings. — A lamp to the path. — Seedtime and harvest.

Tweedie's rights. Albery, J. 15c. .... *De Witt*

Tweedleton's tail-coat. Williams, T. J. 15c. .. *French*

Twelfth-night. *See* Shakespeare, W:

Twells, *Mrs.* J. H. Mills of the gods. [Fiction.] 12° $1.50 .... *Lippincott*

Twelve hints to young men. Ryle, J. C. 10c. .. *Pres. Bd*

Twelve labors of Hercules. Brough, R. B. 15c. *French*

Twelve miles from a lemon. Dodge, M. A. $1.50. *Harper*

Twelve months in Madagascar. Mullens, J. $1.75. *Carter*

Twelve months of matrimony. Carlén, E. F. 50c. *Peterson*

Twelve months' volunteer. Furber, G. C. $3. *U. P. James*

Twelve years with the children. Warren, W. $1.25 *Hoyt, F. & D*

Twenty minutes under an umbrella: farce. 16°. pap. 15c. .... *French*

Twenty minutes with a tiger: farce. 16°. pap., 15c *French*

Twenty sermons for town congregations. Hardwick C. $1.75 .... *Macmillan*

Twenty stories and twenty poems. Parker, C. E. R 80c. .... *Am. Tr*

Twenty straws. Winstanley, E. 30c. ..... *Am. News*

Twenty thousand leagues under the sea. *See* Verne, J

Twenty years after. *See* Dumas, A.

Twenty years ago. *See* Craik, D. M.

Twenty years in the Philippines. La Gironière, P. de $1.50 .... *Harper*

Twenty years on the wing. Spear, J. M. 20c. .. *Colby*

Twenty years with colporteurs. Peabody, C. 25c. 10c. .... *Am. Tr*

Twice crowned. McKeever, H. B. $1.50 .... *Claxton*

Twice found; by author of "Lonely Lily." ill. 16° '75. 75c. .... *Dodd*

Twice killed. Oxenford, J. 15c. ... *De Witt; French*

Twice taken. Hall, C. W. $1.75 .... *Lee & S*

Twice told tale. Wooler, J. P. 15c. .... *French*

Twice told tales. *See* Hawthorne, Natl.

Twice tried. Courtney, E. S. 75c. ....*Claxton.*
Twilight hours. Williams, S. $2.50 ......*Routledge.*
Twilight of faith. Traine, E. $1 ...(?) *H.D.Brown.*
Twilight stories. Cousin Zilpha. 40c. ..*Bost.Am.Tr.*
Twilight stories. *See* Follen, *Mrs.* E. L.
Twilight stories. Miller, O. D. $1 .... *Universalist.*
Twilight stories. Rogers, B. C. 50c. ....*Am. Tr.*
Twilight stories at Overbury Farm. 16°. 50c. *Scribner, W.&A.*
Twin babies. *See* Finley, M. F.
Twin brothers. *See* Baker, *Mrs.* H. N. W.
Twin brothers: farce. 16°. pap., 15c. ....*Happy.*
Twin brothers; or, lessons in charity. 18°. 75c. *Harper.*
Twin brothers; or, Lucius and his children. 32°. 40c. *Scribner, W.&A.*
Twin brothers; or, the victims of the press-gang: romance of land and sea. 8°. pap., 25c. *U.P.James.*
Twin brothers of Everdale. Eden, C. H. $1..*Nelson.*
Twin captains. *See* Dumas, A.
Twin heroes. Reed, F. A. $1.75 ....*Cong.Pub.*
Twin lieutenants. *See* Dumas, A.
Twin roses, and how they were trained. 16°. $1.25. *Am.S.S.*
— *See also* Diamond lib.
Twin sisters. 18°. 35c.; 45c. ....*Am. Bapt.*
Twin sisters. Fleming, M. A. 25c. ....*Beadle.*
Twin sisters. McCalla, M. 50c. ....*Pres.Bd.*
Twin sisters. Saroni, H. S. 50c. ....*Ditson.*
Twin sisters. Sedgwick, A. B. 15c. ....*De Witt.*
Twin sisters. *See* Happy child's lib.
Twin sisters: brief memoir of little Amelia. 18°. '68. 35c. ....*Am.S.S.*
Twining, T: Technical training: suggestive sketch of a national system of industrial instruction founded on a general diffusion of practical science among the people. 8°. '74. $4.50 ....*Macmillan.*
Twins. *See* Baker, *Mrs.* H. N. W.
Twins. *See* Tupper, M. F.
Twins of St. Marcel. Orr, A. S. $1.50..(?) *Shepard.*
Twins of Warsaw. Somerset, C. A. 15c. ...*French.*
Twisted threads. Nauman, M. D. $1.50; $1..*Claxton.*
Twitchell, G: Life, trial and conviction. [In Eng. or Germ.] 8°. pap., 25c. ....*Barclay.*
Two admirals. *See* Cooper, Ja. F.
Two apprentices. *See* Howitt, Ma.
Two Barbaras. Stuart, M. B. $1.50 ......*Carleton.*
Two baronesses. *See* Andersen, H. C.
Two Bens. *See* My holiday books.
Two b'hoys. Dance, C. 15c. ....*French.*
Two birthdays. *See* Baker, *Mrs.* H. N. W.
Two black roses. Stewart, J. C. 15c. ......*De Witt.*
Two blinds: opera bouffe. 16°. pap., 15c. ...*French.*
Two Bonnycastles. Morton, J. M. 15c. .....*French.*
Two books. Davis, C. E. K. $1.15 ....*Hoyt.*
Two boys. Wright, J. McN. $1.50 ....*Souder.*
Two boys, and what they did with a year. McKenzie, A. $1.25 ....*Cong.Pub.*
Two boys saved. Chellis, M. D. $1.25 ...*Cong.Pub.*
Two boys side by side. *See* Cousin Anna's lib.
Two brides. Arthur, T. S. 50c. ....*Peterson.*
Two brothers. Bickersteth, E. H. $2 ....*Carter.*
Two brothers. Power, P. B. 60c. ....*Carter.*
Two brothers. *See* French's serio-comic dramas.
Two brothers. *See* Short stories lib.
Two brothers; or, the little cowslip gatherers. ('63.) 7th ed. ill. 18°. '71. 63c. ....*Perkinpine.*
Two brothers; or, true and false happiness; tr. by A. T. Sadlier. 18°. 50c.; 75c. ....*Sadlier.*
Two Buzzards. Morton, J. M. 15c. ....*French.*
Two by tricks. Yates, E. $1 ....*Routledge.*
Two Cadis. *See* Eichberg, J.
Two can play at that game: comedy. 16°. pap., 15c. *French.*
Two captains. *See* La Motte Fouqué, F. H. C.
Two carpenters; or, the fruits of sloth and thrift illustrated. 18°. 55c. ....*Am.S.S.*
Two chancellors. Klaczko, J. $2 ....*Hurd & H.*
Two children of St. Domingo. Gouraud, J. $1.25; 50c. ....*Scribner, W.&A.*
Two Christmas celebrations. Parker, T. 60c. *Fuller.*
Two Christmas days. Chase, M. G. 60c. ...*Dutton.*
Two Christmas gifts. M'Clellan, K. 60c... *Whittaker.*
Two Christmas trees; or, two Christmas eves with Luther and his children. 18°. 30c. ....*Am.S.S.*
Two college friends. Loring, F. W. $1 ....*Loring.*
Two consciences; or, conscience the moral law, and conscience the witness. 12°. '70. $1..*Claxton.*
Two convicts. *See* Gerstäcker, F:
Two cottagers (The), as related by an old gentleman. 18°. 22c. ....*Am.S.S.*
Two cottages. Fullerton, *Lady* G. 50c. ....*Kenedy.*
Two councils. Trowbridge, C. M. 75c...(?) *Martien.*
Two cousins; or, how to be loved. *See* Theodore Thinker.
Two covenants. Andrews, J. N. 10c. ..*Sev.Day Adv.*
Two daughters. *See* Dickens, C:
Two Dianas. *See* Dumas, A.
Two families. *See* Shaw, A.
Two families: episode in hist. of Chapelton; by author of "Rose Douglas." 12°. '52. $1.50..*Harper.*
Two family mothers. Schwartz, M. S. $1.50; $1..*Porter.*
Two fawns. ill. 24°. '69. 30c. ....*Lothrop.*
Two festivals. Follen, E. L. 50c. ....*Lee & S.*
Two firesides; or, the mechanic and the tradesman. ('65.) 6th ed. ill. 16°. '72. $1.25..*Perkinpine.*
Two flats and a sharp: comedietta. 16°. pap., 15c. *French.*
Two fortune-seekers, and other stories; by R. Johnson, Mrs. L. C. Moulton, E. S. Phelps, E. Farman and others. ill. 16°. '76. $1.50 ..*Lothrop.*
Two fortunes; or, profession and practice. ill. 18°. '73. 45c. ..........*N.Y.Ref.Ch.Bd.; Pres.Com.*
Two friends. ill. 16°. '74. 50c. ....*Nelson.*
Two friends. *See* Greenwell, D.
Two friends. Trowbridge, C. M. $1.25..(?) *Martien.*
Two friends: drama. 16°. pap., 15c. ....*French.*
Two friends; or, religion the best guide for youth. 18°. 30c. ....*Am.S.S.*
Two friends of Forley, and Bessie's two friends. ill. 18°. 50c. ....*Nelson.*
— *Same.* ('73.) New ed. 16°. '75. $1 ......*Hoyt.*
Two galley slaves. Payne, J. H. 15c. ......*French.*
Two gay deceivers. Robertson, T. W., *and* Lacy, T. H. 15c. ....*De Witt; French.*
Two gentlemen at Mivart's: comedietta. 16°. pap., 15c. ....*Happy.*
Two gentlemen in a fix. Suter, W. E. 15c. *French; Lee & S.*
Two gentlemen of Verona. *See* Shakespeare, W:
Two goldfinches. 32°. 20c.; 15c. ....*Dutton.*
Two granddaughters. *See* Chaplin, *Mrs.* J. D.
Two grandmothers. 18°. 17c.; 22c. ......*Am.Bapt.*
Two great captains. Robinson, M. S. 75c...*Tibbals.*
Two great temptations. Vaughan, C. J. $1.25. *Macmillan.*

Two Gregories. Dibdin, T. 15c. .... *French.*
Two guardians. Yonge, C. M. $1 .... *Appleton.*
Two half dollars. 18°. 17c.; 22c. .... *Am. Bapt.*
Two heads better than one. Horne, L. 15c. *French; Lee & S.*
Two heaps, and what Mrs. Brown's Sunday-school class did about them. 18°. '65. 40c. .. *Randolph.*
Two hemispheres. Ruppius, O. $1.50; $1 .. *Claxton.*
Two holidays. Marshall, E. 50c. .... *Carter.*
Two homes compared; or, the advantages of cleanliness. 18°. 25c. .... *Am. S. S.*
Two hundred years ago; or, life in New Sweden; by author of "Over the hedge." 16°. $1 .. *Am. S. S.*
Two idle apprentices. *See* Dickens, C: *and* Collins, W.
Two in the morning. Mathews, C. J. 15c. .. *French.*
Two ladders. *See* Two watches.
Two legends of the Christ-child. Satterlee, M. L. R. *and* W. 60c. .... *Lent.*
Two life-paths. Mundt, C. M. 60c. .... *Appleton.*
Two little Bruces. ('71.) New ed. 16°. '73. $1.25. *Hoyt.*
Two little children. *See* Thomas and Ellen.
Two little cousins. O'Brien, H. 35c. .... *Pres. Bd.*
Two little orioles; or, music in the heart and how to make it. 18°. 45c. .... *Am. S. S.*
Two little yellow jackets. 18°. 75c. ..... (?) *Martien.*
Two lives. McIntosh, M. J. $1.25 .... *Appleton.*
Two lovers; or, a sister's devotion: domestic story, by author of "Twin sisters." 8°. pap., 50c. *Peterson.*
Two loves and a life. Taylor, T., *and* Reade, C. 15c. *French.*
Two Margarets. Marshal, E. 50c. .... *Carter.*
Two marriages. *See* Craik, D. M.
Two marriages; or, Hattie and Nellie. 16°. $1. (?) *Martien.*
Two mechanics. 18°. 30c. .... *Dutton.*
Two merchants. Arthur, T. S. 50c. ...... *Peterson.*
Two mottoes. *See* Bertie's lib.; — Moss rose ser.
Two neighbors. ill. sq. 12°. bds., 50c. .... *Routledge.*
Two New Year's days. Sargent, G. E. $1.15 .. *Hoyt.*
Two opinions. Andrews, L. F. W. 75c. .. *Williamson.*
Two orphans. 18°. 45c.; 55c. .... *Am. Bapt.*
Two orphans. *See* Sherwood, *Mrs.* M. M.
Two paths. Richmond, E. J. $1 .... *Meth. Bk. Conc.*
Two paths. Ruskin, J. $1.25 .... *Wiley.*
Two paths. *See* Tucker, *Mrs.* C.
Two paths; [also] The secret. 18°. 28c.; 35c. *Am. Bapt.*
Two paths; or, history of Mary Lester and Eliza Bruce. ill. 18°. 65c. .... *Am. S. S.*
Two pearls. Crow, *Mrs.* —. 30c. .... *Am. News.*
Two pictures. M'Intosh, M. J. $1 .... *Appleton.*
Two plots: drama. 16°. pap., 15c. .... *French.*
Two plunges for a pearl. Collins, M. 75c. .. *Appleton.*
Two polts. Courtney, J. 15c. .... *De Witt.*
Two Pompeys: Ethiop. drama. 16°. pap., 15c. .. *French.*
Two prima donnas. Sala, G. A. 25c. ...... *Peterson.*
Two prisoners; [also] A night in prison. 32°. 25c. *Pres. Bd.*
Two prodigals. Vincent, M. R. 40c.; 20c. .. *Randolph.*
Two prophets. Baird, A. J. 50c. ... (?) *Cumberland.*
Two Puddifoots. Morton, J. M. 15c. .. *French; Lee & S.*
Two queens. Buckstone, J. B. 15c. .... *French.*
Two rivals; or, man and money. 12°. pap., 20c. *Hurst.*
Two rivulets. Whitman, W. $5 .... *Whitman.*
Two roads. Bourdon, M. F. 30c. .... *O'Shea.*
Two rules. *See* Baker, *Mrs.* H. N. W.

Two Sabbaths. Fuller, E. Q. 60c. .. *Cin. Meth. Bk. Conc.*
Two sailor boys. 18°. 30c. .... *Dutton.*
Two school-boys (Walks, talks, travels and exploits of). *See* Atkinson, J. C.
Two school-girls. *See* Books of blessing.
Two schools. Hughes, M. $1 .... *Cath. Pub.*
Two shawls. 18°. 60c. .... *Cong. Pub.*
Two shipmates. Kingston, W. H. G. 50c. ..... *Pott.*
Two sisters. *See* Baker, *Mrs.* H. N. W.
Two sisters. Southworth, E. D. E. N. $1.75; $1.50. *Peterson.*
Two sons; [also] The prisoner released. 18°. 17c.; 22c. .... *Am. Bapt.*
Two story mittens. *See* Barrow, *Mrs.* F.
Two strings to your bow. Jephson, R. 15c. .. *French.*
Two subprises. Clifton, M. D. 15c. .... *Ames.*
Two sufferers contrasted; or, fear and anguish, and joy and peace. 18°. 50c. .... *Am. S. S.*
Two T. J's. Beecher, M. 15c. .... *Ames.*
Two terms at Olney. Howard, M. 75c. .... *Pres. Bd.*
Two thousand miles on horseback. *See* Meline, Ja. F.
Two thousand years after. Garretson, J. E. $1. *Claxton.*
Two to one: farce. 16°. pap., 15c. .... *French.*
Two tough knots. ('70.) 4th ed. ill. 18°. '74. 50c. *Perkinpine.*
Two victories. Potter, T. J. $1; $1.50 .... *Sadlier.*
Two visions; or, Byron vs. Southey. 18°. pap., 20c. *Mendum.*
Two vocations. Charles, E. $1 .... *Carter.*
Two voyages; or, midnight and daylight. 16°. $1.50. *Pres. Bd.*
Two wallets. O'Brien, H. 50c. .... *Pres. Bd.*
Two watches. 16°. '74. 50c. .... *Nelson.*
Two watches; [also] The two ladders; [also] The drinking fountain. 18°. 35c. .... *Pres. Bd.*
Two ways. *See* Bell, C. D.
Two ways. M., B. V. 40c. .... *West. Tr.*
Two ways and the two ends: hist. of Manlius Spencer and Roland Larkin. ill. 18°. 65c. ...... *Am. S. S.*
Two ways of doing it. Bates, L. $1 .... *J. A. Moore.*
Two ways to begin life. *See* Little Dot ser.
Two weeks in the Yosemite valley. Buckley, J. M. 20c. .... *Meth. Bk. Conc.*
Two wheel-barrows. *See* Abbott, Jac.
Two widows. 18°. 25c. .... *Am. S. S.*
Two widows. Thomas, A. 50c. .... *Harper.*
Two wives. *See* Arthur, T. S.
Two years ago. Kingsley, C. $1.75 ..... *Macmillan.*
Two years before the mast. Dana, R. H., *jr.* $1.50. *Osgood.*
Two years in California. Cone, M. $1.75 ... *Griggs.*
Two years in east Africa. Jouveaux, E. $1.25 .. *Nelson.*
Two years of school life. Pressensé, E. de. $1.25. *Scribner, W. & A.*
Twofold life. Hillern, W. v. $1.75 ..... *Lippincott.*
Twould puzzle a conjurer. Poole, J. 15c. .. *French.*
Twyman Hogue. Hill, W. W. 65c. ...... *Pres. Bd.*
Tyas, Rob. Language of flowers; or, floral emblems of thoughts, feelings and sentiments. col. ill. sm. 4°. $1.75. — (fine ed.) sm. 4°. $5; mor., $10 .... *Routledge.*
— *Same;* ed. by Mrs. L. Burke. 18°. 50c.; $1. — 24°. 20c. .... *Routledge.*
Tyburn tree. 8°. pap., 25c. .... *De Witt.*
Tyerman, Luke. Life and times of J. Wesley. 3 v. por. cr. 8°. $7.50; hf. cf., $13.50 .... *Harper.*
— Oxford Methodists: memories of Clayton, Ingham, Gambold, Hervey and Broughton; with biog. notices of others. por. cr. 8°. $2.50 .. *Harper.*

Tyler, Bennet. Doctrine of perseverance of the saints. *See* Spring, G., Doctrine of election.
— Memoir of Asahel Nettleton. por. 12°. $1.25. *Cong. Pub.*
— Worth of the soul, and other sermons. 12°. $2. *Cong. Pub.*

Tyler, J. *See* Hyde, A., Bliss, F. C., *and* Tyler, J.

Tyler, J. B. *See* How to teach the little folks.

Tyler, Jose. Lyret. [Poem.] ill. 16°. '74. $1.25 . . *Lothrop.*

Tyler, M. A. Egypt, and other poems. 16°. $1 . . *Lippincott.*

Tyler, Mos. Coit. The Brawnville papers. 12°. '69. $1.50 . . . . *Osgood.*

Tyler, Ransom H. American ecclesiastical law: law of relig. societies, church government and creeds, disturbing relig. meetings, and law of burial grounds in U. S. 8°. '66. shp., $5.50 . . . *Gould.*
— Bible and social reform. 12°. '58. $1.75 . . *Challen.*
— Law of boundaries and fences, incl. rights of property on the sea-shore, etc., and law of window lights. 8°. '74. shp., $6.50 . . . . *Gould.*
— Law of infancy, including guardianship and custody of infants, and the law of coverture [in the U. S.] 8°. '73. shp., $7.50 . . . . *Gould.*
— Remedy by ejectment and law of adverse enjoyment in the U. S. 8°. '76. shp., $7.50 . . . . *Gould.*
— Treatise on law of usury, pawns or pledges and maritime loans. 8°. '73. shp., $7.50 . . . . *Gould.*

Tyler, Royall. *See* Vermont, Sup. Court reports.

Tyler, S: Life of Chief Justice Taney. por. 8°. '72. *$5; $6; hf. mor., $7 . . . . *Murphy.*
— Progress of philosophy in the past and future. 12°. $1.75 . . . . *Lippincott.*
— Theory of the beautiful. 12°. '73. 50c.; 75c. *Murphy.*

Tyler, W: Seymour. History of Amherst Coll. during its first half century [1821–1871]. ill. roy. 8°. '73. $5; $6 . . . . (?) *C. W. Bryan*; (?) *Morris.*
— Theology of the Greek poets. 12°. '67. $1.75 . . *Draper.*

Tyler-Smith, W: *See* Smith, W: T.

Tylney Hall. *See* Hood, T:

Tylor, E: B. Early hist. of mankind, and development of civilization. 8°. $2.50 . . . . *Estes.*
— Primitive culture: researches into development of mythology, philosophy, religion, art and custom. 2 v. 8°. $5 . . . . *Estes.*
— *Same.* 2d Am. ed. 2 v. 8°. '73. $5 . . . . *Holt.*
— Stone age, past and present. cr. 8°. '74. pap., 25c. *Estes.*

Tyndale, W: Life and writings. *See* British reformers.

Tyndall, J: Address before the British Assoc., Belfast. 12°. pap., 25c. . . . . *Appleton.*
— Advancement of science: inaug. address at Belfast, 1874, with biog. sketch; [also] opinions of H. Helmholtz and articles of Tyndall and Sir H: Thompson on prayer. 12°. '74. 75c.; pap., 15c.; 35c. . . . . *Somerby.*
— *Same.* por. 12°. $1 . . . . *Mendum.*
— Faraday as a discoverer: memoir. 12°. $1 . . *Appleton.*
— Forms of water. 12°. $1.50; hf. cf., $3.50 . . *Appleton.*
— Fragments of science for unscientific people. 12°. $2 . . . . *Appleton.*
— Heat as a mode of motion. 12°. $2 . . . . *Appleton.*
— Hours of exercise in the Alps. ill. 12°. $2 . . *Appleton.*
— Light and electricity: lectures before the Royal Inst. of Gt. Brit. 12°. $1.25 . . . . *Appleton.*
— Natural philosophy in easy lessons. fp. 8°. $1.25. *Cassell.*
— On sound: lectures at the Royal Inst. of Gt. Brit. ill. 12°. $2 . . . . *Appleton.*
— Radiant heat. 12°. $5; hf. cf., $9 . . . . . . *Appleton.*
— Scientific addresses: 1, On the methods and tendencies of physical investigation; 2, On haze and dust; 3, On the scientific use of the imagination. 12°. '71. 50c.; pap., 25c. . . . . *Van Nostrand.*
— Six lectures on light; delivered in Am. in 1872–'73. ill. 12°. $1; pap., 75c. . . . . *Appleton.*
— *See also* Prayer-gauge debate.

Tyndall banquet: proceedings, N. Y., Feb. 4, 1873. 12°. pap., 50c. . . . . *Appleton.*

Tyng, Dudley Atkins. *See* Massachusetts, Supreme Court reports.

Tyng, Ste. Higginson. Forty years' experience in Sunday-schools. 16°. $1 . . . . *Sheldon.*
— Lectures on the law and the Gospel. 12°. '68. $1.75. *Randolph.*
— Lessons on Acts. 24°. 16c. . . . . *Am. S. S.*
— Memoir of Erasmus J. P. Messinger, missionary in Africa. 18°. 70c. . . . . *Am. S. S.*
— Office and duty of a Christian pastor. 12°. $1.25. *Harper.*
— Prayer-book illustrated by Scripture. 8 nos. 24°. ea., bds., 20c. . . . . *Whittaker.*
— *Same.* 1st ser.: Collects. 18°. '68. 25c. . . *Randolph.*
— Spencers (The). 16°. '69. $1.50 . . . . *Am. Tr.*
— Vow assumed: pastor's address to those who have been confirmed. 32°. 30c. . . . . *Whittaker.*
— *Same.* 32°. '64. 20c. . . . . *Randolph.*

Typee. Melville, H. $1.50 . . . . *Harper.*

Types and emblems. Spurgeon, C. H. $1.25. *Sheldon.*

Typhaines Abbey. Gobineau, A. (*Comte*) de. $1.50; $1 . . . . *Claxton.*

Typical forms and special ends in creation. McCosh, J. $2.50 . . . . *Carter.*

Typographical handbook: information and tables for the apprentice, book and job printer, etc. 32°. '75. 50c. . . . . (?) *Machris.*

Tyrant (The), the slave, the victim and the tar: drama. 16°. pap., 15c. . . . . *French.*

Tyre: its rise, glory and desolation; with notices of the Phœnicians generally. ('60.) 3d ed. 18°. '76. 50c. . . . . *So. Meth.*

Tyrolien lyre. White, E. L., *and* Gould, J. E. $1.50. *Ditson.*

Tyrtæus. War songs. *See* Theocritus, Bion *and* Moschus.

Tyrwhitt, R. St. J: Art teaching of the primitive church, with index of subjects. 12°. $3 . . . *Pott.*
— Christian art and symbolism; with introd. by Ruskin. ill. 12°. '73. $2 . . . . *Roberts.*
— Our sketching club: letters and studies on landscape art. ill. 8°. '75. $2.50 . . . . *Roberts.*
— Schooling of life. fp. 8°. '64. $1 . . . . . . *Macmillan.*

Tyson, G: E. Wonderful drift on the ice-floe. *See* Blake, E. V., Arctic experiences.

Tyson, Ja. Cell doctrine: its hist. and present state, with bibliography of the subject. ill. 8°. '70. $2. *Lindsay.*
— Introduction to study of practical histology. 12°. $1; $1.50 . . . . *Lippincott.*
— Practical guide to examination of urine. ill. 12°. '75. $1.50 . . . . *Lindsay.*
— *See also* Pathological Soc. of Phila.

Tyson, Martha E. Brief account of settlement of Ellicott's mills. *See* Maryland Hist. Soc.

Tyson, *Miss* Ma. L. Queen of the kitchen: coll. of "old Maryland" family receipts for cooking. 12°. $1.75 . . . . *Peterson.*

Tyson, Ph. T. *See* Maryland geol. survey.

Tytler, Alex. Fraser. Universal history, to beginning of 18th cent. 2 v. 8°. '74. shp., $4.50 . . *Claxton.*
— Universal history, to 1820. 6 v. 18°. $4.50 . . *Harper.*

Tytler, Ann Fraser. Leila books. 3 v. ill. 16°. ea., $1.25 . . . . *Porter.*
Cont.: Leila; or, the island. — Leila in England. — Leila at home.

Tytler, C. C. Fraser. Jasmine Leigh. cr. 8°. '71. $1.75 . . . . *Routledge.*
— Jonathan. (Leis. hour ser.) 16°. '76. $1.25 . . *Holt.*
— Margaret. ill. 16°. '73. $1.25 . . . . *Dodd.*
— Mistress Judith. (Leis. hour ser.) ('75.) New ed. 16°. '76. $1.25 . . . . *Holt.*

Tytler, Pat. F. Historical view of progress of discovery on northern coast of Am.; with sketches of natural history of No. Am. regions, by J. Wilson. 18°. 75c. .... *Harper.*

Tytler, Sa. (*pseud.*) *See* Keddie, *Miss* H.

Ubique (*pseud.*) *See* Gillmore, Parker.

Ueberweg, F: History of philosophy; tr. by G. S. Morris; with add. by N. Porter, [and] pref. by H. B. Smith and P. Schaff. ('73.) New ed. 2 v. 8°. '76. $5 .... *Scribner.*

Ugly customer. Williams, T. J. 15c. *French; Lee & S.*

Ugly duck. Andersen, H. C. $1 .... *Miller.*

Ugly duckling. [Toy-book.] ill. 4°. $1; 50c. *Routledge.*

Ugly-girl papers. Powers, S. D. $1 .... *Harper.*

Ugly morsel, and other stories. 24°. 25c. *Bost. Am. Tr.*

— *See also* Banner stories.

Ugolono. Booth, J. B. 15c. .... *French.*

Uhland, L: Gedichte. 12°. 75c.; pap., 50c.; hf. mor., $1 .... *F. W. Thomas.*

Uhlan's (The) wife. Fries, R. 50c. .... *Am. Tr.*

Uhlemann, Max. Syriac grammar; tr. by E. Hutchinson; with exercises in Syriac grammar, chrestomathy and brief lexicon. 2d ed., rev. and enl. 8°. $5 .... *Appleton.*

Uhler, P. R. Report on henioptera. *See* United States, *Corps of Eng.*

Ulbricht, Thdr. *See* Baldauf, J., *and* Ulbricht, T.

Ullathorne, W: B. On the immaculate conception of the mother of God. 18°. '55. 60c.; 80c. *Murphy.*

— *Same.* 18°. '69. 75c. .... *Kelly, P. & Co.*

— Reply to Gladstone. 12°. pap., 25c. .... *Cath. Pub.*

Ullioli, Jos. Fz. Einleitung zur Heiligen Schrift. 18°. 15c. .... *Pres. Bd.*

Ulmann, C: Reformers before the reformation; tr. 2 v. 8°. ea., $3 .... *Scribner, W. & A.*

— Sinlessness of Jesus, an evidence of Christianity; tr. cr. 8°. $3 .... *Scribner, W. & A.*

Ulpe, H: Report on coleoptera. *See* United States, *Corps. of Eng.*

Ulrici, Hm. Shakespeare's dramatic art: hist. and character of [his] plays; tr. by L. D. Schmitz. v. 1. 12°. (Bohn.) '76. $1.25 .. *Little, B. & Co.*

— *Same.* v. 1. 12°. (Bohn.) $1.40 .. *Scribner, W. & A.*

— *Same.* v. 1. 12°. (Bohn.) $1.50 ...... *Lippincott.*

— Strauss as a philosophical thinker: review of "Old faith and the new faith," and confutation of its materialistic views; tr. with introd. by C. P. Krauth. 16°. '74. $1 .... *Smith, E. & Co.*

Ultimate generalization: effort in the philosophy of science. 12°. '76. $1 .... *Somerby.*

Ulysses. Burnand, F. C. 15c. .... *French.*

Um Szepter u. Kronen. Meding, G. 2 v. ea., 50c. *Morwitz.*

Um Thron u. Leben. Hiltl, G. 50c. .... *Morwitz.*

Una (*pseud.*) *See* McMullen, *Miss* Ma. A.

Una and her paupers. Higinbotham, J. M. $2. *Randolph; Routledge.*

Unawares. Peard, F. M. $1.50 .... *Roberts.*

Uncivil liberty. Heywood, E. H. 15c. ..... *Mendum.*

Uncivilized races. *See* Wood, J. G.

Unclaimed: story of Eng. life; by an Eng. woman. 12°. $1.25; pap., $1 .... *Loring.*

Uncle Alick's Sabbath-school. Blackburn, W. M. 60c. *Pres. Bd.*

Uncle Alick's ser. *See* Blackburn, W. M.

Uncle Anthony. Cummings, M. J. $1.25 .. *Lothrop.*

Uncle Austin and his nephews. Alexander, J. W. 75c. *Am. S. S.; N. Y. Ref. Ch. Bd.; Pres. Com.*

Uncle Barnaby; or, recollections of his character and opinions. ill. 18°. '56. 85c. .... *Dodd.*

Uncle Barnaby's budget. 10 v. [2 sets.] ill. 18°. '75. $3.50 .... *Nelson.*

Cont.: Kate Lovell's school days. — Satin dress. — Walter Bradley. — Striving for mastery. — Willie Russell's temptation.

Uncle Barney's fortune. May, C. L. 75c. *H. A. Young.*

Uncle Ben (*pseud.*) Mary Staunton; or, the pupils of Marvel Hall. 12°. $1 .... *Appleton.*

Uncle Ben. Adams, W. T. 45c. .... *Lee & S.*

Uncle Ben and Uncle Levi. *See* Todd, J.

Uncle Charles. Gale, N. $1 .... *Cong. Pub.*

Uncle Crotchet. Phillips, A. 15c. .... *French.*

Uncle Dick. *See* Edmond Darley ser.

Uncle Dick's story. *See* Herd boy ser.

Uncle Downe's home. *See* Bradley, W. I.

Uncle Eph's dream. White, C. 15c. .... *De Witt.*

Uncle Frank's boys and girls' lib. *See* Woodworth, F. C.

Uncle George's stories. *See* Tarbox, Increase N.

Uncle Grandesir's matches. Martineau des Chesnez, E. $1.25 .... *Claxton.*

Uncle Hardy (*pseud.*) Notable shipwrecks. cr. 8°. $2 .... *Cassell.*

Uncle Henry's stories. Bullard, A. 25c. .... *Lee & S.*

Uncle Hugh's house. *See* Hildeburn, *Mrs.* M. J.

Uncle Jabez; or, the history of a man whose boyhood was spent in the school of adversity. ('62.) New ed. ill. 18°. '70. 75c. .... *Hoyt.*

— *Same.* 18°. 60c. .... *Am. S. S.*

Uncle Jack: Christmas story. 18°. 25c. .. *Whittaker.*

Uncle Jack, the fault-killer. 18°. 50c. .. *Carter; Dutton.*

— *Same.* ill. post 18°. 75c. .... *Scribner, W. & A.*

Uncle Jeff: Ethiop. drama. 16°. pap., 15c. *French; Happy.*

Uncle Jerry's blossom. *See* Morning glory lib.

Uncle Jesse (*pseud.*) *See* Babb, C. E.

Uncle Joe's lib. for the younger boys and girls. 24 v. 18°. $13 .... *Am. S. S.*

Uncle Joe's story. 16°. $1 .... (?) *Martien.*

Uncle John (*pseud.*) *See* Aikin, J:

Uncle John. ill. 18°. '68. 25c.; pap., 10c. .. *Am. Tr.*

Uncle John. *See* Llewellyn, E. L.

Uncle John. Melville, G. J. W. $1.25 .... *Appleton.*

Uncle John. Orme, M. 60c. .... *Harper.*

Uncle John's adventures and travels. 16°. 50c. *Scribner, W. & A.*

Uncle John's drolleries. ill. 8°. '76. $1 .. (?) *McLoughlin.*

Uncle John's flower gatherers. Fuller, J. G. $1.25. *Dodd.*

Uncle John's own book of moral and instructive stories. ill. cr. 4°. $1.50; $2 .... *J. E. Potter.*

Uncle Josh's trunk full of fun. Dick, W. B. 15c. *Dick & F.*

Uncle Juvinell (*pseud.*) *See* Thayer, W. M.

Uncle Max. *See* Gladstone, *Mrs.* G.

Uncle Max ser. 4 v. 16°. $3 .... *Lothrop.*

Cont.: Uncle Max. — Fanny's Bible text. — Mattie's home. — Helen's victory.

Uncle Paul's stories. Burnham, S., *jr.* $1. *Bost. Am. Tr.*

Uncle Philip (*pseud.*) *See* Hawks, Fs. Lister.

Uncle Reuben and his budget of stories. *See* Theodore Thinker.

Uncle Reuben ser. 6 v. 18°. $2 .... *Bost. Am. Tr.*

Cont.: Crushed flowers. — Little story book. — Old tales newly told. — Patience and her friend. — Uncle Reuben's tales. — White water lily.

Uncle Reuben's tales. ill. 18°. 35c. .... *Bost. Am. Tr.*

Uncle Rip. Peake, R. B. 15c. .... *French.*

Uncle Robert (*pseud.*) Talks about animals. 18°. 90c. .... *Tibbals.*

Uncle Robert: comedy. 16°. pap., 15c. .... *French.*

Uncle Rod's pet. Emery, S. E. 75c. .... *Dutton.*

Uncle Roland and Mary. Waterbury, J. B. 40c. *Cong. Pub.*
Uncle Silas. Le Fanu, J. S. 75c. .... *Harper.*
Uncle Solomon (*ed.*) Mother Goose's melodies. 16°. pap., 15c. .... *Happy.*
Uncle Toby: drama. 16°. pap., 15c. .... *French.*
Uncle Toby's table talks and reflections; by an attorney at law. 16°. $1.25 .... *Cin. Meth. Bk. Conc.*
Uncle Tom: Ethiop. drama. 16°. pap., 15c. .. *Happy.*
Uncle Tom's cabin. Aiken, G. L. 15c. ...... *French.*
Uncle Tom's cabin. Stowe, H. B. $2 ...... *Osgood.*
Uncle too many. Thomson, J. 15c. .... *French.*
Uncle Walter (*pseud.*) *See* Sleeper, Wa. T.
Uncle William (*pseud.*) Kind words for his young friends. ill. 18°. 40c. .... *Pres. Bd.*
Uncle Willis (*pseud.*) *See* Tilton, S. W.
Uncle Zachary. Oxenford, J. 15c. .... *French.*
Uncle's will. Smith, S. T. 15c. .... *De Witt.*
Uncommercial traveller. *See* Dickens, C:
Unconditional perseverance. Browning, J. W. 60c. *So. Meth.*
Unconscious truth of the four Gospels. Furness, W. H. $1.25 .... *Lippincott.*
Uncrowned kings. Wise, D. $1.25. *Cin. Meth. Bk. Conc.*
Under the apple tree. 18°. 17c.; 22c. .... *Am. Bapt.*
Under the ban. Deléon, *Abbé.* $1.75; $1.25 .. *Harper.*
Under the cedars. Hatch, A. J. $1.50 ...... *Lee & S.*
Under the cross. Peirce, B. K. $4.25 .... *Hoyt.*
Under the earth. Hoffmann, F. 70c. .. (?) *Luth. Pub.*
Under the evergreens. Lorimer, G. C. $1.50. (?) *Shepard.*
Under the fir trees. 16°. $1 .... (?) *Martien.*
Under foot. Clyde, A. 50c. .... *Harper.*
Under the gaslight. Daly, A. 15c. .... *French.*
Under green leaves: book of rural poems. ill. 16°. pap., 30c. .... *Huntington.*
— *See also* Cottage lib.
Under the greenwood tree. Hardy, T. $1.25 .. *Holt.*
Under grey walls. Doudney, S. $1 .... *Nelson.*
Under his banner. Parker, J. M. 90c. ...... *Dutton.*
Under the holly. Hosmer, M., *and* Dunlap, J. $1.25. *Porter.*
Under de kerosene: Ethiop. drama. 16°. pap., 15c. *Happy.*
Under the lime trees; or, grand-mama's stories at Hurst Farm; by author of "Brother Bertie." ill. 12°. $2 .... *Appleton.*
Under the limes. Archer, E. M. $1.75 .. *Macmillan.*
Under lock and key. Speight, T. W. $1.75. *Lippincott.*
Under the microscope. ill. 16°. 75c. .... *Nelson.*
Under the mizzen mast. Adams, N. $1.50 .... *Hoyt.*
Under the oak. Breed, W. P. 75c. .... *Pres. Bd.*
Under the pear tree. Baker, S. 60c. .... *Randolph.*
Under the red dragon. Grant, J. 80c. .... *Routledge.*
Under the rose. Roberts, G. 15c. .... *French.*
Under the sky-light. Sanford, D. P. 50c. ... *Dutton.*
Under the southern cross: tale of the new world; by author of "Spanish brothers." 8°. $2 .. *Nelson.*
Under the spell. Robinson, F. W. 50c. ..... *De Witt.*
Under the storks' nest. Katsch, A. E. $1.25. *Lippincott.*
Under the surface. Connelly, E. M. $1.50 .. *Lippincott.*
Under the trees. Prime, S. I. $2 .... *Harper.*
Under two flags. La Rame, L. de. $1.50 .. *Lippincott.*
Under the vine and under the snow. *See* Maple grove stories.
Under the willow-tree. *See* Andersen, H. C.
Under the willows. Lowell, J. R. $2; $3.50; $4.50. *Osgood.*
Under the wings; or, happy Frank. 18°. 35c. .. *Am. S. S.*
Under the yoke. Wright, J. McN. 90c. .... *West. Tr.*
Undercurrents of Wall St. Kimball, R. B. $1.75. *Carleton.*
Underground. Knox, T. W. *$3.50; $4; $5 .. *Burr.*
Underhill, D. C. Arithmetical primer: tables of arithmetic made easier. New ed., enl. 18°. '75. pap., 4c.; bds., 8c. .... *Collins & Bro.*
Undertones. Buchanan, R. $1.75 .... *Routledge.*
Underwood, Almon. Millennial experience; or, the will of God known and done from moment to moment. ('60.) New ed. 16°. '75. $1.50 .. *Hoyt.*
— Sealing of the Spirit. 18°. '66. 25c. .... *Hoyt.*
Underwood, B. F. Influence of Christianity on civilization. 12°. 25c. .... *Somerby.*
— *See also* Burgess, O. A., *and* Underwood, B. F.
Underwood, Fs. H. Cloud pictures. 16°. $1.50. *Lee & S.*
— Handbook of Eng. literature: Brit. and Am. authors. 2 v. cr. 8°. ea., $2.50; hf. mor., $4.50; mor., $6 .... *Lee & S.*
— Lord of himself. [Fiction.] 12°. $1.75 .... *Lee & S.*
Underwood, Ruf. S. Overcoming. 32°. 20c. .. *Palmer.*
Underwood, W: H. *See* Illinois, Statutes.
Undeveloped west. Beadle, J. H. *$3.75 .. *Nat. Pub.*
Undine. *See* La Motte Fouqué, F. H. K.
Undine. Soane, J. 15c. .... *French.*
Undivine comedy. Krasinski, *Count* Z. N. $2.25. *Lippincott.*
Unendliche Gruss (Der). Stolz, A. 25c. .. *Benziger.*
Unequal match: comedy. 16°. pap., 15c. .... *French.*
Unequal yoke. 18°. 90c. .... *Am. Bapt.*
Unexpected conversions. 24°. 35c.; 45c. ... *Am. S. S.*
Unexpected pleasures. *See* Juvenile classic ser.
Unfinished gentleman. Selby, C. 15c. .... *French.*
Unfortunate maid; or, the miser's fate. 8°. pap., 25c. .... *De Witt.*
Unfortunate Miss Bailey. A'Beckett, G. A. 15c. *French.*
Ungern Sternberg, A. (*Freiherr*) v. The Breughel brothers: an art romance, from the Germ. by G. H. Lodge. ill. 4°. '72. $2 .... *Osgood.*
Ungewitter, Fs. H. Home cyclopedia: manual of European geography and history. 12°. '54. shp., $3 .... *Barnes.*
Ungrateful boy. 18°. 18c. .... *Am. S. S.*
Ungrateful child. *See* Story of William Tyndal.
Ungrateful negro. *See* Edgeworth, *Miss* M.
Unhappy pair: Ethiop. drama. 16°. pap., 15c. .. *Ames.*
Unheimlicher Mann (Ein). *See* Willkomm, E.
Unica. 18°. 35c. .... *Carter; Dutton.*
Unica: story for Sunday. 16°. 50c. .. *Scribner, W. & A.*
Union (The). Cook, T. J. 80c. .... *Huntington.*
Union Bible dictionary; for schools, Bible classes and families. 16°. shp., $2; hf. mor., $2.50; — with maps. 16°. $1.50 .... *Am. S. S.*
Union chant book. Archibald, G. D. 60c.; 50c. *Wilstach.*
Union glee book. Baker, B. F. 85c. .... *Gordon.*
Union hymns. *See* New.
Union or unity. Jarvis, S. F. 10c. ...... *Claremont.*
Union Pacific Railway: 12 views with letter-press. obl. 24°. 75c. .... *Nelson.*
Union prayer book. 12°. '71. $2.50; $4.50; $6.50. *Barnes.*
Union prayer meeting hymns. 32°. 20c.; bds., 15c.; pap., 10c. — New ed. 18°. 50c. ...... *Am. S. S.*
— *Same;* [also] Prayer meeting tune book. 16°. 75c. *Am. S. S.*

Union questions; for Bible classes. 8 v. 24°. ea., 16c. . . . . *Am. S. S.*
— *See also* Teacher's assistant.

Union ser. 4 v. ill. 16°. ea., 75c. . . . . *Fuller.*
Cont.: Boy inventor, by T. Bulfinch. — Alice's dream, by Mrs. Whitaker. — Flowers that never fade. — Pictures and flowers for child lovers, by Mrs. Thurston.

Union speller. 18°. per doz., $1.80 . . . . . . *Meth. Epis.*
— *Same.* 18°. per doz., $2 . . . . *N. Y. Ref. Ch. Bd.*

Union spelling book. 12°. 15c. . . . . *Am. S. S.*

Union star. Baker, B. F., *and* Perkins, W. O. 85c. *Ditson.*

Union temperance song book. 12°. pap., 25c. . . *Ditson.*

United Brethren. Brethren's almanacs, 1873–'76. 4 v. 8°. ea., pap., 10c. . . . . *Brumbaugh.*
— Hymns; arranged for communion service. 32°. 35c. *Clauder.*
— *See also* Moravians.

United Presbyterian Church. Book of discipline; [from Confession of faith]. 16°. 20c.; hf. bd., 25c. *U. P. Bd. of Pub.*
— Confession of faith; cont. Confession, Catechisms and testimony, Discipline, etc. 16°. $1; $2.25; — abridg., 60c. . . . . *U. P. Bd. of Pub.*
— Testimony; [from Confession of faith]. 16°. per doz., pap., $1.20 . . . . *U. P. Bd. of Pub.*
— *See also* Presbyterian Church.

United States.

Note. — The following entries include reports of the U. S. Courts, digests, laws, Acts of Congress, etc., the publication of which is not directly authorized by the government, although it is bibliographically regarded as their author. Below will be found the more important works issued by the various departments of the general government. For Smithsonian publications *see* Smithsonian Institution.

— Admiralty decisions. *See below* District Court reports.
— American chancery digest. *See* Waterman, T. W.
— American reports. *See* Thompson, J. G.
— Annotated internal revenue laws; with decisions of the courts, rulings, etc., by O. F. Bump. 8°. shp., $5 . . . . *Baker, V. & Co.*
— Argument at Geneva: discussions on part of U. S. and Gt. Brit. before tribunal of arbitration under treaty of Washington. 8°. $3.50 . . . . *Appleton.*
— Bankrupt law as cont. in the revised statutes; with amendments. 8°. pap., 75c. . . . . *Baker, V. & Co.*
— *Same;* with rules, forms and notes; [also] acts of 1800 and 1841; by F. C. Brightly. 8°. $3 . . *Kay.*
— — Amendments. 8°. pap., 25c. . . . . *Campbell & Co.*
— — *See also* James, E.; — National bankruptcy register reports; — *and below* Federal; New.
— Cases in prize in Circuit and District Courts for south. dist. of N. Y., decided by Justice Nelson and Judge Betts, 1861–'65; by S. Blatchford. 8°. shp., $7.50 . . . . *Baker, V. & Co.*
— Circuit Court reports for 1st circuit, 1812–'15; by J. Gallison. ('15–'17.) 2d ed., with add. notes and ref. 2 v. 8°. '44 . . . . [*Boston.*]
— *Same.* 1816–'67. 15 v. 8°. ea., shp., $6 . . *Little, B. & Co.*
Cont.: 1816–'30, by W. P. Mason, v. 2–5. — 1830–'39, by C. Sumner, 3 v. — 1839–'45, by W. W. Story, v. 1. — 1845–'47, by C. L. Woodbury and G. L. Minot, 3 v. — 1851–'56, by B. R. Curtis, 2 v. — 1858–'67, by N. Clifford, 2 v.
Note. v. 1 of Mason and v. 2, 3 of Story are o. p.
— Circuit Court reports for 2d circuit, 1810–'40; by E. Paine, jr. 2 v. 8°. '27–'56 . . . . . . [*New York.*]
— *Same.* 1845–'75; by S. Blatchford. 12 v. 8°. ea., shp., $7.50; per set, $78 . . . . *Baker, V. & Co.*
— Circuit Court reports for 3d circuit, 1801; by J. B. Wallace. 8°. '71. shp., $7.50 . . . . *Callaghan.*
— *Same.* 1803–'18; by R. Peters. 8°. '19 . . . [*Phila.*]
— *Same.* 1803–'27; by B. Washington. ('26–'29.) 2d ed. 4 v. 8°. '52–'53 . . . . [*Phila.*]
— *Same.* 1828–'33; by H. Baldwin. 8°. shp., $7.50 . . *Kay.*
— *Same.* 1842–'49; by J. W. Wallace. 8°. '49 . . [*Phila.*]
— *Same.* 1850–'62; by J. W. Wallace. v. 2, 3. 8°. ea., $7.50 . . . . *T. & J. W. Johnson.*
— — *See also below* Reports.

United States, *continued.*
— Circuit Court reports for 4th circuit, 1793–1825; by D. Call. 6 v. 8°. '24–'33. shp., $60 . . *J. W. Randolph*
Note. In Virginia Court of Appeals reports, 1793-1825.
— *Same.* 1802–'33; by J. W. Brockenbrough and J. Marshall. 2 v. 8°. '37. shp., $25 . . *J. W. Randolph*
— *Same.* 1836–'61 (decisions of R. B. Taney); by J. M. Campbell. 8°. shp., $7.50 . . . . *Kay.*
— *Same.* 1865–'69 (decisions of S. P. Chase); by B. T. Johnson. 8°. '76. shp., $7.50 . . . *Ward & P.*
— Circuit Court reports for 5th circuit, 1870–'75; by W. B. Woods. v. 1. 8°. '75. shp., $7.50 . . *Callaghan*
— Circuit Court reports for 6th circuit. *See below* Circuit and Dist. Court reports (Bond).
— Circuit Court reports for (old) 7th circuit, 1829–'55; by J. McLean. 6 v. 8°. shp., $39 . . . . *Clarke.*
— Circuit Court reports for (new) 7th circuit. *See below* Circuit and Dist. Court reports (Bissell).
— Circuit Court reports for 8th circuit, 1863–'69 (decisions by S. F. Miller); by J. M. Woolworth. 8°. '70. shp., $7.50 . . . . *Callaghan.*
— *Same.* 1870–'73; by J. F. Dillon. 2 v. 8°. shp., $15 . . . . *Callaghan.*
— *Same.* 1870–'76; by J. F. Dillon. 3 v. 8°. ea., shp., $7.50 . . . . *Day.*
— Circuit court reports for 9th circuit, 1855–'59; by C. McAllister. 8°. shp., $10 . . . . . . *Baker, V. & Co.*
— — *See also below* Circuit and Dist. Court reports (Deady; Sawyer).
— Circuit Court reports for Dist. of Columbia, 1801–'41; by W. Cranch. 6 v. 8°. '52–'53 . . [*Boston.*]
— Circuit Court rules for south. dist. of N. Y., 1838–'72; coll. by S. Blatchford. 8°. pap., 75c. *Baker, V. & Co.*
— — *See also* Chicago; — *and below* Federal; Rules.
— Circuit and District Court reports, 1863–'71; by B. V. Abbott. ('70.) 2d ed. 2 v. roy. 8°. '75. shp., $15 . . . . *Ward & P.*
— Circuit and District Court reports for 6th circuit, 1855–'71 (decisions of H. H. Leavitt); by L. H. Bond. 2 v. 8°. '72. shp., $14 . . . . *Clarke.*
— Circuit and District Court reports for 7th circuit; by J. H. Bissell. 5 v. 8°. '73–'76. shp., $37.50. *Callaghan.*
— Circuit and District Court reports for 9th circuit, 1859–'69; by M. P. Deady. 8°. '72. shp., $8. *Bancroft.*
— *Same.* 1870–'74; by L. S. B. Sawyer. 2 v. 8°. shp., $15 . . . . *Bancroft.*
— Congress: abridgment of debates of 43d Congress, 2d session; incl. President's messages and proclamations, treaties and list of reports of committees. 8°. '75. $5; shp., $6.50; hf. mor., $7.50. *Holt.*
— — *See also* Benton, T. H.; — Abbott, B. V.
— Constitution; with notes, ref., etc., and index, by E. O. Hinkley. 8°. '53. 75c.; pap., 50c. . . *Murphy.*
— *Same;* with concordance, index and questions by C. W. Stearns. (College ed.) 12°. '72. $1. — (Lib. ed.) 8°. '72. $1.50 . . . . *Mason.*
— — *See also* American constitution; — American text book; — Anderson, J. J.; — Andrews, I. W.; — Burleigh, J. B.; — Constitutions of the several states; — Charters; — Hart, J. S.; — Holmes, G. F.; — *and below* Declaration of independence.
— *Same;* [also] Declaration of independence. 32°. 20c. *Thompson.*
— *Germ.;* nebst Erläutgn. u. Einleitg., bearb. v. J. Hein. 3d ed. 16°. 50c.; bds., 35c. . . . *Morwitz.*
— Court of Claims reports, 1855–'56; by J. C. Devereux. 8°. '56 . . . . [*Washington.*]
— *Same.* 1863–'75. 10 v. 8°. shp., $50 . . *Morrison.*
Cont.: 1-8 (1863-'72), by C. C. Nott and H. Huntington. — 9-10 (1873-'75), by C. C. Nott and A. Hopkins.
— — Digest. *See* Nott, C. C., and Hopkins, A.
— Declaration of independence; [also] Articles of Confederation; [also] Constitution and amendments with index; [also] Washington's Farewell address, Sept. 7, 1796. 8°. '67. pap., 25c. *Clark.*

United States, *continued.*
— — *See also* American text book; — Anderson, J. J.; — Charter; — Constitutions of the several states; — Holmes, G. F.; — *and above* Constitution.
— Digest of criminal decisions. *See* Hanes, J. L.
— Digest of decisions and laws. *See* Brightly, F. C.
— Digest of decisions of courts of common law and admiralty, 1785–1870. 29 v. 8°......[*Boston.*]
Cont.: 1-5 (1785-1846), by T. Metcalf, J. C. Perkins and G. T. Curtis. — 6 (1785-1846), by G. P. Sanger. — 7-15 ('47-'55), by J. P. Putnam. — 16-18 ('56-'58), by G. S. Hale. — 19 ('59), by G. S. Hale and H. F. Smith. — 20-24 ('60-'64), by H. F. Smith. — 25-27 ('65-'67), by H. W. Frost. — 28, 29 ('68-'69), by B. F. Burnham.
— Digest of decisions upon bounty laws. *See* Rapp, S. A.
— Digest of laws. *See* Brightly, F. C.; — Dunlop, J.
— Digest of military laws. *See* Poland, J. S.
— Digest of reports and acts of Cong. *See* Abbott, B. V.
— Digest of statutes relating to revenue, commerce, etc. *See* Heyl, L.
— District and Circuit Court admiralty reports for western lake and river districts, 1857–'75; by H. B. Brown. 8°. '76. shp., $7.50..*Baker, V. & Co.*
— District and Circuit Court reports for the district of Massachusetts, 1865–'71; by J. Lowell. 8°. '72. shp., $6 ....*Little, B. & Co.*
— District Court reports [of land cases] for north. dist. of California, 1835–'58 (determined by O. Hoffman); by N. Hubert. 8°. shp., $7.50..*S. Whitney.*
— District Court reports for dist. of Maine, v. 1 (1822–'39); by A. Ware. 2d ed., rev. 8°. '56. shp., $6 ....*Little, B. & Co.*
— *Same.* v. 2 [of Ware's decisions] (1839–'49); by E. H. Daveis. 8°. '73. shp., $6....*Loring, S. & H.*
— *Same.* v. 3 [of Ware's decisions] (1853–'66); by G. F. Emery. 8°. '74. shp., $6..*Loring, S. & H.*
— District Court reports (admiralty and maritime cases) for dist. of Mass., 1841–'64; by P. Sprague. v. 2. 8°. '68. shp., $5 ....*Little, B. & Co.*
Note. v. 1 is o. p.
— District Court reports (of admiralty cases) for dist. of Mich., north. and south. dist. of Ohio, west. dist. of Penn., west. dist. of Ill., dist. of Mo. and east. dist. of La., 1842–'57; by J. S. Newberry. 8°. '57. ....[*New York.*]
— District Court reports in 2d circuit (N.Y.), 1865–'72; by R. D. Benedict. 7 v. 8°. ea., shp., $9; per set, $56 ....*Baker, V. & Co.*
— District Court reports (of admiralty cases) for south. dist. of N. Y.; by B. V. and A. Abbott. 8°. '57. shp., $6.........................*Little, B. & Co.*
— District Court reports (admiralty cases decided by Judge Betts) for south. dist. of N. Y., 1827–'47; by S. Blatchford, F. Howland and E. R. Olcott. 2 v. 8°. shp., $15 ....*Baker, V. & Co.*
— District Court reports (of prize cases) for N. Y. dist., 1814; by W. P. Van Ness. 8°. '14..[*New York.*]
— District Court reports (of admiralty decisions) for dist. of Penna., 1792–1807; by R. Peters. 2 v. 8°. 1807 ....[*Phila.*]
— *Same.* 1828–'36; by H. D. Gilpin. 8°. '38...[*Phila.*]
— *Same.* 1836–'46; by W. H. Crabbe. 8°. $6.50. *T. & J. W. Johnson.*
— — *See also below* Judgments.
— District Court reports for dist. of So. Carolina, 1792–1805; by T. Bee. 8°. 1810...........[*Phila.*]
— District Court reports for dist. of Vermont.
Note. Included in Vermont Sup. Court reports (v. 20-25).
— District Court rules for south. dist. of N. Y., 1838–'75; coll. and arr. by S. Blatchford. 8°. pap., $1..................................*Baker, V. & Co.*
— — *See also* Chicago; — *and below* Federal; Rules.
— Duties on imports. *See* Heyl, L.; — Morgan, S. T.
— Federal Court rules for Michigan; compr. District and Circuit Court, bankruptcy and admiralty courts. 8°. '73. shp., $3...........*Richmond.*
— Judgments in admiralty of Pennsylvania 1779–'88; by F. Hopkinson. 8°. 1792...........[*Phila.*]

United States, *continued.*
— Laws relating to navy and marine corps, 1776–1865; [with] U. S. Constitution, etc. 8°. '66. shp., $6. *Murphy.*
— Loan acts of Congress relating to national debt and government currency, 1842–1875. 8°. '76. $1.75. *Homans.*
— Messages of the presidents from [Washington] to [Harrison]; [with] Articles of Confederation and Constitution. 8°. '41. shp., $1.25..*I. N. Whiting.*
— Mining acts of July 26, 1866, July 9, 1870, and May 10, 1872; with decisions and forms by H. N. Copp. 8°. '74. shp., $4.50..........*Bancroft.*
— National bank act; with amendments and supplementary acts to 1875 [and] decisions of U. S. Supreme Court and state courts, etc. 8°. '75. $2..*Homans.*
— New rules and orders in bankruptcy, as framed and promulgated by the Supreme Court. 8°. '75. pap., 25c............*Campbell & Co.; Morrison.*
— — *See also above* Bankrupt law.
— Patent and copyright laws. *See* Law, S. D.
— Patent cases. *See* Fisher, S. S.; — Fisher, W. H.; — Whitman, C. S.
— Patent laws. *See* Simonds, W: E.
— Public land laws; with instructions on decisions, practice and forms by J. C. Zabriskie. 8°. '70. shp., $7.50 ....*Bancroft.*
— Reports. *See* American Law Times reports; — Pittsburg reports.
— — Digest. *See* Abbott, B. V.
— Reports of cases in Supreme and Circuit Courts, 1790–1800, and in courts of Penn. before and since the revolution; by A. J. Dallas. 4 v. 8°. $25 ....*T. & J. W. Johnson.*
— Revised statutes, 1873–4, as revised and consolidated by commissioners appointed under act of Congress. 8°. '75. $3.71.....................*Hurd & H.*
— *Same.* roy. 8°. $3.95..................*Morrison.*
— — *See also below* Statutes.
— — Index. *See* Lyman, D.
— Revised statutes rel. to mineral lands, etc. *See* Skidmore, W. A.
— Revised statutes rel. to public lands; with instructions, forms, index, etc. 8°. $1.50..*S. Whitney.*
— Rules of practice of the courts for northern dist. of Ohio. *See* Bill, E.
— Rules of Supreme Court, and for Circuit and District Courts in equity and admiralty cases, etc. 8°. '75. hf. bd., $1.50; pap., $1 ....*Morrison.*
— Secret proceedings and debates of Conv. of 1787, convened for forming Const. of the U. S., incl. the "general information" laid before the legislature of Md. by L. Martin; [with] other documents rel. to the federal compact of the No. Am. union. 12°. mor., $1.25 ....*U. P. James.*
— Stamp duties; with rulings and decisions of the departments and courts. 8°. $1.25; pap., 75c. *Baker, V. & Co.*
— Statutes at large, 1789–1873; ed. by G. P. Sanger, with index. 18 v. roy. 8°. shp., $72..*Little, B. & Co.*
Cont.: v. 1-5. Public statutes at large (1789-1845). — 6. Private statutes (1789-1845). — 7. Treaties with the Indian tribes (1778-1842). — 8. Treaties with foreign powers, with gen. index to v. 1-8 (1778-1845). — 9-17. Public statutes at large (1845-'73). — 18. Index to v. 1-10 (1789-1851).
— — *See also above* Revised statutes.
— Statutes passed at 1st session of 43d Congress, 1873–'74; with recent treaties, postal conventions and exec. proclamations. roy. 8°. $2..*Morrison.*
— Supreme Court reports, 1800–'15; by W. Cranch. 9 v. in 8. 8°. $30............*T. & J. W. Johnson.*
— *Same.* 1816–'27; by H. Wheaton. 12 v. 8°. '21–'29. [*New York.*]
— *Same.* 1790–1827; condensed with notes by R. Peters. 6 v. 8°. '30–'34..............[*Phila.*]
Note. Include Dallas, Cranch and Wheaton.
— *Same.* 1827–'42; by R. Peters. 16 v. 8°...[*Phila.*]
— *Same.* 1843–'57; by B. C. Howard. 17 v. 8°. [*Phila.*]

United States, *continued.*
— *Same.* 1857; by B. C. Howard. 8°. '66. shp., $5. *Little, B. & Co.*
— *Same.* 1858–'60; by B. C. Howard. 6 v. 8°. ea., shp., $5 .... *Morrison.*
— *Same.* 1860–'63; by J. S. Black. 2 v. 8°. ea., shp., $5 .... *Morrison.*
— *Same.* 1863–'75; by J. W. Wallace. 23 v. 8°. ea., shp., $5 .... *Morrison.*
— *Same.* 1875–6; by W. T. Otto. 3 v. 8°. ea., shp., $5 .... *Little, B. & Co.*
— *Same.* 1781–1854; with notes and digest by B. R. Curtis. 5th ed. 22 v. 8°. '70. shp., $88. *Little, B. & Co.*
— *Same.* 1854–'62 (18 Howard to 2 Black); by S. F. Miller. 4 v. 8°. ea., shp., $5 .... *Morrison.*
— — *See also above* Reports.
— — Digest. *See* Curtis, B. R.; — Paschal, G. W.; — Wheaton, H.
— — Rules. *See above* Rules.
— Tariff and internal revenue law, 1872; with alphab. table of the U. S. tariff, table of internal taxes, analyt. index and notes; comp. by H. E. Dresser. 8°. $1; pap., 50c. .... *Harper.*
— *See also* International exhibition; — Opinions of attorneys general.

United States. [**Government Publications.**]
— *Bureau of Medicine and Surgery.* (*Navy Dept.*) Medical essays; comp., from reports by officers of the navy, by A. L. Gihan. 8°. '72. .. *U. S. Govt.*
— — Naval hygiene; by J. Wilson. 8°. '70. *U. S. Govt.*
— *Bureau of Navigation.* Almanac for navigators from "American ephemeris and nautical almanac," 1869–'73. 4 v. 8°. '71–'76 .. *U. S. Govt.*
— — American ephemeris and nautical almanac, 1855–'79. 25 v. 8°. '52–'76 .... *U. S. Govt.*
— — International code of signals. 8°. '73 ... *U. S. Govt.*
— *Coast Survey.* Pacific coast: Coast pilot of Cal., Oregon and Wash. ter.; by G. Davidson. roy. 8°. '69 .... *U. S. Govt.*
— — *Same:* Coast pilot of Alaska (pt. 1) from south. boundary to Cook's Inlet; by G. Davidson. roy. 8°. '69 .... *U. S. Govt.*
— — Plane table (The): its uses in topog. surveying. ill. 8°. '69. $2 .... *Van Nostrand.*
— — Reports of sup't showing progress of survey, 1833–'75. 43 v. [1 v., 8°. and 42 v., 4°.] '34–'76. *U. S. Govt.*
— *Commission of Fish and Fisheries.* Report, 1872–'73, with sup. papers. 8°. '74 .... *U. S. Govt.*
— — *Same.* pt. 3, 1873–4, '75–6. 8°. '76 ... *U. S. Govt.*
— *Corps of Engineers.* Exploration and survey of valley of Great Salt Lake of Utah, etc.; by H. Stansbury. 8°. '52 .... *U. S. Govt.*
— — Geological report of exam., 1834, of elevated country between Missouri and Red Rivers; by G. W. Featherstonhaugh. 8°. '35 .... *U. S. Govt.*
— — Papers on practical engineering. 20 v. 8°. and 4°. '41–'63 .... *U. S. Govt.*

Cont.: 1. Bitumen, its varieties, properties and uses, by H. W. Halleck. — 2. Special report on sea wall for preservation of Ramhead, Mass., by S. Thayer. — 3. Sustaining walls, from a memoir of J. V. Poncelet. — 4. Reports upon physics and hydraulics of Mississippi River, by A. A. Humphreys and H. L. Abbot. — 5. Analytical investigation of resistance of piles, by I. L. Mason. — 6. Report of Gen. J. G. Totten on firing with heavy ordnance. — 7. Treatise on various elements of stability in the well-proportioned arch, by D. P. Woodbury. — 8. Official report of siege of Fort Pulaski, by Gen. Q. A. Gillmore. — 9. Practical treatise on limes, by Q. A. Gillmore. — 12. Tables and formulæ [for] surveying, geodesy, etc., by T. J. Lee. — 13. (Reprint of 4.) — 14. Siege artillery in campaign against Richmond, by H. L. Abbot. — 15. (Appendix.) Practical tables in meteorology and hypsometry, by R. S. Williamson. — 17. Report on certain experimental and theoretical investigations, etc., by W. R. King. — 18. Report on the geolog. exploration of 40th parallel, by C. King; v. 3. Mining industry, by J. D. Hague, 2 v.; v. 5. Botany, by S. Watson, D. C. Eaton and others. — 19. Report on béton aggloméré or coignet-béton, by Q. A. Gillmore. — 20. Report on defenses of Washington, by J. G. Barnard. — 21. Report on fabrication of iron for defensive purposes, etc., by J. G. Barnard, H. G. Wright and P. S. Michie. — 22. Report on North Sea Canal of Holland, etc., by J. G. Barnard.

United States, *continued.*
— — Preliminary report upon a reconnoissance through south. and s. west. Nevada, 1869, by G. M. Wheeler [and] D. W. Lockwood. 4°. '75 .... *U. S. Govt.*
— — Report of an expedition down the Yuni and Colorado Rivers; by L. Sitgreaves. 8°. '53. *U. S. Govt.*
— — Report of explorations across great basin of Utah, etc. 4°. '76 .... *U. S. Govt.*
— — Report of exploring expedition from Sante Fé, New Mex., to junction of Grand and Green Rivers of the Great Colorado, 1859, with geol. report by J. S. Newberry. pl. 4°. '76 .... *U. S. Govt.*
— — Report of geol. explorations of 40th parallel; by Clarence King. v. 3, 5, 6. pl. and maps. 4°. and f°. '70–'76 .... *U. S. Govt.*

Cont.: 3. Mining industry, with atlas, by J. D. Hague. — 5. Botany, by S. Watson, D. C. Eaton and others. — 6. Microscopical petrography.

Note. v. 1, 2, 4, not yet pub.

— — Report of geol. reconnoissance, 1835, by way of Green Bay and Wisconsin to the Coteau de Prairie; by G. W. Featherstonhaugh. 8°. '36 .. *U. S. Govt.*
— — Report of a reconnoissance from Carroll, Montana, to Yellowstone Park, 1875. 4°. '76 .. *U. S. Govt.*
— — Report of a reconnoissance of the basin of the Upper Yellowstone in 1871; by J. W. Barlow, and D. P. Heop. 8°. '72 .... *U. S. Govt.*
— — Report of a reconnoissance of the Black Hills of Dakota, 1874, by W. Ludlow. 4°. '75 .. *U. S. Govt.*
— — Report of a reconnoissance of the Missouri River in 1872; by T. P. Roberts. 8°. '75 .. *U. S. Govt.*
— — Report of a reconnoissance of the Yukon River, Alaska, July–Sept., 1869; by C. W. Raymond. 8°. '71 .... *U. S. Govt.*
— — Report on construction of a milit. road from Fort Walla-Walla to Fort Benton; by J. Mullan. 8°. '63 .... *U. S. Govt.*
— — Report on explor. of the Yellowstone River, by W. F. Raynolds; with geol. report of explor. of Yellowstone and Missouri Rivers, by F. V. Hayden, 1859–'60. 8°. '68–'69 .... *U. S. Govt.*
— — Report to ill. map of hydrog. basin of Upper Missouri River; by J. N. Nicollet. 8°. '45 .. *U. S. Govt.*
— — Report upon geog. and geol. explor. and surveys west of 100th meridian. v. 3, 5. 4°. '75 .. *U. S. Govt.*

Cont.: 3. Report on geol. of portions of Nev., Utah, Cal., Ariz. and New Mex., by G. K. Gilbert; Report on geol. of portions of Utah, Nev. and Ariz., by E. E. Howell; Report upon mineral., etc., conditions, by O. Loew; Report on geol. of route from St. George, Utah, to Gila River, by A. R. Marvine; Report on geol. of a portion of Colorado, by J. J. Stevenson; Report upon henioptera, by P. R. Uhler. — 5. Report upon fishes, by H. C. Yarrow; Synopsis of the reptiles and batrachians of Ariz., by E. Coues; Report upon mammals, by E. Coues and H. C. Yarrow; Report upon hynioptera, by E. T. Cressou; Report upon neuroptera, by H. A. Hagen; Report upon the ornithol. collections, by H. W. Henshaw; Report upon diurnal lepidoptera, by F. L. Mead; Report upon diptera, by C. R. Osten-Sacken; Report upon zygænidæ and lambycidæ, by R. H. Stretch; Report upon orthoptera, by C. Thomas; Report upon coleoptera, by H. Ulpe; Report upon fresh water leeches, by A. E. Verrill; Notes upon geog. distrib. with regard to zool. of west. U. S., by H. C. Yarrow; Report upon batrachians and reptiles, [and] on terrestrial and fluviatile mollusca, by H. C. Yarrow.

— — Report upon reconnoissance of n. west. Wyoming, incl. Yellowstone National Park, etc.; by W. A. Jones. 8°. '75 .... *U. S. Govt.*
— Expedition to the China seas, etc. *See* Hawks, F. L.
— Exploring expedition. *See* Wilkes, C:
— *Geographical and geological survey of the territories,* F. V. Hayden in charge. Reports 1–8. 8°. '67–'76 .... *U. S. Govt.*
— — Exploration of the Colorado River of the west and its tributaries, 1869–'72; by J. W. Powell. 4°. '75. *U. S. Govt.*
— — — *See also* Ives, J. C.
— — Miscellaneous publications. nos. 1–6. 8°. '73–'75 .... *U. S. Govt.*

Cont.: 1. Lists of elevations in U. S. west of Mississippi River, collated by H. Gannett. — 2. Meteorological obs., 1872, in Utah, Idaho and Montana, by H. Gannett. — 3. Birds of the northwest, by E. Coues. — 4. Synopsis of flora of Colorado, by T. C. Porter and J. M. Coulter. — 5. Descript. cat. of photographs of survey of territories, '69–'73, by W. H. Jackson; *Same,* '69–'75, by W. H.

United States, *continued.*
Jackson. — 6. Meteorolog. obs., 1873–4, in Colorado and Montana, [ed.] by G. B. Chittenden.

— — Report of survey of the ter. 2 v. 8°. '73. *U.S. Govt.*
Cont.: v. 1, pt. 1. Contributions to extinct vertebrate fauna of the west. territories, by J. Leidy. — v. 5, pt, 1. Synopsis of the acoididae of No. Am., by C. Thomas.

— — Report on geol. of east. portion of the Uinta Mts.; with atlas by J. W. Powell. 4°. '76.. *U.S. Govt.*

— *Geological Survey of the Territories*, F. V. Hayden in charge. Monograph of geometrical moths or phalænidæ of U. S.; by A. S. Packard, jr. 4°. '76. *U.S. Govt.*

— Report on invertebrate, cretaceous and tertiary fossils of the upper Missouri country; by F. B. Meek. 4°. '76 .... *U.S. Govt.*

— — Vertebrata of the cretaceous formations of the west; by E. D. Cope. 4°. '75 .... *U.S. Govt.*

— *Hydrographic Office.* Sailing directions for the English Channel, pt. 1: south coast of Eng. (no. 34.) 8°. '72 .... *U.S. Govt.*

— Mines and mining. *See* Raymond, R. W.

— *National Museum.* Bulletin. nos. 1–6. 8°. '75–'76. *U.S. Govt.*
Cont.: 1. Check list of No. Am. batrachia and reptilia, by E. D. Cope. — 2. Contributions to nat. hist. of Kerguelen Island, by J. L. Kidder: I. Ornithology, ed. by E. Coues. — 3. *Same:* II. Oology, botany, geology, etc. — 4. Birds of s. west Mexico collected by Fs. E. Sumichrast, by G. N. Lawrence. — 5. Catalogue of fishes of Bermudas, by G. B. Goodé. — 6. International Exhibition, 1876: Classification of the collection to ill. the animal resources of the U. S.

— Naval astron. expedition. *See* Gilliss, J. M.

— *Naval Observatory.* Astronomical obs. at the Observ., 1845–'52, 1861–'74. 20 v. '46–'76.. *U.S. Govt.*

— — Reports on obs. of the total eclipse of the sun, Aug. 7, 1869, under direction of Com. B. F. Sands. 4°. '69 .... *U.S. Govt.*

— — Washington obs. for 1869, app. 1: Reports on obs. of total solar eclipse of Dec. 22, 1870, under direction of Com. B. F. Sands. 4°. '71 .... *U.S. Govt.*

— — Washington obs. for 1869, appendix 2: Zones of stars obs. at the Observatory with the mural circle, 1846–9. 4°. '72 .... *U.S. Govt.*

— — Washington obs. for 1871, appendix 2: Results of obs. with transit instrument and mural circle, 1853–'60; by M. Garnal. 4°. '72..... *U.S. Govt.*

— *Navy Dept.* Manual of boat exercise at U. S. Naval Acad. 18°. '68. 75c. .... *Van Nostrand.*

— — Narrative of north polar expedition, ship Polaris, C. F. Hall commanding; by C. H. Davis. 4°. '76 .... *U.S. Govt.*

— — Ordnance instructions for U. S. navy. ill. 8°. '66. $5 .... *Van Nostrand.*

— — Reports of explorations and surveys for location of a ship-canal bet. Atlantic and Pacific Oceans through Nicaragua, 1872–3. 4°. '74... *U.S. Govt.*

— — Reports of explorations and surveys to ascertain practicability of a ship-canal between Atlantic and Pacific Oceans, by R. W. Shufeldt. 4°. '72. *U.S. Govt.*

— — Scientific results of U.S. Arctic expedition, steamer Polaris, C. F. Hall commanding. v. 1: Physical obs. by E. Bessels. 4°. '76..... *U.S. Govt.*

— *Ordnance Department.* Report of milit. commission to Europe in 1855–6; by A. Mordecai. 4°. '60 .... *U.S. Govt.*

— *Provost Marshal-General's Bureau.* Statistics, medical and anthropological; by J. H. Baxter. 2 v. 4°. '75 .... *U.S. Govt.*

— Report on geol. and topog. of Lake Superior land district. *See* Foster, J. W., *and* Whitney, J. D.

— *Signal Office.* War Department weather map, Nov. 1, 1871–Mar. 31, 1872. 2 v. obl. f°. '71. — *Same.* Apr. 1–Dec. 31, 1872. 3 v. f°. '72. — *Same.* Jan. 1–Sept. 30, 1873. 3 v. f°. '73.. *U.S. Govt.*

— *Surgeon-General's Office.* Cholera epidemic of 1873 in U. S.: reports, prep. by direction of surgeon-general. pl., maps and plans. 8°. '75.. *U.S. Govt.*
Cont.: Hist. of the cholera epidemic of 1873, by Ely McClellan; Hist. of the travels of Asiatic cholera, by J. C. Peters and E. McClellan; Bibliography of cholera by J. S. Billings.

United States, *continued.*

— — Circular no. 1: Report on epidemic cholera and yellow fever in the army of the U. S., 1867; by J. J. Woodward. 4°. '68 .... *U.S. Govt.*

— — Circular no. 2: Report on excisions of the head of the femur for gunshot injury; by G. A. Otis. 4°. '69 .... *U.S. Govt.*

— — Circular no. 3: Report of surg. cases in the U. S. army, 1865–'71; by G. A. Otis. 4°. '71.. *U.S. Govt.*

— — Circular no. 4: Report on barracks and hospitals; by J. S. Billings. 4°. '70 .... *U.S. Govt.*

— — Circular no. 5: Report on epidemic cholera in the U. S. army, 1866; by J. J. Woodward. 4°. '67 .... *U.S. Govt.*

— — Circular no. 6: Report showing materials available in Surgeon-General's Office for pub. of med. and surg. hist. of war. 4°. '66...... *U.S. Govt.*

— — Circular no. 7: Report on amputations at the hip-joint in milit. surgery; [by G. A. Otis]. col. pl. 4°. '67 .... *U.S. Govt.*

— — Circular no. 8: Report on hygiene of U. S. army; by J. S. Billings. pl. and map. 4°. '75.. *U.S. Govt.*

— — Medical and surgical hist. of war of the rebellion; by J. J. Woodward and G. A. Otis. 2 v. 4°. '70–'76 .... *U.S. Govt.*
Cont.: 1. Medical hist. — 2. Surgical hist.

— — Statistical report on sickness and mortality in U. S. army, 1819–'39; by S. Forry. 8°. '40.. *U.S. Govt.*

— — *Same*, 1839–'55; by R. H. Coolidge. 4°. '56. *U.S. Govt.*

— *War Dept.* Artillery tactics; assimilated to tactics of infantry and cavalry. sq. 16°. leath., $2. *Appleton.*

— — Cavalry tactics; assimilated to tactics of infantry and artillery. sq. 16°. leath., $2 .... *Appleton.*

— — *Same.* 3 v. 18°. '63. $3.75 .... *Claxton.*

— — Infantry and rifle tactics: ill. figures of drill manœuvres and positions. sm. 12°. pap., 25c. *Peterson.*

— — Infantry tactics; cont. articles of war and dict. of military terms; with questions by W. B. Wilson. 18°. '64. $1.50 .... *Gleason.*

— — Infantry tactics; incl. infantry of the line, light infantry and riflemen. ill. 16°. $1.25.. *Lippincott.*

— — Instruction for field artillery; prep. by a board of officers. 12°. '60. $3.50 .... *Claxton.*

— — Instruction for heavy artillery; prep. by a board of officers. pl. 12°. '63. $2.50.. *Van Nostrand.*

— — Light infantry drill. 12°. pap., 25c. .. *Peterson.*

— — Ordnance manual for use of officers of U. S. army. ('61.) 4th ed. ill. 12°. '65. $3...... *Claxton.*

— — Reports of experiments on strength, etc., of metals for cannon; with descript. of the machines for testing metals and of the classification of cannon in service. pl. 4°. '56. $10 .... *Baird.*

— — Reports of explorations and surveys to ascertain most practicable route for a railroad from Mississippi River to Pacific Ocean. 2 v. in 13. 4°. '55–'60 .... *U.S. Govt.*

— — Tactics for the instruction, exercise and manœuvres of the soldier, company, line of skirmishers, and battalion; for colored troops. 24°. '63. $1.50. *Van Nostrand.*

United States liquor laws: prohibitory, license, local option and civil damage laws. ('72.) New ed., rev. '74. 12°. 25c. .... *Nat. Temp.*

United States mail: Ethiop. drama. 16°. pap., 15c. *French; Happy.*

United States pharmacopœia. 5th rev., by authority of National Convention for Revision. 12°. $1.75; shp., $2.25; $3.25 .... *Lippincott.*

United States reading books. 2 v. ill. 12°. '67–'68. bds. .... *Am. Tr.*
Cont.: First, 20c. — Second, 40c.

United States Sanitary Commission. Reports. *See* Flint, A.; — Gould, B. A.; — Hamilton, F. H.; — Record of the metropolitan fair; — Stillé, C. J.

United States ser. of readers. *See* Willson, Marcius.

United States songster. 32°. 25c. ..... *U.P. James.*

United States survey field note-book. 8°. '76. $2.50; mor., $5 .... *Winchell.*

United States textile manufacturers' directory; [ed. by J: L. Hayes, etc.] ('74.) New ed. 8°. '75. $5 .... *N.A.of Wool Man.*

Unity and its restoration. Thompson, H. M. 25c. *Dutton.*

Unity in variety. Weldon, G. W. $1.50 .. *Whittaker.*

Unity of history. Freeman, E. A. $1 .... *Macmillan.*

Unity of law. Carey, H. C. $3.50 .... *Baird.*

Universal book of songs. 18°. $1.25 .... *Dick & F.*

Universal history, to accession of Victoria. 7 v. ill. and map. fp. 8°. (Bagster.) $18 ...... *Wiley.*

Universal letter-writer. *See* New.

Universal prayer. *See* Pope, Alex.

Universal reader; comp. for [Cath.] schools. 12°. 50c. *Strong.*

Universal stage. *See* Spencer, W. V.

Universalism against itself. *See* Hall, A.

Universalism, calmly and seriously considered. 18°. 30c. .... *Un.B.Pub.*

Universalism false and unscriptural. Alexander, A. 35c. .... *Pres.Bd.*

Universalism in life and doctrine. Brooks, E. G. $1.25 .... *Williamson.*

Universalism not of the Bible. George, N. D. $1.75. *Meth.Bk.Conc.*

Universalism not of God. Smith, M. H. 50c. .. *Am.Tr.*

Universalist centennial. Proceedings, Gloucester, Mass., Sept. 20–22, 1870. 8°. '70. $1; pap., 50c. *Universalist.*

Universalist register and almanac; ed. by Rev. J. O. Skinner. [Annual.] 12°. pap., 30c. *Universalist.*

University oars. Morgan, J. E. $3 ..... *Macmillan.*

University series. 10 v. 12°. ea., pap., 25c.; — in 2 v., $3 .... *Van Nostrand.*

Cont.: Physical basis of life, by T. H. Huxley. — Correlation of vital and physical forces, by G. F. Barker. — As regards protoplasm, by J. H. Stirling. — Hypothesis of evolution, by E. D. Cope. — Scientific addresses, by J. Tyndall. — Natural selection, by A. R. Wallace. — Spectrum analysis, by Roscoe, Huggins and Lockyer. — Sun, by C. A. Young. — Earth a great magnet, by A. M. Mayer. — Mysteries of the voice and ear, by O. N. Rood.

Unkind brother. 18°. 40c. .... *Cong.Pub.*

Unkind word. *See* Craik, D. M.

Unknown countess. Bennett, E. 25c. .. *U.P.James.*

Unknown path. 32°. 30c. .... *Am.S.S.*

— *See also* Child's lib.

Unknown river. *See* Hamerton, P. G.

Unlimited confidence. Troughton, A. C. 15c. *French.*

Unloved one. Hofland, B. 50c. .... *Harper.*

Unlucky Friday. Craven, H. T. 15c. ...... *French.*

Unnoticed things of Scripture. Kip, W. I. $1.50. *Roman; Widdleton.*

Unpartheissche Lieder-Sammlung. [Hymns.] 32°. leath., 60c. .... *Baer.*

Unpartheyische Gesangbuch (Das). *See* Mennonite Brothers.

Unprotected female. Coyne, J. S. 15c. .... *French.*

Unrecht Gut gedeihet nicht. Nieritz, G. 25c. *Morwitz.*

Unrivalled atlas: 33 maps and chart, with index. 4°. $2.50; $1.75 .... *Scribner, W. & A.*

Unruly tongue. *See* Locust grove stories.

Unschätzbare Schloss (Das). 12°. pap., 15c. *Radde.*

Unseen universe. Tait, P. G., *and* Stewart, B. $1. *Macmillan.*

Unseen world. Fiske, J. $2 .... *Osgood.*

Unseen world in the light of the cross. Stork, T. $1. *Lippincott.*

Unser Vater: Gebet des Herrn. ill. 12°. bds., 38c.; pap., 20c. .... *Radde.*

Unspoken sermons. MacDonald, G. $1.50 .. *Routledge.*

Untearable books. 4 v. 8°. ea., 20c. .... *Hurd & H.*

Cont.: Bo-peep. — Little man and little maid. — Three bears. — Old woman and her pig.

Unto the last. Ruskin, J. $1 .... *Wiley.*

Unto me. *See* Kennedy, *Mrs.* M. G.

Untreue schlägt d. eignen Herrn. *See* Hoffmann, F.

Unwarrantable intrusion. Morton, J. M. 15c. *French.*

Unwelcome child. Wright, H. C. 35c. ...... *Colby.*

Unwritten book: allegory. 18°. 25c. ...... *Am.S.S.*

Unwritten history. Miller, J. *$3; $3.50; $4.50, *Am.Pub.*

Up at the hills. Taylor, T. 15c. .... *French.*

Up the Baltic. Adams, W. T. $1.50 .... *Lee & S.*

Up for the cattle show. Lemon, H. 15c. *De Witt; French.*

Up head: Ethiop. drama. 16°. pap., 15c. .... *Happy.*

Up hill. Phelps, E. S. $1.25 .... *Hoyt.*

Up in the garret. *See* Robin Ranger's lib.

Up the ladder. Baker, H. N. W. $1 .... *H.A.Young.*

Up the Nile by steam. *See* Cook, T:

Up the Rhine. *See* Hood, T:

Up the river. Abbott, J. 90c. .... *Harper.*

Up stairs and down stairs. Brough, W., *and* Halliday, A. 15c. .... *French.*

Up to fifteen; [also] Only me. 16°. '76. $1.50 .. *Hoyt.*

Up to town and back again: [dram.] entertainment. 16°. pap., 15c. .... *French.*

Up a tree: farce. 16°. pap., 15c. .... *French.*

Upfold, G: Manual of devotion for domestic and private use. 16°. $1.25; mor., $3.50 ..... *Appleton.*

Upham, C: Wentworth. Life of Sir H. Vane. *See* Sparks, J., Library of Am. biog.

— Memoir of D. P. King. 8°. '69. pap., 30c. .. *Essex.*

— Memoir of Francis Peabody. 8°. '69. pap., 30c. *Essex.*

— *See also* History of Salem witchcraft; — Pickering, O., *and* Upham, C. W.

Upham, Fs. W. Star of our Lord; or, Christ Jesus, king of all worlds, both of time or space. 12°. '73. $1.75 .... *Meth.Bk.Conc.*

— Wise men: who they were, and how they came to Jerusalem. 12°. '73. $1.25 .... *Meth.Bk.Conc.*

Upham, Ja. B. Art of making wax flowers. 2d ed. ill. 8°. '74. pap., 25c. .... *P.Mason.*

Upham, *Mrs.* P. L. Letters of Madame Guyon. 12°. $1 .... *Palmer.*

— Sacred meditations. 18°. 60c. .... *Harper.*

Upham, T: Cogswell. Book for the home. [Poetry.] ill. 12°. $1.50 .... *Bost.Am.Tr.*

— Christ in the soul. 12°. '72. $1.25 ...... *Crowell.*

— Life and relig. opinions of Mme. Guyon; with account of personal opinions of Abp. Fenélon. 2 v. 12°. $3; hf. cf., $6.50 .... *Harper.*

— Life of faith. 12°. $1.50 .... *Harper.*

— Life of Mme. Catharine Adorna. 16°. 75c. .. *Harper.*

— Mental philosophy. 2 v. 12°. ea., $1.75 .. *Harper.*

— Outlines of imperfect and disordered mental action. 18°. 75c. .... *Harper.*

— Philosophical and practical treatise on the will. 12°. shp., $1.50 .... *Harper.*

— Principles of the interior or hidden life. 12°. $1.50. *Harper.*

— View of the absolute religion, based on philos. principles and doctrines of the Bible. 12°. '73. $1.50 .... *Putnam.*

Upham, W. P. Letters during occupation of Boston by the British, 1775–'76. 8°. '76. 50c. .. *Essex.*

— Memoir of Gen. John Glover of Marblehead. 8°. '63. pap., $1 .... *Essex.*

— Papers relating to Rev. Samuel Skelton. 8°. '75. pap., 10c. .... *Essex.*

Uplands and lowlands. Porter, R. $1.25 .. *Randolph.*

Upon "crawling." 18°. 25c. .... *Am.S.S.*

Upper ten thousand. Thom, A. B. $4 .... *Routledge.*

Upper ten thousand: Ethiop. drama. 16°. pap., 15c. *French.*
Ups and downs. Hale, E. E. $1.50 .... *Roberts.*
Ups and downs of a donkey's life. ill. 16°. $1..*Cassell.*
Ups and downs on land and water. Hoppin, A. $10. *Osgood.*
Upshur, Abel P. Brief inquiry into nature and character of our federal government: review of Story's Commentaries on the U. S. Const. 8°. '62. pap., $1; hf. shp., $1.50 .... *J. Campbell & Son.*
Upside down. Parker, R. A. $1 .... *Lee & S.*
Upton, Emory. Tactics for non-military bodies; for instruction of polit. associations, police forces, fire organizations, etc. 12°. $1; pap., 50c...*Appleton.*
— Tactics, infantry, double and single rank; adapted to American topography and fire-arms. sq. 16°. leath., $2 .... *Appleton.*
Upton, Fs. H. Law of maritime warfare and prize. 3d ed., enl. 8°. shp., $5 .... *Baker, V. & Co.*
— Treatise on law of trade marks. 8°. shp., $4. *W. C. Little.*
Upward and onward. ill. 4°. 25c .... *Am. Bapt.*
Upward and onward. Guernsey, L. E. 85c..*Randolph.*
Upward and onward ser. 4 v. ill. 12°. $6...*Nelson.*
Cont.: Kind words awaken kind echoes. — Youthful diligence, by W. K. Tweedie. — Success in life. — Seed-time and harvest, by W. K. Tweedie.

Upward from sin through grace to glory. Hotchkin, B. B. $1.20 .... *Pres. Bd.*
Upward not inward. 18°. 60c .... *Am. S. S.*
Upward path. Davis, C. E. K. $1.25 .... *Hoyt.*
Upward path. James, A. M. $1.25 .... *Nelson.*
Upwards and downwards. *See* Tucker, *Mrs.* Ctte.
Urbané and his friends. Prentiss, E. $1.25..*Randolph.*
Urbild (Das) des Tartüffe. Gutzkow, K. 25c...*Radde.*
Urbin, E: Practical guide for puddling iron and steel; [also] Comparison of the resisting properties of iron and steel, by A. Brull; tr. by A. A. Fesquet. 8°. '68. $1 .... *Baird.*
Urbino, *Mme.* L. B. *See* Art recreations; — Sewell, *Miss* E. M., *and* Urbino, *Mme.* L. B.
Urbino, *Mrs.* S. R. An American woman in Europe: journal of two years sojourn in France, Switzerland, Italy and Germany. 12°. $1.50...*Lee & S.*
— The princes of art: engravers, painters, sculptors and architects. ill. 12°. $2 .... *Lee & S.*
Urbino series: stories for children; with vocab. for tr. into French. 16°. '69. 60c. .... *Holt.*
Urcullu, Jose de. Gramática inglesa; aument. y rev. por F. Robinson. 12°. $2 .... *Desilver.*
— *See also* Robinson, F., Grammar of the Span. lang.
Ure, And. Cotton manufacture of Gt. Brit. systematically investigated. New ed., rev. by P. L. Simmonds. 2 v. ill. 12°. (Bohn.) ea., $1.75. *Little, B. & Co.*
— *Same.* 2 v. ill. 12°. (Bohn.) ea., $2. *Lippincott; Scribner, W. & A.*
— Dictionary of arts, manufactures and mines. 3 v. 4°. $15; shp., $18; hf. mor., $24 .... *Appleton.*
— *Same.* 6th ed., rev. and enl. by R. Hunt and others. 3 v. ill. 8°. $25 .... *Lee & S.*
- Philosophy of manufactures: expos. of factory system of Gt. Brit. New ed., contin. by P. L. Simmonds. 12°. (Bohn.) $2.75..*Little, B. & Co.*
— *Same.* 12°. (Bohn.) $3..*Lippincott; Scribner, W. & A.*
Urgent private affairs. Coyne, J. S. 15c..... *French.*
Urgeschicht von Meckelnborg. *See* Reuter, F.
Urgos, Francesco. Thrilling incidents in polit. life of an Italian. 16°. '76. $1.25...... *Sev. Day Adv.*
Uriel. Seiss, J. A. $1.25 .... *Luth. Bk. St.*
Urmy, W. S. King of day. 16°. '75. 90c. *Meth. Bk. Conc.*
— Lost and found. 16°. $1.25.... *Cin. Meth. Bk. Conc.*
Urn-burial. *See* Browne, *Sir* T.

Urquhart, D: Pillars of Hercules: narr. of travels in Spain and Morocco in 1848. 2 v. 12°. $3..*Harper.*
Urquhart, J: Memoir. 18°. 55c .... *Am. S. S.*
Ursinus, Zach. Commentary on Heidelberg catechism. 8°. $5 .... *N. Y. Ref. Ch. Bd.*
Ursula. *See* Sewell, E. M.
Ursula's girlhood. 16°. $1 .... *Am. Bapt.*
Ursuline manual: [Cath.] prayers and spiritual exercises; rev. by Bp. England. 18°. '63. 75c.–$35. *Kelly, P. & Co.*
— *Same.* 18°. 75c.–$20 .... *T. Kelly; Strong.*
Urwick, *Rev.* —. A father's letters to his son upon his coming of age. 18°. 75c .... *Nelson.*
Use and abuse of Freemasonry. Smith, G. $1.25; $2.50 .... *Redding.*
Use and abuse of tobacco. Lizars, J. 60c...*Lindsay.*
Use of the body in relation to the mind. Moore, G. $1. *Harper.*
Use of a child. *See* Power, P. B.
Use of tobacco. ('58.) 3d ed. 12°. '75. pap., 10c. *So. Meth.*
Used up. Mathews, C. J. 15c .... *French.*
Useful Christian: memoir of T. Cranfield. 18°. 65c. *Am. S. S.*
Useful disciple. Palmer, P. 65c. .... *Palmer.*
Useful knowledge lib. 4 v. 12°. hf. roxb., $10.75. *Lippincott.*
Cont.: Dictionary of daily knowledge. — Dictionary of medical and surgical knowledge, 2 v. — Dictionary of useful knowledge.

Useful lads; or, friendly advice to boys in business. 18°. 40c. .... *Am. S. S.*
Useful letter-writer. 24°. 75c. 32°. 38c...*Appleton.*
Useful lib. 12 v. 16°. ea., bds. .... *Routledge.*
Cont.: Complete letter-writer, 50c. — Commercial letter-writer, 50c. — White's Landmarks of the hist. of England, 60c. — Questions to Landmarks of the hist. of England, 40c. — White's Landmarks of the history of Greece, 60c. — Edwards' Summary of the hist. of England, 20c. — Edward's Summary of the hist. of France, 50c. — Pedley's Practical housekeeping, 40c. — Manual of weathercasts and storm prognostics, 40c. — How to dress on £15 a year, 50c. — How to economize like a lady, 50c. — Holdsworth's Law of bills of exchange, etc., 50c.

Useful metals and their alloys employed in the conversion of iron, copper, tin, zinc, antimony and lead ores, with their applic. to industrial arts; by J. Scroffren, W. Truran, W. Clay and others. 5th ed. 8°. hf. cf., $3.75 .... *Van Nostrand.*
Useful plants: plants adapted for food of man, described and illustrated. ill. 12°. $1.25....*Nelson.*
Uses of adversity. Hooker, H. 30c. ...... *McCauley.*
Usher, Eliz., Lucy *and* Judith. Extracts from letters. 12°. 35c. .... *Friends Bk. St.*
Using the truth. Henry, S. M. I. $1.25. *Cin. Meth. Bk. Conc.*
Using the weed. Baker, G. M. 15c. .... *Lee & S.*
Usurer's victim. Smith, J. F. 75c. .... *Peterson.*
Ut de Franzosentid. *See* Reuter, F.
Ut mine Festungstid. Reuter, F. $1; 75c. ..*Steiger.*
Ut mine Stromtid. Reuter, F. 3 v. ea., $1; 75c. *Steiger.*

V., A. Three Christmas eves; tr. by L. H. Steiner. ill. 12°. $1.50 .... *Ref. Ch. Pub.*
V., G. L. Jack's story as told by himself. ill. 16°. $1.25. *N. Y. Ref. Ch. Bd.*
V., L. Land battles, from Hastings to Inkermann. ill. 12°. $1.25 .... *Scribner, W. & A.*
— Rhymes for the little ones. 32°. 25c...*Scribner, W. & A.*
— Sea-fights, from Sluys to Navarino. ill. 12°. $1.25. *Scribner, W. & A.*
— Victoria picture reading book. ill. 8°. 50c. *Scribner, W. & A.*
V*n,** W*** O***. Three distinct knocks; or, the door of the most ancient Freemasonry. 12°. pap., 50c. .... *Hurst.*
Vacano, Emile Mario. Die Ehre des Herzens. *See* Samaro, G., Europäische Minen, etc.

Vacation adventures in the wilderness. Murray, W. H. H. $1.50; $2 ....*Osgood.*

Vacation lib. 4 v. ill. 16°. ea., 50c. ....*Pott.*
Cont.: Two shipmates, by W. H. G. Kingston. — Slave dealer, by S. W. Sadler. — Inherited task, by C. H. Eden. — Cotton, by S. W.

Vacation sketches. 18°. '59. 40c........*Randolph.*

Vacation stories. *See* Larned, A.

Vacation story books. 6 v. ill. sq. 16°. ea., 80c. *Lee & S.*
Cont.: Worth not wealth. — Country life. — The charm. — Karl Keigler. — Walter Seyton. — Holidays at Chestnut Hill.

Vaccaj, Nicolo. Practical method of Ital. singing, for soprano; tr. by T. T. Barker. f°. '68. ea., pap., $1.50; — for contralto or bass, $1.50 ....*Ditson.*

— *Same;* tr. by J. C. D. Parker. 2 pts. 4°. ea., pap., $1.50 .............................*G.D.Russell.*

— *Same.* f°. $1.50; — Eng. and Ital., $1.50..*Gordon.*

Vachette, E. ["E. Chavette."] So fair yet false. 12°. $1.75 ....*Carleton.*

Vacquerie, A: Jean Baudry: comédie. With Eng. notes by F. Bôcher. ('67.) New ed. 12°. '70. pap., 40c...............................*Holt.*

Vade-mecum. [Cath. prayer book.] 24°. 75c.–$9. *Cunningham.*

— *See also* Catholic's vade mecum.

Vade mecum ad infirmos pro missionariis Americæ Septenter. [Cath. prayers in Eng. and Germ.] 24°. pap., 15c.........................*Herder.*

Vagabond adventures. Keeler, R. $1.50..**Osgood.*

Vagabond heroine. Edwards, A. $1.25; 75c...*Sheldon.*

Vagabond life in Mexico. Ferry, G. $1.50..*Harper.*

Vagabonds. *See* Trowbridge, J. T.

Vahey, J. W. Julia; or, Sister Agnes. 8°. '76. $1. *Pustet.*

Vaiden, T: J. Bible of rational mind and religion, rational religion and morals: an anal. of functions of mind under operations and directions of reason. 8°. $3 ....*Mendum.*

Vail, S. J. *See* Royal songs.

— *and* Lowry, Rob. Chapel melodies: hymns and tunes. sq. 16°. '68. 50c.; bds., 40c. ....*Biglow.*

Vail family. Theodelinda. 75c. ....*Pres. Bd.*

Vaile, C: A. Galvanized-iron cornice-worker's manual; with tables and pl. 4°. '72. $5.........*Baird.*

Vaille, F: Ozni, *and* Clark, H: A. (*ed.*) Harvard book: hist., biog. and descrip. sketches by various authors. 2 v. imp. 4°. '75. $32; hf. mor., $39; $40; mor., $43; por. and ill., $48. *Williams.*

Vain excuses answered. Bergstresser, P. $1. (?) *Luth. Pub.*

Valance, H: L. Confession of the murder of W: Morgan. 12°. pap., 20c...................*E.A.Cook.*

Valdez, the pirate: his life and adventures. 8°. pap., 50c. ....*Peterson.*

Vale, G. Astronomy and worship of the ancients. 12°. pap., 20c. ....*Mendum.*

— Life of Thomas Paine; with crit. and expl. obs. of his writings. 12°. *net,* $1.............*Mendum.*

Vale of cedars. Aguilar, G. $1............*Appleton.*

Valentin. Kingsley, H. $1.25............*Routledge.*

Valentine, *Mrs.* R. ["Aunt Louisa."] Aunt Louisa's choice books. 13 nos. ill. demy 4°. ea., $2.50. *Scribner, W. & A.*

— Aunt Louisa's Sunday books. 4 nos. demy 4°. ea., $1; bds., 50c..................*Scribner, W. & A.*
Cont.: Joseph and his brethren. — Proverbs of Solomon. — Story of King David. — Wonders of Providence.

— Big picture books. 50 nos. ill. demy 4°. ea., per gross, $24.....................(?) *McLoughlin.*

— Child's delight. ill. 4°. $1.50......(?) *McLoughlin.*

— Cuentos de la tia Luisa. 6 v. ill. 4°. per doz., assorted, $7.50..........................*Appleton.*

— Eastern tales. ill. 12°. $1; $1.50; $1.75; pap., 75c. *Scribner, W. & A.*

— Fairy legends. ill. 4°. $1.50.......(?) *McLoughlin.*

Valentine, *Mrs.* R., *continued.*

— Games for family parties. ill. 12°. $1.25. *Scribner, W. & A.*

— Little treasure. ill. 4°. $1.50......(?) *McLoughlin.*

— London toy books. 45 nos. ill. demy 4°. ea., 50c.; $1 ....*Scribner, W. & A.*

— Nelly, the gipsy girl. 18°. 45c..........*Routledge.*

— Nursery rhymes, tales and jingles. ill. cr. 8°. $3.75. *Scribner, W. & A.*

— Nursery tales. ill. post 18°. 75c...*Scribner, W. & A.*

— Victoria geography. maps and ill. demy 8°. $1. *Scribner, W. & A.*

— Wee-wee stories. ill. 4°. $1.50 ....(?) *McLoughlin.*

Valentine, W. Comic lectures. por. 12°. $1.25; pap., 75c. ....*Dick & F.*

— Comic metamorphoses. por. 12°. $1.25; pap., 75c. *Dick & F.*

Valentine. Brough, W., *and* Halliday, A. 15c. *French.*

Valentine. *See* Cornelio.

Valentine, the countess. Bauer, K. $1.50; 75c.; $1.25..................................*Porter.*

Valentine, the successful student. 18°. pap., 12c. *O'Shea.*

Valentine and his brother. *See* Story of.

Valentine and Orson. Dibdin, T. 15c.......*French.*

Valentine M'Clutchy. *See* Carleton, W:

Valentine Vox. *See* Cockton, H:

Valeria; or, the first Christians; tr. by J. Sadlier. 16°. 50c.; 75c. ....*Sadlier.*

Valerie. *See* Marryat, F:

Valérie. Scribe, E., *and* Duveyrier, A. H. J. 30c. *Holt.*

Valerie Aylmer. Fisher, F. C. $1.50; $1..*Appleton.*

Valerio, *Mrs.* Kath. *See* Washburn, *Mrs.* Kath. S.

Valet de sham. Selby, C. 15c..............*French.*

Valiant woman. Landriot, J. F. $1.50.....*Noonan.*

Vallandigham, Ja. L. Life of Clement L. Vallandigham. 4th ed. 8°. '72. $3; $4; shp., $5; hf. cf., $6 ....*Turnbull.*

Valley. ('56.) 3d ed. 18°. '76. 35c.....*So. Meth.*

Valley farm. Peterson, C. J. 25c.........*Peterson.*

Valley mill; tr. (Fatherland ser.) ill. 16°. $1. (?) *Luth. Pub.*

Valley of Achor. Sheddan, S. S. 35c......*Pres. Bd.*

Valley of lilies. *See* Thomas *a Kempis.*

Valley of pearls. 16°. 25c...............*West. Tr.*

Valley of stains: an allegory, by author of "Clouded gem." 18°. 25c......................*Am. S. S.*

Value, Vct. *See* Ollendorff, H. G.

Vámbérg, Arminius. Travels in central Asia, in 1863. ill. and map. 8°. $4.50; hf. cf., $6.75..*Harper.*

Vampire. Planché, J. R. 15c. ....*French.*

Van Antwerp, D: D. Principles of church hist. 2 v. 12°. '71. ea., $1.75................*De Selding.*

Van Beneden, P. J. Animal parasites and messmates. ill. 12°. '76. $1.50 ....*Appleton.*

Vanbrugh, *Sir* J: *See* Wycherly, W., Congreve, W., Vanbrugh, *Sir* J., *and* Farquhar, G.

— *and* Cibber, C. Provoked husband: comedy. 16°. pap., 15c. ....*French.*

Van Buren, J. D., *jr.* Improvement of water front, N. Y. City. *See* Coryell, M., Conflagration in coal.

— Investigations of formulas for strength of iron parts of steam machinery. ill. 8°. '69. $2.. *Van Nostrand.*

— Quay and other retaining walls. 8°. pap., $1. *Am. Soc. of C. E.*

Van Buren, Mt. Inquiry into origin and course of polit. parties in U. S. 8°. $3.......*Hurd & H.*

Van Buren, W. H. Lectures upon diseases of rectum, Bellevue Hospital Medical College, 1869–'70. 12°. $1.50 ....*Appleton.*

Van Buren, W. H., *continued.*
— *and* Keyes, E. L. Practical treatise on surgical diseases of genito-urinary organs, incl. syphilis. ill. 8°. $5; shp., $6 .... *Appleton.*

Vance, Clara (*pseud.*) *See* Denison, *Mrs.* M. A.

Van Cleef, Pl. D. Discourse in memory of Jacob R. Wortendyke, Dec. 20, 1868. 8°. pap., 25c. *N. Y. Ref. Ch. Bd.*
— Sermon preached in 1st Ref. Prot. Dutch Church of Van Vorst, Jersey City, on 20th anniv. of settlement as pastor, 1870. ill. 8°. pap., 25c. *N. Y. Ref. Ch. Bd.*

Van Cott, *Mrs.* Maggie N. Harvest and the reaper: reminiscences of revival work; with introd. by Bp. Haven. 12°. $1.50; $2 .... *Tibbals.*

Vandeleur, *Maj.* *See* Soldier of the cross.

Vandersloot, J. S: *See* Bible [Whole].
— *and* Simons, M. L. Biblical cyclopedia, instructor and guide. ill. 4°. '76. hf. mor., *$5 .. *F. Scofield.*

Van der Velde, K: Fz. Sämmtliche Schriften. 3 v. 12°. $3.75; pap., $3; hf. mor., $4.50. *F. W. Thomas.*
— Erzählungen u. dramatische Werke. 17 v. 12°. ea., pap., 15c.–30c. .... *F. W. Thomas.*

Cont.: Erzstufen, 30c. — Eroberung v. Mexico, 30c. — Arwed Gyllenstierna, 30c. — Der böhmische Mägdekrieg. — Die Gesandschaftsreise nach China. — Christine u. ihr Hof. — Das Horoscop. — Das Liebhaber-Theater. — Der Maltheser. — Die Lichtensteiner. — Die Patrizier. — Die Wiedertäufer. — Guido. — Prinz Friedrich. — Die Heilung d. Eroberungssucht. — Der Zaubermantel. — Die böhmischen Amazonen, *ea.*, 15c.

Van de Warker, Ely. Detection of criminal abortion, and study of fœticidal drugs. 8°. '72. pap., 50c. *Jas. Campbell.*

Vandewell, H. E., *and* Witham, T. Maxwell. System of figure-skating: theory and practice of the art as developed in England. fp. 8°. $2 .. *Macmillan.*

Van Dieman's land. Moncreiff, W. T. 15c. .. *French.*

Van Doren, W. H. Suggestive commentary on St. Luke. 2 v. cr. 8°. $3 .... *Appleton.*
— Suggestive commentary on Romans. 2 v. 12°. $3. *Appleton.*

Van Dyke, H. J. Lord's prayer. 12°. '71. $1.25. *Carter.*

Vandyke Brown. Troughton, A. C. 15c. *De Witt; French.*

Vane, C: W. Story of the peninsular war. 12°. $1.50; hf. cf., $3.25 .... *Harper.*

Van Evrie, J: H. [Works.] 7 v. 8°. pap. *Van Evrie.*

Cont.: Abolition conspiracy; or, ten years' record of the Repub. party. — Abolition is social death. — Bondholders and bondmen. — Free negroism. — Six species of men, *ea.*, 10c. — History of the Union and the Const. — Subjenation: normal rel. of the races, *ea.*, 25c.

— White supremacy and negro subordination. ill. 12°. $2 .... *Van Evrie.*

Van Horne, T: B. History of the army of the Cumberland; with atlas comp. by E. Ruger. 3 v.: text, 2 v., 8°; atlas, 4°. $8; shp., $10; hf. mor., $12. — (Popular ed.) 2 v. map. 8°. $5; shp., $6; hf. mor., $7 .... *Clarke.*

Vanity and ambition. *See* Cupples, *Mrs.* A. J.

Vanity fair. *See* Thackeray, W: M.

Vanity punished. 32°. 20c.; 15c. .... *Dutton.*

Van Kortland, *Miss* —. Pro aris et focis: plea for our altars and hearths. 12°. '70. $1.25 .... *Virtue.*

Van Lennep, H: J. Bible-lands: their mod. customs and manners ill. of Scripture. ill. and col. maps. 8°. $5; shp., $6; hf. mor., $8 .... *Harper.*
— Ten days among the Greek brigands. 16°. '74. $1.25. *Cong. Pub.*

Van Namee, J. W: Faithless guardian; or, out of the darkness into the light: story of struggles, trials, doubts and triumphs. 12°. '70. $1.50 .. *Colby.*
— Hopedale tavern. ('70.) New ed. 12°. '75. $1. *Nat. Temp.*

Van Ness, W: P. *See* United States, Reports.

Van Nest, Ab. R. Memoir of G: W. Bethune. cr. 8°. $2; hf. cf., $3; mor., $6 .... *Sheldon.*

Vannier, Hip. French pronunciation and spelling. 16°. '52. 60c. .... *G. R. Lockwood.*

Van Norman, D. C. *See* Pujol, L: *and* Van Norman, D. C.

Van Nortwick, W: H. Anti-papal manual: book of ready reference for Am. Protestants. 16°. '76. pap., 25c. .... *Holt Bros.*

Van Nostrand's science series. v. 1–25. 18°. ea., bds., 50c. .... *Van Nostrand.*

Cont.: 1. Chimneys for furnaces, by R. Armstrong. — 2. Steam boiler explosions, by Z. Colburn. — 3. Retaining walls, by A. Jacob. — 4. Proportions of pins used in bridges, by C. E. Bender. — 5. Ventilation of buildings, by W. F. Butler. — 6. Storage reservoirs, by A. Jacob. — 7. Surcharged retaining walls, by J. S. Tate. — 8. Compound engine, by J. Turnbull — 9. Fuel, by C. W. Siemens. — 10. Compound engines, by A. Mallet. — 11. Theory of arches, by W. Allan. — 12. Voussoir arches, by W. Cain. — 13. Gases met with in coal mines, by J. J. Atkinson. — 14. Friction of air in mines, by J. J. Atkinson. — 15. Skew arches, by E. W. Hyde. — 16. Graphic method for solving algebraic questions, by G. L. Vose. — 17. Water supply, by W. H. Corfield. — 18. Sewage utilization, by W. H. Corfield. — 19. Strength of beams, by W. H. Corfield. — 20. Bridge and tunnel centres, by J. B. McMaster. — 21. Safety valves, by R. H. Buel. — 22. High masonry dams, by J. B. McMaster. — 23. Fatigue of metals under repeated strains, by L. Spangenberg. — 24. Treatise on teeth of wheels, by S. W. Robinson. — 25. Theory and calcul. of continuous bridges, by M. Merriman.

Van Oosterzee, Jan. Jac. *See* Oosterzee, J. J. Van.

Van Rensselaer, Cortlandt. Miscellaneous sermons, essays and addresses; ed. by C. Van Rensselaer. 8°. '60. $2.25 .... *Claxton; Lippincott.*

Van Rhyn, G. A. F. What and how to read: guide to recent English literature. 12°. $1; pap., 50c. *Appleton.*

Van Ruyssel, E. Population of an old pear tree; tr. from the French; ed. by C. M. Yonge. ill. 12°. $1.50 .... *Macmillan.*

Vansant, N. Life of H. Mattison, with sketches of sermons; and introd. by E. Thompson. 12°. '70. $1 .... *Tibbals.*

Van Santvoord, C., *and* Lewis, T. Memoir of Eliphalet Nott, for 62 years president of Union Coll. por. 12°. '76. $2 .... *Sheldon.*

Van Santvoord, G: Lives of the chief justices of the U. S. 8°. $3.50 .... *W. C. Little; Scribner.*
— Treatise on practice of N. Y. Supreme Court in equity actions; adapted to the code of procedure. New ed. 2 v. 8°. shp., $15 .... *W. C. Little.*
— Treatise on principles of pleading in civil actions under N. Y. code of procedure. 2 v. 8°. shp., $15. *W. C. Little.*
— *Same.* 3d ed., ed. by N. C. Moak. 8°. '73. shp., $7.50 .... *J. D. Parsons; Weed.*

Vanuxem, Lardner. *See* New York geol. survey.

Van Vechten, Jac. An effective ministry: sermon before classis of Albany, April 21, 1868. 8°. pap., 25c. .... *N. Y. Ref. Ch. Bd.*

Vanzandt, A. B. The elect lady: memoir of Mrs. S. C. Bott. 18°. 60c. .... *Pres. Bd.*
— Power of classis to dissolve the pastoral relation; with remarks by J. Anderson. 8°. pap., 25c. *N. Y. Ref. Ch. Bd.*

Vara; or, the child of adoption. 12°. $1.50 .... *Carter.*

Varia: readings from rare books. 16°. $3. *Scribner, W. & A.*

Variations of popery. Edgar, S. $2.50 .... *So. Meth.*

Variety lib. 5 v. ill. 18°. '65. $3 .... *Meth. Bk. Conc.*

Cont.: Fishermen of Gamp's Island. — Story of May. — Fisherman's children. — Woodbury farm. — Log house by the lake.

Varin, A. *and* E. Picturesque architecture of Switzerland; reproduced by heliotype process. 4°. '75. bds., $12 .... *Osgood.*

Varley, H: The Christian ambassador. 16°. $1. *Willard.*

Varley, Nelson. Album: collection of songs. 4°. $4. *G. D. Russell.*

Varney, G: J. Young people's hist. of Maine, to 1842. 2d ed. 12°. '73. hf. bd., $1.25 .... *Dresser.*

Vasari, Giorgio. Lives of the painters, sculptors and architects; tr. by Mrs. J. Foster. 5 v. 12°. hf. cf., $15 .... *Appleton.*
— *Same.* 5 v. 12°. (Bohn.) ea., $1.25 .... *Little, B. & Co.*
— *Same.* 5 v. 12°. (Bohn.) ea., $1.40 .. *Scribner, W. & A.*
— *Same.* 5 v. 12°. (Bohn.) ea., $1.50 ...... *Lippincott.*

Vasconselos. Simms, W. G. $1.75; 75c. *Widdleton.*

Vashti. Evans, A. J. $2 .... *Carleton.*

Vashti Lethby's heritage. *See* Hamilton, K. W.

Vast army.. 18°. 50c .... *Dutton.*

Vaterunser (Das) in Erzählungen u. Gedichten. Nugel, L. 25c .... *Steiger.*

Vathek. *See* Beckford, W.

Vatican decrees. Gladstone, W. E. 25c ... *Appleton.*

Vaticanism. Gladstone, W. E. 40c .... *Harper.*

Vattel, Emerich. Law of nations: principles of law of nature applied to conduct and affairs of nations and sovereigns. 7th Am. ed.; with notes and ref. by E. D. Ingraham. 8°. '52. $4 .. *T. & J. W. Johnson.*

Vaughan, C: J. Addresses to young clergymen, Salisbury, Sept. 29, 30, Oct. 1, 2, 1875. fp. 8°. '75. $1.50 .... *Macmillan.*
— Book and the life, and other sermons. New ed. fp. 8°. '64. $1.25 .... *Macmillan.*
— Characteristics of Christ's teachings. 16°. $1.50. *Routledge.*
— Christ the light of the world. 16°. $1.50 .. *Routledge.*
— Christ satisfying the instincts of humanity: 8 lectures in Temple Church. 2d ed. fp. 8°. '73. $1.25. *Macmillan.*
— Church of the first days. New ed. 3 ser. fp. 8°. ea., $1.25 .... *Macmillan.*

Cont.: Church of Jerusalem. — Church of the Gentiles. — Church of the world.

— Counsels for young students: sermons before Univ. of Cambridge, 1870–1. fp. 8°. 75c ... *Macmillan.*
— Earnest words for earnest men. 16°. $1.25. *Routledge.*
— Epiphany, Lent and Easter: sermons. 3d ed. cr. 8°. '68. $2.50 .... *Macmillan.*
— Epistles of St. Paul; for Eng. readers. pt. 1: 1st Thessalonians. 2d ed. 8°. pap., 50c. *Macmillan.*
— Family prayers. 16°. '73. $1.25 ...... *Routledge.*
— Foes of faith: sermons before Univ. of Cambridge, 1868. fp. 8°. $1 .... *Macmillan.*
— Half hours in the Temple Church. 16°. '71. $1.25. *Routledge.*
— Last words at the parish church of Doncaster. cr. 8°. $1.50 .... *Routledge.*
— Lectures on Philippians. 3d [chp.] ed. fp. 8°. '72. $1.50 .... *Macmillan.*
— Lectures on Revelation of St. John. 4th ed. 2 v. fp. 8°. '75. $3 .... *Macmillan.*
— Lessons of the cross and passion: lectures in Hereford Cathedral, 1869. fp. 8°. '69. $1 .. *Macmillan.*
— Lessons of life and godliness: sermons in parish church of Doncaster. 4th [chp.] ed. fp. 8°. '70. $1.25. *Macmillan.*
— Life's work and God's discipline: sermons. 2d ed. fp. 8°. '73. $1 .... *Macmillan.*
— Memorials of Harrow Sundays: sermons in Harrow School chapel. 4th ed. cr. 8°. $3 .. *Macmillan.*
— Notes for lectures on confirmation; with suitable prayers. 8th ed. fp. 8°. '72. 50c ... *Macmillan.*
— On public worship and the liturgy; with introd. by H. C. Potter. 16°. '70. $1.25 .... *Dutton.*
— Plain words on Christian living. 16°. $1.50 .. *Routledge.*
— — *See also* Earnest Christian's lib.
— Presence of God in his temple. 16°. '72. $1.25. *Routledge.*
— St. Paul's Epistles to the Romans: Greek text with notes. 8th ed. cr. 8°. '74. $2.25 .. *Macmillan.*
— Sundays in the temple. 16°. '71. $1.25 .. *Routledge.*
— Twelve discourses on subjects connected with liturgy and worship of Church of England. fp. 8°. '67. $1.75 .... *Macmillan.*

Vaughan, C: J., *continued.*
— Two great temptations: temptation of man and temptation of Christ: lectures in Temple Church, 1872. fp. 8°. '72. $1.25 .... *Macmillan.*
— Voices of the prophets on faith, prayer and human life. 16°. $1.50 .... *Routledge.*
— Wholesome words of Jesus Christ: sermons before University of Cambridge, 1866. 2d ed. fp. 8°. $1. *Macmillan.*
— Words from the Gospels: sermons in parish church of Doncaster. 2d ed. fp. 8°. '65. $1.25. *Macmillan.*

Vaughan, D: J. Christian evidences and the Bible. New ed., rev. and enl. fp. 8°. $1.50 .. *Macmillan.*
— Sermons preached in St. John's Church, Leicester, 1855–'56. cr. 8°. $1.50 .... *Macmillan.*

Vaughan, E. T. Some reason of our Christian hope. *See* Hulsean lectures.

Vaughan, H: Poems; with memoir. 18°. $1 .. *Osgood.*

Vaughan, Herb. Reply to Gladstone. 2d ed. 12°. 75c.; pap., 25c .... *Cath. Pub.*
— *and* Ullathorne, W: B. Reply in the Gladstone controversy; [also] Fessler On infallibility, with syllabus. 12°. '75. $1.50 .... *Cath. Pub.*

Vaughan, Vct. C. Osteology and myology of common fowl, gallus domesticus. 12°. '76. $1.50. *Sheehan.*

Vaux, Calvert. Villas and cottages: designs prepared for execution in the U. S. ill. 8°. $3 .. *Harper.*

Vaux, J. E. Sermon notes: helps to young or overworked clergy. 4 v. 8°. '72–'76. ea., $1.75 .. *Pott.*

Vaux, W: Persia, to Arab conquest. (Anc. hist. from the monuments.) ill. 16°. $1 .... *Scribner.*

Vea and her cousins. *See* Cupples, *Mrs.* A. J.

Veazey, Wheelock G. *See* Vermont, Sup. Court reports.

Vedder, N: I. Choice sel. of psalms and hymns and spiritual songs. 32°. 35c .... *U. P. James.*

Vedder lectures. *See* Lewis, Tayler.

Vega Carpio, F. Lope da, *and* Calderon de la Barca, Pedro. Obras maestras. ('52.) New ed., rev. and enl. 12°. '69. $2 .... *Holt.*

Vegetable substances used for food of man. ill. 18°. 75c .... *Harper.*

Veil lifted; or, romance and reality of convent life. ('69.) New ed. ill. 16°. '73. $1.15 ...... *Hoyt.*

Veil on the heart. Phelps, L. L. $1.25 .... *Lothrop.*

Veil withdrawn. Craven, A. $1.50 .... *Cath. Pub.*

Veiled lady. Egan, P. 25c .... *De Witt.*

Veitch, Agnes. Frank Fielding; or, debts and difficulties. 18°. 60c .... (?) *Martien.*
— Woodruff; or, sweetest when crushed: a tale. 16°. 90c .... *Am. Bapt.*

Veitelle, I. de. Mercantile dict. of commercial terms, in Eng., Span. and French. 12°. $2 .. *Appleton.*
— Novísima geografía elemental segum el sistema de Cornell. 3d ed., rev. 4°. 50c .... *Appleton.*

Velásquez de la Cadena, Mariano. Easy introduction to Span. conversation. 18°. 50c ...... *Appleton.*
— New Spanish reader; with notes and vocab. 12°. $1.50 .... *Appleton.*
— Pronouncing dictionary of the Span. and Eng. lang. upon the basis of Sloane's ed. of Neumann and Baretti. 8°. $6 .... *Appleton.*
— *Same*; abridg. 12°. $2.50 .... *Appleton.*
— *See also* Ollendorff, H. G.

Velazquez, *Mme.* Loreta Juaneta. The woman in battle: adventures, exploits and travels of Mme. V., otherwise known as Lieut. Harry T. Buford; ed. by C. J. Worthington. 8°. *$4; hf. mor., $6 .... *So. Pub.*
— *Same.* 8°. *$3.50; leath., $4; hf. mor., $4.50 .. *Belknap.*

Velleius Paterculus, Caius. *See* Sallust.

Velma Lee. Hayward, M. L. 75c .... *Cong. Pub.*

Velpeau, Alfr. Armand L: Marie. Surgical clinic of La Charité : lessons upon diagnosis and treatment of surgical diseases; ed. by A. Regnard; tr. by W. C. B. Fifield. 16°. '66. $1...*Jas. Campbell.*

Velvet-coat, the cat. Dumont, M. 75c.....*Claxton.*

Velvet cushion. 18°. 60c..................*Dutton.*

Venable, C: S. Elementary algebra. 12°. '69. $1.50.
—Key. 12°. '72. $1..............*Univ. Pub.*

— Elements of geometry. cr. 8°. '75. $2..*Univ. Pub.*

— First lessons in numbers. ('66.) Rev. ed. 16°. '70. hf. bd., 30c......................*Univ. Pub.*

— Intermediate arithmetic. ill. 16°. '72. hf. bd., 30c. *Univ. Pub.*

— Key to Practical and Mental arithmetics. 12°. '71. 90c..............................*Univ. Pub.*

— Mental arithmetic; or, oral exercises in abstract and commercial arithmetic. ill. 16°. '66. hf. bd., 45c..............................*Univ. Pub.*

— Practical arithmetic. ('67.) New ed. 12°. '71. hf. bd., $1 ....*Univ. Pub.*

Venable, W. H. Amateur actor. 12°. '74. $1.50. *Wilson, H. & Co.*

— Dramas and dramatic scenes. ill. 12°. '74. $1.50. *Wilson, H. & Co.*

— School history of United States. ill. and maps. 12°. '72. $1.25....................*Wilson, H. & Co.*

— School stage. 12°. '73. $1.25.....*Wilson, H. & Co.*

Vendetta. Peacock, T. B. $1.50..........*Peacock.*

Vendetta, and other tales; tr. by Mrs. J. Sadlier. 16°. 50c.; 75c...........................*Sadlier.*

Venema, H. Institutes of theology; tr. by A. W. Brown. 8°. '73. $2.50...............*Draper.*

Venetia. Disraeli, B. 50c...............*Appleton.*

Venetia Trelawney. Reynolds, G. W. M. $1.75; $1. *Peterson.*

Venetian. Reynoldson, T. H. 15c..........*French.*

Venetian life. Howells, W. D. $2.........*Osgood.*

Venez tous à moi : recueil de prières à l'usage des enfants qui se préparent à la première communion. 32°. *net*, 24c.; 36c..................*Benziger.*

Vengeance of a Jew. Guenot, C. $1.50; $2. *Cummiskey.*

Venice, past and present. ('55.) 3d ed. 18°. '75. 50c. ....*So. Meth.*

Venice preserved. Otway, T. 15c. ....*French.*

Venn, H: Complete duty of man. 12°. '42. 80c. *Am. Tr.*

— Life and letters. 12°. $1..............*McCauley.*

— *See also* Bean, J.

Venn, J: On some characteristics of belief. *See* Hulsean lectures.

Venoni. Lewis, M. G. 15c................*French.*

Ventriloquism made easy. 16°. pap., 15c...*Happy.*

Ventura de Raulica, Joac. Profits and delights of devotion to the Virgin; tr. by Rev. O'Leary. 12°. $1.................................*O'Shea.*

Venus and Adonis. Burnand, F. C. 15c.....*French.*

Venus in arms. Wilson, C. B. 15c. ....*French.*

Vêpres Siciliennes. *See* Verdi, G.

Vera, A: Introduction to speculative philosophy and logic. 8°. '75. $1.50; pap., $1.........*Gray.*

Vera; by author of "Hôtel du Petit St. Jean." [Fiction.] 8°. pap., 40c. ....*Appleton.*

Vercruysse, Bru. New practical meditations for every day on life of Christ. 2 v. 12°. $5....*Benziger.*

Verdant Green. *See* Bradley, E.

Verdi, Giu. Aïda; — Ballo in maschera; — Lombardi (I); — Luisa Miller; — Rigoletto; — Vêpres Siciliennes. *See* Ditson.

— Ernani; with English and Italian words. 4°. bds., $1.50 ....*Ditson.*

— — *See also* Ditson.

— Traviata (La); rendered into Eng. by T. T. Barker. 4°. '59. bds., $1.50......................*Ditson.*

Verdi, Giu., *continued.*

— — *See also* Ditson.

— Trovatore (Il); rendered into Eng. by T. T. Barker. 4°. '57. bds., $1.50...................*Ditson.*

— — *See also* Ditson.

Verdi, T. S. Maternity : popular treatise for wives and mothers. ('70.) 5th ed. 12°. '73. $2.25..*Ford.*

Verdict of reason upon question of future punishment. Dexter, H. M. $1...........*Lockwood, B. & Co.*

Verena, Sophie. Above tempest and tide; tr. by A. Forestier. 12°. $1.50..............*McKinney.*

Verena. Holt, E. S. $1.50................*Carter.*

Verfeindeten Nachbarn (Die). *See* Willkomm, E.

Vergissmeinnicht. Putlitz, G. H. zu. 50c. ...*Holt.*

Vergnaud, Amand Denis. *See* Riffault, J. R. D., Vergnaud, A. D., *and* Toussaint, G. A.

Verhängnissvolle Schmuck (Der). *See* Willkomm, E.

Verklärungen (Die). *See* Zschokke, H.

Verlobung (Die) in der Bleikammer. Vitriolöl, A. 10c..................................*Steiger.*

Verlorene Kind (Das). Schmid, C. v. 20c...*Morwitz.*

Verlorene Sohn (Der). Streckfuss, A. 50c. *Morwitz.*

Verlorene u. wiedergefundene Schäflein (Das). Scriver, C. 50c...........................*Dette.*

Vermilye, Ashbel G. *See* Hymns of the church.

Vermilye, T. E. *See* Bagg, I. N., Account of centennial celebration of West Springfield.

Vermisste Boot (Das). *See* Missing boat.

Vermont. General statutes [to 1862]. 2d ed.; [incl.] laws since 1862. 8°. '70 ....*State.*

— Records of council of safety. *See* Walton, E. P.

— Supreme Court reports, 1789–'91; by N. Chipman. [Reprint.] 8°. '71. shp., $5..........*Tuttle.*

— *Same.* 1789–1825; by D. Chipman. [Reprint.] 2 v. 8°. '64. shp., $10...............*Tuttle.*

— *Same.* 1800–'03; by R. Tyler. 2 v. 8°. 1809–'10. *State.*

— *Same.* 1815–'19; by Wm. Brayton. [Reprint.] 8°. '68. shp., $6 ....*Tuttle.*

— *Same.* 1826–'27; by A. Aiken. 2 v. 8°. '27–'28. *State.*

— *Same.* v. 1–23 (1826–'51). 23 v. 8°. ......*State.*

Cont.: 1–9 (1826–'37), by the judges. — 10, 11 (1836–'39), by G. B. Shaw. — 12–14 (1840–'42), by W. Weston. — 15 (1843), by W. Slade. — 16–23 (1844–'51), by P. T. Washburn.

— *Same.* v. 24–26 (1851–'54); by J. F. Deane. 3 v. 8°. ea., shp., $10 ....*W. C. Little.*

— *Same.* v. 27–29 (1854–'57); by C. L. Williams. 3 v. 8°. shp. ....*Tuttle.*

Note. No regular price.

— *Same.* v. 30–47 (1856–'75). 18 v. 8°. ea., shp., $5. *Tuttle.*

Cont.: 30–35 (1856–'64), by W. G. Shaw. — 36–44 (1865–'72), by W. G. Veazey. — 45–47 (1872–'75), by J. W. Rowell.

— — Digest. *See* Washburn, P: T.

— Twelfth report to legislature relative to registry of births, marriages and deaths in 1868. 8°. '70. $1.50 ....*Tuttle.*

Vermont geological survey. First–fourth reports on geol. of V.; by C. B. Adams. 4 v. 8°. '45–'48. *State.*

— Preliminary report on geol. of V.; by E. Hitchcock. 8°. '59....................................*State.*

— Report on geol. of V.; by E. Hitchcock, E. Hitchcock, jr., A. D. Hager and C. H. Hitchcock. 2 v. maps and ill. 4°. '61. $6...... *Vt. Hist.*

Vermont Historical Society. Collections. 2 v. 8°. '70–'71. ea., $3.50...................*Vt. Hist.*

— Proceedings. 8°. '72. $1.50............*Vt. Hist.*

Vermont wool dealer : farce. 16°. pap., 15c...*French.*

Verne, Jul. Abandoned. *See below* Mysterious island.

— Adventures in the land of the behemoth; tr. ill. sm. 8°. '74. $1 ....(?) *Shepard.*

Note. Same as "Meridiana."

Verne, Jul., *continued.*
— Adventures of Capt. Hatteras; tr. ill. 12°. '75. $3. *Routledge.*
Cont.: pt. 1. Journey to the North pole; pt. 2. Field of ice.
— *Same.* ill. 12°. $3 .... *Osgood.*
— American Gun Club; tr. ill. 12°. '74. $1..*Scribner.*
Note. Part of "From the earth to the moon."
— Around the moon; tr. by E. Roth. ill. 12°. '76. $2. *Cath. Pub.*
Note. Same as "From the earth to the moon."
— Around the world in eighty days; tr. by G. M. Towle. ill. 12°. '73. $1.50 .... *Porter.*
Note. Same as "Tour of the world."
— Baltimore Gun Club; tr. by E. Roth. ill. 12°. '75. $2 .... *Cath. Pub.*
Note. Part of "From the earth to the moon."
— Dr. Ox, and other stories; tr. by G. M. Towle. ill. 12°. $3. — (Saunterer ser.) 18°. $1..*Osgood.*
Note. Same as "From the clouds to the mountains."
— Dropped from the clouds. *See below* Mysterious island.
— Field of ice: sequel to "Journey to the north pole;" tr. ill. 12°. '74. $1.50 .... *Routledge.*
Note. Pt. 2 of "Adventures of Capt. Hatteras."
— Five weeks in a balloon; tr. ill. 12°. $2..*Osgood.*
— Floating city; [also] Blockade runners; tr. ill. 12°. '75. $3 .... *Scribner.*
— From the clouds to the mountains; tr. sq. 16°. '74. $1.50 .... *W. F. Gill.*
Note. Same as "Dr. Ox."
— From the earth to the moon direct in 97 hours and 20 minutes; [also] Trip around it; tr. by L. Mercier and E. E. King. ill. 12°. '74. $3..*Scribner.*
Note. Same as "Around the moon."
— Fur country; or, 70 degrees north latitude; tr. by N. D'Anvers. ill. 8°. '74. $3.50 ....*Osgood.*
— In search of the castaways: romantic narr. of loss of Capt. Grant of the "Britannia," and of adventures of his children and friends in his disc. and rescue; tr. ill. 8°. '73. $3; $3.50..*Lippincott.*
— Journey to the centre of the earth; tr. ill. 12°. '74. $1 .... (?) *Shepard.*
— *Same.* ('74.) New ed. ill. 12°. '75. $3..*Scribner.*
— — *See also below* Stories of adventure.
— Journey to the North Pole; tr. ill. 12°. '74. $1.50. *Routledge.*
Note. Pt. 1 of "Adventures of Capt. Hatteras."
— Meridiana: adventures of three Englishmen and three Russians in south Africa; tr. ill. 12°. '74. $3. *Scribner.*
Note. Same as "Adventures in land of the behemoth."
— — *See also below* Stories of adventure.
— Mysterious island: the modern Robinson Crusoe; tr. by W. H. G. Kingston. 3 v. ill. 12°. '76. ea., $2; — in 1 v. cr. 8°. '76. $3 .... *Scribner.*
Cont.: Dropped from the clouds. — Abandoned. — Secret of the island.
— *Same.* ill. 12°. '76. $1.50 .... *Donnelley.*
— *Same.* pt. 1: Shipwrecked in the air; tr. ill. 12°. '74. $1 .... (?) *Shepard.*
Note. Same as "Dropped from the clouds."
— Secret of the island. *See above* Mysterious island.
— Shipwrecked in the air. *See above* Mysterious island.
— Stories of adventure; tr. 12°. '74. $1.50..*Scribner.*
Compr.: Meridiana; Journey to centre of the earth.
— Tour of the world in eighty days; tr. ill. 4°. '76. pap., 25c. .... *Donnelley.*
Note. Same as "Around the world in eighty days."
— — *See also below* Twenty thousand leagues under the sea.
— Twenty thousand leagues under the sea; tr. ill. 8°. $3. — (Household ed.) ill. 12°. $1.50..*Porter.*
— *Same.* ill. 12°. '75. $1; bds., 75c. .... *Donnelley.*
— *Same;* [also] Tour of the world in eighty days. ill. 12°. $1.50 .... *Donnelley.*
— Wreck of the "Chancellor": diary of J. R. Kazallon, passenger, and Martin Paz; tr. by E. Frewer. (Standard ed.) ill. 12°. $2 .... *Porter.*
Verner's pride. Wood, E. P. $1.75; $1.50..*Peterson.*

Vernon, E: American railroad manual for the U. S. and [Canada]; with maps, railroad directory, etc. 4°. '74 .... (?) *Am. Railroad.*
Vernon, Emily. Gift for young ladies. 32°. *net*, 19c. *Hamersley.*
Vernon, Leicester. Lancers: drama. 16°. pap., 15c. *French.*
Vernon, Ruth (*pseud.*) [Stopford J. Ram.] Bride of love; or, true greatness of female heroism. 12°. *$1.50 .... *Quak. City.*
Vernon. Abbott, J. 90c. .... *Harper.*
Veronica. Trollope, F. E. 50c. .... *Harper.*
Veronica. Zschokke, H. 50c. .... *Harper.*
Veronica; or, devotions to the holy face of our Lord; with prayers and indulgences. 18°. '72. 75c. *Cummiskey.*
Veronica; or, the light-house keeper. [Juvenile.] 18°. 75c. .... *Loring.*
Verplanck, G. C. *See* Brougham, H: (*Lord*), Sedgwick, A., *and* Verplanck, G. C.
Verrill, Addison E. List of the polyps and corals. 8°. '64. pap., 20c. .... *Mus. Comp. Zool.*
— Report on fresh water leeches. *See* United States, *Corps of Eng.*
Vers de société. *See* Jones, C. H.
Versatilities. Newell, R. H. $2 .... *Lee & S.*
Verschleierte Dame (Die). Gerstäcker, F. 20c. *Zickel.*
Verschwörung (Die) d. Fiesko. *See* Schiller, J. F. v.
Verses for holy seasons; by author of "Baron's little daughter." 18°. 60c. .... *McCauley.*
Verses from the "Harvard Advocate." 12°. '76. $1.50. *Sever.*
Verses of many days. Stoddard, W. O. $1.50..*Miller.*
Verstille, *Mrs.* H. W. Southern cookery. 12°. '76. $1.25 .... *Burke.*
Verstossen. König, E. A. 25c. .... *Zickel.*
Vertraue auf Gott, od. Jenney's Schicksale. 24°. 20c. *Kohler.*
Verworfener (Ein). *See* Temme, J. D. H.
Very disobliging. *See* Guilford Street stories.
Very last days of Pompeii: burlesque. 16°. pap., 15c. *French.*
Very little dialogues for very little folks. Holmes, A. 30c.; 50c. .... *Dick & F.*
Very little tales. 2 v. sq. 18°. ea., 60c. .... *Carter.*
Very little tales. *See* Frost, S. Annie.
Very pleasant evening. Suter, W. E. 15c. *French; Lee & S.*
Very serious affair. Harris, A. 15c. .... *French.*
Very simple story. Montgomery, F. 60c. *Randolph.*
Very suspicious. Simpson, J. P. 15c. .... *French.*
Very young Americans. Ledyard, L. W. $1..*Roberts.*
Very young couple; by author of "Mrs. Jerningham's journal." 12°. '74. $1.25 .... *Scribner.*
Vesper psalter; or, psalmody made easy: vesper psalms, with canticles, magnificat, set in mod. notation to Roman psalm tunes, with organ accomp. 4°. '62. $3.50 .... *Kelly, P. & Co.*
Vespucius, Americus. *See* Columbus, Cp., *and* Vespucius, A.
Vessels of the sanctuary: tale of Normandy. 16°. 50c.; 75c. .... *Sadlier.*
Vest pocket ser. v. 1–16. ill. 32°. ea., 50c...*Osgood.*
Cont.: Whittier's Snow-bound. — Longfellow's Evangeline. — Emerson's Power, wealth, illusions. — Emerson's Culture, behavior, beauty. — Longfellow's Courtship of Miles Standish. — Tennyson's Enoch Arden. — Fields' Nathaniel Hawthorne. — Howell's Day's pleasure. — Lowell's Vision of Sir Launfal. — Dickens' Christmas carol. — Mrs. Browning's Lady Geraldine's courtship. — Goldsmith's Deserted village *and* The traveller. — Brown's Rab and his friends *and* Marjorie Fleming. — Coleridge's Rime of the ancient mariner. — Fields' Old acquaintance: Barry Cornwall and his friends. — Keats' Eve of St. Agnes.
Vesta. Benedict, H. A. $1.50 .... *Claxton.*

Vestal. La Grange, A. K. de. $2 .... *O'Shea.*
Vestiges of the natural history of creation; with explan. and defense of the work. 18°. 75c. *Harper.*
— *Same.* 12°. $1.25 .... *U.P.James.*
Vestry harmonies. Adams, J. G. per doz., $6. *Universalist.*
Vestry melodies. Marshall, L. 90c. .... *Graves.*
Veteran of 102. Milner, H. M. 15c. .... *French.*
Vetromile, Eug. Abnakis (The) and their history. 12°. $1.25 .... *Strong.*
— Travels in the east and Holy Land. 8°. $3; $4. *Sadlier.*
Veuillot, L: Life of Christ; tr. by A. Farley. 12°. $2. *Cath.Pub.*
Via sacra. Leonard, W. $1 .... *Dutton.*
Vials of wrath. Crowell, M. R. 25c. .... *Beadle.*
Viardot, L: Wonders of European art; tr. from the Fr. ill. 12°. '74. $1.25 .... *Scribner.*
— Wonders of Italian art; tr. ill. 12°. '75. $1.25. *Scribner.*
— Wonders of sculpture; tr., with chapter on Am. sculpture by C. Cook. ill. 12°. '73. $1.50. *Scribner.*
Viator (*pseud.*) Our roadways: remarks addressed to the commissioners of sewers, municipal corporations, etc. 8°. '76. pap., 20c. .... *Spon.*
Vibbert, W. A. Guide to reading Hebrew text; for beginners. ('72.) New ed. 12°. '76. $1.25 .. *Draper.*
Vicar of Bullhampton. Trollope, A. $1.75; $1.25. *Harper.*
Vicar of Christ. Preston, T. S. $1.50 .. *Coddington.*
Vicar of Wakefield. Coyne, J. S. 15c. ..... *French.*
Vicar of Wakefield. *See* Goldsmith, Ol.
Vicarious sacrifice. Bushnell, H. $2.25 ... *Scribner.*
Vicar's daughter. MacDonald, G. $1.50 .... *Roberts.*
Vicars, Hedley. Leben. 32°. '65. 20c. ..... *Am.Tr.*
Vicissitudes of Bessie Fairfax. Parr, H. $1.50; $1.25; 75c. .... *Porter.*
Vick, Ja. (*pub.*) Vick's flower and vegetable garden. ill. 8°. 65c.; pap., 35c. .... *Vick.*
Vickers, T: *See* Mayo, A. D., *and* Vickers, T.
Vickroy, T. R. English grammar. 12°. '68. 75c. *Keystone.*
Vicomte de Bragelonne. *See* Dumas, A.
Victim bride. Wilmer, L. A. 25c. .... *Barclay.*
Victim's revenge. 8°. pap., 25c. .... *Dick & F.*
Victims. Taylor, T. 15c. .... *French.*
Victims of amusements. Clark, M. 50c. .. *Peterson.*
Victims of ignorance. Stebbins, G. S. $2; $2.50. *D.E.Fisk.*
Victims of the Mamertine prison. O'Reilly, A. J. $2; $2.50 .... *Sadlier.*
Victor, *Mrs.* Fes. Fuller. All over Oregon and Washington. 8°. '72. $3 .... *Carmany.*
— Life of Joseph L. Meek: record of early times in the Rocky Mountains and Oregon. ill. 8°. *$3; shp., $3.50; hf. mor., $5 .... *Col.Bk.*
Victor, *Mrs.* M. V. F. ["Seeley Regester"; "*Mrs.* M: Peabody."] Dead letter. 8°. pap., 25c. . *Beadle.*
— Maum Guinea. 8°. pap., 20c. .... *Beadle.*
— Passing the portal. 12°. $1.50 .... *Carleton.*
— Routledge's recipe book. 16°. 20c. .... *Routledge.*
— Woman's (A) heart. 8°. pap., 25c. .... *Beadle.*
Victor and Hilaria. *See* Maude Grenville lib.
Victor and vanquished. Hay, M. C. 50c. ... *Harper.*
Victor La Tourette. Warriner, E. A. $1.75 .. *Roberts.*
Victor Norman, rector. Denison, M. A. $1.50. *Lippincott.*
Victor vanquished. Dance, C. 15c. .... *French.*
Victoria, *Queen.* Leaves from the journal of our life in the Highlands, 1848–'61; ed. by A. Helps. 12°. $1.75 .... *Harper.*
Victoria. Fleming, M. A. 25c. .... *Beadle.*
Victoria. Henry, S. M. I. $1 .... *Cin.Meth.Bk.Conc.*
Victoria. *See* Sherwood, M. M.
Victoria picture reading book. V., L. 50c. *Scribner, W.& A.*
Victoria picture spelling book. ill. 8°. 50c. *Scribner, W.& A.*
Victories of love. Patmore, C. 50c. ... *H.H.Carter.*
Victorine. Buckstone, J. B. 15c. .... *French.*
Victorinus *Petavionensis.* *See* Tertullian, Q. S. F.
Victor's goat. *See* Witt, *Mme.* H. de.
Victor's stories. Burnham, S., *jr.* $1 .. *Bost.Am.Tr.*
Victor's triumph. Southworth, E. D. E. N. $1.75; $1.50 .... *Peterson.*
Victory. Allen, C. G., *and* Sherwin, W. F. $1.50. *Biglow.*
Victory. *See* Little folks ser.
— *Same;* [also] Even Grip. ill. 18°. '72. 50c. .. *Lothrop.*
Victory Deane. Griffith, C. $1.25 .... *Loring.*
Victory of faith. Hare, J. C. $2.25 ..... *Macmillan.*
Victory of the vanquished. Charles, E. $1 ... *Dodd.*
Victory ser. 12 v. 18°. $6 .... *Lothrop.*
Compr. Victory series for boys; Victory series for girls.
Victory ser. for boys. 6 v. 18°. $3 .... *Lothrop.*
Cont.: Boys and boys; Kindness. — Willie Graham; Among the mountains. — Story of Joseph. — Victory; Even Grip. — Robbie's pets; Nellie's sunbeam. — Plot; Falsely accused.
Victory ser. for girls. 6 v. 18°. $3 .... *Lothrop.*
Cont.: Elsie Wood; Forgiveness. — Naomi's home; Prize. — Neddie and Maggie; Light in the window. — Little Floy. — Peace-maker; Grace Edwards. — A child's companion.
Victory to Jesus Christ: missionary story. 18°. 18c. *Am.S.S.*
Victory won. Marsh, C. 35c. *Carter; N.Y.Ref.Ch.Bd.; Pres.Com.*
Victory won. Miller, C. S. $1 .... *Am.Tr.*
Vidal, A. Treatise on venereal diseases; tr. and ed. by G. C. Blackman. ill. 8°. $4.50 .... *W. Wood.*
Videňský Kat. [Executioner of Vienna.] 2 v. 16°. '75. $5 .... *Geringer.*
Vidocq, Eug. François. Vidocq, the French police spy; by himself. 16°. bds., 80c. .... *Routledge.*
— *Same.* 12°. $1.75; pap., $1.50 .... *Peterson.*
Vieille cousine (La). *See* Souvestre, E.
Viel Lärmen um Nichts. *See* Shakespeare, W:
Viele, Egb. L. Handbook for active service: instructions in campaign duties for volunteers. 12°. '61. $1 .... *VanNostrand.*
Vier amerikanische Gedichte. Metrically tr. into Germ. by C. T. Eben. 16°. '64. pap., 25c. ...... *Holt.*
Vier Blüthen u. Eine Frucht. *See* Schmidt, W.
Vier Haymonskinder (Die). 12°. pap., 25c. .. *Radde.*
Vier Jahreszeiten (Die). ill. 32°. '72. 25c. .. *Am.Tr.*
Vier Schreckenstage (Die) in New York. Winckler, W. 25c. .... *Steiger.*
Vierling, F. *See* Bible [Whole], *Germ.*
Vierundzwanzig Stunden auf d. Stuffenberge; [also] Der Assessor im Wandschrank; [also] Danzig ist über. 12°. '65. pap., 25c. .... *Steiger.*
Vieux Moustache (*pseud.*) *See* Gordon, Clar.
View of Christ. Kimball, D. 40c. .... *Cong.Pub.*
View of the Scripture. Whately, R. $1.50. *Smith, E.& Co.*
Views afoot. Taylor, B. $1.50; $2 .... *Putnam.*
Views from nature. ill. sm. 4°. '64. $1; $1.25 .. *Am.Tr.*
Views from Plymouth rock. Mudge, Z. A. $1.50. *Meth.Bk.Conc.*
Views in Bible lands: 12 views with letter press. obl. 24°. 50c.; 75c. .... *Nelson.*
Views in Jerusalem: 12 views with letter press. obl. 24°. 50c.; 75c. .... *Nelson.*

Views of interesting places in the Holy Land. ill. 8°. 60c. .... *Am.S.S.*

Views of nature. *See* Humboldt, F. H. A. v.

Views of nature. Seaman, E. C. $1 ...... *Scribner*

Vigil of Venus. *See* Catullus, Q. V., *and* Tibullus, A.

Vignettes. Parkes, B. R. $2.50 .... *Routledge.*

Vigny, Alfr. (*Comte*) de. Cinq Mars; or, a conspiracy under Louis XIII.; tr. by W. Hazlitt. [Fiction.] 8°. pap., 50c. .... *Harper.*

— *Same.* 12°. (Bohn.) 80c. .... *Scribner, W.& A.*

Viking heir. Keene, S. F. $1.50 .... *Hoyt.*

Vikram and the vampire. Burton, R. F. $2.50 .. *Appleton.*

Vilikens and his Dinah. White, C. 15c. .... *Happy.*

Villa on the Rhine. Auerbach, B. 2 v. ea., $1.25; in 4 pts., $1.25 .... *Holt.*

Village (Le). Feuillet, O. 25c. .... *Holt.*

Village and family lib. 76 v. 18°. $25 ...... *Am.S.S.*

Village beech tree. ill. 12°. $1.50 .... *Pott.*

Village blacksmith. 18°. '39. 75c..... *Meth.Bk.Conc.*

Village blacksmith. *See* Everett, J.

Village boys; or, sin of profaneness. 18°. 50c... *Am.S.S.*

Village communities in the east and west. *See* Maine, *Sir* H. S.

Village doctor. 18°. 65c. .... *Cong.Pub.*

Village doctor. *See* Arbouville, S. de B.

Village doctor: drama. 16°. pap., 15c. ...... *Happy.*

Village home. 18°. 35c. .... *Carter.*

Village idol. Mackarness, M. A. $1.25 ... *Routledge.*

Village in the mountains. ill. 18°. '40. 30c... *Am.Tr.*

Village innkeeper. Conscience, H. $1; $1.25 .. *Murphy.*

Village lawyer. Lyons, —. 15c. .... *French.*

Village lib. 4 v. 16°. $3. .... *Nelson.*

Cont.: Our village, by J. L. Watson. — Ivan Papof. — Dr. Dunbar, by M. H. Hogg. — The moral wreck, by T. East.

Village lib. 10 v. 18°. $4.80 .... *So.Meth.*

Cont.: Village blacksmith, by J. Everett. — Village Sunday school, by J. C. Symons. — Stories for village lads. — Stories for school boys. — Sketches for youth, by C. Malan. — Sermons to the young. — Short sermons and true tales, by Capers. — Religion in common life, by J. Caird. — Moral lessons. — Wayside flowerets, by Mrs. J. T. H. Cross.

Village missionaries. Brock, C. $1.50 ...... *Nelson.*

Village on the cliff. *See* Thackeray, *Miss* A. I.

Village organist: instruction book with music. obl. 8°. $2.50 .... *Church.*

Village pastor; or, incidents in ministerial life in Great Britain. 16°. $1.50 .... *Pres.Bd.*

Village school. Perring, *Mrs.* —. 45c... *Routledge.*

Village school choir; tr. by A. B. Cooke. ill. 18°. 50c. *J.A.Moore.*

Village schoolmistress. Robbins, S. S. $1.25 .. *Hoyt.*

Village sermons. Burder, G. $2 .... *Claxton.*

Village sermons. Forbes, G. $2 .... *Macmillan.*

Village sermons. Kingsley, C. $1.25 .... *Macmillan.*

Village sketches. Whitehead, T. C. 75c... *Routledge.*

Village steeple. *See* Catholic premium-book lib.

Village Sunday school. *See* Symons, J. C.

Village tale: [dram.] interlude.. 16°. pap., 15c. *French.*

Village teacher. 18°. 25c.; 30c. .... *Am.Bapt.*

Village to court: drama. 16°. pap., 15c. .... *French.*

Villagers of Gilead; or, gathering unto Shiloh: a story. ill. 16°. $1.25 .... *N.Y.Ref.Ch.Bd.*

Villages of the Bible. *See* Cabinet lib. of household reading.

Ville, G: Chemical manures: lectures at experimental farm at Vincennes, 1867; tr. by E. L. Howard. 12°. 50c. .... *Judd.*

— High farming without manure: lectures on agriculture. ('69.) 3d ed. 18°. '72. pap., 40c... *Williams.*

Ville, G: *continued.*

— School of chemical manures; or, elementary principles in the use of fertilizing agents; tr. by A. A. Fesquet. ill. 12°. '72. $1.25 .... *Baird.*

Villefranche, J. M. Cineas; or, Rome under Nero. [Fiction.] 12°. '71. $1.50 .... *Cunningham.*

Villemain, Abel François. Lascaris; ou, les Grecs du 15e siècle. With biog. of V., poems on Greece, and notes by A. Dupuis. sm. 8°. 75c.; pap., 50c. .... *Lippincott.*

Villeta Linden. Bennett, E. $1.50; $1..... *Claxton.*

Villette. *See* Brontë, Ctte.

Villiger, G: Letters addressed to a Protestant friend by a Cath. priest; with pref. by Bp. Becker. 12°. '70. $1.50 .... *Cunningham.*

Villikins and his Dinah. Burnand, F. C. 15c. *French.*

Vincent, Fs. History of Delaware to the present time, cont. full account of first Dutch and Swedish settlements, with descript. of its geog. and geol. v. 1. 8°. '70. *net*, $4.50 .... *J.Campbell & Son.*

Vincent, Fk., *jr.* Land of the white elephant: sights and scenes in southeastern Asia, 1871–'72. maps, plans and ill. cr. 8°. $3.50 .... *Harper.*

— Through and through the tropics: 30,000 miles of travel in Oceanica, Australasia and India. 12°. $1.50 .... *Harper.*

Vincent, H. History of the camp-meeting and grounds at Wesleyan Grove, Martha's Vineyard, for the eleven years ending with 1869; with glances at the earlier years. 16°. $1 .... *Lee & S.*

Vincent, J: *See* Huntington, Jed. Vincent.

Vincent, J: H. Church school and its officers. 16°. '72. 75c. .... *Meth.Bk.Conc.*

— Lesson system: first year with Jesus. 2 v. 12°. ea., 25c. .... *Meth.Bk.Conc.*

— *Same;* second year with Jesus. 2 v. 12°. ea., 25c. *Meth.Bk.Conc.*

— Little foot-prints in Bible lands. 12°. '61. 60c. *Meth.Bk.Conc.*

— Pictorial Bible geog. 4°. '70. $1.... *Meth.Bk.Conc.*

— Sunday-school institutes and normal classes; with introd. by A. Taylor. 12°. '72. 75c. *Meth.Bk.Conc.*

— Year with Moses. 2 nos. 12°. ea., per doz., $3. *Meth.Bk.Conc.*

— *See also* Wise, D., *and* Vincent, J. H.

— *and* Hurlbut, J. L. Lesson compend: notes on International Sunday school lessons for 1876. 12°. 60c. .... *Meth.Bk.Conc.*

— *and* Knapp, *Mrs.* —. Bible-school songs. 18°. 15c. *Meth.Bk.Conc.*

Vincent, Marvin R. Amusement a force in Christian training: discourses. 12°. '67. $1.. *W.H.Young.*

— Gnomon of the New Test. *See* Bengel, J. A.

— The two prodigals. sq. 18°. '76. 40c.; pap., 20c. *Randolph.*

Vincent, Natl. Spirit of prayer. 32°. 30c... *Pres.Bd.*

Vincent, T: Explanation of Assembly's catechism. 18°. 75c. .... *Pres.Bd.*

— Love to Christ; from "True Christian's love of the unseen Christ." 32°. 30c. .... *Pres.Bd.*

Vincent de Paul, *St.* Life. 32°. 45c...... *Cath.Pub.*

— *Same.* 16°. $1; $1.50 .... *Sadlier.*

— Spiritual maxims; arr. for every day in the year by W. Walsh. 32°. 38c. .... *Strong.*

— *See also* St. Vincent de Paul.

Vinci, Leonardo da (*ill.*) The Lord's Supper: photos. with artist's por. by J. Niessen, and text by J. Sighart. 8°. $9 .... *Stroefer.*

— *Germ.* Das Abendmahl des Herrn. Photos., with sketches by J. Niessen and text. roy. 4°. $10; mor., $12 .... *Stroefer.*

Vindication of captors of Major André. Benson, E. $1.50; $3 .... *Sabin.*

Vindication of the true Sabbath. Morton, J. W. 10c. *Sev.DayAdv.*

Vindiciæ ecclesiæ Anglicanæ. *See* Southey, Rob.
Vine, W. R. Latin-English and English-Latin dictionary. 18°. 75c. .... *Routledge.*
Vinegar bitters. White, C. 15c. .... *De Witt.*
Vinegar Hill stories. 3 v. ill. 16°. ea., $1 .... *Carter.*

Cont.: Old church door. — Golden thorns. — An hundred fold.

Vines of Eschol. Robinson, J. B. 75c. ... *Un.B.Pub.*
Vinet, Alex. Rod. Gospel studies; tr. 12°. $1.50 .. *Dodd.*
— History of French literature in 18th cent.; tr. by J. Bruyce. 8°. '57. $3 .... *Draper.*
— Homiletics; or, theory of preaching; tr. and ed. by T. H. Skinner. 12°. '53. $1.75 .... *Ivison.*
— Montaine, and other miscellanies; tr. 12°. $1.75. *Dodd.*
— Outlines of philosophy; tr. and ed. by M. Astie. post 8°. $3.75 .... *Routledge.*
— Outlines of theology; tr. and ed. by M. Astie. post 8°. $3 .... *Routledge.*
— Pastoral theology; or, the theory of evangelical ministry; tr. and ed. by T. H. Skinner. 12°. '53. $1.50 .... *Ivison.*
— *Same;* with introd. by T. O. Summers. ('56.) 2d ed. 12°. '75. $1.50 .... *So.Meth.*
Vineyard of song. Allen, C. G., *and* Seward, T. F. 75c. .... *Biglow.*
Vingut, Francisco J. Compañero del nuevo método de Ollendorff. 12°. '56. $1.75 .. *G.R.Lockwood.*
— Lector y traductor inglés. 12°. '54. $1.50. *G.R.Lockwood.*
— Maestro (El) de francés. [French gram. for Spaniards.] 12°. '71. $2.—Key, $1 .. *G.R.Lockwood.*
— Ollendorff Spanish teacher. 12°. '71. $2. — Key, $1. *G.R.Lockwood.*
— Preceptor (El) ingles elemental. [Eng. gram. for Spaniards.] 12°. '69. $1.50. — Clave. 12°. '69. 75c. .... *G.R.Lockwood.*
— Spanish reader and translator. 12°. '54. $1.50. *G.R.Lockwood.*
— *See also* Ollendorff, H. G.
Vinny Leal's trip to the golden shore. Bigham, R. W. 50c. .... *So.Meth.*
Vinton, Alex. H. Sermons. 4th ed. 12°. '59. $1.50. *Dutton.*
Vinton, Fs. Manual commentary on general canon law and constitution of Prot. Episc. Church in the U. S. 8°. '70. $2.50; $3.50 ...... *Dutton.*
Viola. Abbott, J. 90c. .... *Harper.*
Viola. Bennett, E. $1.75; $1.50 .... *Peterson.*
Viola. Maturin, E. 15c. .... *French.*
Violet. ('65.) New ed. ill. 18°. '75. 50c. ... *Hoyt.*
Violet: drama. 16°. pap., 15c. .... *French.*
Violet: fairy story. ill. 16°. 80c. .... *Lee & S.*
Violet; or, the times we live in. 12°. $1 .. *Lippincott.*
Violet (New). *See* Fillmore, A. D.
Violet and Daisy; or, picture with two sides; by author of "Rosa Lindsay." ill. 16°. $1.15 ... *Crowell.*
— *See also* Apron-strings lib.
Violet and Rose; by author of "Blue bell." ill. 8°. (Lond.) pap., 30c. .... *Am.News.*
Violet Douglas. Marshall, E. $1.50 ...... *Lothrop.*
Violet Fletcher's home work. ill. 16°. '71. $1.25. *Lothrop.*
Violet girls. *See* Baker, *Mrs.* H. N. W.
Violet Lee. Oberholtzer, S. L. $1.25 ... *Lippincott.*
Violet Russell. ill. 16°. 75c. .... *Nelson.*
Violet seller. 18°. 40c. .... *Dutton.*
Violet stories; by Thomas Miller and others. 12 v. 32°. $3 .... *Sheldon.*

Cont.: On the journey. — Walk and a drive. — Ducks and pigs. — Wounded bird. — Sad adventure. — Doctor's visit. — Sheep and lambs. — Young donkey. — Little rabbit-keepers. — Cock of the walk. — Cows in the water. — Young angler.

Violet's idol. Mathews, J. H. 60c. .... *Carter.*
Violin complete: Am. system of teaching art of playing the violin. 4°. '50. bds., $1.25 .... *Ditson.*
Violin made easy. obl. 8°. '51. pap., 75c. .. *Ditson.*
Viollet-le-Duc, Eug. E. Annals of a fortress; tr. ill. 8°. '75. $5 .... *Osgood.*
— Discourses on architecture; tr. with introd. by H. Van Brunt. ill. 8°. '75. $8; hf. cf., $13 .. *Osgood.*
— Habitations of man in all ages; tr. by B. Bucknell. ill. 8°. '76. $5 .... *Osgood.*
— The story of a house; tr. ill. 8°. '74. $5; hf. cf., $8. *Osgood.*
Violoncello without a master; incl. J. A. Hamilton's Complete preceptor. 8°. '56. pap., 75c. .. *Ditson.*
Virchow, Rud. Cellular pathology as based upon physiological and pathological histology: lectures, 1858; tr. by Frank Chance. ill. roy. 8°. '58. $5. *De Witt; Lindsay.*
— Cranial affinities of man and the ape; tr. ill. cr. 8°. '74. pap., 25c. .... *Estes.*
Virgil [*Lat.* Virgilius] Maro, Publius. Opera; ex recensione J. Conington. 18°. 75c. ..... *Harper.*
— *Same;* with notes by F. Bowen. 12°. $2 ... *Dennet.*
— *Same;* with notes by A. H. Bryce. ill. 16°. (Lond.) $2.50. .... *Little, B. & Co.*
— *Same;* interpretatione et notis cur. C. Ruoens. cr. 8°. shp., $2.80 .... *Lippincott.*
— *Same;* text reduced to nat. order of construction, and interlinear tr., by L. Hart and V. R. Osborn. roy. 12°. hf. mor., $2.25 .... *Desilver.*
— *Eng.* Works; literally tr. with notes by Davidson. New ed.; rev. and enl. by T. A. Buckley. 12°. $1.50 .... *Harper.*
— — *Same.* 12°. (Bohn.) $1.25 ...... *Little, B. & Co.*
— — *Same.* 12°. (Bohn.) $1.40 ... *Scribner, W. & A.*
— — *Same.* 12°. (Bohn.) $1.50 .... *Lippincott.*
— *Same;* tr. by J. Dryden. 16°. (Edinb.) '70. $1.50. *Little, B. & Co.*
— — *Same.* 2 v. in 1. 18°. '70. 75c. ...... *Claxton.*
— *Same;* rendered into Eng. prose with introd. analysis and index by J. Lonsdale and S. Lee. 12°. '71. $1.50 .... *Macmillan.*
— [Writings outlined and expl.] by W. L. Collins. (Anc. classics for Eng. readers.) 16°. $1. *Lippincott; Little, B. & Co.*
— Æneid [Lat.]; with notes, metrical index and a dict. ('69.) New ed. map and ill. demy 8°. '70. $1.75; $2 .... *Claxton.*
— *Same;* with notes and index by C. Anthon. ill. 12°. shp., $1.75 .... *Harper.*
— *Same;* with notes, met. index, etc., by T. Chase. ('67.) 7th ed. 16°. '75. hf. leath., $1.50. *Eldredge.*
— *Same;* with notes by Frieze. ill. 12°. $2 .. *Appleton.*
— *Same.* 1st 6 bks.; with notes, lexicon, etc., by T. Chase. ('70.) 6th ed. 16°. '75. hf. leath., $1.25. *Eldredge.*
— — *Same;* with notes, lexicon and app. by E. Searing, and met. index. 8°. '69. $2.25 .... *Barnes.*
— — *Same;* with Latin ordo, notes and index by C. Wiley. ('74.) New ed. 12°. '76. hf. roan, $1.75 .... *Holt.*
— *Eng.* Æneid; tr. by C. P. Cranch. roy. 8°. '72. $4.50; hf. cf., $9; mor., $12.50 .... *Osgood.*
— *Same;* tr. into Eng. octo-syllabic verse by J. Conington. cr. 8°. $2.25; hf. cf., $4 ... *Widdleton.*
— — The Æneids; tr. by W. Morris. 8°. '75. $2.50. *Roberts.*
— Bucolics, Georgics and Æneid [Lat.]; with Eng. notes by E. Moore. 12°. '49. $1.50 .. *Nichols & H.*
— Carmina [Lat.]; ed. by L. Schmitz and C. G. Zumpt. roy. 18°. '53. 85c.; hf. bd., $1 .... *Lea.*
— Eclogues and Georgics [Lat.]; with notes and met. key by E. A. Andrews. 12°. '62. $1.50 .. *Crocker.*
— *Same;* with notes, and met. index, by C. Anthon. 12°. shp., $1.75 .... *Harper.*
— Eclogues, Georgics and Æneid [Lat.]; ed. by L. Schmitz and C. G. Zumpt. 16°. $1 .... *Sheldon.*
— — — *Same;* ed. by T. G. Cooper. 8°. $2.50 .. *Sheldon.*

Virgil [*Lat.* Virgilius] Maro, Publius, *continued.*
— *Eng.* Eclogues, tr. by Wrangham; Georgics, tr. by Sotheby; and Æneid, tr. by Dryden. 2 v. 18°. $1.50 .... *Harper.*
— Eclogues, Georgics and Moretum [Lat.]; with notes, lexicon, etc., by G. Stuart. ('72.) 2d ed. 16°. '75. hf. mor., $1.25 .... *Eldredge.*
— Poems [Lat.] v. 1: Bucolics and bks. 1 to 6 of Æneid; with introds., notes and index. ('74.) 3d ed. 12°. '75. hf. mor., $1.75; without notes, $1 .... *Ginn.*
— *See also* Ovid Naso, P., *and* Virgil.

Virgilia. Grey, G. $1.15 .... *Pres. Bd.*

Virgin Mary. *See* Mary, *Virgin.*

Virgin, W: Wirt. Digest of Maine reports (v. 27–53). 8°. *net*, shp., $7.50 .... *Dresser.*
— Maine civil officer. 3d ed., rev. by B. D. Verrill. 12°. shp., $3.50 .... *Loring, S. & H.*
— Supplemental digest of Maine Sup. Court reports (v. 44–56). 8°. '70. shp., $5.50 .. *Loring, S. & H.*
— *See also* Maine, Sup. Court Reports.

Virgin queen. Smith, J. F. 75c. .... *Dick & F.*

Virgin wife. 8°. pap., 25c. .... *De Witt.*

Virginia, *Cousin (pseud.)* *See* Johnson, V. W.

Virginia. Act of Assembly now in force, 1710, 1759, 1769, 1785, 1794. f°. *or* 8°. $2 .. *J. W. Randolph.*
— *Same.* 1809–'76. 67 v. 8°. ea., hf. shp., $1.25. *J. W. Randolph.*
— *Same.* 1874. 8°. hf. shp., $2.25 ... *J. W. Randolph.*
— *Same.* 1874–'75. 8°. hf. shp., $2 .. *J. W. Randolph.*
— Acts of [Confederate] Assembly, 1861–'64. 4 v. 8°. bds., $6.50 .... *J. W. Randolph.*
— Articles of confederation; Declaration of rights; Constitution; and treaty between Gt. Brit. and the U. S. 12°. 1784. pap., $1 .. *J. W. Randolph.*
— Code of laws, 1803, 1808, 1814, 1819 (2 v.), 1833, 1849, 1860. 8 v. 8°. ea., shp., $2 .... *J. W. Randolph.*
— *Same.* 1849: revisors' reports, 1846–'49. 2 v. 8°. hf. shp., $25 .... *J. W. Randolph.*
— *Same;* incl. legislation to 1874; prep. by G. W. Munford. 8°. '73. shp., $6. *J. W. Randolph; West, J. & Co.*
— Colonial records. 4°. '74. pap., $1.50. *J. W. Randolph; West, J. & Co.*
— Court of Appeals reports, 1790–'96; by B. Washington. 2 v. 8°. '23. shp., $15 .... *J. W. Randolph.*
— *Same.* 1797–1825; by D. Call. 6 v. 8° ..... *State.*
— *Same.* 1809–'20; by W. Munford. 6 v. 8°. '12–'21. shp., $36 .... *J. W. Randolph.*
— *Same.* 1820–'21; by F. W. Gilmer. 8°. '21. cf., $3. *J. W. Randolph.*
— — *See also* United States, Circuit Court reports.
— Court of Appeals and Court of Chancery reports, 1806–'10; by W. W. Hening and W. Munford. 4 v. 8°. 1808–'11. ea., shp., $5; — condensed by L. Minor. 8°. '57. shp., $6 .. *J. W. Randolph.*
— Court of Appeals and General Court reports, 1821–'28; by P. Randolph. 6 v. 8°. cf., $36. *J. W. Randolph.*
— *Same.* 1829–'41; by B. W. Leigh. 12 v. 8°. '30–'75. ea., cf., $5 .... *J. W. Randolph.*
— *Same.* 1842–'44; by C. Robinson. 2 v. 8°. '43–'75. ea., cf., $5 .... *J. W. Randolph.*
— *Same.* 1844–'76; by P. R. Grattan. 26 v. 8°. '45–'76. ea., cf., $6 .... *J. W. Randolph.*
— — Digest. *See* Royal, W. L.
— Digest of civil laws; — of criminal laws. *See* Matthews, J. M.
— Digest of laws. *See* Tate, J.
— Digest of laws resp. real property. *See* Lomax, J. T.
— General Court reports, 1730–'40, and 1768–'72; by T. Jefferson. 8°. '29. hf. cf., $10 .. *J. W. Randolph.*
— *Same.* 1789–1826; by W. Brockenbrough and H. Holmes. 2 v. 8°. '15–'26. shp., $15. *J. W. Randolph.*
— High Court of Chancery reports, 1788–'98; by G. Wythe; with memoir, ref., analysis and index by B. B. Minor and W. Green. 8°. '52. shp., $20. *J. W. Randolph.*

Virginia, *continued.*
— Index to reports. *See* Guigon, A. B.; — Hall, E.; — Munford, W.; — Patton, J. M., *and* Heath, R. B.; — Tate, J.
— Special Court of Appeals reports, 1855–'57; by J. M. Patton and R. B. Heath. 2 v. 8°. '56–'57. shp., $30 .... *J. W. Randolph.*
— Statutes at large: coll. of laws, 1619–1792; ed. by W. W. Hening. 13 v. 8°. 1809–'23. shp., $13. *J. W. Randolph.*
— *Same.* 1792 to 1808; ed. by S. Shepherd. 3 v. 8°. '35–'36. shp., $15 .... *J. W. Randolph.*

Virginia. Abbott, J. 90c. .... *Harper.*

Virginia. Kingston, W. H. G. $1.25 ...... *Lothrop.*

Virginia; or, the power of grace. Baker, H. N. W. 55c. .... *Hoyt.*

Virginia and Maryland; or, the Lord Baltimore's printed case uncased and answered: Lond., 1655. [Reprint.] 4°. pap., $1 .... *Sabin.*

Virginia commissioners' reports on the Maryland and Virginia boundary. 2 v. maps. 8°. '73–'74. hf. shp., $10 .... *J. W. Randolph.*

Virginia convention, 1775–6. Proceedings. 4°. '16. hf. shp., $2 .... *J. W. Randolph.*

Virginia convention, 1788. Journal. 8°. '27. hf. shp., $1.50 .... *J. W. Randolph.*

Virginia convention, 1829–'30. Debates and proceedings. 8°. '30. cf., $5 .... *J. W. Randolph.*

Virginia convention, 1850–51. Journal and documents. 2 v. 8°. cf., $6 .... *J. W. Randolph.*

Virginia convention, 1867–8 [Negro convention]. Debates (partial), journal and documents. 3 v. 8°. hf. shp., $5 .... *J. W. Randolph.*

Virginia debates, 1788. 8°. 1805. shp., $3. *J. W. Randolph.*

Virginia geological survey. Report of the geol. reconnoissance of V.; by W. B. Rogers. 4° ... *State.*
— Reports of progress of geol. survey of V. for 1836–'40; by W. B. Rogers. 5 v. 8°. '38–'41 .. *State.*

Virginia illustrated. Strother, D. H. $3.50; $5.75. *Harper.*

Virginia mummy: Ethiop. drama. 16°. pap., 15c. *French; Happy.*

Virginia railroad scenery: Staunton, Cave of Fountains, and Elliott's Knob. 8°. '74. pap., 25c. *J. W. Randolph.*

Virginia richly valued, by the description of the main land of Florida, her next neighbor; tr. from the Portugese by R. Hacklvyt: Lond., 1609. [Reprint.] 4°. pap., $2 .... *Sabin.*

Virginia selection of psalms, hymns and spiritual songs. Broaddus, A. 75c. .... *Claxton.*

Virginia tourist. Pollard, E. A. $1.75; $1 .. *Lippincott.*

Virginia veteran. Power, J. F. 25c. .... *Lee & S.*

Virginian housewife. Randolph, M. $1 .... *Claxton.*

Virginians (The). *See* Thackeray, W: M.

Virginia's cure. *See* Guilbert, *Bp. of London.*

Virginius. Buckingham, L. 15c. .... *French.*

Virginius. Knowles, J. S. 15c. .... *French.*

Virtue of patience. *See* Yonge, C. M.

Virtue victorious: burlesque. 16°. pap., 15c ... *Happy.*

Virtues and defects of a young girl. 18°. 75c.; $1. *Sadlier.*

Visible speech. Bell, A. M. $5 .... *Burbank.*

Vision of the arch of truth. Knickerbacker, J. F. $1.50 .... *W. H. Young.*

Vision of old Andrew, the weaver. 18°. '72. 60c. *Kenedy.*

Vision of Sir Launfal. *See* Lowell, J. R.

Vision of the three states. 18°. 30c. .... *Dutton.*

Visions of freedom. Baker, G. M. 15c. .... *Lee & S.*

Visit (The): difference between being a good child, and being like a good child. 18°. 35c ... *Am. S. S.*

Visit from St. Nicholas. *See* Moore, C. C.
Visit to ancient Rome. Donaldson, S., *jr.* 30c.; 20c. *Murphy.*
Visit to Aunt Agnes. ill. sq. 12°. '65. $1.. *Meth. Bk. Conc.*
Visit to the catacombs. Bunbury, S. 40c... *So. Meth.*
Visit to the celestial city: allegory. 18°. 30c. *Am. S. S.*
Visit to Derby; or, Minnie and her nurse. 18°. 30c. *Am. S. S.*
Visit to grandmother. ill. 16°. 25c........ *Routledge.*
Visit to the Holy Land, and other stories. ill. 18°. 25c. *Pres. Bd.*
Visit to Ireland. *See* Eddy, D. C.
Visit to the Isle of Wight; by author of "Pierre and his family." 18°. 35c............... *Am. S. S.*
Visit to the mountains. Abbott, J. 50c. .... *Crocker.*
Visit to my birthplace. Bunbury, S. 45c. *Routledge.*
Visit to my discontented cousin: a novelette. 16°. '71. $1 .... *Roberts.*
Visit to some Am. schools and colleges. Jex-Blake, S. $1.75 .... *Macmillan.*
Visit to Uncle Mark's farm. ill. cr. 4°. pap., 20c.; 25c. .... *J. E. Potter.*
Visit to the woods. *See* Llewellyn, E. L.
Visitation manual: [Cath.] prayers and instructions; comp. according to St. Francis de Sales. 24°. '57. $1–$14 .... *Murphy.*
Visitor's book of texts. Bonar, A. A. $1.50.. *Carter.*
Visitor's guide to the Centennial Exhibition and Philadelphia. [In Eng., Germ., Span. or French.] maps. 16°. ea., 50c.; pap., 25c..... *Lippincott.*
Visitor's guide to New Orleans. 16°. '75. pap., 50c. *Waldo.*
Visits to the blessed sacrament. *See* Liguori, A. M. de, *St.*
Visits to Holly Farm. 18°. 17c.; 22c. .... *Am. Bapt.*
Vital godliness. Plumer, W. S. $1.50 ...... *Am. Tr.*
Vital magnetic cure; by a magnetic physician. ('71.) 3d ed. 12°. '73. $1.50 .... *Colby.*
Vital philosophy. Macdonald, J. S. $1.75.. *Lippincott.*
Vital religion. Janney, S. M. *net*, 10c. *Friends Bk. Assoc.*
Vitriolöl, Angelicus (*pseud.*) Die Verlobung in d. Bleikammer: chemische Verbindungs-Komödie in e. schwefelsauren Act. 32°. '75. pap., 10c. *Steiger.*
Vivia. Southworth, E. D. E. N. $1.75; $1.50.. *Peterson.*
Vivia. Wilford, F. 50c.................... *Appleton.*
Vivian. *See* Edgeworth, *Miss* Mar.
Vivian and his friends; or, two hundred years ago. 16°. $1.10 .... *Pres. Bd.*
— *Same.* ('65.) New ed. ill. 16°. '72. $1.25.. *Hoyt.*
Vivian Bertram. Reynolds, G. W. M. 75c. *Peterson.*
Vivian Grey. Disraeli, B. 60c. .... *Appleton.*
Vivian romance (The). Collins, M. 50c. ... *Harper.*
Vivien. *See* Tennyson, Alfr.
Vocalist. Mason, L., *and* Webb, G. J. $1.50. *Ditson; Gordon.*
Vogdes, Fk. W. Architect's and builder's pocket companion and price book. ('71.) 5th ed. ill. 32°. '75. $1.50. — (Pocket ed.), $2......... *Baird.*
Vogdes, W: Elementary treatise on mensuration and practical geometry; with problems in mechanics. 12°. '46. hf. roan, $1.50............ *Fortescue.*
— United States arithmetic. 12°. '57. hf. bd., 70c. — Key. 12°. hf. bd., 45c. .... *Fortescue.*
— *and* Alsop, S: Elements of practical arithmetic. 12°. '60. hf. bd., 40c. — Answers, 20c. *Fortescue.*
Vogel, Alfr. Practical treatise on diseases of children; tr. and ed. by H. Raphael. pl. 8°. $4.50; shp., $5.50.............................. *Appleton.*
Vogel, Hm. Chemistry of light and photography. (Intern. sci. ser.) ill. 12°. $2........ *Appleton.*
— Handbook of photography. 16°. $3.50.. *Benerman.*

Vogel, Hm., *continued.*
— Photographer's pocket reference-book. 12°. $1.50. *Benerman.*
Vögel (Die). *See* Goethe, J. W. v.
Vogelbach, J. Das Leben Martin Luthers. 18°. 25c. *Kohler.*
Vogelhändler (Der). *See* Hoffmann, F.
Vogelhändler (Der) von Imst. Spindler, C. $1.25; $1; $1.50 .... *F. W. Thomas.*
Vogelnestchen (Das). *See* Schmid, C. v.
Voice from the church in Australia. Potter, R. $1.25. *Macmillan.*
Voice from the east to the young. Scudder, J. 60c. *N. Y. Ref. Ch. Bd.*
Voice from the newsboys. Morrow, J. 75c... *Barnes.*
Voice from Olivet. Newton, R. 10c........ *Am. S. S.*
Voice from the pious dead of the medical profession. Brown, H. J. $1.50; $2.......... *Perkinpine.*
Voice from Richmond, and other addresses to children and youth. 18°. 75c................. *Am. S. S.*
Voice of blood. Phillips, S. $2........ *Ref. Ch. Pub.*
Voice of Christian life in song. Charles, E. $1.. *Carter.*
Voice of the church on the coming and kingdom of the Redeemer. Taylor, D. T. $1.25.... *Hastings.*
Voice of flowers. Sigourney, L. H. *net*, 19c. *Hamersley.*
Voice of God in the Psalms. Forbes, G. $2.. *Macmillan.*
Voice of Jesus suffering. Gaudentius, —. $2.. *O'Shea.*
Voice of melody. Armstrong, J. 40c........ *Ditson.*
Voice of the passion flower. *See* What the wind taught.
Voice of praise. Baird, E. T., *and* Converse, C: C. 35c.; 40c.; 20c.; 25c. .... *Pres. Com.*
Voice of praise. Hamilton, E. $1.38........ *Ditson.*
Voice of the seven thunders. Martin, J. L. $1.50. *Cen. Bk.*
Voice of time. Stroud, J. 50c.............. *Cassell.*
Voices from the valley testifying of Jesus. Whitfield, F. 50c............................ *Leighton.*
Voices of comfort. *See* Griswold, R. W.
Voices of the morning. Bush, B. $1.25.. *Lippincott.*
Voices of nature. Bryant, W. C. 75c. ..... *Osgood.*
Voices of the prophets. Gifford, E. H. $2.50. *Scribner, W. & A.*
Voices of the prophets. Vaughan, C. J. $1.50. *Routledge.*
Voices of the soul. Reid, J. $1.75.......... *Carter.*
Volcanoes. ('55.) 2d ed. 18°. '75. 50c.... *So. Meth.*
Volckhausen, Ad. v. Why did he not die? or, the child from the Ebräergang; tr. by Mrs. A. L. Wister. 12°. $1.75................ *Lippincott.*
Volkening, H. (*ed.*) Kleine Missionharfe im Kirchen- u. Volkston. 12°. hf. bd., 25c...... *Volkening.*
Volkening, L. Amerikanische Jugendfreund (Der): Lesebuch f. Oberklassen. 8°. hf. leath., 60c. *Volkening.*
— Amerikanische Kinderfreund (Der): Lesebuch f. Mittelklassen. 8°. hf. leath., 30c.... *Volkening.*
— Lesefibel mit Schreibübungen. 8°. hf. bd., 15c. *Volkening.*
Volkhausen, A. Die Geschichte vom Propheten Jonas. [Satire.] 16°. '76. pap., 25c........... *Besser.*
Volksschul Lesebuch, begründet v. d. ev. Schullehrer-Seminar zu Münsterberg. 3 v. 8°. bds... *Brumder.*
Cont.: Estes Lesebuch, 40c. — Zweites Lesebuch, 60c. — Drittes Lesebuch, $1.
Vollmer, —. Vollständiges deutsches Ver. Staaten Kochbuch. 12°. 60c................... *Kohler.*
— *Eng.* Complete U. S. cook book. 12°. 60c. *Kohler.*
— *Germ and Eng.* 12°. $1.50.............. *Kohler.*
Vollständiges Kochbuch f. d. deutsch-am. Küche. ill. 12°. $1.50................... *F. W. Thomas.*
Volmann, K: Amadeus; or, a night with the spirit. ('52.) New ed. 12°. '53. $1......... *Scribner.*

Volney, Const. François Chassebœuf (*Comte*) de. New researches in anc. hist.; tr. 12°. $1.50..*Mendum.*
— Ruins; or, meditation on revolution of empires; with notes and ill.; [also] Law of nature; with biog. notice by Count Daru; tr. 12°. $1...*Mendum.*
— — *Same;* [also] Controversy between Jos. Priestly and Volney. 16°. $1..................*Miller.*
Voltaire, François Marie Arouet de. Brutus: tragedy; tr. 16°. pap., 15c.....................*French.*
— Henriade (La). 18°. '36. 40c......*G.R.Lockwood.*
— Histoire de Charles XII.; rev. par G. Surenne. 18°. 75c...............................*Appleton.*
— *Same.* 18°. 63c.; — with map and vocab. 12°. hf. roan, $1.25.......................*Lippincott.*
— *Eng.* History of Charles XII. of Sweden. 12°. '68. $1...................................*Claxton.*
— *Same;* with life of V. by Lord Brougham, and crit. notes by Macaulay and Carlyle; ed. by O. W. Wight. cr. 8°. $2.25; hf. cf., $4....*Hurd & H.*
— Ignorant philosopher; [also] Adventures of Pythagoras in India; tr. 8°. pap., 10c...*Mendum.*
— Mérope [Fr.] With notes by C. Delhavé. 16°. 50c.; pap., 25c.........................*Lippincott.*
— Philosophical dictionary; tr. 2 v. in 1. ill. 8°. $5. *Mendum.*
— Siècle de Louis XIV. 12°. $1.50....*G.R.Lockwood.*
Volunteer review. Williams, T. J. 15c.*De Witt; French.*
Von.

Note. For names of writers (not English or American) beginning with *von* look under initial letter of name following this prefix.

Von der Ehe der Christen. 18°. hf. bd., 25c....*Baer.*
Von dem Neffen der seinen Onkel sucht. Oertel, P. F. W. 25c...............................*Steiger.*
Vonneida, S. Collection of hymns for use of United Brethren in Christ. [German.] 18°. 60c.; leath., 75c.; mor., $1.25.................*Un.B.Pub.*
— Harps. [Germ. sing. book.] 24°. shp., 40c.; mor., 75c..............................*Un.B.Pub.*
— Sabbath school songster. [In Eng. or Germ.] 32°. 15c..............................*Un.B.Pub.*
Von Steinwehr, A. *See* Steinwehr, A. v.
Von Toodleburgs (The). Adams, F. C. $1.75. *Claxton.*
Voorhees, Dan. W. Speeches; compiled by C. S. Voorhees, with biog. sketch. 8°. '75. $5..*Clarke.*
Vornehm u. Gering. Lexow, F. 75c.; 50c...*Steiger.*
Vosburg, J: H: Ralph Elmwood: poem. 12°. '74. $1. *Claxton.*
Vose, G: L. Graphic method for solving certain algebraic equations. 18°. '75. bds., 50c. *VanNostrand.*
— Manual for railroad engineers and students: rules and tables for location, construction and equipment of railroads as built in U. S.; with portfolio of plans and maps. ill. 8°. $12.50..*Lee & S.*
— Orographic geology; or, the origin and structure of mountains. 8°. $3.....................*Lee & S.*
Vow assumed. *See* Tyng, S. H.
Vow at the bars. ('66.) New ed. 18°. '75. 40c. *Nat. Temp.*
Vow of the Ornani. Gotthold, J. N. 15c......*Ames.*
Vox (*pseud.*) George Washington Brown: non-partisan polit. satire. ill. 16°. '76. pap., 25c. *Am.News.*
Voyage alone in the yawl "Rob Roy." MacGregor, J. $1.25...............................*Roberts.*
Voyage and venture; or, perils by sea and land. ill. 16°. $1...............................*Routledge.*
Voyage and venture; or, the pleasures and perils of a sailor's life. ill. 12°. $1.25...........*T. Bliss.*
Voyage autour de ma chambre. Maistre, X. de. 50c. *Holt.*
Voyage lib. of adventure. *See* Bowman, Anne.
Voyage of life. 18°. 75c.................*Cong. Pub.*
Voyage of a naturalist. Darwin, C. R. 2 v. $2. *Harper.*
Voyage of the ship Christian. 16°. 20c.; 25c. *Am. Bapt.*
Voyage of the sloop Mary, Quebeck; with account of her wreck off Montauk Point, L. I., 1701; with introd. and notes by E. B. O'Callaghan. sm. 8°. '66. bds., $2.............................*Munsell.*
Voyage of the White Falcon. 16°. $1......*Am.S.S.*
Voyage round the world. Kingston, W. H. G. $2.50. *Nelson.*
Voyage to the Fortunate Isles. Piatt, S. M. B. $1.50. *Osgood.*
Voyages of the slavers St. John and Arms of Amsterdam, 1659–'63; with add. papers ill. of the slave trade under the Dutch; tr. with introd., etc., by E. B. O'Callaghan. sm. 8°. '67. bds., $3..*Munsell.*
Voyages round the world; from death of Capt. Cook to the present time. 18°. 75c..........*Harper.*
Vroom, Garret D. W. *See* New Jersey, Sup. Court reports.
Vroom, P: D. *See* New Jersey, Sup. Court reports.
Vuitel, Jonas. French reading book for schools and families: hist. books of New. Test. in French. 8°. (Bagster.) $1.25.............................*Wiley.*
Vulgar errors. *See* Browne, *Sir* T:
Vulgarisms and other errors of speech; with review of G. W. Moon's "Dean's English" and "Bad English." ('68.) 2d ed. 16°. '69. $1.25..*Claxton.*
Vyhnancův syn. [Son of the exiles.] 16°. '74. $3.40.................................*Geringer.*

W., A. L. Hymns and meditations. ill. 16°. $1. *Routledge.*
— Lizzie Weston's mission and how it was fulfilled. ill. 18°. 60c..........................*Bost.Am.Tr.*
— — *See also* Winter school stories.
W., E. Virginia, more especially the south part thereof, richly and truly valued: Lond., 1650. [Reprint.] 4°. pap., $1..............................*Sabin.*
W., E. A. Ethel Linton; or, the Feversham temper. 16°. $1.25.................*Cin.Meth.Bk.Conc.*
W., F. Big Bruce and little Moss. ill. 18°. 60c...*Crowell.*
— — *See also* Go ahead lib.
W., F. M. C. Little Nellie, the clockmaker's daughter. ('71.) New ed. 16°. '73. $1.25..........*Hoyt.*
W., J. R. The A B C of whist. 48°. 25c. *Scribner, W.& A.*
W., K. M. Ellie; or, nothing perfect here: tale for girls. 16°. $1.50.................(?)*Martien.*
W., M. S. Choice receipts. sq. 4°. '74. $1.50..*Osgood.*
W., S. Cotton. ill. 16°. 50c....................*Pott.*
W—, *Mrs.* C: Haste to the rescue. 18°. '60. 60c.*Am. Tr.*
— *Same.* 18°. 75c.............................*Carter.*
Waagen, Gst. F: *See* Kugler, F. T., Handbook of painting.
Wachenhusen, Hs. For a woman's sake; or, mysteries of the castle; tr. by MS. 8°. '75. $1.50; pap., 75c...................................*W.F.Gill.*
Wackernagel, W., *and* Gruhler, J. Erinnerungen an das heilige Land. 2d ed. 8°. pap., 50c...*Pilger.*
Wacousta. Richardson, J. 50c...........*De Witt.*
Waddell, Mos. Life of Caroline E. Smelt. ill. 18°. '51. 35c.................................*Am Tr.*
— *Same;* with introd by J. N. Waddell. New ed., rev. and enl. 16°. '76. 50c.....*Pres.Com.of Pub.*
— —*See also* Newton, J:
Waddell, W: H: Greek grammar for beginners. 16°. $1.......................................*Harper.*
— Latin grammar for beginners. 16°. $1....*Harper.*
Waddington, G: History of the church, to the reformation. 8°. $2.........................*Harper.*
Waddington, J: John Penry, the Pilgrim martyr, 1559–1593. 18°. 75c..............*Cong. Pub.*
— Path of the Pilgrim church, from its origin to its establ. in New Eng. 16°. 75c.......*Cong. Pub.*
— Track of the hidden church. 12°. $1.25..*Cong. Pub.*

Waddy, Edith. Little trowel. ill. 16°. '75. 90c. *Meth. Bk. Conc.*

Waddy, F: Cartoon portraits and biog. sketches of men of the day. 4°. '75. $7.50 .... *Routledge.*

Wade, E: Code rel. to the poor in state of N. Y.: laws in force in 1870, rel. to support and maintenance of the poor. 8°. '70. shp., $4.50.. *Weed.*

Wadsworth, C: America's mission: Thanksgiving discourse. 8°. pap., 25c. .... *Peterson.*
— Politics in religion. 8°. pap., 12c........ *Peterson.*
— Thankfulness and character: two discourses. 8°. pap., 25c.......................... *Peterson.*
— Thanksgiving: sermon. 8°. pap., 15c.... *Peterson.*

Wadsworth, Olive A. Bill Riggs, jr. ill. 18°. '71. 75c. .... *Lothrop.*
— Homeward bound. 16°. 90c. .... *Pres. Bd.*
— Kit, Fan, Tot and the rest of them: what they did, said and thought about. ill. 16°. $1.25. *Bost. Am. Tr.*

Wadsworth boys. Erickson, D. S. $1.50.. *Lothrop.*

Wag: tale for children. 18°. 25c.... *Scribner, W. & A.*

Wages of sin. Yates, E. 75c............. *W. F. Gill.*

Waggener, Dan. B. Book-keeping simplified: double entry system expl., with rules and tables. 16°. '74. $1; bds., 75c. .... *Waggener.*
— Standard wages tables. obl. 16°. '75. $1.. *Waggener.*

Waggie and Wattie. C., S. T. 75c.....(?) *Martien.*

Waggoner, J. Fred. (*ed.*) Home cook book; comp. from recipes contributed by the ladies of Chicago, etc. 12°. '74. $1.50........... *J. F. Waggoner.*

Waggoner, Ja. H. The atonement: exam. of a remedial system in light of nature and revelation. 16°. '72. 20c........................ *Sev. Day Adv.*

Waggoner, Jos. H. Nature and tendency of modern spiritualism. 16°. '72. 20c. .... *Sev. Day Adv.*
— Refutation of the age to come. 16°. '72. 20c. *Sev. Day Adv.*
— Resurrection of the unjust. 16°. '70. pap., 15c. *Sev. Day Adv.*
— Review of Baird's two sermons on the Sabbath. 16°. pap., 10c........................ *Sev. Day Adv.*
— Wesen (Das) des Sabbaths. 16°. '70. 10c. *Sev. Day Adv*
— *Dutch.* 16°. pap., 10c.............. *Sev. Day Adv.*
— *Eng.* The truth found: nature and obligation of the Sabbath of the fourth commandment. 16°. '76. pap., 10c...................... *Sev. Day Adv.*

Wagner, D: *See* Missouri, Statutes.

Wagner, Ern. Manual of general pathology; tr. from 6th Germ. ed. by J. Van Duyn and E. C. Seguin. 8°. '76. $5.50; leath., $6.50.. *W. Wood.*

Wagner, R: Art life and theories; sel. and tr. by E. L. Burlingame; with pref., catalogue of Wagner's pub. works and drawings of Bayreuth opera house. 12°. '75. $2.................... *Holt.*
— Beethoven; tr. by A. R. Parsons. ('72.) 3d ed., rev. 8°. '73. $1.50; $1.75......... *Benham.*
— Lohengrin. [Music.] 8°. $1.50; pap., $1.25. *Church.*
— — *See also* Ditson.
— Tannhaüser. *See* Ditson.
— — March and chorus. 8°. pap., 30c. ..... *Church.*

Wagner, Rud. Handbook of chemical technology; tr., ed. and enl. from 8th Germ. ed. by W: Crookes. ill. 8°. $5............................ *Appleton.*

Wagner, the wehr wolf. Reynolds, G. W. M. 50c. *De Witt.*

Wagoner of the Alleghanies. *See* Read, T. B.

Wagstaffe, W: Warwick. Student's guide to human osteology. ill. 12°. '76. $3.50...... *Lindsay.*
— *See also* Clark, F. Le G., *and* Wagstaffe, W. W.

Wahl, O. W. Land of the czar. 8°. $5.25. *Scribner, W. & A.*

Wahlverwandtschaften (Die). *See* Goethe, J. W. v.

Wahre geistliche Schild (Der). 18°. $1..... *Radde.*

Wahres u. falsches Wohlthun. Nieritz, G. 25c. *Morwitz.*

Waidmann's Erinnerungen. *See* Pausinger, F. v.

Waifs from the way-bills of an expressman. Tucker, T. W. $1................................ *Lee & S.*

Waifs of the world. Beach, C. A. $1.75. *Scribner, W. & A.*

Waihoura. *See* Kingston, W. H. G.

Waikna. Squier, E. G. $1.50.............. *Harper.*

Wailes, B: L. C. *See* Mississippi agric. and geol. survey.

Wainwright, Jona. M. Family prayers for every day in the week, and for commemoration of holy days, etc. 12°. '61. $1.25................ *Dutton.*
— Life. 18°. 55c.; 60c...................... *Dutton.*
— Music of the church: coll. of psalm, hymn and chant tunes. obl. 8°. '52. $2...... *Ditson; Gordon.*
— Select sermons. 8°. $3................ *Appleton.*
— Short family prayers, for every morning and evening of the week and for particular occasions. 12°. '61. 50c. .... *Dutton.*

Waisbrooker, *Mrs.* Lois. Alice Vale: story for the times. ('69.) 4th ed. 12°. '74. $1.25.. *Colby.*
— Helen Harlow's vow. ('70.) 4th ed. 12°. '75. $1.25. *Colby.*
— Mayweed blossoms. ('71.) 2d ed. 12°. '75. $1.25. *Colby.*
— Nothing like it; or, steps to the kingdom. 12°. '75. $1.50 .... *Colby.*

Waise (Die). Nieritz, G. 25c............ *Morwitz.*

Waisen (Die). *See* Hoffmann, F:

Waisenkind (Das). 24°. 20c............ *Ev. Assoc.*

Wait, W: Law and practice [in N. Y.] in civil actions and proceedings in justice's courts, practice on appeals to county courts, and actions at nisi prius. 3d ed. 2 v. 8°. '74. shp., $15.... *Gould.*
— Practice at law, in equity, and special proceedings in all courts of record in N. Y.; with forms. 6 v. 8°. '72–'75. shp., $45................. *Gould.*
— Table of cases affirmed, reversed, or cited in New York reports. [1794]–1872. 8°. '73. shp., $7.50 .... *Gould.*
— *See also* Clinton, G. W., *and* Wait, W.; — New York State, Code.

Wait for an answer. Lemon, H. 15c........ *French.*

Wait on the Lord. Smith, J. 20c........ *Randolph.*

Wait on the Lord. *See* Winslow, O.

Waite, H: Randall. Carmina collegensia: songs of Am. colleges, with sel. from student songs of Eng. and Germ. universities. ('68.) 2d ed. 8°. '76. $3; $4 .... *Ditson.*

Waite, Otis F. R. New Hampshire in the great rebellion. ill. 8°. $3.50................ *Claremont.*
— *Same.* 8°. '73. *$3.75............... *T. H. Davis.*

Waiting at the cross. Eddy, D. C. $1.50.. *H. A. Young.*

Waiting for a crown; or, early days of King David; by author of "Great things done by little people." ill. 12°. $1.50........................ *Nelson.*

Waiting for the morning. 16°. 90c......... *Am. S. S.*

Waiting for an omnibus. Morton, J. M. 15c... *French.*

Waiting for the verdict. Davis, R. H. $1.75.. *Sheldon.*

Waiting for the verdict: drama. 16°. pap., 15c. *French.*

Waiting hours. *See* Shipton, A.

Waiting race. Yates, E. 75c............. *Appleton.*

Waiting Saviour. Kirk, E. N. 50c..... *Bost. Am. Tr.*

Waiting world. Huntington, W. R. 20c.... *Dutton.*

Wake, C. S. *See* Westropp, H. M., *and* Wake, C. S.

Wake-Robin. Burroughs, J. $1.50...... *Hurd & H.*

Wake up, William Henry! White, C. 15c... *De Witt.*

Wakeley, Jos. B. Anecdotes of the Wesleys. 12°. '69. $1.25......................... *Meth. Bk. Conc.*
— Bold frontier preacher: portraiture of W: Craven. 18°. 50c................. *Cin. Meth. Bk. Conc.*

Wakeley, Jos. B., *continued.*
— Heroes of Methodism. 12°. '56. $1.75..*Meth. Bk. Conc.*
— Prince of pulpit orators: portraiture of G: Whitefield. 12°. '71. $1.25..................*Meth. Bk. Conc.*
— Temperance cyclopædia. 12°. '75. $2..*Nat. Temp.*
— Wesleyan Demosthenes: sel. sermons of Jos. Beaumont, with sketch of his character. 16°. '75. $1.25..........................*Meth. Bk. Conc.*

Waking up. *See* Bright gems for boys and girls; — Little girls' lib.

Walcot, C: M. [Plays.] 4 v. 16°. ea., pap., 15c. *French.*
Cont.: Good fellow: comedy. — Hi-a-wa-tha: extravaganza. — Nothing to nurse: farce. — One coat for two suits.

Walcott, C. H. *See* Buswell, H. F., *and* Walcott, C. H.

Walcott, *Lieut.* G. H. Life. 18°. 50c.....*Cong. Pub.*

Waldauer, A: Fanchon, the cricket: drama. 16°. pap., 15c. ....*French.*
— Little barefoot: drama. 16°. pap., 15c......*French.*

Waldemar Krone's youth. *See* Ewald, H. F.

Walden, Emile de. Ball-room companion; or, dancing made easy. 16°. bds., 50c. ....*Dick & F.*

Walden, J. H. *See* Fisher, E., *and* Walden, J. H.

Walden, Treadwell. Our English Bible and its ancestors. 12°. '71. $1.25 ....*Porter.*
— Sunday school prayer book; with the canticles, hymns and carols of the "Sunday school chant and tune book." Rev. ed. 16°. '63. hf. bd., 40c. ....*Dutton.*
— Sunday school prayer book and the chant and tune book; with the music. 16°. '63. $1; hf. bd., 50c. ....*Dutton.*

Walden; or, life in the woods. Thoreau, H. D. $1.50. *Osgood.*

Waldenses (The). ill. 12°. $1.25........*Pres. Bd.*

Waldeyer, W. *See* Manual of histology.

Waldfried. Auerbach, B. $2.................*Holt.*

Waldkapelle (Die). *See* Schmid, C. v.

Waldlilie (Die). Fleischmann, K. 25c. *Germ. Bapt.*

Waldlilien: Geschichte e. frommen Mädchens. 18°. 30c...................................*Ev. Assoc.*

Waldo; or, a child of the covenant remembered. 18°. 30c.................................*Cong. Pub.*

Waldron, *Mrs.* S. D. Silent musings: book of scraps. 12°. '76. 60c..........................*So. Meth.*

Waldron, W. R. Cartouche, the French robber: drama. 16°. pap., 15c...................*French.*
— Will and the way: drama. 16°. pap., 15c. *French.*
— Worth a struggle: comedy. 16°. pap., 15c...*French.*

Waldron, W: Watson. Atala; or, love in a desert: a metrical Indian legend, and other poems. 16°. '74. 75c.................................*Whittaker.*

Walford, C. Insurance guide and handbook on life, fire, marine, tontine and accident insurance. Am. ed., rev. and enl., with notes. 8°. $4.. *Wynkoop.*

Walford, Edith. Little Content. fp. 8°. 50c...*Cassell.*

Walford, E: *See* Thornbury, W., *and* Walford, E.

Walford, L. B. Mr. Smith: part of his life. (Leis. hour ser.) 16°. '75. $1.25.............*Holt.*

Walk about Zion. Clark, J. A. $1.25 ......*Carter.*

Walk and a talk. *See* Little Rosy's travels.

Walker, A. *See* Bible, Gospels.

Walker, Ab. Jos. *See* Alabama, Code.

Walker, Alex. Intermarriage; or, mode in which, and causes why, beauty, health, intellect result from certain unions, and deformity, disease and insanity from others. ill. 12°. '72. $1.50..*Lindsay.*
— Lady's guide to perfect beauty: anal. and classification of elements of beauty in women. ('60.) New ed. 12°. '68. $1.25 ....*Claxton.*

Walker, Alex. Life of Andrew Jackson. 12°. $1.75. *J. E. Potter.*

Walker, Amasa. Science of wealth: manual of polit. economy. (Student's ed.) 12°. $1.50..*Lippincott.*

Walker, *Miss* Annie L. Plays for children. 16°. bds., 50c..........................*Routledge.*

Walker, C. E. Warlock of the glen: melo-drama. 16°. pap., 15c. ....*French.*

Walker, C. L. *See* Walker, S. R. *and* C. L.

Walker, C: Faith explained. 18°. '50. 25c...*Am. Tr.*
— Repentance explained. 18°. '50. 25c......*Am. Tr.*

Walker, C: Liturgy of the church of Sarum, with [its] calendar; tr. with pref., notes and introd. by T. T. Carter. 4°. $3 ....*Pott.*
— Plain-song "reason why." 12°. '76. $1.75..*Pott.*
— Ritual "reason why:" explan. of meaning of ritual observance. 16°. $1.75..................*Pott.*
— Services of the church, accord. to use of illustrious church of Sarum. 32°. $1.75 ....*Pott.*

Walker, C: D. Memorial of the Virginia Military Institute: sketch of graduates and élèves who fell during the war between the states. 8°. $4; shp., $5..........................*Lippincott.*

Walker, C: M. History of Athens Co., Ohio, and of Ohio Land Co., and first settlement of state at Marietta. map and por. 8°. '69. $6; — large pap. 2 v. imp. 8°. $12..............*Clarke.*

Walker, D. Sepulchre in the garden. 18°. 37c. *Cong. Pub.*

Walker, Don. Manly exercises: skating, riding, driving, etc. New ed., rev. by "Craven." ill. 12°. (Bohn.) $1.75 ....*Little, B. & Co.*
— *Same.* ill. 12°. (Bohn.) $2. *Lippincott; Scribner, W. & A.*

Walker, *Mrs.* E: Ashley. From the crib to the cross: life of Christ in words of one syllable. ill. 16°. $1. *World Pub.*
— *Same;* [also] Pilgrim's progress; in words of one syllable. ill. 12°. '76. $1.50...... *World Pub.*
— Pilgrim's progress; in words of one syllable. ill. 16°. $1.................................*World Pub.*

Walker, Emile. What is free trade? 12°. '67. $1. *Putnam.*

Walker, Fs. Amasa. Some results of the census of 1870; read before Am. Soc. Sci. Assoc., May 15, 1873. 8°. '73. pap., 50c........... *Williams.*
— Statistical atlas of U. S. maps. 4°. '75. hf. mor., *$18.................................*Bien.*
— Treatise on wages and the wages class. 8°. '76. $3.50. *Holt.*

Walker, G: Cribbage made easy. 16°. 75c.; bds., 50c. *Dick & F.*

Walker, Harvey Day. Book-keeping for the million; by single entry. 8°. '69. $2..........*Claxton.*
— Elements of English grammar. ('69.) 2d ed., rev. 12°. '71. 90c.........................*Claxton.*

Walker, H: N. *See* Michigan, Court of Chancery reports.

Walker, J. Bryant, *and* Bates, C. Digest of Ohio decisions. 2 v. roy. 8°. '75. *net,* shp., $12..*Clarke.*

Walker, J. G. Charlie Ashley; or, adventures of an orphan. ill. 12°. 75c...................*Pott.*
— *Same.* 16°. $1 ....(?) *Martien.*

Walker, Ja. Sermons preached in Harvard chapel. 12°. $1.75............................**Osgood.*

Walker, Ja. Barr. Doctrine of the Holy Spirit; or, philos. of divine operation in the redemption of man: v. 2 of Philosophy of the plan of salvation. 4th ed., rev. and enl. 12°. '73. $1.50..*Griggs.*
— Living questions of the age. 12°. $1.50..*Lippincott.*
— Philosophy of plan of salvation; with introd. essay by C. E. Stowe. New ed., with sup. chapter by author. 12°. '74. $1.50..............*Griggs.*
— Poetry of reason and conscience. 12°. $1.50. *Lippincott.*

Walker, Ja. Bradford Richmond. Memorial of the Walkers of the old Plymouth Colony. v. 1. por. 8°. '61. $3; $4; $5.....*J. B. R. Walker.*

Walker, *Mrs.* Ja. B. R. *See* Walker, *Mrs.* Ma. Spring.

Walker, Ja. Perkins. Faith and patience: a story and something more for boys. ill. sq. 16°. 75c. *Fuller.*
— *See also* Altar at home.
Walker, Jeanie Mort. Life of Capt. Jos. Fry, the Cuban martyr. ill. 8°. *$3; $3.50...... *Burr.*
Walker, J: Critical pronouncing dict. and expositor of the Eng. lang. 8°. shp., $2.50 .... *Butler.*
— *Same.* sq. 16°. 75c.................... *Strong.*
— *Same.* 16°. shp., 63c................ *Lippincott.*
— — *See also* Johnson, S: English dict.
— Manual of elocution and oratory; ed. by R: Culver. 12°. 95c........................ *Lippincott.*
— Rhyming, spelling and pronouncing dict. of the Eng. lang. roy. 12°. $3.................. *Dick & F.*
— *Same;* abridg., with index of allowable rhymes. 12°. $1.25 .... *Barnes.*
Walker, J: A. Handbook of Ireland: ill. guide for tourists and travellers. 2d ed. map and pl. 12°. '72. $2 .... *Routledge.*
Walker, *Mrs.* Ma. Spring. Both sides of the street. ('71.) New ed. ill. 16°. '76. $1.60.... *Hoyt.*
— Down in a saloon. ('71.) New ed. 16°. '74. $1.50. *Hoyt.*
— Family doctor; or, Mrs. Barry and her Bourbon. ('68.) New ed. ill. 16°. '76. $1.50..... *Hoyt.*
— Rev. Dr. Willoughby and his wine. ('69.) New ed. 12°. '75. $1.50.................. *Nat. Temp.*
— White robes. 16°. $1.50.............. *Cong. Pub.*
— — *See also* Island home lib.
Walker, P: History and habits of animals; especially of North America and of Scripture. ill. sq. 12°. $1.50 .... *Pres. Bd.*
Walker, R. S. *See* Texas, Sup. Court reports.
Walker, Robt. Ja. *See* Mississippi, Law reports.
Walker, S. R. *and* C. L. Digest of Louisiana Sup. Court reports, 1860–'69. 8°. '70......... *State.*
Walker, T: H. Companion for the afflicted. 12°. '46. $1.10......................... *Meth. Bk. Conc.*
Walker, Tim. Introduction to Am. law: first book for students. 6th ed., rev. by J. B. Walker. 8°. '74. shp., $6 .... *Little, B. & Co.*
Walker, W. B. Cyclical deluges: explication of chief geological phenomena of the globe. 12°. $1.75. *Appleton.*
Walker, W. H. Notes on screw propulsion: its rise and history. 8°. '61. 75c....... *VanNostrand.*
Walker, W: Fruits and flowers: tunes and songs for common and Sunday schools. obl. 12°. bds., 63c. *Lippincott.*
— Southern and western pocket harmonist. [Camp meeting songs.] 18°. $1; hf. roan, 84c.... *Desilver.*
Walker, the filibuster. [Fiction.] 12°. pap., 20c. *Hurst.*
Walking in the light. Buck, D. D. 60c. *Cin. Meth. Bk. Conc.*
Walking in the light. Smith, R. P. 75c.... *Willard.*
Walking with God. Prime, S. I. 60c.; 40c.; 25c. *Randolph.*
Walking with God. Rankin, J. B. 70c. ... *Pres. Bd.*
Walkingame, Fs. Arithmetic; in pounds, shillings and pence. 12°. 30c. .... *Sadlier.*
Walks about Jerusalem. Errett, I. $1 ...... *Chase.*
Walks and talks. *See* Sleeper, W. T.
Walks and talks of an Am. farmer in England. Olmsted, F. L. $1.50.................... *Gleason.*
Walks and talks with grandpapa. *See* Cupples, A. J.
Walks from Eden. Warner, S. $1.50 ...... *Carter.*
Walks in Florence. Horner, S. *and* J. 2 v. $6. *Routledge.*
Walks in London. Mogridge, G. 60c...... *So. Meth.*
Walks in Rome. Hare, A. J. C. $3.50 .. *Routledge.*
Walks of usefulness. 18°. 60c.; 70c...... *Am. Bapt.*
Walks of usefulness in London. Campbell, J. 50c. *Pres. Bd.*
Walks, talks, travels and exploits of two school-boys. Atkinson, J. C. $1.25.............. *Routledge.*
Wall, G: H: The emigrant's lost son; or, life alone in the forest. ill. 16°. 50c............. *Routledge.*
Wall, H: Fashion: satirical poem. 8°. '70. pap., 25c.............................. *West, J. & Co.*
Wall, W: History of infant baptism; with Mr. Gale's reflections, and Dr. Wall's defence; ed. by H. Cotton. 2 v. 8°. $7.................... *Pott.*
Wallace, Ad. Earnest minister (The): biog. of R. V. Lawrence. 12°. '73. $1.50 ..... *A. Wallace.*
— Modern Pentecost (A). 8°. '72. $1.... *A. Wallace.*
— Parson of the islands: biog. of Joshua Thomas. ('60.) New ed. 12°. '72. $1.50.... *A. Wallace.*
Wallace, Alfr. Russell. Contributions to theory of natural selection: essays. 2d ed. cr. 8°. '71. $2 .... *Macmillan.*
— Defence of mod. spiritualism; with Am. pref. by E. Sargent. ('74.) 3d ed. 12°. '75. pap., 25c... *Colby.*
— Malay archipelago, land of the orang-utan and bird of paradise: narr. of travel in 1854–'62, with studies of man and nature. maps and ill. cr. 8°. $2.50 .... *Harper.*
— Natural selection as applied to man. 12°. '71. pap., 25c.......................... *Van Nostrand.*
— *See also* Historical and descriptive account of British India.
Wallace, D. A. Church membership. 18°. 25c. *U. P. Bd. of Pub.*
Wallace, *Mrs.* E. D. Strife: romance of Germany and Italy. 12°. '71. $1.75........... *Claxton.*
— Woman's (A) experiences in Europe; incl. England, France, Germ. and Italy. 12°. $1.50.. *Appleton.*
Wallace, Edn. R. Descriptive guide to Adirondacks, and handbook of travel to Saratoga Springs, Lakes George, Champlain, etc. ('72.) 5th ed. maps and ill. 12°. '76. *$2.......... *Waverley.*
— *See also* Smith, H. P., *and* Wallace, E. R.
Wallace, H: E. *See* Pennsylvania, Constitution; — Philadelphia, Reports.
Wallace, Hor. Binney. Art and scenery in Europe, with other papers. 2d ed. 12°. '56. $2. *Claxton; Lippincott.*
— Literary criticisms, and other papers. 3d ed. 12°. $2.............................. *Lippincott.*
— *See also* Hare, J. I. C., *and* Wallace, H. B.
Wallace, J. A. *See* Engles, J. P., *and* Wallace, J. A.
Wallace, J. J. Little Ruby; or, home jewels: drama. 16°. pap., 15c. .... *De Witt.*
Wallace, J: B. *See* United States, Circuit Court reports.
Wallace, J: H. American trotting register. v. 1. 8°. $10 .... *Woodward.*
— *Same.* v. 2. 8°. '74. $10 .... *Hurd & H.*
— *See also* American stud book.
Wallace, J: W: *See* United States, Sup. Court reports.
Wallace, J: W: *jr.* *See* United States, Circuit Court reports.
Wallace, Lew. The fair god; or, the last of the 'tzins: tale of the conquest of Mexico. 12°. '73. $2; hf. cf., $4......................... *Osgood.*
Wallace, M. A. Well! well! 12°. $1.25; $1.75. *Sadlier.*
Wallace, Rob. Elements of algebra. cr. 8°. 75c. *Cassell.*
— Elements of arithmetic. cr. 8°. 75c....... *Cassell.*
— *See also* De Lolme, J. L., Wallace, R., *and* Bridgeman, H.
Wallace, *Mrs.* Sa. S. T. Boys of Wyoming valley. 18°. 60c........................... *Pres. Bd.*
— Child's (The) mission. 18°. 35c.......... *Pres. Bd.*
— Julia's visit to the asylum. 18°. 35c..... *Pres. Bd.*
— Rosalie's lessons. 18°. 50c. .... *Pres. Bd.*

Wallace, W: Vincent. Amber witch: opera. 8°. '61. $4.50; $6 .... *T.J.Hall.*

Wallace. Abbott, J. 90c. .... *Harper.*

Wallace. Reynolds, G. W. M. $1.75; $1.. *Peterson.*

Wallace, the hero of Scotland. Barrymore, W. 15c. *French.*

Wallamanumps: temperance story. 18°. 75c. *Cong. Pub.*

Wallen, H: D. Service manual for instruction of newly appointed commissioned officers, and rank and file of army. 12°. '69. $1.50.. *Van Nostrand.*

Wallenstein's Lager. *See* Schiller, J. F. v.

Wallenstein's Tod. *See* Schiller, J. F. v.

Waller, *Mrs.* F. Alice and her friends. 16°. '64. 75c. *Dodd.*

— Little Mary's first and last falsehood. ill. 18°. '63. 20c. .... *Am. Tr.*

Waller, Hor. *See* Livingstone, D: Last journals in central Africa.

Waller, J: Open communion; with introd. essay by D. R. Campbell. 12°. 80c. .... *So. Bapt.*

Waller, J: F. Pictures from Eng. literature: ill. by E. M. Ward, J. C. Horsley, W. F. Yeames and others. cr. 4°. $3.50; $5 .... *Cassell.*

— Revelations of Peter Brown, poet and peripatetic, found in his black box. fp. 8°. $1 ...... *Cassell.*

Waller, S. E. Six weeks in the saddle: a painter's journal in Iceland. ill. cr. 8°. '73. $1.75. *Macmillan.*

Wallis, Alex. H. *See* Kelly, J:

Wallis, H. *See* Kramer, H., *and* Wallis, H.

Wallis, Severn T. Address at unveiling of statue of Chief Justice Taney. 8°. '72. 25c. .... *Murphy.*

— Discourse on life and character of G: Peabody. 8°. '70. 50c. .... *Murphy.*

— Glimpses of Spain; or, notes of an unfinished tour in 1847. 12°. $1.50; hf. cf., $3.25 .... *Harper.*

Wall's End miner. Everett, J. 50c. .. *Meth. Bk. Conc.*

Walmesley, C: ["Pastorini."] General history of the Christian church. 12°. $1.25 .... *Sadlier.*

Walmsley, Hu. Mulleneux. Wild sports and savage life in Zulu land. ill. 16°. $1.75.. *Scribner, W.&A.*

Walnut grove ser. 4 v. 16°. $5 .... *H.A. Young.*
Cont.: Good measure, by D. S. Erickson. — Carl Bartlett, by D. S. Erickson. — Little pea-nut merchant. — Making honey.

Walpole, Hor. Anecdotes of painting in England. 12°. $3 .... *Scribner, W.&A.*

— Castle of Otranto. *See* Reeve, C., Old English baron.

— Collected letters. 9 v. 8°. $36; hf. cf., $60. *Scribner, W.&A.*

Walpole. *See* Bulwer-Lytton, *Sir* E. G. E. L.

Walpurgis night. Mendelssohn-Bartholdy, F. $1.25; $1; 80c. .... *Ditson.*

Walpurgisnacht (Die). *See* Zschokke, H:

Walrée, E. C. W. van. ["Christine Müller."] Burgomaster's family; or, weal and woe in a little world; tr. by Sir J. S. Lefevre. 8°. $1.50; pap., $1.25 .... *Scribner.*

— Story of wandering Willie; tr. 8°. pap., 50c. *Scribner.*

Walsh, J: Benn. *See* Ormathwaite, *Lord.*

Walsh, J: H: ["Stonehenge."] British rural sports. 12th ed., enl. ill. 8°. $10.50. *Scribner, W.&A.*

— Dog (The) in health and disease; compr. various modes of breaking and training him for hunting, coursing, shooting, etc. ill. cr. 8°. $3.75.. *Lee & S.*

— Handbook of riding and driving. roy. 32°. bds., 20c. *Routledge.*

— Horse in the stable and the field: his management in health and disease; with notes and add. by R. McClure, and essay on Am. trotting horse by E. Harvey. ill. cr. 8°. '71. $2 .... *Porter.*

— *Same.* cr. 8°. $2.50 .... *Taintor.*

Walsh, J: H: *continued.*

— *Same.* ill. 8°. $3.50 .... *Judd.*

— (*ed.*) Encyclopedia of rural sports. ill. cr. 8°. $4.50 .... *Porter.*

— Every horse owner's cyclopedia; incl. American trotting horse by E. Harvey, Turf and trotting horse of Am. by J. Elderkin, Percheron horse ed. by R. McClure. ill. 8°. '71. $3.75; shp., $4.50; hf. mor., $5.50 .... *Porter.*

— Manual of domestic economy; incl. directions for management of nursery and sick-room, etc. col. pl. and ill. 8°. '73. $5 .... *Routledge.*

— *See also* Athletic sports and manly exercises.

— *and* Forrest, G: Handbook of manly exercises. roy. 32°. bds., 20c. .... *Routledge.*

— *and* Wood, J. G. Handbook of archery, fencing and broadsword. roy. 32°. bds., 20c. .... *Routledge.*

Walsh, J: Tomline. Book of sermons, practical and controversial. roy. 8°. $1.50 .... *Chase.*

— Salvation from sin; or, what must I do to be saved? 24°. pap., 10c. .... *Chase.*

Walsh, M. Chemical and geol. obs. rel. to brick-making in western India. 8°. pap., 40c. ..... *Spon.*

Walsh, Mich. McN. The lawyer in the school room. ('67.) 3d ed. 12°. '71. $1 .... *Schermerhorn.*

Walsh, T: History of the Irish church. 8°. $3.50; hf. mor., $4.50; $5 .... *Sadlier.*

Walsh, W. P. *See* Daily readings for holy seasons.

Walsh, W: Catholic offering. 12°. $1.50 .... *Strong.*

— Eucharistica: pieces, original and translated, on sacrament of the eucharist. 16°. $1 .... *Strong.*

— Lenten manual for passion time and holy week. 24°. 50c. .... *Strong.*

— *See also* Vincent de Paul, *St.*, Spiritual maxims.

Walsh, W: Shepard (*ed.*) Treasure-trove ser.; ed. by R. H. Stoddard. v. 1–3. 16°. '75. ea., $1... *W.F. Gill.*
Cont.: Burlesque. — Travesty. — Story.

Walshe, *Miss* E. H. Golden hills: tale of the Irish famine. 16°. $1.40 .... *Pres. Bd.*

— Manuscript man (The); or, the Bible in India. 16°. $1 .... *Pres. Bd.*

— *Same.* ill. 12°. '70. $1.25 .... *Meth. Bk. Conc.*

Walshe, Wa. Hayle. On disease of the heart and great vessels. 8°. $3 .... *Lea.*

Walsingham, Ctte. Annette; or, the chronicles of Bellevue. 12°. '75. $1.75 .... *Claxton.*

— O'er moor and fen. 12°. '75. $1.50 ...... *Claxton.*

Walten (Das) Gottes. Baumbach, J. 35c.... *Pilger.*

Walter, Jac. (*ed.*) Ancient and mod. music; sel. for use of Cath. Church. f°. bds., $5 ...... *Willig.*

Walter, W: H. Canticles and chants. obl. 16°. 50c. *Gordon.*

— Common prayer (The); with ritual song. 18°. '70. 75c.; pap., 50c. .... *Dutton.*

— Manual of church music. obl. 12°. $1.25.. *Gordon.*

Walter, *Uncle* (*pseud.*) *See* Sleeper, Wa. T.

Walter, the miser. 18°. 17c.; 22c. .... *Am. Bapt.*

Walter and Alice. Eldridge, A. 60c. ...... *Pres. Bd.*

Walter and Frank. Baker, H. N. W. $1.25.. *Graves.*

Walter and the prize, and other stories. ill. 18°. 45c. *Bost. Am. Tr.*

— *Same.* ill. 18°. 50c. .... *Pres. Bd.*

— *Same.* 18°. 60c. .... *Cong. Pub.*

— *See also* Young hero stories.

Walter Binning. *See* Tucker, *Mrs.* C.

Walter Bradley; or, the first lie. 18°. 35c... *Nelson.*

— *See also* Uncle Barnaby's budget.

Walter Ennis. *See* Thrilling stories of the olden time.

Walter Goring. Thomas, A. 75c. .... *Harper.*

Walter in the woods; or, the trees and common objects of the forest described and illustrated. ill. 12°. $1.25 .... *Nelson.*

Walter Lightfoot's pictures. Brown, H. E. 60c. *Bost. Am. Tr.*

Walter Macdonald. T., D. O. $1.50......*Lothrop.*
Walter Milligan. 18°. 30c..................*Dutton.*
Walter Neal's example. Brown, T. $1.25..*Lothrop.*
Walter Ogilby. Kinzie, J. H. $2.......*Lippincott.*
Walter Seyton. ill. 16°. 80c. ....*Lee & S.*
Walter Stockton. Llewellyn, E. 70c......*Pres. Bd.*
Walter Thornley. Sedgwick, T. $1.50 ....*Harper.*
Walter Thornton, and other stories. 32°. 40c. *Scribner, W. & A.*
Walter und die Belohnung. 18°. 30c. ....*Ev. Assoc.*
Walter's escape. De Liefde, J. B. $1.25. *Scribner, W. & A.*
Walter's friend. Adams, H. C. 75c......*Routledge.*
Walter's little lib. *See* Witt, *Mme.* H. de.
Walter's mistake: book for boys. 18°. 75c.....*Nelson.*
Walter's school-days. Adams, H. C. $1.25..*Routledge.*
Walter's tour in the east. *See* Eddy, D. C.
Walter's word. Payn, J. 75c...............*Harper.*
Walters, M. D. C. Harmony of prophecies on restoration of Israel and Judah. cr. 8°. (Bagster.) $1.12 .... *Wiley.*
Walther, C. F. W. Absolution: sermon; tr. 12°. pap., 10c. ....*Luth. Bk. St.*
— Amerikanisch-lutherische Evangelien Postille. ('71.) 5th ed. 4°. '76. $2.50................*Barthel.*
— Amerikanisch-lutherische Pastoraltheologie. ('72.) 2d ed. 8°. '75. $2.25.................*Barthel.*
— Antwort auf die Frage: Warum sind die symbol. Bücher unserer Kirche v. denen, welche Diener derselben werden wollen, unbedingt zu unterschreiben? 8°. 15c..................*Barthel.*
— Doctrine of the Lord's supper, its importance and necessity: sermon; tr. 12°. pap., 10c...*Luth. Bk. St.*
— Evangelische luth. Kirche (Die) die wahre sichtbare Kirche Gottes auf Erden. 8°. '67. 50c...*Barthel.*
— Lutherische Brosamen, Predigten u. Reden, etc. 8°. '76. $3.............................*Barthel.*
— Lutherische Lehre (Die) v. d. Rechtfertigung. 12°. '73. 20c.............................*Barthel.*
— Rechte Gestalt (Die) einer v. Staate unabhängigen Ortsgemeinde. ('62.) 2d ed. 8°. '64. 75c..*Barthel.*
— Stimme (Die) unserer [ev. luth.] Kirche in d. Frage v. Kirche u. Amt. 3d ed. 8°. $2.75....*Barthel.*
Walton, D. Witness of the Spirit. 18°. '46. 50c. *Meth. Bk. Conc.*
Walton, E. P. (*ed.*) Records of council of safety and governor and council of Vermont, 1775–1812. v. 1–4. por. and ill. 8°. '73–'76. ea., $3.. *Vt. Hist.*
Walton, Electa N. L. *See* Walton, G: A. *and* E. N. L.
Walton, Elij. (*ill.*) Alpine and eastern scenery: chromo-liths., with text by T. G. Bonney. roy. 4°. $28; — in 2 v. roy. 8°. ea., $15...*Stroefer.*
— Bernese Oberland: 12 scenes among the peaks and lakes, [with] descrip. text by T. G. Bonney. 4°. $25 .... *Lippincott.*
— English lake scenery: 22 chromo-lith. pl., with text by T. G. Bonney. 4°. $30 ....*Cassell.*
Walton, Emmeline L. (*ed.*) Children's gift: orig. and sel. articles. 16°. *net*, 50c...*Friends Bk. Assoc.*
Walton, G: A. Dictation exercises: key to table for practice in arithmetic. 2 v. 12°. bds., 1, 38c.; 2, 56c. .... *Ware.*
— Key to Written arithmetic and to Dictation exercises. 12°. hf. roan, $1.10 .... *Ware.*
— Metric system of weights and measures. 12°. 20c. *Ware.*
— Written arithmetic. 12°. hf. roan, $1.10.... *Ware.*
— *and* E. N. L. Illustrative pract. arith. 12°. bds., 95c. — Key. 12°. 25c. .... *Ware.*
— — Intellectual arithmetic; with introd. to written arith. 18°. bds.. 42c. .... *Ware.*
— — Manual of arith.; [with] key to illustrative pract. arith. 12°. 75c......................... *Ware.*
— — Pictorial primary arith. 18°. bds., 26c.... *Ware.*
Walton, G: A., *continued.*
— *and* Cogswell, Fs. Book of problems in arith. 12°. bds., 25c.; — with key, 75c.............. *Ware.*
Walton, G: E. Mineral springs of U. S. and Canadas. 12°. $2 ....*Appleton.*
Walton, Haynes. Practical treatise on diseases of the eye. 3d ed., rev. and enl. pl., ill., etc. 8°. '75. $9 ....*Lindsay.*
Walton, Izaak, *and* Cotton, C. Complete angler; or, the contemplative man's recreation: fac-simile of 1st ed., 1653. 16°. '76. bds., $3..*Scribner, W. & A.*
— — *Same.* (Pickering's ed.) 2 v. ill. roy. 8°. $20; hf. cf., $30; cf., $40; — in 1 v. cr. 8°. '75. $3; — ed. by "Ephemera." ill. cr. 8°. $1.25..*Routledge.*
— — *Same;* ed. by J. Major. ill. 18°. '70. $1.50. *Little, B. & Co.*
— — *Same;* with memoirs and notes by Sir H. Nicolas. ill. cr. 8°. $2; hf. cf., $5 ......*Scribner, W. & A.*
— — *Same;* with lives of authors and notes, ed. by E. Jesse; [also] Papers on fishing tackle, by H. G. Bohn. 12°. (Bohn.) $2.50; ill., $3..*Lippincott.*
— — — *Same.* 12°. (Bohn.) $2; ill., $3..*Scribner, W. & A.*
— — *Same;* with notes, bibliog. of fishing and fishing books, and notice of Cotton, by Dr. Bethune; with app. and index. 12°. $3................ *Wiley.*
— — — *See also* British pocket classics.
Walton, Jos. Brief biographies. 12°. pap., 25c. *Friends Bk. St.*
— George Fox's doctrines and ministry. 12°. pap., 8c. *Friends Bk. St.*
Walton, W: Problems and riders. *See* Cambridge Senate-House.
Waltz by Arditi: farce. 16°. pap., 15c......*French.*
Walworth, C. A. Gentle skeptic: essays and conversations of a country justice on authenticity and truthfulness of Old Test. records. 3d ed. 12°. '75. $1.50.........................*Cath. Pub.*
— *Same.* 8°. $1.50; $2.50; hf. cf., $3.75....*O'Shea.*
— *and* Burr, W. H. Doctrine of hell ventilated: discussion. 18°. '74. 60c.............*Cath. Pub.*
Walworth, Mansfield Tracy. [Novels.] 6 v. 12°. ea., $1.75..................................*Carleton.*
Cont.: Beverly. — Delaplaine. — Hotspur. — Lulu. — Stormcliff. — Warwick.
— Mission of death. 16°. 75c.; $1.25 ....*Sadlier.*
Wanastrocht, N. Grammar of the Fr. lang.; with treatise on Fr. versification by M. de Wailly; rev. by N. H. Jerôme. ('37.) New ed. 12°. '54. hf. roan, $1.25............*Claxton; Lippincott.*
— Recueil choisi de traits historiques et de contes moraux. With Eng. notes. New ed., rev. and enl. by P. Mouls. 12°. '44. $1.13..*Claxton; Lippincott.*
Wandelnde Seele. Schabalie, J. P. $1....*Schäfer.*
Wanderer, F. *See* Gallerie Deutscher Dichter.
Wanderer. ill. 18°. '57. 35c. ....*Am. Tr.*
Wanderer. Channing, W. E. $1.25; 75c.; $3; $4. *Osgood.*
Wanderer. Maitland, J. A. $1.75; $1.50..*Peterson.*
Wanderer in Africa. Tucker, C. 50c. ......*Carter.*
Wanderers. Goodrich, S. G. $1.50 ......*Appleton.*
Wandering boys; or, the castle of Olival: drama. 16°. pap., 15c........................*French.*
Wandering heir. *See* Reade, C:
Wandering heiress. Phillips, W. 75c...(?) *O'Kane.*
Wandering Jew. *See* Sue, E.
Wandering May. *See* Library of pleasant stories; — My little corner.
Wandering May; or, come unto me; by author of "Lonely Lily." ill. 16°. '75. 75c........*Dodd.*
Wandering minstrel. Mayhew, E. 15c. ....*French.*
Wandering recollections of a somewhat busy life. Neal, J. $1.50.......................*Roberts.*
Wandering soul. Schabalie, J. P. $1.25.....*Baer.*
Wandering Willie. *See* Story of wandering Willie.

Wanderings in Bible lands. Charles, E. $1... *Carter.*

Wanderings in every clime. Ainsworth, W. F. $10. *Routledge.*

Wanderings in interior of New Guinea. Lawson, J. A. $3 .... *Scribner, W. & A.*

Wanderings in the Isle of Wight. *See* Mogridge, G:

Wanderings in Spain. Hare, A. J. C. $3. *Dodd; Routledge.*

Wanderings of Master Peter. 16°. $1.15.. *Cong. Pub.*

Wanderings of a pilgrim. Harsha, D. A. 40c... *Pres. Bd.*

Wanderings of a pilgrim in the Alps. Cheever, G. B. $1 .... *Wiley.*

Wanderings of the river of the water of life. Cheever, G. B. $1 .... *Wiley.*

Wanderings over Bible lands and seas. *See* Charles, E.

Wanderungen eines Katholiken. 18°. '70. 25c. *Am. Tr.*

Wanklyn, Ja. Alfr. Milk analysis: treatise on exam. of milk and its derivations, cream, butter and cheese. 12°. $1 .... *VanNostrand.*

Wanner, A. The family; or, marriage relation and religious training of children. 12°. 75c. *Ref. Ch. Pub.*

Wanted, a male cook. Baker, G. M. 15c. .. *Lee & S.*

Wanted, a nurse. White, C. 15c........... *De Witt.*

Wanted, a pedigree. Finley, M. F. $2 ..... *Souder.*

Wanted, 1000 milliners. Coyne, J. S. 15c... *French.*

Wanted, a widow. Boucicault, D., *and* Seymour, C. 15c. .... *French.*

Wanted, a young lady. Suter, W. E. 15c. *De Witt; French.*

Wants and wishes. Tonna, C. E. 22c...... *Am. S. S.*

Wapping old stairs. Savill, J. F. 15c. ..... *French.*

War and peace. Tucker, C. 75c. .... *Carter.*

War Department. *See* United States.

War hawk. Armstrong, F. C. 80c. ...... *Routledge.*

War in heaven. Simmons, J. P. $1.50..... *Claxton.*

War lyrics. Brownell, H. H. $1.50 .... **Osgood.*

War lyrics. Ward, T. $1................ *Appleton.*

War of the roses. Baker, G. M. 15c........ *Lee & S.*

War path. Jones, J. B. $1.25; 75c. .... *Lippincott.*

War pictures: sel. of war lyrics. ill. 4°. '64. $1.50; mor., $5 .... *Hurd & H.*

War songs for freemen; with music. 12°. pap., 25c. *Ditson.*

War tiger. *See* Dalton, W.

War to the knife. Byron, H. J. 15c... *De Witt; French.*

War trail. Reid, M. $1.50 .... *Carleton.*

Warburton, Eliot B. G. Darien; or, the merchant prince. [Fiction.] 8°. pap., 50c. .... *Harper.*

— Reginald Hastings: tale of the troubles of 164–. 8°. pap., 50c........................... *Harper.*

— Travels in Egypt and the Holy Land; or, the crescent and the cross. ill. 12°. $1.50..... *T. Bliss.*

Warburton, G: Conquest of Canada. 2 v. 12°. $3; hf. cf., $6.50............................ *Harper.*

Warburton, W. Edward III. 16°. $1........ *Estes.*

Ward, A. E. Arthur's victory. ill. 12°. $1.. *Nelson.*

Ward, Adolphus W. House of Austria in the thirty years' war: lectures. fp. 8°. '69. $1.. *Macmillan.*

Ward, Artemus (*pseud.*) *See* Browne, C: F.

Ward, Aust. N. Male life among the Mormons: moral and social condition of that community from a man's standpoint. ill. 12°. $1.75.... *J. E. Potter.*

Ward, Cath. G. Cottage on the cliff. 8°. '76. pap., 50c. .... *De Witt.*

— Mysterious marriage; or, will of my father. 8°. pap., 25c......................... *Peterson.*

— *Same.* 8°. pap., 50c..................... *De Witt.*

Ward, *Mrs.* Ellen E. Angels' messages; through Mrs. Ward, as medium. 12°. '75. $1.50.. (?) *Sheffield.*

Ward, *Mrs.* F. M. Hardy and Hunter: a boy's own story. ill. 16°. $1.25.............. *Routledge.*

Ward, Fd. DeW. Christian gift; or, pastoral letters upon character. 12°. '69. 60c........ *Darrow.*

— History of churches of Rochester, N. Y. 8°. '71. $1 .... *Darrow.*

— Summer vacation abroad: notes of a visit to England, France, Italy, etc. 12°. '58. $1.25. *Darrow.*

Ward, *Mrs.* Ht. Cape and the Kaffirs. 12°. (Bohn.) 80c........................ *Scribner, W. & A.*

Ward, H: Dana. Faith of Abraham and of Christ, his seed in the coming kingdom of God on earth; with the restitution of all things which God hath spoken. 8°. '71. $1.50............... *Claxton.*

— Gospel of the kingdom: a kingdom not of this world, not in this world, but to come in the heavenly country. 8°. '70. $2.50.............. *Claxton.*

— History of the cross: pagan origin and idolatrous adoption and worship of the image. 3d ed. 8°. '71. $1 .... *Claxton.*

Ward, Hetta L. H. Davy's jacket. ill. 18°. '73. 75c. *Lothrop.*

Ward, Ja. Harman. Manual of naval tactics; with crit. analysis of principal modern naval battles, with app. 8°. '70. $3 .... *VanNostrand.*

— Steam for the million: treatise on steam and its applic. to the useful arts, especially navigation. New ed., rev. 8°. '76. $1...... *VanNostrand.*

Ward, J:. Experiences of a diplomatist: recollections of Germany, founded on diaries kept during 1840–1870. 8°. $3.50.................. *Macmillan.*

Ward, Jul. H. Life of Ja. G. Percival. por. 12°. $3. **Osgood.*

Ward, Mcs. Illuminating: treatise on the art, with examples of styles. sm. 4°. $2.50.. *Scribner, W. & A.*

— Royal illuminated legends. 8 nos. ill. obl. 12°. ea., 50c.; — in 2 v., ea., $2.50...... *Scribner, W. & A.*

— Royal illuminated nursery rhymes. 8 nos. obl. 16°. ea., 25c.; — in 2 v., ea., $1.25.. *Scribner, W. & A.*

Ward, *Mrs.* Mar. Female life among the Mormons: narr. of many years' personal experience among these people. ill. 12°. '63. $1.75... *J. E. Potter.*

Ward, *Mrs.* Ma. O. Home songs. ill. 18°. '73. 70c.; 80c.................................. *Am. Tr.*

— Songs for the little ones at home. ill. 18°. '52. 70c.; 80c. .... *Am. Tr.*

Ward, Natl. ["Theo. de La Guard."] The simple cobler of Aggawam in America: Lond., 1647. [Reprint.] 4°. pap., $1.................. *Sabin.*

Ward, Rob. Plumer. Chatsworth; or, the romance of a week. 8°. pap., 50c.................. *Harper.*

— De Vere; or, the man of independence. 12°. $1.50. *Harper.*

Ward, S: Lyrical recreations. 12°. $2.... *Appleton.*

Ward, Ste. H. On some affections of liver and intestinal canal; with remarks on ague and its sequelæ, scurvy, purpura, etc. 8°. '72. $3 .... *Lindsay.*

Ward, Su. Hayes. Christ at the door. 16°. '72. $1. *Randolph.*

Ward, T: Cantos: England's reformation. 16°. $1. *Sadlier.*

— Errata of the Prot. Bible; or, truths of Eng. translations examined. 8°. $1 .. *Cummiskey; Sadlier.*

— — *See also* Bible [Whole], *Cath.*

Ward, T: War lyrics; or, songs of the south. 16°. $1 .... *Appleton.*

Ward or wife? [Fiction.] ill. 8°. pap., 25c... *Harper.*

Warde, *Mrs.* M. M. Going home. [Fiction.] 12°. $2. *Cummiskey.*

Warden, D: A. Original chants for the Prot. Episc. Church. 8°. bds., 40c.............. *Ditson.*

Warden, F. L. *See* Goodrich, F. B., *and* Warden, F. L.

Warden, J. Excelsior melodeon instructor. f°. $1. *Gordon.*

Warden, Rob. B. Private life and public services of S. P. Chase. por. roy. 8°. '74. $5.50; $6.50; hf. mor., $7.50 .... *Wilstach.*
— *See also* Ohio, Sup. Court reports.
Warden (The). *See* Trollope, A.
Warder, G: W. Poetical fragments of college poems. 12°. $1 .... *S. W. Bk. & Pub.*
Warder, J: A. American pomology: apples. ill. 12°. $3 .... *Judd.*
— Hedges and evergreens. ill. 12°. $1.50 .... *Judd.*
Warder, T. B., *and* Catlett, Ja. M. Battle of Young's Branch or Manassas Plain, July 21, 1861. maps. 18°. '62. pap., $1 .... *J. W. Randolph.*
Wardlaw, Ralph. On miracles. 12°. '53. $1.25. *Carter.*
Wardock Kennilson. Ball, E. 15c. .... *French.*
Ware, Ashur. *See* United States, District Court reports.
Ware, Ht. Life. 18°. 50c. .... *Am. S. S.*
Ware, H: *jr.* Formation of the Christian character; [also] Progress of the Christian life: sequel to "Formation of the Christian character." ('56.) New ed. 16°. '74. 50c. .... *Am. Unit.*
— Hints on extemporaneous preaching. *See* Ripley, H. J., Sacred rhetoric.
— Life of the Saviour. ('33.) 2d ed. 16°. '72. 75c. *Am. Unit.*
— Memoirs of Noah Worcester; with pref., notes and concluding chapter by S. Worcester. 12°. '44. 50c. .... *Am. Unit.*
Ware, J: Hints to young men on true rel. of the sexes. ('50.) New ed. 16°. '67. 40c. .... *Williams.*
— Memoir of H: Ware, jr. ('46.) 5th ed. 12°. '74. $1.25 .... *Am. Unit.*
Ware, J: Life, trial and execution of John Ware, the murderer of his father. [In Eng. or Germ.] 8°. pap., 25c. .... *Barclay.*
Ware, J: F. W. Home life: what it is, and what it needs. 16°. $1.25 .... *Lee & S.*
Ware, Ma. E. Death and life. 16°. $1.25 .. *Lippincott.*
— Elements of character. 16°. $1.25 .... *Lippincott.*
— Thoughts in my garden. 16°. $1.25 .... *Lippincott.*
Ware, T: Autobiography. por. 12°. '39. 90c. *Meth. Bk. Conc.*
Ware, W. Powell. Ten thousand dollar prize rule for equation of payments. ('72.) 3d ed. 18°. '74. $1.25 .... *Claxton.*
Ware, W: Works. 3 v. 12°. ea., $2; per set, hf. cf., $12 .... *Miller.*
Cont.: Aurelian; or, Rome in the 3d cent. — Julian; or, scenes in Judea. — Zenobia; or, fall of Palmyra.
Warfare and work. 18°. 75c. ...... *Carter; Dutton.*
Warfield, *Mrs.* Cath. A. [Novels.] 7 v. 12°. ea., $1.75 .... *Peterson.*
Cont.: Double wedding; or, how she was won. — Hester Howard's temptation. — Household of Bouverie; or, elixir of gold. — Lady Ernestine; or, the absent lord of Rocheforte. — Miriam's memoirs: sequel to "Monfort Hall." — Monfort Hall. — Sea and shore: sequel to "Miriam's memoirs."
— Household of Bouverie; or, the elixir of gold. 12°. $2 .... *Appleton.*
— Miriam Monfort. 12°. $2 .... *Appleton.*
— Romance of Beauseincourt. 12°. $2 .... *Appleton.*
Note. Same as "Miriam's memoirs."
— Romance of the green seal. 8°. pap., 25c. .. *Beadle.*
Waring, *Miss* Anna Letitia. Hymns and meditations; with introd. by Dr. Huntington. 18°. '73. 75c. *Dutton.*
Waring, E: J: Practical therapeutics; chiefly with ref. to articles of the materia medica. 3d Am. ed. 8°. '74. $5; shp., $6 .... *Lindsay.*
Waring, G: E., *jr.* Book of the farm: pract. information in regard to buying or leasing a farm, etc. New ed. ill. 12°. '76. $2 .... *Porter.*
Note. Formerly pub. under title of "Handy book of husbandry."

Waring, G: E., *jr.*, *continued.*
— Draining for profit and draining for health. ill. 12°. $1.50 .... *Judd.*
— Earth closets: how to make them and how to use them. 12°. pap., 50c. .... *Judd.*
— Elements of agriculture. 12°. $1 .... *Judd.*
— Farmer's (A) vacation. ill. sq. 8°. '75. $5 .. *Osgood.*
— Farmers' and mechanics' manual. ('69.) New ed. ill. 8°. '75. *$3; $3.50 .... *Treat.*
— Sanitary drainage of houses and towns; with diagrams. cr. 8°. $2 .... *Hurd & H.*
— Whip and spur. (Saunterer's ser.) 18°. '75. $1.25. *Osgood.*
Waring, Susie M. Diamonds and rubies; or, the home of Santa Claus. 16°. '72. 40c. .... *Dutton.*
— Little Mirabel's fair. ill. 16°. '72. 40c. ... *Dutton.*
Warington, G. Week of creation; or, the cosmogony of Genesis considered in its rel. to modern science. cr. 8°. '70. $1.50 .... *Macmillan.*
Wark, D: Prevention and cure of consumption by the Swedish movement cure; with directions for home applic. 12°. '67. pap., 25c. .... *Wells.*
Warlock of the glen. Walker, C. E. 15c. *French.*
Warn, Reub. H. Sheet-metal worker's instructor; with instructions for boiler making, etc. ('70.) 4th ed. pl. and ill. 8°. '75. $3 .... *Baird.*
Warner, Anna B. ["Amy Lothrop."] Dollars and cents. 12°. '60. $1.75 ... *Claxton; Lippincott.*
— Fourth watch. 32°. '74. 60c.; 75c. .... *Randolph.*
— *Same;* [also] The other shore. sm. 4°. '74. $2. *Randolph.*
— Gardening by myself. ill. 12°. '72. $1.25; pap., 50c. *Randolph.*
— Hymns of the church militant. ('58.) New ed. 16°. '73. $1.50 .... *Carter.*
— Little Jack's four lessons. ('69.) New ed. 18°. '76. 50c. .... *Carter.*
— Melody of 23d Psalm. 24°. '69. 40c.; 75c.; pap., 35c. .... *Randolph.*
— Miss Muff and little Hungry. ill. sq. 8°. 75c. *Pres. Bd.*
— Miss Tiller's vegetable garden, and the money she made out of it. 16°. '72. 90c.; pap., 30c. *Randolph.*
— Other shore (The). 32°. '72. 60c.; 80c. .. *Randolph.*
— — *See also above* Fourth watch.
— Stories of Vinegar Hill. ('71.) New ed. 6 v. 18°. '74. $3 .... *Carter.*
— Three little spades. 16°. $1 .... *Harper.*
— Wayfaring hymns. 24°. '69. 30c.; 50c.; pap., 20c. *Randolph.*
— *See also* Warner, S. *and* A. B.
Warner, C: Dudley. Back-log studies. ill. sm. 4°. '72. $2; hf. cf., $4; mor., $5 .... *Osgood.*
— Baddeck, and that sort of thing. (Saunterer's ser.) 18°. '74. $1 .... *Osgood.*
— My summer in a garden. 16°. '70. $1. — ill. sm. 4°. $3 .... *Osgood.*
— My winter on the Nile among the mummies and Moslems. 8°. '76. *$2.50; $3; hf. mor., $4.50; mor., $7 .... *Am. Pub.*
— Saunterings. (Saunterer's ser.) 18°. '72. $1.25. *Osgood.*
— *See also* Clemens, S. L., *and* Warner, C. D.
Warner, Fannie. Beech bluff. 12°. '71. $1.50. *Cunningham.*
— Hetty Homer. 18°. '70. 50c. ...... *Cunningham.*
Warner, *Mrs.* H. P. Poems of home life. sq. 18°. '71. $1; $1.25; mor., $3; $3.50 ...... *Am. Tr.*
— Round by round. 18°. '75. $1; $1.25 .... *Am. Tr.*
Warner, Ja. F. Dictionary of musical terms. 8°. '72. pap., 60c. .... *Ditson.*
Warner, *Mrs.* S. E. Our baby. ill. 16°. '73. $1.25; $1.50; mor., $3 .... *Am. Tr.*
Warner, *Miss* Su. ["Eliz. Wetherell."] Daisy: sequel to "Melbourne House." 12°. $2 .... *Lippincott.*
— Hills of the Shatemuc. 12°. $1.75 .... *Lippincott.*

Warner, *Miss* Su., *continued.*
— Lessons on the standard-bearers of Old Test. 18°. '72. hf. bd., 35c. . . . . *Randolph.*
— Melbourne House. ('64.) New ed. 12°. '75. $2 . . *Carter.*
— My brother's keeper. 12°. $1.50 . . . . . *Lippincott.*
— Old helmet. ('63.) New ed. 12°. '74. $2.25 . . *Carter.*
— Queechy. 12°. $1.75 . . . . . *Lippincott.*
— Say and do ser. 6 v. 16°. ea., $1.25 . . . . . *Carter.*
Cont.: Little camp on Eagle Hill. — Willow Brook. — Sceptres and crowns. — Flag of truce. — Bread and oranges. — Rapids of Niagara.
— Say and seal. 12°. $2 . . . . . *Lippincott.*
— Story of small beginnings. ('70–'72.) New ed. 4 v. 16°. '74–'75. $5 . . . . . *Carter.*
Cont.: What she could. — Opportunities. — House in town. — Trading.
— Wide, wide world. 12°. $1.75 . . . . . *Lippincott.*
— *and* Anna B. Ellen Montgomery's bookshelf. ('53.) New ed. 5 v. 16°. '74. $5 . . . . . *Carter.*
— — Mr. Rutherford's children. ill. post 18°. 75c. *Scribner, W. & A.*
— — Word ser. ('65–'68.) New ed. 3 v. 16°. '73–'75. ea., $1.50 . . . . . *Carter.*
Cont.: Walks from Eden. — House of Israel. — Star out of Jacob.
— — Wych Hazel. 12°. '76. $2 . . . . . *Putnam.*

Warne's book of poetry for the young; sel. from mod. authors. ill. post 18°. 75c. . . . . *Scribner, W. & A.*

Warne's Chandos juveniles. *See* Chandos juveniles.

Warne's colored gift books. 11 nos. ill. cr. 8°. ea., $1.25 . . . . . *Scribner, W. & A.*
Cont.: Children's delight. — Children's favorite. — Natural hist. pets. — Alexandria nursery book. — Boy's nursery gift. — Home favorites. — Girl's nursery gift. — Bible picture book. — Sunday favorite. — Nursery album. — Alphabet book.

Warne's drolleries. 3 v. ill. demy 4°. ea., $2.50. *Scribner, W. & A.*
Cont.: Naval and military drolleries. — Lear's Book of nonsense. — Book of drolleries.

Warne's drolleries. 5 nos. ill. demy 4°. ea., 50c.; $1. *Scribner, W. & A.*
Cont.: Ten little niggers. — Ten little soldiers. — A frog he would a-wooing go. — Nine niggers more. — Aquarium comicum.

Warne's everlasting Victoria toy books. (Humpty Dumpty ser.) 6 nos. ill. 18°. 75c. — (Little Bo-peep ser.) 6 nos. ill. 18°. 75c. *Scribner, W. & A.*

Warne's favorite fairy tales. 6 v. ill. 12°. ea., $1.75. *Scribner, W. & A.*

Warne's handy atlas. maps. sm. 4°. 50c. *Scribner, W. & A.*

Warne's large type linen alphabet, spelling and reading. ill. cr. 8°. 50c. . . . . *Scribner, W. & A.*

Warne's large type linen primer. 12°. 25c. *Scribner, W. & A.*

Warne's large type primer. cr. 8°. 25c. *Scribner, W. & A.*

Warne's little folks' lib. 8 v. ill. sm. 4°. ea., $1.75. *Scribner, W. & A.*
Cont.: National nursery book. — National natural hist. — Aunt Friendly's holiday album. — Aunt Friendly's nursery keepsake. — Old friends and new friends. — Book of nursery tales. — Aunt Friendly's gift. — Keepsake for the young.

Warne's mounted picture playmates. 6 v. ill. 8°. ea., $2.50 . . . . . *Scribner, W. & A.*

Warne's national nursery lib. 7 nos. ill. 18°. 75c.; bds., 50c. . . . . . *Scribner, W. & A.*
Cont.: Red Riding Hood volume. — Cinderella volume. — Nursery rhymes, songs and ditties. — Æsop's Fables. — Animals. — Birds and animals. — Fishes, insects and reptiles.

Warne's "now and then" picture books. 10 nos. ill. imp. 16°. ea., 50c. . . . . . *Scribner, W. & A.*
Cont.: Alice's new book. — Mina's pets. — Harry's horses. — Honeycomb house. — Little Totty. — A apple pie. — Cock Robin. — Nursery alphabet. — The three bears. — Royal alphabet.

Warne's picture playmates. 7 nos. ill. cr. 8°. ea., $1.75 . . . . . *Scribner, W. & A.*
Cont.: Red Riding Hood playmate. — Natural history playmate. — Jack in the box playmate. — Nursery playmate. — Sunday playmate. — Nursery rhymes playmate. — Alphabet playmate.

Warne's "round the globe" lib. 43 v. 16°. ea., 50c. *Scribner, W. & A.*

Warne's "star of hope" ser. *See* Yonge, C. M.

Warne's Victoria gift books. 20 v. ill. cr. 8°. ea., $2.50 . . . . . *Scribner, W. & A.*
Cont.: Eiloart's Cris Fairlie's boyhood. — Jones' Broad, broad ocean. — Arabian nights. — Andersen's Fairy tales. — Valentine's Sea fights and land battles from Alfred to Victoria. — Holme Lee's Fairy tales. — Grimm's Tales and stories. — Eiloart's Young squire. — Kingston's Adrift in a boat *and* Washed ashore. — Gay's Fables. — Jones' Treasures of the earth. — Romance of history, England. — Romance of history, France. — Romance of history, Italy. — Romance of history, India. — Romance of history, Spain. — Edgeworth's Moral and popular tales. — Edgeworth's Early lessons. — Defoe's Robinson Crusoe. — Swiss family Robinson.

Warne's Victoria tales and stories. 22 sets. 24°. ea., 50c. . . . . . *Scribner, W. & A.*

Warning cry from Niagara. Hall, N. 30c. . . *Pres. Bd.*

Warning from the oak. 18°. 35c. . . . . *Am. S. S.*

Warnings against superstition. Davies, J. L. $1. *Macmillan.*

Warnings of the holy week. Adams, W. $1.50 . . *Pott.*

Warnungsstimmen, od. verschiedene Beispiele göttlicher Gerechtigkeit. 18°. 50c. . . . . *Ev. Assoc.*

Warp and woof. Duffield, S. W. $1.25 . . *Randolph.*

Warrant of faith. Whytehead, R. $2.75 . . . . *Wiley.*

Warren, —. Schulgeographie. 4°. 75c. . . . . *Kohler.*

Warren, Amos W. Young man's guide; or, mathematical compendium. 16°. '72. 75c. . . . . *Tuttle.*

Warren, C. Recovery of Jerusalem. *See* Palestine exploration fund.

Warren, D: M. Brief course in geog ('74.) New ed. 4°. '76. bds., $1.50 . . . . . *Cowperthwait.*
— Common school geog. [Old ser.] ('57.) New ed. 4°. '72. $1.88 . . . . . *Cowperthwait.*
— New common school geog. New series. ('70.) New ed. 4°. '76. bds., $1.88 . . . . . *Cowperthwait.*
— New physical geog. New series. ('69.) New ed. 4°. '76. bds., $1.88 . . . . . *Cowperthwait.*
— New primary geog. New series. ('68.) New ed. sm. 4°. '76. bds., 75c. . . . . . *Cowperthwait.*
— Physical geog. [Old ser.] ('56.) New ed. 4°. '71. $1.88 . . . . . *Cowperthwait.*
— Primary geog. [Old ser.] ('58.) New ed. sm. 4°. '72. 75c. . . . . . *Cowperthwait.*

Warren, E: Life of J: Warren, surgeon in rev. army. por. 8°. '73. $5 . . . . . *Lockwood, B. & Co.*

Warren, Eliz. Bloomfield. ill. 16°. '70. $1.50 . . *Lothrop.*

Warren, H: W. Past successes, future possibilities: centennial sermon. 12°. '76. pap., 25c. *Meth. Bk. Conc.*
— Sights and insights; or, knowledge by travel. ill. 12°. '74. $1.25 . . . . . *Meth. Bk. Conc.*

Warren, Ira, *and* Small, A. E. Household physician. ('59.) New ed., rev. and enl. ill. roy. 8°. '73. shp., *$6 . . . . . *I. Bradley.*

Warren, Isr. P. Chauncey Judd; or, the stolen boy: tale of the revolution. 12°. '74. $1.50 . . *Crowell.*
— Four Gospels; with chronological harmony. ill. 8°. $2. . . . . . *Bost. Am. Tr.*
— Jerusalem, ancient and modern. ill. 8°. '73. $1.25. (?) *Elliott; Estes.*
— Sisters (The): memoir of Eliz. H., Abbie A. and Sa. F. Dickerman. ill. 16°. 80c. . . *Bost. Am. Tr.*
— Snow flakes: chapter from book of nature. ill. sq. 12°. $2.50 . . . . . *Bost. Am. Tr.*
— Sunday school commentary: Gospels and Acts, with notes and ref. ill. 12°. $2 . . . . . *Lee & S.*
— Three judges: story of the men who beheaded their king; with introd. by L. Bacon. ill. 12°. '73. $1.50 . . . . . *Crowell.*
— Wicked not annihilated: refutation of mod. Sadduceeism. 18°. pap., 10c. . . . . *Bost. Am. Tr.*

Warren, *Mrs.* Jane S. Children's picture book. ill. 18°. 40c. . . . . *Bost. Am. Tr.*
— Little Jennie, the minister's daughter. ill. 18°. '63. 40c. . . . . *Crowell.*
— *Same.* ill. 24°. 30c. . . . . *Bost. Am. Tr.*

Warren, *Mrs.* Jane S., *continued.*
— Morning star: hist. of the children's missionary vessel, and the Marquesan and Micronesian missions. ill. 16°. $1 .... *Bost.Am.Tr.*

Warren, J: C. Constipation: its prevention and cure. 16°. 15c. .... **Osgood.*

Warren, J: Leicester. Essay on Greek federal coinage. 8°. '63. $1 .... *Macmillan.*
— Rehearsals: book of verses. 12°. $1.75 .. *Routledge.*
— Searching the net: verses. 12°. '73. $1.75 .. *Routledge.*

Warren, Jona. Mason. Surgical observations; with cases and operations. ill. 8°. $8 ..... *W. Wood.*

Warren, Jos. Beauties for the organ. 2 nos. 8°. ea., pap., 50c. .... *Ditson.*

Warren, *Rev.* Jos. A glance backward at 15 years of missionary life in north India. 12°. 80c. .. *Pres.Bd.*

Warren, Josiah. True civilization. 5th ed. 12°. '75. pap., 30c. .... *B.R.Tucker.*

Warren, Marvin. Ohio criminal law and forms. 3d ed., rev. and enl. 8°. '72. shp., $6.50 .. *Clarke.*

Warren, Mortimer E. Class word speller. 16°. 30c. *Taintor.*
— *and* Edwards, R: Analytical speller. ('71.) New ed. 16°. '76. 25c. .... *Sherwood; Taintor.*

Warren, Nath. B. Anthems arranged for choral service of the church; with biog. notices of composers. 12°. 50c. .... *W.H. Young.*
— The lady of Lawford, and other Christmas stories. ill. 12°. $2.50; $3 .... *Nims.*

Warren, S. M. *See* Swedenborg, E., Compendium of theol. writings.

Warren, S: Diary of a medical student. [Fiction.] 8°. pap., 75c. .... *Peterson.*
— Duties of attorneys and solicitors; with notes and add. cases by [N. C. Moak]. 12°. '70. shp., $2.50. *J.D.Parsons.*
— Passages from the diary of a late physician. [Fiction.] 3 v. 18°. $2.25 .... *Harper.*
— *Same.* 8°. pap., 50c. .... *Peterson.*
— Moral, social and professional duties of attorneys and solicitors. 12°. $1 .... *Harper.*
— Now and then. 12°. $1.25 .... *Harper.*
— Popular and practical introd. to law studies; ed. with alterations, etc., by I. G. Thompson. 12°. '70. $3 .... *J.D.Parsons; Weed.*
— *Same.* 8°. $5 .... *W.C.Little.*
— Ten thousand a year. [Fiction.] 3 v. por. 12°. $6.75 .... *Cockcroft.*
— *Same.* ill. 8°. $2; pap., $1.50 .... *Peterson.*

Warren, S: E: Descriptive geometry, or general problems of orthographic projections. pl. and ill. 8°. $3.50 .... *Wiley.*
— Drafting instruments and operations. ill. 12°. $1.25. *Wiley.*
— Elementary course in free-hand geometrical drawing. 12°. 75c. .... *Wiley.*
— Elementary free-hand geom. drawing; with instructions in lettering. ill. 12°. 75c. .... *Wiley.*
— *Same;* [also] Drafting instruments. 12°. $1.75. *Wiley.*
— Elementary projection drawing. New ed., rev. and enl. ill. 12°. '72. $1.50 .... *Wiley.*
— Elements of machine construction and drawing; with elements of descript. and rational cinematics, cont. principles of gearings, screw propellers, etc. 2 v.: text, 8°.; pl., 4°. $7.50 ...... *Wiley.*
— General problems of shades and shadows. pl. 8°. $3 .... *Wiley.*
— Higher linear perspective. pl. 8°. $3.50 ... *Wiley.*
— Manual of drafting instruments and operations. 12°. $1.25 .... *Wiley.*
— Manual of element. problems in linear perspective of form and shadow. ill. 12°. $1 .... *Wiley.*
— Plane problems in elementary geometry. ill. 12°. $1.25 .... *Wiley.*
— Stone cutting: treatise on graphics and practice of stone cutting. pl. 8°. $2.50 .... *Wiley.*

Warren, T. Robinson. Shooting, boating and fishing. ill. 12°. '71. $1 .... *Scribner.*
— Yachtman's primer. 12°. pap., 50c. ...... *Carleton.*

Warren, W. F. Ministry of evil. 8°. pap., 15c. *Cin.Meth.Bk.Conc.*
— *and* Newhall, F. H., *and* Haven, E. O. Parkerism: discourses delivered on death of Theodore Parker. 12°. '60. 35c. .... *Meth.Bk.Conc.*

Warren, W: These for those: our indebtedness to missions. 12°. $1.50 .... *Hoyt,F.&D.*
— Twelve years with the children. 2d ed. ill. 16°. $1.25 .... *Hoyt,F.&D.*

Warriner, E. A. ["Broad Churchman."] Victor La Tourette. [Fiction.] 16°. '75. $1.75 .. *Roberts.*

Warring, C: B. Mosaic account of creation: miracle of to-day. 12°. '74. $2 .... *Schermerhorn.*

Warrington (*pseud.*) *See* Robinson, W. S.

Warrington ser. 4 v. 12°. $6 .... *Nelson.*

Cont.: Warringtons abroad. — Stories from China. — Stories from the south seas. — Harry Lawton.

Warringtons abroad (The). ill. 12°. $1.50 .. *Nelson.*

Warton, T: Hamlet (The): ode written in Whichwood Forest. ill. 4°. '75. $3 .... *Routledge.*
— History of English poetry, from 11th to 17th centuries. 3 v. in 1. 12°. '70. $4.25; hf. cf., $6.50. *Putnam.*
— *Same.* 12°. $3 .... *Scribner, W.&A.*

Warwick. Walworth, M. T. $1.75 .... *Carleton.*

Warwick woodlands. Herbert, H. W. 75c. .. *Peterson.*

Was he guilty? Dupuy, E. A. $1.75 ...... *Peterson.*

Was he successful? Kimball, R. B. $1.75 .. *Carleton.*

Was I to blame? Rodwell, G. H. 15c. ...... *French.*

Was Ihr wollt. *See* Shakespeare, W:

Was ist des Deutschen Vaterland? für 4 Männerstimmen, arr. v. L. F. Gröbel. 8°. 15c. .... *Kohler.*

Was it an inheritance? Goff, H. N. K. $1.50 .. *Claxton.*

Was Jesus Christ a democrat? Brittan, S. B., *and* Jamieson, W. F. 25c .... *Mendum.*

Was der Mensch säet. *See* Baron, R.

Was she engaged? Jonquil. $1.25 ...... *Lippincott.*

Was sich der Wald erzählt. Putlitz, G. zu. 50c. *Holt.*

Was der Weihnachtsbaum sagt. 24°. 10c. .. *Ev.Assoc.*

Was der Weihnachtsbaum sagt. Bungener, L. L. F. 75c. .... *Ludwig.*

Washburn, Cephas. Reminiscences of the Indians. 12°. '67. $1 ...... *N.Y.Ref.Ch.Bd.; Pres.Com.*

Washburn, C: A. History of Paraguay; with notes of diplomacy under difficulties. 2 v. maps and ill. 8°. $7.50; hf. cf., $15 .... *Lee&S.*

Washburn, E: A. Social law of God: sermons on the ten commandments. 12°. '75. $1.50 .. *Whittaker.*

Washburn, Emory. Law as an element of social science; read at 4th ann. meeeting of the Am. Soc. Sci. Assoc., Boston, Oct. 14, 1868. 8°. '68. pap., 15c. .... *Williams.*
— Lectures on study and practice of law. cr. 8°. '74. $1.75; shp., $2 .... *Little,B.&Co.*
— Treatise on Am. law of easements and servitudes. 3d ed. 8°. '73. shp., $6 .... *Little,B.&Co.*
— Treatise on law of real property. 4th ed. 3 v. 8°. '76. shp., $18 .... *Little,B.&Co.*

Washburn, Fs. T. Sermons and essays. 12°. '76. $1. *Ellis.*

Washburn, Isr., *jr.* History of Livermore [Me.]; or, "notes of Livermore"; [incl.] Story of Thomas Fish [poem], by Mrs. E. A. Allen. 8°. $1.25 .... *Hoyt,F.&D.*

Washburn, J: M. Reason vs. sword; in which it is shown that man has no right to take human life, and that war is violative of laws of nature and of revelation. 12°. '73. $1.75 .... *E.Jones.*
— *Same.* 12°. '73. $2 .... *FriendsPub.H.*

Washburn, *Mrs.* Kath. Sedgwick [*formerly Mrs.* Kath. Valerio]. Ina. [Fiction.] 8°. '71. $1.25; pap., 75c. .... *Estes.*
— Italian girl. 12°. $1.50 .... *Lee & S.*
— Perfect love casteth out fear. 12°. $1.50 .. *Lee & S.*
Washburn, *Miss* Ma. L. Christmas week at grandmother Cheeryheart's. 16°. $1 ..... *Cong. Pub.*
— Everyday Margaret. 12°. $1.25 .... *Cong. Pub.*
Washburn, P: T. Digest of Vermont Supreme Court reports (v. 1–22). 2 v. 8°. '45–'52. shp., $10. *Tuttle.*
— *See also* Vermont, Sup. Court reports.
Washed ashore. *See* Kingston, W. H. G.
Washerwoman's daughter; tr. by A. B. Cooke. ill. 18°. 50c. .... *J. A. Moore.*
Washerwoman's foundling. Gilbert, W. 75c. *Routledge.*
Washington, Bushrod. *See* United States, Circuit Court reports; — Virginia, Court of Appeals reports.
Washington, Eliz. Posie, the minister's daughter. ill. 16°. '71. $1.25 .... *Crowell.*
— — *See also* Posie ser.
Washington, G: Fac-simile of [his] account with the United States, 1775–1783. sm. f°. '76. *$2.50. *Am. Pub.*
— Farewell address. *See* American text book; — Anderson, J. J.; — Burleigh, J. B.; — Charter; — National text book.
— Journal of Maj. Geo. Washington, sent by Rob. Dinwiddie to the commandant of the French forces in Ohio; [with] the governor's letter, and a tr. of the French officer's answer. [Reprint.] map. 8°. $1; large pap., $2 .... *Sabin.*
— Last will and testament of Washington; with schedule of real estate, notes, etc., by W. H. Newton. 8°. '76. $1; pap., 50c. .... *Newton.*
— Life. 18°. 75c. 16°. $1.10 .... *Am. S. S.*
— *Same.* ill. 16°. $1.25 .... *Lee & S.*
— — *See also* National text book.
Washington, Ma. *and* Martha. Lives. ill. 16°. $1.50. *Mason.*
Washington, *Miss* Nina. Ethel's pearls. ill. 16°. '72. 80c. .... *Am. Tr.*
Washington *Territory.* Statutes, 1854–'74. 4 v. 8°. shp., $80 .... *Bancroft.*
— Supreme Court reports to 1864; by E. Evans. 8°. shp., $7.50 .... *Bancroft.*
Washington. Lockwood, I. *50c. .. (?) *I. Lockwood.*
Washington and the generals of the Am. revolution. ('55.) New ed., rev. 2 v. in 1. por. demy 8°. '75. $2.50 .... *Claxton.*
Washington, outside and inside. Townsend, G. A. *$3.50; $4; $5 .... *Betts.*
Wasielwski, Jos. W: v. Life of Robert Schumann; tr. by A. L. Alger. 12°. '71. $1.75 .... *Ditson.*
Wasps (The). *See* Aristophanes.
Wasserfluth am Rhein. *See* Schmid, C. v.
Waste not, want not. *See* Edgeworth, Mar.
Wat Tyler. Southey, R. 20c. .... *Mendum.*
Watch. *See* Picket.
Watch and pray. 18°. 75c. .... *Dutton.*
Watch and wait. Adams, W. T. $1.25 ..... *Lee & S.*
Watch and wait: drama. 16°. pap., 15c. ..... *French.*
Watch dog of Walsingham's: drama. 16°. pap., 15c. *French.*
Watch tower in the wilderness. *See* Shipton, A.
Watchful eye. *See* Dunning, *Mrs.* A. K.
Watching crabs. *See* Herd boy ser.
Watchmaker. Dumas, A. 50c. .... *Routledge.*
Watchman. Maitland, J. A. $1.75; $1.50 .. *Peterson.*
Watchwords for little soldiers. Foster, S. H. 80c. *Am. Unit.*
Watchwords for the warfare of life. Luther, M. $1.75. *Dodd.*
Water babies. *See* Kingsley, C:
Water cress girl. *See* Baker, *Mrs.* H. N. W.
Water cure for the million. Trall, R. T. 50c.; 25c. *Wells.*
Water drops. Sigourney, L. H. 75c. .... *Carter.*
Water-lily. ill. sm. 4°. 60c. .... *Hurd & H.*
— *See also* Little Blue Hood books.
Water lily stories. ('68.) 5th ed. 12 v. ill. 24°. '73. $3 .... *Perkinpine.*
Cont.: Gold bracelet. — Alice and her pupils. — Rose and her troubles. — Charles Morton. — Little forest girl. — Sixpenny calico. — Jan Harmsen. — Betsey Bartlett. — Willie's lessons. — Kate Aubrey's birthday. — Patience and her friend. — Will Thornton, the crow boy.
Water of life. *See* Kennedy, *Mrs.* M. G.
Water of life. Kingsley, C. $1.25 ...... *Macmillan.*
Water waif. Bladen, E. S. 75c. .... *Claxton.*
Water-witch. *See* Cooper, Ja. F.
Water witches. Coyne, J. S. 15c. .... *French.*
Waterbury, Jared B. Advice to a young Christian. ('43.) 2d ed. ill. 18°. '49. 35c. ..... *Am. Tr.*
— *Same;* with introd. by A. Alexander. 18°. '66. 50c. *Pres. Com.*
— Bearing the cross. 18°. 40c. .... *Cong. Pub.*
— Children led to the Saviour. 32°. '64. 20c. *Am. Tr.*
— Considerations for young men. 18°. '51. 35c. *Am. Tr.*
— Cords of love. 18°. 50c. .... *Cong. Pub.*
— Manual of devotion. 16°. $1 .... *Cong. Pub.*
— Memoir of Rev. J: Scudder. por. 12°. $1.75 .. *Harper.*
— Precious Saviour. 24°. '67. $1.25 .... *Randolph.*
— Sabbath abroad. 12°. $1.25 .... *Cong. Pub.*
— Sketches of eloquent preachers. por. 12°. '64. $1. *Am. Tr.*
— Taking up the cross. 18°. 40c. .... *Cong. Pub.*
— To young men. 18°. '70. 25c. .... *Am. Tr.*
— Uncle Roland and Mary. 16°. 40c. ..... *Cong. Pub.*
— Who are the happy? 18°. '51. 35c. .... *Am. Tr.*
— Young woman (The). 18°. '71. 25c. ..... *Am. Tr.*
Waterbury, Jul. H: Songs and anthems. 16°. '71. pap., 15c. .... *Williams.*
Waterbury, Ma. F. Light for little ones. ill. 18°. 50c. .... *Hoyt, F. & D.*
Waterdale neighbors. McCarthy, J. 50c. .. *Harper.*
Waterloo. Erckmann, E., *and* Chatrian, A. $1.25; 75c. .... *Scribner.*
Waterloo soldier. 18°. 25c.; 30c. .... *Am. Bapt.*
Waterloo soldier. Mackenzie, C. A. 40c. .. *Pres. Bd.*
Waterman, Cath. H. Flora's lexicon. 12°. $1.50; mor., $2.50 .... *Nichols & H.*
Waterman, T: Whitney. American chancery digest: index of decisions in equity, in U. S. Courts and in courts of the several states. 3d ed. 3 v. 8°. '51 .... [*New York.*]
— Law of trespass in twofold aspect of the wrong and the remedy. 2 v. 8°. shp., $13; v. 2, sep., shp., $6.50 .... *Baker, V. & Co.*
Cont.: 1. Trespass to the person and trespass in rel. to personal property. — 2. Trespass on real estate.
— Treatise on law of set-off, recoupment and counterclaim. 8°. shp., $6.50 .... *Baker V. & Co.*
Waterman. Dibdin, C. 15c. .... *French.*
Watermelon. *See* Golden stories.
Waters, A. T. Houghton. Diseases of the chest: contributions to their clin. hist., pathology and treatment. 2d ed. 8°. '74. $5 .... *Lindsay.*
Waters (*pseud.*) *See* Russell, W. H. C.
Waters from the well-spring. Bickersteth, E. H. $1. *Carter.*
Watery war. Benedict, F. 10c. .... *So. Bapt.*
Watson, Alex. American home garden: rules for culture of vegetables, flowers, etc.; with notes on farm crops, etc. ill. 12°. $2 .... *Harper.*

Watson, Egb. P. Manual of the hand-lathe. ('69.) 3d ed. ill. 12°. '76. $1.50.............*Baird.*
— Modern practice of Am. machinists and engineers. ('66.) 11th ed. ill. 12°. '74. $2.50....*Baird.*
Watson, Emily H. Child-life in Europe: hist., mythol., fairy and other stories: sequel to "Child-life in Italy." ill. 16°. '74. $1.50..... *W.F. Gill.*
— Child-life in Italy: story of six years abroad. ill. 16°. '74. $1.50.......................*W.F. Gill.*
Watson, H. W. Problems and riders. *See* Cambridge Senate-House.
Watson, H: C. Camp-fires of the revolution. ill. cr. 8°. $2.......................................*Miller.*
— Daring deeds of the revolution. ill. 16°. $1.25..*Lee & S.*
— Heroic women of hist. ill. 12°. $1.75..*J.E. Potter.*
— History of U. S. ill. roy. 8°. $5........*Desilver.*
— Noble deeds of our forefathers. ill. 16°. $1.25..*Lee & S.*
— Six nights in a block house; or, sketches of border life. ill. 12°. $1.75.................*J.E. Potter.*
Watson, J. The secret disciple encouraged to avow his master. sq. 18°. 50c.............*Claxton.*
Watson, J. L. Our village. ill. 16°. '74. 75c...*Nelson.*
— *See also* Keddie, *Miss* H., *and* Watson, J. L.
Watson, Ja. Rowing and athletic manual for 1874. 18°. '74. $1......................(?) *Watson.*
Watson, Ja. C. Popular treatise on comets. ill. 12°. '61. $1.50...........................*Challen.*
— Theoretical astronomy; rel. to motions of heavenly bodies revolving around the sun; with numerical examples and auxiliary tables. roy. 8°. $10. *Lippincott.*
Watson, Ja. Madison. Handbook of calisthenics and gymnastics. ('63.) 2d ed. 8°. '68. $2. *Schermerhorn.*
— [Independent ser. of readers and spellers.] 10 v. '68–'75.......................................*Barnes.*
Cont.: Independent child's speller, 18°, hf. bd., 25c. — element. speller, 18°, hf. bd., 25c. — youth's speller, 12°, hf. bd., 50c. — primary reader, 18°, hf. bd., 25c. — first reader, 18°, hf. bd., 25c. — second, 18°, hf. bd., 50c. — third, 12°, hf. bd., 75c. — fourth, 12°, $1 — fifth, 12°, $1.25 — sixth, 8°, $1.50.
— Manual of calisthenics. 8°. '64. $1.25. *Barnes; Schermerhorn.*
— National elementary speller. 18°. '71. hf. bd., 25c.; 30c. ....*Barnes.*
— Practical elocution. 12°. '68. pap., 15c.....*Barnes.*
— *See also* Parker, R. G., *and* Watson, J. M.
Watson, Ja. V. Helps to promotion of revivals. 12°. '56. $1.........................*Meth. Bk. Conc.*
— Tales and takings. 12°. $1.75..*Cin. Meth. Bk. Conc.*
Watson, Jean L. Round the Grange Farm; or, good old times: stories of Scottish life. ill. 16°. $1.25. *Cin. Meth. Bk. Conc.*
Watson, J: Anniversary discourse: the medical profession in ancient times. 8°. '55. pap., $1. *N.Y. Acad. Med.*
— Anniversary discourse: the true physician. 8°. '60. pap., 25c.....................*N.Y. Acad. Med.*
Watson, J: F. Annals of Phila. and Penna. in the olden time; ill. by T. H. Mumford. 2 v. 8°. $7.50; hf. cf., $12.................*Lippincott.*
Watson, J: L. Memoirs of the Marstons of Salem; with brief genealogy of some of their descendants. sm. 4°. '73. pap., 75c. .... *Williams.*
Watson, J: S. Reasoning power of animals. 8°. $3. *Appleton.*
Watson, J: T. (*ed.*) Dictionary of poetical quotations. ill. 12°. '76. $1.50............... *World Pub.*
Watson, J: W. Beautiful snow! and other poems. ill. 12°. $2; $3; hf. cf., $4...........*Peterson.*
— The outcast, and other poems. 12°. $2; $3; hf. cf., $4..................................*Peterson.*
Watson, *Bp.* R: Apology for the Bible: letters to T: Paine. 18°. '37. 45c............*Meth. Bk. Conc.*
— *Same.* ('56.) 3d ed. 18°. '76. 50c.......*So. Meth.*
— *Same.* 18°. '66. 60c...*N.Y. Ref. Ch. Bd.; Pres. Com.*
— — Reply to Paine. 18°. '57. 40c..........*Am. Tr.*

Watson, *Bp.* R: *continued.*
— — *Germ.* Erwiederung an Paine. 18°. '48. 50c. *Am. Tr.*
Watson, *Rev.* R: Biblical and theolog. dictionary. maps. 8°. '37. $5; cf., $5.75....*Meth. Bk. Conc.*
— *Same;* rev. and enl. by T. O. Summers. ('57.) 5th ed. 8°. '74. shp., $7..............*So. Meth.*
— Conversations for the young. 12°. '37. $1.25. *Meth. Bk. Conc.*
— Exposition of Matthew, Mark, etc. 8°. '37. hf. roan, $1; shp., $3.50................*Meth. Bk. Conc.*
— Life of J: Wesley; with obs. on Southey's Life of Wesley. 12°. '37. $1.25........*Meth. Bk. Conc.*
— *Same;* with notes by T. O. Summers. ('56.) 2d ed. 12°. '76. $2..........................*So. Meth.*
— Sermons and sketches. 2 v. 8°. '37. $6. *Meth. Bk. Conc.*
— *Same;* with biog. introd. and notes by T. O. Summers. 2 v. 8°. '73. shp., $6..........*So. Meth.*
— Theological institutes. 2 v. 8°. '37. $7; cf., $8. *Meth. Bk. Conc.*
— *Same;* ed. by T. O. Summers. ('56.) 6th ed. 8°. '74. shp., $5..........................*So. Meth.*
Watson, S: Clock (The) struck one, and Christian spiritualist: synopsis of investig. of spirit intercourse. ('72.) 3d ed. 12°. '74. $1.50..*Rel. Phil.*
— Clock (The) struck three: review of "Clock struck one," and reply to review. 12°. '74. $1.50. *Rel. Phil.*
— Memphian's trip to Europe. 12°. '74. $1.50..*So. Meth.*
Watson, Sereno. Botany. *See* United States, *Corps of Eng.*
Watson, T: Lectures on principles and practice of physic. New Am. ed., rev.; with add. by H. Hartshorne. 2 v. ill. 8°. $9; leath., $11..*Lea.*
Watson, T: *See* Jaudon, D., Watson, T., *and* Addington, S.
Watson, *Rev.* T: Bible read with profit. 32°. 20c. *Pres. Bd.*
— Body of practical divinity: sermons on Assembly's Catechism. 8°. $3; shp., $3.50..*U.P. Bd. of Pub.*
— *Same.* 8°. '71. $3..........................*Carter.*
Watson, W: Course in descript. geometry for colleges and scientific schools; with app. 4°. pl. and ill. in portfolio. '73. $7...........*Prang.*
Watson, Winslow C. Military and civil hist. of Essex Co., N. Y. 8°. '69. $3...............*Munsell.*
Watson's woods. 18°. '60. $1.25........*Randolph.*
Watt, Alex. Electro-metallurgy practically treated. 12°. '71. 80c.......................... *Virtue.*
Watts, C: *See* Holyoake, A., *and* Watts, C:
Watts, *Miss* Eliz. The poultry yard: management of birds for use and exhibition. ill. 16°. bds., 50c. *Routledge.*
Watts, F: *See* Pennsylvania, Sup. Court reports.
Watts, H: Dictionary of chemistry; with two supplements. 7 v. 8°. $75 ....*R. Worthington.*
Watts, I: Brief memoir. 18°. 25c.........*Am. S. S.*
— Catechisms. *See* Four catechisms.
— *Germ.* Vier Katechismen. 32°. '60. 20c...*Am. Tr.*
— Divine and moral songs. f°. pap., 15c.; 20c. *J.E. Potter.*
— *Same.* 32°. '31. 15c.......*Am. Tr.; Bost. Am. Tr.*
— *Same.* 32°. 25c.; 40c............*Scribner, W. & A.*
— *Same.* 18°. 30c.......................*Whittaker.*
— *Same.* ill. 18°. 40c.......................*Pres. Bd.*
— *Same.* sq. 18°. 60c..........................*Carter.*
— *Same.* ill. 8°. $1; 75c....................*Am. S. S.*
— *Same.* ill. sm. 4°. '71. $2.50. — (chp. ed.) 18°. '71. 45c............................*Routledge.*
— *Same.* ill. sm. 4°. '68. $2; $2.50; mor., $5. *Hurd & H.*
— — *See also below* Horæ lyricæ; Songs.
— Horæ lyricæ; [also] Divine and moral songs for children; with memoir by R. Southey. por. 18°. $1....................................*Osgood.*

Watts, I: *continued.*
— Improvement of the mind. 16°. '49. hf.bd., 50c. *Barnes.*
— *Same.* School ed.; with Denman's questions. 16°. '60. 35c. *Barnes.*
— *Same;* with corrections, questions and sup. by J. Emerson. 18°. bds., 45c. *Ware.*
— Psalms and hymns, with sel. from other authors; ed. by S. M. Worcester. 12°. '34. $1.50–$4.50. — 18°. $1.25–$3.25. — 32°. $1–$2.25. *Crocker.*
— Songs, divine and moral. ill. 18°. 40c. *Am.S.S.*
— *Same.* ill. sq. 16°. 75c. *Nelson.*
— — *See also above* Divine.
— Scripture history. 32°. 50c. *Routledge.*
Watts, I: *See* Ship building.
Watts, J. *See* Collins, T., *and* Watts, J.
Watts, J. G. Life and adventures of a little bird. ill. fp. 8°. 50c. *Cassell.*
Watts, W. Marshall. Elements of organic chemistry. (Element. sci. ser.) 18°. '73. 75c. *Putnam.*
Wau Bun. Kinzie, J. H. $1.75. *Lippincott.*
Wau-nau-gee; or, the massacre at Chicago. 8°. pap., 50c. *Peterson.*
Waverley. Ball, E. 15c. *French.*
Waverley, *See* Scott, *Sir* Wa.
Waverley gallery: eng. ill. of female por. in Sir Wa. Scott's romances: 36 steel eng., and descript. text. imp. 8°. $7.50; mor., $10. *Appleton.*
Wavie, the foundling. 16°. $1. *Cong.Pub.*
Wax flowers: how to make them, with new methods of sheeting wax, etc. ('64.) New ed. 12°. '75. $2. *Tilton.*
Wax matches. *See* Yonge, C. M.
Way, Micajah E. Life. 18°. 17c.; 22c. *Am.Bapt.*
Way and walk. Anderson, G. W. 40c. *Am.Bapt.*
Way down east. Smith, S. $1.75. *J.E.Potter.*
Way for a child to do good. 18°. 22c. *Am.S.S.*
Way home. 18°. 75c. *Carter.*
Way lost and found. Tuttle, J. F. $1.15. *Pres.Bd.*
Way made plain. Brooks, J. H. $1.25. *Am.S.S.*
Way of the cross; or, the fourteen stations of the cross; from the Raccolta. [Cath. prayer book.] 18°. '62. pap., 10c. *Kelly, P.& Co.; Strong.*
Way of faith. *See* Büdinger, M.
Way of heaven. *See* Library of good example.
Way of holiness. Palmer, P. 70c. *Palmer.*
Way of life. *See* Hodge, C.
Way of the world. Adams, W. T. $1.50. *Lee & S.*
Way of the world. Hofland, B. $1. *Nelson.*
Way to be happy. *See* Bell, C. D.
Way to the cross. Dodge, A. A. 85c. *Bost.Am.Tr.*
Way to the cross. *See* Neale, J. M.
Way to do good. Abbott, J. $1.75. *Harper.*
Way to get married. Morton, T. 15c. *French.*
Way to the heart of childhood; or, seed sown in the spring time. 18°. 40c. *Am.S.S.*
Way to heaven. [Cath. prayer book.] 18°. 75c.–$30. — 24°. 50c.–$25. *Sadlier.*
— *Same;* with the Epistles and Gospels. 18°. 75c.–$50. — 24°. 50c.–$60. *Sadlier.*
Way to Jesus. 16°. 30c. *West.Tr.*
Way to keep him. Murphy, A. 15c. *French.*
Way to life. Guthrie, T. $1.50. *Carter.*
Way to mount Zion, and other tales. 16°. $1.35. *Pres.Bd.*
Way to prosper. Arthur, T. S. $1.50. *J.E.Potter.*
Way (The), the truth and the life. Seelye, J. H. $1. *Cong.Pub.*
Way (The), the truth and the life. Staples, N. A. $1.50. *Am.Unit.*
Way we live now. Trollope, A. $2; $1.50. *Harper.*

Wayaffe, —. Mass in C; for three voices; arr. by E. Spoth. f°. '68. pap., $1.25. *Ditson.*
Wayfaring hymns. Warner, A. B. 30c.; 50c.; 20c. *Randolph.*
Wayland, Fs. Elements of intellectual philosophy. 12°. $1.75. *Sheldon.*
— Life of trust. *See* Muller, G.
— Memoir of life and labors of Adoniram Judson. 2 v. in 1. por. 12°. $2.25. *Sheldon.*
— Moral science. 12°. $1.75; — abridg. and adapted to schools and academies. 16°. 70c. *Sheldon.*
— Political economy. 12°. $1.75; — abridg. [for] schools and academies. 16°. 70c. *Sheldon.*
— Principles and practices of the Baptists. 12°. $1.50. *Sheldon.*
— Salvation by Christ: discourses. 12°. '75. $1.50. *Lothrop.*
— Sermons to the churches. 12°. $1. *Sheldon.*
Wayland, Fs., *jr., and* H. L. Memoir of life and labors of Fs. Wayland, incl. sel. from his personal reminiscences and correspondence. 2 v. 12°. $4; hf. cf., $8. *Sheldon.*
Waylland, J: Matthias. Man with the book; or, the Bible among the people. ill. 12°. '73. $1.25. *Meth.Bk.Conc.*
— *Same.* ('72.) New ed. 16°. '73. $1.50. *Hoyt.*
Waymarks for the confirmed. 18°. '75. 40c.; 60c. *Luth.Bk.St.*
Waymarks of the pilgrimage. Cheever, G. B. 50c. *Bost.Am.Tr.*
Wayne, Marion W. Marguerite Kent. [Fiction.] 12°. $2. *Lippincott.*
Ways and ends; or, the two farms at Lynthorpe. 18°. 50c. *Pres.Bd.*
Ways of the hour. *See* Cooper, Ja. F.
Ways of life. Weaver, G. S. 75c. *Wells.*
Ways of Providence. *See* Arthur, T. S.
Ways of women. Smith, J. V. C. *$3; $4; $3.50. *Dustin.*
Wayside blossoms. Booth, M. H. C. $1. *Claxton.*
Wayside cross. Milman, E. H. 25c. *Harper.*
Wayside flowerets. *See* Cross, J. T. H.
Wayside flowers. Dawes, S. E. $1. *Locke.*
Wayside flowers. *See* Better path stories; — Morning glory lib.
Wayside hymns. 16°. '68. 90c. *Randolph.*
Wayside inn. Longfellow, H. W. $1.50; $10. *Osgood.*
Wayside lib. 3 v. 16°. $4. *Hoyt.*
Cont.: Down in a saloon, by M. S. Walker. — Day after to-morrow, by Mrs. Prosser. — Home in a rough suburb, by J. F. Moore.
Wayside pencillings. Moriarty, J. J. 75c. (?) *Van Benthuysen.*
Wayside picture ser. 4 v. ill. 12°. $5. *Nelson.*
Cont.: Pictures of travel in South America. — Pictures of travel in Central America. — Jerusalem and its environs, by W. K. Tweedie. — Rivers and lakes of the Bible, by W. K. Tweedie.
Wayside posies: poems by living authors and pictures eng. by the brothers Dalziel. 4°. $10; mor., $15. *Routledge.*
Wayside service. *See* Shipton, A.
Wayside thoughts. Lloyd, S. H. $1. *Widdleton.*
We all have our little faults. Suter, W. E. 15c. *French.*
We and our neighbors. Stowe, H. B. $1.75. *Ford.*
We're all teetotallers. Baker, G. M. 15c. *Lee & S.*
We girls. Whitney, A. D. T. $1.50. *Osgood.*
We got agate of singing. 18°. 35c. *Carter.*
We love him. *See* Head and heart ser.
We versus I. 18°. 25c. *Am.S.S.*
Weak lungs, and how to make them strong. Lewis, D. $1.50. *Osgood.*
Weak points: comedy. 16°. pap., 15c. *Happy.*
Weakness and strength. Herbert, S. A. F. 70c. *Pres.Bd.*

Wealth and welfare. Bitzius, A. $2......*Routledge.*
Wealth and wine. Chellis, M. D. $1.25..*Nat. Temp.*
Wealth and worth; or, which makes the man? 18°. 75c....*Harper.*
Wealth of nations. *See* Smith, Ad.
Wear and tear. Mitchell, S. W. 50c.; 30c. *Lippincott.*
Wearing of the gray. Cooke, J. E. *$4; $5..*Treat.*
Wearing of the green. *See* Speeches from the dock.
Wearing of the green: burlesque. 16°. pap., 15c. *Happy.*
Wearing of the green song book. 32°. 50c.; pap., 25c. *Noonan.*
Wearithorne. Rodney, M. R. L. $1.50..*Lippincott.*
Weary-foot common. Ritchie, L. $1.25. *Scribner, W. & A.*
Weasel family. f°. pap., 15c.; 20c.; 30c. *J.E. Potter.*
Weathercock. Allingham, J. T. 15c.......*French.*
Weatherley, F. E. Elsie's expedition. ill. sq. 16°. $1.75....*Scribner, W. & A.*
Weatherly, H: Treatise on art of boiling sugar, crystallizing, etc., for confectionery, etc. ('64.) 3d ed. 12°. '75. $2....*Baird.*
Weaver, *Mrs.* —. Tramps in New York. ill. 18°. '63. 40c....*Am. Tr.*
Weaver, Add. The young scamp: Ethiop. drama. 16°. pap., 15c....*De Witt.*
Weaver, G: S. Aims and aids for girls and young women on the various duties of life. 12°. '55. $1.25....*Wells.*
— Christian household. 12°. '54. 75c........*Wells.*
— Hopes and helps for the young of both sexes. 12°. '52. $1.25....*Wells.*
— Mental science, according to philosophy of phrenology. ill. 12°. '51. $1.25....*Wells.*
— Moses and modern science. 12°. $1..*Williamson.*
— Open way (The). 12°. $1.25.......*Williamson.*
— Ways of life; showing right way and wrong way. 12°. '55. 75c....*Wells.*
— Works for the young; embr. Hopes and helps, Aims and aids for girls and young women, Ways of life. 12°. $2.50....*Wells.*
Weaver, J. M. Myrtle question-book. 18°. 25c. *So. Bapt.*
Weaver, Jona. Discourses on the resurrection. 12°. 60c....*Un. B. Pub.*
— Divine Providence: hist. of the doctrine, its nature, reasonableness, etc. 12°. $1.25....*Un. B. Pub.*
Weaver, Josh. Office of devotion for Sunday school; with hymns. 16°. 25c....*Dutton.*
Weaver, W. T. G. Hours of amusement, and other poems. 12°. '76. $2..........*E. H. Cushing.*
Weaver boy: story of Dr. Livingstone. 16°. $1.25. *Carter.*
Weaver of Naumburg; or, the triumph of meekness: story of 14th cent. 18°. 60c.........*So. Bapt.*
Weaver's daughter. 18°. '51. 25c........*Am. Tr.*
Webb, A. C. Historical companion. 2 v. 12°. '76. pt. 1, 60c.; 2, 75c....*Eldredge.*
— Model definer. ('68.) 8th ed. 16°. '75. 25c. *Eldredge.*
— Model etymology. ('68.) 18th ed. 12°. '76. 60c. *Eldredge.*
Webb, A. J. Vocal exercises and solfeggios. f°. $1. *Gordon.*
Webb, C. Belphegor: drama. 16°. pap., 15c. *French.*
Webb, C: H. ["J: Paul."] John Paul's book. ill. 8°. *$3.50; shp., $4; hf. mor., $5.....*Col. Bk.*
— My vacation: sea and shore. 12°. $1.50. *Carleton.*
— Parodies and poems. 12°. $1.50........*Carleton.*
Webb, Edm. F. Railroad laws of Maine. 8°. '76. shp., $7.50....*Dresser.*
Webb, E: Hindoo life; with pictures of men, women and children of India. sq. 8°. 75c....*Pres. Bd.*

Webb, G: F., *and* Power, J. L. Mississippi manual of legal and business forms; with state and federal constitutions, acts of legislature, etc. 3d ed., rev. and enl. 12°. '70. $2....*Power & B.*
Webb, G: Ja. Cantica ecclesiastica. [Anthems.] 8°. '59. bds., $2....*Ditson.*
— Vocal technics: exercises for practice of soprano, contralto, tenor, baritone and bass voices. 4°. '70. bds., $3....*Ditson.*
— Young ladies' vocal class book. f°. $1.25..*Gordon.*
— *See also* Mason, L., *and* Webb, G. J.
— *and* Allen, C. G. Voice culture: concise method for cultivation of the voice; with exercises. obl. 4°. '71. bds., $2.50....*Biglow.*
— *and* Mason, L. New odeon: secular melodies arr. for four voices. obl. 8°. '55. bds., $1.50...*Ditson.*
Webb, *Mrs.* J. B. Alypius of Tagaste. 16°. $1.50. *Pres. Bd.*
— Benaiah: tale of the captivity. ill. 16°. $1. *Scribner, W. & A.*
— *Same.* sq. 12°. $1.25....*Claxton.*
— Helen Mordaunt; or, the standard of life. ill. 16°. $1.25....*Routledge.*
— Ishmael, the Yezidee: tale of Syrian life. ill. 12°. $1.75....*Routledge.*
— Naomi; or, the last days of Jerusalem. 12°. $1. *McCauley.*
— *Same;* with photos. by David Roberts. 4°. '71. $10; mor., $15.—(Popular ed.) ill. cr. 8°. $1.75. *Routledge.*
— Pomponia; or, the Gospel in Cæsar's household. 16°. $1.50....*Pres. Bd.*
— The stitch in time. 32°. 40c.....*Scribner, W. & A.*
Webb, J. Russell. First lessons in lang. and drawing. 16°. '71. 25c....*Andrews.*
— [Model readers.] 4 v. '73–'76........*Sherwood.*
Cont.: Model first reader, 16°, 40c. — second, 16°, 50c. — third, 12°, 75c. — fourth, 12°, $1.25.
— [Normal readers.] 5 v. 12°....*Taintor.*
Cont.: Normal reader, no. 1, 25c. — no. 2, 50c. — no. 3, 75c. — no. 4, $1 — no. 5, $1.25.
— Word method: new method of teaching reading. New ed., rev. 16°. '75. pap., 30c...*E. B. Smith.*
— *See also* Edwards, R., *and* Webb, J. R.
Webb, Ja. *See* Texas, Sup. Court reports.
Webb, *Mrs.* Mar. The Fells of Swarthmore Hall, and their friends. 2d ed. ill. 16°. $1.25..*Lippincott.*
Webb, T: Smith. Freemason's monitor; [with] monitor of the ancient accepted rite, by E. T. Carson. 12°. $1.50....*Pounsford.*
— *Same.* (Miniature ed.) 24°. '75. 75c.; $1. *Masonic; Redding.*
— Miniature monitor; ed. by R. Morris. New ed. 32°. '72. 60c.; $1....*Clark & M.*
Webb, W. C. *See* Kansas, Sup. Court reports.
Webb, W. E. Buffalo land: wealth and wonders of the great west. ill. 8°. '72. *$3.25; $3.75..*Maclean.*
Webb, W: H. Word method primer. 16°. hf. bd., 25c....*Sheldon.*
Webber, C: Wilkins. Old Hicks, the guide: adventures in the Camanche country in search of a gold mine. 12°. $1.50....*Harper.*
— Tales of the southern border. cr. 8°. $2..*Lippincott.*
— Wild scenes and wild hunting; or, the romance of sporting. demy 8°. '75. $2..........*Claxton.*
Webber, H. A. Man and wife: comedy. 16°. pap., 15c....*Ames; French.*
Webber, S. G. *See* Amory, R., *and* Webber, S. G.
Weber, C: Mar. (*Baron*) v. Complete piano works. 8°. $4....*Peters.*
— Mass in E flat; with organ or piano accomp. by V. Novello; with Lat. and Eng. text. 8°. '62. $1; pap., 65c....*Ditson.*
— Mass in G; with organ or piano accomp. by V. Novello; with Lat. and Eng. text. 8°. '62. 90c.; pap., 60c....*Ditson; Gordon.*

Weber, C: Mar., *continued.*
— *Same.* obl. 8°. bds., 75c.; pap., 60c. ...... *Peters.*
— Preciosa; with Eng. version by L. C. Elson. [Opera.] 4°. '70. pap., 75c. ...... *Ditson.*

Weber, F. Family singing book. 8°. '72. pap., 75c. (?) *André.*

Weber, G: Outlines of universal hist.; tr. by M. Behr; with hist. of U. S. by F. Bowen. 8°. hf. roan, $2.50 ...... *Ware.*

Weber, Godf. Theory of musical composition, treated with a view to a naturally consecutive arrangement of topics; tr. with notes by J. F. Warner. 2 v. 8°. $6 ...... *Ditson.*

Weber, K: Iwan, der Leibeigene. 12°. $1; pap., 75c.; hf. mor., $1.25 ...... *F. W. Thomas.*

Weber, Max Mar. v. Carl Maria von Weber: life of an artist; tr. by J. P. Simpson. 2 v. 12°. ea., $1.75 ...... *Ditson.*

Weber, T: R. The Pennsylvania choral harmony: [Moravian] church melodies with German and English text. 10th ed., enl. sm. f°. '75. bds., $1.50 ...... *Clauder.*

Webfoot (*pseud.*) *See* Phelps, W. D.

Webster, Augusta. Auspicious day: dram. poem. fp. 8°. '72. $1.50 ...... *Macmillan.*
— Dramatic studies. fp. 8°. '66. $1.50 ... *Macmillan.*
— Portraits. 2d ed. fp. 8°. $1 ...... *Macmillan.*
— Woman sold (A), and other poems. 12°. '66. $2. *Macmillan.*
— Yu-Pe-Ya's lute: Chinese tale in English verse. fp. 8°. $1 ...... *Macmillan.*

Webster, B: [Plays.] 7 v. 16°. ea., pap., 15c. *French.*

Cont.: Golden farmer: melodrama. — Highways and byways: farce. — Laughing hyena: farce. — My young wife and old umbrella: farce. — One touch of nature. — Paul Clifford. — Swiss swains: farce.

Webster, B: *jr.* Behind time: farce. 16°. pap., 15c. *French.*

Webster, Dan. Life. ill. 16°. $1.25 ...... *Lee & S.*
— Private correspondence with autobiog.; ed. by F. Webster. 2 v. por. 8°. '75. $6 .. *Little, B. & Co.*
— Speeches, forensic arguments and diplomatic papers; with notice of his life and works by E. Everett. 16th ed. 6 v. por. 8°. '72. $18; shp., $24; hf. cf., $30; cf., $36 ...... *Little, B. & Co.*
— *See also* Hudson, H. N., Pamphlet sections.
— *and* Hayne, R. Y. Speeches in U. S. Senate, on Mr. Foot's resolution of January, 1830; [also] Webster's speech in the Senate, March 7, 1850, on the slavery compromise. 8°. pap., 75c.... *Peterson.*

Webster, I. P. The beatitudes: cantata for Sunday schools; with libretto by S. F. Bennett. obl. 16°. '73. pap., 30c. ...... *Ditson.*

Webster, J: Complete works; with account of author and notes by A. Dyce. roy. 8°. $4.50 .. *Routledge.*
— Duchess of Malfi: tragedy. 16°. pap., 15c... *French.*

Webster, Noah. Academic dictionary, explanatory, pronounc., etymol. and synonymous; mainly abridg. from 4° ed. ill. fp. 4°. '67. $2.20 .. *Ivison.*
— American dictionary of the English language; rev. and enl. by C. A. Goodrich and N. Porter. ('65.) New ed. roy. 4°. '76. shp., $12; cf., $20. — 2 v. mor., $16. — 3 v. hf. mor., $18. — 2 v. imp. f°. $30 ...... *Merriam.*

Note. First pub. in N. Y., 1828, in 2 v., 4°. Preceded in 1806 by "Compendious dict. of the Eng. lang.," pub. in Hartford.

— Army and navy dict. ill. 64°. 90c.; $1 .... *Ivison.*
— Common school dictionary, explanatory, pronouncing and synonymous; mainly abridg. from 4° ed. ill. sq. 12°. '57. 94c. ...... *Ivison.*
— Counting-house dict., explanatory, pronounc., etymol. and synonymous; mainly abridg. from 4° ed. ill. 8°. '67. shp., $3.50; hf. mor., $5. ...... *Ivison.*
— Dictionary of the Eng. lang., abridg. by W. A. Wheeler. ('67.) New ed. ill. 8°. '76. $4.50; shp., $5; mor., $6 ...... *Merriam.*

Webster, Noah, *continued.*
— Elementary reader; to follow Elementary speller. 16°. per. doz., *net*, $1.20 ...... *Appleton.*
— Elementary spelling-book. 16°. per. doz., *net*, $1.20. *Appleton.*
— High school dict., explanatory, pronouncing and synonymous; mainly abridg. from 4° ed. ill. sq. 12°. '68. $1.25 ...... *Ivison.*
— History of the U. S.; with hist. account of our [Eng.] ancestors, and of the conquest of So. Am. by the Spaniards. 18°. '41. 37½c... *I. N. Whiting.*
— Pocket dict.; abridg. from 4° ed. ill. 64°. '70. 75c.; 90c.; $1 ...... *Ivison.*
— Primary dict., explanatory, pronouncing and synonymous; mainly abridg. from 4° ed. ill. sq. 16°. '57. 63c. ...... *Ivison.*
— Speller and definer. 12°. bds., 25c. ...... *Morton.*

Webster, T: Encyclopædia of domestic economy; with additions by an Am. physician [D. M. Reese]. ill. 8°. '45. shp., $5 ...... *Harper.*

Webster, *Rev.* T: Woman man's equal; with introd. by Bp. Simpson. 16°. $1.25 .. *Cin. Meth. Bk. Conc.*

Webster's business man; or, counting house correspondent. 12°. '71. 75c. 32°. bds., 50c... *De Witt.*

Webster's chairman's manual and speaker's guide. 12°. '71. 75c.; bds., 50c. ...... *De Witt.*

Webster's little folks' speaker. 12°. 75c. 32°. bds., 50c. ...... *De Witt.*

Webster's practical letter writer. 12°. 75c. 32°. bds., 50c. ...... *De Witt.*

Webster's ready made love letters. 12°. 75c. 32°. bds., 50c. ...... *De Witt.*

Webster's reciter; or, elocution made easy. ill. 12°. 75c. 32°. bds., 50c. ...... *De Witt.*

Webster's youthful speaker. 12°. '76. 75c. 32°. bds., 50c. ...... *De Witt.*

Wedding day. Inchbald, E. 15c. ...... *French.*

Wedding day in all ages and countries. Wood, E. J. $1.25 ...... *Harper.*

Wedding dress. Dumas, A. 25c. ...... *De Witt.*

Wedding garments. McLain, M. W. $1.25 .. *Scribner.*

Wedding guests. Hume-Rothery, M. C. $1.25. *H. H. Carter.*

Wedding party. 48°. '54. 15c. ...... *Meth. Bk. Conc.*

Wedding story. *See* Barker, M. A. (*Lady*).

Wedding wreath. *See* Diamond miniatures.

Wedge of gold. Scott, W. A. 60c. ...... *Pres. Bd.*

Wedgwood, Hensleigh. Dictionary of Eng. etymology. 2d ed., rev. and enl. roy. 8°. $8 ... *Macmillan.*
— *Same*; enl. by G. P. Marsh. imp. 8°. $3 ... *Sheldon.*

Wedgwood, Jla. John Wesley and the evangelical reaction of 18th cent. cr. 8°. $2.50 .. *Macmillan.*

Wedgwood, W: B. Government and law: whole body of Am. law, state and national, with legal hist. of the nation. 8°. shp., $5 ...... *Baker, V. & Co.*
— *Same.* 8°. '66. $3.50 ...... *Schermerhorn.*
— *and* Homans, I: S. Law manual for notaries public and bankers. ('72.) 4th ed. 8°. '73. shp., $6. *Homans.*

Wedl, C: Pathology of the teeth, with special ref. to their anat. and physiol.; tr. by W. E. Boardman, with notes by T. B. Hitchcock. ill. 8°. '72. $4.50; leath., $5.50 ...... *Lindsay.*

Wee Davie. *See* Macleod, N.

Wee Donald: story from real life. ('72.) New ed. 16°. '75. $1.15 ...... *Hoyt.*

Wee Meggie Forsythe. Chaplin, J. D. $1.50. *Bost. Am. Tr.*

Wee-wee songs for our little pets. Lee, L. 75c. *Mason.*

Wee-wee stories. Valentine, R. $1.50. (?) *McLoughlin.*

Weed, H: R. Questions on confessions of faith and form of government of the Presb. Church. 18°. 20c. ...... *Pres. Bd.*

Weed, Truman. Carmina concordiæ: songs of Union College; with music and piano forte accomp. 8°. '75. $1.75 ... *Pond.*

Weed with an ill name. 18°. '64. 45c. *Am.S.S.; Am.Tr.*

Weeden, Jane. The anti-whiskey war. 32°. '74. pap., 10c. ... *Friends Pub.H.*

Weeden, W: B. Morality of prohibitory liquor laws. 16°. '75. $1.25 ... *Roberts.*

Weeds and seeds, and other tales. 18°. 70c. *Pres.Bd.*

Week (The). 18°. 75c. ... *Carter.*

Week (The); or, practical duties of the fourth commandment. 18°. 80c. ... *Am.S.S.*

Week by themselves. Norris, E. M. $1 ... *Nelson.*

Week completed. 18°. 35c. ... *Am.S.S.*

Week completed. Cheap, *Mrs.* — 40c. ... *So.Meth.*

Week day sermons. Dale, R. W. $1.75 .. *Routledge.*

Week day stories for little Ann about poor Jane, told by her mother. 18°. 40c. ... *Am.S.S.*

Week in Lilly's life. Finley, M. F. 60c. ... *Pres.Bd.*

Week in a tent. ill. 18°. '75. 30c. ... *Dodd.*

Week of creation. Warington, G. $1.50. *Macmillan.*

Week on the Concord and Merrimack rivers. Thoreau, H. D. $1.50 ... *Osgood.*

Week with Fanny; or, the fifth commandment enforced. 18°. 35c. ... *Am.S.S.*

Week with Jesus. Lowrie, J. M. $1.50 ... *Pres.Bd.*

Weekly motto verses. 24°. '67. 40c.; 60c. .. *Randolph.*

Week's holiday. Frost, S. A. 75c. ... *Am.Tr.*

Weeks, E: P. *See* Blanchard, G. A., *and* Weeks, E. P.

Weeks, *Mrs.* Helen C. Ainslie ser. 4 v. ill. 16°. '67–'71. $5.25 ... *Hurd & H.*

Cont.: Ainslie stories, $1.50. — Grandpa's house. — White and red. — Four and what they did, *ea.*, $1.25.

Weeks, Jos. D. History of Knights of Pythias; with account of life and times of Damon and Pythias. 3d ed. 12°. $2 ... *J.H.Powers.*

Weeks, Rob. Kelley. Episodes and lyric pieces. 16°. '70. $1.50 ... *Holt.*
— Poems. 16°. '66. $1.25 ... *Holt.*
— Twenty poems. 16°. '76. $1.25 ... *Holt.*

Weems, Mason L. Life of Benjamin Franklin. 12°. $1.25. ... *Lippincott.*
— Life of Fs. Marion. 12°. $1.25 ... *Lippincott.*
— Life of G: Washington. 12°. $1.25 ... *Lippincott.*
— *Germ.* 12°. 50c. ... *I.N. Whiting.*

Weeping willow. Sigourney, L. H. *net*, 19c. *Hamersley.*

Weg zum Himmel. [Cath. prayer book.] 24°. 75c.–$2.50 ... *T.Kelly.*

Wege (Die) des Herrn sind wunderbar. Baumbach, J. 30c. ... *Pilger.*

Wehner, J. H. Principles form character: comedy. 16°. pap., 15c. ... *French.*

Weiberfeind (Der). *See* Benedix, R.

Weiblichen Stufenjahre (Die). *See* Zschokke, H:

Weide für die Lämmer. 18°. 40c. ... *Ev.Assoc.*

Weidemann, J. Make home beautiful: handbook of landscape gardening. col. lith. and eng. 4°. $15. *Judd.*

Weighed in the balance. Robbins, S. S. $1.25 .. *Carter.*

Weightman, C: Art of swimming. 32°. 30c. *De Witt.*

Weihnachten. *See* Hoffmann, F:

Weihnachtsabend (Der). *See* Schmid, C. v.

Weihnachtsblüthen: Taschenbuch. f. d. Jugend. 4 v. ill. 18°. ea., 75c. ... *Radde.*

Weil, Gst. The Bible, the Koran and the Talmud; comp. from Arabic sources, and compared with Jewish traditions. 12°. $1 ... *Harper.*

Weiland, —. New and improved guitar method. f°. $1.50 ... *Gordon.*

Weinland, D. F. Egg tooth of snakes and lizards. 8°. '57. pap., 15c. ... *Essex.*

Weir, Marion Eliza. Rockbourne: a tale. 16°. $1.25. *Carter.*

Weisbach, Albin. Tables for determination of minerals by physical characteristics; tr. by Frazer, jr. 12°. roan, $2 ... *Lippincott.*

Weisbach, Jul. Manual of mechanics of engineering, and of construction of machines; tr. by E. B. Coxe. v. 1: Theoretical mechanics. ill. 8°. '75. $10 ... *Van Nostrand.*

Weise, A. J. History of Troy [N. Y.] from expulsion of Mohegan Indians to 1876; with maps and tables by A. J. Bardin. 8°. '76. $3.50. *W.H. Young.*

Weiss, J: American religion. 16°. '71. $1.50 .. *Roberts.*
— Bible and science. 12°. pap., 10c. ... *Free Rel.*
— Life and correspondence of Theodore Parker. 2 v. por. and eng. 8°. $6; hf. cf., $11 ... *Appleton.*

Weiss, Jul. Harvest of flowers ["Blumenlese"]: operatic Germ. and Ital. melodies [for violins]. 4°. $2.50; — for piano. 4°. $4 ... *Peters.*

Weiss, N. Personal recollections of wreck of the "Ville-du-Havre" and "Loch Earn"; tr. from the Fr. 16°. '75. $1.25 ... *Randolph.*

Weisse Frau (Die). 12°. pap., 15c. ... *Radde.*

Weisse Frau (Die). Mylius, O. $1.50; $1 .. *Zickel.*

Weisse Rose (Die). Ongaro, F. dall'. 40c. *F. W. Thomas.*

Weissenborn, G. American engineering; ill. by large and detailed drawings. 2 v.: text, imp. 8°.; pl., f°. '61. mor., *$38; in 26 nos., ea., $1 .. *Am.Indust.*
— American locomotive engineering; ill. by large and detailed drawings. 2 v.: text, imp. 8°.; pl., f°. '74. mor., *$36; in 24 nos., ea., $1 .. *Am.Indust.*

Weissenburger, Aloys. Hausmannskost f. Gesunde, Hausmittel f. Kranke. 12°. 50c. ... *Benziger.*

Weitbrecht, Ma. Miracles of faith: sketch of Beaté Paulus; with introd. by C. S. Robinson. 18°. '73. 75c. ... *Dodd.*

Weitzmann, C. Gedichte in schwäbischer Mundart. 12°. '70. pap., 45c. ... *Steiger.*

Welch, Adonija S. Analysis of the Eng. sentence. ('62.) New ed., rev. 12°. $1.25 ... *Barnes.*
— Object lessons for primary schools. 12°. '62. $1. *Barnes.*

Welch, Ashbel. Form, weight, [etc.], of rails. *See* Constable, C., Retaining walls; — Hamilton, S., Fabrication of béton blocks.
— *See also* Rapid transit and terminal freight facilities.

Welch, E: J. Cowling. Designing belt gearing. 8°. '75. pap., 20c. ... *Spon.*
— Designing valve gearing. ill. cr. 8°. '75. $2.50 .. *Spon.*

Welch, Orrin. Knights Templars' tactics and drill; with diagrams, etc. 18°. '72. $1 ... *Macoy.*
— *Same.* 16°. '75. $1 ... *Masonic.*
— *Same.* ill. 32°. $1.50 ... *Redding.*

Welch, R. Bethune. Centennial discourse: hereditary interest of the Reformed (Dutch) Church in education, common and collegiate. 8°. '76. pap., 25c. ... (?) *N.Y.Ref.Ch.Bd.*
— Faith and modern thought; with introd. by T. Lewis. 12°. '76. $1.50 ... *Putnam.*

Welcker, W. T. Military lessons; for military schools, colleges and militia. 12°. '74. 75c. ... *Ivison.*

Welcome (The). Kieffer, J. M. 35c. ... *Brainard.*

Welcome (The). Sewall, F. 30c. ... *New Ch.*

Welcome friend: sel. of entertaining and instructive sketches. 12°. $1.25 ... *T.Bliss.*

Welcome guest: coll. of instrumental music. f°. $3; $4; bds., $2.50 ... *Gordon.*

Welcome home. *See* Kennedy, *Mrs.* M. G.

Welcome home: coll. of piano-forte music. 4°. $3; bds., $2.50 ... *G.D.Russell.*

Welcome lib. 10 v. 32°. '66. $2.50.......... *Hoyt.*

Welcome to Jesus. Smith, J. 10c......... *Pres.Bd.*

Weld, Allen H. Latin lessons and reader. ('45.) New ed. 12°. '73. $1.25 .... *Bailey.*

— New English grammar. ('49.) New ed. 12°. '73. hf. bd., 88c. .... *Bailey.*

— Parsing book. ('47.) New ed. 12°. '76. hf. bd., 31c.................................. *Bailey.*

— *See also* Norton, S. A., Weld, A. H., *and* Quackenbos, G: P.

— *and* Quackenbos, G: P. Progressive grammar. ('59.) New ed. 12°. '76. hf. leath., $1.13. *Bailey.*

— — Progressive parsing book. ('59.) New ed. '76. 12°. hf. bd., 31c...................... *Bailey.*

Weldon, G: Warburton. Unity in variety: arguments based on divine workmanship in our planet, constitution of the human mind and inspired hist. of religion. 12°. '71. $1.50 .... *Whittaker.*

Weldon woods; by author of "Soldier's return." ('63.) New ed. ill. 16°. '71. 60c. ...... *Hoyt.*

Welford, R: Griffiths. Practical treatise on equity pleadings; with obs. on orders of 1841, and those orders. 8°. shp., $1.50............ *Kay.*

Well begun is half done; or, the young painter and fiddler; tr. ill. 16°. $1.25 .... *O'Shea.*

Well in the desert. Holt, E. S. $1.25....... *Carter.*

Well in the valley. Smyth, T. $1.25 ...... *Am.S.S.*

Well spent hour. Follen, E. L. $1.25....... *Fuller.*

Well watered plains. Brinsmade, H. N. 35c... *Pres.Bd.*

Well! well! Wallace, M. A. $1.25; $1.75.. *Sadlier.*

Wellard, Ja. James Wellard, companion of John A. Murel. ill. 8°. pap., 25c........... *U.P.James.*

Weller, E: *See* Bartholemew, J., *and* Weller, E.; — Student's atlas of hist. geog.

Weller, S. Clarionet, [fife, flageolet, flute, guitar, melodeon, piano or violin] without a master. 8 nos. obl. 8°. ea., pap., 75c............. *Peters.*

Welles, Gid. Lincoln and Seward: views as to their relative position in the "Lincoln administration." 12°. $1.50; pap., $1 .... *Sheldon.*

Wellesley, Arth. *See* Wellington, *Duke of.*

Wellington, *Duke of.* [Arth. Wellesley.] Military and civil life; by an old soldier, from materials of Maxwell. 12°. (Bohn.) $1.75.. *Little, B.& Co.*

— *Same.* 12°. (Bohn.) $2. *Lippincott; Scribner, W.& A.*

— Words of W.: maxims, reflections, etc. 16°. $1.25. *Scribner, W.& A.*

Wellington, Arth. M. Methods for computation, from diagrams, of preliminary and final estimates of railway earthwork. 12°. $1.50. — pl. f°. $3.50. *Appleton.*

Wellman, J. W. Church polity of the Pilgrims; with app. [Sermon.] 12°. 50c.......... *Cong.Pub.*

Wellmer, Arn. Anna, Countess of Stolberg, superintendent of Bethany Deaconess House at Berlin: story of our own times; tr. by D. M. P. 12°. '73. $1.50........................... *Routledge.*

Wells, C: Grand mass in C minor. f°. $2.. *Gordon.*

Wells, D: Ames. First principles of geology, descriptive and industrial. ill. 12°. '61. $1.25.. *Ivison.*

— Natural philosophy; arr. with special ref. to practical application of physical science. ill. 12°. '57. $1.60 .... *Ivison.*

— Principles of chemistry; arr. with special ref. to pract. applic. to arts and employments of common life. ill. 12°. '58. $1.60 .... *Ivison.*

— Production and distribution of wealth: address, Detroit, May 11, 1875, before Am. Soc. Sci. Assoc. 8°. '75. pap., 20c.................... *Williams.*

— Rational principles of taxation; read May 20, 1874; with discussion on taxation. 8°. '74. pap., 10c. *Williams.*

Wells, D: Ames, *continued.*

— Robinson Crusoe's money; or, the remarkable financial fortunes and misfortunes of a remote island community. ill. 8°. '76. $1; pap., 50c... *Harper.*

— Science of common things: familar explanation of first principles of physical science. ill. 12°. '57. $1.20. *Ivison.*

— Things not generally known: handbook of facts not readily accessible. 12°. $1.75....... *Appleton.*

— *See also* Annual of scientific discovery.

— *and* Dodge, E., *and* Cuyler, G. W. Local taxation: report of commission appointed to revise the [N. Y.] laws for assessment and collection of taxes. 8°. pap., 50c......................... *Harper.*

Wells, J. C. Delineation of law of limitation in Illinois. 8°. '70. shp., $5........... *E.B.Myers.*

— Treatise on questions of law and fact: instructions to juries and bills of exceptions. 8°. '76. shp., $7.50 .... *Cockcroft.*

Wells, J. Soelberg. On long, short and weak sight, and their treatment by scientific use of spectacles. 3d ed., rev. and enl. ill. 8°. '69. $3... *Lindsay.*

— Treatise on diseases of the eye. 3d Lond. ed. ill. 8°. '73. $5; leath., $6.............. *Lea; Lindsay.*

Wells, J: G. Every man his own lawyer, and business form book. 12°. '56. $2.25. *Appleton; Macoy; J. G. Wells.*

— *Germ.* 12°. $2.50...................... *J. G. Wells.*

— The Grange illustrated; or, Patrons' handbook. ill. 12°. '74. $2......................... *J. G. Wells.*

Wells, *Mrs.* Kate G. In the clearings. ('70.) 2d ed. ill. 16°. '72. 80c..................... *Am. Unit.*

Wells, Ralph (*ed.*) Sunday-school teacher's hymn book. 18°. '70. pap., 10c........... *Randolph.*

Wells, S: Roberts. Father Matthew, the temperance apostle: his character and biography. 12°. pap., 10c.................................... *Wells.*

— New physiognomy; or, signs of character, as manifested through the temperament and external forms. ill. 12°. '66. $5; cf., $8; mor., $10.. *Wells.*

— Wedlock; or, the right relations of the sexes; disclosing laws of conjugal selection, etc. 12°. '69. $1.50; $2..................................... *Wells.*

— (*ed.*) Annual of phrenology and physiognomy. 8°. pap., 10c.................................. *Wells.*

— *Same.* 1865–'73. 9 v. in 1. ill. 8°. $2...... *Wells.*

— Wells' new descriptive [phrenological] chart. 12°. '68. 50c.; pap., 25c..................... *Wells.*

Wells, T. Spencer. Diseases of the ovaries. 8°. $4.50................................. *Appleton.*

Wells, W: Heroine of the White Nile; or, what a woman did and dared: travels of Miss Alexina Tinne. ill. 12°. '71. $1........ *Meth.Bk.Conc.*

Wells, W: Harvey. Graded course of instruction for public schools. 12°. '62. $1.25....... *Barnes.*

Wells, W: V. Explorations and adventures in Honduras; compr. travel in gold regions of Olancho, and review of hist. and gen. resources of Central Am. maps and ill. 8°. $3.50.......... *Harper.*

— Life and public services of S: Adams. 3 v. 8°. '65. $12; hf. cf., $18; cf., $21....... *Little, B. & Co.*

Wells of Baca. *See* Macduff, J: R.

Wels, A. Clelia. *See* Bauer, C., Clemence d'Orville.

Wels, C: Church music: coll. of sentences, chants, etc. obl. 4°. '64. $3.................. *Ditson.*

Welsby, W: Newland. *See* England, Exchequer reports.

Welsh, Jane Kilby. Familiar lessons in mineralogy and geology. 2 v. 12°. '33. $1....... *D. Clapp.*

Welsh, Lew. G. Practical guide to business. ('72.) New ed., rev. and enl. ill. 8°. '76. $2.. *Watts.*

— *Same.* ill. 8°. *$2.50........................ *So.Pub.*

Welsh, *Miss* M. J. Baptist denomination. 18°. 60c. *So.Bapt.*

Welsh, W: Women helpers in the church: their sayings and doings. 12°. $1.50....... *Lippincott.*

Welsh girl. Planché, J. R. 15c. . . . . *Lee & S.*

Welstead, H: Giralda: drama. 16°. pap., 15c. *French.*

Welty, *Mrs.* E. A. Self-made; or, living for those we love. [Fiction.] 12°. $1.50 . . . . *Sheldon.*

Wendell, J: L. *See* New York State, Supreme Court reports.

Wendetè, C. W., *and* Perkins, H. S. The sunny side: religious songs for the Sunday school and the home. 16°. '75. bds., 35c. . . . . *Pond.*

Wendling, G: R. Index to Illinois Sup. Court reports to 1873. 8°. shp., $4 . . . . *E.B. Myers.*

Weninger, Fs. Xav. Grosser Katechismus. 16°. 25c. *Benziger.*

— *Eng.* Larger catechism of the Christian doctrine. 24°. bds., 25c.; pap., 15c. . . . . *O'Shea.*

— Herz Jesu Missionsbuch. 18°. leath., $1; $1.35; $1.65 . . . . *Benziger.*

— *Eng.* Sacred heart mission book. 18°. $1–$4 . . *O'Shea.*

— Katholizismus, Protestantismus u. Unglaube. 12°. $1. *Benziger.*

— *Eng.* Catholicity, Protestantism and infidelity. 12°. $1.25 . . . . *O'Shea.*

— Kleiner Katechismus. 18°. 12c. . . . . *Benziger.*

— *Eng.* Smaller catechism of Christian doctrine. 24°. 10c. . . . . *O'Shea.*

— Legende (Die) der Heiligen als christ-kathol. Hausbuch. 2 v. 8°. leath., $8 . . . . *Benziger.*

— Lives of the saints; with a pract. instruction on life of each saint for every day. 12 pts. ill. 8°. ea., $1; in 2 v., $12 . . . . *O'Shea.*

— Monat Mariä (Der). 18°. 65c.; leath., $1.15; $1.35. *Benziger.*

— Ostern im Himmel. 12°. $1 . . . . *Benziger.*

— *Eng.* Easter in heaven. 16°. $1; $1.50 . . *Sadlier.*

— Photographic views; or, relig. and moral truths reflected in the universe. 8°. $2 . . . . *O'Shea.*

— Unfehlbarkeit (Die) des Pabstes. 12°. $1.50. *Benziger.*

— *Eng.* Apostolical and infallible authority of the pope. 12°. $1.50 . . . . *O'Shea.*

— Vollständiges Handb. der christ-kathol. Religion. 12°. hf. mor., $1.75 . . . . *Benziger.*

— *Eng.* Manual of Cath. religion. 12°. $1.50 . . *O'Shea.*

Wenlock of Wenlock. Wilks, T. E. 15c. . . *French.*

Wenonda; or, love conquers. 18°. 30c.; 40c. *Am. Bapt.*

Wentworth, E. Arithmetical problems. 12°. 60c.; — with answers, 75c. . . . . *Harper.*

Wentworth, J: Early Chicago. [Lectures.] por. 12°. '76. pap., 35c. . . . . *Fergus.*

Wentworth, May (*pseud.*) *See* Newman, *Mrs.* M. W.

Wentworth, T: Office and duty of executors; with ref. to Am. cases by E. D. Ingraham. 8°. '32. $3 . . . . *T. & J. W. Johnson.*

Wentworth mystery. Phillips, W. 30c. . . *Am. News.*

Wentworths (The). Pindar, S. C. $1.25 . . *Lothrop.*

Weppner, Margaretha. The north star and the southern cross: personal experiences, impressions and obs. in a two years' journey around the world. 2 v. 12°. '76. $5 . . . . *Weppner.*

Wept of Wish-ton-wish. *See* Cooper, Ja. F.

Wept of Wish-ton-wish: drama. 16°. pap., 15c. *French.*

Wer da steht, der sehe zu, dass er nicht falle. *See* Temme, J. D. H.

Wer Gott vertraut, hat wohl gebaut. ill. 32°. '61. 25c. *Am. Tr.*

Were they miracles? accounts of healing by prayer. sq. 24°. pap., 15c. . . . . *Willard.*

Werner, Ant. Cantate (The): masses, etc., for Cath. service. 2 nos. obl. 8°. '62. ea., bds., $2.25. *Ditson.*

Cont.: 1. Morning service. — 2. Evening service.

— Memorare (The): Cath. music, with organ or piano accomp. obl. 4°. '57. $2.75 . . . . *Ditson.*

— Young beginner's music book; or, Cath. sing. book. 16°. 40c. . . . . *Noonan.*

Werner, D. C. Family dentist: treatise on teeth. 12°. '53. $1.50 . . . . *Wells.*

Werner, Ern. (*pseud.*) *See* Bürstenbinder, E.

Werner. Byron, *Lord.* 15c. . . . . *French.*

Wernli, Jac., *and* Hillmantel, L: Deutsche Schönschreibehefte. obl. 8°. per doz., pap., $1 . . *Enderis.*

Wesley, C: *See* Wesleyan psalter.

Wesley, J: Works. 7 v. 8°. '37. $21; cf., $24.50. *Meth. Bk. Conc.*

— Doctrinal tracts revised. 18°. '36. 75c. *Meth. Bk. Conc.*

— Journal. 2 v. 8°. '37. $6 . . . . *Meth. Bk. Conc.*

— Notes on New Test. 8°. '37. $3.50; cf., $4. — 12°. '45. $1.75 . . . . *Meth. Bk. Conc.*

— Plain account of Christian perfection. 24°. '37. 45c. . . . . *Meth. Bk. Conc.*

— *Same;* ed. by T. O. Summers. 18°. '55. 45c. *So. Meth.*

— *Swed.* 12°. 50c. . . . . *Meth. Bk. Conc.*

— Reasons against separation from Church of England. 8°. '74. pap., 25c. . . . . *Whittaker.*

— Select letters, chiefly on personal religion. 12°. '38. 80c. . . . . *Meth. Bk. Conc.*

— Sermons. 2 v. 8°. '37. $6; cf., $7; $8 . . *Meth. Bk. Conc.*

— *Same.* ('57.) 10th ed. 4 v. 12°. '76. $4.50; shp., $5 . . . . *So. Meth.*

— Sermons on the spiritual life; ed. with introd. by A. Stevens. 3d ed. 12°. '75. $1.50 . . . . *Tibbals.*

Wesley, his own historian. *See* Janes, E. L.

Wesley and his friends. 18°. 60c. . . . . *Am. S. S.*

Wesley and Methodism. Taylor, I. $1.50 . . *Harper.*

Wesleyan Demosthenes. Wakeley, J. B. $1.25. *Meth. Bk. Conc.*

Wesleyan Methodist catechism. 3 pts. 18°. pap., pt. 1, per doz., 50c.; 2, per doz., $1; 3, per doz., $1.35 . . . . *So. Meth.*

Wesleyan minstrel. M'Donald, W. 75c. *Meth. Bk. Conc.*

Wesleyan psalmist. *See* Scudder, M. L.

Wesleyan psalter: poet. version of Book of Psalms by Rev. C. Wesley and others. 18°. '55. 50c.; $1; mor., $2. — 24°. 40c. . . . . *So. Meth.*

Wesleyana: system of Wesleyan theology. 12°. '41. 90c. . . . . *Meth. Bk. Conc.*

Wesley's missionaries to America. Sandford, P. P. 90c. *Meth. Bk. Conc.*

Wessely, J. E. French-English and English-French dictionary. 12°. 75c. . . . . *Routledge.*

— Italian-Eng. and Eng.-Ital. dict. 12°. 75c. . . *Routledge.*

— New pocket dictionary of the English and French lang. 18°. '73. $1 . . . . *Holt.*

— New pocket dictionary of the Germ.-Eng. and Eng.-Germ. lang. 16°. $1 . . . . *Holt.*

— Pocket dictionary of English and Italian lang. 16°. '74. $1 . . . . *Holt.*

— Spanish and Eng. dict. 16°. '74. $1 . . . . *Holt.*

— Spanish-English and English-Spanish dictionary. 12°. 75c. . . . . *Routledge.*

West, Alb. L. Architects and builders' vade mecum and book of reference. 18°. '72. $1.50 . . *Woodhouse.*

West, Anson. State of the dead. 12°. $1.25. *Lippincott.*

West, C: How to nurse sick children. 18°. 50c. *W. Wood.*

— Lectures on diseases of infancy and childhood. 5th Am. ed., enl. 8°. $4.50; leath., $5.50 . . . . *Lea.*

— Lectures on diseases of women. 3d Am. ed. 8°. $3.75; leath., $4.75 . . . . *Lea.*

— On some disorders of the nervous system in childhood. sm. 12°. $1 . . . . *Lea.*

West, J. R. Parish sermons on ascension of our Lord. 16°. '11. $1.25 . . . . *Pott.*

— Short elementary treatise on the eucharist. 16°. '68. $1 . . . . *Pott.*

West, J: B. *See* Shaw, J. C., *and* West, J. B.

West, Mar. A. Romance of missions; or, inside views of life and labor in land of Ararat; with introd. by Mrs. Charles. 12°. '75. $2 . . . . *Randolph.*

West, Rob. A. A father's letters to his daughter. 18°. '65. 35c. . . . . *Am. Tr.*

West End. Boucicault, D. 15c. . . . . *French.*

West India boys. 18°. 50c. . . . . *Am.S.S.*

West India mission; with incidents and notices of converts. 18°. 25c. . . . . *Am.S.S.*

West India pickles. Talboys, W. P. $1.50 . . *Carleton.*

West Indian. Cumberland, R. 15c. . . . . *French.*

West Lawn. Holmes, M. J. $1.50 . . . . *Carleton.*

West Point life: poem read before Dialectic Soc. of U. S. Milit. Acad.; with pen and ink sketches. obl. 8°. '66. $2.50 . . . . *Van Nostrand.*

West Point scrap book. Wood, O. E. $5. *Van Nostrand.*

West Virginia. Acts of Assembly, 1871–2. 2 v. 8°. ea., hf. shp., $1.25. — 1872–3. 8°. hf. shp., $4. — 1875. 8°. pap., 50c. . . . . *J. W. Randolph.*

— Code of laws, 1870. 8°. '71. shp., $3.50. *J. W. Randolph.*

— Constitution and laws, 1861–'66. 8°. shp., $5. *J. W. Randolph.*

— Supreme Court reports, v. 1–5 (1863–'72); by J. M. Hagan. 5 v. 8°. '66–'73. shp., 1, 2, 5, ea., $4; 3, $4.50; 4, $5 . . . . *J. W. Randolph.*

— *Same.* v. 6 (1873); by H. M. Mathews. 8°. '75. shp., $4.50 . . . . *J. W. Randolph.*

Westbrook parsonage. McKeever, H. B. $1.50. *Claxton.*

Westbrooke. *See* Bates, *Miss* L.

Westcott, Brooke Voss. Bible in the Church: account of collection and reception of the Scriptures in the Christian churches. 18°. $1.25 . . *Macmillan.*

— Christian life, manifold and one: six sermons in Peterborough Cathedral. cr. 8°. '69. $1 . . *Macmillan.*

— General survey of the hist. of the canon of the New Test. during the first four centuries. New ed., rev. cr. 8°. $3.50 . . . . *Macmillan.*

— General view of history of the Eng. Bible. 2d ed. cr. 8°. '72. $3.50 . . . . *Macmillan.*

— Gospel of the resurrection: thoughts on its relation to reason and history. 3d ed. cr. 8°. '74. $2. *Macmillan.*

— Introduction to study of the Gospels; with hist. and explan. notes. 8°. '73. $2 . . . . *Dutton.*

— *Same.* 5th ed., rev. cr. 8°. '75. $3.50 . . *Macmillan.*

— On the religious office of the universities: sermons. cr. 8°. '73. $1.75 . . . . *Macmillan.*

Westcott, Marg. Bessie Wilmerton. 12°. $1.75. *Carleton.*

Westcott, Thompson. Centennial portfolio: souvenir of International Exhibition at Phila.: lith. views, with letter press descriptions. obl. 8°. '76. $4.50; pap., $3.50; hf. mor., $7; mor., $10; artist's ed., mor., $20 . . . . *T. Hunter.*

— Life of John Fitch, inventor of the steamboat. 12°. $1.25 . . . . *Lippincott.*

— Names of persons who took oath of allegiance to Penna., 1777–1789; with hist. of test laws of Penna. f°. '65. pap., $10. — 4°. pap., $5. — 8°. pap., $2.50 . . . . *J. Campbell & Son.*

— Official guide book to Phila.; with hist. of the city. maps and ill. 12°. '75. $1.50; mor., $2 . . *Porter.*

Westentaschen-Liederbuch. 48°. 25c.; pap., 15c. *Schäfer.*

Westentaschen-Volks-Liederbuch. 32°. 30c.; pap., 20c. . . . . *Kohler.*

Western adventures. Hunter, F. $1.75 . . *J. E. Potter.*

Western bell. Perkins, E. A., *and* Pease, F. H. $1.50 . . . . *Ditson.*

Western cavaliers. Redford, A. H. $2 . . . . *So. Meth.*

Western farmer and stock grower. Briggs, M. $1.25. *Day.*

Western fruit book. Hooper, E. J. $1.50 . . *Wilstach.*

Western harp. M'Anally, D. R. 65c.; 85c.; $1; $1.50; $2 . . . . *S. W. Bk. & Pub.*

Western harp. Shindler, M. S. B. D. $2; $1.50. *Ditson.*

Western martyrology; or, bloody assizes: lives, trials and dying speeches of those Protestants that suffered in west of Eng. and elsewhere; with life of G: L. Jeffreys. ill. 12°. '74. $2 . . *Routledge.*

Western pilot. Cummings, S. 75c. . . . . *U. P. James.*

Western preacher. Mathes, J. M. $2 . . . . *Cen. Bk.*

Western scenes; or, life on the prairie. ill. 12°. pap., 75c. . . . . *Peterson.*

Western side. 18°. 60c.; 75c. . . . . *Am. Bapt.*

Western Union Telegraph directory: guide to transmission of telegraphic correspondence; with tariff from N. Y. to all parts of the world. 16°. '74. $1 . . . . (?) *West. Un. Tel.*

Western windows. Piatt, J. J. $1.50 . . . . *Hurd & H.*

Western world. Kingston, W. H. G. $2.50 . . *Nelson.*

Westfield, *Mass.* *See* Celebration.

Westlake, J. Willis. How to write letters: manual of correspondence. 16°. $1; $1.50 . . . . *Sower.*

— Three thousand practical words. [Orthography.] ('74.) 5th ed. 16°. '75. 50c. . . . . *Eldredge.*

Westlake, J: Treatise on private international law; or, conflict of laws; with ref. to practice in Eng. and other systems of jurisprudence, and ref. to Am. authorities. 8°. '59. $2.50 . . *T. & J. W. Johnson.*

— — *See also* Law lib.

Westmacott, C. M. Nettlewig Hall: farce. 16°. pap., 15c. . . . . *French.*

Westminster Assembly. Larger catechism. 18°. 20c. . . . . *Pres. Bd.*

— Shorter catechism. 32°. 12c.; — proofs, analysis and notes. 18°. 15c. . . . . *Pres. Bd.*

— — Key. 18°. 30c. . . . . *Carter.*

— *Lat.* 16°. 10c. . . . . *Pres. Bd.*

— *Port.* 16°. 15c. . . . . *Pres. Bd.*

— *Span.* 18°. 10c. . . . . *Pres. Bd.*

— *Welsh.* 18°. 10c. . . . . *Pres. Bd.*

Westmoreland, Mar. Jourdan. Clifford troupe. 12°. $1.75 . . . . *Carleton.*

— Heart hungry. 12°. $1.75 . . . . *Carleton.*

Weston, *Mrs.* D. C. Works. 8 v. 18°. bds. . . *Dutton.*
Cont.: Biog. of New Test. characters, 15c. — Biog. of Old Test. characters, 15c. — Catechism on the church, 25c. — Jewish antiquities, 20c. — Questions on fundamental truths and doctrines of Script., 2 v., *ea.*, 20c. — Synopsis of Bible, 2 v., *ea.*, 20c.

Weston, H. H. Fairy egg and what it held. ill. sq. 16°. $1.25 . . . . *Loring.*

Weston, Mar. D. Henry Roberts. 18°. 40c. . *Cong. Pub.*

Weston, W: *See* Vermont, Sup. Court reports.

Weston, the walkist. Mack, J. 15c. . . . . *De Witt.*

Westropp, Hodder M. Manual of precious stones and antique gems. ill. 12°. $3 . . . . *Scribner, W. & A.*

— *and* Wake, C. S. Ancient symbol worship; with introd., add. notes and app. by A. Wilder. 8°. '74. $2. — 2d ed. ill. 8°. '75. $3 . . . *Bouton.*

Westward Wright, J. McN. $1.10 . . . . *Pres. Bd.*

Westward by rail. Rae, W. F. $2 . . . . *Appleton.*

Westward empire. Magoon, E. L. $1.50 . . *Harper.*

Westward ho! Kingsley, C. $1.75 . . . . *Macmillan.*

Westwood, J: Obadiah. Butterflies of Great Britain. ill. 4°. '72. $6 . . . . *Routledge.*

Wet days at Edgewood. Mitchell, D. G. $1.75. *Scribner.*

Wetenhall, E: Rudiments of the Greek language. 12°. '55. 75c. . . . . *Murphy.*

Wetherel affair. DeForest, J. W. $1.75; $1 . . *Sheldon.*

Wetherell, Eliz. (*pseud.*) *See* Warner, Su.

Wetmore, Ja. Carnahan. Wetmore family of Am. and its collateral branches: geneal., biog. and hist. notices. roy. 8°. '61. hf. roan, $5 . . . *Munsell.*

Wetmore, W: J. The oriental: coll. of eastern melodies. 8°. '73. $1.25 . . . . *Schermerhorn.*

— *See also* Burnap, U. C., *and* Wetmore, W. J.

Wette, W: Mt. L. de. Human life; or, practical ethics; tr. by S. Osgood. 2 v. 12°. $2.50 .... *Dennet.*
— Theodore; or, the skeptic's conversion; tr. from the Germ. 2 v. in 1. 12°. $1.50 .... *Burnham.*
Wey, Fs. Description and recollections of Rome; with 346 wood-eng. by celebrated artists, and a plan of Rome. f°. $30; mor., $40; cf., $45. — (chp. ed.), $15; mor., $30 .... *Appleton.*
Whale and his captors. Cheever, H. T. $1 .. *Harper.*
Whaleman's adventures in the Sandwich Islands. Thomes, W. H. $1.50 .... *Lee & S.*
Wharey, Ja. Sketches of church history. 18°. 65c. *Pres. Bd.*
Wharton, C: Treatment of the horse in the stable and on the road. ill. 12°. $1.25 .. *Judd; Lippincott.*
Wharton, Fs. Commentary on law of agency and agents. 8°. shp., $6.50 .... *Kay.*
— Precedents of indictments and pleas for use in courts of U. S. and in those of the several states; with notes on criminal pleading and practice. 3d ed., rev. 2 v. 8°. shp., $13 .... *Kay.*
— Silence of Scripture. 16°. '68. $1 .... *Dutton.*
— State trials of the U. S. during administrations of Washington and Adams; with ref., etc. 8°. shp., $7.50 .... *W. C. Little.*
— Treatise on conflict of laws, or private international law; incl. a comparative view of Anglo-American, Roman, German and French jurisprudence. 8°. shp., $6.50 .... *Kay.*
— Treatise on criminal law of U. S. 7th ed., rev. 3 v. 8°. shp., $19.50 .... *Kay.*
— Treatise on law of homicide in U. S.; with leading cases. 2d ed. 8°. shp., $6.50 .... *Kay.*
— Treatise on law of negligence; embr. Eng. and Am. authorities. 8°. shp., $6.50 .... *Kay.*
— Treatise on theism, and on modern skeptical theories. 12°. $1.25 .... *Lippincott.*
— *See also* Medical jurisprudence.
Wharton, G: M. A southern medical student's portfolio. ill. 12°. '71. pap., 75c. .... *Claxton.*
Wharton, Grace (*pseud.*) *See* Thomson, *Mrs.* Kath. B.
Wharton, H: Supplement to T. J. Wharton's Digest of Penna. reports, 1852–'62. 8°. '65 ..... *State.*
Wharton, J: J. Smith. Law lexicon; or, dict. of jurisprudence. 2d Am. ed., enl. by E. Hopper. 8°. shp., $6.50 .... *Kay.*
— Principles of conveyancing. *See* Law lib.
Wharton, Ph. (*pseud.*) *See* Thomson, J: C.
Wharton, T: J. Digest of Penna. reports, with some MS. cases, 1754–1852. 2 v. 8°. '53 .... *State.*
— — *See also* Wharton, H:
— *See also* Pennsylvania, Sup. Court reports.
What and how to read. Van Rhyn, G. A. F. $1; 50c. *Appleton.*
What animals do and say. Follen, E. L. 50c. .. *Lee & S.*
What answer? Dickinson, A. E. $1.50 ..... *Osgood.*
What became of Thomas Munce. Naisby, V. 20c. *Barclay.*
What the Bible says about prayer. Moon, G. W. 10c. *Dutton.*
What a boy! Willis, J. A. $1.50 .... *Lippincott.*
What came afterwards. Arthur, T. S. $1.50. *J. E. Potter.*
What can I do? 32°. 15c. .... *Am. S. S.*
What can she do? Roe, E. P. $1.75 .... *Dodd.*
What can woman do? Arthur, T. S. $1.25 .. *J. E. Potter.*
What Catharine did, and what came of it. ill. 18°. '72. 40c. .... *N. Y. Ref. Ch. Bd.; Pres. Com.*
What changed Guy Dennis; or, life at school and at home. 16°. $1 .... *Am. S. S.*
What constitutes a lawful ministry. Ziegenfus, H. L. 15c. .... *Dutton.*
What do I want most? 18°. 50c. .... *Dutton.*
What does a little money cost? 18°. 40c. .. *Cong. Pub.*
What Elise loved best. 18°. 50c. .... *Carter.*
What God does is well done. Salzman, C. G. $1.25. *Cin. Meth. Bk. Conc.*
What good can I do? 18°. 60c. .... *Whittaker.*
What happened after the battle of Dorking. 16°. '71. bds., 25c. .... *Routledge.*
What have I done? drama. 16°. pap., 15c. . *French.*
What he saw and did in Africa. Riley, J. $1.50. *World Pub.*
What I did with my fifty millions. Bagby, G. W. 50c. *Lippincott.*
What I know about Ben Eccles. Holt, J. S. $1.50. *Lippincott.*
What I know of farming. Greeley, H. $1.50 .. *Carleton.*
What is Calvinism? Smith, W. D. 65c. ... *Pres. Bd.*
What is the Centennial? and how to see it. 8°. '76. pap., 50c. .... *Dando.*
What is a child? Groser, W. H. 15c. .. *Meth. Bk. Conc.*
What is confirmation, or the laying on of hands? Haskins, D. G. 12c. .... *Dutton.*
What is Darwinism? Hodge, C. $1.50 .... *Scribner.*
What is faith? Beattie, R. H. 40c. .... *Pres. Bd.*
What is free trade? Walker, E. $1 .... *Putnam.*
What is her name? *See* Edersheim, A.
What is her name? or, the benevolent Jew. 16°. $1. *Am. Bapt.*
What is homœopathy? Holcombe, W. H. 15c. *Boericke.*
What is Judaism? Lewin, R. $1 .... *Appleton.*
What is a little money good for? 18°. 65c. .. *Cong. Pub.*
What is a little money worth? 18°. 40c. .. *Cong. Pub.*
What is music? Rice, I. L. $1; 50c. ...... *Appleton.*
What is Presbyterianism? Hodge, C. 35c. .. *Pres. Bd.*
What is property? Proudhon, P. J. $3.50; $6.50. *B. R. Tucker.*
What is religion? Memminger, R. W. $1.50 .. *Claxton.*
What is revelation? *See* Maurice, F. D.
What is right? Denton, W. 10c. .... *Denton.*
What is spiritualism? Forster, T. G. 25c. .... *Colby.*
What is spiritualism? King, M. M. 25c. ...... *Colby.*
What's to be done? or, the will and the way; by author of "Wealth and worth." 18°. 75c. .... *Harper.*
What is to be, will be. Winstanley, E. 30c. *Am. News.*
What Jesus says. Russell, F. $2 ... (?) *Kalamazoo.*
What Katy did. Woolsey, S. C. $1.50 ..... *Roberts.*
What Katy did at school. Woolsey, S. C. $1.50. *Roberts.*
What made little Mollie so happy. *See* Aunt Alice's lib.
What makes corn grow? *See* Infant school lib.
What makes me grow? or, walks and talks with Amy Dudley. ill. 16°. '68. $1 .... *Putnam.*
What men have said about woman. Southgate, H. $2.50 .... *Routledge.*
What might have been expected. Stockton, F. R. $1.50 .... *Dodd.*
What Minnie found to do. 32°. 20c.; 15c. .. *Dutton.*
What the moon saw. Andersen, H. C. $2.50 .. *Routledge.*
What a mother can endure. *See* Conscience, H.
What must I do to be saved? Peck, J. T. 60c. *Meth. Bk. Conc.*
What my teacher says. 32°. 15c. .... *Am. S. S.*
What now? Deems, C. F. 40c. .... *Am. Tr.*
What of the churches and clergy? 12°. *$1 .. *D. E. Fisk.*
What Robbie was good for. Brine, M. D. 35c. *Am. Tr.*
What shall we believe? Hamilton, D. H. 10c. *D. H. Hamilton.*
What shall we do to-night? or, social amusements for evening parties. ill. 12°. $2 .... *Dick & F.*
What shall we eat: manual for housekeepers. 12°. '68. 75c.; pap., 50c. .... *Putnam.*

What she could. Warner, S. $1.25 .... *Carter.*

What she did with her life. Theed, M. F. $1.25. *Routledge.*

What the swallows sang. Spielhagen, F. $1.25 .. *Holt.*

What then? Gillett, E. H. 25c.; 15c....... *Pres. Bd.*

What think ye? or, questions that must be answered. 18°. 40c. .... *Pres.Bd.*

What to do. Llewellyn, E. L. 55c. .... *Pres. Bd.*

What to do and how to do it. *See* Goodrich, S: G.

What to do and how to do it in case of accident. 12°. '74. 50c. .... *Indust.*

What to do with cold mutton: a book of réchauffés. 12°. $1 .... *Huntington.*

What to observe at the bedside and after death in medical cases. roy. 12°. $1 .... *Lea.*

What to wear? Phelps, E. S. $1; 50c....... *Osgood.*

What the trees taught the little girl. 18°. 25c. *Am.S.S.*

What we saw in Australia. Hill, R. *and* F. $3. *Macmillan.*

What we saw in Egypt. ill. 18°. '74. 50c..... *Nelson.*

What will he do with it? *See* Bulwer-Lytton, *Sir* E. G. E. L.

What'll they say at Brampton? Coyne, J.S. 15c. *French.*

What will the world say? *See* Morenos, O.

What the wind taught; [also] Voice of the passion flower. 32°. 20c.; 15c. .... *Dutton.*

What women should know. Duffey, E. B. $2. *J. M. Stoddart.*

What young people should know. Wilder, B. G. $1.50. *Estes.*

Whately, R: Easy lessons on reasoning; in seventeen lessons. 12°. 90c. .... *Dennet.*
— Elements of logic. 18°. 75c. .... *Harper.*
— *Same.* 12°. $1 .... *Morton.*
— *Same.* 12°. '55. $1.50 .... *So. Meth.*
— *Same.* 12°. $1.75. — Questions, pap., 15c. *Sheldon.*
— Elements of rhetoric. 18°. 75c. .... *Harper.*
— *Same.* 12°. $1 .... *Morton.*
— *Same.* 12°. '58. $1.50 .... *So. Meth.*
— *Same.* 12°. $1.75. — Questions, pap., 15c. *Sheldon.*
— Essays on some of the difficulties in writings of St. Paul. 12°. '65. $1.50 .... *Draper.*
— Essays on some of the peculiarities of the Christian religion; [also] Historic doubts conc. Napoleon. 12°. '70. $1.50 .... *Draper.*
— Evidences of Christianity. 18°. 35c. *Cin. Meth. Bk. Conc.*
— Historic doubts concerning Napoleon. 12°. '70. 50c.; pap., 25c. .... *Draper.*
— — *See also above* Essays.
— Introductory lessons on the mind. 12°. 90c. *Dennet.*
— Introductory lessons on morals and Christian evidences; with pref. by F. D. Huntington. 12°. $1.50 .... *Dennet.*
— Kingdom of Christ. 8°. $1.50 .... *Carter.*
— On corruptions of Christianity. 12°. '76. $1.50. *Tibbals.*
— Selections of Eng. synonymes. 12°. $1..... *Lee & S.*
— View of the Scripture: revelations conc. a future state. 4th ed. 12°. '73. $1.50 .... *Smith, E. & Co.*

Whatever is, is right. Child, A. B. $1 ...... *Colby.*

Wheat, J: T: Preparation for the holy communion. 18°. 60c.; 70c. .... *Dutton.*

Wheat and tares. [Fiction.] 12°. $1.25.... *Harper.*

Wheat or chaff. Ryle, J. C. $1 .... *Carter.*

Wheatland, H: Notice of the Pope family. 8°. '67. pap., 25c. .... *Essex.*

Wheatley, C: Rational illustrations of Book of common prayer. 12°. (Bohn.) $1.25 ..... *Little, B. & Co.*
— *Same.* 12°. (Bohn.) $1.40 .... *Scribner, W. & A.*
— *Same.* 12°. (Bohn.) $1.50 .... *Lippincott.*

Wheatley, R. *See* Palmer, *Mrs.* Phœbe.

Wheaton, H: Digest of U. S. Supreme Court reports (1789–1829). 2 v. 8°. '21–'29 ..... [*New York.*]

Wheaton, H: *continued.*
— *See also* Crichton, A., *and* Wheaton, H.; — Sparks, J., Library of Am. biog.; — United States, Sup. Court reports.

Whedon, Dan. D. Commentaries. 4 v. 12°. '66–'75. ea., $1.75 .... *Meth. Bk. Conc.*

Cont.: Matthew and Mark. — Luke and John. — Acts and Romans. — 1 Corinthians to 2 Timothy.

— Freedom of the will. 12°. '64. $1.75 .. *Meth. Bk. Conc.*
— Public addresses, collegiate and popular. 12°. 75c. *Cin. Meth. Bk. Conc.*
— Question book on Comment. on Matthew and Mark. 18°. per doz., $2.40 .... *Meth. Bk. Conc.*

Wheel of fortune. 32°. 50c. .... *Fisher.*

Wheel of fortune. Baker, H. N. W. $1.25 .. *Graves.*

Wheel of fortune. Cumberland, R. 15c. ..... *French.*

Wheel of the law. Alabaster, H. $7 .. *Scribner, W. & A.*

Wheeler, C: H. Letters from Eden: reminisc. of missionary life in the east. 16°. $1.25 .. *Bost. Am. Tr.*
— Little children in Eden. map and ill. 18°. '76. 75c. *Hoyt, F. & D.*
— Ten years on the Euphrates [Armenia]; or, primitive missionary policy ill.; with introd. by N. G. Clark. ill. 16°. $1.25 .... *Bost. Am. Tr.*

Wheeler, Ella. Drops of water: temperance poems. 12°. '72. 75c. .... *Nat. Temp.*
— Maurine. 8°. '76. $1.50 .... *Cramer.*
— Shells. ('73.) 2d ed. 12°. '74. $1.50 .... *Hauser.*

Wheeler, G: M. Preliminary report upon a reconnoissance in south and southwestern Nevada. *See* United States, *Corps of Eng.*

Wheeler, Gervase. Homes for the people. ill. 12°. $3 .... *Woodward.*
— Rural homes. 12°. $2 .... *Woodward.*

Wheeler, J. Talboys. Analysis and summary of Herodotus. 12°. (Bohn.) $1.75 .... *Little, B. & Co.*
— *Same.* 12°. (Bohn.) $2 .. *Lippincott; Scribner, W. & A.*
— Analysis of Thucydides. 12°. (Bohn.) $1.75. *Little, B. & Co.*
— *Same.* 12°. (Bohn.) $2 .. *Lippincott; Scribner, W. & A.*
— Life and travels of Herodotus in 5th cent. before Christ: imaginary biog. founded on fact. 2 v. map. 12°. $3.50; hf. cf., $7 .... *Harper.*

Wheeler, Jac. D. Reports of criminal law cases decided at N. Y. City Hall, 1776–1823. 3 v. 8°. '23 .. *State.*

Wheeler, J: H. Historical sketches of North Carolina. 8°. $2 .... *Lippincott.*

Wheeler, W: A. Dictionary of noted names of fiction. 12°. '65. $2.50; hf. cf., $4.50 .... *Osgood.*
— *See also* Soule, R. *and* Wheeler, W. A.

Wheelock, E. M. *See* Texas, Sup. Court reports.

Wheelock, E: Willard. *See* Colman, J., *and* Wheelock, E. W.

Wheelwright, Abram. Traditions of Palestine. 16°. 75c. .... *Cong. Pub.*

Wheildon, W: W. American lobster (The), homarus Americanus: natural history and habits. 8°. '75. 25c. .... *Wheildon.*
— Arctic regions. 3 v. 8°. '68–'74. ea., pap., 25c. *Wheildon.*
— Contributions to thought. 12°. '75. $1.50 .. *Wheildon.*
— Letters from Nahant, hist., descript. and miscellaneous. ill. 12°. '48. pap., 25c. .... *Wheildon.*
— Maverick bridge: argument, 1868. 8°. '68. pap., 25c. .... *Wheildon.*
— Memoir of Sol. Willard. pl. 8°. '65. $2.50 .. *Wheildon.*
— New history of battle of Bunker Hill. 8°. '75. 50c. *Wheildon.*
— Scientific excursion across Iowa from Dubuque to Sioux City and Springvale (Humboldt). 8°. '73. 25c. .... *Wheildon.*
— Siege and evacuation of Boston and Charlestown; with account of pre-revolutionary buildings. 8°. '76. 50c. .... *Wheildon.*

Whelpley, S: Compend of hist.; with corrections, add. and improvements by J. Emerson. New ed. 2 v. in 1. 12°. '72. $1.50 .... *Collins & Bro.*
— Letters to Gov. Caleb Strong, showing that retaliation, capital punishment and war are prohibited by the Gospel. 4th ed. 12°. '75. 50c.... *Peace.*
When are we happiest? ill. 18°. '68. 65c... *Perkinpine.*
When I am a man. 18°. 50c............... *Dutton.*
When I was a boy. Tarbox, I. N. 50c. .. *Cong. Pub.*
When I was a girl. Follen, E. L. 50c....... *Lee & S.*
When I was a little girl. Tabor, E. $1.50.. *Macmillan.*
When I was young. Camden, C. $1.25 .. *Routledge.*
When I was young. *See* Old man's stories.
When we were young. Mackarness, M. A. 55c. *Lothrop.*
When were our Gospels written? 18°. 60c... *Cong. Pub.*
When were our Gospels written? Tischendorf, C. 25c. *Am. Tr.*
When women weep. Gotthold, J. N. 15c..... *Ames.*
Where Daisy's doll went. *See* Bertha's rose.
Where is the city? Putnam, E. T. H. $1.25.. *Roberts.*
Where is the harm? Goodale, E. 80c......... *Hoyt.*
Where is he? McConnell, J. S. J. 50c... *Perkinpine.*
Where is Rosa? *See* Maple grove stories.
Where's your wife? Bridgeman, I. V. 15c... *French.*
Where lies the fault? 18°. 35c........... *Cong. Pub.*
Where there's a will there's a way. *See* Haven, *Mrs.* A. B.
Where there's a will there's a way. Morton, J. M. 15c.................................. *French.*
Whewell, W: Astronomy and general physics; considered with ref. to natural theology. (Bridgewater treatise.) 12°. $1............ *Harper.*
— *Same.* 12°. (Bohn.) $1.25 .... *Little, B. & Co.*
— *Same.* 12°. (Bohn.) $1.40....... *Scribner, W. & A.*
— *Same.* 12°. (Bohn.) $1.50 .... *Lippincott.*
— Elements of morality, including polity. 2 v. 12°. $2 .... *Harper.*
— History of inductive sciences. 2 v. 8°. $5. hf. cf., $10 .... *Appleton.*
Which: spiritualism or Christianity? Hull, M., *and* Parker, W. F. 75c.; 50c.............. *Colby.*
Which is the apostolic church? Witherow, T. 50c. *Pres. Bd.*
Which is the church? Southwell, G. W. 12c. *Dutton.*
Which is the heroine? [Fiction.] 8°. pap., 50c. *Harper.*
Which is my likeness? or, seeing others as we see ourselves: book for girls. ill. 12°. $1.50.. *Nelson.*
Which is our Saviour, Christ or the church? Tallaferro, J. H. 10c. .... *So. Bapt.*
Which is the true church? Ellmore, A. 15c. *Cen. Bk.*
Which is which? comedietta. 16°. pap., 15c. *French.*
Which is which? Fullerton, *Lady* G. 25c... *Sadlier.*
Which is wiser? *See* Howitt, Ma.
Which of the two? Morton, J. M. 15c. *De Witt; French.*
Which shall I marry? Suter, W. E. 15c..... *French.*
Which shall it be? Hector, A. F. $1.25....... *Holt.*
Which way? 18°. 30c. .... *Am. S. S.*
Which will have him? vaudeville. 16°. pap., 15c. *Lee & S.*
Which wins? by author of "Robert Joy's victory." ('69.) New ed. ill. 16°. '73. $1.50 ..... *Hoyt.*
Whig almanac. *See* Tribune almanac.
Whig-Examiner. *See* Addison, Jos.
While it was morning. Townsend, V. F. $1.25. *J. E. Potter.*
While they are with us. 18°. '66. 45c. ..... *Am. Tr.*
Whilliden, W. Our great Indian war. 8°. pap., 25c. *Barclay.*
Whim (A) and its consequences. *See* James, G. P. R.
Whims and oddities. *See* Hood, T:

Whip and spur. Waring, G. E., *jr.* $1.25.. *Osgood.*
Whipple, *Miss* Content. Newell boys. ('72.) New ed. 16°. '74. $1.25 .... *Hoyt.*
— Prescotts (The). 18°. '71. 60c. ...... *Garrigues.*
Whipple, Edn. Percy. Works. 6 v. 16°. '50–'71. ea., $1.50; per set, hf. cf., $18 .... *Osgood.*
Cont.: Character and characteristic men. — Essays and reviews, 2 v. — Literature and life. — Literature of age of Elizabeth. — Success and its conditions.

— Washington and the revolution. 16°. 30c... *Osgood.*
Whipple, Squire. Elementary treatise on bridge building. 2d ed., enl. ill. 8°. '73. $4.. *Van Nostrand.*
— Truss bridge building. *See* Craven, A. W., Address to Am. Soc. of Civ. Eng.
— Upright arched bridges. *See* Forshey, C. G., Levees of Mississippi River; — Rapid transit and terminal freight facilities.
— *Same;* [also] Notes on erection of Illinois and St. Louis bridge, by T. Cooper; [also] Education of civil engineers, by T. C. Clarke. 8°. '74. pap., 80c. .... *Am. Soc. of C. E.*
— Utica lift draw bridge. *See* Coryell, M., Conflagration in coal at Kidder Slope.
Whisper to a bride. Sigourney, L. H. *net,* 75c.; $1.67................................ *Hamersley.*
Whispering pine. Kellogg, E. $1.25 .... *Lee & S.*
Whispering pine ser. *See* Kellogg, E.
Whispers from dreamland. Dunning, A. K. 50c. *Pres. Bd.*
Whispers to a bride. *See* Phelps, *Mrs.* A. L.
Whistler. Simonds, W. $1.25............. *Miller.*
Whistler: drama. 16°. pap., 15c. .... *French.*
Whistling Horace. *See* Baker, *Mrs.* H. N. W.
Whitaker, Epher. New fruits from an old field. 12°. '65. $1.50; $2.25 .... *Randolph.*
Whitaker, *Mrs.* Ma. Ann. Alice's dream: tale of Christmas time. ill. 16°. 75c. .... *Fuller.*
— — *See also* Union ser.
Whitcher, B. W. Story of a convent. 12°. $1.. *O'Shea.*
Whitcher, *Mrs.* Fes. M. ["Widow Bedott."] Widow Bedott papers. ill. 12°. $1.75.......... *Mason.*
— Widow Spriggins. 12°. $1.75........... *Carleton.*
Whitcomb, Ida P. Summary of hist. to accompany Lord's "Modern hist." 12°. 60c...... *Desilver.*
White, Alexina B. Little-folk songs. ill. 16°. '71. $1. *Hurd & H.*
White, *Miss* Ambie. Woman in purple and scarlet; or, downfall of Catholicism. 12°. $1.50.. *So. Bapt.*
White, *Rev.* And. Journal of voyage to Maryland, with first expedition of Lord Baltimore, in 1633. 8°. '74. $2; $2.50 .... *Murphy.*
— — *See also* Maryland Hist. Soc.
White, Babington (*pseud.*) Circe; or, three acts in life of an artist. 8°. pap., 50c. .... *Harper.*
White, C. A. Student's mythology. 12°. $1.25. *Widdleton.*
White, C. A., *and* Blake, C. D. School for the reed organ. 4°. '75. bds., $2.50 .... *Pond.*
White, C. I. Life of Mrs. Seton; with extracts from her writings. 7th ed., rev. por. 12°. '56. $2; $2.50 .... *Murphy.*
White, Carlos. Ecce femina: exam. of argument in favor of female suffrage by J. S. Mill and others. 16°. $1.50.............................. *Lee & S.*
White, C: [Ethiop. dramas.] 44 v. 16°. ea., pap., 15c. .... *De Witt.*
Cont.: African box; or, the magician's troubles. — Black chemist. — Black eyed William. — Bogus Injun. — Daguerreotypes; or, the picture gallery. — Damon and Pythias. — Darkey's stratagem. — The draft. — Excise trials. — Fisherman's luck. — Getting square on the call boy. — The ghost. — Going for the cup; or, old Mrs. Williams' dance. — Good night's rest. — Guide to the stage. — Happy couple. — Hippotheatron; or, burlesque circus. — Jealous husband. — Laughing gas. — Lucky job. — Malicious trespass; or, nine points of the law. — Mutton trial. — Night in a strange hotel. — One hundredth night of

White, C: *continued.*

Hamlet. — One night in a bar room. — The policy player. — Pompey's patients. — Recruiting office. — Rival artists. — Sam's courtship. — Sausage makers. — Scampini. — Scenes on the Mississippi. — The serenade. — Siamese twins. — Stage struck couple. — Storming the fort. — Streets of New York. — Stupid servant. — Three strings to one bow. — Uncle Eph's dream. — Vinegar bitters. — Wake up, William Henry. — Wanted, a nurse.

— Black wit and darkey conversations. 18°. pap., 10c. *Dick & F.*
— Joke book. 18°. pap., 10c. *Dick & F.*
— Vilikens and his Dinah: Ethiop. drama. 16°. pap., 15c. *Happy.*

White, C: Abiathar. Manual of physical geog. and institutions of Iowa. ill. 4°. '73. 75c. *Day.*
— Report on geol. survey [1866–'69] of Iowa to 13th Gen. Assembly, 1870. 2 v. ill., maps and diagrams. imp. 8°. $10; hf. mor., $12 *Mills.*
— *See also* Iowa geol. survey.

White, C: J. Elements of theoret. and descript. astronomy. ('69.) 3d ed., rev. 12°. '75. $2 *Claxton.*

White, Dan. Appleton. Covenant of the First Church, Salem, Mass. 8°. '56. pap., 10c. *Essex.*
— New England Congregationalism. 8°. '61. $1 *Essex.*

White, Dan. T. New cook book; embr. temperate and economical receipts for domestic liquors and cookery. 16°. 10c. *U. P. James.*

White, E: L. Boston piano forte instructor; abridg. from Czerny's "Theoretical and practical school for the piano-forte." 4°. bds., $2 *Ditson.*
— Church melodist: collection of sacred music. obl. 8°. '51. bds., $1.50 *Ditson.*
— Melodeon without a master. 8°. '51. pap., 75c. *Ditson.*
— Piano without a master. 8°. '51. pap., 75c. *Ditson.*
— *and* Bissell, T. Seminary class book of music. obl. 16°. '52. bds., 75c. *Ditson.*
— *and* Gould, J. E. Harmonia sacra: coll. of anthems, choruses, etc. obl. 8°. '51. bds., $1.50 *Ditson.*
— — Modern harp; or, Boston sacred melodist: coll. of church music. obl. 8°. '74. bds., $1.50. *Ditson.*
— — Opera chorus book. obl. 4°. '49. bds., $2.50. *Ditson.*
— — Sacred chorus book. obl. 4°. '49. bds., $2.50. *Ditson.*
— — Tyrolien lyre: glee book, with and without pianoforte accomp. obl. 8°. '47. bds., $1.50 *Ditson.*
— *and* Johnson, A. N. Cecilian glee book. obl. 8°. $1.35 *Gordon.*

White, *Mrs.* Ellen G. Spirit of prophecy. v. 1. 16°. '70. $1 *Sev. Day Adv.*
— *Danish.* Prophetien's Aand. 16°. '74. 25c. *Sev. Day Adv.*
— (*ed.*) Sabbath readings. 16°. '73. 60c.; — in 5 v. 16°. pap., 50c. *Sev. Day Adv.*

White, Emerson E. Complete arithmetic; with or without answers. 12°. '70. 90c. *Wilson, H. & Co.*
— Intermediate arithmetic with or without answers. ('70.) New ed. 16°. '73. 45c. *Wilson, H. & Co.*
— Manual of arithmetic: handbook for teachers. 12°. '76. $1 *Wilson, H. & Co.*
— Primary arithmetic. 16°. '68. 30c. *Wilson, H. & Co.*

White, G: Queens and princesses of France. sq. 16°. '60. 60c.; 80c. *Murphy.*

White, G: G. Progressive art studies. 9 sets. ea., 60c. *Ivison.*

Cont.: Elementary ser., 4 sets. — Instrumental ser., 3 sets. — Ornamental ser., 2 sets.

White, Gilb. Natural history of Selborne. ill. 18°. 75c. *Harper.*
— *Same;* with notes by Sir W. Jardine and E. Jesse. ill. 12°. (Bohn.) $1.75; col. ill., $2.75. *Little, B. & Co.*
— — *Same.* ill. 12°. (Bohn.) $2; col. ill., $3. *Scribner, W. & A.*
— — *Same.* ill. 12°. (Bohn.) $2.50; col. ill., $3. *Lippincott.*
— *Same;* with add. notes by J. G. Wood. ill. 16°. $1.25. — ill. 8°. '75. $5 *Routledge.*

White, Gilb., *continued.*
— *Same;* with notes and memoir by Frank Buckland, chapter on antiquities by Lord Selborne, and new letters. ill. 8°. '76. $12; — large pap. ed., with photos. 2 v. 4°. hf. mor., $40 *Macmillan.*
— *See also* Wood, J. G., White, G., *and* Williams, C.

White, H: Massacre of St. Bartholomew; with hist. of religious wars in reign of Charles IX. ill. 8°. $1.75 *Harper.*

White, H: Hopley. *See* Roper, R. S. D., *and* White, H. H.

White, H: Kirke. Poems. (Aldine ed.) 16°. 75c. *Lippincott.*
— *Same;* with memoir. por. 18°. $1 *Osgood.*
— *Same;* with life by R. Southey. (Globe ed.) 16°. $1.25; hf. cf., $3.25; mor., $4 *Appleton.*
— — *Same.* (Household ser.) ill. 16°. $1.50; mor., $3 *Lee & S.*
— — *Same.* (Presentation poets.) ill. 16°. $1.75. *Routledge.*
— *Same;* ed. by R. A. Willmott, with biog. and crit. notice. (British poets.) ill. 12°. $2.25; hf. cf., $3.50; mor., $5 *Routledge.*
— — *See also* Gray, T: Poems; — Rogers, S: Poetical works.

White, Hor. Sophisms of protection. *See* Bastiat, F:

White, Hu. Lawson. Memoir. por. 8°. '56. $2.50. *Claxton; Lippincott.*

White, Ja. Appeal to youth: address at funeral of H: N. White, [with] brief narr. of his life. 16°. '64. pap., 40c. *Sev. Day Adv.*
— Hymns and tunes for those who keep the commandments of God and faith of Jesus. 4th ed. 16°. '76. $1 *Sev. Day Adv.*
— Life of William Miller. 2d ed. por. 16°. '75. $1. *Sev. Day Adv.*
— Our faith and hope. 16°. '70. 20c. *Sev. Day Adv.*
— Second coming of Christ: exposition of Matthew 24. 16°. '76. pap., 10c. *Sev. Day Adv.*

White, *Rev.* Ja. Eighteen Christian centuries; with index. 12°. $2 *Appleton.*
— Feudal times: hist. play. 16°. pap., 15c. *French.*
— History of England, to 1858; with anal., index, etc. cr. 8°. $2.50 *Routledge.*
— History of France, to 1848. 8°. $3 *Appleton.*
— King of commons: play. 16°. pap., 15c. *French.*
— Landmarks of history of England. 16°. bds., 60c. *Routledge.*
— Landmarks of history of Greece. 16°. bds., 60c. *Routledge.*

White, Jason. *See* Johnson, A. N., *and* White, J.

White, J: J. Peace, and other poems. 12°. $1.50. *Lippincott.*

White, J: T. Junior students' Latin-Eng. lexicon. sq. 12°. $3; shp., $3.50 *Ginn.*
— Junior students' Latin-Eng. and Eng.-Lat. lexicon. Rev. ed. sq. 12°. shp., $4.50 *Ginn.*

White, J: Williams. First lessons in Greek; to accompany Goodwin's Greek grammar. 12°. hf. mor., $1.50 *Ginn.*

White, Jos. J. Cranberry culture. ill. 12°. $1.25. *Judd.*

White, Jos. M. New collection of English, Spanish and French laws, and laws of Mexico and Texas, rel. to land titles in their respective colonies, now states or territories of [the U. S.] 2 v. 8°. '39. $10 *T. & J. W. Johnson.*

White, *Miss* M. Agnes. Gordon Lodge; or, retribution: autobiog. 12°. '73. $1.50; $2. *Kelly, P. & Co.*

White, O. W. The common evil. 18°. pap., 10c. *J. A. Clark.*

White, R. Baker. Reason and redemption; or, the Gospel as it attests itself. cr. 8°. $2 *Lippincott.*

White, R: Grant. Chronicles of Gotham: modern satire. 12°. 25c. *Carleton.*
— Fall of man: Darwinian satire. 12°. 50c. *Carleton.*

White, R: Grant, *continued.*
— Memoirs of life of W: Shakespeare; with essay toward expression of his genius, and account of rise and progress of the Eng. drama. cr. 8°. '65. $2.50; large pap., $5; hf. cf., $4; cf., $5; hf. mor., $7.50 .... *Little, B. & Co.*
— Words and their uses. 12°. $2 .... *Sheldon.*
— *See also* Shakespeare, W:
White, W. H. Erection of a bridge over the Danube. *See* Allen, T., Iron hulls.
— European railways. *See* Nickerson, L., Experiments showing neutral axes by polarized light.
White, W: Life of Emanuel Swedenborg, with synopsis of his writings; with introd. by B. F. Barrett. 12°. '66. $1.50 .... *Claxton; Lippincott.*
White, W: Medical electricity. 12°. '72. $2.. *Wells.*
White, Bp. W: Life. 18°. 60c. .... *Dutton.*
White, W: N. Gardening for the south; or, how to grow vegetables and fruits; with add. by J. Van Buren and J. Camak. ill. 12°. $2 .... *Judd.*
White, W: S. The African preacher. 18°. 40c. *Pres. Bd.*
— The Gospel ministry: letters from a father to his sons. 18°. 65c. .... *Pres. Bd.*
White, W: T. Anniversary discourse before N. Y. Acad. of Med. 8°. '76. pap., 20c. *N. Y. Acad. Med.*
White and black lies. Baker, H. N. W. $1.25.. *Hoyt.*
White and red. Weeks, H. C. $1.25 ..... *Hurd & H.*
White as snow. Mayo, I. F. $1 .... *Randolph.*
White Brunswickers. Adams, H. C. $1.50.. *Routledge.*
White castles, and other stories; by popular authors. 16°. '70. 75c. .... *Dutton.*
White cat. Burnand, F. C. 15c. .... *French.*
White cat. Keating, E. H. 15c. .... *French.*
White cat. Planché, J. R. 15c. .... *French.*
White cat. [Toy-book.] ill. 4°. $1; 50c... *Routledge.*
White chief. Belden, G. P. *$2.50 .... *Vent.*
White chief. Reid, M. $1.50 .... *Carleton.*
White chief's bride; or, trappers of Acadie. 8°. pap., 25c. .... *De Witt.*
White chrysanthemum. *See* Shaw, A.
White cockade. *See* Grant, Ja.
White cockade. Phillips, W. 15c. .... *French.*
White cruiser. Judson, E. Z. C. 25c. ..... *Dick & F.*
White dress. 18°. 30c. .... *Am. S. S.*
— *See also* Champney stories.
White dress. *See* Finley, M. F.
White elephant. *See* Dalton, W.
White farm. Lucas, W. J. 15c. .... *French.*
White fawn. Burnand, F. C. 15c. .... *French.*
White fawn; or, the fairies of fire and war. 8°. pap., 25c. .... *De Witt.*
White foreigners. 16°. '69. $1.10 .... *Am. Tr.*
White frock. 18°. 25c. .... *Am. S. S.*
— *See also* Children of Blackberry Hollow.
White gate; or, industry and faith; by author of "Daniel Tracey's store." 18°. 50c. .... *Am. S. S.*
White hand. Farman, E. $1.50 .... *Lothrop.*
White hand; or, jeweled snake. 8°. pap., 25c. *De Witt.*
White Hills. King, T. S. $3 .... *I. N. Andrews; Gill.*
White horse of the Peppers. *See* Lover, S:
White-jacket. Melville, H. $1.50 .... *Harper.*
White kitten. 18°. 60c.; 75c. .... *Am. Bapt.*
White kitten. *See* Golden stories.
White lady. Malen, M. E. O. 30c. ...... *Am. News.*
White lady. Reynolds, G. W. M. 50c. ..... *De Witt.*
White lady slippers. 18°. 22c. .... *Am. S. S.*
White lies. *See* Reade, C:
White milliner. Jerrold, D. 15c. .... *French.*

White Mountain cottage. Porter, A. E. 50c. *Cong. Pub.*
White Oak and its neighbors. Jacobs, S. S. $1.50. *Cong. Pub.*
White phantom. Braddon, M. E. 75c. ...... *De Witt.*
White rabbit. Mathews, J. H. $1 .... *Carter.*
White robes. *See* Walker, *Mrs.* J. B. R.
White Rock Cove; or, long ago at Bray Combe. ('68.) New ed. ill. 16°. '72. $1.15 .... *Hoyt.*
— *Same.* ill. 12°. $1.50 .... *Nelson.*
White rocks; or, the robbers of the Monongahela. Hill, A. F. $1.75 .... *J. E. Potter.*
White roe of Glenmere. *See* Hazelwood ser.
White rose. Hedges, M. J. $1.25 ...... *Nat. Temp.*
White rose. Melville, G. J. W. $1.25 .... *Appleton.*
White rose. *See* Morning glory lib.
White rose and red. Buchanan, R. $1.50.. * *Osgood.*
White rose of Langley. Holt, E. S. $1.50 .. *Carter.*
White rose ser. 4 v. 12°. $5 .... *Nat. Temp.*

Cont.: White rose, by M. J. Hedges. — All for money, by M. D. Chellis. — Wealth and wine, by M. D. Chellis. — Old times, by M. D. Chellis.

White scalper. Aimard, G. 50c. .... *Peterson.*
White secret. 16°. 25c. .... *Bloch.*
White slave; or, the Russian peasant girl. 8°. pap., $1 .... *Harper.*
White squaw. Reid, M. 20c. .... *Beadle.*
White supremacy and negro subordination. Van Evrie, J. H. $2 .... *Van Evrie.*
White swan. *See* Picture stories for little folks.
White water-lily, and other stories. ill. 18°. 35c. *Bost. Am. Tr.*
— *See also* Uncle Reuben ser.
White wolf. 8°. pap., 25c. .... *Dick & F.*
Whitebait at Greenwich. Morton, J. M. 15c. *French.*
Whiteboy (The). Hall, A. M. 50c. .... *Harper.*
Whitecross, J: Anecdotes ill. of sel. passages in each chapter of New Test. 18°. 65c. ...... *Pres. Bd.*
— Anecdotes ill. of sel. passages in each chapter of Old Test. 2 v. 18°. $1.20 .... *Pres. Bd.*
— Anecdotes on Assembly's catechism. 18°. 50c. *Carter.*
— *Same.* 18°. 45c. .... *U. P. Bd. of Pub.*
Whitefield, G: Leben. 24°. 15c. 18°. 30c... *Ev. Assoc.*
— *See also* Gillies, J: Life and sermons.
Whitefriars. *See* Robinson, J.
Whitefriars. Townsend, W. T. 15c. .... *French.*
Whitehall. *See* Robinson, J.
Whitehead, C: Antonio Bishallany. ill. 18°. '63. 45c. *Am. Tr.*
Whitehead, G: Memoirs. 12°. 75c... *Friends Bk. St.*
Whitehead, H: Sermons. 12°. $2 .... *Routledge.*
Whitehead, T. C. Village sketches: club and school festivals, etc. 16°. 75c. .... *Routledge.*
Whitehead, W: A. East Jersey under the proprietary governments; with app. by G: Scot. ('46.) 2d ed., enl. 8°. '75. $4; hf. cf., $5.25 ... *Dennis.*
— — *See also* New Jersey Hist. Soc.
Whiteladies. Oliphant, M. O. W. $1.25 ..... *Holt.*
Whiteley, S. B. *See* Hall, C. H., *and* Whiteley, S. B.
Whiter than snow. ('67.) New ed. ill. 16°. '75. 60c. .... *Hoyt.*
Whitfield, F: Works; ed. by C: W. Quick. 5 v. 12°. ea., 50c. .... *Leighton.*

Cont.: Counsels and knowledge from the words of truth. — Gleanings from Scripture. — Truth in Christ. — Voices from the valley testifying of Jesus. — Word unveiled.

Whitford, O. F. Closing breaks in canals under difficulties. 8°. pap., 25c. .... *Am. Soc. of C. E.*
Whither bound? M., A. M. 55c. .... *Pres. Bd.*
Whiting, G: E. First six months on the organ. 4°. pap., $2 .... *G. D. Russell.*

Whiting, Hattie C. Elmwood; or, the inalienable inheritance. 16°. $1.25 .... *Cong. Pub.*

Whiting, *Mrs.* M. H. Faith White's letter book, 1620–1623. ('66.) New ed. ill. 16°. '75. $1.50; $2 .. *Hoyt.*

Whiting, *Miss* Rachel Augusta. Golden memories of an earnest life: biog. of A. B. Whiting, with sel. from his writings; with introd. by J. M. Peebles. ('72.) 2d ed. por. 12°. '73. $1.50 .... *Colby.*

Whiting, S. K. New crystal spring: temperance melodies. obl. 12°. pap., 35c. .... *G. D. Russell.*

— Pure light: temperance melodies. obl. 16°. pap., 50c. .... *G. D. Russell.*

Whiting, W: Address at Colby University. 8°. pap., 25c. .... *Lee & S.*

— Memoir of Rev. S: Whiting, and of Eliz. St. John. 8°. hf. mor., $10; mor., $12 .... *Lee & S.*

— War powers under the Constitution of the U. S.; [also] War claims of aliens. 8°. $3.50; shp., $4.50 .... *Lee & S.*

Whitman, C: Sidney. Patent cases in the U. S. Sup. Court, [1861–'74]. 8°. '75. $10 .... *Morrison.*

— Patent laws, practices and forms. 8°. '75. shp., $6. *Morrison.*

Whitman, Walt. After all, not to create only. 12°. '71. 30c. .... *Roberts.*

— As a strong bird on pinions free. 12°. '72. 75c. *Somerby.*

— Democratic vistas. 12°. pap., $1 ...... *Whitman.*

— Leaves of grass. ('55.) 6th ed., enl. por. 12°. '76. hf. leath., $5 .... *Whitman.*

— Memoranda during the [civil] war. 12°. $1.50. *Whitman.*

— Passage to India. 12°. '71. $1 .... *Somerby.*

— Two rivulets. por. and autograph. 12°. '76. hf. leath., $5 .... *Whitman.*

Note. Includes "Democratic vistas," "Centennial songs," "Passage to India."

Whitmarsh, Caro. S. Lessons on the Christian life. 18°. per doz., $5 .... *Lee & S.*

— Noisy Herbert, and other stories. ill. sq. 16°. 75c. *Fuller.*

— Summer house stories. 5 v. ill. 16°. $4.50; ea., 90c. .... *Thompson.*

Cont.: Our summer house. — Rainy day stories. — Lives of familiar insects. — Older than Adam. — Wings and webs.

— Sunday lessons for young children. 16°. 15c. *Un. S. S.*

Whitmer, A. C. Child's catechism. 32°. hf. bd., 18c.; pap., 12c. .... *Ref. Ch. Pub.*

— Sacred geography. maps. 24°. 25c. .. *Ref. Ch. Pub.*

Whitmore, W: H. American genealogist. 3d ed., rev. and enl. por. 8°. '75. $3 ...... *Munsell.*

— Elements of heraldry. 8°. $6 .. *Lee & S.; Widdleton.*

— Massachusetts civil list, for the colonial and provincial periods, 1630–1774. 8°. '70. $2 .. *Munsell.*

Whitney, *Mrs.* Adeline D. T. Boys at Chequasset; or, a little leaven. 18°. $1 .... *Loring.*

— Faith Gartney's girlhood. ill. 12°. $1.75 .. *Loring.*

— Gayworthys (The). 12°. $2 .... *Loring.*

— Hitherto: story of yesterdays. 12°. $2 .... *Loring.*

— Mother Goose for grown folks. ill. 12°. $1.50 .. *Loring.*

— Other girls. ill. 12°. '73. $2 .... *Osgood.*

— Pansies. [Poems.] sq. 16°. '72. $1.50; hf. cf., $3; mor., $4 .... *Osgood.*

— Patience Strong's outings. 12°. $1.50 .... *Loring.*

— Real folks. ill. 12°. '71. $1.50 .... *Osgood.*

— Sights and insights. 2 v. 12°. '76. $3 .... *Osgood.*

— Summer in Leslie Goldthwaite's life. ill. 12°. '66. $1.50 .... *Osgood.*

— We girls: a home story. ill. 12°. '70. $1.50 .. *Osgood.*

— Zerub Throop's experiment. sq. 16°. 75c.; pap., 50c. .... *Loring.*

— *See also* Six of one by half a dozen of the other.

Whitney, Dan. H. Defense before Grand Lodge of Illinois. [Masonic.] 12°. pap., 20c. .. *E. A. Cook.*

Whitney, G: H. Handbook of Bible geog. New ed., rev. ill. and maps. 12°. '75. $2.50; mor., $4.50 .... *Meth. Bk. Conc.*

Whitney, J. P. Silver mining regions of Colorado. 12°. '65. pap., 25c. .... *Van Nostrand.*

Whitney, J: R. The last passover: account of closing incidents in life of Christ. 16°. '68. $1 .. *Claxton.*

Whitney, Josiah Dwight. Metallic wealth of the U. S., described and compared with that of other countries. 8°. '54. $3.50 .. *Claxton; Lippincott.*

— *See also* California geol. survey; — Foster, J. W., *and* Whitney, J. D.; — Illinois geol. survey; — Wisconsin geol. survey.

Whitney, S. W. Elements of Eng. grammar. sm. 12°. '75. 45c. .... *Schermerhorn.*

Whitney, T: R. Defence of the Am. policy, as opposed to encroachment of foreign influence, and especially to interference of papacy in polit. interests and affairs of U. S. 12°. $1.50 .. *De Witt.*

Whitney, W: D. Compendious German grammar. ('69.) New ed. 12°. '76. hf. roan, $1.75 .. *Holt.*

— German reader in prose and verse, with notes and vocab. ('69.) New ed. 12°. '76. hf. roan, $2; — in 2 v. 12°. v. 1 [text], $1.50; v. 2 [notes and vocab.], $1 .... *Holt.*

— Language and study of lang.: 12 lectures on principles of linguistic science. ('67.) 5th ed. cr. 8°. '75. $2.50 .... *Scribner.*

— Life and growth of language. 12°. $1.50 .. *Appleton.*

— Oriental and linguistic studies: the Veda, the Avesta, the science of language. ('72.) New ed., with index. cr. 8°. '75. $2.50 .... *Scribner.*

— *Same.* 2d ser.: the east and west; Religion and mythology; Orthography and phonology; Hindoo astronomy. ('74.) New ed., with index. cr. 8°. '75. $2.50 .... *Scribner.*

— *See also* Taittiriya-prâtiçâkhya (The).

Whiton, Ja. Morris. Exercises for tr. into Latin. 18°. '63. *net*, 45c. .... *Peck.*

— First lessons in Greek. 12°. $1.50 .... *Appleton.*

— Handbook of Latin exercises. New ed., rev. 12°. '65. *net*, $1 .... *Peck.*

Whiton, S: J. Glimpses of west Africa; with sketches of missionary labor. ill. 16°. 85c. .. *Bost. Am. Tr.*

Whittaker, F: The red rajah. 8°. pap., 20c. ... *Beadle.*

Whittaker, H: Analysis of recent decisions on practice and pleadings, Jan., 1863 to May, 1867: supplementary to [his] "Practice." 8°. '67. shp., $3 .... *Ward & P.*

Whittelsey, C: C. Missouri civil practice. 8°. '70. shp., $8.50. — Supplement, by W. G. Myer. 8°. $4; — 2 v. in 1. 8°. shp., $9.50 .... *Gilbert.*

— *Same;* [also] Pleading in civil actions, by W. L. McGary. 8°. shp., $12 .... *Gilbert.*

— Missouri form book. 12°. shp., $3 .... *Gilbert.*

— *See also* Missouri, Sup. Court reports.

Whittemore, E. E., *and* Blackman, O. Graded singers. 4 v. 12°. and 8°. $2.50; ea., 25c. *to* $1 .. *Church.*

Whittemore, T: Commentary on Revelation of St. John. 12°. '48. $1 .... *Universalist.*

— Life of Hosea Ballou; with biog. sketches of his seniors and contemporaries in the Universalist ministry. 4 v. por. 12°. '53–'55. $5. *Universalist.*

— Notes and illustrations of parables of the New Test. 12°. '32. $1.25 .... *Universalist.*

— Plain guide to Universalism. 12°. '40. $1. *Universalist.*

Whittier, J: Greenleaf. Complete works. 4 v. 16°. $9; hf. cf., $18; mor., $24 .... *Osgood.*

— Poems. (Amesbury ed.) por. and ill. 8°. '73. $5; hf. cf., $8; mor., $10 .... *Osgood.*

— *Same.* (Blue and gold ed.) 2 v. por. 32°. $2.50; hf. cf., $5; mor., $6 .... *Osgood.*

— *Same.* (Cabinet ed.) 2 v. por. 16°. $3; hf. cf., $6; mor., $8 .... *Osgood.*

— *Same.* (Centennial ed.) ill. 8°. '76. pap., $1 .. *Osgood.*

— *Same.* (Diamond ed.) 18°. $1; hf. cf., $2.25; mor., $3 .... *Osgood.*

Whittier, J: Greenleaf, *continued.*
— *Same.* (Merrimack ed.) 2 v. 16°. '69. $4.50; hf. cf., $9; mor., $12; — in 1 v. por. and ill. 12°. $3.50; hf. cf., $6; mor., $8 .... *Osgood.*
— *Same.* (New household ed.) 12°. '72. $2; hf. cf., $4; mor., $5 .... *Osgood.*
— *Same.* (Red-line ed.) ill. sm. 4°. $3.50; hf. cf., $5; mor., $7 .... *Osgood.*
— Prose works. 2 v. 16°. '66. $4.50; hf. cf., $9; mor., $12 .... *Osgood.*
— Among the hills, and other poems. ill. 16°. '68. $1.50; mor., $4 .... *Osgood.*
— Ballads of New Eng. ill. 8°. '69. $5; mor., $9 .. *Osgood.*
— Child and the poets. *See* Austin, *Mrs.* G. L., Little people of God.
— Child life. ill. 16°. '71. $3; hf. cf., $5; mor., $6. *Osgood.*
— Child life in prose. ill. 16°. '73. $3; hf. cf., $5; mor., $6 .... *Osgood.*
— Hazel blossoms. 16°. '74. $1.50; hf. cf., $3; mor., $4 .... *Osgood.*
— Home ballads and poems. 16°. '60. $1 .... *Osgood.*
— In war-time, and other poems. 16°. '63. $1.25 .. *Osgood.*
— Mabel Martin: harvest idyl. ill. 8°. '75. $5; mor., $9. — ill. 16°. '76. $1.50; mor., $4 .... *Osgood.*
— Maud Muller. ill. 8°. '66. $3.50; mor., $7 .. *Osgood.*
— Miriam, and other poems. 16°. '70. $1.50; mor., $4. *Osgood.*
— National lyrics. ill. sm. 4°. '65. pap., 50c.; — with por., 75c. .... *Osgood.*
— Pennsylvania pilgrim. ill. 16°. '71. $1.50; mor., $4. *Osgood.*
— Snow-bound: winter idyl. por. and ill. 16°. '66. $1.25; mor., $4. — ill. 8°. '67. $5; mor., $9. — (Vest-pocket ser.) ill. 32°. '75. 50c... *Osgood.*
— Tent on the beach, and other poems. 16°. '67. $1.50; mor., $4 .... *Osgood.*
— (*ed.*) Songs of three centuries; selected with introd. essay. 12°. '75. $2; hf. cf., $4; mor., $5. — 8°. $3.50; hf. cf., $7; mor., $9 .... *Osgood.*
— *See also* Companion poets; — Laurel leaves; — Winter poems.

Whittington junior. Reece, R. 15c. .... *French.*

Whittlesey, *Mrs.* —. Aunt Rebecca's charge, and other stories. ('70.) New ed. ill. 16°. '75. $1.25. *Hoyt.*

Whittlesey, C: Ancient mining on the shores of Lake Superior. 4°. '63. pap., 50c. ...... *Smith. Inst.*
— Fluctuations of level in No. Am. lakes. 4°. '60. pap., $1 .... *Smith. Inst.*
— Glacial drift of northwestern states. 4°. '66. pap., $1 .... *Smith. Inst.*

Whittlesey, Elsie Leigh. Helen Ethinger; or, not exactly right. 12°. '71. $1.50 .... *Claxton.*
— Hemlock swamp; [also] Summer at the White Sulphur Springs. 12°. '73. $1.50 .... *Claxton.*

Whittlesey, Sa. J. C. Bertha, the beauty: story of the southern revolution. 12°. '71. $1.50 .... *Claxton.*

Whitty, E: Mich. Bohemians of London; or, knaves and fools. 12°. $1.75; pap., $1.50 ... *Peterson.*

Who are Christians. Denton, W. 10c. ...... *Denton.*

Who are the happy? Waterbury, J. B. 35c. .. *Am. Tr.*

Who breaks, pays. Jenkin, C. $1.25 .... *Holt.*

Who did it? Ogden, R. N. 50c. .... *Claxton.*

Who died first? Leavitt, A. J. 15c. .... *De Witt.*

Who do they take me for? drama. 16°. pap., 15c. *French.*

Who got the pig? Irish [dram.] sketch. 16°. pap., 15c. .... *Happy.*

Who is greatest? *See* Arthur, T. S.

Who is greatest? *See* Howitt, Ma.

Who is he? Smiley, S. F. 75c. .... *Lippincott.*

Who's the heir? March, G. 15c. .... *French.*

Who's my husband? Morton, J. M. 15c. .... *French.*

Who is my neighbor? ill. 18°. '70. 55c. ... *Lothrop.*
— *See also* New holiday lib.

Who is my neighbor? or, the two great commandments; by author of "Little Bob True." 18°. 65c. *Pres. Bd.*

Who is my neighbor? or, the Wilson family. 18°. 35c.; 45c. .... *Am. Bapt.*

Who is to inherit? *See* Lacy's home plays for ladies.

Who's to win him? Williams, T. J. 15c. .... *French.*

Who is who? Williams, T. J. 15c. *De Witt; French; Lee & S.*

Who's your friend? comic drama. 16°. pap., 15c. *Happy.*

Who killed Cock Robin? Mathews, C. J. 15c. .. *French.*

Who shall be greatest? Howitt, M. 75c. .... *Harper.*

Who shall be heir? Pickering, E. 38c. .... *Peterson.*

Who shall be victor? Dupuy, E. A. $1.75 .. *Peterson.*

Who shall publish the glad tidings? *See* Boardman, M. M.

Who speaks first? Dance, C. 15c. .... *French.*

Who speaks next? Follen, E. L. 50c. .... *Lee & S.*

Who stole the chickens? Ethiop. drama. 16°. pap., 15c. .... *French.*

Who stole the pocket book? Morton, J. M. 15c. *French.*

Who stole the spoons? farce. 16°. pap., 15c. .. *Happy.*

Who took those coins? by author of "Nora's life at Derncleugh." 18°. 55c. .... *Am. S. S.*

Who wants a guinea? Colman, G., *jr.* 15c. .. *French.*

Who was the first architect? — the first paper-maker? — were the first builders? — the first miners? — the first weavers? *See* Busy bee lib.

Who was she? or, the soldier's best glory. ('70.) 2d ed. 12°. '72. $1.50 .... *Claxton.*

Who was Swedenborg? Hiller, O. P. 25c. *H. H. Carter; Lippincott.*

Who will win? *See* Cobden, P.

Who won. Robbins, S. S. $1.25 .... *Carter.*

Who won the prize; or, Helen Tracy. 16°. $1. *Am. S. S.*

Who would have thought it. 12°. $1.75 .. *Lippincott.*

Who would not pray? narrative. 18°. 22c. .. *Am. S. S.*

Whole armor. Graham, M. $1.25 .... *Hoyt.*

Wholesome words of Jesus Christ. Vaughan, C. J. $1. *Macmillan.*

Whom to marry and how to get married. *See* Mayhew, H. *and* A.

Why? 18°. 18c. .... *Am. S. S.*

Why am I a Cumberland Presbyterian? 75c.; pap., 40c. .... (?) *Cumberland.*

Why am I a Presbyterian? Campbell, N. W. 75c. (?) *Martien.*

Why and how? Conwell, R. H. $1.50 ...... *Lee & S.*

Why and what am I? Jarves, J. J. $1.50 .. *D. Thomas.*

Why are you a Methodist? Peck, G. 60c. *Meth. Bk. Conc.*

Why delay? Helffenstein, J. 50c. .... *Pres. Bd.*

Why did he marry her? Dupuy, E. A. $1.75 .. *Peterson.*

Why did he not die? Volckhausen, A. v. $1.75. *Lippincott.*

Why did you die? petite comedy. 16°. pap., 15c. *Happy.*

Why do I live? Smyth, T. 40c. .... *Am. Tr.*

Why I am a churchman. Randall, G. M. 12c. *Dutton.*

Why I did not become a sailor. *See* Ballantyne, R. M.

Why is history read so little? address to parents, teachers and members of fashionable society; by a student of hist. 12°. '76. pap., 15c. .. (?) *Wheaton.*

Why men do not believe. Laforet, N. J. $1 .. *Cath. Pub.*

Why the mill was stopped. Grosvenor, H. S. 50c. *Hoyt.*

Why not? Storer, H. R. $1; 50c. .... *Lee & S.*

Why not on Sunday? and other stories. ill. 24°. 25c. *Bost. Am. Tr.*
— *See also* Banner stories.

Why she refused him. Lorraine. $1.75... *Lippincott.*

Why should I be a pastor? Campbell, N. W. 40c. (?) *Martien.*

Why should I be a ruling elder? Campbell, N. W. 40c. (?) *Martien.*

Why was I left? McCalla, M. 60c. *Pres. Bd.*

Why we laugh. Cox, S. S. $1.50 *Harper.*

Why weepest thou? Hall, J. 30c.; 15c... *Randolph.*

Why will ye die? McCord, W. J. 35c. *Pres. Bd.*

Whymper, E: Scrambles among the Alps in 1860–'69. ill. 8°. $2.50; $3 *Lippincott.*

Whymper, F: Heroes of the Arctic. 12°. '76. $1.50. *Pott.*

— Travel and adventure in Alaska. maps and ill. cr. 8°. $2.50 *Harper.*

Whyte, Alex. Duty of prayer. 18°. 60c. *U. P. Bd. of Pub.*

Whytehead, Rob. Warrant of faith. post 8°. (Bagster.) $2.75 *Wiley.*

Whyte-Melville, G: J: *See* Melville, G: J: Whyte.

Wiberg, And. Christian baptism. [In Eng. or Swed.] 16°. 90c. *Am. Bapt.*

Wichert, Ern. The green gate; tr. by Mrs. A. L. Wister. 12°. $1.75 *Lippincott.*

Wichtl, G. Young violinist ["Junge Geiger"], 1st course; [also] Duets by I. Pleyel. 4°. '70. bds., $3 *Church; Ditson; Peters.*

— *Same.* 2d course: practical violin school for amateurs; with Eng., Fr. and Germ. text. 4°. bds., $2.50 *Peters.*

Wicked not annihilated. Warren, I. P. 10c. *Bost. Am. Tr.*

Wicked wife. Courtney, J. 15c. *French.*

Wicked woods of Tobereevil. *See* Mulholland, *Miss* R.

Wicked world: fairy comedy. 16°. pap., 15c. *Happy.*

Wickersham, Ja. Pyle. Methods of instruction. 12°. $1.75 *Lippincott.*

— School economy: treatise on preparation, organization, employments, government and authorities of schools. 12°. $1.50 *Lippincott.*

Wickes, T: Son of man. 16°. $1 *Bost. Am. Tr.*

Wicket gate: narrative of turning of sinners to God. ill. 16°. 80c. *Bost. Am. Tr.*

Wickets in the west. Fitzgerald, R. A. $2.50. *Routledge.*

Wickliffe, J: de. Life and writings. *See* British reformers.

Wicliffe and his times. 18°. 60c. *Am. S. S.*

Widdermer, Irene. Daisy Brentwell. 12°. '76. $1.75. *Putnam.*

Widdifield, Ha. New cook book; or, practical receipts for the housewife. 12°. $1.75.. *Peterson.*

Wide Awake pleasure book. 2 v. ill. 4°. '75–'76. ea., $2; bds., $1.75 *Lothrop.*

Wide, wide world. Warner, S. $1.75.... *Lippincott.*

Widerspenstige (Der). *See* Hoffmann, F:

Widerspenstigen (Der) Zähmung. *See* Shakespeare.

Widow; or, who wins: farce. 16°. pap., 15c. *French.*

Widow and the marquess. *See* Hook, Thdr.

Widow Barnaby. *See* Trollope, *Mrs.* Fes.

Widow Bedott (*pseud.*) *See* Whitcher, *Mrs.* Fes. M.

Widow Bedott papers. Whitcher, F. M. $1.75.. *Mason.*

Widow bewitched: drama. 16°. pap., 15c... *French.*

Widow Davis and young milliners. ill. 18°. '67. 45c. *N. Y. Ref. Ch. Bd.; Pres. Com.*

Widow directed. James, J. A. 50c. *Carter.*

Widow Freeheart: comedy. 16°. pap., 15c... *French.*

Widow Goldsmith's daughter. Smith, J. P. $1.75. *Carleton.*

Widow hunt (A). Coyne, J. S. 15c. *De Witt.*

Widow Lerouge. *See* Gaboriau, E.

Widow Maynard's cow. 18°. 17c.; 22c... *Am. Bapt.*

Widow Rugby's husband. Hooper, J. J. 75c. *Peterson.*

Widow Seymour. Baker, W. E. S. $1.50.. *Wagenseller.*

Widow Spriggins. Whitcher, F. M. $1.75.. *Carleton.*

Widower (The). Smith, J. P. $1.75..... *Carleton.*

Widow's cottage. *See* Nursery lib.

Widow's cow. *See* Little Blue Mantle lib.

Widow's sewing machine: what a helping hand did. ill. 18°. '72. 35c... *N. Y. Ref. Ch. Bd.; Pres. Com.*

Widow's sixpence. Nall, J. 60c. *Pres. Bd.*

Widow's son. ill. 18°. '40. 25c. *Am. Tr.*

Widow's son. 18°. 40c. *Dutton.*

Widow's son. Southworth, E. D. E. N. $1.75; $1.50. *Peterson.*

Widow's souvenir. Rose, A. C. 40c... *Meth. Bk. Conc.*

Widow's victim. Selby, C. 15c. *French.*

Widow's walk. 8°. pap., 25c. *Dick & F.*

Wie einer e. Wallfischfänger wurde. Oertel, P. F. W. 25c. *Steiger.*

Wie es euch gefällt. *See* Shakespeare, W:

Wie Heinrich v. Eichenfels zur Erkenntniss Gottes kam. *See* Schmid, C. v.

Wie man ein Held sein kann. 18°. 30c..... *Ev. Assoc.*

Wie die Saat so die Erndte. *See* Hoffmann, F.

Wiebe, E: Paradise of childhood: manual for self-instruction in Froebel's educational principles, and a practical guide to kinder-gartners. ill. 4°. $3; — in 4 pts., pap., $2.50 *M. Bradley.*

Wiedererstandene Eulenspiegel (Der). 12°. pap., 15c. *F. W. Thomas.*

— *See also* Eulenspiegel (Der).

Wiedertäufer (Die). *See* Van der Velde, K. F.

Wieland. Brown, C. B. $1 *Polock.*

Wife. Knowles, J. S. 15c. *French.*

Wife no. 19. Young, A. E. *$3; $3.50..... *Dustin.*

Wife of seven husbands. Almar, G. 15c..... *French.*

Wife of a vain man. Schwartz, M. S. $1.50; $1. *Porter.*

Wife to order. *See* Gerstäcker, F:

Wife's evidence. Wills, W. G. 50c. *Harper.*

Wife's messenger. Horton, M. B. $1.75.. *Lippincott.*

Wife's secret. Lovell, G. W. 15c... *French; Lee & S.*

Wife's secret. Stephens, A. S. $1.75; $1.50.. *Peterson.*

Wife's sister. Hubback, J. 50c. *Harper.*

Wife's trials. Pardoe, J. 75c. *Peterson.*

Wife's victory. Southworth, E. D. E. N. $1.75; $1.50 *Peterson.*

Wigan, Alfr. Model of a wife: farce. 16°. pap., 15c. *French; De Witt.*

— *See also* Talfourd, F., *and* Wigan, A.

Wigan, Hor. [Comedies.] 6 v. 16°. ea., pap., 15c. *French.*

Cont.: Always intended. — Best way. — Charming woman. — Friends or foes. — Observation and flirtation. — Real and ideal.

— Always intended: comedy. 16°. pap., 15c. *Lee & S.*

— *See also* Oxenford, J., *and* Wigan, H.

Wiggers, G. F. Historical presentation of Augustinism and Pelagianism from orig. sources; tr. with add. by R. Emerson. 8°. '40. $1.50.. *Draper.*

Wiggins, R: New York expositor, or 5th book. [Spelling.] ('42.) New ed. 18°. '71. hf. roan, 45c. *Claxton.*

Wight, P. B. Effects of the fire in Chicago. *See* American Inst. of Arch., Proceedings.

— Remarks on fire-proof construction. 4°. pap., 30c. *Am. Inst. Arch.*

Wight, W: W. Table of cases reported in Burnett, Chandler, Pinney, and in v. 1–37 of Wisconsin reports. 8°. '76. $3 *Callaghan.*

Wightman, W: M. Life of W: Capers; with autobiog. 12°. '58. $2 *So. Meth.*

Wightman, W: M., *continued.*
— Ministerial ability. [Sermon.] 18°. '56. pap., 10c. *So. Meth.*
Wightwick, G: Hints to young architects. New ed., rev. and enl. by G. H. Guillaume. ill. 12°. $2.. *Baird.*
— — *See also* Downing, A. J., Hints to persons about building in the country.
Wigram, *Sir* Ja., *and* O'Hara, J. P. On law of wills. 8°. shp., $6.50 .... *Baker, V. & Co.*
Wigwam and the cabin. Simms, W. G. $1.75; 75c. .... *Widdleton.*
Wikoff, H: The four civilizations of the world: hist. retrospect. 12°. $1.50 .... *Lippincott.*
Wilberforce, J. Inquiry into principles of church authority. 12°. $1.50 .... *Kelly, P. & Co.*
Wilberforce, Rob. I: Preparation for communion; ed. by A. C. Coxe. 12°. 60c.; 70c... *McCauley.*
Wilberforce, S: Heroes of Hebrew history. 12°. $2. *Carter.*
— History of Prot. Episc. Church in America. maps. 16°. $3.50 .... *Pott.*
— Ordination addresses. 12°. $1.50 .... *Carter.*
Wilberforce, W: Children and the lion, and other stories. ill. sq. 12°. '65. $1.25.. *Meth. Bk. Conc.*
— Family prayers. 18°. 37c. .... *J. E. Potter.*
— Memoir. 18°. 75c. .... *Carter.*
— Practical view of the prevailing religious system of professed Christians in the higher and middle classes, contrasted with real Christianity. 12°. $1.25 .... *Carter.*
— Slave-trade: colored race. 18°. '62. pap., 25c.; 15c. *Am. Tr.*
Wilbrandt, Adolph. *See* Reuter, F., Nachgelassene Schriften.
Wilbur, Asa. Biblical standpoint: views of sonship of Christ, Comforter and Trinity; with app. on atonement. 2d ed., enl. 12°. '75. $1.. *Williams.*
Wilbur's trip to the seashore. *See* Pretty little lib.
Wilcox, Cadmus Marcellus. Rifles and rifle practice: elementary treatise on theory of rifle firing. ill. 8°. '61. $2 .... *Van Nostrand.*
Wilcox, J. H., *and* Southard, L. H. Lyra Catholica: masses, hymns, etc. obl. 4°. '66. $2.75; bds., $2.50 .... *Ditson.*
Wilcox, Ja. A. General railroad laws of Ohio in force, Jan. 1, 1874; with other laws and provisions of State constitution affecting railroad corporations. 8°. '74. shp., $5 .... *Clarke.*
Wilcox, Phineas Bacon. Digest of Ohio Sup. Court reports (v. 1–16); with supplement. 2 v. 8°. '44. $1.75 .... *I. N. Whiting.*
— Practical forms in actions personal and real, and in chancery, in Ohio. ('33.) 2d ed. roy. 8°. '49. shp., $4 .... *I. N. Whiting.*
— Practical forms under code of civil procedure [of Ohio]. ('62.) New ed. 8°. '73. $2.25; shp., $3 .... *Gleason.*
— *See also* Ohio, Sup. Court reports.
Wild, E: N. Journal entries under codes of civil and criminal procedure of Ohio, also under several statutes regulating more common proceedings. 8°. '76. shp., $3.50 .... *Clarke.*
Wild, J: One, two, three, or "Bounce": Ethiop. drama. 16°. '76. pap., 15c. .... *De Witt.*
Wild, Jona. *See* Life and adventures of Jona. Wild.
Wild, L. Lesefibel, bearb. nach d. Grundsätzen d. Lautirmethode. 8°. hf. bd., 18c. .... *Vering.*
Wild and domesticated animals: book for young children. ill. 16°. '73. 50c. .... *Routledge.*
Wild and tame: sly peep at four-footed animals, where they live and what they do. 16°. $1.50.. *Am. S. S.*
Wild animals in freedom and captivity. ill. 8°. $2.50. *Scribner, W. & A.*
— *See also* Beeton's boy's own lib.
Wild betrayed. 8°. pap., 25c. .... *De Witt.*
Wild boy of Bohemia: drama. 16°. pap., 15c. *French.*
Wild flower. Robinson, F. W. 50c. .... *De Witt.*
Wild flowers. Hubner, C. W. $1.25; $1.75.. *Authors.*
Wild flowers. M., M. K. 75c. .... *Nelson.*
Wild flowers; or, the May-day walk. 18°. 40c. *Am. S. S.*
Wild a fugitive. 8°. pap., 25c. .... *De Witt.*
Wild huntress. Reid, M. $1.50 .... *Carleton.*
Wild hyacinthe. Randolph, *Mrs.* $1.75.. *Lippincott.*
Wild in limbo. 8°. pap., 25c. .... *De Witt.*
Wild Ireland. Donbavand, R. 35c. .... *Lippincott.*
Wild Irish girl. Morgan, *Lady* S. O. $1.50.. *Haverty.*
Wild Irish girl. Pilgrim, J. 15c. .... *French.*
Wild life. Reid, M. $1.50 .... *Carleton.*
Wild life ser. 5 v. ill. 12°. ea., $1.50 .... *Lee & S.*
Cont.: Wild scenes of a hunter's life. — Bogart's Daniel Boone. — Pioneer mothers of the west. — Arabian nights' entertainments. — Robinson Crusoe.
Wild life under the equator. Du Chaillu, P. B. $1.50. *Harper.*
Wild man. Dibdin, C. 15c. .... *French.*
Wild man of the west. Ballantyne, R. M. $1.25. *Claxton; Porter; Routledge.*
Wild men and wild beasts. Cumming, R. G. $1.50. *Scribner.*
Wild north land. Butler, W. F. $1.75 .... *Porter.*
Wild northern scenes. Hammond, S. H. $1.75. *J. E. Potter.*
Wild oats. O'Keeffe, J. 15c. .... *French.*
Wild Oats songster. ill. 12°. '74. pap., 25c.. *Collin & S.*
Wild oats sown abroad. Witmer, T. B. $1.50.. *Peterson.*
Wild Peggie. *See* Abbott, Jac.
Wild rose. *See* Mackarness, *Mrs.* M. A.
Wild rose and poppies. *See* Flower garlands for little gleaners.
Wild roses. Cousin Sue. 45c. .... *Pres. Bd.*
Wild scenes among the Celts. 18°. 50c.; 55c... *Dutton.*
Wild scenes and wild hunters. Webber, C. W. $2. *Claxton.*
Wild scenes of a hunter's life. Frost, J. $1.50.. *Lee & S.*
Wild southern scenes. Jones, J. B. $1.75; $1.50. *Peterson.*
Wild sports and adventures in Africa. Harris, C. $1.75; $1.50 .... *Peterson.*
Wild sports and savage life in Zulu land. Walmsley, H. M. $1.75 .... *Scribner, W. & A.*
Wild sports in the far west. *See* Gerstäcker, F.
Wild sports of the west. *See* Maxwell, W: H.
Wild sports of the world. Greenwood, J. $2.50. *Harper; Scribner, W. & A.*
Wild swans. *See* Andersen, H. C.
Wild times. Caddell, C. M. $1.50 .... *Cath. Pub.*
Wild western scenes. Jones, J. B. $1.25; 75c. *Lippincott.*
Wildenhahn, C. A. Blind girl of Wittenberg; tr. ill. 16°. $1.50 .... (?) *Luth. Pub.*
— *Same;* tr. by J. G. Morris. New ed. 12°. '76. $1.50 .... *Dodd.*
— Das Leben, oder die Enstehung des Pietismus. 18°. '74. 50c. .... *Am. Tr.*
Wilder, Burt G. Researches and experiments on spider's silk. ill. 8°. '66. 50c. .... *Essex.*
— What young people should know: anat., physiology and hygiene of human reproductive organs. 12°. '75. $1.50 .... *Estes.*
Wilder, Dan. W. Annals of Kansas. 8°. '75. $5. *Martin.*
Wilder, M. H. Congregational polity, as taught in the word of God, and gathered from the approved usages of the Congregational churches. 8°. '69. pap., 15c. .... *Darrow.*

Wilder, Marshall P. Addresses [before] N. E. Historic-Geneal. Soc., Jan. 1 and Jan. 16, 1868; [with] proceedings at these meetings. 8°. '68. pap., 25c. ... *N. E. Hist. Gen.*

— Address [before] N. E. Historic-Geneal. Soc., Jan. 6, 1869; [with] proceedings at that meeting. 8°. '69. pap., 25c. ... *N. E. Hist. Gen.*

— Address [before] N. E. Historic-Geneal. Soc., Jan. 5, 1870; [with] proceedings at that meeting, list of life members, const. and by-laws of the Soc. 8°. '70. pap., 25c. ... *N. E. Hist. Gen.*

Wilder, S: V. S. Memoir. ill. 12°. '65. $1.25; mor., $3.50 ... *Am. Tr.*

Wilder, Solon, *and* Davenport, F: S. Praise of Zion: coll. of music. obl. 8°. '65. bds., $1.50 .. *Ditson.*

Wildermuth, Ottilie. Bärbele's Weihnachten; [also] Brüderchen u. Schwesterchen. 16°. '67. bds., 25c. ... *Steiger.*

— Household stories; tr. by Miss E. Kinmont. 4 v. ill. 16°. ea., $1.25 ... *Cin. Meth. Bk. Conc.*

Cont.: Dwarf's mirror, etc. — Cherubino and seraphina, etc. — Emma's pilgrimage, etc. — Little brother and sister.

— Leon and Zephie; or, the little wanderers; tr. 16°. '68. 75c. ... *Dutton.*

— Ottilie's stories for the little folks; tr. 16°. '66. $1.25 ... *Dutton.*

— Queen (A); tr. by A. B. Cooke. 16°. '65. 75c. *Dutton.*

Wildfell Hall. *See* Brontë, Anne.

Wildfords in India. 16°. $1.25 ... *Pres. Bd.*

Wildmoor. Burckett, F. $2 ... *Lippincott.*

Wilds of London. Greenwood, J. $3 .... *Routledge.*

Wildwood, Warren. Thrilling adventures among the early settlers. ill. 12°. $1.75 ... *J. E. Potter.*

Wiley, A. Life. 12°. 75c. ... *Cin. Meth. Bk. Conc.*

Wiley, Calv. H. Roanoke; or, where is Utopia? ill. 8°. pap., 75c. ... *Peterson.*

— *See also* North Carolina readers.

Wiley, C: A. Elocution and oratory. ('69.) New ed. 12°. '76. $2 ... *Clark & M.*

Wiley, I: W. Religion of the family. 16°. '72. $1; $1.25 ... *Cin. Meth. Bk. Conc.*

Wilford, Flo. Nigel Bartram's ideal. 8°. pap., 50c. *Appleton.*

— Vivia: a modern story. 8°. pap., 50c. .... *Appleton.*

Wilford parsonage. Martyn, S. T. 90c. .... *Am. Tr.*

Wilfred Montressor; or, the secret order of the seven. ill. 8°. $1.75; pap., $1.50 ... *Peterson.*

Wilfrid Cumbermede. *See* Mac Donald, G:

Wilful murder. Higgie, T. 15c. ... *French.*

Wilful Walter. *See* Baker, *Mrs.* H. N. W.

Wilful ward. Wooler, J. P. 15c. ... *French.*

Wilful waste. ill. 24°. '70. 25c. ... *Lothrop.*

Wilhelm, —. Method of teaching vocal music; adapted to use in school room by J. Hullah. 8°. '60. bds., 60c. ... *Ditson.*

— — *See also* Grammar school chorus.

Wilhelm Meister. *See* Goethe, J. W. v.

Wilhem Tell. *See* Hoffmann, Fz.

Wilhelm Tell. *See* Schiller, J. F. v.

Wilhelm Tell. Schmid, C. v. 20c. ... *Morwitz.*

Wilhelmi, A. Einer muss heirathen; [also] Eigensinn, von R. Benedix: Lustspiele. ('66.) New ed. 12°. '75. pap., 40c. ... *Holt.*

Wilkes, C: United States exploring expedition, 1838–'42. 28 v. 4°. and f°. '44–'74 ... *U. S. Govt.*

Cont.: 1-5. Narrative of the expedition, with atlas, by C. Wilkes. — 6. Ethnography and philology, by H. Hale. — 7. Zoophytes, with atlas, by J. D. Dana. — 8. Mammalogy and ornithology, with atlas, by J. Cassin. — 9. Races of man, etc., by C. Pickering. — 10. Geology, with atlas, by J. D. Dana. — 11. Meteorology, by C. Wilkes. — 12. Mollusca and shells, with atlas, by A. A. Gould. — 13, 14. Crustacea, with atlas, by J. D. Dana. — 15. Botany: phanerogamica, with atlas, by A. Gray. — 16. Botany: cryptogamica, filices, incl. lycopodiaceæ and hydropterides, with atlas, by W. D. Brackenridge. — 17. Botany: cryptogamica and phænoganica, ed. by A. Gray. — 20. Herpetology, with atlas, by S. F. Baird and C. Girard. — 23. Hydrography, by C. Wilkes.

Note. The publication of this work has not been completed. v. 18 was to contain Botany, by A. Gray. — 19. Geog. distrib. of animals and plants, by C. Pickering. — 21, 22. Ichthyology, by L. Agassiz. — 24. Physics, by C. Wilkes.

Wilkes, Lanceford B., *and* Ditzler, J. Louisville debate [on baptism]. 2d ed. 8°. '70. $3 .. *Tr. P. & P. Co.*

Wilkes, T: The household: duty of training children in fear of God. 12°. 60c. ... *West. Tr.*

Wilkie, *Sir* D: Wilkie gallery: eng. from paintings of W., with notices. roy. 4°. '73. $30; hf. mor., $35; mor., $45; $50 ... *Gebbie.*

Wilkie gallery: sel. of paintings by W. eng. on steel, with notices. 4°. $40; cf., $45 ... *Appleton.*

Wilkins, A. S. The light of the world: essay. 2d ed. cr. 8°. $1.50 ... *Macmillan.*

Wilkins, E: G. P. My wife's mirror: comedy. 16°. pap., 15c. ... *French.*

— Young New York: comedy. 16°. pap., 15c. .. *French.*

Wilkins, F. How to manage gas. 2d ed. 12°. '68. pap., 20c. ... *Spon.*

Wilkins, J: H. Civilization: play. 16°. pap., 15c. *French.*

— Egyptian: play. 16°. pap., 15c. ... *French.*

Wilkins, *Mrs.* S: F. Kate Parker. 16°. $1.50. *Cong. Pub.*

Wilkins, W. Henri. Rock Allen, the orphan; or, lost and found: comedy. 16°. pap., 15c. ... *Ames.*

Wilkins Wylder. Miller, S. F. $1 ... *Lippincott.*

Wilkinson, —. Problems and riders. *See* Cambridge Senate-House.

Wilkinson, G. H. Break up your fallow ground: help to self-examination. sq. 24°. pap., 20c. .. *Dutton.*

— Guide to a devout life: counsels to the confirmed. sq. 16°. '73. 75c.; pap., 25c. ... *Dutton.*

— Some week-days in Lent. 18°. '72. 75c.; pap., 25c. *Dutton.*

Wilkinson, Garth. Methods of human science and divine revelation. 8°. $5 ... *Lippincott.*

Wilkinson, *Miss* Janet W. Hands not hearts. [Fiction.] 8°. pap., 50c. ... *Harper.*

Wilkinson, *Sir* J: Gardner. Popular account of the ancient Egyptians. 2 v. ill. cr. 8°. (Lond.) '71. $5 ... *Little, B. & Co.*

— *Same*; rev. and abridg. 2 v. ill. 12°. $3.50 .. *Harper.*

Wilkinson, W: Cleaver. Dance of modern society. 16°. '69. 50c.; pap., 25c. ... *Mason.*

— Free lance in field of life and letters. 12°. '74. $1.50.

Wilkinson, W: Fs. Personal names in the Bible interpreted and illustrated. 12°. $2.50 .. *Routledge.*

Wilks, S: Lectures on pathological anatomy. 2d ed., enl. by W. Moxon. ill. 8°. '75. $6.50 .. *Lindsay.*

Wilks, T: Egerton. [Plays.] 24 v. 16°. ea., pap., 15c. *French.*

Cont.: Bamboozling: farce. — Ben, the boatswain. — Black domino. — Captain's not a-miss: farce. — Crown prince. — Dream spectre. — Eily O'Connor. — Halvei, the unknown. — How's your uncle? farce. — Kennyngton Crosse. — King's wager. — Lord Darnley. — Michael Erle: romantic drama. — Miller of Whetstone: burletta. — My wife's dentist: farce. — Raffaelle, the reprobate. — Railroad station: farce. — Roll of the drum. — Seven clerks. — State secrets: farce. — Sudden thoughts: farce. — Wenlock of Wenlock. — Woman's love. — Wren boys; or, the moment of peril.

— Roll of the drum: drama. 16°. pap., 15c. .. *De Witt.*

Will, H: Tables of qualitative chemical anal.; with introd. on course of analysis. ('67.) 2d ed., ed. by C. F. Himes. 8°. '74. $1.50 ... *Baird.*

Will (The). Reynolds, F. 15c. ... *French.*

Will and the donkey. *See* Baker, *Mrs.* H. N. W.

Will and the way. 18°. 35c. ... *Pres. Bd.*

Will and a way. *See* Mudge, Z. A.

Will and the way. Waldron, W. R. 15c. .... *French.*

Will and a way: tales from the Germ. ill. 16°. $1.25. *O'Shea.*
Will Collins. McKeever, H. B. $1............*Hoyt.*
Will Crittenden; or, the lone star of Cuba: romance. 8°. pap., 25c.....................*U.P.James.*
Will-forgers. *See* Tayler, C. B.
Will Foster and my brother Paul; or, real heroes. 16°. '76. $1.50.............................*Hoyt.*
Will o' the wisp. *See* Andersen, H. C.
Will Parsons lib. 8 v. 16°. $4.80...........*Lothrop.*
Cont.: Will Parsons.—Nobody cares, by C. Temple.—Old brown book.—Stick to the raft, by Mrs. G. Gladstone.—Hill farm, by C. Temple.—Dick's strength.—Lost found, by A. Giberne.—Steps downward.
Will Parsons' adventures in the land of the sun. ill. 16°. '76. 60c. ....*Lothrop.*
Will Phillips. R., C. H. $1.50............*Lothrop.*
Will Phillips ser. 4 v. 16°. $6..............*Lothrop.*
Cont.: Will Phillips.—Sure.—The noble printer.—Peter's strange story.
Will Rood's friendship. *See* Bradley, W. I.
Will she have him? Graham, A. 30c.......*Am.News.*
Will Terrill. Ingraham, J. H. 25c..........*De Witt.*
Will Thornton, the crow boy. ill. 24°. 25c. *Perkinpine.*
— *Same.* 18°. 35c......................*Bost.Am.Tr.*
— *See also* Alice and Willie stories.
Will Watch; by author of "Cavendish." 16°. bds., 80c. 12°. bds., $1......................*Routledge.*
Will Watch; or, the bold smuggler. 8°. pap., 25c. *De Witt.*
Willard, *Mrs.* —. Mabel Lee; or, the way to make a thorny path smooth. 18°. 60c........*Cong.Pub.*
Willard, Clara A. Fifty years ago: story of New Eng. life. 12°. '72. $1.50................*Randolph.*
— May Chester; or, home light. 18°. '69. 75c. *Randolph.*
Willard, *Mrs.* Emma. Abridged history of U. S. ('60.) New ed., enl. 12°. $1.40.............*Barnes.*
— *Span.* Compendio de la historia de los Estados Unidos. 12°. '64. $2.................*Barnes.*
— Ancient geog. and atlas. 12°. *net,* 85c...*Hamersley.*
— Astronography; with use of the globes. 12°. $1. *Barnes.*
— Astronomical geography. 12°. bds., 75c.....*Nims.*
— Guide to "Temple of time" and universal hist. 12°. '49. hf. bd., $1 ....*Barnes.*
— History of U. S.; with chronolog. table and maps. ('51.) New ed., enl. 8°. $2.25.........*Barnes.*
— Morals for the young. 12°. '57. 75c. ......*Barnes.*
— Universal history in perspective; with chronological table, maps and ill. ('55.) New ed., rev. 8°. $2.25. *Barnes.*
— *See also* Woodbridge, W. C., *and* Willard, E.
Willard, Fes. E. Hints and helps for woman's Christian temperance work. 12°. 25c.....*Nat.Temp.*
Willard, G: L. Manual of target practice for U. S. army. 18°. '62. 75c. ......*Claxton; Lippincott.*
Willard, J: Equity jurisprudence; ed. by P. Potter. 2d ed. 8°. '75. shp., $7.50............*Banks.*
— Treatise on law of executors, administrators and guardians, and remedies by and against them in surrogates' courts of New York. 8°. '59. shp., $5.50 ....*Gould.*
— Treatise on law of real estate and mode of alienation thereof; with forms and notes adapted to N. Y. 8°. '61. shp., $6.50......................*Gould.*
Willard, J: D. Arion: four part songs for male voices. 5 bks. 16°. '62. $4;—vocal pts. in 4 bks., $3.50; ea., $1.—Piano score, $1.50....*Ditson.*
Willard, Ma. E. Through the wilderness. 16°. $1. *Pres.Bd.*
Willard, X. A. Practical butter book: treatise on butter making at factories and farm dairies. 2d ed. ill. 12°. '75. $1...............*Rural.*
— Practical dairy husbandry. ('71.) 3d ed. ill. 8°. '72. $3.................................*Rural.*
Willcox, Ja. M. Elementary philosophy, pt. 1: science of reasoning and art of correct reasoning. 12°. '75. 75c...........................*Porter.*
Willcox, T: Köstlicher Honigtropfen. 18°. '50. 25c. *Am.Tr.*
Willcox, W. H. Bethesda series for 1875. [S.-school quest. book.] 18°. bds., 15c........*Cong.Pub.*
Wille, Eliz. de. Johannes Olaf: a romance; tr. by F. E. Bunnett. 16°. '73. $2.........*Roberts.*
Willet, J. E. Wonders of insect life. ill. 16°. $1.75. *Am.Bapt.*
Willets, Jac. S. Review of life of William Ladd, apostle of peace. 16°. '75. 35c.; pap., 25c...*Peace.*
Willett, W: M. Messiah. ill. 12°. *$2; hf. mor., $2.75 ....*Russell.*
Willey, B: G. History of White Mountains; with anecdotes ill. life in the backwoods. ('55.) 3d ed. 12°. '70. $1.50 ................*I.N.Andrews.*
Willey, Nath. Instruction book for life insurance agents, canvassers and solicitors. 12°. '75. $1.50 ....*Hine.*
— Principles and practice of life insurance: explan. of computation involved; with tables. ('71.) 2d ed., rev. by R. G. Hann. 8°. '76. $2...*Spectator.*
William, *St.* *See* Lives of the saints.
William *of Malmsbury.* Chronicle of the kings of England [449–1142]; tr. by Sharpe. 12°. (Bohn.) $1.75.................*Little,B.& Co.*
— *Same.* 12°. (Bohn.) $2..*Lippincott; Scribner, W.&A.*
William, *Cousin.* *See* Cousin William.
William, *Uncle.* *See* Uncle William.
William; or, the converted Romanist; tr. from the Fr., rev. by T. O. Summers. ('55.) 3d ed. 18°. '75. 40c. ....*So.Meth.*
William, the converted papist. 18°. 40c....*Am.S.S.*
William, the cottager; by author of "Ellen Herbert." ill. 18°. 75c.........................*Harper.*
William, Prince of Orange; or, the king and the hostage. Merriam, E. E. $1.75 ....*Hoyt.*
William the Silent, and the Netherland war. Barrett, M. $1.50 ....*Lothrop.*
William Allair. Wood, E. P. 25c.........*Peterson.*
William Allen; or, the boy who told the truth, the whole truth, and nothing but the truth. 18°. 35c. *Am.S.S.*
William and Rupert. 18°. 60c...........*Cong.Pub.*
William and Uncle Ben. ill. 16°. 50c.......*Nelson.*
William Bartlett; or, the good son, and other stories. 18°. 40c. ....*Pres.Bd.*
William Beckett; or, the dutiful son. 18°. 17c.; 22c. *Am.Bapt.*
William Freeman. *See* Sunshine and shadow lib.
William Gay; or, play for boys. Abbott, J. 4 v. $2.50 ....*Hurd & H.*
William Henry letters;—and his friends. *See* Diaz, *Mrs.* A. M.
William Herbert; or, religion at school. 18°. 40c. *Am.S.S.*
William Norton. 18°. 40c.................*Dutton.*
William Simpson: comedietta. 16°. pap., 15c. *French.*
William Tell. *See* Brough, Rob. B.
William Tell. Buckingham, L. 15c. ....*French.*
William Tell. *See* Continental lib.
William Tell. Knowles, J. S. 15c..........*French.*
William Tell. *See* Rossini, G.
William Tell. *See* Schiller, J. F. v.
William Tell: Ethiop. drama. 16°. pap., 15c. *Happy.*
William Tell with a vengeance. Byron, H. J. 15c. *De Witt.*
William Thompson: farce. 16°. pap., 15c...*French.*
Williams, A. Liturgical "reason why:" principles of Book of common prayer. 16°. $2 ....*Pott.*

Williams, *Rev.* A. D. Memorials of the Free Communion Baptists. 8°. '73. $1 ...... *Freewill.*
— Rhode Island Freewill Baptist pulpit. 12°. '52. $1 ...... *Freewill.*
Williams, A. D., *M.D.* Diseases of the ear, including necessary anatomy of the organ. ill. 8°. '73. $3.50 ...... *Clarke.*
Williams, A. P. Campbellism exposed. 12°. $1.50. *So. Bapt.*
— The Lord's supper. 18°. 40c. ...... *Am. Bapt.*
Williams, Aar. Woman in the Bible. 16°. $1.50. (?) *Martien.*
Williams, C: Anecdotes of dogs. ill. 16°. 75c. *Routledge.*
— Dogs and their ways. ill. 16°. $1.25 .... *Routledge.*
— Narratives and adventures of travellers in Africa. ill. 12°. $1.25 ...... *Porter.*
— *See also* Wood, J. G., White, G., *and* Williams, C.
Williams, C: J. B. *and* C: T. Pulmonary consumption: its nature, varieties and treatment; with anal. of 1000 cases. 8°. $2.50 ...... *Lea.*
Williams, C: K. (*ed.*) Rutland centennial. 8°. '70. $1.50 ...... *Tuttle.*
Williams, C: Langdon. *See* Vermont, Sup. Court reports.
Williams, C: Thdr. *See* Williams, C: J. B. *and* C: T.
Williams, C: Wye. On heat and steam; embr. new views of vaporization, condensation and explosions. ('64.) 3d ed. ill. 8°. '71. $3.50 .. *Baird.*
Williams, Fs. S. Conversations sur Le grand père. First book in French conversation. 12°. hf. roan, $1.50 ...... *Ware.*
— English into French. 12°. $1.50 ...... *Sheldon.*
— Getting to Paris: practice in French conversation. 12°. $1.75 ...... *Lee & S.*
— Voyage à Paris: la partie française d'un livre d'exercises de conversation française. 12°. $1 .. *Lee & S.*
— *See also* Pussy, *Mme.* F. de.
Williams, Fk. German-English and Eng.-Germ. dictionary. 18°. $1 ...... *Routledge.*
Williams, G. System of penmanship; rev. by D. L. Southerland. 8 nos. sm. 4°. per doz., 1–5, $1.20; with blotters, $1.35; 6–8, $1.80; with blotters, $2 ...... *Scribner.*
Williams, Gus. *See* Gus Williams.
Williams, *Mrs.* H. Dwight. Year in China, and narr. of capture and imprisonment when homeward bound; with introd. note by W. C. Bryant. cr. 8°. '64. $1.50 ...... *Hurd & H.*
— (*ed.*) Leaves of consolation for the afflicted; or, voices from the silent land. 12°. $1 ... *Pres. Bd.*
Williams, H. L., *jr.* Black chap from Whitechapel: Ethiop. drama. 16°. pap., 15c. ...... *De Witt.*
— Serf (The); or, love levels all. [Fiction.] 8°. pap., 25c. ...... *De Witt.*
Williams, H: L. Boys of the Bible. ill. 12°. '67. $1.50 ...... *Allison.*
Williams, H: S. Anatomy of the cat; prepared as a guide to study of vertebrates. 2 v. pl. 4°. '75. $6 ...... *Putnam.*
Williams, H: T. Mysteries of San Francisco. 8°. pap., 75c. ...... *Dick & F.*
— Pacific tourist: ill. trans-continental guide of travel from the Atlantic to the Pacific. ill. 8°. '76. $1.50; $2 ...... *H. T. Williams.*
— Window gardening. 8°. '71. $1.50 .. *H. T. Williams.*
— *See also* Jones, *Mrs.* C. S., *and* Williams, H. T.
— *and* Jones, *Mrs.* C. S. Household elegancies. 8°. '75. $1.50 ...... *H. T. Williams.*
Williams, H: Willard. Our eyes and how to take care of them. 16°. '76. $1 ...... *Hurd & H.*
— Practical guide to study of diseases of the eye. New ed., rev. and enl. cr. 8°. '76. $3 ..... *Hurd & H.*
— Recent advances in ophthalmic science. (Boylston prize essay, 1865.) cr. 8°. '76. pap., $1 .. *Hurd & H.*

Williams, I: Apocalypse; with notes and reflections. 12°. '75. $2.25 ...... *Pott.*
— Baptistry; or, way of eternal life. ill. 16°. '74. $3.75 ...... *Pott.*
— Characters of Old Testament: sermons. 12°. '73. $2.25 ...... *Pott.*
— Devotional comment. on Gospel narrative. 8 v. 12°. '73. ea., $1.25 ...... *Pott.*

Cont.: Thoughts on study of the Gospels. — Harmony of four evangelists. — Our Lord's nativity. — Our Lord's ministry, (2d year). — Our Lord's ministry, (3d year). — Holy week. — Our Lord's passion. — Our Lord's resurrection.

— Female characters of Scripture: sermons. 12°. '73. $2.25 ...... *Pott.*
— Psalms interpreted of Christ: Psalm 1 to 26. 16°. '64. $2.25 ...... *Pott.*
— Sermons on Epistles and Gospels for the Sundays and holy days throughout the year: Advent to Tuesday in Whitsun week. 12°. '75. $2.50 ...... *Pott.*
Williams, J. Life of Alexander the Great. por. 18°. 75c. ...... *Harper.*
Williams, J. Fletcher. History of St. Paul, and of Ramsay Co., Minn. ill. 8°. '76. $3 .. *Minn. Hist.*
— Odd-fellow's minstrel: odes for use of the fraternity. ('64.) New ed. 18°. '76. 60c.; $1.50 .. *R. W. Carroll.*
Williams, Ja. Sermon on Masonry. 12°. pap., 10c. *E. A. Cook.*
Williams, J: Parser's manual: examples in every variety of English construction. 12°. '71. 90c. *Wilson, H. & Co.*
— Readable dictionary; or, topical and synonymic lexicon. 8°. '67. $1.75 ...... *Barnes.*
Williams, J: *of Erromanga.* Life of W., martyr missionary. 18°. 75c. ...... *Am. S. S.*
Williams, J: A: Life of Elder John Smith; with account of rise and progress of current reformation. cr. 8°. $2; shp., $2.50 ...... *Chase.*
Williams, *Sir* J: Bickerton. Memoirs of Mrs. Sarah Savage; [also] Memoirs of Mrs. Ann Hulton and of Mrs. Eleanor Radford, by Matthew Henry. 18°. 75c. ...... *Pres. Bd.*
Williams, J: D., *and* Packard, S. S. Gems of penmanship. obl. 4°. hf. bd., $5 ...... *Appleton.*
— — Guide to penmanship. obl. 4°. $3. *Appleton; Lee & S.*
— — Normal writing speller. obl. 4°. per. doz., $2.40. *Lee & S.*
— — System of penmanship. 12 nos. obl. 4°. per doz., $1.80; with blotters, $2.04 ...... *Lee & S.*
Williams, J: S. History of invasion and capture of Washington, and of events which preceded and followed it. 12°. $1.50; hf. cf., $3.25 .. *Harper.*
Williams, Josh. Principles of law of personal property. 4th ed.; with notes illustrating American law by B. Gerhard and S. Wetherill. 8°. '72. $6 ...... *T. & J. W. Johnson.*
— Principles of law of real property. 4th ed., with notes and Am. ref. by W. H. Rawle and J. T. Mitchell. 8°. '72. $5 ...... *T. & J. W. Johnson.*
Williams, Kath. Tiptoe. ill. 16°. '71. 90c. .. *Am. Tr.*
Williams, Montagu. Fair exchange: comedietta. 16°. pap., 15c. ...... *French.*
— *See also* Burnand, F. C., *and* Williams, M.
— *and* Burnand, F. C. [Plays.] 4 v. 16°. ea., pap., 15c. ...... *French.*

Cont.: B. B.: farce. — Carte de visite: farce. — Isle of St. Tropez. — Turkish bath: farce.

— — Turkish bath: farce. 16°. pap., 15c. .... *Lee & S.*
Williams, Natl. Marshman. Notes on Matthew. ill. 12°. $1.75 ...... *Sheldon.*
— *Same.* 12°. $1.50 ...... *So. Bapt.*
Williams, R: Memoir. 16°. '54. 55c. .. *Meth. Bk. Conc.*
Williams, Rob. Folkestone. Luttrells (The); or, the two marriages. 8°. pap., 50c. ...... *Harper.*
— Secret passion: [sequel to "Youth of Shakespeare"]. 8°. pap., $1 ...... *Peterson.*

Williams, Rob. Folkstone, *continued.*
— Shakespeare and his friends. [Fiction.] 8°. pap., $1 .... *Peterson.*
— Youth of Shakespeare. [Fiction.] 8°. pap., $1. *Peterson.*

Williams, Rog. Bloody tenent of persecution; ed. by S. L. Caldwell. [Reprints of Narragansett Club, v. 3.] sm. 4°. '67. $8. — 4°. $10..... *Tibbitts.*
— Bloody tenent yet more bloody; ed. by S. L. Caldwell. [Reprints of Narragansett Club, v. 4.] sm. 4°. '70. $8. — 4°. $10.......... *Tibbitts.*
— Queries of highest consideration. *See* Cotton, J., Answer to R. Williams.

Williams, S: Two western campaigns in war of 1812. *See* Espy, J., Memorandums of tour in Ohio.

Williams, S: Wells. Middle kingdom: survey of geog., government, education, social life, etc., of China and its inhabitants. 2 v. map. 12°. $4.. *Wiley.*

Williams, Sa. Twilight hours: legacy of verse, with memoir by E. H. Plumptre. cr. 8°. $2.50. *Routledge.*

Williams, Ste. W. Genealogy and hist. of family of Williams in Am., particularly of descendants of Rob. Williams of Roxbury [Mass.] 12°. '47. $5.......... *E. D. Merriam.*

Williams, T: *See* Bible [Whole].

Williams, *Rev.* T: *and* Calvert, J. Fiji and the Fijians, and missionary labors among the cannibals. 3d ed. map and ill. 12°. $2.50...... *Routledge.*

Williams, T: J. [Plays.] 8 v. 16°. ea., pap., 15c. *De Witt.*

Cont.: Cabman 93; or, found in a four-wheeler: farce. — Charming pair: farce. — Dandelion's dodges: farce. — Larkins' love-letters: farce. — One too many for him: farce. — Silent protector: farce. — Volunteer review: farce. — Who is who? or, all in a fog: farce.

— *Same.* 10 v. 16°. ea., pap., 15c.......... *Lee & S.*

Cont.: Dandelion's dodges: farce. — Dunducketty's picnic: farce. — I've written to Browne: farce. — My turn next: farce. — Nursey Chickweed: farce. — Old Gooseberry: farce. — Race for a widow: farce. — Smashington Goit: farce. — An ugly customer: farce. — Who's who? farce.

— *Same.* 33 v. 16°. ea., pap., 15c.......... *French.*

Cont.: Better half: comedietta. — Cabman 93; or, found in a four-wheeler: farce. — Charming pair: farce. — Cure for the fidgets: farce. — Dandelion's dodges: farce. — I've written to Browne: comedietta. — Ici on parle français: farce. — Jack's delight: farce. — Larkins' love-letters: farce. — Lion slayer: farce. — Little Daisy. — Little sentinel: comedietta. — My dress boots: farce. — My turn next: farce. — My wife's maid: farce. — Nursey Chickweed: farce. — Old Gooseberry: farce. — On and off: farce. — One too many for him: farce. — Out to nurse: farce. — Peace and quiet: farce. — Peep show man. — Pipkin's rustic retreat: farce. — Race for a widow: farce. — Silent protector: comedietta. — Silent system: farce. — Terrible tinker: farce. — Turn him out: farce. — Tweedleton's tail-coat: farce. — Ugly customer: farce. — Volunteer review: farce. — Who is who? farce. — Who's to win him? comedietta.

— The better half: comedietta. 16°. pap., 15c... *Ames.*
— *See also* Harris, A., *and* Williams, T. J.
— *and* Harris, A. Cruel to be kind: farce. 16°. pap., 15c.......... *French.*

Williams, W. G. (*ed.*) The Ingham lectures on the evidences of natural and revealed religion. 2d ed. 12°. '72. $1.75.......... *Ingham.*

Williams, W. H. Wreck: farce. 16°. pap., 15c. *French.*

Williams, W: Gloria in excelsis: new church music; with vocal exercises and glees. obl. 8°. '55. bds., $1.......... *Ditson.*
— Our Saviour; with words by E. R. Morse. [Oratorio.] obl. 16°. '56. bds., 45c.......... *Ditson.*
— Singer's manual, sacred and secular. obl. 16°. '58. bds., $1.......... *Ditson.*
— *and* Coule, —. Instruction for the German concertina. obl. 8°. '57. pap., 60c.......... *Ditson.*

Williams, W: Principles and practice of veterinary medicine. 8°. $10.......... *W. Wood.*
— Principles and practice of veterinary surgery. 2d ed. ill. 8°. $10.......... *W. Wood.*

Williams, W: R. Discourse. 18°. '62. 25c... *Am. Tr.*
— God's rescues; or, the lost sheep, the lost coin and the lost son. 16°. '71. 75c.......... *Randolph.*
— Lectures on the Lord's prayer. 12°. $1.25.. *Carter.*
— Religious progress. 12°. $1.25.......... *Carter.*
— *See also* Somers, G. G., Williams, W. R., *and* Hill, L. L.

Williamson, J. D. [Works.] 5 v. 16°.. *Williamson.*

Cont.: Philosophy of Universalism, 40c. — Argument for Christianity. — Endless misery examined and refuted. — Exposition and defence of Universalism. — Sermons for the times and people, *ea.*, 75c.

— Rudiments of theological and moral science. 12°. $2.......... *Williamson.*

Williamson, M. J. Modern diabolism, commonly called modern spiritualism; with new theories of light, heat, electricity and sound. 12°. $2.. *Miller.*

Williamson, Rob. S. On use of barometer on surveys and reconnoissances; with tables and eng. 4°. '68. $15.......... *Van Nostrand.*
— Practical tables in meteorology and hypsometry in connection with use of barometer. 4°. '69. $2.50. *Van Nostrand.*
— *See also* United States, *Corps of Eng.*

Williamson, Wa. Diseases of females and children, and their homœop. treatment. 3d ed., enl. 12°. $1.......... *Boericke.*

Willie, the conqueror. 18°. 30c.......... *Am. S. S.*
Willie and Charlie; or, the way to be happy. ('61.) New ed. ill. 18°. '75. 40c.......... *Hoyt.*
Willie and Clara. *See* Cousin Anna's lib.
Willie and Harry. 18°. 40c.......... *Dutton.*
Willie and his dogs. *See* Infant school lib.
Willie and Katie. 18°. 40c.......... *Cong. Pub.*
Willie and Lillie. 18°. 65c.; 75c.......... *Am. Bapt.*
Willie and Lucy. 18°. 45c.; 55c.......... *Am. Bapt.*
Willie and Lucy at the seaside. *See* Little folk lib.
Willie and Lucy ser. 6 v. ill. sq. 16°. $4.50.. *Nelson.*

Cont.: Willie and Lucy at home, by A. G. — Willie and Lucy abroad, by A. G. — Willie and Lucy at the seaside, by A. G. — Hymns and poems, by H. E. L. — How Patty learnt the alphabet. — Choice poetry.

Willie and the mortgage. Abbott, J. 90c. .. *Harper.*
Willie and Ned. 32°. 25c.......... *Porter.*
Willie and Nellie; or, stories about my canaries. sq. 18°. 90c.......... (?) *Martien.*
Willie and Robert. 18°. 35c.; 40c.......... *Dutton.*
Willie and the scythe. 32°. 20c.; 15c.......... *Dutton.*
Willie and Unica. 18°. 75c.......... *Carter.*
Willie Benton. Doughty, S. P. 50c.... *H. H. Carter.*
Willie books. 5 v. ill. 18°. '59. $3.. *Meth. Bk. Conc.*

Cont.: Willie's lesson. — Willie trying to be manly — to be thorough — wishing to be useful — seeking to be a Christian.

Willie Elton. Finley, M. F. 45c.......... *Pres. Bd.*
Willie Graham; [also] Among the mountains. ill. 18°. '72. 50c.......... *Lothrop.*
— *See also* Little folks ser.
Willie Grant; or, the little Pharisee. 18°. 40c.; 50c. *Am. Bapt.*
Willie Herbert and his six little friends. 16°. 50c. *Scribner, W. & A.*
Willie in search of his grandfather. 16°. $1.. *Am. Bapt.*
Willie Maitland; or, the Lord's prayer illustrated. 18°. 50c.......... *Pres. Bd.*
— *Same.* ill. 18°. '70. 55c.......... *Lothrop.*
Willie Maitland ser. 3 v. 18°. $1.65...... *Lothrop.*

Cont.: Willie Maitland. — Who is my neighbor? — When we were young.

Willie Marsh; or, thou shalt not covet. 18°. 18c. *Am. S. S.*
Willie Russell's temptation. *See* Uncle Barnaby's budget.
Willie seeking to be a Christian; — trying to be manly; — trying to be thorough. *See* Willie books.

Willie Wilson. ('62.) New ed. ill. 18°. '70. 30c. *Hoyt.*
— *See also* Golden stories.

Willie Winkie's nursery rhymes. Silsbee, *Mrs.* —. $1.25 .... **Osgood.*

Willie wishing to be useful. *See* Willie books.

Willie's birthday. 16°. 50c. .... *Scribner, W.& A.*

Willie's disobedience; or, the cottage on the cliff. 18°. 25c. .... *Scribner, W.& A.*

Willie's hyacinth. M'Clellan, K. 40c. .... *Whittaker.*

Willie's lesson. 32°. 20c.; 15c. .... *Dutton.*

Willie's lesson. *See* Willie books.

Willie's lessons. ill. 24°. 25c. .... *Perkinpine.*

Willie's money-box; by author of "Little Redcap." ill. 16°. '74. $1.25 .... *Lothrop.*

Willie's rest: Sunday story. 16°. 50c. *Scribner, W.& A.*

Willie's step-mother: story of domestic life. 18°. 45c. *Am.S.S.*

Willie's trouble; or, the old gig. 18°. 25c. *Scribner, W.& A.*

Willie's trunk; or, Mrs. Lambton's legacy. 18°. 25c. *Scribner, W.& A.*

Willie's western visit. *See* Dot books.

Willie's wish. *See* Bertie's lib.; — Moss rose ser.

Willikind: burlesque. 16°. pap., 15c. ...... *French.*

Willing, *Mrs.* Jennie F. Through the dark to the day. 16°. $1.25 .... *Cin. Meth. Bk. Conc.*

Willing hearts and ready hands. Johnston, J. $1.50. *Nelson.*

Willis, Anson. The nation: its rulers and institutions; or, outlines of the government. [In Eng. and Germ.] por. and ill. 8°. '71. *$2.50; leath., $3 .... *New World.*

Willis, F: L. H. Theodore Parker in spirit life: narr. of personal experiences, inspirationally given. ('74.) 5th ed. 12°. '75. pap., 25c. .. *Colby.*

Willis, Jla. A. What a boy! problems concerning him. 12°. $1.50 .... *Lippincott.*

Willis, Natl. Parker. [Prose works.] 13 v. 12°. ea., $1.75 .... *Scribner.*

Cont.: The convalescent. — Famous persons and places. — Fun jottings. — Health trip to the tropics. — Hurry-graphs. — Life here and there. — Paul Fane. — Pencillings by the way. — People I have met. — Out doors at Idlewild. — The rag-bag. — Rural letters and other records of thoughts at leisure. — Summer cruise.

— Poems. (Blue and gold ed.) ('68.) New ed. por. 24°. '76. $1.50 .... *Clark & M.*
— *Same.* (Cabinet ed.). ('68.) New ed. por. 16°. '76. $1.60; hf. cf., $3; mor., $4 ..... *Clark & M.*
— *Same.* (Ill. ed.) sm. 4°. '59. mor., $10 .. *Clark & M.*
— *Same.* (Red line ed.) ('68.) New ed. ill. and por. sm. 4°. '75. $4; hf. cf., $6; mor., $7.50 .. *Clark & M.*
— Sacred poems. ill. and por. sm. 4°. '68. $2.50; mor., $5 .... *Clark & M.*

Willis, Ol. R. Catalogus plantarum: catalogue of plants growing without cultivation in New Jersey. 8°. '74. $1 .... *Schermerhorn.*
— *Same.* 8°. '74. $1.25 .... *Barnes.*

Willis, Rob., *M.D.* Life, correspondence and ethics of Benedict de Spinoza. 8°. $9 .. *Scribner, W.& A.*

Willis, *Rev.* Rob. Principles of mechanism. 8°. $7.50. *Wiley.*

Willis, *Uncle* (*pseud.*) *See* Tilton, S. W.

Willis, the pilot: sequel to "Swiss family Robinson." ill. 12°. $1; $1.50 .... *Lee & S.*
— *Same.* ill. 16°. $1; $1.75. — 12°. $1.25. *Scribner, W.& A.*

Willis Howard; or, two secrets well kept. 18°. 60c. *Cong. Pub.*

Willison, J: Afflicted man's companion. Rev. ed. por. 18°. '58. 75c. .... *Sower.*
— *Same.* 12°. '51. 75c. .... *Am. Tr.*
— Christian's Scripture directory: thoughts and reflections; [also] Resolutions [for direction of religious life], by J. Edwards. 32°. 25c. .. *Pres. Bd.*

Willison, J: *continued.*
— Sacramental catechism. 18°. 15c. .... *Carter.*
— *Same.* 18°. per 100, $6 .... *N. Y. Ref. Ch. Bd.*
— Sacramental directory: treatise conc. sanctification of a communion Sabbath. 12°. 75c. .. *U. P. Bd. of Pub.*
— Sacramental meditations and advices. 18°. 60c. *U. P. Bd. of Pub.*
— *Same.* 12°. $1.50 .... *Cong. Pub.*

Willison, S. J. *See* Tercentenary book.

Williston, Tim. *See* Liberty or slavery.

Willits, A. A. Miracles of Jesus. ill. imp. 8°. '75. $6; mor., $9 .... *Cowperthwait.*

Willkomm, E. Unheimlicher Mann (Ein). *See* Wartenburg, K., Aus d. Bagno.
— Verfeindeten Nachbarn (Die); [also] Der verhängnissvolle Schmuck. 12°. '65. pap., 35c. .. *Steiger.*

Willmott, Rob. Aris. Pleasures, objects and advantages of literature. 16°. $1 .... *Routledge.*
— Summertime in the country; ill. by B. Foster and others. sm. 4°. $6; mor., $9 .... *Routledge.*
— (*ed.*) English sacred poetry of 16th, 17th, 18th and 19th centuries; ill. by J: Gilbert. 4°. $9; mor., $12 .... *Routledge.*
— Poets of 19th century; with Eng. and Am. add. arranged by E. A. Duyckinck. lli. sm. 4°. $5; hf. cf., $5.50; mor., $9 .... *Harper.*
— *See also* Routledge's British poets.

Willow basket. Wylie, E. J. 45c. .... *Pres. Bd.*

Willow Bend. Luola. 70c. .... *Pres. Bd.*

Willow Brook. Warner, S. $1.25 .... *Carter.*

Willow copse. Boucicault, D. 15c. .... *French.*

Willow Grove Cottage; or, the orphan's victory. 18°. 35c. .... *Am.S.S.*

Willow leaves; or, whispers to the sorrowful. 18°. 50c. .... *Cong. Pub.*

Willow pattern: extravaganza. 16°. pap., 15c. .. *French.*

Willow ser. 4 v. 12°. $6 .... *Nelson.*

Cont.: Traveller's tales. — Elsie's choice. — Sea breezes. — Waiting for a crown.

Wills, Ma. H. A summer in Europe. 12° $1.25. *Lippincott.*

Wills, W: Essay on principles of circumstantial evidence, with cases. 5th Am. ed. 8°. '72. $2. *T. & J. W. Johnson.*

Wills, W: Gorham. Notice to quit. 8°. pap., 50c. *Harper.*
— The wife's evidence. 8°. pap., 50c. ...... *Harper.*

Wills, W: H: Larboard fire: drama. 16°. pap., 15c. *French.*
— Old leaves; gathered from "Household Words." 12°. $1.25 .... *Harper.*

Wills of their own. Tegg, W. 50c. .. *Scribner, W.& A.*

Willshire, W: Hu. Introduction to study and collection of ancient prints. 8°. hf. mor., $10.50. *Scribner, W.& A.*

Willson, E. B. Memoir of Rev. J. L. Russell. 8°. '74. pap., 15c. .... *Essex.*

Willson, Forceythe. Old sergeant, and other poems. 16°. $1.50 .... *Osgood.*

Willson, Marcius. American history: sketches of Indian tribes, hist. of U. S., history of British provinces, early history of Louisiana, etc. ill. 8°. '46. $2 .... *Ivison.*
— Drawing guide: manual to accompany "Industrial draw. ser." 12°. $1 .... *Harper.*
— History of U. S., to 1865; with U. S. Const. ('53.) New ed., rev. ill. 12°. '68. $1.50 ..... *Ivison.*
— Industrial drawing ser. 4 nos. obl. roy. 8°. ea., 40c.; — in 8 pts., ea., 25c. .... *Harper.*
— Manual of information and suggestions for object lessons. 12°. $1.50 .... *Harper.*
— Outlines of general hist.; with geog. and hist. notes and maps. (School ed.) ('54.) New ed. 8°. '72. $2. — (University ed.) 8°. $3 .... *Ivison.*
— Primary Am. hist. 16°. '47. bds., 50c. ... *Ivison.*

Willson, Marcius, *continued.*
— School and family readers. 9 v. 12°. hf. bd. *Harper.*

Cont.: Primer, 25c. — First reader, 40c. — Second, 60c. — Third, 90c. — Fourth, $1.35. — Fifth, $1.80. — Larger speller, 40c. — New speller and analyzer, 45c. — Primary speller, 18°, 20c.

Willy. *See* Hoffmann, F.

Willy Burke. Sadlier, M. A. 60c.......... *Sadlier.*

Willy Graham; or, the disobedient boy. 18°. 22c. *Am.S.S.*

Willy Maitland; or, the Lord's prayer illustrated. ('68.) New ed. ill. 18°. '75. 55c...... *Hoyt.*

Willy Reilly and his dear Coleen bawn. *See* Carleton, W:

Willy's cherry tree. Sanford, D. P. 20c.; 15c. *Dutton.*

Willy's new teacher. Sanford, D. P. 20c.; 15c. *Dutton.*

Willy's winter corner. Sanford, D. P. 20c.; 15c. *Dutton.*

Wilmer, J. The modern vassal: story of Poland. 8°. pap., 25c. .... *Littell & G.*

Wilmer, L. A. Led astray; or, the whole history of Miss Adelaide Fosbenner, and the sad consequences of one false step. [In. Eng. or Germ.] 8°. pap., 25c...................... *Barclay.*
— Victim bride; or, the father's sacrifice. [In Eng. or Germ.] 8°. pap., 25c............... *Barclay.*

Wilmer, Marg. E. Dumb traitor. ('73.) New ed. 12°. '75. $1.25.................... *Nat. Temp.*
— Eva's engagement ring. ('72.) New ed. 12°. '74. 90c. .... *Nat. Temp.*
— Glass cable. ('73.) New ed. 12°. '76. $1.25.. *Nat. Temp.*
— Little girl in black. ('72.) New ed. 12°. '75. 90c. .... *Nat. Temp.*
— Missionary doctor. ill. 18°. 80c... *N. Y. Ref. Ch. Bd.*
— Nine prizes: stories illustrating Beatitudes. ill. 18°. 90c. .... *N. Y. Ref. Ch. Bd.*
— Silver castle. 12°. '76. $1.25 .... *Nat. Temp.*
— Three boys and their stories. 18°. 65c... *Pres. Bd.*
— Wrecker's grandchild. ill. 18°. 80c. *N. Y. Ref. Ch. Bd.*

Wilmingtons (The). Marsh-Caldwell, A. 50c. *Harper.*

Wilmot family. 18°. 70c.; 85c. .... *Am. Bapt.*

Wilmsen, F: Ph. Children's friend's reader. 12°. hf. bd., $1 .... *Sower.*
— Der deutsche Kinderfreund f. Schule u. Haus. 12°. 75c. .... *Radde.*

Wilson, *Mrs.* —. Time will tell. ('72.) New ed. 16°. '74. $1 .... *Nat. Temp.*

Wilson, A. Notes, questions and answers on the parables. 16°. '72. 20c.................. *Pott.*

Wilson, *Mrs.* A. M. Lives of the three Mrs. Judsons, Ann, Sarah and Emily. por. 12°. $1.50.. *Lee & S.*

Wilson, Alex. American ornithology: nat. hist. of birds of U. S.; with contin. by C. L. Bonaparte, with life of author by Geo. Ord. 4 v.: text, 3 v., imp. 8°.; col. pl., 1 v., f°. $95; hf. mor., $100; — in 5 v.: text, 3 v., imp. 8°; pl., 2 v., f°. $97; hf. mor., $110; — pl. (1 v.), $22; hf. mor., $25 .... *Porter.*

Wilson, And. Abode of snow: obs. of a tour from Chinese Tibet to valleys of the Himalaya. map. 18°. '75. $2.25...................... *Putnam.*

Wilson, Ann. Familiar letters of Ann Wilson. 12°. *net*, 75c. .... *Friends Bk. Assoc.*

Wilson, Arth. *See* England, Law reports.

Wilson, *Mrs.* Augusta J. *See* Evans, *Miss* A. J.

Wilson, B: *See* Bible, New Test., *Greek and Eng.*

Wilson, C: Heath. Life and works of Michael Angelo Buonarroti. por. and ill. 8°. '76. $7.50. *Scribner, W. & A.*

Wilson, C: W. Recovery of Jerusalem. *See* Palestine exploration fund.

Wilson, *Mrs.* Cornwell Baron. Venus in arms: farce. 16°. pap., 15c........................ *French.*

Wilson, Dan. Pilgrim fathers. *See* Stowell, W. H., History of Puritans.

Wilson, Dan. Caliban: the missing link. cr. 8°. '73. $2.............................. *Macmillan.*
— Chatterton: a biog. study. cr. 8°. $2.. *Macmillan.*
— Indications of anc. customs suggested by certain cranial forms. *See* American Antiq. Soc.
— Prehistoric annals of Scotland. 2 v. ill. 8°. $8. *Macmillan.*
— Prehistoric man: researches into origin of civilization in the old and the new world. 3d ed., rev. and enl. 2 v. ill. 8°. '76. $12......... *Macmillan.*

Wilson, *Rev.* Dan. On evidences of Christianity. 2 v. 12°. $1.50.......................... *Crocker.*

Wilson, E: L. Lantern journeys. 12°. $2.. *Benerman.*

Wilson, Erasmus. Anatomist's vade mecum. 9th ed., rev. and enl. by G. Buchanan. ill. fp. 8°. '73. $5.50 .... *Lindsay.*
— Healthy skin: treatise on the skin and hair, their preservation and management. 7th ed. 12°. '76. $1.25 .... *Lindsay.*
— On diseases of the skin. 7th ed., enl. ill. 8°. $5; with pl., $10............................ *Lea.*
— Student's book of cutaneous medicine and diseases of the skin. 8°. $3.50............. *Lea; W. Wood.*
— System of human anatomy, general and special; ed. by W. H. Gobrecht. ill. 8°. $4; leath., $5.. *Lea.*

Wilson, Floyd B. Book of recitations and dialogues. 16°. pap., 30c.; bds., 50c............ *Dick & F.*

Wilson, Franklin. Wealth: its acquisition, investment and use. 16°. $1................... *Am. Bapt.*

Wilson, G: Counsels of an invalid: letters on religious subjects. por. fp. 8°. $1.......... *Macmillan.*
— Five gateways of knowledge. fp. 8°. 75c... *Macmillan.*
— Handbook of hygiene and sanitary science. 2d ed., rev. ill. 8°. $2.50 .... *Lindsay.*
— Inorganic chemistry. New ed., enl. by S. Macadam; with new notation. 12°. $1.75..... *Lippincott.*
— Religio chemici. cr. 8°. $2 .... *Macmillan.*
— *and* Geikie, Arch. Life of Edward Forbes. por. 8°. '61. $3 .... *Macmillan.*

Wilson, H: Father Matthew. 12°. pap., 15c. *Nat. Temp.*
— — *Same.* por. 8°. $1.50 .... *Morton.*

Wilson, H: Book of chants. obl. 8°. '72. $2; bds., $1.75 .... *Ditson.*
— Sacred quartet. 2 v. obl. 4°. ea., $2.... *Gordon.*

Wilson, H: Military measures of U. S. Congress, 1861–'65. por. 8°. '66. pap., 50c... *Van Nostrand.*
— Rise and fall of the slave power in Am. [To form 3 v.] v. 1, 2. 8°. '72–'74. $10; shp., $13; hf. cf., $16 .... *Osgood.*
— *See also* Grant, U. S., *and* Wilson, H.

Wilson, H: *and* Caulfield, J. Book of wonderful characters: memoirs and anecdotes of remarkable and eccentric persons. ill. cr. 8°. $3 .... *Routledge.*

Wilson, Hu. Blair. American juror: rules for testing credibility of witnesses and weighing and estimating evidence. 16°. $1.25 .... *Lippincott.*
— United States rifle and light infantry tactics; with questions. 18°. $1.50 .... *Lippincott.*
— *See also* United States, *War Dept.*

Wilson, J. M. Plane geometry; following syllabus of the Geometrical Association. bks. 1–3. 12°. $1.50 .... *Macmillan.*
— Solid geometry and conic sections; with app. on transversals and harmonic division. 2d ed. 12°. '73. $1.25 .... *Macmillan.*

Wilson, J. Vct. Reasons for our hope: Scriptural evidences of final salvation of all the human family. 18°. '46. 75c. .... *Universalist.*

Wilson, Jac. English grammar. 12°. '69. 50c. *Darrow.*

Wilson, Ja. *See* Historical and descriptive account of British India; — Jameson, R., Wilson, J., *and* Murray, H.

Wilson, Ja. Life. 18°. 40c. . . . . *Pres. Bd.*

Wilson, Ja., *and* Gully, Ja. M. Practice of the water-cure. 12°. pap., 50c. . . . . *Wells.*

Wilson, Ja. G. Life and campaigns of U. S. Grant. por. 8°. '68. pap., 25c. . . . . *De Witt.*

— Sketches of illustrious soldiers. por. 12°. '74. $2.25. *Putnam.*

— *See also* Halleck, Fitz-G., Poetical works.

Wilson, Ja. H. Golden fountain; or, Bible truth unfolded. ill. 12°. $1.50 . . . . *Nelson.*

— Gospel and its fruits. 16°. $1.25 . . . . *Carter.*

— Our Father in heaven. 16°. $1.25 . . . . *Carter.*

Wilson, *Miss* Jessie Aitken. Memoir of G: Wilson. 12°. $1.50 . . . . *Macmillan.*

Wilson, J: ["Cp. North."] Lights and shadows of Scottish life. 18°. '70. 75c. . . . . *Claxton.*

— *Same.* 16°. $1 . . . . *Carter.*

— Recreations of Christopher North; [also] Miscellaneous essays of Sir A. Alison. 8°. $2.50; shp., $3.50; hf. cf., $5 . . . . *Appleton.*

— — *See also* Modern Brit. essayists.

— *See also* Noctes ambrosianæ.

Wilson, J: Treatise on Eng. punctuation; with rules on use of capitals, list of abbreviations, etc. ('50.) 20th ed. 12°. $2 . . . . *Potter, A. & Co.*

Wilson, J: (*ed.*) Unitarian principles confirmed by Trinitarian testimonies: sel. from works of theologians belonging to orthodox churches. ('55.) 10th ed. 12°. '76. $1.25 . . . . *Am. Unit.*

Wilson, J: Crawford. Gitanilla: drama. 16°. pap., 15c. . . . . *French.*

Wilson, J: G. Doctrine of baptism. 16°. '71. $1. (?) *Daughaday.*

— Life, character and death of Rev. T. H. Stockton: discourses. 16°. '69. 50c. . . . . *Claxton.*

Wilson, J: Leighton. Western Africa: its hist., condition and prospects. ill. 12°. $1.50 . . . *Harper.*

Wilson, J: Mackey. Tales of the borders and of Scotland, hist., traditionary and imaginative. 5 v. 8°. ea., $2.50 . . . . *Johnson & M.*

— *Same.* 12 v. 16°. hf. cf., $30 . . . . *Routledge.*

Wilson, J: Stainback. Woman's home book of health, embr. her physical life, hygiene and peculiar diseases. 8°. *$2.50 . . . . *So. Pub.*

Wilson, Jos. Naval hygiene. *See* United States, *Bureau of Med. and Surg.*

Wilson, *Rev.* Jos. Selfishness: its nature and remedy. 12°. 80c. . . . . *N. Y. Ref. Ch. Bd.*

Wilson, Jos. G. *See* Oregon, Sup. Court reports.

Wilson, Jos. M. *See* Shinn, E., Smith, W., *and* Wilson, J. M.

Wilson, Jos. W. Elementary algebra. ('71.) 6th ed. 12°. '75. hf. leath., $1.25.—Key, $1.25 . . *Eldredge.*

Wilson, Ol. M. Digest of parliamentary law: rules of the Senate and House of Representatives, with U. S. Constitution. 2d ed. demy 8°. $2.50 . . *Kay.*

— *See also* Indianapolis [Ind.] Sup. Court reports.

Wilson, P. *See* Bible, New Test., *Greek.*

Wilson, Rob. Treatise on steam boilers: their strength, construction and economical working. 16°. (Lond.) '73. $2.50 . . . . *Little, B. & Co.*

— *Same.* ill. 12°. $3 . . . . *Baird.*

Wilson, Rob. Anderson. Mexico: its peasants and its priests; or, adventures and researches in Mexico and its silver mines during parts of 1851–'54; with an exposé of the fabulous character of story of conquest by Cortez. ill. 12°. $1.50 . . *Harper.*

— New history of conquest of Mexico. ill. roy. 8°. '59. $3 . . . . *Challen.*

Wilson, S: Life of George Paull of Benita. 16°. $1.10. *Pres. Bd.*

Wilson, S: F. History of the American revolution; with questions. ('36.) New ed. 12°. hf. roan, '69. $1.50 . . . . *Kelly, P. & Co.*

Wilson, T. P. Frank Oldfield; or, the lost and found. 12°. $1.50 . . . . *Nelson; Tibbals.*

— *Same.* ('70.) New ed. 12°. '73. $1.50 . . *Nat. Temp.*

Wilson, Thdr. D. Ship building, theoretical and practical. ill. 8°. $7.50 . . . . *Wiley.*

Wilson, T: Address to young persons about to be confirmed; ed. by B. Dorr. 32°. 40c. *McCauley.*

— Sacra privata: private meditations and prayers. 32°. 38c. . . . . *Appleton.*

— *Same.* 16°. 50c. . . . . *Claremont.*

— *Same.* 32°. '72. 50c.—12°. '72. $1.25 . . . *Pott.*

— *Same.* 32°. cf., $1 . . . . *Nelson.*

— Short and plain instruction for the better understanding of the Lord's supper. 18°. '68. $1 . . . *Pott.*

— *Same.* 32°. 50c. 24°. cf., $2 . . . . *Nelson.*

— *Same;* with office of holy communion as administered in Prot. Episc. Church in the U. S. 18°. $1; mor., $2.25 . . . . *Claxton; Lippincott.*

— *Same.* 32°. '73. $1; mor., $2.50 . . . . *Dutton.*

— *Same.* 16°. $1.25; cf., $2.50 . . . . *Lee & S.*

Wilson, W. J. Erasmus. *See* Quain, J., *and* Wilson, W. J. E.

Wilson, W. P. Treatise on dynamics. 8°. $3. *Macmillan.*

Wilson, W: Poems; ed. by B. J. Lossing. ('69.) 2d ed. por. 16°. '75. $1.50; $2; mor., $3.50. *A. Wilson.*

Wilson, *Rev.* W: Bible student's guide to the more correct understanding of the Eng. tr. of the Old Test. by ref. to the original Hebrew. 2d ed., rev. 4°. $10 . . . . *Macmillan.*

Wilson, W: Carns. Youthful memoirs. 18°. 45c. *Am. S. S.*

Wilson, W: D. Church identified; by ref. to hist. of its origin, extension and perpetuation; with special ref. to Prot. Episc. Church in U. S. Rev. ed. 12°. '74. $2 . . . . *Dutton.*

— Elementary treatise on logic. 12°. $1.50 . . *Appleton.*

— First principles of political economy. 12°. '75. $2. *Finch.*

— Introduction to metaphysics and study of hist. of philosophy. 12°. '72. $1.25 . . . . *Andrus.*

— Lectures on psychology of thought and action, comparative and human. 12°. '71. $2 . . . . *Andrus.*

— Logic, theoretical and practical. 12°. '72. $1.50. *Andrus.*

Wilson, W: J. Progressive speller. 12°. '70. 25c. *Murphy.*

Wilson's kindling-depot. Parker, C. E. R. 60c. *Am. Tr.*

Wilton Harvey. Sedgwick, C. M. 75c. . . . . *Harper.*

Wimmerstedt, A. E. Flute and piccolo instructor. obl. 8°. pap., 75c. . . . . *Peters.*

— Violin instructor. obl. 8°. pap., 75c. . . . . . *Peters.*

Win and wear. Robbins, S. S. $1.25 . . . . *Carter.*

Win and wear ser. *See* Robbins, S. S.

Winans, Ross. One religion: many creeds. ('70.) 3d ed. 8°. '73. $1.50 . . . . *Des Forges.*

Winans, W: Charity superior to knowledge. [Discourse.] 12°. '51. pap., 20c. . . . . *So. Meth.*

— Discourses on fundamental religious subjects. 8°. '56. $3 . . . . *So. Meth.*

— Gospel ministry. [Sermon.] ('54.) 2d ed. 12°. '76. pap., 10c. . . . . *So. Meth.*

Winantz, W: Erbauliche Predigten. 12°. leath., $1.25 . . . . *Baer.*

Winborough boys. Adams, H. C. $1.75 . . *Routledge.*

Winchell, Alex. Doctrine of evolution: its data, its principles, its speculations and its theistic bearing. 12°. $1 . . . . *Harper.*

— Geology of the stars. cr. 8°. '74. pap., 25c. *Estes.*

— Key to geol. chart. 8°. pap., 25c. . . . . *Harper.*

— Sketches of creation: popular view of some conclusions of the sciences in ref. to hist. of matter and of life. ill. 12°. $2 . . . . *Harper.*

Winchell, S. R. Latin prose composition. *See* Bingham, W., Latin ser.

Winchester, S: Gover. Importance of family religions; with sel. of prayers and hymns, and tables for regular read. of Scriptures. 12°. '68. $1.. *Claxton.*

Winckel, F. Complete treatise on pathology and treatment of childbed; tr. by R. Chadwick. 8°. '76. $4 .... *Lea.*

Winckelmann, J: J. History of ancient art; tr. by G. H. Lodge. 4 v. ill. 8°. '72. ea., $5; hf. cf., $10 .... *Osgood.*

Winckler, Willibald. Lieder e. Wandervogels. por. 12°. (Chicago.) '69. pap., $1.50 .... *Steiger.*

— Vier Schreckenstage (Die) in New York: hist. Novelette. 8°. (Chicago.) '64. pap., 25c. *Steiger.*

Wind spirit and the rain goddess; tr. from the Germ. sq. 16°. 75c. .... *Nichols & H.*

Wind-wafted seed. Macleod, N., *and* Guthrie, T. $2 .... *Routledge.*

Windfalls. Randolph, R. $1 .... *Claxton.*

Windle, *Mrs.* S. Allen. Home pleasures. 32°. 40c. *Scribner, W. & A.*

Windle, W. Scripture text-book for daily use. 16°. '73. 75c. — 24°. 50c.; 75c. .... *Routledge.*

Windmill. Morton, E. 15c. .... *French.*

Window gardener. Rand, E. S., *jr.* $1.. (?) *Shepard.*

Windows of the soul. 18°. 35c. .... *Cong. Pub.*

Windsor Castle. *See* Ainsworth, W: H.

Windsor Castle. Burnand, F. C. 15c. .... *French.*

Wine-cup: temperance [dram.] sketch. 16°. pap., 15c. *Happy.*

Winefred Jones. 16°. 50c.; 75c. .... *Sadlier.*

Winefride, *St.* Life and miracles; [also] Life of St. Catherine. 18°. '71. 60c. .... *Kenedy.*

Wi-ne-ma and her people. Meacham, A. B. *$1. *Am. Pub.*

Winer, G: G. Confessions of Christendom. 8°. $3. *Scribner, W. & A.*

— Grammar of the idiom of the New Test.; prep. as a basis for interpretation of New Test. 7th ed., enl. by G. Lünemann. ('69.) New ed. 8°. '74. $4; shp., $5; hf. goat, $5.75 .... *Draper.*

Wines, Enoch Cobb. Adam and Christ; or, the doctrine of representation stated and explained. 18°. 30c. .... *Pres. Bd.*

— Commentaries on laws of ancient Hebrews. 8°. $2. *Pres. Bd.*

— Essay on temptation. 12°. 75c. .... *Pres. Bd.*

— Prison conference at Brussels, June, 1874; [also] Prison question in Am., by F. B. Sanborn. 8°. '74. pap., 25c. .... *Williams.*

— Promises of God considered in their nature, source, certainty, trueness, etc. 18°. 50c. .... *Pres. Bd.*

— Treatise on regeneration. 12°. 55c. .... *Pres. Bd.*

— True penitent portrayed: exposition of 51st Psalm. sm. 12°. 60c. .... *Pres. Bd.*

Wines, F: Howard. Children in paradise: gift for bereaved parents. 16°. $1 .... (?) *Martien.*

Winfield, A. B. Antidote to errors of Universalism. 18°. 50c. .... *N. Y. Ref. Ch. Bd.*

— Initiatory seal; or, Christian baptism: defence of infant baptism. 8°. pap., 25c. .... *N. Y. Ref. Ch. Bd.*

— Sermon on safety and sure defence of Zion; with hist. of Ref. Dutch Church of Paramus, N. J., 1853. 8°. pap., 25c. .... *N. Y. Ref. Ch. Bd.*

Wing-and-wing. *See* Cooper, Ja. F.

Wingate, G: W. Manual for rifle practice; [with] suggestions for practice at long range and for formation and management of rifle associations. 5th ed., rev. ill. 16°. '75. $1.50.. *W. C. & F. P. Church.*

Winged whale. Aiken, A. W. 20c. .... *Beadle.*

Winged word. Finker, M. A. $1.50 .... *Cath. Pub.*

Wings and stings. *See* Tucker, *Mrs.* Ctte.

Wings and webs. Whitmarsh, C. S. 90c. *Thompson.*

Wings or weights. Montreal, M. 45c. .... *Am. S. S.*

Winifred. Guernsey, L. E. $1.50 .... *Whittaker.*

Winifred, Countess of Nithsdale. Dacre, B. B. (*Lady*). $1.50 .... *Sadlier.*

Winifred Bertram. Charles, E. $1 .... *Dodd.*

Winifred Leigh lib. 4 v. 16°. '67. $4.. *Meth. Bk. Conc.*

Cont.: Winifred Leigh. — Captive boy in Terra del Fuego. — In self and out of self. — Hetty Porter.

Winifred's jewels. Bird, M. A. $1.50 .... *McKinney.*

Winkelman, F: T. Course of exercises in French syntax. 12°. $1.25 .... *Appleton.*

Winket's valentine. ill. 4°. '76. pap., 25c. *Lothrop.*

Winkley, S. H. Question book on life of Jesus. 16°. 12c. .... *Un. S. S.*

— Questions on Gospel of St. John. 16°. 12c. *Un. S. S.*

Winkworth, Cath. Christian singers of Germany. cr. 8°. '69. $1.75 .... *Lippincott; Macmillan.*

Winner, Jos. E. New teacher for the accordeon without a master. obl. 8°. '68. pap., 75c... *Ditson.*

— New teacher for the flute. obl. 8°. '68. pap., 75c. *Ditson.*

Winner, Septimus. Accordion and flutina primer; without a master. obl. 8°. '58. pap., 75c. *Ditson.*

— Accordion songster. obl. 8°. '57. pap., 60c. *Ditson.*

— Cabinet organ tutor. 8°. '67. pap., 75c... *Ditson.*

— Drum book: instruction for drumming. 8°. '61. pap., 25c. .... *Ditson.*

— Easy system for the banjo; — [German accordion; — German concertina]. 3 v. obl. 8°. '69–'70. ea., pap., 50c. .... *Ditson.*

— *Same;* [for the accordion; — flute; — guitar; — violin; — violoncello]. 5 v. obl. 8°. '66–'72. ea., pap., 75c. .... *Ditson.*

— Easy system for the melodeon. 4°. '66. bds., $1.50. *Ditson.*

— Easy system for the piano forte. 4°. '66. bds., $1.50. *Ditson.*

— Guitar primer: method of learning to play the guitar without a master. obl. 8°. '60. pap., 75c. *Ditson.*

— Improved accordion method. obl. 8°. '54. pap., 60c. *Ditson.*

— Improved method for the violin. obl. 8°. '54. pap., 60c. .... *Ditson.*

— Independent accordion player. obl. 8°. 30c. *Gordon.*

— Independent violin player. 12 nos. 8°. ea., 30c. *Gordon.*

— Melodeon primer: method of learning to play melodeon without a master. 8°. '60. pap., 75c. *Ditson.*

— Melodeon tutor. 8°. '67. pap., 75c. .... *Ditson.*

— New German concertina primer. obl. roy. 8°. '64. pap., 75c. .... *Pond.*

— New method for melodeon. obl. 8°. 75c... *Brainard.*

— New method for piano forte. obl. 8°. 75c. *Brainard.*

— New method for reed organ. obl. 8°. 75c. *Brainard.*

— New primer for the accordion; — [banjo; — clarionet; — flute; — German accordion; — guitar; — piano]. 7 v. obl. roy. 8°. '64. ea., pap., 75c. ... *Pond.*

— New school for the accordion; — [banjo; — cabinet organ; — clarionet; — cornet; — fife; — flageolet; — flute; — German accordion; — guitar; — melodeon; — piano forte; — piccolo and böhm flute; — violin]. 14 v. obl. 8°. '61–'72. ea., pap., 75c. .... *Ditson.*

— New teacher for violin; without the aid of a master. obl. 8°. '68. pap., 75c. .... *Ditson.*

— New violin primer. obl. roy. 8°. '64. pap., 75c. *Pond.*

— Perfect guide for the accordion; — [cabinet organ; — clarionet; — fife; — flageolet; — flute; — German concertina; — guitar; — melodeon; — piano; — violin]. 11 v. obl. 8°. '61–'69. ea., pap., 75c. *Ditson.*

— Piano-forte primer. obl. 8°. '60. pap., 75c... *Ditson.*

— Piano tutor. obl. 8°. pap., 75c. .... *Ditson.*

— Pocket preceptor for the violin. obl. 8°. '70. pap., 75c. .... *Ditson.*

— Popular method for the flute. 8°. '54. pap., 60c. *Ditson.*

Winner, Septimus, *continued.*
— Primary school for accordion; — [banjo; — clarionet; — concertina; — cornet; — fife; — flageolet; — flute; — German accordion; — guitar; — violin; — violoncello; — voice]. 13 v. obl. 8°. ea., pap., 75c. . . . . *Brainard.*
— Singing method; with sel. of ballads for single voice. obl. 16°. bds., 60c. . . . . *Ditson.*
Winnie and her grandfather. *See* Martyn, *Mrs.* S. T.
Winnie and his pets. *See* Aunty Ray's little lib.
Winnie and Walter ser. *See* Tarbox, I. N.
Winnie Malone. Porter, A. E. 60c. . . . . *Cong. Pub.*
Winning hazard. Wooler, J. P. 15c. . . . . . . *French.*
Winning his spurs. Kellogg, E. $1.25. . . . . *Lee & S.*
Winning his way. Coffin, C. C. $1.25. . . . . * *Osgood.*
Winning a husband. Macfarren, G. 15c. . . . *French.*
Winning a wife. Lacy, T. H. 15c. . . . . *French.*
Winning souls. Halliday, S. B. $1 . . . . *Ford.*
Winnowed hymns. M'Cabe, C. C., *and* Macfarlan, D. F. 35c.; 25c.; 30c. . . *Biglow; Meth. Bk. Conc.*
Winscom, Jane Anne. Onward; or, the mountain clamberers. 16°. '74. $1.50. . . . . *Dutton.*
Winside Farm; or, the Spensers. 18°. 85c. 16°. $1. *Am. S. S.*
Winslow, C: F: Force and nature: attraction and repulsion: the radical principles of energy discussed in their rel. to physical and morphological development. 8°. '69. $4. . *Lippincott; Macmillan.*
Winslow, Forbes. On obscure diseases of the brain and disorders of the mind. 8°. $4.25. . . . . . *Lea.*
Winslow, Hubbard. Are you a Christian? ('39.) New ed. 32°. '61. 15c. . . . . *Am. Tr.*
— Elements of moral philos. 12°. $1.50. . . . *Appleton.*
— Intellectual philosophy, analytical, synthetical and practical. 8th ed., enl. 12°. $1.65. . . . . . *Ware.*
— Young man's aid to knowledge, virtue and happiness. 24°. '37. 75c. *Crocker.*
Winslow, *Miss* M. E. Barford mills. 12°. '75. $1. *Nat. Temp.*
— More excellent way (A), and other stories. 12°. '76. $1. . . . . *Nat. Temp.*
Winslow, Oct. Works. 13 v. . . . . *Carter.*
Cont.: Declension and revival, 16°, $1. — Foot of the cross, 18°, 75c. — Glory of the Redeemer, 12°, $1.50. — Heaven opened, 16°, $2. — Help heavenward, 18°, 75c. — History of the Jews, 16°, $1.25. — Instant glory, 32°, 30c. — Life of Ma. Winslow, 12°, $1.50. — Man of God, 18°, 75c. — Midnight harmonies, 16°, $1. — Pisgah views, 16°, $1.25. — Precious things, 16°, $1.25. — Sympathy of Christ with man, 16°, $1.25.

Christ ever with you; ill. by experiences drawn from Fulton Street [N. Y.] prayer meeting, and field and hospital life. 18°. 40c. . . . . *N. Y. Ref. Ch. Bd.*
— Danger of rejecting the atonement. 32°. '64. 20c. *Randolph.*
— Go and tell Jesus. 32°. '64. 20c. . . . . *Randolph.*
— — *See also* Hall, N., Come to Jesus.
— *Same;* [also] Wait on the Lord. 24°. '64. 75c. *Randolph.*
— Going home. 32°. '64. 20c. . . . . *Randolph.*
— My time's in God's hands. 32°. '64. 20c. . . *Randolph.*
— — *See also below* None like Christ.
— None like Christ. 32°. '64. 20c. . . . . *Randolph.*
— *Same;* [also] My time's in God's hands. 24°. '64. 75c. *Randolph.*
Winstanley, E. [Novels.] 4 v. ill. 8°. (Lond.) pap. *Am. News.*
Cont.: Carynthia. — Twenty straws. — What is to be, will be, *ea.*, 30c. — Entrances and exits, 60c.
Winston, —. *See* North Carolina, Equity reports; Law reports.
Winter, G. A. Der deutsche Sprachschüler. 16°. '70. bds., 40c. . . . . *Knœfel.*
Winter, Louisa. Memoir. 18°. 22c. . . . . . . *Am. S. S.*
Winter, W: Edwin Booth in twelve dramatic characters: por. by W. J. Hennessy, biog. by W. Winter. 4°. '71. $10. . . . . *Osgood.*

Winter, W: *continued.*
— My witness. [Poetry.] 16°. '71. $1.50; hf. cf., $3; mor., $4. . . . . *Osgood.*
Winter and spring on the shores of the Mediterranean. Bennet, J. H. $3.50. . . . . *Appleton.*
Winter and summer at Burton Hall. *See* Greene, *Mrs.* L. L.
Winter at Woodlawn; or, the armor of light illustrated. ill. sq. 16°. 90c. . . . . *Meth. Bk. Conc.*
Winter days. *See* Robin Ranger's lib.
Winter evening book. *See* Chambers, W. *and* R.
Winter evening lib. 4 v. ill. 16°. ea., 50c. . . . . . *Pott.*
Cont.: Sardinia. — Great czar, by J. F. Cobb. — Faithful servant, by J. B. Cléry. — Pictures from Venice, by C. M. Phillimore.
Winter evening lib. 8 v. ill. 12°. $12. . . . . *Appleton.*
Cont.: Boys at home. — Edgar Clifton. — Prince Charlie. — Louis' school days. — Bertram Noel. — Boy's book of travel. — Sunshine of Greystone. — Mortimer's college life.
Winter evening recreations. *See* Continental lib.
Winter evening tales. Goodrich, S. G. 50c. . . *Desilver.*
Winter evening's conversations on the works of God. 18°. 60c. . . . . *Am. S. S.*
Winter evening's entertainment. Cull, A. $1. . *Ditson.*
Winter fire. Porter, R. $1.25. . . . . *Randolph.*
Winter homes for invalids. Howe, J. W. $1.25. . *Putnam.*
Winter in Florida. Bill, L. $1.25. . . . . . . *Wood & H.*
Winter in Russia. Gautier, T. $2. . . . . *Holt.*
Winter in Spitzbergen. Hildebrant, G. C. $1. . *Dodd.*
Winter poems; by Whittier, Longfellow, Bryant, Lowell and Emerson. ill. 8°. '70. $5; mor., $9. *Osgood.*
Winter school. Brown, H. E. 60c. . . . . *Bost. Am. Tr.*
Winter school stories. 5 v. 18°. $3. . . . *Bost. Am. Tr.*
Cont.: Down in a mine. — Lilian. — Lizzie Weston's mission, by A. L. W. — Lyntonville. — Winter school, by H. E. Brown.
Winter stories. *See* Juvenile picture books.
Winter sunshine. Burroughs, J. $1.50. . . *Hurd & H.*
Winter vacation. 18°. 20c.; 25c. . . . . *Am. Bapt.*
Winterfeld, A. v. Ehefabrikanten (Die); [also] Des Sohnes Heimkehr, v. F. Friedrich. 2 v. 8°. ea., pap., 50c. . . . . *Morwitz.*
— Elephant (Der): komischer Roman. 8°. pap., 50c. *Morwitz.*
— Gross Busekow: Kriegsroman. 8°. pap., 50c. *Morwitz.*
— Lieutenant Falstaff (Der) u. wie es ihm bei den Damen erging. 12°. '65. pap., 25c. . . . *Steiger.*
Wintergreen, the carpet layer. *See* Bright eye ser.
Wintergreen girl. Strong, J. D. 30c. . . . . . *Lothrop.*
Wintermärchen. *See* Heine, H.
Wintermärchen (Das). *See* Shakespeare, W:
Winter's tale. 18°. 40c. . . . . *Dutton.*
Winter's tale. *See* Shakespeare, W:
Winter's wreath. 18°. 35c. . . . . *Routledge.*
— *See also* Moss wreath lib.
Winterslow essays. *See* Hazlitt, W:
Winthorpes (The). Biscoe, E. L. $1.15. . *Bost. Am. Tr.*
Winthrop, Rob. C. Life and letters of John Winthrop, governor of Massachusetts Bay Company, 1588 to 1649. 2d ed., enl. 2 v. por. and ill. 8°. '69. $7. . . . . *Little, B. & Co.*
— Speeches and addresses on various occasions. 2 v. 8°. '52–'67. ea., $3.50. . . . . *Little, B. & Co.*
— Washington, Bowdoin and Franklin, as portrayed in occasional addresses. 8°. '76. $2. . *Little, B. & Co.*
Winthrop, Sophy. Faith and patience; or, the Harrington girls. 18°. '75. $1. . . . . *Randolph.*
Winthrop, Thdr. Works. ('62–'63.) New ed. (Leis. hour ser.) 5 v. 16°. '76. ea., $1.25. . . . . . *Holt.*
Cont.: Canoe and the saddle: adventures among the northwestern rivers and forests; Isthmiana. — Cecil Dreeme; with biog. sketch by G. W. Curtis. — Edwin Brothertoft. — John Brent. — Life in the open air, etc.

Winton, *Mrs.* Nelson W. Drifting anchor. ill. 16°. '72. $1.25 .... *Lothrop.*

Wireman, H: D. Gems of German lyrics; tr. into Eng. verse. 12°. '69. $1.50; $2.50. *Claxton; Kohler.*

— *See also* Bürger, G. A.; — Schiller, J. F. v.

Wirt, A. C. Life. ill. 18°. '58. 35c. .... *Am. Tr.*

Wirt, W: Letters of the British spy; with sketch of author's life. 12°. $1.25 .... *Harper.*

— Sketches of life and character of Patrick Henry. ('18.) 25th ed. 12°. '74. $1.50 .... *Claxton.*

Wirthshaus (Das) zu Cransac. *See* Zschokke, H.

Wisconsin. Laws rel. to organization and government of towns. *See* Spooner, J. C., *and* Bryant, E. E.

— Revised statutes, 1858–'71; by D: Taylor. 2 v. 8°. '71 .... *State.*

— Supreme Court reports, 1842–'76; annotated edition. 41 v. 8°. shp., $246 .... *Callaghan.*

Cont.: Pinney ('42–'52), 3 v. — Smith [1-11 Wis.] ('53–'60), 11 v. — Spooner [12-15 Wis.] ('61–'62), 4 v. — Conover [16-38 Wis.] ('62–'76), 23 v.

Note. Pinney includes Burnett and Chandler, and cases decided from 1842–'49; v. 1-20 repub. with add. notes in '72–'75.

— — Digest. *See* Simmons, J. A.

— Table of cases reported. *See* Wight, W. W.

Wisconsin geological survey. Annual report of geol. survey of W.; by J. G. Percival. 8°. '56 .. *State.*

— *Same;* for 1857; by E. Daniels. 8° .... *State.*

— Report of sup't of geol. survey, 1861. 8°. '61 .. *State.*

— Report on geol. survey of W. v. 1: General geol. and palæont., by J. Hall; On the upper Mississippi lead region, by J. D. Whitney. roy. 8°. '62 .... *State.*

— *See also* Owen, D. D.

Wisdom, folly and prudence, exhibited and contrasted. 18°. 50c. .... *Am. S. S.*

Wisdom from above. Foote, H. W. 30c. .. *Williams.*

Wisdom in miniature. Smith, D. 35c. *Cin. Meth. Bk. Conc.*

Wisdom of experience. *See* Cupples, *Mrs.* A. J.

Wisdom of forethought. *See* Cupples, *Mrs.* A. J.

Wisdom teeth for little people. De Fontaine, F. G. 60c. .... *Hale.*

Wisdom's ways. *See* Head and heart ser.

Wise, Dan. ["Fs. Forrester"; "Lawr. Lancewood."] Bridal greetings: advice to a newly married couple. 24°. '50. 50c.; $1 .... *Meth. Bk. Conc.*

— Christian love; or, charity an essential element of true Christian character. 24°. '50. 40c. *Meth. Bk. Conc.*

— Glen Morris' stories. 5 v. 12°. '74. $6 ... *Meth. Bk. Conc.*

Cont.: Guy Carlton. — Dick Duncan. — Jessie Carlton. — Mattie Sherwood. — Kate Carlton.

— Hollywood ser. ('73.) New ed. 6 v. ill. 16°. '74. $7.50 .... *Perkinpine.*

Cont.: Stephen and his tempter; or, the children of Hollywood. — Florence Baldwin's picnic. — Lionel's courage; or, Clementina's great peril. — Priscilla the beautiful; or, Florence rewarded. — Nat and his chum; or, the friendly rivals. — Elbert's return; or, Foxy at home again.

— Lindendale stories. 5 v. 16°. '65–'69. $6.25. *H. A. Young.*

Cont.: Sidney De Grey; or, the rival schoolboys. — Nellie Warren; or, the lost watch. — Louis Sinclair. — Cousin Clara. — Peter Clinton.

— Little Peachblossom; or, rambles in Central Park. 12°. '73. $1.25 .... *Meth. Bk. Conc.*

— My uncle Toby's lib. 12 v. ill. 16°. $5.63 .. *Thompson.*

Cont.: Arthur Ellerslie. — Minnie Brown. — Arthur's temptation. — A runaway. — Minnie's picnic. — Minnie's playroom. — Redbrook. — Ralph Rattler. — Aunt Amy. — Fretful Lillie. — Cousin Nellie. — Arthur's triumph.

— *Same.* 4 v. 16°. $4 .... *Thompson.*

— Our king; or, story of our Lord's life on earth. ill. 12°. '75. $2 .... *Meth. Bk. Conc.*

— Path of life; or, sketches of the way to glory and immortality. 12°. '48. $1; $1.30 .. *Meth. Bk. Conc.*

— Personal effort explained and enforced. 24°. '45. 30c. *Meth. Bk. Conc.*

Wise, Dan., *continued.*

— Pleasant pathways; or, persuasives to early piety. 12°. '59. $1.25 .... *Meth. Bk. Conc.*

— Questions on Romans. 18°. per doz., $1.80. *Meth. Bk. Conc.*

— Squire of Walton Hall; from life of Charles Waterton. ill. 16°. '74. $1.25 .... *Meth. Bk. Conc.*

— Story of a wonderful life [John Wesley]. 16°. $1.25; $1.50 .... *Cin. Meth. Bk. Conc.*

— Summer days on the Hudson. ill. 12°. '76. $2. *Meth. Bk. Conc.*

— Uncrowned kings. 16°. $1.25 .. *Cin. Meth. Bk. Conc.*

— Young lady's counselor. 12°. '53. $1 .. *Meth. Bk. Conc.*

— Young man's counselor. 12°. '53. $1 .. *Meth. Bk. Conc.*

— *and* Vincent, J. H. Our Sunday school scrap book. 12°. 25c. .... *Meth. Bk. Conc.*

Wise, H: Alex. Seven decades of the Union: the humanities and materialism, ill. by memoir of J: Tyler. 8°. $2 .... *Lippincott.*

Wise, H: A: ["Harry Gringo."] Captain Brand of the "Centipede." ill. 8°. $2; pap., $1.50 .. *Harper.*

Wise, I: M. Combat of the people; or, "Hillel and Herod": historical romance of time of Herod. 16°. 50c. .... *Bloch.*

— Cosmic God: philos. conciliation of religion and science: lectures. 16°. $1.50 .... *Bloch.*

— *Same.* 8°. '76. $1.50 .... *Wise.*

— First of the Maccabees. 16°. 50c. .... *Bloch.*

— History of the Jews of the first commonwealth. 16°. 50c. .... *Bloch.*

— Judaism: its doctrines and duties. 12°. '72. 65c. *Bloch; Wise.*

— Martyrdom of Jesus of Nazareth: hist.-crit. treatise on last chapters of Gospels. 8°. '74. $1 .. *Wise.*

— *Same.* 16°. '74. 75c. .... *Bloch.*

— Three lectures on origin of Christianity: Jesus the Pharisee; The Apostles and the Essenes; Paul and the Mystics. 16°. '70. 35c.; $1.50 .. *Bloch.*

Wise, J: Through the air; or, forty years' experience as an aeronaut. ill. 8°. '74. *$3.50; leath., $4. *Maclean.*

Wise, *Rev.* J: Life. ill. 18°. '53. 35c. .... *Am. Tr.*

— Vindication of government of the New England churches; with introd. by J. S. Clark. 4th ed. 12°. $1.25 .... *Cong. Pub.*

Wise and otherwise. *See* Alden, *Mrs.* I. M.

Wise men. Upham, F. W. $1.25 .... *Meth. Bk. Conc.*

Wise nun of Eastonmere. Taylor, *Miss* —. $1.25. *Kelly, P. & Co.*

Wiseman, Luke H. Agents in the religious revival of the last century. 12°. pap., 10c. .... *So. Meth.*

Wiseman, N: Works. 14 v. 12°. ea., $1.50 .. *O'Shea.*

Cont.: Dramas. — Essays, 6 v. — Lectures on offices and ceremonies of holy week. — Lectures on principal doctrines and practices of the Cath. Church, 2 v. — Lectures on real presence of body and blood of Christ in the eucharist. — Lectures on science and revealed religion, 2 v. — Recollections of last four popes and of Rome in their time.

— Fabiola. 12°. $1.50; $2. .... *Sadlier.*

— Lamp of the sanctuary: Catholic story. 18°. 50c. *Coddington.*

— Lectures on science and religion. 12°. '76. 60c. *Fox.*

— Sermons on moral subjects. 12°. $2; — in 2 v., $4. *Sadlier.*

— Sermons on our Lord and his blessed mother. 12°. $2 .... *Sadlier.*

Wish (The) and the way; or, passages in life of Rose Burgoyne. ill. 12°. $1.75 .... *Nelson.*

Wishing and choosing. *See* Brock, *Mrs.* C.

Wishing and seeking; or, Winnie at the farm. 16°. $1 .... (?) *Martien.*

Wishing and seeking ser. 5 v. 16°. $5 .. (?) *Martien.*

Cont.: Wishing and seeking. — The two marriages. — Agnes Carelton. — Oliver's prisoner. — A rough boy's story.

Wishing cap. 32°. '53. 30c. .... *Am. Tr.*

Wishing-cap papers. Hunt, L. $1.50 ...... *Lee & S.*

Wistar, Caspar. System of anatomy for students of medicine; with notes and add. by W. E. Horner. 9th ed., rev. 2 v. ill. 8°. shp., $5... *Desilver.*

Wister, *Mrs.* A. L. *See* Hillern, W. v.; — John, E.; — Lewald, F.; — Wichert, Ern.; — Volckhausen, Ad. v.

Wit and wisdom of George Eliot. sq. 18°. '73. $1.25. *Roberts.*

Wit bought. *See* Goodrich, S: G.

Witch-Hampton Hall; [also] Lodgings at Knightsbridge. 8°. pap., 25c. ... *Littell & G.*

Witch Hill. Mudge, Z. A. $1.25 .... *Meth. Bk. Conc.*

Witch of Melton Hill. 16°. $1; $1.50..... *Sadlier.*

Witch of Windermere. Selby, C. 15c. ...... *French.*

Witches of New York. Thomson, M. $1.75; $1.50. *Peterson.*

Witcomb, C., *and* Bellenger, H. Guide to French conversation; [with] summary of Fr. grammar, by Delille. ('63.) New ed. 18°. '76. 75c. *Holt.*

With the birds. M., M. R. 75c. ... *Nelson.*

With fate against him. Douglas, A. M. $1.50. *Sheldon.*

With harp and crown. Besant, W., *and* Rice, J. 75c. * *Osgood.*

With a stout heart. Barker, S. $1.25.... *Routledge.*

With the tide. Daryl, S. $1.50 ... *Claxton.*

Witham, T. Maxwell. *See* Vandewell, H. E., *and* Witham, T. M.

Wither, F: C. Church architecture. pl. f°. '74. $15 ... *Bicknell.*

Withered branch revived. Clark, J. A. 25c. *Am. Tr.*

Withered heart. Arthur, T. S. $1.25... *J. E. Potter.*

Witherow, T: Which is the apostolic church? 18°. 50c. ... *Pres. Bd.*

Witherspoon, O. Complete system of S.-school instruction. [To form 10 nos.] 16°. '73. 1-4, pap., 10c.; 5, hf. bd., 20c.; 6, hf. bd., 25c... *M. Taylor.*

— Forms of canonical procedure. 8°. '72. pap., 50c. *M. Taylor.*

— Gloria in excelsis: eight renderings in simple chanting style. 8°. '72. 50c. ... *M. Taylor.*

— New hymnal for Sunday schools; with chants and offices of devotion for opening and closing school. 2d ed. 12°. '75. 25c. ... *M. Taylor.*

Witherspoon, T. D. Children of the covenant; ill. in lives and deaths of A. H., S. W. and M. C. Kerr. 16°. '73. $1 .... *N. Y. Ref. Ch. Bd.; Pres. Com.*

— *Same.* 16°. 50c. ... *West. Tr.*

Within an ace. Jenkin, C. $1.25 ... *Holt.*

Within an inch of his life. *See* Gaboriau, E.

Within and without. MacDonald, G. $1.50.. *Scribner.*

Within the maze. Wood, E. P. $1.75; $1.50.. *Peterson.*

Within sea-walls; or, how the Dutch kept the faith. ill. 18°. $1.25 ... *N. Y. Ref. Ch. Bd.*

Withington, Leon. Song of Solomon. 12°. '61. $1.75 ... *Tilton.*

Without incumbrances. Simpson, J. P. 15c. *French.*

Withrow, T: F. American corporation cases: decisions of U. S. Sup. and Circ. Courts and courts of last resort in the several states, since Jan., 1868, of questions peculiar to law of corporations. 2 v. 8°. '72-'74. ea., shp., $6 ... *E. B. Myers.*
Cont.: Private corporations. — Municipal corporations.

— *See also* Iowa, Sup. Court reports.

— *and* Stiles, E. H. Digest of Iowa Sup. Court reports (v. 1-35, 1839-'72). 2 v. roy. 8°. '75. shp., $15 ... *E. B. Myers.*

Withrow, W. H. Catacombs of Rome, and their testimony relative to primitive Christianity. ill. 12°. '74. $3 ... *Meth. Bk. Conc.*

Witless Willie, the idiot boy. 18°. 50c...(?) *Martien.*

Witmer, Thdr. B. Wild oats sown abroad; or, on and off soundings: European letters. 12°. '72. $1.50. *Peterson.*

Witness of history to Christ. Farrar, F. W. $1.50. *Macmillan.*

Witness of the Spirit. Jackson, W. $1.50..... *Pott.*

Witness of the Spirit. Walton, D. 50c. *Meth. Bk. Conc.*

Witnesses for Christ; or, the poet [Cowper], the hero [Haldane], the statesman [Wilberforce], and the philosopher [Chalmers]. 18°. 35c.... *Pres. Bd.*

Witnesses to the truth. Hanson, J. W. 75c. *Universalist.*

Witnessing church. *See* Harris, J.

Witnessing church. McFerrin, J. B. 15c... *So. Meth.*

Witnessing for Jesus in the homes of the poor. 16°. '68. $1.25 ... *Randolph.*

Wits and beaux of society. *See* Thomson, K. B. *and* J. C.

Witschel, J. H. W. Morgen- u. Abendopfer. 18°. 60c.-$2.50 ... *Kohler.*

Witt, *Mme.* Henriette (*née* Guizot) de. Clara's little lib.; tr. 12 v. 32°. $3 ... (?) *Martien.*
Cont.: Charles, the cheerful giver.—Tom's geranium. —Brave little Louis. — How the boys spent their vacation. — Ronald Cameron. — Victor's goat. — The fireworks. — Little Julia and the cripple. — How Maria's curls made the bracelet. — Arbor the boys built. — Dragon, the faithful shepherd dog. — The picnic.

— Class-book of French poetry for young girls; tr. sm. 8°. $1 ... *Lippincott*

— Derrière les haies. sm. 8°. $1 .... *Lippincott.*

— French country family (A); tr. by D. M. Craik. ill. 12°. $1.50 ... *Harper.*

— *Same.* ill. 12°. $1.50; $1.75 ... *Routledge.*

— Ida's little lib. 6 v. 32°. $1.50...... (?) *Martien.*
Compr. last 6 v. of "Clara's little lib."

— Marie Derville: story of a French boarding school; tr. 12°. $1.50 ... *Lippincott.*

— Motherless; or, a Parisian family; tr. by D. M. Craik. ill. 12°. $1.50 ... *Harper.*

— Walter's little lib. 6 v. 32°. $1.50...(?) *Martien.*
Compr. first 6 v. of "Clara's little lib."

Witt, *Mme.* Pauline de. An only sister; tr. by D. M. Craik. ill. 16°. 90c. ... *Harper.*

— Parents and children: stories for the home circle; tr. ill. 18°. $1 ... *Nelson.*

Witter, C. *See* Köhler, F., *and* Witter, C.

Witter's [arithmetics]. 6 v. 12°. '66-'75... *Witter.*
Cont.: Praktisches Rechenbuch f. d. untern Klassen, 40c.— *Same,* f. d. mittleren Klassen, 50c. —*Same,* f. d. Oberklassen v. P. Roehm, 60c. — Auflösungsheft zu Rechenbuch f. d. mittleren Klassen, 40c. — *Same,* f. d. Oberklassen, v. P. Roehm, 40c. — Müller's Praktische Bruchrechnung, 40c.

Witter's [German spellers and readers]. 5 v. 12°. '73-'76 ... *Witter.*
Cont.: Deutsch-amerik. Elementar- Schüler, od. d. ersten Anschauungs, Schön u. Rechtschreibe-Uebungen, 25c.—Deutsch-amerik. Lese-Schüler, od. d. zweiten Anschauungs, Lese u. Rechtschreibe-Uebungen, 50c. — Drittes Lesebuch f. deutsch-amerik. Schulen, 85c. — Erstes Buch d. Realkenntnisse, ill., 85c. — Zweites Buch d. Realkenntnisse, ill., $1.50.

Witter's Der goldene fertige Rechner in Dollars u. Cents. 16°. '67. 50c. ... *Witter.*

— *Eng.* Ready calculator. 16°. '67. 50c. .. *Witter.*

Witter's neueste Zins-Tabellen. 8°. '67. $1.. *Witter.*

— *Eng.* New interest tables. 8°. '67. $1 .. *Witter.*

Witter's Schönschreibe-Hefte, mit deutschen Vorschriften. 6 nos. 4°. ea., pap., 10c. .. *Witter.*

Wittig, Rud. Excelsior guide for the flute. obl. 8°. '64. pap., 75c. ... *Ditson.*

— Excelsior guide for the violin. obl. 8°. '64. pap., 75c. ... *Ditson.*

Wittikind: extravaganza. 16°. pap., 15c.... *French.*

Wittmaack, Thdr. Populäres Handbuch d. Diätetik. 12°. $1 ... *Radde.*

Witzka, C. B. Mass in G. 4°. pap., $1.25.. *Peters.*

— Tauman's mass in C. 4°. pap., $1.25...... *Peters.*

Wives and daughters. *See* Gaskell, *Mrs.* E. C.

Wives and widows. Stephens, A. S. $1.75; $1.50. *Peterson.*

Wives as they were and maids as they are. Inchbald, E. 15c. ... *French.*

Wizard of the moor. Gott, H. 15c. ....*French.*
Wizard of the mountain. Gilbert, W. 2 v. $5. *Routledge.*
Wizard of the wave. Haines, J. T. 15c.....*French.*
Wizard wand; or, cabinet of conjurations. 3d ed. 32°. '72. pap., 50c......................*Hunter.*
Woans ik tau 'ne Fru kamm. *See* Reuter, F.
Wöhler, F: Handbook of mineral analysis; tr. and ed. by H. B. Nason. ill. 12°. '70. $3.....*Baird.*
— Outlines of organic chemistry; tr. with add. by I. Remsen. roy. 12°. '73. $3 ....*Lea.*
Wohlfahrt, H: Guide to musical composition; tr. by J. S. Dwight. 12°. '59. $1.25.......*Ditson.*
— Young pianist's guide. 4°. *net*, pap., $2..*Schirmer.*
Wolf, C. W. Apis mellifica; or, the poison of the honey bee considered as a therapeutic agent. [Hom.] 12°. pap., 25c. ....*Boericke.*
Wolf, Jos. Life and habits of wild animals; ill. by [his] designs, eng. by J. W. and E. Whymper; with descrip. letter press by D. G. Elliott. 4°. $4 ....*Harper.*
Wolf and the lamb; — and young goat. *See* Stories about animals ser.
Wolf boy. *See* Dalton, W:
Wolf demon. Aiken, A. W. 20c............*Beadle.*
Wolf hunting and wild sport in lower Brittany; by author of "Paul Pendril." cr. 8°. $3..*Scribner, W.& A.*
Wolf Run. Kellogg, E. $1.25..............*Lee & S.*
Wolfe, Helen J. Out in the world; or, a selfish life. 16°. $1.25 ....*Cin. Meth. Bk. Conc.*
Wolfe, J. Rob. Practical Hebrew grammar. post 8°. (Bagster.) $2.50; hf. bd., $3.25........ *Wiley.*
Wolfe, Nap. B. Startling facts in modern spiritualism. ('73.) 2d ed. ill. 12°. '75. $2.....*Rel. Phil.*
Wolfert's roost. *See* Irving, Wash.
Wolfgang, Prince of Anhalt; tr. (Fatherland ser.) ill. 16°. $1.25 ....(?)*Luth. Pub.*
Wolford, G: Statute laws of the several states of U. S. rel. to insurance. 2 v. 8°. '72. shp., $15.. *Weed.*
Wolf's glen. ('67.) New ed. ill. 16°. '71. $1..*Hoyt.*
Wolfsheim, S. M. The child's first piano instructor. 4°. *net*, bds., $1.50................*Schirmer.*
Wollaston, T. V. Lyra Devoniensis. fp. 8°. $1.25. *Macmillan.*
Wolle, P: Hymn tunes; for Church of the United Brethren. obl. 8°. '72. bds., 90c.; — tunes only, bds., 15c. ....*Clauder.*
Wollenweber, L. A. Gemälde a. d. Pennsylvanischen Volksleben. 3d ed. 12°. 50c...*Schäfer.*
Wolliez, *Mme.* —. Edma and Marguerite; tr. from the Fr. 18°. 60c....................*O'Shea.*
Wolseley, *Sir* Garnet J. Soldier's pocket book for public service. 3d ed., rev. and enl. 16°. roan, $1.75 ....*Macmillan.*
Wolstenholme, Jos. Book of mathematical problems on subjects included in Cambridge course. cr. 8°. '67. $3 ....*Macmillan.*
— *See also* Frost, P., *and* Wolstenholme, J.
Woltersdorf, E. G. Kinder-Lieder. 18°. '60. 25c. *Am. Tr.*
— Lieder. 18°. '63. 50c...................*Am. Tr.*
Woltmann, Alfr. Hans Holbein and his time; tr. by F. E. Bunnett. 60 eng. sm. 4°. $10; mor., $15. *Appleton.*
— *See also* Gorling, A., Meyer, E., *and* Woltmann, A.
Woman. Michelet, J. $1.50.............*Carleton.*
Woman, an enigma. McIntosh, M. J. 75c...*Harper.*
Woman: her dignity and sphere. Bates, L. 60c. *Am. Tr.*
Woman: her station providentially appointed. Coxe, M. $1.25.....................*I. N. Whiting.*

Woman and the divine republic. Miller, L. $1.25. (?)*Haas.*
Woman and her master. Smith, J. F. 75c...*Dick & F.*
Woman and the law. Conwell, R. H. 75c. (?)*Russell.*
Woman and the queen. Austin, A. W. 75c. *Williams.*
Woman and the traveller. *See* Stories of the good shepherd.
Woman as God made her. Fulton, J. D. $1.50; $1; 50c....................................*Lee & S.*
Woman as a wife and mother. Chavasse, P. H. $2.50. *Souder.*
Woman her own doctor. McNary, R. B. $1.25. *S. W. Bk. & Pub.*
Woman I adore. Morton, J. M. 15c. ......*French.*
Woman in America. Graves, A. J. 75c....*Harper.*
Woman in American society. Woolson, A. G. $1.50. *Roberts.*
Woman in armor. Hartwell, M. $1.50....*Carleton.*
Woman in battle. *See* Velasquez, *Mme.* L. J.
Woman in the Bible. Williams, A. $1.50..(?)*Martien.*
Woman in black. Sinclair, C. $1.75; $1.50..*Peterson.*
Woman in the case. Turner, B. $1.50....*Carleton.*
Woman in mauve. Phillips, W. 15c........*French.*
Woman in 19th cent. Fuller, M. $1.50 ....*Roberts.*
Woman in purple and scarlet. White, A. $1.50. *So. Bapt.*
Woman in red. 8°. pap., 50c. ....*Peterson.*
Woman in red. *See* Coyne, J. S.
Woman in white. *See* Collins, Wilkie.
Woman's the devil: drama. 16°. pap., 15c...*French.*
Woman, love and marriage. Saunders, F. $1.50. *Carleton.*
Woman man's equal. Webster, T. $1.25. *Cin. Meth. Bk. Conc.*
Woman never vext. Rowley, W. 15c. ......*French.*
Woman of business. Savage, M. W. 75c...*Appleton.*
Woman of fire. Belot, A. 50c.......... *W. F. Gill.*
Woman of honor. Enault, L. 75c.........*Peterson.*
Woman of Samaria. Bennett, W. S. $1.50; $1; — libretto, 12c..........................*Ditson.*
Woman of the world. Cavendish, C. 15c. ..*French.*
Woman on the American frontier. Fowler, W. W. $2.75; $3.50.......................*Scranton.*
Woman (A) sold. Webster, A. $2.....*Macmillan.*
Woman that was a cat. Scribe, E. 15c. ....*French.*
Woman to the rescue. Arthur, T. S. $1.25. *J. M. Stoddart.*
Woman vs. ballot. Fulton, J. D. 15c.......*Lee & S.*
Woman who dared. Sargent, E. $1.50.....*Roberts.*
Woman will be a woman: comedietta. 16°. pap., 15c. *Happy.*
Womanhood. Hooker, I. B. 75c.; 40c.....*Lee & S.*
Woman's defence. Ferrin, M. U. 10c. ....*Mendum.*
Woman's education. Comfort, G. F. *and* A. M. $1. *Durston.*
Woman's experiences in Europe. Wallace, E. D. $1.50 ....*Appleton.*
Woman's friendship. Aguilar, G. $1.....*Appleton.*
Woman's heart. Victor, M. V. F. 25c......*Beadle.*
Woman's kingdom. *See* Craik, D. M.
Woman's life. Carlen, E. F. 75c. ....*Dick & F.*
Woman's love. Dumas, A. 25c...........*Dick & F.*
Woman's love. Smith, J. F. $1.25; 75c. ....*Estes.*
Woman's love. Sue, E. 50c.............*Peterson.*
Woman's love. Wilks, T. E. 15c..........*French.*
Woman's mission and woman's influence. 10th ed. 16°. $1.25.......................*J. E. Potter.*
Woman's pilgrimage to the Holy Land. Griswold, S. M. *$2.50; $2.75....................*Burr.*

Woman's poems. Piatt, S. M. B. $1.50 .... *Osgood.*
Woman's profession as mother and educator. Beecher, C. E. *$1.25 .... *Maclean.*
Woman's ransom. *See* Robinson, F. W.
Woman's record. Hale, S. J. $5–$10 ..... *Harper.*
Woman's temperance crusade. Steele, W. C. 25c. *Nat. Temp.*
Woman's thoughts about women. Craik, D. M. $1.75; $1.50 .... *Peterson.*
Woman's trials. *See* Arthur, T. S.
Woman's vengeance. Payn, J. 50c. .... *Harper.*
Woman's vows and Mason's oaths. Duganne, A. J. H. 15c. .... *De Witt.*
Woman's work in the church. Ludlow, J. M. $2. *Routledge.*
Woman's work in the church. Moore, W. T. 10c. *Chase.*
Woman's worth and worthlessness. Dodge, M. A. $1.50 .... *Harper.*
Woman's wrong. Eiloart, C. J. $1.75; $1.50 .. *Peterson.*
Woman's wrongs. Dodge, M. A. $1.50 ...... *Estes.*
Women; or, chronicles of the late war. Magill, M. T. $1.75 .... *Turnbull.*
Women artists. Ellet, E. F. $1.50 .... *Harper.*
Women before the law. Proffatt, J. $1; $125. *Putnam.*
Women helpers in the church. Welsh, W. $1.50. *Lippincott.*
Women in sacred history. ill. 8°. *$6. — (Imperial ed.) 25 pts. pl. 4°. ea., *50c. .... *Ford.*
Women of the Arabs. Jessup, H. H. $2..... *Dodd.*
Women of the Bible. Adams, C. $1 .. *Meth. Bk. Conc.*
Women of the Bible. Headley, P. C. $1.50 .. *Lee & S.*
Women of the Bible. Martyn, S. T. $3; $5 .. *Am. Tr.*
Women of the century. Hanaford, P. A. *$2.50; $3. *Russell.*
Women of Christianity exemplary for piety and charity. Kavanagh, J. $1 .... *Appleton.*
Women of the covenant. Reed, A. 50c... *Cong. Pub.*
Women of the Gospels. *See* Charles, *Mrs.* E.
Women of Israel. Aguilar, G. 2 v. $2 .. *Appleton.*
Women of Methodism. Stevens, A. $1.50; $2. *Meth. Bk. Conc.*
Women of the south. Forrest, M. $3.50 .. *Univ. Pub.*
Women of the war. Moore, F. $3; $3.50 .. *Scranton.*
Women of worth. *See* Enterprise and adventure lib.
Women's love and life. Schumann, R. $1.50. *Schirmer.*
Women's rights: comedietta. 16°. pap., 15c... *Happy.*
Women's secrets. Capsadell, L. 75c.; 25c... *Authors.*
Women's war on whiskey. Beadle, J. H. 75c.; 50c. *Wilstach.*
Won at last. Reeve, W. 15c......... *Ames; French.*
Won in a canter. 16°. bds., 80c........... *Routledge.*
Won, not wooed. Payn, J. 50c.............. *Harper.*
Wonder. Centlivre, S. 15c................. *French.*
Wonder book. *See* Andersen, H. C.
Wonder book. *See* Hawthorne, Natl.
Wonder case. *See* Newton, R:
Wonder lib. 4 v. 12°. $6 .... *Lothrop.*

Cont.: Earthquakes and volcanoes. — Wonders of the plant world. — Buried cities. — Tombs, temples and monuments of anc. Greece and Rome.

Wonder lib. 5 v. ill. 16°. $3.............. *Nelson.*

Cont.: Nature's wonders. — Wonders of the vegetable world. — Wonders of creation. — Wonders of many lands. — Huc's travels in Tartary, by M. Jones.

Wonder lib. 10 v. 18°. $5.40............ *So. Meth.*

Cont.: Wonders of organic life. — Remarkable delusions. — Remarkable escapes. — Sir Isaac Newton. — Money. — Magic. — Art of printing. — Steam engine. — Mammon, by J. Harris. — Plants and trees of Scripture.

Wonder ser. 4 v. 18°. $3................ *Lothrop.*

Cont.: Wonders of creation. — Wonders of vegetation. — Wonders of nature. — Wonders of many lands.

Wonder stories told for children. *See* Andersen, H. C.
Wonderful adventures among the Modocs. ill. 12°. $1.50 .... *Souder.*
Wonderful adventures among the native tribes of America. 16°. $1.25.............. *Lippincott.*
Wonderful adventures by land and sea of the seven queer travellers who met at an inn. Barnes, J. $1.75 .... *J. E. Potter.*
Wonderful adventures on the ocean. Sleeper, J. S. $1.50 .... *Locke.*
Wonderful animals. [Toy-book.] ill. 8°. $1. (?) *McLoughlin.*
Wonderful bag, and what was in it. 18°. 60c... *Loring.*
Wonderful balloon ascents. Marion, F. $1.25. *Scribner.*
Wonderful bear. *See* New Year lib.
Wonderful cure. *See* Lacy's home plays for ladies.
Wonderful escapes. Bernard, F. $1.25 ... *Scribner.*
Wonderful history. 18°. 15c.; 20c........ *Am. Bapt.*
Wonderful history of the house that Jack built. ill. 4°. pap., 10c.; 15c. .... *J. E. Potter.*
Wonderful lamp. Macleod, A. $1......... *Carter.*
Wonderful lamp; or, light for the darkest path. 18°. 70c. .... *Pres. Bd.*
Wonderful letter. Malan, C. 20c........ *Randolph.*
Wonderful letter-bag. *See* Woodworth, F. C.
Wonderful life. Smith, H. $1.50 .... *Dodd.*
Wonderful life of Ella Cameron. Guyon, G. P. 20c. *Barclay.*
Wonderful machine. *See* My own lib.
Wonderful pocket. Giles, C. $1.......... *New Ch.*
Wonderful Redeemer. 18°. 22c........... *Am. S. S.*
Wonderful stone; or, the curse turned into blessing. 18°. 75c. .... *Pres. Bd.*
Wonderful stories. Banvard, J. 30c.; 40c. *Am. Bapt.*
Wonderful stories of Fuz-Buz, the fly, and Mother Grabem, the spider. ill. 4°. '66. $1. *Claxton; Lippincott.*
Wonderful story of Gentle Hand. Arthur, T. S. $2. *J. M. Stoddart.*
Wonderful tales. *See* Andersen, H. C.
Wonderful woman. Dance, C. 15c......... *French.*
Wonderful woman. Fleming, M. A. $1.75 .. *Carleton.*
Wonderful works; or, the miracles of Christ. ill. 16°. $1 .... *Bost. Am. Tr.*
Wonderful works of Jesus. *See* Clark, M. L.
Wonderland lib. 4 v. ill. 12°. ea., $1.25; $1.50; $2 .... *Lee & S.*

Cont.: Alice's adventures in wonderland. — House on wheels. — Letters everywhere. — Inn of the Guardian Angel.

Wonders and beauties of creation. 12°. '75. $1.50. *Pott.*
Wonders in the air. *See* Books about wonderful and curious things.
Wonders in many lands. ill. 18°. '69. 75c... *Lothrop.* — *See also* Wonder lib.
Wonders near home. *See* Houghton, W.
Wonders of the Arctic world. *See* Sargent, E.
Wonders of art: account of anc. ruins, fortifications, public edifices, etc. 16°. '45. 50c... *W. H. Young.*
Wonders of creation: volcanoes and their phenomena. ill. 18°. '69. 75c..................... *Lothrop.* — *See also* Wonder lib.
Wonders of the deep. DeVere, M. S. $1.50; $2. *Putnam.*
Wonders of European art. Viardot, L. $1.25. *Scribner.*
Wonders of fire and water. *See* Books about wonderful and curious things.
Wonders of geology. Goodrich, S. G. $1 .. *Thompson.*

Wonders of geology. Mantell, G. A. 2 v. ea., $3. *Scribner, W.&A.*

Wonders of glass-making in all ages. Sauzay, A. $1.25 .... *Scribner.*

Wonders of the great deep. Gosse, P. H. *$2; $2.75; $3.50 .... *Quak. City.*

Wonders of insect life. Willet, J. E. $1.75 .. *Am. Bapt.*

Wonders of Italian art. Viardot, L. $1.25 .. *Scribner.*

Wonders of Lourdes. Ségur, L. G. 60c.... *Sadlier.*

Wonders of many lands. *See* Wonder ser.

Wonders of nature. ill. 18°. '69. 75c...... *Lothrop.*

Wonders of nature. Schödler, F. $3.......... *Lea.*

Wonders of organic life; rev. by T. O. Summers. ('58.) 2d ed. 18°. '75. 60c........... *So. Meth.*

Wonders of the physical world. ill. 12°. $1.25 .. *Nelson.*

Wonders of the plant world. ill. 12°. '71. $1.50. *Lothrop; Tibbals.*

Wonders of Providence. demy 4°. $1; bds., 50c. *Scribner, W.&A.*

Wonders of science. *See* Mayhew, H.

Wonders of sculpture. Viardot, L. $1.50 .. *Scribner.*

Wonders of the vegetable world. *See* Wonder lib.

Wonders of vegetation. ill. 18°. '69. 75c... *Lothrop.*

Wonders of vegetation. 18°. 80c.; — in 5 v... *Am. S. S.*
Cont.: Flower, 35c. — Fruit, 40c. — Leaf, 25c. — Seed, 25c. — Various grasses, 40c.

Wonders of water. Tissandier, G. $1.50 .. *Scribner.*

Wonders of the world. ill. 8°. $2.......... *Lee & S.*

Wonders of the world. Rosenberg, C. G. $4; $5. *U. S. Pub.*

Wonders of the Yellowstone. Richardson, J. $1.50. *Scribner.*

Wondrous name. Platt, S. H. 10c. .... *Hope.*

Wondrous strange. Newby, C. J. 50c..... *Peterson.*

Wondrous tale of Alroy. Disraeli, B. 50c. *Appleton.*

Wonliarliarski, W. A. v. Die grosse Dame. 12°. '64. pap., 25c. .... *Steiger.*

Wonneberger, C. Drei Lieder: Festgesänge auf Ostern und Pfingsten. 4°. ea., 25c. .... *Kohler.*

— Sonntags-Schul-Harfe. [Singing book.] 6th ed. 8°. '76. 35c.......... *Pilger.*

Wontus. Runkle, W. M. $1.75 .... *Lippincott.*

Wood, —. Guide to N. Y. City. ill. 12°. $1 .. *Carleton.*

Wood, Alph. American botanist and florist; with analyt. flora. 12°. '70. $2.50 .. *Barnes; Nims.*

— Class book of botany. ('46.) 41st ed., rev. and enl. 2 pts. 12°. $2.50.......... *Barnes.*

— *Same;* with a flora of the U. S. and Canada. 12°. '60. $1.60 .... *Barnes.*

— — *Same.* New ed. 8°. '69. $3.50 .. *Barnes; Nims.*

— Illustrated plant record and guide to analysis. 4°. '76. 75c.......... *Barnes.*

— Leaves and flowers; or, object lessons in botany. ill. 12°. '60. $1.50.......... *Barnes; Nims.*

Wood, Arth. Romantic attachment: comedietta. 16°. pap., 15c.......... *Ames; French.*

Wood, C. A. F. Irish broom maker: farce. 16°. pap., 15c. .... *French.*

Wood, C: H., *and* Long, J. D. Digest of Illinois Supreme Court reports (v. 1–68, 1819–'74). 3d ed., rev. 3 v. roy. 8°. shp., $20 .. *E. B. Myers.*

Wood, De Volson. Backwater in streams as produced by dams. *See* Thurston, R. H., Note on resistance of materials.

— Treatise on bridges. ill. 8°. $3.......... *Wiley.*

— Treatise on resistance of materials, and app. on preservation of timber. 2d ed., rev. 8°. $3 .. *Wiley.*

Wood, E: J. The wedding day in all ages and countries. 12°. $1.25.......... *Harper.*

Wood, *Mrs.* Ellen P. [Novels.] 41 v. 8° .. *Peterson.*
Cont.: Bessie Raue. — Castle's heir; or, Lady Adelaide's oath. — Channings. — Dene Hollow. — Elster's folly. — George Canterbury's will. — Lord Oakburn's daughters; or, the Earl's heirs. — Master of Greylands. — Mildred Arkell. — Oswald Cray. — Red Court Farm. — Roland Yorke. — St. Martin's eve. — Shadow of Ashlydyat. — Squire Trevlyn's heir. — Verner's pride. — Within the maze, *ea.*, $1.75; pap., $1.50. — Edina; or, missing since midnight, $1; pap., 75c. — Mystery; or, Anne Hereford. — Parkwater; or, told in the twilight, *ea.*, pap., 75c. — Haunted tower. — Life's secret. — Lost bank-note. — Lost will. — Orville College, *ea.*, pap., 50c. — Clara Lake's dream. — Cyrilla Maude's first love. — Diamond bracelet. — Five thousand a year. — Foggy night at Offord. — Frances Hildyard. — Light and a dark Christmas. — Marrying beneath your station. — Martyn Ware's temptation. — My cousin Caroline's wedding. — My husband's first love. — Nobleman's wife. — Runaway match. — Self-convicted. — Smuggler's ghost. — William Allair, *ea.*, pap., 25c.

— *Same.* 6 v. 8°. ea., $1.25; pap., 75c. .. *Dick & F.*
Cont.: Barren honor. — Castle Wafer; or, plain gold ring. — East Lynne; or, the earl's daughter. — Heir to Ashley. — Mrs. Halliburton's troubles. — Gervase Castonel; or, the six grey powders, $1.25; pap., 25c.

— Danesbury House. 12°. $1.25.......... *Harper.*

— Out of the deep; or, cast up by the sea. 8°. '75. $1.50; pap., 75c. .... *W. F. Gill.*

Wood, F. Cricket. ill. 48°. 25c.... *Scribner, W.&A.*

Wood, G. Irish doctor: farce. 16°. pap., 15c. *French.*

Wood, G: Gates wide open; or, scenes in another world. 12°. $1.50.......... *Lee & S.*

Wood, G: B. Introductory lectures and addresses. 8°. $3.......... *Lippincott.*

— Practice of medicine. 6th ed., enl. 2 v. 8°. $9; shp., $10.......... *Lippincott.*

— Treatise on practice of medicine. 6th ed. 2 v. 8°. '66. shp., $10.......... *Claxton.*

— Treatise on therapeutics and pharmacology, or materia medica. 3d ed. 2 v. 8°. '67. shp., $10. *Claxton; Lippincott.*

— *and* Bache, Franklin. Dispensatory of the U. S. 13th ed., enl. roy. 8°. shp., $10.... *Lippincott.*

Wood, G: S. Philosophy of creation; by T: Paine through the hand of G: S. Wood. [Spiritism.] ('54.) 6th ed. 12°. '75. 60c.; pap., 35c... *Colby.*

Wood, H. G. Law of nuisances. 8°. '75. shp., $7.50. *J. D. Parsons.*

Wood, H. J. Florence; or, the orphan ward. ill. 16°. 50c. .... *Routledge.*

Wood, H. T. W. Changes in the Eng. lang., 1400–1600. cr. 8°. '71. $1 .... *Macmillan.*

Wood, *Mrs.* H: *See* Wood, *Mrs.* Ellen P.

Wood, Horatio C., *jr.* Fresh-water algæ of No. Am. 4°. '72. pap., $7.50.......... *Smith. Inst.*

— On diagnosis of diseases, etc. *See* Seguin, E. C., Series of Am. clin. lect.

— Phalangeæ of U. S. ill. 8°. '68. $1.50..... *Essex.*

— Thermic fever; or, sunstroke. 12°. $1.25 .. *Lippincott.*

— Toner lecture, 4: fever. 8°. '75. pap., 25c. *Smith. Inst.*

— Treatise on the therapeutics; compr. materia medica and toxicology, with especial ref. to applic. of physiological action of drugs to clinical medicine. 8°. $6; shp., $6.50.......... *Lippincott.*

— Year-book of therapeutics, pharmacy and allied sciences, 1872–3. 2 v. 8°. ea., $2.50 .. *W. Wood.*

Wood, I: Inaugural address before N. Y. Acad. of Med. 8°. '50. pap., 10c. ..... *N. Y. Acad. Med.*

Wood, J. *See* Hildreth, S. P., *and* Wood, J.

Wood, *Mrs.* J. A. A. *See* Lee, Minnie Ma.

Wood, Ja. Iowa justice's form book. 2d ed. 8°. '76. pap., $1.50; leath., $2.......... *Day.*

Wood, *Rev.* Ja. Gospel fountain (The); or, the anxious youth made happy. 18°. 75c. *Pres. Bd.*

— Grace and glory; or, young convert instructed in doctrines of grace: sequel to "Gospel fountain." 18°. 75c. .... *Pres. Bd.*

Wood, J: G: Animal traits and characteristics: 2d ser. of "Sketches and anecdotes of animal life." ill. 16°. $1.25.......... *Routledge.*

— Athletic sports and recreations for boys. ill. 16°. 75c.......... *Routledge.*

Wood, J: G: *continued.*
— — *See also* Boys' treasury of sports and pastimes.
— Bees: their habits, management and treatment. ill. 16°. bds., 50c. ... *Routledge.*
— Bible animals. ('70.) New ed. ill. 8°. '72. $5. *Scribner.*
— *Same;* with articles on evolution by J. M'Cosh; [also] Research and travel in Bible lands by D. March. ill. 8°. *$4.75; leath., $5.50; mor., $6.75 ... *Bradley & G.*
— Boy's own book of natural history. ill. 16°. $1.25. *Routledge.*
— Calendar of the months; or, young naturalist abroad. ill. 16°. '73. $1.25 ... *Routledge.*
— Common moths of Eng. ill. 16°. $1.25 .. *Routledge.*
— Common objects of the country. ill. 16°. $1.25; bds., 50c. ... *Routledge.*
— Common objects of the microscope. ill. 16°. $1.25; bds., 50c. ... *Routledge.*
— Common objects of the seashore; incl. hints for an aquarium. ill. 16°. $1.25; bds., 50c... *Routledge.*
— Croquet. ill. 48°. 25c. ... *Scribner, W. & A.*
— Fresh and salt water aquarium. ill. 16°. $1.25; bds., 50c. ... *Routledge.*
— Homes without hands: habitations of animals. ill. 8°. $4.50; shp., $5; hf. cf., $6.75 ... *Harper.*
— Illustrated natural hist. from designs by Weir, Wolf, Harvey, etc. 3 v. ill. roy. 8°. $21; hf. cf., $28.50; cf., $40; mor., $42.50 ... *Routledge.*
Cont.: Mammalia. — Birds. — Reptiles, fishes, insects, etc.
— Illustrated natural history of man: account of manners and customs of uncivilized races of men; ill. by the Dalziel brothers. 2 v. roy. 8°. $14; hf. cf., $19; cf., $27 ... *Routledge.*
— — *See also below* Uncivilized races.
— Insects at home: account of all insects which are useful or destructive. ill. 8°. '73. *4.75; leath., $5.50; hf. mor., $6.75 ... *Rutter.*
— *Same.* ill. 8°. '72. $5 ... *Scribner.*
— Man and beast, here and hereafter; ill. by original anecdotes. 8°. $1.50. ... *Harper.*
— *Same.* 12°. '75. $3; in 2 v., $5 ... *Routledge.*
— Modern playmate: games, sports and diversions for boys of all ages. ill. sq. cr. 8°. $3 .. *Scribner, W. & A.*
— *Same.* ill. cr. 8°. $5 ... *Lippincott.*
— My feathered friends. ill. 16°. $1.25 ... *Routledge.*
— Natural history. ill. 12°. $1.50 ... *Harper.*
— *Same.* ill. cr. 8°. $2; hf. cf., $3.50 ... *Routledge.*
— Natural history picture-books. 3 v. ill. fp. 4°. ea., $2; in 1 v., $6 ... *Routledge.*
Cont.: Birds. — Mammalia. — Reptiles, fishes and insects.
Note. The 1 v. ed. bears the title "Popular ill. natural hist."
— New illustrated natural hist.; with ill. from designs by Wolf, Zwecker, Weir, etc. 8°. '73. $7; hf. cf., $10; cf., $15 ... *Routledge.*
— Our domestic pets. ill. 16°. $1.25 ... *Routledge.*
— Popular illustrated natural hist. *See above* Natural hist. picture-books.
— Skating and sliding. roy. 32°. bds., 25c... *Routledge.*
— Sketches and anecdotes of animal life. ill. 12°. $1.25. *Routledge.*
— Swimming. ill. 48°. 25c. ... *Scribner, W. & A.*
— Trespassers; showing how inhabitants of earth, air and water are enabled to trespass on domains not their own. ill. 8°. $3 ... *Nelson.*
— Uncivilized races; or, nat. hist. of man. ill. roy. 8°. *$6; leath., $7; hf. mor., $8; mor., $10; — in 2 v., ea., *$3.75; leath., $4.50; hf. mor., $5; mor., $6 ... *Am. Pub.*
— *Same.* ill. roy. 8°. *$6.50; leath., $7.50; hf. mor., $8.50; mor., $10.50; — in 2 v., ea., *$4.25; leath., $4.75; hf. mor., $5.50; mor., $6.50 .. *Burr.*
— — *See also above* Illustrated nat. hist. of man.
— *See also* Athletic sports and manly exercises; — Walsh, J. H., *and* Wood, J. G.
— *and* White, Gilb., *and* Williams, C: Natural hist. youth's ill. lib. 6 v. ill. 16°. $7.50 ... *Routledge.*
Cont.: Dogs and their ways, by Williams. — My feathered friends, by Wood. — Natural hist. of Selborne, by White. — Anecdotes of animal life, by Wood. — Traits and stories of animal life, by Wood. — Boy's own book of nat. hist., by Wood.

Wood, Jla. A. Close communion. 8°. pap., 10c. *Brumbaugh.*
Wood, M. Methodism and the centennial of Am. independence. 12°. '76. $1.75 .. *Meth. Bk. Conc.*
Wood, *Miss* M. F. Harrie Lee; or, the tempter and the tempted. ('63.) New ed. ill. 18°. '75. $1; 65c. ... *Hoyt.*
Wood, Ol. E. West Point scrap book: legends, stories, songs, etc. 2d ed. ill. 8°. '74. $5 .. *Van Nostrand.*
Wood, *Mrs.* R. H. Sunday-school olio: dialogues, etc. 16°. 25c. ... *Meth. Bk. Conc.*
Wood, Shakspere. The new Cvriasvm Urbis: guide to anc. and modern Rome. 12°. '75. $2 ... *Cook.*
Wood, W. S. ["Mat. Merchant."] How Bennie did it. ill. 16°. $1.50 ... *Hoyt, F. & D.*
Wood, W: Manual of physical exercises. ill. 12°. $1.50 ... *Harper.*
Wood, W: Maxwell. Fankwei; or, the "San Jacinto" in the seas of India, China and Japan. 12°. $1.50 ... *Harper.*
Wood carvers; or, a visit to the sea shore. 18°. 45c. *Am. S. S.*
— *Same.* 18°. 60c. ... *Cong. Pub.*
— *See also* Books for children's hour.
Wood violet ser. 4 v. 16°. $3 ... *Nelson.*
Cont.: After the holidays, by Miss Ellis. — Ferryman's family, by E. Leslie. — Young missionaries, by Mrs. Seamer. — Edith Hinton, by Em.
Woodard, Luke. The morning star: treatise on work of Christ. 12°. '75. $1.75; leath., $2.25. *Friends Pub. H.*
Woodbine ser. *See* Baker, *Mrs.* H. N. W.
Woodbridge, S. M. Faith: its true position in life of man. 12°. 25c. ... *N. Y. Ref. Ch. Bd.*
Woodbridge, *Miss* Sa. Mamma's talks with Charlie. ('64.) New ed. ill. 18°. '74. 50c. ... *Hoyt.*
Woodbridge, W: C. Modern school geog. and atlas. 2 v.: text, 8°; atlas, f°. *net*, $1.50 ... *Hamersley.*
— *and* Willard, Emma. Universal geog. and atlas. 2 v. in 1. 12°. *net*, $2.75 ... *Hamersley.*
Woodburn Grange. Howitt, W. $1.75; $1.50. *Peterson.*
Woodbury, A: Maj. Gen. A. E. Burnside and the 9th Army Corps: their campaigns during the [civil] war. por. and maps. roy. 8°. '67. $3 .. *Rider.*
— Narrative of campaign of 1st Rhode Island Reg't in 1861. map and por. 12°. '62. $1.25 ... *Rider.*
— Second Rhode Island Reg't: its military operations during the [civil] war. 12°. '75. $2.50. *Freeman; Rider.*
Woodbury, C: L. *See* United States, Circuit Court reports.
Woodbury, Dan. Phineas. Treatise on elements of stability in well proportioned arch. *See* United States, *Corps of Eng.*
Woodbury, E. K. *See* Woodbury, W. H. *and* E. K.
Woodbury, I: B. Anthem dulcimer; or, New York collection of sacred music. obl. 8°. bds., $1.34. *Huntington.*
— Anthem thanksgiving. obl. 8°. bds., $1.50. *Huntington.*
— Columbian glee book. 8°. hf. bd., $1.50 .. *Thompson.*
— Cythara (The). obl. 8°. bds., $1.50 .. *Huntington.*
— Elements of musical composition and thorough bass; with rules for arranging for full orchestra. 12°. bds., 75c. ... *Ditson.*
— *Same.* 16°. 60c.; 75c. ... *Gordon.*
— Liber musicus. obl. 8°. bds., $1.50 ... *Huntington.*
— Melodeon and seraphine instruction book; with thorough bass instruc. 8°. '50. pap., 50c... *Ditson.*
— New lute of Zion. obl. 8°. bds., $1.50 .. *Huntington.*
— Self instructor for flute. obl. 8°. '53. pap., 50c. *Ditson.*
— Singing-school and music teacher's companion. obl. 8°. bds., 80c. ... *Huntington.*
— Song crown: songs, glees, quartets, etc. obl. 8°. bds., $2 ... *Huntington.*
— Violin instructor. obl. 8°. '53. pap., 50c... *Ditson.*

Woodbury, I: B., *continued.*
— *See also* Benjamin, L. A., *and* Woodbury, I. B.
— *and* Johnson, A. N. New England and Bay State glee book. obl. 8°. 75c. . . . . *Gordon.*
Woodbury, Levi. *See* New Hampshire, Law reports.
Woodbury, W. H. Complete course with German. 12°. '73. $2. — Key, $1 . . . . *Ivison.*
— Eclectic Germ. reader. 12°. '52. $1.25 . . . . *Ivison.*
— Elementary Germ. reader. 12°. '53. $1.25 . . *Ivison.*
— German-Eng. and Eng.-Germ. reader; for Germ. and Eng. S.-schools, etc. 12°. '52. bds., 40c. . . *Ivison.*
— Neue Methode zur Erlernung der engl. Sprache, umgearb. u. verb. nach Woodbury's "Method with German." 12°. '60. $1.40 . . . . *Ivison.*
— New method of learning the Germ. lang. 12°. '55. $1.88. — Key, $1 . . . . *Ivison.*
— Shorter course with the Germ. lang. 12°. '52. $1.25. — Key, $1 . . . . *Ivison.*
— *and* E. K. Easy lessons in German; for beginners. 12°. '75. $1.25 . . . . *Ivison.*
Woodbury Farm. *See* Variety lib.
Woodcliff. McKeever, H. B. $1.50 . . . . *J. A. Moore.*
Woodcliff children. McKeever, H. B. $1 . . *J. A. Moore.*
Woodcock's little game. Morton, J. M. 15c. *De Witt; French.*
Woodcraft. Simms, W. G. $1.75; 75c. . . *Widdleton.*
Woodcutter and exiles. Macduff, J. R. 75c. . . *Carter.*
Woodcutter of Gutech. *See* Laurel ser.
Woodcutter of Lebanon. 18°. 50c. . . . . *Am. S. S.*
Woodd, Basil. Memoirs of J. L. Benn. *See* Newton, J.
Wooden spoon. *See* My own lib.
Woodford, Ja. Russell. Christian sanctity. fp. 8°. '63. $1 . . . . *Macmillan.*
Woodford, Stewart L. *See* Ewing, T., *and* Woodford, S. L.
Woodland cottage, and other tales. 18°. '72. 50c. *Cunningham.*
Woodland lays. Hale, C. L. $2 . . . . *Lippincott.*
Woodland lib. 5 v. ill. 16°. $3.75 . . . . *Nelson.*
Cont.: Things in the forest, by M. and E. Kirby. — Little Lily's travels. — Truth is always best, by M. and E. Kirby. — Frank Martin. — Adventures of Mark Willis, by Mrs. Cupples.
Woodlawn ser. *See* Baker, *Mrs.* H. N. W.
Woodleigh stories. Adams, H. C. $1.75. *Scribner, W. & A.*
Woodman, J. S. Chandler drawing-book. 12°. '72. hf. bd., $1 . . . . *Ginn.*
Woodman, Jona. C. Musical casket: vocal music for soprano and alto voices. obl. 12°. '58. bds., $1. *Ditson.*
Woodman. *See* James, G. P. R.
Woodman's hut. Arnold, W. H. 15c. . . . . . . *French.*
Woodman's Nannette. Baker, S. S. 40c. . . . *Am. Tr.*
Woodman's spell. Stirling, E. 15c. . . . . *French.*
Woodrangers. Reid, M. $1.50 . . . . *Carleton.*
Woodruff, C: S. Legalized prostitution; or, marriage as it is and marriage as it should be, philos. considered. ('62.) 3d ed. 12°. '73. $1 . . . . *Colby.*
Woodruff Hiram. Trotting horse of Am.: how to train and drive him; ed. by C. J. Foster, with introd. by G. Wilkes, and biog. sketch by the editor. ('68.) 18th ed., rev. por. 12°. '74. $2.50 . . . . *Porter.*
Woodruff, J. L. M. ["W. M. L. Jay."] Holden with the cords. 12°. '74. $2 . . . . *Dutton.*
— My winter in Cuba. 12°. '70. $1.50 . . . . . . *Dutton.*
— Shiloh; or, without and within. 12°. '71. $2 . . *Dutton.*
Woodruff, Minnie. Aunt Sarah's stories. 18°. 30c. *Pres. Bd.*
Woodruff. Veitch, A. 90c. . . . . *Am. Bapt.*
Woodruff stories. *See* Goulding, F. R.
Woods, Edg. Golden apples. 16°. $1 . . . . *Carter.*
Woods, Ht. F. Blue book stories. ill. 16°. 70c. *Bost. Am. Tr.*
Woods, Jos. Tourists' flora: descript. catalogue of flowering plants and ferns of British islands, France, Germany, Switzerland, Italy and the Ital. islands. 8°. (Lond.) $9 . . . . *Putnam.*
Woods, *Mrs.* Kate T. The Radical Club. 16°. pap., 25c. . . . . *W. F. Gill.*
Woods, W: B. *See* United States, Circuit Court reports.
Woods and by-ways of New England. Flagg, W. $4; $7 . . . . *Osgood.*
Woods and woodlands: lessons in study of nature and natural hist. ill. 12°. $1 . . . . *Nelson.*
Woodside and seaside, ill. by pen and pencil: eng. from drawings by Birket Foster, Hows and others. 4°. $3; mor., $7 . . . . *Appleton.*
Woodside lib. 6 v. 18°. $5.50 . . . . (?) *Martien.*
Compr.: No lie thrives. — Frank and Rufus. — New York Ned. — Didley Dumps, the newsboy. — Little by little. — Power of gold.
Woodstock. *See* Scott, *Sir* Wa.
Woodville, Jennie (*pseud.*) *See* Stabler, J. L.
Woodville stories. *See* Adams, W: T.
Woodward, Bernard Bolinbroke. *See* Bartlett, W. H., *and* Woodward, B. B.
— *and* Cates, W. L. R. Encyclopedia of chronology, historical and biographical. cr. 8°. $15; shp., $18; hf. cf., $21 . . . . *Lee & S.*
Woodward, E. M. Our campaigns; or, the marches, battles, etc., of our regiment; with sketch of army of the Potomac. 12°. $1.75 . . . . *J. E. Potter.*
Woodward, G: E. Cottages and farm houses: designs, plans, etc. 12°. $1.50 . . . . *Woodward.*
— Country homes: designs, plans, etc. 12°. $1.50. *Woodward.*
— Graperies and horticultural buildings: designs, plans, etc. 12°. $1.50 . . . . *Woodward.*
— National architect: one thousand plans, designs, etc. 4°. $12 . . . . *Woodward.*
— Suburban and country houses: designs, plans, etc. 12°. $1.50 . . . . *Woodward.*
Woodward, J. A. Bouquet: farce. 16°. pap., 15c. *Lee & S.*
Woodward, Jos. Janvier. Hospital steward's manual. 12°. '62. $1.25 . . . . *Claxton.*
— Medical and surgical hist. of war of rebellion. *See* United States, *Surgeon-General's Office.*
— Outlines of chief camp diseases of U. S. armies as observed during the [civil] war. 8°. '63. $2.50. *Claxton; Lippincott.*
— Report on cholera and yellow fever in U. S. army; — Report on epidemic cholera in U. S. army. *See* United States, *Surgeon-General's Office.*
— Toner lecture, 1: cancerous tumors. 8°. '73. pap., 25c. . . . . *Smith Inst.*
Woodworth, Fs. C. Uncle Frank's boys' and girls' lib. ('51.) New ed. 6 v. ill. 16°. '69. $4.50. *Claxton.*
Cont.: Peddler boy. — Poor organ grinder. — Wonderful letter bag. — Diving bell. — Mike Marble. — Our Sue, her motto and its uses.
Woodworth, J: Reminiscences of Troy [N. Y.], 1790–1807. 2d ed., with notes by J. Munsell. map. sq. 8°. '60. $2 . . . . *Munsell.*
Woodworth, S: Forest rose: drama. 16°. pap., 15c. *French.*
Wooed and married. Carey, R. N. $1.75 . . *Lippincott.*
Wooing in jest: comedietta. 16°. pap., 15c. . . *French.*
Wooing o't. Hector, A. F. $1.25 . . . . *Holt.*
Wooing one's wife. Morton, J. M. 15c. . . . . *French.*
Wooing under difficulties. Douglass, J. T. 15c. *Ames.*
Wool gathering. Dodge, M. A. $1.50 . . . . *Estes.*
Woolen and cotton mills reference book. 4°. '68. $50. *J. A. Murphy.*

Wooler, J. P. [Plays.] 5 v. 16°. ea., pap., 15c. *De Witt.*

Cont.: Founded on facts: farce. — Locked in: comedietta. — Marriage at any price: farce. — Orange blossoms: comedietta. — Sisterly service: comedietta.

— *Same.* 19 v. 16°. ea., pap., 15c. .... *French.*

Cont.: Did I dream it? farce. — Founded on facts: farce. — Haunted mill: operetta. — Hunt for a husband: farce. — I'll write to the "Times": farce. — Keep your temper: farce. — Laurence's love suit: comedietta. — Love in livery: farce. — Maid of honour: comedy. — Man without a head: farce. — Marriage at any price: farce. — Model husband: farce. — Old Phil's birthday. — Orange blossoms: comedietta. — Ring and the keeper: operetta.— Sisterly service: comedietta.— Twice-told tale: farce. — Wilful ward: comedietta. — Winning hazard: comedietta.

— Did I dream it? farce. 16°. pap., 15c. ...... *Ames.*

Woolf, B. E. Don't forget your opera glasses: farce. 16°. pap., 15c. .... *French.*

— That nose: farce. 16°. pap., 15c. .... *French.*

Woollett, W: M. Villas and cottages; or, homes for all: plans, views, etc. obl. 8°. '76. $3 .. *Bicknell.*

Woolley, J: Lectures delivered in Australia. cr. 8°. '63. $2 .... *Macmillan.*

Woolly bear. *See* Baker, *Mrs.* H. N. W.

Woolman, J: Journal of [his] life, Gospel labours and Christian experiences. 12°. *net*, shp., $1. *Friends Bk. Assoc.*

— *Same;* with introd. by J. G. Whittier. 16°. '71. $1.50; hf. cf., $3; mor., $4 .... *Osgood.*

— Life. 12°. 75c. .... *Friends Bk. St.*

Woolner, T: My beautiful lady. 3d ed. fp. 8°. $1.50. *Macmillan.*

Woolrych, Hum. W. Treatise on the law of waters. 8°. '53. $3 .... *T. & J. W. Johnson.*

— — *See also* Law lib.

Woolsey, E. J. Specimens of fancy turning executed on hand or foot lathe; by an amateur. photos. 4°. '69. $3 .... *Baird.*

Woolsey, Elij. The supernumerary: lights and shadows of itinerancy. 18°. '44. 50c. .... *Meth. Bk. Conc.*

Woolsey, *Miss* Sa. C. ["Su. Coolidge."] Mischief's Thanksgiving, and other stories. ill. sq. 16°. '74. $1.50 .... *Roberts.*

— New Year's bargain. ill. sq. 16°. '71. $1.50 .. *Roberts.*

— Nine little goslings. ill. 16°. '75. $1.50 ... *Roberts.*

— What Katy did. ill. sq. 16°. '72. $1.50 .... *Roberts.*

— What Katy did at school. ill. sq. 16°. '73. $1.50. *Roberts.*

Woolsey, Thdr. D. Essay on divorce and divorce legislation, with special ref. to U. S. 12°. '69. $1.75 .... *Scribner.*

— Exemption of private property upon the sea from capture; read before the Am. Soc. Sci. Assoc., May 19, 1874. 8°. '74. pap., 15c. .... *Williams.*

— Helpful thoughts for young men. 12°. '74. $1.25. *Lothrop.*

— Introduction to study of international law. ('71.) New ed. cr. 8°. '76. $2.50 .... *Scribner.*

— Relations of honor to political life: address. 8°. 25c. *Judd & W.*

— Religion of the present and of the future: sermons preached chiefly at Yale Coll. ('71.) New ed. cr. 8°. '72. $2; — large pap., $3 ...... *Scribner.*

Woolson, Abba Goold. Dress reform: dress as it affects health of women. ill. 16°. '74. $1.50. *Roberts.*

— Woman in Am. society. 16°. '73. $1.50 .. *Roberts.*

Woolson, Constance F. Castle Nowhere: lake-country sketches. 12°. '75. $2 .... *Osgood.*

Woolworth, Ja. M. *See* Nebraska, Sup. Court reports; — United States, Circuit Court reports.

Worboise, Emma Jane. [Tales.] 4 v. 12°. ea., $1.75. *Routledge.*

Cont.: Campion Court: tale of days of the ejectment, 200 years ago. — Evelyn's story; or, labor and wait. — Lillingstones of Lillingstone. — Lottie Lonsdale; or, chain and its links.

— The Lillingstones of Lillingstone. ill. 16°. '73. $1.25 .... *Dodd.*

Worcester, H: A. Sermons on the Lord's prayer; [with] three sermons on other subjects. 12°. $1.25 .... *Lippincott.*

Worcester, J: Correspondences of the Bible: the animals. 16°. '75. $1.50 ...... *Lockwood, B. & Co.*

— Year's (A) lessons from the Psalms. 18°. '69. 40c. *H. H. Carter.*

Worcester, Jos. E. Comprehensive dictionary of the Eng. lang. ('60.) New ed., rev. ill. 12°. hf. roan, $1.80 .... *Ware.*

— Comprehensive spelling-book. 12°. bds., 31c. .. *Ware.*

— Dictionary of the Eng. lang. roy. 4°. '60. shp., $10; $10.50; hf. mor., $12; mor., $16; $16.33 .. *Ware.*

— Elementary dict. of the Eng. lang. ill. 12°. '60. hf. roan, $1.15 .... *Ware.*

— Elements of hist., anc. and modern.; incl. account of late rebellion. 12°. $1.88 .... *Thompson.*

— Historical atlas: charts of history, mythology, chronology, biography, etc. f°. $2.50 .. *Thompson.*

— Pocket dictionary of the English language; comp. from 4° and school eds. by L. J. Campbell. 32°. '72. 75c. .... *Ware.*

— Primary dict. of the Eng. lang. ('60.) New ed., rev. ill. 18°. '71. hf. roan, 62c. .... *Ware.*

— Primary spelling-book. ill. 16°. bds., 23c. .. *Ware.*

— Pronouncing, explanatory and synonymous dict. of the Eng. lang. 8°. '55. hf. roan, $2.25 .. *Ware.*

— Pronouncing spelling-book. 12°. bds., 35c. .. *Ware.*

— Universal and crit. dict. of the Eng. lang.; [with] Walker's "Key to the pronunciation of classical and Scripture proper names." ('46.) New ed. roy. 8°. '60. shp., $4.37 .... *Ware.*

Worcester, S. T. American spelling-book. 18°. 15c. *Dennet.*

Worcester, T. Illustrations of Scripture; for children of the New Church. 12°. 50c. .... *New Ch.*

Word and the teacher. P., E. H. 75c. .... *Willard.*

Word for the Sabbath. Smith, U. 40c. .. *Sev. Day Adv.*

Word in season. *See* Bright gems for boys and girls; — Little boys' lib.

Word in season. *See* Sargent, L. M.

Word in season; or, the two travellers. 18°. '62. 18c. *Am. S. S.*

Word of God opened. Peirce, B. K. $1.25. *Meth. Bk. Conc.*

Word of life. 18°. '64. 75c. — 16°. $1 .... *Am. S. S.*

Word of life. Brown, C. J. $1.50 .... *Carter.*

Word of the Lord: all the books of the Word. 4°. '69. $7 .... *H. H. Carter.*

Word of promise. Bonar, H. $1 ...... *Bost. Am. Tr.*

Word picture fable book; or, old Æsop in a new dress. ill. roy. 4°. $1.50 .... *Nelson.*

Word pictures. *See* M., E. B.

Word pictures. Strohm, G. $2 .... *Lothrop.*

Word ser. *See* Warner, Su. *and* A. B.

Word to the anxious; or, the soul and its difficulties. 18°. pap., 10c. .... *Am. S. S.*

Word to parents. Bulkeley, H. W. 35c. ... *Pres. Bd.*

Word to the weary. Plumer, W. S. 40c.; 60c. *Randolph.*

Word unveiled. Whitfield, F. 50c. .... *Leighton.*

Words: their use and abuse. Mathews, W. $2; $2.50. *Griggs.*

Words and acts of the Apostles. Faunce, D. W. 15c. *Graves.*

Words and deeds. *See* Biscoe, *Miss* E. L.

Words and mind of Jesus. *See* Macduff, J: R.

Words and places. Taylor, I. $2 ...... *Macmillan.*

Words and their uses. White, R. G. $2 .... *Sheldon.*

Words and works of Jesus. Faunce, D. W. 15c.. *Graves.*

Words for the hour. Howe, J. W. $1 .... * *Osgood.*

Words for the little ones; or, simple lessons on Gospel truths. 18°. 60c. .... *Am. S. S.*

Words for the wise. *See* Arthur, T. S.
Words from the cross as applied to our own death-beds. Nugee, G. $1 .... *Pott.*
Words from the Gospels. Vaughan, C. J. $1.25. *Macmillan.*
Words from the poets; sel. by ed. of "Rays of sun-light." 18°. '70. 50c. .... *Macmillan.*
Words in season. *See* Browning, H. B.
Words in season; for inquirers and the inquiry meeting. sq. 18°. '76. 65c.; pap., 40c. .. *Randolph.*
Words in season for young disciples: daily text book. 32°. 75c. .... *Nelson.*
Words of the angels. Stier, R. $1.25 ... *Routledge.*
Words of the Apostles. *See* Stier, R.
Words of cheer ser. *See* Arthur, T. S.
Words of comfort. Buckner, H. F. 50c.... *Sheldon.*
Words of comfort. Smith, J. 50c.; 75c..... *Am. Tr.*
Words of comfort for days of trial. L., H. L. 90c. *Nelson.*
Words of comfort for doubting hearts. Nevin, A. 50c. *Randolph.*
Words of comfort to bereaved parents. *See* Logan, W:
Words of a friend on the foundation of a religious life. Miles, H. A. $1.25.......... *Lockwood, B. & Co.*
Words of hope. Means, C. A. $2; $3; $4.50 .. *Lee & S.*
Words of Jesus. *See* Macduff, J: R.
Words of Jesus. *See* Stier, R.
Words of peace. Keese, J. 25c.; 40c.; $1 .. *Lothrop.*
Words of the risen Saviour. *See* Stier, R.
Words of truth and love. Plumer, W. S. 55c. *Pres. Bd.*
Words of Wellington. 16°. $1.25 ... *Scribner, W. & A.*
Words of wisdom ill. and applied: sequel to "Little words." 18°. 75c. .... *Pres. Bd.*
Words of the wise; for every day in the year. 24°. '51. 35c. .... *Meth. Bk. Conc.*
Words that shook the world. Adams, C. $1.25. *Meth. Bk. Conc.*
Words to the winners of souls. *See* Bonar, H.
Wordsworth, Cp. Catechesis; or, Christian instruction preparatory to confirmation and first communion. 16°. '69. 50c. .... *Pott.*
— Elements of instruction conc. the church; abridg. from "Theophilus Americanus;" ed. by H. D. Evans. 12°. $1.25 .... *McCauley.*
— Greece, pictorial, descriptive and historical; with hist. of the characteristics of Greek art by G: Scharf. 5th ed. ill. roy. 8°. (Lond.) $9; cf., $17.50 .... *Little, B. & Co.*
— Lectures on the Apocalypse. *See* Hulsean lectures.
— Lectures on inspiration and canon of the Old and New Test. 8°. $2 .... *McCauley.*
— *Same.* 16°. $1 .... *Pott.*
— New Testament in the orig. Greek; with introds. and notes. 2 v. imp. 8°. $25 .... *Scribner, W. & A.*
— Old Testament in the authorized version; with introds., notes and index. 6 v. roy. 8°. $45. *Scribner, W. & A.*
— Theophilus Americanus; or, instructions conc. the church and the Am. branch of it; ed. by H. D. Evans. 12°. $2 .... *McCauley.*
Wordsworth, Dor. Recollections of a tour made in Scotland in 1803, with W: Wordsworth and S: T. Coleridge; ed. by J. C. Shairp. 12°. '74. $2.50. *Putnam.*
Wordsworth, W: Poetical works. 12°. $1.50 .. *Locke.*
— *Same.* 16°. $1.50; mor., $3.75 .... *Appleton.*
— *Same.* (Blue and gold ed.) 18°. $1.25 .. *Nichols & H.*
— *Same.* (Cabinet ed.) 16°. $1.50 ...... *Nichols & H.*
— *Same.* (Chandos classics.) cr. 8°. $1; pap., 75c. *Scribner, W. & A.*
— *Same.* (Chandos poets.) ill. cr. 8°. $3.75; cf., $7.50; mor., $8 .... *Scribner, W. & A.*
— *Same.* (Dick's ed.) ill. 8°. (Lond.) 50c.; pap., 25c. .... *Am. News.*

Wordsworth, W: *continued.*
— *Same.* (Presentation ed.) 16°. $1.75; $3; mor., $3.50 .... *Routledge.*
— *Same.* (Scribner's pop. poets.) ill. 12°. $1.50. *Scribner, W. & A.*
— *Same;* ill. by Foster and Gilbert. 4°. $9; mor., $12 .... *Routledge.*
— *Same;* with memoir. 7 v. por. 18°. $7 .. *Osgood.*
— *Same;* with memoir. (Cabinet ed.) ill. 16°. $1.50; hf. cf., $3 .... *Lippincott.*
— *Same;* with biog. (Household ser.) ill. 16°. $1.50; mor., $3 .... *Lee & S.*
— *Same;* ed. by H. Reed. imp. 8°. '51. mor., $10. *Porter.*
— *Same;* ed. by R. A. Willmott, with biog., etc. (British poets.) ill. 12°. $2.25; hf. cf., $3.50; mor., $5 .... *Routledge.*
— — *See also* Hemans, *Mrs.* F. D., Poems.
— Pastoral poems. ill. 12°. '75. $1.25 ..... *Putnam.*
— Poems for the young. ill. sq. 8°. '74. $2. — sq. 16°. 75c. .... *Routledge.*
— *See also* Hudson, H. N., Pamphlet sections.
Work. Alcott, L. M. $1.75 .... *Roberts.*
Work; or, plenty to do, and how to do it. Brewster, M. M. $1 .... *Randolph.*
Work and conflict. Kennedy, J. $1.25 .... *Pres. Bd.*
Work and no work. *See* Aunt Hattie's stories.
Work and play. 18°. 35c.; 40c. .... *Dutton.*
Work and play. Bushnell, H. $2 .... *Scribner.*
Work and reward. Holt, M. A. 50c. .... *Nat. Temp.*
Work and wages. *See* Howitt, Ma.
Work and wages. Lyman, M. B. $1.25 .. *Cong. Pub.*
Work and win. Adams, W. T. $1.25 .... *Lee & S.*
Work for all; or, Patty Grumbler, and other tales. 16°. '70. $1.25 .... *Dutton.*
Work for all and ways of working. Bush, C. P. 50c. *Pres. Bd.*
Work in the vineyard. Burr, E. F. $2 ..... *Crowell.*
Work of Christ. Davies, J. L. $1.75 .... *Macmillan.*
Work of God in Great Britain. Clark, R. W. $1.50. *Harper.*
Work of preaching Christ. *See* McIlvaine, C. P.
Work, play and profit. Hyde, A. M. $1.25 .. *Lippincott.*
Work to do. Cragin, M. A. $1.25 .... *Cong. Pub.*
Workday Christianity. Clark, A. $1.50 .... *Claxton.*
Workhouse boy. 18°. 60c. .... *Cong. Pub.*
— *See also* River-bank stories.
Working and waiting. Brock, C. 90c. .. (?) *Martien.*
Working and winning. Hedges, M. J. 90c. .. *Am. Tr.*
Working and winning. Thayer, W. M. $1.25 .. *Hoyt.*
Working boy's Sunday improved. 16°. 90c. — 18°. 60c. .... *Am. S. S.*
Working church. 18°. pap., 10c. .... *Pres. Bd.*
Working for God. Morse, F. $1.25 ..... *Macmillan.*
Working for Jesus. *See* Aunt Charity's legacy.
Working for Jesus. Dickson, I. A. R. 25c. .. *Am. Tr.*
Working for Jesus. *See* Kennedy, *Mrs.* M. G.
Working for mama; — for papa. *See* Cousin Belle.
Working man and his friends; or, the story of Archie Tyndal and James Collins. 16°. $1.10 .. *Am. S. S.*
Working man's Sabbath, and how to spend it. 18°. 30c.; pap., 10c. .... *Am. S. S.*
Working to win. *See* Symington, M.
Workingmen and their employers. Gladden, W. $1.75 .... *Lockwood, B. & Co.*
Workingmen's homes. Hale, E. E. $1.25; 75c. *Osgood.*
Works of creation illustrated. ill. sq. 16°. $1.25. *Pres. Bd.*
Workshop receipts. Spon, E. $2 .... *Spon.*
Workwoman's day. 18°. 30c. ...... *U. P. Bd. of Pub.*
— *Same.* 18°. 40c. .... *Am. S. S.*

World (The). *See* Chalmers, A., British essayists.
World and its influences. Engles, W. M. 50c. *Pres. Bd.*
World and its inhabitants. Goodrich, S. G. $1. *Thompson.*
World and stage: comedy. 16°. pap., 15c. . *French.*
World at home. Kirby, M. *and* E. $3 . . . . *Nelson.*
World before the deluge. *See* Figuier, L.
World dictionary: pronounc. dict. of the Eng. lang. ill. 8°. $2; shp., $2.75 . . . . *WorldPub.*
World editions of the poets. 10 v. ill. 8°. ea., $2; roxb., $2.25; shp., $2.75 . . . . *WorldPub.*

Cont.: Burns. — Byron. — Cowper. — Milton. — Moore. — Pope. — Shakespeare. — Scott. — May's Female poets of America. — Bethune's British female poets.

— *Same.* 12 v. ill. 12°. ea., $1.50 . . . . . . *WorldPub.*

Cont.: Byron. — Moore. — Tupper. — Cowper. — Cheever's Poets of America. — Hemans. — Pope. — Shakspeare. — Milton. — Burns. — Scott's Lady of the lake. — Moore's Lalla Rookh.

— *See also* Cabinet ser.; — Pocket ser.
World essays. Reed, W. B. $1.50 . . . . *Hale.*
World famous women. Goodrich, F. B. $6; $9 . . *Rutter.*
World in a pocket book. Crump, W. H. $1.75. *J.E. Potter.*
World noted women; or, types of womanly attributes of all lands and ages. por. imp. 8°. $15. — (chp. ed.) 8°. $5; mor., $6; $7 . . . . *Appleton.*
World of anecdote lib. *See* Hood, E. P.
World of fashion. Oxenford, J. 15c. . . . . *French.*
World of mind. Taylor, I. $1.50 . . . . *Harper.*
World of the sea. Tandon, M. $5 . . . . *Cassell.*
World of waters. *See* Osborne, F.
World of wit and humor. *See* Fenn, G. M.
World of wonders: record of things wonderful in nature, science and art. ill. imp. 8°. *$4; $4.50 . . . . *Cassell.*
— *Same.* ill. imp. 8°. *$4.50; $5; mor., $7.50. *New World.*
World on wheels. Taylor, B. F. $1.50 . . . . . *Griggs.*
World priest. Schefer, L. $2.25 . . . . *Roberts.*
World to blame. Phillips, W. H. $1.50 . . . . *Claxton.*
World we live in. Ansted, D. T. 75c. . . . *Lippincott.*
World we live in. Maury, M. F. $1.25 . . *Univ. Pub.*
World's birthday. Gaussen, L. $1.25 . . . . *Nelson.*
World's laconics. Tryon, E. $1.75 . . . . *Dodd.*
World's own. Howe, J. W. 75c. . . . . *Osgood.*
World's peace jubilee music; performed at the International Musical Festival, Boston, 1872. 8°. '72. bds., $1; pap., 75c. — Supplement, pap., 25c. . . . . *Ditson.*
World's progress. Putnam, G. P. $3.50; $5.50. *Putnam.*
World's sixteen crucified saviors. Graves, K. $2. *Colby.*
Worlds not realized. Gatty, M. 50c. . . . . . . *Carter.*
Wormald, J: Value of artificial fuel. *See* Siemens, C. W., Fuel.
Worman, Ja. H. Collegiate Germ. reader in prose and verse. 12°. '70. $1.75 . . . . *Barnes.*
— Complete grammar of the German language. 8°. '68. $2 . . . . *Barnes.*
— Echo (L') de Paris; or, dialogues to teach French conversation; ed. for Am. students. 12°. '69. $1.25 . . . . *Barnes.*
— Elementary Germ. reader in prose and verse. 12°. '73. $1.25 . . . . *Barnes.*
— Elementary grammar of the Germ. lang. 12°. '68. $1.50 . . . . *Barnes.*
— German echo; or, dialogues to teach Germ. conversation. 12°. '70. $1.25 . . . . *Barnes.*
Wormley, Thdr. G. Micro-chemistry of poisons, incl. their physiological, pathological and legal relations. ill. 8°. $10 . . . . *W. Wood.*
Wornum, Ralph Nicholson. *See* Etchings from the National Gallery; — Lectures on painting; — Turner gallery.
Worrall, H: Guitar school. obl. 8°. bds., $1 . . *Peters.*
— *and* Hayden, W. L. Amateur guitarist: songs, choruses and music. 4°. bds., $2.50 . . . . *Peters.*
Worrell, A. S. Corrective church discipline: review of Mell's "Church discipline," with introd. by Dr. Crawford and app. 18°. 60c. . . . . . *So. Bapt.*
Worship and work. 18°. 60c. . . . . *Cong. Pub.*
Worship of the church in the house; collated chiefly from the liturgy of the Am. church, by a son of the church. 12°. 75c. . . . . *Appleton.*
Worship of God and fellowship among men: sermons on public worship; by Prof. Maurice and others. fp. 8°. 75c. . . . . *Macmillan.*
Worsley, T: Christian drift of Cambridge [Eng.] work: 8 lectures. cr. 8°. '65. $1.75 . . *Macmillan.*
Worssam, S. W., *jr.* On mechanical saws. pl. 8°. $5. *Baird.*
Wort (Ein) ein Mann. *See* Hoffmann, Fz.
Worte des Heiles. *See* Congregation of the Most Holy Redeemer.
Worth, *Mrs.* A. A. Oakwood and its lessons; or, what we can do. 16°. $1.25 . . . . *Cong. Pub.*
Worth, Gorham A. Random recollections of Albany [N. Y.], 1800–'08. 3d ed. pl. 8°. '66. $2.50. *Munsell.*
Worth, *Mrs.* L. L. (*pseud.*) *See* Ellsworth, *Mrs.* —.
Worth and riches. Chase, M. G. 75c. . . . . . . *Dutton.*
Worth and wealth. Baker, H. N. W. $1 . . *H.A. Young.*
Worth, not wealth. Cousin Angie. 80c. . . . . . *Lee & S.*
Worth of the soul. Tyler, B. $2 . . . . *Cong. Pub.*
Worth reading. [Prose selections.] 6 nos. 16°. '75. ea., pap., 10c. . . . . *Tompkins.*
Worth a struggle. Waldron, W. R. 15c. . . . . *French.*
Worth while. Capron, M. J. $1.50 . . . . . . *Cong. Pub.*
Worthen, A: H. *See* Illinois geol. survey.
Worthen, J. W. New method of computing interest and average. 16°. leath., 50c. . . . . . . *Thompson.*
Worthen, W: E. First lessons in mechanics; with pract. applic. for schools. 12°. 75c. . . *Appleton.*
— Rudimentary drawing; for schools. 12°. 75c. *Appleton.*
— (*ed.*) Appleton's cyclopædia of drawing: text book for the mechanic, architect, engineer and surveyor. ill. roy. 8°. $10 . . . . *Appleton.*
— Appleton's dictionary of mechanics, machines, engine work and engineering. 2 v. ill. 8°. hf. mor., $18 . . . . *Appleton.*
— Appleton's scientific ser. 7 v. 8° . . . . *Appleton.*

Cont.: Practical drawing-book, $2. — Practical treatise on mechanical drawing and design, $2. — Practical treatise on arch. drawing and design, $2. — Practical treatise on shading and shadows, $1.50. — Practical treatise on topog. drawing, $1.50. — Practical treatise on perspective and isometrical drawing, $1.50. — Practical treatise on engineering drawing, $2.

— *Same*; in 1 v. 8°. $10 . . . . *Appleton.*
Worthies of All Souls. Burrows, M. $5 . . *Macmillan.*
Wortley, *Lady* Emeline. Travels in the United States. 12°. $1.50 . . . . *Harper.*
Wortmann, W: Rechenbuch f. d. unteren Klassen. 16°. 25c. . . . . *Benziger.*
Wouldst know thyself! Taylor, J. 20c. . . . . *Holmes.*
Wounded bird. *See* Little Rosy's travels.
Wounded boy. *See* Arthur, T. S.
Woven of many threads. *See* Hamilton, C. V.
Wrage, Hm. D. First Germ. reader. 12°. 50c. *Appleton.*
— German primer. 12°. 40c. . . . . *Appleton.*
— Lehrbuch der englischen Sprache. 12°. $1.50. *Appleton.*
— Practical German grammar. 12°. $1.50. — Key. 12°. $1 . . . . *Appleton.*

Wrage, Hm. D., *continued.*
— Progressive German reader. 8°. '71. 40c...*Schmidt.*
— *See also* Ollendorff, H. G.
— *and* Monsanto, H. M. Method of learning Spanish on Ollendorff's system. [For Germans to learn Spanish.] 12°. $1.50. — Key, $1....*Appleton.*
Wragg, J. Flute preceptor. f°. bds., $2....*Ditson.*
Wrangell, Fd. Narrative of an expedition to the Polar sea, in 1820–'23. 18°. 75c.........*Harper.*
Wraxhall, *Sir* F: C: Lascelles. Backwoodsman; or, life on the Indian frontier. 12°. '66. $1.50. *Burnham.*
— Black panther (The); or, a boy's adventures among the redskins. ill. 16°. '64. $1.25....*Burnham.*
— Golden hair: tale of the Pilgrim fathers. ill. 12°. $1.50 ....*Lee & S.*
Wray, C. *See* Simpson, J. P., *and* Wray, C.
Wray, Leon. Practical sugar planter: account of cultivation and manufacture of the sugar cane. ill. 8°. (Lond.) '48. $5 ....*Spon.*
Wreath. 32°. 50c.........................*Nelson.*
Wreath around the cross. Brown, A. M. $1..*Sheldon.*
Wreath of eglantine. Lucas, D. B. $1.50.*Kelly, P. & Co.*
Wreath of gems. Percival, E. $1.50 ...*J. E. Potter.*
Wreath of gems: songs, ballads and duets, with piano accomp. 4°. '68. $3; $4; bds., $2.50..*Ditson.*
Wreath of rhymes. Mayfield, M. $2....*Lippincott.*
Wreath of smoke. Tucker, C. 50c. ....*Carter.*
Wreck, F: Piano and song: how to teach, how to learn, and how to form a judgment of musical performances; tr. by M. P. Nichols. 16°. '75. $1.25.....................*Lockwood, B. & Co.*
Wreck. 18°. 40c...........................*Dutton.*
Wreck. Williams, W. H. 15c.............*French.*
Wreck: Ethiop. drama. 16°. pap., 15c.....*Happy.*
Wreck and the rescue: memoir of Rev. Harrison Fairfield. 18°. 60c....................*Cong. Pub.*
Wreck ashore. Buckstone, J. B. 15c.......*French.*
Wreck of the Chancellor. Verne, J. $2....*Porter.*
Wreck of the Golden Mary. 8°. pap., 25c...*Peterson.*
Wreck of the little ship. sq. 16°. 60c...(?)*Martien.*
Wreck of the Osprey. *See* Ellerslie House lib.
Wrecked heart. Galon, A. 25c..........*Barclay.*
Wrecked in port. Yates, E. 50c..........*Harper.*
Wrecked not lost. *See* Dundas, *Mrs.* —.
Wrecked on a reef. Raynal, F. E. $2......*Nelson.*
Wrecker's grandchild. Wilmer, M. E. 80c. *N. Y. Ref. Ch. Bd.*
Wreckmaster. Knickerbocker, *jr.* $1.25. (?)*Daughaday.*
Wren boys. Wilks, T. E. 15c.............*French.*
Wrench, Mta. The Highland glen; or, plenty and famine. 18°. 35c. *N. Y. Ref. Ch. Bd.; Pres. Com.; Pres. Bd.*
Wrestling Jacob. Hannah, J. 30c....*Meth. Bk. Conc.*
Wright, A. O. Analysis and exposition of the Constitution of Wisconsin. 12°. '73. 50c...*Atwood.*
Wright, A. S. Book of three thousand American receipts. 12°. $1.50.................*Dick & F.*
Wright, Alb. D. Elements of the language; or, analytical orthography. ('42.) New ed. 18°. '70. hf. bd., 25c. ....*Barnes.*
— Primary lessons; or, child's first book. 12°. 25c. *Appleton.*
Wright, Clb. E. Marcus Blair: story of the early times. ill. 12°. $1.25 ....*Lippincott.*
Wright, Dan. Thew. Mrs. Armington's ward; or, the inferior sex. 12°. $1.50..................*Lee & S.*
Wright, Elizur. Elements of life insurance for the use of family banks. 12°. '76. pap., 20c. *Williams.*
— Politics and mysteries of life insurance. 12°. $1.50. *Lee & S.*

Wright, Fes. A few days in Athens. por. 12°. 75c. *Mendum.*
Wright, Hendrick B. Historical sketches of Plymouth, and of the Wyoming valley, Luzerne Co., Penn. por. 12°. $4......................*Peterson.*
Wright, H: C. Empire of the mother over the character and destiny of the race. ('63.) 3d ed. 12°. '74. 75c.; pap., 50c...................*Colby.*
— Errors of the Bible demonstrated by the truths of nature; or, man's only infallible rule of faith and practice. ('67.) 4th ed. 12°. '73. 60c.; pap., 35c. ....*Colby.*
— Kiss for a blow: stories for children. ill. 4°. $1.50; chp. ed., 60c. ....*Lee & S.*
— Living present and dead past; or, God made manifest and useful in living men and women as he was in Jesus. ('65.) 3d ed., rev. 12°. '73. 75c.; pap., 50c..................................*Colby.*
— Unwelcome child; or, crime of an undesigned and undesired maternity. ('58.) 8th ed. 12°. '75. pap., 35c..............................*Colby.*
Wright, H: G. Headaches: their cause and cure. 12°. $1.25 ....*Lindsay.*
Wright, Hor. G. Report on fabrication of iron, etc. *See* United States, *Corps of Eng.*
Wright, J: C. *See* Ohio, Nisi prius reports.
Wright, Josiah. Attic primer; arranged for beginners. 12°. '74. $1.50....................*Macmillan.*
— David, King of Israel: readings for the young. ill. 16°. $1.25..........................*Macmillan.*
— First Latin steps. cr. 8°. '71. $2......*Macmillan.*
— Hellenica: hist. of Greece in Greek, as rel. by Diodorus and Thucydides. fp. 8°. $1....*Macmillan*
— Help to Latin grammar; or, the form and use of words in Lat. cr. 8°. $1.25........*Macmillan.*
— Seven kings of Rome, abridg. from first bk. of Livy. New ed., rev. fp. 8°. $1.25........*Macmillan.*
Wright, *Mrs.* Jla. McNair. Almost a nun. 16°. $1. *Pres. Bd.*
— Cabin in the brush. ill. 18°. 80c. ....*J. A. Moore.*
— Corner stall. ('68.) New ed. ill. 16°. '74. $1.15. *Hoyt.*
— Early church in Britain: its faith and works. 12°. '75. $1.25............*H. E. Simmons; West. Tr.*
— Golden lib. ('67–'68.) New ed. 4 v. ill. 16°. '75. $6.....................................*Hoyt.*
Cont.: Golden heart. — Golden work. — Golden fruit. — Golden life.
— Gospel in the riviera: story of Italy. 12°. 90c. *Un. B. Pub.*
— How could he escape? ('70.) New ed. 12°. '75. $1.25 ....*Nat. Temp.*
— — *See also below* Jug-or-not ser.
— John and the demijohn. ('69.) New ed. ill. 16°. '75. $1.50 ....*Hoyt.*
— Jug-or-not. ('70.) New ed. 12°. '76. $1.25..*Nat. Temp.*
— Jug-or-not ser. ('70–'73.) New ed. 4 v. 12°. '75–'76. $5.25 ....*Nat. Temp.*
Cont.: Jug-or-not. — Nothing to drink. — How could he escape? — Best fellow in the world.
— Life cruise of Capt. Bess Adams. ('74.) 12°. '76. $1.50 ....*Nat. Temp.*
— Lights and shadows of sacred story: anal. of Scripture characters, patriarchs, kings, prophets, warriors, etc. ill. 8°. *$3.50; mor., $5.50..*McCurdy.*
— Mabel and Tura. 16°. $1.25 ....(?)*Martien.*
— Malcolm's cottage and Malcolm's friend. 16°. $1.25. (?)*Martien.*
— Million too much: temperance tale. 16°. '71. $1.25. *Porter.*
— Moth and rust: very plain tale. ('70.) New ed. 16°. '75. $1.60 ....*Hoyt.*
— My five wards; or, Aunt Huldah's homilies. 12°. 90c. ....*Un. B. Pub.*
— New York Bible-woman. 16°. $1.10....*Pres. Bd.*
— New York needle-women; or, Elsie's stars. 16°. 80c. ....*Pres. Bd.*
— Ohio ark, and where it floated. 16°. $1.15..*Pres. Bd.*

Wright, *Mrs.* Jla. McNair, *continued.*
— Our Chatham Street uncle; or, the three golden balls. ('69.) New ed. ill. 16°. '75. $1.50.... *Hoyt.*
— Patriot and Tory one hundred years ago: tale of the revolution. por., ill., etc. 8°. '76. $2.50; hf. mor., $3 .... *Jones.*
— Priest and nun. 12°. $2.25 .... *West. Tr.*
— Secrets of the convent and confessional: exhibition of the influence and workings of papacy upon society and republican institutions; with introd. by D. March. ill. 8°. '70. *$2.75; $3.25 .. *Jones.*
— Shoe-binders of New York; or, fields white to the harvest. 16°. 80c. .... *Pres. Bd.*
— True story lib.: no. 1. 12 v. 32°. $3 ... *Pres. Bd.*

Cont.: Brave Max: story of Captain Hammond. — Good Louise, helper of Oberlin. — Henry Martyn, missionary. — Indians' friend, David Brainerd. — Lizzie, the girl soldier: Mrs. Lizzie Calderwood. — Little king: King Joash. — Our class. — Richard Knill, missionary to India and Russia. — Story of a prophet: Elisha. — Story of a tinker: John Bunyan. — Three seats full. — Tom Scott, the commentator.

— *Same;* no. 2. 12 v. 32°. $3 .... *Pres. Bd.*

Cont.: George Wishart. — John Knox. — William Tyndale. — John Huss. — Martin Luther. — Philip Melancthon. — Queen Margaret. — Renée of Ferrara. — John Calvin. — William Farel. — Admiral Coligny. — Richard Baxter.

— Two boys. ill. 16°. $1.50 .... *Souder.*
— Under the yoke, and other stories. 12°. 90c. *West. Tr.*
— Westward: tale of American emigrant life. 16°. $1.10 .... *Pres. Bd.*

Wright, Lew. Brahma fowl (The): a monograph. 3d ed. pl. cr. 8°. $2.50 .... *Cassell.*
— Illustrated book of poultry: 50 colored portraits of prize birds by J. M. Ludlow. demy 4°. $15; $20 .... *Cassell.*
— Practical poultry keeper. ill. cr. 8°. $2 ... *Cassell.*

Wright, Lorenzo. The great question. *See* Systematic beneficence.

Wright, Mar. Anchor of hope; or, New Test. lessons for children. ill. 16°. 50c. .... *Routledge.*
— Bow of faith; or, Old Test. lessons for children. ill. 16°. 50c. .... *Routledge.*

Wright, R. J. Principia; or, basis of social science. 8°. $3.50 .... *Lippincott.*

Wright, Rob. E. Index to Pennsylvania reports (1 Dallas-20 Smith, 1754-1872). 8°. shp., $10 .. *Welsh.*
— *See also* Pennsylvania, Sup. Court reports.

Wright, Rob. S: On the law of criminal conspiracies and agreements; with Am. notes by E. T. Gardner. 8°. $5 .... *Cockcroft.*

Wright, *Mrs.* S. L. (*ed.*) Now is Christ risen: poems for Eastertide. sq. 16°. '76. $1.25 ...... *Hoyt.*

Wright, *Mrs.* Sa. A. The crimson star; or, the midnight vision. 8°. '75. $1.50 .... *Sickels.*
— The gem of the lake. 8°. '68. pap., 50c. .. *Sickels.*
— The golden ladder; or, the stolen jewel. ill. 12°. '71. $2.50 .... *Sickels.*
— The secret duel; or, the soldier's dream. 12°. '69. pap., 25c. .... *Sickels.*

Wright, T: Caricature history of the four Georges; or, annals of the house of Hanover. ill. 12°. $3. *Appleton; Routledge; Scribner, W. & A.*
— Celt (The), the Roman and the Saxon: hist. of early inhabitants of Britain to conversion of Anglo-Saxons to Christianity. ill. 8°. $4 .. *Lippincott.*
— Dictionary of obsolete and provincial Eng. 12 v. 2°. (Bohn.) ea., $1.75 .... *Little, B. & Co.*
— *Same.* 2 v. 12°. (Bohn.) ea., $2. *Lippincott; Scribner, W. & A.*
— History of caricature and grotesque in literature and art. ill. 12°. '75. $3 .... *Routledge.*
— Homes of other days: history of domestic manners and sentiments in Eng. ill. imp. 8°. $7.50; hf. cf., $10 .... *Appleton.*
— (*ed.*) Early travels in Palestine: Willibald, Sæwulf, Benjamin of Tudela, Mandeville, La Brocquiere and Maundrell. 12°. (Bohn.) $1.75. *Little, B. & Co.*

Wright, T: *continued.*
— *Same.* 12°. (Bohn.) $2 .. *Lippincott; Scribner, W. & A.*
— *See also* Gilray, Ja., Works.

Wright, T: Our new masters. 8°. '73. $2.50 .. *Routledge.*

Wright, W: Arabic grammar. 2 v. 8°. (Lond.) $11. *Wiley.*

Wright, W: National system of bookkeeping. obl. 4°. '66. $1.75 .... *Claxton; Lippincott.*

Wright, W: Oil regions of Pennsylvania. 12°. $1.50. *Harper.*

Wright, W: Aldis. *See* Eastwood, J., *and* Wright, W. A.

Wright, W: B. The brook, and other poems. 12°. '73. $1.50 .... *Scribner.*

Wright, W: C. Piano manual or catechism. 16°. 50c.; bds., 40c. .... *Gordon.*

Wrigley, Edm. Building associations: what they are and how to use them. ('69.) 6th ed. 18°. '74. 75c. .... *J. K. Simon.*
— How to manage building associations. ('72.) 2d ed. 12°. '76. $2 .... *J. K. Simon.*

Wrigley, H: E. *See* Pennsylvania geol. survey.

Wrinkles and recipes. Benjamin, P. $1.50 .. *H. N. Munn.*

Writing on the wall. Morton, T. *and* J. M. 15c. *French.*

Wrong bottle: temperance [dram.] sketch. 16°. pap., 15c. .... *Happy.*

Wrong confessed is half redressed. Neely, K. J. $1. *Lee & S.*

Wrong of slavery. Owen, R. D. $1.25. *Claxton; Lippincott.*

Wrongs of women. Tonna, C. E. 90c. ...... *Dodd.*

Wroxby College. Adams, H. C. $1.75 .. *Routledge.*

Wullschlägel, H: Rob. Die beiden Elsässer. 18°. '73. 35c. .... *Am. Tr.*

Wunderpfeife (Die). Nieritz, G. 25c. ..... *Steiger.*

Wunderweib (Das) v. Eichbühl. 12°. 35c.; pap., 15c. .... *Benziger.*

Würdige Communicant (Der). Seidel, C. T. 75c.; $1; $1.40 .... *Dette.*

Wurst, R. J. Kleine prakt. Sprachdenklehre f. deutsch-am. Schulen bearb. v. J. Straubenmüller. 12°. '65. bds., 50c. .... *Steiger.*

Wurtenburg, K. Aus d. Bagno; [also] Eine junge Frau; [also] Ein unheimlicher Mann, v. E. Willkomm. 12°. '64. pap., 25c. .... *Steiger.*

Wurtz, Ad. History of chemical theory, from age of Lavoisier to present time; tr. by H: Watts. cr. 8°. '69. $2 .... *Macmillan.*

Wuthering Heights. *See* Brontë, E.

Wuttke, Adph. Christian ethics; with pref. by Dr. Reihm and introd. by W. F. Warren; tr. 2 v. 12°. $3.50 .... *Lee & S.*

Cont.: History of ethics. — Pure ethics.

— *Same;* tr. by J. P. Lacroix. 2 v. 12°. '73. $3.50. *Meth. Bk. Conc.*

Wyandotte. *See* Cooper, Ja. F.

Wyatt, *Sir* Mat. Digby. Fine art: sketch of its hist., theory, practice and applic. to industry: lectures at Univ. of Cambridge. 8°. '70. $3 .. *Macmillan.*

Wyatt, *Sir* T: Poems; with memoir. por. 18°. $1. *Osgood.*
— *Same.* (Aldine ed.) 16°. 75c. .... *Lippincott.*

Wyatt, W: E: Christian altar; or, offices of devotion for persons receiving the Lord's supper. 3d ed., rev. and enl. 4°. 50c. .... *Appleton.*
— Parting spirit's address to his mother. 18°. '60. 25c. *Randolph.*
— *Same.* ill. 16°. '62. $1. — 32°. 25c. ..... *Dutton.*

Wych Hazel. Warner, S. *and* A. B. $2 ... *Putnam.*

Wycherley, W: Congreve, W., Vanbrugh, *Sir* J., *and* Farquhar, G. Dramatic works; with notices by L. Hunt. por. 8°. $5 ..... *Routledge.*

Wyckoff, J. F. Christian use of money. 18°. '72. 20c. .... *Am. Tr.*

Wycliffe, J: Life and times. ('57.) 2d ed. 18°. '75. 50c. . . . . *So. Meth.*

Wycliffites (The). Mackay, *Mrs. Col.* $1.25 . . *Carter.*

Wyeth, J: A. Handbook of medical and surgical reference. 18°. $1.25; $1.50 . . . . *W. Wood.*

Wyeth, *Mrs.* M. E. C. Bob Tinker. ill. 18°. '74. 60c. *Am. Tr.*

— Maysie's star. ill. 18°. '74. 25c. . . . . *Am. Tr.*

Wyld, Ja. Scripture atlas: maps and index. 4°. (Bagster.) $3.25 . . . . *Wiley.*

Wylie, *Mrs.* E. J. Willow basket. 18°. 45c. *Pres. Bd.*

Wylie, Ja. Aitken. History of Protestantism. v. 1. ill. cr. 4°. $5 . . . . *Cassell.*

— Journey over the region of fulfilled prophecy. 18°. 50c. . . . . *Carter.*

Wylie, W. T. Lessons and prayers for the schoolroom. 8°. $3 . . . . *Keystone.*

— Worship in the school room. 8°. $1.50; hf. bd., $1; — abridg. 8°. hf. bd., 75c. . . . . *Keystone.*

Wyman, A. P. Piano text book: system of musical notation. 16°. '71. 40c.; bds., 50c. . . . . *Pond.*

Wyman, C. M. The palm. [Hymn book.] 8°. '70. $1.50 . . . . *Church.*

Wyman, Jeffries. Fossil mammals. *See* Gilliss, J. M.

— Fresh water shell mounds of St. John's River, Florida. ill. imp. 8°. '75. pap., $1 . . . *Peabody Acad. of Sci.*

Wymer, W. S. *See* Royal songs.

Wyncote. Erskine, T. $1.25 . . . . *Holt.*

Wynne, E. The old Bible; or, the martyr's gift. ill. 16°. $1 . . . . *Scribner, W. & A.*

Wynne, Faith. Flossy Lee. ill. 18°. 80c. . . *J. A. Moore.*

— Flossy Lee at the mountains. ill. 18°. 80c. *J. A. Moore.*

Wynne, Ja. Private libraries of New York. 8°. $5. (?) *Francis.*

Wynter, And. Borderlands of insanity. 8°. '75. $2. *Putnam.*

Wyoming: a tale. 8°. pap., 50c. . . . . *Harper.*

Wyss, J: Rod., *and* Montolieu, J. I. P. de B. (*Baronne*) de. Swiss family Robinson; or, adventures of a father and mother and four sons on a desert island; [tr.] ill. 12°. $1 . . . . *Lippincott; Porter.*

— — *Same.* ill. 16°. $1; $1.75. — ill. 12°. $1.25; $1.50. — ill. cr. 8°. $2.50 . . . . *Scribner, W. & A.*

— — *Same.* 12°. $1.25 . . . . *Miller.*

— — *Same.* ill. 12°. $1.25. — ill. 16°. $1 . . *Routledge.*

— — *Same.* ill. 16°. $1.50 . . . . *Clark & M.*

— — *Same.* ill. 12°. $1.50. *Appleton; Carleton; World Pub.*

— — *Same.* ill. cr. 8°. $1.50 . . . . *Estes.*

— — *Same.* (Chandos classics.) cr. 8°. $1; pap., 75c. *Scribner, W. & A.*

— — *Same.* ill. 12°. $1.50; $1.25. — (Household ed.) ill. 8°. $2 . . . . *Nelson.*

— — *Same.* (Household ser.) ill. 16°. $1.50; mor., $3 . . . . *Lee & S.*

— — *Same.* (Presentation ed.) ill. 16°. $1.75. *Routledge.*

— — *Same;* ed. and rev. by C. Hartley. ill. cr. 8°. '64. $1.50. — ill. 16°. $1.25 . . . . *Hurd & H.*

— — *Same;* tr. and ed. from Stahl's Fr. ed. by J. Lovell. ill. roy. 8°. $3.50 . . . . *Cassell.*

— — *Same.* 2 v. ill. 18°. $1.50; — sequel. 2 v. 18°. $1.50 . . . . *Harper.*

— — — *See also* Crusoe lib.; — Godolphin, Ma.; — Harper's boys' and girls' lib.; — Library of celebrated books; — Treasure-box of wonder and entertainment.

— — — *French.* 12°. $2 . . . . *Routledge.*

Wythe, G: *See* Virginia, High Court of Chancery reports.

Wythe, Jos. H. Agreement of science and revelation. 12°. $1.75 . . . . *Lippincott.*

— Pastoral office in the Meth. Episc. Church. 18°. '53. 35c. . . . . *Meth. Bk. Conc.*

Wythe, Jos. H., *continued.*

— Physician's pocket dose and symptom book. 11th ed., rev. 18°. '74. $1.25; leath., $1.50 . . *Lindsay.*

Wythe, W. W. Pulpit germs: plans for sermons. 12°. $1.50 . . . . *Lippincott.*

X. Y. Z. Colman, G., *jr.* 15c. . . . . *French.*

Xariffa (*pseud.*) *See* Townsend, M. A.

Xariffa's poems. Townsend, M. A. $1.50 . . *Lippincott.*

Xenophon. Works; tr. by J. S. Watson and H. Dale. 3 v. 12°. (Bohn.) ea., $1.75 . . . . *Little, B. & Co.*

Cont.: Anabasis and Memorabilia. — Cyropædia and Hellenics. — Minor works.

— *Same.* 3 v. 12°. (Bohn.) ea., $2. *Lippincott; Scribner, W. & A.*

— Writings [outlined and expl.] by Sir A. Grant. (Anc. classics for Eng. readers.) 16°. $1. *Lippincott; Little, B. & Co.*

— Anabasis [Gk.]; with Eng. notes by C. Anthon. 12°. shp., $1.50 . . . . *Harper.*

— *Same;* with notes by Boise. 12°. $2 . . . . *Appleton.*

— *Same;* ed. by A. Crosby, with lexicon and notes. 12°. $2.25; — text only, $1.25; — lexicon, $1; — lexicon and notes, $1.25 . . . . *Potter, A. & Co.*

— *Same;* ed. by A. C. Kendrick. 12°. hf. leath., $2. *Sheldon.*

— *Same;* rec. J. F. Macmichael. 18°. 75c. . . *Harper.*

— *Same;* ed. by J. J. Owen. 12°. $2 . . . . *Appleton.*

— *Same;* with interl. tr. for schools by T. Clark. roy. 12°. hf. leath., $2.75 . . . . *Desilver.*

— *Same:* 1st 3 bks., ed. by Boise. 12°. $1.50 . . *Appleton.*

— *Same:* 1st 4 bks., with notes, lexicon, etc., by A. Crosby. 12°. $2 . . . . *Potter, A. & Co.*

— — *Same;* with notes, introd. and vocab., ed. by A. C. Kendrick. 12°. hf. leath., $1.50 . . . . *Sheldon.*

— *Eng.* Anabasis; or, expedition of Cyrus; [also] Memorabilia of Socrates; lit. tr. by J. S. Watson, with geographical comment. by W. F. Ainsworth. 12°. $1.50 . . . . *Harper.*

— — *See also* Kendrick, A. C.

— Cyropædia [Gk.]; ed. by J. J. Owen. 12°. $2.50. *Appleton.*

— *Eng.* History of expedition of Cyrus, and account of institution of Cyrus; tr. by E. Spelman and M. Cooper. 2 v. 18°. $1.50 . . . . *Harper.*

— Memorabilia of Socrates [Gk.]; with Eng. notes by C. Anthon, the prolegomena of Kühner, Wigger's life of Socrates, etc. Rev. and enl. ed. 12°. shp., $1.50 . . . . *Harper.*

— *Same;* with notes by Robbins. 12°. $2 . . *Appleton.*

— *Eng.* Memoirs of Socrates. 16°. $1.25. *Scribner, W. & A.*

Y., J. O. *See* Black, *Mrs.* Sa. S.

Y., T. R. Belle Lovel. 16°. '71. $1.25 . . . *Randolph.*

Yacht club. Adams, W. T. $1.50 . . . . *Lee & S.*

Yacht club ser. *See* Adams, W: T.

Yachtville boys. Davis, C. E. K. 75c. . . . . *Hoyt.*

Yaggy, L. W. Our home counsellor: cyclopedia for daily use: recipes, legal forms, interest tables, etc. 12°. '75. $2.50 . . . . *West. Pub.*

Yahoo (The): a satirical rhapsody; by author of "Great dragon cast out." 12°. 70c. . . *Mendum.*

Yale, Greg. Legal titles to mining claims and water rights in California under mining law of Congress, July, 1866. 8°. '67. leath., $5 . . . . *Roman.*

— *Same.* 8°. '67. shp., $7.50 . . . . *Bancroft.*

Yale College scrapes; or, how the boys go it at New Haven. 8°. pap., 25c. . . . . *Dick & F.*

Yankee among the mermaids. Burton, W. E. 75c. *Peterson.*

Yankee cook book. 16°. pap., 30c.; bds., 50c. *Dick & F.*

Yankee in Canada. Thoreau, H. D. $1.50 . . *Osgood.*

Yankee Jack; or, the perils of a privateersman. 8°. pap., 50c. . . . . *Peterson.*

Yankee land. Logan, C. A. 15c. . . . . *French.*
Yankee middy. Adams, W. T. $1.50 . . . . . . *Lee & S.*
Yankee middy; or, the two frigates. 8°. pap., 50c. *Peterson.*
Yankee pedlar. Barnett, M. 15c. . . . . *French.*
Yankee privateer; or, the traitor merchant. 8°. pap., 25c. . . . . *Dick & F.*
Yankee stories. Haliburton, T. C. $1.75; $1.50. *Peterson.*
Yankee yarns and Yankee letters. Haliburton, T. C. 75c. . . . . *Peterson.*
Yankees in Japan; or, adventures of a sailor. 8°. pap., 50c. . . . . *Peterson.*
Yapp, Alex. ["H. A. Page."] Golden lives: biographies for the day. 2d ed. 12°. '73. $2 . . *Routledge.*
— Noble workers. por. 12°. '75. $2 . . . . *Routledge.*
— Out and all about: stories for children. ill. 12°. '74. $2 . . . . *Routledge.*
Yardley, E. Experiments on cements. 8°. pap., 35c. *Am. Soc. of C. E.*
Yarns of an old mariner. Clarke, M. C. $1.50 . . *Lee & S.*
Yarrow, H: C. Notes on geog. distrib. with regard to zool. of w. U. S.; — Report on batrachians, reptiles and mollusca; — upon fishes; — upon mammals. *See* United States, *Corps of Eng.*
Yateman, *Mrs.* M. R. The double fault. 16°. 90c. *Cong. Pub.*
Yates, Edm. Novels. 8 v. 12°. hf. roxb., $10 . . *Routledge.*
Cont.: Running the gauntlet. — Kissing the rod. — Black sheep. — Broken to harness. — Righted wrong. — Land at last. — Rock ahead. — Forlorn hope.
— *Same.* 5 v. 8°. pap. . . . . *Harper.*
Cont.: Black sheep. — Dr. Wainwright's patient. — Land at last. — Wrecked in port, *ea.*, 50c. — Kissing the rod, 75c.
— Broken to harness: story of Eng. domestic life. 12°. $1.50; pap., $1 . . . . *Loring.*
— Dangerous game. 8°. '74. $1.50; pap., 75c. *W. F. Gill.*
— Forlorn hope. 8°. pap., 50c. . . . . *Loring.*
— Kissing the rod. 12°. $1.25; bds., $1 . . . *Routledge.*
— Nobody's fortune. ill. 8°. (Lond.) pap., 60c. *Am. News.*
— *Same.* 8°. $1.25; pap., 75c. . . . . *Estes.*
— Running the gauntlet. 12°. $1.25; bds., $1 . . *Routledge.*
— *Same.* 12°. $1.50; pap., $1 . . . . *Loring.*
— Silent witness. 8°. '75. $1.50; pap., 75c. *W. F. Gill.*
— Two by tricks. 16°. bds., $1 . . . . *Routledge.*
— Wages of sin. 8°. '75. pap., 50c. . . . . . *W. F. Gill.*
— Waiting race. 8°. pap., 75c. . . . . *Appleton.*
— Yellow flag. 8°. $1.25; pap., 75c. . . . . *Estes.*
— *See also* Harrington, N. H., *and* Yates, E.; — Simpson, J. P., *and* Yates, E.
— *and* Harrington, N. H. Hit him, he has no friends: farce. 16°. pap., 15c. . . . . *French; Lee & S.*
— — My friend from Leatherhead: farce. 16°. pap., 15c. . . . . *French.*
— — Night at Notting Hill: farce. 16°. pap., 15c. *French.*
Yates, J: V. N. *See* New York State, Select cases.
Yatman, J: V. Currency tables; showing value of a greenback dollar note in specie from par to 306 per cent. fp. 12°. '64. pap., 25c. . . . . *Clayton.*
— Tables of specie prices; showing equivalents at various rates of gold, U. S. legal tender currency; also a currency table showing value of a greenback dollar note in specie at various rates. fp. 12°. '64. $1.50 . . . . *Clayton.*
Ye book of sense. ill. obl. 8°. $1.50 . . . . *Porter.*
Ye centennial: a quire booke for folke old and younge; made by ye compiler. obl. 8°. '75. bds., 50c.; pap., 40c. . . . . *Ditson.*
Ye shyp of fooles. Brandt, S. $25; $35; $40; $50. *Appleton.*
Ye will not come; or, the sinner without excuse. 18°. 25c. . . . . *Pres. Bd.*
Yeager, G: Garden of Eden. 12°. 75c. . . *Lippincott.*
Yeakel, R. Biblical riddle school. 18°. 35c. . . *Ev. Assoc.*
Yeaman, G: H. Study of government. 8°. '71. $5. *Little, B. & Co.*

Year (The). Colesworthy, D. C. $1.50 . . . . . *Lee & S.*
Year after marriage. Arthur, T. S. 50c. . . . . *Peterson.*
Year at school. Brown, T. 50c. . . . . *Routledge.*
Year at the shore. Gosse, P. H. $4.50 . . . *Routledge.*
Year book of nature. *See* Draper, J. C.
Year book of therapeutics. *See* Wood, H. C., *jr.*
Year in China. Williams, H. D. $1.50 . . . . *Hurd & H.*
Year in the country. Burton, B. F. $1.25 . . *Lothrop.*
Year in Europe. Cross, J. $2 . . . . *So. Meth.*
Year in Spain. Mackenzie, A. S. 3 v. $3.75 . . *Harper.*
Year in Sunday school; from the journal of an old teacher. 18°. 70c. . . . . *Am. S. S.*
Year of battles. Brockett, L. P. $2.50 . . (?) *Goodspeed.*
Year of Mary. *See* Menghi-D'Arville, *Abbé.*
Year of salvation. Oosterzee, J. J. van. $3.75. *Scribner, W. & A.*
Year of worship. Demarest, G. L. 45c. . . *Universalist.*
Year with the Everards. Butler, C. $1.25 . . *Dutton.*
Year with the Franklins. Cate, E. J. 75c. . . *Harper.*
Year with Gerty West. Griffith, T. H. $1.25 . . *Am. Bapt.*
Year with Maggie and Emma. McIntosh, M. J. 75c. *Appleton.*
Year with Moses. Vincent, J. H. 2 nos. ea., per doz., $3 . . . . *Meth. Bk. Conc.*
Year with St. Paul. Knox, C. E. $1.50 . . *Randolph.*
Years that are told. Porter, R. $1.25 . . . . *Randolph.*
Yeast. Kingsley, C. $1.50 . . . . . *Harper; Macmillan.*
Yeates, Jasp. *See* Pennsylvania, Sup. Court reports.
Yellott, G: The funny philosophers; or, wags and sweethearts. [Fiction.] 12°. $1.50 . . *Lippincott.*
Yellow diamond. Crow, *Mrs.* —. 30c. . . . . *Am. News.*
Yellow dwarf. [Toy-book.] ill. 4°. $1; 50c. *Routledge.*
Yellow dwarf. Keating, E. H. 15c. . . . . *French.*
Yellow dwarf. Planché, J. R. 15c. . . . . *French.*
Yellow flag. *See* Yates, Edm.
Yellow frigate. *See* Grant, Ja.
Yellow mask. *See* Collins, Wilkie.
Yelverton, *Mrs.* Theresa. [*Lady Avonmore.*] Zanita: tale of the Yo-Semite. cr. 8°. '71. $1.50 . . *Hurd & H.*
Yemassee. Simms, W. G. $1.75; 75c. . . *Widdleton.*
Yenni, D. Latin grammar. 8°. $1.75 . . . . . . *Sadlier.*
Yeokel, R., *and* Hoffmann, E. A. Jubeltöne. [Sunday school music.] ('71.) 6th ed. obl. 16°. '75. 40c.; 50c.; 75c. . . . . *Ev. Assoc.*
Yerger, —, Smedes, —, *and* Abbey, R. Debate: Apostolic succession. 18°. '46. 60c. . . . . *So. Meth.*
Yerger, G: S. *See* Tennessee, Law reports.
Yes. Somerset, C. A. 15c. . . . . *French.*
Yes and no. 18°. 12c. . . . . *Cong. Pub.*
Yes and no. 18°. 35c. *Am. S. S.*
Yes and no. ('62.) New ed. ill. 18°. '72. 30c. . . *Hoyt.*
Yesterday, to-day and forever. Bickersteth, E. H. $2; $1.25 . . . . *Carter.*
Yesterdays with authors. Fields, J. T. $2; $4 . . *Osgood.*
Yew tree ruins. Haines, J. T. 15c. . . . . *French.*
Yñiguez, Jose M. Martinez. Crimen, venganza y expiacion ó el beso de Judas. 8°. '74. pap., $1. *Payot.*
Yohn, Alb. B. *See* Monachesi, H. D., *and* Yohn, A. B.
Yoke and burden. Blauvelt, J. R. $1.50 . . . . *Ward.*
Yoland of Groningen. *See* Bresciani, A.
Yônâh, *Rabbî.* Book of Hebrew roots, with extracts from other Hebrew Arabic dictionaries; by Ad. Neubann. 4°. '75. $21. . . . . *Macmillan.*
Yonge, C: Drake. English-Greek lexicon; with Pillon's Greek synonyms and Essay on order of words in Attic-Greek prose, by C. Short; ed. by H. Drisler. 8°. shp., $7 . . . . *Harper.*

Yonge, C: Drake, *continued.*
— Life of Marie Antoinette. 2 v. por. cr. 8°. $6. *Lippincott.*
— Three centuries of Eng. literature. 12°. $2..*Appleton.*
— Three centuries of modern hist. 12°. $2..*Appleton.*

Yonge, *Miss* Ctte. M. Beechcroft. 12°. $1..*Appleton.*
— Ben Sylvester's word. 18°. 60c...*Appleton; Dutton.*
— Book of golden deeds of all times and all countries. 18°. '74. $1.25. — ill. cr. 8°. $2.50..*Macmillan.*
— *Same.* 18°. 75c. — 16°. $1.25..........*Allyn.*
— Book of worthies. 18°. '69. $1.25.....*Macmillan.*
— Caged lion. 12°. $1.25..........*Appleton.*
— *Same.* 3d ed. ill. cr. 8°. $1.75.......*Macmillan.*
— Cameos from Eng. history. 12°. $1......*Appleton.*
— *Same.* 12°. $1.25..........*Lippincott.*
— *Same.* 2 v. 12°. '71. ea., $1.75......*Macmillan.*
Cont.: From Rollo to Edward II. — The wars in France.
— Castle builders. 12°. $1..........*Appleton.*
— Chaplet of pearls. ill. 8°. $1.50; pap., $1..*Appleton.*
— *Same.* 4th ed. cr. 8°. $1.75..........*Macmillan.*
— Chosen people: compend. of sacred and church hist. for school children. 18°. '74. 50c........*Pott.*
— Christmas mummers. 12°. '76. $1.50........*Pott.*
— Clever woman of the family. ill. 8°. $1.50; pap., $1..........*Appleton.*
— *Same.* 3d ed. cr. 8°. '75. $1.75......*Macmillan.*
— Countess Kate: story for girls. 18°. $1...*Loring.*
— Daisy chain; or, aspirations. 12°. $1.75..*Appleton.*
— *Same.* 12th ed. ill. cr. 8°. '74. $1.75..*Macmillan.*
— Dove in the eagle's nest. 12°. $1; pap., 75c. *Appleton.*
— *Same.* 4th ed. cr. 8°. '75. $1.75.....*Macmillan.*
— Dynevor Terrace; or, the clue of life. 12°. $1.75. *Appleton.*
— *Same.* 6th ed. cr. 8°. '73. $1.75.....*Macmillan.*
— Eighteen centuries of beginnings of church hist. 12°. '76. $2..........*Pott.*
— Friarswood post-office: tale for the young. 18°. 60c. *Appleton.*
— Heartsease. 12°. $1.75..........*Appleton.*
— *Same.* 13th ed. ill. cr. 8°. '75. $1.75..*Macmillan.*
— Heir of Redclyffe. 12°. $1.75..........*Appleton.*
— *Same.* 20th ed. ill. cr. 8°. '76. $1.75..*Macmillan.*
— Hopes and fears. 2 v. in 1. 12°. $1.75..*Appleton.*
— *Same.* 4th ed. cr. 8°. '75. $1.75.....*Macmillan.*
— Kenneth; or, the rear guard. 12°. $1...*Appleton.*
— Lady Hester; or, Ursula's narrative. cr. 8°. '74. $1.75..........*Macmillan.*
— Lances of Lynwood. 16°. 75c..........*Appleton.*
— *Same.* 2d ed. col. ill. 12°. '68. $1.50..*Macmillan.*
— Landmarks of history. ('66–'68.) New ed. 3 v. 12°. '76..........*Holt.*
Cont.: Ancient hist., to Mahometan conquest, $1. — Mediæval hist., to the reformation, $1.25. — Modern hist., $1.50.
— Life and letters of J: Coleridge Patteson. 3d ed. 2 v. por., map, and ill. cr. 8°. '75. $5....*Macmillan.*
— Little duke. New ed. 18°. '64. 75c....*Macmillan.*
— Little Lucy's wonderful globe. ill. 4°. '72. 75c.; $1.25..........*Lothrop.*
— *Same.* 2d ed. ill. cr. 4°. $2..........*Macmillan.*
— Musings over the "Christian year," and "Lyra innocentium"; with gleanings of recollections of J: Keble. 12°. $2..........*Appleton.*
— My young Alcides. cr. 8°. '76. $1.75..*Macmillan.*
— P's and Q's; or, the question of putting upon. ill. fp. 8°. '72. $1.50..........*Macmillan.*
— Parallel history of France and England: outlines and dates. obl. 4°. '71. $1.25......*Macmillan.*
— Pigeon pie: tale of Roundhead times. 16°. '64. $1. *Roberts.*
— Pillars of the house; or, under wode, under rode. 2 v. cr. 8°. '74. $3.50..........*Macmillan.*
— Pioneers and founders; or, recent workers in the mission field. cr. 8°. '71. $1.75....*Macmillan.*
— Prince and the page: tale of the last crusade. ill. 18°. '75. 75c..........*Macmillan.*
— Pupils of St. John the divine. ill. 12°. $1.75. *Lippincott.*
— *Same.* cr. 8°. '68. $1.75..........*Macmillan.*

Yonge, *Miss* Ctte. M., *continued.*
— Richard the fearless. 16°. 75c..........*Appleton.*
— — *See also* Fireside lib.
— Scripture readings for schools and families. 12°. '71. 75c.; — with comments. 12°. $1.50..*Macmillan.*
— *Same.* 2d ser.: Joshua to Solomon. 12°. '72. 75c.; — with comments. 12°. $1.50......*Macmillan.*
— *Same.* 3d ser.: Kings and prophets. 12°. '74. 75c.; — with comments. 12°. $1.50......*Macmillan.*
— Six cushions. 16°. $1..........*Lee & S.*
— Stokesley secret; or, how the pig paid the rent. ill. 18°. 60c..........*Appleton.*
— Trial (The): more links of the "Daisy chain." 12°. $1.25..........*Appleton.*
— *Same.* 7th ed. ill. cr. 8°. '74. $1.75...*Macmillan.*
— Two guardians. 12°. $1..........*Appleton.*
— Young stepmother; or, a chronicle of mistakes. 12°. $1.75..........*Appleton.*
— *Same.* 5th ed. cr. 8°. '73. $1.75......*Macmillan.*
— (*ed.*) Star of hope ser. 18 v. 18°. ea., 25c. *Scribner, W. & A.*
Cont.: Bit of fun. — Lost on the line. — Wax matches, etc. — Hunt ribbon. — Girl's adventures. — Virtue of patience. — Alice's watch. — Harry's snow-shoes. — Martin's pet robins. — Henry of Eichenfels. — Red and white roses. — Lost child. — Prasca Loupouloff. — Good beginnings and happy endings. — Alice. — Little Nellie. — Finette. — Story of the venerable Bede.
— Storehouse of stories. 2 ser. fp. 8°. ea., $1.50. *Macmillan.*
— *See also* Sewell, E. M., *and* Yonge, C. M.

Yorke, Ol. (*pseud.*) *See* Mahony, Fs.

You ask! — I'll tell! Chesterman, E. *$2.25; $3..*Flint.*

You can't marry your grandmother. Bayly, T. H. 15c. *French.*

Youatt, W: On the dog; ed. by E. J. Lewis. 8°. $3.75..........*World Pub.*
— On the structure and diseases of the horse; rev. and enl. by W. Watson. ill. 8°. $4........*Lee & S.*
— *Same;* with app. by W. C. Spooner. ill. 8°. $2. *Lippincott.*
— *Same;* with obs. on breeding cavalry horses by Cecil. ill. 16°. bds., 50c..........*Routledge.*
— *Same;* simplified, brought down by W. C. Spooner; with account of breeds in U. S. by H. S. Randall. ill. 12°. $1.50..........*Judd.*
— *Same;* with essay on the ass and mule by J. S. Skinner. ill. 8°. $2..........*World Pub.*
— On sheep: their breeds, management and diseases. ill. 12°. $1..........*Judd.*
— *See also* Farmer's barn book; — New Am. pocket farrier.
— *and* Martin, W. C. L. The hog: treatise on the breeds, management, feeding and medical treatment of swine, etc.; ed. by A. Stevens. ill. 12°. $1..........*Judd.*
— — On cattle: treatise on breeds, management and diseases; ed. by A. Stevens. ill. 12°. $1.50..*Judd.*

Youman, Alex. E. Dictionary of every-day wants. 8°. '72. $4; shp., $4.75..........(?) *F. M. Reed.*

Youmans, E: Livingston. Class-book of chemistry. 12°. $1.75..........*Appleton.*
— *Span.* Elementos de química; tr. por M. A. Rojas. ill. 12°. $2..........*Appleton.*
— Handbook of household science; with questions, (School ed.) 12°. hf. bd., $1.75......*Appleton.*
— (*ed.*) Correlation and conservation of forces: expositions by Grove, Helmholtz, Liebig, Mayer, Faraday and Carpenter. 12°. $2.....*Appleton.*
— Culture demanded by modern life: addresses and arguments on claims of scientific education. 12°. $2..........*Appleton.*

Youmans, Eliza A. First book of botany. ill. 12°. $1..........*Appleton.*
— Second book of botany. 12°. $1.50.....*Appleton.*

Youmans, W: Jay. *See* Huxley, T. H., *and* Youmans, W. J.

Young, Alfr. Office of vespers. 12°. 75c...*Cath. Pub.*
— *See also* Catholic hymns and canticles.

Young, And. History of Wayne Co., Indiana; with biog. and family sketches. por. and views. 8°. '72. $5 ... *Clarke.*

Young, And. W. First book on civil government. ('67.) New ed. 16°. '75. 60c. ... *Clark & M.*

— First lessons in civil government; incl. view of government of New York, and abstract of the laws. ('72.) New ed., rev. 12°. $1.25 ... *Barnes.*

— Government class book. ('75.) New ed. 12°. '76. $1.50 ... *Clark & M.*

Young, Ann Eliza. Wife no. 19; or, story of a life in bondage: [autobiog.]; with notes by J. B. Gough and M. A. Livermore. ill. and por. 8°. '75. *$3; shp., $3.50 ... *Dustin.*

Young, C: A: The sun: sketch of present state of scientific opinion as regards this body. 12°. '72. pap., 25c. ... *Van Nostrand.*

Young, C: F. T. Fouling and corrosion of iron ships: their causes and means of prevention; with mode of applic. to existing ironclads. ill. 8°. (Lond.) '67. $5 ... *Spon.*

Young, Dan. Autobiography. *See* Strickland, W. P.

Young, E: Poems. (Aldine ed.) 2 v. 16°. 75c. *Lippincott.*

— *Same;* with memoir by J. Mitford. 2 v. por. 18°. $2 ... *Osgood.*

— *Same;* [also] Poems, by T. Campbell. ill. 16°. $1.12; $1.35. — 32°. 85c.; $1.12 ... *World Pub.*

— — *See also* Milton, J:

— Night thoughts on life, death and immortality. 18°. 38c. ... *Appleton; Clark & M.; Nichols & H.*

— *Same.* 16°. $1.25 ... *Carter.*

— *Same.* (Blue and gold ed.) 18°. 75c. ... *Appleton.*

— *Same.* (Blue and gold ed.) 24°. 35c.; 75c. *C. H. Davis.*

— *Same;* with memoir, crit. view of writings and notes by J. R. Boyd. 4th ed., rev. 12°. '51. $1.50; — (school ed.), hf. bd., $1.25 ... *Barnes.*

— *Same;* with life and notes by G. Gilfillan. 8°. mor., $6 ... *Appleton.*

— Revenge: tragedy. 16°. pap., 15c. ... *French.*

Young, Fs. Questions to the landmarks of hist. of Eng. 16°. bds., 40c. ... *Routledge.*

Young, G. W. Simple practical methods of calculating strains on girders, arches and trusses; with essay on economy in suspension bridges. 8°. $3.50. *Macmillan.*

Young, Jac. Autobiography of a pioneer. 12°. '44. $1.75 ... *Meth. Bk. Conc.*

Young, J: Christ of history. 12°. $1.25 ... *Carter.*

— *Same.* cr. 8°. $2 ... *Routledge.*

— Creator and the creation. 2d ed. cr. 8°. $2. *Routledge.*

— Life and light of men. cr. 8°. $2.25 ... *Routledge.*

Young, J: Geology. (Adv. sci. ser.) ill. 12°. $1.50. *Putnam.*

— Physical geography. (Adv. sci. ser.) ill. 12°. '73. $1.50 ... *Putnam.*

Young, J: C. Efficacy of prayer. 18°. 35c. ... *Pres. Bd.*

Young, Julian C: Memoir of Charles Mayne Young, tragedian; with extracts from his son's journal. New [chp.] ed. cr. 8°. $2.25 ... *Macmillan.*

— *See also* Stoddard, R. H., Bric-a-brac ser.

Young, Loyal. Commentary on Ecclesiastes; with introd. by A. T. McGill and W. M. Jacobus. 8°. $2.50 ... *Pres. Bd.*

— Communion. 18°. 45c. ... *Pres. Bd.*

— Hidden treasure: allegory. 18°. 35c. ... *Pres. Bd.*

Young, M. J. Familiar lessons in botany; with flora of Texas. 12°. '72. $2 ... *Barnes.*

Young, R. A. Personages. 12°. $1.25 ... *So. Meth.*

Young, Rob. Importance of prayer-meetings. 18°. '41. 35c. ... *Meth. Bk. Conc.*

— Inquirer; [also] New convert. 18°. 25c. *Cin. Meth. Bk. Conc.*

Young, Rob., *continued.*

— Suggestions for conversion of the world. 18°. 40c. *Cin. Meth. Bk. Conc.*

Young, W. Picturesque arch. studies and pract. designs for gate lodges, cottages, cottage hospitals, etc. 50 pl. 4°. '72. $10 ... *Spon.*

— *See also* Spon's builders' pocket-book of prices and memoranda.

Young, W. W. S. (*ed.*) Shipowner's and shipmaster's manual to port of Philadelphia. 8°. '76. pap., 25c. ... *Dando.*

Young actress. Lancaster, E. 15c. ... *French.*

Young adventurer. 16°. $1.25 ... *H. A. Young.*

Young America abroad ser. *See* Adams, W: T.

Young American letter writer. 12°. '69. pap., 10c. *Hunter.*

Young American songster. 12°. '69. pap., 10c. *Hunter.*

Young American's lib. 9 v. 16°. $4.50 ... *Appleton.*
Cont.: Adventures of Capt. Smith. — Adventures of Dan. Boone. — Dawnings of genius. — Adventures of Henry Hudson. — Philip Randolph. — History of French revolution, 2 v. — Southey's Oliver Cromwell. — Adventures of Cortez.

Young American's lib. of eminent statesmen. 6 v. ill. 16°. ea., $1.25 ... *Lee & S.*
Cont.: Benjamin Franklin. — Daniel Webster. — Daring deeds. — William Penn. — Henry Clay. — Noble deeds.

Young American's lib. of famous generals. 6 v. ill. 16°. ea., $1.25 ... *Lee & S.*
Cont.: Gen. Washington. — Gen. Taylor. — Gen. Jackson. — Gen. Lafayette. — Gen. Marion. — Napoleon Bonaparte.

Young Americans abroad; or, vacation in Europe; by J. O. Choules and his pupils. ill. 16°. '74. $1.25. *Lothrop.*

Young analyzer. McElligott, J. N. 30c. ... *Ivison.*

Young and handsome. Planché, J. R. 15c. ... *French.*

Young angler: instructions for preparing rods, lines, hooks, etc. 16°. pap., 10c. ... *Happy.*

Young angler, naturalist and pigeon and rabbit fancier; with hints as to management of silk-worms, aquarium, etc. ill. 16°. 75c. ... *Routledge.*

— *See also* Boy's treasury of sports and pastimes.

Young apprentice. Smith, H. $1.25 ... *Hoyt.*

Young artist. 18°. 50c. ... *O'Shea.*

Young artists; tr. from the Fr. ill. 16°. $1 ... *Routledge.*

Young Benjamin Franklin. Mayhew, H. $1.25 ... *Harper.*

Young bird catcher. *See* Baker, *Mrs.* H. N. W.

Young botanist. Comstock, J. L. 60c. ... *Sheldon.*

Young Brahmin's story. Glandon, A. $1.50 ... *Nelson.*

Young Brown. *See* Murray, G.

Young Calvin in Paris. Blackburn, W. M. 75c. *Pres. Bd.*

Young captives. Newman, —. 50c. ... *Kenedy.*

Young Catholic's manual. [Prayer book.] 32°. 30c.–$2 ... *Noonan.*

— — *See also* Catholic's manual.

Young Catholic's vocal class book. Peters, W. C. 50c. *Peters.*

Young Catholics' lib. 1st ser. 6 v. 18°. '65–'66. ea., 50c. ... *Cunningham.*
Cont.: Cottage evening tales. — Children of the valley. — May Carleton's story; Miller's daughter. — Philip Hartley. — Count Leslie. — A father's tales of the French revolution.

— *Same:* 2d ser. 6 v. 18°. '66. ea., 50c. ... *Cunningham.*
Cont.: Ralph Berrien. — Silver Grange; Phillipine. — Helena Butler. — Charles and Frederick, by J. P. Donnollon. — The Beauforts. — Lauretta and the fables.

— *Same:* 3d ser. 6 v. 18°. '67. ea., 50c. *Cunningham.*
Cont.: Conrad and Gertrude. — Three petitions. — Alice. — Caroline. — Stories of the Commandments. — The seven corporal works of mercy.

— *Same:* 4th ser. 6 v. 18°. '68–'72. ea., 50c. *Cunningham.*
Cont.: Elinor Johnston. — Queen's daughter. — Hetty Homer, by F. Warner. — The Beverly family, by J. R. Chandler. — Aunt Fanny's present. — Woodland cottage, etc.

Young cavalier. Reback, H. 30c. ... *Am. News.*

Young chevalier. Dumas, A. 75c. ... *Dick & F.*

Young child's picture book. *See* Little Alice's lib.

Young Christian. *See* Abbott, Jac.
Young Christian directed. Kimball, D. 60c. *Cong. Pub.*
Young Christian merchant. Barstow, E. 80c. *Bost. Am. Tr.*
Young Christian ser. *See* Abbott, Jac.
Young Christian warned. Rockwell, J. E. 50c. *Pres. Bd.*
Young Christian's manual of devotion. Greenwald, E. 50c. .... *Luth. Bk. St.*
Young Christian's pocket book. 18°. 40c.... *Dutton.*
Young clerk; or, the story of Robert Elliott. 18°. 60c. *Am. S. S.*
Young collegian. Robertson, T. W. 15c.... *De Witt.*
Young colt. *See* Little Blue Mantle lib.
Young comforters. *See* Little Fan's lib.
Young commander. Armstrong, F. C. 80c. *Routledge.*
Young communicant. 24°. '74. 25c.; 40c. — 16°. $1. *Lothrop.*
Young communicant; by author of "Geraldine." 18°. 38c. .... *O'Shea.*
— *See also* Library of good example.
Young communicant's manual. 32°. '76. 30c... *Pott.*
Young composer. Day, H. N. $1 .... *Scribner.*
Young converts. Boyd, R. $1 .... *Revell.*
Young cottager. *See* Richmond, Legh.
Young countess. 18°. 50c. .... *O'Shea.*
Young crusaders. Lautenschlager, —. 50c... *Strong.*
Young Crusoe. Harley, A. J. $1.50........ *Lee & S.*
Young Crusoe. *See* Hofland, B.
Young debater and chairman's assistant: instructions how to form and construct societies, etc.; by an ex-member of the Phila. bar. 16°. pap., 30c.; bds., 50c. .... *Dick & F.*
Young declaimer. Northend, C. 75c. ...... *Barnes.*
Young deliverers. Kellogg, E. $1.25 .... *Lee & S.*
Young detective. Parker, R. A. $1 .... *Lee & S.*
Young disciple. *See* Clark, J: A.
Young disciple's lib. 10 v. 18°. $4.90..... *So. Meth.*
Cont.: Lessons of a disciple. — Creed of all men, by R. Abbey. — Father Reeves, by E. Corderoy. — Cookman's speeches. — Browning On perseverance. — Prayer, by R. Treffry. — Sabbath school offering, by Mrs. M. Martin. — Baxter's call. — Family government, by Andrew. — Language.
Young doctor. Conscience, H. $1; $1.25.. *Murphy.*
Young Dodge Club. *See* DeMille, J.
Young dressmaker. 32°. 20c.; 15c......... *Dutton.*
Young duchess. Reynolds, G. W. M. 50c... *De Witt.*
Young duke. *See* Disraeli, B.
Young eagle; or, forest fortunes; by author of "Amy Russell." 16°. 90c........ *Am. S. S.*
Young engineer: memoir of F. R. Firth, with introd. by E. E. Hale. por. 16°. $1.50 ...... *Lee & S.*
Young England: drama. 16°. pap., 15c. .... *French.*
Young envelope makers. Fry, S. M. 60c. *N. Y. Ref. Ch. Bd.; Pres. Com.*
Young envelope makers; or, prayer and faithfulness rewarded. 18°. '58. 55c. .... *Am. S. S.*
— *See also* Select lib. for girls.
Young exile. *See* Little Fan's lib.
Young exiles. Bowman, A. $1.25 .... *Routledge.*
Young fisherman of Heligoland. ill. 24°. '69. 30c. *Lothrop.*
Young fisherman's narrative. 32°. 20c.; 15c. *Dutton.*
Young folks' companion. *See* Chambers, W. *and* R.
Young folks' glee book. *See* Jarvis, C.
Young forester. *See* Sherwood, *Mrs.* M. M.
Young fortune seekers. *See* Home twilight stories.
Young fortune teller. Gilman, C. 75c.; 60c. *Lee & S.*
Young gold-diggers. Gerstäcker, F. 75c. *Routledge.*
Young governess. *See* Bouquet lib.
Young governess. *See* Janvier, *Mrs.* E. N.
Young governess: tale for girls. ill. 12°. $1.50.. *Nelson.*
Young grey head. Southey, C. B. 10c.... *Randolph.*
Young guest, and other stories. 18°. 50c..... *O'Shea.*
Young heiress; or, building on the sand. 18°. 55c. *Am. S. S.*
Young hero stories. 5 v. 18°. $2.25... *Bost. Am. Tr.*
Cont.: Circus, by A. S. Anthony. — How to be a hero, by E. E. Lay. — Kenny Carle's uniform, by S. J. Pritchard. — Lame Willie, by J. A. Jefferds. — Walter and the prize.
Young hop pickers. *See* Fry, S. M.
Young housekeeper's book. 16°. 10c....... *Dick & F.*
Young housewife's counsellor and friend. Mason, M. $1.75 .... *Hale; Lippincott.*
Young hunter's lib. *See* Lee, *Mrs.* R.
Young husband. Grey, E. C. 50c.......... *Harper.*
Young husband's book: manual of moral, religious and domestic duties. 18°. 75c........ *Miller.*
Young Hussar. Dimond, W. 15c.......... *French.*
Young islanders. *See* Taylor, Jeffries.
Young Jew: memoir of A. M. Myers. 18°. 35c. *Am. S. S.*
Young laborer. 18°. 25c.; 30c........... *Am. Bapt.*
Young ladies' biog. lib. 5 v. 16°. $5....... *Carter.*
Young ladies' companion. Coxe, M. $1; $1.50. *I. N. Whiting.*
Young ladies' friend; ed. and rev. by author of "Unsettled points of etiquette." 12°. $1.50.. *Lippincott.*
Young ladies' harp. Kingsley, G. $1....... *Barnes.*
Young ladies' lib. 3 v. ill. 16°. $3.75.... *Routledge.*
Cont.: Lillieslea, by M. Howitt. — The doctor's ward, by A. Bowman. — How to make the best of it, by M. A. Mackarness.
Young ladies' lib. 4 v. 16°. $5 .... *Lothrop.*
Cont.: Year in the country. — Veil on the heart. — Sybil's way. — Violet Fletcher's home work.
Young ladies' own book. Thornwell, E. $1.75. *J. E. Potter.*
Young ladies' progressive reader; for higher classes in Cath. schools. 12°. $1.25 .... *O'Shea.*
Young lady at home. Arthur, T. S. $1.50.. *J. E. Potter.*
Young lady's book: manual of recreations, arts, sciences and accomplishments. ill. 12°. (Bohn.) $2.75........ *Little, B. & Co.*
— *Same.* ill. 12°. (Bohn.) $3........ *Lippincott.*
— *Same.* ill. 12°. (Bohn.) $3; $3.75.. *Scribner, W. & A.*
Young lady's companion; or, sketches of life, manners and morals at the present day. ill. 12°. $1.25. *T. Bliss.*
Young lady's counselor. Wise, D. $1.. *Meth. Bk. Conc.*
Young lady's delight: parlor companion for Christmas, New Year and all seasons. 12°. $1.25.. *T. Bliss.*
Young lady's guide. ill. 12°. '70. $1.50; $2.. *Am. Tr.*
Young lady's lib. 4 v. 12°. $5.75 .... *Randolph.*
Cont.: Annie Mason. — Fabrics. — Miss Roberts' fortune. — Signal lights.
Young lady's mentor: a guide to the formation of character. ill. 12°. $1.25........ *T. Bliss.*
Young layman. Sanford, D. P. 90c. .... *Dutton.*
Young lieutenant. Adams, W. T. $1.50 .... *Lee & S.*
Young life. Mather, S. A. $1.25.. *Cin. Meth. Bk. Conc.*
Young Magdalen. Smith, F. S. $3; $4 ... *Peterson.*
Young maiden. Muzzey, A. B. $1.25... *Nichols & H.*
Young man. Todd, J. 75c. .... *Bridgman.*
Young man advised. Haven, E. O. $1.25. *Meth. Bk. Conc.*
Young man from home. James, J. A. 45c.... *Am. Tr.*
Young man in the battle of life. Landels, W. $1.50. *Cassell.*
Young man setting out in life. Guest, W. 35c.; 20c. *Am. Tr.*
Young man's book of knowledge. Tegg, T. $1.50. *Sower.*
Young man's counselor. Wise, D. $1.. *Meth. Bk. Conc.*
Young man's friend. Eddy, D. C. $1.50.... *Graves.*

Young man's friend. James, J. A. $1.25.... *Carter.*
Young man's guide to true greatness. Kasey, J. W. $1.25.... *Wilstach.*
Young man's lib. 3 v. 8°. $6 .... *Lothrop.*
Cont.: Knowledge is power. — Every day objects. — Circle of the year.
Young marooners on Florida coast. *See* Goulding, F. R.
Young mechanic: practical carpentry; by author of "Lathe and its uses." ill. sm. 4°. '71. $1.75. *Putnam.*
Young men and maidens. Brown, J. B. 75c. *Randolph.*
Young men of the Bible. Collier, J. A. 60c. *Am. Tr.*
Young men's Bible class. Blacket, W. S. 75c. *Nelson.*
Young men's lib. 25 v. ill. 18°. $25 .... *Am. S. S.*
Young men's singing book. Root, G. F., *and* Mason, L. $1.50.... *Ditson.*
Young Mexican. 18°. 90c.... (?) *Martien.*
Young middy. Armstrong, F. C. $1.50.... *Tilton.*
Young miller. *See* Daisy lib.
Young minister. Magruder, W. H. N. $1.25. *Cin. Meth. Bk. Conc.*
Young minstrel. Johnson, A. N., *and* White, J. 50c. *Gordon.*
Young missionaries. Seamer, F. 75c.... *Nelson.*
Young moose hunters. Stephens, C. A. $1.50. (?) *Shepard.*
Young mother. Selby, C. 15c.... *French.*
Young mother and nurse's oracle. Allen, A. H. $1.25. *Mendenhall.*
Young Muscovite. *See* Brother's (The) lib.
Young naturalist. *See* Loudon, *Mrs.* J. W.
Young New York. Wilkins, E. G. P. 15c... *French.*
Young Nile voyagers. Bowman, A. $1.25.. *Routledge.*
Young observers. Banvard, J. 3 pts. ea., 30c.; 40c. *Am. Bapt.*
Young orator. *See* Simple stories lib.
Young organist. Getze, J. A. $2.50.... *Ditson.*
Young outcast. 18°. 25c.; 30c. .... *Am. Bapt.*
Young outlaw. Alger, H., *jr.* $1.25 .... *Loring.*
Young painter. 18°. 50c.... *O'Shea.*
Young parson. 12°. $1.50.... *Sheldon.*
Young patriot. 18°. 75c.... *Cong. Pub.*
Young people's half hour ser. 4 nos. 12°. '72. ea., pap., 20c.... *Meth. Bk. Conc.*
Cont.: Keep good company, by S. Smiles. — Daniel, the uncompromising young man, by C. H. Payne. — Ten days in Switzerland, by H. B. Ridgaway. — Two weeks in the Yosemite valley, by J. M. Buckley.
Young people's ill. Bible hist.; with introd. by A. Bond. maps and ill. 8°. '72. *$3.75; $4.25; $5.25.... *Henry Bill.*
Young people's lib. 12 v. sq. 16°. $4.50.. *Nichols & H.*
Young people's lib. 30 v. ill. 18°. $10.... *Am. Tr.*
Young people's lib. 40 v. ill. 18°. $30.... *Am. S. S.*
Young pianist. Dressler, W. $2.25; $1.75.. *Peters.*
Young pilgrim. *See* Tucker, *Mrs.* Ctte.
Young potato roasters. 18°. 25c.... *Am. S. S.*
— *See also* Little Blue Mantle lib.
Young prima donna. Grey, E. C. 50c.... *Peterson.*
Young Prince Marigold. Maguire, J. F. $1.50. *Macmillan.*
Young Protestant's lib. 10 v. 18°. $4.65... *So. Meth.*
Cont.: Dialogues on popery, by J. Stanley. — Lives of the popes, 4 v. — The reformation, 2 v. — The inquisition. — William, the converted Romanist. — Memoir of John Huss.
Young Quaker: comedy. 16°. pap., 15c.... *French.*
Young quartermaster: life and death of Lieut. L. M. Bingham, of the 22d South Carolina Vols. 18°. 50c.... *N. Y. Ref. Ch. Bd.*
Young raiders. 16°. 45c.... *Cummiskey.*
Young reader. Pierpont, J. 15c.... *Lippincott.*
Young recruit. 16°. '63. $1.... *Tilton.*
Young recruit. Myers, S. A. 70c.... *Pres. Bd.*
Young recruiting sergeant. ('62.) New ed. ill. 18°. '70. 30c.... *Hoyt.*
Young reefer. Soane, G. 15c.... *French.*
Young reporter; or, how to write short-hand. 16°. bds., 50c. .... *Dick & F.*
Young Rick. *See* Eastman, J. A.
Young Rick lib. 4 v. 16°. $5.50.... *Lothrop.*
Cont.: Young Rick, by J. A. Eastman. — One quiet life, by Mrs. J. J. Colter. — Two fortune seekers, by R. Johnson, etc. — Walter Neal, by T. Brown.
Young ruler. Spencer, J. A. $1.50.... *Randolph.*
Young sailor. Shindler, M. S. B. D. 75c... *Harper.*
Young Sapphira; or, God hears every word we say. ill. 24°. '69. 30c.... *Lothrop.*
Young Savoyard. 16°. 60c.; $1.... *Sadlier.*
Young scamp. Stirling, E. 15c.... *French.*
Young scamp. Weaver, A. 15c.... *De Witt.*
Young schoolmistress. Alden, J. 75c.... *Harper.*
Young seaman's manual; for use of U. S. training ships and marine schools. ill. 8°. '75. hf. roan, $3 .... *Van Nostrand.*
Young sergeant. Denison, M. A. 45c.... *Hoyt.*
Young shawm. Bradbury, W. B. 60c.... *Ditson.*
Young Shetlander and his home. Peirce, D. K. $1.25. *Meth. Bk. Conc.*
Young shipbuilders of Elm Island. Kellogg, E. $1.25. *Lee & S.*
Young singer: school music, original and selected. 2 pts. 16°. '60. ea., 50c.... *Wilson, H. & Co.*
Young singer's manual: new coll., with select. from "Young singer." 16°. '66. 55c... *Wilson, H. & Co.*
Young soldier. 18°. 25c.... *Am. S. S.*
Young speaker. Lovell, J. E. *net*, 85c.... *Peck.*
Young squire. Eiloart, C. J. $2.50.. *Scribner, W. & A.*
Young stepmother. Yonge, C. M. $1.75. *Appleton; Macmillan.*
Young student. Guizot, E. C. P. $1 .... *Appleton.*
Young surveyor. Trowbridge, J. T. $1.25.. *Porter.*
Young teacher. 18°. '46. 25c.... *Am. S. S.*
Young teacher. Hulen, S. E. 75c. .... *Cong. Pub.*
Young Tom Rodman. ill. 8°. (Lond.) 50c... *Am. News.*
Young violinist. *See* Wichtl, G.
Young visitor. 18°. 50c.; 60c.... *Am. Bapt.*
Young voyagers. Adams, W. T. 45c. .... *Lee & S.*
Young voyagers. Reid, M. $1.50 .... *Miller.*
Young whaler. Gerstäcker, F. $1.... *Routledge.*
Young whaler. Kingston, W. H. G. 75c. .. *Lothrop.*
Young widow. Rodwell, T. G. 15c.... *French.*
Young wife's book: a manual of moral, religious and domestic duties. 18°. 75c.... *Miller.*
Young wife's receipt book. 12°. $1.75.... *Peterson.*
Young woman. Waterbury, J. B. 25c.... *Am. Tr.*
Young woman's friend. Eddy, D. C. $1.50.. *Graves.*
Young woman's friend. James, J. A. $1.25.. *Carter.*
Young women's lib. 25 v. ill. 18°. $25.... *Am. S. S.*
Young woodcutter. *See* Little Norwegian.
Young wreckers of the Florida coast. Bache, R. M. $1.50 .... *Claxton.*
Young yachtsman. Bowman, A. $1.25... *Routledge.*
Young yagers. Reid, M. $1.50.... *Miller.*
Younge, E: *See* England, Exchequer reports.
Younger son. Palmer, H. V. 30c.... *Am. News.*
Your life's in danger. Morton, J. M. 15c. *French; Lee & S.*
Your likeness, one shilling. Harrington, N. H., *and* Yates, E. 15c.... *French.*
Your vote and interest: farce. 16°. pap., 15c... *French.*
Yours or mine. Heywood, E. H. 15c. .... *Mendum.*

Youth and manhood of Cyril Thornton. Hamilton, T. $1.50 .... *Harper.*
Youth in earnest. Harbaugh, H. 90c... *Ref. Ch. Pub.*
Youth of Shakespeare. Williams, R. F. $1.. *Peterson.*
Youthful dialogues. 18°. 25c.......... *Am. S. S.*
Youthful diligence. Tweedie, W. K. $1.50.. *Nelson.*
Youthful memories. Wilson, W. C. 45c... *Am. S. S.*
Youthful pilgrim. 18°. 30c.......... *Am. S. S.*
Youthful queen. Shannon, C. 15c. .... *French.*
Youthful voices. Lang, B. J. 60c.; 50c..... *Ditson.*
Youth's Bible and commentator. *See* Cobbin, I.
Youth's book of natural theology. Gallaudet, T. H. 45c. .... *Am. Tr.*
Youth's cabinet. 76 v. ill. 18°. hf. bd., $9.. *Am. Tr.*
Youth's casket of gems and pearls. sq. 16°. 50c. *Pres. Bd.*
Youth's director; or, familiar instructions for young people; tr. by W. Tyler. 18°. 50c..... *Strong.*
Youth's gems. 32 v. ill. 18°. hf. bd., $4.... *Am. Tr.*
Youth's gleaner; or, ripe fruit of piety. 18°. 60c. *Pres. Bd.*
Youth's lib. 50 v. 18°. $25.......... *Cong. Pub.*
Youth's lib. 740 v. 18°. $319.35...... *Meth. Bk. Conc.*
Youth's lib. of biog.; — of hist.; — of literature and science. *See* Goodrich, S: G.
Youth's pictorial lib. 9 v. ill. sq. 16°. '67. $4.50. *Perkinpine.*

Cont.: Stories of foreign countries. — Tales of the great and brave. — Stories of natural history. — Stories of animals. — Christmas stories. — Poems for little folks. — Caspar's adventures. — History of birds. — Fables in verse.

Youth's picture sermons. Andrews, E. 60c.; 80c. *Earle.*
Youth's song book. obl. 16°. bds., 30c... *Huntington.*
Youth's visitor: sel. in prose and verse. ill. sq. 16°. 80c. .... *Pres. Bd.*
Yule, *Mrs.* J. C. Ada Emory; or, the sister's Bible. 16°. $1.50.......... *Am. Bapt.*
Yule log: farce. 16°. pap., 15c.......... *French.*
Yule-tide stories. *See* Thorpe, B.
Yu-Pe-Ya's lute. Webster, A. $1...... *Macmillan.*
Yusef. Browne, J. R. $1.75.......... *Harper.*
Yvan, M., *and* Callery, J. M. History of insurrection in China; ed. by J. Oxenford. 12°. $1.25.. *Harper.*

Zabriskie, Ab. O. *See* New Jersey, Sup. Court reports.
Zabriskie, F. N. Golden fruit from Bible trees. 18°. '62. 50c.......... *Randolph.*
— Precious stones. 18°. '63. 75c........ *Randolph.*
— Story of a soul; or, thoughts on the parable of the prodigal son. 16°. '72. 75c........ *Randolph.*
Zabriskie, Ja. C. *See* United States, Public land laws.
Zaccheus; or, Scripture plan of benevolence. Harris, S. 25c.......... *Am. Tr.*
Zachos, H. *See* Parker, R. G., *and* Zachos, H.
Zachos, J: C. Analytic and phonetic word book. 12°. '59. bds., 30c.......... *Wilstach.*
— Analytic elocution. 8°. '60. $1.50 ...... *Barnes.*
— High school speaker. 12°. '58. $1.25.... *Stevens.*
— New American speaker. 12°. '74. $1.88. *Collins & Bro.*
— Phonic primer, and primary reader. 12°. bds., 35c. *Lee & S.*
— Primary speaker. 16°. '58. 60c........ *Stevens.*
Zadoc Hull (Story of). ill. 16°. 80c. .. *Bost. Am. Tr.*
Zahn, F. L. Zweimal 25 biblische Geschichten; ausgewählt u. mit Fragen versehen, v. E. Bohm. 16°. '71. bds., 45c.......... *Steiger.*
Zaida. *See* Tucker, *Mrs.* Ctte.
Zaidee. Oliphant, M. O. W. 75c........ *Littell & G.*
Zampa. *See* Eiserne Maske.

Zampa. *See* Herold, L. J. F.
Zampa, die Marmorbraut. 12°. pap., 15c..... *Radde.*
Zander, H. J., *and* Howard, T. E. Outlines of composition. 12°. 94c.......... *R. S. Davis (B.)*
Zanita: tale of the Yo-Semite. Yelverton, T. $1.50. *Hurd & H.*
Zanoni. *See* Bulwer-Lytton, *Sir* E. G. E. L.
Zarah, the gipsy: drama. 16°. pap., 15c..... *French.*
Zauberer Virgilius. 12°. pap., 15c.......... *Radde.*
Zaubermantel (Der). *See* Van der Velde, K. F.
Zdrůbka, Fk. B. Druhá čítanka. [Second Bohemian reader.] 16°. '76. 40c.......... *Geringer.*
— Nová anglická mluvnice. [Eng. grammar for Bohemians.] 16°. '73. $1.20......... *Geringer.*
— První čítanka s. obrázky. [First Bohemian reader.] 16°. '75. 40c.......... *Geringer.*
Zelda's fortune. *See* Francillon, R. E.
Zelie, J. H. Critical speller. 16°. 25c. .... *Taintor.*
Zelina. Somerset, C. A. 15c.......... *French.*
Zell (*pseud.*) *See* O'Brien, *Mrs.* H.
Zell's descriptive hand atlas of the world. *See* Bartholomew, J:
Zell's popular encyclopedia. *See* Colange, L.
Zelma. Franklin, J. 83c.......... *Thompson.*
Zend avesta. *See* Avesta.
Zender, Joac. Denis Laurent. Abécédaire français-anglais, illustré. ('53.) New ed. 12°. '70. bds., 50c.......... *Holt.*
Zenner, Gst. Treatise on valve gears, with special consideration of link-motions of locomotive engines; tr. by M. Müller. 3d ed., rev. and enl. pl. 8°. '69. $3.......... *Spon.*
Zenobia. Ware, W. $2.......... *Miller.*
Zerbrochene Kette (Die). 18°. 50c.; 65c... *Ev. Assoc.*
Zerbrochene Krug (Der). *See* Zschokke, H.
Zerub Throop's experiment. Whitney, A. D. T. 75c.; 50c. .... *Loring.*
Zeuner, C: Ancient lyre: coll. of old, new and orig. church music. ('36.) 20th ed., rev. and enl. obl. 8°. bds., $1.50.......... *Ditson.*
— Organ voluntaries. 2 pts. f°. pap., 1, $1.50; 2, $2; 2 pts. in 1 v., bds., $3 .... *Ditson.*
Zicci. *See* Bulwer-Lytton, *Sir* E. G. E. L.
Ziegenfus, H. L. What constitutes a lawful ministry. 12°. pap., 15c.......... *Dutton.*
Ziegler, H: Catechetics, hist., theoretical and practical. 12°. '76. $1.50; $2; shp., $3 .... (?) *Luth. Pub.*
— Pastor (The): his relation to Christ and the church. 12°. '76. $1.50; $2; shp., $3.... (?) *Luth. Pub.*
— Preacher (The): his relation to the study and the pulpit. 12°. '76. $1.50; $2; shp., $3.. (?) *Luth. Pub.*
Ziemssen, H. v. (*ed.*) Cyclopædia of practice of medicine. [To form 17 v.] v. 1-5, 10. roy. 8°. ea., *$5; leath., $6; hf. mor., $7.50...... *W. Wood.*
Ziethe, M. Juliane von Krüdener. 18°. '67. 25c. *Am. Tr.*
— Leben von Anna H. Judson. 18°. '73. 50c. *Am. Tr.*
— Wahrheit (Die) und Herrlichkeit des Christenthums. 18°. '76. 50c.......... *Am. Tr.*
Zigeuner (Der). Glaubrecht, O. 25c...... *Morwitz.*
Zilpha, *Cousin.* *See* Cousin Zilpha.
Zimmerman, Jean Georges. On solitude; prefaced by life of author. por. 18°. 75c....... *Sower.*
Zimmermann, G. A. Handbuch d. deutschen Litera tur Europas u. Amerikas: klassiches Lesebuch. 3 v. 8°. v. 1, 90c.; with Eng. vocab., $1; v. 2, $1.50; v. 3, 90c.......... *Enderis.*
— *Same.* Deutsch-amerikanische Dichter. [App. to v. 2.] 8°. bds., 50c.......... *Enderis.*
Note. v. 2 without app., $1.
Zimmermann, J. A. Bonifazius der Heilige. 12°. 75c. .... *Benziger.*

Zimmers, M. T. Mass; for soprano, tenor and bass. f°. pap., $2 .... *Ditson.*

Zina; or, morning mists; by author of "Story of Aimée." ill. 16°. '73. $1.50 .... *Lothrop.*

Zingee the Hindoo girl. 18°. 18c. .... *Am.S.S.*

Zingra, the gipsy. Maillard, A. M. 50c. .. *U.P.James.*

Zinn, P: Leading and select cases on trusts, with abstracts of other Eng. and Am. cases; with notes and ref., and report of the case of the Covington and Lexington R. R. Co. vs. R. B. Bowler's heirs and others. 8°. '73. shp., $6.50 .... *Clarke.*

Zinsfrage (Die). Fritschel, G. 20c. .... *Brobst.*

Zion. Perkins, W. O. $1.25 .... *G.D.Russell.*

Zion hymn and tune book. Converse, C. C. 25c.; 30c. *Brainard.*

Zion's choral. Tilman, R. 75c. .... *Ditson.*

Zion's harp. Getze, J. A. 60c. .... *Ditson.*

Zion's harp. Pitts, F. E. 60c. .... *Morton.*

Zion's pilgrim. Hawker, R. 45c. .... *Pres.Bd.*

Zion's songster. Mason, T. 50c. .... *Harper.*

Zoa Rodman. Richmond, E. J. $1 ...... *Nat.Temp.*

Zöckler, O: *See* Lange, J. P., Commentary.

Zoe. Jewsbury, G. E. 50c. .... *Harper.*

Zoe's story: allegory. 18°. '63. 50c. .... *Randolph.*

Zollner, C. H. Forty short studies in art of singing; for soprano voice. (op. 50.) f°. $1.50 .. *Brainard.*

— *Same;* for bass voice. (op. 52.) f°. $1.50 .. *Brainard.*

Zoological recreations. Broderip, W. J. $2.50. *Scribner, W.&A.*

Zriny. Körner, C. T. 60c. .... *Holt.*

Zschokke, H: Werke. 46 v. 12°. ea., pap., 10c.–20c. .... *F. W. Thomas.*

Cont.: Addrich im Moos. — Der Freihof v. Aarau. — Lyonel Harlington, *ea.*, 20c. — Alamontade. — Der Creole, *ea.*, 15c. — Die Herrnhuter Familie. — Kleine Ursachen. — Jonathan Frock. — Die Verklärungen. — Blätter a. d. Tagebuche d. armen Pfarrvikars v. Wiltshire. — Ein Narr d. neunzehnten Jahrh. — Die weiblichen Stufenjahre. — Der Millionär. — Der todte Gast. — Der Fürstenblick. — Das Loch im Aermel. — Der Flüchtling im Jura. — Die Irrfarth des Philhelenen. — Florette. — Die Gründung v. Maryland. — Der Pascha v. Buda. — Die Bohne. — Die Nacht in Breczwezmcisl'. — Es ist sehr möglich. — Die Erbschaft. — Das blaue Wunder. — Erzählungen im Nebel. — Die isländischen Briefe. — Das Pfarrhaus. — Bilder a. d. häuslichen Leben. — Die Liebe d. Ausgewanderten. — Tantchen Rosmarin. — Hans Dampf in allen Gassen. — Herrn Quints Verlobung. — Rückwirkungen. — Das Wirthshaus zu Cransac. — Das Abenteuer d. Neujahrsnacht. — Die Walpurgisnacht. — Der Blondin v. Namur. — Kriegerische Abenteuer e. Friedfertigen. — Der Feldweibel. — Die Prinzessin v. Wolfenbüttel. — Agathokles. — Der Pflanzer in Cuba. — Das Goldmacherdorf. — Abellino, *ea.*, 10c.

— Novellen u. Dichtungen. 3 v. 8°. $6; pap., $4.50; hf. mor., $6.75 .... *F. W. Thomas.*

— *Same.* 10 v. 12°. $10; $11; pap., $6.50; hf. mor., $15 .... *Radde.*

— Dead guest (The). 12°. pap., 20c. .... *Radde.*

— *Same;* tr. by G. C. McWhorter. ill. 8°. pap., 50c. *Appleton.*

— History of Switzerland; tr. 12°. $1.75 .... *Mason.*

— Labor stands on golden feet: holiday story for sensible apprentices, journeymen and masters; tr. by J. Yeats. 16°. $1 .... *Cassell.*

— Rose of Disentis; tr. 12°. $1.50; pap., $1 .. *Sheldon.*

— Stunden d. Andacht. 4 v. 8°. $6.50–$20; in 2 v., $6.50–$12 .... *Kohler.*

Zschokke, H: *continued.*

— Veronica; or, the free court of Aarau; tr. 8°. pap., 50c. .... *Harper.*

— Wirthshaus (Das) zu Cransac. ('71.) New ed. 12°. '76. pap., 40c. .... *Schoenhof.*

— Zerbrochene Krug (Der). With Eng. notes. ('71.) New ed. 12°. '76. pap., 30c. .... *Schoenhof.*

Züge aus Havelock's Leben. 32°. '62. 15c. .. *Am.Tr.*

Zulu-land. Grout, L. $1.50 .... *Pres.Bd.*

Zumpt, C: Gli. Latin grammar; adapted to Eng. students by L. Schmitz; rev. and enl. by C. Anthon. 12°. shp., $1.50; — abridg. 12°. shp., $1 .... *Harper.*

— *See also* Schmitz, L., *and* Zumpt, C. G.

Zundel, J: Amateur organist: collection of opening and closing voluntaries. 4°. '53. bds., $2. *Ditson.*

— Choral friend: collection of church music. 8°. '52. $1.25 .... *Barnes.*

— Complete melodeon instructor. 4°. '53. bds., $2.50. *Ditson.*

— First year on the organ. obl. roy. 8°. '69. pap., $1 .... *Pond.*

— Four hundred and forty-four voluntaries and interludes. obl. 8°. $2 .... *Gordon.*

— Modern school for the organ. 4°. '60. bds., $4; — in 3 pts. ea., bds., $2 .... *Ditson.*

— New school reed organ. obl. 4°. $1.50 .... *Gordon.*

— Treatise on harmony and modulation. 16°. $1.50. *Gordon.*

— Two hundred and fifty easy voluntaries and interludes for the organ, melodeon, seraphine, etc. 4°. '51. bds., $2 .... *Ditson.*

— *and* Ryan, Ja. E. School harmonist. 8°. hf. bd., $1.25. — Vocal ed., hf. bd., 90c. .... *Harper.*

Zündt, E. A. Lyrische u. dramatische Dichtungen. 16°. (St. Louis.) '71. $2 .... *Steiger.*

Zung, —. Extracts from Jewish moralists. *See* Hebrew characteristics.

Zurcher, F: *and* Margollé, E. Meteors, aerolites, storms and atmospheric phenomena; tr. by W. Lackland. ill. 12°. '76. $1.50 .... *Scribner.*

— — Volcanoes and earthquakes; tr. by Mrs. N. Lockyer. ill. cr. 8°. $3.75 .... *Lippincott.*

Zurnow, C: The maiden mother; or, Eugenia the guiltless: secrets in the lives of prominent personages of Louisiana. [In Eng. or Germ.] 8°. pap., 25c. .... *Barclay.*

Zwei Freier. *See* Meyr, M.

Zwei heitere Geschichten. Mützelburg, A. 50c. *Morwitz.*

Zwei Kaiser Kronen. Meding, G. 2 v. ea., 50c. *Morwitz.*

Zwei vornehme Ehen. Steinbach, F. 20c. .... *Zickel.*

Zweihundert Erzählungen. Schmid, C. v. 2 v. ea., 20c. .... *Morwitz.*

Zweihundert lehrreiche Erzählungen. Schmid, C. v. 30c.; 15c. .... *Radde.*

Zweimal 25 biblische Geschichten. Zahn, F. L. 45c. *Steiger.*

Zweimal 52 biblische Historien. *See* Hübner, J.

Zwingli, U: Life; with biog. sketch of John Œcolampadius. 18°. 40c. .... *Pres.Bd.*

APPENDIX.

CONTRIBUTED LISTS

OF BOOKS PUBLISHED SINCE 1876,

WITH AUTHOR AND TITLE INDEX.

LIST OF CONTRIBUTORS.

ROBERT CARTER & BROTHERS,

530 Broadway, New York.

July, 1876–1879.

1. **A. L. O. E.** Victory stories. 18°............75c.
2. — Indian stories. 18°.......................75c.
3. — Fritz's victory, and other stories. 18°......50c.
4. — Tiny red night cap, and other stories. 18°..50c.
5. — The truant kitten, and other stories. 18°...50c.
6. — Heroes of Israel. 5 v. in box. 16°......$5.00
7. **Aitken**, *Rev.* W. Hay M. H. What is your life? 12° $1.00
8. **Arnot**, *Rev.* William. Autobiography and memoir. 12°.................................$2.00
9. **Bonar**, *Rev.* And. A. The person of Christ. 18°. 50c.
10. — The brook Besor. 18°....................50c.
11. **Bonar**, Horatius, *D.D.* My old letters. 12°..$2.00
12. — Hymns of the nativity. 16°.............$1.00
13. **Brodie**, Emily. Jean Lindsay, the vicar's daughter. 12°...................................$1.25
14. — The Hamiltons; or, Dora's choice. 16° ..$1.25
15. **Butler**, *Rev.* Wm. Archer. Sermons. 2 v. 12°. $2.50
16. — History of ancient philosophy. 2 v. 12°..$2.50
17. **Charlesworth**, *Miss* M. L. The old looking-glass. 16°....................................$1.00
18. — The broken looking-glass. 16°..........$1.00
19. **Cobden**, Paul. Little lights along shore. 16°. $1.25
20. **Cowper**, William. The task. ill. 8°. $3.50
21. **Culross**, James, *D.D.* John, whom Jesus loved. 12°...................................$1.25
22. **Cunningham**, William, *D.D.* Theological lectures. 8°...............................$3.00
23. **Cuyler**, *Rev.* T. L. Pointed papers. 12°....$1.50
24. **D'Aubigné**, J. H. M., *D.D.* History of reformation in 16th century. 5 v. 12°...........$4.50
25. — *Same.* Time of Calvin. 8 v. 12°........$8.00
26. **Dickson**, *Rev.* Alex. Beauty for ashes. 12°. $2.00
27. **Dinwiddie**, *Rev.* W. Times before the reformation. 16° $1.25
28. **Drinkwater**, Jennie M. Tessa Wadsworth's discipline. 12° $1.50
29. **Dykes**, J. Oswald, *D.D.* Abraham, the friend of God. 12° $1.50
30. **Ella's** half-sovereign. 16° $1.25
31. **Fighting** the foe. 12° $1.50
32. **Fletcher**, Alex., *D.D.* Family devotions. 4°.$5.00
33. **Gabled** farm (The). 12° $1.25
34. **Gale**, *Mrs.* Martha T. The widow's trust. 24°. $1.25
35. **Gray**, Thomas. Elegy. ill. 24°............50c.
36. **Guthrie**, Thomas, *D.D.* Autobiography and life. 12°...................................$2.00
37. **Hamlin**, Cyrus. Among the Turks. 12°...$1.50
38. **Henry**, Matthew. Commentary. 5 v. 4°. $15.00
39. **Hero** in the battle of life. 18°.............50c.
40. **Hester** Trueworthy's royalty. 16° $1.25
41. **Highland** series (The). 6 v. 16°.........$7.50
42. **Hodge**, *Rev.* A. A. Outlines of theology. Revised ed. 8° $3.00
43. **Hodge**, Charles, *D.D.* Commentary on Romans. 12°...................................$1.75
44. **Holt**, Emily Sarah. Clare Avery. 12°.....$1.50
45. — Lettice Eden. 12°......................$1.50
46. — For the Master's sake. 16°..............$1.00
47. — Margery's son. 12° $1.50
48. — Lady Sybil's choice. 12°.................$1.50
49. — The maiden's lodge: a tale of Queen Anne. 12° $1.25
50. **Home** lessons on the old paths. 16°........$1.25
51. **House** in the glen and boys who built it. 12°.$1.25
52. **Jack** O'Lantern. 16°......................$1.25
53. **Jacobus**, M. W., *D.D.* The Christian's heritage. 12° $1.50
54. **Job** (The book of). Illustrated by John Gilbert. 8°....................................$4.50
55. **Lewis**, *Prof.* Tayler. Six days of creation. 12° $1.50
56. **Macduff**, John R., *D.D.* Footsteps of St. Peter. 12°...................................$2.00
57. — Brighter than the sun. 8°..............$2.00
58. — Eventide at Bethel. 12° $1.25
59. — Palms of Elim. 12°....................$1.50
60. — Memories of Patmos. New and cheaper edition. 12°...................................$1.25
61. **Macleod**, Norman, *D.D.* Gold thread, and Wee Davie. 16°..........................75c.
62. **Mathews**, Joanna H. Haps and mishaps. 6 v. 16°...................................$7.50
63. — Milly's whims. 16°....................$1.25
64. — Blackberry jam. 16°...................$1.25
65. — The broken mallet, and The pigeon's eggs. 16°...................................$1.25
66. **Mathews**, Julia A. Uncle Joe's Thanksgiving. 16°...................................$1.25
67. **Meade**, *Miss* L. T. Scamp and I. 12°....$1.25
68. — A knight of to-day. 12°................$1.50
69. — David's little lad. 12°................$1.25
70. — Water gipsies. 16°.....................$1.00
71. — Your brother and mine. 16° $1.00
72. — White lilies. 16° ....60c.
73. — Bel-Marjory. 16° $1.50
74. — Dot and her treasures. 16°.............$1.00
75. — The children's kingdom: the story of a great endeavour. 12° $1.50
76. **Mitchell**, Sam. S., *D.D.* The true man. 12°.$1.50
77. **Moore's** forge: a tale by author of "Win and wear" series. 16° $1.25
78. **Nellie** Arundel; or, the yielded life. 12°...$1.25
79. **Newton**, Richard, *D.D.* The king in his beauty. 16° $1.25
80. — Pebbles from the brook. 16°...........$1.25
81. **Newton**, *Rev.* Wm. Wilberforce. Little and wise. 16°...................................$1.25
82. — The wicket gate. 16°...................$1.25
83. **Old** David's lassie..........................60c.
84. **Patton**, *Rev.* Francis L. Doctrinal sermons.
85. **Peep** of day library. 8 v. 18° $4.50
86. **Pennefather**, *Rev.* William. Life and letters of. 8°....................................$2.50
87. **Pollard**, M. M. Nellie's secret. 16°......$1.00
88. — His grandchild. 16° $1.00
89. **Power**, *Rev.* P. B. Take care of No. 1. 16°...................................$1.00
90. **Prime**, S. Irenæus, *D. D.* Songs of the soul. New ed. 12°.............................$2.00
91. **Rose** Dunbar's mistake. 12° $1.50
92. **Saphir**, *Rev.* Adolph. The hidden life. 12°.$1.50
93. — Our life day. 12° $1.00
94. **Servants** of Christ. 18° ....50c.
95. **Sinclair**, Catherine. Holiday house: a series of tales. 16°...............................$1.25
96. **Springdale** series. 6 v. 18°..............$2.00
97. **Walton**, *Mrs.* O. F. A peep behind the scenes. 16° $1.25
98. — Saved at sea. 18° ....50c.
99. — Was I right? 16° $1.25
100. **Warner**, *Miss* Anna. Blue flag and cloth of gold. 16° $1.25
101. **Warner**, *Miss* Susan. Pine needles. 12°..$1.50
102. — Kingdom of Judah. 16°.................$1.50
103. — Broken walls of Jerusalem. 16°.........$1.25
104. — The king's people. 5 v. 16°............$7.00
105. — My desire. 12° $1.75
106. **Wells**, *Rev.* James. Bible echoes. 16°...$1.25
107. — Bible children. 16°.....................$1.25

ROBERTS BROTHERS,

Boston.

NEW PUBLICATIONS.

1. **Abbott**, Edward. Revolutionary times: sketches of our country, its people and their ways, one hundred years ago. sq. 18° $1.00
2. **Abbott**, Edwin A. How to parse. An attempt to apply the principles of scholarship to English grammar. With appendixes on analysis, spelling and punctuation. 16° $1.00
3. **Afterglow.** A novel. (No name series.) 16°..$1.00
4. **Alcott**, A. Bronson. Table talk. 16°......$1.50
5. **Alcott**, Louisa M. My girls, etc. Being the fourth volume of "Aunt Jo's scrap-bag." 16°....$1.00
6. — Jimmy's cruise in the Pinafore, etc. Being the fifth volume of "Aunt Jo's scrap-bag." 16°. $1.00
7. — Rose in bloom. A sequel to "Eight cousins." 16° $1.50
8. — Under the lilacs. With illustrations. 16°..$1.50
9. **Allen**, Joseph Henry. Hebrew men and times. From the Patriarchs to the Messiah. A new, revised edition. 16° $1.50
10. **Allingham**, William. Songs, ballads and stories. 16°. Gilt edge $2.50
11. **Amateur** poacher (The). By author of "The gamekeeper at home." 12° $1.50
12. **Angell**, H. C. How to take care of our eyes. With advice to parents and teachers in regard to the management of the eyes of children. With illustrations. 16° .... 50c.
13. **Antoninus**, Marcus Aurelius. Selections from the Thoughts of. (Wisdom series.) 18°......50c.
14. **Appleton**, Thomas G. Chequer-work. Tales and essays. 16° $1.50
15. — Syrian sunshine. 16° $1.00
16. — Windfalls. Tales and essays. 16°.......$1.50
17. **Ariosto** (Tales from), retold for children, by a lady. Uniform with "Canterbury chimes." With 3 illustrations. 16° $1.00
18. **Arnold**, Edwin. The light of Asia; or, the great renunciation: being the life and teaching of Gautama, prince of India and founder of Buddhism. 16° $1.50
19. **Atkinson**, W. P. On right use of books. 16° 50c.
20. **Besant**, Walter. Studies in early French poetry. sq. 12° $2.00
21. **Blessed** life (The). Favorite hymns selected by the editor of "Quiet hours." sq. 18°...$1.00
22. **Browne**, *Sir* Thomas. Religio medici: A letter to a friend, Christian morals, Urn-burial, and other papers. With a fine portrait. 16°........$1.25
23. **Bulwer-Lytton.** Poems. (Diamond ed.) mor. antique, $3.75; hf. cf. $3.00
24. **Causerie.** From the "Boston Evening Transcript." sq. 16° $1.00
25. **Chadwick**, J. W. A book of poems. sq. 18°. $1.00
26. — The faith of reason: a series of Sunday lectures on the leading topics of religion. 16°.....$1.00
27. **Chaney**, G. L. Tom: a home story. 16°..$1.25
28. — Aloha: a Hawaiian salutation. With illustrations. 16° $1.50
29. **Child**, Lydia Maria. Aspirations of the world. A chain of opals. 16° $1.25
30. **Collier**, R. Laird. Meditations on the essence of Christianity. 12° $1.25
31. **Colonel's** (The) opera cloak. A novel. (No name (second) series.) 16° $1.00
32. **Coolidge**, Susan (*pseud. of* S. C. Woolsey). Eyebright. A story. With illustrations. sq. 16°..$1.50
33. — For summer afternoons. sq. 18°........$1.25
34. **Deirdrè**: a story in verse. (No name ser.) 16°. $1.00
35. **Delany**, *Mrs.* Autobiography and correspondence of. Revised from Lady Llanover's edition, and edited by Sarah Chauncey Woolsey ("Susan Coolidge"). With portraits. 2 v. 12°....$4.00
36. **Drake**, Samuel Adams. Old landmarks and historic personages of Boston. ill. 12°......$2.00
37. — Old landmarks and historic fields of Middlesex. ill. 12° $2.00
38. **Epic** (The) of Hades. In three books. From the seventh London edition. 16° $1.50
39. **Ewing**, Juliana Horatia. Jan of the windmill. 16° $1.25
40. — Great emergency (A), and other stories. With illustrations. 16° $1.25
41. **Faris**, William W. The children of light. (Second Fletcher prize essay.) 16° $1.50
42. **Fawcett**, Edgar. Fantasy and passion. Poems. 16° $1.25
43. **Fénelon.** Selections from. Edited by the editor of "Quiet hours." (Wisdom series.) 18°....50c.
44. **Gamekeeper** (The) at home. Sketches of natural history and rural life. By the author of "Wild life in a southern county." 12° $1.50
45. — *Same.* With 40 illustrations by Whymper. sm. cr. 8° $4.00
46. **Gemini.** A novel. (No name series.) 16°..$1.00
47. **Great** match (The). A novel. (No name series.) 16° $1.00
48. **Griffin**, R. Andrew. From traditional to rational faith; or, the way I came from Baptist to liberal Christianity. 16° $1.00
49. **Grillparzer**, Franz. Sappho: a tragedy. Translated by Ellen Frothingham. 18°........$1.00
50. **Gwen**: a drama in monologue. By the author of "The epic of Hades." 16° $1.50
51. **H.**, H. (*pseud. of Mrs.* Jackson). Bits of talk in prose and verse for young folks. sq. 18°...$1.00
52. — Bits of travel at home. sq. 18° $1.50
53. — Letters from a cat. Published by her mistress for the benefit of all cats, and the amusement of little children. With seventeen illustrations by Addie Ledyard. sm. 4° $1.25
54. — Nelly's silver mine. A story of Colorado life. With illustrations. 16° $1.50
55. — Verses. hf. cf. $2.75
56. **Hale**, Edward E. The man without a country, and other tales. 16° $1.25
57. — Ninety days' worth of Europe. 16°......$1.50
58. — The Ingham papers. 16° $1.25
59. — Workingmen's homes. ill. 16° $1.25
60. — How to do it. 16° $1.00
61. — His level best. 16° $1.25
62. — The good time coming; or, our new crusade. A temperance story. sq. 18°. pap. .... 50c.
63. — What career? Ten papers on the choice of a vocation and the use of time. 16° $1.25
64. — Mrs. Merriam's scholars. 16° $1.00
65. — G. T. T.; or, the wonderful adventures of a Pullman. 16° $1.00
66. — Stories of war, told by soldiers; ed. by E. E. Hale. 16° $1.00
67. **Hale**, Lucretia P. The Lord's Supper, and its observance. 16° $1.00
68. **Hamerton**, Philip G. Works. 9 v. sq. 12°. hf. cf., gilt, extra $36.00
69. — Wenderholme. A tale of Yorkshire and Lancashire. sq. 12° $2.00
70. — Modern Frenchmen. Five biographies. sq. 12°. $2.00
71. — The life of J. M. W. Turner, R.A. With nine illustrations, after the master's sketches, and four woodcuts. sq. 12°..$2.50; hf. cf., $6; tr. cf., $6.50

ROBERTS BROTHERS,

Continued.

Hamerton, Philip G., *continued.*
72. — Etching and etchers. hf. mor............$8.50
73. **Hedge**, F. H. Ways of the Spirit, and other essays. 16°............................$1.50
74. **Hetty's** strange history. A novel. (No name series.) 16°............................$1.00
75. **His** majesty, myself. A novel. (No name (second) series.) 16°............................$1.00
76. **Holy** songs, carols and sacred ballads. sq. 16°..$1.00
77. **Horne**, R. H. Orion. An epic poem. 12°..$1.50
78. **Houghton**, *Lord.* Poetical works. A new edition, with a preface and a fine steel-engraved portrait of the author. 2 v. 16°................$5.00
79. **Hunt**, Leigh. Book of the sonnet. 2 v. in 1. 16°....................................$2.00
80. — The seer. 2 v. in 1. 16°..............$2.00
81. — *Same.* 2 v. mor.....................$10.00
82. **Ingelow**, Jean. Sarah de Berenger. A novel. 16°....................................$1.50
83. — Poems. (Red line ed.) hf. cf., $6; tr. cf., $7.50
84. — *Same.* (Cabinet ed.) mor. antique, $5; hf. mor., $4; hf. cf.........................$4.00
85. — *Same.* (Household ed.) 16°. $1.50; mor. antique, $4.50; hf. mor., $3.50; hf. cf.......$3.50
86. — *Same.* (Diamond ed.) mor. antique, $3.75; hf. mor., $3; hf. cf., $3; tr. cf...........$4.00
87. **Irene**, the missionary. A novel. 16°......$1.25
88. **Is** that all? A novel. (No name series.) 16°. $1.00
89. **Keats**, John. The poetical works of. Chronologically arranged and edited, with a memoir, by Lord Houghton. 16°. $2; hf. cf. $4.00
90. **Kismet**. A novel. (No name series.) 16°..$1.00
91. **Knappert**, J. The religion of Israel: a manual. Translated from the Dutch by Richard A. Armstrong. 16°..............................$1.00
92. **Joyce**, R. D. Blanid. A poem. By the author of "Deirdrè." 16°....................$1.50
93. **Landor**, Walter S. Imaginary conversations. v. 5. sq. 12°..............................$2.00
94. — *Same.* 5 v. hf. cf. $15.00
95. **Lathrop**, George Parsons. Somebody else. A novel. 16°..............................$1.25
96. **Lear**, Edward. Nonsense songs, stories, botany and alphabets. sq. 12°....................$1.50
97. **Lee**, Holme. Ben Milner's wooing. 16°...$1.00
98. **Legouvé**, Ernest. Reading as a fine art. Translated by Abby L. Alger. 16°...............50c.
99. **Lowell**, Robert T. S. A story or two from an old Dutch town. 16°.......................$1.25
100. **Macpherson**, Gerardine. Memoirs of the life of Anna Jameson, author of "Characteristics of women," etc. With portrait. 8°..........$2.50
101. **Marmorne**. A novel. (No name ser.) 16°..$1.00
102. **Martineau**, James. Hours of thought on sacred things. 16°............................$1.50
103. **Masque** (A) of poets. (No name series.) Red line. 12°. gilt, $1.50; 16° $1.00
104. **Mercy** Philbrick's choice. A novel. (No name series.) 16° $1.00
105. **Mirage**. A novel. (No name series.) 16°..$1.00
106. **Mistral**, F. Mirèio. 12°. cf.,............$5.00
107. **Modern** Mephistopheles (A). A novel. (No name series.) 16°............................$1.00
108. **Molloy**, J. L. Our autumn holiday on French rivers. 16° $1.25
109. **Morris**, William. The story of Sigurd the Volsung, and the fall of the Niblungs. sq. 8°.......$2.50
110. — The decorative arts: their relation to modern life and progress. 16°. pap. ....30c.
111. — Earthly paradise. 3 v. 16°. cf.........$12.00
112. — *Same.* 3 v. 8° cf.....................$15.00
113. **Moulton**, Louise Chandler. Poems. sq. 18°. $1.00
114. **Mountains** (The). A collection of poems, uniform with "Sea and shore." sq. 18°......$1.00
115. **Nieriker**, May Alcott. Studying art abroad, and how to do it cheaply. sq. 16°..............50c.
116. **No** name series: — Mercy Philbrick's choice; Deirdrè; Is that all; Kismet; The great match; A modern Mephistopheles; Afterglow; Hetty's strange history; Will Denbigh, nobleman; The wolf at the door; Marmorne; Mirage; Gemini; A masque of poets. Each, 16°, in black cloth, red and gold lettered $1.00
117. **No** name (second) series: — Signor Monaldini's niece; The colonel's opera cloak; His majesty, myself. Each, 16°, green cloth, black and gold lettered $1.00
118. **Oort**, *Dr.* H., *and* Hooykaas, *Dr.* I. The Bible for learners. Translated from the Dutch by Rev. P. H. Wicksteed, of London. With a comprehensive index, made specially for this edition, and maps.
The Old Testament. 2 v. 12°.........$4.00
The New Testament. 1 v. 12°........$2.50
119. **O'Reilly**, John Boyle. Moondyne. A story of the under-world. 16°....................$1.50
120. **Pascoe**, Charles Eyre. The dramatic list: a record of the principal performances of living actors and actresses of the British stage. cr. 8°. mor., gilt top $5.00
121. **Peard**, Frances M. A winter story. 16° ..$1.00
122. **Philochristus**. Memoirs of a disciple of the Lord. 16°. cl.................................$1.50
123. **Pierce**, Edward L. Memoir and letters of Charles Sumner. With two newly engraved likenesses of Sumner. 2 v. 8°. $6; hf. cf. $10.00
124. **Preston**, Harriet W. Troubadours and trouvères, old and new. sq. 12° $2.00
125. — The biography of Alfred de Musset. By Paul de Musset. Tr. by H. W. Preston. sq. 12°..$2.00
126. **Procter**, Bryan Waller. ["Barry Cornwall."] An autobiographical fragment, and biographical notes, with personal sketches of contemporaries, unpublished lyrics, and letters of literary friends. Edited by Mrs. Procter and Coventry Patmore. sq. 12°................................$2.00
127. **Rossetti**, C. G. Annus Domini. cf.......$2.50
128. **Seeley**, J. R. Life and times of Stein; or, Germany and Prussia in the Napoleonic age. With portrait and maps. 2 v. 8°..............$7.50
129. — The life and adventures of Ernst Moritz Arndt, the singer of the German Fatherland. Preface by J. R. Seeley. cr. 8°..................$2.25
130. **Selections** from the Apocrypha. (Wisdom series.) 18° ....50c.
131. **Selections** from Epictetus. (Wisdom ser.) 18°. 50c.
132. **Selections** from "The imitation of Christ." (Wisdom series.) 18° ....50c.
133. **Shaw**, Flora L. Castle Blair. A story of youthful days. 16°..............................$1.00
134. **Signor** Monaldini's niece. A novel. (No name (second) series.) 16° $1.00
135. **Stevenson**, Robert Louis. Travels with a donkey in the Cevennes. 16° $1.00
136. **Storr**, Francis, *and* Turner, Hawes. Canterbury chimes; or, Chaucer tales retold for children. With ill. from the Ellesmere MS. 16°.....$1.00
137. **Story** (The) of Ruth. From the Holy Bible. With illustrations by Bida. obl. 4°, gilt, and black lettered $5.00
138. **Sunshine** in the soul. Poems sel. by editor of "Quiet hours." (Wisdom series.) 18°.....50c.

ROBERTS BROTHERS,

Continued.

139. **Supernatural** religion. An inquiry into the reality of divine revelation. To which is added the author's preface to the 6th ed. 3 v. 8°..$12.50
140. **Sursum** corda. Hymns for the sick and suffering, compiled by the editor of "Quiet hours," "Sunshine in the soul," etc. 16° $1.25
141. **Tauler**, *Rev. Dr.* John. Life and history of. (Wisdom series.) 18°.......................50c.
142. **Tayler**, John James. Last series of Christian aspects of faith and duty. sq. 12°.........$2.00
143. **Taylor**, J. E. Flowers: their origin, shapes, perfumes and colors. With 32 colored figures by Sowerby, and 161 woodcuts. 12°. full gilt, $2.50
144. **Thorne**, P. Jolly good times at school; also, some times not quite so jolly. ill. sq. 16°.......$1.25
145. **Town** and country series: — Ben Milner's wooing; by Holme Lee. — From traditional to rational faith; by R. Andrew Griffin. — A winter story; by the author of "The rose garden." — Syrian sunshine [and] Notes of travel; by Thomas G. Appleton. — Jan of the windmill; by Mrs. Ewing. — G. T. T.; or, the wonderful adventures of a Pullman; by E. E. Hale. 16°. ea. $1.00
146. **Walker**, James. Reason, faith and duty. Sermons preached chiefly in the college chapel. With portrait. sq. 12°..................$2.00
147. **We** boys; written by one of us for the amusement ment of pa's and ma's in general, Aunt Lovisa in particular. 16°. $1.00
148. **Weiss**, John. Wit, humor, and Shakespeare. sq. 12°...............................$2.00
149. — West-Easterly divan of Goethe. Translated, with an introduction and notes, by John Weiss. sq. 18°...............................$1.25
150. **Wild** life in a Southern county; by the author of "The gamekeeper at home." 16°......$1.25
151. **Will** Denbigh, nobleman. A novel. (No name series.) 16° $1.00
152. **Wisdom** of Jesus, the Son of Sirach; or, Ecclesiasticus. (Wisdom series.) 18°.........50c.
153. **Wisdom** series: — Selections from the Apocrypha. — The wisdom of Jesus, the Son of Sirach; or, Ecclesiasticus. — Selections from the thoughts of Marcus Aurelius Antoninus. — Selections from

Wisdom series, *continued.*
"Imitation of Christ." — Sunshine in the soul: poems selected by the editor of "Quiet hours." — Selections from Epictetus. — The life and history of the Rev. Doctor John Tauler. — Selections from Fénelon. 18°. ea. ....50c.

154. **Wolf** (The) at the door. A novel. (No name series.) 16°..............................$1.00
155. **Wollstonecraft's** (Mary) Letters to Imlay, with prefatory memoir by C. Kegan Paul. Two portraits after Opie. 12°....................$2.00

CHANGES OF PRICE.

156. **Barnes'** Rural poems. (mor. ed.) from $5 to $4
157. **Besant's** French humorists.....from $2.50 to $2
158. **Chaney's** F. Grant & Co. ...from $1.50 to $1.25
159. **Channing's** Thoreau ....from $2 to $1.50
160. **Dimock**, Memoir of.........from $1.25 to $1.50
161. **Freedom** and fellowship in religion. from $2 to $1.50
162. **Frolich's** Picture book.........from $2 to $1.25
163. **Goethe's** Hermann and Dorothea. (mor. ed.) from $5 to $4.50
164. **H. H.** Bits of travel ....from $1.50 to $1.25
165. — Story of Boon ....from 30c. to 35c.
166. **Hale's** Christmas eve..........from 1.50 to $1.25
167. — In his name..............from $1.25 to $1.00
168. — Our new crusade..........from $1.25 to $1.00
169. — Ten times one is ten..........from 88c. to 75c.
170. **Hamerton's** Etching and etchers. from $7.50 to $5
171. — Sylvan year...................from $6 to $5.50
172. **Ingelow's** Off the Skelligs...from $1.75 to $1.50
173. — Fated to be free ....from $1.75 to $1.50
174. — Shepherd lady............from $4.50 to $3.50
175. — *Same.* (mor. ed.)............from $9 to $7.50
176. **Preston's** Aspendale ....from $1.25 to $1.00
177. — Love in the nineteenth century. from $1.25 to $1.00
178. **Quiet** hours.................from $1.25 to $1.00
179. **Sea** and shore ....from $1.25 to $1.00
180. **Thorne's** Jolly good times ...from $1.50 to $1.25
181. **Tytler's** Musical composers ....from $2 to $1.50

AMERICAN UNITARIAN ASSOC.,

7 Tremont Place, Boston.

1. **Endeavors** after the Christian life: discourses by Rev. James Martineau. Reprinted from 6th Eng. ed. 12°, 469 p...........................$1.00
2. **Essentials** and non-essentials in religion. By Rev. James Freeman Clarke, D.D. Being lectures delivered in Music Hall, Boston. sq. 16°, 156 p. cl., 50c.; pap.........................25c.
3. **Hymn** and tune book for the church and the home, and services for congregational worship. Revised ed. sq. 16°, 399 p. mor., $1.25; Tur. mor., gilt edges.........................$3.00
4. — *Same;* with services. sq. 16°, 517 p. mor., $1.50; Tur. mor., gilt..........................$3.50
5. — *Same;* service book, sep. sq. 16°, 118 p. mor., 60c.; Tur. mor., gilt edges............. $2.50
6. **Unitarian** affirmations: seven discourses given in Washington, D. C., by Unitarian ministers. sq. 16°, 175 p. cl., 50c.; pap.................25c.

M. L. HOLBROOK,

13 and 15 Laight St., New York.

1. **Fowler**, Harriet P. Vegetarianism, the radical cure for intemperance ....30c.
2. **Holbrook**, M. L., *M.D.* Hygiene of the brain and nerves and the cure of nervousness; with twenty-eight original letters from leading thinkers and writers concerning their physical and intellectual habits $1.50
3. **Klemm**, C. Muscle beating; or, active and passive gymnastics for healthy and unhealthy people. ill. ....30c.
4. **Meyer**, Bertha. Family government; or, from the cradle to the school, according to Fröbel ..$1.00
5. **Schwab**, Erasmus. The school garden, a practical contribution to the subject of education.....50c.
6. **Schlickeysen**, Gustave. Fruit and bread, a natural and scientific diet..........................$1.00
7. **Studley**, Mary J., *M.D.* What our girls ought to know $1.25

PORTER & COATES,

Cor. of 9th and Chestnut Sts., Philadelphia.

1. **Andersen**, Hans Christian. Stories for the household. ill. cr. 8°. cl. $1.75
2. **Arthur**, T. S. Orange blossoms, fresh and faded. ill. 12°. cl. $1.50
3. — The bar rooms at Brantley; or, the great hotel speculation. ill. 12°. cl. $1.50
4. **Bartlett**, *Mrs.* J. M. D. Until the day break. 12°. cl., $1.50; pap., 75c. — (International ed.)$1.25
5. **Batty**. How to hunt and trap. ill. 12°. cl...$1.50
6. **Baucher**, F. New method of horsemanship. ill. 12°. cl. $1.00
7. **Beers**, Ethel Lynn. All quiet along the Potomac, and other poems. 12°. cl., $1.50; gilt....$1.75
8. **Berthet**, Elie. Prehistoric world. 12°. cl., $1.50
9. **Brontë**, Charlotte. Jane Eyre. (New library edition.) ill. 12°. cl., $1.25; hf. cf., gilt....$3.00
10. — Shirley. (New library edition.) ill. 12°. cl., $1.25; hf. cf., gilt $3.00
11. — Villette. (New library edition.) ill. 12°. cl., $1.25; hf. cf., gilt $3.00
12. — The Professor, Emma and poems. (New library edition.) ill. 12°. cl., $1.25; hf. cf., gilt....$3.00
13. **Brown**, Thomas K. An elementary algebra. 12°. cl. $1.25
14. **Buckwalter**, Geoffrey. A comprehensive spelling-book. 16°. bds. ....30c.
15. — A primary spelling-book. 16°. bds.......22c.
16. **Bunyan**, John. The pilgrim's progress. (Large type.) ill. 12°. cl., $1.25; Tur. mor., ant.$4.00
17. — The holy war. ill. 12°. cl.............$1.25
18. **Burdett**, Charles. Life of Kit Carson. ill. 12°. cl. $1.25
19. **Burnett**, Frances Hodgson. Dolly. 12°. cl., $1.50; pap., 75c. — (International ed.)...........$1.25
20. **Burns**, Robert. Poetical works. With seven engravings on steel. 8°. shp., marb. edges, $3.50; leatherette, gilt side and edges, $4; Tur. mor., antique, gilt edges....................$8.00
21. **Castlemon**, Harry. The buried treasure; or, Old Jordan's "haunt." ill. 16°. cl.......$1.25
22. — The boy trapper; or, how Dave filled the order. ill. 16°. cl. $1.25
23. — The mail carrier. ill. 16°. cl. $1.25
24. — Frank in the forecastle; or, the Sportsman's Club among the whalers. ill. 16°. cl. $1.25
25. — The boy traders; or, the Sportsman's Club among the Boers. ill. 16°. $1.25
26. — George in camp; or, life on the plains. ill. 16°. cl. $1.25
27. **Coates**, Henry T. The children's book of poetry. ill. 4°. cl., gilt side and edges, $3; full Tur. mor., gilt edges $7.50
28. — Fireside encyclopædia of poetry. ill. 8°. cl., gilt edges, $5; hf. cf., gilt, mar. edges, $7.50; full Tur. mor., gilt edges, $10; tree cf., gilt..$12.00
29. **Cordery**, B. Meriton, *and* Phillpotts, J. Surtees. King and commonwealth: a history of Charles I. and the great rebellion. With maps and plans. 12°. cl $1.75
30. **Crockett**, *Col.* David. Life. ill. 12°. cl. ..$1.25
31. **Cummins**, M. S. Mabel Vaughan. 12°. cl., $1.25
32. **Duffey**, E. B. Ladies' and gentlemen's etiquette. 12°. cl. $1.50
33. **Dumas**, Alexandre. The Count of Monte Cristo; ill. by George G. White. 12°. cl.........$1.50
34. — The three guardsmen. ill. 12°. cl.......1.50
35. **Dunglison**, R. J. An elementary physiology. 12°. cl., extra.
36. **Duyckinck**, Evert A. *and* George L. Cyclopedia of American literature; edited to date by M. Laird Simons. ill. with 1000 engravings. 2 v. imp. 8°. cl., $12; shp., $14; hf. mor. ..$16.00
37. **Famous** American race horses. Containing thirty full-page illustrations. 4°. pap............75c.
38. **Famous** American trotting horses. Containing forty-six full-page illustrations of the celebrities of the trotting turf. 4°. pap. ....75c.
39. **Famous** horses of America. Containing the preceding 2 v. bound in one. 4°. cl., extra ...$1.50
40. **Farrar**, *Mrs., and* Moore, *Mrs.* C. J. The young ladies' friend. 12°. cl. $1.50
41. **Fisher**, George P. Life of Benjamin Silliman, M.D., LL. D., late Professor of Chemistry, Mineralogy and Geology, in Yale College. New ed. ill. cr. 8°. cl., uncut edges $2.50
42. **Fleming**, George. A text-book of veterinary obstetrics. 212 ill. 8°. cl. $5.00
43. **Foster**, Charles J. The white horse of Wootton. 12°. cl. $1.50
44. **Garrett**, Rhoda *and* Agnes. House decoration, in painting, woodwork and furniture. ill. 12°. cl., flex. $1.00
45. **Grimm**. Popular tales. Collected by the brothers Grimm. With eighty-five illustrations by Edward H. Wehnert. 12°. cl. $1.25
46. — Stories for the household. Collected by the brothers Grimm. With eighty-five illustrations by Edward H. Wehnert. 12°. cl.............$1.25
47. **Gurney**, Eliza P. The garland: a collection of choice poetry. 12°. cl. $1.50
48. **Happy** days: a story and picture book for boys and girls. ill. 4°. hf. cl., gilt back and illuminated bds., $1.25; cl., black and gold, inlaid side $1.75
49. **Harrison**, Henry W. The battles of the republic by sea and land, from Lexington to the City of Mexico. With one hundred and thirty-five engravings. 12°. cl. $1.25
50. **Hartley**, Cecil B. Life of Daniel Boone, the great western hunter and pioneer. ill. 12°. cl...$1.25
51. **Hazard**, Willis P. Butter and butter making. ill. 12°. pap. ....25c.
52. **Hill**, John Woodroffe. The management and diseases of the dog. With thirty-nine engravings. 12°. cl. $2.00
53. **Holiday** times: a beautiful and profusely illustrated book for boys and girls. 4°. hf. cl., gilt back and illuminated bds., $1.25; cl., black and gold, inlaid side $1.75
54. **Horace**. The odes of Horace. Translated into English verse, with a life and notes, by Theodore Martin. With por. of Horace. 16°. cl...$1.00
55. **Hughes**, Thomas. Tom Brown's school days at Rugby. ill. 12°. cl. $1.00
56. — Tom Brown at Oxford. ill. 12°. cl......$1.50
57. **Hullah**, John, *LL.D.* Music in the house. ill. 12°. cl., flex. ....75c.
58. **Hutton**, Richard Holt. Essays in literary criticism. 12°. cl., gilt $1.50
59. **Johnstone**, H. A. Munro-Butler, *M.P.* A trip up the Volga to the Fair of Nijni-Novgorod. ill. 12°. cl. $1.25
60. **Kames**, *Lord.* An abridgment of the Elements of criticism; edited by John Frost, A.M. 12°. cl. extra, roan back $1.00
61. **Leaders** of France; or, the men of the third republic: reprinted from the *London Daily News.* 12°. cl., extra, black and gold.............$1.25
62. **Leonowens**, *Mrs.* Anna Harriette. The English governess at the Siamese court. With eight full-page illustrations. 12°. cl...............$1.25
63. — The romance of the harem. With eight full-page illustrations. 12°. cl. $1.25

PORTER & COATES,

Continued.

64. **Le Sage.** The adventures of Gil Blas of Santillane. Translated from the French of Le Sage by Tobias Smollett. ill. 12°. cl. $1.50
65. **Lever,** Charles. Charles O'Malley, the Irish dragoon. (New library ed.) 2 original illustrations by F. O. C. Darley. 12°. cl. $1.50
66. — Harry Lorrequer. (New library ed.) 2 original ill. by G. G. White. 12°. cl. $1.50
67. **Loftie,** W. J. A plea for art in the house. ill. 12°. cl., flex. $1.00
68. **Lossing,** Benson J. History of American industries. Illustrated with sixty full-page engravings on steel. 4°. cl., gilt edges, $10; hf. levant, red, gilt edges $15.00
69. **Lover,** Samuel. Handy Andy. (New library ed.) 2 original ill. by G. G. White. 12°. cl. ...$1.50
70. **McKnight,** Charles. Captain Jack, the scout; or, the Indian wars about old Fort Duquesne. ill. 12°. cl. $1.50
71. **Martineau,** Harriet. History of England, from the beginning of the 19th century to the Crimean war. 4 v. cl., per set, $4; shp., mar. edges, per set, $6; hf. cf., gilt, mar. edges $12.00
72. **Merry** times: a story and picture book for boys and girls. ill. 4°. hf. cl., gilt back, and illuminated bds., $1.25; cl., black and gold, inlaid side $1.75
73. **Milton,** John. Poetical works. With a life of the author and notes, by Rev. John Mitford. With engravings on steel. 8°. shp., marbled edges, $3.50; leatherette, gilt side and edges. $4; Tur. mor., gilt edges $8.00
74. **Moore,** Thomas. Poetical works. ill. 8°. shp., mar. edges, $3.50; leatherette, gilt side and edges, $4; Tur. mor., gilt edges $8.00
75. **Munchausen.** The travels and surprising adventures of Baron Munchausen. ill. 12°. cl. ...$1.25
76. **Oliphant,** *Mrs.* Dress. ill. 12°. cl., flex. ....75c.
77. **Orleans.** Memoir of the Duchess of Orleans. By the Marquess de H——. With portrait on steel. 12°. cl. $1.25
78. **Paris,** *Comte de.* History of the Civil War in America. Volumes 1 and 2, embracing, without abridgment, the first four volumes of the French edition. With maps faithfully engraved from the originals, and printed in three colors. 8°. cl., per vol., $3.50; red cl., extra, Roxburgh style, gilt top, uncut edges, $3.50; shp., library style, $4.50; hf. Tur. mor. $6.00
79. **Raub,** Albert N. Elementary arithmetic, oral and written. 16°. bds. ....50c.
80. — Complete arithmetic. 12°. bds. ....88c.
81. — Key to the Complete arithmetic. 16°. cl. ....88c.
82. — Normal first reader. 16°. bds. ....22c.
83. — Normal second reader. 16°. bds. ....38c.
84. — Normal third reader. 16°. bds. ....52c.
85. — Normal fourth reader. 12°. cl., roan back...70c.
86. — Normal fifth reader. cl., roan back ....96c.
87. **Rollin,** Charles. The ancient history of the Egyptians, Carthaginians, Assyrians, Babylonians, Medes and Persians, Grecians and Macedonians; with a life of the author by James Bell. 2 v. roy. 8°. shp., mar. edges, per set $6.00
88. **Scott,** *Sir* Walter. Poetical works. With nine engravings on steel. 8°. shp., marbled edges, $3.50; leatherette, gilt side and edges, $4; Tur. mor., antique, gilt edges $8.00
89. **Scudder,** Horace E. Recollections of Samuel Breck. 12°. cl., extra, gilt top, uncut edges ..$2.00
90. **Seiss,** Joseph A., *D.D.* A miracle in stone; or, the great pyramid of Egypt. ill. 12°. cl. ...$1.25
91. — Voices from Babylon; or, the records of Daniel, the prophet. 12°. cl. $1.50
92. **Sharpless,** Isaac. Elementary plane geometry. 12° ....90c.
93. — Elements of plane and solid geometry. 12°. $1.30
94. **Stothert,** James. French and Spanish painters. Superb etchings after characteristic examples of the famous painters of both schools, etched by well-known masters of the art. 4°. cl., ornate, gilt edges, $10; hf. Levant, $16; a few copies with India proof plates, $15; hf. Levant, $20.00
95. **Trebor.** As it may happen. 12°. cl. $1.50
96. **Verne,** Jules. At the North Pole; or, the voyages and adventures of Capt. Hatteras; with 130 illustrations by Riou. 12°. cl. $1.50
97. — Desert (The) of ice; or, the further adventures of Captain Hatteras; with 126 illustrations by Riou. 12°. cl. $1.50
98. **Ward,** *Mrs.* H. O. Sensible etiquette of the best society. 12°. cl., bevelled bds., gilt top, $2.00
99. **Warren,** Samuel C. Ten thousand a year. New ed., rev. ill. 12°. cl., extra, black and gold, $1.50
100. **Watson,** Henry C. The camp fires of Napoleon. 120 eng. 12°. cl. $1.25
101. **Watson,** John T. Dictionary of poetical quotations. 12°. cl., $1.50; hf. cf., gilt.....$3.00
102. **Westcott,** Thompson. Historic mansions and buildings of Philadelphia, with some notices of their owners and occupants. 77 engravings. sm. 4°. cl., gilt edges $5.00
103. **Willcox,** James M. Elementary rational philosophy. 12°. cl. $1.50
104. **Wilson,** Alexander. Life of; by George F. Ord, F.R.S. imp. 8°. hf. Roxburgh, gilt top, uncut edges $3.00
105. — American ornithology. By Alexander Wilson and Charles Lucien Bonaparte. Popular edition (subscription), complete in one volume, with all the plates contained in the $100 edition, but reduced in size, uncol. imp. 8°. cl., extra, black and gold, $7.50; hf. Tur. mor., gilt $12.00
106. **Youatt,** William. The horse; edited by J. S. Skinner. 8°. cl. $1.75
107. **Young,** L. H. Remarkable events in the world's history. ill. 12°. cl. $1.25

S. R. STODDARD,

Glens Falls, N.Y.

1. **Adirondacks** (The). [Annual.] ill. 50c.; pap. 25c.
2. **Adirondack** wilderness (Stoddard's new tourist's map of) $1.00
3. **Adirondacks:** Souvenir album. 32 views....50c.
4. **Lake** George. [Annual.] ill. 50c.; pap. .....25c.
5. **Ticonderoga,** historical and descriptive ....50c.

MARTIN R. DENNIS & CO.,

Newark, N. J.

1. **Atkinson,** Joseph. History of Newark, from 1666. ill. 8°. $3.50; hf. mor., $5; hf. cf. $6.00
2. **Carmina** Princetonia: songs of Princeton College. 4th ed., enl. 8° $1.50
3. **Ricord,** F. W. English songs from foreign tongues. 12° $2.50
4. **Wickes,** Stephen. History of medicine in N.J., and of its medical men, to 1800. 8° $3.50

BENZIGER BROTHERS,

New York, Cincinnati and St. Louis.

1. **Arnoudt**, F., *S. J.* The Imitation of the Sacred Heart of Jesus, from the Latin of Rev. Fastre. 12°. 798 pp. $2.50
2. **Aufsatzlehre** für Volkschulen, von Sr. Nepomucena, O. S. B. 12°. 59 pp. .... 25c.
3. **Bauhaus**, S. J. Herz-Jesu-Buch zum Beten und Betrachten. 16°. 546 pp. $1.50
4. **Bowden**, H. S. Miniature lives of the saints. 2 v. $2.00
5. **Brennan**, Richard. A popular life of Pope Pius IX. and sketch of his successor Leo XIII. ill. 8°. 288 pp. $1.50
6. — The life of Our Lord and Saviour Jesus Christ and of His Blessed Mother. ill. 4°. 38 pts., ea., 25c.
7. **Businger**, L. C. Das Leben unsers Herrn u. Heilandes Jesus Christus und seiner Jungfr. Mutter Maria. ill. gr. 4°. 1052 pp. ..... $6.50 to $20.00
8. — Christus in seiner Kirche: eine Kirchengeschichte für Schule und Haus. ill. 8°. 276 pp. 75c.
9. **Catechisms.** A short catechism for arch-diocese of Cincinnati. 32°. 64 pp. per 100 ... $2.75 *net.*
10. — Butler's larger catechism, with scriptural catechism. 24°. 124 pp. per 100 .... $3.50 *net.*
11. — A general catechism (National Council). 24°. 96 pp. per 100 .... $2.75 *net.*
12. — Boston catechism. 24°. 107 pp. per 100, $2.75 *net.*
13. **Catholic** premium book library (The). First series. 8°. ea., 50c.: — Anthony; Bertha; Blanche de Massilly; Captain Rougemont; Cassilda; Conversations on home education; Episodes of the Commune; Marcelle; Adventures of a casket; Adventures of a French captain; The better part; The fisherman's daughter; Great-grandmother's secret; The priest of Auvrigny; The village steeple.
14. — Second series. 12°. ea., 35c.: — Life of Our Lord; Life of the Bl. Virgin; Life of St. Patrick; The holy isle; The diary of a confessor; A man at twelve; Lamoriciere.
15. — Third series. 18°. ea., 15c.: — Adolphus; A broken chain; Nicholas; Nina and Pippo; The baker's boy; The last days of the papal army; Zuma.
16. **Day** (The) of first communion: devout prayers, etc. 32°. .... 5c.
17. **De Augustinis**, P. Æmilius M., *S. J.* Prælectiones scholastico-dogmaticæ. De sacramentis in genere, de baptismo, confirmatione, eucharistia. 8° 800 pp. $3.75
18. — De sacramentis in genere, de ordine, extrema unctione, matrimonio. 8°. 800 pp. $3.75
19. **Douglas**, *Lady* Gertrude. Linked lives: a most enthralling story of fiction. 526 pp. $2.00
20. **Epistles** and Gospels for Sundays and Festivals. 32°. 169 pp. .... 30c.
21. **Gibbons**, *Most Rev.* James. Der Glaube unserer Väter, die Lehren und Gebräuche der Kath. Kirche. 8°. 280 pp. $1.00
22. **Gilmour**, R. Catholic national series of readers. 12°: — Primer, 6c.; First reader, 25c.; Second reader, 40c.; Third reader, 75c.; Intermediate third reader; Fourth reader, $1; Fifth reader, $1.25; Speller and word-book .... 25c.
23. **Grammar** (English), by a practical teacher. 12°. 83 pp. .... 25c.
24. **Greetings** to the Christ-child: a collection of Christmas poems for the young. ill. 16° ... $1.00
25. **Hidden** treasure (The), by the Bl. Leonard of Port Maurice. 18°. 188 pp. .... 50c.
26. **Jesuits** (The): their foundation and history. By B. N. 2 v. 8°. 764 pp. $4.50
27. **Keller**, E., *S. J.* The life and acts of Leo XIII. ill. 8°. 350 pp. $2.00
28. **Konings**, A., *C. SS. R.* Theologia moralis novissimi ecclesiæ Doctoris S. Alphonsi, at usui Ven. Cleri Americ. accommodata. 8°. 1066 pp. $5.00
29. — General confessions made easy. 32° ...... 15c.
30. **Kuhn**, *Dr.* Albert, *O. S. B.* Roma, die Denkmale des christl. und des heidnischen Rom in Wort und Bild. ill. gr. 4°. 572 pp. ...... $10.00 to $15.00
31. **Lambing**, A. A. The Sunday-school teacher's manual. 16°. 216 pp. .... 90c.
32. **Lynch**, J. S. M. The rite of ordinations, Latin and English. 16°. 108 pp. .... 75c.
33. **McEvilly**, *Most Rev. Dr* An exposition of the Epistles of St. Paul, and of the Catholic epistles. 2 v. l. 8°. 902 pp. $6.50
34. — An exposition of the Gospels. 8°. Vol. 1, Matthew and Mark. 676 pp. $4.25. Vol. 2, St. Luke. 248 pp. $2.25. Vol. 3, St. John (*in press*).
35. **Mazzella**, P. Camillus, *S. J.* Prælectiones scholastico-dogmaticæ. De Deo creante. 8°. 972 pp. $4.25
36. — De gratia Christi. 8°. 800 pp. $3.75
37. — De virtutibus infusis. 8°. 791 pp. $3.75
38. **Müller**, Mich. New series of catechisms of Christian doctrine. 1. For beginners, 8c.; 2. For parochial and Sunday schools, 15c.; 3. Intermediate, for academies and high schools, 40c.; 4. For the family and students .... 60c.
39. — German edition. (Kleiner.) 1, 10c.; 2 ..... 25c.
40. — God the teacher of mankind: a plain, comprehensive explanation of Christian doctrine. Vol. 1. The church and her enemies. 12°. 602 pp. $2; Vol. 2. The Apostles' creed. 12°. 566 pp., $2; Vol. 3. Grace and the sacraments. 12°. 582 pp. $2.00
41. **Nash**, L. A table-book and introductory arithmetic. 16°. 88 pp. .... 20c.
42. **Paradise** on earth. An eloquent and earnest appeal to a religious life. 32°. 146 pp. ...... 60c.
43. **Pictorial** lives of the saints, with reflections for every day in the year: preface by Dr. E. McGlynn. 8°. 518 pp. $3.50
44. **Pleasant** hours. First lines for young artists: a simple and practical drawing-book. 24 pp. .. 20c.
45. **Popular** hymns for youth; containing 189 of the most popular hymns. 32°. 256 pp. .... 15c.
46. **Prayers** for the children of the Catholic schools. 48°. 192 pp. .... 20c.
47. **Rohner**, Beat., *O. S. B.* Das Leben der allerseligsten Jungfrau Maria und ihres glorreichen Bräutigams St. Joseph. ill. gr. 4°. 1024 pp. from $7.50 to $18.00
48. **Rolfus** und **Braendle.** Die Glaubens- und Sittenlehre der Kathol. Kirche, ein Hand- und Hausbuch für Katecheten und christl. Familien. ill. gr. 4°. 1056 pp. .... from $6.50 to $20.00
49. **Rosecrans**, *Rt. Rev.* S. H. The divinity of Christ, together with thoughts on the passion of Jesus Christ. 16°. 180 pp. .... 60c.
50. **Smith**, S. B. Elements of ecclesiastical law, adapted especially to the discipline of the Church in the United States. 8°. 480 pp. $3.00
51. **Taylor**, Edward I. Souvenir of the novitiate. 32°. 285 pp. $1.00
52. **Van Luytelaar**, *C. SS. R.* Fidei et morum fundamenta. 12°. 56 pp. .... 50c.
53. **Wetzel**, Fr. Xavier. Illustrirte Weltgeschichte in Characterbildern für Schule und Haus. ill. 8°. 400 pp. .... 75c.

BOOKS IN PRESS.

54. **The** story of Jesus for the young.
55. **Sure** path to a happy marriage.
56. **The** Christian mother.
57. **Manual** of the black scapular.

AMERICAN PHILOLOGICAL ASSOCIATION,

Prof. C. R. Lanman, Sec., Baltimore.

1. **American** Philological Association. Transactions, 1869–'78. 9 v. 8°. '71–'79. ea., pap......$2.00

Note.—First volume not sold separately.
Contents of first 9 vols. **1869-'70,** On the nature and theory of the Greek accent, by J. Hadley; On the nature and designation of the accent in Sanskrit, by W. D. Whitney; On the aorist subjunctive and future indicative with ὅπως and οὐ μή, by W. W. Goodwin; On the best method of studying the North American languages, by J. Hammond Trumbull; On the German vernacular of Pennsylvania, by S. S. Haldeman; On the present condition of the question as to the origin of language, by W. D. Whitney; On certain forms of the English verb which were used in the sixteenth and seventeenth centuries, by T. R. Lounsbury; On some mistaken notions of Algonkin grammar, and on mistranslations of words from Eliot's Bible, etc., by J. Hammond Trumbull; Contributions to Creole grammar, by A. Van Name; Proceedings of preliminary meeting ('68), of first annual session ('69), and of second annual session ('70).—**1871,** Studies in Cymric philology, by E. W. Evans; On the so-called Attic second declension, by F. D. Allen; Strictures on the views of August Schleicher respecting the nature of language and kindred subjects, by W. D. Whitney; On English vowel quantity in the thirteenth century and in the nineteenth, by J. Hadley; Anglo-Saxon and Early English pronunciation, by F. A. March; Some notes on Ellis's Early English pronunciation, by C. A. Bristed; On Algonkin names for man, by J. Hammond Trumbull; On some forms of conditional sentences in Latin, Greek and Sanskrit, by J. B. Greenough; Proceedings of third annual session ('71).—**1872,** Studies in Cymric philology, by E. W. Evans; Words derived from Indian languages of North America, by J. Hammond Trumbull; On the Byzantine Greek pronunciation of the tenth century, as illustrated by a manuscript in the Bodleian Library, by J. Hadley; On the substantive use of the Greek participle, by W. A. Stevens; Erroneous and doubtful uses of the word *such*, by C. A. Bristed; Notes on the Lingoa Geral, or Modern Tupí of the Amazonas, by C. F. Hartt; On material and form in language, by W. D. Whitney; Is there an Anglo-Saxon language? by F. A. March; On some irregular verbs in Anglo-Saxon, by F. A. March; Notes on forty versions of the Lord's Prayer in Algonkin languages, by J. Hammond Trumbull; Proceedings.—**1873,** The Epic forms of verbs in άω, by F. D. Allen; Studies in Cymric philology, by E. W. Evans; On Koch's treatment of the Celtic element in English, by J. Hadley; On the pronunciation of Latin, as presented in several recent grammars, by S. S. Haldeman; On some points in the life of Thucydides, by L. R. Packard; On the classification of conditional sentences in Greek syntax, by W. W. Goodwin; Recent discussions of Grimm's Law, by F. A. March; Vocabulary of the language of the Indians of San Blas and Caledonia Bay, Darien, by E. P. Lull; Proceedings.—**1874,** On the prepositions in the Homeric poems, by W. S. Tyler; On the formation of the tenses for completed action in the Latin finite verb, by A. Harkness; On an English vowel-mutation, present in *cag, keg*, by S. S. Haldeman; On a passage in Homer's Odyssey (x. 81–86), by L. R. Packard; On numerals in American Indian languages and the Indian mode of counting, by J. Hammond Trumbull; On the distinction between the subjunctive and optative modes in Greek conditional sentences, by J. B. Sewall; On the age of Xenophon at the time of the Anabasis, by C. D. Morris; Φύσει or θέσει—natural or conventional? by W. D. Whitney; Proceedings.—**1875,** On the formation of the tenses for completed action in the Latin finite verb, by A. Harkness; On an English consonant-mutation, present in *proof, prove*, by S. S. Haldeman; On Begemann's views as to the weak preterit of the Germanic verbs, by F. Carter; On some forms of Greek conditional sentences, by C. D. Morris; On verb-reduplication as a means of expressing completed action, by A. Williams; A grammatical analysis of the Old English poem "The owl and the nightingale," by L. A. Sherman; Proceedings.—**1876,** On εἰ with the future indicative and ἐάν with the subjunctive in the tragic poets, by B. L. Gildersleeve; On Grote's theory of the structure of the Iliad, by L. R. Packard; On negative commands in Greek, by M. W. Humphreys; On Hebrew verb-etymology, by C. H. Toy; A botanico-philological problem, by W. D. Whitney; On *shall* and *should* in protasis, and their Greek equivalents, by W. W. Goodwin; On certain influences of accent in Latin iambic trimeters, by M. W. Humphreys; On the Algonkin verb, by J. Hammond Trumbull; On a supposed mutation between *l* and *u*, by S. S. Haldeman; Proceedings.—**1877,** Notes on certain passages in the Phaedo and the Gorgias of Plato, by L. R. Packard; On the nominal basis of the Hebrew verb, by C. H. Toy; On a certain apparently pleonastic use of ὡς, by F. D. Allen; On the relation of surd and sonant, by W. D. Whitney; On the vocabularies of children under two years of age, by E. S. Holden; On the text and interpretation of certain passages in the Agamemnon of Æschylus, by W. W. Goodwin; On the single case-form in Italian, by A. Stickney; On Willmanns' theory of the authorship of the Nibelungenlied, by F. Carter; On Herodotus's and Æschylus's accounts of the battle of Salamis, by E. G. Sihler; On the principle of economy as a phonetic force, by W. D. Whitney; On the Kürenberg hypothesis, by F. Carter; On dissimilated gemination, by F. A. March; Proceedings.—**1878,** Contributions to the history of the articular infinitive, by B. L. Gildersleeve; The Yoruban language, by C. H. Toy; Influence of accent in Latin dactylic hexameters, by M. W. Humphreys; Observations on Plato's Cratylus, by J. Sachs; On the composition of the Cynegeticus of Xenophon, by T. D. Seymour; Elision, especially in Greek, by M. W. Humphreys; Proceedings.

PETER G. THOMSON,

Arcade Bookstore, 179 Vine Street, Cincinnati, O.

1. **Cincinnati's** beginning: being the early history of the city and the Miami purchase, from hitherto unpublished documents. By Francis W. Miller. large 12°.......................$1.75
2. **Sixteen** Saviours or one? The Gospels not Brahmanic. By John T. Perry, of the Cincinnati "Gazette." 12°. pap., 50c.; cl. ....75c.
3. **Shaw,** W. J. Solomon's story. A novel. ill. 12°. cl. $1.75
4. **Creed** and greed. Lectures by the Rev. Dudley Ward Rhodes, of Cincinnati. 12°. cl., extra. $1.25
5. **Guide** to the examination of urine, with special reference to the diseases of the urinary apparatus. By K. B. Hoffman, Professor of the University of Graz, and R. Ultzmann, Docent at the University of Vienna. From the 2d Germ. ed., translated and edited by F. Forchheimer, M.D., Professor of the Medical College of Ohio. ill. 12°. cl., $1.50; leath.....................$2.00
6. **Healthy** infant (The): a practical treatise on the healthy procreation of the human race. By Tandy L. Dix, M.D. 12°. cl.............$1.25
7. **Dawson,** *Dr.* W. W. A treatise on stone in the bladder 24 col. pl. 8°. cl., $3; leath....$3.75
8. **A** book for every horse-owner. The horse's foot and how to shoe it. Giving the most approved methods of horse-shoeing, together with the anatomy of the horse's foot and its diseases. By J. R. Cole. 42 ill. 8°. cl...............$1.00
9. **Cincinnati** society blue-book and family directory; containing the names of householders, giving their private residences, and exact numbers, together with the names of the adult members of each family, the ladies' reception days, etc., etc. With a complete classification by streets and suburbs. 12°. cl., gilt edges. (By subscription only.)...........................$5.00
10. **Lotos** land, and other poems. By G. S. Ladson. 16°. cl., gilt...........................$1.00
11. **Library** catalogue (The). Ruled and arranged to suit any number of volumes. 4°. cl.......$1.50
12. **Washington** County and the early settlement of Ohio. By Israel Ward Andrews, President of Marietta College. 8°. pap., 75c.; cl. $1.25
13. **Marietta** College in the war of secession, 1861–'65. 8°. pap. ....75c.
14. **References** to the coinage legislation of the United States. By Col. C. W. Moulton. 8°. pap...30c.

AMERICAN BAPTIST PUBLICATION SOCIETY,

1420 Chestnut St., Philadelphia.

1876.

SUNDAY-SCHOOL LIBRARY BOOKS.

1. **Eugene** and his friends. From the French of Mme. E. De Pressensé. By Miss Julia Goodfellow. 16°. 282 pp. $1.25
2. **Charlotte's** friend; or, evil communications corrupt good manners. By Mrs. Bradley. 16°. 255 pp. $1.00
3. **Hoofs** and claws; or, Mrs. Burton's policy. By Sidney Dyer, A.M. 16°. 363 pp. $1.50
4. **Carol** Olmsted. By Mrs. Bradley. 16°. 237 pp. $1.00
5. **Evangel** Wiseman; or, the mother's question. By Sally Rochester Ford. 12°. 507 pp. $1.50
6. **Memoir** of Ann H. Judson, missionary to Burmah. By James D. Knowles. 16°. 354 pp. $1.00

QUESTION BOOK.

7. **Baptist** question book (The) on International Bible-lessons, 1876. By Rev. Granville S. Abbott. 18°. 191 pp. .... 15c.

PICTURE BOOK FOR LITTLE CHILDREN.

8. **Our** little ones. By C. R. Blackall. sm. 4°. 208 pp. .... 75c.

DOCTRINAL AND DENOMINATIONAL.

9. **Baptists** (The) and the national centenary. Edited by Lemuel Moss, D.D. 8° $1.75
10. **Scriptural** terms (The) of admission to the Lord's Supper. By Albert N. Arnold, D. D. 18°. 119 pp. .... 15c.
11. **Trials** and victories of religious liberty in America. By Rev. G. S. Bailey, D.D. 18°. 62 pp. .... 8c.
12. **Baptists** (The) in the United States. By George W. Anderson, D.D. 18°. 72 pp. .... 8c.
13. **Baptism** and baptisteries. By Walfred Nelson Cote. [*In German.*] 18°. 134 pp. .... 55c.
14. **American** Baptist year-book for 1876. 12°. 158 pp. .... 50c.

FOR INQUIRERS.

15. **Baptist** Quarterly. Vol. 9. 8°. 512 pp. .. $3.75
16. **Blood** of Jesus. By Rev. William Reid. [*In German.*] 18°. 132 pp. .... pap., 15c.; cl., 30c.
17. **Bible** (The) in a year; in daily readings. 32°. 16 pp. .... 3c.
18. **German** tract, no. 20: The two covenants. 12°. 20 pp. .... 2c.

1877.

SUNDAY-SCHOOL LIBRARY BOOKS.

19. **Ocean** gardens and palaces; or, the tent on the beach. By Rev. Sidney Dyer, Ph. D. ill. 16°. 304 pp. $1.50
20. **Among** the stars; or, Minnie Weston's astronomy class. By Mrs. M. L. G. Smith. 18°. 180 pp. 70c.
21. **Poor** children's (The) picnic. By Kate Neely Hill. 18°. 108 pp. .... 45c.
22. **Stranger** (The) in his gates. By Mrs. Mary E. Bradley. 16°. 384 pp. $1.50
23. **Way** (The) out; or, how Cornelia Harmon was rescued from a convent. By Justin D. Fulton, D.D. 16°. 352 pp. $1.50

TEACHERS' AIDS AND QUESTION BOOKS.

24. **Notes** on the Gospel of Luke, explanatory and practical. By Rev. Geo. W. Clark, D.D. With illustrations. 12°. 504 pp. $1.50
25. **Baptist** question book (The) on International Bible-lessons, 1877. By Rev. Granville S. Abbott. 18°. 224 pp. .... 15c.
26. **Primary** question book (The) on International Bible-lessons, 1877. By Mrs. M. G. Kennedy. 18°. 160 pp. .... 15c.

PICTURE BOOK FOR LITTLE CHILDREN.

27. **Our** little ones. By C. R. Blackall. sm. 4°. 218 pp. 75c.

DOCTRINAL AND DENOMINATIONAL.

28. **Baptists** (The) in the United States. By Geo. W. Anderson, D.D. 18°. 72 pp. [*In German.*] 8c.
29. **Baptist** doctrine and the pulpit. By Geo. D. B. Pepper, D.D. 18°. 50 pp. .... 8c.
30. **Christianity** susceptible of legal proof. By J. M. Pendleton, D.D. 18°. 50 pp. .... 8c.
31. **Mission** (The) of Baptists. By Rev. Henry M. King. 18°. 36 pp. .... 5c.
32. **Progress** (The) of a century. The Baptists in 1776 and in 1876. By Rev. Alvah Hovey, D.D. 18°. 70 pp. .... 8c.
33. **Young** (The) in our churches. By F. W. Smith, Esq. 18°. 30 pp. .... 5c.
34. **American** Baptist year-book for 1877. 12°. 148 pp. .... 50c.
35. **Baptist** Quarterly. Vol. 10. 8°. 512 pp. .. $3.75

TRACTS,—REGULAR SERIES.

Per 1,000 pp., $1.

36. **New Testament** (The) on baptism. (No. 246.) 12°. 8 pp.
37. **Why** don't you invite us? By J. M. Pendleton, D.D. (No. 247.) 12°. 4 pp.
38. **Soul** saving. By Henry C. Fish, D.D. (No. 248.) 12°. 12 pp.

1878.

DOCTRINAL AND DENOMINATIONAL.

39. **Lectures** on Baptist history. By Wm. R. Williams, D.D. 12°. 360 pp. $1.75
40. **Baptism** (The) of the ages and of the nations. By Rev. W. Cathcart, D.D. 16°. 222 pp. $1.00
41. **Church** (The) in the wilderness; or, the Baptists before the Reformation. By Rev. W. W. Everts, jr. 18°. 52 pp. .... 8c.
42. **Relation** (The) of baptism to the Lord's supper. By Rev. H. L. Gear. 18°. 52 pp. .... 8c.
43. **Restriction** of the Lord's Supper: what it is not, and what it is. By Rev. Henry F. Colby. 18°. 51 pp. .... 8c.
44. **Development** (The) of Baptist principles in Rhode Island. By Rev. C. E. Barrows. 18°. 104 pp. .... 10c.
45. **Baptist** views and doctrinal soundness. By Rev. G. D. B. Pepper, D.D. 18°. 48 pp. .... 8c.
46. **Corrective** church discipline. By Rev. J. M. Pendleton, D.D. 18°. 33 pp. .... 5c.
47. **Convert** culture. By Rev. Granville S. Abbott. [*In German.*] 18°. 48 pp. .... 8c.
48. **Baptist** Quarterly, for 1877 .... $3.75
49. **American** Baptist year-book (The), 1878. 12°. 152 pp. .... 50c.

SUNDAY-SCHOOL LIBRARY BOOKS.

50. **Elmdale** lyceum; or, God's mighty workers. By Rev. Sidney Dyer, Ph. D. 16°. 320 pp. $1.50
51. **Our** home birds. By Ella Rodman Church. 16°. 316 pp. $1.50

AMERICAN BAPTIST PUBLICATION SOCIETY,

Continued.

SUNDAY-SCHOOL QUESTION BOOKS AND LESSONS.

52. **Baptist** question book (The) on International Bible-lessons, 1878. By Rev. Granville S. Abbott. 18°. 150 pp.......................15c.
53. **Primary** question book (The) on International Bible-lessons, 1878. By Mrs. M. G. Kennedy. 18°. 160 pp. ....15c.

PICTURE BOOK FOR LITTLE CHILDREN.

54. **Our** little ones. By C. R. Blackall. sm. 4°. 208 pp. ....75c.

TRACTS.

Per 1,000 pp., $1.

55. **Church** (The) of the New Testament the church of all time.
56. **Baptist** church (A) radically different from pedobaptist churches.
57. **Faith** before church membership.
58. **Pernicious** effects of practice of infant baptism.
59. **Influence** and effects of infant baptism.

1879.

DOCTRINAL AND DENOMINATIONAL.

60. **Christian** doctrines: a compendium of theology. By J. M. Pendleton, D.D. 12°. 426 pp...$1.50
61. **Act** (The) of baptism in the history of the Christian church. By Henry S. Burrage. 16°. 252 pp..................................90c.
62. **Contest** (The) for wealth, and its influence among the churches. By J. F. Wyckoff, Esq. 18°. 68 pp. ....pap., 8c.
63. **American** Baptist year-book, 1879. 12°. ....50c.
64. **The** position of baptism in the Christian system. By Henry H. Tucker. 18°. 52 pp..........8c.

TEACHERS' AIDS AND QUESTION BOOKS.

65. **Notes** on the Gospel of John, explanatory and practical. By Rev. Geo. W. Clark, D.D. With maps and illustrations. 12°. 336 pp.......$1.50
66. **Baptist** question book on the International series, 1879. By Rev. G. S. Abbott. 18°. 152 pp...15c.
67. **Primary** question book (The) on the International ser. By Mrs. M. G. Kennedy. 18°. 152 pp. 15c.
68. **Anniversary** leaves. By Mrs. M. G. Kennedy. 16°. 224 pp.............................$1.00

HYMN AND MUSIC BOOKS.

69. **Hymns** of praise for public worship, prayer-meetings and Sunday schools. 24°. 96 pp. bds., 10c.
70. **The** Gospel hymn and tune book. By Lowry and Doane. 450 hymns. 200 tunes for prayer-meetings and public worship. 224 pp. cl.......50c.

SUNDAY-SCHOOL LIBRARY BOOKS.

71. **The** willows. By L. H. Dayton. 16°. 224 pp.$1.00
72. **That** horrid Sarah. By K. N. Hill. 16°. 206 pp.$1.00
73. **Florence** Walton; or, a question of duty. By May D. McKean. 16°. 535 pp. $1.00
74. **Gems** for the little ones. By C. R. Blackall. sm. 4°. 64 pp...............................15c.

WALTER S. BOOTH,

Township and Law Blank Printer, Rochester, Minn.

BOOTH'S MANUALS (NEW EDITIONS).

1. **Justice's** manual (The): a complete guide for justices of the peace in Minnesota. 5th ed. (July, 1879.) 16°.............................$1.00
2. **Township** manual (The): a complete guide for township officers in Minnesota. 5th ed. 15th thousand. (Aug., 1879.) 16°..............75c.
3. **Constable's** manual (The): a complete guide for constables and collectors in Minnesota. Rev. ed. (April, 1879.) 16°.......................75c.
4. **Highway** manual (The): the road law of Minnesota, complete. 2d ed. (Ready Jan., 1880.) 16°..25c.

E. J. HALE & SON,

17 Murray Street, New York.

1. **Kemper** County vindicated, and a peep at radical rule in Mississippi. By Jas. D. Lynch...$1.50
2. **Angel** (The) in the cloud. A poem. By Edwin W. Fuller. 12°. $1.50. — New ed., with memoir, portrait, and additional poems. 12°. (May, 1878.) $1.50; gilt edge $2.00
3. **Cluster** (A) of poems. By Rev. Dr. Means. 12°. (April, 1878.) plain cl., $1.50; gilt edge..$2.00
4. **Glenalban**, and other poems. By Annie V. Duffy. 12°. (Nov., 1878.) cl...................$1.50
5. **Scattered** leaves. By Mrs. L. M. Leach...$1.50
6. **Poems** of J. De R. Blackwell. v. 1.........$1.50

CARL DOERFLINGER,

Milwaukee, Wis.

1. **Doerflinger**, C. Onkel Karl........$1.50; $2.00
2. **Grohe**, E. Gustav, der kleine Turner..10c.; 18c.
3. — Kurzgefasste Geschichte der Leibesübungen.50c.
4. **Hailmann**, W. N. Lectures on educ...25c.; 40c.
5. **Herwegh**, G. Neue Gedichte $1.35; $1.85
6. **Märklin**, E. Familien-Bilder.........25c.; 50c.
7. **Müller**, W. Schabiade......................75c.
8. **Puchner**, R. Klänge a. d. Westen.........$1.00
9. **Siller**, F. Longfellow's Evangeline in Germ. $1.50
10. **Zündt**, E. A. Dramatische u. lyrische Dichtungen..................................$1.00

DONNELLEY, GASSETTE & LOYD,

Chicago.

1. **Burdette**, R. G. Rise and fall of the mustache, and other Hawk-eyetems.................$1.50
2. **Guiteau**, Charles. The truth: a companion to the Bible......................................50c.
3. **Lynch**, Lawrence L. Shadowed by three; with fifty-five full page illustrations. sq. 16°. 738 p. $1.50
4. **Pierce**, *Col.* Gil A. Zachariah, the Congressman. sq. 16°, 440 p..........................$1.00
5. **Stone**, May E. The doctor's protégé; with nine full-page ill. sq. 16°, 330 p. $1; bds.......75c.
6. **Thompson**, Ray. A respectable family. 552 p. $1.25

THE AMERICAN SUNDAY SCHOOL UNION,

1122 Chestnut Street, Philadelphia.

February, 1876–1879.

1. **Anglo-American** Bible revision. Containing nineteen carefully prepared papers, by members of the American Revision Committee. "It is a book of rare literary merit." 12°..................75c.
2. **Ants** and their works, and what the boys of Brentwood learned of them. 16°..............$1.00
3. **Beginning** life; by a layman. ill. 12°......$1.00
4. **Bible** in the counting-house: lectures to merchants; by H. A. Boardman, D.D. 12°...........75c.
5. **Bible** in the family; or, hints on domestic happiness; by H. A. Boardman, D.D. 12°......75c.
6. **Calvary** songs: a new hymn and tune book for the family and the Sunday-school; by Charles S. Robinson, D.D., and Theodore E. Perkins. 35c.; per 100..............................$30.00
7. **Do** you wear your own clothes? by John R. Whitney. 18°..............................15c.
8. **Dr.** Renwick's medicines: temperance story; by Mrs. A. K. Dunning. 16°...............$1.00
9. **English** woman's (An) work among workingmen; by Ellice Hopkins; with an introduction by Elihu Burritt. 12°...........................35c.
10. **Fatal** inheritance (The); by Mrs. A. K. Dunning. 16°.....................................$1.00
11. **First** lessons for primary classes of Bible persons; arranged in periods, with simple questions and answers; by Mrs. Mary G. Rice. 18°. pap., 3c.; per 100................................$2.50
12. **Flower** mission, and what grew out of it. 16°. cl.......................................$1.00
13. **Foundation** stones for young builders: New Year's book for the boys and girls of America; by Rev. John Hall, D.D. 16°.........................75c.
14. **Grandfather's** last work; by Mary Graham. 18°. cl...40c.
15. **Guernsey** stories. Cont.:—Betsey's bedquilt, and Cub's apple..............................60c.
16. **Harry's** Bible series; by Mrs. Helen E. Brown. Cont.:—Harry's Bible and its little words; Ears to hear; Eyes to see; Lips to speak. 4 v. 18°. cl...$1.40
17. **Historical** foundations of Christianity; by a layman. 16°...............................40c.
18. **How** Jenny kept house, and other stories; by author of "Randolph children." 18°..........60c.
19. **Illustrated** centennial papers for boys and girls; by Rev. Richard Newton:—No. 1, The State House; No. 2, Hall of Independence; No. 3, The prayer in Congress; No. 4, The Declaration of Independence. On sheets 8 by 11 inches, in large type, and printed on toned paper. ea., 4 p. per 100...50c.
20. **Improved** record and roll book for Sunday-schools, primary and infant classes, etc. 4°. cl. for 25 classes, 50c.; for 50 classes, 60c.; chp. ed...30c.

    So arranged as to give the record of twenty-five or fifty classes of twelve scholars each, for a whole year. It is simple, easy to be understood, and contains all the information needed.

21. **Jasper**, the carver; and Aunt Gracie's trust. ill. 16°. cl....................................75c.
22. **Kindling-wood** Jimmy; by Rev. Edward A. Rand. 16°.................................$1.00
23. **Laura's** aspirations; or, the next thing; by E. B. Hollis. 16°. cl..........................$1.25
24. **Little** pilgrim series. Cont.:—The little pilgrim; Little pilgrim and her friends; Little pilgrim at school; Little pilgrim's Christmas; Little pilgrim at Aunt Lou's; Little pilgrim at housekeeping. 6 v. sq. 24°. cl................................$1.50
25. **Loss** and gain; or, great fortunes; by Mrs. A. K. Dunning. 16°................................$1.00
26. **Marcia's** lessons of patience. 18°............35c.
27. **Marie**, the orphan; and other tales...........50c.
28. **Mission-box**; or, doing good and getting good; by L. E. Guernsey. 16°. cl...............90c.
29. **Moral** and religious cards:—No. 1, The three crowns; Earth has a joy unknown in heaven. $3.75 per 100.—No. 2, This is the way, walk ye in it. $3 per 100.—No. 3, Amos Lawrence; Starting just right. $3.75 per 100.—No. 4, Do it now; Do it soon. $3.75 per 100.—No. 5, The street school. $3 per 100.—No. 6, Swearers work cheap. $3 per 100.—No. 7, Aspire and labor to make some spot better. $3 per 100.—No. 8, How to ruin a son. $2.25 per 100.—No. 9, The eyes of the Lord are in every place, beholding the evil and the good. $2.25 per 100.—No. 10, Leave me not, neither forsake me. $2.25 per 100.—No. 11, It shall be well with them that fear God. $2.25 per 100.—No. 12, He hath not dealt with us after our sins. $2.25 per 100. In packages, cont. one each of the above (12 cards). 40c.
30. **Odd** moments of the Willoughby boys; by Mrs. Emily Hartley. 16°. cl.....................90c.
31. **Primary** teachers' manual; for Sunday-school workers; by Mrs. Alice W. Knox..........40c.
32. **Poor** Henry; or, the pilgrim's hut on the Weissenstein; by Dr. Chr. G. Barth. 18°...........40c.
33. **Records** of the Do-Without Society; by Emily Hartley. 16°...........................$1.00
34. **Scholar's** handbook on the International lessons for 1880. By Rev. Edwin W. Rice. New series:—Part I. Studies in Matthew. Part II. Studies in Genesis. 18°. bds., ea., 10c.; per 100....$8.00
35. **Schooner** on the beach; by Rev. Edward A. Rand. 16°......................................$1.00
36. **Setma**, the Turkish maiden; by Dr. Christian G. Barth; tr. from the German. 18°. cl.....40c.
37. **Shawnee** prisoner; by C. F. Guernsey. 16°..$1.25
38. **Sibyl** and the sapphires; or, trading in vanity fair; by C. F. Guernsey. 16°. cl...............$1.25
39. **Silent** comforter, no. 3; from the Psalms....75c.
40. **Soldier-cap** (The); or, I'll be a general. sq. 18°. 50c.
41. **Story** of a Hessian: tale of the revolution in New Jersey; by L. E. Guernsey. 16°...........75c.
42. **Story** of Joseph and his grandfather. sq. 18°..50c.
43. **Talks** with boys and girls; or, wisdom better than gold; by a layman. ill. 12°..............$1.00
44. **Three** girls of the revolution; by author of "Randolph children." 16°.....................$1.50
45. **Thunder-storm**, and other tales. 18°.......50c.
46. **"Tiger Jack;"** from the "Sunday at Home." 18°. cl...35c.
47. **Two** hundred years ago; or, life in New Sweden; by author of "Over the hedge." 16°. cl...$1.00
48. **Views** of heaven. cl., 40c.; gilt...........45c.
49. **Washington** and '76; by L. E. and C. F. Guernsey. ill. 16°................................$1.25
50. **What** will come of it? by E. W. B. ill. 18°. cl..50c.
51. **Wings** or weights; by Mary Montreal. 18°. cl. 45c.

AMERICAN TRACT SOCIETY,

150 Nassau Street, New York.

1. **Apples** of gold. ill. 4°, 208 p. Oct., '79 ....50c.
2. **Balfour**, Clara L. Women worth emulating. ill. 12°, 123 p. Sept., '79 ....80c.
3. **Bible** words for birthdays. 32°, 272 p. '78...50c.
4. **Books** for our birdies. 10 books in box. ill. 32°, ea., 64 p. Sept., '79 ....$1.00
5. **Boyd**, *Mrs.* M. D. R. Grace Ashleigh's life work. ill. 16°, 288 p. Aug., '77................$1.00
6. **Breed**, *Rev.* D. R. Plain progressive talks on the way of salvation. 18°, 56 p. Feb., '78......35c.
7. **Burr**, *Rev.* E. F. Ad fidem; or, parish evidences of the Bible. 12°, 380 p. May, '79 ....$1.50
8. — Ecce cœlum; or, parish astronomy. 12°, 198 p. May, '79..........................$1.00
9. — Pater mundi; or, modern science testifying to the Heavenly Father. 12°, 294 p. May, '79.$1.25
10. — Pater mundi, ser. 2; or, the doctrine of evolution. 12°, 307 p. May, '79..............$1.25
11. **Butts**, *Mrs.* M. F. Frolic and her friends. ill. 16°, 144 p. April, '77......................70c.
12. — Frolic at Maple Grove. ill. 16°, 160 p. '79..75c.
13. **Charlesworth**, *Rev.* V. J. Rowland Hill: life and anecdotes. 16°, 309 p. Jan., '77......$1.00
14. **Chester**, *Miss* S. E. Betty and her cousin Harry. ill. 16°, 235 p. Sept., '77..................$1.00
15. — Handsome Harry. ill. 16°, 294 p. Sept., '78.$1.00
16. — Her little world. ill. 16°, 392 p. Oct., '76.$1.25
17. **Clark**, E. Warren. Life and adventures in Japan. ill. 16°, 247 p. Oct., '78..................$1.25
18. **Cobb**, James F. Heroes of charity. ill. 16°, 216 p. Sept., '78 ....80c.
19. **Cooke**, F. E. Guiding lights: lives of the great and good. ill. 16°, 232 p. Sept., '78 ....80c.
20. **Cutler**, *Rev.* S. A bridal souvenir. 24°, 62 p. July, '79..............................60c.
21. — Name above every name. 18°, 208 p. '77..$1.00
22. — Our little ones in Paradise. 24°, 102 p. '77..60c.
23. **Daily** light on the daily path: evening hour. 32°, 370 p. Sept., '77. mor., $1.50; gilt, 75c.; cl...60c.
24. **Everard**, *Rev.* Geo. Every day life. 24°, 336 p. Sept., '76.............................$1.00
25. **Frost**, S. Annie (*pseud.*) Happy summer. ill. 4°, 183 p. Sept., '76 ....$1.25
26. — Almost a man. ill. 16°, 288 p. Sept., '77..$1.00
27. "**Getting** the better of it." ill. 12°, 192 p. Sept., '79 ....90c.
28. **God's** word, man's light and guide; by Rev. Drs. Taylor, Briggs, Storrs, Crosby, Booth, Porter, Boardman, Washburn and Simpson. 12°, 275 p. July, '77..............................$1.50
29. **Gordon**, Janet. Champions of the Reformation. ill. 16°, 215 p. Sept., '78.................80c.
30. **Gosse**, P. H. Sacred streams and rivers of the Bible. ill. 12°, 433 p. Dec., '77..........$1.75
31. **Haines**, *Mrs.* F. E. H. Jonas King, missionary to Syria and Greece. ill. 12°, 372 p. Mch., '79..$1.50
32. **Harris**, *Mrs.* C. L. Nan's Thanksgiving. ill. 18°, 72 p. April, '78..........................35c.
33. **Harrison**, Jennie (*pseud.*) Up stairs. ill. 16°, 271 p. April, '77......................$1.00
34. **Harvey**, *Mrs.* S. D. Dolly's new shoes. ill. 18°, 48 p. Sept., '77 ....30c.
35. **Henry**, *Mrs.* M. H. (Howe Benning, *pseud.*) Hester Lennox. ill. 16°, 272 p. April, '77 .....$1.00
36. **Hopkins**, *Miss* I. T. Harry Fennimore's principles. ill. 16°, 296 p. April, '77 ....$1.00
37. — The signal flag. ill. 16°, 211 p. Sept., '79..90c.
38. **Houghton**, *Mrs.* L. S. Fifine. ill. 16°, 196 p. Sept., '79 ....90c.
39. **Hunt**, *Mrs.* S. K. Yusuf in Egypt, and his friends. ill. 16°, 220 p. April, '78................$1.00
40. **Jem**, the cobbler. ill. 12°, 192 p. Sept., '79..90c.
41. **Lawrence**, *Mrs.* M. W. The home garden. 24°, 256 p. Sept., '76........................$1.00
42. **Lynnde** Elmer (*pseud.*) Mabel; or, tiny stories for tiny people. ill. 18°, 92 p. April, '79 ....40c.
43. — Daphne stories. 6 books in box. ill. 18°, ea., 48 p. Sept., '79..........................$1.75
44. **McKeever**, *Miss* H. B. Aunt Lou's scrap book. ill. 18°, 59 p. April, '78.....................30c.
45. **Mathews**, *Miss* J. H. Daisybank. ill. 16°, 190 p. Sept., '78..................................90c.
46. — Jim's make up. ill. 18°, 64 p. April, '79....30c.
47. **Miller**, *Mrs.* J. A. ("Faith Latimer.") Dear old stories in parts. 6 books. ill. 4°, ea., 16 p. Sept., '79 ....15c.
48. — Dear old stories told once more. ill. 4°, 164 p. '77.....................................$1.25
49. — Pictures and stories of long ago. ill. 4°, 156 p. Sept., '79..............................$1.25
50. **Miller**, *Mrs.* M. E. Books for bright eyes. 4 vols. in box. ill. 32°, ea., 64 p. Oct., '78.......$1.00
51. **Mortimer**, *Mrs.* M. Apostles preaching to Jews and Gentiles. ill. 18°, 279 p. April, '77 ....60c.
52. — Bible stories. 8 bks. ill. 32°. Sept., '79..75c.
53. **Noble**, *Miss* A. L. Under shelter. ill. 16°, 208 p. Sept., '76..............................$1.00
54. **Packard**, *Miss* C. M. Helen Grey. ill. 16°, 176 p. Mch., '79 ....80c.
55. **Payson**, *Rev.* G. S. All for Christ: the life of Rev. C. H. Payson. ill. 12°, 276 p. '77........$1.50
56. **Raffensperger**, *Mrs.* A. F. Little stories for good little people. ill. 18°, 48 p. Oct., '77.......25c.
57. — Happy home stories. ill. 18°, 48 p. Oct., '79.25c.
58. — Sunny hours. ill. 18°, 48 p. Oct., '79......25c.
59. **Rand**, *Rev.* E. A. Christmas Jack. ill. 16°, 231 p. Sept., '78..............................$1.00
60. — Nellie's New Year. ill. 16°, 351 p. '79..$1.10
61. **Reid**, *Rev.* Wm. Blood of Jesus. 18°, 128 p. July, '78..................................30c.
62. **Romance** of the streets; by a London rambler. ill. 16°, 270 p. Oct., '76...................$1.10
63. **Sangster**, *Mrs.* M. E. May Stanhope and her friends. ill. 16°, 352 p. Sept., '76.........$1.25
64. **Schaff**, Philip, *D.D.* Through Bible lands; or, notes of travel in Egypt, the desert and Palestine. ill. 12°, 413 p. Oct., '78.............$2.25
65. **Stony** road (The). ill. 12°, 192 p. Sept., '79..90c.
66. **Stretton**, Hesba. A night and a day; Apple Tree Court, etc. ill. 16°, 128 p. Oct., '77..........75c.
67. — A man of his word. ill. 16°, 75 p. April, 78..50c.
68. — A thorny path. ill. 16°, 175 p. April, '79..80c.
69. **Thomas**, *Rev.* J. B. The old Bible and the new science. 12°, 224 p. Nov., '77.............$1.50
70. **Thompson**, *Rev.* J. P. The workman, his false friends and his true friends. 16°, 254 p. Aug., '79 ....$1.00
71. **Thoughts** for the day, and Bible readings for a year: wall roll. 4°, 32 p. April, '79 ....75c.
72. **Titterington**, *Mrs.* S. B. Folded hands. 16°, 303 p. April, '78 ....$1.00
73. **Trowbridge**, *Miss* C. M. A crown of glory. ill. 16°, 200 p. Sept., '79 ....90c.
74. — Satisfied. ill. 16°, 214 p. April, '78.......90c.
75. **Tyree**, *Rev.* C. The glorious sufficiency of Christ. 16°, 112 p. June, '79......................60c.
76. **Walton**, *Mrs.* O. F. Angels' Christmas. ill. 18°, 61 p. April, '78 ....30c.
77. **Wheeler**, *Mrs.* S. A. Daughters of Armenia. ill. 16°, 157 p. Sept., '77 ....90c.
78. **Whittelsey**, *Rev.* C. M. Gospel truth and work. 24°, 135 p. '78..............................40c.
79. **Wyeth**, *Mrs.* M. E. C. Margie Hargrave, and the Percy children. ill. 16°, 200 p. Mch., '78..90c.

WARREN F. DRAPER,

Andover, Mass.

NEW PUBLICATIONS.

1. **Cary**, Geo. L. An introduction to the Greek of the New Testament. 12°, 72 p. (Jan., '79.)...75c.
2. **Davies**, Benjamin. A compendious and complete Hebrew and Chaldee lexicon to the Old Testament; with an English-Hebrew index. Carefully revised, with a concise statement of the principles of Hebrew grammar. By Edward C. Mitchell. 8°. (May, '79.) cl., $4.25; mor. backs ...$4.75
3. **Hackett**, Horatio B. A commentary on the original text of the Acts of the Apostles. A reprint of the author's last edition. 8°. (May, '78.)....$3.50
4. **Hill**, Thomas. A statement of the natural sources of theology; with a discussion of their validity, and of modern sceptical objections; to which is added an article on the first chapter of Genesis. 8°. (Dec., '76.) pap., 60c.; cl. flex........80c.
5. **Immer**, A. Hermeneutics of the New Testament. Translated from the German by Rev. Albert H. Newman. With additional notes and full indexes. crown 8°, 413 p. (Oct., '77) $2.25
6. **Mitchell**, Edward C. A concise statement of the principles of Hebrew grammar, for the use of teachers. 8°. (Sept., '79.) pap. ....15c.
7. **Perowne**, J. J. Stewart. The book of Psalms. A new translation, with introductions and notes explanatory and critical. Reprinted from 3d Eng. ed. 2 v. 8°. (Nov., '76.)..............$7.50
8. **Phelps**, Austin. The new birth; or, the work of the Holy Spirit. 16°, 253 p. $1.00
9. **Phocylides'** poem of admonition; with introduction and commentaries. By J. B. Feuling. Translated by H. D. Goodwin. 12°. (Dec., '79.) pap...30c.

IN PRESS.

10. **The** logic of christian evidences. By Rev. G. Frederick Wright. 16°.

CHANGES OF PRICE.

11. **Augustine's**(St.)Confessions. from $1.50 to $1.25
12. **Haley's** Discrepancies........from $2.25 to $2.00
13. **Harris'** Kingdom of Christ ...from $1.75 to $1.50
14. **Haven's** Studies in philosophy and theology. from $2.00 to $1.50
15. **Historical** manual of the South Church. from $1.25 to $1.50
16. **Hymns** and choirs...........from $1.50 to $1.25
17. **Jones'** Hebrew grammar......from $1.75 to $1.50
18. **Lewis'** Church and science....from $1.50 to $1.25
19. **Shadow** of christianity ......from $1.25 to $1.00
20. **Mediation**..................from $1.25 to $1.00
21. **Pond's** Pastoral theology .....from $1.75 to $1.50
22. **Russell's** Pulpit elocution ....from $1.50 to $1.25
23. **Shedd's** Guericke's Ancient church. from $3.00 to $2.75
24. — Mediæval church ....from $1.50 to $1.25
25. **Stuart** On proverbs ....from $1.75 to $1.50
26. **Taylor's** Classical study......from $2.00 to $1.50
27. **Theologia** Germanica........from $1.50 to $1.25
28. **Tyler's** Theology of the Greek poets. from $1.75 to $1.50

CATHOLIC PUBLICATION SOCIETY COMPANY,

9 Barclay Street, New York.

1. **Catholic** Church in the United States. By Rev. I. T. Hecker. pap. ....10c.
2. **History** (A) of the mass and its ceremonies in the eastern and western church. By Rev. J. O'Brien, A.M. 12°. *net*, $1.25; postage ....13c.
3. **Sir** Thomas More: an historical romance ...$1.50
4. **Six** sunny months. By M. A. Tincker. 8°. cl.,$1.50
5. **Letters** of a young Irishwoman to her sister; tr. from the French. 8°. cl., extra.........$1.50
6. **Stray** leaves from a passing life. 8°. cl., extra, $1.50
7. **Alba's** dream, and other stories; original and tr. 8°. cl., extra...........................$1.50
8. **Assunta** Howard, and other stories. 8°. cl., extra. $1.50
9. **Grants** of land and gifts of money to Catholic and Protestant institutions compared. pap......10c.
10. **Trowel** (The) and the cross, by Bolanden. 8°. cl., extra $1.50
11. **Hand-book** of instructions and devotions for the children of Mary; tr. from the French by Rev. J. P. O'Connell, D.D. 32°. cl............60c.
12. **Knowledge** (The) of Mary. By Rev. J. De Concilio $1.50
13. **Frederic** Ozanam, Professor at the Sorbonne: his life and writings. By K. O'Meara........$2.00
14. **Life** of Pope Pius IX. By J. R. G. Hassard..$1.00
15. **Love** of Jesus to penitents. Manning........40c.
16. **Four** seasons (The). By Rev. J. W. Vahey. $1.00
17. **Month** of May. By Father Debussi........50c.
18. **Meditations** and contemplations on the Sacred Passion. By Luis of Granada. 18° ....50c.
19. **One** of God's heroines......................30c.
20. **Sayings** and prayers of Mother McAuley....50c.
21. **Little** treatise on little sufferings. cl. ....30c.
22. **Books** for young girls: — The young girls' month of May; of June; of July; of October; of November; of December; of March. ea. ....10c.
23. **Five-minute** sermons by the Paulists. 16°..$1.00
24. **Illustrated** school books; ed. by Rt. Rev. J. L. Spalding. Readers: — Young Catholic's ill. primer, 20c.; first, 25c.; second, 40c.; third, 60c.; fourth, 75c.; fifth, $1.25; sixth, $1.50; ladies' $1.25
25. — Spellers: — Young Catholic's ill. speller, 25c.; Grammar-school speller and definer ....75c.
26. — Arithmetics: — Ill. table-book; or, first lessons in numbers, 20c.; Standard arithmetic, for schools of all grades, no. 1, 75c.; *Same*, for high schools, colleges, etc., no. 2.......................75c.
27. **Complete** historical catechism, after Fleury..12c.
28. **Deharbe**, Jos. Full catechism of the Catholic religion, no. 1. New ed., rev. and amended by an Am. ecclesiastic, 60c. — Shorter catechism, no. 2, 30c. — Shorter catechism, no. 3.......20c.
29. **History** of the United States for Catholic schools. By J. R. G. Hassard. ill. 12°............$1.50
30. **Introductory** history (An) of the United States, arranged on the catechetical plan; abridg. from larger history of J. R. G. Hassard. ill......40c.
31. **Ancient** history. Translated and adapted from the French of Father Gazeau, S. J. 18°....30c.
32. **Roman** history. Translated and adapted from the French of Father Gazeau, S. J. 18° ....40c.
33. **History** of the middle ages. Translated and adapted from the French of Gazeau. 16°..$1.00
34. **Modern** history. Adapted from the French of Father Gazeau, S.J., and continued.......$1.00

HAPPY HOURS COMPANY,

5 Beekman St., New York.

July, 1876 — Dec., 1879.

BOOKS.

1. **Art** of public speaking. By Samuel Neil. 16°. pap.......25c.
2. **Bottle** (The), in eight plates. By Geo. Cruikshank. 8°. pap.......15c.
3. **Comic** speeches and recitations. By H. Elliott McBride. 16°. pap.......30c.
4. **Dutch** recitations and readings. By André Arnold. 16°. pap.......15c.
5. **Elocution** without a master. By C. W. Smith. 16°. pap.......15c.
6. **Evening** entertainments: plays, charades, etc. 16°. pap.......15c.
7. **How** to join the circus and gymnasium. By Tony Denier. 16°. pap.......25c.
8. **Humorous** dialogues. By H. Elliott McBride. 16°. pap.......30c.
9. **Language** (The) of flowers. 16°. pap.......25c.
10. **Parlor** amusements for the young folks. By G. B. Bartlett. 16°. pap.......30c.
11. **Parlor** tableaux. By Tony Denier. 16°. pap., 25c.
12. **Plays** for young people. By J. Barmby, B.D. 16°. pap.......30c.
13. **Punch** and Judy. ill. 8°. pap.......25c.
14. **Shadow** pantomimes. By Tony Denier. 16°. pap.......25c.
15. **Temperance** dialogues. By H. Elliott McBride. 16°. pap.......30c.

PLAYS.

Each, 16°, pap., 15c.

16. **All's** fair in love and war: comedietta.
17. **Aunt** Betsy's beaux: comedietta.
18. **Aunt** Dinah's pledge: drama, by Harry Seymour.
19. **Aunt** Jerusha's visit: drama.
20. **Babes** (The) in the wood: domestic tragedy.
21. **Bachelor's** (The) bed-room: farce, by C. Mathews.
22. **Bailiff's** (The) daughter: farce.
23. **Beauty** and the beast: juvenile play, by J. Barmby, B.D.
24. **Betsy's** profile: comedietta, by Gustave Droz.
25. **Bric-a-brac**: comedietta, by E. D'Hervilly.
26. **Broken** promises: drama, by S. N. Cook.
27. **Broken** seal: dramatic sketch, by E. Legouvé.
28. **Camille**: play, by Alexander Dumas.
29. **Carried** by assault: comedietta, by E. D'Hervilly.
30. **Champagne**: charade farce.
31. **Changelings** (The); or, which is which? play by Lady Georgiana Fullerton.
32. **Child** (The) of circumstances: sensational drama.
33. **Cinderella**: juvenile play, by J. Barmby, B.D.
34. **Clancarty** (Lady): drama, by Tom Taylor.
35. **Closing** (The) of the "Eagle:" temperance play, by H. Elliott McBride.
36. **Cousin** (A) to them all: comedietta.
37. **Cream** (The) of love: farce.
38. **Cross** purposes: comedietta.
39. **Crumpled** rose leaf (A): comedietta.
40. **Dawn** (The) of love: comedietta, by A. Theuriet.
41. **Diplomacy**: comedietta, by Gustave Droz.
42. **Don't** all speak at once, ladies: comedietta.
43. **Don't** marry a drunkard to reform him: temperance play, by H. Elliott McBride.
44. **Dross** from gold: domestic sketch.
45. **Drunkard's** (The) home: temperance drama.
46. **Drunkard's** (The) warning: temperance drama, by C. W. Taylor.
47. **Family** pictures: farce, by E. Stirling.
48. **Fifteen** years of a drunkard's life: melodrama, by Douglas Jerrold.
49. **Foresight**; or, my daughter's dowry: comedy, by Ernest Legouvé.
50. **Frenchman** (The): charade.
51. **Fruits** of the wine-cup: drama, by John H. Allen.
52. **Furnished** apartments: comic interlude.
53. **Generous** Jew (The): play.
54. **Getting** up in the world: comedy.
55. **Going** through him: monologue.
56. **Gray** mare (A): comedietta, by B. Webster, jr.
57. **Great** Eastern (The): extravaganza, by F. C. Burnand.
58. **Harvest** storm (The): domestic drama.
59. **H. M. S. Pinafore**: comic opera, by W. S. Gilbert and A. Sullivan.
60. **Hob-nobbing**: comedietta.
61. **Hurrah** for Paris! comedietta.
62. **Inhuman**: comedietta.
63. **Is** the man mad? comedietta.
64. **La** Cigale: comedy, by H. Meilhac and L. Halévy.
65. **Les** miserables: Ethiop. farce, by G. W. H. Griffin.
66. **Limerick** boy (The): farce, by James Pilgrim.
67. **Locked** door (The): monologue.
68. **Lord** Dundreary's visit: farce.
69. **Lost** heir (The): historical drama.
70. **Love** and money: comedy, by D. de P. Bourcicault.
71. **Love** flower (The): comedietta, by E. Legouvé and P. Merimée.
72. **Love** master — love man: charade, by H. Hersée.
73. **Love** to music: comedietta.
74. **Male** and female: comedietta.
75. **Married** widows (The): comedietta.
76. **Masquerading** for two: comedietta.
77. **Master-piece**: charade.
78. **Matrimony**: charade.
79. **Maud's** command: temperance play, by H. Elliott McBride.
80. **More** blunders than one: farce, by T. G. Rodwell.
81. **Mothers** and fathers: dramatic sketch.
82. **Mrs.** Sairy Gamp's tea and turn out: a Bozzian sketch, by B. Webster.
83. **Muolo**, the monkey: farce, by Chas. E. Helm.
84. **My** Peter! comedietta, by André Arnold.
85. **My** precious Betsy: farce, by J. M. Morton.
86. **Mystic** spell: pantomime, by C. White.
87. **Oh** my uncle! comedietta.
88. **One** must marry: comedy, by A. Wilhelma.
89. **Our** professor: monologue.
90. **Out** in the streets: play, by S. N. Cook.
91. **Out** of the depths: temperance play, by H. Elliott McBride.
92. **Patches** and powder: a dramatic proverb.
93. **Perfection**; or, the cork leg: farce, by Thomas Haynes Bayley.
94. **Persecuted** Dutchman (The): farce, by S. Barry.
95. **Pet** lamb (The): domestic scene.
96. **Poisoned** darkies (The): temperance play, by H. Elliott McBride.
97. **Princess** (The): juvenile play, by J. Barmby, B.D.
98. **Prison** and palace: comic drama, by J. P. Simpson.
99. **Punch** and Judy: serio-comical tragedy.
100. **Putting** on airs: comedietta.
101. **Queen** Mary: historical drama, by A. Tennyson.
102. **Quite** at home: comedietta, by A. Sketchley.
103. **Ralph** Coleman's reformation: temperance play, by H. Elliott McBride.
104. **Refinement**: charade.

HAPPY HOURS COMPANY,

Continued.

105. **Rob**, the hermit: romantic drama, by C. F. Adams.
106. **Rosebud**; or, the sleeping beauty: juvenile play, by J. Barmby, B. D.
107. **Rumplestiltskin**: extravaganza, by J. Barmby.
108. **Shamrock**: charade, by George Manville Fenn.
109. **Sir** Dagobert and the dragon: romantic extravaganza, by F. C. Burnand.
110. **Skinflint**: charade, by J. Barmby, B. D.
111. **Slight** mistake: comedy, by Emile Souvestre.
112. **Slighted** treasures: petite comedy.
113. **Society** for doing good, but saying bad: comedy.
114. **Stage-struck** Yankee: farce, by O. E. Durivage.
115. **Taken** in and done for: comedietta, by Mrs. Charles Kemble.
116. **Ten** nights in a bar-room: drama, by W. W. Pratt.
117. **Those** "cussed" waves: monologue.
118. **Thoughts** before marriage: monologue.
119. **Three** guesses (The): fairy extravaganza.
120. **Tittlebat** a father: monologue.
121. **To** let, furnished: comedietta, by F. C. Burnand.
122. **Too** windy for an umbrella: petite comedy.
123. **Trip** (A) to Cambridge: comedietta.
124. **Twenty** and forty: comedietta.
125. **Uncle** Jack: comedietta, by S. N. Cook.
126. **Vermont** wool dealer: farce.
127. **Village** belle (The): romantic drama.
128. **Vilikens** and Dinah: farce, by C. White.
129. **Wanderer's** (The) return: drama, by S. N. Cook.
130. **Wardrobe**: charade, by George Manville Fenn.
131. **Whiskey** fiend (The): temperance drama.
132. **Wild** flowers: operetta, by Dr. J. W. Bernhardt.
133. **Wine** cup (The): temperance sketch.
134. **Woman** nature will out: farce.
135. **Woman** (The) of the world: drama.
136. **Woman's** club (The): comedietta, by J. S. Coyne.
137. **Yankee** peddler (The): farce, by M. Barnett.

THE RAILROAD GAZETTE OFFICE,

73 Broadway, New York.

1. **American** Railway Master Mechanics' Assoc., 8th–11th annual reports. 12°. ea., pap...$1.75
2. **Billerica** and Bedford 2-ft. gauge railroad. ill. 8°. pap. .... 25c.
3. **Car-builder's** dictionary; compiled by M. N. Forney, assisted by Leander Garey and Calvin A. Smith. 800 eng. obl. 12°, 490 p. $2.00
4. **Fink**, Albert. Cost of railroad transportation, railroad accounts and governmental regulation of railroad tariffs. 2d ed., with tables. 8°. pap...75c.
5. — Investigation into cost of passenger traffic on American railroads. 8°. pap. .... 75c.
6. **Forney**, M. N. Locomotives for rapid-transit railroads. ill. 12°. pap. .... 40c.
7. **Gieseler**, E. A. Frog angles and distances. 12°. pap. .... 25c.
8. **Jacqmin**, F. Railroad employés in France. 12°, pap. .... 25c.
9. **Kirkman**, Marshall M. Railway accounts: disbursements. obl. 12°, 272 p. $2.00
10. — *Same:* revenue. Enl. and rev. ed. obl. 12°, 514 p. $2.50
11. — Railway baggage-car traffic. obl. 12°, 262 p. $2.00
12. — Railway train and station service. obl. 12°, 280 p. $2.00
13. **Lee**, Francis J. Railroad local passenger traffic. 12°. pap. .... 25c.
14. **Master** Car-Builders' Assoc., 10th–12th annual reports. 12°. ea., pap. .... 25c.
15. **Pocket** railroad report. covers, $1.50; forms, ea., 40c.; per doz. $4.00
16. **Railroad** Gazette: weekly. per year $4.20
17. **Thurston**, Robert H. Friction and lubrication; with new determinations of laws and of coefficients of friction. 12° $1.50
18. **Verrugas** viaduct (The) compared with several other viaducts. 12°. pap. .... 40c.
19. **Weber**, *Baron* M. M. v. Standard gauge and narrow gauge. 12°. pap. .... 25c.
20. **Wellington**, Arthur M. The economic theory of the location of railways. obl. 12°, 250 p...$2.00

CHANGE IN PRICE.

21. **Huntington's** Road-master's assistant. Revised and enlarged by Latimer....... from $1 to $1.50

BICKNELL & COMSTOCK,

27 Warren St., New York.

1. **Ames'** Alphabets $1.50
2. — Compendium of penmanship $5.00
3. **Atwood's** Rules of proportion $1.00
4. **Bicknell's** Cottage and villa architecture ... $6.00
5. — Public buildings $3.50
6. — School-house and church architecture $3.00
7. — Stables, out-buildings, fences, etc. $2.50
8. — Street, store and bank fronts $4.00
9. **Cameron's** Plasterer's manual .... 75c.
10. **Gardner's** Common sense in church building. $1.00
11. **Hussey's** Home building $3.00
12. **Palliser's** American cottage homes $5.00
13. — Builder's specifications .... 75c.
14. — Model homes $1.00
15. **Powell's** Foundation and foundation walls .. $1.50
16. **Woollett's** Old homes made new $1.50

HENRY A. YOUNG & CO.,

13 Bromfield St., Boston.

1. **Barker**, W. R. *and* C. F. The world's checker-book. 16°. '79. 75c.; bds. .... 50c.
2. **Charley** Wheeler's reward. 16°. '78 .... $1.00
3. **Ford**, David B. Studies on the baptismal question. 8°. '79 .... $2.25
4. **Higham**, *Mrs.* Mary R. Our darling's picture stories: — Pet chicken; The rose party; Nannie's present; Little pearl; Rufus' temptation; Dolph's trap; Little comforter: The two robins; Grandma's chest; The golden rule. 10 v. ill. 18°. '78. $3.00
5. — Picture stories for boys; — for girls. ill. 16°. '78. ea. $1.00
6. **Hovey**, Alvah. Manual of systematic theology and Christian ethics. 8°. '77 .... $2.50
7. **Hoyt**, *Mrs.* G. S. ("Marion West.") Sunday school concert book, No. 3. 16°. '79. bds...30c.
8. **Jimmy's** shoes. 16°. '78 .... $1.00
9. **Lacombe**, Paul. Short history of the French people. 12°. '78 .... $1.25
10. **Young's** cheap S.-school libraries: — No. 1. 15 v. ill. 16°. *net*, $9. — No. 2. 16 v. ill. 16°. *net*, $9. — No. 3. 30 v. ill. 18°. *net*, $8. — No. 4. 17 v. 16° $9.00

GEORGE ROUTLEDGE & SONS,

416 Broome Street, New York.

1876.

1. **Modern** magic: a complete manual of conjuring; by Prof. Hoffmann. 300 ill. post 8°. cl...$2.50
2. **Science** in sport made philosophy in earnest; ed. by Robert Routledge. ill. 8°. cl..........$2.50
3. **Every** boy's annual, 1877; cont. stories and tales by the best English juvenile writers, and many hundred engravings. 8°. cl., full gilt $2.50
4. **Doctor's** (The) family; or, the fortunes of the Castels; by J. Girardin. 100 ill. by Emile Bayard. 12°. cl..................................$1.75
5. **Voyage** (A) round the world,—Australia; by Jules Verne. 48 full-page plates. 12° $1.00
6. **Voyage** (A) round the world, — New Zealand; by Jules Verne. 48 full-page plates. 12°....$1.00
7. **From** cadet to colonel: record of a life of active service; by Maj.-Gen. Sir Thomas Seaton, K.C.B. ill. 12° $1.75
8. **Aladdin's** picture book: 24 pages of ill., by Walter Crane; printed in colors. 4°. cl......$2.50
9. **Jack** Horner's picture book: 36 pages of ill.; printed in colors by the Kronheims and Dalziels. demy 4°. cl. $2.50
10. **Baby's** opera: a book of old rhymes, with new dresses, by Walter Crane; eng. and printed in colors by Edmund Evans: music by the earliest masters $1.50
11. **Little** Wide Awake for 1877. 400 ill. sm. 4°. bds., $1.25; cl. $2.00
12. **Routledge's** picture book of animals. 300 ill. sm. 4°. bds., $1.25; cl..................$2.00
13. **Mother** Goose's nursery rhymes: new style. 300 ill. by noted artists. 4°. bds., $1; cl. $1.50
14. **Holiday** album for boys and girls. 192 page pictures. 12°. cl. $1.50
15. **Forget-me-not** (The), and other tales; by author of "Basket of flowers." 16°............$1.25
16. **Minstrel** love: a romance; by De La Motte-Fouqué. ill. 16°...........................$1.25
17. **Thiodolph**, the Icelander; by De La Motte-Fouqué. ill. 16° $1.25
18. **Play-room** album for children: 72 pages of colored plates. sq. 12°. cl.......................$1.25
19. **Walter** Crane's colored picture books for children. Newly arranged in volumes. 8°. ea., cl., $1.25: — Song of sixpence; Chattering Jack; King Luckieboy; Three bears; Marquis of Carabas; Alphabet bee; Blue Beard.
20. **Little** Bright Eyes' picture book. 200 ill. sm. 4°. bds., 60c.; cl..........................$1.00
21. **Little** Golden Locks' picture book. 200 ill. sm. 4°. bds., 60c.; cl..........................$1.00
22. **Animal** picture book. 8 col. plates. sm. 4°. bds...$1.00
23. **Bird** picture book. 10 col. pl. sm. 4°. bds., $1.00
24. **Sunday** evenings at home; by Rev. H. C. Adams. 3 new series. 16°. ea....................75c.
25. **Floral** birthday book: pictures of flowers, printed in colors, by Edmund Evans. 12° $1.00
26. **Story** of a poodle; for boys. 64 ill. 16° ..$1.00
27. **Tom** Thumb's picture book: large type stories and rhymes, and 24 p. of col. ill. sq. 12°......$1.00
28. **Lily's** scrap book, for young children; by Mrs. Sale Barker. 120 ill. 16°. cl.............50c.
29. **Lily's** screen, for young children; by Mrs. Sale Barker. 120 ill. 16°. cl..................50c.
30. **Little** Blossom's picture book. 96 large ill. sq. 12°. bds..75c.
31. **Little** Maybud's picture book. 96 large ill. sq. 12°. bds..75c.
32. **Twin** brothers; by Mrs. Perring. 18°. cl....45c.
33. **Pennell's** (Mr.) new books on angling: — Fly fishing; Bottom fishing; Trolling, or pike fishing. 12°. ea., bds. ....50c.
34. **Floating** city (A); [and] The blockade runners; by Jules Verne. 16°.........................50c.
35. **Bread** and honey; by Mrs. Semple-Garrett. 8 v. 94 ill. 18°. cl. per set $2.00
36. **How** we managed without servants; by a lady who can help. (Useful lib.)..................50c.
37. **Routledge's** 4° toy books; printed in colors by Edmund Evans: — Hind in the wood; Princess Belle Etoile. 50c.; linen...................$1.00
38. **Aunt** Mavor's toy books, in colors: — Sleeping beauty in the wood; A apple pie. 20c.; linen, 40c.
39. **Routledge's** threepenny toy books, in colors: — Jack, the giant-killer; Blue Beard; Aladdin; Forty thieves; Tom Thumb; Sleeping beauty. ea., 12½c.; linen............................25c.

1877.

40. **Art** rambles in the Highlands and islands of Scotland, by John T. Reid: 150 sketches taken from nature, drawn by the author, engraved by the Brothers Dalziel. sm. 4°. cl., gilt edges..$10.00
41. **Seymour's** Humorous sketches: 86 caricature etchings, illustrated in prose and verse by Alfred Crowquill. 8°. cl. $6.00
42. **Birthday** book (The) of flower and song; with selections from the poets, and page ill. printed in colors by Edmund Evans.................$7.50
43. **Heads** of the people; or, portraits of the English; drawn by Kenny Meadows, with essays by W. M. Thackeray, Douglas Jerrold, Mrs. Gore, Mrs. S. C. Hall and others. 2 v. 112 ill. 8°. cl...$7.50
44. **Horne's** Life of Napoleon; ill. by Horace Vernet. 8°. cl..$3.50
45. **Science** (The) of conjuring; by Houdin, with notes by Prof. Hoffmann, author of "Modern magic." 12°. cl.........................$2.50
46. **Records** of the chase and sporting anecdotes; by Cecil. 12°. cl. $2.50
47. **Boys** (The) of Westonbury; by Rev. H. C. Adams; with ill. by A. W. Cooper........$1.75
48. **Christian** year (The): ill. of flowers, designed by W. Foster, and printed in colors by Edmund Evans. 18°. cl. $2.00
49. **Picture-story** album for children. 192 full-page pictures. 12°. cl. $1.50
50. **Lily's** drawing-room book; by Mrs. Sale Barker. 380 engravings, and a colored frontispiece. 12°. cl. $1.25
51. **Little** Wide Awake: new volume for 1878; ed. by Mrs. Sale Barker. sm. 4°. bds., $1.25; cl., $2.00
52. **Little** Blue Bell's picture book; with more than 400 large illustrations by Sir John Gilbert, J. D. Watson, Harrison Weir and other artists, and large-type letter-press. sm. 4°. bds., $1.25; cl. $2.00
53. **Routledge's** picture book of birds. 300 ill. sm. 4°. bds., $1.25; cl. $2.00
54. **Wild** love, and other tales; by De La Motte-Fouqué. ill. 16°..........................$1.25
55. **Our** Little Sunbeam's picture book; by Mrs. Semple Garrett. 150 ill. sm. 4°. bds., $1.00; cl. $1.50
56. **Picture-story** album for boys: 94 full-page pictures from designs by the best artists, and large type. 16°. cl. ....80c.
57. **Picture-story** album for girls: 94 full-page pictures from designs by the best artists, and large type. 16°. cl. ....80c.

GEORGE ROUTLEDGE & SONS,

Continued.

58. **Little** Curly-Pate's story book: 150 ill., and large type. sm. 4°. bds., 60c.; cl. $1.00
59. **Little** Rosy-Cheek's story book: 150 ill., and large type. sm. 4°. bds., 60c.; cl. $1.00
60. **Mother** Goose's jingles: 150 pictures by eminent artists. sm. 4°. bds., 60c.; cl. $1.00
61. **Mother** Goose's melodies: 150 pictures by eminent artists. sm. 4°. bds., 60c.; cl. $1.00
62. **Story** (The) of a wooden horse; tr. from the French by Mrs. Sale Barker. ill. 16°. cl...75c.
63. **Original** Robinson Crusoe (The); by Rev. H. C. Adams. ill. 16°. cl. .... 75c.
64. **Narrative** poetry for the young. 80 ill., eng. by the Brothers Dalziel. 16°. cl. $1.00
65. **Lily** at her grandmamma's; by Mrs. Sale Barker. 120 ill. 16°. cl. .... 50c.
66. **Little** Primrose's picture book. 100 large pictures. sm. 4°. bds., 50c.; cl. .... 75c.
67. **Little** Forget-me-not's picture book. 100 large pictures. sm. 4°. bds., 50c.; cl. .... 75c.
68. **Aunt** Effie's rhymes for little children; ill. by H. K. Browne. sm. 4°. bds. .... 50c.
69. **Hookey-Beak**, the raven; and other tales; with comic ill. by Busch. sm. 4°. bds. .... 50c.
70. **Roses**, and how to grow them. ill. 16°. bds., 50c.
71. **Knots**, splices and ties; by J. T. Burgess. 100 ill. 16°. bds. .... 50c.
72. **Christmas** day and how it was spent: a story. 16°. bds. .... 50c.
73. **Through** the keyhole, a novel; by J. M. Jephson. 16°. pap. .... 50c.
74. **Pleasures** (The) of house-building; by J. Ford Mackenzie. 16°. bds. .... 50c.
75. **Routledge's** forty-five cents series of juvenile books: — Sybil Grey, by Mrs. Perring; Little Davy's new hat, by Robert Bloomfield; Hymns for infant minds, by Ann and Jane Taylor. 18°. ea., cl. .... 45c.
76. **Aunt** Mavor's alphabet; printed in colors by Leighton .... 25c.
77. **Shadowless** man (The); or, the adventures of Peter Schlemihl. 12°. pap. .... 25c.

1878.

78. **Walks** in London; by Augustus J. C. Hare. 2 v. 100 ill. 12°. cl., $5; 2 v. in 1 .... $3.50
79. **Universal** songster (The); or, museum of mirth: woodcuts by George and Robert Cruikshank. 3 v. demy 8°. cl. $7.50
80. **Routledge's** every girl's annual; ed. by Alicia Amy Leith, containing contributions by the Right Hon. Knatchbull-Hugessen, M.P., the author of "The cuckoo clock," etc. 12°. cl. $2.00
81. **Routledge's** every boy's annual for 1879 .... $2.50
82. **Drawing-room** amusements and evening party entertainments; by Prof. Hoffmann, author of "Modern magic," etc. ill. 12°. cl. $2.00
83. **Little** Wide Awake pictures; by Mrs. Sale Barker. 188 pp. of full-page pictures. 4°. cl. $2.00
84. **Golden** light: Scripture history for the young. 80 full-page ill. 4°. bds., $1.25; cl. $1,75
85. **Picture** history (A) of England for the young. 80 full-page pl. 4°. bds., $1.25; cl. $1.75
86. **Uncle** Chesterton's heir; by Madame Colomb. 100 ill. 12°. cl. $1.75
87. **Uncle** Joe's stories; by the Right Hon. Knatchbull-Hugessen, M.P. ill. 12°. cl. $1.75
88. **Baby's** (The) bouquet: Walter Crane's new book. ill. sm. 4°. bds. $1.50
89. **Through** Normandy with my children; by Mrs. Charles Ellis. ill. sq. 12°. cl. $1.50
90. **Picture-book** (A) for laddies and lassies. 160 pages of pictures. cr. 8°. cl. $1.50
91. **Little** Wide Awake for 1879; by Mrs. Sale Barker. 400 ill. sm. 4°. bds., $1.25; cl. $2.00
92. **Picture-book** (The) of fishes, insects, etc.: 240 ill. by Zwecker and others. sm. 4°. bds., $1.25; cl. $2.00
93. **Child's** picture scrap-book (The): about 1,000 ill. f°. fancy bds., $1.25; cl. $2.00
94. **Only** a cat; by Mrs. H. B. Paull. ill. 16°. cl., $1.25
95. **Seven** champions (The) of Christendom. ill. 16°. cl., $1; with 6 col. ill. $1.50
96. **Child's** (The) delight; by Mrs. Adams Acton. ill. 4°. bds., $1; cl. $1.50
97. **Aunt** Effie's nursery rhymes, set to music by Thomas Crampton; ill. by H. K. Browne. sm. 4°. bds., $1; cl. $1.50
98. **Kidnapping** in the Pacific; by W. H. G. Kingston; ill. by Zwecker and others. 16°. cl...75c.
99. **Little** Speckley's adventures. 50 ill. 16°. cl., 75c.
100. **Lily's** holidays; by Mrs. Sale Barker. 120 ill. 16°. cl. .... 50c.
101. **Large** picture primer (The); with full-page pictures. sm. 4°. bds., 50c.; cl. .... 75c.
102. **Little** Violet's picture-book. 100 ill. sm. 4°. bds., 50c.; cl. .... 75c.
103. **Little** Snowdrop's picture-book. 100 ill. sm. 4°. bds., 50c.; cl. .... 75c.
104. **Musical** Cinderella (The): the tale told in verse, interspersed with songs, and colored pictures by Walter Crane .... 50c.
105. **Children's** theatricals; arranged in verse, as easy plays for children to act, by Keith Angus .... 50c.
106. **New** quarto toy-books; each with 6 pages of col. pl., by Caldecott, printed by Edmund Evans: — The house that Jack built; John Gilpin. ea., 50c

1879.

107. **Life** and letters of Baroness Bunsen; by Augustus J. C. Hare. 2 v. 12°. cl., $5; 2 v. in 1, cl., $3.00
108. **Pitty** Patty's library. ea. vol. 24 pages, large picture on each page. 12 v. in set, boxed, and 3 sets in a nest. per set, $1.20: — Merry rhymes for dull times; Lively lays for dreary days; Mignonette for my little pet; Work and play for every day; Little words about little birds; Furze and heather for rainy weather; Little kisses for little misses; A book of joy for mamma's boy; Tit bits for tiny wits; Little mites for tiny sprites; Little jokes for little folks; A welcome guest from robin's nest.
109. **Good** boys' and girls' library. ea. vol. cont. 48 pages, 24 p. of pictures and 24 p. of large type. 8 v. in set, boxed, and 3 sets in a nest. per set, $1.60: — Bright boys' books; Good girl's gift; Tiny Tot's treasure; Pet's picture posies; Little laughter lover; Fun, frolic and fancy; Harry's happy home; Wee Willie Winkie.
110. **Apple** pie (A): new number of Aunt Mavor's toy-books, with 6 pages of colored pictures. 20c.; linen .... 40c.
111. **House** (The) that Jack built: new number of Aunt Mavor's toys. 20c.; linen .... 40c.
112. **Day** dawn library. ea. vol. cont. 32 pages, consisting of 16 pages of pictures and 16 pages of large type. per set, $2.50: — Kind little heart; Mamma's little pet; Happy pet; Red Rover; Baby boy's picture-book; Little sugar plum; The household fairy; Little Ann's picture-book; Nursery pleasures; Happy playtime.

GEORGE ROUTLEDGE & SONS,

Continued.

113. **Little** Rosebud's picture-book. 96 pages, large picture on each page, and large type. sm. 4°. 50c.; cl. ....75c.
114. **Little** Poppy's picture-book. 96 pages, large picture on each page and large type. sm. 4°. 50c.; cl. ....75c.
115. **Dog** picture-book (The); with large pictures and entertaining stories about dogs. sm. 4°. 50c.; cl., 75c.
116. **Cat** picture-book (The); with large pictures and entertaining stories about cats. sm. 4°. 50c.; cl., 75c.
117. **Tiny's** natural history; in words of 4 letters, large type. 80 ill. sm. 4°. 50c.; cl.......75c.
118. **One-syllable** books; ea. vol. cont. 8 full-page pictures. per set, $2.50: — Robinson Crusoe; Swiss family Robinson; Evenings at home; Bunyan's Pilgrim's progress; History of the robins.
119. **Caldecott's** new toy books; by Mr. R. Caldecott; ea. cont. 26 pictures and 6 p. of col. pl. per v., 50c.: — The babes in the wood; Elegy on a mad dog.
120. **John** Brown: essay on working men in America. 16°. pap. ....50c.
121. **Singing** quadrille (The): ill. colored picture-book for children, with popular nursery rhymes set to quadrille music. sm. 4°. pap. ....50c.
122. **Ancient** and modern magic; by a professor. fancy bds. ....50c.
123. **Mrs.** Brown on coöperative stores; by Arthur Sketchley ....50c.
124. **Routledge's** Christmas annual: The stage door, tales by those who enter it; written by the leading actors and actresses of the day ....50c.
125. **Theatrical** scenes, for the performance of children; by Keith Angus ....50c.
126. **Indian** cottage (The); by Bernardin de St. Pierre. 100 ill. 16°. cl...................50c.
127. **Lily's** magic lantern. 128 pages, ill. on each page. 16°. cl. ....50c.
128. **Musical** Red Riding Hood: col. ill. by Walter Crane; words by William Routledge, set to music by Louis N. Parker. 8°. pap.............50c.
129. **Little** Wide Awake's painting-book: col. pictures on one page, and blanks for children to fill in on the opposite page, from designs by Oscar Pletsch. 4°. pap. ....50c.
130. **Little** Silver Locks' story-book for little children. 200 ill. sm. 4°. bds., 60c.; cl. $1.00
131. **Little** Ruby Lips' story-book for little children. 200 ill. sm. 4°. bds., 60c.; cl............$1.00
132. **Good** genius (The) that turned everything into gold; by the Brothers Mayhew; ill. by George Cruikshank ....75c.
133. **Tales** of fairy land; by Tieck.............75c.
134. **Oscar** Pletsch's picture-book: beautiful designs ill. child life, in large type. 4°. bds., $1; cl., $1.50
135. **Birthday** book (A) for the little ones. ill...$1.00
136. **Moore** birthday book (The). sq. 16°. cl...$1.00
137. **Burns** birthday book (The). sq. 16°. cl...$1.00
138. **Bulwer-Lytton** birthday book (The). sq. 16°. cl. $1.00
139. **Art** (The) of practical whist; by Col. A. W. Drayson, R.A., F.R.A.S. $1.00
140. **Red** rose (The) and the white; by W. H. Davenport Adams, with full-page ill. 12°. cl. ..$1.00
141. **Great** civil war (The); by W. H. Davenport Adams, with full-page ill. 12°. cl. $1.00
142. **Wellington's** victories; by W. H. Davenport Adams, with full-page ill. 12°. cl........$1.00
143. **Little** Wide Awake: new volume for 1880. $1.25; cl. $2.00
144. **Little** Robin's picture-book. 400 large ill.; large type. sm. 4°. bds., $1.25; cl............$2.00
145. **Nursery** picture-book. 400 ill. f°. bds., $1.25; cl. $2.00
146. **Boys** (The) of Axleford: a story for boys. ill. 16°. cl. $1.25
147. **Hampdens** (The); by Harriet Martineau. 10 full-page ill. by J. E. Millais, R.A. 12°. cl., $1.50
148. **Noble** boys: their deeds of love and duty; by Wm. Martin. ill. $1.25
149. **Bogatzky's** golden treasury. New edition. 8°. cl., $1.50; gilt $1.75
150. **Willie** Reilly, and his dear Colleen Bawn; by William Carleton. 8 pages of ill..........$1.50
151. **Flower** (The) of Christian chivalry; by Mrs. R. W. Lloyd. 24 ill.........................$1.50
152. **Wave** (The) and the battlefield; by Louisa Stewart. ill. $1.50
153. **Heroines** of the household; by Rev. Wm. Wilson, M.A. 22 ill. $1.50
154. **True** as steel. ill. 12°. cl. $1.75
155. **Gaspar**, the Gaucho; by Capt. Mayne Reid. ill. 12°. cl. $1.75
156. **Roll** (The) of the drum. ill. 12°. cl......$1.75
157. **Waverley** novels. New ed., from new type. 125 ill. by celebrated artists. 25 v. 12°. cl., $25; hf. cf. $62.50
158. **Other** stories; by Right Hon. Knatchbull-Hugessen; with full-page ill. by Ernest Griset....$1.75
159. **Imperial** natural history picture-book (The); ill. with large pictures on natural history. large f°. $1.75; cl. $2.50
160. **Paul** and Virginia; by Bernardin de St. Pierre. ill. 12°. cl. $2.50
161. **Notable** voyages; by W. H. G. Kingston. ill. 12°. cl. $2.00
162. **Under** the window: rhymes for children, cont. 64 pages of exquisite designs by the authoress, Kate Greenaway; printed in colors by Edmund Evans. 8°. bds. $2.50
163. **Caldecott's** picture-book: 128 beautiful designs by R. Caldecott, printed in colors by Edmund Evans. $2.50: — The elegy on a mad dog; John Gilpin; The babes in the wood; The house that Jack built.
164. **Every** boy's annual: volume for 1880 .....$2.50
165. **Every** girl's annual; ed. by Alicia Amy Leith. $2.50
166. **Old** Testament portraits; by Cunningham Geikie, D.D. 50 full-page ill. $3.00
167. **Life** of George Moore; by Samuel Smiles. 12°. cl. $3.00
168. **Spindle** stories; by Ascott R. Hope: original ill. by C. O. Murray, and 6 colored pictures...$3.00
169. **Children** (The) of our village; by Miss Mitford; ill. with about 50 original designs, by the best English artists, engraved by J. D. Cooper. sq. 12°. cl. $3.50
170. **Golden** leaves from celebrated poets: — Golden leaves from the British poets; Golden leaves from the American poets; Golden leaves from the dramatic poets; Golden leaves from the late English poets. $5; gilt $6.00
171. **Bulwer's** Novels. New ed. 8 ill. 8°. cl...$2.50
172. **Fielding's** Works. New ed. 8 ill. 8°. cl...$2.50
173. **Smollett's** Works. New ed. 8 ill. 8°. cl...$2.50
174. **Æsop's** Fables; trans. by George F. Townsend. 50 ill. 16°. cl. ....50c.
175. **Child's** natural history; in words of 4 letters. 108 ill. 16°. cl. ....50c.
176. **Robinson** Crusoe. New ed. 50 ill. 12°. cl. $1.00
177. **Swiss** Family Robinson. New ed. 95 ill. 12°. cl. $1.00
178. **Æsop's** Fables. New ed. 114 ill. 12°. cl., $1.00

THE METHODIST BOOK CONCERN,

805 Broadway, New York.

1. **Other** gipsy (The). ill. 16°.................90c.
2. **Through** the eye to the heart; or, eye-teaching in the Sunday-school. By Rev. W. F. Crafts. Rev. ed. 12°. $1; pap. ....50c.
3. **Old** tales retold from Grecian mythology in talks around the fire. By Augusta Larned. ill. 12°. $2.00
4. **Romans** in Greek (Epistle to the). By H. A. Buttz. 8°. cl., $1; interleaved..........$1.50
5. **Annual** minutes. 8°. pap. $1.00
6. **Official** members of the M. E. Church (Helps to). By James Porter, D.D. 16°...............80c.
7. **Formal** fraternity. Proceedings of the General Conferences of the M. E. Church and of the M. E. Church, South, in 1872, '74 and '76, and of the joint commission of the two churches on fraternal relations, at Cape May, N. J., August 16–23, 1876. 8°. pap., 50c.; flex. cl. ......75c.
8. **Christian** theology (Outlines of). By L. T. Townsend, D.D. 12°.........................40c.
9. **John** Tregenoweth: his mark. By Mark Guy Pearse. sq. 12°. 60c.; pap...............30c.
10. **God's** guide for man's faith and practice: being an arrangement of the Holy Scriptures, under the various aspects of man's belief, duty and privilege, in chronological order. In accordance with design of late James Gilruth. Systematized and collated by J. H. Gilruth. 12°.......$1.50
11. **Pictures** from our portfolio. Arranged by Annie Myrtle. 100 ill. sq. 16°.................$1.50
12. **Queen** of Navarre, the Protestant: the mother of the Bourbons. By Virginia F. Townsend. 4 ill. 16°...................................$1.50
13. **Bears'** (The) den. By Emily Huntington Miller. ill. 16°...............................$1.00
14. **Summer** days at Kirkwood. By Emily Huntington Miller. ill. 16°......................$1.25
15. **Lesson** compend, 1877 and 1878. ea.........60c.
16. **Revivals** of religion; showing their theory, means, obstructions, importations and perversions; with the duty of Christians in regard to them. By James Potter, D.D. Rev. and enl. ed. 12°...................................$1.00
17. **Uncle** Dick's legacy. By Emily Huntington Miller. ill. 16° $1.00
18. **Fighting** the enemy. By Emily Huntington Miller. ill. 16°...........................$1.25
19. **Riverside** Farm (A year at). By Emily Huntington Miller. ill. 16°......................$1.00
20. **Summer** rambles in Europe: a series of sketches of life and travels in Great Britain and upon the continent. By Alexander Clark. 12°.....$1.25
21. **Boys'** (The) pocket library: — v. 1, Rab and his friends; The mountain of miseries, and other stories; — v. 2, Sea-fights; The wreck of the Golden Mary. 24°. ea.......................40c.
22. **Berean** question book, 1877, 1878, and 1879. ea., 20c.
23. **Historical** sketches (Illustrated). By Annie Myrtle. 61 ill. sq. 16°.....................$1.50
24. **Scenes** in my life, occurring during a ministry of nearly half a century in the Methodist Episcopal Church. By Rev. Mark Trafton, D.D. 12°..$1.50
25. **Methodist** almanac, 1877, 1878, and 1879. ea., 10c.
26. **Christmas** chimes; edited by Mrs. E. J. Knowles. ill. sq. 12°. gilt edge, $2.50; mor. $5.00
27. **Chautauqua** text book, no. 2: Studies of the stars: a pocket guide to the science of astronomy. By H. W. Warren, D.D. 24°. pap........10c.
28. **Christian** life and practice in early church..$1.75
29. **Annual** minutes, 1877. shp., $4; pap......$1.00
30. **Mile-stone** papers, doctrinal, ethical and experimental, on Christian progress. By Daniel Steele, D.D. 16°...................................$1.00
31. **Chautauqua** text book, no. 3: Bible studies for little people. By Rev. B. T. Vincent 24°. pap.......................................10c.
32. **Wine** in the word: an inquiry concerning the wine Christ made, the wine of the Supper, etc. By Abraham Coles, M.D., LL.D. 12°. pap., 25c.; flex. cl.......................................40c.
33. **Methodist** Episcopal Church of the United States (Statistics of the). By W. H. De Puy, D.D. 12°. pap....................................20c.
34. **Live** boy (The); or, Charlie's letters. By Edwin A. Johnson, D.D. ill. 16°................$1.00
35. **What** shall I read? Confidential chat on books. 16° ....75c.
36. **Chautauqua** text book, no. 7: Memorial days of the Chautauqua Literary and Scientific Circle. 24°. pap. ....10c.
37. **Chautauqua** text book, no. 4: English history. By J. H. Vincent, D.D. 24°. pap..........10c.
38. **Camp** meetings: their origin, history and utility, also, their perversion and how to correct it; embracing a careful review of the Sabbath question. By Rev. S. C. Swallow. 12°. pap., 20c.; flex. cl. ....30c.
39. **Introduction** to the study of the Holy Scriptures. By Henry M. Harmon, D.D. 8°.........$4.00
40. **Lectures** on preaching, delivered before the theological department of Yale College. By Matthew Simpson, D.D., LL.D. 12°...............$1.50
41. **Christian** theology (Outlines of). By L. T. Townsend, D.D. 12°...........................40c.
42. **Annual** minutes, spring and fall conferences, 1878. ea., pap.....................................75c.
43. **Eddy**, *Rev.* Thomas M., *D.D.* Life of; by Charles N. Sims, D.D. 12°...............$1.75
44. **Commentary** (The people's); including brief notes on the New Testament, with copious references to parallel and illustrative Scripture passages, designed to assist Bible students and common readers to understand the meaning of the inspired word. By Rev. Amos Binney and Daniel Steele, D. D. Revised, with topical index. 12°...$3.00
45. **Bessie**, the cash girl. By Mrs. Mary D. Brine. 18°...50c.
46. **Chautauqua** text book, no. 8: What noted men think of the Bible. By L. T. Townsend, D.D. 24°. pap. ....10c.
47. **Hymnal** of the Methodist Episcopal Church. (Pearl, double column.) cl., 40c.; (superfine pap.) cl., red edges, 50c.; mor., extra gilt edges, $2; cf., flex., $2; cf., circuit, gilt edges...$3.00
48. — *Same.* 24°. cl., 50c.; (superfine pap.) cl., red edges, 65c.; roan, embossed, 75c.; gilt edges, $1; mor., gilt edges, $1.50; gilt edges and clasp, $1.75; extra, $2; gilt clasp, $2.25; antique, $2; gilt clasp, $2.25; cf., flex., $2; silk velvet, with border and clasp..........................$5.00
49. — *Same;* with sections 481–484 of Ritual. 16°. cl., 75c.; (superfine pap.) cl., red edges, $1; roan, embossed, $1.20; gilt edges, $1.50; mor., gilt edges, $2.25; extra, $3; gilt clasp, $3.50; antique, extra, $3; gilt clasp, $3.50; circuit, $6; Russia, panelled sides, $6; cf., flex., $3; silk velvet.......................................$6.00
50. — *Same;* with sections 481–485 of Ritual. 12°. (superfine pap.) shp., $1.50; roan, embossed, $2; gilt edges, $2.40; mor., gilt edges, $3.25; extra, gilt, $4.50; antique........................$4.50
51. — *Same;* with sections 481–484 of Ritual; with tunes. 12°. cl., $1; (superfine pap.) cl., leath. back, red edges, $1.30; mor., gilt edges...$4.00

THE METHODIST BOOK CONCERN,

Continued.

Hymnal of the Meth. Episcopal Church, *continued.*

52. — *Same;* with sections 481–484 of Ritual; with tunes. 8°. (superfine pap.) cl., leath. back, $1.75; mor., extra, $5; French mor., gilt edges, $2.50; mor., circuit, gilt edges, $8; panelled sides, mor., extra, $8; — (Choir ed.) cl., flex. back and sides, $1.50; French mor., flex. back and sides $2.50
53. **Chautauqua** text book, no. 6: Greek literature. By A. D. Vail, D.D. 24°. pap....20c.
54. **Dan'el** Quorm, and his religious notions. By Mark Guy Pearse. ill. 12°....$1.00
55. — *Same.* Second ser. cl. $1.00
56. **Lesson** system (The): story of its origin and inauguration. By Simeon Gilbert. 12°. cl., flex....60c.
57. **Theism** (Studies in). By Borden P. Bowne. 12°....$1.75
58. **Chautauqua** text book, no. 10: What is education? By Wm. F. Phelps, A.M. 24°. pap....10c.
59. **Beyond** the grave: being three lectures before Chautauqua Assembly in 1878, with papers on recognition in the future state, and other addenda. By Bishop Randolph S. Foster. 12°....$1.25
60. **Chautauqua** text book, no. 12: Pestalozzi. By Prof. William F. Phelps, A.M. 24°. pap...10c.
61. **Short** history of the English Bible. By J. M. Freeman, D.D. 12°. flex. cl....50c.
62. **Outlines** of Christian ethics. By John P. Lacroix. 12°. flex. cl....50c.
63. **Chautauqua** text book, no. 11: Socrates. By Prof. William F. Phelps, A.M. 24°. pap...10c.
64. — *Same*, no. 13: Anglo-Saxon. By Prof. Albert S. Cook. 24°. pap....20c.
65. **Chautauqua** library of English history and literature; from the earliest times to the later Norman period. 8°. pap., 60c.; cl....80c.
66. **Annual** minutes, spring conferences, 1879....75c.
67. **Missions** and Missionary Society of the Methodist Episcopal Church. By J. M. Reid, D.D. 2 v. maps and ill....$3.00
68. **Methodism** in the field; or, pastor and people. By J. H. Potts. With an introduction by J. M. Reid, D.D. 16°....$1.25
69. **Atonement** in Christ. By John Miley, D.D. 12°....$1.50
70. **Conrad**: a tale of Wiclif and Bohemia. By Emma Leslie. ill. 12°....$1.50
71. **Margarethe**: tale of 16th century. ill. 12°..$1.50
72. **Cecily**: a tale of the English reformation. By Emma Leslie. ill. 12°....$1.50
73. **Young** folks of Renfrew. (In the interest of the missionary cause.) By Miss Ellen Taneyhill. ill. 16°....$1
74. **Mordecai's** tenants. By Miss A. D. Walker. ill. 16°....75c.
75. **Chautauqua** text book, no. 14: Horace Mann. By Prof. William F. Phelps, A.M. 24°. pap., 10c.
76. — *Same*, no. 15: Fröbel. By Prof. William F. Phelps, A.M. 24°. pap. ....10c.
77. "**Empty** churches and how to fill them." By Rev. J. Benson Hamilton. 12°. flex....25c.
78. **Glenwood.** By Julia K. Bloomfield. 16°..$1.25
79. **Boys'** (The) pocket library: — v. 3, Men of iron; Three great potters; The Prussian vase; — v. 4, Popular delusions; — v. 5, Strange stories about strange people. 24°. ea....40c.
80. **Chautauqua** text book, no. 16: Roman history. By J. H. Vincent, D.D. 24°. pap....10c.
81. — *Same*, no. 17: Roger Ascham and John Sturm. Glimpses of education in 16th century. By Prof. W. F. Phelps. 24°. pap. ....10c.
82. **Chautauqua** text book, no. 18: Christian evidences. By J. H. Vincent, D.D. 24°. pap....10c.
83. **Light** for the little ones. Compiled by Martha Van Marter. Illuminated cover. sq. 12°....$1.25
84. **Blossom** books. 10 v. ill. sq. 4°....$3.00
85. **Methodism** (A hundred years of). By Matthew Simpson, D.D., LL.D. 12°....$1.75
86. **Discipline** of the M. E. Church. 24°. 40c.; mor., tuck, gilt edges....80c.
87. **Chronology** of Bible history, and how to remember it. By Rev. C. Munger. 12°. pap....50c.
88. **Great** republic (The) from the discovery of America to the Centennial, July 4, 1876. By Jesse T. Peck, D.D., LL.D. With 34 steel eng. 8°. cl., $4; shp., $4.50; hf. mor. $5.00
89. **General** conference journals, 1876 ....$4.00
90. **Fleda** and the voice, with other stories. By Mary A. Lathbury (Aunt May). ill, large 8°....$1.50
91. **Rachel** weeping for her children. By Rev. N. Vansant. 18°....75c.
92. **Vanquished** victors; or, sketches of distinguished men who overcame the obstacles in their way to fame, but failed to gain that self-mastery which is the greatest and grandest of all conquests. By Daniel Wise, D.D. ill. 16°....$1.25
93. **Mister** Horn and his friends; or, givers and giving. By Mark Guy Pearse. ill. 12°. $1; pap....50c.
94. **From** Bethlehem to Calvary. By Faith Latimer. ill. 16°....90c.
95. **International** series, 1880: — Senior lesson book (Berean ser., no. 1); no. 2, Berean question book; no. 3, Berean beginner's book. 16°. ea....15c.
96. **Lesson** commentary on International lessons for 1880. By J. H. Vincent and J. L. Hurlbut. 8°. $1.25
97. **Methodist** year book. 12°. pap....10c.

ANNOUNCEMENTS.

98. **Chautauqua** text-book, no. 20: The Chautauqua hand-book. By J. H. Vincent, D.D. 24°. pap., 10c.
99. — *Same*, no. 21: American history. By J. L. Hurlbut, A. M. 24°. pap. ....10c.
100. **Shield** of faith; or, the articles of religion and general rules of the Methodist Episcopal Church, with Scripture proofs. By B. Hawley, D.D.
101. **Whedon's** Commentary. New Testament, v. 5: Titus to Revelations. — Old Testament, v. 5: Psalms; — v. 6: Job, Proverbs, Ecclesiastes, Songs of Solomon.
102. **Concordance** to Hymnal of Methodist Episcopal Church; with indexes. By William Codville.
103. **Library** key and index of general reading. Arranged by F. A. Archibald, A.M.
104. **Dio**, the Athenian; or, from Olympus to Calvary. By Rev. E. F. Burr, D.D.
105. **Recent** travels and explorations in Bible lands. By Frank S. De Hass, D.D.; with maps and eng.
106. **Amy's** probation; or, six months at a convent school: answer to the question, Shall Protestant girls be sent to Roman Catholic schools? By author of "Glaucia," etc.
107. **Wesley** (The) memorial volume; or, Wesley and the Methodist movement, judged by nearly one hundred and fifty writers, living and dead. Edited by Rev. J. O. A. Clark, D.D.
108. **American** (The) conflict: a household story. By Mary S. Robinson. 3 v. ill.
109. **Saxby**: a tale of Old and New England. By Emma Leslie.
110. **Walter**: a tale of the times of Wesley. By Emma Leslie.

THOMAS Y. CROWELL,

744 Broadway, New York.

1. **Almost** too late $1.00
2. **Archie** Vernon's library: — Nita's music lesson; Little housekeeper; Unselfish Freddy; The red apple; The iron boot; A queer lesson. 6 v. 18°, 124 p. $2.40; ea. ....40c.
3. **Aunt** Callie's sunset stories. ill. 4°, 144 p....90c.
4. **Aunt** Ethel's picture gallery. ill. 4°, 288 p...$1.25
5. **British** poets: — Burns, 522 p.; Byron, 720 p.; Campbell, 386 p.; Cowper, 504 p.; Coleridge, 468 p.; Crabbe, 540 p.; Goldsmith, 552 p.; Mrs. Hemans, 394 p.; Thomas Hood, 474 p.; Milton, 552 p.; Moore, 420 p.; Ossian, 492 p.; Pope, 612 p.; Scott, 580 p.; Tennyson, 438 p.; Wordsworth, 539 p. 16°. ea., $1; gilt, red line..$1.25
6. — *Same;* incl. Favorite poems and Shakespeare. 18 vols. $18.25; gilt, red line $22.75
7. **Cliff** Cottage story book. ill. 16°, 190 p.....$1.00
8. **Clover-top** story book. ill. 4°, 144 p........90c.
9. **Conybeare**, W. J., *and* Howson, J. S. Life and Epistles of St. Paul. maps and ill. 12°...$1.50
10. **Crowell's** Sunday-school library, no. 1. 30 v. ill. 18°. $8.75 *net* to schools.
11. — *Same*, no. 2: — Margaret's old home; Nix's offerings; Three judges; White chrysanthemum; Chauncey Judd; Jack Masters; Joanna; Posie; Apron strings; Mrs. Marsh's help; Tover Tangle; Bessie Hartwell; Grace Courtney; Violet and Daisy; Lucy, the light-bearer. 15 v. ill. 16°. $10 *net* to schools.
12. — *Same*, no. 3: — Father Merrill; Lettie Sterling; Newlyn House; Two families; Words and deeds; Laura Linwood; Queer people; Little people; Ollie and the boys; Smith's saloon; Beech Hill; Children of the great king; Johnnie, the railroad boy; Bashie's service; Tell Jesus. 15 v. ill. 16°. $10 *net* to schools.
13. — *Same*, no. 4. For primary and infant scholars. 36 v. ill. 18°. $6.25 *net;* retail..........$10.80
14. — *Same*, no. 5: — Leslie's scholarship; The well-spent hour; The good girl and true woman; The poor boy and merchant prince; Precious gems; The red apple; The iron boot; Unselfish Freddy; Lea's play-ground; The birth-day; Asked of God; Little housekeeper; A queer lesson; Nita's music lesson; Finette. 15 v. ill. 16°. $7.50 *net.*
15. **Curly** and Kitty's library. 6 v. 18°, 64 p...$1.50
16. **Deems**, *Rev.* Chas. F. Jesus. 8°, 750 p....$3.50
17. — Weights and wings. 12°, 272 p...........$1.50
18. — The home altar. 16°....................$1.25
19. — Hymns for all Christians. 16°............$1.00
20. — No room for Jesus. 16°..................40c.
21. **Farmer-boy** (The), and how he became commander-in-chief: life of Washington for American youth; by Uncle Juvinell. 16°, 320 p.....$1.00
22. **Favorite** poems. 16°, 456 p. $1; gilt $1.25
23. **Fleetwood**, John. Life of Christ. ill. 12°. $1.50; gilt $2.00
24. **Foster**, Elon. Cyclopædias: — Prose illustrations; Poetical illustrations; Prose illustrations, 2d ser. 3 v. 8°. ea., $5; shp., $6; hf. mor.......$7.00
25. **Golden** secret library. 6 v. 18°, 64 p.........$1.50
26. **Good** girl (The) and the true woman; or, elements of success drawn from the life of Mary Lyon, and others; by W. M. Thayer. 16°............$1.00
27. **Great** slighted fortune; by J. D. Bell. 12°..$1.50
27. **Hallam**, Henry. Complete works. New and rev. ed. 6 v. cr. 8° $7.50
28. **Harry** and Rover series (The). 6 v. ill. 18°..$1.50
29. **Keeping-on** series (The): — Lost in the snow; Uncle Harry's lesson; Willing to do any thing; The drummer-boy; Both alike; Keeping on. 6 v. ill. 18°. $2.40; ea.............................40c.
30. **Knight**, Chas. A popular history of England from the earliest period to 1867. 8 v. 12°......$10.00
31. **Knowing** and doing $1.00
32. **Laura** Linwood; by author of "The white cross and dove of pearls." 16°, 348 p...........$1.25
33. **Lulu** and Muff series (The). 6 v. ill. 18°...$1.50
34. **Macaulay**, *Lord*. A history of England from the accession of James II. 5 v. 12°...........$5.00
35. — Essays and poems. 3 v. 12° $3.75
36. **Meadow** blossoms; by L. M. Alcott and others. 4° $1.00
37. **Mistress** (The) of the house; by Miss P. B. Chamberlain. 16° $1.25
38. **Nelson**; or, how a country boy made his way in the city; by W. M. Thayer. 16°, 327 p.......$1.25
39. **Nita** and Freddy's library. 6 v. 18°, 64 p...$1.50
40. **Pilgrim's** progress; by John Bunyan. ill. 16°, 491 p. $1; gilt $1.25
41. **Pine** grove picture library. 6 v. 16°, ea., 64 p..$2.40
42. **Plutarch's** Lives; tr. from the Greek, with index and life of Plutarch. New ed. 3 v. 12°....$4.50
43. **Poor** boy (The) and the merchant prince; or, elements of success drawn from life of Amos Lawrence and others; by W. M. Thayer. 16°..$1.00
44. **Portable** commentary: a commentary on the Old and New Testaments; by Jamieson, Fausset and Brown. New ed. maps. cr. 8°, 1421 p.....$3.50
45. **Precious** gems for the Saviour's diadem; by Anna Shipton. 16°. 75c.; pap. ....25c.
46. **Pussy** Dean's library. 6 v. ill. 18° $1.50
47. **Robinson** Crusoe. ill. 12°..................$1.00
48. **Rollin**, Chas. Ancient history. 4 v. 12°...$6.00
49. **Schmitz**, Leonard. Manual of ancient history to 476; with chron. tables. 12°.............$1.25
50. **Sermons** by the Monday Club on the International Sunday-school lessons for 1880. 8°........$1.50
51. **Shakespeare**, Wm. Works; with glossary and indexes. 16°. $1.25; gilt, $1.50; — fine ed. 8°. $2.50; gilt, $3; shp. $3.00
52. **Smith**, Wm. Bible dictionary. maps and ill. 8°, 776 p....................................$2.00
53. **Sparkles** for bright eyes; by L. M. Alcott and others. ill. 4°, 320 p.........................$1.50
54. **Sure** mercies (The) of David; by Anna Shipton. 16°. 75c.; pap...............................25c.
55. **Swiss** family Robinson. ill. 16°............$1.00
56. **Taine's** English literature; tr. H. Van Laun. 12°, 730 p.....................................$1.50
57. **Thackeray**, W. M. Works. 11 v. 12°...$16.50
58. **Tom** Brown's school days at Rugby. ill. 16°..$1.00
59. **Uncle** Richard's stories: — Uncle Richard's stories; Only a blacksmith; Mr. Oliver Penrose; Jeff and Leff; Will Warden and I; A false aim. 6 v. ill. 18°. $2.40; ea. ....40c.
60. **Unswerving**; by Ernest Gilmore. ill. 12°..$1.50
61. **Water** cresses; by L. M. Alcott and others. 4°, 160 p.....................................$1.00
62. **Well-spent** hour library (The): — The well-spent hour, 203 p., $1; Leslie's scholarship, 155 p., 75c.; The birth-day, 198 p., $1; Lea's play-ground, 233 p., $1; Finette, the Norman girl, 185 p., $1. 5 v. 16° $4.75
63. **What** is truth? an inquiry concerning the antiquity and unity of the human race; by Rev. Ebenezer Burgess. 12°, 424 p............$1.50
64. **White** cross (The) and dove of pearls; by author of "Laura Linwood." 12°, 500 p.....$1.50
65. **Year** (A) at Poplar Row; by March Ellenwood. 16° $1.25
66. **Yonge**, Charlotte M. Young folks' histories: — Germany; France; England; Greece; Rome. 5 v. ill. 12°. ea...........................$1.50

A. C. ARMSTRONG & SON,

714 Broadway, New York.

The following list consists chiefly of books formerly published by W. J. Widdleton (and so credited in the Catalogue), but which are now published by A. C. Armstrong & Son.

1. **Aytoun**, Wm. E. Lays of the Scottish cavaliers. 12°. hf. cf., $2.50; cl. $1.25
2. — Bon Gaultier's book of ballads. 12°. hf. cf., $2.50; cl. $1.25
3. **Anderson**, *Rev.* Ja. Ladies of the Scottish covenant. 12°. cl. $1.50
4. **Burton**, Rob. Anatomy of melancholy. New ed., corrected and rev. Original steel frontispiece. 3 v. cr. 8°. hf. cf., $10.50; cl. $5.25
5. **Bird**, *Dr.* R. M. Nick of the woods. ill. 12°. cl. $1.50
6. **Barrington**, *Sir* Jonah. Personal sketches of his own times. ill. 12°. cl. $1.50
7. **Clarke**, Mary Cowden. Girlhood of Shakespeare's heroines. 1st and 2d ser. ill. cr. 8°. ea., cl., $1.75
8. **Conington**, *Rev.* John. Æneid of Virgil: a translation into English. cr. 8°. cl. $1.80
9. **Curran**, John Philpot. Life, by his son; ed. by Dr. Mackenzie. 12°. cl. $1.50
10. **Doran**, *Dr.* Works. New ed.; ed., with memoir, by Richard Henry Stoddard. cr. 8°. hf. cf., $30; cl., gilt top $15.00
11. — Annals of the stage: Thos. Betterton to W. C. Macready. 2 v. cr. 8° $3.50
12. — Table traits, with something on them. cr. 8°. $1.75
13. — Habits and men. cr. 8° $1.75
14. — The queens of the house of Hanover. 2 v. cr. 8° $3.50
15. — Knights and their days. cr. 8° $1.75
16. — Monarchs retired from business. 2 v. cr. 8°. $3.50
17. **Disraeli**, Isaac. Complete works; ed. by B. Disraeli. 9 v. cr. 8°. hf. cf., $30; cl. $15.00
18. — Curiosities of literature, and life of the author. 4 v. cr. 8°. hf. cf., $14; cl. $7.00
19. — Calamities and quarrels of authors, and Memoirs for literary history. 3 v. cr. 8°. hf. cf., $10.50; cl. $5.25
20. — Literary character; or, the history of men of genius. cr. 8° $2.25
21. — Amenities of literature: sketches and character of English literature. 2 v. cr. 8°. hf. cf., $7; cl. $3.50
22. **Duff**, *Rev. Dr.* Alex. Life; by Geo. Smith. 2 portraits and maps. 2 v. 8°. cl. $3.75
23. **Darley**, F. O. C. Thirty outline compositions from Judd's Margaret; engr. by Baker. imp. f°. mor., $25; hf. mor., $20; cl. $15.00
24. **Ellicott**, *Bp.* Homiletical and pastoral lectures delivered before the Church Homiletical Society, London, by Bishops Thompson, Goodwin, Thorold, Titcomb, Walsh, Ryan; Deans Howson, Freemantle, Stewart Perrowne, T. T. Perrowne, Pigou; Canons Barry, Heurtley, Garbett, Bernard, Hoare, Ellison, How, Macdonald, Cadman; with a preface by Rt. Rev. Bishop Ellicott. 12°, 540 p. cl. $1.75
25. **Edwards**, —. History and poetry of finger rings. New ed., with preface by R. H. Stoddard. ill. 12°. cl. $1.25
26. **Gould**, Ed. S. Good English; or, popular errors in English language; with essay on clerical elocution; with 50 p. new matter. 12° $1.25
27. **Gayarre**, Chas. Philip the Second of Spain. por. 8°. cl. $2.50
28. **Hallam**, H. Complete works. Revised and corrected ed. by author. 10 v. cr. 8°. hf. cf., $35; cl. $17.50

(*See No. 61 for cheaper edition of Hallam.*)

Hallam, H., *continued.*

29. — Constitutional history of England: accession of Henry VII. to death of George II. 2 v. cr. 8°. hf. cf., $7; cl. $3.50
30. — View of the state of Europe during the middle ages. 2 v. cr. 8°. hf. cf., $7; cl. $3.50
31. — Introduction to the literature of Europe in 15th, 16th, 17th centuries. 4 v. cr. 8°. hf. cf., $14; cl. $7.00
32. **Kingston**, W. H. G. Hendricks, the hunter: a tale of Zululand. ill. 12°. cl. $1.50
33. **Lamb**, Chas. Complete works; ed. with life, etc., by Sir T. N. Talfourd. Corrected and rev. ed. 5 v. por. cr. 8°. hf. cf., $15; cl. $7.50
34. — Essays of Elia. cr. 8°. cl. $1.50
35. — Eliana: uncollected writings. cr. 8°. cl. .. $1.50
36. **May**, *Sir* T. E. Constitutional history of England since the accession of George III., 1760–1860; with new supplementary chapter, 1861–1871. 2 v. cr. 8°. hf. cf., $7; cl. $3.50
37. — Democracy in Europe: a history. 2 v. 8°. hf. cf., $8; cl. $5.00
38. **Michaud**, J. F. History of the crusades; transl. by W. Robson. 3 v. cr. 8°. cl. $4.50
39. **Milman**, *Dean* H. Hart. Complete works. 14 v. cr. 8°. hf. cf., $49; cl. $24.50
40. — History of Christianity, from the birth of Christ to abolishment of paganism in Roman empire. 3 v. cr. 8°. hf. cf., $10.50; cl. $5.25
41. — History of Latin Christianity, including that of the popes to Nicholas V. 8 v. cr. 8°. hf. cf., $28; cl. $14.00
42. — History of the Jews, from the earliest period to modern times. 3 v. cr. 8°. hf. cf., $10.50; cl., $5.25
43. **Macaulay**, T. B. (*Lord*). Essays, critical, historical and miscellaneous; ed. by E. P. Whipple, with biography and index. 6 v. in 3. por. 12°. cl. $3.75
44. — *Same.* Longman's authorized English ed. cr. 8°. cl. $2.00
45. — Speeches, complete from the standard authority, *Hansard's Parliamentary debates*; arranged in chronological order. 2 v. cr. 8°. cl. $3.00
46. **Moore**, Tom. Life of Richard B. Sheridan. 2 v. por. cr. 8°. cl. $2.50
47. **Mackenzie**, *Dr.* R. S. Bits of blarney. 12°. cl. $1.50
48. **Napier**, *Sir* W. F. P. History of the Peninsula war; with complete index. 55 maps and plans of battles. 5 v. 5 steel por. cr. 8°. cl. .. $10.00
49. **Proctor**, R. A. Flowers of the sky. 54 ill. 12°. cl. $1.00
50. **Praed**, Wm. M. Poems; with memoir by Rev. D. Coleridge. 2 v. por. 12°. cl. $3.00
51. — *Same.* (Blue and gold ed.) 2 v. 32°. cl. .. $2.00
52. **Simms**, W. Gilmore. Works. Comprising: — The partisan; Mellichampe; Katherine Walton; The scout; Woodcraft; The forayers; Eutaw; Guy Rivers; Richard Hurdis; Border beagles; Charlemont; Beauchampe; Confession; The Yemassee; Vasconselos; Southward, ho! The wigwam and the cabin. 17 v. ill. 12°. ea. $1.50
53. **Stanley**, *Dean* A. P. Sinai and Palestine. col. maps and ill. 8° $2.50
54. **Seward**, Wm. H. Works; with memoir, ed. by G. H. Baker. 3 v. por. and ill. 8° $15.00
55. **Sheil**, R. L. Sketches of the Irish bar; with memoir and notes by Dr. R. S. Mackenzie. 2 v. 12° $3.00

A. C. ARMSTRONG & SON,

Continued.

56. **Smith**, Sydney. Wit and wisdom; ed. by E. A. Duyckinck and pref. memoir of Duyckinck by R. H. Stoddard. por. 12°. cl., gilt.......$1.75
57. **Trench**, R. C. Study of words. 12°.......$1.25
58. — *Same;* with 100 pages of additional matter, analysis, etc., by T. D. Suplee. 12°......$1.25
59. **Tupper**, M. F. Poetical works. (Blue and gold ed.) 2 v. por. 32°.....................$2.00
60. — Proverbial philosophy. (Blue and gold ed.) por. 32°............................$1.00
61. **Hallam**, H. Complete works; comprising unabridged editions of The Constitutional history of England, 2 v.; The Middle ages (the state of Europe during the middle ages), 2 v.; Introduction to the literature of Europe, 2 v. Standard ed., rev. and cor. by author. 10 v. in 6. cl., $7.50

A. C. Armstrong & Son are also now the publishers of the list of books formerly published by the late Albert Mason, including: —

62. **Boston** 8vo poets: — Burns, Byron, Cowper, Hemans, Milton, Moore, Scott, Shakespeare. Sheep and morocco.
63. **Bryant & Stratton's** Business arithmetic. 8°. cl......................................$2.50
4. — — Commercial arithmetic. 8°. cl.......$1.88
65. **Constitution** of the United States; with a concordance, classified index and questions for educational purposes, by Chas. W. Stearns. 1 v. 12°. cl...75c.
66. **Hedge**, Levi, *LL.D* Logic. 12°. cl........75c.
67. **Josephus**. Works; with life, explanatory notes and observations, by Wm. Whiston, and index. 4 v. in 2. por. 8°. cl..................$4.50
68. — *Same.* 4 v. 8°. cl....................$9.00
69. **Kinglake**, A. W. Eothen. 12°. cl........$1.00
70. **Martin's** Natural history; translated from the German by Sarah A. Myers. ill. 8°. cl...$3.00
71. **Mitchel**, O. M. Astronomy of the Bible; — Planetary and stellar worlds; — Popular astronomy. ill. 12°. ea...........................$1.50
72. **Saintine**, X. B. Picciola. ill. 12°. cl......75c.
73. **Stael**, *Madame* de. Corinne; translated by Isabel Hill. 12°. cl...........................$1.50
74. **Town**, Salem. Series of readers, analysis, speller and definer.
75. **Whitcher**, Frances M. Widow Bedott papers. ill. 12°.......................................$1.75
76. **Zschokke**, H. History of Switzerland. 12°. cl. $1.50

JOHN WURTELE LOVELL,

24 Bond Street, New York.

1. **Dickens**, Charles. Complete works: — Pickwick papers; David Copperfield; Martin Chuzzelwit; Nicholas Nickleby; Bleak House; Little Dorrit; Dombey & Son; Our mutual friend; Oliver Twist, Pictures from Italy, and American notes; Old curiosity shop, and Hard times; Tale of two cities, and Sketches by Boz; Barnaby Rudge, and Mystery of Edwin Drood; Great expectations, Uncommercial traveller, and Miscellaneous; Christmas stories, and Reprinted pieces; Child's history of England, and Miscellaneous. 15 v. 160 full page ill. by Barnard, Phiz, etc. 12°, ea., 830 p. per v., $1.50; per set (in box) $22.50; hf. cf....................................$45.00
2. — Child's history of England. 12°..........$1.00
3. **Douglas**, James, *Ph. D.* An initiatory grammar for the use of junior pupils. 16°. limp.....25c.
4. **Knight**, Charles. Popular history of England. 8 v. 12°, ea., 600 p. cl., $10; hf. cf.....$20.00
5. **Macaulay**, *Lord.* History of England. 5 v. 12°, ea., 600 p. cl. $5.00
6. — Miscellaneous writings, essays and poems. 3 v. 12°, ea., 800 p. cl. $3.75
7. — Complete works; containing Hist. of England and essays and poems. 8 v. cl., $8; hf. cf., $16.00
8. **McComas**, E. W. The divine problem. 12°, 450 p. cl., gilt...................................$2.00
9. — A rational view of Jesus and religion. 12°, 740 p. cl., gilt $2.00
10. **Plutarch's** Lives; tr. by John Dryden and others, with life of Plutarch. 3 v. 12°, 600 p. ea., cl., $4.50; hf. cf.................................$9.00
11. — *Same.* (Lib. ed.) 3 v. 8°. cl., $6; hf. cf., $12.00
12. **Rollin**, Charles. Ancient history. 4 v. 12°, 800 p. ea., cl., $6; hf. cf..........................$12.00
13. — *Same.* (Lib. ed.) 4 v. 8°. cl., $8; hf. cf., $16.00
14. **Schmitz**, *Dr.* Leonard. Ancient history, to overthrow of Western Empire, A.D. 476; with copious chronological tables. 12°, 580 p. cl.......$1.25
15. — History of early Asiatic nations: being 1st pt. of Ancient history. 12°, 124 p. cl............75c.
16. — History of Greece, Macedonia and the Græco-Macedonian kingdoms: being 2d pt. of Ancient history. 12°. cl..........................75c.
17. — History of Rome, Carthage and Western Empire: being 3d pt. of Ancient history. 12°. cl....75c.
18. **Smith**, *Mrs.* J. Gregory. From dawn to sunrise: a review, historical and philosophical, of the religious ideas of mankind. 12°. cl.........$1.50
19. — *Same.* New ed., revised. ill. 8°. cl......$2.00
20. **Taine**, H. A. History of English literature; tr. by H. Van Laun. New ed. 12°. cl..........$1.50
21. **Thackeray**, W. M. Complete works. *Lovell's popular illustrated edition:* — Vanity fair; The history of Pendennis; The Newcomes; The Virginians; The adventures of Philip, A shabby genteel story; Henry Esmond, Catharine, Denis Duval, and Lovel the widower; Paris, Irish, and Eastern sketches; Barry Lyndon, Great Hoggarty diamond, Character sketches, etc.; Roundabout papers, The four Georges, Critical reviews, etc.; Burlesques, Yellowplush papers, etc.; Christmas books, Book of snobs, and Ballads. 11 v. ill. 12°. ea., cl., $1.50; per set, $16.50; hf. cf....$33.00
22. — Novels: — Vanity fair; History of Pendennis; Newcomes; Virginians; Adventures of Philip, and A shabby genteel story; Henry Esmond, Catharine, Denis Duval, and Lovel the widower. 6 v. (in box). 12°. cl., $9; hf. cf.......$18.00
23. **Todhunter**, I., *M.A.*, *F.R.S.* Elements of Euclid for schools and colleges: 1st 6 bks., and portions of 11th and 12th bks., with notes, appendix and exercises. 16°. cl.................. ...75c.

CALLAGHAN & CO.,

Law Booksellers and Publishers, Chicago, Ill.

1. **American** criminal reports. A series designed to contain the latest and most important criminal cases determined in the federal and state courts in the United States, as well as selected cases, important to American lawyers, from the English, Irish, Scotch and Canadian law reports; with notes and references by J. G. Hawley, late prosecuting attorney at Detroit. 2 vols. (v. 2 now ready.) 8°. 1877–'79. ea. $6.50
2. **Bissell's** Reports. Reports of cases argued and determined in the United States Circuit and District Courts for the Seventh Judicial Circuit, comprising the states of Illinois, Indiana and Wisconsin. By J. H. Bissell. Vols. 6, 7. ea. $7.50
3. **Brandt** On suretyship and guaranty. Being an exposition of the law on the different branches of the subject of sureties and guarantors, as deduced from all the decisions of courts of countries, where the common law prevails, from the earliest period to the present time. By George W. Brandt, of the Chicago bar. 8°, 906 p. 1878 . . $6.50 *net.*
4. **Cooley** On torts. A treatise upon the principles of the law of torts. By Hon. Thomas M. Cooley. 1 vol. 8°. 1879 . . . . $6.50 *net.*
5. **Ewell** On fixtures. A treatise upon the right to things annexed, either actually or constructively to the realty; and upon other property partaking both of a real and personal nature, comprising the law of emblements and other species of property analogous to fixtures. By M. D. Ewell, LL.D., of the Chicago bar. 8°, 600 p. 1876 . . . . $6.00
6. — Evans' Principal and agent. A treatise upon the law of principal and agent, in contract and tort. By William Evans, B.A. Oxon. From the first English edition of 1878, with full notes and references to American cases, adapting it to the practice in the United States. By M. D. Ewell, LL.D. 1 vol. 8°, 850 p. 1879 . . $6.50 *net.*
7. **Gary's** Probate practice. The law and practice in courts of probate, under the statutes and decisions of the Supreme Courts of Wisconsin and Minnesota, with references to the decisions in Michigan, Massachusetts and other states where a similar system prevails, and to decisions elsewhere upon special subjects. By George Gary, Judge of Probate Court of Winnebago County, Wisconsin. 1 vol. 8°, 550 p. 1879 . . . . $5.50 *net.*
8. **Holst's** Political and constitutional history of the United States of America. By Dr. H Von Holst, Prof. of American History in the University of Freiburg. Translated from the German by John J. Lalor and Alfred B. Mason. Vol. 1, 514 p. cl., $3.50; shp., $4; hf. cf., $5; Vol. 2, 720 p. cl., $4.50; shp., $5; hf. cf. $6.00
9. **Hutchinson** On carriers. A treatise on the law of carriers of goods and passengers. By Robert Hutchinson. 1 vol. 8°. 1879 . . . . $6.50 *net.*
10. **Iglehart's** Civil practice. A treatise on the practice in courts of record under the code of civil procedure of the state of Indiana, with forms. By Asa Iglehart. 1 vol. 8°. 1879 . . . . $6.00
11. **Ihering's** Struggle for law. An essay by Dr. Rudolph Von Ihering. Tr. from 5th German ed. by J. J. Lalor. 12°. 1879. cl. $1.50
12. **Moore's** Civil justice. A treatise on the jurisdiction and practice before justices of the peace in civil actions in the state of Illinois. By I. M. Moore. 2d ed. 8°, 1020 p. 1877 . . . . $7.50
13. — Criminal law. A treatise on the practice before justices of the peace and in courts of record in the state of Illinois in criminal cases. By I. M. Moore. 1 vol. 8°. 1876 . . . . $7.50
14. **Moore's** Criminal practice. The law and practice in criminal cases in the courts of Indiana, with references to decisions of other courts when illustrative or applicable. By Alfred Moore. 1 vol. 8°. 1879 . . . . $6.00
15. **Puterbaugh's** Common law pleading and practice. A practical treatise on the forms of common law actions, pleading and practice, in use in Illinois. By S. D. Puterbaugh. 4th ed. 8°. 1876 . . . $7.50
16. **Reynold's** Stephens On evidence. A digest of the law of evidence. By Sir James F. Stephen. Rewritten, revised and adapted to the existing condition of the law in the United States. By William Reynolds, Esq., of the Baltimore bar. 1 vol. 12°. 1879. shp., $2.50; cl. $2.00
17. **Rorer** On judicial sales. A treatise on the law of judicial and execution sales. By David Rorer. 2d ed., rev. and enl. 8°, 665 p. 1878. $6.50 *net.*
18. — On inter-state law. A treatise on American inter-state law, as developed by the statutes and decisions of the state and federal courts. By D. Rorer. 1 vol. 8°. 1879. shp. . . . . $5.00 *net.*
19. **Roscher's** Political economy. The science of political economy historically treated, by Prof. Wilhelm Roscher, of the University of Leipzig. Translated from the 13th German ed., with an introduction to the second French ed. by M. Wolowski, by Jno. J. Lalor. 2 v. 8°. cl., $7; shp., $8; hf. cf. $10.00
20. **Sansum's** Insurance digest. A digest of the law of insurances — accident, fire, life and marine; embracing all the cases in the courts of Great Britain and North America. By O. B. Sansum. 8°. 1876 . . . . $8.00 *net.*
21. **Stager's** Road and bridge laws. The road and bridge laws of Illinois, in counties under township organization, with copious notes and numerous forms. By Walter Stager. 8°. 1878. pap., $2.50; cl., $2.75; full shp. $3.00
22. **Wade** On the law of notice. A treatise on the law of notice, both actual and constructive, embracing the rights and liabilities of purchasers, principals and agents, landlords and tenants, etc., and including the mode by which liabilities are created, modified and extinguished, together with a statement of the law as affecting the dishonor of commercial paper, publication of notices, and all other acts in which notice is essential or important. By William P. Wade. 8°, 800 p. $6.50
23. **Washburn's** Outlines of criminal law. A manual of criminal law, including the mode of procedure by which it is enforced, especially designed for the use of students. By Emory Washburn, LL. D. Edited, with notes, by Marshall D. Ewell, Prof. in Union College of Law, Chicago. 1 vol. 12°, 300 p. . . . . $2.50 *net.*
24. **Wells** On replevin. A treatise upon the law of replevin as deduced from a study of the statutes and decisions of the courts of England, Ireland, Canada and the United States. By H. W. Wells. 1 vol. 8°. 1880 . . . . $6.50 *net.*
25. **Wight's** Table of Wisconsin cases. A table of cases reported in Burnett, Chandler, Pinney and the first 37 volumes of the Wisconsin reports, showing what decisions have been overruled, doubted, questioned, qualified or cited in subsequent decisions. By William W. Wight. 8° $3.00
26. **Wisconsin** reports. Vols. 38 to 46 . . . . $31.50
27. **Woods'** Reports. Reports of cases argued and determined in the Circuit Court of the United States for the Fifth Circuit. By Hon. W. B. Woods. Vols. 2, 3. 8°. ea. $7.50

G. P. PUTNAM'S SONS,

182 Fifth Avenue, New York.

1. **Adams**, Charles F., *jr.* Notes on railroad accidents. 12° $1.25
2. — Railroads and railroad questions. 12° $1.25
3. **Adams**, William D. The secret of success; or, how to get on in the world. sq. 8° $1.50
4. **Alden**, Joseph. Thoughts on the religious life; with introd. by W. C. Bryant. 16° $1.00
5. **Allen**, John. The blessed bees: account of practical bee-keeping. 16° $1.00
6. **Althaus**, J. Diseases of the nervous system. ill. 8° $3.50
7. **Amicis**, Edmondo de. Constantinople; tr. by C. Tilton. 8° $1.75
8. — Studies of Paris. 12° $1.25
9. **Anderson**, Alexander de. The silver country; or, the great southwest. 8° $1.75
10. **B.**, R. G. The Puritan and the Quaker: story of colonial times in New England. 12° $1.50
11. **Bacon**, Francis (*Lord*). Essays; with introd. and notes by H. Lewis. 12° $1.25
12. **Bascom**, John. The principles of ethics. 12° .. $1.25
13. — Principles of psychology. 12° $1.75
14. **Bellamy**, Charles J. The Breton Mills: romance of New England life. 16°. $1; pap., 60c.
15. **Bird**, Isabella. A lady's life in the Rocky Mountains. ill. 8° $1.75
16. **Blanqui**, Jerome Adolphe. History of political economy in Europe; tr. by E. J. Leonard, with introd. by D. A. Wells. 8° $3.50
17. **Bryant**, William C. The flood of years; ill. by W. J. Linton. sq. 8°. $2.50; mor. $5.00
18. — Thanatopsis; ill. by W. J. Linton. 8°. $2.50; mor. $5.00
19. **Burlingame**, Edward L. (*ed.*) Current discussion: — v. 1, International politics; v. 2, Questions of belief. 8°. ea. $1.50
20. **Chadwick**, J. W. The Bible of to-day. 8°. $1.50
21. **Codman**, John. The round trip by way of Panama, through California, Oregon, etc., with notes on railroads, commerce, agriculture, etc. 8° .. $1.50
22. **Couture**, M. Conversations on art; tr. by S. E. Stewart. 12° $1.25
23. **Cutter**, G. R. Dictionary of the German terms used in medicine. 8° $3.00
24. **Day**, Henry N. Ontology; or, the philosophy of knowledge and being. 12° $1.75
25. **Dowse**, Thomas S. Syphilis of the brain and spinal cord. ill. 8° $3.00
26. **Economic** monographs: — 1, Why we trade and how we trade, by D. A. Wells; 2, The silver question, by D. A. Wells; 3, The tariff question, by H. White; 4, Friendly sermons to protectionist manufacturers, by J. S. Moore; 5, Our revenue system and the civil service, by A. L. Earle; 6, Free ships, by Capt. J. Codman; 7, Suffrage in cities, by S. Sterne; 8, Protection and revenue in 1877, by W. G. Sumner; 9, France and the United States, by P. Godwin and others; 10, Essay on free trade, by R. Hawley; 11, Honest money, by C. Schurz; 12, National banking, by M. L. Scudder; 13, Hindrances to prosperity, by S. Sterne; 14, Adulterations in food and medicine, by E. R. Squibb; 15, International copyright, by G. H. Putnam. 8°. ea., pap. .... 25c.
27. **Eggleston**, George Cary. A rebel's recollections. New ed. 16° $1.00
28. **Ewer**, *Rev.* F. C. Catholicity and its relations to Protestantism and Romanism. 12° $1.50
29. **Goodale**, Elaine *and* Dora. Apple blossoms: poems by two children. 2 por. sq. 16° $1.25
30. — — *Same.* (Red line ed.) 8°. $3; mor. .. $6.00
31. — — In Berkshire with the wild flowers; ill. by W. H. Gibson. 8°. $3; mor. $6.00
32. **Green**, Anna Katherine. The Leavenworth case. 16°. $1.25; pap. .... 60c.
33. **Hammond**, William A. Cerebral hyperæmia: results of mental strain, or emotional disturbance. 16° $1.00
34. **Hart**, James M. (*ed.*) German classics for Am. students: — v. 3, Selection from prose of Goethe, 16°, $1; v. 4, Goethe's Faust, pt. 1, 16° ... $1.25
35. **Ireland**, Frederick G. A pocket classical dictionary for ready reference. 16° .... 75c.
36. **Kent**, James. The Johnson manor: tale of New York in early days of the republic. sq. 12° .. $1.25
37. — Sibyl Spencer. 16° $1.25
38. **Klemm**, L. R. Poesie für Haus und Schule. sq. 16° $1.25
39. **Kip**, Leonard. Under the bells. 12° $1.25
40. **Leffingwell**, *Rev.* C. W. Reading-book of English classics. 12° $1.50
41. **Le Goff**, François. Life of Louis Adolph Thiers; tr. by T. Stanton. por. 8° $2.25
42. **Linderman**, Henry R. Money and legal tender in the United States. 12° $1.25
43. **Mallock**, William H. Is life worth living? 4th ed. 8° $1.50
44. **Mann**, D. Manual of prescription writing. 16° .. 90c.
45. **Man's** (A) a man for a' that. $1; pap. ...... 60c.
46. **Mason**, G. C. The old house altered. ill. 8°. $2.50
47. **Mathews**, C. Enchanted moccasins. ill. 8°. $1.50
48. **Mays**, Thomas J. Consumption and how to prevent it. 16° $1.00
49. **Molière**, J. B. P. de. Dramatic works: new tr. in English prose, with short life. 3 v. por. 12°. $4.50
50. **New** Plutarch (The): lives of those who have made the history of the world: — v. 1, Abraham Lincoln, by C. G. Leland; v. 2, Coligny, and the failure of the French reformation, by W. Besant; v. 3, Judas Maccabæus and revival of Jewish nationality, by C. R. Conder. 16°. ea. ... $1.00
51. **Nichols**, George Ward. Pottery: how it is made. ill. 12° $1.25
52. **Oakey**, *Mrs.* From attic to cellar: a book for young housekeepers. 16° .... 75c.
53. **Otis**, F. N. Stricture of male urethra. ill. 8°. $3.00
54. **Pabke**, Marie, *and* Deane, Margery. Wonder world; ill. by L. G. Morse. (Moonfolk ser.) 8°. $1.75
55. **Robinson**, H. M. The great fur land: sketches of life in Hudson's Bay Territory; ill. by Charles Gasche. 12° $1.75
56. **Rossiter**, William. Illustrated dictionary of scientific terms. 8° $1.75
57. **Rydberg**, Viktor. Roman days; tr. by A. C. Clark, with memoir of author by H. A. W. Lindehn. ill. 8° $2.00
58. **Schaffer**, Newton N. Pott's disease: its pathology and mechanical treatment. 8° $1.00
59. **Schmitz**, Leonard. History of Latin literature. 16° $1.00
60. **Smith**, George B. Life of W. E. Gladstone. 2 por. 8° $4.00
61. **Sturtevant**, J. M. Economics; or, the science of wealth. 8° $1.75
62. **Sunderland**, *Rev.* John T. The Bible, what is it? 16° $1.00
63. **Taylor**, Bayard. Studies in German literature; ed. by Marie Taylor, with introd. by G. H. Boker. 8° $2.25
64. **Thwing**, C. F. American colleges: their students and their work. 16° $1.00
65. **Tyler**, Moses Coit. History of American literature: v. 1, 2, 1607–1765. 8° $5; $9.00
66. **Valentin**, W. G. Twenty lessons in inorganic chemistry. 16° $1.00
67. **Value** of life: reply to W. H. Mallock. 8° .. $1.50
68. **Van Laun**, Henri. History of French literature. 3 v. 8°. $7.50; hf. cf. $15.00
69. **Warner**, Susan. Diana. 12° $1.75

CHARLES SCRIBNER'S SONS,

743 and 745 Broadway, New York.

1. **Arnold,** *Rev.* Thomas. Life and correspondence. By Arthur Penrhyn Stanley. 1 v. 8°....$2.50
2. **Bagehot,** Walter. Lombard Street. A description of the money market. 1 v. 12°.....$1.25
3. **Baird,** *Prof.* Henry M. The rise of the Huguenots of France. 2 v. 8°. With map $5.00
4. **Beaconsfield,** *Lord.* The political adventures of. 1 v. 16°. pap., 40c.; cl..................75c.
5. **Bible** commentary (The):—Ezekiel, by G. Currey, D.D.; Daniel, by the late H. J. Rose, B.D., and J. M. Fuller, M.A.; The minor prophets, by Rev. E. Huxtable, M.A., Rev. F. Meyrick, Prof. R. Gandell, Rev. Samuel Clark, Canon F. C. Cook and Rev. W. Drake. 1 v. 8°......$5.00
6. — St. Matthew, by H. Longueville Mansel, D.D., and the editor; St. Mark, by Canon F. C. Cook; St. Luke, by W. Basil Jones, D.D., and Canon Cook. With a general introduction by Wm. Thomson, D.D., Archbishop of York. 1 v. roy. 8°.$5.00
7. **Bismarck,** *Prince.* Letters to his wife, his sister and others, from 1844 to 1870. From the German by Fitz Maxse. 1 v. 12°................$1.00
8. **Blackie,** J. S. The natural history of atheism. 1 v. 12°.................................$1.50
9. — Songs of religion and life. 1 v. 12°.....$1.50
10. **Bonaparte,** *Madame. See* Didier.
11. **Bowen,** *Prof.* Francis. Modern philosophy, from Descartes to Schopenhauer and Hartmann. 1 v. cr. 8°......................................$3.00
12. **Boyesen,** Hjalmar H. Goethe and Schiller: their lives and works, including a commentary on Goethe's Faust. 1 v. 12°...............$2.00
13. — Falconberg. A novel. 1 v. ill. 12°......$1.50
14. — Gunnar: a Norse romance. 1 v. 12°....$1.25
15. — Tales from two hemispheres. 1 v. 12°..$1.25
16. **Brontë,** Charlotte. A monograph. By T. Wemyss Reid. ill. 12°...........................$1.50
17. **Brooks,** Noah. The boy emigrants. ill. 12°..$1.50
18. **Bryant,** William Cullen, *and* Gay, Sidney Howard. A popular illustrated history of the United States. 4 v. ill. roy. 8°. 3 v. now ready. (*Subscription.*) $6.00
19. **Burnett,** Frances Hodgson. That lass o' Lowrie's. 1 v. 12°. pap., 90c.; cl....................$1.50
20. — Haworth's. 1 v. ill. 12°...................$1.50
21. — Surly Tim, and other stories. 1 v. 16°....$1.25
22. — Lindsay's luck. 16°. pap.................30c.
23. — Pretty Polly Pemberton. 16°. pap. ......40c.
24. — Kathleen. 16°. pap.........................40c.
25. — Theo. 16°. pap. ....30c.
26. — Miss Crespigny. 1 v. 16°. pap..........30c.
27. **Busch,** *Dr.* Moritz. Bismarck in the Franco-German war, 1870–'71. (Authorized translation.) 2 v. 12°...................................$4.00
28. — *Same.* 2 v. in 1..........................$1.50
29. **Cable,** George W. Old Creole days. 12°...$1.00
30. **Cahun,** Leon. The adventures of Captain Mago; with 73 ill. 1 v. 8°........................$2.50
31. **Clarke,** Charles *and* Mary Cowden. Recollections of writers. 1 v. $1.75
32. **Cook,** Clarence. The house beautiful; with over 100 illustrations from original drawings. 1 v. sm. 4°. cl., extra.........................$7.50
33. **Cooke,** *Prof.* Josiah P. Religion and chemistry. 1 v. cr. 8°................................$2.50
34. **Cruttwell,** Charles Thomas. The history of Roman literature. 12°.......................$2.50
35. **De Kay,** Charles. The Bohemian: a tragedy in modern life. 1 v. 16° $1.00
36. **De Quincey,** Thomas, His life and writings; with unpublished correspondence. By H. A. Page. 2 v. in 1. por. cr. 8°.............$2.50
37. **Dickens,** Charles. The letters of; ed. by Miss Dickens and Miss Hogarth. 2 v. 12° $3.00
38. **Didier,** Eugene L. The life and letters of Madame Bonaparte. 1 v. 12°.....................$1.50
39. **Dodge,** Mary Mapes. Hans Brinker. New ed., with 12 new illustrations. 1 v. 12°......$1.50
40. — Along the way: a volume of short poems. 1 v. 12°. $1; extra cl. $1.50
41. — Theophilus and others. 1 v. 12°........$1.50
42. **Dorr,** *Mrs.* Julia C. R. Friar Anselmo, and other poems. 1 v. 12°.........................$1.25
43. **Eggleston,** Edward. Roxy: a tale of Indiana life. 1 v. ill. 12°.............................$1.50
44. — The circuit rider. A tale. 1 v. ill. 12°..$1.50

45–51. **Epochs** of modern history. 7 v. maps. 16°. ea......................................$1.00

Cont.: Age of Elizabeth, by M. Creighton.—Fall of the Stuarts and Western Europe, 1678–'97, by E. Hale.—Puritan revolution, by S. R. Gardiner.—Early Plantagenets, by W. Stubbs.—Age of Anne, by E. E. Morris.—Beginning of the middle ages, by R. W. Church.—Normans in Europe, by A. H. Johnson.

52–58. **Epochs** of ancient history. 7 v. maps. 16°. ea......................................$1.00

Cont.: The Greeks and the Persians, by G. W. Cox.—The early empire, by W. W. Capes.—The Athenian empire, by G. W. Cox.—The Roman triumvirates, by C. Merivale.—Early Rome, by W. Ihne.—Age of the Antonines, by W. W. Capes.—The Gracchi, Marius and Sulla, by A. H. Beesly.

59. **Erckmann-Chatrian.** Friend Fritz. A tale of the banks of the Lauter. 1 v. 16°. cl...$1.25
60. **Field,** H. M. From the lakes of Killarney to the Golden Horn. 12°.......................$2.00
61. — From Egypt to Japan. 1 v. 12°........$2.00
62. **Fisher,** *Prof.* George P. Faith and rationalism. 1 v. 12°...............................$1.25
63. — The beginnings of Christianity. 1 v. 8°..$3.00
64. **Froissart** (The boy's); with an introduction by Sidney Lanier; ill. by Alfred Kappes. 1 v. sq. 8° $3.00
65. **Froude,** James Anthony. Life of Julius Cæsar: a sketch. With map. 1 v. 8°............$2.50
66. — Short studies on great subjects. 3d ser. 1 v. cr. 8°......................................$1.50
67. — Thomas à Beckett. Life and times of. 1 v. cr. 8° $1.50
68. **Gilbert,** W. S. Original plays. 1 v. 12°. vellum cl. $1.75
69. **Gilder,** R. W. The poet and his master, and other poems. 1 v. sq. 12° $1.25
70. **Gladstone,** W. E. Gleanings of past years, 1843–'78. 7 v. 16°...............................$7.00
71. **Gould,** J. M. How to camp out. ill. 16°...$1.00
72. **Hale,** *Rev.* E. E. Philip Nolan's friends. 1 v. ill. 12°...$1.75
73. **Harland,** Marion. The dinner year-book. With six full-page col. pl. 1 v. thick 12°, 730 p. bound in cloth, or "kitchen" edition............$2.25
74. **Hodge,** Charles, *D.D., LL.D.* Discussions in church polity; arranged by Rev. William Durant, with a preface by Rev. A. A. Hodge, D.D. 1 v. 8°..$3.50
75. — Conference papers. 1 v. 8° $3.00
76. **Holland,** *Dr.* J. G. Every-day topics; a book of briefs. 1 v. 12°.............................$1.75
77. — Mistress of the manse. A poem. 1 v. 12°..$1.50
78. — *Same.* Illus. ed. 1 v. sm. 4°...........$5.00
79. — Nicholas Minturn. A study in a story. With 11 ill. by C. S. Reinhardt. 1 v. 12°........$1.75
80. — Complete poetical writings. With ill. and por. From new stereotype pl. 1 v. 8°. mor. ant., $9; hf. extra, $7.50; extra cl.........................$5.00
81. **Hunt,** H. G. Bonavia. A concise history of music. 1 v. 16°......................................$1.00

CHARLES SCRIBNER'S SONS,

Continued.

82. **Jerningham's** (John) journal. 1 v. 16°.....75c.
83. **Jerningham's** (Mrs.) journal. 1 v. 12°.....75c.
84. — *Same*: the above 2 v. in 1..............$1.25
85. — Harry. A poem, by the author of "Mrs. Jerningham's Journal." 1 v. 12°...........25c.
86. — A very young couple; by the author of "Mrs. Jerningham's Journal," etc. 1 v. 12° $1.25
87. — Miss Hitchcock's wedding dress; by the author of "Mrs. Jerningham's Journal." 1 v. 12°..$1.25
88. **Keary**, C. F., *M.A.* The dawn of history. An introduction to pre-historic study. 1 v. 12°..$1.25
89. **Keats**, John. Letters to Fanny Brawne. 1 v. 12°. gilt top.........................$1.50
90. **Kingsley**, Charles. His letters and memories of his life; ed. by his wife. 1 v. por. 8°......$2.50
91. — All Saints' day, and other sermons. 1 v. 12°. $1.50
92. **Klunzinger**, *Dr.* C. B. Upper Egypt. The people and products; ill. from original sketches. 1 v. cr. 8°..........................$3.00
93. **Lamb**, Charles *and* Mary. Poetry for children. 1 v. 12°.............................$1.25
94–99. **Lange**, J. P. (*ed.*) Commentary. 6 v. 8°.

Cont.: Exodus, by C. M. Mead; Leviticus, by F. Gardiner; with gen. introd. by Dr. Osgood, $5.—Numbers, by J. P. Lange; Deuteronomy, by F. W. J. Schroeder, $5.—Samuel I. and II., tr., enl. and ed. by C. H. Foy and J. A. Broadus, $5.50.—Chronicles I. and II., by O. Zöckler; Ezra, by F. W. Schultz; Nehemiah, by H. Crosby; Esther, by F. W. Schultz, $5.—Isaiah, by C. W. E. Nagelsbach, $5.—Ezekiel, tr., enl. and ed. by P. Fairbairn and W. Findlay; Daniel, tr., enl. and ed. by J. Strong, $5.

100. **McCosh**, James, *D.D.*, *LL.D.* The emotions. 1 v. cr. 8°............................$2.00
101. **MacDonald**, James M., *D.D.* The life and writings of St. John. Ed. with an introduction by Rev. J. S. Howson, D.D. With 33 ill. and 2 maps. 1 v. 8°.........................$5.00
102. **Macleod**, Rev. Norman, *D.D.* Memoir of; by his brother, Rev. Donald Macleod, M.A. With numerous ill. 2 v. 8°.................$4.50
103. — *Same.* 2 v. in 1.......................$2.50
104. **Marsh**, G. P. The earth as modified by human action. A new edition of "Man and nature," from new stereotyped pl. 1 v. cr. 8°.....$3.00
105. **Metternich**, *Prince.* The autobiography of. 2 v. 8°, with por. and fac-similes..............$5.00
106. **Mitchell**, D. G. About old story tellers. 1 v. ill. 4°. cl., extra gilt top...............$2.00
107. **Müller**, F. Max. Lectures on the origin and growth of religion as illustrated by the religions of India. cr. 8°............................$2.50
108. **Perry**, Arthur Latham. An introduction to political economy. 1 v. 12°..................$1.50
109. **Plato's** best thoughts, as compiled from Prof. Jowett's translation of the Dialogues of Plato. By Rev. C. H. A. Bulkley. 1 v. cr. 8° $2.50
110. **Popular** commentary (The):—1, Matthew, Mark and Luke, with an introduction; by Prof. Philip Schaff, D.D., and Prof. Matthew B. Riddle, D.D. Ill. by 100 original engravings on wood, ten of them full page, 1 steel, and 5 full page maps and plans. 1 v. roy. 8°, 550 p. $6.00
111. — *Same.* 2, John, by Prof. Wm. Milligan and Prof. Wm. F. Moulton, D.D.; Acts of the apostles, by J. S. Howson, D.D., and Canon Donald Spence...................................$6.00
112. **Porter**, Noah, *Pres. of Yale College.* The American colleges and the American public, with afterthoughts on college and school education. 1 v. 12°.......................................$1.50
113. **Prentiss**, S. S. A memoir of. Edited by his brother, George L. Prentiss, D.D. New ed. 2 v. 12°.......................................$2.50
114. **Reid**, T. Wemyss. *See* Brontë.
115. **Robinson**, *Rev.* C. S., *D.D.* Studies in the New Testament. 1 v. 12°........................$1.50
116. **Rousselet**, Louis. The serpent charmer. 1 v. ill. 8° $2.50
117. **Sans** souci series. Haydon's (Benjamin Robert) life, letters and table talk; with 4 por. and autographic letter. 1 v. sq. 12°..............$1.50
118. — Men and manners, one hundred years ago. 1 v. 4 ill. $1.50
119. — Shelley: an anecdote biography of Percy Bysshe Shelley. Compiled by Richard Henry Stoddard. 1 v. ill. 12°....................$1.50
120. **Saxe** Holm's stories. 2d ser. 1 v. 12°....$1.50
121. **Schliemann**, *Dr.* Henry. Ancient Mycenæ: discoveries and researches on the sites of Mycenæ and Tiryns; with preface by Rt. Hon. W. E. Gladstone, M. P. With maps, col. pl., views and cuts, representing several hundred objects of antiquity. 1 v. 4°. cl. extra, gilt top.......$12.00
122. **Schuyler**, Eugene, *Ph.D.* Turkistan: notes of a journey in 1873 in the Russian province of Turkistan, the Khanates of Khokan and Bokhara and provinces of Kuldja. 2 v. ill. 8° $5.00
123. — The Cossacks: a story of Russian life; tr. from the Russian of Count Leo Tolstoy. 1 v. 12°.......................................$1.25
124. **Shakspeare**, Charles. St. Paul at Athens: spiritual Christianity in relation to some aspects of modern thought. 12°.....................$1.25
125. **Shedd**, *Prof.* W. G. T. Theological essays. 1 v. cr. 8°......................................$2.50
126. — Literary essays. 1 v. 8°...............$2.50
127. — A concise analytical commentary on St. Paul's Epistle to the Romans. 1 v. 8°..........$3.00
128. **Shields**, *Prof.* C. W. The final philosophy. 2d ed., rev. 1 v. 8° $3.00
129. **Simon**, Jules. Government of M. Thiers; tr. from the French. 2 v. 8°...................$4 50
130. **Smith**, H. B., *D.D.*, *LL.D.* Faith and philosophy; or, discourses and essays; with an introduction by Rev. Dr. G. L. Prentiss. 1 v. 8°..$3.50
131. **Smith**, Herbert H. Brazil, the Amazons and the coast; ill. from sketches by J. Wells Champney and others. 1 v. 8°........................$5.00
132. **Smyth**, *Rev.* Newman. The religious feeling: a study for faith. 1 v. 12°.................$1.25
133. — Old faiths in new light. 1 v. 12°.........$1.50
134. **Socrates**: a translation of the Apology, Crito and parts of the Phaedo of Plato. 12°........$1.50
135. **Stanley**, Arthur Penrhyn. Lectures on the history of the Jewish church, pt. 3. maps. cr. 8°..$2.50
136. **Stephens**, *Rev.* W. R. W. Christianity and Islam: the Bible and the Koran. 1 v. 12°..$1.25
137. **Stockton**, Frank R. Rudder grange. 1 v. 12° $1.25
138. **Stuart**, Gilbert. Life and works. By George C. Mason. With reproductions of Stuart portraits. 1 v. 4°...................................$10.00
139. **Thompson**, Maurice. The witchery of archery: a complete manual of archery, with an appendix containing directions for the manufacture and use of archery implements, and new chapter on English archery practice. 1 v. ill. 12°........$1.50
140. **Tolstoy**, *Count* Leo. *See* Schuyler.
141. **Trench**, R. C., *Archbishop of Dublin.* Mediæval church history. 1 v. 8°....................$3.00
142. **Tulloch**, *Principal.* The Christian doctrine of sin. 1 v. 12°..............................$1.50
143. **Uhlhorn**, *Dr.* Gerhard. The conflict of Christianity with heathenism; tr. by Prof. Egbert C. Smyth and Prof. C. J. H. Ropes. cr. 8°...$2.50

CHARLES SCRIBNER'S SONS,

Continued.

144. **Van Oosterzee**, J. J., *D.D.* Practical theology. 8°....$3.50
145. **Verne**, Jules. The exploration of the world: 1, Famous travels and travellers; with over 100 full-page ill. 1 v. roy. 8°....$3.50
146. — The mysterious island; with 150 ill. 1 v. $3.00
147. — Hector Servadac. 1 v. 100 ill. 8°....$3.00
148. — Dick Sands. 1 v. 100 full-page cuts. 8°. $3.00
149. — Michael Strogoff; or, the courier of the Czar. 1 v. ill. 8°....$3.00
150. **Vincent**, Marvin R., *D.D.* Gates into the psalm country. 1 v. 12°....$1.50
151. — Faith and character. 1 v. 12°....$1.50
152. **Williams**, S. Wells, *D.D.* Chinese immigration. 1 v. 8°. pap....25c.
153. **Woolsey**, T. D., *D.D.*, *LL.D.* Political science; or, the state, theoretically and practically considered. 2 v. 8°. cl....$7.00
154. — Introduction to the study of international law. New ed., rev. and enl. hf. cf., $4.50; cl. $2.50
155. — Communism and socialism in their history and theory: a sketch. 1 v. 12°....$1.50

R. WORTHINGTON,

750 Broadway, New York.

1. **Addison's** Spectator. 2 v. in 1. 12°. cl., gilt, $1.00
2. **Alden**, W. R. Domestic explosives. cr. 8°. light cl....$1.00
3. **America's** advancement: progress of the United States during their first century; by C. E. Lester; ill. by 100 fine engravings on steel. thick 4°. hf. mor....$12.00
4. **Aunt** Charlotte's nursery book. sm. 4°. bds., 75c.
5. **Aytoun**, William Edmondstoune. Lays of the Scottish cavaliers, and other poems. (Red line.) 12°. cl. extra, full gilt....$1.25
6. **Baby** mine picture book: lithog. covers. 4°..50c.
7. **Baker**, Geo. A., *jr.* Bad habits of good society. sq. 24°. gilt side, red edges....$1.00
8. **Baron** Munchausen. ill. 12°. cl....$1.00
9. **Bartlett**, W. H. History of the United States, from the first settlement of America to the present time; by W. H. Bartlett and B. B. Woodward; ill. with 90 beautiful steel engravings. 3 v. roy. 8°. cl., gilt....$15.00
10. **Boys'** own book: a complete encyclopædia of all athletic, scientific, recreative diversions. cr. 8°. cl., gilt....$1.25
11. **Bunyan's** Pilgrim's progress; containing his authenticated 3d part, "The travels of the ungodly;" with illustrative notes, by Rev. R. Philip. ill. imp. 8°. cl., $3.50; 12°....$1.50
12. **Buttonhole** bouquet: being a choice collection of prose and poetry. 1 v. ill....$1.25
13. **Campbell**, *Sir* George, *M.P.* White and black in the United States. cr. 8°. cl. extra....$1.75
14. **Cesarine** Dietrich; by Geo. Sand. 8°. pap., 50c.
15. **Chatterbox** junior for 1879: an entirely new book both as regards the text and illustrations. 4°. bds....$1.25
16. **Chatterbox** picture book: a collection of pretty pictures, finely engraved on superfine tinted paper. 4°. bds....$1.25
17. **Chatterbox** quartette. imp. 4°....$1.50
18. **Clodd**, Edward, *F.R.S.A.* The childhood of the world. 12°. cl., gilt....$1.00
19. **Clytie**; a story of modern life; by Joseph Hatton. cr. 8°. cl., black and gold....$1.25
20. **Comedy** of the noctes ambrosianæ; by Christopher North (Professor John Wilson). 1 v. 8°. cl....$1.50
21. **Cyprus**, historical and descriptive; with maps and illustrations. 8°. cl., gilt....$1.75
22. **Dark** colleen: a novel; by author of "The queen of Connaught." cr. 8°. cl., black and gold, $1.50
23. **Dufferin**, *Earl of.* Letters from high latitudes. (Authorized edition.) 8°. cl. extra....$1.50
24. **Fairbairn**, A. M. Studies in the philosophy of religion and history. cr. 8°. cl....$1.50
25. **Famous** boys, and how they became famous men. ill. 12°. cl. extra....$1.25
26. **Famous** French authors; by Eugene de Mirecourt. 8°. red cl., gilt top....$1.75
27. **Famous** men; by H. A. Page. por. and ill. 12°. cl., gilt....$1.25
28. **Famous** stories by eminent authors. 2 v. large 12°. cl....$3.00
29. **Fancy's** frolics at Hazel Nook. (New England stories.) 1 v. cl....$1.25
30. **Farmer's** hand-book; by an association of agriculturists. New ed., rev. by J. J. Williams. 8°....$3.50
31. **Fletcher**, *Rev.* Alex., *D.D.* Scripture natural history for the young; ill. with upward of 260 engravings and colored title-page. 2 v. sm. 4°. cl., gilt....$3.00
32. **Foul** play; by Chas. Reade. ill. 8°. pap....50c.
33. **Franklin**, Benjamin. Autobiography. steel por. 1 v. cl....$1.00
34. **Girls'** own book; or, occupation for play hours. ill. 12°. cl., gilt....$1.25
35. **Going** to the bad; by Edm. Yates. 8°. pap...50c.
36. **Gunning**, William D. Life-history of our planet; ill. with 80 illustrations by Mary Gunning. cr. 8°. cl., gilt extra....$1.50
37. **Handsome** Lawrence; by G. Sand. 8°. pap...50c.
38. **Heavy** yokes: romance of southern life. 8°. pap. 50c.
39. **Hero** (A) of the pen; by Ernest Werner. 8°. pap....50c.
40. **Horn** of plenty; by Louisa M. Alcott, and others. ill. sm. 4°. cl., gilt extra....$1.75
41. **Houssaye**, Arsene. Life in Paris: letters on art, literature and society. 12°. cl., gilt....$1.25
42. **Hume**, David. History of England; from the invasion of Julius Cæsar to the Revolution in 1688. (Library ed.) 6 v. 8°. cl. extra....$12.00
43. **Hyneman**, L. History of Freemasonry. 12°. $1.00
44. **Le Brun**, *Madame* Vigée. Souvenirs of. 2 v. in 1. cr. 8°. red cl., gilt top....$1.75
45. **Le chien** d'or (The golden dog); by Wm. Kirby. cr. 8°. cl....$2.00
46. **Little** Buttercup's picture-book: illustrations and interesting stories and poems. 1 v. 4°....$1.25

R. WORTHINGTON,

Continued.

47. **Little** Buttercup's picture-book; with descriptive letter-press. sm. 4° ....50c.
48. **Little** chatterbox for 1879; consisting of bits of natural history, short poems, stories, anecdotes, etc. 4°. bds.............................$1.25
49. **Little** folks' play-book. 4° $1.25
50. **Little** Rosebud's menagerie. sm. 4°.........75c.
51. **Love** and valor; by Tom Hood. 8°. pap.....50c.
52. **Macaulay**, *Lord.* Life and letters; by his nephew, G. Otto Trevelyan. 2 v. 12°. cl. extra...$2.00
53. — *Same.* 2 v. in 1. 12°. cl. extra..........$1.25
54. — Poetical works. 12°. cl., gilt..............$1.25
55. **Marquis** de Villmer; by Geo. Sand. 8°. pap...50c.
56. **Marriage** of Moira Fergus; by Wm. Black. 8°. pap.......................................25c.
57. **Matsell**, Geo. W. The rogues' dictionary. 12°. red cl. $1.50
58. **Medbery**, James K. Men and mysteries of Wall Street. 12°, 350 p.......................$2.00
59. **Member** (The) from Paris; by Grenville Murray. 8°. pap.....................................50c.
60. **Merry** songs for merry singers. 4°. bds...$1.00
61. **Mischief** book (The); by Wm. Busch, author of "Max and Maurice." ill. obl. 8°. bds.....$1.25
62. **Modern** Christianity a civilized heathenism; by the author of "Dame Europa's school." 12° ..$1.00
63. **My** own pet's book of birds. 4° $1.25
64. **My** sister's confession. 8°. pap..............50c.
65. **Mystic** London; by Rev. Charles Maurice Davies, D.D. 8°....................................$1.50
66. **Nichols**, Jas. R., *A.M., M.D.* Fireside science. 1 v. cl.......................... .....$1.25
67. — Science at home. 12°. cl., gilt.........$1.25
68. **O'Halloran**, Silvester. The history of Ireland from the invasion of Henry II. to the present time. 8°. cl., gilt.......................$8.00
69. **Papyrus** leaves; edited by Wm. F. Gill. ill. 4°. cl., full gilt, extra........................$5.00
70. **Peep** show: a handsome volume of amusement and instruction for the young; ill. with pictures and illuminated cover. 4°. bds...............$1.25
71. **Penruddocke**; by Hamilton Aide. 8°. pap...50c.
72. **Punshon**, W. Morley, *D.D.* Lectures and sermons. cr. 8°. cl., gilt...................$1.25
73. **Purdy**, William. London banking life: papers on trade and finance. cr. 8°.............$1.25
74. **Ralston**, W. R. S. Russian folk-tales. cr. 8°. cl. extra....................................$1 50
75. **Ready-money** Mortiboy; by author of "My little girl." 8°. pap.......................75c.
76. **Robinson**, *Prof.* E. A dictionary of the Bible; and a history of the Bible, by Dr. Wm. Smith; with maps and ill. 12°. cl. extra........$1.25
77. **Russell**, W. H. Tour in India; with ill. by Sydney P. Hall. 8°. cl., gilt, extra...... $3.00
78. **Silcote** of Silcote's; by H. Kingsley. 8°. pap. 50c.
79. **Silent** witness; by Edm. Yates. 8°. pap...50c.
80. **Splendid** advantages of being a woman; by C. J. Dunphie. cr. 8°..........................$1.50
81. **Story** of Sibylle; by Oct. Feuillet. 8°. pap...50c.
82. **Swinburne**, A. C. Later poems and ballads. 12°. cl., bev., gilt top..........................$1.75
83. — A study of Shakespeare. 12°. cl., gilt top..$1.75
84. **Tennyson**, A. Lansdowne (red line) edition, complete, finely illustrated and beautifully printed. 12°. cl., gilt, extra gilt edges............$1.25
85. — Octavo edition; illustrated with 24 engravings. Complete in one volume. large 8°. cl. extra, gilt side and gilt top $1.75
86. **Tilton**, Theodore. Thou and I: a lyric of human life; with portrait by Ritchie. 12°. cl., gilt top $1.75
87. **Tomes**, Robert, *M. D.* History of the war with the south; with steel engravings of battle-scenes, plans of cities, portraits, etc. 3 v. roy. 8°. cl. extra...................................$20.00
88. **Verne**, Jules. Tour of the world in eighty days. ill. 16°, 250 p. cl. $1.25
89. — The mysterious island, complete. 3 v. in 1. ill. 16°, 620 p. cl.................................$1.25
90. — Twenty thousand leagues under the sea. ill. 16°, 340 p. cl. $1.25
91. **Walt** Whitman's Leaves of grass. fp. 8°. cl., extra $3.75
92. **Washington** and the American republic; by Benson J. Lossing. 3 v. roy. 8°. cl. $18.00
93. **Washington** (The home of); or, Mount Vernon and its associations; by Benson J. Lossing, LL.D. sm. 4°. cl., gilt edges $3.00
94. **Woodfall's** Junius: Junius' letters, from the latest London edition. 12°, 432 p. cl. extra....$1.50

DODD, MEAD & COMPANY,

751 Broadway, New York.

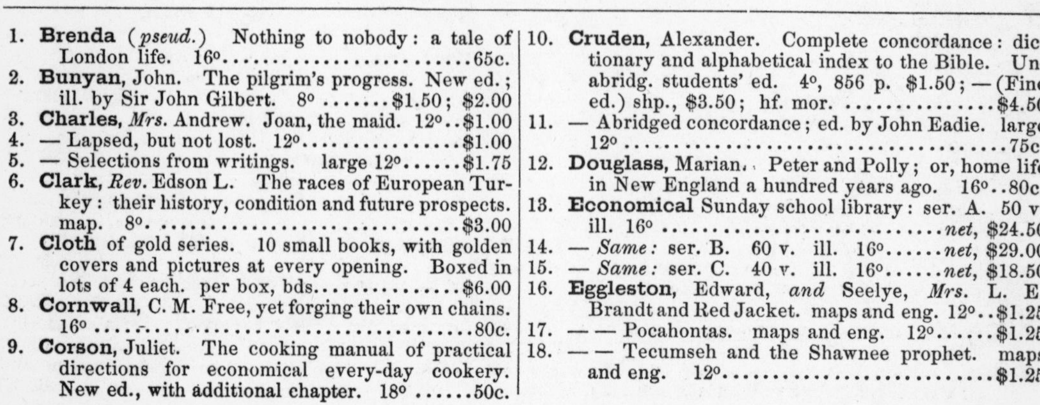

1. **Brenda** (*pseud.*) Nothing to nobody: a tale of London life. 16°..........................65c.
2. **Bunyan**, John. The pilgrim's progress. New ed.; ill. by Sir John Gilbert. 8° $1.50; $2.00
3. **Charles**, *Mrs.* Andrew. Joan, the maid. 12°..$1.00
4. — Lapsed, but not lost. 12°..................$1.00
5. — Selections from writings. large 12°......$1.75
6. **Clark**, *Rev.* Edson L. The races of European Turkey: their history, condition and future prospects. map. 8°....................................$3.00
7. **Cloth** of gold series. 10 small books, with golden covers and pictures at every opening. Boxed in lots of 4 each. per box, bds..................$6.00
8. **Cornwall**, C. M. Free, yet forging their own chains. 16° ....80c.
9. **Corson**, Juliet. The cooking manual of practical directions for economical every-day cookery. New ed., with additional chapter. 18° ......50c.
10. **Cruden**, Alexander. Complete concordance: dictionary and alphabetical index to the Bible. Unabridg. students' ed. 4°, 856 p. $1.50; —(Fine ed.) shp., $3.50; hf. mor. $4.50
11. — Abridged concordance; ed. by John Eadie. large 12° ....75c.
12. **Douglass**, Marian. Peter and Polly; or, home life in New England a hundred years ago. 16°..80c.
13. **Economical** Sunday school library: ser. A. 50 v. ill. 16° ....*net*, $24.50
14. — *Same:* ser. B. 60 v. ill. 16°......*net*, $29.00
15. — *Same:* ser. C. 40 v. ill. 16°......*net*, $18.50
16. **Eggleston**, Edward, *and* Seelye, *Mrs.* L. E. Brandt and Red Jacket. maps and eng. 12°..$1.25
17. — — Pocahontas. maps and eng. 12°........$1.25
18. — — Tecumseh and the Shawnee prophet. maps and eng. 12°..................................$1.25

DODD, MEAD & COMPANY,

Continued.

19. **Eggleston**, George Cary. Red eagle. maps and eng. 12°........................$1.25
20. **Finley**, Martha. Casella: tale of the Waldenses. 16°........................80c.
21. — Elsie's children. 16°........................$1.25
22. — Elsie's motherhood. 16°........................$1.25
23. — Mildred Keith: v. 1 of a companion ser. to the "Elsie books." 16°........................$1.25
24. — Mildred at Roselands: v. 2 of the Mildred ser. 16°........................$1.25
25. — Signing the contract and what it cost: a novel. 12°........................$1.00
26. — Wanted, a pedigree: a novel. large 12°, 600 p........................$1.00
27. **Foster**, Emilie. Teddy and his friends. ill. sq. 8°........................bds., $1.00
28. **Garrett**, Edward. The house by the works. New ed. ill. 12°........................$1.00
29. **Gilman**, Arthur. Shakespeare's morals: suggestive selections, with brief collateral readings and Scriptural references. 12°........................$1.50
30. **Hall**, Theresa Oakey. Little Miss Fancy. ill. sq. 8°........................$1.50
31. **Josephus**, Flavius. Complete works; tr. by William Whiston, with notes, observations and index. 2 v. 4°........................$6.00
32. **Kingsley**, Henry. Austin Elliot. 12°......$1.00
33. — Hillyars and the Burtons. 12°..........$1.00
34. — Leighton Court. 12°........................$1.00
35. — Ravenshoe. 12°........................$1.00
36. — Recollections of Geoffrey Hamlyn. 12°...$1.00
37. **Land** and sea: — The ocean; Builders of the sea; Frozen north; Ancient Egypt; India. ill. 16°........................$2.50
38. **Liefde**, J. B. de. The maid of Stralsund: historical novel of the Thirty Years' War. 12°...$1.00
39. **Lübke**, Wilhelm. Outlines of the history of art: new tr. from 7th Germ. ed.; ed. with notes by Clarence Cook. 2 v. ill. roy. 8°........$14.00
40. **Maberly**, J. The print collector: an introd. to knowledge of ancient prints, with suggestions as

Maberly, J., *continued.*
to mode of collecting; ed. with introd. and notes and an account of some principal modern etchers and their works, by Robert Hoe, jr. ill. 8°. $6.00

41. **Markham**, Richard. Around the Yule log. ill. sq. 8°........................$1.50
42. **Master** (The) and his friends in art and song: steel eng. of paintings by the old masters. sq. 8°........................$3.00
43. **Moffat**, *Rev.* James C. A comparative history of religions. 2 v. in 1. 12°................$2.50
44. **Niebuhr**, Barthold George. Greek hero stories; tr. by B. Hoppin; ill. by A. Hoppin. 16°..$1.00
45. **Nordhoff**, Charles. Sailor life ser.: — Man-of-war life; Merchant vessel; Whaling and fishing. ill. 16°. ea........................$1.00
46. **Primary** class economical Sunday-school library. 40 v. ill. 18°........................*net*, $7.50
47. **Roe**, *Rev.* Edward P. A face illumined. 12°..$1.50
48. — A knight of the 19th century. 12°........$1.50
49. — Near to nature's heart. 12°............$1.50
50. **Rollin**, Charles. Ancient history; with tr. of such notes and quotations as are not rendered in the text. New ed. 2 v. 4°................$6.00
51. **Schaff**, *Rev.* Philip. The harmony of the reformed confessions, as related to the present state of evangelical theology. 12°................60c.
52. **Spear**, *Rev.* Samuel T. Religion and the state. 12°........................$1.50
53. **Stretton**, Hesba. Crew of the Dolphin. 16°.65c.
54. — In prison and out. 12°................$1.00
55. — Through a needle's eye. 12°............$1.00
56. **Stuart**, Esmé. The little brown girl. 16°....80c.
57. **Sunlight** through the mist: lessons from the lives of great and good men. 16°................65c.
58. **Towner**, Ausburn. Chedayne of Kotono: a story of the early days of the republic. 12°.....$1.50
59. **Whately**, M. L. Letters from Egypt. ill. 16°. 65c.
60. **Woltman**, Alfred, *and* Wörmann, Karl. A history of painting in all ages; tr. by Sidney Colvin. 2 v. ill. roy. 8°.

G. & C. MERRIAM,

Springfield, Mass.

1. **Webster**, Noah. Unabridged dictionary. New ed., now added a supplement of over 4600 new words and meanings, also a new biographical dictionary of over 9700 names. 3000 eng. and 4 p. of col. pl. 4°, 1928 p. shp., mar. edge, $12; cl., 3 v. (for mailing), $12; hf. Tur., extra, mar. edge, $13.50; hf. Rus., mar. edge, $13.50; full Rus., mar. edge, $16; full Rus., vermilion edge, $16.50; Tur. mor., vermilion edge, $16.50; Tur. mor., gilt..$20.00
2. — National pictorial dictionary. 600 eng. 8°, 1040 p. cl., $4.50; shp., $5; hf. Tur., verm. edge, $6.00
3. **Chitty**, Joseph. Pleadings. New ed., from later English work, thoroughly revised and Americanized, with notes and references brought down to present time, by Hon. J. C. Perkins, LL.D. 2 v. 8°. '76........................$16.00
4. — On contracts. New ed. [Published by Houghton, Osgood & Co., but supplied by G. & C. Merriam.] 2 v. 8°........................$15.00
5. — On bills; ed. by J. C. Perkins. 8°........$8.00

UNITED PRESBYTERIAN BOARD OF PUBLICATION,

55 Ninth Street, Pittsburgh, Pa.

1. **Bible** songs: selections from the Psalms .....25c.
2. **Guthrie**, *Rev.* Wm. Trial of saving faith....75c.
3. **Leaders** of our church universal $3.00
4. **Luther** on Galatians. $1.30; shp...........$1.50
5. **School** Bible. 16°. *net*, shp., 50c.; roan....60c.
6. **Teacher's** Bible; with Bagster's references, tables of Jewish offices, weights and measures, etc. 16°. Tur. mor., flex., ribbon edges............$3.00
7. **Thompson**, E. A. Four evangelists ....60c.
8. **United** Presbyterian digest of actions of General Assembly, 1859–1878........................$1.50
9. **Young**, E. H. The olive tree................40c.

WILLIAM LINDEMANN,

32 Avenue A, New York.

1. The fresco manual: a collection of 500 designs for usual decorations. 31 pl. obl. f°.........$4.00

D. APPLETON & CO.,

1, 3 and 5 Bond St., New York.

1. **Abbey,** Henry. Poems. 12°..............$1.25
2. **Abney,** W. de W. Treatise on photography. ill. 12°..........................$1.50
3. **Alden,** Joseph. Studies in Bryant. 18°.....45c.
4. **All** the way round; or, what a boy saw and heard on his way round the world. 12°.........$1.50
5. **Allen,** Grant. Physiological æsthetics. 12°.$1.50
6. **Allen,** Zach. Solar light and heat. ill. 8°..$1.50
7. **American** annual cyclopædia. v. 16–18. 8°. ea., $5; shp., $6; hf. mor., $7; hf. rus......$8.00
8. **American** girl (An) and her four years in a boys' college. By Sola. 12°..................$1.25
9. **American** painters: eighty-three engravings from pictures by native artists; by G. W. Sheldon. 4°. $7; mor...........................$13.00
10. **Appletons'** dictionary of New York and vicinity. maps. sq. 12°. pap.....................30c.
11. **Appletons'** general guide to the United States and Canada:—New England and Middle states and Canada; Western and Southern states. maps and ill. 16°. ea., roan, $1.25; in 1 v., roan...$2.50
12. **Appletons'** hand-atlas of ancient geography. 28 maps. 4°..............................$3.00
13. **Appletons'** hand-book of American cities. New ed., rev. ill. large 12°. pap.............50c.
14. **Appletons'** hand-book of summer resorts. New ed., rev. for the summer of 1879. maps and ill. large 12°. 75c.; pap......................50c.
15. **Appletons'** hand-book of winter resorts; for tourists and invalids. New ed., rev. for winter of '78–'79. maps and ill. large 12°. 75c.; pap., 50c.
16. **Arab** wife (The): a romance of the Polynesian seas. 18°. pap...........................25c.
17. **Armstrong,** H. E. Introduction to the study of organic chemistry. 12°...................$1.50
18. **Arnold,** Thomas. English literature, from 596 to 1832; from "Encyclopædia Britannica." 18°. pap.....................................25c.
19. **Arnott,** Neil. Elements of physics; or, natural philosophy. 7th ed. 12°................$3.00
20. **Ayres,** George B. How to paint photographs in water-colors and in oil. 12°..............$2.00
21. **Azarias,** *Brother*. The development of English literature: Old English period. 12°......$1.25
22. **Bagehot,** Walter. The English constitution, and other political essays. New ed., rev. 12°.$2.00
23. **Bain,** Alex. Education as a science. 12°...$1.75
24. **Ballard,** Harlan H. Pieces to speak and how to speak them. no. 1.......................25c.
25. — Word-writer: exercise book to accompany "Words, and how to put them together."....15c.
26. — Words, and how to put them together. 18°..40c.
27. **Barnum,** *Rev.* Samuel W. A vocabulary of English rhymes, arranged on a new plan. 16°..$2.50
28. **Barry,** John W. Railway appliances. 12°..$1.50
29. **Beaumont** *and* Fletcher. Works. 2 v. large 8°. $5; hf. cf.........................$12.00
30. — — *Same;* with notes and biog. memoir, by Rev. Alexander Dyce. 4 v. 8°..............$5.00
31. **Beckwith,** Arthur. Majolica and fayence; with photo-engravings. 12°......................$1.00
32. **Beecher,** *Rev.* Edward. History of opinions on the Scriptural doctrine of retribution. 12°....$1.25
33. **Beecher,** *Rev.* Henry Ward. Twelve lectures to young men on various important subjects. Rev. ed. 12°................................$1.50
34. **Beecher,** *Mrs.* Henry Ward. All around the house; or, how to make homes happy. 12°.$1.50
35. — Letters from Florida. ill. 16°...........50c.
36. **Belèze,** G. Historia sagrada para los niños..30c.
37. **Benjamin,** S. G. W. The multitudinous seas. 18°. 60c.; pap................................25c.

Benjamin, S. G. W., *continued.*

38. — The world's paradises; or, sketches of life, scenery and climate in noted sanitaria. 18°. 60c.; pap......................................30c.
39. **Bentzon,** Th. Remorse; from the French. 16°. 75c.; pap.................................50c.
40. **Bernstein,** Julius. Five senses of man. 12°..$1.75
41. **Blaserna,** Pietro. The theory of sound in its relation to music. 12°......................$1.50
42. **Boardman,** *Rev.* George D. Epiphanies of the risen Lord. 12°.........................$1.25
43. — Studies in the creative week. 12°........$1.25
44. — Studies in the model prayer. 12°........$1.25
45. **Broughton,** *Miss* Rhoda. Joan: a novel. 8°. pap......................................75c.
46. **Brown,** John J. The American angler's guide; or, complete fisher's manual for the U. S. ill. 12°.....................................$2.00
47. **Bryant,** William Cullen. Poetical works. (Household ed.) 12°.........................$2.00
48. **Buchanan,** Robert. The shadow of the sword: romance. 8°. pap........................75c.
49. **Buckley,** Arabella B. The fairy-land of science. ill. 12°.................................$1.50
50. **Bunce,** John Thackray. Fairy-tales: their origin and meaning. 18°. 60c.; pap.............25c.
51. **Bunyan,** John. The pilgrim's progress; in French and English. (Polyglot ed.) ill. 12°...$1.25
52. **Butler,** J. Glentworth. Bible readers' commentary. New Testament: v. 1, The fourfold Gospel; v. 2, Acts, Epistles and Revelations. ill., maps and diagrams. 8°. ea., $5; shp., $6; hf. mor., $7; mor......................................$10.00
53. **Cambridge,** Ada. My guardian: novel. ill. 12°. pap......................................60c.
54. **Carpenter,** W. B. Mesmerism, spiritualism, etc., hist. and scientifically considered. 12°....$1.25
55. **Cartilla** y doctrina cristiana....................5c.
56. **Cats,** Jacob, *and* Farlie, Robert. Moral emblems, with aphorisms, adages and proverbs of all ages and nations; with ill. from designs in their works by John Leighton; tr. and ed. by R. Pigot. 4°. mor.....................................$20.00
57. **Cernuschi,** Henri. Nomisma; or, "legal tender." 12°.....................................$1.25
58. **Cervantes.** Don Quixote de la Mancha. [Spanish.] ill. 8°. $2.50.—12°..............$1.50
59. **Chambers,** Julius. A mad world and its inhabitants. 12°..............................$1.25
60. **Cherbuliez,** Victor. Jean Têterol's idea; from the French. 16°. $1; pap..................60c.
61. — Meta Holdenis: novel, from the French. 16°. 75c.; pap.................................50c.
62. — Samuel Brohl and Company; from the French. 16°. $1; pap.............................60c.
63. **Church,** Alfred J. Stories from Homer. 24 col. ill. from Flaxman's designs. 12°..........$2.00
64. **Classical** studies, as information or as training; by a Scotch graduate. 8°..................50c.
65. **Classical** writers; ed. by J. R. Green:—1, Milton, by Stopford A. Brooke; 2, Euripides, by J. P. Mahaffy. 16°. ea.........................60c.
66. **Colin,** Alfred. Universal metric system. 12°..50c.
67. **Collins,** Wilkie. A rogue's life: from his birth to his marriage. 18°. pap...................25c.
68. — The yellow mask. 18°. pap..............25c.
69. **Compendio** de la gramática de la lengua castellana..25c.
70. **Conant,** *Rev.* T. J. *and* Blandina. A general and analytical index to the American cyclopædia. large 8°, 810 p. $5; shp., $6; hf. mor., $7; hf. rus....................................$8.00

D. APPLETON & CO.,

Continued.

71. **Conder,** Claude Reignier. Tent-work in Palestine: record of discovery and adventure. 2 v. ill. and maps. 8°.......$6.00
72. **Conocimiento** de las tablas de sumar, restar, multiplicar, y dividir, para uso de las escuelas.....5c.
73. **Cooley's** Cyclopædia of practical receipts and collateral information in the arts, manufactures, professions and trades. 6th ed., rev. by R. V. Tuson. v. 1. 8°.......$4.50
74. **Cooper,** J. Fenimore. Novels. (New illustrated ed.) 64 eng. on steel from drawings by F. O. C. Darley. 16 v.......$16.00
75. — Sea tales. Complete in 1 v. ill. 8°. $4; shp., $5; hf. cf.......$6.50
76. **Cowles,** *Rev.* Henry. The book of Job....$1.50
77. — The Epistle to the Hebrews; with notes, critical, explanatory and practical. 12°.......$1.50
78. — The minor prophets. 12°.......$2.00
79. — The shorter Epistles; with notes. 12°...$2.00
80. **Curtis,** George Ticknor. The last years of Daniel Webster: a monograph. 8°. pap.......50c.
81. **Curtis,** T. F. The human element in the inspiration of the sacred Scriptures. 12°.......$2.00
82. **Dale,** R. W. Impressions of America; from the "Nineteenth Century." 18°. pap.......30c.
83. **Damon,** Wm. E. Ocean wonders. ill. 12°..$1.50
84. **Darwin,** Charles Robert. Different forms of flowers on plants of the same species. ill. 12°. $1.50; hf. cf.......$3.50
85. — The effects of cross and self fertilization in the vegetable kingdom. 12°. $2; hf. cf.....$4.00
86. — The various contrivances by which orchids are fertilized by insects. 2d ed., rev. ill. 12°. $1.75; hf. cf.......$3.75
87. **De Koven,** *Rev.* James. Sermons preached on various occasions; with introd. by Rev. Morgan Dix. por. 12°.......$1.50
88. **Dickens,** Charles. Works. (New household ed.): — American notes, and Pictures from Italy; Child's history of England; Christmas books; Uncommercial traveller, *ea.*, $1.25; pap., 75c.; Dombey and son; Edwin Drood, Reprinted pieces, and other stories, *ea.*, $1.75; pap., $1.25; Old curiosity shop; Sketches by Boz, *ea.*, $1.50; pap., $1; Hard times, $1; pap.......50c.
90. **Dunman,** Thomas. A glossary of biological, anatomical and physiological terms. sm. 8°. $1.00
91. **Edwardes,** *Mrs.* Annie. Jet: her face or her fortune? a story. 18°. pap.......30c.
92. — Vivian, the beauty. 18°. 60c.; pap......30c.
93. **Elliott,** Charles Wyllys. Pottery and porcelain, from early times down to the Philadelphia Exhibition. ill. 8°. $5; mor.......$10.00
94. **Elliott,** S. B. The Felmeres: novel. 12°..$1.50
95. **Farragut,** Loyall. Life of David Glasgow Farragut. por., maps and ill. 8°.......$4.00
96. **Ferris,** George T. The great German composers. 18°. 60c.; pap.......30c.
97. — The great Italian and French composers. 18°. 60c.; pap.......30c.
98. **Feuillet,** Octave. The diary of a woman; from the French. 16°. 75c.; pap.......50c.
99. **Field,** David Dudley. The vote that made the president, 1877. 8°. pap.......25c.
100. **Fisher,** George Park (*ed.*) Early Christian literature primers: — v. 1, Apostolic fathers and apologists of the 2d century, A. D. 95–180; by Rev. Geo. A. Jackson. 18°.......60c.
101. **Flint,** Austin, *jr.* On the source of muscular power. 12°.......$1.00

Flint, Austin, *jr.*, *continued.*

102. — A text-book of human physiology; ill. by 3 lithographic pl. and 313 woodcuts. imp. 8°. $6; shp.......$7.00
103. **Francillon,** R. E. Rare good luck: a fortune in seven strokes. 8°. pap.......50c.
104. **Gamgee,** John. Yellow fever a nautical disease: its origin and prevention. 8°.......$1.50
105. **Garrigues,** Henry J. On gastro-elytrotomy. 8°. pap.......50c.
106. **Gautier,** Théophile. Spirite: a fantasy, from the French. 16°. 75c.; pap.......50c.
107. **Geikie,** *Rev.* Cunningham. The English reformation: how it came about, and why we should uphold it. 12°.......$2.00
108. — The life and words of Christ. 12 eng. on steel. 2 v. $8; hf. cf., $15; mor.......$20.00
109. **Gems** of American poets. 32°. 38c. — 24°..75c.
110. **Gems** of the Centennial Exhibition. 100 ill. f°. $6.00
111. **German** home life; from "Fraser's Magazine." 12°.......$1.50
112. **Gilmore,** J. H. The English language, and its early literature. 12°.......60c.
113. — Outlines of logic. 12°.......75c.
114. **Globe** edition of the poets: — Burns, pap., 60c.; Butler's Hudibras; Campbell, pap., 60c.; Chaucer; Cowper; Dante, pap., 60c.; Dryden, pap., 60c.; Hemans, 2 v.; Herbert; Kirke White, pap., 60c.; Milton, pap., 60c.; Pope, pap., 60c.; Scott, pap., 60c.; Spenser; Tasso, pap., 60c. ill. 16°. ea., $1.25; hf. cf., $3.25; ant. mor., $4.00
115. **Gobineau,** *Comte* de. Romances of the east; from the French. 16°. $1; pap.......60c.
116. **Goldsmith,** Oliver. Complete works. 4 v. 8°. $15; hf. cf.......$25.00
117. **Gore,** G. The art of electro-metallurgy; including all known of electro-deposition. ill.......$2.50
118. **Gray,** Asa. Darwiniana: essays and reviews pertaining to Darwinism. 12°.......$2.00
119. **Greene,** F. V. The Russian army and its campaigns in Turkey in 1877–'78; with atlas. 8°. $6.00
120. **Greene,** George Washington. Primary drawing cards. 2 pts. ea.......12c.
121. **Gréville,** Henry. Ariadne; from the French. 75c.; pap.......50c.
122. **Guernsey,** Alfred H. Thomas Carlyle: his life, his books, his theories. 18°. 60c.; pap....30c.
123. **H.,** K. C. Janet and her friends. 4°.......$3.00
124. **Häckel,** Ernest. Evolution of man: popular exposition of the principal points of human ontogeny and phylogeny. 2 v. ill. 12°.....$5.00
125. — Freedom in science and teaching; with prefatory note by T. H. Huxley. 12°.......$1.00
126. **Hall,** Henry. American navigation; with some account of the causes of its former prosperity and present decline. 8°. pap.......50c.
127. **Haller,** Gustave. Renee and Franz Le Bleuet; from the French. 16°. 75c.; pap.......50c.
128. **Hardy,** T. The distracted young preacher; [also] Hester, by Beatrice May Butt. 18°. pap...25c.
129. **Harkness,** Albert. Cicero; with notes and dictionary. 12°.......$1.50
130. — New Latin reader.......$1.10
131. — Preparatory course in Latin prose authors; with notes, ill., map and dictionary. 12°..$1.75
132. — Sallust's Catiline; with notes and vocabulary. 12°.......$1.15
133. **Harris,** William T., Rickoff, Andrew J., *and* Bailey, Mark. Appleton's school readers: — Appleton's first reader, 25c.; second, 40c.; third, 56c.; fourth, 70c.; fifth.......$1.25

D. APPLETON & CO.,

Continued.

134. **Harvey**, Alexander. First lines of therapeutics. 12°....$1.50
135. **Hawthorne**, Julian. Garth: a novel. 8°. $1.25; pap....75c.
136. — Mrs. Gainsborough's diamonds. 18°. pap., 20c.
137. **Health** primers; ed. by J. Langdon Down, Henry Power, J. Mortimer-Granville and John Tweedy: — 1, Exercise and training; 2, Alcohol: its use and abuse; 3, Premature death: its promotion and prevention; 4, The house and its surroundings; 5, Personal appearance in health and disease; 6, Baths and bathing; 7, The skin and its troubles. 7 v. sq. 16°. ea....40c.
138. **Heilprin**, Michael. The historical poetry of the ancient Hebrews; tr. and critically examined. v. 1. cr. 8°....$2.00
139. **Henry**, *Rev.* C. S. The endless future of the human race. 12°....75c.
140. **Heyse**, Paul. In paradise; from the German. 2 v. 16°. $2; pap....$1.20
141. — Tales; from the German. 16°. $1; pap., 60c.
142. **Hillern**, Wilhelmine v. Geier-wally: tale of the Tyrol; from the German. 18°. 60c.; pap...30c.
143. **History** primers; ed. by J. R. Green: — Greece, by C. A. Fyffe; Rome, by M. Creighton; Europe, by E. A. Freeman; Old Greek life, by J. P. Mahaffy; Geography, by G. Grove; Roman antiquities, by A. S. Wilkins. 18°. ea....45c.
144. **Hofmann**, K. B., *and* Ultzmann, R. Analysis of the urine; with special reference to diseases of the genito-urinary organs. col. pl. 8°....$2.00
145. **Hughes**, William. The treasury of geography, physical, historical, descriptive and political. 12°. $3; hf. cf....$4.00
146. **Hunt**, Leigh. Table-talk, and Imaginary conversations of Pope and Swift. 18°. 60c.; pap...30c.
147. **Huxley**, Thomas H. American addresses; with a lecture on the study of biology. 12°....$1.25
148. — Manual of the anatomy of invertebrated animals. 12°....$2.50
149. — Physiography: an introduction to the study of nature. ill. and col. pl. 12°....$2.50
150. **Jennings**, Louis J. Field-paths and green lanes: being country walks, chiefly in Surrey and Sussex; with ill. by J. H. Whymper. 12°....$1.50
151. **Johnston**, William Preston. Life of Gen. Albert Sidney Johnston. maps, por. and ill. large 8°, 774 p. $5; shp., $6; hf. tur....$7.00
152. **Johonnot**, James. Principles and practice of teaching. 12°....$1.50
153. **Jones**, Thomas. History of New York during the revolutionary war, and of the leading events in the other colonies at that period; ed. by Edward F. De Lancy, with notes. 2 v. maps and por. 8°....$15.00
154. **Kavanagh**, Julia. Two lilies: a novel. 12°. $1.25; pap....50c.
155. **Ketchum**, *Mrs.* Chambers. Lotos flowers, gathered in sun and shadow....$1.50
156. **Keyes**, E. L. The tonic treatment of syphilis. 8°....$1.00
157. **Kip**, *Rt. Rev.* William Ingraham. The church of the Apostles. 12°....$1.25
158. **Kramer**, John W. A manual for visitors of the poor. 16°. 50c.; pap....25c.
159. **Kroeh**, Charles F. The first German reader. 12°. bds....35c.
160. **Krüsi**, Hm. Perspectiva. 4 nos. ea....27c.
161. — Manual del maestro....50c.
162. — Manuals: — Elementary mechanical drawing, by F. B. Morse, 6 pts., 1, 4, 6, ea., 45c.; 2, 3, 5, ea., 25c.; per set, $2; — Elementary architecture, by C. Babcock, 9 pts., ea., 45c.; per set, $4; — Textile designs, for calico and other print goods, etc., by C. Kastner, 6 pts., 1, 2, 3, 4, ea., 30c.; 5, 6, ea., 40c.; per set, $2; — Relief designs, representing architect. and sculptural ornaments, etc., 6 pts., 1, 30c.; 2, 3, ea., 45c.; 4, 5, 6, ea., 40c.; per set....$2.00
163. **Lacroix**, Paul. Science and literature in the middle ages, and at the period of the renaissance. ill. 8°. $12; hf. cf., $15; levant mor....$25.00
164. **Lamb**, Charles. Essays of Elia. 1st ser. 18°. pap....30c.
165. — The last essays of Elia. 18°. 60c.; pap...30c.
166. **Lamb**, *Mrs.* Martha J. (*ed.*) The homes of America; with 103 ill. on wood. 4°. $6; mor....$12.00
167. **Landscape** in American poetry; ill. from drawings by J. A. Brown: descriptive text by Lucy Larcom. large 8°. $4; mor....$8.00
168. **Lecky**, William E. H. History of England in the eighteenth century. 2 v. 8°....$5.00
169. **Le Conte**, Joseph. Elements of geology: text-book for colleges and the general reader. ill. 12°....$4.00
170. **Le Fanu**, J. Sheridan. The bird of passage: a story. 18°. pap....25c.
171. **Lights** of the old English stage: biographical and anecdotal sketches of famous actors of the old English stage; reprinted from "Temple Bar." 18°. pap....30c.
172. **Lindau**, Rudolph. Gordon Baldwin; [also] The philosopher's pendulum. 18°. pap....25c.
173. — Liquidated; [also] The seer. 18°. pap...25c.
174. **Linton**, Ethel Lynn. Misericordia: a story. 18°. pap....20c.
175. **Literature** primers; ed. by J. R. Green: — English grammar, by R. Morris; English literature, by Stopford Brooke; Philology, by J. Peile; Classical geography, by H. F. Tozer; Shakespeare, by Edward Dowden; Studies in Bryant, by J. Alden; Greek literature, by R. C. Jebb; English grammar exercises, by Morris and Bowman; Homer, by W. E. Gladstone; English composition, by John Nichol. 18°. ea....45c.
176. **Lockyer**, J. Norman. Studies in spectrum analysis. ill. 12°....$2.50
177. **Lubbock**, *Sir* John. Prehistoric times, as illustrated by ancient remains and the manners and customs of modern savages. New ed., rev. ill. 8°....$5.00
178. **Lubomirski**, *Prince.* Safar-Hadgi; or, Russ and Turcoman; from the French. 16°. $1; pap....60c.
179. **Macaulay**, *Lord.* Essays, critical and miscellaneous. New ed. 2 v. 8°....$2.50
180. — Miscellaneous essays and poems. New ed. 7 v. in 4. 12°....$4.00
181. **Macfarlane**, James. American geological railway guide, giving the geological formation at every railway station. 8°....$1.50
182. **Macquoid**, Katharine S. The fisherman of Ange: a story. 18°. pap....20c.
183. — My story: novel. 8°. pap....$1.00
184. **McSherry**, Richard. Health, and how to promote it. 12°....$1.25
185. **Marryat**, Florence. My own child: novel. 8°. pap....75c.
186. **Martin**, Theodore. Life of the Prince Consort. 4 v. por. 12°. ea....$2.00
187. **Masson**, Gustave. Compendious dictionary of the French language: French-English and English-French. 12°....$1.70

D. APPLETON & CO.,

Continued.

188. **Mathers,** *Miss* H. Comin' thro' the rye: novel. 8°. pap....75c.
189. — Cherry ripe: novel. 8°. pap....50c.
190. **Matthews,** J. Brander (*ed.*) Comedies for amateur acting. 18°. 60c.; pap....30c.
191. **Maunder,** Samuel. The biographical treasury: dictionary of universal biog.; rev. and partly rewritten by L. R. Cates. 16°. $3; hf. cf...$4.00
192. — The scientific and literary treasury; rev. and partly rewritten by J. Y. Johnson. 16°. $3; hf. cf....$4.00
193. — The treasury of history. 16°. $3; hf. cf...$4.00
194. — The treasury of knowledge and library of reference; rev. by B. B. Woodward, John Morris and W. Hughes. 16°. $3; hf. cf....$4.00
195. — The treasury of natural history; or, a popular dictionary of zoölogy; rev., with an extra supplement, by E. W. H. Holdsworth. 16°. $3; hf. cf....$4.00
196. **Mayer,** Alfred Marshall. Sound: series of experiments in the phenomena of sound for use of students of every age: v. 2 of Experimental science series. ill. 12°....$1.00
197. — *and* Barnard, Charles. Light: a series of experiments in the phenomena of light: v. 1 of Experimental science series....$1.00
198. **Merivale,** *Rev.* Charles. History of the Romans under the empire. (Popular ed.) 7 v. in 4. 12°. $7; hf. cf....$15.00
199. **Miles,** Manly. Stock breeding. ill. 12°...$1.50
200. **Minturn,** Robert B. From New York to Delhi by way of Rio de Janeiro, Australia and China. 12°....$1.75
201. **Mivart,** St. George. Contemporary evolution: essay on some recent social changes. 12°..$1.50
202. **Model** copy books. 6 nos. per doz....$1.50
203. **Modern** fishers of men among the various sexes, sects and sets of Chartville Church and community. 12°. pap....50c.
204. **Morgan,** H. H. Representative names in the history of English literature. 8°....$1.00
205. **Morris,** *Rev.* David. A class-book history of England; ill. with woodcuts and historical maps. 1st Am. from 15th Eng. ed. 12°....$1.25
206. **Morris,** *Rev.* Richard. Elementary lessons in historical English grammar; cont. accidence and word-formation. 18°....$1.00
207. **Motteau,** Achille. Petits causeries; or, element. English and French conversations. ill. 12°. $1.25
208. "**My** queen:" novel. 18°. pap....25c.
209. **Nevin,** *Rev.* R. J. St. Paul's within the walls: account of the American chapel at Rome, Italy, with sermons preached in connection with its consecration. 12°....$1.50
210. **New** York Medical Journal. General index, April, 1865, to June, 1876 (23 v.)....75c.
211. **Nicholson,** H. Alleyne. The ancient life history of the earth: comprehensive outline of the principles and leading facts of palæontological science. ill. sm. 8°....$2.00
212. **Nightingale,** A. F. Handbook of requirements for admission to the colleges of the U. S. large 8°....$1.00
213. **North** American Review (Essays from); collected by A. T. Rice. 12°....$2.00
214. **Northend,** Charles. Choice thoughts. bds., 30c.
215. — Memory gems for the young. bds....20c.
216. — Gems of thought: collection of selections, or aphorisms. 12°....75c.
217. **Ophthalmological** Congress (Report of the fifth International), held in New York, Sept., 1876. 8°....$2.50
218. **Otological** Society (Report of the first Congress of), New York, Sept., 1876. 8°. pap....$2.00
219. **Payer,** Julius. New lands within the Arctic circle: narrative of the discoveries of the Austrian ship Tegetthoff in 1872–'74. maps and ill. 8°....$3.50
220. **Peschel,** Oscar. The races of man and their geographical distribution. 12°....$2.25
221. **Peters,** *Rev.* Samuel. General history of Connecticut, from first settlement to latest period of amity with Great Britain. Lond., 1781....$1.50
222. **Pettingell,** J. H. Homiletical index: hand-book of texts, themes and authors, for use of preachers and Bible scholars; with introd. by George E. Day. 8°. $3; interleaved....$4 00
223. **Phillips,** Barnet. A struggle: a story. 18°. pap....25c.
224. **Picturesque** America; ed. by W. C. Bryant. 2 v. f°. (*Subscription.*) hf. mor., $36; mor., $44.00
225. **Picturesque** Europe; ed. by Bayard Taylor. 3 v. f°. (*Subscription.*) hf. mor., $48; mor., $54; mor., gilt, extra....$57.00
226. **Preece,** W. H., *and* Sivewright, J. Telegraphy. 12°....$1.50
227. **Prendergast,** Thomas. Handbook to the Mastery series. 12°....45c.
228. **Prescott,** George S. The speaking telephone, electric light, and other recent electrical inventions. New ed., including ill. description of all of Edison's inventions. ill. 8°....$4.00
229. **Presidential** counts. 8°. $3.50; pap....$3.00
230. **Primary** copy books: model series. 6 nos., with Wakeman's sliding copies. per doz....90c.
231. **Quackenbos,** G. P. Illustrated lessons in our language; or, how to speak and write correctly. 12°....55c.
232. **Quatrefages,** A. de. The human species. 12°. $2.00
233. **Radcliffe,** A. G. Schools and masters of painting, with an appendix on the principal galleries of Europe. ill. 12°. $3; hf. cf....$5.00
234. **Raymond,** Rossiter W. The book of Job: essays and a metrical paraphrase; with introd. note by Rev. T. J. Conant. 12°....$1.25
235. **Reade,** Charles. Christie Johnstone. 18°. 60c.; pap....30c.
236. — Peg Woffington. 18°. 60c.; pap....30c.
237. **Reeves,** Marian C. L. Old Martin Boscawen's jest: a novel. 8°. pap....50c.
238. **Reid,** Christian. Bonny Kate: a novel. 8°. $1.25; pap....75c.
239. — A gentle belle: novel. 8°. pap....50c.
240. — A summer idyl. 18°. pap....30c.
241. **Rémusat,** *Madame* de. Memoirs, 1802–1808; with pref. and notes by her grandson; from the French. v. 1. pap....50c.
242. **Reybaud,** *Mme.* Charles. The goldsmith's wife; from the French. 18°. pap....25c.
243. — A thorough Bohemienne: tale, from the French. 18°. 60c.; pap....30c.
244. — Uncle Cesar; from the French. 18°. pap...25c.
245. **Richards,** Eugene L. Elements of plane trigonometry. 12°. hf. bd....75c.
246. — Elements of plane and spherical trigonometry. 12°. hf. bd....$1.00
247. — The elements of spherical trigonometry. 12°. hf. bd....75c.
248. **Richardson,** Benjamin Ward. A ministry of health, and other addresses. 12°....$1.50
249. **Richardson,** H. W. Paper money: a collection of the principal historical facts bearing upon the current financial discussion. 12°. pap....15c.

D. APPLETON & CO.,

Continued.

250. **Rideing**, William H. (*ed.*) The alpenstock: a book about the Alps and Alpine adventure. 18°. 60c.; pap. .... 30c.
251. — A-saddle in the wild west: a glimpse of travel. 18°. 60c.; pap. .... 25c.
252. **Righted** at last: novel. 8°. $1.25; pap. ... 75c.
253. **Ripalda**, Gerónimo. Catecismo y exposicion breve de la doctrina cristiana. 18°, 96 p. ... 18c.
254. **Rollin**, Horace J. Studio, field and gallery: manual of painting for the student and amateur. 12° $1.50
255. **Rood**, Ogden N. Modern chromatics, with applications to art and industry. ill. 12° $2.00
256. **Roscoe**, H. E., *and* Schorlemmer, C. Treatise on chemistry: v. 1, Non-metallic elements. ill. 8°. $5; — v. 2, pt. 1, Metals. ill. 8° $3.00
257. **Ruskin**, John. On painting; with a biographical sketch. 18°. 60c.; pap. .... 30c.
258. **Rutley**, Frank. The study of rocks: elementary text-book in petrology. ill. 16° $1.75
259. **Sand**, George. The tower of Percemont; from the French. 16°. 75c.; pap. .... 50c.
260. **Schücking**, Levin. Fire and flame: novel. 8°. pap. .... 75c.
261. **Science** primers: — Chemistry, by H. E. Roscoe; Physics, by B. Stewart; *same* in Span., 30c.; *same* in Portuguese, 30c.; Physical geography, by A. Geikie; Geology, by A. Geikie; *same* in Span., 30c.; Physiology, by M. Foster; Astronomy, by J. N. Lockyer; Botany, by J. D. Hooker; Logic, by W. S. Jevons; *same* in Span., 30c.; Inventional geometry, by W. G. Spencer; Pianoforte playing, by F. Taylor; Political economy, by W. S. Jevons; *same* in Span., 30c.; Natural resources of the U. S., by J. N. Patton. 18°. ea. .... 45c.
262. **Sewall**, Frank. The Latin speaker: easy dialogues and other sel. for memorizing and declaiming in the Latin tongue. 12° $1.00
263. **Seward**, William H. Autobiography (1801–1834), with a later memoir by his son Frederic W. Seward. (*Subscription.*) $4.25; shp., $5.25; hf. tur., $6.25; tur. $8.25
264. **Sherman**, John. Selected speeches and reports on finance and taxation, 1859 to 1878. 8°. $2.50
265. **Sherwood**, *Mrs.* The sarcasm of destiny. $1.50
266. **Simmonds**, P. L. The commercial products of the sea; or, marine contributions to food, industry and art. ill. 12° $1.75
267. **Social** etiquette of New York. 18° $1.00
268. **Souvestre**, Emil. An attic philosopher in Paris; or, a peep at the world from a garret; from the French. 18°. 60c.; pap. .... 25c.
269. **Spencer**, Herbert. The data of ethics: 1st part of "Principles of morality." 12° $1.25
270. — Descriptive sociology; or, groups of sociological facts: — no. 4, African races, comp. and abstracted by D. Duncan; no. 5, Asiatic races, comp. and abstracted by D. Duncan; no. 6, North and South American races, comp. and abstracted by D. Duncan. obl. f°. ea., bds $4.00
271. **Stanley**, Edwin J. Rambles in wonderland; or, up the Yellowstone, and among the geysers. map and ill. large 12°. $1.25; pap. .... 75c.
272. **Stebbing**, W. Analysis of Mill's System of logic. 12° $1.50
273. **Stickney**, J. H. Child's book of language: graded ser. of lessons and blanks: — 1, Stories in pictures; 2, Studies in animals; 3, Studies in plants; 4, Studies of words. ea., 10c.; teachers' ed. .... 35c.
274. **Stretton**, Hesba. The doctor's dilemma: novel. ill. 8°. pap. .... 75c.
275. **Sturgis**, Julian. An accomplished gentleman: novel. 18°. 60c.; pap. .... 30c.
276. — John-a-dreams: a tale. 18°. pap. .... 30c.
277. **Talcott**, *Mrs.* H. B. Fortunes of Miss Follen: novel. 12° $1.50
278. **Tardieu**, Jules. Money: a tale, from the French. 18°. pap. .... 25c.
279. **Taylor**, *Lieut.-Gen.* Richard. Destruction and reconstruction: personal experiences of the late war. 8°, 274 p. $2.00
280. **Taylor**, Walter H. Four years with Gen. Lee. 8° $2.00
281. **Theuriet**, André. Antoinette: a story, from the French. 18°. pap. .... 20c.
282. — Gérard's marriage: a novel, from the French. 16°. 75c.; pap. .... 50c.
283. — The godson of a marquis; from the French. 16°. 75c.; pap. .... 50c.
284. — The house of the two Barbels; from the French. 18°. pap. .... 20c.
285. — Raymonde: a tale, from the French. 18°. pap. .... 30c.
286. — Young Maugars; from the French. 16°. $1; pap. .... 60c.
287. **Thornton**, M. J. Di Cary: novel of life in Virginia since the war. 8°. pap. .... 75c.
288. **Thorpe**, T. E., *and* Muir, M. M. P. Qualitative chemical analysis and laboratory practice. 12°. $1.50
289. **Thurston**, Robert H. A history of the growth of the steam-engine. ill. 12° $2.50
290. **Tilden**, W. A. Introduction to the study of chemical philosophy. 12° $1.50
291. **Towle**, George M. Beaconsfield: sketch of the literary and political career of Benjamin Disraeli. 18°. pap. .... 25c.
292. **Trollope**, Frances Eleanor. Black spirits and white: novel. ill. 8°. pap. .... 75c.
293. — Mrs. Jack: a story. 18°. pap. .... 20c.
294. **Turner** gallery (The): series of one hundred and twenty engravings on steel, from works of J. M. W. Turner. 2 v. f°. (*Subscription.*) hf. mor., $32; mor. $36.00
295. **Tyndall**, John. Contributions to molecular physics in the domain of radiant heat. 12° ... $5.00
296. — Lessons in electricity, at the Royal Institution, 1875–'76. 12° $1.00
297. **Ulbach**, Louis. Madame Gosselin; from the French. 16°. $1; pap. .... 60c.
298. **Unwin**, W. C. Elements of machine design. 12°. $1.50
299. **Upton**, Emory. The armies of Asia and Europe; accompanied by letters descriptive of a journey from Japan to the Caucasus. 8° $3.00
300. **Vail**, *Rt. Rev.* Thomas H. The comprehensive church; or, Christian unity and ecclesiastical union in the Prot. Episcopal Church. 12° .. $1.25
301. **Van Laun**, Henri. The French revolutionary epoch: history of France from beginning of the first French revolution to end of the second empire. 2 v. 12° $3.50
302. **Vasquez**, M. Guia de los masones libres, en los tres grados simbólicos del rito escoces antiguo y aceptado ó sea manual del maestro perfecto. 12°, 265 p. $1.50
303. **Vogel**, Theodor. A century of discovery. ill. 12° $1.75
304. **Vors**, Frédéric. Bibelots and curios: manual for collectors; with a glossary of technical terms. 16° .... 75c.

D. APPLETON & CO.,

Continued.

305. **Walker,** A. C. The correct card; or, how to play at whist. 18° $1.00
306. **Webber,** Samuel. Manual of power, for machines, shafts and belts; with a history of cotton manufacture in the U. S. 8° $3.50
307. **Welby,** A. B. Poems by Amelia. 12°....$1 50
308. **White,** Andrew D. Paper money inflation in France: how it came, what it brought and how it ended. 8°. pap. ....50c.
309. — The warfare of science. 12°. $1; pap...50c.
310. **White,** Henry Kirke. Poetical works. Chp. ed. pap. ....60c.
311. **Wiedemann,** Francisco. Libro primero de aritmética para niños ....30c.
312. **Wilkes,** George. Shakespeare, from an American point of view. 8° $3.50
313. **Willard,** Samuel. General history, from B. C. 800 to A. D. 1876; outlined in diagrams and tables. 8° $2.00
314. **Williamson,** Benj. Differential calculus..$3.75
315. — Elementary treatise on integral calculus..$3.75
316. **Woodward,** J. D. Scenery of the Pacific railways and Colorado. map and ill. sm. 4°, 90 p. $1.25; pap. ....75c.
317. **Woolson,** Constance Fenimore. Two women, 1862: poem. 16° $1.00
318. **Wylie,** W. Gill. Hospitals: their history, organization and construction. 8° $2.50
319. **Xenophon.** Five books of Anabasis; with notes and lexicon by J. R. Boise. 12° $1.70
320. **Yonge,** *Miss* Charlotte M. The three brides. 12° $1.75
321. — The disturbing element. 18°. pap. ......30c.
322. **Youmans,** Eliza A. Key to Botanical charts. 25c.
323. — Lessons in cookery: handbook of the National Training-School for Cookery, South Kensington, London; added, Principles of diet in health and disease, by Thomas K. Chambers. 12°....$1.50

ANSON D. F. RANDOLPH & CO.,

900 Broadway, New York.

1876–1879.

1. **Avis** Benson. Mrs. E. Prentiss. 16°......$1.25
2. **Agatha** Lee's inheritance. M. R. Higham. 18°. 60c.
3. **At** the beautiful gate. 18° ....75c.
4. **At** the beautiful gate, Unto the desired haven, The palace of the king. 16° $2.50
5. **Ages** (The) before Moses. John Monro Gibson, D.D. 12° $1.25
6. **A** life worth living: memorials of Emily Bliss Gould. By L. W. Bacon. 12° $1.50
7. **Beatific** vision (The). W. S. Plumer. 32°..50c.
8. **Bessie** Harrington's venture. Julia A. Mathews. 16° $1.25
9. **Blessed** company (The) of all faithful people. Harriet McEwen Kimball. 18° ....50c.
10. **Concordance** (A) to the Psalms. 16°......$1.00
11. **Comfort.** K. H. J. 16° ....75c.
12. **Christ** his own witness. Rev. E. Ballantine. 12°. $1.50
13. **Counsels** to the confirmed. 32° ....45c.
14. **Count** Agénor de Gasparin. 16° $1.00
15. **Christ,** the consoler. Ellice Hopkins. 16°..$1.25
16. **Communion** (The) of saints. 32° ....50c.
17. **Canterbury** pilgrimage (The). G. T. Bedell, D.D. 12° $1.25
18. **David** Fleming's forgiveness. Margaret M. Robertson. 16° $1.25
19. **Fulness** of blessing. Sarah F. Smiley. 12°..$1.50
20. **Four** lectures on epochs of early church history. Charles Merivale. 12° $1.50
21. **Glimpses** of the coming. Richard G. Greene. 12°. $1.00
22. **Gentleman** Jim. Mrs. E. Prentiss. 18°....50c.
23. **Holy** cross. W. C. Prime. 16° $1.00
24. **Handbook** (A) to the Bible. F. R. Conder and C. R. Conder. 12° $2.25
25. **Home** life in song. 16°. $1.50; 4° $2.50
26. **In** the mist. Rose Porter. 12° $1.25
27. **Jack** Granger's cousin. Julia A. Mathews. 16°. $1.00
28. **Kept** for the Master's use. F. R. Havergal. 18°. 50c.
29. **Ladies'** crochet-book. E. M. C. pap., 25c.; cl., 40c.
30. **Ladies'** knitting-book. E. M. C. pap., 25c.; cl., 40c.
31. **Life** of Prof. Albert Hopkins. Albert C. Sewall. 12° $1.50
32. **Life** mosaic. F. R. Havergal. 4° $4.00
33. **Life** of the Rev. George Whitefield. L. Tyerman. 2 v. 8° $4.00
34. **Life** of our Lord. 18° $1.00
35. **Land** and the life. Albert Z. Gray. 12° .....50c.
36. **Little** sanctuary (The). Dr. Alexander Raleigh. 16° $1.25
37. **Lay** effort. H. C. Haydn. 16° ....75c.
38. **Morning** stars. F. R. Havergal. 32° ....40c.
39. **Ministry** of song. F. R. Havergal. 32°....75c.
40. **Morning** bells, and Little pillows. F. R. Havergal. 60c.
41. **My** king. F. R. Havergal. 18° ....40c.
42. **Name** of Jesus. Caroline M. Noel. 18°...$1.00
43. **Other** house (The). M. R. Higham. 16°..$1.00
44. **Osego** chronicles. Mary B. Sleight. 16°..$1.25
45. **Our** theological century. John F. Hurst. 12°..75c.
46. **Palace** (The) of the king. 18° 75c.; $1.50
47. **Psalter** (The). Talbot W. Chambers. 12°..$1.25
48. **Pemaquid.** Mrs. E. Prentiss. 12° $1.50
49. **Pilgrim** Psalms. Rev. Samuel Cox. 12°...$1.00
50. **Polished** diamonds. John Todd. 18° ......50c.
51. **Red-letter** days. F. R. Havergal. 24° ......85c.
52. **Royal** invitation (The); and Loyal responses. F. R. Havergal. 18° ....85c.
53. **Royal** commandments; and Royal bounty. 18°. 85c.
54. **Story** of creation. S. M. Campbell, D.D. 12°.
55. **Secret** drawer (The). 18° ....50c.
56. **Song** and a sigh. Rose Porter. 12° $1.25
57. **Stranger** and guest. Marvin R. Vincent. 18°..75c.
58. **Star** (The) and the cloud. 18° ....75c.
59. **Stepping-stones.** Sarah Doudney. 16°...$1.00
60. **Socialism.** Roswell D. Hitchcock. 12° .....50c.
61. **Unto** the desired haven. 18° ....75c.
62. **Under** gray walls. Sarah Doudney. 18° ....50c.
63. **Who** is he? Sarah F. Smiley. 16° ....65c.

CASSELL, PETTER, GALPIN & CO.,

596 Broadway, New York.

For the corrected prices of books noted in the main body of this work see Cassell, Petter, Galpin & Company's descriptive catalogue.

1. **Adams,** W. Davenport. Dictionary of English literature. New [chp.] ed. cr. 8°, 776 p...$2.00
2. **Arabian** nights. New ed. ill. cr. 4°, 760 p. $4; hf. cf., $7; mor....................$10.00
3. **Archer,** Thomas. Decisive events in history. ill. fp. 4°..............................$1.75
4. **Ashworth,** Henry. Recollections of Richard Cobden, and the Anti-corn-law League........$3.50
5. **Barnard,** Fred. Character sketches from Charles Dickens. 6 pl. in a portfolio............$6.00
6. **Blakston,** W. A. Canaries and cage birds..$15.00
7. **Breeders'** and fanciers' pedigree book. 4°, 64 p. $1.25
8. **Bright** Sundays; by Mrs. Heild. ill........$1.00
9. **Broglie,** *Duc* de. The king's secret: secret correspondence of Louis xv. with his diplomatic agents, 1732 to 1774. 2 v. 8°, 935 p.............$5.00
10. **Browne,** Phillis. Field friends and forest foes: description of domestic and wild animals. ill. 192 p...$2.00
11. — *Same.* New ed. bds....................$1.25
12. **Bunyan,** John. Pilgrim's progress, and Holy war. 12 chromo pl. and 200 ill. demy 4°, 820 p. $12.50; mor. antique....................$22.00
13. **Butler,** James. European ferns; with col. pl. painted from nature by D. Blair, and wood eng. To be complete in about 30 pts. ea. ....25c.
14. **Caird,** James. The landed interest and supply of food. cr. 8°..........................$2.50
15. **Cassell's** ill. almanac for 1880. demy 4°.....25c.
16. **Cathrop,** *Rev.* Gordon. Flowers from the garden of God: book of children's sermons. fp. 8°, 224 p...$1.25
17. **Cervantes.** Don Quixote; with 400 ill. by G. Doré. Cheaper ed. demy 4°, 884 p......$7.50
18. **Chadwick,** *Rev.* G. A. Christ bearing witness to himself. cr. 8°, 176 p.................$1.50
19. **Cheerful** songs for young folks. ill. cr. 8°...50c.
20. **Childhood's** happy hours: short stories. ill. bds. 75c.
21. **Defoe,** Daniel. Life and adventures of Robinson Crusoe. 100 ill. imp. 8°............$3; $4.00
22. **Dictionary** of cookery: 9,000 receipts. ill. and col. pl. roy. 8°, 1178 p. hf. roxb. $6.50
23. **Diseases** of women: their causes, symptoms and treatment; by a physician. fp. 8°.........$2.50
24. **Domestic** dictionary (The). roy. 8°, 1280 p. hf. roan.......................................$6.50
25. **Doudney,** *Miss* Sarah. Stories of girlhood; or, the brook and the river. ill. fp. 4°, 192 p...$2.00
26. **Durant,** *Dr.* Ghislani. Horse-back riding from a medical point of view. 12°, 137 p.........$1.25
27. — Hygiene of the voice: its physiology and anatomy. 12°..$1.50
28. **Educational** year book for 1879 ....$2.50
29. **Ellicott,** *Rev.* C. J. (*ed.*) Handy commentary; ed. for schools, with col. maps: — Gospel of Matthew, by E. H. Plumptre, $1.25; Gospel of Luke, by E. H. Plumptre, $1.25; Gospel of John, by H. W. Watkins, $1.25; Corinthians i., by T. T. Shore, 75c.; Acts, by E. H. Plumptre, $1.25; Gospel of Mark, by E. H. Plumptre................$1.25
30. — Some present dangers of the Church of England, and other papers. cr. 8°.................$1.25
31. **Family** physician: manual of domestic medicine; by physicians and surgeons of the London Hospital. roy. 8°..........................$5.00
32. **Farrar,** *Rev.* Fred. William. Life and works of St. Paul. 2 v. 8°............................$6.00
33. **Flower,** E. F. Bits and bearing reins, and horses and harness. 2d ed. pl. and por. ....50c.
34. **Garrett,** Edward. The magic flower pot, and other stories. cr. 8°, 272 p...............$1.50
35. **Gillmore,** Parker. The great thirst land: a ride through Natal, Orange Free State, Transvaal, Kalahari. demy 8°, 480 p. $3.50
36. **Gospel** for the nineteenth century, leaving us an example, is it living, and why? inquiry suggested by certain passages in Mill's "Essays on religion"...$5.00
37. **Grant,** James. History of India. 2 v. por. and ill. cr. 4°, ea., 576 p. $8; hf. cf........$12.00
38. **Great** industries of Great Britain. v. 1, 2. ill. cr. 4°. ea. $3.00
39. **Greenaway,** Kate. Painting book for "Little folks:" ser. of outline drawing. 2d ed. ....50c.
40. **Griffith,** *Major.* The English army: its past history, present condition and future prospects. demy 8°...$5.00
41. **Haile,** Ellen. Three brown boys, and other happy children. ill. fp. 4°, 228 p. $1.75; bds. $1.25
42. **Heild,** *Mrs.* Pet's posy of pictures and stories. ill. 16°, 180 p. $1.00
43. **Heroes** of Britain in peace and war. v. 1. 150 ill. cr. 4°, 320 p. $3; in pts., ea. ....25c.
44. **Hibberd,** Shirley. Familiar garden flowers; with 40 col. pl. by F. Edward Hulme. cl., $5; tr. cf., $7.50; mor.............................$7.50
45. **Holiday** album for little folks: collection of stories. ill. cr. 4°.......................$1.25
46. **Home** songs and melodies: 33 pieces of music and 250 ill. New ed.........................$2.00
47. **Hulme,** F. E. Familiar wild flowers, figured and described. 40 col. pl. 12°. $5; tr. cf., $7.50; mor...$7.50
48. **Hunt,** Madeline B. Little hinges; with ill. by M. E. Edwards. roy. 16°..................$1.50
49. **Infant** Jesus, and other stories. ill. 64 p. bds., 25c.
50. **International** portrait gallery: each pt. cont. a por. in color, with biog. sketches: monthly pts. ea...25c.
51. **Jackson,** Thomas. Stories about animals. 150 ill. fp. 4°, 253 p.........................$2.00
52. **Jones,** *Mrs.* Little talks with little people: short stories. ill. 16°..........................$1.00
53. **Joshua** commanding the sun, and other stories. ill. 64 p. bds...................................25c.
54. **Kirby,** Mary *and* Elizabeth. Stories about birds of land and water. ill. fp. 4°, 250 p.....$2.00
55. **Kirby,** W. F. European butterflies and moths: monthly pts. col. pl. ea.......................25c.
56. **Ladies'** (The) physician: guide for women in the treatment of their ailments............$2.50
57. **Latin** Testament. roan........................$1.00
58. **Little** folks; for 1879. ill. 400 p. $1.75; bds., $1.00
59. **Little** folks picture album: companion to "Little folks picture gallery." 200 ill. cr. 4°. bds., $1.25
60. **Little** folks' picture gallery. New ed. ill. cr. 4°. bds.......................................$1.25
61. **Little** stories for little people. ill. 12°, 64 p. bds...25c.
62. **Live** Stock Journal almanac for 1880........50c.
63. **Living** pages from many ages. cr. 4°, 332 p. $2.50
64. **Mamma's** stories for her pets. ill. 64 p. bds., 25c.
65. **Mason,** James (*ed.*) The old fairy tales. New ed. ill. $1.00

CASSELL, PETTER, GALPIN & CO.,

Continued.

66. **Mateaux,** Clara L. Around and about old England. ill. fp. 4°, 248 p. $2.00
67. — Odd folks at home. ill. fp. 4°, 192 p.....$2.00
68. — Peeps abroad for folks at home. ill. fp. 4°, 256 p. bds..................................$1.25
69. — Wee Willie Winkle: story of a boy who was found. ill. 16°..........................$1.00
70. — Woodland romances; or, fables and fancies. ill. fp. 4°, 192 p. $2.00
71. **Morley,** Henry. Chicken market (The), and other fairy tales; with ill. by C. H. Bennett. cr. 8°, 368 p..............................$1.75
72. — Library of English literature: — v. 1, Shorter English poems, 512 p.; v. 2, Illustrations of English religion; v. 3, English plays; v. 4, Shorter prose works. ill. cr. 4°. ea.......$5.00
73. — Palissy, the potter. New ed. cr. 8° $2.00
74. **Moulton,** *Rev.* W. F. The history of the English Bible. cr. 8°, 240 p. $1.50
75. **Natural** history of the ancients. cr. 8°, 240 p. $1.75
76. **Ned,** *Uncle*. The little chatterer. ill. 8°, 96 p. bds..50c.
77. — Little playfellows. ill. 8°, 96 p. bds. ....50c.
78. **Norman,** C. B. The campaign in Armenia in 1877. maps and plans. demy 8° $4.00
79. **Northcott,** W. H. Theory and action of the steam engine; with numbers, diagrams and tables. demy 8°, 224 p. $3.50
80. **Old** and new London: narrative of its history, people and places: — v. 1, 2, History of London east of Temple Bar, by W. Thornbury; v. 3, 4, History of London west of Temple Bar, by E. Walford; v. 5, Western and northern suburbs, by E. Walford; v. 6, The southern suburbs. 6 v. maps and ill. cr. 4°, ea., 576 p., $4.50; per set, hf. mor., $39; — maps...........$1.25
81. **Ollier,** Edmund. History of the Russo-Turkish war. 2 v...............................$8.00
82. — *and* Chester, J. L. History of the United States, from earliest discoveries to the present time. 3 v. ea., $4.50; per set, hf. cf. ..$19.50
83. **Our** own country: illustrated geographical and historical description of the chief places of interest in Great Britain. v. 1. ill. demy 4°...$3.00
84. **Palmer,** *Mrs.* Common sense papers on housekeeping. ill. fp. 8°, 256 p. $1.25
85. **Papa's** stories for his darlings. ill. 12°, 64 p...25c.
86. **Parlor** menagerie (The); wherein are exhibited in a descriptive and anecdotal form the habits, resources, and mysterious instincts of the more interesting portion of the animal creation; with ill. by T. Bewick and W. Hawes. 8°, 520 p. $1.50
87. **Paws** and claws. New ed. ill. fp. 4°. bds...$1.25
88. **Payne,** A. G. Common sense papers on cooking. ill fp. 8°, 256 p..........................$1.25
89. **Pictures** and stories for our darlings. ill. cr. 4°. bds. $1.00
90. **Pleasant** stories and pictures. ill. 64 p. bds., 25c.
91. **Pretty** poems for little people. ill. cr. 8°...40c.
92. **Pretty** stories for tiny folks. ill. 64 p.....25c.
93. **Rimmer,** W. A. Pleasant spots around Oxford. 70 ill. fp. 4°. $6; tur. mor.............$12.00
94. **Robinson,** J. Forbes. Great painters of Christendom. ill. roy. 4°, 448 p. $20; hf. mor., $25; mor. $30.00
95. **Ruth** gleaning, and other stories. ill. 64 p...25c.
96. **Saunders,** William. Through the light continent; or, the United States in 1877-'78. 8°. 420 p...$5.00
97. **Sergeant,** L. New Greece. map. demy 8°.$3.50
98. **Shakespeare,** William. The Leopold Shakspere. 400 ill. sm. 4°, 1184 p. $4.50; hf. cf., $7; hf. mor., $7; mor., $10; tr. cf. $10; $11.00
99. **Shaw,** Vero, *and* Stables, *Dr.* Gordon. The illustrated book of the dog; with 30 fac-simile col. pl. To be complete in about 30 pts. ea., 40c.
100. **Shelton,** J. P. Dairy farming; with col. pl. and wood. eng. To be complete in about 25 pts. ea., 40c.
101. **Shore,** *Rev.* T. Teignmouth. Life of the world to come, and other subjects. post 8°......$1.50
102. — Some difficulties of belief. post 8°.......$1.50
103. **Silver** wings and golden scales: description of butterflies, bees, wasps, grasshoppers, etc. ill. fp. 4°, 192 p. $2.00
    — *Same.* New ed. bds. $1.25
104. **Simple** rhymes for happy times. ill. cr. 8°..50c.
105. **Simple** stories for the little ones. ill. 12°, 64 p. bds...25c.
106. **Sportsman's** year-book. demy 8°, 272 p...$2.50
107. **Stables,** Gordon. Dogs in their relation to the public, social, sanitary and legal...........75c.
108. — Jungle, peak and plain: a boy's book of hunting and adventure. ill. fp. 4°, 192 p..........$2.00
109. — The practical kennel guide; with plain instructions how to rear and breed dogs for pleasure, show and profit. ill. 12°, 192 p...........$1.50
110. **Stainer,** *Dr.* Music of the Bible. cr. 8°, 196 p. $1.50
111. **Storer,** *Rev.* John. Wild white cattle of Great Britain. 8°..............................$8.00
112. **Sunny** days for little people: short stories. ill. fp. 4°, 128 p. bds.........................75c.
113. **Teacher's** illustrated Bible; with references. 1000 orig. ill. cr. 4°, 1248 p. $5; col. maps, leath., $8; mor., $10; levant $12.00
114. **Tuneful** lays for merry days. ill. sq. cr. 8°..50c.
115. **Whymper,** Fred. The sea: its stirring story of adventure, peril and heroism. v. 1, 2. ill. cr. 4°. ea...$3.00
116. **Wilson,** Alexander, *and* Bonaparte, *Prince* Charles Lucien. American ornithology; or, the natural history of the birds of the U. S.; with notes and life of author by Sir William Jardine. 3 v. 103 col. plates. $18; hf. mor., $20; hf. cf......$24
117. **Wise** king (The), and other stories. ill. 64 p. bds...25c.
118. **Wood,** J. G. Field naturalist's handbook..$2.00
119. **World** (The) of wonders: record of things wonderful in nature, science and art. ill. imp. 8°, 500 p. $4..............................$4.50
120. **Wray,** *Rev.* J. Jackson. A man every inch of him; or, the story of Frank Fullerton's school days. ill. cr. 8°, 216 p...................$1.50
121. — Matthew Mellowdew. cr. 8°, 384 p......$2.00
122. — Nestleton Magna: story of Yorkshire Methodism. cr. 8°..........................$1.50
123. — Peter Pengelley; or, true as the clock. ill. 90c.
124. **Wright,** Louis. Practical pigeon keeper. ill. cr. 8°, 232 p...............................$1.50
125. **Wright,** Perceval. Animal life described and illustrated. ill. roy. 8°, 608 p.............$5.00
126. **Wylie,** *Rev.* J. A. The history of Protestantism, from the earliest period to the present time. 3 v. ill. cr. 4°, ea., 600 p. $15; hf. cf. $21.00

HOUGHTON, OSGOOD & CO.,

Boston, Mass.

1. **Aldrich**, T. B. The queen of Sheba. 16°..$1.50
2. — Flower and thorn. Later poems. 16°....$1.25
3. — Tom Bailey's adventures. pap..........50c.
4. — Baby Bell. A holiday volume. sm. 4°..$1.50
5. — The story of a cat. Tr. from the French by T. B. Aldrich. ill. 12°..................$1.00
6. **Allen**, Grant. Color-sense: its origin and development. 8°..............................$3.50
7. **American** poems. Selected from the works of Longfellow, Whittier, Bryant, Holmes, Lowell and Emerson. 16°......................$1.25
8. **Attwood**, F. G. Manners and customs of ye Harvard studente. f°..................$1.50
9. **Avery**, B. P. Californian pictures. 4°......$5.00
10. **Bacon**, Francis. An account of his life and times. Abridged from the "Life and letters of Bacon," by James Spedding. 2 v. cr. 8°........$5.00
11. — Works. Popular edition. Based upon the complete edition of Spedding, Ellis and Heath. 2 v. cr. 8°..................................$5.00
12. **Beers**, H. A. Odds and ends. 18°........$1.25
13. **Bishop**, W. H. Detmold: a romance. 18°..$1.25
14. **Browning**, Robt. Pacchiarotto, and other poems. 16°......................................$1.50
15. **Burning** of the convent. 18°..............$1.00
16. **Burroughs**, John. Birds and poets. 16°..$1.50
17. — Locusts and wild honey. 16°...........$1.50
18. **Caton**, John Dean. The antelope and deer of America. ill. 8°..........................$4.00
19. — Miscellanies. por. 8°..................$2.00
20. **Chaucer**, Geoffrey. Poetical works. Edited, with memoir, by Arthur Gilman; with full index and por. (Riverside ed.) 3 v. cr. 8°.......$5.25
21. **Christmastide.** Holiday volume, comprising "The river path," "Excelsior," "The rose," and "Baby Bell." 8°................................$5.00
22. **Clapp**, H. C., *M.D.* Tabular handbook of auscultation and percussion. 4 plates. 8°.......$1.50
23. **Clarke**, E. H. Visions. With introduction by Dr. O. W. Holmes. por. 16°..............$1.50
24. **Clarke**, J. F. Memorial and biographical sketches. 12°......................................$2.00
25. **Clement**, Clara E., *and* Hutton, Laurence. Artists of 19th cent. and their works. 2 v. cr. 8°. $5.00
26. **College** book. Containing historical sketches of 24 leading American colleges. sq. 8°....$10.00
27. **Cook**, Joseph. Biology. 3 ill. 12°.......$1.50
28. — Transcendentalism. 12°..................$1.50
29. — Orthodoxy. 12°..........................$1.50
30. — Conscience. 12°.........................$1.50
31. — Heredity. 12°...........................$1.50
32. — Marriage. 12°...........................$1.50
33. — Labor. 12°..............................$1.50
34. **Cooper**, J. Fenimore. Complete works. (Globe ed.) 16 v.................................$16.00
35. **Curtis**, B. R. Dottings round the circle. ill. 8°. $2.50
36. **Darley**, F. O. C. Compositions in outline from Hawthorne's "Scarlet letter." large folio. $10.00
37. **Dhammapada**: Buddhist canon. cr. 8°....$2.50
38. **Diaz**, *Mrs.* A. M. The Jimmyjohns. 16°..$1.50
39. **Dresden** gallery (The): 24 heliotypes of famous pictures in the Dresden gallery. large 4°..$10.00
40. **Dwight**, Thomas. The anatomy of the head. 6 plates. 8°..............................$2.50
41. **Earnest** trifler (An). Novel. 16°.........$1.25
42. **Edkins**, Joseph. Religion in China. 8°....$2.50
43. **Emerson**, R. W. Fortune of the republic. 16°. pap., 25c.; cl..............................50c.
44. — Works. ("Little classic" ed.) 9 v. ea...$1.50
45. — *Same.* (Fireside ed.) 5 v. 16°..........$10.00
46. **Faed** gallery: 24 heliotypes of the best pictures of Thomas Faed. large 4°..............$10.00
47. **Fields**, J. T. Underbrush. 18°..........$1.25
48. — *and* Whipple, E. P. Family library of British poetry, from Chaucer to the present time. 12 por. roy. 8°, 1028 p.........................$5.00
49. **Forster**, E. J. Manual for medical officers of U. S. militia.................................$2.00
50. **Gallery** of great artists: 24 heliotypes. 4°..$10.00
51. **Gardner**, E. C. Home interiors. 16°......$1.50
52. **Garland**, G. M. Pneumono-dynamics. pap., $1.50; cl..$2.00
53. **Garrison**, W. L. Tributes to. por.....50c.; 75c.
54. **Ghiberti** gates: 33 heliotypes representing "the Ghiberti gates" of the baptistery of St. John, Florence.................................$10.00
55. **Gibbon**, Edward. Mahomet. 18°...........60c.
56. **Goethe's** Faust. Translated by B. Taylor. 1 v. 12°.......................................$3.50
57. **Goethe** gallery. The female characters of Goethe. By Wilhelm Kaulbach. Heliotypes......$10.00
58. **Gordon**, George H. History of the campaign of the Army of Virginia. maps. 8°........$4.00
59. **Gray** engravings. 24 heliotypes. large 4°..$10.00
60. **Greene**, Harris R. English language: its grammatical and logical principles. 12°...........$1.05
61. **Greg**, W. R. Creed of Christendom. 2 v. cr. 8°. $5.00
62. **Gynecological** transactions. v. 1, $5; v 2, $6.50; v. 3..$5.00
63. **Hamilton**, J. C. Life of Alexander Hamilton. 7 v. 40 por. 8°..........................$25.00
64. **Harrison**, J. A. Greek vignettes. 18°.....$1.25
65. — Spain in profile. 18°....................$1.50
66. **Harte**, Bret. Thankful Blossom. 18°......$1.25
67. — Two men of Sandy Bar. 18°............$1.00
68. — The story of a mine. 18°...............$1.00
69. — Drift from two shores. 18°.............$1.25
70. — The twins of Table Mountain. 18°........$1.25
71. **Harvard** book (The): historical, biographical and descriptive sketches. By Samuel Eliot, J. F. Clarke, A. P. Peabody, Samuel Longfellow, Edmund Quincy, E. E. Hale, O. W. Holmes, R. H. Dana, jr., J. R. Lowell, T. W. Higginson and many others. 2 v. 57 por. and 110 views, fac-similes, etc. large 4°. levant cl.....$30.00
72. **Haug**, Martin. Essays on the sacred language, writings and religion of the Parsis. Ed. by E. W. West. cr. 8°...........................$4.50
73. **Hawthorne**, N. Works. ("Little classic" ed.) 23 v. 18°. ea.............................$1.25
74. — *Same.* (Fireside ed.) 12 v. 16°......$20.00
75. **Heaton**, George. The cure of rupture, reducible and irreducible; also, of varicocele. Ed. by J. Henry Davenport, M.D. 16°.............$1.50
76. **Hodge**, H. C. Arizona as it is. map. 12°..$1.50
77. **Holmes**, Oliver Wendell. The school boy. ill. $4.00
78. — John Lothrop Motley. 16°..............$1.50
79. **Howe**, J. B. Political economy of Great Britain, the United States and France, in the use of money. 8°...............................$3.50
80. — Monetary and industrial fallacies. 8°....$1.50
81. — Mono-metalism and bi-metalism. 8°......$1.00
82. **Howells**, W. D. The parlor car: farce. 32°. 50c.
83. — Out of the question: comedy. 18°......$1.25
84. — A counterfeit presentment: comedy. 18°..$1.25
85. — (*ed.*) Choice autobiography, with critical and biographical essays. ("Little classic" ed.) per v. $1.25: — 1, 2, Memoirs of Frederica Sophia Wilhelmina, Margravine of Baireuth; 3, Lord Herbert of Cherbury and Thomas Ellwood; 4, Vittorio Alfieri; 5, Carlo Goldoni; 6, Edward Gibbon; 7, 8, François Marmontel.
86. **Hughes**, Thos. Manliness of Christ. 16°..$1.00

HOUGHTON, OSGOOD & CO.,

Continued.

87. **Hunt,** W. M. Talks on art. 8°.........$1.00
88. **James,** Henry. Society the redeemed form of man, and the earnest of God's omnipotence in human nature. 8°.............................$2.00
89. **James,** Henry, *jr.* The American. 12°....$2.00
90. —Watch and ward. ("Little classic" ed.) 18°. $1.25
91. —The Europeans. 12°..................$1.50
92. — Confidence $1.50
93. **Jeffries,** B. Joy. Color blindness: its dangers and its detection. ill. 12°..................$2.00
94. **Jewett,** Sarah O. Deephaven. 18°......$1.25
95. — Old friends and new. 18°.............$1.25
96. — Play days. Stories for children. sq. 16°..$1.50
97. **Johnson,** Helen K. Tears for the little ones. 12°. $2.00
98. **Johnson,** Samuel. Oriental religions: China. 8°. $5.00
99. **Jones,** L. A. A treatise on the law of mortgages of real property. 2 v. 8°.............$13.00
100. —A treatise on the law of railroad and other corporate securities, including also municipal aid bonds. 8° $6.50
101. **King,** T. Starr. Christianity and humanity; with memoir by E. P. Whipple. por. 12°..$2.00
102. — Substance and show, and other lectures. 12°. $2.00
103. **Klaczko,** Julian. Two chancellors: Prince Gortchakof and Prince Bismarck. cr. 8°.......$2.00
104. **Knowlton,** Helen M. Hints for pupils in drawing and painting: 20 heliotypes of drawings by Wm. M. Hunt. 16°....................$2.00
105. **Koran** (Selections from). By Stanley Lane Poole. 8° $3.50
106. **Lamartine,** A. de. Oliver Cromwell. 18°..60c.
107. — Mary Stuart. 18°......................60c.
108. **Lange,** F. A. History of materialism. v. 1 and 2. 8°. ea...............................$3.50
109. **Larcom,** Lucy (*ed.*) Hillside and seaside in poetry. 18°..........................$1.00
110. **Lewes,** G. H. Physical basis of life. 8°..$3.00
111. — The study of psychology. 8°...........$2.00
112. — Problems of life and mind. 3d ser......$3.00
113. **Lippitt,** F. J. Criminal law as administered in Mass. 8°.............................$5.00
114. **Longfellow,** H. W. Poems. (Illustrated library ed.) 8°...............................$4.00
115. — Kéramos, and other poems. 16°........$1.25
116. — The skeleton in armor. ill. 8°..........$5.00
117. — Excelsior. ill. sq. 16° $1.50
118. — (*ed.*) Poems of places. 31 v. 18°. ea., $1; per set, $25: —1–4, England and Wales; 5, Ireland; 6–8, Scotland, Denmark, Iceland, Norway and Sweden; 9, 10, France and Savoy; 11–13, Italy; 14, 15, Spain, Portugal, Belgium and Holland; 16, Switzerland and Austria; 17, 18, Germany; 19, Greece and Turkey (in Europe); 20, Russia, including Asiatic Russia; 21–23, Asia; 24, Africa; 25, 26, New England; 27, Middle states; 28, Southern states; 29, Western states; 30, British America, Mexico, South America; 31, Oceanica.
119. **Lowell,** J. R. The rose. ill. sq. 16°....$1.50
120. **Magitot,** E. Treatise on dental caries. Experimental and therapeutic investigations. Tr. by Thos. H. Chandler, D.M.D. 8°..........$2.50
121. **Martineau,** Harriet. Autobiography; with memorials by Mrs. M. W. Chapman. 2 v. por. 8°. $6.00
122. — Household education. 18°.............$1.25
124. **Meredith,** Owen. Poems. (Illustrated library ed.) 8°...............................$4.00
125. **Michelet,** Jules. Joan of Arc. 18°.......60c.
126. **Millais** gallery. Heliotypes of the best pictures by J. E. Millais: por., descriptive letter-press. large 4°...............................$10.00
127. **Narjoux,** Felix. Notes and sketches of an architect during a tour in the northwest of Europe. ill. 8° $3.00
128. **Omar Khayyam.** Rubaiyat. sq. 16°......$1.00
129. **One** year abroad; by the author of "One summer." 18° $1.25
130. **Orth,** Johannes. A compend. of diagnosis in pathological anatomy; trans. 8°.........$3.50
131. **Page,** H. A. Thoreau: his life and aims. 18°. $1.00
132. **Paige,** Lucius R. History of Cambridge, Mass. maps. 8° $6.00
133. **Palfrey,** Francis W. Memoir of William Francis Bartlett. por. 16° $1.50
134. **Parloa,** M. First principles of household management and cookery. 18° ....75c.
135. **Parton,** James. The French Parnassus. 12°. $2. 8°....................................$3.50
136. **Peace** parliament (The); or, the reconstruction creed of christendom. 16°....................50c.
137. **Perkins,** Charles C. Raphael and Michael Angelo. A critical and biog. essay. ill. 8° ..$5.00
138. **Perry,** Nora. Her lover's friend. 16°.....$1.50
139. **Phelps,** Eliz. S. Sealed orders. 16°......$1.50
140. **Physicus.** A candid examination of theism. 8°.......................................$2.50
141. **Piatt,** J. J. Poems of house and home. 16°. $1.50
142. **Piatt,** *Mrs.* S. M. B. That new world. 16°. $1.50
143. — Dramatic persons and moods. 16°......$1.25
144. **Pole,** William. Philosophy of music. 8°..$3.50
145. **Poore,** Ben. Perley. Political register and Congressional directory. 8° $6.00
146. **Pratt,** C. E. The American bicycler. ill. ..75c.
147. **Princeton** book. Containing the history of the College of New Jersey. 69 fine illustrations, including portraits, buildings, views, etc. 1 v. large 4°. sheets, $18; cl. $20.00
148. **Public** Health Association. Reports and papers. v. 1, $6.50; 2, $6.50; 3, $4; 4...........$5.00
149. **Putnam,** Geo. Sermons. steel por. 16°..$1.75
150. **Raymond,** George L. Ideals made real, and Haydn. 16° $1.25
151. — Colony ballads. 16° ....75c.
152. **Richardson,** Chas. F. A primer of American literature. 18°..........................50c.
153. **Riola,** E. How to learn Russian: manual. 12°. $3.00
154. — Key to manual $1.25
155. **Rochefoucauld,** *Mme.* de la (*Duchess of Doudeauville*). Life. 16° $1.25
156. **Schwartze,** Hermann. Pathological anatomy of the ear. Tr. by J. Orne Green, M.D. 8°..$2.00
157. **Scott,** Walter. Waverley novels. (Globe ed.) 13 v....................................$13.00
158. **Scudder,** H. E. The Bodleys telling stories. 81 ill. sm. 4°.............................$1.50
159. — The Bodleys on wheels. 77 ill. sm. 4°..$1.50
160. — The Bodleys afoot. 79 ill. sm. 4°......$1.50
161. **Severance,** Mark Sibley. Hammersmith: his Harvard days. 12°.......................$2.00
162. **Shairp,** J. C. Poetic interpretation of nature. 16°.......................................$1.25
163. **Shaler,** N. S. Thoughts on the nature of intellectual property, and its importance to the state. 8°.......................................75c.
164. **Shea,** George. Alexander Hamilton. por. 8°. $4.50
165. **Simcox,** Edith. Natural law: a study in ethics. 8°.......................................$3.50
166. **Sime,** James. Lessing: his life and writings. 2 v. por. 8°...........................$7.00

HOUGHTON, OSGOOD & CO.,

Continued.

167. **Smith**, Baxter P. History of Dartmouth College; with portraits of the presidents. 8° $5.00
168. **Smith**, Stephen. Manual of the principles and practice of operative surgery. ill. cr. 8°. cl., $4; roan $4.50
169. **Stebbins**, Emma. Charlotte Cushman: her letters and memories of her life. por. 12°.. $2.50
170. **Stedman**, E. C. Hawthorne and other poems. 16° $1.25
171. **Sterne**, Stuart. Angelo: a poem. 16° $1.00
172. **Stowe**, Harriet B. Uncle Tom's cabin. (Holiday ed.) Introduction, 30 pages, and bibliography. ill. 8° $3.50
173. **Sweetser**, M. F. Artist biographies. 15 v. 18°. ea., cl., 50c.: — Titian; Albert Dürer; Rembrandt; Sir Joshua Reynolds; Guido Reni; Turner; Leonardo da Vinci; Raphael; Murillo; Claude Lorraine; Michael Angelo; Van Dyck; Fra Angelico; Landseer; Washington Allston. The set of 15 volumes, in box $7.50
174. — *Same.* (Illustrated ed.) 5 v. 16°, each containing 12 heliotype engravings, $1.50; per set, $7.50: — (1) Raphael, Leonardo da Vinci, Michael Angelo; (2) Titian, Guido, Claude Lorraine; (3) Reynolds, Turner, Landseer; (4) Dürer, Rembrandt, Van Dyck; (5) Fra Angelico, Murillo, Allston.
176. **Tanagra** figurines. ill. 16° $1.50
177. **Taylor**, Bayard. Poetical works. (Household ed.) 12° $2.00
178. — The Echo Club, and other literary diversions. 18° $1.25
179. — Prince Deukalion: a lyrical drama. 4°.. $3.00
180. **Tennyson**, Alfred. Poems. (Illustrated library ed.) 8° $4.00
181. — *Same.* (Universal ed.) ill. sq. 16° ...... 75c.
182. — *Same.* (Shawmut ed.) ill. cr. 8°. full gilt, $1.50; plain edges $1.00
183. — *Same.* (Hazelmere ed.) Ornamental borders. sm. 4° $1.50
184. — Harold: a drama. 16° $1.00
185. — *Same.* ill. 12° $2.00
186. **Thacher**, Mary P. Seashore and prairie. 18°. $1.00
187. **Thaxter**, Celia. Drift-weed: poems. 18°.. $1.50
188. **Thompson**, J. P. Lectures on the centennial of American independence. cr. 8° $2.50
189. **Tiele**, C. P. Outlines of the history of religion to the spread of the universal religions. 8°. $2.50
190. **Titian** gallery (The). Containing 24 heliotypes of the most famous of Titian's paintings. large 4° $10.00
191. **Trollope**, T. A. Vittoria Colonna. 18° .... 60c.
193. **Waring**, Geo. E., *jr.* Village improvements and farm villages. ill. 18° ...... 75c.
194. — The bride of the Rhine. ill $1.50
195. **Warner**, C. D. In the Levant. 12° $2.00
196. — Being a boy; ill. by "Champ." sq. 16°.. $1.50
197. — In the wilderness. 18° ...... 75c.
198. **Warren**, George Washington. History of the Bunker Hill Monument Association during the first century of the United States of America. ill. and fac-similes. 8° $6.00
199. **Weber**, Albrecht. History of Indian literature. cr. 8° $5.00
200. **Whitman**, Sarah Helen. Poems. por. 16°. $1.50
201. **Whitney**, *Mrs.* A. D. T. Just how: a key to the cook-books. 16° $1.00
202. **Whittier**, John G. Poems. (Illustrated library ed.) 8° $4.00
203. — The vision of Echard. 16° $1.25
204. — The river path. ill. sq. 16° $1.50
205. **Wilson**, Henry. Rise and fall of the slave power in America. vol. 3. 8°. $5; per set (3 v.).. $15.00
206. **Winsor**, Justin. Reader's handbook of the American revolution. 16° $1.25
207. **Wyman**, Morrill. Autumnal catarrh. (Hay fever.) Illustrative maps and tables. 8° ... $2.00

CHANGES OF PRICE.

208. **Andersen's** Works. 10 v... from $16.50 to $15.00
209. **Andrews'** Latin reader ...... from $1.12 to 87c.
210. — Latin lessons ...... from 88c. to 70c.
211. — Viri Romæ ...... from $1.25 to $1.00
212. — *and* Stoddard's Latin grammar. from $1.50 to $1.05
213. **Carlyle's** Essays. 4 v ...... from $9.00 to $7.50
214. **Cooper's** Works. (Household ed.) 32 v. per v. from $1.25 to $1.00
215. **Cummins'** Lamplighter ...... from $1.75 to $1.50
216. — El Fureidis ...... from $1.75 to $1.50
217. **De Stael's** Germany ...... from $3.00 to $2.50
218. **Dickens'** Works. (Library ed.) 29 v. per v. from $2.00 to $1.50
219. **Gesenius'** Hebrew lexicon... from $7.50 to $6.00
220. **Montaigne's** Works. 4 v... from $9.00 to $7.50
221. **Parton's** Works ...... per v. from $3.00 to $2.00
222. **Pierce's** Dickens dictionary.. from $3.00 to $2.00
223. **Prayers** of the ages ...... from $2.50 to $1.50
224. **Red-line** poets ...... from $3.50 to $2.50
225. **Robinson's** (Crabb) Diary, now in 1 v. ...., $2.50
226. **Scott's** Waverley novels. (Library ed.) 25 v. ea., from $1.50 to $1.00
227. **Waring's** A farmer's vacation. from $5.00 to $3.00
228. **Whitney's** (*Mrs.* A. D. T.) Stories, to uniform price ...... per v. $1.50

NEW CHURCH BOARD OF PUB.

20 Cooper Union, New York.

1. **Swedenborg**, Emanuel. True Christian religion. Rotch ed. 3 v. 12°. cl., $3.75; hf. cf. $7.50
2. — Divine Providence. Rotch ed. 12°. cl., $1.50; hf. cf. $2.25
3. — Compendium of his theological writings; compiled by Rev. Samuel M. Warren; with biog. introd. by Hon. John Bigelow. large 12°, 852 p. cl. $3.00
4. **Book** of rites and sacraments. cl., 45c.; mor., $1.00
5. **Hosanna** (The): a book of hymns, songs, chants and anthems. sq. 12°, 218 p. cl., 75c.; mor., $2.00

F. H. THOMAS & CO.,

208 S. Fourth St., St. Louis.

1. **Bay**, W. V. V. Reminiscences of bench and bar of Missouri. 8° $3.00
2. **Bishop**, J. P. Law of contracts; condensed. 8°. $3.50
3. **Dunlap**, M. E. Abridgment of Blackstone. 24°. $1.25
4. **Lieber**. Hermeneutics; or, principles of interpretation. New Am. ed., with notes by Prof. W. G. Hammond. (*In press.*) *net* ...... $2.50 *or* $3.00
5. **Mills**, H. E. Treatise on law of eminent domain. 8° $4.75
6. **Wade**, William P. Retroactive laws. 8°, 425 p. *net* $4.75

CLAXTON, REMSEN & HAFFELFINGER,

624–628 Market Street, Philadelphia.

1. **Arlt**, Ferdinand v. Injuries of the eye, and their medico-legal aspects; tr. by Charles S. Turnbull. 12°....$1.25
2. **Barrett**, B. F. New Church (The): its nature and whereabouts. 12°....$1.00
3. — New view of hell; showing its nature, whereabouts, duration and how to escape it. 12°..$1.00
4. — Swedenborg and Channing. 12°....$1.00
5. **Baum**, *Rev.* Henry Mason. The rights and duties of rectors, churchwardens and vestrymen in the American church. 12°....$1.50
6. **Beard**, James Melville. K. K. K. sketches, humorous and didactic. 12°....$1.50
7. **Bennett**, *Rev.* William W. Narrative of the great revival which prevailed in the southern armies during the late civil war between the states of the federal union. ill. 12°....$1.50
8. **Bilgram**, Hugo. Slide-valve gears. 16°....$1.00
9. **Bladen**, Elizabeth S. Water waif: a story of the revolution. 16°....75c.
10. **Bruner**, Jane W. Free prisoners: a story of California life. 12°....$1.50
11. **Centennial** frog, and other stories. ill. 16°..$1.00
12. **Child** hunters; by a friend of Italy. ill. 16°..$1.00
13. **Clifford**, *Mrs.* Josephine. Overland tales. 12°..$1.50
14. **Comly**, John. Comly's primer; or, the first book for children....4c.
15. **Cooper**, John H. Treatise on the use of belting. 8°....$3.50
16. **Dartt**, Mary. On the plains, and among the peaks; or, how Mrs. Maxwell made her natural history collection. 2d ed. ill. $1; fancy pap....50c.
17. **Davenport**, —. Anderson's History of the United States. New ed., rev. 16°....90c.
18. **Davis**, Thomas J. Sketch of the life, character and public services of Thos. Jefferson. 16°. $1.00
19. **Drayton**, Henry S. Light in dark places; or, how the Camps lived in their poverty; with ill. by F. A. Chapman. 16°....$1.25
20. **Elliott**, *Mrs.* Sarah A. Mrs. Elliott's housewife: practical receipts on cookery. 12°....$1.50
21. **Ferguson**, —. Anecdotical guide to Mexico; with a map of the railways: historical, geological, archæological and critical. 12°. pap....$1.00
22. **Freedley**, Edwin T. Common sense in business: practical answers to practical questions. 12°. $1.50
23. — Home comforts; or, things worth knowing in every household. 12°....$1.50
24. **Gentry**, Thomas G. The house sparrow at home and abroad. demy 8°....$2.00
25. **Gobright**, L. A. Echoes of childhood: old friends in new costumes. ill. sq. 16°....$1.00
26. **Goulding**, F. R. The Woodruff stories. New issue. 3 v. in 1. ill....$1.50
27. **Hays**, *Rev.* George P. Every-day reasoning; or, the science of inductive logic. 12°....$1.50
28. **Hobson**, Arthur H. G. The amateur mechanic's practical handbook. 12°....$1.25
29. **Ingersoll**, L. D. History of the War Department of the United States; with biog. sketches of the different secretaries. demy 8°....$3.50
30. **Irving**, Washington. Rip Van Winkle; tr. into French by Maj. L. Du Bos. ill. 16°. 75c.; hf. bd....60c.
31. **Ives**, Charles L. The Bible doctrine of the soul; or, man's nature and destiny as revealed. 12°. 75c.; pap....50c.
32. **Jackson**, Andrew. Complete memoirs. 18°..75c.
33. **Keyser**, Charles S. Fairmount Park and the International Exhibition at Philadelphia. 6th ed. 12°. $1; fancy pap....50c.
34. **King**, H. T. The egotist. 12°....$1.50
35. **Legouve**, Ernest. Art of reading; with notes mainly biog. or critical; tr. by Edw. Roth. por. 12°....$1.50
36. **Lewis**, *Rev.* W. P. Lectionaries, English and Irish. 12°....$2.00
37. **M.**, A. B. Essay contributing to a philosophy of literature. 2d ed. 12°....$1.50
38. **McKay**, *Mrs.* C. E. Stories of hospital and camp. 12°....$1.25
39. **Marchmont**, John. Thirty-four years: an American story of southern life. 12°....$1.50
40. **Memminger**, *Rev.* R. W. Reflections of a recluse. 12°....$1.25
41. **Morris**, Margaret E. Heavenly dawn: original and selected pieces. 16°....$1.25
42. **Morton**, James. The system of calculating diameter, circumference, area and squaring the circle. 12°....$1.00
43. **My** intimate enemy: a story. 16°....$1.00
44. **Peabody**, S. H. Cecil's books of natural history. New issue. ill. 16°....$1.75
45. **Phelps**, *Mrs.* Lincoln. The Blue Ribbon Society; or, the school girls' rebellion. 12°....75c.
46. **Riddell**, Robert. The artisan; illustrated by forty plates of geometric drawings, showing the most practical methods that may be applied to works of building and other constructions. f°....$5.00
47. — The carpenter and joiner modernized. 3d ed., rev. ill. 4°....$7.50
48. — Lessons on hand-railing for learners. 3d ed. 4°. $5.00
49. — Mechanic's geometry. ill. 4°....$5.00
50. **Roper**, Stephen. Handbook of modern steam fire engines. 12°....$3.50
51. — Use and abuse of the steam-boiler. ill. 18°. $2.00
52. **Roth**, Edward. A short geography. pt. 1: The hemispheres. 18°. text, 20c.; chart....30c.
53. — A short Latin grammar. pt. 1: The declensions. 18°. hf. bd., 50c.; — pt. 2: The cases, the adjectives, the pronouns. 18°. pap....25c.
54. **Sayen**, W. H. The Grand International Chess Congress, held in Philadelphia, in August, 1876. 12°....$2.00
55. **Shakspeare**, William. Complete dramatic and poetical works, with outline of life, and description of his portraits; collected by John S. Hart. (Avon ed.) ill. imp. 8°, 966 double-column p. cl., $3; cl., extra, gilt edge, $3.75; shp., $3.50; hf. tur., $5.50; tur....$8.00
56. — *Same;* in 2 v. cl., $3.75; cl., extra, gilt edge, $4.50; shp....$4.25
57. — *Same.* Fine ed., printed on toned paper: 20 large and striking full page Boydell ill. cl., $5; law shp., $6; hf. tur., $8.50; tur....$9.50
58. **Sheely**, Aaron (*ed.*) Anecdotes and humors of school life. 12°. $1.50....$2.25
59. **Simonin**, L. A French view of the Grand International Exposition of 1876; tr. by Samuel H. Needles. 8°. pap....50c.
60. **Spang**, Henry W. Practical treatise on lightning protection. ill. 12°....$1.50
61. **Spur** of Monmouth; or, Washington in arms: hist. and centennial romance of the revolution; by an ex-pension agent. 12°....$1.75
62. **Swedenborg** library; ed. by B. F. Barrett: — v. 2, Heaven; v. 3, Freedom, rationality and catholicity; v. 4, Divine Providence and its laws. 16°. ea....75c.
63. **Teasdale**, *Rev.* Thomas C. Revised edition of Revival discourses. 12°....$1.25
64. **Thomas**, E. A. At swords' points: novel. 12°. $1.50

CLAXTON, REMSEN & HAFFELFINGER,

Continued.

65. **Trautwine,** John C. Civil engineer's pocket book of mensuration, trigonometry, etc. 4th ed., rev. (10th thousand.) 12°, 648 p. mor.......$5.00
66. — The field practice of laying out circular curves for railroads. 10th ed., rev. and enl. 12°..$2.00
67. **Two** years behind the plough; or, the experience of a Pennsylvania farm boy. 12°.........$1.00
68. **Verne,** Jules. Off on a comet, a journey through planetary space: sequel to "To the sun"; tr. by Edward Roth. ill. 12°...................$1.50
69. — To the sun; or, a journey through planetary space; tr. by Edward Roth. ill. 12°......$1.50
70. **Voltaire.** Life of Charles XII. 12°........$1.00
71. **White,** Charles J. Elements of theoretical and descriptive astronomy. 3d ed. ill. demy 8°. $2.00
72. **Whittlesey,** Elsie L. Elyria: a novel. 12°. $1.00
73. **Woolever,** Adam. Treasury of wisdom, wit and humor, odd comparisons and proverbs. roy. 8°. $2.50; shp., $3.50; tur.................$6.00
74. **Word** of God on true marriage: new issue of Opinions concerning the Bible law of marriage. 12°...............................$1.00

D. VAN NOSTRAND,

23 Murray St., New York.

1. **Dubois,** A. J. Graphical statics. 8°. cl...$1.50
2. **Eddy,** H. T. Graphical statics. 8°. cl.....$1.50
3. **Naquet,** A. Legal chemistry. 12°. cl.....$2.00
4. **Prescott,** A. B. Qualitative chemical analysis. 8°. cl...................................$3.50
5. — First book in qual. chemistry. 12°.......$1.50
6. **Mott,** H. A. Chemists' manual. 8°. cl....$6.00
7. **Caldwell,** G. C., *and* Breneman, A. A. Chemical practice. 8°. cl......................$1.50
8. **Gillmore,** Q. A. Roads, streets and pavements. 12mo. cl.............................$2.00
9. **Davis,** C. H., *and* Rae, F. B. Electrical diagrams. 8°. cl........................$2.00
10. **Rose,** J. Pattern maker. 8°. cl..........$2.50
11. **Fanning,** J. F. Water supply. 8°. cl.....$6.00
12. **Plympton,** G. W. Planisphere or star finder. $1.00
13. **Schuman,** F. Heating and ventilation. 12°..$1.50
14. **Clark,** D. K. Manual of rules and tables. 8°. cl....................................$7.50
15. — Fuel: its combustion, etc. 12°. cl.......$1.50
16. **Weyrauch,** J. J. Iron and steel construction. 12°. cl................................$1.00
17. **Jannetaz,** E. Determination of rocks. 12°..$1.50
18. **Shield,** J. E. Engineering construction. 12°. cl....................................$1.50
19. **Shunk,** W. F. Engineer's pocket book. 12°. tuck..................................$2.50
20. **Adams,** J. Sewers and drains. 8°. cl.....$2.50
21. **McElroy,** S. Hempstead storage reservoir...50c.
22. **Spinoza,** B. Ethics; from the Latin. 8°..$3.00
23. **Van Nostrand,** D. Science series. nos. 21–49. 18°. ea., bds..........................50c.
24. **Fry,** J. B. History of brevet rank. 8°. cl...$3.50
25. — Army sacrifices. 12°. cl..............$1.00
26. **Arnold,** F. S. Discipline and drill of militia. 12°. cl.................................$2.00
27. **Roberts,** J. Hand book of artillery. 18°....$2.00
28. **Roberts,** W. H. Hints and helps for national guardsmen. 12°. cl...................
29. **Parker,** F. A. The galley period. 8°. cl...$5.00
30. **Hamersly,** L. B. Records of officers of U. S. N. 8°. cl.................................$5.00
31. **Moore,** Frank. Rebellion record. 12 v. 8°..$60.00
32. **Van Nostrand,** D. Engineering Magazine. v. 14–21. 8°. ea.........................$3.00
33. **Wheeler,** J. B. Art and science of war. 12°. $1.75
34. **Watt,** A. Electro-metallurgy. 12°. cl.....$1.00
35. **Ives,** R. A. Military law. 8°. shp.........$4.00
36. **Wainwright,** W. P. Animal locomotion. 12°. cl.

WILLIAM WARE & CO.,

Boston, Mass.

1. **Seaver** *and* Walton's Franklin primary arithmetic. 20c. — Elementary arithmetic. 35c. — Written arithmetic...............................75c.
2. — — Metric system.........................15c.
3. **Walton's** Arithmetical table. per 100......$7.20
4. **Walton** *and* Cogswell's Book of problems....18c.
5. **Hill's** First lessons in geometry..............33c.
6. — Second book in geometry.................54c.
7. **Farrar's** Arithmetical problems..............54c.
8. **Worcester's** New primary spelling book.....18c.
9. — New pronouncing spelling book...........25c.
10. **Adams'** Spelling book for advanced classes...25c.
11. **Eliot's** Manual of U. S. history. (Revised ed.)$1.35
12. **Weber's** Outlines of universal history......$1.80
13. **Smith's** History of Greece. (Felton's ed.)..$2.00
14. **Blair's** Outlines of chronology...............36c.
15. **Edwards,** Amelia B. Outlines of Eng. hist...22c.
16. **Winslow's** Intellectual philosophy........$1.20
17. **Emerson's** Watts On the mind..............33c.
18. **Bowen's** Metaphysical and ethical science...$1.35
19. **Allen's** Classical hand-book................62c.
20. **Sophocles'** Modern Greek grammar........$1.80

THOMPSON, BROWN & CO.,

23 Hawley Street, Boston.

WHOLESALE PRICES.

1. **Bradbury,** William F. Bradbury's Eaton's practical arithmetic. 12°. '79. 75c.; — Key of answers, 20c.; — Key of solutions....................75c.
2. — Elementary geometry. (University ed.) 12°. '77.......................................$1.28
3. — Metric system. (*In press.*)
4. **Eaton,** James S. Primary arithmetic. Revised ed. 18°. '77...................................18c.
5. **Meservey,** A. B. Book-keeping, containing single and double entry, for high schools and academies. 12°. '77. 80c.; blanks, 72c.; — Key...80c.
6. **Stone,** A. P. History of England; based on and retaining portions of Worcester's History. 12°. '79...66c.
7. — History of United States. (*In press.*)
8. **Tilden,** W. S. The musical guide. 12°. '79..55c.

RETAIL PRICE.

9. **Cushing,** Luther S. Manual of parliamentary practice. Revised ed. 16°. '77................75c.

HARPER & BROTHERS,

Franklin Square, New York.

1. **Alden**, W. L. Canoe and flying proa. 32°. pap. 25c.
2. **Ames**, Fisher. Modern whist. 32°. pap....20c.
3. **Anthon**, *Prof.* Charles. Livy. 12°........$1.40
4. — Commentary to Euripides. 18°..........$1.05
5. **Arnold**, A. Through Persia by caravan. 12°..$1.75
6. **Arnold**, Matthew. Poems. 4°. pap.........10c.
7. **Atkinson**, E. Labor and capital. 32°. pap...20c.
8. **Austen**, Jane. Sense and sensibility. 4°. pap. 15c.
9. **Autenrieth's** Homeric dictionary. ill. post 8°. $1.30
10. **Bachelor** of the Albany. 4°. pap. ....10c.
11. **Baird**, S. F. Records of science and industry for 1876, 1877, 1878. 3 v. 12°. per v.........$2.00
12. **Baker**, W. M. Virginians in Texas. 8°. pap...75c.
13. **Ballads** of battle and bravery. 32°. pap.....25c.
14. **Bartlett**, S. C. Egypt to Palestine. ill. 8°..$3.50
15. **Bayne**, P. Lessons from my masters. 12°..$1.75
16. **Beale**, Anne. Rose Mervin. 4°. pap. ......15c.
17. **Beard**, G. M. Hay fever. 12°.............$2.00
18. **Benjamin**, S. G. W. Art in America. ill. 8°..$4.00
19. — Contemporary art in Europe. ill. 8°......$3.50
20. — The Atlantic islands. ill. 8° $3.00
21. **Besant**, Walter. Life of Coligny. 32°. pap...25c.
22. **Biart**, L. Involuntary voyage. ill. 12°.....$1.25
23. **Black**, C. A Sussex idyl. 32°. pap.........25c.
24. **Black**, Wm. Green pastures and Piccadilly. 8°. pap., 50c.; 12°.......................$1.25
25. — Macleod of Dare. 4°. pap., 10c.; ill. 8°. pap. 60c.; 12°...............................$1.25
26. — Madcap Violet. 8°. pap., 50c.; 12°.....$1.25
27. — Sketch of Goldsmith. 12°...............75c.
28. — Novels. (Library edition.) 9 v. 12°. per v...$1.25
29. **Blackmore**, R. D. Erema. 8°. pap.........50c.
30. — Cripps, the carrier. ill. 8°. pap...........50c.
31. **Blaikie**, Wm. How to get strong. ill. 12°..$1.00
32. **Blunt**, *Lady* Anne. Bedouin tribes of Euphrates. 8°.....................................$2.50
33. **Bonner**, Sherwood. Like unto like. 8°. pap...75c.
34. **Bourne**, H. R. F. Life of Locke. 2 v. 8°..$5.00
35. **Bowra**, H. A young wife's story. 8°. pap...25c.
36. **Braddon**, M. E. An open verdict. 8°. pap...35c.
37. — Joshua Haggard's daughter. ill. 8°. pap...50c.
38. — The cloven foot. 4°. pap.................15c.
39. — Vixen. 4°. pap. ....15c.
40. — Weavers and weft. 8°. pap...............25c.
41. **Brambach's** Latin orthography. sq. 16°....$1.17
42. **Brontë**, Charlotte. Jane Eyre. 4°. pap......15c.
43. **Brook**, L. A beautiful woman. 4°. pap......10c.
44. **Bryce**, James. Constantinople. 32°. pap....15c.
45. **Bulwer's** Last days of Pompeii. 4°. pap.....15c.
46. **Burnaby**, F. Ride to Khiva. 12°..........$2.00
47. **Burney**, *Miss.* Evelina. 4°. pap............15c.
48. **Butt**, Geraldine. Dieudonnée. 32°. pap.....20c.
49. — The time of roses. 32°. pap...............20c.
50. **Buxton**, B. H. Nell. 4°. pap...............15c.
51. **Calder**, A. Miriam's heritage. 8°. pap......75c.
52. **Cameron's** Across Africa. 8°..............$5.00
53. **Cameron**, *Mrs.* H. L. Juliet's guardian. 8°. pap. 40c.
54. — Deceivers ever. 8°. pap. ....30c.
55. **Capes'** University life in ancient Athens. 32°. pap....................................25c.
56. **Carleton**, Will. Young folks' centennial rhymes. ill. post 8°............................$1.50
57. **Carnochan's** Operative surgery. 4°. pap. pts. 1 and 2 together, $1; pt. 3, 75c.; pts. 4 and 5 together, $1; pt. 6............................75c.
58. **Cesnola**, L. P. di. Cyprus. ill. 8° $7.50
59. **China** Hunters' Club. ill. post 8° $1.75
60. **Church**, *Dean.* Sketch of Spenser. 12°.....75c.
61. **Church**, A. J. Stories from Homer. ill. 16°. $1.25
62. — Stories from Virgil. 32°. pap............25c.
63. **Cicero.** Text.
64. Epistles; ed. by Klotz. 18°. pap., 42c.; cl., 65c.
65. Tusculan disputations; ed. by Dr. Anthon. 12°. shp....................................$1.30
66. Tusculan disputations; ed. by Klotz. 18°. pap., 42c.; cl.................................65c.
67. De natura deorum, De divinatione, De fato. 18°. pap., 42c.; cl..........................65c.
68. **Clayton**, C. Azalea. 8°. pap. ....30c.
69. **Coffin**, C. C. Boys of '76. ill. 8°.........$3.00
70. — The story of liberty. 8°................$3.00
71. **Coleridge's** Ancient mariner. ill. by Doré. f°. $10.00
72. **Collins**, W. Man and wife. 4°. pap. .....15c.
73. — My lady's money. 32°. pap.............25c.
74. — Percy and the prophet. 32°. pap. ....20c.
75. — The two destinies. ill. 8°. pap., 35c. 12°. $1.25
76. **Colonel** Dunwoddie, millionaire. 8°. pap. ..75c.
77. **Conant**, *Mrs.* H. S. Primers of German and Spanish literature. 32°. pap., per v...........25c.
78. **Constable**, A. G. Afghanistan. 32°. pap. .15c.
79. **Cooke**, J. E. Professor Pressensee. 32°. pap..25c.
80. — Mr. Grantley's idea. 32°. pap. ....25c.
81. — Stories of the Old Dominion. 12°.......$1.50
82. **Cooking** receipts from "Harper's Bazar." 32°. pap.....................................25c.
83. **Cooper**, V. K. Tales from Euripides. 32°. pap. .20c.
84. **Cowper's** The task. 32°. pap. ....20c.
85. **Cox's** school history of Greece. 16°........70c.
86. **Crabb's** Synonymes. New ed. 12°.......$2.50
87. **Craik**, G. M. Dorcas. 4°. pap. ....15c.
88. — Anne Warwick. 8°. pap. ....25c.
89. **Creighton**, M. Half-hour history of England. 32°. pap.....................................25c.
90. **Crommelin**, May. Orange lily. 4°. pap...10c.
91. **Cupples**, George. Green hand. 4°. pap. ..15c.
92. — The sunken rock. 32°. pap. ....15c.
93. **D'Israeli**, Benj. Young duke. 4°. pap. ....15c.
94. — Life of. 4°. pap. ....10c.
95. **Daudet**, Ernest. Henriette; trans. 4°. pap. ..10c.
96. **Dawson**, J. W. Origin of the world. 12°..$2.00
97. **Defoe's** Journal of plague in London. 4°. pap..10c.
98. **De Leon**, E. The Khedive's Egypt. ill. 12°..$1.50
99. **De Mille**, James. Elements of rhetoric. 12°.$1.40
100. **Denison**, *Mrs.* Old Slip warehouse. 8°. pap...60c.
101. **Desart**, *Earl of.* Kelverdale. 4°. pap.....15c.
102. **Deshler**, C. D. Afternoons with the poets. post 8°.....................................$1.75
103. **Despard**, Matilda. Kilrogan Cottage. 8°. pap...60c.
104. **Dickens**, Chas. Pickwick papers. 4°. pap. ..20c.
105. **Dickinson**, Anna E. Ragged register. 12°..$1.00
106. **Douglas**, G. Mar's white witch. 8°. pap. ..15c.
107. **Drake**, S. A. Captain Nelson. 8°. pap....75c.
108. **Draper**, J. W. Scientific memoirs. 8°....$3.00
109. **Duffs'** Book-keeping. 20th ed. 8°........$2.63
110. **Eaton**, D. B. Civil service in Great Britain. 8°. $2.50
111. **Edwards**, M. B. Holidays in eastern France. 32°. pap. ....25c.
112. **Egleston's** Villages and village life. post 8°..$1.75
113. **Eliot**, George. Daniel Deronda. 8°. pap., 50c. 2 v. 12°. per v...........................$1.25
114. — Theophrastus Such. 4°. pap., 10c. 12°..$1.25
115. — Amos Barton. 32°. pap. ....20c.
116. — Mr. Gilfil's love story. 32°. pap.........20c.
117. — Janet's repentance. 32°. pap. ....20c.
118. — Brother Jacob; The lifted veil. 32°. pap....20c.
119. **English**, T. D. American ballads. 32°. pap...25c.
120. **Epochs** of English history. 8 v. 32°. pap. per v.......................................25c.

HARPER & BROTHERS,

Continued.

121. **Farjeon**, B. L. Bells of Penraven. 4°. pap...10c.
122. — Duchess of Rosemary Lane. 8°. pap.....35c.
123. — Shadows on the snow. ill. 8°. pap........30c.
124. **Fenn**, G. M. Parson O'Dumford. 4°. pap...15c.
125. **Petherstonhaugh**, *Hon. Mrs.* Kingsdene. 4°. pap.......................................10c.
126. **First** century of the Republic. ill. 8°......$5.00
127. **Fitzpatrick**, W. J. Life of Lever. 4°. pap...15c.
128. **Freeman**, E. Turks in Europe. 32°. pap...15c.
129. — Origin of English nation. 32°. pap.......25c.
130. **Geary**, G. Asiatic Turkey. 4°. pap.......15c.
131. **Goldsmith's** Plays. 32°. pap.............25c.
132. — Poems. 32°. pap.......................20c.
133. — Vicar of Wakefield. 32°. pap...........25c.
134. **Green**, J. R. History of the English people. vols. I., II. and III. 8°. per v.............$2.50
135. — Readings from English history. 12°.....$1.50
136. **Greenwood**, J. Reuben Davidger. 4°. pap...15c.
137. **Griffis**, W. E. Mikado's empire. ill. 8°...$4.00
138. **Guernsey**, A. H. Spanish armada. 32°. pap. 20c.
139. **Hackländer**, F. W. Behind blue glasses; tr. 32°. pap.................................20c.
140. **Hale**, E. E. Back to back. 32°. pap.......25c.
141. **Hamley**, Chas. Wassail. 32°. pap........20c.
142. **Hamley**, E. B. Lady Lee's widowhood. 4°. pap. 15c.
143. **Hamley**, W. G. House of Lys. 4°. pap...15c.
144. **Harper's** Latin dictionary. roy. 8°. shp...$9.50
145. **Harwood**, J. B. Paul Knox Pitman. 4°. pap. 10c.
146. **Haweis**, *Mrs.* Art of beauty. sq. 16°....$1.75
147. **Hay**, Mary Cecil. Arundel motto. 8°. pap...25c.
148. — Back to the old home. 32°. pap.........20c.
149. — Dark inheritance. 32°. pap.............15c.
150. — Nora's love test. 8°. pap................25c.
151. — Reaping the whirlwind. 32°. pap.........20c.
152. — Shadow on the threshold. 32°. pap......20c.
153. — Sorrow of a secret. 32°. pap............15c.
154. **Hays**, *Mrs.* Princess Idleways. sq. 16°....75c.
155. **Henderson**, Mary F. Practical cooking. ill. 12°. $1.50
156. **Hepworth**, G. H. Starboard and port. ill. 12°. $1.75
157. **Hill**, A. S. Principles of rhetoric. 12°. hf. leath. $1.17
158. **Hoey**, *Mrs.* All or nothing. 4°. pap.......15c.
159. — Kate Cronin's dowry. 32°. pap..........15c.
160. **Hoffman**, W. Camp, court and siege. 12°..$1.25
161. **Holly**, H. H. Modern dwellings. ill. sq. 8°..$4.00
162. **Hopkins**, E. Rose Turquand. 8°. pap.....35c.
163. **Horsley's** Text-book of harmony. 12° .....88c.
164. **Hugessen**, E. H. K. Oliver Cromwell. 32°. pap. 20c.
165. **Hugo**, V. History of a crime. ill. 4°. pap., 10c.; 2 v. 8°. pap..................................50c.
166. **Hume's** England. (New lib. ed.) 6 v. 8° $12.00
167. **Hunt**, *Mrs.* Basildon. 4°. pap..............10c.
168. **Hurst** and Whiting's Seneca. 12°.........$1.52
169. **Hutton**, R. H. Sketch of Scott. 12°.......75c.
170. **Huxley**, *Professor*. Sketch of Hume. 12°..75c.
171. **Irene** Macgillicuddy. 32°. pap. ....15c.
172. **James**, G. P. R. Bride of Landeck. 32°. pap., 20c.
173. — The gypsy. 4°. pap........................15c.
174. **James**, Henry, *jr.* Daisy Miller. 32°. pap...20c.
175. — An international episode. 32°. pap.......20c.
176. **Jenkin**, F. Healthy houses. 32°. pap.....25c.
177. **Jenkins**, E. Haverholme. 4°. pap........10c.
178. **Jewel** of a girl. 8°. pap....................35c.
179. **Johnson**, *Dr.* Words and ways. 12°....$1.50
180. **Johnson**, V. W. Miss Nancy's pilgrimage. 8°. pap.....................................40c.
181. **Justine's** lovers. 8°. pap..................60c.
182. **Keary**, *Miss.* A doubting heart. 4°. pap...15c.
183. **Keep**, R. P. Stories from Herodotus. 16°..$1.50
184. **Kennedy**, J. School and family. 16°....$1.00
185. **King**, K. Bubble reputation. 4°. pap.....15c.
186. **Kinglake's** Eothen. 4°. pap...............10c.
187. **Knox**, T. W. John 32°. pap...............20c.
188. — The boy travellers. ill. 8°..............$3.00
189. **Lady** Carmichael's will, etc. 32°. pap.....15c.
190. **Lamb**, Chas. Adventures of Ulysses. 32°. pap. 25c.
191. — *and* Mary. Tales from Shakespeare. 2 v. 32°. pap. per v..................................25c.
192. **Lane**, L. M. My sister's keeper. 32°. pap...25c.
193. **Lawrence**, E. Historical studies. 8°......$3.00
194. — Primers of English literature. 3 v. 32°. pap. per v......................................25c.
195. — Primer of Latin literature. 32°. pap....25c.
196. — Primer of Greek literature. 32°. pap....25c.
197. — Primer of mediæval literature. 32°. pap...25c.
198. — Jews and their persecutors. 32°. pap....20c.
199. **Lawrence**, G. A. Guy Livingstone. 4°. pap., 10c.
200. **Leith-Adams**, *Mrs.* Winstowe. 8°. pap...25c.
201. — Georgie's wooer. 32°. pap...............20c.
202. **Liddell** *and* Scott's Greek lexicon. New ed. 4° shp.......................................$11.00
203. — *Same*; abridged. 4°. hf. leath.........$2.35
204. **Linton**, E. L. Our professor. 32°. pap....15c.
205. — From dreams to waking. 8°. pap.......20c.
206. **Lockhart**, L. W. M. Mine is thine. 8°. pap., 40c.
207. **Long's** Central Africa. ill. 8°.............$2.50
208. **Lucas'** Zulus and British frontier. 4°. pap....10c.
209. **McCarthy**, Justin. History of our own times. no. 1. 4°. pap. ....20c.
210. — Donna Quixote. 4°. pap....................15c.
211. **Macaulay's** England. (New ed.) 5 v. 8°..$10.00
212. — Life and letters. (Popular ed.) 12°....$1.75
213. — Essays. 14 v. 32°. pap. per v........25c.
214. — Selections from. 8°.........................$2.50
215. **Macdonnell**, A. Quaker cousins. 4°. pap...15c.
216. **Macquoid**, *Mrs.* The awakening. 32°. pap...15c.
217. — Elinor Dryden. 4°. pap.....................20c.
218. — The mill of St. Herbot. 32°. pap.......20c.
219. **Madge** Dunraven. 4°. pap....................10c.
220. **Mag**. 8°. pap....................................50c.
221. **Manning**, E. Six months on a slaver. 32°. pap. 20c.
222. **Martin**, *Mrs.* "Bonnie Lesley." 4°. pap...15c.
223. — "For a dream's sake." 4°. pap.........15c.
224. **Mathews**, C. J. Life of. 4°. pap..........15c.
225. **Meade**, L. T. David's little lad. 32°. pap...25c.
226. **Mediæval** and modern saints and miracles. 12°. $1.50
227. **Meredith**, Geo. The egoist. 4°. pap.....15c.
228. — House on the beach. 32°. pap...........20c.
229. **Merivale's** School history of Rome. 16°....90c.
230. **Minto**, W. Sketch of Defoe. 12°..........75c.
231. **Mistletoe** bough for 1878. 4°. pap........15c.
232. **Mistletoe** bough for 1879. 4°. pap..........10c.
233. **Mitford**, *Miss.* Our village. 32°. pap.....25c.
234. **Modern** minister. ill. v. 1. 8°. pap., 35c. v. 2. 8°. pap..40c.
235. **Moltke's** Letters from Russia. 32°. pap....25c.
236. **Moncel**, *Count* du. Telephone, microphone and phonograph. ill. 12°.........................$1.25
237. **Morison**, J. C. Sketch of Gibbon. 12°.....75c.
238. **Morley**, John. Burke. 12°....................75c.
239. **Morse**, Clara F. Blush roses. 8°. pap. ...50c.
240. **Motley's** Dutch republic. New ed. 3 v. 8°..$6.00
241. — United Netherlands. New ed. 4 v. 8°..$8.00
242. — John of Barneveld. New ed. 2 v. 8°...$4.00
243. — Peter the Great. 32°. pap...................25c.

HARPER & BROTHERS,

Continued.

244. **Moy** O'Brien. 4°. pap. ....10c.
245. **Mulock,** *Miss.* A legacy. 12° $1.25
246. — John Halifax, gentleman. 4°. pap. 15c
247. — The laurel bush. ill. 8°. pap., 25c. 12°..$1.25
248. — Young Mrs. Jardine. 4°. pap., 10c. 12°..$1.25
249. **My** heart's in the Highlands. 4°. pap. ....10c.
250. **Newcomb,** Simon. Popular astronomy. 8°..$4.00
251. — A B C of finance. 32°. pap. ....25c.
252. **Newman,** *Mrs.* Last of the Haddons. 8°. pap...25c.
253. **Nichols,** G. W. Art education. ill. 8°...$4.00
254. **Norris,** W. E. Heaps of money. 8°. pap. ..25c.
255. **Notley,** F. E. M. Love's crosses. 4°. pap...15c.
256. — Time shall try. 4°. pap. ....15c.
257. **O'Brien,** C. G. Light and shade. 4°. pap...10c.
258. **O'Flanagan,** J. R. Irish bar. 4°. pap. ....15c.
259. — Munster Circuit. 4°. pap. ....15c.
260. **Oliphant,** *Mrs.* Caritá. ill. 8°. pap.......50c.
261. — Mrs. Arthur. 8°. pap. ....40c.
262. — Phœbe, junior. 8°. pap. ....35c.
263. — The fugitives. 4°. pap. ....10c.
264. — The primrose path. 8°. pap. ....50c.
265. — Within the precincts. 4°. pap. ....15c.
266. — Young Musgrave. 8°. pap. ....40c.
267. **Orred,** Meta. Honor's worth. 4°. pap. ....15c.
268. — A long time ago. 8°. pap. ....25c.
269. **Our** children's songs. ill. 8°.............$1.00
270. **Parton,** Jas. History of caricature. ill. 8°..$5.00
271. **Pattison,** Mark. Sketch of Milton. 12°....75c.
272. **Patrick,** Mary. Marjorie Bruce's lovers. 8°. pap. ....25c.
273. — Christine Brownlee's ordeal. 4°. pap. ...15c.
274. **Payn,** Jas. By proxy. 8°. pap. ....35c.
275. — High spirits. 4°. pap. ....15c.
276. — Less black than we're painted. 8°. pap...35c.
277. — Under one roof. 4°. pap. ....15c.
278. — What he cost her. 8°. pap. ....40c.
279. **People** of Turkey. 4°. pap. ....15c.
280. **Perry's** English church history. cr. 8°.....$2.50
281. **Perry,** Alice. Esther Pennefather. 8°. pap. ..75c.
282. **Phillips,** B. Burning their ships. 32°. pap. ..20c.
283. **Pike,** J. S. The new puritan. 12°........$1.00
284. **Platonis** Dialogi VI. 16°. pap., 42c.; cl. ..65c.
285. **Porter,** *Mrs.* Cousin Polly's gold mine. 8°. pap., 40c.
286. **Prime,** W. C. Pottery and porcelain. ill. 8°..$7.00
287. **Quackenbos'** Ancient literature. ill. 12°...$1.50
288. **Rare** pale Margaret. 4°. pap. ....10c.
289. **Reade,** Chas. Woman hater. ill. 8°. pap., 60c. 12° $1.00
290. — The coming man. 32°. pap. ....20c.
291. — The jilt. ill. 32°. pap. ....20c.
292. — Novels. (Harper's household edition.) 12 v. 12°. per v. $1.00
293. **Rémusat,** Memoirs of Madame de. Part I. 4°. pap. ....10c.
294. **Rice** *and* Besant's golden butterfly. 8°. pap...40c.
295. — When the ship comes home. 32°. pap. ..25c.
296. — 'Twas in Trafalgar's Bay. 32°. pap. ....20c.
297. — Sweet Nelly. 4°. pap. ....10c.
298. — Shepherds all and maidens fair. 32°. pap., 25c.
299. — By Celia's arbor. ill. 8°. pap. ....50c.
300. **Robinson,** F. W. Coward conscience. 4°. pap., 15c.
301. — Poor Zeph. 32°. pap. ....20c.
302. — As long as she lived. 8°. pap. ....50c.
303. — The bar maid at Battleton. 32°. pap......15c.
304. — The romance of a back street. 32°. pap...15c.
305. **Rolfe's** Shakespeare; with notes and ill.: — Merchant of Venice; Tempest; Hamlet; Henry VIII.; Julius Cæsar; Twelfth night; Richard II.; Romeo and Juliet; Macbeth; Midsummer night's dream; Winter's tale; Othello; Henry V.; As you like it; Much ado about nothing. 16°. per v. ....70c.
306. **Roquette's** Curate of Orsièrres; trans. 32°. pap. 20c.
307. **Russell,** W. C. Auld lang syne. 4°. pap...10c.
308. — Wreck of the "Grosvenor." 8°. pap.....30c.
309. **Russians** of to-day. 4°. pap. ....10c.
310. **Sadlier,** A. T. Seven years and mair. 32°. pap. 20c.
311. **Saunders,** J. The Sherlocks. 4°. pap.....15c.
312. — Israel Mort, overman. 8°. pap..........50c.
313. **Schaff,** P. Creeds of Christendom. 3 v. 8°. $15.00
314. **Scott,** *Sir* W. Marmion. 32°. pap.......25c.
315. — The lady of the lake. 32°. pap.........25c.
316. — The lay of the last minstrel. 32°. pap.....20c.
317. — The talisman. 4°. pap. ....15c.
318. — The Waverley novels:
319. Thistle edition. 48 v. per v.........$1.00
320. Holyrood edition. 48 v. per v.........75c.
321. Popular edition. 24 v. per v.........$1.25
322. **Seeman's** Mythology. ill. 16°.............70c.
323. **Shairp's** Sketch of Burns. 12°.............75c.
324. **Sheridan's** The rivals; The school for scandal. 32°. pap. ....25c.
325. **Short,** J. T. North Americans of antiquity. 8°. $3.00
326. **Sir** John. 4°. pap. ....15c.
327. **Sir** Roger de Coverley. 32°. pap...........25c.
328. **Smiles,** S. Scotch geologist. ill. 12°....$1.50
329. — Scotch naturalist. ill. 12°..............$1.50
330. **Smith,** P. Student's ecclesiastical history. ill. 12°.....................................$1.75
331. **Smith,** W. Student's smaller classical dictionary. ill. 12°.................................$1.46
332. — German principia. pt. 2. 12°............94c.
333. **Sparkes,** J. C. L. Pottery painting. 32°. pap. 20c.
334. **Spender,** Emily. True marriage. 4°. pap...15c.
335. **Spofford,** *Mrs.* Art decoration. ill. 8°..$4.00
336. **Sport** and work on Nepaul frontier. 4°. pap...10c.
337. **Spry's** Voyage of Challenger. ill. cr. 8°...$2.00
338. **Squire,** E. G. Peru. ill. 8°..............$5.00
339. **Stanley,** H. M. Through the dark continent. 2 v. ill. 8°. (*Sold by subscription*).....$10.00
340. **Stephen,** Leslie. Sketch of Johnson. 12°..75c.
341. **Sterndale,** R. A. Afghan's knife. 4°. pap...15c.
342. **Stickney,** A. True republic. 12°........$1.00
343. **Stirling,** M. C. Grahams of Invermoy. 4°. pap. 15c.
344. **Stone,** O. C. New Guinea. 4°. pap.......10c.
345. **Student's** French grammar. 12°..........$1.40
346. **Sun**-maid (The). 8°. pap..................35c.
347. **Symond,** J. A. Sketch of Shelley. 12°....75c.
348. — Studies of the Greek poets. 2 v. sq. 16°..$3.50
349. **Tabor,** Eliza. Last of her line. 4°. pap....15c.
350. — Little Miss Primrose. 4°. pap...........15c.
351. **Taylor,** W. M. Daniel the beloved. 12°..$1.50
352. — Moses the law-giver. 12°...............$1.50
353. — Peter the apostle. 12°..................$1.50
354. **Tennyson's** Songs; set to music. ill. 4°..$5.00
355. — Lover's tale. 32°. pap..................10c.
356. **Thackeray,** *Miss.* Da Capo. 32°. pap.....20c.
357. **Thackeray,** W. M. Henry Esmond. 4°. pap. 15c.
358. — The four Georges. 32°. pap.............25c.
359. — The English humorists. 2 v. 32°. pap. per v. ....25c.
360. — Works. (Harper's household ed.) 11 v. ill. 12°. per v. $1.25
361. **That** artful vicar. 4°. pap. ....15c.
362. **Thompson,** R. W. Papacy and civil powers. cr. 8° $3.00
363. **Thompson,** *Sir* Henry. Food and feeding. 32°. pap. ....20c.

HARPER & BROTHERS,

Continued.

364. **Thomson,** *Sir* W. The Atlantic. 2 v. ill. 8°. $12.00
365. **Towle's** Modern France. 32°. pap........25c.
366. **Treat,** Mary. Chapters on ants. 32°. pap...20c.
367. **Trollope,** A. John Caldigate. 4°. pap.....15c.
368. — An eye for an eye. 4°. pap.............10c.
369. — Cousin Henry. 4°. pap.................10c.
370. — Framley Parsonage. 4°. pap...........15c.
371. — Is he Popinjoy? 4°. pap................15c.
372. — Sketch of Thackeray. 12° ....75c.
373. — The American senator. 8°. pap..........50c.
374. — The Bertrams. 4°. pap. ....15c.
375. — The lady of Launay. 32°. pap...........20c.
376. — Thompson Hall. ill. 32°. pap............20c.
377. **Trollope,** F. E. Among aliens. ill. 4°. pap...15c.
378. **Trowbridge,** J. T. Book of gold. ill. 8°...$2.50
379. **Two** Miss Flemings. 4°. pap. ....15c.
380. **Two** tales of married life. 8°. pap. ....30c.
381. **Virginia**: a Roman sketch. 32°. pap. .....25c.
382. **Walker,** A. Hints to women on care of property. 32°. pap. ....20c.
383. **Wallace,** A. R. Geographical distribution of animals. 2 v. ill. 8° $10.00
384. **Waring,** Geo. E., *jr.* Tyrol. 8° $3.00
385. **Warren,** H. W. Recreations in astronomy. 12°. $1.75
386. **Warring's** Squire Paul; tr. 32°. pap. ....25c.
387. **Weston,** A. H. Rifle club and range. ill. 12°. $1.00
388. **What** Mr. Darwin saw. ill. 8°............$3.00
389. **Whipple,** E. P. Recollections of Choate. 32°. pap..15c.
390. **Wilson,** J. G. Poets and poetry of Scotland. 2 v. 8° $10.00
391. **Winchell,** A. Reconciliation of science and religion. 12° $2.00
392. **Within** sound of the sea. 4°. pap.........10c.
393. **Wordsworth's** Poems. 4°. pap. ....15c.
394. **Yonge,** C. D. Life of Marie Antoinette. cr. 8°. $2.50
395. **Yonge,** C. M. Christians and Moors of Spain. 4°. pap. ....10c.
396. **Yorke,** S. Cleveden. 4°. pap...............10c.
397. **Young,** *Miss* J. J. Ceramic art. 8° $5.00
398. **Youth's** health book. 32°. pap. ....25c.

S. T. GORDON & SON,

13 East Fourteenth Street, New York.

OPERAS, ORATORIOS AND CANTATAS.

1. **Bridal** (The); by Ch. Edward Horsley. (C.) retail, $1; trade..........................75c.
2. **H. M. S. Pinafore** complete vocal score by A. S. Sullivan. (C.) retail, 50c.; trade ....33c.
3. — *Same.* (C.) bds., retail, 75c.; trade......50c.
4. — *Same:* vocal selection. retail, 25c.; trade..10c.

SABBATH-SCHOOL BOOKS.

5. **New** song: complete. 256 p. (C.) pap., retail, 45c.; trade ....40c.
6. — — *Same.* (C.) bds., retail, 50c.; trade, 45c.; cl., retail, 55c.; trade ....50c.
7. — *Same:* miniature. 128 p. (C.) pap., retail, 25c.; trade ....20c.
8. — — *Same.* (D.) bds., retail, 30c.; trade, 25c.; cl., retail, 35c.; trade ....30c.

GLEE AND CHORUS BOOKS.

9. **Sparkling** stream: temperance glee book. (C.) retail, 50c.; trade ....40c.

COLLECTIONS OF CHURCH MUSIC.

10. **Millard's** Selections. vol. 2. (C.) bds., retail, $2; trade.....................................$1.50
11. — *Same.* (C.) cl., retail, $2.50; trade $2.00
12. **Oriental**; by Burnap and Wetmore. (C.) retail, $1.25; trade..............................94c.

MASSES, CATHOLIC MUSIC, ETC.

13. **Millard's** Mass in B flat (new). (C.) pap., retail, $1; trade..................................75c.
14. — *Same.* (C.) cl., retail, $1.25; trade $1.00

PIANOFORTE METHODS.

15. **Schmidt,** J. Method: 1st course, foreign fingering. (A.) retail, $2; trade.............$1.00

COLLECTION OF PIANO AND VOCAL MUSIC.

16. **Gems** of American song. (B.) bds., retail, $2; trade $1.25
17. — *Same.* (B.) cl., retail, $2.50; trade $1.75
18. — *Same.* (B.) gilt, retail, $3; trade $2.25

PIANO STUDIES.

19. **Couppez** (Le) l'alphabet: 25 études: op. 17. (A.) retail, $1.50; trade ....75c.
20. **Wieck's** Piano studies. (B.) pap., retail, 75c.; trade ....38c.
21. — *Same.* (B.) bds., retail, $1; trade.......50c.

ORGAN AND MELODEON INSTRUCTORS.

22. **Getze's** New and improved school for parlor organ. retail, $2.50; trade...................80c.

VOCAL EXERCISES AND METHODS.

23. **Bassini,** Carlo. Education of the voice. (B.) retail, $1.50; trade......................$1.00
24. **Godoy,** J. Vocal exercises: selected. (A.) retail, $1.50; trade.........................75c.
25. **Savinelli,** Angelo. Twelve vocalizes for the highest style of perfection. (A.) 2 bks. ea., retail, $1.50; trade ....75c.

SCHOOL MUSIC BOOKS.

26. **Athenaeum**; for female voices; by Burnap. (C.) bds., retail, $1; trade ....67c.
27. **Little** Red Riding Hood: operetta; by H. Millard. (C.) retail, 25c.; trade..................20c.
28. **Queen** of the bird: a musical charade; by H. Millard. (C.) retail, 25c.; trade..........20c.

J. B. LIPPINCOTT & CO.,

715 and 717 Market St., Philadelphia.

1. **Adams,** John Quincy. Memoirs. 12 v. 8°. ea., cl. $5.00
2. **Agnew,** D. Hayes, *M.D.* The principles and practice of surgery. v. 1. cl., $7.50; shp. $8.50
3. **Airy** fairy Lilian; by author of "Molly Bawn." cl., $1.25; pap. . . . . 60c.
4. **All** things pertaining to life; by C. T. Anderson. 16° $1.00
5. **All** wrong. 12°. cl. $1.00
6. **Allen** Bay; by S. O. Stedman. 16°. cl. . . . $1.25
7. **Allibone,** S. Austin. Great authors of all ages. 8°. cl., $5; shp., $6; cl. gilt $5.50
8. **American** college fraternities; by Wm. R. Baird. 12°. cl. $1.50
9. **Angelo** and Ariel; by F. Sewall. 16°. cl. . . $1.00
10. **Annotated** poems of English authors; ed. by Rev. E. T. Stevens and Rev. D. Morris: — Gray's Elegy in a country churchyard, 20c.; Goldsmith's Deserted village, 20c.; Goldsmith's Traveller, 25c.; Cowper's Task, 25c.; Scott's Lady of the lake, 25c.; — in 1 v. cl. $1.00
11. **Ariadne;** by Ouida. 12°. cl. $1.50
12. **At** the councillor's; by E. Marlitt. 12°. cl. . . $1.50
13. **Audubon,** the naturalist; by Mrs. H. St. John. 12°. cl. $1.25
14. **Barker,** *Lady.* Letters from South Africa. 8°. cl. $1.00
15. **Batterson,** *Rev.* H. G. The American episcopate. 8°. cl., red edges $2.00
16. **Beyond** the Sierras; by A. H. Tevis. 12° . . $1.50
17. **Bodines;** or, camping on the Lycoming; by T. S. Up de Graff. 12°. cl. $1.50
18. **Bolles,** A. S. Labor and capital. 12°. pap., 75c.; cl. $1.50
19. **Brewer,** E. Cobham. The reader's handbook. 12°. hf. roan $3.50
20. **Brookes,** C. B. A guide to the popular terms in science and art. 12°. cl. $1.50
21. **Brother** and sister; by H. Glyndon. 16°. cl., $1.25
22. **Brown,** Henry A. Memoir of; by J. M. Hoppin. 12°. cl. $2.50
23. **Budget** (The); by Uncle Herbert. 4°. hf. bd., $1.25; cl. $1.75
24. **Byron,** *Lord.* Complete works; with life, ed. by Thos. Moore. (Illustrated ed.) 4 v. 12°. cl., $10; hf. cf., $16; shp. $12.00
25. — *Same.* Cheap ed. cl., $5; shp. $6.00
25. — Don Juan. 12°. cl. $1.25
26. **Castle** Hohenwald: tr. by Mrs. A. L. Wister. 12°. cl. $1.50
27. **Century** (The): its fruits and its festival; by E. C. Bruce. cl. $3.00
28. **Change;** by W. Leighton. 12°. cl. $1.50
29. **Christ,** the teacher of men; by A. W. Pitzer. 12°. cl. $1.25
30. **Christian** (The); by Rev. W. S. Plumer. 12° . . $1.00
31. **Clare** and Bebé. 12°. cl., $1.25; pap. . . . . . 60c.
32. **Clifton** picture (The); by author of "The odd trump." 8°. cl., $1.25; pap. . . . . 75c.
33. **Contanseau's** French and English dictionary for schools. cr. 8°. hf. roan $2.50
34. — Pocket French and English dictionary. 18°. $1.50; — 2 v. in case. cl. flex. $1.75
35. **Cook,** J. C. Holiday tour in Europe. 16°. cl., $1; pap. . . . . 75c.
36. **Courtship** in 1720 and in 1860; by Hawley Smart. 16° $1.00
37. **Cross** (The); by C. F. Richardson. 16°. cl. . . 60c.
38. **Cross** (The) above the crescent; by H. Southgate. 12°. cl. $1.50
39. **Derry,** —. Georgia: a guide to its cities, towns, etc. 12°. cl., $1; pap. . . . . 75c.
40. **Dick** Rodney; by James Grant. 12°. cl. . . $1.25
41. **Doctor** Hildreth; by A. L. White. 12°. cl. . . $1.50
42. **Duhring,** Julia. Gentlefolks and others. 12°. cl. $2.00
43. **Duhring,** L. A. Atlas of skin diseases. [To form 10 pts.] pts. 1–5. ea. $2.50
44. — Diseases of the skin. 8°. cl. $6.00
45. **Earthly** suffering and heavenly glory; by Rev. H. A. Boardman. 12°. cl. $2.00
46. **Elsa;** by A. C. Hogbin. 12°. cl. $1.50
47. **Family** feud (A); tr. by Mrs. A. L. Wister. 12°. cl. $1.25
48. **Five** weeks in a balloon; by Jules Verne. 12°. cl. $1.25
49. **Florida** (Handbook of); by Sidney Lanier. 12°. pap., $1; cl., ill. $1.75
50. **For** Percival: a novel. 8°. cl., $1.25; pap. . . 75c.
51. **Foreign** classics for English readers. 10 v. 16°. ea. $1.00
52. **Forrester,** *Mrs.* Diana Carew; or, for a woman's sake. 12°. cl. $1.50
53. **Francesca** of Rimini: a poem, by A. S. H. 12°. cl. 75c.
54. **Frank** Wildman's adventures; by Frederick Gerstaecker. 12°. cl. $1.25
55. **French** and Belgians; by P. C. Gibbons. 12°. cl. $2.00
56. **Friendship;** by Ouida. 12°. cl. $1.50
57. **Furness,** H. H. Variorum ed. of Shakespeare: — Hamlet, 2 v.; King Lear, 1 v. roy. 8°. ea., cl., $4.00
58. **Gallatin,** Albert. Writings of; by H. Adams. 3 v. 8°. cl. $15.00
59. — Life of; by H. Adams. 8°. cl. $5.00
60. **Genevieve** of Brabant; by Mrs. C. Willing. 4°. cl. gilt, $2.50; tur. $6.50
61. **Ghost** (The) of Redbrook. 8°. cl., $1.25; pap., 75c.
62. **Girl** of the period; by Garry Gaines. 16°. cl., $1; pap. . . . . 50c.
63. **Grandpapa's** stories; or, dame nature; by P. B. Saintine. 12°. cl. $1.25
64. **Grant,** General (With), in the East; by Dr. J. M. Keating. 12°. cl. $1.50
65. **Grey** Abbey. 16° $1.00
66. **Guatemozin:** a drama; by M. Macdonald. 16°. cl. $1.00
67. **Haldeman,** S. S. Outlines of etymology. 12°. cl. 90c.
68. **Handbook** of nursing. cl. flex., $1; cl. . . . $1.25
69. **Harvey** and his discovery; by Dr. J. M. Da Costa. 12°. cl. . . . . 75c.
70. **Her** lovers; by S. H. Clagett. 12°. cl. $1.50
71. **High-water-mark;** by F. Jerome. 12°. cl., $1.50
72. **Highways** and byways of American travel; by Ed. Strahan. 8°. cl. $2.00
73. **Hilda:** a poem. 12°. cl. $1.25
74. **Hobbs,** J. H. Architectural designs for country and suburban residences. 8°. cl. $3.00
75. **Hovelacque,** A. Science of language. 12°. cl. $1.75
76. **Hymns** and carols for church and Sunday school; by Alice Nevin. cr. 8°. cl., 80c.; bds. . . . . 50c.
77. **Image** of air, and other poems; by A. S. Logan. 12°. cl. . . . . 75c.
78. **In** the meshes; by C. McKenzie. 12°. cl. . $1.50
79. **Iris:** the romance of an opal ring; by Mrs. Toland. 8°. cl. gilt, $3; antique $7.50
80. **It** is the fashion; by Mrs. Elgard. 16° $1.00
81. **Jean;** by B. Westcott. 12°. cl. $1.25
82. **Kate** Weathers; by Frank Vaughan. 12°. cl., $1.50
83. **King's** rifle; from the Atlantic to the Indian Ocean, etc.; by Maj. Pinto. (*In press.*)
84. **Klein,** E. Atlas of histology. 12 pts. ea., $1.75

J. B. LIPPINCOTT & CO.,

Continued.

85. **Ladye** Chace; by Bishop Coxe. 18°. cl.....75c.
86. **Laidley**, *Col.* T. T. S. Instructions in rifle firing. $1.50
87. **Law** unto herself; by R. H. Davis. 8°. cl., $1; pap., 50c.
88. **Lectures** on popular and scientific subjects; by the Earl of Caithness. 12°. cl..........$1.00
89. **Leeds**, J. W. History of the United States. 12°. cl. $1.75
90. **Leighton**, Wm. At the court of King Edwin. 16°. cl..........$1.25
91. **Letorneau**, C. Biology: v. 2 of Contemporary science library. 12°. cl..........$1.75
92. **Life's** promise to pay; by Clara Conway. 12°. cl. $1.50
93. **Lil**; by Hon. Mrs. Fetherstonhaugh. 16°..$1.00
94. **Longman's** pocket German and English dictionary. 18°. cl..........$1.50
95. — *Same.* 2 v. in case. cl. flex. $1.75
96. **Lord** Stirling's stand, and other poems; by W. H. Babcock. 12°. cl. $1.50
97. **Lost** truths of Christianity. 12°. cl.......$1.25
98. **Love** in idleness; by E. W. Olney. 8°. cl., $1; pap. ....50c.
99. **McKnight**, D. A. The electoral system of the U. S. 8°. cl..........$3.00
100. **Maclean**, J. History of the College of New Jersey. 2 v. 8°. cl..........$7.00
101. **Madelon** Lemoine; by Mrs. Leith Adams. 12°. cl., $1.50; pap. ....75c.
102. **Marable** family (The); by S. Hillyer $1.50
103. **Margaret** Chetwynd; by Susan Morley. 12°. cl. $1.50
104. **Margarethe**; from the German of E. Juncker, by Mrs. A. L. Wister. 12°. cl..........$1.50
105. **Mark** Seaworth: a tale of the Indian ocean; by W. H. G. Kingston. 12°. cl..........$1.25
106. **Marks**, Wm. D. The steam engine. 12°. cl., $1.50
107. **Marlitt**, E. In the Schillingscourt. 12°. cl., $1.50
108. **Marquis** of Lossie; by G. Macdonald. 8°. cl., $1.25; pap. ....75c.
109. **Maud**; by A. Tennyson; ill. by H. A. Herr. 4°. cl., gilt..........$2.50
110. **Mere** adventurer (A); by E. Hay. 8°. cl., $1.25; pap..........75c.
111. **Methodism**, old and new; by J. R. Flanigen. 12°..........$1.50
112. **Midshipman** (The), Marmaduke Merry; by W. H. G. Kingston. 12°. cl..........$1.25
113. **Mignon**; by Mrs. Forrester. 12°. cl. $1.50
114. **Mitchell**, S. W. Fat and blood. 16°. cl. ..$1.25
115. — Nurse and patient. 18°. cl. ....50c.
116. **Molly** Bawn; by the author of "Phyllis." 12°. cl., $1.25; pap..........60c.
117. **Molly** Maguires (The); by F. P. Dewees. 12°. cl. $1.50
118. **Mother** Goose's melodies. 4°, 96 p. bds., 50c. 4°, 48 p. linen..........60c.
119. **Moths**; by Ouida. 12°. cl. $1.25
120. **My** intimate friend; by F. Duncan. 12°. cl., $1.50
121. **My** mother's manuscript; by M. L. Helper. 12°. cl. $1.25
122. **Mystery** of life; by T. Parsons. 12°. cl...$1.25
123. **Nellie's** memoires; by R. N. Carey. 12°. cl., $1.25; pap..........75c.
124. **New** Ireland; by A. M. Sullivan. Cheap ed. 12°. cl. $1.00
125. **Nile** days; or, Egyptian bonds; by E. K. Bates. 12°. cl., $1; pap..........50c.
126. **Olivia** Raleigh; by W. W. F. Synge. 16°...$1.00
127. **O'Neil**, T. Warren. The refutation of Darwinism. 8°. cl..........$2.50
128. **Out** of the shadows; by J. B. Kenyon. 12°. $1.00
129. **Outlying** Europe and the nearer Orient; by Joseph Moore. (*In press.*)
130. **Parson** (The) on dancing; by Rev. J. B. Gross. 12°. cl..........$1.00
131. **Pastor** (The); by Rev. G. T. Bedell. 12°..$2.00
132. **Pathological** Society. Transactions. v. 4–8. 8°. v. 4, 5, ed. by J. Tyson, ea., $4; v. 6, ed. by J. Tyson, $3; v. 7, 8, ed. by J. H. C. Simes, ea. $3.00
133. **Paul** Blake (Surprising adventures of); by Alf. Elewes. 12°. cl..........$1.25
134. **Paul** Faber; by G. Macdonald. 8°. cl., $1.25; pap..........75c.
135. **Pegasus** re-saddled; by H. C. Pennell. 4°. cl., gilt $2.00
136. **Pepper**, *Dr.* Wm. The climate of America. (*In press.*)
137. **Persons**, places and things. 8°. cl. $3.00
138. **Peter**, the whaler; by W. H. G. Kingston. 12°. cl..........$1.25
139. **Philip** Van Artevelde; by Henry Taylor. 16°. cl..........$1.25
140. **Phyllis**; by the Duchess. 12°. cl., $1.25; pap. 50c.
141. **Playmate** (The). 4°. cl., $1.75; hf. bd., $1.25
142. **Powell**, T. W. Analysis of American law. New ed. 8°. cl., $3; shp..........$4.00
143. **Power** (The) of the spirit; by W. H. Furness. 12°. cl..........$1.50
144. **Privateersman** (The); by Captain Marryat. 12°. cl. $1.25
145. **Questions** awakened by the Bible; by Rev. J. Miller. 12°. cl..........$1.50
146. **Random** arrows; by F. Hempstead. cl...$1.00
147. **Reason** and religion; by P. Connelly. 16° ..$1.00
148. **Red** Eric (The); by R. M. Ballantyne. 12°..$1.25
149. **Reiter**, W. C. Monograph on diphtheria. cl. flex..........60c.
150. **Rhona**; by Mrs. Forrester. 12°. cl. $1.50
151. **Roberts**, J. B. Paracentesis of the pericardium. 8°. cl..........$1.25
152. **Romance** (The) of natural history; by P. H. Gosse. 12°. cl..........$1.25
153. **Round** the world; by W. H. G. Kingston. 12°. cl..........$1.25
154. **Salt** water; by W. H. G. Kingston. 12°. cl...$1.25
155. **Samson**, G. W. The atonement. 16°. cl...$1.00
156. **Sanford**, S. P., *A. M.* Elementary algebra. 12°. hf. roan $1.25
157. **School** story (A); or, three years at Wolverton. 12°. cl..........$1.25
158. **Schweigger**, *Prof.* C. Handbook of ophthalmology; tr. by P. Farley. 8°. cl........$4.50
159. **Science** and revelation; by Rev. Joseph H. Wythe. 12°. cl..........$1.75
160. **Scott**, *Sir* Walter. The lady of the lake. 4°. cl., gilt, $3.50. 12°. cl..........$1.25
161. **Seaforth**; by Florence Montgomery. 12°. cl. $1.25
162. **Searcy**, W. E. H. Lessons in phonography. 12°. cl..........$2.00
163. **Second** coming of the Lord; by Rev. C. Giles. 12°. cl..........$1.25
164. **Seiss**, J. A. The last times. 12°. cl.....$1.50
165. **Smith**, T. L. Elements of the laws. 12°. cl. $1.50
166. **Sons** (The) of Godwin; by Wm. Leighton. 12°. cl. $1.25
167. **Souci**; by Mrs. J. H. Twells. 12°. cl.....$1.50
168. **Southall**, J. C. Epoch of the mammoth. 12°. cl. $2.50

J. B. LIPPINCOTT & CO.,

Continued.

169. **Southern** household companion; by M. L. Edgeworth. 12°. cl....$1.25
170. **Stoneridge**; by Rev. C. A. Smith. 12°. cl., $1.25
171. **Storm-driven**; by Mary Healy. 16°....$1.00
172. **Studies** in verse; by Charles Quiet. 12°. cl., $1.00
173. **Tales** of Old Thule; by J. M. Smith. 12°. cl. $1.50
174. **Thackeray's** Ballads. 4°. cl. gilt....$5.00
175. **Thebes**, and other poems; by Chas. S. Larned. (*In press.*)
176. **Thirty** years at sea; by E. Shippen. 12°..$1.50
177. **Through** winding ways; by E. W. Olney. 8°. cl., $1.25; pap. ....75c.
178. **Ticknor**, F. O. Poems. 12°. cl. $1.50
179. **Tiger** prince (The); by Wm. Dalton. 16°. $1.25
180. **Too** rich; from the German, by Mrs. A. L. Wister. 12°. cl. $1.50
181. **Topnard**, Paul. Anthropology: v. 3 of Contemporary science library. 12°. cl....$2.00
182. **Tupper**, M. F. Proverbial philosophy. 16°. cl. $1.00
183. **Twice** defeated; by R. Edwards. 12°. cl., $1.75
184. **Two** Americas (The); by Sir Rose Price. 8°. cl. $2.00
185. **Under** the tricolor; by Lucy H. Hooper. 12°. cl. $1.25
186. **United** States dispensatory; by Wood and Bache. shp....$7.50
187. **Viking** (The); by C. E. Spencer. 12°. cl., $1.75
188. **Virgil's** Æneid; tr. by H. B. Pierce. 12°. cl. $2.00
189. **Viva**; by Mrs. Forrester. 12°. cl. $1.50
190. **Walker**, J. B., *D.D.* Living questions of the age. 12°. cl. $1.50
191. **Wanderings** in four continents. 8°. cl...$3.00
192. **War** tiger (The); by Wm. Dalton. 16°...$1.25
193. **Wax** flowers; by F. I. Duncan. 12°. cl...$1.00
194. **We** four; by L. L. Rees. 12° $1.25
195. **Webster**, Daniel. Life of; by S. M. Smucker. 12°. cl. $1.25
196. **White** elephant (The); by Wm. Dalton. 16°. $1.25
197. **Who** and what; by A. de P. Miller. 12°..$1.75
198. **Wolf** boy (The) of China; by Wm. Dalton. 16°. $1.25
199. **Women's** husbands. 8°. cl., $1; pap. ....50c.
200. **Wonders** of the great deep; by P. H. Gosse. 12°. cl. $1.25
201. **Wood**, H. C., *jr.*, *M.D.* Physician's visiting list and vade-mecum. 16°. roan....$1.25
202. **World** well lost; by E. Lynn Lynton. 12°. cl., $1.25; pap. ....75c.
203. **Worthy** women of our first century; ed. by Mrs. Owen J. Wister and Agnes Irwin. cr. 8°..$2.00
204. **Wrecked**, but not lost; by F. Templeton. 12°. cl. $1.50
205. **Wurtz**, Ad. Elements of modern chemistry; tr. by W. H. Greene. 12°. cl., $2.50; shp..$3.00
206. **Young** foresters; by W. H. G. Kingston. 12°. cl. $1.25
207. **Young** islanders (The); or, school-boy Crusoes. 12°....$1.25

S. R. WELLS & CO.,

737 Broadway, New York.

1. **Æsop**. Fables. (People's ed.) ill. 12°. bds...25c.
2. **American** Phrenological Journal and Science of Health: monthly. 8°. per year, $2; ea. ..20c.
3. **Baker**, Arthur M. How to learn shorthand; or, the stenographic instructor. obl. 12°. pap....25c.
4. **Bray**, Charles. The education of the feelings and affections; ed., with notes and ill. from 3d Lond. ed., by Nelson Sizer. 12°....$1.50
5. **Daniell**, W. H. How to sing; or, the voice and how to use it. 12°. 75c.; pap....50c.
6. **Deluze**, J. P. F. Practical instructions in animal magnetism; tr. by T. C. Hartshorn. New ed., rev. with notes by the translator, and letters. 12°, 524 p. $2.00
7. **Drayton**, H. S. How to study phrenology; with suggestions to students, lists of best works, constitutions for societies, etc. 12°. pap....10c.
8. — *and* McNeill, James. Brain and mind; or, mental science considered in accordance with the principles of phrenology and in relation to modern physiology. ill. 12°. cl....$1.50
9. **Fairchild**, M. Augusta, *M.D.* How to be well; or, common-sense medical hygiene: directions for treatment of acute diseases without drug medicines; also, hints on health. 12° $1.00
10. **Harmony** of phrenology and the Bible. pap., 10c.
11. **How** to conduct a public meeting: chairman's guide for conducting meetings. 12°. pap...15c.
12. **Jacques**, D. H. How to grow handsome; or, hints toward physical perfection, and the philosophy of human beauty, showing how to acquire and retain bodily symmetry, health and vigor, secure long life, etc. New ed. 12°, 244 p. $1.00

Jacques, D. H., *continued.*

13. — The temperaments; or, varieties of physical constitution in man, considered in their relation to mental character and affairs of life; with introd. by H. S. Drayton. ill. 12°, 350 p...$1.50
14. **Kirby**, G. B. Transmission; or, variations of character through the mother. 12°. 50c.; pap., 25c.
15. **Mitchell**, *Rev.* Thomas. Key to ghostism: science and art unlock its mysteries. 12°. cl. $1.50
16. **Petit**, Amelie V. How to read, what and why; or, hints in choosing the best books, with classified list of best works in biography, criticism, fine arts, history, novels, etc. 12°....$1.00
17. **Pope**, Alexander. Essay on man; with ill. and notes by S. R. Wells. (People's ed.) 12°. bds., 25c.
18. **Sizer**, Nelson. Choice of pursuits; or, what to do and why; with port. and biog. of many successful thinkers and workers. 12°, 508 p....$1.75
19. — How to teach according to temperament and mental development; or, phrenology in the schoolroom and the family. ill. 12°, 351 p....$1.50
20. **Thwing**, *Prof.* E. P. Facts about tobacco. 12°. pap....25c.
21. **Trall**, R. T., *M.D.* The true temperance platform: exposition of the fallacy of alcoholic medication: being the substance of lectures delivered in the Queen's Concert Rooms, London. 12°, 162 p. 50c.
22. **Turner**, T. Phrenology: its history and important principles. 12°. pap....10c.
23. **Wilson**, James Victor. How to magnetize; or, magnetism and clairvoyance: treatise on choice, management and capabilities of subjects, with instructions on method of procedure. 18°...25c.

HENRY HOLT & CO.,

12 East 23d St., Madison Square, New York.

1. **Albemarle**, *Earl of.* Fifty years of my life. large 12° $2.50
2. **Alexander**, *Mrs.* (*pseud.*) *See* Hector, *Mrs.* Annie F.
3. **Auerbach**, Brth. Aloys. 16°. (Leis. ho. ser.) $1.00
4. — Convicts (The) and their children. 16°. (Leis. ho. ser.) $1.00
5. — Landolin. Tr. by Annie B. Irish. 16°. (Leis. ho. ser.) $1.00
6. — Lorley and Reinhard. 16°. (Leis. ho. ser.) $1.00
7. — Poet and merchant. 16°. (Leis. ho. ser.) ..$1.00
8. **Ammen**, S. Z. Latin grammar for beginners. 12°. 75c.
9. **Baker**, H. B. English actors. 2 v. 12°....$3.50
10. **Baker**, James. Turkey. 8°, with two maps..$4.00
11. **Ball**, R. S., *LL.D.*, *F.R.S.* Astronomy; revised by Simon Newcomb. 16°....60c.
12. — Mechanics. 16° ....60c.
13. **Beerbohm**, Julius. Wanderings in Patagonia. 16°. (Leis. ho. ser.) $1.00
14. **Beers**, Henry A. A century of American literature. 16°. (Leis. ho. ser.) $1.00
15. **Bessey**, C. E. Botany. (Am. science ser.)
16. **Bellows**, John. French and English dictionary. 32° $3.00
17. **Below**, Otto v. Latin chart ....50c.
18. **Berlioz**, Hector. Selections from his writings. 12° $2.00
19. **Brassey**, *Mrs.* Around the world in the yacht "Sunbeam." 8°....$2.00
20. — Sunshine and storm in the East. 8°......$3.50
21. **Butt**, Bee. May. Delicia: a novel. 16°. (Leis. ho. ser.) $1.00
22. — Eugénie. 16°. (Leis. ho. ser.) $1.00
23. **Cadell**, *Mrs.* H. M. Ida Craven: a novel. 16°. (Leis. ho. ser.) $1.00
24. **Carlyle**, Thomas. Anthology. 12°....$2.00
25. **Champlin**, John D., *jr.* The young folks' cyclopædia of common things. large 12°....$3.00
26. — The child's catechism of common things. 16°. 60c.
27. **College** hymnal (The). 18°....$1.25
28. **Conway**, M. D. Demonology and devil lore. 2 v. 8° $7.00
29. — Idols and ideals. 12°....$1.50
30. — The sacred anthology. 12°....$2.00
31. **Corkran**, Alice. Bessie Lang: a novel. 16°. (Leis. ho. ser.) $1.00
32. **Cox**, *Sir* Geo. W., *M.A.* Popular romances of the middle ages. large 12°....$2.25
33. **Creasy**, *Sir* Edward S. History of the Ottoman Turks. large 12° $2.50
34. **Escott**, T. H. S. England: her people, polity and pursuits. 8°....$3.50
35. **Farrar**, James A. Primitive manners and customs. 12°....$1.75
36. **Fothergill**, Jessie. The first violin. 16°. (Leis. ho. ser.) $1.00
37. — Probation: a novel. 16°. (Leis. ho. ser.)..$1.00
38. **Freeman's** Historical course.
39. Thompson's History of England. 16°....$1.10
40. Yonge's History of France. 16°....$1.00
41. **Gasc**, F. E. A. Dictionary of the French and English languages. 8°....$3.75
42. — Improved modern pocket dictionary of the French and English languages....$1.40
43. — *Same.* Tourists' ed. 2 v. in case 18°....$1.60
44. **Görner**, C. A. Englisch: ein Lustspiel....30c.
45. **Goodholme**, Todd S. Domestic cyclopædia. 8°. $5.00
46. **Grohman**, W. A. Baillie. Gaddings with a primitive people. 16°. (Leis. ho. ser.) $1.00
47. **Griffiths**, Arthur. Lola. 16°. (Leis. ho. ser.) $1.00
48. **Guthrie**, Frederick. Practical physics: molecular physics and sound. 16° ....60c.
49. **Hardy**, Thomas. The return of the native. 16°. (Leis. ho. ser.) $1.00
50. **Hector**, *Mrs.* Annie F. ("Mrs. Alexander".) Heritage of Langdale. 16°. (Leis. ho. ser.) $1.00
51. — Maid, wife, or widow? 16°. (Leis. ho. ser.) $1.00
52. **Heness**, Gottlieb. Der Sprechlehrer unter seinen Schülern. 12°....$1.35
53. **James**, Henry A. Communism in America. 8°. pap., $1; cloth $1.25
54. **Janes**, E. French grammar. 12°....$1.25
55. **Johnson**, Elizabeth Winthrop. The studio arts. 16° ....60c.
56. **Johnson**, Rossiter. Single famous poems; coll. and ed. by Rossiter Johnson. sq. 12°. gilt..$2.00
57. — Play-day poems; coll. and ed. by Rossiter Johnson. 16°. (Leis. ho. ser.) $1.00
58. **Johnson**, *Dr.* Samuel. Chief lives of the poets. large 12° $2.00
59. **Johnston**, Alexander. History of American politics. 16° ....60c.
60. **Kavanagh**, Julia *and* Bridget. The pearl fountain. 8° $1.50
61. **Kemble**, Frances Ann. Records of a girlhood. large 12°, with por....$2.50
62. **Klemm**, L. R. New German text books: —
63. 5. Kreis. 12°. *wholesale price*, bds....45c.
64. 6. Kreis. 12°. *wholesale price*, bds....50c.
65. 7. Kreis. 12°. *wholesale price*, bds....60c.
66. 8. Kreis (or circle). Abriss der Geschichte der deutschen Literatur. 12°. *retail*, cl..$1.50
67. **Koehler**, *Dr.* A. Practical botany. large 12°..$2.50
68. **Lacombe**, Paul. Histoire du peuple français. 12°. 75c.
69. **Laffan**, May. The Hon. Miss Ferrard. 16°. (Leis. ho. ser.) $1.00
70. **Lewes**, G. H. On actors and the art of acting. 12°....$1.50
71. **Lounsbury**, Thomas R. History of the English language. 16°....$1.00
72. **Macalister**, Alex. Zoölogy of the invertebrate animals; rev. for America by Prof. A. S. Packard, jr. 16°....60c.
73. — Zoölogy of the vertebrate animals. 16°...60c.
74. — The above two volumes in one. 16°......$1.00
75. **McCoan**, J. C. Egypt. 8° $3.75
76. **McKnight**, George. Life and faith: sonnets. sq. 16° $2.00
77. **McNab**, William Ramsay. Botany. 16°....$1.00
78. **Majendie**, *Lady* Margaret. Giannetto. 16°. (Leis. ho. ser.) $1.00
79. — Dita. 16°. (Leis. ho. ser.)....$1.00
80. **Molesworth**, *Mrs.* Hathercourt. 16°. (Leis. ho. ser.) $1.00
81. **Morgan**, L. H. Ancient society. 8° $4.00
82. **Newcomb**, Simon, *and* Holden, Edward S. Astronomy. large 12° $2.50
83. **Nesbitt**, M. L. Grammar-land. sq. 16° ...$1.25
84. **Otto**, *Dr.* Emil. A first book in French for young pupils. 12°. bds....35c.
85. — Introductory French lessons $1.25
86. — Introductory French reader. 12°....$1.00
87. — Exercises for translating English into German. 12°....$1.00
88. **Packard**, A. S., *jr.* Zoölogy; for students and general readers. large 12°....$3.00
89. **Plays** for private acting. 16°. (Leis. ho. ser.) $1.00
90. **Reid**, Whitelaw. Some newspaper tendencies. 16°. pap. ....50c.

HENRY HOLT & CO.,

Continued.

91. **Roberts,** *Miss.* Noblesse oblige. 16°. (Leis. ho. ser.) $1.00
92. **Roscher,** —. Political economy; tr. by J. J. Lalor. 2 v. 8° $7.00
93. **Rydberg,** Viktor. Magic of the middle ages. 12° $1.50
94. **Sauveur,** *Dr.* L. Fables de La Fontaine; avec notes $1.50
95. — Introduction to the teaching of ancient languages. 12°. pap .... 25c.
96. — Talks with Cæsar De bello Gallico. 12°. cl. $1.50
97. — Vade mecum of the Latinist. 12°. pap., 25c.
98. — Word (A) for word rendering into English of C. Julii Cæsar Comentarii de bello Gallico, book I. 12°. pap. .... 25c.
99. **Scrivener,** F. H. Greek Testament, with lexicon. 16° $2.50
100. **Smith,** J. Moyr. Prince of Argolis. sq. 12°. $2.00
101. **Stern,** S. M. Studien und Plaudereien. 12°. $1.35
102. **Symonds,** J. A. Renaissance in Italy: the fine arts. 8° $3.50
103. **Taine,** H. A. English literature. (Popular ed.) 8° $1.25
104. — French revolution. v. 1. large 12° $2.50
105. **Tautphœus,** *Baroness.* Novels: The initials, 2 v.; Quits, 2 v.; Cyrilla, 2 v.; At odds, 2 v. 16°. ea. $1.00
106. **Thornbury,** Walter. Life of Turner. 12°..$2.75
107. **Tolhausen,** A. Technological dictionary:—pt. 1, French-German-English; pt. 2, English-German-French; pt. 3, German-English-French. 8°. ea., cl. $3.50
108. **Turgenieff,** Ivan. Virgin soil. 16°. (Leis. ho. ser.) $1.00
109. **Tylor,** E. B. Early history of mankind. 8°..$3.50
110. **Villari,** Linda. In change unchanged. 16°. (Leis. ho. ser.) $1 00
111. **Walford,** L. B. Pauline. 16°. (Leis. ho. ser.) $1.00
112. — Cousins. 16°. (Leis. ho. ser.) $1.00
113. **Wallace,** D. Mackenzie. Russia. 8° $4.00
114. **White,** C. A. Classic literature. large 12°. $2.25
115. **Walker,** F. A. Money. 8° $4.00
116. — Money in its relations to trade and industry. 12° $1.25
117. **Whitney,** *Prof.* W. D. A compendious German dictionary. sm. 8°. hf. bound $3.50
118. — *Same.* 2 v. sm. 8°. hf. bound, in a box..$5.50
119. — Goethe's Faust. Ed. by Prof. W. D. Whitney. 12°. cl. $1.20
120. — Goethe's Iphigenie auf Tauris. Annotated by Prof. Franklin Carter, of Yale College, and ed. by Prof. W. D. Whitney. 12°. cl. .... 95c.
121. — Lessing's Minna von Barnhelm. Annotated by W. D. Whitney. 12°. cl. .... 95c.
122. — Schiller's Maria Stuart. Annotated by E. S. Joynes, Professor in Vanderbilt University, and ed. by Prof. W. D. Whitney. 12°. cl. ..$1.10
123. — Schiller's Wilhelm Tell. Ed. by Prof. W. D. Whitney. 12°. cl. $1.00
124. **Wright,** Chauncey. Philosophical discussions. 8° $3.50
125. **Yale** College: a sketch of its history, etc.; ed. by W. L. Kingsley. 2 v. ill. 4°. sheets, $35; cl., $37; hf. mor., $45; full mor., $50; full rus. $55.00

G. I. JONES & CO.,

St. Louis.

1. **Bateman's** Political and constitutional law of the United States. The political and constitutional law of the United States of America. By Wm. O. Bateman. 8°, 400 p. cl. $3.00
2. **Hosmer's** Short history of German literature. A short history of German literature from the earliest period to the present time. By Prof. James K. Hosmer. 2d ed. 12°, 644 p. $2.00
3. **Jameson's** Rhetorical method. A concise treatment of the topics belonging to rhetoric and composition; for use in schools and academies. By Henry W. Jameson, B.A. 12°, 108 p. ..75c.
4. **Loud's** Geometry. An elementary geometry on the analytic plan. By Prof. F. H. Loud. 8°. cl...$1.25
5. **Morgan's** Topical Shakespeariana. A collection of English Shakespeariana, arranged under headings to facilitate reference to special subjects of investigation. By Horace H. Morgan. 8°. cl...$2.00
6. **Rosenkranz's** Pedagogics. Pedagogics as a system, by Karl Rosenkranz. Translated from the German by Anna C. Brackett. 8°. cl. $2.00
7. **Shirley's** Dartmouth College causes. The Dartmouth College causes and the Supreme Court of the United States. By John M. Shirley. 12°, 470 p. leath. $2.50
8. **Snider's** System of Shakespeare's dramas. The aim of this work is to show each drama as a whole, in its thought, organization and characters. By Denton J. Snider. 2 v. 12°, 458, 460 p. cl., $4; 2 v. in 1 .... $2.50
9. **Soule's** "Hamlet revamped": a travesty ...50c.
10. **Soule's** "Romeo and Juliet": a travesty ....50c.

UNIVERSALIST PUB. HOUSE,

16 Bromfield St., Boston.

1. **Memoir** of Thomas Whittemore, D.D.; by John G. Adams, D.D. 12°. cl., $1.50; cl., gilt, $1.75
2. **Services** for the days of the Christian year, specially observed by the Universalist Church. per doz., bds., $3.60; ea. .... 35c.
3. **The** old forts taken: five lectures on endless punishment and future life; by Rev. A. A. Miner, D.D. 16°. cl. .... 50c.
4. **The** latest word of Universalism: thirteen essays by thirteen clergymen. 3d ed. 16°. cl. $1 00
5. **The** Universalism of the Lord's prayer; by Rev. John G. Adams, D.D. 16°. cl. .... 50c.
6. **Sunday** school harmonies. 32 p. per 100, pap., $10; ea. .... 10c.
7. **Endless** punishment in the very words of its advocates; by Rev. Thomas J. Sawyer, S. T. D. 16°. cl. $1.00
8. **At** our best, and other essays; by Rev. Sumner Ellis. cl. $1.00
9. **Memoir** of Rev. E. Fisher, D.D.; by Rev. G. H. Emerson, D.D. cl. $1.00

CHANGES IN PRICE.

10. **Our** new departure .... from $1.75 to $1.25
11. **Ely** *and* Thomas' Discussion ..... from 65c. to 75c.
12. **Primitive** Christianity and its corruptions. from $1.50 to $1.00
13. **A century** of Universalism..from $1.50 to $1.00
14. **Crown** of thorns, from $1.25 to $1; gilt edge, $1.25

LITTLE, BROWN & CO.,

Boston, Mass.

1. **Otto's** U. S. Supreme Court reports. v. 1–9. 8°. ea., shp....$4.00
2. **Hamilton,** Alexander. Life; by John T. Morse, jr. 2 v. 12°. cl....$4.50
3. **Holmes'** U. S. Circuit Court reports. v. 1. 8°. shp....$6.00
4. **Smith,** *Dr.* Wm. Dictionary of Christian biography. v. 1. 8°. cl....$5.50
5. **Cabot,** George. Life; by H. C. Lodge. 8°. cl.,$3.50
6. **Parkman,** Francis. Count Frontenac and New France under Louis XIV. sm. 8°. cl....$2.50
7. **Lowell's** U. S. District Court decisions. v. 2. 8°. shp....$6.00
8. **Stephens'** Digest of the law of evidence. (May's edition.) 12°. leatherette, $2.50; shp....$3.00
9. **American** Law Review. v. 11, 12, 13. 8°. ea., shp....$4.00
10. **Pomeroy,** J. W. Remedies and remedial rights. 8°. shp....$6.00
11. **Bancroft,** George. History of the United States. Centenary ed., rev. 6 v. cr. 8°. cl....$13.50
12. **United** States digest. New series. v. 5–9. roy. 8°. ea., shp....$6.00
13. **Ewell,** M. D. Leading cases on the disabilities incident to infancy, etc. 8°. shp....$6.00
14. **Bowditch,** H. I. Hygiene in America. 12°. cl.,$2.50
15. **Webster,** Daniel, Reminiscences and anecdotes of; by Peter Harvey. por. 8°. cl....$3.00
16. **Anglo-Saxon** law (Essays in). 8°. cl....$4.00
17. **Bigelow,** M. M. Law of fraud. 8°. shp...$6.00
18. **Adams,** Henry. New England federalism. 8°. cl....$4.00
19. **Bigelow,** M. M. Elementary treatise on the law of torts. 12°. leatherette, $2.50; shp....$3.00
20. **Clifford's** U. S. Circuit Court reports. v. 3. 8°. shp....$6.00
21. **Williams,** G. F. Massachusetts citations. roy. 8°. shp....$6.00
22. **Forbes,** R. B. Personal reminiscences. 12°. cl., $2.00
23. **Choate,** Rufus. Addresses and orations. cr. 8°. cl....$2.25
24. **United** States digest. First series, v. 15: Table of cases. roy. 8°. shp....$6.00
25. **Shelley,** Percy B. Minor poems. 16°. cl...$1.75
26. **Heard,** F. F. Criminal law. 8°. shp....$6.00
27. **Drone,** E. S. Law of copyright, literary and dramatic. 8°. shp....$6.00
28. **Webster,** Daniel. Great speeches; with an essay by E. P. Whipple. roy. 8°. cl....$3.00
29. **Winthrop,** Robert C. Addresses and speeches. v. 3, 1869–'79. 8°. cl....$3.50
30. **Smith's** New Hampshire reports, 1802–1816. 8°. shp....$5.00
31. **Abbott,** B. V. Law dictionary. 2 v. 8°. shp., $12.00
32. **Bouvier,** John. Institutes of American law. 2 v. roy. 8°. shp....$12.00
33. — Law dictionary. 2 v. roy. 8°. shp....$12.00
34. **Bigelow,** M. M. Elements of equity. 12°. leatherette, $2.50; shp....$3.00
35. **Heard,** F. F. Criminal pleading. 12°. leatherette, $2.50; shp....$3.00
36. **Bigelow,** M. M. Placita Anglo Normannica. 8°. cl....$4.00
37. **Curtis,** *Hon.* B. R. Life and writings. 2 v. 8°. cl....$6.00
38. **Massachusetts** reports, v. 126; by John Lathrop. 8°. shp....$3.25
39. **Rimmer,** *Dr.* Wm. Art anatomy. obl. 4°. hf. mor., $35. (*Reduced from* $50.)
40. **Pickering,** Charles. History of plants. 4°..$15.00
41. **United** States digest. First series; with table of cases. 15 v. roy. 8°. shp....$90.00
42. **Encyclopædia** Britannica. Ninth ed. v. 1–10. 4°. ea., cl., $8; hf. rus....$10.00
43. **Scott,** *Sir* Walter. Waverley novels. (Illustrated centenary ed.) 25 v. 134 steel plates. cr. 8°. cl....$31.25
44. **Mississippi** reports, v. 53, 54; by J. A. Brown. 8°. ea., shp....$6.00
45. **Schouler,** James. Law of personal property. v. 2. 8°. shp....$6.00
46. **Mason,** Joseph. Practice in the common law courts of New England. 8°. shp....$6.00
47. **Preble,** W. B., jr. Patent case index. 12°. shp., $5.00
48. **Schouler,** James. Law of bailments. 8°. shp., $6.00
49. **Amos,** Sheldon. Fifty years of the English constitution, 1830–'80. 12°. cl....$3.00
50. **Todd,** Alpheus. Parliamentary government in the British colonies. 8°. cl....$5.00

NEW EDITIONS, 1876–1880.

51. **Washburn's** Real property. 4th ed. 3 v...$18.00
52. **Smith's** Probate law. 3d ed....$2.50
53. **Greenleaf's** Evidence. 13th ed. 3 v....$18.00
54. **Story's** Equity jurisprudence. 12th ed. 2 v. $12.00
55. **Bishop's** Criminal law. 6th ed. 2 v....$12.00
56. **Angell's** Law of carriers. 5th ed....$6.00
57. — Law of watercourses. 7th ed....$6.00
58. **Redfield's** Wills. v. 1, 4th ed.; v. 2, 3, 3d ed. 3 v....$18.00
59. **Angell's** Law of limitations. 6th ed....$6.00
60. **Bartlett's** Americanisms. 4th ed....$4.00
61. **Cooley's** Constitutional limitations. 4th ed. $6.00
62. **Walker's** American law. 7th ed....$6.00
63. **Story's** Bailments. 9th ed....$6.00
64. **Drake's** Attachment. 5th ed....$6.00
65. **Choate's** Life. 3d ed....$2.25
66. **Story's** Promissory notes. 7th ed....$6.00
67. **Taylor's** Landlord and tenant. 7th ed....$6.00
68. **Fletcher** *and* Kidder's Brazil. 9th ed....$4.00
69. **Morse's** Law of banks and banking. 2d ed...$6.00
70. **Langdell,** C. C. Cases on contracts, with summary. 2d ed. 2 v....$10.00
71. **Parkman's** Great west. La Salle and the discovery of the great west. 11th ed....$2.50
72. **Story's** Equity pleading. 9th ed....$6.00
73. **Emerson's** Trees and shrubs. 3d ed. 2 v. ill. $12; with col. pl....$20.00
74. **Parsons'** Partnership. 3d ed....$6.00
75. **Herrick's** Town officer. 2d ed. cl., $2.50; shp. $3.00
76. **Daniell's** Chancery. 5th ed. 3 v....$18.00

REDUCTIONS IN PRICE.

77. **Burke's** Works. 12 v....$18.00 to $15.00
78. **Choate's** Life.... $2.50 to $2.25
79. **Plutarch's** Lives. 5 v....$15.00 to $10.00
80. — *Same.* 1 v. ed.... $4.00 to $3.00
81. — Morals. 5 v....$15.00 to $10.00
82. **White's** Shakespeare. 12 v....$18.00 to $15.00
83. **Brougham's** Writings. 11 v....$19.25 to $13.75
84. **Campbell's** Chief justices. 4 v... $8.00 to $7.00
85. — Lord chancellors. 10 v....$20.00 to $17.50
86. **Clarke's** Shakespeare concordance. $9.00 to $7.50
87. **Dickens'** Works. ill. 30 v....$60.00 to $52.50
88. **Encyclopædia** Britannica. 9th ed. cloth, per v., $9 to $8; hf. rus., per v....$11.00 to $10.00
89. **Fergusson's** History of architecture. 4 v. $53.00 to $48.00
90. **Gibbon's** Rome. 8 v....$22.50 to $20.00
91. **Grote's** Greece. 12 v....$21.00 to $18.00
92. **Hallam's** Works. per v.... $1.75 to $1.50

LITTLE, BROWN & CO.,

Continued.

93. **Jameson's** Italian painters ...... $4.50 to $4.00
94. **Kugler's** German schools. 2 v... $9.00 to $8.00
95. **Kugler's** Italian schools. 2 v....$11.00 to $10.00
96. **Mahon's** England and Queen Anne. per v. $1.75 to $1.50
97. **Milman's** Works. per v.........$1.75 to $1.50
98. **Mill's** Political economy........ $2.50 to $2.00
99. **Pole** On Whist.................. $1.00 to 75c.
100. **Scott's** Poems, Life, and Tales of a grandfather. (Centenary ed.) per v...........$1.25 to $1.00
101. **Waverley** novels. (Centenary ed.) per v. $1.25 to $1.00

LOCKWOOD, BROOKS & CO.,

381 Washington St., Boston.

1. **Allen**, J. A. Westboro' State Reform School reminiscences. 16°, 94 p. flex. cl., 50c.; pap., 30c.
2. **Ball**, B. L. Three days on the White Mountains. 16°, 72 p. pap. ....25c.
3. **Bartlett**, M. C. Little figures, and other stories. 16°, 245 p..............................$1.25
4. — Real boys and girls. 16°, 189 p. cl......$1.00
5. **Benjamin**, S. G. W. What is art? 8°, 57 p...75c.
6. **Brown**, H. N. Sunday stories. 16°, 220 p...$1.00
7. **Bullard**, A. Fifty years with the Sabbath schools. por. 12°, 336 p. cl.....................$1.75
8. **Bynner**, E. L. Nimport: novel. sq. 16°, 494 p. $1.25
9. — Tritons: novel. 16°, 406 p. cl..........$1.25
10. **Champney**, L. W. All around a palette. ill. sm. 4°, 314 p. cl. $1.50
11. — Bourbon lilies. 16°, 388 p. cl., $1.25; pap., 75c.
12. — In the sky-garden. ill. sm. 4°, 211 p. cl...$1.50
13. **Clarke**, J. F. Astronomical lantern........$3.50
14. — How to find the stars. 16°, 47 p. pap.....50c.
15. **Craigin**, L. T. Cedars (The). ill. 16°, 297 p. cl..$1.25
16. — Long ago. ill. 16°, 240 p. cl............$1.25
17. **Gladden**, W. Was Bronson Alcott's school a type of God's moral government? 16°, 64 p. pap...40c.
18. **Glumer**, C. v. The Frau Domina: novel. 16°, 250 p. flex. cl. $1.50
19. **Gospel** invitation (The). sm. 8°, 332 p. cl...$1.50
20. **Hale**, E. E. In His name. 8°, 89 p. pap.....40c.
21. **Long**, J. D. Æneid of Virgil; tr. into Eng. blank verse. cr. 8°, 431 p. cl. $2.00
22. **Lord**, J. Ancient history. New ed., rev. 12°, 569 p. cl....................................$1.50
23. **Loring**, G. B. Farm-yard Club of Jotham. ill. 8°, 603 p. extra cl...........................$3.00
24. **May**, A. W. Essay on dress. 8°, 27 p. pap...20c.
25. **Mears**, D. O. Life of Edw. N. Kirk, D.D. ill. and por. 8°, 448 p. cl., $3; hf. cf., $5; hf. mor., extra...............................$5.50
26. **Miles**, H. A. Birth of Jesus. 12°, 211 p....$1.50
27. **Monday** Club. Sermons on International lessons, 1877. cr. 8°, 448 p. cl.................$1.50
28. **Robbins**, *Mrs.* S. S. One happy winter; or, a visit to Florida. ill. 16°, 240 p. $1.25
29. **Roberts**, R. H. Harry Holbrooke, of Holbrooke Hall: novel. ill. sq. 16°, 215 p. flex. cl...$1.25
30. **Savage**, M. J. Life questions. 12°, 159 p...$1.00
31. — Light on the cloud; or, hints of comfort for hours of sorrow. 18°, 170 p. cl., gilt.....$1.25
32. — Religion of evolution. 12°, 253 p. cl.....$1.50
33. **Sears**, E. H. Christ in the life. 12°, 278 p...$1.25
34. **Tripp**, G. H. Student life at Harvard. 12°, 518 p. cl., $1.75; pap..........................$1.00
35. **Whiton**, J. M. Is "eternal" punishment endless? sq. 16°, 116 p. cl., $1; pap. ....75c.
36. **Wieck**, F. Piano and song. 16°, 199 p. cl., $1.25
37. **Zylyff**. The Ponca chiefs; or, Indians' attempt to appeal from the tomahawk to the courts. 16°, 146 p. pap.................................50c.

J. M. STODDART & CO.,

727 Chestnut St., Philadelphia.

1. **Croasdale's** system of industrial art drawing; by Miss E. Croasdale: —
   Elementary series; in 5 nos. per no. ....25c.
   Architectural series; in 5 nos. per no. ......35c.
   Ornamentation series; in 5 nos. per no......35c.
   Plane geometry; in 5 nos. per no...........25c.
   Perspective; in 4 nos. per no...............35c.
   Object drawing; in 3 nos. per no...........25c.
   Landscape; in 3 nos. per no. ....50c.
   Easy lessons cards for blackboard or slate; in boxes....................................25c.
2. **Musical** cabinet (The); compiled by Eastburn: a series of new and valuable music books: — Vocal: Choice parlor ballads, Pleasant pastime, Songs of affections, Gems of Germany, Select contralto or baritone songs; — Instrumental: Fireside gems, Beauties of Dorn, Favorite dances, Sparks of melody, Gathered pearls, Circlet of brilliants, Beauties of Strauss. 4°. bds., $1; cl., extra $1.50
3. **New** organ book; compiled by Eastburn. 4°. bds., $1.50; full cl., extra.....................$2.00
4. **Night-express** (The); by Jas. D. McCabe. Illuminated cover. 12°..........................25c.
5. **What** came of it; or, the strike at Tivoli Mills; by T. S. Arthur. 12°. pap., 25c.; cl...........50c.

OLIVER DITSON & CO.,

Boston.

1. **The** temple: singing class and choir book; by W. O. Perkins. $1; per doz.................$9.00
2. **The** voice of worship: choir and singing class book; by L. O. Emerson. $1; per doz..........$9.00
3. **White** robes: Sunday school song book; by A. J. Abbey and M. J. Munger. 30c.; per doz...$3.00
4. **Temperance** jewels: temperance song book; by J. H. Tenney. 35c.; per doz. $3.60
5. **American** anthem book: book of easy anthems; by A. N. Johnson, J. H. Tenney and A. J. Abbey. $1.25; per doz. $12.00
6. **Emerson's** anthem book: new coll. of anthems; by L. O. Emerson. $1.25; per doz......$12.00
7. **Parlor** organ instruction book; for teaching both light and sacred music on the reed organ; by A. N. Johnson..............................$1.60
8. **Doctor** of Alcantara: comic opera, by Eichberg: new arrangement............................$1.50
9. **Student's** life in song; with introd. by C. D. Warner $1.50
10. **Dow's** sacred quartets for male voices: general collection, also Masonic; by Howard M. Dow. $2; per doz..............................$18.00

SHELDON & CO.,

8 Murray St., New York.

July, 1876–1879.

1. **Avery**, *Prof.* Elroy M. Elements of natural philosophy $1.30
2. — Elements of chemistry. (*In press.*)
3. — First lessons in natural philosophy. (*In press.*)
4. — Teacher's handbook to accompany Avery's "Natural philosophy"; containing solutions of problems, practical suggestions and additional matter on electric light. 12°. bds. .... 75c.
5. **Broadus**, John A., *D.D.* Lectures on the history of preaching. 12°. cl. $1.50
6. **Chapin**, *Prest.* A. L. Elements of political economy by Francis Wayland, recast $1.75
7. — First principles of political econ. 16°. cl. .. 75c.
8. **Cuthbert**, J. H., *D.D.* Life of Richard Fuller, D.D. 12°. cl. $1.50
9. **Ford**, Sallie R. Ernest Quest. 12°. cl. ... $1.50
10. **Faunce**, W. D. A young man's difficulties with his Bible. 12°. cl. $1.25
11. **Gregory**, *Rev.* D. S. Why four Gospels. 12°. $1.50
12. **Hill**, *Prest.* D. J. Life of Washington Irving. 12°. cl. $1.00
13. — Life of William Cullen Bryant. 12°. cl. .. $1.00
14. — The science of rhetoric. 12°. hf. leath. .. $1.25
15. — The elements of logic. (*In press.*)
16. — The elements of rhetoric and composition. 12°. hf. leath. $1.25
17. **Haven**, Joseph, *D.D.* History of ancient and modern philosophy. 12°. $2.00
18. **Krauth**, Chas. P., *S.T.D., LL.D.* A vocabulary of the philosophical sciences, including mental, moral and metaphysical. 8° $3.50
19. **Mell**, P. H. A manual of parliamentary practice. New ed., rev. 16°. cl. .... 75c.
20. — The doctrine of prayer. 16°. cl. .... 60c.
21. **Murray**, David. Manual of land surveying. 8°. $2.00
22. **Olney**, *Prof.* Edward. A pract. arith. 12°.. 75c.
23. — The science of arithmetic. 12° $1.25
24. **Otis**, *Col.* E. S. The Indian question. 12°... $1.50
25. **Palmer**, *Prof.* Joseph H. Elements of book-keeping .... 90c.
26. — Blanks to book-keeping. 5 nos. ea. .... 10c.
27. **Rusling**, *Gen.* Jas. F. The great west and Pacific coast. 8° $2.50
28. **Service** of song: hymns and tunes. (Centennial edition.) sq. 12°. hf. leath. $1.25
29. — *Same:* hymns only .... 60c.
30. **Spurgeon**, *Rev.* Chas. H. Commenting and commentaries. 12°. cl. $1.25
31. — The matchless mystery, and other sermons. 12°. cl. $1.50
32. **Tyler**, Moses Coit. A manual of English literature. 8° $3.00

Note. This book has been prepared by using "Morley's First sketch of English literature" as a basis, Prof. Morley's consent having been obtained.

33. **Wilkinson**, *Capt.* J. The narrative of a blockade runner. 12°. cl. $1.25
34. **Whittaker**, *Capt.* F. A popular life of Gen. Geo. A. Custer. ill. 8° $3.00
35. — The cadet's button: a story of American army life. 12° $1.50

FORDS, HOWARD & HULBERT,

27 Park Place, New York.

1. **Abbott**, Lyman. The Gospel history. *See* Gilmore, James R.
2. **Bryant**, W: Cullen. A new library of poetry and song. More than 2,000 selections from above 700 of the best poets of England, Scotland, Ireland and America, together with numerous translations from Sanskrit, Persian, Chinese, Latin, Greek, French, German, Spanish and Italian authors of note. Prefaced with a treatise by Mr. Bryant on the "Poets and poetry of the English language." (*Completed, Dec.*, 1877.) Including also the "New biographical memoir of Bryant," by James Grant Wilson. (*Added, Sept.*, 1878.) Illustrated with 69 plates, steel portraits, wood engravings, etc. 1,060 pp. 4°. in 21 parts. ea., pap., 50c.; or, 2 v. cl., gilt, $14; hf. mor., $18; full mor., $22. (*Subscription.*)
3. **Fool's** (A) errand. By one of the fools. A novel, giving the true and startling adventures of a northern settler in one of the southern states since the "late unpleasantness." 16°. (*Nov.*, 1879.) cl. $1.00
4. **Gilmore**, James R. (*See also* Edmund Kirke.) The Gospel history. Being a complete connected narrative of the life of our Lord, woven from the text of the four evangelists. With notes, original and selected; indexes of texts and topics; and a table of lessons. By James R. Gilmore and Lyman Abbott, D.D. 16°. over 600 pp. (*Dec.*, 1879.) cl., flex.; red edges.
5. **Goodwin**, *Rev.* T. A. The mode of man's immortality; or, the when, where and how of the future life. By the author of "The perfect man." New (third) edition, with additional chapters on "Future punishment" and "The ministry of angels"; also a full index. 12°. (*Sept.*, 1879.) cl. $1.25
6. **Kirke**, Edmund (*pseud. of* J. R. Gilmore). The workingman's paradise; or, West Virginia as a home. With hints to new settlers. 32°. (*Aug.*, 1879.) pap. .... 15c.
7. **Lives** and portraits of the one hundred greatest men of history. 7 v. in portfolio. ea., $7.50. (*Subscription.*)
8. **O'Reilly**, Bernard. Heroic women of the Bible and the church. Narrative biographies of grand female characters of the Old and New Testaments, and of saintly women of the Christian church, both in earlier and later ages. Illustrated with 25 plates in oil colors from celebrated paintings. (*Completed, Mar.*, 1878.) Issued in 25 parts. ea., pap., 50c.; or, 1 v., hf. mor., $18.00; full mor., $21.00. (*Subscription.*)
9. **Raymond**, Rossiter W. Camp and cabin: sketches of life and travel in the west. 32°. (*Dec.*, 1879.) cl., red edges $1.25
10. — Merry-go-round (The): stories for boys and girls. ill. sm. 4°. (*Nov.*, 1879.) cl. $1.50
11. **Stowe**, Harriet Beecher. Poganuc people: their loves and lives. A novel. ill. 12°. (*May*, 1878.) cl. $1.50
12. **Tourgee**, Albion W. Figs and thistles: a western story. 12°. (*Sept.*, 1879.) cl. $1.00
13. — Toinette: a tale of the south. New ed., with new preface on the race-problem of the south. (*Sept.*, 1879.) [Originally pub. 1874 under *pseudonym* "Henry Churton."] cl. $1.00

CHANGES OF PRICE.

14. **Stowe's** (H.B.) My wife and I. from $1.75 to $1.50
15. — We and our neighbors ..... from $1.75 to $1.50

S. C. GRIGGS & CO.,

25 Washington St., Chicago.

1. **Blanc**, Charles. Grammar of painting and engraving; tr. from the French by Mrs. Kate N. Doggett; with the orig. ill. 3d ed. 8° $3.00
2. **Brown**, Marshall. Wit and humor: a choice collection. 6th ed. ill. 12° $1.50
3. **Buckingham**, C. P. Elements of differential and integral calculus; by a new method without use of infinitesimals or limits. 12° $2.00
4. **Carew**, Rachel. Tangled: a novel. sq. 16°. $1.00
5. **Cross**, J. G. Eclectic short-hand. 2d ed. 12°. $2.00
6. **Dement**, R. S. Ingersoll, Beecher and dogma; or, a few simple truths and their logical deductions. 2d ed. 12° $1.00
7. **Edda** (The Younger), also called Snorre's Edda, or the prose Edda; with introd., notes, vocab. and index, by R. B. Anderson. 12° $2.00
8. **Fawcett**, W. L. Hand-book of finance; with over 80 tables and diagrams. 2d ed. 12° $1.75
9. **Forestier**, Auber. Echoes from mist-land; or, the Nibelungen lay revealed to lovers of romance and chivalry. 12° $1.50
10. **Freeman**, *Mrs.* A. M. Somebody's Ned: a novel. 12° $1.00
11. **Hathaway**, Benjamin. Art-life, and other poems. 12°. $1; gilt $1.25
12. **Hudson**, S. A. Law for the clergy. 16° ... $1.00
13. **Jones**, Elisha. Exercises in Latin prose composition. 3d ed. 12° $1.00
14. — First lessons in Latin. 13th ed. 12° $1.25
15. **Jones**, Wm. P. Myth of Stone Idol: a love legend of Dakota. sm. 4° $1.00
16. **Jousset**, P. Clinical lectures; tr. from the French by R. Ludlam. 8°. cl., $4.50; hf. mor. $5.50
17. **Kippax**, John R. Churchyard literature: collection of American epitaphs. 12° $1.50
18. **Lie**, Jonas. The barque Future: a Norseland story; tr. by Mrs. Ole Bull. 12° $1.00
19. — The pilot and his wife: a Norse love story; tr. by Mrs. Ole Bull. 12° $1.50
20. **Maertz**, Louise. New method for study of English literature. 12°. interleaved $1.00
21. **Mathews**, William. Hours with men and books. 12° $2.00
22. — Oratory and orators. 12° $2.00
23. **Miller**, Emily Huntington. What Tommy did. ill. 16°. $1; pap. .... 50c.
24. **Raymond**, Geo. L. The orator's manual: treatise on vocal culture, emphasis and gesture, with selections. 2d ed. 12° $1.50
25. **Robert**, H. M. Rules of order for deliberative assemblies. (Pocket ed.) .... 75c.
26. **Rogers**, May. The Waverley dictionary: alphabetical arrangement of all characters in Scott's novels, with analysis of each, and selections from text. 12° $2.00
27. **Sainte-Beuve**, C. A. Monday chats; sel. and tr. by W. Mathews. 3d ed. 12° $2.00
28. **Taylor**, Benj. F. Between the gates. 12° .. $1.50
29. — Summer savory. 12° $1.00
30. **Tegnér**, Esaias. Fridthjof's saga; tr. by T. A. E. and M. A. L. Holcomb. 12° $1.50
31. **Viking** tales of the north: Sagas of Thorstein, viking's son, and Fridthjof the Bold; tr. from the Icelandic by R. B. Anderson; [also] Tegnér's Fridthjof's saga; tr. by G. Stephens. 12° .. $2.00
32. **Zur** Brücke, —. German without grammar or dictionary. pt. 1. 6th ed. 12° .... 50c.
33. — *Same.* pt. 2. 12° $1.25

SOWER, POTTS & CO.,

530 Market St., Philadelphia.

NET RETAIL PRICES.

1. **Brooks**, Edward. Union arithmetic: part 1 (primary). 16° .... 25c.
2. — — Part 2. 12° .... 45c.
3. — — Part 3. 12° .... 45c.
4. — Union arithmetic complete [pts. 2 and 3 bd. together]. 12° .... 90c.
5. — — Key. 12° $1.00
6. — New primary arithmetic. 16° .... 22c.
7. — New mental arithmetic. 16° .... 35c.
8. — — Key. 16° .... 38c.
9. — New written arithmetic. 12° .... 80c.
10. — — Key. 12° $1.00
11. — Higher arithmetic. 12° $1.25
12. — — Key. 12° $1.25
13. — Key to Geometry and trigonometry. 12° .. $1.00
14. — Philosophy of arithmetic. 12° $2.25
15. — Normal methods of teaching. 12° $1.75
16. **Lyte**, E. O. Institute glee book. pap., 20c.; bds., 38c.
17. — Institute songs. pap., 20c.; bds. .... 38c.
18. — School-room songs .... 15c.
19. **Montgomery**, J. V. Normal union system of drawing: primary series. nos. 1–8 .... ea., 10c.
20. — *Same:* 2d series. nos. 9–12 .... ea, 25c.
21. — Teacher's manual of drawing. 12° $1.50
22. **Westlake**, J. Willis. Common school literature. 16° .... 50c.

ADAMS & BISHOP,

46 Beekman Street, New York.

1. **The** Ladies' Floral Cabinet: a monthly journal devoted to floriculture and the household. per year $1.25
2. **Williams'** Pacific tourist and guide across the continent. cl., $2; flex. $1.50
3. **Window** gardening; by Henry T. Williams. cl. $1.50
4. **Household** elegancies; by H. T. Williams and Mrs. C. S. Jones. cl. $1.50
5. **Beautiful** homes; by H. T. Williams. cl. .. $1.50
6. **Ladies'** fancy work; by Mrs. C. S. Jones and Henry T. Williams. cl. $1.50
7. **Evening** amusements; or, how to entertain company; by Henry T. Williams and S. Annie Frost. cl. $1.50
8. **Ladies'** guide to needlework; by S. Annie Frost. cl., $1; pap. .... 50c.
9. **Williams'** Designs for needlework. 3 v. ea. 30c.
10. **Every** woman her own flower gardener; by Mrs. S. O. Johnson .... $1; 50c.
11. **Insects** on plants and how to destroy them. pap. 30c.
12. **Household** hints and recipes; by Mrs. S. O. Johnson. cl., $1; pap. .... 50c.

THOMAS NELSON & SONS,

42 Bleecker Street, New York.

1877.

1. **Arctic** world (The) illustrated. f°. cl...$6.50
2. **Bible** pictures for our pets. pt. 1: Old Testament pictures. pt. 2: New Testament pictures. ea., bds., $1; in 1 v., cl., gilt..................$2.00
3. **Birdie** and her dog. ill. 4°. cl.............$1.00
4. **Children's** (The) wreath. col. ill. 4°. bds...$1.25
5. **Crescent** library (The). 4 v. ill. 18°. cl...$2.00
6. **Daisy** chain (The). col. ill. 4°. bds........$1.25
7. **English** pictures; by Rev. Sam'l Manning, LL.D. 8°. cl., gilt..........................$3.50
8. **Forest**, jungle and prairie (The). 12°. cl...$1.00
9. **Great** shipwrecks, 1544 to 1877. ill. 8°. cl...$2.50
10. **Help** by the way: a daily monitor. 18° $1.00
11. **Little** Clara's picture gallery. ill. 4°. bds....50c.
12. **Little** Snowflake's album. ill. 4°. bds.......40c.
13. **Little** Sunbeam. ill. 4°. bds..............$1.00
14. **Medical** information and advice (Book of); by the late Dr. J. Warburton Bigbie, of Edinburgh. New and improved ed. 12°. cl. $1.25
15. **Mediterranean** (The): illustrated picturesque views, and descriptions of its cities, shores and islands. f°. cl., extra, full gilt $6.00
16. **Natural** history of the Bible; by M.K.M. 18°..$1.25
17. **Our** pet's library. 4 v. ill. 18°. cl. $3.00
18. **Pendower**: a story of Cornwall in the time of Henry VIII.; by M. Filleul. 12°. cl.......$2.00
19. **Recent** polar voyages: a record of adventure and discovery. 62 ill. and map. 8°. cl.......$2.50
20. **Scenes** with the hunter and trapper in many lands: stories of adventure with wild animals. 12°..$2.50
21. **Shakespeare's** Dramatic works. Annotated household ed.; with 370 ill. by the late Frank Howard, R.A. 8°. gilt................$3.50
22. **Story** of Sir Humphrey Davy. 18°. cl........50c.
23. **Story** of Benvenuto Cellini. 18°. cl., extra..50c.
24. **Turkish** empire (The): the sultans, the territory and the people; by Rev. T. Milner. New ed. 12°. cl. $1.50
25. **Twice** lost: a story of shipwreck and adventure in the wilds of Australia; by Kingston. 8° ..$2.00
26. **Wonders** of the heavens: — Nebulæ and comets; The planetary system; The sun and moon; The stars. ill. 18°. ea., cl. ....50c.
27. **Young** Llanero (The): a story of war and wild life in South America; by Kingston. 8° ..$2.00
28. **Nelly's** teachers and what they learned. 8°..$1.50

1878.

29. **A. L. O. E.** The children's posey. col. ill...$1.25
30. **All** pictures and stories. ill. 4°. bds.........50c.
31. **Arnot**, *Rev.* Wm. "Lessons from life:" stories and teachings for the young. 12°. cl......$1.00
32. **Ballantyne**, R. M. Stories for boys. New ed. ill. 12°. ea.............................$1.25
33. Deep down.
34. Golden dream (The).
35. In the track of the troops.
36. Life boat (The): a tale of our coast heroes.
37. Lighthouse (The); or, the story of a great fight between man and the sea.
38. Norseman (The) in the west; or, America before Columbus.
39. Pirate city: an Algerine tale.
40. Rivers of ice: a tale illustrative of Alpine adventure and glacier action.
41. **Barbauld**, *Mrs.* Hymns in prose for children; with 100 ill. by Giacomelli. 18°. cl., gilt $1.00
42. **Bird** world (The) described with pen and pencil; by W. H. Davenport Adams. (Uniform with Michelet's Bird.) 8°. cl., gilt $5.00
43. **Children's** birthday text book. (Interleaved.) 32°. cl..................................40c.
44. **Culross**, *Rev.* J. The home at Bethany: its joys, its sorrows and its divine guest. 12°. cl.....$1.25
45. "**Dew** drop series." 48 v. (assorted). 32°. per set, bds.......................................$4.80
46. **Favorite** nursery series. 10 v. ill. 4°. bds. ..$2.50
47. **Happy** hours in picture land. ill. 4°. bds. ..50c.
48. **Kingston**, W. H. G. In the Rocky Mountains: a tale of adventure. 41 ill. 12°. cl........$1.50
49. **Kiss** for a blow series. 24 v. ill. 32°. cl...$3.60
50. **Little** Lottie's picture gallery. ill. 4° ....50c.
51. **Manning**, *Rev.* S. French pictures illustrated by pen and pencil. ill. imp. 8°. cl., gilt $3.50
52. **My** own library. 6 v. ill. 16°. cl. $3.00
53. **National** nursery album. 96 col. ill. 18°. cl. ..$1.00
54. **Natural** history album. 500 col. ill. 18°. cl. ..$1.00
55. **Our** favorite nursery rhymes. 100 ill. 4°. cl. ..75c.
56. **Story** after story, of land, sea and beast. ill. 4°. cl. $1.25
57. **Symington**, *Rev.* A. M. The story of Esther, the queen; with an introduction. 12°. cl.....$1.25
58. **Tales** for the young. 14 v. ill. 16°. cl.....$2.80
59. **Young** rover (A). ill. 4°. bds............50c.
60. **Willing** heart series. 5 v. ill. 16°. cl.....$2.50
61. **Good** out of evil: a tale for children; by Mrs. Surr. 32 ill. 16°. cl......................75c.

1879.

62. **Aunt** Louisa's golden gift. col. ill. 4°. cl., $2.50
63. **Archie** Dunn's stories. ill. 12°. cl.........$1.00
64. **Basil** Grey; or, tried and true; by Rev. W. J. Bettison, M.A. ill. 12°. cl., extra........$1.00
65. **Bickersteth**, *Rev.* E. Family prayers. 12°..$1.25
66. **Boundary** tree (The), and other stories. 12°..50c.
67. **Christian** leaders (The) of the last century; or, England a hundred years ago; by Rev. J. C. Ryle, B.A. 8°. cl., extra....................$2.25
68. **Church** and state: three lectures delivered in St. George's Church, Edinburgh; by Robt. Rainy, D.D., Hon. Lord Moncreiff, A. Taylor Innes, Esq. 12°. cl................................$3.00
69. **Duff**, Alexander, *D.D., LL.D.* Recollections of, and of the mission college which he founded in Calcutta; by Rev. Lal Behari Day. 16°. cl...$1.50
70. **Euphrates** (The) and Tigris: narrative of discovery and adventure, with a description of the ruins of Babylon and Nineveh. ill. 16°...80c.
71. **Elijah** and Elisha; adapted to the use of Sunday school teachers. 12°. cl.................$1.25
72. **Eva** and Bertie: a tale for little children. ill. 12°. cl. ....50c.
73. **Esther** Ray, the hop-picker. ill. 12°. cl......50c.
74. **From** day to day; or helpful words for Christian life: (daily readings for a year); by Robert Macdonald, D.D. 8°. cl.................$2.00
75. **Famous** parks and gardens of the world, described and ill. 4°. cl., gilt.....................$6.50
76. **Galileo**, the astronomer of Pisa. col. frontispiece. 18°. cl......................................50c.
77. **Grace** Dermott; or, help for the afflicted. ill. 12°. cl., extra.................................50c.
78. **Gibraltar** and its sieges; with a description of its natural features. ill. 16°. cl. ....60c.
79. **Greatness** (The) of little things; by James Culross, D.D. 12°. cl...........................$1.25
80. **Golden** mushroom; by Sarah M. Fry. ill. 16°. cl. 50c.
81. **Golden** sheaves; or, Grace Reynolds. ill. 12°. cl., gilt $1.25

THOMAS NELSON & SONS,

Continued.

82. **Horæ** Paulinæ; by William Paley, M.A.; with an introduction by Wm. Binnie, D.D. 12°. cl...75c.
83. **In** the far east: a narrative of exploration and adventure in Cochin-China, Cambodia, Laos and Siam. ill. 16°. cl., extra....80c.
84. **In** the woods; by M. K. M.; with 34 ill. by Giacomelli. 12°. cl....$1.00
85. **Little** Tot's album. 130 ill. 4°. cl., extra..$1.50
86. **Little** Robin's picture book. ill. 4°. bds., 75c.; cl., extra....$1.00
87. **Little** Susy's picture album. ill. 4°. bds....75c.
88. **Little** things in daily life. 18°. cl., bev.....50c.
89. **Lionel** Franklin's victory; by E. Van Sommer. ill. post 8°. cl., extra....$1.25
90. **Little** May; or, of what use am I? ill. 12°..75c.
91. **Lillian**: a tale of three hundred years ago; by G. E. Sargent. ill. 12°. cl., extra....75c.
92. **Lands** of Scripture (The); compr. Those holy fields, The land of the Pharaohs, Pictures from Bible lands; by Rev. S. Manning, LL.D., and S. G. Green, D.D. ill. 8°. cl., gilt.....$10.00
93. **My** first story book. ill. 4°. bds., 75c.; cl. ..$1.00
94. **My** pretty book of pictures. ill. 4°. bds.....75c.
95. **Mount** Sinai, Petra and the Desert. 23 ill...80c.
96. **Mustard** and Cress: their surprising adventures, and the downfall of Burdock; by C. O. Murray. 24 col. ill. bds....$1.00
97. **New** Granada (In); or, heroes and patriots; by Kingston. ill. 12°. cl., extra....$1.50
98. **Nineteenth** century (The): a history, by Robert Mackenzie. 8°....$2.50
99. **Post** haste; by Ballantyne. ill. 12°. cl., extra $1.50
100. **Patty** Bailey; or, who knows best. ill. 12°. cl. 50c.
101. **Pictures** from Bible lands drawn with pen and pencil. ill. imp. 8°. cl., gilt....$3.50
102. **Royal** banner (The); or, gold and rubies. ill. 12°. cl....80c.
103. **River** Amazon (The) and its wonders; by author of "The Arctic world." ill. 16°. cl.......60c.
104. **Swedish** twins (The): a tale for the young; by author of "The babes in the basket." ill. 16°. cl....60c.
105. **Saved** at sea: a light-house story; by the author of "Chrystie's old organ." ill. sq. 16°....75c.
106. **Sought** and saved; by M. A. Paull. ill. 12°..$1.25
107. **Sir** David Wilkie (Story of): his life and works. ill. 16°. cl....80c.
108. **Shepherd's** call; by Rev. Robert Balgamie. ill. 12°. cl....$1.50
109. **True** to his colours; or, the life that wears best; by Rev. T. P. Wilson, M.A. 6 ill. 12°. cl., $1.25
110. **Tiny** workers; or, man's little rivals in the animal world. ill. 18°. cl. ....60c.
111. **Two** little Turks; or, getting into mischief. ill. 16°. cl....80c.
112. **Wenzel's** inheritance: a story of Bohemia in the 15th century; by Annie Lucas. 12°. cl., $2.00
113. **Was** I right? by Mrs. O. F. Walton. 16°..$1.75
114. **Women** worth emulating: a companion volume to "Men worth imitating." ill. 12°. cl...$1.00
115. **Wood** carvers (The). ill. 12°. cl. ....50c.
116. **While** they are with us; by Mrs. Coates. 12°..50c.
117. **Weir**, Harrison. Pictures of animals. 24 col. ill. large 4°. cl. $2.50
118. **Young** rebels (The). ill. 12°. cl.........$1.00
119. "**Good** time" series. 10 v. ill. 18°. cl. ..$2.00
120. **My** book shelf. 4 v. ill. 18°. cl.........$1.60
121. "**Little** Sunshine" series. 12 v. ill. 18°. bds., $4.20
122. **My** story box. 12 v. ill. 18°. cl.........$2.40
123. **Garland** series (The). 10 v. ill. 18°. cl. ..$2.50
124. **Lilydale** series (The). 6 v. 18°. cl. $2.10
125. **Short** story series. 24 v. ill. 32°. bds. ..$3.60
126. **Picture** album series (The). 12 v. 16°...$3.60
127. **Library** of pictures and stories. 6 v. 16°..$2.10
128. **Child's** (The) favorite series. 6 v. ill. 4°..$3.00
129. **Little** Snowball series. 6 v. ill. 4°. cl. ..$4.50
130. **Bluff** crag series (The). 10 v. ill. 18°. cl...$3.00
131. "**Herschel**" series (The). 4 v. ill. 16°....$2.00
132. "**May** flower" series (The). 4 v. ill. 16°. cl., $2.00
133. "**Robin**" series (The). 4 v. ill. 16°. cl. ..$2.00
134. **Library** of travel and adventure. 6 v....$4.80
135. **Picture** gift-book series (The). 20 v. 32°..$3.50
136. "**Amazon**" series (The). 4 v. ill. 16°. cl. ..$3.20
137. **Little** Susy's series. 4 v. ill. 4°. bds. ...$3.00
138. **Nelson's** Sunday-school library. 35 v. ill. 18°. cl., extra....$12.00

J. W. BOUTON,

706 Broadway, New York.

1876–1880.

1. **Inman**, Thomas, *M.D.* Ancient faiths and modern. 8°. 1876. cl....$5.00
2. **Unger**, William. Works: 72 etchings after the old masters. 10 pts. f°. 1876....$60.00
3. **Planché**, J. R. Encyclopædia of costume. 4°. 1877. hf. mor....$25.00
4. **Mackenzie**, K. R. H. Royal Masonic cyclopædia. 8°. 1877. cl....$7.00
5. **Caxton**, William. Dictes and sayings of the philosophers: facsimile of ed. of 1477. 4°. 1877. cl....$10.00
6. **Michelet**, Jules. Bible of humanity. 8°. 1877. cl....$3.00
7. **Simpson**, Richard. School of Shakspere. 2 v. 12°. 1878. cl....$4.00
8. **Yarker**, John. Mysteries of antiquity. 2d ed. 12°. 1878. cl....$2.00
9. **Kelley**, E. G., *M.D.* Philosophy of existence. 8°. 1878. cl....$5.00
10. **Loubat**, J. F., *LL.D.* Medallic history of the United States. 2 v. ill. 4°. 1878. cl. ..$30.00
11. **Stanfield**, Clarkson. Coast scenery of England. 4°. 1879. cl....$5.0
12. **Weisse**, John A., *M.D.* Origin and progress of English language. 8°. 1879. cl....$5.00
13. **Jennings**, Hargrave. Rosicrucians. 2d ed. 12°. 1879. cl....$2.50
14. **Blavatzky**, *Mme.* Isis unveiled. 4th ed. 2 v. 8°. 1879. cl....$7.50
15. **Inman**, Thomas, *M.D.* Ancient pagan symbolism. 3d ed. 8°. 1880. cl....$3.00
16. **Our** early emigrant ancestors. 2d ed. 4°. 1880. cl....$5.00
17. **Jones**, Owen. Grammar of ornament. 28 pts. f°. 1880....$28.00
18. **Rowlandson**, the caricaturist. 2 v. 400 ill. 4°. 1880....$20.00

POTT, YOUNG & CO.,

Cooper Union, New York.

1. **Ancient** history from the monuments. ill. 16°. ea., cl. ....75c.
2. Assyria, from the earliest times to the fall of Nineveh; by the late George Smith.
3. Babylonia (History of); by the late George Smith; ed. by Rev. A. H. Sayce.
4. Egypt, from the earliest times to B. C. 300; by S. Birch, LL.D.
5. Greek cities and islands of Asia Minor; by W. S. W. Vaux, M.A., F.R.S.
6. Persia, from the earliest period to the Arab conquest; by W. S. W. Vaux, M.A., F.R.S.
7. Sinai, from the fourth Egyptian dynasty to the present day; by Major H. S. Palmer; with map and ill.
8. **Commentary** on the Holy Bible, according to the authorized version, with a brief commentary; by various authors. Old Testament. v. 1, Pentateuch; v. 2, Historical books, Joshua to Esther; v. 3, Poetical books, Job to Song of Solomon. New Testament. v. 1, Four Gospels; v. 2, Acts to Revelations. maps and plans. 12°. cl., red edges, per v............................$2.00
9. **Conversion** of the West. maps. 16°. ea., cl., 75c.
10. The continental Teutons; by Dean Merivale.
11. The Celts; by Rev. G. F. Maclear.
12. The Northmen; by Rev. G. F. Maclear.
13. The English; by Rev. G. F. Maclear.
14. The Slavs; by Rev. G. F. Maclear.
15. **Cutts**, *Rev.* E. L. Turning points of English church history. 12°. cl.................$1.25
16. — Turning points of general church history. 12°. cl...$1.50
17. **Early** chroniclers of Europe. 12°. ea., cl....$1.50
18. England; by James Gairdner.
19. France; by Gustave Masson.
20. **Fathers** (The) for English readers. 16°. ea.,cl.,75c.
21. The Apostolic fathers; by Rev. H. S. Holland.
22. The defenders of the faith; or, the Christian apologists of the second and third centuries; by Rev. F. Watson.
23. Saint Augustine; by Rev. W. B. Clark, M.A.
24. Saint Jerome; by Rev. E. L. Cutts.
25. Saint Basil; by Rev. Canon Smith.
26. Saint Ambrose; by Rev. R. Thornton, D.D.
27. Gregory the Great; by Rev. J. Barmby.
28. The Venerable Bede; by Professor Brown.
29. **Heathen** world (The) and St. Paul. maps. fp. 8°. ea., cl. ....75c.
30. St. Paul in Damascus and Arabia; by Rev. George Rawlinson, M.A.
31. St. Paul in Greece; by Rev. G. S. Davies, M.A.
32. St. Paul at Rome; by Very Rev. Charles Merivale, D.D.
33. St. Paul in Asia Minor and at the Syrian Antioch; by Rev. E. H. Plumptre, M.A.
34. **Home** library (The). 12°. ea., cl.........$1.50
35. House of God (The) the home of man; by Rev. G. E. Jelf, M.A.
36. Inner life (The), as revealed in the correspondence of celebrated Christians; edited by the late Rev. T. Erskine.
37. Savonarola: his life and times; by Rev. William R. Clark, M.A.
38. Great English churchmen; or, memorable names in English church history and literature; by W. H. Davenport Adams.
39. Narcissus: a tale of early Christian times; by Rev. W. Boyd Carpenter, M.A.
40. The military religious orders of the middle ages; by F. C. Woodhouse, M.A.
41. **Non-Christian** religious systems. maps. 8°. ea., cl. $1.25
42. Buddhism: sketch of the life and teachings of Gautama the Buddha; by J. W. Rhys Davids.
43. Hinduism; by Monier Williams.
44. Islam and its founder; by J. W. H. Stobart.
45. The Corân: its composition and teaching, and the testimony it bears to Holy Scriptures; by Sir William Muir.
46. Confucianism and Taouism; by Robert K. Douglas.

E. STEIGER,

25 Park Place, New York.

1. **Ahn-Henn's** German reading charts........$1.00
2. **Ahn**, F: [German series, ed.] by P. Henn. 12°.
   Cont.: Synopsis of German grammar, bds., 60c.; hf. roan, 80c. — Second German reader, with notes and vocab., or with foot notes and vocab., ea., bds., $1; hf. roan, $1.20. — Key, bds., 50c.
3. **Ahn's** German dialogues. no. 1. 12°. bds., 25c.; cl. ....35c.
4. **Ahn**, F: [French series, ed.] by P. Henn. 12°.
   Cont.: Elements of French grammar, bds., 35c. — Second French reader, with notes and vocab., or with foot notes and vocab., ea., bds., 80c.; hf. roan, $1. — Key, bds., 40c.
5. **Ahn-Henn's** French reading charts........$1.00
6. **Ahn's** French dialogues. no. 1. 12°. bds., 30c.; no. 2, bds., 25c.; no. 3, bds. ....30c.
7. **Ahn-Oehlschläger's** pronouncing method of the German language. (Edition of 1879.) 8°.
   Cont.: First part, bds., 80c.; hf. roan, $1.— Second, bds., 40c.; hf. roan, 60c. — Complete, bds., $1.15; hf. roan, $1.40. — Key, bds., 40c.
8. **Ahn-Henn's** Latin wall charts.............$1.50
9. **Ahn**, F: [Latin series, ed.] by P. Henn. 12°.
   Cont.: First Latin book, bds., 60c.; cl., 70c. — Key, bds., 40c.— Second Latin book, bds., 70c.; cl., 80c. — Key, bds., 40c. — Latin vocabulary for beginners, methodical and etymological, bds., 60c.; cl., 70c.
10. **Freut** euch des Lebens! Taschenliederbuch. 32°. bds., 40c.; cl.................................60c.
11. **Kraus-Boelte**, M., *and* J. Kraus. Kindergarten guide. no. 1. ill. 8°. pap., 35c.; cl., 65c.; no. 2, pap., 70c.; cl., $1; no. 3, pap., 50c.; cl., 80c.; no. 4, pap., 70c.; cl. $1.00
12. **Peabody**, E. P., *and* Mary Mann. Guide to the kindergarten. 12°.......................$1.35
13. — — After kindergarten, what? a primer of reading. 12°. bds................................45c.
14. **Reffelt**, H. Fünftes Buch für Schule und Haus. 12°. bds..75c.
15. — Wandtafeln für den Unterricht im Lesen und Schreiben $1.00
16. **Schumacher**, Herm. A. Petrus Martyr, der Geschichtsschreiber des Weltmeeres. 4°. pap., $1.25; limp cl...................................$1.75
17. **Steiger's** designs for kindergarten occupations. 12 nos. ea.......................................30c.
18. **Steiger's** educational directory for 1878. 8°. limp cl..$1.50
19. **Watson**, J. Madison. Handbook of calisthenics and gymnastics. ill. 8°. $2. — Manual of calisthenics. ill. 8°.................................$1.20
20. **Year-book** (The) of education for 1878. 8°. cl. $2. — for 1879. cl...............................$2.00

JOHN E. POTTER & CO.,

617 Sansom Street, Philadelphia.

1. **Affection's** gift. 32° ....50c.
2. **Album** (The) of love. 32° ....50c.
3. **Barnwell**, R. Grant. The Russo-Turkish war; with the Servian insurrection, massacre of Christians, etc. maps, plans and eng. 12° $2.50
4. **Blackwood**, *Rev.* William (*ed.*) Potter's popular encyclopedia of universal religious knowledge. 6 v. 4°. $5. 3 v. hf. tur.............$12.00
5. **Blair**, Hugh. Beauties of Blair. 32°........50c.
6. **Bridal** wreath (The). 32°..................50c.
7. **Burke**, Edmund. Beauties of. 32°.........50c.
8. **Butterworth**, John. Concordance to the Holy Scriptures. New ed., enl. by Dr. Adam Clarke. 8°. $1.50; shp. $2.00
9. **Clark**, W. Gaylord. Select poems. 32° .....50c.
10. **Fenno**, Frank H. Science and art of elocution: how to read and speak. 12°.............$1.25
11. **Floral** gift (The). 32° ....50c.
12. **Gerard** the lion slayer, and other stories; or, the romance of adventure. ill. 16°...........$1.25
13. **Heart's-ease**: a floral offering. 32° .... 50c.
14. **Hemans**, *Mrs.* Felicia. Poetical works; ed. by Rufus W. Griswold. 12°. $2; full gilt...$2.50
15. **Hillyard**, W. Heard. The little trapper, and other stories. ill. 16° $1.25
16. **Homer.** Iliad; tr. by Alexander Pope; with notes, ed. by W. C. Armstrong. 12°. $2; gilt..$2.50
17. — Odyssey; tr. by Alexander Pope; with notes, ed. by W. C. Armstrong. 12°. $2; gilt......$2.50
18. **Illustrated** handbook to all religions. 12°...$2.00
19. **Josephus**, Flavius. Complete works; with index. por. 8°. $3; shp. $3.50
20. **Keepsake** (The). 32°.....................50c.
21. **Language** (The) of flowers. 32° ....50c.
22. **Language** (The) of love. 32° ....50c.
23. **More**, Hannah. Letters to young ladies. 32°..50c.
24. **Lily** (The) of the valley. 32°..............50c.
25. **Maria** Celeste, *Sister*. Private life of Galileo; compiled by his eldest daughter. 12°......$1.50
26. **Men** who have risen: biographies of inventors, discoverers, merchants, etc. ill. 16° $1.25
27. **Montgomery**, James. Poetical works. steel eng. 8°. $2.50; gilt.........................$3.00
28. **Moore**, Thomas. Poetical works. New Am. ed. 12°. $2; full gilt $2.50
29. **Morier**, James. Hajji Baba in Persia, Turkey and Russia. ill. 12°........................$1.75
30. **Napoleon** and his campaigns, his army and his generals. eng. 12° $1.75
31. **Osgood**, *Mrs.* Frances Sargent. Poetical works. steel pl. 12°. $2; full gilt $2.50
32. **Poetical** fortune-teller (The). 32°..........50c.
33. **Poetry** (The) of love. 32° ....50c.
34. **Proctor**, *Major* George. History of the crusades. ill. 12° $1.75
35. **Raum**, John O. History of New Jersey from its earliest settlement to the present time. 2 v. 8°. ea., $3; shp., $4; hf. tur., roxb..........$5.00
36. **Robert** Warren; or, the Texan refugee: story of the late civil war. 12°..................$1.75
37. **Shakespeare**, William. Dramatic and poetical works; with notes and comments, and biog. sketch by J. Payne Collier. 8 v. in 4. 12°. $2; full gilt $2.50
38. **Stolz**, John. Cause and cure of crime. 12°..$1.75
39. **That** mother-in-law of mine. 16° $1.00
40. **Verne**, Jules. A winter amid the ice, and other stories. ill. 12° $1.75
41. **Violet**; or, thoughts among flowers. 32°.....50c.
42. **Sigourney**, *Mrs.* L. H. Poetical works. 12°. $2; full gilt $2.50
43. **Tupper**, Martin Farquhar, *A.M.F.R.S.* Proverbial philosophy, Thousand lines, Hactenus, etc. 12°. $2; full gilt..........................$2.50
44. **Atlantis**, *Mrs.* A. A. Mildred Brainridge. 16°. $1.25
45. **Dashwell**, *Rev.* The new minister at Hampton. 16° $1.00
46. **Bonsall**, J. Northern tourist's book of summer travel. 150 ill. 8°. 50c.; cl. $1.00

PUBLICATIONS OF

THE BANKER'S MAGAZINE OFFICE

(Formerly I. S. Homans),

251 Broadway, New York.

1. **Banker's** (The) Almanac and Register, 1851–'80. 8°. per v..............................$2.00
2. **Banker's** (The) Magazine and Statistical Register, 1846–'79: monthly. $5 per year; per no. ..50c.
3. **Chappell**, Philip E. Bond, stock and note values; at any rate of interest, 6 mos. to 20 yrs. 4°.$3.00
4. **Cook**, C. C. The rate-inlaid interest tables (4 to 10%) and account averager. 4° $6.00
5. **Diggs**, D. W. Money of all nations equalized, and currency rates of sterling exchange. 12°....$1.00
6. **Legal-tender** cases of 1871: decisions of the U. S. Supreme Court, Dec. term, 1870; with notes of 44 cases quoted or referred to in the opinions. 8°......................................$1.50
7. **Lovett**, Robert K. Manual of foreign exchange. 8°.......................................$1.50
8. **Macleod**, Henry Dunning. Economics for beginners. sm. cr. 8°.......................$1.00
9. **National** bank laws of the United States, arranged in topical and numerical order; with index. 8°. $1; gilt $1.25
10. **Thompson**, A. S. Common-sense time-tables, showing maturities at 30, 60, 90, or 120 days. 8°...$1.00
11. **Tower**, J. V. R. Premium tables for buying and selling gold, bonds and stocks. 4° $2.00
12. **Weston**, George M. The silver question. 8°. $1.25

S. E. CASSINO,

299 Washington St., Boston.

1. **Butler**, S. Evolution, old and new. 12°....$2.50
2. **Eaton**, D. C. Ferns of North America. 2 v. col. pl. 4° $30.00
3. **Emerton**, J. H. Structure and habits of spiders. ill. 12° $1.50
4. **Gentry**, T. G. Life-histories of birds. 2 v. 12°. $4.00
5. **Goodale**, G. L. Wild flowers of America. pts. 1-9. ill. 4°. ea. $1.50
6. **Granville**, J. M. Common mind troubles. 3d ed. fp. 8° ....50c.
7. — Secret of a clear head. 3d ed. fp. 8°......50c.
8. **Minot**, H. D. Land-birds and game-birds of New England. ill. 8°, 456 p.................$3.00
9. **Robinson**, J. Ferns in their homes and ours. ill. 12°..$1.50

SCRIBNER & CO.,

743 and 745 Broadway, New York.

1. **Baby** days: a selection of songs, stories and pictures from St. Nicholas. New ed., with music. 8°. '79, $2.00.
2. **Portfolio** of proof impressions; selected from Scribner's Monthly and St. Nicholas: 102 proofs, 14 × 11. 4°. '79. cl., $10.00.
3. **Robinson**, C. S. Spiritual songs, with music, for the church and the choir. 8°, 441 p. '79. cl., $1.50; flex. leath., $1.75; silk, $2.50; rus., $5.00
4. — Spiritual songs for social worship. (An abridgment of Spiritual songs, with some additions, for use in prayer-meetings.) 8°, 237 p. '79. cl., 75c.; silk, $1.25.
5. — *and* R. S. MacArthur. The Calvary selection of spiritual songs, with music, for the church and the choir; for use in Baptist churches. 8°, 441 p. '79. cl., $1.50; flex. leath., $1.75; silk, $2.50; rus., $5.00.
6. **Scribner's** Monthly Illustrated Magazine; conducted by J. G. Holland: monthly. 8°, 160 p.; begun in '70. Yearly subscriptions, $4; single nos., 35c.; — bound vols., 6 months, cl., $3; mor. backs, $4.00.
7. **Index** to Scribner's Monthly Illustrated Magazine (v. 1–10). 8°. '76. pap., $1.50; cl., $2; mor. backs, $3.00.
   (An Index to the first 20 vols. will be ready during 1880.)
8. **St. Nicholas**: Scribner's illustrated magazine for girls and boys: conducted by Mary Mapes Dodge: monthly. 8°, 80 p., begun in '73. Yearly subscriptions, $3; single nos., 25c.; — bound vols., 12 months, cl., $4; cl. gilt, $5.00.

ST. NICHOLAS GAMES.

9. **Protean** cards: fifty games in one box; by the editor of St. Nicholas: 104 cards, with book of directions, 56 p. New ed. '80. pasteboard boxes, $1; ebonized wood boxes, $1.50.
10. **Stratford** game of characters and quotations, and the Stratford Solitaire. New ed. '80. 50 cards, in pasteboard boxes, 75c.

Books formerly published by A. S. Barnes & Co., plates and copyrights purchased by Scribner & Co., May, 1879.

11. **Robinson**, C. S. Chapel songs: selections from "Songs for the sanctuary." 8°, 218 p. '74. cl., $1; leath. gilt, $2; rus., $4; bds., 80c.; — (with Psalter), $1.40; $2.50; $5; bds., $1.10.
12. — Memorial pulpit: 52 sermons. 2 v. 12°, 636 p. '73. cl., $3.00.
13. — Psalms and hymns and spiritual songs: hymns and tunes. 8°, 535 p. '75. cl., $2; leath., gilt, $3.75; rus., $5.60; — (with Psalter), $2.25; $4; $5.90. — (Hymns only.) 12°, 290 p. cl., 60c.
14. — Songs for the sanctuary [Cong., Pres. and Bapt. eds.]; or, hymns and tunes for Christian worship. 8°, 482 p. '72. cl., $2; leath. gilt, $3.75; rus., $5.60; — (with Psalter), $2.25; $4; $5.90. — (Hymns only.) 12°, 846 p. '70. $2; $3.75; $5.60. — (Hymns only.) 16°, 827 p. '77. $1.25; $2.50; $4.00.
15. — Songs for Christian worship in the chapel and family. (An abridgment of Songs of the church.) 8°, 302 p. '69. cl., $1.50; leath., gilt, $3.50; rus., $5.50.
16. — Songs of the church; or, hymns and tunes for Christian worship. [Cong. and Pres. eds.] 8°, 396 p. '62. cl., $2; leath., gilt, $3.50; rus., $5.50.
17. **The Psalter**; for responsive reading. 8°, 86 p. '72. cl., 50c.; rus., $2.50.

IVISON, BLAKEMAN, TAYLOR & CO.,

138 and 140 Grand Street, New York.

1. **American** educational phonic charts: 4 in set, on rollers; with hand-book. per set..........60c.
2. **Bryant**, H. B., *and* Stratton, H. D. New counting-house bookkeeping. 8°..............$2.00
3. **Institute** reader. 12°......................25c.
4. **Lockwood**, John. Topical brief of Swinton's Outlines of history. 12°..............30c.
5. **Loomis**, George B. Progressive chorus and glee book. bk. 5. 8°..........................84c.
6. **Monsanto**, H. M. French student's assistant. 12°. 35c.
7. **Parshall**, N. C. Graded exercises in English grammar. 12°................................36c.
8. **Robinson**, Horatio N. Elements of arithmetic. 12°..40c.
9. **Spencer**, Lyman P. Spencerian copy books: shorter course. 7 nos. per doz., 84c.; covers, per 100......................................80c.
10. — Spencerian (New) compendium of penmanship. pts. 1, 2. 4°. ea..........................50c.
11. **Swett**, John. Normal word book. 12°......18c.
12. **Swinton**, William. New word analysis. 12°.35c.
13. — Primary geography. 8°......................54c.
14. **Webster**, Noah. Diacritical charts, in sheets, 30c.; on bds...60c.
15. **Wells**, David A. Natural philosophy. New ed. 12°. pt. 1, 55c.; pt. 2, 65c.; in 1 v........$1.15
16. **White**, George G. Industrial drawing series: — Primary drawing books, 1, 2, per doz., 84c.; Primary drawing, 12 cards, per set, 18c.; Dictation lessons, 30c.; Drawing books, no. 1, 2, 3, ea., 12c.; no. 4, 5, 6, ea., 15c.; Exercise book, large, per doz., $1; small, per doz. ....85c.
17. — Geometrical drawing books. 2 nos. ea.....15c.
18. — Model and object drawing books. no. 11, 18c.; no. 12..25c.
19. — Perspective drawing books. 2 nos. ea. ...18c.
20. — Primary cards, 22c.; Manual, 22c.; Practice paper, per pack.............................15c.
21. — Progressive art studies: — Elementary series, 4 nos., ea., 30c.; Manual for same, 10c.; Ornamental, 2 nos., ea., 30c.; Manual, 10c.; Ornamental C. (2 nos. in 1 v.) 50c.; Manual, 10c.; Landscape ser., 3 nos., ea., 30c.; Manual, 10c.; Instrumental ser., 4 nos., ea., 30c.; Manual, 10c.; Drawing paper, per pack ....26c.

ESTES & LAURIAT,

301 Washington St., Boston.

1. **American** Art Review (The): a journal devoted to the practice, theory, history and archæology of art. per year.......................$12.00
2. **Baby's** pleasure book; by author of "Holidays at home." ill. large 8°. bds..................75c.
3. **Butterworth,** H. Zigzag journeys in Europe: vacation rambles in historic lands, with stories and legends connected with the scenes visited. ill. sm. 4°. $1.50; cl., $2; cl. gilt $2.25
4. **Chatterbox** for 1879: an authorized reprint from duplicates of the original English plates. 4°. bds., $1.25; cl., $1.75; cl. gilt............$2.25
5. **De Colange,** L. The dictionary of commerce, manufactures, commercial law, banking, exchange, insurance (fire, marine and life), patents, canals, commercial geography of the world, etc. To form 25 nos. ill. sup. roy. 8°. ea., 50c.; — in 2 v. cl., $13.50; shp., $15; hf. mor....$16.50
6. **Dickens,** Charles. Works. New ed., printed from new plates. 15 v. ill. $22.50; hf. cf., or hf. mor...............................$50.00
7. **Drake,** Samuel Adams. History of Middlesex County, Mass., from the earliest times to the present day. 2 v. ill. large roy. 8°. ea., cl., $7.50; hf. mor...............................$10.00
8. **Ferns** (The) of North America; cont. ill. and descript. of every species known to inhabit the U. S.; with pl. drawn and col. after nature by J. H. Emerton: text by Prof. D. C. Eaton and other naturalists. 2 v...................$30.00
9. **Findlay,** Philip. Our baby's primer and pretty picture book for the youngest children. ill. sm. 4°. bds.................................30c.
10. **Granville,** J. M. Common mind troubles: essays on failings, defects of memory, confusions of thought, sleeplessness from thought, etc. 16°. 50c.
11. **Half-hour** recreations in popular science: second ser.: — Transmission of sound by the atmosphere, by John Tyndall; Gigantic cuttle-fish, by Saville Kent; The glacial epoch of our globe, by Alexander Braun; The sun and the earth, by Prof. Balfour Stewart; The ice age in Britain, by Prof. Geikie; Plant life in the sea, by L. Kny; The telephone and the phonograph, by Prof. F. J. Garbit; The use and abuse of food, Ozone, Dew; The levelling power of rain, by Richard A. Proctor; The succession of life on the earth, by Prof. W. C. Williamson; What the earth is composed of, by Prof. Roscoe; Notes on tree growth, by Prof. Asa Gray; Science and war, by H. Baden Pritchard; Existence of glacial action upon the summit of Mt. Washington, N. H., by Prof. C. H. Hitchcock. large 12°. cl......$2.50
12. **Hamilton,** Gail. Our common school system. 16°. cl..................................$1.50
13. **Home** book (The) of poetry: compilation from the best Eng. and Am. poets. New ed. 22 steel pl. sm. 4°. cl. gilt, $5; tr. cf. $10.00
14. **Lallanne,**—. On etching: complete exposition of the processes employed, with 10 ill. plates by the author: text tr. by S. R. Koehler, with an introd. chapter. Authorized ed., with pl. from the originals: pl. on Holland pap. 8°. $3.50; limited ed., 100 copies only, India proof pl........$6.00
15. **Lilly's** day and what she did with it: one day's life of little Lilly, with her haps and mishaps. ill. sm. 4°. bds.............................50c.
16. **Little** Jack's adventures: story of a little Breton boy. ill. sm. 4°. bds....................50c.
17. **Little** May and her lost A: the wonderful adventures of a very little girl. ill. sm. 4°. bds...50c.
18. **Masson,** Gustave. Outlines of the history of France, from the earliest times to the outbreak of the revolution: abridgment of Guizot's "Popular history of France from the earliest times;" for schools, colleges and families; with maps, chronological index, historical and genealogical tables, por., etc. 8°. cl.........................$3.00
19. **Original** Chatterbox album (The) of animals: a series of Chatterbox pictures, illustrating the life of our domestic animals, and descript. of some queer creatures of the animal world. ill. roy. 8°. bds., $1.25; cl. $1.75
20. **Original** Chatterbox picture gallery (The): a series of the best pictures sel. from the past vols. of the Chatterbox; with verse to each picture. ill. roy. 8°. bds., $1.25; cl. $1.75
21. **Original** Chatterbox stories (The): 200 Chatterbox ill. and text. 4°. bds...............$1.00
22. **Rambaud,**—. Popular history of Russia, from the earliest times to 1880. 3 v. roy. 8°. ea., $5.50; shp., $6.50; hf. cf., $7.50; hf. mor........$7.50
23. **Richards,** Laura E. The little tyrant: story with a moral. ill. sm. 4°. bds. ....50c.
24. **Walter,** *Rev.* J. E. The perception of space and matter: a review of the theories of Reid, Hamilton, Bain and Spencer, and an independent discussion of the cognition of space and matter. cr. 8°. cl...............................$2.00
25. **White,** Alexina B. Little-folk songs: nursery ditties. ill. sm. 4°. bds.....................75c.
26. **Wild** flowers (The) of America; with ill. from original water-color paintings by Isaac Sprague, and text, with scientific and popular nomenclature, by George Goodale. To form 25 parts. ea.......................................$1.50
27. **World's** (The) worship in stone, temple, cathedral and mosque: 150 ill., cont. accurate views of some of the most noted monuments of architectural art of all ages and countries; with descript. text by M. M. Ripley. large 4°. cl.......$6.00
28. **Yonge,** Charlotte M. Histories for young folks: — Young folks' history of France; Rome; America; Germany; Greece; England. ill. 16°. ea...$1.50

INDEX

TO BOOKS CONTAINED IN APPENDIX.

AUTHORS AND TITLES.

To facilitate reference, the books of each publisher have been numbered consecutively and the number included in the Index reference. For list of publishers (giving page number) see first part of Appendix.

T5-ANX-581

The Best Teachers' Test Preparation for the

GACE®

Basic Skills

TestWare® Edition

Judith F. Robbins, Ph.D.
Susan T. Franks, Ed.D.
Dana Sparkman, Ph.D.
Kymberly A. Harris, Ph.D.
Georgia Southern University
Statesboro, GA

Visit our Educator Support Center at:
www.REA.com/teacher

Research & Education Association
61 Ethel Road West
Piscataway, New Jersey 08854
E-mail: info@rea.com

The Best Teachers' Test Preparation for the
Georgia GACE® Basic Skills Test
With TestWare® on CD-ROM

Published 2011

Printed in the United States of America

Library of Congress Control Number 2008942502

ISBN-13: 978-0-7386-0512-8
ISBN-10: 0-7386-0512-3

G10-0101

About Research & Education Association

Founded in 1959, Research & Education Association is dedicated to publishing the finest and most effective educational materials—including software, study guides, and test preps—for students in middle school, high school, college, graduate school, and beyond.

REA's Test Preparation series includes books and software for all academic levels in almost all disciplines. Research & Education Association publishes test preps for students who have not yet entered high school, as well as for high school students preparing to enter college. Students from countries around the world seeking to attend college in the United States will find the assistance they need in REA's publications. For college students seeking advanced degrees, REA publishes test preps for many major graduate school admission examinations in a wide variety of disciplines, including engineering, law, and medicine. Students at every level, in every field, with every ambition can find what they are looking for among REA's publications.

REA's practice tests are always based upon the most recently administered exams and include every type of question that you can expect on the actual exams.

REA's publications and educational materials are highly regarded and continually receive an unprecedented amount of praise from professionals, instructors, librarians, parents, and students. Our authors are as diverse as the fields represented in the books we publish. They are well-known in their respective disciplines and serve on the faculties of prestigious high schools, colleges, and universities throughout the United States and Canada.

Today, REA's wide-ranging catalog is a leading resource for teachers, students, and professionals.

We invite you to visit us at *www.rea.com* to find out how REA is making the world smarter.

Acknowledgments

We would like to thank Larry Kling, Vice President, Editorial, for his editorial direction; Pam Weston, Vice President, Publishing, for setting the quality standards for production integrity and managing the publication to completion; John Cording, Vice President, Technology, for coordinating the design, development, and testing of REA's TestWare® software; Alice Leonard, Senior Editor, for project management and preflight editorial review; Diane Goldschmidt, Senior Editor, for post-production quality assurance; Amy Jamison and Heena Patel, Technology Project Managers, for their software testing efforts; Christine Saul, Senior Graphic Artist, for cover design; Rachel DiMatteo, Graphic Artist, for test design; and Jeff LoBalbo, Senior Graphic Artist, for post-production file mapping.

We also gratefully acknowledge Christina Alex and Anne McGowan for copyediting, Kathy Caratozzolo of Caragraphics for typesetting, Ellen Gong for proofreading, and Brooke Graves for indexing the manuscript.

About the Authors

Dr. Susan Franks, the coauthor of the reading section of this test preparation book, has a distinguished career as an Associate Professor of Early Childhood Education in the Department of Teaching and Learning at Georgia Southern University, Statesboro, Georgia. Dr. Franks earned her Ed.D. from Virginia Polytechnic Institute and State University in Elementary Education with a specialty in Curriculum and Instruction. Dr. Franks is a frequent presenter at national and international conferences. She has an ongoing program of consultant work with classroom teachers.

In her early career, Dr. Franks played a major role in the development and implementation of a formal, written K–8 curriculum for the Choctaw Tribal School District, Choctaw, Mississippi.

Dr. Judith F. Robbins, coauthor of the GACE Basic Skills reading section, enjoys a long-term career as an Associate Professor of Early Childhood Education at the College of Education at Georgia Southern University where she conducts courses in Language Arts, with the additional focus on Lab School participation by student teachers. In addition, Dr. Robbins is a faculty member at the Center for Excellence in Teaching at Georgia Southern University. The center is a uniquely faculty-driven institution that is dedicated to the inspiration and advancement of outstanding and innovative teachers. Her Ph.D. was earned at Florida State University with a major in Reading and Language Arts. Dr. Robbins is frequently invited to be a presenter at national and international conferences.

Drs. Franks and Robbins collaborate often on programs and publications for teachers.

Dr. Dana Sparkman, author of the mathematics portion of this book, has devoted her career to the education of teachers. Dr. Sparkman earned her Ph.D., with a major in Elementary Education, from the University of Alabama. As an Assistant Professor in the Department of Teaching and Learning at Georgia Southern University, Dr. Sparkman teaches a full range of mathematics courses for future teachers. She is a current member of the Georgia Council of Teachers of Mathematics, and the Georgia Educational Research Association. Dr. Sparkman often presents papers at international and national conferences.

Dr. Kymberly A. Harris, author of the writing portion of this book, earned her Ph.D. with a special emphasis on Interdisciplinary Education, at the University of Alabama. She is also a member of the Teaching and Learning Department at Georgia Southern University where she teaches, among others, the Practicum and Field Study courses. Dr. Harris is a frequent presenter at national and international conferences.

Contents

CHAPTER

Introduction

1

About This Book and TestWare®

REA's *The Best Teachers' Test Preparation for the GACE Basic Skills Test* with TestWare® on CD-ROM is a comprehensive guide designed to assist you in preparing to take the GACE Basic Skills Test, which is a requirement to teach in Georgia (unless an exemption is granted). To help you to succeed in this important step toward your teaching career in Georgia schools, this test guide, along with REA's exclusive TestWare® software, features:

- An accurate and complete overview of the GACE Basic Skills Test
- The information you need to know about the exam
- A targeted review of each subarea
- Tips and strategies for successfully completing standardized tests
- Diagnostic tools to identify areas of strength and weakness
- Two full-length, true-to-format practice tests based on the most recently administered GACE Basic Skills Test
- Detailed explanations for each answer on the practice tests. These allow you to identify correct answers and understand not only why they are correct but also why the other answer choices are incorrect.

When creating this test prep, the authors and editors considered the most recent test administrations and professional standards. They also researched information from the Georgia Department of Education, professional journals, textbooks, and educators. The result is the best GACE test preparation materials based on the latest information available.

About Test Selection

The GACE are conducted during morning and afternoon test sessions. Test sessions are four hours in length. The morning session has a reporting time of 7:45 A.M. and ends at approximately 12:30 P.M. The afternoon session has a reporting time of 1:00 P.M. and ends at approximately 5:45 P.M. You may select tests for a single test session or for both the morning and afternoon test sessions.

The number of tests you may register to take in one test session is determined by the assessment(s) for which you are registering. Each assessment consists of one or more tests. Because you are registering for an assessment that includes multiple tests, you may take one, two, or all three Basic Skills Tests in the same test session.

About the GACE Basic Skills Test

The purpose of the GACE Basic Skills Test is to assess the knowledge and skills of prospective Georgia teachers in the areas of reading, mathematics, and writing. The GACE Basic Skills Test contains these three sections:

- Reading: Test code 200 (approximately 42 selected-response questions)
- Mathematics: Test code 201 (approximately 48 selected-response questions)
- Writing: Test code 202 (approximately 42 selected-response questions and a constructed-response assignment)

What Does the Test Cover?

The following table lists the objectives used as the basis for the GACE Basic Skills Test and the approximate number of questions in the Reading, Math, and Writing tests. A thorough review of all the specific skills is the focus of this book.

Test Framework

Basic Skills	Objectives	Skill	Approximate Number of Selected-Response Questions
Reading Test I (Test Code 200)	0001	Understand the main idea and supporting details in written material.	**42**
	0002	Identify a writer's purpose and point of view.	
	0003	Analyze the relationship among ideas in written material.	
	0004	Use critical reasoning skills to evaluate written material.	
	0005	Use reading strategies to comprehend written materials.	
	0006	Determine the meaning of words and phrases.	
Mathematics Test II (Test Code 201)	0007	Understand number properties and number operations.	**48**
	0008	Understand measurement concepts and principles of geometry.	
	0009	Understand statistical concepts and data analysis and interpretation.	
	0010	Understand problem-solving principles and techniques.	
Writing Test III (Test Code 202)	0011	Recognize unity, focus, and development in writing.	**42** (60% of Test Score) Constructed-Response Assignments: 1 (40% of Score)
	0012	Recognize effective organization in writing.	
	0013	Recognize effective sentences.	
	0014	Recognize Standard American English usage.	
	0015	Demonstrate the ability to prepare a developed composition on a given topic using language and style appropriate to a given audience, purpose, and occasion.	

How Is the GACE Basic Skills Test Scored?

Your total raw score is converted to a scaled score. A scaled score is a combination of the number of scorable questions you answer correctly on the selected-response section of the test and the scores you received on any constructed-response assignments and then converted to a scale from 100 to 300. The score of 220 is the passing score for any GACE test. The passing score for each test is established by the Georgia Professional Standards Commission and is based on the professional judgments and recommendations of Georgia educators. "Pass" or "Did Not Pass" status is based on your total score for each test. If you meet the passing score, your total test scaled score is not reported in order to preclude the use of GACE scores for purposes other than Georgia educator certification (e.g., employment, college admission screening).

What Is the Passing Score for the GACE Basic Skills Test?

The passing scaled score for each part is 220. There is no composite or combining all three tests. Each must be passed.

When Will I Receive My Score Report, and What Will It Look Like?

Your scores are reported directly to the Georgia Professional Standards Commission and are automatically added to your certification application file. Your scores are also reported to the Georgia institution of higher education or other agency that you indicated when you registered. Of course, as with any important document, you should keep a copy for your permanent records.

Unofficial test scores are posted on the Internet at 5:00 P.M. Eastern Time on the score report dates listed on *www.gace.nesinc.com/GA3_testdates.asp*. For each test date, the unofficial scores are kept on the Internet for approximately two weeks. You may only view these scores once during the posting period for security reasons.

Can I Retake the Test?

If you wish to retake a test, you may do so at any subsequent test administration. Please consult the GACE website at *www.gace.nesinc.com* for information about test registration. The GACE website also includes information regarding test retakes and score reports.

Who Administers the Test?

The Georgia Professional Standards Commission (PSC) has contracted with Evaluation Systems to assist in the development and administration of the Georgia Assessments for the Certification of Educators® (GACE®). The GACE tests are aligned with state and national standards for educator preparation and with state standards for the P–12 student curriculum (Georgia Performance Standards).

For additional information you can contact:

GACE Program
Evaluation Systems
Pearson
P.O. Box 660
Amherst, MA 01004-9002
(800) 523-7064 or **(413) 256-2894**

For operator assistance, call between 9:00 A.M.–5:00 P.M., Eastern Time, Monday through Friday, excluding holidays.

The Automated Information System is available 24 hours daily.

Fax: (413) 256-7082 (Registration forms may not be transmitted by fax.)

When Should I Take the Test?

Georgia law requires that teachers demonstrate mastery of basic skills, professional knowledge, and the content area in which they are specializing.

To receive information on upcoming administrations of the GACE Basic Skills Test, consult the GACE website at *www.gace.nesinc.com.*

Do I Pay a Registration Fee?

To take the GACE, you must pay a registration fee. For information about the fees, log on to *http://www.gace.nesinc.com/GA3_testfees.asp.*

How to Use This Book and TestWare®

When Should I Start Studying?

It is never too early to start studying for the GACE Basic Skills Test. The earlier you begin, the more time you will have to sharpen your skills. Do not procrastinate! Cramming is not an effective way to study because it does not allow you the time you need to think about the content, review the subareas, and take the practice tests.

What Should I Study First?

We strongly recommend that you begin your preparation with the TestWare® tests. The software provides the added benefits of instantaneous, accurate scoring and enforced time conditions.

What Do the Review Sections Cover?

The targeted review in this book is designed to help you sharpen the basic skills you need to approach the GACE Basic Skills Test, as well as provide strategies for attacking the questions.

Each teaching area included in the GACE Basic Skills Test is examined in a separate chapter. The skills required for all three areas are extensively discussed to optimize your understanding of what the examination covers.

Your schooling has taught you most of the information you need to answer the questions on the test. The education classes you took should have provided you with the know-how to make important decisions about situations you will face as a teacher. The review sections in this book are designed to help you fit the information you have acquired into the competencies specified on the GACE. Going over your class notes and textbooks together with the reviews provided here will give you an excellent springboard for passing the examination.

Studying for the GACE Basic Skills Test

Choose the time and place for studying that works best for you. Some people set aside a certain number of hours every morning to study, while others prefer to study at night before going to sleep. Other people study off and on during the day—for instance, while waiting for a bus or during a lunch break. Only you can determine when and where your study time will be most effective. Be consistent and use your time efficiently. Work out a study routine and stick to it.

When you take the practice tests, simulate the conditions of the actual test as closely as possible. Turn off your television and radio, and sit down at a table in a quiet room, free from distraction. On completing a practice test, score it and thoroughly review the explanations to the questions you answered incorrectly; however, do not review too much at any one time. Concentrate on one problem area at a time by reviewing the question and explanation, and by studying the review in this guide until you are confident that you have mastered the material.

Keep track of your scores so you can gauge your progress and discover general weaknesses in particular sections. Give extra attention to the reviews that cover your areas of difficulty, so you can build your skills in those areas. Many have found the use of study or note cards very helpful for this review.

How Can I Use My Study Time Efficiently?

The following study schedule allows for thorough preparation for the GACE Basic Skills Test. The course of study presented here is seven weeks, but you can condense or expand the timeline to suit your personal schedule. It is vital that you adhere to a structured plan and set aside ample time each day to study. The more time you devote to studying, the more prepared and confident you will be on the day of the test.

Study Schedule

Week 1	After having read this first chapter to understand the format and content of this exam, take the first practice test for each of the three subject areas on CD-ROM. Your scores will help you pinpoint your strengths and weaknesses. Make sure you simulate real exam conditions when you take the tests. Afterward, score them and review the explanations, especially for questions you answered incorrectly.
Week 2	Review the explanations for the questions you missed, and review the appropriate chapter sections. Useful study techniques include highlighting key terms and information, taking notes as you review each section, and putting new terms and information on note cards to help retain the information.
Weeks 3 and 4	Reread all your note cards, refresh your understanding of the competencies and skills included in the exam, review your college textbooks, and read over notes you took in your college classes. This is also the time to consider any other supplementary materials that your counselor or the Georgia Department of Education suggests. Review the department's website at *http://www.gace.nesinc.com*.
Week 5	Begin to condense your notes and findings. A structured list of important facts and concepts, based on your note cards and the GACE Basic Skills competencies, will help you thoroughly review for the test. Review the answers and explanations for any questions you missed.
Week 6	Have someone quiz you using the note cards you created. Take the second set of practice tests on CD-ROM, adhering to the time limits and simulated test day conditions.
Week 7	Using all your study materials, review areas of weakness revealed by your score on the second set of practice tests. Then retake sections of the practice tests printed in this book as needed.

Format of the GACE Basic Skills Test

What Types of Questions Are on the Test?

- The Reading test has approximately 42 selected-response (multiple-choice) questions.
- The Mathematics test has approximately 48 selected-response questions.
- The Writing test has approximately 42 selected-response questions and one constructed-response question.

Can I Take the Test Online?

As of this writing, computer-based testing is not available for the GACE Basic Skills Test. For the latest update, go to *www.gace.nesinc.com/GA3_internet_based_testing.asp*.

Test-Taking Tips

Although you may not be familiar with tests like the GACE, this book will acquaint you with this type of exam and help alleviate your test-taking anxieties. By following the seven suggestions listed here, you can become more relaxed about taking the GACE, as well as other tests.

Tip 1. Acquaint yourself with the format of the GACE. When you are practicing, stay calm and pace yourself. After simulating the test only once, you will boost your chances of doing well, and you will be able to sit down for the actual GACE with much more confidence.

Tip 2. Read all the possible answers. Just because you think you have found the correct response, do not automatically assume that it is the best answer. Read through each choice to be sure that you are not making a mistake by jumping to conclusions.

Tip 3. Use the process of elimination. Go through each answer to a question and eliminate as many of the answer choices as possible. If you can eliminate two answer choices, you have given yourself a better chance of getting the item correct, because only two choices are left from which to make your guess. Do not leave an answer blank; it is better to guess than not to answer a question on the GACE test because there is no penalty for guessing.

Tip 4. Place a question mark in your answer booklet next to the answers you guessed, and then recheck them later if you have time.

Tip 5. Work quickly and steadily. You will have four hours to complete the entire test, so the amount of time you spend will depend upon whether you take all three subarea tests in one test session. Taking the practice tests in this book will help you learn to budget your precious time.

Tip 6. Learn the directions and format of the test. This will not only save time but also will help you avoid anxiety (and the mistakes caused by being anxious).

Tip 7. When taking the multiple-choice portion of the test, be sure that the answer oval you fill in corresponds to the number of the question in the test booklet. The multiple-choice test is graded by machine, and marking one wrong answer can throw off your answer key and your score. Be extremely careful.

The Day of the Test

Before the Test

On the morning of the test, be sure to dress comfortably so you are not distracted by being too hot or too cold while taking the test. Plan to arrive at the test center early. This will allow you to collect your thoughts and relax before the test and will also spare you the anguish that comes with being late. You should check your GACE Registration Bulletin to find out what time to arrive at the center.

What to Bring

Before you leave for the test center, make sure that you have your admission ticket. Your admission ticket lists your test selection, test site, test date, and reporting time. See the Test Selection options at *www.gace.nesinc.com/GA3_testselection.asp*.

You must also bring personal identification that includes one piece of current, government-issued identification, in the name in which you registered, bearing your photograph and signature and one additional piece of identification (with or without a photograph). If the name on your identification differs from the name in which you are registered, you must bring official verification of the change (e.g., marriage certificate, court order).

If for any reason you do not have proper identification or your admission ticket, you will need to report immediately and directly to the Information Table at the test site. You may be required to complete additional paperwork, which may reduce your available testing time.

You must bring several sharpened No. 2 pencils with erasers, because none will be provided at the test center. If you like, you can wear a watch to the test center. However, you cannot wear one that makes noise, because it might disturb the other test takers. Dictionaries, textbooks, notebooks, calculators, cell phones, beepers, PDAs, scratch paper, listening and recording devices, briefcases, or packages are not permitted. Drinking, smoking, and eating during the test are prohibited.

You may bring a water bottle into the testing room, as long as it is clear (without a label) but with a tight lid. During testing, you will have to store your bottle under your seat.

Security Measures

As part of the identity verification process, your thumbprint will be taken at the test site. Thumbprints will be used only for the purpose of identity verification. If you do not provide a thumbprint, you will not be allowed to take the test. No refund or credit of any kind will be given. This thumbprint does not take the place of the complete fingerprint set requirement for Georgia teacher certification.

Enhanced security measures, including additional security screenings, may be required by test site facilities. If an additional screening is conducted, only screened persons will be admitted to the test site. If you do not proceed through the security screening, you will not be allowed to take the test and you will not receive a refund or credit of any kind.

Late Arrival Policy

If you are late for a test session, you may not be admitted. If you are permitted to enter, you will not be given any additional time for the test session. You will be required to sign a statement acknowledging this.

If you arrive late and are not admitted, you will be considered absent and will not receive a refund or credit of any kind. You will need to register and pay again to take the test at a future administration.

Absentee Policy

If you are absent, you will not receive a refund or credit of any kind. You will need to register and pay again to take the test at a future administration.

During the Test

The GACE Basic Skills Test is given in one sitting, with no breaks. However, during testing, you may take restroom breaks. Any time that you take for restroom breaks is considered part of the available testing time. Procedures will be followed to maintain test security. Once you enter the test center, follow all the rules and instructions given by the test supervisor. If you do not, you risk being dismissed from the test and having your score canceled.

When all the materials have been distributed, the test instructor will give you directions for completing the informational portion of your answer sheet. Fill out the sheet carefully, because the information you provide will be printed on your score report.

Once the test begins, mark only one answer per question, completely erase unwanted answers and marks, and fill in answers darkly and neatly.

After the Test

When you finish your test, hand in your materials and you will be dismissed. Then, go home and relax—you deserve it!

CHAPTER

Reading

2

The reading portion of the GACE Basic Skills Test **assesses critical reading and reading comprehension skills.** Test takers will be asked to read a passage and answer questions about the material included in that passage. It is comprised of 42 selected-response/multiple-choice questions.

This review is designed to prepare you for the reading section. You will be guided through a review of the content related to the test objectives. A step-by-step approach to help you analyze and answer questions about reading passages, as well as tips to help you quickly and accurately answer the questions, are also included. By studying this review, you will greatly increase your chances of achieving a good score on the reading section of the GACE.

I. GACE Reading Objectives

Remember, the more you know about the skills tested, the better you will perform on the test. The objectives on which you will be tested are contained in the following list:

- 0001 Understand the main idea and supporting details in written material.
- 0002 Identify a writer's purpose and point of view.

- 0003 Analyze the relationship among ideas in written material.
- 0004 Use critical reasoning skills to evaluate written material.
- 0005 Use reading strategies to comprehend written materials.
- 0006 Determine the meaning of words and phrases.

Now that you know what the objectives are, let's look at them more closely. This section will provide a review of the important information about each of the objectives.

Objective 0001: Understand the main idea and supporting details in written material.

The first objective deals with the main idea and the supporting details. The main idea is the topic discussed in the passage. Supporting details explain the main ideas providing support for the main idea statement. They illustrate or elaborate on the main idea of a paragraph. It is important to find the main idea of the passage because it helps you remember important information.

This is evident in the following passage.

> Experienced lawyers know that most lawsuits are won or lost before they are ever heard in court. Thus, successful lawyers prepare their cases carefully, undertaking exhaustive research and investigation prior to going to court.
>
> Interviews and statements taken from all available witnesses ascertain those who are likely to be called to support the other side. This time provides opportunities for strategy planning in the building of the case; decisions about which expert witnesses to call (such as doctors, chemists, or others who have special knowledge of the subject matter); books and articles to be read pertaining to the subject matter of the case; and meetings with witnesses to prepare them for possible questions by the opposing lawyers and to review the case.
>
> Finally, a trial memorandum of law is handed to the judge at the outset of the trial. As a result of this thorough preparation, experienced lawyers know their strong and weak points and can serve their clients well.

The main idea expressed in this passage is the importance of pretrial preparation by lawyers. It is not explicitly stated, but it becomes apparent as you read the passage.

A description of the importance of conducting interviews and gathering statements from witnesses, the function of expert witnesses, and the importance of the trial memorandum are all details that support the main idea.

Objective 0002: Identify a writer's purpose and point of view.

The second objective deals with a writer's purpose and point of view. The following questions are helpful in order to determine the author's purpose. Ask yourself if the relationship between the writer's main idea and the evidence the writer uses answers one of the following four questions:

- What is the writer's primary goal or overall objective?
- Is the writer trying to persuade me by using facts to make a case for an idea?
- Is the writer trying only to inform and enlighten me about an idea, object, or event?
- Is the writer attempting to amuse me or to keep me fascinated or laughing?

Read the following examples and see whether you can decide what the primary purpose of the statements might be.

Example 1 Jogging too late in life can cause more health problems than it solves. I will allow that the benefits of jogging are many: lowered blood pressure, increased vitality, better cardiovascular health, and better muscle tone. However, an older person may have a history of injury or chronic ailments that makes jogging counterproductive. For example: the elderly jogger may have hardening of the arteries, emphysema, or undiscovered aneurysms just waiting to burst and cause stroke or death. Chronic arthritis in the joints will only be aggravated by persistent irritation and use. Moreover, for those of us with injuries sustained in our youth—such as torn Achilles tendons or knee cartilage—jogging might just make a painful life more painful, canceling out the benefits the exercise is intended to produce.

Example 2 Jogging is a sporting activity that exercises all the main muscle groups of the body. That the voluntary muscles in the arms, legs, buttocks, and torso are engaged goes without question. Running down a path makes you move your upper body as well as your lower body muscles. People do not often take into account, however, how the involuntary muscle system is also put through its paces. The heart, diaphragm, and even the eye and facial muscles take part as we hurl our bodies through space at speeds up to five miles per hour over distances as long as 26 miles and more for some.

Example 3 It seems to me that jogging styles are as identifying as fingerprints! People seem to be as individual in the way they run as they are in personality. Here comes the Duck, waddling down the track, little wings going twice as fast as the feet in an effort to stay upright. At about the quarter-mile mark I see the Penguin, quite natty in the latest jogging suit, stiff as a board from neck to ankles and the ankles flexing a mile a minute to cover the yards. And down there at the half-mile post—there goes the Giraffe—a tall fellow in a spotted electric yellow outfit, whose long strides cover about a dozen yards each, and whose neck waves around under some old army camouflage hat that may have served its time in a surplus store in the Bronx or in the Arabian desert. If you see the animals in the jogger woods once, you can identify them from miles away just by seeing their gait. By the way, be careful whose hoof you step on; it may be mine!

Good arguments are not just based on one's opinion.

In Example 1 the writer makes a statement that a number of people would debate and that isn't clearly demonstrated by science or considered common knowledge. In fact, common wisdom usually maintains the opposite. Many would say that jogging improves the health of the aging—even to the point of slowing the aging process. As soon as you see a writer point to or identify *an issue open to debate* that stands in need of proof, he or she is setting out to persuade you that one side or the other is the more justified position. You'll notice too that the writer takes a stand here. It's almost as if he or she is saying, "I have concluded that. ..." But a thesis or arguable idea is only a *hypothesis* until evidence is summoned by the writer to prove it. Effective arguments are based on serious, factual, or demonstrable evidence, not merely opinion.

In Example 2 the writer is just stating fact. This is not a matter for debate. From here, the writer's evidence is to *explain* and *describe* what is meant by the fact. This is accomplished by analyzing (breaking down into its constituent elements) the way the different muscle groups come into play or do work when jogging, thus explaining the fact stated as a main point in the opening sentence. The assertion that jogging exercises all of the muscle groups is not in question or a matter of debate. Besides taking the form of explaining how something works or what parts it comprises (for example, the basic parts of a bicycle are …), writers may show how the idea, object, or event functions. A writer may use this information to prove something. But if the writer doesn't argue to provide a debatable point one way or the other, then the purpose must be either to inform (as here) or to entertain.

In example 3 the writer is taking a stand yet not attempting to prove anything; a light-hearted observation is made and nothing more. In addition, all of the examples used to support the statement are fanciful, funny, odd, or peculiar to the writer's particular vision. Joggers aren't *really* animals, after all.

As you read the information regarding jogging, make sure you examine all of the facts that the author uses to support the main idea. This will allow you to decide whether or not the writer has made a case, and what sort of purpose it supports. Look for supporting details—facts, examples, illustrations, testimony, or research of experts—that are relevant to the topic in question and show what the writer says is so. In fact, paragraphs and theses consist of *show* and *tell*. The writer *tells* you something is so or not so and then *shows* you the facts, illustrations, expert testimony, or experiences to back up whatever is asserted.

It is also important to recognize the author's implied audience and the effect that the writer's language choices will have on that audience. The author's choice of style and content is affected by the intended audience. You will notice that Examples 1 and 2 are more formal, and include technical terms, whereas the third example is informal. Example 1 includes terms such as "arteries, emphysema, or undiscovered aneurysms," while Example 3 compares a jogger to a "duck, waddling down the track." The differences between the third passage and the first two suggest different audiences.

The style an author uses is dependent upon her audience.

Objective 0003: Analyze the relationship among ideas in written material.

The third objective deals with analyzing the relationship among ideas in written material. This objective includes various types of relationships such as cause and effect, analogies, or classification. It also involves analyzing relationships between or among similar ideas or ideas in opposition.

Other examples of content that may be covered under this objective include identifying a sequence of events or steps, predicting outcomes, and drawing conclusions based on the information stated or implied in the passage.

As you read, you should note the structure of the paragraphs. There are several common structures for passages some of which are included on the GACE. A number of these structures are described below.

Main Types of Paragraph Structures

1. Main idea plus supporting arguments
2. Main idea plus examples
3. Comparisons or contrasts
4. Pro and con structure
5. Cause and effect
6. Chronological or sequence of events
7. A structure that has several different aspects of one idea

For example, a paragraph on education in the United States in the 1600s and 1700s might define education, describe colonial education, give information about separation of church and state, and then outline the opposing and supporting arguments regarding taxation as a source of educational funding. Being able to recognize these structures will help you recognize how the author has organized the passage, and more easily determine the given facts.

If you see a writer using a transitional pattern that reflects a sequence moving forward in time, such as "In 1982 ... Then, in the next five years ... A decade later, in 1997, the ... ," chances are the writer is telling a story, history, or the like. Writers often use transitions of classification to analyze an idea, object, or event. They may say something like, "The first part ... Secondly ... Thirdly ... Finally ... " You may then ask yourself what the analysis is for. Is it to explain or to persuade you of something? These transitional patterns may also help reveal the relationship of one part of a passage to another. For example, a writer may be writing, "On the one hand ... On the other hand ... " This should alert you to the fact that the writer is comparing or contrasting two things. What for? Is one better than the other? Is one worse?

By understanding the relationship among the main point, transitions, and supporting information, you may more readily determine the pattern of organization as well as the writer's purpose in a given piece of writing.

As with the earlier paragraph showing the difference among possible purposes of education in the United States in the 1600s and 1700s, you must look at the relationship between the facts or information presented (that's the show part) and what the writer is trying to point out to you (that's the tell part) with that data. For example, a discussion presented about education in the 1600s might be used to:

1. Prove that it was a failure (a form of argument).
2. Show that it consisted of these elements (an analysis of the status of education during that time).
3. Show that education during that time was silly.

To understand the author's purpose, the main point and the supporting evidence must be considered together. To be meaningful, a controlling or main point is needed. You need to know if that main point is missing. You need to be able to distinguish between the writer showing data and the writer making a point.

Objective 0004: Use critical reasoning skills to evaluate written material.

The fourth objective deals with the use of critical reasoning skills to evaluate written material. These skills are used in a number of possible ways. This might include evaluating the stated or implied assumptions upon which the validity of a writer's argument depends. The reader must judge the relevance or importance of facts, examples, or graphic data used by the writer to make a point. The reader must also evaluate the logic of a writer's argument and the validity of analogies, distinguish between fact and opinion, and assess the credibility or objectivity of a writer or source of written material.

Compare the two paragraphs that follow and note the different assumptions made by the authors. In the second paragraph the controlling statement changes the discussion from explanation to argument.

1. Colonial education was different than today's education and consisted of several elements. Education in those days meant primarily studying the three "R's" (Reading, 'Riting, and 'Rithmetic) and the Bible. The church and state were more closely aligned

with one another. Education was, after all, for the purpose of serving God better, not to make more money.

2. Colonial "education" was really just a way to create a captive audience for churches. Education in those days meant studying the three "R's" in order to learn God's word—the Bible—not commerce. The churches and the state were closely aligned with one another, and what was good for the church was good for the state—or else you were excommunicated, which kept you out of Heaven for sure.

The same informational areas are brought up in both paragraphs, but in paragraph 1 the writer treats it more analytically ("consisted of several elements"). However, the controlling statement in paragraph 2 puts forth a more volatile hypothesis, and then uses the same information to support that hypothesis.

It is also important to be able to recognize the difference between the statements of fact presented versus statements of the author's opinion. Look at the following examples. In each case ask yourself whether you are reading a fact or an opinion.

GACE Tip

It is important to be able to recognize the difference between fact and opinion.

1. Some roses are red.
2. Roses are the most beautiful flower on earth.
3. After humans smell roses they fall in love.
4. Roses are the worst plants to grow in your backyard.

Item 1 is a fact. All you have to do is look at the evidence. Go to a florist; you will see that Item 1 is true. A fact is anything that can be demonstrated to be objectively true in reality or which has been demonstrated to be true in reality and is documented by others. For example, the moon is orbiting about 250,000 miles from the earth.

Item 2 is an opinion. The writer claims this as truth but since it is a subjective quality (beauty), it remains to be seen. Others may hold different opinions. This is a matter of taste, not fact.

Item 3 is an opinion. There is probably some time-related coincidence between these two but there is no verifiable, repeatable, or observable evidence that this is always true. It is certainly not true in the way that if you throw a ball into the air, it will come back down to earth if left on its own without interference. Opinions have a way of sounding absolute; they are held by the writer with confidence, but are not facts that provide evidence.

Item 4, though perhaps sometimes true, is nevertheless a matter of opinion. Many variables contribute to the health of a plant in a garden: soil, temperature range, amount of moisture, and number and kinds of bugs. This is a debatable point for which the writer would have to provide evidence.

Objective 0005: Use reading strategies to comprehend written materials.

Strategic reading is vital in comprehending what was read. This might include organizing and summarizing information, following directions or instructions, or interpreting visual information presented in charts, graphs, or tables.

Organizing and summarizing information is essential to the comprehension of passages. Read the following passage about water and, as you read, consider the topics that best organize the information in the passage.

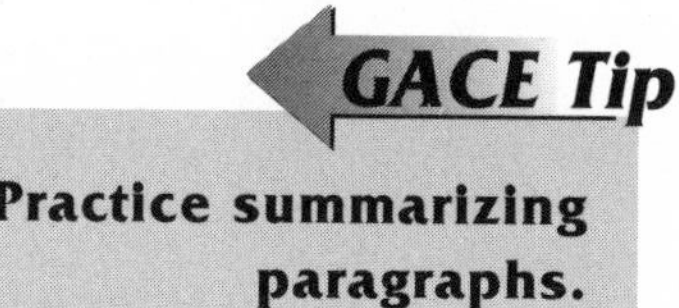

Water

The most important source of sediment is earth and rock material carried to the sea by rivers and streams; glaciers and winds may also have transported the same materials. Other sources are volcanic ash and lava, shells and skeletons of organisms, chemical precipitates in seawater, and particles from outer space.

Water is a most unusual substance because it exists on the surface of the earth in its three physical states: ice, water, and water vapor. There are other substances that might exist in a solid, liquid, or gaseous state at temperatures normally found at the earth's surface, but there are fewer substances that occur in all three states.

Water is odorless, tasteless, and colorless. It is the only substance known to exist in a natural state as a solid, liquid, or gas on the surface of the earth. It is a universal solvent. Water does not corrode, rust, burn, or separate into its components easily. It is chemically indestructible. It can corrode almost any metal and erode the most solid rock. A unique property of water is that it expands and floats on water when frozen or in the solid state. Water has a freezing point of 0°C and a boiling point of 100°C. Water has the capacity for absorbing great quantities of heat with relatively little increase in temperature. When ***distilled***, water is a poor conductor of electricity but when salt is added, it is a good conductor of electricity.

Sunlight is the source of energy for temperature change, evaporation, and currents for water movement through the atmosphere. Sunlight controls the rate of photosynthesis for all marine plants, which are directly or indirectly the source of food for all marine animals. Migration, breeding, and other behaviors of marine animals are affected by light.

Water, as the ocean or sea, is blue because of the molecular scattering of sunlight. Blue light, being of short wavelength, is scattered more effectively than light of longer wavelengths. Variations in color may be caused by particles suspended in water, water depth, cloud cover, temperature, and other variable factors. Heavy concentrations of dissolved materials cause a yellowish hue, while algae will cause the water to look green. Heavy populations of plant and animal materials will cause the water to look brown.

After reading the passage above you will recognize that it can be organized according to topics. The writer discusses the physical states of water, the properties of water, the effects of the sun on water, and the reasons for color variation in water. Organizing information in this manner will assist you in comprehending material.

Reading directions correctly is a comprehension skill.

Comprehension also involves the ability to follow a set of directions or a list of instructions. Carefully read the following instructions for absentee voting.

Instructions for Absentee Voting

These instructions describe conditions under which voters were permitted to register for, or request absentee ballots to vote in, the November 4, 2008 election.

(1) If you moved on or prior to October 6, 2008, and did not register to vote at your new address, you are not eligible to vote in this election.

(2) If you move after this date, you may vote via absentee ballot or at your polling place, using your previous address as your address of registration for this election.

(3) You must register at your new address to vote in future elections.

(4) The last day to request an absentee ballot is October 31, 2008.

(5) You must be a registered voter in the county.

(6) You must make a separate request for each election.

(7) The absentee ballot shall be issued to the requesting voter in person or by mail.

After carefully reading the instructions for absentee voting, you should be able to answer questions regarding information presented. For example, consider the following item:

A voter will be able to participate in the November 4, 2008, election as an absentee if he or she

A. requested an absentee ballot on November 1, 2008

B. voted absentee in the last election.

C. moved as a registered voter on October 13, 2008.

D. moved on October 5, 2008.

Upon reading the passage, you will note that a voter will be able to participate as an absentee if he or she moved as a registered voter on October 13, 2008. Statement #1 and Statement #2 above provide the information that if you move after October 5, you may vote via absentee ballot.

Another important comprehension skill involves reading information presented in graphic form. Graphs are used to produce visual aids for sets of information. Often, the impact of numbers and statistics is diminished by an overabundance of tedious numbers. A graph helps a reader rapidly visualize or organize irregular information, as well as trace long periods of decline or increase. The following is a guide to reading the three main graphic forms that you may encounter when taking the GACE.

Line Graphs

Line graphs are used to track multiple elements of one or more subjects. One element is usually a time factor, over whose span the other element increases, decreases, or remains static. The lines that compose such graphs are connected points that are displayed on the chart through each integral stage. For example, look at the following immigration graph.

The average number of immigrants from 1820 to 1830 is represented at one point; the average number of immigrants from 1831 to 1840 is represented at the next. The line that connects these points is used only to ease the visual gradation between the points. It is not

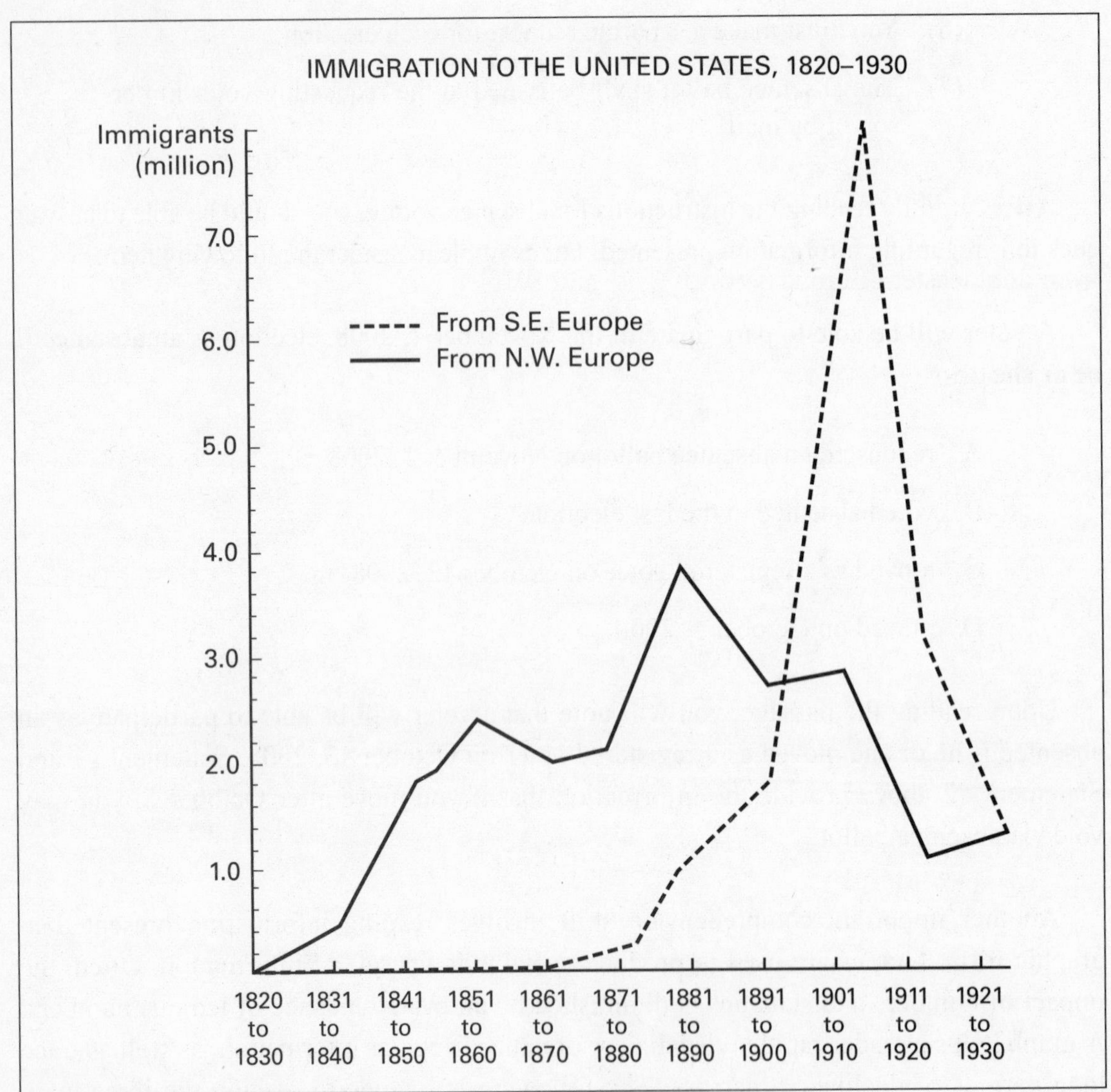

meant to give a strictly accurate representation for every year between the two decades. If it were, the line would not be a straight, even progression from year to year as these lines demonstrate. The purpose of the graph is to plot the average increases or decreases from point to point. When dealing with more than one subject, a line graph must use either different colored lines or different types of lines if the graph is black-and-white. In the graph, the dark bold line represents immigration from Northwestern Europe and the broken line represents immigration from Southeastern Europe.

To read a line graph, find the point of change that interests you. For example, if you want to trace immigration from Northwestern Europe from 1861-1870, you would find the position of the dark line on that point. Next, trace the position to the vertical information on the chart. In this instance, one would discover that approximately two million immigrants arrived from Northwestern Europe in the period of time from 1861 to 1890. If you want to know when the number of immigrants reached four million, you would find four million on the vertical side of the graph and read across. Between 1881 and 1890, four million immigrants arrived from Northwestern Europe, and the same number arrived from Southeastern Europe between 1891 and 1910.

Bar Graphs

Bar graphs are also used to plot two dynamic elements of a subject. However, unlike a line graph, the bar graph usually deals with only one subject. The exception to this is when the graph is three-dimensional and the bars take on the dimension of depth. However, because we will only be looking at two-dimensional graphs, we will be working with only

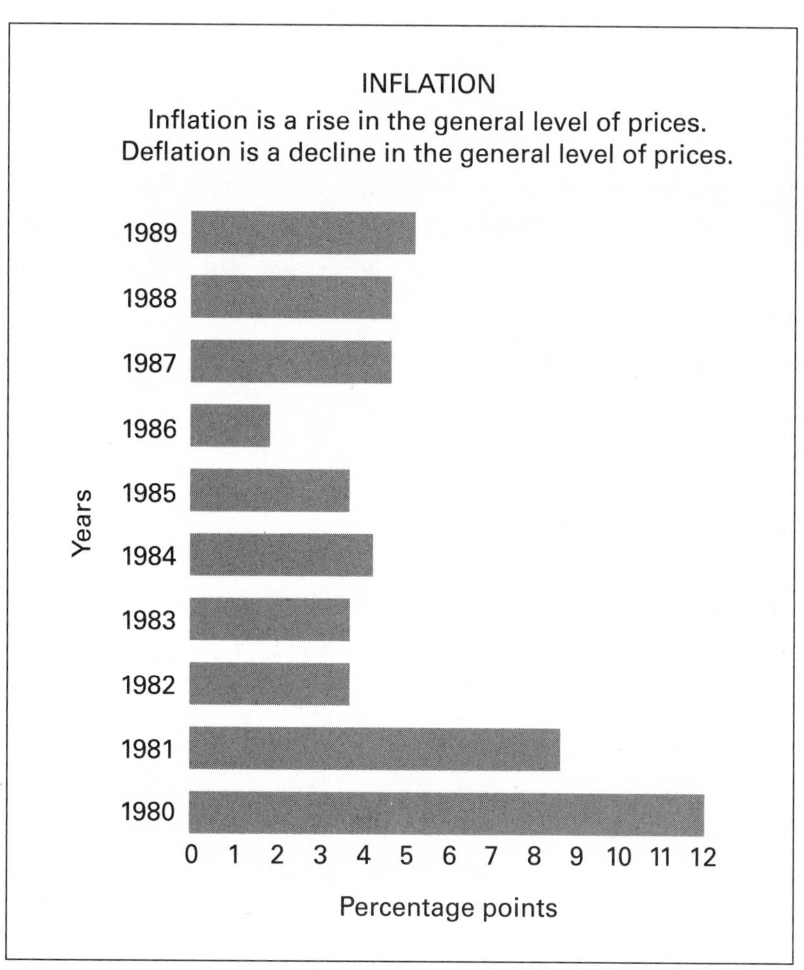

a single subject. The other difference between a line and a bar graph is that a bar graph usually calls for a single element to be traced in terms of another, whereas a line graph usually plots either of the two elements with equal interest. For example, in the bar graph, inflation and deflation are being marked over a span of years.

Percentage points are assigned to each year's level of prices, and that percentage decreases (deflation) from 1980 to 1981 and from 1981 to 1982. The price level is static from 1982 to 1983, then increases (inflation) from 1983 to 1984. Therefore, it is obvious that the bar graph is read strictly in terms of the changes exhibited over a period of time or against some other element. Conversely, a line graph is used to plot two dynamic elements of equal interest to the reader (e.g., either number of immigrants or the particular decade in question).

To read a bar graph, simply begin with the element at the base of a bar and trace the bar to its full length. Once you reach its length, cross-reference the other element of information that matches the length of the bar.

Pie Charts

Pie charts differ greatly from line graphs and bar graphs. Pie charts are used to help a reader visualize percentages of information with many elements to the subject. An entire "pie" represents 100 percent of a given quality of information. The pie is the sliced into measurements that correspond to each piece's share of the 100 percent. For example, in the pie chart that follows, Jason's rent occupies a slice greater than any other in the pie, because no other element equals or exceeds 25 percent of Jason's monthly budget.

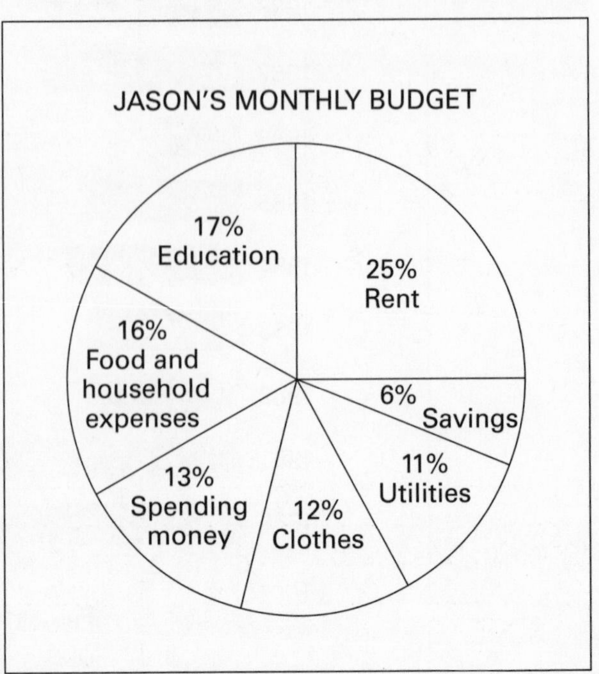

Another aspect of pie charts is that the smaller-percentage elements are moved consecutively to the larger elements. Therefore, the largest element in the chart will necessarily be adjacent to the smallest element in the chart, while the line that separates them is the beginning or endpoint of the chart. From this point the chart fans out to the other elements of the chart, moving from the smallest percentages to the largest.

To read a pie chart, choose the element of the subject that interests you and compare its size to those of the other elements. In cases where the elements are similar in size, do not assume that they are equal. The exact percentage of the element will be listed within that slice of the chart. For example, Jason's utilities, clothes, and spending money are all similar in size, but it is clear when reading the chart that each possesses a different value.

Reading Tables

Tables are useful because they relate large bodies of information within a confined area. To read a table, cross-reference the column headings that run horizontally across the top of the table with the row headings that run vertically down the left side of the table.

Drug	Psychological Dependence	Physical Dependence	Physical Withdrawal Effects	Development of Tolerance
Depressants				
Alcohol	Mild to very strong	Very strong	Severe/ dangerous	Minimal
Barbiturates	Develops slowly	Develops slowly	Death possible	Minimal
Narcotics				
Opiates (heroin, morphine)	Very strong; develops rapidly	Rapid/ increases with dosage	Frightening symptoms but not dangerous	Very high; goes down quickly after withdrawal (Danger if user returns to original dose)
Stimulants				
Amphetamines	Strong	Not in formal sense, but body seeks "rush"	Mild	Extremely high
Cocaine	Very strong	None	None (can cause heart spasms and instant death even if healthy)	None
Crack	Strong	Strong	Mild	High
Psychedelics				
LSD	Unpredictable	None	None	Extremely high
Marijuana	Mild to strong	Some, in high doses	None	None (Some to high doses)

Scan the table for overall information to the appropriate headings of the table to interpret the information listed. Note that some tables possess horizontal subheadings, which further clarify the different areas of information.

To use the preceding table, one should simply choose a particular drug, and then find the appropriate information needed about that drug through the headings listed at the top of the table. For example, the physical withdrawal effects of amphetamines, a stimulant drug, are mild.

Objective 0006: Determine the meaning of words and phrases.

Objective six deals with the use of context clues to determine the meaning of words, phrases, or figurative expressions. This involves using surrounding words in the sentence or passage in order to determine the meaning of an unknown word or phrase.

Consider again the third paragraph from the passage on water used earlier.

> Water is odorless, tasteless, and colorless. It is the only substance known to exist in a natural state as a solid, liquid, or gas on the surface of the earth. It is a universal solvent. Water does not corrode, rust, burn, or separate into its components easily. It is chemically indestructible. It can corrode almost any metal and erode the most solid rock. A unique property of water is that it expands and floats on water when frozen or in the solid state. Water has a freezing point of 0°C and a boiling point of 100° C. Water has the capacity for absorbing great quantities of heat with relatively little increase in temperature. When ***distilled,*** water is a poor conductor of electricity, but when salt is added, it is a good conductor of electricity.

You will notice that the last sentence includes the word ***distilled***. As you read the sentence try to determine the meaning of the word from the surrounding context clues.

The words, "but when salt is added," give the reader a clue that distilled may best be defined as "free of salt content."

II. Strategies for Taking the Reading Test

To help you further master these skills, the remainder of this chapter provides practice using the types of passages and questions that you will encounter on the GACE reading test. Each question is tied directly to one of the six GACE objectives identified and explained in the previous section.

The Passages

The passages in the reading section of the GACE include very diverse subjects. Although you will not be expected to have prior knowledge of the information presented in the passages, you will be expected to know the fundamental reading comprehension techniques presented in this chapter. Only your ability to read and comprehend material will be tested.

The Questions

Each passage will be followed by a number of questions. The questions will ask you to make determinations based on what you have read. You will commonly encounter questions that will ask you to:

1. Determine which of the given answer choices best expresses the main idea of the passage. (objective 0001)
2. Determine which details best support the writer's main idea. (objective 0001)
3. Determine the author's purpose in writing the passage. (objective 0002)
4. Analyze cause-and-effect relationships based on information in the passage. (objective 0003)
5. Use critical reasoning skills to evaluate the validity of an argument. (objective 0004)
6. Know the difference between fact and opinion in a statement. (objective 0004)
7. Determine the organization of the information in the passage. (objective 0005)

8. Determine which of the answer choices best summarizes the information presented in the passage. (objective 0005)
9. Answer a question based on information presented in a graphic form. (objective 0005)
10. Determine the definition of a word as it is used in the passage. (objective 0006)

Test-Taking Strategies and Tips

In order to make the most out of the time allotted, it is important to read strategically. The following is a recommended plan of attack to follow when reading the passages and answering the questions in the reading section.

1. Read over the *questions* (the questions only, not the possible answers) before reading the passage. This will help you to focus on the purpose for reading.
2. Read the passage while keeping the questions in mind.
3. Uncover the main idea or theme of the passage. It is often contained within the first few lines of the passage.
4. Uncover the main idea of each paragraph. Usually it is contained in either the first or last sentence of the paragraph.
5. Skim over the detailed points of the passage while circling key words or phrases. These are words or phrases such as *but, on the other hand, although, however, yet,* and *except.* These key words give clues to the organization of the information and important points to recall.
6. When answering the questions, approach each question one at a time. Read each carefully, selecting the one "best answer."
7. If the question is asking for an answer that can only be found in a specific place in the passage, save it for last since this type of question requires you to go back to the passage and therefore takes more of your time.

Additional Tips

- Look over all the passages first and then attack the passages that seem easiest and most interesting.

- Read the directions carefully.
- Identify and underline what sentences are the main ideas of each paragraph.
- If a question asks you to draw inferences, your answer should reflect what is implied in the passage, rather than what is directly stated.
- Use the context of the sentence to find the meaning of an unfamiliar word.
- Identify what sentences are example sentences and label them with an "E."
- Determine whether or not the writer is using facts or opinions.
- Circle key transitions and identify dominant patterns of organization.
- Make your final response and move on. Don't linger over or get frustrated by the really difficult passages. If you haven't gotten answers after two attempts, answer as best you can and move on. You are not penalized for guessing.
- If you have time at the end, go back to the passages that were difficult and review them again.

A Four-Step Approach

When you take the reading section of the GACE, you will have two basic tasks: 1) to read the passage and 2) to answer the questions.

Carefully reading the passage is the more important of the two. Answering the questions is based on an understanding of the passage. What follows is a four-step approach to reading:

Step 1: Preview the passage.

Step 2: Read actively.

Step 3: Review the passage.

Step 4: Answer the questions.

The following exercises will help prepare you to use these four steps when you complete the reading section of the GACE.

Step 1: Preview the Passage

A preview of the reading passage will give you a purpose and a reason for reading. It is a good strategy to use when taking a test. Before beginning to read the passage, you should take about 30 seconds to look over the passage and questions. An effective way to preview the passage is to quickly read the first sentence of each paragraph, the concluding sentence of the passage, and the questions (but not the answers) following the passage. The sample passage below will allow you to practice this skill. Practice previewing the passage by reading the first sentence of each paragraph and the last line of the passage.

Passage

That obscenity and pornography are difficult areas for the Supreme Court is well documented. The Court's numerous attempts to define obscenity have proven unworkable and left the decision to the subjective preferences of the justices. Perhaps Justice Stewart put it best when, after refusing to define obscenity, he declared, but "I know it when I see it." Does the Court literally have to see it to know it? Specifically, what role does the fact-pattern, including the materials' medium, play in the Court's decisions?

Several recent studies employ fact-pattern analysis in modeling the Court's decision making. These studies examine the fact-pattern or case characteristics, often with ideological and attitudinal factors, as a determinant of the decision reached by the Court. In broad terms, these studies owe their theoretical underpinnings to attitude theory. As the name suggests, attitude theory views the Court's attitudes as an explanation of its decisions.

These attitudes, however, do not operate in a vacuum. As Spaeth explains, "the activation of an attitude involves both an object and the situation in which that object is encountered." The objects to which the court directs its attitudes are litigants. The situation—the subject matter of the case—can be defined in broad or narrow terms. One may define the situation as an entire area of the law (e.g., civil liberties issues). On an even broader scale, the situation may be defined as the decision to grant certiorari or whether to defect from a minimum-winning coalition.

Defining the situation with such broad strokes, however, does not allow one to control for case content. In many specific issue areas, the cases present strikingly similar patterns. In examining the Court's search and seizure decisions, Segal found that a relatively small number of situational and case characteristic variables explain a high proportion of the Court's decisions.

Despite Segal's success, efforts to verify the applicability of fact-pattern analysis in other issue areas and using broad-based factors have been slow. Renewed interest in obscenity and pornography by federal and state governments as a result of lobbying campaigns by fundamentalist groups, the academic community, and other anti-pornography interest groups pro and con indicate that the Court's decisions in this area deserve closer examination.

The Court's obscenity and pornography decisions also present an opportunity to study the Court's behavior in an area where the Court has granted significant decision-making authority to the states. In *Miller v. California* (1973), the Court announced the importance of local community standards in obscenity determinations. The Court's subsequent behavior may suggest how the Court will react in other areas where it has chosen to defer to the states (e.g., abortion).

Questions

1. The main idea of the passage is best stated in which of the following?

   A. The Supreme Court has difficulty convicting those who violate obscenity laws.

   B. The current definitions for obscenity and pornography provided by the Supreme Court are unworkable.

   C. Fact-pattern analysis is insufficient for determining the attitude of the Court toward the issues of obscenity and pornography.

   D. Despite the difficulties presented by fact-pattern analysis, Justice Segal found the solution in the patterns of search-and-seizure decisions.

2. Of the following, which fact best supports the writer's contention that the Court's decisions in the areas of obscenity and pornography deserve closer scrutiny?

   A. The fact that a Supreme Court Justice said, "I know it when I see it."

   B. Recent studies that employ fact-pattern analysis in modeling the Court's decision-making process

C. The fact that attitudes do not operate in a vacuum

D. The fact that federal and state governments, interested groups, and the academic community show renewed interest in the obscenity and pornography decisions by the Supreme Court

3. The writer's main purpose in this passage is to

A. convince the reader that the Supreme Court is making decisions about obscenity based on their subjective views alone.

B. explain to the reader how fact-pattern analysis works with respect to cases of obscenity and pornography.

C. define obscenity and pornography for the layperson.

D. demonstrate the role fact-pattern plays in determining the Supreme Court's attitude about cases in obscenity and pornography.

4. Based on the data in the passage, what would most likely be the major cause for the difficulty in pinning down the Supreme Court's attitude toward cases of obscenity and pornography?

A. The personal opinions of the Court justices

B. The broad nature of the situations of the cases

C. The ineffective logistics of certiorari

D. The inability of the Court to resolve the variables presented by individual case content

5. Based on the passage, the rationale for fact-pattern analyses arises out of what theoretical groundwork?

A. Subjectivity theory

B. The study of cultural norms

C. Attitude theory

D. Cybernetics

6. Which of the following statements express the writer's opinion rather than a fact?

A. It is well documented that the area of obscenity and pornography is a difficult one for the Supreme Court.

B. The objects to which a court directs its attitudes are the litigants.

C. In many specific issue areas, the cases present strikingly similar fact-patterns.

D. The Court's subsequent behavior may suggest how it will react in other legal areas.

7. Which group of topics best reflects the organization of the passage?

A. I. The difficulties of the Supreme Court
II. Several recent studies
III. Spaeth's definition of *attitude*
IV. The similar patterns of cases
V. Other issue areas
VI. The case of *Miller v. California*

B. I. The Supreme Court, obscenity, and fact-pattern analysis
II. Fact-pattern analyses and attitude theory
III. The definition of *attitude* for the Court
IV. The definition of *situation*
V. The breakdown in fact-pattern analysis
VI. Studying Court behavior

C. I. Justice Stewart's view of pornography
II. Theoretical underpinnings
III. A minimum-winning coalition
IV. Search-and-seizure decisions
V. Renewed interest in obscenity and pornography
VI. The importance of local community standards

D. I. The Court's numerous attempts to define obscenity
II. Case characteristics
III. The subject matter of cases
IV. The Court's proportion of decisions
V. Broad-based factors
VI. Obscenity determination

8. Which of the following paragraphs is the best summary of the passage?

A. The Supreme Court's decision-making process with respect to obscenity and pornography has become too subjective. Fact-pattern analyses used to determine the overall attitude of the Court reveal only broad-based attitudes on the part of the Court toward the situations of obscenity cases. But these patterns cannot fully account for the Court's attitudes toward case content. Research is not conclusive on whether fact-pattern analyses work when applied to legal areas. Renewed public and local interest suggests continued study and close examination of how the Court makes decisions. Delegating authority to the states may reflect patterns for Court decisions in other socially sensitive areas.

B. Though subjective, the Supreme Court decisions are well documented. Fact-pattern analyses reveal the attitude of the Supreme Court toward its decisions in cases. Spaeth explains that an attitude involves both an object and a situation. For the Court, the situation may be defined as the decision to grant certiorari. Cases present strikingly similar patterns, and a small number of variables explain a high proportion of the Court's decisions. Segal has made an effort to verify the applicability of fact-pattern analysis with some success. The Court's decisions on obscenity and pornography suggest weak Court behavior, such as in *Miller v. California*.

C. To determine what obscenity and pornography mean to the Supreme Court, we must operate in a vacuum. The litigants and the subject matter of cases are defined in broad terms (such as an entire area of law) to reveal the Court's decision-making process. Search-and-seizure cases reveal strikingly similar patterns, leaving the Court open to grant certiorari effectively. Renewed public interest in the Court's decisions proves how the Court will react in the future.

D. Supreme Court decisions about pornography and obscenity are under examination and are out of control. The Court has to see the case to know it. Fact-pattern analyses reveal that the Court can only define cases in narrow terms, thus revealing individual egotism on the part of the Justices. As a result of strikingly similar patterns in search-and-seizure cases, the Court should be studied further for its weakness in delegating authority to state courts, as in the case of *Miller v. California*.

9. In the context of the passage, *subjective* might be more closely defined as

   A. personal.
   B. wrong.
   C. focused.
   D. objective.

By previewing the passage you should have read the following:

- It is well documented that the areas of obscenity and pornography are difficult ones for the Supreme Court.
- Several recent studies employ fact-pattern analysis in modeling the Court's decision making.
- These attitudes, however, do not operate in a vacuum.
- Defining the situation with such broad strokes, however, does not allow one to control for case content.
- Despite Segal's success, efforts to verify the applicability of fact-pattern analysis in other issue areas and using broad-based factors have been slow in coming.
- The Court's obscenity and pornography decisions also present an opportunity to study the Court's behavior in an area where the Court has granted significant decision-making authority to the states.
- The Court's subsequent behavior may suggest how the Court will react in other areas where it has chosen to defer to the states (e.g., abortion).

These few sentences tell you much about the entire passage. As you begin to examine the passage, you should first determine the main idea of the passage and underline it so you can easily refer to it if a question requires you to do so (see question 1). *The main idea should be found in the first paragraph of the passage, and may even be the first sentence*. From what you have read thus far, you now know that the main idea of this passage is that the Supreme Court has difficulty in making static decisions about obscenity and pornography.

In addition, there are many details that support the main idea (see question 2). By reading further in the passage you know that recent studies have used fact-pattern analysis in modeling the Court's decision. You have learned that attitudes do not operate independently and that case content is important. The feasibility of using fact-pattern analysis in other areas and using broad-based factors has not been quickly verified. To study the behavior of the Court in an area in which they have granted significant decision-making authority to the states, one has only to consider the obscenity and pornography decisions. In summary, the author suggests that the Court's subsequent behavior may suggest how the Court will react in those other areas in which decision-making authority has previously been ceded to the states. As you can see, having this information will make the reading of the passage much easier.

You should have also looked at the stem of the question in your preview. You do not need to spend time reading the answers to each question in your preview. The stem alone can help to guide you as you read.

The stems in this case are as follows:

1. The main idea of the passage is best stated in which of the following?
2. Of the following, which fact best supports the writer's contention that the Court's decisions in the areas of obscenity and pornography deserve closer scrutiny?
3. The writer's main purpose in this passage is to _____.
4. Based on the data in the passage, what would most likely be the major cause for the difficulty in pinning down the Supreme Court's attitude toward cases of obscenity and pornography?
5. Based on the passage, the rationale for fact-pattern analyses arises out of what theoretical groundwork?
6. Which of the following statements express the writer's opinion rather than a fact?
7. Which group of topics best reflect the organization of the passage?
8. Which of the following paragraphs is the best summary of the passage?
9. In the context of the passage, *subjective* might be more closely defined as ____.

Step 2: Read Actively

After you preview you are now ready to read actively. This means that, as you read, you will be engaged in such things as underlining important words, topic sentences, main ideas, and words denoting the tone of the passage. If you think underlining can help you save time and help you remember the main ideas, feel free to use your pencil.

Read the first sentence of each paragraph carefully, since this often contains the topic of the paragraph. You may wish to underline each topic sentence.

During this stage you should also determine the writer's purpose in writing the passage (see question 3), as this will help you focus on the main points and the writer's key points in the organization of a passage.

Step 3: Review the Passage

After you finish reading actively, take 10 or 20 seconds to look over the main idea and the topic sentences that you have underlined, and the key words and phrases you have marked. Now you are ready to enter Step 4 and answer the questions.

Step 4: Answer the Questions

In Step 2, you gathered enough information from the passage to answer questions dealing with the objectives. Let's look again at these questions.

Main Idea Questions (Objective 0001)

Looking back at the questions that followed the passage, you should see that question 1 is a main idea question.

1. The main idea of the passage is best stated in which of the following?

    A. The Supreme Court has difficulty convicting those who violate obscenity laws.

    B. The current definitions for obscenity and pornography provided by the Supreme Court are unworkable.

    C. Fact-pattern analysis is insufficient for determining the attitude of the Court toward the issues of obscenity and pornography.

    D. Despite the difficulties presented by fact-pattern analysis, Justice Segal found the solution in the patterns of search-and-seizure decisions.

In answering the question, you see that choice C is the correct answer. The writer uses the second, third, fourth, and fifth paragraphs to show how fact-pattern analysis is an ineffective determinant of the Supreme Court's attitudes toward obscenity and pornography.

Choice A is incorrect. Nothing is ever said directly about *convicting* persons accused of obscenity, only that the Court has difficulty defining it.

Choice B is also incorrect. Though the writer states it as a fact, it is only used as an effect that leads the writer to examine how fact-pattern analysis does or does not work to reveal the "cause" or attitude of the Court toward obscenity and pornography.

Also, answer choice D is incorrect. The statement is contrary to what Segal found when he examined search-and-seizure cases.

Supporting Details Questions (Objective 0001)

Question 2 requires you to analyze the author's supporting details.

2. Of the following, which fact best supports the writer's contention that the Court's decisions in the areas of obscenity and pornography deserve closer scrutiny?

   A. The fact that a Supreme Court Justice said, "I know it when I see it."

   B. Recent studies that employ fact-pattern analysis in modeling the Court's decision-making process

   C. The fact that attitudes do not operate in a vacuum

   D. The fact that federal and state governments, interested groups, and the academic community show renewed interest in the obscenity and pornography decisions by the Supreme Court.

Look at the answer choices to answer this question. Choice D must be correct. In the fifth paragraph, the writer states that the "renewed interest"—a real and observable fact—from these groups "indicates the Court's decisions … deserve closer examination," another way of saying scrutiny.

Choice A is incorrect. The writer uses this remark to show how the Court cannot effectively define obscenity and pornography, relying on "subjective preferences" to resolve issues.

In addition, choice B is incorrect because the writer points to the data in D, not fact-pattern analyses, to prove this. Choice C is also incorrect. Although it is true, the writer makes this point to show how fact-pattern analysis doesn't help clear up the real-world situations in which the Court must make its decisions.

As you determine where the author's supporting details are, you may want to label them with an "S" so that you can refer back to them easily when answering questions.

Purpose Questions (Objective 0002)

In examining question 3 you will see that you must determine the author's purpose in writing the passage.

3. The writer's main purpose in this passage is to

   A. convince the reader that the Supreme Court is making decisions about obscenity based on their subjective views alone.

   B. explain to the reader how fact-pattern analysis works with respect to cases of obscenity and pornography.

   C. define obscenity and pornography for the layperson.

   D. demonstrate the role fact-pattern plays in determining the Supreme Court's attitude about cases in obscenity and pornography.

Looking at the answer choices you should see that choice D is correct. Though the writer never states it directly, the data is consistently summoned to show that fact-pattern analysis only gives us part of the picture, or "broad strokes" about the Court's attitude, but cannot account for the attitude toward individual cases.

Choice A is incorrect. The writer doesn't try to convince us of this fact, but merely states it as an opinion resulting from the evidence derived from the "well-documented" background of the problem.

B is also incorrect. The writer not only explains the role of fact-pattern analysis but also rather shows how it cannot fully apply.

The passage is about the Court's difficulty in defining these terms, not the man or woman on the street. Nowhere do definitions for these terms appear. Therefore, choice C is incorrect.

Cause and Effect Questions (Objective 0003)

Question 4 requires you to analyze a cause-and-effect relationship.

4. Based on the data in the passage, what would most likely be the major cause for the difficulty in pinning down the Supreme Court's attitude toward cases of obscenity and pornography?

   A. The personal opinions of the Court justices

   B. The broad nature of the situations of the cases

   C. The ineffective logistics of certiorari

   D. The inability of the Court to resolve the variables presented by individual case content

Choice D is correct, as it is precisely what fact-pattern analyses cannot resolve.

Response A is incorrect because no evidence is presented for it; all that is mentioned is that they do make personal decisions. Answer choice B is incorrect because it is one way in which fact-pattern analysis can be helpful. Finally, C is only a statement about certiorari being difficult to administer. The author never claimed this about it in the first place.

Critical Reasoning Questions (Objective 0004)

To answer question 5 you must be able to recall information from the passage as you use critical reasoning skills to evaluate written material.

5. Based on the passage, the rationale for fact-pattern analyses arises out of what theoretical groundwork?

   A. Subjectivity theory

   B. The study of cultural norms

   C. Attitude theory

   D. Cybernetics

The easiest way to answer this question is to refer back to the passage. In the second paragraph the writer states that recent studies using fact-pattern analyses—"owe their theoretical underpinnings to attitude theory." Therefore, we can conclude that response C is correct.

Answer choices A, B, and D are incorrect, as they are never mentioned or discussed by the writer.

Fact vs. Opinion Questions (Objective 0004)

By examining question 6, you can see that you are required to know the difference between fact and opinion.

6. Which of the following statements express the writer's opinion rather than a fact?

   A. It is well documented that the area of obscenity and pornography is a difficult one for the Supreme Court.

   B. The objects to which a court directs its attitudes are the litigants.

   C. In many specific issue areas, the cases present strikingly similar fact-patterns.

   D. The Court's subsequent behavior may suggest how the Court will react in other legal areas.

Keeping in mind that an opinion is something that is yet to be proven to be the case, you can determine that choice D is correct. It is the only statement among the four for which evidence is yet to be gathered. It is the writer's opinion that this may be a way to predict the Court's attitudes.

Choices A, B, and C are all derived from verifiable data or documentation, and are therefore incorrect.

Organization Questions (Objective 0005)

Question 7 asks you to organize given topics to reflect the organization of the passage.

7. Which group of topics best reflect the organization of the passage?

   A. I. The difficulties of the Supreme Court

      II. Several recent studies

      III. Spaeth's definition of *attitude*

      IV. The similar patterns of cases

      IV. Other issue areas

      V. The case of *Miller v. California*

B. I. The Supreme Court, obscenity, and fact-pattern analysis.
   II. Fact-pattern analyses and attitude theory
   III. The definition of *attitude* for the Court
   IV. The definition of *situation*
   V. The breakdown in fact-pattern analysis
   VI. Studying Court behavior

C. I. Justice Stewart's view of pornography
   II. Theoretical underpinnings
   III. A minimum-winning coalition
   IV. Search-and-seizure decisions
   V. Renewed interest in obscenity and pornography
   VI. The importance of local community standards

D. I. The Court's numerous attempts to define obscenity
   II. Case characteristics
   III. The subject matter of cases
   IV. The Court's proportion of decisions
   V. Broad-based factors
   VI. Obscenity determination

After examining all of the choices you will determine that choice B is the correct response. These topical areas lead directly to the implied thesis that the "role" of fact-pattern analysis is insufficient to determine the attitude of the Supreme Court in the areas of obscenity and pornography.

Choice A is incorrect because the first topic stated in the list is not the topic of the first paragraph. It is too global. The first paragraph is about the difficulties the Court has with defining obscenity and how fact-pattern analysis might be used to determine the Court's attitude and clear up the problem.

Choice C is incorrect because each of the items listed in this topic list represents supporting evidence or data for the real topic of each paragraph. (See the list in B for correct topics.) For example, Justice Stewart's statement about pornography is only cited to indicate the nature of the problem the Court has with obscenity. It is not the focus of the paragraph itself.

Finally, choice D is incorrect. As with choice C, these are all incidental pieces of information or data used to support broader points.

Summarization Questions (Objective 0005)

To answer question 8 you must be able to summarize the passage.

8. Which of the following paragraphs is the best summary of the passage?

   A. The Supreme Court's decision-making process with respect to obscenity and pornography has become too subjective. Fact-pattern analyses used to determine the overall attitude of the Court reveal only broad-based attitudes on the part of the Court toward the situations of obscenity cases. But these patterns cannot fully account for the Court's attitudes toward case content. Research is not conclusive on whether fact-pattern analyses work when applied to legal areas. Renewed public and local interest suggests continued study and close examination of how the Court makes decisions. Delegating authority to the states may reflect patterns for Court decisions in other socially sensitive areas.

   B. Though subjective, the Supreme Court decisions are well documented. Fact-pattern analyses reveal the attitude of the Supreme Court toward its decisions in cases. Spaeth explains that an attitude involves both an object and a situation. For the Court, the situation may be defined as the decision to grant certiorari. Cases present strikingly similar patterns, and a small number of variables explain a high proportion of the Court's decisions. Segal has made an effort to verify the applicability of fact-pattern analysis with some success. The Court's decisions on obscenity and pornography suggest weak Court behavior, such as in *Miller v. California.*

   C. To determine what obscenity and pornography mean to the Supreme Court, we must operate in a vacuum. The litigants and the subject matter of cases are defined in broad terms (such as an entire area of law) to reveal the Court's decision-making process. Search-and-seizure cases reveal strikingly similar patterns, leaving the Court open to grant certiorari effectively. Renewed public interest in the Court's decisions proves how the Court will react in the future.

   D. Supreme Court decisions about pornography and obscenity are under examination and are out of control. The Court has to see

> the case to know it. Fact-pattern analyses reveal that the Court can only define cases in narrow terms, thus revealing individual egotism on the part of the justices. As a result of strikingly similar patterns in search-and-seizure cases, the Court should be studied further for its weakness in delegating authority to state courts, as in the case of *Miller v. California.*

The paragraph that best and most accurately reports what the writer demonstrated based on the implied thesis is choice C. That is the correct answer to question 8.

Choice A is incorrect. It reflects some of the evidence presented in the passage, but the passage does not imply that all Court decisions are subjective, just the ones about pornography and obscenity. Similarly, the writer does not suggest that ceding authority to the states (as in *Miller v. California*) is a sign of some weakness, but merely that it is worthy of study as a tool for predicting or identifying the Court's attitude.

Response B is also incorrect. The writer repeatedly shows how fact-pattern analysis cannot pin down the Court's attitude toward case content.

D is incorrect. Nowhere does the writer say or suggest that the justice system is "out of control" or that the justices are "egotists," only that they are liable to be reduced to being "subjective" rather than having a cogent and identifiable shared standard.

Definition Questions (Objective 0006)

Question 9 requires you to determine the meaning of words in context.

9. In the context of the passage, *subjective* might be more closely defined as

   A. personal.
   B. wrong.
   C. focused.
   D. objective.

Choice A is the best answer. We can see from the example that Justice Stewart's comment is not an example of right or wrong. Most of the time if we are talking about people's "preferences," they are usually about taste or quality. They are usually not a result of scientific study and sometimes not even clear reasoning. They arise out of personal taste, idiosyncratic intuitions, etc. Thus, A is the most likely choice.

Choice C is incorrect because the Court's focus is already in place: on obscenity and pornography. Choice B is incorrect. Nothing is implied or stated about the rightness or wrongness of the decisions themselves. Rather it is the definition of obscenity that seems "unworkable." D is also incorrect. Objective is an antonym of subjective in this context.

To reason based on the object of study is the opposite of reasoning based upon the beliefs, opinions, or ideas of the one viewing the object rather than the evidence presented by the object.

You may not have been familiar with the word *subjective*, but from your understanding of the writer's intent, you should have been able to figure out what was being sought. Surrounding words and phrases almost always offer you some clues in determining the meaning of a word. In addition, any examples that appear in the text may also provide some hints.

Interpretation of Graphic Information Questions (Objective 0005)

Graphs, charts, and tables may also play a large part on the GACE, and you should be familiar with them. More than likely, you will encounter at least one passage that is accompanied by some form of graphic information. You will then be required to answer any question(s) based on the interpretation of the information presented in the graph, chart, or table as described in section one of this chapter.

Helpful Hints for Reading Graphic Information

You should approach any graphic information you encounter as a key to a larger body of information in abbreviated form. Be sure to use the visual aids of the graphics (e.g., the size of slices on pie charts) *as aids only*; do not ignore the written information listed on the graph or table, etc.

Note especially the title and headings so that you know exactly at what you are looking. Also, be aware of the source of the information, where applicable. Know what each element of the graphic information represents; this will help you compare how drastic or subtle any changes are, and over what span of time they take place. Be sure you realize what the actual numbers represent: whether it is dollars, so many thousands of people, millions of shares, and so forth. Finally, note the way in which the graphic information relates to the text it seeks to illustrate. Know in what ways the graphic information supports the arguments of the author of the given passage.

Conclusion

This review was designed to prepare you for the reading section of the GACE Basic Skills Test. **You were guided through a review of content related to the GACE reading objectives.** When taking the test you should utilize the step-by-step approach from this chapter. It will help you as you analyze the reading passages and answer the questions about those passages.

Remember, the more you know about the skills tested, the better you will perform on the test. By studying this review, you have greatly increased your chances of achieving a good score on the reading section of the GACE.

CHAPTER

Mathematics

3

The mathematics portion of the GACE Basic Skills Test reviews **basic math skills for teachers**. Test takers will be required to answer 48 selected-response/multiple-choice questions.

This review is designed to prepare you for the mathematics section with a healthy review of the content related to the test objectives. Helpful tips are also included. By studying this review, you will greatly increase your chances of achieving a good score on the mathematics section of the GACE.

2. GACE Mathematics Objectives

0007 Understand number properties and number operations.

For example:

- identifying mathematically equivalent ways of representing numbers
- performing operations on integers, fractions, decimals, and percents
- applying number properties (e.g., distributive, order of operations) to simplify numerical expressions

0008 Understand measurement concepts and principles of geometry.

For example:

- applying knowledge of measurement concepts (e.g., time, space, and money)
- selecting and converting units within and between standard and metric measurement
- applying knowledge of the language of geometry (e.g., points, lines, angles, and distance) in various situations
- analyzing fundamental properties of basic geometric shapes
- determining the length, perimeter, area, and volume of geometric shapes or figures

0009 Understand statistical concepts and data analysis and interpretation.

For example:

- interpreting information presented in tables
- interpreting information presented in line graphs, scatter plots, pictographs, bar graphs, histograms, and pie graphs
- determining the theoretical probability of simple events
- demonstrating knowledge of measures of central tendency (e.g., mean, median) and variability (e.g., range, deviation from the mean)
- demonstrating knowledge of the use of statistical concepts in real-world situations

0010 Understand problem-solving principles and techniques.

For example:

- identifying missing terms in numerical and graphical patterns
- solving problems and drawing conclusions using deductive reasoning

- solving word problems involving integers, fractions, decimals, and percents
- applying number properties and geometric principles to solve a variety of problems
- following a set of instructions to perform a given computation
- evaluating an algebraic expression by substituting numbers for variables
- solving algebraic equations and inequalities
- estimating results and determining reasonableness

0007 Number Properties and Operations

This section includes: mathematically equivalent ways of representing numbers; adding, subtracting, multiplying, and dividing fractions, decimals, and integers; number properties such as the distributive property and order of operations; applying number properties to simplify and solve numerical expressions; solving problems with percents and ratios; performing computation with exponents and scientific notation; estimating solutions to problems; and using the concepts of "less than" and "greater than."

Computation with Fractions

There are three steps involved in adding and subtracting fractions. First, make sure that the denominators of both fractions are the same. Then, add the numerators and write that answer over the denominator. Finally, simplify the fraction if needed.

When adding and subtracting fractions that have unlike denominators, a common denominator must be obtained by changing the given fractions to equivalent fractions with the same denominator. These equivalent fractions will have the same value as the original fractions, and they can be easily added or subtracted because they have the same denominator.

For example, to add $\frac{1}{2}$ and $\frac{2}{3}$, the lowest common denominator is 6, because the least common multiple of the denominators (2 and 3) is 6. Therefore, $\frac{1}{2}$ can be written

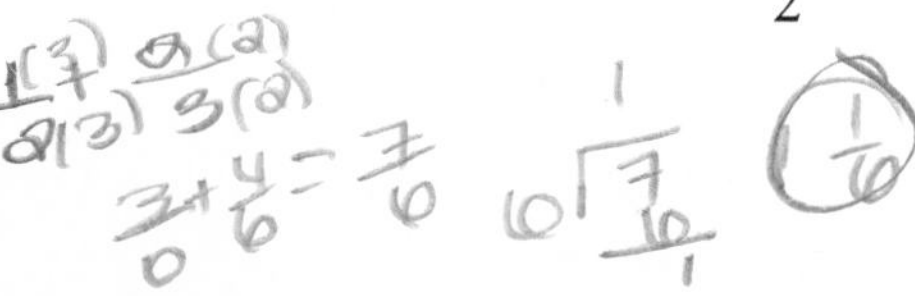

as $\frac{3}{6}$, and $\frac{2}{3}$ can be written as $\frac{4}{6}$. After changing $\frac{1}{2}+\frac{2}{3}$ to $\frac{3}{6}+\frac{4}{6}$, we can easily add the numerators together, arriving at the answer of $\frac{7}{6}$, or $1\frac{1}{6}$.

To add mixed numbers (those made up of a whole number and a fraction), add the fractions first, then the whole numbers. If the fractions sum to more than 1, add the 1 to the whole number sum (as if you were "carrying" to the next column when adding).

Subtracting fractions is much the same as adding. If the denominators are the same, simply subtract the numerators and simplify the fraction. If the denominators are not the same, a common denominator must be obtained. One challenge occurs when subtracting mixed numbers such as $3\frac{2}{5}$ and $1\frac{4}{5}$. Because $\frac{4}{5}$ cannot be subtracted from $\frac{2}{5}$, we must rename $3\frac{2}{5}$ to $2\frac{7}{5}$. We arrive at this renamed number by "borrowing" one whole, or $\frac{5}{5}$ from the 3, and adding the $\frac{5}{5}$ to the existing $\frac{2}{5}$. The new problem, then, is $2\frac{7}{5}$ minus $1\frac{4}{5}$, which equals $1\frac{3}{5}$.

GACE Tip

You don't need common denominators to multiply or divide fractions.

Multiplying and dividing fractions does not require the use of common denominators. When multiplying fractions, simply multiply the numerators together, multiply the denominators together, and then simplify the resulting fraction. For example, $\frac{2}{5}\times\frac{3}{4}$ equals $\frac{6}{20}$, or $\frac{3}{10}$.

To multiply whole numbers, change the whole numbers to improper fractions, such as $\frac{10}{3}$, and then follow the procedure described above.

To divide fractions, "flip," or invert, the divisor (2nd fraction), and multiply. For example, in the case of $\frac{1}{2}$ divided by $\frac{3}{8}$, change the problem to read $\frac{1}{2}\times\frac{8}{3}$. After multiplying, the answer is $\frac{8}{6}$ or $1\frac{1}{3}$.

Computation with Decimals

Decimal numbers are another way of representing fractions in which denominators are powers of ten (tenths, hundredths, and thousandths). For example, $\frac{12}{100}$ is written as 0.12, $\frac{4}{1000}$ is written as 0.004, and so on.

To add or subtract decimal numbers, simply arrange them vertically, with the decimal points aligned. Then add or subtract as with whole numbers. Remember that a whole number can be written as a decimal number by placing a decimal point at the end of the number, and then adding zeroes as needed. Therefore, 3 becomes 3.0, or 3.00, etc.

When you add or subtract decimal numbers, align the decimals.

To multiply decimal numbers, arrange the numbers vertically, with alignment on the right side (or "right justified"). Multiply the numbers as if they were whole numbers. Count the number of digits to the right of the decimal point in each of the two factors. Starting at the right side of the product, move the decimal point that many places to the left (ensuring that there are the same number of digits to the right of the decimal in the answer as there were in the factors together). Here is an example:

1.64	Multiply the numbers as if they were whole numbers.
× 0.3	Since there are 3 digits to the right of the decimal in the factors, make
.492	sure that the decimal in the product also has 3 digits to the right of the decimal.

To divide decimal numbers, set up the problem as a traditional whole-number division problem. In the divisor, move the decimal all the way to the right, making it appear as a whole number. Count the number of "places" the decimal was moved. Now, in the dividend, move the decimal the same number of places to the right. Move the decimal directly upward, and write it into the quotient spot. Finally, divide the numbers as if they were whole numbers to arrive at the answer. Here is an example:

$0.3\overline{)1.44}$	Move the decimal point in the divisor one place to the right, so it appears as a whole number. Then move the decimal point in the dividend one place to the right as well.
$\begin{array}{r} 4.8 \\ 0.3\overline{)1.44} \end{array}$	Write the decimal point in the quotient above where it appears in the dividend. Divide as if the numbers were whole numbers.

Careful placement of digits and decimal points when writing the problem and the quotient help ensure a correct answer.

Computation with Integers

The rules for performing operations on integers (positive and negative whole numbers), and on fractions and decimal numbers in which at least one is negative, are typically the same as the rules for performing operations on non-negative numbers. Pay close attention to the sign (positive or negative value) of each number, and the answer. The rule for multiplication and division is that two positives or two negatives result in a positive answer, whereas "mixing" a positive and a negative gives a negative answer ($-5 \times 3 = -15$, for example). Adding and subtracting with positive and negative numbers is somewhat different. When negative numbers are involved, think of the values as money, with "adding" being thought of as "gaining" and "subtracting" being thought of as "losing." Further, positive numbers can be seen as "credits" and negative numbers, "debts." (Be careful: adding or "gaining" –5, is like *losing* 5).

Percent

Percent is a way of representing a number "out of 100." In fact, the word "percent" literally means "per 100." It is easy to write a percent number as a fraction or a decimal. For example, 25% is the same as $\frac{25}{100}$ and 0.25.

GACE Tip

Percent means *per 100.*

There are three types of percent problems: finding a percent of a number, finding what percent one number is of another number, and finding the total when the percentage is known.

Finding a percent of a number

First, write the percent as a decimal. To do this, simply replace the % sign with a decimal, and move it two places to the left. For example, 25% would be written as .25.

Second, multiply the decimal and the given number. Place the decimal point as described in the multiplying decimals section above.

Example What is 60% of 24?

Write the percent as a decimal. .60

Multiply the decimal and the given number. .60 × 24

Place the decimal point in the correct place. 14.40

Finding what percent one number is of another number

Set up an equation: __ percent times the total number is the smaller number? It helps to write the percent number as a fraction or decimal.

Example What percentage of 120 is 48?

Write the equation: $\frac{n}{100} \times 120 = 48$

Solve the equation: $1.2n = 48$

$n = 40$

Therefore, 48 is 40% of 120.

Finding the total when the percent is known

Write a proportion. (Percentage is $\frac{n}{100}$; set it equal to the given number over the unknown number.)

Solve the proportion.

Example 15 is 6% of what number?

Write the proportion: $\frac{15}{n} = \frac{6}{100}$

Solve the proportion by cross-multiplying: $6n = 15 \times 100$

$6n = 1500$

$n = 250$

Therefore, 15 is 6% of 250.

Solving and Simplifying Equations

Mathematical expressions and equations often include several operations. When simplifying those expressions and equations, there is a specific order in which each operation is done. The steps in the "order of operations" are:

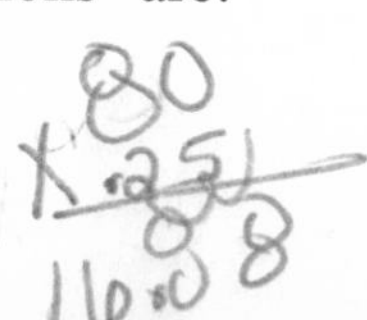

1. Perform the operations inside parentheses and brackets.
2. Clear the exponents.
3. Multiply and divide, from left to right.
4. Add and subtract, from left to right.

GACE Tip

To simplify equations, use the mnemonic: *Please Excuse My Dear Aunt Sally.*

The mnemonic "Please Excuse My Dear Aunt Sally" (which stands for "parentheses, exponents, multiply, divide, add, subtract") is a device that helps with remembering the order of operations. Here is an example:

Example 1	$4 + 9 \times 3 - 2 = 29$	Multiply 9 by 3 *before* doing the addition and subtraction.
Example 2	$3(4 + 1)^2 = 75$	Add the numbers inside the parentheses, which is 5; clear the exponent next by squaring 5 to equal 25; then multiply left to right so that $3 \times 25 = 75$.

Sometimes, mathematical expressions are represented in a shortened form. *Exponential notation* is a way to show repeated multiplication. For example, $3 \times 3 \times 3$ may be written as 3^3, which is equal to 27. Be mindful that 3^3 does not mean 3×3, but the use of 3 as a factor 3 times.

Scientific notation is a way to show numbers using exponents, particularly very large or very small numbers. A number is in scientific notation when it is shown as a number between 1 and 10 times a power of 10. Therefore, the number 75,000 in scientific notation is shown as 7.5×10^4.

Other common mathematical notation symbols include the following:

Symbol	Meaning	Examples		
$<$	less than	$.412 < .43$	$-35 < -7$	$\frac{1}{3} < \frac{1}{2}$
$>$	greater than	$.792 > .692$	$5 > -3$	$\frac{4}{5} > \frac{2}{3}$
$\neq$	not equal to	$.5 \neq .4$	$-7 \neq 7$	$\frac{2}{5} \neq \frac{1}{3}$

0008 Geometry and Measurement

This section involves applying knowledge of measurement concepts (such as time, space, and money) to solve problems; selecting and converting units within and between the standard and metric measurement systems; using the language of geometry (such as points, lines, angles, and distance) with a variety of problems; analyzing fundamental properties of basic geometric shapes; and finding the length, perimeter, area, and volume of geometric shapes and figures.

When you take the GACE, a page of mathematical definitions and formulas will be provided. This section is a review of the information needed to address geometry and measurement questions.

Definitions

π	pi	This symbol indicates the ratio between a circle's circumference and its diameter, and is commonly rounded to 3.14.
$\angle$	angle	There are three types of angles: (a) acute, in which the degree measure is less than 90°, (b) right, in which the degree measure is exactly 90°, and (c) obtuse, in which the degree measure is greater than 90°.
$\angle ABC$	angle ABC	In this notation, the angle has vertex B, and is formed by rays BA and BC.
∟	right angle	This symbol indicates a right angle, which measures exactly 90°.
$\overline{AB}$	line segment AB	The line over AB indicates a line segment, which has two endpoints.
$\overleftrightarrow{AB}$	line AB	The line with arrows on both ends over AB indicates a line that continues forever.
$\overrightarrow{AB}$	ray AB	This ray starts at endpoint A, continues through point B, and continues forever.
$\cong$	congruent	Figures, angles, or line segments that are congruent are exactly the same shape and the same size.
$\sim$	similar	Figures that are similar have the same shape, but not the same size. The corresponding sides of similar figures are proportional.

The following are formulas for finding the areas of basic polygons (informally defined as closed, coplanar geometric figures with three or more straight sides). Abbreviations used are as follows: A stands for area, l stands for length, w stands for width, h stands for height, and b stands for length of the base.

Triangle (a three-sided polygon): $A = \frac{b \times h}{2}$. (Note that, as shown in the figure that follows, the height of a triangle is not necessarily the same as the length of any of its sides.)

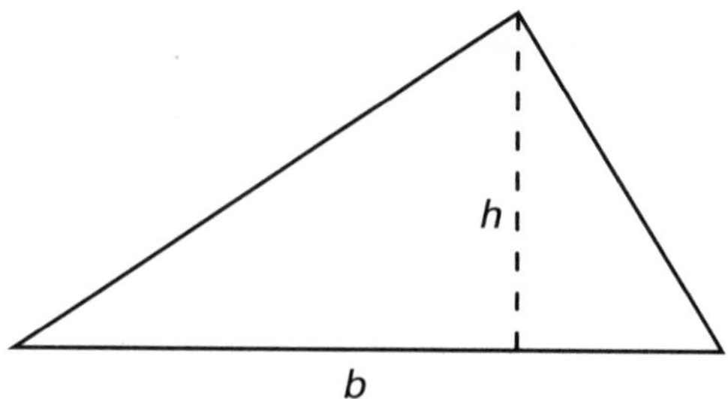

Rectangle (a four-sided polygon with four right angles): $A = l \times w$

Parallelogram (a four-sided polygon with two pairs of parallel sides): $A = l \times w$. (Note that, as with triangles, and as shown in the figure below, the height of a parallelogram is not necessarily the same as the length of its sides.)

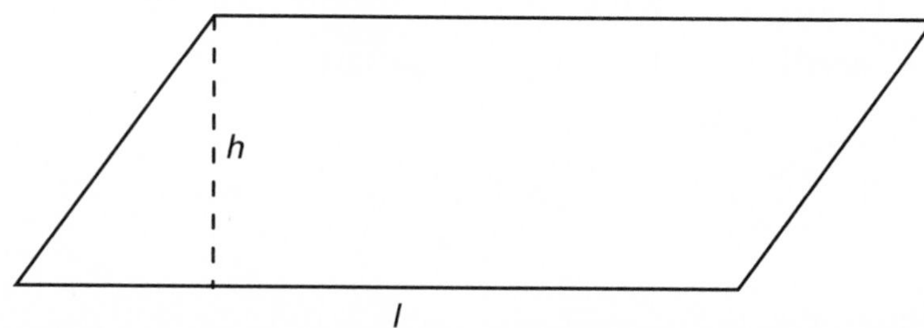

The area of a circle can be found by squaring the length of its radius, then multiplying that product by π. The formula is given as $A = \pi r^2$. (π, or pi, is the ratio of a circle's circumference to its diameter. The value of π is the same for all circles; approximately 3.14159. The approximation 3.14 is adequate for many calculations.) The approximate area of the circle shown below can be found by squaring 6 (giving 36), then multiplying 36 by 3.14, giving an area of about 113 square units.

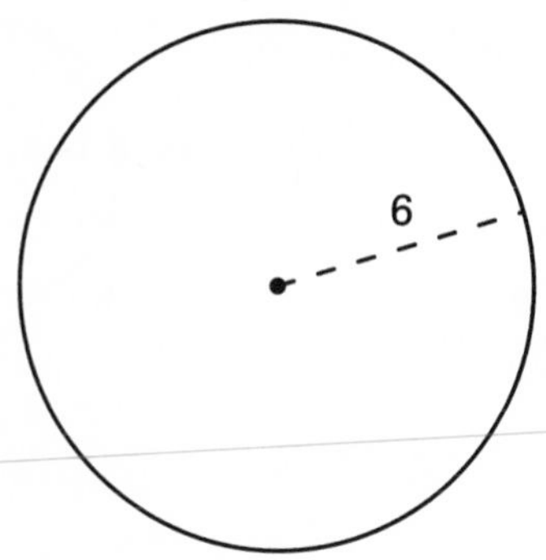

Here are several commonly used volume formulas:

The volume of a rectangular solid is equal to the product of its length, width, and height—$A = l \times w \times h$. (A rectangular solid can be thought of as a box, wherein all intersecting edges form right angles.)

A prism is a polyhedron with two congruent, parallel faces (called bases) and whose lateral (side) faces are parallelograms. The volume of a prism can be found by multiplying the area of the prism's base by its height. The volume of the triangular prism shown hereafter is 60 cubic units. (The area of the triangular base is 10 square units, and the height is 6 units.)

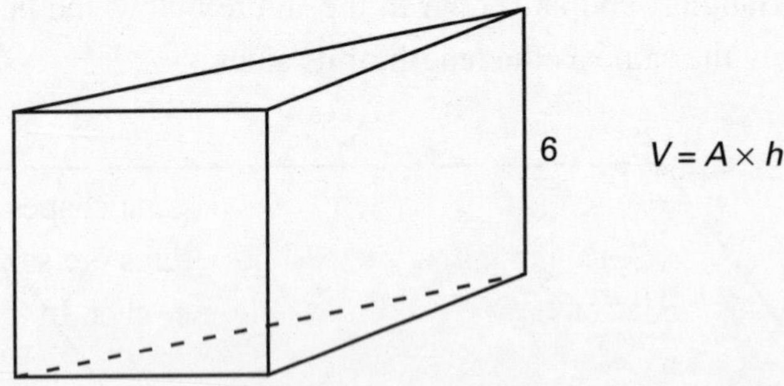

A cylinder is like a prism in that it has parallel faces, but its rounded "side" is smooth. The formula for finding the volume of a cylinder is the same as the formula for finding the volume of a prism: The area of the cylinder's base is multiplied by the height. The volume of the cylinder in the following figure is approximately 628 cubic units. $(5 \times 5 \times \pi \times 8)$.

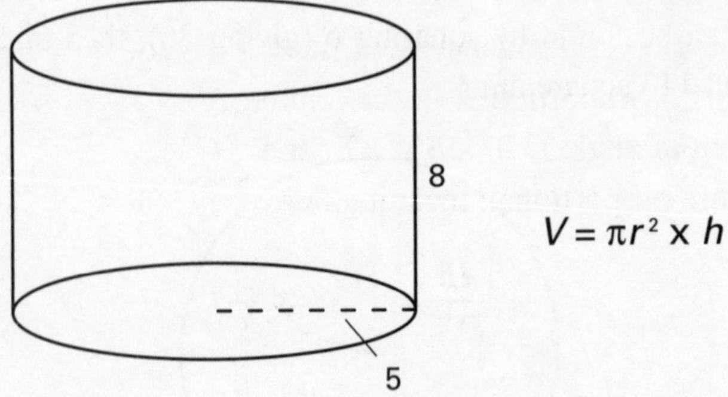

A property of all triangles is that the sum of the measures of the three angles is 180°. If, therefore, the measures of two angles are known, the third can be deduced using addition, and then subtraction.

Right triangles (those with a right angle) have several special properties. A chief property is described by the Pythagorean Theorem, which states that in any right triangle with legs (shorter sides) a and b, and hypotenuse (the longest side) c, the sum of the squares of the sides will be equal to the square of the hypotenuse ($a^2 + b^2 = c^2$). Note that in the right triangle shown here, $3^2 + 4^2 = 5^2$.

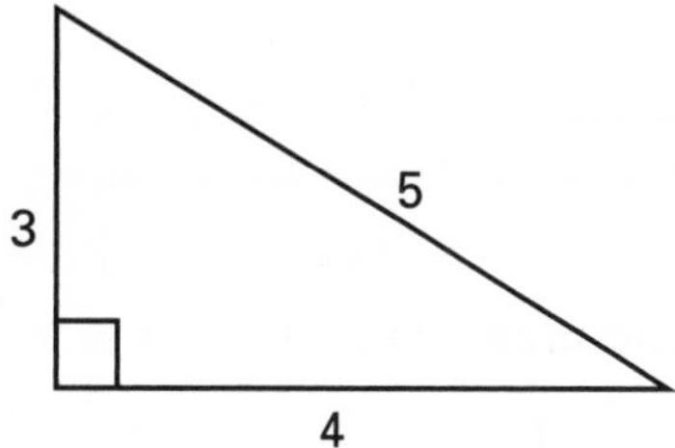

Applying Reasoning Skills

Geometric figures are *similar* if they have the exact same shapes, even if they do not have the same sizes. In transformational geometry, two figures are said to be similar if and only if a similarity transformation maps one figure onto the other. In the figure that follows, triangles A and B are similar.

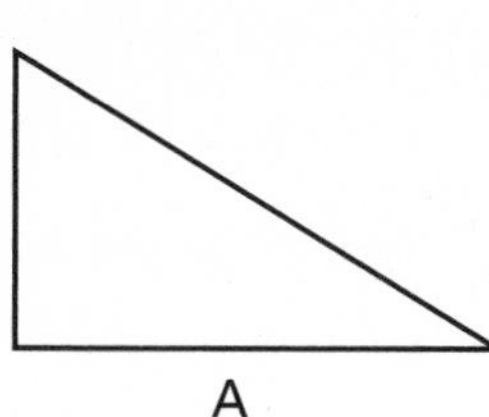

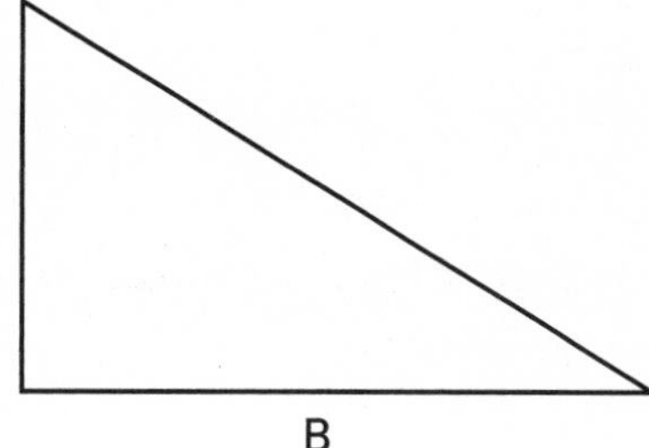

Corresponding angles of similar figures have the same measure, and the lengths of corresponding sides are proportional. In the similar triangles below, $\angle A \cong \angle D$ (meaning "angle A is congruent to angle D"), $\angle B \cong \angle E$, and $\angle C \cong \angle F$. The corresponding sides of the triangles below are proportional, meaning that:

$$\frac{AB}{DE} = \frac{BC}{EF} = \frac{CA}{DF}$$

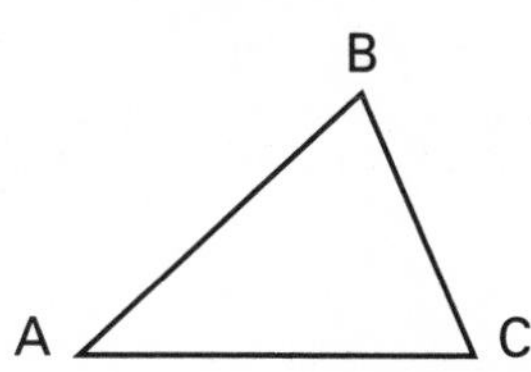

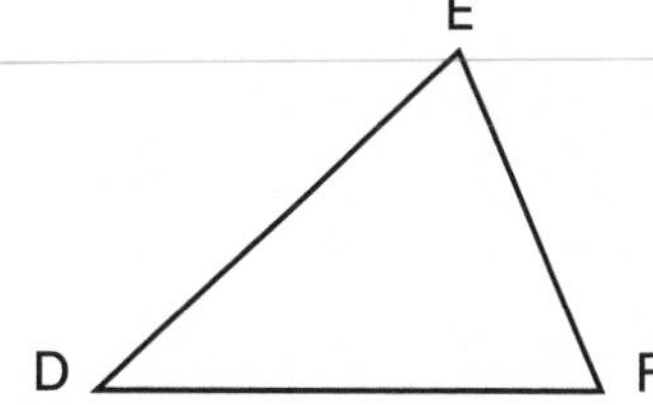

Figures are *congruent* if they have the same shape *and* size. (Congruent figures are also similar.) In the figure below, rectangles A and B are congruent.

Straight lines within the same plane that have no points in common (that is, they never cross) are parallel lines. Note that the term *parallel* is used to describe the relationship between two coplanar lines that do not intersect. Lines that are not coplanar—although they never cross—are not considered to be parallel. Coplanar lines crossing at right angles (90°) are perpendicular.

When presented with math or logic problems, including geometry problems, *deductive reasoning* may be helpful. Deductive reasoning is reasoning from the general to the specific, and is supported by deductive logic. Here is an example of deductive reasoning:

> All humans who have walked on the moon are males (a general proposition). Neil Armstrong walked on the moon, therefore he is a male (a specific proposition).

Note that conclusions reached via deductive reasoning are sound only if the original assumptions are actually true.

With *inductive* reasoning, a general rule is inferred from specific observations (which may be limited). Moving from the statement "All fish I have ever seen have fins" (specific but limited observations) to "All fish have fins" (a general proposition) is an example of inductive reasoning. Conclusions arrived at via inductive reasoning are not necessarily true.

An example of how logical reasoning can be used to solve a geometry problem is given hereafter. (In this case *deductive* reasoning is used to find the measure of $\angle J$.)

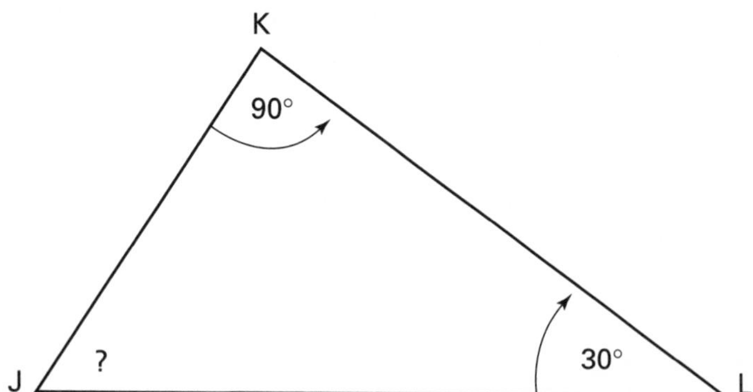

The sum of the measures of the three angles of any triangle is 180° (a general proposition). The sum of the measures of ∠K and ∠L is 120°; therefore, the measure of ∠J is 60° (a specific proposition).

Some problems may require you to make conversions for units of measurement (distance, volume, and mass) in both the standard system and the metric system. These are the most common conversions:

Distance	1 foot = 12 inches	**Volume**	1 gallon = 4 quarts
	1 yard = 3 feet		1 quart = 2 pints (32 ounces)
	1 mile = 5280 feet		
			1 liter = 1000 milliliters
	1 kilometer = 1000 meters		1 cubic centimeter = 1 milliliter
	1 meter = 100 centimeters		
	1 centimeter = 10 millimeters		1 quart = 0.95 liters
	1 inch = 2.54 centimeters		
Mass	1 pound = 16 ounces	**Time**	1 minute = 60 seconds
	1 ton = 2000 pounds		1 hour = 60 minutes
			1 day = 24 hours
	1 gram = 1000 milligrams		1 year = 365 days
	1 kilogram = 1000 grams		1 year = 52 weeks
	1 kilogram = 2.2 pounds		

Examples:

12 ft. = _____ yd.	Since there are 3 feet in 1 yard, 12 divided by 3 = 4 yards.
450 cm = _____ m	Since there are 100 centimeters in 1 meter, 450 divided by 100 = 4.5 meters.
64 oz. = _____ lbs.	Since there are 16 ounces in 1 pound, 64 divided by 16 = 4 pounds.
7200 g = _____ kg	Since there are 1000 grams in 1 kilogram, 7200 divided by 1000 = 7.2 kilograms.
7 gal. = _____ qt.	Since there are 4 quarts in 1 gallon, $7 \times 4 = 28$ quarts.
8300 ml = _____ l	Since there are 1000 milliliters in 1 liter, 8300 divided by 1000 = 8.3 liters.
7 hours = _____ min.	Since there are 60 minutes in 1 hour, $7 \times 60 = 420$ minutes.
45 min. = _____ hr.	There are 60 minutes in one hour. 45 minutes is less than one hour, so set up a fraction to show 45 out of 60 minutes $\left(\frac{45}{60} = \frac{3}{4}\right)$. Therefore, 45 minutes is $\frac{3}{4}$ of an hour.

0009 Data Analysis and Statistics

This section includes interpreting information presented in tables, line graphs, scatter plots, pictographs, bar graphs, histograms, and pie charts; determining the theoretical probability of simple events; demonstrating knowledge of measures of central tendency (mean, median), and variability (range, deviation from the mean); and demonstrating knowledge of the use of statistical concepts to solve real-world problems.

Graphs, tables, and charts come in many different forms; most of these represent numerical data in easy-to-read visual formats. A bar graph, like the one below, typically shows "how much" for each category.

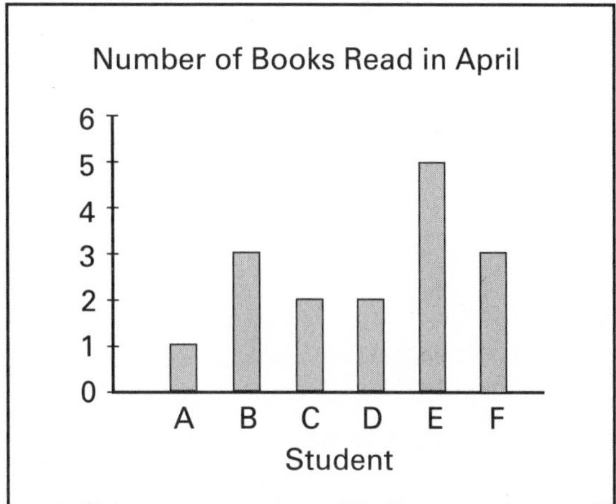

Line graphs, like the one below, are well suited to indicate *change over time.* These graphs indicate time (in months, years, etc.) on the bottom or horizontal axis. We use line graphs to show trends in data.

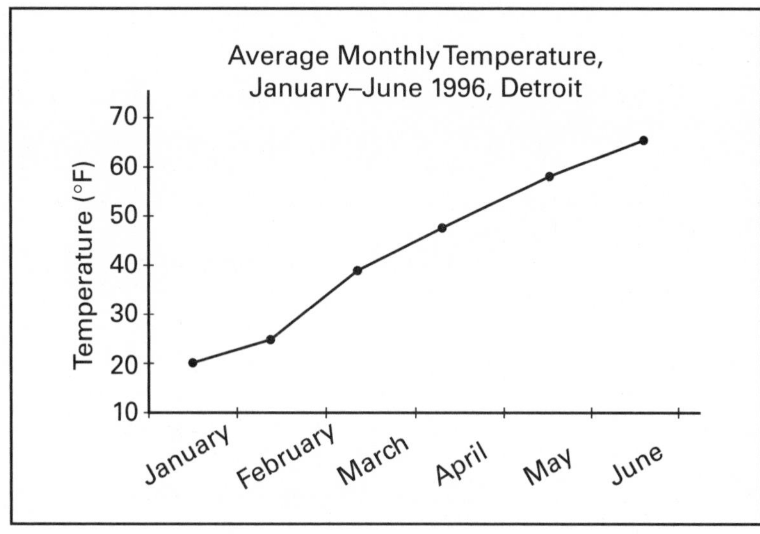

Pie graphs (also called circle graphs or pie charts) show how a quantity is "split up." As with the example below, pie graphs may not necessarily be accompanied by specific numeric values. These graphs are particularly effective for showing relative amounts at a glance.

Scatter plots are used to investigate relationships between two variables. The scatter plot below shows height (in centimeters) in relation to arm span (in centimeters). As might be expected, as a person's height increases, their arm span tends to increase as well.

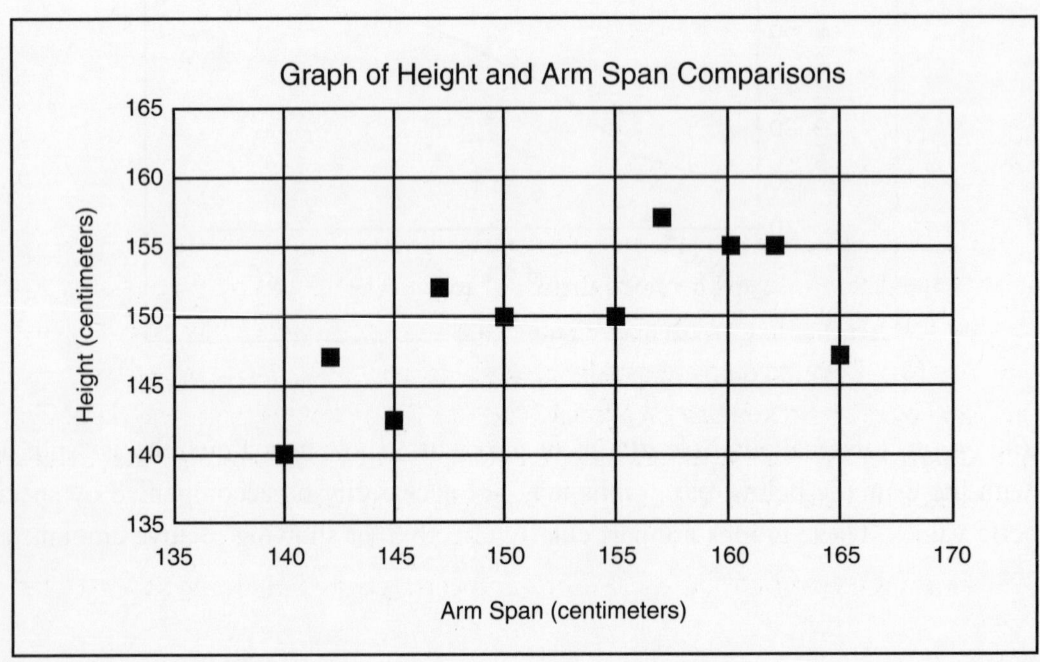

Histograms are graphs that use vertical columns to show frequencies. The histogram below shows the number of students who made particular scores on a quiz.

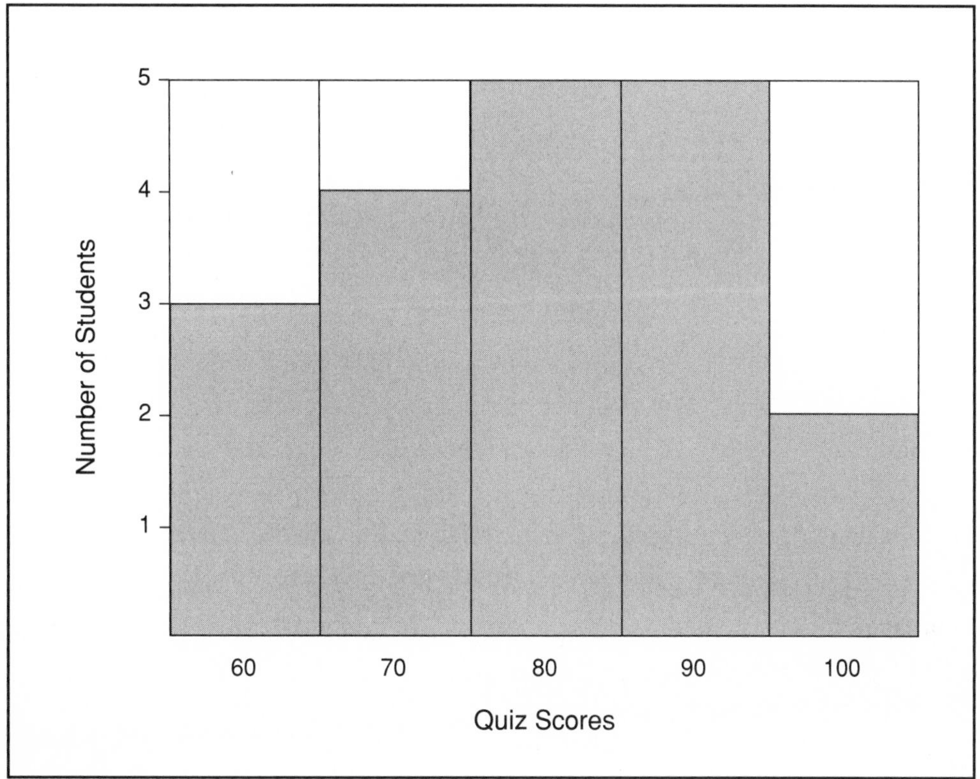

Statistical Concepts

Data can be represented in *discrete* or *continuous* form, depending on what they represent. Discrete data have gaps between them. A bar graph is a common way to show discrete data. For example, the bar graph above shows the number of students who made particular scores on a test. Discrete data are usually obtained by counting. Continuous data are usually represented by an unbroken line on a graph, and usually are obtained by measuring. The line graph on page 65, shows the average monthly temperature over time. The data are continuous, because there are no gaps in the months or in the temperatures.

There are a number of statistical terms and concepts that you may need to know for the test:

GACE Tip

Mean: average
Median: center number
Mode: occurs most often

Mean

Commonly known as the "average," the mean is the sum of a set of numbers divided by the quantity of numbers in the set. To find the mean, add all of the numbers together, and divide by how many numbers are given.

For example, suppose you are given the following data set:

16, 9, 11, 19, 12, 16, 22

To find the mean, add all the numbers together (16 + 9 + 11 + 19 + 12 + 16 + 22 = 105). Then, divide the sum (105) by the quantity of numbers in the data set (7).

105 divided by 7 = 15. The mean of this data set is 15.

Median

The median is the center value in a set of numbers; to find the median, list the numbers from smallest to largest, and locate the number in the middle. If there are two middle numbers, compute their average.

Given the same data set as above, list the numbers from smallest to largest.

9, 11, 12, 16, 16, 19, 22

The number in the middle is 16, which is the median.

Mode

A measure of central tendency, the mode is the value in a set of numbers that occurs most often.

Given the same data set as above, we see that 16 occurs twice in the data set, and all of the other numbers occur once. Therefore, 16 is the mode.

Range

The range is the measure of the variation (spread) that is the difference between the largest value and smallest value in a set of data. To find the range, subtract the smallest number in the set from the largest number.

Sample

A sample is a survey of the population made by taking a set that is judged to be representative of the population. Choosing the sample in a randomized way is essential for validity and believability.

Standard Deviation

Standard deviation is the most commonly used expression of spread, or variation, of data. The higher the standard deviation, the higher is the degree of spread around the center of the data (that is, the data are more inconsistent with each other).

Percentiles

A percentile is a ranking or measure of where a piece of data stands in relation to the other data in the set. Percentiles tell how many other data are lower in value. For example, a person might score 75% on a test, but rank in the 90 percentile. This means that 89% of all other test takers received a lower score. The median occurs at the 50 percentile.

Frequency Distributions

Frequency distributions represent the likelihood that a statistic of interest will fall in a certain interval; for example, the height of a person chosen at random may follow the normal distribution (also called a standard distribution, or "bell-shaped curve"). These are some types of distributions:

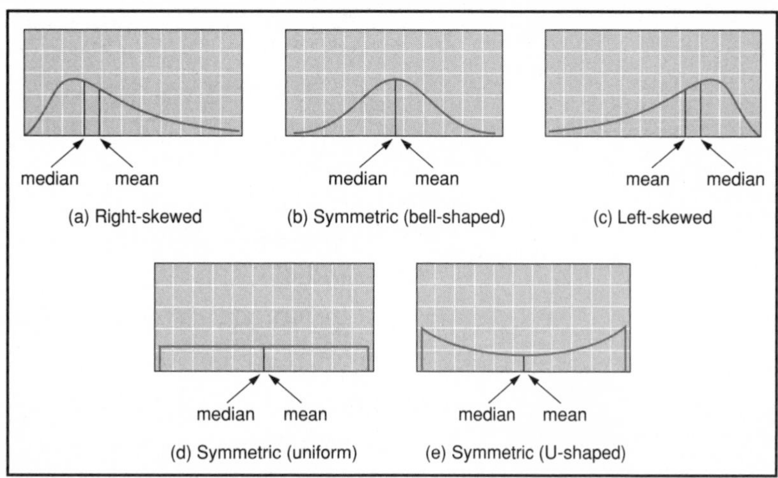

(a) Right-skewed (b) Symmetric (bell-shaped) (c) Left-skewed

(d) Symmetric (uniform) (e) Symmetric (U-shaped)

Figure (b) is the normal distribution, on which tests are often said to be graded. In this figure, more scores fall in the middle than on the high or low ends. In the right-skewed distribution in Figure (a), more of the scores are low, and in the left-skewed distribution in Figure (c), more of the scores are high. The distribution in Figure (d) shows that all scores are distributed equally from high to low, and Figure (e) shows a distribution in which most scores were either high or low, with fewer in the average range. Notice the location of the mean and median in each figure.

Correlation

Correlation is the relationship between two variables. For example, a graph of tar and nicotine in cigarettes might look like this:

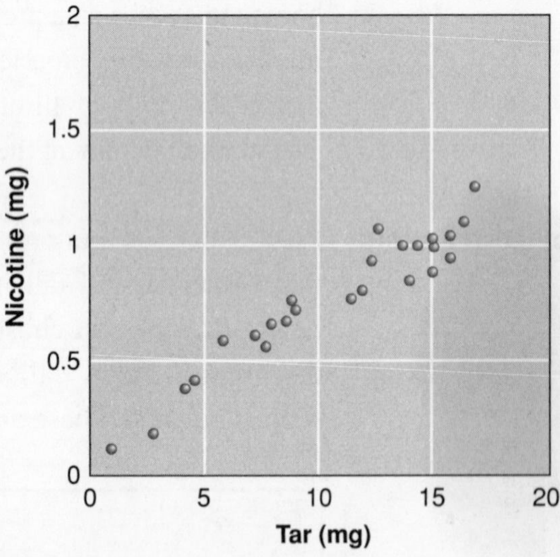

Each dot represents a particular cigarette, and the placement of the dot depends on the amounts of its tar (x-axis) and nicotine (y-axis). Drawings like this are called *scatter plots*. You could draw a straight line through this scatter plot, and it would go up and to the right, because, in general, the higher the amount of tar, the higher the amount of nicotine. The amounts of tar and nicotine are thus *positively correlated.* Some variables are *negatively correlated*; for instance, the weight of a vehicle would be negatively correlated with gas mileage if several models of vehicle were plotted in a scatter plot.

Here are some other scatter plots with varying kinds of correlation:

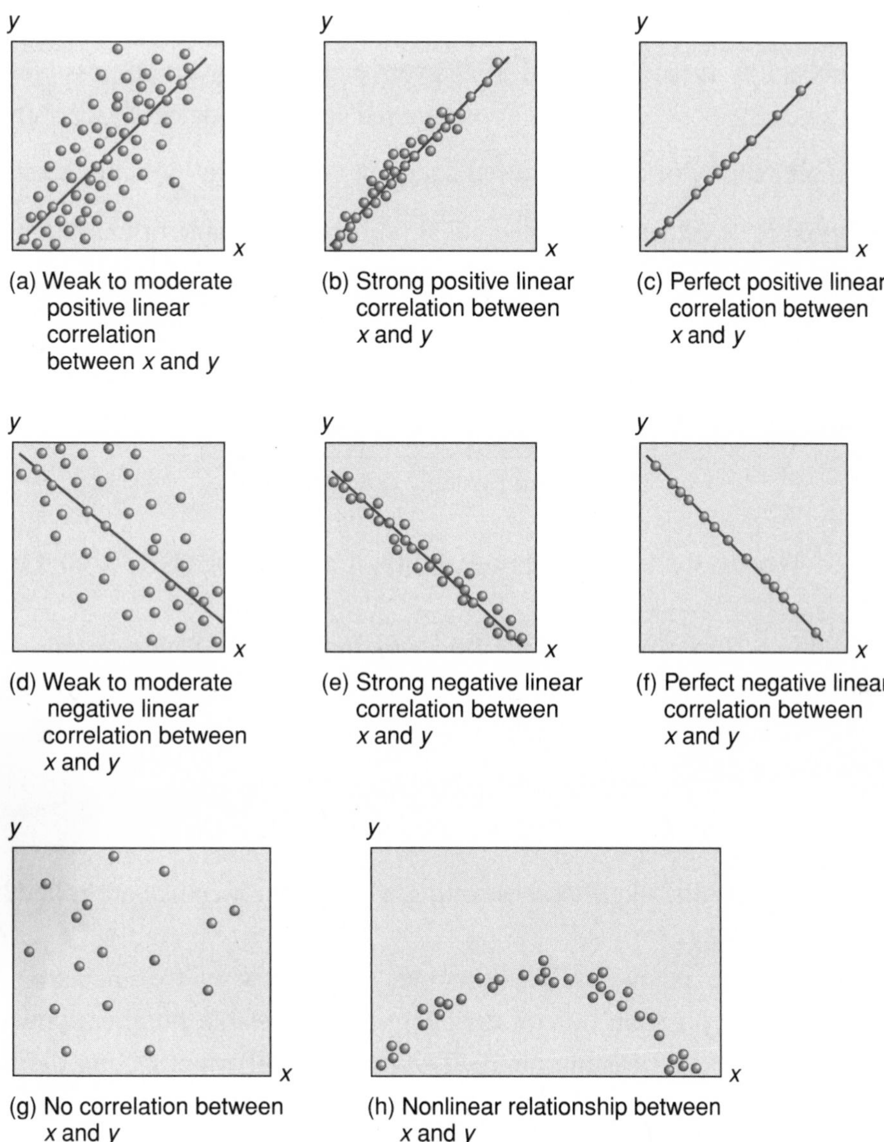

(a) Weak to moderate positive linear correlation between x and y

(b) Strong positive linear correlation between x and y

(c) Perfect positive linear correlation between x and y

(d) Weak to moderate negative linear correlation between x and y

(e) Strong negative linear correlation between x and y

(f) Perfect negative linear correlation between x and y

(g) No correlation between x and y

(h) Nonlinear relationship between x and y

When a correlation is linear or almost linear, you can use the graph to make predictions. For example, in the graph of tar and nicotine above, you could predict with a fair amount of certainty that a cigarette with 10 mg of tar would have between 0.7 and 0.8 mg of nicotine. In scatterplots without a linear correlation [(*g*) and (*h*) above], it's much harder to predict the value of y, given the value of x, in fact, in graph (*g*) it's nearly impossible.

Probability

One probability concept that may be addressed on the test is *theoretical probability*. Theoretical probability is the likelihood of an event occurring, given all possible outcomes. For example, given the possibilities of choosing a red candy, a blue candy, or a green candy, the theoretical probability of choosing a red candy is $\frac{1}{3}$. The total possible outcomes of an event are required for calculations of theoretical probability. A table or chart that shows the possibilities may be helpful.

To find the theoretical probability of an event, make a fraction:

$$\frac{\text{number of ways the event can occur}}{\text{total possible outcomes}}$$

Example 1 What is the theoretical probability of getting "heads" if a coin is tossed?

When you flip a coin, there are only 2 possible outcomes—heads or tails. Two is the denominator of the fraction. The number of ways that you could get "heads" is 1 (only 1 side is a "head"). One is the numerator of the fraction. Therefore, the theoretical probability is $\frac{1}{2}$ or 50%.

Example 2 What is the likelihood of rolling a "7" when two dice are rolled?

First, determine how many possible outcomes there are when two dice are rolled. The chart below shows the possible outcomes. There are 6 possible numbers you could roll when rolling die #1, and 6 possible numbers you could roll when rolling die #2. Therefore, there are 36 possible combinations or outcomes ($6 \times 6 = 36$). This is the denominator of the fraction.

Second, find the number of ways the event can occur. In this case, the sum of "7" appears 6 times. Six is the numerator of the fraction. Therefore, the theoretical probability is $\frac{6}{36}$, or $\frac{1}{6}$, or 16.6%.

Possible Outcomes – Die #1							
Possible Outcomes – Die #2		**1**	**2**	**3**	**4**	**5**	**6**
	1	2	3	4	5	6	7
	2	3	4	5	6	7	8
	3	4	5	6	7	8	9
	4	5	6	7	8	9	10
	5	6	7	8	9	10	11
	6	7	8	9	10	11	12

Example 3 Look at the spinner below. Assume that each section in the spinner is equal in area. What is the likelihood of getting a 1 on the first spin and a 2 on the second spin?

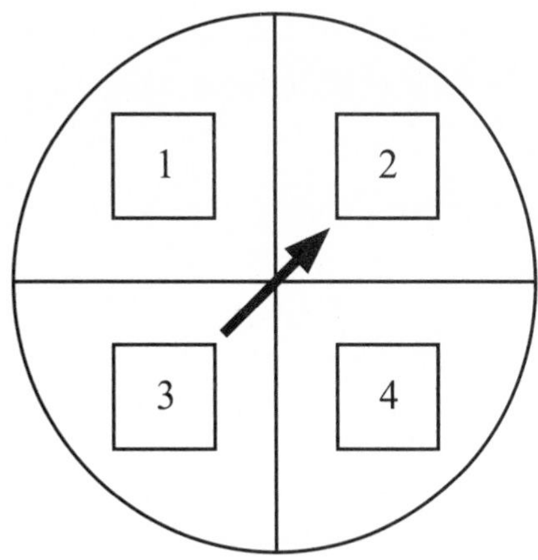

First, determine the number of possible outcomes when spinning a spinner twice. The ordered pairs below show the possibilities (outcome of spin 1, outcome of spin 2).

(1, 1)	(2, 1)	(3, 1)	(4, 1)
(1, 2)	(2, 2)	(3, 2)	(4, 2)
(1, 3)	(2, 3)	(3, 3)	(4, 3)
(1, 4)	(2, 4)	(3, 4)	(4, 4)

Sixteen possible outcomes exist. This is the denominator of the fraction.

Only *one* of the outcomes (1, 2) illustrates the possibility of getting a 1 with the first spin and a 2 with the second spin. One is the numerator of the fraction.

Therefore, the theoretical probability of getting a 1 with the first spin and a 2 with the second spin is $\frac{1}{16}$ or 6.25%.

0010 Problem-Solving Principles and Techniques

This section includes identifying missing terms in numerical and graphic patterns; solving word problems involving integers, fractions, decimals, and percents; solving problems and drawing conclusions using a variety of problem-solving techniques; evaluating and solving algebraic expressions, equations, and inequalities; and estimating results and determining whether the answer is reasonable.

GACE Tip

When you have finished a problem, always check to see that your answer makes sense.

There are two keys to successfully solving word problems: setting up the problem correctly (using the correct operations) and ensuring that your answer is reasonable. Read word problems carefully; often, particular words and phrases in word problems translate into numbers and operation symbols. Consider this word problem:

Roberto babysat for the Yagers one evening. They paid him $5 just for coming over to their house, plus $7 for every hour of babysitting. How much was he paid if he babysat for 4 hours?

In this problem, "plus" indicates addition, and "for every hour" suggests multiplication. Thus, the equation for this problem can be set up like this: $5 + (7 \times 4)$ = Roberto's earnings.

There are a number of "clue words" that suggest which operations should be used. The chart below contains a sample of these words.

Addition Clue Words	Subtraction Clue Words
add altogether in all plus sum total	difference have left how much/many more less than remain
Multiplication Clue Words	**Division Clue Words**
for every multiplied by product of times	as much divided equally parts separated split sharing something

Although these clue words suggest which operation is appropriate, each word problem requires an individual approach. Keeping in mind the reasonableness of the computational setup should be helpful.

It may also be helpful to use a variety of problem-solving strategies. These may include drawing a picture, making a chart or table, looking for a pattern, logical reasoning, or working backwards.

CHAPTER

Writing

4

The writing portion of the GACE Basic Skills Test **assesses the test-taker's ability to recognize well-written compositions and Standard American English usage as well as to compose a written response to a given topic.** When you take this test, you will be asked to read a passage and answer questions about the words or punctuation included in that passage. You may also be asked to fill in the blank with a sentence or phrase that makes the passage more effective.

The GACE Writing Test is divided into two sections. The first section includes approximately 42 selected-response (multiple-choice) test items. The second Section requires you to demonstrate the ability to prepare an essay (constructed-response) on a given prompt.

When you take the second section of the Writing Test you will be directed to write a written response on a given topic. Your composition will be evaluated on the following criteria: **appropriateness** (how well your response addresses the topic and is appropriate for the audience, purpose, and occasion); your **focus** and **organization** (logical sequence of thoughts and ideas, and overall clarity); your **support** (how well you have used details to support your thesis statement); your **grammar**, **sentence structure**, and **usage** (the extent to which your response has no errors in usage, and the precision of your word choice); and your **use of conventions** (the extent to which your response has no errors in spelling, capitalization, and punctuation). Your responses will be rated on a four-point scale from "4" to "1." Other possible scores you could receive would be: "unscorable" or "blank."

This review is designed to prepare you for the multiple-choice questions in the Test III (Writing) subarea. The review will help you to recognize good writing and give you pointers on how to write a well-developed composition on a given subject. Tips to help you quickly and accurately answer the questions are also included. By studying this review, you will greatly increase your chances of achieving a good score on the GACE.

3. GACE Writing Skills Objectives

Skills Covered in Selected-Response Questions

0011 Recognize unity, focus, and development in writing

For example:

- recognizing unnecessary shifts in point of view or distracting details that impair the development of the main idea in a piece of writing
- recognizing revisions that improve the unity and focus of a piece of writing
- recognizing thesis statements, topic sentences, and supporting elements

0012 Recognize effective organization in writing

For example:

- recognizing methods of paragraph organization
- recognizing the use of transitional words or phrases
- reorganizing sentences to improve cohesion and the effective sequence of ideas

0013 Recognize effective sentences

For example:

- recognizing redundancy
- identifying structures (e.g., sentences, fragments, run-on sentences)
- identifying standard subject-verb agreement
- identifying double negatives, parallel structure, and standard placement of modifiers

0014 Recognize Standard American English usage

For example:

- recognizing the standard use of verb forms and cases
- recognizing the standard use of pronouns/antecedents and plural and possessive forms of nouns
- recognizing the standard use and formations of adverbs and adjectives
- recognizing standard punctuation and capitalization

Skills Covered in Constructed-Response Questions

0015 Demonstrate the ability to prepare a developed composition on a given topic using language and style appropriate to a given audience, purpose, and occasion

- composing a coherent, focused, and sustained composition on a given topic using language and style appropriate to a specified audience, purpose, and occasion
- stating and maintaining a clear thesis statement using organizational strategies to enhance meaning and clarity
- providing reasoned support and/or specific examples to maintain the thesis statement
- using effective sentence structure, word choice, and mechanics (e.g., grammar, syntax)
- using spelling, capitalization, and punctuation according to the conventions of Standard American English

The Passages

The reading passages in this part of your test will be based on many different subjects. Although you will not be expected to know the content presented in the passages, you will be expected to recognize correct writing techniques and select appropriate revisions to sections that are not grammatically correct. Each passage will be followed by a number of questions. Some questions may ask you to find mistakes in Standard American English usage; others may ask you to supply appropriate words or phrases in blanks.

Objective 0011 Recognize unity, focus and development in writing

Recognizing unnecessary shifts in point of view or distracting details that impair the development of the main idea in a piece of writing

Point of view is the relationship of the writer to the written piece. The point of view in a particular passage must be consistent throughout the passage. Unnecessary shifts in the point of view come about by the change in the number of the noun or pronoun. Points of view may be considered one of three *persons:*

- First person singular or plural (*I*, *we*): the narrator is part of the composition
- Second person singular or plural (*you*): the narrator is addressing the reader
- Third person singular or plural (*he*, *she*, *it*, *they*): the narrator is not a part of the composition, but an observer of it

For example, this text is written in *second person* (*you*) which addresses the reader directly. Generally, it is best to stay in the point of view, or the correct person, in which you begin the passage. The most common shift in point of view in college writing is from first or third person to second person. Consider the following:

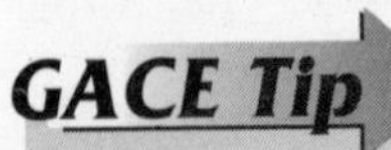

Stay with the same person that you started with.

"Just trying to figure out which college to attend is a big challenge. The prospective college student must take into consideration cost and available majors, as well as location of the school. Once the list has been narrowed down by these factors, you might want to take into account where your parents might like you to go."

Because the writer began in the third person, in this instance the point of view should remain in the third person. The writer could make the following changes to correct the unnecessary shift in point of view. The second sentence could be changed:

"You, the prospective college student, must take into consideration cost and available majors, as well as location of the school."

Or the *third:*

> "Once the list has been narrowed down by these factors, he or she might want to take into account where his or her parents might like him or her to go." OR "Once the list has been narrowed down by these factors, students might want to take into account where their parents might like them to go."

You can see that the replacement to third person singular in this instance can be somewhat stilted, but selection of the point of view is more dependent on the audience and the purpose of the passage.

On the test, you will be asked to recognize these inconsistencies in point of view and select corrections that provided consistency across the passage. In this example, as you will see in the test, it is necessary to read the entire passage to determine the appropriate point of view.

This descriptive statement that accompanies Objective 0011 also focuses on the importance of being able to recognize *distracting details*. These are sentences or phrases within the passage that do not address the main idea. Again, it is essential to read the entire passage to be able able to recognize information that does not fit into the passage.

Recognizing revisions that improve the unity and focus of a piece of writing

You will be asked to select answers that will provide revisions to the passages given. You need to be able to identify revisions that improve the *unity and focus* of a piece of writing. The unity of a composition is that quality in which all the sentences support the main idea and the parts fit together in a complete, self-contained whole. The focus of a composition is that quality in which the position or proposition of the writer is clearly evident. Consider this passage:

All of the sentences in a composition need to support the main idea.

> In 1867 Congress passed the Fourteenth Amendment, which granted citizenship to "all persons born or naturalized in the United States." This included former slaves recently freed. The Fourteenth Amendment

> also gave "equal protection of the laws" to all citizens and declared that no state could deny anyone "life, liberty or property" without due process. Due process means that everyone has equal protection under the law, and people may not be treated differently, or discriminated against. The 14th Amendment made it illegal for states to discriminate against anyone based on race. However, a number of white southerners did not want to give African Americans real freedom and, as a result, most southern states adopted black codes to limit the freedoms of African Americans.

This passage has both unity and focus because all of the sentences are supportive of the main idea of the historical delivery of equal rights under the law to African Americans. The passage addresses the constitutional law and the measures taken to violate that law.

Recognizing thesis statements, topic sentences, and supporting elements

A **thesis statement** is a position or proposition advanced by a writer and all the information in an essay supports or elaborates on this idea. The **topic sentence** is one that states the main idea of a paragraph, while the **supporting elements** are facts, examples, details, illustrations, testimony, or the research of experts that verify or add credence to a main idea.

A successful thesis statement can be recognized by asking these questions about the passage:

1. What was the central idea that guided the passage?
2. What questions were answered in the passage?
3. What significant ideas surfaced in the passage?
4. What did I find out after I read the passage?

When you are reading to locate the thesis statements, topic sentences, and supporting elements, look for the main idea and be wary of irrelevant ideas. Take the following example:

> [1]After 1870, many northerners grew tired of trying to force change on the South. [2]They felt that it was time to forget the Civil War and let southerners run their own governments, even if that meant African Americans might lose the rights they had so recently gained. [3]Many changes occurred during Reconstruction that were meant to help the former slaves and

freedmen. [4]Without federal protection, the Reconstruction governments that were supportive of African American civil rights fell in 1877.

Sentence 3 is not a supporting element of this passage. While sentence 4 does mention Reconstruction, the thesis of this passage does not focus on the changes that occurred during Reconstruction, but rather how those changes were abandoned. The proposition advanced by this writer within the passage is that when northerners grew tired of supporting the Reconstruction governments in the south, these governments fell. The reasons why the northerners no longer supported the Reconstruction governments, such as they grew tired of trying to force change and that they felt it was time to forget the Civil War, act as supporting elements.

Objective 0012 Recognize effective organization in writing

Recognizing methods of paragraph organization

Good writing is evidenced by a coherent composition, which has a systematic order of ideas. Coherent writing is recognized by the connections between one sentence or paragraph and the next. Sentences and paragraphs should be arranged in such a way that it is easy to determine the intent of the writer. This arrangement should be clear and logical so that the flow of the information is easy to follow.

Different types of compositions use different orders of paragraphs, but usually there is an introductory paragraph followed by supporting paragraphs that further describe the supporting elements, and a concluding paragraph. The order in which the information is presented may be affected by the content of the composition. Some paragraphs will be written in chronological order, some in spatial order, and some compositions may be written to compare or contrast objects and events, and this order will be presented.

Well-organized writing includes an introductory paragraph, supporting paragraphs, and a concluding paragraph.

The following example uses **spatial order** in the first paragraph, **chronological order** in the second, and **compare and contrast** in the third.

1. My best friend and I handed over our tickets and headed into the stadium. Immediately in front of us was the concession stand, but we headed up the long ramp on our right to

the upper level. Once on the upper level, another concession stand stood in front of us, but we went instead to the stairs between the concession stand and the restrooms to get to our seats.

2. Before we arrived at our assigned row, we first greeted other season ticket holders who we had seen at previous games. We then inched our way to our seats while trying not to step on anyone's toes. When we got to our seats, we once again greeted familiar faces and then adjusted our seat cushions. Before we sat down, we got the vendor's attention for some hot dogs and cold drinks. Finally we were ready.

3. This game was unlike any game last season: we could feel the excitement in the air. Last year we rarely saw the stadium filled before kickoff, but at this game, every seat was filled by the time the team hit the field for warm-ups. This game reminded me of games during the season when we won the national championship, which meant that everyone was up and cheering from the beginning to the end. Unlike last year when some fans left at halftime, this year fans stayed after the game to continue to show support for the team.

Recognizing the use of transitional words or phrases

A **transition** is a connecting word or phrase that clarifies the relationship of other words or ideas. Transitional words and phrases show the relationship between details and help make these relationships clear. Consider these commonly used transitions and the relationships they illustrate:

Time: *after, always, before, finally, first, immediately, later, meanwhile, now, sometimes, soon, until*

Place: *above, ahead, around, below, down, far, here, inside, near, next, opposite, outside, over, parallel, there, under, vertically, within*

Order of importance: *first, latter, primarily, secondarily*

Cause and effect: *as a result, because, by, so, then, therefore*

Comparison and contrast: *but, even more, however, just as, like, on the other hand, unlike*

Example: *for example, for instance, namely, that is*

In the previous passages, note the words and phrases in the first paragraph that identify the place (in front, between), the second paragraph that illustrate the order in which the events occurred (before, first), and the third paragraph that compare and contrast (unlike, but).

Reorganizing sentences to improve cohesion and the effective sequence of ideas

The key to cohesion is **organization**. The logical sequence of ideas, coupled with transitional words and phrases to keep connections clear, is the mainstay of coherent writing. It is a sign of good writing when paragraphs are arranged so that one leads logically to the next and sentences within paragraphs are ordered so that readers can easily follow the flow of ideas. Consider the following example:

> LBJ pushed to have the civil rights bill passed. It had passed in the House of Representatives, in February 1964, but was stalled in the Senate where southern segregationists intended to kill it. After President Kennedy's assassination on November 22, 1963, President Lyndon Johnson was determined to continue Kennedy's civil rights policies. Johnson was aided in his goal to pass the civil rights bill by national remorse over Kennedy's assassination. President Johnson took advantage of the public mood and on July 2, 1964, he signed into law the Civil Rights Act of 1964. Even though Johnson was from the South, he had broken with the segregationists.

While the content and ideas are presented within the example, it is difficult to follow chronologically or through the order of importance. Here is the passage reorganized with the ideas more effectively sequenced:

> After President Kennedy's assassination on November 22, 1963, President Lyndon Johnson was determined to continue Kennedy's civil rights policies. He pushed to have the civil rights bill passed. Though it had passed in the House of Representatives in February 1964, it was stalled in the Senate, where southern segregationists intended to kill it. Even though Johnson was from the South, he had broken with the segregationists. Johnson was aided in his goal to pass the civil rights bill by national remorse over Kennedy's assassination. President Johnson took advantage of public mood and on July 2, 1964, he signed into law the Civil Rights Act of 1964.

The rearrangement of the sentences, and the addition of one transition word, helps the reader to understand the progression of the information.

Objective 0013 Recognize effective sentences

Recognizing redundancy

Often in college writing, the same point will be restated in more than one question. You will encounter test questions that will gauge your ability to detect redundancies (unnecessary repetitions). These questions require you to select sentences that use only those necessary words to convey a message clearly. Effective writing is concise writing, but this doesn't mean that short sentences are better than long ones simply because they are brief. Repetition of words, sounds, and phrases should be used only for emphasis. Consider the following example:

> **GACE Tip**
>
> **Effective writing is concise writing.**

> Often, anxiety before a competition can promote poor performance in football players, especially quarterbacks. Being nervous can cause players to forget plays, throw to covered receivers, and move too quickly from behind center.

"Anxiety" in the first sentence and "being nervous" in the second means essentially the same thing, as do "quarterbacks" and "players." These two sentences can be combined and reworked to offer a more concise thesis and supporting details.

> "Anxiety in quarterbacks can have disastrous results when their nervousness promotes poor performance like forgetting plays, throwing to covered receivers, and moving too quickly from behind center."

Identifying structures (e.g., sentences, fragments, run-on sentences)

A **sentence** is a group of words that expresses a complete thought and can be classified by structure (simple, compound, complex, compound-complex). Every sentence has two basic parts, a subject and a predicate.

Sentence fragments are incomplete sentences that either 1) lack a subject or a verb or 2) are preceded by a subordinating conjunction (e.g., *after*, *before*, *since*, *until*). A **run-on sentence** is two or more complete sentences written as though they were one sentence.

Consider how sentences can be identified from existing fragments or run-on sentences:

Fragment that lacks a subject:

Incorrect Kitty has several ideas about teaching reading to young children. That won't cost much to implement.

Correct Kitty has several ideas that won't cost much to implement about teaching reading to young children.

Fragment that is a subordinate clause:

Incorrect Jemella went to the later show. Because it was a romance.

Correct Jemella went to the later show because it was a romance. OR

Jemella went to the later show. It was a romance.

Run-on sentence as a comma splice (two main clauses separated only by a comma):

Incorrect I did not see her come in, she was late.

Correct I did not see her come in. She was late. OR

I did not see her come in; she was late. OR

I did not see her come in, but she was late.

Two main clauses without a comma before the coordinating conjunction:

Incorrect I usually buy my airplane ticket early but I thought I would wait this year.

Correct I usually buy my airplane ticket early, but I thought I would wait this year.

Identifying standard subject-verb agreement

There are **two basic rules of subject and verb agreement** that govern all the other rules:

1. a singular subject must have a singular verb.
2. a plural subject must have a plural verb.

A verb must agree with its subject in person and number, and this is often where students make mistakes. It is good practice to identify the real subject of a sentence and then determine whether the verb form should be singular or plural.

Every English verb has five forms, two of which are the bare form (plural and the –s form (singular). In other words, singular verb forms end in –s; plural forms do not.

Here are the **rules governing subject verb agreement in action**:

Intervening Phrases and Clauses

A verb must agree with the subject of the sentence, not with the object of the preposition. Do not mistake a word in an intervening clause for the subject of a sentence.

Example The collection of baseball cards *was* very valuable. (The subject is *collection,* a singular noun. *Of baseball cards* is a prepositional phrase with a plural object. The verb *was* agrees with the singular noun *collection.)*

Prepositional phrases beginning with compound prepositions such as *along with, together with, in addition to,* and *as well as* introduce phrases that modify the subject without changing the number. Although their meaning is similar to that of *and*, these expressions don't form compound sentences.

Example The newspapers, together with the aluminum, are ready to be recycled. (The subject is *newspapers,* a plural noun. *Together with the aluminum* is a prepositional phrase with a singular object. The verb *are* agrees with the plural noun *newspapers.*)

Appositives and adjective clauses give information about the subject but don't change its number. Make sure you don't mistake a word in an appositive of an adjective clause for the subject of the sentence.

Example *Sharon*, one of my sisters, *cooks* for the entire family during the holidays. (singular)

Example The *states* that border Florida *are* Alabama and Georgia. (plural)

Compound Subjects

A compound subject is joined by *and* or *both*. It takes a plural verb unless its parts belong to one unit or they both refer to the same thing.

Examples The *Tigris* and the *Euphrates flow* through southwestern Asia. (plural)

Both *rivers* and *streams provide* irrigation for farmland. (plural)

Examples *Peanut butter* and *jelly is* my favorite sandwich. (singular)

Her *lord* and *master is* the dog. (singular)

When compound subjects are joined by *or* or *nor* (or by *either* ... *or* or *neither* ... *nor*), the verb agrees with the subject closer to it.

Examples *Raisins* or an *apple makes* a good snack. (singular)

Neither the *equipment* nor the *uniforms have arrived* yet. (plural)

Collective Nouns

When a **collective noun refers to a group as a whole**, it requires a singular verb. When a collective noun refers to each member of a group individually, it requires a plural verb.

Examples The *chorus performs* beautifully. (singular)

The *chorus are staying* at different hotels. (plural)

When deciding the number of the verb needed for a collective noun, it is helpful to look for the pronouns *its* and *their*. When a collective noun is referred to by *its*, the collective noun requires a singular verb. When a collective noun is referred to by *their,* the collective noun needs a plural verb.

***Its* takes a singular verb; *their* requires a plural verb.**

Some nouns ending in *–s*, such as *mumps, measles*, *news*, and *mathematics*, take singular verbs. Other nouns ending in *–s*, *like scissors, pants, binoculars*, and *eyeglasses,* take plural verbs. Many nouns that end in *–ics* are either singular or plural, depending on the context. In general, if the noun refers to a whole, like a disease or science, it requires a singular verb. If it is referring to qualities, activities, or individual items, it requires a plural verb.

Examples *Measles is* usually a childhood disease. (singular)

His *pants were wrinkled* from sitting for so long. (plural)

Statistics is one of my favorite courses. (singular)

Statistics are the basis of much research. (plural)

Nouns of Amount

When a plural noun of amount refers to one unit, it acts as a singular subject. When it refers to individual units, it acts as a plural subject.

Examples Two *weeks is* not enough time to see China. (singular)

Your five *days* of quarantine *are* up. (plural)

When a fraction or a percentage refers to a singular word, it requires a singular verb. When it refers to a plural word, it requires a plural verb.

Examples Fifty *percent* of the *money was used* for bribes. (singular)

Fifty *percent* of the *voters are* in line. (plural)

A unit of measurement usually requires a singular verb.

Examples Sixteen by twenty *inches is* a standard size for a picture frame. (singular)

Ten *yards is needed* for a first down. (singular)

Indefinite Pronouns

Some indefinite pronouns are always singular, some are always plural, and others may be singular or plural depending on their use.

Indefinite Pronouns

Singular	Another, anyone, anybody, anything, each, either, everybody, everyone, everything, neither, nobody, no one, nothing, one, other, somebody, someone, something
Plural	Both, few, many, others, several
Singular or Plural	All, any, enough, most, much, none, some

Singular indefinite pronouns require singular verbs and **plural indefinite pronouns** require plural verbs. For those indefinite pronouns that can be either singular or plural, subject-verb agreement depends on the nouns to which they refer.

Examples *Everyone wants* a ticket to the concert. (singular)

Few of us *believe* we will get tickets. (plural)

Most of the stadium *was* completely full. (*Most* refers to the singular noun *stadium*.)

Most of the attendees *were* young adults. (*Most* refers to the plural noun *attendees*.)

Phrases and Clauses as Subjects

Whenever a phrase or a clause acts as a subject, the verb must be singular.

Examples *Running laps is* good exercise. (The gerund phrase *running laps* functions as the subject and agrees with the singular verb *is*.)

To worry about grades is ineffectual. (The infinitive phrase *to worry about grades* functions as the subject and agrees with the singular verb *is*.)

Whoever makes the most pies wins the blue ribbon. (The noun clause *whoever makes the most pies* functions as the subject and agrees with the singular verb *wins*.)

Adjective Clauses

When the subject of an adjective clause is a relative pronoun, the verb in the clause must agree with the word to which the relative pronoun refers.

If the relative pronoun is the subject of the clause and it refers to a singular word, the verb in the adjective clause must be singular.

Example The woman who teaches my cooking class dresses in white. (singular)

If the relative pronoun is the subject of the adjective clause and it refers to a plural word, then the verb in the adjective clause must be plural

Example Coffee shops that have the Internet are convenient. (plural)

If an adjective clause is preceded by *the only one of* (plural word), the relative pronoun will refer to the word *one*, and the verb in the clause must be singular.

Example Dennis is the only one of my brothers who has children. (The antecedent of *who* is *one*, not *brothers*, because only one brother has children. Since *one* is singular, *who* is considered singular, and the verb in the adjective clause, *has,* must also be singular.)

If an adjective clause is preceded by *one of* (plural word), then the relative pronoun will refer to the plural word, and the verb in the clause must be plural.

Example Beijing was one of my favorite places that were included on our itinerary. (The antecedent of *that* is *places*, not *one*, because there were other places on the itinerary. Since *places* is plural, *that* is considered plural and the verb in the adjective clause, *were,* must also be plural.)

Identifying double negatives, parallel structure, and standard placement of modifiers

A double negative is two or more negative words used to express the same idea. Use only one negative word to express a negative idea.

Incorrect	I don't have no cell phone service in this area.
Correct	I don't have any cell phone service in this area. OR
Correct	I have no cell phone service in this area.

Some sentences can correctly contain more than one negative word. Notice in the example below, however, that each clause only contains one negative word.

Examples The girls *didn't* go to the movie because they had *no* money.

Parallel Structure

Parallel structure is expressing similar details using similar grammatical structures. Parallel structures often contain conjunctions and words, phrases or sentences that have similar grammatical form. Parallel structure refers to the grammatical balance of a series of any of the following:

Phrases. The boy rode *up the street, toward the town*, and *away from his incomplete chores.*

Adjectives. The university has been *historically nondiscriminatory, traditionally liberal*, and *unconventionally civil.*

Nouns. The luncheon consisted of *casseroles, a meat dish*, and *dessert.*

Verbs. The contestant *bit, chewed,* and *swallowed* the hot dog in less than five seconds.

Verbals. *Collaborating, planning*, and *implementing* are all parts of a successful team goal.

Correlative Conjunctions. *Either* we will finish this tonight, *or* we will come back tomorrow and complete it.

Sometimes a **string of grammatical structures** seem to be parallel because they address the same type of thought. Remember to look for structures that are similar, not the thought behind the structure.

Incorrect	The man was heroic and a credit to his division.
Correct	The man was a hero and a credit to his division.

Modifiers

Modifiers are words used to describe other words in sentences. Modifiers that modify the wrong word or seem to modify more than one word in a sentence are called misplaced modifiers. Modifiers should be placed as close as possible to the words they modify in order to make the meaning of the sentence clear.

Incorrect	At the last meeting, the governor discussed the cost of filling potholes in the interstate with members of his budgetary team. (prepositional phrase incorrectly modifying *filling potholes)*
Correct	At the last meeting, the governor discussed with members of his budgetary team the cost of filling potholes in the interstate. (prepositional phrase correctly modifying *discussed*)
Incorrect	Swimming effortlessly and easily, the coach cheered the relay team. (participial phrase incorrectly modifying *the coach*)
Correct	The coach cheered the relay team swimming effortlessly and easily. (participial phrase correctly modifying *the relay team*)

Dangling modifiers seem logically to modify no word at all. To correct a sentence that has a dangling modifier, you must supply a word that the dangling modifier can sensibly modify.

Incorrect	Sailing the ship to the north, a storm was avoided.
Correct	A storm was avoided because the captain sailed the ship to the north. OR
Correct	Sailing the ship to the north, the captain avoided the storm.

Objective 0014 Recognizing Standard American English usage

Recognizing the standard use of verb forms and cases

Most college writers can identify the regular verbs that form the past tense by adding the suffix *–ed.* Irregular verbs seem to offer up the most problem because there is no rule to determine how the past and past participle forms are created.

Base Form	Past Form	Past Participle (have, has, had)
be, am, are, is	was, were	been
swim	swam	swum
put	put	put
write	wrote	written
lie	lay	lain

Strategies for the Essay

To give yourself the best chance of writing a good constructed response, it is important to understand the assignment directions and have a pretty good idea of what the graders are looking for. Since you have four hours to complete all sections of the GACE Basic Skills Assessment, you should set aside approximately 60 minutes to complete this task. Remember this time schedule is only a suggestion and each writer should adjust this based on his or her own strengths.

0015 Demonstrate the ability to prepare a developed composition on a given topic using language and style appropriate to a given audience, purpose, and occasion.

For example:

- Composing a coherent, focused, and sustained composition on a given topic using language and style appropriate to a specified audience, purpose, and occasion

The writing prompts on the GACE are designed to measure your knowledge of expository writing. Expository writing is that writing which informs an audience by presenting information and explaining concepts and ideas. Effective expository writing enables readers to understand information by taking them down a logical step-by-step path. When you write your answer you should pay special attention to the following criteria:

1. Respond directly to the prompt.
2. Make your writing thoughtful and interesting.
3. Vary word and sentence choice for the purpose and audience named in the response.
4. Choose a method of organization that allows you to present details in a logical sequence.
5. Stay focused on your purpose for writing by appraising whether every sentence you write is a worthy contribution to your composition.
6. Use appropriate transitions to support the flow of ideas.
7. Elaborate through effective use of detail.

8. Communicate your response effectively by using correct spelling, capitalization, punctuation, grammar, usage, and sentence structure.

It is important that you know exactly what a writing prompt of the constructed-response assignment asks for. After reading the prompt, quickly jot down the ideas that immediately occur to you. Look for the exact words within the prompt that specify audience and purpose.

There are particular strategies that will be helpful in composing a well developed essay for the constructed-response assignment. These steps are prewriting, drafting, and revising, editing, and proofreading. You should carefully consider these steps and practice using them before you take the test.

Prewriting

Prewriting is beginning to gather and organize details before you write. Allow close to one-fourth of your time for prewriting.

- Consider your audience. Some questions you might ask are: What does the reader need and want to know? What information will require more explanation? What details will interest or influence my audience. Because your audience may be unfamiliar with your perspective on the topic, it is important to provide an explanation to guarantee that your audience will understand your ideas.
- Consider your purpose. Does the writing prompt ask you to inform the audience? Persuade the audience? Entertain the audience? Your purpose should factor into the planning of your writing just as the audience does.
- Organize the information you want to include in your response. Identify how you want to present the information: compare-and-contrast, cause-and-effect, problem-and solution.
- Plan a structure before you draft your essay. This will keep you on track and help you address all points you want to discuss in your response. Remember your outline is not part of your grade, so do not spend time creating an elaborate structure, but instead strive to get the ideas down and leave yourself enough time to develop a strong response. For each section of your outline, jot down the main ideas you want to include, using key words or details.

- You may do your prewriting on scratch paper but you must use the booklet provided to submit your complete response.

The next objective listed for the constructed-response assignment addresses formulating a thesis and supporting statements. It will help you if you think of this as the actual drafting of the essay.

- **Stating and maintaining a clear thesis statement using organizational strategies to enhance meaning and clarity**
- **Providing reasoned support and/or specific examples to maintain the thesis statement**

Drafting

Drafting is getting your ideas down in roughly the format you intend. Allow about half of your time for drafting.

- Once you have chosen your organization, identify a focus for your response. Consider the type of writing you are creating and draft a simple statement to direct your writing.
- Your essay should have three parts: an introduction that addresses the question and states the thesis; a body which should present at least two main points to support your thesis; and a conclusion that will restate the answer expressed in the thesis and sum up the main points in the body of the essay.
- Your opening paragraph should include a thesis statement to focus the attention of your audience immediately. Remember that the introduction foreshadows the basic structure of the constructed-response assignment.
- Explain your points clearly and in logical order. The types of paragraphs you write depend on the topic and the purpose for writing. Back up your thesis with support from your memory or your own personal experience, Here are some types of details you can use in your response:
    - Facts, incidents or trends
    - Specific examples
    - Descriptive details

- Your conclusion should reemphasize the main points of the essay, and it should also explore their implications.

The next step in preparing your structured-response answer is the nuts-and-bolts of writing. In this step you will revise, edit, and proofread your response before you submit it. When you view this as a process, you will be able to strengthen your response to the writing prompt. Remember, the organization of your writing is the framework for the entire submission. You may decide to strengthen the structure by reordering or adding paragraphs.

- Using effective sentence structure, word choice, and mechanics (i.e., grammar, syntax)
- Using spelling, capitalization, and punctuation according to the conventions of Standard American English

Revising, editing, and proofreading

Revising is correcting any major errors and proofreading is fixing errors in grammar, spelling and grammar. Allow almost one fourth of your time to revise and edit. Use the last few minutes to proofread your work.

- Review your response. Decide whether everything is clearly defined. Neatly cross out any details that do not support your purpose.
- Make sure that you have used transitions to show the connections among your ideas and help the reader in following your line of thinking. You may use transitions either at the beginnings of paragraphs, or you may use them to show the connections among ideas within a single paragraph.
- Check for errors in spelling, grammar, and punctuation. To help with spelling, consider looking at each word, starting with the last word in each paragraph and moving toward the first. If you are unsure of the spelling, consider replacing the word in question with a word you know how to spell correctly.
- Look for common grammar errors in your writing. For example, check subject-verb agreement, make sure each sentence expresses a complete thought and verify that you have used pronouns correctly.
- When making changes, place one line through the text you want eliminated. Use a carat [^] to indicate the placement of added words.
- Since this constructed-response assignment may be hand-written, make sure that each word is legible.

Practice Test 1
Part 1: Reading

GACE Basic Skills

This test is also on CD-ROM in our special interactive TestWare® for the GACE Basic Skills. It is highly recommended that you first take this exam on computer. You will then have the additional study features and benefits of enforced timed conditions and instantaneous, accurate scoring. See page 6 for instructions on how to get the most out of REA's TestWare®.

ANSWER SHEET
PRACTICE TEST 1, PART 1: READING

1 _____	11 _____	22 _____	33 _____
2 _____	12 _____	23 _____	34 _____
3 _____	13 _____	24 _____	35 _____
4 _____	14 _____	25 _____	36 _____
5 _____	15 _____	26 _____	37 _____
6 _____	16 _____	27 _____	38 _____
7 _____	17 _____	28 _____	39 _____
8 _____	18 _____	29 _____	40 _____
9 _____	19 _____	30 _____	41 _____
10 _____	20 _____	31 _____	42 _____
	21 _____	32 _____	

PRACTICE TEST 1, PART 1: READING

PART 1: **Reading**
42 questions

Read the passage below; then answer the two questions that follow.

America's national bird, the mighty bald eagle, is being threatened by a new menace. Once decimated by hunters and loss of habitat, this newest danger is suspected to be from the intentional poisoning by livestock ranchers. Authorities have found animal carcasses injected with restricted pesticides. These carcasses are suspected to have been placed to attract and kill predators such as the bald eagle in an effort to preserve young grazing animals. It appears that the eagle is being threatened again by the consummate predator, humans.

1. One can conclude from this passage that

   A. the pesticides used are detrimental to the environment.
   B. the killing of eagles will protect the rancher's rangeland.
   C. ranchers must obtain licenses to use the pesticides.
   D. the poisoning could result in the extinction of the bald eagle.

2. The author's attitude is one of

   A. detached observation.
   B. concerned interest.
   C. informed acceptance.
   D. unbridled anger.

Questions 3, 4, and 5 refer to the graph below.

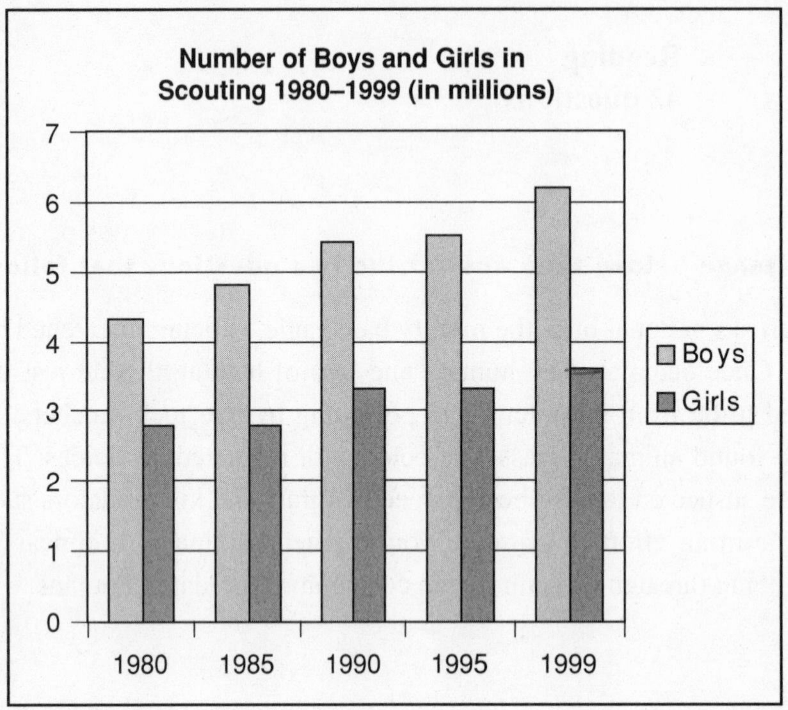

Source: United States Census Bureau

3. In what year was the involvement in scouting closest to being equal between girls and boys?

   A. 1980
   B. 1985
   C. 1990
   D. 1995

4. What was the difference (in millions) between the number of boys and the number of girls involved in scouting in 1999?

   A. 1.6 million
   B. .9 million
   C. 2.6 million
   D. 2.0 million

5. What year had the greatest discrepancy between the involvement of boys and the involvement of girls in scouting?

   A. 1980

   B. 1985

   C. 1990

   D. 1999

Read the passage below; then answer the six questions that follow.

Frederick Douglass

1 Frederick Douglass was born Frederick Augustus Washington Bailey in 1817 to a white father and a slave mother. Frederick was raised by his grandmother on a Maryland plantation until he was eight. It was then that he was sent to Baltimore by his owner to be a servant to the Auld family. Mrs. Auld recognized Frederick's intellectual acumen and defied the law of the state by teaching him to read and write. When Mr. Auld warned that education would make the boy unfit for slavery, Frederick sought to continue his education in the streets. When his master died, Frederick was returned to the plantation to work in the fields at age 16. Later, he was hired out to work in the shipyards in Baltimore as a ship caulker. He plotted an escape but was discovered before he could get away. Five years later he was able to pay his way to New York City and then to New Bedford, Massachusetts. He eluded slave hunters by changing his name to Douglass.

2 At an 1841 antislavery meeting in Massachusetts, Douglass was invited to give a talk about his experiences under slavery. His impromptu speech was so powerful and so eloquent that it thrust him into a career as an agent for the Massachusetts Anti-Slavery Society.

3 Douglass wrote his autobiography in 1845 primarily to counter those who doubted his authenticity as a former slave. This work became a classic in American literature and a primary source about slavery from the point of view of a slave. Douglass went on a two-year speaking tour abroad to avoid recapture by his former owner and to win new friends for the abolition movement. He returned with funds to purchase his freedom and to start his own antislavery newspaper. He became a consultant to Abraham Lincoln and throughout Reconstruction fought doggedly for full civil rights for freedmen. He also supported the women's rights movement.

6. According to the passage, Douglass's autobiography was motivated by

   A. the desire to make money for his antislavery movement.
   B. the desire to start a newspaper.
   C. his interest in authenticating his life as a slave.
   D. his desire to educate people about slavery.

7. The central idea of the passage is that Frederick Douglass

   A. was influential in changing the laws regarding the education of slaves.
   B. was one of the most eminent human rights leaders of the century.
   C. was a personal friend and confidant to a president.
   D. wrote a classic in American literature.

8. According to the author of this passage, Mrs. Auld taught Frederick to read because

   A. Frederick wanted to learn like the other boys.
   B. she recognized his natural ability.
   C. he needed to read to work in the home.
   D. she obeyed her husband's wishes in the matter.

9. The title that best expresses the ideas of this passage is

   A. The History of the Anti-Slavery Movement.
   B. The Dogged Determination of Frederick Douglass.
   C. Frederick Douglass's Contributions to Freedom.
   D. The Oratorical and Literary Brilliance of Frederick Douglass.

10. In the context of the passage, <u>impromptu</u> is closest in meaning to

   A. unprepared.
   B. in a quiet manner.
   C. forceful.
   D. elaborate.

11. This passage is most likely written for an audience of
    - A. textbook publishers.
    - B. general readers.
    - C. biographers.
    - D. feminists.

Read the passage below; then answer the three questions that follow.

1 One of the many tragedies of the Civil War was the housing and care of prisoners. The Andersonville prison, built by the Confederates in 1864 to accommodate 10,000 Union prisoners, was not yet completed when prisoners began arriving. Five months later, the total number of men incarcerated there had risen to 31,678.

2 The sounds of death and dying were not diminished by the surrender of weapons to a captor. Chances of survival for prisoners in Andersonville were not much better than in the throes of combat. Next to overcrowded, inadequate shelter caused unimaginable suffering. The Confederates were not equipped with the manpower, tools or supplies necessary to house such a population of captives. Prisoners themselves gathered lumber, logs, anything they could find to construct some sort of protection from the elements. Some prisoners dug holes in the ground, risking suffocation from cave-ins, but many hundreds were left exposed to the wind, rain, cold, and heat.

3 Daily food rations were exhausted by the sheer numbers that had to be served, resulting in severe dietary deficiencies. The overcrowding, meager rations, and deplorable unsanitary conditions resulted in rampant disease and a high mortality rate. The consequences of a small scratch or wound could result in death in Andersonville. During the prison's 13-month existence, more than 12,000 prisoners died and were buried in the Andersonville cemetery. Most of the deaths were caused by diarrhea, dysentery, gangrene, and scurvy that could not be treated due to inadequate staff and supplies.

12. What is the central idea of the passage?

    A. The prison was never fully completed.
    B. Prison doctors were ill-equipped to handle emergencies.
    C. Andersonville prison was not adequate to care for three times as many prisoners as it could hold.
    D. Many prisoners died as a result of shelter cave-ins.

13. From this passage the author's attitude toward the Confederates is one of

    A. impartiality.
    B. contempt.
    C. indifference.
    D. denial.

14. In the context of the passage, the word *throes* is closest in meaning to

    A. area.
    B. midst.
    C. times.
    D. vicinity.

Read the passage below; then answer the three questions that follow.

1 To the Shakers, perfection was found in the creation of an object that was both useful and simple. Their Society was founded in 1774 by Ann Lee, an Englishwoman from the working classes, who arrived in New York with eight followers. "Mother Ann" established her religious community on the belief that worldly interests were evil.

2 To gain entrance into the Society, believers had to remain celibate, have no private possessions, and avoid contact with outsiders. The order came to be called "Shakers" because of the feverish dance the group performed at their meetings. Another characteristic of the group was the desire to seek perfection in their work.

3 Shaker furniture was created to exemplify specific characteristics: simplicity of design, quality craftsmanship, harmony of proportion, and usefulness. While the Shakers did not create any innovations in furniture designs, they were known for fine craftsmanship. In their work, the major emphasis was on function, and not on excessive or elaborate decorations that they believed contributed nothing to the product's usefulness.

15. The passage indicates that members of the religious order were called the Shakers because

A. they shook hands at their meetings.
B. they did a shaking dance at their meetings.
C. they took their name from the founder.
D. they were named after the township where they originated.

16. Which of the following is the most appropriate substitute for the use of the term innovations in the third paragraph?

A. corrections
B. changes
C. functions
D. brocades

17. Which of the following does the passage suggest about the Shakers?

A. Shakers believed in form over function in their designs.
B. Shaker furniture has seen a surge in popularity.
C. Shakers appeared to believe that form follows function.
D. Shaker furniture is noted for the use of brass hardware.

Read the passage below; then answer the three questions that follow.

Benjamin Franklin began writing his autobiography in 1771, but he set it aside to assist the colonies in gaining independence from England. After a hiatus of 13 years, he returned to chronicle his life, addressing his message to the younger generation. In this significant literary work of the early United States, Franklin portrays himself as benign, kindhearted, practical, and hardworking. He established a list of ethical conduct and recorded his transgressions when he was successful in overcoming temptation. Franklin wrote that he was unable to arrive at perfection, ". . . yet I was, by the endeavor, a better and happier man then I otherwise should have been if I had not attempted it."

18. Which of the following is the LEAST appropriate substitute for the use of the term <u>ethical</u> near the end of the passage?

    A. moral
    B. depraved
    C. virtuous
    D. qualified

19. The passage suggests which of the following about Franklin's autobiography?

    A. It was representative of early American literature.
    B. It fell short of being a major work of literary quality.
    C. It personified Franklin as a major political figure.
    D. It was a notable work of early American literature.

20. Which of the following slogans best describes Franklin's assessment of the usefulness of attempting to achieve perfection?

    A. Cleanliness is next to Godliness.
    B. Nothing ventured, nothing gained.
    C. Ambition is its own reward.
    D. Humility is everything.

Questions 21, 22, and 23 refer to the graph below.

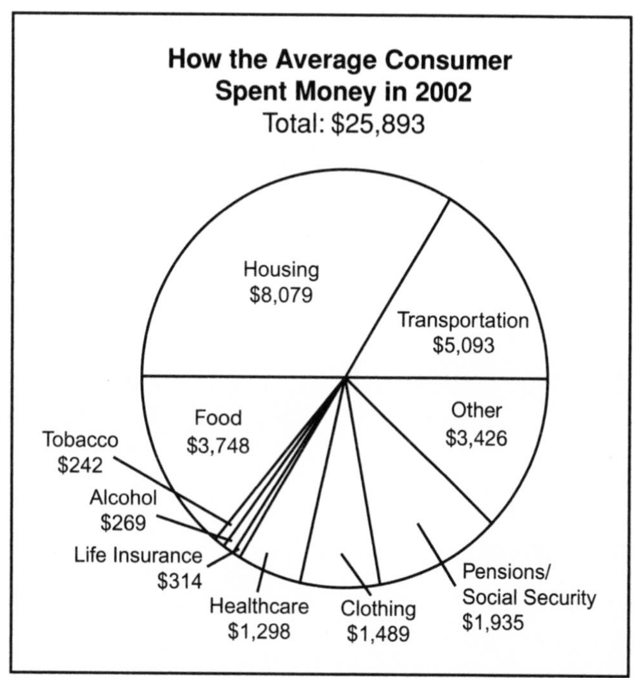

Source: Census Bureau's Statistical Abstract of the U.S.

21. According to the graph, the average consumer spent approximately 50 percent of her/his earnings on

    A. housing and healthcare costs.
    B. transportation and housing.
    C. food.
    D. transportation and pensions.

22. After transportation, the next greatest amount of money was spent on

    A. clothing.
    B. other.
    C. food.
    D. pensions/social security.

23. According to the graph, expenditure on health care was approximately equal to

    A. clothing.
    B. pensions.
    C. food.
    D. other.

Read the passage below; then answer the three questions that follow.

Georgia and peaches are synonymous. The peach is practically a symbol of Georgia. The peach, being the state fruit, adorns all things in the state. The main growing area in the state consists of a band of counties running diagonally through the center of the state. These central counties of Crawford, Houston, Macon, Monroe, Peach, and Taylor are home to over 1½ million peach trees. They produce 100 million pounds of peaches annually. These peaches are sold as fresh fruit and canned. They are processed as jellies, preserves, peach cider, ice cream, hot sauce, chutney, and anything else that can benefit from the peach's tangy, sweet taste. There are over 40 varieties of peaches grown in Georgia. They are available 16 weeks of the year.

24. The central idea of the passage is that the Georgia peach

    A. is practically a symbol of Georgia.
    B. is available 16 weeks of the year.
    C. is grown in 6 central counties of Georgia.
    D. is processed in a variety of ways.

25. In the passage, the word <u>synonymous</u> is closest in meaning to

    A. the same.
    B. the opposite.
    C. equivalent in connotation.
    D. alike.

26. According to the passage, how many varieties of peaches are grown in Georgia?

    A. Less than 30
    B. More than 100
    C. Over 40
    D. A dozen

Read the passage below; then answer the five questions that follow.

1 Spa water quality is maintained through a filter to ensure cleanliness and clarity. Wastes such as perspiration, hairspray, and lotions, which cannot be removed by the spa filter, can be controlled by shock treatment or super chlorination every other week. Although the filter traps most of the solid material to control bacteria and algae and to oxidize any organic material, the addition of disinfectants such as bromine or chlorine is necessary.

2 As all water solutions have a pH that controls corrosion, proper pH balance is also necessary. A pH measurement determines if the water is acid or alkaline. Based on a 14-point scale, a pH reading of 7.0 is considered neutral while a lower reading is considered acidic, and a higher reading indicates alkalinity or basic. High pH (above 7.6) reduces sanitizer efficiency, clouds water, promotes scale formation on surfaces and equipment, and interferes with filter operation. When pH is high, add a pH decrease more rapidly. A weekly dose of a stain and scale fighter also will help to control this problem. Low pH (below 7.2) is equally damaging, causing equipment corrosion, water that is irritating, and rapid sanitizer dissipation. To increase pH, add sodium bicarbonate (e.g., *Spa Up*).

3 The recommended operating temperature of a spa (98°–104°) is a fertile environment for the growth of bacteria and viruses. This growth is prevented when appropriate sanitizer levels are continuously monitored. Bacteria can also be controlled by maintaining a proper bromine level of 3.0 to 5.0 parts per million (ppm) or a chlorine level of 1.0–2.0 ppm. As bromine tablets should not be added directly to the water, a bromine floater will properly dispense the tablets. Should chlorine be the chosen sanitizer, a granular form is recommended, as liquid chlorine or tablets are too harsh for the spa.

27. Although proper chemical and temperature maintenance of spa water is necessary, the most important condition to monitor is the

    A. prevention of the growth of bacteria and viruses.
    B. prevention of the corrosion of equipment.
    C. prevention of the formation of scales.
    D. prevention of cloudy water.

28. Of the chemical and temperature conditions in a spa, the condition most dangerous to one's health is

    A. spa water temperature above 104°.
    B. bromine level between 3.0 and 5.0.
    C. pH level below 7.2.
    D. spa water temperature between 90° and 104°.

29. The primary purpose of the passage is to

    A. relate that maintenance of a spa can negate the full enjoyment of the spa experience.
    B. convey that the maintenance of a spa is expensive and time consuming.
    C. explain the importance of proper spa maintenance.
    D. detail proper spa maintenance.

30. The spa filter can be relied upon to

    A. control algae and bacteria.
    B. trap most solid material.
    C. assure an adequate level of sanitation.
    D. maintain clear spa water.

31. Which chemical should one avoid when maintaining a spa?

A. liquid chlorine

B. bromine

C. sodium bisulfate

D. baking soda

Read the passage below; then answer the three questions that follow.

1 There is an importance of learning communication and meaning in language. Yet the use of notions such as communication and meaning as the basic criteria for instruction, experiences, and materials in classrooms may misguide a child in several respects. Communication in the classroom is vital. The teacher should use communication to help students develop the capacity to make their private responses become public responses. Otherwise, one's use of language would be in danger of being what the younger generation refers to as mere words, mere thoughts, and mere feelings.

2 Learning theorists emphasize specific components of learning; behaviorists stress behavior in learning; humanists stress the affective in learning; and cognitivists stress cognition in learning. All three of these components occur simultaneously and cannot be separated from each other in the learning process. In 1957, Festinger referred to dissonance as the lack of harmony between what one does (behavior) and what one believes (attitude). Attempts to separate the components of learning either knowingly or unknowingly create dissonances wherein language, thought, feeling, and behavior become diminished of authenticity. As a result, ideas and concepts lose their content and vitality, and the manipulation and politics of communication assume prominence.

32. Which of the following best describes the author's attitude toward the subject discussed?

A. A flippant disregard

B. A mild frustration

C. A passive resignation

D. An informed concern

33. The primary purpose of the passage is to

A. discuss the relationships between learning and communication.

B. assure teachers that communication and meaning are the basic criteria for learning in classrooms.

C. stress the importance of providing authentic communication in classroom learning.

D. address the role of communication and meaning in classrooms.

34. Which of the following is the most complete and accurate definition of the term <u>mere</u> as used in the passage?

A. small

B. minor

C. little

D. insignificant

Read the passage below; then answer the five questions that follow.

The Beginnings of the Submarine

A submarine was first used as an offensive weapon during the American Revolutionary War. The *Turtle*, a one-man submersible designed by an American inventor named David Bushnell and hand-operated by a screw propeller, attempted to sink a British man-of-war in New York Harbor. The plan was to attach a charge of gunpowder to the ship's bottom with screws and explode it with a time fuse. After repeated failures to force the screws through the copper sheathing of the hull of the H.M.S. *Eagle*, the submarine gave up and withdrew, exploding its powder a short distance from the *Eagle*. Although the attack was unsuccessful, it caused the British to move their blockading ships from the harbor to the outer bay.

On February 17, 1864, a Confederate craft, a hand-propelled submersible, carrying a crew of eight men, sank a Federal corvette that was blockading Charleston Harbor. The hit was accomplished by a torpedo suspended ahead of the Confederate *Hunley* as she rammed the Union frigate *Housatonic*, and is the first recorded instance of a submarine sinking a warship.

The submarine first became a major component in naval warfare during World War I, when Germany demonstrated its full potential. Wholesale sinking of Allied shipping by the German U-boats almost swung the war in favor of the Central Powers. Then, as now, the submarine's greatest advantage was that it could operate beneath the ocean surface where detection was difficult. Sinking a submarine was comparatively easy, once it was found—but finding it before it could attack was another matter.

During the closing months of World War I, the Allied Submarine Devices Investigation Committee was formed to obtain from science and technology more effective underwater detection equipment. The committee developed a reasonablely accurate device for locating a submerged submarine. This device was a trainable hydrophone, which was attached to the bottom of the ASW ship, and used to detect screw noises and other sounds that came from a submarine. Although the committee disbanded after World War I, the British made improvements on the locating device during the interval between then and World War II, and named it *ASDIC* after the committee.

American scientists further improved on the device, calling it SONAR, a name derived from the underlined initials of the words **so**und **na**vigation and **r**anging.

At the end of World War II, the United States improved the snorkel (a device for bring air to the crew and engines when operating submerged on diesels) and developed the *Guppy* (short for greater underwater propulsion power), a conversion of the fleet-type submarine of World War II fame. The superstructure was changed by reducing the surface area and streamlining the metal fairing. Performance increased greatly with improved electronic equipment, additional battery capacity, and the addition of the snorkel.

35. The passage implies that one of the most pressing modifications needed for the submarine was to

A. streamline its shape.

B. enlarge the submarine for accommodating more torpedoes and men.

C. reduce the noise caused by the submarine.

D. add a snorkel.

36. It is inferred that

    A. ASDIC was formed to obtain technology for underwater detection.
    B. ASDIC developed an accurate device for locating submarines.
    C. the hydrophone was attached to the bottom of the ship.
    D. ASDIC was formed to develop technology to define U.S. shipping.

37. SONAR not only picked up the sound of submarines moving through the water but also

    A. indicated the speed at which the sub was moving.
    B. gave the location of the submarine.
    C. indicated the speed of the torpedo.
    D. placed the submarine within a specified range.

38. According to the passage, the submarine's success was due in part to its ability to

    A. strike and escape undetected.
    B. move swifter than other vessels.
    C. submerge to great depths while being hunted.
    D. run silently.

39. From the passage, one can infer that

    A. David Bushnell was indirectly responsible for the sinking of the Federal corvette in Charleston Harbor.
    B. David Bushnell invented the *Turtle*.
    C. the *Turtle* was a one-man submarine.
    D. the *Turtle* sank the *Eagle* on February 17, 1864.

Read the passage below; then answer the three questions that follow.

1 In 1975, Sinclair observed that it had often been supposed that the main factor in learning to talk is being able to imitate. Schlesinger (1975) noted that at certain stages of learning to speak, a child tends to imitate everything an adult says to him or her, and it therefore seems reasonable to accord to such imitation an important role in the acquisition of language.

2 Moreover, various investigators have attempted to explain the role of imitation in language. In his discussion of the development of imitation and cognition of adult speech sounds, Nakazema (1975) stated that although the parent's talking stimulates and accelerates the infant's articulatory activity, the parent's phoneme system does not influence the child's articulatory mechanisms. Slobin and Welsh (1973) suggested that imitation is the reconstruction of the adult's utterance and that the child does so by employing the grammatical rules that he has developed at a specific time. Schlesinger proposed that by imitating the adult the child practices new grammatical constructions. Brown and Bellugi (1964) noted that a child's imitations resemble spontaneous speech in that they drop inflections, most function words, and sometimes other words. However, the word order of imitated sentences usually was preserved. Brown and Bellugi assumed that imitation is a function of what the child attended to or remembered. Shipley et al. (1969) suggested that repeating an adult's utterance assists the child's comprehension. Ervin (1964) and Braine (1971) found that a child's imitations do not contain more advanced structures than his or her spontaneous utterances; thus, imitation can no longer be regarded as the simple behavioristic act that scholars assumed it to be.

40. The author of the passage would tend to agree with which of the following statements?

A. Apparently, children require practice with more advanced structures before they are able to imitate.

B. Apparently, children only imitate what they already do, using whatever is in their repertoire.

C. Apparently, the main factor in learning to talk remains being able to imitate.

D. Apparently, children cannot respond meaningfully to a speech situation until they have reached a stage at which they can make symbol-orientation responses.

41. The primary purpose of the passage is to

A. explain the role of imitation in language acquisition.

B. assure parents of their role in assisting imitation in language acquisition.

C. relate the history of imitation in language acquisition.

D. discuss relationships between psychological and physiological processes in language acquisition.

42. An inference that parents may make from the passage is that they should

A. be concerned when a child imitates their language.

B. focus on developing imitation in their child's language.

C. realize that their child's imitations may reflect several aspects of language acquisition.

D. realize that their talking may over-stimulate their child's articulatory activity.

ANSWER KEY – READING PRACTICE TEST 1

Question	Answer	Objective	
1	**D**	0001	Understand the main idea and supporting details in written material.
2	**B**	0002	Identify a writer's purpose and point of view.
3	**A**	0004	Use critical reasoning skills to evaluate written material.
4	**C**	0004	Use critical reasoning skills to evaluate written material.
5	**D**	0004	Use critical reasoning skills to evaluate written material.
6	**C**	0003	Analyze the relationship among ideas in written material.
7	**B**	0001	Understand the main idea and supporting details in written material.
8	**B**	0003	Analyze the relationship among ideas in written material.
9	**C**	0001	Understand the main idea and supporting details in written material.
10	**A**	0006	Determine the meaning of words and phrases.
11	**B**	0002	Identify a writer's purpose and point of view.
12	**C**	0001	Understand the main idea and supporting details in written material.
13	**A**	0002	Identify a writer's purpose and point of view.
14	**B**	0006	Determine the meaning of words and phrases.
15	**B**	0003	Analyze the relationship among ideas in written material.
16	**B**	0006	Determine the meaning of words and phrases.

Question	Answer	Objective	
17	**C**	0004	Use critical reasoning skills to evaluate written material.
18	**B**	0006	Determine the meaning of words and phrases.
19	**D**	0004	Use critical reasoning skills to evaluate written material.
20	**B**	0004	Use critical reasoning skills to evaluate written material.
21	**B**	0001	Understand the main idea and supporting details in written material.
22	**C**	0001	Understand the main idea and supporting details in written material.
23	**A**	0001	Understand the main idea and supporting details in written material.
24	**A**	0001	Understand the main idea and supporting details in written material.
25	**C**	0006	Determine the meaning of words and phrases.
26	**C**	0005	Use reading strategies to comprehend written materials.
27	**A**	0005	Use reading strategies to comprehend written materials.
28	**A**	0005	Use reading strategies to comprehend written materials.
29	**C**	0001	Understand the main idea and supporting details in written materials.
30	**B**	0005	Use reading strategies to comprehend written materials.
31	**A**	0005	Use reading strategies to comprehend written materials.
32	**D**	0002	Identify a writer's purpose and point of view.

Question	Answer	Objective	
33	**C**	0001	Understand the main idea and supporting details in written material.
34	**D**	0006	Determine the meaning of words and phrases.
35	**A**	0004	Use critical reasoning skills to evaluate written material.
36	**D**	0004	Use critical reasoning skills to evaluate written material.
37	**D**	0005	Use reading strategies to comprehend written materials.
38	**A**	0005	Use reading strategies to comprehend written materials.
39	**A**	0004	Use critical reasoning skills to evaluate written material.
40	**B**	0002	Identify a writer's purpose and point of view.
41	**A**	0001	Understand the main idea and supporting details in written material.
42	**C**	0004	Use critical reasoning skills to evaluate written material.

Practice Test 1, Part 1 Progress Chart

0001 Understand the Main Idea and Supporting Details in Written Material —/11

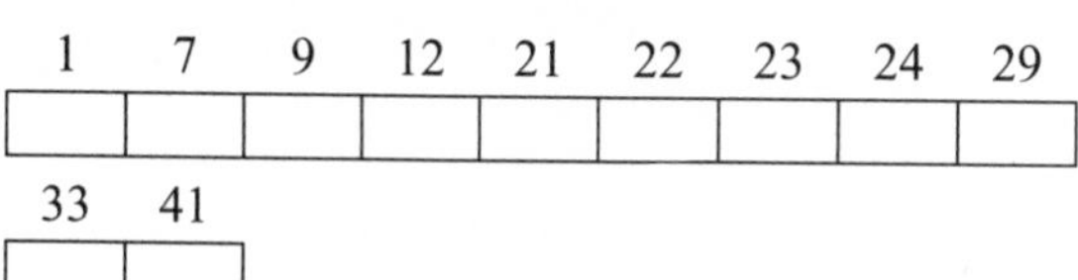

0002 Identify a Writer's Purpose and Point of View —/5

0003 Analyze the Relationship Among Ideas in Written Material —/3

6	8	15

0004 Use Critical Reasoning Skills to Evaluate Written Material —/10

3	4	5	17	19	20

35	36	39	42

0005 Use Reading Strategies to Comprehend Written Materials —/7

26	27	28	30	31	37	38

0006 Determine the Meaning of Words and Phrases —/6

10	14	16	18	25	34

Detailed Explanations for Practice Test 1, Part 1: Reading

1. **D**

It is implied that the poisoning of animal carcasses in the habitat of bald eagles presents a new danger of extinction for America's symbol. Choices A and C are not mentioned in the passage. Choice B suggests a reason for the poisoning; however, the overall focus of the passage does not support this answer.

2. **B**

The author's use of words such as "mighty bald eagle" and "threatened by a new menace" supports concern for the topic. Therefore, choices A and C are not applicable. The author appears for the most part to be objective. Choice D is too strong to be correct.

3. **A**

In 1980, the difference between the number of boys and girls involved in scouting was 1.5 million. This represents the closest margin.

4. **C**

In 1999, the difference between the number of boys and girls involved in scouting was 2.6 million.

5. **D**

The greatest difference between the number of boys and the number of girls involved in scouting was in 1999, at 2.6 million. There were almost twice as many boys as there were girls.

6. **C**

Douglass was interested in raising social consciousness about slavery. The passage stresses his interest in refuting those who doubted his claim to have been a slave.

7. **B**

Choice A is not supported by the text. Choices C and D, while true, are irrelevant to the question.

8. **B**

This choice is supported by the statement, "Mrs. Auld recognized Frederick's intellectual acumen. . . ." Choice D contradicts information in the passage. The passage does not support choices A and C.

9. **C**

Choices A and B are either too broad or too general. Choice D is too specific and limited to cover the information in the passage.

10. **A**

An *impromptu* speech is one given off-the-cuff.

11. **B**

The writer's accessible style, use of easy-to-understand supporting details and examples, and avoidance of technical language indicate that the passage was most likely written for an audience of general readers.

12. **C**

The passage states that housing of prisoners was "one of the many tragedies of the Civil War," and that "overcrowding, meager rations… resulted in rampant disease and a high mortality rate," implying that the prison facility was inadequate for the number of prisoners. All other choices are discussed, but the main issue is overcrowded conditions.

13. **A**

The author emphasizes a lack of supplies and manpower to care for the prisoners, not a lack of interest in doing so by the Confederates. Hence, choices B, C, and D are not appropriate.

14. **B**

In the *midst* of combat is closest in meaning to *throes*. The area and the vicinity of combat are not as close to the meaning of *throes*. The time of combat is not as important as actually being in the midst of battle.

15. **B**

This choice is supported by the second paragraph of the passage. All other choices are irrelevant to information in the passage.

16. **B**

Innovations means changes or new features that have been introduced.

17. **C**

The passage discusses the importance of usefulness as well as simplicity to the Shakers; therefore, the function of the piece of furniture would be more important than the particular form. Choices A and D are contradictory to the information given, while choice B is beyond the information given in the text.

18. **B**

Depraved means "corrupted" or "perverted." All other choices have to do with accepted standards of conduct.

19. **D**

The author states that Franklin's work was a "significant literary work of early United States." Each of the other choices is not supported by the text.

20. **B**

The final sentence of the paragraph supports this choice. Choice C might apply, but choice B is closest to the overall mood of the passage. Choices A and D are not relevant to the question.

21. **B**

Transportation and housing total about half of the $25,892.

22. **C**

According to the graph, food is next, after transportation, in amount of money spent by the consumer.

23. **A**

According to the graph, healthcare was closest to clothing in total amount spent.

24. **A**

The central idea of the passage is that the Georgia peach is practically a symbol of Georgia. Choices B, C, and D do not reflect the central idea. They are details in the passage.

25. **C**

Synonymous is closest in meaning to *equivalent* in connotation.

26. **C**

This choice is clearly stated in the passage.

27. **A**

Choices B, C, and D present minor problems in spa maintenance. If bacteria and viruses are allowed to grow, they can become a possible source of health problems. They are controlled by both temperature and chemicals.

28. **A**

Choices B, C, and D are correct levels or degrees.

29. **C**

Choices A and B represent an inference that goes beyond the scope of the passage and would indicate a bias on the part of the reader. Although the passage explains spa maintenance, in choice D, the information is not adequate to serve as a detailed guide.

30. **B**

The other choices, A and C, refer to chemical or temperature maintenance. Although choice D helps to ensure clarity, choice B is explicitly stated in the passage.

31. **A**

Choices B, C, and D are appropriate chemicals. Although chlorine is an alternative to bromine, this passage indicates it should be granular as indicated in choice A.

32. **D**

Choices A, B, and C all connote extreme or inappropriate attitudes not expressed in the passage. The author presents an informed concern—choice D.

33. **C**

For the other choices, A, B, and D, the criteria, the role, the discussion, and the assurance for communication or learning are not provided in the passage. The passage stresses the importance of authenticity in communication—choice C.

34. **D**

Each of the choices is a possible definition, but the passage overall suggests that communication needs to be developed so that students' responses may become more significant and authentic—choice D.

35. **A**

Answer A is correct because of the importance of streamlining mentioned in the final paragraph. B and C are not suggested in the paragraph, and D is secondary in importance to A.

36. **D**

Since it may be inferred from the general purpose of underwater detection equipment, D is correct. While A and B are true statements, they are not inferences. C is not implied in the passage.

37. **D**

Answer D is correct because the "R" in SONAR stands for "Ranging." A, B, and C are neither mentioned nor implied by the passage.

38. **A**

As was mentioned in the third sentence of the third paragraph, A is correct. B, C, and D are not mentioned in the passage.

39. **A**

It may be inferred that Bushnell's invention led to the success of the later version of the submarine. B and C are true, but are not inferences because they are directly stated in the first paragraph. D is not a true statement; the *Turtle* had no direct link to the 1864 incident.

40. **B**

Choices A and D are not supported by the passage. Choice C represents an incorrect conclusion. Choice B is supported by the various investigators' explanations.

41. **A**

As stated explicitly in the passage, the various investigators have attempted to explain the role of imitation in language—choice A. The other choices go beyond the scope of the passage.

42. **C**

As the investigators studied different aspects of language while attempting to explain the role of imitation in language, choice C is correct. The other choices go beyond the scope of the passage.

Practice Test 1
Part 2: Mathematics

GACE Basic Skills

This test is also on CD-ROM in our special interactive TestWare® for the GACE Basic Skills. It is highly recommended that you first take this exam on computer. You will then have the additional study features and benefits of enforced timed conditions and instantaneous, accurate scoring. See page 6 for instructions on how to get the most out of REA's TestWare®.

ANSWER SHEET
PRACTICE TEST 1, PART 2: MATHEMATICS

1 _____	13 _____	25 _____	37 _____
2 _____	14 _____	26 _____	38 _____
3 _____	15 _____	27 _____	39 _____
4 _____	16 _____	28 _____	40 _____
5 _____	17 _____	29 _____	41 _____
6 _____	18 _____	30 _____	42 _____
7 _____	19 _____	31 _____	43 _____
8 _____	20 _____	32 _____	44 _____
9 _____	21 _____	33 _____	45 _____
10 _____	22 _____	34 _____	46 _____
11 _____	23 _____	35 _____	47 _____
12 _____	24 _____	36 _____	48 _____

DEFINITIONS AND FORMULAS

Measurement

U.S. Standard Metric

Distance

1 inch = 2.54 centimeters
12 inches = 1 foot
3 feet = 1 yard
5280 feet = 1 mile
1 centimeter = 10 millimeters
1 meter = 100 centimeters
1 kilometer = 1000 meters

Volume (liquid)

1 quart = 32 ounces
1 quart ≈ 0.95 liters
1 gallon = 4 quarts
1 liter = 1000 milliliters
1 cubic centimeter = 1 milliliter

Mass

1 pound = 16 ounces
1 ton = 2000 pounds
2.2 pounds ≈ 1 kilogram
1 gram = 1000 milligrams
1 kilogram = 1000 grams

Time

1 minute = 60 seconds
1 hour = 60 minutes
1 day = 24 hours
1 year = 365 days
1 year = 52 weeks

Definitions

$=$	equal to
$>$	greater than
$<$	less than
$\geq$	greater than or equal to
$\leq$	less than or equal to
π	≈ 3.14
$\angle$	angle
$m\angle$	measure of angle
⊾	right angle
$\overline{AB}$	line segment
AB	length of line segment AB
$\angle ABC$	angle with vertex B formed by rays BA and BC

Formulas

Square

Area = s^2
Perimeter = $4s$

Rectangle

Area = bw
Perimeter = $2b + 2w$

Triangle

Area = $\frac{1}{2}bh$
Sum of the interior angles = 180°

Right triangle

Pythagorean formula: $c^2 = a^2 + b^2$

Circle

Area = πr^2
Circumference = $2\pi r$
Diameter = $2r$

Right cylinder

Surface area = $2\pi rh + 2\pi r^2$
Volume = $\pi r^2 h$

Cube

Surface area = $6s^2$
Volume = s^3

Rectangular solid

Surface area = $2bw + 2bh + 2wh$
Volume = bwh

PRACTICE TEST 1, PART 2: MATHEMATICS

PART 2: **Mathematics**
48 questions

1. Multiply $\frac{2}{3}$ by $\frac{4}{5}$. Show your answer in simplified (reduced) form.

   A. $\frac{6}{8}$

   B. $\frac{6}{15}$

   C. $\frac{8}{15}$

   D. 1

2. Add $2\frac{3}{4}$ and $1\frac{1}{2}$.

   A. $3\frac{4}{6}$

   B. $3\frac{1}{2}$

   C. $3\frac{5}{4}$

   D. $4\frac{1}{4}$

3. Subtract $3\frac{2}{3}$ from $7\frac{1}{2}$.

   A. $4\frac{1}{6}$

   B. $3\frac{5}{6}$

   C. 4

   D. $3\frac{1}{6}$

4. Divide $\frac{2}{3}$ by $\frac{4}{5}$. Choose the answer in simplest form.

A. $\frac{8}{15}$

B. $\frac{2}{15}$

C. $\frac{10}{12}$

D. $\frac{5}{6}$

5. Perform the indicated operation.

$$(-16) - (-5)$$

A. –11

B. 11

C. 21

D. –21

6. Divide 8.2 by 0.05.

A. 1.64

B. 164

C. 16.4

D. .164

7. The number 14 is approximately 22% of which of the following numbers?

A. 56

B. 60

C. 308

D. 64

8. Simplify to a single term in scientific notation.

$$(2 \times 10^3) \times (6 \times 10^4)$$

A. 12×10^7
B. 12×10^{12}
C. 1.2×10^8
D. 1.2×10^{12}

9. Simplify: $3 + 2 \times 5 - 4$

A. 21
B. 9
C. 5
D. –5

10. Select the number that is missing in the problem below.

$$1{,}806 - \underline{\qquad} = 358$$

A. 2,164
B. 1,552
C. 1,458
D. 1,448

11. Bob gets $6 an hour for babysitting. His sister Jana gets $7 an hour. One evening Bob babysat for 4 hours, while Jana babysat for half that long. How much money did they earn altogether for the evening?

A. $24
B. $38
C. $14
D. $19

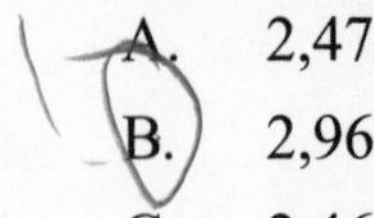

12. The population of the city of Fairview increased by approximately 0.5% last year. If the population at the beginning of the year was 2,460, what was the approximate population at the end of the year?

A. 2,472
B. 2,960
C. 2,465
D. 2,510

13. A red rose bush is 39 inches tall and a yellow rose bush is $36\frac{3}{4}$ inches tall. The red rose bush is growing at a rate of $\frac{1}{2}$ of an inch per week, and the yellow rose bush is growing at a rate of $\frac{3}{4}$ of an inch per week. How long will it be before they are the same height?

A. 6 weeks
B. 8 weeks
C. 9 weeks
D. 12 weeks

14. Sarah began studying at 11:20 a.m. She took a break from 2:05 to 2:20, then studied until 3:15. How much time did she spend studying?

A. 3 hours 55 minutes
B. 2 hours 50 minutes
C. 3 hours 45 minutes
D. 3 hours 40 minutes

15. Convert: 120 mg = _____ g

A. 0.12
B. 1.20
C. 12
D. .012

16. Convert: 5.6 km = _____ cm

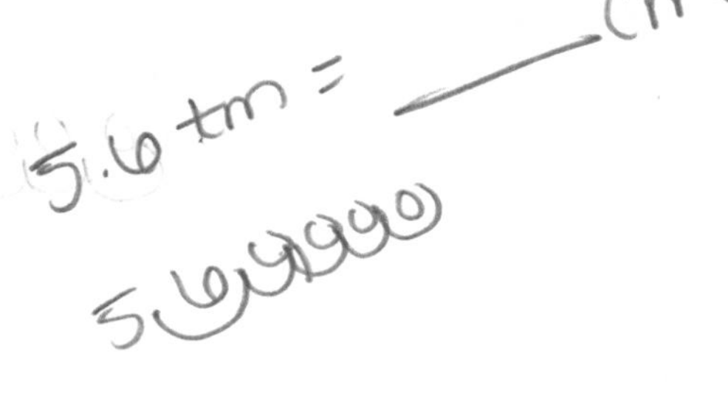

A. 560
B. 5,600
C. 56,000
D. 560,000

17. Convert: 14 feet = _____ inches

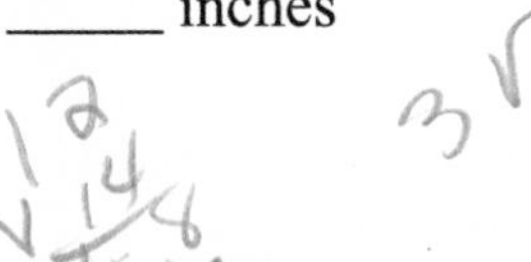

A. 42 inches
B. 520 inches
C. 168 inches
D. 84 inches

18. Convert: 4 feet 3 inches = _____ inches

A. 48 inches
B. 51 inches
C. 54 inches
D. 16 inches

19. Use the figure below to answer the question.

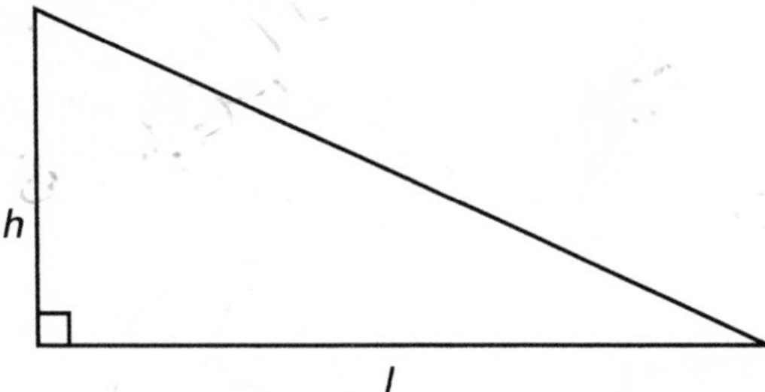

Which formula can be used to find the area of the triangle?

A. $A = \frac{(l \times h)}{2}$

B. $A = \frac{(l + h)}{2}$

C. $A = 2(l + h)$

D. $A = 2(l \times h)$

20. What is the area of a triangle with a base length of 20 inches and a height of 8 inches?

    A. 80 square inches
    B. 120 square inches
    C. 40 square inches
    D. 28 square inches

21. You have a square piece of paper that has a perimeter of 20 cm. What is the area of the paper?

    A. 400 square cm
    B. 25 square cm
    C. 16 square cm
    D. 24 square cm

22. A circle has a radius of 4 cm. What is the area of the circle? (Use 3.14 as an approximation for pi.)

    A. 12.56 square centimeters
    B. 25.12 square centimeters
    C. 37.68 square centimeters
    D. 50.24 square centimeters

23. What is the approximate volume of the following cylinder? (Use 3.14 as an approximation for pi.)

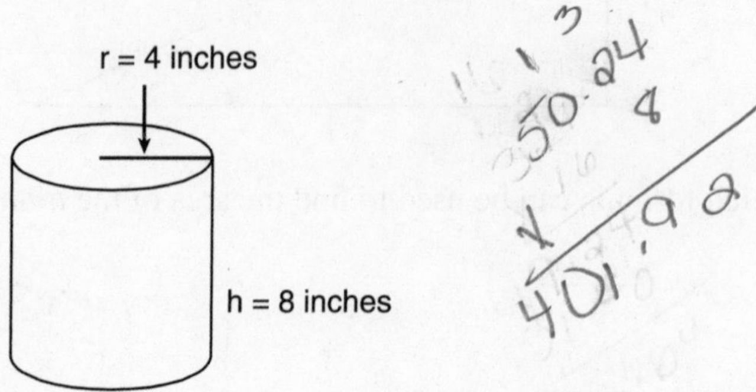

    A. 401.92 cubic inches
    B. 3215.36 cubic inches
    C. 37.68 cubic inches
    D. 100.48 cubic inches

24. Use the figures given to answer the question that follows.

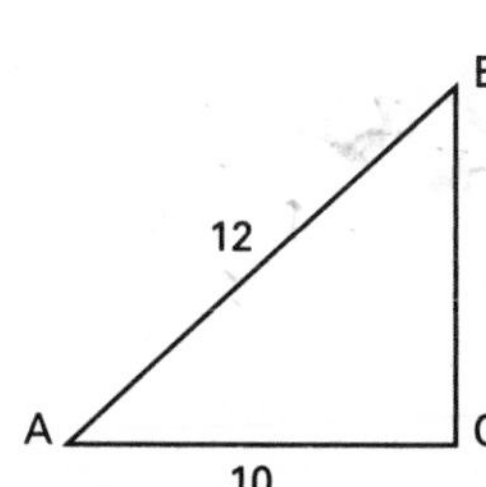

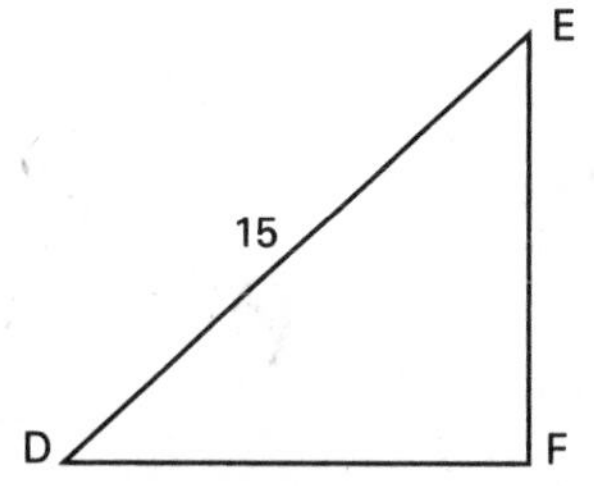

If the two triangles are similar, what is the length of side DF?

A. 12.5 units

B. 13 units

C. 12 units

D. 13.5 units

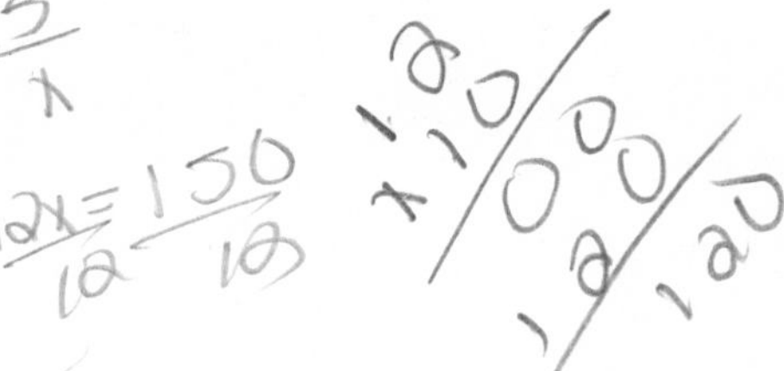

25. Use the figure given to answer the question that follows. Assume that AD is a line.

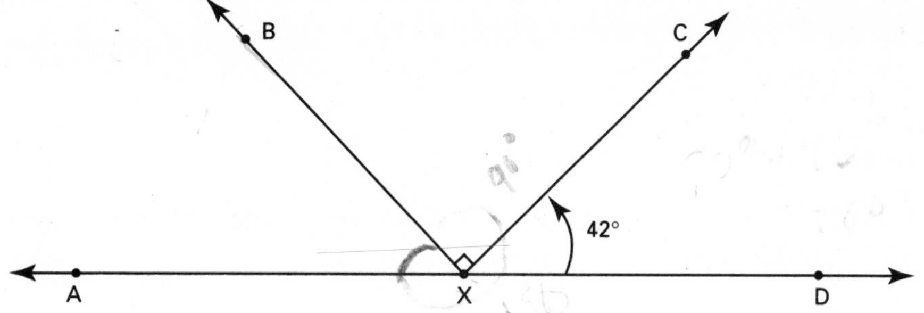

What is the measure of angle AXB?

A. 48°

B. 90°

C. 42°

D. There is not enough information to answer the question.

26. The daily high temperatures in Frostbite, Minnesota, for one week in January were as follows:

Sunday:	–2°F
Monday:	3°F
Tuesday:	0°F
Wednesday:	–4°F
Thursday:	–5°F
Friday:	–1°F
Saturday:	2°F

What was the average (mean) daily high temperature for that week?

A. 7

B. –7

C. –1

D. 1

27. In 4 practice runs on a 100 m track, a sprinter has times of 12.4 seconds, 11.95 seconds, 12.25 seconds, and 13.0 seconds. What was the average practice time of the sprinter?

A. 12.6 seconds

B. 12.4 seconds

C. 12.55 seconds

D. 12.3 seconds

28. James has 15 pennies in his pocket. The mint date on 3 of the pennies is 2003. If James randomly chooses one penny out of his pocket, what is the probability that the penny will have the date of 2003?

A. 15%

B. 20%

C. 25%

D. 3%

29. A bag contains 9 red chips, 7 blue chips, and 8 white chips. Without looking at the color, you choose one marble from the bag. What is the approximate likelihood that the marble is white?

A. 50%

B. 38%

C. 33%

D. 29%

30. The following table lists the gross income and profit for the Bailey Company.

Year	2000	2001	2002	2003	2004	2005	2006
Gross Income	1,315	1,625	2,018	2,758	3,566	4,459	5,034
Profit	143	172	222	1,327	1,464	1,562	2,709

In which year was the difference between gross income and profit the greatest?

A. 2001

B. 2003

C. 2005

D. 2006

31. Use the graph to answer the question that follows.

Which of the following scenarios could be represented by the graph above?

A. Mr. Cain mowed grass at a steady rate for a while, then took a short break, and then finished the job at a steady but slower rate.

B. Mr. Cain mowed grass at a steady rate for a while, and then mowed at a steady slower rate, then he took a break.

C. Mr. Cain mowed grass at a variable rate for a while, then took a short break, and then finished the job at a variable rate.

D. Mr. Cain mowed grass at a steady rate for a while, then took a short break, and then finished the job at a steady but faster pace.

32. Use the bar graph that follows to answer the question.

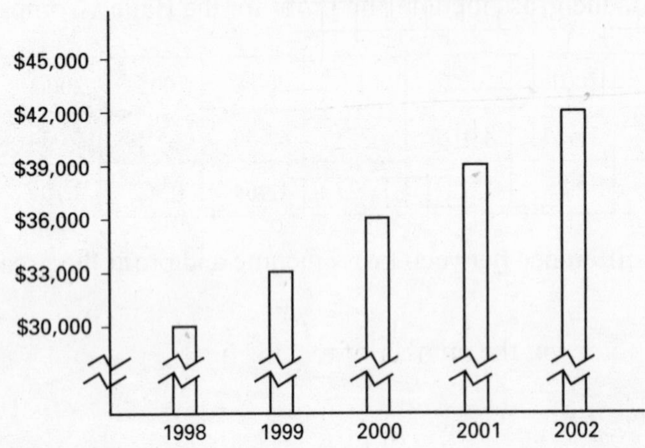

Only one of the statements below is necessarily true. Which one?

A. The range of Ms. Patton's earnings for the years shown is $15,000.

B. Ms. Patton's annual pay increases were consistent over the years shown.

C. Ms. Patton earned $45,000 in 2003.

D. Ms. Patton's average income for the years shown was $38,000.

33. The scatter plot below shows the relationship between grade level and hours of reading each week. Which statement describes this relationship?

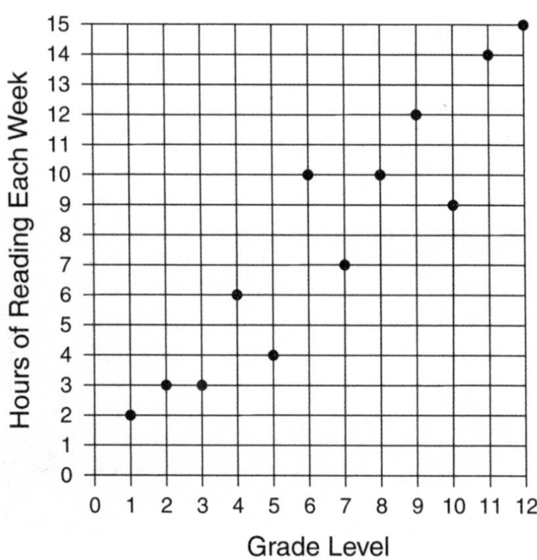

A. As grade level goes down, the number of reading hours goes up.

B. As grade level goes up, the number of reading hours goes down.

C. As grade level goes up, the number of reading hours goes up.

D. Grade level and reading hours are unrelated.

34. Use the pie chart below to answer the question that follows.

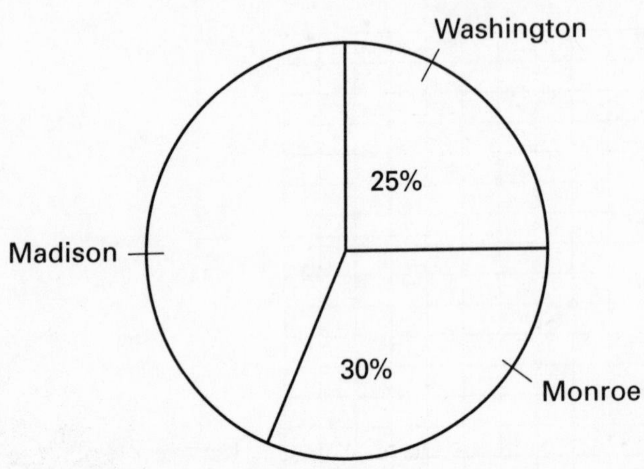

If the total number of people voting was 600, which of the following statements are true?

I. Madison received more votes than Monroe and Washington combined.

II. Madison received 45% of the votes.

III. Monroe received 180 votes.

IV. Madison received 330 votes.

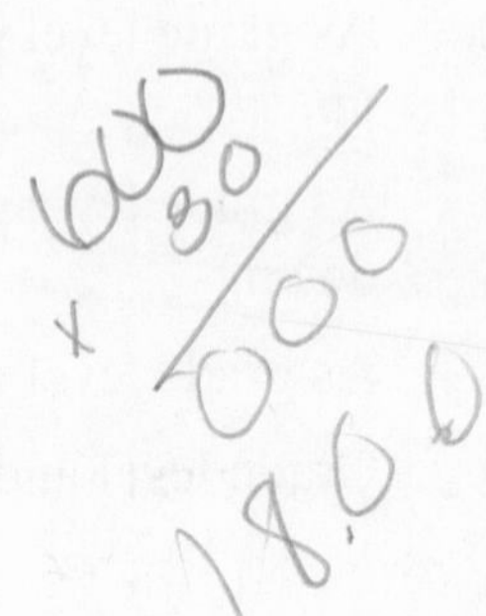

A. I and III only

B. I and IV only

C. II and III only

D. II and IV only

35. The following plot represents an individual's shoe size and height.

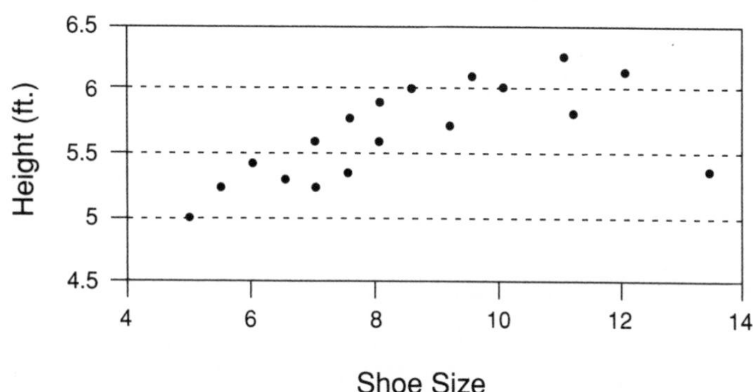

Which of the following best describes the relationship between shoe size and height?

A. There appears to be no relationship between shoe size and height.

B. An increase in height causes an increase in shoe size.

C. There appears to be a negative relationship between shoe size and height.

D. There appears to be a positive relationship between shoe size and height.

36. What is the next number in this sequence?

4096, 1024, 256, 64, _____

A. 4

B. 8

C. 16

D. 32

37. What is the next number in this sequence?

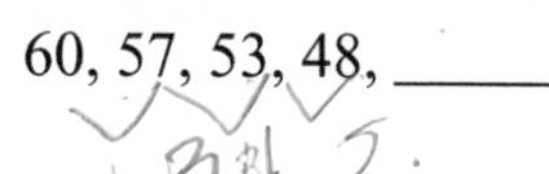

60, 57, 53, 48, _____

A. 45

B. 44

C. 43

D. 42

38. To convert from a Celsius temperature to a Fahrenheit temperature, multiply the Celsius temperature by $\frac{9}{5}$ and add 32. Find the Fahrenheit temperature that is equal to –20° Celsius.

A. –4 degrees Fahrenheit
B. 0 degrees Fahrenheit
C. 4 degrees Fahrenheit
D. 8 degrees Fahrenheit

39. Bridal Veil Falls in California is 189 meters high. Niagara Falls, between New York and Ontario, is $\frac{2}{7}$ the height of Bridal Veil Falls. How high is Niagara Falls?

A. 378 meters
B. 54 meters
C. 60 meters
D. 108 meters

40. Camille bought a bracelet from her favorite store. The price of the bracelet was \$31.99, and sales tax was 6.5%. She paid for her purchase with \$35.00. How much change did Camille receive?

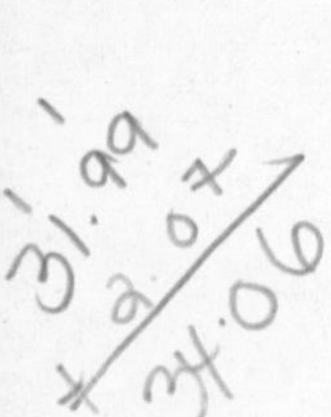

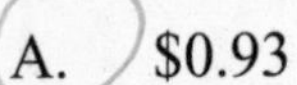

A. \$0.93
B. \$0.78
C. \$1.12
D. \$1.03

41. A survey was taken to determine the amount of time children spent watching TV each day. The results were 1 hour or less (18.4%), between 1 and 5 hours (68.8%), and 5 or more hours (12.8%). If you considered 415 children, about how many would you expect to watch television for 1 hour or less each day?

A. 72
B. 76
C. 80
D. 84

42. Bev, Kim, Lee, Ron, and Sue each have a favorite sport. No two of them have the same favorite sport. Using the following clues, find Bev's favorite sport.

- Ron's favorite sport is not basketball.
- Bev does not like basketball or soccer.
- Sue's favorite sport is volleyball.
- Kim does not like golf.
- Lee's favorite sport is the sport that Kim does not like.
- Three of the sports are basketball, soccer, and tennis.

A. Bev's favorite sport is volleyball.
B. Bev's favorite sport is golf.
C. Bev's favorite sport is tennis.
D. It is impossible to determine Bev's favorite sport from the information given.

43. Simplify the following expression. Then evaluate it when $x = 3$.

$$5x + 3 + (-8) + (-3x)$$

A. 1
B. 17
C. 19
D. 35

44. Evaluate the following expression using the following values: $x = 3$, $y = 4$, and $z = 6$.

$$2x\,(z + 3y)$$

A. 108
B. 120
C. 216
D. 432

45. Solve for q:

$$\frac{1}{4}q - 9 = 3$$

A. $q = 12$

B. $q = 27$

C. $q = 48$

D. $q = 108$

46. What are the solutions of this equation?

$$3x^2 - 11 = 1$$

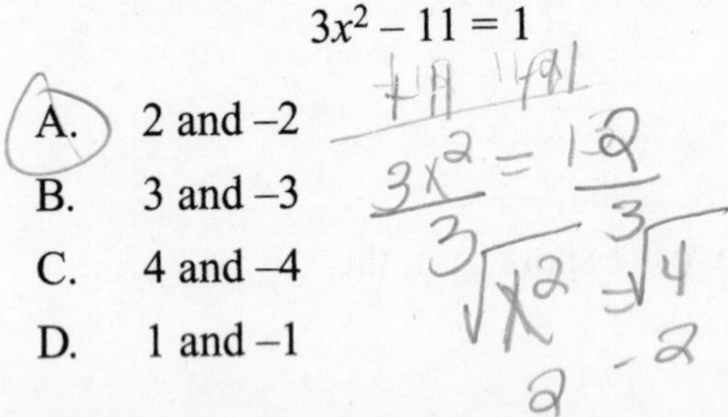

A. 2 and –2

B. 3 and –3

C. 4 and –4

D. 1 and –1

47. Solve the following inequality:

$$2(x + 1) \geq 3x - 2$$

A. $x \geq 2$

B. $x \geq 4$

C. $x \leq 2$

D. $x \leq 4$

48. Which equation could be used to solve the following problem?

"Three consecutive odd numbers add up to 117. What are they?"

A. $x + (x + 2) + (x + 4) = 117$

B. $x + 3x + 5x = 117$

C. $x + x + x = 117$

D. $x + (x + 1) + (x + 3) = 117$

ANSWER KEY – MATHEMATICS PRACTICE TEST 1

Question	Answer	Objective	
1	**C**	0007	Understand number properties and number operations.
2	**D**	0007	Understand number properties and number operations.
3	**B**	0007	Understand number properties and number operations.
4	**D**	0007	Understand number properties and number operations.
5	**A**	0007	Understand number properties and number operations.
6	**B**	0007	Understand number properties and number operations.
7	**D**	0007	Understand number properties and number operations.
8	**C**	0007	Understand number properties and number operations.
9	**B**	0007	Understand number properties and number operations.
10	**D**	0007	Understand number properties and number operations.
11	**B**	0010	Understand problem-solving principles and techniques.
12	**A**	0010	Understand problem-solving principles and techniques.
13	**C**	0010	Understand problem-solving principles and techniques.
14	**D**	0010	Understand problem-solving principles and techniques.

Question	Answer	Objective	
15	**A**	0008	Understand measurement concepts and principles of geometry.
16	**D**	0008	Understand measurement concepts and principles of geometry.
17	**C**	0008	Understand measurement concepts and principles of geometry.
18	**B**	0008	Understand measurement concepts and principles of geometry.
19	**A**	0008	Understand measurement concepts and principles of geometry.
20	**A**	0008	Understand measurement concepts and principles of geometry.
21	**B**	0008	Understand measurement concepts and principles of geometry.
22	**D**	0008	Understand measurement concepts and principles of geometry.
23	**A**	0008	Understand measurement concepts and principles of geometry.
24	**A**	0008	Understand measurement concepts and principles of geometry.
25	**A**	0008	Understand measurement concepts and principles of geometry.
26	**C**	0007	Understand number properties and number operations.
27	**B**	0010	Understand problem-solving principles and techniques.
28	**B**	0010	Understand problem-solving principles and techniques.
29	**C**	0010	Understand problem-solving principles and techniques.
30	**C**	0009	Understand statistical concepts and data analysis and interpretation.

Question	Answer	Objective	
31	**A**	0009	Understand statistical concepts and data analysis and interpretation.
32	**B**	0009	Understand statistical concepts and data analysis and interpretation.
33	**C**	0009	Understand statistical concepts and data analysis and interpretation.
34	**C**	0009	Understand statistical concepts and data analysis and interpretation.
35	**D**	0009	Understand statistical concepts and data analysis and interpretation.
36	**C**	0007	Understand number properties and number operations.
37	**D**	0007	Understand number properties and number operations.
38	**A**	0009	Understand statistical concepts and data analysis and interpretation.
39	**B**	0010	Understand problem-solving principles and techniques.
40	**A**	0010	Understand problem-solving principles and techniques.
41	**B**	0010	Understand problem-solving principles and techniques.
42	**C**	0010	Understand problem-solving principles and techniques.
43	**A**	0007	Understand number properties and number operations.
44	**A**	0007	Understand number properties and number operations.

Question	Answer	Objective	
45	**C**	0007	Understand number properties and number operations.
46	**A**	0007	Understand number properties and number operations.
47	**D**	0007	Understand number properties and number operations.
48	**A**	0007	Understand number properties and number operations.

Practice Test 1, Part 2 Progress Chart

0007 Understand Number Properties and Number Operations —/19

1	2	3	4	5	6	7	8	9	10

26	36	37	43	44	45	46	47	48

0008 Understand Measurement Concepts and Principles of Geometry —/11

15	16	17	18	19	20	21	22	23	24	25

0009 Understand Statistical Concepts and Data Analysis and Interpretation —/7

30	31	32	33	34	35	38

0010 Understand Problem-Solving Principles and Techniques —/11

11	12	13	14	27	28	29	39	40	41	42

Detailed Explanations for Practice Test 1, Part 2: Mathematics

1. **C**

The traditional approach to multiplying simple fractions (those between 0 and 1) is to first multiply the numerators together and then multiply the denominators together to find the product. In this case, $\frac{2}{3} \times \frac{4}{5} = \frac{8}{15}$.

2. **D**

When solving addition or subtraction problems with fractions, first compute the fractional part. In this case, add $\frac{3}{4}$ and $\frac{1}{2}$. To do this, you must find equivalent fractions with common denominators. The common denominator here is 4, so the fraction $\frac{3}{4}$ stays the same, and the fraction $\frac{1}{2}$ is changed to $\frac{2}{4}$. Adding the fractions together results in $\frac{5}{4}$, or $1\frac{1}{4}$. Add $1\frac{1}{4}$ to the whole numbers (2 + 1), arriving at the answer of $4\frac{1}{4}$.

3. **B**

When subtracting mixed numbers, the first step is to subtract the fractions (in this case, $\frac{1}{2} - \frac{2}{3}$). Because the denominators are different, equivalent fractions with a common denominator must be obtained. The least common denominator is 6, so $\frac{1}{2}$ converts to $\frac{3}{6}$ (making the top number $7\frac{3}{6}$) and $\frac{2}{3}$ converts to $\frac{4}{6}$ (making the bottom number $3\frac{4}{6}$). It is impossible to subtract $\frac{4}{6}$ from $\frac{3}{6}$, so we must rename the top number by "borrowing" one whole from the 7 and adding $\frac{6}{6}$ to the fraction. This results in the problem now reading $6\frac{9}{6} - 3\frac{4}{6}$. We are able to easily subtract now, arriving at the answer of $3\frac{5}{6}$.

4. **D**

When dividing fractions, the traditional algorithm involves inverting, or "flipping," the second fraction and multiplying. Therefore, the algorithm would read

$\frac{2}{3} \times \frac{5}{4}$. Multiply the numerators, and then multiply the denominators. The resulting fraction is $\frac{10}{12}$, which, in simplest form, is $\frac{5}{6}$.

5. **A**

To subtract a negative number, think first about subtracting a number, and what that would look like on a number line. If this problem read –16 – 5, we would move to the left on the number line (as we do when we subtract), and the answer would be –21 (which is answer choice C; thus you can eliminate that answer choice). If one subtracts a negative number, we must move to the right on the number line, because you are subtracting the opposite. Therefore, –16 – (–5) may be thought of as –16 + 5. Therefore, the appropriate answer choice is A, –11.

6. **B**

The first step when dividing decimals is to make the divisor appear as a whole number by moving the decimal point to the right. In this problem, move the decimal point in the divisor two places to the right, to make the divisor read 5. Then, move the decimal point in the dividend two places to the right. The dividend now looks like 820. Move the decimal point straight up from the end of the 820 into the same spot in the quotient. Divide normally to reach the answer of 164.

7. **D**

To solve this problem, you must set up an equation. The easiest way to do so is to write the equation as it is read: 14 = 22%n (with n being the unknown number). Rewrite the 22% as .22, and you have 14 = .22n. Divide both sides by .22 to isolate the unknown number. The result is 63.63, which is approximately 64, thus answer D.

8. **C**

To solve this problem in scientific notation, simply multiply the first two digits inside each group of parentheses (2 × 6 = 12). To multiply the 10s notations, simply add the exponents ($10^3 \times 10^4$, add the 3 and 4, which results in 10^7). Thus far, the solution reads: 12×10^7. In scientific notation, however, the initial factor must be greater than zero and less than ten. Therefore, we change the 12. 12 = 1.2 × 10. This gives us another power of ten, which changes the 10^7 to 10^8. The simplified answer to this problem, therefore, is 1.2×10^8.

9. **B**

The order of operations is used to solve this problem. Multiplication comes before addition and subtraction, so the first step is to multiply 2 × 5, which equals 10. Then, add and subtract left to right (3 + 10 – 4 = 9).

10. **D**

This problem simply requires that you know how to find a missing number in an equation. To solve this problem, start with 1,806 and subtract 358 to find the missing number, which is 1,448.

11. **B**

To find how much money Bob and Jana made together, you must first determine how much each made separately, then add those numbers together. Bob babysat for 4 hours and received $6 per hour, which is $24. Jana babysat for half as long as Bob – 2 hours – and received $7 per hour, which is $14. The total that the two made together was $38.

12. **A**

First, find the number of people that a 0.5% increase in population illustrates. To find that amount, multiply the population by the increase (2,460 × 0.005), which equals 12.3. Add the increase (12.3) to the original population (2,460) to reach the answer of 2,472.3, which, when rounded to the nearest person (whole number), would give an approximate population of 2,472.

13. **C**

One way to solve this problem is to draw a chart that shows the growth of each rose bush.

Week	**1**	**2**	**3**	**4**	**5**	**6**	**7**	**8**	**9**
Red 39 in.	$39\frac{1}{2}$	40	$40\frac{1}{2}$	41	$41\frac{1}{2}$	42	$42\frac{1}{2}$	43	$43\frac{1}{2}$
Yellow $36\frac{3}{4}$ in.	$37\frac{1}{2}$	$38\frac{1}{4}$	39	$39\frac{3}{4}$	$40\frac{1}{2}$	$41\frac{1}{4}$	42	$42\frac{3}{4}$	$43\frac{1}{2}$

Track the rate of the red rose bush by adding $\frac{1}{2}$ an inch for each week, and do the same for the yellow rose bush at the rate of $\frac{3}{4}$ of an inch per week. At the 9th week, both bushes are the same height: $43\frac{1}{2}$ inches.

14. **D**

To solve this problem, consider the total amount of time illustrated in the problem, including the 15-minute break that Sarah took from 2:05–2:20. From 11:20 to 3:15 is 3 hours 55 minutes. Subtract the 15-minute break that Sarah took to arrive at the answer of 3 hours 40 minutes.

15. **A**

To solve this problem, consider the following:

1000 milligrams = 1 gram

The problem is: 120 milligrams = ___ grams

One way to do this problem is to set up and solve a ratio.

$$\frac{120 \text{ milligrams}}{1000 \text{ milligrams}} = \frac{x \text{ grams}}{1 \text{ gram}}$$

$120 = 1000x$ Then divide both sides by 1000.

$$\frac{120}{1000} = \frac{1000x}{1000} = 0.12 \text{ grams}$$

16. **D**

To solve this problem, consider that 1km = 1000 m and 1 m = 100 cm.
First, change 5.6 km to meters (5.6 × 1000 = 5600).
Then, change 5,600 m to cm (5600 × 100 = 560,000).
Thus, answer D.

17. **C**

Since there are 12 inches in a foot, simply multiply 14 feet by 12 inches to reach the answer of 168 inches.

18. **B**

To convert 4 feet 3 inches to inches only, first convert the 4 feet to inches ($4 \times 12 = 48$ inches), and then add the extra 3 inches to arrive at the answer of 51 inches.

19. **A**

The area of any rectangle is equal to the measure of its length times the measure of its width (or to say it differently, the measure of its base times the measure of its height). A right triangle can be seen as half of a rectangle (sliced diagonally). Answer A represents, in effect, a rectangle's area cut in half (i.e., divided by two).

20. **A**

The formula used for finding the area of a triangle is $\frac{1}{2} \times$ base $\times$ height. In this case:

$$\frac{1}{2} \times (8 \times 20)$$

$$\frac{1}{2} \times (160) = 80 \text{ square inches}$$

21. **B**

If a square has a perimeter of 20 centimeters, that means that the length of each side is 5 centimeters. To find the area of a square, multiply the length (5) by the width (5) to reach the answer of 25 square centimeters.

22. **D**

To find the area of a circle, use the formula πr^2. In this problem, substitute 4 for r, and the result is: 16π. When you use 3.14 for pi and multiply that by 16, the answer is 50.24 square centimeters.

23. **A**

To find the volume of a cylinder, use the formula $\pi r^2 \times h$. Substitute 3.14 for pi, 4 for r, and 8 for h.

$3.14 \times 4^2 \times 8$ $\quad$ $3.14 \times 16 \times 8 = 401.92$ cubic inches

24. **A**

If two triangles are similar, that means that they have the exact same shape (although not necessarily the same size). It also means that the corresponding angles of the two triangles have the same measure, and that corresponding sides are proportional.

One way to find the solution to this problem is to set up a proportion with one corner being the unknown value (x), and then solve the proportion:

$$\frac{12}{10} = \frac{15}{x}$$

This can be read as "12 is to 10 as 15 is to x". The problem can be solved using cross-multiplication, then finding the unknown value.

$$12x = 15x \times 10$$
$$12x = 150$$
$$x = 12.5$$

25. **A**

There are two things one must know in order to answer the question. One is the meaning of the small square at the vertex of angle BXC. That symbol tells you that angle BXC is a right angle (which measures 90º). A straight line can be thought of as an angle that measures 180º. This is a straight angle.

In the figure in problem 25, therefore, the sum of the angles DXC (42º) and BXC (90º) is 132º. That means that the remaining angle on the line must have a measure of 48º (180º – 132º).

26. **C**

To find the average (mean) of a set of values, first add them together. In this case, the negative and positive integers should be added together separately. Those two sums are –12 and 5. (The 0 may be ignored, since it does not affect either sum.) Then –12 and 5 should be added together for a sum of –7.

To complete the work, the sum of –7 must be divided by the number of values (7), giving –1.

27. **B**

To find the average trial time for the sprinter, add all four values together, and then divide by the number of trials (4).

11.95 + 12.25 + 12.4 + 13 = 49.6
49.6 divided by 4 = 12.4 seconds

28. **B**

To find the likelihood, set up a fraction that shows the number of desired outcomes (3 pennies with the date of 2003) over the total possibilities (15 pennies in all).

$$\frac{3}{15} = \frac{1}{5} \text{ or } 20\%$$

29 **C**

To find the likelihood of drawing a white marble, set up a fraction that shows the number of desired outcomes (8 white marbles) over the total possibilities (24 marbles in all).

$$\frac{8}{24} = \frac{1}{3} \text{ or } 33\%.$$

30. **C**

The difference in gross income and profits in the year 2005 was 2,897 (4,459 – 1,562), which is the largest difference of all the years shown.

31. **A**

The somewhat steep straight line to the left shows that Mr. Cain worked at a steady rate for awhile. The completely flat lines in the middle shows that he stopped for a while. The line doesn't go up because no grass was cut then. Finally, the line continues upward (after his break) less steeply (and therefore more flatly), indicating that he was working at a slower rate.

32. **B**

Because Ms. Patton's increases were consistent ($3,000 yearly), and because the directions tell you that only one statement is true, answer B must be correct. Consider:

The range of Ms. Patton's earnings is $12,000 (the jump from $30,000 to $42,000), so answer A cannot be correct.

Although Ms. Patton may have earned $45,000 in 2003, you don't know that, so answer C cannot be correct.

Answer D gives the incorrect earnings average; it was $36,000, not $38,000.

33. **C**

Draw a line through the set of data points. Notice that low grade levels go with low hours of reading, and that high grade levels go with high hours of reading. Next, evaluate the truth of each possible answer. The graph shows that as the grade level goes up, the number of reading hours goes up.

34. **C**

The chart shows that Madison received less than half of the votes (this slice takes up less than half of the pie), so statement I cannot be true.

Washington and Monroe together received 55% of the votes, and everyone else voted for Madison, so Madison must have received 45% of the votes (all of the candidates' percentages must add up to 100%). Therefore, statement II is true.

Monroe received 30% of the 600 votes. 0.30 times 600 is 180, so statement III is true.

Madison received 45% of the vote, and 45% of 600 is 270, so statement IV is false.

35. **D**

D is the correct solution. We can see from the figure that as shoe size increases so does height, so there is a positive relationship which rules out (A) and (C). The problem with (B) is that neither variable causes a change in the other variable.

36. **C**

In this sequence, the pattern is "divided by 4" to reach the next number.

4096 divided by 4 is 1024
1024 divided by 4 is 256
256 divided by 4 is 64
64 divided by 4 is 16; thus answer C is correct.

37. **D**

In this sequence, the pattern is progressive. Each number is the result of subtraction by a larger number each time.

60 minus 3 = 57
57 minus 4 = 53
53 minus 5 = 48
48 minus 6 = 42; therefore, D is the correct answer.

38. **A**

To convert a Celsius temperature to a Fahrenheit temperature, multiply the Celsius value by $\frac{9}{5}$, then add 32. Thus:

$$\left(\frac{9}{5}\times -20\right) + 32 = \_\_\_\_ \text{ degrees Fahrenheit}$$

$-36 + 32 = -4$ degrees Fahrenheit (therefore, answer A is correct).

39. **B**

To find the height of Niagara Falls, multiply $\frac{2}{7}$ by the height of Bridal Veil Falls (189 meters).

(2 × 189) divided by 7 = height of Niagara Falls
378 divided by 7 = 54 meters (answer B).

40. **A**

To find the amount of tax, multiply the tax rate of 6.5% (.065 in decimal form) by \$31.99, the cost of the bracelet. (.065 × \$31.99 = 2.079, which rounds to \$2.08.) Therefore, the total cost of the bracelet with tax is \$34.07. If she paid with \$35.00, subtracting \$34.07 from that amount will give the change she should receive (\$0.93, answer choice A).

41. **B**

To determine the number of children in the entire sample of 415 that would watch TV for an hour or less, multiply 415 by the percentage in the survey who answered "one hour or less" (18.4%).

415 × .184 = 76.36

Because we cannot have .36 of a person, round the answer to 76; thus answer B is correct.

42. **C**

One way to solve this deductive reasoning problem is to draw a chart, and use the clues to "rule out" sports that are not favorites, or identify which sports are favorites. First, read through all of the clues to determine the possibilities for favorite sports and list them across the top of the chart. Then, list the names of the people identified. When you "rule out" a sport for each person, mark an X in the chart.

	Basketball	Soccer	Volleyball	Golf	Tennis
Sue			O	X	
Ron	X		X	X	
Bev	X	X	X	X	
Kim			X	X	
Lee			X	O	

Ron's favorite sport is not basketball. Put an X beside Ron's name under basketball.

Bev's favorite sport is not basketball or soccer, so put an X beside her name under those two sports.

Sue's favorite sport is volleyball. Put an O beside her name in volleyball to show that it is her favorite.

Because we know that volleyball is Sue's favorite, put an X under volleyball beside everyone else's name.

Kim doesn't like golf. Put an X beside Kim's name under golf.

Lee's favorite sport is the one that Kim does not like (golf), so put an O beside his name under golf, and an X beside everyone else's name under golf.

Looking beside Bev's name, all of the sports have an X except tennis. Therefore, tennis is her favorite sport (answer choice C).

43. **A**

First, simplify the expression. Combine like terms $[5x + (-3x)]$ and $[3 + (-8)]$.

$5x - 3x = 2x$ $\quad\quad$ $3 - 8 = -5$

Therefore, the expression becomes: $2x - 5$

Substitute 3 for x, and the result is: $2(3) - 5$ or $6 - 5 = 1$ (answer A).

44. **A**

To solve this expression, substitute the given numbers for the variables in the expression, then use the order of operations to solve.

$2x\,(z + 3y) = 2(3)\,(6 + 3(4))$
$= 6\,(6 + 12)$
$= 6\,(18)$
$= 108$ (therefore, answer A is correct.)

45. **C**

To solve this equation for q, first you must isolate the term that contains q. In this example, add 9 to both sides.

$$\frac{1}{4}q - 9 = 3$$

$$\frac{1}{4}q - 9 + 9 = 3 + 9$$

Combine like terms: $\frac{1}{4}q = 12$

Multiply both sides by 4 to eliminate the fraction. $(4)\ \frac{1}{4}q = 12\ (4)$

Therefore, $q = 48$ (answer choice C).

46. **A**

To solve this equation for x, first add 11 to each side, which gives $3x^2 = 12$.

Dividing both sides by 3 gives $x^2 = 4$.

Find the square roots of 4; 2 and –2.

The solutions can be checked by substituting them (one at a time) into the original question to see if they work. In this case, both 2 and –2 work.

47. **D**

To solve this inequality, treat it as a typical equation and solve it.

$$2(x + 1) \geq 3x - 2$$

First, use the distributive property to simplify the left side.

$$2x + 2 \geq 3x - 2$$

To isolate the variable terms, subtract $2x$ from each side.

$$2x + 2 - 2x \geq 3x - 2 - 2x$$

Combine like terms: $2 \geq x - 2$

Add 2 to both sides to isolate the variable completely: $2 + 2 \geq x$

The answer currently reads $4 \geq x$. We typically read the expression with the variable first, in which case, we must "flip" the sign. The answer, then, is $x \leq 4$.

48. **A**

You know that the correct equation must show three consecutive odd numbers being added to give 117. Odd numbers (just like even numbers) are each two apart from each other. Only the three values given in answer A are each two apart.

Because the numbers being sought are odd, one might be tempted to choose answer D. However, the second value in answer D ($x + 1$) is not two numbers apart from the first value (x); it is different by only one.

Practice Test 1
Part 3: Writing

GACE Basic Skills

This test is also on CD-ROM in our special interactive TestWare® for the GACE Basic Skills. It is highly recommended that you first take this exam on computer. You will then have the additional study features and benefits of enforced timed conditions and instantaneous, accurate scoring. See page 6 for instructions on how to get the most out of REA's TestWare®.

ANSWER SHEET
PRACTICE TEST 1, PART 3: WRITING

1 _____	11 _____	22 _____	33 _____
2 _____	12 _____	23 _____	34 _____
3 _____	13 _____	24 _____	35 _____
4 _____	14 _____	25 _____	36 _____
5 _____	15 _____	26 _____	37 _____
6 _____	16 _____	27 _____	38 _____
7 _____	17 _____	28 _____	39 _____
8 _____	18 _____	29 _____	40 _____
9 _____	19 _____	30 _____	41 _____
10 _____	20 _____	31 _____	42 _____
	21 _____	32 _____	

PRACTICE TEST 1, PART 3: WRITING

PART 3: Writing
42 questions

Read the passage below; then answer the three questions that follow.

[1]Actually, the term "Native American" is incorrect. [2]Indians migrated to the North American continent from other areas, just earlier than Europeans did. [3]The ancestors of the Anasazi—Indians of the four-state area of Colorado, New Mexico, Utah, and Arizona—probably crossed from Asia into Alaska. [4]About 25,000 years ago, while the continental land bridge still existed. [5]This land bridge arched across the Bering Strait in the last Ice Age. [6]About 500 C.E. the ancestors of the Anasazi moved onto the Mesa Verde, a high plateau in the desert country of Colorado. [7]The Wetherills, five brothers who ranched in the area, are general given credit for the first exploration of the ruins in the 1870s and 1880s. [8]There were some 50,000 Anasazi thriving successfully in the four-corners area by the 1200s C.E. [9] At their zenith, 700 to 1300 C.E., the Anasazi had established widespread communities and built thousands of sophisticated structures—cliff dwellings, pueblos, and kivas. [10]They even engaged in trade with Indians in surrounding regions by exporting pottery and other goods.

1. Which of the following number parts is a sentence fragment?

   A. Part 1

   B. Part 2

   C. Part 4

   D. Part 5

2. Which of the following draws attention away from the main idea of the paragraph?

   A. Part 3

   B. Part 4

   C. Part 7

   D. Part 8

3. Which of the following changes is needed to make the passage conform to the conventions of Standard American English?

   A. Part 2: Change "earlier" to "more early."
   B. Part 3: Change "probably" to "more probably."
   C. Part 7: Change "general" to "generally."
   D. Part 8: Change "successfully" to "most successful."

Read the passage below; then answer the three questions that follow.

[1]Many events happened in both the South and the North to prevent African Americans from gaining civil rights. [2]Many whites did not want to associate with former slaves and were supportive of segregating the races. [3]The laws that were passed to keep the races segregated were known as Jim Crow laws which made it illegal for blacks to go to white public facilities like hospitals, libraries, schools and parks as well as private facilities like restaurants and churches. [4]The Jim Crow laws and other legal segregation are known as *de jure* segregation, meaning by law segregation another type of segregation is *de facto* segregation which is the segregation that occurs when people follow unwritten rules or customs that segregate the races. [5]When these laws were brought before the Supreme Court as a violation of the 14th Amendment, the Supreme Court ruled that the 14th Amendment had only prohibited states, not individuals or businesses, from discriminating against blacks.

[6]Booker T. Washington, who founded the Tuskegee Institute, believed that fighting discrimination should occur through economic advancement. [7]He believed that if African Americans learned skills through education, they would make themselves equal to whites economically and this would help them to become socially equal. [8]He argued that protesting against discrimination only increased white's hostility toward the blacks. [9]Even though there were few changes in the lives of many African Americans changes were coming. [10]Many African Americans sought to further the black cause by trying to get along with the white population.

4. Which of the following changes is needed to improve the unity and focus of the second paragraph?

   A. Reverse the order of Parts 7 and 8

   B. Delete Part 7

   C. Reverse the order of Parts 8 and 9

   D. Delete Part 10

5. Which of the following numbered parts of the passage is a run-on sentence?

   A. Part 3

   B. Part 4

   C. Part 5

   D. Part 7

6. Which of the following changes is needed to correct an error in punctuation?

   A. Part 1: Insert a comma after "North."

   B. Part 5: Insert a comma after "Court."

   C. Part 7: Insert a comma after "believed."

   D. Part 9: Insert a comma after "Americans."

Read the passage below; then answer the three questions that follow.

[1]Being an optimist or pessimist may have a weighty effect on your health, emotional state of mind, and longevity. [2]A thirty-year study of patients who were being treated at the Mayo Clinic provide insight into what it means to have a sunny disposition. [3]Researchers followed up with patients to whom they had given a personality test thirty years previously. [4]After thirty years, those patients who had reported being more optimistic had lived longer than expected, while the pessimists had a shorter-than-expected lifespan.

[5]Other research that promotes having a brighter outlook on life has found that people who described himself as being pessimistic have higher blood pressure and are more likely to have increased anxiety and depression. [6]An optimist can expect to recover more quickly after being sick and he or she is also less likely to get sick in the first place. [7]If you have a better outlook on life, you are likely to be in better physical and mental health, and possibly live longer.

7. Which of the following changes is needed to correct an error in subject/verb agreement?

   A. Part 2: Change "provide" to "provides."
   B. Part 3: Change "followed" to "follows."
   C. Part 6: Change "expect" to "expects."
   D. Part 7: Change "are" to "were."

8. Which of the following changes is needed to correct an error in noun/pronoun agreement?

   A. Part 3: Change "they" to "he or she."
   B. Part 5: Change "himself" to "themselves."
   C. Part 6: Change "he or she" to "they."
   D. Part 7: Change "you" to "him."

9. What is the thesis of this passage?

   A. After thirty years, those patients who had reported being more optimistic had lived longer than expected, while the pessimists had a shorter-than-expected lifespan.
   B. An optimist can expect to recover more quickly after being sick and he or she is also less likely to get sick in the first place.
   C. Researchers followed up with patients to whom they had given a personality test thirty years previously
   D. Being an optimist or pessimist may have a weighty effect on your health, emotional state of mind, and longevity.

Read the passage below; then answer the three questions that follow.

[1]Savannah, Georgia, founded in 1733, was the first colonial and state capital of Georgia. [2]It has long been recognized as one of the most beautiful and most walkable cities in America and has a large National Historical Landmark district that includes the 22 squares that were originally laid out by the British philanthropist James Oglethorpe. [3]He originally envisioned founding the colony of Georgia with colonists that had been imprisoned for their inability to pay their debts. [4]Oglethorpe had experienced the loss of a good friend, not just a good friend but his best friend, who had died in a debtors' prison. [5]Oglethorpe

wanted to create a colony that would give people a fresh start. [6]While this vision of shipping debtors on a large scale to Georgia was never realized, the city of Savannah continues to celebrate the altruism of James Oglethorpe and one of the most lavish squares contains a larger-than-life statue of him. [7]Most of the other squares have only a fountain at their center, but Chippewa Square (not Oglethorpe Square as one might expect) has a statue of General Oglethorpe that was sculpted by the same artist, Daniel Chester French, who created the seated Lincoln in Washington D.C. [8]It is often referred to as the most beautiful when compared to the Gordon monument in Wright Square.

10. Which of the following parts contains redundant phrasing?

   A. Part 2
   B. Part 4
   C. Part 6
   D. Part 7

11. Which of the following parts contains a nonstandard pronoun use?

   A. Part 2
   B. Part 3
   C. Part 6
   D. Part 7

12. Which of the following contains a nonstandard use of a comparative form?

   A. Part 1
   B. Part 2
   C. Part 6
   D. Part 8

Read the passage below; then answer the three questions that follow.

[1]The Lincoln Cent was first struck in 1909 to celebrate the 100th Anniversary of the birth of Abraham Lincoln. [2]The coin carried the motto "In God We Trust"—the first time it appeared on this denomination coin. [3]Though we might not think so at first glance, the lowly Cent is a fitting memorial for the great

man whose profile graces this most common coin of the realm, and a tolerable symbol for the nation whose commerce it serves.

[4]The obverse has the profile of Lincoln as he looked during the trying years of the Civil War. [5]Faced with the immense problems of a divided nation, the prevention of the split between North and South was difficult. [6]With the outbreak of hostilities at Fort Sumter. Lincoln was saddened to see his beloved country caught up in the senseless violence that is war. [7]Throughout America, war captured the attention of people: the woman who saved the lives of the wounded, the soldier waiting to go into battle, the bewildered child trying hard to understand the loss of a parent.

[8]Barely a month before the end of the war, Lincoln took the oath of office a secondly time as President. [9]With the war still raging, his inaugural address took on added meaning: [10]"With malice toward none, with charity for all, with firmness in the right as God gives us to see the right, let us strive on to finish the work we are in, to bind up the nations wounds, to care for him who shall have borne the battle and his widow and his orphan, to do all which may achieve and cherish a just and lasting peace among ourselves and with all nations."

13. Which of the following changes is needed in the third paragraph?

    A. Part 8: Change "end" to "climax."

    B. Part 8: Change "secondly" to "second."

    C. Part 9: Change "With" to "Of."

    D. Part 9: Change "on" to "in."

14. Which of the following changes is needed in the second paragraph?

    A. Part 4: Change "has" to "had."

    B. Part 5: Change "the prevention of the split between North and South was difficult" to "Lincoln found it difficult to prevent the split between North and South."

    C. Part 7: Change "waiting" to "waited."

    D. Part 7: Change "captured" to "captures."

15. Which of the following is a nonstandard sentence?

    A. Part 2

    B. Part 3

    C. Part 6

    D. Part 8

Read the passage below; then answer the three questions that follow.

[1]The Tuskegee Experiment's true nature had to be hidden from the subjects to ensure their cooperation. [2]The sharecroppers' grossly disadvantaged lot in life made them easy to manipulate. [3]Pleased at the prospect of free medical care—almost none of them had ever seen a doctor before—these unsophisticated and trusting men became the dupes in what has been identified as a "long-standing misuse of the therapeutic medical model".

[4]The study was meant to discover how syphilis affected African Americans as opposed to whites—the theory being that whites experienced more neurological complications from syphilis whereas African Americans were more susceptible to cardiovascular damage. [5]____. [6]Although scientists touted the study as one of great scientific merit, from the outset its actual benefits were unclear. [7]It took almost forty years before someone involved in the study took a hard and honest look at the end result, there was no interest in the study or its participants outside of a small group of doctors and civil right activists.

16. Which of the following sentences, if inserted as Part 5, would be most consistent with the writer's purpose and intended audience?

    A. If the theory had been proven, much would have changed in the clinical treatment of syphilis.

    B. How this knowledge would have changed the clinical treatment of syphilis is uncertain.

    C. On the other hand, neurological complications were much more important to the scientists.

    D. We will never know what the racist scientists of the 1920s were thinking when they devised this theory.

17. Which of the numbered parts should be revised to correct a nonstandard use of a comma?

    A. Part 2
    B. Part 4
    C. Part 6
    D. Part 7

18. Which of the following changes is needed in the first paragraph?

    A. Part 1: Change "Experiment's" to "Experiments"
    B. Part 3: Change "had" to "has."
    C. Part 2: Change "easy to manipulate" to "easily manipulated."
    D. Part 3: Move the period at the end inside the quotation mark.

Read the passage below; then answer the three questions that follow.

[1]The zoning regulations of Westside have long been a thorn in the side of local real estate developers. [2]The authors of those regulations apparently believed that their regulations would be appropriate in perpetuity, because they ______________________ to amend. [3]The result is a growing area of blight bounded on the north by Forrest Drive and on the east by Cascade Circle.

[4]The Westside's city council has a chance to bring the zoning practices into the twenty-first century. [5]The decisive votes will come from Council members Nelson and Crawford. [6]The votes of these two in particular will be of interest to their constituents, because the residents of their districts would stand to gain a great deal from rezoning. [7]The proposed changes would bring the Fifth District some much-needed commerce in the currently run-down Forrest Drive area and would help _________ the Fifth District's steady population loss. [8]Although each of these self-styled "progressives" have displayed reluctance to vote for anything that would spur development in the recent past, both have strong opposition in the upcoming election and would do well to consider how their votes on this issue will impact the results of that election.

19. Which of the following changes is needed in the previous passage?

    A. Part 1: Change "have" to "has."

    B. Part 4: Change "Westside's" to "Westside."

    C. Part 8: Change the comma after "past" to a semicolon.

    D. Part 8: Change "how" to "that."

20. Which of the numbered sentences should be revised to correct an error in verb form?

    A. Part 3

    B. Part 5

    C. Part 6

    D. Part 8

21. Which of the following phrases, if inserted into the blank in Part 2, would make sense and would be free of errors?

    A. made the regulations very easy

    B. ensured that the provisions would be difficult

    C. made them almost impossible

    D. said the zoning ordinances would be hard

Read the passage below; then answer the three questions that follow.

[1]Water is a most unusual substance because it exists on the surface of the Earth in it's three physical states: ice, water, and water vapor. [2]There are other substances that exist in a solid and liquid and gaseous state at temperatures normally found at the Earth's surface, but there are fewer substances that occur in all three states.

[3]Water is odorless, tasteless, and colorless. [4]It is the only substance known to exist in a natural state as a solid, liquid, or gas on the surface of the Earth. [5]It is a universal solvent. [6]Water does not corrode, rust, burn, or separate into its components easily. [7]It is chemically indestructible. [8]It can corrode almost any metal and erode the most solid rock. [9]A unique property of water is that, when frozen in its solid state, it expands and floats on water. [10]Water has a freezing

point of 0°C and a boiling point of 100°C. [11]Water has the capacity to absorb great quantities of heat with relatively little increase in temperature. [12]When distilled, water is a poor conductor of electricity but when salt is added, it is a good conductor of electricity.

22. The writer's main purpose in this passage is to

    A. explain the taste of water.

    B. examine the effects of water on solids.

    C. define the properties of water.

    D. describe the three physical states of all liquids.

23. Which of the following changes is needed in the passage above?

    A. Part 1: Change "it's" to "its."

    B. Part 2: Change "exist" to "exists."

    C. Part 6: Change "its" to "it's."

    D. Part 9: Change "its" to "it's."

24. Which of the following changes is needed in Part 2?

    A. There are other substances that exist in a solid, liquid, and gaseous state at temperatures normally found at the Earth's surface, but there are fewer substances that occur in all three states.

    B. There are other substances that exist in a solid and liquid or gaseous state at temperatures normally found at the Earth's surface, but there are fewer substances that occur in all three states.

    C. There are other substances that exist in a solid or liquid or gaseous state at temperatures normally found at the Earth's surface, but there are fewer substances that occur in all three states.

    D. There are other substances that exist in a solid, liquid, and gaseous state at temperatures normally found at the Earth's surface, but there are fewer substances that occur in all three states.

Read the passage below; then answer the three questions that follow.

[1]A submarine was first used as a military weapon during the American Revolutionary War. [2]The *Turtle*, a one-man submersible designed by an American named David Bushnell and hand-operated by a screw propeller, attempted to sink a British warship in New York Harbor. [3]The plan was to attach a charge of gunpowder to the ship's bottom with screws and explode it with a time fuse. [4]After repeated failures to force the screws through the copper sheathing of the H.M.S. *Eagle*, the submarine was giving up and withdrew, exploding its powder a short distance from the *Eagle*. [5]Although the attack was unsuccessful, it caused the British to move their blockading ships from the harbor to the outer bay.

[6]On February 17, 1864, a Confederate craft, a hand-propelled submersible carrying a crew of eight men, sank a Federal corvette that was blockading Charleston Harbor. [7]The crew hadn't no hope of coming close enough to the corvette to fire upon it with a cannon, so the submarine was used to stealthily approach the ship. [8]The hit was accomplished by a torpedo suspended ahead of the Confederate *Hunley* as she rammed the union frigate *Housatonic*, and is the first recorded instance of a submarine sinking a warship.

25. Which of the following is a nonstandard sentence?

    A. Part 3

    B. Part 5

    C. Part 7

    D. Part 8

26. Which of the following contains nonstandard capitalization?

    A. Part 1

    B. Part 5

    C. Part 6

    D. Part 8

27. Which of the following changes is needed for Part 4?

    A. Change "force" to "forcing."
    B. Change "was giving up" to "gave up."
    C. Change "withdrew" to "withdraw."
    D. Change "exploding" to "exploded."

Read the passage below; then answer the three questions that follow.

[1]The dismissal of Dr. Dennis Griffin has brought many of the students and faculty together to fight for this beloved professor. [2]It does not promote a feeling of academic freedom to know that a tenured professor can be run out of his post because he disagrees with the Board of Regents. [3]True, his was the only negative vote on the retirement fund issue promoted by the university system. [4]However, since when has a dissenting opinion been the prompt for persecution of faculty members on this campus? [5]________________. [6]English professors, especially, have traditionally had the reputation of fighting courageously for out-of-the-box thinking and innovative approaches to problem solving. [7]They have also historically been the school's champion against injustice.

[8]There cannot be an issue closer to the basis of America's founding principles than this one because the foundation of America is based on the freedom of speech. [9]The students of this university need to know whose to blame for the loss of Dr. Griffin. [10]He is a stimulating speaker, an engaging person, and one of the finest teachers. [11]Where will this issue come to a halt? [12]Will other tenured professors now be more intimidated and hesitate to express those views not consistent with the general consensus of opinion? [13]Will students receive a quality education from a university that infringes on freedom of speech?

28. Which of the following requires revision for redundancy?

    A. Part 3
    B. Part 6
    C. Part 8
    D. Part 12

29. Which of the following, if added between sentences 4 and 6, best supports the writer's purpose and audience?

   A. We should allow teachers to express their own opinions regardless of what we ourselves think.

   B. This university has always prided itself on instructors who are rather maverick in their thinking.

   C. Don't you think this is a pitiful way to treat a fine instructor?

   D. One must acknowledge that university professors, as a whole, should support the opinions of fellow faculty members.

30. Which one of the following changes is needed?

   A. Part 8: Change "closer" to "closest."

   B. Part 9: Change "whose" to "who's."

   C. Part 10: Change "finest" to "finer."

   D. Part 11: Change "Where" to "When."

Read the passage below; then answer the three questions that follow.

[1]Madison County's business and professional community along with the Price College faculty and staff donated a record $1.4 million to the 35th annual Scholarship Fund Drive. [2]The total marks the 10th straight year the one-day fundraising drive has topped $1 million in contributions to Price College. [3]The scholarship fund drive helps meet the scholarship commitments of Price College that are not met by state funding. [4]Proceeds from the program go to support both academic and athletic scholarship programs. [5]While the local businesses have often been recognized for their support of the College, the Scholarship Fund Drive demonstrates what a giving community this is, especially in its maintenance of those scholarships available to students within Madison County. [6]Several new endowments were created to be used specific for students who graduate from Madison County public and private high schools. [7]The Eleanor A. Harper Scholarship was established in memory of the former principle of Madison High School and a Price College graduate. [8]This annual scholarship is available to those students who graduate from Madison High School and wish to pursue a degree in education. [9]The legacy of generosity by the members of this community is part and parcel of what makes this such a great place to live and raise a family.

31. Which of the following changes is needed?

    A. Part 5: Change "its" to "it's."
    B. Part 6: Change "specific" to "specifically."
    C. Part 8: Change "available" to "availability."
    D. Part 9: Change "generosity" to "generous."

32. Which of these is the best way to rewrite Part 7?

    A. The Eleanor A. Harper Scholarship was established in memory of the former principal of Madison High School and a former Price College graduate.
    B. The Eleanor A. Harper Scholarship was established in memory of the former principal of Madison High School who was also a Price College graduate.
    C. The Eleanor A. Harper Scholarship was established in memory of the former principal of Madison High School and a graduate of Price College.
    D. The Eleanor A. Harper Scholarship was established in memory of the former principal of Madison High School, a Price College graduate.

33. Which of the following parts contains a distracting detail that impairs the development of the main idea of this passage?

    A. Part 2
    B. Part 4
    C. Part 8
    D. Part 9

Read the passage below; then answer the three questions that follow.

[1]About 3,000 years ago in the Zhou dynasty, the Chinese government began to establish specialized institutions to train blind music officials who were appointed to record history and it was common to find blind scholars, story-tellers and musicians in ancient China. [2]The famous Confucian classic 'Book of Rites' advocated that the government should be responsible for the care and well-being of those who were disabled and sick. [3]A few Chinese scholars claimed that the humanistic attitude and treatment to people with disabilities

under the influence of Confucian philosophy in ancient China were about 10 centuries earlier than the advocacy of liberty and humanity initiated during the Renaissance in the West. [4]Despite the fact that discrimination, alienation, and stigma of people with disabilities characterized the early history of China most of them survived with the support of family, government, and the society at large. [5]A social attitude of sympathy towards people with disabilities had been carefully nurtured, and it was so deeply rooted in Chinese society that we cannot ignore its strong influence today.

[6]Nevertheless, people with disabilities were kept at the bottom of the hierarchical feudal pyramid under this philosophy and a culture of sympathy instead of education was adopted to respond to the needs of those with disabilities in China. [7]Special education institutions began to be established by the American and European missionaries in China after 1840. [8]When Chairman Mao founded the People's Republic of China in 1949, 42 special schools were serving more than 2,000 students with blindness and deafness. [9]The open reform policy under Deng Xiaoping's leadership in the 1980s resulted in tremendous social and political changes as well as economic growth. [10]This encouraged more governmental attention to the rights of people with disabilities. [11]However, the enrollment rate of students with disabilities has since become a nationwide quality index of school district performance.

34. Which of the following contains nonstandard comma use?

A. Part 1

B. Part 2

C. Part 4

D. Part 5

35. Which of the following changes needs to be made?

A. Part 3: Change "to" to "of."

B. Part 5: Change "sympathy" to "sympathetic."

C. Part 8: Change "were" to "are."

D. Part 10: Change "to" to "for."

36. Which of the following contains an error in transitional phrasing?

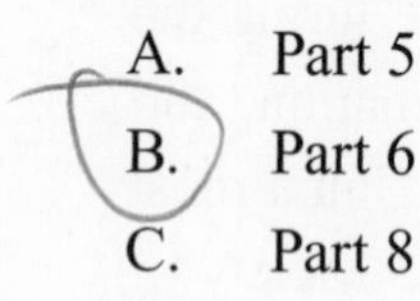

A. Part 5

B. Part 6

C. Part 8

D. Part 11

Read the passage below; then answer the three questions that follow.

[1]Students who are placed in residential programs for behavior or emotional problems or who are adjudicated into detention centers historically have not experienced success in school. [2]These students usually do not have a consistent record of school attendance; their absenteeism can be for more than an entire school year, as they often have been moved from different placements or institutions. [3]Residential treatment provides the longest period of secondary school attendance for many of the students. [4] ______________________________ [5]Students who are incarcerated have not experienced classroom involvement or positive teacher interaction prior to their detainment; this may be the only time they have ever been in a setting where they feel that the teacher recognizes them. [6]For some of them, their incarceration or admission to a residential treatment facility afford them opportunities to participate in appropriate relationships with teachers.

[7]Transitioning back to public schools, where they have not had success should be addressed by the school to which they are returning as well as the facility from which they are leaving. [8]This reintegration is essential in providing students with opportunities for success and a full measure of participation in the educational community; the students' success can be a measure of society's willingness to work with at-risk students.

[9]Academic achievement is related not only to delinquency; but also to recidivism. [10]The ability for students to quickly reintegrate into a public school promotes continued academic effort and better relationships within the school setting. [11]It may be possible in fact, to reduce recidivism by providing necessary skills for academic achievement such as self-advocacy and self-determination, two skills used in developing transition plans for students.

37. Which of the following, if added between sentences 3 and 5, best supports the writer's purpose and audience?

    A. As such, it provides an opportune setting for many of these students to experience some type of academic success both within the content area coursework and in their relationships with educators.

    B. No one knows how long these students have been absent.

    C. But, it isn't the answer to poor judgment by the student.

    D. Residential treatment first came to the forefront of treatment facilities with the onset of drug treatment facilities in the 1960s.

38. Which of the following contains nonstandard semicolon use?

    A. Part 2

    B. Part 5

    C. Part 8

    D. Part 9

39. Which of the following changes needs to be made in the first paragraph?

    A. Part 1: Change "who" to "whom."

    B. Part 3: Change "provides" to "provide."

    C. Part 5: Change "feel" to "feels."

    D. Part 6: Change "afford" to "affords."

Read the passage below; then answer the three questions that follow.

[1]The situation for men has changed as a result of women's massive entry into the workforce for the better. [2]Men who would have felt unrelenting pressure to remain with one firm and climb the career ladder are often freed up by a second income to change careers in midlife. [3]They enjoy greatest intimacy and involvement with their children.

[4]The benefits for business are also readily apparent. [5]No senior manager in the country would deny that the huge generation of women who entered management a decade ago has functioned superbly, often outperforming men.

[6]Yet the prevailing message from the media on the subject of women and business is one filled with pessimism. [7]We hear about women leaving their employers in the lurch when they go on maternity leave. [8]Or we hear the flip side, that women are overly committed to their careers and neglectful of their families. [9]And, in fact, it is true that problems arising from women's new work force role do exist, side by side with the benefits.

[10]The problems hurt business as well as individuals and their families, affordable quality childcare, for one example is still a distant dream. [11]Some women are distracted at work, and men who would have felt secure about their children when their wives were home are also anxious and distracted. [12]Distraction also impedes the productivity of some high-achieving women with the birth of their first child and causes some to depart with the birth of their second.

40. Which of the following sentences displays a nonstandard placement of a modifying phrase?

A. Part 1
B. Part 2
C. Part 5
D. Part 11

41. Which of the following sentences displays a nonstandard use of a comparative form?

A. Part 2

B. Part 3
C. Part 7
D. Part 9

42. Which of the following sentences is a nonstandard sentence?

A. Part 8
B. Part 9
C. Part 10
D. Part 12

Constructed-Response Assignment Directions

For the constructed-response assignment, you are asked to prepare a written response and record it on the pages that you are given in your Written Response Booklet.

Be sure to read the assignment carefully and plan your response before you start to write. You may use any blank space provided in the test booklet following the question to outline your ideas or simply to jot down notes. **However, when you take the GACE Basic Skills, you must write your final version on the pages that the test administrators provide in the test booklet.**

Test scorers use the following criteria to evaluate your constructed-response submission:

- Appropriateness of your response in that you address the topic directly and use language that would be appropriate for the specified occasion, audience, and purpose
- Your focus and organization in sticking to your topic and providing a logical flow to your reasoning
- The support you give to your thesis in the examples you provide
- Your use of correct grammar, sentence structure, and word usage
- Your use of conventions, which include spelling, punctuation, and capitalization

Constructed-Response Question

Writing Assignment

Many scholars note the decline in the use of research resources that are only available in print form. With the onset of the availability of many resources such as journal articles, encyclopedias, and other sources such as public records and almanacs online, the use of libraries by individuals who are seeking information has also declined.

In an essay written to an English instructor, argue whether you feel the trend of accessing research resources online versus physically visiting a library is commendable or contemptible. Reflect on modern research techniques and the effects of a strictly online environment on the culture of academic investigation. Discuss the advantages and/or disadvantages of researching a topic that excludes or minimizes the need to physically search for resources. Finally, draw upon your own exposure to and attitude toward online resources and print copy resources, respectively.

ANSWER KEY – WRITING PRACTICE TEST 1

Question	Answer	Objective	
1	C	**0013**	Recognize effective sentences.
2	C	**0011**	Recognize unity, focus, and development in writing.
3	C	**0014**	Recognize Standard American English usage.
4	D	**0011**	Recognize unity, focus, and development in writing.
5	B	**0013**	Recognize effective sentences.
6	D	**0014**	Recognize Standard American English usage.
7	A	**0014**	Recognize Standard American English usage.
8	B	**0013**	Recognize effective sentences.
9	D	**0011**	Recognize unity, focus, and development in writing.
10	B	**0013**	Recognize effective sentences.
11	B	**0014**	Recognize Standard American English usage.
12	D	**0014**	Recognize Standard American English usage.
13	B	**0013**	Recognize effective sentences.
14	B	**0014**	Recognize Standard American English usage.
15	C	**0014**	Recognize Standard American English usage.
16	B	**0011**	Recognize unity, focus, and development in writing.
17	D	**0014**	Recognize Standard American English usage.
18	D	**0014**	Recognize Standard American English usage.
19	B	**0013**	Recognize effective sentences.
20	D	**0013**	Recognize effective sentences.

Question	Answer	Objective	
21	B	0012	Recognize effective organization in writing.
22	C	0011	Recognize unity, focus, and development in writing.
23	A	0014	Recognize Standard American English usage.
24	B	0011	Recognize unity, focus, and development in writing.
25	C	0013	Recognize effective sentences.
26	D	0014	Recognize Standard American English usage.
27	B	0013	Recognize effective sentences.
28	C	0013	Recognize effective sentences.
29	B	0011	Recognize unity, focus, and development in writing.
30	B	0013	Recognize effective sentences.
31	B	0014	Recognize Standard American English usage.
32	B	0011	Recognize unity, focus, and development in writing.
33	D	0011	Recognize unity, focus, and development in writing.
34	C	0014	Recognize Standard American English usage.
35	A	0013	Recognize effective sentences.
36	D	0012	Recognize effective organization in writing.
37	A	0011	Recognize unity, focus, and development in writing.
38	D	0014	Recognize Standard American English usage.
39	D	0013	Recognize effective sentences.
40	A	0014	Recognize Standard American English usage.
41	B	0014	Recognize Standard American English usage.
42	C	0013	Recognize effective sentences.

Practice Test 1, Part 3 Progress Chart

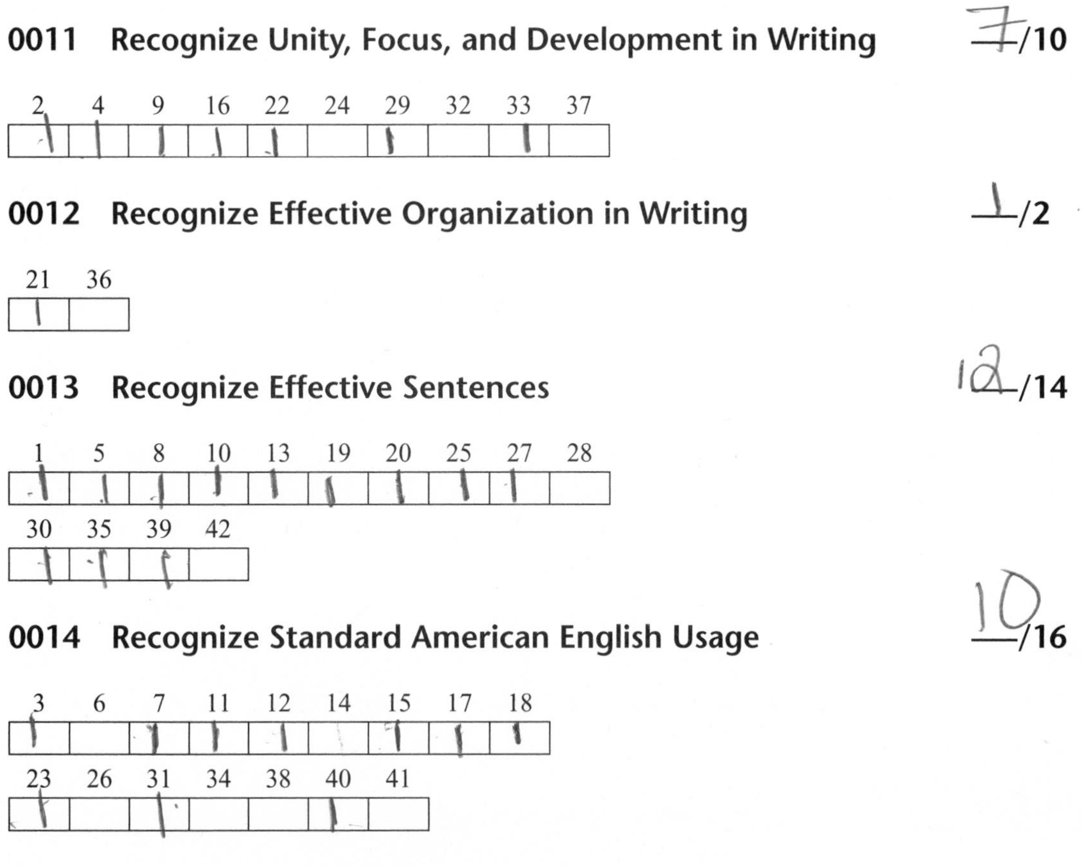

0011 Recognize Unity, Focus, and Development in Writing 7/10

2 4 9 16 22 24 29 32 33 37

0012 Recognize Effective Organization in Writing 1/2

21 36

0013 Recognize Effective Sentences 12/14

1 5 8 10 13 19 20 25 27 28

30 35 39 42

0014 Recognize Standard American English Usage 10/16

3 6 7 11 12 14 15 17 18

23 26 31 34 38 40 41

0015 Demonstrate the Ability to Prepare a Developed Composition on a Given Topic Using Language and Style Appropriate to a Given Audience, Purpose, and Occasion **—/Constructed Response**

Detailed Explanations for Practice Test 1, Part 3: Writing

1. **C**

Choice C is a prepositional phrase, "About 25,000 years ago," which is followed by a subordinate clause. This part should be linked to the previous sentence as it is integral to the migration of the Anasazi. Choices A, B, and D are all complete sentences.

2. **C**

Choice C has to do with the later history of the Mesa Verde area, after the Anasazi had abandoned it. Since this is so far removed chronologically, Part 7 should be deleted or further developed in a third paragraph. Choices A and B discuss the very early history of the Indians. Choice D follows the chronological time order from 500 C.E. and leads into a discussion of the height of the Anasazi civilization.

3. **C**

Choice C indicates the change of the incorrect word "general" to an adverb form "generally" to modify the verb phrase "are given." Choices A, B, and D would all change a correct comparison phrase to an incorrect one.

4. **D**

Choice D is a sentence that does not add to the focus of the second paragraph. Choice A would not continue the thesis statement introduced in Part 6. Choice B would remove a necessary piece of information that supports the thesis statement. Choice C would place the sentences out of a coherent order.

5. **B**

Choice B has two distinct sentences contained in a single sentence. A period should be placed between "segregation" and "another." Choices A, C, and D are all single ideas represented in single sentences.

6. **D**

Choice D contains a subordinate phrase that occurs at the beginning of the sentence and should be offset with a comma. Any comma added to the suggested places in Choices A, B, and C would create a comma splice.

7. **A**

Choice A will change the verb to "provide," which will make it agree with the subject of the sentence "study," which is singular. Choice B would make the verb an incorrect tense. Choice C would make the verb plural, which would create an error with the singular subject "optimist." Choice D would make the verb an incorrect tense.

8. **B**

Choice C changes the pronoun to a plural one, making it agree with the noun "people." Choices A, C, and D are all correct noun/pronoun agreement.

9. **D**

The thesis in this passage occurs at the beginning and is restated again at the end. Choices A, B, and C are supporting details for the thesis.

10. **B**

The sentence contains a restatement of "good friend" as "best friend" and is unnecessary. No redundancy occurs in Choices A, C, and D.

11. **B**

Part 3 contains the indirect pronoun "that" when referring to the noun "colonists." Standard American English requires the use of the pronoun "who" when referring to people. Choices A, C, and D contain standard pronoun use.

12. **D**

Choice D contains a comparison of only two subjects, the Oglethorpe statue and the Gordon monument, but the superlative case "most beautiful" is used rather than the correct comparative form "more beautiful." Choice A does not contain a comparative form. Choice C uses the superlative forms "most beautiful" and "most walkable" to compare Savannah to all other cities in America. Choice C uses the superlative form "most lavish" to compare Chippewa Square with all the other squares.

13. **B**

The adjective form "second" not the adverbial form "secondly" is appropriate here, since it modifies a noun, not a verb.

14. **B**

The opening verb phrase is a dangling modifier. "Prevention" is not "faced with" anything; Lincoln is. All the other choices are standard American English sentences.

15. **C**

"With the outbreak . . . " is a prepositional phrase that is stopped with a period. It has no subject and is not a standard American English sentence. All the rest are correct.

16. **B**

Part 6 begins with "Although"—used for mentioning the scientists' public statements—and refers to the "hazy" benefits derived from the study. Thus, the sentence has to deal with speculation about the "uncertain" benefits. Choice D fits in the paragraph's development fairly well, but it is not the best answer because the pejorative word "racist" would not generally be used to characterize someone.

17. **D**

Part 7 contains a comma splice. The sentence has two independent clauses, and they are not joined by a coordinating conjunction. They, therefore, must be separated by a semicolon, not a comma.

18. **D**

By convention in Standard American English, periods and commas are always placed inside of quotation marks except in certain technical copy.

19. **B**

The presence of "the" before "Westside's" means that the reference is *the* council, not to a council belonging to Westside. The other choices are all correct, and changing them would make them nonstandard.

20. **D**

The subject of the first clause is "each" which is singular, so the verb should be "has."

21. **B**

Choice A is wrong because it makes no sense within the sentence; the zoning regulations cannot be easy to change. Choice C makes no sense, its use of "them" is ambiguous—does it refer to the authors or the regulations? Choice D is wrong because, if the authors *said* the regulations would be hard to change, the word *apparently* earlier in the sentence would make no sense. Thus, Choice B is the best answer.

22. **C**

The writer's didactic summary of water's properties is the only perspective found in the passage. Choice A refers to only one property of water and Choice B is the subject of a single paragraph. An in-depth discussion of the physical states of liquids is not offered within the passage.

23. **A**

The contraction "it's" is used to replace "it is" and is not the possessive form of "it." Choice B would change the number of the verb to singular, and the subject "substances" is plural. Choices C and D would change the correct possessive form "its" to the incorrect contraction "it's."

24. **B**

The writer is stating that it is possible for substances to occur in two states: a solid and either a liquid or gas. Choice A infers that substances occur in all three states. Choice C infers that substances are found in only one state. Choice D infers that a single state can have all three properties.

25. **C**

Part 7 contains the double negative "hadn't no." It should read either "the crew had no hope…" or "the crew hadn't any hope…" Choices A, B, and D are all standard sentences.

26. **D**

"Union" should be capitalized because it refers to a part of the United States during the Civil War. You will note that earlier in the same sentence the word "Confederate" is capitalized.

27. **B**

It is necessary to change the verb phrase so it is parallel with the verb "withdrew." Choices A, C, and D would each change the tense of the sentence.

28. **C**

Choice C unnecessarily repeats the words "basis," "based," "founding," and "foundation." These forms need not be repeated and the sentence should be condensed. Choices A, B, and D are all well-worded sentences.

29. **B**

Choice B fits between sentence 4 and sentence 6. Sentence 4 mentions the topic of dissenting opinion, and sentence 6 elaborates by stating the position that English professors have always been outspoken. This idea is continued in sentence 7. Choice A changes the voice to plural first-person "we," which is out of place in this passage. Choice C is too casual. Choice D directly contradicts the thesis of the letter.

30. **B**

Choice B contains an inappropriate use of words. The contraction for "who is" should be used to make the sentence correct. The possessive "whose" is not correct in this context. Choice A correctly uses the comparative degree. Choice C correctly uses the superlative degree. Choice D does not make a needed change.

31. **B**

An adverb form is needed to modify the verb phrase "to be used." The word "specific" in its current form serves as an adjective. Choice A correctly uses the possessive form of "its." Choice C would change the adjective "available" which is describing the noun "scholarship," to an incorrect noun form "availability." Choice D would change the noun "generosity" to the incorrect adjective form "generous."

32. **B**

Choice B is a revision that makes clear that the scholarship was named for a woman who was both a principal and a graduate. Choice A does not provide clarity on whether the scholarship was named for one or two people. Choice C only changes the order of the second noun phrase. Choice D could be used, but is still somewhat unclear about the person's role.

33. **D**

Choice D is not congruent with the focus of the passage. While there is some mention of the generosity of the community, this doesn't promote the idea that it is a great place to raise a family. Choices A, B, and C all provide details that are related to the thesis of the passage.

34. **C**

Part 4 begins with a insubordinate clause, "Despite the fact that discrimination, alienation, and stigma of people with disabilities characterized the early history of China" and should be offset by a comma. Choices A, B, and D all contain standard comma use.

35. **A**

The preposition "to" is incorrect because the sentence is referring to "treatment" and "attitudes" of one person. Choice B would change the noun form "sympathy" to the incorrect adjective form "sympathetic." Choice C would incorrectly change tense. Choice D would create an error in direction of the government's attention.

36. **D**

The transitional word "However" should be used to compare and contrast different viewpoints. The transition that is needed is cause and effect because the cause is the increased attention by the government and the effect is the use of enrollment rate as a way to determine school district performance. Choice A does not contain transitional phrasing. Choice B uses the transitional word "Nevertheless" to point out a comparison between the sympathetic attitude and the continued poor lot of people with disabilities. Choice C does not contain a transition word.

37. **A**

Choice A contains the transition phrase "As such" which is referring to residential treatment and it further supports Part 5 which mentions both academic success and relationships with teachers. Choice B is a detail that is unnecessary and may not be true. Choice C draws the focus away from the characteristics of residential treatment and onto the student. Choice D could be expanded in another paragraph, but does not lend itself to further focus on the topic.

38. **D**

Semicolons are used to separate main clauses that can stand alone as sentences. The subordinate clause "but also to recidivism" cannot stand alone as a sentence and should be offset by a comma, not a semicolon. Choices A, B, and C all contain semicolons that are separating main clauses.

39. **D**

Choice D changes the plural verb "affords" to a correct singular verb "afford" so that it will agree with the singular subject "incarceration or admission." Choice A correctly uses the pronoun form. Choice B correctly uses the singular verb form. Choice C correctly uses the plural verb form.

40. **A**

It is not the workforce that is "for the better," but the situation for men. This is also supported by the rest of the evidence offered in the paragraph. The other sentences have their modifying phrases directly related to the idea they qualify.

41. **B**

The writer is comparing the situation before and after the appearance of women in management. That's only two things—therefore, the comparative form, not the superlative, is correct: greater. Choices A, C, and D are all incorrect responses: they have no comparative adjectives, just adverbs used as qualifiers, e.g., "overly." These are used in a standard way.

42. **C**

Part 10 is a run-on sentence, incorrectly punctuated with a comma after "families" instead of a period or a semicolon (i.e., it's a comma splice). The rest of the choices are all standard sentences.

Sample Response for Constructed-Response Question

Writing Sample with a Score of 4

The ability to search for resources for research papers at any time of the day or night makes the online environment very appealing. Not having to be restricted by library hours or reserving computer time in the labs means that an individual can complete assignments that require research whenever he or she feels like it. Being able to search for appropriate supporting documentation whether in one's pajamas or dressed for work is a very liberating idea and also provides the opportunity to more quickly locate needed citations through a variety of helpful search engines.

Unfortunately, much can be lost through this ease-of-use research modality. Libraries themselves in many ways promote a sense of academic integrity that cannot be experienced by simply searching for a topic online. When unsure of a topic or thesis, roaming through the stacks of journals contained within a library's research section often provide inspiration that cannot be found with the electronic version of a journal. Many times the topic selection and all supporting details can be located within a relatively short period of time if the existing catalogs are used. The librarians are real people who are familiar with the available resources and can point the would-be researcher in the right direction. This human touch can often provide clarification on topic selection as well as provide insight into resources that the researcher might not have considered.

Research in many ways is meant to be excavated, discovered, and illuminated through the skill of the researcher, not masticated, reconstituted and regurgitated through the wonders of modern technology. A research topic that allows the researcher to use only resources available online reduces input from other sources that may support or refute whatever the topic is that has been selected.

While this essay does not support the abandonment of the use of the internet to search for supporting documentation, it is more important to search all possible resources rather than just those available online.

Considering this practice of using online sources exclusively for research purposes brings to mind the question of whether libraries may eventually be abandoned. The peculiar experience afforded by going to a library to study or to conduct research cannot be replaced by sitting in front of a computer. The ease of skimming through a wide range of printed resources versus reading from a computer screen means that the individual can quickly decide if the resource is viable or not and move on without having to click one's way back to a list. Unfortunately, the library and librarian may indeed be a thing of the past. With the onset of strictly online coursework and degrees, more and more journals may be transposed to online availability and the days of searching through the stacks of journals in the library for a particular issue may be over.

Features of the Writing Sample Scoring 4

Appropriateness—The essay addressed the topic of whether it was better to use online sources exclusively or if going to the library to do a thorough search of all sources was more appropriate. While the topic paragraph did promote the idea that there were advantages to using online resources, the remainder of the essay was focused on how going to the library to find print sources added to the total research experience.

Focus and Organization—The essay followed the prompts as given and the opinion of the writer, that the sources found in print were important, was the evident focus of the essay. The organization went from refuting the advantages of using online sources to the less tangible advantages of studying and researching in a library.

Support—The writer provides a strong argument that all possible resources should be investigated and utilized, and not just those that may be found online. The writer also puts forth the point that by searching through the connections available in printed text, the researcher strengthens his or her own researching techniques, something that cannot be done as easily by using search engines.

Grammar, Sentence Structure, and Usage—The sentences contain appropriate grammar and are standardized and vary in form with the use of different phrases to begin sentences ("While this essay . . . ," "With the onset . . . ") to add interest. The use of vivid imagery (working in pajamas, roaming through journal stacks) also adds to the readability of the essay. The comparison of researching using the printed word as a discovery as compared to researching using the computer and simply eating is easy to follow.

Conventions—Spelling and punctuation are mostly standard throughout the essay. There are some lengthy sentences throughout the essay, but for the most part all sentences and transitions can be easily followed.

Writing Sample with a Score of 2 or 1

It is obvious to nearly everyone that nobody uses the library to do research papers any more and that most people preefer to just search for the topic online. The time it takes to gather up paper and pencil and drive to the library is a waist of time and most people end up just searching for stuff on the computer when they get to the library. Almost everything you need can be found through online sources and those journals that aren't online don't have to be used.

Using the research online makes it easier and quicker to do assignments. Having to find information in journals and magazines can be hard to do if you don't know how to use the card catalog and who wants to ask the librarian? Not me. It makes more sense to use the computer to find the research that is out there and put that in your paper. Using online resourses helps the writer use your time more efficienly and finish more quicker. Most topics have already been completely researched, so the technique of doing research is to find what has already been done and paraphrase it. There is plenty of research out there to support whatever topic you want to write about, so going to the library to try and find more just doesn't make any sense to me.

Using online sources esclusively from here on out to write about whatever topic is assigned is the way of the future and soon everything will be online so there's no real need to figure out how to use the library and the Dewey decimal system and all that other stuff anyway. There's no reason to ever bother to go to the library to write a research paper again.

Features of the Writing Sample Scoring 2 or 1

Appropriateness—The writer uses only one argument, that everything necessary to write a research paper is online. This argument fails to properly embrace the topic, which is the advantages and disadvantages of the process of online research versus using the printed text. The language used is also not appropriate for the audience, an English instructor, as it is too informal. There are also examples of colloquialisms ("from here on out," "all that stuff") that are not appropriate for a formal paper.

Focus and Organization—The thesis statement is that all resources to complete research are easily found online, but there is no clarity about what that means or how that comes about. The paragraphs and sentences within the paragraphs do restate this single thesis, but the thesis itself is unclear and unfounded.

Support—There is no reasoned support or specific examples given to develop the thesis. The support that is given, that the existing information about any given topic can be taken and paraphrased and so there is no need for any input from the researcher, is nonsensical and doesn't portray a mature attitude toward the process of conducting research.

Grammar, Sentence Structure, and Usage—Sentence 5 in the second paragraph has an incorrect use of comparison ("more quicker" instead of "more quickly") and Sentence 3, which answers the question at the end of Sentence 2, is a fragment. The first sentence of the third paragraph is a run-on sentence even with the use of "and." There are several instances of switching from point of view (Sentence 5 switches from the third person "the writer" to second person "your.") and the use of first and second persons throughout the essays adds to the informal tone.

Conventions—Spelling is generally badly attempted. This appears to be an obvious lack of care on the part of the test-taker. Samples of misspelling would be: "preefer" for "prefer;" "resourses" for "resources;" "waist" for "waste;" "efficienly" for "efficiently;" "esclusively" for "exclusively."

Practice Test 2
Part 1: Reading

GACE Basic Skills

This test is also on CD-ROM in our special interactive TestWare® for the GACE Basic Skills. It is highly recommended that you first take this exam on computer. You will then have the additional study features and benefits of enforced timed conditions and instantaneous, accurate scoring. See page 6 for instructions on how to get the most out of REA's TestWare®.

ANSWER SHEET
PRACTICE TEST 2, PART 1: READING

1 _____	11 _____	22 _____	33 _____
2 _____	12 _____	23 _____	34 _____
3 _____	13 _____	24 _____	35 _____
4 _____	14 _____	25 _____	36 _____
5 _____	15 _____	26 _____	37 _____
6 _____	16 _____	27 _____	38 _____
7 _____	17 _____	28 _____	39 _____
8 _____	18 _____	29 _____	40 _____
9 _____	19 _____	30 _____	41 _____
10 _____	20 _____	31 _____	42 _____
	21 _____	32 _____	

PRACTICE TEST 2, PART 1: READING

Part 1: **Reading**
42 questions

Read the passage below; then answer the three questions that follow.

In view of the current emphasis on literature-based reading instruction, a greater understanding by teachers of variance in cultural, language, and story components should assist in narrowing the gap between reader and text and improve reading comprehension. Classroom teachers should begin with students' meaning and intentions about stories before moving students to the commonalities of story meaning based on common background and culture. With teacher guidance, students should develop a fuller understanding of how complex narratives are when they are writing stories as well as when they are reading stories.

1. Which of the following is the intended audience for the passage?

   A. Teachers using literature-based curriculum
   B. Professors teaching a literature course
   C. Parents concerned about their child's comprehension of books
   D. Teacher educators teaching reading methods course

2. Which of the following is the most complete and accurate definition of the term variance as used in the passage?

   A. change
   B. fluctuations
   C. diversity
   D. deviation

3. The passage supports a concept of meaning primarily residing in

   A. culture, language, and story components.
   B. comprehension.
   C. students' stories only.
   D. students and narratives.

Read the passage below; then answer the four questions that follow.

As noted by Favat in 1977, the study of children's stories has been an ongoing concern of linguists, anthropologists, and psychologists. The past decade has witnessed a surge of interest in children's stories from researchers in these and other disciplines. The use of narratives for reading and reading instruction has been commonly accepted by the educational community. The notion that narrative is highly structured and that children's sense of narrative structure is more highly developed than expository structure has been proposed by some researchers.

Early studies of children's stories followed two approaches for story analysis: The analysis of story content or the analysis of story structure. Story content analysis has centered primarily on examining motivational and psychodynamic aspects of story characters as noted in the works of Erikson and Pitcher and Prelinger in 1963 and Ames in 1966. These studies have noted that themes or topics predominate and the themes change with age.

Early research on story structure focused on formal models of structure, such as story grammar and story schemata. These models specified basic story elements and formed sets of rules similar to sentences grammar for ordering the elements.

The importance or centrality of narrative in a child's development of communicative ability has been proposed by Halliday (1976) and Hymes (1975). Thus, the importance of narrative for language communicative ability and for reading and reading instruction has been well documented. However, the question still remains about how these literacy abilities interest and lead to conventional reading.

4. This passage is most probably directed at which of the following audiences?

   A. reading educators

   B. linguists

   C. psychologists

   D. reading researchers

5. According to the passage, future research should address

   A. how story structure and story schema interact with comprehension.

   B. how children's use and understanding of narrative interacts and leads to conventional reading.

   C. how story content interacts with story comprehension.

   D. how narrative text structure differs from expository text structure.

6. The major distinction between story content and story structure is that

   A. story content focuses on motivational aspects whereas story structure focuses on rules similar to sentence grammar.

   B. story content focuses on psychodynamic aspects whereas story structure focuses on formal structural models.

   C. story content and story structure essentially refer to the same concepts.

   D. story content focuses primarily on characters whereas story structure focuses on story grammar and schemata.

7. Which of the following is the most complete and accurate definition of the term surge as used in the first paragraph?

   A. a heavy swell

   B. a sudden rise

   C. a sudden increase

   D. a sudden rush

Read the passage below; then answer the four questions that follow.

Throughout its history, the American school system has often been the target of demands that it change to meet the social priorities of the times. This theme has been traced to the following significant occurrences in education: Benjamin Franklin's advocacy in 1749 for a more useful type of education; Horace Mann's zealous proposals in the 1830s espousing the tax supported public school; John Dewey's early twentieth century attack on traditional schools for not developing the child effectively for his or her role in society; the post-Sputnik pressure for academic rigor; the prolific criticism and accountability pressures of the 1970s; and the ensuing disillusionment and continued criticism of school through the last decade of the twentieth century. Indeed, the waves of criticism about American education have reflected currents of social dissatisfaction for any given period of this country's history.

As dynamics of change in the social order result in demands for change in the American educational system, so in turn insistence has developed for revision of teacher education (witness the more recent Holmes report [1986]). Historically, the education of American teachers has reflected evolving attitudes about public education. With slight modifications, the teachers' education pattern established following the demise of the normal school during the early 1900s has persisted in most teacher preparation programs. The pattern has been one requiring certain academic and professional (educational) courses often resulting in teachers prone to teach as they had been taught.

8. The author of this passage would probably agree with which of the following statements?

   A. Social dissatisfaction should drive change in the American school systems.

   B. Schools were eliminated.

   C. Critics of American education reflect vested interests.

   D. Teachers' teaching methods tend to reflect what they have learned in their academic and professional courses.

9. The evolving attitudes about public schools are

   A. stated.

   B. unstated.

   C. alluded.

   D. unwarranted.

10. One possible sequence of significant occurrences in education noted in the passage is

    A. Mann's tax-supported public school, post-Sputnik pressures for academic rigor, and the Holmes' report.

    B. Franklin's more useful type of education, Dewey's educating children for their role in society, and Mann's tax supported public schools.

    C. Franklin's more useful type of education, the Holmes' report, and accountability pressures of the 1970s.

    D. Mann's tax-supported public schools, accountability pressures of the 1970s, and the post-Sputnik pressures for academic rigor.

11. Which of the following statements most obviously implies dissatisfaction with the preparation of teachers in the United States?

    A. Demands for change in the American education system led to the insistence for revision of teacher education programs.

    B. The pattern of teacher education requires certain academic and professional education courses.

    C. The education of U.S. teachers has reflected evolving attitudes about public education.

    D. Teacher education has changed very little since the decline of the normal school.

Read the passage below; then answer the four questions that follow.

Hawk on a Freshly Plowed Field

My Lord of the Field, proudly perched on the sod,
You eye with disdain
And mutter with wings
As steadily each furrow I tractor-plod.
"Intruder!" You glare, firmly standing your ground,
Proclaim this fief yours
By Nature so willed—
Yet bound to the air on my very next round.
You hover and soar, skimming close by the earth,
Distract me from work
To brood there with you
Of changes that Man wrought your land—for his worth.
In medieval days, lords were god over all:
Their word was the law.
Yet here is this hawk
A ruler displaced—Man and Season forestall.
My Lord of the Field, from sight you have flown.
For purpose untold,
When brave, you return
And perch once again, still liege-lord—but Alone.

Jacqueline K. Hultquist (1952)

12. Which of the following is the most complete and accurate definition of the term liege-lord as used in the passage?

    A. monarch

    B. king

    C. sovereign

    D. master

13. Which of the following best describes the author's attitude toward the hawk?

    A. Romantic
    B. Pensive
    C. Intimidating
    D. Fearful

14. Which of the following groups of words about the hawk carry human qualities?

    A. Mutter, brood, and ruler
    B. Brave, disdain, and perch
    C. Brave, brood, and distract
    D. Mutter, disdain, and skimming

15. Which of the following is the most complete and accurate definition of the term medieval as used in the passage?

    A. antiquated
    B. feudal
    C. old
    D. antediluvian

Read the passage below; then answer the three questions that follow.

Representatives of the world's seven richest and most industrialized nations held a three-day economic summit in London on July 14–16, 1991. On the second day of the summit, Mikhail Gorbachev, of the Soviet Union, who appealed for help, was offered support by the seven leaders for his economic reforms and his "new thinking" regarding political reforms. However, because the allies were split on giving a big aid package to Gorbachev, the seven leaders decided to provide help in the form of technical assistance in fields such as banking and energy, rather than in hard cash.

16. Which of the following statements bests synthesizes what the passage is about?

    A. A seven-nation economic summit was held in London in July 1991.

    B. Mikhail Gorbachev appealed for help and the seven leaders agreed to support his economic reforms.

    C. At a three-day economic summit held in London in July 1991, leaders of the world's seven richest and most industrialized nations agreed to provide technical assistance to Gorbachev.

    D. Representatives of the world's seven most industrialized nations, at a summit conference in London, were split on giving Gorbachev assistance in the form of hard cash.

17. The passage implies that

    A. under the leadership of Gorbachev, the Soviet Union was faced with a financial crisis.

    B. Gorbachev's "new thinking" on democratic reforms needed support from the seven nations meeting in London.

    C. the seven leaders meeting in London were split on giving Gorbachev economic and political support.

    D. with the support of political and economic reforms along with provisions for technical assistance from the seven nations that met in London, the Soviet Union, under the leadership of Gorbachev, would be able to achieve political and economic stability.

18. The passage suggests that technical assistance would be provided to the Soviet Union

    A. only in the fields of banking and energy.

    B. in the fields of banking and energy and possibly other fields.

    C. by the U.S. in the fields of banking and energy.

    D. by all seven nations—U.S., Great Britain, France, Germany, Italy, Canada, and Japan.

Read the passage below; then answer the three questions that follow.

A follow-up survey of the 2000 census showed an estimated undercount of 5.2 million people nationwide. This "undercount" was greatest in California, where approximately 1.1 million people were not recorded. This estimated undercount was based on a post-census survey of 171,390 households nationwide. Failure to achieve an accurate count would affect federal funding and political representation. If the higher numbers were used, California would gain eight congressional seats instead of seven and about $1 billion in federal funds. In July 2001, however, the Commerce Secretary decided to stick to the original figures of the 2000 census.

19. Which of the following statements gives the main idea of the passage you just read?

    A. California would have gained an additional congressional seat and more federal money if the 1.1 million people undercounted in the census were included.

    B. An undercount in the census, if not considered, would be a disadvantage to any state.

    C. A post-census survey would be necessary to get to a more accurate population figure for the states.

    D. California suffered the most due to the 1.1 million undercount in the 2000 census.

20. If the 1.1 million undercount was considered for California,

    A. it would settle any political dispute arising from the undercount.

    B. it would give California eight congressional seats and one billion dollars in federal funds.

    C. it would discourage the practice of a post-census survey.

    D. it would reverse the decision made by the Commerce Secretary.

21. What would it mean for California if the original figures of the 2000 census were to remain the same?

A. No additional federal funding would be given.

B. There would be no additional political representation.

C. The amount of federal funding and number of congressional seats would remain the same.

D. The results of the follow-up survey of the 2000 census would be meaningless.

Read the passage below; then answer the four questions that follow.

A toxic spill took place on the upper Sacramento River in California when a slow-moving Southern Pacific train derailed north of the town of Dunsmuir. A tank car containing 19,500 gallons of pesticide broke open and spilled into the river. This pesticide is used to kill soil pests. Since the spill, thousands of trout and other fish were poisoned along a 45-mile stretch of a river. In addition, 190 people were treated at a local hospital for respiratory and related illnesses. Residents along the river were warned to stay away from the tainted water. Once this water reached Lake Shasta, a source of water for millions of Californians, samples were taken to assess the quality of the water.

22. Which of the following statements conveys the message in the passage?

A. Pesticides intended to kill pests can be dangerous to all living things.

B. Water uncontaminated by pesticides is safe to drink.

C. Take every precaution not to come in contact with pesticide-infected water.

D. Pesticides that killed thousands of trout and other fish would not necessarily kill human beings.

23. The Southern Pacific train that derailed was

    A. a passenger train.
    B. a freight train.
    C. a freight and passenger train.
    D. a special train.

24. The most serious problem that could have come about as a result of the toxic spill was

    A. possible movement of residents in Dunsmuir to another place of residence.
    B. the negative effects on those whose livelihood depended on the fishing industry.
    C. when the tainted water reached Lake Shasta, which is a source of water supply for millions of Californians.
    D. the uncertain length of time it would take to make the tainted water safe and healthy again.

25. This unfortunate incident of a toxic spill resulting from a train derailment implies

    A. that there is the need for more environmental protection.
    B. that other means for transporting pesticides need to be considered.
    C. that there should be an investigation as to the cause of the train derailment and that effective measures to prevent its occurrence again should be applied.
    D. that there should be research on how to expedite making infected water safe and healthy again.

Read the passage below; then answer the three questions that follow.

Labor Day, a national holiday observed in the United States, is really a day we should remember to give thanks to the labor unions. In the days before the unions became effective, a holiday meant a day off, but also the loss of a day's pay to working people. It was not until World War II that unions succeeded, through negotiations with the federal government, in making paid holidays a common practice.

26. The main idea in the passage you just read is

    A. the role labor unions played in employer-employee relations.

    B. that Labor Day as a national holiday in the U.S.

    C. the role labor unions played in effecting paid holidays.

    D. the dispute between granting paid and unpaid holidays.

27. The passage implies that before World War II

    A. a holiday gave working people a chance to rest from work.

    B. Labor Day meant losing a day's pay.

    C. a holiday was a day to make up for upon returning to work.

    D. labor unions were ineffective.

28. As a national holiday, Labor Day should really be a day to remember and be thankful for

    A. working people.

    B. paid holidays.

    C. labor unions.

    D. a free day.

Read the passage below; then answer the three questions that follow.

Ash from Mt. Pinatubo in the Philippines has been found to contain gold and other precious metals. However, officials warned against any hopes of a new "gold rush." They found gold content of only 20 parts per billion, which is far below commercial levels. Other metals found were chromium, copper, and lithium.

29. The passage indicates

    A. the possibility of existing gold mines beneath Mt. Pinatubo.

    B. the need for further exploration of what else lies beneath the volcano.

    C. that other active volcanoes might be worth exploring as possible gold resources.

    D. that the gold content of the ash from Mt. Pinatubo does not warrant a commercial level.

30. Which of the following makes a good title for the passage you just read?

    A. A New Gold Rush

    B. Ash Content from Mt. Pinatubo

    C. A Philippine Discovery

    D. Precious Metals

31. What might be a possible research project resulting from the ash contents finding of Mt. Pinatubo?

    A. Research on the ash content from the eruption of Mt. Fujiyama in Japan

    B. Potential market value of the gold and other metal contents in the volcanic ash from Mt. Pinatubo

    C. Further excavation into possible gold underneath Mt. Pinatubo

    D. Research on what lies underneath active volcanoes

Read the passage below; then answer the four questions that follow.

Lead poisoning is considered by health authorities to be the most common and devastating environmental disease of young children. According to studies made, it affects 15% to 20% of urban children and from 50% to 75% of inner-city, poor children. As a result of a legal settlement, all of California's medical-eligible children, ages one through five, will now be routinely screened annually for lead poisoning. Experts estimate that more than 50,000 cases will be detected in California because of the newly mandated tests. This will halt at an early stage a disease that leads to learning disabilities and life-threatening disorders.

32. Lead poisoning among young children, if not detected early, can lead to

    A. physical disabilities.

    B. mental disabilities.

    C. learning disabilities.

    D. death.

33. The mandate to screen all young children for lead poisoning is required of

    A. all young children in California.

    B. all children with learning disabilities.

    C. all medical-eligible children, ages one through five, in California.

    D. all school-age children in California.

34. According to findings, more cases of lead poisoning are found among

    A. urban children.

    B. inner-city, poor children.

    C. immigrant children.

    D. children in rural areas.

35. The implication of this mandate in California regarding lead poisoning is that

    A. non-eligible children will not be screened.
    B. children older than five years will not be screened.
    C. middle-class children will not be screened.
    D. thousands of young children in California will remain at risk for lead poisoning.

Read the passage below; then answer the three questions that follow.

The U.S. Postal Service issued a 50-cent stamp in Anchorage, Alaska, on October 12, 1991, to commemorate the 500th anniversary of the arrival of the Italian explorer Christopher Columbus in the New World. The stamp series showed the pre-Columbian voyages of discovery. The stamp depicts how America may have appeared to Asians crossing the Bering Strait.

36. Which of the following makes an appropriate title for the passage?

    A. The Discovery of the Americas
    B. The 500th Anniversary of the Discovery of America
    C. The Significance of the Bering Strait
    D. A New Commemorative U.S. Postal Stamp

37. The passage implies that

    A. historical facts need to be verified.
    B. Christopher Columbus was not the first to arrive in the New World.
    C. Native Americans came from Asia.
    D. history books need to be rewritten.

38. Which of the following would you consider as the most historically significant?

    A. Asians crossed over the Bering Strait to the New World before Columbus came.

    B. It has been 500 years since Christopher Columbus arrived in the New World.

    C. A tribute to Christopher Columbus was held on October 12, 1991.

    D. There were other voyages undertaken before Christopher Columbus'.

Read the passage below; then answer the four questions that follow.

Assignment: Research for a White Paper Proposing U.S. Foreign Policy

Imagine you are in charge (or assigned to) a foreign policy desk in the U.S. Department of State. First, select one of the following regions (descriptors are merely suggestions):

Western Europe—A Changing Alliance
Eastern Europe—Out from Behind the Iron Curtain
The Middle East—Still an Enigma
Africa—Rising Expectations in the Postwar Continent
South and Southeast Asia—Unrest in Far Away Places
The Far East—Alienation and Alliance
The Western Hemisphere—Neighbors; Pro and Con

After selecting one of the regions above, conduct research and prepare a White Paper for the area that will indicate:

1. a General Policy Statement toward the nations of that region;

2. a statement as to how World War II set the stage for that policy;

3. a summary of the major events since 1945 in that region which have affected U.S. foreign policy; and

4. a list of suggested problems and/or possibilities for near-future interactions of that region and the U.S.

39. In order to complete this assignment, it is necessary to

    A. select a region and use the descriptor given with that region before conducting research.

    B. select a region and conduct research to prepare the White Paper.

    C. conduct research and choose a region in the world of your choice before writing the White Paper.

    D. interview someone familiar with the history of the region before conducting research.

40. Which of the following is the most complete and accurate definition of the term *enigma* as used in the passage?

    A. Riddle

    B. Puzzle

    C. Secret

    D. Mystery

41. Which of the following is the most appropriate secondary school audience for the assignment?

    A. Students in a World Geography class

    B. Students in a World History class

    C. Students in an Economics class

    D. Students in an American Government class

42. Which of the following statements is not part of the directions provided?

    A. The White Paper should include a General Policy Statement toward the nations of the region selected.

    B. The White Paper should include one of the seven regions that are listed.

    C. If the Middle East is chosen, the descriptor "Still an Enigma" must be used.

    D. The White Paper must indicate a statement as to how World War II set the stage for the policy.

ANSWER KEY – READING PRACTICE TEST 2

Question	Answer	Objective	
1	A	**0002**	Identify a writer's purpose and point of view.
2	C	**0006**	Determine the meaning of words and phrases.
3	D	**0004**	Use critical reasoning skills to evaluate written material.
4	D	**0002**	Identify a writer's purpose and point of view.
5	B	**0004**	Use critical reasoning skills to evaluate written material.
6	B	**0003**	Analyze the relationship among ideas in written material.
7	C	**0006**	Determine the meaning of words and phrases.
8	D	**0002**	Identify a writer's purpose and point of view.
9	B	**0004**	Use critical reasoning skills to evaluate written material.
10	A	**0003**	Analyze the relationship among ideas in written material.
11	D	**0004**	Use critical reasoning skills to evaluate written material.
12	D	**0006**	Determine the meaning of words and phrases.
13	B	**0002**	Identify a writer's purpose and point of view.
14	A	**0006**	Determine the meaning of words and phrases.
15	B	**0006**	Determine the meaning of words and phrases.
16	C	**0001**	Understand the main idea and supporting details in written material.
17	D	**0003**	Analyze the relationship among ideas in written material.
18	B	**0004**	Use critical reasoning skills to evaluate written material.

Question	Answer	Objective	
19	A	**0001**	Understand the main idea and supporting details in written material.
20	B	**0001**	Understand the main idea and supporting details in written material.
21	C	**0004**	Use critical reasoning skills to evaluate written material.
22	C	**0001**	Understand the main idea and supporting details in written material.
23	B	**0004**	Use critical reasoning skills to evaluate written material.
24	C	**0003**	Analyze the relationship among ideas in written material.
25	C	**0003**	Analyze the relationship among ideas in written material.
26	C	**0001**	Understand the main idea and supporting details in written material.
27	B	**0003**	Analyze the relationship among ideas in written material.
28	C	**0004**	Use critical reasoning skills to evaluate written material.
29	D	**0004**	Use critical reasoning skills to evaluate written material.
30	B	**0001**	Understand the main idea and supporting details in written material.
31	B	**0004**	Use critical reasoning skills to evaluate written material.
32	D	**0003**	Analyze the relationship among ideas in written material.
33	C	**0004**	Use critical reasoning skills to evaluate written material.
34	B	**0004**	Use critical reasoning skills to evaluate written material.

Question	Answer	Objective	
35	D	**0003**	Analyze the relationship among ideas in written material.
36	D	**0001**	Understand the main idea and supporting details in written material.
37	B	**0003**	Analyze the relationship among ideas in written material.
38	A	**0004**	Use critical reasoning skills to evaluate written material.
39	B	**0005**	Use reading strategies to comprehend written materials.
40	B	**0006**	Determine the meaning of words and phrases.
41	D	**0002**	Identify a writer's purpose and point of view.
42	C	**0005**	Use reading strategies to comprehend written materials.

Practice Test 2, Part 1 Progress Chart

0001 Understand the Main Idea and Supporting Details in Written Material —/7

16	19	20	22	26	30	36

0002 Identify a Writer's Purpose and Point of View —/5

1	4	8	13	41

0003 Analyze the Relationship Among Ideas in Written Material —/9

6	10	17	24	25	27	32	35	37

0004 Use Critical Reasoning Skills to Evaluate Written Material —/13

3	5	9	11	18	21	23	28	29

31	33	34	38

0005 Use Reading Strategies to Comprehend Written Materials —/2

39	42

0006 Determine the Meaning of Words and Phrases —/6

2	7	12	14	15	40

Detailed Explanations for Practice Test 2, Part 1: Reading

1. **A**

Although audiences in choices B, C, and D may benefit from the information provided in the passage, the passage explicitly states that a greater understanding of the information in the passage should assist teachers—choice A.

2. **C**

Each of the choices is a definition of variance. However, for this passage, choice C is the most appropriate.

3. **D**

Although meaning is found in the components of each choice, the passage states that we should begin with students' meaning before moving to the commonalities of story meaning—choice D.

4. **D**

As the passage presents information by various researchers on children's stories, the passage ends with an unanswered question that still needs to be addressed by reading researchers as provided in choice D.

5. **B**

Although more information may be needed about story content and story structure as indicated in choices A, C, and D, the main question that remains to be answered is choice B.

6. **B**

Each choice provides partially correct information about story content and story structure; choice B provides the most complete response.

7. **C**

Each choice is a possible definition. However, choice C is most appropriate as there was an increased interest by researchers in these and other areas even though it has been an ongoing concern of some researchers.

8. **D**

Choice B is not supported by the passage. Choices A and C go beyond the passage. The last sentence states, "The pattern … resulting in teachers prone to teach as they had been taught"—thus choice D.

9. **B**

The other choices, A, C, and D, are not supported by the passage. Although the passage mentions that teacher education has reflected evolving attitudes about education, the attitudes are not spelled out—choice B.

10. **A**

Only choice A has the correct sequence; the other sequences are incorrect.

11. **D**

Choices A, B, and C are statements about education in general, teacher education, and teachers. Choice D's statement that teacher education has changed very little implies that this lack of change could be a source of dissatisfaction.

12. **D**

Choices A, B, and C suggest rights either by heredity or supreme authority. The hyphenated term *liege-lord* connotes both entitled rights and power to command respect. Thus choice D, "master" (one who assumes authority and property rights through ability and power to control), best represents the hawk.

13. **B**

Choices C and D are not supported by the passage. Choice A represents a possible conclusion, but choice B suggests real thought about the hawk.

14. **A**

Each of the other choices contains a term that does not refer to human qualities. The other qualities may refer to the hawk, e.g., *perch*, or to the author of the passage, e.g., disdain.

15. **B**

Choice D is incorrect because of definition. Choices A and C are possible definitions, but *feudal* most clearly denotes an association to the Middle Ages.

16. **C**

The question asks for the best synthesis of the passage and C is the best and most complete answer. Choices A, B, and D are not as complete. For example, A left out the duration of the conference, B left out both the duration of the conference and the number of the nations represented at the summit, and D left out the number of nations represented and support for Gorbachev's "new thinking."

17. **D**

Of the choices provided, D gives the most logical and sound implication of the passage. A falls short of the capabilities of Gorbachev's leadership; in B the "new thinking" referred to already had the support of the seven leaders at the summit; and C is a rather sweeping, unfair statement.

18. **B**

The mention of banking and energy does not rule out technical assistance in other fields, hence, B is the correct answer. Choice A limited the assistance to only the fields of banking and energy; in C the statement is only partly true—the U.S. is not alone in providing support; and in D technical assistance could likewise come from other nations outside of the seven.

19. **A**

The question asks for the main idea in the passage and A gives the best and complete main idea. Choices B and C are generalizations derived from the passage and D, while it is true and specific to the passage, is stated in the negative.

20. **B**

B gives the most specific consequence for California. The other choices, while all plausible or possible answers, do not get to the root of the issue specific to California.

21. **C**

Based on the passage read, the answer to this question is C—two things are mentioned that could affect California and these are federal funding and the number of congressional seats. While A and B are correct, they are incomplete. Choice D is a consequential generalization that is correct but lacks the preciseness of C.

22. **C**

The question asks for the "message" conveyed in the passage. Choice C is the correct answer, as it gives a warning. In choice A, pesticides cannot necessarily be dangerous to all living things—some are good for the protection of plants, for example; in B, water can be contaminated by something other than pesticides; and the statement in choice D may be true, but it is certainly not the best answer.

23. **B**

The train is definitely a freight train; hence, B is the correct answer. In A, if it were a passenger train, hundreds would have been killed; in C, according to the clues, the choices here don't apply; and in D, the answer used "special train" but could have appropriately used "freight train" instead.

24. **C**

The question here asks for the most "serious problem" that could have come about; so, of all the choices, C provides the most serious problem resulting from the pesticide spill for Californians. Choices A, B, and D are not life-threatening; C is.

25. **C**

C is the most logical and straightforward answer. C prioritizes which action should be taken first, and is therefore the correct answer. While the choices in A, B, and D are sound answers, they don't list the most urgent thing to do.

26. **C**

The correct answer here is C because this choice synthesizes the key or main idea in the passage. The other choices, while partly true, don't give the main idea.

27. **B**

Before World War II, during the depression years, one can easily presume that people were more practical or money minded; hence, Labor Day, as celebrated then, could mean the loss of a day's pay for working people. Thus, B is the correct answer. While choices A, C, and D are also possible answers, they don't get to the root of the issue.

28. **C**

Explicitly given in the passage is C, the correct answer. Choices A, B, and D, while they may all be true and correct, are not what is precisely given in the passage.

29. **D**

The gold content found in the volcanic ash from Mt. Pinatubo could easily stir or trigger a "gold rush." However, people are warned that the gold content found is not at a "commercial level." Hence, D is the correct answer. The other choices provided are all mere speculations.

30. **B**

Choice B is the most appropriate answer—it also synthesizes the content of the reading passage; hence, it is the correct answer. Choice A is incorrect. Choices C and D are somewhat applicable as titles but do not really synthesize the main idea of the passage as choice B.

31. **B**

If priorities have to be established to determine the most immediate research needed on the ash content from Mt. Pinatubo, choice B will have to be the most logical choice because there is already some data with which to work. Other research possibilities such as those in choices A, C, and D would have to come later.

32. **D**

All the choices in this question are possible answers; however, since the question asks what lead poisoning, if not detected early, "can lead to," it calls for the ultimate consequence. Hence, D is the correct answer inasmuch as the passage states "life-threatening disorders" as among the possible consequences.

33. **C**

The correct answer to this question is choice C—it gives the complete and precise category. Other choices are incomplete—A left out the age group and the medical eligibility; B is narrowed down and all-inclusive of "children with learning disabilities;" and choice D is incorrect.

34. **B**

As indicated by figures in the passage, the correct answer is B. Other choices A, C, and D are obviously incorrect. This is an example of a question in which the incorrect choices are not possible answers. The correct answer is derived from the figures provided in the passage.

35. **D**

The implications provided in choices A through D are correct. However, each of the implications for A through C is narrowed down to only one specific category of children—not any one is inclusive of all that needs to be addressed. Hence, D is the best answer because it addresses the thousands who will not be screened, which include those in choices A through C.

36. **D**

A title is supposed to synthesize the main idea and D does. Choice A leaves out the main idea of a commemorative stamp; choice B is incorrect because it implies Columbus discovered the Americas; choice C is not the main idea of the passage.

37. **B**

The underlying fact behind the passage is heavily implied; therefore, B is the correct answer. Choice A, while true, is a generalized implication, not addressing the specific issue; choice C is debatable; choice D, like A, is also a generalized implication.

38. **A**

Of the choices given, A is the most historically significant, and, therefore, the correct answer. Choice B is significant but leaves out the fact that Columbus was not the first to arrive in the New World, the main point in the passage; choice C is a mere commemoration day; and choice D is not specific enough as an historically significant fact.

39. **B**

B is the most appropriate choice. A is incorrect because the descriptors are only suggestions. Likewise, C is incorrect because the list of regions is given. There are no directions that state someone must be interviewed; hence, D is also not a correct answer.

40. **B**

Although each definition appears appropriate, choices A, C, and D assume that a solution is known, or had been known at one time, and could be solved. Choice B suggests a situation that is intricate enough to perplex the mind. Choice B is the most appropriate for this passage, as one definition of *enigma* is "an inexplicable situation."

41. **D**

Although choices A, B, and C may touch on such a topic, the roles and functions of governmental offices and departments are generally addressed in an American Government class. Thus, choice D is correct.

42. **C**

C is not part of the directions. "Still an Enigma" is suggested, but not required. The other choices, A, B, and D are part of the directions.

Practice Test 2
Part 2: Mathematics

GACE Basic Skills

This test is also on CD-ROM in our special interactive TestWare® for the GACE Basic Skills. It is highly recommended that you first take this exam on computer. You will then have the additional study features and benefits of enforced timed conditions and instantaneous, accurate scoring. See page 6 for instructions on how to get the most out of REA's TestWare®.

ANSWER SHEET
PRACTICE TEST 2, PART 2: MATHEMATICS

1 _____	13 _____	25 _____	37 _____
2 _____	14 _____	26 _____	38 _____
3 _____	15 _____	27 _____	39 _____
4 _____	16 _____	28 _____	40 _____
5 _____	17 _____	29 _____	41 _____
6 _____	18 _____	30 _____	42 _____
7 _____	19 _____	31 _____	43 _____
8 _____	20 _____	32 _____	44 _____
9 _____	21 _____	33 _____	45 _____
10 _____	22 _____	34 _____	46 _____
11 _____	23 _____	35 _____	47 _____
12 _____	24 _____	36 _____	48 _____

DEFINITIONS AND FORMULAS

Measurement

U.S. Standard Metric

Distance
1 inch = 2.54 centimeters
12 inches = 1 foot
3 feet = 1 yard
5280 feet = 1 mile
1 centimeter = 10 millimeters
1 meter = 100 centimeters
1 kilometer = 1000 meters

Volume (liquid)
1 quart = 32 ounces
1 quart ≈ 0.95 liters
1 gallon = 4 quarts
1 liter = 1000 milliliters
1 cubic centimeter = 1 milliliter

Mass
1 pound = 16 ounces
1 ton = 2000 pounds
2.2 pounds ≈ 1 kilogram
1 gram = 1000 milligrams
1 kilogram = 1000 grams

Time
1 minute = 60 seconds
1 hour = 60 minutes
1 day = 24 hours
1 year = 365 days
1 year = 52 weeks

Definitions

$=$	equal to
$>$	greater than
$<$	less than
$\geq$	greater than or equal to
$\leq$	less than or equal to
π	≈ 3.14
$\angle$	angle
$m\angle$	measure of angle
∟	right angle
$\overline{AB}$	line segment
AB	length of line segment AB
$\angle ABC$	angle with vertex B formed by rays BA and BC

Formulas

Square
Area = s^2
Perimeter = $4s$

Rectangle
Area = bw
Perimeter = $2b + 2w$

Triangle
Area = $\frac{1}{2}bh$
Sum of the interior angles = 180°

Right triangle
Pythagorean formula: $c^2 = a^2 + b^2$

Circle
Area = πr^2
Circumference = $2\pi r$
Diameter = $2r$

Right cylinder
Surface area = $2\pi rh + 2\pi r^2$
Volume = $\pi r^2 h$

Cube
Surface area = $6s^2$
Volume = s^3

Rectangular solid
Surface area = $2bw + 2bh + 2wh$
Volume = bwh

PRACTICE TEST 2, PART 2: MATHEMATICS

PART 2: **Mathematics**
48 questions

1. Multiply $\frac{2}{5}$ by $\frac{3}{4}$. Show your answer in simplified (reduced) form.

   A. $\frac{5}{9}$

   B. $\frac{6}{20}$

   C. $\frac{5}{20}$

   D. $\frac{3}{10}$

2. Add $3\frac{2}{3}$ and $1\frac{1}{2}$. Show your answer in simplified (reduced) form.

   A. $5\frac{1}{6}$

   B. $4\frac{2}{5}$

   C. $4\frac{3}{5}$

   D. $4\frac{7}{6}$

3. Subtract $1\frac{2}{5}$ from $6\frac{1}{3}$.

   A. $4\frac{5}{15}$

   B. $5\frac{5}{15}$

C. $4\frac{14}{15}$

D. $4\frac{1}{3}$

4. Divide 6 by $\frac{3}{5}$

A. $\frac{2}{5}$

B. $\frac{3}{5}$

C. 10

D. $3\frac{3}{5}$

5. Perform the indicated operation.

$$(-25) - 7$$

A. –32

B. 32

C. –18

D. 18

6. Multiply 1.35 by 0.06.

A. 0.81

B. 0.081

C. 8.1

D. 0.0081

7. What percentage of 120 is 36?

A. 24%

B. 30%

C. 36%

D. 40%

8. Simplify to a single term in scientific notation.

$$(3 \times 10^4) \times (7 \times 10^5)$$

A. 21×10^{20}

B. 21×10^9

C. 2.1×10^9

D. 2.1×10^{10}

9. Simplify: $7 \times 2 + \frac{4}{4}$

A. 10

B. 14

C. 15

D. 21

10. Select the number that is missing in the problem below.

348 + _______ = 1,961

A. 1613

B. 1623

C. 1627

D. 2309

11. Williams Clothing Store sold sweaters for $70 at the beginning of September. In October, the price of the sweaters was raised by 10%. In December, the sweaters were placed on sale for 25% off. What was the price of the sweaters in December?

A. $59.50

B. $57.75

C. $55.00

D. $52.50

12. Three pounds of peanuts cost $4.65. What would five pounds cost (at the same price per pound)?

    A. $5.45

    B. $6.20

    C. $7.75

    D. $9.30

13. At 11:00 A.M., the temperature was 86º in San Francisco and was decreasing at a rate of 4 degrees per hour. At the same time, the temperature was 56º in Saint Louis and was increasing at the rate of 2 degrees per hour. At what time (San Francisco time) will the temperatures be the same?

    A. 3:00 P.M.

    B. 4:00 P.M.

    C. 5:00 P.M.

    D. The temperatures don't reach the same point on that day.

14. Steven began working on a project at 8:00 A.M. He worked until 12:30 P.M. Steven is paid $9.50 per hour for his work. How much did he make working on this project?

    A. $36.00

    B. $38.00

    C. $42.75

    D. $47.50

15. Convert: 123 ml = _____ liters

    A. 0.0123 l

    B. 0.123 l

    C. 1.23 l

    D. 12.3 l

16. Convert: 45.6 m = _____ centimeters

    A. 456 cm

    B. 4,560 cm

    C. 45,600 cm

    D. 456,000 cm

17. Convert: 64 fluid ounces = _____ pints

    A. 4
    B. 8
    C. 12
    D. 16

18. Convert: 12000 pounds = _____ tons

    A. 2
    B. 3
    C. 4
    D. 6

19. What is the area of a triangle that has a base length of 12 cm and a height of 6 cm?

    A. 72 square centimeters
    B. 36 square centimeters
    C. 18 square centimeters
    D. 60 square centimeters

20. What is the length of the base of a triangle with height 18 cm and an area measure of 252 square centimeters?

    A. 14 cm
    B. 20 cm
    C. 24 cm
    D. 28 cm

21. A rectangle is 5 inches wide. The area of the rectangle is 30 square inches. What is the perimeter of the rectangle?

    A. 30 inches
    B. 22 inches
    C. 20 inches
    D. There is not enough information given to determine the perimeter.

22. Use the figure below to answer the question.

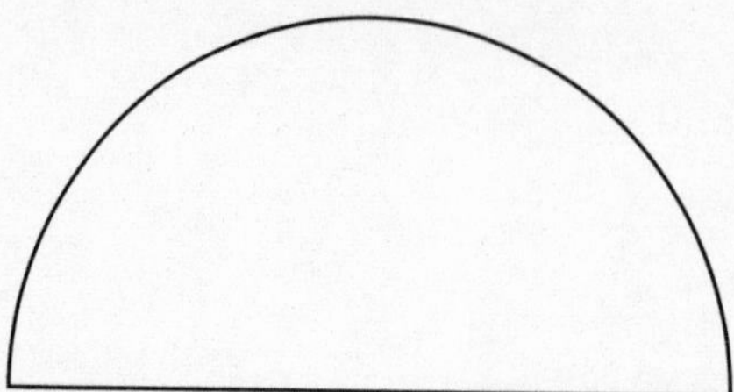

Which formula can be used to find the area of the figure? (Assume the curve is *half* of a circle.)

A. $A = \pi r$

B. $A = 2\pi r^2$

C. $A = \pi r^2$

D. $A = \dfrac{\pi r^2}{2}$

23. What is the approximate volume of the following cylinder?

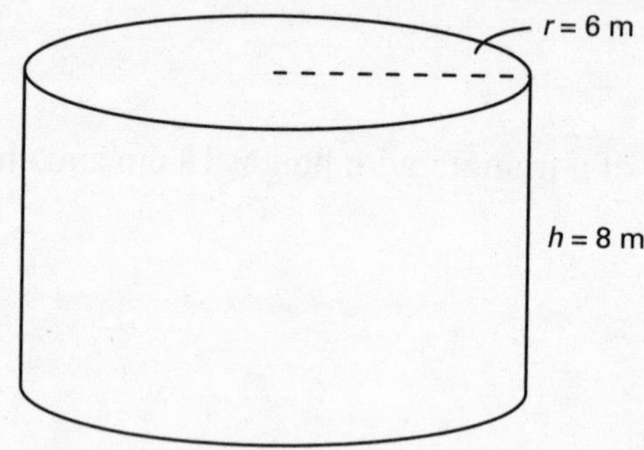

A. 904 cm^3

B. 301 cm^3

C. 151 cm^3

D. 452 cm^3

24. Use the Pythagorean theorem to answer this question: Which answer comes closest to the actual length of side x in the triangle below?

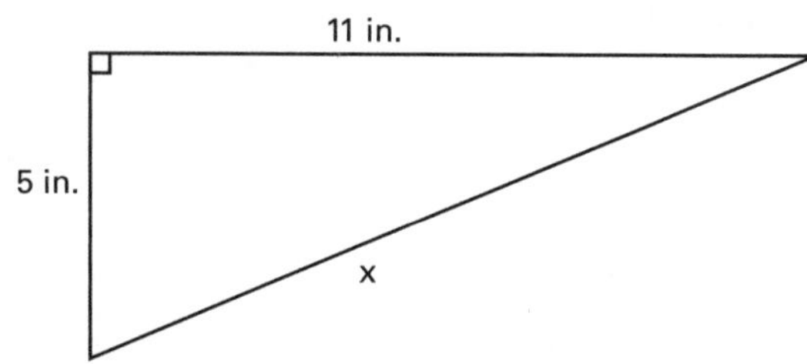

A. 14 in.

B. 12 in.

C. 11 in.

D. 13 in.

25. Use the figures to answer the question that follows.

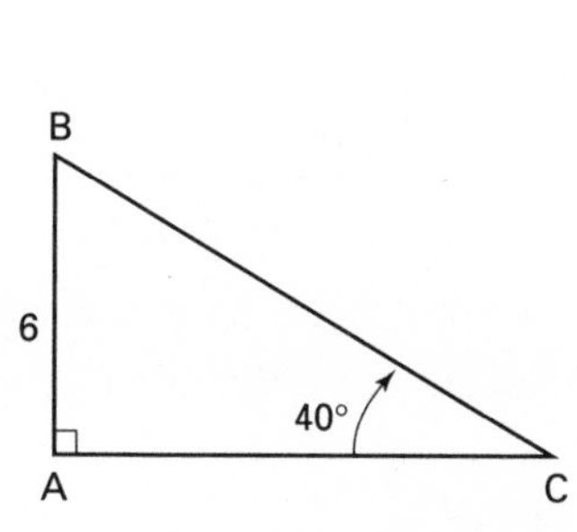

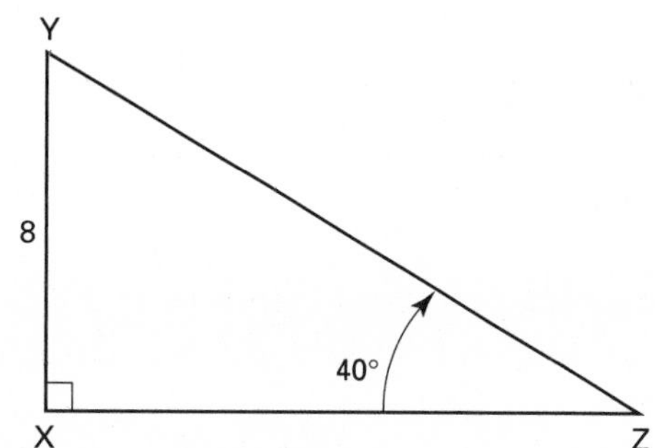

Which of the following statements about the two triangles are true?

I. The triangles are similar.
II. The triangles are congruent.
III. The measures of angles ABC and XYZ are the same.
IV. The lengths of sides BC and YZ are the same.

A. I and III only

B. I and IV only

C. II and III only

D. II and IV only

26. Mr. Johnson coaches the school's wrestling team. During the month of January, the 10 members of the team recorded the following weight gains and losses (in pounds):

$$-3, -5, 0, 2, -2, -4, -2, -5, 3, -4$$

What was the average weight gain or loss per team member?

A. Gain of 2 pounds

B. Gain of 1 pound

C. There was no loss or gain

D. Loss of 2 pounds

27. At a neighborhood pond, you measure the pH level of the water each day for 10 days. The measurements were:

7.1, 6.9, 6.7, 6.5, 6.3, 6.9, 6.8, 6.5, 6.3, 6.1

What is the median pH level of the water?

A. 6.6

B. 6.4

C. 6.5

D. 6.2

28. Olivia took a poll to find out how many days each week that college students exercise. She asked 300 students and obtained the following data.

Number of Exercise Days	Number of Respondents
0	18
1	34
2	48
3	65
4	84
5	35
6	13
7	3

If Olivia asked another student how many days each week he or she exercises, what is the probability that the answer will be four or more days?

A. 25%

B. 35%

C. 45%

D. 50%

29. Erica's change purse has 28 quarters, 13 dimes, 21 nickels, and 18 pennies. When she picked up her purse, a single coin fell out. What is the likelihood that the coin was a quarter?

A. 30%

B. 35%

C. 28%

D. 40%

30. Use the table below to answer the question that follows.

Minutes Spent in Instruction

	Monday	Tuesday	Wednesday	Thursday	Friday
Reading	45	50	50	45	30
Math	35	50	40	45	25
Science	30	25	35	20	25
Social Studies	20	30	25	40	40

Which of the following is true?

A. The largest variation in time spent teaching is in math.

B. Exactly twice as much time is spent in teaching reading as in teaching social studies.

C. The greatest increase in time spent teaching occurred from Tuesday to Wednesday in science.

D. The greatest decrease in time spent teaching occurred from Thursday to Friday in reading.

31. The following graph shows the distribution of test scores in Ms. Alvarez's class.

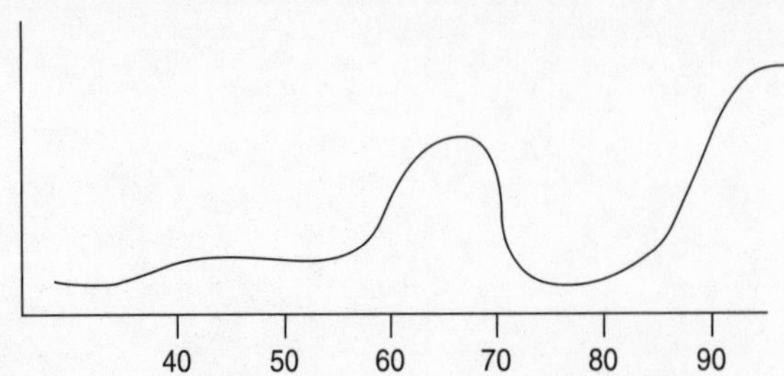

Which of the following statements do you know to be true?

I. The majority of students scored higher than 60.
II. The test was a fair measure of ability.
III. The mean score is probably higher than the median.
IV. The test divided the class into distinct groups.

A. I and II only
B. I and IV only
C. I, III, and IV only
D. IV only

32. According to the graph below, which one of the following statements is true?

Households by Income Class

Percentage Distribution of Households and Discretionary Income
(Total U.S. = 100 percent)

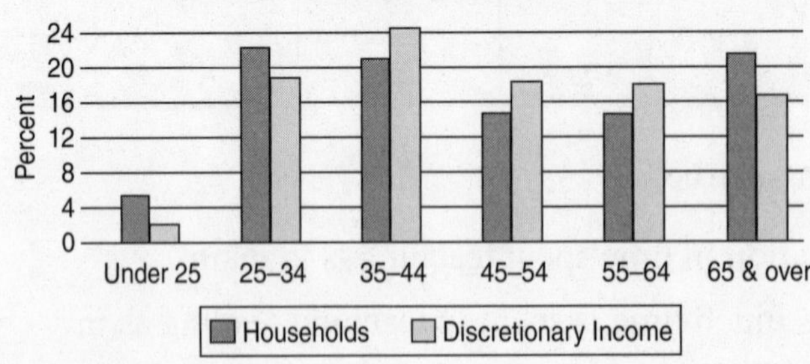

A. Middle-age households tend to have greater discretionary income.
B. The youngest have the most discretionary income.
C. The oldest have the most discretionary income.
D. The older one gets, the less discretionary income one has.

33. According to the graph, the profit for Kay's Computers in 2006 was what percent increase over the profit in 2003?

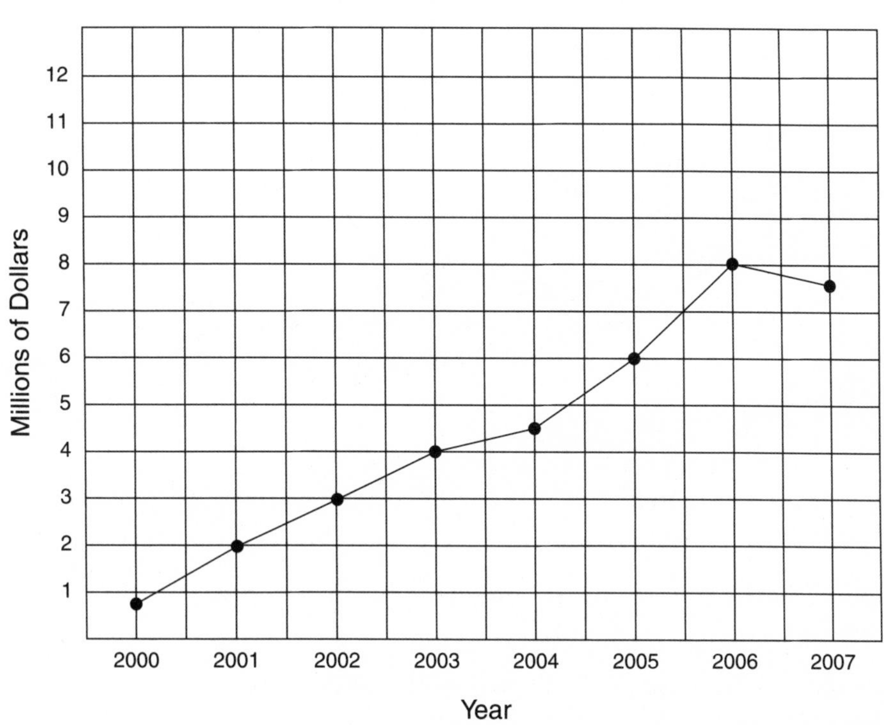

A. 50%

B. 100%

C. 150%

D. 200%

34.

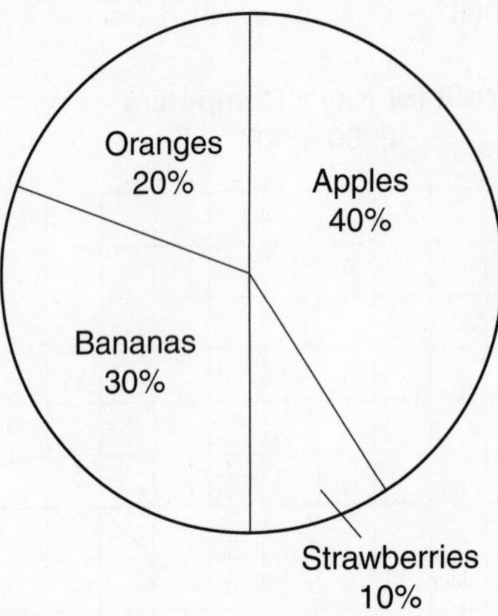

Based on the circle graph above, which of the following is an accurate statement about fruit sales in the United States?

A. Apples have the most positive effect on the health of the consumer.

B. Oranges and bananas make up half of the daily nutritional requirements of the average consumer.

C. More apples are sold than any other fruit.

D. Without the sales of oranges, the fruit industry would not be profitable.

35. The members of the Striders walking team participated in a 5K Fun Run. The scatter plot below represents the relationship between the age of the participants and their race completion times. Which statement best describes this relationship?

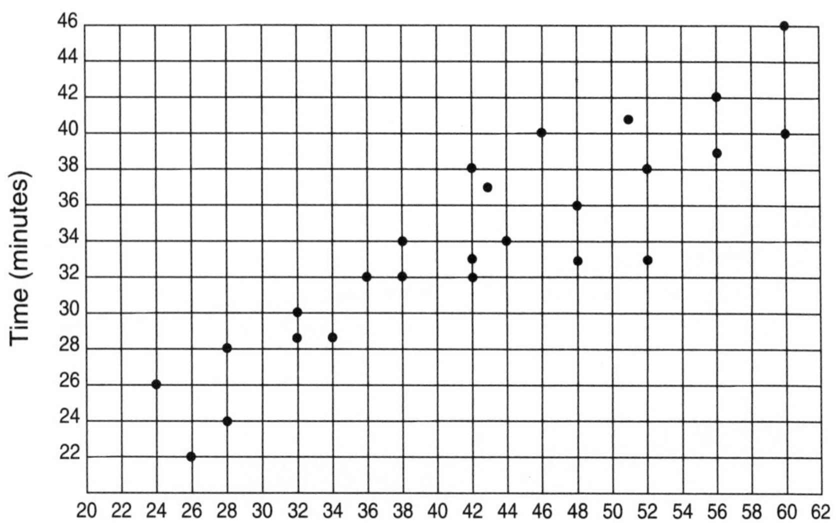

A. There appears to be no relationship between the participants' age and race completion time.

B. There appears to be a negative relationship between age and race completion time.

C. There appears to be a positive relationship between age and race completion time.

D. There is no way to accurately describe the relationship between the two variables using the diagram given.

36. What is the next number in this sequence?

1, 5, 2, 6, _____

A. 3

B. 4

C. 7

D. 8

37. What is the next number in this sequence?

100, 81, 64, 49, _____

A. 40

B. 36

C. 25

D. 20

38. Eileen's club is sponsoring a dance at school. The expenses of the dance include $600 for a disk jockey, $75 for security, $40 for advertisements, and $120 for refreshments. Eileen plans to charge $6 per person. What is the minimum number of people that will need to attend for Eileen's club to show a profit from the dance?

A. 100

B. 125

C. 140

D. 155

39. Kay bought $1\frac{3}{4}$ pounds of apples, $2\frac{1}{2}$ pounds of bananas, and $3\frac{2}{5}$ pounds of oranges. How much fruit did she buy in all?

A. $6\frac{1}{2}$ pounds

B. $6\frac{6}{11}$ pounds

C. $7\frac{1}{10}$ pounds

D. $7\frac{13}{20}$ pounds

40. Jared obtained a loan in the amount of $1200 from a local bank. At the end of a year, he will pay back all of the loan, plus interest, at the rate of 9.25%. How much will he owe at the end of a year?

A. $1209.25

B. $1292.50

C. $1311.00

D. $1320.00

41. Michael works for a newpaper that has 60,000 subscriptions: 31,500 for the morning paper, 10,000 for the evening paper, and 18,500 for the Sunday paper. About what percentage of the subscriptions are for the morning paper?

A. 50%

B. 53%

C. 60%

D. 62%

42. There are 6 people who attend a meeting. Everyone shakes hands with all of the other attendees. How many handshakes is that in all?

A. 36

B. 30

C. 15

D. 384

43. Evaluate the expression when $n = 4$.

$$\frac{1}{4}(n \times 8)$$

A. 2

B. 8

C. 14

D. 16

44. Evaluate the following expression using the following values: $x = 3$, $y = 4$, and $z = 6$.

$$4y(x + y + z + 3)$$

A. 128

B. 200

C. 256

D. 272

45. Simplify: $(-2b^5)(6a^2)(2a)$

A. $24a^2b^5$

B. $-25a^2b^5$

C. $-24a^3b^5$

D. $6a^3b^5$

46. Find the sum of $3c^2 + 12c - 4$ and $6c^2 + 11c - 7$.

A. $9c^2 - c + 11$

B. $9c^2 + 23c + 3$

C. $9c^2 + 23c - 11$

D. $3c^2 + 23c - 11$

47. Solve the following inequality:

$$13n + 6 \leq 97$$

A. $n \geq 7$

B. $n \leq 7$

C. $n \geq 6$

D. $n \leq 5$

48. Amelia, Jackie, Carla, and Kim are in a leadership club at State University. One is majoring in education, one is majoring in English, one is majoring in business, and one is majoring in theater. Amelia and Jackie have an 8:00 class with the education major. Carla and Kim commute with the theater major. Jackie eats lunch with the theater major.

Who is majoring in theater?

A. Amelia

B. Carla

C. Kim

D. It is impossible to determine the theater major with the information provided.

ANSWER KEY – MATHEMATICS PRACTICE TEST 2

Question	Answer	Objective	
1	**D**	0007	Understand number properties and number operations.
2	**A**	0007	Understand number properties and number operations.
3	**C**	0007	Understand number properties and number operations.
4	**C**	0007	Understand number properties and number operations.
5	**A**	0007	Understand number properties and number operations.
6	**B**	0007	Understand number properties and number operations.
7	**B**	0007	Understand number properties and number operations.
8	**D**	0007	Understand number properties and number operations.
9	**C**	0007	Understand number properties and number operations.
10	**A**	0007	Understand number properties and number operations.
11	**B**	0010	Understand problem-solving principles and techniques.
12	**C**	0010	Understand problem-solving principles and techniques.
13	**B**	0010	Understand problem-solving principles and techniques.
14	**C**	0010	Understand problem-solving principles and techniques.

Question	Answer	Objective	
15	**B**	0008	Understand measurement concepts and principles of geometry.
16	**B**	0008	Understand measurement concepts and principles of geometry.
17	**A**	0008	Understand measurement concepts and principles of geometry.
18	**D**	0008	Understand measurement concepts and principles of geometry.
19	**B**	0008	Understand measurement concepts and principles of geometry.
20	**D**	0008	Understand measurement concepts and principles of geometry.
21	**B**	0008	Understand measurement concepts and principles of geometry.
22	**D**	0008	Understand measurement concepts and principles of geometry.
23	**A**	0008	Understand measurement concepts and principles of geometry.
24	**B**	0008	Understand measurement concepts and principles of geometry.
25	**A**	0008	Understand measurement concepts and principles of geometry.
26	**D**	0010	Understand problem-solving principles and techniques.
27	**A**	0009	Understand statistical concepts and data analysis and interpretation.
28	**C**	0009	Understand statistical concepts and data analysis and interpretation.

Question	Answer	Objective	
29	**B**	0009	Understand statistical concepts and data analysis and interpretation.
30	**A**	0009	Understand statistical concepts and data analysis and interpretation.
31	**B**	0009	Understand statistical concepts and data analysis and interpretation.
32	**A**	0009	Understand statistical concepts and data analysis and interpretation.
33	**B**	0009	Understand statistical concepts and data analysis and interpretation.
34	**C**	0009	Understand statistical concepts and data analysis and interpretation.
35	**C**	0009	Understand statistical concepts and data analysis and interpretation.
36	**A**	0007	Understand number properties and number operations.
37	**B**	0007	Understand number properties and number operations.
38	**C**	0010	Understand problem-solving principles and techniques.
39	**D**	0010	Understand problem-solving principles and techniques.
40	**C**	0010	Understand problem-solving principles and techniques.
41	**B**	0010	Understand problem-solving principles and techniques.
42	**C**	0010	Understand problem-solving principles and techniques.

Question	Answer	Objective	
43	**B**	0007	Understand number properties and number operations.
44	**C**	0007	Understand number properties and number operations.
45	**C**	0007	Understand number properties and number operations.
46	**C**	0007	Understand number properties and number operations.
47	**B**	0007	Understand number properties and number operations.
48	**A**	0010	Understand problem-solving principles and techniques.

Practice Test 2, Part 2 Progress Chart

0007 Understand Number Properties and Number Operations —/17

1	2	3	4	5	6	7	8	9	10

36	37	43	44	45	46	47

0008 Understand Measurement Concepts and Principles of Geometry —/11

15	16	17	18	19	20	21	22	23	24	25

0009 Understand Statistical Concepts and Data Analysis and Interpretation —/9

27	28	29	30	31	32	33	34	35

0010 Understand Problem-Solving Principles and Techniques —/11

11	12	13	14	26	38	39	40	41	42	48

Detailed Explanations for Practice Test 2, Part 2: Mathematics

1. **D**

The traditional approach to multiplying simple fractions (those between 0 and 1) is to first multiply the numerators together and then multiply the denominators together to find the product. In this case, $\frac{2}{5}\times\frac{3}{4}=\frac{6}{20}$. Written in simplified form, $\frac{6}{20}=\frac{3}{10}$.

2. **A**

To add mixed numbers, first address the fractions. To add $\frac{2}{3}$ and $\frac{1}{2}$, find a common denominator, which in this case is 6. Equivalent fractions for $\frac{2}{3}$ and $\frac{1}{2}$ with the denominator of 6 are $\frac{4}{6}$ and $\frac{3}{6}$, respectively. Add the two fractions together to reach $\frac{7}{6}$. Simplified, $\frac{7}{6}$ equals $1\frac{1}{6}$. Add the one to the other whole numbers (therefore, 1 + 3 + 1) to reach 5. The final, simplified answer is $5\frac{1}{6}$, answer A.

3. **C**

When subtracting mixed numbers, the first step is to subtract the fractions (in this case, $\frac{1}{3}-\frac{2}{5}$). Because the denominators are different, equivalent fractions with a common denominator must be obtained. The least common denominator of these fractions is 15, so $\frac{1}{3}$ converts to $\frac{5}{15}$ (making the top number $\frac{6}{15}$) and $\frac{2}{5}$ converts to $\frac{6}{15}$ (making the bottom number $1\frac{6}{15}$). It is impossible to subtract $\frac{6}{15}$ from $\frac{5}{15}$, so we must rename the top number by "borrowing" one whole from the 6, and adding $\frac{15}{15}$ to the fraction. This results in the problem now reading $5\frac{20}{15}-1\frac{6}{15}$. We are able to easily subtract now, arriving at the answer of $4\frac{14}{15}$.

4. **C**

When dividing fractions, the traditional algorithm involves inverting, or "flipping," the second fraction and multiplying. Therefore, the algorithm would read $6 \times \frac{5}{3}$. It is easier to think of 6 as $\frac{6}{1}$, so that you may multiply the numerators (6×5) and then the denominators (1×3). The answer, therefore, is $\frac{30}{3}$, which, when simplified, is 10.

5. **A**

To subtract a negative number, think first about what subtraction looks like on a number line. When we subtract on a number line, we move to the left. Beginning at –25 and moving left (in the negative direction) 7 results in the answer of –32.

6. **B**

When multiplying decimals, set up the problem vertically, aligned on the right, then multiply regularly.

$$\begin{array}{r} 1.35 \\ \underline{\times .06} \\ 810 \\ \underline{+0000} \\ .0810 \end{array}$$

Count the number of digits to the right of the decimal in the original problem (in this case, 4 digits are to the right). Beginning at the far right of the answer, move the decimal point so that there will be 4 digits to the right of the decimal, making the answer .0810, which is equal to 0.081 (answer choice B).

7. **B**

To solve this problem, you must set up an equation. The easiest way to do so is to write the equation as it is read: What percentage $\left(\frac{n}{100}\right)$ of 120 (× 120) is 36 (=36)?

$\frac{x}{100} \times 120 = 36$

Multiply both sides by 100 to eliminate the fraction: $100\left(\frac{n}{100}\right) \times 120 = 36 \times 100$

Simplify: $n \times 120 = 3600$

$120n = 3600$

Divide both sides by 120: $n = 30$

Therefore, 30% of 120 = 36, answer B.

8. **D**

To solve this problem in scientific notation, simply multiply the first two digits inside each group of parentheses ($3 \times 7 = 21$). To multiply the 10's notations, simply add the exponents ($10^4 \times 10^5 = 10^9$). Thus far, the solution reads: 21×10^9. However, in scientific notation, the initial factor must be greater than zero and less than ten. Therefore, we change the 21 to 2.1, and increase the power of ten in the second factor by one. 21 changes to 2.1 and 10^9 changes to 10^{10}. The simplified answer to this problem, therefore, is 2.1×10^{10}.

9. **C**

The order of operations is used to solve this problem. Multiplication comes before addition, so the first step is to multiply 7×2, which equals 14. Then add $\frac{4}{4}$ (or 1), which brings the answer to 15.

10. **A**

This problem simply requires that you understand that to find a missing number in an addition sentence, you simply subtract the smaller from the larger of the two given numbers. In this case, 1,961 – 348 equals 1,613.

11. **B**

First, find the cost of the sweaters when the price was increased by 10% ($70.00 × 0.10 = $7.00 increase). Therefore, after the price increase, sweaters cost $77.00. Then, to find the sale price, first find the amount that 25% off would be by multiplying $77.00 by 0.25, which is $19.25. Subtract $19.25 from $77.00, which equals $57.75, answer B.

12. **C**

To solve this problem, first find the cost of 1 pound of peanuts. The problem says that 3 pounds of peanuts cost \$4.65. Therefore, to find the cost of one pound, divide \$4.65 by 3, which equals \$1.55 per pound. To find the cost of five pounds, then, multiply \$1.55 × 5, which equals \$7.75.

13. **B**

The easiest way to solve this problem is to make a chart showing the temperature changes by the hour. The first row shows the hourly temperature change for San Francisco (a decrease of 4° per hour) and the second row shows the hourly temperature change for St. Louis (an increase of 2° per hour). The temperatures are the same at 4:00 P.M., thus answer B.

City	11:00 A.M.	12:00 noon	1:00 P.M.	2:00 P.M.	3:00 P.M.	4:00 P.M.
San Francisco	86°	82°	78°	74°	70°	66°
St. Louis	56°	58°	60°	62°	64°	66°

14. **C**

To solve this problem, first determine the number of hours that Steven worked, which is $4\frac{1}{2}$ (or 4.5). Then, multiply his time (4.5) by his rate of pay per hour (\$9.50) to find that for this project, he earned \$42.75.

15. **B**

To solve this problem, consider that: 1 liter = 1000 milliliters.

The easiest way to solve this problem is to think in terms of a ratio:

$$\frac{123 \text{ milliliters}}{1000 \text{ milliliters}} = \frac{n \text{ liters}}{1}$$

Cross multiply to set up the equation: $123 = 1000n$

$$\frac{123}{1000} = \frac{1000n}{1000}$$ Divide both sides by 1000.

$n = 0.123$

16. **B**

Because there are 100 centimeters in 1 meter, simply multiply 100 by the number of meters given (in this case, 45.6) to obtain the answer of 4,560 cm.

17. **A**

In capacity conversions, 1 pint equals 16 ounces. To find how many pints are in 64 ounces, divide 64 ounces by the number of ounces in a pint (16), which results in the answer of 4 pints.

18. **D**

In weight conversions, 1 ton equals 2000 pounds. Therefore, to find how many tons equal 12,000 pounds, divide 12,000 pounds by the number of pounds in a ton (2000) to obtain the answer of 6 tons.

19. **B**

The formula used for finding the area of a triangle is $\frac{1}{2} \times \text{base} \times \text{height}$. In this case:

$$\frac{1}{2} \times (12 \times 6)$$

$$\frac{1}{2} \times 72 = 36$$

Note that area is always reported in square units.

20. **D**

To solve this problem, recall the formula used for finding the area of a triangle $\left(\frac{1}{2} \times \text{base} \times \text{height}\right)$. In the given problem, the base (b) is unknown.

Substitute the numbers that you know. $\frac{1}{2}(b \times 18) = 252$

Multiply both sides by 2 to eliminate the fraction. $(2)\,\frac{1}{2}(b \times 18) = 252\,(2)$

$b \times 18 = 504$

Divide both sides by 18 to determine the base (b). $b = 28$

21. **B**

To find the perimeter of any figure, you must know the length of each side. In this case, the width of the rectangle is given (5 inches). To find the perimeter, we must find the length. The area of the rectangle is 30 square inches.

Set up an equation using the area formula.	A = length × width
In this case:	30 = length × 5
Divide both sides by 5.	6 = length

Now we know the dimensions of the rectangle. Two sides are length, and two sides are width; therefore, 6 + 6 + 5 + 5 = 22 inches, answer B.

22. **D**

The formula for finding the area of any circle is pi (3.14) times the length of the radius times itself. In thise case, you need to take half of pi × r^2; hence, the answer D.

23. **A**

The formula for finding the volume of a cylinder is: V = pi (r^2) × h.

This means that the volume is equal to pi (about 3.14) times the measure of the radius squared times the height of the cylinder. In this case, that is:

$$3.14 \times 6^2 \times 8 \quad \text{or} \quad 3.14 \times 36 \times 8$$

or about 904. (Note that the final answer is given in cubic centimeters.)

24. **B**

Use the Pythagorean theorem to compute the length of any side of any right triangle, as long as you know the lengths of the other two sides. Here is the theorem:

For any right triangle with side lengths of a, b, and c, and where the length of the hypotenuse (the longest side, and the one opposite the right angle) equals $a^2 + b^2 = c^2$.

Substituting the given values for a and b for problem 24:

$$11^2 + 5^2 = c^2$$

or

$$121 + 25 = c^2$$

or

$$146 = c^2$$

To complete the work, take the square root of 146, which is approximately 12.

25. **A**

If you know the measure of two angles of any triangle, you can calculate the measure of the third angle. (The sum of the three angles is always 180º.) So the measure of the third angle in both of the triangles is 50º, and statement III is correct.

If two triangles have the same degree measures (as established above), then they are similar triangles (which means they have the same shape). Statement I is therefore correct.

Triangles are congruent only if they are exactly the same shape and size. One triangle is larger than the other, so statement II is false.

Because the second triangle is larger than the first, and they are the same shape, there is no way that sides BC and YZ could be the same length. Therefore, statement IV is false.

26. **D**

To find the average (mean) of a set of values, first add them together. In this case, the negative and positive integers should be added together separately. Those two sums are –25 and 5. (The 0 may be ignored, since it does not affect either sum.) Then –25 and 5 should be added together for a sum of –20.

To complete the work, the sum of –20 must be divided by the number of values (10), giving –2, or a weight *loss* of 2 pounds.

27. **A**

To find the median of a set of data, list the values from smallest to largest. In this case, the list would be:

6.1, 6.3, 6.3, 6.5, 6.5, 6.7, 6.8, 6.9, 6.9, 7.1

The two middle values are 6.5 and 6.7. To find the median, take the average of those two values; hence, the answer is 6.6.

28. **C**

To solve this problem, you must find the total number of students who responded "4 days or more," which is 135 of the 300. To find the percentage, divide 135 by 300, which equals .45 or 45%. If another student is asked, there is a 45% chance that he or she will answer 4 days or more.

29. **B**

To solve this problem, find the total number of coins in Erica's purse, which is 80. The percentage of quarters in her purse is 28/80 or .35. Therefore, if one coin falls from her purse, the likelihood it will be a quarter is 35%.

30. **A**

Consider statement A: The range (which is the amount of variation in a data set) of time spent teaching mathematics is from 25 minutes on Friday to 50 minutes on Tuesday, which is a range of 25 minutes. The range of time spent for reading instruction is 20 minutes, for science instruction is 15 minutes, and for social studies instruction is 20 minutes. Therefore, statement A is true.

Statement B says that twice as much time is spent teaching reading as social studies. The total time for teaching reading is 220 minutes, and the total time for social studies instruction is 155 minutes, which is not exactly half of 220. Therefore, statement B is false.

Statement C says that the greatest increase in time spent teaching occurred from Tuesday to Wednesday in science. That increase in time was 10 minutes, which is less than the increase in math instruction between Monday and Tuesday. Therefore, statement C is false.

Statement D says that the greatest decrease in time spent teaching occurred from Thursday to Friday in reading. This decrease was 15 minutes, while the decrease in math instruction on those days was 20 minutes. Therefore, statement D is false.

31. **B**

Just from looking at the graph, it is clear that most of the space under the curve is past the 60 mark on the x-axis. Answer D is eliminated because it doesn't include statement I.

Statement II can't be answered by what the graph shows. It appears possible that certain questions were too hard for many in the class and that there weren't enough questions to differentiate B students from C students, but perhaps the class performed exactly as it should have, given the students' ability and Ms. Alvarez's teaching. The distribution can give a teacher many clues about the test, the students, and herself, but by itself it tells us nothing about the fairness of the test. Thus, answer A can be eliminated.

Statement III is also false; in left-skewed distributions such as this one, the median is higher than the mean. This is true because the mean is lowered by the lowest scores while the median is relatively unaffected by them.

Statement IV is true; one fairly large group has scored in the high 80s and 90s and another discernible group in the low to mid-60s, whereas a few students fall outside these two groups. Thus, the answer has to be B.

32. **A**

Graph reading and interpretation is the primary focus of this question. Choice B is obviously wrong because the bar representing the discretionary income of the youngest households ("Under 25") is the shortest bar on the chart, indicating that this group has the least discretionary income. Choices C and D are also incorrect. The oldest group has less discretionary income than those between 25 and 65, but more than those under 25.

33. **B**

This graph shows that the profit in 2003 was $4 million and the profit in 2006 was $8 million. Because the profit in 2006 is exactly double the profit of 2003, that shows that the company made 100% additional profit, therefore, answer B.

34. **C**

The title of the graph indicates that the graph shows fruit sales. Therefore, any question that is not specifically about fruit sales may be eliminated. Both A and B are about health and nutrition, so they may be eliminated. We do not know how the sales of oranges affect profits, so we can eliminate D. We can see that the largest section (40%) of the circle graph represents apples, so C is the correct answer.

35. **C**

From the graph, we can see that as age increases, so does the race completion time. Therefore, there is a positive relationship, which rules out A and B. The problem with D is that any scatter plot shows either a positive relationship, a negative relationship, or no relationship. No relationship between the variables is still an accurate way to describe variables in a scatter plot graph. Therefore, the correct answer is C.

36. **A**

In this sequence, the pattern is plus 4, minus 3. ($1 + 4 = 5$; $5 - 3 = 2$; $2 + 4 = 6$) So, the next part of the pattern is minus 3; therefore, $6 - 3 = 3$.

37. **B**

In this sequence, the pattern is perfect squares, decreasing. The first number is 100 or 10^2, the second number is 81 or 9^2, the third number is 64 or 8^2, the fourth number is 49 or 7^2. Following this pattern, the next number would be 6^2, or 36.

38. **C**

To solve this problem, first find the total amount of expenses ($600 + 75 + 40 + 120), which equals $835. If each person is going to pay $6 to enter the dance, divide $835 by $6 to determine how many people need to attend for the club to make that amount.

$$\$835 \div \$6 = 139.1666$$

Rounded up, this means that 140 people must attend the dance for Eileen's club to make a profit. (140 × $6 = $840, which would be a profit of $5.)

39. **D**

To find out how many total pounds were purchased, add all of the values together. When adding mixed numbers, address the fractions first. In this problem, you must find a common denominator for $\frac{3}{4}$, $\frac{1}{2}$, and $\frac{2}{5}$. The least common denominator of those fractions is 20.

Change the given fractions to equivalent fractions with a denominator of 20. $\frac{3}{4}=\frac{15}{20}$ $\frac{1}{2}=\frac{10}{20}$ $\frac{2}{5}=\frac{8}{20}$

Add the fractions together. $\frac{15}{20}+\frac{10}{20}+\frac{8}{20}=\frac{33}{20}$

$\frac{33}{20}$ changes to the mixed number $1\frac{13}{20}$.

Add the 1 from the mixed number to the other whole number in the problem (1, 2, and 3) to reach the whole number of 7. Combine that with the fraction to obtain the answer of $7\frac{13}{20}$.

40. **C**

To find the amount of interest that will be due with Jared's loan, multiply the amount of the loan ($1200) by the amount of interest (it is easiest if you change the 9.25% to a decimal – 0.0925).

$$\$1200 \times 0.0925 = \$111$$

Add the amount of interest ($111) to the principal amount of the loan ($1200) to get the total amount due of $1311.

41. **B**

To find the percentage of subscriptions that are for the morning paper, make a fraction that shows the number of morning paper subscriptions over the total subscriptions:

$\frac{31,500}{60,000}$ Divide 31,500 by 60,000 = 0.525, which is 52.5%. The closest answer to this number is answer B, 53%.

42. **C**

The easiest way to solve this problem is to develop a chart or a diagram. In chart form, the problem looks like this:

Shakes hands with	Person 1	Person 2	Person 3	Person 4	Person 5	Person 6
Person 1	Can't shake with himself	X	X	X	X	X
Person 2	Already shaken with person 1	Can't shake with himself	X	X	X	X
Person 3	Already shaken with person 1	Already shaken with person 2	Can't shake with himself	X	X	X
Person 4	Already shaken with person 1	Already shaken with person 2	Already shaken with person 3	Can't shake with himself	X	X
Person 5	Already shaken with person 1	Already shaken with person 2	Already shaken with person 3	Already shaken with person 4	Can't shake with himself	X
Person 6	Already shaken hands with everyone else.					

Count the X's to show 15 total handshakes.

43. **B**

To solve this problem, apply the order of operations and substitute 4 for n.

$$\frac{1}{4}(4\times 8)=\frac{1}{4}(32)=8$$

44. **C**

To solve this problem, apply the order of operations and substitute the given values.

$$4(4)\,(3+4+6+3)=16\,(16)$$
$$=256$$

Therefore, answer C is correct.

45. **C**

$$(-2b^5)(6a^2)(2a)$$

To simplify this expression, first multiply the whole numbers $(-2\times 6\times 2)$ to get -24. Then combine like terms $(a^2\times a=a^3)$. There is only one b term (b^5). Put the constant and variables together, which results in the answer $-24a^3b^5$.

46. **C**

To add $3c^2+12c-4$ and $6c^2+11c-7$, simply combine the two expressions into one, keeping the signs as they are. Note: if you were subtracting the second expression, you would need to change the signs for each variable and constant.

Therefore: $3c^2+12c-4+6c^2+11c-7$

Combine like terms: $3c^2+6c^2=9c^2$
$12c+11c=23c$
$-4+(-7)=-11$

Put the expressions together to get the answer of $9c^2+23c-11$.

47. **B**

To solve this inequality, treat it like a regular algebraic equation and solve for n.

$$13n+6\le 97$$

Subtract 6 from both sides: $13n+6-6\le 97-6$

Simplify: $13n\le 91$

Divide both sides by 13 to isolate the variable: $\frac{13n}{13}\le\frac{91}{13}$

$n\le 7$

48. **A**

To solve this problem, make a chart showing all the possibilities.

	Education Major	English Major	Business Major	Theater Major
Amelia	X			
Jackie	X			X
Carla				X
Kim				X

Using the clues, put an X in each column when a person can be eliminated from consideration for that particular major. First, Amelia and Jackie have an 8:00 class with the education major. Therefore, put an X under education major for Amelia and Jackie. Second, Carla and Kim commute with the theater major. So, put an X under theater major for Carla and Kim. Finally, Jackie eats lunch with the theater major, so she cannot be majoring in theater; therefore, put an X beside her name under theater major, leaving Amelia as the only possible theater major.

Practice Test 2
Part 3: Writing

GACE Basic Skills

This test is also on CD-ROM in our special interactive TestWare® for the GACE Basic Skills. It is highly recommended that you first take this exam on computer. You will then have the additional study features and benefits of enforced timed conditions and instantaneous, accurate scoring. See page 6 for instructions on how to get the most out of REA's TestWare®.

ANSWER SHEET
PRACTICE TEST 2, PART 3: WRITING

1 _____	11 _____	22 _____	33 _____
2 _____	12 _____	23 _____	34 _____
3 _____	13 _____	24 _____	35 _____
4 _____	14 _____	25 _____	36 _____
5 _____	15 _____	26 _____	37 _____
6 _____	16 _____	27 _____	38 _____
7 _____	17 _____	28 _____	39 _____
8 _____	18 _____	29 _____	40 _____
9 _____	19 _____	30 _____	41 _____
10 _____	20 _____	31 _____	42 _____
	21 _____	32 _____	

PRACTICE TEST 2, PART 3: WRITING

PART 3: Writing
42 questions

Read the passage below; then answer the three questions that follow.

[1]The campaign against smoking has intensified in the last forty years, with special focus now on stopping young people from ever starting to smoke. [2]Since research has linked smoking to cancer, heart disease, and emphysema, it is somewhat mystifying as to why anyone would want to smoke in the first place. [3]Many groups, including the American Cancer Society, have worked to raise awareness of the dangers of smoking cigarettes. [4]Because of the efforts of groups like this, the Surgeon General placed the following warning on cigarette packaging: "The Surgeon General has determined that cigarette smoking is dangerous to your health." [5]The Surgeon General is appointed by the President.

[6]Even with the well-documented links between smoking and disease, people continue to smoke. [7]______________________________ [8]While more people may not be starting to smoke, it is concerning that them who do smoke may, in fact, be smoking more.

[9]There is a growing body of research that links smoke from cigarettes to cancer in individuals who do not smoke themselves. [10]This threat from secondhand smoke has led to bans against smoking in most federal and state buildings and requirements that restaurants and other businesses set aside nonsmoking areas. [11]Some smokers do claim that this is a form of discrimination, but it is hard to argue that one person's right to smoke is more important than the health of others who may come in contact with secondhand smoke.

1. Which of the following, if added between sentences 6 and 8, best supports the writer's purpose and audience?

   A. There is some information that indicates that the daily consumption of cigarettes is on the increase.

   B. These people who smoke are just killing themselves.

   C. Maybe some people are unconcerned with the research and enjoy smoking.

   D. It is hard to quit smoking cigarettes.

2. Which of the following contains nonstandard pronoun use?

   A. Part 2
   B. Part 4
   C. Part 8
   D. Part 11

3. Which of the following number parts draws attention away from the main idea of the first paragraph of the passage?

   A. Part 1
   B. Part 2
   C. Part 4
   D. Part 5

Read the passage below; then answer the three questions that follow.

[1]The influx of immigrants that America had been experiencing slowed during the conflicts with France and England, but the flow increased between 1815 and 1837, when an economic downturn sharply reduced their numbers. [2]Thus, the overall rise in population during these years was due more to incoming foreigners than to a natural, domestically derived increase. [3]Most of the newcomers were from Britain, Germany, and Southern Ireland.[4] The Germans usually fared best. [5]Since they brought more money and more skills. [6]Discrimination was common in the job market, primarily directed against the Catholics. [7]"Irish Need Not Apply" signs were common. [8]However, the persistent labor shortage prevented the natives from totally excluding the foreign elements. [9]These newcomers huddled in ethnic neighborhoods in the cities, or those who could moved on westward to try their hand at farming.

[10]The rapid growth in urban areas was not matched by the growth of services. [11]Clean water, removing the trash, housing, and public transportation all lagged behind the growing need for these services. [12]Bad water and poor sanitation produced poor health, and epidemics of typhoid fever, typhus, and cholera were common. [13]Police and fire protection were usually inadequate and the development of professional forces was resisted because of the cost.

4. Which of the following is a sentence fragment?

   A. Part 2
   B. Part 5
   C. Part 8
   D. Part 12

5. Which of the following changes is needed in Part 11?

   A. Change "clean water" to "cleaning the water."
   B. Change "removing the trash" to "trash removal."
   C. Change "housing" to "providing housing."
   D. Change "public transportation" to "busing."

6. Which of the following contains an error in capitalization?

   A. Part 3
   B. Part 4
   C. Part 6
   D. Part 7

Read the passage below; then answer the three questions that follow.

[1]Language not only expresses an individual's ideology, it also sets perimeters while it persuades and influences the discourse in the community that hears and interprets its meaning. [2]Therefore, the language of failure should not be present in the learning environment because it will have a prohibitive impact on the students' desire to learn as well as a negative influence on the students' self-esteem. [3]Failure can be defined as a lack of success. [4]When students do not immediately succeed, we award a failing grade to those students. [5]As educators we might well ask ourselves if this is the type of doctrine who we want to permeate our classrooms.

[6]One must remain aware that individuals acquire knowledge at independent rates of speed and everyone learns at a particular pace that is unique unto himself or herself. [7]Certainly no one would suggest that one infant "failed" the art of learning to walk because she acquired the skill two months behind her infant peer. [8]Would anyone suggest that infant number one failed walking? [9]What would a mentor project to either toddler were he to suggest that a slower acquisition of walking skills implied failure? [10]Sometimes we as educators feel the need to suggest Student A failed due to the slower procurement of abstract concepts it is essential to shift the learning focus from failure to success.

7. Which of the following requires revision for redundancy?

   A. Part 2

   B. Part 4

   C. Part 6

   D. Part 8

8. Which of the following changes is needed?

   A. Part 1: Change "individual's" to "individuals'"

   B. Part 4: Change "students" to "student's"

   C. Part 5: Change "who" to "that"

   D. Part 7: Change "no one" to "anyone."

9. Which of the following numbered parts of the passage is a run-on sentence?

   A. Part 1

   B. Part 5

   C. Part 6

   D. Part 10

Read the passage below; then answer the three questions that follow.

[1]Vitamins were once thought to be a cure all for a wide range of illnesses and symptoms. [2]It was also believed that vitamins could provide preventative powers if taken prior to high-risk exposure. [3]Now findings by long-term trials indicate that vitamin C, vitamin E, and selenium supplements do not reduce the risk of being diagnosed with lung or pancreatic cancer as once believed. [4]Other research has found no connection between over-the-counter vitamins and minerals and reducing risk of stroke or cardiovascular disease.

[5]It might be a better plan to forego a regimen of vitamins and minerals and focus instead on eating a healthy diet. [6]All necessary vitamins can be ingested by making healthy choices for meals and snacks. [7] ____________________ [8]Probably the best advice to follow when choosing foods to meet suggested vitamin requirements is to follow the food pyramid. [9]And choose wisely.

10. Which of the following sentences, if inserted as Part 7, would best fit the writer's organizational pattern in the second paragraph of the passage?

    A. A healthy diet involves one that is high in unprocessed fruits and vegetables and low in foods that contain sugars and fats.

    B. Until there is more support for taking vitamins, just eat right.

    C. While there is conflicting reports about the advantages of over-the-counter vitamins and minerals, everyone knows about vegetables.

    D. You could be on the safe side and eat healthy and take vitamins.

11. Which of the following changes needs to be made?

    A. Part 1: Change "wide" to "wider."

    B. Part 3: Change "being diagnosed" to "diagnosis."

    C. Part 4: Change "reducing" to "reduced."

    D. Part 8: Change "best" to "better."

12. Which of the numbered sentences is a nonstandard sentence?

    A. Part 3

    B. Part 4

    C. Part 8

    D. Part 9

Read the passage below; then answer the three questions that follow.

[1]Hillary Rodham Clinton, born in Park Ridge, Illinois, grew up in a relatively affluent family, the youngest daughter of a textile magnate. [2]She was a student leader in high school and campaigned for presidential candidate Barry Goldwater in 1964 as the chair of the local Young Republicans chapter. [3]The political upheaval and unrest of the 1960s, as evidenced by the assignation of John F. Kennedy, Martin Luther King, Jr., and Robert Kennedy, led Clinton to change her political activism. [4]During her college career at Wellesley College, she campaigned for the Democratic anti-war candidate Eugene McCarthy.

[5]It was at Yale attending law school that Hillary Rodham Clinton first became interested in family law and children's issues. [6]It was also while at Yale that she first met her future husband, Bill Clinton. [7]The two followed separate paths after graduation from Yale, while Hillary continuing her focus on children by working on the Children's Defense Fund. [8]She moved to Arkansas to teach at the University of Arkansas Law School in 1974, in what has been referred to as the more important turning point of her career. [9]It is during this period that she began her courtship with Bill Clinton, who she married in 1975. [10]By marrying Bill Clinton, a political power couple was created.

[11]In 2001 Hillary Rodham Clinton became the first first lady elected to public office. [12]She successfully ran for office as the junior senator from New York but was unsuccessful in her bid for president in 2008. [13]She was nominated by President-Elect Barack Obama as secretary of state, a position that requires Senate confirmation, which she received.

13. Which of the following changes needs to be made in the second paragraph?

    A. Part 5: Change "became" to "becomes."
    B. Part 6: Change "first" to "then."
    C. Part 7: Change "while" to "with."
    D. Part 9: Change "who" to "whom."

14. Which of the following displays a nonstandard use of a comparative form?

    A. Part 1
    B. Part 8
    C. Part 10
    D. Part 12

15. Which of the following sentences displays a nonstandard use of a modifying phrase?

    A. Part 10
    B. Part 11
    C. Part 12
    D. Part 13

Read the passage below; then answer the three questions that follow.

[1]If you ever visit the outside market in Charleston, South Carolina, be sure to visit one of the many booths where women can be witnessed weaving sweet-grass baskets, much as she did in the antebellum period. [2]These baskets and the art of making them represents one of the oldest remaining authentic African-American crafts left in this country. [3]The baskets were originally woven by slaves brought to the Charleston area from the West Indies. [4]The slaves were first brought to South Carolina to work on the rice plantations; the baskets were used in the harvesting of rice, a process known as "winnowing." [5]The baskets had other uses and were also used as containers for bread, cornmeal, and sewing materials.

[6]The baskets are woven from a type of grass called "sweetgrass" (*Muhlenbergia filipes*) so called because of its fragrance, which reminds me of sweet hay. [7]The grasses are indigenous to the area around Charleston; they can be found in the marsh and coastal areas. [8]Modern-day basket weavers still harvest these grasses; though private development of the coast has reduced the area in which the grasses can be found. [9]Because the baskets are made from marsh grasses, they are impervious to water and can be washed without any harm being done to the basket. [10]The baskets illustrate the long-standing usefulness of an item that has been tested over time; the baskets are still used on small rice farms to harvest rice.

16. Which of the following sentences displays a nonstandard use of a semicolon?

    A. Part 4
    B. Part 7
    C. Part 8
    D. Part 10

17. Which of the numbered sentences should be revised to correct an error in noun/pronoun agreement?

    A. Part 1
    B. Part 2
    C. Part 7
    D. Part 9

18. Which of the following is the best way to rewrite Part 6?

    A. The baskets are woven from a type of grass called "sweetgrass" (*Muhlenbergia filipies*) so called because of its fragrance, which reminds us all of sweet hay.
    B. The baskets are woven from a type of grass called "sweetgrass" (*Muhlenbergia filipies*) so called because of its fragrance, which is a reminder of sweet hay.
    C. [6]The baskets are woven from a type of grass called "sweetgrass" (*Muhlenbergia filipies*) so called because of its fragrance which is reminiscent of sweet hay.

D. Reminding me of sweet hay, the baskets are woven from a type of grass called "sweetgrass" (*Muhlenbergia filipies*) so called because of its fragrance.

Read the passage below; then answer the three questions that follow.

[1]The domestication of dogs marks the first domestication of any wild animal and probably occurred sometime between 20,000 and 15,000 years ago. [2]During the Mesolithic era, early man began using dogs for hunting and when livestock was domesticated approximately 7000 to 9000 years ago, there is an indication that dogs were used in herding. [3]The skeletal remains of dogs reveal that by the bronze age, the following five types of domestic dogs were in existence: pointers, shepherds, mastiffs, greyhounds, and wolf-types. [4]There is evidence that the Romans had bred guard dogs sometime around the 4th century B.C.E., and Aristotle listed known breeds of dogs as early as 350 B.C.E.

[5]As the Roman Empire spread across Europe, so did the breeds of dogs the Romans had developed. [6]As the Romans took their dogs throughout Europe, other breeds arose as a result of cross-breeding the Roman breeds with the existing dogs found on the continent of Europe. [7]Most of these dog breeds were advanced to provide assistance to their owners when hunting, but the rise of dogs for other purposes such as companionship was evident by the 4th century.

[8]After the fall of the Roman Empire, the struggle for survival became more important to the population than breeding dogs. [9]What eventually saved the dog-breeding craft was the dog's useful in the hunt and assisting his human counterpart in locating food.

19. Which of the following methods of organization does the writer use in the passage?

    A. Order of importance

    B. Explain a process

    C. Cause and effect

    D. Spatial relationships

20. Which of the following changes is needed for Part 9?

    A. Change "eventually" to "eventual."
    B. Change "saved" to "saves."
    C. Change "useful" to "usefulness."
    D. Change "assisting" to "assists."

21. Which of the following contains nonstandard capitalization?

    A. Part 2
    B. Part 3
    C. Part 5
    D. Part 8

Read the passage below; then answer the three questions that follow.

[1]No one wants to anticipate the trouble and stress that accompanies a flat tire, but a little forethought and preplanning can make the tire change less troublesome. [2]_____, be sure that all of the necessary tools and essentials are found in the trunk of the car so that the process of changing the tire can begin. [3]These essentials include the spare tire, the car jack, and tire iron.

[4]To begin changing the tire, the car should be parked, with the parking brake engaged, on the most level ground that is feasible. [5]If on a busy highway, it is often suggested that you open the hood to indicate that the car is in some type of disrepair. [6]Retrieve the tools and spare and remove the hubcap if necessary. [7]Loosen the lug nuts, which hold the tire in place, before elevating the car with the jack. [8]Before jacking the car up, be sure to check the owner's manual for the specific placement of the jack. [9]Jack the car up a little higher than the flat tire to have enough room to replace it with the full tire. [10]Remove the lug nuts and replace the flat tire with the new tire, making sure the valve on the tire is facing out. [11]Replace the lug nuts. [12]Tighten them in the opposite direction than they were removed. [13]Slowly lower the jack, remove it, and tighten the lug nuts again when the car is completely on the ground. [14]Now replace the hubcap and feel secure that you have correctly changed your flat tire.

22. Which of the following methods of organization does the writer use in the passage?

    A. Order of importance
    B. Explain a process
    C. Cause and effect
    D. Spatial relationships

23. Which of the following changes is needed to correct an error in sentence structure?

    A. Combine Parts 4 and 5 into a single sentence.
    B. Divide Part 10 into two sentences.
    C. Combine Parts 11 and 12 into a single sentence.
    D. Divide Part 13 into two sentences.

24. Which of the following transition words, if inserted into the blank in Part 2, would provide a more effective sequence of ideas?

    A. Next
    B. Then
    C. First
    D. Finally

Read the passage below; then answer the three questions that follow.

[1]There is a common misconception that the vice-president of the United States lives in separate quarters contained within the White House. [2]Many would be surprised to find out that the vice-president did not have a designated residence in Washington, D.C., until 1974. [3]Prior to 1974, the vice-president either lived in hotels or bought a home for himself and his family. [4]The vice-president's family were often moved from location to location during his tenure in office.

[5]In 1974, congress designated a house on the grounds of the U.S. Naval Observatory as the official residence of the vice-president. [6]The house was originally built in 1893 for the Superintendent of the Observatory and is built in the Victorian style of "Queen Anne" country home. [7]It was not designed for the vice-president as his residence. [8]The three-story residence has twelve rooms and six bathrooms, and covers 9,150 square feet.

[9]Gerald Ford was the first vice-president eligible to take up residence in the "Admiral's House," so called because the chief officer of the Naval Observatory lived there beginning in 1929. [10]The resignation of Richard Nixon preempted Ford's move to the newly renovated residence. [11]The next eligible vice-president was Nelson Rockefeller, who already maintained a home in Washington, D.C., and therefore used the residence mainly for entertaining. [12]The first full-time resident of the home was Walter Mondale, Jimmy Carter's vice-president, in 1976. [13]Since that time, all vice-presidents and their families have maintained the former "Admiral's House" as their home during their tenure.

25. Which of the following changes is needed to make the passage conform to the conventions of Standard American English?

    A. Part 3: Change "lived" to "lives."

    B. Part 4: Change "were" to "was."

    C. Part 8: Change "has" to "had."

    D. Part 9: Change "was" to "is"

26. Which of the following draws attention away from the main idea of the passage?

    A. Part 2

    B. Part 3

    C. Part 5

    D. Part 6

27. Which of the following sentences contains nonstandard capitalization?

    A. Part 2

    B. Part 5

    C. Part 9

    D. Part 12

Read the passage below; then answer the three questions that follow.

[1]The carousel, or merry-go-round, is a contraption that we remember as part of our elementary school days on the playground. [2]Riding the rotating platform with its six metal bars provided a common recess experience. [3]What a surprise to discover that the lowly merry-go-round was actually first developed as a tool to aid soldiers in the art of war! [4]The carousel was originally developed to provide practice for the cavalry.

[5]The original design was used by Turkish and arab horsemen as a military exercise meant to provide practice for combat done on the backs of horses. [6]The earliest known pictures of carousels depict baskets large enough for one man suspended from an innermost pole. [7]The baskets would be propelled around the pole and the warrior would attempt to joust stationary opponents or spear rings that were suspended from a rope. [8]The Europeans first observed this training exercise during the Crusades and brought the carousel (from the Spanish word *carosella*, meaning "little war") back to the royalty and nobility, where the humble carousel enjoyed elevated status as a form of entertainment.

[9]With its newfound popularity, carousels were created with elaborate horses and animals, though the game of ring tilt, where the riders attempt to grab golden rings, remained an integral part of the carousel riding event. [10]These types of carousels are what many people remember from city parks or county fairs. [11]It is interesting that what was first designed as a tool to aid warriors ended up as a beloved amusement ride and an integral part of urban culture.

28. What is the thesis statement of the passage?

    A. The earliest known pictures of carousels depict baskets large enough for one man suspended from an innermost pole.

    B. The carousel was originally developed to provide practice for the cavalry.

    C. These types of carousels are what many people remember from city parks or county fairs.

    D. The carousel, or merry-go-round, is a contraption that we remember as part of our elementary school days on the playground.

29. Which of the following contains nonstandard capitalization?

   A. Part 4
   B. Part 5
   C. Part 8
   D. Part 11

30. Which of the following changes is needed for Part 9?

   A. Change "were created" to "create."
   B. Change "though" to "although."
   C. Change "attempt" to "attempted."
   D. Change "remained" to "remains."

Read the passage below; then answer the three questions that follow.

[1]The health of students and their families depends not only on individual and family decisions, but on the factors involving the wider society. [2]One of these factors is advertising which often encourages children to make unhealthy decisions. [3]Students as young as kindergarten and first grade can learn how to recognize advertisements (e.g., for candy or sugar-laden cereal) that might lead him or her to unhealthy behavior. [4]By third of fourth grade, they should be able to demonstrate that they are able to make health-related decisions regarding advertisements in various media.

[5]In addition, any studies of the physical environment—in science, social studies, or other subjects—should be related to health whenever possible. [6]Examples include the effects of pollution on health, occupational-related disease, and the differences in healthcare options available to people in different parts of the world and in different economic circumstances.

[7]Differentiation between communicable and noncommunicable disease can be taught at the youngest grade levels.[8]______________________________ [9]Older children should be able to explain the transmission and prevention of communicable disease, and all children should learn which diseases cannot be transmitted through casual contact.

31. Which of the following, if inserted as Part 8, best supports the writer's purpose and audience?

    A. Very young children should learn to wash their hands frequently, for instance.

    B. Another aspect of physical education concerns awareness and avoidance of the health risks that are present in our everyday lives.

    C. Unfortunately, because of the presence of peer pressure and lack of parental control, the effect of education is sometimes not enough.

    D. It can be difficult to stress the importance of good hygiene.

32. Which of the following parts contains a nonstandard pronoun use?

    A. Part 1

    B. Part 2

    C. Part 3

    D. Part 4

33. Which of the following changes is needed to correct an error in punctuation?

    A. Part 1: Insert a comma after "individual."

    B. Part 2: Insert a comma after "advertising."

    C. Part 6: Insert a comma after "include."

    D. Part 9: Insert a comma after "prevention."

Read the passage below; then answer the three questions that follow.

[1]Folk dances are cultural dances that have remained quite stable for a long period of time. [2]The music has remained constant and the movements have changed little over the years. [3]It is also valuable to learn folk dances from other cultures. [4]Folk dances usually reflect the national traditions of various cultures they evoke pride in people's traditions and culture by keeping alive the dances of their ancestors. [5]Folk dances are usually about the group, not the specific dancer or couple. [6]Folk dance is a solid connection to the past and a vehicle for "belonging." [7]When one dances a folk dance, you belong to the group that

has danced that dance throughout the ages. [8]For some cultures that are being absorbed into western society and swallowed by global culture, such as the Inuit of northern Canada, languages are gradually lost, traditional crafts are lost and ancient religion is lost, but the folk dances are the last to go. [9]People cling to their dances as the last remnant of a shared past. [10]People dance their own culture's folk dance to understand who they are and where they came from.

34. Which of the following changes is needed to improve the unity and focus of the essay?

    A. Reverse the order of Parts 8 and 9.

    B. Delete Part 3.

    C. Reverse the order of Parts 7 and 8.

    D. Delete Part 4.

35. Which of the following numbered parts of the passage is an unnecessary shift in point of view?

    A. Part 4

    B. Part 5

    C. Part 7

    D. Part 10

36. Which of the following numbered parts is a run-on sentence?

    A. Part 2

    B. Part 4

    C. Part 5

    D. Part 7

Read the passage below; then answer the three questions that follow.

[1]The beloved Vulcan statue located in Vulcan Park located atop Red Mountain in Birmingham Alabama has been completely renovated and returned to its rightful spot. [2]The statue was removed from its pedestal in 1999 and recast and restored by Robinson Iron and Steel of Alexander City, Alabama. [3]It was a long and arduous process that took a total of four years, but the City of Birmingham is glad of his return.

[4]The statue was originally cast in 1904 as an entry to the 1905 World's Fair in St. Louis, Missouri. [5]It was commissioned by the city to promote Birmingham and the state of Alabama to the world and the god Vulcan was chosen to advertise the city's industrial might in the iron and steel business. [6]The sculptor, Giuseppe Moretti, cast the 56-foot iron statue in 21 pieces and then each piece was shipped to St. Louis for assembly. [7]The sculpture continues to reign as the largest iron structure in the world. [8]The statue of Vulcan was awarded the Grand Prize at the 1905 World's Fair.

[9]The years between Vulcan's return to Birmingham and 1999 were not kind to the statue, and a nonprofit organization was formed to return the symbol of Birmingham's steel industry to its former glory. [10]Funds were raised to not only refurbish the statue but to create a Vulcan Park where the Greek god could revel in his uniqueness. [11]It is to the park he returned in 2003, after a cost of $14 million, and the homecoming was celebrated on the 100th anniversary of the original dedication of the statue. [12]Vulcan now stands atop Red Mountain, a symbol of an industrial age that has since passed.

37. The writer's main purpose in writing this passage is to

    A. explain how iron statues are made.

    B. examine the cost of refurbishing landmarks.

    C. define the importance of maintaining landmarks.

    D. describe the statue and its restoration.

38. Which of the following changes is needed to correct an error in punctuation?

    A. Part 1: Insert a comma after "Birmingham" and after "Alabama."

    B. Part 2: Insert a comma after "Steel."

    C. Part 6: Insert a comma after "St. Louis."

    D. Part 10: Insert a comma after "Vulcan Park."

39. Which of the following changes is needed to improve the unity and focus of the second paragraph?

    A. Reverse the order of Parts 4 and 5.

    B. Delete Part 6.

    C. Reverse the order of Parts 7 and 8.

    D. Delete Part 8.

Read the passage below; then answer the three questions that follow.

[1]There is a continuing controversy about the existence of global warming, but if one chooses to look at the causes of global warming, it is easiest to assume that global warming does exist. [2]There are both natural and man-made causes of global warming, and it is important to examine both of these to get the total picture of the problem at hand. [3]Some causes of global warming can be eliminated, and some cannot.

[4]The natural causes of global warming include the release of methane gas from arctic tundra and wetlands. [5]The methane gas is a powerful greenhouse gas and serves to contain heat within the earth's atmosphere. [6]Another natural cause of global warming is the cyclical nature of climate change. [7]Every 40,000 years, the earth experiences a climate change, and this could be what is occurring now.

[8]There is little debate regarding whether human beings have added to the causes of global warming. [9]It is evident that the burning of fossil fuels has also created the release of increased amounts of CO_2 into the atmosphere, which is another greenhouse gas. [10]Human beings also promote the release of more methane gas into the atmosphere by the rise of population, creating a rise in food production. [11]Increased population also adds to the CO_2 problem because more people mean the exhalation of more of that gas also.

[12]Some of these causes can be reversed. [13]It is possible to reduce the amount of greenhouse gases emitted by using reusable energy and using fossil fuels more efficiently. [14]Planting more trees will also help by reducing CO_2 and increasing the oxygen in the atmosphere. [15]In short, those of us living on the planet need to reduce emission of fossil fuels and take better care of our environment.

40. Which of the following contains a nonstandard use of a comparative form?

    A. Part 1
    B. Part 2
    C. Part 11
    D. Part 15

41. Which of the following methods of organization does the writer use in the passage?

    A. Chronological order
    B. Spatial relationships
    C. Explain a process
    D. Cause and effect

42. What is the thesis statement of the passage?

    A. There is a continuing controversy about the existence of global warming, but if one chooses to look at the causes of global warming, it is easiest to assume that global warming does exist.
    B. Some causes of global warming can be eliminated, and some cannot.
    C. The natural causes of global warming include the release of methane gas from arctic tundra and wetlands.
    D. There is little debate regarding whether human beings have added to the causes of global warming.

Constructed-Response Assignment Directions

For the constructed-response assignment, you are asked to prepare a written response and record it on the pages that you are given in your Written Response Booklet.

Be sure to read the assignment carefully and plan your response before you start to write. You may use any blank space provided in the test booklet following the question to outline your ideas or simply to jot down notes. **However, when you take the GACE Basic Skills Test, you must write your final version on the pages that the test administrators provide in the test booklet.**

Test scorers use the following criteria to evaluate your constructed-response submission:

- Appropriateness of your response in that you address the topic directly and use language that would be appropriate for the specified occasion, audience and, purpose
- Your focus and organization in sticking to your topic and providing a logical flow to your reasoning
- The support you give to your thesis in the examples you provide
- Your use of correct grammar, sentence structure, and word usage
- Your use of conventions, which include spelling, punctuation, and capitalization

Constructed-Response Question

Writing Assignment

Of all general reference materials, a dictionary is the one probably used most often. If a dictionary is used to merely check the meaning or spelling of words, it is not being utilized to its full value. Write an essay to be read by a college instructor, in which you describe additional uses for the dictionary beyond that of finding word meanings. Identify which usage you think is the most important and provide support for this, using specific examples.

ANSWER KEY – WRITING PRACTICE TEST 2

Question	Answer	Objective	
1	A	**0011**	Recognize unity, focus, and development in writing.
2	C	**0014**	Recognize Standard American English usage.
3	D	**0011**	Recognize unity, focus, and development in writing.
4	B	**0013**	Recognize effective sentences.
5	B	**0013**	Recognize effective sentences.
6	A	**0014**	Recognize Standard American English usage.
7	C	**0013**	Recognize effective sentences.
8	C	**0014**	Recognize Standard American English usage.
9	D	**0014**	Recognize Standard American English usage.
10	A	**0012**	Recognize effective organization in writing.
11	C	**0013**	Recognize effective sentences.
12	D	**0013**	Recognize effective sentences.
13	C	**0012**	Recognize effective organization in writing.
14	B	**0014**	Recognize Standard American English usage.
15	A	**0013**	Recognize effective sentences.
16	C	**0014**	Recognize Standard American English usage.
17	A	**0014**	Recognize Standard American English usage.
18	C	**0011**	Recognize unity, focus, and development in writing.
19	B	**0011**	Recognize unity, focus, and development in writing.
20	C	**0014**	Recognize Standard American English usage.

Question	Answer	Objective	
21	B	**0014**	Recognize Standard American English usage.
22	B	**0011**	Recognize unity, focus, and development in writing.
23	C	**0013**	Recognize effective sentences.
24	C	**0012**	Recognize effective organization in writing.
25	B	**0013**	Recognize effective sentences.
26	D	**0013**	Recognize effective sentences.
27	B	**0014**	Recognize Standard American English usage.
28	B	**0012**	Recognize effective organization in writing.
29	B	**0014**	Recognize Standard American English usage.
30	C	**0014**	Recognize Standard American English usage.
31	A	**0012**	Recognize effective organization in writing.
32	C	**0013**	Recognize effective sentences.
33	B	**0014**	Recognize Standard American English usage.
34	B	**0011**	Recognize unity, focus, and development in writing.
35	C	**0013**	Recognize effective sentences.
36	B	**0013**	Recognize effective sentences.
37	D	**0011**	Recognize unity, focus, and development in writing.
38	A	**0014**	Recognize Standard American English usage.
39	C	**0012**	Recognize effective organization in writing.
40	A	**0013**	Recognize effective sentences.
41	D	**0012**	Recognize effective organization in writing.
42	B	**0011**	Recognize unity, focus, and development in writing.

Practice Test 2, Part 3 Progress Chart

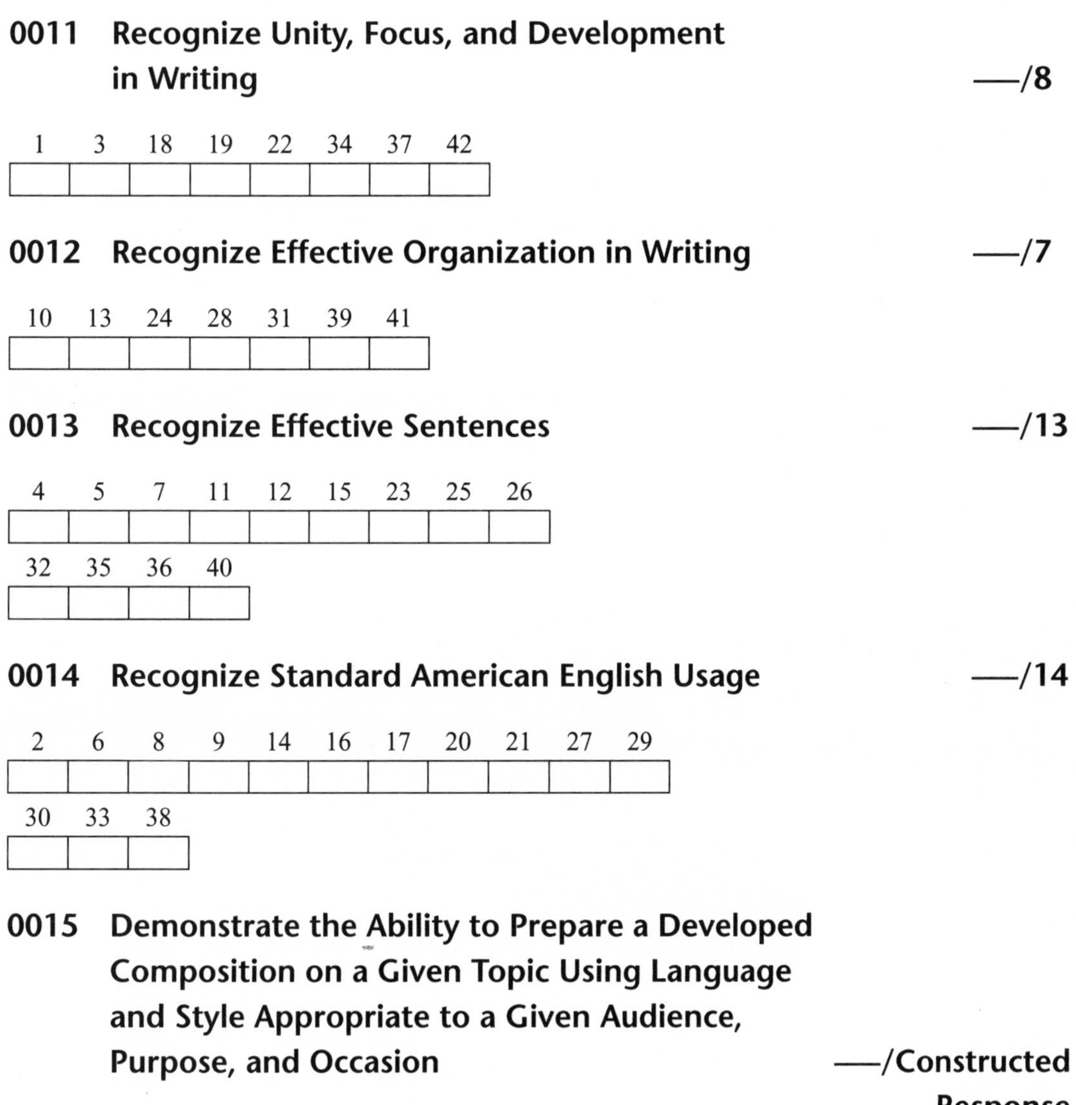

0011 Recognize Unity, Focus, and Development in Writing —/8

1	3	18	19	22	34	37	42

0012 Recognize Effective Organization in Writing —/7

10	13	24	28	31	39	41

0013 Recognize Effective Sentences —/13

4	5	7	11	12	15	23	25	26

32	35	36	40

0014 Recognize Standard American English Usage —/14

2	6	8	9	14	16	17	20	21	27	29

30	33	38

0015 Demonstrate the Ability to Prepare a Developed Composition on a Given Topic Using Language and Style Appropriate to a Given Audience, Purpose, and Occasion —/Constructed Response

Detailed Explanations for Practice Test 2, Part 3: Writing

1. **A**

Choice A contains information regarding the rise of cigarette use, which leads to the proposition in the next sentence regarding the concern that more cigarettes are being smoked. Choices B and C do not promote transition between the first and third sentences in the paragraph. Choice D does not support the thesis of the passage.

2. **C**

The pronoun "them" is usually used in the subjective case. Here the demonstrative pronoun needed is "those." Choices A, B, and D are all standard pronoun use.

3. **D**

Choice D does not provide information that is relevant to the issue of smoking. Choices A, B, and C all provide supporting details to the topic.

4. **B**

Part 5 is a prepositional phrase, "Since they brought . . . ," which is followed by a subordinate clause. This part should be linked to the previous sentence. Choices A, C, and D are all complete sentences.

5. **B**

Choice B provides parallel structure in the listing of the services to be provided: all the services are nouns or compound nouns. The other choices would create non-parallel structures within the sentence.

6. **A**

The direction or area of a country is only capitalized if it is a geographical name of the area (i.e., South Carolina, Southern Hemisphere) or a compass point (the Southeast), but not if it is a nonspecific direction or region (southern Ireland).

7. **C**

The sentence contains the words "rates of speed" and "particular pace" which have the same meaning, as well as "acquire knowledge" and "learns" which are also repetitive. No redundancy occurs in Choices A, B, and D.

8. **C**

The pronoun "who" is used to refer to people and the use of the demonstrative pronoun "that" is confusing in its reference. Choice A would change a correct possessive form to an incorrect plural form. Choice C would change the correct plural form to an incorrect possessive form, and Choice D would change the indefinite pronouns in such a way that the sentence would be nonsensical.

9. **D**

Part 10 is two sentences that should be separated by a period between "concepts" and "it" to make two independent sentences. The rest of the choices are all standard sentence structure.

10. **A**

Choice A provides information that is needed for the transition from the idea that vitamins can be found by choosing the correct diet and following the food pyramid. Choice B is too informal for the tone of the passage. Choice C assumes information that may not be correct. Choice D demonstrates change of person and does not provide a sensible transition to Part 8.

11. **C**

Choice C provides agreement in parallel structures of the noun phrase "over-the-counter vitamins and minerals" and "reduced risk." Choices A and D would create an incorrect comparative structure. Choice B would change the existing verb phrase to a noun, which would be nonstandard sentence structure.

12. **D**

Choice D is a sentence fragment with no connection to the preceding sentence. All other choices are complete sentences.

13. **C**

Choice C changes the prepositions so that the sentence transitions from the additional service that Clinton acquired. Choice A creates a change of tense midsentence. Choice B changes transitions so that the information in the sentence is incorrect. Choice D would make the pronoun form incorrect.

14. **B**

Choice B contains the comparison of more than two subjects: that is, moving to Arkansas and every other "turning point," but the incorrect comparative case "more important" is used rather than the correct superlative form "most important." Choices A and C do not contain a comparative form. Choice D uses the correct positive form "unsuccessful."

15. **A**

The opening verb phrase is a dangling modifier. It is unclear who is marrying Bill Clinton or who is creating a power couple. A correct revision would include "A political power couple was created with the marriage of Hillary Rodham to Bill Clinton." All the other choices are Standard American English sentences.

16. **C**

Semicolons are used to separate main clauses that can stand alone as sentences. The subordinate clause "though private development of the coast…" cannot stand alone as a sentence and should be offset by a comma, not a semicolon. Choices A, B, and D all contain semicolons that are separating main clauses.

17. **A**

Choice A should be revised so that the singular pronoun "she" is changed to agree with the plural noun "women." Choices B, C, and D are all correct noun/pronoun agreement and require no revision.

18. **C**

The revision in Choice C retains the existing third person point of view. Choices A and D change the point of view to first person, and Choice B has incorrect word choice of the noun "reminder" instead of the more appropriate adjective "reminiscent."

19. **B**

The writer organizes the passage from the beginning of the domestication of dogs through the fall of the Roman Empire, which is chronological. Choice A suggests that some part of the breeding of dogs was more important, which is not stated in the passage. Choice C would describe perhaps how the domestication of dogs came about, but this is not stated in the passage. Choice D would be correct if the original area in which dogs were bred was described.

20. **C**

Choice C changes the incorrect adjective form "useful" to the correct noun form "usefulness." Choice A would change the correct adverb form to the incorrect adjective form. Choices B and D would create incorrect changes of tense in the sentence.

21. **B**

Part 3 contains the capitalization error "bronze age." Historical events, eras, and calendar items are all capitalized in Standard American English.

22. **B**

The passage is organized to explain how to change a tire. Choice A is incorrect because there is no singular important event that occurs in changing a tire. Choice C is incorrect, as no mention is made of the cause of the flat tire. Though there are some descriptions ordered spatially, Choice D is incorrect because the passage itself is not organized this way.

23. **C**

The very brief Part 11 should be combined with Part 12 with the addition of the conjunction "and." Choice A would create too many ideas within a single sentence. Choices B and D would create incomplete sentences.

24. **C**

Choice C offers the transition word "First" that should be used to emphasize the first event to occur. Choices A and B provide transitions that would promote the following steps, not the initial step. Choice D is a transition word for the last step in the process.

25. **B**

The noun "family" is a group noun used as a single entity, so the singular verb "was" is correct. Choices A, C, and D are incorrect changes in tense.

26. **D**

Choice D is redundant and it has already been stated that the residence was built for another purpose. Choice A would remove a supporting statement of the thesis. Choice B provides information that is further explained in the following sentence. Choice C substantiates the original idea that the home was built for another purpose and gives specific details about the home.

27. **B**

Part 5 contains the word "congress," which should be capitalized as an institution.

28. **B**

The focus of the passage is on the origin of the carousel. Choice A provides interesting support for how the carousel was originally designed, but no supporting information is provided. Choices C and D provide personal insight into carousels and the shared experience, but are not the focus of the history of the carousel.

29. **B**

Part 5 contains the word "arab," which should be capitalized as an ethnic or national group or language.

30. **C**

Choice C makes the sentence consistent in past verb tense. Choices A and D provide incorrect verb tense. Choice B would do nothing to change the logic of the sentence and is unnecessary.

31. **A**

Part 7 states that information should be provided to children "at the youngest grade levels" and this statement is supported by the information in Choice A. Choice B does not provide support for the information in the paragraph. Choice C could be a paragraph unto itself, but does not provide transition between Parts 7 and 9. Choice D is important, but does not support the information that follows.

32. **C**

Part 3 contains a plural noun "students" with incorrect objective personal singular pronouns "him" and "her." The other choices are all correct noun/pronoun agreement.

33. **B**

Choice B inserts a comma to set off the participial phrase "which often encourages . . . " Any comma added to the suggested places in Choices A, C, and D would create a comma splice.

34. **B**

Choice B has to do with cultural awareness of others outside the culture, not of those within. This is far removed from the focus of the paragraph. Part 3 should be deleted or further developed in a second paragraph. Choices A and C would put the ideas out of sequence. Choice D would remove the thesis statement from the paragraph.

35. **C**

Part 7 changes from third person "one" to second person "you" within the sentence. The other choices maintain third person point of view.

36. **B**

Choice B has two distinct sentences contained in a single sentence. A period should be placed between "cultures" and "they." Choices A, C, and D are all single ideas represented in single sentences.

37. **D**

The writer's description of the statue and its restoration is the only perspective found in the passage. Choice A is not mentioned in the passage, and Choice B is the subject of a single sentence. An in-depth discussion of the importance of maintaining landmarks is not offered within the passage.

38. **A**

A comma is placed between a city and state. All other choices would create a comma splice.

39. **C**

Part 8, which describes the award given at the World's Fair, should be closer to supporting elements about that event. Part 7 is a good concluding sentence for that paragraph and should occur last. Choice A would place information out of sequence. Choices B and D would remove necessary information that gives unity to the passage.

40. **A**

Choice A contains a comparison of only two subjects, to examine or not examine the causes of global warming, but the superlative case "easiest" is used rather than the correct comparative form "easier." Choice B does not contain a comparative form. Choice C uses the correct comparative adjective "more" modifying the noun "people." Choice D contains the correct comparative adjective "better" modifying the noun "care."

41. **D**

The writer organizes the paragraphs to illustrate the causes of global warming. Choice A would suggest that the passage had been organized to illustrate the history of global warming, which it is not. Choice B is incorrect because there is no description regarding the environment of global warming other than the atmosphere. Choice C is incorrect because even though the passage does offer examples of greenhouse gases and how it is produced, the process itself is not the focus of the passage, but rather the effect that greenhouse gases have on global warming.

42. **B**

The thesis in this passage is stated in Part 2 and repeated in Part 3. Choices A, C, and D are all supporting elements for the thesis statement.

Sample Response for Constructed-Response Question

Writing Sample with a Score of 4

Dictionaries contain a wealth of information about words and can be used for many different purposes besides finding words' meanings. One of the best dictionaries to use when conducting research is an unabridged dictionary because of the exhaustive listing of words found and the other useful tools about the words. An unabridged dictionary will provide much more information about words than simply the word meaning. Unabridged dictionaries can be used to determine the syllables of words, the pronunciation of words, the spelling of the plural or inflected form of the word, and their etymology.

One important use of an unabridged dictionary is to determine the syllabication of a word. When writing, it is important to correctly break words at the end of lines by dividing the word into the correct syllables. The dictionary will illustrate these syllables by using dots, spaces, or slashes where the word may be divided into syllables. Using a dictionary to check the correct syllabication will ensure that mistakes are avoided in written work.

Another important use of the unabridged dictionary is the pronunciation guide which accompanies the entry word. While sometimes the dictionary is used to provide a guide to spelling, the dictionary also provides a guide to how to say the particular word. The pronunciation guide uses symbols to indicate the syllabus that gets the most stress, and other symbols to indicate particular sounds. Using a dictionary to check the pronunciation of a word can help in pronouncing the word correctly and may help an individual recognize a word with which they are unfamiliar.

Perhaps the least appreciated use of the unabridged dictionary could be the inclusion of the plural forms of nouns and the inflected forms of verbs. This tool provides insight into the variations in the tense or number of an entry word. This use of the dictionary provides the irregular spelling of words and is helpful in the correct spelling of rarely used words.

Dictionaries often provide the etymology of the word. Etymologies are a valuable aid for extending vocabulary. Knowing a word's origin can help in remembering the word and also provide insight into the meanings of related words with a common origin. Using a dictionary to check the etymology of a word can open up a larger range of words with the same foundation.

Of all of the uses of the dictionary, besides finding the meaning of a word, it is the etymology of the word that can be the most useful. Identifying the age of a word by recognizing that it might have originated in during the Middle Ages often allows the writer to recognize how long particular ideas or actions have been in use. The word "jury," for example, comes from the Latin word meaning "to swear an oath," and in serving on a jury one swears to be nonbiased. The same etymology is evident in the words juror, jurisdiction, and jurisprudence. All of these words entail the use of an oath or the swearing in of something related to expressing an oath.

Dictionaries do provide definitions and are not intended as an encyclopedia, but knowing the different parts and uses of the dictionary can extend its usefulness beyond that of a simple definition provider. The dictionary is intended to provide clear and accurate information about words but also does a good job of providing information that assists individuals in both reading and writing. As such, a dictionary supplies multiple, easy-to-use research tools in a single resource.

Features of the Writing Sample Scoring 4

Appropriateness—The paper's topic and the writer's viewpoint are both well laid out in the first paragraph. The four uses of the dictionary are listed in the topic paragraph and are explored in deeper detail throughout the essay. The language and style fit the writer's audience. The style is formal, but possesses a personalized voice.

Focus and Organization—The writer follows the cues of the writing assignment closely, structuring his or her essay around the specific prompts found therein. The essay follows the course presented in the last sentence of the topic paragraph, and each of the uses of the dictionary is given a complete explanation in the paragraphs that follow, and in the order in which they were initially listed. Different uses for each of the components are examined, but the general focus remains on the use of the dictionary as a research tool.

Support—Each paragraph gives a full explanation of the listed component and the concluding paragraph uses a common sense argument to draw all the parts together. The sixth paragraph clearly offers the writer's choice of the most important use and the examples used support the choice.

Grammar, Sentence Structure, and Usage—The sentences are standardized and vary in form, and the consistent use of the active voice ("Dictionaries provide...," and "The word comes from. . .") make the essay easy to read. There is some stiltedness found in the repetition of "the use of" and "provides" but for the most part the essay is constructed of a variety of sentence forms.

Conventions—Spelling, punctuation, and capitalization are mostly standard throughout the essay.

Writing Sample with a Score of 2 or 1

Besides using the dictionary for looking up definitions of words, it can be used to figure out how to spell words. This is probably how most people got their first taste of the dictionary. Whenever kids ask how to spell something, they are usually told to look it up in the dictionary. Which usually doesn't help much if you don't know how to spell it in the first place.

I am not sure that the inventors of the dictionary meant for it to be used for correct spelling, but that is how it is used these days. Most of us were taught to look up spelling words in the dictionary and then were told to look up a word whenever we didn't know how to spell something. So, we are pretty good at using the dictionary this way.

You can usually get pretty close to the spelling of a word by just saying it out loud and then using those sounds to locate the first part of the word using the guide words at the top of the pages in the dictionary. Sometimes it can be tricky if it is one of those words that have a strange sound and you don't know what the letter is, exactly. It can be a guessing game that takes a long time when you don't know what you are looking for.

Luckily now there are dictionaries built right in the computer software programs that find the misspelled words for you. Sometimes the computer does it for you and automatically changes the spelling of words you use alot. Sometimes you can just right click on it and it will give a whole bunch of words that are close to your word and you pick the one that looks write.

There are other uses of the dictionary, but using it to help you spell is the next most important one after finding out definitions. It was how you first started using the dictionary, and can still be used for that same purpose. The spell checker feature on the computer is an automatic dictionary that is the same purpose as looking words up yourself.

Features of the Writing Sample Scoring 2 or 1

Appropriateness—The writer misconstrues the prompt and writes about only a single use of the dictionary. The prompt does not call for how to use the dictionary for a single purpose; it calls for different uses for the dictionary besides finding word meanings. This essay investigates a single use for the dictionary and while it does offer some support for this point of view, the writer doesn't offer a distinct rationale for using the dictionary to check the spelling of the word, but instead provides instruction in how to use the dictionary for this purpose. The prompt initially points out that using the dictionary to check the spelling of words constitutes a minor use of the possible range of uses, but the writer uses this single usage as the topic of this essay. The writer uses informal language with colloquialisms and idiomatic expressions.

Focus and Organization—While the focus seems to be on the singular use of the dictionary as a way to check spelling, the writer becomes tangential with the introduction of the spellcheck option found on most computers. The writer makes some historical references that are probably common experiences for most readers (asking how to spell a word, only to be told to look it up in the dictionary, trying to determine particular sounds of words), but these experiences don't lend any credence to this selection as the most useful utilization of the dictionary. There is mention of "other uses of the dictionary," but none is explored.

Support—The support seems to be that using the dictionary to check spelling is the most common exercise with which readers are familiar, but there isn't any support to indicate that this is the most appropriate use of the dictionary as a reference material. There is no connection to the usefulness of checking word spelling to writing or researching.

Grammar, Sentence Structure, and Usage—Most sentences follow standard sentence structure, but the opening sentence of the essay has an unclear insubordinate clause and the use of "it" is confusing. Switching from second person to third person throughout the essay makes it very difficult to follow and the use of second person adds to the informality of the essay. There is a sentence fragment in the last line of the first paragraph. There is the use of the word "pretty" as an adverb ("pretty good" and "pretty close") and incorrect noun/verb agreement in the third paragraph ("...it is one of those words that have a strange sound," should be "has").

Conventions—There is an incorrect homonym use ("write" should be "right" in the fourth paragraph) and the word "alot" is two words (a lot)—and probably should not be used at all in formal writing. There is nonstandard comma use before the word "exactly" in the third paragraph.

Index

N

O

P

Q

R

S

T

V

Pages for Constructed-Response Answers

Pages for Constructed-Response Answers

Pages for Constructed-Response Answers

Pages for Constructed-Response Answers

Installing REA's TestWare®

SYSTEM REQUIREMENTS

Pentium 75 MHz (300 MHz recommended) or a higher or compatible processor; Microsoft Windows 98 or later; 64 MB available RAM; Internet Explorer 5.5 or higher.

INSTALLATION

1. Insert the GACE Basic Skills CD-ROM into the CD-ROM drive.
2. If the installation doesn't begin automatically, from the Start Menu choose the RUN command. When the RUN dialog box appears, type d:\setup (where d is the letter of your CD-ROM drive) at the prompt and click OK.
3. The installation process will begin. A dialog box proposing the directory "C:\Program Files\REA\GACE_BasicSkills\" will appear. If the name and location are suitable, click OK. If you wish to specify a different name or location, type it in and click OK.
4. Start the GACE Basic Skills TestWare® application by double-clicking on the icon.

REA's GACE Basic Skills TestWare® is **EASY** to **LEARN AND USE**. To achieve maximum benefits, we recommend that you take a few minutes to go through the on-screen tutorial on your computer. The "screen buttons" are also explained here to familiarize you with the program.

TECHNICAL SUPPORT

REA's TestWare® is backed by customer and technical support. For questions about **installation or operation of your software**, contact us at:

Research & Education Association
Phone: (732) 819-8880 (9 a.m. to 5 p.m. ET, Monday–Friday)
Fax: (732) 819-8808
Website: www.rea.com
E-mail: info@rea.com

Note to Windows XP Users: In order for the TestWare® to function properly, please install and run the application under the same computer administrator-level user account. Installing the TestWare® as one user and running it as another could cause file-access path conflicts.